# Contents

P9-DFF-245

**Section**

Indexes

# Acknowledgements and Advisements

## Acknowledgements

The AHA Guide® to the Health Care Field is published annually by Health Forum LLC, an affiliate of the American Hospital Association. Contributions are made by Information Systems and Technology, Member Relations, Office of the President, Office of the Secretary, Printing Services Group, AHA Resource Center and the following participants:

| | |
|---|---|
| Grant Denten | Maura Kennedy |
| Matthew Diener | Peter Kralovec |
| Dianna Doyle | Mary Krzywicki |
| DeAnn Ellis | Andrea Liebig |
| Joan Finn | Denise Loggins |
| Deanna Frazier | Kathy Poole |
| Robyn Gray | Christine Remedios |
| Tan Harris | Jennifer Sikora |
| Stella Hines | Susan Sheffey |
| Clisby Jackson | Elaine Singh |
| Danny Jackson | Marty Weitzel |
| Kimberly Jackson | |

Health Forum LLC acknowledges the cooperation given by many professional groups and government agencies in the health care field, particularly the following: American College of Surgeons; American Medical Association; Blue Cross and Blue Shield Association; Council of Teaching Hospitals of the Association of American Medical Colleges; The Joint Commission; DNV Healthcare Inc.; Center for Improvement in Healthcare Quality; Accreditation Commission for Education in Nursing; Commission on Accreditation of Rehabilitation Facilities; American Osteopathic Association, Centers for Medicare & Medicaid Services; and various offices within the U.S. Department of Health and Human Services.

## Advisements

The data published here should be used with the following advisements: The data is based on replies to an annual survey that seeks a variety of information, not all of which is published in this book. The information gathered by the survey includes specific services, but not all of each hospital's services. Therefore, the data does not reflect an exhaustive list of all services offered by all hospitals. For information on the availability of additional data and products, please contact Health Forum LLC at 800/821–2039, or visit our web site.

Health Forum LLC does not assume responsibility for the accuracy of information voluntarily reported by the individual institutions surveyed. **The purpose of this publication is to provide basic data reflecting the delivery of health care in the United States and associated areas, and is not to serve as an official and all inclusive list of services offered by individual hospitals. The information reflected is based on data collected as of August 31, 2015.**

## An Introduction to *AHA Guide*®

Welcome, and thank you for purchasing the 2016 edition of *AHA Guide*®. This section is designed to aid you in using the book. While the primary focus of *AHA Guide* is on hospitals, it also contains information on other areas of the health care field, divided across its two major sections:

A.  Hospitals
B.  Health care systems, networks, and alliances

The information contained within this publication was compiled using AHA membership, and the AHA Annual Survey of Hospitals. *AHA Guide* is the leading hospital directory and represents hospitals with or without AHA membership.

Additional information contained in the front of AHA Guide includes:

* A section by section table of contents
* Recognition of the source of data in the *Acknowledgements and Advisements* section
* Information on AHA's history as well as a listing of our awards in *AHA Offices, Officers, Historical Data, and Awards*

**2016
AHA Guide
Code Chart**

**Sample Hospital Listing:**

## Getting Started: The AHA Guide Code Chart

Open the front cover and *AHA Guide* begins with the *2016 AHA Guide Code Chart*. This two page section (front and back) explains how to find and understand the most important elements of each hospital's listing. The chart is specially perforated and is meant to be extracted and used alongside Section A as a resource. The information found on these pages is repeated in the first section, so don't worry about removing the chart.

The *Code Chart* is a very useful tool to have when reading. It allows new users to become familiar with the data, and it aids returning users in understanding the new design and layout of *AHA Guide*. At the top of the chart, there is a sample listing. If you have used this publication before, you will notice the new columnar listing of all hospital entries by city. The city and county names are highlighted in gray, and all hospitals within the city follow. After the hospital name, you will find the address, telephone number, approval, facility and service codes, and health care systems to which the hospital belongs. Following this are the chief administrators and classifications for the hospital. Utilization data for the hospital is found in the box at the bottom of each hospital's entry in *AHA Guide*.

The chart further demonstrates how to understand these important elements:

1. **Approval codes** refer to certifications held by a hospital; they represent information supplied by various national approving and reporting bodies. For example, code A–3 indicates accreditation under one of the programs of the Accreditation Council for Graduate Medical Education, evidence that the hospital has been approved for participation in residency training.
2. **Physician codes** represent the different types of arrangements the hospital participates in with its physicians. In this section, code P-1 signifies a closed physician-hospital organization.
3. **Health Care System names** reference specific health care system headquarters to which the hospital belongs. The presence of a system name indicates that the hospital is a member. If no names are listed, the hospital does not belong to a system.
4. **Titles of Chief Administrators** including the Chief Executive Officer and, when available, other C-Suite officers such as the Chief Financial Officer, Chief Information Officer, Chief Medical Officer, Chief Operating Officer, Chief Human Resources Officer, and Chief Nursing Officer.
5. **Classification** refers to two items in *AHA Guide*. **Control** classification indicates the

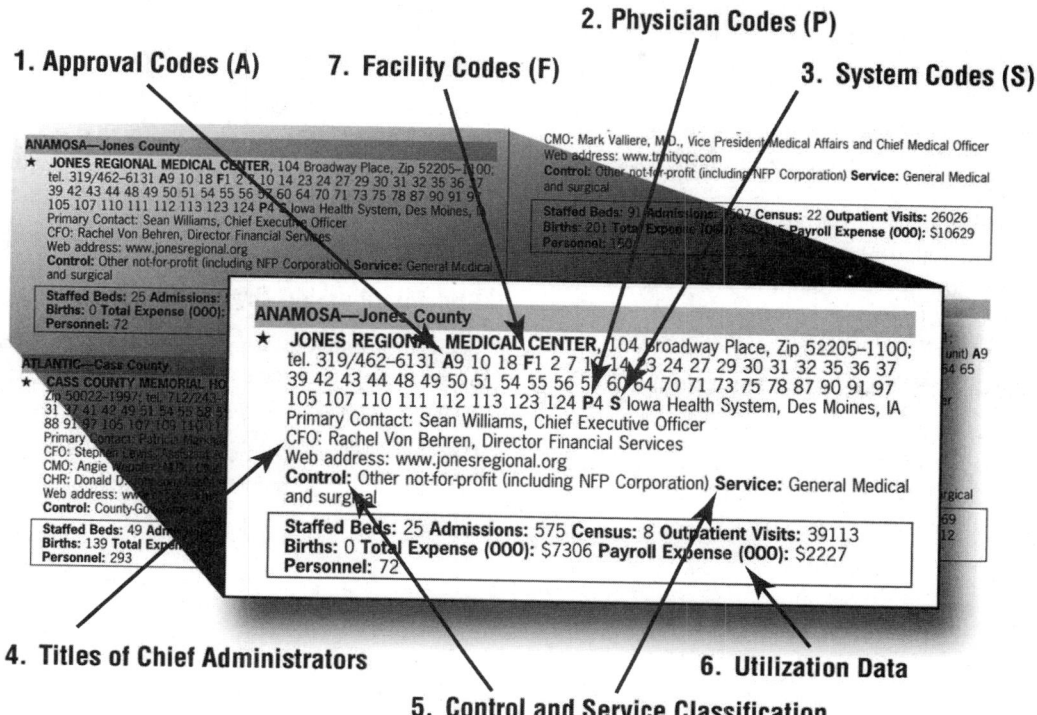

**1. Approval Codes (A)**

**7. Facility Codes (F)**

**2. Physician Codes (P)**

**3. System Codes (S)**

**4. Titles of Chief Administrators**

**5. Control and Service Classification**

**6. Utilization Data**

organization that operates the hospital, and **Service** classification refers to the type of service the hospital offers. Previously, this section utilized numerical codes corresponding with a literal value, but the new design of *AHA Guide* bypasses the codes and instead displays the literal classifications for control and service.

- **Control:** In this section, organizations are divided among nonfederal government hospitals, nongovernment not-for-profit hospitals, investor owned for-profit hospitals, and federal government hospitals.
- **Service:** This section displays the primary type of service that a hospital offers. The most common value is general hospital. Among the other services listed in this section are specialties such as psychiatric hospitals or children's hospitals.

6. **Utilization Data** contains the statistics related to the day-to-day and cumulative operation of the hospital. The information included in this section consists of:
- **Beds:** Number of beds regularly maintained.
- **Admissions:** Amount of patients accepted for inpatient services over a 12-month period.

- **Census:** Average number of patients receiving care each day.
- **Outpatient Visits:** Amount of visits by patients not lodged in the hospital while receiving care.
- **Births:** Number of infants born in the hospital and accepted for service in a newborn infant bassinet.
- **Expense:** Includes all expenses (including payroll) that the hospital had over the 12-month period.
- **Personnel:** Represents personnel situations as they existed at the end of the reporting period. In this area, full time equivalency is calculated on the basis that two part-time persons equal one full-time person.

7. **Facility codes** provide a description of the specific services offered by a hospital. Code F-14, for instance, indicates that the hospital contains a Blood Donor Center.

## How To Use This Book

Section A begins with the *AHA Guide Hospital Listing Requirements.* This explains the requisite accreditations or characteristics a hospital must meet to be included in *AHA Guide.*

After this there is *An Explanation of the Hospital Listings*. These two pages review the information included in the Code Chart and are a vital resource in identifying the information, symbols, and codes for each hospital's listing.

Next up are the *Annual Survey* definitions, which go into even greater detail in explaining the facility and physician codes. Please note that these are arranged alphabetically and numerically to correspond with the code chart. Also included here are the definitions of the terms for Control and Service found in the Classification section. The listings of *Hospitals in the United States, by State* follow the definitions.

## Finding Hospitals & Health Care Professionals in Section A

There are two ways to locate hospitals in the print version of *AHA Guide*. One is by the hospital's geographic classification. In Section A, hospitals are arranged alphabetically by state and then by city. The second method is through the *Hospital Index* that appears directly after the listings.

There is also an *Index of Health Care Professionals* which begins after the first index that lists key people from hospitals and health systems. Look for fold out tabs and tabs on the sides of pages that mark the indices.

## AHA Membership Organizations

Section A ends with a description of the AHA Membership categories along with a listing of various AHA Membership organizations.

For more information on Systems, Networks, and Alliances, please read the introduction to Section B.

# AHA Offices, Officers, and Historical Data

**Chicago:** 155 N. Wacker Drive, Chicago, IL 60606; tel. 312/422–3000

**Washington:** 800 10th Street, N.W., Two CityCenter, Suite 400, Washington, DC 20001; tel. 202/638–1100

**Chairman of the Board of Trustees:** James H. Skogsbergh, Advocate Health Care, 3075 Highland Parkway, Suite 600, Downers Grove, IL 60515
**Chairman–Elect of the Board of Trustees:** Eugene A. Woods, CHRISTUS Health, 919 Hidden Ridge, Irving, TX 75038

**Immediate Past Chairman of the Board of Trustees:** Jonathan B. Perlin, MD, HCA, One Park Plaza, 1–4W, Nashville, TN 37203
**President & CEO:** Richard J. Pollack , 800 10th Street, NW, Two CityCenter, Suite 400, Washington, DC 20001

**Senior Vice President and Secretary:** Gail Lovinger Goldblatt, 155 N. Wacker Drive, Chicago, IL 60606
**Senior Vice President and Treasurer:** John Evans, 155 N. Wacker Drive, Chicago, IL 60606

## Past Presidents/Chairs†

| | | | | | |
|---|---|---|---|---|---|
| 1899 | ★James S. Knowles | 1939 | ★G. Harvey Agnew, M.D. | 1979 | W. Daniel Barker |
| 1900 | ★James S. Knowles | 1940 | ★Fred G. Carter, M.D. | 1980 | ★Sister Irene Kraus |
| 1901 | ★Charles S. Howell | 1941 | ★B. W. Black, M.D. | 1981 | ★Bernard J. Lachner |
| 1902 | ★J. T. Duryea | 1942 | ★Basil C. MacLean, M.D. | 1982 | ★Stanley R. Nelson |
| 1903 | ★John Fehrenbatch | 1943 | ★James A. Hamilton | 1983 | Elbert E. Gilbertson |
| 1904 | ★Daniel D. Test | 1944 | ★Frank J. Walter | 1984 | Thomas R. Matherlee |
| 1905 | ★George H. M. Rowe, M.D. | 1945 | ★Donald C. Smelzer, M.D. | 1985 | ★Jack A. Skarupa |
| 1906 | ★George P. Ludlam | 1946 | ★Peter D. Ward, M.D. | 1986 | Scott S. Parker |
| 1907 | ★Renwick R. Ross, M.D. | 1947 | ★John H. Hayes | 1987 | Donald C. Wegmiller |
| 1908 | ★Sigismund S. Goldwater, M.D. | 1948 | ★Graham L. Davis | 1988 | Eugene W. Arnett |
| 1909 | ★John M. Peters, M.D. | 1949 | ★Joseph G. Norby | 1989 | Edward J. Connors |
| 1910 | ★H. B. Howard, M.D. | 1950 | ★John N. Hatfield | 1990 | David A. Reed |
| 1911 | ★W. L. Babcock, M.D. | 1951 | ★Charles F. Wilinsky, M.D. | 1991 | C. Thomas Smith |
| 1912 | ★Henry M. Hurd, M.D. | 1952 | ★Anthony J. J. Rourke, M.D. | 1992 | D. Kirk Oglesby, Jr. |
| 1913 | ★F. A. Washburn, M.D. | 1953 | ★Edwin L. Crosby, M.D. | 1993 | Larry L. Mathis |
| 1914 | ★Thomas Howell, M.D. | 1954 | ★Ritz E. Heerman | 1994 | Carolyn C. Roberts |
| 1915 | ★William O. Mann, M.D. | 1955 | ★Frank R. Bradley | 1995 | Gail L. Warden |
| 1916 | ★Winford H. Smith, M.D. | 1956 | ★Ray E. Brown | 1996 | Gordon M. Sprenger |
| 1917 | ★Robert J. Wilson, M.D. | 1957 | ★Albert W. Snoke, M.D. | 1997 | Reginald M. Ballantyne III |
| 1918 | ★A. B. Ancker, M.D. | 1958 | ★Tol Terrell | 1998 | John G. King |
| 1919 | ★A. R. Warner, M.D. | 1959 | ★Ray Amberg | 1999 | Fred L. Brown |
| 1920 | ★Joseph B. Howland, M.D. | 1960 | ★Russell A. Nelson, M.D. | 2000 | ★Carolyn Boone Lewis |
| 1921 | ★Louis B. Baldwin, M.D. | 1961 | ★Frank S. Groner | 2001 | Gary A. Mecklenburg |
| 1922 | ★George O'Hanlon, M.D. | 1962 | ★Jack Masur, M.D. | 2002 | Sr. Mary Roch Rocklage, RSM |
| 1923 | ★Asa S. Bacon | 1963 | ★T. Stewart Hamilton, M.D. | 2003 | Dennis R. Barry |
| 1924 | ★Malcolm T. MacEachern, M.D. | 1964 | ★Stanley A. Ferguson | 2004 | David L. Bernd |
| 1925 | ★E. S. Gilmore | 1965 | ★Clarence E. Wonnacott | 2005 | George F. Lynn |
| 1926 | ★Arthur C. Bachmeyer, M.D. | 1966 | ★Philip D. Bonnet, M.D. | **January–April 2006** | Richard J. Umbdenstock |
| 1927 | ★R. G. Brodrick, M.D. | 1967 | ★George E. Cartmill | **April–December 2006** | George F. Lynn |
| 1928 | ★Joseph C. Doane, M.D. | 1968 | ★David B. Wilson, M.D. | 2007 | Kevin E. Lofton |
| 1929 | ★Louis H. Burlingham, M.D. | 1969 | ★George William Graham, M.D. | 2008 | William D. Petasnick |
| 1930 | ★Christopher G. Parnall, M.D. | 1970 | ★Mark Berke | 2009 | Thomas M. Priselac |
| 1931 | ★Lewis A. Sexton, M.D. | 1971 | ★Jack A. L. Hahn | 2010 | Richard P. de Filippi |
| 1932 | ★Paul H. Fesler | 1972 | ★Stephen M. Morris | 2011 | John W. Bluford |
| 1933 | ★George F. Stephens, M.D. | 1973 | ★John W. Kauffman | 2012 | Teri G. Fontenot |
| 1934 | ★Nathaniel W. Faxon, M.D. | 1974 | ★Horace M. Cardwell | 2013 | Benjamin K. Chu, MD |
| 1935 | ★Robert Jolly | 1975 | Wade Mountz | 2014 | James H. Hinton |
| 1936 | ★Robin C. Buerki, M.D. | 1976 | H. Robert Cathcart | 2015 | Jonathan B. Perlin, MD, PhD |
| 1937 | ★Claude W. Munger, M.D. | 1977 | ★John M. Stagl | | |
| 1938 | ★Robert E. Neff | 1978 | ★Samuel J. Tibbitts | | |

## Chief Executive Officers

| | | | | | |
|---|---|---|---|---|---|
| 1917–18 | ★William H. Walsh, M.D. | 1954–72 | ★Edwin L. Crosby, M.D. | 1991–2007 | Richard J. Davidson |
| 1919–24 | ★Andrew Robert Warner, M.D. | 1972 | Madison B. Brown, M.D. (acting) | 2007–2015 | Richard J. Umbdenstock |
| 1925–27 | ★William H. Walsh, M.D. | 1972–86 | J. Alexander McMahon | 2015 | Richard J. Pollack (current) |
| 1928–42 | ★Bert W. Caldwell, M.D. | 1986–91 | Carol M. McCarthy, Ph.D., J.D. | | |
| 1943–54 | ★George Bugbee | 1991 | Jack W. Owen (acting) | | |

## Distinguished Service Award

The award recognizes significant lifetime contributions and service to health care institutions and associations.

| | | | | | |
|---|---|---|---|---|---|
| 1934 | Matthew O. Foley | 1965 | Albert W. Snoke, M.D. | 1992 | David H. Hitt |
| 1939 | Malcolm T. MacEachern, M.D. | 1966 | Frank S. Groner | 1993 | Edward J. Connors |
| 1940 | Sigismund S. Goldwater, M.D. | 1967 | Rev. John J. Flanagan, S.J. | | Jack W. Owen |
| 1941 | Frederic A. Washburn, M.D. | 1968 | Stanley W. Martin | 1994 | George Adams |
| 1942 | Winford H. Smith, M.D. | 1969 | T. Stewart Hamilton, M.D. | 1995 | Scott S. Parker |
| 1943 | Arthur C. Bachmeyer, M.D. | 1970 | Charles Patteson Cardwell, Jr. | 1996 | John A. Russell |
| 1944 | Rt. Rev. Msgr. Maurice F. Griffin, LL.D. | 1971 | Mark Berke | 1997 | D. Kirk Oglesby, Jr. |
| 1945 | Asa S. Bacon | 1972 | Stanley A. Ferguson | 1998 | Henry B. Betts, M.D. |
| 1946 | George F. Stephens, M.D. | 1973 | Jack A. L. Hahn | 1999 | Mitchell T. Rabkin, M.D. |
| 1947 | Robin C. Buerki, M.D. | 1974 | George William Graham, M.D. | 2000 | Gail L. Warden |
| 1948 | James A. Hamilton | 1975 | George E. Cartmill | 2001 | Gordon M. Sprenger |
| 1949 | Claude W. Munger, M.D. | 1976 | D. O. McClusky, Jr. | 2002 | Carolyn Boone Lewis |
| 1950 | Nathaniel W. Faxon, M.D. | 1977 | Boone Powell | 2003 | C. Thomas Smith |
| 1951 | Bert W. Caldwell, M.D. | 1978 | Richard J. Stull | 2004 | Michael C. Waters |
| 1952 | Fred G. Carter, M.D. | 1979 | Horace M. Cardwell | 2005 | John G. King |
| 1953 | Basil C. MacLean, M.D. | 1980 | Donald W. Cordes | 2006 | Gary A. Mecklenburg |
| 1954 | George Bugbee | 1981 | Sister Mary Brigh Cassidy | | Sr. Mary Roch Rocklage, RSM |
| 1955 | Joseph G. Norby | 1982 | R. Zach Thomas, Jr. | 2007 | Richard J. Davidson |
| 1956 | Charles F. Wilinsky, M.D. | 1983 | H. Robert Cathcart | 2008 | Fred L. Brown |
| 1957 | John H. Hayes | 1984 | Matthew F. McNulty, Jr., Sc.D. | 2009 | George F. Lynn |
| 1958 | John N. Hatfield | 1985 | J. Alexander McMahon | 2010 | James J. Mongan, M.D. |
| 1959 | Edwin L. Crosby, M.D. | 1986 | Sister Irene Kraus | 2011 | Thomas C. Royer, M.D. |
| 1960 | Oliver G. Pratt | 1987 | W. Daniel Barker | 2012 | Karen Davis, Ph.D. |
| 1961 | E. M. Bluestone, M.D. | 1988 | Elbert E. Gilbertson | 2013 | Thomas C. Dolan, Ph.D., FACHE |
| 1962 | Mother Loretto Bernard, S.C., R.N. | 1989 | Donald G. Shropshire | 2014 | Thomas M. Priselac |
| 1963 | Ray E. Brown | 1990 | John W. Colloton | 2015 | Richard P. de Filippi |
| 1964 | Russell A. Nelson, M.D. | 1991 | Carol M. McCarthy, Ph.D., J.D. | | |

★Deceased

†On June 3, 1972, the House of Delegates changed the title of the chief elected officer to chairman of the Board of Trustees, and the title of president was conferred on the chief executive officer of the Association.

# Award of Honor

Awarded to individuals, organizations, or groups to recognize an exemplary contribution to the health and well being of the people through leadership on a major health policy or social initiative.

| | | | | | |
|---|---|---|---|---|---|
| 1966 | Senator Lister Hill | 1997 | Paul B. Batalden, M.D. | | Stanley F. Hupfeld |
| 1967 | Emory W. Morris, D.D.S. | | Habitat for Humanity International | 2008 | Regina M. Benjamin, MD, MBA |
| 1971 | Special Committee on Provision of Health | 1998 | John E. Curley, Jr. | | Alfred G. Stubblefield |
| | Services (staff also) | | National Civic League | 2009 | The Center to Advance Palliative Care |
| 1982 | Walter J. McNemey | 1999 | Joseph Cardinal Bernardin, Literacy Volunteers | | Paul B. Hofmann, Dr.PH |
| 1989 | Ruth M. Rothstein | | of America | 2010 | Jack Bovender |
| 1990 | Joyce C. Clifford, R.N. | 2000 | Institute for Safe Medication Practices | 2011 | Cary Medical Center, Caribou, ME |
| 1991 | Haynes Rice | 2001 | Dennis R. Barry | 2012 | Ronald McDonald House Charities |
| 1992 | Donald W. Dunn | 2002 | Donald M. Berwick, M.D. | | The Schwartz Center for Compassionate |
| | Ira M. Lane, Jr. | 2003 | Steven A. Schroeder, M.D. | | Healthcare |
| 1993 | Elliott C. Roberts, Sr. | | Dan S. Wilford | 2013 | George C. Halvorson |
| | William A. Spencer, M.D. | 2004 | Ron J. Anderson, M.D. | | Reach Out and Read |
| 1994 | Robert A. Derzon | | Johnson & Johnson | 2014 | Rhonda Anderson, RN |
| 1995 | Russell G. Mawby, Ph.D. | 2005 | Sr. Mary Jean Ryan | | Ohio Hospital Association |
| | John K. Springer | 2006 | Jordan J. Cohen, M.D. | 2015 | Spencer C. Johnson |
| 1996 | Stephen J. Hegarty | | James W. Varnum | | Robert Wood Johnson Foundation |
| | Mothers Against Drunk Driving (MADD) | 2007 | Edward A. Eckenhoff | | |

# Justin Ford Kimball Innovators Award

Recognition to individuals or organizations that have made outstanding, innovative contributions to health care financing and/or delivery that improves access or coordination of care.

| | | | | | |
|---|---|---|---|---|---|
| 1958 | E. A. van Steenwyk | 1974 | William H. Ford, Ph.D. | 1995 | E. George Middleton, Jr. |
| 1959 | George A. Newbury | 1975 | Earl H. Kammer | | Glenn R. Mitchell |
| 1960 | C. Rufus Rorem, Ph.D. | 1976 | J. Ed McConnell | 1997 | Harvey Pettry |
| 1961 | James E. Stuart | 1978 | Edwin R. Werner | | D. David Sniff |
| 1962 | Frank Van Dyk | 1979 | Robert M. Cunningham, Jr. | 1998 | Montana Health Research and Education |
| 1963 | William S. McNary | 1981 | Maurice J. Norby | | Foundation |
| 1964 | Frank S. Groner | 1982 | Robert E. Rinehimer | 1999 | Kenneth W. Kizer, M.D. |
| 1965 | J. Douglas Colman | 1983 | John B. Morgan, Jr. | 2002 | David M. Lawrence, M.D. |
| 1967 | Walter J. McNemey | 1984 | Joseph F. Duplinsky | 2003 | Lowell C. Kruse |
| 1968 | John W. Paynter | 1985 | David W. Stewart | 2006 | Spencer Foreman, M.D. |
| 1970 | Edwin L. Crosby, M.D. | 1988 | Ernest W. Saward, M.D. | 2009 | On Lok |
| 1971 | H. Charles Abbott | 1990 | James A. Vohs | 2012 | Thomas S. Nesbitt, M.D. |
| 1972 | John R. Mannix | 1993 | John C. Lewin, M.D. | 2015 | Glenn D. Steele, Jr., MD |
| 1973 | Herman M. Somers | 1994 | Donald A. Brennan | | |

# Board of Trustees Award

Individuals or groups who have made substantial and noteworthy contributions to the work of the American Hospital Association.

| | | | | | |
|---|---|---|---|---|---|
| 1959 | Joseph V. Friel | 1981 | Vernon A. Knutson | | Stephen Rogness |
| | John H. Hayes | | John E. Sullivan | 2000 | Dennis May |
| 1960 | Duncan D. Sutphen, Jr. | 1982 | John Bigelow | 2001 | Spencer C. Johnson |
| 1963 | Eleanor C. Lambertsen, R.N., Ed.D. | | Robert W. O'Leary | | Michael M. Mitchel |
| 1964 | John R. Mannix | | Jack W. Owen | 2002 | Victor L. Campbell |
| 1965 | Albert G. Hahn | 1984 | Howard J. Berman | | Joseph A. Parker |
| | Maurice J. Norby | | O. Ray Hurst | 2003 | J. Richard Gaintner, M.D. |
| 1966 | Madison B. Brown, M.D. | | James R. Neely | | Donald A. Wilson |
| | Kenneth Williamson | 1985 | James E. Ferguson | 2004 | Richard L. Clarke |
| 1967 | Alanson W. Wilcox | | Cleveland Rodgers | | Thelma Traut |
| 1968 | E. Dwight Barnett, M.D. | 1986 | Rex N. Olsen | 2005 | Merrill Gappmayer |
| 1969 | Vane M. Hoge, M.D. | 1987 | Michael Lesparre | | Leo Greenawalt |
| | Joseph H. McNinch, M.D. | 1988 | Barbara A. Donaho, R.N. | 2006 | Robert L. Harman |
| 1972 | David F. Drake, Ph.D. | 1989 | Walter H. MacDonald | | Kenneth G. Stella |
| | Paul W. Earle | | Donald R. Newkirk | 2007 | Deborah Freund, Ph.D. |
| | Michael Lesparre | 1990 | William T. Robinson | | Michael D. Stephens |
| | Andrew Pattullo | 1992 | Jack C. Bills | 2008 | James R. Castle |
| 1973 | Tilden Cummings | | Anne Hall Davis | 2009 | Richard M. Knapp, Ph.D. |
| | Edmond J. Lanigan | 1993 | Theodore C. Eickhoff, M.D. | 2010 | Fred Hessler |
| 1974 | James E. Hague | | Stephen W. Gamble | | John G. O'Brien |
| | Sister Marybelle | | Yoshi Honkawa | 2011 | Carolyn F. Scanlan |
| 1975 | Helen T. Yast | 1994 | Roger M. Busfield, Jr., Ph.D. | | Charlotte S. Yeh, MD |
| 1976 | Boynton P. Livingston | 1995 | Stephen E. Dorn | 2012 | Larry S. Gage |
| | James Ludlam | | William L. Yates | | Larry McAndrews |
| | Helen McGuire | 1996 | Leigh E. Morris | 2013 | Jeffrey D. Selberg |
| 1979 | Newton J. Jacobson | | John Quigley | 2014 | Russell D. Harrington, Jr. |
| | Edward W. Weimer | 1998 | John D. Leech | | Daniel Sisto |
| 1980 | Robert B. Hunter, M.D. | 1999 | Sister Carol Keehan | 2015 | Todd C. Linden |
| | Samuel J. Tibbitts | | C. Edward McCauley | | R. Timothy Rice |

# Citation for Meritorious Service

| | | | | | |
|---|---|---|---|---|---|
| 1968 | F. R. Knautz | | Gordon McLachlan | 1983 | David M. Kinzer |
| | Sister Conrad Mary, R.N. | 1977 | Theodore Cooper, M.D. | 1984 | Donald L. Custis, M.D. |
| 1971 | Hospital Council of Southern California | 1979 | Norman D. Burkett | 1985 | John A. D. Cooper, M.D. |
| 1972 | College of Misericordia, Dallas, PA | | John L. Quigley | | Imperial Council of the Ancient Arabic Order of |
| 1973 | Madison B. Brown, M.D. | | William M. Whelan | | the Nobles of the Mystic Shrine for North |
| | Samuel J. Tibbitts | 1980 | Sister Grace Marie Hiltz | | America |
| 1975 | Kenneth B. Babcock, M.D. | | Leo J. Gehrig, M.D. | 1986 | Howard F. Cook |
| | Sister Mary Maurita Sengelaube | 1981 | Richard Davi | 1987 | David H. Hitt |
| 1976 | Chaiker Abbis | | Pearl S. Fryar | | Lucile Packard |
| | Susan Jenkins | 1982 | Jorge Brull Nater | | |

This citation is no longer awarded

# AHA NOVA Awards

This award honors effective, collaborative programs focused on improving community health status.

## 1994

**Health Partners of Philadelphia (PA):** Albert Einstein Medical Center, Episcopal Hospital, Frankford Hospital, Medical College of Pennsylvania Hospital, St. Christopher's Hospital for Children, Temple University Hospital

**Decker Family Development Center:** Children's Hospital Medical Center of Akron (OH)
**Denver (CO) School–Based Clinics:** The Children's Hospital
**Basic Health Plan:** Dominican Network; Mount Carmel Hospital, Colville, WA; St. Joseph's

Hospital, Chewelah, WA; and Holy Family Hospital, Spokane, WA
**HealthLink:** Lakes Region General Hospital, Laconia, NH

## 1995

**Bladen Community Care Network:** Bladen County Hospital, Elizabethtown, NC
**Building a Healthier Community:** Community–Kimball Health Care System, Toms River, NJ

**Injury Prevention Program:** Harlem Hospital Center, New York City, NY
**The Community Ministries & Outreach Program:** Reaching Out to Our Vickery/Meadow

Neighborhood: Presbyterian Healthcare System, Dallas, TX
**"CHOICES":** Shriners Hospitals for Crippled Children, Tampa, FL

## 1996

**Lincoln and Sunnyslope:** John C. Lincoln Hospital and Health Center, Sunnyslope, AZ
**Growing into Life Task Force:** Aiken (SC) Regional Medical Centers

**People Caring for People:** Beatrice (NE) Community Hospital and Health Center
**Injury Prevention Center of the Greater Dayton (OH) Area:** The Children's Medical Center, Good

Samaritan Hospital and Health Center, Grandview Hospital, Kettering Memorial Hospital, Miami Valley Hospital, and St. Elizabeth Medical Center
**Family Road:** Hutzel Hospital, Detroit, MI

## 1997

**Health Promotion Schools of Excellence Program:** Alliant Health System and Kosair Children's Hospital, Louisville, KY
**Health, Outreach, Prevention, and Education (HOPE):** Health First Holmes Regional Medical Center, Melbourne, FL

**Healthy Community Initiative:** Roper Care Alliance, Charleston, SC
**Obstetrical Care and Prenatal Counseling Program:** St. Alexius Medical Center, Bismarck, ND
**HIV/AIDS Neighborhood Service Program:** Yale–New Haven Hospital, New Haven, CT

## 1998

**Partners for a Healthier Community:** Evergreen Community Health Care, Group Health Cooperative of Puget Sound, Overlake Hospital Medical Center, Providence Health System/Medalia HealthCare, Seattle, WA
**Glenwood–Lyndale Community Clinic:** Hennepin County Medical Center, Minneapolis, MN

**Greater Dallas (TX) Injury Prevention Center:** Parkland Health & Hospital System, Children's Medical Center of Dallas, Baylor Health Care System, Methodist Hospitals of Dallas, and Presbyterian Healthcare System
**Network of Trust:** Phoebe Putney Memorial Hospital, Albany, GA

**The Lauderdale Court:** A Community Partnership: St. Joseph Hospital and Health Centers, Memphis, TN

## 1999

**Making a Case for Community Health:** Middletown (OH) Regional Hospital
**The Family Resource Center:** Mount Carmel Medical Center, Pittsburg, KS

**The Health Neighborhood Project:** St. Patrick Hospital, Missoula, MT
**Kids for Health:** Washington Regional Medical Center, Fayetteville, AR

**Children's Village:** Yakima Memorial Hospital, Yakima, WA

## 2000

**Community Healthcare Network:** Columbus (GA) Regional Healthcare System
**Pasadena County Asthma Project:** Huntington Memorial Hospital, Pasadena, CA

**Ashe County Health Council "Health Carolinias Task Force":** Ashe Memorial Hospital, Jefferson, NC
**Caritas–Connection Project:** St. Mary's Hospital, Passaic, NJ

**Correctional Health Care Program:** Baystate Health System, Springfield, MA

## 2001

**J.C. Lewis Health Center:** Memorial Health and St. Joseph's Candler Health System, Savannah, GA
**Project C.A.R.E.:** Mercy Medical Center, Canton, OH

**TeenHealthFX.com:** Atlantic Health System, Florham Park, NJ

**Vista ElderCARE:** Vista Health, Waukegan, IL

**Western Village Enterprise School:** INTEGRIS Health, Oklahoma City, OK

## 2002

**Chester Community Connections:** Crozer–Keystone Health System, Springfield, PA
**The Hope Street Family Center:** California Hospital Medical Center, Los Angeles, CA
**Mobile Health Outreach Ministry:** St. Vincent's Health System, Jacksonville, FL

**Operation Access:** Kaiser Foundation Hospitals, Oakland; Sutter Health, Sacramento; San Francisco General Hospital, San Francisco; St. Rose Hospital, Hayward; and Santa Rosa Memorial Hospital, Santa Rosa, CA

**Wilmington Health Access for Teens:** New Hanover Health Network, Wilmington, NC

## 2003

**C.O.A.C.H. for Kids:** Cedars–Sinai Medical Center, Los Angeles, CA
**Community Action Network:** Trinity Regional Medical Center, Fort Dodge, IA

**Hearts N' Health:** Glendale Adventist Medical Center, Glendale, CA
**Saint Joseph Health Center:** Saint Joseph Regional Medical Center, South Bend, IN

**St. Mary Medical Center Bensalem Ministries:** St. Mary Medical Center, Langhorne, PA

## 2004

**Better Beginnings:** Brockton Hospital, Brockton, MA
**Buffalo County Community Health Partners:** Good Samaritan Health Systems, Kearney, NE

**Quad City Health Initiative:** Genesis Health System, Davenport, IA and Trinity Regional Health System, Rock Island, IL
**Quality of Life in the Truckee Meadows:** Washoe Health System, Reno, NV

**Solano Coalition for Better Health, Inc.:** NorthBay Healthcare Group, Fairfield, CA; Sutter Solano Medical Center, Vallejo, CA; and Kaiser Permanente, Martinez, CA

## 2005

**Children's Health Connection:** McKay-Dee Hospital Center, Ogden, UT
**Palmetto Health's Vision Health Initiative:** Palmetto Health, Columbia, SC

**Project Dulce, Whittier Institute for Diabetes:** Scripps Health, San Diego, CA
**Toledo/Lucas County CareNet:** Mercy Health Partners, ProMedica Health System, and Medical

University of Ohio, all of Toledo, OH and St. Luke's Hospital, Maumee, OH
**Volunteer Health Advisor (VHA) Program:** Cambridge Health Alliance, Cambridge, MA

**2006**

**Healthy Learners, Columbia, SC:** Allendale County Hospital, Fairfax, SC; McLeod Medical Center–Dillon, Dillon, SC; Sisters of Charity Providence Hospitals, Columbia, SC; and Self Regional Healthcare, Greenwood, SC

**Primary Care Access Network (PCAN):** Health Central, Ocoee, FL; Florida Hospital, Winter Park, FL; and Orlando Regional Healthcare, Orlando, FL
**ProHealth Care Community Health Outreach Initiative:** ProHealth Care, Waukesha, WI

**St. Joseph Mobile Health Services:** Saint Joseph HealthCare Inc., Lexington, KY
**Yonkers Childhood Health Initiative:** St. John's Riverside, Yonkers, NY

**2007**

**Medical-Legal Partnership for Children:** Boston Medical Center, Boston, MA
**NOW (Nutritional Options for Wellness) Program:** Spectrum Health, Grand Rapids, MI

**Richland Care:** Palmetto Health, Columbia, SC
**Trauma Nurses Talk Tough:** Legacy Health System, Portland, OR

**UMass Memorial Medical Center Healthy Youth Development Initiative:** UMass Memorial Health Care, Worcester, MA
**Youth Health Partnership-Patee Market Youth Dental Clinic:** Heartland Health, St. Joseph, MO

**2008**

**Partnership for Community Health:** California Pacific Medical Center, San Francisco, CA
**Every Child Succeeds:** Cincinnati Children's Hospital Medical Center, Cincinnati, OH

**Memorial Hermann Health Centers for Schools:** Memorial Hermann, Houston, TX
**Nutrition Center of Maine:** Saint Mary's Health System, Lewiston, ME

***ENERGIZE!* Pediatric Diabetes Intervention Program:** WakeMed Health & Hospitals, Raleigh, NC

**2009**

**Lighten Up 4 Life:** Mission Health System, Asheville, NC
**Project BRIEF:** Jacobi Medical Center and North Central Bronx Hospital, Bronx, NY

**Really Awesome Health (RAH) and Wholesome Routines:** Duke Raleigh Hospital, Raleigh, NC
**Student Success Jobs Program:** Brigham and Women's Hospital, Boston, MA

**Taos First Steps Program:** Holy Cross Hospital, Taos, NM

**2010**

**Community-Based Alternatives to the Emergency Room:** Lee Memorial Health System, Fort Meyers, FL
**Health-e-Access Telemedicine:** University of Rochester Medical Center, Rochester, NY

**Healthy Futures:** Munson Healthcare System, Traverse City, MI
**Healthy San Francisco:** San Francisco General Hospital, University of California Medical Center, Chinese Hospital, California Pacific Medical Center,

Saint Francis Memorial Hospital, St. Mary's Medical Center, and Kaiser Permanente, San Francisco, CA
**Pediatric Asthma Program:** Sinai Health System, Chicago, IL

**2011**

**Emergency Department Consistent Care Program:** Providence St. Peter Hospital, Olympia, WA
**Integrated Community Nursing Program at Parkview Health:** Parkview Health, Fort Wayne, IN

**Milwaukee Health Care Partnership:** Aurora Health Care, Children's Hospital & Health System, Inc., Columbia St. Mary's, and Froedtert Health, all of Milwaukee, WI, and Wheaton Franciscan Healthcare, Glendale, WI

**The Diabetes Collaborative:** Northwestern Memorial Hospital, Chicago, IL
**Rochester Youth Violence Partnership:** University of Rochester Medical Center and Rochester General Health System, Rochester, NY

**2012**

**The Beth Embraces Wellness: An Integrated Approach to Prevention in the Community:** Newark Beth Israel Medical Center and Children's Hospital of New Jersey, Newark, NJ

**CARE Network:** St. Joseph Health Queen of the Valley Medical Center, Napa, CA
**Fitness in the City:** Boston Children's Hospital, Boston, MA

**Puff City:** Henry Ford Health System, Detroit, MI
**Rural Health Initiative:** Shawano Medical Center of ThedaCare, Shawano, WI

**2013**

**Bangor Beacon Community:** EMHS, Brewer, ME and St. Joseph Healthcare, Bangor, ME
**Chippewa Health Improvement Partnership (CHIP):** St. Joseph's Hospital, Chippewa Falls, WI

**Core Health Program of Healthier Communities:** Spectrum Health, Grand Rapids, MI
**Free Preventive Screenings Program:** Good Samaritan Hospital, Vincennes, IN

**Hope Clinic and Pharmacy:** Ephraim McDowell Health, Danville, KY

**2014**

**FirstReach:** FirstHealth of the Carolinas, Pinehurst, NC
**Children's Hospital Center for Pediatric Medicine Asthma Action Team:** Greenville Health System, Greenville, SC

**Let's Go!:** The Barbara Bush Children's Hospital at Maine Medical Center, Portland, ME
**Hearts Beat Back:** The Heart of New Ulm (HONU) Project: New Ulm Medical Center, part of Allina Health, New Ulm, MN

**Finney County Community Health Coalition:** St. Catherine Hospital, Garden City, KS

**2015**

**Activate Whittier:** PIH Health, Whittier, Calif. and Kaiser Permanente Downey Medical Center, Downey, CA
**Bithlo Transformation Effort:** Florida Hospital, Orlando, FL

**Blood Pressure Advocate Program:** University of Rochester Medical Center, Rochester, NY
**Community Health:** Healthy Eating: Presbyterian Healthcare Services, Albuquerque, NM

**Mayor's Healthy City Initiative (Healthy BR):** Baton Rouge General Medical Center, Ochsner Medical Center-Baton Rouge, Our Lady of the Lake Regional Medical Center and Woman's Hospital, Baton Rouge, LA

# The Carolyn Boone Lewis Living the Vision Award

Organizations and individuals living AHA's vision of a society of healthy communities where all individuals reach their highest potential for health.

| | | | | | |
|---|---|---|---|---|---|
| **1998** | Memorial Healthcare System, Hollywood, FL Baptist Health System, Montgomery, AL | **2003** | Franklin Memorial Hospital, Farmington, ME | **2013** | St. Joseph's Hospital Health Center, Syracuse, NY |
| **1999** | Robert A. DeVries, Battle Creek, MI Memorial Health System, South Bend, IN | **2004** | Jamaica Hospital Medical Center, Jamaica, New York | | Cheshire Medical Center/Dartmouth–Hitchcock Keene, Keene, NH |
| **2000** | Rockingham Memorial Hospital, Harrisonburg, VA | **2005** | Fairbanks Memorial Hospital, Fairbanks, AK Boston Medical Center, Boston, MA | **2014** | TPR Collaborative, Maryland |
| **2001** | Salina Regional Health Center, Salina, KS | **2010** | Lehigh Valley Health Network, Allentown, PA | | |
| **2002** | Health Improvement Collaborative of Greater Cincinnati, Cincinnati, OH | **2011** | Alaska Native Tribal Health Consortium, Anchorage, AK | | |

# Circle of Life Award

This award celebrates innovation in palliative and end-of-life care.

**2000**

| | | |
|---|---|---|
| Improving Care through the End of Life, Franciscan Health System, Gig Harbor, WA | The Hospice of The Florida Suncoast, Largo, FL | Louisiana State Penitentiary Hospice Program, Angola, LA |

**2001**

| | | |
|---|---|---|
| Department of Pain Medicine and Palliative Care, Beth Israel Medical Center, New York, NY | Palliative CareCenter & Hospice of the North Shore, Evanston , IL | St. Joseph's Manor, Trumbull, CT |

**2002**

| | | |
|---|---|---|
| Children's Program of San Diego Hospice and Children's Hospital and Health Center of San Diego, San Diego, CA | Hospice of the Bluegrass, Lexington, KY<br>Project Safe Conduct, Hospice of the Western Reserve and Ireland Cancer Center, Cleveland, OH | **Special Circle of Life Award** Population–based Palliative Care Research Network (PoPCRN), Denver, CO |

**2003**

| | | |
|---|---|---|
| Hospice & Palliative CareCenter, Winston–Salem, NC | Providence Health System, Portland, OR | University of California Davis Health System, Sacramento, CA |

**2004**

| | | |
|---|---|---|
| Hope Hospice and Palliative Care, Fort Myers, FL | St. Mary's Healthcare System for Children, Bayside, NY | University of Texas M.D. Anderson Cancer Center Palliative Care, Houston, TX |

**2005**

| | | |
|---|---|---|
| High Point Regional Health System, High Point, NC | Palliative and End-of-life Care Program, Hoag Memorial Hospital Presbyterian, Newport Beach, CA | Thomas Palliative Care Unit, VCU Massey Cancer Center, Richmond, VA |

**2006**

| | | |
|---|---|---|
| Continuum Hospice Care, New York, NY | Mercy Supportive Care, St. Joseph Mercy Oakland, Pontiac, MI | Transitions and Life Choices, Fairview Health Services, Minneapolis, MN |

**2007**

| | | |
|---|---|---|
| UCSF Palliative Care Program, San Francisco, CA | Covenant Hospice, Pensacola, FL | Woodwell: A Program of Presbyterian SeniorCare and Family Hospice and Palliative Care, Oakmont, PA |

**2008**

| | | |
|---|---|---|
| Children's Hospitals and Clinics of Minnesota, Pain and Palliative Care Program, Minneapolis, MN | Haven Hospice, Gainesville, FL | The Pediatric Advanced Care Team, The Children's Hospital of Philadelphia, Philadelphia, PA |

**2009**

| | | |
|---|---|---|
| Four Seasons, Flat Rock, NC | Oregon Health and Science University Palliative Medicine & Comfort Care Program, Portland, OR | Wishard Health Services Palliative Care Program, Indianapolis, IN |

**2010**

| | | |
|---|---|---|
| Department of Veteran Affairs, VA New York/New Jersey Healthcare Network, Brooklyn, NY | Kansas City Hospice & Palliative Care, Kansas City, MO | Snohomish Palliative Partnership, Everett, WA |

**2011**

| | | |
|---|---|---|
| The Center for Hospice & Palliative Care, Cheektowaga, NY | Gilchrist Hospice Care, Hunt Valley, MD | St. John Providence Health System, Detroit, MI |

**2012**

| | | |
|---|---|---|
| Haslinger Family Pediatric Palliative Care Center, Akron Children's Hospital, Akron, OH | Calvary Hospital, Bronx, NY | Sharp HealthCare, San Diego, CA |

**2013**

| | | |
|---|---|---|
| The Denver Hospice and Optio Health Services, Denver, CO | Hertzberg Palliative Care Institute at the Mount Sinai Medical Center, New York, NY | UnityPoint Health, Iowa and Illinois |

**2014**

| | | |
|---|---|---|
| OACIS/Palliative Medicine, Lehigh Valley Health Network, Allentown, PA | Supportive & Palliative Care, Baylor Health Care System, Dallas, TX | Yakima Valley Memorial Hospital, Yakima, WA |

**2015**

Care Dimensions, Danvers, MA

# The American Hospital Association–McKesson Quest for Quality Prize

Honoring Leadership and Innovation in Patient Care Quality, Safety, and Commitment

**2002**

| | | |
|---|---|---|
| Missouri Baptist Medical Center, St. Louis, MO | **Finalist:** Fairview Hospital, Greater, Barrington, MA | **Finalist:** Minnesota Children's Hospital and Clinics, Minneapolis, MN |

**2003**

| | | |
|---|---|---|
| Abington Memorial Hospital, Abington, PA | **Finalist:** Beaumont Hospitals, Royal Oak, MI | **Finalist:** University of Wisconsin Hospital and Clinics, Madison, WI |

**2004**

| | | |
|---|---|---|
| Sentara Norfolk General Hospital, Norfolk, VA | **Finalist:** The Johns Hopkins Hospital, Baltimore, MD | **Finalist:** Mary Lanning Memorial Hospital, Hastings, NE |

**2005**

| | | |
|---|---|---|
| North Mississippi Medical Center, Tupelo, MS | **Finalist:** El Camino Hospital, Mountain View, CA | **Finalist:** NewYork-Presbyterian Hospital, New York, NY |

**2006**

Cincinnati Children's Hospital Medical Center, Cincinnati, OH

**2007**
Columbus Regional Hospital, Columbus, IN

**Finalist:** Cedars-Sinai Medical Center, Los Angeles, CA

**Finalist:** INTEGRIS Baptist Medical Center, Oklahoma City, OK

---

**2008**
Munson Medical Center, Traverse City, MI

**Finalist:** University of Michigan Hospitals & Health Centers, Ann Arbor, MI

---

**2009**
Bronson Methodist Hospital, Kalamazoo, MI

**Finalist:** Beth Israel Deaconess Medical Center, Boston, MA

---

**2010**
McLeod Regional Medical Center, Florence, SC

**Finalist:** Henry Ford Hospital, Detroit, MI

---

**2011**
Memorial Regional Hospital, Hollywood, FL

**Finalist:** AtlantiCare Regional Medical Center, Atlantic City, NJ

**Finalist:** Northwestern Memorial Hospital, Chicago, IL

---

**2012**
University Hospitals Case Medical Center, Cleveland, OH

**Finalist:** Lincoln Medical and Mental Health Center, Bronx, NY

**Finalist:** University of North Carolina Hospitals, Chapel Hill, NC and Life Choices, Fairview Health Services, Minneapolis, MN

---

**2013**
Beth Israel Deaconess Medical Center, Boston, MA

**Finalist:** Franklin Woods Community Hospital, Johnson City, TN

---

**2014**
VCU Medical Center, Richmond, VA

Finalist: Carolinas Medical Center-Northeast, Concord, NC

---

**2015**
Children's Hospital Colorado in Aurora, CO

**Finalist** Duke University Hospital, Durham, NC

---

# Foster G. McGaw Prize

Honors health delivery organizations that have demonstrated exceptional commitment to community service.

| | | | | | |
|---|---|---|---|---|---|
| **1986** | Lutheran Medical Center, Brooklyn, NY | **1996** | St. Mary's Hospital, Rochester, NY | **2006** | Memorial Healthcare System, Hollywood, FL |
| **1987** | Copley Hospital, Morrisville, VT | **1997** | Bladen County Hospital Rural Health Network, | **2007** | Harborview Medical Center, Seattle, WA |
| | Mount Sinai Hospital, Hartford, CT | | Elizabethtown, NC | **2008** | St. Mary's Health System, Lewiston, ME |
| **1988** | MetroHealth System, Cleveland, OH | **1998** | Allina Health System, Minneapolis, MN | **2009** | Heartland Health, St. Joseph, MO |
| **1989** | Greater Southeast Healthcare System, Washington, DC | **1999** | LAC+USC Healthcare Network, Los Angeles, CA | **2010** | Allegiance Health, Jackson, MI |
| **1990** | Mount Zion Medical Center of The University of California-San Francisco, San Francisco, CA | **2000** | Kaweah Delta Health Care District, Visalia, CA | **2011** | Mt. Ascutney Hospital and Health Center, Windsor, VT |
| **1991** | Franklin Regional Hospital, Franklin, NH | **2001** | Memorial Hospital of South Bend, South Bend, IN | **2012** | St. Joseph's/Candler Health System, Savannah, GA |
| **1992** | Mount Sinai Hospital Medical Center of Chicago, Chicago, IL | **2002** | John C. Lincoln Health Network, Phoenix, AZ | **2013** | Crozer–Keystone Health System, Delaware County, PA |
| **1993** | The Cambridge Hospital, Cambridge, MA | **2003** | Phoebe Putney Memorial Hospital, Albany, GA | | |
| **1994** | Parkland Memorial Hospital, Dallas, TX | **2004** | Henry Ford Health System, Detroit, MI | **2014** | Palmetto Health, Columbia, SC |
| **1995** | Our Lady of Lourdes Medical Center, Camden, NJ | **2005** | Venice Family Clinic, Venice, CA | | |

---

# Dick Davidson Quality Milestone Award for Allied Association Leadership

The award recognizes state, regional or metropolitan hospital association leadership in improving health care quality.

| | | | | | |
|---|---|---|---|---|---|
| **2011** | Michigan Health & Hospital Association | **2013** | Florida Hospital Association | **2015** | Minnesota Hospital Association |
| | South Carolina Hospital Association | | Tennessee Hospital Association | | |
| **2012** | Iowa Hospital Association | **2014** | Connecticut Hospital Association | | |
| | Washington State Hospital Association | | Wisconsin Hospital Association | | |

---

# AHA Equity of Care Award

The award is presented to hospitals or care systems that are noteworthy leaders and examples to the field in the area of equitable care.

**2014** Massachusetts General Hospital, Boston, MA
**2015** Henry Ford Health System, Detroit, MI
Robert Wood Johnson University Hospital, New Brunswick, NJ

 **A**

# AHA Guide
# Hospital Listing Requirements

An institution may be listed by the American Hospital Association if it is accredited as a hospital by The Joint Commission, American Osteopathic Association, DNV Healthcare accredited, or Medicare certified as a provider of acute service under Title 18 of the Social Security Act. Membership in the American Hospital Association is not a prerequisite.

If none of the four conditions mentioned above are satisfied, an insitiution licensed as a hospital by the appropriate state agency may be registered by AHA as a hospital by meeting the following alernative requirements:

**Function:** The primary function of the institution is to provide patient services, diagnostic and therapeutic, for particular or general medical conditions.

1. The institution shall maintain at least six inpatient beds, which shall be continuously available for the care of patients who are nonrelated and who stay on the average in excess of 24 hours per admission.
2. The institution shall be constructed, equipped, and maintained to ensure the health and safety of patients and to provide uncrowded, sanitary facilities for the treatment of patients.
3. There shall be an identifiable governing authority legally and morally responsible for the conduct of the hospital.
4. There shall be a chief executive to whom the governing authority delegates the continuous responsibility for the operation of the hospital in accordance with established policy.
5. There shall be an organized medical staff of fully licensed physicians* that may include other licensed individuals permitted by law and by the hospital to provide patient care services independently in the hospital. The medical staff shall be accountable to the governing authority for maintaining proper standards of medical care, and it shall be governed by bylaws adopted by said staff and approved by the governing authority.
6. Each patient shall be admitted on the authority of a member of the medical staff who has been granted the privilege to admit patients to inpatient services in accordance with state law and criteria for standards of medical care established by the individual medical staff. Each patient's general medical condition is the responsibility of a qualified physician member of the medical staff. When nonphysician members of the medical staff are granted privileges to admit patients, provision is made for prompt medical evaluation of these patients by a qualified physician. Any graduate of a foreign medical school who is permitted to assume responsibilities for patient care shall possess a valid license to practice medicine, or shall be certified by the Educational Commission for Foreign Medical Graduates, or shall have qualified for and have successfully completed an academic year of supervised clinical training under the direction of a medical school approved by the Liaison Committee on GAT Medical Education.
7. Registered nurse supervision and other nursing services are continuous.
8. A current and complete medical record shall be maintained by the institution for each patient and shall be available for reference.
9. Pharmacy service shall be maintained in the institution and shall be supervised by a registered pharmacist.
10. The institution shall provide patients with food service that meets their nutritional and therapeutic requirements; special diets shall also be available.

---

\* Physician–Term used to describe an individual with an M.D. or D.O. degree who is fully licensed to practice medicine in all its phases.

‡ The completed records in general shall contain at least the following: the patient's identifying data and consent forms, medical history, record of physical examination, physicians' progress notes, operative notes, nurses' notes, routine x–ray and laboratory reports, doctors' orders, and final diagnosis.

# Types of Hospitals

In addition to meeting these 10 general requirements, hospitals are listed as one of four types of hospitals: general, special, rehabilitation and chronic disease, or psychiatric. The following definitions of function by type of hospital and special requirements are:

## General

The primary function of the institution is to provide patient services, diagnostic and therapeutic, for a variety of medical conditions. A general hospital also shall provide:

- diagnostic x–ray services with facilities and staff for a variety of procedures
- clinical laboratory service with facilities and staff for a variety of procedures and with anatomical pathology services regularly and conveniently available
- operating room service with facilities and staff.

## Special

The primary function of the institution is to provide diagnostic and treatment services for patients who have specified medical conditions, both surgical and nonsurgical. A special hospital also shall provide:

- such diagnostic and treatment services as may be determined by the Executive Committee of the Board of Trustees of the American Hospital Association to be appropriate for the specified medical conditions for which medical services are provided shall be maintained in the institution with suitable facilities and staff. If such conditions do not normally require diagnostic x–ray service, laboratory service, or operating room service, and if any such services are therefore not maintained in the institution, there shall be written arrangements to make them available to patients requiring them.
- clinical laboratory services capable of providing tissue diagnosis when offering pregancy termination services.

## Rehabilitation and Chronic Disease

The primary function of the institution is to provide diagnostic and treatment services to handicapped or disabled individuals requiring restorative and adjustive services. A rehabilitation and chronic disease hospital also shall provide:

- arrangements for diagnostic x–ray services, as required, on a regular and conveniently available basis
- arrangements for clinical laboratory service, as required on a regular and conveniently available basis
- arrangements for operating room service, as required, on a regular and conveniently available basis
- a physical therapy service with suitable facilities and staff in the institution
- an occupational therapy service with suitable facilities and staff in the institution

- arrangements for psychological and social work services on a regular and conveniently available basis
- arrangements for educational and vocational services on a regular and conveniently available basis
- written arrangements with a general hospital for the transfer of patients who require medical, obstetrical, or surgical services not available in the institution.

## Psychiatric

The primary function of the institution is to provide diagnostic and treatment services for patients who have psychiatric–related illnesses. A psychiatric hospital also shall provide:

- arrangements for clinical laboratory service, as required, on a regular and conveniently available basis
- arrangements for diagnostic x–ray services, as required on a regular and conveniently available basis
- psychiatric, psychological, and social work service with facilities and staff in the institution
- arrangements for electroencephalograph services, as required, on a regular and conveniently available basis.
- written arrangements with a general hospital for the transfer of patients who require medical, obstetrical, or surgical services not available in the institution.

The American Hospital Association may, at the sole discretion of the Executive Committee of the Board of Trustees, grant, deny, or withdraw the listing of an institution.

---

\* Physician–Term used to describe an individual with an M.D. or D.O. degree who is fully licensed to practice medicine in all its phases.

‡ The completed records in general shall contain at least the following: the patient's identifying data and consent forms, medical history, record of physical examination, physicians' progress notes, operative notes, nurses' notes, routine x–ray and laboratory reports, doctors' orders, and final diagnosis.

---

# Explanation
# of Hospital Listings

## Sample Hospital Listing:

**ANYTOWN, Universal County**

⊠ **ANYTOWN HOSPITAL & CLINICS (777777)**, (Formerly Anytown Area
Community Hospital and Clinic), 100 South Main Street, Zip 12345–6789;
tel. 123/456–7890 **A**9 10 ] ①
**F**10 12 23 24 29 30 31 37 39 49 51 55 57 64 65 66 68 70 71 72 77
78 83 87 88 91 96 97 106 107 110 111 113 124 **P**1 2 3 **S** Universal — ⑦
County Health System ② ③
Primary Contact: Ann M. Generic, Chief Executive Officer
COO: Ann M. Generic
CFO: Michael M. Generic ④
CMO: Peterl Van Generic, President Medical Staff
CHR: Jerry Generic, Human Resources Director
CNO: Danielle Generic, R.N., Chief Nursing Officer
Web address: www.website.org
**Control:** Other not–for–profit (including NFP Corporation) **Service:** General ] ⑤
Medical and Surgical

**Staffed Beds:** 25 **Admissions:** 892 **Census:** 9 **Outpatient Visits:** 44014
**Births:** 51 **Total Expense ($000):** 19210 **Payroll Expense ($000):** 5864 ⑥
**Personnel:** 182

**ANYTOWN, Universal County**

⊠ **ANYTOWN HOSPITAL & CLINICS (777777)**, (Formerly Anytown Area
Community Hospital and Clinic), 100 South Main Street, Zip 12345–6789;
tel. 123/456–7890 **A**9 10

① = **Approval Codes**
② = **Physician Codes**
③ = **Health Care System Name**
④ = **Titles of Chief Administrators**
⑤ = **Control and Service Classifications**
⑥ = **Utilization Data**
⑦ = **Facility Codes**

---

**Hospital, Medicare Provider Number, Address, Telephone, Approval, Facility, and Physician Codes, Health Care System**

★ American Hospital Association (AHA) membership  ○ Healthcare Facilities Accreditation Program  ⇑ Center for Improvement in Healthcare Quality Accreditation
□ The Joint Commission accreditation  ◇ DNV Healthcare Inc. accreditation  △ Commission on Accreditation of Rehabilitation Facilities (CARF) accreditation

---

### ① Approval Codes

*Reported by the approving bodies specified, as of the dates noted.*

**1** Accreditation under the hospital program of The Joint Commission (April 2015).
**2** Cancer program approved by American College of Surgeons (May 2015).
**†3** Approval to participate in residency training, by the Accreditation Council for Graduate Medical Education (July 2015).
**†5** Medical school affiliation, reported to the American Medical Association (June 2015).
**6** Hospital–controlled professional nursing school, reported by Accreditation Commission for Education in Nursing (August 2015).
**7** Accreditation by Commission on Accreditation of Rehabilitation Facilities (March 2015).

**8** Member of Council of Teaching Hospitals of the Association of American Medical Colleges (April 2015).
**9** Hospitals contracting or participating in a Plan, reported by the Blue Cross and Blue Shield Association (April 2014).
**10** Certified for participation in the Health Insurance for the Aged (Medicare) Program by the Centers for Medicare and Medical Services (April 2015).
**11** Healthcare Facilities Accreditation Program (April 2015).
**12** Internship approved by American Osteopathic Association (April 2015).

**13** Residency approved by American Osteopathic Association (April 2015).
**18** Critical Access Hospitals (April 2015).
**19** Rural Referral Center (April 2015).
**20** Sole Community Provider (April 2015).
**21** Accreditation by DNV Healthcare Inc. (April 2015).
**22** Accreditation by Center for Improvement in Healthcare Quality (May 2015).

**Nonreporting** indicates that the 2014 Annual Survey questionnaire for the hospital was not received prior to publication.

---

### ② Physician Codes

*Actually available within, and reported by the institution; for definitions, see page A12.*

**(Alphabetical/Numerical Order)**

**1** Closed physician–hospital organization (PHO)
**2** Equity model
**3** Foundation

**4** Group practice without walls
**5** Independent practice association (IPA)
**6** Integrated salary model

**7** Management service organization (MSO)
**8** Open physician–hospital organization (PHO)

---

### ③ Health Care System Name

*The inclusion of the letter "S" (1) indicates that the hospital belongs to a health care system and (2) identifies the specific system to which the hospital belongs.*

---

### ④ Titles of Chief Administrators

### ⑤ Control and Service Classification

*For a list of control and service classifications, see page A13.*

**Control–**The type of organization that is responsible for establishing policy for overall operation of the hospital.

**Service–**The type of service the hospital provides to the majority of admissions.

---

### ⑥ Utilization Data

*Definitions are based on the American Hospital Association's Hospital Administration Terminology. In completing the survey, hospitals were requested to report data for a full year, in accord with their fiscal year, ending in 2014.*

**Beds–**Number of beds regularly maintained (set up and staffed for use) for inpatients as of the close of the reporting period. Excludes newborn bassinets.

**Admissions–**Number of patients accepted for inpatient service during a 12–month period; does not include newborn.

**Census–**Average number of inpatients receiving care each day during the 12–month reporting period; does not include newborn.

**Outpatient Visits–**A visit by a patient who is not lodged in the hospital while receiving medical, dental, or other services. Each appearance of an outpatient in each unit constitutes one visit regardless of the number of diagnostic and/or therapeutic treatments that a patient receives.

**Births–**Number of infants born in the hospital and accepted for service in a newborn infant bassinet during a 12–month period; excludes stillbirths.

**Expense:** Expense for a 12–month period; both total expense and payroll components are shown. Payroll expenses include all salaries and wages.

**Personnel:** Represents personnel situations as they existed at the end of the reporting period; includes full-time equivalents of part–time personnel. Full–time equivalents were calculated on the basis that two part–time persons equal one full–time person.

---

†Data from the Graduate Medical Education Database, Copyright 2015, American Medical Association, Chicago, Illinois.

## Sample Hospital Listing:

**ANYTOWN, Universal County**

⊠ **ANYTOWN HOSPITAL & CLINICS (777777)**, (Formerly Anytown Area Community Hospital and Clinic), 100 South Main Street, Zip 12345–6789; tel. 123/456–7890 **A**9 10 ] ①
**F**10 12 23 24 29 30 31 37 39 49 51 55 57 64 65 66 68 70 71 72 77 78 83 87 88 91 96 97 106 107 110 111 113 124 **P**1 2 3 **S** Universal ⑦
County Health System ② ③
Primary Contact: Ann M. Generic, Chief Executive Officer
COO: Ann M. Generic
CFO: Michael M. Generic ④
CMO: Peterl Van Generic, President Medical Staff
CHR: Jerry Generic, Human Resources Director
CNO: Danielle Generic, R.N., Chief Nursing Officer
Web address: www.website.org
**Control:** Other not–for–profit (including NFP Corporation) **Service:** General ⑤
Medical and Surgical

**Staffed Beds:** 25 **Admissions:** 892 **Census:** 9 **Outpatient Visits:** 44014
**Births:** 51 **Total Expense ($000):** 19210 **Payroll Expense ($000):** 5864 ⑥
**Personnel:** 182

**ANYTOWN, Universal County**

⊠ **ANYTOWN HOSPITAL & CLINICS (777777)**, (Formerly Anytown Area Community Hospital and Clinic), 100 South Main Street, Zip 12345–6789; tel. 123/456–7890 **A**9 10

① = Approval Codes
② = Physician Codes
③ = Health Care System Name
④ = Titles of Chief Administrators
⑤ = Control and Service Classifications
⑥ = Utilization Data
⑦ = Facility Codes

---

**Hospital, Medicare Provider Number, Address, Telephone, Approval, Facility, and Physician Codes, Health Care System**

★ American Hospital Association (AHA) membership    ◯ Healthcare Facilities Accreditation Program    ⇑ Center for Improvement in Healthcare Quality Accreditation
☐ The Joint Commission accreditation    ◇ DNV Healthcare Inc. accreditation    △ Commission on Accreditation of Rehabilitation Facilities (CARF) accreditation

---

## ⑦ Facility Codes

*Provided directly by the hospital; for definitions, see page A6.*

### (Numerical Order)

1. Acute long-term care
2. Adult day care program
3. Airborne infection isolation room
4. Alcoholism-drug abuse or dependency inpatient services
5. Alcoholism-drug abuse or dependency outpatient services
6. Alzheimer center
7. Ambulance services
8. Ambulatory surgery center
9. Arthritis treatment center
10. Assisted living
11. Auxiliary
12. Bariatric/weight control services
13. Birthing room-LDR room-LDRP room
14. Blood donor center
15. Breast cancer screening/mammograms
16. Burn care services
17. Cardiac intensive care
18. Adult cardiology services
19. Pediatric cardiology services
20. Adult diagnostic catheterization
21. Pediatric diagnostic catheterization
22. Adult interventional cardiac catheterization
23. Pediatric interventional cardiac catheterization
24. Adult cardiac surgery
25. Pediatric cardiac surgery
26. Adult cardiac electrophysiology
27. Pediatric cardiac electrophysiology
28. Cardiac rehabilitation
29. Case management
30. Chaplaincy/pastoral care services
31. Chemotherapy
32. Children's wellness program
33. Chiropractic services
34. Community health education
35. Community outreach
36. Complementary and alternative medicine services
37. Computer assisted orthopedic surgery (CAOS)
38. Crisis prevention
39. Dental services
40. Emergency department
41. Pediatric emergency department
42. Satellite emergency department
43. Trauma center (certified)
44. Enabling services
45. Optical colonoscopy
46. Endoscopic ultrasound
47. Ablation of Barrett's esophagus
48. Esophageal impedance study
49. Endoscopic retrograde cholangiopancreatography (ERCP)
50. Enrollment assistance services
51. Extracorporeal shock wave lithotripter (ESWL)
52. Fertility clinic
53. Fitness center
54. Freestanding outpatient care center
55. Genetic testing/counseling
56. Geriatric services
57. Health fair
58. Health research
59. Health screenings
60. Hemodialysis
61. HIV–AIDS services
62. Home health services
63. Hospice program
64. Hospital–based outpatient care center services
65. Immunization program
66. Indigent care clinic
67. Intermediate nursing care
68. Linguistic/translation services
69. Meals on wheels
70. Medical surgical intensive care services
71. Mobile health services
72. Neonatal intensive care
73. Neonatal intermediate care
74. Neurological services
75. Nutrition programs
76. Obstetrics
77. Occupational health services
78. Oncology services
79. Orthopedic services
80. Other special care
81. Outpatient surgery
82. Pain management program
83. Inpatient palliative care unit
84. Palliative care program
85. Patient controlled analgesia (PCA)
86. Patient education center
87. Patient representative services
88. Pediatric intensive care services
89. Pediatric medical–surgical care
90. Physical rehabilitation inpatient services
91. Assistive technology center
92. Electrodiagnostic services
93. Physical rehabilitation outpatient services
94. Prosthetic and orthotic services
95. Robot-assisted walking therapy
96. Simulated rehabilitation environment
97. Primary care department
98. Psychiatric care
99. Psychiatric child–adolescent services
100. Psychiatric consultation–liaison services
101. Psychiatric education services
102. Psychiatric emergency services
103. Psychiatric geriatric services
104. Psychiatric outpatient services
105. Psychiatric partial hospitalization services
106. Psychiatric residential treatment
107. CT scanner
108. Diagnostic radioisotope facility
109. Electron beam computed tomography (EBCT)
110. Full–field digital mammography (FFDM)
111. Magnetic resonance imaging (MRI)
112. Intraoperative magnetic resonance imaging
113. Magnetoencephalography (MEG)
114. Multi–slice spiral computed tomography (MSCT) (<64 slice CT)
115. Multi–slice spiral computed tomography (64 + slice CT)
116. Positron emission tomography (PET)
117. Positron emission tomography/CT (PET/CT)
118. Single photon emission computerized tomography (SPECT)
119. Ultrasound
120. Image–guided radiation therapy (IGRT)
121. Intensity–modulated radiation therapy (IMRT)
122. Proton beam therapy
123. Shaped beam radiation therapy
124. Stereotactic radiosurgery
125. Retirement housing
126. Robotic surgery
127. Rural health clinic
128. Skilled nursing care
129. Sleep center
130. Social work services
131. Sports medicine
132. Support groups
133. Swing bed services
134. Teen outreach services
135. Tobacco treatment/cessation program
136. Bone marrow transplant services
137. Heart transplant
138. Kidney transplant
139. Liver transplant
140. Lung transplant
141. Tissue transplant
142. Other transplant
143. Transportation to health services
144. Urgent care center
145. Virtual colonoscopy
146. Volunteer services department
147. Women's health center/services
148. Wound management services

# Annual Survey

Each year, an annual survey of hospitals is conducted by the American Hospital Association through its Health Forum affiliate.

The facilities and services found below are provided by the hospital. For data products reflecting the services provided by a hospital through its health care system, or network or through a formal arrangement with another provider contact Health Forum at 800/821–2039, or visit www.healthforum.com.

The AHA Guide to the Health Care Field does not include all data collected from the 2014 Annual Survey. Requests for purchasing other Annual Survey data should be directed to Health Forum LLC, an affiliate of the American Hospital Association, 155 N. Wacker Drive, Chicago, IL 60606, 800/821–2039.

## Definitions of Facility Codes

1. **Acute long–term care.** Provides specialized acute hospital care to medically complex patients who are critically ill, have multisystem complications and/or failure, and require hospitalization averaging 25 days, in a facility offering specialized treatment programs and therapeutic intervention on a 24–hour/7 day a week basis.

2. **Adult day care program.** Program providing supervision, medical and psychological care, and social activities for older adults who live at home or in another family setting, but cannot be alone or prefer to be with others during the day. May include intake assessment, health monitoring, occupational therapy, personal care, noon meal, and transportation services.

3. **Airborne infection isolation room.** A single–occupancy room for patient care where environmental factors are controlled in an effort to minimize the transmission of those infectious agents, usually spread person to person by droplet nuclei associated with coughing and inhalation. Such rooms typically have specific ventilation requirements for controlled ventilation, air pressure and filtration.

4. **Alcoholism–drug abuse or dependency inpatient unit.** Provides diagnosis and therapeutic services to patients with alcoholism or other drug dependencies. Includes care for inpatient/residential treatment for patients whose course of treatment involves more intensive care than provided in an outpatient setting or where patient requires supervised withdrawal.

5. **Alcoholism–drug abuse or dependency outpatient unit.** Organized hospital services that provide medical care and/or rehabilitative treatment services to outpatients for whom the primary diagnosis is alcoholism or other chemical dependency.

6. **Alzheimer center.** Facility that offers care to persons with Alzheimer's disease and their families through an integrated program of clinical services, research, and education.

7. **Ambulance services.** Provision of ambulance services to the ill and injured who require medical attention on a scheduled or unscheduled basis.

8. **Ambulatory surgery center.** Facility that provides care to patients requiring surgery who are admitted and discharged on the same day. Ambulatory surgery centers are distinct from same day surgical units within the hospital outpatient departments for purposes of Medicare payments.

9. **Arthritis treatment center.** Specifically equipped and staffed center for the diagnosis and treatment of arthritis and other joint disorders.

10. **Assisted living.** A special combination of housing, supportive services, personalized assistance and health care designed to respond to the individual needs of those who need help in activities of daily living and instrumental activities of daily living. Supportive services are available, 24 hours a day, to meet scheduled and unscheduled needs, in a way that promotes maximum independence and dignity for each resident and encourages the involvement of a resident's family, neighbor and friends.

11. **Auxiliary.** A volunteer community organization formed to assist the hospital in carrying out its purpose and to serve as a link between the institution and the community.

12. **Bariatric/weight control services.** Bariatrics is the medical practice of weight reduction.

13. **Birthing room–LDR room–LDRP room.** A single room–type of maternity care with a more homelike setting for families than the traditional three–room unit (labor/delivery/recovery) with a separate postpartum area. A birthing room combines labor and delivery in one room. An LDR room accommodates three stages in the birthing process—labor, delivery, and recovery. An LDRP room accommodates all four stages of the birth process—labor, delivery, recovery and postpartum.

14. **Blood donor center.** A facility that performs, or is responsible for the collection, processing, testing or distribution of blood and components.

15. **Breast cancer screening/mammograms.** Mammography screening–the use of breast x–ray to detect unsuspected breast cancer in asymptomatic women. Diagnostic mammography–the x–ray imaging of breast tissue in symptomatic women who are considered to have a substantial likelihood of having breast cancer already.

16. **Burn care services.** Provides care to severely burned patients. Severely burned patients are those with any of the following: 1. Second–degree burns of more than 25% total body surface area for adults or 20% total body surface area for children; 2. Third–degree burns of more than 10% total body surface area; 3. Any severe burns of the hands, face, eyes, ears or feet or; 4. All inhalation injuries, electrical burns, complicated burn injuries involving fractures and other major traumas, and all other poor risk factors.

17. **Cardiac intensive care.** Provides patient care of a more specialized

nature than the usual medical and surgical care, on the basis of physicians' orders and approved nursing care plans. The unit is staffed with specially trained nursing personnel and contains monitoring and specialized support or treatment equipment for patients who, because of heart seizure, open–heart surgery, or other life–threatening conditions, require intensified, comprehensive observation and care. May include myocardial infarction, pulmonary care, and heart transplant units.

18. **Adult cardiology services.** An organized clinical service offering diagnostic and interventional procedures to manage the full range of adult heart conditions.

19. **Pediatric cardiology services.**

20. **Adult diagnostic catheterization.** (also called coronary angiography or coronary arteriography) is used to assist in diagnosing complex heart conditions. Cardiac angiography involves the insertion of a tiny catheter up into the artery in the groin then carefully threading the catheter up into the aorta where the coronary arteries originate. Once the catheter is in place, a dye is injected which allows the cardiologist to see the size, shape and distribution of the coronary arteries. These images are used to diagnose heart disease and to determine, among other things, whether or not surgery is indicated.

21. **Pediatric diagnostic catheterization.** (also called coronary angiography or coronary arteriography) is used to assist in diagnosing complex heart conditions. Cardiac angiography involves the insertion of a tiny catheter up into the artery in the groin then carefully threading the catheter up into the aorta where the coronary arteries originate. Once the catheter is in place, a dye is injected which allows the cardiologist to see the size, shape and distribution of the coronary arteries. These images are used to diagnose heart disease and to determine, among other things, whether or not surgery is indicated.

22. **Adult interventional cardiac catheterization.** Nonsurgical procedure that utilizes the same basic principles as diagnostic cathereterization and then uses advanced the techniques to improve the heart's function. It can be less invasive alternative to heart surgery.

23. **Pediatric diagnostic catheterization.** Nonsurgical

procedure that utilizes the same basic principles as diagnostic cathereterization and then uses advanced the techniques to improve the heart's function. It can be less invasive alternative to heart surgery.

24. **Adult cardiac surgery.** Includes minimally invasive procedures that include surgery done with only a small incision or no incision at all, such as through a laparoscope or an endoscope and more invasive major surgical procedures that include open chest and open heart surgery.

25. **Pediatric cardiac surgery.** Includes minimally invasive procedures that include surgery done with only a small incision or no incision at all, such as through a laparoscope or an endoscope and more invasive major surgical procedures that include open chest and open heart surgery defibrillator implantation and follow-up.

26. **Adult cardiac electrophysiology.** Evaluation and management of patients with complex rhythm or conduction abnormalities, including diagnostic testing, treatment of arrhythmias by catheter ablation or drug therapy, and pacemaker/defibrillator implantation and follow-up.

27. **Pediatric cardiac electrophysiology.**

28. **Cardiac rehabilitation.** A medically supervised program to help heart patients recover quickly and improve their overall physical and mental functioning. The goal is to reduce risk of another cardiac event or to keep an already present heart condition from getting worse. Cardiac rehabilitation programs include: counseling to patients, an exercise program, helping patients modify risk factors such as smoking and high blood pressure, providing vocational guidance to enable the patient to return to work, supplying information on physical limitations and lending emotional support.

29. **Case management.** A system of assessment, treatment planning, referral and follow–up that ensures the provision of comprehensive and continuous services and the coordination of payment and reimbursement for care.

30. **Chaplaincy/pastoral care services.** A service ministering religious activities and providing pastoral counseling to patients, their families,

and staff of a health care organization.

31. **Chemotherapy.** An organized program for the treatment of cancer by the use of drugs or chemicals.

32. **Children's wellness program.** A program that encourages improved health status and a healthful lifestyle of children through health education, exercise, nutrition and health promotion.

33. **Chiropractic services.** An organized clinical service including spinal manipulation or adjustment and related diagnostic and therapeutic services.

34. **Community health education.** Education that provides health information to individuals and populations as well as support for personal, family and community health decisions with the objective of improving health status.

35. **Community outreach.** A program that systematically interacts with the community to identify those in need of services, alerting persons and their families to the availability of services, locating needed services, and enabling persons to enter the service delivery system.

36. **Complementary and alternative medicine services.** Organized hospital services or formal arrangements to providers that provide care or treatment not based solely on traditional western allopathic medical teachings as instructed in most U.S. medical schools. Includes any of the following; acupuncture, chiropractic, homeopathy, osteopathy, diet and lifestyle changes, herbal medicine, massage therapy, etc.

37. **Computer assisted orthopedic surgery (CAOS).** Orthopedic surgery using computer technology, enabling three–dimensional graphic models to visualize a patient's anatomy.

38. **Crisis prevention** Services provided in order to promote physical and mental well being and the early identification of disease and ill health prior to the onset and recognition of symptoms so as to permit early treatment.

39. **Dental services.** An organized dental service, not necessarily involving special facilities, that provides dental or oral services to inpatients or outpatients.

40. **Emergency department.** Hospital facilities for the provision of

unscheduled outpatient services to patients whose conditions require immediate care. Must be staffed 24 hours a day.

41. **Pediatric emergency department.** Hospital facilities for the provision of unscheduled outpatient services to patients whose conditions require immediate care.

42. **Satellite emergency department.** A facility owned and operated by the hospital but physically separate from the hospital for the provision of unscheduled outpatient services to patients whose conditions require.

43. **Trauma center (certified).** A facility certified to provide emergency and specialized intensive care to critically ill and injured patients.

44. **Enabling services.** A program that is designed to help the patient access health care services by offering any of the following linguistic services, transportation services, and/or referrals to local social services agencies.

45. **Optical colonoscopy.** An examination of the interior of the colon using a long, flexible, lighted tube with a small built-in camera.

46. **Endoscopic ultrasound.** Specially designed endoscope that incorporates an ultrasound transducer used to obtain detailed images of organs in the chest and abdomen. The endoscope can be passed through the mouth or the anus. When combined with needle biopsy the procedure can assist in diagnosis and staging of cancer.

47. **Ablation of Barrett's esophagus.** Premalignant condition that can lead to adenocarcinoma of the esophagus. The non surgical ablation of the premalignant tissue in Barrett's esophagus by the application of thermal energy or light through an endoscope passed from the mouth into the esophagus.

48. **Esophageal impedance study.** A test in which a catheter is placed through the nose into the esophagus to measure whether gas or liquids are passing from the stomach into the esophagus and causing symptoms.

49. **Endoscopic retrograde cholangiopancreatography (ERCP).** A procedure in which a catheter is introduced through an endoscope into the bile ducts and pancreatic ducts. Injection of contrast materials permits detailed x–ray of these structures. The procedure is used diagnostically as

well as therapeutically to relieve obstruction or remove stones

50. **Enrollment assistance services.** A program that provides enrollment assistance for patients who are potentially eligible for public health insurance programs such as Medicaid, State Children's Health Insurance, or local/state indigent care programs. The specific services offered could include explanation of benefits, assist applicants in completing the application and locating all relevant documents, conduct eligibilty interviews, and/or forward applications and documentation to state/local social service or health agency.

51. **Extracorporeal shock wave lithotripter (ESWL).** A medical device used for treating stones in the kidney or urethra. The device disintegrates kidney stones noninvasively through the transmission of acoustic shock waves directed at the stones.

52. **Fertility clinic.** A specialized program set in an infertility center that provides counseling and education as well as advanced reproductive techniques such as: injectable therapy, reproductive surgeries, treatment for endometriosis, male factor infertility, tubal reversals, in vitro fertilization (IVF), donor eggs, and other such services to help patients achieve successful pregnancies.

53. **Fitness center.** Provides exercise, testing, or evaluation programs and fitness activities to the community and hospital employees.

54. **Freestanding outpatient care center.** A facility owned and operated by the hospital, but physically separate from the hospital, that provides various medical treatments on an outpatient basis only. In addition to treating minor illnesses or injuries, the center will stabilize seriously ill or injured patients before transporting them to a hospital. Laboratory and radiology services are usually available.

55. **Genetic testing/counseling** A service equipped with adequate laboratory facilities and directed by a qualified physician to advise parents and prospective parents on potential problems in cases of genetic defects. A genetic test is the analysis of human DNA, RNA, chromosomes, proteins, and certain metabolites in order to detect heritable disease–related genotypes, mutations,

phenotypes, or karyotypes for clinical purposes. Genetic tests can have diverse purposes, including the diagnosis of genetic diseases in newborns, children, and adults; the identification of future health risks; the prediction of drug responses; and the assessment of risks to future children.

56. **Geriatric services.** The branch of medicine dealing with the physiology of aging and the diagnosis and treatment of disease affecting the aged. Services could include: Adult day care program; Alzheimer's diagnostic–assessment services; Comprehensive geriatric assessment; Emergency response system; Geriatric acute care unit; and/or Geriatric clinics.

57. **Health fair.** Community health education events that focus on the prevention of disease and promotion of health through such activities as audiovisual exhibits and free diagnostic services.

58. **Health research.** Organized hospital research program in any of the following areas: basic research, clinical research, community health research, and/or research on innovative health care delivery.

59. **Health screenings.** A preliminary procedure, such as a test or examination to detect the most characteristic sign or signs of a disorder that may require further investigation.

60. **Hemodialysis.** Provision of equipment and personnel for the treatment of renal insufficiency on an inpatient or outpatient basis.

61. **HIV–AIDS services.** Services may include one or more of the following: HIV–AIDS unit (special unit or team designated and equipped specifically for diagnosis, treatment, continuing care planning, and counseling services for HIV–AIDS patients and their families.) General inpatient care for HIV–AIDS (inpatient diagnosis and treatment for human immunodeficiency virus and acquired immunodeficiency syndrome patients, but dedicated unit is not available.) Specialized outpatient program for HIV–AIDS (special outpatient program providing diagnostic, treatment, continuing care planning, and counseling for HIV–AIDS patients and their families.)

62. **Home health services.** Service providing nursing, therapy, and

health–related homemaker or social services in the patient's home.

63. **Hospice program.** A program providing palliative care, chiefly medical relief of pain and supportive services, addressing the emotional, social, financial, and legal needs of terminally ill patients and their families. Care can be provided in a variety of settings, both inpatient and at home.

64. **Hospital–based outpatient care center services.** Organized hospital health care services offered by appointment on an ambulatory basis. Services may include outpatient surgery, examination, diagnosis, and treatment of a variety of medical conditions on a nonemergency basis, and laboratory and other diagnostic testing as ordered by staff or outside physician referral.

65. **Immunization program.** Program that plans, coordinates and conducts immunization services in the community.

66. **Indigent care clinic.** Health care services for uninsured and underinsured persons where care is free of charge or charged on a sliding scale. This would include "free clinics" staffed by volunteer practitioners, but could also be staffed by employees with sponsoring health care organizations subsidizing the cost of service.

67. **Intermediate nursing care.** Provides health–related services (skilled nursing care and social services) to residents with a variety of physical conditions or functional disabilities. These residents do not require the care provided by a hospital or skilled nursing facility, but do need supervision and support services.

68. **Linguistic/translation services.** Services provided by the hospital designed to make health care more accessible to non–English speaking patients and their physicians.

69. **Meals on wheels.** A hospital sponsored program which delivers meals to people, usually the elderly, who are unable to prepare their own meals. Low cost, nutritional meals are delivered to individuals' homes on a regular basis.

70. **Medical surgical intensive care services.** Provides patient care of a more intensive nature than the usual medical and surgical care, on the basis of physicians' orders and approved nursing care plans. These units are staffed with specially trained nursing personnel and contain monitoring and specialized support equipment of patients who, because of shock, trauma, or other life–threatening conditions, require intensified, comprehensive observation and care. Includes mixed intensive care units.

71. **Mobile health services.** Vans and other vehicles used to deliver primary care services.

72. **Neonatal intensive care.** A unit that must be separate from the newborn nursery providing intensive care to all sick infants including those with the very lowest birth weights (less that 1500 grams). NICU has potential for providing mechanical ventilation, neonatal surgery, and special care for the sickest infants born in the hospital or transferred from another institution. A full–time neonatologist serves as director of the NICU.

73. **Neonatal intermediate care.** A unit that must be separate from the normal newborn nursery and that provides intermediate and/or recovery care and some specialized services, including immediate resuscitation, intravenous therapy, and capacity for prolonged oxygen therapy and monitoring.

74. **Neurological services.** Services provided by the hospital dealing with the operative and nonoperative management of disorders of the central, peripheral, and autonomic nervous system.

75. **Nutrition programs.** Those services within a health care facility which are designed to provide inexpensive, nutritionally sound meals to patients.

76. **Obstetrics.** Levels should be designated: (1) unit provides services for uncomplicated maternity and newborn cases; (2) unit provides services for uncomplicated cases, the majority of complicated problems, and special neonatal services; and (3) unit provides services for all serious illnesses and abnormalities and is supervised by a full–time maternal/fetal specialist.

77. **Occupational health services.** Includes services designed to protect the safety of employees from hazards in the work environment.

78. **Oncology services.** Inpatient and outpatient services for patients with cancer, including comprehensive care, support and guidance in addition to patient education and preventiion, chemotherapy, counseling, and other treatment methods.

79. **Orthopedic services.** Services provided for the prevention or correction of injuries or disorders of the skeletal system and associated muscles, joints, and ligaments.

80. **Other special care.** Provides care to patients requiring care more intensive than that provided in the acute area, yet not sufficiently intensive to require admission to an intensive care unit. Patients admitted to the area are usually transferred here from an intensive care unit once their condition has improved. These units are sometimes referred to as definitive observation, step–down, or progressive care units.

81. **Outpatient surgery.** Scheduled surgical services provided to patients who do not remain in the hospital overnight. The surgery may be performed in operating suites also used for inpatient surgery, specially designated surgical suites for outpatient surgery, or procedure rooms within an outpatient care facility.

82. **Pain management program.** A hospital wide formalized program that includes staff education for the management of chronic and acute pain based on guidelines and protocols like those developed by the agency for Health Care Policy Research, etc.

83. **Inpatient palliative care unit.** An inpatient palliative care ward is a physically discreet, inpatient nursing unit where the focus is palliative care. The patient care focus is on symptom relief for complex patients who may be continuing to undergo primary treatment. Care is delivered by palliative medicine specialists.

84. **Palliative care program.** An organized program providing specialized medical care, drugs or therapies for the management of acute or chronic pain and/or the control of symptoms adminstered by specially trained physicians and other clinicians; and supportive care services, such as counseling on advanced directives, spiritual care, and social services, to patients with advanced disease and their families.

85. **Patient controlled analgesia (PCA).** Patient Controlled Analgesia (PCA) is intravenously administered pain medicine under the patient's control. The patient has a button on the end of a cord than can be pushed at will, whenever more pain medicine is desired. This button will only deliver more pain medicine at pre–

determined intervals, as programmed by the doctor's order.

86. **Patient education center.** Written goals and objectives for the patient and/or family related to therapeutic regimens, medical procedures, and self care.

87. **Patient representative services.** Organized hospital services providing personnel through whom patients and staff can seek solutions to institutional problems affecting the delivery of high–quality care and services.

88. **Pediatric intensive care services.** Provides care to pediatric patients that is of a more intensive nature than that usually provided to pediatric patients. The unit is staffed with specially trained personnel and contains monitoring and specialized support equipment for treatment of patients who, because of shock, trauma, or other life–threatening conditions, require intensified, comprehensive observation and care.

89. **Pediatric medical–surgical care.** Provides acute care to pediatric patients on the basis of physicians' orders and approved nursing care plans.

90. **Physical rehabilitation inpatient services.** Provides care encompassing a comprehensive array of restoration services for the disabled and all support services necessary to help patients attain their maximum functional capacity.

91. **Assistive technology center.** A program providing access to specialized hardware and software with adaptations allowing individuals greater independence with mobility, dexterity, or increased communication options.

92. **Electrodiagnostic services.** Diagnostic testing services for nerve and muscle function including services such as nerve conduction studies and needle electromyography.

93. **Physical rehabilitation outpatient services.** Outpatient program providing medical, health–related, therapy, social, and/or vocational services to help disabled persons attain or retain their maximum functional capacity.

94. **Prosthetic and orthotic services.** Services providing comprehensive prosthetic and orthotic evaluation, fitting, and training.

95. **Robot-assisted walking therapy.** A form of physical therapy that uses a robotic device to assist patients who are relearning how to walk.

96. **Simulated rehabilitation environment.** Rehabilitation focused on retraining functional skills in a contextually appropriate environment (simulated home and community settings) or in a traditional setting (gymnasium) using motor learning principles.

97. **Primary care department.** A unit or clinic within the hospital that provides primary care services (e.g. general pediatric care, general internal medicine, family practice and gynecology) through hospital–salaried medical and or nursing staff, focusing on evaluating and diagnosing medical problems and providing medical treatment on an outpatient basis.

98. **Psychiatric care.** Provides acute or long–term care to emotionally disturbed patients, including patients admitted for diagnosis and those admitted for treatment of psychiatric problems, on the basis of physicians' orders and approved nursing care plans. Long–term care may include intensive supervision to the chronically mentally ill, mentally disordered, or other mentally incompetent persons.

99. **Psychiatric child–adolescent services.** Provides care to emotionally disturbed children and adolescents, including those admitted for diagnosis and those admitted for treatment.

100. **Psychiatric consultation–liaison services.** Provides organized psychiatric consultation/liaison services to nonpsychiatric hospital staff and/or department on psychological aspects of medical care that may be generic or specific to individual patients.

101. **Psychiatric education services.** Provides psychiatric educational services to community agencies and workers such as schools, police, courts, public health nurses, welfare agencies, clergy and so forth. The purpose is to expand the mental health knowledge and competence of personnel not working in the mental health field and to promote good mental health through improved understanding, attitudes, and behavioral patterns.

102. **Psychiatric emergency services.** Services or facilities available on a 24–hour basis to provide immediate unscheduled outpatient care, diagnosis, evaluation, crisis intervention, and assistance to persons suffering acute emotional or mental distress.

103. **Psychiatric geriatric services.** Provides care to emotionally disturbed elderly patients, including those admitted for diagnosis and those admitted for treatment.

104. **Psychiatric outpatient services.** Provides medical care, including diagnosis and treatment of psychiatric outpatients.

105. **Psychiatric partial hospitalization services.** Organized hospital services of intensive day/evening outpatient services of three hours or more duration, distinguished from other outpatient visits of one hour.

106. **Psychiatric residential treatment.**

107. **CT scanner.** Computed tomographic scanner for head and whole body scans.

108. **Diagnostic radioisotope facility.** The use of radioactive isotopes (Radiopharmaceutical) as tracers or indicators to detect an abnormal condition or disease.

109. **Electron beam computed tomography (EBCT).** A high tech computed tomography scan used to detect coronary artery disease by measuring coronary calcifications. This imaging procedure uses electron beams which are magnetically steered to produce a visual of the coronary artery and the images are produced faster than conventional CT scans.

110. **Full–field digital mammography (FFDM).** Combines the x–ray generators and tubes used in analog screen–film mammography (SFM) with a detector plate that converts the x–rays into a digital signal.

111. **Magnetic resonance imaging (MRI).** The use of a uniform magnetic field and radio frequencies to study tissue and structure of the body. This procedure enables the visualization of biochemical activity of the cell in vivo without the use of ionizing radiation, radioisotopic substances, or high–frequency sound.

112. **Intraoperative magnetic resonance imaging.** An integrated surgery system which provides an MRI system in an operating room. The system allows for immediate evaluation of the degree to tumor resection while the patient is undergoing a surgical resection. Intraoperative MRI exists when a MRI (low–field or high–field) is placed in the operating theater and is

used during surgical resection without moving the patient from the operating room to the diagnostic imaging suite.

**113. Magnetoencephalography (MEG).** A noninvasive neurophysiological measurement tool used to study magnetic fields generated by neuronal activity of the brain. MEG provides direct information about the dynamics of evoked and spontaneous neural activity and the location of their sources in the brain. The primary uses of MEG include assisting surgeons in localizing the source of epilepsy, sensory mapping and the study of brain function. When it is combined with structural imaging, it is known as magnetic source imaging (MSI).

**114. Multi–slice spiral computed tomography (MSCT) (<64 slice CT).** A specialized computed tomography procedure that provides three–dimensional processing and allows narrower and multiple slices with increased spatial resolution and faster scanning times as compared to a regular computed tomography scan.

**115. Multi–slice spiral computed tomography (64 + slice CT).** Involves the acquisition of volumetric tomographic x–ray absorption data expressed in Hounsfield units using multiple rows of detectors. 64+ systems reconstruct the equivalent of 64 or greater slices to cover the imaged volume.

**116. Positron emission tomography (PET).** A nuclear medicine imaging technology which uses radioactive (positron emitting) isotopes created in a cyclotron or generator and computers to produce composite pictures of the brain and heart at work. PET scanning produces sectional images depicting metabolic activity or blood flow rather than anatomy.

**117. Positron emission tomography/CT (PET/CT).** Provides metabolic functional information for the monitoring of chemotherapy, radiotherapy and surgical planning.

**118. Single photon emission computerized tomography (SPECT).** A nuclear medicine imaging technology that combines existing technology of gamma camera imaging with computed tomographic imaging technology to provide a more precise and clear image.

**119. Ultrasound.** The use of acoustic waves above the range of 20,000 cycles per second to visualize internal body structures.

**120. Image–guided radiation therapy (IGRT).** Automated system for image–guided radiation therapy that enables clinicians to obtain high–resolution x–ray images to pinpoint tumor sites, adjust patient positioning when necessary, and complete a treatment, all within the standard treatment time slot, allowing for more effective cancer treatments.

**121. Intensity–modulated radiation Therapy (IMRT).** A type of three–dimensional radiation therapy, which improves the targeting of treatment delivery in a way that is likely to decrease damage to normal tissues and allows varying intensities diagnosis of genetic diseases in newborns, children, and adults; the identification of future health risks; the prediction of drug responses; and the assessment of risks to future children.

**122. Proton beam therapy.** A form of radiation therapy which administers proton beams. While producing the same biologic effects as x–ray beams, the energy distribution of protons differs from conventional x–ray beams in that they can be more precisely focused in tissue volumes in a three–dimensional pattern resulting in less surrounding tissue damage than conventional radiation therapy permitting administration of higher doses.

**123. Shaped beam radiation therapy.** A precise, non–invasive treatment that involves targeting beams of radiation that mirror the exact size and shape of a tumor at a specific area of a tumor to shrink or destroy cancerous cells. This procedure delivers a therapeutic dose of radiation that conforms precisely to the shape of the tumor, thus minimizing the risk to nearby tissues.

**124. Stereotactic radiosurgery.** Stereotactic radiosurgery (SRS) is a radiotherapy modality that delivers a high dosage of radiation to a discrete treatment area in as few as one treatment session. Includes gamma knife, cyberknife, etc.

**125. Retirement housing.** A facility which provides social activities to senior citizens, usually retired persons, who do not require health care but some short–term skilled nursing care may be provided. A retirement center may furnish housing and may also have acute hospital and long–term care facilities, or it may arrange for acute and long term care through affiliated institutions.

**126. Robotic surgery.** The use of mechanical guidance devices to remotely manipulate surgical instrumentation.

**127. Rural health clinic.** A clinic located in a rural, medically under–served area in the United States that has a separate reimbursement structure from the standard medical office under the Medicare and Medicaid programs.

**128. Skilled nursing care.** Provides non–acute medical and skilled nursing care services, therapy, and social services under the supervision of a licensed registered nurse on a 24–hour basis.

**129. Sleep center.** Specially equipped and staffed center for the diagnosis and treatment of sleep disorders.

**130. Social work services.** Services may include one or more of the following: Organized social work services (services that are properly directed and sufficiently staffed by qualified individuals who provide assistance and counseling to patients and their families in dealing with social, emotional, and environmental problems associated with illness or disability, often in the context of financial or discharge planning coordination.) Outpatient social work services (social work services provided in ambulatory care areas.) Emergency department social work services (social work services provided to emergency department patients by social workers dedicated to the emergency department or on call.)

**131. Sports medicine.** Provision of diagnostic screening and assessment and clinical and rehabilitation services for the prevention and treatment of sports–related injuries.

**132. Support groups.** A hospital sponsored program which allows a group of individuals with the same or similar problems who meet periodically to share experiences, problems, and solutions, in order to support each other.

**133. Swing bed services.** A hospital bed that can be used to provide either acute or long–term care depending on community or patients needs. To be eligible a hospital must have a Medicare provider agreement in place, have fewer than 100 beds, be located in a rural area, not have a 24 hour nursing service waiver in effect, have not been terminated from the program in the prior two years, and meet various service conditions.

**134. Teen outreach services.** A program focusing on the teenager which encourages an improved health status and a healthful lifestyle including physical, emotional, mental, social, spiritual and economic health through education, exercise, nutrition and health promotion.

**135. Tobacco treatment/cessation program.** Organized hospital services with the purpose of ending tobacco–use habits of patients addicted to tobacco/nicotine.

**136.–142. Transplant services.** The branch of medicine that transfers an organ or tissue from one person to another or from one body part to another to replace a diseased structure or to restore function or to change appearance. Services could include: Bone marrow transplant program **(136. Bone marrow)**; heart **(137. Heart transplant)**, kidney **(138. Kidney transplant)**, liver **(139. Liver transplant)** lung **(140. Lung transplant)**, tissue **(141. Tissue**

transplant). Please include heart/lung or other multi– transplant surgeries in other **(142. Other Transplant)**.

**143. Transportation to health services.** A long–term care support service designed to assist the mobility of the elderly. Some programs offer improved financial access by offering reduced rates and barrier–free buses or vans with ramps and lifts to assist the elderly or handicapped; others offer subsidies for public transport systems or operate mini–bus services exclusively for use by senior citizens.

**144. Urgent care center.** A facility that provides care and treatment for problems that are not life–threatening but require attention over the short term. These units function like emergency rooms but are separate from hospitals with which they may have backup affiliation arrangements.

**145. Virtual colonoscopy.** Noninvasive screening procedure used to visualize, analyze and detect cancerous or potentially cancerous polyps in the colon.

**146. Volunteer services department.** An organized hospital department responsible for coordinating the services of volunteers working within the institution.

**147. Women's center.** An area set aside for coordinated education and treatment services specifically for and promoted by women as provided by this special unit. Services may or may not include obstetrics but include a range of services other than OB.

**148. Wound management services.** Services for patients with chronic wounds and non–healing wounds often resulting from diabetes, poor circulation, improper seating and immunocompromising conditions. The goals are to progress chronic wounds through stages of healing, reduce and eliminate infections, increase physical function to minimize complications from current wounds and prevent future chronic wounds. Wound management services are provided on an inpatient or outpatient basis, depending on the intensity of service needed.

# Definitions of Physician Codes

1. **Closed physician–hospital organization (PHO).** A PHO that restricts physician membership to those practitioners who meet criteria for cost effectiveness and/or high quality.

2. **Equity model.** Allows established practitioners to become shareholders in a professional corporation in exchange for tangible and intangible assets of their existing practices.

3. **Foundation.** A corporation, organized either as a hospital affiliate or subsidiary, which purchases both the tangible and intangible assets of one or more medical group practices. Physicians remain in a separate corporate entity but sign a professional services agreement with the foundation.

4. **Group practice without walls.** Hospital sponsors the formation of, or

provides capital to physicians to establish, a 'quasi' group to share administrative expenses while remaining independent practitioners.

5. **Independent practice association (IPA).** A legal entity that hold managed care contracts. The IPA then contracts with physicians, usually in solo practice, to provide care either on a fee–for–services or capitated basis. The purpose of an IPA is to assist solo physicians in obtaining managed care contracts.

6. **Integrated salary model.** Physicians are salaried by the hospital or another entity of a health system to provide medical services for primary care and specialty care.

7. **Management services organization (MSO).** A corporation, owned by the

hospital or a physician/hospital joint venture, that provides management services to one or more medical group practices. The MSO purchases the tangible assets of the practices and leases them back as part of a full–service management agreement, under which the MSO employs all non–physician staff and provides all supplies/administrative systems for a fee.

8. **Open physician–hospital organization (PHO).** A joint venture between the hospital and all members of the medical staff who wish to participate. The PHO can act as a unified agent in managed care contracting, own a managed care plan, own and operate ambulatory care centers or ancillary services projects, or provide administrative services to physician members.

# Control and Service Classifications

## Control

### Government, nonfederal
State
County
City
City–county
Hospital district or authority

### Nongovernment not–for–profit
Church operated
Other

### Investor–owned (for–profit)
Individual
Partnership
Corporation

### Government, federal
Air Force
Army
Navy
Public Health Service other than 47
Veterans Affairs

Federal other than 41–45, 47–48
Public Health Service Indian Service
Department of Justice

### Osteopathic
Church operated
Other not–for–profit
Other
Individual for–profit
Partnership for–profit
Corporation for–profit

## Service

General medical and surgical
Hospital unit of an institution
  (prison hospital, college infirmary, etc.)
Hospital unit within a facility for persons
  with intellectual disabilities
Surgical
Psychiatric
Tuberculosis and other respiratory
  diseases
Cancer
Heart

Obstetrics and gynecology
Eye, ear, nose, and throat
Rehabilitation
Orthopedic
Chronic disease
Other specialty
Children's general
Children's hospital unit of an institution
Children's psychiatric
Children's tuberculosis and other
  respiratory diseases
Children's eye, ear, nose, and throat

Children's rehabilitation
Children's orthopedic
Children's chronic disease
Children's other specialty
Intellectual disabilities
Long–Term Acute Care
Alcoholism and other chemical
  dependency
Children's Long–Term Acute Care
Children's Cancer
Children's Heart

# ALABAMA

## ALABASTER—Shelby County

☐ **NOLAND HOSPITAL SHELBY (012013)**, 1000 First Street North, 3rd Floor, Zip 35007–8703; tel. 205/620–8641 **A**1 9 10 **F**3 26 28 29 30 60 61 75 77 79 84 91 92 103 107 111 119 148 **S** Noland Health Services, Inc., Birmingham, AL
Primary Contact: Laura S. Wills, Administrator
Web address: www.nolandhospitals.com
**Control:** Other not–for–profit (including NFP Corporation) **Service:** Long–Term Acute Care hospital

> **Staffed Beds:** 52 **Admissions:** 134 **Census:** 9 **Outpatient Visits:** 0 **Births:** 0 **Total Expense ($000):** 3964 **Payroll Expense ($000):** 1468

☐ **SHELBY BAPTIST MEDICAL CENTER (010016)**, 1000 First Street North, Zip 35007–8703; tel. 205/620–8100, (Nonreporting) **A**1 3 9 10 **S** Baptist Health System, Birmingham, AL
Primary Contact: Robert Phillips, President
CFO: Jennifer Pittman, Chief Financial Officer
CMO: Mark Scofield, M.D., Chief Medical Officer
CIO: Mike Nighman, Facility Coordinator Information Systems
CHR: Cindy Nicholson, Director Human Resources
CNO: Martha Seahorn, R.N., Chief Nurse Office
Web address: www.bhsala.com/shelby/Home.aspx
**Control:** Church–operated, Nongovernment, not–for profit **Service:** General Medical and Surgical

> **Staffed Beds:** 206

## ALEXANDER CITY—Tallapoosa County

⊞ **RUSSELL MEDICAL CENTER (010065)**, 3316 Highway 280, Zip 35010–3369, Mailing Address: P.O. Box 939, Zip 35011–0939; tel. 256/329–7100, (Nonreporting) **A**1 9 10 19
Primary Contact: Lother E. Peace, III, President and Chief Executive Officer
CFO: Timothy J. Thornton, Chief Financial Officer
CMO: Michele Goldhagen, M.D., Chief of Staff
CIO: Tommy Spraggins, Director Information Services
CHR: Mary Shockley, Director Human Resources
Web address: www.russellmedcenter.com
**Control:** Other not–for–profit (including NFP Corporation) **Service:** General Medical and Surgical

> **Staffed Beds:** 69

## ANDALUSIA—Covington County

⊞ **ANDALUSIA REGIONAL HOSPITAL (010036)**, 849 South Three Notch Street, Zip 36420–5325, Mailing Address: P.O. Box 760, Zip 36420–1214; tel. 334/222–8466, (Nonreporting) **A**1 9 10 **S** LifePoint Health, Brentwood, TN
Primary Contact: John C. Yanes, Chief Executive Officer
COO: Melissa Davis, Chief Operating Officer
CFO: Shirley M. Smith, Chief Financial Officer
CIO: Matthew Perry, Director Information Systems
CHR: Kaci Daughtry, Director Human Resources
Web address: www.andalusiaregionalhospital.com
**Control:** Corporation, Investor–owned, for–profit **Service:** General Medical and Surgical

> **Staffed Beds:** 88

## ANNISTON—Calhoun County

☐ **NOLAND HOSPITAL ANNISTON (012011)**, 400 East 10th Street, 4th Floor, Zip 36207–4716; tel. 256/741–6141, (Nonreporting) **A**1 9 10 **S** Noland Health Services, Inc., Birmingham, AL
Primary Contact: Bill Mitchell, Administrator
Web address: www.nolandhealth.com
**Control:** Other not–for–profit (including NFP Corporation) **Service:** Long–Term Acute Care hospital

> **Staffed Beds:** 38

⊞ **NORTHEAST ALABAMA REGIONAL MEDICAL CENTER (010078)**, 400 East Tenth Street, Zip 36207–4716, Mailing Address: P.O. Box 2208, Zip 36202–2208; tel. 256/235–5121, (Nonreporting) **A**1 2 9 10
Primary Contact: Louis A. Bass, Chief Executive Officer
CMO: David Zinn, M.D., Vice President Medical Affairs
CIO: Pete Furlow, Director Information Technology Services
CHR: Michael S. Simms, Sr., Vice President Human Resources
CNO: Elaine Davis, Chief Nursing Officer and Vice President Patient Services
Web address: www.rmccares.org
**Control:** Hospital district or authority, Government, nonfederal **Service:** General Medical and Surgical

> **Staffed Beds:** 276

⊞ **STRINGFELLOW MEMORIAL HOSPITAL (010038)**, 301 East 18th Street, Zip 36207–3952; tel. 256/235–8900, (Nonreporting) **A**1 9 10 **S** Community Health Systems, Inc., Franklin, TN
Primary Contact: Jay Hinesley, Chief Executive Officer
CIO: Peggy Henderson, Director Health Information
CHR: Tamatha Johnson, Director Human Resources
Web address: www.stringfellowhealth.com
**Control:** Corporation, Investor–owned, for–profit **Service:** General Medical and Surgical

> **Staffed Beds:** 75

## ASHLAND—Clay County

★ **CLAY COUNTY HOSPITAL (010073)**, 83825 Highway 9, Zip 36251–7981, Mailing Address: P.O. Box 1270, Zip 36251–1270; tel. 256/354–2131, (Nonreporting) **A**9 10
Primary Contact: Linda U. Jordan, Administrator
COO: Linda U. Jordan, Administrator
CFO: Kerry W. Tomlin, Associate Administrator
CMO: John Fischer, Director Medical Staff
CIO: Brad Strother, Director Information Technology
CHR: Linda T. Smith, Director Human Resources
CNO: Charles Griffin, Director of Nursing
Web address: www.claycountyhospital.com
**Control:** County–Government, nonfederal **Service:** General Medical and Surgical

> **Staffed Beds:** 124

## ATHENS—Limestone County

☐ **ATHENS–LIMESTONE HOSPITAL (010079)**, 700 West Market Street, Zip 35611–2457, Mailing Address: P.O. Box 999, Zip 35612–0999; tel. 256/233–9292 **A**1 5 9 10 **F**3 7 8 11 13 15 18 28 29 34 35 40 46 48 50 51 53 54 56 57 58 59 64 68 70 73 75 76 77 79 81 84 85 86 87 89 93 98 107 108 109 110 111 114 115 118 119 129 130 131 132 143 144 146 147 **S** Huntsville Hospital Health System, Huntsville, AL
Primary Contact: David Pryor, President
COO: Randy Comer, Chief Operating Officer
CFO: Randy Comer, Chief Financial Officer
CMO: Jon Bignault, M.D., Chief of Staff
CIO: Kim Hoback, Supervisor Information Systems
CHR: Rachel Frey, Director Human Resources
CNO: Jan Lenz, Chief Nursing Officer
Web address: www.athenslimestonehospital.com
**Control:** Hospital district or authority, Government, nonfederal **Service:** General Medical and Surgical

> **Staffed Beds:** 101 **Admissions:** 3764 **Census:** 40 **Outpatient Visits:** 160892 **Births:** 469 **Total Expense ($000):** 65123 **Payroll Expense ($000):** 27718 **Personnel:** 699

---

**Hospital, Medicare Provider Number, Address, Telephone, Approval, Facility, and Physician Codes, Health Care System**

★ American Hospital Association (AHA) membership
☐ The Joint Commission accreditation
◯ Healthcare Facilities Accreditation Program
◇ DNV Healthcare Inc. accreditation
⇑ Center for Improvement in Healthcare Quality Accreditation
△ Commission on Accreditation of Rehabilitation Facilities (CARF) accreditation

---

## ATMORE—Escambia County

★ **ATMORE COMMUNITY HOSPITAL (010169)**, 401 Medical Park Drive,
Zip 36502–3091; tel. 251/368–2500, (Nonreporting) **A**9 10
Primary Contact: A. William Perkins, Administrator
CFO: Keith Strickling, Chief Financial Officer
CHR: Linda Lowrey, Human Resources Officer
CNO: Ashley Chunn, Director of Nursing
Web address: www.ebaptisthealthcare.org/AtmoreCommunityHospital/
**Control:** Other not–for–profit (including NFP Corporation) **Service:** General
Medical and Surgical

**Staffed Beds:** 49

## BAY MINETTE—Baldwin County

**NORTH BALDWIN INFIRMARY (010129)**, 1815 Hand Avenue,
Zip 36507–4110, Mailing Address: P.O. Box 1409, Zip 36507–1409;
tel. 251/937–5521, (Nonreporting) **A**9 10 **S** Infirmary Health System, Mobile, AL
Primary Contact: Ben K. Hansart
CFO: J. Patrick Murphy, Chief Financial Officer
Web address: www.mobileinfirmary.org
**Control:** Other not–for–profit (including NFP Corporation) **Service:** General
Medical and Surgical

**Staffed Beds:** 50

## BESSEMER—Jefferson County

☐ **MEDICAL WEST (010114)**, 995 Ninth Avenue S.W., Zip 35022–4527;
tel. 205/481–7000 **A**1 3 9 10 **F**3 11 13 15 18 29 30 31 34 40 43 45 49 50
57 59 60 64 68 70 74 75 76 77 78 79 80 81 82 85 86 90 92 93 94 96 98
100 101 102 103 104 107 108 110 111 114 115 118 119 129 130 132 143
146 147 148 **P**6 **S** UAB Health System, Birmingham, AL
Primary Contact: Brian Keith Pennington, President and Chief Executive Officer
COO: Sean Tinney, FACHE, Chief Operating Officer
CFO: Brandon H. Slocum, Senior Vice President and Chief Financial Officer
CMO: Conrad De Los Santos, President Medical Staff
CIO: Bob Duckworth, Director Information Systems
CHR: Gannon Davis, Director Human Resources
CNO: Pamela Spencer Autrey, R.N., Chief Nursing Officer
Web address: www.medicalwesthospital.org
**Control:** Hospital district or authority, Government, nonfederal **Service:** General
Medical and Surgical

**Staffed Beds:** 231 **Admissions:** 6539 **Census:** 106 **Outpatient Visits:**
214550 **Births:** 548 **Total Expense ($000):** 105530 **Payroll Expense**
**($000):** 42941 **Personnel:** 992

## BIRMINGHAM—Jefferson County

✠ **BIRMINGHAM VETERANS AFFAIRS MEDICAL CENTER**, 700 South 19th
Street, Zip 35233–1927; tel. 205/933–8101, (Nonreporting) **A**1 2 3 5 8
**S** Department of Veterans Affairs, Washington, DC
Primary Contact: William F. Harper, M.D., Acting Director
COO: Phyllis J. Smith, Associate Director
CFO: Mary S. Mitchell, Chief Resource Management Services
CMO: William F. Harper, M.D., Chief of Staff
CIO: Antonia Mohamed, Acting Chief Information Officer
CHR: Jacqueline Caron, Chief Human Resources
CNO: Cynthia Cleveland, Ph.D., Associate Director for Patient Care Services and
Nurse Executive
Web address: www.birmingham.va.gov/
**Control:** Veterans Affairs, Government, federal **Service:** General Medical and
Surgical

**Staffed Beds:** 151

✠ **BROOKWOOD MEDICAL CENTER (010139)**, 2010 Brookwood Medical Center
Drive, Zip 35209–6875; tel. 205/877–1000 **A**1 2 3 5 10 **F**3 11 12 13 15 17
18 20 22 24 26 29 30 31 34 35 38 40 43 45 46 47 48 49 50 56 57 58 59
64 70 72 74 75 76 78 79 81 82 85 86 87 90 98 100 101 102 103 104 105
107 108 109 110 111 114 115 116 117 118 119 120 121 123 124 126 129
130 132 135 145 146 147 148 **S** TENET Healthcare Corporation, Dallas, TX
Primary Contact: Charles A. Stark, FACHE, President and Chief Executive Officer
COO: Brenda H. Carlisle, R.N., Chief Operating Officer
CFO: Doug Carter, Chief Financial Officer
CMO: Bradley Dennis, M.D., Chief Medical Officer
CIO: Manuel Price, Director Information Systems
CHR: Ronnelle Stewart, SPHR, Chief Human Resources Officer
CNO: Jacquelyn Martinek, R.N., Chief Nursing Officer
Web address: www.bwmc.com
**Control:** Corporation, Investor–owned, for–profit **Service:** General Medical and
Surgical

**Staffed Beds:** 645 **Admissions:** 25029 **Census:** 366 **Outpatient Visits:**
109209 **Births:** 3995 **Total Expense ($000):** 324660 **Payroll Expense**
**($000):** 102281 **Personnel:** 1925

✠ **CHILDREN'S OF ALABAMA (013300)**, 1600 Seventh Avenue South,
Zip 35233–1785; tel. 205/638–9100 **A**1 3 5 9 10 **F**3 7 8 11 12 16 17 19 21
23 25 27 29 30 31 32 34 35 38 39 40 41 43 46 48 49 50 54 55 57 58 59
60 61 64 65 68 72 74 75 77 78 79 80 81 82 84 85 86 87 88 89 92 93 94
96 97 98 99 100 101 102 104 107 108 109 111 114 115 116 117 118 119
129 130 131 132 134 135 136 137 138 139 142 143 144 146 148
Primary Contact: Wm. Michael Warren, Jr., Chief Executive Officer
COO: Tom Shufflebarger, Chief Operating Officer
CFO: Dawn Walton, Chief Financial Officer
CMO: Crayton A. Fargason, M.D., Medical Director
CIO: Mike McDevitt, Chief Information Officer
CHR: Douglas B. Dean, Chief Human Resources Officer
CNO: Deb Wesley, MSN, Chief Nursing Officer
Web address: www.childrensal.org
**Control:** Other not–for–profit (including NFP Corporation) **Service:** Children's
general

**Staffed Beds:** 351 **Admissions:** 13676 **Census:** 232 **Outpatient Visits:**
653926 **Total Expense ($000):** 667588 **Payroll Expense ($000):** 239616
**Personnel:** 3959

✠ **HEALTHSOUTH LAKESHORE REHABILITATION HOSPITAL (013025)**, 3800
Ridgeway Drive, Zip 35209–5599; tel. 205/868–2000, (Nonreporting) **A**1 9 10
**S** HEALTHSOUTH Corporation, Birmingham, AL
Primary Contact: Vickie Demers, Chief Executive Officer
CFO: Kimberly Thrasher, Controller
CMO: Michael Rosemore, M.D., Medical Director
CHR: Julie Smith, Director Human Resources
CNO: April Cobb, Chief Nursing Officer
Web address: www.healthsouthlakeshorerehab.com
**Control:** Corporation, Investor–owned, for–profit **Service:** Rehabilitation

**Staffed Beds:** 100

☐ **HILL CREST BEHAVIORAL HEALTH SERVICES (014000)**, 6869 Fifth Avenue
South, Zip 35212–1866; tel. 205/833–9000, (Nonreporting) **A**1 9 10 **S** Universal
Health Services, Inc., King of Prussia, PA
Primary Contact: Steve McCabe, Chief Executive Officer
CFO: Mark Teske, Chief Financial Officer
Web address: www.hillcrestbhs.com
**Control:** Corporation, Investor–owned, for–profit **Service:** Psychiatric

**Staffed Beds:** 89

☐ **NOLAND HOSPITAL BIRMINGHAM (012009)**, 50 Medical Park East Drive, 8th
Floor, Zip 35235; tel. 205/808–5100, (Nonreporting) **A**1 9 10 **S** Noland Health
Services, Inc., Birmingham, AL
Primary Contact: Laura S. Wills, Administrator
COO: Sharon Engle, Director Clinical Services
CMO: Mark Middlebrooks, M.D., Medical Director
CHR: Ashley Clark, Coordinator Human Resources
CNO: Rachel Chapman, Nurse Manager
Web address: www.nolandhealth.com
**Control:** Other not–for–profit (including NFP Corporation) **Service:** Long–Term
Acute Care hospital

**Staffed Beds:** 45

☐ **PRINCETON BAPTIST MEDICAL CENTER (010103)**, 701 Princeton Avenue
S.W., Zip 35211–1303; tel. 205/783–3000, (Nonreporting) **A**1 2 3 5 9 10
**S** Baptist Health System, Birmingham, AL
Primary Contact: Betsy Postlethwait, President
COO: Sarah Nunnelly, Chief Operating Officer
CFO: Beverly Haymon, Chief Financial Officer
CMO: Alan Craig, M.D., Chief Medical Officer
CNO: Paula Davenport, Chief Nursing Officer
Web address: www.bhsala.com
**Control:** Church–operated, Nongovernment, not–for profit **Service:** General
Medical and Surgical

**Staffed Beds:** 295

✠ **SELECT SPECIALTY HOSPITAL–BIRMINGHAM (012008)**, 800 Montclair
Road, 9th Floor, Zip 35213–1908; tel. 205/599–4600, (Nonreporting) **A**1 9 10
**S** Select Medical Corporation, Mechanicsburg, PA
Primary Contact: Andrea White, Chief Executive Officer
CMO: Allan Goldstein, M.D., Medical Director and Chief of Staff
Web address: www.selectspecialtyhospitals.com/company/locations/birmingham.
aspx
**Control:** Corporation, Investor–owned, for–profit **Service:** Long–Term Acute Care
hospital

**Staffed Beds:** 38

✠ **ST. VINCENT'S BIRMINGHAM (010056)**, 810 St. Vincent's Drive,
Zip 35205–1695, Mailing Address: P.O. Box 12407, Zip 35202–2407;
tel. 205/939–7000 **A**1 2 3 5 9 10 **F**3 11 13 15 17 18 20 22 24 26 28 29 30
31 34 35 37 40 43 45 50 53 54 57 58 59 60 62 65 66 68 70 72 74 75 76
77 78 79 81 82 84 85 86 87 91 93 94 107 108 110 111 114 115 119 120
121 123 126 129 130 131 135 146 147 **S** Ascension Health, Saint Louis, MO
Primary Contact: Evan Ray, FACHE, President
COO: Andy Davis, Chief Operating Officer
CFO: Wilma Newton, Executive Vice President and Chief Financial Officer
CMO: Gregory L. James, D.O., Chief Medical Officer
CIO: Timothy Stettheimer, Vice President and Chief Information Officer
CHR: Michelle Galipeau, Director Human Resources
Web address: www.stvhs.com
**Control:** Other not–for–profit (including NFP Corporation) **Service:** General Medical and Surgical

> **Staffed Beds:** 409 **Admissions:** 19520 **Census:** 254 **Outpatient Visits:** 190506 **Births:** 3644 **Total Expense ($000):** 360888 **Payroll Expense ($000):** 101272 **Personnel:** 1782

✠ **ST. VINCENT'S EAST (010011)**, 50 Medical Park East Drive, Zip 35235–9987;
tel. 205/838–3000 **A**1 2 3 5 9 10 **F**3 11 12 13 17 18 20 22 24 26 28 29 30
31 34 35 40 43 44 45 46 47 49 50 51 53 54 57 58 59 60 64 65 70 72 74
76 77 78 79 81 85 86 87 90 93 94 98 100 101 102 103 104 107 108 111
114 119 121 123 126 129 130 131 132 135 146 **S** Ascension Health, Saint Louis, MO
Primary Contact: Michael Korpiel, FACHE, President and Chief Operating Officer
COO: Andrew Gnann, Vice President Operations
CFO: Jan DiCesare, Vice President Financial Operations
CMO: Frank Malensek, M.D., Chief Medical Officer
CIO: Beverly Golightly, Director Information Technology
CHR: Carol Maietta, Vice President Human Resources and Chief Learning Officer
CNO: Amy Shelton, Chief Nursing Officer
Web address: www.stvhs.com
**Control:** Other not–for–profit (including NFP Corporation) **Service:** General Medical and Surgical

> **Staffed Beds:** 362 **Admissions:** 15771 **Census:** 249 **Outpatient Visits:** 129681 **Births:** 1067 **Total Expense ($000):** 214729 **Payroll Expense ($000):** 71086 **Personnel:** 1212

✠ **GRANDVIEW MEDICAL CENTER (010104)**, 800 Montclair Road,
Zip 35213–1984; tel. 205/592–1000 **A**1 2 3 5 9 10 13 **F**3 11 12 13 15 17 18
20 22 24 26 28 29 30 31 34 35 40 43 45 46 47 48 49 50 51 53 54 57 58
59 64 70 72 73 74 75 76 77 78 79 81 82 84 85 90 93 96 98 99 102 103
106 107 108 109 110 111 114 115 116 117 118 119 120 122 124 126 129
130 131 132 135 146 147 148 **S** Community Health Systems, Inc., Franklin, TN
Primary Contact: Keith Granger, President and Chief Executive Officer
COO: Drew Mason, Chief Operating Officer
CFO: Julie Soekoro, Chief Financial Officer
CMO: Hugh O'Shields, M.D., President Medical Staff
CIO: Tim Townes, Director Information Systems
CHR: Joel R. Windham, Director Human Resources
CNO: Andy Romine, Chief Nursing Officer
Web address: www.grandviewhealth.com
**Control:** Corporation, Investor–owned, for–profit **Service:** General Medical and Surgical

> **Staffed Beds:** 379 **Admissions:** 11374 **Census:** 185 **Outpatient Visits:** 294670 **Births:** 483 **Total Expense ($000):** 211949 **Payroll Expense ($000):** 78694 **Personnel:** 1369

**UAB HIGHLANDS** See University of Alabama Hospital

✠ **UNIVERSITY OF ALABAMA HOSPITAL (010033)**, 619 19th Street South,
Zip 35249–1900; tel. 205/934–4011, (Includes UAB HIGHLANDS, 1201 11th
Avenue South, Zip 35205–5299; tel. 205/930–7000; Anthony Patterson, Chief
Operating Officer) **A**1 2 3 5 8 9 10 **F**3 4 5 6 8 9 11 12 13 15 16 17 18 19 20
21 22 23 24 25 26 27 28 29 30 31 33 34 35 37 38 39 40 43 44 45 46 47
48 49 50 52 53 54 55 56 57 58 59 60 61 62 64 65 66 68 70 71 72 73 74
75 77 78 79 81 82 83 84 85 86 87 90 91 92 93 94 95 96 97 98 99 100
101 102 103 104 107 108 110 111 114 115 116 117 118 119 120 121 123
124 126 129 130 131 132 135 136 137 138 139 140 141 142 143 144 145
146 147 148 **P**3 **S** UAB Health System, Birmingham, AL
Primary Contact: Anthony Patterson, FACHE, Senior Vice President Inpatient Services
CFO: Mary Beth Briscoe, Chief Financial Officer
CMO: Loring Rue, M.D., Senior Vice President, Quality Patient Safety and Clinical Effectiveness
CIO: Joan Hicks, Chief Information Officer
CHR: Alesia Jones, Chief Human Resources Officer
CNO: Terri Lyn Poe, Interim Chief Nursing Officer
Web address: www.uabmedicine.org
**Control:** State–Government, nonfederal **Service:** General Medical and Surgical

> **Staffed Beds:** 1191 **Admissions:** 73500 **Census:** 913 **Outpatient Visits:** 608344 **Births:** 4163 **Total Expense ($000):** 1286784 **Payroll Expense ($000):** 479534 **Personnel:** 8184

**VETERANS AFFAIRS MEDICAL CENTER** See Birmingham Veterans Affairs Medical Center

### BOAZ—Marshall County

☐ **MARSHALL MEDICAL CENTER SOUTH (010005)**, U.S. Highway 431 North,
Zip 35957–0999, Mailing Address: P.O. Box 758, Zip 35957–0758;
tel. 256/593–8310 **A**1 9 10 19 **F**3 7 8 11 12 13 15 18 20 22 26 28 29 31 32
34 35 37 40 43 45 46 50 53 54 57 59 64 68 70 74 75 76 78 79 81 85 86
87 92 93 100 107 108 110 111 114 115 117 119 121 123 129 130 131
132 135 141 145 146 147 148 **S** Marshall Health System, Guntersville, AL
Primary Contact: John D. Anderson, FACHE, Administrator
CFO: Kathy Nelson, Chief Financial Officer
Web address: www.mmcenters.com//index.php/facilities/marshall_south
**Control:** Hospital district or authority, Government, nonfederal **Service:** General Medical and Surgical

> **Staffed Beds:** 114 **Admissions:** 4760 **Census:** 47 **Outpatient Visits:** 271045 **Births:** 629 **Total Expense ($000):** 85698 **Payroll Expense ($000):** 30314 **Personnel:** 566

### BREWTON—Escambia County

☐ **D. W. MCMILLAN MEMORIAL HOSPITAL (010099)**, 1301 Belleville Avenue,
Zip 36426–1306, Mailing Address: P.O. Box 908, Zip 36427–0908;
tel. 251/867–8061 **A**1 9 10 **F**3 7 11 13 15 31 34 35 40 45 57 59 62 64 70
75 76 78 79 81 85 86 89 93 100 107 108 111 114 119 127 129 130 131
132 133 135 143 146 **P**6
Primary Contact: Christopher B. Griffin, Chief Executive Officer
CFO: Rick Owens, Chief Financial Officer
CIO: Ian Vickery, Director Information Technology
CHR: Autherine Davis, Director Human Resources
CNO: Bob Ellis, Director of Nursing
Web address: www.dwmmh.org
**Control:** Hospital district or authority, Government, nonfederal **Service:** General Medical and Surgical

> **Staffed Beds:** 49 **Admissions:** 1601 **Census:** 17 **Outpatient Visits:** 48157 **Births:** 243 **Total Expense ($000):** 25584 **Payroll Expense ($000):** 10134 **Personnel:** 229

### BUTLER—Choctaw County

★ **CHOCTAW GENERAL HOSPITAL (011304)**, 401 Vanity Fair Avenue,
Zip 36904–3032; tel. 205/459–9100, (Nonreporting) **A**9 10 18 **S** Rush Health Systems, Meridian, MS
Primary Contact: J. W. Cowan, Administrator
Web address: www.choctawgeneral.com/cgh/
**Control:** Corporation, Investor–owned, for–profit **Service:** General Medical and Surgical

> **Staffed Beds:** 25

### CAMDEN—Wilcox County

**J. PAUL JONES HOSPITAL (010102)**, 317 McWilliams Avenue,
Zip 36726–1610; tel. 334/682–4131 **A**9 10 20 **F**15 29 40 107 119 125
127 133
Primary Contact: Elizabeth M. Kennedy, Administrator
CMO: Willie White, M.D., Director Medical Staff
CIO: Jill Smith, Administrative Coordinator
CHR: Jill Smith, Administrative Coordinator
**Control:** City–County, Government, nonfederal **Service:** General Medical and Surgical

> **Staffed Beds:** 21 **Admissions:** 213 **Census:** 2 **Outpatient Visits:** 15460 **Births:** 0 **Total Expense ($000):** 3659 **Payroll Expense ($000):** 1662 **Personnel:** 49

### CARROLLTON—Pickens County

**PICKENS COUNTY MEDICAL CENTER (010109)**, 241 Robert K. Wilson Drive,
Zip 35447, Mailing Address: P.O. Box 478, Zip 35447–0478;
tel. 205/367–8111, (Nonreporting) **A**9 10 20
Primary Contact: Jim Marshall, CEO
CFO: Janice Winters, Controller
CMO: William R. Brooke, M.D., President Medical Staff
CHR: Dottie D. Wilson, Director Human Resources
Web address: www.dchsystem.com
**Control:** County–Government, nonfederal **Service:** General Medical and Surgical

> **Staffed Beds:** 52

## CENTRE—Cherokee County

☒ **CHEROKEE MEDICAL CENTER (010022)**, 400 Northwood Drive, Zip 35960–1023; tel. 256/927–5531 **A**1 9 10 **F**3 11 15 29 30 35 40 43 45 48 57 59 64 70 75 77 81 85 87 92 93 96 107 108 114 119 127 129 130 131 133 146 **P**6 **S** Community Health Systems, Inc., Franklin, TN
Primary Contact: Terry Long, Chief Executive Officer
CFO: Zac Allen, CPA, Chief Financial Officer
CHR: Marlene Benefield, Director Human Resources
Web address: www.cherokeemedicalcenter.com
**Control:** Corporation, Investor–owned, for–profit **Service:** General Medical and Surgical

**Staffed Beds:** 45 **Admissions:** 864 **Census:** 13 **Outpatient Visits:** 20164 **Births:** 0 **Total Expense ($000):** 16026 **Payroll Expense ($000):** 5148 **Personnel:** 141

## CENTREVILLE—Bibb County

**BIBB MEDICAL CENTER (010058)**, 208 Pierson Avenue, Zip 35042–2918; tel. 205/926–4881, (Total facility includes 131 beds in nursing home–type unit) **A**3 9 10 13 **F**3 11 15 29 35 40 50 57 59 64 81 93 107 114 119 125 127 128 130 133 143 144 146
Primary Contact: Joseph Marchant, Administrator
CFO: Heather Desmond, Chief Financial Officer
CMO: John Meigs, Jr., M.D., Chief of Staff
CHR: Kim Hayes, Director Human Resources
Web address: www.bibbmedicalcenter.com
**Control:** County–Government, nonfederal **Service:** General Medical and Surgical

**Staffed Beds:** 161 **Admissions:** 671 **Census:** 128 **Outpatient Visits:** 42994 **Births:** 0 **Total Expense ($000):** 16235 **Payroll Expense ($000):** 8294 **Personnel:** 205

## CHATOM—Washington County

★ **WASHINGTON COUNTY HOSPITAL (011300)**, 14600 St. Stephens Avenue, Zip 36518–9998, Mailing Address: P.O. Box 1299, Zip 36518–1299; tel. 251/847–2223 **A**9 10 18 **F**29 34 40 57 59 64 89 107 114 119 128 133 148 **P**6
Primary Contact: Douglas Tanner, Chief Executive Officer
CFO: Alyson Overstreet, Chief Financial Officer
CMO: Steve Donald, M.D., Chief of Staff
CIO: Brady Wright, Information Technology Network Administrator
CHR: Linda Randolph, Director Personnel Services
CNO: Michelle Alford, R.N., Director of Nursing
Web address: www.wchnh.org
**Control:** County–Government, nonfederal **Service:** General Medical and Surgical

**Staffed Beds:** 25 **Admissions:** 197 **Census:** 5 **Outpatient Visits:** 10786 **Births:** 0 **Total Expense ($000):** 7256 **Payroll Expense ($000):** 2848 **Personnel:** 84

## CULLMAN—Cullman County

☐ **CULLMAN REGIONAL MEDICAL CENTER (010035)**, 1912 Alabama Highway 157, Zip 35055, Mailing Address: P.O. Box 1108, Zip 35056–1108; tel. 256/737–2000 **A**1 9 10 **F**3 7 11 12 13 15 16 17 18 19 20 22 26 28 29 30 34 35 37 40 43 45 46 49 50 51 53 57 59 62 63 70 71 74 75 76 79 81 82 83 84 85 86 87 89 93 97 107 108 110 111 114 118 119 121 129 130 131 132 133 134 135 146 147 148
Primary Contact: James Clements, Chief Executive Officer
CFO: Nesha Donaldson, Chief Financial Officer
CMO: Bill Smith, M.D., Chief of Staff
CIO: Nancy Zavatchen, Director Information Technology
CHR: Toni Geddings, Director Human Resources
CNO: Cheryl Bailey, R.N., Chief Nursing Officer Vice President Patient Care Services
Web address: www.crmchospital.com
**Control:** Other not–for–profit (including NFP Corporation) **Service:** General Medical and Surgical

**Staffed Beds:** 115 **Admissions:** 6408 **Census:** 64 **Outpatient Visits:** 91767 **Births:** 683 **Total Expense ($000):** 96018 **Payroll Expense ($000):** 37085 **Personnel:** 847

## DADEVILLE—Tallapoosa County

**LAKE MARTIN COMMUNITY HOSPITAL (010052)**, 201 Mariarden Road, Zip 36853–6251, Mailing Address: P.O. Box 629, Zip 36853–0629; tel. 256/825–7821, (Nonreporting) **A**9 10
Primary Contact: Michael D. Bruce, Chief Executive Officer
CHR: Karen Treadwell, Director Human Resources
Web address: www.lakemartincommunityhospital.com
**Control:** Partnership, Investor–owned, for–profit **Service:** General Medical and Surgical

**Staffed Beds:** 26

## DAPHNE—Baldwin County

☒ **EASTPOINTE HOSPITAL (014017)**, 7400 Roper Lane, Zip 36526–5274; tel. 251/378–6500 **A**1 9 10 **F**50 98 130 143 **P**6 **S** AltaPointe Health Systems, Mobile, AL
Primary Contact: Philip L. Cusa, Administrator
CFO: Kevin Markham, Chief Financial Officer
CMO: Sandra K. Parker, M.D., Chief Medical Officer
CIO: Steve Dolan, Chief Information Officer
CHR: Alicia Donoghue, Director Human Resources
Web address: www.altapointe.org/eastpointe.php
**Control:** Other not–for–profit (including NFP Corporation) **Service:** Psychiatric

**Staffed Beds:** 66 **Admissions:** 1642 **Census:** 49 **Outpatient Visits:** 0 **Births:** 0

## DECATUR—Morgan County

☐ **DECATUR MORGAN HOSPITAL (010085)**, 1201 Seventh Street S.E., Zip 35601–3303, Mailing Address: P.O. Box 2239, Zip 35609–2239; tel. 256/341–2000, (Includes DECATUR MORGAN HOSPITAL PARKWAY CAMPUS, 1874 Beltline Road S.W., Zip 35601–5509, Mailing Address: P.O. Box 2239, Zip 35609–2239; tel. 256/350–2211; DECATUR MORGAN HOSPITAL–WEST, 2205 Beltline Road S.W., Zip 35601–3687, Mailing Address: P.O. Box 2240, Zip 35609–2240; tel. 256/306–4000), (Nonreporting) **A**1 5 9 10 **S** Huntsville Hospital Health System, Huntsville, AL
Primary Contact: Nathaniel Richardson, Jr., President
CFO: Kim Shrewsbury, Vice President and Chief Financial Officer
CMO: Allen J. Schmidt, M.D., President, Medical Staff
CIO: Mark Megehee, Vice President and Chief Information Officer
CNO: Anita Walden, Vice President and Chief Nursing Officer
Web address: www.decaturgeneral.org
**Control:** Hospital district or authority, Government, nonfederal **Service:** General Medical and Surgical

**Staffed Beds:** 132

**PARKWAY MEDICAL CENTER** See Decatur Morgan Hospital Parkway Campus

## DEMOPOLIS—Marengo County

**BRYAN W. WHITFIELD MEMORIAL HOSPITAL (010112)**, 105 U.S. Highway 80 East, Zip 36732–3616, Mailing Address: P.O. Box 890, Zip 36732–0890; tel. 334/289–4000, (Nonreporting) **A**3 9 10 20
Primary Contact: Arthur D. Evans, Chief Executive Officer and Administrator
CHR: Danny Smith, Director Human Resources
Web address: www.bwwmh.com
**Control:** Hospital district or authority, Government, nonfederal **Service:** General Medical and Surgical

**Staffed Beds:** 68

## DOTHAN—Houston County

☒ **FLOWERS HOSPITAL (010055)**, 4370 West Main Street, Zip 36305–4000, Mailing Address: P.O. Box 6907, Zip 36302–6907; tel. 334/793–5000 **A**1 2 9 10 **F**3 4 12 13 15 16 17 18 19 20 22 24 26 28 29 31 34 35 40 43 46 48 49 50 51 56 57 59 60 61 64 67 68 70 74 75 76 77 78 79 81 82 85 86 87 89 90 92 93 97 98 100 107 108 110 111 114 115 116 117 118 119 126 128 129 132 134 135 146 147 148 **P**6 **S** Community Health Systems, Inc., Franklin, TN
Primary Contact: Suzanne Woods, President and Chief Executive Officer
COO: Barry Moss, Assistant Chief Executive Officer
CFO: Talana Bell, Chief Financial Officer
CIO: Matthew Garrett, Director Information Systems
CHR: Jennifer Odom, Interim Director Human Resources
CNO: Dan L. Cumbie, Chief Nursing Officer
Web address: www.flowershospital.com
**Control:** Corporation, Investor–owned, for–profit **Service:** General Medical and Surgical

**Staffed Beds:** 141 **Admissions:** 10465 **Census:** 126 **Outpatient Visits:** 128762 **Births:** 1298 **Total Expense ($000):** 165506 **Payroll Expense ($000):** 52443 **Personnel:** 1109

☒ **HEALTHSOUTH REHABILITATION HOSPITAL (013030)**, 1736 East Main Street, Zip 36301–3040, Mailing Address: P.O. Box 6708, Zip 36302–6708; tel. 334/712–6333, (Nonreporting) **A**1 9 10 **S** HEALTHSOUTH Corporation, Birmingham, AL
Primary Contact: Margaret A. Futch, Chief Executive Officer
CFO: Heath Watson, Controller
CHR: Lydia Christion, Director Human Resources
Web address: www.healthsouthdothan.com
**Control:** Corporation, Investor–owned, for–profit **Service:** Rehabilitation

**Staffed Beds:** 39

*Many Facility Codes have changed. Please refer to the AHA Guide Code Chart.*

© 2015 AHA Guide

☐ **LAUREL OAKS BEHAVIORAL HEALTH CENTER (014013)**, 700 East Cottonwood Road, Zip 36301–3644; tel. 334/794–7373, (Nonreporting) **A**1 9 10 **S** Universal Health Services, Inc., King of Prussia, PA
Primary Contact: Derek Johnson, Chief Executive Officer
CMO: Nelson Handol, M.D., Medical Director
CHR: Lorrie Evans, Director Human Resources
Web address: www.laureloaksbhc.com
**Control:** Corporation, Investor–owned, for–profit **Service:** Children's hospital psychiatric

**Staffed Beds: 38**

☐ **NOLAND HOSPITAL DOTHAN (012010)**, 1108 Ross Clark Circle, 4th Floor, Zip 36301–3022; tel. 334/699–4300, (Nonreporting) **A**1 9 10 **S** Noland Health Services, Inc., Birmingham, AL
Primary Contact: Kaye Burke, Administrator
Web address: www.nolandhealth.com
**Control:** Other not–for–profit (including NFP Corporation) **Service:** Long–Term Acute Care hospital

**Staffed Beds: 35**

☒ ◇ **SOUTHEAST ALABAMA MEDICAL CENTER (010001)**, 1108 Ross Clark Circle, Zip 36301–3024, Mailing Address: P.O. Box 6987, Zip 36302–6987; tel. 334/793–8111 **A**1 2 9 10 13 21 **F**3 8 12 13 15 18 20 22 24 26 28 29 30 31 32 34 35 37 40 43 44 45 49 50 51 53 54 56 57 59 60 62 63 64 68 70 71 74 75 76 77 78 79 81 82 84 85 86 87 89 92 93 94 98 100 101 102 103 104 105 107 108 110 111 114 115 116 117 118 119 120 121 123 124 126 127 129 130 132 135 146 147 148
Primary Contact: Ronald S. Owen, FACHE, Chief Executive Officer
COO: Charles C. Brannen, Senior Vice President and Chief Operating Officer
CFO: Derek Miller, Senior Vice President and Chief Financial Officer
CMO: Charles Harkness, D.O., Vice President Medical Affairs
CIO: Eric Allen Daffron, Division Director, Information Systems
CHR: Tony Welch, Vice President Human Resources
CNO: Diane Buntyn, MSN, Vice President Patient Care Services
Web address: www.samc.org
**Control:** Hospital district or authority, Government, nonfederal **Service:** General Medical and Surgical

**Staffed Beds: 420 Admissions: 18986 Census: 262 Outpatient Visits: 147544 Births: 1471 Total Expense ($000): 307464 Payroll Expense ($000): 135820 Personnel: 2463**

### ENTERPRISE—Coffee County

☒ **MEDICAL CENTER ENTERPRISE (010049)**, 400 North Edwards Street, Zip 36330–2510; tel. 334/347–0584, (Nonreporting) **A**1 9 10 **S** Community Health Systems, Inc., Franklin, TN
Primary Contact: Richard Ellis, Chief Executive Officer
CFO: Greg McGilvray, Chief Financial Officer
CMO: Rick Harrelson, M.D., President Medical Staff
CIO: Stephen Smothers, Director Information Systems
CHR: Toni Kaminski, Director Human Resources
CNO: Bobby Phillips, Chief Nursing Officer
Web address: www.mcehospital.com
**Control:** Corporation, Investor–owned, for–profit **Service:** General Medical and Surgical

**Staffed Beds: 117**

### EUFAULA—Barbour County

**MEDICAL CENTER BARBOUR (010069)**, 820 West Washington Street, Zip 36027–1899; tel. 334/688–7000 **A**9 10 **F**3 11 15 29 30 34 35 40 45 46 50 57 59 64 68 70 81 85 98 103 107 119 127 133 135 146
Primary Contact: Ralph H. Clark, Jr., FACHE, Chief Executive Officer
CFO: Debbie Norton, Chief Financial Officer
CHR: Cindy Griffin, Director Human Resources
CNO: Kathy Wilder, R.N., Chief Clinical Officer
Web address: www.medctrbarbour.org
**Control:** Hospital district or authority, Government, nonfederal **Service:** General Medical and Surgical

**Staffed Beds: 47 Admissions: 1639 Census: 25 Outpatient Visits: 38331 Births: 0 Total Expense ($000): 16527 Payroll Expense ($000): 7359 Personnel: 190**

### EUTAW—Greene County

★ **GREENE COUNTY HEALTH SYSTEM (010051)**, 509 Wilson Avenue, Zip 35462–1099; tel. 205/372–3388, (Nonreporting) **A**9 10
Primary Contact: Elmore Patterson, Chief Executive Officer
Web address: www.gcheutaw.com
**Control:** County–Government, nonfederal **Service:** General Medical and Surgical

**Staffed Beds: 20**

### EVERGREEN—Conecuh County

**EVERGREEN MEDICAL CENTER (010148)**, 101 Crestview Avenue, Zip 36401–3333, Mailing Address: P.O. Box 706, Zip 36401–0706; tel. 251/578–2480, (Nonreporting) **A**9 10 **S** Gilliard Health Services, Montgomery, AL
Primary Contact: Tom McLendon, Administrator
CFO: Sharon Jones, Chief Financial Officer
CMO: William Farmer, M.D., Chief of Staff
CHR: Tracey Rhodes, Coordinator Human Resources
CNO: Angie Hendrix, Director of Nursing
Web address: www.evergreenmedical.org
**Control:** Partnership, Investor–owned, for–profit **Service:** General Medical and Surgical

**Staffed Beds: 44**

### FAIRHOPE—Baldwin County

☐ **THOMAS HOSPITAL (010100)**, 750 Morphy Avenue, Zip 36532–1812, Mailing Address: P.O. Box 929, Zip 36533–0929; tel. 251/928–2375, (Nonreporting) **A**1 9 10 19 **S** Infirmary Health System, Mobile, AL
Primary Contact: Ormand Thompson
COO: Douglas Garner, Vice President
CMO: Michael McBrearty, M.D., Vice President Medical Affairs
CNO: Julie Rowell, R.N., Chief Nursing Officer
Web address: www.thomashospital.com
**Control:** Other not–for–profit (including NFP Corporation) **Service:** General Medical and Surgical

**Staffed Beds: 136**

### FAYETTE—Fayette County

☐ **FAYETTE MEDICAL CENTER (010045)**, 1653 Temple Avenue North, Zip 35555–1314, Mailing Address: P.O. Drawer 710, Zip 35555–0710; tel. 205/932–5966, (Nonreporting) **A**1 9 10 **S** DCH Health System, Tuscaloosa, AL
Primary Contact: Donald J. Jones, FACHE, Administrator
CFO: Jeff Huff, Assistant Administrator Finance
CHR: Felicia Solomon–Owens, Director Human Resources
Web address: www.dchsystem.com
**Control:** Hospital district or authority, Government, nonfederal **Service:** General Medical and Surgical

**Staffed Beds: 167**

### FLORENCE—Lauderdale County

☐ **ELIZA COFFEE MEMORIAL HOSPITAL (010006)**, 205 Marengo Street, Zip 35630–6033, Mailing Address: P.O. Box 818, Zip 35631–0818; tel. 256/768–9191, (Nonreporting) **A**1 9 10 **S** RegionalCare Hospital Partners, Brentwood, TN
Primary Contact: Russell Pigg, Chief Executive Officer
COO: Mike Howard, Associate Administrator
CFO: Steve E. Hobbs, Chief Financial Officer
CMO: Oliver Matthews, M.D., Chief Medical Officer
CIO: William Johnson, Director Information Systems
CHR: Cheryl Lee, Director Human Resources
CNO: Marye Elliott, Chief Nursing Officer
Web address: www.chgroup.org
**Control:** Hospital district or authority, Government, nonfederal **Service:** General Medical and Surgical

**Staffed Beds: 278**

### FOLEY—Baldwin County

☒ **SOUTH BALDWIN REGIONAL MEDICAL CENTER (010083)**, 1613 North McKenzie Street, Zip 36535–2299; tel. 251/949–3400, (Nonreporting) **A**1 9 10 19 **S** Community Health Systems, Inc., Franklin, TN
Primary Contact: Keith Newton, Chief Executive Officer
CFO: Brad Hardcastle, Chief Financial Officer
CMO: John Campbell, Chief Medical Officer
CHR: Pam Brunson, Director Human Resources
CNO: Margaret Roley, Chief Nursing Officer
Web address: www.southbaldwinrmc.com
**Control:** Corporation, Investor–owned, for–profit **Service:** General Medical and Surgical

**Staffed Beds: 112**

---

**Hospital, Medicare Provider Number, Address, Telephone, Approval, Facility, and Physician Codes, Health Care System**

★ American Hospital Association (AHA) membership
☐ The Joint Commission accreditation
○ Healthcare Facilities Accreditation Program
◇ DNV Healthcare Inc. accreditation
⇑ Center for Improvement in Healthcare Quality Accreditation
△ Commission on Accreditation of Rehabilitation Facilities (CARF) accreditation

## FORT PAYNE—Dekalb County

⊞ **DEKALB REGIONAL MEDICAL CENTER (010012)**, 200 Medical Center Drive, Zip 35968–3458, Mailing Address: P.O. Box 680778, Zip 35968–1608; tel. 256/845–3150, (Nonreporting) **A**1 9 10 20 **S** Community Health Systems, Inc., Franklin, TN
Primary Contact: Corey Ewing, FACHE, Chief Executive Officer
CFO: Chris Benson, Chief Financial Officer
CMO: Anthony Sims, M.D., Chief of Staff
CIO: Joseph Helms, Director Information Systems
CHR: Diane McMichen, Director Human Resources
CNO: Marquita Bailey, Chief Nursing Officer
Web address: www.dekalbregional.com
**Control:** Corporation, Investor–owned, for–profit **Service:** General Medical and Surgical

**Staffed Beds:** 121

## GADSDEN—Etowah County

⊞ **GADSDEN REGIONAL MEDICAL CENTER (010040)**, 1007 Goodyear Avenue, Zip 35903–1195; tel. 256/494–4000 **A**1 2 9 10 **F**3 11 13 15 18 20 22 24 29 30 31 34 35 40 43 45 50 56 57 59 60 64 68 70 74 76 77 78 79 80 81 89 93 98 99 102 103 105 107 108 111 112 113 114 115 121 124 126 129 130 131 146 147 148 **S** Community Health Systems, Inc., Franklin, TN
Primary Contact: Stephen G. Pennington, Chief Executive Officer
COO: Paul Theriot, Chief Operating Officer
CFO: Michael Cotton, Chief Financial Officer
CMO: William Haller, III, M.D., Chief of Staff
CIO: Glenn Phillips, Director Information Systems
CHR: Gale H. Sanders, Director
CNO: Donna Nicholson, Chief Nursing Officer
Web address: www.gadsdenregional.com
**Control:** Corporation, Investor–owned, for–profit **Service:** General Medical and Surgical

**Staffed Beds:** 268 **Admissions:** 13862 **Census:** 196 **Outpatient Visits:** 74771 **Births:** 1041 **Total Expense ($000):** 144386 **Payroll Expense ($000):** 53777 **Personnel:** 1125

⊞ **HEALTHSOUTH REHABILITATION OF GADSDEN (013032)**, 801 Goodyear Avenue, Zip 35903–1133; tel. 256/439–5000 **A**1 9 10 **F**28 90 91 93 95 96 148 **S** HEALTHSOUTH Corporation, Birmingham, AL
Primary Contact: Kayla Feazell, Chief Executive Officer
COO: Kayla Feazell, Chief Executive Officer
CFO: Lori Norman, Chief Financial Officer
CMO: Diem Yeung, M.D., Medical Director
CIO: Lori Norman, Chief Financial Officer
CHR: Heather Blevins, Director Human Resources
CNO: Barry Eads, Chief Nursing Officer
Web address: www.healthsouthgadsden.com
**Control:** Corporation, Investor–owned, for–profit **Service:** Rehabilitation

**Staffed Beds:** 44 **Admissions:** 1036 **Census:** 38 **Outpatient Visits:** 1951 **Births:** 0 **Total Expense ($000):** 11072 **Payroll Expense ($000):** 6282 **Personnel:** 154

☐ **MOUNTAIN VIEW HOSPITAL (014006)**, 3001 Scenic Highway, Zip 35904–3047, Mailing Address: P.O. Box 8406, Zip 35902–8406; tel. 256/546–9265 **A**1 9 10 **F**2 54 98 99 104 105 130 132
Primary Contact: G. Michael Shehi, M.D., Interim Chief Executive Officer
COO: Sara Romano, R.N., Vice President
CFO: Mary Jensen, Controller
CMO: G. Michael Shehi, M.D., Medical Director
CHR: Dave Jensen, Director Human Resources, Performance Improvement and Risk Management
Web address: www.mtnviewhospital.com
**Control:** Individual, Investor–owned, for–profit **Service:** Psychiatric

**Staffed Beds:** 68 **Admissions:** 1183 **Census:** 31 **Outpatient Visits:** 30591 **Births:** 0 **Total Expense ($000):** 11763 **Payroll Expense ($000):** 6865 **Personnel:** 206

⊞ **RIVERVIEW REGIONAL MEDICAL CENTER (010046)**, 600 South Third Street, Zip 35901–5399; tel. 256/543–5200 **A**1 9 10 **F**5 8 12 15 17 18 20 22 24 26 29 30 34 37 40 41 45 46 47 48 49 50 51 56 57 59 60 68 69 70 74 75 77 79 81 85 87 91 92 93 94 97 103 107 108 109 110 111 114 115 118 119 120 126 129 130 146 148 **S** Prime Healthcare Services, Ontario, CA
Primary Contact: Thomas Roddy, Interim Chief Executive Officer
COO: Thomas Roddy, Chief Operating Officer
CIO: Jay Terrell, Manager Management Information Systems
CHR: Leslie Morton, Manager Human Resources
CNO: Tammy Harlow, Chief Nurse Executive
Web address: www.riverviewregional.com
**Control:** Corporation, Investor–owned, for–profit **Service:** General Medical and Surgical

**Staffed Beds:** 175 **Admissions:** 6101 **Census:** 104 **Outpatient Visits:** 64252 **Births:** 0 **Total Expense ($000):** 84384 **Payroll Expense ($000):** 27898 **Personnel:** 661

## GENEVA—Geneva County

★ **WIREGRASS MEDICAL CENTER (010062)**, 1200 West Maple Avenue, Zip 36340–1694; tel. 334/684–3655, (Nonreporting) **A**9 10
Primary Contact: Samuel Johnson, Chief Executive Officer
CFO: Gloria McGowan, Chief Financial Officer
CIO: Tom Garske, Director Information Systems
CHR: Pam Phillips, Chief Human Resource Officer
CNO: Craig Cassady, Director of Nursing
Web address: www.alaweb.com/~tgarske
**Control:** Hospital district or authority, Government, nonfederal **Service:** General Medical and Surgical

**Staffed Beds:** 49

## GEORGIANA—Butler County

**GEORGIANA HOSPITAL (010047)**, 515 Miranda Street, Zip 36033–4519, Mailing Address: P.O. Box 548, Zip 36033–0548; tel. 334/376–2205, (Nonreporting) **A**9 10
Primary Contact: Harry Cole, Jr., Administrator
**Control:** Partnership, Investor–owned, for–profit **Service:** General Medical and Surgical

**Staffed Beds:** 22

## GREENSBORO—Hale County

**HALE COUNTY HOSPITAL (010095)**, 508 Green Street, Zip 36744–2316; tel. 334/624–3024, (Nonreporting) **A**9 10
Primary Contact: Shay Whaley, Administrator
Web address: www.halecountyhospital.com
**Control:** Hospital district or authority, Government, nonfederal **Service:** General Medical and Surgical

**Staffed Beds:** 20

## GREENVILLE—Butler County

⊞ **L. V. STABLER MEMORIAL HOSPITAL (010150)**, 29 L. V. Stabler Drive, Zip 36037–3800; tel. 334/382–2671, (Nonreporting) **A**1 5 9 10 **S** Community Health Systems, Inc., Franklin, TN
Primary Contact: Donald R. Rentfro, Chief Executive Officer
CFO: Vann Windham, Chief Financial Officer
CMO: Norman F. McGowin, III, M.D., Chief of Staff
CIO: Doug Burkett, Manager Information Technology
CHR: Robert Foster, Director Human Resources
CNO: Kimberli Weaver, Chief Nursing Officer
Web address: www.lvstabler.com
**Control:** Corporation, Investor–owned, for–profit **Service:** General Medical and Surgical

**Staffed Beds:** 61

## GROVE HILL—Clarke County

★ **GROVE HILL MEMORIAL HOSPITAL (010091)**, 295 South Jackson Street, Zip 36451–3231, Mailing Address: P.O. Box 935, Zip 36451–0935; tel. 251/275–3191, (Nonreporting) **A**9 10
Primary Contact: Emily Steadham, Administrator
CFO: Elaine Averett, Chief Financial Officer
CMO: Eniola Fagbongbe, M.D., Chief Medical Staff
CIO: Aaron Harrell, Director
CHR: Aubrey Sheffield, Administrative Assistant Human Resources and Public Relations
CNO: Karen Coleman, Director of Nursing
Web address: www.grovehillmemorial.org
**Control:** City–Government, nonfederal **Service:** General Medical and Surgical

**Staffed Beds:** 33

## GUNTERSVILLE—Marshall County

**MARSHALL MEDICAL CENTER NORTH (010010)**, 8000 Alabama Highway 69, Zip 35976; tel. 256/753–8000 **A**5 9 10 **F**3 8 11 12 13 15 26 28 29 32 34 35 37 38 40 43 45 49 50 51 53 54 57 59 64 68 70 74 75 76 79 81 82 85 86 87 92 93 99 100 102 103 104 107 108 110 111 114 115 119 130 131 132 133 135 141 146 147 **S** Marshall Health System, Guntersville, AL
Primary Contact: Cheryl M. Hays, FACHE, Administrator
COO: Cheryl M. Hays, FACHE, Administrator and Chief Operating Officer
CFO: Kathy Nelson, Chief Financial Officer
CIO: Kim Bunch, Director Information Technology
CHR: Jeff Stone, Director Human Resources
CNO: Kathy Woodruff, R.N., Chief Nursing Officer
Web address: www.mmcenters.com
**Control:** Hospital district or authority, Government, nonfederal **Service:** General Medical and Surgical

**Staffed Beds:** 90 **Admissions:** 4163 **Census:** 53 **Outpatient Visits:** 160459 **Births:** 370 **Total Expense ($000):** 55706 **Payroll Expense ($000):** 21378 **Personnel:** 339

*Many Facility Codes have changed. Please refer to the AHA Guide Code Chart.*   © 2015 AHA Guide

## HALEYVILLE—Winston County

✠ **LAKELAND COMMUNITY HOSPITAL (010125)**, Highway 195 East,
Zip 35565–9536, Mailing Address: P.O. Box 780, Zip 35565–0780;
tel. 205/486–5213, (Nonreporting) **A**1 9 10 **S** Curae Health, Clinton, TN
Primary Contact: Cynthia Nichols, R.N., MSN, Chief Executive Officer
CFO: Penny Westmoreland, Chief Financial Officer
Web address: www.lakelandcommunityhospital.com/
**Control:** Corporation, Investor–owned, for–profit **Service:** General Medical and
Surgical

**Staffed Beds:** 56

## HAMILTON—Marion County

✠ **MARION REGIONAL MEDICAL CENTER (010044)**, 1256 Military Street South,
Zip 35570–5003; tel. 205/921–6200, (Nonreporting) **A**1 9 10 **S** North
Mississippi Health Services, Inc., Tupelo, MS
Primary Contact: Tanya Brasher, Administrator
CMO: Jarred Sartain, M.D., President Medical Staff
CHR: Anne Lawler, Director Human Resources
CNO: Jennifer Cagle, Director of Nursing
Web address: www.nmhs.net
**Control:** Other not–for–profit (including NFP Corporation) **Service:** General
Medical and Surgical

**Staffed Beds:** 36

## HUNTSVILLE—Madison County

**BEHAVIORAL HEALTHCARE CENTER AT HUNTSVILLE (014018)**, 5315
Millennium Drive N.W., Zip 35806–2458; tel. 256/964–6700, (Nonreporting) **A**10
**S** Tennessee Health Management, Parsons, TN
Primary Contact: Bradley Moss, Administrator
Web address: www.tnhealthmanagement.com/bhc/huntsville
**Control:** Corporation, Investor–owned, for–profit **Service:** Psychiatric

**Staffed Beds:** 20

✠ **CRESTWOOD MEDICAL CENTER (010131)**, One Hospital Drive,
Zip 35801–3403; tel. 256/429–4000, (Nonreporting) **A**1 5 9 10 **S** Community
Health Systems, Inc., Franklin, TN
Primary Contact: Pamela Hudson, M.D., Chief Executive Officer
COO: Bobby Ginn, Chief Operating Officer
CFO: Sherry J. Jones, Chief Financial Officer
CHR: Elyria Sinclair, Director Human Resources
CNO: Martha Delaney Walls, R.N., Chief Nursing Officer
Web address: www.crestwoodmedcenter.com
**Control:** Corporation, Investor–owned, for–profit **Service:** General Medical and
Surgical

**Staffed Beds:** 150

✠ **HEALTHSOUTH REHABILITATION HOSPITAL OF NORTH ALABAMA
(013029)**, 107 Governors Drive S.W., Zip 35801–4326; tel. 256/535–2300,
(Nonreporting) **A**1 9 10 **S** HEALTHSOUTH Corporation, Birmingham, AL
Primary Contact: Douglas H. Beverly, Chief Executive Officer
Web address: www.healthsouthhuntsville.com
**Control:** Corporation, Investor–owned, for–profit **Service:** Rehabilitation

**Staffed Beds:** 70

☐ **HUNTSVILLE HOSPITAL (010039)**, 101 Sivley Road S.W., Zip 35801–4470;
tel. 256/265–1000, (Includes HUNTSVILLE HOSPITAL FOR WOMEN AND
CHILDREN, 911 Big Cove Road S.E., Zip 35801–3784; tel. 256/265–1000;
MADISON HOSPITAL, 8375 Highway 72 West, Madison, Zip 35758–9573;
tel. 256/265–2012; Mary Lynne Wright, R.N., President) **A**1 2 3 5 10 **F**5 7 8 12
13 14 15 17 18 19 20 21 22 23 24 25 26 28 29 30 31 35 37 38 39 40 41
43 48 49 50 51 53 54 56 57 59 60 63 64 68 70 71 72 73 76 78 79 80 81
82 84 85 88 89 93 96 98 99 100 101 102 103 104 105 107 108 109 110
111 114 115 116 117 118 119 126 129 130 131 142 145 146 147 148
**S** Huntsville Hospital Health System, Huntsville, AL
Primary Contact: David S. Spillers, Chief Executive Officer
COO: Jeff Samz, Chief Operating Officer
CFO: Kelli Powers, Chief Financial Officer
CMO: Robert Chappell, M.D., Chief Medical Officer and Chief Quality Officer
CIO: Rick Corn, Chief Information Officer
CHR: Andrea P. Rosler, Vice President Human Resources
CNO: Karol Jones, Chief Nursing Officer
Web address: www.huntsvillehospital.org
**Control:** Hospital district or authority, Government, nonfederal **Service:** General
Medical and Surgical

**Staffed Beds:** 877 **Admissions:** 42735 **Census:** 565 **Outpatient Visits:**
753873 **Births:** 5189 **Total Expense ($000):** 733395 **Payroll Expense
($000):** 295335 **Personnel:** 6440

## JACKSON—Clarke County

**JACKSON MEDICAL CENTER (010128)**, 220 Hospital Drive, Zip 36545–2459,
Mailing Address: P.O. Box 428, Zip 36545–0428; tel. 251/246–9021,
(Nonreporting) **A**9 10 **S** Gilliard Health Services, Montgomery, AL
Primary Contact: Amy Gibson, Chief Executive Officer
COO: Jennifer M. Ryland, R.N., Chief Administrative Officer
CFO: Amy Gibson, Chief Executive Officer
CHR: Kathy Jones, Director Human Resources
Web address: www.jacksonmedicalcenter.org
**Control:** Partnership, Investor–owned, for–profit **Service:** General Medical and
Surgical

**Staffed Beds:** 26

## JACKSONVILLE—Calhoun County

☐ **RMC JACKSONVILLE (010146)**, 1701 Pelham Road South, Zip 36265–3399,
Mailing Address: P.O. Box 999, Zip 36265–0999; tel. 256/435–4970 **A**1 9 10
**F**3 4 5 29 30 34 35 40 42 45 48 50 51 56 57 59 64 65 68 69 76 79 81 82
85 93 98 103 107 108 111 114 119 120 135 146
Primary Contact: Joe Weaver, Chief Executive Officer
COO: Carlos Farmer, R.N., Director Clinical Operations
CFO: Robbin Curlee, Controller
CMO: Rey Gavino, M.D., Chief of Staff
CIO: Richard Maust, Chief Information Officer
CHR: Doug Scott, Director Human Resources
CNO: Jean Ann McMurrey, R.N., Chief Nursing Officer
Web address: www.jmchealth.com
**Control:** Hospital district or authority, Government, nonfederal **Service:** General
Medical and Surgical

**Staffed Beds:** 70 **Admissions:** 1702 **Census:** 23 **Outpatient Visits:** 45863
**Births:** 343 **Total Expense ($000):** 21115 **Payroll Expense ($000):** 9030
**Personnel:** 179

## JASPER—Walker County

☐ **WALKER BAPTIST MEDICAL CENTER (010089)**, 3400 Highway 78 East,
Zip 35501–8907, Mailing Address: P.O. Box 3547, Zip 35502–3547;
tel. 205/387–4000, (Nonreporting) **A**1 9 10 20 **S** Baptist Health System,
Birmingham, AL
Primary Contact: Robert Phillips, Administrator
CFO: John Langlois, Chief Financial Officer
CIO: Kenny Horton, Director Information Systems
CHR: Pat Morrow, Director Human Resources
CNO: Robbie Hindman, Vice President Patient Care Services and Chief Nursing
Officer
Web address: www.bhsala.com
**Control:** Church–operated, Nongovernment, not–for profit **Service:** General
Medical and Surgical

**Staffed Beds:** 236

## LUVERNE—Crenshaw County

☐ **BEACON CHILDREN'S HOSPITAL (014015)**, 150 Hospital Drive, Zip 36049;
tel. 334/335–5040, (Nonreporting) **A**1 9 10
Primary Contact: Lee Anne Montgomery, Administrator
Web address: www.beaconchildrenshospital.com
**Control:** Other not–for–profit (including NFP Corporation) **Service:** Children's
hospital psychiatric

**Staffed Beds:** 24

**CRENSHAW COMMUNITY HOSPITAL (010008)**, 101 Hospital Circle,
Zip 36049–7344; tel. 334/335–3374, (Nonreporting) **A**9 10
Primary Contact: Bradley Eisemann, Administrator
COO: Victoria Lawrenson, Chief Operating Officer
CMO: Charles Tompkins, M.D., Chief of Staff
CHR: Patricia Jarry, Manager Human Resources
**Control:** Corporation, Investor–owned, for–profit **Service:** General Medical and
Surgical

**Staffed Beds:** 49

## MADISON—Madison County

**BRADFORD HEALTH SERVICES AT HUNTSVILLE**, 1600 Browns Ferry Road,
Zip 35758–9601, Mailing Address: P.O. Box 1488, Zip 35758–0176;
tel. 256/461–7272, (Nonreporting) **S** Bradford Health Services, Birmingham, AL
Primary Contact: Bob Hinds, Executive Director
Web address: www.bradfordhealth.com
**Control:** Corporation, Investor–owned, for–profit **Service:** Alcoholism and other
chemical dependency

**Staffed Beds:** 84

---

**Hospital, Medicare Provider Number, Address, Telephone, Approval, Facility, and Physician Codes, Health Care System**

★ American Hospital Association (AHA) membership
☐ The Joint Commission accreditation
○ Healthcare Facilities Accreditation Program
◇ DNV Healthcare Inc. accreditation
⇑ Center for Improvement in Healthcare Quality Accreditation
△ Commission on Accreditation of Rehabilitation Facilities (CARF) accreditation

**MOBILE—Mobile County**

**BAYPOINTE BEHAVIORAL HEALTH (014014)**, 5800 Southland Drive, Zip 36693–3313; tel. 251/661–0153, (Nonreporting) **A**3 9 10 **S** AltaPointe Health Systems, Mobile, AL
Primary Contact: Jack Lungu, Administrator
Web address: www.altapointe.org
**Control:** Corporation, Investor–owned, for–profit **Service:** Psychiatric

Staffed Beds: 60

**INFIRMARY LONG TERM ACUTE CARE HOSPITAL (012006)**, 5 Mobile Infirmary Circle, Zip 36607–3513, Mailing Address: P.O. Box 2226, Zip 36652–2226; tel. 251/660–5239, (Nonreporting) **A**1 9 10 **S** Infirmary Health System, Mobile, AL
Primary Contact: Susanne Marmande, Administrator
Web address: www.theinfirmary.com/
**Control:** Other not–for–profit (including NFP Corporation) **Service:** Long–Term Acute Care hospital

Staffed Beds: 38

△ **MOBILE INFIRMARY MEDICAL CENTER (010113)**, 5 Mobile Infirmary Drive North, Zip 36607–3513, Mailing Address: P.O. Box 2144, Zip 36652–2144; tel. 251/435–2400, (Includes ROTARY REHABILITATION HOSPITAL, 5 Mobile Infirmary Circle, Zip 36607, Mailing Address: P.O. Box 2144, Zip 36652; tel. 251/435–3400), (Nonreporting) **A**1 2 3 5 7 9 10 **S** Infirmary Health System, Mobile, AL
Primary Contact: Jennifer Eslinger, Administrator
CFO: Joe Denton, Executive Vice President and Chief Financial Officer
CIO: Eddy Stephens, Vice President Information Technology
CHR: Sheila Young, Vice President Human Resources
CNO: Suzanne C. Bird, R.N., Chief Nursing Officer
Web address: www.infirmaryhealth.org
**Control:** Other not–for–profit (including NFP Corporation) **Service:** General Medical and Surgical

Staffed Beds: 517

**PROVIDENCE HOSPITAL (010090)**, 6801 Airport Boulevard, Zip 36608–3785, Mailing Address: P.O. Box 850429, Zip 36685–0429; tel. 251/633–1000 **A**1 2 3 5 9 10 **F**3 11 13 15 17 18 20 22 24 26 28 29 30 31 34 35 40 44 45 49 50 51 53 54 55 57 58 59 60 61 64 65 68 70 73 74 75 76 77 78 79 80 81 82 83 84 85 86 87 89 92 93 96 102 107 108 110 111 114 115 117 119 120 121 124 126 129 130 131 132 135 142 146 148 **P**5 6 **S** Ascension Health, Saint Louis, MO
Primary Contact: Todd Kennedy, President and Chief Executive Officer
COO: Todd S. Kennedy, Executive Vice President and Chief Operating Officer
CFO: C. Susan Cornejo, Senior Vice President Finance and Chief Financial Officer
CMO: William M. Lightfoot, M.D., Vice President Medical Services
CIO: Kathy Ross, Chief Information Officer
CHR: Christopher Cockrell, Executive Director Human Resources
CNO: Peter Lindquist, Vice President and Chief Nursing Officer
Web address: www.providencehospital.org
**Control:** Church–operated, Nongovernment, not–for profit **Service:** General Medical and Surgical

Staffed Beds: 302 Admissions: 15148 Census: 207 Outpatient Visits: 145560 Births: 1902 Total Expense ($000): 202432 Payroll Expense ($000): 69136 Personnel: 1279

**ROTARY REHABILITATION HOSPITAL** See Mobile Infirmary Medical Center

**SPRINGHILL MEMORIAL HOSPITAL (010144)**, 3719 Dauphin Street, Zip 36608–1798, Mailing Address: P.O. Box 8246, Zip 36689–0246; tel. 251/344–9630 **A**1 9 10 **F**11 13 15 17 18 20 22 24 26 28 29 30 31 34 40 46 47 49 50 51 57 60 70 74 75 76 77 78 79 81 82 85 86 87 88 89 93 107 110 111 115 118 119 126 127 129 130 132 146 147 148
Primary Contact: Jeffery M. St. Clair, President and Chief Executive Officer
COO: Jeffery M. St Clair, President and Chief Executive Officer
CFO: Jan Grigsby, Vice President and Chief Financial Officer
CMO: Liston Jones, M.D., Medical Director
CIO: Mark Kilborn, Director Information Systems
CHR: Daniela Batchelor, Director Human Resources
CNO: Paul Read, R.N., Vice President and Chief Nursing Officer
Web address: www.springhillmemorial.com
**Control:** Corporation, Investor–owned, for–profit **Service:** General Medical and Surgical

Staffed Beds: 196 Admissions: 10078 Census: 140 Outpatient Visits: 167895 Births: 630 Total Expense ($000): 140448 Payroll Expense ($000): 44939 Personnel: 1079

⊠ **UNIVERSITY OF SOUTH ALABAMA CHILDREN'S AND WOMEN'S HOSPITAL (013301)**, (Childrens and Womens), 1700 Center Street, Zip 36604–3301; tel. 251/415–1000 **A**1 3 5 9 10 **F**3 7 11 13 15 21 27 29 30 31 40 48 49 52 55 58 59 64 72 73 74 75 76 77 78 79 81 85 86 87 88 89 93 107 111 114 119 130 143 146 147 **S** University of South Alabama Hospitals, Mobile, AL
Primary Contact: Owen Bailey, Administrator
CFO: William B. Bush, CPA, Chief Financial Officer
CIO: Mark Lauteren, Chief Information Officer
CHR: Janice Rehm, Manager Human Resources
CNO: Carol Druckenmiller, R.N., Assistant Administrator and Chief Nursing Officer
Web address: www.usahealthsystem.com/usacwh
**Control:** State–Government, nonfederal **Service:** Other specialty

Staffed Beds: 198 Admissions: 9559 Census: 168 Outpatient Visits: 64587 Births: 2857 Total Expense ($000): 122643 Payroll Expense ($000): 51813 Personnel: 1138

⊠ **UNIVERSITY OF SOUTH ALABAMA MEDICAL CENTER (010087)**, 2451 Fillingim Street, Zip 36617–2293; tel. 251/471–7000 **A**1 2 3 5 8 9 10 **F**3 11 16 17 18 20 22 24 26 29 31 34 40 43 46 49 57 58 59 60 61 64 70 74 78 79 81 85 87 107 108 111 114 115 119 130 146 148 **S** University of South Alabama Hospitals, Mobile, AL
Primary Contact: A. Elizabeth Anderson, FACHE, Administrator
CFO: William B. Bush, CPA, Chief Financial Officer
CIO: Mark Lauteren, Chief Information Officer
CHR: Anita Shirah, Director Human Resources
CNO: Lisa Mestas, Chief Nursing Officer and Assistant Administrator Clinical Services
Web address: www.usahealthsystem.com/usamc
**Control:** State–Government, nonfederal **Service:** General Medical and Surgical

Staffed Beds: 132 Admissions: 6407 Census: 108 Outpatient Visits: 53702 Births: 1 Total Expense ($000): 212305 Payroll Expense ($000): 117976 Personnel: 1348

**MONROEVILLE—Monroe County**

**MONROE COUNTY HOSPITAL (010120)**, 2016 South Alabama Avenue, Zip 36460–3044, Mailing Address: P.O. Box 886, Zip 36461–0886; tel. 251/575–3111, (Nonreporting) **A**1 9 10 20
Primary Contact: Jeffrey M. Brannon, Chief Executive Officer
CFO: Wes Nall, Chief Financial Officer
CMO: David Stallworth, M.D., Chief of Staff
CIO: Jody Falkenberry, Director Information Systems
CHR: Tara Nowling, Director Human Resources
CNO: Barbara Harned, R.N., Chief Nursing Officer
Web address: www.mchcare.com
**Control:** Hospital district or authority, Government, nonfederal **Service:** General Medical and Surgical

Staffed Beds: 44

**MONTGOMERY—Montgomery County**

**BAPTIST MEDICAL CENTER EAST (010149)**, 400 Taylor Road, Zip 36117–3512, Mailing Address: P.O. Box 241267, Zip 36124–1267; tel. 334/277–8330 **A**1 3 9 10 **F**3 11 12 13 15 29 30 34 35 40 44 45 47 49 50 56 57 63 64 68 70 72 73 75 76 77 79 81 82 85 86 89 90 93 94 107 108 111 114 115 119 126 129 130 132 135 146 147 **S** Baptist Health, Montgomery, AL
Primary Contact: Jeff G. Rains, Chief Executive Officer
CFO: Katrina Belt, Chief Financial Officer
CHR: Kay Bennett, Vice President Human Resources
CNO: Kathy Gaston, Chief Nursing Officer
Web address: www.baptistfirst.org
**Control:** Hospital district or authority, Government, nonfederal **Service:** General Medical and Surgical

Staffed Beds: 164 Admissions: 9392 Census: 116 Outpatient Visits: 91329 Births: 3526 Total Expense ($000): 99430 Payroll Expense ($000): 39589 Personnel: 819

**BAPTIST MEDICAL CENTER SOUTH (010023)**, 2105 East South Boulevard, Zip 36116–2409, Mailing Address: Box 11010, Zip 36111–0010; tel. 334/288–2100 **A**1 3 5 9 10 **F**3 5 11 12 13 15 17 18 20 22 24 26 28 29 30 31 34 35 40 44 45 47 49 50 56 57 58 59 60 61 63 64 68 70 72 74 75 76 78 79 81 82 84 85 86 87 89 90 93 94 98 100 101 102 103 104 105 107 108 110 111 114 115 116 117 118 119 126 129 130 131 132 135 146 147 148 **S** Baptist Health, Montgomery, AL
Primary Contact: J. Peter Selman, FACHE, Chief Executive Officer
CFO: Melissa Johnson, Chief Financial Officer
CMO: Donovan Kendrick, M.D., Chief Medical Officer
CIO: Steve Miller, Director Information Systems
CHR: Kay Bennett, System Director Human Resources
CNO: Karen McCaa, R.N., Vice President Patient Care Services and Chief Nursing Officer
Web address: www.baptistfirst.org
**Control:** Hospital district or authority, Government, nonfederal **Service:** General Medical and Surgical

Staffed Beds: 372 Admissions: 17396 Census: 242 Outpatient Visits: 248186 Births: 777 Total Expense ($000): 362372 Payroll Expense ($000): 88823 Personnel: 1791

*Many Facility Codes have changed. Please refer to the AHA Guide Code Chart.*

© 2015 AHA Guide

✠ **CENTRAL ALABAMA VETERANS HEALTH CARE SYSTEM**, 215 Perry Hill Road, Zip 36109–3798; tel. 334/272–4670, (Includes MONTGOMERY DIVISION, 215 Perry Hill Road, tel. 334/272–4670; TUSKEGEE DIVISION, 2400 Hospital Road, Tuskegee, Zip 36083–5001; tel. 334/727–0550), (Nonreporting) **A**1 3 **S** Department of Veterans Affairs, Washington, DC
Primary Contact: Robin Jackson, Ph.D., Interim Director
CFO: Debra Nicholson, Manager Finance
CMO: Cliff Robinson, M.D., Chief of Staff
CIO: Rhoda Tyson, Chief Information Officer
CHR: Janice Hardy, Chief Human Resource Management Service
Web address: www.centralalabama.va.gov/
**Control:** Veterans Affairs, Government, federal **Service:** General Medical and Surgical

| Staffed Beds: 261 |
|---|

✠ **HEALTHSOUTH REHABILITATION HOSPITAL OF MONTGOMERY (013028)**, 4465 Narrow Lane Road, Zip 36116–2900; tel. 334/284–7700 **A**1 9 10 **F**3 9 28 29 34 35 54 56 57 59 64 74 75 77 86 90 93 95 130 131 132 143 146 148 **P**5 **S** HEALTHSOUTH Corporation, Birmingham, AL
Primary Contact: Thomas Roddy, Chief Executive Officer
CFO: Heath Watson, Controller
CMO: Jeffrey Eng, M.D., Medical Director
CIO: Anidra Billingslea, Health Insurance Management
CHR: Kim McDaniel, Director Human Resources
CNO: Lee Anne Montgomery, R.N., Chief Nursing Officer
Web address: www.healthsouthmontgomery.com
**Control:** Corporation, Investor–owned, for–profit **Service:** Rehabilitation

| Staffed Beds: 70 Admissions: 1810 Census: 62 Outpatient Visits: 4539 Births: 0 Total Expense ($000): 18079 Payroll Expense ($000): 10764 Personnel: 185 |
|---|

✠ **JACKSON HOSPITAL AND CLINIC (010024)**, 1725 Pine Street, Zip 36106–1117; tel. 334/293–8000, (Nonreporting) **A**1 3 9 10
Primary Contact: Joe B. Riley, FACHE, President and Chief Executive Officer
COO: Michael James, Chief Operations Officer
CFO: Paul Peiffer, Chief Financial Officer and Vice President
CHR: Gilbert Darrington, Director Human Resources
CNO: Sharon A. Goodison, R.N., Chief Nursing Officer
Web address: www.jackson.org
**Control:** Other not–for–profit (including NFP Corporation) **Service:** General Medical and Surgical

| Staffed Beds: 251 |
|---|

**LONG TERM CARE HOSPITAL** See Noland Hospital Montgomery

**MONTGOMERY DIVISION** See Central Alabama Veterans Health Care System

☐ **NOLAND HOSPITAL MONTGOMERY (012007)**, 1725 Pine Street, 5 North, Zip 36106–1109; tel. 334/240–0532, (Nonreporting) **A**1 9 10 **S** Noland Health Services, Inc., Birmingham, AL
Primary Contact: Susan E. Legg, Interim Administrator
Web address: www.nolandhealth.com
**Control:** Other not–for–profit (including NFP Corporation) **Service:** Long–Term Acute Care hospital

| Staffed Beds: 65 |
|---|

**MOULTON—Lawrence County**

☐ **LAWRENCE MEDICAL CENTER (010059)**, 202 Hospital Street, Zip 35650–1218, Mailing Address: P.O. Box 39, Zip 35650–0039; tel. 256/974–2200, (Nonreporting) **A**1 9 10 **S** Huntsville Hospital Health System, Huntsville, AL
Primary Contact: Kyle Buchanan, Chief Executive Officer
CFO: Jim Crawford, Chief Financial Officer
CIO: Jeremy Duncan, Director Information Systems
CHR: Diane K. Secor, Director Human Resources
CNO: Sherry Jolley, Chief Clinical Officer
Web address: www.lawrencemedicalcenter.com
**Control:** County–Government, nonfederal **Service:** General Medical and Surgical

| Staffed Beds: 43 |
|---|

**MUSCLE SHOALS—Colbert County**

☐ **SHOALS HOSPITAL (010157)**, 201 Avalon Avenue, Zip 35661–2805, Mailing Address: P.O. Box 3359, Zip 35662–3359; tel. 256/386–1600, (Nonreporting) **A**1 9 10 **S** RegionalCare Hospital Partners, Brentwood, TN
Primary Contact: Jeff Jennings, FACHE, Chief Executive Officer
CFO: Steve E. Hobbs, Chief Financial Officer
CMO: Terry TRUE, M.D., Chief of Staff
CIO: William Johnson, Director Information Systems
CHR: Nancy Bowling, Director Human Resources
CNO: Denida A. Cox, Chief Nursing Officer
Web address: www.shoalshospital.com
**Control:** Hospital district or authority, Government, nonfederal **Service:** General Medical and Surgical

| Staffed Beds: 137 |
|---|

**NORTHPORT—Tuscaloosa County**

**NORTHPORT MEDICAL CENTER (010145)**, 2700 Hospital Drive, Zip 35476–3360; tel. 205/333–4500, (Nonreporting) **A**5 **S** DCH Health System, Tuscaloosa, AL
Primary Contact: Luke Standeffer, Administrator
CFO: Nina Dusang, Chief Financial Officer
CMO: Kenneth Aldridge, M.D., Vice President Medical Affairs
CIO: Kim Ligon, Director Information Services
CHR: Peggy Sease, Vice President Human Resources
CNO: Lorraine Yehlen, R.N., Chief Nursing Officer
Web address: www.dchsystem.com
**Control:** Hospital district or authority, Government, nonfederal **Service:** General Medical and Surgical

| Staffed Beds: 196 |
|---|

**ONEONTA—Blount County**

✠ **ST. VINCENT'S BLOUNT (010050)**, 150 Gilbreath, Zip 35121–2827, Mailing Address: P.O. Box 1000, Zip 35121–0013; tel. 205/274–3000 **A**1 9 10 **F**3 11 15 18 29 30 35 40 43 45 57 59 64 65 70 75 77 78 79 81 82 85 86 87 91 93 107 108 110 119 133 135 **S** Ascension Health, Saint Louis, MO
Primary Contact: Michael Korpiel, FACHE, President
CFO: David Cauble, Chief Financial Officer
CMO: David R. Wilson, M.D., Chief of Staff
CIO: John Laliberte, Chief Information Officer
CHR: Carol Maietta, Vice President and Talent Resource Officer Human Resources and Learning
CNO: Amy Shelton, Vice President Patient Care Services
Web address: www.stvhs.com
**Control:** Other not–for–profit (including NFP Corporation) **Service:** General Medical and Surgical

| Staffed Beds: 25 Admissions: 1096 Census: 14 Outpatient Visits: 35668 Births: 0 Total Expense ($000): 19238 Payroll Expense ($000): 6661 Personnel: 129 |
|---|

**OPELIKA—Lee County**

✠ **EAST ALABAMA MEDICAL CENTER (010029)**, 2000 Pepperell Parkway, Zip 36801–5452; tel. 334/749–3411, (Includes EAST ALABAMA MEDICAL CENTER–LANIER, 4800 48th Street, Valley, Zip 36854–3666; tel. 334/756–9180; Greg Nichols, Chief Executive Officer), (Nonreporting) **A**1 2 9 10 19
Primary Contact: Terry W. Andrus, President
COO: Laura D. Grill, R.N., Executive Vice President and Administrator
CFO: Sam Price, Executive Vice President Finance/Chief Financial Officer
CMO: Michael Lisenby, M.D., Vice President and Chief Medical Officer
CIO: Sarah Gray, Vice President Information Services
CHR: Susan Johnston, Vice President Human Resources
CNO: Jane Fullum, Vice President Patient Care Services
Web address: www.eamc.org
**Control:** Hospital district or authority, Government, nonfederal **Service:** General Medical and Surgical

| Staffed Beds: 544 |
|---|

| **Hospital, Medicare Provider Number, Address, Telephone, Approval, Facility, and Physician Codes, Health Care System** |
|---|
| ★ American Hospital Association (AHA) membership    ○ Healthcare Facilities Accreditation Program    ⇧ Center for Improvement in Healthcare Quality Accreditation |
| ☐ The Joint Commission accreditation    ◇ DNV Healthcare Inc. accreditation    △ Commission on Accreditation of Rehabilitation Facilities (CARF) accreditation |

## OPP—Covington County

★ **MIZELL MEMORIAL HOSPITAL (010007)**, 702 Main Street, Zip 36467–1626,
Mailing Address: P.O. Box 1010, Zip 36467–1010; tel. 334/493–3541,
(Nonreporting) **A**9 10
Primary Contact: Jana Wyatt, Chief Executive Officer
CFO: Amy Bess, Chief Financial Officer
CIO: Elizabeth Cook, Chief Information Officer
CHR: Dianne Morrison, Director Human Resources
CNO: Steven Skeen, R.N., Chief Nursing Officer
Web address: www.mizellmh.com
**Control:** Other not–for–profit (including NFP Corporation) **Service:** General
Medical and Surgical

| Staffed Beds: 58 |
|---|

## OZARK—Dale County

**DALE MEDICAL CENTER (010021)**, 126 Hospital Avenue, Zip 36360–2080;
tel. 334/774–2601, (Nonreporting) **A**9 10
Primary Contact: Vernon Johnson, Administrator
CFO: Brad Hull, Chief Financial Officer
CMO: Steve Brandt, M.D., Chief of Staff
CHR: Sheila Dunn, Assistant Administrator Human Resources
Web address: www.dalemedical.org
**Control:** Corporation, Investor–owned, for–profit **Service:** General Medical and
Surgical

| Staffed Beds: 75 |
|---|

## PELL CITY—St. Clair County

☒ **ST. VINCENT'S ST. CLAIR (010130)**, 7063 Veterans Parkway,
Zip 35125–1499; tel. 205/814–2105 **A**1 9 10 **F**3 11 15 29 30 34 35 40 43
50 57 59 64 65 66 68 70 74 77 78 79 81 87 107 111 119 130 135 146 148
**S** Ascension Health, Saint Louis, MO
Primary Contact: Michael Korpiel, President
CFO: Jason Lynn, Director Finance
Web address: www.stvhs.com
**Control:** Other not–for–profit (including NFP Corporation) **Service:** General
Medical and Surgical

| Staffed Beds: 40 Admissions: 2181 Census: 25 Outpatient Visits: 48317 |
|---|
| Births: 0 Total Expense ($000): 27568 Payroll Expense ($000): 9890 |
| Personnel: 172 |

## PHENIX CITY—Russell County

☐ **JACK HUGHSTON MEMORIAL HOSPITAL (010168)**, 4401 Riverchase Drive,
Zip 36867–7483; tel. 334/732–3000 **A**1 3 9 10 13 **F**3 29 40 70 79 81 107
111 115 119 131
Primary Contact: Mark A. Baker, Chief Executive Officer
COO: Rachel H. Crenshaw, Chief Operating Officer
CFO: Angela Hodzeda, Chief Financial Officer
CMO: Lamar Carden, M.D., Chief Medical Officer
CHR: Lana Thomas–Folds, System Director Human Resources
CNO: Sylvia Thomas, Chief Nursing Officer
Web address: www.jackhughstonmemorialhospital.com
**Control:** Corporation, Investor–owned, for–profit **Service:** General Medical and
Surgical

| Staffed Beds: 35 Admissions: 2249 Census: 20 Outpatient Visits: 22254 |
|---|
| Births: 0 Total Expense ($000): 41246 Payroll Expense ($000): 12208 |
| Personnel: 258 |

☒ **REGIONAL REHABILITATION HOSPITAL (013033)**, 3715 Highway 280/431
North, Zip 36867; tel. 334/732–2200 **A**1 9 10 **F**3 29 30 90 93 95 132
**S** HEALTHSOUTH Corporation, Birmingham, AL
Primary Contact: Michael Bartell, CEO
CFO: Bobby Edmondson, Controller
CMO: Nitin Desei, M.D., Medical Director
CIO: Jacki Cuevas, Director Health Information Services
CHR: Cindy Glynn, Director Human Resources
CNO: Wendy Lee, Chief Nursing Officer
Web address: www.regionalrehabhospital.com
**Control:** Partnership, Investor–owned, for–profit **Service:** Rehabilitation

| Staffed Beds: 48 Admissions: 1198 Census: 44 Outpatient Visits: 3546 |
|---|
| Births: 0 Total Expense ($000): 18450 Payroll Expense ($000): 7881 |
| Personnel: 156 |

## PRATTVILLE—Autauga County

☐ **PRATTVILLE BAPTIST HOSPITAL (010108)**, 124 South Memorial Drive,
Zip 36067–3619, Mailing Address: P.O. Box 681630, Zip 36068–1638;
tel. 334/365–0651 **A**1 3 9 10 **F**3 11 12 15 18 29 30 34 35 40 44 45 50 56
57 59 60 63 64 68 70 74 75 81 82 84 85 86 87 93 107 111 114 119 129
132 146 **S** Baptist Health, Montgomery, AL
Primary Contact: Eric Morgan, Interim Chief Executive Officer
CFO: LaDonna McDaniel, Financial Manager
CIO: B. Blaine Brown, Vice President and General Counsel
CHR: Kymberli Skipper, Manager Human Resources
Web address: www.baptistfirst.org/facilities/prattville–baptist–hospital/default.aspx
**Control:** Hospital district or authority, Government, nonfederal **Service:** General
Medical and Surgical

| Staffed Beds: 50 Admissions: 2535 Census: 30 Outpatient Visits: 68620 |
|---|
| Births: 0 Total Expense ($000): 35186 Payroll Expense ($000): 12518 |
| Personnel: 244 |

## RED BAY—Franklin County

★ **RED BAY HOSPITAL (011302)**, 211 Hospital Road, Zip 35582–3858, Mailing
Address: P.O. Box 490, Zip 35582–0490; tel. 256/356–9532 **A**9 10 18 **F**15 29
30 34 35 39 40 45 53 56 57 59 64 65 68 75 77 81 87 91 93 107 119 127
128 130 131 133 135 146 **S** Huntsville Hospital Health System, Huntsville, AL
Primary Contact: Glen M. Jones, FACHE, Administrator
CFO: Penny Westmoreland, Chief Financial Officer
CMO: Kristy Crandell, M.D., Medical Staff President
CHR: Amy Leigh Bishop, Director Human Resources
CNO: Margaret Thorn, Interim Director of Nursing
Web address: www.redbayhospital.com
**Control:** Hospital district or authority, Government, nonfederal **Service:** General
Medical and Surgical

| Staffed Beds: 25 Admissions: 396 Census: 9 Outpatient Visits: 12136 |
|---|
| Births: 0 Total Expense ($000): 8166 Payroll Expense ($000): 3483 |
| Personnel: 82 |

## RUSSELLVILLE—Franklin County

☒ **RUSSELLVILLE HOSPITAL (010158)**, 15155 Highway 43, Zip 35653–1975,
Mailing Address: P.O. Box 1089, Zip 35653–1089; tel. 256/332–1611,
(Nonreporting) **A**1 9 10 **S** Curae Health, Clinton, TN
Primary Contact: Christine R. Stewart, FACHE, Chief Executive Officer
CFO: Penny Westmoreland, Chief Financial Officer
CHR: Stephen Proctor, Director of Human Resources/Risk
CNO: Belinda Johnson, R.N., Chief Nursing Officer/Chief Clinical Officer
Web address: www.russellvillehospital.com
**Control:** Partnership, Investor–owned, for–profit **Service:** General Medical and
Surgical

| Staffed Beds: 92 |
|---|

## SCOTTSBORO—Jackson County

☐ **HIGHLANDS MEDICAL CENTER (010061)**, 380 Woods Cove Road,
Zip 35768–2428, Mailing Address: P.O. Box 1050, Zip 35768–1050;
tel. 256/259–4444, (Nonreporting) **A**1 5 9 10 20
Primary Contact: Kim Bryant, Chief Executive Officer
CFO: Dan Newell, Chief Financial Officer
CIO: Doug Newby, Chief Information Officer
CHR: Susanna S. Sivley, Chief Personnel Officer
Web address: www.highlandsmedcenter.com
**Control:** Hospital district or authority, Government, nonfederal **Service:** General
Medical and Surgical

| Staffed Beds: 92 |
|---|

## SELMA—Dallas County

☒ **VAUGHAN REGIONAL MEDICAL CENTER (010118)**, 1015 Medical Center
Parkway, Zip 36701–6352; tel. 334/418–4100, (Nonreporting) **A**1 3 5 9 10
**S** LifePoint Health, Brentwood, TN
Primary Contact: Roy Vinson, Interim Chief Executive Officer
COO: Debbie Pace, Chief Operating Officer
CFO: Kelly Penton, Chief Financial Officer
CMO: Walid Freij, M.D., Chief of Staff
CIO: Matthew McHugh, Director Information Services
CHR: Dionne Williams, Director Human Resources
CNO: Genesia L. Rucker, MSN, Chief Nursing Officer
Web address: www.vaughanregional.com
**Control:** Corporation, Investor–owned, for–profit **Service:** General Medical and
Surgical

| Staffed Beds: 175 |
|---|

*Many Facility Codes have changed. Please refer to the AHA Guide Code Chart.*   © 2015 AHA Guide

## SHEFFIELD—Colbert County

☐ **HELEN KELLER HOSPITAL (010019)**, 1300 South Montgomery Avenue, Zip 35660–6334, Mailing Address: P.O. Box 610, Zip 35660–0610; tel. 256/386–4196 **A**1 9 10 **F**3 7 8 11 13 15 18 20 21 28 29 30 31 34 35 40 45 47 49 50 51 53 57 59 60 64 65 68 70 74 75 76 77 78 79 80 81 82 83 84 85 86 87 89 91 92 93 94 107 108 110 111 114 115 117 118 119 126 129 130 131 132 135 145 146 147 148 **S** Huntsville Hospital Health System, Huntsville, AL
Primary Contact: Paul Storey, FACHE, President and Chief Executive Officer
CFO: Morris S. Strickland, Chief Financial Officer
CHR: Pam Bryant, Director Human Resources
Web address: www.helenkeller.com
**Control:** Hospital district or authority, Government, nonfederal **Service:** General Medical and Surgical

**Staffed Beds:** 145 **Admissions:** 6719 **Census:** 70 **Outpatient Visits:** 111726 **Births:** 915 **Total Expense ($000):** 89103 **Payroll Expense ($000):** 30722 **Personnel:** 688

## SYLACAUGA—Talladega County

☐ **COOSA VALLEY MEDICAL CENTER (010164)**, 315 West Hickory Street, Zip 35150–2996; tel. 256/401–4000, (Nonreporting) **A**1 9 10
Primary Contact: Glenn C. Sisk, President
CFO: Janice Brown, Chief Financial Officer
CIO: Sandra Murchison, Director Medical Records
CHR: Christy Knowles, Chief Human Resources Officer
Web address: www.cvhealth.net
**Control:** Other not–for–profit (including NFP Corporation) **Service:** General Medical and Surgical

**Staffed Beds:** 101

## TALLADEGA—Talladega County

☐ **CITIZENS BAPTIST MEDICAL CENTER (010101)**, 604 Stone Avenue, Zip 35160–2217, Mailing Address: P.O. Box 978, Zip 35161–0978; tel. 256/362–8111, (Nonreporting) **A**1 9 10 19 **S** Baptist Health System, Birmingham, AL
Primary Contact: Joel Taylor, Administrator
CFO: Zach Abercrombie, Chief Financial Officer
CHR: Sandra Willis, Manager Human Resources
CNO: Ann McEntire, MSN, Chief Nursing Officer
Web address: www.bhsala.com/home_citizens.cfm?id=38
**Control:** Church–operated, Nongovernment, not–for profit **Service:** General Medical and Surgical

**Staffed Beds:** 116

## TALLASSEE—Elmore County

★ **COMMUNITY HOSPITAL (010034)**, 805 Friendship Road, Zip 36078–1234; tel. 334/283–6541, (Nonreporting) **A**9 10
Primary Contact: Jennie R. Rhinehart, Administrator and Chief Executive Officer
Web address: www.chal.org
**Control:** Other not–for–profit (including NFP Corporation) **Service:** General Medical and Surgical

**Staffed Beds:** 47

## TROY—Pike County

☐ **TROY REGIONAL MEDICAL CENTER (010126)**, 1330 Highway 231 South, Zip 36081–3058; tel. 334/670–5000, (Nonreporting) **A**1 9 10
Primary Contact: Teresa G. Grimes, Chief Executive Officer
COO: Josh Hester, Chief Operating Officer
CFO: Janet Smith, Chief Financial Officer
CMO: Paul Dulaney, M.D., Chief of Staff
CIO: Michael Moore, Director Information Systems
CHR: Beth Nissen, Director Human Resources
CNO: Amy Minor, Chief Nursing Officer
Web address: www.troymedicalcenter.com
**Control:** Corporation, Investor–owned, for–profit **Service:** General Medical and Surgical

**Staffed Beds:** 78

## TUSCALOOSA—Tuscaloosa County

☐ **BRYCE HOSPITAL (014007)**, 200 University Boulevard, Zip 35401–1294; tel. 205/507–8299, (Nonreporting) **A**1 3 5 10
Primary Contact: Shelia Penn, Facility Director
CFO: Wendell Summerville, Chief Financial Officer
CMO: Cynthia Moore Sledge, M.D., Medical Director
CIO: Ronene Howell, Director Health Information Management
CHR: Jim Elliott, Director Human Resources
Web address: www.mh.alabama.gov/
**Control:** State–Government, nonfederal **Service:** Psychiatric

**Staffed Beds:** 820

☐ **DCH REGIONAL MEDICAL CENTER (010092)**, 809 University Boulevard East, Zip 35401–2029; tel. 205/759–7111 **A**1 2 3 5 9 10 20 **F**3 11 12 13 15 17 18 20 22 24 26 28 29 30 31 35 38 40 43 45 48 49 50 51 57 59 60 61 62 64 66 68 70 72 74 75 76 77 78 79 81 82 86 87 88 89 90 93 94 96 98 100 101 102 103 104 105 106 107 108 110 111 114 115 116 117 118 119 121 126 129 130 131 132 146 147 148 **P**8 **S** DCH Health System, Tuscaloosa, AL
Primary Contact: William H. Cassels, Administrator
CFO: Nina Dusang, Vice President Finance and Chief Financial Officer
CMO: Kenneth Aldridge, M.D., Vice President Medical Affairs
CIO: Kim Ligon, Director Information Services
CHR: Peggy Sease, Vice President Human Resources
CNO: Lorraine Yehlen, R.N., Vice President Patient Care Services
Web address: www.dchsystem.com
**Control:** Hospital district or authority, Government, nonfederal **Service:** General Medical and Surgical

**Staffed Beds:** 684 **Admissions:** 31452 **Census:** 448 **Outpatient Visits:** 456254 **Births:** 3431 **Total Expense ($000):** 438085 **Payroll Expense ($000):** 193346 **Personnel:** 3729

☐ **MARY S HARPER GERIATRIC PSYCHIATRY CENTER (014012)**, 200 University Boulevard, Zip 35401–1250; tel. 205/759–0900, (Nonreporting) **A**1 10
Primary Contact: Beverly White, MS, Facility Director
CFO: Sarah Mitchell, Director Finance
CMO: Robin Barton Lariscy, M.D., Medical Director
CIO: Sarah Mitchell, Director Finance
CHR: Jim Elliott, Director Human Resources
Web address: www.mh.alabama.gov
**Control:** Corporation, Investor–owned, for–profit **Service:** Psychiatric

**Staffed Beds:** 96

☐ **NOLAND HOSPITAL TUSCALOOSA (012012)**, 809 University Boulevard E, 4th Floor, Zip 35401–2029; tel. 205/759–7241, (Nonreporting) **A**1 9 10 **S** Noland Health Services, Inc., Birmingham, AL
Primary Contact: Dale Jones, Administrator
Web address: www.nolandhealth.com
**Control:** Other not–for–profit (including NFP Corporation) **Service:** Long–Term Acute Care hospital

**Staffed Beds:** 32

☐ **TAYLOR HARDIN SECURE MEDICAL FACILITY (014011)**, 1301 Jack Warner Parkway, Zip 35404–1060; tel. 205/556–7060, (Nonreporting) **A**1 10
Primary Contact: Barbara Jackson, Acting Facility Director
Web address: www.mh.alabama.gov/
**Control:** Corporation, Investor–owned, for–profit **Service:** Psychiatric

**Staffed Beds:** 114

⊠ **TUSCALOOSA VETERANS AFFAIRS MEDICAL CENTER**, 3701 Loop Road East, Zip 35404–5015; tel. 205/554–2000, (Nonreporting) **A**1 5 **S** Department of Veterans Affairs, Washington, DC
Primary Contact: John F. Merkle, Acting Medical Center Director
COO: Gary D. Trende, FACHE, Associate Director
CFO: Angelia Stevenson, Manager Finance
CMO: Carlos E. Berry, M.D., Acting Chief of Staff
Web address: www.tuscaloosa.va.gov
**Control:** Veterans Affairs, Government, federal **Service:** Psychiatric

**Staffed Beds:** 366

## TUSKEGEE—Macon County

**TUSKEGEE DIVISION** See Central Alabama Veterans Health Care System, Montgomery

---

**Hospital, Medicare Provider Number, Address, Telephone, Approval, Facility, and Physician Codes, Health Care System**

★ American Hospital Association (AHA) membership
☐ The Joint Commission accreditation
◯ Healthcare Facilities Accreditation Program
◇ DNV Healthcare Inc. accreditation
⇑ Center for Improvement in Healthcare Quality Accreditation
△ Commission on Accreditation of Rehabilitation Facilities (CARF) accreditation

---

**UNION SPRINGS—Bullock County**

**BULLOCK COUNTY HOSPITAL (010110)**, 102 West Conecuh Avenue,
Zip 36089–1303; tel. 334/738–2140, (Nonreporting) **A**9 10 20
Primary Contact: Jacques Jarry, Administrator
COO: Victoria Lawrenson, Chief Operating Officer
CMO: Maria Bernardo, M.D., Chief of Staff
Web address: www.unionspringsalabama.com/
**Control:** Corporation, Investor–owned, for–profit **Service:** General Medical and
Surgical

**Staffed Beds:** 54

---

**WARRIOR—Jefferson County**

**BRADFORD HEALTH SERVICES AT WARRIOR LODGE**, 1189 Allbritt Road,
Zip 35180, Mailing Address: P.O. Box 129, Zip 35180–0129;
tel. 205/647–1945, (Nonreporting) **S** Bradford Health Services, Birmingham, AL
Primary Contact: Roy M. Ramsey, Executive Director
Web address: www.bradfordhealth.com
**Control:** Corporation, Investor–owned, for–profit **Service:** Alcoholism and other
chemical dependency

**Staffed Beds:** 100

---

**WEDOWEE—Randolph County**

**WEDOWEE HOSPITAL (010032)**, 209 North Main Street, Zip 36278–7428,
Mailing Address: P.O. Box 307, Zip 36278–0307; tel. 256/357–2111,
(Nonreporting) **A**9 10
Primary Contact: Michael D. Alexander, MS, Administrator
Web address: www.wedoweehospital.org/
**Control:** County–Government, nonfederal **Service:** General Medical and Surgical

**Staffed Beds:** 26

---

**WETUMPKA—Elmore County**

**ELMORE COMMUNITY HOSPITAL (010097)**, 500 Hospital Drive,
Zip 36092–1625, Mailing Address: P.O. Box 130, Zip 36092–0003;
tel. 334/567–4311, (Nonreporting) **A**9 10
Primary Contact: Gordon Faulk, Administrator
CFO: Mike Bruce, Chief Financial Officer
CHR: Cindy Futral, Director Human Resources
Web address: www.elmorehospital.com/
**Control:** Partnership, Investor–owned, for–profit **Service:** General Medical and
Surgical

**Staffed Beds:** 49

---

**WINFIELD—Marion County**

⊞ **NORTHWEST MEDICAL CENTER (010086)**, 1530 U.S. Highway 43,
Zip 35594–5056; tel. 205/487–7000, (Nonreporting) **A**1 9 10 **S** Curae Health,
Clinton, TN
Primary Contact: Michael D. Windham, Chief Executive Officer
CFO: James Gory, Chief Financial Officer
CMO: Gary Fowler, M.D., Chief of Staff Family Practice
Web address: www.northwestmedcenter.com
**Control:** Corporation, Investor–owned, for–profit **Service:** General Medical and
Surgical

**Staffed Beds:** 66

---

**YORK—Sumter County**

**HILL HOSPITAL OF SUMTER COUNTY (010138)**, 751 Derby Drive,
Zip 36925–2121; tel. 205/392–5263, (Nonreporting) **A**9 10
Primary Contact: Loretta Wilson, Administrator
CFO: Joyce Wedgeworth, Financial Clerk
CMO: Gary Walton, M.D., Chief Medical Officer
CNO: Cynthia Brown, Director of Nursing
**Control:** Other not–for–profit (including NFP Corporation) **Service:** General
Medical and Surgical

**Staffed Beds:** 33

---

# ALASKA

## ANCHORAGE—Anchorage Division

☒ **ALASKA NATIVE MEDICAL CENTER (020026)**, 4315 Diplomacy Drive,
Zip 99508–5926; tel. 907/563–2662, (Nonreporting) **A**1 3 5 10
Primary Contact: Roald Helgesen, Chief Executive Officer
CMO: Paul Franke, M.D., Chief Medical Officer
CHR: Sonya Conant, Senior Director Human Resources
Web address: www.anmc.org
**Control:** Other not–for–profit (including NFP Corporation) **Service:** General
Medical and Surgical

**Staffed Beds: 138**

☐ **ALASKA PSYCHIATRIC INSTITUTE (024002)**, 3700 Piper Street,
Zip 99508–4677; tel. 907/269–7100 **A**1 10 **F**99 100 103
Primary Contact: Melissa Ring, Ph.D., M.D., Chief Executive Officer
COO: Ron Hale, Administrator
CFO: Tina Williams, Chief Financial Officer
CIO: Stephen Schneider, Manager Information Services
CHR: Jason Goodenbery, Administrative Assistant III
CNO: Sharon Bergstedt, Director of Nursing
Web address: www.hss.state.ak.us/dbh/API/
**Control:** State–Government, nonfederal **Service:** Psychiatric

**Staffed Beds: 80 Admissions: 1595 Census: 58 Outpatient Visits: 0 Births:**
0

☒ **ALASKA REGIONAL HOSPITAL (020017)**, 2801 Debarr Road,
Zip 99508–2997, Mailing Address: P.O. Box 143889, Zip 99514–3889;
tel. 907/264–1754, (Nonreporting) **A**1 2 9 10 **S** HCA, Nashville, TN
Primary Contact: Julie Taylor, FACHE, Chief Executive Officer
COO: Victor Rosenbaum, Chief Operating Officer
CFO: Lynn Kennington, Chief Financial Officer
CMO: David Cadogan, Chief Medical Officer
CIO: Gene Kaplanis, Director Information Technology
CHR: Tammy Kaminski, Director Human Resources
CNO: Linda Doughty, Chief Nursing Officer
Web address: www.alaskaregional.com
**Control:** Corporation, Investor–owned, for–profit **Service:** General Medical and
Surgical

**Staffed Beds: 132**

☒ **NORTH STAR BEHAVIORAL HEALTH SYSTEM (024001)**, 2530 DeBarr Circle,
Zip 99508–2948; tel. 907/258–7575, (Includes NORTH STAR BEHAVIORAL
HEALTH, 1650 South Bragaw, Zip 99508–3467; tel. 907/258–7575) **A**1 3 5 9
10 **F**98 99 106 130 **S** Universal Health Services, Inc., King of Prussia, PA
Primary Contact: Andrew Mayo, Ph.D., Chief Executive Officer and Managing
Director
CFO: Alan Barnes, Chief Financial Officer
CMO: Ruth Dukoff, M.D., Medical Director
CIO: Brian O'Connell, Director Information Services
CHR: Sabrina Ben, Director Human Resources
CNO: Brandy Proctor, Director of Nursing
Web address: www.northstarbehavioral.com
**Control:** Corporation, Investor–owned, for–profit **Service:** Children's hospital
psychiatric

**Staffed Beds: 200 Admissions: 1094 Census: 168 Outpatient Visits: 0**
**Births:** 0 **Total Expense ($000):** 30220 **Payroll Expense ($000):** 16506
**Personnel:** 268

☒ **PROVIDENCE ALASKA MEDICAL CENTER (020001)**, 3200 Providence Drive,
Zip 99508–4615, Mailing Address: P.O. Box 196604, Zip 99519–6604;
tel. 907/562–2211, (Includes CHILDREN'S HOSPITAL AT PROVIDENCE, 3200
Providence Drive, Zip 99508; tel. 907/212–3130) **A**1 2 3 5 9 10 13 **F**3 8 11 12
13 17 18 19 20 21 22 24 25 26 28 29 30 31 34 35 38 39 40 41 43 45 46
47 49 50 53 55 56 57 58 59 60 62 63 65 67 68 70 72 74 75 76 77 78 79
81 82 83 84 85 86 87 88 89 90 92 93 94 97 98 99 100 101 102 104 105
106 107 108 111 115 118 119 120 121 123 124 126 130 131 132 146 148
**S** Providence Health & Services, Renton, WA
Primary Contact: Richard Mandsager, M.D., Executive Officer
CFO: Anthony Dorsch, Chief Financial Officer
CMO: Roy Davis, M.D., Chief Medical Officer
CIO: Stephanie Morton, Chief Information Officer
CHR: Scott Jungwirth, Chief Human Resources Officer
Web address: www.providence.org/alaska/pamc/default.htm
**Control:** Church–operated, Nongovernment, not–for profit **Service:** General
Medical and Surgical

**Staffed Beds: 401 Admissions: 16648 Census: 270 Outpatient Visits:**
401660 **Births: 2982 Total Expense ($000): 540295 Payroll Expense**
**($000): 190266 Personnel: 2488**

☒ **ST. ELIAS SPECIALTY HOSPITAL (022001)**, 4800 Cordova Street,
Zip 99503–7218; tel. 907/561–3333, (Nonreporting) **A**1 9 10
Primary Contact: Sharon H. Kurz, Ph.D., Chief Executive Officer
Web address: www.st–eliashospital.com
**Control:** Other not–for–profit (including NFP Corporation) **Service:** Long–Term
Acute Care hospital

**Staffed Beds: 59**

## BARROW—North Slope Division

☒ **SAMUEL SIMMONDS MEMORIAL HOSPITAL (021312)**, 7000 Uulu Street,
Zip 99723, Mailing Address: P.O. Box 29, Zip 99723–0029; tel. 907/852–4611,
(Nonreporting) **A**1 9 10 18
Primary Contact: Richard Hall, Interim Chief Executive Officer
CMO: Devon Allen, M.D., Chief of Medical Staff
Web address: www.arcticslope.org
**Control:** Other not–for–profit (including NFP Corporation) **Service:** General
Medical and Surgical

**Staffed Beds: 14**

## BETHEL—Bethel Division

☒ **YUKON–KUSKOKWIM DELTA REGIONAL HOSPITAL (020018)**, 700 Chief
Eddie Hoffman Highway, Zip 99559–3000, Mailing Address: P.O. Box 528,
Zip 99559–0528; tel. 907/543–6300, (Nonreporting) **A**1 3 5 10
Primary Contact: Dan Winkelman, President and Chief Executive Officer
CFO: Vanetta Van Cleave, Chief Financial Officer
CIO: William Pearch, Chief Information Officer
Web address: www.ykhc.org
**Control:** Other not–for–profit (including NFP Corporation) **Service:** General
Medical and Surgical

**Staffed Beds: 37**

## CORDOVA—Valdez–Cordova Division

★ **CORDOVA COMMUNITY MEDICAL CENTER (021307)**, 602 Chase Avenue,
Zip 99574, Mailing Address: P.O. Box 160, Zip 99574–0160;
tel. 907/424–8000, (Nonreporting) **A**9 10 18
Primary Contact: Stephen Sundby, Ph.D., Administrator and Chief Executive
Officer
CFO: Tiffany G. Varnadoe, Director Finance
CMO: James Dudley, M.D., Medical Director
CHR: Laura Cloward, Human Resources Coordinator
Web address: www.cdvcmc.com
**Control:** City–Government, nonfederal **Service:** General Medical and Surgical

**Staffed Beds: 23**

---

**Hospital, Medicare Provider Number, Address, Telephone, Approval, Facility, and Physician Codes, Health Care System**

★ American Hospital Association (AHA) membership    ○ Healthcare Facilities Accreditation Program    ⇑ Center for Improvement in Healthcare Quality Accreditation
☐ The Joint Commission accreditation    ◇ DNV Healthcare Inc. accreditation    △ Commission on Accreditation of Rehabilitation Facilities (CARF) accreditation

**AK**

### DILLINGHAM—Dillingham Division

✠ **BRISTOL BAY AREA HEALTH CORPORATION (021309)**, 6000 Kanakanak Road, Zip 99576, Mailing Address: P.O. Box 130, Zip 99576–0130; tel. 907/842–5201, (Nonreporting) **A**1 9 10 18
Primary Contact: Robert J. Clark, President and Chief Executive Officer
COO: Lucrecia Scotford, Executive Vice President and Chief Operations Officer
CFO: David Morgan, Vice President and Chief Financial Officer
CMO: Arnold Loera, M.D., Clinical Director
CIO: Bill Wilcox, Chief Information Technology Officer
CHR: John Davis, Chief Human Resources Officer
CNO: Starla Fox, Director of Nursing
Web address: www.bbahc.org
**Control:** Other not–for–profit (including NFP Corporation) **Service:** General Medical and Surgical

**Staffed Beds:** 16

### ELMENDORF AFB—Anchorage Division

✠ **U. S. AIR FORCE REGIONAL HOSPITAL**, 5955 Zeamer Avenue, Zip 99506–3702; tel. 907/580–3006, (Nonreporting) **A**1 5 **S** Department of the Air Force, Washington, DC
Primary Contact: Major Mark Lamey, Commander
COO: Colonel Rebecca Seese, Chief Operating Officer
CFO: Major Felicia Burks, Chief Financial Officer
CMO: Colonel Marriner Oldham, M.D., Chief Medical Officer
CIO: Major Phillip Oliphant, Chief Information Officer
CHR: Mark Clark, Human Resources Liaison
Web address: www.elmendorf.af.mil/
**Control:** Air Force, Government, federal **Service:** General Medical and Surgical

**Staffed Beds:** 64

### FAIRBANKS—Fairbanks North Star Division

✠ **FAIRBANKS MEMORIAL HOSPITAL (020012)**, 1650 Cowles Street, Zip 99701–5998; tel. 907/452–8181, (Total facility includes 90 beds in nursing home–type unit) **A**1 2 3 5 9 10 **F**3 13 15 18 20 22 28 29 30 34 35 40 45 48 50 51 57 60 62 63 64 67 68 70 74 75 76 77 78 79 80 81 82 85 86 87 93 96 98 100 101 103 107 108 110 111 114 115 119 120 121 126 128 129 130 132 146 148 **P**6 **S** Banner Health, Phoenix, AZ
Primary Contact: Sheldon Stadnyk, M.D., Interim Chief Executive Officer
CFO: Jim Lynch, Chief Financial Officer
CMO: Gregory Johnson, D.D.S., Medical Director
CIO: Carl J. Kegley, System Director Information Technology
CHR: Carol Barnett, Chief Human Resources Officer
CNO: Gena Edmiston, R.N., Chief Nursing Officer
Web address: www.bannerhealth.com/locations/alaska/fairbanks+memorial+Hospital
**Control:** Other not–for–profit (including NFP Corporation) **Service:** General Medical and Surgical

**Staffed Beds:** 217 **Admissions:** 4820 **Census:** 130 **Outpatient Visits:** 325570 **Births:** 1067 **Total Expense ($000):** 210474 **Payroll Expense ($000):** 84312 **Personnel:** 1061

### FORT WAINWRIGHT—Fairbanks North Star Division

✠ **BASSETT ARMY COMMUNITY HOSPITAL**, 1060 Gaffney Road, Box 7400, Zip 99703–5001, Mailing Address: 1060 Gaffney Road, Box 7440, Zip 99703–5001; tel. 907/361–4000, (Nonreporting) **A**1 **S** Department of the Army, Office of the Surgeon General, Falls Church, VA
Primary Contact: Timothy Bergeron, Deputy Commander, Administration
CMO: Colonel Leo Bennett, M.D., Deputy Commander Clinical Services
CHR: Terri Morefield, Deputy Chief Human Resources Division
Web address: www.alaska.amedd.army.mil
**Control:** Army, Government, federal **Service:** General Medical and Surgical

**Staffed Beds:** 24

### HOMER—Kenai Peninsula Division

★ **SOUTH PENINSULA HOSPITAL (021313)**, 4300 Bartlett Street, Zip 99603–7000; tel. 907/235–8101, (Total facility includes 28 beds in nursing home–type unit) **A**9 10 18 **F**3 13 15 18 29 30 31 34 35 36 40 45 50 56 57 59 62 64 65 67 68 70 75 76 77 78 79 81 82 85 87 91 92 93 94 97 100 107 110 111 115 119 128 129 130 133 147 148 **P**6 8
Primary Contact: Robert F. Letson, FACHE, Chief Executive Officer
CFO: Lori Meyer, Interim Chief Financial Officer
CMO: Hal Smith, M.D., Chief of Staff
CIO: Jim Bartilson, Manager Information Systems
CHR: Cindy H. Brinkerhoff, Director Human Resources
CNO: Shara Sutherlin, R.N., Director Patient Care Services
Web address: www.sphosp.org
**Control:** Hospital district or authority, Government, nonfederal **Service:** General Medical and Surgical

**Staffed Beds:** 50 **Admissions:** 977 **Census:** 35 **Outpatient Visits:** 46080 **Births:** 127 **Total Expense ($000):** 54064 **Payroll Expense ($000):** 23134 **Personnel:** 334

### JUNEAU—Juneau Division

✠ **BARTLETT REGIONAL HOSPITAL (020008)**, 3260 Hospital Drive, Zip 99801–7808; tel. 907/796–8900 **A**1 9 10 20 **F**3 4 5 13 15 28 29 30 31 34 40 43 57 59 70 77 81 85 86 91 93 98 99 100 102 104 105 107 108 110 111 114 115 119 120 129 130 135 148 **P**6
Primary Contact: Charles E. Bill, Chief Executive Officer
CFO: Alan Germany, Interim Chief Financial Officer
CMO: Amy Dressel, M.D., Chief of Staff
CIO: Martha Palicka, Interim Manager Information Systems
CHR: Mila Cosgrove, Manager Human Resources
CNO: William Gardner, Chief Nursing Officer
Web address: www.bartletthospital.org
**Control:** City–Government, nonfederal **Service:** General Medical and Surgical

**Staffed Beds:** 73 **Admissions:** 2301 **Census:** 34 **Outpatient Visits:** 133697 **Births:** 372 **Total Expense ($000):** 87844 **Payroll Expense ($000):** 34133 **Personnel:** 403

### KETCHIKAN—Ketchikan Gateway Division

★ ◇ **PEACEHEALTH KETCHIKAN MEDICAL CENTER (021311)**, 3100 Tongass Avenue, Zip 99901–5746; tel. 907/225–5171, (Nonreporting) **A**5 9 10 18 21 **S** PeaceHealth, Vancouver, WA
Primary Contact: Ken Tonjes, Interim Chief Administrative Officer
CFO: Ken Tonjes, Chief Financial Officer
CMO: Peter Rice, M.D., Medical Director
CIO: Tim Walker, Manager Information Services
CHR: Lanetta Lundberg, Vice President Culture and People
Web address: www.peacehealth.org
**Control:** Other not–for–profit (including NFP Corporation) **Service:** General Medical and Surgical

**Staffed Beds:** 54

### KODIAK—Kodiak Island Division

✠ **PROVIDENCE KODIAK ISLAND MEDICAL CENTER (021306)**, 1915 East Rezanof Drive, Zip 99615–6602; tel. 907/486–3281, (Nonreporting) **A**1 9 10 18 **S** Providence Health & Services, Renton, WA
Primary Contact: Barbara Bigelow, Administrator
COO: Brenda Zawacki, Chief Operating Manager
CFO: Timothy Hocum, Chief Financial Officer
CMO: Steve Smith, M.D., Chief of Staff
CIO: David Johnson, Manager Information Services
CNO: LeeAnn Horn, Chief Nurse Executive
Web address: www.providence.org
**Control:** Other not–for–profit (including NFP Corporation) **Service:** General Medical and Surgical

**Staffed Beds:** 25

### KOTZEBUE—Northwest Arctic Division

☐ **MANIILAQ HEALTH CENTER (021310)**, 436 5th Avenue, Zip 99752–0043, Mailing Address: P.O. Box 43, Zip 99752–0043; tel. 907/442–7344, (Nonreporting) **A**1 5 9 10 18
Primary Contact: Paul Hansen, Administrator
COO: Timothy Schuerch, President and Chief Executive Officer
CFO: Lucy Nelson, Director Finance, Vice President
CMO: Patricia Clancy, M.D., Director Medical Services
CIO: Eugene Smith, Chief Information Officer
CHR: Gerty Gallahom, Director Human Resources
CNO: Commander Donna K. Biagioni, R.N., Director of Nursing
Web address: www.maniilaq.org
**Control:** Other not–for–profit (including NFP Corporation) **Service:** General Medical and Surgical

**Staffed Beds:** 17

### NOME—Nome Division

✠ **NORTON SOUND REGIONAL HOSPITAL (021308)**, Bering Straits, Zip 99762, Mailing Address: P.O. Box 966, Zip 99762–0966; tel. 907/443–3311, (Nonreporting) **A**1 9 10 18
Primary Contact: Angela Gorn, Vice President
COO: Roy Agloinga, Chief Administrative Officer
CMO: David Head, M.D., Chief Medical Staff
CIO: Dan Bailey, Director Information Systems
CHR: Tiffany Martinson, Director Human Resources
Web address: www.nortonsoundhealth.org
**Control:** Other not–for–profit (including NFP Corporation) **Service:** General Medical and Surgical

**Staffed Beds:** 36

*Many Facility Codes have changed. Please refer to the AHA Guide Code Chart.* © 2015 AHA Guide

## PALMER—Matanuska–Susitna Division

✠ **MAT-SU REGIONAL MEDICAL CENTER (020006)**, 2500 South Woodworth Loop, Zip 99645–8984, Mailing Address: P.O. Box 1687, Zip 99645–1687; tel. 907/861–6000 **A**1 3 9 10 20 **F**3 8 13 15 18 19 20 22 26 28 29 30 31 34 35 38 39 40 43 45 46 47 48 50 51 54 55 56 57 59 64 65 68 70 74 75 76 77 78 79 81 85 86 87 91 93 96 97 99 102 107 108 110 111 114 115 119 124 126 128 129 130 132 133 135 144 146 148 **P**6 **S** Community Health Systems, Inc., Franklin, TN
Primary Contact: John R. Lee, Chief Executive Officer
CMO: Christopher Sahlstrom, M.D., Chief of Staff
CIO: Bryan Meurer, Director Information Systems
CHR: Cathy Babuscio, Director Human Resources
CNO: Emily Stevens, Chief Nursing Officer
Web address: www.matsuregional.com
**Control:** Partnership, Investor–owned, for-profit **Service:** General Medical and Surgical

**Staffed Beds: 74 Admissions:** 4245 **Census:** 41 **Outpatient Visits:** 100535 **Births:** 728 **Total Expense ($000):** 100256 **Payroll Expense ($000):** 41906 **Personnel:** 457

## PETERSBURG—Wrangell–Petersburg Division

★ **PETERSBURG MEDICAL CENTER (021304)**, 103 Fram Street, Zip 99833, Mailing Address: Box 589, Zip 99833–0589; tel. 907/772–4291, (Total facility includes 15 beds in nursing home–type unit) **A**9 10 18 **F**15 31 34 40 45 57 59 62 63 64 67 79 81 84 85 93 97 107 114 119 133 146 148
Primary Contact: Elizabeth Woodyard, R.N., MSN, Chief Executive Officer
CFO: Doran Hammett, Chief Financial Officer
CHR: Cynthia Newman, Manager Human Resources
CNO: Jennifer Bryner, Director Nursing
Web address: www.pmc-health.com
**Control:** City–County, Government, nonfederal **Service:** General Medical and Surgical

**Staffed Beds: 27 Admissions:** 176 **Census:** 21 **Outpatient Visits:** 14723 **Births:** 0 **Total Expense ($000):** 14033 **Payroll Expense ($000):** 6131 **Personnel:** 99

## SEWARD—Kenai Peninsula Division

★ **PROVIDENCE SEWARD MEDICAL CENTER (021302)**, 417 First Avenue, Zip 99664, Mailing Address: P.O. Box 365, Zip 99664–0365; tel. 907/224–5205, (Total facility includes 40 beds in nursing home–type unit) **A**9 10 18 **F**3 29 30 40 50 57 64 93 107 114 119 128 133 146 148 **P**6 **S** Providence Health & Services, Renton, WA
Primary Contact: Joseph Fong, Administrator
Web address: www.providence.org
**Control:** Other not–for–profit (including NFP Corporation) **Service:** General Medical and Surgical

**Staffed Beds: 46 Admissions:** 151 **Census:** 34 **Outpatient Visits:** 26436 **Births:** 0 **Total Expense ($000):** 15679

## SITKA—Sitka Division

✠ **SEARHC MT. EDGECUMBE HOSPITAL (020027)**, 222 Tongass Drive, Zip 99835–9416; tel. 907/966–2411 **A**1 5 9 10 **F**3 5 13 15 29 30 34 35 39 40 43 45 48 50 57 59 61 64 65 70 75 76 81 82 85 87 93 97 99 100 102 103 104 107 110 111 115 119 130 131 135 143 144 147
Primary Contact: Charles Clement, Chief Executive Officer
COO: Daniel P. Neumeister, Chief Operating Officer
CFO: Barbara Searls, Chief Financial Officer
CMO: David Vastola, Medical Director
CIO: Bob Cita, Chief Information Officer
CHR: Peggy Bernhardt–Kadlec, Chief Human Resources Officer
CNO: Patricia L. Giampa, Chief Nursing Officer
Web address: www.searhc.org
**Control:** Other not–for–profit (including NFP Corporation) **Service:** General Medical and Surgical

**Staffed Beds: 27 Admissions:** 583 **Census:** 9 **Outpatient Visits:** 33042 **Births:** 49 **Total Expense ($000):** 111089 **Payroll Expense ($000):** 42028 **Personnel:** 316

★ **SITKA COMMUNITY HOSPITAL (021303)**, 209 Moller Avenue, Zip 99835–7142; tel. 907/747–3241, (Total facility includes 15 beds in nursing home–type unit) **A**9 10 18 **F**3 11 13 15 28 29 31 32 33 34 35 40 43 44 45 50 53 56 59 62 64 65 75 76 77 78 79 81 82 84 85 87 89 90 93 94 96 97 102 107 110 114 119 128 130 131 133 135 148
Primary Contact: Rob Allen, Chief Executive Officer
CFO: Lee W. Bennett, Chief Financial Officer
CHR: Shannon Callahan, Director Human Resources
Web address: www.sitkahospital.org
**Control:** City–Government, nonfederal **Service:** Long–Term Acute Care hospital

**Staffed Beds: 28 Admissions:** 269 **Census:** 13 **Outpatient Visits:** 2479 **Births:** 35 **Total Expense ($000):** 25804 **Payroll Expense ($000):** 10832 **Personnel:** 138

## SOLDOTNA—Kenai Peninsula Division

✠ **CENTRAL PENINSULA GENERAL HOSPITAL (020024)**, 250 Hospital Place, Zip 99669–6999; tel. 907/714–4404, (Total facility includes 58 beds in nursing home–type unit) **A**1 9 10 20 **F**3 4 5 11 13 15 28 29 30 31 34 35 36 38 40 45 46 47 48 49 57 59 65 68 70 74 75 76 77 78 79 81 82 84 85 86 87 93 97 99 100 102 103 104 105 106 107 108 110 111 115 119 128 129 130 131 132 133 134 135 145 146 147 148
Primary Contact: Richard Davis, Chief Executive Officer
COO: Matt Dammeyer, Ph.D., Chief Operating Officer
CFO: Shaun Keef, Chief Financial Officer
CMO: Gregg Motonaga, M.D., Chief of Staff
CIO: Bryan Downs, Director Information Systems
CHR: John Dodd, Vice President Human Resources
Web address: www.cpgh.org
**Control:** Other not–for–profit (including NFP Corporation) **Service:** General Medical and Surgical

**Staffed Beds: 117 Admissions:** 2632 **Census:** 81 **Outpatient Visits:** 86256 **Births:** 429 **Total Expense ($000):** 113392 **Payroll Expense ($000):** 51562 **Personnel:** 682

## VALDEZ—Valdez–Cordova Division

★ **PROVIDENCE VALDEZ MEDICAL CENTER (021301)**, 911 Meals Avenue, Zip 99686–0550, Mailing Address: P.O. Box 550, Zip 99686–0550; tel. 907/835–2249, (Nonreporting) **A**9 10 18 **S** Providence Health & Services, Renton, WA
Primary Contact: Barbara Bigelow, Administrator
CFO: Jeremy O'Neil, Manager Finance
CMO: John Cullen, M.D., Chief of Staff and Medical Director Long Term Care
CHR: Maureen Radotich, Director Human Resources
Web address: www.providence.org/alaska
**Control:** City–Government, nonfederal **Service:** General Medical and Surgical

**Staffed Beds: 21**

## WRANGELL—Wrangell–Petersburg Division

★ **WRANGELL MEDICAL CENTER (021305)**, First Avenue & Bennett Street, Zip 99929, Mailing Address: P.O. Box 1081, Zip 99929–1081; tel. 907/874–7000, (Nonreporting) **A**9 10 18
Primary Contact: Marla I. Sanger, R.N., Chief Executive Officer
CIO: Cathy Gross, Director Health Information Management Systems
Web address: www.wrangellmedicalcenter.com
**Control:** City–Government, nonfederal **Service:** General Medical and Surgical

**Staffed Beds: 22**

---

**Hospital, Medicare Provider Number, Address, Telephone, Approval, Facility, and Physician Codes, Health Care System**

★ American Hospital Association (AHA) membership
☐ The Joint Commission accreditation
○ Healthcare Facilities Accreditation Program
◇ DNV Healthcare Inc. accreditation
⇧ Center for Improvement in Healthcare Quality Accreditation
△ Commission on Accreditation of Rehabilitation Facilities (CARF) accreditation

# ARIZONA

**AZ**

## APACHE JUNCTION—Pinal County

☒ **BANNER GOLDFIELD MEDICAL CENTER (030134)**, 2050 West Southern Avenue, Zip 85120–7305; tel. 480/733–3300 **A**1 10 **F**3 13 18 29 30 34 36 40 41 44 45 47 49 50 61 68 75 76 77 79 80 81 82 85 86 87 89 92 100 102 107 111 114 119 130 132 135 136 140 141 145 146 147 148 **S** Banner Health, Phoenix, AZ
Primary Contact: Julie Nunley, R.N., Chief Executive Officer
CFO: Tracy French, Chief Financial Officer
CMO: Devin Minior, M.D., Interim Chief Medical Officer
CHR: Janine Polito, Chief Human Resources Officer
CNO: Terri Paulus, Chief Nursing Officer
Web address: www.bannerhealth.com/Locations/Arizona/Banner+Goldfield+Medical+Center/_Welcome+to+Banner+Goldfield.htm
**Control:** Other not–for–profit (including NFP Corporation) **Service:** General Medical and Surgical

> **Staffed Beds: 30 Admissions: 658 Census: 6 Total Expense ($000):** 19002 **Payroll Expense ($000):** 8200 **Personnel:** 105

## BENSON—Cochise County

★ **BENSON HOSPITAL (031301)**, 450 South Ocotillo Street, Zip 85602–6403, Mailing Address: P.O. Box 2290, Zip 85602–2290; tel. 520/586–2261 **A**9 10 18 **F**3 11 29 30 34 40 43 50 57 59 64 75 77 87 107 114 119 132 133 146 148
Primary Contact: Richard Polheber, Chief Executive Officer
CFO: Ken Goranson, Chief Financial Officer
CIO: Rob Roberts, Director Information Technology
CHR: Isabel Dominguez, Director Human Resources
Web address: www.bensonhospital.org
**Control:** Other not–for–profit (including NFP Corporation) **Service:** General Medical and Surgical

> **Staffed Beds: 22 Admissions: 361 Census: 3 Outpatient Visits:** 14722 **Births: 3 Total Expense ($000):** 13020 **Payroll Expense ($000):** 6447 **Personnel:** 125

## BISBEE—Cochise County

★ **COPPER QUEEN COMMUNITY HOSPITAL (031312)**, 101 Cole Avenue, Zip 85603–1399; tel. 520/432–5383 **A**9 10 18 **F**1 3 11 15 18 29 30 40 43 45 46 62 74 75 77 81 85 93 107 110 114 119 127 130 133 135 147
Primary Contact: James J. Dickson, Administrator and Chief Executive Officer
COO: Daniel Roe, M.D., Chief Operating Officer
CFO: James Ehasz, Chief Financial Officer
CMO: Daniel Roe, M.D., Chief Medical Officer
CIO: David Chmura, Chief Information Officer
CHR: Virginia Martinez, Director of Human Resources
CNO: Linda Morin, Director of Nursing
Web address: www.cqch.org
**Control:** Other not–for–profit (including NFP Corporation) **Service:** General Medical and Surgical

> **Staffed Beds: 14 Admissions: 327 Census: 4 Outpatient Visits:** 36975 **Births: 6 Total Expense ($000):** 22411 **Payroll Expense ($000):** 11334 **Personnel:** 178

## BULLHEAD CITY—Mohave County

☒ **WESTERN ARIZONA REGIONAL MEDICAL CENTER (030101)**, 2735 Silver Creek Road, Zip 86442–8303; tel. 928/763–2273, (Nonreporting) **A**1 9 10 19 **S** Community Health Systems, Inc., Franklin, TN
Primary Contact: Alex Villa, Chief Executive Officer
Web address: www.warmc.com
**Control:** Corporation, Investor–owned, for–profit **Service:** General Medical and Surgical

> **Staffed Beds:** 139

## CASA GRANDE—Pinal County

★ ◇ **BANNER CASA GRANDE MEDICAL CENTER (030016)**, 1800 East Florence Boulevard, Zip 85122–5399; tel. 520/381–6300 **A**9 10 21 **F**3 13 15 18 20 22 29 30 34 40 45 49 50 51 57 59 64 68 70 74 75 76 78 79 81 85 87 89 92 93 100 107 108 110 111 114 115 117 118 119 129 130 132 144 145 146 147 148 **S** Banner Health, Phoenix, AZ
Primary Contact: Rona Curphy, President and Chief Executive Officer
CFO: Robert Bender, Chief Financial Officer
CMO: Devin Minior, M.D., Chief Medical Officer
CHR: Carol D'Souza, Chief Human Resources Officer
CNO: Kelley Kieffer, Chief Nursing Officer
Web address: www.https://www.bannerhealth.com/Locations/Arizona/Banner+Casa+Grande+Medical+Center/_Banner+Casa+Grande+Medical+Center.htm
**Control:** Other not–for–profit (including NFP Corporation) **Service:** General Medical and Surgical

> **Staffed Beds: 87 Admissions: 3642 Census: 36 Outpatient Visits:** 62125 **Births:** 394

## CHANDLER—Maricopa County

☐ **ARIZONA ORTHOPEDIC SURGICAL HOSPITAL (030112)**, 2905 West Warner Road, Zip 85224–1674; tel. 480/603–9000, (Nonreporting) **A**1 9 10 **S** United Surgical Partners International, Addison, TX
Primary Contact: Patricia Alice, Chief Executive Officer
Web address: www.azosh.com
**Control:** Corporation, Investor–owned, for–profit **Service:** Surgical

> **Staffed Beds:** 24

☒ **CHANDLER REGIONAL MEDICAL CENTER (030036)**, 1955 West Frye Road, Zip 85224–6282; tel. 480/728–3000 **A**1 3 9 10 **F**3 8 11 13 15 17 18 20 22 24 26 28 29 30 31 32 34 35 37 40 41 42 43 44 45 46 47 48 49 50 51 54 57 58 59 60 64 65 66 68 70 71 72 73 74 75 76 77 78 79 81 82 83 84 85 86 87 93 96 107 108 110 111 114 115 119 126 130 131 132 135 143 144 146 147 148 **P**6 **S** Dignity Health, San Francisco, CA
Primary Contact: Tim Bricker, President and Chief Executive Officer
COO: Peter Menor, Vice President Operations
CFO: Mark Kem, Vice President Finance and Chief Financial Officer
CMO: Terry J. Happel, M.D., Vice President and Chief Medical Officer
CHR: Renea Brunke, Vice President Human Resources
CNO: Peg Smith, Vice President and Chief Nursing Officer
Web address: www.chandlerregional.com
**Control:** Other not–for–profit (including NFP Corporation) **Service:** General Medical and Surgical

> **Staffed Beds: 243 Admissions: 18526 Census: 199 Outpatient Visits:** 165148 **Births: 3780 Total Expense ($000):** 331897 **Payroll Expense ($000):** 133816 **Personnel:** 1838

## CHINLE—Apache County

☒ **CHINLE COMPREHENSIVE HEALTH CARE FACILITY (030084)**, Highway 191, Zip 86503, Mailing Address: P.O. Drawer PH, Zip 86503–8000; tel. 928/674–7011, (Nonreporting) **A**1 5 9 10 **S** U. S. Indian Health Service, Rockville, MD
Primary Contact: Ronald Tso, Chief Executive Officer
COO: Shirley Lewis, Administrative Officer
CFO: Philene Tyler, Chief Finance Officer
CMO: Kevin Rand, M.D., Clinical Director
CIO: Perry Francis, Supervisory Information Technology Specialist
CHR: Lorraine Smith, Supervisory Human Resource Specialist
CNO: Patricia Gorman, Chief Nurse Executive
Web address: www.ihs.gov
**Control:** PHS, Indian Service, Government, federal **Service:** General Medical and Surgical

> **Staffed Beds:** 60

## COTTONWOOD—Yavapai County

★ ◇ **VERDE VALLEY MEDICAL CENTER (030007)**, 269 South Candy Lane, Zip 86326–4170; tel. 928/639–6000 **A**9 10 13 20 21 **F**3 8 11 13 15 18 19 20 22 28 29 30 31 32 34 35 36 40 44 46 47 48 49 50 53 57 59 60 64 68 70 75 76 77 78 79 81 82 85 86 87 89 93 98 100 101 102 103 107 108 110 111 114 115 118 119 120 121 123 124 129 130 131 132 135 143 145 146 147 148 **S** Northern Arizona Healthcare, Flagstaff, AZ
Primary Contact: Susanne Maiden, Interim Administrator
CFO: Gregory Kuzma, Vice President and Chief Financial Officer
CMO: Harry Alberti, M.D., Chief Medical Officer and Vice President Medical Affairs
CIO: Marilynn Black, Chief Information Officer
CHR: Lori L. Jackson, Director Human Resources
CNO: Jennifer Brewer, R.N., Chief Nursing Officer and Vice President Nursing Services
Web address: www.nahealth.com
**Control:** Other not–for–profit (including NFP Corporation) **Service:** General Medical and Surgical

> **Staffed Beds: 110 Admissions: 4571 Census: 49 Outpatient Visits:** 98927 **Births: 565 Total Expense ($000):** 129041 **Payroll Expense ($000):** 51090 **Personnel:** 831

*Many Facility Codes have changed. Please refer to the AHA Guide Code Chart.*  © 2015 AHA Guide

## FLAGSTAFF—Coconino County

★ ◇ **FLAGSTAFF MEDICAL CENTER (030023)**, 1200 North Beaver Street, Zip 86001–3118; tel. 928/779–3366 **A**3 5 9 10 21 **F**3 5 7 8 11 13 15 17 18 20 22 24 26 28 29 30 31 32 34 35 37 40 43 44 45 49 50 54 57 58 59 60 61 64 65 66 68 70 72 75 76 77 78 79 81 82 84 85 86 87 88 89 93 94 98 99 100 101 102 103 104 105 107 108 111 114 115 116 117 118 119 120 121 123 124 126 130 131 132 145 146 147 148 **S** Northern Arizona Healthcare, Flagstaff, AZ
Primary Contact: Richard Langosch, President and Chief Executive Officer
CFO: Richard Langosch, Interim Chief Financial Officer
CMO: Bert McKinnon, M.D., Interim Chief Medical Officer
CIO: Marilynn Black, Chief Information Officer and Vice President
CHR: Ann M. Bollone, Vice President Human Resources
CNO: Lindy M. Parker, Interim Chief Nursing Officer and Vice President Patient Care Services
Web address: www.flagstaffmedicalcenter.com
**Control:** Other not–for–profit (including NFP Corporation) **Service:** General Medical and Surgical

**Staffed Beds:** 267 **Admissions:** 14833 **Census:** 168 **Outpatient Visits:** 69842 **Births:** 1224 **Total Expense ($000):** 334619 **Payroll Expense ($000):** 126943 **Personnel:** 1970

☐ **GUIDANCE CENTER (034023)**, 2187 North Vickey Street, Zip 86004–6121; tel. 928/527–1899, (Nonreporting) **A**1 10
Primary Contact: Karissa Nisted, Interim Chief Executive Officer
Web address: www.tgcaz.org
**Control:** Other not–for–profit (including NFP Corporation) **Service:** Psychiatric

**Staffed Beds:** 10

## FLORENCE—Pinal County

◇ **FLORENCE HOSPITAL AT ANTHEM (030132)**, 4545 North Hunt Highway, Zip 85132–6937; tel. 520/868–3333, (Nonreporting) **A**10 21
Primary Contact: Bryan J. Hastings, Interim Chief Executive Officer
CFO: T. Patrick Clune, Chief Financial Officer
CNO: Kimberly Fawley, Chief Nursing Officer
Web address: www.fhanthem.com
**Control:** Partnership, Investor–owned, for–profit **Service:** General Medical and Surgical

**Staffed Beds:** 36

## FORT DEFIANCE—Apache County

★ **TSEHOOTSOOI MEDICAL CENTER (030071)**, Highway 12 & Bonito Drive, Zip 86504, Mailing Address: P.O. Box 649, Zip 86504–0649; tel. 928/729–8000, (Nonreporting) **A**10 **S** U. S. Indian Health Service, Rockville, MD
Primary Contact: Leland Leonard, Ph.D., Chief Executive Officer
COO: Valonia Hardy, Chief Healthy Living Officer
CFO: Rachel Sorrell, Chief Financial Officer
CMO: Michael Tutt, M.D., Chief Medical Officer
CIO: Virgil Chavez, Director Information Technology
CHR: Vivian Santistevan, Chief Human Resources
CNO: Tori Davidson, R.N., Chief Nursing Officer
Web address: www.fdihb.org
**Control:** PHS, Indian Service, Government, federal **Service:** General Medical and Surgical

**Staffed Beds:** 39

## FORT MOHAVE—Mohave County

☒ **VALLEY VIEW MEDICAL CENTER (030117)**, 5330 South Highway 95, Zip 86426–9225; tel. 928/788–2273, (Nonreporting) **A**1 9 10 **S** LifePoint Health, Brentwood, TN
Primary Contact: Fred Capozello, Jr., Chief Executive Officer
CHR: Susan L. Scharles, Director Human Resources
Web address: www.valleyviewmedicalcenter.net
**Control:** Corporation, Investor–owned, for–profit **Service:** Other specialty

**Staffed Beds:** 90

## GANADO—Apache County

☒ **SAGE MEMORIAL HOSPITAL (031309)**, Highway 264, Zip 86505, Mailing Address: P.O. Box 457, Zip 86505–0457; tel. 928/755–4500 **A**1 9 10 18 **F**1 5 7 11 18 29 32 34 35 39 40 50 53 54 57 59 62 64 65 68 75 100 101 104 107 119 127 133 134 144
Primary Contact: Christi J. El–Meligi, R.N., Chief Executive Officer
COO: Netrisha Dalgai, Director of Operations
CFO: Michael Katigbak, Chief Financial Officer
CMO: Jeremy Wray, D.O., Medical Director
CIO: Michael Katigbak, Director Computer Services
CHR: Gary Pahe, Manager Human Resources
CNO: Ernasha McIntosh, Interim Director of Nursing
Web address: www.sagememorial.com
**Control:** Other not–for–profit (including NFP Corporation) **Service:** General Medical and Surgical

**Staffed Beds:** 25 **Admissions:** 426 **Census:** 7 **Total Expense ($000):** 29379 **Payroll Expense ($000):** 9739

## GILBERT—Maricopa County

☒ **BANNER GATEWAY MEDICAL CENTER (030122)**, 1900 North Higley Road, Zip 85234–1604; tel. 480/543–2000 **A**1 3 9 10 **F**3 12 13 15 29 30 31 34 35 36 40 45 46 47 48 49 50 54 55 57 58 59 60 64 68 70 75 76 77 78 79 80 81 82 84 85 86 87 92 97 100 107 108 109 110 111 114 115 116 117 118 119 120 121 123 124 126 130 131 132 133 135 136 146 147 148 **S** Banner Health, Phoenix, AZ
Primary Contact: Todd S. Werner, Chief Executive Officer
CFO: Claire Agnew, Chief Financial Officer
CMO: David Edwards, M.D., Chief Medical Officer
CHR: Amber R. Kovacs, Chief Human Resources Officer
Web address: www.bannerhealth.com/Locations/Arizona/Banner+Gateway+Medical+Center/
**Control:** Other not–for–profit (including NFP Corporation) **Service:** General Medical and Surgical

**Staffed Beds:** 177 **Admissions:** 13459 **Census:** 129 **Births:** 4102 **Total Expense ($000):** 289657 **Payroll Expense ($000):** 82282 **Personnel:** 1434

**GILBERT HOSPITAL (030120)**, 5656 South Power Road, Zip 85295–8487; tel. 480/984–2000 **A**9 10 **F**3 29 34 40 41 45 49 50 59 70 79 81 82 87 107 108 111 114 119
Primary Contact: Bryan J. Hargis, FACHE, Chief Executive Officer
CFO: Dennis E. Rutherford, CPA, Chief Financial Officer
CMO: Timothy Johns, M.D., Chief Medical Officer
CIO: Michelle Cianfrani, Director Information Technology
CNO: Marla Meggers, R.N., Chief Nursing Officer
Web address: www.gilberter.com
**Control:** Corporation, Investor–owned, for–profit **Service:** General Medical and Surgical

**Staffed Beds:** 19 **Admissions:** 502 **Census:** 4

☒ **MERCY GILBERT MEDICAL CENTER (030119)**, 3555 South Val Vista Road, Zip 85297–7323; tel. 480/728–8000 **A**1 9 10 **F**3 8 11 13 15 18 20 22 26 28 29 30 31 32 34 35 37 38 40 41 42 44 45 46 47 49 50 51 57 58 59 60 64 65 66 68 70 73 74 75 76 77 78 79 81 82 83 84 85 86 87 96 100 101 102 103 107 108 110 111 114 115 119 126 129 130 131 132 135 144 145 146 147 148 **P**6 **S** Dignity Health, San Francisco, CA
Primary Contact: Tim Bricker, President and Chief Executive Officer
COO: Jane E. Hanson, R.N., Chief Operating Officer
CFO: Chuck Sowers, Vice President Finance and Chief Financial Officer
CMO: Phil Fracica, M.D., Vice President and Chief Medical Officer
CIO: Larissa Spraker, Vice President Business Development and Chief Strategy Officer
CHR: Anita Harger, Director Human Resources
CNO: Julie Hoffman, Vice President Patient Care Services and Chief Nursing Officer
Web address: www.mercygilbert.org
**Control:** Other not–for–profit (including NFP Corporation) **Service:** General Medical and Surgical

**Staffed Beds:** 220 **Admissions:** 13565 **Census:** 131 **Outpatient Visits:** 86923 **Births:** 3087 **Total Expense ($000):** 222313 **Payroll Expense ($000):** 84817

**Hospital, Medicare Provider Number, Address, Telephone, Approval, Facility, and Physician Codes, Health Care System**

★ American Hospital Association (AHA) membership
☐ The Joint Commission accreditation
○ Healthcare Facilities Accreditation Program
◇ DNV Healthcare Inc. accreditation
⇑ Center for Improvement in Healthcare Quality Accreditation
△ Commission on Accreditation of Rehabilitation Facilities (CARF) accreditation

**AZ**

### GLENDALE—Maricopa County

☒ **ARROWHEAD HOSPITAL (030094)**, 18701 North 67th Avenue, Zip 85308–7100; tel. 623/561–1000 **A**1 3 9 10 **F**3 11 13 15 17 18 20 22 24 26 28 29 30 31 34 35 37 40 41 45 46 47 48 49 57 59 64 70 72 74 75 76 77 78 79 81 85 87 107 108 110 111 113 118 119 130 146 148 **S** TENET Healthcare Corporation, Dallas, TX
Primary Contact: Frank L. Molinaro, Chief Executive Officer
CMO: Patrick Smith, M.D., Chief Medical Officer
CHR: Sharon M. Chadwick, Director Human Resources
Web address: www.arrowheadhospital.com
**Control:** Corporation, Investor–owned, for–profit **Service:** General Medical and Surgical

**Staffed Beds:** 234 **Admissions:** 13304 **Census:** 124 **Births:** 3168 **Total Expense ($000):** 143172 **Payroll Expense ($000):** 55856 **Personnel:** 901

☐ **AURORA BEHAVIORAL HEALTH SYSTEM WEST (034024)**, 6015 West Peoria Avenue, Zip 85302–1213; tel. 623/344–4400 **A**1 9 10 **F**4 5 29 50 68 87 98 99 100 101 103 104 105 130 133 **S** Signature Healthcare Services, Corona, CA
Primary Contact: Bruce Waldo, Chief Executive Officer
CFO: Rebekah Francis, JD, Chief Financial Officer
CHR: Vicki Thomsen, Director Human Resources
CNO: Lori Milus, R.N., Director of Nursing
Web address: www.aurorabehavioral.com
**Control:** Corporation, Investor–owned, for–profit **Service:** Psychiatric

**Staffed Beds:** 90 **Admissions:** 4003 **Census:** 90 **Births:** 0

☒ **BANNER THUNDERBIRD MEDICAL CENTER (030089)**, 5555 West Thunderbird Road, Zip 85306–4696; tel. 602/865–5555, (Includes BANNER BEHAVIORAL HEALTH CENTER–THUNDERBIRD CAMPUS, 5555 West Thunderbird Road, Zip 85306; tel. 602/588–5555) **A**1 9 10 **F**3 5 13 15 17 18 19 20 22 24 26 28 29 30 31 34 35 36 37 38 39 40 41 44 45 46 49 50 51 59 60 61 64 68 70 72 73 74 75 76 77 78 79 80 81 82 85 86 87 88 89 90 91 92 93 94 96 98 100 101 102 104 105 107 108 110 111 114 115 116 117 118 119 120 121 123 124 126 130 131 132 134 135 145 146 147 148 **S** Banner Health, Phoenix, AZ
Primary Contact: Thomas C. Dickson, Chief Executive Officer
CFO: Richard Miller, Administrator Finance
CMO: Kathryn Perkins, M.D., Chief Medical Officer
CHR: Laura Witt, Administrator Human Resources
Web address: www.bannerhealth.com/Locations/Arizona/Banner+Thunderbird+Medical+Center/
**Control:** Other not–for–profit (including NFP Corporation) **Service:** General Medical and Surgical

**Staffed Beds:** 474 **Admissions:** 29174 **Census:** 367 **Births:** 5076 **Total Expense ($000):** 441700 **Payroll Expense ($000):** 157544 **Personnel:** 2564

☒ **HEALTHSOUTH VALLEY OF THE SUN REHABILITATION HOSPITAL (033032)**, 13460 North 67th Avenue, Zip 85304–1042; tel. 623/878–8800 **A**1 9 10 **F**29 62 64 75 90 93 132 **S** HEALTHSOUTH Corporation, Birmingham, AL
Primary Contact: Beth Bacher, Chief Executive Officer
CFO: Kathryn Haney, Controller
CMO: Michael Kravetz, M.D., Medical Director
CHR: Danette Garcia, Director Human Resources
CNO: Stephanie Palmer, Chief Nursing Officer
Web address: www.healthsouthvalleyofthesun.com
**Control:** Corporation, Investor–owned, for–profit **Service:** Rehabilitation

**Staffed Beds:** 75 **Admissions:** 1196 **Census:** 44 **Births:** 0 **Total Expense ($000):** 18711 **Payroll Expense ($000):** 9213 **Personnel:** 151

### GLOBE—Gila County

**COBRE VALLEY COMMUNITY HOSPITAL** See Cobre Valley Regional Medical Center

★ **COBRE VALLEY REGIONAL MEDICAL CENTER (031314)**, 5880 South Hospital Drive, Zip 85501–9454; tel. 928/425–3261 **A**9 10 18 **F**3 11 12 13 15 18 29 30 34 35 40 43 45 46 49 51 57 59 64 70 74 75 78 79 81 82 87 92 93 97 107 108 110 111 115 117 118 119 127 129 130 133 135 146 147 148 **P**5 **S** HealthTech Management Services, Brentwood, TN
Primary Contact: Neal Jensen, Chief Executive Officer
CFO: Frank Napier, Interim Chief Financial Officer
CIO: Sharon Bennett, Manager Information Systems
CHR: Rita Murphy, Director Human Resources
Web address: www.cvrmc.org
**Control:** Other not–for–profit (including NFP Corporation) **Service:** General Medical and Surgical

**Staffed Beds:** 25 **Admissions:** 1602 **Census:** 14 **Outpatient Visits:** 52949 **Births:** 331 **Total Expense ($000):** 38741 **Payroll Expense ($000):** 16404 **Personnel:** 257

### GOODYEAR—Maricopa County

☒ **WEST VALLEY HOSPITAL (030110)**, 13677 West McDowell Road, Zip 85395–2635; tel. 623/882–1500, (Nonreporting) **A**1 9 10 **S** TENET Healthcare Corporation, Dallas, TX
Primary Contact: Stan V. Holm, FACHE, Chief Executive Officer
CFO: Richard Franco, Chief Financial Officer
CMO: Ron Kenneth, M.D., Chief Medical Officer
Web address: www.wvhospital.com
**Control:** Corporation, Investor–owned, for–profit **Service:** General Medical and Surgical

**Staffed Beds:** 106

☒ **WESTERN REGIONAL MEDICAL CENTER (030127)**, 14200 West Celebrate Life way, Zip 85338–3005; tel. 623/207–3000 **A**1 10 **F**3 15 29 30 31 33 34 36 46 47 49 53 55 57 64 68 70 75 77 78 79 81 82 83 84 85 86 87 93 96 100 104 107 108 110 111 114 115 116 117 118 119 120 121 123 124 126 129 130 132 135 144 146 148 **P**6 **S** Cancer Treatment Centers of America, Schaumburg, IL
Primary Contact: Matthew McGuire, President and Chief Executive Officer
Web address: www.cancercenter.com/western–hospital.cfm
**Control:** Corporation, Investor–owned, for–profit **Service:** Cancer

**Staffed Beds:** 24 **Admissions:** 640 **Census:** 9 **Outpatient Visits:** 33643 **Births:** 0 **Personnel:** 621

### KEAMS CANYON—Navajo County

☒ **HOPI HEALTH CARE CENTER (031305)**, Highway 264 Mile Marker 388, Zip 86042, Mailing Address: P.O. Box 4000, Polacca, Zip 86042–4000; tel. 928/737–6000, (Nonreporting) **A**1 10 18 **S** U. S. Indian Health Service, Rockville, MD
Primary Contact: Daryl Melvin, Chief Executive Officer
COO: Leonard H. Lopez, Chief Operating Officer
CFO: Dorothy Sulu, Budget Analyst
CMO: Darren Vicenti, M.D., Clinical Director
CHR: Trudy Begay, Human Resources Specialist
CNO: Melissa Wyaco, Chief Nurse Executive
Web address: www.ihs.gov/index.asp
**Control:** PHS, Indian Service, Government, federal **Service:** General Medical and Surgical

**Staffed Beds:** 15

### KINGMAN—Mohave County

★ ◇ **KINGMAN REGIONAL MEDICAL CENTER (030055)**, 3269 Stockton Hill Road, Zip 86409–3691; tel. 928/757–2101 **A**9 10 13 21 **F**3 11 13 15 17 18 22 24 28 29 30 31 34 35 40 42 43 49 51 53 57 59 60 62 63 64 70 74 75 76 77 78 79 81 82 84 85 86 87 89 90 93 97 107 108 110 111 114 115 116 117 118 119 121 123 127 129 130 132 135 143 144 146 147 148 **P**6 7
Primary Contact: Brian Turney, Chief Executive Officer
COO: Ryan Kennedy, Chief Operating Officer
CFO: Timothy D. Blanchard, Chief Financial Officer
CMO: Thomas Gaughan, M.D., Chief Medical Officer
CIO: Robert (Bob) Sarnecki, Chief Information Officer
CHR: Heather N. Crowl, Chief Human Resources Officer
CNO: Kimberly Miyauchi, R.N., Chief Nursing Officer
Web address: www.azkrmc.com
**Control:** Hospital district or authority, Government, nonfederal **Service:** General Medical and Surgical

**Staffed Beds:** 180 **Admissions:** 9280 **Census:** 120 **Outpatient Visits:** 390869 **Births:** 668 **Total Expense ($000):** 228980 **Payroll Expense ($000):** 98732 **Personnel:** 1641

### LAKE HAVASU CITY—Mohave County

☒ **HAVASU REGIONAL MEDICAL CENTER (030069)**, 101 Civic Center Lane, Zip 86403–5683; tel. 928/855–8185, (Nonreporting) **A**1 9 10 **S** LifePoint Health, Brentwood, TN
Primary Contact: Michael N. Patterson, Chief Executive Officer
CFO: Christopher Flores, Chief Financial Officer
CMO: Michael Rosen, M.D., Chief Medical Officer
CIO: Linda Toy, Director Information Systems
Web address: www.havasuregional.com
**Control:** Corporation, Investor–owned, for–profit **Service:** General Medical and Surgical

**Staffed Beds:** 162

### LAKESIDE—Navajo County

**CCC AT PINEVIEW HOSPITAL (034027)**, 1920 West Commerce Drive, Zip 85929; tel. 928/368–4110, (Nonreporting) **A**9 10
Primary Contact: Michelle Witt, Administrator
Web address: www.ccc–az.org
**Control:** Other not–for–profit (including NFP Corporation) **Service:** Psychiatric

**Staffed Beds:** 16

*Many Facility Codes have changed. Please refer to the AHA Guide Code Chart.*   © 2015 AHA Guide

## LAVEEN—Maricopa County

☐ **DIGNITY HEALTH ARIZONA GENERAL HOSPITAL (030136)**, 7171 South 51st Avenue, Zip 85339–2923; tel. 623/584–5100, (Nonreporting) **A1**
Primary Contact: Robert C. Honeycutt, Chief Executive Officer
CMO: David K. Butler, M.D., Chief Medical Officer
CNO: Kevin Lee Meek, R.N., Chief Nursing Officer
Web address: www.dignityhealth.org/arizonageneral/
**Control:** Other not–for–profit (including NFP Corporation) **Service:** Long–Term Acute Care hospital

**Staffed Beds:** 16

## MESA—Maricopa County

☐ **ARIZONA SPINE AND JOINT HOSPITAL (030107)**, 4620 East Baseline Road, Zip 85206–4624; tel. 480/832–4770 **A1** 9 10 **F**29 34 77 79 81 82 85 146 **S** National Surgical Healthcare, Chicago, IL
Primary Contact: Todd Greene, Chief Executive Officer
CHR: Diane Hearne, Director Human Resources
CNO: Stacy Hayes, R.N., Chief Nursing Officer
Web address: www.azspineandjoint.com
**Control:** Corporation, Investor–owned, for–profit **Service:** Orthopedic

**Staffed Beds:** 23 **Admissions:** 933 **Census:** 5 **Outpatient Visits:** 3929 **Births:** 0 **Total Expense ($000):** 21083 **Payroll Expense ($000):** 5894 **Personnel:** 82

✠ **BANNER BAYWOOD MEDICAL CENTER (030088)**, 6644 East Baywood Avenue, Zip 85206–1797; tel. 480/321–2000 **A1** 9 10 **F**3 13 15 18 29 30 31 34 36 37 40 41 44 45 47 48 49 50 51 56 57 59 60 61 64 68 70 74 75 76 77 78 79 80 81 82 84 85 86 87 90 91 92 94 96 100 102 103 107 108 110 111 113 114 118 119 126 129 130 132 135 136 146 147 148 **P**8 **S** Banner Health, Phoenix, AZ
Primary Contact: Laura Robertson, R.N., Chief Executive Officer
CFO: Stanley Adams, Chief Financial Officer
CMO: Larry Spratling, M.D., Chief Medical Officer
CIO: Janice Hoppe, Vice President Information Technology System
CHR: Pam Cannon, Chief Human Resources Officer
CNO: Cynthia Helmich, R.N., Chief Nursing Officer
Web address: www.bannerhealth.com/locations/Arizona/banner+baywood+medical+center
**Control:** Other not–for–profit (including NFP Corporation) **Service:** General Medical and Surgical

**Staffed Beds:** 388 **Admissions:** 18391 **Census:** 231 **Births:** 810 **Total Expense ($000):** 246043 **Payroll Expense ($000):** 92970 **Personnel:** 1624

**BANNER CHILDREN'S HOSPITAL** See Cardon Children's Medical Center

✠ **BANNER DESERT MEDICAL CENTER (030065)**, 1400 South Dobson Road, Zip 85202–4707; tel. 480/412–3000, (Includes CARDON CHILDREN'S MEDICAL CENTER, 1400 South Dobson Road, tel. 480/412–3000; Rhonda Anderson, R.N., FACHE, Chief Executive Officer; SAMARITAN BEHAVIORAL HEALTH CENTER–DESERT SAMARITAN MEDICAL CENTER, 2225 West Southern Avenue, Zip 85202; tel. 602/464–4000) **A1** 3 5 9 10 **F**3 13 18 19 20 21 22 23 24 25 26 27 28 29 30 31 32 34 36 37 40 41 43 44 45 46 47 48 49 50 51 57 58 59 60 61 64 68 70 71 72 74 75 76 77 78 79 81 82 84 85 86 87 88 89 91 92 93 96 100 102 107 108 111 114 115 117 118 119 121 123 124 126 129 130 131 132 135 146 148 **S** Banner Health, Phoenix, AZ
Primary Contact: Laura Robertson, R.N., Chief Executive Officer
CFO: Scott Leckey, Chief Financial Officer
CMO: Tanya Kne, M.D., Chief Medical Officer
CIO: Stacey Hinkle, Director Information Technology
CHR: Kevin McVeigh, Chief Human Resources Officer
Web address: www.bannerhealth.com/Locations/Arizona/Banner+Desert+Medical+Center
**Control:** Other not–for–profit (including NFP Corporation) **Service:** General Medical and Surgical

**Staffed Beds:** 579 **Admissions:** 34046 **Census:** 387 **Births:** 4742 **Total Expense ($000):** 527239 **Payroll Expense ($000):** 186561 **Personnel:** 3106

✠ **BANNER HEART HOSPITAL (030105)**, 6750 East Baywood Avenue, Zip 85206–1749; tel. 480/854–5000 **A**1 9 10 **F**3 17 18 20 22 24 26 28 29 30 34 36 44 45 50 51 56 57 59 60 61 64 68 74 75 77 78 81 82 84 85 86 87 92 94 100 103 113 119 126 130 132 135 146 147 148 **S** Banner Health, Phoenix, AZ
Primary Contact: Laura Robertson, R.N., Chief Executive Officer
CFO: Stanley Adams, Chief Financial Officer
CMO: Mark Starling, M.D., Chief Medical Officer
CIO: Janice Hoppe, Vice President, Information Technology System
CHR: Pam Cannon, Chief Human Resources Officer
CNO: Cynthia Helmich, R.N., Chief Nursing Officer
Web address: www.bannerhealth.com/Locations/Arizona/Banner+Heart+Hospital/
**Control:** Other not–for–profit (including NFP Corporation) **Service:** Heart

**Staffed Beds:** 111 **Admissions:** 5074 **Census:** 59 **Births:** 0 **Total Expense ($000):** 102196 **Payroll Expense ($000):** 27569 **Personnel:** 448

**CARDON CHILDREN'S MEDICAL CENTER** See Banner Desert Medical Center

✠ **HEALTHSOUTH EAST VALLEY REHABILITATION HOSPITAL (033037)**, 5652 East Baseline Road, Zip 85206–4713; tel. 480/567–0350 **A**1 9 10 **F**28 29 64 74 75 77 79 82 90 91 93 94 95 96 130 132 148 **S** HEALTHSOUTH Corporation, Birmingham, AL
Primary Contact: Jerry Gray, Interim Chief Executive Office Officer
CMO: Martin Yee, M.D., Medical Director
CHR: Nancy Pickler, Director of Human Resources
CNO: Hope Dunn, Chief Nursing Officer
Web address: www.healthsoutheastvalley.com
**Control:** Corporation, Investor–owned, for–profit **Service:** Rehabilitation

**Staffed Beds:** 60 **Admissions:** 1291 **Census:** 49 **Births:** 0 **Personnel:** 153

★ ◇ **MOUNTAIN VISTA MEDICAL CENTER (030121)**, 1301 South Crismon Road, Zip 85209–3767; tel. 480/358–6100, (Nonreporting) **A**9 10 13 21 **S** IASIS Healthcare, Franklin, TN
Primary Contact: Anthony Marinello, Chief Executive Officer
CNO: Bill Southwick, R.N., Chief Nursing Officer
Web address: www.mvmedicalcenter.com
**Control:** Corporation, Investor–owned, for–profit **Service:** General Medical and Surgical

**Staffed Beds:** 172

**PROMISE HOSPITAL OF PHOENIX (032006)**, 433 East 6th Street, Zip 85203–7104; tel. 480/427–3000, (Nonreporting) **A**10 **S** Promise Healthcare, Boca Raton, FL
Primary Contact: Scott Floden, Chief Executive Officer
COO: Wendy Larson, Chief Clinical Officer
CFO: Theo Clark, Director Financial Services
CMO: Syed Shahryar, M.D., Medical Director
CHR: Christie Brea, Manager Human Resources
Web address: www.promise–phoenix.com
**Control:** Corporation, Investor–owned, for–profit **Service:** Long–Term Acute Care hospital

**Staffed Beds:** 40

**SAMARITAN BEHAVIORAL HEALTH CENTER–DESERT SAMARITAN MEDICAL CENTER** See Banner Desert Medical Center

**TRILLIUM SPECIALTY HOSPITAL–EAST VALLEY** See Acuity Specialty Hospital of Arizona at Mesa

## NOGALES—Santa Cruz County

✠ **CARONDELET HOLY CROSS HOSPITAL (031313)**, 1171 West Target Range Road, Zip 85621–2415; tel. 520/285–3000 **A**1 3 9 10 18 **F**3 11 13 29 30 31 32 34 35 40 50 51 56 57 59 64 65 68 70 75 77 79 81 85 86 87 93 107 111 119 130 132 133 134 135 146 **S** Ascension Health, Saint Louis, MO
Primary Contact: Debbie Knapheide, MSN, Site Administrator, Chief Nursing Officer and Chief Operating Officer
COO: Debbie Knapheide, MSN, Site Administrator, Chief Nursing Officer and Chief Operating Officer
CFO: Alan Strauss, Chief Financial Officer
CMO: Roy Farrell, M.D., Chief Medical Officer
CNO: Debbie Knapheide, MSN, Site Administrator, Chief Nursing Officer and Chief Operating Officer
Web address: www.carondelet.org
**Control:** Church–operated, Nongovernment, not–for profit **Service:** General Medical and Surgical

**Staffed Beds:** 25 **Admissions:** 1038 **Census:** 6 **Outpatient Visits:** 36319 **Births:** 714 **Total Expense ($000):** 21798 **Payroll Expense ($000):** 9568 **Personnel:** 142

---

**AZ**

### ORO VALLEY—Pima County

☒ **ORO VALLEY HOSPITAL (030114)**, 1551 East Tangerine Road,
Zip 85755–6213; tel. 520/901–3500 **A**1 9 10 **F**3 15 17 18 20 22 27 29 30
34 35 40 48 49 50 51 59 60 70 74 79 81 85 87 90 91 93 107 108 110 111
114 115 119 129 144 146 147 **S** Community Health Systems, Inc., Franklin, TN
Primary Contact: Jae Dale, Chief Executive Officer
CFO: Maurene Polashek, Chief Financial Officer
CNO: Julie Hunt, R.N., Chief Nursing Officer
Web address: www.orovalleyhospital.com
**Control:** Corporation, Investor–owned, for–profit **Service:** General Medical and
Surgical

**Staffed Beds:** 144 **Admissions:** 5174 **Census:** 57 **Total Expense ($000):**
94518 **Payroll Expense ($000):** 39285 **Personnel:** 564

### PAGE—Coconino County

☒ **PAGE HOSPITAL (031304)**, 501 North Navajo Drive, Zip 86040, Mailing
Address: P.O. Box 1447, Zip 86040–1447; tel. 928/645–2424 **A**1 9 10 18 **F**3
11 13 15 29 31 34 35 39 40 45 53 54 59 64 76 78 79 80 81 82 85 87 93
107 108 110 111 114 117 118 133 143 146 **P**7 **S** Banner Health, Phoenix, AZ
Primary Contact: Sandy Haryasz, R.N., Chief Executive Officer
CFO: Darcy Robertson, Chief Financial Officer
CMO: Thomas Wood, M.D., Chief Medical Officer
CIO: Paul Caldwell, Facility Coordinator Information Technology Customer
Relations
CHR: Ed Franklin, Chief Human Resources Officer
CNO: Susan Eubanks, Chief Nursing Officer
Web address: www.bannerhealth.com/Locations/Arizona/Page+Hospital
**Control:** Other not–for–profit (including NFP Corporation) **Service:** General
Medical and Surgical

**Staffed Beds:** 25 **Admissions:** 512 **Census:** 3 **Births:** 202 **Total Expense
($000):** 12542 **Payroll Expense ($000):** 5695 **Personnel:** 89

### PARKER—La Paz County

**LA PAZ REGIONAL HOSPITAL (031317)**, 1200 West Mohave Road,
Zip 85344–6349; tel. 928/669–9201 **A**9 10 18 **F**1 3 4 11 15 16 17 18 20 22
26 28 29 34 35 39 40 45 46 50 51 53 57 59 65 66 67 68 70 72 73 75 76
78 79 80 81 82 85 87 88 89 90 93 97 98 102 107 110 111 114 115 119
127 128 130 132 133 135 144 146 148
Primary Contact: Vickie Clark, Interim Chief Executive Officer
CFO: Steve Stewart, Chief Financial Officer
CMO: Jack Dunn, M.D., Chief of Staff
CHR: Regina M. Martinez, Director Human Resources
CNO: Bonnie Viloria, Chief Nursing Officer
Web address: www.lapazhospital.org
**Control:** Other not–for–profit (including NFP Corporation) **Service:** General
Medical and Surgical

**Staffed Beds:** 25 **Admissions:** 779 **Census:** 7 **Outpatient Visits:** 28624
**Births:** 0 **Total Expense ($000):** 22703 **Payroll Expense ($000):** 9171

☒ **U. S. PUBLIC HEALTH SERVICE INDIAN HOSPITAL (031307)**, 12033 Agency
Road, Zip 85344–7718; tel. 928/669–2137, (Nonreporting) **A**1 9 10 18 **S** U. S.
Indian Health Service, Rockville, MD
Primary Contact: Ronald Milford, Chief Executive Officer
CFO: Robin Tahbo, Financial Management Officer
CMO: Laurence Norick, M.D., Clinical Director
CIO: JayLynn Saavedra, Chief Information Officer
Web address: www.ihs.gov
**Control:** Public Health Service, Government, federal **Service:** General Medical
and Surgical

**Staffed Beds:** 20

### PAYSON—Gila County

☒ **PAYSON REGIONAL MEDICAL CENTER (030033)**, 807 South Ponderosa
Street, Zip 85541–5599; tel. 928/474–3222 **A**1 9 10 20 **F**13 15 18 29 30 35
37 40 51 70 75 76 77 78 79 81 82 85 86 87 91 93 96 107 110 111 113
119 132 146 147 148 **S** Community Health Systems, Inc., Franklin, TN
Primary Contact: Lance Porter, Chief Executive Officer
CFO: Peter Finelli, Chief Financial Officer
CMO: John Vandruff, M.D., Chief of Staff
CIO: Nick Vandermeer, Director Information Systems
CHR: Shawn M. Thomas, Director Human Resources
CNO: Hart Hintze, Chief Nursing Officer
Web address: www.paysonhospital.com
**Control:** Corporation, Investor–owned, for–profit **Service:** General Medical and
Surgical

**Staffed Beds:** 39 **Admissions:** 1851 **Census:** 13 **Births:** 182

### PEORIA—Maricopa County

**KINDRED HOSPITAL ARIZONA–NORTHWEST PHOENIX** See Kindred Hospital
Arizona–Phoenix, Phoenix

### PHOENIX—Maricopa County

☒ **ABRAZO MARYVALE CAMPUS (030001)**, 5102 West Campbell Avenue,
Zip 85031–1799; tel. 623/848–5000 **A**1 9 10 **F**3 13 18 20 22 26 29 34 35
40 45 49 59 68 70 73 74 75 76 81 85 86 107 108 111 119 130 146 147
**S** TENET Healthcare Corporation, Dallas, TX
Primary Contact: Crystal Hamilton, R.N., Chief Executive Officer
COO: Scott Morey, Chief Nursing Officer
CFO: Julie Hastings–Smith, Chief Financial Officer
CMO: Lynette Watkins, M.D., Chief Medical Officer
CHR: Erin Gonzalez, Director Chief Human Resources
CNO: Scott Morey, Chief Nursing Officer
Web address: www.maryvalehospital.com
**Control:** Corporation, Investor–owned, for–profit **Service:** General Medical and
Surgical

**Staffed Beds:** 100 **Admissions:** 4730 **Census:** 51 **Outpatient Visits:** 46293
**Births:** 468 **Total Expense ($000):** 53140 **Payroll Expense ($000):** 30573
**Personnel:** 348

☒ **ABRAZO SCOTTSDALE CAMPUS (030083)**, 3929 East Bell Road,
Zip 85032–2196; tel. 602/923–5000, (Nonreporting) **A**1 9 10 **S** TENET
Healthcare Corporation, Dallas, TX
Primary Contact: David Tupponce, M.D., Chief Executive Officer
CFO: Jeffrey Zyla, Chief Financial Officer
CMO: David Tupponce, M.D., Chief Medical Officer
CHR: Kendrick Russell, Chief Human Resources Officer
CNO: Vicki Lynn Huber, R.N., Chief Nursing Officer
Web address: www.abrazoscottsdale.com
**Control:** Corporation, Investor–owned, for–profit **Service:** General Medical and
Surgical

**Staffed Beds:** 142

☐ **ARIZONA STATE HOSPITAL (034021)**, 2500 East Van Buren Street,
Zip 85008–6079; tel. 602/244–1331 **A**1 10 **F**3 29 30 39 53 57 59 65 68 75
77 94 98 130 135 143 146 **P**6
Primary Contact: Ann M. Froio, Interim Chief Executive Officer
COO: Donna Noriega, Chief Operating Officer
CFO: Donna Noriega, Chief Operating Officer
CMO: Steve Dingle, M.D., Chief Medical Officer
CIO: Bruce Randolph, Chief Information Technology
CHR: Jeanine Decker, Manager Human Resources
Web address: www.hs.state.az.us
**Control:** State–Government, nonfederal **Service:** Psychiatric

**Staffed Beds:** 299 **Admissions:** 79 **Census:** 243 **Outpatient Visits:** 0 **Births:**
0 **Total Expense ($000):** 58750 **Payroll Expense ($000):** 29964
**Personnel:** 493

☒ **BANNER ESTRELLA MEDICAL CENTER (030115)**, 9201 West Thomas Road,
Zip 85037–3332; tel. 623/327–4000 **A**1 3 9 10 **F**3 12 13 18 20 22 24 28 29
30 31 34 35 36 37 38 40 43 44 45 46 49 50 51 57 58 59 60 61 64 68 70
74 75 76 77 78 79 80 81 82 85 86 87 91 94 96 102 107 108 111 114 115
119 126 130 132 135 144 145 146 147 148 **P**5 6 **S** Banner Health,
Phoenix, AZ
Primary Contact: Debra J. Krmpotic, R.N., Chief Executive Officer
COO: Gary Foster, R.N., Assistant Administrator
CFO: Dean Shepardson, Chief Financial Officer
CMO: Timothy Ranney, M.D., Chief Medical Officer
CHR: JoAnn Odell, Chief People Resource Officer
CNO: Nancy Adamson, R.N., Chief Nursing Officer
Web address: www.bannerhealth.com/Locations/Arizona/Banner+Estrella+
Medical+Center/
**Control:** Other not–for–profit (including NFP Corporation) **Service:** General
Medical and Surgical

**Staffed Beds:** 266 **Admissions:** 16701 **Census:** 163 **Births:** 4415 **Total
Expense ($000):** 202883 **Payroll Expense ($000):** 84488 **Personnel:** 1381

★ △ **BANNER GOOD SAMARITAN MEDICAL CENTER (030002)**, 1111 East
McDowell Road, Zip 85006–2666, Mailing Address: P.O. Box 2989,
Zip 85062–2989; tel. 602/239–2000 **A**2 3 5 7 8 9 10 **F**3 8 13 15 18 20 22
24 26 28 29 30 31 34 35 36 37 39 40 43 44 45 46 47 49 50 51 52 53 55
56 57 58 59 60 61 64 66 68 70 72 74 75 76 77 78 79 81 82 83 84 85 86
87 90 91 92 93 94 96 97 98 100 101 102 103 104 107 108 110 111 114
115 116 117 118 119 120 121 123 124 126 130 131 132 135 138 139 141
142 145 146 147 148 **S** Banner Health, Phoenix, AZ
Primary Contact: Steve Narang, M.D., Chief Executive Officer
CFO: Kathy Kotin, Chief Financial Officer
CMO: Paul Stander, M.D., Chief Medical Officer
CIO: Michael S. Warden, Senior Vice President Information Technology
CHR: Michael Fleming, Chief People Officer
Web address: www.bannerhealth.com/Locations/Arizona/Banner+Good+
Samaritan+Medical+Center
**Control:** Other not–for–profit (including NFP Corporation) **Service:** General
Medical and Surgical

**Staffed Beds:** 685 **Admissions:** 34020 **Census:** 475 **Births:** 5998 **Total
Expense ($000):** 670724 **Payroll Expense ($000):** 244773 **Personnel:**
3565

*Many Facility Codes have changed. Please refer to the AHA Guide Code Chart.*
© 2015 AHA Guide

**HAVEN SENIOR HORIZONS (034020)**, 1201 South 7th Avenue, Suite 200, Zip 85007–4076; tel. 623/236–2000 **A**10 **F**42 56 68 98 100 101 102 103 **P**5 **S** Haven Behavioral Healthcare, Nashville, TN
Primary Contact: Kathy Shaw, Chief Executive Officer
CHR: Erin McEldowney, Manager Human Resources
CNO: Char Ralstin, Director of Nursing
Web address: www.havenbehavioral.com
**Control:** Corporation, Investor–owned, for–profit **Service:** Psychiatric

**Staffed Beds:** 30 **Admissions:** 764 **Census:** 27 **Outpatient Visits:** 0 **Births:** 0 **Personnel:** 72

★ ○ ◇ **HONORHEALTH DEER VALLEY MEDICAL CENTER (030092)**, 19829 North 27th Avenue, Zip 85027–4002; tel. 623/879–6100 **A**9 10 11 21 **F**3 8 15 17 18 20 22 24 26 28 33 34 35 40 41 43 45 46 49 50 54 55 57 58 59 60 64 70 74 75 77 78 79 81 85 87 89 92 107 108 111 114 115 118 119 126 130 132 145 146 147 148 **S** HonorHealth, Scottsdale, AZ
Primary Contact: John L. Harrington, Jr., FACHE, Chief Executive Officer
CMO: Mary Ann Turley, D.O., Medical Director
CHR: Frank L. Cummins, Vice President Human Resources
CNO: Jessica Rivas, R.N., Vice President and Chief Nursing Officer
Web address: www.jcl.com
**Control:** Other not–for–profit (including NFP Corporation) **Service:** General Medical and Surgical

**Staffed Beds:** 204 **Admissions:** 12016 **Census:** 123 **Personnel:** 1881

★ ◇ **HONORHEALTH JOHN C. LINCOLN MEDICAL CENTER (030014)**, 250 East Dunlap Avenue, Zip 85020–2825; tel. 602/943–2381 **A**9 10 13 21 **F**3 11 15 17 18 20 22 24 26 28 29 30 31 34 37 40 43 45 46 47 49 50 53 54 57 58 59 60 64 68 70 74 75 77 78 79 81 85 92 107 108 111 114 115 116 119 126 130 132 135 145 146 147 148 **S** HonorHealth, Scottsdale, AZ
Primary Contact: Margaret Elizabeth Griffin, Chief Executive Officer
CFO: Todd La Porte, Chief Financial Officer
CMO: Christopher Shearer, M.D., Chief Medical Officer
CHR: Carol Henderson, Senior Vice President, Chief Talent Officer
CNO: Jelden Arcilla, R.N., Vice President and Chief Nursing Officer
Web address: www.jcl.com
**Control:** Other not–for–profit (including NFP Corporation) **Service:** General Medical and Surgical

**Staffed Beds:** 262 **Admissions:** 14033 **Census:** 174

☒ **KINDRED HOSPITAL ARIZONA–PHOENIX (032000)**, 40 East Indianola Avenue, Zip 85012–2059; tel. 602/280–7000, (Includes KINDRED HOSPITAL ARIZONA–NORTHWEST PHOENIX, 13216 North Plaza Del Rio Boulevard, Peoria, Zip 85381–4907; tel. 623/974–5463; Karen Shammas, Chief Executive Officer), (Nonreporting) **A**1 10 **S** Kindred Healthcare, Louisville, KY
Primary Contact: Karen Cawley, Chief Executive Officer
Web address: www.khphoenix.com/
**Control:** Corporation, Investor–owned, for–profit **Service:** Long–Term Acute Care hospital

**Staffed Beds:** 166

**LOS NINOS HOSPITAL (033301)**, 2303 East Thomas Road, Zip 85016–7827; tel. 602/954–7311, (Nonreporting) **A**10
Primary Contact: William Timmons, Chief Executive Officer
Web address: www.losninoshospital.com
**Control:** Other not–for–profit (including NFP Corporation) **Service:** Children's other specialty

**Staffed Beds:** 15

★ ◇ **MARICOPA INTEGRATED HEALTH SYSTEM (030022)**, 2601 East Roosevelt Street, Zip 85008–4956; tel. 602/344–5011, (Includes ARIZONA CHILDREN'S CENTER, 2601 East Roosevelt Street, Zip 85008–4973; tel. 602/344–5051) **A**3 5 8 9 10 21 **F**3 12 13 15 16 17 18 20 22 26 28 29 30 31 34 35 36 39 40 41 42 43 44 45 46 47 48 49 51 53 54 57 58 59 60 61 64 66 68 70 72 73 74 75 76 77 78 79 81 85 86 87 88 89 93 94 97 98 100 102 103 104 105 107 108 110 111 114 115 116 117 118 119 130 132 134 135 144 145 146 147 148 **P**1
Primary Contact: Stephen A. Purves, FACHE, President and Chief Executive Officer
COO: William F. Vanaskie, Executive Vice President and Chief Operating Officer
CFO: Michael Ayres, Senior Vice President and Chief Financial Officer
CMO: Robert Fromm, M.D., Chief Medical Officer
CIO: Kelly Summers, Chief Information Officer
CHR: Marshall Jones, Senior Vice President Human Resources
CNO: Sherry Stotler, R.N., Chief Nursing Officer
Web address: www.mihs.org
**Control:** Hospital district or authority, Government, nonfederal **Service:** General Medical and Surgical

**Staffed Beds:** 522 **Admissions:** 16697 **Census:** 365 **Outpatient Visits:** 483471 **Births:** 2733 **Total Expense ($000):** 540997 **Payroll Expense ($000):** 236725 **Personnel:** 3847

☒ **MAYO CLINIC HOSPITAL (030103)**, 5777 East Mayo Boulevard, Zip 85054–4502; tel. 480/515–6296 **A**1 2 3 5 9 10 **F**3 6 8 9 12 15 17 18 20 22 24 26 28 29 30 31 34 35 36 37 39 40 45 46 47 48 49 50 51 54 55 56 58 59 60 61 64 68 70 74 75 77 78 79 80 81 82 84 85 86 87 90 92 93 96 97 100 103 104 107 108 110 111 112 114 115 116 117 118 119 120 121 123 124 126 129 130 131 132 135 136 137 138 139 141 142 145 146 147 148 **P**6 **S** Mayo Clinic, Rochester, MN
Primary Contact: Darin Goss, Administrator
CFO: Jeffrey R. Froisland, Chief Financial Officer
CMO: Jeff T. Mueller, M.D., Chief Medical Officer, Medical Director
CIO: Amy Z. Vrabel, Chief Information Officer
CHR: Nichelle A. Baker, Chair Human Resources
CNO: Teresa Connolly, R.N., Chief Nursing Officer
Web address: www.mayoclinic.org/arizona/
**Control:** Other not–for–profit (including NFP Corporation) **Service:** General Medical and Surgical

**Staffed Beds:** 268 **Admissions:** 13347 **Census:** 179 **Outpatient Visits:** 57916 **Births:** 0 **Personnel:** 2749

☐ **OASIS HOSPITAL (030131)**, 750 North 40th Street, Zip 85008–6486; tel. 602/797–7700, (Nonreporting) **A**1 3 9 10
Primary Contact: James Flinn, JD, FACHE, Chief Executive Officer
Web address: www.oasishospital.com
**Control:** Partnership, Investor–owned, for–profit **Service:** Orthopedic

**Staffed Beds:** 64

☒ **PHOENIX BAPTIST HOSPITAL (030030)**, 2000 West Bethany Home Road, Zip 85015–2443; tel. 602/249–0212, (Includes ARIZONA HEART HOSPITAL, 1930 East Thomas Road, Zip 85016; tel. 602/532–1000; Danny L. Jones, Jr., FACHE, Chief Executive Officer), (Nonreporting) **A**1 3 5 9 10 **S** TENET Healthcare Corporation, Dallas, TX
Primary Contact: Danny L. Jones, Jr., FACHE, Chief Executive Officer
COO: Chris Bird, Chief Operating Officer
CFO: Leanne Krush, Chief Financial Officer
CMO: Lynnette Watkins, M.D., Chief Medical Officer
CHR: Lois Dopler, Interim Director Human Resources
CNO: Lorna Maxson, R.N., Chief Nursing Officer
Web address: www.phoenixbaptisthospital.com
**Control:** Corporation, Investor–owned, for–profit **Service:** General Medical and Surgical

**Staffed Beds:** 215

☒ **PHOENIX CHILDREN'S HOSPITAL (033302)**, 1919 East Thomas Road, Zip 85016–7710; tel. 602/546–1000 **A**1 3 5 9 10 **F**3 8 11 15 17 19 21 23 25 27 29 30 31 32 34 35 37 38 39 40 41 42 43 44 46 48 49 50 54 55 57 58 59 60 61 64 65 66 68 71 72 73 74 75 77 78 79 81 82 84 85 86 87 88 89 91 92 93 94 96 97 98 99 100 101 102 104 105 107 108 111 113 114 115 116 117 118 119 129 130 131 132 134 135 136 138 144 146 148 **P**6
Primary Contact: Robert L. Meyer, President and Chief Executive Officer
COO: Betsy Kuzas, Executive Vice President and Chief Operating Officer
CFO: Craig L. McKnight, Senior Vice President and Chief Financial Officer
CMO: Murray Pollack, M.D., Vice President and Chief Medical Officer
CIO: David Higginson, Senior Vice President and Chief Information Officer
CHR: Thomas Diederich, Senior Vice President Human Resources
CNO: Pam Carlson, Senior Vice President and Chief Nursing Officer
Web address: www.phoenixchildrens.com
**Control:** Other not–for–profit (including NFP Corporation) **Service:** Children's general

**Staffed Beds:** 331 **Admissions:** 13333 **Census:** 205 **Outpatient Visits:** 237514 **Births:** 0 **Total Expense ($000):** 661678 **Payroll Expense ($000):** 269810 **Personnel:** 3295

☒ **PHOENIX VETERANS AFFAIRS HEALTH CARE SYSTEM**, 650 East Indian School Road, Zip 85012–1892; tel. 602/277–5551, (Nonreporting) **A**1 2 3 5 9 **S** Department of Veterans Affairs, Washington, DC
Primary Contact: Glen W. Grippen, Interim Medical Center Director
CFO: Christine Hollingsworth, Chief Financial Officer
CMO: Raymond Chung, M.D., Chief of Staff
Web address: www.phoenix.va.gov/
**Control:** Veterans Affairs, Government, federal **Service:** General Medical and Surgical

**Staffed Beds:** 197

☒ **SELECT SPECIALTY HOSPITAL–PHOENIX (032001)**, 350 West Thomas Road, 3rd Floor Main, Zip 85013–4409; tel. 602/406–6802, (Nonreporting) **A**1 10 **S** Select Medical Corporation, Mechanicsburg, PA
Primary Contact: Sharon Anthony, Chief Executive Officer
Web address: www.selectspecialtyhospitals.com/company/locations/phoenix.aspx
**Control:** Corporation, Investor–owned, for–profit **Service:** Long–Term Acute Care hospital

**Staffed Beds:** 48

**AZ**

---

**Hospital, Medicare Provider Number, Address, Telephone, Approval, Facility, and Physician Codes, Health Care System**

★ American Hospital Association (AHA) membership
☐ The Joint Commission accreditation
○ Healthcare Facilities Accreditation Program
◇ DNV Healthcare Inc. accreditation
⇑ Center for Improvement in Healthcare Quality Accreditation
△ Commission on Accreditation of Rehabilitation Facilities (CARF) accreditation

**AZ**

SELECT SPECIALTY HOSPITAL–PHOENIX DOWNTOWN See Select Specialty Hospital–Scottsdale, Scottsdale

⊞ △ **ST. JOSEPH'S HOSPITAL AND MEDICAL CENTER (030024)**, 350 West Thomas Road, Zip 85013–4496, Mailing Address: P.O. Box 2071, Zip 85001–2071; tel. 602/406–3000, (Includes CHILDREN'S HEALTH CENTER, 350 West Thomas Road, Zip 85013–4409) **A**1 2 3 5 7 8 9 10 19 **F**3 6 11 12 13 15 17 18 20 22 24 26 29 30 31 34 35 40 43 45 46 47 48 49 51 53 55 56 57 58 59 64 66 68 70 71 72 73 74 75 76 77 78 79 81 82 83 84 85 86 87 90 91 92 93 94 96 97 100 101 102 103 104 107 108 110 111 114 115 116 117 118 119 120 121 123 124 126 127 130 131 140 141 146 147 148 **P**5 6 **S** Dignity Health, San Francisco, CA
Primary Contact: Patty White, R.N., MS, President
CFO: John Peters, Chief Financial Officer
CHR: Maureen Sterbach, Vice President Human Resources
CNO: Julie Ward, MSN, Chief Nursing Officer
Web address: www.stjosephs-phx.org
**Control:** Other not–for–profit (including NFP Corporation) **Service:** General Medical and Surgical

**Staffed Beds:** 595 **Admissions:** 29513 **Census:** 402 **Outpatient Visits:** 497605 **Births:** 4624 **Total Expense ($000):** 887910 **Payroll Expense ($000):** 350760 **Personnel:** 4713

☐ **ST. LUKE'S BEHAVIORAL HEALTH CENTER (034013)**, 1800 East Van Buren, Zip 85006–3742; tel. 602/251–8546, (Nonreporting) **A**1 9 10 **S** IASIS Healthcare, Franklin, TN
Primary Contact: Gregory L. Jahn, R.N., Chief Executive Officer
CFO: Ruby Majhail, Chief Financial Officer
CMO: Mario Tafur, M.D., Chief of Staff
CIO: Chris Ulrey, Director Management Information Systems
CHR: Amy M. Howell, Director Human Resources
Web address: www.iasishealthcare.com
**Control:** Corporation, Investor–owned, for–profit **Service:** Psychiatric

**Staffed Beds:** 85

★ ◇ **ST. LUKE'S MEDICAL CENTER (030037)**, 1800 East Van Buren Street, Zip 85006–3742; tel. 602/251–8100, (Includes TEMPE ST. LUKE'S HOSPITAL, 1500 South Mill Avenue, Tempe, Zip 85281–6699; tel. 480/784–5510; Dale Larson, Administrator) **A**3 9 10 21 **F**3 12 13 18 20 22 24 26 29 37 40 45 47 49 50 51 56 60 64 68 70 74 76 79 81 82 85 87 90 91 92 98 100 103 107 108 111 114 115 118 119 126 129 130 131 133 134 135 146 148 **P**4 **S** IASIS Healthcare, Franklin, TN
Primary Contact: Christopher Hill, Chief Executive Officer
CFO: Ken Walsh, Chief Financial Officer
CHR: Trinise Thompson, Director Human Resources
Web address: www.stlukesmedcenter.com
**Control:** Corporation, Investor–owned, for–profit **Service:** General Medical and Surgical

**Staffed Beds:** 284 **Admissions:** 7996 **Census:** 112 **Outpatient Visits:** 76743 **Births:** 429 **Total Expense ($000):** 150620 **Payroll Expense ($000):** 55820 **Personnel:** 790

☐ **THE SURGICAL HOSPITAL OF PHOENIX (030108)**, 6501 North 19th Avenue, Zip 85015–1646; tel. 602/795–6020, (Nonreporting) **A**1 9 10
Primary Contact: Eric Tomlon, Chief Executive Officer
CFO: Marcus Losada, Controller
CMO: Christopher A. Yeung, M.D., Chief of Staff
CHR: Deby Tooker, Director Human Resources
CNO: Deborah Roberts, R.N., Chief Nursing Officer
Web address: www.sshaz.com
**Control:** Corporation, Investor–owned, for–profit **Service:** Surgical

**Staffed Beds:** 33

⊞ **U. S. PUBLIC HEALTH SERVICE PHOENIX INDIAN MEDICAL CENTER (030078)**, 4212 North 16th Street, Zip 85016–5389; tel. 602/263–1200, (Nonreporting) **A**1 5 9 10 **S** U. S. Indian Health Service, Rockville, MD
Primary Contact: Captain Michael Weahkee, Chief Executive Officer
CFO: Geraldine Harney, Chief Financial Officer
CMO: Dave Civic, M.D., Associate Director Clinical Services
CIO: Vina Montour, Director Information Technology
CHR: Betty Weston, Chief Human Resources Officer
Web address: www.ihs.gov
**Control:** PHS, Indian Service, Government, federal **Service:** General Medical and Surgical

**Staffed Beds:** 127

☐ **VALLEY HOSPITAL PHOENIX (034026)**, 3550 East Pinchot Avenue, Zip 85018–7434; tel. 602/957–4000, (Nonreporting) **A**1 9 10 **S** Universal Health Services, Inc., King of Prussia, PA
Primary Contact: Michelle David, Chief Executive Officer
Web address: www.valleyhospital-phoenix.com
**Control:** Corporation, Investor–owned, for–profit **Service:** Psychiatric

**Staffed Beds:** 122

**PRESCOTT—Yavapai County**

⊞ **NORTHERN ARIZONA VETERANS AFFAIRS HEALTH CARE SYSTEM**, 500 Highway 89 North, Zip 86313–5000; tel. 928/445–4860, (Total facility includes 90 beds in nursing home–type unit) **A**1 9 **F**3 4 5 6 15 18 20 22 29 30 31 34 35 36 38 39 40 45 50 54 56 57 59 62 63 64 65 66 71 75 77 78 79 82 83 84 86 87 91 93 94 97 100 101 102 103 104 106 107 108 111 115 119 127 130 132 133 135 143 146 147 148 **P**6 **S** Department of Veterans Affairs, Washington, DC
Primary Contact: Donna K. Jacobs, FACHE, Director
COO: James Belmont, Associate Director
CFO: Ame Callahan, Acting Manager Resource Management Service
CMO: A. Panneer Selvam, M.D., Chief of Staff
CIO: Scott McCrimmon, Manager Information Technology
CHR: Jane Lewerke, Manager Human Resources
Web address: www.prescott.va.gov/
**Control:** Veterans Affairs, Government, federal **Service:** General Medical and Surgical

**Staffed Beds:** 147 **Admissions:** 1334 **Census:** 106 **Outpatient Visits:** 275542 **Births:** 0 **Total Expense ($000):** 180933 **Payroll Expense ($000):** 67183

★ **YAVAPAI REGIONAL MEDICAL CENTER (030012)**, 1003 Willow Creek Road, Zip 86301–1668; tel. 928/445–2700 **A**9 10 **F**3 11 15 17 18 20 22 24 28 29 30 31 32 34 35 40 45 46 50 53 54 57 59 60 64 68 70 74 75 77 78 79 81 82 84 85 86 87 91 93 107 108 111 114 118 119 130 131 132 135 146 148 **P**6
Primary Contact: John Amos, President and Chief Executive Officer
COO: Larry P. Burns, Jr., Chief Operating Officer
CFO: Lee Livin, Chief Financial Officer
CMO: Joseph Goldberger, M.D., Chief Medical Officer
CHR: Mark Timm, Director Human Resources
CNO: Diane Drexler, R.N., Chief Nursing Officer
Web address: www.yrmc.org
**Control:** Other not–for–profit (including NFP Corporation) **Service:** General Medical and Surgical

**Staffed Beds:** 134 **Admissions:** 6426 **Census:** 70 **Outpatient Visits:** 75792 **Births:** 0 **Total Expense ($000):** 175263 **Payroll Expense ($000):** 58194 **Personnel:** 955

**PRESCOTT VALLEY—Yavapai County**

☐ **MOUNTAIN VALLEY REGIONAL REHABILITATION HOSPITAL (033036)**, 3700 North Windsong Drive, Zip 86314–1253; tel. 928/759–8800, (Nonreporting) **A**1 9 10 **S** Ernest Health, Inc., Albuquerque, NM
Primary Contact: Judy Baum, Chief Executive Officer
Web address: www.mvrrh.ernesthealth.com
**Control:** Corporation, Investor–owned, for–profit **Service:** Rehabilitation

**Staffed Beds:** 16

**WINDHAVEN PSYCHIATRIC HOSPITAL (034025)**, 3347 North Windsong Drive, Zip 86314–2283, Mailing Address: 3343 North Windsong Drive, Zip 86314–1213; tel. 928/445–5211 **A**9 10 **F**29 98 99 100 **P**6
Primary Contact: Larry D. Green, Jr., Chief Executive Officer
COO: Pamela Pierce, Deputy Chief Executive Officer
CFO: Doug Oliver, Chief Financial Officer
CMO: Shane Russell–Jenkins, M.D., Medical Director
CIO: Laura Norman, Chief Development and Information Officer
CHR: Pamela Pierce, Deputy Chief Executive Officer
CNO: Ebony Forrey, Director of Nursing
Web address: www.wygc.org
**Control:** Other not–for–profit (including NFP Corporation) **Service:** Psychiatric

**Staffed Beds:** 16 **Admissions:** 805 **Census:** 16 **Outpatient Visits:** 0 **Births:** 0 **Total Expense ($000):** 3761 **Payroll Expense ($000):** 2378 **Personnel:** 24

★ **YAVAPAI REGIONAL MEDICAL CENTER – EAST (030118)**, 7700 East Florentine Road, Zip 86314–2245; tel. 928/445–2700 **A**9 10 **F**3 11 13 15 29 30 31 40 68 70 72 75 76 77 78 81 84 85 86 87 89 93 107 108 111 114 116 117 118 119 130 146 147 148
Primary Contact: John Amos, Chief Executive Officer
CFO: Lee Livin, Chief Financial Officer
CMO: Joseph Goldberger, M.D., Chief Medical Officer
CHR: Mark Timm, Director Human Resources
CNO: Diane Drexler, R.N., Chief Nursing Officer
Web address: www.yrmc.org
**Control:** Other not–for–profit (including NFP Corporation) **Service:** General Medical and Surgical

**Staffed Beds:** 72 **Admissions:** 3812 **Census:** 31 **Outpatient Visits:** 56203 **Births:** 1096 **Total Expense ($000):** 54412 **Payroll Expense ($000):** 24685 **Personnel:** 406

## SACATON—Pinal County

⊠ **HUHUKAM MEMORIAL HOSPITAL (031308)**, 483 West Seed Farm Road, Zip 85147, Mailing Address: P.O. Box 38, Zip 85147–0001; tel. 602/528–1200, (Nonreporting) **A**1 3 9 10 18
Primary Contact: Lorrie Henderson, Ph.D., Chief Executive Officer
COO: Pamela Thompson, Chief Operations Officer
CMO: Noel Habib, M.D., Chief Medical Officer
CHR: Michael Freeman, Director Human Resources
Web address: www.grhc.org
**Control:** Other not–for–profit (including NFP Corporation) **Service:** General Medical and Surgical

**Staffed Beds:** 12

## SAFFORD—Graham County

★ **MT. GRAHAM REGIONAL MEDICAL CENTER (030068)**, 1600 South 20th Avenue, Zip 85546–4097; tel. 928/348–4000 **A**3 9 10 20 **F**3 11 13 15 18 29 30 31 34 35 40 43 45 48 49 50 57 59 62 63 64 65 66 70 75 76 77 78 79 81 85 87 97 107 108 110 111 114 119 127 129 130 133 135 146 147 **P**6
Primary Contact: Mark E. Marchetti, President and Chief Executive Officer
CFO: Keith Bryce, Vice President Finance and Chief Financial Officer
CIO: Anthon Ellsworth, Director Information Technology
CHR: Irvan Wick Lewis, Vice President Human Resources
CNO: Lori Burress, Vice President Patient Services and Chief Nursing Officer
Web address: www.mtgraham.org
**Control:** Hospital district or authority, Government, nonfederal **Service:** General Medical and Surgical

**Staffed Beds:** 49 **Admissions:** 1819 **Census:** 14 **Outpatient Visits:** 69719 **Births:** 654 **Total Expense ($000):** 57467 **Payroll Expense ($000):** 24789 **Personnel:** 454

## SAN CARLOS—Gila County

⊠ **U. S. PUBLIC HEALTH SERVICE INDIAN HOSPITAL (030077)**, 238 Cibeque Circle, Zip 85550, Mailing Address: P.O. Box 208, Zip 85550–0208; tel. 928/475–2371, (Nonreporting) **A**1 10 **S** U. S. Indian Health Service, Rockville, MD
Primary Contact: Deven Parlikar, President and Chief Executive Officer
CFO: Vivie Hosteenez, Chief Financial Officer
CMO: Douglas Brinkerhoff, M.D., Clinical Director
CIO: Nimmy Mathews, Acting Director Quality Management
CHR: Shirley M. Boni, Administrative Officer
Web address: www.ihs.gov
**Control:** PHS, Indian Service, Government, federal **Service:** General Medical and Surgical

**Staffed Beds:** 8

## SAN TAN VALLEY—Pinal County

⊠ **BANNER IRONWOOD MEDICAL CENTER (030130)**, 37000 North Gantzel Road, Zip 85140–7303; tel. 480/394–4000 **A**1 9 10 **F**3 13 18 29 30 34 36 40 41 44 45 47 49 50 61 68 75 76 77 79 80 81 82 85 86 87 89 92 100 102 107 111 114 119 130 132 135 136 141 142 145 146 147 148 **S** Banner Health, Phoenix, AZ
Primary Contact: Julie Nunley, R.N., Chief Executive Officer
CFO: Tracy French, Chief Financial Officer
CMO: Darren West, M.D., Interim Chief Medical Officer
CHR: Janine Polito, Chief Human Resources Officer
CNO: Terri Paulus, Chief Nursing Officer
Web address: www.bannerhealth.com/Locations/Arizona/Banner+Ironwood/
**Control:** Other not–for–profit (including NFP Corporation) **Service:** General Medical and Surgical

**Staffed Beds:** 53 **Admissions:** 2700 **Census:** 23 **Births:** 914 **Total Expense ($000):** 59574 **Payroll Expense ($000):** 18528 **Personnel:** 287

## SCOTTSDALE—Maricopa County

⊠ **BANNER BEHAVIORAL HEALTH HOSPITAL – SCOTTSDALE (034004)**, 7575 East Earll Drive, Zip 85251–6915; tel. 480/941–7500 **A**1 3 9 10 **F**5 29 30 34 35 36 43 44 50 57 68 75 86 87 98 99 101 102 104 105 106 130 132 134 135 146 **P**5 **S** Banner Health, Phoenix, AZ
Primary Contact: Cherie Martin, R.N., MSN, FACHE, Chief Executive Officer
CFO: Michael A. Cimino, Jr., Chief Financial Officer
CMO: Clifford Zeller, M.D., Chief Medical Officer
CHR: Kevin McVeigh, Interim Chief Human Resources Officer
CNO: Cherri Anderson, Chief Nursing Officer
Web address: www.bannerhealth.com/Locations/Arizona/Banner+Behavioral+Health
**Control:** Other not–for–profit (including NFP Corporation) **Service:** Psychiatric

**Staffed Beds:** 95 **Admissions:** 3949 **Census:** 83 **Births:** 0 **Total Expense ($000):** 32730 **Payroll Expense ($000):** 16410 **Personnel:** 296

★ ◇ **FREEDOM PAIN HOSPITAL (030135)**, (Pain Specialty), 17500 North Perimeter Drive, Zip 85255–7808; tel. 480/586–2300 **A**10 21 **F**29 33 34 36 58 64 80 81 82 85 87
Primary Contact: Steven M. Siwek, M.D., President and Chief Executive Officer
COO: Michael Adams, Chief Operating Officer
CFO: Douglas B. Kell, Chief Financial Officer
CMO: Natalie Shand, M.D., Vice President Integrative Medicine and Chief Medical Officer
CIO: Milad Najjar, Information Technology
CHR: Samantha Mendez, Human Resources
CNO: Jani Manseau, Vice President Operations and Chief Nursing Officer
Web address: www.freedompainhospital.com
**Control:** Corporation, Investor–owned, for–profit **Service:** Other specialty

**Staffed Beds:** 12 **Admissions:** 56 **Census:** 1 **Births:** 0 **Total Expense ($000):** 11394 **Payroll Expense ($000):** 2887

⊠ **HEALTHSOUTH SCOTTSDALE REHABILITATION HOSPITAL (033025)**, 9630 East Shea Boulevard, Zip 85260–6267; tel. 480/551–5400, (Nonreporting) **A**1 9 10 **S** HEALTHSOUTH Corporation, Birmingham, AL
Primary Contact: Timothy T. Poore, Chief Executive Officer
CFO: Lisa Barrick, Controller
CMO: Keith W. Cunningham, M.D., Medical Director
CHR: Mary Beth Giczi, Director Human Resources
CNO: Diane M. Caruso, MSN, Chief Nursing Officer
Web address: www.healthsouthscottsdale.com
**Control:** Corporation, Investor–owned, for–profit **Service:** Rehabilitation

**Staffed Beds:** 60

★ ◇ **HONORHEALTH REHABILITATION HOSPITAL (033038)**, 8850 East Pima Center Parkway, Zip 85258–4619; tel. 480/800–3900, (Nonreporting) **A**10 11 **S** Select Medical Corporation, Mechanicsburg, PA
Primary Contact: Scott R. Keen, Chief Executive Officer
Web address: www.scottsdale–rehab.com/
**Control:** Partnership, Investor–owned, for–profit **Service:** Rehabilitation

**Staffed Beds:** 50

★ ◇ **HONORHEALTH SCOTTSDALE OSBORN MEDICAL CENTER (030038)**, 7400 East Osborn Road, Zip 85251–6403; tel. 480/882–4000, (Nonreporting) **A**2 3 5 8 9 10 21 **S** HonorHealth, Scottsdale, AZ
Primary Contact: Bruce Pearson, Senior Vice President and Chief Executive Officer
CFO: Todd La Porte, Senior Vice President and Chief Financial Officer
CMO: James Burke, M.D., Senior Vice President and Chief Medical Officer
CIO: James R. Cramer, Vice President and Chief Information Officer
CHR: Carol Henderson, Vice President Human Resources
Web address: www.shc.org
**Control:** Other not–for–profit (including NFP Corporation) **Service:** General Medical and Surgical

**Staffed Beds:** 347

★ ◇ **HONORHEALTH SCOTTSDALE SHEA MEDICAL CENTER (030087)**, 9003 East Shea Boulevard, Zip 85260–6771; tel. 480/323–3000, (Nonreporting) **A**2 3 5 9 10 21 **S** HonorHealth, Scottsdale, AZ
Primary Contact: Gary E. Baker, Senior Vice President and Chief Executive Officer
CFO: Todd La Porte, Senior Vice President and Chief Financial Officer
CMO: James Burke, M.D., Senior Vice President and Chief Medical Officer
CIO: James R. Cramer, Vice President and Chief Information Officer
CHR: Carol Henderson, Senior Vice President and Chief Talent Officer
CNO: Joanne T. Clavelle, R.N., Senior Vice President and Chief Clinical Officer
Web address: www.shc.org
**Control:** Other not–for–profit (including NFP Corporation) **Service:** General Medical and Surgical

**Staffed Beds:** 409

★ ◇ **HONORHEALTH SCOTTSDALE THOMPSON PEAK MEDICAL CENTER (030123)**, 7400 East Thompson Peak Parkway, Zip 85255–4109; tel. 480/324–7000, (Nonreporting) **A**9 10 21 **S** HonorHealth, Scottsdale, AZ
Primary Contact: Kimberly Post, R.N., Vice President and Administrator
CFO: Todd La Porte, Chief Financial Officer
CMO: James Burke, M.D., Senior Vice President and Chief Medical Officer
CIO: James R. Cramer, Chief Information Officer
CHR: Carol Henderson, Vice President Human Resources
Web address: www.shc.org
**Control:** Other not–for–profit (including NFP Corporation) **Service:** General Medical and Surgical

**Staffed Beds:** 64

---

**Hospital, Medicare Provider Number, Address, Telephone, Approval, Facility, and Physician Codes, Health Care System**

★ American Hospital Association (AHA) membership
□ The Joint Commission accreditation
◇ Healthcare Facilities Accreditation Program
◇ DNV Healthcare Inc. accreditation
⇑ Center for Improvement in Healthcare Quality Accreditation
△ Commission on Accreditation of Rehabilitation Facilities (CARF) accreditation

**AZ**

✠ **SELECT SPECIALTY HOSPITAL–SCOTTSDALE (032005)**, 7400 East Osborn Road, 3 West, Zip 85251–6432; tel. 480/882–4360, (Includes SELECT SPECIALTY HOSPITAL–PHOENIX DOWNTOWN, 1012 East Wiletta Street, 4th Floor, Phoenix, Zip 85006; tel. 602/239–6134; Sharon Anthony, Interim Chief Executive Officer), (Nonreporting) **A**1 10 **S** Select Medical Corporation, Mechanicsburg, PA
Primary Contact: Anthony Martino, Chief Executive Officer
Web address: www.selectspecialtyhospitals.com/company/locations/scottsdale.aspx
**Control:** Corporation, Investor–owned, for–profit **Service:** Long–Term Acute Care hospital

Staffed Beds: 62

**SELLS—Pima County**

✠ **U. S. PUBLIC HEALTH SERVICE INDIAN HOSPITAL–SELLS (030074)**, Highway 86 & Topawa Road, Zip 85634, Mailing Address: P.O. Box 548, Zip 85634–0548; tel. 520/383–7251, (Nonreporting) **A**1 9 10 **S** U. S. Indian Health Service, Rockville, MD
Primary Contact: Priscilla Whitethorne, Chief Executive Officer
COO: Diane Shanley, Deputy Service Unit Director
CFO: Vivian Draper, Chief Financial Officer
CMO: Peter Ziegler, M.D., Acting Chief Medical Officer
CIO: Karen Wade, Chief Information Officer
CNO: Donna Hobbs, Nurse Executive
Web address: www.ihs.gov
**Control:** PHS, Indian Service, Government, federal **Service:** General Medical and Surgical

Staffed Beds: 12

**SHOW LOW—Navajo County**

★ **SUMMIT HEALTHCARE REGIONAL MEDICAL CENTER (030062)**, 2200 East Show Low Lake Road, Zip 85901–7800; tel. 928/537–4375 **A**9 10 20 **F**3 11 15 18 20 22 28 29 30 31 32 34 35 36 38 40 41 43 45 46 47 53 54 57 59 64 65 68 70 71 73 75 76 77 78 79 81 82 92 93 107 108 110 111 113 114 119 121 127 129 130 131 132 135 146
Primary Contact: Ronald L. McArthur, Chief Executive Officer
COO: Doug Gilchrist, Chief Operating Officer
CFO: Kurt Loveless, Chief Financial Officer
CMO: Alan Neil DeWitt, Chief Medical Officer
CIO: Aaron Young, Chief Information Officer
CHR: Connie Kakavas, Chief Human Resources Officer
CNO: Cynthia Ebert–Loomis, R.N., Chief Nursing Officer
Web address: www.summithealthcare.net
**Control:** Other not–for–profit (including NFP Corporation) **Service:** General Medical and Surgical

Staffed Beds: 89 Admissions: 4113 Census: 34 Births: 940

**SIERRA VISTA—Cochise County**

☐ **CANYON VISTA MEDICAL CENTER (030043)**, 5700 East Highway 90, Zip 85635–9110; tel. 520/263–2000 **A**1 9 10 13 20 **F**3 11 13 15 18 20 22 27 28 29 30 34 35 40 41 45 46 48 49 50 51 57 60 63 64 70 73 75 76 77 79 81 82 85 86 89 93 107 111 114 115 118 119 127 130 145 146 148 **S** RegionalCare Hospital Partners, Brentwood, TN
Primary Contact: Jeff Egbert, Interim Chief Executive Officer
COO: Bruce J. Norton, Senior Vice President and Chief Operating Officer
CFO: Steve Calabrese, Vice President and Chief Financial Officer
CMO: Steven Mehta, M.D., Chief Medical Officer
CIO: Jorge Moreno, Director Information Technology Operations
CHR: Traci Meyer, Director Human Resources and Public Relations Officer
CNO: Cynthia Lewis, Chief Nursing Officer
Web address: www.svrhc.org
**Control:** Other not–for–profit (including NFP Corporation) **Service:** General Medical and Surgical

Staffed Beds: 83 Admissions: 4720 Census: 37 Births: 1049 Personnel: 495

**SPRINGERVILLE—Apache County**

**WHITE MOUNTAIN REGIONAL MEDICAL CENTER (031315)**, 118 South Mountain Avenue, Zip 85938–5104; tel. 928/333–4368, (Nonreporting) **A**9 10 18
Primary Contact: Gregory J. Was, CPA, Chief Executive Officer
CFO: James Hamblin, Chief Financial Officer
CMO: Scott Hamblin, M.D., President Medical Staff
Web address: www.wmrmc.com
**Control:** Other not–for–profit (including NFP Corporation) **Service:** General Medical and Surgical

Staffed Beds: 20

**SUN CITY—Maricopa County**

✠ **BANNER BOSWELL MEDICAL CENTER (030061)**, 10401 West Thunderbird Boulevard, Zip 85351–3004, Mailing Address: P.O. Box 1690, Zip 85372–1690; tel. 623/832–4000, (Total facility includes 78 beds in nursing home–type unit) **A**1 2 3 9 10 **F**3 11 15 18 20 22 24 26 28 29 30 31 34 35 36 37 40 44 45 46 47 48 49 50 51 53 56 57 58 59 60 61 64 65 69 70 74 75 78 79 81 84 85 86 87 90 91 92 93 94 96 107 108 110 111 114 115 117 118 119 124 126 130 132 135 141 143 145 146 147 148 **S** Banner Health, Phoenix, AZ
Primary Contact: David Cheney, Chief Executive Officer
CFO: Jeremy Williams, Chief Financial Officer
CMO: Kathryn Perkins, M.D., Chief Medical Officer
CHR: Brenda Dietrich, Chief Human Resources Officer
Web address: www.bannerhealth.com/Locations/Arizona/Banner+Boswell+Medical+Center
**Control:** Other not–for–profit (including NFP Corporation) **Service:** General Medical and Surgical

Staffed Beds: 377 Admissions: 17857 Census: 261 Outpatient Visits: 82499 Total Expense ($000): 278579 Payroll Expense ($000): 100513 Personnel: 1681

**TRILLIUM SPECIALTY HOSPITAL–WEST VALLEY** See Acuity Specialty Hospital of Sun City

**SUN CITY WEST—Maricopa County**

✠ **BANNER DEL E. WEBB MEDICAL CENTER (030093)**, 14502 West Meeker Boulevard, Zip 85375–5299, Mailing Address: P.O. Box 5169, Zip 85376–5169; tel. 623/214–4000 **A**1 3 9 10 **F**3 5 8 9 13 15 18 20 22 28 29 30 31 34 35 36 37 39 40 41 44 45 46 47 48 49 50 51 56 57 58 59 60 61 64 65 68 70 74 75 76 77 78 79 80 81 82 84 85 86 87 90 91 92 93 94 96 98 100 102 103 104 105 107 108 110 111 114 115 118 119 126 130 131 132 135 145 146 147 148 **P**1 8 **S** Banner Health, Phoenix, AZ
Primary Contact: Debbie Flores, Chief Executive Officer
CMO: Michel Dagher, D.O., Vice President and Chief Medical Officer
CIO: David Runt, Chief Information Officer
Web address: www.bannerhealth.com/Locations/Arizona/Banner+Del+Webb+Medical+Center/
**Control:** Other not–for–profit (including NFP Corporation) **Service:** General Medical and Surgical

Staffed Beds: 373 Admissions: 15523 Census: 186 Outpatient Visits: 110374 Births: 1736 Total Expense ($000): 243906 Payroll Expense ($000): 85069 Personnel: 1398

**TEMPE—Maricopa County**

☐ **AURORA BEHAVIORAL HEALTH SYSTEM EAST (034028)**, 6350 South Maple Street, Zip 85283–2857; tel. 480/345–5400, (Nonreporting) **A**1 9 10 **S** Signature Healthcare Services, Corona, CA
Primary Contact: Bruce Waldo, Chief Executive Officer
CFO: Rebekah Francis, JD, Chief Financial Officer
CMO: Jason Friday, M.D., Medical Director
CHR: Vicki Thomsen, Director Human Resources
Web address: www.auroraarizona.com
**Control:** Partnership, Investor–owned, for–profit **Service:** Psychiatric

Staffed Beds: 70

**TUBA CITY—Coconino County**

✠ **TUBA CITY REGIONAL HEALTH CARE CORPORATION (030073)**, 167 Main Street, Zip 86045–0611, Mailing Address: P.O. Box 600, Zip 86045–0600; tel. 928/283–2501 **A**1 3 5 9 10 **F**3 5 8 9 11 13 14 15 18 26 27 28 29 30 31 32 34 35 36 38 39 40 41 43 44 45 46 47 48 50 52 53 54 55 56 57 58 59 60 61 62 63 64 65 66 68 70 71 74 75 76 77 79 80 81 82 83 84 85 86 87 89 90 91 92 93 94 95 96 97 99 100 101 102 103 104 107 108 110 111 114 115 119 124 127 128 130 131 132 133 134 135 141 142 143 144 145 146 147 148 **P**1 6 7
Primary Contact: Lynette Bonar, Chief Executive Officer
CFO: Clifford Lee Olsson, Chief Financial Officer
CMO: Alan Spacone, M.D., Chief Medical Officer
CHR: John S. Pemberton, Director Human Resources
Web address: www.tchealth.org
**Control:** Other not–for–profit (including NFP Corporation) **Service:** General Medical and Surgical

Staffed Beds: 53 Admissions: 2162 Census: 29 Outpatient Visits: 745369 Births: 435 Total Expense ($000): 151241 Payroll Expense ($000): 74955 Personnel: 910

*Many Facility Codes have changed. Please refer to the AHA Guide Code Chart.* © 2015 AHA Guide

**TUCSON—Pima County**

☒ **BANNER – UNIVERSITY MEDICAL CENTER SOUTH (030111)**, 2800 East Ajo Way, Zip 85713–6289; tel. 520/874–2000 **A**1 3 5 9 10 **F**3 11 12 15 18 20 22 26 29 30 34 35 36 38 40 43 44 50 51 54 55 56 57 58 59 61 64 65 68 70 74 75 77 79 81 82 85 87 93 97 98 100 101 102 103 104 107 110 111 114 115 119 127 130 131 135 145 146 147 148 **P**4 **S** Banner Health, Phoenix, AZ
Primary Contact: Sarah Frost, Administrator
COO: Sarah Frost, Administrator and Chief Operating Officer
CFO: Misty Hansen, Chief Financial Officer
CMO: John Kettelle, M.D., Chief Medical Officer
CIO: Dan Critchley, Chief Information Officer
CHR: John Marques, Vice President Chief Human Resources Officer
Web address: www.uahealth.com
**Control:** Other not–for–profit (including NFP Corporation) **Service:** General Medical and Surgical

**Staffed Beds:** 161 **Admissions:** 7554 **Census:** 111 **Outpatient Visits:** 206867 **Births:** 0 **Total Expense ($000):** 154869 **Payroll Expense ($000):** 53208 **Personnel:** 784

☒ **BANNER – UNIVERSITY MEDICAL CENTER TUCSON (030064)**, 1501 North Campbell Avenue, Zip 85724–5128; tel. 520/694–0111, (Includes DIAMOND CHILDREN'S HOSPITAL, 1501 North Campbell Avenue, Zip 85724–0001; tel. 520/694–0111) **A**1 3 5 8 9 10 **F**3 8 11 12 13 17 18 19 20 21 22 23 24 25 26 27 28 29 30 31 32 34 35 36 37 38 40 41 43 44 45 46 47 48 49 50 53 54 57 58 59 60 61 62 64 67 68 69 70 72 74 75 76 77 78 79 81 84 85 86 87 88 89 92 93 97 100 101 102 107 108 111 114 115 116 117 118 119 120 121 123 124 126 129 130 132 135 136 137 138 139 140 141 142 145 146 147 148 **P**4 6 **S** Banner Health, Phoenix, AZ
Primary Contact: Thomas C. Dickson, Chief Executive Officer
COO: Sarah Frost, Chief Operating Officer and Administrator, University of Arizona Medical Center – South Campus
CFO: Misty Hansen, Chief Financial Officer
CMO: Andreas Theodorou, Chief Medical Officer
CIO: Dan Critchley, Chief Information Officer
CHR: John Marques, Vice President Human Resources
Web address: www.uahealth.com
**Control:** Other not–for–profit (including NFP Corporation) **Service:** General Medical and Surgical

**Staffed Beds:** 479 **Admissions:** 22630 **Census:** 365 **Outpatient Visits:** 424326 **Births:** 1901 **Total Expense ($000):** 700088 **Payroll Expense ($000):** 215122 **Personnel:** 3207

☒ **CARONDELET ST. JOSEPH'S HOSPITAL (030011)**, 350 North Wilmot Road, Zip 85711–2678; tel. 520/873–3000 **A**1 5 9 10 **F**3 5 11 12 13 18 20 22 28 29 30 31 34 35 38 40 44 45 46 47 49 50 57 59 60 61 64 68 69 70 72 74 75 76 77 78 79 81 82 83 84 85 86 87 90 92 93 98 100 101 102 103 104 105 107 108 114 115 118 119 126 129 130 132 135 145 146 147 148 **S** Ascension Health, Saint Louis, MO
Primary Contact: Tony Fonze, President and Chief Executive Officer
CFO: Alan Strauss, Chief Financial Officer
CMO: Donald Denmark, M.D., Chief Medical Officer
CIO: Sally Zambrello, Chief Information Officer
CHR: Igor Shegolev, Vice President Human Resources
CNO: Robin Conklin, R.N., Chief Nursing Officer
Web address: www.carondelet.org
**Control:** Church–operated, Nongovernment, not–for profit **Service:** General Medical and Surgical

**Staffed Beds:** 486 **Admissions:** 16372 **Census:** 218 **Outpatient Visits:** 129990 **Births:** 2586 **Total Expense ($000):** 261216 **Payroll Expense ($000):** 89114 **Personnel:** 1416

☒ **CARONDELET ST. MARY'S HOSPITAL (030010)**, 1601 West St. Mary's Road, Zip 85745–2682; tel. 520/872–3000 **A**1 3 5 9 10 **F**3 11 15 17 18 20 22 24 26 28 29 30 31 34 38 40 44 45 46 47 49 50 51 56 57 58 59 60 61 63 64 68 70 74 77 78 79 81 82 84 85 87 90 92 93 96 98 100 101 102 103 107 108 110 111 114 115 118 119 129 130 131 132 146 148 **S** Ascension Health, Saint Louis, MO
Primary Contact: Amy Beiter, M.D., President and Chief Executive Officer
CMO: Donald Denmark, M.D., Chief Medical Officer
Web address: www.carondelet.org
**Control:** Church–operated, Nongovernment, not–for profit **Service:** General Medical and Surgical

**Staffed Beds:** 300 **Admissions:** 11102 **Census:** 152 **Outpatient Visits:** 183247 **Births:** 0 **Total Expense ($000):** 198404 **Payroll Expense ($000):** 72908 **Personnel:** 1184

☐ **CORNERSTONE HOSPITAL OF SOUTHEAST ARIZONA (032004)**, 7220 East Rosewood Drive, Zip 85710–1350; tel. 520/546–4595 **A**1 10 **F**1 29 30 75 77 82 84 85 90 **S** Cornerstone Healthcare Group, Dallas, TX
Primary Contact: Louise Cassidy, Chief Executive Officer
CFO: Kurt Schultz, Group Chief Financial Officer
CMO: Haroon Haque, M.D., Medical Director
CIO: Adam Davis, Director Information Technology
CHR: Debra Ramage, Director Human Resources and Payroll
CNO: Robert Labowitz, Chief Nursing Officer
Web address: www.chghospitals.com
**Control:** Corporation, Investor–owned, for–profit **Service:** Long–Term Acute Care hospital

**Staffed Beds:** 34 **Admissions:** 291 **Census:** 20 **Personnel:** 83

☒ **HEALTHSOUTH REHABILITATION HOSPITAL OF SOUTHERN ARIZONA (033029)**, 1921 West Hospital Drive, Zip 85704–7806; tel. 520/742–2800 **A**1 9 10 **F**3 29 34 59 64 69 90 93 95 96 130 131 132 143 148 **S** HEALTHSOUTH Corporation, Birmingham, AL
Primary Contact: Donna Beifus, Chief Executive Officer
CFO: Kaleigh Hotchkiss, Controller
CMO: Susan Bulen, M.D., Medical Director
CHR: Neil Cullen, Director Human Resources
CNO: Cheryl Nelson, Chief Nursing Officer
Web address: www.healthsouthsouthernarizona.com
**Control:** Corporation, Investor–owned, for–profit **Service:** Rehabilitation

**Staffed Beds:** 60 **Admissions:** 1084 **Census:** 34 **Births:** 0 **Total Expense ($000):** 13265 **Payroll Expense ($000):** 6856

☒ **HEALTHSOUTH REHABILITATION INSTITUTE OF TUCSON (033028)**, 2650 North Wyatt Drive, Zip 85712–6108; tel. 520/325–1300 **A**1 9 10 **F**29 34 35 62 90 93 96 130 132 **S** HEALTHSOUTH Corporation, Birmingham, AL
Primary Contact: Jeffrey Christensen, Chief Executive Officer
CFO: Mary Donovan, Controller
CMO: Jon Larson, M.D., Medical Director
CHR: Dawn Mosier, Director Human Resources
Web address: www.rehabinstituteoftucson.com
**Control:** Corporation, Investor–owned, for–profit **Service:** Rehabilitation

**Staffed Beds:** 80 **Admissions:** 1382 **Census:** 51 **Outpatient Visits:** 0 **Births:** 0 **Total Expense ($000):** 19084 **Payroll Expense ($000):** 11013 **Personnel:** 190

☒ **KINDRED HOSPITAL–TUCSON (032002)**, 355 North Wilmot Road, Zip 85711–2601; tel. 520/584–4500, (Nonreporting) **A**1 10 **S** Kindred Healthcare, Louisville, KY
Primary Contact: Marc Lemon, Chief Executive Officer
CFO: Lynn Myers, Controller
CMO: Sunil Natrajan, M.D., Medical Director
CNO: Annette Lindeman, Chief Clinical Officer
Web address: www.khtucson.com
**Control:** Corporation, Investor–owned, for–profit **Service:** Long–Term Acute Care hospital

**Staffed Beds:** 51

☒ **NORTHWEST MEDICAL CENTER (030085)**, 6200 North La Cholla Boulevard, Zip 85741–3599; tel. 520/742–9000 **A**1 3 5 9 10 **F**3 8 12 13 15 17 18 19 20 22 24 26 28 29 30 31 34 35 37 40 49 53 57 59 68 70 72 74 75 76 78 79 81 85 91 93 102 107 108 110 111 113 114 118 119 126 130 135 144 146 147 148 **S** Community Health Systems, Inc., Franklin, TN
Primary Contact: Kevin Stockton, Chief Executive Officer
CFO: Ronald Patrick, Chief Financial Officer
CIO: David Bullock, Director Information Services
CNO: Kay Stubbs, Chief Nursing Officer
Web address: www.northwestmedicalcenter.com
**Control:** Corporation, Investor–owned, for–profit **Service:** General Medical and Surgical

**Staffed Beds:** 270 **Admissions:** 16479 **Census:** 170 **Births:** 2881 **Total Expense ($000):** 274561 **Payroll Expense ($000):** 114758 **Personnel:** 1695

**PALO VERDE MENTAL BEHAVIORAL HEALTH (034030)**, 2695 North Craycroft Road, Zip 85712–2244; tel. 520/322–2888, (Nonreporting) **A**9 10 **S** Universal Health Services, Inc., King of Prussia, PA
Primary Contact: P. Jay Frayser, Chief Executive Officer
CFO: Richard N. England, Chief Financial Officer
CHR: Michelle Carrasco, Director Human Resources
Web address: www.paloverdebh.com/
**Control:** Other not–for–profit (including NFP Corporation) **Service:** Psychiatric

**Staffed Beds:** 48

**AZ**

---

**Hospital, Medicare Provider Number, Address, Telephone, Approval, Facility, and Physician Codes, Health Care System**

★ American Hospital Association (AHA) membership
☐ The Joint Commission accreditation
○ Healthcare Facilities Accreditation Program
◇ DNV Healthcare Inc. accreditation
⇧ Center for Improvement in Healthcare Quality Accreditation
△ Commission on Accreditation of Rehabilitation Facilities (CARF) accreditation

**AZ**

☐ **SIERRA TUCSON**, 39580 South Lago Del Oro Parkway, Zip 85739–1091; tel. 520/624–4000 **A**1 **F**4 29 33 35 36 53 75 80 82 98 106 118 135 **P**6 **S** CRC Health Group, Inc., Cupertino, CA
Primary Contact: Stephen P. Fahey, Executive Director
COO: Stephen P. Fahey, Executive Director
CFO: Amy Fritton, Controller
CMO: Jerome Lerner, M.D., Medical Director
CHR: Betty Dickens, Director Human Resources
CNO: Sue Menzie, R.N., Director Patient Care
Web address: www.sierratucson.com
**Control:** Corporation, Investor–owned, for–profit **Service:** Psychiatric

**Staffed Beds:** 139 **Admissions:** 1022 **Census:** 81 **Outpatient Visits:** 0 **Births:** 0

☐ **SONORA BEHAVIORAL HEALTH HOSPITAL (034022)**, 6050 North Corona Road, #3, Zip 85704–1096; tel. 520/469–8700 **A**1 3 9 10 **F**1 4 5 16 17 29 67 70 72 73 76 80 88 89 90 98 99 100 103 104 105 128 **P**6 **S** Acadia Healthcare Company, Inc., Franklin, TN
Primary Contact: Edeli Kinsala, Chief Executive Officer
CMO: Steven Bupp, M.D., Medical Director
CHR: Ciria Soto, Director Human Resources
CNO: Angel Payne, Clinical Director, Director of Nursing
**Control:** Corporation, Investor–owned, for–profit **Service:** Psychiatric

**Staffed Beds:** 72 **Admissions:** 2450 **Census:** 63 **Outpatient Visits:** 3837 **Births:** 0

✉ △ **SOUTHERN ARIZONA VETERANS AFFAIRS HEALTH CARE SYSTEM**, 3601 South 6th Avenue, Zip 85723–0002; tel. 520/792–1450, (Nonreporting) **A**1 3 5 7 8 9 **S** Department of Veterans Affairs, Washington, DC
Primary Contact: Jonathan H. Gardner, FACHE, Director
CFO: Larry Korn, Manager Finance
CMO: Jayendra H. Shah, M.D., Chief Medical Officer
CIO: John Walston, Chief Information Officer
CHR: Patrice Craig, Manager Human Resources
Web address: www.tucson.va.gov
**Control:** Veterans Affairs, Government, federal **Service:** General Medical and Surgical

**Staffed Beds:** 285

**TMC FOR CHILDREN** See TMC Healthcare

★ **TMC HEALTHCARE (030006)**, 5301 East Grant Road, Zip 85712–2874; tel. 520/327–5461, (Includes TMC BEHAVIORAL HEALTH CENTER, 2601 North Cornerstone Drive, Sherman, Texas, Zip 75092–2551; tel. 903/416–3000; Jennifer Wiggins, Chief Executive Officer; TMC FOR CHILDREN, 5301 East Grant Road, Zip 85712–2805; tel. 520/327–5461) **A**3 5 9 10 **F**3 11 12 13 15 17 18 19 20 22 24 26 28 29 30 31 32 34 35 37 40 41 45 46 47 48 49 50 51 53 56 57 58 59 60 62 63 64 65 68 69 72 74 75 76 77 78 79 81 82 84 85 87 88 89 100 102 104 107 108 110 111 115 118 119 124 126 129 130 146 148 **P**6
Primary Contact: Judy F. Rich, President and Chief Executive Officer
COO: Cheryl Meadows, Executive Assistant to the President
CFO: Stephen Bush, Chief Financial Officer
CMO: Rick Anderson, M.D., Senior Vice President and Chief Medical Officer
CIO: Frank Marini, Vice President and Chief Information Officer
CHR: Richard W. Lawley, Vice President Human Resources
CNO: Elizabeth Maish, R.N., Vice President and Chief Nursing Officer
Web address: www.tmcaz.com
**Control:** Other not–for–profit (including NFP Corporation) **Service:** General Medical and Surgical

**Staffed Beds:** 570 **Admissions:** 29983 **Census:** 341 **Outpatient Visits:** 153457 **Births:** 5527 **Total Expense ($000):** 443395 **Payroll Expense ($000):** 174555 **Personnel:** 3050

**WHITERIVER—Navajo County**

☐ **U. S. PUBLIC HEALTH SERVICE INDIAN HOSPITAL–WHITERIVER (030113)**, 200 West Hospital Drive, Zip 85941–0860, Mailing Address: State Route 73, Box 860, Zip 85941–0860; tel. 928/338–4911 **A**1 10 **F**3 8 13 29 32 34 35 36 38 39 40 44 45 46 50 53 54 56 57 59 61 64 65 66 68 75 76 78 79 81 82 84 85 86 87 89 91 93 94 97 100 101 104 107 115 119 130 131 132 135 144 146 147 148 **S** U. S. Indian Health Service, Rockville, MD
Primary Contact: Michelle Martinez, Chief Executive Officer
COO: Brian Campbell, Director Professional Services
CFO: Desdemona Leslie, Finance Officer
CMO: John Umhau, M.D., Clinical Director
CIO: Russell Barker, Information Officer
CHR: Lena Fasthorse, Supervisor Human Resource
CNO: Jana Towne, Nurse Executive
Web address: www.ihs.gov
**Control:** PHS, Indian Service, Government, federal **Service:** General Medical and Surgical

**Staffed Beds:** 35 **Admissions:** 910 **Census:** 12 **Outpatient Visits:** 120000 **Births:** 54 **Personnel:** 417

**WICKENBURG—Maricopa County**

★ **WICKENBURG COMMUNITY HOSPITAL (031300)**, 520 Rose Lane, Zip 85390–1447; tel. 928/684–5421 **A**9 10 18 **F**11 15 34 40 53 57 59 63 65 90 93 107 110 111 115 117 119 127 133 146 148
Primary Contact: James Tavary, Chief Executive Officer
CFO: Mike Ellis, Chief Financial Officer
CMO: Clifford Ball, D.O., Medical Director Emergency Room
CIO: Michael McKay, Chief Information Officer
CHR: Kate Pina, Director Human Resources
CNO: Linda Brockwell, Chief Nursing Officer
Web address: www.wickhosp.com
**Control:** Other not–for–profit (including NFP Corporation) **Service:** General Medical and Surgical

**Staffed Beds:** 19 **Admissions:** 676 **Census:** 8 **Births:** 2 **Total Expense ($000):** 17940 **Payroll Expense ($000):** 9565 **Personnel:** 168

**WILLCOX—Cochise County**

★ **NORTHERN COCHISE COMMUNITY HOSPITAL (031302)**, 901 West Rex Allen Drive, Zip 85643–1009; tel. 520/384–3541, (Total facility includes 24 beds in nursing home–type unit) **A**9 10 18 **F**29 34 35 40 43 56 57 59 64 65 77 90 93 107 110 111 115 119 127 128 133 146
Primary Contact: Roland Knox, Chief Executive Officer
CFO: Dana Strong, Chief Financial Officer
CMO: Hisham Hamam, M.D., Chief of Staff
CIO: Dennis Drury, Director Information Technology
CNO: Pam Noland, Director of Nursing
Web address: www.ncch.com
**Control:** Hospital district or authority, Government, nonfederal **Service:** General Medical and Surgical

**Staffed Beds:** 48 **Admissions:** 464 **Census:** 21 **Outpatient Visits:** 16236 **Births:** 0 **Total Expense ($000):** 17012 **Payroll Expense ($000):** 7712 **Personnel:** 163

**WINSLOW—Navajo County**

★ **LITTLE COLORADO MEDICAL CENTER (031311)**, 1501 Williamson Avenue, Zip 86047–2797; tel. 928/289–4691 **A**9 10 18 **F**29 34 40 50 65 79 81 107 127 130 133
Primary Contact: John J. Dempsey, Chief Executive Officer
CFO: Gina Reffner, Chief Financial Officer
CMO: Perry Mitchell, M.D., Chief of Staff
CHR: Nina L. Ferguson, Director Human Resources
Web address: www.lcmcwmh.com
**Control:** Other not–for–profit (including NFP Corporation) **Service:** General Medical and Surgical

**Staffed Beds:** 25 **Admissions:** 1279 **Census:** 10 **Births:** 208 **Total Expense ($000):** 28313 **Payroll Expense ($000):** 12098 **Personnel:** 209

**YUMA—Yuma County**

★ **YUMA REGIONAL MEDICAL CENTER (030013)**, 2400 South Avenue A, Zip 85364–7170; tel. 928/344–2000 **A**2 3 5 9 10 **F**3 8 12 13 15 18 20 22 24 26 28 29 30 31 32 34 35 39 40 41 45 46 47 48 49 50 54 57 58 59 64 65 68 70 72 74 75 76 77 78 79 81 82 83 84 85 86 87 89 93 97 100 104 107 108 109 110 111 114 115 116 117 118 119 120 121 122 123 124 130 132 141 144 147 148
Primary Contact: Robert Trenschel, D.O., President and Chief Executive Officer
CFO: David Willie, Chief Financial Officer
CMO: Carl Myers, M.D., Vice President Medical Affairs and Chief Medical Officer
CIO: Gene Shaw, Chief Information Officer
CHR: Sharon R. Gardner, Vice President Human Resources
CNO: Deborah Carver, R.N., Vice President Patient Care Services
Web address: www.yumaregional.org
**Control:** Other not–for–profit (including NFP Corporation) **Service:** General Medical and Surgical

**Staffed Beds:** 406 **Admissions:** 17073 **Census:** 189 **Outpatient Visits:** 175070 **Births:** 3348 **Total Expense ($000):** 319965 **Payroll Expense ($000):** 116059 **Personnel:** 1767

✉ **YUMA REHABILITATION HOSPITAL (033034)**, 901 West 24th Street, Zip 85364–6384; tel. 928/726–5000, (Nonreporting) **A**1 9 10 **S** HEALTHSOUTH Corporation, Birmingham, AL
CFO: Larry Barclift, Chief Financial Officer
CMO: Rinely Aguiar–Olsen, M.D., Medical Director
CHR: Linda Woen, Director Human Resources
CNO: Kristin Parra, Chief Nursing Officer
Web address: www.yumarehabhospital.com
**Control:** Corporation, Investor–owned, for–profit **Service:** Rehabilitation

**Staffed Beds:** 41

*Many Facility Codes have changed. Please refer to the AHA Guide Code Chart.* © 2015 AHA Guide

# ARKANSAS

## ARKADELPHIA—Clark County

☒ **BAPTIST HEALTH MEDICAL CENTER–ARKADELPHIA (041321)**, 3050 Twin Rivers Drive, Zip 71923–4299; tel. 870/245–2622, (Nonreporting) **A**1 9 10 18 **S** Baptist Health, Little Rock, AR
Primary Contact: John Bowen, Assistant Vice President and Administrator
CFO: Robert C. Roberts, Vice President and Chief Financial Officer
CMO: Eddie Phillips, M.D., Chief Medical Officer
CIO: David House, Vice President and Chief Information Officer
CHR: Anthony Kendall, Vice President Human Resources
Web address: www.baptist-health.com/locations/accesspoint.aspx?accessPointID=187
**Control:** Other not–for–profit (including NFP Corporation) **Service:** General Medical and Surgical

**Staffed Beds:** 25

## ASHDOWN—Little River County

★ **LITTLE RIVER MEMORIAL HOSPITAL (041320)**, 451 West Locke Street, Zip 71822–3325; tel. 870/898–5011 **A**9 10 18 **F**2 3 15 29 30 40 56 57 59 62 63 75 77 86 87 91 92 93 97 107 110 114 119 130 148
Primary Contact: James Dowell, Administrator and Chief Executive Officer
CFO: Jackie Rainey, Chief Financial Officer
CIO: Mitchell Jones, Director Information Technology
CHR: Vicki Keener, Administrative Assistant and Director Human Resources
CNO: Cynthia Metzger, Chief Nursing and Operations Officer
**Control:** County–Government, nonfederal **Service:** General Medical and Surgical

**Staffed Beds:** 25 **Admissions:** 218 **Census:** 2 **Outpatient Visits:** 7842 **Births:** 0 **Total Expense ($000):** 11001 **Payroll Expense ($000):** 5990 **Personnel:** 59

## BARLING—Sebastian County

☐ **VALLEY BEHAVIORAL HEALTH SYSTEM (044006)**, 10301 Mayo Drive, Zip 72923–1660; tel. 479/494–5700 **A**1 9 10 **F**5 40 98 99 100 101 102 103 104 105 106 **P**6 **S** Acadia Healthcare Company, Inc., Franklin, TN
Primary Contact: Anthony Walters, Chief Executive Officer
CFO: Paul D. Ervin, Chief Financial Officer
CMO: Richard Livingston, M.D., Medical Director
CHR: Patricia J. Moore, Director Human Resource
CNO: Landon Horton, Director of Nursing
Web address: www.valleybehavioral.com
**Control:** Corporation, Investor–owned, for–profit **Service:** Psychiatric

**Staffed Beds:** 75 **Admissions:** 1726 **Census:** 64 **Births:** 0

## BATESVILLE—Independence County

★ **WHITE RIVER MEDICAL CENTER (040119)**, 1710 Harrison Street, Zip 72501–7303, Mailing Address: P.O. Box 2197, Zip 72503–2197; tel. 870/262–1200, (Total facility includes 11 beds in nursing home–type unit) **A**9 10 **F**3 8 11 12 13 15 17 20 22 28 29 30 31 34 35 38 40 42 43 44 45 48 50 51 56 57 59 60 64 68 70 74 75 76 77 78 79 81 82 85 86 87 90 93 98 100 101 103 104 107 108 110 111 114 115 119 121 126 127 128 129 130 131 132 135 144 146 147 148 **P**6 **S** White River Health System, Batesville, AR
Primary Contact: Gary Bebow, FACHE, Administrator and Chief Executive Officer
CFO: Phillip Hacker, Chief Financial Officer
CMO: Doug Bernard, M.D., Chief Medical Officer
CIO: Gary Paxson, Chief Information Officer
CHR: Gary McDonald, Associate Administrator Human Resources
CNO: Dede Strecker, Chief Nursing Officer
Web address: www.whiteriverhealthsystem.com
**Control:** Other not–for–profit (including NFP Corporation) **Service:** General Medical and Surgical

**Staffed Beds:** 210 **Admissions:** 7959 **Census:** 107 **Outpatient Visits:** 217771 **Births:** 675 **Total Expense ($000):** 154605 **Payroll Expense ($000):** 57043 **Personnel:** 1119

## BENTON—Saline County

☐ **RIVENDELL BEHAVIORAL HEALTH SERVICES OF ARKANSAS (044007)**, 100 Rivendell Drive, Zip 72019–9100; tel. 501/316–1255, (Nonreporting) **A**1 9 10 **S** Universal Health Services, Inc., King of Prussia, PA
Primary Contact: Jay Schehi, Chief Executive Officer
CFO: Mike Rainbolt, Chief Financial Officer
Web address: www.rivendellofarkansas.com
**Control:** Corporation, Investor–owned, for–profit **Service:** Children's hospital psychiatric

**Staffed Beds:** 77

★ **SALINE MEMORIAL HOSPITAL (040084)**, 1 Medical Park Drive, Zip 72015–3354; tel. 501/776–6000, (Nonreporting) **A**9 10
Primary Contact: Bob Trautman, Chief Executive Officer
COO: Carla Robertson, Chief Operating Officer and Chief Financial Officer
CFO: Carla Robertson, Chief Operating Officer and Chief Financial Officer
CIO: Andy Dick, Director Information Services
CHR: Carol Matthews, Director Human Resources
CNO: Debbie Burrow, R.N., Chief Nursing Officer
Web address: www.salinememorial.org
**Control:** Other not–for–profit (including NFP Corporation) **Service:** General Medical and Surgical

**Staffed Beds:** 139

## BERRYVILLE—Carroll County

☒ **MERCY HOSPITAL BERRYVILLE (041329)**, 214 Carter Street, Zip 72616–4303; tel. 870/423–3355 **A**1 9 10 18 **F**3 11 15 28 29 30 31 34 35 40 43 45 46 48 50 57 59 61 64 75 77 78 81 85 93 107 108 114 119 129 130 131 132 133 146 148 **P**6 **S** Mercy Health, Chesterfield, MO
Primary Contact: Douglas M. Stroemel, Administrator
CFO: Sherry Clouse Day, Vice President Finance
CHR: Taya James, Director
CNO: Michele Gann, Vice President Patient Services
Web address: www.mercy.net/berryvillear
**Control:** Church–operated, Nongovernment, not–for profit **Service:** General Medical and Surgical

**Staffed Beds:** 25 **Admissions:** 724 **Census:** 7 **Outpatient Visits:** 28694 **Births:** 0 **Total Expense ($000):** 16707 **Payroll Expense ($000):** 7726 **Personnel:** 147

## BLYTHEVILLE—Mississippi County

☒ **GREAT RIVER MEDICAL CENTER (040069)**, 1520 North Division Street, Zip 72315–1448, Mailing Address: P.O. Box 108, Zip 72316–0108; tel. 870/838–7300 **A**1 9 10 **F**11 13 15 28 29 34 45 46 53 57 59 64 68 70 75 76 79 81 89 93 97 107 108 111 114 119 120 130 135 146 147 **P**7 **S** QHR, Brentwood, TN
Primary Contact: Ralph E. Beaty, Chief Executive Officer
COO: Chris Raymer, R.N., Chief Operating Officer and Chief Nursing Officer
CFO: Randy Nichols, Chief Financial Officer
CMO: Sia Shahriari, M.D., Chief of Staff
CIO: Tammy Bratcher, System Information Technology Director
CHR: Cheri Blurton, Director Human Resources, HIPAA Privacy Officer
CNO: Chris Raymer, R.N., Chief Operating Officer and Chief Nursing Officer
Web address: www.mchsys.org
**Control:** County–Government, nonfederal **Service:** General Medical and Surgical

**Staffed Beds:** 73 **Admissions:** 2143 **Census:** 15 **Outpatient Visits:** 30188 **Births:** 520 **Total Expense ($000):** 19439 **Payroll Expense ($000):** 8856 **Personnel:** 211

---

**Hospital, Medicare Provider Number, Address, Telephone, Approval, Facility, and Physician Codes, Health Care System**

★ American Hospital Association (AHA) membership
☐ The Joint Commission accreditation
○ Healthcare Facilities Accreditation Program
◇ DNV Healthcare Inc. accreditation
⇑ Center for Improvement in Healthcare Quality Accreditation
△ Commission on Accreditation of Rehabilitation Facilities (CARF) accreditation

**AR**

### BOONEVILLE—Logan County

★ **MERCY HOSPITAL BOONEVILLE (041318)**, 880 West Main Street, Zip 72927–3443, Mailing Address: P.O. Box 290, Zip 72927–0290; tel. 479/675–2800 **A**9 10 18 **F**3 35 40 43 45 57 59 64 65 68 81 85 107 119 127 129 133 **S** Mercy Health, Chesterfield, MO
Primary Contact: David Hill, Regional Administrator
CFO: J. Stuart Lisko, Regional Director Operations, Critical Access Hospital Operations
CMO: Michael Miranda, Chief of Staff
CHR: Doris Whitaker, Vice President and Manager
CNO: Candace Bollinger, Director of Nursing
Web address: www.mercy.net
**Control:** Church–operated, Nongovernment, not–for profit **Service:** General Medical and Surgical

**Staffed Beds:** 25 **Admissions:** 183 **Census:** 2 **Outpatient Visits:** 8856 **Births:** 0 **Total Expense ($000):** 5206 **Payroll Expense ($000):** 1905 **Personnel:** 67

### CALICO ROCK— County

**COMMUNITY MEDICAL CENTER OF IZARD COUNTY (041306)**, 61 Grasse Street, Zip 72519, Mailing Address: P.O. Box 438, Zip 72519–0438; tel. 870/297–3726 **A**9 10 18 **F**3 11 15 29 30 34 35 40 43 45 47 57 64 81 93 107 111 119 127 128 130 133 146
Primary Contact: Kim Skidmore, Chief Executive Officer
COO: Cathy Franks, RN, Chief Operating Officer
CMO: Bethany Knight, M.D., Chief of Staff
CIO: Quentin Wildhagen, Systems Administrator
CHR: Crystal R. Moody, Director Human Resources
CNO: Dana Hicks, Director of Nursing
Web address: www.cmcofic.org
**Control:** Other not–for–profit (including NFP Corporation) **Service:** General Medical and Surgical

**Staffed Beds:** 25 **Admissions:** 490 **Census:** 6 **Outpatient Visits:** 3500 **Births:** 0 **Total Expense ($000):** 6053 **Payroll Expense ($000):** 2731 **Personnel:** 74

### CAMDEN—Ouachita County

★ **OUACHITA COUNTY MEDICAL CENTER (040050)**, 638 California Avenue S.W., Zip 71701–4699, Mailing Address: P.O. Box 797, Zip 71711–0797; tel. 870/836–1000 **A**9 10 20 **F**3 4 5 7 8 11 13 15 29 31 34 40 41 43 46 48 49 50 57 59 62 63 64 65 68 69 70 75 76 77 78 79 81 85 87 89 93 98 100 102 103 107 108 111 114 115 119 127 129 130 132 133 135 146 148 **P**8
Primary Contact: Peggy L. Abbott, President and Chief Executive Officer
CFO: Robert Anders, Chief Financial Officer
CIO: Kenny Frachiseur, Chief Information Officer
CHR: Mary Bridges, Director Human Resources
CNO: Diane Isaacs, Director of Nursing
Web address: www.ouachitamedcenter.com
**Control:** Other not–for–profit (including NFP Corporation) **Service:** General Medical and Surgical

**Staffed Beds:** 65 **Admissions:** 2104 **Census:** 18 **Outpatient Visits:** 35000 **Births:** 214 **Total Expense ($000):** 32914 **Payroll Expense ($000):** 14514 **Personnel:** 398

**OUACHITA MEDICAL CENTER** See Ouachita County Medical Center

### CLARKSVILLE—Johnson County

★ **JOHNSON REGIONAL MEDICAL CENTER (040002)**, 1100 East Poplar Street, Zip 72830–4419, Mailing Address: P.O. Box 738, Zip 72830–0738; tel. 479/754–5454 **A**5 9 10 **F**2 3 7 11 29 34 39 40 43 45 51 57 59 62 64 70 75 76 77 79 81 90 93 96 98 103 104 107 108 110 111 114 119 129 130 132 147 148
Primary Contact: Albert Pilkington, III, Chief Executive Officer
CFO: Edward Anderson, Chief Financial Officer
CIO: Scott Cook, Chief Information Officer
CHR: Betty Collier, Director Human Resources
CNO: Michael E. Zielaskiewicz, R.N., Interim Chief Nursing Officer
Web address: www.jrmc.com
**Control:** Other not–for–profit (including NFP Corporation) **Service:** General Medical and Surgical

**Staffed Beds:** 80 **Admissions:** 2324 **Census:** 28 **Outpatient Visits:** 38086 **Births:** 330 **Total Expense ($000):** 32242 **Payroll Expense ($000):** 13695

### CLINTON—Van Buren County

**OZARK HEALTH MEDICAL CENTER (041313)**, Highway 65 South, Zip 72031–9045, Mailing Address: P.O. Box 206, Zip 72031–0206; tel. 501/745–7000, (Total facility includes 118 beds in nursing–type unit) **A**10 18 **F**11 15 28 29 34 35 40 43 45 57 59 62 64 65 75 79 81 93 107 110 111 114 119 128 132 133 146
Primary Contact: David Deaton, Chief Executive Officer
CFO: Mike Deaton, Chief Financial Officer
CMO: Steve Schoettle, M.D., Chief Medical Staff
CHR: Sally Cassell, Manager Human Resources
CNO: Edna Prosser, Chief Nursing Officer
Web address: www.ozarkhealthinc.com
**Control:** Other not–for–profit (including NFP Corporation) **Service:** General Medical and Surgical

**Staffed Beds:** 143 **Admissions:** 845 **Census:** 97 **Outpatient Visits:** 27316 **Births:** 3 **Total Expense ($000):** 19758 **Payroll Expense ($000):** 8820 **Personnel:** 216

### CONWAY—Faulkner County

⊞ **CONWAY REGIONAL MEDICAL CENTER (040029)**, 2302 College Avenue, Zip 72034–6297; tel. 501/329–3831 **A**1 9 10 **F**3 8 11 13 15 17 18 20 22 24 28 29 30 31 35 40 43 45 49 50 51 53 56 57 59 60 62 64 70 74 75 77 78 79 81 84 85 87 90 93 103 107 108 110 111 115 117 119 120 127 130 131 132 146 147 148 **P**8
Primary Contact: Matthew Troupe, Chief Executive Officer
COO: Alan Finley, Chief Operating Officer
CFO: Steven P. Rose, Chief Financial Officer
CMO: James France, M.D., Chief of Staff
CHR: Richard Tyler, Corporate Director Human Resources
CNO: Jacquelyn Wilkerson, R.N., Chief Nursing Officer
Web address: www.conwayregional.org
**Control:** Other not–for–profit (including NFP Corporation) **Service:** General Medical and Surgical

**Staffed Beds:** 154 **Admissions:** 7899 **Census:** 83 **Outpatient Visits:** 105587 **Births:** 1807 **Total Expense ($000):** 139053 **Payroll Expense ($000):** 48356 **Personnel:** 1039

**CONWAY REGIONAL REHAB HOSPITAL (043033)**, 2210 Robinson Street, Zip 72034–4943; tel. 501/932–3500, (Nonreporting) **A**9 10
Primary Contact: Alicia Kunert, Executive Director
Web address: www.conwayregional.org
**Control:** Partnership, Investor–owned, for–profit **Service:** Rehabilitation

**Staffed Beds:** 24

### CROSSETT—Ashley County

★ **ASHLEY COUNTY MEDICAL CENTER (041323)**, 1015 Unity Road, Zip 71635–9443, Mailing Address: P.O. Box 400, Zip 71635–0400; tel. 870/364–4111 **A**9 10 18 **F**3 11 13 15 18 29 30 31 34 35 40 45 50 53 56 57 59 62 64 68 70 75 76 77 78 79 81 85 93 98 100 103 104 105 107 108 110 111 115 119 127 129 130 132 133 148
Primary Contact: Phillip K. Gilmore, FACHE, Chief Executive Officer
CFO: Bill Couch, Chief Financial Officer
CMO: Brad Walsh, M.D., Chief of Staff
CIO: Dan Austin, Manager Data Processing
CHR: Shirley White, Director Human Resources
CNO: Emily Bendinelli, Director of Nurses
Web address: www.acmconline.org
**Control:** Other not–for–profit (including NFP Corporation) **Service:** General Medical and Surgical

**Staffed Beds:** 33 **Admissions:** 1257 **Census:** 16 **Outpatient Visits:** 87442 **Births:** 138 **Total Expense ($000):** 25511 **Payroll Expense ($000):** 11773 **Personnel:** 246

### DANVILLE—Yell County

★ **CHAMBERS MEMORIAL HOSPITAL (040011)**, Highway 10 at Detroit, Zip 72833, Mailing Address: P.O. Box 639, Zip 72833–0639; tel. 479/495–2241 **A**9 10 20 **F**3 11 15 29 34 35 40 43 45 57 59 62 81 93 97 107 114 119 128 130 133
Primary Contact: Michael Scott Peek, Chief Executive Officer
CMO: John Westwood, M.D., Chief of Staff
CIO: Ken Masters, Director Information Technology
CHR: Stacey Lane, Executive Assistant Human Resources
CNO: Joeann Bowerman, Director of Nursing Services
Web address: www.chambershospital.com
**Control:** Other not–for–profit (including NFP Corporation) **Service:** General Medical and Surgical

**Staffed Beds:** 41 **Admissions:** 1994 **Census:** 17 **Outpatient Visits:** 26542 **Births:** 0 **Total Expense ($000):** 19255 **Payroll Expense ($000):** 8974 **Personnel:** 177

*Many Facility Codes have changed. Please refer to the AHA Guide Code Chart.*

**DARDANELLE—Yell County**

**RIVER VALLEY MEDICAL CENTER (041302)**, 200 North Third Street,
Zip 72834–3802, Mailing Address: P.O. Box 578, Zip 72834–0578;
tel. 479/229–4677, (Nonreporting) **A**9 10 18 **S** Allegiance Health Management,
Shreveport, LA
Primary Contact: Christopher L. Bariola, Chief Executive Officer
CMO: William P. Scott, M.D., Chief of Staff
CHR: Kathy Hastin, Administrative Assistant Human Resources
**Control:** Corporation, Investor–owned, for–profit **Service:** General Medical and
Surgical

**Staffed Beds:** 35

**DE QUEEN—Sevier County**

**DE QUEEN MEDICAL CENTER (041319)**, 1306 Collin Raye Drive,
Zip 71832–2502; tel. 870/584–4111 **A**9 10 18 **F**3 11 15 29 40 41 57 59 75
77 90 93 107 114 119 129 133 146 148
Primary Contact: Jeremy Icenhower, Administrator and Chief Executive Officer
CFO: Vicky Kelly, Chief Financial Officer
CMO: Jason Lofton, M.D., Medical Director
CIO: David Harris, Director Information Systems
CHR: Ramona Driver, Director Human Resources
CNO: Kristy Richardson, Director of Nursing
Web address: www.dequeenhospital.com
**Control:** Corporation, Investor–owned, for–profit **Service:** General Medical and
Surgical

**Staffed Beds:** 35 **Admissions:** 526 **Census:** 13 **Outpatient Visits:** 64095
**Births:** 0 **Personnel:** 161

**DE WITT—Arkansas County**

★ **DEWITT HOSPITAL (041314)**, Highway 1 and Madison Street,
Zip 72042–9481, Mailing Address: P.O. Box 32, Zip 72042–0032;
tel. 870/946–3571, (Total facility includes 60 beds in nursing home–type unit) **A**9
10 18 **F**3 7 11 29 34 35 40 57 59 62 64 107 119 127 128 133 143 145 **P**6
Primary Contact: Larry Morse, Interim Chief Executive Officer
CMO: Stan Burleson, M.D., Chief Medical Staff
CIO: Jonathan Fuchs, Chief Information Officer
CHR: Hannah Hackney, Director Accounting and Human Resources
CNO: Rosie Killion, R.N., Chief Nursing Officer
Web address: www.dhnh.org
**Control:** Other not–for–profit (including NFP Corporation) **Service:** General
Medical and Surgical

**Staffed Beds:** 85 **Admissions:** 367 **Census:** 51 **Outpatient Visits:** 10430
**Births:** 0 **Total Expense ($000):** 11017 **Payroll Expense ($000):** 6338
**Personnel:** 194

**DUMAS—Desha County**

**DELTA MEMORIAL HOSPITAL (041326)**, 811 South Highway 65,
Zip 71639–3006, Mailing Address: P.O. Box 887, Zip 71639–0887;
tel. 870/382–4303 **A**9 10 18 **F**3 11 13 15 29 34 35 40 45 50 55 57 59 62
64 68 75 76 77 78 81 86 87 93 97 107 114 119 120 127 128 130 133 134
135 148 **P**6
Primary Contact: Cris Bolin, Chief Executive Officer
CMO: Thomas Lewellen, D.O., Chief of Staff
CIO: Chris McTigrit, Manager Information Technology
CHR: Doris Fortenberry, Coordinator Human Resources
CNO: Dana Miles, Chief Nursing Officer and Chief Clinical Officer
Web address: www.deltamem.org
**Control:** Other not–for–profit (including NFP Corporation) **Service:** General
Medical and Surgical

**Staffed Beds:** 25 **Admissions:** 756 **Census:** 7 **Outpatient Visits:** 30566
**Births:** 97 **Total Expense ($000):** 12407 **Payroll Expense ($000):** 5563
**Personnel:** 146

**EL DORADO—Union County**

✠ **MEDICAL CENTER OF SOUTH ARKANSAS (040088)**, 700 West Grove Street,
Zip 71730–4416; tel. 870/863–2000 **A**1 9 10 **F**3 11 13 15 17 18 20 22 24
28 29 31 34 35 40 43 45 46 50 56 57 59 64 70 73 75 76 77 78 79 80 81
82 85 87 89 90 93 107 108 110 111 114 115 119 130 131 146 147 148 **P**7
8 **S** Community Health Systems, Inc., Franklin, TN
Primary Contact: Robert Rupp, Chief Executive Officer
COO: Ross Korkmas, Assistant Chief Executive Officer
CFO: Dale Maddox, Chief Financial Officer
CMO: Robert A. Watson, II, M.D., Chief of Staff
CIO: Rob Robison, Director Information Technology
CHR: LaKeitha Davis, Director Human Resources
CNO: Kathy Degenstein Gartman, Chief Nursing Officer
Web address: www.themedcenter.net
**Control:** Corporation, Investor–owned, for–profit **Service:** General Medical and
Surgical

**Staffed Beds:** 120 **Admissions:** 4084 **Census:** 42 **Outpatient Visits:** 53744
**Births:** 598 **Total Expense ($000):** 62918 **Payroll Expense ($000):** 22497
**Personnel:** 501

**EUREKA SPRINGS—Carroll County**

**EUREKA SPRINGS HOSPITAL (041304)**, 24 Norris Street, Zip 72632–3541;
tel. 479/253–7400, (Nonreporting) **A**9 10 18 **S** Allegiance Health Management,
Shreveport, LA
Primary Contact: Christopher L. Bariola, Chief Executive Officer
CFO: Sondra Wear, Director Financial Services
CMO: Gregory Kresse, M.D., Chairman Medical Staff
CIO: Drew Wood, Director Information Technology
CHR: Jodi Smith, Administrative Assistant Human Resources
CNO: Vicki Andert, Chief Nursing Officer
Web address: www.eurekaspringshospital.com
**Control:** Corporation, Investor–owned, for–profit **Service:** General Medical and
Surgical

**Staffed Beds:** 15

**FAYETTEVILLE—Washington County**

✠ **HEALTHSOUTH REHABILITATION HOSPITAL (043032)**, 153 East Monte
Painter Drive, Zip 72703–4002; tel. 479/444–2200 **A**1 9 10 **F**3 29 34 57 59
75 77 79 90 91 92 93 94 95 96 **P**8 **S** HEALTHSOUTH Corporation,
Birmingham, AL
Primary Contact: Jack C. Mitchell, FACHE, Chief Executive Officer
CFO: Robbi Hudson, Chief Financial Officer
CMO: Marty Hurlbut, M.D., Medical Director
CHR: Missy Cole, Director Human Resources
CNO: Miriam Irvin, CNO
Web address: www.healthsouthfayetteville.com
**Control:** Corporation, Investor–owned, for–profit **Service:** Rehabilitation

**Staffed Beds:** 60 **Admissions:** 1425 **Census:** 48 **Outpatient Visits:** 1879
**Births:** 0 **Total Expense ($000):** 13526 **Payroll Expense ($000):** 7771
**Personnel:** 163

○ **PHYSICIANS' SPECIALTY HOSPITAL (040152)**, 3873 North Parkview Drive,
Zip 72703, Mailing Address: 3875 North Parkview Drive, Zip 72703;
tel. 479/571–7070 **A**3 9 10 11 **F**12 29 40 45 79 81 82 85 107 111 114 119
131 **P**2
Primary Contact: Rhonda McCabe, Chief Executive Officer
CFO: Rhonda McCabe, Chief Financial Officer
CIO: Walter Beadle, Chief Information Officer
CHR: Deborah Austin, Chief People Officer
CNO: Kelley Oliver, R.N., Chief Nursing Officer
Web address: www.pshfay.com
**Control:** Corporation, Investor–owned, for–profit **Service:** Surgical

**Staffed Beds:** 21 **Admissions:** 1082 **Census:** 5 **Outpatient Visits:** 15706
**Births:** 0 **Total Expense ($000):** 32341 **Payroll Expense ($000):** 9307
**Personnel:** 192

□ **SPRINGWOODS BEHAVIORAL HEALTH HOSPITAL (044019)**, 1955 West
Truckers Drive, Zip 72704–5637; tel. 479/973–6000 **A**1 9 10 **F**5 34 38 56 57
98 99 100 101 103 104 105 106 130 132 134 **P**6
Primary Contact: Mark Bethell, Chief Executive Officer
Web address: www.springwoodsbehavioral.com
**Control:** Corporation, Investor–owned, for–profit **Service:** Psychiatric

**Staffed Beds:** 80 **Admissions:** 2205 **Census:** 42 **Outpatient Visits:** 948
**Births:** 0 **Total Expense ($000):** 12732 **Payroll Expense ($000):** 4999
**Personnel:** 170

**AR**

---

**AR**

☐ **VANTAGE POINT OF NORTHWEST ARKANSAS (044004)**, 4253 North Crossover Road, Zip 72703–4596; tel. 479/521–5731 **A**1 9 10 **F**5 87 98 99 100 101 102 103 104 106 130 132 **P**6 **S** Acadia Healthcare Company, Inc., Franklin, TN
Primary Contact: Connie Borengasser, Chief Executive Officer
CFO: Ben Winbery, Chief Financial Officer
CMO: Norman Snyder, M.D., Medical Director
CIO: Margaret Brown, Director Medical Records
CHR: Kathy Vickers, Director Human Resources
CNO: Suzette Branscum, Director of Nursing
Web address: www.vantagepointnwa.com
**Control:** Corporation, Investor–owned, for–profit **Service:** Psychiatric

**Staffed Beds:** 114 **Admissions:** 2183 **Census:** 89 **Outpatient Visits:** 144477 **Births:** 0 **Total Expense ($000):** 24948 **Payroll Expense ($000):** 14686 **Personnel:** 307

☒ **VETERANS HEALTH CARE SYSTEM OF THE OZARKS**, 1100 North College Avenue, Zip 72703–1944; tel. 479/443–4301, (Nonreporting) **A**1 2 3 **S** Department of Veterans Affairs, Washington, DC
Primary Contact: Mark Worley, Interim Director
COO: Doris B. Cassidy, Associate Director
CMO: Bonnie Baker, M.D., Chief Medical Services
CIO: Michael Gracie, Chief Information Officer
CHR: Kathryn L. Barker, Chief Human Resources Management
Web address: www.fayettevillear.va.gov
**Control:** Veterans Affairs, Government, federal **Service:** General Medical and Surgical

**Staffed Beds:** 72

☒ **WASHINGTON REGIONAL MEDICAL CENTER (040004)**, 3215 North Hills Boulevard, Zip 72703–4424; tel. 479/463–1000 **A**1 3 9 10 **F**3 9 11 12 13 14 17 18 20 22 24 26 28 29 30 31 34 35 39 40 43 45 46 47 48 49 50 51 53 54 56 57 58 59 60 61 62 63 64 68 70 71 72 73 74 75 76 77 78 79 80 81 82 83 84 85 86 87 89 92 93 97 100 102 107 108 111 115 118 119 126 129 130 131 132 135 144 146 147 148 **P**6 8
Primary Contact: William L. Bradley, President and Chief Executive Officer
CFO: Dan Eckels, Chief Financial Officer
CMO: David Ratcliff, M.D., Chief Medical Affairs
CIO: Becky Magee, Chief Information Officer
CHR: Steve Percival, Director Human Resources
CNO: Beverly Winney, Chief Nursing Officer
Web address: www.wregional.com
**Control:** Other not–for–profit (including NFP Corporation) **Service:** General Medical and Surgical

**Staffed Beds:** 288 **Admissions:** 13191 **Census:** 149 **Outpatient Visits:** 147152 **Births:** 1196 **Total Expense ($000):** 198435 **Payroll Expense ($000):** 75106 **Personnel:** 1931

**FORDYCE—Dallas County**

★ **DALLAS COUNTY MEDICAL CENTER (041317)**, 201 Clifton Street, Zip 71742–3099; tel. 870/352–6300 **A**9 10 18 **F**11 29 30 34 35 40 43 45 57 59 64 81 86 93 107 127 133 146
Primary Contact: Kenneth Sanders, Interim Administrator and Chief Executive Officer
CFO: Billie Launius, Director Business Finance
CMO: Michael Payne, M.D., Chief of Staff
CHR: Audrey Allen, Coordinator Benefits
CNO: Hollie Raney, Director of Nursing
Web address: www.dallascountymedicalcenter.com
**Control:** County–Government, nonfederal **Service:** General Medical and Surgical

**Staffed Beds:** 22 **Admissions:** 318 **Census:** 2 **Outpatient Visits:** 37942 **Births:** 0 **Total Expense ($000):** 8655 **Payroll Expense ($000):** 3161 **Personnel:** 82

**FORREST CITY—St. Francis County**

☒ **FORREST CITY MEDICAL CENTER (040019)**, 1601 Newcastle Road, Zip 72335–2218; tel. 870/261–0000 **A**1 9 10 20 **F**3 7 11 13 15 18 29 40 45 50 57 59 70 76 79 81 85 93 103 107 108 111 114 118 119 130 133 135 145 146 **P**6 **S** Community Health Systems, Inc., Franklin, TN
Primary Contact: Kevin Decker, Chief Executive Officer
CFO: Todd Williams, Interim Chief Financial Officer
CMO: James Meredith, M.D., Chief of Staff
CIO: Scott Miller, Director Information Services
CHR: Sherry McLaughlin, Director Human Resources
CNO: Rhonda Nelson, Chief Nursing Officer
Web address: www.forrestcitymedicalcenter.com
**Control:** Corporation, Investor–owned, for–profit **Service:** General Medical and Surgical

**Staffed Beds:** 61 **Admissions:** 2396 **Census:** 22 **Outpatient Visits:** 32596 **Births:** 777 **Total Expense ($000):** 27650 **Payroll Expense ($000):** 9441 **Personnel:** 240

**FORT SMITH—Sebastian County**

☒ **CHRISTUS DUBUIS HOSPITAL OF FORT SMITH (042008)**, 7301 Rogers Avenue, 4th Floor, Zip 72903–4100; tel. 479/314–4900 **A**1 9 10 **F**1 3 29 30 68 75 77 82 84 85 91 130 148 **S** CHRISTUS Health, Irving, TX
Primary Contact: Keith Rogers, Interim Administrator
CFO: Paul Veillon, CPA, Chief Financial Officer
Web address: www.christusdubuis.org/fortsmith
**Control:** Church–operated, Nongovernment, not–for profit **Service:** Long–Term Acute Care hospital

**Staffed Beds:** 25 **Admissions:** 255 **Census:** 18 **Outpatient Visits:** 0 **Births:** 0 **Total Expense ($000):** 7768 **Payroll Expense ($000):** 2975 **Personnel:** 56

☒ **HEALTHSOUTH REHABILITATION HOSPITAL OF FORT SMITH (043028)**, 1401 South J Street, Zip 72901–5155; tel. 479/785–3300 **A**1 9 10 **F**28 29 34 35 77 90 91 93 94 95 96 130 131 132 **S** HEALTHSOUTH Corporation, Birmingham, AL
Primary Contact: Dawn Watts, Chief Executive Officer
CFO: Brenda Forbes, Controller
CMO: Cygnet Schroeder, D.O., Medical Director
CIO: Donna England, Director Medical Records
CHR: S. Janette Daniels, Director Human Resources
CNO: Jacqueline Floyd, Chief Nursing Officer
Web address: www.healthsouthfortsmith.com
**Control:** Corporation, Investor–owned, for–profit **Service:** Rehabilitation

**Staffed Beds:** 60 **Admissions:** 1252 **Census:** 40 **Outpatient Visits:** 5282 **Births:** 0 **Total Expense ($000):** 14568 **Payroll Expense ($000):** 7367 **Personnel:** 154

☒ **MERCY HOSPITAL FORT SMITH (040062)**, 7301 Rogers Avenue, Zip 72903–4189, Mailing Address: P.O. Box 17000, Zip 72917–7000; tel. 479/314–6000 **A**1 2 9 10 **F**3 12 13 15 17 18 20 22 24 26 28 29 30 31 32 34 35 36 38 40 43 44 45 49 50 53 55 56 57 58 59 60 61 62 63 64 65 68 70 71 72 73 74 75 76 77 78 79 81 82 83 84 85 86 87 89 90 92 93 95 96 102 107 108 110 111 114 115 119 120 121 123 124 126 129 130 134 135 143 146 147 148 **P**6 8 **S** Mercy Health, Chesterfield, MO
Primary Contact: Ryan Gehrig, President
COO: Brent Hubbard, Chief Operating Officer
CFO: Greta Wilcher, Senior Vice President and Chief Financial Officer
CMO: David Hunton, M.D., Chief Medical Officer
CHR: Bryan Brown, Executive Director
CNO: Marianne Rataj, R.N., Chief Nursing Officer
Web address: www.mercy.net/fortsmithar
**Control:** Church–operated, Nongovernment, not–for profit **Service:** General Medical and Surgical

**Staffed Beds:** 344 **Admissions:** 14196 **Census:** 192 **Outpatient Visits:** 152177 **Births:** 2346 **Total Expense ($000):** 239060 **Payroll Expense ($000):** 71296 **Personnel:** 1534

**MERCY ORTHOPEDIC HOSPITAL FORT SMITH**, 3601 South 79th Street, Zip 72903–6255; tel. 479/709–8500, (Nonreporting) **S** Mercy Health, Chesterfield, MO
Primary Contact: Ryan Gehrig, President
Web address: www.mercy.net/practice/mercy–orthopedic–hospital–fort–smith
**Control:** Other not–for–profit (including NFP Corporation) **Service:** Orthopedic

**Staffed Beds:** 24

☒ **SELECT SPECIALTY HOSPITAL–FORT SMITH (042006)**, 1001 Towson Avenue, 6 Central, Zip 72901–4921; tel. 479/441–3960 **A**1 9 10 **F**1 3 29 34 45 46 56 57 74 75 78 79 94 148 **S** Select Medical Corporation, Mechanicsburg, PA
Primary Contact: Cindy McLain, Chief Executive Officer
Web address: www.selectspecialtyhospitals.com/company/locations/fortsmith.aspx
**Control:** Corporation, Investor–owned, for–profit **Service:** Long–Term Acute Care hospital

**Staffed Beds:** 34 **Admissions:** 419 **Census:** 29 **Outpatient Visits:** 0 **Births:** 0 **Total Expense ($000):** 13196 **Payroll Expense ($000):** 4818 **Personnel:** 86

*Many Facility Codes have changed. Please refer to the AHA Guide Code Chart.*  © 2015 AHA Guide

✠ **SPARKS REGIONAL MEDICAL CENTER (040055)**, 100 Towson Avenue, Zip 72901–2632, Mailing Address: P.O. Box 2406, Zip 72917–7006; tel. 479/441–4000 **A**1 3 9 10 **F**3 8 12 13 14 15 17 18 20 21 22 24 26 28 29 30 31 34 35 40 45 46 47 48 49 50 51 53 54 56 58 59 60 62 64 67 70 72 74 75 77 78 79 81 82 85 86 87 89 93 97 98 103 107 108 109 110 111 112 113 114 115 117 119 120 121 122 124 126 127 129 130 144 146 147 148 **P**8 **S** Community Health Systems, Inc., Franklin, TN
Primary Contact: Daniel E. McKay, Chief Executive Officer
COO: Jeremy Drinkwitz, Chief Operating Officer
CMO: Katherine Irish–Clardy, M.D., Chief Medical Officer
CIO: Tom Sallis, Director Information Systems
CHR: Robert Freeman, Director Human Resources
CNO: Cindy Slaydon, Chief Nursing Executive
Web address: www.sparks.org
**Control:** Corporation, Investor–owned, for–profit **Service:** General Medical and Surgical

**Staffed Beds:** 303 **Admissions:** 16333 **Census:** 214 **Outpatient Visits:** 181931 **Births:** 1389 **Total Expense ($000):** 235316 **Payroll Expense ($000):** 65527 **Personnel:** 1874

GRAVETTE—Benton County

**OZARKS COMMUNITY HOSPITAL (041331)**, 1101 Jackson Street Sw, Zip 72736–9121; tel. 479/787–5291 **A**9 10 18 **F**3 29 40 44 45 50 59 64 65 75 82 85 87 89 93 96 97 100 107 111 114 119 127 128 129 130 133 143 148 **P**6
Primary Contact: Paul Taylor, Administrator
Web address: www.ochonline.com/
**Control:** Corporation, Investor–owned, for–profit **Service:** General Medical and Surgical

**Staffed Beds:** 25 **Admissions:** 669 **Census:** 18 **Outpatient Visits:** 38731 **Births:** 0 **Total Expense ($000):** 16987 **Payroll Expense ($000):** 8576 **Personnel:** 158

HARRISON—Boone County

★ **NORTH ARKANSAS REGIONAL MEDICAL CENTER (040017)**, 620 North Main Street, Zip 72601–2911; tel. 870/414–4000 **A**9 10 **F**3 7 8 11 13 15 17 18 24 28 29 30 31 34 35 39 40 41 43 45 53 56 57 59 62 63 64 65 68 70 73 75 76 77 78 79 81 82 85 86 87 89 92 93 97 98 100 101 102 103 107 108 110 111 114 115 118 119 120 121 123 127 129 130 131 132 135 144 146 147 148 **P**8
Primary Contact: Vincent Leist, President and Chief Executive Officer
CFO: Debbie Henry, Vice President Financial Services
CIO: William J. Bogle, Director Information Systems
CHR: Linda Dickey Melton, Vice President Human Resources
CNO: Sammie Cribbs, Vice President Patient Care Services
Web address: www.narmc.com
**Control:** Other not–for–profit (including NFP Corporation) **Service:** General Medical and Surgical

**Staffed Beds:** 127 **Admissions:** 4226 **Census:** 36 **Outpatient Visits:** 135328 **Births:** 776 **Total Expense ($000):** 76777 **Payroll Expense ($000):** 32225 **Personnel:** 704

HEBER SPRINGS—Cleburne County

✠ **BAPTIST HEALTH MEDICAL CENTER–HEBER SPRINGS (041312)**, 1800 Bypass Road, Zip 72543–9135; tel. 501/887–3000 **A**1 9 10 18 **F**3 8 11 15 28 29 30 31 34 35 36 40 43 45 48 50 51 57 59 64 68 74 75 77 78 79 81 85 93 102 107 110 111 115 116 117 119 127 129 131 132 133 134 135 143 146 **S** Baptist Health, Little Rock, AR
Primary Contact: Edward L. Lacy, FACHE, Vice President and Administrator
Web address: www.baptist–health.com/maps–directions/bhmc–heber–springs
**Control:** Other not–for–profit (including NFP Corporation) **Service:** General Medical and Surgical

**Staffed Beds:** 25 **Admissions:** 894 **Census:** 7 **Outpatient Visits:** 34499 **Births:** 0 **Total Expense ($000):** 18544 **Payroll Expense ($000):** 5806 **Personnel:** 138

HELENA—Phillips County

✠ **HELENA REGIONAL MEDICAL CENTER (040085)**, 1801 Martin Luther King Drive, Zip 72342, Mailing Address: P.O. Box 788, Zip 72342–0788; tel. 870/338–5800 **A**1 9 10 20 **F**3 11 13 15 28 29 34 40 43 50 59 62 70 73 74 75 76 79 81 82 87 89 93 97 107 108 114 119 132 133 135 145 146 147 148 **S** Community Health Systems, Inc., Franklin, TN
Primary Contact: Leah Osbahr, M.P.H., Chief Executive Officer
CFO: Amy Rice, Chief Financial Officer
CIO: Robert White, Director Information Technology
CHR: Juril Fonzie, Director Human Resources
CNO: Jodi Love, R.N., Chief Nursing Officer
Web address: www.helenarmc.com
**Control:** Corporation, Investor–owned, for–profit **Service:** General Medical and Surgical

**Staffed Beds:** 105 **Admissions:** 1756 **Census:** 12 **Outpatient Visits:** 26260 **Births:** 208 **Total Expense ($000):** 27809 **Payroll Expense ($000):** 7423 **Personnel:** 138

HOPE—Hempstead County

◇ **WADLEY REGIONAL MEDICAL CENTER AT HOPE (040153)**, 2001 South Main Street, Zip 71801–8194; tel. 870/722–3800 **A**9 10 21 **F**3 11 15 18 29 34 35 40 56 57 59 64 70 86 93 98 103 107 110 111 114 119 127 130 **S** IASIS Healthcare, Franklin, TN
Primary Contact: Thomas D. Gilbert, FACHE, Chief Executive Officer
CFO: Bonny Sorensen, Chief Financial Officer
CIO: Matt Kesterson, Director Information Services
CHR: Debby Butler, Director Human Resources
CNO: Shelly Strayhorn, R.N., Chief Nursing Officer
Web address: www.wadleyhealthathope.com
**Control:** Corporation, Investor–owned, for–profit **Service:** General Medical and Surgical

**Staffed Beds:** 79 **Admissions:** 1067 **Census:** 17 **Outpatient Visits:** 24117 **Births:** 0 **Total Expense ($000):** 13802 **Payroll Expense ($000):** 5612 **Personnel:** 130

HOT SPRINGS—Garland County

✠ **CHI ST. VINCENT HOT SPRINGS (040026)**, 300 Werner Street, Zip 71913–6406; tel. 501/622–1000, (Includes HEALTHPARK HOSPITAL, 1636 Higdon Ferry Road, Hot Springs National Park, Zip 71913; tel. 501/520–2000) **A**1 2 9 10 19 **F**3 11 12 13 15 17 18 20 22 24 26 28 29 30 31 34 35 37 38 40 43 49 50 56 57 59 62 64 65 66 68 69 70 71 74 75 76 77 78 79 81 85 86 87 89 90 92 93 98 103 107 108 110 111 112 114 115 116 117 118 119 120 121 124 126 129 130 132 134 135 146 147 148 **P**6 **S** Catholic Health Initiatives, Englewood, CO
Primary Contact: Anthony Houston, President
COO: Andrew Runge, Chief Operating Officer
CFO: Sarah Bradey, Vice President Finance
CIO: Bill Perry, Director Information Systems
Web address: www.chistvincent.com/Hospitals/st–vincent–hot–springs
**Control:** Church–operated, Nongovernment, not–for profit **Service:** General Medical and Surgical

**Staffed Beds:** 282 **Admissions:** 12172 **Census:** 163 **Outpatient Visits:** 163981 **Births:** 993 **Total Expense ($000):** 175824 **Payroll Expense ($000):** 65652 **Personnel:** 1068

☐ **NATIONAL PARK MEDICAL CENTER (040078)**, 1910 Malvern Avenue, Zip 71901–7799; tel. 501/321–1000 **A**1 9 10 19 **F**3 11 13 15 17 18 20 22 24 28 29 30 31 34 35 40 45 46 47 49 56 57 59 64 70 73 74 75 76 78 79 81 85 87 89 90 91 92 93 94 98 103 107 110 111 119 124 129 130 131 132 146 147 148 **P**1 **S** Capella Healthcare, Franklin, TN
Primary Contact: Jerry D. Mabry, FACHE, Chief Executive Officer
COO: Brian Bell, Associate Administrator and Chief Operating Officer
CFO: Robbie Pettey, Chief Financial Officer
CMO: Robert Breving, M.D., Chief of Staff
CIO: Brian Coffman, Director Information System
CHR: Tina Albright, Director Human Resources
CNO: Patsy Sue Crumpton, R.N., Chief Nursing Officer
Web address: www.nationalparkmedical.com
**Control:** Corporation, Investor–owned, for–profit **Service:** General Medical and Surgical

**Staffed Beds:** 193 **Admissions:** 6179 **Census:** 89 **Outpatient Visits:** 53995 **Births:** 430 **Total Expense ($000):** 69137 **Payroll Expense ($000):** 25208 **Personnel:** 577

---

**Hospital, Medicare Provider Number, Address, Telephone, Approval, Facility, and Physician Codes, Health Care System**

★ American Hospital Association (AHA) membership
☐ The Joint Commission accreditation
○ Healthcare Facilities Accreditation Program
◇ DNV Healthcare Inc. accreditation
⇑ Center for Improvement in Healthcare Quality Accreditation
△ Commission on Accreditation of Rehabilitation Facilities (CARF) accreditation

**HOT SPRINGS NATIONAL PARK—Garland County**

⊠ **CHRISTUS DUBUIS HOSPITAL OF HOT SPRINGS (042004)**, 300 Werner Street, 3rd Floor East, Zip 71913–6406; tel. 501/609–4300 **A**1 9 10 **F**1 3 29 30 45 68 77 79 85 87 118 130 135 148
Primary Contact: Keith Rogers, Administrator
CFO: Paul Veillon, CPA, Chief Financial Officer
CIO: David Cook, Manager Information Systems
Web address: www.christusdubuis.org/hotsprings
**Control:** Church–operated, Nongovernment, not–for profit **Service:** Long–Term Acute Care hospital

| | |
|---|---|
| **Staffed Beds:** 26 **Admissions:** 164 **Census:** 11 **Outpatient Visits:** 0 **Births:** 0 **Total Expense ($000):** 5681 **Payroll Expense ($000):** 2204 **Personnel:** 49 | |

★ **LEVI HOSPITAL (040132)**, 300 Prospect Avenue, Zip 71901–4097; tel. 501/624–1281 **A**9 10 **F**40 57 59 64 93 98 102 103 104 107 130 131 132
Primary Contact: Patrick G. McCabe, Jr., FACHE, President and Chief Executive Officer
CFO: Stuart Lisko, Vice President, Chief Financial Officer and Compliance Officer
CMO: P. Ross Bandy, M.D., Chief Medical Officer and Chief of Staff
CIO: Stuart Lisko, Vice President, Chief Financial Officer and Compliance Officer
CHR: Susan Kramer, Director of Human Resources
CNO: Steven Boyd, R.N., Nurse Executive
Web address: www.levihospital.com
**Control:** Other not–for–profit (including NFP Corporation) **Service:** Psychiatric

| | |
|---|---|
| **Staffed Beds:** 50 **Admissions:** 1273 **Census:** 19 **Outpatient Visits:** 18504 **Births:** 0 **Total Expense ($000):** 7152 **Payroll Expense ($000):** 4237 **Personnel:** 97 | |

**JACKSONVILLE—Pulaski County**

**ALLEGIANCE SPECIALTY HOSPITAL OF LITTLE ROCK** See Cornerstone Hospital of North Little Rock

**CORNERSTONE HOSPITAL OF NORTH LITTLE ROCK (042010)**, 9601 Interstate 630, Exit 7, 10th Floor, Zip 72076–3721; Mailing Address: Little Rock, tel. 501/265–0600 **A**9 10 **F**1 3 18 29 59 65 75 148 **S** Cornerstone Healthcare Group, Dallas, TX
Primary Contact: James H. Rogers, FACHE, Chief Executive Officer
CNO: Joy Miller, Chief Nursing Officer
Web address: www.chghospitals.com/littlerock/
**Control:** Corporation, Investor–owned, for–profit **Service:** Long–Term Acute Care hospital

| | |
|---|---|
| **Staffed Beds:** 40 **Admissions:** 314 **Census:** 21 **Outpatient Visits:** 0 **Births:** 0 **Total Expense ($000):** 9556 **Payroll Expense ($000):** 4300 **Personnel:** 84 | |

**NORTH METRO MEDICAL CENTER (040074)**, 1400 West Braden Street, Zip 72076–3788; tel. 501/985–7000 **A**9 10 **F**3 11 15 17 29 34 35 40 43 50 56 57 59 62 64 68 70 79 80 81 85 103 104 107 108 110 111 115 118 119 129 130 132 146 148 **P**8 **S** Allegiance Health Management, Shreveport, LA
Primary Contact: Joe Farrer, Interim Administrator
CFO: Lynn Muller, Chief Financial Officer
CMO: Ann Layton, M.D., Chief of Staff
CHR: Jane Rockwell, Director Support Services
Web address: www.northmetromed.com
**Control:** Corporation, Investor–owned, for–profit **Service:** General Medical and Surgical

| | |
|---|---|
| **Staffed Beds:** 73 **Admissions:** 1199 **Census:** 25 **Outpatient Visits:** 44015 **Births:** 0 **Personnel:** 308 | |

**JONESBORO—Craighead County**

⊠ **HEALTHSOUTH REHABILITATION HOSPITAL OF JONESBORO (043029)**, 1201 Fleming Avenue, Zip 72401–4311, Mailing Address: P.O. Box 1680, Zip 72403–1680; tel. 870/932–0440, (Nonreporting) **A**1 9 10 **S** HEALTHSOUTH Corporation, Birmingham, AL
Primary Contact: Donna Harris, Chief Executive Officer
CFO: Allan Jones, Controller
CMO: Terence Braden, III, D.O., Medical Director
CHR: Tammy Barley, Director, Human Resources
Web address: www.healthsouthjonesboro.com
**Control:** Corporation, Investor–owned, for–profit **Service:** Rehabilitation

| | |
|---|---|
| **Staffed Beds:** 67 | |

⊠ **NEA BAPTIST MEMORIAL HOSPITAL (040118)**, 4800 East Johnson Avenue, Zip 72401–8413; tel. 870/936–1000 **A**1 3 9 10 **F**3 11 12 13 15 17 18 20 22 24 26 28 29 30 31 34 39 40 43 45 46 48 49 57 59 60 74 75 76 77 78 79 81 82 84 85 86 87 89 93 107 108 110 111 115 118 119 120 121 123 124 126 130 135 146 148 **P**8 **S** Baptist Memorial Health Care Corporation, Memphis, TN
Primary Contact: Brad Parsons, FACHE, Administrator and Chief Executive Officer
CFO: Kyle Sanders, Chief Financial Officer
CMO: Stephen Woodruff, M.D., Chief Medical Officer
CIO: Terry Crider, Information Technology Site Manager
CHR: James Keller, Director Human Resources
CNO: Paula Grimes, R.N., Chief Nursing Officer
Web address: www.neabaptist.com
**Control:** Other not–for–profit (including NFP Corporation) **Service:** General Medical and Surgical

| | |
|---|---|
| **Staffed Beds:** 181 **Admissions:** 8332 **Census:** 91 **Outpatient Visits:** 65480 **Births:** 763 **Total Expense ($000):** 149417 **Payroll Expense ($000):** 46963 **Personnel:** 921 | |

⊠ **ST. BERNARDS MEDICAL CENTER (040020)**, 225 East Jackson Avenue, Zip 72401–3119; tel. 870/207–4100 **A**1 2 3 9 10 19 **F**3 5 11 12 13 15 17 18 19 20 22 24 26 27 28 29 30 31 32 34 35 38 39 40 43 45 46 49 50 51 53 54 56 57 59 60 62 63 64 68 70 71 72 74 75 76 77 78 79 81 82 84 85 86 87 89 92 93 98 99 100 101 102 103 104 105 107 108 109 110 111 114 115 116 117 118 119 120 121 123 126 129 130 131 132 135 141 145 146 147 148 **P**1 6 7
Primary Contact: Chris B. Barber, FACHE, President and Chief Executive Officer
COO: Michael K. Givens, FACHE, Administrator
CFO: Harry Hutchison, Vice President Fiscal Services
CMO: Shane Speights, M.D., Vice President Medical Affairs
CIO: Josh Melton, Chief Information Officer
CHR: Jacque Ballard, Vice President Human Resources
CNO: Susan Greenwood, R.N., Vice President and Chief Nursing Officer
Web address: www.stbernards.info
**Control:** Church–operated, Nongovernment, not–for profit **Service:** General Medical and Surgical

| | |
|---|---|
| **Staffed Beds:** 386 **Admissions:** 16785 **Census:** 190 **Outpatient Visits:** 246030 **Births:** 1317 **Total Expense ($000):** 254709 **Payroll Expense ($000):** 87065 **Personnel:** 1965 | |

**LAKE VILLAGE—Chicot County**

★ **CHICOT MEMORIAL MEDICAL CENTER (041328)**, 2729 Highway 65 and 82 South, Zip 71653; tel. 870/265–5351 **A**9 10 18 **F**3 7 11 13 15 18 29 34 35 36 40 43 45 50 53 57 59 62 64 71 75 77 81 82 85 87 93 107 111 114 119 129 130 132 133 146 147 148
Primary Contact: David Mantz, Chief Executive Officer
CFO: Vicki Allen, Chief Financial Officer
CMO: Michael Bradley Mayfield, M.D., Chief of Staff
CIO: David Andrews, Manager Information Systems
CHR: Bobbie Ivey, Director Human Resources
CNO: Eric Selby, R.N., Chief Nursing Officer
Web address: www.chicotmemorial.com
**Control:** Other not–for–profit (including NFP Corporation) **Service:** General Medical and Surgical

| | |
|---|---|
| **Staffed Beds:** 25 **Admissions:** 1045 **Census:** 11 **Outpatient Visits:** 21231 **Births:** 84 **Total Expense ($000):** 16447 **Payroll Expense ($000):** 7188 **Personnel:** 176 | |

**SOUTHEAST REHABILITATION HOSPITAL (043034)**, 2729–A Highway 65 and 82 South, Zip 71653; tel. 870/265–4333 **A**10 **F**3 90
Primary Contact: Stacy Noble, Administrator
Web address: www.lakevilleclinic.com/southeast–rehabilitation–hospital.html
**Control:** Partnership, Investor–owned, for–profit **Service:** Rehabilitation

| | |
|---|---|
| **Staffed Beds:** 15 **Admissions:** 257 **Census:** 8 **Outpatient Visits:** 0 **Births:** 0 **Total Expense ($000):** 3919 **Payroll Expense ($000):** 2478 **Personnel:** 47 | |

**LITTLE ROCK—Pulaski County**

⊠ **ARKANSAS CHILDREN'S HOSPITAL (043300)**, 1 Children's Way, Zip 72202–3500; tel. 501/364–1100 **A**1 3 5 8 9 10 **F**3 7 8 9 11 12 16 17 19 21 23 25 27 28 29 30 31 32 34 35 38 39 40 41 43 45 46 48 50 53 55 57 58 59 60 61 64 68 71 72 73 74 75 77 78 79 80 81 82 84 85 86 87 88 89 90 91 93 94 97 99 100 102 107 108 111 114 115 116 117 118 119 126 129 130 131 132 135 136 137 138 143 146 **P**8
Primary Contact: Marcella Doderer, FACHE, President and Chief Executive Officer
COO: David Berry, Senior Vice President and Chief Operating Officer
CFO: Gena Wingfield, Senior Vice President and Chief Financial Officer
CMO: Jay Deshpande, M.D., Chief Quality Officer and Chief Medical Officer
CIO: Darrell Leonhardt, Senior Vice President Information Systems
CHR: Andree Trosclair, Vice President Human Resources
Web address: www.archildrens.org
**Control:** Other not–for–profit (including NFP Corporation) **Service:** Children's general

| | |
|---|---|
| **Staffed Beds:** 342 **Admissions:** 14550 **Census:** 218 **Outpatient Visits:** 343369 **Births:** 0 **Total Expense ($000):** 494201 **Payroll Expense ($000):** 213763 **Personnel:** 4835 | |

**AR**

AR

⊠ **ARKANSAS HEART HOSPITAL (040134)**, 1701 South Shackleford Road, Zip 72211–4335; tel. 501/219–7000 **A**1 3 5 9 10 **F**3 11 17 18 20 22 24 26 29 30 34 35 40 57 58 59 64 70 74 75 81 85 86 102 107 111 114 119 127 129 130 132 148
Primary Contact: Bruce Murphy, M.D., President and Chief Executive Officer
CHR: Brent Davis, Human Resources Team Leader
Web address: www.arheart.com
**Control:** Partnership, Investor–owned, for–profit **Service:** Heart

**Staffed Beds:** 112 **Admissions:** 4397 **Census:** 50 **Outpatient Visits:** 12155 **Births:** 0 **Total Expense ($000):** 135699 **Payroll Expense ($000):** 37111 **Personnel:** 770

☐ **ARKANSAS STATE HOSPITAL (044011)**, 305 South Palm Street, Zip 72205–5432; tel. 501/686–9000 **A**1 3 5 9 10 **F**29 30 53 98 99 103 106 130 143 **P**6
Primary Contact: Steve Henson, Chief Executive Officer
CFO: Gary W. Hollis, Comptroller
CMO: Steven Domon, M.D., Medical Director
CIO: Tina Grissom, Chief Information Technology Officer
CHR: Donna Sadler, Director Human Resources
CNO: James Scoggins, Director of Nursing
Web address: www.state.ar.us/dhs/dmhs
**Control:** State–Government, nonfederal **Service:** Psychiatric

**Staffed Beds:** 222 **Admissions:** 692 **Census:** 202 **Outpatient Visits:** 0 **Births:** 0 **Total Expense ($000):** 50343 **Payroll Expense ($000):** 24807 **Personnel:** 605

★ **BAPTIST HEALTH EXTENDED CARE HOSPITAL (042012)**, 9601 Interstate 630, Exit 7, 10th Floor, Zip 72205–7202; tel. 501/202–1070 **A**9 10 **F**1 3 29 31 77 87 130 148 **S** Baptist Health, Little Rock, AR
Primary Contact: Mike Perkins, Vice President and Administrator
CFO: Robert C. Roberts, Vice President
CIO: David House, Vice President
CHR: Anthony Kendall, Vice President Human Resources
CNO: Diane Smith, Chief Nursing Officer
Web address: www.baptist–health.com/maps–directions/bh_extended_care/default.aspx
**Control:** Other not–for–profit (including NFP Corporation) **Service:** Long–Term Acute Care hospital

**Staffed Beds:** 55 **Admissions:** 333 **Census:** 25 **Outpatient Visits:** 0 **Births:** 0 **Total Expense ($000):** 13125 **Payroll Expense ($000):** 5073 **Personnel:** 96

⊠ **BAPTIST HEALTH MEDICAL CENTER–LITTLE ROCK (040114)**, 9601 Interstate 630, Exit 7, Zip 72205–7299; tel. 501/202–2000 **A**1 3 5 6 9 10 **F**3 4 5 7 8 11 12 13 15 17 18 20 22 24 26 28 29 30 31 32 34 35 36 37 38 40 43 44 45 49 50 54 56 57 58 59 60 61 62 64 65 67 68 70 72 73 74 75 76 77 78 79 81 82 84 85 86 87 89 93 98 99 100 101 102 103 104 107 108 110 111 114 118 119 126 128 129 130 131 132 134 135 137 138 143 144 146 147 148 **S** Baptist Health, Little Rock, AR
Primary Contact: Greg Crain, FACHE, Vice President and Administrator
CFO: Robert C. Roberts, Senior Vice President Financial Services
CMO: Anthony Bennett, M.D., Chief Clinical Affairs
CIO: David House, Vice President and Chief Information Officer
CHR: Anthony Kendall, Vice President Human Resources
CNO: Jill Massiet, R.N., Vice President Patient Care
Web address: www.baptist–health.org/maps–directions/bhmc–lr
**Control:** Other not–for–profit (including NFP Corporation) **Service:** General Medical and Surgical

**Staffed Beds:** 688 **Admissions:** 28692 **Census:** 392 **Births:** 3420 **Total Expense ($000):** 423698 **Payroll Expense ($000):** 132811 **Personnel:** 2497

⊠ △ **BAPTIST HEALTH REHABILITATION INSTITUTE (043026)**, 9601 Interstate 630, Exit 7, Zip 72205–7202; tel. 501/202–7000 **A**1 3 5 7 9 10 **F**29 30 34 35 50 53 64 75 86 87 90 91 93 95 96 130 132 143 **S** Baptist Health, Little Rock, AR
Primary Contact: Lee Gentry, FACHE, Vice President and Administrator
CFO: Robert C. Roberts, Senior Vice President
CIO: David House, Vice President and Chief Information Officer
CHR: Anthony Kendall, Vice President Human Resources
Web address: www.baptist–health.com/locations/accesspoint.aspx?accessPointID=202
**Control:** Other not–for–profit (including NFP Corporation) **Service:** Rehabilitation

**Staffed Beds:** 90 **Admissions:** 1416 **Census:** 49 **Outpatient Visits:** 66474 **Births:** 0 **Total Expense ($000):** 28038 **Payroll Expense ($000):** 13500 **Personnel:** 225

⊠ △ **CENTRAL ARKANSAS VETERANS HEALTHCARE SYSTEM**, 4300 West Seventh Street, Zip 72205–5446; tel. 501/257–1000, (Includes NORTH LITTLE ROCK DIVISION, 2200 Fort Roots Drive, North Little Rock, Zip 72114–1706; tel. 501/661–1202), (Nonreporting) **A**1 2 3 5 7 8 **S** Department of Veterans Affairs, Washington, DC
Primary Contact: Cyril Ekeh, Interim Director
CFO: Colonel Nate Todd, Chief Financial Officer
CMO: Margie Scott, M.D., Chief of Staff
CIO: Jim Hall, Acting Chief Information Officer
CHR: Richard Nelson, Chief of Human Resources Management Services
Web address: www.littlerock.va.gov/
**Control:** Veterans Affairs, Government, federal **Service:** General Medical and Surgical

**Staffed Beds:** 551

⊠ **CHI ST. VINCENT INFIRMARY MEDICAL CENTER (040007)**, Two St. Vincent Circle, Zip 72205–5499; tel. 501/552–3000 **A**1 3 5 9 10 **F**3 11 13 17 18 20 22 24 26 27 28 29 30 31 34 35 37 40 43 44 45 46 48 49 50 51 53 54 56 57 58 59 60 61 64 68 70 72 74 75 76 77 78 79 80 81 82 83 84 85 86 87 91 92 93 96 97 98 100 101 102 107 108 109 110 111 112 114 115 116 117 118 119 124 126 129 130 132 135 143 146 147 148 **P**1 6 7 **S** Catholic Health Initiatives, Englewood, CO
Primary Contact: Polly J. Davenport, FACHE, R.N., President, CHI St. Vincent Infirmary
COO: Polly J. Davenport, FACHE, President, CHI St. Vincent Infirmary
CFO: Tadd M. Richert, CPA, Senior Vice President and Chief Financial Officer
CMO: Thomas H. Cummins, M.D., Senior Vice President and Chief Medical Officer
CHR: Tim Osterholm, Senior Vice President and Chief People Officer
CNO: Brenda Baird, Senior Vice President and Chief Nursing Officer
Web address: www.chistvincent.com/
**Control:** Church–operated, Nongovernment, not–for profit **Service:** General Medical and Surgical

**Staffed Beds:** 447 **Admissions:** 20391 **Census:** 296 **Outpatient Visits:** 154432 **Births:** 1375 **Total Expense ($000):** 379142 **Payroll Expense ($000):** 130343 **Personnel:** 1969

☐ **PINNACLE POINTE HOSPITAL (044013)**, 11501 Financial Center Parkway, Zip 72211–3715; tel. 501/223–3322 **A**1 9 10 **F**29 34 98 99 101 102 105 106 130 **S** Universal Health Services, Inc., King of Prussia, PA
Primary Contact: Shane Frazier, Chief Executive Officer
CFO: Gina Dailey, Chief Financial Officer
CMO: Ben Nimmo, M.D., Medical Director
CIO: James L. Howe, Director Human Resources
CHR: James L. Howe, Director Human Resources
CNO: Bobby Alexander, R.N., Chief Nursing Officer
Web address: www.pinnaclepointehospital.com
**Control:** Corporation, Investor–owned, for–profit **Service:** Children's hospital psychiatric

**Staffed Beds:** 124 **Admissions:** 2693 **Census:** 110 **Outpatient Visits:** 0 **Births:** 0 **Total Expense ($000):** 17366 **Payroll Expense ($000):** 10150 **Personnel:** 217

⊠ **UAMS MEDICAL CENTER (040016)**, 4301 West Markham Street, Zip 72205–7101; tel. 501/686–7000 **A**1 3 5 8 9 10 13 **F**3 11 12 13 15 17 18 20 22 24 26 29 30 31 34 40 43 44 45 46 47 48 49 50 52 53 54 55 56 57 58 59 60 61 64 67 68 70 72 73 74 75 76 77 78 79 81 82 84 85 86 87 91 92 93 94 96 97 98 99 100 101 102 103 104 107 108 110 111 114 115 116 117 118 119 120 121 123 124 126 129 130 131 132 136 138 139 141 142 145 146 147 148 **P**6
Primary Contact: Roxane A. Townsend, M.D., Chief Executive Officer
COO: Melissa Fontaine, Chief Operating Officer
CFO: William Bowes, Chief Financial Officer
CMO: Nicholas P. Lang, M.D., Chief Medical Officer
CIO: David L. Miller, Chief Information Officer
CHR: Jeff Risinger, Director Human Resources
CNO: Mary Helen Forrest, R.N., Chief Nursing Officer
Web address: www.uams.edu/medcenter
**Control:** State–Government, nonfederal **Service:** General Medical and Surgical

**Staffed Beds:** 464 **Admissions:** 22903 **Census:** 386 **Outpatient Visits:** 447161 **Births:** 3018 **Total Expense ($000):** 599298 **Payroll Expense ($000):** 196595 **Personnel:** 3830

| Hospital, Medicare Provider Number, Address, Telephone, Approval, Facility, and Physician Codes, Health Care System |
| --- |

★ American Hospital Association (AHA) membership
☐ The Joint Commission accreditation
◯ Healthcare Facilities Accreditation Program
◇ DNV Healthcare Inc. accreditation
⇧ Center for Improvement in Healthcare Quality Accreditation
△ Commission on Accreditation of Rehabilitation Facilities (CARF) accreditation

**AR**

### MAGNOLIA—Columbia County

★ **MAGNOLIA REGIONAL MEDICAL CENTER (040067)**, 101 Hospital Drive, Zip 71753–2415, Mailing Address: P.O. Box 629, Zip 71754–0629; tel. 870/235–3000 **A**3 9 10 20 **F**3 11 13 15 29 31 34 35 40 43 57 59 62 64 70 75 76 77 81 86 87 91 93 97 107 108 110 111 115 119 129 130 132 133 146 147 148
Primary Contact: Margaret M. West, MS, Chief Executive Officer
CMO: John Alexander, Jr., M.D., Chief of Staff
CHR: Shawnee Hicks, Director Human Resources
Web address: www.magnoliahospital.org
**Control:** City–Government, nonfederal **Service:** General Medical and Surgical

**Staffed Beds:** 49 **Admissions:** 1406 **Census:** 12 **Outpatient Visits:** 107324 **Births:** 313 **Total Expense ($000):** 24131 **Payroll Expense ($000):** 11078 **Personnel:** 252

### MALVERN—Hot Spring County

★ **BAPTIST HEALTH MEDICAL CENTER–HOT SPRING COUNTY (040076)**, 1001 Schneider Drive, Zip 72104–4811; tel. 501/332–1000 **A**9 10 **F**3 11 15 17 18 29 34 40 43 45 57 59 62 70 75 81 89 98 106 107 110 111 115 119 129 130 146 148 **S** Baptist Health, Little Rock, AR
Primary Contact: Sheila Williams, Vice President and Administrator
CMO: Allen Gerber, M.D., Chief of Staff
CHR: Kelli Hopkins, Director Human Resources
CNO: Dee Schall, R.N., Chief Nursing Officer
Web address: www.https://www.baptist-health.org
**Control:** Other not–for–profit (including NFP Corporation) **Service:** General Medical and Surgical

**Staffed Beds:** 72 **Admissions:** 2240 **Census:** 24 **Outpatient Visits:** 27288 **Births:** 0 **Total Expense ($000):** 20831 **Payroll Expense ($000):** 9740 **Personnel:** 300

### MAUMELLE—Pulaski County

☐ **METHODIST BEHAVIORAL HOSPITAL OF ARKANSAS (044017)**, 1601 Murphy Drive, Zip 72113–6187; tel. 501/803–3388 **A**1 9 10 **F**30 32 38 50 54 64 75 86 87 98 99 102 104 106 130 **P**1
Primary Contact: Andy Altom, Chief Executive Officer
Web address: www.umch.org
**Control:** Other not–for–profit (including NFP Corporation) **Service:** Children's hospital psychiatric

**Staffed Beds:** 60 **Admissions:** 1308 **Census:** 57 **Outpatient Visits:** 83565 **Births:** 0 **Total Expense ($000):** 16194 **Payroll Expense ($000):** 8294 **Personnel:** 130

### MCGEHEE—Desha County

★ **MCGEHEE–DESHA COUNTY HOSPITAL (041308)**, 900 South Third, Zip 71654–2562, Mailing Address: P.O. Box 351, Zip 71654–0351; tel. 870/222–5600 **A**9 10 18 **F**3 11 29 40 57 59 62 64 68 107 114 119 132 133 135 146 148
Primary Contact: John E. Heard, Chief Executive Officer
CFO: Teresa Morgan, Chief Financial Officer
CMO: James Young, M.D., Chief of Staff
CIO: Shaun Perry, Chief Information Officer
CNO: Sarah Calvert, Chief Nursing Officer
**Control:** Other not–for–profit (including NFP Corporation) **Service:** General Medical and Surgical

**Staffed Beds:** 25 **Admissions:** 245 **Census:** 2 **Outpatient Visits:** 7002 **Births:** 0 **Total Expense ($000):** 8847 **Payroll Expense ($000):** 4351 **Personnel:** 116

### MENA—Polk County

★ **MENA REGIONAL HEALTH SYSTEM (040015)**, 311 North Morrow Street, Zip 71953–2516; tel. 479/394–6100, (Nonreporting) **A**9 10 20
Primary Contact: Jay Quebedeaux, Chief Executive Officer
COO: Richard A. Billingsley, MSN, Chief Operating Officer and Chief Nursing Officer
CFO: Laura Allen, Chief Financial Officer
CMO: Thomas Sullivan, M.D., Chief of Staff
CIO: Nicholas Dunn, Director Information Systems
CHR: Amy Jarman, Director Human Resources
CNO: Richard A. Billingsley, MSN, Chief Operating Officer and Chief Nursing Officer
Web address: www.menaregional.com
**Control:** City–Government, nonfederal **Service:** General Medical and Surgical

**Staffed Beds:** 35

### MONTICELLO—Drew County

★ **DREW MEMORIAL HOSPITAL (040051)**, 778 Scogin Drive, Zip 71655–5729; tel. 870/367–2411 **A**9 10 20 **F**3 11 13 15 29 31 34 35 40 43 45 50 57 59 62 64 68 70 75 76 77 78 81 82 86 87 91 93 94 96 100 103 107 110 111 115 119 128 129 130 132 133 147 148
Primary Contact: Scott G. Barrilleaux, FACHE, Chief Executive Officer
CMO: Jeffery Reinhart, M.D., Chief of Staff
CIO: Rusty Bryant, Director Information Technology
CHR: Keith Van Dee, Director Human Resources
CNO: Linda Orrell, Interim Chief Nursing Officer
Web address: www.drewmemorial.org
**Control:** Other not–for–profit (including NFP Corporation) **Service:** General Medical and Surgical

**Staffed Beds:** 49 **Admissions:** 2346 **Census:** 21 **Outpatient Visits:** 31369 **Births:** 349 **Total Expense ($000):** 27217 **Payroll Expense ($000):** 11473 **Personnel:** 272

### MORRILTON—Conway County

**ST. ANTHONY'S MEDICAL CENTER** See St. Vincent Morrilton

★ **ST. VINCENT MORRILTON (041324)**, 4 Hospital Drive, Zip 72110–4510; tel. 501/977–2300 **A**9 10 18 **F**3 11 15 28 29 30 34 40 44 45 50 57 59 62 64 70 77 79 80 81 85 87 93 97 107 110 111 119 127 130 133 145 146 **P**1 6 **S** Catholic Health Initiatives, Englewood, CO
Primary Contact: Leslie Arnold, Chief Executive Officer and Administrator
CFO: Amanda George, Assistant Controller
CMO: Charles Howard, M.D., Chief of Staff
CHR: Tammy Smith, Director Human Resources
Web address: www.stanthonysmorrilton.com/
**Control:** Church–operated, Nongovernment, not–for profit **Service:** General Medical and Surgical

**Staffed Beds:** 25 **Admissions:** 808 **Census:** 8 **Outpatient Visits:** 32407 **Births:** 0 **Total Expense ($000):** 15706 **Payroll Expense ($000):** 6155 **Personnel:** 122

### MOUNTAIN HOME—Baxter County

★ **BAXTER REGIONAL MEDICAL CENTER (040027)**, 624 Hospital Drive, Zip 72653–2955; tel. 870/508–1000 **A**9 10 20 **F**7 11 13 15 17 18 20 22 24 28 29 30 31 36 40 41 43 45 46 47 49 53 57 59 62 63 64 70 71 76 77 78 79 81 82 84 85 86 87 90 93 98 103 104 107 108 111 114 115 119 124 126 127 129 130 132 135 146 147 148 **P**6 8
Primary Contact: Ron Peterson, FACHE, President and Chief Executive Officer
COO: Rudy Darling, Chief Operating Officer
CFO: Ivan Holleman, Chief Financial Officer
CHR: Karen Adams, Vice President Human Resources
Web address: www.baxterregional.org
**Control:** Other not–for–profit (including NFP Corporation) **Service:** General Medical and Surgical

**Staffed Beds:** 209 **Admissions:** 8190 **Census:** 106 **Outpatient Visits:** 114054 **Births:** 682 **Total Expense ($000):** 160079 **Payroll Expense ($000):** 64320 **Personnel:** 1262

### MOUNTAIN VIEW—Stone County

★ **STONE COUNTY MEDICAL CENTER (041310)**, 2106 East Main Street, Zip 72560–6439, Mailing Address: P.O. Box 510, Zip 72560–0510; tel. 870/269–4361 **A**9 10 18 **F**3 8 11 15 29 34 35 40 43 57 59 64 79 81 91 93 107 110 111 114 119 128 133 146 147 148 **S** White River Health System, Batesville, AR
Primary Contact: Stanley Townsend, Chief Executive Officer
CFO: Jana Richardson, Chief Financial Officer
CIO: Gary Paxson, Associate Administrator Information Systems
CHR: Gary McDonald, Associate Administrator Human Resources
CNO: Diana Shelden, Chief Nursing Officer
Web address: www.whiteriverhealthsystem.com
**Control:** Other not–for–profit (including NFP Corporation) **Service:** General Medical and Surgical

**Staffed Beds:** 25 **Admissions:** 745 **Census:** 7 **Outpatient Visits:** 20162 **Births:** 0 **Total Expense ($000):** 13663 **Payroll Expense ($000):** 4700 **Personnel:** 104

### NASHVILLE—Howard County

★ **HOWARD MEMORIAL HOSPITAL (041311)**, 130 Medical Circle, Zip 71852–8606; tel. 870/845–4400 **A**9 10 18 **F**3 11 15 29 30 34 35 40 43 45 50 53 57 64 65 70 77 81 85 87 93 102 107 108 110 115 119 133 146
Primary Contact: Debra J. Wright, R.N., Chief Executive Officer
CFO: William J. Craig, Chief Financial Officer
CMO: John Hearnsberger, M.D., Chief of Staff
CHR: Gayla Lacefield, Director Human Resources
CNO: Alesha Danielle Collins, MSN, Chief Nursing Officer
Web address: www.howardmemorial.com
**Control:** Other not–for–profit (including NFP Corporation) **Service:** General Medical and Surgical

**Staffed Beds:** 20 **Admissions:** 530 **Census:** 6 **Outpatient Visits:** 29247 **Births:** 0 **Total Expense ($000):** 14740 **Payroll Expense ($000):** 6308 **Personnel:** 140

## NORTH LITTLE ROCK—Pulaski County

☐ **ARKANSAS SURGICAL HOSPITAL (040147)**, 5201 North Shore Drive, Zip 72118–5312; tel. 501/748–8000 **A**1 9 10 **F**3 29 35 40 74 75 79 81 82 85 87 107 111 114 119 131 146
Primary Contact: Carrie Helm, Chief Executive Officer
CFO: Charles Powell, Chief Financial Officer
CMO: Kenneth A. Martin, M.D., Chief of Staff
CIO: Scott Davis, Manager Information Technology
CNO: Judy Jones, Chief Clinical Officer
Web address: www.ArkSurgicalHospital.com
**Control:** Corporation, Investor–owned, for–profit **Service:** General Medical and Surgical

**Staffed Beds:** 51 **Admissions:** 3186 **Census:** 18 **Outpatient Visits:** 15747 **Births:** 0 **Total Expense ($000):** 48552 **Payroll Expense ($000):** 11542 **Personnel:** 217

⊞ △ **BAPTIST HEALTH MEDICAL CENTER – NORTH LITTLE ROCK (040036)**, 3333 Springhill Drive, Zip 72117–2922; tel. 501/202–3000 **A**1 3 7 9 10 **F**3 8 11 13 15 17 18 20 22 24 26 28 29 30 31 38 40 43 45 46 47 49 50 53 54 56 59 60 64 65 70 72 73 74 75 76 77 78 79 81 85 86 87 89 90 93 94 107 108 110 111 114 115 116 117 118 119 124 126 129 130 135 146 147 148 **S** Baptist Health, Little Rock, AR
Primary Contact: Harrison M. Dean, FACHE, Senior Vice President and Administrator
CFO: Robert C. Roberts, Senior Vice President Financial Services
CMO: Eddie Phillips, M.D., Chief Medical Affairs
CIO: David House, Vice President and Chief Information Officer
CHR: Anthony Kendall, Vice President Human Resources
CNO: Kathy Martin, Vice President Patient Care
Web address: www.baptist–health.com/locations/accesspoint.aspx?accessPointID=190
**Control:** Other not–for–profit (including NFP Corporation) **Service:** General Medical and Surgical

**Staffed Beds:** 225 **Admissions:** 12514 **Census:** 146 **Outpatient Visits:** 69366 **Births:** 1585 **Total Expense ($000):** 165747 **Payroll Expense ($000):** 54680 **Personnel:** 936

**NORTH LITTLE ROCK DIVISION** See Central Arkansas Veterans Healthcare System, Little Rock

☐ **THE BRIDGEWAY (044005)**, 21 Bridgeway Road, Zip 72113–9516; tel. 501/771–1500 **A**1 9 10 **F**4 5 98 99 104 105 106 **P**5 **S** Universal Health Services, Inc., King of Prussia, PA
Primary Contact: Jason Miller, M.P.H., Chief Executive Officer
CFO: Fred Woods, Chief Financial Officer
CMO: Philip L. Mizell, M.D., Medical Director
CHR: Neely Robison, Director Human Resources
CNO: Sherrie James, R.N., Director of Nursing
Web address: www.thebridgeway.com
**Control:** Corporation, Investor–owned, for–profit **Service:** Psychiatric

**Staffed Beds:** 103 **Admissions:** 4549 **Census:** 88 **Outpatient Visits:** 11316 **Births:** 0 **Total Expense ($000):** 17411 **Payroll Expense ($000):** 8352 **Personnel:** 199

## OSCEOLA—Mississippi County

⊞ **SOUTH MISSISSIPPI COUNTY REGIONAL MEDICAL CENTER (041316)**, 611 West Lee Avenue, Zip 72370–3001, Mailing Address: P.O. Box 108, Blytheville, Zip 72316–0108; tel. 870/563–7000 **A**1 9 10 18 **F**29 40 50 57 59 68 75 81 93 107 114 130 133 146 **S** QHR, Brentwood, TN
Primary Contact: Ralph E. Beaty, Chief Executive Officer
COO: Chris Raymer, R.N., Chief Operating Officer and Chief Nursing Officer
CFO: Randy Nichols, Chief Financial Officer
CMO: Pratapji Thakor, M.D., Chief of Staff
CIO: Tammy Bratcher, Director Information Technology
CHR: Cheri Blurton, Director Human Resources
CNO: Chris Raymer, R.N., Chief Operating Officer and Chief Nursing Officer
Web address: www.mchsys.org
**Control:** County–Government, nonfederal **Service:** General Medical and Surgical

**Staffed Beds:** 25 **Admissions:** 631 **Census:** 6 **Outpatient Visits:** 12618 **Births:** 0 **Total Expense ($000):** 8911 **Payroll Expense ($000):** 3850 **Personnel:** 71

## OZARK—Franklin County

★ **MERCY HOSPITAL OZARK (041303)**, 801 West River Street, Zip 72949–3023; tel. 479/667–4138 **A**9 10 18 **F**3 18 20 22 24 26 28 34 35 40 43 45 57 59 64 68 81 85 107 119 133 **S** Mercy Health, Chesterfield, MO
Primary Contact: Teresa Williams, R.N., Administrator and Director of Nursing
COO: Brent Hubbard, Chief Operating Officer
CMO: John Lachowsky, M.D., Chief Medical Officer
CIO: Tiana Bolduc, Chief Information Officer
Web address: www.mercy.net/northwestarar/practice/mercy–hospital–ozark
**Control:** Church–operated, Nongovernment, not–for profit **Service:** General Medical and Surgical

**Staffed Beds:** 25 **Admissions:** 333 **Census:** 4 **Outpatient Visits:** 12324 **Births:** 0 **Total Expense ($000):** 10052 **Payroll Expense ($000):** 3633 **Personnel:** 53

## PARAGOULD—Greene County

⊞ △ **ARKANSAS METHODIST MEDICAL CENTER (040039)**, 900 West Kingshighway, Zip 72450–5942, Mailing Address: P.O. Box 339, Zip 72451–0339; tel. 870/239–7000 **A**1 7 9 10 19 **F**3 7 10 11 13 15 18 20 22 28 29 32 34 35 39 40 43 45 49 50 51 53 54 57 59 62 64 68 70 75 76 78 79 81 85 86 87 89 90 93 97 107 108 110 111 114 115 119 125 129 130 131 132 133 135 146 147 148 **P**6 8
Primary Contact: Barry L. Davis, FACHE, President and Chief Executive Officer
CFO: Brad Bloemer, Vice President Finance and Chief Financial Officer
CMO: John Hines, M.D., Chief of Staff
CIO: Mardy Holmes, Director Information Technology
CHR: Kevin Thielemier, Director Human Resources
CNO: Lana R. Williams, Chief Nursing Officer
Web address: www.arkansasmethodist.org
**Control:** Other not–for–profit (including NFP Corporation) **Service:** General Medical and Surgical

**Staffed Beds:** 125 **Admissions:** 4079 **Census:** 52 **Outpatient Visits:** 115806 **Births:** 506 **Total Expense ($000):** 56897 **Payroll Expense ($000):** 23902 **Personnel:** 543

## PARIS—Logan County

★ **MERCY HOSPITAL PARIS (041300)**, 500 East Academy, Zip 72855–4040; tel. 479/963–6101 **A**9 10 18 **F**3 35 40 43 57 59 64 65 68 81 85 107 119 133 **S** Mercy Health, Chesterfield, MO
Primary Contact: Sharon D. Sorey, R.N., Administrator
COO: Brent Hubbard, Chief Operating Officer
Web address: www.mercy.net/fortsmithar
**Control:** Church–operated, Nongovernment, not–for profit **Service:** General Medical and Surgical

**Staffed Beds:** 16 **Admissions:** 154 **Census:** 2 **Outpatient Visits:** 13450 **Births:** 0 **Total Expense ($000):** 8306 **Payroll Expense ($000):** 3454 **Personnel:** 50

## PIGGOTT—Clay County

★ **PIGGOTT COMMUNITY HOSPITAL (041330)**, 1206 Gordon Duckworth Drive, Zip 72454–1911; tel. 870/598–3881 **A**9 10 18 **F**7 11 15 18 29 34 35 40 43 57 59 62 64 77 81 93 107 111 114 119 127 129 130 133 143 146 148
Primary Contact: James L. Magee, Executive Director
CFO: Linda Ort, Chief Financial Officer
Web address: www.piggottcommunityhospital.com
**Control:** City–Government, nonfederal **Service:** General Medical and Surgical

**Staffed Beds:** 25 **Admissions:** 889 **Census:** 13 **Outpatient Visits:** 14159 **Births:** 0 **Total Expense ($000):** 14981 **Payroll Expense ($000):** 7337 **Personnel:** 196

## PINE BLUFF—Jefferson County

**ARKANSAS DEPARTMENT OF CORRECTION HOSPITAL**, 7500 Correctional Circle, Zip 71603–1438; tel. 870/267–6999, (Nonreporting) **A**3 5
Primary Contact: Roland Anderson, M.D., Medical Director
**Control:** State–Government, nonfederal **Service:** Hospital unit of an institution (prison hospital, college infirmary, etc.)

**Staffed Beds:** 27

---

**Hospital, Medicare Provider Number, Address, Telephone, Approval, Facility, and Physician Codes, Health Care System**

★ American Hospital Association (AHA) membership
☐ The Joint Commission accreditation
○ Healthcare Facilities Accreditation Program
◇ DNV Healthcare Inc. accreditation
⇑ Center for Improvement in Healthcare Quality Accreditation
△ Commission on Accreditation of Rehabilitation Facilities (CARF) accreditation

**AR**

★ △ **JEFFERSON REGIONAL MEDICAL CENTER (040071)**, 1600 West 40th Avenue, Zip 71603–6301; tel. 870/541–7100 **A**3 5 6 7 9 10 20 **F**3 8 11 13 15 17 18 20 22 24 28 29 30 31 34 35 40 43 45 46 48 49 50 51 53 54 56 57 59 60 61 64 65 70 72 73 74 75 76 77 78 79 81 85 86 87 89 90 96 97 98 100 101 102 103 107 108 110 111 114 115 116 118 119 124 128 130 131 132 135 143 144 145 146 147 148 **P**7
Primary Contact: Walter E. Johnson, Jr., President and Chief Executive Officer
COO: Brian N. Thomas, Senior Vice President and Chief Operating Officer
CFO: Bryan G. Jackson, Vice President and Chief Financial Officer
CMO: John Lytle, M.D., Chief of Staff
CIO: Patrick Neece, Chief Information Officer
CHR: M Daryl Scott, Assistant Vice President
CNO: Louise Hickman, R.N., Vice President of Patient Care Services
Web address: www.jrmc.org
**Control:** Other not–for–profit (including NFP Corporation) **Service:** General Medical and Surgical

**Staffed Beds: 333 Admissions: 9137 Census: 140 Outpatient Visits:** 194146 **Births:** 818 **Total Expense ($000):** 167398 **Payroll Expense ($000):** 72666 **Personnel:** 1229

### POCAHONTAS—Randolph County

**FIVE RIVERS MEDICAL CENTER (040047)**, 2801 Medical Center Drive, Zip 72455–9436; tel. 870/892–6000 **A**9 10 20 **F**3 11 18 29 40 43 45 47 50 57 59 62 70 79 81 85 93 98 103 107 111 113 115 119 130 133 146
Primary Contact: Luther J. Lewis, FACHE, Chief Executive Officer
CFO: Joey Radcliff, Chief Financial Officer
CHR: Anita Dickson, Director Human Resources
CNO: Paula Lewis, Interim Chief Nursing Officer
Web address: www.fiveriversmc.com
**Control:** Other not–for–profit (including NFP Corporation) **Service:** General Medical and Surgical

**Staffed Beds: 46 Admissions: 838 Census: 13 Outpatient Visits:** 19028 **Births:** 0 **Total Expense ($000):** 15369 **Payroll Expense ($000):** 7866 **Personnel:** 118

### ROGERS—Benton County

⊠ **MERCY HOSPITAL ROGERS (040010)**, 2710 Rife Medical Lane, Zip 72758–1452; tel. 479/338–8000 **A**1 9 10 **F**3 8 11 12 13 15 17 18 20 22 24 26 28 29 30 40 43 45 46 49 54 57 59 62 64 68 70 71 72 74 75 76 77 79 81 82 85 86 89 93 103 107 108 110 111 115 118 119 129 130 131 135 146 147 148 **S** Mercy Health, Chesterfield, MO
Primary Contact: Eric Pianalto, President
COO: Brenda Chase, Chief Operating Officer
CFO: Benny Stover, Vice President Finance
CMO: Chris Johnson, M.D., Chief of Staff
CHR: Rick Barclay, Vice President Support Services
CNO: Michele Diedrich, R.N., Chief Nursing Officer
Web address: www.mercyhealthnwa.smhs.com
**Control:** Church–operated, Nongovernment, not–for profit **Service:** General Medical and Surgical

**Staffed Beds: 162 Admissions: 11497 Census: 97 Outpatient Visits:** 205560 **Births:** 1430 **Total Expense ($000):** 156281 **Payroll Expense ($000):** 47704 **Personnel:** 998

### RUSSELLVILLE—Pope County

☐ **SAINT MARY'S REGIONAL MEDICAL CENTER (040041)**, 1808 West Main Street, Zip 72801–2724; tel. 479/968–2841 **A**1 9 10 19 **F**3 11 13 15 18 20 22 29 34 35 40 43 45 50 51 53 54 56 57 59 64 68 70 74 75 76 78 79 81 85 86 87 89 90 93 98 102 107 108 109 110 111 114 115 118 119 120 121 123 127 129 130 131 132 146 147 148 **S** Capella Healthcare, Franklin, TN
Primary Contact: Mike McCoy, Interim Chief Executive Officer
COO: Mike McCoy, Chief Operating Officer
CFO: Wendell VanEs, Chief Financial Officer
CMO: Doug Kerin, M.D., Chief of Staff
CHR: Connie Gragg, Director Human Resources
CNO: Pat Torrico, R.N., Chief Nursing Officer
Web address: www.saintmarysregional.com
**Control:** Corporation, Investor–owned, for–profit **Service:** General Medical and Surgical

**Staffed Beds: 151 Admissions: 5800 Census: 69 Outpatient Visits:** 83236 **Births:** 1038 **Total Expense ($000):** 72833 **Payroll Expense ($000):** 23780 **Personnel:** 505

### SALEM—Fulton County

**FULTON COUNTY HOSPITAL (041322)**, 679 North Main Street, Zip 72576–9451, Mailing Address: P.O. Box 517, Zip 72576–0517; tel. 870/895–2691 **A**9 10 18 **F**3 7 11 28 29 30 34 40 43 45 57 59 75 107 114 119 133 146 148
Primary Contact: Charles Willett, Administrator and Chief Executive Officer
Web address: www.fultoncountyhospital.org
**Control:** County–Government, nonfederal **Service:** General Medical and Surgical

**Staffed Beds: 25 Admissions: 1012 Census: 15 Outpatient Visits:** 7631 **Births:** 0 **Total Expense ($000):** 9485 **Payroll Expense ($000):** 4152 **Personnel:** 143

### SEARCY—White County

**ADVANCED CARE HOSPITAL OF WHITE COUNTY (042011)**, 1200 South Main Street, Zip 72143–7321; tel. 501/278–3155, (Nonreporting) **A**9 10
Primary Contact: Terri L. Parsons, Administrator
CMO: Miguel Aguinaga, M.D., Medical Director
CNO: Kathy DeVore, R.N., Director Patient Services
Web address: www.advancedcarehospital.com
**Control:** Other not–for–profit (including NFP Corporation) **Service:** Long–Term Acute Care hospital

**Staffed Beds: 27**

★ **UNITY HEALTH WHITE COUNTY MEDICAL CENTER (040014)**, 3214 East Race Avenue, Zip 72143–4810; tel. 501/268–6121, (Includes UNITY HEALTH HARRIS MEDICAL CENTER, 1205 McLain Street, Newport, Zip 72112–3533; tel. 870/523–8911; LaDonna Johnston, Interim Administrator; UNITY HEALTH SPECIALTY CARE, 1200 South Main Street, Zip 72143–7397; tel. 501/278–3100) **A**9 10 13 20 **F**1 3 11 12 13 17 18 20 22 24 28 29 30 31 34 35 39 40 43 45 51 54 57 59 61 62 64 68 70 74 75 76 77 78 79 81 86 87 89 90 93 98 100 102 103 105 107 108 111 115 119 126 129 130 131 132 134 135 145 146 147 148 **P**2 6
Primary Contact: Raymond W. Montgomery, II, FACHE, President and Chief Executive Officer
CFO: Stuart Hill, Vice President and Treasurer
CMO: John Henderson, M.D., Chief Medical Officer
CIO: Kevin Hoofman, Director Management Information
CHR: Pamela G. Williams, Director Human Resources
CNO: Peggy Turner, Assistant Vice President and Director of Nursing
Web address: www.wcmc.org
**Control:** Other not–for–profit (including NFP Corporation) **Service:** General Medical and Surgical

**Staffed Beds: 286 Admissions: 12008 Census: 153 Outpatient Visits:** 93515 **Births:** 1196 **Total Expense ($000):** 184988 **Payroll Expense ($000):** 83138 **Personnel:** 1539

### SHERWOOD—Pulaski County

★ **CHI ST. VINCENT MEDICAL CENTER–NORTH (040137)**, 2215 Wildwood Avenue, Zip 72120–5089; tel. 501/552–7100 **A**9 10 **F**3 11 18 20 22 26 29 30 35 40 43 44 45 50 64 68 70 74 79 81 85 87 107 110 111 115 118 119 129 130 146 **P**1 6 **S** Catholic Health Initiatives, Englewood, CO
Primary Contact: Polly J. Davenport, FACHE, R.N., President
CFO: Tadd M. Richert, CPA, Senior Vice President and Chief Financial Officer
CMO: Thomas H. Cummins, M.D., Senior Vice President and Chief Medical Officer
CHR: Tim Osterholm, Senior Vice President and Chief People Officer
CNO: Brenda Baird, Senior Vice President and Chief Nursing Officer
Web address: www.stvincenthealth.com
**Control:** Church–operated, Nongovernment, not–for profit **Service:** General Medical and Surgical

**Staffed Beds: 58 Admissions: 1483 Census: 13 Outpatient Visits:** 28391 **Births:** 0 **Total Expense ($000):** 23704 **Payroll Expense ($000):** 7344 **Personnel:** 137

⊠ **ST. VINCENT REHABILITATION HOSPITAL (043031)**, 2201 Wildwood Avenue, Zip 72120–5074; tel. 501/834–1800 **A**1 9 10 **F**29 50 60 68 90 91 95 96 130 132 143 148 **S** HEALTHSOUTH Corporation, Birmingham, AL
Primary Contact: Lisa Watson, Chief Executive Officer
CFO: Stacy Shilling, Controller
CMO: Kevin J. Collins, M.D., Medical Director
CNO: Shannon Moreno–Cook, Chief Nursing Officer
Web address: www.stvincenthealth.com/svrehabhospital/index.html
**Control:** Corporation, Investor–owned, for–profit **Service:** Rehabilitation

**Staffed Beds: 60 Admissions: 1602 Census: 52 Outpatient Visits:** 6532 **Births:** 0 **Total Expense ($000):** 22101 **Payroll Expense ($000):** 10899 **Personnel:** 194

### SILOAM SPRINGS—Benton County

⊠ **SILOAM SPRINGS REGIONAL HOSPITAL (040001)**, 603 North Progress Avenue, Zip 72761–4352; tel. 479/524–4141, (Nonreporting) **A**1 9 10 **S** Community Health Systems, Inc., Franklin, TN
Primary Contact: Patrick Kerwood, Chief Executive Officer
CFO: James E. Little, Chief Financial Officer
CMO: Hunt Cooper, M.D., Chief of Staff
CHR: Carmen Burasco, Director Human Resources
Web address: www.ssrh.net/Pages/home.aspx
**Control:** Corporation, Investor–owned, for–profit **Service:** General Medical and Surgical

**Staffed Beds: 43**

*Many Facility Codes have changed. Please refer to the AHA Guide Code Chart.* © 2015 AHA Guide

**SPRINGDALE—Washington County**

✠ **NORTHWEST MEDICAL CENTER – SPRINGDALE (040022)**, 609 West Maple Avenue, Zip 72764–5394, Mailing Address: P.O. Box 47, Zip 72765–0047; tel. 479/751–5711, (Includes NORTHWEST MEDICAL CENTER – BENTONVILLE, 3000 Medical Center Parkway, Bentonville, Zip 72712; tel. 479/553–1000; Benjamin Casmer, Chief Operating Officer; WILLOW CREEK WOMEN'S HOSPITAL, 4301 Greathouse Springs Road, Johnson, Zip 72741–0544, Mailing Address: P.O. Box 544, Zip 72741–0544; tel. 479/684–3000; Debbie A. Crandall, Administrative Director) **A**1 3 9 10 **F**3 8 11 12 13 15 17 18 20 22 24 26 28 29 30 40 43 45 46 47 48 49 50 51 56 60 61 70 72 74 76 77 79 81 82 85 86 87 90 91 92 93 96 98 102 107 108 110 111 114 115 118 119 124 126 129 130 131 135 146 147 148 **P**5 8 **S** Community Health Systems, Inc., Franklin, TN
Primary Contact: Harrison Kiser, Interim Chief Executive Officer
CFO: Steve Flader, Chief Financial Officer
CMO: Robert Petrino, M.D., Chief of Staff
CIO: Paul DeMay, Chief Information Officer
Web address: www.northwesthealth.com
**Control:** Corporation, Investor–owned, for–profit **Service:** General Medical and Surgical

| | |
|---|---|
| **Staffed Beds:** 295 **Admissions:** 16166 **Census:** 164 **Outpatient Visits:** 150529 **Births:** 3603 **Total Expense ($000):** 202221 **Payroll Expense ($000):** 71856 **Personnel:** 1481 | |

✠ **REGENCY HOSPITAL OF NORTHWEST ARKANSAS – SPRINGDALE (042009)**, 609 West Maple Avenue, 6th Floor, Zip 72764; tel. 479/757–2600, (Nonreporting) **A**1 10 **S** Select Medical Corporation, Mechanicsburg, PA
Primary Contact: Jerry Alexander, Chief Executive Officer
COO: Ruth Jones, Chief Clinical Officer
CMO: Gary Templeton, M.D., Medical Director
CHR: Melissa Ross–Cole, Director Human Resources
Web address: www.regencyhospital.com
**Control:** Corporation, Investor–owned, for–profit **Service:** Long–Term Acute Care hospital

| |
|---|
| **Staffed Beds:** 25 |

**STUTTGART—Arkansas County**

★ **BAPTIST HEALTH MEDICAL CENTER–STUTTGART (040072)**, North Buerkle Road, Zip 72160–3420, Mailing Address: P.O. Box 1905, Zip 72160–1905; tel. 870/673–3511 **A**9 10 **F**3 11 13 15 18 29 30 34 35 39 40 43 53 57 59 64 68 70 75 78 79 81 85 87 93 97 107 111 114 119 127 128 129 130 133 135 146 148 **S** Baptist Health, Little Rock, AR
Primary Contact: Harrison M. Dean, FACHE, Interim Administrator
CMO: Christopher Morgan, M.D., Chief of Staff
CIO: Warren Horton, Information Technologist
CNO: Susan Williams, R.N., Chief Nursing Officer
Web address: www.baptist-health.org/maps–directions/bhmc–stuttgart/default.aspx
**Control:** Other not–for–profit (including NFP Corporation) **Service:** General Medical and Surgical

| |
|---|
| **Staffed Beds:** 49 **Admissions:** 1386 **Census:** 13 **Outpatient Visits:** 13396 **Births:** 207 **Total Expense ($000):** 25619 **Payroll Expense ($000):** 8800 **Personnel:** 153 |

**TEXARKANA—Miller County**

☐ **RIVERVIEW BEHAVIORAL HEALTH (044020)**, 701 Arkansas Boulevard, Zip 71854–2105; tel. 870/772–5028, (Nonreporting) **A**1 9 10 **S** Acadia Healthcare Company, Inc., Franklin, TN
Primary Contact: Michael A. Truman, Chief Executive Officer
CFO: Kimberly Hibschman, Chief Financial Officer
CMO: John Gary Tharp, M.D., Medical Director
CIO: Jim Cruson, Chief Information Officer
CHR: Roberta Bachman, Director Human Resources
CNO: Carrie Gray, Director of Nursing
Web address: www.riverviewbehavioralhealth.com
**Control:** Corporation, Investor–owned, for–profit **Service:** Psychiatric

| |
|---|
| **Staffed Beds:** 50 |

**VAN BUREN—Crawford County**

✠ **SPARKS MEDICAL CENTER – VAN BUREN (040018)**, East Main and South 20th Streets, Zip 72956–5715, Mailing Address: P.O. Box 409, Zip 72957–0409; tel. 479/474–3401 **A**1 9 10 **F**3 8 11 12 15 18 29 30 34 35 40 43 45 48 49 50 51 56 57 58 59 64 65 68 70 74 75 77 79 81 82 85 86 87 93 97 100 107 108 110 111 114 119 130 131 132 135 144 146 **P**6 **S** Community Health Systems, Inc., Franklin, TN
Primary Contact: Daniel E. McKay, Chief Executive Officer
CHR: James Ford, Director Human Resources
CNO: Shelly L. Cordum, R.N., Administrator and Chief Nursing Executive
Web address: www.sparkshealth.com/locations/sparks–medical–center–van–buren
**Control:** Corporation, Investor–owned, for–profit **Service:** General Medical and Surgical

| |
|---|
| **Staffed Beds:** 103 **Admissions:** 1377 **Census:** 11 **Outpatient Visits:** 32866 **Births:** 0 **Total Expense ($000):** 20314 **Payroll Expense ($000):** 6742 **Personnel:** 125 |

**WALDRON—Scott County**

★ **MERCY HOSPITAL WALDRON (041305)**, 1341 West 6th Street, Zip 72958–7642; tel. 479/637–4135 **A**9 10 18 **F**3 35 40 43 45 57 59 64 65 68 81 85 107 119 127 129 133 **P**6 8 **S** Mercy Health, Chesterfield, MO
Primary Contact: Dorothy O'Bar, R.N., Administrator
COO: Brent Hubbard, Chief Operating Officer
CFO: Greta Wilcher, Senior Vice President and Chief Financial Officer
CMO: Nathan Bennett, M.D., Chief Medical Officer
CNO: Dorothy O'Bar, R.N., Regional Administrator
Web address: www.stedwardmercy.com
**Control:** Church–operated, Nongovernment, not–for profit **Service:** General Medical and Surgical

| |
|---|
| **Staffed Beds:** 24 **Admissions:** 336 **Census:** 4 **Outpatient Visits:** 17444 **Births:** 0 **Total Expense ($000):** 11177 **Payroll Expense ($000):** 4128 **Personnel:** 60 |

**WALNUT RIDGE—Lawrence County**

✠ **LAWRENCE MEMORIAL HOSPITAL (041309)**, 1309 West Main, Zip 72476–1430, Mailing Address: P.O. Box 839, Zip 72476–0839; tel. 870/886–1200, (Includes LAWRENCE HALL NURSING HOME ), (Total facility includes 179 beds in nursing home–type unit) **A**1 9 10 18 **F**3 11 15 28 29 32 34 35 40 45 46 47 57 59 84 85 97 107 111 114 119 127 128 129 130 133 135 146
Primary Contact: Gary R. Sparks, Interim President
COO: Junior Briner, Chief Operating Officer
CFO: Vanessa Wagner, Chief Financial Officer
CMO: Kevin Diamond, M.D., Chief of Staff
CHR: Donna Carter, Director Human Resources
CNO: Rosalind Casillas, Director of Nursing
Web address: www.lawrencehealth.net
**Control:** County–Government, nonfederal **Service:** General Medical and Surgical

| |
|---|
| **Staffed Beds:** 204 **Admissions:** 1145 **Census:** 148 **Outpatient Visits:** 31392 **Births:** 0 **Total Expense ($000):** 19747 **Payroll Expense ($000):** 10044 **Personnel:** 296 |

**WARREN—Bradley County**

★ **BRADLEY COUNTY MEDICAL CENTER (041327)**, 404 South Bradley Street, Zip 71671–3493; tel. 870/226–3731 **A**9 10 18 **F**3 11 13 15 29 30 34 35 40 45 49 50 56 57 59 62 68 81 87 89 93 98 103 104 107 108 111 115 118 119 129 130 131 132 133 147 **P**6
Primary Contact: Rex Jones, Chief Executive Officer
CFO: Brandon Gorman, Controller
CMO: Joe H. Wharton, M.D., Chief of Staff
CHR: Angela Lochridge, Director Human Resources
CNO: Tiffany Holland, Chief Nursing Officer
Web address: www.bradleycountymedicalcenter.com
**Control:** Other not–for–profit (including NFP Corporation) **Service:** General Medical and Surgical

| |
|---|
| **Staffed Beds:** 33 **Admissions:** 1342 **Census:** 14 **Outpatient Visits:** 64676 **Births:** 167 **Total Expense ($000):** 20963 **Payroll Expense ($000):** 8909 **Personnel:** 206 |

**AR**

**WYNNE—Cross County**

✠ **CROSSRIDGE COMMUNITY HOSPITAL (041307)**, 310 South Falls Boulevard,
Zip 72396–3013, Mailing Address: P.O. Box 590, Zip 72396–0590;
tel. 870/238–3300 **A**1 9 10 18 **F**3 11 15 28 34 35 40 43 50 57 59 62 64 68
69 75 77 81 93 107 110 111 114 119 130 133 135 146
Primary Contact: Gary R. Sparks, Administrator
COO: Bryan Mattes, Associate Administrator
CFO: Janice Morris, Accountant
CIO: Gail Copeland, Director Management Information Systems
CHR: Bertha Ragle, Director Personnel
CNO: Amelia Davis, Director of Nursing
**Control:** Church–operated, Nongovernment, not–for profit **Service:** General
Medical and Surgical

**Staffed Beds:** 15 **Admissions:** 625 **Census:** 7 **Outpatient Visits:** 17674
**Births:** 0 **Total Expense ($000):** 14087 **Payroll Expense ($000):** 5586
**Personnel:** 137

**AR**

# CALIFORNIA

## ALAMEDA—Alameda County

★ **ALAMEDA HOSPITAL (050211)**, 2070 Clinton Avenue, Zip 94501–4397; tel. 510/522–3700, (Total facility includes 181 beds in nursing home–type unit) (Data for 61 days) **A**9 10 **F**3 11 15 17 18 29 31 34 35 36 39 40 43 46 50 57 58 59 70 77 78 79 81 82 85 93 97 107 108 110 114 118 119 128 130 131 132 146 147 148 **S** Alameda Health System, San Leandro, CA
Primary Contact: Bonnie Panlasigui, Chief Administrative Officer
CFO: Robert C. Anderson, Interim Chief Financial Officer
CMO: Aika Sharma, M.D., President Medical Staff
CIO: Robert Lundy–Paine, Director Information Systems
CHR: Phyllis Weiss, Director Human Resources
Web address: www.alamedahospital.org
**Control:** Hospital district or authority, Government, nonfederal **Service:** General Medical and Surgical

Staffed Beds: 246 Admissions: 522 Census: 187 Outpatient Visits: 6075
Births: 0 Total Expense ($000): 19360 Payroll Expense ($000): 7764
Personnel: 494

## ALHAMBRA—Los Angeles County

☐ **ALHAMBRA HOSPITAL MEDICAL CENTER (050281)**, 100 South Raymond Avenue, Zip 91801–3199, Mailing Address: P.O. Box 510, Zip 91802–2510; tel. 626/570–1606, (Nonreporting) **A**1 9 10 **S** AHMC & Healthcare, Inc., Alhambra, CA
Primary Contact: Iris Lai, Chief Executive Officer
CFO: Linda Marsh, Vice President Financial Services and Chief Financial Officer
CMO: Stephen Chen, M.D., Chief Medicare
CIO: Johnson Legaspi, Director Information Systems
CHR: Elizabeth Sabandit, Director Human Resources
CNO: Eleanor Martinez, Chief Nursing Officer
Web address: www.alhambrahospital.com
**Control:** Partnership, Investor–owned, for–profit **Service:** General Medical and Surgical

Staffed Beds: 144

## ALTURAS—Modoc County

**MODOC MEDICAL CENTER (051330)**, 228 West McDowell Avenue, Zip 96101–3934; tel. 530/233–5131, (Total facility includes 71 beds in nursing home–type unit) **A**9 10 18 **F**7 29 34 35 40 46 57 65 81 93 114 119 127 128 130 133 146 **P**5
Primary Contact: Kevin Kramer, Chief Executive Officer
CMO: Ed Richert, M.D., Chief of Staff
CHR: Diane Hagelthorn, Human Resources Generalist
Web address: www.modocmedicalcenter.org
**Control:** Hospital district or authority, Government, nonfederal **Service:** General Medical and Surgical

Staffed Beds: 87 Admissions: 256 Census: 48 Outpatient Visits: 39863
Births: 0 Total Expense ($000): 14333 Payroll Expense ($000): 5797

## ANAHEIM—Orange County

☐ **AHMC ANAHEIM REGIONAL MEDICAL CENTER (050226)**, 1111 West La Palma Avenue, Zip 92801–2881; tel. 714/774–1450, (Nonreporting) **A**1 9 10 **S** AHMC & Healthcare, Inc., Alhambra, CA
Primary Contact: Patrick A. Petre, Chief Executive Officer
COO: Deborah G. Webber, Chief Operating Officer
CFO: Michael Chung, Chief Financial Officer
CMO: Amitabh Prakash, M.D., Chief Medical Officer
CIO: Jeff DesRoches, Manager Information Systems
CHR: Kathy Doi, Executive Director Human Resources
CNO: Phyllis Snyder, Chief Nursing Officer
Web address: www.anaheimregionalmc.com
**Control:** Other not–for–profit (including NFP Corporation) **Service:** General Medical and Surgical

Staffed Beds: 223

**ANAHEIM MEDICAL CENTER** See Kaiser Permanente Orange County Anaheim Medical Center

⊠ **KAISER PERMANENTE ORANGE COUNTY ANAHEIM MEDICAL CENTER (050609)**, 3440 East La Palma Avenue, Zip 92806–2020; tel. 714/644–2000, (Includes ORANGE COUNTY IRVINE MEDICAL CENTER, 6640 Alton Parkway, Irvine, Zip 92618; tel. 949/932–5000; Mark E. Costa, Executive Director) **A**1 3 5 10 **F**3 13 14 15 17 18 19 20 29 30 31 35 37 40 44 45 46 47 48 49 50 59 61 62 63 64 65 68 70 72 74 75 76 78 79 80 81 82 84 85 87 89 92 93 100 107 108 111 114 115 119 130 135 143 146 148 **S** Kaiser Foundation Hospitals, Oakland, CA
Primary Contact: Mark E. Costa, Executive Director
COO: Margie Harrier, MSN, Medical Center Chief Operations Officer
CFO: Marcus Hoffman, Area Chief Financial Officer
CMO: Nancy Gin, M.D., Area Associate Medical Director
CIO: James Brady, Area Information Officer
CHR: Jocelyn A. Herrera, Director Human Resources
CNO: Martha Dispoto, I, R.N., Chief Nurse Executive, Anaheim Medical Center
Web address: www.kp.org
**Control:** Other not–for–profit (including NFP Corporation) **Service:** General Medical and Surgical

Staffed Beds: 436 Admissions: 24989 Census: 289 Outpatient Visits:
393682 Births: 5875 Personnel: 2476

☐ **WEST ANAHEIM MEDICAL CENTER (050426)**, 3033 West Orange Avenue, Zip 92804–3183; tel. 714/827–3000 **A**1 10 13 **F**3 11 15 17 18 20 22 24 29 40 45 49 70 79 81 85 98 103 105 107 108 111 114 119 128 130 146 **S** Prime Healthcare Services, Ontario, CA
Primary Contact: Virgis Narbutas, Chief Executive Officer
CFO: Kora Guoyavatin, Chief Financial Officer
CMO: Hassan Alkhouli, M.D., Chief Medical Officer
CIO: Vic Mahan, Director Information Technology
CHR: Stephanie Sioson, Director Human Resources
CNO: Virginia Edward, R.N., Administrator and Chief Nursing Officer
Web address: www.westanaheimmedctr.com
**Control:** Partnership, Investor–owned, for–profit **Service:** General Medical and Surgical

Staffed Beds: 219 Admissions: 5926 Census: 92 Outpatient Visits: 67187
Births: 0 Personnel: 669

☐ **WESTERN MEDICAL CENTER ANAHEIM (050744)**, 1025 South Anaheim Boulevard, Zip 92805–5806; tel. 714/533–6220, (Nonreporting) **A**1 9 10 **S** Integrated Healthcare, Santa Ana, CA
Primary Contact: Suzanne Richards, R.N., M.P.H., FACHE, Chief Executive Officer
CMO: Harmohinder Gogia, M.D., Chief Medical Officer
CIO: Nova Stewart, Chief Information Officer
Web address: www.westernmedanaheim.com
**Control:** Corporation, Investor–owned, for–profit **Service:** General Medical and Surgical

Staffed Beds: 188

## ANTIOCH—Contra Costa County

⊠ **KAISER PERMANENTE ANTIOCH MEDICAL CENTER (050760)**, 4501 Sand Creek Road, Zip 94531–8687; tel. 925/813–6500, (Nonreporting) **A**1 10 **S** Kaiser Foundation Hospitals, Oakland, CA
Primary Contact: Colleen McKeown, Senior Vice President and Area Manager
COO: Jeanette Engle-Ramirez, Chief Operating Officer
CFO: Kerry Easthope, Area Finance Officer
CMO: Dale Poppert, Chief Financial Officer
CIO: Lynda K. Roseman, Area Information Officer
CNO: Janet Julie, Chief Nursing Officer
Web address: www.https://health.kaiserpermanente.org/wps/portal/facility/100382
**Control:** Other not–for–profit (including NFP Corporation) **Service:** General Medical and Surgical

Staffed Beds: 150

---

| Hospital, Medicare Provider Number, Address, Telephone, Approval, Facility, and Physician Codes, Health Care System |
|---|
| ★ American Hospital Association (AHA) membership    ○ Healthcare Facilities Accreditation Program    ⇑ Center for Improvement in Healthcare Quality Accreditation |
| ☐ The Joint Commission accreditation    ◇ DNV Healthcare Inc. accreditation    △ Commission on Accreditation of Rehabilitation Facilities (CARF) accreditation |

**CA**

⊠ **SUTTER DELTA MEDICAL CENTER (050523)**, 3901 Lone Tree Way, Zip 94509–6253; tel. 925/779–7200 **A**1 9 10 **F**3 8 11 13 15 18 20 22 26 29 30 31 34 35 40 41 45 47 49 50 51 60 64 65 66 68 70 72 74 75 76 77 78 79 81 82 83 84 85 86 93 96 107 108 110 111 114 115 119 127 130 132 146 147 148 **S** Sutter Health, Sacramento, CA
Primary Contact: Dori Stevens, Chief Executive Officer
CFO: Julie Peterson, Chief Financial Officer
CMO: Anupam Mapara, M.D., Chief of Staff
CIO: Kathy Frederickson, Information Systems Site Lead
CHR: Noemi Whitehead, Administrative Director Human Resources
CNO: James Christopher Reedy, Chief Nursing Officer
Web address: www.sutterdelta.org
**Control:** Other not–for–profit (including NFP Corporation) **Service:** General Medical and Surgical

**Staffed Beds:** 132 **Admissions:** 9133 **Census:** 89 **Outpatient Visits:** 76208 **Births:** 1000 **Total Expense ($000):** 157819 **Payroll Expense ($000):** 58293 **Personnel:** 700

### APPLE VALLEY—San Bernardino County

★ ○ **ST. MARY MEDICAL CENTER (050300)**, 18300 Highway 18, Zip 92307–2206, Mailing Address: P.O. Box 7025, Zip 92307–0725; tel. 760/242–2311 **A**9 10 11 **F**8 11 13 15 18 20 22 24 26 28 29 30 34 35 40 45 46 50 57 59 60 64 65 68 70 71 72 75 76 77 78 79 81 82 83 84 85 86 87 89 93 107 108 111 115 119 126 127 130 132 135 143 146 148 **P**3 5 **S** St. Joseph Health, Irvine, CA
Primary Contact: Alan H. Garrett, Chief Executive Officer
COO: Kelly Linden, Senior Vice President, Chief Operating Officer
CFO: Tracey Fernandez, Chief Financial Officer
CMO: Dennis Haghighat, M.D., Vice President Medical Affairs
CIO: Doug Kleine, IT Director
CHR: Joseph Turco, Director Human Resources
CNO: Marilyn Drone, R.N., Vice President, CNO
Web address: www.stmaryapplevalley.com/
**Control:** Church–operated, Nongovernment, not–for profit **Service:** General Medical and Surgical

**Staffed Beds:** 210 **Admissions:** 15711 **Census:** 176 **Outpatient Visits:** 143697 **Births:** 2396 **Total Expense ($000):** 270234 **Payroll Expense ($000):** 96587 **Personnel:** 1453

### ARCADIA—Los Angeles County

⊠ **METHODIST HOSPITAL OF SOUTHERN CALIFORNIA (050238)**, 300 West Huntington Drive, Zip 91007–3473, Mailing Address: P.O. Box 60016, Zip 91066–6016; tel. 626/898–8000, (Total facility includes 26 beds in nursing home–type unit) **A**1 2 3 9 10 **F**3 12 13 14 15 17 18 20 22 24 26 28 29 30 31 34 35 37 38 40 45 46 48 49 50 51 55 56 57 58 59 60 64 65 68 70 72 73 74 75 76 77 78 79 81 82 84 85 86 87 90 92 94 100 102 107 108 111 114 115 117 119 120 121 123 128 130 132 135 146 147 148
Primary Contact: Dan F. Ausman, President and Chief Executive Officer
COO: Steven A. Sisto, Senior Vice President and Chief Operating Officer
CFO: William E. Grigg, Senior Vice President and Chief Financial Officer
CHR: Gwen Chambers, Executive Director Human Resources
Web address: www.methodisthospital.org
**Control:** Other not–for–profit (including NFP Corporation) **Service:** General Medical and Surgical

**Staffed Beds:** 335 **Admissions:** 17018 **Census:** 220 **Outpatient Visits:** 75365 **Births:** 2023 **Total Expense ($000):** 260539 **Payroll Expense ($000):** 120680 **Personnel:** 1569

### ARCATA—Humboldt County

○ **MAD RIVER COMMUNITY HOSPITAL (050028)**, 3800 Janes Road, Zip 95521–4788, Mailing Address: P.O. Box 1115, Zip 95518–1115; tel. 707/822–3621 **A**9 10 11 **F**2 3 13 15 18 29 30 34 35 36 40 41 45 46 48 50 53 54 56 57 59 62 64 65 66 68 70 75 76 77 78 79 81 82 85 87 89 93 97 107 108 110 111 114 118 119 127 130 131 133 135 144 146 147 148 **P**5
Primary Contact: Douglas A. Shaw, Chief Executive Officer
COO: Steve Engle, Chief Operations Officer
CFO: Michael Young, Chief Financial Officer
CMO: Ronald Berman, M.D., Chief of Staff
CIO: Steve Engle, Chief Operations Officer
CHR: Peggy Shea, Human Resources Lead
CNO: Ken Terpening, Chief Nursing Officer
Web address: www.madriverhospital.com
**Control:** Corporation, Investor–owned, for–profit **Service:** General Medical and Surgical

**Staffed Beds:** 42 **Admissions:** 2058 **Census:** 22 **Outpatient Visits:** 115168 **Births:** 614 **Total Expense ($000):** 52458 **Payroll Expense ($000):** 20982 **Personnel:** 456

### ARROYO GRANDE—San Luis Obispo County

★ **ARROYO GRANDE COMMUNITY HOSPITAL (050016)**, 345 South Halcyon Road, Zip 93420–3896; tel. 805/489–4261, (Total facility includes 14 beds in nursing home–type unit) **A**9 10 **F**8 11 15 29 30 34 35 37 40 50 51 54 57 59 64 68 70 75 77 78 79 81 84 87 90 93 94 96 100 107 108 109 110 111 114 117 118 119 129 130 132 146 148 **S** Dignity Health, San Francisco, CA
Primary Contact: Kenneth Dalebout, Administrator and Chief Executive Officer
CHR: Ami Padilla, Director Human Resources
Web address: www.arroyograndehospital.org
**Control:** Other not–for–profit (including NFP Corporation) **Service:** General Medical and Surgical

**Staffed Beds:** 67 **Admissions:** 2746 **Census:** 39 **Outpatient Visits:** 56410 **Births:** 0 **Total Expense ($000):** 76696 **Payroll Expense ($000):** 27093 **Personnel:** 305

### ATASCADERO—San Luis Obispo County

☐ **ATASCADERO STATE HOSPITAL**, 10333 El Camino Real, Zip 93422–5808, Mailing Address: P.O. Box 7001, Zip 93423–7001; tel. 805/468–2000 **A**1 **F**3 29 30 31 34 38 39 53 57 59 75 82 86 87 98 102 103 130 132 144 146 **P**6
Primary Contact: Linda Persons, Executive Director
COO: David Landrum, Chief Police Services
CFO: Janie Pagnini, Administrator Accounting
CMO: David Fennell, M.D., Acting Medical Director
CIO: James Grover, Manager Data Processing
CHR: Elizabeth Andres, Director Human Resources
CNO: Liz Souza, Coordinator Nursing Services
Web address: www.dmh.ca.gov/statehospitals/atascadero
**Control:** State–Government, nonfederal **Service:** Psychiatric

**Staffed Beds:** 1275 **Admissions:** 1204 **Census:** 1069 **Outpatient Visits:** 0 **Births:** 0 **Total Expense ($000):** 211854 **Payroll Expense ($000):** 136094 **Personnel:** 1871

### AUBURN—Placer County

⊠ **SUTTER AUBURN FAITH HOSPITAL (050498)**, 11815 Education Street, Zip 95602–2410; tel. 530/888–4500 **A**1 2 9 10 **F**3 8 11 12 15 17 18 20 28 29 30 31 34 35 37 39 40 44 45 47 49 50 57 58 59 62 63 64 68 70 74 75 78 79 81 85 86 87 92 93 107 108 110 111 114 119 130 132 135 145 146 147 148 **S** Sutter Health, Sacramento, CA
Primary Contact: Mitchell J. Hanna, Chief Executive Officer
CFO: Gary Hubschman, Administrative Director Finance
CMO: John Mesic, M.D., Chief Medical Officer
CIO: Tom Ream, Regional Chief Information Officer
CHR: Yvette Martinez, Director Human Resources
CNO: Gina Temple, Chief Nurse Executive
Web address: www.sutterhealth.org
**Control:** Other not–for–profit (including NFP Corporation) **Service:** General Medical and Surgical

**Staffed Beds:** 72 **Admissions:** 3354 **Census:** 31 **Outpatient Visits:** 67187 **Births:** 0 **Total Expense ($000):** 113935 **Payroll Expense ($000):** 36220 **Personnel:** 411

### AVALON—Los Angeles County

★ **CATALINA ISLAND MEDICAL CENTER (051307)**, 100 Falls Canyon Road, Zip 90704, Mailing Address: P.O. Box 1563, Zip 90704–1563; tel. 310/510–0700 **A**9 10 18 **F**3 11 18 28 34 36 40 50 57 64 65 66 75 93 96 107 113 119 127 128 130 133 146
Primary Contact: Bryan M. Ballard, Interim Chief Executive Officer
CFO: John Lovrich, Chief Financial Officer
CMO: Monte Mellon, M.D., Chief of Staff
CIO: Jami Fuller, Manager Information Technology
CHR: Krista Steuter, Director Human Resources
CNO: David Hamlin, Chief Patient Care Services
Web address: www.catalinaislandmedicalcenter.org
**Control:** Other not–for–profit (including NFP Corporation) **Service:** General Medical and Surgical

**Staffed Beds:** 12 **Admissions:** 10 **Census:** 6 **Outpatient Visits:** 6861 **Births:** 0 **Total Expense ($000):** 7505 **Payroll Expense ($000):** 3058 **Personnel:** 56

### BAKERSFIELD—Kern County

☐ **BAKERSFIELD HEART HOSPITAL (050724)**, 3001 Sillect Avenue, Zip 93308–6337; tel. 661/316–6000, (Nonreporting) **A**1 10
Primary Contact: Michelle Oxford, Chief Operating Officer, Acting Chief Executive Officer
COO: Michelle Oxford, Chief Operating Officer, Acting Chief Executive Officer
CFO: Vickie Scharr, Chief Financial Officer
CMO: Brijesh Bhambi, M.D., Chief Medical Officer
CIO: Peter Mayer, Director Information Systems
CHR: Linda Hansen, Director Human Resources
Web address: www.bakersfieldhearthospital.com
**Control:** Partnership, Investor–owned, for–profit **Service:** Heart

**Staffed Beds:** 47

*Many Facility Codes have changed. Please refer to the AHA Guide Code Chart.* © 2015 AHA Guide

☒ **BAKERSFIELD MEMORIAL HOSPITAL (050036)**, 420 34th Street, Zip 93301–2237; tel. 661/327–1792 **A**1 3 5 9 10 13 **F**3 11 13 15 17 18 20 22 24 26 28 29 30 31 37 40 45 50 60 68 70 72 74 75 76 77 78 79 81 84 85 86 88 89 93 107 108 109 111 114 119 120 124 126 130 146 147 148 **S** Dignity Health, San Francisco, CA
Primary Contact: Jon Van Boening, President and Chief Executive Officer and Senior Vice President Operations Dignity Health Central Va
COO: Bruce Peters, Vice President and Chief Operating Officer
CFO: Jesica Hanson, Vice President and Chief Financial Officer
CMO: Rodney Mark Root, D.O., Vice President Medical Affairs
CHR: Sheri Comaianni, Vice President Human Resources
Web address: www.bakersfieldmemorial.org
**Control:** Other not–for–profit (including NFP Corporation) **Service:** General Medical and Surgical

**Staffed Beds:** 406 **Admissions:** 14878 **Census:** 171 **Outpatient Visits:** 141213 **Births:** 3173 **Total Expense ($000):** 325960 **Payroll Expense ($000):** 128485 **Personnel:** 1398

☐ **GOOD SAMARITAN HOSPITAL (050257)**, 901 Olive Drive, Zip 93308–4144, Mailing Address: P.O. Box 85002, Zip 93380–5002; tel. 661/399–4461 **A**1 9 10 **F**2 4 5 18 29 35 45 64 70 75 81 85 98 99 100 101 102 103 104 107 119 148 **P**8
Primary Contact: Ganesh Acharya, Chief Executive Officer
COO: Noel Cabezzas, Chief Operating Officer
CFO: Vicki Nguyen, Chief Financial Officer
CMO: Ronnie Claiborne, M.D., Chief Medical Officer
CIO: Anand Manohara, Associate Administrator
CHR: Milissa Newton, Supervisor Human Resources
**Control:** Partnership, Investor–owned, for–profit **Service:** General Medical and Surgical

**Staffed Beds:** 154 **Admissions:** 686 **Census:** 42 **Outpatient Visits:** 14692 **Births:** 0 **Personnel:** 361

☒ **HEALTHSOUTH BAKERSFIELD REHABILITATION HOSPITAL (053031)**, 5001 Commerce Drive, Zip 93309–0689; tel. 661/323–5500, (Nonreporting) **A**1 9 10 **S** HEALTHSOUTH Corporation, Birmingham, AL
Primary Contact: Martha Samora, R.N., FACHE, Chief Executive Officer
CFO: Robert Mosesian, Controller
CMO: Chris Yoon, M.D., Medical Director
CHR: Lori Brackett, Director Human Resources
CNO: Kathleen Szura, R.N., Chief Nursing Officer
Web address: www.healthsouthbakersfield.com
**Control:** Corporation, Investor–owned, for–profit **Service:** Rehabilitation

**Staffed Beds:** 66

☐ **KERN MEDICAL CENTER (050315)**, 1700 Mount Vernon Avenue, Zip 93306–4018; tel. 661/326–2000, (Nonreporting) **A**1 2 3 5 9 10
Primary Contact: Russell V. Judd, Chief Executive Officer
CMO: Eugene Kercher, M.D., Chief Medical Officer
CIO: Bill Fawns, Interim Manager Information Systems
CHR: Steve O'Connor, Manager Human Resources
Web address: www.kernmedicalcenter.com
**Control:** County–Government, nonfederal **Service:** General Medical and Surgical

**Staffed Beds:** 188

☒ **MERCY HOSPITALS OF BAKERSFIELD (050295)**, 2215 Truxtun Avenue, Zip 93301–3698, Mailing Address: P.O. Box 119, Zip 93302–0119; tel. 661/632–5000, (Includes MERCY SOUTHWEST HOSPITAL, 400 Old River Road, Zip 93311; tel. 661/663–6000), (Nonreporting) **A**1 2 3 9 10 **S** Dignity Health, San Francisco, CA
Primary Contact: Bruce Peters, Chief Executive Officer
CFO: Rodney Winegarner, Chief Financial Officer
CIO: Jeff Vague, Regional Manager Information Systems
CHR: Jay King, Vice President Human Resources
Web address: www.mercybakersfield.org
**Control:** Church–operated, Nongovernment, not–for profit **Service:** General Medical and Surgical

**Staffed Beds:** 222

☒ **SAN JOAQUIN COMMUNITY HOSPITAL (050455)**, 2615 Chester Avenue, Zip 93301–2014, Mailing Address: P.O. Box 2615, Zip 93303–2615; tel. 661/395–3000 **A**1 9 10 **F**3 8 11 12 13 15 16 18 20 22 24 26 28 29 30 31 34 35 36 40 45 46 47 48 49 50 51 54 55 56 57 59 64 65 68 70 71 72 74 75 76 77 78 79 81 82 84 85 86 87 91 107 108 110 111 114 115 116 117 118 119 120 121 123 124 126 130 132 135 146 147 148 **S** Adventist Health, Roseville, CA
Primary Contact: Douglas Duffield, President and Chief Executive Officer
CFO: Brent Soper, Chief Financial Officer
CHR: Marlene Kreidler, Executive Director Human Resources
Web address: www.sanjoaquinhospital.org
**Control:** Church–operated, Nongovernment, not–for profit **Service:** General Medical and Surgical

**Staffed Beds:** 254 **Admissions:** 19051 **Census:** 201 **Outpatient Visits:** 175307 **Births:** 3469 **Total Expense ($000):** 344999 **Payroll Expense ($000):** 126251 **Personnel:** 1865

### BALDWIN PARK—Los Angeles County

**BALDWIN PARK MEDICAL CENTER** See Kaiser Permanente Baldwin Park Medical Center

☒ **KAISER PERMANENTE BALDWIN PARK MEDICAL CENTER (050723)**, 1011 Baldwin Park Boulevard, Zip 91706–5806; tel. 626/851–1011 **A**1 3 10 **F**3 8 13 15 18 29 30 31 34 35 40 41 49 56 57 58 59 60 61 62 63 64 65 68 70 72 74 75 76 77 78 79 81 82 84 85 86 87 93 94 107 111 119 130 146 147 148 **S** Kaiser Foundation Hospitals, Oakland, CA
Primary Contact: Margaret H. Pierce, Executive Director
COO: Payman Roshan, Chief Operating Officer
CFO: Rebecca Wheeler, Director Finance
CMO: John Bigley, M.D., Medical Director
CIO: Linda C. Salazar, Information Technology Leader
CNO: Michelle Nowicki, R.N., Chief Nurse Executive
Web address: www.kp.org
**Control:** Other not–for–profit (including NFP Corporation) **Service:** General Medical and Surgical

**Staffed Beds:** 254 **Admissions:** 12588 **Census:** 118 **Outpatient Visits:** 344666 **Births:** 2836

☒ **KINDRED HOSPITAL–BALDWIN PARK (052045)**, 14148 Francisquito Avenue, Zip 91706–6120; tel. 626/388–2700 **A**1 9 10 **F**1 29 45 60 84 107 111 119 130 148 **S** Kindred Healthcare, Louisville, KY
Primary Contact: Fiona Basa–Reyes, Chief Executive Officer
COO: Dina Garrow, Chief Nursing Officer and Chief Operating Officer
CFO: Christine Saltonstall, Chief Financial Officer
CMO: Anil Gupta, M.D., Chief of Staff
CHR: Antoinette Bibal, Director Human Resources
CNO: Dina Garrow, Chief Nursing Officer and Chief Operating Officer
Web address: www.khbaldwinpark.com
**Control:** Corporation, Investor–owned, for–profit **Service:** Long–Term Acute Care hospital

**Staffed Beds:** 91 **Admissions:** 941 **Census:** 69 **Outpatient Visits:** 0 **Births:** 0 **Total Expense ($000):** 32411 **Payroll Expense ($000):** 17680

**VISTA SPECIALTY HOSPITAL OF SAN GABRIEL VALLEY** See Kindred Hospital–Baldwin Park

### BANNING—Riverside County

☒ **SAN GORGONIO MEMORIAL HOSPITAL (050054)**, 600 North Highland Springs Avenue, Zip 92220–3046; tel. 951/845–1121 **A**1 9 10 **F**3 8 11 13 15 18 28 29 30 34 35 40 45 49 56 57 68 70 76 79 81 82 85 87 104 107 108 110 115 119 130 146 147 148
Primary Contact: Mark S. Turner, Chief Executive Officer
CFO: David Recupero, Chief Financial Officer
CMO: Richard Sheldon, M.D., Vice President Medical Affairs
CIO: Linda Palmer, Coordinator Medical Records
CHR: Annah Karam, Director Human Resources
CNO: Pat Brown, R.N., Chief Nursing Officer
Web address: www.sgmh.org
**Control:** Hospital district or authority, Government, nonfederal **Service:** General Medical and Surgical

**Staffed Beds:** 71 **Admissions:** 3706 **Census:** 40 **Outpatient Visits:** 43830 **Births:** 397 **Total Expense ($000):** 68395 **Payroll Expense ($000):** 27522 **Personnel:** 456

**CA**

---

**Hospital, Medicare Provider Number, Address, Telephone, Approval, Facility, and Physician Codes, Health Care System**

★ American Hospital Association (AHA) membership
☐ The Joint Commission accreditation
◯ Healthcare Facilities Accreditation Program
◇ DNV Healthcare Inc. accreditation
⇑ Center for Improvement in Healthcare Quality Accreditation
△ Commission on Accreditation of Rehabilitation Facilities (CARF) accreditation

**CA**

### BARSTOW—San Bernardino County

✠ **BARSTOW COMMUNITY HOSPITAL (050298)**, 820 East Mountain View Street, Zip 92311–3004; tel. 760/256–1761, (Nonreporting) **A**1 9 10 20 **S** Community Health Systems, Inc., Franklin, TN
Primary Contact: Steven Foster, Chief Executive Officer
CFO: Carrie Howell, Chief Financial Officer
CIO: Scott Bullock, Director Information Systems
CNO: Donna M. Smith, Chief Nursing Officer
Web address: www.barstowhospital.com
**Control:** Corporation, Investor–owned, for–profit **Service:** General Medical and Surgical

**Staffed Beds:** 30

### BERKELEY—Alameda County

✠ △ **ALTA BATES SUMMIT MEDICAL CENTER (050305)**, 2450 Ashby Avenue, Zip 94705–2067; tel. 510/204–4444, (Includes ALTA BATES MEDICAL CENTER–HERRICK CAMPUS, 2001 Dwight Way, Zip 94704; tel. 510/204–4444) **A**1 3 5 7 9 10 **F**3 5 8 11 13 15 17 18 20 22 26 28 29 30 31 34 35 36 37 40 45 46 47 49 51 55 56 57 58 59 60 61 64 68 70 72 74 75 77 78 79 81 82 84 85 87 90 93 98 99 100 103 104 105 107 108 110 111 114 116 117 118 119 120 121 123 124 130 132 135 136 146 147 148 **S** Sutter Health, Sacramento, CA
Primary Contact: Charles Prosper, Chief Executive Officer
CFO: Robert Petrina, Chief Financial Officer
CMO: John Gentile, M.D., Vice President Medical Affairs
Web address: www.altabates.com
**Control:** Other not–for–profit (including NFP Corporation) **Service:** General Medical and Surgical

**Staffed Beds:** 441 **Admissions:** 17750 **Census:** 280 **Outpatient Visits:** 173118 **Births:** 6513 **Total Expense ($000):** 598817 **Payroll Expense ($000):** 174998 **Personnel:** 1550

### BIG BEAR LAKE—San Bernardino County

★ **BEAR VALLEY COMMUNITY HOSPITAL (051335)**, 41870 Garstin Drive, Zip 92315, Mailing Address: P.O. Box 1649, Zip 92315–1649; tel. 909/866–6501, (Total facility includes 21 beds in nursing home–type unit) **A**9 10 18 20 **F**3 15 29 33 34 35 39 40 50 54 56 57 59 64 81 82 93 97 107 119 128 129 133 146
Primary Contact: David Faulkner, Interim Chief Executive Officer
COO: Wade Sturgeon, Chief Operating Officer and Chief Financial Officer
CFO: Wade Sturgeon, Chief Operating Officer and Chief Financial Officer
CMO: Michael Norman, M.D., Chief Medical Staff
CHR: Kathy Norris, Director Human Resources
CNO: Mary Norman, R.N., Chief Nursing Officer
Web address: www.bvchd.org
**Control:** Hospital district or authority, Government, nonfederal **Service:** General Medical and Surgical

**Staffed Beds:** 30 **Admissions:** 169 **Census:** 17 **Outpatient Visits:** 17193 **Births:** 0 **Total Expense ($000):** 20286 **Payroll Expense ($000):** 9040

### BISHOP—Inyo County

✠ **NORTHERN INYO HOSPITAL (051324)**, 150 Pioneer Lane, Zip 93514–2599; tel. 760/873–5811, (Nonreporting) **A**1 9 10 18
Primary Contact: Victoria Alexander–Lane, Chief Executive Officer
COO: Leon Freis, Chief Operating Officer
CMO: Thomas Boo, M.D., Chief of Staff
CIO: Adam Taylor, Manager Information Technology
CHR: Georgan L. Stottlemyre, Director Human Resources
CNO: Kathy Decker, Interim Chief Nursing Officer
Web address: www.nih.org
**Control:** Hospital district or authority, Government, nonfederal **Service:** General Medical and Surgical

**Staffed Beds:** 25

### BLYTHE—Riverside County

◇ **PALO VERDE HOSPITAL (050423)**, 250 North First Street, Zip 92225–1702; tel. 760/922–4115, (Nonreporting) **A**9 10 20 21
Primary Contact: Sandra J. Anaya, R.N., Chief Executive Officer
CFO: Christa Ronde, Assistant Chief Financial Officer
CMO: Hossain Sahlolbei, M.D., Chief of Staff
CIO: Jerome Learson, Manager Information Technology and Chief Security Officer
CHR: Myrna Davis, Manager Human Resources
CNO: Nena Foreman, Chief Nursing Officer
Web address: www.paloverdehospital.org
**Control:** Hospital district or authority, Government, nonfederal **Service:** General Medical and Surgical

**Staffed Beds:** 35

### BRAWLEY—Imperial County

★ ◇ **PIONEERS MEMORIAL HEALTHCARE DISTRICT (050342)**, 207 West Legion Road, Zip 92227–7780; tel. 760/351–3333 **A**3 9 10 21 **F**3 11 13 15 18 26 29 30 31 34 35 40 43 45 46 49 51 56 57 59 64 65 70 73 74 75 78 79 81 82 85 86 91 93 97 107 108 110 111 115 119 127 130 144 146 147
Primary Contact: Lawrence E. Lewis, Chief Executive Officer
COO: Stephen J. Campbell, Chief Operating Officer
CFO: Roger Armstrong, Interim Chief Financial Officer
CMO: Kestutis V. Kuraitis, M.D., Chief of Staff
CIO: Kathleen S. McKernan, Director Information Systems
CHR: Julie Cunningham, Associate Administrator and Chief Human Resources Officer
CNO: Robyn Atadero, R.N., Chief Nursing Officer
Web address: www.pmhd.org
**Control:** Hospital district or authority, Government, nonfederal **Service:** General Medical and Surgical

**Staffed Beds:** 107 **Admissions:** 5283 **Census:** 43 **Outpatient Visits:** 104145 **Births:** 1845 **Total Expense ($000):** 93241 **Payroll Expense ($000):** 38943 **Personnel:** 677

### BREA—Orange County

✠ **KINDRED HOSPITAL–BREA (052039)**, 875 North Brea Boulevard, Zip 92821–2699; tel. 714/529–6842, (Nonreporting) **A**1 9 10 **S** Kindred Healthcare, Louisville, KY
Primary Contact: Diane Zeoli, Chief Executive Officer
COO: Denise Jenkins, Chief Clinical Officer
CFO: John Browne, Assistant Administrator Finance
CMO: Jyotika Wali, M.D., Chief of Staff
Web address: www.kindredhospitalbrea.com/
**Control:** Corporation, Investor–owned, for–profit **Service:** Long–Term Acute Care hospital

**Staffed Beds:** 48

### BURBANK—Los Angeles County

✠ △ **PROVIDENCE SAINT JOSEPH MEDICAL CENTER (050235)**, 501 South Buena Vista Street, Zip 91505–4866; tel. 818/843–5111 **A**1 2 3 7 9 10 **F**3 7 11 12 13 14 15 17 18 20 22 24 26 29 30 31 34 35 36 38 39 40 41 45 46 47 48 49 50 51 53 55 56 57 58 59 60 62 64 65 70 72 74 75 76 77 78 79 81 82 83 84 85 86 87 90 92 93 94 97 100 101 107 108 110 111 114 115 116 117 119 120 121 122 123 124 126 128 130 131 132 145 146 147 148 **S** Providence Health & Services, Renton, WA
Primary Contact: Julie Sprengel, Chief Executive Officer
COO: David Emter, Chief Operating Officer
CFO: Glenn Bales, Chief Financial Officer
CMO: Nick Testa, M.D., Chief Medical Officer
CIO: Anne Marie Brody, Director Information Systems Customer Service
CHR: LaDonna Najieb, Service Area Director Human Resources
CNO: Valarie Fleming, R.N., Chief Nursing Officer
Web address: www.providence.org
**Control:** Church–operated, Nongovernment, not–for profit **Service:** General Medical and Surgical

**Staffed Beds:** 383 **Admissions:** 16544 **Census:** 203 **Outpatient Visits:** 240605 **Births:** 2518 **Total Expense ($000):** 287275 **Payroll Expense ($000):** 142180 **Personnel:** 2164

### BURLINGAME—San Mateo County

✠ **MILLS–PENINSULA HEALTH SERVICES (050007)**, 1501 Trousdale Drive, Zip 94010–3282; tel. 650/696–5400, (Includes MILLS HEALTH CENTER, 100 South San Mateo Drive, San Mateo, Zip 94401; tel. 650/696–4400; Janet Wagner, R.N., Chief Executive Officer; MILLS–PENINSULA MEDICAL CENTER, 1501 Trousdale Drive, Zip 94010–3205; tel. 650/696–5400; Janet Wagner, R.N., Chief Executive Officer), (Total facility includes 62 beds in nursing home–type unit) **A**1 2 9 10 **F**2 3 4 5 6 8 9 11 12 13 15 17 18 20 22 24 26 28 29 30 31 34 35 36 37 38 40 45 46 47 48 49 51 53 54 55 56 57 58 59 60 64 65 66 68 72 74 75 76 77 78 79 81 84 85 86 87 91 93 94 97 98 99 100 102 103 104 105 107 108 110 111 114 115 116 117 118 119 120 121 123 124 126 128 130 132 134 135 146 147 148 **S** Sutter Health, Sacramento, CA
Primary Contact: Janet Wagner, R.N., Chief Executive Officer
COO: Dolores S. Gomez, R.N., Chief Operating Officer
CFO: Catherine Messman, Chief Financial Officer
CMO: Ranjit Hundal, M.D., Chief Medical Executive
CIO: Michael Reandeau, Chief Information Officer
CHR: Claudia Christensen, Director, Human Resources
CNO: Vicki White, R.N., Chief Nurse Executive
Web address: www.mills–peninsula.org
**Control:** Other not–for–profit (including NFP Corporation) **Service:** General Medical and Surgical

**Staffed Beds:** 320 **Admissions:** 13646 **Census:** 160 **Outpatient Visits:** 331051 **Births:** 2060 **Total Expense ($000):** 467131 **Payroll Expense ($000):** 144259 **Personnel:** 1494

*Many Facility Codes have changed. Please refer to the AHA Guide Code Chart.*     © 2015 AHA Guide

## CAMARILLO—Ventura County

★ **ST. JOHN'S PLEASANT VALLEY HOSPITAL (050616)**, 2309 Antonio Avenue, Zip 93010–1414; tel. 805/389–5800, (Nonreporting) **A**9 10 **S** Dignity Health, San Francisco, CA
Primary Contact: Darren W. Lee, President and Chief Executive Officer
COO: Kim A. Wilson, R.N., Chief Operating Officer
CMO: Eugene Fussell, M.D., Chief Medical Officer
CIO: Jeff Perry, Director Information Technology
CHR: Ed Gonzales, Vice President Human Resources
CNO: Raye Burkhardt, Chief Nursing Officer
Web address: www.stjohnshealth.org
**Control:** Other not–for–profit (including NFP Corporation) **Service:** General Medical and Surgical

**Staffed Beds:** 127

## CAMP PENDLETON—San Diego County

✉ **NAVAL HOSPITAL CAMP PENDLETON**, Santa Margarita Road, Building H100, Zip 92055–5191, Mailing Address: P.O. Box 555191, Zip 92055–5191; tel. 760/725–1304, (Nonreporting) **A**1 3 5 **S** Bureau of Medicine and Surgery, Department of the Navy, Washington, DC
Primary Contact: Captain Lisa Mulligan, Commanding Officer
CFO: Commander Gordon Blighton, Director Resource Management
CIO: Gabe Vallido, Chief Information Officer
CHR: Lieutenant Jet Ramos, Head Staff Administration
Web address: www.cpen.med.navy.mil/
**Control:** Navy, Government, federal **Service:** General Medical and Surgical

**Staffed Beds:** 72

## CANOGA PARK—Los Angeles County, See Los Angeles

## CARMICHAEL—Sacramento County

✉ **MERCY SAN JUAN MEDICAL CENTER (050516)**, 6501 Coyle Avenue, Zip 95608–0306, Mailing Address: P.O. Box 479, Zip 95609–0479; tel. 916/537–5000 **A**1 2 3 5 9 10 **F**3 8 11 12 13 15 17 18 20 22 24 26 28 29 30 31 34 35 37 40 43 45 47 48 49 50 51 57 58 62 63 64 70 72 74 75 76 77 78 79 81 82 83 84 85 89 92 93 100 107 108 111 114 115 118 119 126 129 130 132 135 146 148 **S** Dignity Health, San Francisco, CA
Primary Contact: Brian K. Ivie, President
COO: Paul R. Luehrs, Chief Operating Officer
CFO: Robert Pascuzzi, Chief Financial Officer
CMO: Mark Owens, M.D., Vice President Medical Affairs
CHR: Donna Utley, Vice President Human Resources
Web address: www.mercysanjuan.org
**Control:** Church–operated, Nongovernment, not–for profit **Service:** General Medical and Surgical

**Staffed Beds:** 370 **Admissions:** 23027 **Census:** 278 **Outpatient Visits:** 124195 **Births:** 2191 **Personnel:** 2241

## CASTRO VALLEY—Alameda County

✉ **EDEN MEDICAL CENTER (050488)**, 20103 Lake Chabot Road, Zip 94546–5305; tel. 510/537–1234 **A**1 2 3 9 10 **F**3 11 13 15 18 29 30 31 34 35 38 40 43 46 47 49 50 51 53 54 56 57 58 59 60 65 68 70 74 75 76 77 78 79 81 84 85 87 93 100 101 102 107 108 110 111 115 117 118 119 120 121 124 130 132 135 144 146 147 148 **S** Sutter Health, Sacramento, CA
Primary Contact: Theresa Glubka, R.N., Chief Executive Officer
Web address: www.edenmedcenter.org
**Control:** Other not–for–profit (including NFP Corporation) **Service:** General Medical and Surgical

**Staffed Beds:** 130 **Admissions:** 8739 **Census:** 101 **Outpatient Visits:** 83370 **Births:** 1393 **Total Expense ($000):** 283250 **Payroll Expense ($000):** 92078 **Personnel:** 896

## CEDARVILLE—Modoc County

**SURPRISE VALLEY HEALTH CARE DISTRICT (051308)**, 741 North Main Street, Zip 96104, Mailing Address: P.O. Box 246, Zip 96104–0246; tel. 530/279–6111, (Nonreporting) **A**9 10 18
Primary Contact: Richard Cornwell, Chief Executive Officer
CFO: Renae Sweet, Chief Financial Officer
CMO: Chuck Colas, M.D., Medical Director
CHR: William Bostic, Administrative Assistant Human Resources
Web address: www.svhospital.org/
**Control:** Hospital district or authority, Government, nonfederal **Service:** General Medical and Surgical

**Staffed Beds:** 4

## CERRITOS—Los Angeles County

☐ **COLLEGE HOSPITAL CERRITOS (054055)**, 10802 College Place, Zip 90703–1579; tel. 562/924–9581, (Nonreporting) **A**1 9 10 **S** College Health Enterprises, Santa Fe Springs, CA
Primary Contact: Stephen Witt, President and Chief Executive Officer
CFO: Roderick Bell, Chief Financial Officer
CHR: Holly Risha, Administrative Director Human Resources
Web address: www.collegehospitals.com
**Control:** Corporation, Investor–owned, for–profit **Service:** Psychiatric

**Staffed Beds:** 157

## CHESTER—Plumas County

★ **SENECA HEALTHCARE DISTRICT (051327)**, 130 Brentwood Drive, Zip 96020–0737, Mailing Address: P.O. Box 737, Zip 96020–0737; tel. 530/258–2151, (Nonreporting) **A**9 10 18
Primary Contact: Linda S. Wagner, MSN, FACHE, Chief Executive Officer
CFO: Carlene Slusher, Director Finance
CMO: Dana Ware, M.D., Chief of Staff
CIO: Elizabeth Steffen, Director Information Technology
CHR: Marie Stuersel, Director Human Resources
CNO: Teresa L. Whitfield, MS, Chief Nursing Officer
Web address: www.senecahospital.org
**Control:** Hospital district or authority, Government, nonfederal **Service:** General Medical and Surgical

**Staffed Beds:** 26

## CHICO—Butte County

✉ **ENLOE MEDICAL CENTER (050039)**, 1531 Esplanade, Zip 95926–3386; tel. 530/332–7300, (Includes ENLOE MEDICAL CENTER–COHASSET, 560 Cohasset Road, Zip 95926; tel. 530/332–7300), (Nonreporting) **A**1 9 10
Primary Contact: Michael C. Wiltermood, President and Chief Executive Officer
CMO: Forrest Olson, M.D., Chief Medical Officer
CHR: Carol Linscheid, Vice President Human Resources
Web address: www.enloe.org
**Control:** Other not–for–profit (including NFP Corporation) **Service:** General Medical and Surgical

**Staffed Beds:** 263

## CHINO—San Bernardino County

☐ **CANYON RIDGE HOSPITAL (054111)**, 5353 G Street, Zip 91710–5250; tel. 909/590–3700 **A**1 3 9 10 **F**5 29 98 99 101 102 104 105 **P**5 **S** Universal Health Services, Inc., King of Prussia, PA
Primary Contact: Jeff McDonald, Chief Executive Officer
CFO: Burt Harris, Chief Financial Officer
CMO: Mir Ali–Khan, M.D., Medical Director
CIO: Maria Patterson, Manager Health Information Management
CHR: Ericca Lopez, Director Human Resources
Web address: www.canyonridgehospital.com
**Control:** Corporation, Investor–owned, for–profit **Service:** Psychiatric

**Staffed Beds:** 106 **Admissions:** 5857 **Census:** 85 **Outpatient Visits:** 11315 **Births:** 0

★ ○ **CHINO VALLEY MEDICAL CENTER (050586)**, 5451 Walnut Avenue, Zip 91710–2672; tel. 909/464–8600, (Nonreporting) **A**10 11 12 13 **S** Prime Healthcare Services, Ontario, CA
Primary Contact: James M. Lally, D.O., President and Chief Medical Officer
CFO: Gregory Brentano, Chief Financial Officer
CIO: Vic Mahan, Chief Information Officer
Web address: www.cvmc.com
**Control:** Corporation, Investor–owned, for–profit **Service:** General Medical and Surgical

**Staffed Beds:** 112

## CHULA VISTA—San Diego County

**SCRIPPS MERCY HOSPITAL CHULA VISTA** See Scripps Mercy Hospital, San Diego

---

**Hospital, Medicare Provider Number, Address, Telephone, Approval, Facility, and Physician Codes, Health Care System**

★ American Hospital Association (AHA) membership   ○ Healthcare Facilities Accreditation Program   ⇑ Center for Improvement in Healthcare Quality Accreditation
☐ The Joint Commission accreditation   ◇ DNV Healthcare Inc. accreditation   △ Commission on Accreditation of Rehabilitation Facilities (CARF) accreditation

✠ **SHARP CHULA VISTA MEDICAL CENTER (050222)**, 751 Medical Center Court, Zip 91911–6699, Mailing Address: P.O. Box 1297, Zip 91912–1297; tel. 619/502–5800, (Total facility includes 100 beds in nursing home–type unit) **A**1 2 9 10 **F**8 11 12 13 15 17 18 20 22 24 26 28 29 30 31 34 35 40 46 47 49 51 53 54 57 59 60 63 64 65 70 72 75 76 77 78 79 81 82 85 86 87 93 107 108 110 111 114 115 118 119 120 121 123 124 126 128 130 132 143 146 147 148 **P**5 **S** Sharp HealthCare, San Diego, CA
Primary Contact: Pablo Velez, Chief Executive Officer
CMO: Lynn Welling, M.D., Chief Medical Officer
CHR: Zoe Gardner, Manager Human Resources
Web address: www.sharp.com
**Control:** Other not–for–profit (including NFP Corporation) **Service:** General Medical and Surgical

**Staffed Beds:** 343 **Admissions:** 14894 **Census:** 268 **Outpatient Visits:** 128166 **Births:** 2680 **Total Expense ($000):** 303877 **Payroll Expense ($000):** 130624 **Personnel:** 1547

### CLEARLAKE—Lake County

✠ **ST. HELENA HOSPITAL CLEAR LAKE (051317)**, 15630 18th Avenue, Zip 95422–9336, Mailing Address: P.O. Box 6710, Zip 95422; tel. 707/994–6486 **A**1 9 10 18 **F**18 34 40 45 50 57 62 70 76 81 87 93 97 107 108 110 111 113 116 118 127 130 133 134 143 144 **P**3 **S** Adventist Health, Roseville, CA
Primary Contact: David Santos, President and Chief Executive Officer
COO: David Santos, President Chief Executive Officer
CFO: Buck McDonald, Chief Financial Officer
CMO: Marc Shapiro, M.D., Chief Medical Officer
CIO: Joshua Cowan, Chief Information Officer
CHR: Audrey Barrall, Director Human Resources
CNO: Colleen Assavapisitkul, Chief Nursing Officer
Web address: www.adventisthealth.org
**Control:** Church–operated, Nongovernment, not–for profit **Service:** General Medical and Surgical

**Staffed Beds:** 25 **Admissions:** 1391 **Census:** 14 **Outpatient Visits:** 150683 **Births:** 166 **Total Expense ($000):** 68695 **Payroll Expense ($000):** 24400 **Personnel:** 383

### CLOVIS—Fresno County

**CLOVIS COMMUNITY MEDICAL CENTER (050492)**, 2755 Herndon Avenue, Zip 93611–6801; tel. 559/324–4000, (Nonreporting) **A**9 10 **S** Community Medical Centers, Fresno, CA
Primary Contact: Craig Castro, Chief Executive Officer
CFO: Tracy Kiritani, Vice President and Chief Financial Officer
CIO: George Vasquez, Chief Technology Officer
CHR: Ginny Burdick, Senior Vice President and Chief Human Resources Officer
Web address: www.communitymedical.org
**Control:** Other not–for–profit (including NFP Corporation) **Service:** General Medical and Surgical

**Staffed Beds:** 109

### COALINGA—Fresno County

**COALINGA REGIONAL MEDICAL CENTER (050397)**, 1191 Phelps Avenue, Zip 93210–9636; tel. 559/935–6400, (Total facility includes 99 beds in nursing home–type unit) **A**9 10 20 **F**15 32 35 40 41 50 57 59 65 66 68 89 90 93 102 107 110 115 119 127 128 130 143 148
Primary Contact: Sharon A. Spurgeon, Chief Executive Officer
CFO: Sandra Earls, Chief Financial Officer
CMO: Lymar Bik, M.D., Medical Director
CIO: Chris Burrage, Manager Information Technology
CHR: Lucia Lopez, Manager Human Resources
Web address: www.coalingamedicalcenter.com
**Control:** Hospital district or authority, Government, nonfederal **Service:** General Medical and Surgical

**Staffed Beds:** 123 **Admissions:** 297 **Census:** 77 **Outpatient Visits:** 26103 **Births:** 0 **Total Expense ($000):** 21174 **Payroll Expense ($000):** 9477 **Personnel:** 191

### COLTON—San Bernardino County

★ ○ **ARROWHEAD REGIONAL MEDICAL CENTER (050245)**, 400 North Pepper Avenue, Zip 92324–1819; tel. 909/580–1000 **A**2 3 5 9 10 11 12 13 **F**3 8 13 15 16 18 20 22 28 29 30 31 32 34 35 36 39 40 43 45 47 49 50 51 52 54 55 56 57 60 64 66 68 70 71 72 74 75 76 77 78 79 81 82 84 85 86 87 89 91 92 93 97 98 100 101 102 107 108 110 111 114 115 116 118 119 120 121 130 132 135 146 147 148 **P**5
Primary Contact: William L. Gilbert, Hospital Director
CFO: Frank Arambula, Chief Financial Officer
CMO: Richard Pitts, D.O., Medical Director
CIO: Felix Ekpo, Manager, Information Systems
CHR: William Berkley, Director Human Resources
CNO: Michelle Sayre, R.N., Chief Nursing Officer
Web address: www.arrowheadmedcenter.org
**Control:** County–Government, nonfederal **Service:** General Medical and Surgical

**Staffed Beds:** 436 **Admissions:** 22381 **Census:** 321 **Outpatient Visits:** 313443 **Births:** 2529 **Total Expense ($000):** 561968 **Payroll Expense ($000):** 179750 **Personnel:** 2903

### COLUSA—Colusa County

⇑ **COLUSA REGIONAL MEDICAL CENTER (050434)**, 199 East Webster Street, Zip 95932–2954; tel. 530/458–5821, (Total facility includes 6 beds in nursing home–type unit) **A**9 10 20 22 **F**40 43 53 54 57 59 62 64 65 75 77 81 84 107 119 129 130 133 144 146
Primary Contact: Walter G. Beck, Chief Executive Officer
CFO: Gary Pea, Chief Financial Officer
CMO: Gregory Burt, M.D., Chief Medical Officer
CIO: Rachel Betke–Mena, Director Health Information Management
CHR: Dierdre Athenais, Director Human Resources
CNO: Katherine Hughes, R.N., Chief Nursing Officer
Web address: www.colusamedicalcenter.org
**Control:** Other not–for–profit (including NFP Corporation) **Service:** General Medical and Surgical

**Staffed Beds:** 30 **Admissions:** 925 **Census:** 10 **Outpatient Visits:** 46129 **Total Expense ($000):** 21262 **Payroll Expense ($000):** 9651

### CONCORD—Contra Costa County

✠ **JOHN MUIR BEHAVIORAL HEALTH CENTER (054131)**, 2740 Grant Street, Zip 94520–2265; tel. 925/674–4100, (Nonreporting) **A**1 9 10 **S** John Muir Health, Walnut Creek, CA
Primary Contact: Cindy Bolter, Chief Nursing and Operations Officer
COO: O. B. Towery, M.D., Chief of Staff
CFO: Michael Moody, Senior Vice President and Chief Financial Officer
CMO: O. B. Towery, M.D., Chief of Staff
CIO: Jim Wesley, Senior Vice President and Chief Information Officer
CHR: Lisa Foust, Senior Vice President Human Resources
CNO: Cindy Bolter, Chief Nursing and Operations Officer
Web address: www.johnmuirhealth.com
**Control:** Other not–for–profit (including NFP Corporation) **Service:** Psychiatric

**Staffed Beds:** 70

✠ **JOHN MUIR MEDICAL CENTER, CONCORD (050496)**, 2540 East Street, Zip 94520–1906; tel. 925/682–8200 **A**1 2 9 10 **F**3 12 15 17 18 20 22 24 26 28 29 30 31 34 37 39 40 44 45 46 47 48 49 50 55 56 57 58 59 61 64 68 70 74 75 77 78 79 80 81 82 83 84 85 86 87 93 100 102 108 110 118 119 120 121 123 126 130 132 135 141 145 146 148 **P**3 5 **S** John Muir Health, Walnut Creek, CA
Primary Contact: Michael S. Thomas, President and Chief Administrative Officer
COO: Michael S. Thomas, President and Chief Administrative Officer
CFO: Chris Pass, Interim Chief Financial Officer
CMO: John Merson, M.D., Chief of Staff
CIO: Jon Russell, Senior Vice President and Chief Information Officer
CHR: Lisa Foust, Senior Vice President Human Resources
CNO: Donna Brackley, R.N., Senior Vice President Patient Care Services
Web address: www.johnmuirhealth.com
**Control:** Other not–for–profit (including NFP Corporation) **Service:** General Medical and Surgical

**Staffed Beds:** 183 **Admissions:** 9828 **Census:** 119 **Outpatient Visits:** 168191 **Births:** 0 **Total Expense ($000):** 380985 **Payroll Expense ($000):** 143127 **Personnel:** 1018

### CORONA—Riverside County

☐ **CORONA REGIONAL MEDICAL CENTER (050329)**, 800 South Main Street, Zip 92882–3400; tel. 951/737–4343, (Includes CORONA REGIONAL MEDICAL CENTER–REHABILITATION, 730 Magnolia Avenue, Zip 92879; tel. 951/736–7200) **A**1 9 10 **F**3 13 15 20 22 26 29 30 34 35 40 42 45 46 59 62 63 70 74 76 79 81 84 85 87 89 97 98 101 102 104 105 107 110 111 119 128 130 135 146 148 **S** Universal Health Services, Inc., King of Prussia, PA
Primary Contact: Mark H. Uffer, Chief Executive Officer
COO: Parrish Scarboro, Chief Operating Officer
CFO: Frederick J. Drewette, Chief Financial Officer
CMO: Nalin Nanayakkara, M.D., Chief of Staff
CIO: Irv Hoff, Director Information Systems
CHR: Berninia Bradley, Director, Human Resources
Web address: www.coronaregional.com
**Control:** Corporation, Investor–owned, for–profit **Service:** General Medical and Surgical

**Staffed Beds:** 238 **Admissions:** 8477 **Census:** 136 **Outpatient Visits:** 68004 **Births:** 1043 **Total Expense ($000):** 137411 **Payroll Expense ($000):** 61257

*Many Facility Codes have changed. Please refer to the AHA Guide Code Chart.* © 2015 AHA Guide

**CORONADO—San Diego County**

☒ **SHARP CORONADO HOSPITAL AND HEALTHCARE CENTER (050234)**, 250 Prospect Place, Zip 92118–1999; tel. 619/522–3600, (Total facility includes 122 beds in nursing home–type unit) **A**1 9 10 **F**3 11 15 29 30 34 35 36 37 40 45 53 57 59 60 64 65 68 69 70 74 75 77 79 81 82 85 86 87 93 107 111 114 119 126 128 130 135 146 148 **S** Sharp HealthCare, San Diego, CA
Primary Contact: Susan Stone, R.N., Ph.D., Senior Vice President and Chief Executive Officer
CFO: Victoria Day, Chief Financial Officer and Vice President of Ancillary Services
CNO: Nancy Lee, Chief Nursing Officer
Web address: www.sharp.com
**Control:** Other not–for–profit (including NFP Corporation) **Service:** General Medical and Surgical

**Staffed Beds:** 181 **Admissions:** 2329 **Census:** 116 **Outpatient Visits:** 63292 **Births:** 0 **Total Expense ($000):** 78110 **Payroll Expense ($000):** 34898 **Personnel:** 426

**COSTA MESA—Orange County**

☐ **COLLEGE HOSPITAL COSTA MESA (050543)**, 301 Victoria Street, Zip 92627–7131; tel. 949/642–2734, (Nonreporting) **A**1 9 10 **S** College Health Enterprises, Santa Fe Springs, CA
Primary Contact: Susan L. Taylor, Chief Executive Officer
CFO: Dale Bracy, Chief Financial Officer
CMO: Michael Schwartz, M.D., Chief of Staff
CIO: Eladio Aldana, Manager Information Systems
CHR: Sharon DuBruyne, Director Human Resources
Web address: www.collegehospitals.com/cosHome
**Control:** Corporation, Investor–owned, for–profit **Service:** Psychiatric

**Staffed Beds:** 122

**COVINA—Los Angeles County**

☐ **AURORA CHARTER OAK HOSPITAL (054069)**, (BEHAVIORAL HEALTH), 1161 East Covina Boulevard, Zip 91724–1599; tel. 626/966–1632 **A**1 9 10 **F**4 5 29 35 87 98 101 102 104 105 130 135 **S** Signature Healthcare Services, Corona, CA
Primary Contact: Todd A. Smith, Chief Executive Officer
COO: Sheila Cordova, Director Clinical Services and Chief Operating Officer
CMO: Adib Bitar, M.D., Medical Director
CHR: Christine de la Paz, Director Human Resources
CNO: Jackie Curtin, Director of Clinical Services
Web address: www.charteroakhospital.com
**Control:** Corporation, Investor–owned, for–profit **Service:** Other specialty

**Staffed Beds:** 146 **Admissions:** 6887 **Census:** 125 **Outpatient Visits:** 16079 **Births:** 0

★ **CITRUS VALLEY MEDICAL CENTER–INTER COMMUNITY CAMPUS (050382)**, 210 West San Bernardino Road, Zip 91723–1515, Mailing Address: P.O. Box 6108, Zip 91722–5108; tel. 626/331–7331, (Includes CITRUS VALLEY MEDICAL CENTER–INTER–COMMUNITY CAMPUS, 210 West San Bernardino Road, Mailing Address: P.O. Box 6108, Zip 91722–5108; tel. 626/331–7331; CITRUS VALLEY MEDICAL CENTER–QUEEN OF THE VALLEY CAMPUS, 1115 South Sunset Avenue, West Covina, Zip 91790–3940, Mailing Address: P.O. Box 1980, Zip 91793–1980; tel. 626/962–4011) **A**9 10 **F**3 7 8 11 13 18 20 22 24 25 26 27 28 29 30 31 32 34 35 40 41 44 45 46 47 49 50 51 55 56 57 59 64 65 68 69 70 71 72 74 75 76 77 78 79 80 81 82 83 84 85 86 87 89 90 92 93 96 98 102 103 105 107 108 110 114 115 118 119 120 121 124 126 128 129 130 131 132 135 143 146 147 148 **P**5 **S** Citrus Valley Health Partners, Covina, CA
Primary Contact: Robert H. Curry, President and Chief Executive Officer
CFO: Roger Sharma, Chief Financial Officer
CIO: Pavel Bindra, M.D., Chief Medical Officer and Chief Information Officer
CHR: Paul Heredia, Chief Human Resources Officer
CNO: Diana Lugo–Zenner, R.N., Chief Nursing Officer
Web address: www.cvhp.org
**Control:** Other not–for–profit (including NFP Corporation) **Service:** General Medical and Surgical

**Staffed Beds:** 327 **Admissions:** 24916 **Census:** 287 **Outpatient Visits:** 160468 **Births:** 4049 **Total Expense ($000):** 370374 **Payroll Expense ($000):** 126265 **Personnel:** 1600

**CRESCENT CITY—Del Norte County**

☒ **SUTTER COAST HOSPITAL (050417)**, 800 East Washington Boulevard, Zip 95531–8359; tel. 707/464–8511 **A**1 9 10 20 **F**3 8 11 13 15 29 30 34 35 40 43 45 46 47 48 50 51 54 57 59 62 68 70 75 76 77 79 81 82 84 85 87 93 97 107 108 110 111 114 118 119 127 130 132 144 146 148 **S** Sutter Health, Sacramento, CA
Primary Contact: Mitchell J. Hanna, Interim Chief Executive Officer
Web address: www.sutterhealth.org
**Control:** Other not–for–profit (including NFP Corporation) **Service:** General Medical and Surgical

**Staffed Beds:** 49 **Admissions:** 2091 **Census:** 18 **Outpatient Visits:** 44801 **Births:** 302 **Total Expense ($000):** 59528 **Payroll Expense ($000):** 19754 **Personnel:** 312

**CULVER CITY—Los Angeles County**

**SOUTHERN CALIFORNIA HOSPITAL AT CULVER CITY (050752)**, 3828 Delmas Terrace, Zip 90232–6806; tel. 310/836–7000, (Nonreporting) **A**9
Primary Contact: Michael T. Phillips, FACHE, Administrator
CFO: Vincent Rubin, Chief Financial Officer
CMO: Martha Sonnenberg, M.D., Chief of Staff
CIO: Carrie Bonar, Chief Information Officer
CHR: Betty J. Harris, Director Human Resources
Web address: www.sch–culvercity.com
**Control:** Corporation, Investor–owned, for–profit **Service:** General Medical and Surgical

**Staffed Beds:** 239

**DALY CITY—San Mateo County**

☒ **SETON MEDICAL CENTER (050289)**, 1900 Sullivan Avenue, Zip 94015–2229; tel. 650/992–4000, (Total facility includes 116 beds in nursing home–type unit) **A**1 2 3 9 10 **F**3 8 17 18 20 22 24 26 28 29 30 31 34 35 40 45 46 49 53 54 57 59 60 64 65 66 68 70 71 72 74 75 77 78 79 81 82 84 87 93 107 110 111 114 115 116 117 118 119 120 121 123 124 128 130 133 135 146 147 148 **P**3 **S** Daughters of Charity Health System, Los Altos Hills, CA
Primary Contact: John Ferrell, President and Chief Executive Officer
COO: Stephanie Mearns, Vice President Patient Care Services and Chief Nurse Executive
CFO: Richard Wood, Chief Financial Officer
CMO: David Goldschmid, M.D., President Medical Staff
CHR: Patricia White, Vice President Human Resources
Web address: www.setonmedicalcenter.org
**Control:** Church–operated, Nongovernment, not–for profit **Service:** General Medical and Surgical

**Staffed Beds:** 423 **Admissions:** 6234 **Census:** 231 **Outpatient Visits:** 186318 **Births:** 579 **Total Expense ($000):** 282933 **Payroll Expense ($000):** 128466

**DAVIS—Yolo County**

☒ **SUTTER DAVIS HOSPITAL (050537)**, 2000 Sutter Place, Zip 95616–6201, Mailing Address: P.O. Box 1617, Zip 95617–1617; tel. 530/756–6440 **A**1 3 5 9 10 **F**3 8 11 13 15 18 28 29 30 31 40 45 47 48 49 57 65 70 76 78 79 81 83 85 86 87 92 107 108 111 119 124 130 131 141 142 146 147 **S** Sutter Health, Sacramento, CA
Primary Contact: Jennifer Maher, Chief Executive Officer
CFO: Brett Moore, Chief Financial Officer
CMO: Deven Merchant, M.D., Chief Medical Executive
CHR: Don Hartman, Director Human Resources
CNO: Myrna Chang, Chief Nursing Executive
Web address: www.sutterhealth.org
**Control:** Other not–for–profit (including NFP Corporation) **Service:** General Medical and Surgical

**Staffed Beds:** 48 **Admissions:** 3380 **Census:** 22 **Outpatient Visits:** 47024 **Births:** 1521 **Total Expense ($000):** 82127 **Payroll Expense ($000):** 27891 **Personnel:** 341

**DELANO—Kern County**

○ **DELANO REGIONAL MEDICAL CENTER (050608)**, 1401 Garces Highway, Zip 93215–3690, Mailing Address: P.O. Box 460, Zip 93216–0460; tel. 661/725–4800, (Nonreporting) **A**9 10 11
Primary Contact: Bahram Ghaffari, President
CFO: Bahram Ghaffari, President
CIO: Sandy Bakich, Director Information Management
CHR: Del Garbanzos, Director Human Resources
CNO: Amy Scroggs, Chief Nursing Officer
Web address: www.drmc.com
**Control:** Other not–for–profit (including NFP Corporation) **Service:** General Medical and Surgical

**Staffed Beds:** 100

**CA**

---

**Hospital, Medicare Provider Number, Address, Telephone, Approval, Facility, and Physician Codes, Health Care System**

★ American Hospital Association (AHA) membership    ○ Healthcare Facilities Accreditation Program    ⇑ Center for Improvement in Healthcare Quality Accreditation
☐ The Joint Commission accreditation    ◇ DNV Healthcare Inc. accreditation    △ Commission on Accreditation of Rehabilitation Facilities (CARF) accreditation

© 2015 AHA Guide    *Many Facility Codes have changed. Please refer to the AHA Guide Code Chart.*    Hospitals **A59**

**CA**

## DOWNEY—Los Angeles County

✠ **KAISER PERMANENTE DOWNEY MEDICAL CENTER (050139)**, 9333 Imperial Highway, Zip 90242–2812; tel. 562/657–9000 **A**1 3 10 **F**3 8 13 15 18 19 29 30 31 35 38 40 45 46 49 50 58 60 64 65 68 70 72 74 75 76 78 79 81 82 83 84 85 87 88 89 92 100 107 110 111 114 115 119 126 130 132 146 148 **S** Kaiser Foundation Hospitals, Oakland, CA
Primary Contact: James Branchick, R.N., MS, Executive Director
CNO: Patricia J. Clausen, R.N., Chief Nurse Executive
Web address: www.kaiserpermanente.org
**Control:** Other not–for–profit (including NFP Corporation) **Service:** General Medical and Surgical

**Staffed Beds:** 342 **Admissions:** 18687 **Census:** 198 **Outpatient Visits:** 191433 **Births:** 3741

★ ◇ **PIH HEALTH HOSPITAL – DOWNEY (050393)**, 11500 Brookshire Avenue, Zip 90241–4917; tel. 562/904–5000 **A**9 10 12 13 21 **F**3 13 15 17 18 19 20 22 24 29 30 40 41 42 45 47 48 49 50 57 70 72 74 75 76 77 79 81 85 91 92 93 97 102 107 108 110 111 115 118 119 130 132 145 146 148 **P**3 5 **S** PIH Health, Whittier, CA
Primary Contact: James R. West, President and Chief Executive Officer
COO: Robert Fuller, Executive Vice President and Chief Operating Officer
CFO: Ed King, Chief Financial Officer
CIO: Nick Pappas, Chief Information Officer
CHR: Carole Everhart, Administrative Director Human Resources
CNO: Heather Conwell, Chief Nursing Officer
Web address: www.PIHHealth.org
**Control:** Other not–for–profit (including NFP Corporation) **Service:** General Medical and Surgical

**Staffed Beds:** 192 **Admissions:** 8154 **Census:** 95 **Outpatient Visits:** 82554 **Births:** 1154 **Total Expense ($000):** 187919 **Payroll Expense ($000):** 64465 **Personnel:** 1068

☐ △ **RANCHO LOS AMIGOS NATIONAL REHABILITATION CENTER (050717)**, 7601 East Imperial Highway, Zip 90242–3496; tel. 562/401–7111, (Nonreporting) **A**1 3 5 7 9 10 **S** Los Angeles County–Department of Health Services, Los Angeles, CA
Primary Contact: Jorge Orozco, Chief Executive Officer
COO: Benjamin Ovando, Chief Operations Officer
CFO: Robin Bayus, Chief Financial Officer
CMO: Mindy Aisen, M.D., Chief Medical Officer
CIO: Francis Tang, Chief Information Officer
CHR: Elizabeth Jacobi, Associate Director Human Resources
CNO: Aries Limbaga, R.N., Chief Nursing Officer
Web address: www.rancho.org
**Control:** County–Government, nonfederal **Service:** Rehabilitation

**Staffed Beds:** 207

## DUARTE—Los Angeles County

✠ **CITY OF HOPE'S HELFORD CLINICAL RESEARCH HOSPITAL (050146)**, 1500 East Duarte Road, Zip 91010–3012; tel. 626/256–4673 **A**1 2 3 5 8 9 10 **F**3 8 11 14 15 18 26 29 30 31 34 35 36 38 44 45 46 47 49 50 55 56 57 58 59 61 63 64 68 70 74 75 77 78 79 80 81 82 84 85 86 87 88 89 92 93 96 99 100 101 102 103 104 107 108 110 111 115 117 118 119 120 121 123 124 126 130 132 134 135 136 141 142 144 145 146 147 148 **P**3
Primary Contact: Robert Stone, President and Chief Executive Officer
COO: Marty Sargeant, Chief Operating Officer
CFO: Gary F. Conner, Chief Financial Officer
CMO: Alexandra Levine, M.D., Chief Medical Officer
CIO: Paul Conocenti, Chief Information Officer
CHR: Stephanie Neuvirth, Chief Human Resource and Diversity Officer
Web address: www.cityofhope.org
**Control:** Other not–for–profit (including NFP Corporation) **Service:** Cancer

**Staffed Beds:** 193 **Admissions:** 5876 **Census:** 159 **Outpatient Visits:** 199943 **Births:** 0 **Total Expense ($000):** 719904 **Payroll Expense ($000):** 250529 **Personnel:** 3019

## EL CENTRO—Imperial County

✠ **EL CENTRO REGIONAL MEDICAL CENTER (050045)**, 1415 Ross Avenue, Zip 92243–4398; tel. 760/339–7100 **A**1 9 10 **F**3 11 13 15 18 26 29 30 31 34 40 43 45 46 47 48 49 50 51 54 57 59 60 64 66 70 74 75 76 78 79 81 82 85 86 87 89 93 97 107 108 110 111 114 115 116 117 119 126 127 130 131 145 146 147 148
Primary Contact: Tomas Virgen, R.N., MSN, Interim Chief Executive Officer
COO: Tomas Virgen, R.N., Chief Operating Officer
CFO: Kathleen Farmer, Assistant Administrator Finance and Chief Financial Officer
CIO: John Gaede, Director Information Systems
CHR: Bill Moore, Human Resources
Web address: www.ecrmc.org
**Control:** City–Government, nonfederal **Service:** General Medical and Surgical

**Staffed Beds:** 161 **Admissions:** 8382 **Census:** 60 **Outpatient Visits:** 198530 **Births:** 1131 **Total Expense ($000):** 121460 **Payroll Expense ($000):** 47119

## ELDRIDGE—Sonoma County

**SONOMA DEVELOPMENTAL CENTER (050547)**, 15000 Arnold Drive, Zip 95431–8900, Mailing Address: P.O. Box 1493, Zip 95431–1493; tel. 707/938–6000, (Nonreporting) **A**10
Primary Contact: Karen Faria, Executive Director
COO: Karen Clark, Director Administrative Services
CMO: Carol Castillo, Medical Director
CHR: Brenda Dukes, Director Human Resources
Web address: www.dds.ca.gov/sonoma
**Control:** State–Government, nonfederal **Service:** Intellectual Disabilities

**Staffed Beds:** 546

## ENCINITAS—San Diego County

✠ △ **SCRIPPS MEMORIAL HOSPITAL–ENCINITAS (050503)**, 354 Santa Fe Drive, Zip 92024–5182, Mailing Address: P.O. Box 230817, Zip 92023–0817; tel. 760/633–6501 **A**1 2 7 9 10 **F**3 8 11 13 14 15 18 20 22 26 29 30 31 34 35 40 44 49 54 57 58 59 64 65 68 70 74 75 76 77 78 79 81 82 84 85 86 87 90 91 92 93 94 96 107 108 111 114 115 118 119 130 132 141 146 148 **P**3 5 **S** Scripps Health, San Diego, CA
Primary Contact: Carl J. Etter, Chief Executive and Senior Vice President
COO: Rebecca Cofinas, Vice President and Chief Operating Executive Operations
CFO: Sharon Creal, Vice President Financial Operations
CHR: Cara Williams, Director Human Resources
Web address: www.scripps.org
**Control:** Other not–for–profit (including NFP Corporation) **Service:** General Medical and Surgical

**Staffed Beds:** 194 **Admissions:** 9930 **Census:** 113 **Outpatient Visits:** 69157 **Births:** 2052 **Total Expense ($000):** 213513 **Payroll Expense ($000):** 82860 **Personnel:** 1017

## ENCINO—Los Angeles County, See Los Angeles

## ESCONDIDO—San Diego County

✠ △ **PALOMAR MEDICAL CENTER (050115)**, 2185 West Citracado Parkway, Zip 92029–4159; tel. 760/739–3000 **A**1 3 5 7 9 10 **F**3 11 12 13 15 17 18 20 22 24 26 28 29 30 31 40 42 43 45 46 47 50 51 62 64 68 70 74 75 76 77 78 79 81 84 85 86 87 90 93 96 97 98 100 102 103 104 105 107 108 111 112 114 115 119 120 121 123 124 126 129 130 131 146 147 148 **P**3 **S** Palomar Health, Escondido, CA
Primary Contact: Mariellena Sudak, R.N., Interim Vice President and Chief Nursing Officer
CMO: Duane Buringrud, M.D., Chief Medical and Quality Officer
CIO: Prudence August, Chief Information Officer
CHR: Brenda C. Turner, Chief Human Resources Officer
CNO: Mariellena Sudak, R.N., Chief Nursing Officer
Web address: www.palomarhealth.org
**Control:** Hospital district or authority, Government, nonfederal **Service:** General Medical and Surgical

**Staffed Beds:** 287 **Admissions:** 22979 **Census:** 258 **Outpatient Visits:** 190546 **Births:** 3165 **Total Expense ($000):** 463750 **Payroll Expense ($000):** 179821 **Personnel:** 1344

## EUREKA—Humboldt County

**HUMBOLDT COUNTY MENTAL HEALTH (054124)**, 720 Wood Street, Zip 95501–4413; tel. 707/268–2900 **A**10 **F**5 7 29 38 98 99 100 101 102 103 104 105 **P**4
Primary Contact: Jet L. DeKruse, Administrator
CMO: Harpreet Duggal, M.D., Medical Director, Department of Health and Human Services
CNO: Sherry Gallagher, Director Nursing, Department of Health and Human Services
Web address: www.https://co.humboldt.ca.us/hhs/mhb/
**Control:** County–Government, nonfederal **Service:** Psychiatric

**Staffed Beds:** 16 **Admissions:** 614 **Census:** 12 **Outpatient Visits:** 0 **Births:** 0

★ ◇ **ST. JOSEPH HOSPITAL (050006)**, 2700 Dolbeer Street, Zip 95501–4799; tel. 707/445–8121, (Includes GENERAL HOSPITAL, 2200 Harrison Avenue, Zip 95501–3299; tel. 707/445–5111) **A**2 9 10 11 19 **F**3 8 11 12 13 15 17 18 20 22 24 26 28 29 30 31 35 39 40 45 46 47 48 49 53 54 62 63 64 68 70 72 74 75 76 78 79 81 82 84 85 86 87 90 93 96 107 108 110 111 114 115 118 119 120 121 123 124 129 130 131 146 148 **P**5 **S** St. Joseph Health, Irvine, CA
Primary Contact: David O'Brien, M.D., President
CFO: Mich Riccioni, Chief Financial Officer
CMO: Mathew Miller, M.D., Vice President and Chief Medical Officer
CIO: Wendy Thorpe, Area Director Information Systems
CHR: Linda Cook, Vice President Human Resources
CNO: Carol Reeder, R.N., Chief Nursing Officer
Web address: www.stjosepheureka.org
**Control:** Church–operated, Nongovernment, not–for profit **Service:** General Medical and Surgical

**Staffed Beds:** 153 **Admissions:** 6346 **Census:** 85 **Outpatient Visits:** 174340 **Births:** 520 **Total Expense ($000):** 196999 **Payroll Expense ($000):** 55299 **Personnel:** 1030

*Many Facility Codes have changed. Please refer to the AHA Guide Code Chart.*
© 2015 AHA Guide

## FAIRFIELD—Solano County

⊞ **NORTHBAY MEDICAL CENTER (050367)**, 1200 B. Gale Wilson Boulevard, Zip 94533–3587; tel. 707/646–5000, (Includes NORTHBAY VACAVALLEY HOSPITAL, 1000 Nut Tree Road, Vacaville, Zip 95687–4100; tel. 707/624–7000; B. Konard Jones, President, Hospital Division) **A**1 2 5 9 10 **F**2 3 6 8 11 13 17 18 19 20 22 24 26 28 29 30 31 32 35 36 40 41 43 44 46 49 50 51 54 56 59 62 63 64 65 70 72 73 74 75 76 77 78 79 80 81 82 84 85 87 89 92 93 94 96 97 100 104 107 114 115 118 119 121 130 131 132 146 147 148 **P**3
Primary Contact: B. Konard Jones, President, Hospital Division
CFO: Arthur E. DeNio, Vice President and Chief Financial Officer
CIO: Christopher Timbers, Vice President and Chief Information Officer
CHR: Ken McCollum, Vice President, Human Resources
Web address: www.northbay.org
**Control:** Other not–for–profit (including NFP Corporation) **Service:** General Medical and Surgical

**Staffed Beds:** 170 **Admissions:** 8695 **Census:** 101 **Outpatient Visits:** 284540 **Births:** 1332 **Total Expense ($000):** 399160 **Payroll Expense ($000):** 182643 **Personnel:** 1343

## FALL RIVER MILLS—Shasta County

★ **MAYERS MEMORIAL HOSPITAL DISTRICT (051305)**, 43563 Highway 299 East, Zip 96028–0459, Mailing Address: P.O. Box 459, Zip 96028–0459; tel. 530/336–5511, (Total facility includes 87 beds in nursing home–type unit) **A**9 10 18 **F**3 7 13 40 45 50 56 57 59 63 64 75 76 79 81 85 93 107 114 119 128 130 132 133 146 148
Primary Contact: Louis James Ward, Interim Chief Executive Officer
COO: Louis James Ward, Chief Operating Officer
CFO: Travis Lakey, Chief Financial Officer
CMO: Thomas Watson, M.D., Chief of Staff
CIO: Chris Broadway, Manager Information Technology
CHR: Julie Thompson, Manager Personnel and Payroll
CNO: Sherry Wilson, R.N., Chief Nursing Officer
Web address: www.mayersmemorial.com
**Control:** Hospital district or authority, Government, nonfederal **Service:** General Medical and Surgical

**Staffed Beds:** 97 **Admissions:** 390 **Census:** 76 **Outpatient Visits:** 20295 **Births:** 59

## FOLSOM—Sacramento County

⊞ **MERCY HOSPITAL OF FOLSOM (050414)**, 1650 Creekside Drive, Zip 95630–3400; tel. 916/983–7400 **A**1 5 9 10 **F**3 8 11 12 13 29 30 34 35 36 37 39 40 49 57 59 60 64 66 68 70 74 75 77 81 82 84 85 86 93 107 108 114 115 118 119 130 132 146 147 148 **P**3 4 5 **S** Dignity Health, San Francisco, CA
Primary Contact: Edmundo Castaneda, President
COO: Randall Castillo, Vice President, Operations
CFO: Robin Rogness, Vice President and Chief Financial Officer
CHR: Anthony Robinson, Manager, Human Resources
CNO: Josh Freilich, Vice President and Chief Nurse Executive
Web address: www.mercyfolsom.org
**Control:** Church–operated, Nongovernment, not–for profit **Service:** General Medical and Surgical

**Staffed Beds:** 106 **Admissions:** 6116 **Census:** 55 **Outpatient Visits:** 54016 **Births:** 939 **Total Expense ($000):** 146175 **Payroll Expense ($000):** 60774 **Personnel:** 523

⊞ **VIBRA HOSPITAL OF SACRAMENTO (052033)**, 330 Montrose Drive, Zip 95630–2720; tel. 916/351–9151, (Nonreporting) **A**1 9 10 **S** Vibra Healthcare, Mechanicsburg, PA
Primary Contact: Janet Biedron, R.N., Chief Executive Officer
CFO: Bruce MacNeill, Chief Financial Officer
CMO: Alan Cubre, M.D., Medical Director
CHR: Michael G. Fanselau, District Director Human Resources
Web address: www.vhsacramento.com
**Control:** Corporation, Investor–owned, for–profit **Service:** Long–Term Acute Care hospital

**Staffed Beds:** 37

## FONTANA—San Bernardino County

⊞ **KAISER PERMANENTE FONTANA MEDICAL CENTER (050140)**, 9961 Sierra Avenue, Zip 92335–6794; tel. 909/427–5000, (Includes KAISER PERMANENTE ONTARIO MEDICAL CENTER, 2295 South Vineyard Avenue, Ontario, Zip 91761–7925; tel. 909/724–5000; Greg Christian, Executive Director) **A**1 3 5 10 **F**3 4 8 11 13 15 17 18 20 22 24 28 29 30 31 35 40 41 44 48 49 50 51 52 57 58 59 60 62 63 64 65 68 70 72 73 74 75 76 77 78 79 81 82 84 85 86 87 88 89 100 102 107 108 110 111 114 115 117 118 119 130 132 135 141 145 146 148 **S** Kaiser Foundation Hospitals, Oakland, CA
Primary Contact: Greg Christian, Executive Director
COO: Ray Hahn, Chief Operating Officer
CFO: Donald P. Bernard, Chief Financial Officer
CMO: David Quam, M.D., Area Medical Director
CIO: David Young, M.D., Area Information Officer
CHR: Kimberly Labiaga, Human Resources Leader
CNO: Toni Andersen, R.N., Chief Nurse Executive
Web address: www.kaiserpermanente.org
**Control:** Other not–for–profit (including NFP Corporation) **Service:** General Medical and Surgical

**Staffed Beds:** 490 **Admissions:** 27798 **Census:** 315 **Outpatient Visits:** 158827 **Births:** 5954 **Personnel:** 4253

## FORT BRAGG—Mendocino County

⊞ **MENDOCINO COAST DISTRICT HOSPITAL (051325)**, 700 River Drive, Zip 95437–5495; tel. 707/961–1234, (Nonreporting) **A**1 9 10 18
Primary Contact: Bob S. Edwards, Jr., FACHE, Chief Executive Officer
CFO: Wayne Allen, Chief Financial Officer
CMO: John Kermen, D.O., Chief Medical Staff
CIO: Jeff Edwards, Manager Information Services
CHR: Scott Kidd, Director Human Resources
CNO: Bonnie Kittner, R.N., Chief Nursing Officer
Web address: www.mcdh.org
**Control:** Hospital district or authority, Government, nonfederal **Service:** General Medical and Surgical

**Staffed Beds:** 25

## FORT IRWIN—San Bernardino County

⊞ **WEED ARMY COMMUNITY HOSPITAL**, Inner Loop Road and 4th Street, Building 166, Zip 92310–5065, Mailing Address: P.O. Box 105109, Zip 92310–5109; tel. 760/380–3108, (Nonreporting) **A**1 **S** Department of the Army, Office of the Surgeon General, Falls Church, VA
Primary Contact: Colonel Cheryl Taylor–Whitehead, Commander
CIO: Michael Haenelt, Chief Information Management
Web address: www.irwin.amedd.army.mil
**Control:** Army, Government, federal **Service:** General Medical and Surgical

**Staffed Beds:** 27

## FORTUNA—Humboldt County

★ **REDWOOD MEMORIAL HOSPITAL (051318)**, 3300 Renner Drive, Zip 95540–3198; tel. 707/725–3361 **A**2 9 10 18 **F**3 11 13 15 17 18 29 30 34 35 39 40 45 50 53 56 57 59 63 64 68 70 75 76 77 79 81 82 84 85 86 93 107 110 114 119 130 131 132 133 146 **S** St. Joseph Health, Irvine, CA
Primary Contact: David O'Brien, M.D., President
COO: Joseph J. Rogers, Vice President and Chief Operating Officer
CFO: Andrew Rybolt, Vice President and Chief Financial Officer
CHR: Bob Sampson, Vice President Human Resources
Web address: www.redwoodmemorial.org/
**Control:** Church–operated, Nongovernment, not–for profit **Service:** General Medical and Surgical

**Staffed Beds:** 25 **Admissions:** 1448 **Census:** 13 **Outpatient Visits:** 45209 **Births:** 330 **Total Expense ($000):** 36045 **Payroll Expense ($000):** 12899 **Personnel:** 167

## FOUNTAIN VALLEY—Orange County

⊞ **FOUNTAIN VALLEY REGIONAL HOSPITAL AND MEDICAL CENTER (050570)**, 17100 Euclid Street, Zip 92708–4043; tel. 714/966–7200, (Nonreporting) **A**1 2 5 9 10 **S** TENET Healthcare Corporation, Dallas, TX
Primary Contact: B. Joseph Badalian, Chief Executive Officer
CFO: Ken Jordan, Chief Financial Officer
CMO: E. V. Sunderrajan, M.D., Chief of Staff
CIO: Freddie Sanchez, Director Information Systems
CHR: Tim Howard, Chief Human Resources Officer
CNO: Mary Botticella, R.N., Chief Nursing Officer
Web address: www.fountainvalleyhospital.com
**Control:** Corporation, Investor–owned, for–profit **Service:** General Medical and Surgical

**Staffed Beds:** 242

**CA**

---

**Hospital, Medicare Provider Number, Address, Telephone, Approval, Facility, and Physician Codes, Health Care System**

★ American Hospital Association (AHA) membership
□ The Joint Commission accreditation
○ Healthcare Facilities Accreditation Program
◇ DNV Healthcare Inc. accreditation
⇑ Center for Improvement in Healthcare Quality Accreditation
△ Commission on Accreditation of Rehabilitation Facilities (CARF) accreditation

☒ **ORANGE COAST MEMORIAL MEDICAL CENTER (050678)**, 9920 Talbert Avenue, Zip 92708–5115; tel. 714/378–7000 **A**1 2 9 10 **F**3 8 11 12 13 15 18 20 22 24 26 28 29 30 31 34 35 38 40 44 45 46 47 48 49 50 51 53 55 56 57 58 59 64 65 68 70 72 74 75 76 77 78 79 81 82 84 85 86 87 93 107 108 110 111 114 115 116 117 118 119 124 126 130 131 132 135 143 145 146 147 **S** MemorialCare, Fountain Valley, CA
Primary Contact: Marcia Manker, Chief Executive Officer
COO: Emily Randle, Vice President Operations
CFO: Steve McNamara, Chief Financial Officer
CIO: Scott Raymond, Director Information Systems
CHR: Michelle Gutierrez, Executive Director Human Resources
CNO: Dale Vital, Chief Nursing Officer
Web address: www.memorialcare.org
**Control:** Other not–for–profit (including NFP Corporation) **Service:** General Medical and Surgical

**Staffed Beds: 218 Admissions: 12112 Census: 122 Outpatient Visits: 78428 Births: 1580 Total Expense ($000): 259441 Payroll Expense ($000): 72021 Personnel: 1055**

### FREMONT—Alameda County

☒ **FREMONT HOSPITAL (054110)**, 39001 Sundale Drive, Zip 94538–2005; tel. 510/796–1100 **A**1 9 10 **F**3 5 29 30 38 68 98 99 100 101 102 103 104 105 130 132 135 143 **S** Universal Health Services, Inc., King of Prussia, PA
Primary Contact: John C. Cooper, Chief Executive Officer
CMO: Vikas Duvvuri, M.D., Medical Director
CHR: Tom Piz, Director Human Resources
Web address: www.fremonthospital.com
**Control:** Corporation, Investor–owned, for–profit **Service:** Psychiatric

**Staffed Beds: 96 Admissions: 4354 Census: 87 Outpatient Visits: 11999 Births: 0 Total Expense ($000): 23459 Payroll Expense ($000): 14149 Personnel: 264**

☒ **FREMONT MEDICAL CENTER (050512)**, 39400 Paseo Padre Parkway, Zip 94538–2310; tel. 510/248–3000, (Nonreporting) **A**1 10 **S** Kaiser Foundation Hospitals, Oakland, CA
Primary Contact: Victoria O'Gorman, Administrator
Web address: www.kp.org
**Control:** Other not–for–profit (including NFP Corporation) **Service:** General Medical and Surgical

**Staffed Beds: 106**

☒ **WASHINGTON HOSPITAL HEALTHCARE SYSTEM (050195)**, 2000 Mowry Avenue, Zip 94538–1746; tel. 510/797–1111, (Nonreporting) **A**1 2 9 10
Primary Contact: Nancy D. Farber, Chief Executive Officer
COO: Edward J. Fayen, Associate Administrator Operations and Support
CFO: Chris Henry, Associate Administrator and Chief Financial Officer
CMO: Albert Brooks, M.D., Chief Medical Staff Services
CIO: Robert Thorwald, Chief Information Officer
CHR: Bryant Welch, Chief Human Resources
CNO: Stephanie Williams, R.N., Chief Nursing Officer
Web address: www.whhs.com
**Control:** Hospital district or authority, Government, nonfederal **Service:** General Medical and Surgical

**Staffed Beds: 269**

### FRENCH CAMP—San Joaquin County

☐ **SAN JOAQUIN GENERAL HOSPITAL (050167)**, 500 West Hospital Road, Zip 95231–9693, Mailing Address: P.O. Box 1020, Stockton, Zip 95201–3120; tel. 209/468–6000, (Nonreporting) **A**1 3 5 10
Primary Contact: David K. Culberson, Chief Executive Officer
CFO: Ron Kreutner, Chief Financial Officer
CMO: Sheela Kapre, M.D., Chief Medical Officer
CIO: Don Johnston, Chief Information Officer
CHR: Lisa M. Lopez, Director Human Resources
CNO: Erlinda Bolor, R.N., Chief Nursing Officer
Web address: www.sjgeneral.org/
**Control:** County–Government, nonfederal **Service:** General Medical and Surgical

**Staffed Beds: 110**

### FRESNO—Fresno County

**COMMUNITY BEHAVIORAL HEALTH CENTER**, 7171 North Cedar Avenue, Zip 93720–3311; tel. 559/449–8000 **A**9 **F**29 87 98 102 130 **S** Community Medical Centers, Fresno, CA
Primary Contact: Craig Wagoner, Chief Executive Officer
CFO: Stephen Walter, Senior Vice President and Chief Financial Officer
CMO: Tom Utecht, M.D., Senior Vice President and Chief Quality Officer
CIO: George Vasquez, Vice President Information Services
CHR: Ginny Burdick, Vice President Human Resources
CNO: Karen L. Buckley, R.N., Chief Nursing Officer
Web address: www.communitymedical.org
**Control:** Other not–for–profit (including NFP Corporation) **Service:** Psychiatric

**Staffed Beds: 61 Admissions: 3680 Census: 52 Outpatient Visits: 0 Births: 0 Total Expense ($000): 18435 Payroll Expense ($000): 9581 Personnel: 124**

☐ **COMMUNITY REGIONAL MEDICAL CENTER (050060)**, 2823 Fresno Street, Zip 93721–1324, Mailing Address: P.O. Box 1232, Zip 93715–1232; tel. 559/459–6000, (Nonreporting) **A**1 2 3 5 8 9 10 **S** Community Medical Centers, Fresno, CA
Primary Contact: Craig Wagoner, Chief Executive Officer
COO: Patrick W. Rafferty, Executive Vice President and Chief Operating Officer
CFO: Stephen Walter, Senior Vice President and Chief Financial Officer
CMO: Tom Utecht, M.D., Chief Medical and Quality Officer
CIO: Craig Castro, Chief Information Officer
CHR: Ginny Burdick, Vice President Human Resources
Web address: www.communitymedical.org
**Control:** Other not–for–profit (including NFP Corporation) **Service:** General Medical and Surgical

**Staffed Beds: 793**

☐ **FRESNO HEART AND SURGICAL HOSPITAL (050732)**, 15 East Audubon Drive, Zip 93720–1542; tel. 559/433–8000, (Nonreporting) **A**1 3 9 10 **S** Community Medical Centers, Fresno, CA
Primary Contact: Wanda Holderman, R.N., Chief Executive Officer
CFO: Ben Armfield, Chief Financial Officer
CMO: Tom Utecht, M.D., Corporate Chief Quality Officer
CIO: George Vasquez, Corporate Chief Information Officer
CHR: Julie Adair, Interim Corporate Chief Human Resources Officer
CNO: Heather Rodriguez, Chief Nursing Officer
Web address: www.fresnoheartandsurgical.org
**Control:** Corporation, Investor–owned, for–profit **Service:** Heart

**Staffed Beds: 60**

**FRESNO MEDICAL CENTER** See Kaiser Permanente Fresno Medical Center

☐ **FRESNO SURGICAL HOSPITAL (050708)**, 6125 North Fresno Street, Zip 93710–5207; tel. 559/431–8000, (Nonreporting) **A**1 9 10
Primary Contact: Kristine Kassahn, Chief Executive Officer
CFO: Bruce Cecil, Chief Financial Officer
CMO: Bruce Witmer, M.D., Medical Director
CHR: Laura Patillo, Manager Human Resources
Web address: www.fresnosurgicalhospital.com
**Control:** Partnership, Investor–owned, for–profit **Service:** General Medical and Surgical

**Staffed Beds: 16**

☒ **KAISER PERMANENTE FRESNO MEDICAL CENTER (050710)**, 7300 North Fresno Street, Zip 93720–2942; tel. 559/448–4500 **A**1 3 10 **F**3 4 8 12 13 15 29 30 31 35 40 45 49 51 53 59 63 64 68 70 72 73 74 76 77 78 79 81 82 83 84 85 86 87 90 93 96 97 98 102 107 108 110 111 114 116 117 118 119 124 128 130 135 144 146 148 **S** Kaiser Foundation Hospitals, Oakland, CA
Primary Contact: Debbie Hemker, Senior Vice President and Area Manager
CFO: Richard Alves, Chief Financial Officer
CMO: Varouj Altebarmakian, M.D., Physician in Chief
CIO: Brad Bain, Information Systems Leader
Web address: www.kaiserpermanente.org
**Control:** Other not–for–profit (including NFP Corporation) **Service:** General Medical and Surgical

**Staffed Beds: 169 Admissions: 4020 Census: 67 Outpatient Visits: 848178 Births: 1051**

☒ **SAINT AGNES MEDICAL CENTER (050093)**, 1303 East Herndon Avenue, Zip 93720–3397; tel. 559/450–3000 **A**1 2 9 10 **F**3 8 11 13 15 17 18 20 22 24 26 28 29 30 31 34 35 37 40 44 45 46 47 49 50 51 55 56 57 58 59 61 64 66 70 74 75 76 77 78 79 81 82 84 85 86 87 91 92 93 94 95 96 97 102 107 108 110 111 112 113 114 115 116 117 118 119 120 121 123 124 126 130 132 135 146 147 148 **P**1 5 **S** Trinity Health, Livonia, MI
Primary Contact: Nancy Hollingsworth, R.N., MSN, President and Chief Executive Officer
COO: Mark T. Bateman, Interim Chief Operating Officer
CFO: Phil Robinson, Chief Financial Officer
CMO: Stephen Soldo, M.D., Chief Medical Officer
CIO: Irfan Ali, Director Information Services
CHR: Stacy Vaillancourt, Vice President Marketing, Communications, Advocacy and Human Resources
Web address: www.samc.com
**Control:** Church–operated, Nongovernment, not–for profit **Service:** General Medical and Surgical

**Staffed Beds: 436 Admissions: 20628 Census: 234 Outpatient Visits: 221849 Births: 3102 Total Expense ($000): 400433 Payroll Expense ($000): 146596 Personnel: 1814**

☒ △ **SAN JOAQUIN VALLEY REHABILITATION HOSPITAL (053032)**, 7173 North Sharon Avenue, Zip 93720–3329; tel. 559/436–3600, (Nonreporting) **A**1 7 9 10 **S** Vibra Healthcare, Mechanicsburg, PA
Primary Contact: Mary Jo Jacobson, Chief Executive Officer
CFO: Margaret Casarez, Chief Financial Officer
CMO: Michael Azevedo, M.D., Medical Director
CIO: Christi Rolff, Director Business Development
CHR: Jennifer Morrow, Director Human Resources
Web address: www.sanjoaquinrehab.com
**Control:** Corporation, Investor–owned, for–profit **Service:** Rehabilitation

**Staffed Beds: 62**

*Many Facility Codes have changed. Please refer to the AHA Guide Code Chart.* © 2015 AHA Guide

**✠ VETERANS AFFAIRS CENTRAL CALIFORNIA HEALTH CARE SYSTEM**, 2615 East Clinton Avenue, Zip 93703–2223; tel. 559/225–6100, (Nonreporting) **A**1 3 5 **S** Department of Veterans Affairs, Washington, DC
Primary Contact: Wessel H. Meyer, M.D., Acting Director
CMO: Wessel H. Meyer, M.D., Chief of Staff
CHR: Sandra Stein, Chief Human Resources Management
Web address: www.fresno.va.gov/
**Control:** Veterans Affairs, Government, federal **Service:** General Medical and Surgical

**Staffed Beds:** 117

## FULLERTON—Orange County

**✠ △ ST. JUDE MEDICAL CENTER (050168)**, 101 East Valencia Mesa Drive, Zip 92835–3875; tel. 714/992–3000 **A**1 2 3 5 7 9 10 **F**2 3 8 9 11 12 13 15 18 20 22 24 26 28 29 30 31 32 34 35 36 39 40 43 44 45 46 47 48 49 50 51 53 54 55 56 57 58 59 60 61 62 63 64 65 66 68 70 71 72 74 75 76 77 78 79 81 82 83 84 85 86 87 90 91 92 93 95 96 97 100 107 108 109 110 111 112 114 115 116 117 118 119 120 121 123 124 126 129 130 131 132 134 135 143 146 147 148 **P**3 5 **S** St. Joseph Health, Irvine, CA
Primary Contact: Lee Penrose, President and Chief Executive Officer
COO: Brian Helleland, Executive Vice President and Chief Operating Officer
CFO: Ed Salvador, Chief Financial Officer
CIO: Ryan Olsen, Vice President of Operations
CHR: Mark Jablonski, Vice President Mission Integration
CNO: Linda Jenkins, R.N., Vice President Patient Care Services
Web address: www.stjudemedicalcenter.org
**Control:** Church–operated, Nongovernment, not–for profit **Service:** General Medical and Surgical

**Staffed Beds:** 329 **Admissions:** 12583 **Census:** 166 **Outpatient Visits:** 426732 **Births:** 2100 **Total Expense ($000):** 430761 **Payroll Expense ($000):** 135378 **Personnel:** 1797

## GARBERVILLE—Humboldt County

**JEROLD PHELPS COMMUNITY HOSPITAL (051309)**, 733 Cedar Street, Zip 95542–3292; tel. 707/923–3921, (Nonreporting) **A**9 10 18
Primary Contact: Harry Jasper, Administrator
COO: Kent Scown, Director Operations and Information Services
CFO: Harry Jasper, Chief Financial Officer
CMO: Marcin Matuszkiewicz, M.D., Chief of Staff and Medical Director
CIO: Kent Scown, Director Operations and Information Services
CHR: Dee Way, Director Human Resources
CNO: Sarah Beach, Director of Nursing
Web address: www.shchd.org
**Control:** Hospital district or authority, Government, nonfederal **Service:** General Medical and Surgical

**Staffed Beds:** 16

## GARDEN GROVE—Orange County

**☐ GARDEN GROVE HOSPITAL AND MEDICAL CENTER (050230)**, 12601 Garden Grove Boulevard, Zip 92843–1959; tel. 714/537–5160, (Nonreporting) **A**1 9 10 **S** Prime Healthcare Services, Ontario, CA
Primary Contact: Edward Mirzabegian, Chief Executive Officer
CFO: Kora Guoyavatin, Chief Financial Officer
CMO: Hassan Alkhouli, M.D., Chief Medical Officer
CIO: Vic Mahan, Director Information Systems
CHR: Stephanie Sioson, Director Human Resources
CNO: Wanda Ruben, R.N., Chief Nursing Officer
Web address: www.gardengrovehospital.com
**Control:** Corporation, Investor–owned, for–profit **Service:** General Medical and Surgical

**Staffed Beds:** 167

## GARDENA—Los Angeles County

**✠ KINDRED HOSPITAL SOUTH BAY (052050)**, 1246 West 155th Street, Zip 90247–4062; tel. 310/323–5330, (Nonreporting) **A**1 9 10 **S** Kindred Healthcare, Louisville, KY
Primary Contact: Lourene Money, R.N., Interim Chief Executive Officer
COO: Michael Grubb, Chief Operating Officer and Chief Financial Officer
CFO: Michael Grubb, Chief Operating Officer and Chief Financial Officer
CHR: Michelle Parra, Director Human Resources
Web address: www.khsouthbay.com/
**Control:** Corporation, Investor–owned, for–profit **Service:** Long–Term Acute Care hospital

**Staffed Beds:** 84

**☐ MEMORIAL HOSPITAL OF GARDENA (050468)**, 1145 West Redondo Beach Boulevard, Zip 90247–3528; tel. 310/532–4200, (Nonreporting) **A**1 9 10 **S** Avanti Hospitals, El Segundo, CA
Primary Contact: Josh D. Luke, Ph.D., FACHE, Interim Chief Executive Officer
CFO: Daniel R. Heckathorne, Chief Financial Officer
CMO: Nosratian Farshao, M.D., Chief Medical Staff
CHR: Matthew Kempiak, Director Human Resources and Administrative Services
CNO: Glenda Luce, Chief Nursing Officer
Web address: www.mhglax.com/
**Control:** Corporation, Investor–owned, for–profit **Service:** General Medical and Surgical

**Staffed Beds:** 172

**VISTA HOSPITAL OF SOUTH BAY** See Kindred Hospital South Bay

## GILROY—Santa Clara County

**✠ SAINT LOUISE REGIONAL HOSPITAL (050688)**, 9400 No Name Uno, Zip 95020–3528; tel. 408/848–2000 **A**1 9 10 **F**3 11 13 15 17 29 30 31 34 35 37 40 41 45 46 47 50 54 57 59 60 64 68 69 70 75 76 78 79 81 82 85 107 108 111 114 118 130 132 135 143 144 146 148 **S** Daughters of Charity Health System, Los Altos Hills, CA
Primary Contact: Sister Margaret Keaveney, Chief Executive Officer
COO: Carol Furgurson, Chief Operating Officer
CFO: Nicole Thomson, Chief Financial Officer
CIO: Dick Hutsell, Vice President Information Technology Services
CHR: Lin Velasquez, Vice President Human Resources
CNO: Marilyn Gerrior, R.N., Chief Nursing Executive
Web address: www.dochs.org
**Control:** Church–operated, Nongovernment, not–for profit **Service:** General Medical and Surgical

**Staffed Beds:** 93 **Admissions:** 2361 **Census:** 29 **Outpatient Visits:** 49956 **Births:** 566 **Total Expense ($000):** 92197 **Payroll Expense ($000):** 42596

## GLENDALE—Los Angeles County

**✠ GLENDALE ADVENTIST MEDICAL CENTER (050239)**, 1509 Wilson Terrace, Zip 91206–4098; tel. 818/409–8000 **A**1 2 3 5 9 10 **F**3 5 8 13 15 17 18 20 22 24 26 28 29 30 31 32 34 35 36 37 40 44 45 46 47 48 49 51 53 54 56 57 58 59 64 65 68 70 71 72 74 75 76 77 78 79 81 82 83 84 85 86 87 90 91 92 93 96 98 102 103 104 105 106 107 108 109 110 111 114 115 117 118 119 120 121 124 126 128 129 130 131 132 135 145 146 147 148 **P**3 **S** Adventist Health, Roseville, CA
Primary Contact: Kevin A. Roberts, FACHE, President and Chief Executive Officer
COO: Warren Tetz, Senior Vice President and Chief Operating Officer
CFO: Kelly Turner, Senior Vice President Finance and Chief Financial Officer
CMO: Arby Nahapetian, M.D., Vice President Medical Affairs and Quality
CIO: Sharon Correa, Vice President and Chief Information Officer
CHR: Susan Crabtree, Director Human Resources
CNO: Judy Blair, Senior Vice President Clinical Services and Chief Nursing Officer
Web address: www.glendaleadventist.com
**Control:** Church–operated, Nongovernment, not–for profit **Service:** General Medical and Surgical

**Staffed Beds:** 462 **Admissions:** 19675 **Census:** 277 **Outpatient Visits:** 266585 **Births:** 2427 **Total Expense ($000):** 404801 **Payroll Expense ($000):** 142846 **Personnel:** 2075

**✠ GLENDALE MEMORIAL HOSPITAL AND HEALTH CENTER (050058)**, 1420 South Central Avenue, Zip 91204–2594; tel. 818/502–1900 **A**1 9 10 **F**12 13 15 17 18 20 22 24 26 28 29 30 31 34 35 40 41 45 46 47 49 50 51 53 58 64 68 70 72 73 74 75 76 78 79 81 84 85 88 89 90 91 92 93 98 99 102 107 108 110 111 114 115 119 120 128 130 131 132 146 147 148 **S** Dignity Health, San Francisco, CA
Primary Contact: Jack Ivie, President
CFO: Rebecca Cheng, Chief Financial Officer
CIO: Brian Gregor, Manager Information Technology Operations
CHR: Nga Nguyen, Manager Human Resources and Organizational Development
CNO: Claire H. Hanks, R.N., Vice President and Chief Nursing Officer
Web address: www.glendalememorial.com
**Control:** Other not–for–profit (including NFP Corporation) **Service:** General Medical and Surgical

**Staffed Beds:** 334 **Admissions:** 9388 **Census:** 124 **Outpatient Visits:** 100065 **Births:** 1871 **Total Expense ($000):** 213472 **Payroll Expense ($000):** 85876 **Personnel:** 1092

CA

---

**Hospital, Medicare Provider Number, Address, Telephone, Approval, Facility, and Physician Codes, Health Care System**

★ American Hospital Association (AHA) membership   ○ Healthcare Facilities Accreditation Program   ⇑ Center for Improvement in Healthcare Quality Accreditation
☐ The Joint Commission accreditation   ◇ DNV Healthcare Inc. accreditation   △ Commission on Accreditation of Rehabilitation Facilities (CARF) accreditation

★ ◇ **USC VERDUGO HILLS HOSPITAL (050124)**, 1812 Verdugo Boulevard, Zip 91208–1409; tel. 818/790–7100 **A**9 10 21 **F**12 13 14 15 17 28 29 30 31 34 35 36 37 38 40 41 45 46 47 48 49 50 51 56 57 59 60 63 68 70 74 75 76 77 79 81 83 84 85 87 91 93 98 101 103 104 105 107 108 110 111 115 119 124 128 130 132 145 146 147 148 **P**8 **S** Keck Medicine of USC, Los Angeles, CA
Primary Contact: Paul A. Craig, R.N., JD, Chief Executive Officer
COO: Paul M. Czajka, Chief Operating Officer
CFO: Mark Overeem, Chief Financial Officer
CMO: Donald Larsen, M.D., Chief Medical Officer
CHR: Eva Herberger, Administrator Human Resources
CNO: Janet Brooks, Chief Nursing Officer
Web address: www.uscvhh.org
**Control:** Other not–for–profit (including NFP Corporation) **Service:** General Medical and Surgical

**Staffed Beds: 75 Admissions: 5775 Census: 75 Outpatient Visits: 65842 Births: 581 Total Expense ($000): 83929 Payroll Expense ($000): 36678 Personnel: 633**

### GLENDORA—Los Angeles County

⊞ **FOOTHILL PRESBYTERIAN HOSPITAL (050597)**, 250 South Grand Avenue, Zip 91741–4218; tel. 626/963–8411 **A**1 9 10 **F**3 7 11 13 15 17 18 29 30 31 34 35 40 41 44 45 49 50 51 60 64 65 70 74 75 76 77 78 79 81 85 86 87 107 108 114 119 130 131 143 146 **S** Citrus Valley Health Partners, Covina, CA
Primary Contact: Robert H. Curry, President and Chief Executive Officer
COO: Elvia Foulke, Executive Vice President and Chief Operating Officer
CMO: John DiMare, M.D., Medical Director
CIO: David McCobb, Chief Information Officer
Web address: www.cvhp.org/Our_Facilities/Foothill_Presbyterian.aspx
**Control:** Other not–for–profit (including NFP Corporation) **Service:** Obstetrics and gynecology

**Staffed Beds: 69 Admissions: 5177 Census: 52 Outpatient Visits: 54172 Births: 771 Total Expense ($000): 77729 Payroll Expense ($000): 30469 Personnel: 371**

◯ **GLENDORA COMMUNITY HOSPITAL (050205)**, 150 West Route 66, Zip 91740–6207; tel. 626/852–5000, (Nonreporting) **A**9 10 11
Primary Contact: Edward Mirzabegian, Chief Executive Officer
CFO: Robert Bonner, Chief Financial Officer
CMO: Oliver Solomon, M.D., Chief Medical Officer
CIO: Jeffrey Cox, Chief Information Officer
CHR: Diana Cancel, Director Human Resources
CNO: Mary Ann Bennett, Chief Nursing Officer
Web address: www.evhmc.com
**Control:** Other not–for–profit (including NFP Corporation) **Service:** General Medical and Surgical

**Staffed Beds: 118**

### GRANADA HILLS—Los Angeles County, See Los Angeles

### GRASS VALLEY—Nevada County

⊞ **SIERRA NEVADA MEMORIAL HOSPITAL (050150)**, 155 Glasson Way, Zip 95945–5723, Mailing Address: P.O. Box 1029, Zip 95945–1029; tel. 530/274–6000, (Nonreporting) **A**1 2 9 10 19 **S** Dignity Health, San Francisco, CA
Primary Contact: Katherine A. Medeiros, President and Chief Executive Officer
CFO: Carolyn Canady, Chief Financial Officer
CMO: Brian Evans, M.D., Chief of Medicine
CHR: Terri Labriola, Human Resources Officer
CNO: Jill McWilliams, Chief Nursing Officer
Web address: www.snmh.org
**Control:** Other not–for–profit (including NFP Corporation) **Service:** General Medical and Surgical

**Staffed Beds: 121**

### GREENBRAE—Marin County

⊞ **MARIN GENERAL HOSPITAL (050360)**, 250 Bon Air Road, Zip 94904–1784, Mailing Address: P.O. Box 8010, San Rafael, Zip 94912–8010; tel. 415/925–7000 **A**1 2 10 **F**3 8 13 15 18 20 22 24 26 28 29 30 31 34 35 36 37 40 43 45 47 49 57 58 59 60 68 70 72 74 75 76 77 78 79 81 84 85 86 87 89 93 98 100 104 105 107 108 110 111 114 115 116 117 118 119 120 121 123 124 126 130 132 141 146 148 **P**3 4 5
Primary Contact: Lee Domanico, Chief Executive Officer
CFO: David W. Cox, Chief Financial Officer
CMO: Joel Sklar, M.D., Chief Medical Officer
CIO: Mark Zielazinski, Chief Information and Technology Integration Officer
CHR: Linda Lang, Chief Human Resources Officer
Web address: www.maringeneral.org
**Control:** Other not–for–profit (including NFP Corporation) **Service:** General Medical and Surgical

**Staffed Beds: 173 Admissions: 8977 Census: 108 Outpatient Visits: 174786 Births: 1416 Total Expense ($000): 329531 Payroll Expense ($000): 142227 Personnel: 1229**

### GRIDLEY—Butte County

★ ◇ **ORCHARD HOSPITAL (051311)**, 240 Spruce Street, Zip 95948–2216, Mailing Address: P.O. Box 97, Zip 95948–0097; tel. 530/846–5671, (Nonreporting) **A**9 10 18 21
Primary Contact: Steve Stark, Chief Executive Officer
COO: Tracy Atkins, Chief Operating and Nursing Officer
CMO: Henry Starkes, M.D., Medical Director
CIO: Ryan Quist, Administrative Assistant
CNO: Tracy Atkins, Chief Operating and Nursing Officer
Web address: www.bgmh.us.com/
**Control:** Other not–for–profit (including NFP Corporation) **Service:** General Medical and Surgical

**Staffed Beds: 45**

### HANFORD—Kings County

⊞ **ADVENTIST MEDICAL CENTER – HANFORD (050121)**, 115 Mall Drive, Zip 93230–3513; tel. 559/582–9000, (Includes ADVENTIST MEDICAL CENTER–SELMA, 1141 Rose Avenue, Selma, Zip 93662–3241; tel. 559/891–1000; Richard L. Rawson, President and Chief Executive Officer) **A**1 3 10 **F**3 8 13 14 15 20 22 29 30 34 35 40 56 57 59 68 70 76 79 81 93 106 107 111 119 130 146 147 148 **S** Adventist Health, Roseville, CA
Primary Contact: Wayne Ferch, President and Chief Executive Officer
CIO: Michael Aubry, Director Information Systems
Web address: www.adventisthealthcv.com/hospital_newhanfordhospital.aspx
**Control:** Church–operated, Nongovernment, not–for profit **Service:** General Medical and Surgical

**Staffed Beds: 199 Admissions: 9398 Census: 108 Outpatient Visits: 239513 Births: 300 Total Expense ($000): 216750 Payroll Expense ($000): 79401 Personnel: 1358**

⊞ **CENTRAL VALLEY GENERAL HOSPITAL (050196)**, 1025 North Douty Street, Zip 93230–3722, Mailing Address: P.O. Box 480, Zip 93232–2113; tel. 559/583–2100 **A**1 3 9 10 **F**8 13 18 129 39 34 39 50 54 57 59 64 65 76 87 97 107 109 110 111 114 119 129 130 135 144 146 147 **P**3 **S** Adventist Health, Roseville, CA
Primary Contact: Wayne Ferch, President and Chief Executive Officer
Web address: www.hanfordhealth.com
**Control:** Church–operated, Nongovernment, not–for profit **Service:** General Medical and Surgical

**Staffed Beds: 49 Admissions: 2227 Census: 12 Outpatient Visits: 386183 Births: 2129 Total Expense ($000): 99523 Payroll Expense ($000): 33064 Personnel: 720**

### HARBOR CITY—Los Angeles County, See Los Angeles

### HAWAIIAN GARDENS—Los Angeles County

◇ **GARDENS REGIONAL HOSPITAL AND MEDICAL CENTER (050575)**, 21530 South Pioneer Boulevard, Zip 90716–2608; tel. 562/860–0401, (Nonreporting) **A**9 10 21
Primary Contact: James Sherman, President and Chief Executive Officer
CMO: Derek Dobalian, M.D., Chief of Staff
CIO: Anthony Carrasco, Director Information Systems
CHR: Gregg W. Yost, Chief Human Resources Officer
CNO: Juliet Miranda, Chief Nursing Officer
Web address: www.grhmc.org
**Control:** Other not–for–profit (including NFP Corporation) **Service:** General Medical and Surgical

**Staffed Beds: 107**

### HAYWARD—Alameda County

☐ **ST. ROSE HOSPITAL (050002)**, 27200 Calaroga Avenue, Zip 94545–4383; tel. 510/264–4000, (Nonreporting) **A**1 9 10
Primary Contact: Lex Reddy, President and Chief Executive Officer
CFO: Michael Taylor, Vice President Financial Services and Chief Financial Officer
CMO: Charles S. Feldstein, M.D., Vice President Medical Affairs
CHR: John Davini, Vice President
Web address: www.srhca.org
**Control:** Church–operated, Nongovernment, not–for profit **Service:** General Medical and Surgical

**Staffed Beds: 150**

### HEALDSBURG—Sonoma County

◇ **HEALDSBURG DISTRICT HOSPITAL (051321)**, 1375 University Avenue, Zip 95448–3382; tel. 707/431–6500, (Nonreporting) **A**9 10 18 21
Primary Contact: Nancy Schmid, Chief Executive Officer
COO: Regina Novello, R.N., Chief Operating Officer
CFO: John S. Parigi, II, Interim Chief Financial Officer
CMO: Judy Widger, M.D., Chief of Staff
CIO: Steven Hansen, Director Information Technology
CHR: Kristina Holloway, Chief Human Resources Officer
CNO: Susan G. Spoelma, MSN, Chief Nursing Officer
Web address: www.nschd.org
**Control:** Hospital district or authority, Government, nonfederal **Service:** General Medical and Surgical

**Staffed Beds: 24**

*Many Facility Codes have changed. Please refer to the AHA Guide Code Chart.*

**HEMET—Riverside County**

☐ **HEMET VALLEY MEDICAL CENTER (050390)**, 1117 East Devonshire Avenue, Zip 92543–3083; tel. 951/652–2811, (Nonreporting) **A**1 9 10 12 13 **S** Physicians for Healthy Hospitals, Hemet, CA
Primary Contact: Joel M. Bergenfeld, Chief Hospital Executive Officer
CFO: John R. Collins, Chief Financial Officer
CHR: Michele Bird, Chief Human Resources Officer
CNO: Kathryn McLaughlin, Chief Nursing Officer
Web address: www.physiciansforhealthyhospitals.com
**Control:** Hospital district or authority, Government, nonfederal **Service:** General Medical and Surgical

Staffed Beds: 238

**HOLLISTER—San Benito County**

☒ **HAZEL HAWKINS MEMORIAL HOSPITAL (050296)**, 911 Sunset Drive, Zip 95023–5695; tel. 831/637–5711, (Includes WILLIAM AND INEZ MABIE SKILLED NURSING FACILITY, 911 Sunset Drive, Zip 95023; tel. 408/637–5711), (Nonreporting) **A**1 9 10
Primary Contact: Ken Underwood, Chief Executive Officer
CFO: Mark Robinson, Associate Administrator and Chief Financial Officer
CIO: Julio Gil, Manager Information Services
CHR: Ysidro Gallardo, Associate Administrator Human Resources
Web address: www.hazelhawkins.com
**Control:** Hospital district or authority, Government, nonfederal **Service:** General Medical and Surgical

Staffed Beds: 113

**HOLLYWOOD—Los Angeles County, See Los Angeles**

**HUNTINGTON BEACH—Orange County**

☐ **HUNTINGTON BEACH HOSPITAL (050526)**, 17772 Beach Boulevard, Zip 92647–6896; tel. 714/843–5000, (Nonreporting) **A**1 10 **S** Prime Healthcare Services, Ontario, CA
Primary Contact: Kevan Metcalfe, Chief Executive Officer
CFO: Alan H. Smith, Chief Financial Officer
CMO: Hassan Alkhouli, M.D., Medical Director
CIO: Adam Morquecho, Director Information Technology
CHR: Stephanie Sioson, Director Human Resources
CNO: Sofia Abrina, Administrator and Chief Nursing Officer
Web address: www.hbhospital.com
**Control:** Other not-for-profit (including NFP Corporation) **Service:** General Medical and Surgical

Staffed Beds: 131

**HUNTINGTON PARK—Los Angeles County**

**COMMUNITY AND MISSION HOSPITALS OF HUNTINGTON PARK** See Community Hospital of Huntington Park

○ **COMMUNITY HOSPITAL OF HUNTINGTON PARK (050091)**, 2623 East Slauson Avenue, Zip 90255–2926; tel. 323/583–1931 **A**10 11 **F**3 29 40 41 49 70 79 81 89 107 108 119 130 148 **S** Avanti Hospitals, El Segundo, CA
Primary Contact: Araceli Lonergan, Chief Executive Officer
CFO: Cheryl Tong, Corporate Chief Financial Officer
CMO: Jose Rivas, M.D., Chief of Staff
CIO: Jason Cervantes, Corporate Chief Information Officer
CHR: Paul Celuch, Corporate Human Resources Director
CNO: Lisa Jacobson, Director of Nursing
Web address: www.chhplax.com
**Control:** Corporation, Investor-owned, for-profit **Service:** General Medical and Surgical

Staffed Beds: 81 Admissions: 3497 Census: 37 Outpatient Visits: 39914 Births: 0 Total Expense ($000): 37226 Payroll Expense ($000): 20000

**INDIO—Riverside County**

☒ **JOHN F. KENNEDY MEMORIAL HOSPITAL (050534)**, 47111 Monroe Street, Zip 92201–6799; tel. 760/347–6191 **A**1 9 10 **F**3 8 18 20 29 30 34 35 37 40 46 47 48 49 50 54 56 57 59 64 65 67 85 87 89 97 107 108 111 118 119 126 130 146 148 **S** TENET Healthcare Corporation, Dallas, TX
Primary Contact: Gary Honts, Chief Executive Officer
COO: Patrick Caster, Chief Operating Officer
CFO: Lorna Curtis, Chief Financial Officer
CHR: Raymond Konieczek, Chief Human Resources Officer
CNO: Barbara Eusebio, Chief Nursing Officer
Web address: www.jfkmemorialhosp.com
**Control:** Corporation, Investor-owned, for-profit **Service:** General Medical and Surgical

Staffed Beds: 112 Admissions: 7796 Census: 70 Outpatient Visits: 54425 Births: 2214 Total Expense ($000): 118576 Payroll Expense ($000): 54600 Personnel: 579

**INGLEWOOD—Los Angeles County**

☐ **CENTINELA HOSPITAL MEDICAL CENTER (050739)**, 555 East Hardy Street, Zip 90301–4011, Mailing Address: P.O. Box 720, Zip 90312–6720; tel. 310/673–4660, (Nonreporting) **A**1 10 **S** Prime Healthcare Services, Ontario, CA
Primary Contact: Linda Bradley, Chief Executive Officer
CFO: Paul Sennett, Chief Financial Officer
CMO: Paryus Patel, M.D., Chief Medical Officer
CIO: Martin Cordova, Director Information Services
CHR: George Akopyan, Director Human Resources
CNO: Mohammad Abdelnaser, Chief Nursing Officer
Web address: www.centinelamed.com
**Control:** Corporation, Investor-owned, for-profit **Service:** General Medical and Surgical

Staffed Beds: 353

**IRVINE—Orange County**

◇ **HOAG ORTHOPEDIC INSTITUTE (050769)**, 16250 Sand Canyon Avenue, Zip 92618–3714; tel. 949/517–3149, (Nonreporting) **A**3 21
Primary Contact: Deressa Reid, Interim Chief Executive Officer
Web address: www.hoag.org/Locations/Pages/HoagHospOrthoInstitute.aspx
**Control:** Other not-for-profit (including NFP Corporation) **Service:** Orthopedic

Staffed Beds: 20

**ORANGE COUNTY IRVINE MEDICAL CENTER** See Kaiser Permanente Orange County Anaheim Medical Center, Anaheim

**JACKSON—Amador County**

☒ **SUTTER AMADOR HOSPITAL (050014)**, 200 Mission Boulevard, Zip 95642–2564; tel. 209/223–7500 **A**1 5 9 10 20 **F**29 34 35 40 46 47 49 54 59 64 65 70 75 76 77 78 79 81 85 87 93 102 107 108 110 111 115 119 129 130 132 146 148 **S** Sutter Health, Sacramento, CA
Primary Contact: Anne Platt, Chief Executive Officer
CFO: Brett Moore, CPA, Assistant Administrator Finance
CMO: Ron Hood, M.D., Chief of Staff
CIO: Joy Bailey, Director Information Technology
CHR: Beverly Revels, Director Human Resources
CNO: Nikki Allen, Patient Care Executive
Web address: www.sutteramador.org
**Control:** Other not-for-profit (including NFP Corporation) **Service:** General Medical and Surgical

Staffed Beds: 52 Admissions: 2495 Census: 23 Outpatient Visits: 41678 Births: 319 Total Expense ($000): 64514 Payroll Expense ($000): 21012 Personnel: 267

**JOSHUA TREE—San Bernardino County**

☒ **HI-DESERT MEDICAL CENTER (050279)**, 6601 White Feather Road, Zip 92252–6607; tel. 760/366–3711, (Total facility includes 120 beds in nursing home-type unit) **A**1 9 10 20 **F**8 11 13 15 18 29 30 34 35 39 40 45 46 50 54 57 59 62 63 64 65 66 68 70 77 79 81 82 93 94 97 104 107 110 111 115 119 127 128 130 135 146 148 **S** TENET Healthcare Corporation, Dallas, TX
Primary Contact: Randall L. Kelley, FACHE, Interim Chief Executive Officer
CMO: Sumit Mahajan, M.D., Chief Medical Staff
CHR: Barbara Staresinic, Director Human Resources
Web address: www.hdmc.org
**Control:** Hospital district or authority, Government, nonfederal **Service:** General Medical and Surgical

Staffed Beds: 179 Admissions: 3693 Census: 132 Outpatient Visits: 122543 Births: 405 Total Expense ($000): 65447 Payroll Expense ($000): 27565 Personnel: 446

**KENTFIELD—Marin County**

☒ **KENTFIELD REHABILITATION AND SPECIALTY HOSPITAL (052043)**, 1125 Sir Francis Drake Boulevard, Zip 94904–1455; tel. 415/456–9680 **A**1 9 10 **F**1 29 54 77 93 119 148 **P**6 8 **S** Vibra Healthcare, Mechanicsburg, PA
Primary Contact: Ann Gors, Chief Executive Officer
CFO: Stephanie Lawrence, Chief Financial Officer
CMO: Curtis Roebken, M.D., Chief Medical Staff
CHR: Julene English, Director Human Resources
Web address: www.kentfieldrehab.com
**Control:** Corporation, Investor-owned, for-profit **Service:** Long-Term Acute Care hospital

Staffed Beds: 48 Admissions: 424 Census: 48 Outpatient Visits: 15310 Births: 0 Total Expense ($000): 33937 Payroll Expense ($000): 15696 Personnel: 227

CA

---

**Hospital, Medicare Provider Number, Address, Telephone, Approval, Facility, and Physician Codes, Health Care System**

★ American Hospital Association (AHA) membership
☐ The Joint Commission accreditation
○ Healthcare Facilities Accreditation Program
◇ DNV Healthcare Inc. accreditation
⇑ Center for Improvement in Healthcare Quality Accreditation
△ Commission on Accreditation of Rehabilitation Facilities (CARF) accreditation

**CA**

## KING CITY—Monterey County

☐ **MEE MEMORIAL HOSPITAL (050189)**, 300 Canal Street, Zip 93930–3431; tel. 831/385–6000, (Nonreporting) **A**1 9 10 20
Primary Contact: Lex Smith, Chief Executive Officer
CFO: Gary L. Wangsmo, Chief Financial Officer
CMO: Schindelheim Roy, M.D., Chief of Staff
CIO: Mike McNamara, Chief Information Officer
CHR: Karen Wong, Chief Human Resources Officer
Web address: www.meememorial.com
**Control:** Other not–for–profit (including NFP Corporation) **Service:** General Medical and Surgical

**Staffed Beds: 119**

## LA JOLLA—San Diego County

⌧ **SCRIPPS GREEN HOSPITAL (050424)**, 10666 North Torrey Pines Road, Zip 92037–1093; tel. 858/455–9100 **A**1 2 5 8 9 10 **F**3 8 11 12 14 15 17 18 20 22 24 26 28 29 30 31 34 35 36 37 44 45 46 47 49 50 51 54 57 58 59 61 64 68 70 74 75 77 78 79 80 81 82 84 85 86 87 93 107 108 110 111 113 114 115 117 118 119 120 121 123 124 126 130 131 132 136 138 139 141 142 146 148 **P**3 **S** Scripps Health, San Diego, CA
Primary Contact: Robin Brown, Chief Executive, Senior Vice President
CFO: Richard Rothberger, Corporate Executive Vice President and Chief Financial Officer
CMO: James LaBelle, M.D., Chief Medical Officer
CIO: Patric Thomas, Corporate Vice President Information Services
CHR: Victor Buzachero, Corporate Senior Vice President for Innovation, Human Resources and Performance Management
Web address: www.scrippshealth.org
**Control:** Other not–for–profit (including NFP Corporation) **Service:** General Medical and Surgical

**Staffed Beds: 173 Admissions: 9216 Census: 103 Outpatient Visits: 86204 Births: 0 Total Expense ($000): 311722 Payroll Expense ($000): 96621 Personnel: 1314**

⌧ **SCRIPPS MEMORIAL HOSPITAL–LA JOLLA (050324)**, 9888 Genesee Avenue, Zip 92037–1200, Mailing Address: P.O. Box 28, Zip 92038–0028; tel. 858/626–4123 **A**1 2 3 5 9 10 **F**3 5 8 11 12 13 14 15 17 18 20 22 24 26 28 29 30 31 34 40 43 44 45 46 48 49 51 53 54 55 57 58 59 64 65 68 70 74 75 76 77 78 79 81 82 84 85 86 87 91 92 93 94 100 101 102 107 108 110 111 114 115 117 118 119 124 126 130 132 141 145 146 147 148 **P**3 5 **S** Scripps Health, San Diego, CA
Primary Contact: Gary G. Fybel, Chief Executive, Senior Vice President
COO: Cindy Steckel, Vice President Chief Nurse and Operations Executive
CFO: Linda Honaker, Vice President Financial Operations
CMO: James LaBelle, M.D., Chief Medical Officer
CHR: Shelly Blazakis, Director Human Resources Services
CNO: Cindy Steckel, Vice President Chief Nurse and Operations Executive
Web address: www.scripps.org/locations/hospitals__scripps–memorial–hospital–la–jolla
**Control:** Other not–for–profit (including NFP Corporation) **Service:** General Medical and Surgical

**Staffed Beds: 194 Admissions: 15604 Census: 180 Outpatient Visits: 94772 Births: 3911 Total Expense ($000): 420359 Payroll Expense ($000): 148256 Personnel: 1937**

## LA MESA—San Diego County

☐ **ALVARADO PARKWAY INSTITUTE BEHAVIORAL HEALTH SYSTEM (054075)**, 7050 Parkway Drive, Zip 91942–1535; tel. 619/465–4411 **A**1 9 10 **F**4 5 29 30 34 35 38 50 59 64 68 75 82 87 98 100 101 103 104 105 130 132 135
Primary Contact: Patrick C. Ziemer, Chief Executive Officer
CFO: Chad Engbrecht, Chief Financial Officer
CMO: Saleem Ishaque, M.D., Executive Medical Director
CNO: Bonnie Asada, Director of Nursing
Web address: www.apibhs.com
**Control:** Corporation, Investor–owned, for–profit **Service:** Psychiatric

**Staffed Beds: 66 Admissions: 2254 Census: 60 Outpatient Visits: 102380 Births: 0 Total Expense ($000): 23821 Payroll Expense ($000): 12156 Personnel: 243**

⌧ △ **SHARP GROSSMONT HOSPITAL (050026)**, 5555 Grossmont Center Drive, Zip 91942–3019, Mailing Address: P.O. Box 158, Zip 91944–0158; tel. 619/740–6000, (Total facility includes 30 beds in nursing home–type unit) **A**1 2 3 7 9 10 **F**3 8 11 13 15 17 18 20 22 24 26 28 29 30 31 34 35 38 40 43 44 45 46 47 48 49 50 54 55 56 57 58 59 60 61 62 63 64 65 66 68 70 72 74 75 76 77 78 79 80 81 82 83 84 85 86 87 90 91 92 93 94 96 97 98 99 100 101 102 103 104 105 107 108 109 110 111 114 115 116 117 118 119 120 121 123 124 126 128 129 130 132 135 141 143 145 146 147 148 **S** Sharp HealthCare, San Diego, CA
Primary Contact: Scott Evans, FACHE, PharmD, Senior Vice President and Chief Executive Officer
COO: Maryann Cone, Chief Operating Officer
CFO: Kari Cornicelli, Chief Financial Officer
CMO: Michael Murphy, M.D., Chief Medical Officer
CIO: Kenneth Lawonn, Senior Vice President and Chief Information Officer
CHR: George Holtz, Director Human Resources
Web address: www.sharp.com
**Control:** Other not–for–profit (including NFP Corporation) **Service:** General Medical and Surgical

**Staffed Beds: 490 Admissions: 28842 Census: 343 Outpatient Visits: 320634 Births: 3883 Total Expense ($000): 579921 Payroll Expense ($000): 245688 Personnel: 2841**

## LA MIRADA—Los Angeles County

⌧ **KINDRED HOSPITAL–LA MIRADA (052038)**, 14900 East Imperial Highway, Zip 90638–2172; tel. 562/944–1900, (Includes KINDRED HOSPITAL SAN GABRIEL VALLEY, 845 North Lark Ellen Avenue, West Covina, Zip 91791–1069; tel. 626/339–5451; Eleyce Winn, Chief Executive Officer; KINDRED HOSPITAL SANTA ANA, 1901 North College Avenue, Santa Ana, Zip 92706–2334; tel. 714/564–7800; Victor Carrasco, Chief Executive Officer), (Nonreporting) **A**1 9 10 **S** Kindred Healthcare, Louisville, KY
Primary Contact: April Myers, Administrator
CFO: Rishab Punjabi, Chief Financial Officer
CMO: Prakash Chandra Patel, M.D., Chief of Staff
CHR: Susan Bergquist, Human Resources Generalist
CNO: Esperanza Sanchez, Chief Clinical Officer
Web address: www.kindredlamirada.com/
**Control:** Corporation, Investor–owned, for–profit **Service:** Long–Term Acute Care hospital

**Staffed Beds: 216**

## LA PALMA—Orange County

☐ **LA PALMA INTERCOMMUNITY HOSPITAL (050580)**, 7901 Walker Street, Zip 90623–1764; tel. 714/670–7400 **A**1 10 **F**3 8 13 15 17 18 20 22 29 35 40 41 45 49 56 59 60 64 70 76 77 79 81 85 91 98 101 102 103 104 105 107 108 111 114 119 130 146 147 148 **S** Prime Healthcare Services, Ontario, CA
Primary Contact: Virgis Narbutas, Chief Executive Officer
CFO: Alan H. Smith, Chief Financial Officer
CMO: Sami Shoukair, M.D., Chief Medical Officer
CIO: Vic Mahan, Director Information Technology
CHR: Stephanie Sioson, Director Human Resources
CNO: Hilda Manzo–Luna, Chief Nursing Officer
Web address: www.lapalmaintercommunityhospital.com
**Control:** Other not–for–profit (including NFP Corporation) **Service:** General Medical and Surgical

**Staffed Beds: 141 Admissions: 2899 Census: 48 Outpatient Visits: 27215 Births: 463 Personnel: 312**

## LAGUNA HILLS—Orange County

⌧ **SADDLEBACK MEMORIAL MEDICAL CENTER (050603)**, 24451 Health Center Drive, Zip 92653–3689; tel. 949/837–4500, (Includes SADDLEBACK MEMORIAL MEDICAL CENTER – SAN CLEMENTE CAMPUS, 654 Camino De Los Mares, San Clemente, Zip 92673–2827; tel. 949/496–1122) **A**1 2 9 10 **F**3 11 12 13 14 16 18 20 22 24 26 28 29 30 31 34 35 36 38 40 44 45 46 47 48 49 50 51 53 54 55 56 57 58 59 62 63 64 65 68 70 72 74 75 76 77 78 79 81 82 84 85 86 87 93 94 96 100 107 108 110 111 114 115 116 117 118 119 120 121 123 124 126 130 132 135 141 142 143 145 146 147 148 **P**7 **S** MemorialCare, Fountain Valley, CA
Primary Contact: Steve Geidt, Chief Executive Officer
COO: Cheryl Jacob, Chief Operating Officer
CFO: Adolfo Chanez, Vice President Finance and Chief Financial Officer
CMO: Ernest Hayward, M.D., Chief of Staff
CIO: J. Scott Joslyn, Senior Vice President and Chief Information Officer
CHR: Kayce H. Hudson, Executive Director Human Resources
CNO: Kathy Dawson, R.N., Chief Nursing Officer
Web address: www.memorialcare.org
**Control:** Other not–for–profit (including NFP Corporation) **Service:** General Medical and Surgical

**Staffed Beds: 313 Admissions: 14708 Census: 149 Outpatient Visits: 271963 Births: 2751 Total Expense ($000): 345685 Payroll Expense ($000): 115442 Personnel: 1426**

**CA**

## LAKE ARROWHEAD—San Bernardino County

✠ **SAN BERNARDINO MOUNTAINS COMMUNITY HOSPITAL DISTRICT (051312)**, 29101 Hospital Road, Zip 92352–9706, Mailing Address: P.O. Box 70, Zip 92352–0070; tel. 909/336–3651, (Nonreporting) **A**1 9 10 18
Primary Contact: Charles Harrison, Chief Executive Officer
COO: Terry Pena, Chief Operating Officer and Chief Nursing Officer
CFO: Yvonne Waggener, Chief Financial Officer
CMO: Lawrence Walker, M.D., Chief of Staff
CIO: Patrick Miller, Technology Coordinator
CHR: Julie Atwood, Director Human Resources
CNO: Terry Pena, Chief Operating Officer and Chief Nursing Officer
Web address: www.mchcares.com
**Control:** Hospital district or authority, Government, nonfederal **Service:** General Medical and Surgical

| **Staffed Beds: 37** |
| --- |

## LAKE ISABELLA—Kern County

**KERN VALLEY HEALTHCARE DISTRICT (051314)**, 6412 Laurel Avenue, Zip 93240–9529, Mailing Address: P.O. Box 1628, Zip 93240–1628; tel. 760/379–2681, (Nonreporting) **A**9 10 18
Primary Contact: Timothy McGlew, Chief Executive Officer
CFO: Chester Beedle, Chief Financial Officer
CMO: Gary A. Finstad, M.D., Chief of Staff
CIO: Paul Quinn, Information Systems Manager
CHR: Debra Hoffman, Manager Human Resources
CNO: Mark Gordon, Chief Nursing Officer
Web address: www.kvhd.org
**Control:** Hospital district or authority, Government, nonfederal **Service:** General Medical and Surgical

| **Staffed Beds: 99** |
| --- |

## LAKEPORT—Lake County

✠ **SUTTER LAKESIDE HOSPITAL (051329)**, 5176 Hill Road East, Zip 95453–6300; tel. 707/262–5000 **A**1 9 10 18 **F**3 8 11 13 15 18 29 30 34 35 36 40 43 45 46 51 53 54 56 57 59 61 64 65 66 68 70 71 74 75 76 79 81 82 85 86 87 91 93 96 97 107 110 111 114 118 119 127 130 131 133 135 146 147 148 **S** Sutter Health, Sacramento, CA
Primary Contact: Siri Nelson, Chief Administrative Officer
CFO: Linnea Humble, Director of Finance
CMO: Diane Pege, M.D., Vice President Medical Affairs
CIO: Jack Buell, Director Information Services
CHR: Brenda DeRamus, Manager Human Resources
CNO: Teresa Campbell, R.N., Chief Nursing Executive
Web address: www.sutterlakeside.org
**Control:** Other not–for–profit (including NFP Corporation) **Service:** General Medical and Surgical

| **Staffed Beds: 25 Admissions: 1802 Census: 17 Outpatient Visits: 74907 Births: 306 Total Expense ($000): 70226 Payroll Expense ($000): 23251 Personnel: 296** |
| --- |

## LAKEWOOD—Los Angeles County

✠ **LAKEWOOD REGIONAL MEDICAL CENTER (050581)**, 3700 East South Street, Zip 90712–1498, Mailing Address: P.O. Box 6070, Zip 90714–6070; tel. 562/531–2550 **A**1 9 10 **F**3 11 15 17 18 20 22 24 26 29 30 34 35 38 40 45 49 50 51 57 59 64 68 70 74 75 77 81 85 87 93 107 108 109 111 115 118 119 120 126 130 132 143 146 148 **S** TENET Healthcare Corporation, Dallas, TX
Primary Contact: Timothy P. Menton, Interim Chief Executive Officer
CFO: Eric Delgado, Chief Financial Officer
CMO: Ronald L. Kaufman, M.D., Chief Medical Officer
CIO: Pat Pierce, Director Information Systems
CHR: Mary Okuhara, Director Human Resources
CNO: Terri Newton, Chief Nursing Officer
Web address: www.lakewoodregional.com
**Control:** Corporation, Investor–owned, for–profit **Service:** General Medical and Surgical

| **Staffed Beds: 153 Admissions: 8090 Census: 108 Outpatient Visits: 64598 Births: 0 Total Expense ($000): 141959 Payroll Expense ($000): 67499 Personnel: 752** |
| --- |

## LANCASTER—Los Angeles County

✠ **ANTELOPE VALLEY HOSPITAL (050056)**, 1600 West Avenue J, Zip 93534–2894; tel. 661/949–5000, (Nonreporting) **A**1 3 5 9 10
Primary Contact: Jack J. Burke, MS, R.N., Interim Chief Executive Officer
COO: Jack J. Burke, MS, Chief Operating Officer and Chief Nursing Officer
CFO: Paul Brydon, Chief Financial Officer
CMO: Radha Krishnan, M.D., Chief Medical Officer
CIO: Dale Lepper, Interim Chief Information Officer
CHR: George Leisher, Chief Human Resources Officer
CNO: Jack J. Burke, MS, Chief Operating Officer and Chief Nursing Officer
Web address: www.avhospital.org
**Control:** Hospital district or authority, Government, nonfederal **Service:** General Medical and Surgical

| **Staffed Beds: 368** |
| --- |

## LIVERMORE—Alameda County

**VALLEY MEMORIAL** See Stanford Health Care – ValleyCare, Pleasanton

**VETERANS AFFAIRS PALO ALTO HEALTH CARE SYSTEM, LIVERMORE DIVISION** See VA Palo Alto Health Care System, Palo Alto

## LODI—San Joaquin County

✠ **LODI MEMORIAL HOSPITAL (050336)**, 975 South Fairmont Avenue, Zip 95240–5118, Mailing Address: P.O. Box 3004, Zip 95241–1908; tel. 209/334–3411, (Includes LODI MEMORIAL HOSPITAL WEST, 800 South Lower Sacramento Road, Zip 95242; tel. 209/333–0211) **A**1 3 9 10 **F**3 11 12 13 15 18 29 30 32 34 35 40 45 46 47 49 50 53 55 56 57 59 60 62 64 66 68 70 74 75 76 77 79 81 82 83 84 85 86 87 90 91 92 93 96 97 107 108 114 115 119 120 121 126 127 130 131 132 135 144 146 148 **S** Adventist Health, Roseville, CA
Primary Contact: Daniel Wolcott, President and Chief Executive Officer
CFO: Terry Deak, Chief Financial Officer
CHR: Mark T. Wallace, Director Human Resources
CNO: Debbie Moreno, Chief Nursing Officer
Web address: www.lodihealth.org
**Control:** Other not–for–profit (including NFP Corporation) **Service:** General Medical and Surgical

| **Staffed Beds: 190 Admissions: 7034 Census: 86 Outpatient Visits: 238811 Births: 1048 Total Expense ($000): 164425 Payroll Expense ($000): 68367 Personnel: 1125** |
| --- |

## LOMA LINDA—San Bernardino County

**LOMA LINDA UNIVERSITY CHILDREN'S HOSPITAL** See Loma Linda University Medical Center

**LOMA LINDA UNIVERSITY HEART & SURGICAL HOSPITAL** See Loma Linda University Medical Center

✠ △ **LOMA LINDA UNIVERSITY MEDICAL CENTER (050327)**, 11234 Anderson Street, Zip 92354–2804, Mailing Address: P.O. Box 2000, Zip 92354–0200; tel. 909/558–4000, (Includes LOMA LINDA UNIVERSITY CHILDREN'S HOSPITAL, 11234 Anderson Street, tel. 909/558–8000; LOMA LINDA UNIVERSITY EAST CAMPUS HOSPITAL, 25333 Barton Road, Zip 92354–3053; tel. 909/558–6000; LOMA LINDA UNIVERSITY HEART & SURGICAL HOSPITAL, 26780 Barton Road, Zip 92354; tel. 909/583–2900) **A**1 2 3 5 7 8 9 10 **F**2 3 5 11 12 13 15 17 18 19 20 21 22 23 24 25 26 27 28 29 30 31 32 34 35 37 40 41 43 45 46 47 48 49 50 54 57 59 60 62 64 65 68 70 72 74 75 76 77 78 79 81 82 84 85 86 87 88 89 90 91 92 93 94 107 108 110 111 114 115 117 118 119 120 121 122 123 124 126 129 130 132 134 136 137 138 139 141 142 143 144 146 147 148 **P**3 **S** Loma Linda University Adventist Health Sciences Center, Loma Linda, CA
Primary Contact: Kerry Heinrich, JD, Chief Executive Officer
CFO: Steve Mohr, Senior Vice President Finance and Chief Financial Officer
CMO: H. Roger Hadley, M.D., Vice President, Medical Affairs
CIO: Mark Zirkelbach, Chief Information Officer
CHR: Della G. Stange, Executive Director, People Services
CNO: Judith Storfjell, Ph.D., Senior Vice President and Chief Nursing Officer
Web address: www.llumc.edu
**Control:** Other not–for–profit (including NFP Corporation) **Service:** General Medical and Surgical

| **Staffed Beds: 850 Admissions: 31094 Census: 556 Outpatient Visits: 707168 Births: 2781 Total Expense ($000): 1238420 Payroll Expense ($000): 452383 Personnel: 7123** |
| --- |

| **Hospital, Medicare Provider Number, Address, Telephone, Approval, Facility, and Physician Codes, Health Care System** |
| --- |
| ★ American Hospital Association (AHA) membership   ◯ Healthcare Facilities Accreditation Program   ⇑ Center for Improvement in Healthcare Quality Accreditation |
| ☐ The Joint Commission accreditation   ◇ DNV Healthcare Inc. accreditation   △ Commission on Accreditation of Rehabilitation Facilities (CARF) accreditation |

★ △ **VETERANS AFFAIRS LOMA LINDA HEALTHCARE SYSTEM**, 11201 Benton Street, Zip 92357–1000; tel. 909/825–7084, (Nonreporting) **A**1 2 3 5 7 8 **S** Department of Veterans Affairs, Washington, DC
Primary Contact: Barbara Fallen, FACHE, Director
COO: Shane Elliott, Associate Director Administration
CFO: Eric C. Sorenson, Chief Financial Officer
CMO: Dwight Evans, M.D., Chief of Staff
CIO: Doug Wirthgen, Facility Chief Information Officer
CHR: Eugene Wylie, Chief Human Resources Officer
CNO: Anne Gillespie, R.N., Associate Director Patient Care and Nursing Services
Web address: www.lomalinda.va.gov
**Control:** Veterans Affairs, Government, federal **Service:** General Medical and Surgical

**Staffed Beds:** 270

## LOMPOC—Santa Barbara County

CA

★ ⥣ **LOMPOC VALLEY MEDICAL CENTER (050110)**, 1515 East Ocean Avenue, Zip 93436–7092, Mailing Address: P.O. Box 1058, Zip 93438–1058; tel. 805/737–3300, (Nonreporting) **A**9 10 22
Primary Contact: James J. Raggio, Chief Executive Officer
COO: Naishadh Buch, Chief Operating Officer
CFO: Robert M. Baden, Chief Financial Officer
CMO: Randall Michel, M.D., Chief of Staff
CIO: Jim White, Chief Information Officer
CHR: Edwin R. Braxton, Director Human Resources
CNO: Jayne Scalise, R.N., Chief Nursing Executive
Web address: www.lompocvmc.com
**Control:** Hospital district or authority, Government, nonfederal **Service:** General Medical and Surgical

**Staffed Beds:** 140

## LONE PINE—Inyo County

★ **SOUTHERN INYO HEALTHCARE DISTRICT (051302)**, 501 East Locust Street, Zip 93545–1009, Mailing Address: P.O. Box 1009, Zip 93545–1009; tel. 760/876–5501, (Nonreporting) **A**9 10 18
Primary Contact: Lee Barron, Chief Executive Officer
CFO: Lee Barron, Chief Executive Officer
CIO: Patricia M. Murray, Information Officer
CHR: Ashley Williams, Manager Human Resources
Web address: www.sihd.org
**Control:** Hospital district or authority, Government, nonfederal **Service:** General Medical and Surgical

**Staffed Beds:** 4

## LONG BEACH—Los Angeles County

◇ **COLLEGE MEDICAL CENTER (050277)**, 2776 Pacific Avenue, Zip 90806–2699, Mailing Address: P.O. Box 1268, Zip 90801–1268; tel. 562/595–1911, (Nonreporting) **A**9 10 12 13 21
Primary Contact: Joseph Avelino, Chief Executive Officer
COO: Jennifer Ensminger, Chief Operating Officer
CFO: Jim Canedo, Chief Financial Officer
CMO: Luke Watson, M.D., Chief of Staff
CIO: Rohan Corea, Director Healthcare Information Technology
CHR: Ann Mattia Schiller, Vice President Human Resources
Web address: www.phlb.org
**Control:** Other not–for–profit (including NFP Corporation) **Service:** General Medical and Surgical

**Staffed Beds:** 184

☐ **COMMUNITY HOSPITAL LONG BEACH (050727)**, 1720 Termino Avenue, Zip 90804–2104; tel. 562/498–1000 **A**1 5 9 10 **F**3 5 11 12 14 18 26 28 29 30 31 34 35 38 40 45 46 49 50 53 54 56 57 59 64 65 68 70 71 75 77 79 81 82 85 86 87 93 98 100 101 102 103 104 105 107 108 111 115 119 130 132 135 146 148 **S** MemorialCare, Fountain Valley, CA
Primary Contact: Diana Hendel, PharmD, Chief Executive Officer
COO: Diane DeWalsche, R.N., Chief Operating Officer
CMO: Dennis Parmer, M.D., Chief Medical Staff
CIO: Robert Klingseis, Manager Information Systems
CHR: Valene J. Martin, Administrative Director Human Resources
Web address: www.memorialcare.org
**Control:** Other not–for–profit (including NFP Corporation) **Service:** General Medical and Surgical

**Staffed Beds:** 148 **Admissions:** 4584 **Census:** 54 **Outpatient Visits:** 25936 **Births:** 0 **Total Expense ($000):** 60311 **Payroll Expense ($000):** 24368 **Personnel:** 452

★ △ **LONG BEACH MEMORIAL MEDICAL CENTER (050485)**, 2801 Atlantic Avenue, Zip 90806–1701, Mailing Address: P.O. Box 1428, Zip 90801–1428; tel. 562/933–2000 **A**1 2 3 5 7 8 9 10 **F**3 9 11 12 14 15 17 18 20 22 24 26 28 29 30 31 34 35 36 37 38 39 40 43 44 45 47 48 49 50 52 53 55 56 57 58 59 61 63 64 65 68 70 74 75 77 78 79 81 82 84 85 86 87 90 93 96 97 107 108 110 111 114 115 116 117 118 119 120 121 123 124 126 128 129 130 131 132 135 141 142 143 144 146 147 148 **S** MemorialCare, Fountain Valley, CA
Primary Contact: Tammie McMann Brailsford, Interim Chief Executive Officer
COO: Tamra Kaplan, Chief Operating Officer
CFO: John Bishop, Chief Financial Officer
CMO: Susan Melvin, D.O., Chief Medical Officer
CIO: Danny Asaoka, Executive Director Information Systems
CNO: Judith A. Fix, R.N., Senior Vice President and Chief Nursing Officer
Web address: www.memorialcare.org/LongBeach
**Control:** Other not–for–profit (including NFP Corporation) **Service:** General Medical and Surgical

**Staffed Beds:** 458 **Admissions:** 21182 **Census:** 267 **Outpatient Visits:** 186110 **Births:** 0 **Total Expense ($000):** 529494 **Payroll Expense ($000):** 167312 **Personnel:** 3226

☐ **MILLER CHILDREN'S & WOMEN'S HOSPITAL LONG BEACH (053309)**, 2801 Atlantic Avenue, Zip 90806–1701; tel. 562/933–5437 **A**1 2 3 5 9 10 **F**3 11 12 13 14 15 19 21 23 25 27 29 30 31 32 34 35 36 37 38 40 41 43 44 45 47 48 49 50 52 53 54 55 57 58 59 61 64 65 66 68 72 74 75 76 77 78 79 81 82 84 85 86 87 88 89 93 96 97 99 100 101 102 104 107 108 111 114 115 116 117 118 119 120 121 123 124 126 129 130 132 134 135 141 142 143 144 146 147 148 **S** MemorialCare, Fountain Valley, CA
Primary Contact: Diana Hendel, PharmD, Chief Executive Officer
Web address: www.memorialcare.org
**Control:** Other not–for–profit (including NFP Corporation) **Service:** Children's general

**Staffed Beds:** 371 **Admissions:** 15922 **Census:** 190 **Outpatient Visits:** 100879 **Births:** 5987 **Total Expense ($000):** 360426 **Payroll Expense ($000):** 128629 **Personnel:** 1237

★ **ST. MARY MEDICAL CENTER (050191)**, 1050 Linden Avenue, Zip 90813–3321, Mailing Address: P.O. Box 887, Zip 90801–0887; tel. 562/491–9000 **A**1 2 3 5 9 10 **F**3 8 12 13 15 17 18 19 20 22 24 26 28 29 30 31 34 35 38 39 40 43 45 46 47 48 49 50 54 55 57 58 59 60 61 64 65 66 68 70 71 72 74 75 76 77 78 79 81 82 84 85 86 87 89 90 93 97 102 107 108 110 111 114 115 118 119 120 121 125 130 143 145 146 147 148 **P**5 **S** Dignity Health, San Francisco, CA
Primary Contact: Joel P. Yuhas, FACHE, President and Chief Executive Officer
COO: Gail Daly, Chief Nursing Officer and Chief Operating Officer
CFO: Harold Way, Chief Financial Officer
CMO: Andrew Burg, M.D., Chief of Staff
CIO: Rich Patla, Site Director
CHR: Bob Bokern, Director Human Resources
CNO: Gail Daly, Chief Nursing Officer and Chief Operating Officer
Web address: www.stmarymedicalcenter.org
**Control:** Other not–for–profit (including NFP Corporation) **Service:** General Medical and Surgical

**Staffed Beds:** 135 **Admissions:** 11104 **Census:** 135 **Outpatient Visits:** 242345 **Births:** 2743 **Total Expense ($000):** 233180 **Payroll Expense ($000):** 99356 **Personnel:** 1203

★ △ **VA LONG BEACH HEALTHCARE SYSTEM**, 5901 East 7th Street, Zip 90822–5201; tel. 562/826–8000, (Nonreporting) **A**1 2 3 5 7 8 **S** Department of Veterans Affairs, Washington, DC
Primary Contact: Michael W. Fisher, Director
COO: Anthony DeFrancesco, Associate Director
CFO: Michael J. Rupert, Chief Financial Officer
CMO: Sandor Szabo, M.D., Chief of Staff
CIO: Rodney Sagmit, Chief Information Management
CHR: Mary E. McCartan, Manager Human Resources
Web address: www.longbeach.va.gov/
**Control:** Veterans Affairs, Government, federal **Service:** General Medical and Surgical

**Staffed Beds:** 356

## LOS ALAMITOS—Orange County

★ **LOS ALAMITOS MEDICAL CENTER (050551)**, 3751 Katella Avenue, Zip 90720–3164; tel. 562/598–1311 **A**1 9 10 13 **F**3 8 11 13 15 17 18 20 22 28 29 31 34 35 40 41 44 45 49 50 51 54 55 56 57 59 64 65 66 68 70 75 76 77 78 79 81 82 85 86 87 98 103 107 108 109 110 111 112 114 115 117 118 119 120 121 124 126 130 132 142 143 146 148 **P**2 3 5 **S** TENET Healthcare Corporation, Dallas, TX
Primary Contact: Kent G. Clayton, Chief Executive Officer
CFO: Dave Vickers, Chief Financial Officer
CIO: Sally Andrada, Chief Information Officer
CHR: Angie Driscoll, Director Human Resources
Web address: www.losalamitosmedctr.com
**Control:** Corporation, Investor–owned, for–profit **Service:** General Medical and Surgical

**Staffed Beds:** 167 **Admissions:** 9507 **Census:** 117 **Outpatient Visits:** 85134 **Births:** 1373 **Total Expense ($000):** 159140 **Payroll Expense ($000):** 72749 **Personnel:** 875

**LOS ANGELES—Los Angeles County**

(Mailing Addresses - Canoga Park, Encino, Granada Hills, Harbor City, Hollywood, Mission Hills, North Hollywood, Northridge, Panorama City, San Pedro, Sepulveda, Sherman Oaks, Sun Valley, Sylmar, Tarzana, Van Nuys, West Hills, West Los Angeles, Woodland Hills)

✠ **BARLOW RESPIRATORY HOSPITAL (052031)**, 2000 Stadium Way, Zip 90026–2696; tel. 213/250–4200 **A**1 9 10 **F**1 3 14 29 30 35 45 46 64 68 84 93 103 130 132 148
Primary Contact: Margaret W. Crane, Chief Executive Officer
COO: Alex Villarruz, Chief Operating Officer
CFO: Edward Engesser, Chief Financial Officer and Chief Information Officer
CMO: David Nelson, M.D., Medical Director
CIO: Edward Engesser, Chief Financial Officer and Chief Information Officer
CHR: Rashawn Woods, Vice President Human Resources
CNO: Gladys D'Souza, Chief Nursing Officer
Web address: www.barlow2000.org
**Control:** Other not–for–profit (including NFP Corporation) **Service:** Long–Term Acute Care hospital

**Staffed Beds:** 105 **Admissions:** 730 **Census:** 64 **Outpatient Visits:** 0 **Births:** 0 **Total Expense ($000):** 50414 **Payroll Expense ($000):** 22367 **Personnel:** 269

✠ **CALIFORNIA HOSPITAL MEDICAL CENTER (050149)**, 1401 South Grand Avenue, Zip 90015–3010; tel. 213/748–2411, (Total facility includes 31 beds in nursing home–type unit) **A**1 3 5 9 10 **F**3 11 17 29 30 31 34 35 40 43 45 49 51 53 57 59 64 70 72 76 78 79 81 84 89 102 107 108 111 114 119 121 130 132 135 143 146 147 **S** Dignity Health, San Francisco, CA
Primary Contact: Margaret R. Peterson, Ph.D., R.N., President
COO: Harold Newton, Chief Operating Officer
CFO: Rebecca Cheng, Chief Financial Officer
CMO: Joseph Nussbaum, M.D., Chief of Staff
CIO: Rich Patla, Director Information Technology
CHR: Lisa Guzman, Director Human Resources
Web address: www.chmcla.org
**Control:** Other not–for–profit (including NFP Corporation) **Service:** General Medical and Surgical

**Staffed Beds:** 318 **Admissions:** 15830 **Census:** 172 **Outpatient Visits:** 92679 **Births:** 3984 **Total Expense ($000):** 329160 **Payroll Expense ($000):** 129141 **Personnel:** 1473

✠ △ **CEDARS–SINAI MEDICAL CENTER (050625)**, 8700 Beverly Boulevard, Zip 90048–1865, Mailing Address: Box 48750, Zip 90048–0750; tel. 310/423–5000 **A**1 2 3 5 7 8 9 10 **F**3 5 6 8 9 11 12 13 14 15 17 18 19 20 21 22 23 24 25 26 27 28 29 30 31 32 33 34 35 36 37 38 43 44 45 46 47 48 49 50 51 52 53 54 55 56 57 58 59 60 61 64 65 66 68 69 70 71 72 74 75 76 77 78 79 81 82 83 84 85 86 87 88 89 90 91 92 93 96 97 100 102 107 108 109 110 111 112 113 114 115 116 117 118 119 120 121 122 123 124 126 130 131 132 133 134 135 136 137 138 139 140 141 142 145 146 147 148 **P**3 4 5 8
Primary Contact: Thomas M. Priselac, President and Chief Executive Officer
COO: Mark R. Gavens, Senior Vice President Clinical Care Services and Chief Operating Officer
CFO: Edward M. Prunchunas, Senior Vice President and Chief Financial Officer
CMO: Michael L. Langberg, M.D., Senior Vice President Medical Affairs and Chief Medical Officer
CIO: Darren Dworkin, Senior Vice President and Chief Information Officer
CHR: Jeanne Flores, Senior Vice President Human Resources and Organizational Development
CNO: Linda Burnes Bolton, R.N., Vice President and Chief Nursing Officer
Web address: www.cedars–sinai.edu
**Control:** Other not–for–profit (including NFP Corporation) **Service:** General Medical and Surgical

**Staffed Beds:** 882 **Admissions:** 45268 **Census:** 642 **Outpatient Visits:** 747137 **Births:** 6718 **Total Expense ($000):** 2457372 **Payroll Expense ($000):** 927194 **Personnel:** 11246

✠ **CHILDREN'S HOSPITAL LOS ANGELES (053302)**, 4650 West Sunset Boulevard, Zip 90027–6062, Mailing Address: 4650 West Sunset Boulevard, MS #1, Zip 90027–6062; tel. 323/660–2450 **A**1 3 5 9 10 **F**3 5 8 14 17 19 21 23 25 27 29 30 31 32 34 35 36 38 39 40 41 43 44 45 46 49 50 51 54 55 57 58 59 60 61 64 68 71 72 74 75 77 78 79 80 81 82 84 85 86 87 88 89 90 93 99 100 104 107 108 111 114 115 116 117 118 119 120 121 122 123 124 126 129 130 131 132 134 135 136 137 138 139 141 146 148
Primary Contact: Paul S. Viviano, President and Chief Executive Officer
CFO: Lannie Tonnu, Senior Vice President and Chief Financial Officer
CMO: Brent Polk, M.D., Chair Department of Pediatrics and Vice President Academic Affairs
CIO: TJ Malseed, Vice President and Chief Information Officer
CHR: Myra Gregorian, Vice President and Chief Human Resources Officer
CNO: Mary Dee Hacker, R.N., Vice President, Patient Care Services and Chief Nursing Officer
Web address: www.chla.org
**Control:** Other not–for–profit (including NFP Corporation) **Service:** Children's general

**Staffed Beds:** 347 **Admissions:** 14615 **Census:** 277 **Outpatient Visits:** 316734 **Births:** 0

☐ **EAST LOS ANGELES DOCTORS HOSPITAL (050641)**, 4060 Whittier Boulevard, Zip 90023–2526; tel. 323/268–5514, (Nonreporting) **A**1 9 10 **S** Avanti Hospitals, El Segundo, CA
Primary Contact: Araceli Lonergan, Chief Executive Officer
CFO: Daniel R. Heckathorne, System Chief Financial Officer
CMO: Michael Austerlitz, M.D., Chief of Staff
CIO: Jason Cervantes, Chief Information Officer
CHR: Paul Celuch, Chief Human Resource Officer
CNO: Nadine A. Mariotti, R.N., Chief Nursing Officer
Web address: www.elalax.com
**Control:** Partnership, Investor–owned, for–profit **Service:** General Medical and Surgical

**Staffed Beds:** 127

☐ **ENCINO HOSPITAL MEDICAL CENTER (050158)**, 16237 Ventura Boulevard, Encino, Zip 91436–2272; tel. 818/995–5000, (Nonreporting) **A**1 10 **S** Prime Healthcare Services, Ontario, CA
Primary Contact: Bockhi Park, Chief Executive Officer
CFO: Kanner Tillman, Chief Financial Officer
CMO: Muhammad Anwar, M.D., Chief Medical Officer
CIO: Edward Barrera, Director Communications
CHR: Barbara Back, Manager Human Resources
CNO: Vilma L. Dinham, R.N., Chief Nursing Officer
Web address: www.encinomed.com
**Control:** Other not–for–profit (including NFP Corporation) **Service:** General Medical and Surgical

**Staffed Beds:** 66

○ **GATEWAYS HOSPITAL AND MENTAL HEALTH CENTER (054028)**, 1891 Effie Street, Zip 90026–1793; tel. 323/644–2000 **A**10 11 **F**29 35 77 94 98 99 100 101 104 106 130 **P**6
Primary Contact: Mara Pelsman, Chief Executive Officer
COO: Jeff Emery, Chief Financial Officer and Chief Operating Officer
CFO: Jeff Emery, Chief Financial Officer and Chief Operating Officer
CMO: Mark Hantoot, M.D., Medical Director
CIO: Jeff Emery, Chief Financial Officer and Chief Operating Officer
CHR: Melanie Van Heusen, Director Human Resources
Web address: www.gatewayshospital.org
**Control:** Other not–for–profit (including NFP Corporation) **Service:** Psychiatric

**Staffed Beds:** 55 **Admissions:** 1012 **Census:** 37 **Outpatient Visits:** 115778 **Births:** 0 **Personnel:** 305

**GENERAL HOSPITAL** See LAC/University of Southern California Medical Center

**CA**

---

**Hospital, Medicare Provider Number, Address, Telephone, Approval, Facility, and Physician Codes, Health Care System**

★ American Hospital Association (AHA) membership
☐ The Joint Commission accreditation
○ Healthcare Facilities Accreditation Program
◇ DNV Healthcare Inc. accreditation
⇑ Center for Improvement in Healthcare Quality Accreditation
△ Commission on Accreditation of Rehabilitation Facilities (CARF) accreditation

☐ **GOOD SAMARITAN HOSPITAL (050471)**, 1225 Wilshire Boulevard, Zip 90017–2395; tel. 213/977–2121 **A**1 2 3 5 9 10 **F**3 7 8 11 13 14 15 17 18 20 22 24 26 28 29 30 31 34 35 36 37 40 43 45 46 47 48 49 50 51 53 57 58 59 60 64 65 68 70 72 74 75 76 77 78 79 81 85 86 87 93 107 108 110 111 114 115 117 118 119 120 121 123 124 126 129 130 132 143 145 146 148 **P**5
Primary Contact: Andrew B. Leeka, President and Chief Executive Officer
COO: Dan C. McLaughlin, Vice President Professional Services
CFO: Alan Ino, Chief Financial Officer
CMO: Margaret Bates, Chief of Staff
CIO: Dean Campbell, Vice President Information Services and Chief Information Officer
CHR: Lexie Schuster, Vice President Human Resources
CNO: Margaret Pfeiffer, R.N., Vice President Patient Care Services
Web address: www.goodsam.org
**Control:** Other not–for–profit (including NFP Corporation) **Service:** General Medical and Surgical

**Staffed Beds: 374 Admissions: 12809 Census: 155 Outpatient Visits: 91297 Births: 3858 Total Expense ($000): 269470 Payroll Expense ($000): 116969 Personnel: 1314**

☒ **HOLLYWOOD PRESBYTERIAN MEDICAL CENTER (050063)**, 1300 North Vermont Avenue, Zip 90027–6306; tel. 213/413–3000 **A**1 3 5 9 10 **F**3 8 13 15 17 18 20 22 24 26 29 30 31 34 40 41 45 46 49 50 51 56 57 59 60 61 64 68 70 72 74 75 76 77 78 79 80 81 85 87 89 90 92 93 96 97 107 108 110 111 115 119 130 132 146 147 148 **P**3 5
Primary Contact: Allen Stefanek, Chief Executive Officer
COO: Allen Stefanek, Chief Operating Officer
CFO: Michael Almanzor, Chief Financial Officer
CMO: John Gentile, M.D., Chief Medical Officer
CIO: Steve Giles, Chief Information Officer
CHR: Norma Braun, Vice President Human Resources
CNO: Julieta M. Padilla, Chief Nursing Officer
Web address: www.hollywoodpresbyterian.com
**Control:** Partnership, Investor–owned, for–profit **Service:** General Medical and Surgical

**Staffed Beds: 434 Admissions: 12961 Census: 229 Outpatient Visits: 58818 Births: 3583 Total Expense ($000): 233472 Payroll Expense ($000): 95123 Personnel: 1174**

**KAISER FOUNDATION MENTAL HEALTH CENTER** See Kaiser Permanente Los Angeles Medical Center

☒ **KAISER PERMANENTE LOS ANGELES MEDICAL CENTER (050138)**, 4867 Sunset Boulevard, Zip 90027–5961; tel. 323/783–4011, (Includes KAISER FOUNDATION MENTAL HEALTH CENTER, 765 West College Street, Zip 90012; tel. 213/580–7200) **A**1 3 5 8 10 **F**3 5 8 13 15 17 18 19 20 21 22 23 24 26 28 29 30 31 35 36 38 40 44 45 46 47 49 50 51 54 55 56 57 58 59 60 61 62 63 64 65 66 68 70 72 73 74 75 76 77 78 79 80 81 82 83 84 85 86 87 88 89 92 93 94 97 98 99 100 101 102 103 104 105 106 107 108 109 110 111 113 114 115 118 119 120 121 122 123 124 126 129 130 131 132 135 144 146 147 148 **P**6 **S** Kaiser Foundation Hospitals, Oakland, CA
Primary Contact: William N. Grice, Executive Director
COO: Derek Berz, Chief Operating Officer
CFO: Brad Malsed, Area Chief Financial Officer
CMO: Michael Tome, M.D., Medical Director
CIO: David Strickland, Area Information Officer
CHR: Paul J. Martin, Director Human Resources
Web address: www.kaiserpermanente.org
**Control:** Other not–for–profit (including NFP Corporation) **Service:** General Medical and Surgical

**Staffed Beds: 528 Admissions: 22197 Census: 317 Outpatient Visits: 2378828 Births: 2488 Personnel: 6061**

☒ **KAISER PERMANENTE PANORAMA CITY MEDICAL CENTER (050137)**, 13652 Cantara Street, Panorama City, Zip 91402–5497; tel. 818/375–2000, (Nonreporting) **A**1 3 5 10 **S** Kaiser Foundation Hospitals, Oakland, CA
Primary Contact: Dennis C. Benton, Executive Director
COO: Murtaza Sanwari, Chief Operating Officer
CFO: Karla Valle–Smith, Area Chief Finance Officer
CMO: Mary L. Wilson, M.D., Area Medical Director
CIO: Earle Johnson, Area Information Officer
CHR: Carole L. Erken, Human Resources Leader
CNO: Celeste Farugia, R.N., Chief Nurse Executive
Web address: www.kaiserpermanente.org
**Control:** Other not–for–profit (including NFP Corporation) **Service:** General Medical and Surgical

**Staffed Beds: 154**

☒ **KAISER PERMANENTE SOUTH BAY MEDICAL CENTER (050411)**, 25825 Vermont Avenue, Harbor City, Zip 90710–3599; tel. 310/325–5111 **A**1 3 10 **F**3 12 13 15 17 18 29 30 31 34 35 40 44 45 46 47 48 49 50 57 58 59 60 61 64 65 68 70 72 74 75 76 78 79 81 82 84 85 86 87 88 94 130 135 146 147 148 **P**6 **S** Kaiser Foundation Hospitals, Oakland, CA
Primary Contact: Lesley A. Wille, Administrator and Executive Director
Web address: www.kaiserpermanente.org
**Control:** Other not–for–profit (including NFP Corporation) **Service:** General Medical and Surgical

**Staffed Beds: 180 Admissions: 11894 Census: 113 Outpatient Visits: 66844 Births: 2293**

☒ **KAISER PERMANENTE WEST LOS ANGELES MEDICAL CENTER (050561)**, 6041 Cadillac Avenue, Zip 90034–1700; tel. 323/857–2201 **A**1 3 5 10 **F**3 12 13 14 15 29 30 31 34 35 37 40 45 46 47 48 49 50 55 56 59 60 61 64 65 68 70 72 74 75 76 78 79 81 82 84 85 86 87 107 108 110 111 114 115 116 117 119 126 130 132 135 141 146 147 148 **P**6 **S** Kaiser Foundation Hospitals, Oakland, CA
Primary Contact: Georgina R. Garcia, R.N., Executive Director
CFO: Alice H. Issai, Business Strategy and Finance Leader
CMO: Fred Alexander, M.D., Medical Director
CIO: Gregory M. Sincock, Information Technology Leader
Web address: www.kaiserpermanente.org
**Control:** Other not–for–profit (including NFP Corporation) **Service:** General Medical and Surgical

**Staffed Beds: 130 Admissions: 15568 Census: 127 Outpatient Visits: 78045 Births: 2241 Total Expense ($000): 1093133 Payroll Expense ($000): 104529 Personnel: 1337**

☒ **KAISER PERMANENTE WOODLAND HILLS MEDICAL CENTER (050677)**, 5601 DeSoto Avenue, Woodland Hills, Zip 91367–6798; tel. 818/719–2000 **A**1 3 5 10 **F**3 13 14 15 17 18 29 30 31 34 40 41 45 48 49 50 51 55 56 57 60 61 64 65 68 70 73 74 75 76 77 78 79 80 81 82 84 85 86 87 89 92 93 100 102 103 107 108 110 111 114 115 117 119 124 130 132 141 146 147 148 **P**6 **S** Kaiser Foundation Hospitals, Oakland, CA
Primary Contact: Michael C. Carter, Executive Director
COO: Richard Trogman, FACHE, Chief Operating Officer
CFO: Marilou Cheung, Assistant Administrator Finance
CMO: Shirley Suda, M.D., Area Medical Director
CIO: David Snow, Area Information Officer
CHR: Cathy Cousineau, Director Human Resources
CNO: Nancy Tankel, R.N., Chief Nurse Executive
Web address: www.kaiserpermanente.org
**Control:** Other not–for–profit (including NFP Corporation) **Service:** General Medical and Surgical

**Staffed Beds: 158 Admissions: 11350 Census: 116 Outpatient Visits: 45292 Births: 1460 Personnel: 1480**

☒ **KECK HOSPITAL OF USC (050696)**, 1500 San Pablo Street, Zip 90033–5313; tel. 323/442–8500 **A**1 3 5 8 9 10 **F**3 6 8 9 11 12 15 17 18 20 22 24 26 28 29 30 31 34 35 36 37 38 39 44 45 46 47 48 49 50 51 53 54 55 56 57 58 59 60 61 64 65 68 70 71 74 75 77 78 79 81 82 84 85 86 87 90 92 93 96 97 100 101 104 107 108 110 111 114 115 116 117 118 119 120 121 123 124 126 129 130 131 132 135 136 137 138 139 140 141 142 143 145 146 147 148 **P**1 **S** Keck Medicine of USC, Los Angeles, CA
Primary Contact: Rodney Hanners, Chief Executive Officer
CFO: Robert Allen, Chief Financial Officer
CMO: Donald Larsen, M.D., Chief Medical Officer
CIO: Mark Amey, Chief Information Officer
CHR: Matthew McElrath, Chief Human Resources Officer
Web address: www.keckhospitalofusc.org
**Control:** Other not–for–profit (including NFP Corporation) **Service:** General Medical and Surgical

**Staffed Beds: 240 Admissions: 11143 Census: 218 Outpatient Visits: 217440 Births: 0 Total Expense ($000): 707735 Payroll Expense ($000): 221753 Personnel: 2913**

**KEDREN COMMUNITY MENTAL HEALTH CENTER (054083)**, 4211 South Avalon Boulevard, Zip 90011–5699; tel. 323/233–0425 **A**10 **F**29 30 31 35 64 68 98 99 100 101 104 105
Primary Contact: John H. Griffith, Ph.D., President & Chief Executive Officer
COO: Madeline Valencerina, Chief Operating Officer
CFO: Rizwan A. Uraizee, Chief Financial Officer
CMO: Frank L. Williams, Executive Vice President/ Medical Director
CNO: Essie Adams, Director of Nursing
Web address: www.kedrenmentalhealth.com
**Control:** Other not–for–profit (including NFP Corporation) **Service:** Psychiatric

**Staffed Beds: 72326 Admissions: 850 Census: 66 Outpatient Visits: 0 Births: 0 Total Expense ($000): 29667 Payroll Expense ($000): 18834 Personnel: 283**

☒ **KINDRED HOSPITAL–LOS ANGELES (052032)**, 5525 West Slauson Avenue, Zip 90056–1067; tel. 310/642–0325, (Nonreporting) **A**1 9 10 **S** Kindred Healthcare, Louisville, KY
Primary Contact: Phillip R. Wolfe, Administrator
CFO: Charles Natcher, Chief Financial Officer
Web address: www.kindredhospitalla.com/
**Control:** Corporation, Investor–owned, for–profit **Service:** Long–Term Acute Care hospital

**Staffed Beds: 81**

*Many Facility Codes have changed. Please refer to the AHA Guide Code Chart.*    © 2015 AHA Guide

☐ **LAC–OLIVE VIEW–UCLA MEDICAL CENTER (050040)**, 14445 Olive View Drive, Sylmar, Zip 91342–1438; tel. 818/364–1555 **A**1 3 5 10 **F**3 13 15 18 19 20 22 26 29 30 31 40 41 45 46 48 49 50 51 58 59 60 61 62 63 64 65 66 68 70 72 74 76 78 79 81 83 84 85 87 89 93 94 97 98 100 102 103 104 105 107 108 110 111 114 115 116 117 118 119 130 143 144 146 147 148 **S** Los Angeles County–Department of Health Services, Los Angeles, CA
Primary Contact: Carolyn F. Rhee, Chief Executive Officer
COO: Niloo Shahi, Chief Operating Officer
CFO: Anthony Gray, Chief Financial Officer
CMO: Shannon Thyne, Chief Medical Officer
CIO: Susan Aintablian, Chief Information Officer
CHR: Thomas Beggane, Manager Human Resources
CNO: Dellone Pascascio, Chief Nursing Officer
Web address: www.ladhs.org
**Control:** County–Government, nonfederal **Service:** General Medical and Surgical

**Staffed Beds:** 190 **Admissions:** 12612 **Census:** 185 **Outpatient Visits:** 244168 **Births:** 569 **Total Expense ($000):** 446795 **Payroll Expense ($000):** 177082 **Personnel:** 2240

☐ **LAC/UNIVERSITY OF SOUTHERN CALIFORNIA MEDICAL CENTER (050373)**, 1200 North State Street, Zip 90033–1029; tel. 323/226–2622, (Includes GENERAL HOSPITAL, 1200 North State Street, Zip 90033; WOMEN'S AND CHILDREN'S HOSPITAL, 1240 North Mission Road, Zip 90033) **A**1 2 3 5 8 9 10 **F**7 13 14 15 16 17 18 19 20 21 22 23 24 25 26 27 28 29 30 31 34 35 36 38 39 40 41 43 44 45 46 47 48 49 50 51 53 54 55 56 57 58 59 60 61 63 64 65 66 68 69 70 71 72 74 75 76 77 78 79 80 81 82 83 84 85 86 87 88 89 91 92 93 94 97 98 99 100 101 102 103 104 105 107 108 109 110 111 112 113 115 116 117 118 119 121 122 123 124 129 130 131 133 134 135 144 145 146 147 148 **P**6 **S** Los Angeles County–Department of Health Services, Los Angeles, CA
Primary Contact: Dan Castillo, Chief Executive Officer
COO: Henry Ornelas, Chief Operating Officer
CFO: Mark Corbet, Interim Chief Financial Officer
CMO: Hal F. Yee, Jr., M.D., Interim Chief Medical Officer
CIO: Oscar Austelli, Chief Information Officer
CHR: Elizabeth Jacobi, Human Resources Director
CNO: Isabel Milan, R.N., Chief Nursing Officer
Web address: www.lacusc.org
**Control:** County–Government, nonfederal **Service:** General Medical and Surgical

**Staffed Beds:** 664 **Admissions:** 30923 **Census:** 532 **Outpatient Visits:** 576754 **Births:** 985 **Total Expense ($000):** 1375844 **Payroll Expense ($000):** 505872

◇ **LOS ANGELES COMMUNITY HOSPITAL AT LOS ANGELES (050663)**, 4081 East Olympic Boulevard, Zip 90023–3330; tel. 323/267–0477, (Includes LOS ANGELES COMMUNITY HOSPITAL OF NORWALK, 13222 Bloomfield Avenue, Norwalk, Zip 90650; tel. 562/863–4763), (Nonreporting) **A**10 21 **S** Alta Healthcare System, Los Angeles, CA
Primary Contact: Omar Ramirez, Chief Executive Officer
CFO: Johnnette Chong, Chief Financial Officer
**Control:** Corporation, Investor–owned, for–profit **Service:** General Medical and Surgical

**Staffed Beds:** 180

**LOS ANGELES COUNTY CENTRAL JAIL HOSPITAL**, 441 Bauchet Street, Zip 90012–2906; tel. 213/473–6100, (Nonreporting)
Primary Contact: Tom Flaherty, Assistant Administrator
**Control:** County–Government, nonfederal **Service:** Hospital unit of an institution (prison hospital, college infimary, etc.)

**Staffed Beds:** 190

**LOS ANGELES MEDICAL CENTER** See Kaiser Permanente Los Angeles Medical Center

**MARTIN LUTHER KING, JR. COMMUNITY HOSPITAL**, 1680 East 120th Street, Zip 90059–3026; tel. 424/338–8000, (Nonreporting)
Primary Contact: Elaine Batchlor, M.D., M.P.H., Chief Executive Officer
COO: Myrna Allen, R.N., Chief Operating and Nursing Officer
CMO: John Fisher, M.D., Chief Medical Officer
CIO: Sajid Ahmed, Chief Information and Innovation Officer
CHR: Susan M. Burrows, Vice President Human Resources
CNO: Myrna Allen, R.N., Chief Operating and Nursing Officer
Web address: www.mlkcommunityhospital.org/about–hospital
**Control:** Other not–for–profit (including NFP Corporation) **Service:** General Medical and Surgical

**Staffed Beds:** 131

☐ **MIRACLE MILE MEDICAL CENTER (050751)**, 6000 San Vicente Boulevard, Zip 90036–4404; tel. 323/930–1040, (Nonreporting) **A**1 9 10
Primary Contact: Gil Tepper, M.D., Chief Executive Officer
COO: Liz Cheever, Administrator
CFO: Bert Roberts, Controller
CMO: Gil Tepper, M.D., Chief of Staff
CIO: Jonathan Lindell, Director Information Technology
CHR: Liz Cheever, Administrator
CNO: Melody Bradley, Chief Nursing Officer
Web address: www.miraclemilemedicalcenter.com
**Control:** Individual, Investor–owned, for–profit **Service:** General Medical and Surgical

**Staffed Beds:** 17

☐ **MISSION COMMUNITY HOSPITAL (050704)**, 14850 Roscoe Boulevard, Panorama City, Zip 91402–4677; tel. 818/787–2222, (Nonreporting) **A**1 5 9 10
Primary Contact: James Theiring, Chief Executive Officer
CMO: Glenn Marshak, M.D., Chief of Staff
CIO: Dustin Fennell, Director Information Systems
CHR: Carolyn Fish, Director Human Resources
CNO: Gwendolyn Dianne Wagner, R.N., Chief Nursing Officer
Web address: www.mchonline.org
**Control:** Other not–for–profit (including NFP Corporation) **Service:** General Medical and Surgical

**Staffed Beds:** 145

**MOTION PICTURE AND TELEVISION FUND HOSPITAL AND RESIDENTIAL SERVICES (050552)**, 23388 Mulholland Drive, Woodland Hills, Zip 91364–2792; tel. 818/876–1888, (Nonreporting) **A**9 10
Primary Contact: Bob Beitcher, Chief Executive Officer
COO: David Asplund, Chief Operating Officer
CFO: Frank Guarrera, Executive Vice President and Chief Financial Officer
CHR: Nancy Rubin, Vice President Human Resources
Web address: www.mptvfund.org
**Control:** Other not–for–profit (including NFP Corporation) **Service:** General Medical and Surgical

**Staffed Beds:** 20

⊞ △ **NORTHRIDGE HOSPITAL MEDICAL CENTER (050116)**, 18300 Roscoe Boulevard, Northridge, Zip 91328–4167; tel. 818/885–8500 **A**1 2 3 5 7 9 10 **F**1 2 3 5 8 11 12 13 14 15 17 18 20 22 24 26 28 29 30 31 34 35 38 40 41 43 48 49 56 57 58 59 60 61 64 68 70 72 73 74 75 76 77 78 79 81 82 84 85 86 87 88 89 90 93 97 98 99 100 101 102 103 104 105 107 108 110 111 114 117 118 119 121 124 126 129 130 132 134 146 147 148 **S** Dignity Health, San Francisco, CA
Primary Contact: Saliba Salo, President
CFO: Michael Taylor, Vice President Finance
CHR: Susan Paulsen, Director Human Resources
CNO: Mary Jane Jones, R.N., Vice President Nursing Operations
Web address: www.northridgehospital.org
**Control:** Other not–for–profit (including NFP Corporation) **Service:** General Medical and Surgical

**Staffed Beds:** 371 **Admissions:** 14374 **Census:** 176 **Outpatient Visits:** 61102 **Births:** 1422 **Total Expense ($000):** 324040 **Payroll Expense ($000):** 134878 **Personnel:** 1646

◇ **OLYMPIA MEDICAL CENTER (050742)**, 5900 West Olympic Boulevard, Zip 90036–4671; tel. 310/657–5900, (Nonreporting) **A**3 9 10 21
Primary Contact: John A. Calderone, Ph.D., Chief Executive Officer
CFO: Matthew Williams, R.N., Chief Financial Officer
CMO: Panch Jeyakumar, M.D., Chief of Staff
CIO: Jason Williams, Director Information Systems
CHR: Joseph Ambrosini, Director Human Resources
CNO: Sylvia A. Ventura, R.N., Chief Nursing Officer
Web address: www.olympiamc.com
**Control:** Partnership, Investor–owned, for–profit **Service:** General Medical and Surgical

**Staffed Beds:** 204

☐ **PACIFIC ALLIANCE MEDICAL CENTER (050018)**, 531 West College Street, Zip 90012–2385; tel. 213/624–8411, (Nonreporting) **A**1 9 10
Primary Contact: John R. Edwards, Administrator and Chief Executive Officer
CFO: Allan Shubin, Chief Financial Officer
CIO: John D. Brown, Director Information Systems
Web address: www.pamc.net
**Control:** Partnership, Investor–owned, for–profit **Service:** General Medical and Surgical

**Staffed Beds:** 138

**CA**

---

**Hospital, Medicare Provider Number, Address, Telephone, Approval, Facility, and Physician Codes, Health Care System**

★ American Hospital Association (AHA) membership
☐ The Joint Commission accreditation
○ Healthcare Facilities Accreditation Program
◇ DNV Healthcare Inc. accreditation
⇑ Center for Improvement in Healthcare Quality Accreditation
△ Commission on Accreditation of Rehabilitation Facilities (CARF) accreditation

**CA**

☐ **PACIFICA HOSPITAL OF THE VALLEY (050378)**, 9449 San Fernando Road, Sun Valley, Zip 91352–1489; tel. 818/767–3310, (Nonreporting) **A**1 9 10
Primary Contact: Ayman Mousa, R.N., Ph.D., Chief Executive Officer
COO: Daniel Santos, Director Ancillary Services
CFO: Eileen Fisler, Chief Financial Officer
CMO: Joseph Eipe, M.D., Chief Medical Officer
CIO: Mubashir Hashmi, Chief Information Officer
CHR: Patti Alonzo, Manager Human Resources
CNO: Janet B. Latto, Chief Nursing Officer and Disaster Officer
Web address: www.pacificahospital.com
**Control:** Corporation, Investor–owned, for–profit **Service:** General Medical and Surgical

Staffed Beds: 231

**PANORAMA CITY MEDICAL CENTER** See Kaiser Permanente Panorama City Medical Center

☐ **PROMISE HOSPITAL OF EAST LOS ANGELES (052046)**, 443 South Soto Street, Zip 90033–4398; tel. 323/261–1181, (Includes PROMISE HOSPITAL OF EAST LOS ANGELES, SUBURBAN MEDICAL CENTER CAMPUS, 16453 South Colorado Avenue, Paramount, Zip 90723–5000; tel. 562/531–3110; Michael D. Kerr, Chief Executive Officer) **A**1 9 10 **F**3 29 30 31 35 36 42 56 57 59 60 61 63 65 68 70 74 75 77 78 79 81 82 84 85 86 87 91 92 100 101 103 107 108 119 143 148 **P**1 **S** Promise Healthcare, Boca Raton, FL
Primary Contact: Michael D. Kerr, Chief Executive Officer
Web address: www.promiseeastla.com
**Control:** Corporation, Investor–owned, for–profit **Service:** Long–Term Acute Care hospital

Staffed Beds: 199 **Admissions:** 1956 **Census:** 161 **Outpatient Visits:** 0
Births: 0 **Total Expense ($000):** 80974 **Payroll Expense ($000):** 43906
Personnel: 665

☒ △ **PROVIDENCE HOLY CROSS MEDICAL CENTER (050278)**, 15031 Rinaldi Street, Mission Hills, Zip 91345–1207; tel. 818/365–8051, (Total facility includes 48 beds in nursing home–type unit) **A**1 2 7 9 10 **F**3 8 11 13 15 17 18 20 22 24 26 28 29 30 31 34 35 36 40 41 43 44 45 46 49 50 54 56 57 58 59 60 61 64 65 68 70 71 72 74 75 76 77 78 79 81 82 84 85 87 89 90 93 94 97 107 108 110 111 114 115 116 117 119 120 121 123 124 126 128 130 131 132 133 143 146 147 148 **S** Providence Health & Services, Renton, WA
Primary Contact: Bernard Klein, M.D., Chief Executive
CFO: Dave Mast, Chief Financial Officer
CHR: Lori Curry, Regional Chief Human Resources Officer
CNO: Ann Dechairo–Marino, R.N., Chief Nursing Officer
Web address: www.https://california.providence.org/holy–cross/Pages/default.aspx
**Control:** Church–operated, Nongovernment, not–for profit **Service:** General Medical and Surgical

Staffed Beds: 377 **Admissions:** 16144 **Census:** 248 **Outpatient Visits:** 101301 **Births:** 3121 **Total Expense ($000):** 261956 **Payroll Expense ($000):** 131369 **Personnel:** 1996

☒ △ **PROVIDENCE LITTLE COMPANY OF MARY MEDICAL CENTER SAN PEDRO (050078)**, 1300 West Seventh Street, San Pedro, Zip 90732–3505; tel. 310/832–3311, (Total facility includes 106 beds in nursing home–type unit) **A**1 7 9 10 **F**2 3 4 5 11 13 14 15 18 29 30 32 34 35 40 43 44 45 49 50 51 57 59 60 65 66 68 70 71 74 75 76 77 78 79 81 82 84 85 86 87 90 92 93 94 96 98 100 101 102 103 104 107 108 110 111 119 120 123 128 130 131 132 133 135 145 146 **S** Providence Health & Services, Renton, WA
Primary Contact: Mary Kingston, Chief Executive Officer
COO: Carlos W. Priestley, Chief Operating Officer
CFO: Elizabeth Zuanich, Chief Financial Officer
CMO: Herbert Webb, M.D., Chief Medical Officer
CIO: Rachel Sanchez, Director Information Systems
CHR: Andreas Viggers, Director Human Resources
Web address: www.https://california.providence.org/san–pedro
**Control:** Church–operated, Nongovernment, not–for profit **Service:** General Medical and Surgical

Staffed Beds: 307 **Admissions:** 6736 **Census:** 187 **Outpatient Visits:** 44986 **Births:** 597 **Total Expense ($000):** 117467 **Payroll Expense ($000):** 65150 **Personnel:** 1066

☒ **PROVIDENCE TARZANA MEDICAL CENTER (050761)**, 18321 Clark Street, Tarzana, Zip 91356–3521; tel. 818/881–0800 **A**1 9 10 **F**3 7 13 15 17 18 19 20 22 24 26 28 29 30 31 34 35 40 41 45 46 49 50 55 56 57 59 61 63 64 65 70 72 74 75 76 77 78 79 81 82 83 84 85 86 87 88 89 91 92 93 97 107 108 110 111 114 115 119 126 130 131 132 143 145 146 147 148 **S** Providence Health & Services, Renton, WA
Primary Contact: Dale Surowitz, Chief Executive
COO: Phyllis Bushart, R.N., Chief Operating Officer
CFO: Ted Wang, Chief Financial Officer
CIO: Alex Nury, Chief Information Officer
CHR: Wendy Regal, Director Human Resources
Web address: www.providence.org/tarzana.com
**Control:** Church–operated, Nongovernment, not–for profit **Service:** General Medical and Surgical

Staffed Beds: 249 **Admissions:** 13171 **Census:** 161 **Outpatient Visits:** 60100 **Births:** 2217 **Total Expense ($000):** 184518 **Payroll Expense ($000):** 97667 **Personnel:** 1286

☒ **RONALD REAGAN UCLA MEDICAL CENTER (050262)**, 757 Westwood Plaza, Zip 90095–8358; tel. 310/825–9111, (Includes MATTEL CHILDREN'S HOSPITAL, 10833 Le Conte Avenue, Zip 90024; tel. 310/825–9111) **A**1 3 5 8 9 10 **F**3 6 7 8 9 11 12 13 14 15 17 18 19 20 21 22 23 24 25 26 27 28 29 30 31 32 34 35 36 40 41 43 44 45 46 47 48 49 50 51 52 54 55 56 57 58 59 61 62 64 65 66 68 70 71 72 74 75 76 77 78 79 81 82 83 84 85 86 87 88 89 90 92 93 94 96 97 102 107 108 110 111 112 113 114 115 116 117 118 119 120 121 123 124 126 129 130 131 132 135 136 137 138 139 140 141 142 143 145 146 147 148 **P**6 **S** University of California Systemwide Administration, Oakland, CA
Primary Contact: James Atkinson, M.D., Interim President
CFO: Paul Staton, Chief Financial Officer
CMO: J. Thomas Rosenthal, M.D., Chief Medical Officer
CIO: Virginia McFerran, Chief Information Officer
CHR: Mark Speare, Senior Associate Director Human Resources
CNO: Heidi M. Crooks, R.N., Senior Associate Director, Outpatient and Patient Care Services
Web address: www.uclahealth.org
**Control:** State–Government, nonfederal **Service:** General Medical and Surgical

Staffed Beds: 466 **Admissions:** 23442 **Census:** 453 **Outpatient Visits:** 526575 **Births:** 1924 **Total Expense ($000):** 1505160 **Payroll Expense ($000):** 590860 **Personnel:** 7421

☐ **SHERMAN OAKS HOSPITAL (050755)**, 4929 Van Nuys Boulevard, Sherman Oaks, Zip 91403–1777; tel. 818/981–7111, (Total facility includes 12 beds in nursing home–type unit) **A**1 5 10 **F**17 20 29 31 34 35 38 40 56 57 59 61 64 70 75 77 78 79 81 82 85 98 103 104 105 107 108 118 119 128 130 131 132 146 148 **S** Prime Healthcare Services, Ontario, CA
Primary Contact: Bockhi Park, Chief Executive Officer
CFO: Daniel Leon, Chief Financial Officer
CMO: Michael Malamed, M.D., Chief of Staff
Web address: www.shermanoakshospital.com
**Control:** Other not–for–profit (including NFP Corporation) **Service:** General Medical and Surgical

Staffed Beds: 91 **Admissions:** 6039 **Census:** 84 **Outpatient Visits:** 26128 **Births:** 0 **Total Expense ($000):** 80355 **Payroll Expense ($000):** 30677 **Personnel:** 631

☒ **SHRINERS HOSPITALS FOR CHILDREN–LOS ANGELES (053310)**, 3160 Geneva Street, Zip 90020–1199; tel. 213/388–3151, (Nonreporting) **A**1 3 5 9 10 **S** Shriners Hospitals for Children, Tampa, FL
Primary Contact: Lou Lazatin, Administrator
CFO: David Burkitt, Director Fiscal Services
CMO: Hugh Watts, M.D., Chief of Staff
CIO: Mark Garrett, Chief Information Officer
Web address: www.shrinershospitalsforchildren.org/Hospitals/Locations/Losangeles.aspx
**Control:** Other not–for–profit (including NFP Corporation) **Service:** Children's rehabilitation

Staffed Beds: 60

☐ **SILVER LAKE MEDICAL CENTER (050763)**, 1711 West Temple Street, Zip 90026–5421; tel. 213/989–6100, (Includes SILVER LAKE MEDICAL CENTER–INGLESIDE HOSPITAL, 7500 East Hellman Avenue, Rosemead, Zip 91770; tel. 626/288–1160), (Nonreporting) **A**1 10 **S** Success Healthcare, Boca Raton, FL
Primary Contact: Brent A. Cope, Chief Executive Officer
CFO: John Cowles, Chief Financial Officer
CMO: Louis Acosta, M.D., Chief of Staff
CIO: Scott Musack, Chief Information Officer
CHR: Sylvia Cloud, Director Human Resources
Web address: www.silverlakemc.com
**Control:** Corporation, Investor–owned, for–profit **Service:** General Medical and Surgical

Staffed Beds: 150

◇ **SOUTHERN CALIFORNIA HOSPITAL AT HOLLYWOOD (050135)**, 6245 De Longpre Avenue, Zip 90028–9001; tel. 323/462–2271, (Includes SOUTHERN CALIFORNIA HOSPITAL AT VAN NUYS, 14433 Emelita Street, Van Nuys, Zip 91401; tel. 818/787–1511), (Nonreporting) **A**10 21 **S** Alta Healthcare System, Los Angeles, CA
Primary Contact: Bruce P. Grimshaw, FACHE, Chief Executive Officer
Web address: www.hollywoodcommunityhospital.org/
**Control:** Corporation, Investor–owned, for–profit **Service:** General Medical and Surgical

Staffed Beds: 45

**SOUTHERN CALIFORNIA HOSPITAL AT VAN NUYS** See Southern California Hospital at Hollywood

*Many Facility Codes have changed. Please refer to the AHA Guide Code Chart.* © 2015 AHA Guide

✠ **ST. VINCENT MEDICAL CENTER (050502)**, 2131 West Third Street, Zip 90057–1901, Mailing Address: P.O. Box 57992, Zip 90057–0992; tel. 213/484–7111, (Total facility includes 27 beds in nursing home–type unit) **A**1 3 9 10 **F**3 11 15 17 18 20 22 24 26 29 30 31 34 35 36 40 45 47 49 50 54 57 58 59 60 63 64 65 68 70 71 74 75 77 78 79 80 81 82 85 87 90 91 93 96 107 108 110 111 116 118 119 120 121 125 128 130 136 138 142 143 146 148 **P**5 **S** Daughters of Charity Health System, Los Altos Hills, CA
Primary Contact: Catherine Fickes, R.N., President and Chief Executive Officer
CFO: Michael Garko, Chief Financial Officer
CMO: Brian Itagaki, M.D., Chief of Staff
CIO: Dan Robbins, Information Technology and Account Executive
CHR: Gail Watts, Director
CNO: Judy McCurdy, R.N., Vice President and Chief Nursing Officer
Web address: www.stvincentmedicalcenter.com
**Control:** Church–operated, Nongovernment, not–for profit **Service:** General Medical and Surgical

**Staffed Beds:** 271 **Admissions:** 7629 **Census:** 95 **Outpatient Visits:** 93136 **Births:** 0 **Total Expense ($000):** 226224 **Payroll Expense ($000):** 70826 **Personnel:** 947

✠ **STEWART & LYNDA RESNICK NEUROPSYCHIATRIC HOSPITAL AT UCLA (054009)**, 150 UCLA Medical Plaza, Zip 90095–8353; tel. 310/825–9989 **A**1 3 5 9 10 **F**3 5 6 29 30 35 40 42 43 55 56 64 68 77 86 87 98 99 100 101 102 103 104 105 130 132 134 147 **P**1 **S** University of California Systemwide Administration, Oakland, CA
Primary Contact: Peter Whybrow, M.D., Chief Executive Officer
COO: Ruth Irwin, Associate Director Clinical Operations
CHR: Cindy Cohen, Director Human Resources
Web address: www.semel.ucla.edu/resnick
**Control:** State–Government, nonfederal **Service:** Psychiatric

**Staffed Beds:** 74 **Admissions:** 2214 **Census:** 69 **Outpatient Visits:** 21567 **Births:** 0 **Total Expense ($000):** 56044 **Payroll Expense ($000):** 32885 **Personnel:** 345

✠ **UNIVERSITY OF SOUTHERN CALIFORNIA–NORRIS CANCER HOSPITAL (050660)**, 1441 Eastlake Avenue, Zip 90089–0112; tel. 323/865–3000 **A**1 2 3 5 8 9 10 **F**3 8 11 15 29 30 31 34 35 36 38 39 45 46 47 48 49 50 54 55 56 57 58 59 60 61 64 65 68 70 74 75 77 78 79 81 82 84 85 86 87 92 93 96 100 101 104 107 108 110 111 114 115 118 119 120 121 123 124 130 132 135 136 143 145 146 147 148 **P**1 **S** Keck Medicine of USC, Los Angeles, CA
Primary Contact: Rodney Hanners, Chief Executive Officer
COO: Tarek Salaway, Chief Operating Officer
CFO: Robert Allen, Chief Financial Officer
CMO: Stephanie Hall, M.D., Medical Director
CIO: Joshua Lee, Chief Information Officer
CHR: Matthew McElrath, Chief Human Resources Officer
CNO: Annette Sy, R.N., Chief Nursing Officer
Web address: www.uscnorriscancerhospital.org
**Control:** Other not–for–profit (including NFP Corporation) **Service:** Cancer

**Staffed Beds:** 60 **Admissions:** 1342 **Census:** 27 **Outpatient Visits:** 97026 **Births:** 0 **Total Expense ($000):** 141769 **Payroll Expense ($000):** 33295 **Personnel:** 407

**USC UNIVERSITY HOSPITAL** See Keck Hospital of USC

✠ △ **VA GREATER LOS ANGELES HEALTHCARE SYSTEM**, 11301 Wilshire Boulevard, Zip 90073–1003; tel. 310/478–3711, (Nonreporting) **A**1 5 7 8 **S** Department of Veterans Affairs, Washington, DC
Primary Contact: Donna M. Beiter, R.N., MSN, Director
COO: Lynn Carrier, Associate Director Administration and Support
CFO: Olivia Ortiz–Bitner, Acting Chief Financial Officer
CMO: Dennis Schaberg, M.D., Chief Medicine
CIO: Eugene Archey, Chief Information Technology
CHR: Harold Goings, Chief Human Resources
Web address: www.losangeles.va.gov/
**Control:** Veterans Affairs, Government, federal **Service:** General Medical and Surgical

**Staffed Beds:** 1087

★ ◇ **VALLEY PRESBYTERIAN HOSPITAL (050126)**, 15107 Vanowen Street, Van Nuys, Zip 91405–4597; tel. 818/782–6600 **A**5 9 10 21 **F**3 13 18 20 22 24 28 29 31 34 40 44 45 46 49 50 53 57 59 64 65 70 72 74 75 76 77 78 79 81 85 86 87 88 89 90 96 107 108 109 114 115 119 130 145 146 147 148 **P**5
Primary Contact: Gustavo A. Valdespino, President and Chief Executive Officer
COO: Gayathri S. Jith, M.P.H., Senior Vice President Strategy and Operations
CFO: Lori Cardle, Senior Vice President, Chief Financial Officer
CIO: Jeff Allport, Vice President, Chief Information Officer
CHR: Jonathan Wu, Vice President Human Resources
CNO: Lori Burnell, R.N., Senior Vice President and Chief Nursing Officer
Web address: www.valleypres.org
**Control:** Other not–for–profit (including NFP Corporation) **Service:** General Medical and Surgical

**Staffed Beds:** 350 **Admissions:** 15402 **Census:** 189 **Outpatient Visits:** 105835 **Births:** 3524 **Total Expense ($000):** 273784 **Payroll Expense ($000):** 110271 **Personnel:** 1464

✠ **WEST HILLS HOSPITAL AND MEDICAL CENTER (050481)**, 7300 Medical Center Drive, West Hills, Zip 91307–1900; tel. 818/676–4000, (Nonreporting) **A**1 9 10 **S** HCA, Nashville, TN
Primary Contact: Douglas Long, President and Chief Executive Officer
COO: Omar Chughtai, Vice President and Chief Operating Officer
CFO: Tony Lopez, Vice President and Chief Financial Officer
CMO: Ron Chitayat, M.D., Chief Medical Staff
CIO: Tony Lopez, Chief Financial Officer
CHR: Edward Battista, Vice President Human Resources
CNO: Janet Brooks, R.N., Vice President and Chief Nursing Officer
Web address: www.westhillshospital.com
**Control:** Corporation, Investor–owned, for–profit **Service:** General Medical and Surgical

**Staffed Beds:** 225

**WEST LOS ANGELES MEDICAL CENTER** See Kaiser Permanente West Los Angeles Medical Center

✠ **WHITE MEMORIAL MEDICAL CENTER (050103)**, 1720 Cesar Chavez Avenue, Zip 90033–2414; tel. 323/268–5000, (Total facility includes 27 beds in nursing home–type unit) **A**1 2 3 5 9 10 **F**3 11 13 15 17 18 19 20 22 24 26 27 28 29 30 31 34 35 40 41 45 46 47 48 49 50 51 53 57 58 59 64 68 70 72 74 75 76 78 79 81 82 84 85 86 87 88 89 90 91 92 93 96 98 99 102 103 107 108 109 110 111 114 115 116 117 118 119 120 121 123 128 130 131 132 146 147 148 **S** Adventist Health, Roseville, CA
Primary Contact: John G. Raffoul, President and Chief Executive Officer
CFO: John Raffoul, Senior Vice President Finance
CIO: Ralf Weissenberger, Director Information Systems
CHR: Natasha Milatovich, Association Vice President Human Resources
CNO: Patricia Stone, R.N., Senior Vice President Operations and Chief Nursing Officer
Web address: www.whitememorial.com
**Control:** Church–operated, Nongovernment, not–for profit **Service:** General Medical and Surgical

**Staffed Beds:** 353 **Admissions:** 19995 **Census:** 238 **Outpatient Visits:** 68523 **Births:** 3749 **Total Expense ($000):** 382448 **Payroll Expense ($000):** 124831 **Personnel:** 1514

**WOMEN'S AND CHILDREN'S HOSPITAL** See LAC/University of Southern California Medical Center

**WOODLAND HILLS MEDICAL CENTER** See Kaiser Permanente Woodland Hills Medical Center

**LOS BANOS—Merced County**

✠ **MEMORIAL HOSPITAL LOS BANOS (050528)**, 520 West I Street, Zip 93635–3498; tel. 209/826–0591 **A**1 9 10 20 **F**3 11 13 15 18 29 30 34 35 40 45 46 49 50 57 59 64 66 68 77 76 81 85 87 107 108 111 115 119 127 130 132 135 146 **S** Sutter Health, Sacramento, CA
Primary Contact: Ash Gokli, M.D., Chief Executive Officer
CFO: Timothy J. Noakes, Chief Financial Officer
CHR: Shawn Garcia, Manager Human Resources
CNO: Kristie Marion, Chief Nurse Executive
Web address: www.memoriallosbanos.org/
**Control:** Other not–for–profit (including NFP Corporation) **Service:** General Medical and Surgical

**Staffed Beds:** 36 **Admissions:** 1488 **Census:** 10 **Outpatient Visits:** 57048 **Births:** 695 **Total Expense ($000):** 43526 **Payroll Expense ($000):** 14016 **Personnel:** 217

**CA**

---

**Hospital, Medicare Provider Number, Address, Telephone, Approval, Facility, and Physician Codes, Health Care System**

★ American Hospital Association (AHA) membership   ○ Healthcare Facilities Accreditation Program   ⇑ Center for Improvement in Healthcare Quality Accreditation
□ The Joint Commission accreditation   ◇ DNV Healthcare Inc. accreditation   △ Commission on Accreditation of Rehabilitation Facilities (CARF) accreditation

**LYNWOOD—Los Angeles County**

☒ **ST. FRANCIS MEDICAL CENTER (050104)**, 3630 East Imperial Highway, Zip 90262–2636; tel. 310/900–8900, (Nonreporting) **A**1 9 10 **S** Daughters of Charity Health System, Los Altos Hills, CA
Primary Contact: Gerald T. Kozai, President and Chief Executive Officer
COO: Kurt Weinmeister, Chief Operating Officer
CFO: Nancy Wilson, Senior Vice President and Chief Financial Officer
CIO: Judi Binderman, Chief Information Technology Officer and Chief Medical Informatics Officer
CHR: Laura Kato, Vice President Human Resources
CNO: Mary Lynne Knighten, R.N., Chief Nursing Officer and Vice President Patient Care Services
Web address: www.dochs.org
**Control:** Church–operated, Nongovernment, not–for profit **Service:** General Medical and Surgical

**Staffed Beds:** 323

**MADERA—Madera County**

○ **MADERA COMMUNITY HOSPITAL (050568)**, 1250 East Almond Avenue, Zip 93637–5696, Mailing Address: P.O. Box 1328, Zip 93639–1328; tel. 559/675–5501 **A**9 10 11 19 **F**13 29 30 34 35 40 45 46 47 48 49 54 59 64 65 70 74 75 76 79 81 82 87 107 108 110 111 119 127 132 146 148 **P**5
Primary Contact: Evan J. Rayner, Chief Executive Officer
COO: Karen Paolmelli, Chief Operating Officer
CFO: Mark Foote, Chief Financial Officer
CIO: Jerry Kovalski, Director Information Systems
CHR: Christine M. Watts–Johnson, Assistant Vice President
CNO: Meri Combs, R.N., Vice President and Chief Nursing Officer
Web address: www.maderahospital.org
**Control:** Other not–for–profit (including NFP Corporation) **Service:** General Medical and Surgical

**Staffed Beds:** 106 **Admissions:** 4301 **Census:** 53 **Outpatient Visits:** 144498 **Births:** 1604 **Total Expense ($000):** 75937 **Payroll Expense ($000):** 33171 **Personnel:** 724

□ △ **VALLEY CHILDREN'S HOSPITAL (053300)**, 9300 Valley Children's Place, Zip 93636–8761; tel. 559/353–3000 **A**1 3 5 7 9 10 **F**3 8 9 11 19 21 23 25 27 28 29 30 31 32 34 35 38 40 41 44 46 48 50 54 55 57 58 59 60 61 62 64 65 68 72 73 74 75 77 78 79 81 82 84 85 86 87 88 89 90 93 94 97 107 108 111 114 115 119 127 129 130 131 132 134 143 146 147 148
Primary Contact: Todd A. Suntrapak, President and Chief Executive Officer
CFO: Michele Waldron, Senior Vice President and Chief Financial Officer
CMO: David Christensen, M.D., Senior Vice President and Chief Medical Officer
CHR: Nat Ponticello, Vice President Human Resources
CNO: Beverly P. Hayden–Pugh, R.N., Senior Vice President and Chief Nursing Officer
Web address: www.valleychildrens.org
**Control:** Other not–for–profit (including NFP Corporation) **Service:** Children's general

**Staffed Beds:** 356 **Admissions:** 12695 **Census:** 210 **Outpatient Visits:** 250191 **Births:** 0 **Total Expense ($000):** 422898 **Payroll Expense ($000):** 176656 **Personnel:** 1920

**MAMMOTH LAKES—Mono County**

◇ **MAMMOTH HOSPITAL (051303)**, 85 Sierra Park Road, Zip 93546–2073, Mailing Address: P.O. Box 660, Zip 93546–0660; tel. 760/934–3311 **A**9 10 18 21 **F**3 11 13 15 18 29 31 34 35 39 40 45 46 50 53 57 59 64 65 68 70 74 75 76 77 78 79 81 82 85 93 97 99 104 107 110 111 114 119 127 131 132 146 147
Primary Contact: Gary Myers, Chief Executive Officer
CFO: Melanie Van Winkle, Chief Financial Officer
CMO: Tomi Bortolazzo, M.D., Chief of Staff
CIO: Mark Lind, Director Information Technology
CHR: Jeff Byberg, Manager Human Resources
CNO: Kathleen Alo, R.N., Chief Nursing Officer
Web address: www.mammothhospital.com
**Control:** Hospital district or authority, Government, nonfederal **Service:** General Medical and Surgical

**Staffed Beds:** 17 **Admissions:** 580 **Census:** 3 **Outpatient Visits:** 73566 **Births:** 100 **Total Expense ($000):** 51258 **Payroll Expense ($000):** 17384

**MANTECA—San Joaquin County**

☒ **DOCTORS HOSPITAL OF MANTECA (050118)**, 1205 East North Street, Zip 95336–4900; tel. 209/823–3111 **A**1 9 10 **F**3 11 12 13 15 29 31 34 35 40 45 49 50 51 64 75 76 78 79 81 85 102 107 108 110 111 115 116 117 118 119 130 132 146 147 148 **S** TENET Healthcare Corporation, Dallas, TX
Primary Contact: Carmen Silva, R.N., Interim Chief Executive Officer
COO: Carmen Silva, R.N., Chief Operating Officer
CFO: Michael Szymanski, Chief Financial Officer
CHR: Traci Holzer, Chief Human Resources Officer
CNO: Kathy Daley, R.N., Chief Nursing Officer
Web address: www.doctorsmanteca.com
**Control:** Corporation, Investor–owned, for–profit **Service:** General Medical and Surgical

**Staffed Beds:** 73 **Admissions:** 3641 **Census:** 37 **Outpatient Visits:** 64387 **Births:** 686 **Total Expense ($000):** 71332 **Payroll Expense ($000):** 36517 **Personnel:** 403

☒ **KAISER PERMANENTE MANTECA MEDICAL CENTER (050748)**, 1777 West Yosemite Avenue, Zip 95337–5187; tel. 209/825–3700, (Includes MODESTO MEDICAL CENTER, 4601 Dale Road, Modesto, Zip 95356–9718; tel. 209/735–5000; Corwin N. Harper, Administrator), (Nonreporting) **A**1 10 **S** Kaiser Foundation Hospitals, Oakland, CA
Primary Contact: Deborah G. Friberg, Interim Senior Vice President and Area Manager
COO: Corwin N. Harper, Senior Vice President and Area Manager
CFO: Debra L. Brown, Area Financial Officer
CMO: Moses D. Elam, M.D., Physician–in–Chief
CIO: Tom J. Osteen, Director Area Technology
CHR: Pat McKeldin, Human Resource Business Partner
Web address: www.kaiserpermanente.org
**Control:** Other not–for–profit (including NFP Corporation) **Service:** General Medical and Surgical

**Staffed Beds:** 184

**MARINA DEL REY—Los Angeles County**

□ **MARINA DEL REY HOSPITAL (050740)**, 4650 Lincoln Boulevard, Zip 90292–6306; tel. 310/823–8911, (Nonreporting) **A**1 9 10
Primary Contact: Sean Fowler, Chief Executive Officer
COO: Phyllis Buchart, Chief Operating Officer
CFO: Stephen A. Hargett, Senior Vice President and Chief Financial Officer
Web address: www.marinahospital.com
**Control:** Corporation, Investor–owned, for–profit **Service:** General Medical and Surgical

**Staffed Beds:** 40

**MARIPOSA—Mariposa County**

★ **JOHN C. FREMONT HEALTHCARE DISTRICT (051304)**, 5189 Hospital Road, Zip 95338–9524, Mailing Address: P.O. Box 216, Zip 95338–0216; tel. 209/966–3631, (Nonreporting) **A**9 10 18
Primary Contact: Alan MacPhee, Chief Executive Officer
CFO: Matthew Matthiessen, Chief Financial Officer
CMO: Joseph E.C. Rogers, M.D., Chief of Staff
CIO: Phil Blas, Chief Information Officer
CNO: Theresa Loya, R.N., Chief Nursing Officer
Web address: www.jcf-hospital.com
**Control:** Hospital district or authority, Government, nonfederal **Service:** General Medical and Surgical

**Staffed Beds:** 34

**MARTINEZ—Contra Costa County**

☒ **CONTRA COSTA REGIONAL MEDICAL CENTER (050276)**, 2500 Alhambra Avenue, Zip 94553–3156; tel. 925/370–5000 **A**1 2 3 10 **F**3 11 13 15 18 30 31 36 39 40 41 44 45 49 50 52 54 56 58 59 61 62 64 65 66 68 70 71 72 73 74 75 76 77 78 79 81 82 84 85 86 87 92 93 96 97 98 100 102 103 104 107 108 109 110 111 114 119 130 132 143 146 147 148 **P**6
Primary Contact: Anna M. Roth, R.N., MS, M.P.H., Chief Executive Officer
COO: Timothy Thompson–Cook, Chief Operating Officer
CFO: Patrick Godley, Chief Financial Officer
CMO: David Goldstein, M.D., Chief Medical Officer
CNO: Jaspreet Benepal, Chief Nursing Officer
Web address: www.cchealth.org/medical_center/
**Control:** County–Government, nonfederal **Service:** General Medical and Surgical

**Staffed Beds:** 113 **Admissions:** 8753 **Census:** 113 **Outpatient Visits:** 434875 **Births:** 1994 **Total Expense ($000):** 471425 **Payroll Expense ($000):** 159609 **Personnel:** 1858

**KAISER FOUNDATION HOSPITAL** See Kaiser Permanente Walnut Creek Medical Center, Walnut Creek

CA

**MARYSVILLE—Yuba County**

★ **RIDEOUT MEMORIAL HOSPITAL (050133)**, 726 Fourth Street,
Zip 95901–5600; tel. 530/749–4300, (Includes FREMONT MEDICAL CENTER,
970 Plumas Street, Yuba City, Zip 95991–4087; tel. 530/751–4000) **A**2 9 10
20 **F**3 8 13 15 17 18 19 20 22 23 24 28 29 30 31 40 43 45 47 49 54 59 61 64
68 70 72 74 76 77 78 79 81 82 85 89 93 94 96 97 107 110 111 114 115
117 119 120 121 123 124 130 147 148 **P**3
Primary Contact: Robert E. Chason, Interim Chief Executive Officer
CMO: Robert Plass, M.D., Chief Medical Officer
CIO: Tarun Ghosh, Chief Information Officer
CHR: Tresha Moreland, MS, Vice President Human Resources
Web address: www.frhg.org
**Control:** Other not–for–profit (including NFP Corporation) **Service:** General
Medical and Surgical

**Staffed Beds:** 233 **Admissions:** 11927 **Census:** 144 **Outpatient Visits:**
163914 **Births:** 2035 **Total Expense ($000):** 294318 **Payroll Expense
($000):** 88794

**MENLO PARK—San Mateo County**

✠ **MENLO PARK SURGICAL HOSPITAL (050754)**, 570 Willow Road,
Zip 94025–2617; tel. 650/324–8500 **A**1 9 10 **F**3 18 35 64 68 79 81 82 85
**S** Sutter Health, Sacramento, CA
Primary Contact: Kathleen Palange, R.N., Chief Administrative Officer
CMO: Andrew Gutow, M.D., Medical Director
CNO: Marjorie Eckford, Chief Nursing Officer
Web address: www.pamf.org/mpsh
**Control:** Other not–for–profit (including NFP Corporation) **Service:** General
Medical and Surgical

**Staffed Beds:** 12 **Admissions:** 193 **Census:** 1 **Outpatient Visits:** 3234
**Births:** 0 **Total Expense ($000):** 13511 **Payroll Expense ($000):** 4307
**Personnel:** 44

**MERCED—Merced County**

✠ **MERCY MEDICAL CENTER MERCED (050444)**, 333 Mercy Avenue,
Zip 95340–8319; tel. 209/564–5000, (Includes MERCY MEDICAL CENTER
MERCED–DOMINICAN CAMPUS, 2740 M Street, Zip 95340–2880;
tel. 209/384–6444; Charles Kassis, President) **A**1 3 5 9 10 19 **F**1 3 4 13 15 16
17 18 20 26 28 29 30 34 35 39 40 41 42 45 49 50 57 59 62 64 65 66 67
68 70 72 73 74 75 76 77 79 80 81 84 85 86 87 88 89 90 93 96 97 98 107
108 110 111 115 119 127 128 130 132 146 148 **P**3 **S** Dignity Health, San
Francisco, CA
Primary Contact: Charles Kassis, President
CFO: Michael Strasser, Vice President and Chief Financial Officer
CMO: Robert Streeter, M.D., Vice President Medical Affairs
CIO: Daniel Andresen, Chief information Officer
CHR: Julie Rocha, Vice President Human Resources
CNO: Greg Rouleau, Vice President Nursing
Web address: www.mercymercedcares.org
**Control:** Other not–for–profit (including NFP Corporation) **Service:** General
Medical and Surgical

**Staffed Beds:** 186 **Admissions:** 10709 **Census:** 115 **Outpatient Visits:**
196111 **Births:** 785 **Total Expense ($000):** 245574 **Payroll Expense
($000):** 93745 **Personnel:** 1085

**MISSION HILLS—Los Angeles County, See Los Angeles**

**MISSION VIEJO—Orange County**

☐ **CHOC CHILDREN'S AT MISSION HOSPITAL (053306)**, 27700 Medical Center
Road, Zip 92691–6426; tel. 949/364–1400 **A**1 5 9 10 **F**3 11 36 72 74 79 81
85 88 89 146
Primary Contact: Kimberly C. Cripe, President and Chief Executive Officer
COO: Matthew S. Gerlach, Chief Operating Officer
CFO: Kerri Ruppert Schiller, Senior Vice President and Chief Financial Officer
CMO: Maria Minon, M.D., Vice President Medical Affairs and Chief Medical Officer
CIO: Mark Headland, Chief Information Officer
CHR: Mamoon Syed, Vice President Human Resources
Web address: www.choc.org
**Control:** Other not–for–profit (including NFP Corporation) **Service:** Children's
general

**Staffed Beds:** 54 **Admissions:** 1836 **Census:** 21 **Outpatient Visits:** 23727
**Births:** 0 **Total Expense ($000):** 46860 **Payroll Expense ($000):** 8555
**Personnel:** 98

✠ △ **MISSION HOSPITAL (050567)**, 27700 Medical Center Road,
Zip 92691–6474; tel. 949/364–1400, (Includes MISSION HOSPITAL LAGUNA
BEACH, 31872 Coast Highway, Laguna Beach, Zip 92651–6775;
tel. 949/499–1311; Kenneth D. McFarland, President and Chief Executive Officer)
**A**1 2 7 9 10 **F**3 4 5 8 11 13 14 15 17 18 20 22 24 26 28 29 30 31 34 35 36
40 43 44 45 46 47 48 49 50 53 54 57 58 59 64 65 66 68 70 74 75 76 77
78 79 80 81 82 84 85 86 87 90 92 93 96 98 100 101 104 105 107 108 110
111 114 115 116 117 118 119 120 121 123 126 129 130 131 132 134 135
141 143 145 146 147 148 **P**3 5 **S** St. Joseph Health, Irvine, CA
Primary Contact: Kenneth D. McFarland, President and Chief Executive Officer
COO: Michael D. Beck, Vice President Operations
CFO: Eileen Haubl, Senior Vice President and Chief Financial Officer
CMO: Linda Sieglen, M.D., Chief Medical Officer
CIO: Bill Russell, Senior Chief Information Officer
CHR: Terri Covert, Vice President Human Resources
CNO: Linda Johnson, R.N., Chief Clinical Officer
Web address: www.mission4health.com
**Control:** Church–operated, Nongovernment, not–for profit **Service:** General
Medical and Surgical

**Staffed Beds:** 228 **Admissions:** 19778 **Census:** 227 **Outpatient Visits:**
188568 **Births:** 2772 **Total Expense ($000):** 429050 **Payroll Expense
($000):** 135964 **Personnel:** 1721

**MODESTO—Stanislaus County**

★ ◇ **CENTRAL VALLEY SPECIALTY HOSPITAL (052055)**, 730 17th Street,
Zip 95354–1209; tel. 209/248–7700, (Nonreporting) **A**21
Primary Contact: Gia Smith, Chief Executive Officer
Web address: www.centralvalleyspecialty.org/CVSH/
**Control:** Partnership, Investor–owned, for–profit **Service:** Long–Term Acute Care
hospital

**Staffed Beds:** 100

✠ **DOCTORS MEDICAL CENTER (050464)**, 1441 Florida Avenue,
Zip 95350–4418, Mailing Address: P.O. Box 4138, Zip 95352–4138;
tel. 209/578–1211 **A**1 2 3 9 10 **F**3 13 17 18 20 22 24 26 28 29 31 35 40 41
43 45 46 48 49 50 51 55 57 59 60 65 70 72 74 75 76 77 78 79 80 81 85
89 98 102 103 107 108 109 110 111 112 113 114 115 116 117 118 119
126 130 132 146 147 **S** TENET Healthcare Corporation, Dallas, TX
Primary Contact: Warren J. Kirk, Chief Executive Officer
COO: Mike King, Chief Operating Officer
CFO: Greg Berry, Chief Financial Officer
CIO: Debbie Fuller, Director Health Information Systems and Chief Information
Officer
CHR: Michele Bava, Director Human Resources
CNO: Lani Dickinson, R.N., Chief Nursing Officer
Web address: www.dmc–modesto.com
**Control:** Corporation, Investor–owned, for–profit **Service:** General Medical and
Surgical

**Staffed Beds:** 455 **Admissions:** 24628 **Census:** 344 **Outpatient Visits:**
139070 **Births:** 3975 **Total Expense ($000):** 413413 **Payroll Expense
($000):** 199475 **Personnel:** 2260

✠ **MEMORIAL MEDICAL CENTER (050557)**, 1700 Coffee Road,
Zip 95355–2869, Mailing Address: P.O. Box 942, Zip 95353–0942;
tel. 209/526–4500, (Includes MEMORIAL MEDICAL CENTER, 1700 Coffee Road,
Zip 95355, Mailing Address: Box 942, Zip 95353; tel. 209/526–4500) **A**1 2 9
10 **F**3 8 11 12 13 15 17 18 20 22 24 28 29 30 43 45 46 47 48
49 50 51 57 58 59 60 62 64 66 68 70 73 74 75 76 77 78 79 81 82 84 85
86 87 89 107 108 111 114 115 118 119 120 121 124 130 146 148 **S** Sutter
Health, Sacramento, CA
Primary Contact: Daryn J. Kumar, Chief Executive Officer
COO: Steve Mitchell, Chief Operating Officer
CFO: Eric Dalton, Chief Financial Officer
CIO: Patrick Anderson, Chief Information Officer
CHR: Paula Rafala, Director, Human Resources
CNO: Sandra Proctor, R.N., Chief Nurse Executive
Web address: www.memorialmedicalcenter.org
**Control:** Other not–for–profit (including NFP Corporation) **Service:** General
Medical and Surgical

**Staffed Beds:** 230 **Admissions:** 16861 **Census:** 213 **Outpatient Visits:**
108853 **Births:** 2029 **Total Expense ($000):** 495938 **Payroll Expense
($000):** 158116 **Personnel:** 2056

**MODESTO MEDICAL CENTER** See Kaiser Permanente Manteca Medical Center,
Manteca

**CA**

**CA**

**STANISLAUS SURGICAL HOSPITAL (050726)**, 1421 Oakdale Road, Zip 95355–3356; tel. 209/572–2700 **A**5 9 10 **F**3 15 45 46 47 51 74 79 81 82 93 107 111 116 117 119 147 148
Primary Contact: Douglas V. Johnson, Chief Executive Officer
CFO: Richard Hart, Chief Financial Officer
CMO: Wesley Kinzie, M.D., Chief of Staff
CIO: Richard Hart, Chief Financial Officer
CHR: Tyson Hubbard, Director Human Resources
CNO: Susan Gonzalez, Director of Clinical Services
Web address: www.stanislaussurgical.com
**Control:** Corporation, Investor–owned, for–profit **Service:** Surgical

**Staffed Beds:** 23 **Admissions:** 555 **Census:** 4 **Outpatient Visits:** 27072
**Births:** 0 **Total Expense ($000):** 28988 **Payroll Expense ($000):** 9270
**Personnel:** 216

### MONROVIA—Los Angeles County

○ **MONROVIA MEMORIAL HOSPITAL (052054)**, 323 South Heliotrope Avenue, Zip 91016–2914; tel. 626/408–9800, (Nonreporting) **A**9 10 11
Primary Contact: Ron Kupferstein, Chief Executive Officer
Web address: www.monroviamemorial.com
**Control:** Partnership, Investor–owned, for–profit **Service:** Long–Term Acute Care hospital

**Staffed Beds:** 49

### MONTCLAIR—San Bernardino County

☐ **MONTCLAIR HOSPITAL MEDICAL CENTER (050758)**, 5000 San Bernardino Street, Zip 91763–2326; tel. 909/625–5411, (Nonreporting) **A**1 10 **S** Prime Healthcare Services, Ontario, CA
Primary Contact: Gregory Brentano, Chief Executive Officer
CFO: Robert Bonner, Chief Financial Officer
CMO: Joseph Hourany, Chief Medical Officer
CNO: Gail Aviado, Chief Nursing Officer
Web address: www.montclair–hospital.com
**Control:** Other not–for–profit (including NFP Corporation) **Service:** General Medical and Surgical

**Staffed Beds:** 102

### MONTEBELLO—Los Angeles County

◇ **BEVERLY HOSPITAL (050350)**, 309 West Beverly Boulevard, Zip 90640–4308; tel. 323/726–1222, (Nonreporting) **A**9 10 21
Primary Contact: Alice Cheng, President and Chief Executive Officer
CFO: Larry Pugh, Vice President and Chief Financial Officer
CIO: Mark Turner, Director Information Systems
CHR: John Barnes, Administrative Director Human Resources
CNO: Kathy Wojno, Vice President Nursing Services and Chief Nursing Officer
Web address: www.beverly.org
**Control:** Other not–for–profit (including NFP Corporation) **Service:** General Medical and Surgical

**Staffed Beds:** 102

### MONTEREY—Monterey County

⊠ **COMMUNITY HOSPITAL OF THE MONTEREY PENINSULA (050145)**, 23625 Holman Highway, Zip 93940–5902, Mailing Address: Box 'HH', Zip 93942–6032; tel. 831/624–5311, (Total facility includes 28 beds in nursing home–type unit) **A**1 2 9 10 **F**3 5 11 12 13 15 17 18 20 22 24 26 28 29 30 31 32 34 35 37 40 44 45 46 47 48 49 50 51 53 54 57 58 59 60 61 62 63 64 68 70 73 74 75 76 77 78 79 81 82 83 84 85 87 89 90 91 92 93 94 96 98 99 100 101 102 103 104 105 107 110 111 114 115 116 117 118 119 120 121 123 124 128 129 130 132 134 135 145 146 148
Primary Contact: Steven J. Packer, M.D., President and Chief Executive Officer
CFO: Laura Zehm, Vice President and Chief Financial Officer
CMO: Anthony D. Chavis, M.D., Vice President Enterprise Medical Officer, Community Hospital Foundation
Web address: www.chomp.org
**Control:** Other not–for–profit (including NFP Corporation) **Service:** General Medical and Surgical

**Staffed Beds:** 248 **Admissions:** 11633 **Census:** 163 **Outpatient Visits:** 299431 **Births:** 1115 **Total Expense ($000):** 423875 **Payroll Expense ($000):** 151730 **Personnel:** 1685

### MONTEREY PARK—Los Angeles County

☐ **GARFIELD MEDICAL CENTER (050737)**, 525 North Garfield Avenue, Zip 91754–1205; tel. 626/573–2222, (Nonreporting) **A**1 9 10 **S** AHMC & Healthcare, Inc., Alhambra, CA
Primary Contact: David J. Batista, Chief Executive Officer
COO: David J. Batista, Chief Operating Officer
CFO: Steve Maekawa, Chief Financial Officer
CMO: Terry Lee, M.D., Chief of Staff
CIO: Ann Curnutt, Director Information Systems
CHR: Rebecca R. Ricartti, Interim Director Human Resources
CNO: Shirley Tang, R.N., Chief Nursing Officer
Web address: www.garfieldmedicalcenter.com
**Control:** Partnership, Investor–owned, for–profit **Service:** General Medical and Surgical

**Staffed Beds:** 210

☐ **MONTEREY PARK HOSPITAL (050736)**, 900 South Atlantic Boulevard, Zip 91754–4780; tel. 626/570–9000 **A**1 9 10 **F**3 15 29 34 35 40 49 50 57 59 60 70 75 76 81 86 87 89 107 113 114 119 130 142 143 146 **S** AHMC & Healthcare, Inc., Alhambra, CA
Primary Contact: Philip A. Cohen, Chief Executive Officer
COO: Ericka Smith, Chief Operating Officer
CFO: Daniel Song, Chief Financial Officer
CMO: Azucena Porral, M.D., Chief of Staff
CIO: Angelica Ching, Director Information Systems
CNO: Evelyn Ku, Chief Nursing Officer
Web address: www.montereyparkhosp.com
**Control:** Partnership, Investor–owned, for–profit **Service:** General Medical and Surgical

**Staffed Beds:** 101 **Admissions:** 5077 **Census:** 45 **Outpatient Visits:** 22893
**Births:** 1757 **Total Expense ($000):** 74163 **Payroll Expense ($000):** 20962
**Personnel:** 281

### MORENO VALLEY—Riverside County

⊠ **KAISER PERMANENTE MORENO VALLEY MEDICAL CENTER (050765)**, 27300 Iris Avenue, Zip 92555–4800; tel. 951/243–0811 **A**1 10 **F**3 13 17 29 30 35 40 44 45 46 49 50 59 60 64 65 68 70 75 76 77 79 81 84 85 87 97 100 102 107 108 109 111 115 119 130 135 146 148 **S** Kaiser Foundation Hospitals, Oakland, CA
Primary Contact: Corey A. Seale, Chief Executive Officer
**Control:** Other not–for–profit (including NFP Corporation) **Service:** General Medical and Surgical

**Staffed Beds:** 71 **Admissions:** 6679 **Census:** 44 **Outpatient Visits:** 38306
**Births:** 1145 **Personnel:** 244

⊠ **RIVERSIDE COUNTY REGIONAL MEDICAL CENTER (050292)**, 26520 Cactus Avenue, Zip 92555–3911; tel. 951/486–4000 **A**1 3 5 10 12 13 **F**3 8 11 13 15 29 30 31 32 35 39 40 43 44 46 47 49 50 56 57 58 59 64 65 66 68 70 71 72 74 75 76 77 78 79 81 82 85 87 88 89 93 94 97 98 99 100 101 102 103 104 107 108 111 114 118 119 130 135 143 146 147 148
Primary Contact: Zareh Sarrafian, Chief Executive Officer
CFO: Christopher Hans, Chief Financial Officer
CMO: Arnold Tabuenca, M.D., Medical Director
CNO: Judi Nightingale, R.N., Chief Nursing Officer
Web address: www.rcrmc.org
**Control:** County–Government, nonfederal **Service:** General Medical and Surgical

**Staffed Beds:** 439 **Admissions:** 20830 **Census:** 314 **Outpatient Visits:** 265383 **Births:** 2144 **Total Expense ($000):** 478240 **Payroll Expense ($000):** 194456 **Personnel:** 3028

### MOUNT SHASTA—Siskiyou County

⊠ **MERCY MEDICAL CENTER MOUNT SHASTA (051319)**, 914 Pine Street, Zip 96067–2143; tel. 530/926–6111 **A**1 9 10 18 **F**3 11 13 15 29 30 35 40 43 50 53 56 57 59 62 63 64 68 70 75 76 77 79 81 82 84 89 93 107 108 110 111 114 118 119 121 127 130 131 132 133 143 146 148 **S** Dignity Health, San Francisco, CA
Primary Contact: Kenneth E. S. Platou, President
CFO: Kimberly Miranda, Chief Financial Officer
CMO: Gary Herfindahl, M.D., Chief of Staff
CHR: Michelle Michl, Director Human Resources
CNO: Sherie Ambrose, Vice President Patient Care Services
Web address: www.mercymtshasta.org
**Control:** Other not–for–profit (including NFP Corporation) **Service:** General Medical and Surgical

**Staffed Beds:** 33 **Admissions:** 1015 **Census:** 7 **Outpatient Visits:** 63957
**Births:** 135 **Total Expense ($000):** 51683 **Payroll Expense ($000):** 19531
**Personnel:** 207

*Many Facility Codes have changed. Please refer to the AHA Guide Code Chart.* © 2015 AHA Guide

**CA**

## MOUNTAIN VIEW—Santa Clara County

✠ **EL CAMINO HOSPITAL (050308)**, 2500 Grant Road, Zip 94040–4302, Mailing Address: P.O. Box 7025, Zip 94039–7025; tel. 650/940–7000, (Includes EL CAMINO HOSPITAL LOS GATOS, 815 Pollard Road, Los Gatos, Zip 95032–1438; tel. 408/378–6131) **A**1 2 3 9 10 **F**3 5 11 12 13 15 16 17 18 20 22 24 26 28 29 30 31 34 35 40 45 46 49 50 51 54 55 56 57 58 59 60 64 65 70 72 74 75 76 77 78 79 81 82 84 85 86 87 89 90 93 98 101 102 103 104 105 107 108 110 111 114 115 116 117 118 119 120 121 123 124 126 129 130 132 135 143 146 147
Primary Contact: Tomi S. Ryba, President and Chief Executive Officer
COO: Mike Zdeblick, Chief Operating Officer
CFO: Iftikhar Hussain, Chief Financial Officer
CMO: Eric Pifer, M.D., Chief Medical Officer
CIO: Greg Walton, Chief Information Officer
CHR: Kathryn M. Fisk, Chief Human Resources Officer
CNO: Cheryl Reinking, R.N., Chief Nursing Officer
Web address: www.elcaminohospital.org
**Control:** Hospital district or authority, Government, nonfederal **Service:** General Medical and Surgical

> **Staffed Beds:** 420 **Admissions:** 18567 **Census:** 238 **Outpatient Visits:** 296707 **Births:** 5239 **Total Expense ($000):** 669679 **Payroll Expense ($000):** 299156 **Personnel:** 1549

## MURRIETA—Riverside County

☐ **LOMA LINDA UNIVERSITY MEDICAL CENTER–MURRIETA (050770)**, 28062 Baxter Road, Zip 92563–1401; tel. 951/290–4000 **A**1 9 10 **F**3 12 13 15 18 20 22 24 25 26 28 29 30 34 35 38 40 44 45 46 48 49 51 57 59 64 70 74 75 76 77 78 79 81 85 87 91 93 107 108 110 111 114 115 116 117 118 119 120 121 126 130 132 141 142 146 148 **P**5 **S** Loma Linda University Adventist Health Sciences Center, Loma Linda, CA
Primary Contact: Richard L. Rawson, Chief Executive Officer
COO: Richard M. Tibbits, Vice President and Chief Operating Officer
CFO: James Uli, Chief Financial Officer
CMO: Jeff Conner, M.D., Chief Medical Staff
Web address: www.llumcmurrieta.org
**Control:** Church–operated, Nongovernment, not–for profit **Service:** General Medical and Surgical

> **Staffed Beds:** 106 **Admissions:** 7739 **Census:** 85 **Outpatient Visits:** 68722 **Births:** 1176 **Total Expense ($000):** 198270 **Payroll Expense ($000):** 52320

☐ **SOUTHWEST HEALTHCARE SYSTEM (050701)**, 25500 Medical Center Drive, Zip 92562–5965; tel. 951/696–6000, (Includes INLAND VALLEY MEDICAL CENTER, 36485 Inland Valley Drive, Wildomar, Zip 92595–9700; tel. 951/677–1111; Bradley D. Neet, FACHE, Chief Executive Officer; RANCHO SPRINGS MEDICAL CENTER, 25500 Medical Center Drive, tel. 951/696–6000) **A**1 9 10 **F**11 12 13 15 18 20 29 30 34 35 37 40 43 45 50 51 60 70 76 78 79 81 85 87 107 111 115 116 117 126 130 146 148 **S** Universal Health Services, Inc., King of Prussia, PA
Primary Contact: Bradley D. Neet, FACHE, Chief Executive Officer
COO: Jared Giles, Chief Operating Officer
CFO: Jon Zilkow, Chief Financial Officer
CMO: Yara Gorski, M.D., Chief of Staff
CIO: Jeffrey Upcraft, Director Information Services
CHR: Della G. Stange, Director Human Resources
CNO: Kristen Johnson, Chief Nursing Officer
Web address: www.swhealthcaresystem.com/
**Control:** Corporation, Investor–owned, for–profit **Service:** General Medical and Surgical

> **Staffed Beds:** 252 **Admissions:** 14894 **Census:** 148 **Outpatient Visits:** 87896 **Births:** 3163 **Total Expense ($000):** 209218 **Payroll Expense ($000):** 96086 **Personnel:** 1140

## NAPA—Napa County

☐ **NAPA STATE HOSPITAL (054122)**, 2100 Napa–Vallejo Highway, Zip 94558–6293; tel. 707/253–5000 **A**1 3 5 10 **F**30 39 53 56 59 61 67 68 77 86 98 103 128 130 132 135 146 **P**6
Primary Contact: Dolly Matteucci, Executive Director
COO: Dolly Matteucci, Executive Director
Web address: www.dmh.ca.gov
**Control:** State–Government, nonfederal **Service:** Psychiatric

> **Staffed Beds:** 1284 **Admissions:** 667 **Census:** 1151 **Outpatient Visits:** 0 **Births:** 0 **Total Expense ($000):** 273760 **Payroll Expense ($000):** 171766 **Personnel:** 2248

✠ **QUEEN OF THE VALLEY MEDICAL CENTER (050009)**, 1000 Trancas Street, Zip 94558–2906, Mailing Address: P.O. Box 2340, Zip 94558–0688; tel. 707/252–4411 **A**1 2 9 10 **F**3 13 15 17 18 20 22 24 26 29 30 31 32 34 35 37 39 40 41 43 44 45 46 47 48 49 50 51 54 57 59 64 68 70 72 74 75 76 77 78 79 81 84 85 86 87 89 90 91 92 93 96 97 102 107 108 110 111 114 115 116 117 118 119 120 121 123 126 130 132 135 146 **P**3 5 **S** St. Joseph Health, Irvine, CA
Primary Contact: Walt Mickens, FACHE, President and Chief Executive Officer
COO: Vincent Morgese, M.D., Executive Vice President, Chief Operating Officer and Chief Medical Officer
CFO: Mich Riccioni, Vice President and Chief Financial Officer, Northern California Region
CMO: Vincent Morgese, M.D., Executive Vice President, Chief Operating Officer and Chief Medical Officer
CHR: Robert A. Eisen, Vice President Human Resources, Northern California Region
Web address: www.thequeen.org
**Control:** Church–operated, Nongovernment, not–for profit **Service:** General Medical and Surgical

> **Staffed Beds:** 174 **Admissions:** 7154 **Census:** 89 **Outpatient Visits:** 185690 **Births:** 795 **Total Expense ($000):** 252460 **Payroll Expense ($000):** 88001 **Personnel:** 1059

## NATIONAL CITY—San Diego County

☐ △ **PARADISE VALLEY HOSPITAL (050024)**, 2400 East Fourth Street, Zip 91950–2099; tel. 619/470–4321, (Includes BAYVIEW BEHAVIORAL HEALTH CAMPUS, 330 Moss Street, Chula Vista, Zip 91911–2005; tel. 619/426–6311; George Lewis, Executive Director), (Nonreporting) **A**1 3 7 9 10 **S** Prime Healthcare Services, Ontario, CA
Primary Contact: Neerav Jadeja, Administrator
CFO: Janet L. Caceres, Chief Financial Officer
CMO: Genaro Fernandez, M.D., Chief of Staff
CIO: Amanda Kaems, Manager Information Systems
CHR: Lorraine Villegas, Manager Human Resources
Web address: www.paradisevalleyhospital.org
**Control:** Corporation, Investor–owned, for–profit **Service:** General Medical and Surgical

> **Staffed Beds:** 205

## NEEDLES—San Bernardino County

★ **COLORADO RIVER MEDICAL CENTER (051323)**, 1401 Bailey Avenue, Zip 92363–3198; tel. 760/326–7100 **A**9 10 18 **F**1 3 4 16 17 29 30 34 35 40 45 50 53 57 59 65 67 68 70 72 73 77 79 80 81 87 88 89 90 98 102 107 114 119 128 130 145 146 148 **P**4
Primary Contact: Steve Lopez, Chief Executive Officer
COO: Knaya Tabora, Chief Operating Officer and Chief Nursing Officer
CFO: Steve Lopez, Chief Executive Officer
CMO: Robert Strecker, M.D., Chief of Staff
CIO: Ron Chieffo, Chief Information Officer
CHR: Pam Barrett, Human Resources Director
CNO: Knaya Tabora, Chief Operating Officer and Chief Nursing Officer
Web address: www.crmccares.com
**Control:** Other not–for–profit (including NFP Corporation) **Service:** General Medical and Surgical

> **Staffed Beds:** 25 **Admissions:** 597 **Census:** 5 **Outpatient Visits:** 9886 **Births:** 0 **Total Expense ($000):** 8517 **Payroll Expense ($000):** 4295

## NEWPORT BEACH—Orange County

★ ◇ **HOAG MEMORIAL HOSPITAL PRESBYTERIAN (050224)**, One Hoag Drive, Zip 92663–4120, Mailing Address: P.O. Box 6100, Zip 92658–6100; tel. 949/764–4624, (Includes HOAG HOSPITAL IRVINE, 16200 Sand Canyon Avenue, Irvine, Zip 92618–3714; tel. 949/764–8240) **A**3 5 9 10 21 **F**3 4 5 8 11 13 14 15 17 18 20 22 24 26 28 29 30 31 34 35 36 37 40 44 45 46 47 48 49 50 51 53 54 55 57 58 59 60 64 68 70 71 72 74 75 76 77 78 79 81 82 84 85 87 92 93 94 96 97 100 102 103 107 108 110 111 113 114 115 116 117 118 119 120 121 123 124 126 129 130 131 132 135 141 143 144 145 146 147 148
Primary Contact: Robert Braithwaite, President and Chief Executive Officer
CFO: Jennifer C. Mitzner, Senior Vice President Finance and Chief Financial Officer
CMO: Jack Cox, M.D., Senior Vice President and Chief Quality Officer
CIO: Tim Moore, R.N., Senior Vice President and Chief Information Officer
CHR: Jan L. Blue, Vice President Human Resources
CNO: Richard A. Martin, MSN, Senior Vice President and Chief Nursing Officer
Web address: www.hoaghospital.org
**Control:** Other not–for–profit (including NFP Corporation) **Service:** General Medical and Surgical

> **Staffed Beds:** 414 **Admissions:** 17988 **Census:** 207 **Outpatient Visits:** 280483 **Births:** 4553 **Total Expense ($000):** 605091 **Payroll Expense ($000):** 215043 **Personnel:** 4041

---

**Hospital, Medicare Provider Number, Address, Telephone, Approval, Facility, and Physician Codes, Health Care System**

★ American Hospital Association (AHA) membership
☐ The Joint Commission accreditation
◯ Healthcare Facilities Accreditation Program
◇ DNV Healthcare Inc. accreditation
⇑ Center for Improvement in Healthcare Quality Accreditation
△ Commission on Accreditation of Rehabilitation Facilities (CARF) accreditation

**NEWPORT BAY HOSPITAL (054135)**, 1501 East 16th Street,
Zip 92663–5924; tel. 949/650–9750, (Nonreporting) **A**10
Primary Contact: James E. Parkhurst, President and Chief Executive Officer
COO: Garry Hardwick, R.N., Chief Operating Officer
CFO: Rocky Gentner, Chief Financial Officer
CMO: Jason Kellogg, M.D., Chief of Staff
CIO: Nina Swenson, Director Business Services
CHR: Phyllis Parkhurst, Vice President Support Services
Web address: www.newportbayhospital.com
**Control:** Corporation, Investor–owned, for–profit **Service:** Psychiatric

| Staffed Beds: 34 |
|---|

**NORTH HOLLYWOOD—Los Angeles County, See Los Angeles**

**NORTHRIDGE—Los Angeles County, See Los Angeles**

**NORWALK—Los Angeles County**

**COAST PLAZA DOCTORS HOSPITAL** See Coast Plaza Hospital

☐ **COAST PLAZA HOSPITAL (050771)**, 13100 Studebaker Road,
Zip 90650–2500; tel. 562/868–3751, (Nonreporting) **A**1 10 **S** Avanti Hospitals,
El Segundo, CA
Primary Contact: Richard Rowe, PharmD, Chief Executive Officer
CFO: Mihi Lee, Chief Financial Officer
CMO: Galal S. Gough, M.D., Chief of Staff
CIO: Linda K. Roman, Administrator
Web address: www.coastplaza.com
**Control:** Partnership, Investor–owned, for–profit **Service:** General Medical and
Surgical

| Staffed Beds: 123 |
|---|

**LOS ANGELES COMMUNITY HOSPITAL OF NORWALK** See Los Angeles
Community Hospital at Los Angeles, Los Angeles

☐ **METROPOLITAN STATE HOSPITAL (054133)**, 11401 Bloomfield Avenue,
Zip 90650–2015; tel. 562/863–7011, (Nonreporting) **A**1 10
Primary Contact: Michael Barsom, M.D., Executive Director
CFO: Maybelle Manlagnit, Senior Accounting Officer
CIO: Paul Mello, Manager Data Processing
CHR: Jorge Banuedos, Director Human Resources
Web address: www.dmh.ca.gov
**Control:** State–Government, nonfederal **Service:** Psychiatric

| Staffed Beds: 657 |
|---|

**NOVATO—Marin County**

✠ **NOVATO COMMUNITY HOSPITAL (050131)**, 180 Rowland Way,
Zip 94945–5009, Mailing Address: P.O. Box 1108, Zip 94948–1108;
tel. 415/209–1300 **A**1 9 10 **F**3 15 18 26 29 30 31 34 40 45 49 50 51 54 56
59 60 64 68 70 74 75 77 78 79 81 84 85 87 93 107 108 111 115 119 130
131 132 134 143 144 146 148 **S** Sutter Health, Sacramento, CA
Primary Contact: Brian Alexander, Chief Administrative Officer
CMO: Barbara Nylund, M.D., Chief of Staff
CIO: Kathryn Graham, Director Communications and Community Relations
CHR: Diana G. Johnson, Acting Chief Human Resources Officer
Web address: www.novatocommunity.sutterhealth.org
**Control:** Other not–for–profit (including NFP Corporation) **Service:** General
Medical and Surgical

| Staffed Beds: 40 Admissions: 1466 Census: 13 Outpatient Visits: 83528 |
|---|
| Births: 0 Total Expense ($000): 68867 Payroll Expense ($000): 21026 |
| Personnel: 227 |

**OAKDALE—Stanislaus County**

✠ **OAK VALLEY HOSPITAL DISTRICT (050067)**, 350 South Oak Avenue,
Zip 95361–3581; tel. 209/847–3011, (Nonreporting) **A**1 9 10
Primary Contact: John McCormick, President and Chief Executive Officer
CFO: Alberto Diaz, Chief Financial Officer
CMO: Albert Gelders, M.D., Chief of Staff
CIO: Sherry Peral, Manager Information Systems
CHR: Brian Beck,PHR,MHROD, Vice President Human Resources
CNO: Joann L. Saporito, R.N., Vice President Nursing Services
Web address: www.oakvalleycares.org
**Control:** Hospital district or authority, Government, nonfederal **Service:** General
Medical and Surgical

| Staffed Beds: 150 |
|---|

**OAKLAND—Alameda County**

✠ **ALTA BATES SUMMIT MEDICAL CENTER – SUMMIT CAMPUS (050043)**,
350 Hawthorne Avenue, Zip 94609–3100; tel. 510/655–4000 **A**1 2 5 9 10 **F**3 8
11 12 15 17 18 20 22 24 26 29 30 34 35 36 40 45 46 47 49 51 56 57 58
59 60 61 64 68 70 74 75 77 78 79 81 82 85 86 87 90 97 107 108 111 114
115 116 117 118 119 120 121 123 124 126 130 132 135 146 148 **S** Sutter
Health, Sacramento, CA
Primary Contact: Charles Prosper, Chief Executive Officer
CMO: John Gentile, M.D., Vice President Medical Affairs
CHR: Mark Beiting, Vice President Human Resources
Web address: www.altabatessummit.com
**Control:** Other not–for–profit (including NFP Corporation) **Service:** General
Medical and Surgical

| Staffed Beds: 326 Admissions: 10885 Census: 166 Outpatient Visits: |
|---|
| 126349 Births: 0 Total Expense ($000): 358889 Payroll Expense ($000): |
| 116200 Personnel: 1523 |

☐ **CHILDREN'S HOSPITAL AND RESEARCH CENTER OAKLAND (053301)**,
(Pediatrics), 747 52nd Street, Zip 94609–1859; tel. 510/428–3000 **A**1 3 5 9
10 **F**19 21 23 25 29 30 32 34 35 38 40 41 43 44 45 46 50 54 55 57 58 59
61 65 66 68 72 74 75 77 78 79 81 84 86 87 88 90 93 97 99 100 101 102
104 107 111 127 129 130 131 132 134 136 143 146
Primary Contact: Bertram Lubin, M.D., President and Chief Executive Officer
CFO: Doug Myers, Senior Vice President and Chief Financial Officer
CIO: Don Livsey, Vice President and Chief Information Officer
Web address: www.childrenshospitaloakland.org
**Control:** Other not–for–profit (including NFP Corporation) **Service:** Children's
general

| Staffed Beds: 190 Admissions: 10452 Census: 137 Outpatient Visits: |
|---|
| 239420 Births: 0 Total Expense ($000): 520013 Payroll Expense ($000): |
| 233830 Personnel: 2181 |

✠ **HIGHLAND HOSPITAL (050320)**, 1411 East 31st Street, Zip 94602–1018;
tel. 510/437–4800, (Includes FAIRMONT HOSPITAL, 15400 Foothill Boulevard,
San Leandro, Zip 94578–1009; tel. 510/895–4200; James E. T. Jackson,
M.P.H., Chief Administrative Officer; JOHN GEORGE PSYCHIATRIC HOSPITAL,
2060 Fairmont Drive, San Leandro, Zip 94578–1001; tel. 510/346–1300; Guy
C. Qvistgaard, Chief Executive Officer) **A**1 3 5 10 **F**3 5 11 13 15 18 20 22 28
29 30 31 32 34 35 36 38 39 40 43 44 45 46 49 50 54 56 57 58 59 60 61
64 65 66 68 70 71 73 74 75 76 77 78 79 81 82 84 85 86 87 90 92 93 94
96 97 98 100 101 102 104 105 107 111 112 114 115 119 128 130 132
134 135 142 143 144 146 147 148 **P**6 **S** Alameda Health System, San
Leandro, CA
Primary Contact: Delvecchio Finley, Chief Executive Officer
CFO: Marion Schales, Chief Financial Officer
CMO: Sang–ick Chang, M.D., Chief Medical Officer
CHR: Jeanette L. Louden Corbett, Chief Human Resources Officer
Web address: www.alamedahealthsystem.org
**Control:** Hospital district or authority, Government, nonfederal **Service:** General
Medical and Surgical

| Staffed Beds: 380 Admissions: 15234 Census: 313 Outpatient Visits: |
|---|
| 414643 Births: 1131 Total Expense ($000): 651003 Payroll Expense |
| ($000): 303785 Personnel: 2441 |

✠ **KAISER PERMANENTE OAKLAND MEDICAL CENTER (050075)**, 3600
Broadway, Zip 94611–5693; tel. 510/752–1000, (Includes KAISER PERMANENTE
RICHMOND MEDICAL CENTER, 901 Nevin Avenue, Richmond, Zip 94801–2555;
tel. 510/307–1500), (Nonreporting) **A**1 3 5 8 10 **S** Kaiser Foundation Hospitals,
Oakland, CA
Primary Contact: Odette Bolano, R.N., Senior Vice President and Area Manager
CFO: Dennis Morris, Area Finance Officer
CMO: John Loftus, M.D., Chief of Staff
CIO: Johnny Law, Area Information Officer
CHR: Rick Mead, Human Resources Leader
CNO: Charlene Boyer, Chief Nursing Officer
Web address: www.kaiserpermanente.org
**Control:** Other not–for–profit (including NFP Corporation) **Service:** General
Medical and Surgical

| Staffed Beds: 267 |
|---|

**OAKLAND MEDICAL CENTER** See Kaiser Permanente Oakland Medical Center

☐ **TELECARE HERITAGE PSYCHIATRIC HEALTH CENTER (054146)**, 2633 East
27th Street, Zip 94601–1912; tel. 510/535–5115 **A**1 9 10 **F**98 103 **P**5
Primary Contact: Anne L. Bakar, President and Chief Executive Officer
Web address: www.tbhcare.com/
**Control:** Corporation, Investor–owned, for–profit **Service:** Psychiatric

| Staffed Beds: 26 Admissions: 1276 Census: 20 Outpatient Visits: 0 Births: |
|---|
| 0 Personnel: 53 |

**OCEANSIDE—San Diego County**

✠ **TRI–CITY MEDICAL CENTER (050128)**, 4002 Vista Way, Zip 92056–4593; tel. 760/724–8411 **A**1 2 3 5 9 10 **F**3 5 8 11 12 13 15 18 20 22 24 26 28 29 30 31 34 35 36 37 38 39 40 41 45 46 47 48 49 51 53 57 59 60 61 62 64 65 68 70 72 74 75 76 77 78 79 81 82 84 85 86 87 90 91 92 93 94 97 98 99 100 101 102 104 105 107 108 109 110 111 112 113 114 115 116 117 118 119 120 121 122 123 124 126 130 131 132 135 143 146 147 148
Primary Contact: Timothy M. Moran, Chief Executive Officer
COO: Casey Fatch, Chief Operating Officer
CFO: Steve Dietlin, Chief Financial Officer
CMO: Scott Worman, Chief of Staff
CIO: Kim Cook, Interim Clinical Applications Services Manager
CHR: Esther Beverly, Vice President Human Resources
CNO: Sharon A. Schultz, MSN, Chief Nurse Executive and Vice President
Web address: www.tricitymed.org
**Control:** Hospital district or authority, Government, nonfederal **Service:** General Medical and Surgical

> **Staffed Beds:** 330 **Admissions:** 15332 **Census:** 193 **Outpatient Visits:** 178877 **Births:** 2576 **Total Expense ($000):** 325810 **Payroll Expense ($000):** 141727 **Personnel:** 1692

**ONTARIO—San Bernardino County**

✠ **KINDRED HOSPITAL–ONTARIO (052037)**, 550 North Monterey Avenue, Zip 91764–3399; tel. 909/391–0333, (Nonreporting) **A**1 9 10 **S** Kindred Healthcare, Louisville, KY
Primary Contact: Vincent Trac, Chief Executive Officer
CFO: Omar Oregel, Controller
CMO: Marc Lynch, D.O., Chief of Staff
CHR: Laurel Scharber, Administrative Assistant and Coordinator Human Resources
CNO: Holly Ramos, R.N., Chief Clinical Officer
Web address: www.khontario.com/
**Control:** Corporation, Investor–owned, for–profit **Service:** Long–Term Acute Care hospital

> **Staffed Beds:** 91

**ORANGE—Orange County**

☐ **CHAPMAN MEDICAL CENTER (050745)**, 2601 East Chapman Avenue, Zip 92869–3296; tel. 714/633–0011, (Nonreporting) **A**1 9 10 **S** Integrated Healthcare, Santa Ana, CA
Primary Contact: Don Kreitz, Chief Executive Officer
COO: Ada Yeh, R.N., Chief Operating Officer and Chief Nursing Officer
CFO: Robert Heinemeier, Chief Financial Officer
CMO: Steven Duckor, M.D., Chief of Staff
CIO: Sri Yarramsetti, Chief Information Officer
CHR: JoAnne Suehs, Manager Human Resources
CNO: Ada Yeh, R.N., Chief Operating Officer and Chief Nursing Officer
Web address: www.chapmanmedicalcenter.com
**Control:** Corporation, Investor–owned, for–profit **Service:** General Medical and Surgical

> **Staffed Beds:** 100

☐ **CHILDREN'S HOSPITAL OF ORANGE COUNTY (053304)**, 1201 West La Veta Avenue, Zip 92868–4203, Mailing Address: PO Box 5700, Zip 92863–5700; tel. 714/997–3000 **A**1 3 5 9 10 **F**3 14 17 19 21 23 25 27 29 30 31 32 34 35 40 41 50 55 57 58 59 61 64 65 66 68 71 72 74 75 77 78 79 81 85 86 87 88 89 91 92 93 97 104 107 111 113 114 115 116 117 118 119 120 121 123 126 129 130 131 132 134 136 146 **P**5
Primary Contact: Kimberly C. Cripe, President and Chief Executive Officer
COO: Matthew S. Gerlach, Chief Operating Officer
CFO: Kerri Ruppert Schiller, Senior Vice President and Chief Financial Officer
CMO: Maria Minon, M.D., Vice President Medical Affairs and Chief Medical Officer
CIO: Mark Headland, Chief Information Officer
CHR: Mamoon Syed, Vice President Human Resources
CNO: Melanie Patterson, R.N., Vice President Patient Care Services and Chief Nursing Officer
Web address: www.choc.org
**Control:** Other not–for–profit (including NFP Corporation) **Service:** Children's general

> **Staffed Beds:** 279 **Admissions:** 11246 **Census:** 156 **Outpatient Visits:** 206964 **Births:** 0 **Total Expense ($000):** 549190 **Payroll Expense ($000):** 164403 **Personnel:** 2435

◇ **HEALTHBRIDGE CHILDREN'S HOSPITAL (053308)**, 393 South Tustin Street, Zip 92866–2501; tel. 714/289–2400 **A**9 10 21 **F**3 29 64 65 75 77 90 93 128 130 132 146 148 **S** Nexus Health Systems, Houston, TX
Primary Contact: Brian Cotter, Chief Executive Officer
Web address: www.HealthBridgeOrange.com
**Control:** Partnership, Investor–owned, for–profit **Service:** Children's rehabilitation

> **Staffed Beds:** 27 **Admissions:** 137 **Census:** 25 **Outpatient Visits:** 0 **Births:** 0 **Total Expense ($000):** 10506 **Payroll Expense ($000):** 5775 **Personnel:** 113

✠ **ST. JOSEPH HOSPITAL (050069)**, 1100 West Stewart Drive, Zip 92868–3849, Mailing Address: P.O. Box 5600, Zip 92863–5600; tel. 714/633–9111 **A**1 2 3 5 9 10 **F**3 5 8 12 13 14 15 17 18 19 20 21 22 23 24 25 26 27 28 29 30 31 34 35 37 39 40 41 45 46 47 49 50 51 53 54 55 57 58 59 60 64 65 66 68 69 70 71 74 75 76 77 78 79 80 81 82 84 85 86 87 91 92 93 98 100 102 104 105 107 108 109 110 111 113 114 115 116 117 118 119 120 121 123 124 126 129 130 131 132 135 138 141 146 147 148 **P**3 5 **S** St. Joseph Health, Irvine, CA
Primary Contact: Steven C. Moreau, President and Chief Executive Officer
COO: Jeremy Zoch, Executive Vice President and Chief Operating Officer
CFO: Kristi Liberatore, Vice President and Chief Financial Officer
CMO: Paul Beck, Chief Medical Officer
CIO: Jeremy Zoch, Executive Vice President and Chief Operating Officer
CHR: Mary P. Leahy, Vice President Human Resources
CNO: Katie Skelton, MSN, Vice President Nursing and Chief Nursing Officer
Web address: www.sjo.org
**Control:** Other not–for–profit (including NFP Corporation) **Service:** General Medical and Surgical

> **Staffed Beds:** 379 **Admissions:** 20324 **Census:** 211 **Outpatient Visits:** 314187 **Births:** 5543 **Total Expense ($000):** 585840 **Payroll Expense ($000):** 177989 **Personnel:** 2385

✠ **UC IRVINE MEDICAL CENTER (050348)**, 101 The City Drive South, Zip 92868–3298; tel. 714/456–6011 **A**1 2 3 5 8 9 10 **F**3 6 8 9 11 12 13 14 15 16 17 18 20 22 24 26 28 29 30 31 32 34 35 36 37 39 40 43 44 45 46 47 48 49 50 51 53 54 55 56 57 58 59 60 61 64 65 66 68 70 71 72 74 75 76 77 78 79 80 81 82 84 85 86 87 90 91 92 93 96 97 98 99 100 101 102 104 105 107 108 110 111 112 115 116 117 118 119 120 121 123 124 126 130 131 132 134 135 138 141 142 145 146 147 148 **P**6 **S** University of California Systemwide Administration, Oakland, CA
Primary Contact: Terry A. Belmont, Chief Executive Officer
COO: Alice H. Issai, Chief Operating Officer
CFO: Morris J. Frieling, Chief Financial Officer
CMO: Doug Merill, M.D., Chief Medical Officer
CIO: Scott Cebula, Interim Chief Information Officer
CHR: Susi Takeuchi, Chief Human Resources Officer
CNO: Karen A. Grimley, R.N., Chief Nursing Officer
Web address: www.ucihealth.com
**Control:** State–Government, nonfederal **Service:** General Medical and Surgical

> **Staffed Beds:** 411 **Admissions:** 19287 **Census:** 295 **Outpatient Visits:** 592526 **Births:** 1492 **Total Expense ($000):** 828705 **Payroll Expense ($000):** 337195 **Personnel:** 4326

**OROVILLE—Butte County**

**OROVILLE HOSPITAL (050030)**, 2767 Olive Highway, Zip 95966–6118; tel. 530/533–8500 **A**9 10 **F**3 5 11 13 15 18 19 26 28 29 30 31 32 33 34 35 36 38 39 40 41 43 44 45 46 47 48 49 50 51 52 54 56 57 59 60 61 62 63 64 65 66 68 70 74 75 76 77 78 79 81 82 83 84 85 86 87 91 93 94 96 97 107 108 110 111 114 115 116 117 118 119 120 121 123 124 126 127 129 130 131 132 134 135 144 145 146 147 148
Primary Contact: Robert J. Wentz, President and Chief Executive Officer
COO: Scott Chapple, Chief Operating Officer
CFO: Ashok Khanchandani, Chief Financial Officer
CMO: Mathew N. Fine, M.D., Chief Medical Officer
CIO: Denise LeFevre, Chief Information Officer
CHR: Scott Chapple, Chief Operating Officer
CNO: Carol Speer–Smith, R.N., Chief Nursing Officer
Web address: www.orovillehospital.com
**Control:** Other not–for–profit (including NFP Corporation) **Service:** General Medical and Surgical

> **Staffed Beds:** 133 **Admissions:** 10967 **Census:** 109 **Outpatient Visits:** 343345 **Births:** 441 **Total Expense ($000):** 202739 **Payroll Expense ($000):** 78787 **Personnel:** 1072

**OXNARD—Ventura County**

✠ **ST. JOHN'S REGIONAL MEDICAL CENTER (050082)**, 1600 North Rose Avenue, Zip 93030–3723; tel. 805/988–2500, (Nonreporting) **A**1 2 9 10 **S** Dignity Health, San Francisco, CA
Primary Contact: Darren W. Lee, President and Chief Executive Officer
CIO: Jeff Perry, Director Information Technology
CHR: Ed Gonzales, Vice President Human Resources
Web address: www.stjohnshealth.org
**Control:** Other not–for–profit (including NFP Corporation) **Service:** General Medical and Surgical

> **Staffed Beds:** 266

**CA**

---

**Hospital, Medicare Provider Number, Address, Telephone, Approval, Facility, and Physician Codes, Health Care System**

★ American Hospital Association (AHA) membership
☐ The Joint Commission accreditation
○ Healthcare Facilities Accreditation Program
◇ DNV Healthcare Inc. accreditation
⇑ Center for Improvement in Healthcare Quality Accreditation
△ Commission on Accreditation of Rehabilitation Facilities (CARF) accreditation

## PALM SPRINGS—Riverside County

☒ **DESERT REGIONAL MEDICAL CENTER (050243)**, 1150 North Indian Canyon Drive, Zip 92262–4872, Mailing Address: P.O. Box 2739, Zip 92263–2739; tel. 760/323–6511, (Total facility includes 30 beds in nursing home–type unit) **A**1 2 3 9 10 13 **F**3 12 13 14 15 17 18 20 22 24 26 28 29 30 31 34 35 40 43 45 46 47 48 49 50 51 52 53 54 55 56 57 58 59 60 61 62 64 65 68 70 72 74 75 76 77 78 79 81 82 85 86 87 89 90 92 93 94 100 102 107 108 109 110 111 114 115 116 119 120 124 126 128 130 131 132 144 146 147 148 **S** TENET Healthcare Corporation, Dallas, TX
Primary Contact: Carolyn P. Caldwell, Chief Executive Officer
COO: Jeffrey Patterson, Chief Operating Officer
CFO: Richard Phillips, Chief Financial Officer
CMO: Charles Anderson, M.D., Chief Medical Officer
CIO: Robert Klingseis, Director Information Systems
CHR: Frederick K. Owusu, Chief Human Resources Officer
CNO: Kristin Schmidt, R.N., Chief Nursing Officer
Web address: www.desertregional.com
**Control:** Individual, Investor–owned, for–profit **Service:** General Medical and Surgical

**Staffed Beds:** 382 **Admissions:** 18130 **Census:** 223 **Outpatient Visits:** 151067 **Births:** 3277 **Total Expense ($000):** 332360 **Payroll Expense ($000):** 156782 **Personnel:** 1731

## PALMDALE—Los Angeles County

☐ **PALMDALE REGIONAL MEDICAL CENTER (050204)**, 38600 Medical Center Drive, Zip 93551–4483; tel. 661/382–5000, (Nonreporting) **A**1 9 10 **S** Universal Health Services, Inc., King of Prussia, PA
Primary Contact: Richard Allen, Chief Executive Officer
COO: Karen Faulis, Chief Operating Officer
CFO: Kurt Broten, Chief Financial Officer
CIO: Roy Singleton, Director Computer Information Systems
CHR: Karen Hickling, Director Human Resources
CNO: Pat McClendon, MSN, Chief Nursing Officer
Web address: www.palmdaleregional.com
**Control:** Corporation, Investor–owned, for–profit **Service:** General Medical and Surgical

**Staffed Beds:** 157

## PALO ALTO—Santa Clara County

☒ **LUCILE SALTER PACKARD CHILDREN'S HOSPITAL STANFORD (053305)**, 725 Welch Road, Zip 94304–1614; tel. 650/497–8000 **A**1 3 5 9 10 **F**3 7 11 12 13 15 17 19 25 27 28 29 30 31 32 34 35 36 38 43 44 45 46 47 48 49 50 52 54 55 57 58 59 60 61 62 64 65 66 68 71 72 73 74 75 76 77 78 79 80 81 82 84 85 86 87 88 89 91 92 93 96 97 100 101 104 107 111 115 119 124 126 129 130 131 132 134 136 137 138 139 140 141 142 144 145 146 148 **P**3 **S** Stanford Health Care, Palo Alto, CA
Primary Contact: Christopher G. Dawes, President and Chief Executive Officer
COO: Anne McCune, Chief Operating Officer
CMO: Kenneth Cox, M.D., Chief Medical Officer
CIO: James McCaughey, Chief Strategy Officer
CHR: Greg Souza, Vice President Human Resources
CNO: Susan Costello, Chief Nursing Officer
Web address: www.stanfordchildrens.org
**Control:** Other not–for–profit (including NFP Corporation) **Service:** Children's general

**Staffed Beds:** 302 **Admissions:** 13028 **Census:** 224 **Outpatient Visits:** 202523 **Births:** 4277 **Total Expense ($000):** 864157 **Payroll Expense ($000):** 284430 **Personnel:** 3009

☒ **STANFORD HEALTH CARE (050441)**, 300 Pasteur Drive, Suite H3200, Zip 94304–2203; tel. 650/723–4000 **A**1 3 5 8 9 10 **F**3 5 6 7 8 9 11 12 14 15 17 18 20 21 22 23 24 26 27 28 29 30 31 33 34 35 36 37 38 39 40 41 43 44 45 46 47 48 49 50 52 53 54 55 56 57 58 59 60 65 66 68 70 74 75 77 78 79 80 81 82 84 85 86 87 91 92 93 94 95 96 97 98 100 101 102 103 104 107 110 111 114 115 117 118 119 120 121 123 124 126 129 130 131 132 135 136 137 138 139 140 141 142 143 144 145 146 147 148 **P**3 5 6 **S** Stanford Health Care, Palo Alto, CA
Primary Contact: Amir Dan Rubin, President and Chief Executive Officer
COO: James Hereford, Chief Operating Officer
CFO: Daniel Morrissette, Chief Financial Officer
CMO: Norman Rizk, M.D., Chief Medical Officer
CIO: Pravene Nath, Chief Information Officer
CHR: Kety Duron, Vice President Human Resources
CNO: Nancy Lee, R.N., Vice President Patient Care Services and Chief Nursing Officer
Web address: www.stanfordhealthcare.org
**Control:** Other not–for–profit (including NFP Corporation) **Service:** General Medical and Surgical

**Staffed Beds:** 481 **Admissions:** 25092 **Census:** 397 **Outpatient Visits:** 1182926 **Births:** 0 **Total Expense ($000):** 2498440 **Payroll Expense ($000):** 771347 **Personnel:** 7845

☒ △ **VA PALO ALTO HEALTH CARE SYSTEM**, 3801 Miranda Avenue, Zip 94304–1207; tel. 650/493–5000, (Includes PALO ALTO DIVISION, 3801 Miranda Avenue, tel. 650/493–5000; VETERANS AFFAIRS PALO ALTO HEALTH CARE SYSTEM, LIVERMORE DIVISION, 4951 Arroyo Road, Livermore, Zip 94550; tel. 510/447–2560), (Nonreporting) **A**1 2 3 5 7 **S** Department of Veterans Affairs, Washington, DC
Primary Contact: Elizabeth Joyce Freeman, FACHE, Director
CFO: Mel Niese, Chief Fiscal Service
CMO: Lawrence Leung, M.D., Chief of Staff
CIO: Doug Wirthgen, Chief Information Officer
CHR: Lori Peery, Chief Human Resource Management Services
Web address: www.paloalto.va.gov/
**Control:** Veterans Affairs, Government, federal **Service:** General Medical and Surgical

**Staffed Beds:** 808

## PANORAMA CITY—Los Angeles County, See Los Angeles

## PARADISE—Butte County

☒ **FEATHER RIVER HOSPITAL (050225)**, 5974 Pentz Road, Zip 95969–5593; tel. 530/877–9361, (Nonreporting) **A**1 2 9 10 **S** Adventist Health, Roseville, CA
Primary Contact: Kevin R. Erich, President and Chief Executive Officer
CFO: Dan Gordon, Chief Financial Officer
CMO: Anthony Nasr, M.D., Chief Medical Staff
CIO: Dan Gordon, Chief Financial Officer
CHR: Denton Gruzensky, Director Human Resources
Web address: www.frhosp.org
**Control:** Church–operated, Nongovernment, not–for profit **Service:** General Medical and Surgical

**Staffed Beds:** 54

## PASADENA—Los Angeles County

☒ **HUNTINGTON MEMORIAL HOSPITAL (050438)**, 100 West California Boulevard, Zip 91105–3097, Mailing Address: P.O. Box 7013, Zip 91109–7013; tel. 626/397–5000 **A**1 2 3 5 9 10 **F**3 4 5 8 11 12 13 14 15 18 20 22 24 26 28 29 30 31 34 35 37 40 41 43 44 45 46 47 48 49 50 51 53 56 58 59 60 61 63 64 65 66 68 70 72 74 75 76 77 78 79 81 82 84 86 87 88 89 90 92 93 97 98 100 101 102 103 104 105 106 107 108 111 114 115 118 119 120 121 123 126 129 130 132 146 147 148 **P**3 5 7
Primary Contact: Stephen A. Ralph, President and Chief Executive Officer
COO: James S. Noble, Chief Operating Officer
CFO: Eugene Gutierrez, Vice President Finance
CMO: Paula Verrette, M.D., Senior Vice President Quality and Physician Services and Chief Medical Officer
CIO: Debbie Tafoya, Vice President and Chief Information Officer
CHR: Debbie Ortega, Chief Human Resource Officer and Vice President Administrative Services
CNO: Gloria Sanchez–Rico, Chief Nursing Officer and Vice President
Web address: www.huntingtonhospital.com
**Control:** Other not–for–profit (including NFP Corporation) **Service:** General Medical and Surgical

**Staffed Beds:** 556 **Admissions:** 25686 **Census:** 310 **Outpatient Visits:** 146023 **Births:** 3283 **Total Expense ($000):** 554373 **Payroll Expense ($000):** 196503 **Personnel:** 2832

☐ **LAS ENCINAS HOSPITAL (054078)**, 2900 East Del Mar Boulevard, Zip 91107–4399; tel. 626/795–9901, (Nonreporting) **A**1 9 10 **S** Signature Healthcare Services, Corona, CA
Primary Contact: Gerard Conway, Chief Executive Officer
CMO: Daniel Suzuki, M.D., Medical Director
CIO: Eric Kim, Chief Information Officer
CHR: Veronica Herrera, Director Human Resources
Web address: www.lasencinashospital.com
**Control:** Corporation, Investor–owned, for–profit **Service:** Psychiatric

**Staffed Beds:** 138

## PATTON—San Bernardino County

☐ **PATTON STATE HOSPITAL**, 3102 East Highland Avenue, Zip 92369–7813; tel. 909/425–7000 **A**1 3 **F**3 29 30 39 53 57 58 59 61 65 74 75 77 86 87 98 100 101 103 130 132 135 143 146
Primary Contact: Harry Oreol, Acting Chief Executive Officer
CFO: Kathleen Gamble, Fiscal Officer
CMO: George Christison, M.D., Medical Director
CIO: Cindy Barrett, Administrative Assistant
CHR: Nancy Varela, Director Human Resources
Web address: www.dmh.cahwnet.gov/statehospitals/patton
**Control:** State–Government, nonfederal **Service:** Psychiatric

**Staffed Beds:** 1528 **Admissions:** 1321 **Census:** 1506 **Births:** 0 **Total Expense ($000):** 308107 **Payroll Expense ($000):** 192389 **Personnel:** 2283

*Many Facility Codes have changed. Please refer to the AHA Guide Code Chart.* © 2015 AHA Guide

**CA**

## PERRIS—Riverside County

★ ○ **KINDRED HOSPITAL RIVERSIDE (052052)**, 2224 Medical Center Drive, Zip 92571–2638; tel. 951/436–3535, (Nonreporting) **A**9 10 11 **S** Kindred Healthcare, Louisville, KY
Primary Contact: Jonathan Jean–Marie, Administrator and Chief Executive Officer
COO: Guay Khim Fugate, Chief Operations Officer
CFO: John Browne, Senior Chief Financial Officer
CHR: Tom Wright, Director Human Resources
Web address: www.khriverside.com
**Control:** Corporation, Investor–owned, for–profit **Service:** Long–Term Acute Care hospital

Staffed Beds: 40

## PETALUMA—Sonoma County

⊞ **PETALUMA VALLEY HOSPITAL (050136)**, 400 North McDowell Boulevard, Zip 94954–2366; tel. 707/778–1111 **A**1 9 10 **F**3 11 13 15 29 30 31 35 40 44 45 46 49 50 51 57 60 63 64 68 70 74 75 76 77 78 79 81 84 85 87 91 92 93 100 107 108 110 111 115 119 130 146 148 **S** St. Joseph Health, Irvine, CA
Primary Contact: Todd Salnas, President
COO: David Ziolkowski, Chief Operating Officer
CFO: Mich Riccioni, Chief Financial Officer
CIO: Patrick Wylie, Director Information Systems
Web address: www.stjosephhealth.org/About–Us/Facilities/Petaluma–Valley–Hospital.aspx
**Control:** Other not–for–profit (including NFP Corporation) **Service:** General Medical and Surgical

Staffed Beds: 38 Admissions: 2608 Census: 23 Outpatient Visits: 59462 Births: 457 Total Expense ($000): 76457 Payroll Expense ($000): 27686 Personnel: 301

## PLACENTIA—Orange County

⊞ **PLACENTIA–LINDA HOSPITAL (050589)**, 1301 North Rose Drive, Zip 92870–3899; tel. 714/993–2000 **A**1 9 10 **F**3 7 11 12 15 17 18 29 30 34 35 40 45 46 47 48 49 54 56 57 59 65 70 75 79 81 82 85 87 93 97 107 108 110 111 118 119 130 131 132 135 144 146 148 **P**3 5 **S** TENET Healthcare Corporation, Dallas, TX
Primary Contact: Audrey Gregory, R.N., MSN, Chief Executive Officer
COO: Dwayne Richardson, Chief Operating Officer
CFO: Brittany Whitaker, Chief Financial Officer
CIO: Eleanor Laneaux, Director Information Systems
CHR: Diane Worthington, Chief Human Resources Officer
CNO: Fred Valtairo, Chief Nursing Officer
Web address: www.placentialinda.com
**Control:** Corporation, Investor–owned, for–profit **Service:** General Medical and Surgical

Staffed Beds: 114 Admissions: 3182 Census: 30 Outpatient Visits: 69087 Births: 0 Total Expense ($000): 57271 Payroll Expense ($000): 30757 Personnel: 383

## PLACERVILLE—El Dorado County

⊞ **MARSHALL MEDICAL CENTER (050254)**, 1100 Marshall Way, Zip 95667–5722; tel. 530/622–1441, (Nonreporting) **A**1 2 9 10
Primary Contact: James Whipple, Chief Executive Officer
CFO: Laurie Eldridge, Chief Financial Officer
CMO: Rene Orona, M.D., Chief of Staff
CIO: Mike Jones, Director Information Services
CHR: Scott Comer, Director Administrative Services
Web address: www.marshallmedical.org
**Control:** Other not–for–profit (including NFP Corporation) **Service:** General Medical and Surgical

Staffed Beds: 105

## PLEASANTON—Alameda County

⊞ **STANFORD HEALTH CARE – VALLEYCARE (050283)**, 5555 West Las Positas Boulevard, Zip 94588–4000; tel. 925/847–3000, (Includes VALLEY MEMORIAL, 1111 East Stanley Boulevard, Livermore, Zip 94550–4115; tel. 925/447–7000), (Nonreporting) **A**1 2 9 10 **S** Stanford Health Care, Palo Alto, CA
Primary Contact: Scott Gregerson, President and Chief Executive Officer
COO: Cindy Noonan, Chief Operating Officer
CMO: Dat Nguyen, M.D., Chief of Staff
CIO: Bob Woods, Chief Information Officer
CHR: Chris Faber, Human Resources Analyst
Web address: www.valleycare.com
**Control:** Other not–for–profit (including NFP Corporation) **Service:** General Medical and Surgical

Staffed Beds: 207

## POMONA—Los Angeles County

⊞ △ **CASA COLINA HOSPITAL AND HEALTH SYSTEMS (053027)**, 255 East Bonita Avenue, Zip 91767–1923, Mailing Address: P.O. Box 6001, Zip 91769–6001; tel. 909/596–7733 **A**1 7 9 10 13 **F**2 3 16 29 30 34 35 44 53 54 56 58 59 64 65 68 74 75 79 86 87 90 91 92 93 95 96 97 104 107 110 111 115 119 130 131 132 134 146 148
Primary Contact: Felice L. Loverso, Ph.D., President and Chief Executive Officer
CFO: David Morony, Chief Financial Officer
CMO: Christopher Chalian, M.D., Medical Director
CIO: Ross Lesins, Chief Information Officer
CHR: Karen Du Pont, Chief Human Resource Officer
CNO: Kathryn Johnson, Chief Nursing Officer
Web address: www.casacolina.org
**Control:** Other not–for–profit (including NFP Corporation) **Service:** Rehabilitation

Staffed Beds: 68 Admissions: 1364 Census: 60 Outpatient Visits: 76666 Births: 0 Total Expense ($000): 42611 Payroll Expense ($000): 25159

⊞ **POMONA VALLEY HOSPITAL MEDICAL CENTER (050231)**, 1798 North Garey Avenue, Zip 91767–2918; tel. 909/865–9500 **A**1 2 3 5 10 **F**3 11 13 15 17 18 20 22 24 26 28 29 30 31 34 35 40 41 45 46 47 49 50 51 53 54 55 57 58 59 60 61 63 64 68 69 70 72 74 75 76 77 78 79 81 84 85 89 92 93 107 108 110 111 114 115 116 117 118 119 120 121 123 124 126 129 130 131 132 135 144 145 146 147 148 **P**5 7
Primary Contact: Richard E. Yochum, FACHE, President and Chief Executive Officer
CFO: Michael Nelson, Executive Vice President and Chief Financial Officer
CMO: Kenneth Nakamoto, M.D., Vice President Medical Affairs
CIO: Kent Hoyos, Chief Information Officer
CHR: Ray Inge, Vice President Human Resources
CNO: Darlene Scafiddi, R.N., Vice President Nursing and Patient Care Services
Web address: www.pvhmc.org
**Control:** Other not–for–profit (including NFP Corporation) **Service:** General Medical and Surgical

Staffed Beds: 399 Admissions: 20118 Census: 249 Outpatient Visits: 507438 Births: 7124 Total Expense ($000): 478785 Payroll Expense ($000): 210754 Personnel: 2442

## PORTERVILLE—Tulare County

**PORTERVILLE DEVELOPMENTAL CENTER (050546)**, 26501 Avenue 140, Zip 93257–9109, Mailing Address: P.O. Box 2000, Zip 93258–2000; tel. 559/782–2222, (Nonreporting) **A**10
Primary Contact: Theresa Billeci, Executive Director
COO: Betty Davis, Director Administrative Services
CFO: Karen Warren, Fiscal Officer
CMO: Joseph Mendoza, M.D., Medical Director
CIO: Vincent Chandler, Director Information Services
CHR: Shawna Gregg, Director Human Resources
CNO: Tom Shelton, Coordinator of Nursing Services
Web address: www.pdc.dds.ca.gov/
**Control:** State–Government, nonfederal **Service:** Intellectual Disabilities

Staffed Beds: 753

☐ **SIERRA VIEW MEDICAL CENTER (050261)**, 465 West Putnam Avenue, Zip 93257–3320; tel. 559/784–1110, (Total facility includes 35 beds in nursing home–type unit) **A**1 9 10 **F**3 13 15 29 30 31 34 35 40 42 45 47 49 54 57 59 60 65 68 70 75 76 78 79 81 85 87 89 93 107 108 110 111 115 119 121 123 130 132 135 146 147 148
Primary Contact: Donna J. Hefner, R.N., President and Chief Executive Officer
CFO: John Chivers, Senior Vice President Finance
CHR: Sharon Brown, Vice President Human Resources
Web address: www.sierra–view.com
**Control:** Hospital district or authority, Government, nonfederal **Service:** General Medical and Surgical

Staffed Beds: 156 Admissions: 6147 Census: 98 Outpatient Visits: 143890 Births: 1590 Total Expense ($000): 123588 Payroll Expense ($000): 45965

## PORTOLA—Plumas County

**EASTERN PLUMAS HEALTH CARE (051300)**, 500 First Avenue, Zip 96122–9406; tel. 530/832–6500, (Nonreporting) **A**9 10 18
Primary Contact: Thomas P. Hayes, Chief Executive Officer
CFO: Jeri Nelson, Chief Financial Officer
CMO: Eric Bugna, M.D., Chief of Staff
CHR: Cathy Conant, Chief Human Resources and Personnel
Web address: www.ephc.org
**Control:** Hospital district or authority, Government, nonfederal **Service:** General Medical and Surgical

Staffed Beds: 10

---

**Hospital, Medicare Provider Number, Address, Telephone, Approval, Facility, and Physician Codes, Health Care System**

★ American Hospital Association (AHA) membership  ○ Healthcare Facilities Accreditation Program  ⇑ Center for Improvement in Healthcare Quality Accreditation
☐ The Joint Commission accreditation  ◇ DNV Healthcare Inc. accreditation  △ Commission on Accreditation of Rehabilitation Facilities (CARF) accreditation

## POWAY—San Diego County

⊠ **POMERADO HOSPITAL (050636)**, 15615 Pomerado Road, Zip 92064–2460; tel. 858/613–4000, (Total facility includes 127 beds in nursing home–type unit) **A**1 9 10 **F**3 11 12 13 14 18 20 29 30 31 34 35 36 38 40 45 46 47 50 51 54 55 56 57 58 59 62 64 65 68 70 72 74 75 76 77 78 79 81 82 84 85 87 97 98 100 101 102 103 107 110 111 119 120 128 130 131 132 133 143 144 146 147 148 **P**3 **S** Palomar Health, Escondido, CA
Primary Contact: Cheryl Olson, Chief Administrative Officer
CIO: Steven Tanaka, Chief Information Officer
CHR: Brenda C. Turner, Chief Human Resources Officer
Web address: www.pph.org
**Control:** Hospital district or authority, Government, nonfederal **Service:** General Medical and Surgical

**Staffed Beds:** 201 **Admissions:** 6718 **Census:** 188 **Outpatient Visits:** 74286 **Births:** 1399 **Total Expense ($000):** 153682 **Payroll Expense ($000):** 61772 **Personnel:** 538

## QUINCY—Plumas County

☐ **PLUMAS DISTRICT HOSPITAL (051326)**, 1065 Bucks Lake Road, Zip 95971–9599; tel. 530/283–2121, (Nonreporting) **A**1 9 10 18
Primary Contact: Jeffrey Kepple, M.D., Chief Executive Officer
CMO: Vincent Frantz, M.D., Chief of Staff
CIO: Brenda Compton, Manager Information Technology
CHR: Denise Harding, Director Human Resources
Web address: www.pdh.org
**Control:** Hospital district or authority, Government, nonfederal **Service:** General Medical and Surgical

**Staffed Beds:** 25

## RANCHO CUCAMONGA—San Bernardino County

★ ○ **KINDRED HOSPITAL RANCHO (052049)**, 10841 White Oak Avenue, Zip 91730–3811; tel. 909/581–6400, (Nonreporting) **A**9 10 11 **S** Kindred Healthcare, Louisville, KY
Primary Contact: Jeanette Williams, Interim Chief Executive Officer
COO: Jody Knox, Chief Operating Officer
Web address: www.khrancho.com
**Control:** Corporation, Investor–owned, for–profit **Service:** Long–Term Acute Care hospital

**Staffed Beds:** 55

## RANCHO MIRAGE—Riverside County

⊠ △ **EISENHOWER MEDICAL CENTER (050573)**, 39000 Bob Hope Drive, Zip 92270–3221; tel. 760/340–3911 **A**1 2 3 7 9 10 **F**2 3 9 11 12 15 17 18 20 22 24 26 28 29 30 31 34 35 37 40 41 45 47 49 50 53 54 56 57 58 59 60 61 64 65 68 70 74 75 77 78 79 81 82 84 85 86 87 89 90 93 96 97 100 101 102 104 107 108 109 110 111 112 114 115 116 117 118 119 120 121 123 124 126 129 130 131 132 135 144 145 146 147 148 **P**3
Primary Contact: G. Aubrey Serfling, President and Chief Executive Officer
COO: Martin Massiello, Executive Vice President and Chief Operating Officer
CFO: Ken Wheat, Senior Vice President and Chief Financial Officer
CMO: Alan Williamson, M.D., Chief Medical Officer
CIO: David Perez, Vice President and Chief Information Officer
CHR: Liz Guignier, Vice President Human Resources
CNO: Ann R. Mostofi, MSN, Vice President Patient Care and Chief Nursing Officer
Web address: www.emc.org
**Control:** Other not–for–profit (including NFP Corporation) **Service:** General Medical and Surgical

**Staffed Beds:** 367 **Admissions:** 17620 **Census:** 194 **Outpatient Visits:** 627222 **Births:** 0 **Total Expense ($000):** 543510 **Payroll Expense ($000):** 188239 **Personnel:** 2771

## RED BLUFF—Tehama County

⊠ **ST. ELIZABETH COMMUNITY HOSPITAL (050042)**, 2550 Sister Mary Columba Drive, Zip 96080–4397; tel. 530/529–8000 **A**1 9 10 20 **F**3 7 8 11 13 15 29 30 34 35 40 43 45 51 54 62 63 64 68 70 75 76 81 82 84 85 89 93 107 108 110 111 114 119 130 131 132 133 145 146 148 **P**3 **S** Dignity Health, San Francisco, CA
Primary Contact: G. Todd Smith, President
CFO: Gina Anderson, Chief Financial Officer
CMO: James DeSoto, M.D., Vice President Medical Affairs
CIO: Henry Niessink, Senior Manager Information Technology Systems
CHR: Denise Little, Director Human Resources
Web address: www.mercy.org
**Control:** Church–operated, Nongovernment, not–for profit **Service:** General Medical and Surgical

**Staffed Beds:** 65 **Admissions:** 3225 **Census:** 22 **Outpatient Visits:** 65089 **Births:** 666 **Total Expense ($000):** 78112 **Payroll Expense ($000):** 32777 **Personnel:** 375

## REDDING—Shasta County

⊠ **MERCY MEDICAL CENTER REDDING (050280)**, 2175 Rosaline Avenue, Zip 96001–2549, Mailing Address: P.O. Box 496009, Zip 96049–6009; tel. 530/225–6000 **A**1 2 3 5 9 10 **F**2 3 7 11 13 15 17 18 20 22 24 28 29 30 31 34 35 37 40 43 45 46 47 48 49 50 54 57 59 61 62 63 64 66 68 70 72 75 76 77 78 79 81 82 84 85 89 91 97 107 108 111 114 115 118 119 126 130 132 135 143 144 145 146 147 148 **S** Dignity Health, San Francisco, CA
Primary Contact: Mark D. Korth, President
COO: Patrick Varga, Chief Operating Officer
CFO: Kimberly Miranda, Regional Vice President Finance and Chief Financial Officer
CMO: James DeSoto, M.D., Vice President Medical Affairs
CIO: Henry Niessink, Regional Director Information Technology Services
CHR: Stephan Hosler, Vice President Human Resources
CNO: Kimberly Shaw, Vice President Patient Care and Chief Nursing Executive
Web address: www.mercy.org
**Control:** Church–operated, Nongovernment, not–for profit **Service:** General Medical and Surgical

**Staffed Beds:** 267 **Admissions:** 12917 **Census:** 156 **Outpatient Visits:** 137846 **Births:** 1999 **Total Expense ($000):** 368028 **Payroll Expense ($000):** 134698 **Personnel:** 1506

**NORTHERN CALIFORNIA REHABILITATION HOSPITAL** See Vibra Hospital of Northern California

**PATIENTS' HOSPITAL OF REDDING (050697)**, 2900 Eureka Way, Zip 96001–0220; tel. 530/225–8700, (Nonreporting) **A**9 10
Primary Contact: Shari Lejsek, Administrator
CFO: Kim Needles, Manager Business Office
CMO: James Tate, M.D., Chief of Staff
CIO: Kim Cameron, Manager Health Information Services
CHR: Brenda Meline, Manager Human Resources
CNO: Diane Rieke, Director Patient Care Services
Web address: www.patientshospital.com
**Control:** Individual, Investor–owned, for–profit **Service:** Surgical

**Staffed Beds:** 10

⊠ **SHASTA REGIONAL MEDICAL CENTER (050764)**, 1100 Butte Street, Zip 96001–0853, Mailing Address: P.O. Box 496072, Zip 96049–6072; tel. 530/244–5400, (Nonreporting) **A**1 5 9 10 **S** Prime Healthcare Services, Ontario, CA
Primary Contact: Cynthia Gordon, R.N., Chief Executive Officer
COO: Becky Levy, Chief Operating Officer
CFO: Becky Levy, Chief Financial Officer
CMO: Marcia McCampbell, M.D., Chief Medical Officer
CIO: Tony VanBoekel, Director Information Systems
CHR: Andrew Torge, Director Human Resources
CNO: Leslie Woodson, R.N., Chief Nursing Officer
Web address: www.shastaregional.com
**Control:** Corporation, Investor–owned, for–profit **Service:** General Medical and Surgical

**Staffed Beds:** 120

⊠ **VIBRA HOSPITAL OF NORTHERN CALIFORNIA (052047)**, 2801 Eureka Way, Zip 96001–0222; tel. 530/246–9000, (Total facility includes 32 beds in nursing home–type unit) **A**1 9 10 **F**1 29 30 64 77 93 119 128 130 148 **S** Vibra Healthcare, Mechanicsburg, PA
Primary Contact: Chris Jones, Chief Executive Officer
COO: Lisa Stevens, Chief Clinical Officer and Chief Operating Officer
CFO: Rebecca Andrews, Chief Financial Officer
CMO: Nanda Kumar, M.D., Chief of Staff
CIO: Mark Cardenas, Director Plant Operations
CHR: Wendy Tempest, Director Human Resources
Web address: www.norcalrehab.com
**Control:** Corporation, Investor–owned, for–profit **Service:** Long–Term Acute Care hospital

**Staffed Beds:** 88 **Admissions:** 1173 **Census:** 75 **Outpatient Visits:** 2801 **Births:** 0 **Total Expense ($000):** 32104 **Payroll Expense ($000):** 15193 **Personnel:** 245

## REDLANDS—San Bernardino County

⊠ **LOMA LINDA UNIVERSITY BEHAVIORAL MEDICINE CENTER (054093)**, 1710 Barton Road, Zip 92373–5304; tel. 909/558–9200 **A**1 5 9 10 **F**4 5 29 34 35 57 87 98 99 100 101 102 103 104 105 130 132 **S** Loma Linda University Adventist Health Sciences Center, Loma Linda, CA
Primary Contact: Edward Field, Administrator
COO: Ruthita J. Fike, Chief Executive Officer
CFO: Steve Mohr, Senior Vice President Finance and Chief Financial Officer
CMO: William Murdoch, M.D., Medical Director
CIO: Mark Zirkelback, Chief Information Officer
CHR: Mark Hubbard, Vice President Risk Management
CNO: Norie Lee Reyes Bencito Aca–ac, R.N., Director of Nursing
Web address: www.llu.edu
**Control:** Other not–for–profit (including NFP Corporation) **Service:** Psychiatric

**Staffed Beds:** 89 **Admissions:** 4559 **Census:** 71 **Outpatient Visits:** 35775 **Births:** 0 **Total Expense ($000):** 32844 **Payroll Expense ($000):** 15348

*Many Facility Codes have changed. Please refer to the AHA Guide Code Chart.*   © 2015 AHA Guide

**CA**

☒ **REDLANDS COMMUNITY HOSPITAL (050272)**, 350 Terracina Boulevard, Zip 92373–0742, Mailing Address: P.O. Box 3391, Zip 92373–0742; tel. 909/335–5500, (Total facility includes 16 beds in nursing home–type unit) **A**1 3 9 10 **F**3 11 13 15 18 20 28 29 30 31 34 35 40 45 46 47 49 54 57 59 62 63 64 65 66 68 70 72 74 76 77 78 79 81 82 84 85 87 93 96 97 98 102 104 105 107 108 110 111 114 115 116 117 119 121 126 128 130 132 143 146 147 148 **P**5
Primary Contact: James R. Holmes, President and Chief Executive Officer
CFO: Michelle Mok, Chief Financial Officer
CNO: Lauren Spilsbury, R.N., Vice President for Patient Care Services
Web address: www.redlandshospital.org
**Control:** Other not–for–profit (including NFP Corporation) **Service:** General Medical and Surgical

**Staffed Beds:** 197 **Admissions:** 11990 **Census:** 124 **Outpatient Visits:** 162850 **Births:** 2601 **Total Expense ($000):** 288935 **Payroll Expense ($000):** 92991 **Personnel:** 1370

**REDWOOD CITY—San Mateo County**

☒ **KAISER PERMANENTE REDWOOD CITY MEDICAL CENTER (050541)**, 1150 Veterans Boulevard, Zip 94063–2087; tel. 650/299–2000, (Nonreporting) **A**1 3 5 10 **S** Kaiser Foundation Hospitals, Oakland, CA
Primary Contact: Frank T. Beirne, FACHE, Senior Vice President and Area Manager
COO: Maureen O'Brien, Chief Operating Officer
CFO: Tim O'Connor, Area Finance Officer
CMO: James O'Donnell, Physician in Chief
CHR: Sharon Barncord, Business Partner Human Resources
Web address: www.kaiserpermanente.org
**Control:** Other not–for–profit (including NFP Corporation) **Service:** General Medical and Surgical

**Staffed Beds:** 213

☒ **SEQUOIA HOSPITAL (050197)**, 170 Alameda De Las Pulgas, Zip 94062–2799; tel. 650/369–5811 **A**1 9 10 **F**11 12 13 15 18 20 22 24 26 28 29 30 31 32 34 35 37 40 45 46 49 50 53 57 59 60 64 68 70 74 75 76 77 78 79 81 84 86 87 92 93 94 107 108 110 111 114 115 118 119 120 121 123 126 129 130 132 135 146 147 148 **P**3 **S** Dignity Health, San Francisco, CA
Primary Contact: Bill Graham, President
COO: Sherie C. Hickman, Vice President Operations and Chief Operating Officer
CFO: Gratia Barton, Chief Financial Officer
CMO: Christopher Dunn, M.D., Vice President Medical Affairs
CIO: Gracie O'Brien, Chief Information Officer
CHR: Linde Cheema, Vice President Human Resources
CNO: Sherry Eldridge, Vice President Patient Care Services and Chief Nurse Executive
Web address: www.sequoiahospital.org
**Control:** Other not–for–profit (including NFP Corporation) **Service:** General Medical and Surgical

**Staffed Beds:** 131 **Admissions:** 5458 **Census:** 56 **Outpatient Visits:** 101223 **Births:** 1614 **Total Expense ($000):** 220525 **Payroll Expense ($000):** 80609 **Personnel:** 735

**REEDLEY—Fresno County**

☒ **ADVENTIST MEDICAL CENTER–REEDLEY (050192)**, 372 West Cypress Avenue, Zip 93654–2199; tel. 559/638–8155 **A**1 3 9 10 **F**13 15 29 30 40 45 50 64 76 77 81 87 107 110 111 114 119 127 133 135 **P**3 **S** Adventist Health, Roseville, CA
Primary Contact: Wayne Ferch, President and Chief Executive Officer
CFO: Teresa Jacques, Interim Chief Financial Officer
CMO: Todd Spencer, M.D., Chief Medical Staff
CIO: Valerie Alvarez, Executive Assistant
CHR: Ramona Alvarado, Interim Manager Human Resources
Web address: www.skdh.org
**Control:** Church–operated, Nongovernment, not–for profit **Service:** General Medical and Surgical

**Staffed Beds:** 49 **Admissions:** 2614 **Census:** 12 **Outpatient Visits:** 173081 **Births:** 1430 **Total Expense ($000):** 56260 **Payroll Expense ($000):** 21664 **Personnel:** 455

**RESEDA—Los Angeles County**

☐ **JOYCE EISENBERG–KEEFER MEDICAL CENTER (054147)**, 7150 Tampa Avenue, Zip 91335–3700; tel. 818/774–3000, (Total facility includes 228 beds in nursing home–type unit) **A**1 10 **F**30 39 50 53 56 62 63 65 68 74 75 77 82 84 98 101 103 125 128 130 132 143 146 148
Primary Contact: Molly Forrest, President and Chief Executive Officer
CNO: Haya Berci, Executive Director of Nursing
Web address: www.jha.org
**Control:** Other not–for–profit (including NFP Corporation) **Service:** Psychiatric

**Staffed Beds:** 235 **Admissions:** 592 **Census:** 235 **Outpatient Visits:** 0 **Births:** 0 **Total Expense ($000):** 38465 **Payroll Expense ($000):** 15172 **Personnel:** 369

**RICHMOND—Contra Costa County**

**KAISER PERMANENTE RICHMOND MEDICAL CENTER** See Kaiser Permanente Oakland Medical Center, Oakland

**RIDGECREST—Kern County**

★ ◇ **RIDGECREST REGIONAL HOSPITAL (051333)**, 1081 North China Lake Boulevard, Zip 93555–3130; tel. 760/446–3551, (Total facility includes 125 beds in nursing home–type unit) **A**9 10 18 21 **F**3 8 11 13 15 18 28 29 30 32 34 35 39 40 41 43 45 50 56 57 59 62 63 64 66 68 70 75 76 77 79 81 84 85 87 89 93 97 104 107 108 110 111 114 115 119 127 128 129 130 131 133 134 144 146 147 148
Primary Contact: James A. Suver, FACHE, Chief Executive Officer
CFO: Lois Johnson, Administrator Fiscal Services
CMO: Victoria Schauf, M.D., Chief of Staff
CIO: Randy Ferguson, Chief Information Officer
CHR: Dave Shary, Administrator Human Resources
Web address: www.rrh.org
**Control:** Other not–for–profit (including NFP Corporation) **Service:** General Medical and Surgical

**Staffed Beds:** 150 **Admissions:** 1851 **Census:** 21 **Outpatient Visits:** 123324 **Births:** 455 **Total Expense ($000):** 85257 **Payroll Expense ($000):** 30257 **Personnel:** 671

**RIVERSIDE—Riverside County**

☒ **KAISER PERMANENTE RIVERSIDE MEDICAL CENTER (050686)**, 10800 Magnolia Avenue, Zip 92505–3000; tel. 951/353–2000 **A**1 3 5 10 **F**3 13 15 17 28 29 30 31 34 35 40 44 45 46 48 49 50 51 59 60 62 63 64 65 68 70 72 74 75 76 77 78 79 81 82 84 85 86 87 89 92 93 97 100 102 107 108 109 110 111 114 115 117 118 119 130 144 146 147 148 **S** Kaiser Foundation Hospitals, Oakland, CA
Primary Contact: Vita M. Willett, Executive Director
COO: Robin D. Mackenroth, Chief Operating Officer
CFO: JiJi Abraham, Chief Financial Officer
CMO: Frank M. Flowers, M.D., Area Medical Director
CIO: Alfred T. Velasquez, Area Information Officer
CHR: Michelle Skipper, Director Human Resources
CNO: Rosemary M. Butler, R.N., Chief Nurse Executive
Web address: www.kaiserpermanente.org
**Control:** Other not–for–profit (including NFP Corporation) **Service:** General Medical and Surgical

**Staffed Beds:** 226 **Admissions:** 14697 **Census:** 131 **Outpatient Visits:** 151040 **Births:** 3023 **Personnel:** 860

☐ **PACIFIC GROVE HOSPITAL (054130)**, 5900 Brockton Avenue, Zip 92506–1862; tel. 951/275–8400 **A**1 9 10 **F**4 5 34 35 68 86 98 101 102 103 104 105 130 132 **P**5 **S** Acadia Healthcare Company, Inc., Franklin, TN
Primary Contact: Brent J. Bryson, Chief Executive Officer
Web address: www.pacificgrovehospital.com
**Control:** Corporation, Investor–owned, for–profit **Service:** Psychiatric

**Staffed Beds:** 68 **Admissions:** 1146 **Census:** 18 **Outpatient Visits:** 4591 **Births:** 0 **Personnel:** 60

☐ **PARKVIEW COMMUNITY HOSPITAL MEDICAL CENTER (050102)**, 3865 Jackson Street, Zip 92503–3998; tel. 951/688–2211 **A**1 9 10 **F**3 8 11 12 13 15 29 34 35 40 45 46 49 50 57 59 60 62 64 68 70 72 74 76 77 79 81 84 85 86 87 89 100 107 108 111 114 115 119 130 132 146 147 148
Primary Contact: Steven Popkin, Chief Executive Officer
COO: Robert Brown, Chief Operating Officer
CFO: Patti Lepe, Chief Financial Officer
CMO: Dong Kim, M.D., Chief of Staff
CIO: John Ciccarelli, Director Information Technology
CHR: Lizette O. Norton, Vice President Human Resources
CNO: Thomas Santos, R.N., Chief Nursing Officer
Web address: www.pchmc.org
**Control:** Other not–for–profit (including NFP Corporation) **Service:** General Medical and Surgical

**Staffed Beds:** 193 **Admissions:** 10058 **Census:** 112 **Outpatient Visits:** 75150 **Births:** 2353 **Total Expense ($000):** 144893 **Payroll Expense ($000):** 57493 **Personnel:** 1029

**RIVERSIDE CENTER FOR BEHAVIORAL MEDICINE** See Pacific Grove Hospital

CA

**Hospital, Medicare Provider Number, Address, Telephone, Approval, Facility, and Physician Codes, Health Care System**

★ American Hospital Association (AHA) membership    ○ Healthcare Facilities Accreditation Program    ⇧ Center for Improvement in Healthcare Quality Accreditation
☐ The Joint Commission accreditation    ◇ DNV Healthcare Inc. accreditation    △ Commission on Accreditation of Rehabilitation Facilities (CARF) accreditation

**CA**

✠ **RIVERSIDE COMMUNITY HOSPITAL (050022)**, 4445 Magnolia Avenue, Zip 92501–4199, Mailing Address: P.O. Box 1669, Zip 92502–1669; tel. 951/788–3000, (Nonreporting) **A**1 2 5 9 10 **S** HCA, Nashville, TN
Primary Contact: Patrick D. Brilliant, President and Chief Executive Officer
COO: Daniel Bowers, Chief Operating Officer
CFO: Russell T. Young, Chief Financial Officer
CMO: Lawrence Clark, M.D., President Medical Staff
CIO: Cae Swanger, Chief Information Officer
CHR: Nathan Bigler, Vice President Human Relations
CNO: Francine Paschall, R.N., Chief Nursing Officer
Web address: www.riversidecommunityhospital.com
**Control:** Corporation, Investor–owned, for–profit **Service:** General Medical and Surgical

Staffed Beds: 373

**RIVERSIDE MEDICAL CENTER** See Kaiser Permanente Riverside Medical Center

### ROSEMEAD—Los Angeles County

☐ **BHC ALHAMBRA HOSPITAL (054032)**, 4619 North Rosemead Boulevard, Zip 91770–1478, Mailing Address: P.O. Box 369, Zip 91770–0369; tel. 626/286–1191, (Nonreporting) **A**1 9 10 **S** Universal Health Services, Inc., King of Prussia, PA
Primary Contact: Peggy Minnick, R.N., Chief Executive Officer
CFO: Michelle Jackson, Chief Financial Officer
CMO: Wakelin McNeel, M.D., Medical Director
CIO: Debbie Irvin, Director Health Information Management
CHR: Venus Taylor, Director Human Resources
Web address: www.bhcalhambra.com
**Control:** Corporation, Investor–owned, for–profit **Service:** Psychiatric

Staffed Beds: 97

**SILVER LAKE MEDICAL CENTER–INGLESIDE HOSPITAL** See Silver Lake Medical Center, Los Angeles

### ROSEVILLE—Placer County

✠ **KAISER PERMANENTE ROSEVILLE MEDICAL CENTER (050772)**, 1600 Eureka Road, Zip 95661–3027; tel. 916/784–4000, (Nonreporting) **A**1 2 5 10 **S** Kaiser Foundation Hospitals, Oakland, CA
Primary Contact: Jeffrey A. Collins, M.D., Senior Vice President and Area Manager
Web address: www.kp.org
**Control:** Other not–for–profit (including NFP Corporation) **Service:** General Medical and Surgical

Staffed Beds: 340

✠ △ **SUTTER ROSEVILLE MEDICAL CENTER (050309)**, One Medical Plaza Drive, Zip 95661–3037; tel. 916/781–1000 **A**1 2 5 7 9 10 **F**3 8 12 13 15 18 20 22 28 29 30 31 34 35 40 43 45 46 50 55 56 58 59 60 63 64 65 68 70 72 74 75 76 78 79 81 82 84 85 89 90 93 94 96 107 108 109 111 114 116 119 126 130 131 132 141 146 147 148 **S** Sutter Health, Sacramento, CA
Primary Contact: Patrick R. Brady, Chief Executive Officer
COO: Dionne Miller, Chief Operating Officer
CFO: Gary Hubschman, Administrative Director Finance
CMO: Stuart Bostrom, M.D., Director Medical Affairs
CIO: Nancy Turner, Director Communications
CHR: Lynda Dasaro, Director Human Resources
CNO: Barbara J. Nelson, Ph.D., Chief Nursing Executive
Web address: www.sutterroseville.org
**Control:** Other not–for–profit (including NFP Corporation) **Service:** General Medical and Surgical

Staffed Beds: 328 Admissions: 19179 Census: 222 Outpatient Visits: 209658 Births: 2987 Total Expense ($000): 431636 Payroll Expense ($000): 136572 Personnel: 1442

### SACRAMENTO—Sacramento County

☐ **HERITAGE OAKS HOSPITAL (054104)**, 4250 Auburn Boulevard, Zip 95841–4164; tel. 916/489–3336 **A**1 3 5 9 10 **F**2 3 5 38 64 87 98 99 100 101 102 103 104 105 130 **P**8 **S** Universal Health Services, Inc., King of Prussia, PA
Primary Contact: Shawn Silva, Chief Executive Officer
CFO: Art Wong, Chief Financial Officer
CMO: Joseph Sison, M.D., Medical Director
CHR: Lisa Myers, Director Human Resources
Web address: www.heritageoakshospital.com
**Control:** Corporation, Investor–owned, for–profit **Service:** Psychiatric

Staffed Beds: 120 Admissions: 4155 Census: 106 Outpatient Visits: 19617 Births: 0 Total Expense ($000): 22343 Payroll Expense ($000): 12898

✠ **KAISER PERMANENTE SACRAMENTO MEDICAL CENTER (050425)**, 2025 Morse Avenue, Zip 95825–2100; tel. 916/973–5000, (Nonreporting) **A**1 2 3 5 10 **S** Kaiser Foundation Hospitals, Oakland, CA
Primary Contact: Sandy Sharon, Senior Vice President and Area Manager
CFO: Jim Eldridge, Area Financial Officer
CMO: Chris Palkowski, M.D., Physician in Chief
CIO: Philip Fasano, Chief Information Officer
CHR: Gay Westfall, Senior Vice President Human Resources
Web address: www.kp.org
**Control:** Other not–for–profit (including NFP Corporation) **Service:** General Medical and Surgical

Staffed Beds: 287

✠ **KAISER PERMANENTE SOUTH SACRAMENTO MEDICAL CENTER (050674)**, 6600 Bruceville Road, Zip 95823–4691; tel. 916/688–2430 **A**1 3 5 10 **F**3 8 12 13 15 20 22 29 30 31 34 35 40 43 44 45 49 50 58 59 61 62 63 64 65 68 70 73 74 75 76 77 78 79 81 82 84 85 86 87 93 96 97 100 104 107 108 109 110 111 114 115 119 126 129 130 131 134 135 144 146 147 148 **S** Kaiser Foundation Hospitals, Oakland, CA
Primary Contact: Patricia M. Rodriguez, Senior Vice President and Area Manager
CIO: Kathleen McKenna, Public Affairs Leader
Web address: www.kp.org
**Control:** Other not–for–profit (including NFP Corporation) **Service:** General Medical and Surgical

Staffed Beds: 181 Admissions: 11357 Census: 120 Outpatient Visits: 111828 Births: 2491 Personnel: 1642

✠ △ **MERCY GENERAL HOSPITAL (050017)**, 4001 J Street, Zip 95819–3600; tel. 916/453–4545 **A**1 2 3 5 7 9 10 **F**3 8 11 13 15 17 18 20 22 24 26 28 29 30 31 34 35 36 37 38 39 40 44 45 46 47 48 49 50 51 53 56 57 58 59 63 64 66 68 70 74 75 76 77 78 79 81 82 84 85 86 87 90 91 93 94 96 99 100 107 108 109 111 114 115 119 124 126 130 131 132 135 143 145 146 **P**3 5 **S** Dignity Health, San Francisco, CA
Primary Contact: Edmundo Castaneda, President
COO: Patricia Monczewski, Chief Operating Officer
CFO: Ronald Kroll, Chief Financial Officer
CMO: Robert Wiebe, M.D., Chief Medical Officer
CHR: Cyndi Kirch, Vice President Human Resources
Web address: www.mercygeneral.org
**Control:** Other not–for–profit (including NFP Corporation) **Service:** General Medical and Surgical

Staffed Beds: 394 Admissions: 16042 Census: 189 Outpatient Visits: 60212 Births: 2094 Total Expense ($000): 472491 Payroll Expense ($000): 177335 Personnel: 1447

✠ **METHODIST HOSPITAL OF SACRAMENTO (050590)**, 7500 Hospital Drive, Zip 95823–5477; tel. 916/423–3000, (Total facility includes 170 beds in nursing home–type unit) **A**1 3 5 9 10 **F**3 8 11 12 17 29 30 34 35 37 39 40 41 47 49 50 56 57 58 60 61 64 68 70 72 74 75 77 79 81 84 85 86 87 93 96 97 102 107 108 111 115 119 128 130 131 132 146 147 148 **P**5 **S** Dignity Health, San Francisco, CA
Primary Contact: Brian K. Ivie, President and Chief Executive Officer
COO: Anita J. Kennedy, Vice President Operations
CFO: Bonnie Jenkins, Chief Financial Officer
CMO: Amir Sweha, M.D., Vice President Medical Administration
CHR: Cyndi Kirch, Vice President Human Resources
CNO: Martina Evans–Harrison, R.N., Chief Nurse Executive
Web address: www.methodistsacramento.org
**Control:** Other not–for–profit (including NFP Corporation) **Service:** General Medical and Surgical

Staffed Beds: 281 Admissions: 10305 Census: 257 Outpatient Visits: 90881 Births: 1792 Total Expense ($000): 253926 Payroll Expense ($000): 113911 Personnel: 869

☐ **SHRINERS HOSPITALS FOR CHILDREN–NORTHERN CALIFORNIA (053311)**, 2425 Stockton Boulevard, Zip 95817–2215; tel. 916/453–2000, (Nonreporting) **A**1 3 5 9 10 **S** Shriners Hospitals for Children, Tampa, FL
Primary Contact: Margaret Bryan, Administrator
COO: Margaret Bryan, Administrator
CFO: William Dalby, Director Fiscal Services
CIO: John Bevel, Manager Information Systems
CHR: Deborah Rubens, Director Human Resources
Web address: www.shrinershospitalsforchildren.org/Hospitals/Locations/NorthernCalifornia.aspx
**Control:** Other not–for–profit (including NFP Corporation) **Service:** Children's general

Staffed Beds: 70

☐ **SIERRA VISTA HOSPITAL (054087)**, 8001 Bruceville Road, Zip 95823–2329;
tel. 916/288–0300 **A**1 9 10 **F**4 5 29 35 38 50 64 98 99 101 102 104 105
130 **S** Universal Health Services, Inc., King of Prussia, PA
Primary Contact: Mike Zauner, Chief Executive Officer
CFO: Nicole Sinclair, Chief Financial Officer
CMO: Okechukwu Nwangburuka, M.D., Medical Director
CIO: Ixel Morell, Director Business Development
CNO: Gwen Hubbard, Director of Nursing
Web address: www.sierravistahospital.com
**Control:** Corporation, Investor–owned, for–profit **Service:** Psychiatric

**Staffed Beds:** 120 **Admissions:** 5424 **Census:** 112 **Outpatient Visits:** 0
**Births:** 0 **Total Expense ($000):** 18752 **Payroll Expense ($000):** 12899
**Personnel:** 287

**SOUTH SACRAMENTO MEDICAL CENTER** See Kaiser Permanente South
Sacramento Medical Center

☒ **SUTTER CENTER FOR PSYCHIATRY (054096)**, 7700 Folsom Boulevard,
Zip 95826–2608; tel. 916/386–3000 **A**1 9 10 **F**29 30 34 35 68 98 99 100
101 104 105 130 132 133 134 143 **S** Sutter Health, Sacramento, CA
Primary Contact: John W. Boyd, PsyD, Chief Administrative Officer
CFO: Pamela Ansley, Director Finance
CMO: Cindy Thygeson, M.D., Director Medical Affairs
CHR: Kristin Daniels, Manager Human Resources
Web address: www.sutterpsychiatry.org
**Control:** Other not–for–profit (including NFP Corporation) **Service:** Psychiatric

**Staffed Beds:** 71 **Admissions:** 3201 **Census:** 54 **Outpatient Visits:** 5158
**Births:** 0 **Total Expense ($000):** 23536 **Payroll Expense ($000):** 11880
**Personnel:** 180

☒ **SUTTER MEDICAL CENTER, SACRAMENTO (050108)**, 2801 L Street,
Zip 95816–5680; tel. 916/454–3333, (Includes SUTTER CHILDREN'S CENTER,
5151 F. Street, Zip 95819–3223; tel. 800/478–8837; SUTTER GENERAL
HOSPITAL, 2801 L Street, Zip 95816; tel. 916/454–2222) **A**1 2 3 5 9 10 **F**3 11
12 15 17 18 19 20 21 22 23 24 25 26 27 28 29 30 31 34 35 36 37 40 45
46 48 49 52 55 56 58 59 61 63 64 68 70 72 74 75 76 77 78 79 81 84 85
86 87 88 89 93 102 107 108 111 114 115 118 119 124 126 129 130 132
134 136 137 146 147 148 **S** Sutter Health, Sacramento, CA
Primary Contact: Carrie Owen–Plietz, Chief Executive Officer
COO: Faraaz Yousuf, Chief Operating Officer
CFO: Richard SooHoo, Chief Financial Officer
CMO: Muhammed Afzal, M.D., Chief of Staff
CIO: Jim Mills, Regional Director Information Technology
CHR: Colleen Peschel, Director Human Resources
CNO: Marchelle M. McGriff, Chief Nursing Executive
Web address: www.sutterhealth.org
**Control:** Other not–for–profit (including NFP Corporation) **Service:** General
Medical and Surgical

**Staffed Beds:** 512 **Admissions:** 28539 **Census:** 334 **Outpatient Visits:**
214742 **Births:** 5397 **Total Expense ($000):** 827086 **Payroll Expense
($000):** 256438 **Personnel:** 2889

☒ **UNIVERSITY OF CALIFORNIA, DAVIS MEDICAL CENTER (050599)**, 2315
Stockton Boulevard, Zip 95817–2282; tel. 916/734–2011, (Includes UNIVERSITY
OF CALIFORNIA DAVIS CHILDREN'S HOSPITAL, 2315 Stockton Boulevard,
Zip 95817–2201; tel. 800/282–3284) **A**1 2 3 5 8 9 10 **F**3 6 8 9 11 12 13 15
16 17 18 19 20 21 22 23 24 25 26 27 28 29 30 31 33 34 35 36 37 38 39
40 41 43 44 45 46 47 48 49 50 51 53 54 55 56 57 58 59 60 61 62 63 64
65 66 68 70 71 72 73 74 75 76 77 78 79 81 82 84 85 86 87 88 89 90 91
92 93 94 96 97 99 100 102 103 104 107 108 110 111 114 115 116 117
118 119 120 121 123 124 126 129 130 131 132 134 135 136 138 141 142
143 144 145 146 147 148 **P**6 **S** University of California Systemwide
Administration, Oakland, CA
Primary Contact: Ann Madden Rice, Chief Executive Officer
COO: Vincent Johnson, Chief Operating Officer
CFO: Timothy Maurice, Chief Financial Officer
CMO: J. Douglas Kirk, M.D., Chief Medical Officer
CIO: Michael N. Minear, Chief Information Officer
CHR: Stephen Chilcott, Associate Director Human Resources
CNO: Carol Robinson, R.N., Chief Patient Care Services Officer
Web address: www.ucdmc.ucdavis.edu
**Control:** Other not–for–profit (including NFP Corporation) **Service:** General
Medical and Surgical

**Staffed Beds:** 581 **Admissions:** 31346 **Census:** 481 **Outpatient Visits:**
1200027 **Births:** 1884 **Total Expense ($000):** 1547960 **Payroll Expense
($000):** 666731 **Personnel:** 7585

☒ **ST. HELENA HOSPITAL NAPA VALLEY (050013)**, 10 Woodland Road,
Zip 94574–9554; tel. 707/963–3611 **A**1 9 10 **F**3 4 5 8 15 17 18 20 22 24 26
28 29 31 34 35 36 37 40 42 45 47 50 51 53 57 58 59 60 62 64 65 70
74 75 76 77 78 79 81 82 84 85 86 87 92 97 98 99 100 101 102 104 105
107 108 110 111 115 117 119 120 121 126 130 131 135 146 147 148 **P**3
**S** Adventist Health, Roseville, CA
Primary Contact: Steven Herber, M.D., FACS, President and Chief Executive
Officer
CFO: Brandon Parker, Vice President
CMO: Steven Herber, M.D., President and Chief Executive Officer
CIO: Mark Heringer, Interim Director Information Systems
CHR: Stacy Nelson, II, Director Human Resources
CNO: Nia Lendaris, Regional Vice President Patient Care
Web address: www.sthelenahospital.org
**Control:** Church–operated, Nongovernment, not–for profit **Service:** General
Medical and Surgical

**Staffed Beds:** 116 **Admissions:** 5066 **Census:** 60 **Outpatient Visits:** 96225
**Births:** 256 **Total Expense ($000):** 194068 **Payroll Expense ($000):** 57002
**Personnel:** 813

☒ **NATIVIDAD MEDICAL CENTER (050248)**, 1441 Constitution Boulevard,
Zip 93906–3100, Mailing Address: P.O. Box 81611, Zip 93912–1611;
tel. 831/647–7611 **A**1 3 5 9 10 **F**3 5 9 12 13 15 18 19 29 30 34 35 37 40 45
46 47 48 49 50 51 57 59 61 64 65 68 70 72 74 75 76 78 79 81 82 84 85
86 87 89 90 91 92 93 96 97 98 100 102 107 108 111 114 118 119 130
132 133 143 146 147 148 **P**6
Primary Contact: Gary Gray, D.O., Interim Chief Executive Officer and Chief
Medical Officer
CMO: Gary Gray, D.O., Chief Medical Officer
CIO: Kirk Larson, Chief Information Officer
CHR: Lawanda Janine Bouyea, Director Human Resources
Web address: www.natividad.com
**Control:** County–Government, nonfederal **Service:** General Medical and Surgical

**Staffed Beds:** 137 **Admissions:** 7410 **Census:** 93 **Outpatient Visits:** 149961
**Births:** 2813 **Total Expense ($000):** 184860 **Payroll Expense ($000):**
60167 **Personnel:** 779

☒ **SALINAS VALLEY MEMORIAL HEALTHCARE SYSTEM (050334)**, 450 East
Romie Lane, Zip 93901–4098; tel. 831/757–4333 **A**1 2 9 10 **F**3 13 15 17 18
19 20 22 24 26 28 29 31 34 35 37 40 45 46 49 50 57 58 59 64 68 70 72
74 75 76 77 78 79 81 84 85 87 89 107 108 110 111 115 118 119 126 129
130 146 148
Primary Contact: Pete Delgado, President and Chief Executive Officer
COO: Luis Fonseca, Chief Operating Officer
CFO: Augustine Lopez, Chief Financial Officer
CMO: Allen Radner, M.D., Chief Medical Officer
CIO: Audrey Parks, Senior Administrative Director Information Technology
CHR: Michelle B. Childs, Senior Administrative Director Human Resources
CNO: Christie Gonder, Chief Nursing Officer
Web address: www.svmh.com
**Control:** Hospital district or authority, Government, nonfederal **Service:** General
Medical and Surgical

**Staffed Beds:** 185 **Admissions:** 9961 **Census:** 120 **Outpatient Visits:** 93954
**Births:** 1812 **Total Expense ($000):** 318333 **Payroll Expense ($000):**
145974 **Personnel:** 1015

☒ **MARK TWAIN MEDICAL CENTER (051332)**, 768 Mountain Ranch Road,
Zip 95249–9998; tel. 209/754–3521 **A**1 9 10 18 **F**3 8 11 12 15 18 28 29 30
31 33 34 35 36 38 40 41 44 45 46 47 48 49 50 53 54 56 57 59 64 65 66
68 70 74 75 77 78 79 81 82 83 84 85 86 87 91 92 93 96 97 102 104 107
108 110 111 115 117 119 127 130 131 132 133 144 145 146 147 148 **P**6
**S** Dignity Health, San Francisco, CA
Primary Contact: Craig J. Marks, FACHE, President
CFO: Jacob Lewis, Chief Financial Officer
CHR: Nancy Vargas, Director Human Resources
Web address: www.marktwainhospital.com
**Control:** Other not–for–profit (including NFP Corporation) **Service:** General
Medical and Surgical

**Staffed Beds:** 25 **Admissions:** 1160 **Census:** 12 **Outpatient Visits:** 84391
**Births:** 0 **Total Expense ($000):** 60165 **Payroll Expense ($000):** 24458
**Personnel:** 253

---

**Hospital, Medicare Provider Number, Address, Telephone, Approval, Facility, and Physician Codes, Health Care System**

★ American Hospital Association (AHA) membership    ○ Healthcare Facilities Accreditation Program    ⇑ Center for Improvement in Healthcare Quality Accreditation
☐ The Joint Commission accreditation    ◇ DNV Healthcare Inc. accreditation    △ Commission on Accreditation of Rehabilitation Facilities (CARF) accreditation

**SAN BERNARDINO—San Bernardino County**

☒ △ **BALLARD REHABILITATION HOSPITAL (053037)**, 1760 West 16th Street, Zip 92411–1160; tel. 909/473–1200 **A**1 7 9 10 **F**29 34 35 50 64 79 90 93 96 130 132 135 148 **S** Vibra Healthcare, Mechanicsburg, PA
Primary Contact: Mary Miles Hunt, Chief Executive Officer
COO: Mary Miles Hunt, Chief Executive Officer
CFO: Jonathan Silver, Chief Financial Officer
CMO: Van Chen, M.D., Medical Director
CNO: Chris Bauman, Director of Nursing
Web address: www.ballardrehab.com
**Control:** Corporation, Investor–owned, for–profit **Service:** Rehabilitation

**Staffed Beds:** 45 **Admissions:** 1170 **Census:** 45 **Outpatient Visits:** 2663 **Births:** 0 **Total Expense ($000):** 19241 **Payroll Expense ($000):** 11273

☒ **COMMUNITY HOSPITAL OF SAN BERNARDINO (050089)**, 1805 Medical Center Drive, Zip 92411–1214; tel. 909/887–6333, (Total facility includes 122 beds in nursing home–type unit) **A**1 9 10 **F**8 11 13 15 20 28 29 30 31 32 34 35 40 45 46 47 48 49 50 57 59 60 65 68 70 72 74 75 76 77 79 81 82 86 87 89 94 98 100 101 104 107 108 111 119 128 130 132 135 146 147 148 **S** Dignity Health, San Francisco, CA
Primary Contact: June Collison, President
CFO: Ed Sorenson, Vice President Finance and Chief Financial Officer
CIO: Robert Redden, Site Director Information Technology
CHR: Denice C. Findlay, Director Human Resources
Web address: www.chsb.org
**Control:** Other not–for–profit (including NFP Corporation) **Service:** General Medical and Surgical

**Staffed Beds:** 379 **Admissions:** 11629 **Census:** 249 **Outpatient Visits:** 76592 **Births:** 2961 **Total Expense ($000):** 219319 **Payroll Expense ($000):** 96445 **Personnel:** 1136

☒ **ST. BERNARDINE MEDICAL CENTER (050129)**, 2101 North Waterman Avenue, Zip 92404–4855; tel. 909/883–8711 **A**1 2 3 9 10 **F**3 8 11 12 15 17 18 20 22 24 26 28 29 30 31 34 35 40 45 46 47 49 50 54 58 60 64 65 68 70 72 74 75 76 77 78 79 81 84 85 86 87 92 93 100 102 107 108 110 111 114 115 119 120 121 126 130 131 132 134 143 144 146 147 148 **P**3 8 **S** Dignity Health, San Francisco, CA
Primary Contact: Darryl VandenBosch, President
CMO: Betty Daniels, M.D., Chief of Staff
CIO: James Croker, Director Information Systems
CHR: Dee Webb, Vice President Human Resources
Web address: www.stbernardinemedicalcenter.com
**Control:** Other not–for–profit (including NFP Corporation) **Service:** General Medical and Surgical

**Staffed Beds:** 342 **Admissions:** 15707 **Census:** 204 **Outpatient Visits:** 83994 **Births:** 2028 **Total Expense ($000):** 333128 **Payroll Expense ($000):** 135517 **Personnel:** 1548

**SAN DIEGO—San Diego County**

☒ **ALVARADO HOSPITAL MEDICAL CENTER (050757)**, 6655 Alvarado Road, Zip 92120–5208; tel. 619/287–3270, (Nonreporting) **A**1 2 3 9 10 **S** Prime Healthcare Services, Ontario, CA
Primary Contact: Robin Gomez, R.N., MSN, Administrator
CFO: Brian Kleven, Chief Financial Officer
CMO: Larry Emdur, D.O., Chief Medical Officer
CIO: Wayne Bartlett, Director Information Systems
CHR: Sara Turner, Director Human Resources
CNO: Peggy Jezsu, Chief Nursing Officer
Web address: www.alvaradohospital.com
**Control:** Corporation, Investor–owned, for–profit **Service:** General Medical and Surgical

**Staffed Beds:** 83

☐ **AURORA SAN DIEGO HOSPITAL (054095)**, 11878 Avenue of Industry, Zip 92128–3490; tel. 858/487–3200 **A**1 9 10 **F**4 5 34 35 82 98 99 101 103 104 105 130 132 **S** Signature Healthcare Services, Corona, CA
Primary Contact: James S. Plummer, Chief Executive Officer
COO: Barbara Kennison, Director Clinical Services
CFO: Gene Fantano, Chief Financial Officer
CMO: Thomas Flanagan, M.D., Medical Director
CIO: Alain Azcona, Director Business Development
CHR: Susan Haas, Director Human Resources
Web address: www.sandiego.aurorabehavioral.com/
**Control:** Individual, Investor–owned, for–profit **Service:** Psychiatric

**Staffed Beds:** 80 **Admissions:** 3264 **Census:** 70 **Outpatient Visits:** 15214 **Births:** 0 **Personnel:** 242

☒ **KAISER PERMANENTE SAN DIEGO MEDICAL CENTER (050515)**, 4647 Zion Avenue, Zip 92120–2507; tel. 619/528–5000 **A**1 3 5 10 **F**3 8 13 14 15 29 30 31 41 45 46 47 48 49 50 51 54 55 56 58 59 60 61 62 63 64 65 68 70 71 72 74 75 76 77 78 79 81 82 83 84 85 86 87 89 97 100 102 103 104 107 108 111 114 115 117 118 119 130 131 132 144 146 148 **S** Kaiser Foundation Hospitals, Oakland, CA
Primary Contact: E. Jane Finley, Senior Vice President and Executive Director
CFO: Lynette Seid, Area Chief Financial Officer
CMO: Paul E. Bernstein, M.D., Area Medical Director
CIO: Matthew T. Ebaugh, Area Information Officer
CHR: Cherie L. Sampson, Director Human Resources
Web address: www.kaiserpermanente.org
**Control:** Other not–for–profit (including NFP Corporation) **Service:** General Medical and Surgical

**Staffed Beds:** 414 **Admissions:** 29518 **Census:** 287 **Outpatient Visits:** 130118 **Births:** 4248 **Personnel:** 3534

☒ **KINDRED HOSPITAL–SAN DIEGO (052036)**, 1940 El Cajon Boulevard, Zip 92104–1096; tel. 619/543–4500, (Nonreporting) **A**1 9 10 **S** Kindred Healthcare, Louisville, KY
Primary Contact: Natalie Germuska, R.N., MSN, Market Chief Executive Officer
CMO: Davies Wong, M.D., Medical Director
CHR: Jody Dewen Moore, District Director Human Resources
CNO: Maureen Bodine, Chief Clinical Officer
Web address: www.kindredsandiego.com
**Control:** Corporation, Investor–owned, for–profit **Service:** Long–Term Acute Care hospital

**Staffed Beds:** 70

☒ **NAVAL MEDICAL CENTER SAN DIEGO**, 34800 Bob Wilson Drive, Zip 92134–5000; tel. 619/532–6400, (Nonreporting) **A**1 2 3 5 **S** Bureau of Medicine and Surgery, Department of the Navy, Washington, DC
Primary Contact: Captain Jose' A. Acosta, MC, USN, Commanding Officer
CFO: Captain O. G. Haugen, Director Resources
CIO: Lieutenant D. V. Gonzales, Head Information Technology Management
Web address: www.med.navy.mil/sites/nmcsd/Pages/default.aspx
**Control:** Navy, Government, federal **Service:** General Medical and Surgical

**Staffed Beds:** 285

☐ **PROMISE HOSPITAL OF SAN DIEGO (052051)**, 5550 University Avenue, Zip 92105–2307; tel. 619/582–3800, (Nonreporting) **A**1 9 10 **S** Promise Healthcare, Boca Raton, FL
Primary Contact: Chuck Smith, Interim Chief Executive Officer
CFO: Kevin Ohler, Director of Finance
CMO: Larry Emdur, D.O., Chief of Staff
CIO: Jim Wilson, Vice President Information Technology
CHR: Kathleen Greene, Director Human Resources
CNO: Kevin Wood, Interim Chief Clinical Officer
Web address: www.promisesandiego.com
**Control:** Corporation, Investor–owned, for–profit **Service:** Long–Term Acute Care hospital

**Staffed Beds:** 100

☒ **RADY CHILDREN'S HOSPITAL – SAN DIEGO (053303)**, 3020 Childrens Way, Zip 92123–4223; tel. 858/576–1700, (Total facility includes 43 beds in nursing home–type unit) **A**1 3 5 9 10 **F**1 3 4 7 8 9 10 11 12 16 17 19 20 21 22 23 24 25 26 27 28 29 30 31 32 34 35 36 38 39 40 41 43 45 46 47 48 50 54 55 57 58 59 60 62 63 64 65 67 68 70 72 73 74 75 77 78 79 80 81 82 83 84 85 86 87 88 89 90 91 92 93 94 98 99 100 101 102 104 105 106 107 108 111 114 115 118 119 122 124 128 129 130 131 132 133 134 135 136 137 138 139 141 143 144 145 146 148 **P**3 5
Primary Contact: Donald Kearns, M.D., President and Chief Executive Officer
COO: Meg Norton, Executive Vice President and Chief Administrative Officer
CFO: Roger Roux, Chief Financial Officer
CMO: Irvin A. Kaufman, M.D., Chief Medical Officer
CIO: Albert Oriol, Vice President Information Management and Chief Information Officer
CHR: Mamoon Syed, Vice President Human Resources
CNO: Mary Fagan, MSN, Chief Nursing Officer
Web address: www.rchsd.org
**Control:** Other not–for–profit (including NFP Corporation) **Service:** Children's general

**Staffed Beds:** 377 **Admissions:** 18260 **Census:** 245 **Outpatient Visits:** 299690 **Births:** 0 **Total Expense ($000):** 801417 **Payroll Expense ($000):** 288858 **Personnel:** 4031

**RADY CHILDREN'S HOSPITAL AND HEALTH CENTER** See Rady Children's Hospital – San Diego

☐ **SAN DIEGO COUNTY PSYCHIATRIC HOSPITAL (054114)**, 3853 Rosecrans Street, Zip 92110–3115, Mailing Address: P.O. Box 85524, Zip 92186–5524; tel. 619/692–8211, (Nonreporting) **A**1 10
Primary Contact: Izabela Karmach, R.N., Administrator
COO: Izabela Karmach, R.N., Administrator
CFO: Raul J. Loyo–Rodriguez, Administrative Analyst III
CMO: Michael Krelstein, M.D., Medical Director
CIO: Linda Cannon, Chief Medical Records Services
CHR: Francisco Puentes, Human Resource Officer
Web address: www.sdcounty.ca.gov
**Control:** County–Government, nonfederal **Service:** Psychiatric

**Staffed Beds:** 357

**SAN DIEGO MEDICAL CENTER** See Kaiser Permanente San Diego Medical Center

✠ **SCRIPPS MERCY HOSPITAL (050077)**, 4077 Fifth Avenue, Zip 92103–2105; tel. 619/294–8111, (Includes SCRIPPS MERCY HOSPITAL CHULA VISTA, 435 H Street, Chula Vista, Zip 91912–6617, Mailing Address: P.O. Box 1537, Zip 91910–1537; tel. 619/691–7000) **A**1 2 3 5 9 10 **F**3 8 11 12 13 14 15 17 18 20 22 24 26 28 29 30 33 40 43 44 45 46 49 50 51 54 55 57 58 59 61 64 65 66 68 70 73 74 75 76 77 78 79 81 82 84 85 86 87 92 93 97 98 100 101 102 103 104 105 107 108 110 111 114 115 118 119 126 129 130 132 134 135 141 146 147 148 **P**3 5 **S** Scripps Health, San Diego, CA
Primary Contact: Thomas A. Gammiere, Chief Executive, Senior Vice President
CFO: Edward Turk, Vice President Finance
CMO: Davis Cracroft, M.D., Senior Director Medical Affairs
CIO: Drexel DeFord, Chief Information Officer
Web address: www.scrippshealth.org
**Control:** Other not–for–profit (including NFP Corporation) **Service:** General Medical and Surgical

**Staffed Beds:** 436 **Admissions:** 32221 **Census:** 391 **Outpatient Visits:** 169462 **Births:** 3610 **Total Expense ($000):** 611319 **Payroll Expense ($000):** 243575 **Personnel:** 3161

✠ △ **SHARP MEMORIAL HOSPITAL (050100)**, 7901 Frost Street, Zip 92123–2701; tel. 858/939–3400 **A**1 2 3 7 9 10 **F**3 8 11 12 15 17 18 20 22 24 26 28 29 30 31 33 34 35 36 40 43 44 45 46 49 50 56 57 58 59 60 62 64 65 68 70 74 75 77 78 79 81 82 84 85 86 87 90 93 107 108 110 114 115 117 118 119 120 121 123 124 126 129 130 131 132 135 137 138 142 143 145 146 148 **S** Sharp HealthCare, San Diego, CA
Primary Contact: Tim Smith, Senior Vice President and Chief Executive Officer
COO: Janie Kramer, Chief Operating Officer
CFO: Kari Cornicelli, Chief Financial Officer
CMO: Geoffrey Stiles, M.D., Chief Medical Officer
CIO: Kenneth Lawonn, Senior Vice President and Chief Information Officer
CHR: Connie Duquette, Director Human Resources
CNO: Pamela Wells, R.N., Chief Nursing Officer
Web address: www.sharp.com
**Control:** Other not–for–profit (including NFP Corporation) **Service:** General Medical and Surgical

**Staffed Beds:** 394 **Admissions:** 18714 **Census:** 270 **Outpatient Visits:** 389501 **Births:** 0 **Total Expense ($000):** 629139 **Payroll Expense ($000):** 239279 **Personnel:** 3221

✠ **SHARP MESA VISTA HOSPITAL (054145)**, 7850 Vista Hill Avenue, Zip 92123–2717; tel. 858/278–4110, (Includes SHARP MCDONALD CENTER, 7989 Linda Vista Road, Zip 92111–5106; tel. 858/637–6920) **A**1 9 10 **F**4 5 11 29 30 34 35 37 40 43 49 56 57 58 59 64 68 87 98 99 101 102 103 104 105 130 132 135 143 146 **S** Sharp HealthCare, San Diego, CA
Primary Contact: Kathi Lencioni, Senior Vice President and Chief Executive Officer
CFO: Kari Cornicelli, Chief Financial Officer
CMO: Michael Plopper, M.D., Chief Medical Officer
CIO: Kenneth Lawonn, Senior Vice President Information Systems
CHR: Carlisle Lewis, III, Senior Vice President Legal and Human Resources
CNO: Cheryl Odell, R.N., Chief Nursing Officer
Web address: www.sharp.com
**Control:** Other not–for–profit (including NFP Corporation) **Service:** Psychiatric

**Staffed Beds:** 163 **Admissions:** 5875 **Census:** 113 **Outpatient Visits:** 93412 **Births:** 0 **Total Expense ($000):** 67966 **Payroll Expense ($000):** 39423 **Personnel:** 545

✠ **UC SAN DIEGO HEALTH (050025)**, 200 West Arbor Drive, Zip 92103–9000; tel. 619/543–6222, (Includes THORNTON HOSPITAL, 9300 Campus Point Drive, La Jolla, Zip 92037–1300; tel. 858/657–7000; UC SAN DIEGO SHILEY EYE INSTITUTE, 9415 Campus Point Drive, Room 2411 Dept Of, La Jolla, Zip 92093–0946, Mailing Address: 9415 Campus Point Drive, Zip 92093–0946; tel. 858/534–6290; Karen Anisko Ryan, Director Business Development and Communications) **A**1 2 3 5 8 9 10 **F**3 6 9 11 12 13 15 16 17 18 20 22 24 26 29 30 31 34 36 37 40 43 44 45 46 47 48 49 50 51 54 55 56 57 58 59 60 61 64 65 66 68 70 72 73 74 75 76 77 78 79 80 81 82 84 85 86 87 91 92 93 97 98 99 100 101 102 103 107 108 109 110 111 113 114 115 117 118 119 120 121 123 124 126 129 130 131 132 136 137 138 139 140 141 142 145 147 148 **P**1 **S** University of California Systemwide Administration, Oakland, CA
Primary Contact: Patty Maysent, Interim Chief Executive Officer
COO: Margarita Baggett, MSN, Interim Chief Operating Officer
CFO: Lori Donaldson, Chief Financial Officer
CMO: Angela Scioscia, M.D., Chief Medical Officer
CIO: Ed Babakanian, Chief Information Officer
CHR: William J. Murin, Chief Human Resources Officer
CNO: Margarita Baggett, MSN, Chief Nursing Officer
Web address: www.health.ucsd.edu
**Control:** State–Government, nonfederal **Service:** General Medical and Surgical

**Staffed Beds:** 530 **Admissions:** 27650 **Census:** 446 **Outpatient Visits:** 678870 **Births:** 2560 **Total Expense ($000):** 1152590 **Payroll Expense ($000):** 409511 **Personnel:** 5379

**UNIVERSITY OF CALIFORNIA SAN DIEGO MEDICAL CENTER** See UC San Diego Health

✠ △ **VA SAN DIEGO HEALTHCARE SYSTEM**, 3350 LaJolla Village Drive, Zip 92161–0002; tel. 858/552–8585, (Total facility includes 39 beds in nursing home–type unit) **A**1 3 5 7 8 **F**1 3 4 5 12 15 18 20 22 24 26 29 30 34 35 36 37 38 39 40 44 45 46 47 48 49 50 54 55 56 57 58 59 60 61 62 63 64 65 68 71 74 75 77 79 81 82 83 84 85 86 87 90 91 92 93 94 95 96 97 98 100 101 102 103 104 105 106 107 110 111 114 115 116 117 118 119 126 129 130 132 135 143 144 145 146 147 148 **S** Department of Veterans Affairs, Washington, DC
Primary Contact: Jeffrey T. Gering, FACHE, Director
COO: Cynthia Abair, Associate Director
CFO: Ronald Larson, Chief Financial Officer
CMO: Robert M. Smith, M.D., Chief of Staff
CIO: Ruey Keller, Acting Chief Information Officer
CHR: Stephanie Wright, Director Human Resources Management
Web address: www.sandiego.va.gov
**Control:** Veterans Affairs, Government, federal **Service:** General Medical and Surgical

**Staffed Beds:** 216 **Admissions:** 9067 **Census:** 160 **Outpatient Visits:** 922532 **Births:** 0 **Total Expense ($000):** 643432 **Payroll Expense ($000):** 247058 **Personnel:** 2785

✠ **VIBRA HOSPITAL OF SAN DIEGO (052044)**, 555 Washington Street, Zip 92103–2294; tel. 619/260–8300 **A**1 9 10 **F**1 3 64 70 91 148 **P**5 **S** Vibra Healthcare, Mechanicsburg, PA
Primary Contact: Yameeka Jones, Chief Executive Officer
CFO: Mike Gonzales, Chief Financial Officer
CMO: John Fox, M.D., Medical Director
CHR: Tania Khalique, Director Human Resources
Web address: www.vhsandiego.com/
**Control:** Partnership, Investor–owned, for–profit **Service:** Long–Term Acute Care hospital

**Staffed Beds:** 110 **Admissions:** 930 **Census:** 69 **Outpatient Visits:** 1371 **Births:** 0 **Total Expense ($000):** 35832 **Payroll Expense ($000):** 16661 **Personnel:** 330

**SAN DIMAS—Los Angeles County**

☐ **SAN DIMAS COMMUNITY HOSPITAL (050588)**, 1350 West Covina Boulevard, Zip 91773–3219; tel. 909/599–6811 **A**1 9 10 **F**3 8 13 15 29 30 40 45 46 49 50 56 70 74 76 79 81 85 107 108 110 115 119 126 130 146 148 **S** Prime Healthcare Services, Ontario, CA
Primary Contact: Gregory Brentano, Chief Executive Officer
CFO: Robert Bonner, Chief Financial Officer
CMO: Zuhair Yahya, M.D., Chief Medical Officer
CIO: Jason Beckett, Director Information Services
Web address: www.sandimashospital.com/
**Control:** Corporation, Investor–owned, for–profit **Service:** General Medical and Surgical

**Staffed Beds:** 101 **Admissions:** 3712 **Census:** 40 **Outpatient Visits:** 24176 **Births:** 575 **Total Expense ($000):** 55455 **Payroll Expense ($000):** 20005 **Personnel:** 419

**CA**

| Hospital, Medicare Provider Number, Address, Telephone, Approval, Facility, and Physician Codes, Health Care System | |
|---|---|
| ★ American Hospital Association (AHA) membership | ◯ Healthcare Facilities Accreditation Program    ⇑ Center for Improvement in Healthcare Quality Accreditation |
| ☐ The Joint Commission accreditation | ◇ DNV Healthcare Inc. accreditation    △ Commission on Accreditation of Rehabilitation Facilities (CARF) accreditation |

**SAN FRANCISCO—San Francisco County**

⊞ △ **CALIFORNIA PACIFIC MEDICAL CENTER (050047)**, 2333 Buchanan Street, Zip 94115–1925, Mailing Address: P.O. Box 7999, Zip 94120–7999; tel. 415/600–6000, (Includes CALIFORNIA PACIFIC MEDICAL CENTER–DAVIES CAMPUS, Castro and Duboce Streets, Zip 94114; tel. 415/565–6000), (Total facility includes 53 beds in nursing home–type unit) **A**1 2 3 5 7 8 9 10 **F**2 3 6 7 8 12 13 15 18 19 20 22 24 26 28 29 30 31 32 34 35 36 37 38 39 40 41 46 47 48 49 50 51 52 55 56 57 58 59 60 61 63 65 68 70 72 74 75 76 77 78 79 81 82 83 84 85 86 87 88 89 90 91 92 93 96 97 98 99 100 101 102 104 107 108 110 111 114 115 116 117 118 119 120 121 123 124 126 128 130 132 133 135 137 138 139 141 142 143 144 145 146 147 148 **S** Sutter Health, Sacramento, CA
Primary Contact: Warren S. Browner, M.D., M.P.H., Chief Executive Officer
CFO: John Gates, Vice President Finance and Chief Financial Officer
CMO: Allan Pont, M.D., Vice President Medical Affairs
CIO: Craig Vercruysse, Chief Information Officer
CNO: Diana M. Karner, R.N., Chief Nursing Officer
Web address: www.cpmc.org
**Control:** Other not–for–profit (including NFP Corporation) **Service:** General Medical and Surgical

**Staffed Beds:** 644 **Admissions:** 25343 **Census:** 398 **Outpatient Visits:** 467978 **Births:** 4973 **Total Expense ($000):** 1037710 **Payroll Expense ($000):** 343760 **Personnel:** 3804

⊞ **CHINESE HOSPITAL (050407)**, 845 Jackson Street, Zip 94133–4899; tel. 415/982–2400 **A**1 9 10 **F**3 11 15 18 29 30 31 34 35 40 45 47 49 50 57 59 60 64 65 70 75 77 78 79 81 86 87 97 107 110 115 118 119 130 132 135 145 146 147 **P**5
Primary Contact: Brenda Yee, R.N., MSN, Chief Executive Officer
COO: Jian Q. Zhang, MSN, Chief Operating Officer
CFO: Thomas Bolger, Chief Financial Officer
CMO: William Chung, M.D., Chief of Staff
CIO: Keith Minard, Chief Information Officer
CHR: Lydia Mahr–Chan, Director of Human Resources
CNO: Peggy Cmiel, R.N., Chief Nursing Officer
Web address: www.chinesehospital-sf.org
**Control:** Other not–for–profit (including NFP Corporation) **Service:** General Medical and Surgical

**Staffed Beds:** 25 **Admissions:** 1787 **Census:** 22 **Outpatient Visits:** 78693 **Births:** 0 **Total Expense ($000):** 104637 **Payroll Expense ($000):** 31095 **Personnel:** 320

**JEWISH HOME OF SAN FRANCISCO (054089)**, 302 Silver Avenue, Zip 94112–1510; tel. 415/334–2500, (Total facility includes 362 beds in nursing home–type unit) **A**10 **F**6 58 98 103 128 130 143 146 148 **P**5
Primary Contact: Daniel R. Ruth, President and Chief Executive Officer
COO: Kevin Ward, Chief Operating Officer
CFO: Victor E. Meinke, Chief Financial Officer
CNO: Edwin Cabigao, Chief Nursing Officer
Web address: www.jhsf.org
**Control:** Other not–for–profit (including NFP Corporation) **Service:** Psychiatric

**Staffed Beds:** 374 **Admissions:** 1137 **Census:** 348 **Outpatient Visits:** 0 **Births:** 0 **Total Expense ($000):** 53119 **Payroll Expense ($000):** 27415

⊞ **KAISER PERMANENTE SAN FRANCISCO MEDICAL CENTER (050076)**, 2425 Geary Boulevard, Zip 94115–3358; tel. 415/833–2000 **A**1 3 5 10 **F**3 8 13 15 17 18 19 20 21 24 26 28 29 30 31 32 33 35 40 41 44 45 46 49 50 52 60 61 62 64 65 66 68 70 72 74 75 76 77 78 79 81 82 84 85 86 87 89 100 107 108 111 119 126 130 141 146 **S** Kaiser Foundation Hospitals, Oakland, CA
Primary Contact: Christine Robisch, Senior Vice President and Area Manager
COO: Helen Archer–Duste, Chief Operating Officer
CFO: Alex Khoo, Interim Area Finance Officer
CMO: Robert Mithun, M.D., Physician in Chief
CIO: Peti Arunamata, Interim Area Director Information Technology
CHR: Diane J. Easterwood, Human Resources Business Partner
Web address: www.kaiserpermanente.org
**Control:** Other not–for–profit (including NFP Corporation) **Service:** General Medical and Surgical

**Staffed Beds:** 215 **Admissions:** 11828 **Census:** 147 **Outpatient Visits:** 49230 **Births:** 2956

★ **LAGUNA HONDA HOSPITAL AND REHABILITATION CENTER (050668)**, (General Acute Care Hospital), 375 Laguna Honda Boulevard, Zip 94116–1499; tel. 415/759–2300, (Total facility includes 769 beds in nursing home–type unit) **A**10 **F**3 29 30 53 56 61 63 64 65 68 74 75 77 82 83 84 90 92 93 94 96 100 103 104 127 128 130 132 135 146 148 **P**1
Primary Contact: Mivic Hirose, Executive Administrator
COO: Michael R. Llewellyn, Chief Operating Officer
CFO: Tess Navarro, Chief Financial Officer
CMO: Colleen Riley, M.D., Medical Director
CIO: Pat Skala, Chief Information Officer
CHR: Willie Ramirez, Manager Labor Relations
Web address: www.lagunahonda.org/
**Control:** City–County, Government, nonfederal **Service:** Other specialty

**Staffed Beds:** 780 **Admissions:** 991 **Census:** 756 **Outpatient Visits:** 5170 **Births:** 0 **Total Expense ($000):** 241027 **Payroll Expense ($000):** 114808 **Personnel:** 1393

⊞ △ **SAINT FRANCIS MEMORIAL HOSPITAL (050152)**, 900 Hyde Street, Zip 94109–4899, Mailing Address: P.O. Box 7726, Zip 94120–7726; tel. 415/353–6000, (Nonreporting) **A**1 2 3 7 9 10 **S** Dignity Health, San Francisco, CA
Primary Contact: James P. Houser, Interim Chief Executive Officer
CFO: Alan Fox, Chief Financial Officer
CHR: Richard Mead, Senior Director Human Resources
Web address: www.saintfrancismemorial.org
**Control:** Other not–for–profit (including NFP Corporation) **Service:** General Medical and Surgical

**Staffed Beds:** 239

⊞ **SAN FRANCISCO GENERAL HOSPITAL AND TRAUMA CENTER (050228)**, 1001 Potrero Avenue, Zip 94110–3594; tel. 415/206–8000 **A**1 2 3 5 8 10 **F**3 13 15 17 18 20 22 29 30 34 35 36 38 39 40 43 44 45 46 47 48 49 50 57 58 59 60 61 64 65 68 70 71 72 74 75 76 77 78 79 81 82 83 84 86 87 89 92 93 94 97 98 99 100 102 105 107 108 110 111 119 128 129 130 131 132 135 144 146 147 148
Primary Contact: Roland Pickens, Interim Chief Executive Officer
COO: Iman Nazeeri–Simmons, Chief Operating Officer
CFO: Valerie Inouye, Chief Financial Officer
CMO: Todd May, M.D., Chief Medical Officer
CIO: Winona Windolovich, Director Applications
CHR: Elaine Lee, Manager Human Resources
CNO: Terry Dentoni, Chief Nursing Officer
Web address: www.sfdph.org
**Control:** City–County, Government, nonfederal **Service:** General Medical and Surgical

**Staffed Beds:** 441 **Admissions:** 16227 **Census:** 311 **Outpatient Visits:** 580637 **Births:** 1123 **Total Expense ($000):** 787659 **Payroll Expense ($000):** 295965

**SAN FRANCISCO MEDICAL CENTER** See Kaiser Permanente San Francisco Medical Center

⊞ **SAN FRANCISCO VA MEDICAL CENTER**, 4150 Clement Street, Zip 94121–1545; tel. 415/221–4810, (Nonreporting) **A**1 2 3 5 **S** Department of Veterans Affairs, Washington, DC
Primary Contact: Bonnie S. Graham, Director
CFO: Brian Kelly, Acting Chief Fiscal Service
CMO: C. Diana Nicoll, M.D., Chief of Staff
CIO: Ryan Chun, Information Resources Management
CHR: Jerry Mills, Chief Human Resources Management Services
CNO: Shirley Pikula, MSN, Associate Director Patient Center Care
Web address: www.sanfrancisco.va.gov/
**Control:** Veterans Affairs, Government, federal **Service:** General Medical and Surgical

**Staffed Beds:** 244

⊞ **ST. LUKE'S HOSPITAL (050055)**, 3555 Cesar Chavez Street, Zip 94110–4403; tel. 415/600–6000, (Total facility includes 39 beds in nursing home–type unit) **A**1 3 5 10 **F**3 8 13 18 29 30 34 35 40 50 55 63 64 66 67 68 70 72 75 76 77 78 79 81 82 85 89 93 97 100 107 108 110 111 114 118 119 128 130 143 146 147 148 **S** Sutter Health, Sacramento, CA
Primary Contact: Warren S. Browner, M.D., M.P.H., Chief Executive Officer
COO: Rick Stevens, Chief Administrative Officer
CFO: John Gates, Chief Financial Officer
CMO: Jerome Franz, M.D., Chief Medical Staff
CIO: Rob Seide, Manager Marketing and Communications
CHR: Linda Isaacs, Vice President Human Resources
Web address: www.stlukes–sf.org
**Control:** Other not–for–profit (including NFP Corporation) **Service:** General Medical and Surgical

**Staffed Beds:** 175 **Admissions:** 3936 **Census:** 83 **Outpatient Visits:** 74439 **Births:** 954 **Total Expense ($000):** 140493 **Payroll Expense ($000):** 46465 **Personnel:** 496

⊞ **ST. MARY'S MEDICAL CENTER (050457)**, 450 Stanyan Street, Zip 94117–1079; tel. 415/668–1000, (Nonreporting) **A**1 2 3 5 9 10 **S** Dignity Health, San Francisco, CA
Primary Contact: Anna Cheung, President
COO: Deborah Kolhede, Vice President and Chief Operating Officer
CFO: Eric Brettner, Vice President and Chief Financial Officer
CMO: Francis Charlton, Jr., M.D., Chief Medical Staff
CHR: Barbara Morrissett, Vice President Human Resources
CNO: Barbara Eusebio, R.N., Vice President, Chief Nurse Executive
Web address: www.stmarysmedicalcenter.com
**Control:** Other not–for–profit (including NFP Corporation) **Service:** General Medical and Surgical

**Staffed Beds:** 232

*Many Facility Codes have changed. Please refer to the AHA Guide Code Chart.* © 2015 AHA Guide

**⊞ UCSF MEDICAL CENTER (050454)**, 500 Parnassus Avenue, Zip 94143–0296, Mailing Address: 500 Parnassus Avenue, Box 0296, Zip 94143–0296; tel. 415/476–1000, (Includes UCSF BENIOFF CHILDREN'S HOSPITAL, 500 Parnassus Avenue, Zip 94143–2203, Mailing Address: 505 Parnassus Avenue, Zip 94143–2203; tel. 888/689–8273; UCSF MEDICAL CENTER MISSION BAY, 1975 4th Street, Zip 94158–2351; tel. 415/353–3000) **A**1 2 3 5 8 9 10 **F**3 6 7 8 9 11 12 13 14 15 17 18 19 20 21 22 23 24 25 26 27 29 30 31 32 33 34 35 36 37 39 40 41 43 44 45 46 47 48 49 50 51 52 53 54 55 56 57 58 59 60 61 62 63 64 65 66 68 70 72 74 75 76 77 78 79 81 82 83 84 85 86 87 88 89 92 93 94 97 99 100 101 102 103 104 105 107 108 110 111 112 113 114 115 116 117 119 120 121 123 124 126 129 130 131 132 134 135 136 137 138 139 140 141 142 144 145 146 147 148 **S** University of California Systemwide Administration, Oakland, CA
Primary Contact: Mark R. Laret, Chief Executive Officer
COO: Ken M. Jones, Chief Operating Officer
CFO: Barrie Strickland, Chief Financial Officer
CMO: Josh Adler, M.D., Chief Medical Officer
CIO: Joe Bergfort, Chief Information Officer
CHR: David Odato, Chief Administrative and Chief Human Resources Officer
CNO: Sheila Antrum, R.N., Chief Nursing Officer, Director Patient Care Services
Web address: www.ucsfhealth.org
**Control:** Other not–for–profit (including NFP Corporation) **Service:** General Medical and Surgical

> **Staffed Beds:** 650 **Admissions:** 29175 **Census:** 490 **Outpatient Visits:** 959322 **Births:** 2228 **Total Expense ($000):** 2236314 **Payroll Expense ($000):** 819158 **Personnel:** 7471

**VETERANS AFFAIRS MEDICAL CENTER** See San Francisco VA Medical Center

### SAN GABRIEL—Los Angeles County

**☐ SAN GABRIEL VALLEY MEDICAL CENTER (050132)**, 438 West Las Tunas Drive, Zip 91776–1216, Mailing Address: P.O. Box 1507, Zip 91778–1507; tel. 626/289–5454 **A**1 9 10 **F**13 15 18 29 31 34 35 36 40 44 45 49 51 56 57 59 60 64 68 74 75 78 79 81 85 87 102 103 107 108 111 115 119 130 143 146 147 148 **S** AHMC & Healthcare, Inc., Alhambra, CA
Primary Contact: Howard Ternes, Chief Executive Officer
COO: Karen Price–Gharzeddine, R.N., Chief Nursing Officer and Chief Operating Officer
CFO: Andrew Grim, Chief Financial Officer
CIO: Bernie Sauer, Director Information Technology
CHR: Victor Voisard, Director Human Resources
CNO: Karen Price–Gharzeddine, R.N., Chief Operating Officer and Chief Nursing Officer
Web address: www.sgvmc.org
**Control:** Partnership, Investor–owned, for–profit **Service:** General Medical and Surgical

> **Staffed Beds:** 273 **Admissions:** 9965 **Census:** 165 **Outpatient Visits:** 27879 **Births:** 3023

### SAN JOSE—Santa Clara County

**⊞ GOOD SAMARITAN HOSPITAL (050380)**, 2425 Samaritan Drive, Zip 95124–3997, Mailing Address: P.O. Box 240002, Zip 95154–2402; tel. 408/559–2011 **A**1 2 3 9 10 **F**2 3 5 8 11 12 13 15 17 18 19 20 21 22 23 24 25 26 27 28 29 30 31 34 35 37 38 40 44 45 46 47 48 49 50 54 57 58 59 60 63 64 67 68 70 73 74 75 76 77 78 79 81 82 83 84 85 86 87 89 90 93 96 98 101 102 104 105 107 108 110 111 114 115 116 117 118 119 120 123 124 126 130 135 146 147 148 **S** HCA, Nashville, TN
Primary Contact: Paul Beaupre, M.D., Chief Executive Officer
COO: Jordan Herget, Chief Operating Officer
CFO: Lana Arad, Chief Financial Officer
CMO: Bruce Wilbur, M.D., Chief Medical Officer
CIO: Darrell O'Dell, Director Information Services
CHR: Edward Battista, Vice President Human Resources
CNO: Darina Kavanagh, R.N., Chief Nursing Officer
Web address: www.goodsamsanjose.com
**Control:** Corporation, Investor–owned, for–profit **Service:** General Medical and Surgical

> **Staffed Beds:** 332 **Admissions:** 16417 **Census:** 222 **Outpatient Visits:** 132943 **Births:** 3593 **Total Expense ($000):** 331339 **Payroll Expense ($000):** 189922 **Personnel:** 1115

**⊞ KAISER PERMANENTE SAN JOSE MEDICAL CENTER (050604)**, 250 Hospital Parkway, Zip 95119–1199; tel. 408/972–7000 **A**1 5 10 **F**3 8 13 17 18 20 22 29 30 31 35 40 46 49 51 56 68 70 73 74 76 78 79 81 82 84 85 87 104 107 108 110 111 114 115 119 130 141 146 148 **S** Kaiser Foundation Hospitals, Oakland, CA
Primary Contact: Irene Chavez, Senior Vice President and Area Manager
COO: Irene Chavez, Senior Vice President and Area Manager
CFO: Stephen L. Kalsman, Area Finance Officer
CMO: Raj Bhandari, M.D., Physician–in–Chief
CIO: Greg Tuck, Area Information Officer
CHR: Susan Franzella, Human Resource Business Partner
CNO: Theresa R. Nero, R.N., Chief Nursing Officer
Web address: www.kaiserpermanente.org
**Control:** Other not–for–profit (including NFP Corporation) **Service:** General Medical and Surgical

> **Staffed Beds:** 217 **Admissions:** 10692 **Census:** 110 **Outpatient Visits:** 285386 **Births:** 2136 **Personnel:** 1495

**⊞ O'CONNOR HOSPITAL (050153)**, 2105 Forest Avenue, Zip 95128–1471; tel. 408/947–2500 **A**1 2 3 5 9 10 **F**1 3 8 11 13 15 18 19 20 22 24 26 28 29 30 31 34 35 37 40 44 46 48 49 50 53 54 57 59 60 64 66 68 70 72 74 75 76 77 78 79 81 84 85 86 87 89 93 97 100 107 108 110 111 114 116 117 118 119 121 123 128 130 131 132 135 146 147 148 **S** Daughters of Charity Health System, Los Altos Hills, CA
Primary Contact: Sister Margaret Keaveney, President and Chief Executive Officer
CIO: Richard Hutsell, Vice President and Chief Information Officer, Daughters of Charity Health System
CHR: Julie Hatcher, Vice President Human Resources
CNO: Dawn Marie Goeringer, Chief Clinical Care Officer
Web address: www.oconnorhospital.org
**Control:** Other not–for–profit (including NFP Corporation) **Service:** General Medical and Surgical

> **Staffed Beds:** 202 **Admissions:** 10991 **Census:** 136 **Outpatient Visits:** 180125 **Births:** 3019 **Total Expense ($000):** 315990 **Payroll Expense ($000):** 142568 **Personnel:** 943

**⊞ REGIONAL MEDICAL CENTER OF SAN JOSE (050125)**, 225 North Jackson Avenue, Zip 95116–1603; tel. 408/259–5000, (Nonreporting) **A**1 2 9 10 **S** HCA, Nashville, TN
Primary Contact: Michael T. Johnson, FACHE, President and Chief Executive Officer
COO: Brian J. Knecht, Chief Operating Officer
CFO: Raju Iyer, Chief Financial Officer
CMO: William Scott, M.D., Vice President Medical Affairs
CIO: Shirley Joyal, Director Information Systems
CHR: Nancy Clark, Vice President Human Resources
Web address: www.regionalmedicalsanjose.com
**Control:** Partnership, Investor–owned, for–profit **Service:** General Medical and Surgical

> **Staffed Beds:** 193

**SAN JOSE MEDICAL CENTER** See Kaiser Permanente San Jose Medical Center

**☐ △ SANTA CLARA VALLEY MEDICAL CENTER (050038)**, 751 South Bascom Avenue, Zip 95128–2699; tel. 408/885–5000 **A**1 3 5 7 9 10 **F**3 5 9 12 13 15 16 17 18 19 20 21 22 23 24 25 26 27 28 29 30 31 32 34 35 39 40 43 45 46 47 48 49 50 51 52 55 56 58 59 60 61 63 64 65 66 68 70 71 72 73 74 75 76 77 79 80 81 82 83 84 85 86 87 88 89 90 92 93 97 98 99 100 101 102 103 104 107 108 109 110 111 112 114 115 116 117 118 119 120 121 122 123 124 129 130 131 132 134 135 142 143 144 146 147 148 **P**6
Primary Contact: Paul E. Lorenz, Chief Executive Officer
COO: Benita McLarin, Chief Operating Officer
CMO: Jeffrey Arnold, M.D., Chief Medical Officer
CIO: Lee Herrmann, Chief Healthcare Technology Officer
CHR: David Manson, Manager Human Resources
CNO: Trudy Johnson, RN, R.N., Chief Nursing Officer
Web address: www.scvmed.org
**Control:** County–Government, nonfederal **Service:** General Medical and Surgical

> **Staffed Beds:** 342 **Admissions:** 22442 **Census:** 332 **Outpatient Visits:** 802648 **Births:** 3387 **Total Expense ($000):** 1243998 **Payroll Expense ($000):** 464991

### SAN LEANDRO—Alameda County

**FAIRMONT HOSPITAL** See Highland Hospital, Oakland

**⊞ KAISER PERMANENTE SAN LEANDRO MEDICAL CENTER (050777)**, 2500 Merced Street, Zip 94577–4201; tel. 510/454–1000, (Nonreporting) **A**1 10 **S** Kaiser Foundation Hospitals, Oakland, CA
Primary Contact: Thomas S. Hanenburg, Senior Vice President and Area Manager
Web address: www.kaiserpermanente.org
**Control:** Other not–for–profit (including NFP Corporation) **Service:** General Medical and Surgical

> **Staffed Beds:** 264

CA

---

**Hospital, Medicare Provider Number, Address, Telephone, Approval, Facility, and Physician Codes, Health Care System**

★ American Hospital Association (AHA) membership
☐ The Joint Commission accreditation
○ Healthcare Facilities Accreditation Program
◇ DNV Healthcare Inc. accreditation
⇑ Center for Improvement in Healthcare Quality Accreditation
△ Commission on Accreditation of Rehabilitation Facilities (CARF) accreditation

**CA**

✠ **KINDRED HOSPITAL–SAN FRANCISCO BAY AREA (052034)**, 2800 Benedict Drive, Zip 94577–6840; tel. 510/357–8300, (Nonreporting) **A**1 9 10 **S** Kindred Healthcare, Louisville, KY
Primary Contact: Jacob M. McCarty, Chief Executive Officer
CFO: Ziba Aflak, Chief Financial Officer
CHR: Erin Greene, Coordinator Human Resources
CNO: Emily Gard, Chief Clinical Officer
Web address: www.kindredhospitalsfba.com
**Control:** Corporation, Investor–owned, for–profit **Service:** Long–Term Acute Care hospital

**Staffed Beds:** 99

☐ **SAN LEANDRO HOSPITAL (050773)**, 13855 East 14th Street, Zip 94578–2600; tel. 510/357–6500, (Data for 242 days) **A**1 10 **F**3 15 18 29 30 34 35 40 44 45 50 57 60 68 70 77 79 81 107 108 110 111 114 130 146 **S** Alameda Health System, San Leandro, CA
Primary Contact: James E. T. Jackson, M.P.H., Chief Administrative Officer
Web address: www.sanleandrohospital.org
**Control:** Hospital district or authority, Government, nonfederal **Service:** General Medical and Surgical

**Staffed Beds:** 42 **Admissions:** 1775 **Census:** 31 **Outpatient Visits:** 19897 **Births:** 0 **Total Expense ($000):** 51288 **Payroll Expense ($000):** 24562 **Personnel:** 525

☐ **WILLOW ROCK CENTER (054149)**, 2050 Fairmont Drive, Zip 94578–1001; tel. 510/895–5502 **A**1 10 **F**29 34 57 98 99 101
Primary Contact: Anne L. Bakar, President and Chief Executive Officer
Web address: www.tbhcare.com
**Control:** Individual, Investor–owned, for–profit **Service:** Children's hospital psychiatric

**Staffed Beds:** 16 **Admissions:** 626 **Census:** 10 **Outpatient Visits:** 0 **Births:** 0 **Total Expense ($000):** 5695 **Payroll Expense ($000):** 1089

**SAN LUIS OBISPO—San Luis Obispo County**

**CALIFORNIA MENS COLONY CORRECTIONAL TREATMENT CENTER**, Highway 1, Zip 93409–8101, Mailing Address: P.O. Box 8101, Zip 93403–8101; tel. 805/547–7913, (Nonreporting)
Primary Contact: Martha Wallace, Administrator
CFO: William Cook, Associate Warden Business Service
CIO: Terry Knight, Public Information Officer and Administrative Assistant
Web address: www.yaca.ca.gov/visitors/fac_prison_cmc.html
**Control:** State–Government, nonfederal **Service:** Hospital unit of an institution (prison hospital, college infirmary, etc.)

**Staffed Beds:** 39

✠ **FRENCH HOSPITAL MEDICAL CENTER (050232)**, 1911 Johnson Avenue, Zip 93401–4197; tel. 805/543–5353 **A**1 2 9 10 **F**8 11 15 18 20 22 24 28 29 30 34 35 40 46 50 53 54 57 59 64 68 70 75 76 77 78 79 81 84 85 86 87 89 97 100 107 108 110 111 114 115 119 124 130 132 134 146 147 148 **S** Dignity Health, San Francisco, CA
Primary Contact: Alan Iftiniuk, Chief Executive Officer
COO: Carla A. Adams, Chief Nursing Officer and Chief Operating Officer
CFO: Sue Andersen, Chief Financial Officer
CMO: Scott Smelser, M.D., Chief of Staff
CIO: Cyndi Lang, Director Information Services
CHR: Barry Nateman, Manager Human Resources
CNO: Carla A. Adams, Chief Nursing Officer and Chief Operating Officer
Web address: www.frenchmedicalcenter.org
**Control:** Other not–for–profit (including NFP Corporation) **Service:** General Medical and Surgical

**Staffed Beds:** 112 **Admissions:** 4083 **Census:** 39 **Outpatient Visits:** 64702 **Births:** 561 **Total Expense ($000):** 106176 **Payroll Expense ($000):** 39819 **Personnel:** 401

✠ **SIERRA VISTA REGIONAL MEDICAL CENTER (050506)**, 1010 Murray Avenue, Zip 93405–1806, Mailing Address: P.O. Box 1367, Zip 93406–1367; tel. 805/546–7600 **A**1 2 9 10 19 **F**3 13 15 17 18 20 29 30 31 34 40 43 45 46 49 50 57 59 64 65 70 72 73 74 75 76 77 78 79 80 81 84 85 86 89 107 108 110 114 115 119 126 130 131 132 145 146 147 148 **S** TENET Healthcare Corporation, Dallas, TX
Primary Contact: Joseph DeSchryver, Chief Executive Officer
COO: Ike MMeje, Chief Operating Officer
CFO: Rollie Pirkl, Chief Financial Officer
CIO: Robert Leonard, Director Information Services
CHR: Kristin Flynn, Chief Human Resources Officer
CNO: Nicki E. Edwards, Ph.D., Interim Chief Nursing Officer
Web address: www.sierravistaregional.com
**Control:** Corporation, Investor–owned, for–profit **Service:** General Medical and Surgical

**Staffed Beds:** 164 **Admissions:** 5169 **Census:** 61 **Outpatient Visits:** 42109 **Births:** 1247 **Total Expense ($000):** 113641 **Payroll Expense ($000):** 52419 **Personnel:** 576

**SAN MATEO—San Mateo County**

**MILLS HEALTH CENTER** See Mills–Peninsula Health Services, Burlingame

☐ **SAN MATEO MEDICAL CENTER (050113)**, 222 West 39th Avenue, Zip 94403–4398; tel. 650/573–2222, (Total facility includes 31 beds in nursing home–type unit) **A**1 3 5 9 10 **F**3 15 18 19 29 30 31 32 39 40 45 47 49 51 54 56 59 60 61 64 65 66 68 69 70 71 74 75 78 79 81 82 84 85 87 89 90 93 97 98 100 101 102 103 104 105 107 115 119 128 130 134 146 147 148 **P**8
Primary Contact: Susan P. Ehrlich, M.D., Chief Executive Officer
COO: John Thomas, Chief Operating Officer
CFO: David S. McGrew, Chief Financial Officer
CMO: Chester Kunnappilly, M.D., Chief Medical Officer and Chief Quality Officer
CIO: Michael Aratow, M.D., Chief Information Officer
CHR: Angela Gonzales, Manager Human Resources
CNO: Joan G. Spicer, R.N., Chief Nursing Officer
Web address: www.sanmateomedicalcenter.org
**Control:** County–Government, nonfederal **Service:** General Medical and Surgical

**Staffed Beds:** 90 **Admissions:** 3537 **Census:** 83 **Outpatient Visits:** 494694 **Births:** 0 **Total Expense ($000):** 252870 **Payroll Expense ($000):** 90475 **Personnel:** 1050

**SAN PEDRO—Los Angeles County, See Los Angeles**

**SAN RAFAEL—Marin County**

✠ **KAISER PERMANENTE SAN RAFAEL MEDICAL CENTER (050510)**, 99 Montecillo Road, Zip 94903–3397; tel. 415/444–2000, (Nonreporting) **A**1 10 **S** Kaiser Foundation Hospitals, Oakland, CA
Primary Contact: Judy Coffey, R.N., Senior Vice President and Area Manager
CFO: John Groesbeck, Area Finance Officer
CMO: Gary Mizono, M.D., Physician–in–Chief
CIO: Stanley Dobrawa, Area Technology Director
CHR: Rudy Collins, Human Resources Business Partner
CNO: Judy Coffey, R.N., Senior Vice President and Area Manager
Web address: www.kaiserpermanente.org
**Control:** Other not–for–profit (including NFP Corporation) **Service:** General Medical and Surgical

**Staffed Beds:** 116

**SAN RAMON—Contra Costa County**

✠ **SAN RAMON REGIONAL MEDICAL CENTER (050689)**, 6001 Norris Canyon Road, Zip 94583–5400; tel. 925/275–9200 **A**1 9 10 **F**3 8 11 13 15 18 20 22 24 26 28 29 30 31 34 35 37 40 45 46 47 48 49 53 57 59 64 70 72 75 77 78 79 81 85 86 87 93 107 108 110 118 119 126 130 131 132 146 147 148 **S** TENET Healthcare Corporation, Dallas, TX
Primary Contact: Gary Sloan, Chief Executive Officer
CFO: Beenu Chadha, Chief Financial Officer
CMO: Erik Gracer, M.D., Chief of Staff
CIO: Asa Mandale, Interim Director Information Systems and Telecommunications
CHR: Dennis Mills, Director Human Resources
CNO: Pam Pshea, R.N., Chief Nursing Officer
Web address: www.sanramonmedctr.com
**Control:** Partnership, Investor–owned, for–profit **Service:** General Medical and Surgical

**Staffed Beds:** 123 **Admissions:** 4500 **Census:** 45 **Outpatient Visits:** 73950 **Births:** 755 **Total Expense ($000):** 131557 **Payroll Expense ($000):** 60806 **Personnel:** 521

**SANTA ANA—Orange County**

☐ **COASTAL COMMUNITIES HOSPITAL (050747)**, 2701 South Bristol Street, Zip 92704–6278; tel. 714/754–5454, (Nonreporting) **A**1 9 10 **S** Integrated Healthcare, Santa Ana, CA
Primary Contact: Don Kreitz, Interim Chief Executive Officer
CFO: Robert Heinemeier, Chief Financial Officer
CHR: Debby Riester, Manager Human Resources
Web address: www.coastalcommhospital.com
**Control:** Corporation, Investor–owned, for–profit **Service:** General Medical and Surgical

**Staffed Beds:** 178

☐ **ORANGE COUNTY GLOBAL MEDICAL CENTER, INC. (050746)**, 1001 North Tustin Avenue, Zip 92705–3577; tel. 714/953–3500, (Nonreporting) **A**1 3 5 9 10 **S** Integrated Healthcare, Santa Ana, CA
Primary Contact: Suzanne Richards, R.N., M.P.H., FACHE, Chief Executive Officer
COO: Ann Abe, Administrator and Chief Operating Officer
CFO: John Collins, Chief Financial Officer
CMO: Seifolah Esfandiari, M.D., Chief of Staff
CIO: Sri Yarramsetti, Chief Information Officer
CHR: Darcy Castro, Director, Human Resources
CNO: Shela Kaneshiro, Chief Nursing Officer
Web address: www.orangecounty-gmc.com
**Control:** Corporation, Investor–owned, for–profit **Service:** General Medical and Surgical

**Staffed Beds:** 282

*Many Facility Codes have changed. Please refer to the AHA Guide Code Chart.* © 2015 AHA Guide

## SANTA BARBARA—Santa Barbara County

**COTTAGE REHABILITATION HOSPITAL** See Santa Barbara Cottage Hospital

✠ **GOLETA VALLEY COTTAGE HOSPITAL (050357)**, 351 South Patterson Avenue, Zip 93111–2496, Mailing Address: Box 6306, Zip 93160–6306; tel. 805/967–3411 **A**1 9 10 **F**8 11 12 15 29 40 65 68 70 79 81 107 110 114 119 124 130 148 **S** Cottage Health System, Santa Barbara, CA
Primary Contact: Ronald C. Werft, President and Chief Executive Officer
COO: Steven A. Fellows, Executive Vice President and Chief Operating Officer
CFO: Joan Bricher, Senior Vice President Finance and Chief Financial Officer
CMO: Edmund Wroblewski, M.D., Vice President Medical Affairs and Chief Medical Officer
CIO: Alberto Kywi, Chief Information Officer
CHR: Patrice Ryan, Vice President Human Resources
Web address: www.sbch.org
**Control:** Other not–for–profit (including NFP Corporation) **Service:** General Medical and Surgical

**Staffed Beds:** 80 **Admissions:** 1626 **Census:** 38 **Outpatient Visits:** 39511 **Births:** 0 **Total Expense ($000):** 65343 **Payroll Expense ($000):** 24690 **Personnel:** 279

✠ △ **SANTA BARBARA COTTAGE HOSPITAL (050396)**, 400 West Pueblo Street, Zip 93105–4390, Mailing Address: P.O. Box 689, Zip 93102–0689; tel. 805/682–7111, (Includes COTTAGE CHILDREN'S HOSPITAL, 400 West Pueblo Street, Zip 93105–4353; tel. 877/247–3260; COTTAGE REHABILITATION HOSPITAL, 2415 De la Vina Street, Zip 93105–3819; tel. 805/687–7444; Melinda Staveley, President and Chief Executive Officer) **A**1 2 3 5 7 8 9 10 **F**3 4 5 8 11 12 13 15 17 18 20 22 24 26 28 29 30 31 34 35 40 42 43 46 50 53 54 57 58 59 60 64 65 68 70 72 74 75 76 78 79 81 84 86 88 89 90 91 92 93 96 98 100 102 103 104 106 107 108 111 114 115 117 119 126 130 132 135 146 148 **S** Cottage Health System, Santa Barbara, CA
Primary Contact: Ronald C. Werft, President and Chief Executive Officer
COO: Steven A. Fellows, Executive Vice President and Chief Operating Officer
CFO: Joan Bricher, Senior Vice President Finance and Chief Financial Officer
CMO: Edmund Wroblewski, M.D., Vice President Medical Affairs and Chief Medical Officer
CIO: Alberto Kywi, Chief Information Officer
CHR: Patrice Ryan, Vice President Human Resources
CNO: Herb J. Geary, R.N., Vice President Patient Care Services and Chief Nursing Officer
Web address: www.cottagehealthsystem.org
**Control:** Other not–for–profit (including NFP Corporation) **Service:** General Medical and Surgical

**Staffed Beds:** 351 **Admissions:** 18105 **Census:** 230 **Outpatient Visits:** 132097 **Births:** 2398 **Total Expense ($000):** 560343 **Payroll Expense ($000):** 177441 **Personnel:** 2186

**SANTA BARBARA COUNTY PSYCHIATRIC HEALTH FACILITY (054125)**, 315 Camino Del Remedio, Zip 93110–1332; tel. 805/681–5244, (Nonreporting) **A**10
Primary Contact: Takashi Wada, Interim Director
CFO: Michael C. Evans, Chief Executive Officer and Deputy Director of Finance and Administration
CMO: Ole Behrendtsen, M.D., Medical Director
CIO: Dana Fahey, Manager Management Information Systems
CHR: Elena Molelus, Manager Human Resources
Web address: www.countyofsb.org
**Control:** County–Government, nonfederal **Service:** Psychiatric

**Staffed Beds:** 16

## SANTA CLARA—Santa Clara County

✠ **KAISER PERMANENTE SANTA CLARA MEDICAL CENTER (050071)**, 700 Lawrence Expressway, Zip 95051–5173; tel. 408/851–1000 **A**1 2 3 5 10 **F**3 5 8 11 12 15 17 18 19 20 21 22 23 24 26 29 40 41 44 45 48 49 50 51 52 53 54 55 56 57 58 59 60 61 62 63 64 65 68 70 71 72 74 75 76 77 78 79 81 82 83 84 85 86 87 88 89 91 92 93 94 96 97 99 100 101 104 107 108 109 110 111 114 115 116 117 118 119 120 121 123 124 126 129 130 131 132 134 135 144 146 147 148 **P**3 **S** Kaiser Foundation Hospitals, Oakland, CA
Primary Contact: Christopher L. Boyd, Senior Vice President and Area Manager
COO: Pamela Lindemoen, Chief Operating Officer
CFO: Sean Fitzpatrick, Area Finance Officer
CMO: Susan Smarr, M.D., Physician–in–Chief
CIO: Scott May, Area Director Technology
CHR: Robert Hyde, Human Resources Business Partner
CNO: Anne M. Goldfisher, R.N., Chief Nursing Officer
Web address: www.kaiserpermanente.org
**Control:** Other not–for–profit (including NFP Corporation) **Service:** General Medical and Surgical

**Staffed Beds:** 327 **Admissions:** 19207 **Census:** 221 **Outpatient Visits:** 1043871 **Births:** 4462

## SANTA CRUZ—Santa Cruz County

✠ **DOMINICAN HOSPITAL (050242)**, 1555 Soquel Drive, Zip 95065–1794; tel. 831/462–7700 **A**1 2 9 10 **F**3 7 8 11 13 15 17 18 20 22 24 26 28 29 30 31 34 35 37 40 45 46 53 57 59 60 62 64 65 66 68 70 71 72 74 75 76 77 78 79 81 82 83 84 85 86 87 89 90 91 92 93 95 107 111 112 114 115 116 117 119 126 130 146 147 148 **S** Dignity Health, San Francisco, CA
Primary Contact: Nanette Mickiewicz, M.D., President
COO: Chris Wernke, Chief Operating Officer
CFO: Rick Harron, Chief Financial Officer
CMO: Freddie Weinstein, M.D., Chief Medical Officer
CIO: Lee Vanderpool, Vice President
CHR: Vicki Miranda, Vice President Human Resources
Web address: www.dominicanhospital.org
**Control:** Other not–for–profit (including NFP Corporation) **Service:** General Medical and Surgical

**Staffed Beds:** 223 **Admissions:** 10363 **Census:** 129 **Outpatient Visits:** 200575 **Births:** 835 **Total Expense ($000):** 325716 **Payroll Expense ($000):** 147871 **Personnel:** 1118

✠ **SUTTER MATERNITY AND SURGERY CENTER OF SANTA CRUZ (050714)**, 2900 Chanticleer Avenue, Zip 95065–1816; tel. 831/477–2200 **A**1 9 10 **F**3 13 34 45 51 57 76 79 81 85 119 126 132 146 **S** Sutter Health, Sacramento, CA
Primary Contact: Stephen Gray, Chief Administrative Officer
CFO: Bonnie Liang, Divisional Finance Officer
CMO: Joseph Fabry, D.O., Chief of Staff
CIO: Ann Barr, Chief Information Officer, Sutter Health Bay Area
CHR: Maynard Jenkins, Regional Vice President Human Resources
CNO: Sherri Stout–Torres, R.N., Chief Nursing Executive
Web address: www.suttersantacruz.org
**Control:** Other not–for–profit (including NFP Corporation) **Service:** General Medical and Surgical

**Staffed Beds:** 30 **Admissions:** 1573 **Census:** 11 **Outpatient Visits:** 11447 **Births:** 1035 **Total Expense ($000):** 55735 **Payroll Expense ($000):** 18622 **Personnel:** 192

## SANTA MARIA—Santa Barbara County

✠ **MARIAN REGIONAL MEDICAL CENTER (050107)**, 1400 East Church Street, Zip 93454–5906; tel. 805/739–3000, (Total facility includes 95 beds in nursing home–type unit) **A**1 2 3 9 10 13 **F**3 8 11 12 13 15 17 18 20 22 24 28 29 30 31 34 35 36 37 39 40 43 46 49 50 53 54 56 57 58 59 60 62 63 64 65 66 68 69 72 74 75 76 77 78 79 81 82 84 85 86 87 89 93 97 100 107 108 110 111 114 115 116 117 118 119 126 127 128 129 130 132 134 135 143 146 147 148 **S** Dignity Health, San Francisco, CA
Primary Contact: Charles J. Cova, President and Chief Executive Officer
COO: Kerin Mase, R.N., Chief Operating Officer and Chief Nursing Officer
CFO: Sue Andersen, Vice President and Service Area and Chief Financial Officer
CMO: Chuck Merrill, M.D., Vice President Medical Affairs
CIO: Patricia Haase, Director Information Technology and Communications
CHR: Ed Gonzales, Vice President Human Resources
CNO: Kerin Mase, R.N., Chief Operating Officer and Chief Nursing Officer
Web address: www.marianmedicalcenter.org
**Control:** Church–operated, Nongovernment, not–for profit **Service:** General Medical and Surgical

**Staffed Beds:** 286 **Admissions:** 11312 **Census:** 186 **Outpatient Visits:** 227176 **Births:** 3811 **Total Expense ($000):** 356480 **Payroll Expense ($000):** 124600 **Personnel:** 1365

## SANTA MONICA—Los Angeles County

✠ **SAINT JOHN'S HEALTH CENTER (050290)**, 2121 Santa Monica Boulevard, Zip 90404–2091; tel. 310/829–5511 **A**1 2 9 10 **F**1 3 4 8 11 13 14 15 16 17 18 20 22 24 26 29 30 31 34 35 37 40 41 45 46 49 56 58 64 67 70 72 73 74 76 78 79 80 81 82 84 85 88 89 90 93 97 98 107 108 110 111 118 119 120 121 123 124 126 128 130 131 132 135 146 147 **S** Providence Health & Services, Renton, WA
Primary Contact: Marcel C. Loh, FACHE, Chief Executive Officer
COO: Kenneth L. Meehan, Interim Chief Operating Officer
CFO: Michelle Mok, Chief Financial Officer
CIO: Martha Ponce, Director Information Technologies and Telecommunications
CHR: Steven Sharrer, Vice President Human Resources
CNO: Dawna Hendel, R.N., Chief Nursing Officer and Vice President Patient Care Services
Web address: www.newstjohns.org/home.aspx
**Control:** Church–operated, Nongovernment, not–for profit **Service:** General Medical and Surgical

**Staffed Beds:** 234 **Admissions:** 10266 **Census:** 117 **Outpatient Visits:** 148089 **Births:** 1830 **Total Expense ($000):** 202874 **Payroll Expense ($000):** 92271 **Personnel:** 1252

**CA**

---

**Hospital, Medicare Provider Number, Address, Telephone, Approval, Facility, and Physician Codes, Health Care System**

★ American Hospital Association (AHA) membership  ◯ Healthcare Facilities Accreditation Program  ⇧ Center for Improvement in Healthcare Quality Accreditation
☐ The Joint Commission accreditation  ◇ DNV Healthcare Inc. accreditation  △ Commission on Accreditation of Rehabilitation Facilities (CARF) accreditation

**CA**

✉ **SANTA MONICA–UCLA MEDICAL CENTER AND ORTHOPAEDIC HOSPITAL (050112)**, 1250 16th Street, Zip 90404–1249; tel. 310/319–4000 **A**1 3 5 9 10 **F**3 8 9 11 12 13 15 18 20 22 24 26 27 29 30 31 34 35 37 40 41 45 46 47 48 49 50 52 54 55 56 57 58 59 64 65 68 70 72 74 75 76 78 79 81 82 84 85 86 87 89 93 96 97 102 107 108 110 111 114 115 116 117 118 119 130 131 143 145 146 147 **P**6 **S** University of California Systemwide Administration, Oakland, CA
Primary Contact: Paul Watkins, Chief Administrative Officer
COO: Posie Carpenter, R.N., Chief Administrative Officer
CFO: Paul Staton, Chief Financial Officer
CMO: James Atkinson, M.D., Medical Director
CIO: Virginia McFerran, Chief Information Officer
CHR: Mark Speare, Senior Associate Director Patient Relations and Human Resources
Web address: www.healthcare.ucla.edu
**Control:** State–Government, nonfederal **Service:** General Medical and Surgical

**Staffed Beds:** 265 **Admissions:** 18380 **Census:** 211 **Outpatient Visits:** 165542 **Births:** 1673 **Total Expense ($000):** 396330 **Payroll Expense ($000):** 156430 **Personnel:** 1712

### SANTA ROSA—Sonoma County

✉ **KAISER PERMANENTE SANTA ROSA MEDICAL CENTER (050690)**, 401 Bicentennial Way, Zip 95403–2192; tel. 707/571–4000, (Nonreporting) **A**1 3 10 **S** Kaiser Foundation Hospitals, Oakland, CA
Primary Contact: Judy Coffey, R.N., Senior Vice President and Area Manager
COO: Vicky Locey, R.N., Chief Operating and Chief Nursing Officer
CFO: John Groesbeck, Area Finance Officer
CMO: Kirk Pappas, M.D., Physician–in–Chief
CIO: Stanley Dobrawa, Area Technology Director
CHR: Rudy Collins, Human Resources Business Partner
CNO: Vicky Locey, R.N., Chief Operating and Chief Nursing Officer
Web address: www.kaiserpermanente.org
**Control:** Other not–for–profit (including NFP Corporation) **Service:** General Medical and Surgical

**Staffed Beds:** 117

✉ **SANTA ROSA MEMORIAL HOSPITAL (050174)**, 1165 Montgomery Drive, Zip 95405–4897, Mailing Address: P.O. Box 522, Zip 95402–0522; tel. 707/546–3210 **A**1 2 9 10 **F**2 3 8 11 13 15 18 20 22 24 26 29 30 31 32 34 35 40 42 43 45 46 47 49 50 54 58 59 62 63 64 65 66 68 70 71 72 74 75 76 77 78 79 81 82 83 84 85 87 89 90 91 93 94 100 104 107 108 110 111 114 115 116 117 118 119 120 121 123 129 130 132 143 144 146 148 **S** St. Joseph Health, Irvine, CA
Primary Contact: Todd Salnas, President
COO: David Ziolkowski, Chief Operating Officer
CFO: Mich Riccioni, Chief Financial Officer
CMO: Richard Carvolth, M.D., Chief Medical Officer
CIO: Terri Oliver, Interim Executive Director Information Systems
CHR: Robert A. Eisen, Vice President Human Resources
CNO: Tiffany Oliver, Chief Nursing Officer
Web address: www.stjosephhealth.org
**Control:** Other not–for–profit (including NFP Corporation) **Service:** General Medical and Surgical

**Staffed Beds:** 278 **Admissions:** 12384 **Census:** 156 **Outpatient Visits:** 186704 **Births:** 925 **Total Expense ($000):** 364459 **Payroll Expense ($000):** 109638 **Personnel:** 1449

✉ **SUTTER SANTA ROSA REGIONAL HOSPITAL (050291)**, 30 Mark West Springs Road, Zip 95403; tel. 707/576–4000, (Includes WARRACK CAMPUS, 2449 Summerfield Road, Zip 95405–7815; tel. 707/576–4200) **A**1 3 5 9 10 **F**3 11 12 13 15 18 20 22 24 26 29 31 34 35 36 39 40 49 50 51 56 59 60 61 64 65 68 70 72 74 75 76 77 78 79 81 82 84 85 87 107 108 111 119 130 146 148 **S** Sutter Health, Sacramento, CA
Primary Contact: Mike Purvis, Chief Administrative Officer
CMO: William Carroll, M.D., Chief Medical Executive
Web address: www.sutterhealth.org
**Control:** Other not–for–profit (including NFP Corporation) **Service:** General Medical and Surgical

**Staffed Beds:** 84 **Admissions:** 6389 **Census:** 68 **Outpatient Visits:** 52268 **Births:** 1691 **Total Expense ($000):** 197208 **Payroll Expense ($000):** 68371 **Personnel:** 631

### SEPULVEDA—Los Angeles County, See Los Angeles

### SHERMAN OAKS—Los Angeles County, See Los Angeles

### SIMI VALLEY—Ventura County

✉ **SIMI VALLEY HOSPITAL (050236)**, 2975 North Sycamore Drive, Zip 93065–1277; tel. 805/955–6000 **A**1 2 9 10 **F**3 8 15 20 22 28 29 30 31 34 35 40 45 46 49 57 59 60 62 64 72 76 78 81 93 107 108 111 112 114 119 146 147 **P**3 **S** Adventist Health, Roseville, CA
Primary Contact: Jennifer Swenson, President and Chief Executive Officer
CFO: Crystal Ruditsky, Interim Vice President and Chief Financial Officer
CMO: John Dingilian, M.D., Chief Medical Officer
CIO: Bridget Nakamura, Director Information Systems
CHR: Sandra Werner, Director Human Resources
CNO: Caroline Esparza, Senior Vice President and Chief Nurse Executive
Web address: www.simivalleyhospital.com
**Control:** Church–operated, Nongovernment, not–for profit **Service:** General Medical and Surgical

**Staffed Beds:** 144 **Admissions:** 5822 **Census:** 70 **Outpatient Visits:** 81821 **Births:** 691 **Total Expense ($000):** 129485 **Payroll Expense ($000):** 53320

### SOLVANG—Santa Barbara County

✉ **SANTA YNEZ VALLEY COTTAGE HOSPITAL (051331)**, 2050 Viborg Road, Zip 93463–2295; tel. 805/688–6431 **A**1 9 10 18 **F**15 28 40 57 68 81 85 107 111 114 119 143 146 **S** Cottage Health System, Santa Barbara, CA
Primary Contact: Ronald C. Werft, President and Chief Executive Officer
COO: Steven A. Fellows, Executive Vice President and Chief Operating Officer
CFO: Joan Bricher, Senior Vice President Finance and Chief Financial Officer
CMO: Edmund Wroblewski, M.D., Vice President Medical Affairs and Chief Medical Officer
CIO: Alberto Kywi, Chief Information Officer
CHR: Patrice Ryan, Vice President Human Resources
Web address: www.cottagehealthsystem.org
**Control:** Other not–for–profit (including NFP Corporation) **Service:** General Medical and Surgical

**Staffed Beds:** 11 **Admissions:** 223 **Census:** 2 **Outpatient Visits:** 17820 **Births:** 0 **Total Expense ($000):** 14239 **Payroll Expense ($000):** 6573 **Personnel:** 63

### SONOMA—Sonoma County

★ ⑴ **SONOMA VALLEY HOSPITAL (050090)**, 347 Andrieux Street, Zip 95476–6811, Mailing Address: P.O. Box 600, Zip 95476–0600; tel. 707/935–5000, (Total facility includes 27 beds in nursing home–type unit) **A**9 10 22 **F**3 11 12 13 15 29 34 35 40 44 45 49 50 57 59 62 63 68 70 76 77 79 81 84 85 93 107 111 117 119 128 130 147 148 **S** Sonoma Valley Health Care District
Primary Contact: Kelly Mather, Chief Executive Officer
CFO: Jeanette Tarver, Director of Finance
CMO: Robert Cohen, M.D., Chief Medical Officer
CIO: Fe Sendaydiego, Director Information Systems
CHR: Paula M. Davis, Chief Human Resources Officer
CNO: Leslie Lovejoy, R.N., Chief Nursing and Quality Officer
Web address: www.svh.com
**Control:** Hospital district or authority, Government, nonfederal **Service:** General Medical and Surgical

**Staffed Beds:** 75 **Admissions:** 1534 **Census:** 33 **Outpatient Visits:** 61448 **Births:** 148 **Total Expense ($000):** 54922 **Payroll Expense ($000):** 24237 **Personnel:** 325

### SONORA—Tuolumne County

✉ **SONORA REGIONAL MEDICAL CENTER (050335)**, 1000 Greenley Road, Zip 95370–4819; tel. 209/536–5000, (Total facility includes 68 beds in nursing home–type unit) **A**1 9 10 **F**3 8 11 13 15 17 18 20 28 29 30 31 34 35 37 39 40 45 49 53 54 56 57 59 62 63 64 70 71 75 76 77 78 79 81 84 85 86 87 92 93 97 107 108 110 111 114 115 117 118 119 120 121 122 123 127 128 130 131 132 133 135 143 144 146 148 **P**6 **S** Adventist Health, Roseville, CA
Primary Contact: Andrew Jahn, President and Chief Executive Officer
CFO: Greg McCulloch, CPA, Vice President of Finance and Chief Financial Officer
CMO: Ed Clinite, D.O., Chief of Staff
CNO: Julie Kline, Senior Vice President Patient Services
Web address: www.sonoramedicalcenter.org/
**Control:** Church–operated, Nongovernment, not–for profit **Service:** General Medical and Surgical

**Staffed Beds:** 152 **Admissions:** 4951 **Census:** 112 **Outpatient Visits:** 287204 **Births:** 533 **Total Expense ($000):** 214422 **Payroll Expense ($000):** 76619 **Personnel:** 1057

*Many Facility Codes have changed. Please refer to the AHA Guide Code Chart.* © 2015 AHA Guide

**SOUTH EL MONTE—Los Angeles County**

☐ **GREATER EL MONTE COMMUNITY HOSPITAL (050738)**, 1701 Santa Anita Avenue, Zip 91733–3411; tel. 626/579–7777 **A**1 9 10 **F**3 13 17 18 19 29 34 35 40 49 56 57 59 65 68 70 76 81 87 89 93 107 119 128 130 143 146 **S** AHMC & Healthcare, Inc., Alhambra, CA
Primary Contact: Stanley Toy, Jr., M.D., Chief Executive Officer
COO: Jose Ortega, Chief Operating Officer
CFO: Michael Chung, Chief Financial Officer
CMO: Dilip Patel, M.D., Chief of Staff
CIO: Jay Geldhof, Director Information Systems
CHR: Jason Jaquez, Director Human Resources
CNO: Evelyn Calubaquib, Chief Nursing Officer
Web address: www.greaterelmonte.com
**Control:** Hospital district or authority, Government, nonfederal **Service:** General Medical and Surgical

**Staffed Beds:** 117 **Admissions:** 3564 **Census:** 42 **Outpatient Visits:** 18008
**Births:** 520 **Personnel:** 281

**SOUTH LAKE TAHOE—El Dorado County**

✠ **BARTON MEMORIAL HOSPITAL (050352)**, 2170 South Avenue, Zip 96150–7026, Mailing Address: P.O. Box 9578, Zip 96158–9578; tel. 530/541–3420, (Total facility includes 48 beds in nursing home–type unit) **A**1 5 9 10 20 **F**3 8 11 13 15 18 29 30 32 34 35 38 40 45 46 47 48 50 54 57 59 62 63 64 65 66 68 70 75 76 77 79 81 82 83 84 85 86 87 89 90 92 93 94 96 97 99 100 104 107 109 110 111 112 113 114 115 116 117 118 119 121 122 123 124 126 127 128 129 130 131 132 135 143 144 146 147 148
Primary Contact: John G. Williams, President and Chief Executive Officer
COO: Kathy Cocking, R.N., Vice President Operations
CFO: Richard P. Derby, Vice President Finance
CMO: Clint Purvance, M.D., Chief Medical Officer
CHR: LeAnne Kankel, Vice President Human Relations
Web address: www.bartonhealth.org
**Control:** Other not–for–profit (including NFP Corporation) **Service:** General Medical and Surgical

**Staffed Beds:** 111 **Admissions:** 2200 **Census:** 64 **Outpatient Visits:** 70127
**Births:** 348 **Total Expense ($000):** 105567 **Payroll Expense ($000):** 45710
**Personnel:** 758

**SOUTH SAN FRANCISCO—San Mateo County**

✠ **KAISER PERMANENTE SOUTH SAN FRANCISCO (050070)**, 1200 El Camino Real, Zip 94080–3208; tel. 650/742–2000, (Nonreporting) **A**1 3 10 **S** Kaiser Foundation Hospitals, Oakland, CA
Primary Contact: Frank T. Beirne, FACHE, Senior Vice President and Area Manager
CMO: Michelle Caughey, M.D., Physician In Chief
CIO: Angel Shew, Director Area Technology
CHR: Sharon Barncord, Human Resource Business Partner
Web address: www.kaiserpermanente.org
**Control:** Other not–for–profit (including NFP Corporation) **Service:** General Medical and Surgical

**Staffed Beds:** 120

**STOCKTON—San Joaquin County**

☐ **DAMERON HOSPITAL (050122)**, 525 West Acacia Street, Zip 95203–2484; tel. 209/944–5550, (Nonreporting) **A**1 9 10
Primary Contact: Lorraine P. Auerbach, FACHE, President and Chief Executive Officer
COO: Michael Glasberg, Senior Vice President, Chief Operating Officer
CFO: Elizabeth R. Propp, Vice President Finance and Chief Financial Officer
CMO: Bradley Reinke, M.D., Vice President Medical Affairs and Chief Medical Officer
CIO: David Kerrins, Vice President Information Services and Chief Information Officer
CHR: Tresha Moreland, MS, Regional Vice President Human Resources
CNO: Janine Hawkins, R.N., Vice President Patient Care Services and Chief Nursing Officer
Web address: www.dameronhospital.org
**Control:** Other not–for–profit (including NFP Corporation) **Service:** General Medical and Surgical

**Staffed Beds:** 202

✠ **ST. JOSEPH'S BEHAVIORAL HEALTH CENTER (054123)**, 2510 North California Street, Zip 95204–5568; tel. 209/461–2000 **A**1 9 10 **F**5 29 38 68 98 100 101 103 104 105 130 132 143 146 **S** Dignity Health, San Francisco, CA
Primary Contact: Paul Rains, R.N., MSN, President
CFO: Doreen Hartmann, Chief Financial Officer
CMO: David Robinson, D.O., Medical Director
CHR: Nancy Vargas, Chief Human Resources
CNO: Benny Lee Lucas, Jr., Chief Nursing Executive
Web address: www.stjosephscanhelp.org
**Control:** Church–operated, Nongovernment, not–for profit **Service:** Psychiatric

**Staffed Beds:** 35 **Admissions:** 1863 **Census:** 32 **Outpatient Visits:** 9222
**Births:** 0 **Total Expense ($000):** 15766 **Payroll Expense ($000):** 9022

✠ **ST. JOSEPH'S MEDICAL CENTER (050084)**, 1800 North California Street, Zip 95204–6019, Mailing Address: P.O. Box 213008, Zip 95213–9008; tel. 209/943–2000, (Nonreporting) **A**1 2 3 9 10 **S** Dignity Health, San Francisco, CA
Primary Contact: Donald J. Wiley, President and Chief Executive Officer
COO: Michael R. Ricks, Chief Operating Officer
CFO: Nikki Ochoa, Interim Chief Financial Officer
CMO: Susan McDonald, M.D., Vice President
CIO: Randall Gamino, Director Perot Site
CHR: Nancy Vargas, Vice President Human Resources
Web address: www.stjosephsCARES.org
**Control:** Church–operated, Nongovernment, not–for profit **Service:** General Medical and Surgical

**Staffed Beds:** 273

**SUN CITY—Riverside County**

☐ **MENIFEE VALLEY MEDICAL CENTER (050684)**, 28400 McCall Boulevard, Zip 92585–9537; tel. 951/679–8888 **A**1 9 10 **F**11 12 14 15 29 30 31 34 35 40 45 46 47 49 50 51 57 59 70 78 79 81 82 107 108 114 119 130 **S** Physicians for Healthy Hospitals, Hemet, CA
Primary Contact: Joel M. Bergenfeld, Chief Hospital Executive Officer
CHR: Michele Bird, Chief Human Resources Officer
Web address: www.valleyhealthsystem.com
**Control:** Partnership, Investor–owned, for–profit **Service:** General Medical and Surgical

**Staffed Beds:** 74 **Admissions:** 2927 **Census:** 32 **Outpatient Visits:** 17814
**Births:** 0 **Total Expense ($000):** 40234 **Payroll Expense ($000):** 15982

**SUN VALLEY—Los Angeles County, See Los Angeles**

**SUSANVILLE—Lassen County**

✠ **BANNER LASSEN MEDICAL CENTER (051320)**, 1800 Spring Ridge Drive, Zip 96130–6100; tel. 530/252–2000 **A**1 9 10 18 **F**3 13 15 18 29 31 34 40 45 46 48 49 50 57 59 64 65 68 75 76 78 79 81 87 90 91 92 93 107 108 110 111 114 115 119 124 129 130 133 146 147 148 **S** Banner Health, Phoenix, AZ
Primary Contact: Catherine S. Harshbarger, R.N., Chief Executive Officer
CFO: Jon R. McMillan, Chief Financial Officer
CMO: Hal Meadows, M.D., Chief Medical Officer
CHR: Roberto Martinez, Chief Human Resources Officer
CNO: Kathy H. Virgil–Belding, Chief Nursing Officer
Web address: www.bannerhealth.com/Locations/California/Banner+Lassen+Medical+Center
**Control:** Other not–for–profit (including NFP Corporation) **Service:** General Medical and Surgical

**Staffed Beds:** 25 **Admissions:** 1209 **Census:** 11 **Outpatient Visits:** 30907
**Births:** 281 **Total Expense ($000):** 32676 **Payroll Expense ($000):** 13599
**Personnel:** 179

**SYLMAR—Los Angeles County, See Los Angeles**

**TARZANA—Los Angeles County, See Los Angeles**

**CA**

---

**Hospital, Medicare Provider Number, Address, Telephone, Approval, Facility, and Physician Codes, Health Care System**

★ American Hospital Association (AHA) membership   ◯ Healthcare Facilities Accreditation Program   ⇑ Center for Improvement in Healthcare Quality Accreditation
☐ The Joint Commission accreditation   ◇ DNV Healthcare Inc. accreditation   △ Commission on Accreditation of Rehabilitation Facilities (CARF) accreditation

**TEHACHAPI—Kern County**

★ ◇ **TEHACHAPI VALLEY HEALTHCARE DISTRICT (051301)**, 115 West E Street, Zip 93561–1607, Mailing Address: P.O. Box 1900, Zip 93581–1900; tel. 661/823–3000 **A**9 10 18 21 **F**29 40 54 57 59 64 65 66 68 82 93 107 119 127 130 132 133
Primary Contact: Eugene Suksi, Interim Chief Executive Officer
CFO: Chester Beedle, Interim Chief Financial Officer
CMO: Susan Cribbs, D.O., Chief of Staff
CIO: Dusty Colvard, Manager Information Technology
CHR: Susan Nelson–Jones, Director Human Resources
CNO: Juliana Kay Kirby, R.N., Chief Nursing Officer
Web address: www.tvhd.org
**Control:** Hospital district or authority, Government, nonfederal **Service:** General Medical and Surgical

Staffed Beds: 24 **Admissions:** 122 **Census:** 1 **Births:** 3 **Total Expense ($000):** 21702 **Payroll Expense ($000):** 9150

**TEMECULA—Riverside County**

☒ **TEMECULA VALLEY HOSPITAL (050775)**, 31700 Temecula Parkway, Zip 92592–5896; tel. 951/331–2216, (Nonreporting) **A**1 10 **S** Universal Health Services, Inc., King of Prussia, PA
Primary Contact: Darlene Wetton, R.N., Chief Executive Officer
Web address: www.temeculavalleyhospital.com
**Control:** Corporation, Investor–owned, for–profit **Service:** General Medical and Surgical

Staffed Beds: 140

**TEMPLETON—San Luis Obispo County**

☒ **TWIN CITIES COMMUNITY HOSPITAL (050633)**, 1100 Las Tablas Road, Zip 93465–9796; tel. 805/434–3500 **A**1 9 10 **F**3 8 13 18 29 30 31 34 37 39 40 45 46 47 48 49 50 55 56 57 59 60 64 67 68 70 74 75 76 77 78 79 81 84 85 87 107 108 111 115 119 130 146 148 **S** TENET Healthcare Corporation, Dallas, TX
Primary Contact: Mark P. Lisa, FACHE, Chief Executive Officer
COO: Mike Lane, Chief Operating Officer
CFO: Paul Posmoga, Chief Financial Officer
CIO: Don Wheeler, Director Information Systems
CHR: Eloise Rendon, Director Human Resources
CNO: Carol Howland, Chief Nursing Officer
Web address: www.twincitieshospital.com
**Control:** Corporation, Investor–owned, for–profit **Service:** General Medical and Surgical

Staffed Beds: 89 **Admissions:** 4415 **Census:** 47 **Outpatient Visits:** 45904 **Births:** 662 **Total Expense ($000):** 79842 **Payroll Expense ($000):** 36986 **Personnel:** 408

**THOUSAND OAKS—Ventura County**

☒ **LOS ROBLES HOSPITAL AND MEDICAL CENTER (050549)**, 215 West Janss Road, Zip 91360–1899; tel. 805/497–2727, (Includes THOUSAND OAKS SURGICAL HOSPITAL, 401 Rolling Oaks Drive, Zip 91361–1050; tel. 805/497–2727; Natalie Mussi, President and Chief Executive Officer), (Total facility includes 42 beds in nursing home–type unit) **A**1 2 9 10 **F**3 11 12 13 15 17 18 19 20 22 24 26 28 29 31 34 35 40 41 43 46 47 48 49 50 54 59 64 65 69 70 72 74 75 76 77 78 79 81 82 84 85 87 89 90 91 100 110 111 114 119 126 128 130 131 132 135 146 147 148 **S** HCA, Nashville, TN
Primary Contact: Natalie Mussi, President and Chief Executive Officer
COO: Norair Jemjemian, Chief Operating Officer
CMO: Hannah Grossman, M.D., Chief Medical Officer
CIO: Alex Bryer, Director Information Management
CHR: John Bibby, Vice President Human Resources
CNO: Cynthia J. Johnson, R.N., Chief Nursing Officer
Web address: www.losrobleshospital.com
**Control:** Corporation, Investor–owned, for–profit **Service:** General Medical and Surgical

Staffed Beds: 367 **Admissions:** 15377 **Census:** 238 **Outpatient Visits:** 88374 **Births:** 1997

**TORRANCE—Los Angeles County**

☐ **DEL AMO HOSPITAL (054053)**, 23700 Camino Del Sol, Zip 90505–5000; tel. 310/530–1151, (Nonreporting) **A**1 9 10 **S** Universal Health Services, Inc., King of Prussia, PA
Primary Contact: Lisa K. Montes, Chief Executive Officer
Web address: www.delamohospital.com
**Control:** Corporation, Investor–owned, for–profit **Service:** Psychiatric

Staffed Beds: 70

☐ **HARBOR–UCLA MEDICAL CENTER (050376)**, 1000 West Carson Street, Zip 90502–2059; tel. 310/222–2345 **A**1 2 3 5 8 10 **F**3 11 12 13 14 15 17 18 19 20 22 24 25 26 29 30 31 32 34 35 39 40 41 43 44 45 46 47 48 49 52 55 56 57 59 60 61 64 66 68 70 72 74 76 77 78 79 81 82 84 85 87 88 89 93 97 98 100 101 102 107 108 110 114 115 116 118 119 120 129 130 131 132 134 135 138 141 144 146 147 148 **P**3 **S** Los Angeles County–Department of Health Services, Los Angeles, CA
Primary Contact: Delvecchio Finley, Chief Executive Officer
COO: Kimberly McKenzie, R.N., Chief Nursing Officer and Chief Operations Officer
CFO: Jody Nakasuji, Chief Financial Officer
CMO: Timothy Van Natta, M.D., Chief Medical Officer
CIO: Sandy Mungovan, Chief Information Officer
CHR: Karyl Smith, Director Human Resources
CNO: Kimberly McKenzie, R.N., Chief Nursing Officer and Chief Operations Officer
Web address: www.humc.edu
**Control:** County–Government, nonfederal **Service:** General Medical and Surgical

Staffed Beds: 397 **Admissions:** 19478 **Census:** 325 **Outpatient Visits:** 403524 **Births:** 805 **Total Expense ($000):** 763669 **Payroll Expense ($000):** 300104 **Personnel:** 3744

☒ **PROVIDENCE LITTLE COMPANY OF MARY MEDICAL CENTER – TORRANCE (050353)**, 4101 Torrance Boulevard, Zip 90503–4664; tel. 310/540–7676, (Total facility includes 77 beds in nursing home–type unit) **A**1 2 9 10 **F**3 8 11 13 14 15 18 19 20 22 24 26 28 29 30 31 34 35 37 44 45 46 49 50 51 57 59 60 62 64 68 70 72 74 75 76 77 78 79 81 82 84 85 86 87 89 91 92 93 100 107 108 110 111 114 115 116 117 118 119 120 121 123 126 128 130 131 132 133 143 145 146 147 148 **S** Providence Health & Services, Renton, WA
Primary Contact: Elizabeth Dunne, Chief Executive
CFO: Elizabeth Zuanich, Chief Financial Officer
CMO: Laurence Eason, M.D., Chief Medical Officer
Web address: www.lcmweb.org
**Control:** Church–operated, Nongovernment, not–for profit **Service:** General Medical and Surgical

Staffed Beds: 376 **Admissions:** 19781 **Census:** 245 **Outpatient Visits:** 205608 **Births:** 2656 **Total Expense ($000):** 249999 **Payroll Expense ($000):** 134520 **Personnel:** 2191

☒ **TORRANCE MEMORIAL MEDICAL CENTER (050351)**, 3330 Lomita Boulevard, Zip 90505–5073; tel. 310/325–9110 **A**1 2 9 10 **F**3 5 8 11 12 13 14 15 16 17 18 19 20 22 24 26 28 29 30 31 32 34 35 36 37 39 40 41 44 45 46 47 48 49 50 51 55 57 58 59 60 61 62 63 64 68 70 72 74 75 76 77 78 79 81 82 83 84 85 86 87 89 91 92 93 96 107 108 109 110 111 114 115 116 117 118 119 120 121 123 124 126 128 129 130 132 134 135 141 143 145 146 147 148 **P**3 5 7
Primary Contact: Craig Leach, President and Chief Executive Officer
CFO: Bill Larson, Chief Financial Officer
CMO: John McNamara, M.D., Chief Medical Officer
CIO: Bernadette Reid, Chief Information Officer
CHR: Debra Ambriz, Director Human Resources
Web address: www.torrancememorial.org
**Control:** Other not–for–profit (including NFP Corporation) **Service:** General Medical and Surgical

Staffed Beds: 378 **Admissions:** 23847 **Census:** 266 **Outpatient Visits:** 352499 **Births:** 3198 **Total Expense ($000):** 491884 **Payroll Expense ($000):** 186875 **Personnel:** 2698

**TRACY—San Joaquin County**

☒ **SUTTER TRACY COMMUNITY HOSPITAL (050313)**, 1420 North Tracy Boulevard, Zip 95376–3497; tel. 209/835–1500 **A**1 9 10 **F**3 11 13 15 18 29 30 31 34 35 39 40 45 46 49 50 54 57 59 60 64 68 70 74 75 76 77 78 79 81 82 85 86 87 93 107 108 110 111 115 119 124 130 135 146 148 **S** Sutter Health, Sacramento, CA
Primary Contact: David M. Thompson, Chief Executive Officer
COO: Doug Archer, Assistant Administrator
CFO: Eric Dalton, Chief Financial Officer
CIO: Catherine M. Larsen, Director Marketing
CHR: Melanie Wallace, Manager Human Resources
Web address: www.suttertracy.org
**Control:** Other not–for–profit (including NFP Corporation) **Service:** General Medical and Surgical

Staffed Beds: 78 **Admissions:** 3978 **Census:** 34 **Outpatient Visits:** 75875 **Births:** 700 **Total Expense ($000):** 97170 **Payroll Expense ($000):** 33983 **Personnel:** 459

**TRAVIS AFB—Solano County**

☒ **DAVID GRANT USAF MEDICAL CENTER**, 101 Bodin Circle, Zip 94535–1809; tel. 707/423–7300, (Nonreporting) **A**1 3 5 **S** Department of the Air Force, Washington, DC
Primary Contact: Colonel Brian T. Hayes, Commander
CFO: Major Jonathan Richards, Chief Financial Officer
CMO: Colonel Chris Scharenbrock, M.D., Chief Medical Staff
Web address: www.travis.af.mil/units/dgmc/index.asp
**Control:** Air Force, Government, federal **Service:** General Medical and Surgical

Staffed Beds: 116

**CA**

## TRUCKEE—Nevada County

★ **TAHOE FOREST HOSPITAL DISTRICT (051328)**, 10121 Pine Avenue, Zip 96161–4856, Mailing Address: P.O. Box 759, Zip 96160–0759; tel. 530/587–6011, (Total facility includes 37 beds in nursing home–type unit) **A**2 3 5 9 10 18 **F**11 70 76 128 129 **S** Tahoe Forest Health System, Truckee, CA
Primary Contact: Jake Dorst, Interim Chief Executive Officer
CFO: Crystal Betts, Chief Financial Officer
CMO: Richard Ganong, M.D., Chief of Staff
CIO: Mark Griffiths, Chief Systems Innovation Officer
CHR: Marcie Mortensson, Chief Human Resources Officer
Web address: www.tfhd.com
**Control:** Hospital district or authority, Government, nonfederal **Service:** General Medical and Surgical

**Staffed Beds:** 62 **Admissions:** 1695 **Census:** 47 **Outpatient Visits:** 61482
**Births:** 375 **Total Expense ($000):** 111789 **Payroll Expense ($000):** 40486
**Personnel:** 567

## TULARE—Tulare County

★ ◇ **TULARE REGIONAL MEDICAL CENTER (050359)**, 869 North Cherry Street, Zip 93274–2287; tel. 559/688–0821 **A**9 10 21 **F**3 11 13 15 20 26 29 34 35 40 45 46 47 48 49 50 53 56 57 59 60 62 64 65 66 68 70 71 73 74 75 76 77 79 81 85 86 89 93 97 107 108 110 111 119 126 127 129 130 131 132 135 146 147 148
Primary Contact: Paul A. Walker, FACHE, Interim Chief Executive Officer
CFO: Michael Bernstein, Chief Financial Officer
CMO: Pradeep Kamboj, M.D., Chief Medical Staff
CIO: Jim Peelgren, Chief Information Officer
CHR: John Barbadian, Vice President Human Resources
CNO: Patricia Mathewson, Chief Nursing Officer
Web address: www.tulareregional.org
**Control:** Hospital district or authority, Government, nonfederal **Service:** General Medical and Surgical

**Staffed Beds:** 103 **Admissions:** 3786 **Census:** 39 **Outpatient Visits:** 102463
**Births:** 1167 **Total Expense ($000):** 70247 **Payroll Expense ($000):** 22983
**Personnel:** 430

## TURLOCK—Stanislaus County

⊞ **EMANUEL MEDICAL CENTER (050179)**, 825 Delbon Avenue, Zip 95382–2016, Mailing Address: P.O. Box 819005, Zip 95381–9005; tel. 209/667–4200 **A**1 2 9 10 **F**3 8 11 15 18 20 22 24 26 29 30 31 34 35 40 47 48 49 54 59 60 64 68 70 73 75 76 77 78 79 81 89 93 97 107 108 110 111 114 115 118 119 120 121 123 130 132 146 147 148 **S** TENET Healthcare Corporation, Dallas, TX
Primary Contact: Susan C. Micheletti, Chief Executive Officer
CFO: David Neapolitan, Chief Financial Officer
CHR: Terry Gray, Vice President Human Resources
CNO: Constance Fairchilds, R.N., Vice President Patient Care Services
Web address: www.emanuelmed.com
**Control:** Corporation, Investor–owned, for–profit **Service:** General Medical and Surgical

**Staffed Beds:** 209 **Admissions:** 9068 **Census:** 209 **Outpatient Visits:** 128221 **Births:** 1336 **Total Expense ($000):** 184522 **Payroll Expense ($000):** 67971 **Personnel:** 977

## TUSTIN—Orange County

⊞ **HEALTHSOUTH TUSTIN REHABILITATION HOSPITAL (053034)**, 14851 Yorba Street, Zip 92780–2925; tel. 714/832–9200, (Nonreporting) **A**1 9 10 **S** HEALTHSOUTH Corporation, Birmingham, AL
Primary Contact: Diana C. Hanyak, Chief Executive Officer
CFO: Paula Redmond, Controller
CMO: Rodric Bell, M.D., Medical Director
CHR: JoAnn Roiz, PHR, Director Human Resources
Web address: www.tustinrehab.com
**Control:** Corporation, Investor–owned, for–profit **Service:** Rehabilitation

**Staffed Beds:** 48

**NEWPORT SPECIALTY HOSPITAL (052053)**, 14662 Newport Avenue, Zip 92780–6064; tel. 714/838–9600, (Nonreporting) **A**9 10
Primary Contact: Barbara Schneider, R.N., Chief Executive Officer
COO: Kara Bourne, R.N., Chief Nursing Officer and Chief Operating Officer
CIO: Darla Kennedy, Chief Information Officer
CHR: Aprille Major, Director Human Resources
Web address: www.newportspecialtyhospital.com/
**Control:** Corporation, Investor–owned, for–profit **Service:** Long–Term Acute Care hospital

**Staffed Beds:** 42

## TWENTYNINE PALMS—San Bernardino County

⊞ **ROBERT E. BUSH NAVAL HOSPITAL**, 1145 Sturgis Road, Zip 92278, Mailing Address: Box 788250, MCAGCC, Zip 92278–8250; tel. 760/830–2190, (Nonreporting) **A**1 3 **S** Bureau of Medicine and Surgery, Department of the Navy, Washington, DC
Primary Contact: Captain Jay C. Sourbeer, Commanding Officer
CHR: Virginia Ward, Human Resources Officer
CNO: Captain Sandra Mason, MSN, Director Nursing Services and Senior Nurse Executive
Web address: www.med.navy.mil/sites/nhtp/Pages/default.aspx
**Control:** Navy, Government, federal **Service:** General Medical and Surgical

**Staffed Beds:** 29

## UKIAH—Mendocino County

⊞ **UKIAH VALLEY MEDICAL CENTER (050301)**, 275 Hospital Drive, Zip 95482–4531; tel. 707/462–3111 **A**1 5 9 10 **F**3 8 11 12 13 15 18 29 30 31 32 34 35 38 40 44 45 46 48 49 50 51 54 57 59 60 64 65 68 70 72 75 76 77 78 79 81 82 84 85 86 87 93 94 97 107 108 110 111 114 115 116 117 118 119 127 130 131 132 135 144 146 147 148 **S** Adventist Health, Roseville, CA
Primary Contact: Gwen Matthews, R.N., MSN, Chief Executive Officer
CIO: David Eastman, Site Director
CHR: Rebecca Ryan, Interim Director Human Resources and Employee Health
Web address: www.adventisthealth.org
**Control:** Church–operated, Nongovernment, not–for profit **Service:** General Medical and Surgical

**Staffed Beds:** 50 **Admissions:** 3707 **Census:** 33 **Outpatient Visits:** 204306
**Births:** 813 **Total Expense ($000):** 122401 **Payroll Expense ($000):** 41001
**Personnel:** 607

## UPLAND—San Bernardino County

⊞ **SAN ANTONIO COMMUNITY HOSPITAL (050099)**, 999 San Bernardino Road, Zip 91786–4920, Mailing Address: Box 5001, Zip 91785–5001; tel. 909/985–2811 **A**1 2 9 10 **F**3 8 11 13 15 17 18 20 22 24 26 28 29 31 35 38 40 45 46 49 50 54 57 59 60 61 64 65 69 70 72 74 75 76 77 78 79 80 81 82 83 84 85 86 87 89 91 92 93 94 107 108 110 111 114 115 118 119 121 123 124 130 132 146 147 148
Primary Contact: Harris F. Koenig, President and Chief Executive Officer
CFO: Wah Chung Hsu, Senior Vice President Finance
CMO: Jay Shah, M.D., President Medical Staff
CIO: Kamel Pandya, Director Information Services
CHR: Lynn Kelly, Vice President Human Resources
CNO: Liz Aragon, R.N., Vice President, Chief Nursing Officer
Web address: www.sach.org
**Control:** Other not–for–profit (including NFP Corporation) **Service:** General Medical and Surgical

**Staffed Beds:** 279 **Admissions:** 15590 **Census:** 151 **Outpatient Visits:** 213116 **Births:** 2253 **Total Expense ($000):** 280806 **Payroll Expense ($000):** 118557 **Personnel:** 1594

## VACAVILLE—Solano County

**CALIFORNIA MEDICAL FACILITY**, 1600 California Drive, Zip 95687; tel. 707/448–6841, (Nonreporting)
Primary Contact: Mary Lou Dunlap, Correctional Health Services Administrator
CMO: Raymond Andreasen, M.D., Chief Medical Officer–Inpatient
Web address: www.cya.ca.gov/visitors/fac_prison_cmf.html
**Control:** State–Government, nonfederal **Service:** Hospital unit of an institution (prison hospital, college infimary, etc.)

**Staffed Beds:** 215

⊞ **KAISER PERMANENTE VACAVILLE MEDICAL CENTER (050767)**, 1 Quality Drive, Zip 95688–9494; tel. 707/624–4000, (Nonreporting) **A**1 3 10 **S** Kaiser Foundation Hospitals, Oakland, CA
Primary Contact: Corwin N. Harper, Senior Vice President and Area Manager
Web address: www.kp.org
**Control:** Other not–for–profit (including NFP Corporation) **Service:** General Medical and Surgical

**Staffed Beds:** 64

**NORTHBAY VACAVALLEY HOSPITAL** See NorthBay Medical Center, Fairfield

---

**Hospital, Medicare Provider Number, Address, Telephone, Approval, Facility, and Physician Codes, Health Care System**

★ American Hospital Association (AHA) membership  ○ Healthcare Facilities Accreditation Program  ⇑ Center for Improvement in Healthcare Quality Accreditation
□ The Joint Commission accreditation  ◇ DNV Healthcare Inc. accreditation  △ Commission on Accreditation of Rehabilitation Facilities (CARF) accreditation

## VALENCIA—Los Angeles County

✠ **HENRY MAYO NEWHALL MEMORIAL HOSPITAL (050624)**, 23845 McBean Parkway, Zip 91355–2083; tel. 661/253–8000 **A**1 2 9 10 **F**3 7 8 9 11 15 17 18 20 22 24 26 28 29 30 31 34 35 38 40 41 43 45 49 50 54 55 57 59 60 64 70 72 74 76 77 78 79 81 82 84 85 86 87 90 93 94 98 99 100 101 102 103 104 105 107 108 109 110 114 115 118 119 130 132 135 146 147 148
Primary Contact: Roger E. Seaver, President and Chief Executive Officer
COO: John V. Schleif, Senior Vice President and Chief Operating Officer
CFO: C. R. Hudson, Senior Vice President and Chief Financial Officer
CMO: Richard Frankenstein, M.D., Vice President and Chief Medical Officer
CIO: Cindy Peterson, Vice President and Chief Information Officer
CHR: Mark Puleo, Vice President and Chief Human Resources Officer
CNO: Larry R. Kidd, R.N., Vice President and Chief Nursing Officer
Web address: www.henrymayo.com
**Control:** Other not–for–profit (including NFP Corporation) **Service:** General Medical and Surgical

**Staffed Beds:** 238 **Admissions:** 12457 **Census:** 151 **Outpatient Visits:** 102189 **Births:** 1319 **Total Expense ($000):** 244640 **Payroll Expense ($000):** 83242 **Personnel:** 1396

## VALLEJO—Solano County

✠ △ **KAISER PERMANENTE VALLEJO MEDICAL CENTER (050073)**, 975 Sereno Drive, Zip 94589–2441; tel. 707/651–1000, (Nonreporting) **A**1 3 5 7 10 **S** Kaiser Foundation Hospitals, Oakland, CA
Primary Contact: Corwin N. Harper, Senior Vice President and Area Manager
COO: Karen Grisnak, R.N., Chief Operating Officer and Assistant Administrator Quality Services
CFO: Joseph D'Angina, Area Finance Officer
CMO: Steven Stricker, M.D., Physician in Chief
CIO: Gale Austin–Moore, Director Area Technology
CHR: Sherri Stegge, Director Human Resources
Web address: www.kaiserpermanente.org
**Control:** Other not–for–profit (including NFP Corporation) **Service:** General Medical and Surgical

**Staffed Beds:** 287

✠ **ST. HELENA HOSPITAL–CENTER FOR BEHAVIORAL HEALTH (054074)**, 525 Oregon Street, Zip 94590–3201; tel. 707/648–2200 **A**1 9 10 **F**29 30 50 64 65 68 98 99 104 105 130 146 **S** Adventist Health, Roseville, CA
Primary Contact: Patricia Williams, Regional VP for Behavioral Medicine and Population Health
CFO: Edward A. McDonald, Chief Financial Officer
Web address: www.sthelenahospitals.org/location/center–for–behavioral–health
**Control:** Other not–for–profit (including NFP Corporation) **Service:** Psychiatric

**Staffed Beds:** 61 **Admissions:** 2404 **Census:** 54 **Outpatient Visits:** 4220 **Births:** 0 **Total Expense ($000):** 21841 **Payroll Expense ($000):** 10627 **Personnel:** 112

✠ **SUTTER SOLANO MEDICAL CENTER (050101)**, 300 Hospital Drive, Zip 94589–2574, Mailing Address: P.O. Box 3189, Zip 94590–0669; tel. 707/554–4444 **A**1 2 9 10 **F**3 8 11 13 15 18 26 29 30 31 34 35 40 45 49 50 55 57 59 64 68 70 74 75 76 77 78 79 81 84 85 86 87 100 107 108 110 111 114 118 119 120 121 123 124 130 132 146 **S** Sutter Health, Sacramento, CA
Primary Contact: John W. Boyd, PsyD, Chief Executive Officer
CFO: Cynthia van Hoff, Chief Financial Officer
CHR: Jean Willhite, Director Human Resources
Web address: www.suttersolano.org
**Control:** Other not–for–profit (including NFP Corporation) **Service:** General Medical and Surgical

**Staffed Beds:** 102 **Admissions:** 4098 **Census:** 44 **Outpatient Visits:** 64536 **Births:** 561 **Total Expense ($000):** 125849 **Payroll Expense ($000):** 43059 **Personnel:** 467

## VAN NUYS—Los Angeles County, See Los Angeles

## VENTURA—Ventura County

★ ◇ **COMMUNITY MEMORIAL HEALTH SYSTEM (050394)**, 147 North Brent Street, Zip 93003–2809; tel. 805/652–5011, (Includes COMMUNITY MEMORIAL HOSPITAL, 147 North Brent Street, Zip 93003–2854; tel. 805/652–5011; OJAI VALLEY COMMUNITY HOSPITAL, 1306 Maricopa Highway, Ojai, Zip 93023–3163; tel. 805/646–1401; Haady Lashkari, Chief Administrative Officer), (Total facility includes 66 beds in nursing home–type unit) **A**2 3 5 9 10 13 21 **F**3 8 11 12 13 15 17 18 19 20 22 24 26 28 29 30 31 32 34 35 40 45 46 47 48 49 53 54 57 59 64 65 66 68 70 71 72 74 75 77 78 79 81 82 83 84 85 86 91 93 97 104 107 108 110 111 115 118 119 126 127 128 130 131 132 144 145 146 147 148 **P**4 7
Primary Contact: Gary Wilde, President and Chief Executive Officer
COO: Adam Thunell, Chief Operating Officer and Vice President Operations
CFO: David Glyer, Vice President Finance
CMO: Stanley Frochtzwajg, M.D., Chief Medical Officer
CIO: Ron Sandifer, Chief Information Officer
CHR: Diany Klein, Vice President Human Resources
Web address: www.cmhshealth.org
**Control:** Other not–for–profit (including NFP Corporation) **Service:** General Medical and Surgical

**Staffed Beds:** 284 **Admissions:** 13172 **Census:** 202 **Outpatient Visits:** 483402 **Births:** 2965 **Total Expense ($000):** 311309 **Payroll Expense ($000):** 111388 **Personnel:** 1553

☐ **VENTURA COUNTY MEDICAL CENTER (050159)**, 3291 Loma Vista Road, Zip 93003–3099; tel. 805/652–6000, (Nonreporting) **A**1 3 9 10
Primary Contact: Kim S. Milstien, Chief Executive Officer
CMO: Bryan Wong, M.D., Medical Director
CIO: Terry Theobald, Chief Information Officer
CHR: Tim Rhyne, Personnel Officer
CNO: Susan Scott, Chief Nurse Executive
Web address: www.vchca.org
**Control:** County–Government, nonfederal **Service:** General Medical and Surgical

**Staffed Beds:** 160

☐ **VISTA DEL MAR HOSPITAL (054077)**, 801 Seneca Street, Zip 93001–1411; tel. 805/653–6434, (Nonreporting) **A**1 9 10 **S** Signature Healthcare Services, Corona, CA
Primary Contact: Mayla Krebsbach, Chief Executive Officer
COO: Sherri Block, Chief Operating Officer
CFO: Steve Ruths, M.D., Medical Director
Web address: www.vistadelmarhospital.com
**Control:** Corporation, Investor–owned, for–profit **Service:** Psychiatric

**Staffed Beds:** 87

## VICTORVILLE—San Bernardino County

★ ○ **DESERT VALLEY HOSPITAL (050709)**, 16850 Bear Valley Road, Zip 92395–5795; tel. 760/241–8000 **A**9 10 11 **F**3 13 15 18 20 22 24 26 29 30 31 34 35 37 38 40 45 46 49 50 51 56 57 58 59 61 64 65 68 70 79 81 82 85 107 108 111 114 115 119 126 129 130 135 144 146 148 **S** Prime Healthcare Services, Ontario, CA
Primary Contact: Fred Hunter, R.N., Chief Executive Officer
COO: Luis Leon, Chief Operating Officer
CFO: Martin Mansukhani, Chief Financial Officer
CIO: Sreekant Gotti, Director Information Systems
CNO: Patrick Reinhard, R.N., Chief Nursing Officer
Web address: www.dvmc.com
**Control:** Corporation, Investor–owned, for–profit **Service:** General Medical and Surgical

**Staffed Beds:** 110 **Admissions:** 9787 **Census:** 91 **Outpatient Visits:** 70759 **Births:** 938 **Total Expense ($000):** 113810 **Payroll Expense ($000):** 35263 **Personnel:** 686

☐ ○ **VICTOR VALLEY GLOBAL MEDICAL CENTER (050517)**, 15248 Eleventh Street, Zip 92395–3704; tel. 760/245–8691 **A**1 9 10 11 **F**3 8 11 15 29 30 34 35 40 46 50 57 59 68 70 73 75 76 81 89 96 107 111 115 130 144 148
Primary Contact: Suzanne Richards, R.N., M.P.H., FACHE, Chief Executive Officer
COO: Doreen Dann, R.N., Chief Operating Officer
CIO: Joe Archer, Chief Information Officer
CHR: Cesar Lugo, Director Human Resources
Web address: www.vvgmc.com
**Control:** State–Government, nonfederal **Service:** General Medical and Surgical

**Staffed Beds:** 101 **Admissions:** 3486 **Census:** 63 **Outpatient Visits:** 50661 **Births:** 1289 **Total Expense ($000):** 81571 **Payroll Expense ($000):** 37720 **Personnel:** 523

**CA**

**CA**

## VISALIA—Tulare County

⊞ △ **KAWEAH DELTA MEDICAL CENTER (050057)**, 400 West Mineral King Boulevard, Zip 93291–6263; tel. 559/624–2000, (Includes SOUTH CAMPUS, 1633 South Court Street, Zip 93277; tel. 559/624–6090) **A**1 5 7 9 10 **F**3 13 15 17 18 20 22 24 26 28 29 30 31 34 35 40 41 43 45 49 50 51 53 54 56 57 59 60 62 63 64 65 68 70 73 74 75 76 77 78 79 81 82 84 85 86 87 89 90 93 97 98 99 100 101 102 103 104 107 108 110 111 114 116 117 118 119 123 124 126 127 128 129 130 131 132 134 135 144 146 147 148 **P**7
Primary Contact: Lindsay K. Mann, Chief Executive Officer
COO: Thomas J. Rayner, Senior Vice President and Chief Operating Officer
CFO: Gary Herbst, Senior Vice President and Chief Financial Officer
CMO: James Paskert, M.D., Vice President Chief Medical and Quality Officer
CIO: Mike Mistretta, Vice President and Chief Information Officer
CNO: Regina Sawyer, Vice President Chief Nursing Officer
Web address: www.kaweahdelta.org
**Control:** Hospital district or authority, Government, nonfederal **Service:** General Medical and Surgical

**Staffed Beds:** 421 **Admissions:** 22336 **Census:** 363 **Outpatient Visits:** 599397 **Births:** 4264 **Total Expense ($000):** 464779 **Payroll Expense ($000):** 196486 **Personnel:** 3209

## WALNUT CREEK—Contra Costa County

⊞ △ **JOHN MUIR MEDICAL CENTER, WALNUT CREEK (050180)**, 1601 Ygnacio Valley Road, Zip 94598–3194; tel. 925/939–3000 **A**1 2 7 9 10 **F**3 11 13 15 17 18 19 20 22 24 26 28 29 30 31 32 34 35 37 39 40 43 44 45 46 47 48 49 50 54 55 56 57 58 59 61 62 64 65 68 70 72 74 75 76 77 78 79 80 81 82 83 84 85 86 87 88 89 90 93 96 100 102 108 110 118 119 120 121 123 124 126 130 131 132 135 141 145 146 147 148 **P**3 5 **S** John Muir Health, Walnut Creek, CA
Primary Contact: Jane Willemsen, Chief Administrative Officer
COO: Raymond Nassief, Senior Vice President Operations and Clinical Transformation
CFO: Michael Moody, Senior Vice President and Chief Financial Officer
CMO: Irving Pike, M.D., Chief Medical Officer
CIO: Jim Wesley, Interim Chief Information Officer
CHR: Alice A. Villanueva, Senior Vice President Human Resources
CNO: Debra Pendergast, Senior Vice President Patient Care Services and Chief Nursing Officer
Web address: www.jmmdhs.com/index.php/jmmdhs_jmmc.html
**Control:** Other not–for–profit (including NFP Corporation) **Service:** General Medical and Surgical

**Staffed Beds:** 383 **Admissions:** 17515 **Census:** 242 **Outpatient Visits:** 314508 **Births:** 2901 **Total Expense ($000):** 689217 **Payroll Expense ($000):** 242398 **Personnel:** 1950

⊞ **KAISER PERMANENTE WALNUT CREEK MEDICAL CENTER (050072)**, 1425 South Main Street, Zip 94596–5300; tel. 925/295–4000, (Includes KAISER FOUNDATION HOSPITAL, 200 Muir Road, Martinez, Zip 94553–4696; tel. 510/372–1000), (Nonreporting) **A**1 2 3 5 10 **S** Kaiser Foundation Hospitals, Oakland, CA
Primary Contact: Colleen McKeown, Senior Vice President and Area Manager
CFO: Yakesun Wing, Business Strategy and Finance Leader
CIO: Kevin Wheeler, Information Technology Leader
Web address: www.kaiserpermanente.org
**Control:** Other not–for–profit (including NFP Corporation) **Service:** General Medical and Surgical

**Staffed Beds:** 233

## WATSONVILLE—Santa Cruz County

⊞ **WATSONVILLE COMMUNITY HOSPITAL (050194)**, 75 Nielson Street, Zip 95076–2468; tel. 831/724–4741 **A**1 9 10 **F**3 11 13 15 18 20 29 34 35 40 45 49 50 51 57 60 64 68 70 72 74 76 77 79 81 87 89 93 97 107 111 115 119 130 144 146 148 **S** Community Health Systems, Inc., Franklin, TN
Primary Contact: Audra Earle, FACHE, Chief Executive Officer
CFO: Dennis T. Bynum, Interim Chief Financial Officer
CMO: Robert Weber, M.D., Chief Medical Staff
CIO: Sergio Nell, Director Information Systems
CHR: Jeri Gilbert, Director Human Resources
Web address: www.watsonvillehospital.com
**Control:** Corporation, Investor–owned, for–profit **Service:** General Medical and Surgical

**Staffed Beds:** 106 **Admissions:** 4733 **Census:** 47 **Outpatient Visits:** 65443 **Births:** 1331 **Total Expense ($000):** 119663 **Payroll Expense ($000):** 50334

## WEAVERVILLE—Trinity County

**TRINITY HOSPITAL (051315)**, 60 Easter Avenue, Zip 96093, Mailing Address: P.O. Box 1229, Zip 96093–1229; tel. 530/623–5541, (Total facility includes 26 beds in nursing home–type unit) **A**9 10 18 **F**3 11 29 30 34 40 45 57 62 64 81 107 114 119 127 128 130 133
Primary Contact: Stanley C. Oppegard, Chief Executive Officer
CFO: Kathy Walker, Chief Financial Officer
CMO: Donald Krouse, M.D., Chief of Staff
CIO: Jennifer Van Matre, Director Finance
CHR: Heidi Corrigan, Manager Human Resources
CNO: Judy Nordlund, R.N., Chief Nursing Officer
Web address: www.mcmedical.org
**Control:** Hospital district or authority, Government, nonfederal **Service:** General Medical and Surgical

**Staffed Beds:** 47 **Admissions:** 335 **Census:** 22 **Births:** 0 **Total Expense ($000):** 14220 **Payroll Expense ($000):** 6278 **Personnel:** 135

## WEST COVINA—Los Angeles County

☐ **DOCTORS HOSPITAL OF WEST COVINA (050096)**, 725 South Orange Avenue, Zip 91790–2614; tel. 626/338–8481, (Nonreporting) **A**1 9 10
Primary Contact: Gerald H. Wallman, Administrator
CFO: Kami Horvat, Chief Financial Officer
CMO: Nashat Ateia, M.D., Chief of Staff
CHR: Lourdes Meza, Coordinator Human Resources
CNO: Rita Lawrence, Director of Nursing
**Control:** Corporation, Investor–owned, for–profit **Service:** General Medical and Surgical

**Staffed Beds:** 51

## WEST HILLS—Los Angeles County, See Los Angeles

## WEST LOS ANGELES—Los Angeles County, See Los Angeles

## WESTMINSTER—Orange County

⊞ **KINDRED HOSPITAL–WESTMINSTER (052035)**, 200 Hospital Circle, Zip 92683–3910; tel. 714/893–4541, (Nonreporting) **A**1 9 10 **S** Kindred Healthcare, Louisville, KY
Primary Contact: Brooke Saunders, Administrator
CFO: Dale Wagner, Chief Financial Officer
Web address: www.khwestminster.com/
**Control:** Corporation, Investor–owned, for–profit **Service:** Long–Term Acute Care hospital

**Staffed Beds:** 109

## WHITTIER—Los Angeles County

⊞ **PIH HEALTH HOSPITAL–WHITTIER (050169)**, 12401 Washington Boulevard, Zip 90602–1099; tel. 562/698–0811, (Total facility includes 35 beds in nursing home–type unit) **A**1 2 3 5 9 10 **F**3 11 12 13 14 15 17 18 20 22 24 26 28 29 30 31 34 35 36 37 40 44 45 46 49 50 51 54 55 56 57 58 59 60 61 62 63 64 65 66 68 69 70 71 72 74 75 76 77 78 79 81 84 85 86 87 89 90 92 93 96 107 108 110 111 114 115 116 117 118 119 120 121 123 124 128 130 131 132 135 143 145 146 147 148 **P**3 5 **S** PIH Health, Whittier, CA
Primary Contact: James R. West, President and Chief Executive Officer
COO: Reanna Thompson, R.N., Chief Operating Officer and Chief Nursing Officer
CMO: Rosalio J. Lopez, M.D., Senior Vice President and Chief Medical Officer
CIO: Jason Fischer, Chief Information Officer
CHR: Sherri Hollingsworth, Chief Human Resources Officer
CNO: Reanna Thompson, R.N., Chief Operating Officer and Chief Nursing Officer
Web address: www.PIHHealth.org
**Control:** Other not–for–profit (including NFP Corporation) **Service:** General Medical and Surgical

**Staffed Beds:** 242 **Admissions:** 20374 **Census:** 242 **Outpatient Visits:** 274410 **Births:** 4219 **Total Expense ($000):** 494245 **Payroll Expense ($000):** 182202 **Personnel:** 2879

☐ **WHITTIER HOSPITAL MEDICAL CENTER (050735)**, 9080 Colima Road, Zip 90605–1600; tel. 562/945–3561, (Nonreporting) **A**1 9 10 **S** AHMC & Healthcare, Inc., Alhambra, CA
Primary Contact: Richard Castro, Chief Executive Officer
COO: Mary Anne Monje, Chief Financial Officer and Chief Operating Officer
CFO: Mary Anne Monje, Chief Financial Officer and Chief Operating Officer
CIO: Jay Geldhof, Director Information Systems
CHR: Martha Salado, Interim Director Human Resources
Web address: www.whittierhospital.com
**Control:** Corporation, Investor–owned, for–profit **Service:** General Medical and Surgical

**Staffed Beds:** 81

---

**Hospital, Medicare Provider Number, Address, Telephone, Approval, Facility, and Physician Codes, Health Care System**

★ American Hospital Association (AHA) membership
☐ The Joint Commission accreditation
○ Healthcare Facilities Accreditation Program
◇ DNV Healthcare Inc. accreditation
⇑ Center for Improvement in Healthcare Quality Accreditation
△ Commission on Accreditation of Rehabilitation Facilities (CARF) accreditation

## WILLITS—Mendocino County

☒ **FRANK R. HOWARD MEMORIAL HOSPITAL (051310)**, One Madrone Street,
Zip 95490–4298; tel. 707/459–6801 **A**1 9 10 18 **F**11 15 29 30 34 35 40 57
59 68 70 75 79 81 93 107 110 111 115 119 131 132 133 135 146 147 148
**S** Adventist Health, Roseville, CA
Primary Contact: Rick Bockmann, Chief Executive Officer
CFO: Chris Sauder, Chief Financial Officer
CMO: Kimberly Faucher, M.D., Chief Medical Officer
CIO: Nick Bejarano, Regional Marketing Manager
CHR: Darcy De Leon, Executive Director, Human Resources
CNO: Karen M. Scott, Vice President Patient Care
Web address: www.howardhospital.com
**Control:** Church–operated, Nongovernment, not–for profit **Service:** General
Medical and Surgical

**Staffed Beds:** 25 **Admissions:** 1496 **Census:** 16 **Outpatient Visits:** 34431
**Births:** 1 **Total Expense ($000):** 45072 **Payroll Expense ($000):** 18112
**Personnel:** 233

## WILLOWS—Glenn County

**GLENN MEDICAL CENTER (051306)**, 1133 West Sycamore Street,
Zip 95988–2745; tel. 530/934–1800, (Nonreporting) **A**9 10 18
Primary Contact: Barbara Rydgren, Administrator
CFO: John Lovrich, Chief Financial Officer
CHR: Deborah McMillan, Director Human Resources
Web address: www.glennmed.org
**Control:** Other not–for–profit (including NFP Corporation) **Service:** General
Medical and Surgical

**Staffed Beds:** 15

## WOODLAND—Yolo County

☒ **WOODLAND HEALTHCARE (050127)**, 1325 Cottonwood Street,
Zip 95695–5199; tel. 530/662–3961, (Nonreporting) **A**1 5 9 10 **S** Dignity
Health, San Francisco, CA
Primary Contact: H. Kevin Vaziri, President
Web address: www.woodlandhealthcare.org
**Control:** Other not–for–profit (including NFP Corporation) **Service:** General
Medical and Surgical

**Staffed Beds:** 111

## WOODLAND HILLS—Los Angeles County, See Los Angeles

## YREKA—Siskiyou County

☐ **FAIRCHILD MEDICAL CENTER (051316)**, 444 Bruce Street, Zip 96097–3450;
tel. 530/842–4121, (Nonreporting) **A**1 9 10 18
Primary Contact: Jonathon Andrus, Chief Executive Officer
CFO: Kelly Martin, Chief Financial Officer
CMO: David Della Lana, M.D., Chief of Staff
CIO: Joan Munson, Manager Information Systems
CHR: Joann Sarmento, Manager Human Resources
CNO: Kathy Shelvock, R.N., Assistant Administrator Patient Care Services
Web address: www.fairchildmed.org
**Control:** Other not–for–profit (including NFP Corporation) **Service:** General
Medical and Surgical

**Staffed Beds:** 25

## YUBA CITY—Sutter County

**FREMONT MEDICAL CENTER** See Rideout Memorial Hospital, Marysville

☐ **SUTTER SURGICAL HOSPITAL – NORTH VALLEY (050766)**, 455 Plumas
Boulevard, Zip 95991–5074; tel. 530/749–5700 **A**1 9 10 **F**3 26 29 30 34 37
57 64 68 74 79 81 85 86 111 146
Primary Contact: Shawndra Simpson, Interim Chief Executive Officer
CHR: Michelle Guina, Manager Human Resources
CNO: David Cooke, Chief Nursing Officer
Web address: www.sshnv.org
**Control:** Corporation, Investor–owned, for–profit **Service:** Surgical

**Staffed Beds:** 14 **Admissions:** 514 **Census:** 4 **Outpatient Visits:** 4706
**Births:** 0 **Total Expense ($000):** 20676 **Payroll Expense ($000):** 4933
**Personnel:** 74

*Many Facility Codes have changed. Please refer to the AHA Guide Code Chart.* © 2015 AHA Guide

# COLORADO

### ALAMOSA—Alamosa County

★ **SAN LUIS VALLEY HEALTH (060008)**, 106 Blanca Avenue, Zip 81101–2393; tel. 719/589–2511 **A**9 10 20 **F**3 7 11 13 15 29 30 31 33 40 43 45 53 70 74 75 76 77 78 79 81 85 93 107 108 110 111 114 119 129 130 131 133 146 147 148 **P**6 **S** San Luis Valley Health, Alamosa, CO
Primary Contact: Konnie Martin, Chief Executive Officer
COO: Patti Thompson, Chief Operating Officer
CFO: Shane Mortensen, Chief Financial Officer
CMO: Gregory McAuliffe, M.D., Chief Medical Officer
CIO: Chuck Laufle, Director of Information Services
CHR: Mandy Lee Crockett, Director Human Resources
Web address: www.slvrmc.org
**Control:** Other not–for–profit (including NFP Corporation) **Service:** General Medical and Surgical

**Staffed Beds:** 44 **Admissions:** 1919 **Census:** 15 **Outpatient Visits:** 123739 **Births:** 528 **Total Expense ($000):** 68610 **Payroll Expense ($000):** 34056 **Personnel:** 569

### ASPEN—Pitkin County

⊞ **ASPEN VALLEY HOSPITAL DISTRICT (061324)**, 401 Castle Creek Road, Zip 81611–1159; tel. 970/925–1120 **A**1 9 10 18 **F**3 7 8 10 13 15 18 28 29 31 34 35 40 43 57 59 64 68 70 75 76 77 78 79 81 82 85 86 87 89 93 94 107 108 110 111 115 118 119 131 132 133 135 144 146 148
Primary Contact: Daniel J. Bonk, Chief Executive Officer
CFO: Terry Collins, Chief Financial Officer
CMO: J. Christopher Beck, D.O., President Medical Staff
CIO: Ginny Dyche, Director Community Relations
CHR: Alicia Miller, Director Human Resources
CNO: Elaine Gerson, Chief Clinical Officer and General Counsel
Web address: www.avhaspen.org
**Control:** Hospital district or authority, Government, nonfederal **Service:** General Medical and Surgical

**Staffed Beds:** 25 **Admissions:** 1043 **Census:** 7

### AURORA—Adams County

⊞ **CHILDREN'S HOSPITAL COLORADO (063301)**, 13123 East 16th Avenue, Zip 80045–7106; tel. 720/777–1234, (Includes CHILDREN'S HOSPITAL OF COLORADO AT MEMORIAL, 1400 East Boulder Street, Colorado Springs, Zip 80909–5533; tel. 719/365–5000) **A**1 3 5 9 10 **F**3 11 12 13 14 17 19 21 23 25 27 28 29 30 31 32 34 35 36 38 39 40 41 42 43 44 45 46 48 49 50 53 54 55 58 59 60 61 64 65 66 68 71 72 74 75 76 77 78 79 80 81 82 84 85 86 87 88 89 91 92 93 95 96 97 98 99 100 101 102 104 105 106 107 108 111 114 115 116 117 119 126 129 130 131 132 134 136 137 138 139 141 144 146 147 148 **P**8
Primary Contact: Jena Hausmann, President and Chief Executive Officer
COO: Jena Hausmann, President and Chief Operating Officer
CFO: Jeff Harrington, Chief Financial Officer
CMO: Joan Bothner, M.D., Chief Medical Officer
CIO: Mary Anne Leach, Vice President and Chief Information Officer
CHR: Nita Mosby Henry, Vice President Human Resources
CNO: Kelly Marie Johnson, R.N., Senior Vice President Patience Care Services and Chief Nursing Officer
Web address: www.thechildrenshospital.org
**Control:** Other not–for–profit (including NFP Corporation) **Service:** Children's general

**Staffed Beds:** 486 **Admissions:** 18528 **Census:** 305 **Outpatient Visits:** 685046 **Births:** 146 **Total Expense ($000):** 873539 **Payroll Expense ($000):** 372071 **Personnel:** 5025

⊞ **KINDRED HOSPITAL–AURORA (062013)**, 700 Potomac Street 2nd Floor, Zip 80011–6844; tel. 720/857–8333, (Nonreporting) **A**1 9 10 **S** Kindred Healthcare, Louisville, KY
Primary Contact: Adolphe Edward, Market Chief Executive Officer
CMO: Eric Yaeger, M.D., Chief Medical Officer
CHR: Becky Small, Chief Human Resources Officer
CNO: Paul Green, Chief Clinical Officer
Web address: www.khaurora.com/
**Control:** Corporation, Investor–owned, for–profit **Service:** Long–Term Acute Care hospital

**Staffed Beds:** 37

⊞ **MEDICAL CENTER OF AURORA (060100)**, 1501 South Potomac Street, Zip 80012–5411; tel. 303/695–2600, (Includes MEDICAL CENTER OF AURORA NORTH, 700 Potomac Street, Zip 80011–6792; tel. 303/363–7200; SOUTH CAMPUS, 1501 South Potomac, Zip 80012; tel. 303/695–2600) **A**1 2 9 10 **F**3 8 11 13 15 17 18 20 22 24 26 28 29 30 31 34 35 37 39 40 42 43 45 46 47 48 49 53 54 56 57 59 63 64 68 70 72 74 75 76 77 78 79 81 82 84 85 86 87 89 92 98 103 107 108 110 111 114 115 117 118 119 126 129 130 132 135 146 147 148 **P**6 8 **S** HCA, Nashville, TN
Primary Contact: Ryan Simpson, Interim Chief Executive Officer
COO: Mary Berrigan, Chief Operating Officer
CFO: Bryce DeHaven, Chief Financial Officer
CMO: Dianne McCallister, M.D., Chief Medical Officer
Web address: www.auroramed.com
**Control:** Corporation, Investor–owned, for–profit **Service:** General Medical and Surgical

**Staffed Beds:** 303 **Admissions:** 14953 **Census:** 203

⊞ △ **SPALDING REHABILITATION HOSPITAL (063027)**, 900 Potomac Steet, Zip 80011–6716; tel. 303/367–1166, (Nonreporting) **A**1 7 10 **S** HCA, Nashville, TN
Primary Contact: Mark S. Deno, Chief Executive Officer
COO: Debbie Petersen, R.N., Chief Operating Officer and Chief Nursing Officer
CFO: Joyce Webber, Chief Financial Officer
CHR: Donna Greeley, Director Human Resources
CNO: Debbie Petersen, R.N., Chief Operating Officer and Chief Nursing Officer
Web address: www.spaldingrehab.com
**Control:** Partnership, Investor–owned, for–profit **Service:** Rehabilitation

**Staffed Beds:** 40

⊞ **UNIVERSITY OF COLORADO HOSPITAL (060024)**, 12605 East 16th Avenue, Zip 80045–2545; tel. 720/848–0000 **A**1 2 3 5 8 9 10 **F**3 4 5 6 8 9 11 12 13 15 16 17 18 20 22 24 26 28 29 30 31 33 34 35 36 37 38 40 43 44 45 46 47 48 49 50 52 53 54 55 56 57 58 59 60 61 64 65 68 70 71 72 74 75 76 77 78 79 81 82 84 85 86 87 90 91 92 93 94 96 97 100 101 102 103 104 107 108 110 111 113 114 115 117 118 119 120 121 123 124 126 130 131 132 134 135 136 137 138 139 140 141 142 146 147 148 **S** University of Colorado Health, Fort Collins, CO
Primary Contact: Elizabeth B. Concordia, Interim President and Chief Executive Officer
COO: Thomas Gronow, Chief Operating Officer
CFO: Barbara Carveth, Chief Financial Officer
CMO: Jean Kutner, M.D., Chief Medical Officer
CIO: Steve Hess, Vice President Information Services and Chief Information Officer
CNO: Carolyn Lucey Sanders, Senior Vice President Patient Services and Chief Nursing Officer
Web address: www.uch.edu
**Control:** Hospital district or authority, Government, nonfederal **Service:** General Medical and Surgical

**Staffed Beds:** 648 **Admissions:** 26966 **Census:** 449 **Outpatient Visits:** 927481 **Births:** 3015 **Total Expense ($000):** 1037783 **Payroll Expense ($000):** 361674 **Personnel:** 4911

### BOULDER—Boulder County

⊞ △ **BOULDER COMMUNITY HEALTH (060027)**, 1100 Balsam Avenue, Zip 80304–3496, Mailing Address: P.O. Box 9019, Zip 80301–9019; tel. 303/440–2273, (Includes BOULDER COMMUNITY FOOTHILLS HOSPITAL, 4747 Arapahoe Avenue, Zip 80303–1133, Mailing Address: P.O. Box 9047, Zip 80301–9047; tel. 720/854–7000) **A**1 2 3 5 7 9 10 **F**70 72 76 90 98
Primary Contact: Robert Vissers, M.D., Interim Chief Executive Officer
COO: Robert Vissers, M.D., Executive Vice President and Chief Operating Officer
CFO: Bill Munson, Vice President and Chief Financial Officer
CNO: Jacqueline M. Attlesey–Pries, R.N., Chief Nursing Officer, Vice President
Web address: www.bch.org
**Control:** Other not–for–profit (including NFP Corporation) **Service:** General Medical and Surgical

**Staffed Beds:** 167 **Admissions:** 7990 **Census:** 95 **Outpatient Visits:** 412684 **Births:** 1262 **Total Expense ($000):** 308257 **Payroll Expense ($000):** 129982 **Personnel:** 1764

**CO**

---

**Hospital, Medicare Provider Number, Address, Telephone, Approval, Facility, and Physician Codes, Health Care System**

★ American Hospital Association (AHA) membership
□ The Joint Commission accreditation
○ Healthcare Facilities Accreditation Program
◇ DNV Healthcare Inc. accreditation
⇑ Center for Improvement in Healthcare Quality Accreditation
△ Commission on Accreditation of Rehabilitation Facilities (CARF) accreditation

## BRIGHTON—Adams County

✖ **PLATTE VALLEY MEDICAL CENTER (060004)**, 1600 Prairie Center Parkway, Zip 80601–4006; tel. 303/498–1600 **A**1 5 9 10 **F**3 7 13 15 18 20 22 26 28 29 30 31 34 35 40 43 45 49 57 68 70 72 74.75 76 77 78 79 81 85 87 89 90 92 93 107 108 110 111 115 119 130 132 135 146 147 148 **P**5
Primary Contact: John R. Hicks, President and Chief Executive Officer
COO: Kurt Gensert, R.N., Vice President Operations
CFO: Harold Dupper, Chief Financial Officer
CMO: Kirk Quackenbush, M.D., Chief of Staff
CIO: Darrell Messersmith, Director Information Systems
CHR: Jackie J. Dunkin, Director Human Resources
Web address: www.pvmc.org
**Control:** Other not–for–profit (including NFP Corporation) **Service:** General Medical and Surgical

| | |
|---|---|
| **Staffed Beds:** 70 **Admissions:** 3090 **Census:** 26 **Outpatient Visits:** 70631 **Births:** 925 **Total Expense ($000):** 103772 **Payroll Expense ($000):** 37246 **Personnel:** 513 | |

## BRUSH—Morgan County

★ **EAST MORGAN COUNTY HOSPITAL (061303)**, 2400 West Edison Street, Zip 80723–1640; tel. 970/842–6200 **A**9 10 18 **F**3 11 15 28 29 34 35 40 43 45 50 53 57 59 64 68 75 77 79 81 85 93 107 115 119 127 130 132 133 148 **P**6 **S** Banner Health, Phoenix, AZ
Primary Contact: Linda Thorpe, Chief Executive Officer
CFO: Thomas Loff, Chief Financial Officer
CMO: Lawrence Schoelkopf, M.D., Chief Medical Officer
CIO: Michael S. Warden, Senior Vice President and Chief Information Officer
CHR: Gracie Ramos, Human Resource Generalist
CNO: Roberta Bean, R.N., Interim Chief Nursing Officer
Web address: www.emchbrush.com
**Control:** Other not–for–profit (including NFP Corporation) **Service:** General Medical and Surgical

| | |
|---|---|
| **Staffed Beds:** 19 **Admissions:** 466 **Census:** 6 **Outpatient Visits:** 25125 **Births:** 0 **Total Expense ($000):** 24616 **Payroll Expense ($000):** 11775 **Personnel:** 134 | |

## BURLINGTON—Kit Carson County

★ **KIT CARSON COUNTY HEALTH SERVICE DISTRICT (061313)**, 286 16th Street, Zip 80807–1697; tel. 719/346–5311 **A**9 10 18 **F**3 13 15 29 31 34 35 40 43 45 47 48 57 75 76 78 79 81 84 93 107 110 111 127 128 130 133 **P**6
Primary Contact: Myra L. Evans, Interim Chief Executive Officer
CMO: Bong Pham, Chief Medical Officer
CIO: Paul Velasco, IT Manager
CHR: Robin Konecne, Manager Human Resources
CNO: Kandi Kuper, Chief Nursing Officer
Web address: www.kcchsd.org
**Control:** Hospital district or authority, Government, nonfederal **Service:** General Medical and Surgical

| | |
|---|---|
| **Staffed Beds:** 19 **Admissions:** 379 **Census:** 4 **Births:** 84 **Total Expense ($000):** 15480 **Payroll Expense ($000):** 5756 | |

## CANON CITY—Fremont County

✖ **ST. THOMAS MORE HOSPITAL (060016)**, 1338 Phay Avenue, Zip 81212–2302; tel. 719/285–2000 **A**1 9 10 20 **F**3 8 11 12 13 15 29 30 34 35 40 43 51 53 57 59 64 66 69 70 75 76 77 79 81 82 85 86 87 89 93 97 107 108 110 111 119 127 128 129 131 132 133 135 146 147 148 **S** Catholic Health Initiatives, Englewood, CO
Primary Contact: Sheri Trahern, CPA, FACHE, Chief Executive Officer
COO: Dennis Bruens, Vice President Operations
CFO: Gwenyth Howard, Vice President Finance
CMO: Kern Low, M.D., Chief Medical Officer
CIO: Jillian Maes, Director Marketing and Public Relations
CHR: Janet Reedy, Manager Human Resources
CNO: Jodee Trainor, Chief Nursing Officer
Web address: www.stmhospital.org
**Control:** Church–operated, Nongovernment, not–for profit **Service:** General Medical and Surgical

| | |
|---|---|
| **Staffed Beds:** 55 **Admissions:** 1731 **Census:** 17 **Outpatient Visits:** 39615 **Births:** 240 **Total Expense ($000):** 39178 **Payroll Expense ($000):** 15972 **Personnel:** 363 | |

## CASTLE ROCK—Douglas County

✖ **CASTLE ROCK ADVENTIST HOSPITAL (060125)**, 2350 Meadows Boulevard, Zip 80109–8405; tel. 720/455–5000, (Data for 334 days) **A**1 10 **F**3 11 13 15 18 20 22 29 30 32 34 35 37 38 40 43 45 48 49 50 57 59 60 62 64 65 67 68 70 72 74 75 76 77 79 81 85 86 87 89 91 93 102 107 108 110 111 114 115 118 119 129 130 131 135 146 147 148 **P**6 **S** Adventist Health System Sunbelt Health Care Corporation, Altamonte Springs, FL
Primary Contact: Todd Folkenberg, Chief Executive Officer
CFO: Jeremy Pittman, Chief Financial Officer
Web address: www.castlerockhospital.org
**Control:** Church–operated, Nongovernment, not–for profit **Service:** General Medical and Surgical

| | |
|---|---|
| **Staffed Beds:** 48 **Admissions:** 1727 **Census:** 16 **Outpatient Visits:** 19465 **Births:** 333 **Total Expense ($000):** 179626 **Payroll Expense ($000):** 66032 **Personnel:** 321 | |

## CHEYENNE WELLS—Cheyenne County

★ **KEEFE MEMORIAL HOSPITAL (060043)**, 602 North 6th Street West, Zip 80810, Mailing Address: P.O. Box 578, Zip 80810–0578; tel. 719/767–5661 **A**9 10 20 **F**3 15 29 34 35 36 40 43 45 57 59 64 65 68 93 97 107 108 110 114 119 127 133 147 **P**6
Primary Contact: Virginia Hallagin, Chief Executive Officer
CFO: Stella Worley, Manager Revenue Cycle Team
CMO: Christine Connolly, M.D., Chief of Staff
CIO: Jeanne Moffat, Manager Information Technology
CHR: Karli Strobel, Director Human Resources
CNO: Jesse Smith, Director of Nursing
Web address: www.keefememorial.com
**Control:** County–Government, nonfederal **Service:** General Medical and Surgical

| | |
|---|---|
| **Staffed Beds:** 11 **Admissions:** 54 **Census:** 1 **Outpatient Visits:** 3252 **Births:** 0 **Personnel:** 48 | |

## COLORADO SPRINGS—El Paso County

☐ **CEDAR SPRINGS HOSPITAL (064009)**, 2135 Southgate Road, Zip 80906–2693; tel. 719/633–4114, (Nonreporting) **A**1 9 10 **S** Universal Health Services, Inc., King of Prussia, PA
Primary Contact: A. Elaine Crnkovic, Chief Executive Officer
CFO: Cynthia D. Deboer, Chief Financial Officer
CMO: Larry Shores, M.D., Executive Medical Director
CHR: Jessica McCoy, Director Human Resources
CNO: Jodi Mattson, Director of Nursing
Web address: www.cedarspringsbhs.com
**Control:** Corporation, Investor–owned, for–profit **Service:** Psychiatric

| | |
|---|---|
| **Staffed Beds:** 110 | |

✖ **HEALTHSOUTH REHABILITATION HOSPITAL OF COLORADO SPRINGS (063030)**, 325 Parkside Drive, Zip 80910–3134; tel. 719/630–8000 **A**1 10 **F**29 30 54 62 64 100 132 **S** HEALTHSOUTH Corporation, Birmingham, AL
Primary Contact: Stephen Schaefer, Chief Executive Officer
CFO: Stephanie Davis, Controller
CHR: Diana Crepeau, Director Human Resources
Web address: www.healthsouthcoloradosprings.com
**Control:** Corporation, Investor–owned, for–profit **Service:** Rehabilitation

| | |
|---|---|
| **Staffed Beds:** 56 **Admissions:** 1087 **Census:** 40 **Births:** 0 | |

✖ △ **MEMORIAL HOSPITAL (060022)**, 1400 East Boulder Street, Zip 80909–5599; tel. 719/365–9888 **A**1 2 7 9 10 **F**3 8 11 12 13 15 17 18 19 20 21 22 23 24 26 27 28 29 30 31 34 35 36 40 41 43 44 45 46 48 49 55 57 58 59 64 68 70 72 74 76 77 78 79 81 82 84 85 86 87 88 90 92 93 94 96 97 107 108 109 110 111 114 115 116 117 118 119 120 121 123 124 126 129 130 132 135 141 144 146 148 **P**6 8 **S** University of Colorado Health, Fort Collins, CO
Primary Contact: George E. Hayes, FACHE, President and Chief Executive Officer
CFO: Dan Rieber, Chief Financial Officer
CMO: Patrick O. Faricy, M.D., Chief Medical Officer
CHR: Jeffrey Johnson, Vice President
CNO: Michelle Smith, R.N., Chief Clinical Officer
Web address: www.uchealth.org/southerncolorado
**Control:** Other not–for–profit (including NFP Corporation) **Service:** General Medical and Surgical

| | |
|---|---|
| **Staffed Beds:** 448 **Admissions:** 19261 **Census:** 211 **Outpatient Visits:** 556671 **Births:** 4375 **Total Expense ($000):** 568378 **Payroll Expense ($000):** 235794 **Personnel:** 2800 | |

◇ **PEAK VIEW BEHAVIORAL HEALTH (064026)**, 7353 Sisters Grove, Zip 80923–2615; tel. 719/444–8484 **A**9 10 13 21 **F**98 **P**7 **S** Strategic Behavioral Health, LLC, Memphis, TN
Primary Contact: Lana Currance, R.N., MSN, Chief Executive Officer
Web address: www.strategicbh.com/peakview.html
**Control:** Corporation, Investor–owned, for–profit **Service:** Psychiatric

| | |
|---|---|
| **Staffed Beds:** 92 **Admissions:** 3456 **Census:** 75 **Outpatient Visits:** 0 **Births:** 0 | |

**CO**

*Many Facility Codes have changed. Please refer to the AHA Guide Code Chart.* © 2015 AHA Guide

⊠ △ **PENROSE–ST. FRANCIS HEALTH SERVICES (060031)**, 2222 North Nevada Avenue, Zip 80907–6799, Mailing Address: P.O. Box 7021, Zip 80933–7021; tel. 719/776–5000, (Includes PENROSE HOSPITAL, 2215 North Cascade Avenue, Zip 80907, Mailing Address: P.O. Box 7021, Zip 80933–7021; tel. 719/776–5000; ST. FRANCIS MEDICAL CENTER, 6001 East Woodmen Road, Zip 80923–2601; tel. 719/776–5000) **A**1 2 7 9 10 19 **F**3 5 11 12 13 14 15 17 18 20 22 24 28 29 30 31 34 35 36 38 39 40 41 42 43 44 45 46 47 48 49 50 52 53 54 55 56 57 58 59 61 62 64 65 68 70 71 72 74 75 76 77 78 79 81 82 84 85 86 87 89 90 91 93 96 97 99 100 101 102 103 107 108 110 114 115 118 119 120 121 123 124 126 127 129 130 131 132 135 144 146 147 148 **P**5 **S** Catholic Health Initiatives, Englewood, CO
Primary Contact: Margaret D. Sabin, President and Chief Executive Officer
COO: Andrea C. Coleman, Chief Operating Officer
CIO: Tanya Bell, Public Information Officer
CHR: James Humphrey, Vice President Talent Resources and Human Resources for South Side Operating Group
Web address: www.penrosestfrancis.org
**Control:** Church–operated, Nongovernment, not–for profit **Service:** General Medical and Surgical

**Staffed Beds:** 417 **Admissions:** 22735 **Census:** 256 **Outpatient Visits:** 162682 **Births:** 2930 **Total Expense ($000):** 417482 **Payroll Expense ($000):** 134189 **Personnel:** 2179

⊠ **SELECT LONG TERM CARE HOSPITAL – COLORADO SPRINGS (062016)**, 6001 East Woodmen Road, 6th Floor, Zip 80923–2601; tel. 719/571–6000, (Nonreporting) **A**1 9 10 **S** Select Medical Corporation, Mechanicsburg, PA
Primary Contact: Kent Helwig, Chief Executive Officer
CMO: Dave Call, M.D., Medical Director
CHR: Lisa Gayler, Director Human Resources
CNO: Jodie L. Green, Chief Nursing Officer
Web address: www.coloradosprings.selectspecialtyhospitals.com/
**Control:** Corporation, Investor–owned, for–profit **Service:** Long–Term Acute Care hospital

**Staffed Beds:** 30

### CORTEZ—Montezuma County

★ ◇ **SOUTHWEST MEMORIAL HOSPITAL (061327)**, 1311 North Mildred Road, Zip 81321–2299; tel. 970/565–6666 **A**9 10 18 21 **F**3 7 11 13 15 28 29 31 34 35 40 47 48 50 54 59 64 65 70 75 76 79 81 82 85 86 87 93 94 97 107 108 110 111 115 119 127 129 130 131 132 133 135 146 147 148 **P**1
Primary Contact: W. Kent Rogers, Chief Executive Officer
CFO: John Nadone, Chief Financial Officer
CIO: David Cabana, Director Management Information Systems
CHR: Jim Bob Wynes, Director Human Resources
CNO: Liz Sellers, R.N., Chief Nursing Officer
Web address: www.swhealth.org
**Control:** Other not–for–profit (including NFP Corporation) **Service:** General Medical and Surgical

**Staffed Beds:** 25 **Admissions:** 1150 **Census:** 9 **Outpatient Visits:** 51140 **Births:** 193 **Total Expense ($000):** 47568 **Payroll Expense ($000):** 22036 **Personnel:** 306

### CRAIG—Moffat County

⊠ **THE MEMORIAL HOSPITAL AT CRAIG (061314)**, 750 Hospital Loop, Zip 81625–8750; tel. 970/824–9411 **A**1 9 10 18 **F**3 7 11 13 15 18 29 31 32 34 35 40 43 45 49 50 51 57 59 68 70 75 77 78 79 81 85 86 87 91 93 97 102 107 108 110 111 112 114 119 129 130 131 132 133 135 146 147 148 **S** QHR, Brentwood, TN
Primary Contact: John Rossfeld, Chief Executive Officer
CFO: Tim Howard, Interim Chief Financial Officer
CMO: Scott Ellis, D.O., Chief Medical Officer
CIO: Jennifer Riley, Chief of Marketing and Business Development
CHR: Jill Spencer, Chief Human Resource Officer
CNO: Christopher Kalinowski, Chief Nursing Officer
Web address: www.thememorialhospital.com
**Control:** County–Government, nonfederal **Service:** General Medical and Surgical

**Staffed Beds:** 25 **Admissions:** 675 **Census:** 6 **Outpatient Visits:** 22817 **Births:** 131

### DEL NORTE—Rio Grande County

★ **RIO GRANDE HOSPITAL (061301)**, 310 County Road 14, Zip 81132–8758; tel. 719/657–2510 **A**9 10 18 **F**34 40 43 57 65 81 93 107 111 115 119 127 129 133 **P**6
Primary Contact: Arlene Harms, Chief Executive Officer
CFO: Greg Porter, Chief Financial Officer
CMO: Heidi E. Helgeson, M.D., Chief Medical Officer
CIO: Yael DeFaye, Director, Information Technology
CHR: Paula Warner–Pacheco, Chief Human Resources
CNO: Beverly Martinez, Director of Nursing
Web address: www.rio–grande–hospital.org/
**Control:** Other not–for–profit (including NFP Corporation) **Service:** General Medical and Surgical

**Staffed Beds:** 17 **Admissions:** 479 **Census:** 3

### DELTA—Delta County

⊠ **DELTA COUNTY MEMORIAL HOSPITAL (060071)**, 1501 East 3rd Street, Zip 81416–2815, Mailing Address: P.O. Box 10100, Zip 81416–0008; tel. 970/874–7681 **A**1 9 10 **F**3 11 13 15 28 29 30 31 34 40 43 45 50 57 59 62 70 75 76 77 78 79 81 85 87 93 107 108 110 111 114 115 119 124 127 129 146 147 148 **P**5 8
Primary Contact: Jason Cleckler, Chief Executive Officer
CFO: Bev Carlson, Chief Financial Officer
CMO: John P. Knutson, M.D., Chief Medical Staff
CIO: Mitch Van Scoyk, Manager Information Systems
CHR: Larry Vincent, Director Human Resources
Web address: www.deltahospital.org
**Control:** Hospital district or authority, Government, nonfederal **Service:** General Medical and Surgical

**Staffed Beds:** 49 **Admissions:** 1825 **Census:** 15 **Outpatient Visits:** 83460 **Births:** 241 **Total Expense ($000):** 64885 **Payroll Expense ($000):** 25043

### DENVER—Denver, Adams and Arapaho Coun Counties

⊠ **COLORADO ACUTE LONG TERM HOSPITAL (062012)**, 1690 North Meade Street, Zip 80204–1552; tel. 303/264–6900, (Nonreporting) **A**1 9 10 **S** LifeCare Management Services, Plano, TX
Primary Contact: Craig Bailey, MS, Administrator
Web address: www.lifecare–hospitals.com/hospital/colorado
**Control:** Corporation, Investor–owned, for–profit **Service:** Long–Term Acute Care hospital

**Staffed Beds:** 63

☐ **COLORADO MENTAL HEALTH INSTITUTE AT FORT LOGAN (064003)**, 3520 West Oxford Avenue, Zip 80236–3197; tel. 303/866–7066, (Nonreporting) **A**1 3 5 10
Primary Contact: Christopher D. Burke, Director
CFO: Sabina Genesio, Finance Officer for Institutes
CMO: Bruce Leonard, M.D., Medical Director and Chief of Psychiatry
CNO: Nancy Kehiayan, Director of Nursing
Web address: www.cdhs.state.co.us/cmhifl
**Control:** State–Government, nonfederal **Service:** Psychiatric

**Staffed Beds:** 297

⊠ **DENVER HEALTH (060011)**, 777 Bannock Street, Zip 80204–4507; tel. 303/436–6000 **A**1 3 5 8 9 10 **F**3 5 7 8 11 12 13 15 18 19 20 22 26 28 29 30 31 32 34 35 37 38 39 40 41 42 43 44 45 46 49 50 52 53 54 55 56 57 58 59 60 61 64 65 66 68 70 71 72 74 75 76 77 78 79 80 81 82 84 85 86 87 88 89 90 92 93 94 97 98 99 100 102 103 104 107 108 110 111 114 115 119 127 129 130 131 132 134 135 143 144 146 147 148 **P**6
Primary Contact: Arthur A. Gonzalez, Dr.PH, FACHE, Chief Executive Officer
COO: Stephanie Thomas, Chief Operating Officer
CFO: Peg Burnette, Chief Financial Officer
CMO: Thomas MacKenzie, M.D., Medical Director, Chief of Clinical Operations
CIO: Jeff Pelot, Interim Chief Information Officer
CHR: Greg Rossman, Chief Human Resource Officer
CNO: Kathy Boyle, R.N., Chief Nursing Officer
Web address: www.denverhealth.org
**Control:** Hospital district or authority, Government, nonfederal **Service:** General Medical and Surgical

**Staffed Beds:** 407 **Admissions:** 21858 **Census:** 295 **Outpatient Visits:** 901569 **Births:** 3314 **Total Expense ($000):** 855258 **Payroll Expense ($000):** 389402 **Personnel:** 5418

**CO**

---

**Hospital, Medicare Provider Number, Address, Telephone, Approval, Facility, and Physician Codes, Health Care System**

★ American Hospital Association (AHA) membership  ○ Healthcare Facilities Accreditation Program  ⇑ Center for Improvement in Healthcare Quality Accreditation
☐ The Joint Commission accreditation  ◇ DNV Healthcare Inc. accreditation  △ Commission on Accreditation of Rehabilitation Facilities (CARF) accreditation

**CO**

⊠ **KINDRED HOSPITAL–DENVER (062009)**, 1920 High Street, Zip 80218–1213; tel. 303/320–5871 **A**1 9 10 **F**1 119 130 148 **S** Kindred Healthcare, Louisville, KY
Primary Contact: Adolphe Edward, Market Chief Executive Officer
CFO: Tim Stecker, Chief Financial Officer
CMO: Eric Yaeger, M.D., Medical Director
Web address: www.kh–denver.com
**Control:** Individual, Investor–owned, for–profit **Service:** Long–Term Acute Care hospital

**Staffed Beds:** 68 **Admissions:** 430 **Census:** 5 **Outpatient Visits:** 0 **Births:** 0

⊠ **NATIONAL JEWISH HEALTH (060107)**, (Respiratory), 1400 Jackson Street, Zip 80206–2762; tel. 303/388–4461 **A**1 3 5 9 10 **F**3 9 11 12 18 20 28 29 30 31 32 34 35 36 44 45 46 47 48 50 53 54 55 57 58 59 61 62 64 65 66 68 70 74 75 77 78 84 86 87 89 90 93 96 97 98 99 100 101 104 107 108 111 114 115 116 117 118 119 127 129 130 132 134 135 143 145 146 147 **P**6
Primary Contact: Michael Salem, M.D., President and Chief Executive Officer
COO: Ron Berge, Executive Vice President and Chief Operating Officer
CFO: Christine Forkner, Executive Vice President and Chief Financial Officer
CMO: Gary Cott, M.D., Executive Vice President Medical and Clinical Services
CIO: Lots Pook, Chief Information Officer
CHR: Sarah Taylor, Chief Human Resources
CNO: Jeff Downing, R.N., Chief Nursing Officer
Web address: www.njhealth.org
**Control:** Other not–for–profit (including NFP Corporation) **Service:** Respiratory

**Staffed Beds:** 76 **Admissions:** 71 **Census:** 1 **Outpatient Visits:** 93918 **Births:** 0 **Total Expense ($000):** 219402 **Payroll Expense ($000):** 109380 **Personnel:** 1492

⊠ **PORTER ADVENTIST HOSPITAL (060064)**, 2525 South Downing Street, Zip 80210–5876; tel. 303/778–1955 **A**1 2 9 10 **F**3 4 5 8 11 15 17 18 20 22 24 26 28 29 30 31 34 35 36 37 38 40 44 45 46 47 48 49 50 53 54 55 56 57 58 59 60 63 64 65 68 70 74 75 77 78 79 81 82 83 84 85 86 87 90 91 92 93 94 96 97 98 100 101 102 103 104 105 106 107 108 109 110 111 112 114 115 116 117 118 119 120 121 122 123 124 126 129 130 132 135 138 139 141 142 146 147 148 **P**6 **S** Adventist Health System Sunbelt Health Care Corporation, Altamonte Springs, FL
Primary Contact: Morre Dean, Chief Executive Officer
COO: David Dookeeram, Chief Operating Officer
CFO: Andrew Gaasch, Chief Financial Officer
CHR: Oz Muller, Director Human Resources
CNO: Sharon H. Pappas, Ph.D., Chief Nursing Officer
Web address: www.porterhospital.org/poh/home/
**Control:** Church–operated, Nongovernment, not–for profit **Service:** General Medical and Surgical

**Staffed Beds:** 250 **Admissions:** 9608 **Census:** 132 **Outpatient Visits:** 60450 **Births:** 0 **Total Expense ($000):** 236872 **Payroll Expense ($000):** 80326 **Personnel:** 1139

⊠ △ **PRESBYTERIAN–ST. LUKE'S MEDICAL CENTER (060014)**, 1719 East 19th Avenue, Zip 80218–1281; tel. 303/839–6000, (Includes ROCKY MOUNTAIN HOSPITAL FOR CHILDREN, 1719 East 19th Avenue, Zip 80218–1235; tel. 720/754–1000; Maureen Tarrant, President and Chief Executive Officer) **A**1 2 3 5 7 9 10 **F**3 8 11 12 13 14 15 18 19 20 21 22 23 24 25 26 27 28 29 30 31 34 35 36 37 40 41 43 44 45 46 47 48 49 50 54 55 56 58 59 60 61 64 65 66 68 70 72 73 74 75 76 78 79 80 81 82 84 85 86 87 88 89 91 92 93 94 95 96 97 102 107 108 110 111 115 116 117 118 119 120 121 123 126 129 130 131 132 134 136 138 146 147 148 **P**2 4 6 **S** HCA, Nashville, TN
Primary Contact: Maureen Tarrant, Chief Executive Officer
CFO: Shari Collier, Chief Financial Officer
CMO: Steve Quach, M.D., Chief Medical Officer
CIO: Jason Brakenhoff, Director Information Services
CHR: Keri Moore, Vice President Human Resources and Support Services
CNO: Margaret Scheaffel, R.N., Chief Nursing Officer
Web address: www.pslmc.com
**Control:** Corporation, Investor–owned, for–profit **Service:** General Medical and Surgical

**Staffed Beds:** 399 **Admissions:** 11081 **Census:** 213 **Outpatient Visits:** 68989 **Births:** 1494

⊠ **ROSE MEDICAL CENTER (060032)**, 4567 East Ninth Avenue, Zip 80220–3941; tel. 303/320–2121 **A**1 2 3 5 9 10 **F**3 8 9 11 12 13 15 18 20 22 24 26 28 29 30 31 34 35 40 43 44 45 46 49 50 52 53 54 55 58 59 60 61 64 68 70 72 74 75 76 77 78 79 81 82 84 85 86 87 91 92 93 94 97 100 101 102 107 108 110 111 112 114 115 116 117 118 119 120 121 122 123 126 129 130 131 132 135 146 147 148 **P**6 8 **S** HCA, Nashville, TN
Primary Contact: Kenneth H. Feiler, Chief Executive Officer
COO: Ryan Tobin, Chief Operating Officer
CFO: Jac Connelly, Chief Financial Officer
CMO: Andrew Ziller, M.D., Chief Medical Officer
CIO: Dave Trevathan, Director Information Systems
CHR: Clarence McDavid, Vice President Human Resources
CNO: Lynne Wagner, R.N., Chief Nursing Officer
Web address: www.rosebabies.com
**Control:** Corporation, Investor–owned, for–profit **Service:** General Medical and Surgical

**Staffed Beds:** 262 **Admissions:** 12155 **Census:** 124 **Outpatient Visits:** 54835 **Births:** 3734 **Total Expense ($000):** 235060 **Payroll Expense ($000):** 85788 **Personnel:** 1014

⊠ **SAINT JOSEPH HOSPITAL (060028)**, 1835 Franklin Street, Zip 80218–1126; tel. 303/837–7111 **A**1 2 3 5 9 10 **F**3 8 11 12 13 15 18 20 22 24 26 28 29 30 31 34 35 37 40 43 45 46 49 50 55 58 60 63 64 66 68 70 71 72 74 75 77 78 79 81 82 84 85 87 93 107 108 110 111 115 116 117 119 120 121 123 124 126 130 145 146 **P**6 7 **S** SCL Health, Broomfield, CO
Primary Contact: Bain J. Farris, President and Chief Executive Officer
COO: Barbara A. Jahn, Chief Operating Officer
CFO: Buzz Binder, Vice President Finance
CMO: Shawn Dufford, M.D., Vice President Medical Affairs and Chief Medical Officer
CHR: William R. Gould, Vice President Human Resources
CNO: Mary Shepler, R.N., Vice President and Chief Nursing Officer
Web address: www.exempla.org
**Control:** Other not–for–profit (including NFP Corporation) **Service:** General Medical and Surgical

**Staffed Beds:** 400 **Admissions:** 17839 **Census:** 225 **Outpatient Visits:** 149597 **Births:** 4016 **Total Expense ($000):** 455497 **Payroll Expense ($000):** 155531 **Personnel:** 2372

**SELECT SPECIALTY HOSPITAL DENVER SOUTH** See Select Specialty Hospital–Denver

⊠ **SELECT SPECIALTY HOSPITAL–DENVER (062015)**, 1719 East 19th Avenue, 5B, Zip 80218–1235; tel. 303/563–3700, (Includes SELECT SPECIALTY HOSPITAL DENVER SOUTH, 2525 South Downing Street, 3 South, Zip 80210–5817; tel. 303/715–7373; George Welton, Chief Executive Officer) **A**1 9 10 **F**1 29 77 85 87 91 148 **S** Select Medical Corporation, Mechanicsburg, PA
Primary Contact: George Welton, Chief Executive Officer
Web address: www.selectspecialtyhospitals.com/company/locations/denver.aspx
**Control:** Individual, Investor–owned, for–profit **Service:** Long–Term Acute Care hospital

**Staffed Beds:** 22 **Admissions:** 238 **Census:** 17 **Outpatient Visits:** 0 **Births:** 0

⊠ △ **VETERANS AFFAIRS EASTERN COLORADO HEALTH CARE SYSTEM**, 1055 Clermont Street, Zip 80220–3877; tel. 303/399–8020, (Total facility includes 100 beds in nursing home–type unit) **A**1 3 5 7 **F**3 18 20 22 24 26 29 30 31 35 36 38 39 40 44 45 47 48 49 50 53 54 55 56 57 58 59 60 61 62 63 64 65 68 70 74 75 77 78 79 80 81 82 83 84 85 87 90 91 92 93 94 95 96 97 98 100 101 102 103 104 106 107 108 111 114 115 119 126 127 128 129 130 132 135 144 146 147 148 **S** Department of Veterans Affairs, Washington, DC
Primary Contact: Lynette A. Roff, Director
CFO: Eliott R. Vanderstek, Chief Fiscal Service
CMO: Ellen Mangione, M.D., Chief of Staff
CIO: Don Huckaby, Chief Information Management Service
CHR: Lorene Connel, Chief Human Resources Management Service
Web address: www.denver.va.gov/
**Control:** Veterans Affairs, Government, federal **Service:** General Medical and Surgical

**Staffed Beds:** 271 **Admissions:** 5899 **Census:** 99 **Births:** 0

**DURANGO—La Plata County**

**ANIMAS SURGICAL HOSPITAL (060117)**, 575 Rivergate Lane, Zip 81301–7487; tel. 970/247–3537, (Nonreporting) **A**9 10
Primary Contact: Brett Gosney, Chief Executive Officer
Web address: www.animassurgical.com/
**Control:** Corporation, Investor–owned, for–profit **Service:** Surgical

**Staffed Beds:** 12

⊠ **MERCY REGIONAL MEDICAL CENTER (060013)**, 1010 Three Springs Boulevard, Zip 81301–8296; tel. 970/247–4311 **A**1 2 9 10 20 **F**11 13 15 17 18 20 22 24 26 27 28 29 30 31 35 36 40 42 43 45 49 50 59 60 61 66 70 72 73 76 78 79 81 84 85 87 89 94 96 97 107 111 115 119 126 127 129 130 131 132 133 135 146 147 148 **P**6 **S** Catholic Health Initiatives, Englewood, CO
Primary Contact: Thomas Gessel, FACHE, President and Chief Executive Officer
COO: William McConnell, Ph.D., Vice President Operations and Strategic Outreach
CFO: Jane Strobel, Vice President and Chief Financial Officer
CMO: William Plauth, M.D., Vice President Operations and Chief Medical Officer
CIO: Neil Stock, Director Technology and Facilities
CHR: Cathy Roberts, Vice President Mission Integration and Human Resources
CNO: Nancy Hoyt, R.N., Vice President Operations/Clinical and Chief Nursing Officer
Web address: www.mercydurango.org
**Control:** Church–operated, Nongovernment, not–for profit **Service:** General Medical and Surgical

**Staffed Beds:** 82 **Admissions:** 4180 **Census:** 37 **Outpatient Visits:** 116301 **Births:** 930 **Total Expense ($000):** 110450 **Payroll Expense ($000):** 38342 **Personnel:** 901

*Many Facility Codes have changed. Please refer to the AHA Guide Code Chart.*        © 2015 AHA Guide

## EADS—Kiowa County

★ **WEISBROD MEMORIAL COUNTY HOSPITAL (061300)**, 1208 Luther Street, Zip 81036, Mailing Address: P.O. Box 817, Zip 81036–0817; tel. 719/438–5401 **A**9 10 18 **F**7 29 30 34 40 57 59 64 75 82 87 93 96 97 127 133 135 143 148
Primary Contact: Tristen Sheridan, Chief Executive Officer and Administrator
CFO: Shannon Dixon, Manager Business Office
CMO: Jeff Waggoner, M.D., Chief of Staff
CHR: Shannon Dixon, Manager Business Office
CNO: Wendy McDowell, R.N., Director of Nursing
Web address: www.kchd.org
**Control:** Hospital district or authority, Government, nonfederal **Service:** General Medical and Surgical

| | |
|---|---|
| **Staffed Beds:** 25 **Admissions:** 108 **Census:** 1 **Outpatient Visits:** 8148 **Births:** 0 | |

## ENGLEWOOD—Arapahoe County

⊞ **CRAIG HOSPITAL (062011)**, 3425 South Clarkson Street, Zip 80113–2899; tel. 303/789–8000 **A**1 3 5 9 10 **F**29 30 34 35 36 44 50 53 58 64 68 74 75 77 81 86 87 90 91 93 95 96 97 100 104 130 132 146 148
Primary Contact: Michael L. Fordyce, President and Chief Executive Officer
COO: Dana Polonsky, Vice President of Clinical Services
CFO: Julie Keegan, Vice President Finance
CMO: Thomas E. Balazy, M.D., Medical Director
CIO: Chris Watkins, Director of Information Technology
CHR: Stacy L. Abel, Director Human Resources
CNO: Diane Reinhard, R.N., Vice President of Patient Care Services
Web address: www.craighospital.org
**Control:** Other not–for–profit (including NFP Corporation) **Service:** Rehabilitation

| | |
|---|---|
| **Staffed Beds:** 87 **Admissions:** 519 **Census:** 75 **Outpatient Visits:** 9761 **Births:** 0 **Total Expense ($000):** 76900 **Payroll Expense ($000):** 37299 **Personnel:** 591 | |

⊞ **SWEDISH MEDICAL CENTER (060034)**, 501 East Hampden Avenue, Zip 80113–2702; tel. 303/788–5000 **A**1 2 3 5 9 10 13 **F**3 7 8 11 12 13 15 18 20 22 24 26 29 30 31 34 35 38 39 40 42 43 44 45 47 48 49 50 53 55 57 58 59 60 64 66 68 70 72 73 74 75 76 77 78 79 81 82 84 85 86 87 88 89 90 92 97 102 107 108 109 111 114 115 116 117 118 119 120 121 122 123 124 126 129 130 131 132 146 147 148 **P**8 **S** HCA, Nashville, TN
Primary Contact: Mary M. White, Chief Executive Officer
COO: Daniel Miller, Chief Operating Officer
CFO: Kathy Ashenfelter, Chief Financial Officer
CMO: Paul Hancock, M.D., Chief Medical Officer
CIO: Jeff Schnoor, Director Information Systems
CHR: Lisa Morris, Vice President Human Resources
CNO: Shari Chavez, Chief Nursing Officer
Web address: www.swedishhospital.com
**Control:** Partnership, Investor–owned, for–profit **Service:** General Medical and Surgical

| | |
|---|---|
| **Staffed Beds:** 363 **Admissions:** 20384 **Census:** 268 **Outpatient Visits:** 137546 **Births:** 2121 **Personnel:** 1707 | |

## ESTES PARK—Larimer County

★ **ESTES PARK MEDICAL CENTER (061312)**, 555 Prospect Avenue, Zip 80517–6312, Mailing Address: P.O. Box 2740, Zip 80517–2740; tel. 970/586–2317, (Nonreporting) **A**9 10 18
Primary Contact: Brian J. Herwig, Chief Executive Officer
CFO: Ryan White, Chief Financial Officer
CMO: Paul Fonken, M.D., Chief of Staff
CIO: Gary Hall, Vice President of Information Technology
CHR: Charles Frye, Director Human Resources
CNO: Cynthia Standlee, R.N., Chief Nursing Officer
Web address: www.epmedcenter.com
**Control:** Hospital district or authority, Government, nonfederal **Service:** General Medical and Surgical

| | |
|---|---|
| **Staffed Beds:** 68 | |

## FORT CARSON—El Paso County

⊞ **EVANS U. S. ARMY COMMUNITY HOSPITAL**, 1650 Cochrane Circle, Building 7500, Zip 80913–4613; tel. 719/526–7200 **A**1 3 9 **F**3 7 8 11 12 15 18 29 30 32 33 34 35 36 38 40 44 45 46 47 48 49 50 51 53 54 56 57 58 59 64 65 68 70 74 75 76 77 79 81 82 85 86 87 91 92 93 94 96 97 98 99 100 101 102 104 105 107 110 111 115 118 119 126 129 130 132 134 135 143 146 147 148 **P**6 **S** Department of the Army, Office of the Surgeon General, Falls Church, VA
Primary Contact: Colonel Dennis P. LeMaster, Commander
CFO: Major Bradley Robinson, Chief Financial Officer
CHR: Lieutenant Colonel Lory Gurr, Chief Human Resources Division
Web address: www.evans.amedd.army.mil
**Control:** Army, Government, federal **Service:** General Medical and Surgical

| | |
|---|---|
| **Staffed Beds:** 69 **Admissions:** 4629 **Census:** 28 **Outpatient Visits:** 887814 **Births:** 2035 **Total Expense ($000):** 233128 **Payroll Expense ($000):** 92592 **Personnel:** 2049 | |

## FORT COLLINS—Larimer County

★ **BANNER FORT COLLINS MEDICAL CENTER**, 4700 Lady Moon Drive, Zip 80528–4426; tel. 970/229–4000, (Nonreporting) **S** Banner Health, Phoenix, AZ
Primary Contact: Rick Sutton, Chief Executive Officer Northern Colorado
COO: Marilyn Fain, R.N., Chief Operating Officer
CFO: Lori Sehrt, Associate Chief Financial Officer Northern Colorado
CMO: Bert Honea, M.D., Associate Chief Medical Officer Northern Colorado
CHR: Kelly Hurt, Chief Human Resources Officer Northern Colorado and Western Region
CNO: Roberta Bean, R.N., Associate Chief Nursing Officer
Web address: www.bannerhealth.com/Locations/Colorado/Banner+Fort+Collins+Medical+Center
**Control:** Other not–for–profit (including NFP Corporation) **Service:** General Medical and Surgical

| | |
|---|---|
| **Staffed Beds:** 24 | |

⊞ **POUDRE VALLEY HOSPITAL (060010)**, 1024 South Lemay Avenue, Zip 80524–3998; tel. 970/495–7000, (Includes MOUNTAIN CREST HOSPITAL, 4601 Corbett Drive, Zip 80525; tel. 970/270–4800) **A**1 2 3 5 9 10 19 **F**3 5 7 11 12 13 14 15 18 20 22 28 29 30 31 32 34 35 38 39 40 43 44 45 46 47 48 49 50 53 54 55 57 58 59 60 61 64 65 66 68 69 70 72 73 74 75 76 77 78 79 80 81 82 84 85 86 87 89 92 93 98 99 100 101 102 103 104 105 106 107 108 110 111 114 115 118 119 120 121 123 124 126 129 130 131 132 134 135 143 146 147 148 **P**5 6 **S** University of Colorado Health, Fort Collins, CO
Primary Contact: Kevin L. Unger, FACHE, President and Chief Executive Officer
CFO: Stephanie Doughty, Chief Financial Officer
CMO: William Neff, M.D., Chief Medical Officer
CIO: Fernando Pedroza, Vice President Information Technology
CHR: Anjanette Mosebar, Director Human Resources
CNO: Donna D. Poduska, MS, Chief Nursing Officer
Web address: www.uchealth.org
**Control:** Other not–for–profit (including NFP Corporation) **Service:** General Medical and Surgical

| | |
|---|---|
| **Staffed Beds:** 226 **Admissions:** 13404 **Census:** 128 **Outpatient Visits:** 269962 **Births:** 2388 **Total Expense ($000):** 385406 **Payroll Expense ($000):** 141268 **Personnel:** 1908 | |

## FORT MORGAN—Morgan County

⊞ **COLORADO PLAINS MEDICAL CENTER (060044)**, 1000 Lincoln Street, Zip 80701–3298; tel. 970/867–3391 **A**1 9 10 20 **F**3 11 13 15 28 29 31 34 35 40 43 44 45 46 47 48 50 51 53 56 57 59 62 64 65 70 75 76 77 79 80 81 86 87 89 93 94 97 98 100 101 103 104 105 107 108 110 111 114 119 129 130 131 133 146 147 148 **P**6 **S** LifePoint Health, Brentwood, TN
Primary Contact: Gene L. O'Hara, Interim Chief Executive Officer
CFO: Christina Patton, Chief Financial Officer
CHR: Janet Brinkman, Director Human Resources
CNO: Sonya Bass, MS, Chief Nursing Officer
Web address: www.coloradoplainsmedicalcenter.com
**Control:** Corporation, Investor–owned, for–profit **Service:** General Medical and Surgical

| | |
|---|---|
| **Staffed Beds:** 50 **Admissions:** 1558 **Census:** 20 **Outpatient Visits:** 40716 **Births:** 398 **Total Expense ($000):** 33059 **Payroll Expense ($000):** 13247 **Personnel:** 224 | |

**CO**

---

**Hospital, Medicare Provider Number, Address, Telephone, Approval, Facility, and Physician Codes, Health Care System**

★ American Hospital Association (AHA) membership
☐ The Joint Commission accreditation
◯ Healthcare Facilities Accreditation Program
◇ DNV Healthcare Inc. accreditation
⇑ Center for Improvement in Healthcare Quality Accreditation
△ Commission on Accreditation of Rehabilitation Facilities (CARF) accreditation

**CO**

### FRISCO—Summit County

⊠ **ST. ANTHONY SUMMIT MEDICAL CENTER (060118)**, 340 Peak One Drive, Zip 80443, Mailing Address: P.O. Box 738, Zip 80443–0738; tel. 970/668–3300 **A**1 9 10 **F**3 34 40 42 43 45 57 59 68 70 75 76 77 79 81 82 84 85 97 107 110 111 119 129 130 132 144 146 147 **S** Catholic Health Initiatives, Englewood, CO
Primary Contact: Paul J. Chodkowski, Chief Executive Officer
COO: Mary L. Henrikson, Chief Nursing Officer and Chief Operating Officer
CFO: David Thompson, Chief Financial Officer
CMO: Alan Dulit, M.D., Chief Medical Officer
CHR: Dana Laverdiere, Director Human Resources
CNO: Mary L. Henrikson, Chief Nursing Officer and Chief Operating Officer
Web address: www.summitmedicalcenter.org
**Control:** Church–operated, Nongovernment, not–for profit **Service:** General Medical and Surgical

**Staffed Beds: 34 Admissions: 1176 Census: 9 Outpatient Visits: 19304 Births: 339 Total Expense ($000): 40153 Payroll Expense ($000): 14862 Personnel: 214**

### FRUITA—Mesa County

★ **FAMILY HEALTH WEST (061302)**, 300 West Ottley Avenue, Zip 81521–2118, Mailing Address: P.O. Box 130, Zip 81521–0130; tel. 970/858–9871, (Total facility includes 90 beds in nursing home–type unit) **A**9 10 18 **F**3 6 9 10 15 29 34 35 39 40 41 43 45 49 50 56 59 64 65 66 68 74 75 79 81 82 85 86 87 90 91 93 107 110 111 115 119 124 128 130 132 133 135 143 146 147 148 **P**6
Primary Contact: Mark J. Francis, President, Chief Executive Officer and Hospital Administrator
CFO: Mark J. Francis, President, Chief Executive Officer and Hospital Administrator
CMO: Christopher Wibblesman, M.D., Chief of Staff
CIO: Patrick Yount, Director Information Services
CHR: Kelly Murphy, Director Human Resources
CNO: Lori Henderson, Chief Nursing Officer, Vice President Clinical
Web address: www.fhw.org
**Control:** Other not–for–profit (including NFP Corporation) **Service:** General Medical and Surgical

**Staffed Beds: 106 Admissions: 560 Census: 92 Outpatient Visits: 33244 Births: 0 Total Expense ($000): 35258 Payroll Expense ($000): 14267 Personnel: 274**

### GLENWOOD SPRINGS—Garfield County

⊠ **VALLEY VIEW HOSPITAL (060075)**, 1906 Blake Avenue, Zip 81601–4259; tel. 970/945–6535 **A**1 9 10 20 **F**3 4 11 13 14 15 18 20 22 28 29 30 31 32 34 35 36 40 43 45 49 50 51 54 57 58 59 68 69 70 74 75 76 77 78 79 81 85 86 87 93 104 107 108 110 111 114 115 117 118 119 120 121 123 124 126 129 130 131 132 135 145 146 147 148
Primary Contact: Gary L. Brewer, Chief Executive Officer
COO: Dewane Pace, Chief of Ancillary Operations
CFO: Larry L. Dupper, Chief Financial Officer
CMO: Al Saliman, M.D., Chief Medical Officer
CIO: Richard S. Escue, Director Information Technology
CHR: Daniel Biggs, Director Human Resources
CNO: Sandra Hurley, MS, Chief Nursing Officer
Web address: www.vvh.org
**Control:** Other not–for–profit (including NFP Corporation) **Service:** General Medical and Surgical

**Staffed Beds: 56 Admissions: 2810 Census: 29 Outpatient Visits: 102430 Births: 736 Total Expense ($000): 161560 Payroll Expense ($000): 66429 Personnel: 773**

### GRAND JUNCTION—Mesa County

⊠ ○ **COMMUNITY HOSPITAL (060054)**, 2021 North 12th Street, Zip 81501–2999; tel. 970/242–0920 **A**1 9 10 11 **F**3 8 12 15 29 30 34 35 40 47 48 49 50 57 59 62 64 70 75 77 79 81 85 86 87 93 97 107 108 110 111 114 115 119 129 130 131 132 144 146 147 148 **P**8 **S** QHR, Brentwood, TN
Primary Contact: Chris Thomas, FACHE, President and Chief Executive Officer
CMO: Donald Nicolay, M.D., Chief Medical Officer
CIO: Mike Kansgen, Director Information Services
CNO: Kristin Gundt, Chief Nursing Officer
Web address: www.yourcommunityhospital.com
**Control:** Other not–for–profit (including NFP Corporation) **Service:** General Medical and Surgical

**Staffed Beds: 42 Admissions: 1585 Census: 15**

⊠ **GRAND JUNCTION VETERANS HEALTH CARE SYSTEM**, 2121 North Avenue, Zip 81501–6428; tel. 970/242–0731, (Nonreporting) **A**1 **S** Department of Veterans Affairs, Washington, DC
Primary Contact: Marc Magill, Medical Center Director
COO: Patricia A. Hitt, Associate Director
CFO: Laquita Gruver, Fiscal Officer
CMO: William R. Berryman, M.D., Chief of Staff
CIO: Craig Frerichs, Chief Information Technology Service
CHR: William Chester, Manager Human Resources
Web address: www.grandjunction.va.gov/
**Control:** Veterans Affairs, Government, federal **Service:** General Medical and Surgical

**Staffed Beds: 23**

⊠ **ST. MARY'S MEDICAL CENTER (060023)**, 2635 North 7th Street, Zip 81501–8209, Mailing Address: P.O. Box 1628, Zip 81502–1628; tel. 970/298–2273 **A**1 2 3 10 **F**3 7 12 13 14 15 17 18 20 22 24 26 28 29 30 31 34 35 37 40 43 44 45 46 48 49 50 51 53 54 55 57 58 59 60 61 64 65 67 68 69 70 72 74 75 76 77 78 79 81 82 85 86 87 89 90 91 92 93 96 97 100 102 107 108 109 110 111 112 114 115 116 117 119 120 121 122 123 124 126 129 130 131 132 135 143 145 146 147 148 **P**6 **S** SCL Health, Broomfield, CO
Primary Contact: Michael J. McBride, FACHE, President and Chief Executive Officer
COO: Reza Kaleel, Executive Vice President and Chief Operating Officer
CFO: Terri Chinn, Vice President Finance
CIO: John Bullard, Director Information Technology
CHR: Judy White House, Vice President Human Resources
CNO: Shelley Peterson, R.N., Vice President Patient Services and Chief Nursing Officer
Web address: www.stmarygj.com
**Control:** Church–operated, Nongovernment, not–for profit **Service:** General Medical and Surgical

**Staffed Beds: 346 Admissions: 12599 Census: 173 Outpatient Visits: 199336 Births: 2101 Total Expense ($000): 330607 Payroll Expense ($000): 102753 Personnel: 1627**

**VETERANS AFFAIRS MEDICAL CENTER** See Grand Junction Veterans Health Care System

**WEST SPRINGS HOSPITAL (064023)**, 515 28 3/4 Road, Zip 81501–5016; tel. 970/263–4918, (Nonreporting) **A**9 10
Primary Contact: Sharon Raggio, President and Chief Executive Officer
CFO: Scott Miller, Chief Financial Officer
CMO: Jules Rosen, M.D., Chief Medical Officer
CHR: Karen Birmingham, Director Human Resources
CNO: Deborah Sharpe, RN, R.N., Director of Nursing
Web address: www.WestSpringsHospital.org
**Control:** Other not–for–profit (including NFP Corporation) **Service:** Psychiatric

**Staffed Beds: 32**

### GREELEY—Weld County

⊠ **NORTH COLORADO MEDICAL CENTER (060001)**, 1801 16th Street, Zip 80631–5154; tel. 970/352–4121 **A**1 2 3 9 10 **F**3 7 8 11 13 14 15 18 20 22 24 26 28 29 30 31 34 35 38 40 42 43 46 49 50 51 53 54 55 56 57 58 59 60 61 64 65 68 70 73 74 75 76 77 78 79 80 81 82 84 85 86 87 89 93 100 107 108 110 111 114 115 116 117 118 119 120 121 123 126 127 129 130 131 132 133 135 141 143 146 148 **P**6 8 **S** Banner Health, Phoenix, AZ
Primary Contact: Richard O. Sutton, Chief Executive Officer
COO: Wendy Sparks, Chief Operating Officer
CFO: Mary McCabe, Chief Financial Officer
CHR: Jeannie Gallagher, Chief Human Resource Officer
CNO: Tiffany Erin Hettinger, Associate Chief Nursing Officer
Web address: www.ncmcgreeley.com
**Control:** Other not–for–profit (including NFP Corporation) **Service:** General Medical and Surgical

**Staffed Beds: 225 Admissions: 11941 Census: 125 Outpatient Visits: 156820 Births: 1503 Total Expense ($000): 323170 Payroll Expense ($000): 96950 Personnel: 1692**

### GUNNISON—Gunnison County

⊠ **GUNNISON VALLEY HOSPITAL (061320)**, 711 North Taylor Street, Zip 81230–2296; tel. 970/641–1456, (Nonreporting) **A**1 9 10 18
Primary Contact: Robert J. Santilli, Chief Executive Officer
CFO: James P. Barbuat, Chief Financial Officer
CIO: Trevor Smith, Chief Management Information Services
CHR: Christina Lovelace, Director Human Resources
CNO: Lisa Loughran, Chief Nursing Officer
Web address: www.gvh–colorado.org
**Control:** County–Government, nonfederal **Service:** General Medical and Surgical

**Staffed Beds: 24**

*Many Facility Codes have changed. Please refer to the AHA Guide Code Chart.* © 2015 AHA Guide

## HAXTUN—Phillips County

★ **HAXTUN HOSPITAL DISTRICT (061304)**, 235 West Fletcher Street,
Zip 80731–2737; tel. 970/774–6123 **A**9 10 18 **F**7 40 43 54 59 64 65 75 87
97 107 114 119 133 146
Primary Contact: Larry E. Schrage, FACHE, Chief Executive Officer
CFO: Rick Lee Nader, Chief Financial Officer
CMO: Colby Jolley, D.O., Acting Chief of Staff
CIO: Andrea Evers, Director Information Technology
CHR: Randy Brigham, Director Human Resources
CNO: Gail Phelps, R.N., Chief Nursing Officer
Web address: www.haxtunhealth.org
**Control:** Hospital district or authority, Government, nonfederal **Service:** General
Medical and Surgical

**Staffed Beds: 25 Admissions: 44 Census: 22**

## HOLYOKE—Phillips County

★ **MELISSA MEMORIAL HOSPITAL (061305)**, 1001 East Johnson Street,
Zip 80734–1854; tel. 970/854–2241 **A**9 10 18 **F**3 7 15 28 29 34 35 40 43
45 50 57 59 64 68 75 77 81 84 85 93 97 107 110 111 114 119 127 129
133 146 148 **P**6
Primary Contact: Jim Murphy, Interim Chief Executive Officer
CFO: Melissa Prante, Chief Financial Officer
CMO: Dennis Jelden, M.D., Chief of Staff
CIO: David Bickford, Chief Information Officer
CHR: Sharon Greenman, Director Human Resources
CNO: Pat Notter, R.N., Chief Nursing Officer and Director Quality
Web address: www.melissamemorial.org
**Control:** Hospital district or authority, Government, nonfederal **Service:** General
Medical and Surgical

**Staffed Beds: 15 Admissions: 120 Census: 1 Outpatient Visits: 10993
Births: 0 Personnel: 94**

## HUGO—Lincoln County

**LINCOLN COMMUNITY HOSPITAL AND NURSING HOME (061306)**, 111 6th
Street, Zip 80821–0248, Mailing Address: P.O. Box 248, Zip 80821–0248;
tel. 719/743–2421, (Nonreporting) **A**9 10 18
Primary Contact: Kevin M. Stansbury, Chief Executive Officer
CFO: Patsy Shields, Chief Financial Officer
CMO: Mark Olson, M.D., Chief of Staff
CIO: Michael Gaskins, Director Information Technology
CNO: Dan Walker, Chief Nursing Officer
Web address: www.lincolncommunityhospital.com
**Control:** County–Government, nonfederal **Service:** General Medical and Surgical

**Staffed Beds: 50**

## JOHNSTOWN—Larimer County

☐ **NORTHERN COLORADO LONG TERM ACUTE HOSPITAL (062017)**, 4401
Union Street, Zip 80534; tel. 970/619–3663, (Nonreporting) **A**1 9 10 **S** Ernest
Health, Inc., Albuquerque, NM
Primary Contact: Lamar McBride, Chief Operating Officer
Web address: www.ncltah.ernesthealth.com/
**Control:** Partnership, Investor–owned, for–profit **Service:** Long–Term Acute Care
hospital

**Staffed Beds: 40**

⊠ **NORTHERN COLORADO REHABILITATION HOSPITAL (063033)**, 4401 Union
Street, Zip 80534–2800; tel. 970/619–3400 **A**1 10 **F**29 90 91 92 93 96 119
132 **S** Ernest Health, Inc., Albuquerque, NM
Primary Contact: Elizabeth Bullard, Chief Operating Officer
CFO: Ken R. Derrington, Chief Financial Officer
CMO: Indria S. Lanig, M.D., Medical Director
CHR: Jill Scanlon, Director Human Resources
CNO: Rhonda Carolus, Director of Nursing Operations
Web address: www.ncrh.ernesthealth.com
**Control:** Corporation, Investor–owned, for–profit **Service:** Rehabilitation

**Staffed Beds: 40 Admissions: 930 Census: 35 Births: 0**

## JULESBURG—Sedgwick County

**SEDGWICK COUNTY HEALTH CENTER (061310)**, 900 Cedar Street,
Zip 80737–1199; tel. 970/474–3323, (Total facility includes 52 beds in nursing
home–type unit) **A**9 10 18 **F**10 13 15 31 32 34 40 45 53 56 57 59 64 65 66
67 76 81 89 107 110 111 114 119 127 128 131 133 148 **P**6
Primary Contact: David Garnas, Chief Executive Officer
COO: David Garnas, Chief Executive Officer
CFO: Karla Dunker, Director Finance
CMO: Donald Regier, M.D., Chief Medical Officer
CHR: Sonja Bell, Coordinator Human Resources
**Control:** County–Government, nonfederal **Service:** General Medical and Surgical

**Staffed Beds: 67 Admissions: 153 Census: 51 Outpatient Visits: 13682
Births: 15 Total Expense ($000): 9085 Payroll Expense ($000): 4648
Personnel: 83**

## KREMMLING—Grand County

★ **MIDDLE PARK MEDICAL CENTER–KREMMLING (061318)**, 214 South Fourth
Street, Zip 80459, Mailing Address: P.O. Box 399, Zip 80459–0399;
tel. 970/724–3442, (Nonreporting) **A**9 10 18
Primary Contact: David Ross, Chief Executive Officer
COO: Trampas Hutches, Chief Operating Officer
CFO: Brendan Gale, Chief Financial Officer
CMO: Jason Stuerman, M.D., Chief of Staff
CIO: Trampas Hutches, Chief Operations Officer and Chief Information Officer
CHR: Jason Bryan, Director Human Resources
CNO: Carmen Covington, Chief Nursing Officer
Web address: www.mpmc.org
**Control:** Hospital district or authority, Government, nonfederal **Service:** General
Medical and Surgical

**Staffed Beds: 19**

## LA JARA—Conejos County

★ **SAN LUIS VALLEY HEALTH CONEJOS COUNTY HOSPITAL (061308)**, 19021
U.S. Highway 285, Zip 81140–0639, Mailing Address: P.O. Box 639,
Zip 81140–0639; tel. 719/274–5121 **A**9 10 18 **F**3 29 40 43 54 56 59 64 70
87 93 97 107 114 119 127 128 133 **S** San Luis Valley Health, Alamosa, CO
Primary Contact: Kelly Gallegos, Administrator
CFO: Shane Mortensen, Chief Financial Officer
CMO: Gregory McAuliffe, M.D., Chief Medical Officer
CIO: Kathy Rogers, Vice President Marketing
CHR: Mandy Lee Crockett, Director Human Resources
CNO: Tandra Dunn, Director of Nursing
Web address: www.sanluisvalleyhealth.org/locations/conejos–county–hospital
**Control:** Other not–for–profit (including NFP Corporation) **Service:** General
Medical and Surgical

**Staffed Beds: 17 Admissions: 115 Census: 1**

## LA JUNTA—Otero County

⊠ **ARKANSAS VALLEY REGIONAL MEDICAL CENTER (060036)**, 1100 Carson
Avenue, Zip 81050–2799; tel. 719/383–6000, (Total facility includes 99 beds in
nursing home–type unit) **A**1 9 10 20 **F**3 8 11 13 15 29 31 34 35 40 43 45 57
59 64 67 68 70 75 76 77 78 79 81 84 85 86 87 89 93 97 107 108 110 111
115 118 119 128 129 130 132 145 147 148 **P**6 **S** QHR, Brentwood, TN
Primary Contact: Lynn Crowell, Chief Executive Officer
CFO: Janette Bender, Chief Financial Officer
CMO: Michael Morley, M.D., Chief of Staff
CIO: Annette Cook, Application Support Specialist
CHR: Leigh Fitzpatrick, Director Human Resources
Web address: www.avrmc.org
**Control:** Other not–for–profit (including NFP Corporation) **Service:** General
Medical and Surgical

**Staffed Beds: 163 Admissions: 2053 Census: 77**

CO

**LAFAYETTE—Boulder County**

⊞ **GOOD SAMARITAN MEDICAL CENTER (060116)**, 200 Exempla Circle, Zip 80026–3370; tel. 303/689–4000 **A**1 2 9 10 **F**3 11 12 13 15 18 20 22 24 28 29 30 31 34 35 36 40 43 45 46 49 51 55 57 59 60 63 64 68 70 72 74 75 76 77 78 79 80 81 84 85 86 87 91 92 93 94 100 102 107 108 110 111 114 115 119 126 130 132 143 145 146 147 148 **P**6 **S** SCL Health, Broomfield, CO
Primary Contact: David Hamm, President and Chief Executive Officer
COO: Beth Forsyth, Chief Operating Officer
CFO: John Higgins, Vice President and Chief Financial Officer
CMO: Todd Mydler, M.D., Vice President and Chief Medical Officer
CHR: Amy Pacey, Vice President Human Resources
CNO: Susan Kerschen, MS, Vice President and Chief Nursing Officer
Web address: www.exempla.org
**Control:** Other not–for–profit (including NFP Corporation) **Service:** General Medical and Surgical

**Staffed Beds:** 183 **Admissions:** 12422 **Census:** 139 **Outpatient Visits:** 97392 **Births:** 2513 **Total Expense ($000):** 254001 **Payroll Expense ($000):** 82376 **Personnel:** 1099

**LAKEWOOD—Jefferson County**

☐ **ORTHOCOLORADO HOSPITAL (060124)**, 11650 West 2nd Place, Zip 80228–1527; tel. 720/321–5000, (Nonreporting) **A**1 9 10
Primary Contact: Jude Torchia, Chief Executive Officer
Web address: www.orthocolorado.org
**Control:** Partnership, Investor–owned, for–profit **Service:** Orthopedic

**Staffed Beds:** 48

⊞ **ST. ANTHONY HOSPITAL (060015)**, 11600 West Second Place, Zip 80228–1527; tel. 720/321–0000 **A**1 2 3 5 9 10 13 **F**3 7 11 12 17 18 20 22 24 26 28 29 30 31 34 35 36 40 43 45 46 47 48 49 50 53 56 57 59 64 65 68 70 74 75 76 77 78 79 81 82 84 85 87 90 92 93 96 97 102 107 108 111 114 115 116 117 118 119 120 121 123 124 126 129 130 132 133 134 135 146 147 148 **S** Catholic Health Initiatives, Englewood, CO
Primary Contact: Jeffrey Brickman, FACHE, President and Chief Executive Officer
COO: Patrick Green, Chief Operating Officer
CFO: David Thompson, Chief Financial Officer
CMO: Winston Tripp, II, M.D., Chief Medical Officer
CIO: Dana Moore, Senior Vice President Information Services
CHR: Michelle Fornier–Johnson, Group Vice President Human Resources
CNO: Cindy Parrott, R.N., Chief Nursing Officer
Web address: www.stanthonyhosp.org
**Control:** Church–operated, Nongovernment, not–for profit **Service:** General Medical and Surgical

**Staffed Beds:** 224 **Admissions:** 10708 **Census:** 157 **Outpatient Visits:** 77570 **Births:** 0 **Total Expense ($000):** 296101 **Payroll Expense ($000):** 90051 **Personnel:** 1503

**LAMAR—Prowers County**

★ **PROWERS MEDICAL CENTER (061323)**, 401 Kendall Drive, Zip 81052–3993; tel. 719/336–4343 **A**9 10 18 **F**3 11 13 15 18 20 28 29 31 34 35 40 45 50 56 57 59 62 64 65 66 68 78 81 85 86 93 97 107 111 119 127 130 133 146 147 148 **P**6 **S** QHR, Brentwood, TN
Primary Contact: Craig Loveless, Chief Executive Officer
COO: Karen Bryant, Chief Support Services Officer
CFO: Audrey Kane, Interim Chief Financial Officer
CMO: Barry Portner, M.D., Chief of Staff
CIO: Jason Spano, Manager Information Technology
CHR: Karen Bryant, Chief Support Services Officer
Web address: www.prowersmedical.com
**Control:** Hospital district or authority, Government, nonfederal **Service:** General Medical and Surgical

**Staffed Beds:** 25 **Admissions:** 894 **Census:** 9 **Outpatient Visits:** 43976 **Births:** 168 **Total Expense ($000):** 24051 **Payroll Expense ($000):** 10405 **Personnel:** 235

**LEADVILLE—Lake County**

★ **ST. VINCENT GENERAL HOSPITAL DISTRICT (061319)**, 822 West 4th Street, Zip 80461–3897; tel. 719/486–0230, (Nonreporting) **A**9 10 18
Primary Contact: Sam Radke, Interim Chief Executive Officer and Interim Chief Financial Officer
CFO: Sam Radke, Interim Chief Executive Officer and Interim Chief Financial Officer
CMO: Gary Petry, M.D., Chief of Staff
CHR: Cheryl Snider, Director Human Resources
CNO: Von Kilpatrick, Chief Nursing Officer
Web address: www.svghd.org
**Control:** Hospital district or authority, Government, nonfederal **Service:** General Medical and Surgical

**Staffed Beds:** 25

**LITTLETON—Jefferson County**

**FEDERAL CORRECTIONAL INSTITUTE HOSPITAL**, 9595 West Quincy Street, Zip 80123–1159; tel. 303/985–1566, (Nonreporting)
Primary Contact: Mike Hudson, Administrator
**Control:** Department of Justice, Government, federal **Service:** Hospital unit of an institution (prison hospital, college infirmary, etc.)

**Staffed Beds:** 6

⊞ **HEALTHSOUTH REHABILITATION HOSPITAL OF DENVER (063034)**, 1001 West Mineral Avenue, Zip 80120–4507; tel. 303/334–1100, (Nonreporting) **A**1 10 **S** HEALTHSOUTH Corporation, Birmingham, AL
Primary Contact: David H. Shefte, Chief Executive Officer
CFO: Liz Freudenberg, Chief Financial Officer
CMO: Jill Castro, M.D., Medical Director
CHR: Sarah Thomas, Director of Human Resources
CNO: Carol Anne Banville, Chief Nursing Officer
Web address: www.healthsouthdenver.com
**Control:** Corporation, Investor–owned, for–profit **Service:** Rehabilitation

**Staffed Beds:** 40

☐ **HIGHLANDS BEHAVIORAL HEALTH SYSTEM (064024)**, 8565 South Poplar Way, Zip 80130–3602; tel. 720/348–2800, (Nonreporting) **A**1 9 10 **S** Universal Health Services, Inc., King of Prussia, PA
Primary Contact: Paul Sexton, Chief Executive Officer
Web address: www.highlandsbhs.com
**Control:** Corporation, Investor–owned, for–profit **Service:** Psychiatric

**Staffed Beds:** 86

⊞ **LITTLETON ADVENTIST HOSPITAL (060113)**, 7700 South Broadway Street, Zip 80122–2628; tel. 303/730–8900 **A**1 2 5 9 10 **F**3 11 13 15 17 18 20 22 29 30 31 34 35 36 37 40 41 43 45 46 47 48 49 53 54 55 57 59 64 68 70 72 74 75 76 77 78 79 81 82 83 84 85 87 89 90 92 93 97 107 108 110 111 114 115 116 117 118 119 126 129 130 131 132 135 146 147 148 **P**6 **S** Adventist Health System Sunbelt Health Care Corporation, Altamonte Springs, FL
Primary Contact: Brett Spenst, Chief Executive Officer
COO: Geoff Lawton, Vice President Operations
CFO: Cheryl Curry, Chief Financial Officer
CMO: Lawrence Wood, M.D., Chief Medical Officer
CHR: Rita K. Arthur, Director Human Resources
CNO: Rhonda Ward, R.N., Chief Nursing Officer
Web address: www.centura.org
**Control:** Church–operated, Nongovernment, not–for profit **Service:** General Medical and Surgical

**Staffed Beds:** 201 **Admissions:** 9192 **Census:** 115 **Outpatient Visits:** 58343 **Births:** 1470 **Total Expense ($000):** 179626 **Payroll Expense ($000):** 66032 **Personnel:** 913

**LONE TREE—Douglas County**

⊞ **SKY RIDGE MEDICAL CENTER (060112)**, 10101 Ridge Gate Parkway, Zip 80124–5522; tel. 720/225–1000 **A**1 2 5 9 10 12 13 **F**3 8 12 13 15 17 18 20 22 28 29 30 31 34 35 36 37 40 41 43 45 46 47 48 49 54 59 64 70 72 73 74 75 76 77 78 79 81 82 84 85 86 87 89 93 97 107 108 111 114 115 119 120 121 123 126 129 130 131 132 135 146 147 148 **P**8 **S** HCA, Nashville, TN
Primary Contact: Susan Hicks, Chief Executive Officer
CFO: Craig Sammons, Chief Financial Officer
CMO: David Markenson, M.D., Chief Medical Officer
CIO: Evan Tice, Director Information Technology and Systems
CHR: Jim Ritchey, Director Human Resources
CNO: Marian Savitsky, R.N., Chief Nursing Officer
Web address: www.skyridgemedcenter.com
**Control:** Corporation, Investor–owned, for–profit **Service:** General Medical and Surgical

**Staffed Beds:** 275 **Admissions:** 13532 **Census:** 128 **Outpatient Visits:** 91434 **Births:** 3336 **Personnel:** 1022

CO

*Many Facility Codes have changed. Please refer to the AHA Guide Code Chart.* © 2015 AHA Guide

**LONGMONT—Boulder County**

✠ **LONGMONT UNITED HOSPITAL (060003)**, 1950 West Mountain View Avenue, Zip 80501–3162, Mailing Address: P.O. Box 1659, Zip 80502–1659; tel. 303/651–5111, (Total facility includes 15 beds in nursing home–type unit) **A**1 2 9 10 **F**2 3 11 13 15 18 20 22 28 29 30 31 34 35 36 37 39 40 43 44 45 47 49 50 53 54 56 57 59 61 64 68 70 73 74 75 76 77 78 79 81 82 84 85 86 87 89 92 93 107 108 110 111 114 115 118 119 121 123 126 128 129 130 131 132 135 146 148 **P**6
Primary Contact: Mitchell C. Carson, President and Chief Executive Officer
CFO: Neil W. Bertrand, Chief Financial Officer
CMO: Amy Johnson, M.D., Chief of Staff
CIO: Michael Jefferies, Vice President Information Systems
CHR: Warren Laughlin, Vice President Human Resources
CNO: Nancy Driscoll, R.N., Chief Nursing Officer
Web address: www.luhcares.org
**Control:** Other not–for–profit (including NFP Corporation) **Service:** General Medical and Surgical

**Staffed Beds: 146 Admissions: 7173 Census: 86 Outpatient Visits: 176085 Births: 1009 Total Expense ($000): 172990 Payroll Expense ($000): 69475 Personnel: 1074**

**LOUISVILLE—Boulder County**

✠ **AVISTA ADVENTIST HOSPITAL (060103)**, 100 Health Park Drive, Zip 80027–9583; tel. 303/673–1000 **A**1 9 10 **F**3 8 11 13 15 17 18 20 22 28 29 30 34 40 43 44 45 47 48 49 50 56 59 60 62 63 64 68 70 72 74 75 76 77 79 81 82 84 85 86 87 89 93 107 108 111 114 115 119 129 130 131 132 135 146 147 **P**4 6 **S** Adventist Health System Sunbelt Health Care Corporation, Altamonte Springs, FL
Primary Contact: Dennis Barts, Chief Executive Officer
CFO: Brent Davis, Chief Financial Officer
CMO: David Ehrenberger, M.D., Chief Medical Officer
CHR: Becky Ortega, Director Human Resources
Web address: www.avistahospital.org
**Control:** Church–operated, Nongovernment, not–for profit **Service:** General Medical and Surgical

**Staffed Beds: 114 Admissions: 4118 Census: 36 Outpatient Visits: 44526 Births: 1965 Total Expense ($000): 81052 Payroll Expense ($000): 32703 Personnel: 412**

☐ **CENTENNIAL PEAKS HOSPITAL (064007)**, 2255 South 88th Street, Zip 80027–9716; tel. 303/673–9990, (Nonreporting) **A**1 9 10 **S** Universal Health Services, Inc., King of Prussia, PA
Primary Contact: Elicia Bunch, Chief Executive Officer
COO: Lisa Strub, Chief Operating Officer
CFO: Tim Ryan, Chief Financial Officer
CMO: Konoy Mandal, M.D., Medical Director
CHR: Suzanne Martinez, Director Human Resources
CNO: Donia L. Andersen, Director of Nursing
Web address: www.centennialpeaks.com
**Control:** Other not–for–profit (including NFP Corporation) **Service:** Psychiatric

**Staffed Beds: 72**

**LOVELAND—Larimer County**

✠ **MCKEE MEDICAL CENTER (060030)**, 2000 Boise Avenue, Zip 80538–4281; tel. 970/669–4640 **A**1 2 9 10 **F**2 3 8 11 12 13 15 18 20 22 28 29 30 31 34 35 38 40 43 46 49 50 54 56 57 59 60 61 62 64 68 70 74 75 76 77 78 79 80 81 82 85 86 87 93 97 104 107 108 110 111 114 115 119 120 121 123 124 126 129 130 132 134 135 146 147 148 **P**1 6 **S** Banner Health, Phoenix, AZ
Primary Contact: Julie Klein, Chief Operating Officer
CFO: Lori Sehrt, Chief Financial Officer
CMO: Bert Honea, M.D., Medical Director
CIO: Steve Rains, Director Information Services
CHR: Jeannie Gallagher, jeanie.gallagher@bannerhealth.com
CNO: Kelly Sturler, Chief Nursing Officer
Web address: www.mckeeloveland.com
**Control:** Other not–for–profit (including NFP Corporation) **Service:** General Medical and Surgical

**Staffed Beds: 105 Admissions: 4350 Census: 34 Outpatient Visits: 89802 Births: 817 Total Expense ($000): 120774 Payroll Expense ($000): 35234 Personnel: 569**

✠ **MEDICAL CENTER OF THE ROCKIES (060119)**, 2500 Rocky Mountain Avenue, Zip 80538–9004; tel. 970/624–2500 **A**1 3 5 9 10 **F**3 8 11 13 14 15 17 18 20 22 24 26 28 29 30 31 32 34 35 38 39 40 42 43 44 45 47 49 50 54 55 57 58 59 60 61 64 65 68 70 74 75 76 77 78 79 80 81 82 83 84 85 86 87 89 90 91 92 93 96 100 107 108 110 111 114 115 118 119 126 129 130 131 132 134 135 143 146 147 148 **P**5 6 **S** University of Colorado Health, Fort Collins, CO
Primary Contact: Kevin L. Unger, FACHE, President and Chief Executive Officer
CFO: Stephanie Doughty, Chief Financial Officer
CMO: William Neff, M.D., Chief Medical Officer
CIO: Steve Hess, Vice President & Chief Information Officer
Web address: www.medctrrockies.org
**Control:** Other not–for–profit (including NFP Corporation) **Service:** General Medical and Surgical

**Staffed Beds: 166 Admissions: 9681 Census: 113 Births: 1144 Total Expense ($000): 289208 Payroll Expense ($000): 86103 Personnel: 1105**

**MEEKER—Rio Blanco County**

★ **PIONEERS MEDICAL CENTER (061325)**, 345 Cleveland Street, Zip 81641–3238; tel. 970/878–5047, (Includes WALBRIDGE MEMORIAL CONVALESCENT WING ), (Total facility includes 30 beds in nursing home–type unit) **A**9 10 18 **F**3 15 28 29 34 35 40 45 50 53 56 57 59 62 63 64 65 68 69 75 77 79 81 82 84 85 87 91 93 97 100 102 103 107 110 111 114 119 127 128 130 131 132 133 135 143 146 147 148 **P**6 **S** QHR, Brentwood, TN
Primary Contact: Kenneth Harman, Chief Executive Officer
COO: Drew Varland, Chief Nursing Officer and Chief Operating Officer
CFO: James W. Worrell, Chief Financial Officer
CMO: Albert Krueger, M.D., Chief of Staff
CIO: Curtis Cooper, Manager Information Systems
CHR: Twyla Jensen, Director Human Resources
Web address: www.pioneershospital.org
**Control:** Hospital district or authority, Government, nonfederal **Service:** General Medical and Surgical

**Staffed Beds: 40 Admissions: 151 Census: 22 Outpatient Visits: 10378 Births: 0 Total Expense ($000): 13433 Payroll Expense ($000): 6466 Personnel: 108**

**MONTROSE—Montrose County**

✠ **MONTROSE MEMORIAL HOSPITAL (060006)**, 800 South Third Street, Zip 81401–4212; tel. 970/249–2211 **A**1 3 9 10 20 **F**3 12 15 18 20 28 29 30 31 34 35 40 43 45 46 51 57 66 70 73 74 75 77 79 80 81 82 85 88 89 90 93 107 108 110 111 114 119 126 127 129 130 131 146 **S** QHR, Brentwood, TN
Primary Contact: Steven Hannah, Chief Executive Officer
COO: Mary E. Snyder, Chief Operations Officer
CFO: Stephan A. Wilson, Chief Financial Officer
CMO: Richard Shannon, M.D., Chief of Staff
CIO: Carlos Lovera, Director Information Systems
CHR: Kathy McKie, Director Human Resources
Web address: www.montrosehospital.com
**Control:** Other not–for–profit (including NFP Corporation) **Service:** General Medical and Surgical

**Staffed Beds: 69 Admissions: 2878 Census: 28 Outpatient Visits: 101903 Births: 445 Total Expense ($000): 82244 Payroll Expense ($000): 29153**

**PAGOSA SPRINGS—Archuleta County**

**PAGOSA SPRINGS MEDICAL CENTER (061328)**, 95 South Pagosa Boulevard, Zip 81147–8329; tel. 970/731–3700, (Nonreporting) **A**9 10 18
Primary Contact: Bradley Cochennet, Chief Executive Officer
**Control:** Other not–for–profit (including NFP Corporation) **Service:** General Medical and Surgical

**Staffed Beds: 11**

**PARKER—Douglas County**

✠ **PARKER ADVENTIST HOSPITAL (060114)**, 9395 Crown Crest Boulevard, Zip 80138–8573; tel. 303/269–4000 **A**1 2 9 10 **F**3 11 12 13 15 20 22 29 30 31 35 36 38 40 43 45 46 49 50 54 55 57 59 64 70 72 73 74 75 76 77 78 79 81 82 83 84 85 87 93 96 97 107 110 111 114 115 116 117 119 120 126 129 130 131 132 146 147 148 **P**6 **S** Adventist Health System Sunbelt Health Care Corporation, Altamonte Springs, FL
Primary Contact: Morre Dean, Chief Executive Officer
CFO: Andrew Gaasch, Chief Financial Officer
Web address: www.parkerhospital.org
**Control:** Church–operated, Nongovernment, not–for profit **Service:** General Medical and Surgical

**Staffed Beds: 145 Admissions: 6890 Census: 73 Outpatient Visits: 61048 Births: 1750 Total Expense ($000): 149190 Payroll Expense ($000): 50216 Personnel: 745**

CO

---

**Hospital, Medicare Provider Number, Address, Telephone, Approval, Facility, and Physician Codes, Health Care System**

★ American Hospital Association (AHA) membership
☐ The Joint Commission accreditation
◯ Healthcare Facilities Accreditation Program
◇ DNV Healthcare Inc. accreditation
⇑ Center for Improvement in Healthcare Quality Accreditation
△ Commission on Accreditation of Rehabilitation Facilities (CARF) accreditation

CO

## PUEBLO—Pueblo County

☐ **COLORADO MENTAL HEALTH INSTITUTE AT PUEBLO (060115)**, 1600 West 24th Street, Zip 81003–1499; tel. 719/546–4000, (Nonreporting) **A**1 3 5 10
Primary Contact: John R. DeQuardo, M.D., Superintendent
CFO: Jim Duff, Chief Financial Officer
CMO: Al Singleton, M.D., Chief Psychiatry and Chief Medical Staff
CIO: Eunice Wolther, Public Information Officer
CHR: Mary Young, Director Human Resources
Web address: www.cdhs.state.co.us/cmhip
**Control:** State–Government, nonfederal **Service:** Psychiatric

**Staffed Beds:** 514

☐ **HAVEN BEHAVIORAL WAR HEROES HOSPITAL (064025)**, 1008 Minnequa Avenue, Suite 6100, Zip 81004–3733; tel. 719/546–6000, (Nonreporting) **A**1 10
**S** Haven Behavioral Healthcare, Nashville, TN
Primary Contact: Carrin Harper, M.D., Chief Executive Officer
**Control:** Corporation, Investor–owned, for–profit **Service:** Psychiatric

**Staffed Beds:** 20

✉ △ **PARKVIEW MEDICAL CENTER (060020)**, 400 West 16th Street, Zip 81003–2781; tel. 719/584–4000, (Total facility includes 20 beds in nursing home–type unit) **A**1 7 9 10 13 **F**2 3 4 5 8 11 13 15 18 20 22 24 28 29 30 31 34 35 37 38 40 42 43 45 46 49 50 51 53 56 57 58 59 62 64 70 73 74 75 76 78 79 81 82 84 85 86 87 89 90 93 94 95 96 97 98 99 100 101 102 103 104 105 107 108 111 114 115 116 119 128 129 130 131 132 135 141 146 147 148 **P**6 8
Primary Contact: Michael T. Baxter, Chief Executive Officer
CFO: Leslie Barnes, Chief Financial Officer
CMO: Steve Nafziger, M.D., Vice President Medical Affairs
CIO: Steve Shirley, Chief Information Officer
CHR: Darrin Smith, Vice President Human Resources
CNO: Linda Flores, R.N., Vice President Nursing Services
Web address: www.parkviewmc.org
**Control:** Other not–for–profit (including NFP Corporation) **Service:** General Medical and Surgical

**Staffed Beds:** 370 **Admissions:** 14437 **Census:** 231 **Outpatient Visits:** 208835 **Births:** 1443 **Total Expense ($000):** 262450 **Payroll Expense ($000):** 109861 **Personnel:** 2293

✉ **ST. MARY–CORWIN MEDICAL CENTER (060012)**, 1008 Minnequa Avenue, Zip 81004–3798; tel. 719/557–4000 **A**1 2 3 9 10 13 **F**3 13 15 18 20 22 26 28 29 30 31 34 35 40 43 45 47 48 49 50 51 53 55 57 58 59 64 68 70 72 73 75 76 78 79 81 82 84 85 86 87 89 90 107 108 110 111 114 115 117 119 120 121 123 124 126 129 130 131 132 135 146 147 148 **P**6 **S** Catholic Health Initiatives, Englewood, CO
Primary Contact: Brian Moore, President and Chief Executive Officer
COO: Michael Cafasso, Vice President Operations
CFO: Vanessa Kochevar, Chief Financial Officer
CMO: Charles Raye, M.D., Chief Medical Officer
CHR: Timea Kennedy, Director Human Resources
CNO: Donna Fisher, R.N., Chief Nursing Officer
Web address: www.centura.org
**Control:** Church–operated, Nongovernment, not–for profit **Service:** General Medical and Surgical

**Staffed Beds:** 153 **Admissions:** 5895 **Census:** 71 **Outpatient Visits:** 88179 **Births:** 641 **Total Expense ($000):** 143436 **Payroll Expense ($000):** 51194 **Personnel:** 750

## RANGELY—Rio Blanco County

★ **RANGELY DISTRICT HOSPITAL (061307)**, 225 Eagle Crest Drive, Zip 81648–2104; tel. 970/675–5011, (Nonreporting) **A**9 10 18
Primary Contact: Nick Goshe, Chief Executive Officer
CFO: Jim Dillon, Chief Financial Officer
CMO: S. Kathleen Rieves, M.D., Chief Medical Officer
CHR: Cynthia S. Stults, Executive Assistant and Human Resources Director
CNO: Sharma Vaughn, Chief Nursing Officer
Web address: www.rangelyhospital.com
**Control:** Hospital district or authority, Government, nonfederal **Service:** General Medical and Surgical

**Staffed Beds:** 25

## RIFLE—Garfield County

★ **GRAND RIVER HOSPITAL DISTRICT (061317)**, 501 Airport Road, Zip 81650–8510, Mailing Address: P.O. Box 912, Zip 81650–0912; tel. 970/625–1510, (Total facility includes 57 beds in nursing home–type unit) **A**9 10 18 **F**3 11 12 15 29 34 35 39 40 41 43 45 50 55 57 59 64 68 69 75 77 79 81 85 87 93 96 97 107 108 110 111 112 115 118 119 127 128 129 130 131 132 133 144 145 146 148 **P**6
Primary Contact: James Coombs, Chief Executive Officer
COO: Bill Noel, Chief Operating Officer
CFO: Ed Johlman, Chief Financial Officer
CMO: Gary Meyer, M.D., Chief Medical Officer
CIO: Diana Murray, Director Information Systems
CHR: Dawn Hodges, Director Human Resources
Web address: www.grhd.org
**Control:** Hospital district or authority, Government, nonfederal **Service:** General Medical and Surgical

**Staffed Beds:** 70 **Admissions:** 541 **Census:** 50 **Outpatient Visits:** 144654 **Births:** 0 **Total Expense ($000):** 59318 **Payroll Expense ($000):** 29528 **Personnel:** 426

## SALIDA—Chaffee County

★ **HEART OF THE ROCKIES REGIONAL MEDICAL CENTER (061322)**, 1000 Rush Drive, Zip 81201–9627, Mailing Address: P.O. Box 429, Zip 81201–0429; tel. 719/530–2200 **A**9 10 18 **F**3 5 11 13 15 28 29 31 34 35 40 43 45 50 54 57 64 68 70 74 75 76 77 78 79 81 82 85 93 97 99 104 107 110 111 114 117 119 127 129 130 131 133 135 146 147 148
Primary Contact: Robert A. Morasko, Chief Executive Officer
CFO: Lesley Fagerberg, Vice President Fiscal Services
CMO: James Wigington, M.D., Chief of Staff
CIO: Andy Waldbart, Department Manager
CHR: Barbara J. Abel, Vice President Human Resources
CNO: Linda Johnson, R.N., Vice President, Patient Services and Chief Nursing Officer
Web address: www.hrrmc.com
**Control:** Hospital district or authority, Government, nonfederal **Service:** General Medical and Surgical

**Staffed Beds:** 25 **Admissions:** 1081 **Census:** 11 **Outpatient Visits:** 56010 **Births:** 121 **Total Expense ($000):** 42462 **Payroll Expense ($000):** 19630 **Personnel:** 323

## SPRINGFIELD—Baca County

★ **SOUTHEAST COLORADO HOSPITAL DISTRICT (061311)**, 373 East Tenth Avenue, Zip 81073–1699; tel. 719/523–4501, (Total facility includes 56 beds in nursing home–type unit) **A**9 10 18 **F**3 6 7 11 29 34 35 40 42 45 50 56 57 62 63 66 68 81 93 97 107 127 133 147 148 **P**6
Primary Contact: Jerry Jasper, Chief Executive Officer and Administrator
CFO: Dorothy Burke, Chief Financial Officer
CMO: Jerry Flynn, M.D., Chief of Staff
CIO: Chris Westphal, Chief Information Technology Officer
CHR: Sherrilyn Turner, Director Human Resources
Web address: www.sechosp.org
**Control:** Hospital district or authority, Government, nonfederal **Service:** General Medical and Surgical

**Staffed Beds:** 79 **Admissions:** 195 **Census:** 31

## STEAMBOAT SPRINGS—Routt County

✉ **YAMPA VALLEY MEDICAL CENTER (060049)**, 1024 Central Park Drive, Zip 80487–8813; tel. 970/879–1322, (Total facility includes 59 beds in nursing home–type unit) **A**1 2 9 10 20 **F**3 13 15 18 28 29 30 31 34 35 36 40 43 45 46 48 49 50 51 57 64 68 70 73 75 76 77 78 79 81 82 84 85 86 87 93 97 107 110 111 115 119 126 128 129 130 131 132 133 135 143 146 147
Primary Contact: Frank May, Chief Executive Officer
COO: David Garner, Chief Operating Officer
CIO: Mark Clark, Chief Information Officer
CHR: Soniya Fidler, Chief Human Resources and Compliance Officer
CNO: Marie Timlin, R.N., Chief Nursing Officer
Web address: www.yvmc.org
**Control:** Other not–for–profit (including NFP Corporation) **Service:** General Medical and Surgical

**Staffed Beds:** 98 **Admissions:** 1330 **Census:** 16 **Outpatient Visits:** 64465 **Births:** 273 **Total Expense ($000):** 77656 **Payroll Expense ($000):** 25375 **Personnel:** 382

*Many Facility Codes have changed. Please refer to the AHA Guide Code Chart.* © 2015 AHA Guide

**STERLING—Logan County**

✠ **STERLING REGIONAL MEDCENTER (060076)**, 615 Fairhurst Street, Zip 80751–4523; tel. 970/522–0122 **A**1 9 10 20 **F**13 15 18 28 29 30 31 34 35 36 40 43 45 50 51 57 59 64 68 69 70 75 76 77 78 79 81 85 87 93 94 97 107 108 109 110 111 114 115 119 127 129 130 131 146 148 **P**6 **S** Banner Health, Phoenix, AZ
Primary Contact: Sharon Lind, MSN, FACHE, Interim Chief Executive Officer
CFO: Pamela Stieb, Chief Financial Officer
CMO: Jeff Bacon, D.O., Medical Director
CHR: Cynda Eklund, Chief Human Resources Officer
CNO: Wade Alan Tyrrell, RN, Chief Nursing Officer
Web address: www.bannerhealth.com/Locations/Colorado/Sterling+Regional+MedCenter
**Control:** Other not–for–profit (including NFP Corporation) **Service:** General Medical and Surgical

**Staffed Beds:** 25 **Admissions:** 1114 **Census:** 9 **Births:** 260 **Total Expense ($000):** 40610 **Payroll Expense ($000):** 14891 **Personnel:** 209

**THORNTON—Adams County**

✠ **NORTH SUBURBAN MEDICAL CENTER (060065)**, 9191 Grant Street, Zip 80229–4341; tel. 303/451–7800 **A**1 9 10 **F**3 11 12 13 15 18 20 22 29 30 35 40 43 45 59 60 64 68 70 72 74 75 76 79 80 81 82 84 85 87 89 107 108 111 115 119 129 130 132 135 146 **S** HCA, Nashville, TN
Primary Contact: Jennifer Alderfer, Chief Executive Officer
CFO: Deborah Hart, Chief Financial Officer
CIO: Jeff Schnoor, Director Information Technology and Systems
CHR: Suzanne Kelley, Director Human Resources
Web address: www.northsuburban.com
**Control:** Corporation, Investor–owned, for–profit **Service:** General Medical and Surgical

**Staffed Beds:** 115 **Admissions:** 6704 **Census:** 71

✠ **VIBRA HOSPITAL OF DENVER (062014)**, 8451 Pearl Street, Zip 80229–4804; tel. 303/288–3000, (Nonreporting) **A**1 9 10 **S** Vibra Healthcare, Mechanicsburg, PA
Primary Contact: Austin B. Cleveland, Chief Executive Officer
CMO: John Buckley, M.D., President Medical Staff
CHR: Lorna Fulton, Director Human Resources
Web address: www.vhdenver.com
**Control:** Corporation, Investor–owned, for–profit **Service:** Long–Term Acute Care hospital

**Staffed Beds:** 71

**TRINIDAD—Las Animas County**

**MT. SAN RAFAEL HOSPITAL (061321)**, 410 Benedicta Avenue, Zip 81082–2093; tel. 719/846–9213 **A**9 10 18 **F**3 15 28 34 40 45 46 50 65 75 81 82 85 89 93 94 96 97 107 111 114 119 127 129 133 146 147 148
Primary Contact: John Tucker, Chief Executive Officer
CFO: David W. Rollins, Chief Financial Officer
CMO: Thomas Goodell, M.D., Chief of Staff
CIO: Michael Archuleta, Chief Information Technology Officer
CHR: Tammy Rogers, Director Human Resources
CNO: Denise C. Clark, R.N., Chief Clinical Officer
Web address: www.msrhc.org
**Control:** Other not–for–profit (including NFP Corporation) **Service:** General Medical and Surgical

**Staffed Beds:** 18 **Admissions:** 776 **Census:** 6

**VAIL—Eagle County**

✠ **VAIL VALLEY MEDICAL CENTER (060096)**, 181 West Meadow Drive, Zip 81657–5242, Mailing Address: P.O. Box 40000, Zip 81658–7520; tel. 970/476–2451, (Nonreporting) **A**1 3 9 10 20
Primary Contact: Doris Kirchner, Chief Executive Officer
CFO: Charles Crevling, Senior Vice President and Chief Financial Officer
CMO: Barry Hammaker, M.D., Chief Medical Officer and Chief Clinical Officer
CIO: Brian Foster, Chief Information Officer
CHR: Rick Smith, Senior Vice President Human Resources and Chief Administrative Officer
CNO: Sheila Sherman, Vice President Patient Care Services
Web address: www.vvmc.com
**Control:** Other not–for–profit (including NFP Corporation) **Service:** General Medical and Surgical

**Staffed Beds:** 58

**WALSENBURG—Huerfano County**

★ **SPANISH PEAKS REGIONAL HEALTH CENTER (061316)**, 23500 U.S. Highway 160, Zip 81089–9524; tel. 719/738–5100 **A**9 10 18 **F**11 28 34 35 39 40 43 45 50 57 59 64 79 81 82 85 93 97 107 110 111 115 119 127 129 131 133 147 148 **P**6
Primary Contact: Todd Oberheu, Chief Executive Officer
CFO: Richard L. Corradino, Chief Financial Officer
CMO: Thomas Hoffeld, M.D., Chief of Staff
CIO: Jose Camacho, Director Information Technology
CHR: Tony Marostica, Director Human Resources
CNO: Sherry Gomez, Chief Nursing Officer
Web address: www.sprhc.org
**Control:** Hospital district or authority, Government, nonfederal **Service:** General Medical and Surgical

**Staffed Beds:** 20 **Admissions:** 226 **Census:** 3

**WESTMINSTER—Jefferson County**

**CLEO WALLACE CENTERS HOSPITAL**, 8405 Church Ranch Boulevard, Zip 80021–3918; tel. 303/466–7391, (Nonreporting) **A**9
Primary Contact: Perry May, Executive Director
Web address: www.devereuxco.org
**Control:** Other not–for–profit (including NFP Corporation) **Service:** Children's hospital psychiatric

**Staffed Beds:** 61

✠ **ST. ANTHONY NORTH HEALTH CAMPUS (060104)**, 14300 Orchard Parkway, Zip 80023–9206; tel. 720/627–0000 **A**1 2 3 9 10 **F**3 11 13 15 18 20 22 26 28 29 30 31 34 35 36 40 43 45 49 54 57 60 63 64 65 68 70 72 74 75 76 77 78 79 81 82 84 85 87 92 93 97 102 107 108 110 114 115 119 130 146 147 148 **S** Catholic Health Initiatives, Englewood, CO
Primary Contact: Carole Peet, R.N., MSN, President and Chief Executive Officer
CFO: Alison Mizer, Chief Financial Officer
CIO: Dana Moore, Senior Vice President Information Services
CHR: Robert Archibold, Director, Human Resources
CNO: Carol A. Butler, R.N., VP Patient Care Services & Operations
Web address: www.stanthonynorth.org
**Control:** Church–operated, Nongovernment, not–for profit **Service:** General Medical and Surgical

**Staffed Beds:** 122 **Admissions:** 5792 **Census:** 61 **Outpatient Visits:** 55926 **Births:** 744 **Total Expense ($000):** 115917 **Payroll Expense ($000):** 40895 **Personnel:** 728

**WHEAT RIDGE—Jefferson County**

✠ **LUTHERAN MEDICAL CENTER (060009)**, 8300 West 38th Avenue, Zip 80033–6005; tel. 303/425–4500, (Includes EXEMPLA WEST PINES, 3400 Lutheran Parkway, Zip 80033; tel. 303/467–4000), (Total facility includes 120 beds in nursing home–type unit) **A**1 2 3 9 10 **F**3 4 5 10 11 13 15 18 20 22 24 26 28 29 30 31 33 34 35 36 40 43 45 47 48 49 50 54 55 58 59 60 62 63 64 67 68 70 72 74 75 76 77 78 79 81 84 85 86 87 94 98 100 101 102 103 104 105 107 108 110 111 114 115 119 120 121 123 124 125 126 128 129 130 132 137 146 147 148 **P**6 **S** SCL Health, Broomfield, CO
Primary Contact: Grant Wicklund, President and Chief Executive Officer
COO: Peggy Cain Price, Vice President and Chief Operating Officer
CFO: Karen Scremin, Vice President Finance
CMO: Christina Johnson, M.D., Vice President and Chief Clinical and Quality Officer
CHR: Scott Day, Vice President Human Resources
CNO: Geraldine Towndrow, R.N., Senior Vice President Nursing
Web address: www.exempla.org
**Control:** Other not–for–profit (including NFP Corporation) **Service:** General Medical and Surgical

**Staffed Beds:** 475 **Admissions:** 15160 **Census:** 319 **Outpatient Visits:** 206181 **Births:** 2669 **Total Expense ($000):** 273458 **Payroll Expense ($000):** 90138 **Personnel:** 1519

**WOODLAND PARK—Teller County**

◇ **PIKES PEAK REGIONAL HOSPITAL (061326)**, 16420 West Highway 24, Zip 80863; tel. 719/687–9999 **A**9 10 18 21 **F**3 15 29 30 34 40 41 43 45 50 57 59 64 65 68 75 77 79 80 81 85 97 107 110 111 114 119 129 131 133 146 148 **P**6 **S** IASIS Healthcare, Franklin, TN
Primary Contact: Terry Buckner, Chief Executive Officer
CFO: Kimberly Monvesky, Chief Financial Officer
CMO: Kurt Wever, M.D., Chief of Staff
CHR: Arianne Randolph, Director Human Resources
CNO: Rodney Bice, R.N., Chief Nursing Officer
Web address: www.pprmc.org
**Control:** Corporation, Investor–owned, for–profit **Service:** General Medical and Surgical

**Staffed Beds:** 15 **Admissions:** 536 **Census:** 4 **Outpatient Visits:** 29482 **Births:** 0 **Total Expense ($000):** 18320 **Payroll Expense ($000):** 6613 **Personnel:** 119

CO

---

**Hospital, Medicare Provider Number, Address, Telephone, Approval, Facility, and Physician Codes, Health Care System**

★ American Hospital Association (AHA) membership
□ The Joint Commission accreditation
○ Healthcare Facilities Accreditation Program
◇ DNV Healthcare Inc. accreditation
⇑ Center for Improvement in Healthcare Quality Accreditation
△ Commission on Accreditation of Rehabilitation Facilities (CARF) accreditation

**WRAY—Yuma County**

★ **WRAY COMMUNITY DISTRICT HOSPITAL (061309)**, 1017 West 7th Street,
Zip 80758–1420; tel. 970/332–4811, (Nonreporting) **A**3 9 10 18
Primary Contact: Jennie Sullivan, Chief Executive Officer
CMO: Monte Uyemura, M.D., Chief of Staff
Web address: www.wraycommunitydistricthospital.com/
**Control:** Hospital district or authority, Government, nonfederal **Service:** General
Medical and Surgical

**Staffed Beds:** 15

**YUMA—Yuma County**

★ **YUMA DISTRICT HOSPITAL (061315)**, 1000 West 8th Avenue,
Zip 80759–2641; tel. 970/848–5405 **A**9 10 18 **F**3 11 13 15 28 29 30 31 34
35 36 40 43 44 50 53 57 59 62 64 65 68 74 75 77 78 79 81 82 87 93 97
99 101 102 103 104 107 111 115 119 127 130 133 148 **P**6
Primary Contact: John Gardner, Chief Executive Officer
CFO: Cathy Wolff, Vice President Financial Services and Chief Financial Officer
CMO: John Wolz, M.D., Chief Medical Staff
CIO: Jason Hawley, Manager Information Services
CHR: Gini Adams, Director Employee and Public Relations
CNO: Beth Saxton, R.N., Vice President Patient Care Services
Web address: www.yumahospital.org
**Control:** Hospital district or authority, Government, nonfederal **Service:** General
Medical and Surgical

**Staffed Beds:** 12 **Admissions:** 240 **Census:** 2 **Outpatient Visits:** 42970
**Births:** 0 **Total Expense ($000):** 21276 **Payroll Expense ($000):** 9213
**Personnel:** 118

**CO**

# CONNECTICUT

## BETHLEHEM—Litchfield County

**WELLSPRING FOUNDATION**, 21 Arch Bridge Road, Zip 06751–1612, Mailing
Address: P.O. Box 370, Zip 06751–0370; tel. 203/266–7235, (Nonreporting) **A**9
Primary Contact: Richard E. Beauvais, Ph.D., Chief Executive Officer
CFO: Richard E. Beauvais, Ph.D., Chief Executive Officer
Web address: www.wellspring.org
**Control:** Other not–for–profit (including NFP Corporation) **Service:** Psychiatric

**Staffed Beds:** 36

## BRANFORD—New Haven County

☐ **THE CONNECTICUT HOSPICE (070038)**, 100 Double Beach Road,
Zip 06405–4909; tel. 203/315–7500, (Nonreporting) **A**1 10
Primary Contact: Rosemary Johnson Hurzeler, President and Chief Executive
Officer
Web address: www.hospice.com
**Control:** Other not–for–profit (including NFP Corporation) **Service:** Other specialty

**Staffed Beds:** 52

## BRIDGEPORT—Fairfield County

⊞ **BRIDGEPORT HOSPITAL (070010)**, 267 Grant Street, Zip 06610–2805,
Mailing Address: P.O. Box 5000, Zip 06610–0120; tel. 203/384–3000 **A**1 2 3 5
6 8 9 10 **F**3 5 6 8 11 12 13 14 15 16 18 19 20 22 24 26 28 29 30 31 32 34
35 36 38 39 40 41 43 44 45 46 47 48 49 50 51 52 54 55 56 57 58 59 61
64 65 66 68 70 74 75 76 77 78 79 80 81 82 84 85 86 87 90 93 96 97 98
99 100 101 102 103 104 105 107 108 110 111 114 115 116 117 118 119
120 121 123 124 126 129 130 131 132 134 135 144 145 146 147 148 **P**3
**S** Yale New Haven Health System, New Haven, CT
Primary Contact: William M. Jennings, President and Chief Executive Officer
CFO: Patrick McCabe, Senior Vice President Finance and Chief Financial Officer
CMO: Michael Ivy, M.D., Senior Vice President for Medical Affairs and Chief
Medical Officer
CIO: Daniel Barchi, Senior Vice President, Technical Services and Chief
Information Officer
CHR: Melissa Turner, Senior Vice President Human Resources
CNO: MaryEllen Kosturko, R.N., Senior Vice President Patient Care Operations and
Chief Nursing Officer
Web address: www.bridgeporthospital.org
**Control:** Other not–for–profit (including NFP Corporation) **Service:** General
Medical and Surgical

**Staffed Beds:** 357 **Admissions:** 16256 **Census:** 255 **Outpatient Visits:**
331419 **Births:** 2341 **Total Expense ($000):** 426496 **Payroll Expense
($000):** 153451 **Personnel:** 2086

☐ **SOUTHWEST CONNECTICUT MENTAL HEALTH SYSTEM (074012)**, 1635
Central Avenue, Zip 06610–2717; tel. 203/551–7400, (Nonreporting) **A**1 9 10
**S** Connecticut Department of Mental Health and Addiction Services, Hartford, CT
Primary Contact: Daniel Wartenberg, PsyD, M.P.H., Chief Executive Officer
COO: Cindy Perjon, Associate Director
CFO: Linda Woznikaitis, Chief Financial Officer
CMO: Sandra Gomez–Luna, Medical Director
CIO: Bernetta Witcher–Boateng, Ph.D., Director Quality Improvement Services and
Compliance
CHR: Nancy Derman, Director Human Resources
Web address: www.ct.gov/dmhas/cwp/view.asp?a=2946&q=378936
**Control:** State–Government, nonfederal **Service:** Psychiatric

**Staffed Beds:** 62

⊞ **ST. VINCENT'S MEDICAL CENTER (070028)**, 2800 Main Street,
Zip 06606–4292; tel. 203/576–5454, (Includes ST. VINCENT'S BEHAVIORAL
HEALTH, 47 Long Lots Road, Westport, Zip 06880–3800; tel. 203/221–8813;
Margaret Hardy, R.N., MS, Vice President and Executive Director) **A**1 2 3 5 9 10
**F**3 4 5 8 12 13 15 17 18 20 22 24 26 28 29 30 31 34 35 36 38 40 43 44
45 46 47 48 49 50 53 54 55 56 57 58 59 60 61 63 64 65 66 68 70 71 74
75 76 77 78 79 80 81 82 83 84 85 86 87 90 91 92 93 96 97 98 99 100
101 102 103 104 105 106 107 108 110 111 114 115 117 118 119 120 121
123 124 126 130 132 134 143 144 145 146 147 148 **P**1 **S** Ascension Health,
Saint Louis, MO
Primary Contact: Stuart G. Marcus, M.D., FACS, President and Chief Executive
Officer
COO: Dale G. Danowski, R.N., Senior Vice President Chief Operating Officer and
Chief Nursing Officer
CFO: John Gleckler, Chief Financial Officer
CMO: Larry Schek, M.D., Senior Vice President Chief Medical Director and Vice
President Cardiology
CIO: Rick McCarthy, Chief Information Officer
CHR: Wayne Rustin, Vice President, Chief Human Resources Officer
CNO: Dale G. Danowski, R.N., Senior Vice President Chief Operating Officer and
Chief Nursing Officer
Web address: www.stvincents.org
**Control:** Other not–for–profit (including NFP Corporation) **Service:** General
Medical and Surgical

**Staffed Beds:** 413 **Admissions:** 17762 **Census:** 302 **Outpatient Visits:**
627936 **Births:** 1058 **Total Expense ($000):** 433464 **Payroll Expense
($000):** 189454 **Personnel:** 2053

## BRISTOL—Hartford County

⊞ **BRISTOL HOSPITAL (070029)**, Brewster Road, Zip 06011, Mailing Address:
P.O. Box 977, Zip 06011–0977; tel. 860/585–3000, (Nonreporting) **A**1 2 5 9 10
Primary Contact: Kurt A. Barwis, FACHE, President and Chief Executive Officer
COO: Marc D. Edelman, Vice President Operations
CFO: Peter Freytag, Senior Vice President Finance and Chief Financial Officer
CMO: Leonard Banco, M.D., Senior Vice President and Chief Medical Officer
CIO: David Rackliffe, Assistant Vice President Information Services
CHR: Jeanine Reckdenwald, Vice President Human Resources and Support
Services
Web address: www.bristolhospital.org
**Control:** Other not–for–profit (including NFP Corporation) **Service:** General
Medical and Surgical

**Staffed Beds:** 134

## DANBURY—Fairfield County

⊞ **DANBURY HOSPITAL (070033)**, 24 Hospital Avenue, Zip 06810–6099;
tel. 203/739–7000, (Includes NEW MILFORD HOSPITAL, 21 Elm Street, New
Milford, Zip 06776–2993; tel. 860/355–2611; John M. Murphy, M.D., President
and Chief Executive Officer, Western Connecticut Health Network) **A**1 2 3 5 8 9
10 **F**3 5 8 9 12 13 14 15 17 18 20 22 24 26 28 29 30 31 32 34 35 36 37
38 39 40 43 44 45 46 47 48 49 50 51 54 55 56 57 58 59 61 64 65 66 68
70 72 74 75 76 77 78 79 81 82 83 84 85 86 87 89 90 91 92 93 94 96 97
98 99 100 101 102 103 104 105 107 108 109 110 111 112 114 115 116
117 118 119 120 121 123 124 126 129 130 131 132 134 135 144 145 146
147 148 **P**8 **S** Western Connecticut Health Network, Danbury, CT
Primary Contact: John M. Murphy, M.D., President and Chief Executive Officer,
Western Connecticut Health Network
COO: Michael Daglio, President – Norwalk Hospital – SVP, WCHN
CFO: Steven Rosenberg, Chief Financial Officer
CMO: Matthew Miller, M.D., Chief Medical Officer – WCHN
CIO: Kathleen DeMatteo, Chief Information Officer
CNO: Moreen Donahue, R.N., Chief Nursing Executive
Web address: www.danburyhospital.org
**Control:** Other not–for–profit (including NFP Corporation) **Service:** General
Medical and Surgical

**Staffed Beds:** 342 **Admissions:** 16513 **Census:** 243 **Outpatient Visits:**
403297 **Births:** 2023 **Total Expense ($000):** 516771 **Payroll Expense
($000):** 193413 **Personnel:** 2206

---

**Hospital, Medicare Provider Number, Address, Telephone, Approval, Facility, and Physician Codes, Health Care System**

★ American Hospital Association (AHA) membership    ○ Healthcare Facilities Accreditation Program    ⇑ Center for Improvement in Healthcare Quality Accreditation
☐ The Joint Commission accreditation    ◇ DNV Healthcare Inc. accreditation    △ Commission on Accreditation of Rehabilitation Facilities (CARF) accreditation

**DERBY—New Haven County**

⊞ **GRIFFIN HOSPITAL (070031)**, 130 Division Street, Zip 06418–1326;
tel. 203/735–7421 **A**1 2 3 5 9 10 **F**3 5 8 12 13 15 18 28 29 30 34 35 36 38
40 45 49 50 51 53 56 57 58 59 64 65 68 70 71 74 75 76 77 78 79 81 82
84 85 86 87 93 94 96 97 98 99 100 101 102 103 104 105 107 108 110
111 114 116 117 118 119 120 121 129 130 132 134 135 144 146 147 148
Primary Contact: Patrick Charmel, President and Chief Executive Officer
CMO: Kenneth V. Schwartz, M.D., Medical Director
CIO: George Tomas, Director Information Services
CHR: Steve Mordecai, Director Human Resources
CNO: Barbara J. Stumpo, R.N., Vice President Patient Care Services
Web address: www.griffinhealth.org
**Control:** Other not–for–profit (including NFP Corporation) **Service:** General
Medical and Surgical

> **Staffed Beds:** 111 **Admissions:** 6310 **Census:** 81 **Outpatient Visits:** 191250
> **Births:** 662 **Total Expense ($000):** 130275 **Payroll Expense ($000):** 55697
> **Personnel:** 966

**FARMINGTON—Hartford County**

⊞ **UNIVERSITY OF CONNECTICUT HEALTH CENTER, JOHN DEMPSEY
HOSPITAL (070036)**, 263 Farmington Avenue, Zip 06032–1941;
tel. 860/679–2000 **A**1 2 3 5 8 9 10 12 13 19 **F**3 5 6 7 8 9 11 12 13 15 18
20 22 24 26 29 30 31 34 35 36 37 38 39 40 44 45 46 47 52
54 55 56 57 58 59 60 61 63 64 65 66 68 70 74 75 76 77 78 79 81 82 83
84 85 86 87 91 92 93 94 97 98 99 100 101 102 103 104 105 107 108 110
111 114 115 117 118 119 120 121 123 124 126 127 129 130 131 132 134
135 143 144 145 146 147 148 **P**6
Primary Contact: Anne Diamond, JD, Chief Executive Officer
CFO: John Biancamano, Chief Financial Officer
CMO: Richard Simon, M.D., Chief of Staff
CIO: Sandra Armstrong, Chief Information Officer
CHR: Carolle Andrews, Interim Chief Human Resources Officer
CNO: Ellen Leone, R.N., Chief Nursing Officer
Web address: www.uchc.edu
**Control:** State–Government, nonfederal **Service:** General Medical and Surgical

> **Staffed Beds:** 174 **Admissions:** 8109 **Census:** 103 **Outpatient Visits:**
> 288049 **Births:** 468 **Total Expense ($000):** 331950 **Payroll Expense ($000):** 104623 **Personnel:** 1355

**GREENWICH—Fairfield County**

⊞ **GREENWICH HOSPITAL (070018)**, 5 Perryridge Road, Zip 06830–4697;
tel. 203/863–3000 **A**1 2 3 5 9 10 **F**3 5 8 11 12 13 14 15 18 20 22 26 28 29
30 31 32 34 35 36 37 38 39 40 44 45 46 47 48 49 50 51 52 53 54 55 56
57 58 59 61 63 64 65 66 68 70 72 74 75 76 77 78 79 80 81 82 84 85 86
87 89 93 96 97 99 100 101 102 103 104 107 108 109 110 111 114 115
116 117 118 119 120 121 123 124 126 129 130 131 132 134 135 146 147
148 **P**2 3 5 **S** Yale New Haven Health System, New Haven, CT
Primary Contact: Norman G. Roth, Chief Executive Officer
COO: Norman G. Roth, Interim Chief Operating Officer
CFO: Eugene Colucci, Vice President Finance
CMO: A. Michael Marino, M.D., Senior Vice President Medical Administration
Web address: www.greenhosp.org
**Control:** Other not–for–profit (including NFP Corporation) **Service:** General
Medical and Surgical

> **Staffed Beds:** 184 **Admissions:** 10306 **Census:** 130 **Outpatient Visits:**
> 289874 **Births:** 2519 **Total Expense ($000):** 317854 **Payroll Expense ($000):** 113219 **Personnel:** 1518

**HARTFORD—Hartford County**

⊞ **CONNECTICUT CHILDREN'S MEDICAL CENTER (073300)**, 282 Washington
Street, Zip 06106–3322; tel. 860/545–9000, (Nonreporting) **A**1 3 5 9 10
Primary Contact: Martin J. Gavin, President and Chief Executive Officer
CFO: Gerald J. Boisvert, Vice President and Chief Financial Officer
CMO: Paul Dworkin, M.D., Physician–in–Chief
CIO: Kelly R. Styles, Vice President and Chief Information Officer
CHR: Elizabeth Rudden, Vice President Human Resources
Web address: www.ccmckids.org
**Control:** Other not–for–profit (including NFP Corporation) **Service:** Children's
general

> **Staffed Beds:** 182

⊞ **HARTFORD HOSPITAL (070025)**, 80 Seymour Street, Zip 06102–8000,
Mailing Address: P.O. Box 5037, Zip 06102–5037; tel. 860/545–5000, (Includes
INSTITUTE OF LIVING, 400 Washington Street, Zip 06106–3392;
tel. 860/545–7000), (Total facility includes 104 beds in nursing home–type unit)
**A**1 2 3 5 9 10 **F**2 3 5 6 7 8 9 10 11 12 13 15 17 18 20 22 24 26 28 29 30
31 34 35 36 37 38 39 40 43 44 45 46 47 48 49 50 51 53 54 55 56 57
58 59 60 61 63 64 65 66 68 70 71 74 75 76 77 78 79 80 81 82 83 84 85
86 87 91 92 93 94 96 97 98 99 100 101 102 103 104 105 106 107 108
110 111 114 115 116 117 118 119 120 121 123 124 125 126 128 129 130
131 132 135 137 138 139 141 145 146 147 148 **P**6 8 **S** Hartford HealthCare,
Hartford, CT
Primary Contact: Stuart Markowitz, M.D., President
CMO: Stuart Markowitz, M.D., Chief Medical Officer
CIO: Stephan O'Neill, Vice President Information Services
CHR: Richard McAloon, Vice President Human Resources
Web address: www.harthosp.org
**Control:** Other not–for–profit (including NFP Corporation) **Service:** General
Medical and Surgical

> **Staffed Beds:** 898 **Admissions:** 38934 **Census:** 712 **Outpatient Visits:**
> 232801 **Births:** 3763 **Total Expense ($000):** 1037033 **Payroll Expense ($000):** 435885 **Personnel:** 6053

⊞ **MOUNT SINAI REHABILITATION HOSPITAL (073025)**, 490 Blue Hills Avenue,
Zip 06112–1513; tel. 860/714–3500 **A**1 10 **F**29 30 34 54 58 59 64 68 74 75
82 90 91 92 93 94 95 96 130 131 132 **P**8 **S** Saint Francis Care, Inc.,
Hartford, CT
Primary Contact: Robert J. Krug, M.D., Chief Executive Officer
CFO: David Bittner, Chief Financial Officer
Web address: www.stfranciscare.org
**Control:** Other not–for–profit (including NFP Corporation) **Service:** Rehabilitation

> **Staffed Beds:** 30 **Admissions:** 660 **Census:** 23 **Outpatient Visits:** 38853
> **Births:** 0 **Total Expense ($000):** 28854 **Payroll Expense ($000):** 11794
> **Personnel:** 200

⊞ **SAINT FRANCIS HOSPITAL AND MEDICAL CENTER (070002)**, 114
Woodland Street, Zip 06105–1208; tel. 860/714–4000 **A**1 2 3 5 8 9 10 **F**3 8
11 12 13 15 17 18 20 22 24 26 28 29 30 31 34 35 36 38 39 40 43 46 47
48 49 50 53 54 55 56 57 58 59 61 64 65 66 68 70 72 74 75 76 77 78 79
81 82 84 85 87 91 92 93 94 95 96 97 98 99 100 101 102 103 104 107 111
115 117 118 119 120 121 123 124 126 129 130 131 132 134 135 144 145
146 147 148 **P**8 **S** Saint Francis Care, Inc., Hartford, CT
Primary Contact: Christopher M. Dadlez, President and Chief Executive Officer
COO: Kathleen M. Roche, R.N., Executive Vice President and Chief Operating
Officer
CFO: John N. Giamalis, Senior Vice President and Chief Financial Officer
CMO: Rolf W. Knoll, M.D., Senior Vice President and Chief Medical Officer
CIO: Linda Shanley, Vice President and Chief Information Officer
CHR: Dawn L. Bryant, Senior Vice President and Chief Human Resource Officer
Web address: www.saintfranciscare.com
**Control:** Church–operated, Nongovernment, not–for profit **Service:** General
Medical and Surgical

> **Staffed Beds:** 612 **Admissions:** 28594 **Census:** 399 **Outpatient Visits:**
> 267480 **Births:** 2933 **Total Expense ($000):** 666789 **Payroll Expense ($000):** 254219 **Personnel:** 4545

**MANCHESTER—Hartford County**

⊞ **MANCHESTER MEMORIAL HOSPITAL (070027)**, 71 Haynes Street,
Zip 06040–4188; tel. 860/646–1222 **A**1 2 5 9 10 12 13 **F**3 4 5 11 13 15 18
26 28 29 30 31 34 35 36 38 39 40 41 44 45 46 47 49 50 51 57 58 59 61
63 64 66 70 71 72 73 74 75 76 77 78 79 80 81 84 85 86 87 91 93 98 99
100 101 102 103 104 105 107 108 110 111 114 118 119 126 129 130 131
132 134 135 141 142 143 145 146 148 **P**3 5 6 8 **S** Eastern Connecticut
Health Network, Manchester, CT
Primary Contact: Peter J. Karl, President and Chief Executive Officer
CFO: Michael D. Veillette, Senior Vice President and Chief Financial Officer
CMO: Joel R. Reich, M.D., Senior Vice President Medical Affairs
CIO: Richard Daigle, Director Information Technology
CHR: Deborah Gogliettino, Senior Vice President Human Resources
CNO: Mary Powers, MSN, Senior Vice President and Chief Nursing Officer
Web address: www.echn.org
**Control:** Other not–for–profit (including NFP Corporation) **Service:** General
Medical and Surgical

> **Staffed Beds:** 156 **Admissions:** 7840 **Census:** 111 **Outpatient Visits:**
> 320570 **Births:** 1248 **Total Expense ($000):** 185310 **Payroll Expense ($000):** 83606 **Personnel:** 1060

CT

*Many Facility Codes have changed. Please refer to the AHA Guide Code Chart.*

## MANSFIELD CENTER—Tolland County

☒ **NATCHAUG HOSPITAL (074008)**, 189 Storrs Road, Zip 06250–1683;
tel. 860/456–1311 **A**1 9 10 **F**5 98 99 100 104 105 106 **S** Hartford HealthCare,
Hartford, CT
Primary Contact: Stephen W. Larcen, Ph.D., President
COO: David Klein, Ph.D., Vice President Operations, Behavioral Health Network
CFO: Paul V. Maloney, Vice President Finance, Behavioral Health Network
CMO: Deborah Weidner, M.D., Medical Director
CIO: Mark Olson, Interim Chief Information Officer, Behavioral Health Network
CHR: Janet Keown, Vice President Human Resources, Behavioral Health Network
CNO: Justin Sleeper, Vice President Clinical Operations, Behavioral Health Network
Web address: www.natchaug.org
**Control:** Other not–for–profit (including NFP Corporation) **Service:** Psychiatric

**Staffed Beds:** 57 **Admissions:** 2035 **Census:** 52 **Outpatient Visits:** 59049
**Births:** 0 **Total Expense ($000):** 47873 **Payroll Expense ($000):** 28615
**Personnel:** 322

## MERIDEN—New Haven County

☒ **MIDSTATE MEDICAL CENTER (070017)**, 435 Lewis Avenue, Zip 06451–2101;
tel. 203/694–8200 **A**1 2 9 10 **F**3 11 12 13 15 18 28 29 30 31 34 35 36 38
39 40 43 44 45 46 47 48 49 50 51 53 54 56 57 59 61 63 64 68 70 74 75
76 78 79 81 82 84 85 86 87 97 98 102 107 108 110 111 114 115 117 118
119 120 121 123 124 126 129 130 131 132 144 145 146 147 148 **P**5
**S** Hartford HealthCare, Hartford, CT
Primary Contact: Lucille A. Janatka, President and Chief Executive Officer,
Hartford HealthCare Central Region
CMO: Kenneth R. Kurz, M.D., Chief of Staff
CIO: Jennifer Comerford, Manager Information Services
CHR: Ken Cesca, Vice President Human Resources
Web address: www.midstatemedical.org
**Control:** Other not–for–profit (including NFP Corporation) **Service:** General
Medical and Surgical

**Staffed Beds:** 98 **Admissions:** 8341 **Census:** 102 **Outpatient Visits:** 161185
**Births:** 929 **Total Expense ($000):** 216615 **Payroll Expense ($000):** 69745
**Personnel:** 932

## MIDDLETOWN—Middlesex County

☐ **ALBERT J. SOLNIT PSYCHIATRIC CENTER – SOUTH CAMPUS**, 915 River
Road, Zip 06457–3921, Mailing Address: P.O. Box 2792, Zip 06457–9292;
tel. 860/704–4000, (Nonreporting) **A**1 3 5
Primary Contact: Michelle Sarofin, Superintendent
CFO: Connie Tessarzik, Business Manager
CMO: Lesley Siegel, M.D., Medical Director
CIO: Andrew J A Kass, M.D., Assistant Superintendent
Web address: www.ct.gov/
**Control:** State–Government, nonfederal **Service:** Children's hospital psychiatric

**Staffed Beds:** 102

☐ **CONNECTICUT VALLEY HOSPITAL (074003)**, Eastern Drive,
Zip 06457–3947, Mailing Address: P.O. Box 351, Zip 06457–3947;
tel. 860/262–5000, (Includes WHITING FORENSIC DIVISION OF CONNECTICUT
VALLEY HOSPITAL, O'Brien Drive, Zip 06457, Mailing Address: Box 70,
Zip 06457–3942; tel. 203/344–2541) **A**1 3 5 9 10 **F**3 4 29 30 34 36 39 50
53 56 57 58 59 60 61 65 68 74 75 77 82 84 86 87 90 91 94 97 98 99 100
101 102 103 106 119 130 132 135 144 146 148 **S** Connecticut Department of
Mental Health and Addiction Services, Hartford, CT
Primary Contact: Helene M. Vartelas, Chief Executive Officer
COO: John D'Evano, Chief Operating Officer
CFO: Michael Schuberth, Director, Fiscal Services and Plant Operations
CMO: Thomas Pisano, M.D., Chief Professional Services
CIO: Kathryn Connelly, Manager Information Technology
CHR: Cheryl Thompson, Facility Director Human Resources
CNO: Jerilynn Lamb–Pagone, Nurse Executive
Web address: www.ct.gov/dmhas/cwp/view.asp?a=3519&q=416778
**Control:** State–Government, nonfederal **Service:** Psychiatric

**Staffed Beds:** 596 **Admissions:** 3563 **Census:** 558 **Outpatient Visits:** 0
**Births:** 0 **Total Expense ($000):** 160007 **Payroll Expense ($000):** 129562
**Personnel:** 1429

☒ **MIDDLESEX HOSPITAL (070020)**, 28 Crescent Street, Zip 06457–3650;
tel. 860/358–6000 **A**1 2 3 5 9 10 **F**3 5 12 13 15 18 20 22 24 28 29 30 31
32 34 35 36 38 40 42 45 46 47 49 50 51 54 55 57 58 59 60 62 63 64 65
68 70 74 75 76 77 78 79 81 83 84 85 86 87 89 92 93 94 97 98 99 100
101 102 103 104 105 107 108 110 111 114 115 116 117 118 119 120 121
123 124 126 129 130 131 132 134 135 145 146 147 148 **P**6
Primary Contact: Vincent G. Capece, Jr., President and Chief Executive Officer
CFO: Susan Martin, Vice President Finance
CMO: Arthur V. McDowell, III, M.D., Vice President Clinical Affairs
CIO: Ludwig Johnson, Vice President Information Technology
CHR: Gregory Nokes, Vice President Human Resources
CNO: Jacquelyn Calamari, MSN, Vice President and Chief Nursing Officer
Web address: www.middlesexhospital.org
**Control:** Other not–for–profit (including NFP Corporation) **Service:** General
Medical and Surgical

**Staffed Beds:** 237 **Admissions:** 13197 **Census:** 154 **Outpatient Visits:**
580594 **Births:** 1120 **Total Expense ($000):** 345861 **Payroll Expense
($000):** 164846 **Personnel:** 1789

**WHITING FORENSIC DIVISION OF CONNECTICUT VALLEY HOSPITAL** See
Connecticut Valley Hospital

## MILFORD—New Haven County

☒ **MILFORD HOSPITAL (070019)**, 300 Seaside Avenue, Zip 06460–4603;
tel. 203/876–4000 **A**1 9 10 **F**3 8 11 13 15 29 32 34 35 37 38 40 45 46 49
50 54 57 58 59 63 64 68 70 74 75 76 78 79 81 82 85 87 89 102 107 108
111 114 118 119 126 130 132 135 144 146
Primary Contact: Joseph Pelaccia, President and Chief Executive Officer
COO: Lloyd Friedman, M.D., Vice President Medical Affairs and Chief Operating
Officer
CFO: Joseph Pelaccia, President and Chief Executive Officer
CMO: Lloyd Friedman, M.D., Vice President Medical Affairs and Chief Operating
Officer
CIO: Marilyn Christensen, Director Information Technology
CHR: Jeffrey Komornik, Director Human Resources
CNO: Beverly Lyon, R.N., Vice President Nursing
Web address: www.milfordhospital.org
**Control:** Other not–for–profit (including NFP Corporation) **Service:** General
Medical and Surgical

**Staffed Beds:** 48 **Admissions:** 3119 **Census:** 34 **Outpatient Visits:** 52219
**Births:** 128 **Total Expense ($000):** 72077 **Payroll Expense ($000):** 35687
**Personnel:** 519

## NEW BRITAIN—Hartford County

☒ △ **HOSPITAL FOR SPECIAL CARE (072004)**, 2150 Corbin Avenue,
Zip 06053–2298; tel. 860/223–2761 **A**1 3 5 7 10 **F**1 3 11 29 30 35 39 53 56
64 90 91 92 93 96 119 130 131 132 135 146 148
Primary Contact: John J. Votto, D.O., President and Chief Executive Officer
CFO: Laurie A. Whelan, Senior Vice President Finance and Chief Financial Officer
CMO: Paul Scalise, M.D., Chief Pulmonary Medicine and Internal Medicine
CIO: Stan Jankowski, Vice President and Chief Information Officer
CHR: Judi Trczinski, Vice President and Chief Human Resources Officer
Web address: www.hfsc.org
**Control:** Other not–for–profit (including NFP Corporation) **Service:** Long–Term
Acute Care hospital

**Staffed Beds:** 225 **Admissions:** 609 **Census:** 197 **Outpatient Visits:** 22019
**Births:** 0 **Total Expense ($000):** 92698 **Payroll Expense ($000):** 52866
**Personnel:** 750

☒ **THE HOSPITAL OF CENTRAL CONNECTICUT (070035)**, 100 Grand Street,
Zip 06052–2017, Mailing Address: P.O. Box 100, Zip 06052–2017;
tel. 860/224–5011, (Includes BRADLEY MEMORIAL, 81 Meriden Avenue,
Southington, Zip 06489–3297; tel. 860/276–5000; NEW BRITAIN GENERAL, 100
Grand Street, Mailing Address: P.O. Box 100, Zip 06050–0100;
tel. 860/224–5011) **A**1 2 3 5 9 10 **F**3 11 12 13 15 18 20 22 28 29 30 31 34
35 38 40 44 45 49 50 51 53 54 57 58 59 60 61 64 65 66 68 70 72 74 75
76 77 78 79 81 84 85 86 87 89 93 97 98 99 100 101 102 103 104 105 107
108 110 111 114 115 117 118 119 120 121 123 124 126 129 130 132 135
144 146 147 148 **P**6 **S** Hartford HealthCare, Hartford, CT
Primary Contact: Lucille A. Janatka, President and Chief Executive Officer,
Hartford HealthCare Central Region
CFO: Brian Rogoz, Vice President Finance and Treasurer
CIO: Frank Pinto, Chief Information Officer
CHR: Elizabeth A. Lynch, Vice President Human Resources
Web address: www.thocc.org
**Control:** Other not–for–profit (including NFP Corporation) **Service:** General
Medical and Surgical

**Staffed Beds:** 188 **Admissions:** 14292 **Census:** 180 **Outpatient Visits:**
403555 **Births:** 1587 **Total Expense ($000):** 359304 **Payroll Expense
($000):** 148416 **Personnel:** 1813

**CT**

---

**Hospital, Medicare Provider Number, Address, Telephone, Approval, Facility, and Physician Codes, Health Care System**

★ American Hospital Association (AHA) membership    ○ Healthcare Facilities Accreditation Program    ⇧ Center for Improvement in Healthcare Quality Accreditation
☐ The Joint Commission accreditation    ◇ DNV Healthcare Inc. accreditation    △ Commission on Accreditation of Rehabilitation Facilities (CARF) accreditation

**NEW CANAAN—Fairfield County**

☐ **SILVER HILL HOSPITAL (074014)**, 208 Valley Road, Zip 06840–3899;
tel. 203/966–3561, (Nonreporting) **A**1 9 10
Primary Contact: Sigurd H. Ackerman, M.D., President and Chief Executive Officer
COO: Elizabeth Moore, Chief Operating Officer
CFO: Ruurd Leegstra, Chief Financial Officer
CMO: Sigurd H. Ackerman, M.D., President and Chief Executive Officer
CIO: Maria Klinga, Director Management Information Systems
CHR: Rich Juliana, Director Human Resources
Web address: www.silverhillhospital.org
**Control:** Other not–for–profit (including NFP Corporation) **Service:** Psychiatric

**Staffed Beds:** 60

**NEW HAVEN—New Haven County**

☐ **CONNECTICUT MENTAL HEALTH CENTER (074011)**, 34 Park Street,
Zip 06519–1109, Mailing Address: P.O. Box 1842, Zip 06508–1842;
tel. 203/974–7144, (Nonreporting) **A**1 3 5 9 10 **S** Connecticut Department of
Mental Health and Addiction Services, Hartford, CT
Primary Contact: Michael Sernyak, M.D., Director
COO: Robert Cole, Chief Operating Officer
CFO: Robert Cole, Chief Operating Officer
CMO: Jeanne Steines, D.O., Medical Director
CIO: Paul Moore, Chief Information Officer
CHR: Carolyn Wallace, Director Human Resources
Web address: www.ct.gov/dmhas/cwp/view.asp?a=2906&q=334596
**Control:** State–Government, nonfederal **Service:** Psychiatric

**Staffed Beds:** 39

**HOSPITAL OF SAINT RAPHAEL** See Yale–New Haven Hospital–Saint Raphael
Campus

☒ **YALE–NEW HAVEN HOSPITAL (070022)**, 20 York Street, Zip 06510–3202;
tel. 203/688–4242, (Includes YALE–NEW HAVEN CHILDREN'S HOSPITAL, 1 Park
Street, Zip 06504–8901; tel. 203/688–4242; YALE–NEW HAVEN
HOSPITAL–SAINT RAPHAEL CAMPUS, 1450 Chapel Street, Zip 06511–4405;
tel. 203/789–3000; Christopher M. O'Connor, President and Chief Executive
Officer; YALE–NEW HAVEN PSYCHIATRIC HOSPITAL, 184 Liberty Street,
Zip 06519–1625; tel. 203/688–9704; Paul Haeberle, Executive Director), (Total
facility includes 114 beds in nursing home–type unit) **A**1 2 3 5 8 9 10 **F**3 5 6 8
9 11 12 13 14 15 17 18 19 20 21 22 23 24 25 26 27 28 29 30 31 32 34 35
36 37 38 39 40 41 42 43 44 45 46 47 48 49 50 51 52 53 54 55 56 57 58
59 61 64 65 66 68 70 71 72 73 74 75 76 77 78 79 80 81 82 84 85 86 87
88 89 90 91 92 93 94 96 97 98 99 100 101 102 103 104 105 107 108 109
110 111 112 114 115 116 117 118 119 120 121 123 124 126 128 129 130
131 132 134 135 136 137 138 139 141 142 143 144 145 146 147 148 **P**2
3 5 6 **S** Yale New Haven Health System, New Haven, CT
Primary Contact: Marna P. Borgstrom, Chief Executive Officer
COO: Richard D'Aquila, President and Chief Operating Officer
CFO: James Staten, Senior Vice President Finance
CMO: Peter N. Herbert, M.D., Senior Vice President Medical Affairs and Chief of
Staff
CIO: Daniel Barchi, Senior Vice President Information Systems and Chief
Information Officer
CHR: Kevin A. Myatt, Senior Vice President Human Resources
CNO: Patricia Sue Fitzsimons, R.N., Senior Vice President Patient Services
Web address: www.ynhh.org
**Control:** Other not–for–profit (including NFP Corporation) **Service:** General
Medical and Surgical

**Staffed Beds:** 1576 **Admissions:** 73786 **Census:** 1199 **Outpatient Visits:**
1187405 **Births:** 5536 **Total Expense ($000):** 2303625 **Payroll Expense
($000):** 821315 **Personnel:** 11530

**NEW LONDON—New London County**

☒ △ **LAWRENCE + MEMORIAL HOSPITAL (070007)**, 365 Montauk Avenue,
Zip 06320–4769; tel. 860/442–0711, (Nonreporting) **A**1 2 3 7 9 10 **S** L+M
Healthcare, New London, CT
Primary Contact: Bruce D. Cummings, President and Chief Executive Officer
COO: Daniel Rissi, M.D., Vice President, Chief Medical and Clinical Operations
Officer
CFO: Lugene A. Inzana, Vice President and Chief Financial and Support Services
Officer
CMO: Daniel Rissi, M.D., Chief Medical and Clinical Operations
CIO: Kimberly Kalajainen, Vice President Operations and Chief Information Officer
CHR: Donna Epps, Vice President and Chief Human Resources Officer
CNO: Lauren Williams, R.N., Vice President of Professional Services and Chief
Nursing Officer
Web address: www.lmhospital.org
**Control:** Other not–for–profit (including NFP Corporation) **Service:** General
Medical and Surgical

**Staffed Beds:** 256

**NORWALK—Fairfield County**

☒ **NORWALK HOSPITAL (070034)**, 34 Maple Street, Zip 06850–3894;
tel. 203/852–2000 **A**1 2 3 5 9 10 **F**3 5 7 8 11 12 13 15 17 18 20 22 26 28
29 30 31 34 35 36 39 40 43 44 45 46 47 48 49 50 51 53 54 55 57 58 59
64 66 68 70 72 74 75 76 77 78 79 80 81 82 84 85 87 89 90 93 96 98 100
101 102 103 104 105 107 108 110 111 114 115 117 118 119 120 121 123
124 126 129 130 131 132 135 145 146 148 **P**8
Primary Contact: Michael Daglio, President
CFO: Michael Kruzick, Acting Chief Financial Officer
CMO: Michael Marks, M.D., Chief of Staff
CHR: Anthony Aceto, Vice President Human Resources
Web address: www.norwalkhospital.org
**Control:** Other not–for–profit (including NFP Corporation) **Service:** General
Medical and Surgical

**Staffed Beds:** 313 **Admissions:** 11907 **Census:** 153 **Outpatient Visits:**
262363 **Births:** 1367 **Total Expense ($000):** 311061 **Payroll Expense
($000):** 133022 **Personnel:** 1635

**NORWICH—New London County**

☒ **THE WILLIAM W. BACKUS HOSPITAL (070024)**, 326 Washington Street,
Zip 06360–2740; tel. 860/889–8331 **A**1 2 3 5 9 10 **F**3 9 11 12 13 15 18 20
26 28 29 30 31 34 35 36 40 42 43 45 46 49 50 51 54 57 58 59 61 62 63
64 65 70 71 74 75 76 78 79 81 82 84 85 86 87 89 92 93 97 98 100 101
102 103 104 105 107 108 110 111 114 115 116 117 118 119 120 121 126
130 132 134 135 144 145 146 147 148 **S** Hartford HealthCare, Hartford, CT
Primary Contact: David A. Whitehead, President, Hartford HealthCare East Region
COO: Carolyn Trantalis, R.N., Regional Vice President, Clinical Services and
Operations
CFO: Daniel E. Lohr, Regional Vice President Finance
CMO: Robert Sidman, M.D., Regional Vice President, Medical Affairs
CIO: Angie Mathieu, System Director Information Technology and Regional Chief
Information Officer
CHR: Karen James, Regional Director, Human Resources
CNO: Carolyn Trantalis, R.N., Regional Vice President, Clinical Services and
Operations
Web address: www.backushospital.org
**Control:** Other not–for–profit (including NFP Corporation) **Service:** General
Medical and Surgical

**Staffed Beds:** 184 **Admissions:** 9801 **Census:** 128 **Outpatient Visits:**
489134 **Births:** 896 **Total Expense ($000):** 251772 **Payroll Expense
($000):** 110167 **Personnel:** 1338

**PUTNAM—Windham County**

☒ **DAY KIMBALL HOSPITAL (070003)**, 320 Pomfret Street, Zip 06260–1836,
Mailing Address: P.O. Box 6001, Zip 06260–0901; tel. 860/928–6541,
(Nonreporting) **A**1 5 9 10
Primary Contact: Robert E. Smanik, FACHE, President and Chief Executive Officer
COO: Donald St. Onge, Chief Operating Officer
CFO: Douglas Glazier, Interim Chief Financial Officer
CMO: John Graham, M.D., Vice President Medical Affairs
CIO: Odile Romanick, Chief information Officer
CHR: John Miller, Director Human Resources
CNO: Donald St. Onge, Chief Operating Officer
Web address: www.daykimball.org
**Control:** Other not–for–profit (including NFP Corporation) **Service:** General
Medical and Surgical

**Staffed Beds:** 63

**ROCKY HILL—Hartford County**

☐ **CONNECTICUT VETERANS HOME AND HOSPITAL (072006)**, 287 West
Street, Zip 06067–3501; tel. 860/616–3606, (Nonreporting) **A**10
Primary Contact: Babatunde O. Green, Chief Executive Officer
CFO: Michael Clark, Fiscal Administrative Manager
CMO: Vamseedhar Alla, M.D., Director Medical Staff
CIO: Sheri DeVaux, Information Technology Manager
CHR: Noreen Sinclair, Human Resources Administrator
CNO: Jeff Lord, Director of Nursing
Web address: www.ct.gov/ctva
**Control:** State–Government, nonfederal **Service:** Long–Term Acute Care hospital

**Staffed Beds:** 125

**SHARON—Litchfield County**

☐ **SHARON HOSPITAL (070004)**, 50 Hospital Hill Road, Zip 06069–2096, Mailing
Address: P.O. Box 789, Zip 06069–0789; tel. 860/364–4000, (Nonreporting) **A**1
9 10 20 **S** RegionalCare Hospital Partners, Brentwood, TN
Primary Contact: Kim Lumia, President and Chief Executive Officer
CMO: Michael Parker, M.D., Chief of Staff
CHR: Kathleen Berlinghoff, Director Human Resources
Web address: www.sharonhospital.com
**Control:** Corporation, Investor–owned, for–profit **Service:** General Medical and
Surgical

**Staffed Beds:** 78

*Many Facility Codes have changed. Please refer to the AHA Guide Code Chart.*

## SOMERS—Tolland County

**CONNECTICUT DEPARTMENT OF CORRECTION'S HOSPITAL**, 100 Bilton Road, Zip 06071–1059, Mailing Address: P.O. Box 100, Zip 06071–0100; tel. 860/749–8391, (Nonreporting)
Primary Contact: Edward A. Blanchette, M.D., Director
**Control:** State–Government, nonfederal **Service:** Hospital unit of an institution (prison hospital, college infimary, etc.)

**Staffed Beds:** 29

## SOUTHINGTON—Hartford County

**BRADLEY MEMORIAL** See The Hospital of Central Connecticut, New Britain

## STAFFORD SPRINGS—Tolland County

☐ **JOHNSON MEMORIAL MEDICAL CENTER (070008)**, 201 Chestnut Hill Road, Zip 06076–4005; tel. 860/684–4251, (Nonreporting) **A**1 2 9 10
Primary Contact: Stuart E. Rosenberg, President and Chief Executive Officer
CFO: John Grish, Chief Financial Officer
CMO: Ian Tucker, M.D., Vice President Medical Affairs
CHR: Donna M. Megliola, Assistant Vice President
CNO: Patricia Jagoe, Assistant Vice President Patient Care
Web address: www.jmmc.com
**Control:** Other not–for–profit (including NFP Corporation) **Service:** General Medical and Surgical

**Staffed Beds:** 88

## STAMFORD—Fairfield County

☒ **STAMFORD HOSPITAL (070006)**, 30 Shelburne Road, Zip 06902–3628, Mailing Address: P.O. Box 9317, Zip 06904–9317; tel. 203/276–1000 **A**1 2 3 5 8 9 10 **F**3 8 11 12 13 15 17 18 19 20 22 24 26 28 29 30 31 32 34 35 36 37 38 40 41 43 44 45 46 47 48 49 50 52 53 54 55 56 57 58 59 60 61 64 65 66 68 70 71 72 73 74 75 76 77 78 79 81 82 84 85 86 87 89 90 91 92 93 95 96 97 98 100 101 102 103 104 107 108 110 111 114 115 116 117 118 119 120 121 123 124 126 129 130 131 132 135 144 145 146 147 148 **P**6
Primary Contact: Brian G. Grissler, President and Chief Executive Officer
COO: Kathleen A. Silard, R.N., Executive Vice President Operations and Chief Operating Officer
CFO: Kevin Gage, Chief Financial Officer
CMO: Sharon Kiely, M.D., Senior Vice President Medical Affairs and Chief Medical Officer
CIO: John Rossi, Vice President Information Systems and Chief Information Officer
CHR: Elaine Guglielmo, Vice President Human Resources and Organizational Development
CNO: Ellen M. Komar, R.N., Vice President Patient Care Services
Web address: www.stamhealth.org
**Control:** Other not–for–profit (including NFP Corporation) **Service:** General Medical and Surgical

**Staffed Beds:** 305 **Admissions:** 12766 **Census:** 178 **Outpatient Visits:** 431915 **Births:** 2082 **Total Expense ($000):** 443491 **Payroll Expense ($000):** 183394 **Personnel:** 2382

## TORRINGTON—Litchfield County

☐ **THE CHARLOTTE HUNGERFORD HOSPITAL (070011)**, 540 Litchfield Street, Zip 06790–6679, Mailing Address: P.O. Box 988, Zip 06790–0988; tel. 860/496–6666 **A**1 2 9 10 **F**13 15 18 28 29 30 31 32 34 35 38 40 42 45 47 48 49 50 51 57 59 60 63 64 68 70 74 75 76 78 79 80 81 82 83 85 87 89 93 94 97 98 99 100 102 104 105 107 108 110 115 116 118 119 120 121 123 129 130 131 132 135 144 145 146 148 **P**6
Primary Contact: Daniel J. McIntyre, President and Chief Executive Officer
CFO: Susan Schapp, Vice President Finance and Treasurer
CMO: Mark Prete, M.D., Vice President Medical Affairs
CHR: R. James Elliott, Vice President Human Resources
Web address: www.charlottehungerford.org
**Control:** Other not–for–profit (including NFP Corporation) **Service:** General Medical and Surgical

**Staffed Beds:** 76 **Admissions:** 5660 **Census:** 67 **Outpatient Visits:** 274002 **Births:** 446 **Total Expense ($000):** 121999 **Payroll Expense ($000):** 56703 **Personnel:** 675

## VERNON—Tolland County

☒ **ROCKVILLE GENERAL HOSPITAL (070012)**, 31 Union Street, Zip 06066–3160; tel. 860/872–0501 **A**1 5 10 **F**3 11 15 18 26 28 29 30 34 35 36 38 39 40 41 44 45 46 47 49 50 51 54 57 59 61 63 64 66 70 74 75 77 79 81 82 84 85 86 87 89 93 107 108 110 111 114 118 119 124 130 131 132 135 141 142 144 145 146 147 148 **P**3 5 6 8 **S** Eastern Connecticut Health Network, Manchester, CT
Primary Contact: Peter J. Karl, President and Chief Executive Officer
CFO: Michael D. Veillette, Senior Vice President and Chief Financial Officer
CMO: Joel R. Reich, M.D., Senior Vice President Medical Affairs
CIO: James Weeks, Interim Chief Information Officer
CHR: Deborah Gogliettino, Senior Vice President Human Resources
CNO: Mary Powers, MSN, Senior Vice President Patient Care Services
Web address: www.echn.org
**Control:** Other not–for–profit (including NFP Corporation) **Service:** General Medical and Surgical

**Staffed Beds:** 47 **Admissions:** 2343 **Census:** 31 **Outpatient Visits:** 113438 **Births:** 0 **Total Expense ($000):** 72160 **Payroll Expense ($000):** 32460 **Personnel:** 296

## WALLINGFORD—New Haven County

☐ △ **GAYLORD HOSPITAL (072003)**, Gaylord Farm Road, Zip 06492–7048, Mailing Address: P.O. Box 400, Zip 06492–7048; tel. 203/284–2800 **A**1 5 7 10 **F**1 29 30 31 34 35 53 54 59 60 64 74 75 82 84 87 91 93 94 95 96 107 114 119 129 130 131 132 146 148
Primary Contact: George M. Kyriacou, President and Chief Executive Officer
CFO: Art Tedesco, Interim Chief Financial Officer
CMO: Stephen Holland, M.D., Vice President Chief Medical Officer and Medical Director
CIO: Gerry Maroney, Chief Information Officer and Security Officer
CHR: Wally G. Harper, Vice President Human Resources
CNO: Virginia Staubach, R.N., Chief Nursing Officer and Senior Director of Nursing Services
Web address: www.gaylord.org
**Control:** Other not–for–profit (including NFP Corporation) **Service:** Long–Term Acute Care hospital

**Staffed Beds:** 137 **Admissions:** 1446 **Census:** 111 **Outpatient Visits:** 59720 **Births:** 0 **Total Expense ($000):** 75602 **Payroll Expense ($000):** 41237 **Personnel:** 453

★ **MASONICARE HEALTH CENTER (070039)**, 22 Masonic Avenue, Zip 06492–3048, Mailing Address: P.O. Box 70, Zip 06492–7001; tel. 203/679–5900, (Nonreporting) **A**3 5 10
Primary Contact: Stephen B. McPherson, President and Chief Executive Officer
COO: Jon–Paul Venoit, Chief Operating Officer
CFO: Raymond Scott Thelen, Vice President and Chief Financial Officer
CMO: Ronald Schwartz, M.D., Medical Director
CIO: Michael Nichols, Chief Information Officer
CHR: Edward Dooling, Vice President, Human Resources
CNO: Patti Russell, Vice President Nursing
Web address: www.masonicare.org
**Control:** Other not–for–profit (including NFP Corporation) **Service:** Other specialty

**Staffed Beds:** 65

## WATERBURY—New Haven County

☒ **SAINT MARY'S HOSPITAL (070016)**, 56 Franklin Street, Zip 06706–1281; tel. 203/709–6000 **A**1 2 3 5 9 10 **F**3 5 8 11 12 13 15 17 18 20 22 24 28 29 30 31 32 34 35 36 37 39 40 41 43 45 46 47 49 50 51 53 54 55 57 59 64 70 72 73 74 75 76 77 78 79 80 81 85 87 92 93 96 98 100 102 104 107 108 110 111 114 115 118 119 126 129 130 132 135 144 145 146 147 148 **P**6
Primary Contact: Chad W. Wable, President and Chief Executive Officer
COO: Charles Flinn, Vice President, Chief Operating Officer
CFO: Ralph W. Becker, Vice President, Chief Financial Officer
CMO: Steven E. Schneider, M.D., Chief Medical Officer
CIO: Michael Novak, Vice President, Operations and Chief Information Officer
CHR: M. Clark Kearney, Vice President Human Resources
CNO: Elizabeth Bozzuto, R.N., Chief Nursing Officer and Vice President
Web address: www.stmh.org
**Control:** Church–operated, Nongovernment, not–for profit **Service:** General Medical and Surgical

**Staffed Beds:** 168 **Admissions:** 10757 **Census:** 134 **Outpatient Visits:** 242659 **Births:** 1089 **Total Expense ($000):** 227227 **Payroll Expense ($000):** 85350 **Personnel:** 1273

CT

---

**Hospital, Medicare Provider Number, Address, Telephone, Approval, Facility, and Physician Codes, Health Care System**

★ American Hospital Association (AHA) membership
☐ The Joint Commission accreditation
○ Healthcare Facilities Accreditation Program
◇ DNV Healthcare Inc. accreditation
⇑ Center for Improvement in Healthcare Quality Accreditation
△ Commission on Accreditation of Rehabilitation Facilities (CARF) accreditation

✦ **WATERBURY HOSPITAL (070005)**, 64 Robbins Street, Zip 06708–2600; tel. 203/573–6000 **A**1 2 3 5 9 10 19 **F**3 5 9 12 13 15 17 18 20 22 24 28 29 30 31 34 35 38 40 41 43 44 45 47 49 50 51 53 55 57 59 61 64 68 70 72 73 74 75 76 78 79 81 82 84 85 87 96 97 98 99 100 101 102 103 104 105 107 108 111 115 119 129 130 131 132 145 146 148
Primary Contact: Darlene Stromstad, FACHE, President and Chief Executive Officer
CFO: Colleen M. Scott, Vice President Finance
CMO: David Puzzuto, M.D., Vice President Medical Affairs and Chief Medical Officer
CIO: Michael J. Cemeno, Chief Information Officer
CHR: Diane Woolley, Vice President Human Resources
CNO: Sandra Ladarola, Chief Nursing Officer
Web address: www.waterburyhospital.org
**Control:** Other not–for–profit (including NFP Corporation) **Service:** General Medical and Surgical

**Staffed Beds:** 176 **Admissions:** 10708 **Census:** 154 **Outpatient Visits:** 199897 **Births:** 1059 **Total Expense ($000):** 216453 **Payroll Expense ($000):** 83909 **Personnel:** 1111

### WEST HARTFORD—Hartford County

★ **THE HOSPITAL AT HEBREW HEALTH CARE (070040)**, 1 Abrahms Boulevard, Zip 06117–1525; tel. 860/523–3800, (Nonreporting) **A**10
Primary Contact: Bonnie B. Gauthier, President and Chief Executive Officer
COO: Marcia H. Hickey, Senior Vice President Operations
CFO: David Houle, Executive Vice President and Chief Financial Officer
CMO: Ava Pannullo, M.D., Vice President Medical Services and Physician in Chief
CHR: Sam Vogt, Manager Human Resources
Web address: www.hebrewhealthcare.org
**Control:** Other not–for–profit (including NFP Corporation) **Service:** Other specialty

**Staffed Beds:** 332

### WEST HAVEN—New Haven County

✦ **VETERANS AFFAIRS CONNECTICUT HEALTHCARE SYSTEM**, 950 Campbell Avenue, Zip 06516–2770; tel. 203/932–5711, (Includes WEST HAVEN DIVISION, 950 Campbell Avenue, Zip 06516–2700; tel. 203/932–5711), (Nonreporting) **A**1 2 3 5 8 **S** Department of Veterans Affairs, Washington, DC
Primary Contact: Gerald F. Culliton, Medical Center Director
CFO: Joseph LaMadeleine, Chief Financial Officer
CMO: Michael Ebert, M.D., Chief of Staff
CIO: Joseph Erdos, M.D., Chief Information Officer
CHR: Mark Bain, Chief Human Resources
Web address: www.connecticut.va.gov
**Control:** Veterans Affairs, Government, federal **Service:** General Medical and Surgical

**Staffed Beds:** 197

### WESTPORT—Fairfield County

**ST. VINCENT'S BEHAVIORAL HEALTH** See St. Vincent's Medical Center, Bridgeport

### WILLIMANTIC—Windham County

**WINDHAM COMMUNITY MEMORIAL HOSPITAL** See Windham Hospital

✦ **WINDHAM HOSPITAL (070021)**, 112 Mansfield Avenue, Zip 06226–2040; tel. 860/456–9116 **A**1 2 5 9 10 **F**3 8 11 12 13 14 15 17 18 28 29 30 31 32 34 35 36 40 45 48 50 51 54 56 57 59 60 61 63 64 65 66 68 69 70 74 75 76 77 78 79 81 82 83 84 85 86 87 89 93 94 100 102 107 108 110 111 115 116 117 118 119 129 130 131 132 134 135 144 146 147 148 **S** Hartford HealthCare, Hartford, CT
Primary Contact: David A. Whitehead, President, Hartford HealthCare East Region
COO: Carolyn Trantalis, R.N., Chief Operating Officer, East Region
CFO: Daniel E. Lohr, Regional Vice President Finance
CMO: Nadia Nashid, M.D., Chief of Staff
CHR: Theresa L. Buss, Regional Vice President Human Resources
Web address: www.windhamhospital.org
**Control:** Other not–for–profit (including NFP Corporation) **Service:** General Medical and Surgical

**Staffed Beds:** 56 **Admissions:** 3080 **Census:** 34 **Outpatient Visits:** 91730 **Births:** 389 **Total Expense ($000):** 86793 **Payroll Expense ($000):** 38236 **Personnel:** 461

*Many Facility Codes have changed. Please refer to the AHA Guide Code Chart.*
© 2015 AHA Guide

# DELAWARE

## DOVER—Kent County

☒ **BAYHEALTH MEDICAL CENTER (080004)**, 640 South State Street, Zip 19901–3530; tel. 302/674–4700, (Includes BAYHEALTH MEDICAL CENTER AT KENT GENERAL, 640 South State Street, Zip 19901–3597; BAYHEALTH MEDICAL CENTER, MILFORD MEMORIAL HOSPITAL, 21 West Clarke Avenue, Milford, Zip 19963–1840, Mailing Address: P.O. Box 199, Zip 19963–0199; tel. 302/430–5738; Michael Ashton, Administrator) **A**1 2 3 5 9 10 **F**3 8 11 12 13 15 17 18 20 22 24 26 28 29 30 31 32 34 35 38 40 41 42 43 44 45 47 48 49 50 51 53 54 55 57 58 59 60 61 62 64 67 68 70 72 73 74 75 76 77 78 79 81 82 84 85 86 87 89 90 93 94 98 99 100 101 102 103 104 107 108 110 111 114 115 117 118 119 120 121 123 124 126 129 130 131 132 134 135 144 146 147 148
Primary Contact: Terry Murphy, President and Chief Executive Officer
COO: Deborah Watson, Senior Vice President and Chief Operating Officer
CFO: Mike Tretina, Senior Vice President and Chief Financial Officer
CMO: Gary M. Siegelman, M.D., Senior Vice President and Chief Medical Officer
CIO: Richard Mohnk, Vice President Corporate Services
CHR: Shana Ross, Vice President Human Resources
CNO: Bonnie I. Perratto, MSN, Senior Vice President, Chief Nurse Executive
Web address: www.bayhealth.org
**Control:** Other not–for–profit (including NFP Corporation) **Service:** General Medical and Surgical

**Staffed Beds: 347 Admissions: 18581 Census: 272 Outpatient Visits: 568266 Births: 2272 Total Expense ($000): 481846 Payroll Expense ($000): 220793 Personnel: 2932**

☐ **DOVER BEHAVIORAL HEALTH SYSTEM (084004)**, 725 Horsepond Road, Zip 19901–7232; tel. 302/741–0140, (Nonreporting) **A**1 9 10 **S** Universal Health Services, Inc., King of Prussia, PA
Primary Contact: Jean–Charles Constant, Administrator
Web address: www.doverbehavioral.com
**Control:** Corporation, Investor–owned, for–profit **Service:** Psychiatric

**Staffed Beds: 72**

## LEWES—Sussex County

☒ **BEEBE HEALTHCARE (080007)**, 424 Savannah Road, Zip 19958–1462; tel. 302/645–3300 **A**1 2 3 6 9 10 19 **F**2 3 8 11 12 13 15 17 18 20 22 24 26 28 29 30 31 32 34 35 36 38 40 43 45 46 49 50 51 54 55 56 57 58 59 60 61 62 64 65 68 70 74 75 76 77 78 79 80 81 83 84 85 87 89 93 97 100 107 108 110 111 114 115 116 117 118 119 120 121 123 124 130 131 132 134 143 146 147 148 **P**4
Primary Contact: Jeffrey M. Fried, FACHE, President and Chief Executive Officer
CFO: Paul Pernice, Vice President Finance
CMO: Jeffrey Hawtof, M.D., Vice President Medical Operations and Informatics
CIO: Michael Maksymow, Vice President Information Systems
CHR: Catherine Halen, Vice President Human Resources
CNO: Steve Rhone, R.N., Vice President Patient Care Services
Web address: www.beebemed.org
**Control:** Other not–for–profit (including NFP Corporation) **Service:** General Medical and Surgical

**Staffed Beds: 155 Admissions: 9978 Census: 112 Outpatient Visits: 459008 Births: 856 Total Expense ($000): 278248 Payroll Expense ($000): 103240 Personnel: 1743**

## MILFORD—Sussex County

**BAYHEALTH MEDICAL CENTER, MILFORD MEMORIAL HOSPITAL** See Bayhealth Medical Center, Dover

## NEW CASTLE—New Castle County

☐ **DELAWARE PSYCHIATRIC CENTER (084001)**, 1901 North Dupont Highway, Zip 19720–1199; tel. 302/255–2700 **A**1 3 5 10 **F**30 34 39 58 59 65 68 75 86 87 98 100 101 103 106 130 132 135 143 **P**1
Primary Contact: Melissa A. Smith, Deputy Director
CIO: James Nau, Manager Computer and Applications Support
Web address: www.dhss.delaware.gov
**Control:** State–Government, nonfederal **Service:** Psychiatric

**Staffed Beds: 169 Admissions: 498 Census: 113 Outpatient Visits: 0 Births: 0 Total Expense ($000): 35389 Payroll Expense ($000): 16985 Personnel: 397**

☐ **MEADOW WOOD BEHAVIORAL HEALTH SYSTEM (084003)**, 575 South Dupont Highway, Zip 19720–4606; tel. 302/328–3330, (Nonreporting) **A**1 9 10 **S** Acadia Healthcare Company, Inc., Franklin, TN
Primary Contact: Bill A. Mason, Chief Executive Officer
CFO: Maria Valdenegro, Chief Financial Officer
Web address: www.meadowwoodhospital.com
**Control:** Corporation, Investor–owned, for–profit **Service:** Psychiatric

**Staffed Beds: 53**

## NEWARK—New Castle County

☒ **CHRISTIANA CARE HEALTH SYSTEM (080001)**, 4755 Ogletown–Stanton Road, Zip 19718–0002, Mailing Address: P.O. Box 6001, Zip 19714–6001; tel. 302/733–1000, (Includes CHRISTIANA HOSPITAL, 201 South Broom Street, Wilmington, Zip 19805, Mailing Address: P.O. Box 2653, Zip 19805; tel. 302/658–6711; WILMINGTON HOSPITAL, 501 West 14th Street, Wilmington, Zip 19801, Mailing Address: Box 1668, Zip 19899; tel. 302/733–1000) **A**1 2 3 5 8 9 10 12 13 **F**2 3 6 7 8 11 12 13 15 17 18 20 22 24 26 28 29 30 31 32 34 35 36 37 38 39 40 41 42 43 44 45 46 47 48 49 50 51 53 54 55 56 57 58 59 60 61 62 64 65 66 68 70 72 74 75 76 77 78 79 80 81 82 84 85 86 87 88 89 90 92 93 94 96 97 98 99 100 101 102 103 104 105 107 108 110 111 114 115 116 117 118 119 120 121 123 124 126 129 130 131 132 134 135 136 138 143 145 146 147 148 **P**5 6 **S** Christiana Care Health System, Wilmington, DE
Primary Contact: Janice E. Nevin, M.D., M.P.H., Chief Executive Officer
COO: Gary W. Ferguson, Executive Vice President and Chief Operating Officer
CFO: Thomas L. Corrigan, Senior Vice President Finance, Managed Care and Chief Financial Officer
CIO: Randall Gaboriault, Chief Information Officer
CHR: Audrey C. Van Luven, Senior Vice President and Chief Human Resources Officer
CNO: Diane P. Talarek, R.N., Chief Nursing Officer
Web address: www.christianacare.org
**Control:** Other not–for–profit (including NFP Corporation) **Service:** General Medical and Surgical

**Staffed Beds: 1007 Admissions: 52779 Census: 764 Outpatient Visits: 582257 Births: 6427 Total Expense ($000): 1460347 Payroll Expense ($000): 705510 Personnel: 9455**

☐ **ROCKFORD CENTER (084002)**, 100 Rockford Drive, Zip 19713–2121; tel. 302/996–5480 **A**1 9 10 **F**98 99 103 104 105 **P**6 8 **S** Universal Health Services, Inc., King of Prussia, PA
Primary Contact: John F. McKenna, Chief Executive Officer and Managing Director
CFO: Kumar Purohit, Chief Financial Officer
CHR: Jessi Stewart, Director Human Resources
CNO: Michelle Singletary–Twyman, Chief Nursing Officer
Web address: www.rockfordcenter.com
**Control:** Corporation, Investor–owned, for–profit **Service:** Psychiatric

**Staffed Beds: 118 Admissions: 4552 Census: 120 Outpatient Visits: 15867 Births: 0**

## SEAFORD—Sussex County

☒ **NANTICOKE MEMORIAL HOSPITAL (080006)**, 801 Middleford Road, Zip 19973–3636; tel. 302/629–6611 **A**1 2 9 10 **F**3 12 13 15 18 22 28 29 30 31 32 34 35 37 40 43 45 50 51 54 57 59 60 64 65 68 70 74 75 76 77 78 79 81 84 85 86 87 89 91 93 107 108 111 114 115 117 119 120 121 123 129 130 131 132 135 144 146 147 148 **P**6
Primary Contact: Steven A. Rose, R.N., President and Chief Executive Officer
COO: Penny Short, R.N., Chief Operating Officer
CFO: Denise Jester, Chief Financial Officer
CMO: Robert Ferber, M.D., Chief Clinical Innovation Officer
CIO: Susan Godesky, Director Information Technology
CHR: Barbara A. Hendricks, Vice President, Human Resources
CNO: Lori L. Lee, Assistant Vice President Nursing
Web address: www.nanticoke.org
**Control:** Other not–for–profit (including NFP Corporation) **Service:** General Medical and Surgical

**Staffed Beds: 99 Admissions: 5278 Census: 55 Outpatient Visits: 126025 Births: 882 Total Expense ($000): 110724 Payroll Expense ($000): 41583 Personnel: 853**

**DE**

---

**Hospital, Medicare Provider Number, Address, Telephone, Approval, Facility, and Physician Codes, Health Care System**

★ American Hospital Association (AHA) membership  ○ Healthcare Facilities Accreditation Program  ⇑ Center for Improvement in Healthcare Quality Accreditation
☐ The Joint Commission accreditation  ◇ DNV Healthcare Inc. accreditation  △ Commission on Accreditation of Rehabilitation Facilities (CARF) accreditation

## WILMINGTON—New Castle County

☒ △ **ALFRED I. DUPONT HOSPITAL FOR CHILDREN (083300)**, 1600 Rockland Road, Zip 19803–3616, Mailing Address: Box 269, Zip 19899–0269; tel. 302/651–4000 **A**1 3 5 7 10 **F**3 8 11 12 17 18 19 20 21 22 23 24 25 26 27 29 30 31 32 34 35 36 37 39 40 41 43 44 45 48 50 53 54 55 56 57 58 59 60 61 64 65 68 72 73 74 75 77 78 79 80 81 82 84 85 86 87 88 89 90 91 92 93 94 96 97 99 100 101 102 104 107 111 115 118 119 126 127 129 130 131 132 136 137 138 139 143 146 148 **S** Nemours, Jacksonville, FL
Primary Contact: Roy Proujansky, M.D., Chief Executive Officer
COO: Paul D. Kempinski, Chief Operating Officer
CFO: William N. Britton, Associate Administrator Finance
CMO: Brent R. King, Chief Medical Officer and Chief Physician
CIO: Ann Altoe, Senior Director Information Systems and Security Officer
Web address: www.nemours.org
**Control:** Other not–for–profit (including NFP Corporation) **Service:** Children's general

**Staffed Beds:** 196 **Admissions:** 8715 **Census:** 133 **Outpatient Visits:** 165172 **Births:** 0 **Total Expense ($000):** 381615 **Payroll Expense ($000):** 127770 **Personnel:** 2034

**CHRISTIANA HOSPITAL** See Christiana Care Health System, Newark

☒ **SELECT SPECIALTY HOSPITAL–WILMINGTON (082000)**, 701 North Clayton Street, 5th Floor, Zip 19805–3948; tel. 302/421–4545 **A**1 10 **F**1 29 130 148 **S** Select Medical Corporation, Mechanicsburg, PA
Primary Contact: Donna Gares, R.N., FACHE, MSN, Chief Executive Officer
CFO: David Huffman, Vice President and Controller
CMO: Hummayun Ismail, M.D., Medical Director
CHR: Barbara A. Foster, Regional Human Resources Director
Web address: www.wilmington.selectspecialtyhospitals.com
**Control:** Corporation, Investor–owned, for–profit **Service:** Long–Term Acute Care hospital

**Staffed Beds:** 35 **Admissions:** 337 **Census:** 30 **Outpatient Visits:** 0 **Births:** 0 **Total Expense ($000):** 15244 **Payroll Expense ($000):** 6840 **Personnel:** 92

☒ **ST. FRANCIS HOSPITAL (080003)**, Seventh and Clayton Streets, Zip 19805–0500, Mailing Address: P.O. Box 2500, Zip 19805–0500; tel. 302/421–4100, (Nonreporting) **A**1 2 3 5 9 10 **S** Trinity Health, Livonia, MI
Primary Contact: Brian E. Dietz, FACHE, Interim President and Chief Executive officer
CIO: Paul W. Rowe, Director Information Technology
CHR: Charlene J. Wilson, Vice President Human Resources
Web address: www.stfrancishealthcare.org
**Control:** Other not–for–profit (including NFP Corporation) **Service:** General Medical and Surgical

**Staffed Beds:** 214

**WILMINGTON HOSPITAL** See Christiana Care Health System, Newark

☒ **WILMINGTON VETERANS AFFAIRS MEDICAL CENTER**, 1601 Kirkwood Highway, Zip 19805–4989; tel. 302/994–2511, (Nonreporting) **A**1 2 3 5 8 **S** Department of Veterans Affairs, Washington, DC
Primary Contact: Robin C. Aube–Warren, Director
CFO: Mary Ann Kozel, Chief Fiscal
CMO: Enrique Guttin, M.D., Chief of Staff
CIO: Scott Vlars, Chief Information Technology Services
CHR: Louis McCloskey, Chief Human Resources
Web address: www.va.gov/wilmington
**Control:** Veterans Affairs, Government, federal **Service:** General Medical and Surgical

**Staffed Beds:** 60

# DISTRICT OF COLUMBIA

**WASHINGTON—District Of Columbia County**

✠ **CHILDREN'S NATIONAL MEDICAL CENTER (093300)**, 111 Michigan Avenue N.W., Zip 20010–2916; tel. 202/476–5000 **A**1 3 5 8 9 10 **F**3 5 7 8 11 12 14 17 18 19 21 23 25 27 29 30 31 32 34 35 36 38 39 40 41 42 43 44 45 46 48 49 50 51 54 55 57 58 59 60 61 64 65 66 68 71 72 74 75 77 78 79 81 82 83 84 85 86 87 88 89 92 93 94 96 97 98 99 100 102 104 107 111 112 115 116 117 118 119 126 129 130 131 132 134 136 137 138 141 142 146 148 **P**6
Primary Contact: Kurt Newman, M.D., President and Chief Executive Officer
COO: Kathleen Gorman, MSN, Executive Vice President Patient Care Services and Chief Operating Officer
CFO: Douglas Myers, Executive Vice President and Chief Financial Officer
CMO: Mark L. Batshaw, M.D., Physician–in–Chief, Executive Vice President and Chief Academic Officer
CIO: Brian Jacobs, M.D., Vice President Chief Information Officer and Chief Medical Information Officer
CHR: Darryl Varnado, Executive Vice President and Chief People Officer
CNO: Linda Talley, MS, Vice President and Chief Nursing Officer
Web address: www.childrensnational.org
**Control:** Other not–for–profit (including NFP Corporation) **Service:** Children's general

**Staffed Beds:** 303 **Admissions:** 14580 **Census:** 224 **Outpatient Visits:** 505848 **Births:** 0 **Total Expense ($000):** 723882 **Payroll Expense ($000):** 327006 **Personnel:** 5338

✠ △ **GEORGE WASHINGTON UNIVERSITY HOSPITAL (090001)**, 900 23rd Street N.W., Zip 20037–2342; tel. 202/715–4000, (Nonreporting) **A**1 2 3 5 7 8 9 10 **S** Universal Health Services, Inc., King of Prussia, PA
Primary Contact: Barry A. Wolfman, Chief Executive Officer and Managing Director
COO: Kimberly Russo, Chief Operating Officer
CFO: Richard Davis, Chief Financial Officer
CMO: Gary Little, M.D., Medical Director
CIO: Louis Duhe, Senior Director Information Technology
CHR: Erin Fagan, Manager Human Resources
Web address: www.gwhospital.com
**Control:** Partnership, Investor–owned, for–profit **Service:** General Medical and Surgical

**Staffed Beds:** 363

**GEORGETOWN UNIVERSITY HOSPITAL** See MedStar Georgetown University Hospital

✠ **HOWARD UNIVERSITY HOSPITAL (090003)**, 2041 Georgia Avenue N.W., Zip 20060–0002; tel. 202/865–6100 **A**1 2 3 5 8 9 10 **F**3 8 12 13 15 17 18 24 26 28 29 30 31 32 34 35 36 38 39 40 41 43 44 45 46 50 54 55 56 57 58 59 60 61 64 65 66 68 70 71 72 73 74 75 76 77 78 79 81 82 85 86 87 89 93 97 98 99 100 101 102 103 104 107 108 110 111 114 115 118 119 123 124 129 130 132 146 147 148 **P**4
Primary Contact: James D. Edwards, Chief Executive Officer
COO: Paul Mullings, Chief Operating Officer
CMO: Thomas E. Gaiter, M.D., Chief Medical Officer
CIO: Bernie Galla, Interim Director Management Information Systems
CHR: Anthony Jacks, Director Human Resources
Web address: www.huhealthcare.com
**Control:** Other not–for–profit (including NFP Corporation) **Service:** General Medical and Surgical

**Staffed Beds:** 280 **Admissions:** 8525 **Census:** 127 **Outpatient Visits:** 167102 **Births:** 956 **Total Expense ($000):** 307544 **Payroll Expense ($000):** 129904 **Personnel:** 1901

✠ **MEDSTAR GEORGETOWN UNIVERSITY HOSPITAL (090004)**, 3800 Reservoir Road N.W., Zip 20007–2197; tel. 202/444–2000 **A**1 2 3 5 8 9 10 **F**3 9 11 13 15 18 20 26 28 29 30 31 32 34 35 37 40 43 44 45 46 47 48 49 50 51 55 57 58 59 60 61 64 65 66 68 70 71 72 73 74 75 77 78 79 80 81 82 84 85 86 87 88 89 92 93 94 97 98 99 100 102 103 104 105 107 108 109 110 111 114 115 116 117 118 119 120 121 123 124 126 129 130 131 132 134 136 138 139 142 145 146 147 148 **P**6 **S** MedStar Health, Columbia, MD
Primary Contact: Richard L. Goldberg, M.D., President
COO: Michael Sachtleben, Chief Operating Officer
CFO: Paul Warda, Chief Financial Officer
CMO: Lisa Boyle, M.D., Vice President Medical Affairs and Medical Director
CIO: Catherine Szenczy, Senior Vice President and Chief Information Officer
CHR: Mary Jo Schweickhardt, Vice President Human Resources
CNO: Eileen Brennan Ferrell, MS, Vice President and Chief Nursing Officer
Web address: www.georgetownuniversityhospital.org
**Control:** Other not–for–profit (including NFP Corporation) **Service:** General Medical and Surgical

**Staffed Beds:** 399 **Admissions:** 16496 **Census:** 315 **Outpatient Visits:** 811423 **Births:** 1116 **Total Expense ($000):** 855864 **Payroll Expense ($000):** 402581 **Personnel:** 4483

✠ △ **MEDSTAR NATIONAL REHABILITATION HOSPITAL (093025)**, 102 Irving Street N.W., Zip 20010–2949; tel. 202/877–1000 **A**1 3 5 7 9 10 **F**3 11 28 29 30 34 35 36 44 54 58 60 64 68 74 75 77 78 79 82 86 87 90 91 92 93 94 95 96 119 129 130 131 132 146 148 **P**6 **S** MedStar Health, Columbia, MD
Primary Contact: John D. Rockwood, President
CFO: Michael Boemmel, Vice President and Chief Financial Officer
CMO: Michael R. Yochelson, M.D., Vice President and Medical Director
CHR: Pamela Ashby, Vice President Human Resources
CNO: Rosemary C. Welch, R.N., Vice President and Chief Nursing Officer
Web address: www.medstarnrh.org
**Control:** Other not–for–profit (including NFP Corporation) **Service:** Rehabilitation

**Staffed Beds:** 137 **Admissions:** 2221 **Census:** 105 **Outpatient Visits:** 278119 **Births:** 0 **Total Expense ($000):** 107669 **Payroll Expense ($000):** 60281 **Personnel:** 1204

✠ **MEDSTAR WASHINGTON HOSPITAL CENTER (090011)**, 110 Irving Street N.W., Zip 20010–3017; tel. 202/877–7000 **A**1 2 3 5 8 9 10 **F**3 5 7 9 12 13 15 16 17 18 20 22 24 26 28 29 30 31 34 35 36 37 38 39 40 43 44 45 46 47 48 49 50 51 54 55 56 57 58 59 60 61 62 63 64 65 66 68 70 72 73 74 75 76 77 78 79 80 81 82 84 85 86 87 92 97 98 100 101 102 103 104 105 107 108 109 110 111 112 114 115 116 117 118 119 120 121 124 126 130 131 132 135 137 138 142 144 146 147 148 **P**1 **S** MedStar Health, Columbia, MD
Primary Contact: John Sullivan, President
COO: Robert Ross, Chief Operating Officer
CFO: William Gayne, Chief Financial Officer
CMO: Gregory J. Argyros, M.D., Senior Vice President, Medical Affairs & Chief Medical Officer
CIO: Joe Brothman, Assistant Vice President, Information Systems
CHR: James P. Hill, Senior Vice President Administrative Services
CNO: Susan E. Eckert, R.N., Senior Vice President and Chief Nursing Officer
Web address: www.whcenter.org
**Control:** Other not–for–profit (including NFP Corporation) **Service:** General Medical and Surgical

**Staffed Beds:** 763 **Admissions:** 35795 **Census:** 593 **Outpatient Visits:** 384112 **Births:** 3305 **Total Expense ($000):** 1086489 **Payroll Expense ($000):** 495851 **Personnel:** 5397

**NATIONAL REHABILITATION HOSPITAL** See MedStar National Rehabilitation Hospital

**DC**

---

**Hospital, Medicare Provider Number, Address, Telephone, Approval, Facility, and Physician Codes, Health Care System**

★ American Hospital Association (AHA) membership
☐ The Joint Commission accreditation
○ Healthcare Facilities Accreditation Program
◇ DNV Healthcare Inc. accreditation
⇑ Center for Improvement in Healthcare Quality Accreditation
△ Commission on Accreditation of Rehabilitation Facilities (CARF) accreditation

✠ **PROVIDENCE HOSPITAL (090006)**, 1150 Varnum Street N.E.,
Zip 20017–2104; tel. 202/269–7000, (Total facility includes 252 beds in nursing
home–type unit) **A**1 2 3 5 9 10 **F**3 4 5 12 13 15 17 20 26 29 30 31 34 35 40
42 43 44 45 46 49 50 53 54 56 57 59 61 64 65 66 68 69 70 72 74 75 76
77 78 79 81 82 83 84 85 86 87 91 92 93 94 95 96 97 98 102 103 104 105
106 107 108 111 112 114 118 119 126 128 129 130 131 132 134 135 143
146 147 148 **S** Ascension Health, Saint Louis, MO
Primary Contact: Amy E. Freeman, President and Chief Executive Officer
CFO: Rick Talento, Senior Vice President and Chief Financial Officer
CMO: Raymond L. Cox, M.D., Chief Medical Officer
CIO: Alan Wyman, Chief Information Officer
CHR: Matt Lasecki, Interim Vice President Human Resources
CNO: Thedosia Munford, Senior Vice President and Chief Nursing Officer
Web address: www.provhosp.org
**Control:** Other not–for–profit (including NFP Corporation) **Service:** General
Medical and Surgical

**Staffed Beds:** 438 **Admissions:** 11279 **Census:** 374 **Outpatient Visits:**
105537 **Births:** 2113 **Total Expense ($000):** 200244 **Payroll Expense
($000):** 83617 **Personnel:** 1594

☐ **PSYCHIATRIC INSTITUTE OF WASHINGTON (094004)**, 4228 Wisconsin
Avenue N.W., Zip 20016–2138; tel. 202/885–5600, (Nonreporting) **A**1 5 9 10
Primary Contact: Charles J. Baumgardner, President and Chief Executive Officer
COO: Carol Desjeunes, Vice President and Chief Operating Officer
CFO: Aarti Subramanian, Vice President and Chief Financial Officer
CMO: Howard Hoffman, M.D., Medical Director
CIO: Ray Santina, Director Information Systems
CHR: Dawn Hatterer–Hoag, Director Human Resources
Web address: www.psychinstitute.com
**Control:** Corporation, Investor–owned, for–profit **Service:** Psychiatric

**Staffed Beds:** 104

★ **SAINT ELIZABETHS HOSPITAL (094001)**, 1100 Alabama Avenue S.E.,
Zip 20032–4540; tel. 202/299–5000 **A**3 5 10 **F**30 39 56 59 65 74 75 86 91
98 99 103 130 135 146 148
Primary Contact: Beth Gouse, Ph.D., Interim Chief Executive Officer
CFO: James V. Jackson, Budget Director
CMO: Bernard Arons, M.D., Director Medical Affairs
CNO: Clotilde Vidoni–Clark, R.N., Chief Nurse Executive
Web address: www.dbh.dc.gov/
**Control:** State–Government, nonfederal **Service:** Psychiatric

**Staffed Beds:** 292 **Admissions:** 434 **Census:** 264 **Outpatient Visits:** 0
**Births:** 0 **Personnel:** 776

✠ **SIBLEY MEMORIAL HOSPITAL (090005)**, 5255 Loughboro Road N.W.,
Zip 20016–2633; tel. 202/537–4000, (Total facility includes 45 beds in nursing
home–type unit) **A**1 2 3 5 9 10 **F**3 6 8 10 12 13 14 15 17 18 19 20 29 30 31
34 35 36 40 46 47 48 51 53 55 56 57 58 59 60 62 63 64 65 68 70 74 75
76 77 78 79 81 82 84 85 86 87 92 93 96 98 100 102 103 105 107 108 109
110 111 114 117 119 120 121 123 126 128 129 130 131 132 135 141 145
146 147 148 **S** Johns Hopkins Health System, Baltimore, MD
Primary Contact: Richard O. Davis, Ph.D., President
COO: Sanjay K. Saha, Chief Operating Officer
CFO: Marty Basso, Chief Financial Officer
CMO: M. Therese McDonnell, M.D., Interim Vice President Patient Safety, Quality
and Medical Affairs
CIO: Christopher T. Timbers, Chief Information Officer
CHR: Queenie C. Plater, Vice President Human Resources for JHM Community
Division
CNO: Lynn Meuer, Interim Chief Nursing Officer
Web address: www.sibley.org
**Control:** Other not–for–profit (including NFP Corporation) **Service:** General
Medical and Surgical

**Staffed Beds:** 246 **Admissions:** 11676 **Census:** 157 **Outpatient Visits:**
95325 **Births:** 3398 **Total Expense ($000):** 272166 **Payroll Expense
($000):** 116498 **Personnel:** 1533

☐ **SPECIALTY HOSPITAL OF WASHINGTON (092002)**, 700 Constitution Avenue
N.E., Zip 20002–6058; tel. 202/546–5700, (Nonreporting) **A**1 10 **S** Specialty
Hospitals of America, LLC, Portsmouth, NH
Primary Contact: Susan P. Bailey, R.N., Chief Executive Officer
CFO: Ed Clark, Vice President Finance
CMO: Manisha Singal, M.D., Medical Director
CHR: Margaret A. Fisher, Executive Director Human Resources
Web address: www.specialtyhospitalofwashington.com
**Control:** Corporation, Investor–owned, for–profit **Service:** Long–Term Acute Care
hospital

**Staffed Beds:** 177

☐ **SPECIALTY HOSPITAL OF WASHINGTON–HADLEY (092003)**, 4601 Martin
Luther King Jr. Avenue, S.W., Zip 20032–1131; tel. 202/574–5700,
(Nonreporting) **A**1 10 **S** Specialty Hospitals of America, LLC, Portsmouth, NH
Primary Contact: Cathy Borris–Hale, Chief Executive Officer
CFO: Ronald Davis, Chief Financial Officer
CMO: Samir Al–Khouri, M.D., Medical Director
CHR: Bing Lechoco, Director Human Resources
**Control:** Corporation, Investor–owned, for–profit **Service:** Long–Term Acute Care
hospital

**Staffed Beds:** 82

✠ △ **THE HSC PEDIATRIC CENTER**, 1731 Bunker Hill Road N.E.,
Zip 20017–3096; tel. 202/832–4400 **A**1 7 9 **F**12 29 31 32 34 35 39 50 54
58 64 65 68 71 75 80 83 84 86 90 91 93 94 96 130 132 143 146 148 **P**6
Primary Contact: John Mathewson, Interim Chief Operating Officer
COO: John Mathewson, Interim Chief Operating Officer
CFO: Nancy J. Southers, Vice President and Chief Financial Officer
CMO: Robert Blake, M.D., Chief Medical Officer
CHR: Lynne Hostetter, Vice President Human Resources
CNO: Debbie C. Holson, R.N., Vice President Patient Care Services and Chief
Nursing Officer
Web address: www.hscpediatriccenter.org/
**Control:** Other not–for–profit (including NFP Corporation) **Service:** Children's
chronic disease

**Staffed Beds:** 118 **Admissions:** 279 **Census:** 39 **Outpatient Visits:** 11954
**Births:** 0 **Total Expense ($000):** 39531 **Payroll Expense ($000):** 17397
**Personnel:** 239

✠ **UNITED MEDICAL CENTER (090008)**, 1310 Southern Avenue S.E.,
Zip 20032–4623; tel. 202/574–6000, (Total facility includes 120 beds in nursing
home–type unit) **A**1 9 10 **F**3 13 15 18 20 22 29 30 34 35 40 45 50 57 59 60
61 64 65 68 70 74 75 76 77 78 79 81 85 87 91 93 96 97 98 100 102 107
108 110 111 114 119 128 130 146 147 148
Primary Contact: Andrew L. Davis, Jr., Interim Chief Executive Officer
COO: Pamela R. Lee, Executive Vice President Operations and Chief Quality
Officer
CFO: Barbara Roberson, Interim Chief Financial Officer
CMO: Julian R. Craig, Chief Medical Officer
CIO: Thomas Hallisey, Chief Information Officer
CHR: Jackie Johnson, Executive Vice President Human Resources
CNO: Maribel Torres, Executive Vice President Patient Care Services and Chief
Nursing Officer
Web address: www.united–medicalcenter.com
**Control:** Other not–for–profit (including NFP Corporation) **Service:** General
Medical and Surgical

**Staffed Beds:** 354 **Admissions:** 6794 **Census:** 106 **Outpatient Visits:** 91540
**Births:** 483 **Total Expense ($000):** 102975 **Payroll Expense ($000):** 46540
**Personnel:** 690

**VETERANS AFFAIRS MEDICAL CENTER** See Washington DC Veterans Affairs
Medical Center

✠ △ **WASHINGTON DC VETERANS AFFAIRS MEDICAL CENTER**, 50 Irving
Street N.W., Zip 20422–0002; tel. 202/745–8000, (Nonreporting) **A**1 2 3 5 7 9
**S** Department of Veterans Affairs, Washington, DC
Primary Contact: Brian A. Hawkins, Director
CFO: Frank Filosa, Fiscal Manager
CIO: Amanda Graves, Chief Information Systems
Web address: www.washingtondc.va.gov/
**Control:** Veterans Affairs, Government, federal **Service:** General Medical and
Surgical

**Staffed Beds:** 291

**WASHINGTON HOSPITAL CENTER** See MedStar Washington Hospital Center

# FLORIDA

## ALTAMONTE SPRINGS—Seminole County

**FLORIDA HOSPITAL–ALTAMONTE** See Florida Hospital, Orlando

☐ **HEALTHSOUTH REHABILITATION HOSPITAL OF ALTAMONTE SPRINGS**, 831 South State Road 434, Zip 32714–3502; tel. 407/587–8600, (Nonreporting) **A**1 **S** HEALTHSOUTH Corporation, Birmingham, AL
Primary Contact: Jill Jordan, Chief Executive Officer
Web address: www.healthsouthaltamontesprings.com
**Control:** Corporation, Investor–owned, for–profit **Service:** Rehabilitation

**Staffed Beds: 50**

## APALACHICOLA—Franklin County

**GEORGE E. WEEMS MEMORIAL HOSPITAL (101305)**, 135 Avenue G., Zip 32320–1613, Mailing Address: P.O. Box 580, Zip 32329–0580; tel. 850/653–8853, (Nonreporting) **A**9 10 18
Primary Contact: Mike Cooper, Chief Executive Officer
CFO: James Robinson, Chief Financial Officer
CIO: Dennis Peterson, Chief Information Officer
CHR: Ginny Grimer, Director Human Resources
Web address: www.weemsmemorial.com
**Control:** Partnership, Investor–owned, for–profit **Service:** General Medical and Surgical

**Staffed Beds: 23**

## APOPKA—Orange County

**FLORIDA HOSPITAL–APOPKA** See Florida Hospital, Orlando

## ARCADIA—Desoto County

☐ **DESOTO MEMORIAL HOSPITAL (100175)**, 900 North Robert Avenue, Zip 34266–8712, Mailing Address: P.O. Box 2180, Zip 34265–2180; tel. 863/494–3535, (Nonreporting) **A**1 9 10 20
Primary Contact: Vincent A. Sica, President and Chief Executive Officer
CFO: Dan Hogan, Chief Financial Officer
CMO: Steven Mishkind, M.D., Chief of Staff
CIO: Kristen Spahr, Director of Marketing
CHR: Lois Hilton, Director Human Resources
CNO: Joseph La Cava, Chief Nursing Officer and Director Of Anesthesia
Web address: www.dmh.org
**Control:** Other not–for–profit (including NFP Corporation) **Service:** General Medical and Surgical

**Staffed Beds: 49**

## ATLANTIS—Palm Beach County

✠ **JFK MEDICAL CENTER (100080)**, 5301 South Congress Avenue, Zip 33462–1197; tel. 561/965–7300, (Nonreporting) **A**1 2 3 5 9 10 **S** HCA, Nashville, TN
Primary Contact: Gina Melby, Chief Executive Officer
CFO: Jim Leamon, Chief Financial Officer
CIO: Jane Stewart, Director Information Services
CHR: Trudy Bromley, Vice President Human Resources
Web address: www.jfkmc.com
**Control:** Corporation, Investor–owned, for–profit **Service:** General Medical and Surgical

**Staffed Beds: 424**

## AVENTURA—Miami-Dade County

✠ **AVENTURA HOSPITAL AND MEDICAL CENTER (100131)**, 20900 Biscayne Boulevard, Zip 33180–1407; tel. 305/682–7000, (Nonreporting) **A**1 2 3 9 10 **S** HCA, Nashville, TN
Primary Contact: Dianne Goldenberg, Chief Executive Officer
COO: Lorna Kernizan, Chief Operating Officer
CFO: Alisa Bert, Chief Financial Officer
CMO: Martin Grossman, Chief of Staff
CHR: Denver Hopkins, Director of Human Resources
CNO: Karen Bibbo, R.N., Chief Nursing Officer
Web address: www.aventurahospital.com
**Control:** Corporation, Investor–owned, for–profit **Service:** General Medical and Surgical

**Staffed Beds: 359**

## BARTOW—Polk County

✠ **BARTOW REGIONAL MEDICAL CENTER (100121)**, 2200 Osprey Boulevard, Zip 33830–3308, Mailing Address: P.O. Box 1050, Zip 33831–1050; tel. 863/533–8111, (Nonreporting) **A**1 9 10 **S** Community Health Systems, Inc., Franklin, TN
Primary Contact: Philip Minden, Chief Executive Officer
CFO: Michael Boscia, Chief Financial Officer
CMO: Stuart Patterson, M.D., Chief of Staff
CIO: Vilakon Champavannarath, Director Information Systems
CHR: Marie Horton, Director Associate Relations
Web address: www.bartowregional.com
**Control:** Corporation, Investor–owned, for–profit **Service:** General Medical and Surgical

**Staffed Beds: 72**

## BAY PINES—Pinellas County

✠ △ **BAY PINES VETERANS AFFAIRS HEALTHCARE SYSTEM**, 10000 Bay Pines Boulevard, Zip 33744–8200, Mailing Address: P.O. Box 5005, Zip 33744–5005; tel. 727/398–6661, (Total facility includes 112 beds in nursing home–type unit) **A**1 2 3 5 7 9 **F**3 4 5 8 12 15 18 20 22 26 28 29 30 31 36 38 39 40 45 46 47 49 51 53 54 56 57 58 59 60 61 62 63 64 65 68 70 74 75 77 78 79 81 82 83 84 85 86 87 90 91 93 94 97 98 100 101 102 103 104 105 106 107 108 110 111 114 115 116 117 118 119 120 121 123 128 129 130 131 132 135 143 144 146 147 148 **P**6 **S** Department of Veterans Affairs, Washington, DC
Primary Contact: Suzanne M. Klinker, Director
COO: Kris Brown, Associate Director
CFO: Jeanine Ergle, Chief Financial Officer
CMO: George F. Van Buskirk, M.D., Chief of Staff
CIO: John Williams, Chief Information Officer
CHR: Paula Buchele, Chief Human Resources
Web address: www.baypines.va.gov/
**Control:** Veterans Affairs, Government, federal **Service:** General Medical and Surgical

**Staffed Beds: 396 Admissions: 10991 Census: 320 Outpatient Visits: 1382369 Births: 0 Total Expense ($000): 689681 Payroll Expense ($000): 285018 Personnel: 4017**

## BELLE GLADE—Palm Beach County

**GLADES GENERAL HOSPITAL** See Lakeside Medical Center

✠ **LAKESIDE MEDICAL CENTER (100130)**, 39200 Hooker Highway, Zip 33430–5368; tel. 561/996–6571 **A**1 9 10 13 **F**3 11 13 15 29 34 35 40 50 56 57 68 70 76 80 81 85 87 89 91 92 93 107 108 109 110 111 114 119 130 135 146
Primary Contact: Thomas J. Leach, Administrator
COO: Darcy Davis, Chief Financial Officer
CFO: Darcy Davis, Chief Financial Officer
CMO: Ron Wiewora, M.D., Chief Medical Officer
CIO: Rick Roche, Director Human Resources and Information Systems
CHR: Rick Roche, Director Human Resources and Information Systems
Web address: www.lakesidemedical.org
**Control:** Hospital district or authority, Government, nonfederal **Service:** General Medical and Surgical

**Staffed Beds: 70 Admissions: 2641 Census: 26 Outpatient Visits: 33780 Births: 479 Total Expense ($000): 42807 Payroll Expense ($000): 16287 Personnel: 293**

## BLOUNTSTOWN—Calhoun County

**CALHOUN–LIBERTY HOSPITAL (101304)**, 20370 N.E. Burns Avenue, Zip 32424–1045, Mailing Address: P.O. Box 419, Zip 32424–0419; tel. 850/674–5411 **A**9 10 18 **F**3 7 15 29 34 40 45 50 54 57 59 107 110 114 119 127 128 133
Primary Contact: Phillip Hill, Chief Executive Officer
CFO: Nathan Ebersole, Controller
CIO: Michael Flowers, Director Information Management
CHR: Lynn Pitts, Director Human Resources
CNO: Debra Summers, Chief Nursing Officer
Web address: www.calhounlibertyhospital.com
**Control:** Other not–for–profit (including NFP Corporation) **Service:** General Medical and Surgical

**Staffed Beds: 25 Admissions: 677 Census: 15 Outpatient Visits: 23167 Births: 1 Total Expense ($000): 9937 Payroll Expense ($000): 5496 Personnel: 159**

**FL**

---

**Hospital, Medicare Provider Number, Address, Telephone, Approval, Facility, and Physician Codes, Health Care System**

★ American Hospital Association (AHA) membership
☐ The Joint Commission accreditation
○ Healthcare Facilities Accreditation Program
◇ DNV Healthcare Inc. accreditation
⇑ Center for Improvement in Healthcare Quality Accreditation
△ Commission on Accreditation of Rehabilitation Facilities (CARF) accreditation

## BOCA RATON—Palm Beach County

**BOCA RATON COMMUNITY HOSPITAL** See Boca Raton Regional Hospital

☐ **BOCA RATON REGIONAL HOSPITAL (100168)**, 800 Meadows Road, Zip 33486–2368; tel. 561/955–7100 **A**1 2 3 5 9 10 **F**3 6 8 11 12 13 15 17 18 20 22 24 26 28 29 30 31 34 35 36 37 40 44 45 46 47 48 49 50 51 53 54 55 56 57 58 59 60 61 62 64 68 70 71 72 74 75 76 77 78 79 81 82 84 85 86 87 91 92 93 94 96 97 100 102 103 107 108 109 110 111 112 114 115 116 117 118 119 120 121 123 124 126 130 131 132 135 144 145 146 147 148 **P**6
Primary Contact: Jerry J. Fedele, President and Chief Executive Officer
COO: Karen Poole, Chief Operating Officer
CFO: Dawn Jauersack, Vice President and Chief Financial Officer
CMO: Charles Posternack, M.D., Vice President
CIO: Robin Hildwein, Chief Information Officer
CHR: Mindy Raymond, Vice President Human Resources
CNO: Melissa Durbin, R.N., Chief Nursing Officer
Web address: www.brrh.com
**Control:** Other not-for-profit (including NFP Corporation) **Service:** General Medical and Surgical

**Staffed Beds:** 413 **Admissions:** 17018 **Census:** 219 **Outpatient Visits:** 342462 **Births:** 2093 **Total Expense ($000):** 365699 **Payroll Expense ($000):** 141793 **Personnel:** 2133

✠ **WEST BOCA MEDICAL CENTER (100268)**, 21644 State Road 7, Zip 33428–1899; tel. 561/488–8000 **A**1 5 9 10 **F**8 13 15 18 19 29 31 35 39 40 41 49 54 57 64 70 72 74 76 79 80 81 85 86 88 89 93 107 108 109 110 111 114 115 117 118 119 126 129 130 131 147 148 **P**4 5 **S** TENET Healthcare Corporation, Dallas, TX
Primary Contact: Mitchell S. Feldman, Chief Executive Officer
COO: Laura A. Cillo, Chief Operating Officer
CFO: Brook Thomas, Chief Financial Officer
CMO: Jack L. Harari, M.D., Chief Medical Officer
CIO: Lauren McCauley, Marketing Director
CHR: Stephanie Sherman, Chief Human Resources Officer
CNO: Ruth Schwarzkopf, R.N., Chief Nursing Officer
Web address: www.westbocamedctr.com
**Control:** Corporation, Investor-owned, for-profit **Service:** General Medical and Surgical

**Staffed Beds:** 195 **Admissions:** 9985 **Census:** 111 **Outpatient Visits:** 68752 **Births:** 1990 **Total Expense ($000):** 116941 **Payroll Expense ($000):** 50542 **Personnel:** 628

## BONIFAY—Holmes County

☐ **DOCTORS MEMORIAL HOSPITAL (101307)**, 2600 Hospital Drive, Zip 32425–4264, Mailing Address: P.O. Box 188, Zip 32425–0188; tel. 850/547–8000 **A**1 9 10 18 **F**3 11 15 29 30 40 45 50 57 59 64 70 77 81 90 93 107 110 114 119 131 133 146 148
Primary Contact: Joann Baker, Administrator
CFO: Celia F. Ward, Controller and Chief Financial Officer
CMO: Leisa Bailey, M.D., Chief of Staff
CIO: Rohan Anderson, Chief Information Officer
CHR: Christy Booth, Chief Human Resources Officer
CNO: Karla Rockwell, Director of Nursing
Web address: www.doctorsmemorial.org
**Control:** Hospital district or authority, Government, nonfederal **Service:** General Medical and Surgical

**Staffed Beds:** 20 **Admissions:** 539 **Census:** 6 **Births:** 0 **Total Expense ($000):** 12076 **Payroll Expense ($000):** 4785

## BOYNTON BEACH—Palm Beach County

☐ **BETHESDA HOSPITAL EAST (100002)**, 2815 South Seacrest Boulevard, Zip 33435–7995; tel. 561/737–7733 **A**1 3 5 9 10 **F**3 8 12 13 17 18 20 22 24 26 28 29 30 31 35 40 41 45 46 49 50 51 56 58 60 61 64 68 70 72 74 75 76 77 78 79 81 86 87 88 89 90 93 94 96 107 110 111 114 115 119 120 121 123 124 126 129 130 131 132 133 143 146 148 **P**6
Primary Contact: Roger L. Kirk, President and Chief Executive Officer
COO: Gary Nordmark, Administrator and Vice President Operations
CFO: Joanne Aquilina, Vice President Finance and Chief Financial Officer
CMO: Albert Biehl, M.D., Vice President Medical Affairs
CIO: Leslie Albright, Vice President Information Systems
CHR: Regina Bellway, Vice President Human Resources
CNO: Geralyn Lunsford, R.N., Administration and Vice President Patient Services
Web address: www.bethesdaweb.com
**Control:** Other not-for-profit (including NFP Corporation) **Service:** General Medical and Surgical

**Staffed Beds:** 481 **Admissions:** 19813 **Census:** 286 **Outpatient Visits:** 239540 **Births:** 3022 **Total Expense ($000):** 273617 **Payroll Expense ($000):** 101745 **Personnel:** 1845

## BRADENTON—Manatee County

✠ △ **BLAKE MEDICAL CENTER (100213)**, 2020 59th Street West, Zip 34209–4669; tel. 941/792–6611 **A**1 2 7 9 10 **F**3 11 15 17 18 20 22 24 26 27 28 29 30 31 34 35 40 43 45 48 49 50 57 58 59 64 68 70 74 75 77 78 79 80 81 85 87 90 91 92 93 94 96 100 107 108 110 111 114 115 118 119 126 129 130 131 132 146 147 148 **S** HCA, Nashville, TN
Primary Contact: Daniel J. Friedrich, III, Chief Executive Officer
COO: Valerie L. Powell–Stafford, Chief Operating Officer
CMO: Kirk Cianciolo, D.O., Chief Medical Officer
CIO: Shannon Piatkowski, Director Information Technology
CHR: Veronica Lequeux, Vice President Human Resources
Web address: www.blakemedicalcenter.com
**Control:** Corporation, Investor–owned, for–profit **Service:** General Medical and Surgical

**Staffed Beds:** 377 **Admissions:** 15314 **Census:** 205 **Births:** 0 **Personnel:** 1051

☐ **LAKEWOOD RANCH MEDICAL CENTER (100299)**, 8330 Lakewood Ranch Boulevard, Zip 34202–5174; tel. 941/782–2100, (Nonreporting) **A**1 9 10 **S** Universal Health Services, Inc., King of Prussia, PA
Primary Contact: Linda S. Widra, FACHE, Ph.D., R.N., Interim Chief Executive Officer
COO: Linda S. Widra, FACHE, Chief Operating Officer
CFO: Gerald Christine, Chief Financial Officer
CHR: Trish Morales, Director Human Resources
Web address: www.lakewoodranchmedicalcenter.com
**Control:** Corporation, Investor–owned, for–profit **Service:** General Medical and Surgical

**Staffed Beds:** 120

**MANATEE GLENS HOSPITAL AND ADDICTION CENTER (104040)**, (Substance Abuse, Mental Health and Addictions), 2020 26th Avenue East, Zip 34208–7753, Mailing Address: P.O. Box 9478, Zip 34206–9478; tel. 941/782–4600 **A**9 10 13 **F**4 5 38 44 50 61 98 99 100 101 102 103 104 132 134 135
Primary Contact: Mary Ruiz, Chief Executive Officer
CFO: Sean Gingras, CPA, Chief Financial Officer
CMO: Ranjay Halder, M.D., Chief Medical Director
CIO: Heidi L. Blair, Vice President Administration
CHR: Colleen O'Connor, Director Human Resources
Web address: www.manateeglens.org
**Control:** Other not–for–profit (including NFP Corporation) **Service:** Other specialty

**Staffed Beds:** 30 **Admissions:** 3877 **Census:** 30 **Outpatient Visits:** 0 **Births:** 0 **Total Expense ($000):** 4780 **Payroll Expense ($000):** 3152

☐ **MANATEE MEMORIAL HOSPITAL (100035)**, 206 Second Street East, Zip 34208–1000; tel. 941/746–5111, (Nonreporting) **A**1 2 5 9 10 12 13 **S** Universal Health Services, Inc., King of Prussia, PA
Primary Contact: Kevin DiLallo, Chief Executive Officer
CFO: Mark A. Tierney, Chief Financial Officer
CMO: Linda Christmann, M.D., Chief of Staff
CIO: Troy Beaubien, Director Information Services
CHR: Sheree Threewits, Director Human Resources
CNO: Darlette Tice, Chief Nursing Officer
Web address: www.manateememorial.com
**Control:** Partnership, Investor–owned, for–profit **Service:** General Medical and Surgical

**Staffed Beds:** 319

☐ **SUNCOAST BEHAVIORAL HEALTH CENTER**, 4480 51st Street West, Zip 34210–2855; tel. 941/251–5000, (Nonreporting) **A**1 9 **S** Universal Health Services, Inc., King of Prussia, PA
Primary Contact: Brandy Hamilton, Chief Executive Officer
CFO: Linda Weymouth, Chief Financial Officer
CMO: Jaime Barker, M.D., Medical Director
Web address: www.suncoastbhc.com
**Control:** Corporation, Investor–owned, for–profit **Service:** Children's hospital psychiatric

**Staffed Beds:** 60

## BRANDON—Hillsborough County

✠ **BRANDON REGIONAL HOSPITAL (100243)**, 119 Oakfield Drive, Zip 33511–5779; tel. 813/681–5551, (Nonreporting) **A**1 5 9 10 **S** HCA, Nashville, TN
Primary Contact: Bland Eng, Chief Executive Officer
CFO: Michael T. Terrell, Chief Financial Officer
CMO: Joseph C. Corcoran, Chief Medical Officer
CIO: Aaron Fountain, Chief Information Officer
CHR: Doug Goodman, Vice President Human Resources
CNO: Chris Taramasco, R.N., Chief Nursing Officer
Web address: www.brandonhospital.com
**Control:** Corporation, Investor–owned, for–profit **Service:** General Medical and Surgical

**Staffed Beds:** 407

**FL**

*Many Facility Codes have changed. Please refer to the AHA Guide Code Chart.* © 2015 AHA Guide

## BROOKSVILLE—Hernando County

⊠ **BAYFRONT HEALTH BROOKSVILLE (100071)**, 17240 Cortez Boulevard, Zip 34601–8921, Mailing Address: P.O. Box 37, Zip 34605–0037; tel. 352/796–5111, (Includes BAYFRONT HEALTH SPRING HILL, 10461 Quality Drive, Spring Hill, Zip 34609–9634; tel. 352/688–8200; Patrick Maloney, Market Chief Executive Officer), (Nonreporting) **A**1 9 10 **S** Community Health Systems, Inc., Franklin, TN
Primary Contact: Kenneth R. Wicker, Chief Executive Officer
COO: Scott Hartsell, Chief Operating Officer
CFO: Matthew Seagroves, Chief Financial Officer
CMO: Mohammad A. Joud, M.D., Chief of Staff
CIO: Lee Burch, Director Management Information Systems
CHR: Claudia L. Jack, Director Associate Relations
Web address: www.brooksvilleregionalhospital.org
**Control:** Corporation, Investor–owned, for–profit **Service:** General Medical and Surgical

**Staffed Beds:** 120

⊠ **HEALTHSOUTH REHABILITATION HOSPITAL OF SPRING HILL (103042)**, 12440 Cortez Boulevard, Zip 34613–2628; tel. 352/592–4250, (Nonreporting) **A**1 9 10 **S** HEALTHSOUTH Corporation, Birmingham, AL
Primary Contact: Lori Bedard, Chief Executive Officer
CFO: Kimberly Lunt, Controller
CMO: Mira Zelin, D.O., Medical Director
CIO: Myra Merillo, Supervisor Health Information Management
CHR: Mary Salamanca, Director Human Resources
CNO: Edwin Montanez, R.N., Chief Nursing Officer
Web address: www.healthsouthspringhill.com
**Control:** Corporation, Investor–owned, for–profit **Service:** Rehabilitation

**Staffed Beds:** 80

⊠ **OAK HILL HOSPITAL (100264)**, 11375 Cortez Boulevard, Zip 34613–5409; tel. 352/596–6632 **A**1 2 3 9 10 **F**3 11 15 18 20 22 24 26 29 30 31 34 35 40 41 45 46 48 49 50 51 56 57 59 64 70 74 75 77 78 79 81 85 87 93 107 108 110 111 114 115 116 119 126 130 131 132 146 147 148 **P**6 **S** HCA, Nashville, TN
Primary Contact: Mickey Smith, Chief Executive Officer
COO: Sonia I. Wellman, R.N., Chief Operating Officer
CFO: Matt Romero, Chief Financial Officer
CMO: Mike Torres, M.D., Chief Medical Officer
CIO: Cindy Peters, Chief Information Officer
CHR: Charles Snider, Vice President Human Resources
CNO: Leanne Salazar, Chief Nursing Officer
Web address: www.oakhillhospital.com
**Control:** Corporation, Investor–owned, for–profit **Service:** General Medical and Surgical

**Staffed Beds:** 262 **Admissions:** 15110 **Census:** 181 **Outpatient Visits:** 81456 **Births:** 0 **Total Expense ($000):** 162763 **Payroll Expense ($000):** 57353 **Personnel:** 989

☐ **SPRINGBROOK HOSPITAL (104057)**, 7007 Grove Road, Zip 34609–8610; tel. 352/596–4306 **A**1 9 10 **F**4 98 106 135
Primary Contact: James E. O'Shea, Administrator
Web address: www.springbrookhospital.org/
**Control:** Corporation, Investor–owned, for–profit **Service:** Psychiatric

**Staffed Beds:** 66 **Admissions:** 2601 **Census:** 65 **Outpatient Visits:** 0 **Births:** 0 **Total Expense ($000):** 12033 **Payroll Expense ($000):** 5321 **Personnel:** 114

## CAPE CORAL—Lee County

★ ◇ **CAPE CORAL HOSPITAL (100244)**, 636 Del Prado Boulevard, Zip 33990–2695; tel. 239/424–2000 **A**9 10 21 **F**3 11 13 14 15 17 18 20 28 29 30 34 35 40 43 45 46 48 50 51 52 53 56 57 59 60 65 66 68 70 74 75 76 77 79 81 82 84 85 86 87 89 94 97 107 108 110 111 114 129 130 132 135 146 147 148 **S** Lee Memorial Health System, Fort Myers, FL
Primary Contact: James R. Nathan, President and Chief Executive Officer
COO: Lawrence Antonucci, M.D., Chief Operating Officer
CFO: Mike German, Chief Financial Officer
CMO: Mark Greenberg, M.D., Chief Medical Officer
CIO: Mike Smith, Chief Information Officer
CHR: Jon C. Cecil, Chief Human Resource Officer
CNO: 
Web address: www.leememorial.org
**Control:** Hospital district or authority, Government, nonfederal **Service:** General Medical and Surgical

**Staffed Beds:** 291 **Admissions:** 16266 **Census:** 183 **Outpatient Visits:** 242184 **Births:** 1395

## CELEBRATION—Osceola County

**FLORIDA HOSPITAL CELEBRATION HEALTH** See Florida Hospital, Orlando

## CHATTAHOOCHEE—Gadsden County

**FLORIDA STATE HOSPITAL (104000)**, U.S. Highway 90 East, Zip 32324–1000, Mailing Address: P.O. Box 1000, Zip 32324–1000; tel. 850/663–7536, (Nonreporting) **A**10
Primary Contact: Diane R. James, Administrator
CFO: Denise Smith, Director Financial Services
Web address: www.dcf.state.fl.us/institutions/fsh
**Control:** State–Government, nonfederal **Service:** Psychiatric

**Staffed Beds:** 987

## CHIPLEY—Washington County

☐ **NORTHWEST FLORIDA COMMUNITY HOSPITAL (101308)**, 1360 Brickyard Road, Zip 32428–6303, Mailing Address: P.O. Box 889, Zip 32428–0889; tel. 850/638–1610 (Total facility includes 34 beds in nursing home-type unit) **A**1 9 10 18 **F**3 11 15 18 29 30 34 35 40 45 57 59 62 68 81 82 85 93 104 107 111 114 119 127 128 129 130 131 133 135 146 148 **S** Alliant Management Services, Louisville, KY
Primary Contact: Mark E. Bush, Chief Executive Officer
COO: Janet Kinney, Chief Operating Officer
CFO: Marcey Black, Chief Financial Officer
CHR: Shelia Schiefelbein, Coordinator Human Resources
CNO: Joan Beard, Chief Nursing Officer
Web address: www.nfch.org
**Control:** Corporation, Investor–owned, for–profit **Service:** General Medical and Surgical

**Staffed Beds:** 59 **Admissions:** 844 **Census:** 44 **Outpatient Visits:** 53432 **Births:** 0 **Total Expense ($000):** 23179 **Payroll Expense ($000):** 9258 **Personnel:** 193

## CLEARWATER—Pinellas County

⊠ **MORTON PLANT HOSPITAL (100127)**, 300 Pinellas Street, Zip 33756–3804, Mailing Address: P.O. Box 210, Zip 33757–0210; tel. 727/462–7000, (Total facility includes 120 beds in nursing home–type unit) **A**1 2 3 5 9 10 **F**3 5 6 9 11 13 15 17 18 20 22 24 26 28 29 30 31 34 35 37 38 40 42 45 46 48 49 50 51 53 54 55 56 57 58 59 60 61 62 64 65 66 68 70 72 74 75 76 77 78 79 80 81 82 84 85 86 87 98 99 100 101 102 103 104 107 108 109 110 111 114 115 116 117 118 119 120 121 123 124 126 128 129 130 131 132 143 144 145 146 147 148 **P**6 **S** Morton Plant Mease Health Care, Clearwater, FL
Primary Contact: N. Kristopher Hoce, President
CFO: Carl Tremonti, Chief Financial Officer
CMO: Jeff Jensen, D.O., Vice President, Medical Affairs
CHR: Angel Brown, Director Human Resources
CNO: Lisa Johnson, R.N., Chief Nursing Executive
Web address: www.mortonplant.com
**Control:** Other not–for–profit (including NFP Corporation) **Service:** General Medical and Surgical

**Staffed Beds:** 662 **Admissions:** 24194 **Census:** 300 **Outpatient Visits:** 327512 **Births:** 2249 **Total Expense ($000):** 406411 **Payroll Expense ($000):** 126949 **Personnel:** 2239

☐ **WINDMOOR HEALTHCARE OF CLEARWATER (104017)**, 11300 U.S. 19 North, Zip 33764; tel. 727/541–2646, (Nonreporting) **A**1 9 10 **S** Universal Health Services, Inc., King of Prussia, PA
Primary Contact: Wendy Merson, Chief Executive Officer
Web address: www.windmoor.com
**Control:** Corporation, Investor–owned, for–profit **Service:** Psychiatric

**Staffed Beds:** 100

## CLERMONT—Lake County

☐ **SOUTH LAKE HOSPITAL (100051)**, 1900 Don Wickham Drive, Zip 34711–1979; tel. 352/394–4071 **A**1 9 10 **F**3 8 11 13 15 18 20 22 26 28 29 30 31 32 34 35 37 40 45 46 47 48 49 50 51 53 54 57 59 60 62 64 66 68 70 74 75 76 77 78 79 81 82 85 86 87 89 92 93 107 108 110 111 114 115 116 117 119 124 126 127 130 131 132 135 145 146 147 148 **P**6 **S** Orlando Health, Orlando, FL
Primary Contact: John Moore, President
COO: Paul Johns, Chief Operating Officer
CFO: Lance Sewell, Chief Financial Officer
CHR: Sue Brown, Administrator Human Resources
CNO: Linda Walton, R.N., Chief Nursing Officer
Web address: www.southlakehospital.com
**Control:** Hospital district or authority, Government, nonfederal **Service:** General Medical and Surgical

**Staffed Beds:** 122 **Admissions:** 8490 **Census:** 93 **Outpatient Visits:** 105585 **Births:** 598 **Total Expense ($000):** 135246 **Payroll Expense ($000):** 52575 **Personnel:** 999

**FL**

---

**Hospital, Medicare Provider Number, Address, Telephone, Approval, Facility, and Physician Codes, Health Care System**

★ American Hospital Association (AHA) membership
☐ The Joint Commission accreditation
◯ Healthcare Facilities Accreditation Program
◇ DNV Healthcare Inc. accreditation
⇑ Center for Improvement in Healthcare Quality Accreditation
△ Commission on Accreditation of Rehabilitation Facilities (CARF) accreditation

## CLEWISTON—Hendry County

✠ **HENDRY REGIONAL MEDICAL CENTER (101309)**, 524 West Sagamore Avenue, Zip 33440–3514; tel. 863/902–3000 **A**1 9 10 18 **F**3 11 15 18 29 34 35 40 45 50 57 59 64 65 68 70 75 77 79 81 82 85 91 93 97 107 110 111 114 119 127 130 133 135 146 **P**6 **S** QHR, Brentwood, TN
Primary Contact: R. D. Williams, Chief Executive Officer
CFO: John Beltz, Chief Financial Officer
CMO: Karim Kaki, M.D., Chief Medical Director
CIO: Leon Hoover, Director Information Systems
CHR: Lisa Miller, Director Human Resources
CNO: Sandra E. Viall, MSN, Chief Nursing Officer
Web address: www.hendryregional.org
**Control:** Hospital district or authority, Government, nonfederal **Service:** General Medical and Surgical

**Staffed Beds:** 25 **Admissions:** 722 **Census:** 6 **Outpatient Visits:** 33538 **Births:** 0 **Total Expense ($000):** 27517 **Payroll Expense ($000):** 11975 **Personnel:** 208

## COCOA BEACH—Brevard County

✠ **HEALTH FIRST CAPE CANAVERAL HOSPITAL (100177)**, 701 West Cocoa Beach Causeway, Zip 32931–5595, Mailing Address: P.O. Box 320069, Zip 32932–0069; tel. 321/799–7111 **A**1 9 10 **F**3 11 13 15 18 20 22 26 29 30 31 34 35 40 43 44 45 46 47 48 49 51 54 56 57 59 60 62 64 65 68 70 74 75 78 79 83 86 87 91 92 93 103 107 108 110 111 114 115 119 124 129 130 132 143 146 147 **P**6 7 **S** Health First, Inc., Rockledge, FL
Primary Contact: William Calhoun, President, Community Hospitals
CFO: Joseph G. Felkner, Senior Vice President Finance and Chief Financial Officer
CMO: Jeffrey Stalnaker, M.D., Vice President, Medical Affairs
CIO: Lori Delone, Senior Vice President Support Services and Chief Information Officer
CHR: Paula Just, Vice President Human Resources
CNO: Connie Bradley, R.N., Chief Nursing Officer
Web address: www.health-first.org
**Control:** Other not–for–profit (including NFP Corporation) **Service:** General Medical and Surgical

**Staffed Beds:** 145 **Admissions:** 6814 **Census:** 76 **Outpatient Visits:** 105332 **Births:** 645 **Total Expense ($000):** 83250 **Payroll Expense ($000):** 37050 **Personnel:** 466

## CORAL GABLES—Miami–Dade County

✠ **BAPTIST HEALTH SOUTH FLORIDA, DOCTORS HOSPITAL (100296)**, 5000 University Drive, Zip 33146–2094; tel. 786/308–3000 **A**1 3 5 9 10 **F**3 11 18 29 30 31 34 35 37 40 45 47 49 53 57 58 59 60 63 64 68 70 74 75 77 78 79 81 82 84 85 86 87 93 94 100 102 107 108 111 114 115 119 124 126 130 131 132 135 143 146 148 **P**8 **S** Baptist Health South Florida, Coral Gables, FL
Primary Contact: Nelson Lazo, Chief Executive Officer
CFO: Maria J. Yanez, Chief Financial Officer
Web address: www.baptisthealth.net
**Control:** Other not–for–profit (including NFP Corporation) **Service:** General Medical and Surgical

**Staffed Beds:** 146 **Admissions:** 5874 **Census:** 82 **Outpatient Visits:** 66918 **Births:** 0 **Total Expense ($000):** 179894 **Payroll Expense ($000):** 55303 **Personnel:** 871

✠ **CORAL GABLES HOSPITAL (100183)**, 3100 Douglas Road, Zip 33134–6914; tel. 305/445–8461, (Nonreporting) **A**1 9 10 **S** TENET Healthcare Corporation, Dallas, TX
Primary Contact: Patrick Downes, Chief Executive Officer
COO: Cristina Jimenez, Chief Operating Officer
CFO: Henry Capote, Interim Chief Financial Officer
CMO: Pedro Friarte, Director of Physician Services
CIO: Mercy Hermosa, Director of Information System
CHR: Ana Paguaga, Director of Human Resources
CNO: David O'Brien, Chief Nursing Officer
Web address: www.coralgableshospital.com
**Control:** Corporation, Investor–owned, for–profit **Service:** General Medical and Surgical

**Staffed Beds:** 256

## CORAL SPRINGS—Broward County

✠ **BROWARD HEALTH CORAL SPRINGS (100276)**, 3000 Coral Hills Drive, Zip 33065–4108; tel. 954/344–3000 **A**1 9 10 **F**3 11 12 13 15 17 20 29 31 34 35 40 41 48 51 55 57 58 59 61 63 64 66 68 70 72 74 75 76 77 78 79 80 81 82 84 85 86 87 88 89 93 96 107 108 111 114 115 118 119 126 129 130 131 132 143 146 147 148 **S** Broward Health, Fort Lauderdale, FL
Primary Contact: Drew Grossman, Chief Executive Officer
COO: Kimberley Graham, R.N., Chief Nursing Officer and Chief Operating Officer
CFO: Arthur Wallace, Chief Financial Officer
CMO: Azeem Sachedina, M.D., Chief of Staff
CHR: Eileen O'Brien, Director Human Resources
CNO: Kimberley Graham, R.N., Chief Nursing Officer and Chief Operating Officer
Web address: www.browardhealth.org
**Control:** Hospital district or authority, Government, nonfederal **Service:** General Medical and Surgical

**Staffed Beds:** 182 **Admissions:** 13240 **Census:** 138 **Outpatient Visits:** 137579 **Births:** 2341 **Total Expense ($000):** 144241 **Payroll Expense ($000):** 59330 **Personnel:** 932

## CRESTVIEW—Okaloosa County

✠ **NORTH OKALOOSA MEDICAL CENTER (100122)**, 151 Redstone Avenue S.E., Zip 32539–6026; tel. 850/689–8100 **A**1 9 10 **F**3 8 11 13 15 18 20 22 28 29 30 34 40 45 50 51 54 57 59 64 70 74 75 76 77 78 79 81 85 86 87 89 90 93 96 97 107 108 110 111 114 115 116 117 119 124 126 127 129 130 131 132 146 147 148 **S** Community Health Systems, Inc., Franklin, TN
Primary Contact: Ronnie Daves, Chief Executive Officer
COO: Heath Evans, Assistant Chief Executive Officer
CFO: Jim Andrews, Chief Financial Officer
CMO: Michael Foley, M.D., Chief Medical Officer
CIO: Jenny Zeitler, Network Administrator
CHR: Melody M. Miller–Collette, Director Human Resources
CNO: Nina Perez, R.N., Chief Nursing Officer
Web address: www.northokaloosa.com
**Control:** Corporation, Investor–owned, for–profit **Service:** General Medical and Surgical

**Staffed Beds:** 110 **Admissions:** 5253 **Census:** 53 **Outpatient Visits:** 118051 **Births:** 526 **Personnel:** 502

## CRYSTAL RIVER—Citrus County

✠ **SEVEN RIVERS REGIONAL MEDICAL CENTER (100249)**, 6201 North Suncoast Boulevard, Zip 34428–6712; tel. 352/795–6560, (Nonreporting) **A**1 9 10 19 **S** Community Health Systems, Inc., Franklin, TN
Primary Contact: Joyce A. Brancato, Chief Executive Officer
COO: Austin Brown, Chief Operating Officer
CFO: Vickie Magurean, Chief Financial Officer
CHR: Joann Mramor, Director Human Resources
CNO: Cynthia Heitzman, R.N., Chief Nursing Officer
Web address: www.srrmc.com
**Control:** Corporation, Investor–owned, for–profit **Service:** General Medical and Surgical

**Staffed Beds:** 128

## CUTLER BAY—Miami–Dade County

**HEALTHSOUTH REHABILITATION HOSPITAL** See HEALTHSOUTH Rehabilitation Hospital of Miami

★ **HEALTHSOUTH REHABILITATION HOSPITAL OF MIAMI (103038)**, 20601 Old Cutler Road, Zip 33189–2400; tel. 305/251–3800 **A**9 10 **F**3 29 77 86 90 91 96 130 132 135 148 **S** HEALTHSOUTH Corporation, Birmingham, AL
Primary Contact: Elizabeth L. Izquierdo, CPA, Chief Executive Officer
CFO: Reyna Hernandez, Chief Financial Officer
CIO: Miguel Cruz, Medical Staff Credentialing Coordinator
CHR: Susan Riley, Director Human Resources
CNO: Ellen Romanowski, Chief Nursing Officer
Web address: www.healthsouthmiami.com
**Control:** Corporation, Investor–owned, for–profit **Service:** Rehabilitation

**Staffed Beds:** 60 **Admissions:** 1362 **Census:** 43 **Outpatient Visits:** 0 **Births:** 0 **Total Expense ($000):** 15832 **Payroll Expense ($000):** 7809 **Personnel:** 151

## DADE CITY—Pasco County

✠ **BAYFRONT HEALTH DADE CITY (100211)**, 13100 Fort King Road, Zip 33525–5294; tel. 352/521–1100, (Nonreporting) **A**1 9 10 **S** Community Health Systems, Inc., Franklin, TN
Primary Contact: Shauna McKinnon, Chief Executive Officer
CFO: Linda Stockton, Chief Financial Officer
CMO: Petros Tsambiras, M.D., Chief of Staff
CIO: Cheryl Kaufman, Director Health Information Management
CHR: Tabatha Wallace, Director Human Resources
Web address: www.pascoregionalmc.com
**Control:** Corporation, Investor–owned, for–profit **Service:** General Medical and Surgical

**Staffed Beds:** 120

**FL**

*Many Facility Codes have changed. Please refer to the AHA Guide Code Chart.* © 2015 AHA Guide

## DAVENPORT—Polk County

✠ **HEART OF FLORIDA REGIONAL MEDICAL CENTER (100137)**, 40100 Highway 27, Zip 33837–5906; tel. 863/422–4971 **A**1 9 10 **F**3 11 12 13 15 17 18 20 22 29 30 34 40 49 50 51 57 59 60 64 70 74 75 76 77 79 81 85 87 89 107 110 111 114 115 119 126 130 135 144 146 147 148 **S** Community Health Systems, Inc., Franklin, TN
Primary Contact: Ann Barnhart, Chief Executive Officer
CFO: Tonja Mosley, Chief Financial Officer
CMO: Claudio Manubens, M.D., Chief of Staff
CIO: Louis Jones, Director Management Information Systems
CHR: Joan Allard, Director Human Resources
CNO: Dottie Mileto, Chief Nursing Officer
Web address: www.heartofflorida.com
**Control:** Corporation, Investor–owned, for–profit **Service:** General Medical and Surgical

**Staffed Beds:** 193 **Admissions:** 8984 **Census:** 91 **Births:** 987 **Total Expense ($000):** 105378 **Payroll Expense ($000):** 33418

## DAYTONA BEACH—Volusia County

✠ **FLORIDA HOSPITAL MEMORIAL MEDICAL CENTER (100068)**, 301 Memorial Medical Parkway, Zip 32117–5167; tel. 386/676–6000, (Includes FLORIDA HOSPITAL–OCEANSIDE, 264 South Atlantic Avenue, Ormond Beach, Zip 32176–8192; tel. 386/672–4161) **A**1 2 9 10 **F**2 3 11 12 13 15 17 18 20 22 24 26 28 29 30 31 32 34 35 38 40 42 45 46 47 49 50 54 57 58 59 60 65 68 70 71 74 75 76 77 78 79 81 82 85 86 87 90 91 92 93 96 97 100 107 108 109 110 111 112 114 115 116 117 119 120 121 123 124 130 131 132 135 146 147 148 **P6 S** Adventist Health System Sunbelt Health Care Corporation, Altamonte Springs, FL
Primary Contact: Daryl Tol, Chief Executive Officer
COO: Darlinda Copeland, Chief Operating Officer
CFO: Debora Thomas, Chief Financial Officer
CMO: Ron Jimenez, M.D., Chief Medical Officer
CHR: Opal R. Howard, Executive Director Human Resources
CNO: Michele Goeb–Burkett, R.N., Chief Nursing Officer
Web address: www.floridahospitalmemorial.org
**Control:** Church–operated, Nongovernment, not–for profit **Service:** General Medical and Surgical

**Staffed Beds:** 358 **Admissions:** 13853 **Census:** 191 **Outpatient Visits:** 210488 **Births:** 1533 **Total Expense ($000):** 257933 **Payroll Expense ($000):** 99224 **Personnel:** 1755

☐ **HALIFAX HEALTH MEDICAL CENTER OF DAYTONA BEACH (100017)**, 303 North Clyde Morris Boulevard, Zip 32114–2700; tel. 386/254–4000, (Includes HALIFAX BEHAVIORAL SERVICES, 841 Jimmy Ann Drive, Zip 32117–4599; tel. 904/274–5333; HALIFAX HEALTH MEDICAL CENTER OF PORT ORANGE, 1041 Dunlawton Avenue, Port Orange, Zip 32127; tel. 386/322–4700; Ann Martorano, Chief Operatiang Officer) **A**1 2 3 5 9 10 **F**3 11 12 13 17 18 20 22 24 26 28 29 30 31 40 42 43 45 46 47 49 50 53 55 60 65 70 72 76 77 78 79 81 85 86 87 88 89 90 91 93 94 96 97 98 99 100 101 102 103 107 108 111 114 115 118 119 120 121 123 124 126 130 131 132 135 138 146 147 148
Primary Contact: Jeff Feasel, Chief Executive Officer
COO: Ann Martorano, Chief Operating Officer
CFO: Eric Peburn, Chief Financial Officer
CMO: Donald Stoner, M.D., Chief Medical Officer
CIO: Tom Stafford, Chief Information Officer
CHR: Kimberly Fulcher, Chief Human Resources Officer
Web address: www.halifax.org
**Control:** Hospital district or authority, Government, nonfederal **Service:** General Medical and Surgical

**Staffed Beds:** 678 **Admissions:** 22380 **Census:** 333 **Outpatient Visits:** 253258 **Births:** 2010 **Total Expense ($000):** 412099 **Payroll Expense ($000):** 181605 **Personnel:** 3192

**SELECT SPECIALTY HOSPITAL DAYTONA BEACH**, 301 Memorial Medical Parkway, 11th Floor, Zip 32117–5167; tel. 386/231–3436, (Nonreporting) **S** Select Medical Corporation, Mechanicsburg, PA
Primary Contact: Adrianne Lutes, Chief Executive Officer
Web address: www.daytonabeach.selectspecialtyhospitals.com
**Control:** Corporation, Investor–owned, for–profit **Service:** Long–Term Acute Care hospital

**Staffed Beds:** 34

## DEERFIELD BEACH—Broward County

★ △ **BROWARD HEALTH NORTH (100086)**, 201 East Sample Road, Zip 33064–3502; tel. 954/941–8300 **A**2 7 10 **F**3 6 11 15 17 18 20 28 29 30 31 34 35 37 40 43 45 46 49 51 55 57 58 59 60 61 64 66 68 70 74 75 77 78 79 80 81 82 83 84 85 86 87 90 92 93 94 96 100 107 108 110 111 114 115 117 118 119 120 121 123 124 129 130 131 132 143 145 146 148 **S** Broward Health, Fort Lauderdale, FL
Primary Contact: Pauline Grant, FACHE, Chief Executive Officer
COO: Kevin Fusco, Chief Operating Officer
CFO: Robert Bugg, Chief Financial Officer
CMO: Darren Hoffberger, D.O., Chief of Staff
CIO: Doris Crain, Vice President and Chief Information Officer
CHR: Grace King, Regional Director Human Resources
CNO: Bettiann S. Ruditz, MS, Chief Nursing Officer
Web address: www.browardhealth.org
**Control:** Hospital district or authority, Government, nonfederal **Service:** General Medical and Surgical

**Staffed Beds:** 334 **Admissions:** 13803 **Census:** 213 **Outpatient Visits:** 105508 **Births:** 0 **Total Expense ($000):** 219911 **Payroll Expense ($000):** 80641 **Personnel:** 1237

## DEFUNIAK SPRINGS—Walton County

**HEALTHMARK REGIONAL MEDICAL CENTER (100081)**, 4413 U.S. Highway 331 South, Zip 32435–6307; tel. 850/951–4500 **A**9 10 **F**3 40 45 62 64 65 70 75 81 87 93 94 97 107 111 114 115 119 127 133 143 146 **P**6
Primary Contact: James H. Thompson, Ph.D., FACHE, Owner and Chief Executive Officer
COO: Gerald C. Beard, Chief Operating Officer
CFO: Jim Brewer, M.P.H., Chief Financial Officer
CMO: Edward Tenewitz, M.D., Chief of Staff
CIO: Ray Downs, Senior Staff Accountant
CHR: Debra Tiller, Director Personnel and Administrative Secretary
Web address: www.healthmarkregional.com
**Control:** Individual, Investor–owned, for–profit **Service:** General Medical and Surgical

**Staffed Beds:** 50 **Admissions:** 874 **Census:** 11 **Births:** 0 **Total Expense ($000):** 11191 **Payroll Expense ($000):** 5010

## DELAND—Volusia County

★ **FLORIDA HOSPITAL DELAND (100045)**, 701 West Plymouth Avenue, Zip 32720–3236; tel. 386/943–4522 **A**2 9 10 **F**3 4 13 15 18 20 22 26 28 29 30 31 34 35 37 38 40 45 46 47 48 49 50 54 55 56 57 58 59 60 64 70 74 75 76 77 78 79 80 81 84 85 86 87 93 97 98 100 102 107 108 109 110 111 112 114 115 116 117 119 120 121 124 126 129 130 131 132 135 146 147 **P6 S** Adventist Health System Sunbelt Health Care Corporation, Altamonte Springs, FL
Primary Contact: Timothy W. Cook, President and CEO
COO: Hector M. De Jesus, Chief Operating Officer
CFO: Nigel Hinds, Chief Financial Officer
CMO: Samuel Edwards, M.D., Chief of Staff
CIO: Kevin Piper, Director Information Systems
CHR: Stefanie Audet, Director Human Resources
CNO: Patricia Ann Stark, R.N., CNO
Web address: www.fhdeland.org
**Control:** Other not–for–profit (including NFP Corporation) **Service:** General Medical and Surgical

**Staffed Beds:** 156 **Admissions:** 8550 **Census:** 98 **Outpatient Visits:** 122911 **Births:** 472 **Total Expense ($000):** 111014 **Payroll Expense ($000):** 42765 **Personnel:** 851

## DELRAY BEACH—Palm Beach County

✠ **DELRAY MEDICAL CENTER (100258)**, 5352 Linton Boulevard, Zip 33484–6580; tel. 561/498–4440, (Includes FAIR OAKS PAVILION, 5440 Linton Boulevard, Zip 33484–6578; tel. 561/495–1000; PINECREST REHABILITATION HOSPITAL, 5360 Linton Boulevard, Zip 33484–6538; tel. 561/495–0400) **A**1 3 5 9 10 **F**3 4 11 12 15 17 18 20 22 24 26 29 31 34 35 37 38 40 41 43 45 46 49 50 51 56 57 58 59 60 64 65 67 70 74 75 77 78 79 80 81 82 83 84 85 87 90 91 93 94 96 97 98 100 101 102 103 104 107 108 111 115 118 119 126 129 130 132 133 135 143 144 146 147 148 **S** TENET Healthcare Corporation, Dallas, TX
Primary Contact: Mark Bryan, Chief Executive Officer
CMO: Anthony Dardano, M.D., Chief Medical Officer
CIO: Robens Rosena, Director Information Systems
CHR: Shannon Wills, Director Human Resources
Web address: www.delraymedicalctr.com
**Control:** Corporation, Investor–owned, for–profit **Service:** General Medical and Surgical

**Staffed Beds:** 439 **Admissions:** 19943 **Census:** 299 **Outpatient Visits:** 69750 **Births:** 0 **Personnel:** 1280

FL

---

**Hospital, Medicare Provider Number, Address, Telephone, Approval, Facility, and Physician Codes, Health Care System**

★ American Hospital Association (AHA) membership ☐ The Joint Commission accreditation ○ Healthcare Facilities Accreditation Program ◇ DNV Healthcare Inc. accreditation ⇑ Center for Improvement in Healthcare Quality Accreditation △ Commission on Accreditation of Rehabilitation Facilities (CARF) accreditation

## DUNEDIN—Pinellas County

☐ **BAYCARE ALLIANT HOSPITAL (102021)**, 601 Main Street, Zip 34698–5848; tel. 727/736–9999 **A**1 9 10 **F**1 3 28 29 130 148
Primary Contact: Jacqueline Arocho, Administrator
CFO: John Proni, CPA, Manager Finance
CMO: Leonard Dunn, M.D., Chief Medical Officer
CHR: Darlene Shelton, Coordinator Team Resources
Web address: www.baycare.org
**Control:** Other not–for–profit (including NFP Corporation) **Service:** Long–Term Acute Care hospital

**Staffed Beds:** 38 **Admissions:** 381 **Census:** 28 **Outpatient Visits:** 0 **Births:** 0 **Total Expense ($000):** 16319 **Payroll Expense ($000):** 5832 **Personnel:** 76

✠ **MEASE DUNEDIN HOSPITAL (100043)**, 601 Main Street, Zip 34698–5891, Mailing Address: P.O. Box 760, Zip 34697–0760; tel. 727/733–1111 **A**1 9 10 **F**3 12 15 17 18 26 29 30 31 34 37 40 44 49 60 62 68 70 75 78 79 81 84 85 86 87 98 99 100 102 103 105 107 108 110 111 114 118 119 130 132 145 146 **S** Morton Plant Mease Health Care, Clearwater, FL
Primary Contact: Lou Galdieri, R.N., President
CFO: Carl Tremonti, Chief Financial Officer
CMO: Donald Pocock, M.D., Chief Medical Officer
CHR: Sharon Collotta, Director Human Resources
Web address: www.mpmhealth.com
**Control:** Other not–for–profit (including NFP Corporation) **Service:** General Medical and Surgical

**Staffed Beds:** 120 **Admissions:** 4889 **Census:** 59 **Outpatient Visits:** 30760 **Births:** 0 **Total Expense ($000):** 68666 **Payroll Expense ($000):** 27588 **Personnel:** 405

## EGLIN AFB—Okaloosa County

✠ **U. S. AIR FORCE REGIONAL HOSPITAL**, 307 Boatner Road, Suite 114, Zip 32542–1282; tel. 850/883–8221, (Nonreporting) **A**1 3 5 **S** Department of the Air Force, Washington, DC
Primary Contact: Colonel Gianna Zeh, Commander
Web address: www.eglin.af.mil
**Control:** Air Force, Government, federal **Service:** General Medical and Surgical

**Staffed Beds:** 57

## ENGLEWOOD—Sarasota County

✠ **ENGLEWOOD COMMUNITY HOSPITAL (100267)**, 700 Medical Boulevard, Zip 34223–3978; tel. 941/475–6571, (Nonreporting) **A**1 9 10 **S** HCA, Nashville, TN
Primary Contact: Dale Alward, Chief Executive Officer
COO: Alex Chang, Chief Operating Officer
CMO: Eric Pressman, D.O., Chair Department of Medicine
CHR: Tony Welch, Vice President, Human Resources
CNO: Kathleen Pace, MSN, Chief Nursing Officer
Web address: www.englewoodcommunityhospital.com
**Control:** Corporation, Investor–owned, for–profit **Service:** General Medical and Surgical

**Staffed Beds:** 100

## FERNANDINA BEACH—Nassau County

✠ **BAPTIST MEDICAL CENTER NASSAU (100140)**, 1250 South 18th Street, Zip 32034–3098; tel. 904/321–3500 **A**1 9 10 **F**3 11 13 15 18 26 29 30 34 35 40 45 49 64 70 74 76 79 81 82 85 91 92 93 102 107 108 110 111 114 115 119 124 129 132 146 148 **S** Baptist Health, Jacksonville, FL
Primary Contact: Stephen Lee, FACHE, President
COO: Patricia K. Hausauer, Director Finance
CFO: Patricia K. Hausauer, Director Finance
CHR: Jodi Atkins, Human Resources Specialist
CNO: Barbara S. Gingher, R.N., Assistant Administrator for Patient Care Services
Web address: www.baptistjax.com/locations/baptist–medical–center–nassau
**Control:** Other not–for–profit (including NFP Corporation) **Service:** General Medical and Surgical

**Staffed Beds:** 52 **Admissions:** 3277 **Census:** 30 **Births:** 567 **Total Expense ($000):** 48584 **Payroll Expense ($000):** 19270

## FORT LAUDERDALE—Broward County

☐ **ATLANTIC SHORES HOSPITAL (104065)**, 4545 North Federal Highway, Zip 33308–5274; tel. 954/771–2711, (Nonreporting) **A**1 9 10 **S** Universal Health Services, Inc., King of Prussia, PA
Primary Contact: Manuel R. Llano, Chief Executive Officer
COO: Karin Carol, Chief Operating Officer
Web address: www.atlanticshoreshospital.com
**Control:** Corporation, Investor–owned, for–profit **Service:** Psychiatric

**Staffed Beds:** 72

✠ **BROWARD HEALTH IMPERIAL POINT (100200)**, 6401 North Federal Highway, Zip 33308–1495; tel. 954/776–8500 **A**1 9 10 **F**3 11 12 15 20 29 31 34 35 40 45 51 53 55 57 58 59 61 63 64 66 68 70 74 75 77 78 79 80 81 82 84 85 86 87 93 98 100 102 104 105 107 108 111 114 115 118 119 126 129 130 131 132 143 146 147 148 **S** Broward Health, Fort Lauderdale, FL
Primary Contact: Alice Taylor, R.N., MSN, Chief Executive Officer
COO: Sandra Todd–Atkinson, Chief Operating Officer and Chief Nursing Officer
CFO: Susan Newton, Chief Financial Officer
CHR: Carl McDonald, Regional Director Human Resources
CNO: Sandra Todd–Atkinson, Chief Operating Officer and Chief Nursing Officer
Web address: www.browardhealth.org
**Control:** Hospital district or authority, Government, nonfederal **Service:** General Medical and Surgical

**Staffed Beds:** 180 **Admissions:** 8353 **Census:** 99 **Outpatient Visits:** 88471 **Births:** 0 **Total Expense ($000):** 106151 **Payroll Expense ($000):** 41146 **Personnel:** 677

✠ **BROWARD HEALTH MEDICAL CENTER (100039)**, 1600 South Andrews Avenue, Zip 33316–2510; tel. 954/355–4400, (Includes CHRIS EVERT CHILDRENS HOSPITAL, 1600 South Andrews Avenue, tel. 954/355–4400; Calvin E. Glidewell, Jr., Chief Executive Officer) **A**1 2 3 5 9 10 12 13 **F**3 11 13 15 17 18 20 22 24 26 28 29 30 31 34 35 40 41 43 45 48 49 51 53 57 59 60 61 62 63 64 65 66 68 70 71 72 73 74 75 76 77 78 79 80 81 82 83 84 85 87 88 89 93 94 98 100 102 105 107 108 110 111 114 115 116 117 119 120 121 126 129 130 139 146 147 **S** Broward Health, Fort Lauderdale, FL
Primary Contact: Calvin E. Glidewell, Jr., Chief Executive Officer
COO: Natassia Orr, Chief Operating Officer
CFO: Alexander Fernandez, Chief Financial Officer
CMO: Louis Yogel, M.D., Chief of Staff
CIO: Doris Crain, Vice President Information Services
CHR: Dionne Wong, Vice President and Chief Human Resources Officer
CNO: Robyn Farrington, Chief Nursing Officer
Web address: www.browardhealth.org
**Control:** Hospital district or authority, Government, nonfederal **Service:** General Medical and Surgical

**Staffed Beds:** 648 **Admissions:** 27116 **Census:** 409 **Outpatient Visits:** 251757 **Births:** 3357 **Total Expense ($000):** 445152 **Payroll Expense ($000):** 175834 **Personnel:** 2881

**FLORIDA MEDICAL CENTER** See Florida Medical Center – A Campus of North Shore

★ **FLORIDA MEDICAL CENTER – A CAMPUS OF NORTH SHORE**, 5000 West Oakland Park Boulevard, Zip 33313–1585; tel. 954/735–6000, (Nonreporting) **A**9 **S** TENET Healthcare Corporation, Dallas, TX
Primary Contact: Gabrielle Finley–Hazle, Chief Executive Officer
Web address: www.fmc–campus.com
**Control:** Partnership, Investor–owned, for–profit **Service:** General Medical and Surgical

**Staffed Beds:** 459

☐ **FORT LAUDERDALE HOSPITAL (104026)**, 1601 East Las Olas Boulevard, Zip 33301–2393; tel. 954/463–4321 **A**1 9 10 **F**4 5 38 98 99 102 103 104 105 130 132 135 **S** Universal Health Services, Inc., King of Prussia, PA
Primary Contact: Manuel R. Llano, Chief Executive Officer
CFO: Gina Lee, Chief Financial Officer
Web address: www.fortlauderdalehospital.org
**Control:** Corporation, Investor–owned, for–profit **Service:** Psychiatric

**Staffed Beds:** 100 **Admissions:** 5479 **Census:** 91 **Births:** 0 **Total Expense ($000):** 18160 **Payroll Expense ($000):** 8917

✠ **HOLY CROSS HOSPITAL (100073)**, 4725 North Federal Highway, Zip 33308–4668, Mailing Address: P.O. Box 23460, Zip 33307–3460; tel. 954/771–8000 **A**1 2 3 5 9 10 **F**3 8 11 12 13 15 17 18 20 22 24 26 28 29 30 31 32 34 35 36 37 39 40 44 45 46 47 48 49 50 51 53 54 56 57 58 59 61 62 64 65 66 67 68 70 71 72 73 74 75 76 77 78 79 80 81 82 84 85 86 87 90 91 92 93 95 96 97 100 107 108 110 111 114 115 116 117 118 119 120 121 123 124 126 129 130 131 132 134 143 144 145 146 147 **P**6 **S** Trinity Health, Livonia, MI
Primary Contact: Patrick Taylor, M.D., President and Chief Executive Officer
COO: Luisa Gutman, Senior Vice President and Chief Operating Officer
CFO: Linda Wilford, CPA, Senior Vice President and Chief Financial Officer
CMO: Kenneth Homer, M.D., Chief Medical Officer
CIO: Jeff Smith, Chief Information Officer
CNO: Taren Ruggiero, R.N., Vice President and Chief Nursing Officer
Web address: www.holy-cross.com
**Control:** Other not–for–profit (including NFP Corporation) **Service:** General Medical and Surgical

**Staffed Beds:** 359 **Admissions:** 16929 **Census:** 221 **Outpatient Visits:** 266376 **Births:** 1339 **Total Expense ($000):** 298676 **Payroll Expense ($000):** 105530 **Personnel:** 2580

**IMPERIAL POINT MEDICAL CENTER** See Broward Health Imperial Point

*Many Facility Codes have changed. Please refer to the AHA Guide Code Chart.* © 2015 AHA Guide

⊠ **KINDRED HOSPITAL SOUTH FLORIDA–FORT LAUDERDALE (102010)**, 1516 East Las Olas Boulevard, Zip 33301–2399; tel. 954/764–8900, (Includes KINDRED HOSPITAL SOUTH FLORIDA–CORAL GABLES, 5190 S.W. Eighth Street, Coral Gables, Zip 33134–2495; tel. 305/445–1364; Charles Doten, Chief Executive Officer; KINDRED HOSPITAL SOUTH FLORIDA–HOLLYWOOD, 1859 Van Buren Street, Hollywood, Zip 33020–5127; tel. 954/920–9000; Craig A. Hoover, Administrator), (Nonreporting) **A**1 9 10 **S** Kindred Healthcare, Louisville, KY
Primary Contact: Michael S. Roffelsen, Chief Executive Officer
CFO: Dean Card, Chief Financial Officer
Web address: www.khfortlauderdale.com/
**Control:** Corporation, Investor–owned, for–profit **Service:** Long–Term Acute Care hospital

**Staffed Beds:** 123

### FORT MYERS—Lee County

**CHILDREN'S HOSPITAL OF SOUTHWEST FLORIDA** See Lee Memorial Hospital

★ ◇ **GULF COAST MEDICAL CENTER (100220)**, 13681 Doctor's Way, Zip 33912–4300; tel. 239/343–1000 **A**9 10 21 **F**3 11 13 17 18 20 22 24 26 28 29 30 40 45 46 49 60 64 70 74 77 79 80 81 84 85 86 87 91 93 102 107 108 111 115 118 119 130 138 146 **S** Lee Memorial Health System, Fort Myers, FL
Primary Contact: James R. Nathan, President and Chief Executive Officer
COO: Lawrence Antonucci, M.D., Chief Operating Officer
CFO: Ben Spence, Chief Financial Officer
CMO: Mark Greenberg, M.D., Medical Director
CIO: Mike Smith, Chief Information Officer
CHR: Jon C. Cecil, Chief Human Resource Officer
CNO: Donna Giannuzzi, R.N., Chief Patient Care Officer
Web address: www.leememorial.org
**Control:** Hospital district or authority, Government, nonfederal **Service:** General Medical and Surgical

**Staffed Beds:** 349 **Admissions:** 22033 **Census:** 262 **Outpatient Visits:** 66232 **Births:** 1589

★ △ ◇ **LEE MEMORIAL HOSPITAL (100012)**, 2776 Cleveland Avenue, Zip 33901–5855, Mailing Address: P.O. Box 2218, Zip 33902–2218; tel. 239/332–1111, (Includes CHILDREN'S HOSPITAL OF SOUTHWEST FLORIDA, 9981 South HealthPark Drive, Zip 33908; tel. 239/433–7799; James R. Nathan, Chief Executive Officer; HEALTHPARK MEDICAL CENTER, 9981 South HealthPark Drive, Zip 33908; tel. 239/433–7799; James R. Nathan, Chief Executive Officer; THE REHABILITATION HOSPITAL, 2776 Cleveland Avenue, Zip 33901; tel. 239/332–1111; James R. Nathan, Chief Executive Officer), (Total facility includes 112 beds in nursing home–type unit) **A**2 3 7 9 10 21 **F**3 11 13 14 15 17 18 19 20 21 22 24 26 28 29 30 31 32 34 35 38 40 41 43 45 48 50 51 53 54 56 57 58 59 61 62 64 65 68 70 72 73 74 75 76 77 78 79 80 81 82 84 85 86 87 88 89 90 93 94 97 100 102 103 104 105 106 107 108 110 111 113 114 115 116 117 119 128 129 130 131 132 134 135 146 147 148 **S** Lee Memorial Health System, Fort Myers, FL
Primary Contact: James R. Nathan, President and Chief Executive Officer
COO: Lawrence Antonucci, M.D., Chief Operating Officer
CFO: Ben Spence, Chief Financial Officer
CMO: Chuck Krivenko, M.D., Chief Medical Officer, Clinical and Quality Services
CIO: Mike Smith, Chief Information Officer
CHR: Jon C. Cecil, Chief Human Resource Officer
CNO: Donna Giannuzzi, R.N., Chief Nursing Officer
Web address: www.leememorial.org
**Control:** Hospital district or authority, Government, nonfederal **Service:** General Medical and Surgical

**Staffed Beds:** 835 **Admissions:** 37864 **Census:** 517 **Outpatient Visits:** 166511 **Births:** 2833

☐ **PARK ROYAL HOSPITAL (104074)**, 9241 Park Royal Drive, Zip 33908–9204; tel. 239/985–2700, (Nonreporting) **A**1 9 10 **S** Acadia Healthcare Company, Inc., Franklin, TN
Primary Contact: Michael K. Evans, Chief Executive Officer
CFO: Amy Ciampa, Chief Financial Officer
CHR: Robert Raynor, Human Resources Director
Web address: www.ParkRoyalHospital.com
**Control:** Corporation, Investor–owned, for–profit **Service:** Psychiatric

**Staffed Beds:** 76

**PROMISE HOSPITAL OF FORT MYERS**, 3050 Champion Ring Road, Zip 33905–5599; tel. 239/313–2900, (Nonreporting) **S** Promise Healthcare, Boca Raton, FL
Primary Contact: Patrick G. Ryan, Chief Executive Officer
Web address: www.promisefortmyers.com
**Control:** Corporation, Investor–owned, for–profit **Service:** Long–Term Acute Care hospital

**Staffed Beds:** 60

### FORT PIERCE—St. Lucie County

⊠ **LAWNWOOD REGIONAL MEDICAL CENTER & HEART INSTITUTE (100246)**, 1700 South 23rd Street, Zip 34950–4803; tel. 772/461–4000, (Includes LAWNWOOD PAVILION, 1860 North Lawnwood Circle, Zip 34950, Mailing Address: P.O. Box 1540, Zip 34954–1540; tel. 361/466–1500), (Nonreporting) **A**1 9 10 **S** HCA, Nashville, TN
Primary Contact: Greg Lowe, Chief Executive Officer
CFO: Robert Dunwoody, Chief Financial Officer
CIO: Eric Castle, Director Information Services
CHR: Pam Burchell, Director Human Resources
Web address: www.lawnwoodmed.com
**Control:** Corporation, Investor–owned, for–profit **Service:** General Medical and Surgical

**Staffed Beds:** 331

### FORT WALTON BEACH—Okaloosa County

⊠ **FORT WALTON BEACH MEDICAL CENTER (100223)**, 1000 Mar–Walt Drive, Zip 32547–6795; tel. 850/862–1111, (Nonreporting) **A**1 2 3 9 10 **S** HCA, Nashville, TN
Primary Contact: Mitchell P. Mongell, FACHE, Chief Executive Officer
COO: Jeremy Gray, Chief Operating Officer
CFO: Jeffrey Steve Moore, Chief Financial Officer
CMO: Colonel Tama Van Decar, M.D., Chief Medical Officer
CIO: Amy Caldeira, Director Information Technology and Systems
CHR: Julia Truman, Vice President Human Resources
CNO: Holly McGucken, R.N., Chief Nursing Officer
Web address: www.fwbmc.com
**Control:** Corporation, Investor–owned, for–profit **Service:** General Medical and Surgical

**Staffed Beds:** 257

### GAINESVILLE—Alachua County

⊠ **NORTH FLORIDA REGIONAL MEDICAL CENTER (100204)**, 6500 Newberry Road, Zip 32605–4392, Mailing Address: P.O. Box 147006, Zip 32614–7006; tel. 352/333–4000 **A**1 2 3 9 10 **F**3 12 13 15 17 18 20 22 24 26 28 29 30 31 34 35 37 40 42 45 46 48 49 50 51 56 57 59 60 64 70 72 74 75 76 77 78 79 80 81 85 86 87 98 107 108 109 110 111 113 114 115 116 117 118 119 120 121 123 124 126 129 130 132 135 145 146 147 148 **S** HCA, Nashville, TN
Primary Contact: Brian Cook, Chief Executive Officer
COO: Thibaut vanMarcke, Chief Operating Officer
CFO: Jay St Pierre, Chief Financial Officer
CMO: Ann Weber, M.D., Chief Medical Officer
CIO: Eric Strand, Director Information Services
CNO: Scarlott Mueller, Chief Nursing Officer
Web address: www.nfrmc.com
**Control:** Corporation, Investor–owned, for–profit **Service:** General Medical and Surgical

**Staffed Beds:** 432 **Admissions:** 24252 **Census:** 268 **Outpatient Visits:** 126326 **Births:** 2727 **Total Expense ($000):** 282377 **Payroll Expense ($000):** 95974 **Personnel:** 1606

⊠ **NORTH FLORIDA/SOUTH GEORGIA VETERAN'S HEALTH SYSTEM**, 1601 S.W. Archer Road, Zip 32608–1135; tel. 352/376–1611, (Includes GAINESVILLE VETERANS AFFAIRS MEDICAL CENTER, 1601 S.W. Archer Road, Zip 32608–1197; tel. 352/376–1611; LAKE CITY VETERANS AFFAIRS MEDICAL CENTER, 619 South Marion Avenue, Lake City, Zip 32025–5898; tel. 386/755–3016), (Total facility includes 250 beds in nursing home–type unit) **A**1 3 5 8 9 10 11 12 15 17 18 20 22 24 26 28 29 30 31 33 34 35 36 38 39 40 44 45 46 47 48 49 51 54 55 56 57 58 59 60 61 62 63 64 65 66 68 70 74 75 77 78 79 81 82 83 84 85 86 87 91 92 93 94 97 98 100 101 102 103 104 105 106 107 108 109 110 111 114 115 116 117 118 119 127 129 130 131 132 133 135 136 141 143 144 145 146 147 148 **P**6 **S** Department of Veterans Affairs, Washington, DC
Primary Contact: Thomas Wisnieski, FACHE, Director
COO: Thomas Sutton, Associate Director
CFO: Jim Taylor, Chief Business Office
CMO: Brad Bender, M.D., Chief of Staff
CIO: Deborah Michel-Ogborn, Chief Information Resource Management
CHR: Michelle Manderino, Chief Human Resources
Web address: www.northflorida.va.gov
**Control:** Veterans Affairs, Government, federal **Service:** General Medical and Surgical

**Staffed Beds:** 623 **Admissions:** 14783 **Census:** 623 **Outpatient Visits:** 873462 **Births:** 0 **Total Expense ($000):** 905251 **Personnel:** 4901

**FL**

---

| **Hospital, Medicare Provider Number, Address, Telephone, Approval, Facility, and Physician Codes, Health Care System** |

★ American Hospital Association (AHA) membership  ◯ Healthcare Facilities Accreditation Program  ⇑ Center for Improvement in Healthcare Quality Accreditation
☐ The Joint Commission accreditation  ◇ DNV Healthcare Inc. accreditation  △ Commission on Accreditation of Rehabilitation Facilities (CARF) accreditation

⌧ **SELECT SPECIALTY HOSPITAL–GAINESVILLE (102022)**, 2708 S.W. Archer Road, Zip 32608–1316; tel. 352/337–3240, (Nonreporting) **A**1 9 10 **S** Select Medical Corporation, Mechanicsburg, PA
Primary Contact: Kristopher Kitzke, Chief Executive Officer
Web address: www.selectspecialtyhospitals.com/company/locations/gainesville. aspx
**Control:** Corporation, Investor–owned, for–profit **Service:** Long–Term Acute Care hospital

**Staffed Beds:** 44

⌧ △ **UF HEALTH SHANDS HOSPITAL (100113)**, 1600 S.W. Archer Road, Zip 32610–3003, Mailing Address: P.O. Box 100326, Zip 32610–0326; tel. 352/265–0111, (Includes UF HEALTH SHANDS CANCER HOSPITAL, 1515 S.W. Archer Road, Zip 32608–1134, Mailing Address: PO BOX 100014, Zip 32610–0014; tel. 352/265–0111; Edward Jimenez, Chief Executive Officer; UF HEALTH SHANDS CHILDREN'S HOSPITAL, 1600 S.W. Archer Road, Mailing Address: PO BOX 100326, Zip 32610–0326; tel. 352/265–0111; Edward Jimenez, Chief Executive Officer; UF HEALTH SHANDS PSYCHIATRIC HOSPITAL, 4101 N.W. 89th Boulevard, Zip 32606; tel. 352/265–5481; Marina T. Cecchini, Administrator; UF HEALTH SHANDS REHAB HOSPITAL, 4101 N.W. 89th Boulevard, Zip 32606–3813; tel. 352/265–5499; Marina T. Cecchini, Administrator) **A**1 2 3 5 7 8 9 10 **F**2 3 4 5 6 7 8 9 10 11 12 13 14 15 16 17 18 19 20 21 22 23 24 25 26 27 29 30 31 32 34 35 36 37 38 39 40 41 42 43 44 45 46 47 48 49 50 51 52 53 54 55 56 57 58 59 60 61 62 64 65 66 68 69 70 72 73 74 75 76 77 78 79 80 81 82 83 84 85 86 87 88 89 90 91 93 94 96 97 98 99 100 101 102 103 104 105 107 108 109 110 111 114 115 116 117 118 119 120 121 123 124 126 129 130 131 132 134 135 136 137 138 139 140 141 142 143 144 145 146 147 148 **P**6 **S** UF Health Shands, Gainesville, FL
Primary Contact: Edward Jimenez, Chief Executive Officer
CFO: James J. Kelly, Jr., Interim Senior Vice President and Chief Financial Officer
CMO: Timothy C. Flynn, M.D., Chief of Staff
CIO: Kari Cassel, Senior Vice President and Chief Information Officer
CHR: Janet L. Christie, Senior Vice President Human Resources
CNO: Irene Alexaitis, MSN, Vice President Nursing and Chief Nursing Officer
Web address: www.https://ufhealth.org/
**Control:** Other not–for–profit (including NFP Corporation) **Service:** General Medical and Surgical

**Staffed Beds:** 973 **Admissions:** 44630 **Census:** 776 **Outpatient Visits:** 889279 **Births:** 2807 **Total Expense ($000):** 1133360 **Payroll Expense ($000):** 412517 **Personnel:** 7767

**UF HEALTH SHANDS REHAB HOSPITAL** See UF Health Shands Hospital

### GRACEVILLE—Jackson County

**CAMPBELLTON GRACEVILLE HOSPITAL (101302)**, 5429 College Drive, Zip 32440–1897; tel. 850/263–4431 **A**9 10 18 **F**3 28 29 30 34 35 40 54 59 63 64 65 67 77 83 84 94 97 107 119 127 128 130 133 135 148
Primary Contact: H. D. Cannington, Administrator
CFO: Dena Cooper, Chief Financial Officer
CMO: Steve Davis, M.D., Chief Medical Officer
CHR: Judy Austin, Director Human Resources
Web address: www.c-ghospital.com
**Control:** Hospital district or authority, Government, nonfederal **Service:** General Medical and Surgical

**Staffed Beds:** 25 **Admissions:** 131 **Census:** 1 **Births:** 0

### GREEN COVE SPRINGS—Clay County

⌧ **KINDRED HOSPITAL NORTH FLORIDA (102015)**, 801 Oak Street, Zip 32043–4317; tel. 904/284–9230 **A**1 9 10 **F**1 18 28 29 30 31 46 84 107 119 **S** Kindred Healthcare, Louisville, KY
Primary Contact: Susan Drago, R.N., Chief Executive Officer
CFO: Steve Hart, Controller
CMO: Lionel J. Gatien, D.O., Chief of Staff
CIO: Rick Chapman, Chief Information Officer
CNO: Susan Drago, R.N., Chief Clinical Officer
Web address: www.khnorthflorida.com
**Control:** Corporation, Investor–owned, for–profit **Service:** Long–Term Acute Care hospital

**Staffed Beds:** 80 **Admissions:** 644 **Census:** 56 **Outpatient Visits:** 0 **Births:** 0 **Total Expense ($000):** 30621 **Payroll Expense ($000):** 10261

### GULF BREEZE—Santa Rosa County

⌧ **GULF BREEZE HOSPITAL (100266)**, 1110 Gulf Breeze Parkway, Zip 32561–4884; tel. 850/934–2000 **A**1 3 9 10 **F**3 8 11 15 17 20 26 29 30 31 40 44 45 46 50 54 57 59 64 68 70 71 74 75 78 79 81 82 84 85 86 91 93 107 108 110 111 114 119 120 121 123 129 130 131 132 143 146 147 148 **S** Baptist Health Care Corporation, Pensacola, FL
Primary Contact: Scott Raynes, President
CFO: Kerry Vermillion, Senior Vice President Finance and Chief Financial Officer
Web address: www.ebaptisthealthcare.org/GulfBreezeHospital/
**Control:** Other not–for–profit (including NFP Corporation) **Service:** General Medical and Surgical

**Staffed Beds:** 77 **Admissions:** 4035 **Census:** 42 **Outpatient Visits:** 114126 **Births:** 0 **Total Expense ($000):** 87846 **Payroll Expense ($000):** 24165 **Personnel:** 452

### HIALEAH—Miami–Dade County

⌧ **HIALEAH HOSPITAL (100053)**, 651 East 25th Street, Zip 33013–3878; tel. 305/693–6100 **A**1 9 10 **F**3 12 13 15 18 24 29 34 40 41 45 49 50 56 57 59 60 61 65 68 70 72 74 76 77 79 81 82 85 87 93 98 102 103 107 108 110 111 114 115 118 119 126 129 130 147 148 **S** TENET Healthcare Corporation, Dallas, TX
Primary Contact: Ben A. Rodriguez, Chief Executive Officer
CFO: Gary Nymoen, Chief Financial Officer
CMO: Orlando Garcia, M.D., Chief Medical Officer
CHR: Yamila Herrera, Director Human Resources
CNO: Lourdes Camps, R.N., Chief Nursing Officer
Web address: www.hialeahhosp.com
**Control:** Corporation, Investor–owned, for–profit **Service:** General Medical and Surgical

**Staffed Beds:** 172 **Admissions:** 12523 **Census:** 143 **Outpatient Visits:** 37787 **Births:** 1264 **Personnel:** 646

☐ **PALM SPRINGS GENERAL HOSPITAL (100050)**, 1475 West 49th Street, Zip 33012–3275, Mailing Address: P.O. Box 2804, Zip 33012–2804; tel. 305/558–2500, (Nonreporting) **A**1 10
Primary Contact: Nicholas T. Smith, Chief Executive Officer
CFO: Tony Milian, Chief Financial Officer
CHR: Lourdes Anton, Director Human Resources
Web address: www.psghosp.com
**Control:** Corporation, Investor–owned, for–profit **Service:** General Medical and Surgical

**Staffed Beds:** 190

⌧ **PALMETTO GENERAL HOSPITAL (100187)**, 2001 West 68th Street, Zip 33016–1898; tel. 305/823–5000, (Nonreporting) **A**1 5 9 10 12 13 **S** TENET Healthcare Corporation, Dallas, TX
Primary Contact: Ana J. Mederos, Chief Executive Officer
COO: Georgina Diaz, Chief Operating Officer
CFO: Oscar Vicente, Chief Financial Officer
CMO: Eloy Roman, M.D., Chief of Staff
CHR: Ana Gonzalez–Fajardo, Human Resources Director
Web address: www.palmettogeneral.com
**Control:** Corporation, Investor–owned, for–profit **Service:** General Medical and Surgical

**Staffed Beds:** 360

**SOUTHERN WINDS HOSPITAL** See Westchester General Hospital, Miami

### HOLLYWOOD—Broward County

☐ **LARKIN BEHAVIORAL HEALTH SERVICES (104015)**, 1201 North 37th Avenue, Zip 33021–5498; tel. 954/962–1355 **A**1 9 **F**98
Primary Contact: Iris Berges, Chief Executive Officer
COO: Christopher Gabel, Chief Operating Officer
CFO: Rocky Davidson, Chief Financial Officer
CHR: Len Alpert, Director Human Resources
Web address: www.hollywoodpavilion.com
**Control:** Corporation, Investor–owned, for–profit **Service:** Psychiatric

**Staffed Beds:** 50 **Admissions:** 76 **Census:** 4 **Births:** 0 **Total Expense ($000):** 2215 **Payroll Expense ($000):** 1044

⌧ △ **MEMORIAL REGIONAL HOSPITAL (100038)**, 3501 Johnson Street, Zip 33021–5421; tel. 954/987–2000, (Includes JOE DIMAGGIO CHILDREN'S HOSPITAL, 1000 Joe DiMaggio Drive, Zip 33021–5426; tel. 954/987–2000; Chantal Leconte, Chief Executive Officer; MEMORIAL REGIONAL HOSPITAL SOUTH, 3600 Washington Street, Zip 33021–8216; tel. 954/966–4500; Douglas Zaren, FACHE, Administrator) **A**1 2 3 5 7 9 10 **F**3 4 5 11 12 13 15 17 18 19 20 21 22 23 24 25 26 27 28 29 30 31 32 34 37 38 39 40 41 43 44 45 46 47 49 50 51 53 55 56 57 58 59 60 61 64 65 66 68 70 71 72 73 74 75 76 77 78 79 81 82 84 85 87 88 89 90 91 93 95 96 97 98 99 100 101 102 103 104 105 107 108 110 111 114 115 119 120 121 123 126 129 130 131 132 134 135 137 145 146 147 148 **S** Memorial Healthcare System, Hollywood, FL
Primary Contact: Zeff Ross, FACHE, Senior Vice President and Chief Executive Officer
CFO: David Smith, Chief Financial Officer
CMO: Stanley Marks, M.D., Chief Medical Officer
CIO: Forest Blanton, Administrator Process Engineering
CHR: Ray Kendrick, Chief Human Resources Officer
CNO: Maggie Hansen, R.N., Chief Nursing Officer
Web address: www.mhs.net
**Control:** Hospital district or authority, Government, nonfederal **Service:** General Medical and Surgical

**Staffed Beds:** 1037 **Admissions:** 34597 **Census:** 542 **Outpatient Visits:** 411504 **Births:** 4788 **Total Expense ($000):** 747289 **Payroll Expense ($000):** 304266 **Personnel:** 4411

☐ **SOUTH FLORIDA STATE HOSPITAL (104001)**, 800 East Cypress Drive, Zip 33025–4543; tel. 954/392–3000, (Nonreporting) **A**1 10
Primary Contact: Lee Packer, Administrator
Web address: www.geocarellc.com/Locations/SouthFloridaStateHospital
**Control:** State–Government, nonfederal **Service:** Psychiatric

**Staffed Beds:** 355

*Many Facility Codes have changed. Please refer to the AHA Guide Code Chart.*   © 2015 AHA Guide

## HOMESTEAD—Miami–Dade County

✠ **BAPTIST HEALTH SOUTH FLORIDA, HOMESTEAD HOSPITAL (100125)**, 975 Baptist Way, Zip 33033–7600; tel. 786/243–8000 **A**1 9 10 **F**3 11 13 15 18 29 30 31 34 35 40 41 45 47 49 50 51 53 57 58 59 60 61 63 64 68 70 74 75 76 78 79 81 82 84 85 86 87 89 93 102 107 108 110 111 114 115 119 129 130 131 132 134 135 145 146 147 148 **P**8 **S** Baptist Health South Florida, Coral Gables, FL
Primary Contact: William M. Duquette, Chief Executive Officer
COO: Kenneth R. Spell, Vice President Operations
CFO: Erik Long, Controller
CMO: Steven Fletcher, M.D., Chief of Staff
CIO: Mimi Taylor, Corporate Vice President Information Technology
CHR: Corey Heller, Corporate Vice President and Chief Human Resources Officer
CNO: Nancy Gail Gordon, R.N., CNO and VP of Nursing
Web address: www.baptisthealth.net
**Control:** Other not–for–profit (including NFP Corporation) **Service:** General Medical and Surgical

**Staffed Beds: 142 Admissions: 9769 Census: 89 Outpatient Visits:** 131795 **Births:** 1577 **Total Expense ($000):** 209573 **Payroll Expense ($000):** 71728 **Personnel:** 1091

## HUDSON—Pasco County

✠ **REGIONAL MEDICAL CENTER BAYONET POINT (100256)**, 14000 Fivay Road, Zip 34667–7199; tel. 727/869–5400 **A**1 2 9 10 13 **F**3 17 18 20 22 24 26 28 29 30 31 34 35 40 41 43 45 46 48 49 50 51 56 57 58 59 60 64 70 74 75 77 78 79 81 84 85 86 87 91 94 100 107 108 109 111 114 115 118 119 129 130 132 135 141 143 146 148 **S** HCA, Nashville, TN
Primary Contact: Shayne George, Chief Executive Officer
COO: Shalin Shah, Chief Operating Officer
CFO: Thomas Lawhorne, Chief Financial Officer
CMO: Joseph Pino, M.D., Chief Medical Officer
CIO: Mike Wilms, Director Information Systems
CHR: Geoffrey A. Washburn, Vice President
CNO: Tanya Simpson, Chief Nursing Officer
Web address: www.rmchealth.com
**Control:** Corporation, Investor–owned, for–profit **Service:** General Medical and Surgical

**Staffed Beds: 290 Admissions: 14049 Census: 180 Outpatient Visits:** 71555 **Births:** 0 **Total Expense ($000):** 156464 **Payroll Expense ($000):** 54565 **Personnel:** 832

## INVERNESS—Citrus County

✠ **CITRUS MEMORIAL HEALTH SYSTEM (100023)**, 502 West Highland Boulevard, Zip 34452–4754; tel. 352/726–1551, (Nonreporting) **A**1 9 10 19 **S** HCA, Nashville, TN
Primary Contact: Ralph A. Aleman, President and Chief Executive Officer
CFO: Mark Williams, Chief Financial Officer
CMO: C. Toumbis, M.D., Chief of Staff
CIO: Nick Brooks, Director of Information Systems
CHR: Lee Glotzback, Director Human Resources
CNO: Linda M. McCarthy, R.N., VP/ Chief Nursing Officer
Web address: www.citrusmh.com
**Control:** Other not–for–profit (including NFP Corporation) **Service:** General Medical and Surgical

**Staffed Beds: 198**

## JACKSONVILLE—Duval County

✠ **BAPTIST MEDICAL CENTER JACKSONVILLE (100088)**, 800 Prudential Drive, Zip 32207–8202; tel. 904/202–2000, (Includes BAPTIST MEDICAL CENTER SOUTH, 14550 St. Augustine Road, Zip 32258–2160; tel. 904/821–6000; Ronald G. Robinson, Administrator; WOLFSON CHILDREN'S HOSPITAL, 800 Prudential Drive, Zip 32207; tel. 904/202–8000; Michael D. Aubin, President) **A**1 2 3 5 9 10 **F**3 5 6 8 11 12 13 15 17 19 20 21 22 23 24 25 26 27 28 30 31 32 34 35 36 37 38 39 40 41 42 45 46 47 48 49 50 51 53 55 56 57 58 59 60 61 62 64 68 70 72 73 74 75 76 78 79 80 81 82 83 85 86 87 88 89 92 93 94 98 99 100 101 102 103 104 105 107 108 109 110 111 112 113 114 115 116 117 118 119 120 121 123 124 126 129 130 132 134 135 136 146 147 148 **P**6 **S** Baptist Health, Jacksonville, FL
Primary Contact: Michael A. Mayo, FACHE, President
COO: John F. Wilbanks, FACHE, Chief Operating Officer
CFO: Scott Wooten, Senior Vice President and Chief Financial Officer
CMO: Keith L. Stein, M.D., Senior Vice President Medical Affairs and Chief Medical Officer
CIO: Roland Garcia, Senior Vice President and Chief Information Officer
CHR: M. Beth Mehaffey, Vice President Human Resources
Web address: www.e–baptisthealth.com
**Control:** Other not–for–profit (including NFP Corporation) **Service:** General Medical and Surgical

**Staffed Beds: 901 Admissions: 47788 Census: 612 Outpatient Visits:** 588424 **Births:** 4386 **Total Expense ($000):** 803989 **Payroll Expense ($000):** 274796 **Personnel:** 5305

✠ △ **BROOKS REHABILITATION HOSPITAL (103039)**, 3599 University Boulevard South, Zip 32216–4252; tel. 904/345–7600 **A**1 3 7 9 10 **F**10 29 30 54 62 64 90 91 93 95 96 130 132 146
Primary Contact: Douglas M. Baer, Chief Executive Officer
COO: Michael Spigel, Executive Vice President & Chief Operating Officer
CMO: Trevor Paris, M.D., Medical Director
CIO: Karen Green, Chief Information Officer
CHR: Karen Gallagher, Vice President Human Resources and Learning
CNO: Joanne Hoertz, Vice President of Nursing
Web address: www.brookshealth.org
**Control:** Other not–for–profit (including NFP Corporation) **Service:** Rehabilitation

**Staffed Beds: 140 Admissions: 3161 Census: 130 Outpatient Visits:** 262866 **Births:** 0 **Total Expense ($000):** 76720 **Payroll Expense ($000):** 30784 **Personnel:** 438

★ **MAYO CLINIC JACKSONVILLE (100151)**, 4500 San Pablo Road South, Zip 32224–1865; tel. 904/953–2000 **A**2 3 5 9 10 **F**3 6 8 9 11 12 14 15 17 18 20 22 24 26 28 29 30 31 34 35 36 37 39 40 45 46 47 48 49 50 51 54 55 56 57 58 59 60 61 63 64 65 70 74 75 77 78 79 80 81 82 84 85 86 87 91 92 93 96 97 100 104 105 107 108 110 111 112 114 115 116 117 118 119 120 121 123 124 126 129 130 131 132 135 136 137 138 139 140 141 142 145 146 148 **P**6 **S** Mayo Clinic, Rochester, MN
Primary Contact: Gianrico Farrugia, M.D., Vice President and Chief Executive Officer
COO: Hilary G. Mathews, MS, Administrator
CFO: Kevin Lockett, Interim Chief Financial Officer
CMO: Nancy Dawson, M.D., Medical Director
CIO: John Crooks, Chair Information Services
CHR: Daniel Tomlinson, Chair Human Resources
CNO: Debra Harrison, MS, Chief Nursing Officer
Web address: www.mayoclinic.org/jacksonville/
**Control:** Other not–for–profit (including NFP Corporation) **Service:** General Medical and Surgical

**Staffed Beds: 249 Admissions: 12355 Census: 162 Outpatient Visits:** 44325 **Births:** 0 **Personnel:** 2585

✠ **MEMORIAL HOSPITAL JACKSONVILLE (100179)**, 3625 University Boulevard South, Zip 32216–4207, Mailing Address: P.O. Box 16325, Zip 32245–6325; tel. 904/399–6111 **A**1 2 3 9 10 **F**3 4 11 12 13 15 17 18 20 22 24 26 28 29 30 31 32 34 35 38 40 41 42 45 51 52 53 54 55 57 58 59 64 65 70 72 74 75 77 78 79 81 82 84 87 97 98 100 101 102 103 104 105 107 111 126 130 143 146 147 148 **S** HCA, Nashville, TN
Primary Contact: James F. O'Loughlin, President and Chief Executive Officer
COO: Bobby McCullough, Chief Operating Officer
CFO: Andy Miller, Chief Financial Officer
CMO: Aaron West, M.D., Chief Medical Officer
CIO: Lance Penton, Director, Information Services
CHR: Stuart Thompson, Vice President Human Resources
CNO: Suzanne Woods, Senior Vice President of Nursing
Web address: www.memorialhospitaljax.com
**Control:** Corporation, Investor–owned, for–profit **Service:** General Medical and Surgical

**Staffed Beds: 418 Admissions: 21872 Census: 271 Births: 1502 Total Expense ($000):** 292069 **Payroll Expense ($000):** 92261

✠ **NAVAL HOSPITAL JACKSONVILLE**, 2080 Child Street, Zip 32214–5000; tel. 904/542–7300, (Nonreporting) **A**1 3 5 **S** Bureau of Medicine and Surgery, Department of the Navy, Washington, DC
Primary Contact: Commander Darryl Green, Director Administration
CFO: Lieutenant Commander Michael Gregonis, Comptroller
CMO: Captain Christopher Quarles, M.D., Director Medical Services
CIO: Mike Haytaian, Head Director Information Resources Management
CHR: Captain Ruby Tennyson, Director Administration
Web address: www.med.navy.mil/SITES/NAVALHOSPITALJAX/Pages/default.aspx
**Control:** Navy, Government, federal **Service:** General Medical and Surgical

**Staffed Beds: 64**

☐ **RIVER POINT BEHAVIORAL HEALTH (104016)**, 6300 Beach Boulevard, Zip 32216–2782; tel. 904/724–9202, (Nonreporting) **A**1 9 10 **S** Universal Health Services, Inc., King of Prussia, PA
Primary Contact: Kevin McGee, Chief Executive Officer
CFO: Jenni Stackhouse, Chief Financial Officer
CIO: Bill Willis, Director Information Technology
CHR: Cathy Calhoun, Director Human Resources
Web address: www.riverpointbehavioral.com
**Control:** Corporation, Investor–owned, for–profit **Service:** Psychiatric

**Staffed Beds: 92**

FL

---

**Hospital, Medicare Provider Number, Address, Telephone, Approval, Facility, and Physician Codes, Health Care System**

★ American Hospital Association (AHA) membership ○ Healthcare Facilities Accreditation Program ⇑ Center for Improvement in Healthcare Quality Accreditation
☐ The Joint Commission accreditation ◇ DNV Healthcare Inc. accreditation △ Commission on Accreditation of Rehabilitation Facilities (CARF) accreditation

✠ **SPECIALTY HOSPITAL JACKSONVILLE (102012)**, 4901 Richard Street, Zip 32207–7328; tel. 904/737–3120 **A**1 9 10 **F**1 18 29 60 75 85 119 130 148 **S** HCA, Nashville, TN
Primary Contact: Barbara McCarthy, Chief Executive Officer
CFO: Joshua Szostek, Chief Financial Officer
CMO: Wendell H. Williams, Jr., M.D., Medical Director
CIO: Lance Penton, Director, Information Services
CHR: Lisa Ayala, R.N., Director Human Resources
Web address: www.specialtyhospitaljax.com
**Control:** Corporation, Investor–owned, for–profit **Service:** Long–Term Acute Care hospital

**Staffed Beds:** 62 **Admissions:** 672 **Census:** 49 **Outpatient Visits:** 0 **Births:** 0 **Personnel:** 202

✠ **ST. VINCENT'S MEDICAL CENTER RIVERSIDE (100040)**, 1 Shircliff Way, Zip 32204–4748, Mailing Address: P.O. Box 2982, Zip 32203–2982; tel. 904/308–7300 **A**1 2 3 9 10 13 **F**3 7 11 12 13 15 17 18 20 22 24 26 28 29 30 31 34 35 36 38 40 44 45 46 47 48 49 50 51 53 54 55 56 57 58 59 60 61 64 65 66 68 70 71 72 74 75 76 78 79 81 82 84 85 86 87 91 93 94 96 97 107 108 110 111 114 115 117 118 119 120 121 123 124 126 130 131 132 133 135 143 144 145 146 147 148 **S** Ascension Health, Saint Louis, MO
Primary Contact: Donnie Romine, Interim President and Chief Executive Officer
COO: Donnie Romine, System Chief Operating Officer and President St. Vincent's Medical Center Riverside
CFO: Kimberly Hodgkinson, Chief Financial Officer
CMO: Kenneth Rothfield, System Vice President and Chief Medical Officer
CIO: Ann Carey, Vice President and Chief Information Officer
CHR: Janice G. Lipsky, R.N., System Vice President Human Resources and Organizational Development
CNO: Gail P. Green, R.N., Chief Nursing Officer
Web address: www.jaxhealth.com
**Control:** Church–operated, Nongovernment, not–for profit **Service:** General Medical and Surgical

**Staffed Beds:** 528 **Admissions:** 25395 **Census:** 332 **Outpatient Visits:** 141449 **Births:** 1755 **Total Expense ($000):** 413352 **Payroll Expense ($000):** 125449 **Personnel:** 2294

✠ **ST. VINCENT'S MEDICAL CENTER SOUTHSIDE (100307)**, 4201 Belfort Road, Zip 32216–1431; tel. 904/296–3700 **A**1 5 9 10 **F**3 12 13 15 18 20 22 26 29 30 31 34 35 37 40 44 45 47 49 51 57 59 60 64 65 70 72 74 75 76 78 79 81 82 85 86 87 93 96 107 108 110 111 114 115 119 126 128 129 130 131 132 143 146 147 148 **S** Ascension Health, Saint Louis, MO
Primary Contact: Donnie Romine, Interim President and Chief Executive Officer
COO: Kyle Sanders, Chief Operating Officer
CFO: Kimberly Hodgkinson, Chief Financial Officer
CIO: Beth Fagin, Manager Information Systems
CHR: Edwina Coulliette, Manager Human Resources
CNO: Lorraine Keith, FACHE, Chief Nursing Officer
Web address: www.jaxhealth.com
**Control:** Church–operated, Nongovernment, not–for profit **Service:** General Medical and Surgical

**Staffed Beds:** 288 **Admissions:** 11951 **Census:** 140 **Outpatient Visits:** 42433 **Births:** 1454 **Total Expense ($000):** 156623 **Payroll Expense ($000):** 43917 **Personnel:** 784

✠ **UF HEALTH JACKSONVILLE (100001)**, 655 West Eighth Street, Zip 32209–6595; tel. 904/244–0411, (Total facility includes 56 beds in nursing home–type unit) **A**1 2 3 5 8 9 10 **F**3 5 8 11 12 13 15 17 18 19 20 22 24 25 26 28 29 30 31 32 33 34 35 36 38 39 40 41 43 44 45 46 47 49 50 51 52 53 54 56 57 58 59 60 61 62 64 65 66 68 70 71 72 73 74 75 76 77 78 79 80 81 82 84 85 86 87 88 89 92 93 94 96 97 98 99 100 101 102 103 104 105 107 108 109 110 111 114 115 116 117 118 119 120 121 123 124 126 128 129 130 131 132 134 135 141 145 146 147 148 **S** UF Health Shands, Gainesville, FL
Primary Contact: Russell Armistead, Chief Executive Officer
COO: Greg Miller, Senior Vice President Operations
CFO: Mike Gleason, Vice President and Chief Financial Officer
CMO: David Vukich, M.D., Senior Vice President, Chief Medical Officer and Chief Quality Officer
CIO: Kari Cassel, Senior Vice President and Chief Information Officer
CHR: Lesli Ward, Vice President Human Resources
CNO: Patrice I. Jones, R.N., Vice President and Chief Nursing Officer
Web address: www.ufhealthjax.org/
**Control:** Other not–for–profit (including NFP Corporation) **Service:** General Medical and Surgical

**Staffed Beds:** 620 **Admissions:** 24858 **Census:** 456 **Outpatient Visits:** 423353 **Births:** 2865 **Total Expense ($000):** 541491 **Payroll Expense ($000):** 192350 **Personnel:** 4221

☐ **WEKIVA SPRINGS (104069)**, 3947 Salisbury Road, Zip 32216–6115; tel. 904/296–3533, (Nonreporting) **A**1 9 10 **S** Universal Health Services, Inc., King of Prussia, PA
Primary Contact: Sheila Carr, Chief Executive Officer
Web address: www.wekivacenter.com
**Control:** Other not–for–profit (including NFP Corporation) **Service:** Psychiatric

**Staffed Beds:** 60

✠ **BAPTIST MEDICAL CENTER BEACHES (100117)**, 1350 13th Avenue South, Zip 32250–3205; tel. 904/627–2900 **A**1 9 10 **F**3 8 11 13 15 18 20 28 29 30 31 36 40 43 45 49 50 53 54 57 59 61 64 74 75 76 77 78 79 80 81 82 85 86 93 107 108 110 111 114 115 118 119 126 129 130 146 147 148 **S** Baptist Health, Jacksonville, FL
Primary Contact: Joseph M. Mitrick, FACHE, President
COO: John F. Wilbanks, FACHE, Chief Operating Officer
CFO: Scott Wooten, Senior Vice President and Chief Financial Officer
CMO: Keith L. Stein, M.D., Chief Medical Officer
CIO: Roland Garcia, Senior Vice President and Chief Information Officer
CHR: Dana Voisele, Director Human Resources
Web address: www.community.e–baptisthealth.com/bmc/beaches/index.html
**Control:** Other not–for–profit (including NFP Corporation) **Service:** General Medical and Surgical

**Staffed Beds:** 136 **Admissions:** 7635 **Census:** 80 **Outpatient Visits:** 84068 **Births:** 1159 **Total Expense ($000):** 105144 **Payroll Expense ($000):** 35107 **Personnel:** 666

★ **JAY HOSPITAL (100048)**, 14114 South Alabama Street, Zip 32565–1219; tel. 850/675–8000 **A**9 10 **F**3 11 15 18 29 30 34 35 40 45 46 48 49 50 57 59 64 75 77 81 82 85 93 107 114 119 130 132 133 135 146 147 **S** Baptist Health Care Corporation, Pensacola, FL
Primary Contact: Michael T. Hutchins, Administrator
CFO: Keith Strickling, Chief Accountant
CMO: Scott Moore, Chief of Staff
CHR: Heather Suggs, Manager Human Resources
CNO: Patsy Jackson, Director of Nursing
Web address: www.bhcpns.org/jayhospital/
**Control:** Other not–for–profit (including NFP Corporation) **Service:** General Medical and Surgical

**Staffed Beds:** 49 **Admissions:** 536 **Census:** 7 **Outpatient Visits:** 22438 **Births:** 0 **Total Expense ($000):** 10910 **Payroll Expense ($000):** 4850 **Personnel:** 101

✠ **JUPITER MEDICAL CENTER (100253)**, 1210 South Old Dixie Highway, Zip 33458–7299; tel. 561/747–2234 **A**1 2 9 10 **F**3 8 11 12 13 15 18 20 22 28 29 30 31 34 35 36 37 40 47 48 49 50 53 54 55 57 58 59 66 70 71 74 75 76 77 78 79 80 81 82 84 85 86 87 93 107 108 109 110 111 114 115 116 117 118 119 120 121 123 126 129 130 132 135 143 144 146 147 148 **P**6
Primary Contact: John D. Couris, President and Chief Executive Officer
CFO: Dale E. Hocking, Chief Financial Officer
CIO: Tom Crawford, Chief Information Officer
CHR: Peter Gloggner, Chief Human Resources Officer
Web address: www.jupitermed.com
**Control:** Other not–for–profit (including NFP Corporation) **Service:** General Medical and Surgical

**Staffed Beds:** 163 **Admissions:** 9925 **Census:** 118 **Outpatient Visits:** 132406 **Births:** 1154 **Total Expense ($000):** 175880 **Payroll Expense ($000):** 66308 **Personnel:** 1227

✠ **LOWER KEYS MEDICAL CENTER (100150)**, 5900 College Road, Zip 33040–4396, Mailing Address: P.O. Box 9107, Zip 33041–9107; tel. 305/294–5531, (Includes DE POO HOSPITAL, 1200 Kennedy Drive, Zip 33041; tel. 305/294–4692), (Nonreporting) **A**1 9 10 19 **S** Community Health Systems, Inc., Franklin, TN
Primary Contact: Nicki L. Will–Mowery, Ph.D., Chief Executive Officer
COO: Meylan Love–Watler, Chief Operating Officer
CFO: Dale Guffey, Chief Financial Officer
CMO: Jerome Covington, M.D., Chief Medical Officer
CIO: Les Jackson, Manager Information Systems
CHR: Donald Canalejo, Director Human Resources
Web address: www.lkmc.com
**Control:** Corporation, Investor–owned, for–profit **Service:** General Medical and Surgical

**Staffed Beds:** 90

**FLORIDA HOSPITAL KISSIMMEE** See Florida Hospital, Orlando

✠ **OSCEOLA REGIONAL MEDICAL CENTER (100110)**, 700 West Oak Street, Zip 34741–4996; tel. 407/846–2266, (Nonreporting) **A**1 2 3 5 9 10 13 **S** HCA, Nashville, TN
Primary Contact: Robert M. Krieger, Chief Executive Officer
CFO: Glenn Romig, Chief Financial Officer
CMO: Aida Sanchez–Jimenez, M.D., Chief Medical Officer
CHR: Sylvia Lollis, Director Human Resources
CNO: Sonya Quintana, R.N., Chief Nursing Officer
Web address: www.osceolaregional.com
**Control:** Corporation, Investor–owned, for–profit **Service:** General Medical and Surgical

**Staffed Beds:** 235

**FL**

✠ **POINCIANA MEDICAL CENTER (100320)**, 325 Cypress Parkway, Zip 34758; tel. 407/530–2000, (Nonreporting) **A**1 10 **S** HCA, Nashville, TN
Primary Contact: Joanna J. Conley, FACHE, Chief Executive Officer
Web address: www.poincianamedicalcenter.com
**Control:** Corporation, Investor–owned, for–profit **Service:** General Medical and Surgical

**Staffed Beds: 24**

### LAKE BUTLER—Union County

**LAKE BUTLER HOSPITAL HAND SURGERY CENTER (101303)**, 850 East Main Street, Zip 32054–1353, Mailing Address: P.O. Box 748, Zip 32054–0748; tel. 386/496–2323, (Nonreporting) **A**9 10 18
Primary Contact: Pamela B. Howard, R.N., Chief Executive Officer, Administrator and Risk Manager
COO: Jennifer Thomas, Chief Operating Officer and Director of Public Relations
CFO: Paula Webb, Chief Financial Officer and Compliance Officer
CMO: Cynthia Larimer, M.D., Chief of Staff
CIO: Diane Cason, Chief Information Officer, Controller and Director Human Resources
CNO: Mandy Dicks, Director of Nursing
Web address: www.lakebutlerhospital.com
**Control:** Corporation, Investor–owned, for–profit **Service:** General Medical and Surgical

**Staffed Beds: 25**

**RECEPTION AND MEDICAL CENTER**, State Road 231 South, Zip 32054, Mailing Address: P.O. Box 628, Zip 32054–0628; tel. 386/496–6000, (Nonreporting)
Primary Contact: Maxine Streeter, Administrator
Web address: www.dc.state.fl.us
**Control:** State–Government, nonfederal **Service:** Hospital unit of an institution (prison hospital, college infirmary, etc.)

**Staffed Beds: 120**

### LAKE CITY—Columbia County

✠ **LAKE CITY MEDICAL CENTER (100156)**, 340 N.W. Commerce Drive, Zip 32055–4709; tel. 386/719–9000, (Nonreporting) **A**1 9 10 **S** HCA, Nashville, TN
Primary Contact: Mark Miller, FACHE, Chief Executive Officer
COO: Jennifer B. Adams, Chief Operating Officer and Chief Financial Officer
CFO: Jennifer B. Adams, Chief Operating Officer and Chief Financial Officer
CMO: Miguel Tepedino, M.D., Chief Medicine
CIO: Taylor Dickerson, Chief Information Officer
CHR: Steve Gordon, Director Human Resources
Web address: www.lakecitymedical.com
**Control:** Corporation, Investor–owned, for–profit **Service:** General Medical and Surgical

**Staffed Beds: 67**

✠ **SHANDS LAKE SHORE REGIONAL MEDICAL CENTER (100102)**, 368 N.E. Franklin Street, Zip 32055–3047; tel. 386/292–8000, (Nonreporting) **A**1 3 9 10 **S** Community Health Systems, Inc., Franklin, TN
Primary Contact: Rhonda Kay Sherrod, R.N., MSN, Administrator
CMO: Ricardo Rosato, M.D., President Medical Staff
CHR: Janice Jackson, Director Human Resources
Web address: www.shandslakeshore.com
**Control:** Partnership, Investor–owned, for–profit **Service:** General Medical and Surgical

**Staffed Beds: 85**

**VETERANS AFFAIRS MEDICAL CENTER** See Lake City Veterans Affairs Medical Center

### LAKE WALES—Polk County

✠ **LAKE WALES MEDICAL CENTER (100099)**, 410 South 11th Street, Zip 33853–4256; tel. 863/676–1433 **A**1 9 10 **F**3 11 15 18 20 29 30 34 35 40 45 46 49 50 56 57 59 64 70 74 75 79 81 82 85 86 87 89 91 92 93 94 96 98 103 107 108 110 111 114 115 119 124 129 131 132 146 147 148 **S** Community Health Systems, Inc., Franklin, TN
Primary Contact: Andrew Howard, Interim Chief Executive Officer
CFO: Danny Warren, Chief Financial Officer
CMO: Sunil Nihalani, M.D., Chief Medical Staff
CIO: Erwin Jaropillo, Director Information Systems
CHR: Renee Latterner, Director Human Resources
CNO: Lee Clack, R.N., Chief Nursing Officer
Web address: www.lakewalesmedicalcenter.com
**Control:** Corporation, Investor–owned, for–profit **Service:** General Medical and Surgical

**Staffed Beds: 131 Admissions: 4251 Census: 51 Outpatient Visits: 47979 Births: 0 Total Expense ($000): 52796 Payroll Expense ($000): 20939 Personnel: 445**

### LAKE WORTH—Palm Beach County

✠ **SELECT SPECIALTY HOSPITAL–PALM BEACH (102023)**, 3060 Melaleuca Lane, Zip 33461–5174; tel. 561/357–7200, (Nonreporting) **A**1 9 10 **S** Select Medical Corporation, Mechanicsburg, PA
Primary Contact: Larry Melby, Chief Executive Officer
Web address: www.selectspecialtyhospitals.com/company/locations/palmbeach.aspx
**Control:** Corporation, Investor–owned, for–profit **Service:** Long–Term Acute Care hospital

**Staffed Beds: 60**

### LAKELAND—Polk County

✠ **LAKELAND REGIONAL HEALTH (100157)**, 1324 Lakeland Hills Boulevard, Zip 33805–4543, Mailing Address: P.O. Box 95448, Zip 33804–5448; tel. 863/687–1100 **A**1 2 3 5 9 10 **F**3 4 11 13 18 20 22 24 26 28 29 30 31 34 37 38 40 41 43 44 45 46 47 49 51 55 56 57 58 59 60 61 64 65 66 67 70 71 72 74 75 76 77 78 79 80 81 82 83 84 85 86 87 88 89 90 93 98 99 100 101 102 103 104 107 108 109 110 111 114 115 118 119 120 121 123 124 126 130 132 135 143 144 146 147 148 **P**6
Primary Contact: Mack Reavis, M.D., President and Chief Medical Officer
CFO: Evan Jones, Chief Financial Officer
CMO: Mack Reavis, M.D., President and Chief Medical Officer
CIO: Elizabeth Kerns, Chief Information Officer
CHR: Amy C. Barry, Senior Vice President and Chief Human Resources Officer
Web address: www.lrmc.com
**Control:** Other not–for–profit (including NFP Corporation) **Service:** General Medical and Surgical

**Staffed Beds: 820 Admissions: 41091 Census: 530 Outpatient Visits: 252731 Births: 3147 Total Expense ($000): 566868 Payroll Expense ($000): 227108 Personnel: 4402**

### LAND O'LAKES—Pasco County

✠ **FLORIDA HOSPITAL AT CONNERTON LONG TERM ACUTE CARE (102026)**, 9441 Health Center Drive, Zip 34637–5837; tel. 813/903–3701 **A**1 9 10 **F**3 29 30 34 70 107 119 146 148 **S** Adventist Health System Sunbelt Health Care Corporation, Altamonte Springs, FL
Primary Contact: Brian Adams, President and Chief Executive Officer
COO: Debora Martoccio, R.N., Chief Operating Officer
CMO: Sharad Patel, M.D., Medical Director
CNO: Rafael Padilla, R.N., Chief Nursing Officer
Web address: www.elevatinghealthcare.org
**Control:** Church–operated, Nongovernment, not–for profit **Service:** Long–Term Acute Care hospital

**Staffed Beds: 50 Admissions: 661 Census: 48 Outpatient Visits: 0 Births: 0 Total Expense ($000): 23157 Payroll Expense ($000): 9889 Personnel: 180**

### LARGO—Pinellas County

✠ **HEALTHSOUTH REHABILITATION HOSPITAL (103037)**, 901 North Clearwater–Largo Road, Zip 33770–4126; tel. 727/586–2999, (Nonreporting) **A**1 9 10 **S** HEALTHSOUTH Corporation, Birmingham, AL
Primary Contact: Tripp Smith, Chief Executive Officer
CFO: Judith Johnson, Controller
CMO: Richard A. Liles, M.D., Medical Director
CHR: Jackie Chalk, Director Human Resources
CNO: Pattie Brenner, R.N., Chief Nursing Officer
Web address: www.healthsouthlargo.com
**Control:** Corporation, Investor–owned, for–profit **Service:** Rehabilitation

**Staffed Beds: 70**

FL

---

**Hospital, Medicare Provider Number, Address, Telephone, Approval, Facility, and Physician Codes, Health Care System**

★ American Hospital Association (AHA) membership
☐ The Joint Commission accreditation
○ Healthcare Facilities Accreditation Program
◇ DNV Healthcare Inc. accreditation
⇧ Center for Improvement in Healthcare Quality Accreditation
△ Commission on Accreditation of Rehabilitation Facilities (CARF) accreditation

☒ **LARGO MEDICAL CENTER (100248)**, 201 14th Street S.W., Zip 33770–3133; tel. 727/588–5200, (Includes LARGO MEDICAL CENTER – INDIAN ROCKS, 2025 Indian Rocks Road, Zip 33774–1096, Mailing Address: P.O. Box 2025, Zip 33779–2025; tel. 727/581–9474), (Nonreporting) **A**1 2 5 9 10 12 13 **S** HCA, Nashville, TN
Primary Contact: Anthony M. Degina, President and Chief Executive Officer
CFO: Robert E. Billings, Chief Financial Officer
CMO: David Weiland, M.D., Chief Medical Officer
CIO: David Saly, Director, Information Services
CNO: Brenda Simpson, R.N., Chief Nursing Officer
Web address: www.largomedical.com
**Control:** Corporation, Investor–owned, for–profit **Service:** General Medical and Surgical

**Staffed Beds:** 243

### LAUDERDALE LAKES—Broward County

☐ △ **ST. ANTHONY'S REHABILITATION HOSPITAL (103027)**, 3485 N.W. 30th Street, Zip 33311–1890; tel. 954/739–6233 **A**1 7 9 10 **F**28 29 30 34 35 60 64 68 74 79 90 91 93 94 95 96 130 131 132 148 **S** Catholic Health Services, Lauderdale Lakes, FL
Primary Contact: Joseph M. Catania, Chief Executive Officer
Web address: www.catholichealthservices.org
**Control:** Church–operated, Nongovernment, not–for profit **Service:** Rehabilitation

**Staffed Beds:** 26 **Admissions:** 506 **Census:** 19 **Outpatient Visits:** 1382 **Births:** 0 **Total Expense ($000):** 8355 **Payroll Expense ($000):** 3756 **Personnel:** 77

### LEESBURG—Lake County

☒ △ **LEESBURG REGIONAL MEDICAL CENTER (100084)**, 600 East Dixie Avenue, Zip 34748–5999; tel. 352/323–5762 **A**1 2 7 9 10 **F**3 8 11 13 15 17 18 20 22 24 26 28 29 30 31 34 35 40 45 47 48 49 53 54 57 59 64 68 70 74 75 76 77 78 79 81 82 84 85 87 89 90 93 96 107 108 110 111 114 115 119 130 132 135 144 146 147 **P**6 7 **S** Central Florida Health Alliance, Leesburg, FL
Primary Contact: Donald G. Henderson, FACHE, President and Chief Executive Officer
COO: Saad Ehtisham, R.N., Vice President and Chief Operating Officer
CFO: Diane P. Harden, Chief Financial Officer
CIO: David Steele, Vice President Information Technology
CHR: Amie Richason, Vice President Human Resources
CNO: Teri Keel, Vice President Chief Clinical Officer
Web address: www.cfhalliance.org
**Control:** Other not–for–profit (including NFP Corporation) **Service:** General Medical and Surgical

**Staffed Beds:** 331 **Admissions:** 15191 **Census:** 201 **Outpatient Visits:** 81071 **Births:** 1545 **Total Expense ($000):** 199233 **Payroll Expense ($000):** 75193 **Personnel:** 1272

**LIFESTREAM BEHAVIORAL CENTER (104018)**, 2020 Tally Road, Zip 34748–3426, Mailing Address: P.O. Box 491000, Zip 34749–1000; tel. 352/315–7500 **A**9 10 **F**5 29 34 35 50 56 57 59 66 68 87 99 100 101 102 103 104 106 130 132 134 **P**1
Primary Contact: Jonathan M. Cherry, President and Chief Executive Officer
COO: Howard Weiner, Senior Vice President Administrative Services
CFO: Carol Dozier, Chief Financial Officer
CMO: T. J. Valente, M.D., Medical Director
CHR: Ben Hargrove, Human Resources Director
Web address: www.lsbc.net
**Control:** Other not–for–profit (including NFP Corporation) **Service:** Psychiatric

**Staffed Beds:** 46 **Admissions:** 2478 **Census:** 33 **Births:** 0 **Total Expense ($000):** 34974 **Payroll Expense ($000):** 2911

### LEHIGH ACRES—Lee County

☒ **LEHIGH REGIONAL MEDICAL CENTER (100107)**, 1500 Lee Boulevard, Zip 33936–4835; tel. 239/369–2101, (Nonreporting) **A**1 10 **S** Community Health Systems, Inc., Franklin, TN
Primary Contact: Joanie Jeannette, MSN, Chief Executive Officer
CFO: Osman Gruhonjic, Chief Financial Officer
CMO: Joe Lemmons, D.O., Chief of Staff
CIO: Jeff Hampton, Director Information Systems
CHR: Mary Gray, Director Human Resources
CNO: Julie G. Banker, R.N., Chief Nursing Officer
Web address: www.lehighregional.com
**Control:** Corporation, Investor–owned, for–profit **Service:** General Medical and Surgical

**Staffed Beds:** 88

### LIVE OAK—Suwannee County

☒ **SHANDS LIVE OAK REGIONAL MEDICAL CENTER (101301)**, 1100 S.W. 11th Street, Zip 32064–3608; tel. 386/362–0800 **A**1 9 10 18 **F**15 18 29 34 35 40 41 45 50 54 56 57 59 64 68 75 81 91 92 93 97 102 107 108 110 111 119 127 135 146 147 **S** Community Health Systems, Inc., Franklin, TN
Primary Contact: Richard Huth, Chief Executive Officer
CFO: Mihn Dang–Do, Chief Financial Officer
CMO: Andrew C. Bass, M.D., Medical Director
CIO: Scott Thompson, Market Management Information System Director
CHR: Angela Altman, Market Human Resources Director
CNO: Jana Rolerson, Chief Nursing Officer
Web address: www.shandsliveoak.com/
**Control:** Corporation, Investor–owned, for–profit **Service:** General Medical and Surgical

**Staffed Beds:** 25 **Admissions:** 1327 **Census:** 13 **Births:** 0 **Total Expense ($000):** 16677 **Payroll Expense ($000):** 7051

### LOXAHATCHEE—Palm Beach County

☒ **PALMS WEST HOSPITAL (100269)**, 13001 Southern Boulevard, Zip 33470–9203; tel. 561/798–3300 **A**1 9 10 **F**3 8 13 15 18 19 20 22 29 30 31 34 35 39 40 41 45 46 49 50 51 56 57 58 60 61 64 68 70 74 75 76 77 78 79 80 81 82 84 85 86 87 88 89 93 107 108 110 111 114 115 119 124 126 130 131 141 146 147 148 **S** HCA, Nashville, TN
Primary Contact: Eric Goldman, Chief Executive Officer
COO: Madeline Nava, Chief Operating Officer
CFO: Steven Burroughs, Chief Financial Officer
CIO: Martha Stinson, Director of Information Technology
CHR: Marcy Mills–Mathews, Director Human Resources
CNO: Silvia Stradi, Chief Nursing Officer
Web address: www.palmswesthospital.com
**Control:** Corporation, Investor–owned, for–profit **Service:** General Medical and Surgical

**Staffed Beds:** 204 **Admissions:** 12558 **Census:** 139 **Outpatient Visits:** 74958 **Births:** 1333 **Total Expense ($000):** 125637 **Payroll Expense ($000):** 51676 **Personnel:** 466

### MACCLENNY—Baker County

**ED FRASER MEMORIAL HOSPITAL AND BAKER COMMUNITY HEALTH CENTER (100134)**, 159 North Third Street, Zip 32063–2103, Mailing Address: P.O. Box 484, Zip 32063–0484; tel. 904/259–3151, (Nonreporting) **A**9 10 20
Primary Contact: Dennis R. Markos, Chief Executive Officer
CFO: W. Steve Dudley, CPA, Chief Financial Officer
CMO: Mark Hardin, M.D., Medical Director
CIO: Ernie Waller, Director Information Technology
CHR: Stacey Conner, Director Personnel
CNO: Valerie Markos, Chief Nursing Officer
Web address: www.bcmedsvcs.com
**Control:** Other not–for–profit (including NFP Corporation) **Service:** General Medical and Surgical

**Staffed Beds:** 68

### MADISON—Madison County

**MADISON COUNTY MEMORIAL HOSPITAL (101311)**, 224 N.W. Crane Avenue, Zip 32340–2561; tel. 850/973–2271, (Nonreporting) **A**9 10 18
Primary Contact: Tammy Stevens, Chief Executive Officer
CFO: Patrick Halfhill, Chief Financial Officer
CMO: Brett Perkins, M.D., Chief Medical Staff
CIO: Patrick Stiff, Coordinator Information Technology
CHR: Cindi Burnett, Chief Human Resources Officer
Web address: www.mcmh.us/
**Control:** Other not–for–profit (including NFP Corporation) **Service:** General Medical and Surgical

**Staffed Beds:** 25

### MARATHON—Monroe County

☒ **FISHERMEN'S HOSPITAL (101312)**, 3301 Overseas Highway, Zip 33050–2329; tel. 305/743–5533 **A**1 9 10 18 **F**3 11 15 17 18 29 34 35 40 45 46 50 51 57 59 64 68 70 75 79 81 82 85 91 93 107 108 110 111 114 119 124 130 133 141 146 **P**8 **S** QHR, Brentwood, TN
Primary Contact: Hal W. Leftwich, FACHE, Chief Executive Officer
COO: Lynn Mauck, R.N., Chief Operating Officer and Chief Nursing Officer
CFO: Scott Merkle, Chief Financial Officer
CMO: Ronald Samess, M.D., Chief of Staff
CIO: Joe Brake, Director Information Services
CNO: Lynn Mauck, R.N., Chief Operating Officer and Chief Nursing Officer
Web address: www.fishermenshospital.org
**Control:** Other not–for–profit (including NFP Corporation) **Service:** General Medical and Surgical

**Staffed Beds:** 25 **Admissions:** 650 **Census:** 5 **Outpatient Visits:** 10972 **Births:** 0 **Total Expense ($000):** 24862 **Payroll Expense ($000):** 10948 **Personnel:** 207

FL

*Many Facility Codes have changed. Please refer to the AHA Guide Code Chart.*   © 2015 AHA Guide

## MARGATE—Broward County

✠ **NORTHWEST MEDICAL CENTER (100189)**, 2801 North State Road 7, Zip 33063–5727; tel. 954/974–0400 **A**1 3 9 10 **F**3 8 11 12 13 15 17 18 22 24 26 29 31 34 35 40 41 44 45 46 47 49 50 53 56 57 59 60 61 63 64 65 68 70 73 74 75 76 77 78 79 80 81 82 83 85 86 87 89 93 107 108 110 111 114 115 117 118 119 126 129 130 131 132 135 146 147 148 **S** HCA, Nashville, TN
Primary Contact: Erica Gulrich, Chief Executive Officer
CFO: Ananda Rampat, Chief Financial Officer
CMO: Jose Martinez, M.D., Chief Medical Officer
CIO: David Irizarri, Director Information Technology
CHR: Lynda Bryan, Vice President Human Resources
CNO: Sandra Emeott, R.N., Chief Nursing Officer
Web address: www.northwestmed.com
**Control:** Corporation, Investor–owned, for–profit **Service:** General Medical and Surgical

**Staffed Beds:** 223 **Admissions:** 14259 **Census:** 145 **Births:** 1685 **Total Expense ($000):** 163185 **Payroll Expense ($000):** 50056

## MARIANNA—Jackson County

✠ **JACKSON HOSPITAL (100142)**, 4250 Hospital Drive, Zip 32446–1917, Mailing Address: P.O. Box 1608, Zip 32447–5608; tel. 850/526–2200 **A**1 9 10 20 **F**3 11 13 15 18 29 30 31 34 35 40 45 49 50 53 57 59 70 75 76 78 81 85 86 87 89 97 107 108 110 111 114 119 120 127 130 132 133 135 144 146 147 **S** QHR, Brentwood, TN
Primary Contact: Larry Meese, Chief Executive Officer
CFO: Kevin Rovito, Chief Financial Officer
CMO: Doyle Bosse, M.D., Chief Medical Officer
CIO: Beth Medlock, Manager Information Technology
CHR: Brooke G. Donaldson, Assistant Administrator Human Resources
CNO: Robbin K. Catt, Chief Nursing Officer
Web address: www.jacksonhosp.com
**Control:** Hospital district or authority, Government, nonfederal **Service:** General Medical and Surgical

**Staffed Beds:** 68 **Admissions:** 2805 **Census:** 35 **Births:** 451 **Total Expense ($000):** 47331 **Payroll Expense ($000):** 20916

## MELBOURNE—Brevard County

☐ **CIRCLES OF CARE (104024)**, 400 East Sheridan Road, Zip 32901–3184; tel. 321/722–5200, (Nonreporting) **A**1 5 9 10
Primary Contact: James B. Whitaker, President
CFO: David L. Feldman, Executive Vice President and Treasurer
CMO: Jose Alvarez, M.D., Chief Medical Staff
CHR: Linda Brannon, Vice President Human Resources
Web address: www.circlesofcare.org
**Control:** Other not–for–profit (including NFP Corporation) **Service:** Psychiatric

**Staffed Beds:** 134

**DEVEREUX HOSPITAL AND CHILDREN'S CENTER OF FLORIDA**, 8000 Devereux Drive, Zip 32940–7907; tel. 321/242–9100, (Nonreporting) **S** Devereux, Villanova, PA
Primary Contact: Steven Murphy, Executive Director
COO: Eva Horner, Assistant Executive Director Operations
CFO: Kelly Messer, Director of Finance
CMO: Manal Durgin, Network Medical Director
CIO: Diana Deitrick, Director Information Services
CHR: Tim Dillion, Vice President of Human Resources
Web address: www.devereux.org
**Control:** Other not–for–profit (including NFP Corporation) **Service:** Children's hospital psychiatric

**Staffed Beds:** 100

✠ **HEALTH FIRST HOLMES REGIONAL MEDICAL CENTER (100019)**, 1350 South Hickory Street, Zip 32901–3224; tel. 321/434–7000 **A**1 5 9 10 **F**3 7 11 13 15 17 18 20 22 24 26 29 30 31 34 40 43 45 46 47 48 49 56 57 59 60 65 68 70 72 73 74 75 76 77 78 79 81 82 83 84 85 87 89 91 92 93 100 107 108 110 111 114 115 116 117 118 119 124 126 129 130 132 146 147 148 **P**6 7 **S** Health First, Inc., Rockledge, FL
Primary Contact: Sean Gregory, President
CFO: Joseph G. Felkner, Executive Vice President, Finance and Chief Financial Officer
CMO: Joseph Albert Gurri, Vice President of Medical Affairs
CIO: Dustin Leek, Vice President of Enterprise Technical Services
CHR: Paula Just, Chief Human Resources Officer
CNO: Kelly Breedlove, Vice President of Nursing
Web address: www.health–first.org
**Control:** Other not–for–profit (including NFP Corporation) **Service:** General Medical and Surgical

**Staffed Beds:** 514 **Admissions:** 27247 **Census:** 357 **Outpatient Visits:** 222944 **Births:** 2925 **Total Expense ($000):** 360596 **Payroll Expense ($000):** 146138 **Personnel:** 1946

☐ **HEALTH FIRST VIERA HOSPITAL (100315)**, 8745 North Wickham Road, Zip 32940–5997; tel. 321/434–9164 **A**1 5 9 10 **F**3 11 12 15 18 29 30 31 34 35 40 41 44 45 46 47 48 49 50 57 59 60 64 68 70 74 77 78 79 81 85 86 87 93 97 107 108 110 111 115 117 118 119 126 129 130 132 146 148 **P**6 **S** Health First, Inc., Rockledge, FL
Primary Contact: William Calhoun, President, Community Hospitals
COO: Deborah Angerami, Chief Operating Officer
CFO: Joseph G. Felkner, Executive Vice President and Chief Financial Officer
CMO: Scott Gettings, M.D., Senior Vice President and Chief Medical Officer
CIO: Lori Delone, Senior Vice President and Chief Information Officer
CHR: Paula Just, Chief Human Resources Officer
CNO: Connie Bradley, R.N., Senior Vice President and Chief Nursing Officer
Web address: www.vierahospital.org
**Control:** Other not–for–profit (including NFP Corporation) **Service:** General Medical and Surgical

**Staffed Beds:** 84 **Admissions:** 3759 **Census:** 40 **Outpatient Visits:** 52138 **Births:** 0 **Total Expense ($000):** 74685 **Payroll Expense ($000):** 22982 **Personnel:** 347

✠ **HEALTHSOUTH SEA PINES REHABILITATION HOSPITAL (103034)**, 101 East Florida Avenue, Zip 32901–8301; tel. 321/984–4600 **A**1 9 10 **F**29 34 59 62 64 68 79 82 86 87 91 93 94 95 96 130 132 148 **S** HEALTHSOUTH Corporation, Birmingham, AL
Primary Contact: Denise B. McGrath, Chief Executive Officer
CFO: Dana Edwards, Chief Financial Officer
CMO: Juan Lebron, M.D., Medical Director
CHR: James L. Henry, Director Human Resources
Web address: www.healthsouthseapines.com
**Control:** Corporation, Investor–owned, for–profit **Service:** Rehabilitation

**Staffed Beds:** 90 **Admissions:** 1527 **Census:** 57 **Outpatient Visits:** 4136 **Births:** 0 **Total Expense ($000):** 19086 **Payroll Expense ($000):** 11678 **Personnel:** 190

✠ **KINDRED HOSPITAL MELBOURNE (102027)**, 765 West Nasa Boulevard, Zip 32901–1815; tel. 321/733–5725 **A**1 9 10 **F**1 3 29 70 107 114 148 **S** Kindred Healthcare, Louisville, KY
Primary Contact: Joyce Baldrica, Chief Executive Officer
Web address: www.khmelbourne.com
**Control:** Corporation, Investor–owned, for–profit **Service:** Long–Term Acute Care hospital

**Staffed Beds:** 60 **Admissions:** 397 **Census:** 32 **Outpatient Visits:** 0 **Births:** 0 **Total Expense ($000):** 19793 **Payroll Expense ($000):** 7031

✠ **WUESTHOFF MEDICAL CENTER – MELBOURNE (100291)**, 250 North Wickham Road, Zip 32935–8625; tel. 321/752–1200, (Nonreporting) **A**1 9 10 **S** Community Health Systems, Inc., Franklin, TN
Primary Contact: Richard Frank, Chief Executive Officer
CFO: Steve Bender, Chief Financial Officer
Web address: www.wuesthoff.com/locations/wuesthoff–medical–center–melbourne
**Control:** Corporation, Investor–owned, for–profit **Service:** General Medical and Surgical

**Staffed Beds:** 119

## MIAMI—Miami–Dade County

✠ △ **BAPTIST HEALTH SOUTH FLORIDA, BAPTIST HOSPITAL OF MIAMI (100008)**, 8900 North Kendall Drive, Zip 33176–2197; tel. 786/596–1960, (Includes BAPTIST CHILDREN'S HOSPITAL, 8900 North Kendall Drive, Zip 33176–2118; tel. 786/596–1960) **A**1 2 3 5 7 9 10 **F**3 8 11 13 15 17 18 19 20 22 24 26 28 29 30 31 32 34 35 40 41 45 46 47 49 50 51 53 54 55 56 57 58 59 60 61 62 63 64 66 68 70 72 73 74 75 76 77 78 79 81 82 84 85 86 87 88 89 90 91 92 93 96 100 102 107 108 109 110 111 114 115 116 117 118 119 120 121 123 124 126 129 130 132 135 144 145 146 147 148 **P**8 **S** Baptist Health South Florida, Coral Gables, FL
Primary Contact: Albert Boulenger, Chief Executive Officer
COO: Randall Lee, Vice President and Chief Operating Officer
CFO: Ralph E. Lawson, Executive Vice President and Chief Financial Officer
CMO: Mark J. Hauser, M.D., Chief Medical Officer
CIO: Mimi Taylor, Corporate Vice President Information Technology
Web address: www.baptisthealth.net
**Control:** Other not–for–profit (including NFP Corporation) **Service:** General Medical and Surgical

**Staffed Beds:** 672 **Admissions:** 33545 **Census:** 499 **Outpatient Visits:** 375785 **Births:** 4400 **Total Expense ($000):** 772523 **Payroll Expense ($000):** 267954 **Personnel:** 4141

**FL**

---

**Hospital, Medicare Provider Number, Address, Telephone, Approval, Facility, and Physician Codes, Health Care System**

★ American Hospital Association (AHA) membership
☐ The Joint Commission accreditation
○ Healthcare Facilities Accreditation Program
◇ DNV Healthcare Inc. accreditation
⇧ Center for Improvement in Healthcare Quality Accreditation
△ Commission on Accreditation of Rehabilitation Facilities (CARF) accreditation

⊞ **BAPTIST HEALTH SOUTH FLORIDA, SOUTH MIAMI HOSPITAL (100154)**, 6200 S.W. 73rd Street, Zip 33143–4679; tel. 786/662–4000 **A**1 2 3 9 10 **F**3 5 11 12 13 15 17 18 20 22 24 26 28 29 30 31 34 35 36 40 46 48 49 50 51 52 53 54 57 58 59 60 61 64 68 70 72 74 75 76 77 78 79 81 82 84 85 86 87 93 107 108 110 111 114 115 116 117 118 119 120 121 123 124 126 129 130 132 135 144 146 147 148 **P**8 **S** Baptist Health South Florida, Coral Gables, FL
Primary Contact: Lincoln S. Mendez, Chief Executive Officer
COO: Jeanette Stone, Vice President Operations
CFO: Berta Rufat, Controller
CMO: Jeremy Tabak, M.D., President Medical Staff
CIO: Mimi Taylor, Vice President Information Technology
CHR: Diana Montenegro, Director Human Resources
CNO: Kathy Sparger, R.N., Chief Nursing Officer
Web address: www.baptisthealth.net
**Control:** Other not–for–profit (including NFP Corporation) **Service:** General Medical and Surgical

**Staffed Beds:** 335 **Admissions:** 16739 **Census:** 223 **Outpatient Visits:** 267603 **Births:** 4740 **Total Expense ($000):** 452665 **Payroll Expense ($000):** 151370 **Personnel:** 2247

⊞ **BAPTIST HEALTH SOUTH FLORIDA, WEST KENDALL BAPTIST HOSPITAL (100314)**, 9555 S.W. 162nd Avenue, Zip 33196–6408; tel. 786/467–2000 **A**1 3 10 **F**3 11 13 18 19 29 30 31 34 35 40 41 45 49 50 51 53 57 58 59 60 63 64 68 70 74 75 76 78 79 81 82 84 85 86 87 93 100 102 107 108 109 111 114 115 119 126 130 131 132 135 146 147 148 **P**8 **S** Baptist Health South Florida, Coral Gables, FL
Primary Contact: Javier Hernandez–Lichtl, Chief Executive Officer
CFO: Odalys Remigio, Assistant Vice President, Finance
CMO: Juan–Carlos Verdeja, M.D., President of Medical Staff
CHR: Hilde Zamora de Aguero, Human Resources Site Director
CNO: Denise H. Harris, R.N., Chief Nursing Officer
Web address: www.baptisthealth.net/en/facilities/West–Kendall–Baptist–Hospital/Pages/default.aspx
**Control:** Other not–for–profit (including NFP Corporation) **Service:** General Medical and Surgical

**Staffed Beds:** 133 **Admissions:** 7297 **Census:** 79 **Outpatient Visits:** 69141 **Births:** 831 **Total Expense ($000):** 175078 **Payroll Expense ($000):** 57618 **Personnel:** 931

⊞ **BASCOM PALMER EYE INSTITUTE–ANNE BATES LEACH EYE HOSPITAL (100240)**, 900 N.W. 17th Street, Zip 33136–1199, Mailing Address: Box 016880, Zip 33101–6880; tel. 305/326–6000 **A**1 3 5 9 10 **F**3 8 29 34 38 40 41 50 54 57 58 59 64 66 68 71 78 79 80 81 86 87 93 94 111 119 129 130 141 142 144 146 **P**6 **S** University of Miami Health System, Miami, FL
Primary Contact: Michael B. Gittelman, Administrator
COO: Charles Pappas, M.D., Chief Operating Officer
CFO: Harry Rohrer, Chief Financial Officer
CMO: Eduardo Alfonso, M.D., Chairman Ophthalmology
CHR: Paul Hudgins, Associate Vice President Human Resources
Web address: www.bascompalmer.org
**Control:** Other not–for–profit (including NFP Corporation) **Service:** Eye, ear, nose, and throat

**Staffed Beds:** 56 **Admissions:** 74 **Census:** 1 **Outpatient Visits:** 210097 **Births:** 0 **Total Expense ($000):** 102395 **Payroll Expense ($000):** 29888 **Personnel:** 592

**HIGHLAND PARK HOSPITAL** See Jackson Health System

☐ △ **JACKSON HEALTH SYSTEM (100022)**, 1611 N.W. 12th Avenue, Zip 33136–1005; tel. 305/585–1111, (Includes HIGHLAND PARK HOSPITAL, 1695 N.W. Ninth Avenue, Zip 33136; tel. 305/355–8234; HOLTZ CHILDREN'S HOSPITAL, 1611 N.W. 12th Avenue, tel. 305/585–5437; Daniel Armstrong, Chief Administrative Officer; JACKSON MEMORIAL HOSPITAL, 1611 N.W. 12th Avenue, Zip 33136; tel. 305/585–6661; Alex Contreras–Soto, Senior Vice President and Chief Administrative Officer; JACKSON NORTH MEDICAL CENTER, 160 N.W. 170th Street, North Miami Beach, Zip 33169–5576; tel. 305/651–1100; Sandy Sears, Senior Vice President and Chief Administrative Officer; JACKSON SOUTH COMMUNITY HOSPITAL, 9333 S.W. 152nd Street, Zip 33157–1780; tel. 305/251–2500; Martha Garcia, Senior Vice President and Chief Administrative Officer), (Total facility includes 342 beds in nursing home–type unit) **A**1 3 5 7 8 9 10 **F**1 3 4 5 8 11 12 13 15 16 17 18 19 20 21 22 23 24 25 26 27 28 29 30 31 34 35 38 39 40 41 43 44 45 49 50 54 55 56 58 63 64 65 66 67 68 70 71 72 74 75 76 77 78 79 80 81 82 83 84 85 86 87 88 89 90 93 94 96 97 98 99 100 101 102 103 104 106 107 108 109 110 111 114 115 116 117 118 119 120 121 123 126 128 129 130 131 132 135 136 137 138 139 140 141 142 146 147 148 **P**6
Primary Contact: Carlos A. Migoya, President and Chief Executive Officer
COO: Don S. Steigman, Chief Operating Officer
CFO: Mark T. Knight, Executive Vice President and Chief Financial Officer
CMO: Michael K. Butler, M.D., Executive Vice President and Chief Medical Officer
CIO: Fernando Martinez, Vice President and Chief Information Officer
CHR: Trummell Valdera, Senior Vice President and Chief Human Resources Officer
Web address: www.um–jmh.org
**Control:** County–Government, nonfederal **Service:** General Medical and Surgical

**Staffed Beds:** 1953 **Admissions:** 56880 **Census:** 1386 **Outpatient Visits:** 545177 **Births:** 6188 **Total Expense ($000):** 1522887 **Payroll Expense ($000):** 710037 **Personnel:** 8813

**JACKSON SOUTH COMMUNITY HOSPITAL** See Jackson Health System

⊞ **KENDALL REGIONAL MEDICAL CENTER (100209)**, 11750 Bird Road, Zip 33175–3530; tel. 305/223–3000, (Nonreporting) **A**1 3 9 10 **S** HCA, Nashville, TN
Primary Contact: Scott A. Cihak, Chief Executive Officer
COO: Elizabeth Durrence, Chief Operating Officer
CFO: Scott Herndon, Chief Financial Officer
CIO: Francis Tezanos, Director Information Technology and Services
CHR: Knicole S. White, Director Human Resources
CNO: Wendy Stuart, Chief Nursing Officer
Web address: www.kendallmed.com
**Control:** Partnership, Investor–owned, for–profit **Service:** General Medical and Surgical

**Staffed Beds:** 300

☐ **MIAMI JEWISH HOME AND HOSPITAL FOR AGED (100277)**, 5200 N.E. Second Avenue, Zip 33137–2706; tel. 305/751–8626, (Nonreporting) **A**1 3 5 10
Primary Contact: Jeffrey P. Freimark, Chief Executive Officer
CFO: Lisa Jo Desmarteau, Chief Financial Officer
CMO: Brian Kiedrowski, M.D., Chief Medical Director
CHR: Larry McDonald, Director Human Resources
Web address: www.mjhha.org
**Control:** Other not–for–profit (including NFP Corporation) **Service:** General Medical and Surgical

**Staffed Beds:** 32

⊞ △ **MIAMI VETERANS AFFAIRS HEALTHCARE SYSTEM**, 1201 N.W. 16th Street, Zip 33125–1624; tel. 305/575–7000, (Nonreporting) **A**1 3 5 7 **S** Department of Veterans Affairs, Washington, DC
Primary Contact: Paul M. Russo, FACHE, Director
COO: Lance Davis, Associate Director
CFO: Albert Tucker, Chief Financial Officer
CMO: Vincent DeGennaro, M.D., Chief of Staff
CIO: Anthony Brooks, Chief Information Officer
CHR: Loyman Marin, Chief Human Resources
CNO: Marcia C. Lysaght, R.N., Associate Director Patient Care Services
Web address: www.miami.va.gov/
**Control:** Veterans Affairs, Government, federal **Service:** General Medical and Surgical

**Staffed Beds:** 401

⊞ **NICKLAUS CHILDREN'S HOSPITAL (103301)**, 3100 S.W. 62nd Avenue, Zip 33155–3009; tel. 305/666–6511 **A**1 2 3 5 8 9 10 12 13 **F**1 3 4 7 8 9 16 17 18 19 20 21 22 23 24 25 26 27 29 30 31 32 34 35 36 38 39 40 41 42 43 44 45 46 48 50 53 54 55 57 58 59 60 61 64 65 66 67 68 70 71 72 73 74 75 77 78 79 80 81 82 85 86 87 88 89 90 93 97 98 99 100 101 102 104 105 107 108 111 114 115 116 117 118 119 128 129 130 131 132 134 136 143 144 146 **P**6 7
Primary Contact: M. Narendra Kini, M.D., President and Chief Executive Officer
COO: Martha McGill, Executive Vice President and Chief Operating Officer
CFO: Timothy L. Birkenstock, Chief Financial Officer
CMO: Deise Granado–Villar, M.D., Chief Medical Officer and Senior Vice President Medical Affairs
CIO: Edward Martinez, Chief Information Officer
CHR: Michael S. Kushner, Senior Vice President and Chief Talent Officer
CNO: Jacqueline Gonzalez, Senior Vice President and Chief Nursing Officer
Web address: www.mch.com
**Control:** Other not–for–profit (including NFP Corporation) **Service:** Children's general

**Staffed Beds:** 272 **Admissions:** 10899 **Census:** 165 **Outpatient Visits:** 447619 **Births:** 0 **Total Expense ($000):** 519406 **Payroll Expense ($000):** 241886 **Personnel:** 3140

⊞ **NORTH SHORE MEDICAL CENTER (100029)**, 1100 N.W. 95th Street, Zip 33150–2098; tel. 305/835–6000, (Nonreporting) **A**1 9 10 **S** TENET Healthcare Corporation, Dallas, TX
Primary Contact: Manuel Linares, Chief Executive Officer
COO: Shana Crittenden, Chief Operating Officer
CFO: Howard Brown, Chief Financial Officer
CMO: Marcia Bierman, M.D., Chief of Staff
CIO: Luis Estrada, Director Multifacility Information Systems
CHR: Carmen Gomez, Director Human Resources
CNO: Patrick Beaver, Chief Nursing Officer
Web address: www.northshoremedical.com
**Control:** Corporation, Investor–owned, for–profit **Service:** General Medical and Surgical

**Staffed Beds:** 357

**PROMISE HOSPITAL OF MIAMI**, 14001 N.W. 82nd Avenue, Zip 33158; tel. 786/609–9200, (Nonreporting) **S** Promise Healthcare, Boca Raton, FL
Primary Contact: Theodore L. Welding, Chief Executive Officer
Web address: www.promise–miami.com
**Control:** Corporation, Investor–owned, for–profit **Service:** Long–Term Acute Care hospital

**Staffed Beds:** 60

*Many Facility Codes have changed. Please refer to the AHA Guide Code Chart.*  © 2015 AHA Guide

✠ **SELECT SPECIALTY HOSPITAL–MIAMI (102001)**, 955 N.W. 3rd Street, Zip 33128–1274; tel. 305/416–5700, (Nonreporting) **A**1 9 10 **S** Select Medical Corporation, Mechanicsburg, PA
Primary Contact: Dionisio Bencomo, Chief Executive Officer
Web address: www.selectspecialtyhospitals.com/company/locations/miami.aspx
**Control:** Corporation, Investor–owned, for–profit **Service:** Long–Term Acute Care hospital

**Staffed Beds:** 47

☐ **SISTER EMMANUEL HOSPITAL (102016)**, 3663 South Miami Avenue, Zip 33133–4253; tel. 305/285–2939 **A**1 9 10 **F**1 3 29 30 31 60 75 77 78 79 82 92 93 148
Primary Contact: Miguel Vasquez, Chief Executive Officer
CFO: Miguel Vasquez, Chief Financial Officer
CMO: Hugo Gonzalez, M.D., Chief Medical Officer
CIO: Macarena Restrepo, Manager Business Office
CHR: Kathy Mainieri, Human Resource Specialist
Web address: www.sisteremmanuelhospital.org/
**Control:** Corporation, Investor–owned, for–profit **Service:** Long–Term Acute Care hospital

**Staffed Beds:** 29 **Admissions:** 339 **Census:** 27 **Births:** 0 **Total Expense ($000):** 13026 **Payroll Expense ($000):** 4830

✠ **UNIVERSITY OF MIAMI HOSPITAL (100009)**, 1400 N.W. 12th Avenue, Zip 33136–1003; tel. 305/325–5511 **A**1 2 3 5 9 10 **F**3 11 12 15 17 18 20 22 24 26 29 30 31 34 35 38 39 40 43 44 45 46 47 48 49 50 51 54 57 58 59 60 63 64 65 68 70 71 74 75 77 78 79 80 81 82 84 85 86 87 90 91 92 93 97 98 100 101 102 103 104 105 107 108 109 110 111 113 114 115 117 118 119 120 121 123 124 126 130 131 135 141 146 148 **S** University of Miami Health System, Miami, FL
Primary Contact: David Zambrana, R.N., Chief Executive Officer
CFO: Harry Rohrer, Chief Financial Officer
CMO: Francisco Kerdel, M.D., President Medical Staff
CIO: Craig Scott, Interim Director Management Information Systems
CHR: Errol Douglas, Director Human Resources
Web address: www.umiamihospital.com
**Control:** Other not–for–profit (including NFP Corporation) **Service:** General Medical and Surgical

**Staffed Beds:** 514 **Admissions:** 21260 **Census:** 326 **Outpatient Visits:** 146174 **Births:** 0 **Total Expense ($000):** 367887 **Payroll Expense ($000):** 113757 **Personnel:** 2037

✠ **UNIVERSITY OF MIAMI HOSPITAL AND CLINICS (100079)**, 1475 N.W. 12th Avenue, Zip 33136–1002; tel. 305/243–4000 **A**1 2 3 5 9 10 **F**3 9 11 12 14 15 18 19 29 30 31 32 34 35 36 38 44 45 46 47 48 49 50 52 54 55 57 58 59 61 64 65 68 70 74 75 77 78 79 80 81 82 84 85 86 87 91 92 93 97 99 100 101 103 104 107 108 110 111 114 115 117 118 119 120 121 123 124 126 130 132 135 136 141 145 146 147 148 **P**6 **S** University of Miami Health System, Miami, FL
Primary Contact: Richard R. Ballard, Chief Executive Officer and Administrator
COO: Joseph B. Natoli, Senior Vice President Business and Finance and Chief Financial Officer
CFO: Harry Rohrer, Chief Financial Officer
CMO: W. Jarrad Goodwin, M.D., Director
CHR: Paul Hudgins, Associate Vice President Human Resources
Web address: www.uhealthsystem.com
**Control:** Other not–for–profit (including NFP Corporation) **Service:** Cancer

**Staffed Beds:** 40 **Admissions:** 1485 **Census:** 30 **Outpatient Visits:** 340574 **Births:** 0 **Total Expense ($000):** 334030 **Payroll Expense ($000):** 68024 **Personnel:** 1182

**VETERANS AFFAIRS MEDICAL CENTER** See Miami Veterans Affairs Healthcare System

✠ △ **WEST GABLES REHABILITATION HOSPITAL (103036)**, 2525 S.W. 75th Avenue, Zip 33155–2800; tel. 305/262–6800 **A**1 7 9 10 **F**7 29 90 91 93 148 **S** Select Medical Corporation, Mechanicsburg, PA
Primary Contact: Walter Concepcion, Chief Executive Officer
CFO: Sara Reohr, Regional Controller
CMO: Jose L. Vargas, M.D., Medical Director
CHR: Barbara Etchason, HR Manager
CNO: Constance Hughes, Director of Nursing
Web address: www.westgablesrehabhospital.com/
**Control:** Corporation, Investor–owned, for–profit **Service:** Rehabilitation

**Staffed Beds:** 60 **Admissions:** 1698 **Census:** 52 **Births:** 0

○ **WESTCHESTER GENERAL HOSPITAL (100284)**, 2500 S.W. 75th Avenue, Zip 33155–2805; tel. 305/264–5252, (Includes SOUTHERN WINDS HOSPITAL, 4225 West 20th Street, Hialeah, Zip 33012–5835; tel. 305/558–9700) **A**9 10 11 12 13 **F**3 15 18 29 31 40 45 49 56 65 70 74 75 77 78 79 81 85 87 98 99 100 102 103 107 108 110 114 115 119 130
Primary Contact: Gilda Baldwin, Chief Executive Officer
CFO: Joel Snook, Chief Financial Officer
CMO: Rogelio Zaldivar, M.D., Medical Director
CHR: Alicia Lund, Director Human Resources
Web address: www.westchesterhospital.com
**Control:** Corporation, Investor–owned, for–profit **Service:** General Medical and Surgical

**Staffed Beds:** 197 **Admissions:** 9608 **Census:** 142 **Outpatient Visits:** 35647 **Births:** 0 **Total Expense ($000):** 67604 **Payroll Expense ($000):** 33522 **Personnel:** 645

**MIAMI BEACH—Dade County**

**MIAMI HEART CAMPUS AT MOUNT SINAI MEDICAL CENTER** See Mount Sinai Medical Center

☐ △ **MOUNT SINAI MEDICAL CENTER (100034)**, 4300 Alton Road, Zip 33140–2948; tel. 305/674–2121, (Includes MIAMI HEART CAMPUS AT MOUNT SINAI MEDICAL CENTER, 4701 North Meridian Avenue, Zip 33140–2910; tel. 305/672–1111) **A**1 2 3 5 7 8 9 10 13 **F**1 3 4 6 8 12 13 14 15 16 17 18 19 20 22 24 26 28 29 30 31 34 35 36 37 38 39 40 41 42 44 45 46 47 48 49 50 51 53 54 55 56 57 58 59 60 61 62 63 64 65 66 67 68 70 71 72 73 74 75 76 77 78 79 80 81 82 83 84 85 86 87 88 89 90 91 92 93 96 97 98 100 101 102 103 104 107 108 110 111 112 114 115 118 119 120 121 123 124 126 128 129 130 131 132 135 143 145 146 147 148 **P**6
Primary Contact: Steven D. Sonenreich, President and Chief Executive Officer
COO: Angel Pallin, Senior Vice President of Operations
CFO: Alex A. Mendez, Executive Vice President of Operations and Chief Financial Officer
CMO: Robert Goldszer, M.D., Senior Vice President and Chief Medical Officer
CIO: Tom Gillette, Senior Vice President and Chief Information Officer
CHR: Georgia McLean, Director Human Resources
CNO: Karen W. Moyer, R.N., Senior Vice President and Chief Nursing Officer
Web address: www.msmc.com
**Control:** Other not–for–profit (including NFP Corporation) **Service:** General Medical and Surgical

**Staffed Beds:** 608 **Admissions:** 22613 **Census:** 369 **Outpatient Visits:** 181225 **Births:** 2822 **Total Expense ($000):** 443858 **Payroll Expense ($000):** 171955 **Personnel:** 3514

**MIDDLEBURG—Clay County**

✠ **ST. VINCENT'S MEDICAL CENTER CLAY COUNTY (100321)**, 1670 St. Vincent's Way, Zip 32068–8427, Mailing Address: 1670 St. Vincents Way, Zip 32068–8447; tel. 904/602–1000, (Data for 273 days) **A**1 10 **F**3 15 18 20 29 30 34 40 49 50 51 57 60 64 65 70 74 75 77 79 81 84 85 86 87 92 93 102 103 107 108 110 111 114 115 118 119 124 129 130 132 146 147 148 **S** Ascension Health, Saint Louis, MO
Primary Contact: Blain Claypool, President
Web address: www.jaxhealth.com/
**Control:** Church–operated, Nongovernment, not–for profit **Service:** General Medical and Surgical

**Staffed Beds:** 64 **Admissions:** 3208 **Census:** 43 **Outpatient Visits:** 27523 **Births:** 0 **Total Expense ($000):** 40738 **Payroll Expense ($000):** 15729 **Personnel:** 337

**MILTON—Santa Rosa County**

✠ **SANTA ROSA MEDICAL CENTER (100124)**, 6002 Berryhill Road, Zip 32570–5062; tel. 850/626–7762 **A**1 9 10 **F**3 11 13 15 18 20 29 30 34 35 40 45 49 54 57 59 64 65 74 75 76 77 79 81 85 87 97 107 108 111 115 119 126 129 130 132 135 144 146 147 148 **S** Community Health Systems, Inc., Franklin, TN
Primary Contact: Doug Sills, Chief Executive Officer
CFO: Jared Whipkey, Chief Financial Officer
CIO: Rick Payne, Director Information Systems
CHR: Christopher Foreman, Director Human Resources
CNO: Trish Davis, Chief Nursing Officer
Web address: www.santarosamedicalcenter.org
**Control:** Corporation, Investor–owned, for–profit **Service:** General Medical and Surgical

**Staffed Beds:** 68 **Admissions:** 3522 **Census:** 35 **Births:** 354 **Total Expense ($000):** 49135 **Payroll Expense ($000):** 15435

**FL**

---

**Hospital, Medicare Provider Number, Address, Telephone, Approval, Facility, and Physician Codes, Health Care System**

★ American Hospital Association (AHA) membership
☐ The Joint Commission accreditation
○ Healthcare Facilities Accreditation Program
◇ DNV Healthcare Inc. accreditation
⇑ Center for Improvement in Healthcare Quality Accreditation
△ Commission on Accreditation of Rehabilitation Facilities (CARF) accreditation

**WEST FLORIDA COMMUNITY CARE CENTER (104027)**, 5500 Stewart Street, Zip 32570–4304; tel. 850/983–5500 **A**10 **F**29 30 106 130 132 143 **P**6
Primary Contact: Carmen Paroby, Administrator
**Control:** State–Government, nonfederal **Service:** Psychiatric

**Staffed Beds:** 80 **Admissions:** 158 **Census:** 87 **Outpatient Visits:** 0 **Births:** 0

### MIRAMAR—Broward County

☒ **MEMORIAL HOSPITAL MIRAMAR (100285)**, 1901 S.W. 172nd Avenue, Zip 33029–5592; tel. 954/538–5000 **A**1 9 10 **F**3 13 15 29 30 40 41 45 49 50 57 59 61 64 68 70 72 74 75 76 78 79 81 82 85 86 87 91 93 107 108 110 111 114 115 118 119 126 130 131 132 145 146 147 **S** Memorial Healthcare System, Hollywood, FL
Primary Contact: Leah A. Carpenter, Administrator and Chief Executive Officer
CFO: Judy Sada, Chief Financial Officer
CMO: Stanley Marks, M.D., Chief Medical Officer
CIO: Forest Blanton, Senior VP and Chief Information Officer
CHR: Ray Kendrick, Chief Human Resources Officer
CNO: Denise Reynolds, Chief Nursing Officer
Web address: www.mhs.net
**Control:** Hospital district or authority, Government, nonfederal **Service:** General Medical and Surgical

**Staffed Beds:** 178 **Admissions:** 8427 **Census:** 85 **Outpatient Visits:** 118579 **Births:** 3056 **Total Expense ($000):** 124032 **Payroll Expense ($000):** 59083 **Personnel:** 765

### MIRAMAR BEACH—Walton County

☒ **SACRED HEART HOSPITAL ON THE EMERALD COAST (100292)**, 7800 Highway 98 West, Zip 32550; tel. 850/278–3000 **A**1 9 10 **F**3 11 13 15 18 20 22 26 28 29 30 31 34 35 36 40 44 49 50 51 53 57 58 59 60 64 68 70 74 75 76 78 79 81 82 84 85 86 87 93 96 107 108 110 111 114 115 118 119 121 123 124 130 132 135 146 147 148 **P**7 **S** Ascension Health, Saint Louis, MO
Primary Contact: Roger L. Hall, President
CMO: Gary M. Pablo, M.D., Chief Medical Officer
Web address: www.sacredheartemerald.org
**Control:** Other not–for–profit (including NFP Corporation) **Service:** General Medical and Surgical

**Staffed Beds:** 58 **Admissions:** 4765 **Census:** 39 **Births:** 1159 **Total Expense ($000):** 84120 **Payroll Expense ($000):** 25578

### NAPLES—Collier County

**LANDMARK HOSPITAL OF SOUTHWEST FLORIDA**, 1285 Creekside Boulevard East, Zip 34108; tel. 239/529–1800, (Nonreporting) **S** Landmark Hospitals, Cape Girardeau, MO
Primary Contact: Jimmy Dascani, Chief Executive Officer
Web address: www.landmarkhospitals.com/naples.aspx
**Control:** Partnership, Investor–owned, for–profit **Service:** Long–Term Acute Care hospital

**Staffed Beds:** 50

☒ △ **NCH DOWNTOWN NAPLES HOSPITAL (100018)**, 350 Seventh Street North, Zip 34102–5754, Mailing Address: P.O. Box 413029, Zip 34101–3029; tel. 239/624–4000, (Includes NCH NORTH NAPLES HOSPITAL, 11190 Health Park Boulevard, Zip 34110–5729, Mailing Address: 11190 Health Park Boulevard, Zip 34110–5729; tel. 239/552–7000) **A**1 2 7 9 10 **F**3 11 13 14 17 18 20 22 24 26 28 29 30 31 34 37 40 41 45 47 49 50 53 57 59 64 68 70 72 74 75 76 77 78 79 81 84 85 86 87 88 89 90 92 93 95 96 98 100 102 103 107 108 111 114 115 119 126 130 135 146 147 148
Primary Contact: Allen S. Weiss, M.D., President and Chief Executive Officer
COO: Phillip C. Dutcher, Chief Operating Officer
CFO: Mike Stephens, Chief Financial Officer
CMO: Doug Ardion, M.D., Chief Medical Officer
CHR: John McGirl, Chief Human Resources Officer
CNO: Michele Thoman, R.N., Chief Nursing Officer
Web address: www.nchmd.org
**Control:** Other not–for–profit (including NFP Corporation) **Service:** General Medical and Surgical

**Staffed Beds:** 713 **Admissions:** 29438 **Census:** 354 **Outpatient Visits:** 281730 **Births:** 3418 **Total Expense ($000):** 367803 **Payroll Expense ($000):** 141733 **Personnel:** 2544

☒ **PHYSICIANS REGIONAL – PINE RIDGE (100286)**, 6101 Pine Ridge Road, Zip 34119–3900; tel. 239/348–4000, (Includes PHYSICIANS REGIONAL, 8300 Collier Boulevard, Zip 34114; tel. 239/354–6000; C. Scott Campbell, Market Chief Executive Officer), (Nonreporting) **A**1 9 10 **S** Community Health Systems, Inc., Franklin, TN
Primary Contact: Scott Lowe, Interim Market Chief Executive Officer
COO: Susan Takacs, Market Chief Operating Officer
CFO: Ken Warriner, Market Chief Financial Officer
CHR: Jill Gaffoli, Director Human Resources
CNO: Judy C. Paull, R.N., Market Chief Nursing Executive
Web address: www.physiciansregional.com
**Control:** Corporation, Investor–owned, for–profit **Service:** General Medical and Surgical

**Staffed Beds:** 201

☐ **THE WILLOUGH AT NAPLES (104063)**, 9001 Tamiami Trail East, Zip 34113–3304; tel. 239/775–4500, (Nonreporting) **A**1 9 10
Primary Contact: James E. O'Shea, Administrator
CFO: Steve Baldwin, Vice President Finance
Web address: www.thewilloughatnaples.com/
**Control:** Corporation, Investor–owned, for–profit **Service:** Psychiatric

**Staffed Beds:** 80

### NEW PORT RICHEY—Pasco County

☒ △ **MORTON PLANT NORTH BAY HOSPITAL (100063)**, 6600 Madison Street, Zip 34652–1900; tel. 727/842–8468 **A**1 7 9 10 **F**3 11 18 20 22 29 30 31 34 35 40 44 45 47 48 49 50 57 58 59 64 68 70 74 75 78 79 81 84 85 86 87 90 91 93 96 98 99 100 102 107 108 111 114 115 118 119 129 130 132 135 143 146 147 148 **S** Morton Plant Mease Health Care, Clearwater, FL
Primary Contact: Michael Yungmann, President
CFO: Carl Tremonti, Chief Financial Officer
CMO: Andrew Fink, Vice President Medical Affairs
CHR: Angel Brown, Director Team Resources
CNO: Shannon L. Hancock, Director, Patient Services
Web address: www.mpmhealth.com
**Control:** Other not–for–profit (including NFP Corporation) **Service:** General Medical and Surgical

**Staffed Beds:** 226 **Admissions:** 10892 **Census:** 143 **Outpatient Visits:** 34283 **Births:** 0 **Total Expense ($000):** 107034 **Payroll Expense ($000):** 42905 **Personnel:** 567

### NEW SMYRNA BEACH—Volusia County

☒ **BERT FISH MEDICAL CENTER (100014)**, 401 Palmetto Street, Zip 32168–7399; tel. 386/424–5000 **A**1 9 10 **F**3 11 15 18 20 22 28 29 30 33 34 40 45 46 49 50 57 59 60 66 68 70 74 78 79 81 84 93 107 108 110 111 114 115 119 120 121 135 148 **P**5
Primary Contact: Steven W. Harrell, FACHE, Interim Chief Executive Officer
COO: Steven W. Harrell, FACHE, Chief Operating Officer
CFO: Al W. Allred, Chief Financial Officer
CMO: Eric Lo, M.D., Chief Medical Staff
CIO: Calvin Patrick, II, Director Information Services
CHR: Nancy K. Evolga, Executive Director Human Resources
CNO: Linda G. Breum, R.N., Chief Nursing Officer
Web address: www.bertfish.com
**Control:** Hospital district or authority, Government, nonfederal **Service:** General Medical and Surgical

**Staffed Beds:** 112 **Admissions:** 3891 **Census:** 47 **Births:** 0 **Total Expense ($000):** 88852 **Payroll Expense ($000):** 31993

### NICEVILLE—Okaloosa County

☒ **TWIN CITIES HOSPITAL (100054)**, 2190 Highway 85 North, Zip 32578–1045; tel. 850/678–4131 **A**1 9 10 **F**3 29 34 35 45 50 59 70 75 79 81 82 85 93 107 108 110 111 115 119 124 147 **S** HCA, Nashville, TN
Primary Contact: David Whalen, Chief Executive Officer
CFO: Mark Day, Chief Financial Officer
CHR: Cyndi Ronca, Director Human Resources
Web address: www.tchealthcare.com
**Control:** Corporation, Investor–owned, for–profit **Service:** General Medical and Surgical

**Staffed Beds:** 65 **Admissions:** 1976 **Census:** 20 **Births:** 0 **Total Expense ($000):** 37384 **Payroll Expense ($000):** 10994

### NORTH MIAMI—Miami–Dade County

☐ △ **ST. CATHERINE'S REHABILITATION HOSPITAL (103026)**, 1050 N.E. 125th Street, Zip 33161–5881; tel. 305/357–1735, (Nonreporting) **A**1 7 9 10 **S** Catholic Health Services, Lauderdale Lakes, FL
Primary Contact: Jaime Gonzalez, Administrator
COO: Jim Ball, Chief Operating Officer
CFO: Mary Jo Frick, Director Finance
CMO: Miriam Feliz, M.D., Medical Director
Web address: www.catholichealthservices.org
**Control:** Other not–for–profit (including NFP Corporation) **Service:** Rehabilitation

**Staffed Beds:** 60

### NORTH MIAMI BEACH—Dade County

**JACKSON NORTH MEDICAL CENTER** See Jackson Health System, Miami

### OCALA—Marion County

☒ **HEALTHSOUTH REHABILITATION HOSPITAL OF OCALA (103043)**, 2275 S.W. 22nd Lane, Zip 34471–7710; tel. 352/282–4000, (Nonreporting) **A**1 10 **S** HEALTHSOUTH Corporation, Birmingham, AL
Primary Contact: Ellen Witterstaeter, FACHE, Chief Executive Officer
CFO: Sammy King, Controller
CMO: Amy Clunn, M.D., Medical Director
CHR: Tracy Sapp, Director Human Resources
CNO: Wendy Milam, Chief Nursing Officer
Web address: www.healthsouthocala.com
**Control:** Corporation, Investor–owned, for–profit **Service:** Rehabilitation

**Staffed Beds:** 40

**FL**

*Many Facility Codes have changed. Please refer to the AHA Guide Code Chart.* © 2015 AHA Guide

✠ **KINDRED HOSPITAL OCALA (102019)**, 1500 S.W. 1st Avenue,
Zip 34471–6504; tel. 352/369–0513, (Nonreporting) **A**1 9 10 **S** Kindred
Healthcare, Louisville, KY
Primary Contact: Merlene Bhoorasingh, Administrator
CFO: Dean Cocchi, Chief Financial Officer
Web address: www.kindredocala.com/
**Control:** Corporation, Investor–owned, for–profit **Service:** Long–Term Acute Care
hospital

**Staffed Beds:** 31

✠ **MUNROE REGIONAL MEDICAL CENTER (100062)**, 1500 S.W. 1st Avenue,
Zip 34471–6504, Mailing Address: P.O. Box 6000, Zip 34478–6000;
tel. 352/351–7200 **A**1 3 5 9 10 **F**3 8 11 12 13 15 17 18 20 22 24 26 28 29
30 34 35 38 40 41 42 44 45 49 50 51 53 57 58 59 60 64 65 67 68 70 74
75 76 77 79 81 85 86 87 89 91 93 100 107 108 109 110 111 112 113 114
115 119 120 124 126 130 131 135 136 141 146 147 148 **S** Community
Health Systems, Inc., Franklin, TN
Primary Contact: Bob Moore, FACHE, Chief Executive Officer
COO: Philoron A. Wright, II, FACHE, Chief Operating Officer
CFO: Eric LaChance, Chief Financial Officer
CMO: Lon McPherson, M.D., Senior Vice President Medical Affairs and Chief
Quality Officer
CIO: Carl Candullo, Chief Information Officer
CNO: Pamela W. Michell, R.N., Vice President, Chief Nursing Officer
Web address: www.munroeregional.com
**Control:** Corporation, Investor–owned, for–profit **Service:** General Medical and
Surgical

**Staffed Beds:** 420 **Admissions:** 28011 **Census:** 237 **Outpatient Visits:**
136732 **Births:** 2015 **Total Expense ($000):** 209220 **Payroll Expense
($000):** 77619 **Personnel:** 1975

✠ **OCALA REGIONAL MEDICAL CENTER (100212)**, 1431 S.W. First Avenue,
Zip 34471–6500, Mailing Address: P.O. Box 2200, Zip 34478–2200;
tel. 352/401–1000, (Includes WEST MARION COMMUNITY HOSPITAL, 4600 S.W.
46th Court, Zip 34474; tel. 352/291–3000), (Nonreporting) **A**1 2 3 9 10 13
**S** HCA, Nashville, TN
Primary Contact: Randy McVay, Chief Executive Officer
CMO: Art Osberg, M.D., Chief Medical Officer
CIO: Brandon Holbert, Director, Information Services
CHR: Wayne Nielsen, Director Human Resources
Web address: www.ocalaregional.com
**Control:** Corporation, Investor–owned, for–profit **Service:** General Medical and
Surgical

**Staffed Beds:** 270

**THE CENTERS (104068)**, 5664 S.W. 60th Avenue, Zip 34474–5677;
tel. 352/291–5500, (Nonreporting) **A**9 10
Primary Contact: Timothy Cowart, Chief Executive Officer
Web address: www.thecenters.us
**Control:** Other not–for–profit (including NFP Corporation) **Service:** Psychiatric

**Staffed Beds:** 40

**THE VINES (104071)**, 3130 S.W. 27th Avenue, Zip 34471–4306;
tel. 352/671–3130 **A**9 10 **F**4 5 98 99 101 102 103 104 105 106 **S** Universal
Health Services, Inc., King of Prussia, PA
Primary Contact: Stephen Quintyne, Chief Executive Officer
Web address: www.thevineshospital.com
**Control:** Corporation, Investor–owned, for–profit **Service:** Psychiatric

**Staffed Beds:** 64 **Admissions:** 2571 **Census:** 64 **Outpatient Visits:** 3886
**Births:** 0 **Total Expense ($000):** 15049 **Payroll Expense ($000):** 5930
**Personnel:** 136

**OCOEE—Orange County**

✠ **HEALTH CENTRAL HOSPITAL (100030)**, 10000 West Colonial Drive,
Zip 34761–3499; tel. 407/296–1000, (Total facility includes 228 beds in nursing
home–type unit) **A**1 9 10 **F**3 8 11 12 13 15 16 17 18 20 22 26 28 29 30 34
35 37 40 42 44 49 50 51 57 59 60 70 73 74 76 79 81 82 85 86 87 88 89
90 93 97 107 108 110 111 115 118 119 128 129 130 132 144 146 148 **P**6
**S** Orlando Health, Orlando, FL
Primary Contact: Gregory P. Ohe, President
COO: Rick Smith, Chief Operating Officer
CFO: Michael E. Mueller, Chief Financial Officer
CMO: James Barton Rodier, M.D., Chief Quality Officer
CIO: John T. Sills, Chief Information Officer
CHR: Nancy Dinon, Vice President Human Resources
CNO: Christina McGuirk, Chief Nursing Officer
Web address: www.healthcentral.org
**Control:** Other not–for–profit (including NFP Corporation) **Service:** General
Medical and Surgical

**Staffed Beds:** 399 **Admissions:** 12247 **Census:** 341 **Outpatient Visits:**
105495 **Births:** 748 **Total Expense ($000):** 179877 **Payroll Expense
($000):** 77353 **Personnel:** 1197

**OKEECHOBEE—Okeechobee County**

✠ **RAULERSON HOSPITAL (100252)**, 1796 Highway 441 North,
Zip 34972–1918, Mailing Address: P.O. Box 1307, Zip 34973–1307;
tel. 863/763–2151, (Nonreporting) **A**1 9 10 20 **S** HCA, Nashville, TN
Primary Contact: Robert H. Lee, President
CFO: Heather Garvey, Chief Financial Officer
CMO: Mohammad Riaz, M.D., Chief of Staff
CIO: Doug Schneider, Director Information Systems
CHR: Janis Stevens, Director Human Resources
Web address: www.raulersonhospital.com
**Control:** Corporation, Investor–owned, for–profit **Service:** General Medical and
Surgical

**Staffed Beds:** 100

**ORANGE CITY—Volusia County**

✠ **FLORIDA HOSPITAL FISH MEMORIAL (100072)**, 1055 Saxon Boulevard,
Zip 32763–8468; tel. 386/917–5000 **A**1 9 10 **F**1 3 4 11 15 16 17 20 28 29
30 31 34 35 37 40 45 48 49 59 64 67 70 72 73 74 75 77 78 79 80 81 82
85 87 88 89 90 91 92 93 98 100 104 107 108 110 111 114 115 116 117
118 119 120 121 128 129 130 132 135 144 146 147 148 **P**8 **S** Adventist
Health System Sunbelt Health Care Corporation, Altamonte Springs, FL
Primary Contact: Ed Noseworthy, President and Chief Executive Officer
COO: Danielle Johnson, Chief Operating Officer
CFO: Eric Osterly, Chief Financial Officer
CMO: Leighton Smith, M.D., Chief Medical Officer
CHR: Bonne S. Macpherson, Director Human Resources
CNO: Jennifer Shull, R.N., Chief Nursing Officer
Web address: www.fhfishmemorial.org
**Control:** Church–operated, Nongovernment, not–for profit **Service:** General
Medical and Surgical

**Staffed Beds:** 175 **Admissions:** 8797 **Census:** 109 **Births:** 0 **Total Expense
($000):** 128111 **Payroll Expense ($000):** 50669

**ORANGE PARK—Clay County**

✠ **ORANGE PARK MEDICAL CENTER (100226)**, 2001 Kingsley Avenue,
Zip 32073–5156; tel. 904/639–8500 **A**1 2 3 9 10 **F**3 8 11 15 17 18 20 22 24
26 28 29 30 31 34 35 40 45 46 48 49 50 60 67 68 70 72 74 76 77 79 81
84 85 87 93 94 97 98 100 101 102 103 104 107 108 110 111 114 115 118
119 126 131 132 135 146 147 148 **S** HCA, Nashville, TN
Primary Contact: Chad Patrick, President and Chief Executive Officer
COO: Christopher J. Mosley, Chief Operating Officer
CFO: Fred Ashworth, Chief Financial Officer
CMO: Lawrence Coots, M.D., Chief Medical Officer
CHR: Chris Marlin, Director Human Resources
CNO: Kathy Hester, Chief Nursing Officer
Web address: www.opmedical.com
**Control:** Corporation, Investor–owned, for–profit **Service:** General Medical and
Surgical

**Staffed Beds:** 297 **Admissions:** 16470 **Census:** 189 **Births:** 2184 **Total
Expense ($000):** 193885 **Payroll Expense ($000):** 61835

**ORLANDO—Orange County**

**ARNOLD PALMER CHILDREN'S HOSPITAL** See Orlando Regional Medical
Center

**ASPIRE HEALTH PARTNERS (104067)**, 1800 Mercy Drive, Zip 32808–5646;
tel. 407/875–3700, (Nonreporting) **A**9 10
Primary Contact: Jerry Kassab, President and Chief Executive Officer
Web address: www.lakesidecares.org
**Control:** Other not–for–profit (including NFP Corporation) **Service:** Psychiatric

**Staffed Beds:** 54

☐ **CENTRAL FLORIDA BEHAVIORAL HOSPITAL (104072)**, 6601 Central Florida
Parkway, Zip 32821–8064; tel. 407/370–0111 **A**1 5 9 10 **F**98 99 101 102 103
105 130 **S** Universal Health Services, Inc., King of Prussia, PA
Primary Contact: Vickie Lewis, Chief Executive Officer
CFO: Marsha Burick, Chief Financial Officer
Web address: www.centralfloridabehavioral.com
**Control:** Corporation, Investor–owned, for–profit **Service:** Psychiatric

**Staffed Beds:** 126 **Admissions:** 6093 **Census:** 112 **Outpatient Visits:** 0
**Births:** 0 **Personnel:** 173

**FL**

★ △ ◇ **FLORIDA HOSPITAL (100007)**, 601 East Rollins Street, Zip 32803–1248; tel. 407/303–6611, (Includes FLORIDA HOSPITAL CELEBRATION HEALTH, 400 Clebration Place, Celebration, Zip 34747; tel. 407/303–4000; Monica Reed, M.D., Administrator; FLORIDA HOSPITAL EAST ORLANDO, 7727 Lake Underhill Drive, Zip 32822; tel. 407/277–8110; FLORIDA HOSPITAL FOR CHILDREN–WALT DISNEY PAVILION, 601 East Rollins Street, tel. 407/303–9732; Lars D. Houmann, President; FLORIDA HOSPITAL KISSIMMEE, 2450 North Orange Blossom Trai, Kissimmee, Zip 34741; tel. 407/846–4343; William Haupt, Administrator; FLORIDA HOSPITAL–ALTAMONTE, 601 East Altamonte Drive, Altamonte Springs, Zip 32701; tel. 407/830–4321; Rob Fulbright, Administrator; FLORIDA HOSPITAL–APOPKA, 201 North Park Avenue, Apopka, Zip 32703; tel. 407/889–2566; Verbelee Neilsen Swanson, Administrator; WINTER PARK MEMORIAL HOSPITAL, 200 North Lakemont Avenue, Winter Park, Zip 32792–3273; tel. 407/646–7000; Ken Bradley, Administrator) **A**2 3 5 7 8 9 10 21 **F**3 6 7 9 11 12 13 15 17 18 19 20 21 22 23 24 25 26 27 28 29 30 31 32 34 35 36 37 38 39 40 41 44 45 46 47 48 49 50 51 53 54 56 57 58 59 60 61 62 64 65 66 68 70 71 72 73 74 75 76 77 78 79 80 81 82 84 85 86 87 88 89 90 91 93 96 97 98 100 101 102 103 104 107 108 110 111 112 113 114 115 116 117 118 119 120 121 123 124 126 129 130 131 132 134 135 136 137 138 139 140 141 142 145 146 147 148 **P**1 6 **S** Adventist Health System Sunbelt Health Care Corporation, Altamonte Springs, FL
Primary Contact: Lars D. Houmann, President
COO: Brian Paradis, Chief Operating Officer
CFO: Eddie Soler, Chief Financial Officer
CMO: David Moorhead, M.D., Chief Medical Officer
CHR: Sheryl Dodds, Chief Clinical Officer
Web address: www.flhosp.org
**Control:** Other not–for–profit (including NFP Corporation) **Service:** General Medical and Surgical

**Staffed Beds:** 2478 **Admissions:** 146388 **Census:** 1878 **Outpatient Visits:** 971869 **Births:** 10643 **Total Expense ($000):** 3786669 **Payroll Expense ($000):** 977087 **Personnel:** 17860

☒ **NEMOURS CHILDREN'S HOSPITAL (103304)**, 13535 Nemours Parkway, Zip 32827–7402; tel. 407/567–4000 **A**1 5 9 10 **F**3 19 29 30 31 32 34 35 36 39 40 41 42 45 46 48 50 53 54 55 57 58 59 60 61 64 65 68 71 72 73 74 75 78 79 81 82 85 86 87 88 89 91 92 93 94 97 99 100 101 104 107 108 111 115 119 124 129 130 131 132 143 144 146 **S** Nemours, Jacksonville, FL
Primary Contact: Roger A. Oxendale, Chief Executive Officer
CMO: Lane Donnelly, M.D., Chief Medical Officer
CNO: Barbara Meeks, MSN, Chief Nurse Executive
Web address: www.nemours.org
**Control:** Other not–for–profit (including NFP Corporation) **Service:** Children's

**Staffed Beds:** 64 **Admissions:** 2399 **Census:** 27 **Outpatient Visits:** 30873 **Births:** 0 **Total Expense ($000):** 145398 **Payroll Expense ($000):** 35597 **Personnel:** 505

☒ **ORLANDO REGIONAL MEDICAL CENTER (100006)**, 1414 Kuhl Avenue, Zip 32806–2093; tel. 407/841–5111, (Includes ARNOLD PALMER CHILDREN'S HOSPITAL, 92 West Miller Street, Zip 32806; tel. 407/649–6960; Kathy Swanson, President; WINNIE PALMER HOSPITAL FOR WOMEN AND BABIES, 83 West Miller Street, Zip 32806; tel. 321/843–2201; Kathy Swanson, President), (Nonreporting) **A**1 2 3 5 8 9 10 **S** Orlando Health, Orlando, FL
Primary Contact: Mark A. Jones, President
CFO: Paul Goldstein, Vice President Finance and Chief Financial Officer
CMO: Timothy Bullard, M.D., Chief of Staff
CIO: Rick Schooler, Vice President and Chief Information Officer
CHR: Nancy Dinon, Vice President Human Resources
Web address: www.orlandohealth.com/facilities/orlando–regional–medical–center
**Control:** Other not–for–profit (including NFP Corporation) **Service:** General Medical and Surgical

**Staffed Beds:** 1468

☒ **SELECT SPECIALTY HOSPITAL–ORLANDO (102003)**, 2250 Bedford Road, Zip 32803–1443; tel. 407/303–7869, (Includes SELECT SPECIALTY HOSPITAL–ORLANDO SOUTH, 5579 South Orange Avenue, Zip 32809–3493; tel. 407/241–4800), (Nonreporting) **A**1 9 10 **S** Select Medical Corporation, Mechanicsburg, PA
Primary Contact: Nellie Castroman, Chief Executive Officer
COO: James Whitacre, Chief Operating Officer
Web address: www.selectspecialtyhospitals.com/company/locations/orlando.aspx
**Control:** Corporation, Investor–owned, for–profit **Service:** Long–Term Acute Care hospital

**Staffed Beds:** 75

**SELECT SPECIALTY HOSPITAL–ORLANDO SOUTH** See Select Specialty Hospital–Orlando

**WINNIE PALMER HOSPITAL FOR WOMEN AND BABIES** See Orlando Regional Medical Center

**PROMISE HOSPITAL OF FLORIDA AT THE VILLAGES (102028)**, 5050 County Road, Zip 34484; tel. 352/689–6400 **A**10 **F**1 18 26 28 29 30 31 34 57 84 90 98 130 **P**5 **S** Promise Healthcare, Boca Raton, FL
Primary Contact: Hoyt Ross, Chief Executive Officer
CNO: Janice M. McCoy, MS, Chief Clinical Officer
Web address: www.promise–villages.com
**Control:** Corporation, Investor–owned, for–profit **Service:** Long–Term Acute Care hospital

**Staffed Beds:** 40 **Admissions:** 475 **Census:** 35 **Outpatient Visits:** 0 **Births:** 0 **Total Expense ($000):** 13388 **Payroll Expense ($000):** 6066

☒ **PUTNAM COMMUNITY MEDICAL CENTER (100232)**, Highway 20 West, Zip 32177–8118, Mailing Address: P.O. Box 778, Zip 32178–0778; tel. 386/328–5711 **A**1 9 10 19 **F**3 11 13 15 18 20 22 28 29 30 34 35 40 45 46 50 51 54 57 59 60 64 70 74 75 76 77 79 81 85 87 93 107 108 110 111 114 115 119 129 130 133 135 146 147 148 **S** LifePoint Health, Brentwood, TN
Primary Contact: Christopher J. Mosley, Chief Executive Officer
CFO: Debra Noyes, Chief Financial Officer
CMO: Joseph Stillword, Chief of Staff
CIO: Yvette A. Jones, HIM Director
CHR: John Schneider, Human Resources Director
CNO: Carol Negoshian, MSN, Chief Nursing Officer
Web address: www.pcmcfl.com
**Control:** Corporation, Investor–owned, for–profit **Service:** General Medical and Surgical

**Staffed Beds:** 99 **Admissions:** 4873 **Census:** 57 **Births:** 393 **Total Expense ($000):** 71848 **Payroll Expense ($000):** 23564

☐ **HEALTH FIRST PALM BAY HOSPITAL (100316)**, 1425 Malabar Road N.E., Zip 32907–2506; tel. 321/434–8000 **A**1 5 10 **F**3 11 18 20 29 30 34 40 43 45 49 51 53 57 59 60 65 68 70 74 75 79 81 84 85 87 91 92 107 108 110 111 114 115 118 119 130 132 143 145 146 **P**6 7 **S** Health First, Inc., Rockledge, FL
Primary Contact: William Calhoun, President, Community Hospitals
COO: Judy Gizinski, Chief Operating Officer
CFO: Joseph G. Felkner, Executive Vice President and Chief Financial Officer
CMO: Scott Gettings, M.D., Senior Vice President and Chief Medical Officer
CIO: Alex Popowycz, Senior Vice President / Chief Information Officer
CHR: Paula Just, Chief Human Resources Officer
CNO: Connie Bradley, R.N., Senior Vice President and Chief Nursing Officer
Web address: www.health–first.org/hospitals_services/pbch/index.cfm
**Control:** Other not–for–profit (including NFP Corporation) **Service:** General Medical and Surgical

**Staffed Beds:** 119 **Admissions:** 6065 **Census:** 75 **Outpatient Visits:** 79301 **Births:** 0 **Total Expense ($000):** 72204 **Payroll Expense ($000):** 32393 **Personnel:** 347

☒ **PALM BEACH GARDENS MEDICAL CENTER (100176)**, 3360 Burns Road, Zip 33410–4323; tel. 561/622–1411, (Nonreporting) **A**1 9 10 **S** TENET Healthcare Corporation, Dallas, TX
Primary Contact: Jeffrey M. Welch, Chief Executive Officer
CFO: Judi Stimson, Chief Financial Officer
CIO: James Vega, Director Information Systems
CHR: Kevin Caracciolo, Chief Human Resources Officer
CNO: Ed Price, R.N., Chief Nursing Officer
Web address: www.pbgmc.com
**Control:** Corporation, Investor–owned, for–profit **Service:** General Medical and Surgical

**Staffed Beds:** 199

☒ **FLORIDA HOSPITAL–FLAGLER (100118)**, 60 Memorial Medical Parkway, Zip 32164–5980; tel. 386/586–2000 **A**1 2 9 10 **F**11 15 18 20 22 28 29 30 31 34 35 40 45 46 47 49 50 51 54 57 59 60 62 63 64 68 70 74 75 77 78 79 81 85 86 87 93 97 107 108 110 111 114 115 117 119 120 121 123 124 126 130 132 135 144 146 147 **P**6 **S** Adventist Health System Sunbelt Health Care Corporation, Altamonte Springs, FL
Primary Contact: Kenneth R. Mattison, Chief Executive Officer
CFO: Valerie Ziesmer, Chief Financial Officer
CMO: John Walsh, M.D., Chief Medical Officer
CHR: Joshua I. Champion, Director
Web address: www.floridahospitalflagler.com/
**Control:** Church–operated, Nongovernment, not–for profit **Service:** General Medical and Surgical

**Staffed Beds:** 99 **Admissions:** 7341 **Census:** 87 **Outpatient Visits:** 249828 **Births:** 0 **Total Expense ($000):** 141365 **Payroll Expense ($000):** 61190 **Personnel:** 871

**FL**

## PANAMA CITY—Bay County

✠ **BAY MEDICAL CENTER SACRED HEART HEALTH SYSTEM (100026)**, 615 North Bonita Avenue, Zip 32401–3600, Mailing Address: P.O. Box 59515, Zip 32412–0515; tel. 850/769–1511, (Nonreporting) **A**1 2 9 10 **S** LHP Hospital Group, Plano, TX
Primary Contact: Stephen Grubbs, Chief Executive Officer
CFO: Mark Spafford, Interim Chief Financial Officer
CHR: Donna Baird, Vice President Corporate Services
CNO: Jan Thornton, Chief Nursing Officer
Web address: www.baymedical.org
**Control:** Hospital district or authority, Government, nonfederal **Service:** General Medical and Surgical

**Staffed Beds:** 273

☐ **EMERALD COAST BEHAVIORAL HOSPITAL (104073)**, 1940 Harrison Avenue, Zip 32405–4542; tel. 850/763–0017, (Nonreporting) **A**1 9 10 **S** Universal Health Services, Inc., King of Prussia, PA
Primary Contact: Tim Bedford, Chief Executive Officer
Web address: www.emeraldcoastbehavioral.com
**Control:** Corporation, Investor–owned, for–profit **Service:** Psychiatric

**Staffed Beds:** 86

✠ **GULF COAST REGIONAL MEDICAL CENTER (100242)**, 449 West 23rd Street, Zip 32405–4593, Mailing Address: P.O. Box 15309, Zip 32406–5309; tel. 850/769–8341 **A**1 2 9 10 **F**3 8 12 13 15 20 22 26 29 30 31 34 35 37 39 40 41 46 47 48 49 51 54 56 57 59 60 64 68 70 72 74 75 76 77 78 79 80 81 85 86 87 89 93 107 108 109 111 114 116 117 118 119 126 130 131 132 135 144 146 147 148 **S** HCA, Nashville, TN
Primary Contact: Carlton Ulmer, Chief Executive Officer
COO: Holly Jackson, Chief Operating Officer
CFO: Laurie Haynes, Chief Financial Officer
CHR: Tracy McGlon, Director Human Resources
CNO: Mary Reval, R.N., Chief Nursing Officer
Web address: www.egulfcoastmedical.com
**Control:** Corporation, Investor–owned, for–profit **Service:** General Medical and Surgical

**Staffed Beds:** 176 **Admissions:** 11550 **Census:** 121 **Births:** 2325 **Total Expense ($000):** 146569 **Payroll Expense ($000):** 43051

✠ **HEALTHSOUTH EMERALD COAST REHABILITATION HOSPITAL (103040)**, 1847 Florida Avenue, Zip 32405–4640; tel. 850/914–8600 **A**1 9 10 **F**3 28 29 34 57 59 68 75 77 85 86 87 90 91 95 96 130 131 132 148 **S** HEALTHSOUTH Corporation, Birmingham, AL
Primary Contact: Tony N. Bennett, Chief Executive Officer
CFO: Bradley Tilghman, Controller
CMO: Michael Hennigan, M.D., Medical Director
CHR: Traci Powell, Director Human Resources
CNO: Sharon Hamilton, Chief Nursing Officer
Web address: www.healthsouthpanamacity.com
**Control:** Corporation, Investor–owned, for–profit **Service:** Rehabilitation

**Staffed Beds:** 75 **Admissions:** 1569 **Census:** 53 **Outpatient Visits:** 0 **Births:** 0 **Total Expense ($000):** 18792 **Payroll Expense ($000):** 9415 **Personnel:** 206

✠ **SELECT SPECIALTY HOSPITAL–PANAMA CITY (102017)**, 615 North Bonita Avenue, 3rd Floor, Zip 32401–3623; tel. 850/767–3180 **A**1 9 10 **F**1 3 29 148 **S** Select Medical Corporation, Mechanicsburg, PA
Primary Contact: Randal S. Hamilton, Chief Executive Officer
CMO: Amir Manzoor, M.D., Medical Director
Web address: www.selectspecialtyhospitals.com/company/locations/panamacity.aspx
**Control:** Corporation, Investor–owned, for–profit **Service:** Long–Term Acute Care hospital

**Staffed Beds:** 30 **Admissions:** 432 **Census:** 29 **Outpatient Visits:** 0 **Births:** 0 **Total Expense ($000):** 10652 **Payroll Expense ($000):** 5516

## PEMBROKE PINES—Broward County

✠ **MEMORIAL HOSPITAL PEMBROKE (100230)**, 7800 Sheridan Street, Zip 33024–2536; tel. 954/883–8482 **A**1 9 10 **F**3 12 17 29 30 34 40 42 44 45 46 47 48 49 50 51 59 64 65 66 70 74 75 79 81 82 85 86 87 107 108 111 114 115 119 126 130 132 144 146 148 **S** Memorial Healthcare System, Hollywood, FL
Primary Contact: Mark Doyle, Chief Executive Officer
CFO: Joseph Stuczynski, Assistant Administrator Finance and Support
CMO: Stanley Marks, M.D., Chief Medical Officer
CIO: Forest Blanton, Chief Information Officer
CNO: Judy Frum, R.N., Chief Nursing Officer
Web address: www.memorialpembroke.com/
**Control:** Hospital district or authority, Government, nonfederal **Service:** General Medical and Surgical

**Staffed Beds:** 149 **Admissions:** 5764 **Census:** 69 **Outpatient Visits:** 59242 **Births:** 0 **Total Expense ($000):** 118116 **Payroll Expense ($000):** 49360 **Personnel:** 734

✠ **MEMORIAL HOSPITAL WEST (100281)**, 703 North Flamingo Road, Zip 33028–1014; tel. 954/436–5000 **A**1 2 9 10 **F**3 12 13 15 17 18 20 22 26 28 29 30 31 34 35 36 40 41 45 46 47 49 51 53 55 56 57 58 59 60 61 64 68 70 72 74 75 76 78 79 81 82 84 85 87 91 92 93 107 108 110 111 114 115 118 119 120 121 123 124 126 130 131 132 136 145 146 147 148 **S** Memorial Healthcare System, Hollywood, FL
Primary Contact: C. Kennon Hetlage, FACHE, Administrator and Chief Executive Officer
CFO: Walter Bussell, Chief Financial Officer
CMO: Eric Freling, M.D., Director Medical Staff Affairs
CIO: Forest Blanton, Chief Information Officer
CHR: Maria Naranjo, Director Human Resources
CNO: Grisel Fernandez–Bravo, R.N., Chief Nursing Officer
Web address: www.mhs.net
**Control:** Hospital district or authority, Government, nonfederal **Service:** General Medical and Surgical

**Staffed Beds:** 384 **Admissions:** 20944 **Census:** 258 **Outpatient Visits:** 271218 **Births:** 4180 **Total Expense ($000):** 351294 **Payroll Expense ($000):** 140894 **Personnel:** 1960

## PENSACOLA—Escambia County

✠ **BAPTIST HOSPITAL (100093)**, 1000 West Moreno, Zip 32501–2316, Mailing Address: P.O. Box 17500, Zip 32522–7500; tel. 850/434–4011 **A**1 2 3 9 10 **F**3 8 11 12 13 15 17 18 19 20 22 24 26 28 29 30 31 34 35 37 40 43 45 46 47 48 49 50 51 54 55 56 57 58 59 60 61 63 64 67 70 71 74 75 76 77 78 79 80 81 82 84 85 86 87 92 93 97 98 99 100 101 102 103 104 107 108 110 111 114 115 116 117 118 119 120 121 123 124 126 129 130 131 132 135 144 146 147 148 **P**4 6 **S** Baptist Health Care Corporation, Pensacola, FL
Primary Contact: Scott Raynes, President
CFO: Sharon Nobles, Interim Chief Financial Officer
CMO: Mike Oleksyk, M.D., Vice President and Chief Medical Officer
CIO: Steven Sarros, Vice President and Chief Information Officer
CHR: Darlene Stone, Vice President Human Resources
CNO: Cynde Gamache, R.N., Vice President and Chief Nursing Officer
Web address: www.ebaptisthealthcare.org
**Control:** Other not–for–profit (including NFP Corporation) **Service:** General Medical and Surgical

**Staffed Beds:** 339 **Admissions:** 17995 **Census:** 227 **Outpatient Visits:** 257336 **Births:** 899 **Total Expense ($000):** 264353 **Payroll Expense ($000):** 84682 **Personnel:** 1537

✠ **NAVAL HOSPITAL PENSACOLA**, 6000 West Highway 98, Zip 32512–0003; tel. 850/505–6413, (Nonreporting) **A**1 3 5 **S** Bureau of Medicine and Surgery, Department of the Navy, Washington, DC
Primary Contact: Commander Devin Morrison, Director Administration
COO: Commander Devin Morrison, Director for Administration
CMO: Commander Carolyn Rice, M.D., Director Medical Services
CIO: Lieutenant Commander William Berg, Chief Information Officer
CHR: Commander Devin Morrison, Director for Administration
CNO: Captain Amy Tarbay, Director Nursing Services
Web address: www.med.navy.mil/sites/pcola/Pages/default.aspx
**Control:** Navy, Government, federal **Service:** General Medical and Surgical

**Staffed Beds:** 28

**REHABILITATION INSTITUTE OF WEST FLORIDA** See West Florida Hospital

---

**Hospital, Medicare Provider Number, Address, Telephone, Approval, Facility, and Physician Codes, Health Care System**

★ American Hospital Association (AHA) membership
☐ The Joint Commission accreditation
○ Healthcare Facilities Accreditation Program
◇ DNV Healthcare Inc. accreditation
⇑ Center for Improvement in Healthcare Quality Accreditation
△ Commission on Accreditation of Rehabilitation Facilities (CARF) accreditation

☒ **SACRED HEART HOSPITAL OF PENSACOLA (100025)**, 5151 North Ninth Avenue, Zip 32504–8795, Mailing Address: P.O. Box 2700, Zip 32513–2700; tel. 850/416–7000 **A**1 2 3 5 9 10 13 **F**3 8 12 13 15 17 18 19 20 21 22 24 26 28 29 30 31 34 35 40 41 43 45 46 47 48 49 50 54 55 57 58 59 60 61 65 66 70 71 72 73 74 75 76 77 78 79 81 82 84 85 87 88 89 90 92 93 96 97 107 108 110 111 112 114 116 117 119 120 124 126 128 130 131 132 135 144 145 146 147 148 **S** Ascension Health, Saint Louis, MO
Primary Contact: Henry Stovall, President
CFO: C. Susan Cornejo, Chief Financial Officer
CMO: Stephanie J. Duggan, M.D., Vice President and Chief Medical Officer
CIO: Kathy Ross, Chief Information Officer
CHR: Carol Whittington, Chief Human Resources Officer
CNO: Amy Wilson, Vice President and Chief Nursing Officer
Web address: www.sacred–heart.org
**Control:** Other not–for–profit (including NFP Corporation) **Service:** General Medical and Surgical

**Staffed Beds:** 560 **Admissions:** 22823 **Census:** 268 **Births:** 3856 **Total Expense ($000):** 364566 **Payroll Expense ($000):** 110165

☒ **SELECT SPECIALTY HOSPITAL–PENSACOLA (102024)**, 7000 Cobble Creek Drive, Zip 32504–8638; tel. 850/473–4800, (Nonreporting) **A**1 9 10 **S** Select Medical Corporation, Mechanicsburg, PA
Primary Contact: David Goodson, Chief Executive Officer
CMO: John Bray, M.D., Medical Director
Web address: www.selectspecialtyhospitals.com/company/locations/pensacola.aspx
**Control:** Corporation, Investor–owned, for–profit **Service:** Long–Term Acute Care hospital

**Staffed Beds:** 75

☒ **WEST FLORIDA HOSPITAL (100231)**, 8383 North Davis Highway, Zip 32514–6088; tel. 850/494–4000, (Includes REHABILITATION INSTITUTE OF WEST FLORIDA, 8383 North Davis Highway, Zip 32514, Mailing Address: P.O. Box 18900, Zip 32523; tel. 850/494–6000; THE PAVILION, 8383 North Davis Highway, Zip 32523, Mailing Address: P.O. Box 18900, Zip 32523; tel. 904/494–5000), (Nonreporting) **A**1 2 9 10 **S** HCA, Nashville, TN
Primary Contact: Brian Baumgardner, Chief Executive Officer
COO: Kenneth C. Donahey, Chief Operating Officer
CFO: Randy Butler, Chief Financial Officer
CMO: Terry Stallings, M.D., Chief Medical Officer
CIO: Jeff Amerson, Director Information System
CHR: Wanda Salley, Vice President Human Resources
CNO: Karen White–Trevino, Chief Nursing Officer
Web address: www.westfloridahospital.com
**Control:** Corporation, Investor–owned, for–profit **Service:** General Medical and Surgical

**Staffed Beds:** 339

PERRY—Taylor County

★ **DOCTOR'S MEMORIAL HOSPITAL (100106)**, 333 North Byron Butler Parkway, Zip 32347–2300; tel. 850/584–0800 **A**9 10 20 **F**3 7 11 15 29 30 34 35 40 45 50 57 59 62 70 81 85 89 90 93 107 110 111 114 119 127 129 132 133 146 **P**6
Primary Contact: Mary Lescher, Interim Chief Executive Officer
CMO: Ron Emerick, M.D., Chief of Staff
CHR: Sarah Brus, Director Human Resources
CNO: Mary Lescher, Chief Clinical Officer
Web address: www.doctorsmemorial.com
**Control:** Other not–for–profit (including NFP Corporation) **Service:** General Medical and Surgical

**Staffed Beds:** 45 **Admissions:** 1056 **Census:** 10 **Births:** 6 **Total Expense ($000):** 26628 **Payroll Expense ($000):** 12094

PLANT CITY—Hillsborough County

☒ **SOUTH FLORIDA BAPTIST HOSPITAL (100132)**, 301 North Alexander Street, Zip 33563–4303; tel. 813/757–1200 **A**1 9 10 **F**3 11 12 15 18 20 22 28 29 30 31 34 35 40 41 44 45 47 48 49 51 57 59 64 70 74 75 76 77 78 79 81 85 86 87 89 93 94 107 108 110 111 114 115 118 119 124 126 130 131 132 135 146 148 **S** Trinity Health, Livonia, MI
Primary Contact: Karen Kerr, R.N., President and Chief Executive Officer
CFO: Carl Tremonti, Chief Financial Officer
CMO: Mark Vaaler, M.D., Chief Medical Officer
CHR: Pat Teeuwen, Director Team Resources
CNO: Teresa Colletti, Director Patient Services
Web address: www.sjbhealth.org
**Control:** Other not–for–profit (including NFP Corporation) **Service:** General Medical and Surgical

**Staffed Beds:** 115 **Admissions:** 6283 **Census:** 69 **Outpatient Visits:** 56372 **Births:** 592 **Total Expense ($000):** 92300 **Payroll Expense ($000):** 36379 **Personnel:** 484

PLANTATION—Broward County

☒ **PLANTATION GENERAL HOSPITAL (100167)**, 401 N.W. 42nd Avenue, Zip 33317–2882; tel. 954/587–5010, (Includes MERCY HOSPITAL – A CAMPUS OF PLANTATION GENERAL HOSPITAL, 3663 South Miami Avenue, Miami, Zip 33133–4237; tel. 305/854–4400; Barbara Simmons, R.N., Chief Executive Officer), (Nonreporting) **A**1 2 3 9 10 **S** HCA, Nashville, TN
Primary Contact: Randy Gross, Chief Executive Officer
COO: Kristen Lindenboom, Chief Operating Officer
CFO: Irfan Mirza, Chief Financial Officer
CIO: Mia McGlynn, Director Management Information Systems
CHR: Jennifer Allen, Vice President Human Resources
Web address: www.plantationgeneral.com
**Control:** Corporation, Investor–owned, for–profit **Service:** General Medical and Surgical

**Staffed Beds:** 264

☒ **WESTSIDE REGIONAL MEDICAL CENTER (100228)**, 8201 West Broward Boulevard, Zip 33324–2701; tel. 954/473–6600 **A**1 9 10 **F**3 8 11 15 17 18 20 22 24 26 29 30 31 34 35 40 44 45 49 50 57 59 60 68 70 74 75 77 78 79 80 81 82 85 86 87 93 107 108 110 111 114 115 117 119 126 129 130 131 132 145 146 148 **S** HCA, Nashville, TN
Primary Contact: Barbara Simmons, Chief Executive Officer
COO: Shana Sappington–Crittenden, Chief Operating Officer
CFO: Kevin Corcoran, Chief Financial Officer
CMO: Brian Weinstein, M.D., Chief of Staff
CIO: Andres Blanco, Director Management Information Systems
CHR: Maria Rivera, Director Human Resources
Web address: www.westsideregional.com
**Control:** Corporation, Investor–owned, for–profit **Service:** General Medical and Surgical

**Staffed Beds:** 215 **Admissions:** 14247 **Census:** 170 **Outpatient Visits:** 58528 **Births:** 0 **Total Expense ($000):** 145083 **Payroll Expense ($000):** 56101

PORT CHARLOTTE—Charlotte County

☒ **BAYFRONT HEALTH PORT CHARLOTTE (100077)**, 2500 Harbor Boulevard, Zip 33952–5000; tel. 941/766–4122 **A**1 5 9 10 **F**8 17 18 20 22 24 26 29 30 40 45 48 70 72 76 79 81 89 93 107 111 114 119 126 146 147 **S** Community Health Systems, Inc., Franklin, TN
Primary Contact: Richard H. Satcher, Chief Executive Officer
COO: Brian Cruddas, Chief Operating Officer
CFO: Jeffrey Mullis, Interim Chief Financial Officer
CMO: Thomas Noone, M.D., Chief Medical Officer
CHR: Karen Gardiner, Human Resources Director
CNO: Debra Clark, Chief Nursing Officer
Web address: www.bayfrontcharlotte.com
**Control:** Corporation, Investor–owned, for–profit **Service:** General Medical and Surgical

**Staffed Beds:** 254 **Admissions:** 10885 **Census:** 136 **Births:** 1338 **Total Expense ($000):** 122963 **Payroll Expense ($000):** 40841

☒ △ **FAWCETT MEMORIAL HOSPITAL (100236)**, 21298 Olean Boulevard, Zip 33952–6765; tel. 941/629–1181 **A**1 2 7 9 10 **F**3 8 15 18 20 22 26 29 30 31 34 35 40 45 46 47 48 49 51 57 59 64 70 74 75 77 78 79 81 85 86 87 90 91 93 96 107 108 110 111 114 119 131 132 146 147 148 **S** HCA, Nashville, TN
Primary Contact: Thomas J. Rice, FACHE, President and Chief Executive Officer
CFO: Phillip Baker, Vice President and Chief Financial Officer
CHR: Tony Welch, Vice President Human Resources
CNO: Kathleen Pace, MSN, Vice President and Chief Nursing Officer
Web address: www.fawcetthospital.com
**Control:** Corporation, Investor–owned, for–profit **Service:** General Medical and Surgical

**Staffed Beds:** 238 **Admissions:** 11238 **Census:** 156 **Births:** 0 **Total Expense ($000):** 141083 **Payroll Expense ($000):** 47015

PORT ST. JOE—Gulf County

☒ **SACRED HEART HOSPITAL ON THE GULF (100313)**, 3801 East Highway 98, Zip 32456–5318; tel. 850/229–5600 **A**1 9 10 20 **F**1 3 4 11 15 16 17 29 30 31 34 35 40 44 45 48 50 54 57 59 64 67 68 70 72 73 79 80 81 85 88 89 90 93 98 107 110 111 114 119 128 130 131 133 146 147 **P**7 **S** Ascension Health, Saint Louis, MO
Primary Contact: Roger L. Hall, President
CNO: Katherine L. Chastain, R.N., Chief Nursing Officer
Web address: www.sacred–heart.org/gulf/
**Control:** Other not–for–profit (including NFP Corporation) **Service:** General Medical and Surgical

**Staffed Beds:** 19 **Admissions:** 655 **Census:** 7 **Births:** 1 **Total Expense ($000):** 19355 **Payroll Expense ($000):** 5910

**FL**

## PORT ST. LUCIE—St. Lucie County

☐ **PORT ST. LUCIE HOSPITAL (104070)**, 2550 S.E. Walton Road,
Zip 34952–7168; tel. 772/335–0400, (Nonreporting) **A**1 9 10
Primary Contact: John Sannuto, Chief Executive Officer
Web address: www.portstluciehospitalinc.com
**Control:** Other not–for–profit (including NFP Corporation) **Service:** Psychiatric

**Staffed Beds: 75**

✠ **ST. LUCIE MEDICAL CENTER (100260)**, 1800 S.E. Tiffany Avenue,
Zip 34952–7521; tel. 772/335–4000, (Nonreporting) **A**1 2 9 10 13 **S** HCA,
Nashville, TN
Primary Contact: Jay Finnegan, Chief Executive Officer
COO: Calvin Thomas, IV, Chief Operating Officer
CFO: Kevin Keeling, Chief Financial Officer
Web address: www.stluciemed.com
**Control:** Corporation, Investor–owned, for–profit **Service:** General Medical and
Surgical

**Staffed Beds: 194**

## PUNTA GORDA—Charlotte County

✠ **BAYFRONT HEALTH PUNTA GORDA (100047)**, 809 East Marion Avenue,
Zip 33950–3819, Mailing Address: P.O. Box 51–1328, Zip 33951–1328;
tel. 941/639–3131 **A**1 9 10 **F**3 17 18 29 30 31 34 35 36 38 39 40 44 45 50
53 54 56 57 59 60 64 68 70 74 75 77 78 79 81 85 86 87 93 94 98 100
101 102 103 107 108 110 111 115 118 119 126 130 131 132 135 146 148
**S** Community Health Systems, Inc., Franklin, TN
Primary Contact: Brandon W. Downey, Chief Executive Officer
Web address: www.bayfrontcharlotte.com
**Control:** Corporation, Investor–owned, for–profit **Service:** General Medical and
Surgical

**Staffed Beds: 208 Admissions: 5202 Census: 93 Births: 0 Total Expense
($000): 63201 Payroll Expense ($000): 22405**

## RIVIERA BEACH—Palm Beach County

✠ **KINDRED HOSPITAL THE PALM BEACHES (102025)**, 5555 West Blue Heron
Boulevard, Zip 33418–7813; tel. 561/840–0754 **A**1 9 10 **F**1 3 18 29 30 45 48
70 74 75 77 79 82 84 85 91 97 100 107 114 145 148 **S** Kindred Healthcare,
Louisville, KY
Primary Contact: Timothy Page, Chief Executive Officer
Web address: www.khthepalmbeaches.com/
**Control:** Corporation, Investor–owned, for–profit **Service:** Long–Term Acute Care
hospital

**Staffed Beds: 70 Admissions: 455 Census: 37 Outpatient Visits: 0 Births:
0 Total Expense ($000): 20473 Payroll Expense ($000): 8215**

## ROCKLEDGE—Brevard County

✠ **WUESTHOFF MEDICAL CENTER – ROCKLEDGE (100092)**, 110 Longwood
Avenue, Zip 32955–2887, Mailing Address: P.O. Box 565002, Mail Stop 1,
Zip 32956–5002; tel. 321/636–2211 **A**1 2 9 10 **F**3 15 17 18 19 20 22 24 26
28 29 30 31 35 40 46 49 50 51 59 60 64 68 70 72 74 75 76 78 79 81 82
84 85 89 93 102 107 111 114 115 117 119 126 130 131 132 135 146 147
148 **S** Community Health Systems, Inc., Franklin, TN
Primary Contact: Gary Malaer, Interim Chief Executive Officer
CFO: Richard Haun, Chief Financial Officer
CMO: Vinay Mehindru, M.D., Medical Director
CIO: David Barnhart, Director Information Systems
CHR: Marchita H. Marino, Vice President Human Resources
Web address: www.wuesthoff.org
**Control:** Corporation, Investor–owned, for–profit **Service:** General Medical and
Surgical

**Staffed Beds: 298 Admissions: 11786 Census: 148 Births: 595 Total
Expense ($000): 135847 Payroll Expense ($000): 50537 Personnel: 1063**

## SAFETY HARBOR—Pinellas County

✠ **MEASE COUNTRYSIDE HOSPITAL (100265)**, 3231 McMullen–Booth Road,
Zip 34695–6607, Mailing Address: P.O. Box 1098, Zip 34695–1098;
tel. 727/725–6222 **A**1 2 9 10 **F**3 8 13 15 17 18 20 22 26 28 29 30 31 34 35
37 40 41 44 46 49 51 59 60 62 64 68 70 72 73 75 76 77 78 79 81 84 85
86 87 89 107 108 109 111 114 115 116 117 118 119 126 129 130 131
132 145 146 147 148 **S** Morton Plant Mease Health Care, Clearwater, FL
Primary Contact: Lou Galdieri, R.N., President
CFO: Carl Tremonti, Chief Financial Officer
CMO: Donald Pocock, M.D., Chief Medical Officer
CHR: Sharon Collotta, Director Human Resources
Web address: www.mpmhealth.com
**Control:** Other not–for–profit (including NFP Corporation) **Service:** General
Medical and Surgical

**Staffed Beds: 311 Admissions: 16639 Census: 204 Outpatient Visits:
113285 Births: 2168 Total Expense ($000): 232923 Payroll Expense
($000): 83222 Personnel: 1168**

## SAINT AUGUSTINE—St. Johns County

☐ **FLAGLER HOSPITAL (100090)**, 400 Health Park Boulevard, Zip 32086–5784;
tel. 904/819–5155 **A**1 2 5 9 10 20 **F**1 3 5 8 11 12 13 14 15 18 20 22 24 28
29 30 31 34 35 38 40 45 49 56 57 58 59 60 65 67 70 72 73 74 75 76 78
79 80 81 82 85 86 87 89 90 93 98 100 101 102 104 105 106 107 108 110
111 114 115 119 120 126 128 129 130 131 132 135 146 **P**8
Primary Contact: Joseph S. Gordy, President
COO: Jason P. Barrett, Chief Operating Officer
CFO: Lynda I. Kirker, Chief Financial Officer
CMO: Douglas Dew, M.D., President Medical Staff
CIO: Bill Rieger, Chief Information Officer
CHR: Jeff Hurley, Vice President Human Resources
Web address: www.flaglerhospital.org
**Control:** Other not–for–profit (including NFP Corporation) **Service:** General
Medical and Surgical

**Staffed Beds: 318 Admissions: 13486 Census: 159 Births: 1436 Total
Expense ($000): 213170 Payroll Expense ($000): 76837**

## SAINT CLOUD—Osceola County

✠ **ST. CLOUD REGIONAL MEDICAL CENTER (100302)**, 2906 17th Street,
Zip 34769–6099; tel. 407/892–2135 **A**1 9 10 **F**3 15 18 29 30 34 35 40 45
46 49 51 57 59 70 74 75 77 78 79 81 82 85 86 87 91 93 94 96 97 107
108 110 111 115 119 146 **S** Community Health Systems, Inc., Franklin, TN
Primary Contact: Brent Burish, Chief Executive Officer
CFO: Jordan Ohman, Chief Financial Officer
CMO: Scott Wurm, M.D., Chief Medical Officer
CIO: James Devlin, Director Information Systems
CHR: Bethany Meadows, Director Human Resources
CNO: Inna Makievsky, FACHE, Chief Nursing Officer
Web address: www.stcloudregional.com
**Control:** Corporation, Investor–owned, for–profit **Service:** General Medical and
Surgical

**Staffed Beds: 84 Admissions: 3774 Census: 46 Births: 0 Total Expense
($000): 43836 Payroll Expense ($000): 16944**

## SAINT PETERSBURG—Pinellas County

✠ **ALL CHILDREN'S HOSPITAL JOHNS HOPKINS MEDICINE (103300)**, 501 6th
Avenue South, Zip 33701–4634; tel. 727/898–7451 **A**1 3 5 8 9 10 **F**3 11 17
18 19 20 21 22 23 24 25 26 27 29 30 31 32 34 35 36 37 39 40 41 43 44
45 46 47 48 49 50 54 55 57 58 59 60 61 64 65 68 72 73 74 75 77 78 79
81 82 85 86 87 88 89 92 93 96 97 99 100 107 111 114 115 116 118
119 129 130 131 132 134 135 136 137 141 142 143 144 146 148 **S** Johns
Hopkins Health System, Baltimore, MD
Primary Contact: Jonathan M. Ellen, M.D., President
CFO: Nancy Templin, Vice President Finance and Chief Financial Officer
CMO: Michael Epstein, M.D., Senior Vice President Medical Affairs
CIO: Cal Popovich, Vice President Information Technology
CHR: Jay Kuhns, Vice President Human Resources
Web address: www.allkids.org
**Control:** Other not–for–profit (including NFP Corporation) **Service:** Children's
general

**Staffed Beds: 259 Admissions: 7607 Census: 188 Outpatient Visits:
369512 Births: 0 Total Expense ($000): 399416 Payroll Expense ($000):
160966 Personnel: 2762**

FL

---

**Hospital, Medicare Provider Number, Address, Telephone, Approval, Facility, and Physician Codes, Health Care System**

★ American Hospital Association (AHA) membership    ○ Healthcare Facilities Accreditation Program    ⇑ Center for Improvement in Healthcare Quality Accreditation
☐ The Joint Commission accreditation    ◇ DNV Healthcare Inc. accreditation    △ Commission on Accreditation of Rehabilitation Facilities (CARF) accreditation

☒ **BAYFRONT HEALTH ST. PETERSBURG (100032)**, 701 Sixth Street South, Zip 33701–4891; tel. 727/823–1234, (Nonreporting) **A**1 3 5 9 10 **S** Community Health Systems, Inc., Franklin, TN
Primary Contact: Kathryn Gillette, President and Chief Executive Officer
COO: Lavah Lowe, Executive Vice President and Chief Operating Officer
CFO: Eric Smith, Chief Financial Officer
CIO: Kevin Murphy, Director, Information Technology Services
CHR: Jim Reames, Director Human Resources
CNO: Karen Long, R.N., Vice President Nursing
Web address: www.bayfrontstpete.com
**Control:** Corporation, Investor–owned, for–profit **Service:** General Medical and Surgical

**Staffed Beds:** 382

☒ **NORTHSIDE HOSPITAL (100238)**, 6000 49th Street North, Zip 33709–2145; tel. 727/521–4411 **A**1 9 10 12 13 **F**3 17 18 20 22 24 26 28 29 30 31 34 35 40 45 49 50 51 53 56 57 58 59 60 64 65 70 74 75 77 78 79 81 85 92 93 107 108 111 114 115 118 119 135 146 **S** HCA, Nashville, TN
Primary Contact: Dia Nichols, Chief Executive Officer
COO: Jayme Chancellor, Chief Operating Officer
CFO: Gary Searls, Chief Financial Officer
CMO: Ira Siegman, M.D., Chief Medical Officer
CIO: Kirk Hendrick, Director Information Systems
CHR: Maggie Miklos, Director Human Resources
CNO: Wendy Lincoln, Chief Nursing Officer
Web address: www.northsidehospital.com
**Control:** Corporation, Investor–owned, for–profit **Service:** General Medical and Surgical

**Staffed Beds:** 227 **Admissions:** 9384 **Census:** 121 **Births:** 0 **Total Expense ($000):** 138750 **Payroll Expense ($000):** 46763

☒ **PALMS OF PASADENA HOSPITAL (100126)**, 1501 Pasadena Avenue South, Zip 33707–3798; tel. 727/381–1000, (Nonreporting) **A**1 9 10 **S** HCA, Nashville, TN
Primary Contact: Sharon Hayes, Chief Executive Officer
CFO: James B. Gilbert, Chief Financial Officer
CMO: George Hutter, M.D., Chief of Staff
CIO: Danny Waters, Director, Information Services
CHR: Karen Casteel, Director Human Resources
CNO: Andrea Clyne, R.N., Chief Nursing Officer
Web address: www.palmspasadena.com
**Control:** Corporation, Investor–owned, for–profit **Service:** General Medical and Surgical

**Staffed Beds:** 307

☒ **ST. ANTHONY'S HOSPITAL (100067)**, 1200 Seventh Avenue North, Zip 33705–1388, Mailing Address: P.O. Box 12588, Zip 33733–2588; tel. 727/825–1100, (Total facility includes 28 beds in nursing home–type unit) **A**1 2 5 9 10 **F**3 11 12 15 17 18 20 22 26 28 29 30 31 34 35 40 44 45 46 49 51 57 59 60 64 68 70 74 75 77 78 79 81 84 85 86 87 93 98 100 102 103 107 108 110 111 114 115 117 118 119 121 123 124 126 129 130 131 132 135 146 148 **S** Trinity Health, Livonia, MI
Primary Contact: William G. Ulbricht, President
COO: Ronald J. Colaguori, Vice President Operations
CFO: Carl Tremonti, Chief Financial Officer
CMO: James McClintic, M.D., Vice President Medical Affairs
CIO: Tim Thompson, Vice President Information Services
CHR: James S. Bacon, Director Team Resources
Web address: www.stanthonys.com/
**Control:** Other not–for–profit (including NFP Corporation) **Service:** General Medical and Surgical

**Staffed Beds:** 393 **Admissions:** 17186 **Census:** 261 **Outpatient Visits:** 81942 **Births:** 0 **Total Expense ($000):** 223931 **Payroll Expense ($000):** 92114 **Personnel:** 1437

☒ **ST. PETERSBURG GENERAL HOSPITAL (100180)**, 6500 38th Avenue North, Zip 33710–1629; tel. 727/384–1414, (Nonreporting) **A**1 2 9 10 12 13 **S** HCA, Nashville, TN
Primary Contact: Janice Balzano, Chief Executive Officer
COO: Stephanie McNulty, Chief Operating Officer
CFO: Shawn Gregory, Chief Financial Officer
CMO: George Hutter, M.D., Chief Medical Officer
CHR: Jennifer B. Robinson, Vice President Human Resources
CNO: JoAnne Cattell, Chief Nursing Officer
Web address: www.stpetegeneral.com
**Control:** Corporation, Investor–owned, for–profit **Service:** General Medical and Surgical

**Staffed Beds:** 219

**SANFORD—Seminole County**

☒ △ **CENTRAL FLORIDA REGIONAL HOSPITAL (100161)**, 1401 West Seminole Boulevard, Zip 32771–6764; tel. 407/321–4500, (Nonreporting) **A**1 7 9 10 **S** HCA, Nashville, TN
Primary Contact: Wendy H. Brandon, Chief Executive Officer
COO: Glenn Carney, Chief Operating Officer
CFO: Richard Read, Chief Financial Officer
CIO: Jerry Ballard, Director Information Systems
CHR: Linda V. Smith, Vice President Human Resources
CNO: Maria Calloway, R.N., Chief Nursing Officer
Web address: www.centralfloridaregional.com
**Control:** Corporation, Investor–owned, for–profit **Service:** General Medical and Surgical

**Staffed Beds:** 226

**SARASOTA—Sarasota County**

☒ **COMPLEX CARE HOSPITAL AT RIDGELAKE (102018)**, 6150 Edgelake Drive, Zip 34240–8803; tel. 941/342–3000 **A**1 10 **F**1 3 60 85 107 114 130 **S** LifeCare Management Services, Plano, TX
Primary Contact: Danny R. Edwards, Administrator
CFO: Leah Drabant, Director of Finance
CMO: Craig Harcup, M.D., Hospital Medical Director
CHR: Jennifer Sparks, Human Resources Generalist
CNO: Timothy Mitchell, R.N., Chief Nursing Officer
Web address: www.lifecare–hospitals.com/hospital.php?id=23
**Control:** Corporation, Investor–owned, for–profit **Service:** Long–Term Acute Care hospital

**Staffed Beds:** 40 **Admissions:** 447 **Census:** 33 **Outpatient Visits:** 0 **Births:** 0

☒ **DOCTORS HOSPITAL OF SARASOTA (100166)**, 5731 Bee Ridge Road, Zip 34233–5056; tel. 941/342–1100, (Nonreporting) **A**1 2 9 10 **S** HCA, Nashville, TN
Primary Contact: Robert C. Meade, Chief Executive Officer
COO: Stephen W. Young, Chief Operating Officer
CFO: Charles Schwaner, III, Chief Financial Officer
CMO: Thomas Trinchetto, M.D., Chief Medical Officer
CHR: Theresa Levering, Director Human Resources
CNO: Kathy Mitchell, R.N., Chief Nursing Officer
Web address: www.doctorsofsarasota.com
**Control:** Corporation, Investor–owned, for–profit **Service:** General Medical and Surgical

**Staffed Beds:** 168

☒ △ **HEALTHSOUTH REHABILITATION HOSPITAL OF SARASOTA (103031)**, 6400 Edgelake Drive, Zip 34240–8813; tel. 941/921–8600, (Nonreporting) **A**1 7 9 10 **S** HEALTHSOUTH Corporation, Birmingham, AL
Primary Contact: Marcus Braz, Chief Executive Officer
CFO: Barbara Bierut, Chief Financial Officer
CMO: Alexander De Jesus, M.D., Medical Director
CHR: Brenda Benner, Director Human Resources
CNO: Jacqueline Juenger, R.N., Chief Nursing Officer
Web address: www.healthsouthsarasota.com
**Control:** Corporation, Investor–owned, for–profit **Service:** Rehabilitation

**Staffed Beds:** 96

**HEALTHSOUTH RIDGELAKE HOSPITAL** See Complex Care Hospital at Ridgelake

☐ △ **SARASOTA MEMORIAL HEALTH CARE SYSTEM (100087)**, 1700 South Tamiami Trail, Zip 34239–3555; tel. 941/917–9000 **A**1 2 3 5 7 9 10 **F**3 6 7 8 11 12 13 15 17 18 20 22 24 26 28 29 30 31 32 34 35 36 37 38 39 40 42 44 45 46 47 48 49 50 51 53 54 55 56 57 58 59 60 61 64 66 68 70 72 73 74 75 76 77 78 79 80 81 82 84 85 86 87 89 90 91 93 95 96 98 99 100 101 102 103 107 108 110 111 114 115 116 117 118 119 124 126 129 130 131 132 135 143 144 145 146 147 148
Primary Contact: David Verinder, Interim Chief Executive Officer
COO: David Verinder, Chief Operating Officer
CFO: Bill Woeltjen, Chief Financial Officer
CMO: Steve Taylor, M.D., Chief Medical Officer
CIO: Denis Baker, Chief Information Officer
CHR: Laurie Bennett, Director Human Resources
CNO: Jan Mauck, R.N., Chief Nursing Officer
Web address: www.smh.com
**Control:** Hospital district or authority, Government, nonfederal **Service:** General Medical and Surgical

**Staffed Beds:** 635 **Admissions:** 27488 **Census:** 353 **Outpatient Visits:** 520425 **Births:** 3097 **Total Expense ($000):** 496766 **Payroll Expense ($000):** 183448 **Personnel:** 3845

FL

## SEBASTIAN—Indian River County

✠ **SEBASTIAN RIVER MEDICAL CENTER (100217)**, 13695 North U.S. Highway 1, Zip 32958–3230, Mailing Address: Box 780838, Zip 32978–0838; tel. 772/589–3186, (Total facility includes 31 beds in nursing home–type unit) **A**1 9 10 **F**3 11 12 15 18 20 22 28 29 30 31 34 40 41 45 46 49 50 51 57 59 60 62 63 64 65 68 70 74 75 77 78 79 81 82 83 84 85 86 87 89 91 92 93 107 110 111 114 115 116 117 119 126 128 129 130 132 133 145 146 148 **P**8 **S** Community Health Systems, Inc., Franklin, TN
Primary Contact: Kelly Enriquez, Chief Executive Officer
CFO: John McEachern, Controller
CMO: Ralph Geiger, M.D., Chief of Staff
CHR: Kam Storey, Director Human Resources
Web address: www.sebastianrivermedical.com
**Control:** Corporation, Investor–owned, for–profit **Service:** General Medical and Surgical

**Staffed Beds:** 140 **Admissions:** 4560 **Census:** 66 **Outpatient Visits:** 22000 **Births:** 0

## SEBRING—Highlands County

✠ **FLORIDA HOSPITAL HEARTLAND MEDICAL CENTER (100109)**, 4200 Sun'n Lake Boulevard, Zip 33872–1986, Mailing Address: P.O. Box 9400, Zip 33871–9400; tel. 863/314–4466, (Includes FLORIDA HOSPITAL LAKE PLACID, 1210 U.S. 27 North, Lake Placid, Zip 33852–7948; tel. 863/465–3777; Eric Stevens, Chief Executive Officer) **A**1 9 10 19 **F**11 13 15 18 20 22 24 26 28 29 30 34 35 37 40 44 45 49 50 51 53 54 57 59 60 62 64 70 75 76 79 81 86 87 89 97 98 100 101 103 104 107 108 110 111 114 115 116 117 118 119 126 127 129 130 132 133 135 146 147 148 **P**6 **S** Adventist Health System Sunbelt Health Care Corporation, Altamonte Springs, FL
Primary Contact: Eric Stevens, Chief Executive Officer
CFO: Rosalie Oliver, Chief Financial Officer
CMO: Jorge F. Gonzalez, M.D., Chief Medical Officer
CHR: Anthony Stahl, Vice President
CNO: Gloria N. Santos, R.N., Chief Nursing Officer
Web address: www.fhheartland.org/
**Control:** Church–operated, Nongovernment, not–for profit **Service:** General Medical and Surgical

**Staffed Beds:** 214 **Admissions:** 11477 **Census:** 153 **Outpatient Visits:** 158538 **Births:** 920 **Total Expense ($000):** 179104 **Payroll Expense ($000):** 78660 **Personnel:** 1346

✠ **HIGHLANDS REGIONAL MEDICAL CENTER (100049)**, 3600 South Highlands Avenue, Zip 33870–5495, Mailing Address: Drawer 2066, Zip 33871–2066; tel. 863/471–5800 **A**1 9 10 19 **F**3 11 13 18 20 22 29 34 40 45 49 50 51 57 59 64 70 76 79 81 85 87 93 97 107 108 110 114 119 124 129 146 **S** Community Health Systems, Inc., Franklin, TN
Primary Contact: Joseph Bernard, Chief Executive Officer
CFO: John D. Montois, Interim Chief Financial Officer
CIO: Nate Johnson, Chief Information Officer
CHR: John D. Ware, Human Resources Director
CNO: Adam Kless, Chief Nursing Officer
Web address: www.highlandsregional.com
**Control:** Corporation, Investor–owned, for–profit **Service:** General Medical and Surgical

**Staffed Beds:** 116 **Admissions:** 3425 **Census:** 37 **Births:** 376 **Total Expense ($000):** 55091 **Payroll Expense ($000):** 16310

## SOUTH MIAMI—Miami–Dade County

✠ **LARKIN COMMUNITY HOSPITAL (100181)**, 7031 S.W. 62nd Avenue, Zip 33143–4781; tel. 305/284–7500 **A**1 3 9 10 12 13 **F**3 5 8 10 11 15 29 34 35 37 38 40 44 45 49 54 56 57 58 59 60 62 64 65 68 70 71 74 75 77 78 79 81 82 84 85 87 91 92 93 96 97 98 100 101 102 103 104 105 107 108 110 111 114 117 118 119 124 126 129 130 131 132 133 135 143 145 146 148
Primary Contact: Sandra Sosa–Guerrero, Chief Executive Officer
COO: George J. Michel, Chief Operating Officer
CFO: Edgar Castillo, Chief Financial Officer
CMO: Mario Almeida–Suarez, M.D., Chief of Staff
CIO: Orlando Suarez, Director Information Technology
CHR: Carolina Pena, Assistant Director Administrator
CNO: Mercedes Perez, Vice President Nursing
Web address: www.larkinhospital.com
**Control:** Individual, Investor–owned, for–profit **Service:** General Medical and Surgical

**Staffed Beds:** 146 **Admissions:** 5535 **Census:** 90 **Outpatient Visits:** 29906 **Births:** 0 **Total Expense ($000):** 98008 **Payroll Expense ($000):** 42778 **Personnel:** 767

## STARKE—Bradford County

**SHANDS STARKE** See Shands Starke Regional Medical Center

✠ **SHANDS STARKE REGIONAL MEDICAL CENTER (101310)**, 922 East Call Street, Zip 32091–3699; tel. 904/368–2300 **A**1 3 9 10 18 **F**3 11 15 29 30 34 35 40 44 45 50 57 59 64 68 74 75 77 81 85 93 97 107 111 114 119 127 129 131 132 135 **P**6 **S** Community Health Systems, Inc., Franklin, TN
Primary Contact: Rhonda Kay Sherrod, R.N., MSN, Interim Chief Executive Officer
Web address: www.shands.org
**Control:** Partnership, Investor–owned, for–profit **Service:** General Medical and Surgical

**Staffed Beds:** 49 **Admissions:** 1401 **Census:** 13 **Births:** 0 **Total Expense ($000):** 25272 **Payroll Expense ($000):** 10325

## STUART—Martin County

✠ **HEALTHSOUTH REHABILITATION HOSPITAL AT MARTIN HEALTH (103044)**, 5850 S.E. Community Drive, Zip 34997–6420; tel. 772/324–3500, (Nonreporting) **A**1 10 **S** HEALTHSOUTH Corporation, Birmingham, AL
Primary Contact: Ivette Miranda, Chief Executive Officer
CFO: Dawn Salas, Controller
CMO: Stephen L. Chastain, M.D., Chief Medical Officer
CHR: Annette DiPiero, Human Resource Director
Web address: www.healthsouthmartin.com
**Control:** Corporation, Investor–owned, for–profit **Service:** Rehabilitation

**Staffed Beds:** 34

✠ **MARTIN HEALTH SYSTEM (100044)**, 200 S.E. Hospital Avenue, Zip 34994–2346, Mailing Address: P.O. Box 9010, Zip 34995–9010; tel. 772/287–5200, (Includes MARTIN MEMORIAL HOSPITAL SOUTH, 2100 S.E. Salerno Road, Zip 34997; tel. 772/223–2300; Mark E. Robitaille, President and Chief Executive Officer) **A**1 2 9 10 **F**3 8 11 12 13 15 17 18 20 22 24 26 28 29 30 31 35 36 37 40 42 45 46 47 49 50 51 53 55 60 64 68 70 72 73 74 75 76 77 78 79 81 82 85 86 87 91 93 94 95 107 108 110 111 115 116 117 118 119 120 121 123 124 126 129 130 132 143 144 146 **P**6
Primary Contact: Mark E. Robitaille, President and Chief Executive Officer
COO: Robert L. Lord, JD, Senior Vice President and Chief Operating Officer
CFO: Chuck Cleaver, Vice President and Chief Financial Officer
CMO: Fernando Petry, M.D., Vice President and Chief Medical Officer
CIO: Edmund Collins, Chief Information Officer
CHR: Angie L. Metcalf, Vice President and Chief Human Resource Officer
CNO: Mary Elizabeth Flippo, R.N., Vice President and Chief Nursing Officer
Web address: www.martinhealth.org
**Control:** Other not–for–profit (including NFP Corporation) **Service:** General Medical and Surgical

**Staffed Beds:** 335 **Admissions:** 22310 **Census:** 275 **Outpatient Visits:** 122829 **Births:** 2226 **Total Expense ($000):** 377660 **Payroll Expense ($000):** 158741 **Personnel:** 2961

## SUN CITY CENTER—Hillsborough County

✠ **SOUTH BAY HOSPITAL (100259)**, 4016 Sun City Center Boulevard, Zip 33573–5298; tel. 813/634–3301 **A**1 9 10 **F**3 15 18 29 30 31 34 35 37 40 45 49 50 57 59 64 68 70 74 75 77 78 79 81 82 85 86 87 93 107 108 110 111 114 118 119 132 146 148 **S** HCA, Nashville, TN
Primary Contact: Sharon L. Roush, Chief Executive Officer
COO: Gary Malaer, Chief Operating Officer
CFO: Shawn Gregory, Chief Financial Officer
CIO: Danny Waters, Director Information Technology and Systems
CHR: Megan Dean, Director Human Resources
CNO: Terrie Jefferson, R.N., Chief Nursing Officer
Web address: www.southbayhospital.com
**Control:** Corporation, Investor–owned, for–profit **Service:** General Medical and Surgical

**Staffed Beds:** 112 **Admissions:** 8023 **Census:** 97 **Births:** 0 **Total Expense ($000):** 74845 **Payroll Expense ($000):** 26448

## SUNRISE—Broward County

✠ **HEALTHSOUTH SUNRISE REHABILITATION HOSPITAL (103028)**, 4399 North Nob Hill Road, Zip 33351–5899; tel. 954/749–0300 **A**1 3 10 **F**3 29 62 82 90 91 93 95 96 132 148 **S** HEALTHSOUTH Corporation, Birmingham, AL
Primary Contact: Stacy Modlin, Chief Executive Officer
COO: Jay de los Reyes, Chief Operating Officer
CFO: Ruth Goodstein, Controller
CMO: Scott Tannenbaum, M.D., Medical Director
CIO: Angela Manning, Director Health Information Services
CHR: Barbara Dunkiel, Director Human Resources
CNO: Omaira D. Riano, Chief Nursing Officer
Web address: www.healthsouthsunrise.com
**Control:** Corporation, Investor–owned, for–profit **Service:** Rehabilitation

**Staffed Beds:** 126 **Admissions:** 2288 **Census:** 86 **Births:** 0 **Total Expense ($000):** 37305 **Payroll Expense ($000):** 17907

**FL**

---

**Hospital, Medicare Provider Number, Address, Telephone, Approval, Facility, and Physician Codes, Health Care System**

★ American Hospital Association (AHA) membership ○ Healthcare Facilities Accreditation Program ⇑ Center for Improvement in Healthcare Quality Accreditation
□ The Joint Commission accreditation ◇ DNV Healthcare Inc. accreditation △ Commission on Accreditation of Rehabilitation Facilities (CARF) accreditation

## TALLAHASSEE—Leon County

☒ **CAPITAL REGIONAL MEDICAL CENTER (100254)**, 2626 Capital Medical Boulevard, Zip 32308–4499; tel. 850/325–5000, (Nonreporting) **A**1 2 9 10 **S** HCA, Nashville, TN
Primary Contact: Mark Robinson, FACHE, Chief Executive Officer
CMO: Steve West, M.D., Chief Medical Officer
CIO: Robert A. Steed, Director Information Systems
CHR: Louise Truitt, Vice President Human Resources
Web address: www.capitalregionalmedicalcenter.com
**Control:** Individual, Investor–owned, for–profit **Service:** General Medical and Surgical

**Staffed Beds:** 198

**EASTSIDE PSYCHIATRIC HOSPITAL (104059)**, 2634 Capital Circle N.E., Zip 32308–4106; tel. 850/523–3333, (Nonreporting) **A**9 10
Primary Contact: Jay A. Reeve, President and Chief Executive Officer
COO: Sue Conger, Chief Operating Officer
CFO: Virginia Kelly, Chief Financial Officer
CMO: Ludmila de Faria, M.D., Chief Medical Officer
CIO: Thad Moorer, Chief Information Officer
CHR: Candy Landry, Chief Human Resource Officer
CNO: Judy Goreau, R.N., Director of Nursing
Web address: www.apalacheecenter.org
**Control:** Other not–for–profit (including NFP Corporation) **Service:** Psychiatric

**Staffed Beds:** 24

☒ **HEALTHSOUTH REHABILITATION HOSPITAL OF TALLAHASSEE (103033)**, 1675 Riggins Road, Zip 32308–5315; tel. 850/656–4800, (Nonreporting) **A**1 9 10 **S** HEALTHSOUTH Corporation, Birmingham, AL
Primary Contact: K. Dale Neely, FACHE, Chief Executive Officer
CFO: David Applewood, Controller
CMO: Robert Rowland, M.D., Medical Director
CIO: Kamilah Lawson, Health Information Management Services Director
CHR: Carol Bugayong, Human Resources Director
CNO: Elizabeth Squires, Chief Nursing Officer
Web address: www.healthsouthtallahassee.com
**Control:** Corporation, Investor–owned, for–profit **Service:** Rehabilitation

**Staffed Beds:** 76

☒ **SELECT SPECIALTY HOSPITAL–TALLAHASSEE (102020)**, 1554 Surgeons Drive, Zip 32308–4631; tel. 850/219–6800, (Nonreporting) **A**1 9 10 **S** Select Medical Corporation, Mechanicsburg, PA
Primary Contact: Lora Davis, Chief Executive Officer
Web address: www.tallahassee.selectspecialtyhospitals.com/
**Control:** Corporation, Investor–owned, for–profit **Service:** Long–Term Acute Care hospital

**Staffed Beds:** 29

☒ **TALLAHASSEE MEMORIAL HEALTHCARE (100135)**, 1300 Miccosukee Road, Zip 32308–5054; tel. 850/431–1155, (Total facility includes 42 beds in nursing home–type unit) **A**1 2 3 5 7 9 10 **F**2 3 5 6 8 11 12 15 17 18 19 20 22 24 26 28 29 30 31 34 35 37 40 42 43 45 46 47 49 50 51 53 54 55 56 57 58 59 60 61 62 64 65 68 70 72 73 74 75 76 77 78 79 80 81 82 84 85 86 87 88 89 91 93 96 97 98 99 100 102 103 104 107 108 110 113 114 115 117 118 119 120 121 123 124 126 127 128 129 130 131 132 135 143 144 146 147 148 **P**6
Primary Contact: G. Mark O'Bryant, President and Chief Executive Officer
COO: Jason H. Moore, Vice President and Chief Operating Officer
CFO: William A. Giudice, Vice President and Chief Financial Officer
CMO: Dean Watson, M.D., Chief Medical Officer
CIO: Don Lindsey, Vice President and Chief Information Officer
CHR: Steven W. Adriaanse, Vice President and Chief Human Resources Officer
Web address: www.tmh.org
**Control:** Other not–for–profit (including NFP Corporation) **Service:** General Medical and Surgical

**Staffed Beds:** 491 **Admissions:** 26333 **Census:** 358 **Outpatient Visits:** 637671 **Births:** 3700 **Total Expense ($000):** 508035 **Payroll Expense ($000):** 217338 **Personnel:** 3674

## TAMARAC—Broward County

☒ **UNIVERSITY HOSPITAL AND MEDICAL CENTER (100224)**, 7201 North University Drive, Zip 33321–2996; tel. 954/721–2200, (Includes UNIVERSITY PAVILION, 7425 North University Drive, Zip 33328; tel. 305/722–9933), (Nonreporting) **A**1 9 10 **S** HCA, Nashville, TN
Primary Contact: Joseph D. Melchiode, Chief Executive Officer
CFO: Aurelio Gonzalez, Chief Financial Officer
CMO: Ran Abrahamy, M.D., Chief of Staff
CIO: Tom Scharff, Director Information Services
Web address: www.uhmchealth.com
**Control:** Corporation, Investor–owned, for–profit **Service:** General Medical and Surgical

**Staffed Beds:** 317

## TAMPA—Hillsborough County

☒ **FLORIDA HOSPITAL CARROLLWOOD (100069)**, 7171 North Dale Mabry Highway, Zip 33614–2665; tel. 813/932–2222 **A**1 3 10 **F**3 8 11 15 20 26 29 30 31 34 35 40 44 45 48 49 50 53 54 56 57 58 59 60 61 64 65 68 70 74 75 77 78 79 80 81 82 85 86 87 92 93 97 107 110 111 114 119 130 131 132 143 146 148 **S** Adventist Health System Sunbelt Health Care Corporation, Altamonte Springs, FL
Primary Contact: Joe Johnson, Chief Executive Officer
COO: Mary C. Whillock, R.N., Associate Nursing Officer and Chief Operating Officer
CFO: Marvin A. Kurtz, Chief Financial Officer
Web address: www.elevatinghealthcare.org/locations/carrollwood
**Control:** Church–operated, Nongovernment, not–for profit **Service:** General Medical and Surgical

**Staffed Beds:** 90 **Admissions:** 4584 **Census:** 47 **Outpatient Visits:** 66217 **Births:** 0 **Total Expense ($000):** 106605 **Payroll Expense ($000):** 30485 **Personnel:** 411

☒ △ **FLORIDA HOSPITAL TAMPA (100173)**, 3100 East Fletcher Avenue, Zip 33613–4688; tel. 813/971–6000 **A**1 2 3 5 7 10 **F**3 12 13 15 16 17 18 19 20 21 22 24 25 26 27 28 29 30 31 34 35 37 40 41 44 45 46 47 48 49 50 54 57 58 59 60 64 65 70 72 74 75 76 77 78 79 80 81 82 84 85 86 87 89 90 91 92 93 96 107 108 109 110 111 112 114 115 116 117 118 119 120 121 123 124 126 129 130 132 135 143 144 146 147 148 **P**6 7 **S** Adventist Health System Sunbelt Health Care Corporation, Altamonte Springs, FL
Primary Contact: Brian Adams, President and CEO
COO: Dick Tibbits, Vice President and Chief Operating Officer
CFO: Dima Didenko, Chief Financial Officer
CMO: Brad Bjornstad, M.D., Vice President and Chief Medical Officer
CHR: Dick Tibbits, Vice President and Chief Operating Officer
CNO: Joy B. Solomita, R.N., Vice President and Chief Nursing Officer
Web address: www.floridahospital.com/tampa
**Control:** Other not–for–profit (including NFP Corporation) **Service:** General Medical and Surgical

**Staffed Beds:** 493 **Admissions:** 20148 **Census:** 301 **Outpatient Visits:** 108898 **Births:** 1448 **Total Expense ($000):** 324498 **Payroll Expense ($000):** 118247 **Personnel:** 2253

☒ **H. LEE MOFFITT CANCER CENTER AND RESEARCH INSTITUTE (100271)**, 12902 Magnolia Drive, MBC Diversity, Zip 33612–9497; tel. 813/972–4673 **A**1 2 3 5 9 10 **F**3 8 11 15 26 29 30 31 34 35 36 37 38 44 45 46 47 48 49 50 54 55 56 57 58 59 63 64 68 70 71 74 75 77 78 79 81 82 83 84 85 86 87 91 92 93 96 97 100 101 103 104 107 108 109 110 111 113 114 115 116 117 118 119 120 121 123 124 126 130 132 134 135 136 141 144 146 147 148 **P**6
Primary Contact: Alan F. List, M.D., President and Chief Executive Officer
COO: John A. Kolosky, Executive Vice President and Chief Operating Officer
CFO: Janene Culumber, Vice President and Chief Financial Officer
CMO: W. Michael Alberts, M.D., Vice President Medical Affairs
CIO: Mark Hulse, Vice President and Chief Information Officer
CHR: Yvette Tremonti, Vice President Human Resources
Web address: www.moffitt.org
**Control:** Other not–for–profit (including NFP Corporation) **Service:** Cancer

**Staffed Beds:** 206 **Admissions:** 9153 **Census:** 162 **Outpatient Visits:** 339565 **Births:** 0 **Total Expense ($000):** 834459 **Payroll Expense ($000):** 340328 **Personnel:** 4703

☒ △ **JAMES A. HALEY VETERANS' HOSPITAL–TAMPA**, 13000 Bruce B. Downs Boulevard, Zip 33612–4745; tel. 813/972–2000, (Total facility includes 64 beds in nursing home–type unit) **A**1 3 5 7 8 **F**3 5 9 12 15 17 18 20 22 24 26 28 29 30 31 33 34 35 36 38 39 40 44 46 47 48 49 50 51 53 54 55 56 57 58 59 60 61 62 63 64 65 70 71 74 75 77 78 79 80 81 82 83 84 85 86 87 90 91 92 93 94 95 96 97 98 100 101 102 103 104 105 106 107 108 109 110 111 113 114 115 116 117 118 119 120 121 123 127 128 129 130 131 132 135 143 144 146 147 148 **P**1 **S** Department of Veterans Affairs, Washington, DC
Primary Contact: Kathleen R. Fogarty, Director
CFO: Robert Konkel, Manager Finance
CMO: Edward Cutolo, Jr., M.D., Chief of Staff
CIO: Jose Seymour, Chief Information Resource Management
CHR: Neal C. Hamilton, Chief Human Resources
CNO: Laureen Doloresco, R.N., Associate Director for Patient Care and Nursing Services
Web address: www.tampa.va.gov/
**Control:** Veterans Affairs, Government, federal **Service:** General Medical and Surgical

**Staffed Beds:** 499 **Admissions:** 11787 **Census:** 314 **Outpatient Visits:** 1224618 **Births:** 0 **Total Expense ($000):** 842159 **Payroll Expense ($000):** 363282 **Personnel:** 4705

FL

*Many Facility Codes have changed. Please refer to the AHA Guide Code Chart.* © 2015 AHA Guide

✠ **KINDRED HOSPITAL BAY AREA–TAMPA (102009)**, 4555 South Manhattan Avenue, Zip 33611–2397; tel. 813/839–6341, (Includes KINDRED HOSPITAL–BAY AREA ST. PETERSBURG, 3030 Sixth Street South, Saint Petersburg, Zip 33705–3720; tel. 727/894–8719; Debra Plummer, Chief Executive Officer) **A**1 10 **F**1 3 18 29 34 59 60 70 74 75 85 87 130 148 **S** Kindred Healthcare, Louisville, KY
Primary Contact: Sandra Morgan, Chief Executive Officer
CFO: Frank Billy, Chief Financial Officer
CHR: Deborah Basria, Human Resources Payroll Administrator
Web address: www.khtampa.com/
**Control:** Hospital district or authority, Government, nonfederal **Service:** Long–Term Acute Care hospital

**Staffed Beds:** 73 **Admissions:** 481 **Census:** 48 **Births:** 0 **Total Expense ($000):** 25531 **Payroll Expense ($000):** 9739

✠ **KINDRED HOSPITAL CENTRAL TAMPA (102013)**, 4801 North Howard Avenue, Zip 33603–1411; tel. 813/874–7575, (Nonreporting) **A**1 9 10 **S** Kindred Healthcare, Louisville, KY
Primary Contact: Ralph Selner, Chief Executive Officer
CFO: John Miner, Chief Financial Officer
Web address: www.kindredcentraltampa.com/
**Control:** Corporation, Investor–owned, for–profit **Service:** Long–Term Acute Care hospital

**Staffed Beds:** 102

✠ **MEMORIAL HOSPITAL OF TAMPA (100206)**, 2901 Swann Avenue, Zip 33609–4057; tel. 813/873–6400, (Nonreporting) **A**1 5 9 10 **S** HCA, Nashville, TN
Primary Contact: Ward Boston, III, Chief Executive Officer
CFO: Shelley V. Kolseth, Chief Financial Officer
CIO: John Riton, Director Information Services
Web address: www.memorialhospitaltampa.com
**Control:** Corporation, Investor–owned, for–profit **Service:** General Medical and Surgical

**Staffed Beds:** 139

☐ **SHRINERS HOSPITALS FOR CHILDREN–TAMPA (103303)**, 12502 USF Pine Drive, Zip 33612–9499; tel. 813/972–2250 **A**1 3 5 9 10 **F**3 34 35 50 57 64 68 74 77 79 81 85 89 91 93 94 107 131 146 **S** Shriners Hospitals for Children, Tampa, FL
Primary Contact: Jeannette Skinner, R.N., FACHE, Administrator
CFO: Ruth Gregos, Director Finance
CMO: Maureen Maciel, M.D., Chief of Staff
CHR: Amy Schenker, Human Resources Director
Web address: www.shrinershospitalsforchildren.org/Hospitals/Locations/Tampa.aspx
**Control:** Other not–for–profit (including NFP Corporation) **Service:** Children's orthopedic

**Staffed Beds:** 60 **Admissions:** 217 **Census:** 1 **Births:** 0 **Total Expense ($000):** 20391 **Payroll Expense ($000):** 8726

✠ **ST. JOSEPH'S HOSPITAL (100075)**, 3001 West Martin Luther King Jr. Boulevard, Zip 33607–6387, Mailing Address: P.O. Box 4227, Zip 33677–4227; tel. 813/870–4000, (Includes ST. JOSEPH'S CHILDREN'S HOSPITAL, 3001 Dr. Martin Luther King Jr. Boulevard, Zip 33607; tel. 813/554–8500; ST. JOSEPH'S HOSPITAL – NORTH, 4211 Van Dyke Road, Lutz, Zip 33558–8005; tel. 813/443–7000; Paula McGinnis, Chief Executive Officer; ST. JOSEPH'S HOSPITAL BEHAVIORAL HEALTH CENTER, 4918 North Habana Avenue, Zip 33614–6815; tel. 813/870–4300; ST. JOSEPH'S HOSPITAL–SOUTH, 6901 Simmons Loop, Riverview, Zip 33578–9498; tel. 813/302–8000; Scott Smith, Chief Executive Officer; ST. JOSEPH'S WOMEN'S HOSPITAL, 3030 West Dr. Martin L. King Boulevard, Zip 33607–6394; tel. 813/872–2950; Kimberly Guy, Chief Operating Officer) **A**1 2 3 5 9 10 **F**3 7 11 12 13 15 17 18 20 21 22 23 24 25 26 27 28 29 30 31 33 34 35 37 39 40 41 43 44 45 46 48 49 51 55 57 58 59 64 65 66 68 70 71 72 73 74 75 76 77 78 79 81 82 84 85 86 87 88 89 93 94 98 99 100 101 102 107 108 110 111 114 115 118 119 120 121 123 124 126 127 129 130 131 132 135 145 146 147 148 **S** Trinity Health, Livonia, MI
Primary Contact: Lorraine Lutton, President
CFO: Cathy Yoder, Chief Financial Officer
CMO: Mark Vaaler, M.D., Vice President Medical Staff Affairs
CIO: Lindsey Jarrell, Vice President Information Services
CHR: Pat Teeuwen, Director Team Resources
Web address: www.sjbhealth.org
**Control:** Other not–for–profit (including NFP Corporation) **Service:** General Medical and Surgical

**Staffed Beds:** 1006 **Admissions:** 47337 **Census:** 621 **Outpatient Visits:** 419956 **Births:** 8000 **Total Expense ($000):** 740828 **Payroll Expense ($000):** 272085 **Personnel:** 3354

✠ **TAMPA COMMUNITY HOSPITAL (100255)**, 6001 Webb Road, Zip 33615–3291; tel. 813/888–7060 **A**1 5 9 10 **F**3 4 5 15 18 20 29 40 45 46 47 48 49 70 74 79 81 82 85 92 93 98 102 103 107 110 111 114 115 118 119 126 128 130 146 148 **P**4 5 **S** HCA, Nashville, TN
Primary Contact: Jacob Fisher, Chief Executive Officer
COO: Paulina Tam, Vice President of Operations
CIO: Albert Lacy, Associate Director of Information Technology
CHR: Stephanie Kunkel, Vice President of Human Resources
CNO: Susan Laber, R.N., Chief Nursing Officer
Web address: www.tampacommunityhospital.com/
**Control:** Corporation, Investor–owned, for–profit **Service:** General Medical and Surgical

**Staffed Beds:** 201 **Admissions:** 4687 **Census:** 59 **Births:** 0 **Total Expense ($000):** 63879 **Payroll Expense ($000):** 21241

✠ △ **TAMPA GENERAL HOSPITAL (100128)**, 1 Tampa General Circle, Zip 33606–3571, Mailing Address: P.O. Box 1289, Zip 33601–1289; tel. 813/844–7000, (Includes TAMPA GENERAL HOSPITAL CHILDREN'S MEDICAL CENTER, 1 Tampa General Circle, tel. 813/844–7000) **A**1 3 5 7 8 9 10 **F**3 7 8 9 11 12 13 15 16 17 18 19 20 22 24 26 28 29 30 31 32 34 35 36 37 38 40 41 43 44 45 46 47 48 49 50 51 52 54 55 56 57 58 59 60 61 62 63 64 65 66 68 70 72 73 74 75 76 77 78 79 81 82 83 84 85 86 87 88 89 90 91 92 93 94 96 97 100 101 102 103 107 108 109 110 111 112 114 115 119 120 121 123 124 126 129 130 131 132 134 135 137 138 139 140 141 142 143 145 146 147 148 **P**6
Primary Contact: James R. Burkhart, FACHE, President and Chief Executive Officer
COO: Deana Nelson, FACHE, Executive Vice President and Chief Operating Officer
CFO: Steve Short, Executive Vice President Finance and Administration and Chief Financial Officer
CMO: Sally Houston, M.D., Executive Vice President and Chief Medical Officer
CIO: Scott Arnold, Senior Vice President Information Systems
CHR: Chris Roederer, Senior Vice President Human Resources
CNO: Janet Davis, R.N., Senior Vice President and Chief Nursing Officer
Web address: www.tgh.org
**Control:** Other not–for–profit (including NFP Corporation) **Service:** General Medical and Surgical

**Staffed Beds:** 1011 **Admissions:** 45077 **Census:** 736 **Outpatient Visits:** 319566 **Births:** 5281 **Total Expense ($000):** 1029471 **Payroll Expense ($000):** 387142 **Personnel:** 6716

**TARPON SPRINGS—Pinellas County**

✠ **FLORIDA HOSPITAL NORTH PINELLAS (100055)**, 1395 South Pinellas Avenue, Zip 34689–3790; tel. 727/942–5000 **A**1 5 9 10 **F**3 11 13 15 17 18 20 22 26 28 29 30 31 34 35 40 45 46 48 49 50 57 59 64 70 71 75 76 78 79 81 93 94 96 97 107 108 110 111 114 115 117 119 126 128 129 130 131 132 146 147 148 **S** Adventist Health System Sunbelt Health Care Corporation, Altamonte Springs, FL
Primary Contact: Bruce Bergherm, Chief Executive Officer
CFO: Michael Mewhirter, Chief Financial Officer
CMO: Paul Arnold, M.D., Chief of Medical Staff
CIO: Brett Peterson, Director of Information Services
CHR: Vernon Elarbee, Director of Human Resources
CNO: Karen Owensby, R.N., Chief Clinical Officer
Web address: www.fhnorthpinellas.com/
**Control:** Church–operated, Nongovernment, not–for profit **Service:** General Medical and Surgical

**Staffed Beds:** 168 **Admissions:** 4779 **Census:** 65 **Outpatient Visits:** 41098 **Births:** 248 **Total Expense ($000):** 88296 **Payroll Expense ($000):** 28648 **Personnel:** 530

**TAVARES—Lake County**

✠ **FLORIDA HOSPITAL WATERMAN (100057)**, 1000 Waterman Way, Zip 32778–5266; tel. 352/253–3333 **A**1 2 9 10 **F**3 11 13 15 17 18 20 22 24 26 28 29 30 31 34 35 37 40 45 49 50 53 54 57 59 62 64 66 70 74 75 76 77 78 79 81 85 89 93 107 108 110 111 114 115 116 117 118 119 120 121 123 132 135 144 146 148 **P**8 **S** Adventist Health System Sunbelt Health Care Corporation, Altamonte Springs, FL
Primary Contact: David Ottati, Chief Executive Officer
COO: Carrie L. Fish, Senior Vice President and Chief Operating Officer
CFO: Frances H. Crunk, Vice President and Chief Financial Officer
CMO: Vinay Mehindru, M.D., Vice President/Chief Medical Officer
CHR: Madge Springer, Director Human Resources
CNO: Patricia R. Dolan, R.N., Vice President/ Chief Nursing Officer
Web address: www.fhwat.org
**Control:** Church–operated, Nongovernment, not–for profit **Service:** General Medical and Surgical

**Staffed Beds:** 269 **Admissions:** 14237 **Census:** 173 **Births:** 492 **Total Expense ($000):** 197220 **Payroll Expense ($000):** 78090

---

**Hospital, Medicare Provider Number, Address, Telephone, Approval, Facility, and Physician Codes, Health Care System**

★ American Hospital Association (AHA) membership    ○ Healthcare Facilities Accreditation Program    ⇑ Center for Improvement in Healthcare Quality Accreditation
☐ The Joint Commission accreditation    ◇ DNV Healthcare Inc. accreditation    △ Commission on Accreditation of Rehabilitation Facilities (CARF) accreditation

**FL**

**TAVERNIER—Monroe County**

☒ **BAPTIST HEALTH SOUTH FLORIDA, MARINERS HOSPITAL (101313)**, 91500 Overseas Highway, Zip 33070–2547; tel. 305/434–3000 **A**1 9 10 18 **F**3 11 15 18 28 29 30 31 34 35 40 45 47 50 53 57 59 68 70 74 75 78 79 81 84 85 93 97 102 107 108 110 111 114 115 119 129 130 131 132 133 145 146 147 148 **P**8 **S** Baptist Health South Florida, Coral Gables, FL
Primary Contact: Rick Freeburg, Chief Executive Officer
CFO: Erik Long, Controller
CIO: Mimi Taylor, Vice President Information Technology
CHR: John Williamson, Human Resources Site Manager
Web address: www.baptisthealth.net/en/facilities/mariners–hospital/Pages/default.aspx
**Control:** Other not–for–profit (including NFP Corporation) **Service:** General Medical and Surgical

**Staffed Beds:** 25 **Admissions:** 567 **Census:** 6 **Outpatient Visits:** 21208 **Births:** 0 **Total Expense ($000):** 46539 **Payroll Expense ($000):** 14750 **Personnel:** 195

**THE VILLAGES—Sumter County**

☒ **THE VILLAGES REGIONAL HOSPITAL (100290)**, 1451 El Camino Real, Zip 32159–0041; tel. 352/751–8000 **A**1 2 9 10 **F**3 8 11 15 18 20 22 24 28 29 30 31 34 35 40 45 51 54 57 59 64 68 70 74 75 77 78 79 81 84 85 87 93 107 108 110 111 114 115 116 119 130 132 135 144 146 **P**6 **S** Central Florida Health Alliance, Leesburg, FL
Primary Contact: Donald G. Henderson, FACHE, President and Chief Executive Officer
COO: Saad Ehtisham, R.N., Vice President and Chief Operating Officer
CFO: Diane P. Harden, Senior Vice President and Chief Financial Officer
CHR: Amie Richason, Vice President Human Resources
CNO: Mary Jane Curry–Pelyak, R.N., Vice President and Chief Clinical Officer
Web address: www.cfhalliance.org
**Control:** Other not–for–profit (including NFP Corporation) **Service:** General Medical and Surgical

**Staffed Beds:** 223 **Admissions:** 13833 **Census:** 156 **Outpatient Visits:** 69806 **Births:** 0 **Total Expense ($000):** 138561 **Payroll Expense ($000):** 51882 **Personnel:** 870

**TITUSVILLE—Brevard County**

☐ **PARRISH MEDICAL CENTER (100028)**, 951 North Washington Avenue, Zip 32796–2163; tel. 321/268–6111 **A**1 2 9 10 **F**3 11 13 15 18 20 22 28 29 30 34 35 40 45 47 50 51 53 54 56 57 59 60 62 64 68 69 70 74 75 76 77 78 79 80 81 82 83 84 85 86 87 89 92 93 94 107 108 110 111 116 126 129 130 132 134 135 143 144 146 147 148
Primary Contact: George Mikitarian, Jr., Chief Executive Officer
CFO: Timothy K. Skeldon, Senior Vice President and Chief Financial Officer
CMO: Lisa Alexanda, M.D., Vice President Medical Affairs
CIO: William Moore, Chief Information Officer
CHR: Roberta Chaildin, Manager Human Resources
Web address: www.parrishmed.com
**Control:** Hospital district or authority, Government, nonfederal **Service:** General Medical and Surgical

**Staffed Beds:** 210 **Admissions:** 6581 **Census:** 75 **Births:** 652 **Total Expense ($000):** 170699 **Payroll Expense ($000):** 65775

**TRINITY—Pasco County**

**COMMUNITY HOSPITAL** See Medical Center of Trinity

☒ **MEDICAL CENTER OF TRINITY (100191)**, 9330 State Road 54, Zip 34655–1808; tel. 727/834–4900 **A**1 2 10 **F**8 11 13 15 18 20 22 26 29 30 31 34 35 38 40 45 46 47 48 49 57 59 60 67 68 70 74 75 76 77 78 79 80 81 82 84 85 86 87 93 94 98 102 103 107 108 110 111 119 126 130 132 135 146 147 148 **S** HCA, Nashville, TN
Primary Contact: Leigh Massengill, Chief Executive Officer
COO: Kenneth West, Chief Operating Officer
CFO: Michael Wyers, Chief Financial Officer
CMO: Linda Badillo, M.D., Chief of Medical Staff
CIO: Kurt Hornung, Director
CHR: Christena Miano, Human Resources Director
CNO: Nancy Maysilles, R.N., Chief Nursing Officer
Web address: www.medicalcentertrinity.com
**Control:** Corporation, Investor–owned, for–profit **Service:** General Medical and Surgical

**Staffed Beds:** 282 **Admissions:** 13211 **Census:** 152 **Births:** 1079 **Total Expense ($000):** 185009 **Payroll Expense ($000):** 58470

**VENICE—Sarasota County**

☒ **VENICE REGIONAL BAYFRONT HEALTH (100070)**, 540 The Rialto, Zip 34285–2900; tel. 941/485–7711 **A**1 9 10 **F**3 8 11 12 15 17 18 20 22 24 26 28 29 30 31 34 35 37 40 45 46 47 49 50 51 54 56 57 59 60 64 70 74 77 78 79 81 82 87 93 96 107 108 110 111 114 118 119 126 129 130 144 146 148 **S** Community Health Systems, Inc., Franklin, TN
Primary Contact: Jeff Reece, Interim Chief Executive Officer
COO: Kristen Gentry, Chief Operating Officer
CFO: Brian Hess, Chief Financial Officer
CIO: Eloy Rivas, Director of Information Systems
CHR: Faye Peraza, Director Human Resources
CNO: Cathy Carr, MSN, Chief Nursing Officer
Web address: www.veniceregional.com
**Control:** Corporation, Investor–owned, for–profit **Service:** General Medical and Surgical

**Staffed Beds:** 312 **Admissions:** 10316 **Census:** 126 **Outpatient Visits:** 117474 **Births:** 0 **Total Expense ($000):** 148034 **Payroll Expense ($000):** 50197

**VERO BEACH—Indian River County**

☒ **HEALTHSOUTH TREASURE COAST REHABILITATION HOSPITAL (103032)**, 1600 37th Street, Zip 32960–4863; tel. 772/778–2100 **A**1 9 10 **F**12 29 34 90 91 148 **S** HEALTHSOUTH Corporation, Birmingham, AL
Primary Contact: Michael Kissner, Chief Executive Officer
CFO: Kevin Hardy, Chief Financial Officer
CMO: Jimmy Wayne Lockhart, M.D., Medical Director
CHR: Linda Rinehart, Director Human Resources
Web address: www.healthsouthtreasurecoast.com
**Control:** Corporation, Investor–owned, for–profit **Service:** Rehabilitation

**Staffed Beds:** 80 **Admissions:** 1525 **Census:** 56 **Outpatient Visits:** 0 **Births:** 0 **Total Expense ($000):** 19957 **Payroll Expense ($000):** 9704

☒ **INDIAN RIVER MEDICAL CENTER (100105)**, 1000 36th Street, Zip 32960–6592; tel. 772/567–4311 **A**1 2 9 10 **F**3 11 12 13 17 18 20 22 24 26 28 29 30 31 34 35 37 40 44 45 49 50 51 57 58 59 60 61 64 70 74 75 76 77 78 79 80 81 82 83 84 85 86 87 89 92 93 96 97 98 99 100 101 102 103 104 107 108 110 111 114 115 116 117 118 119 120 121 124 126 129 130 131 132 135 144 146 147 148 **P**6
Primary Contact: Jeffrey L. Susi, President and Chief Executive Officer
COO: Steven Salyer, Senior Vice President and Chief Operating Officer
CFO: Greg Gardner, Senior Vice President and Chief Financial Officer
CMO: Charles Mackett, M.D., Senior Vice President and Chief Medical Officer
CIO: William Neil, Vice President and Chief Information Officer
CNO: Lynn Hubbard, R.N., Vice President and Chief Nursing Officer
Web address: www.irmc.cc
**Control:** Other not–for–profit (including NFP Corporation) **Service:** General Medical and Surgical

**Staffed Beds:** 197 **Admissions:** 13347 **Census:** 164 **Outpatient Visits:** 130034 **Births:** 1048 **Total Expense ($000):** 202420 **Payroll Expense ($000):** 90898 **Personnel:** 1512

**WAUCHULA—Hardee County**

☒ **FLORIDA HOSPITAL WAUCHULA (101300)**, 533 West Carlton Street, Zip 33873–3407; tel. 863/773–3101 **A**1 9 10 18 **F**3 29 40 107 110 111 127 129 130 133 **P**6 **S** Adventist Health System Sunbelt Health Care Corporation, Altamonte Springs, FL
Primary Contact: Denise Grimsley, Administrator
CFO: Rosalie Oliver, Senior Vice President and Chief Financial Officer
CMO: Jorge F. Gonzalez, M.D., Vice President and Chief Nursing Officer
CIO: Jeff McDonald, Information Technology Manager
CHR: Michelle F. Myers, Director Human Resources
CNO: Gloria N. Santos, R.N., Vice President and Chief Nursing Officer
Web address: www.fh.floridahospital.com/heartland/home.aspx
**Control:** Church–operated, Nongovernment, not–for profit **Service:** General Medical and Surgical

**Staffed Beds:** 25 **Admissions:** 852 **Census:** 21 **Outpatient Visits:** 27730 **Births:** 0 **Total Expense ($000):** 23302 **Payroll Expense ($000):** 7850 **Personnel:** 118

**WESLEY CHAPEL—Pasco County**

★ ◇ **FLORIDA HOSPITAL WESLEY CHAPEL (100319)**, 2600 Bruce B. Downs Boulevard, Zip 33544–9207; tel. 813/929–5000 **A**5 9 10 21 **F**3 11 13 15 18 20 22 26 29 30 34 35 40 45 51 53 57 59 60 64 70 74 77 79 81 86 93 107 108 110 111 115 117 119 126 131 145 146 147 **S** Adventist Health System Sunbelt Health Care Corporation, Altamonte Springs, FL
Primary Contact: Denyse Bales–Chubb, Chief Executive Officer
Web address: www.https://www.floridahospital.com/wesley–chapel
**Control:** Other not–for–profit (including NFP Corporation) **Service:** General Medical and Surgical

**Staffed Beds:** 83 **Admissions:** 5191 **Census:** 53 **Outpatient Visits:** 51290 **Births:** 327 **Total Expense ($000):** 111065 **Payroll Expense ($000):** 32890 **Personnel:** 570

**FL**

☐ **NORTH TAMPA BEHAVIORAL HEALTH (104075)**, 29910 State Road 56, Zip 33543–8800; tel. 813/922–3300, (Nonreporting) **A**1 10 **S** Acadia Healthcare Company, Inc., Franklin, TN
Primary Contact: Michael Ham, Chief Executive Officer
Web address: www.northtampabehavioralhealth.com
**Control:** Corporation, Investor–owned, for–profit **Service:** Psychiatric

Staffed Beds: 75

**WEST PALM BEACH—Palm Beach County**

⊞ **GOOD SAMARITAN MEDICAL CENTER (100287)**, 1309 North Flagler Drive, Zip 33401–3499; tel. 561/655–5511, (Nonreporting) **A**1 2 5 9 10 **S** TENET Healthcare Corporation, Dallas, TX
Primary Contact: Mark Nosacka, Chief Executive Officer
CFO: Cynthia McCauley, Chief Financial Officer
CIO: Candace Helms, Director Information Services
CHR: Amy Linsin, Chief Human Resources Officer
Web address: www.goodsamaritanmc.com
**Control:** Corporation, Investor–owned, for–profit **Service:** General Medical and Surgical

Staffed Beds: 174

☐ **JEROME GOLDEN CENTER FOR BEHAVIORAL HEALTH, INC. (104008)**, 1041 45th Street, Zip 33407–2494; tel. 561/383–8000, (Nonreporting) **A**1 10
Primary Contact: Linda De Piano, Ph.D., Chief Executive Officer
CFO: Dominic Paris, Chief Financial Officer
CMO: Suresh Rajpara, M.D., Chief Medical Officer
CIO: Iris Garcia, Director, Information Services
CHR: Patricia Squire, Director Human Resources
CNO: Al Ricketts, Director of Nursing
Web address: www.goldenctr.org
**Control:** Other not–for–profit (including NFP Corporation) **Service:** Psychiatric

Staffed Beds: 44

**PALM BEACH CHILDREN'S HOSPITAL** See St. Mary's Medical Center

⊞ △ **ST. MARY'S MEDICAL CENTER (100288)**, 901 45th Street, Zip 33407–2495; tel. 561/844–6300, (Includes PALM BEACH CHILDREN'S HOSPITAL, 901 45th Street, Zip 33407; tel. 561/844–6300) **A**1 7 9 10 **F**3 6 8 11 12 13 15 17 18 19 20 21 22 23 24 25 29 30 31 34 35 38 39 40 41 43 44 45 47 48 49 50 51 56 57 58 59 60 64 65 68 70 72 73 74 75 76 77 78 79 81 85 86 87 88 89 90 92 93 94 96 98 100 101 102 103 107 108 110 111 114 115 119 120 121 123 130 131 132 134 135 146 147 148 **S** TENET Healthcare Corporation, Dallas, TX
Primary Contact: Joey Bulfin, R.N., Interim Chief Executive Officer
COO: Joey Bulfin, R.N., Chief Operating Officer
CFO: Tom Schlemmer, Chief Financial Officer
CMO: Jeffrey Davis, D.O., Chief Medical Officer
CIO: Rich Avato, Director
CHR: Thomas J. Piszczatoski, Chief Human Resource Officer
CNO: Donna Small, R.N., Chief Nursing Officer
Web address: www.stmarysmc.com
**Control:** Corporation, Investor–owned, for–profit **Service:** General Medical and Surgical

Staffed Beds: 464 Admissions: 18239 Census: 290 Outpatient Visits: 117623 Births: 3289 Total Expense ($000): 245373 Payroll Expense ($000): 100389 Personnel: 1480

**VETERANS AFFAIRS MEDICAL CENTER** See West Palm Beach Veterans Affairs Medical Center

☐ **WELLINGTON REGIONAL MEDICAL CENTER (100275)**, 10101 Forest Hill Boulevard, Zip 33414–6199; tel. 561/798–8500, (Nonreporting) **A**1 9 10 12 13 **S** Universal Health Services, Inc., King of Prussia, PA
Primary Contact: Robbin Lee, Chief Executive Officer
COO: Pamela S. Tahan, Chief Operating Officer
CFO: Joseph Paul, Chief Financial Officer
CMO: Richard Hays, M.D., Chief of Staff
CIO: Pierre Bergeron, Director Information Services
CHR: Mary Jo Caracciolo, Director Human Resources
CNO: Asenath Cassel, Chief Nursing Officer
Web address: www.wellingtonregional.com
**Control:** Corporation, Investor–owned, for–profit **Service:** General Medical and Surgical

Staffed Beds: 108

⊞ **WEST PALM BEACH VETERANS AFFAIRS MEDICAL CENTER**, 7305 North Military Trail, Zip 33410–6400; tel. 561/422–8262, (Total facility includes 120 beds in nursing home–type unit) **A**1 3 5 9 **F**1 3 11 15 18 20 28 29 30 31 33 34 35 36 38 39 40 44 45 47 49 50 51 56 57 59 60 61 62 63 64 65 68 70 71 74 75 77 78 79 81 82 83 84 85 86 87 91 92 93 94 96 97 98 100 101 102 103 104 105 106 107 109 110 111 115 116 117 118 119 120 121 122 123 127 129 130 132 135 146 147 148 **S** Department of Veterans Affairs, Washington, DC
Primary Contact: Charleen R. Szabo, FACHE, Director
CFO: Lori Hancock, Chief Business Officer
CMO: Deepak Mandi, M.D., Chief of Staff
CIO: Karen Gabaldon, Chief Management Information Systems
CHR: David Green, Chief Human Resources
Web address: www.westpalmbeach.va.gov/
**Control:** Veterans Affairs, Government, federal **Service:** General Medical and Surgical

Staffed Beds: 300 Admissions: 8295 Census: 230 Outpatient Visits: 731958 Births: 0 Total Expense ($000): 425727 Payroll Expense ($000): 178215 Personnel: 2894

⊞ ○ **WEST PALM HOSPITAL (100234)**, 2201 45th Street, Zip 33407–2047; tel. 561/842–6141 **A**1 9 10 11 **F**3 29 34 35 40 45 49 57 59 60 70 79 81 82 93 98 99 101 102 103 104 105 107 110 111 119 146 148 **S** HCA, Nashville, TN
Primary Contact: Dana Oaks, Chief Executive Officer
COO: Patrick Chapman, Assistant Vice President Operations
CMO: Paul Seltzer, M.D., Chief of Staff
CIO: Kenneth Vasquez, Associate Director
CHR: Donna Boyle, Director
CNO: Geraldine DeStefano, R.N., Chief Nursing Officer
Web address: www.westpalmhospital.com
**Control:** Corporation, Investor–owned, for–profit **Service:** General Medical and Surgical

Staffed Beds: 245 Admissions: 9355 Census: 111 Births: 0 Total Expense ($000): 88339 Payroll Expense ($000): 30129

**WESTON—Broward County**

⊞ **CLEVELAND CLINIC FLORIDA (100289)**, 2950 Cleveland Clinic Boulevard, Zip 33331–3602; tel. 954/659–5000 **A**1 2 3 5 9 10 **F**3 8 9 12 15 17 18 20 22 24 26 28 29 30 31 34 35 37 39 40 44 45 46 47 48 49 50 51 54 55 56 57 58 59 60 61 63 64 65 68 70 74 75 77 78 79 80 81 82 84 85 86 87 91 92 93 96 97 100 101 107 108 109 110 111 114 115 116 119 126 129 130 131 132 135 137 138 139 141 145 146 147 148 **P**6 **S** Cleveland Clinic Health System, Cleveland, OH
Primary Contact: Wael Barsoum, Interim Chief Executive Officer
CFO: Keith Nilsson, Chief Financial Officer
CMO: Raul Rosenthal, M.D., Interim Chief of Staff
CIO: John Santangelo, Director Information Technology
CHR: Becky Caputo, Interim Director Human Resources
CNO: Kerry Major, R.N., Chief Nursing Officer
Web address: www.clevelandclinic.org/florida
**Control:** Other not–for–profit (including NFP Corporation) **Service:** General Medical and Surgical

Staffed Beds: 155 Admissions: 10320 Census: 127 Outpatient Visits: 173444 Births: 0 Total Expense ($000): 196519 Payroll Expense ($000): 71504 Personnel: 2115

**WILLISTON—Levy County**

**NATURE COAST REGIONAL HOSPITAL** See Regional General Hospital

**REGIONAL GENERAL HOSPITAL (100322)**, 125 S.W. Seventh Street, Zip 32696–2403; tel. 352/528–2801, (Nonreporting) **A**9 10
Primary Contact: Davie Lloyd, FACHE, Chief Executive Officer
CFO: Barbara Miller, Manager Business Office
CMO: Jeremie Young, M.D., Chief of Staff
CHR: Karla Dass, Director Human Resources
Web address: www.tricountyhosp.com/
**Control:** Partnership, Investor–owned, for–profit **Service:** General Medical and Surgical

Staffed Beds: 20

FL

| | | |
|---|---|---|
| **Hospital, Medicare Provider Number, Address, Telephone, Approval, Facility, and Physician Codes, Health Care System** | | |
| ★ American Hospital Association (AHA) membership | ○ Healthcare Facilities Accreditation Program | ⇧ Center for Improvement in Healthcare Quality Accreditation |
| ☐ The Joint Commission accreditation | ◇ DNV Healthcare Inc. accreditation | △ Commission on Accreditation of Rehabilitation Facilities (CARF) accreditation |

## WINTER HAVEN—Polk County

✠ △ **WINTER HAVEN HOSPITAL (100052)**, 200 Avenue F. N.E.,
Zip 33881–4193; tel. 863/293–1121 **A**1 7 9 10 **F**3 8 11 13 14 15 17 18 20
22 24 26 28 29 30 31 34 40 45 49 52 57 58 59 60 64 68 70 72 73 74 75
76 77 78 79 81 82 84 85 86 87 89 90 93 94 98 100 101 102 103 104 107
108 110 111 114 115 118 119 121 123 126 130 132 135 144 146 147 148
**P**6 7
Primary Contact: Stephen A. Nierman, President
COO: David Libby, Vice President Operations
CFO: Tina Solomon, Executive Director Finance
CMO: Donald I. Gale, M.D., Vice President Medical Affairs
CIO: Cal Cole, Director Information Systems
CHR: Andrea K. Williams, Manager, Employee Relations
CNO: Mary Jo Schreiber, R.N., Vice President Patient Services
Web address: www.winterhavenhospital.org
**Control:** Other not–for–profit (including NFP Corporation) **Service:** General
Medical and Surgical

**Staffed Beds:** 529 **Admissions:** 16749 **Census:** 232 **Outpatient Visits:**
301421 **Births:** 1607 **Total Expense ($000):** 266379 **Payroll Expense
($000):** 120512 **Personnel:** 1995

## WINTER PARK—Orange County

**WINTER PARK MEMORIAL HOSPITAL** See Florida Hospital, Orlando

## ZEPHYRHILLS—Pasco County

✠ **FLORIDA HOSPITAL ZEPHYRHILLS (100046)**, 7050 Gall Boulevard,
Zip 33541–1399; tel. 813/788–0411 **A**1 5 9 10 **F**3 12 13 14 15 17 18 20 22
24 26 28 29 30 31 32 34 35 37 40 44 45 46 47 48 49 51 53 54 56 57 59
60 62 63 64 68 70 74 76 77 79 81 82 83 86 87 91 92 93 97 107 108 110
111 114 116 119 124 126 129 130 132 133 135 146 147 148 **S** Adventist
Health System Sunbelt Health Care Corporation, Altamonte Springs, FL
Primary Contact: Randy Surber, Chief Executive Officer
COO: Donald E. Welch, Chief Operating Officer
CFO: Bill Heinrich, Chief Financial Officer
CMO: Hugar McNamee, D.O., Chief Medical Officer
CIO: Kelley Sasser, Director Information Systems
CHR: Laura Asaftei, Administrative Director
CNO: Gwen Alonso, Chief Nursing Officer
Web address: www.fhzeph.org
**Control:** Church–operated, Nongovernment, not–for profit **Service:** General
Medical and Surgical

**Staffed Beds:** 139 **Admissions:** 8022 **Census:** 92 **Outpatient Visits:** 115222
**Births:** 526 **Total Expense ($000):** 129147 **Payroll Expense ($000):** 49395
**Personnel:** 873

**FL**

*Many Facility Codes have changed. Please refer to the AHA Guide Code Chart.*

# GEORGIA

## ADEL—Cook County

⊠ **COOK MEDICAL CENTER–A CAMPUS OF TIFT REGIONAL MEDICAL CENTER (110101)**, 706 North Parrish Avenue, Zip 31620–1511; tel. 229/896–8000, (Total facility includes 95 beds in nursing home–type unit) **A**1 9 10 **F**11 15 29 30 34 35 40 45 46 47 48 56 57 59 64 65 68 75 77 81 84 85 86 87 93 97 98 103 107 108 110 111 114 118 119 127 129 130 133 135 146 147 148 **P**4 5 **S** Tift Regional Health System, Tifton, GA
Primary Contact: Michael L. Purvis, Chief Executive Officer
COO: Kim Wills, Chief Operating Officer
CIO: Barry Medley, Director Information Systems
CHR: Shirley Padgett, Director Human Resources
Web address: www.cookmedicalcenter.com
**Control:** Hospital district or authority, Government, nonfederal **Service:** General Medical and Surgical

**Staffed Beds:** 155 **Admissions:** 707 **Census:** 91 **Outpatient Visits:** 17794 **Births:** 0 **Total Expense ($000):** 16680 **Payroll Expense ($000):** 7281 **Personnel:** 199

## ALBANY—Dougherty County

★ ◇ **PHOEBE PUTNEY MEMORIAL HOSPITAL (110007)**, 417 West Third Avenue, Zip 31701–1943, Mailing Address: P.O. Box 3770, Zip 31706–3770; tel. 229/312–4100, (Includes PHOEBE NORTH, 2000 Palmyra Road, Zip 31701–1528, Mailing Address: P.O. Box 1908, Zip 31702–1908; tel. 229/434–2000) **A**2 3 5 9 10 21 **F**3 5 7 11 12 13 15 17 18 20 22 24 26 28 29 30 31 34 35 40 45 46 49 50 51 53 54 56 57 59 60 62 63 64 68 70 72 73 74 75 76 77 78 79 81 82 83 84 85 86 87 89 90 92 93 94 96 97 98 100 101 102 103 104 105 107 108 110 111 114 115 116 117 118 119 120 121 123 124 126 127 129 130 131 132 134 135 136 144 145 146 147 148 **P**1 7 **S** Phoebe Putney Health System, Albany, GA
Primary Contact: Joel Wernick, President and Chief Executive Officer
COO: Joe Austin, Executive Vice President and Chief Operating Officer
CFO: Kerry Loudermilk, Senior Vice President and Chief Financial Officer
CMO: Frank Middleton, M.D., Interim Chief Medical Officer
CIO: Jesse Diaz, Chief Information Officer
CHR: David J. Baranski, Vice President Human Resources
CNO: Laura Shearer, R.N., Senior Vice President and Chief Nursing Officer
Web address: www.phoebeputney.com
**Control:** Other not–for–profit (including NFP Corporation) **Service:** General Medical and Surgical

**Staffed Beds:** 526 **Admissions:** 20195 **Census:** 310 **Outpatient Visits:** 901809 **Births:** 2494 **Total Expense ($000):** 506928 **Payroll Expense ($000):** 177437 **Personnel:** 2718

## ALMA—Bacon County

⊠ **BACON COUNTY HOSPITAL AND HEALTH SYSTEM (111327)**, 302 South Wayne Street, Zip 31510–2922, Mailing Address: P.O. Drawer 1987, Zip 31510–0987; tel. 912/632–8961, (Nonreporting) **A**1 9 10 18
Primary Contact: Cindy R. Turner, Chief Executive Officer
COO: Cindy R. Turner, Chief Executive Officer
CFO: Kyle Kimmel, Chief Financial Officer
CMO: Lou Ellen Hutcheson, M.D., Chief of Staff
CIO: Neil O'Steen, Director Information Technology
CHR: Kerry Hancock, Director Human Resources
CNO: Deanna Hoff, R.N., Director of Nursing
Web address: www.baconcountyhospital.com
**Control:** Other not–for–profit (including NFP Corporation) **Service:** General Medical and Surgical

**Staffed Beds:** 113

## AMERICUS—Sumter County

★ ◇ **PHOEBE SUMTER MEDICAL CENTER (110044)**, 126 Highway 280 West, Zip 31719; tel. 229/924–6011, (Nonreporting) **A**9 10 21 **S** Phoebe Putney Health System, Albany, GA
Primary Contact: Brandi Lunneborg, Chief Executive Officer
CMO: Andrew Carlson, M.D., Vice President Medical Staff Services
CIO: Becky Lightner, Director Information Systems
CHR: Deatrice Harris, Supervisor Human Resources and Employment
Web address: www.phoebesumter.org
**Control:** Other not–for–profit (including NFP Corporation) **Service:** General Medical and Surgical

**Staffed Beds:** 45

## ATHENS—Clarke County

⊠ **ATHENS REGIONAL MEDICAL CENTER (110074)**, 1199 Prince Avenue, Zip 30606–2797; tel. 706/475–7000 **A**1 2 3 9 10 **F**3 8 11 13 15 17 18 20 22 24 26 28 29 30 31 32 34 35 36 40 43 45 46 47 48 49 50 51 54 56 57 58 59 60 61 62 68 70 71 72 73 74 76 77 78 79 80 81 83 84 85 86 87 89 92 93 94 96 100 107 108 110 111 115 116 117 118 119 120 121 123 124 129 130 131 132 135 145 146 147 148
Primary Contact: Charles A. Peck, M.D., Interim President and Chief Executive Officer
CFO: Wendy J. Cook, Senior Vice President and Chief Financial Officer
CMO: James L. Moore, M.D., Senior Vice President and Chief Medical Officer
CIO: Mike Koehler, Interim Chief Information Officer
CHR: Robert D. Finch, Vice President Human Resources
CNO: Lori Giles, Interim Chief Nursing Officer
Web address: www.armc.org
**Control:** Other not–for–profit (including NFP Corporation) **Service:** General Medical and Surgical

**Staffed Beds:** 343 **Admissions:** 18512 **Census:** 230 **Outpatient Visits:** 315243 **Births:** 2538 **Total Expense ($000):** 377395 **Payroll Expense ($000):** 149283 **Personnel:** 2374

☐ **LANDMARK HOSPITAL OF ATHENS (112017)**, 775 Sunset Drive, Zip 30606–2211; tel. 706/425–1500 **A**1 10 **F**1 3 29 30 45 84 119 130 148 **S** Landmark Hospitals, Cape Girardeau, MO
Primary Contact: Tommy Jackson, Chief Executive Officer
Web address: www.landmarkhospitals.com
**Control:** Individual, Investor–owned, for–profit **Service:** Long–Term Acute Care hospital

**Staffed Beds:** 42 **Admissions:** 541 **Census:** 33 **Outpatient Visits:** 0 **Births:** 0 **Personnel:** 113

⊠ △ **ST. MARY'S HEALTH CARE SYSTEM (110006)**, 1230 Baxter Street, Zip 30606–3791; tel. 706/389–3000 **A**1 3 7 9 10 **F**3 11 12 13 15 18 19 20 22 26 28 29 30 34 35 40 41 45 46 48 49 50 51 53 54 57 58 59 61 62 63 64 68 70 72 74 75 76 77 79 80 81 83 84 85 87 90 93 94 97 107 110 111 114 115 119 126 129 130 131 132 135 141 145 146 147 148 **P**5 **S** Trinity Health, Livonia, MI
Primary Contact: Donald McKenna, President and Chief Executive Officer
CFO: Marty Hutson, Chief Financial Officer
CMO: Bruce Middendorf, M.D., Chief Medical Officer
CIO: Kerry Vaughn, Chief Information Officer
CHR: Jeff English, Vice President Human Resources
CNO: Nina Evans, R.N., Vice President and Chief Nursing Officer
Web address: www.stmarysathens.com
**Control:** Church–operated, Nongovernment, not–for profit **Service:** General Medical and Surgical

**Staffed Beds:** 179 **Admissions:** 8443 **Census:** 107 **Outpatient Visits:** 168114 **Births:** 1349 **Total Expense ($000):** 158659 **Payroll Expense ($000):** 57772 **Personnel:** 1055

## ATLANTA—Fulton and De Kalb County

☐ **ANCHOR HOSPITAL (114032)**, 5454 Yorktowne Drive, Zip 30349–5317; tel. 770/991–6044 **A**1 9 10 **F**4 98 99 103 105 130 **S** Universal Health Services, Inc., King of Prussia, PA
Primary Contact: Jason McPherson, Chief Executive Officer and Managing Director
CFO: Pamela Whitehead, Chief Financial Officer
CMO: Shailesh Patel, M.D., Medical Director
CIO: Michael Delpleache, Specialist Information Technology
CHR: Ebuni McFall–Roberts, Director Human Resources
CNO: Kim Butts, System Nurse Executive
Web address: www.anchorhospital.com
**Control:** Corporation, Investor–owned, for–profit **Service:** Psychiatric

**Staffed Beds:** 122 **Admissions:** 4203 **Census:** 106 **Outpatient Visits:** 13356 **Births:** 0 **Total Expense ($000):** 19597 **Payroll Expense ($000):** 8850 **Personnel:** 245

**GA**

---

**Hospital, Medicare Provider Number, Address, Telephone, Approval, Facility, and Physician Codes, Health Care System**

★ American Hospital Association (AHA) membership
☐ The Joint Commission accreditation
◇ Healthcare Facilities Accreditation Program
◇ DNV Healthcare Inc. accreditation
⇑ Center for Improvement in Healthcare Quality Accreditation
△ Commission on Accreditation of Rehabilitation Facilities (CARF) accreditation

⊞ **ATLANTA MEDICAL CENTER (110115)**, 303 Parkway Drive N.E.,
Zip 30312–1212; tel. 404/265–4000, (Includes ATLANTA MEDICAL CENTER –
SOUTH CAMPUS, 1170 Cleveland Avenue, Zip 30344–3665; tel. 404/466–1170;
Daniel Jackson, Chief Administrative Officer), (Nonreporting) **A**1 2 3 5 8 9 10
**S** TENET Healthcare Corporation, Dallas, TX
Primary Contact: Thomas E. Casaday, Chief Executive Officer
COO: Douglas Brewer, Chief Operating Officer
CFO: Jay M. Pennisson, Chief Financial Officer
CMO: Albert Barrocas, M.D., Chief Medical Officer
CIO: Maryland McCarty, Director Information Systems
CHR: Jimmy Duncan, Chief Human Resources Officer
CNO: Patricia Feilmeier, R.N., Chief Nurse Executive
Web address: www.atlantamedcenter.com
**Control:** Corporation, Investor–owned, for–profit **Service:** General Medical and
Surgical

**Staffed Beds:** 403

☐ △ **CHILDREN'S HEALTHCARE OF ATLANTA (113301)**, 1600 Tullie Circle,
N.E., Zip 30329–2303; tel. 404/785–7000, (Includes CHILDREN'S HEALTHCARE
OF ATLANTA AT EGLESTON, 1600 Tullie Circle, Zip 30329; tel. 404/325–6000;
CHILDREN'S HEALTHCARE OF ATLANTA AT HUGHES SPALDING, 35 Jesse Hill Jr.
Drive, S.E., Zip 30303–3032; tel. 404/785–9500; CHILDREN'S HEALTHCARE OF
ATLANTA AT SCOTTISH RITE, 1001 Johnson Ferry Road N.E., Zip 30342–1600;
tel. 404/256–5252), (Nonreporting) **A**1 3 5 7 8 9 10
Primary Contact: Donna W. Hyland, President and Chief Executive Officer
COO: Carolyn Kenny, Executive Vice President Clinical Care
CFO: Ruth Fowler, Senior Vice President and Chief Financial Officer
CMO: Daniel Salinas, M.D., Senior Vice President and Chief Medical Officer
CIO: Allana Cummings, Chief Information Officer
CHR: Linda Matzigkeit, Senior Vice President Human Resources
Web address: www.choa.org
**Control:** Other not–for–profit (including NFP Corporation) **Service:** Children's
general

**Staffed Beds:** 496

⊞ **EMORY REHABILITATION HOSPITAL (113031)**, 1441 Clifton Road N.E.,
Zip 30322–1004; tel. 404/712–5512, (Nonreporting) **A**1 10 **S** Emory Healthcare,
Atlanta, GA
Primary Contact: Michael Eric Garrard, Chief Executive Officer
CMO: S. Byron Milton, M.D., Medical Director
CHR: Janine Diaz, Human Resources Manager
CNO: Deborah Almauhy, R.N., Chief Nursing Officer
Web address: www.emoryhealthcare.org/rehabilitation
**Control:** Corporation, Investor–owned, for–profit **Service:** Rehabilitation

**Staffed Beds:** 56

⊞ **EMORY SAINT JOSEPH'S HOSPITAL OF ATLANTA (110082)**, 5665
Peachtree Dunwoody Road N.E., Zip 30342–1701; tel. 678/843–7001 **A**1 2 3 9
10 **F**3 11 15 17 18 20 22 24 26 28 29 30 31 34 35 37 40 44 45 46 47 49
50 51 53 54 55 57 58 59 60 64 68 70 71 74 75 77 78 79 81 82 84 85 87
93 107 108 110 111 114 115 116 117 118 119 120 121 123 124 126 130
132 135 145 146 147 148 **P**6 **S** Emory Healthcare, Atlanta, GA
Primary Contact: Craig McCoy, Chief Executive Officer
CFO: Kevin Brenan, Chief Financial Officer
CMO: Paul Scheinberg, M.D., Chief of Staff
CIO: Dedra Cantrell, Chief Information Officer
CHR: Audra Farish, Vice President Human Resources
Web address: www.stjosephsatlanta.org
**Control:** Other not–for–profit (including NFP Corporation) **Service:** General
Medical and Surgical

**Staffed Beds:** 250 **Admissions:** 13486 **Census:** 182 **Outpatient Visits:**
110200 **Births:** 0 **Total Expense ($000):** 303239 **Payroll Expense ($000):**
92188 **Personnel:** 1474

⊞ **EMORY UNIVERSITY HOSPITAL (110010)**, 1364 Clifton Road N.E.,
Zip 30322; tel. 404/712–2000, (Includes EMORY UNIVERSITY ORTHOPAEDIC
AND SPINE HOSPITAL, 1455 Montreal Road, Tucker, Zip 30084;
tel. 404/251–3600; June Conner, R.N., Chief Operating Officer; EMORY WESLEY
WOODS GERIATRIC HOSPITAL, 1821 Clifton Road N.E., Atlanta, Zip 30329–4021;
tel. 404/728–6200; Jennifer Schuck, Associate Administrator) **A**1 2 3 5 8 9 10
**F**3 11 12 15 17 18 20 22 24 26 28 29 30 31 34 35 36 38 39 40 44 45 46
47 48 49 50 55 56 57 58 59 60 61 63 64 68 70 74 75 77 78 79 80 81 82
84 85 86 87 93 98 100 101 102 103 104 105 107 108 109 110 111 114
115 116 117 118 119 120 121 123 124 126 129 130 131 132 135 136 137
138 139 140 141 142 145 146 147 148 **P**6 **S** Emory Healthcare, Atlanta, GA
Primary Contact: Bryce Gartland, Chief Executive Officer
CFO: Greg E. Anderson, Chief Financial Officer, Emory Health System
CMO: Ira Horowitz, M.D., Chief Medical Officer
CIO: Dedra Cantrell, Chief Information Officer
CHR: Mary Beth Allen, Vice President Human Resources
CNO: Nancye R. Feistritzer, Chief Nursing Officer
Web address: www.emoryhealthcare.org
**Control:** Other not–for–profit (including NFP Corporation) **Service:** General
Medical and Surgical

**Staffed Beds:** 550 **Admissions:** 24393 **Census:** 440 **Outpatient Visits:**
158506 **Births:** 0 **Total Expense ($000):** 712761 **Payroll Expense ($000):**
222514 **Personnel:** 3601

⊞ **EMORY UNIVERSITY HOSPITAL MIDTOWN (110078)**, 550 Peachtree Street
N.E., Zip 30308–2247; tel. 404/686–4411 **A**1 2 3 5 8 9 10 **F**3 11 12 13 15
17 18 20 22 24 26 28 29 30 31 34 35 36 38 40 44 45 46 47 48 49 50 51
52 55 57 58 59 60 61 63 64 68 70 72 73 74 75 76 77 78 79 81 82 84 85
86 87 92 93 100 102 104 107 108 110 111 114 115 116 117 118 119 120
121 123 124 126 130 131 132 135 141 146 147 148 **P**6 **S** Emory
Healthcare, Atlanta, GA
Primary Contact: Daniel Owens, Chief Executive Officer
CMO: James P. Steinberg, M.D., Chief Medical Officer
CIO: Dedra Cantrell, Chief Information Officer
CHR: Dallis Howard–Crow, Chief Human Resources Officer
Web address: www.emoryhealthcare.org
**Control:** Other not–for–profit (including NFP Corporation) **Service:** General
Medical and Surgical

**Staffed Beds:** 458 **Admissions:** 20676 **Census:** 345 **Outpatient Visits:**
191919 **Births:** 3596 **Total Expense ($000):** 560944 **Payroll Expense**
**($000):** 165099 **Personnel:** 2558

⊞ **GRADY MEMORIAL HOSPITAL (110079)**, 80 Jesse Hill Jr. Drive S.E.,
Zip 30303–3031, Mailing Address: P.O. Box 26189, Zip 30303–0004;
tel. 404/616–1000, (Total facility includes 261 beds in nursing home–type unit)
**A**1 2 3 5 8 9 10 **F**2 3 7 8 13 15 16 17 18 20 22 24 26 29 30 31 34 35 39
40 43 45 46 47 49 50 51 52 53 54 55 56 57 58 59 60 61 62 63 64 65 66
68 70 72 73 74 75 76 77 78 79 80 81 82 84 85 86 87 93 94 97 98 100
101 102 103 104 105 107 108 109 110 111 112 113 114 115 116 117 118
119 120 121 128 129 130 132 134 135 143 144 146 147 148
Primary Contact: John M. Haupert, FACHE, Chief Executive Officer
COO: Christopher R. Mosley, FACHE, Chief Operating Officer
CFO: Mark Meyer, Chief Financial Officer
CMO: Curtis Lewis, M.D., Chief of Staff
CIO: Deborah Cancilla, Chief Information Officer
CHR: Larry A. Callahan, Senior Vice President Human Resources
CNO: Rhonda A. Scott, Ph.D., Chief Nursing Officer and Executive Vice President
Web address: www.gradyhealthsystem.org
**Control:** Other not–for–profit (including NFP Corporation) **Service:** General
Medical and Surgical

**Staffed Beds:** 896 **Admissions:** 27989 **Census:** 719 **Outpatient Visits:**
604739 **Births:** 3135 **Total Expense ($000):** 827697 **Payroll Expense**
**($000):** 309797 **Personnel:** 4736

⊞ **KINDRED HOSPITAL–ATLANTA (112004)**, 705 Juniper Street N.E.,
Zip 30308–1307; tel. 404/873–2871, (Nonreporting) **A**1 9 10 **S** Kindred
Healthcare, Louisville, KY
Primary Contact: Robert Russell, Chief Executive Officer
CFO: Michael Nelson, Chief Financial Officer
CMO: David N. DeRuyter, M.D., President Medical Staff
CHR: Armetria Gibson, Human Resources Generalist
CNO: Annette Harrilson, Chief Clinical Officer
Web address: www.kindredatlanta.com/
**Control:** Partnership, Investor–owned, for–profit **Service:** Long–Term Acute Care
hospital

**Staffed Beds:** 70

⊞ **NORTHSIDE HOSPITAL (110161)**, 1000 Johnson Ferry Road N.E.,
Zip 30342–1611; tel. 404/851–8000 **A**1 2 3 9 10 **F**3 5 8 11 12 13 15 17 18
20 22 26 28 29 30 31 34 35 37 40 44 45 46 47 48 49 50 54 55 57 58 59
60 64 68 70 71 72 73 74 75 76 77 78 79 80 81 82 84 85 86 87 93 100
104 105 107 108 110 111 114 115 117 118 119 120 121 123 124 126 129
130 132 135 136 145 146 147 148 **S** Northside Healthcare System,
Atlanta, GA
Primary Contact: Robert Quattrocchi, President and Chief Executive Officer
CFO: Debbie Mitcham, Chief Financial Officer
CIO: Tina Wakim, Vice President Information
Web address: www.northside.com
**Control:** Other not–for–profit (including NFP Corporation) **Service:** General
Medical and Surgical

**Staffed Beds:** 587 **Admissions:** 35492 **Census:** 459 **Outpatient Visits:**
710567 **Births:** 15175 **Total Expense ($000):** 1416822 **Payroll Expense**
**($000):** 417101 **Personnel:** 7157

☐ **PEACHFORD BEHAVIORAL HEALTH SYSTEM (114010)**, 2151 Peachford
Road, Zip 30338–6599; tel. 770/455–3200, (Nonreporting) **A**1 9 10 **S** Universal
Health Services, Inc., King of Prussia, PA
Primary Contact: Matthew Crouch, Chief Executive Officer and Managing Director
COO: Sharon Stackhouse, Assistant Administrator and Director Risk Management
CFO: April Hughes, Chief Financial Officer
CMO: Asaf Aleem, M.D., Medical Director
CHR: Clay Boyles, Director Human Resources
Web address: www.peachfordhospital.com
**Control:** Corporation, Investor–owned, for–profit **Service:** Psychiatric

**Staffed Beds:** 246

GA

*Many Facility Codes have changed. Please refer to the AHA Guide Code Chart.*    © 2015 AHA Guide

★ ◇ **PIEDMONT HOSPITAL (110083)**, 1968 Peachtree Road N.W., Zip 30309–1281; tel. 404/605–5000 **A**2 3 5 9 10 21 **F**3 8 11 12 13 15 17 18 20 22 24 26 28 29 30 31 34 35 40 45 46 47 48 49 50 51 53 54 55 56 57 58 59 60 63 64 65 68 70 72 73 74 75 76 77 78 79 81 82 83 84 85 86 87 93 107 110 111 114 115 116 117 118 119 120 121 123 124 126 129 130 131 132 135 137 138 139 142 143 146 147 148 **S** Piedmont Healthcare, Atlanta, GA
Primary Contact: Leslie A. Donahue, President and Chief Executive Officer
COO: Ed Lovern, Chief Operating Officer
CFO: Thomas Arnold, Chief Financial Officer
CMO: Mark Cohen, M.D., Chief Medical Officer
CHR: Rick Springfield, Vice President Human Resources
CNO: Kelly Hulsey, Chief Nursing Officer
Web address: www.piedmonthospital.org
**Control:** Other not–for–profit (including NFP Corporation) **Service:** General Medical and Surgical

**Staffed Beds:** 510 **Admissions:** 27649 **Census:** 414 **Outpatient Visits:** 298630 **Births:** 3538

**SAINT JOSEPH'S HOSPITAL OF ATLANTA** See Emory Saint Joseph's Hospital of Atlanta

⊠ **SELECT SPECIALTY HOSPITAL – NORTHEAST ATLANTA (112005)**, 1821 Clifton Road N.E., 2nd Floor, Zip 30329–4021; tel. 404/728–6200, (Nonreporting) **A**1 10 **S** Select Medical Corporation, Mechanicsburg, PA
Primary Contact: Matthew Paul Pearson, Chief Executive Officer
CFO: Theodore Saunders, Assistant Controller
CMO: Jeffrey Mikell, M.D., Chief Medical Officer
CIO: Vicky Goziah, Software Administrator
CNO: Annette Branan, Chief Nursing Officer and Vice President Patient Care Services
Web address: www.selectspecialtyhospitals.com/
**Control:** Corporation, Investor–owned, for–profit **Service:** Long–Term Acute Care hospital

**Staffed Beds:** 18

⊠ **SELECT SPECIALTY HOSPITAL–ATLANTA (112009)**, 550 Peachtree Street N.E., Zip 30308–2247; tel. 404/815–0348, (Nonreporting) **A**1 9 10 **S** Select Medical Corporation, Mechanicsburg, PA
Primary Contact: Dwayne Hooks, Jr., R.N., Chief Executive Officer
Web address: www.selectspecialtyhospitals.com/company/locations/atlanta.aspx
**Control:** Corporation, Investor–owned, for–profit **Service:** Long–Term Acute Care hospital

**Staffed Beds:** 30

☐ **SHEPHERD CENTER (112003)**, 2020 Peachtree Road N.W., Zip 30309–1465; tel. 404/352–2020, (Nonreporting) **A**1 3 5 9 10
Primary Contact: Gary R. Ulicny, Ph.D., President and Chief Executive Officer
COO: Sarah Morrison, Vice President Clinical Services
CFO: Stephen B. Holleman, Chief Financial Officer
CMO: Donald P. Leslie, M.D., Medical Director
CIO: Michael L. Jones, Ph.D., Chief Information Officer
CHR: Betsy Fox, Director Human Resources
CNO: Tamara King, R.N., Chief Nurse Executive
Web address: www.shepherd.org
**Control:** Other not–for–profit (including NFP Corporation) **Service:** Long–Term Acute Care hospital

**Staffed Beds:** 100

**WESLEY WOODS GERIATRIC HOSPITAL OF EMORY UNIVERSITY** See Emory Wesley Woods Geriatric Hospital

**WESLEY WOODS LONG TERM CARE HOSPITAL** See Select Specialty Hospital – Northeast Atlanta

### AUGUSTA—Richmond County

⊠ △ **CHARLIE NORWOOD VETERANS AFFAIRS MEDICAL CENTER**, 1 Freedom Way, Zip 30904–6285; tel. 706/733–0188, (Nonreporting) **A**1 2 3 5 7 8 **S** Department of Veterans Affairs, Washington, DC
Primary Contact: Maria R. Andrews, Director
COO: John D. Stenger, Acting Associate Director
CFO: Earline Corder, Chief Fiscal
CIO: Sandy Williford, Chief Health Information Management and Revenue Administration
CHR: Roger W. Buterbaugh, Chief Human Resources Officer
CNO: Michelle Cox–Henley, R.N., Associate Director for Patient and Nursing Services
Web address: www.augusta.va.gov/
**Control:** Veterans Affairs, Government, federal **Service:** General Medical and Surgical

**Staffed Beds:** 338

⊠ **DOCTORS HOSPITAL (110177)**, 3651 Wheeler Road, Zip 30909–6426; tel. 706/651–3232, (Nonreporting) **A**1 2 3 5 9 10 **S** HCA, Nashville, TN
Primary Contact: Douglas Welch, Chief Executive Officer
CIO: Dona Hornung, Director Information and Technology Services
Web address: www.doctors–hospital.net
**Control:** Corporation, Investor–owned, for–profit **Service:** General Medical and Surgical

**Staffed Beds:** 307

☐ **EAST CENTRAL REGIONAL HOSPITAL (114029)**, 3405 Mike Padgett Highway, Zip 30906–3897; tel. 706/790–2011, (Includes EAST CENTRAL REGIONAL HOSPITAL, 100 Myrtle Boulevard, Gracewood, Zip 30812–1299; tel. 706/790–2011), (Total facility includes 250 beds in nursing home–type unit) **A**1 3 5 10 **F**29 34 38 39 59 65 67 75 77 86 87 96 98 101 128 130 132 143 **P**6
Primary Contact: Paul Bruck, Administrator
CFO: Candace Walker, Chief Financial Officer
Web address: www.dbhdd.ga.gov
**Control:** State–Government, nonfederal **Service:** Psychiatric

**Staffed Beds:** 467 **Admissions:** 791 **Census:** 345 **Outpatient Visits:** 0 **Births:** 0 **Total Expense ($000):** 89504 **Payroll Expense ($000):** 33718 **Personnel:** 1239

⊠ **GEORGIA REGENTS MEDICAL CENTER (110034)**, 1120 15th Street, Zip 30912–0004; tel. 706/721–0211, (Includes CHILDREN'S HOSPITAL OF GEORGIA, 1446 Harper Street, Zip 30912–0012; tel. 706/721–5437), (Nonreporting) **A**1 2 3 5 8 9 10 13
Primary Contact: Peter Buckley, M.D., Interim Chief Executive Officer
COO: Steven Scott, Chief Operating Officer
CFO: Greg Damron, Vice President Finance and Chief Financial Officer
CMO: William Kanto, M.D., Senior Vice President and Chief Medical Officer
CIO: Charles Enicks, Chief Information Officer
CHR: Susan Norton, Vice President Human Resources
CNO: Laura E. Brower, R.N., Chief Nursing Officer
Web address: www.grhealth.org
**Control:** Other not–for–profit (including NFP Corporation) **Service:** General Medical and Surgical

**Staffed Beds:** 460

⊠ **HEALTHSOUTH WALTON REHABILITATION HOSPITAL (113030)**, 1355 Independence Drive, Zip 30901–1037; tel. 706/724–7746, (Nonreporting) **A**1 3 5 9 10 **S** HEALTHSOUTH Corporation, Birmingham, AL
Primary Contact: Eric Crossan, Chief Executive Officer
CMO: Pamela Salazar, M.D., Chief of Staff
CIO: Ann Keller, Supervisor Health Information Management
CHR: Volante Henderson, Director Human Resources
CNO: Lynn Beaulieu, R.N., Chief Nursing Officer
Web address: www.healthsouthwalton.com/
**Control:** Corporation, Investor–owned, for–profit **Service:** Rehabilitation

**Staffed Beds:** 58

**MEDICAL COLLEGE OF GEORGIA HEALTH** See Georgia Regents Medical Center

⊠ **SELECT SPECIALTY HOSPITAL–AUGUSTA (112013)**, 1537 Walton Way, Zip 30904–3764; tel. 706/731–1200, (Nonreporting) **A**1 9 10 **S** Select Medical Corporation, Mechanicsburg, PA
Primary Contact: Curtis L. Roberts, Chief Executive Officer
CHR: Terrie Richardson, Coordinator Human Resources
CNO: Kim Pippin, Chief Nursing Officer
Web address: www.augusta.selectspecialtyhospitals.com
**Control:** Corporation, Investor–owned, for–profit **Service:** Long–Term Acute Care hospital

**Staffed Beds:** 80

⊠ **TRINITY HOSPITAL OF AUGUSTA (110039)**, 2260 Wrightsboro Road, Zip 30904–4726; tel. 706/481–7000, (Nonreporting) **A**1 3 9 10 **S** Community Health Systems, Inc., Franklin, TN
Primary Contact: Jason Studley, Chief Executive Officer
CFO: Kevin Cargill, Chief Financial Officer
CMO: Niti Carlson, M.D., Chief of Staff
CIO: Charlotte Choate, Director Information Systems
CHR: Diana Maxson, Director Human Resources
CNO: Debbie Spells–Wilson, R.N., Chief Nursing Officer
Web address: www.trinityofaugusta.com
**Control:** Corporation, Investor–owned, for–profit **Service:** General Medical and Surgical

**Staffed Beds:** 105

GA

---

**Hospital, Medicare Provider Number, Address, Telephone, Approval, Facility, and Physician Codes, Health Care System**

★ American Hospital Association (AHA) membership ☐ The Joint Commission accreditation ◯ Healthcare Facilities Accreditation Program ◇ DNV Healthcare Inc. accreditation ⇑ Center for Improvement in Healthcare Quality Accreditation △ Commission on Accreditation of Rehabilitation Facilities (CARF) accreditation

✠ **UNIVERSITY HOSPITAL (110028)**, 1350 Walton Way, Zip 30901–2629; tel. 706/722–9011 **A**1 2 3 5 9 10 **F**3 12 13 15 17 18 20 22 24 26 28 29 30 31 34 35 37 38 40 41 44 48 49 50 54 56 57 59 60 62 63 64 68 70 72 73 74 75 76 77 78 79 80 81 82 83 84 85 86 87 89 93 97 100 107 108 110 111 114 115 116 117 118 119 126 129 130 132 134 135 144 146 147 148 **P**8 **S** University Health Care System, Augusta, GA
Primary Contact: James R. Davis, Chief Executive Officer
CFO: David Belkoski, Executive Vice President and Chief Financial Officer
CMO: William L. Farr, M.D., Chief Medical Officer
CIO: Shirley Gabriel, Vice President and Chief Information Officer
CHR: Laurie Ott, Vice President Human Resources and President University Health Care Foundation
CNO: Lynda Watts, R.N., Vice President Patient Care Services
Web address: www.universityhealth.org
**Control:** Other not–for–profit (including NFP Corporation) **Service:** General Medical and Surgical

**Staffed Beds:** 477 **Admissions:** 22580 **Census:** 314 **Outpatient Visits:** 449599 **Births:** 3103 **Total Expense ($000):** 377434 **Payroll Expense ($000):** 141917 **Personnel:** 2327

**VETERANS AFFAIRS MEDICAL CENTER** See Charlie Norwood Veterans Affairs Medical Center

**WALTON REHABILITATION HOSPITAL** See HEALTHSOUTH Walton Rehabilitation Hospital

### AUSTELL—Cobb County

✠ △ **WELLSTAR COBB HOSPITAL (110143)**, 3950 Austell Road, Zip 30106–1121; tel. 770/732–4000 **A**1 2 3 7 9 10 **F**3 4 11 13 15 16 17 18 20 22 26 28 29 30 31 37 38 40 41 44 45 48 49 50 51 53 54 55 58 59 60 61 62 64 66 68 70 72 73 74 76 77 78 79 80 81 82 84 85 86 87 90 93 94 96 98 100 101 102 103 104 105 107 108 110 111 114 115 118 119 126 130 132 135 141 146 147 148 **P**5 6 **S** WellStar Health System, Marietta, GA
Primary Contact: Kem Mullins, FACHE, Senior Vice President and Hospital President
COO: Kevin Deter, Chief Operating Officer
CFO: Darold Etheridge, Vice President and Chief Financial Officer
CMO: Thomas McNamara, D.O., Vice President Medical Affairs
CIO: Jonathan B. Morris, M.D., Senior Vice President and Chief Information Officer
CHR: Joseph W. Herzberg, Assistant Vice President Human Resources
Web address: www.wellstar.org
**Control:** Other not–for–profit (including NFP Corporation) **Service:** General Medical and Surgical

**Staffed Beds:** 362 **Admissions:** 20099 **Census:** 267 **Outpatient Visits:** 221506 **Births:** 3529 **Personnel:** 1918

### BAINBRIDGE—Decatur County

◇ **MEMORIAL HOSPITAL AND MANOR (110132)**, 1500 East Shotwell Street, Zip 39819–4256; tel. 229/246–3500, (Nonreporting) **A**9 10 21
Primary Contact: William J. Walker, Jr., Chief Executive Officer
COO: Lee Harris, Assistant Administrator Support Services
CFO: Karen Faircloth, Chief Financial Officer
CMO: Shawn Surratt, M.D., Chief of Staff
CIO: Nelda Moore, Director Data Processing
CHR: Angel Sykes, Director Human Resources
CNO: Cynthia Vickers, R.N., Assistant Administrator for Nursing Services
Web address: www.mh–m.org
**Control:** Hospital district or authority, Government, nonfederal **Service:** General Medical and Surgical

**Staffed Beds:** 80

### BAXLEY—Appling County

◇ **APPLING HEALTHCARE SYSTEM (110071)**, 163 East Tollison Street, Zip 31513–0120; tel. 912/367–9841, (Total facility includes 101 beds in nursing home–type unit) **A**9 10 20 21 **F**1 7 8 11 15 29 30 40 47 56 60 68 70 75 76 77 80 81 91 98 103 107 111 119 127 133 143 146 147 148 **P**6
Primary Contact: Peyton A. Smith, Chief Executive Officer
COO: Judy M. Long, R.N., Chief Nursing Officer and Chief Operating Officer
CFO: Raymond J. Leadbetter, Jr., Revenue Cycle Consultant
CMO: Garland Martin, M.D., Chief of Staff
CIO: Gary Gower, Chief Information Officer
CHR: Carla McLendon, Director Human Resources
CNO: Judy M. Long, R.N., Chief Nursing Officer and Chief Operating Officer
Web address: www.appling–hospital.org
**Control:** County–Government, nonfederal **Service:** General Medical and Surgical

**Staffed Beds:** 150 **Admissions:** 1629 **Census:** 128 **Outpatient Visits:** 29820 **Births:** 95 **Total Expense ($000):** 33242 **Payroll Expense ($000):** 14909 **Personnel:** 378

### BLAIRSVILLE—Union County

✠ **UNION GENERAL HOSPITAL (110051)**, 35 Hospital Road, Zip 30512–3139; tel. 706/745–2111, (Nonreporting) **A**1 9 10 20 **S** Union General Hospital, Inc., Blairsville, GA
Primary Contact: Mike Gowder, Chief Executive Officer
COO: Lewis Kelley, Chief Operating Officer
CFO: Stephanie L. Fletcher, CPA, Chief Financial Officer
CMO: Andre Schaeffer, M.D., Chief of Staff
CIO: Mike Johnston, Director Facilities Operations
CHR: Kathy Hood, Administrative Assistant Human Resources
CNO: Julia Barnett, Chief Nursing Officer
Web address: www.uniongeneralhospital.com
**Control:** Hospital district or authority, Government, nonfederal **Service:** General Medical and Surgical

**Staffed Beds:** 195

### BLAKELY—Early County

★ ◇ **PIONEER COMMUNITY HOSPITAL OF EARLY (111314)**, 11740 Columbia Street, Zip 39823–2574; tel. 229/723–4241, (Nonreporting) **A**9 10 18 21 **S** Pioneer Health Services, Magee, MS
Primary Contact: Allen J. Gamble, Chief Executive Officer
Web address: www.pchearly.com
**Control:** Corporation, Investor–owned, for–profit **Service:** General Medical and Surgical

**Staffed Beds:** 25

### BLUE RIDGE—Fannin County

✠ **FANNIN REGIONAL HOSPITAL (110189)**, 2855 Old Highway 5, Zip 30513–6248; tel. 706/632–3711, (Nonreporting) **A**1 9 10 **S** Community Health Systems, Inc., Franklin, TN
Primary Contact: David S. Sanders, Chief Executive Officer
CFO: Phillip Fouts, Chief Financial Officer
CIO: Timothy Snider, Manager Information Systems
CHR: Terrasina Ensley, Director Human Resources
CNO: Jason L. Jones, R.N., Chief Nursing Officer
Web address: www.fanninregionalhospital.com
**Control:** Corporation, Investor–owned, for–profit **Service:** General Medical and Surgical

**Staffed Beds:** 50

### BRASELTON—Hall County

**NORTHEAST GEORGIA MEDICAL CENTER BRASELTON**, 1400 River Place, Zip 30517–5600; tel. 770/219–9000, (Nonreporting)
Primary Contact: Anthony Williamson, President
Web address: www.nghs.com/locations/braselton
**Control:** Other not–for–profit (including NFP Corporation) **Service:** General Medical and Surgical

**Staffed Beds:** 773

### BREMEN—Haralson County

✠ **HIGGINS GENERAL HOSPITAL (111320)**, 200 Allen Memorial Drive, Zip 30110–2012; tel. 770/824–2000, (Nonreporting) **A**1 9 10 18 **S** Tanner Health System, Carrollton, GA
Primary Contact: Michael D. Alexander, MS, Administrator
CIO: Dianne Reed, Director Information Systems
CHR: Vivian C. Barr, Director Human Resources
Web address: www.tanner.org/Main/HigginsGeneralHospitalBremen.aspx
**Control:** Other not–for–profit (including NFP Corporation) **Service:** General Medical and Surgical

**Staffed Beds:** 25

### BRUNSWICK—Glynn County

✠ **SOUTHEAST GEORGIA HEALTH SYSTEM BRUNSWICK CAMPUS (110025)**, 2415 Parkwood Drive, Zip 31520–4722, Mailing Address: P.O. Box 1518, Zip 31521–1518; tel. 912/466–7000, (Total facility includes 220 beds in nursing home–type unit) **A**1 2 9 10 **F**3 6 11 12 13 15 17 18 20 22 26 28 29 30 31 34 35 37 40 44 45 46 47 48 49 50 51 54 57 59 64 66 68 70 71 74 75 76 77 78 79 81 84 85 86 87 89 91 93 94 96 100 107 108 110 111 114 115 117 119 120 121 124 126 129 131 132 135 144 146 147 148 **P**5 **S** Southeast Georgia Health System, Brunswick, GA
Primary Contact: Michael D. Scherneck, Interim Chief Executive Officer
CFO: Michael D. Scherneck, Executive Vice President and Chief Financial Officer
CIO: Chuck Bumgardner, Director Information Systems
CHR: Patrick D. Ebri, Ph.D., Vice President, Human Resources
CNO: Elizabeth Gunn, R.N., Vice President, Patient Care Services
Web address: www.sghs.org
**Control:** Hospital district or authority, Government, nonfederal **Service:** General Medical and Surgical

**Staffed Beds:** 469 **Admissions:** 11433 **Census:** 373 **Outpatient Visits:** 217560 **Births:** 1291 **Total Expense ($000):** 298166 **Payroll Expense ($000):** 128927 **Personnel:** 1417

*Many Facility Codes have changed. Please refer to the AHA Guide Code Chart.*

© 2015 AHA Guide

**GA**

## CAIRO—Grady County

✠ **GRADY GENERAL HOSPITAL (110121)**, 1155 Fifth Street S.E.,
Zip 39828–3142, Mailing Address: P.O. Box 360, Zip 39828–0360;
tel. 229/377–1150 **A**1 9 10 **F**3 11 13 15 18 28 29 34 35 40 45 50 57 59 68
70 76 79 81 85 86 87 91 92 93 107 110 111 115 119 130 133 146 **P**6
**S** Archbold Medical Center, Thomasville, GA
Primary Contact: Crystal Ramm, Administrator
COO: Jim Carter, Chief Operating Officer
CFO: Skip Hightower, Chief Financial Officer
CIO: Tracy Gray, Chief Information Officer
CHR: Michelle Pledger, Coordinator Human Resources
CNO: Tammy Harlow, Director of Nursing
Web address: www.archbold.org
**Control:** Hospital district or authority, Government, nonfederal **Service:** General
Medical and Surgical

**Staffed Beds:** 48 **Admissions:** 1183 **Census:** 16 **Outpatient Visits:** 47896
**Births:** 170 **Total Expense ($000):** 21141 **Payroll Expense ($000):** 8072
**Personnel:** 134

## CALHOUN—Gordon County

✠ ○ **GORDON HOSPITAL (110023)**, 1035 Red Bud Road, Zip 30701–2082,
Mailing Address: P.O. Box 12938, Zip 30703–7013; tel. 706/629–2895 **A**1 2 9
10 11 19 **F**3 7 11 13 15 18 20 29 30 31 34 35 37 40 46 57 59 62 64 70 75
76 77 78 79 81 82 85 86 87 93 107 108 111 115 119 120 121 123 129
130 135 144 146 147 148 **P**1 6 **S** Adventist Health System Sunbelt Health Care
Corporation, Altamonte Springs, FL
Primary Contact: Pete M. Weber, President and Chief Executive Officer
COO: Brandon M. Nudd, Chief Operating Officer
CFO: Cory Reeves, Chief Financial Officer
CMO: Will Theus, M.D., Chief of Staff
CHR: Jeni Hasselbrack, Director Human Resources
CNO: Amy Jordan, Chief Nursing Officer/Vice President of Nursing
Web address: www.gordonhospital.com
**Control:** Church–operated, Nongovernment, not–for profit **Service:** General
Medical and Surgical

**Staffed Beds:** 85 **Admissions:** 4032 **Census:** 43 **Outpatient Visits:** 258888
**Births:** 559 **Total Expense ($000):** 105613 **Payroll Expense ($000):** 43586
**Personnel:** 894

## CAMILLA—Mitchell County

✠ **MITCHELL COUNTY HOSPITAL (111331)**, 90 East Stephens Street,
Zip 31730–1836, Mailing Address: P.O. Box 639, Zip 31730–0639;
tel. 229/336–5284, (Total facility includes 156 beds in nursing home–type unit)
**A**1 9 10 18 **F**3 11 15 18 29 34 35 40 50 57 59 68 75 87 107 110 111 114
119 127 128 130 133 146 **P**6 **S** Archbold Medical Center, Thomasville, GA
Primary Contact: James Womack, Administrator
COO: LaDon Toole, Vice President Network Operations
CFO: Skip Hightower, Senior Vice President and Chief Financial Officer
CMO: Jason Smith, M.D., Chief of Staff
CIO: Tracy Gray, Chief Information Officer
CHR: Vickie County–Teemer, Coordinator Human Resources
CNO: Carla Beasley, Director of Nursing
Web address: www.archbold.org
**Control:** Hospital district or authority, Government, nonfederal **Service:** General
Medical and Surgical

**Staffed Beds:** 181 **Admissions:** 544 **Census:** 168 **Outpatient Visits:** 12262
**Births:** 0 **Total Expense ($000):** 26689 **Payroll Expense ($000):** 11172
**Personnel:** 131

## CANTON—Cherokee County

✠ **NORTHSIDE HOSPITAL–CHEROKEE (110008)**, 201 Hospital Road,
Zip 30114–2408, Mailing Address: P.O. Box 906, Zip 30169–0906;
tel. 770/720–5100 **A**1 9 10 **F**3 8 11 12 13 15 18 20 22 26 28 29 30 31 34
35 40 44 45 49 50 54 57 59 60 64 68 70 73 74 75 76 78 79 81 82 85 86
87 93 107 108 110 111 114 119 120 121 123 126 129 130 132 144 145
146 147 148 **S** Northside Healthcare System, Atlanta, GA
Primary Contact: William M. Hayes, Chief Executive Officer
COO: Mike Patterson, Director of Operations
CFO: Brian Jennette, Chief Financial Officer
CMO: Alexander Kessler, M.D., Chief of Staff
CIO: Bill Dunford, Manager
CHR: Roslyn Roberts, Manager
CNO: Jan Johnson, R.N., Chief Nursing Officer
Web address: www.northside.com
**Control:** Other not–for–profit (including NFP Corporation) **Service:** General
Medical and Surgical

**Staffed Beds:** 88 **Admissions:** 6058 **Census:** 78 **Outpatient Visits:** 97854
**Births:** 1120 **Total Expense ($000):** 155532 **Payroll Expense ($000):**
67777 **Personnel:** 1132

## CARROLLTON—Carroll County

✠ **TANNER MEDICAL CENTER–CARROLLTON (110011)**, 705 Dixie Street,
Zip 30117–3818; tel. 770/836–9666, (Nonreporting) **A**1 2 9 10 **S** Tanner Health
System, Carrollton, GA
COO: James D. Griffith, Chief Operating Officer
CHR: Vivian C. Barr, Director Human Resources
Web address: www.tanner.org
**Control:** Other not–for–profit (including NFP Corporation) **Service:** General
Medical and Surgical

**Staffed Beds:** 201

## CARTERSVILLE—Bartow County

✠ **CARTERSVILLE MEDICAL CENTER (110030)**, 960 Joe Frank Harris Parkway,
Zip 30120–2129; tel. 770/382–1530, (Nonreporting) **A**1 2 9 10 **S** HCA,
Nashville, TN
Primary Contact: Keith Sandlin, Chief Executive Officer
COO: Lori Rakes, Chief Operating Officer
Web address: www.cartersvillemedical.com
**Control:** Corporation, Investor–owned, for–profit **Service:** General Medical and
Surgical

**Staffed Beds:** 80

## CEDARTOWN—Polk County

✠ **POLK MEDICAL CENTER (111330)**, 2360 Rockmart Highway,
Zip 30125–6029; tel. 770/748–2500 **A**1 10 18 **F**3 15 28 29 30 34 35 40 50
56 57 59 64 68 75 77 93 103 107 108 110 114 119 129 130 132 133 135
143 146 147 148
Primary Contact: Matt Gorman, Administrator
CFO: Rick Sheerin, Chief Financial Officer
CHR: Jeanna Smith, Administrative Assistant and Human Resources Officer
CNO: Charmaine Thomas, R.N., Chief Nursing Officer
Web address: www.polkhospital.org
**Control:** Hospital district or authority, Government, nonfederal **Service:** General
Medical and Surgical

**Staffed Beds:** 25 **Admissions:** 228 **Census:** 5 **Outpatient Visits:** 31691
**Births:** 0 **Total Expense ($000):** 14031 **Payroll Expense ($000):** 6434
**Personnel:** 110

## CHATSWORTH—Murray County

✠ **MURRAY MEDICAL CENTER (110050)**, 707 Old Dalton Ellijay Road,
Zip 30705–2060, Mailing Address: P.O. Box 1406, Zip 30705–1406;
tel. 706/695–4564 **A**1 9 10 **F**3 7 15 29 40 81 107 111 119 146 **S** Adventist
Health System Sunbelt Health Care Corporation, Altamonte Springs, FL
Primary Contact: Hal Coble, Administrator
CMO: Blaine Minor, M.D., Chief of Staff
CIO: Jose C. Rios, Director Information Services
CHR: Brandy Rymer, Coordinator Human Resources
CNO: Susan Shook, Interim Chief Executive officer
Web address: www.murraymedical.org/
**Control:** Hospital district or authority, Government, nonfederal **Service:** General
Medical and Surgical

**Staffed Beds:** 33 **Admissions:** 369 **Census:** 3 **Outpatient Visits:** 29355
**Births:** 0 **Total Expense ($000):** 11988 **Payroll Expense ($000):** 5979
**Personnel:** 119

## CLAXTON—Evans County

✠ **EVANS MEMORIAL HOSPITAL (110142)**, 200 North River Street,
Zip 30417–1659, Mailing Address: P.O. Box 518, Zip 30417–0518;
tel. 912/739–2611 **A**1 9 10 **F**3 15 29 34 40 45 53 57 59 68 75 81 93 97
107 108 110 119 127 130 133 135 146
Primary Contact: Nikki NeSmith, Interim Chief Operating Officer
CFO: John Wiggins, Chief Financial Officer
CMO: Kyle Parks, M.D., Chief of Staff
CIO: Steve Schmidt, Director Information Systems
CHR: Gina Waters, Director Human Resources
CNO: Nikki NeSmith, Chief Nursing Officer
Web address: www.evansmemorial.org/Pages/default.aspx
**Control:** Hospital district or authority, Government, nonfederal **Service:** General
Medical and Surgical

**Staffed Beds:** 9 **Admissions:** 716 **Census:** 7 **Outpatient Visits:** 30101
**Births:** 0 **Total Expense ($000):** 14769 **Payroll Expense ($000):** 7169
**Personnel:** 141

GA

**Hospital, Medicare Provider Number, Address, Telephone, Approval, Facility, and Physician Codes, Health Care System**

★ American Hospital Association (AHA) membership  ○ Healthcare Facilities Accreditation Program  ⇑ Center for Improvement in Healthcare Quality Accreditation
□ The Joint Commission accreditation  ◇ DNV Healthcare Inc. accreditation  △ Commission on Accreditation of Rehabilitation Facilities (CARF) accreditation

## CLAYTON—Rabun County

**MOUNTAIN LAKES MEDICAL CENTER (111336)**, 196 Ridgecrest Circle, Zip 30525–4111; tel. 706/782–4233, (Nonreporting) **A**9 10 18
Primary Contact: Joseph Forese, Chief Executive Officer
CFO: Jimmy Norman, Chief Financial Officer
CHR: Charles Harbaugh, Director Human Resources
Web address: www.mountainlakesmedicalcenter.com
**Control:** Hospital district or authority, Government, nonfederal **Service:** General Medical and Surgical

**Staffed Beds:** 24

## COCHRAN—Bleckley County

◇ **BLECKLEY MEMORIAL HOSPITAL (111302)**, 145 East Peacock Street, Zip 31014–7846, Mailing Address: P.O. Box 536, Zip 31014–0536; tel. 478/934–6211, (Nonreporting) **A**9 10 18 21
Primary Contact: Nikki Paulk, Chief Executive Officer
Web address: www.bleckleymemorial.com
**Control:** Hospital district or authority, Government, nonfederal **Service:** General Medical and Surgical

**Staffed Beds:** 25

## COLQUITT—Miller County

◇ **MILLER COUNTY HOSPITAL (111305)**, 209 North Cuthbert Street, Zip 39837–3518, Mailing Address: P.O. Box 7, Zip 39837–0007; tel. 229/758–3305, (Total facility includes 163 beds in nursing home–type unit) **A**9 10 18 21 **F**8 29 30 34 35 39 40 44 45 50 56 57 59 64 65 66 68 75 77 81 85 87 93 97 103 104 107 108 114 119 127 128 129 130 133 135 143 146 148
Primary Contact: Robin Rau, Chief Executive Officer
CFO: Jill Brown, Chief Financial Officer
CMO: William Swofford, M.D., Chief of Staff
CIO: Keith Lovering, Information Technician
CHR: Karie Spence, Director Human Resources
CNO: Shawn Whittaker, Chief Nursing Officer
Web address: www.millercountyhospital.com
**Control:** Hospital district or authority, Government, nonfederal **Service:** General Medical and Surgical

**Staffed Beds:** 188 **Admissions:** 633 **Census:** 148 **Outpatient Visits:** 34368 **Births:** 1 **Total Expense ($000):** 25196 **Payroll Expense ($000):** 12852 **Personnel:** 334

## COLUMBUS—Muscogee County

**BRADLEY CENTER OF ST. FRANCIS** See St. Francis Hospital

✠ **COLUMBUS SPECIALTY HOSPITAL (112012)**, 616 19th Street, Zip 31901–1528, Mailing Address: P.O. Box 910, Zip 31902–0910; tel. 706/494–4075 **A**1 9 10 **F**1 3 28 29 130 148
Primary Contact: Robert Saulnier, R.N., MSN, Chief Executive Officer
CFO: William Eckstein, Chief Financial Officer
CHR: Myra Whitley, Director Human Resources
CNO: Carol George, Chief Nursing Officer
Web address: www.columbusspecialtyhospital.net
**Control:** Other not–for–profit (including NFP Corporation) **Service:** Long–Term Acute Care hospital

**Staffed Beds:** 33 **Admissions:** 297 **Census:** 23 **Outpatient Visits:** 0 **Births:** 0 **Total Expense ($000):** 12815 **Payroll Expense ($000):** 4748

**MIDTOWN MEDICAL CENTER WEST**, 616 19th Street, Zip 31901–1528, Mailing Address: P.O. Box 2188, Zip 31902–2188; tel. 706/494–4262, (Nonreporting) **A**9 **S** Columbus Regional Healthcare System, Columbus, GA
Primary Contact: Ryan Chandler, Chief Executive Officer
CMO: Thomas L. Theus, M.D., Chief of Medicine
CIO: Ryan Sanders, Director Information Services
Web address: www.columbusregional.com
**Control:** Other not–for–profit (including NFP Corporation) **Service:** General Medical and Surgical

**Staffed Beds:** 171

**HUGHSTON HOSPITAL** See Northside Medical Center

☐ **NORTHSIDE MEDICAL CENTER (110200)**, 100 Frist Court, Zip 31909–3578, Mailing Address: P.O. Box 7188, Zip 31908–7188; tel. 706/494–2100, (Nonreporting) **A**1 3 9 10 **S** Columbus Regional Healthcare System, Columbus, GA
Primary Contact: Stan Hickson, FACHE, Chief Executive Officer
COO: Michelle Breitfelder, Chief Operating Officer
CFO: Roland Thacker, Chief Financial Officer
CMO: Lyle Norwood, M.D., Chief of Staff
CIO: Douglas Colburn, Chief Information Officer
CHR: Becky Augustyniak, Director Human Resources
Web address: www.columbusregional.com
**Control:** Hospital district or authority, Government, nonfederal **Service:** Orthopedic

**Staffed Beds:** 100

✠ **ST. FRANCIS HOSPITAL (110129)**, 2122 Manchester Expressway, Zip 31904–6878, Mailing Address: P.O. Box 7000, Zip 31908–7000; tel. 706/596–4000, (Includes BRADLEY CENTER OF ST. FRANCIS, 2000 16th Avenue, Zip 31906–0308; tel. 706/320–3700) **A**1 3 9 10 **F**3 10 11 13 15 17 18 20 22 24 26 28 29 30 31 34 35 40 45 46 49 50 51 53 54 56 57 58 59 60 63 64 70 74 75 76 77 78 79 81 85 86 91 92 93 94 98 99 100 101 102 103 104 105 106 107 108 110 111 115 119 126 129 130 131 144 145 146 147 148 **P**6 7
Primary Contact: Kirk G. Wilson, Interim Chief Executive Officer
COO: Kevin Sass, FACHE, Senior Vice President Human Resources, Organization and Cultural Development
CFO: Matthew Moore, Executive Vice President and Chief Integration Officer
CMO: Bobbi Farber, M.D., Chief Medical Officer
CIO: Chuck Christian, Vice President Chief Information Officer
CHR: E. Rick Lowe, FACHE, Operations Support Risk Management and Compliance
CNO: Deborah Bostic, MSN, Senior Vice President Hospital Operations and Chief Nursing Officer
Web address: www.sfhga.com
**Control:** Other not–for–profit (including NFP Corporation) **Service:** General Medical and Surgical

**Staffed Beds:** 329 **Admissions:** 15694 **Census:** 222 **Outpatient Visits:** 170985 **Births:** 1435 **Total Expense ($000):** 254305 **Payroll Expense ($000):** 91570 **Personnel:** 2428

☐ **THE MEDICAL CENTER (110064)**, 710 Center Street, Zip 31901–1527, Mailing Address: P.O. Box 951, Zip 31902–0951; tel. 706/571–1000, (Nonreporting) **A**1 2 3 5 9 10 12 13 **S** Columbus Regional Healthcare System, Columbus, GA
Primary Contact: Ryan Chandler, President and Chief Executive Officer
Web address: www.columbusregional.com
**Control:** Other not–for–profit (including NFP Corporation) **Service:** General Medical and Surgical

**Staffed Beds:** 497

☐ **WEST CENTRAL GEORGIA REGIONAL HOSPITAL (114013)**, 3000 Schatulga Road, Zip 31907–3117, Mailing Address: P.O. Box 12435, Zip 31917–2435; tel. 706/568–5000, (Nonreporting) **A**1 10
Primary Contact: John L. Robertson, Administrator
COO: Larmar Cunningham, Chief Operating Officer
CMO: Abiodun Famakinwa, M.D., Acting Clinical Director
CIO: Ron Buchanan, Director Information Services
CHR: Coreg Burns, Human Resources Lead
Web address: www.wcgrh.org
**Control:** State–Government, nonfederal **Service:** Psychiatric

**Staffed Beds:** 145

## COMMERCE—Jackson County

✠ **NORTHRIDGE MEDICAL CENTER (110040)**, 70 Medical Center Drive, Zip 30529–1078; tel. 706/335–1000, (Total facility includes 167 beds in nursing home–type unit) **A**1 9 10 **F**3 11 15 17 18 29 30 34 40 45 53 56 57 59 70 79 81 82 85 89 90 93 98 103 107 108 110 111 114 119 128 130 133 146 **P**6
Primary Contact: Larry W. Ebert, Jr., Chief Operating Officer and Chief Financial Officer
CFO: Larry W. Ebert, Jr., Chief Operating Officer and Chief Financial Officer
CMO: Narasimhulu Neelagaru, M.D., Chief of Staff
CNO: Maura Cobb, R.N., Chief Nursing Officer
Web address: www.northridgemc.com
**Control:** Corporation, Investor–owned, for–profit **Service:** General Medical and Surgical

**Staffed Beds:** 257 **Admissions:** 1321 **Census:** 173 **Outpatient Visits:** 25231 **Births:** 0 **Total Expense ($000):** 26401 **Payroll Expense ($000):** 11935 **Personnel:** 354

## CONYERS—Rockdale County

✠ **ROCKDALE MEDICAL CENTER (110091)**, 1412 Milstead Avenue N.E., Zip 30012–3877; tel. 770/918–3000 **A**1 5 9 10 **F**3 11 13 15 18 20 28 29 30 34 35 36 40 45 46 47 49 57 59 64 70 72 73 74 75 76 79 81 82 85 86 87 92 93 107 108 110 111 114 115 118 119 126 130 131 132 135 145 146 147 148 **S** LifePoint Health, Brentwood, TN
Primary Contact: Deborah Armstrong, Chief Executive Officer
COO: James Atkins, Chief Operating Officer
CFO: Diane Roth, Chief Financial Officer
CMO: Lisa Gillespie, M.D., Chief Medical Officer
CIO: Gail Waldo, Director Information Technology
CHR: Marianne Freeman, Vice President Human Resources
CNO: Eleanor Post, R.N., Chief Nursing Officer
Web address: www.rockdalemedicalcenter.org
**Control:** Corporation, Investor–owned, for–profit **Service:** General Medical and Surgical

**Staffed Beds:** 138 **Admissions:** 9045 **Census:** 110 **Outpatient Visits:** 116108 **Births:** 1805 **Total Expense ($000):** 120741 **Payroll Expense ($000):** 46705 **Personnel:** 718

*Many Facility Codes have changed. Please refer to the AHA Guide Code Chart.* © 2015 AHA Guide

GA

## CORDELE—Crisp County

✠ **CRISP REGIONAL HOSPITAL (110104)**, 902 North Seventh Street, Zip 31015–3234; tel. 229/276–3100, (Total facility includes 243 beds in nursing home–type unit) **A**1 3 9 10 20 **F**3 10 11 13 15 28 29 30 31 34 35 40 43 44 45 48 50 51 54 56 57 58 59 60 61 62 63 64 65 68 70 75 76 77 78 79 81 84 85 86 87 89 90 93 96 97 107 108 110 111 115 125 127 128 129 132 133 135 144 146 147 148 **P**2 8
Primary Contact: Steven Gautney, Chief Executive Officer
COO: Mary Jim Montgomery, R.N., Chief Operating Officer
CFO: Jessica Y. Carter, Chief Financial Officer
CMO: David Kavtaradze, M.D., Chief of Staff
CHR: George M. Laurin, Interim Director Human Resources
CNO: Marsha L. Mulderig, R.N., Chief Nursing Officer
Web address: www.crispregional.org
**Control:** County–Government, nonfederal **Service:** General Medical and Surgical

> **Staffed Beds:** 316 **Admissions:** 2896 **Census:** 140 **Outpatient Visits:** 88728 **Births:** 318 **Personnel:** 542

## COVINGTON—Newton County

✠ **NEWTON MEDICAL CENTER (110018)**, 5126 Hospital Drive, Zip 30014–2567; tel. 770/786–7053 **A**1 9 10 **F**7 11 12 13 15 18 20 28 29 30 31 34 35 40 49 59 62 64 70 72 74 75 78 79 81 82 85 87 93 97 107 108 111 119 130 131 132 141 142 146 147 148
Primary Contact: James F. Weadick, Administrator and Chief Executive Officer
CFO: Troy Brooks, Assistant Administrator Fiscal Services
CMO: B. Carter Rogers, Chief of Staff
CIO: Brad Collier, Director
CHR: Greg H. Richardson, Assistant Administrator Human Resources
CNO: Patricia A. Waller, R.N., Assistant Administrator Patient Care Services
Web address: www.newtonmedical.com
**Control:** Other not–for–profit (including NFP Corporation) **Service:** General Medical and Surgical

> **Staffed Beds:** 101 **Admissions:** 4765 **Census:** 43 **Outpatient Visits:** 238641 **Births:** 840 **Total Expense ($000):** 81983 **Payroll Expense ($000):** 37004 **Personnel:** 666

## CUMMING—Forsyth County

✠ **NORTHSIDE HOSPITAL–FORSYTH (110005)**, 1200 Northside Forsyth Drive, Zip 30041–7659; tel. 770/844–3200 **A**1 9 10 **F**3 8 11 12 13 15 18 20 22 26 28 29 30 31 34 35 37 40 44 45 48 49 50 54 57 59 60 64 68 70 71 72 73 74 75 76 78 79 81 82 85 86 87 93 107 108 110 111 114 115 117 119 120 121 123 124 126 129 130 132 135 144 145 146 147 148 **S** Northside Healthcare System, Atlanta, GA
Primary Contact: Lynn Jackson, Administrator
CFO: Eric Caldwell, Director Finance
Web address: www.northside.com
**Control:** Other not–for–profit (including NFP Corporation) **Service:** General Medical and Surgical

> **Staffed Beds:** 252 **Admissions:** 13006 **Census:** 184 **Outpatient Visits:** 192024 **Births:** 2863 **Total Expense ($000):** 317319 **Payroll Expense ($000):** 113554 **Personnel:** 2011

## CUTHBERT—Randolph County

★ ◇ **SOUTHWEST GEORGIA REGIONAL MEDICAL CENTER (111300)**, 361 Randolph Street, Zip 39840–6127; tel. 229/732–2181, (Nonreporting) **A**9 10 18 21 **S** Phoebe Putney Health System, Albany, GA
Primary Contact: Kim Gilman, Chief Executive Officer and Chief Nursing Officer
CFO: Brent Rigsby, Chief Financial Officer
CNO: Amy Cason, Chief Executive Officer and Chief Nursing Officer
Web address: www.phoebeputney.com/
**Control:** Hospital district or authority, Government, nonfederal **Service:** General Medical and Surgical

> **Staffed Beds:** 105

## DAHLONEGA—Lumpkin County

☐ **CHESTATEE REGIONAL HOSPITAL (110187)**, 227 Mountain Drive, Zip 30533–1606; tel. 706/864–6136 **A**1 9 10 **F**2 3 15 29 34 49 50 54 56 57 59 64 65 79 81 85 86 87 98 103 105 107 108 110 111 114 119 127 129 130 133 143 147 **P**8 **S** Sunlink Health Systems, Atlanta, GA
Primary Contact: Jason Cox, Chief Executive Officer
CFO: Molly Lindquist, Interim Chief Financial Officer
CMO: Richard Wherry, M.D., Chief of Staff
CHR: Barbara Patrick, Director Human Resources
CNO: Barbara Arnau, R.N., Chief Nursing Officer
Web address: www.chestateeregionalhospital.com
**Control:** Corporation, Investor–owned, for–profit **Service:** General Medical and Surgical

> **Staffed Beds:** 49 **Admissions:** 1000 **Census:** 12 **Outpatient Visits:** 18986 **Births:** 0 **Total Expense ($000):** 16378 **Payroll Expense ($000):** 6696 **Personnel:** 142

## DALTON—Whitfield County

✠ **HAMILTON MEDICAL CENTER (110001)**, 1200 Memorial Drive, Zip 30720–2529, Mailing Address: P.O. Box 1168, Zip 30722–1168; tel. 706/272–6000 **A**1 2 9 10 19 **F**3 4 5 8 12 13 15 18 20 22 26 28 29 30 31 34 35 40 43 44 45 46 47 48 49 50 51 53 54 57 59 60 62 63 64 68 70 72 73 74 75 76 77 78 79 81 82 83 84 85 86 87 89 93 96 97 98 100 101 102 103 104 105 107 108 110 111 114 115 116 117 118 119 120 121 123 126 129 130 131 132 135 144 146 147 148
Primary Contact: Jeffrey D. Myers, President and Chief Executive Officer
COO: Sandra D. McKenzie, Executive Vice President and Chief Operating Officer
CFO: Gary L. Howard, Senior Vice President and Chief Financial Officer
CMO: Stephen G. Rohn, M.D., Vice President and Chief Medical Officer
CIO: John M. Forrester, Director Information Services
CHR: Jason Hopkins, Director, Human Resources
CNO: Cathy Ferguson, R.N., Vice President and Chief Nursing Officer
Web address: www.hamiltonhealth.com
**Control:** Other not–for–profit (including NFP Corporation) **Service:** General Medical and Surgical

> **Staffed Beds:** 230 **Admissions:** 10220 **Census:** 129 **Outpatient Visits:** 275470 **Births:** 1824 **Personnel:** 1069

## DECATUR—Dekalb County

✠ **ATLANTA VETERANS AFFAIRS MEDICAL CENTER**, 1670 Clairmont Road, Zip 30033–4004; tel. 404/321–6111, (Nonreporting) **A**1 2 3 5 8 **S** Department of Veterans Affairs, Washington, DC
Primary Contact: Leslie Wiggins, Director
CFO: Pamela Watkins, Chief Financial Officer
CMO: David Bower, M.D., Chief of Staff
CIO: William Brock, Chief Information Officer
CHR: Zeta Ferguson, Chief Human Resources
CNO: Sandy Leake, MSN, Associate Director, Nursing and Patient Care Services
Web address: www.atlanta.va.gov/
**Control:** Veterans Affairs, Government, federal **Service:** General Medical and Surgical

> **Staffed Beds:** 239

☐ **DEKALB MEDICAL AT DOWNTOWN DECATUR (112006)**, 450 North Candler Street, Zip 30030–2671; tel. 404/501–6700 **A**1 5 9 10 **F**1 3 11 29 30 35 50 82 90 146 148 **S** DeKalb Regional Health System, Decatur, GA
Primary Contact: John Shelton, President and Chief Executive Officer
COO: John Shelton, Executive Vice President and Chief Operating Officer
CMO: David Snyder, M.D., Chief of Staff
CHR: Tom Crawford, Vice President Human Resources
Web address: www.dekalbmedicalcenter.org
**Control:** Other not–for–profit (including NFP Corporation) **Service:** Long–Term Acute Care hospital

> **Staffed Beds:** 44 **Admissions:** 336 **Census:** 25 **Outpatient Visits:** 0 **Births:** 0 **Total Expense ($000):** 17501 **Payroll Expense ($000):** 7369 **Personnel:** 113

**GA**

✠ **DEKALB MEDICAL AT NORTH DECATUR (110076)**, 2701 North Decatur Road, Zip 30033–5995; tel. 404/501–1000 **A**1 2 3 9 10 **F**3 12 13 15 18 20 22 26 28 29 30 31 34 35 36 37 40 45 48 49 50 53 55 56 57 58 59 60 70 71 72 73 74 75 76 77 78 79 81 82 85 86 87 90 93 97 98 100 102 105 107 108 111 114 115 117 119 120 121 124 126 129 130 131 132 134 135 146 148 **S** DeKalb Regional Health System, Decatur, GA
Primary Contact: John Shelton, President and Chief Executive Officer
COO: Dane Henry, Executive Vice President and Chief Operating Officer
CFO: John Katsianis, Senior Vice President and Chief Financial Officer
CIO: Beth Patino, Chief Information Officer
CHR: LeRoy Walker, Vice President Human Resources
CNO: Susan Breslin, R.N., Vice President Patient Care Services and Chief Nursing Officer
Web address: www.dekalbmedical.org
**Control:** Other not–for–profit (including NFP Corporation) **Service:** General Medical and Surgical

**Staffed Beds:** 417 **Admissions:** 19673 **Census:** 240 **Outpatient Visits:** 165660 **Births:** 4470 **Total Expense ($000):** 304384 **Payroll Expense ($000):** 107494 **Personnel:** 2239

☐ **GEORGIA REGIONAL HOSPITAL AT ATLANTA (114019)**, 3073 Panthersville Road, Zip 30034–3828; tel. 404/243–2100, (Nonreporting) **A**1 3 5 10
Primary Contact: Susan Trueblood, Chief Executive Officer
COO: Sonny Slate, Chief Operating Officer
CFO: Reginald Jones, Business Manager
CMO: Emile Risby, M.D., Clinical Director
CIO: Elfie Early, Manager Data Services
CHR: Lorraine Farr, Manager Human Resources
Web address: www.atlantareg.dhr.state.ga.us
**Control:** State–Government, nonfederal **Service:** Psychiatric

**Staffed Beds:** 319

**VETERANS AFFAIRS MEDICAL CENTER** See Atlanta Veterans Affairs Medical Center

**DEMOREST—Habersham County**

★ ◇ **HABERSHAM MEDICAL CENTER (110041)**, 541 Historic Highway 441, Zip 30535–3118, Mailing Address: P.O. Box 37, Zip 30535–0037; tel. 706/754–2161, (Nonreporting) **A**9 10 21
Primary Contact: Jerry R. Wise, Chief Executive Officer
COO: Michael Gay, Chief Operating Officer
CFO: Barbara Duncan, Chief Financial Officer
CMO: Josh Garrett, Chief of Staff
CHR: Ryan Snow, Director Human Resources
Web address: www.habershammedical.com/
**Control:** Hospital district or authority, Government, nonfederal **Service:** General Medical and Surgical

**Staffed Beds:** 137

**DONALSONVILLE—Seminole County**

◇ **DONALSONVILLE HOSPITAL (110194)**, 102 Hospital Circle, Zip 39845–1199; tel. 229/524–5217, (Nonreporting) **A**9 10 21
Primary Contact: Charles H. Orrick, Administrator
CFO: James Moody, Chief Financial Officer
CMO: C. O. Walker, M.D., Chief of Staff
CHR: Jo Adams, Director Human Resources
**Control:** Other not–for–profit (including NFP Corporation) **Service:** General Medical and Surgical

**Staffed Beds:** 140

**DOUGLAS—Coffee County**

✠ **COFFEE REGIONAL MEDICAL CENTER (110089)**, 1101 Ocilla Road, Zip 31533–2207, Mailing Address: P.O. Box 1287, Zip 31534–1287; tel. 912/384–1900, (Nonreporting) **A**1 9 10 20
Primary Contact: Vicki Lewis, R.N., MS, FACHE, President and Chief Executive Officer
CFO: Donald C. Lewis, Jr., Vice President and Chief Financial Officer
CHR: Laura Bloom, Director Human Resources
Web address: www.coffeeregional.org
**Control:** Other not–for–profit (including NFP Corporation) **Service:** General Medical and Surgical

**Staffed Beds:** 88

**DOUGLASVILLE—Douglas County**

★ **WELLSTAR DOUGLAS HOSPITAL (110184)**, 8954 Hospital Drive, Zip 30134–2282; tel. 770/949–1500 **A**2 9 10 **F**3 11 13 15 18 20 22 28 29 30 31 37 38 40 44 45 48 49 50 51 54 58 59 60 61 64 68 70 74 75 76 77 78 79 81 82 85 86 87 93 94 102 107 108 110 111 114 115 117 118 119 129 130 132 135 146 147 148 **P**5 6 **S** WellStar Health System, Marietta, GA
Primary Contact: Craig A. Owens, President
CFO: Bradley Greene, Chief Financial Officer
CMO: Noel Holtz, M.D., Chief Medical Officer
CHR: Danyale Ziglor, Assistant Director Human Resources
Web address: www.wellstar.org
**Control:** Other not–for–profit (including NFP Corporation) **Service:** General Medical and Surgical

**Staffed Beds:** 108 **Admissions:** 6608 **Census:** 72 **Outpatient Visits:** 130387 **Births:** 461 **Personnel:** 743

**YOUTH VILLAGES INNER HARBOUR CAMPUS**, 4685 Dorsett Shoals Road, Zip 30135–4999; tel. 770/942–2391, (Nonreporting)
Primary Contact: Patrick Lawler, Chief Executive Officer
CFO: J. Steve Lewis, Director Finance
CIO: Laura Sellers, Director Information Systems
CHR: Sherry Kollmeyer, Vice President Human Resources
Web address: www.innerharbour.org
**Control:** Other not–for–profit (including NFP Corporation) **Service:** Children's hospital psychiatric

**Staffed Beds:** 176

**DUBLIN—Laurens County**

✠ **CARL VINSON VETERANS AFFAIRS MEDICAL CENTER**, 1826 Veterans Boulevard, Zip 31021–3620; tel. 478/272–1210, (Nonreporting) **A**1 **S** Department of Veterans Affairs, Washington, DC
Primary Contact: Captain Maryalice Morro, Director
COO: Gerald M. DeWorth, Associate Director
CFO: Kathy Stephens, Chief Financial Officer
CIO: Mark Cowart, Chief Information Officer
CHR: Kurt Oster, Human Resources Officer
Web address: www.dublin.va.gov/
**Control:** Veterans Affairs, Government, federal **Service:** General Medical and Surgical

**Staffed Beds:** 178

✠ **FAIRVIEW PARK HOSPITAL (110125)**, 200 Industrial Boulevard, Zip 31021–2997, Mailing Address: P.O. Box 1408, Zip 31040–1408; tel. 478/275–2000, (Nonreporting) **A**1 9 10 19 **S** HCA, Nashville, TN
Primary Contact: Donald R. Avery, FACHE, President and Chief Executive Officer
COO: Matthew Steven Hasbrouck, Chief Operating Officer
CFO: Ted Short, Chief Financial Officer
CMO: Jeri Miller, M.D., President Medical Staff
CIO: Marsha Morris, Manager Information Services
CHR: Jeff Bruton, Director Human Resources
CNO: Donna Trickey, R.N., Chief Nursing Officer
Web address: www.fairviewparkhospital.com
**Control:** Corporation, Investor–owned, for–profit **Service:** General Medical and Surgical

**Staffed Beds:** 168

**DULUTH—De Kalb County**

**GWINNETT MEDICAL CENTER–DULUTH** See Gwinnett Hospital System, Lawrenceville

**EAST POINT—Fulton County**

✠ **REGENCY HOSPITAL OF SOUTH ATLANTA (112014)**, 1170 Cleveland Avenue, 4th Floor, Zip 30344–3615; tel. 404/466–6250, (Nonreporting) **A**1 3 10 **S** Select Medical Corporation, Mechanicsburg, PA
Primary Contact: Lorie Powell, Interim Chief Executive Officer
Web address: www.regencyhospital.com
**Control:** Corporation, Investor–owned, for–profit **Service:** Long–Term Acute Care hospital

**Staffed Beds:** 40

*Many Facility Codes have changed. Please refer to the AHA Guide Code Chart.* © 2015 AHA Guide

**GA**

## EASTMAN—Dodge County

◇ **DODGE COUNTY HOSPITAL (110092)**, 901 Griffin Avenue, Zip 31023–6720, Mailing Address: PO BOX 4309, Zip 31023–4309; tel. 478/374–4000 **A**9 10 21 **F**3 11 13 15 29 30 31 40 45 53 57 59 64 69 70 75 76 79 81 85 86 107 108 110 111 114 119 146 147
Primary Contact: Kevin Bierschenk, Chief Executive Officer
CFO: Jan Hamrick, Chief Financial Officer
CIO: Victor Woodard, Manager Information Technology
CHR: Wendy Selph, Director Human Resources
CNO: Sandra M. Campbell, R.N., Chief Nursing Officer
Web address: www.dodgecountyhospital.com
**Control:** Hospital district or authority, Government, nonfederal **Service:** General Medical and Surgical

> **Staffed Beds:** 25 **Admissions:** 1604 **Census:** 17 **Outpatient Visits:** 34474
> **Births:** 130 **Total Expense ($000):** 20157 **Payroll Expense ($000):** 8521
> **Personnel:** 235

## EATONTON—Putnam County

☐ **PUTNAM GENERAL HOSPITAL (111313)**, 101 Lake Oconee Parkway, Zip 31024–6054; tel. 706/485–2711, (Nonreporting) **A**1 9 10 18
Primary Contact: Darrell M. Oglesby, Administrator
CFO: Brenda Jarrett, Chief Financial Officer
CMO: Omar Akhras, M.D., Chief of Staff
CIO: Steven Cason, Chief Information Officer
CHR: Ellen Ellard, Director Human Resources
Web address: www.putnamgeneral.com
**Control:** Hospital district or authority, Government, nonfederal **Service:** General Medical and Surgical

> **Staffed Beds:** 25

## ELBERTON—Elbert County

⊞ **ELBERT MEMORIAL HOSPITAL (110026)**, 4 Medical Drive, Zip 30635–1897; tel. 706/283–3151, (Nonreporting) **A**1 9 10
Primary Contact: Brandon Clary, Chief Executive Officer
CIO: Greg Fields, Director Information Technology
CHR: Georgian Walton, Director Human Resources
CNO: Dede Arnau, R.N., Chief Nursing Officer
Web address: www.emhcare.net
**Control:** Hospital district or authority, Government, nonfederal **Service:** General Medical and Surgical

> **Staffed Beds:** 42

## ELLIJAY—Gilmer County

☐ **NORTH GEORGIA MEDICAL CENTER (110205)**, 1362 South Main Street, Zip 30540–5410, Mailing Address: P.O. Box 2239, Zip 30540–0025; tel. 706/276–4741, (Total facility includes 100 beds in nursing home–type unit) **A**1 9 10 **F**3 11 15 29 30 32 34 35 40 42 44 45 46 48 50 54 56 57 59 64 65 68 70 74 75 77 79 81 82 86 87 90 91 92 93 97 103 107 108 110 111 114 119 120 127 128 129 130 131 132 133 135 143 145 146 **P**1 4 **S** Sunlink Health Systems, Atlanta, GA
Primary Contact: Earl S. Whiteley, FACHE, Chief Executive Officer
COO: Earl S. Whiteley, FACHE, Chief Executive Officer
CFO: Debbie Self, Chief Financial Officer
CMO: Brian Rowan, Chief of Staff
CHR: Mary Beth Ralston, Human Resources Director
CNO: Katie Lancey, Chief Nursing Officer
Web address: www.northgeorgiamedicalcenter.com
**Control:** Corporation, Investor–owned, for–profit **Service:** General Medical and Surgical

> **Staffed Beds:** 135 **Admissions:** 925 **Census:** 104 **Outpatient Visits:** 31250
> **Births:** 3

## FAYETTEVILLE—Fayette County

★ ◇ **PIEDMONT FAYETTE HOSPITAL (110215)**, 1255 Highway 54 West, Zip 30214–4526; tel. 770/719–7000 **A**2 3 9 10 21 **F**3 11 13 15 18 20 22 24 26 28 29 30 31 34 35 40 41 45 46 47 48 49 50 51 53 55 57 59 64 70 72 73 74 75 76 77 78 79 81 84 85 87 93 96 107 108 111 114 115 119 121 122 123 124 126 129 130 135 146 147 148 **S** Piedmont Healthcare, Atlanta, GA
Primary Contact: Michael Burnett, Chief Executive Officer
CFO: Sheryl Klink, Chief Financial Officer
CMO: Frederick Willms, M.D., Chief Medical Officer
CHR: Holly Sawyer, Director and Human Resources Business Partner
CNO: Judy M. Long, R.N., Chief Nursing Officer and Vice President Patient Care Services
Web address: www.piedmont.org
**Control:** Other not–for–profit (including NFP Corporation) **Service:** General Medical and Surgical

> **Staffed Beds:** 172 **Admissions:** 12321 **Census:** 144 **Outpatient Visits:** 147252 **Births:** 2325 **Total Expense ($000):** 181042 **Payroll Expense ($000):** 77046 **Personnel:** 1082

## FITZGERALD—Ben Hill County

◇ **DORMINY MEDICAL CENTER (110073)**, 200 Perry House Road, Zip 31750–8857, Mailing Address: P.O. Box 1447, Zip 31750–1447; tel. 229/424–7100, (Nonreporting) **A**9 10 21
Primary Contact: Mel Pyne, Chief Executive Officer
CFO: Paige Wynn, Chief Financial Officer
CMO: Stephen Thombley, M.D., Chief of Staff
CIO: Chris Ward, Director Management Information Systems
CHR: Denise Steverson, Director Human Resources
CNO: Staci Mims, Chief Nursing Officer
Web address: www.dorminymedical.org
**Control:** Hospital district or authority, Government, nonfederal **Service:** General Medical and Surgical

> **Staffed Beds:** 67

## FORSYTH—Monroe County

☐ **MONROE COUNTY HOSPITAL (111318)**, 88 Martin Luther King Jr. Drive, Zip 31029–1682, Mailing Address: P.O. Box 1068, Zip 31029–1068; tel. 478/994–2521 **A**1 9 10 18 **F**3 11 15 29 35 40 57 59 68 75 77 81 107 110 111 114 119 132 133 146 148 **P**1 2 3
Primary Contact: Kay A. Floyd, R.N., Chief Executive Officer
CFO: Marlene McLennan, Controller
CMO: Jeremy Goodwin, M.D., President, Medical Staff
CIO: Donna Hogg, Supervisor Medical Records
CHR: Deborah Flowers, Director Human Resources
CNO: Casey Fleckenstein, Medical and Surgical Nurse Manager
Web address: www.monroehospital.org
**Control:** Hospital district or authority, Government, nonfederal **Service:** General Medical and Surgical

> **Staffed Beds:** 25 **Admissions:** 499 **Census:** 8 **Outpatient Visits:** 16958
> **Births:** 0 **Total Expense ($000):** 10786 **Payroll Expense ($000):** 4340
> **Personnel:** 115

## FORT BENNING—Muscogee County

⊞ **MARTIN ARMY COMMUNITY HOSPITAL**, 7950 Martin Loop, Zip 31905–5648, Mailing Address: 7950 Martin Loop, B9200, Room 010, Zip 31905–5648; tel. 706/544–2516, (Nonreporting) **A**1 3 5 **S** Department of the Army, Office of the Surgeon General, Falls Church, VA
Primary Contact: Colonel Scott B. Avery, Commander
CHR: Major Bernita Hightower, Chief Human Resources
Web address: www.martin.amedd.army.mil
**Control:** Army, Government, federal **Service:** General Medical and Surgical

> **Staffed Beds:** 57

## FORT GORDON—Richmond County

⊞ **DWIGHT DAVID EISENHOWER ARMY MEDICAL CENTER**, 300 West Hospital Road, Zip 30905–5741; tel. 706/787–5811, (Nonreporting) **A**1 2 3 5 **S** Department of the Army, Office of the Surgeon General, Falls Church, VA
Primary Contact: Colonel John P. Lamoureux, Commander
CMO: Colonel James M. Baunchalk, Deputy Chief Clinical Services
CIO: Major Joseph A. Ponce, Chief Information Management
CHR: Elizabeth Shelt, Civilian Personnel Officer
Web address: www.ddeamc.amedd.army.mil
**Control:** Army, Government, federal **Service:** General Medical and Surgical

> **Staffed Beds:** 107

GA

---

**Hospital, Medicare Provider Number, Address, Telephone, Approval, Facility, and Physician Codes, Health Care System**

★ American Hospital Association (AHA) membership    ◯ Healthcare Facilities Accreditation Program    ⇑ Center for Improvement in Healthcare Quality Accreditation
☐ The Joint Commission accreditation    ◇ DNV Healthcare Inc. accreditation    △ Commission on Accreditation of Rehabilitation Facilities (CARF) accreditation

## FORT OGLETHORPE—Catoosa County

☐ **HUTCHESON MEDICAL CENTER (110004)**, 100 Gross Crescent Circle,
Zip 30742–3669; tel. 706/858–2000, (Nonreporting) **A**1 9 10 **S** Erlanger Health
System, Chattanooga, TN
Primary Contact: Farrell Hayes, President and Chief Executive Officer
COO: Kevin Hopkins, Vice President of Operations
CFO: Farrell Hayes, Chief Financial Officer
CMO: John Erdman, M.D., Chief of Staff
CIO: Ruth Wright–Whitaker, Director Information Services
CHR: Cathy Hulsey, Manager of Human Resources
CNO: Sandra Siniard, Vice President of Patient Care Services
Web address: www.hutcheson.org
**Control:** Hospital district or authority, Government, nonfederal **Service:** General
Medical and Surgical

| Staffed Beds: 185 |
|---|

## FORT VALLEY—Peach County

◇ **MEDICAL CENTER OF PEACH COUNTY, NAVICENT HEALTH (111310)**, 601
Blue Bird Boulevard, Zip 31030–4599, Mailing Address: P.O. Box 1799,
Zip 31030–1799; tel. 478/825–8691, (Nonreporting) **A**9 10 18 21 **S** Navicent
Health, Macon, GA
Primary Contact: Darren Pearce, Administrator and Chief Executive Officer
CFO: Lisa Urbindosto, Chief Financial Officer
CMO: Crystal Brown, M.D., Medical Director
CNO: Brenda Goodman, Chief Nursing Officer
Web address: www.navicenthealth.org
**Control:** Hospital district or authority, Government, nonfederal **Service:** General
Medical and Surgical

| Staffed Beds: 25 |
|---|

## GAINESVILLE—Hall County

★ △ ◇ **NORTHEAST GEORGIA MEDICAL CENTER (110029)**, 743 Spring
Street N.E., Zip 30501–3899; tel. 770/219–3553, (Total facility includes 53
beds in nursing home–type unit) **A**2 7 9 10 19 21 **F**3 4 5 7 11 12 13 15 17 18
20 22 24 26 28 29 30 31 34 35 38 39 40 43 44 45 46 47 48 49 50 51 54
56 57 58 59 60 61 63 64 65 66 68 70 72 73 74 75 76 77 78 79 81 82 84
85 86 87 89 90 93 98 99 100 101 102 103 104 105 106 107 108 110 111
114 115 116 117 119 120 121 123 124 126 128 129 130 131 132 143 144
146 147 148 **P**6
Primary Contact: Carol H. Burrell, President and Chief Executive Officer
CFO: Tony Herdener, Vice President Systems and Finance
CMO: Jim Bailey, M.D., Chief Medical Officer
CIO: Mark Jennings, Director Information Systems
Web address: www.nghs.com
**Control:** Other not–for–profit (including NFP Corporation) **Service:** General
Medical and Surgical

| Staffed Beds: 773 Admissions: 28895 Census: 619 Outpatient Visits:<br>351388 Births: 3675 Total Expense ($000): 609697 Payroll Expense<br>($000): 227768 Personnel: 5845 |
|---|

## GRACEWOOD—Richmond County

**EAST CENTRAL REGIONAL HOSPITAL** See East Central Regional Hospital,
Augusta

## GREENSBORO—Greene County

⌧ **ST. MARY'S GOOD SAMARITAN HOSPITAL (111329)**, 5401 Lake Oconee
Parkway, Zip 30642–4232; tel. 706/453–7331 **A**1 9 10 18 **F**3 11 15 26 29 30
34 35 40 45 50 51 57 59 64 65 68 74 75 77 79 81 85 87 93 107 108 115
119 129 130 133 146 **S** Trinity Health, Livonia, MI
Primary Contact: D. Montez Carter, President
CMO: Dave Ringer, M.D., Chief of Staff
CNO: Celia Covington, MSN, Director of Nursing
Web address: www.stmarysgoodsam.org
**Control:** Church–operated, Nongovernment, not–for profit **Service:** General
Medical and Surgical

| Staffed Beds: 25 Admissions: 716 Census: 14 Outpatient Visits: 22777<br>Births: 0 Total Expense ($000): 16370 Payroll Expense ($000): 6867<br>Personnel: 140 |
|---|

## GRIFFIN—Spalding County

⌧ **SPALDING REGIONAL MEDICAL CENTER (110031)**, 601 South Eighth Street,
Zip 30224–4294, Mailing Address: P.O. Drawer V, Zip 30224–1168;
tel. 770/228–2721 **A**1 2 9 10 **F**3 7 11 13 15 18 20 22 29 30 31 34 35 40 49
50 51 53 54 57 59 64 70 73 74 75 76 77 78 79 81 85 87 89 93 107 108
110 111 114 115 119 129 130 131 135 143 146 147 148 **P**8 **S** TENET
Healthcare Corporation, Dallas, TX
Primary Contact: John A. Quinn, Chief Executive Officer
COO: Tamara Ison, Chief Operating Officer
CFO: Cameron Pophan, Chief Financial Officer
CMO: Philip Osehobo, M.D., Chief Medical Officer
CIO: Steve Brown, Director Information Systems
CHR: Amanda Remington, Director Human Resources
CNO: Wadra McCullough, Chief Nursing Officer
Web address: www.spaldingregional.com
**Control:** Corporation, Investor–owned, for–profit **Service:** General Medical and
Surgical

| Staffed Beds: 160 Admissions: 8477 Census: 100 Outpatient Visits: 99376<br>Births: 947 Total Expense ($000): 97945 Payroll Expense ($000): 41716<br>Personnel: 707 |
|---|

## HAWKINSVILLE—Pulaski County

◇ **TAYLOR REGIONAL HOSPITAL (110135)**, Macon Highway, Zip 31036, Mailing
Address: P.O. Box 1297, Zip 31036–7297; tel. 478/783–0200, (Nonreporting)
**A**3 9 10 21
Primary Contact: Nicole Paulk, President
CFO: Lisa Halliday, Director Accounting Services
CMO: Al Baggett, M.D., Interim Chief of Staff
CIO: Dawn Warnock, Director Medical Records
Web address: www.taylorregional.org
**Control:** Other not–for–profit (including NFP Corporation) **Service:** General
Medical and Surgical

| Staffed Beds: 57 |
|---|

## HAZLEHURST—Jeff Davis County

☐ **JEFF DAVIS HOSPITAL (111333)**, 1215 South Tallahassee Street,
Zip 31539–2921, Mailing Address: P.O. Box 1690, Zip 31539–1690;
tel. 912/375–7781, (Nonreporting) **A**1 9 10 18
Primary Contact: Michael Layfield, Chief Executive Officer
Web address: www.jeffdavishospital.org/getpage.php?name=2013HF
**Control:** Hospital district or authority, Government, nonfederal **Service:** General
Medical and Surgical

| Staffed Beds: 25 |
|---|

## HIAWASSEE—Towns County

**CHATUGE REGIONAL HOSPITAL AND NURSING HOME (111324)**, 110 Main
Street, Zip 30546–3408, Mailing Address: P.O. Box 509, Zip 30546–0509;
tel. 706/896–2222, (Total facility includes 112 beds in nursing home–type unit)
**A**9 10 18 **F**3 11 15 29 30 34 40 57 59 65 70 75 77 89 90 93 107 108 110
111 114 119 128 130 132 133 135 143 145 146 **P**4 **S** Union General
Hospital, Inc., Blairsville, GA
Primary Contact: John Mark Gordon, Administrator
CFO: Tim Henry, Accountant
CMO: Robert F. Stahlkuppe, M.D., Chief of Staff
CIO: Walt Stafford, Director Information Technology
CHR: Rita Bradshaw, Director Human Resources
Web address: www.chatugeregionalhospital.org
**Control:** Hospital district or authority, Government, nonfederal **Service:** General
Medical and Surgical

| Staffed Beds: 137 Admissions: 520 Census: 114 Outpatient Visits: 24698<br>Births: 0 Total Expense ($000): 13353 Payroll Expense ($000): 8338<br>Personnel: 223 |
|---|

## HINESVILLE—Liberty County

☐ **LIBERTY REGIONAL MEDICAL CENTER (111335)**, 462 Elma G. Miles
Parkway, Zip 31313–4000, Mailing Address: P.O. Box 919, Zip 31310–0919;
tel. 912/369–9400, (Nonreporting) **A**1 9 10 18
Primary Contact: Donna Cochrane, Interim Chief Executive Officer
Web address: www.libertyregional.org
**Control:** Hospital district or authority, Government, nonfederal **Service:** General
Medical and Surgical

| Staffed Beds: 25 |
|---|

*Many Facility Codes have changed. Please refer to the AHA Guide Code Chart.* © 2015 AHA Guide

✠ **WINN ARMY COMMUNITY HOSPITAL**, 1061 Harmon Avenue,
Zip 31314–5641, Mailing Address: 1061 Harmon Avenue, Suite 2311B,
Zip 31314–5641; tel. 912/435–6965 **A**1 3 5 **F**3 7 12 13 15 29 30 32 33 34
35 36 38 39 40 41 44 45 50 51 54 57 59 61 64 65 68 70 71 74 75 76 77
79 81 82 85 87 89 92 93 97 98 99 100 101 102 104 107 110 111 119 130
132 135 143 144 146 147 **P**6 **S** Department of the Army, Office of the Surgeon
General, Falls Church, VA
Primary Contact: Colonel Kirk W. Eggleston, Commanding Officer
CIO: Arthur N. Kirshner, Chief Information Management
CHR: Major Yvette McCrea, Chief Human Resources
CNO: Colonel Sharon Brown, Deputy Commander Nursing
Web address: www.winn.amedd.army.mil/
**Control:** Army, Government, federal **Service:** General Medical and Surgical

> **Staffed Beds:** 37 **Admissions:** 3145 **Census:** 22 **Outpatient Visits:** 671400
> **Births:** 1159

### HIRAM—Paulding County

✠ **WELLSTAR PAULDING HOSPITAL (110042)**, 2518 Jimmy Lee Smith Parkway,
Zip 30141; tel. 470/644–7000, (Total facility includes 182 beds in nursing
home–type unit) **A**1 2 9 10 **F**3 11 15 18 20 28 29 30 31 37 38 40 41 44 45
49 50 54 55 59 61 64 68 70 75 77 78 79 80 81 82 85 86 87 93 102 107
108 110 111 114 118 119 120 121 123 128 129 130 135 146 148 **P**5 6
**S** WellStar Health System, Marietta, GA
Primary Contact: Mark Haney, President
COO: Lindsay Rehn, Executive Director of Financial Operations
CFO: Lindsay Rehn, Executive Director of Financial Operations
CMO: Guillermo Pierluisi, Vice President of Medical Affairs
CHR: Jessica Bedsole, Director, Human Resources
CNO: Vicky Hogue, R.N., Vice President Patient Services and Chief Nursing Officer
Web address: www.wellstar.org
**Control:** Other not–for–profit (including NFP Corporation) **Service:** General
Medical and Surgical

> **Staffed Beds:** 238 **Admissions:** 2678 **Census:** 195 **Outpatient Visits:**
> 101722 **Births:** 0 **Personnel:** 622

### HOMERVILLE—Clinch County

★ **CLINCH MEMORIAL HOSPITAL (111308)**, 1050 Valdosta Highway,
Zip 31634–9701, Mailing Address: P.O. Box 516, Zip 31634–0516;
tel. 912/487–5211 **A**9 10 18 **F**3 7 11 15 34 40 45 57 59 64 77 91 93 107
111 114 119 129 130 133 135 145 146
Primary Contact: Greg Brown, Chief Executive Officer
COO: Greg Brown, Chief Executive Officer
CFO: Sandra Hughes, Chief Financial Officer
CMO: Samuel Cobarrubias, M.D., Chief of Staff
CIO: Shelly Studebaker, Director Management Information Systems
CHR: Shelly Studebaker, Manager Human Resources
CNO: Wayne Lee, Director of Nursing
Web address: www.sgmc.org/healthsystem/clinchmemorial.htm
**Control:** County–Government, nonfederal **Service:** General Medical and Surgical

> **Staffed Beds:** 25 **Admissions:** 240 **Census:** 3 **Outpatient Visits:** 12743
> **Births:** 0 **Total Expense ($000):** 10086 **Payroll Expense ($000):** 3679
> **Personnel:** 106

### JACKSON—Butts County

★ **SYLVAN GROVE HOSPITAL (111319)**, 1050 McDonough Road,
Zip 30233–1599; tel. 770/775–7861 **A**9 10 18 **F**15 29 34 35 40 50 57 59 68
77 93 107 119 130 133 **S** TENET Healthcare Corporation, Dallas, TX
Primary Contact: John A. Quinn, Chief Executive Officer
CFO: Tamara Ison, Chief Financial Officer
CIO: Steve Brown, Chief Information Officer
CHR: Amanda Remington, Director Human Resources
Web address: www.sylvangrovehospital.com
**Control:** Corporation, Investor–owned, for–profit **Service:** General Medical and
Surgical

> **Staffed Beds:** 24 **Admissions:** 495 **Census:** 14 **Outpatient Visits:** 18475
> **Births:** 0 **Total Expense ($000):** 8773 **Payroll Expense ($000):** 4928
> **Personnel:** 72

### JASPER—Pickens County

★ ◇ **PIEDMONT MOUNTAINSIDE HOSPITAL (110225)**, 1266 Highway 515
South, Zip 30143–4872; tel. 706/692–2441 **A**9 10 21 **F**3 13 15 20 28 29 34
35 40 41 45 46 49 53 57 59 64 70 76 77 79 81 85 107 108 110 111 114
115 119 129 130 132 135 148 **S** Piedmont Healthcare, Atlanta, GA
Primary Contact: Denise Ray, President and Chief Executive Officer
CFO: Frank R. Powell, Chief Financial Officer
CIO: Geoffrey Brown, Chief Information Officer
CHR: Connie McLendon, Director Human Resources
CNO: Michelle Breitfelder, Chief Nursing Officer
Web address: www.piedmontmountainsidehospital.org
**Control:** Other not–for–profit (including NFP Corporation) **Service:** General
Medical and Surgical

> **Staffed Beds:** 52 **Admissions:** 2879 **Census:** 28 **Outpatient Visits:** 56425
> **Births:** 318 **Total Expense ($000):** 46888 **Payroll Expense ($000):** 20904
> **Personnel:** 373

### JESUP—Wayne County

☐ **WAYNE MEMORIAL HOSPITAL (110124)**, 865 South First Street,
Zip 31545–0210, Mailing Address: P.O. Box 410, Zip 31598–0410;
tel. 912/427–6811, (Nonreporting) **A**1 9 10 20
Primary Contact: Joseph P. Ierardi, Chief Executive Officer
CFO: Greg Jones, Chief Financial Officer
CMO: Dan Collipp, M.D., Chief of Staff
CIO: Deborah Six, Coordinator Data Processing
CHR: John McIwain, Director Human Resources
Web address: www.wmhweb.com
**Control:** County–Government, nonfederal **Service:** General Medical and Surgical

> **Staffed Beds:** 84

### JOHNS CREEK—Fulton County

✠ **EMORY JOHNS CREEK HOSPITAL (110230)**, 6325 Hospital Parkway,
Zip 30097–5775; tel. 678/474–7000 **A**1 2 3 10 **F**3 11 12 13 15 18 20 22 26
29 30 31 34 35 36 40 45 49 50 54 57 59 60 64 68 70 72 73 74 75 76 77
78 79 81 82 85 87 93 107 108 110 111 115 116 117 119 126 129 130 131
132 141 146 147 148 **P**6 **S** Emory Healthcare, Atlanta, GA
Primary Contact: Marilyn Margolis, Chief Executive Officer
COO: Laurie Hansen, Associate Administrator
CFO: JoAnn Manning, Chief Financial Officer
CMO: Adedapo Odetoyinbo, M.D., Chief Medical Office
CIO: Brad Foresythe, Director Information Systems
CHR: Jennifer Elizabeth Garber, Vice President Human Resources
CNO: Marilyn Margolis, Chief Nursing Officer
Web address: www.emoryjohnscreek.com
**Control:** Other not–for–profit (including NFP Corporation) **Service:** General
Medical and Surgical

> **Staffed Beds:** 113 **Admissions:** 5934 **Census:** 68 **Outpatient Visits:** 58759
> **Births:** 1080 **Total Expense ($000):** 114114 **Payroll Expense ($000):**
> 37250 **Personnel:** 584

### KENNESAW—Cobb County

**DEVEREUX GEORGIA TREATMENT NETWORK**, 1291 Stanley Road N.W.,
Zip 30152–4359; tel. 770/427–0147 **F**98 99 106 **S** Devereux, Villanova, PA
Primary Contact: Gwendolyn Skinner, Executive Director
COO: Mary H. Esposito, Assistant Executive Director
CFO: Kathy Goggin, Director Administrative Services
CMO: Yolanda Graham, M.D., Medical Director
CIO: Sam Maguta, Coordinator Information Systems
CHR: Rudie Delien, Director Human Resources
CNO: Debra Sharpton, Director of Nursing
Web address: www.devereuxga.org
**Control:** Other not–for–profit (including NFP Corporation) **Service:** Children's
hospital psychiatric

> **Staffed Beds:** 100 **Admissions:** 162 **Census:** 74 **Outpatient Visits:** 62
> **Births:** 0 **Total Expense ($000):** 16657 **Payroll Expense ($000):** 9177
> **Personnel:** 33

**GA**

---

**Hospital, Medicare Provider Number, Address, Telephone, Approval, Facility, and Physician Codes, Health Care System**

★ American Hospital Association (AHA) membership    ○ Healthcare Facilities Accreditation Program    ⇑ Center for Improvement in Healthcare Quality Accreditation
☐ The Joint Commission accreditation    ◇ DNV Healthcare Inc. accreditation    △ Commission on Accreditation of Rehabilitation Facilities (CARF) accreditation

**GA**

## LAGRANGE—Troup County

✠ **WEST GEORGIA HEALTH (110016)**, 1514 Vernon Road, Zip 30240–4131; tel. 706/882–1411, (Total facility includes 260 beds in nursing home–type unit) **A**1 2 9 10 19 **F**3 8 11 12 13 15 18 20 22 26 28 29 30 31 34 35 40 47 48 49 50 54 56 57 58 59 62 63 64 66 68 70 73 74 75 76 77 78 79 80 81 82 84 85 86 89 92 93 96 102 107 108 110 111 114 115 119 120 121 123 128 129 130 132 135 146 147 148 **P**6
Primary Contact: Gerald N. Fulks, President and Chief Executive Officer
COO: Charis Acree, Senior Vice President
CFO: Paul R. Perrotti, CPA, Chief Financial Officer
CIO: Jack Storey, Chief Information Officer
CHR: Tommy Britt, Vice President of Human Resources
CNO: Tracy Gynther, R.N., Vice President and Chief Nursing Officer
Web address: www.wghealth.org/
**Control:** Other not–for–profit (including NFP Corporation) **Service:** General Medical and Surgical

**Staffed Beds: 389 Admissions: 7081 Census: 310 Outpatient Visits: 139282 Births: 991 Total Expense ($000): 182109 Payroll Expense ($000): 72868 Personnel: 1280**

## LAKELAND—Lanier County

✠ **SOUTH GEORGIA MEDICAL CENTER LANIER CAMPUS (111326)**, 116 West Thigpen Avenue, Zip 31635–1011; tel. 229/482–3110, (Nonreporting) **A**1 9 10 18
Primary Contact: C. Richard Dwozan, Administrator
CFO: Libby Flemming, Controller and Chief Information Officer
CMO: Bruce Herrington, M.D., Chief Medical Officer
CIO: Libby Flemming, Controller and Chief Information Officer
CHR: Vicki Dinkins, Director Human Resources
Web address: www.sgmc.org
**Control:** Other not–for–profit (including NFP Corporation) **Service:** Other specialty

**Staffed Beds: 87**

## LAVONIA—Franklin County

★ ◇ **ST. MARY'S SACRED HEART HOSPITAL (110027)**, 367 Clear Creek Parkway, Zip 30553–4173; tel. 706/356–7800, (Nonreporting) **A**9 10 21 **S** Trinity Health, Livonia, MI
Primary Contact: Jeff English, Interim Chief Executive Officer
CIO: Tim Vickery, Chief Information Officer
CHR: Lauren Papka, Chief Administrative Officer
CNO: Evelyn Murphy, R.N., Chief Nursing Officer
Web address: www.stmaryssacredheart.org/
**Control:** Other not–for–profit (including NFP Corporation) **Service:** General Medical and Surgical

**Staffed Beds: 35**

## LAWRENCEVILLE—Gwinnett County

✠ **GWINNETT HOSPITAL SYSTEM (110087)**, 1000 Medical Center Boulevard, Zip 30046–7694, Mailing Address: P.O. Box 348, Zip 30046–0348; tel. 678/312–1000, (Includes GWINNETT MEDICAL CENTER, 1000 Medical Center Boulevard, Zip 30245, Mailing Address: Box 348, Zip 30246; tel. 678/312–1000; Thomas Shepherd, Executive Vice President and Chief Operating Officer; GWINNETT MEDICAL CENTER–DULUTH, 3620 Howell Ferry Road, Duluth, Zip 30096; tel. 678/312–6800), (Total facility includes 89 beds in nursing home–type unit) **A**1 2 9 10 19 **F**3 8 11 12 13 15 17 18 20 22 24 26 28 29 30 31 34 35 36 37 38 40 41 43 44 45 46 47 48 49 50 54 55 56 58 59 64 67 68 70 71 72 73 74 75 76 77 78 79 81 82 84 85 86 87 90 93 96 97 107 108 110 111 114 115 116 117 118 119 126 128 129 130 131 132 134 135 146 147 148 **P**8
Primary Contact: Philip R. Wolfe, President and Chief Executive Officer
COO: Thomas Shepherd, Executive Vice President and Chief Operating Officer
CFO: Thomas Y. McBride, III, Executive Vice President and Chief Financial Officer
CMO: Alan Bier, M.D., Executive Vice President and Chief Medical Officer
CIO: Patricia A. Lavely, FACHE, Senior Vice President and Chief Information Officer
CHR: Steve Nadeau, Senior Vice President Human Resources
CNO: Carol Danielson, R.N., Senior Vice President and Chief Nursing Officer
Web address: www.gwinnettmedicalcenter.org
**Control:** Other not–for–profit (including NFP Corporation) **Service:** General Medical and Surgical

**Staffed Beds: 552 Admissions: 27991 Census: 466 Outpatient Visits: 357365 Births: 4970 Total Expense ($000): 607464 Payroll Expense ($000): 237197 Personnel: 3918**

☐ **SUMMITRIDGE HOSPITAL (114004)**, 250 Scenic Highway, Zip 30046–5675; tel. 678/442–5800, (Nonreporting) **A**1 10
Primary Contact: Jeff Pritchard, Chief Executive Officer
Web address: www.summitridgehospital.net
**Control:** Other not–for–profit (including NFP Corporation) **Service:** Psychiatric

**Staffed Beds: 25**

## LITHONIA—Dekalb County

☐ **DEKALB MEDICAL AT HILLANDALE (110226)**, 2801 DeKalb Medical Parkway, Zip 30058–4996; tel. 404/501–8700 **A**1 9 10 **F**3 11 15 18 29 30 34 35 40 45 48 49 50 56 57 59 60 70 74 75 77 78 79 81 82 85 86 87 93 107 108 111 114 119 120 121 130 146 **S** DeKalb Regional Health System, Decatur, GA
Primary Contact: John Shelton, President and Chief Executive Officer
COO: John Shelton, Chief Operating Officer
CMO: Duane Barclay, D.O., Chief Medical Officer
CIO: Mark Trocino, Chief Information Officer
CHR: Tom Crawford, Vice President Human Resources
Web address: www.dekalbmedical.org
**Control:** Other not–for–profit (including NFP Corporation) **Service:** General Medical and Surgical

**Staffed Beds: 80 Admissions: 4605 Census: 53 Outpatient Visits: 95059 Births: 0 Total Expense ($000): 70728 Payroll Expense ($000): 25914 Personnel: 418**

## LOUISVILLE—Jefferson County

**JEFFERSON HOSPITAL (110100)**, 1067 Peachtree Street, Zip 30434–1599; tel. 478/625–7000, (Nonreporting) **A**9 10 20
Primary Contact: James Heitzenrater, Chief Executive Officer
CMO: James Polhill, M.D., Chief Medical Officer
CHR: Catherine Hall, Manager Human Resources
CNO: Ben Doyle, R.N., Director of Nursing
Web address: www.jeffersonhosp.com
**Control:** City–County, Government, nonfederal **Service:** General Medical and Surgical

**Staffed Beds: 37**

## MACON—Bibb County

✠ **COLISEUM MEDICAL CENTERS (110164)**, 350 Hospital Drive, Zip 31217–3871; tel. 478/765–7000, (Includes COLISEUM CENTER FOR BEHAVIORAL HEALTH, 340 Hospital Drive, Zip 31217–3838; tel. 478/741–1355; Lance Jones, Chief Executive Officer), (Nonreporting) **A**1 2 9 10 **S** HCA, Nashville, TN
Primary Contact: Lance Jones, Chief Executive Officer
COO: Todd Dixon, R.N., Chief Operating Officer
CFO: Heath King, Chief Financial Officer
CMO: Michael Thornsberry, M.D., Chief Medical Officer
CIO: Joan Morstad, Director Information Systems
CHR: Laura Booras, Vice President Human Resources
CNO: Candice R. Carroll, Chief Nursing Officer
Web address: www.coliseumhealthsystem.com
**Control:** Corporation, Investor–owned, for–profit **Service:** General Medical and Surgical

**Staffed Beds: 227**

✠ **COLISEUM NORTHSIDE HOSPITAL (110201)**, 400 Charter Boulevard, Zip 31210–4853, Mailing Address: P.O. Box 4627, Zip 31208–4627; tel. 478/757–8200, (Nonreporting) **A**1 9 10 **S** HCA, Nashville, TN
Primary Contact: Stephen J. Daugherty, Chief Executive Officer
COO: Todd Dixon, R.N., Chief Operating Officer
CFO: Heath King, Chief Financial Officer
CHR: Laura Booras, Director of Human Resources
CNO: Patricia Derrico, FACHE, Chief Nursing Officer
Web address: www.coliseumhealthsystem.com
**Control:** Corporation, Investor–owned, for–profit **Service:** General Medical and Surgical

**Staffed Beds: 103**

★ ◇ **MEDICAL CENTER, NAVICENT HEALTH (110107)**, 777 Hemlock Street, Zip 31201–2155; tel. 478/633–1000, (Includes CHILDREN'S HOSPITAL, 777 Hemlock Street, tel. 478/633–1000) **A**2 3 5 8 9 10 21 **F**3 5 7 8 11 12 13 14 15 17 18 20 22 24 26 28 29 30 31 32 34 35 36 39 40 43 44 45 46 47 48 49 50 51 53 54 56 57 58 59 60 61 62 63 64 65 66 68 70 72 73 74 75 76 77 78 79 81 82 83 84 85 86 87 88 89 92 93 94 97 98 99 100 101 102 103 104 105 107 108 110 111 114 115 119 126 130 132 135 143 144 145 146 147 148 **P**1 **S** Navicent Health, Macon, GA
Primary Contact: Ninfa Saunders, Chief Executive Officer
COO: Tejas Gandhi, Chief Administrative Officer
CFO: Rhonda Perry, Chief Financial Officer
CMO: Fady Wanna, M.D., Chief Clinical Officer and Chief Medical Officer
CIO: William Avenel, Assistant Vice President Information Services
CHR: Bernard J. Price, Assistant Vice President
CNO: Tracey Blalock, Chief Nursing Officer
Web address: www.mccg.org
**Control:** Other not–for–profit (including NFP Corporation) **Service:** General Medical and Surgical

**Staffed Beds: 659 Admissions: 30714 Census: 477 Outpatient Visits: 377328 Births: 1710 Total Expense ($000): 592657 Payroll Expense ($000): 224972 Personnel: 3467**

*Many Facility Codes have changed. Please refer to the AHA Guide Code Chart.*
© 2015 AHA Guide

⊞ **REGENCY HOSPITAL OF CENTRAL GEORGIA (112016)**, 535 Coliseum Drive, Zip 31217–0104; tel. 478/803–7300, (Nonreporting) **A**1 9 10 **S** Select Medical Corporation, Mechanicsburg, PA
Primary Contact: Michael S. Boggs, Chief Executive Officer
Web address: www.regencyhospital.com
**Control:** Corporation, Investor–owned, for–profit **Service:** Long–Term Acute Care hospital

**Staffed Beds:** 60

★ ◇ **REHABILITATION HOSPITAL, NAVICENT HEALTH (113029)**, 3351 Northside Drive, Zip 31210–2587; tel. 478/201–6500 **A**3 9 10 21 **F**90 93 95 132 143 148 **S** Navicent Health, Macon, GA
Primary Contact: Elbert T. McQueen, President and Chief Executive Officer
COO: Darren Pearce, Executive Director
CFO: Beverly Owens, Controller
CMO: Allison Scheetz, M.D., Medical Director
Web address: www.centralgarehab.com
**Control:** Hospital district or authority, Government, nonfederal **Service:** Rehabilitation

**Staffed Beds:** 58 **Admissions:** 1039 **Census:** 39 **Outpatient Visits:** 12135 **Births:** 0 **Total Expense ($000):** 14925 **Payroll Expense ($000):** 8326

### MADISON—Morgan County

☐ **MORGAN MEMORIAL HOSPITAL (111304)**, 1077 South Main Street, Zip 30650–2073, Mailing Address: P.O. Box 860, Zip 30650–0860; tel. 706/342–1667, (Nonreporting) **A**1 9 10 18
Primary Contact: Ralph A. Castillo, CPA, Chief Executive Officer
CFO: Kyle Wilkinson, Chief Financial Officer
CMO: Dan Zant, M.D., Chief of Staff
CIO: Patrick Cook, Vice President Support Services
CHR: Sarah Phillips, Manager Human Resources
CNO: Beth O'Neill, Chief Nursing Officer
Web address: www.mmh.org
**Control:** Hospital district or authority, Government, nonfederal **Service:** General Medical and Surgical

**Staffed Beds:** 38

### MARIETTA—Cobb County

⊞ △ **WELLSTAR KENNESTONE HOSPITAL (110035)**, 677 Church Street, Zip 30060–1148; tel. 770/793–5000 **A**1 2 3 5 7 9 10 **F**3 8 10 11 12 13 15 17 18 20 22 24 26 28 29 30 31 36 37 38 40 41 43 44 45 46 47 48 49 50 51 53 54 55 58 59 60 61 64 66 68 70 72 73 74 75 76 77 78 79 80 81 82 84 85 86 87 90 93 94 96 100 102 107 108 110 111 114 115 117 118 119 120 121 123 124 125 126 129 130 132 135 141 146 147 148 **P**5 6 **S** WellStar Health System, Marietta, GA
Primary Contact: Dan Woods, President
COO: Monte Wilson, Chief Operating Officer
CFO: Marty Gutkin, Vice President Finance and Chief Financial Officer
CMO: Robert Lubitz, M.D., Vice President of Medical Affairs
CIO: Jonathan B. Morris, M.D., Senior Vice President and Chief Information Officer
CHR: Bobby DeCoux, Assistant Vice President Human Resources
CNO: Laura J. Caramanica, Ph.D., Vice President and Chief Nursing Officer
Web address: www.wellstar.org
**Control:** Other not–for–profit (including NFP Corporation) **Service:** General Medical and Surgical

**Staffed Beds:** 633 **Admissions:** 37292 **Census:** 494 **Outpatient Visits:** 406051 **Births:** 5382 **Personnel:** 3952

⊞ **WELLSTAR WINDY HILL HOSPITAL (112007)**, 2540 Windy Hill Road, Zip 30067–8632; tel. 770/644–1000 **A**1 2 9 10 **F**1 3 5 11 15 29 30 44 45 50 51 60 61 64 68 75 77 79 81 85 86 87 93 100 101 107 108 110 111 114 118 119 129 130 135 141 146 148 **P**5 6 **S** WellStar Health System, Marietta, GA
Primary Contact: Kem Mullins, FACHE, President
CFO: Marsha Burke, Senior Vice President and Chief Financial Officer
CMO: Larry Haldeman, M.D., Executive Vice President and Chief Medical Officer
CIO: Leigh Cox, Chief Information Officer
Web address: www.wellstar.org
**Control:** Other not–for–profit (including NFP Corporation) **Service:** Long–Term Acute Care hospital

**Staffed Beds:** 55 **Admissions:** 360 **Census:** 33 **Outpatient Visits:** 35448 **Births:** 0 **Personnel:** 303

### METTER—Candler County

☐ **CANDLER COUNTY HOSPITAL (111334)**, 400 Cedar Street, Zip 30439–3338, Mailing Address: P.O. Box 597, Zip 30439–0597; tel. 912/685–5741, (Nonreporting) **A**1 9 10 18
Primary Contact: Mel Pyne, Chief Executive Officer
Web address: www.candlercountyhospital.com
**Control:** Hospital district or authority, Government, nonfederal **Service:** General Medical and Surgical

**Staffed Beds:** 25

### MILLEDGEVILLE—Baldwin County

☐ **CENTRAL STATE HOSPITAL**, 620 Broad Street, Zip 31062–0001; tel. 478/445–4128, (Total facility includes 18 beds in nursing home–type unit) **A**1 3 9 **F**30 39 57 59 75 86 87 97 98 100 128 130
Primary Contact: Susan Trueblood, Regional Hospital Administrator
COO: Terry McGee, Chief Operations Officer
CMO: Scott VanSant, M.D., Chief Medical Officer
CIO: Betsy Bradley, Coordinator Performance Improvement
CHR: Myra Holloway, Director Human Resources Management
Web address: www.centralstatehospital.org
**Control:** State–Government, nonfederal **Service:** Psychiatric

**Staffed Beds:** 202 **Admissions:** 77 **Census:** 177 **Outpatient Visits:** 0 **Births:** 0 **Total Expense ($000):** 77123 **Payroll Expense ($000):** 30450 **Personnel:** 812

☐ **OCONEE REGIONAL MEDICAL CENTER (110150)**, 821 North Cobb Street, Zip 31061–2351, Mailing Address: P.O. Box 690, Zip 31059–0690; tel. 478/454–3505, (Total facility includes 15 beds in nursing home–type unit) **A**1 9 10 19 **F**3 11 13 15 28 29 30 31 34 35 37 40 45 46 49 50 51 53 57 59 60 64 68 70 75 76 78 79 80 81 82 85 86 87 89 92 93 107 108 110 111 114 116 117 119 120 121 123 128 129 132 135 146 147 148 **S** Oconee Regional Health Systems, Milledgeville, GA
Primary Contact: Randy Hoover, Interim President and Chief Executive Officer
CFO: Brenda Qualls, Chief Financial Officer
CHR: Scott Parton, Director Human Resources
CNO: Deborah Block, Vice President Nursing and Chief Nursing Officer
Web address: www.oconeeregional.com
**Control:** Other not–for–profit (including NFP Corporation) **Service:** General Medical and Surgical

**Staffed Beds:** 90 **Admissions:** 3483 **Census:** 49 **Outpatient Visits:** 119239 **Births:** 600 **Total Expense ($000):** 71642 **Payroll Expense ($000):** 25145 **Personnel:** 493

### MILLEN—Jenkins County

**OPTIM MEDICAL CENTER – JENKINS (111311)**, 931 East Winthrope Avenue, Zip 30442–1839; tel. 478/982–4221 **A**9 10 18 **F**11 15 29 34 40 45 50 57 59 64 65 75 77 79 81 82 90 93 97 107 119 127 133 146 **S** National Surgical Healthcare, Chicago, IL
Primary Contact: Robert R. Sellers, Administrator
CFO: Marsha Carroll, Director of Fiscal Services
CIO: Rob Snipes, Chief Information Officer
CHR: Natalie Peterson, Director of Human Resources
CNO: S. Lagina Evans, R.N., Assistant Chief Nursing Officer
Web address: www.optimhealth.com
**Control:** Corporation, Investor–owned, for–profit **Service:** General Medical and Surgical

**Staffed Beds:** 25 **Admissions:** 287 **Census:** 3 **Outpatient Visits:** 19012 **Births:** 0 **Total Expense ($000):** 8773 **Payroll Expense ($000):** 3972

### MONROE—Walton County

⊞ **CLEARVIEW REGIONAL MEDICAL CENTER (110046)**, 2151 West Spring Street, Zip 30655–3115, Mailing Address: PO BOX 1346, Zip 30655–1346; tel. 770/267–8461, (Nonreporting) **A**1 9 10 **S** Community Health Systems, Inc., Franklin, TN
Primary Contact: James Machado, Chief Executive Officer
CFO: Charlie Brinkley, Chief Financial Officer
CMO: Douglas Miller, M.D., Chief of Medical Staff
CIO: Ashley Henry, Director Information Systems
CHR: Michele Monsrud, Director Human Resources
CNO: Sharon H. Queen, R.N., Chief Nursing Officer
Web address: www.clearviewregionalmedicalcenter.com/
**Control:** Corporation, Investor–owned, for–profit **Service:** General Medical and Surgical

**Staffed Beds:** 77

**GA**

**Hospital, Medicare Provider Number, Address, Telephone, Approval, Facility, and Physician Codes, Health Care System**

★ American Hospital Association (AHA) membership  ○ Healthcare Facilities Accreditation Program  ⇑ Center for Improvement in Healthcare Quality Accreditation
☐ The Joint Commission accreditation  ◇ DNV Healthcare Inc. accreditation  △ Commission on Accreditation of Rehabilitation Facilities (CARF) accreditation

© 2015 AHA Guide  *Many Facility Codes have changed. Please refer to the AHA Guide Code Chart.*  Hospitals **A161**

## MONTEZUMA—Macon County

☐ **FLINT RIVER COMMUNITY HOSPITAL (110190)**, 509 Sumter Street,
Zip 31063–1733, Mailing Address: P.O. Box 770, Zip 31063–2502;
tel. 478/472–3100, (Nonreporting) **A**1 9 10
Primary Contact: Michael C. Patterson, Chief Executive Officer
CMO: Quincy Jordan, M.D., Chief of Staff
CHR: Vicki Stotts, Coordinator Human Resources
CNO: Lee Hughes, R.N., Chief Nursing Officer
Web address: www.flintriverhospital.com/
**Control:** Corporation, Investor–owned, for–profit **Service:** General Medical and
Surgical

**Staffed Beds:** 49

## MONTICELLO—Jasper County

**JASPER MEMORIAL HOSPITAL (111303)**, 898 College Street,
Zip 31064–1258; tel. 706/468–6411, (Total facility includes 55 beds in nursing
home–type unit) **A**9 10 18 **F**11 18 29 34 40 57 59 65 77 93 97 107 111 119
128 133 146 148 **P**6 **S** Oconee Regional Health Systems, Milledgeville, GA
Primary Contact: Jan Gaston, Administrator
CFO: Stuart Abney, Controller
CHR: Laura Hammonds, Assistant Administrator
CNO: Tammy Honeycutt, R.N., Director of Nursing
Web address: www.jaspermemorialhospital.org
**Control:** Other not–for–profit (including NFP Corporation) **Service:** General
Medical and Surgical

**Staffed Beds:** 67 **Admissions:** 170 **Census:** 57 **Outpatient Visits:** 8449
**Births:** 0 **Total Expense ($000):** 9182 **Payroll Expense ($000):** 4480
**Personnel:** 116

## MOULTRIE—Colquitt County

⊞ ○ **COLQUITT REGIONAL MEDICAL CENTER (110105)**, 3131 South Main
Street, Zip 31768–6925, Mailing Address: P.O. Box 40, Zip 31776–0040;
tel. 229/985–3420 **A**1 9 10 11 **F**3 7 11 12 13 15 17 20 29 30 31 32 34 35
39 40 45 47 48 49 56 57 59 60 61 62 63 65 68 70 74 75 76 77 78 79 81
82 85 86 87 89 91 93 97 107 108 110 111 115 119 126 127 129 130 131
132 135 143 144 146 147 148
Primary Contact: James L. Matney, President and Chief Executive Officer
COO: W. Larry Sims, Chief Operating Officer
CFO: Shamb Purohit, Chief Financial Officer
CMO: Andy Wills, M.D., Medical Director
CIO: Bill Bishop, Chief Information Officer
CHR: Dawn Johns, Director Human Resources
CNO: Dena Zinker, MSN, Vice President Patient Services
Web address: www.colquittregional.com
**Control:** Hospital district or authority, Government, nonfederal **Service:** General
Medical and Surgical

**Staffed Beds:** 99 **Admissions:** 4470 **Census:** 52 **Outpatient Visits:** 127481
**Births:** 553 **Total Expense ($000):** 81302 **Payroll Expense ($000):** 33877
**Personnel:** 835

**TURNING POINT HOSPITAL (110209)**, 3015 Veterans Parkway South,
Zip 31788–6705, Mailing Address: P.O. Box 1177, Zip 31776–1177;
tel. 229/985–4815 **A**9 10 **F**4 5 30 75 87 98 105 130 135 143 **P**6 **S** Universal
Health Services, Inc., King of Prussia, PA
Primary Contact: Ben Marion, Chief Executive Officer and Managing Director
COO: Judy Payne, R.N., Chief Operating Officer
CFO: Edwin Bennett, Controller
CHR: Jennifer Azar, Director Human Resources
CNO: Faith Connell, Director of Nursing
Web address: www.turningpointcare.com
**Control:** Corporation, Investor–owned, for–profit **Service:** Alcoholism and other
chemical dependency

**Staffed Beds:** 59 **Admissions:** 3161 **Census:** 50 **Outpatient Visits:** 22206
**Births:** 0 **Total Expense ($000):** 20152 **Payroll Expense ($000):** 10890
**Personnel:** 206

## NASHVILLE—Berrien County

⊞ **SOUTH GEORGIA MEDICAL CENTER BERRIEN CAMPUS (110234)**, 1221
East McPherson Avenue, Zip 31639–2326, Mailing Address: P.O. Box 665,
Zip 31639–0665; tel. 229/543–7100 **A**1 9 10 **F**3 15 29 34 35 38 40 45 50
56 57 59 68 75 77 78 86 87 93 98 103 107 108 110 111 115 119 130
135 146
Primary Contact: C. Richard Dwozan, Administrator
Web address: www.berrienhospital.com
**Control:** Hospital district or authority, Government, nonfederal **Service:** General
Medical and Surgical

**Staffed Beds:** 39 **Admissions:** 576 **Census:** 13 **Outpatient Visits:** 16493
**Births:** 0 **Total Expense ($000):** 7900 **Payroll Expense ($000):** 3423
**Personnel:** 86

## NEWNAN—Coweta County

★ ◇ **PIEDMONT NEWNAN HOSPITAL (110229)**, 745 Poplar Road,
Zip 30265–1618; tel. 770/400–1000 **A**9 10 21 **F**11 13 15 18 20 28 29 30 31
34 35 40 45 46 49 51 53 57 59 60 64 68 70 74 75 76 78 79 81 84 85 86
87 93 107 108 110 111 114 115 116 117 118 119 120 121 123 126 129
130 132 135 146 148 **S** Piedmont Healthcare, Atlanta, GA
Primary Contact: Michael Robertson, Chief Executive Officer
COO: Nathan Nipper, Vice President and Chief Operating Officer
CFO: John Miles, Chief Financial Officer
CMO: Jeffrey R. Folk, M.D., Vice President Medical Affairs and Chief Medical
Officer
CIO: Henry Scott, Executive Director, Technical Services
CHR: Clay Boyles, Executive Director, Human Resources
CNO: Jason Smith, Chief Nursing Officer
Web address: www.piedmontnewnan.org
**Control:** Other not–for–profit (including NFP Corporation) **Service:** General
Medical and Surgical

**Staffed Beds:** 130 **Admissions:** 7539 **Census:** 83 **Outpatient Visits:** 99597
**Births:** 1162 **Total Expense ($000):** 112492 **Payroll Expense ($000):**
44684

☐ **SOUTHEASTERN REGIONAL MEDICAL CENTER (110233)**, 600 Celebrate Life
Parkway, Zip 30265–8000; tel. 770/400–6000 **A**1 10 **F**3 15 29 30 33 34
35 36 38 45 46 47 49 55 57 58 64 67 68 70 75 77 78 81 82 83 84 85 86
87 93 104 107 108 109 110 111 114 115 116 117 118 119 120 121 123
124 126 130 132 135 146 148 **P**6 **S** Cancer Treatment Centers of America,
Schaumburg, IL
Primary Contact: Anne Meisner, MSN, President and Chief Executive Officer
COO: David Kent, Chief Operating Officer
CFO: Scott Walker, Chief Financial Officer
CNO: Gloria V. Barnes, MSN, Assistant Vice President Patient Care Services
Web address: www.cancercenter.com/southeastern–hospital.cfm
**Control:** Corporation, Investor–owned, for–profit **Service:** Cancer

**Staffed Beds:** 50 **Admissions:** 774 **Census:** 13 **Outpatient Visits:** 72116
**Births:** 0 **Personnel:** 754

## OCILLA—Irwin County

⊞ **IRWIN COUNTY HOSPITAL (110130)**, 710 North Irwin Avenue,
Zip 31774–5011; tel. 229/468–3800, (Nonreporting) **A**1 9 10
Primary Contact: Sue Spivey, Administrator
CFO: Tami Gray, Chief Financial Officer
CMO: Ashfaq Saiyed, M.D., Medical Director
CHR: Becky Edwards, Manager Human Resources
Web address: www.irwincntyhospital.com
**Control:** County–Government, nonfederal **Service:** General Medical and Surgical

**Staffed Beds:** 64

## PERRY—Houston County

⊞ **PERRY HOSPITAL (110153)**, 1120 Morningside Drive, Zip 31069–2906;
tel. 478/987–3600 **A**1 9 10 **F**3 11 16 18 29 30 34 35 39 40 45 48 50 56 57
58 59 61 68 70 75 79 81 82 85 86 87 89 100 107 110 111 114 115 119
129 130 131 132 133 134 135 146 147 148 **S** Houston Healthcare System,
Warner Robins, GA
Primary Contact: David Campbell, Administrator
CFO: Sean Whilden, Chief Financial Officer
CMO: Jefferson Davis, M.D., Medical Director
CIO: George Curtis, Director Information Systems
CHR: Michael O'Hara, Senior Executive Director
CNO: Melinda D. Hartley, R.N., Vice President Patient Care Services
Web address: www.hhc.org
**Control:** Other not–for–profit (including NFP Corporation) **Service:** General
Medical and Surgical

**Staffed Beds:** 39 **Admissions:** 1552 **Census:** 22 **Outpatient Visits:** 37394
**Births:** 0 **Total Expense ($000):** 24110 **Payroll Expense ($000):** 9232
**Personnel:** 211

## QUITMAN—Brooks County

⊞ **BROOKS COUNTY HOSPITAL (111332)**, 903 North Court Street,
Zip 31643–1315, Mailing Address: P.O. Box 5000, Zip 31643–5000;
tel. 229/263–4171 **A**1 9 10 18 **F**11 15 18 29 34 35 40 50 57 59 68 75 86
87 97 107 110 111 119 127 130 133 135 146 **P**6 **S** Archbold Medical Center,
Thomasville, GA
Primary Contact: Kenneth D. Rhudy, Chief Executive Officer
CFO: Skip Hightower, Chief Financial Officer
CMO: Michael Sopt, M.D., Chief of Staff
CHR: Janet Eldridge, Director Human Resources and Personnel
CNO: June Furney, R.N., Director of Nursing
Web address: www.archbold.org
**Control:** Hospital district or authority, Government, nonfederal **Service:** General
Medical and Surgical

**Staffed Beds:** 25 **Admissions:** 474 **Census:** 16 **Outpatient Visits:** 13572
**Births:** 0 **Total Expense ($000):** 12341 **Payroll Expense ($000):** 5413
**Personnel:** 89

**GA**

*Many Facility Codes have changed. Please refer to the AHA Guide Code Chart.*
© 2015 AHA Guide

## REIDSVILLE—Tattnall County

★ **OPTIM MEDICAL CENTER – TATTNALL (111323)**, 247 South Main Street, Zip 30453–4605; tel. 912/557–1000 **A**9 10 18 **F**3 8 11 15 29 34 35 37 40 45 46 50 54 59 64 74 75 77 79 81 82 85 86 87 90 91 93 94 96 97 107 111 114 119 127 129 130 131 133 146 **S** National Surgical Healthcare, Chicago, IL
Primary Contact: Brad Trower, Administrator
Web address: www.tattnallhospital.com
**Control:** Corporation, Investor–owned, for–profit **Service:** General Medical and Surgical

**Staffed Beds:** 25 **Admissions:** 1282 **Census:** 9 **Outpatient Visits:** 27815 **Births:** 0 **Total Expense ($000):** 46834 **Payroll Expense ($000):** 16587 **Personnel:** 152

## RIVERDALE—Clayton County

☐ **RIVERWOODS BEHAVIORAL HEALTH SYSTEM (114035)**, 233 Medical Center Drive, Zip 30274–2640; tel. 770/991–8500, (Nonreporting) **A**1 5 10 **S** Acadia Healthcare Company, Inc., Franklin, TN
Primary Contact: Kirk Kureska, Chief Executive Officer
COO: Jenifer Harcourt, Chief Operating Officer
CFO: Tricia Nelson, Chief Financial Officer
CIO: Hema Patel, Director Medical Records
CHR: Tareka Beasley, Director Human Resources
Web address: www.riverwoodsbehavioral.com
**Control:** Corporation, Investor–owned, for–profit **Service:** Psychiatric

**Staffed Beds:** 75

⊞ **SOUTHERN CRESCENT HOSPITAL FOR SPECIALTY CARE (112015)**, 11 Upper Riverdale Road S.W., 6th Floor, Zip 30274–2615; tel. 770/897–7600 **A**1 10 **F**1 29 30 35 44 75 77 82 84 87 148 **S** CHRISTUS Health, Irving, TX
Primary Contact: Jeff Denney, Administrator
Web address: www.christusdubuis.org/SouthernCrescentHospitalforSpecialtyCare
**Control:** Church–operated, Nongovernment, not–for profit **Service:** Long–Term Acute Care hospital

**Staffed Beds:** 30 **Admissions:** 250 **Census:** 20 **Outpatient Visits:** 0 **Births:** 0 **Total Expense ($000):** 10605 **Payroll Expense ($000):** 3939 **Personnel:** 69

☐ **SOUTHERN REGIONAL MEDICAL CENTER (110165)**, 11 Upper Riverdale Road S.W., Zip 30274–2615; tel. 770/991–8000, (Nonreporting) **A**1 2 3 5 9 10
Primary Contact: Kimberly Ryan, Administrator
COO: Therese O. Sucher, Senior Vice President Operations
CFO: Richard G. Stovall, Senior Vice President Fiscal Services and Chief Financial Officer
CMO: Willie Cochran, Jr., M.D., Chief of Staff
CIO: Karen Moore, Vice President Information Technology and Chief Information Officer
CHR: Norma Adams, Director Human Resources
Web address: www.southernregional.org
**Control:** Other not–for–profit (including NFP Corporation) **Service:** General Medical and Surgical

**Staffed Beds:** 274

## ROME—Floyd County

⊞ **FLOYD MEDICAL CENTER (110054)**, 304 Turner McCall Boulevard, Zip 30165–5621, Mailing Address: P.O. Box 233, Zip 30162–0233; tel. 706/509–5000 **A**1 2 3 5 9 10 13 19 **F**3 4 5 6 7 8 9 11 12 13 15 17 18 20 22 26 28 29 30 31 32 34 35 36 37 38 39 40 43 44 45 46 48 49 50 51 53 54 56 57 58 59 61 63 64 65 66 68 70 71 72 74 75 76 77 78 79 81 82 84 85 86 87 88 89 90 93 96 97 98 100 101 102 103 104 107 108 110 111 114 115 118 119 129 130 131 132 134 135 143 144 146 147 148
Primary Contact: Kurt Stuenkel, FACHE, President and Chief Executive Officer
COO: Warren Alston Rigas, Executive Vice President and Chief Operating Officer
CFO: Rick Sheerin, Vice President Fiscal Services
CMO: Joseph Biuso, M.D., Vice President and Chief of Medical Affairs
CIO: Jeff Buda, Chief Information Officer
CHR: Beth Bradford, Director Human Resources
CNO: Sheila Bennett, R.N., Vice President & Chief Nursing Officer
Web address: www.floyd.org
**Control:** Other not–for–profit (including NFP Corporation) **Service:** General Medical and Surgical

**Staffed Beds:** 327 **Admissions:** 13885 **Census:** 205 **Outpatient Visits:** 252392 **Births:** 2203 **Total Expense ($000):** 326480 **Payroll Expense ($000):** 140660 **Personnel:** 2329

⊞ **KINDRED HOSPITAL ROME (112010)**, 304 Turner McCall Boulevard, Zip 30165–5621; tel. 706/378–6800, (Nonreporting) **A**1 9 10 **S** Kindred Healthcare, Louisville, KY
Primary Contact: Chad Lovett, Chief Executive Officer
CFO: Julia Smith, Chief Financial Officer
CMO: Brij Singh, Medical Staff Director
CHR: Holly Murdock, Human Resources Coordinator
CNO: Jennifer Johnstone, Chief Clinical Officer
Web address: www.kindredrome.com
**Control:** Corporation, Investor–owned, for–profit **Service:** Long–Term Acute Care hospital

**Staffed Beds:** 45

⊞ **REDMOND REGIONAL MEDICAL CENTER (110168)**, 501 Redmond Road, Zip 30165–1415, Mailing Address: P.O. Box 107001, Zip 30165–7001; tel. 706/291–0291, (Nonreporting) **A**1 2 9 10 19 **S** HCA, Nashville, TN
Primary Contact: John Quinlivan, Chief Executive Officer
COO: Patrick Trammell, Chief Operating Officer
CFO: Ken Metteauer, Chief Financial Officer
CMO: Julie Coffman Barnes, M.D., Chief Medical Officer
CIO: Brad Treglown, Director Information Systems
CHR: Patsy Adams, Vice President Human Resources
CNO: Lisa Wallace, R.N., Chief Nursing Officer
Web address: www.redmondregional.com
**Control:** Corporation, Investor–owned, for–profit **Service:** General Medical and Surgical

**Staffed Beds:** 230

**SPECIALTY HOSPITAL** See Kindred Hospital Rome

## ROSWELL—Fulton County

⊞ **NORTH FULTON REGIONAL HOSPITAL (110198)**, 3000 Hospital Boulevard, Zip 30076–3899; tel. 770/751–2500, (Nonreporting) **A**1 2 3 9 10 13 **S** TENET Healthcare Corporation, Dallas, TX
Primary Contact: Deborah C. Keel, Chief Executive Officer
COO: Teresa C. Urquhart, Chief Operating Officer
CFO: Lyra Howalt, Chief Financial Officer
CMO: Karim Godamunne, M.D., Chief Medical Officer
CHR: Susan Brown, Chief Human Resources Officer
CNO: Nancy Melcher, Chief Nursing Officer
Web address: www.northfultonregional.com
**Control:** Corporation, Investor–owned, for–profit **Service:** General Medical and Surgical

**Staffed Beds:** 196

## SAINT MARYS—Camden County

⊞ **SOUTHEAST GEORGIA HEALTH SYSTEM CAMDEN CAMPUS (110146)**, 2000 Dan Proctor Drive, Zip 31558–3810; tel. 912/576–6200 **A**1 9 10 20 **F**3 11 13 15 29 30 31 34 35 40 45 46 47 48 49 50 54 57 59 64 68 70 71 75 77 78 79 81 85 86 87 93 94 96 107 108 110 111 114 116 117 119 120 129 130 131 132 146 **P**5 **S** Southeast Georgia Health System, Brunswick, GA
Primary Contact: Howard W. Sepp, Jr., FACHE, Vice President and Administrator
CFO: Michael D. Scherneck, Executive Vice President and Chief Financial Officer
CMO: Christian Smith, Chief of Staff
CIO: Chuck Bumgardner, Director
CHR: Patrick D. Ebri, Ph.D., Vice President Human Resources
Web address: www.sghs.org
**Control:** City–County, Government, nonfederal **Service:** General Medical and Surgical

**Staffed Beds:** 40 **Admissions:** 1848 **Census:** 17 **Outpatient Visits:** 80977 **Births:** 733 **Total Expense ($000):** 37889 **Payroll Expense ($000):** 14637 **Personnel:** 271

## SAINT SIMONS ISLAND—Glynn County

☐ **SAINT SIMONS BY–THE–SEA HOSPITAL (114016)**, 2927 Demere Road, Zip 31522–1620; tel. 912/638–1999, (Nonreporting) **A**1 9 10 **S** Universal Health Services, Inc., King of Prussia, PA
Primary Contact: Tim Merritt, Chief Executive Officer
CMO: Kim Masters, M.D., Medical Director
CIO: Chisty Mosely, Director Information Management
Web address: www.ssbythesea.com
**Control:** Corporation, Investor–owned, for–profit **Service:** Psychiatric

**Staffed Beds:** 101

**GA**

---

**Hospital, Medicare Provider Number, Address, Telephone, Approval, Facility, and Physician Codes, Health Care System**

★ American Hospital Association (AHA) membership  ○ Healthcare Facilities Accreditation Program  ⇑ Center for Improvement in Healthcare Quality Accreditation
☐ The Joint Commission accreditation  ◇ DNV Healthcare Inc. accreditation  △ Commission on Accreditation of Rehabilitation Facilities (CARF) accreditation

## SANDERSVILLE—Washington County

☐ **WASHINGTON COUNTY REGIONAL MEDICAL CENTER (110086)**, 610 Sparta Road, Zip 31082–1860, Mailing Address: P.O. Box 636, Zip 31082–0636; tel. 478/240–2000, (Nonreporting) **A**1 9 10 20
Primary Contact: Jimmy Childre, Jr., Interim Chief Executive Officer
CFO: Cythia Parker, Fiscal Director
CMO: Robert Wright, M.D., Chief of Staff
CHR: Gayle Prince, Director Human Resources
Web address: www.wcrmc.com
**Control:** Hospital district or authority, Government, nonfederal **Service:** General Medical and Surgical

**Staffed Beds:** 116

## SAVANNAH—Chatham County

☒ △ **CANDLER HOSPITAL (110024)**, 5353 Reynolds Street, Zip 31405–6015; tel. 912/819–6000, (Total facility includes 11 beds in nursing home–type unit) **A**1 7 9 10 **F**2 3 11 13 15 18 20 29 30 31 32 34 35 36 37 38 39 40 44 45 46 47 48 49 50 53 54 57 58 59 60 61 64 65 68 70 71 73 74 75 76 77 78 80 81 82 84 85 86 87 89 90 93 94 96 107 108 110 111 115 117 118 119 120 121 123 124 126 128 129 130 131 132 135 146 147 148
Primary Contact: Paul P. Hinchey, President and Chief Executive Officer
CFO: Gregory J. Schaack, CPA, Vice President and Chief Financial Officer
CMO: James Scott, M.D., Vice President Medical Affairs
CIO: George Evans, Vice President and Chief Information Officer
CHR: Don Stubbs, Vice President Human Resources
CNO: Sherry Danello, MSN, Vice President and Chief Nursing Officer
Web address: www.sjchs.org
**Control:** Church–operated, Nongovernment, not–for profit **Service:** General Medical and Surgical

**Staffed Beds:** 286 **Admissions:** 12224 **Census:** 190 **Outpatient Visits:** 229388 **Births:** 3009 **Total Expense ($000):** 235098 **Payroll Expense ($000):** 90789 **Personnel:** 1675

☐ **COASTAL HARBOR TREATMENT CENTER (114008)**, 1150 Cornell Avenue, Zip 31406–2702; tel. 912/354–3911 **A**1 9 10 **F**5 98 99 103 105 106 **S** Universal Health Services, Inc., King of Prussia, PA
Primary Contact: Sally Perry, Chief Executive Officer
COO: Ray Heckerman, Chief Executive Officer and Managing Director
CFO: Brad Lavoie, Chief Financial Officer
CMO: Reemon Bishara, M.D., Medical Director
CHR: Kellie Carlson, Director Human Resources
CNO: Jillisa Thornton, Director of Nursing
Web address: www.coastalharbor.com
**Control:** Corporation, Investor–owned, for–profit **Service:** Psychiatric

**Staffed Beds:** 193 **Admissions:** 2972 **Census:** 127 **Outpatient Visits:** 21310 **Births:** 0 **Total Expense ($000):** 28864 **Payroll Expense ($000):** 12242 **Personnel:** 301

**GEORGE AND MARIE BACKUS CHILDREN'S HOSPITAL** See Memorial Children's Hospital

☐ **GEORGIA REGIONAL HOSPITAL AT SAVANNAH (114028)**, 1915 Eisenhower Drive, Zip 31406–5098; tel. 912/356–2011, (Nonreporting) **A**1 10
Primary Contact: Andy Mannich, Regional Administrator
COO: Thomas F. Kurtz, Jr., Chief Operating Officer
CFO: Janet Edenfield, Director Financial Services
CMO: Donald Manning, M.D., Clinical Director
CHR: Jamekia Powers, Assistant Director Human Resources
Web address: www.garegionalsavannah.com
**Control:** State–Government, nonfederal **Service:** Psychiatric

**Staffed Beds:** 105

⇧ **LANDMARK HOSPITAL OF SAVANNAH (110235)**, 800 East 68th Street, Zip 31405–4710; tel. 912/298–1000, (Nonreporting) **A**22 **S** Landmark Hospitals, Cape Girardeau, MO
Primary Contact: John Salandi, Chief Executive Officer
Web address: www.landmarkhospitals.com/savannah
**Control:** Partnership, Investor–owned, for–profit **Service:** Long–Term Acute Care hospital

**Staffed Beds:** 50

☒ △ **MEMORIAL HEALTH (110036)**, 4700 Waters Avenue, Zip 31404–6283, Mailing Address: P.O. Box 23089, Zip 31403–3089; tel. 912/350–8000, (Includes MEMORIAL CHILDREN'S HOSPITAL, 4700 Waters Avenue, Zip 31404–6220, Mailing Address: PO Box 23089, Zip 31403–3089; tel. 912/350–7337) **A**1 2 3 5 7 8 10 **F**3 8 11 12 13 14 15 17 18 19 20 22 24 26 28 29 30 31 32 34 35 36 37 39 40 41 43 44 45 46 49 50 53 54 55 56 57 59 60 61 64 65 66 68 70 71 72 73 74 75 76 77 78 79 80 81 82 83 84 85 86 87 88 89 90 92 93 96 97 98 100 101 102 103 104 107 110 111 115 117 118 119 120 121 122 123 124 126 129 130 131 132 135 143 144 146 147 148 **P**6
Primary Contact: Margaret Gill, President and Chief Executive Officer
COO: Mary Chatman, Ph.D., Senior Vice President, Chief Operating Officer and Chief Nursing Officer
CFO: Laura Dow, Vice President, Finance
CMO: Ramon V. Meguiar, M.D., Chief Medical Officer
CIO: Kathryn McClellan, Vice President and Chief Information Officer
CHR: Jonathan Small, Vice President, Human Resources
CNO: Mary Chatman, Ph.D., Senior Vice President, Chief Operating Officer and Chief Nursing Officer
Web address: www.memorialhealth.com
**Control:** Other not–for–profit (including NFP Corporation) **Service:** General Medical and Surgical

**Staffed Beds:** 534 **Admissions:** 25666 **Census:** 425 **Outpatient Visits:** 235699 **Births:** 2885 **Total Expense ($000):** 457272 **Payroll Expense ($000):** 166285 **Personnel:** 3600

☒ **SELECT SPECIALTY HOSPITAL–SAVANNAH (112011)**, 5353 Reynolds Street, 4 South, Zip 31405–6015; tel. 912/819–7972, (Nonreporting) **A**1 9 10 **S** Select Medical Corporation, Mechanicsburg, PA
Primary Contact: Patrick McVey, Chief Executive Officer
Web address: www.selectspecialtyhospitals.com/company/locations/savannah.aspx
**Control:** Corporation, Investor–owned, for–profit **Service:** Long–Term Acute Care hospital

**Staffed Beds:** 40

**ST. JOSEPH'S CANDLER HOSPITAL** See Candler Hospital

☐ △ **ST. JOSEPH'S HOSPITAL (110043)**, 11705 Mercy Boulevard, Zip 31419–1791; tel. 912/819–4100, (Total facility includes 11 beds in nursing home–type unit) **A**1 2 7 9 10 **F**3 11 15 17 18 20 22 24 26 28 29 30 34 35 36 37 38 39 40 41 42 44 45 49 50 56 57 58 59 60 65 68 70 74 75 77 79 80 81 82 84 85 86 87 90 93 94 96 107 108 110 114 115 119 126 128 130 131 132 135 146 148
Primary Contact: Paul P. Hinchey, President and Chief Executive Officer
COO: Kyle McCann, Chief Operating Officer
CFO: Gregory J. Schaack, CPA, Vice President and Chief Financial Officer
CMO: James Scott, M.D., Vice President Medical Affairs
CIO: Nolan Henessee, Vice President and Chief Information Officer
CHR: Steve Pound, Vice President Human Resources
CNO: Sherry Danello, MSN, Vice President and Chief Nursing Officer
Web address: www.sjchs.org
**Control:** Church–operated, Nongovernment, not–for profit **Service:** General Medical and Surgical

**Staffed Beds:** 238 **Admissions:** 11096 **Census:** 175 **Outpatient Visits:** 78629 **Births:** 0 **Total Expense ($000):** 183123 **Payroll Expense ($000):** 65618 **Personnel:** 1254

## SMYRNA—Cobb County

☒ **RIDGEVIEW INSTITUTE (114012)**, 3995 South Cobb Drive S.E., Zip 30080–6397; tel. 770/434–4567 **A**1 5 9 10 **F**4 5 29 35 38 75 87 98 99 100 101 103 104 105 130 132 147 **P**8
Primary Contact: Frank Sartor, President and Chief Executive Officer
CFO: Ruth Jenkins, Chief Financial Officer
CMO: Thomas Bradford Johns, M.D., Medical Director
CIO: Lynn Leger, Director Information Systems
CHR: Betty Sonderman, Manager Human Resources
Web address: www.ridgeviewinstitute.com
**Control:** Other not–for–profit (including NFP Corporation) **Service:** Psychiatric

**Staffed Beds:** 102 **Admissions:** 4622 **Census:** 75 **Outpatient Visits:** 39246 **Births:** 0 **Total Expense ($000):** 30627 **Payroll Expense ($000):** 18012 **Personnel:** 327

## SNELLVILLE—Gwinnett County

☒ **EASTSIDE MEDICAL CENTER (110192)**, 1700 Medical Way, Zip 30078–2195; tel. 770/979–0200, (Nonreporting) **A**1 2 9 10 **S** HCA, Nashville, TN
Primary Contact: Scott Schmidly, Chief Executive Officer
COO: Callie Andrews, Chief Operating Officer
CMO: Michael O'Neill, M.D., Chief Medical Officer
CIO: Pattie Page, Director Marketing and Public Relations
Web address: www.eastsidemedical.com
**Control:** Corporation, Investor–owned, for–profit **Service:** General Medical and Surgical

**Staffed Beds:** 247

**GA**

## SPRINGFIELD—Effingham County

✠ **EFFINGHAM HOSPITAL (111306)**, 459 Highway 119 South, Zip 31329–3021, Mailing Address: P.O. Box 386, Zip 31329–0386; tel. 912/754–6451, (Total facility includes 105 beds in nursing home–type unit) **A**1 9 10 18 **F**3 6 11 15 18 26 27 29 32 34 35 40 43 45 49 50 54 56 57 59 61 64 74 77 79 81 85 86 97 107 110 111 114 119 127 128 130 133 134 135 146 147 148 **P**6
Primary Contact: Norma J. Morgan, Chief Executive Officer
COO: Tammy Mims, Chief Operating Officer
CMO: James Cornwell, M.D., Chief Medical Staff
CIO: Mary Pizzino, Chief Information Officer
CHR: Vicky Little, Director Human Resources
CNO: Marie Livingstone, R.N., Chief Nursing Officer
Web address: www.effinghamhospital.org
**Control:** Hospital district or authority, Government, nonfederal **Service:** General Medical and Surgical

> **Staffed Beds:** 130 **Admissions:** 930 **Census:** 108 **Outpatient Visits:** 42872 **Births:** 0 **Total Expense ($000):** 36154 **Payroll Expense ($000):** 16161 **Personnel:** 324

## STATESBORO—Bulloch County

✠ **EAST GEORGIA REGIONAL MEDICAL CENTER (110075)**, 1499 Fair Road, Zip 30458–1683, Mailing Address: P.O. Box 1048, Zip 30459–1048; tel. 912/486–1000 **A**1 9 10 19 **F**3 11 13 15 18 20 22 26 29 35 37 40 45 46 47 48 49 51 54 57 59 60 64 67 68 70 74 75 76 77 78 79 81 82 85 87 89 93 107 108 110 111 112 114 115 116 117 118 119 126 129 132 145 146 147 148 **P**5 **S** Community Health Systems, Inc., Franklin, TN
Primary Contact: Robert F. Bigley, President and Chief Executive Officer
COO: Heath Evans, Chief Operating Officer
CFO: Elmer Polite, Chief Financial Officer
CMO: Alan Scott, M.D., Chief of Staff
CIO: Conan Stuart, Director Information Services
CHR: Michael Black, Director Human Resources
CNO: Heidi Malez Coffee, Chief Nursing Officer
Web address: www.eastgeorgiaregional.com
**Control:** Corporation, Investor–owned, for–profit **Service:** General Medical and Surgical

> **Staffed Beds:** 149 **Admissions:** 7524 **Census:** 79 **Outpatient Visits:** 50464 **Births:** 1509 **Personnel:** 604

**WILLINGWAY HOSPITAL**, 311 Jones Mill Road, Zip 30458–4765; tel. 912/764–6236 **A**3 9 **F**4 5
Primary Contact: Barbara S. Reid, Chief Executive Officer
CMO: Robert W. Mooney, M.D., Medical Director
Web address: www.willingway.com
**Control:** Corporation, Investor–owned, for–profit **Service:** Alcoholism and other chemical dependency

> **Staffed Beds:** 40 **Admissions:** 414 **Census:** 31 **Outpatient Visits:** 9098 **Births:** 0 **Total Expense ($000):** 8240 **Payroll Expense ($000):** 3908 **Personnel:** 94

## STOCKBRIDGE—Henry County

★ ◇ **PIEDMONT HENRY HOSPITAL (110191)**, 1133 Eagle's Landing Parkway, Zip 30281–5099; tel. 678/604–1000 **A**2 9 10 21 **F**3 8 11 13 15 18 20 22 26 29 30 31 34 35 37 40 45 46 49 53 54 57 59 61 64 70 72 73 74 75 76 77 78 79 81 82 84 85 86 87 93 100 107 108 110 111 114 115 118 119 120 121 122 124 130 132 135 144 146 147 148 **P**3 **S** Piedmont Healthcare, Atlanta, GA
Primary Contact: Charles F. Scott, President and Chief Executive Officer
COO: Jeff Cooper, Chief Operating Officer
CFO: Sherry Henderson, Chief Financial Officer
CMO: Jagdeep Singh, M.D., Chief Medical Officer
CHR: Virgil Holder, Human Resources Business Partner
CNO: Frances Marthone, R.N., Chief Nursing Officer
Web address: www.piedmonthenry.org
**Control:** Other not–for–profit (including NFP Corporation) **Service:** General Medical and Surgical

> **Staffed Beds:** 214 **Admissions:** 12363 **Census:** 152 **Outpatient Visits:** 141474 **Births:** 2304 **Total Expense ($000):** 159538 **Payroll Expense ($000):** 63698 **Personnel:** 1064

## SWAINSBORO—Emanuel County

◇ **EMANUEL MEDICAL CENTER (110109)**, 117 Kite Road, Zip 30401–3231, Mailing Address: P.O. Box 879, Zip 30401–0879; tel. 478/289–1100, (Nonreporting) **A**9 10 20 21
Primary Contact: Mel Pyne, Chief Executive Officer
CFO: Rhonda Durden, Chief Financial Officer
CMO: Cedric Porter, M.D., President Medical Staff
CIO: Dave Flanders, Director Information Technology Systems
CHR: Ellen Boyd, Director Human Resources
Web address: www.emanuelmedical.org
**Control:** Hospital district or authority, Government, nonfederal **Service:** General Medical and Surgical

> **Staffed Beds:** 91

## SYLVANIA—Screven County

★ **OPTIM MEDICAL CENTER – SCREVEN (111312)**, 215 Mims Road, Zip 30467–2097; tel. 912/564–7426 **A**9 10 18 **F**3 11 15 29 34 35 40 45 50 59 64 65 75 77 79 81 82 90 93 97 107 119 133 146 **S** National Surgical Healthcare, Chicago, IL
Primary Contact: Robert R. Sellers, Administrator
CFO: Marsha Carroll, Director Financial Services
CIO: Rob Snipes, Chief Information Officer
CHR: Natalie Peterson, Human Resources Director
CNO: S. Lagina Evans, R.N., Assistant Chief Nursing Officer
Web address: www.optimhealth.com
**Control:** Corporation, Investor–owned, for–profit **Service:** General Medical and Surgical

> **Staffed Beds:** 25 **Admissions:** 267 **Census:** 4 **Outpatient Visits:** 16019 **Births:** 0 **Total Expense ($000):** 9581 **Payroll Expense ($000):** 4803

## SYLVESTER—Worth County

★ ◇ **PHOEBE WORTH MEDICAL CENTER (111328)**, 807 South Isabella Street, Zip 31791–7554, Mailing Address: P.O. Box 545, Zip 31791–0545; tel. 229/776–6961, (Nonreporting) **A**9 10 18 21 **S** Phoebe Putney Health System, Albany, GA
Primary Contact: Kim Gilman, Chief Executive Officer
CFO: Candace Guarnieri, Chief Financial Officer
CMO: Natu M. Patel, M.D., Chief of Staff
CHR: Clay Jones, Regional Director of Human Resources
Web address: www.phoebeputney.com
**Control:** Other not–for–profit (including NFP Corporation) **Service:** General Medical and Surgical

> **Staffed Beds:** 25

## THOMASTON—Upson County

★ ◇ **UPSON REGIONAL MEDICAL CENTER (110002)**, 801 West Gordon Street, Zip 30286–3426, Mailing Address: P.O. Box 1059, Zip 30286–0027; tel. 706/647–8111 **A**9 10 20 21 **F**3 11 13 15 28 29 30 31 34 35 36 40 45 46 49 50 57 59 61 64 70 76 78 79 80 81 82 85 86 87 89 107 108 111 114 115 118 119 124 130 131 132 135 148 **P**6 **S** HealthTech Management Services, Brentwood, TN
Primary Contact: David L. Castleberry, FACHE, Chief Executive Officer
CFO: John Williams, Chief Financial Officer
CIO: Douglas Thompson, Chief Information Officer
CHR: Rich Williams, Director Human Resources
CNO: Marilyn Ray, MSN, Chief Nursing Officer
Web address: www.urmc.org
**Control:** Other not–for–profit (including NFP Corporation) **Service:** General Medical and Surgical

> **Staffed Beds:** 77 **Admissions:** 3056 **Census:** 32 **Outpatient Visits:** 76078 **Births:** 390 **Total Expense ($000):** 58980 **Payroll Expense ($000):** 22640 **Personnel:** 472

**GA**

---

**Hospital, Medicare Provider Number, Address, Telephone, Approval, Facility, and Physician Codes, Health Care System**

★ American Hospital Association (AHA) membership
□ The Joint Commission accreditation
◯ Healthcare Facilities Accreditation Program
◇ DNV Healthcare Inc. accreditation
⇑ Center for Improvement in Healthcare Quality Accreditation
△ Commission on Accreditation of Rehabilitation Facilities (CARF) accreditation

## THOMASVILLE—Thomas County

✠ **JOHN D. ARCHBOLD MEMORIAL HOSPITAL (110038)**, 915 Gordon Avenue, Zip 31792–6614, Mailing Address: P.O. Box 1018, Zip 31799–1018; tel. 229/228–2000, (Total facility includes 64 beds in nursing home–type unit) **A**1 2 9 10 19 **F**3 5 8 11 13 15 18 20 22 26 28 29 34 35 36 40 43 45 46 47 48 49 50 51 57 59 60 64 67 68 70 74 75 76 77 78 79 81 82 84 85 86 87 89 90 93 98 101 102 103 104 106 107 108 110 111 114 115 117 118 119 121 123 124 126 128 129 130 131 132 143 144 146 147 148 **P**6 **S** Archbold Medical Center, Thomasville, GA
Primary Contact: J. Perry Mustian, President and Chief Executive Officer
CFO: Skip Hightower, Senior Vice President and Chief Financial Officer
CIO: Tracy Gray, Senior Vice President Information Services
CHR: Zach Wheeler, Senior Vice President Human Resources
CNO: Amy Griffin, Vice President Patient Care Services
Web address: www.archbold.org
**Control:** Other not–for–profit (including NFP Corporation) **Service:** General Medical and Surgical

**Staffed Beds:** 302 **Admissions:** 10080 **Census:** 216 **Outpatient Visits:** 223993 **Births:** 841 **Total Expense ($000):** 217766 **Payroll Expense ($000):** 73941 **Personnel:** 1752

## THOMSON—McDuffie County

★ ◇ **UNIVERSITY HOSPITAL MCDUFFIE (110111)**, 2460 Washington Road, N.E., Zip 30824; tel. 706/595–1411 **A**9 10 21 **F**3 11 15 29 30 34 40 45 50 57 59 64 68 79 81 87 107 110 114 119 129 130 132 146 148 **S** University Health Care System, Augusta, GA
Primary Contact: Sandra I. McVicker, R.N., MSN, President and Chief Nursing Officer
CFO: Dave Belkoski, Chief Financial Officer
CIO: Lisa Sanderlin, Chief Information Officer
CHR: Belinda H. Campbell, Director Human Resources, Legal Compliance and Risk Management
CNO: Sandra I. McVicker, R.N., President and Chief Nursing Officer
Web address: www.universityhealth.org/mcduffie
**Control:** Other not–for–profit (including NFP Corporation) **Service:** General Medical and Surgical

**Staffed Beds:** 25 **Admissions:** 613 **Census:** 5 **Outpatient Visits:** 26516 **Births:** 0 **Total Expense ($000):** 14756 **Payroll Expense ($000):** 6125 **Personnel:** 83

## TIFTON—Tift County

✠ **TIFT REGIONAL MEDICAL CENTER (110095)**, 901 East 18th Street, Zip 31794–3648, Mailing Address: Drawer 747, Zip 31793–0747; tel. 229/382–7120, (Total facility includes 15 beds in nursing home–type unit) **A**1 2 9 10 19 **F**3 8 9 11 12 13 15 18 20 22 26 28 29 31 33 34 35 40 45 47 49 50 54 57 59 60 63 64 68 70 74 75 76 77 78 79 81 82 84 85 86 87 89 92 93 97 107 108 110 111 114 115 118 119 120 121 123 126 128 129 130 132 135 143 144 146 147 148 **P**6 **S** Tift Regional Health System, Tifton, GA
Primary Contact: William T. Richardson, President and Chief Executive Officer
COO: Christopher Dorman, Senior Vice President/Chief Operating Officer
CFO: Dennis L. Crum, Senior Vice President and Chief Financial Officer
CMO: William Guest, M.D., Senior Vice President and Chief Medical Officer
CIO: Guy McAllister, Vice President and Chief Information Officer
CHR: Lori S. Folsom, Assistant Vice President Human Resources
CNO: Carol Smith, Vice President Patient Care and Chief Nursing Officer
Web address: www.tiftregional.com
**Control:** Hospital district or authority, Government, nonfederal **Service:** General Medical and Surgical

**Staffed Beds:** 191 **Admissions:** 9354 **Census:** 119 **Outpatient Visits:** 179856 **Births:** 1271 **Total Expense ($000):** 262151 **Payroll Expense ($000):** 111546 **Personnel:** 1816

## TOCCOA—Stephens County

✠ **STEPHENS COUNTY HOSPITAL (110032)**, 163 Hospital Drive, Zip 30577–6820; tel. 706/282–4200, (Total facility includes 92 beds in nursing home–type unit) **A**1 9 10 **F**3 7 11 13 15 28 30 34 35 40 51 57 59 60 64 68 70 75 76 77 79 81 85 86 89 93 107 110 111 115 119 125 129 130 146 148
Primary Contact: Edward C. Gambrell, Jr., Administrator
CFO: Jeff Laird, Controller
CHR: Diane Hardeman, Director Personnel
CNO: Faye M. Taylor, R.N., Director of Nursing
Web address: www.stephenscountyhospital.com
**Control:** Hospital district or authority, Government, nonfederal **Service:** General Medical and Surgical

**Staffed Beds:** 188 **Admissions:** 2275 **Census:** 123 **Outpatient Visits:** 35404 **Births:** 374 **Total Expense ($000):** 46823 **Payroll Expense ($000):** 21198 **Personnel:** 485

## VALDOSTA—Lowndes County

☐ **GREENLEAF CENTER (114036)**, 2209 Pineview Drive, Zip 31602–7316; tel. 229/247–4357, (Nonreporting) **A**1 10 **S** Acadia Healthcare Company, Inc., Franklin, TN
Primary Contact: Stephen Register, Chief Executive Officer
Web address: www.greenleafcounseling.net
**Control:** Corporation, Investor–owned, for–profit **Service:** Psychiatric

**Staffed Beds:** 50

✠ **SOUTH GEORGIA MEDICAL CENTER (110122)**, 2501 North Patterson Street, Zip 31602–1735, Mailing Address: P.O. Box 1727, Zip 31603–1727; tel. 229/333–1000, (Includes SMITH NORTHVIEW HOSPITAL, 4280 North Valdosta Road, Zip 31602, Mailing Address: P.O. Box 10010, Zip 31604; tel. 229/671–2000; Leonard Carter, Campus Administrator) **A**1 2 9 10 19 **F**3 7 8 11 13 15 17 18 20 22 24 26 28 29 30 31 32 34 35 39 40 45 46 47 49 50 51 54 57 58 59 60 64 68 70 72 73 74 75 76 77 78 79 81 82 84 85 86 87 89 90 96 107 108 110 111 113 114 115 117 118 119 120 121 123 124 126 129 130 131 132 135 143 144 146 147 148 **P**6
Primary Contact: Raymond A. Snead, Chief Executive Officer and Administrator
COO: Andrew Flemer, Chief Operating Officer
CFO: Raymond A. Snead, Jr., FACHE, Interim Chief Financial Officer
CMO: Kimberly Megow, M.D., Chief Medical Officer
CIO: Bob Foster, Chief Information Officer
CHR: Johnny Percy Ball, III, Assistant Administrator Human Resources
Web address: www.sgmc.org
**Control:** Hospital district or authority, Government, nonfederal **Service:** General Medical and Surgical

**Staffed Beds:** 302 **Admissions:** 14996 **Census:** 174 **Outpatient Visits:** 251891 **Births:** 2212 **Total Expense ($000):** 302743 **Payroll Expense ($000):** 95604 **Personnel:** 2299

## VIDALIA—Toombs County

✠ **MEADOWS REGIONAL MEDICAL CENTER (110128)**, One Meadows Parkway, Zip 30474–8759, Mailing Address: P.O. Box 1048, Zip 30475–1048; tel. 912/535–5555 **A**1 9 10 20 **F**11 13 15 18 20 22 29 30 31 34 35 37 40 43 45 46 47 50 51 53 54 57 59 60 62 64 68 70 74 75 77 78 79 81 85 86 87 93 97 107 108 110 111 115 118 119 124 127 129 130 131 132 146 147 148
Primary Contact: Alan Kent, Chief Executive Officer
COO: Shirley Hoskins, Chief Operating Officer
CFO: John Cornell, Vice President Finance
CIO: Charles Bondurant, Chief Information Officer
Web address: www.meadowsregional.org
**Control:** Other not–for–profit (including NFP Corporation) **Service:** General Medical and Surgical

**Staffed Beds:** 57 **Admissions:** 4202 **Census:** 42 **Outpatient Visits:** 78155 **Births:** 793 **Total Expense ($000):** 97910 **Payroll Expense ($000):** 33640 **Personnel:** 653

## VILLA RICA—Carroll County

✠ **TANNER MEDICAL CENTER–VILLA RICA (110015)**, 601 Dallas Road, Zip 30180–1202; tel. 770/456–3000, (Nonreporting) **A**1 9 10 **S** Tanner Health System, Carrollton, GA
Primary Contact: Bonnie Boles, M.D., Administrator
Web address: www.tanner.org
**Control:** Other not–for–profit (including NFP Corporation) **Service:** General Medical and Surgical

**Staffed Beds:** 39

## WARM SPRINGS—Meriwether County

☐ **ROOSEVELT WARM SPRINGS REHABILITATION AND SPECIALTY HOSPITALS – LTAC (112000)**, 6135 Roosevelt Highway, Zip 31830–2757, Mailing Address: P.O. Box 280, Zip 31830–2757; tel. 706/655–5000 **A**1 10 **F**1 29 30 35 57 59 60 74 75 77 85 86 87 100 119 146 148 **P**6
Primary Contact: David L. Mork, Jr., FACHE, Chief Executive Officer
CFO: Laura Stokes, Director Financial Services
CMO: W. Burton McDaniel, Jr., M.D., Physician Executive
CHR: Laura Stokes, Director Human Resources
Web address: www.grhealth.org
**Control:** State–Government, nonfederal **Service:** Long–Term Acute Care hospital

**Staffed Beds:** 20 **Admissions:** 155 **Census:** 13 **Outpatient Visits:** 0 **Births:** 0 **Total Expense ($000):** 9072 **Payroll Expense ($000):** 4262 **Personnel:** 110

**GA**

*Many Facility Codes have changed. Please refer to the AHA Guide Code Chart.*   © 2015 AHA Guide

⊠ **ROOSEVELT WARM SPRINGS REHABILITATION AND SPECIALTY HOSPITALS – REHAB (113028)**, 6135 Roosevelt Highway, Zip 31830–2757, Mailing Address: P.O. Box 280, Zip 31830–0280; tel. 706/655–5515 **A**1 9 10 **F**29 30 35 57 59 60 74 75 77 85 86 87 90 100 119 146 148 **P**6
Primary Contact: David L. Mork, Jr., FACHE, Executive Director and Chief Operating Officer
CFO: Laura Stokes, Director Financial Services
CMO: Burton McDaniel, M.D., Medical Director
CIO: Christen Carter, Director Public Relations
CHR: Laura Stokes, Director Human Resources
Web address: www.rooseveltrehab.org
**Control:** State–Government, nonfederal **Service:** Rehabilitation

**Staffed Beds:** 32 **Admissions:** 335 **Census:** 14 **Outpatient Visits:** 0 **Births:** 0 **Total Expense ($000):** 9998 **Payroll Expense ($000):** 4262 **Personnel:** 137

⊠ **WARM SPRINGS MEDICAL CENTER (111316)**, 5995 Spring Street, Zip 31830–2149, Mailing Address: P.O. Box 8, Zip 31830–0008; tel. 706/655–3331, (Total facility includes 79 beds in nursing home–type unit) **A**1 9 10 18 **F**3 8 15 29 30 40 45 46 49 57 59 75 79 81 93 107 114 119 128 130 133 146
Primary Contact: Karen Daniel, Chief Executive Officer
CFO: Patrick Flynn, Chief Financial Officer
CMO: Alan Thompson, M.D., President Medical Staff
CIO: Milo Varnadoe, Director Information Systems
CHR: Theresa Passarelli, Human Resources Generalist
CNO: Lynda Ligon, Chief Nursing Officer
Web address: www.warmspringsmc.org
**Control:** Partnership, Investor–owned, for–profit **Service:** General Medical and Surgical

**Staffed Beds:** 104 **Admissions:** 326 **Census:** 78 **Outpatient Visits:** 14173 **Births:** 0 **Total Expense ($000):** 12373 **Payroll Expense ($000):** 5503 **Personnel:** 145

**WARNER ROBINS—Houston County**

⊠ **HOUSTON MEDICAL CENTER (110069)**, 1601 Watson Boulevard, Zip 31093–3431, Mailing Address: P.O. Box 2886, Zip 31099–2886; tel. 478/922–4281 **A**1 9 10 13 **F**3 11 13 15 18 20 22 26 28 29 30 31 34 35 38 39 40 45 46 48 49 50 51 54 56 57 58 59 60 61 64 68 70 73 75 76 79 81 82 85 86 87 89 92 93 98 100 102 103 107 108 110 111 114 115 118 119 129 130 131 132 134 135 144 146 147 148 **P**6 **S** Houston Healthcare System, Warner Robins, GA
Primary Contact: Cary Martin, Chief Executive Officer
CFO: Sean Whilden, Chief Financial Officer
CIO: George Curtis, Chief Information Officer
CHR: Michael O'Hara, Senior Executive Director Human Resources
Web address: www.hhc.org
**Control:** Other not–for–profit (including NFP Corporation) **Service:** General Medical and Surgical

**Staffed Beds:** 237 **Admissions:** 14498 **Census:** 174 **Outpatient Visits:** 222689 **Births:** 1988 **Total Expense ($000):** 198610 **Payroll Expense ($000):** 78890 **Personnel:** 1880

**WASHINGTON—Wilkes County**

☐ **WILLS MEMORIAL HOSPITAL (111325)**, 120 Gordon Street, Zip 30673–1602, Mailing Address: P.O. Box 370, Zip 30673–0370; tel. 706/678–2151, (Nonreporting) **A**1 9 10 18
Primary Contact: Jane Echols, Chief Executive Officer
CFO: Tracie Burriss, Chief Financial Officer
CMO: Robert J. Williams, M.D., Chief Medical Staff
CIO: Reed Hawkes, Chief Information Officer
CHR: Tom Urban, Director Human Resources
CNO: Ann Harrison, R.N., Director of Nursing
Web address: www.willsmemorialhospital.com
**Control:** Hospital district or authority, Government, nonfederal **Service:** General Medical and Surgical

**Staffed Beds:** 25

**WAYCROSS—Ware County**

⊠ **MAYO CLINIC HEALTH SYSTEM IN WAYCROSS (110003)**, 410 Darling Avenue, Zip 31501–6357, Mailing Address: P.O. Box 139, Zip 31502–0139; tel. 912/283–3030, (Nonreporting) **A**1 2 3 5 9 10 **S** Mayo Clinic, Rochester, MN
Primary Contact: John Presutti, D.O., Chief Executive Officer
COO: Mary Hoffman, Chief Administrative Officer and Chief Financial Officer
CFO: Mary Hoffman, Chief Administrative Officer and Chief Financial Officer
CIO: Barry Rudd, Chief Information Officer
CHR: Brigitte Churchill, Director of Human Resources
CNO: Holli Sweat, Associate Administrator and Chief Nursing Officer
Web address: www.mayoclinichealthsystem.org
**Control:** Other not–for–profit (including NFP Corporation) **Service:** General Medical and Surgical

**Staffed Beds:** 199

**WAYNESBORO—Burke County**

☐ **BURKE MEDICAL CENTER (110113)**, 351 Liberty Street, Zip 30830–9686; tel. 706/554–4435, (Nonreporting) **A**1 9 10
Primary Contact: Karen ONeal, Chief Executive Officer
CFO: Karen ONeal, Chief Financial Officer
CHR: Kim Anthony, Director Human Resources
CNO: Debra Burch, Chief Nursing Officer
Web address: www.burkemedical.net
**Control:** Hospital district or authority, Government, nonfederal **Service:** General Medical and Surgical

**Staffed Beds:** 40

**WINDER—Barrow County**

⊠ **BARROW REGIONAL MEDICAL CENTER (110045)**, 316 North Broad Street, Zip 30680–2150, Mailing Address: P.O. Box 688, Zip 30680–0688; tel. 770/867–3400 **A**1 9 10 **F**3 11 13 15 29 30 34 35 40 45 50 51 57 59 60 68 70 74 75 76 77 79 81 82 85 93 97 107 108 110 111 114 118 119 124 130 131 132 135 143 146 147 148 **S** Community Health Systems, Inc., Franklin, TN
Primary Contact: Chad Hatfield, Chief Executive Officer
CMO: William Lytollis, M.D., Chief of Staff
CIO: Ed Stanley, Director Information Systems
CHR: Tina Jackson, Director Human Resources
Web address: www.barrowregional.com
**Control:** Corporation, Investor–owned, for–profit **Service:** General Medical and Surgical

**Staffed Beds:** 56 **Admissions:** 1940 **Census:** 17 **Outpatient Visits:** 26536 **Births:** 118 **Personnel:** 235

**GA**

---

| **Hospital, Medicare Provider Number, Address, Telephone, Approval, Facility, and Physician Codes, Health Care System** |
| --- |

★ American Hospital Association (AHA) membership
☐ The Joint Commission accreditation
○ Healthcare Facilities Accreditation Program
◇ DNV Healthcare Inc. accreditation
⇑ Center for Improvement in Healthcare Quality Accreditation
△ Commission on Accreditation of Rehabilitation Facilities (CARF) accreditation

# HAWAII

## AIEA—Honolulu County

✠ **PALI MOMI MEDICAL CENTER (120026)**, 98–1079 Moanalua Road, Zip 96701–4713; tel. 808/486–6000 **A**1 2 5 9 10 **F**3 8 12 15 18 20 22 26 29 30 31 32 34 35 40 45 46 47 49 50 57 58 59 64 67 68 69 70 74 75 77 78 79 81 82 83 84 85 86 87 92 107 110 111 114 115 119 126 130 131 132 135 142 143 146 147 148 **P**5 8 **S** Hawaii Pacific Health, Honolulu, HI
Primary Contact: Art Gladstone, R.N., President and Chief Executive Officer
CFO: David Okabe, Executive Vice President, Chief Financial Officer and Treasurer
CMO: James Kakuda, M.D., Chief of Staff
CIO: Steve Robertson, Senior Vice President
CHR: Gail Lerch, R.N., Vice President Human Resources
CNO: Brigitte McKale, MSN, Vice President and Chief Nurse Executive
Web address: www.palimomi.org
**Control:** Other not–for–profit (including NFP Corporation) **Service:** General Medical and Surgical

**Staffed Beds:** 128 **Admissions:** 6797 **Census:** 121 **Outpatient Visits:** 167103 **Births:** 0 **Total Expense ($000):** 206884 **Payroll Expense ($000):** 78183 **Personnel:** 1105

## EWA BEACH—Honolulu County

✠ **KAHI MOHALA BEHAVIORAL HEALTH (124001)**, 91–2301 Old Fort Weaver Road, Zip 96706–3602; tel. 808/671–8511 **A**1 3 9 10 **F**29 35 44 68 98 99 100 101 103 104 105 106 127 130 132 133 143 **S** Sutter Health, Sacramento, CA
Primary Contact: Leonard Licina, Chief Executive Officer
CFO: Rose Choy, Chief Financial Officer
CMO: Steven Chaplin, M.D., Medical Director
CHR: Christina Enoka, Director Human Resources and Risk Management
Web address: www.kahimohala.org
**Control:** Other not–for–profit (including NFP Corporation) **Service:** Psychiatric

**Staffed Beds:** 76 **Admissions:** 678 **Census:** 69 **Outpatient Visits:** 3143 **Births:** 0 **Total Expense ($000):** 20948 **Payroll Expense ($000):** 9886 **Personnel:** 180

## HILO—Hawaii County

✠ **HILO MEDICAL CENTER (120005)**, 1190 Waianuenue Avenue, Zip 96720–2089; tel. 808/932–3000, (Nonreporting) **A**1 3 5 9 10 20 **S** Hawaii Health Systems Corporation, Honolulu, HI
Primary Contact: Dan Brinkman, R.N., Interim Chief Executive Officer
COO: Dan Brinkman, R.N., Chief Operating Officer
CFO: Money Atwal, Chief Financial Officer
CMO: Ted Peskin, M.D., Acute Care Medical Director
CIO: Money Atwal, Chief Information Officer
CHR: Holly Ka'Akimaka, Director Human Resources
CNO: Arthur Sampaga, Assistant Director Nursing
Web address: www.hmc.hhsc.org
**Control:** State–Government, nonfederal **Service:** General Medical and Surgical

**Staffed Beds:** 276

## HONOKAA—Hawaii County

★ **HALE HO'OLA HAMAKUA (121307)**, 45–547 Plumeria Street, Zip 96727–6902; tel. 808/932–4100, (Nonreporting) **A**5 9 10 18 **S** Hawaii Health Systems Corporation, Honolulu, HI
Primary Contact: David Culbreth, Administrator
CMO: Bruce Graves, M.D., Chief of Staff
CNO: Faith Olivera, R.N., Interim Director of Nursing
Web address: www.hhh.hhsc.org/
**Control:** State–Government, nonfederal **Service:** General Medical and Surgical

**Staffed Beds:** 52

## HONOLULU—Honolulu County

✠ **KAISER PERMANENTE MEDICAL CENTER (120011)**, 3288 Moanalua Road, Zip 96819–1469; tel. 808/432–0000, (Total facility includes 28 beds in nursing home–type unit) **A**1 3 5 10 **F**3 4 12 13 15 17 18 19 20 21 22 24 26 29 30 31 32 34 35 36 38 40 41 45 46 47 48 49 50 51 54 55 56 57 58 59 60 61 62 64 65 68 70 71 72 74 75 76 77 78 79 81 82 83 84 85 86 87 88 89 92 93 94 97 99 100 101 104 107 108 110 111 115 116 117 119 128 129 130 131 133 134 135 144 146 148 **P**1 **S** Kaiser Foundation Hospitals, Oakland, CA
Primary Contact: Linda Puu, Hospital Administrator
CFO: Thomas Risse, Chief Financial Officer and Vice President Business Services
CMO: Keith Ogasawara, M.D., Associate Medical Director and Professional Chief of Staff
CIO: Brian Yoshii, Vice President Information Technology
CHR: Jean Melnikoff, Vice President Human Resources
Web address: www.kaiserpermanente.org
**Control:** Other not–for–profit (including NFP Corporation) **Service:** General Medical and Surgical

**Staffed Beds:** 235 **Admissions:** 10222 **Census:** 167 **Outpatient Visits:** 60518 **Births:** 1481 **Personnel:** 1547

☐ **KAPIOLANI MEDICAL CENTER FOR WOMEN & CHILDREN (123300)**, 1319 Punahou Street, Zip 96826–1001; tel. 808/983–6000, (Nonreporting) **A**1 2 3 5 9 10 **S** Hawaii Pacific Health, Honolulu, HI
Primary Contact: Martha Smith, Chief Executive Officer
CFO: David Okabe, Senior Vice President, Chief Financial Officer and Treasurer
CIO: Steve Robertson, Vice President
CHR: Gail Lerch, R.N., Vice President
Web address: www.kapiolani.org
**Control:** Other not–for–profit (including NFP Corporation) **Service:** Children's general

**Staffed Beds:** 225

✠ **KUAKINI MEDICAL CENTER (120007)**, 347 North Kuakini Street, Zip 96817–2381; tel. 808/536–2236 **A**1 2 3 5 9 10 **F**3 15 17 18 20 22 24 26 28 29 31 34 35 40 45 46 49 57 58 59 60 68 70 74 75 77 78 79 80 81 82 85 86 87 107 108 110 111 114 115 117 118 119 121 129 130 131 132 145 146 147 148 **P**1
Primary Contact: Gary K. Kajiwara, President and Chief Executive Officer
CFO: Quin Ogawa, Vice President Finance and Chief Financial Officer
CMO: Nobuyuki Miki, M.D., Vice President Medical Services and Chief Medical Officer
CIO: Gary K. Kajiwara, President and Chief Executive Officer
CHR: Ann N. Choy, Manager Human Resources and Payroll
CNO: Virginia Walker, Vice President Nursing Services and Chief Nursing Officer
Web address: www.kuakini.org
**Control:** Other not–for–profit (including NFP Corporation) **Service:** General Medical and Surgical

**Staffed Beds:** 87 **Admissions:** 4884 **Census:** 82 **Outpatient Visits:** 56585 **Births:** 0 **Total Expense ($000):** 135779 **Payroll Expense ($000):** 61067 **Personnel:** 985

★ **LEAHI HOSPITAL (122001)**, 3675 Kilauea Avenue, Zip 96816–2398; tel. 808/733–8000, (Nonreporting) **A**9 10 **S** Hawaii Health Systems Corporation, Honolulu, HI
Primary Contact: Reid Kondo, Interim Chief Executive Officer
CFO: Edward Chu, Chief Financial Officer
CMO: Albert Yazawa, M.D., Regional Medical Director
CHR: Russel Higa, JD, Regional Director Human Resources
CNO: Amy Vasunaga, Chief Nurse Executive
Web address: www.hhsc.org
**Control:** State–Government, nonfederal **Service:** Long–Term Acute Care hospital

**Staffed Beds:** 164

**HI**

⊠ **QUEEN'S MEDICAL CENTER (120001)**, 1301 Punchbowl Street, Zip 96813–2499; tel. 808/691–5100, (Includes QUEEN'S MEDICAL CENTER – WEST OAHU, 91–2141 Fort Weaver Road, Ewa Beach, Zip 96706–1993; tel. 808/691–3000; Susan R. Murray, Chief Operating Officer), (Total facility includes 28 beds in nursing home–type unit) **A**1 2 3 5 9 10 **F**3 5 11 12 13 15 17 18 20 22 24 26 28 29 31 34 35 37 38 39 40 43 44 45 46 47 48 49 50 51 55 56 57 58 59 60 61 62 63 64 66 68 70 73 74 75 76 77 78 79 81 82 84 85 86 87 93 96 97 98 99 100 101 102 103 104 105 107 108 110 111 115 117 118 119 120 121 124 126 128 129 130 131 132 135 138 139 143 146 147 148 **S** Queen's Health Systems, Honolulu, HI
Primary Contact: Arthur A. Ushijima, FACHE, President
COO: Mark Yamakawa, Chief Operating Officer
CFO: Robert Nobriga, Executive Vice President and Chief Financial Officer
CMO: Leslie Chun, M.D., Vice President Medical Staff and Chief Quality Officer
CIO: Hunter Praywell, Vice President Information Technology and Chief Information Officer
CHR: Nona Tamanaha, Vice President Human Resources
CNO: Cynthia Kamikawa, R.N., Vice President Nursing Emergency Department and Trauma and Chief Nursing Officer
Web address: www.queensmedicalcenter.org
**Control:** Other not–for–profit (including NFP Corporation) **Service:** General Medical and Surgical

**Staffed Beds: 512 Admissions: 26060 Census: 433 Outpatient Visits: 383746 Births: 2231 Total Expense ($000): 817227 Payroll Expense ($000): 338246 Personnel: 3928**

⊠ **REHABILITATION HOSPITAL OF THE PACIFIC (123025)**, 226 North Kuakini Street, Zip 96817–2488; tel. 808/531–3511 **A**1 9 10 **F**3 11 28 29 34 36 44 54 58 64 68 74 75 77 79 90 91 93 94 95 96 130 131 132 135 143 146 147 148
Primary Contact: Timothy J. Roe, M.D., President and Chief Executive Officer
CFO: Wendy Manuel, Vice President and Chief Financial Officer
CMO: Jason Chang, M.D., Chief Medical Director
CIO: Scott Morimoto, Director Clinical Informatics
CHR: Faye Miyamoto, Vice President Human Resources
CNO: Amy Parungao, Director of Nursing
Web address: www.rehabhospital.org
**Control:** Other not–for–profit (including NFP Corporation) **Service:** Rehabilitation

**Staffed Beds: 70 Admissions: 1544 Census: 53 Outpatient Visits: 42369 Births: 0 Total Expense ($000): 40682 Payroll Expense ($000): 19717 Personnel: 279**

☐ **SHRINERS HOSPITALS FOR CHILDREN–HONOLULU (123301)**, 1310 Punahou Street, Zip 96826–1099; tel. 808/941–4466 **A**1 3 5 9 10 **F**29 35 39 53 58 64 74 75 77 79 81 93 94 119 130 132 146 **P**6 **S** Shriners Hospitals for Children, Tampa, FL
Primary Contact: John R. White, Administrator
CFO: Patricia Miyasawa, CPA, Director Fiscal Service
CMO: Craig Ono, M.D., Chief of Staff
CIO: Gregory A. Wolf, Director Information Systems
CHR: Derek Ito, Director Human Resources
CNO: Andrea Kubota, R.N., Director Patient Care Services
Web address: www.shrinershospitalsforchildren.org/Hospitals/Locations/Honolulu.aspx
**Control:** Other not–for–profit (including NFP Corporation) **Service:** Children's orthopedic

**Staffed Beds: 16 Admissions: 162 Census: 3 Outpatient Visits: 9343 Births: 0**

☐ **STRAUB CLINIC & HOSPITAL (120022)**, 888 South King Street, Zip 96813–3097; tel. 808/522–4000 **A**1 2 3 5 9 10 **F**3 11 15 16 18 20 21 22 23 24 26 27 28 29 30 31 34 40 44 45 47 49 50 54 56 57 59 64 65 68 70 74 75 77 78 79 80 81 84 85 86 87 92 93 97 100 104 107 108 110 111 114 118 119 129 130 131 132 135 143 144 145 146 147 148 **P**6 **S** Hawaii Pacific Health, Honolulu, HI
Primary Contact: Art Gladstone, R.N., Chief Executive Officer
COO: Maureen Flannery, Vice President Clinic Operations
CFO: David Okabe, Executive Vice President, Chief Financial Officer and Treasurer
CMO: Randy Yates, M.D., Chief Medical Officer
CIO: Steve Robertson, Executive Vice President and Chief Information Officer
CHR: Gail Lerch, R.N., Executive Vice President Human Resources
CNO: Patricia Boeckmann, R.N., Vice President Operations and Chief Nursing Officer
Web address: www.straubhealth.org
**Control:** Other not–for–profit (including NFP Corporation) **Service:** General Medical and Surgical

**Staffed Beds: 129 Admissions: 6908 Census: 116 Outpatient Visits: 832453 Births: 0 Total Expense ($000): 376351 Payroll Expense ($000): 169663 Personnel: 1672**

⊠ **TRIPLER ARMY MEDICAL CENTER**, 1 Jarret White Road, Zip 96859–5001; tel. 808/433–6661 **A**1 2 3 5 **F**3 7 8 12 13 14 15 18 19 20 21 22 23 24 25 26 27 29 30 31 32 33 34 35 36 38 39 40 41 43 44 45 46 47 48 49 50 51 52 53 54 55 56 57 58 59 60 64 65 67 68 70 72 74 75 76 77 78 79 81 82 85 86 87 88 89 91 92 93 94 96 97 98 99 100 101 102 103 104 105 106 107 108 110 111 115 116 117 118 119 120 121 123 124 126 127 129 130 131 132 133 134 135 143 144 145 146 147 148 **S** Department of the Army, Office of the Surgeon General, Falls Church, VA
Primary Contact: Colonel David K. Dunning, Commanding Officer
COO: Major Elias B. Lozano, Executive Officer
CFO: Lieutenant Colonel Christopher A. Wodarz, Chief, Resource Management Division
CMO: Captain Andrew L. Findlay, Deputy Commander Clinical Services
CIO: Lieutenant Colonel Donna E. Beed, Chief Information Management Division
CHR: Colonel James N. Davidson, Troop Commander
CNO: Colonel Jennifer L. Bedick, Deputy Commander Nursing
Web address: www.tamc.amedd.army.mil
**Control:** Army, Government, federal **Service:** General Medical and Surgical

**Staffed Beds: 194 Admissions: 13892 Census: 144 Outpatient Visits: 888687 Births: 3088**

★ **VETERANS AFFAIRS PACIFIC ISLANDS HEALTH CARE SYSTEM**, 459 Patterson Road, Zip 96819; tel. 808/433–0600, (Nonreporting) **S** Department of Veterans Affairs, Washington, DC
Primary Contact: James E. Hastings, M.D., Director
Web address: www.hawaii.va.gov/
**Control:** Veterans Affairs, Government, federal **Service:** General Medical and Surgical

**Staffed Beds: 0**

**KAHUKU—Honolulu County**

⊠ **KAHUKU MEDICAL CENTER (121304)**, 56–117 Pualalea Street, Zip 96731–2052; tel. 808/293–9221, (Total facility includes 8 beds in nursing home–type unit) **A**9 10 18 **F**3 29 34 35 40 41 59 64 69 75 82 86 87 91 93 97 107 108 114 119 128 130 132 133 146 148 **P**6
Primary Contact: Stephany Vaioleti, Administrator
CFO: Francis Daquioag, Controller
CMO: P. Douglas Nielson, M.D., Chief of Staff
Web address: www.hhsc.org/oahu/kahuku/index.html
**Control:** Other not–for–profit (including NFP Corporation) **Service:** General Medical and Surgical

**Staffed Beds: 21 Admissions: 107 Census: 18 Outpatient Visits: 5662 Births: 0 Total Expense ($000): 11091 Payroll Expense ($000): 4613 Personnel: 75**

**KAILUA—Honolulu County**

⊠ **CASTLE MEDICAL CENTER (120006)**, 640 Ulukahiki Street, Zip 96734–4454; tel. 808/263–5500 **A**1 3 9 10 **F**8 12 13 15 18 20 22 24 29 30 31 34 35 37 40 45 49 51 57 59 64 68 70 74 75 77 78 79 81 84 85 87 93 98 102 107 108 111 115 119 126 130 132 135 146 147 148 **P**8 **S** Adventist Health, Roseville, CA
Primary Contact: Kathryn A. Raethel, R.N., M.P.H., President and Chief Executive Officer
CMO: Alan Cheung, M.D., Vice President Medical Affairs
CIO: Brian Rothe, Site Director Information Systems
CHR: Todd Reese, Director Human Resources
CNO: Laura R. Westphal, Vice President Patient Care Services
Web address: www.castlemed.org
**Control:** Church–operated, Nongovernment, not–for profit **Service:** General Medical and Surgical

**Staffed Beds: 160 Admissions: 7598 Census: 92 Outpatient Visits: 99157 Births: 1067 Total Expense ($000): 144595 Payroll Expense ($000): 57274 Personnel: 779**

**KAMUELA—Hawaii County**

⊠ **NORTH HAWAII COMMUNITY HOSPITAL (120028)**, 67–1125 Mamalahoa Highway, Zip 96743–8496; tel. 808/885–4444, (Data for 181 days) **A**1 9 10 20 **F**3 8 13 15 18 26 29 30 31 34 35 36 40 43 45 46 49 50 53 57 58 59 62 64 68 70 75 76 77 78 79 81 84 85 93 97 107 108 110 111 115 119 130 131 146 147 148 **P**6 **S** Queen's Health Systems, Honolulu, HI
Primary Contact: Kenneth D. Graham, FACHE, President
CFO: Marilynn Hata, Vice President Finance and Operations
CMO: Gary Goldberg, M.D., Chief Medical Officer
CHR: Gary Sirman, Chief Human Resource Officer
CNO: Miquel Noelani Simms, Chief Nursing Officer
Web address: www.nhch.com
**Control:** Other not–for–profit (including NFP Corporation) **Service:** General Medical and Surgical

**Staffed Beds: 35 Admissions: 931 Census: 18 Outpatient Visits: 31867 Births: 272 Total Expense ($000): 26490 Payroll Expense ($000): 11984 Personnel: 290**

HI

---

**Hospital, Medicare Provider Number, Address, Telephone, Approval, Facility, and Physician Codes, Health Care System**

★ American Hospital Association (AHA) membership
☐ The Joint Commission accreditation
○ Healthcare Facilities Accreditation Program
◇ DNV Healthcare Inc. accreditation
⇑ Center for Improvement in Healthcare Quality Accreditation
△ Commission on Accreditation of Rehabilitation Facilities (CARF) accreditation

## KANEOHE—Honolulu County

☐ **HAWAII STATE HOSPITAL**, 45–710 Keaahala Road, Zip 96744–3597;
tel. 808/247–2191, (Nonreporting) **A**1 3 5
Primary Contact: William J. May, Administrator
COO: Anthony Fraiola, Associate Administrator Administrative and Support Services
CFO: Anthony Fraiola, Business Manager
CMO: William Sheehan, M.D., Medical Director
CIO: John Jansen, Management Information Specialist
CHR: Karen Hara, Personnel Management Specialist
CNO: Lani Tsuneishi, Chief Nursing Unit
Web address: www.hawaii.gov/health/
**Control:** State–Government, nonfederal **Service:** Psychiatric

**Staffed Beds:** 178

## KAPAAU—Kauai County

★ **SAMUEL MAHELONA MEMORIAL HOSPITAL (121306)**, 4800 Kawaihau Road,
Zip 96746–1971; tel. 808/822–4961, (Nonreporting) **A**9 10 18 **S** Hawaii Health Systems Corporation, Honolulu, HI
Primary Contact: Peter Klune, Chief Executive Officer
CFO: Michael Perel, Regional Chief Financial Officer
CMO: Gerald Tomory, M.D., Regional Medical Director
CIO: Sandra McMaster, Regional Chief Information Officer
CHR: Lani Aranio, Regional Director Human Resources
Web address: www.smmh.hhsc.org
**Control:** State–Government, nonfederal **Service:** General Medical and Surgical

**Staffed Beds:** 80

## KAUNAKAKAI—Maui County

⊠ **MOLOKAI GENERAL HOSPITAL (121303)**, 280 Home Olu Place,
Zip 96748–0408, Mailing Address: P.O. Box 408, Zip 96748–0408;
tel. 808/553–5331 **A**1 9 10 18 **F**3 15 29 34 35 40 41 44 50 57 59 63 64 65 66 68 69 75 77 78 82 84 87 91 93 97 107 110 115 119 127 130 132 133 134 135 147 148 **P**6 **S** Queen's Health Systems, Honolulu, HI
Primary Contact: Janice Kalanihuia, President
CFO: Zessica L. Apiki, Accountant
CMO: William Thomas, Jr., M.D., Medical Director Clinical and Internal Affairs
CIO: Sampson Wescoatt, Manager Information Technology
CHR: Alicia Teves, Coordinator Human Resources
Web address: www.queens.org
**Control:** Other not–for–profit (including NFP Corporation) **Service:** General Medical and Surgical

**Staffed Beds:** 15 **Admissions:** 131 **Census:** 1 **Outpatient Visits:** 29854
**Births:** 36 **Total Expense ($000):** 13008 **Payroll Expense ($000):** 4719
**Personnel:** 76

## KEALAKEKUA—Hawaii County

⊠ **KONA COMMUNITY HOSPITAL (120019)**, 79–1019 Haukapila Street,
Zip 96750–7920; tel. 808/322–9311 **A**1 9 10 20 **F**3 11 12 13 15 29 30 31 34 35 40 43 44 47 50 68 70 76 77 78 79 81 84 98 107 108 109 111 115 119 120 121 123 128 130 133 **S** Hawaii Health Systems Corporation, Honolulu, HI
Primary Contact: Jay E. Kreuzer, FACHE, Chief Executive Officer
CFO: Dean Herzog, Chief Financial Officer
CMO: Richard McDowell, M.D., Medical Director
CHR: Kathryn Salomon, Director Human Resources
CNO: Patricia Kalua, Chief Nurse Executive
Web address: www.kch.hhsc.org
**Control:** State–Government, nonfederal **Service:** General Medical and Surgical

**Staffed Beds:** 94 **Admissions:** 3532 **Census:** 48 **Outpatient Visits:** 38700
**Births:** 528 **Total Expense ($000):** 84027 **Payroll Expense ($000):** 32300
**Personnel:** 476

## KOHALA—Hawaii County

★ **KOHALA HOSPITAL (121302)**, (Critical Access Hospital), 54–383 Hospital
Road, Zip 96755, Mailing Address: P.O. Box 10, Kapaau, Zip 96755–0010;
tel. 808/889–6211, (Total facility includes 24 beds in nursing home–type unit) **A**9 10 18 **F**40 80 108 130 133 **P**6 **S** Hawaii Health Systems Corporation, Honolulu, HI
Primary Contact: Eugene Amar, Jr., Administrator
CMO: Silvia Sonnenschein, M.D., Chief of Staff
Web address: www.koh.hhsc.org
**Control:** State–Government, nonfederal **Service:** Other specialty

**Staffed Beds:** 28 **Admissions:** 31 **Census:** 21 **Outpatient Visits:** 2090
**Births:** 0 **Total Expense ($000):** 7664 **Payroll Expense ($000):** 3120
**Personnel:** 59

## KULA—Maui County

★ **KULA HOSPITAL (121308)**, 100 Keokea Place, Zip 96790–7450;
tel. 808/878–1221, (Nonreporting) **A**9 10 18 **S** Hawaii Health Systems Corporation, Honolulu, HI
Primary Contact: Darren Kasai, Assistant Administrator
CFO: Nerissa Garrity, Chief Financial Officer
CMO: Nicole Apoliona, M.D., Medical Director
Web address: www.hhsc.org
**Control:** State–Government, nonfederal **Service:** General Medical and Surgical

**Staffed Beds:** 6

## LANAI CITY—Maui County

★ **LANAI COMMUNITY HOSPITAL (121305)**, 628 Seventh Street,
Zip 96763–0650, Mailing Address: P.O. Box 630650, Zip 96763–0650;
tel. 808/565–8450, (Nonreporting) **A**9 10 18 **S** Hawaii Health Systems Corporation, Honolulu, HI
Primary Contact: Darren Kasai, Assistant Administrator
Web address: www.lch.hhsc.org
**Control:** Other not–for–profit (including NFP Corporation) **Service:** General Medical and Surgical

**Staffed Beds:** 24

## LIHUE—Kauai County

☐ **WILCOX MEMORIAL HOSPITAL (120014)**, 3–3420 Kuhio Highway,
Zip 96766–1099; tel. 808/245–1100 **A**1 2 9 10 20 **F**3 13 15 18 28 29 30 31 34 35 40 43 46 47 48 49 50 57 59 60 64 68 70 74 75 76 77 78 79 81 84 85 91 93 97 102 107 108 110 111 114 115 119 130 133 135 146 147 148 **S** Hawaii Pacific Health, Honolulu, HI
Primary Contact: Jen Chahanovich, President and Chief Executive Officer
CFO: David Okabe, Executive Vice President, Chief Financial Officer and Treasurer
CMO: Craig Netzer, M.D., President Medical Staff
CIO: Steve Robertson, Executive Vice President Revenue Cycle Management and Chief Information Officer
CNO: Mary Ann England, Chief Nurse Executive
Web address: www.wilcoxhealth.org
**Control:** Other not–for–profit (including NFP Corporation) **Service:** General Medical and Surgical

**Staffed Beds:** 65 **Admissions:** 3447 **Census:** 43 **Outpatient Visits:** 87887
**Births:** 550 **Total Expense ($000):** 92656 **Payroll Expense ($000):** 31428
**Personnel:** 442

## PAHALA—Hawaii County

★ **KAU HOSPITAL (121301)**, 1 Kamani Street, Zip 96777, Mailing Address: P.O.
Box 40, Zip 96777–0040; tel. 808/932–4200, (Total facility includes 16 beds in nursing home–type unit) **A**9 10 18 **F**40 59 64 97 127 128 133 146 **S** Hawaii Health Systems Corporation, Honolulu, HI
Primary Contact: Merilyn Harris, Administrator
CFO: Money Atwal, Chief Financial Officer
CMO: Clifford Field, M.D., Medical Director
Web address: www.hhsc.org
**Control:** State–Government, nonfederal **Service:** General Medical and Surgical

**Staffed Beds:** 21 **Admissions:** 30 **Census:** 14 **Outpatient Visits:** 7244
**Births:** 0 **Total Expense ($000):** 7825 **Payroll Expense ($000):** 5273
**Personnel:** 55

## WAHIAWA—Honolulu County

⊠ **WAHIAWA GENERAL HOSPITAL (120004)**, 128 Lehua Street,
Zip 96786–2036; tel. 808/621–8411, (Total facility includes 107 beds in nursing home–type unit) **A**1 3 5 9 10 **F**1 3 4 8 11 15 16 17 29 31 40 56 62 67 70 72 73 75 76 77 78 79 80 81 85 86 87 88 89 90 93 96 98 103 107 108 109 110 115 119 128 130 132 145 146 147 148 **P**8
Primary Contact: R. Don Olden, Chief Executive Officer
COO: R. Don Olden, Chief Executive Officer
CMO: Manuel Abundo, M.D., Chief of Staff
CIO: Jason Fujinaka, Manager Information System
CHR: Bert Shimabukuro, Director Human Resources
CNO: Tammy Kohrer, Director of Nursing–Acute
Web address: www.wahiawageneral.org
**Control:** Other not–for–profit (including NFP Corporation) **Service:** General Medical and Surgical

**Staffed Beds:** 160 **Admissions:** 2530 **Census:** 134 **Outpatient Visits:** 31906
**Births:** 0 **Total Expense ($000):** 62058 **Payroll Expense ($000):** 29506
**Personnel:** 365

## WAILUKU—Maui County

⊠ **MAUI MEMORIAL MEDICAL CENTER (120002)**, 221 Mahalani Street,
Zip 96793–2581; tel. 808/244–9056, (Nonreporting) **A**1 9 10 20 **S** Hawaii Health Systems Corporation, Honolulu, HI
Primary Contact: Wesley Lo, Regional Chief Executive Officer
CIO: Dana Mendoza, Chief Information Officer
Web address: www.mmmc.hhsc.org
**Control:** State–Government, nonfederal **Service:** General Medical and Surgical

**Staffed Beds:** 213

**HI**

✠ **KAUAI VETERANS MEMORIAL HOSPITAL (121300)**, Waimea Canyon Road,
Zip 96796, Mailing Address: P.O. Box 337, Zip 96796–0337;
tel. 808/338–9431, (Total facility includes 20 beds in nursing home–type unit) **A**1
9 10 18 **F**1 11 13 15 17 40 67 70 76 79 81 89 93 107 110 111 114 119
128 130 133 147 **S** Hawaii Health Systems Corporation, Honolulu, HI
Primary Contact: Peter Klune, Chief Executive Officer
CFO: Michael Perel, Regional Chief Financial Officer
CMO: Gerald Tomory, M.D., Regional Medical Director
CIO: Sandra McMaster, Regional Chief Information Officer
CHR: Solette Perry, Regional Director Human Resources
Web address: www.kvmh.hhsc.org
**Control:** State–Government, nonfederal **Service:** General Medical and Surgical

**Staffed Beds:** 45 **Admissions:** 800 **Census:** 26 **Outpatient Visits:** 7899
**Births:** 275 **Total Expense ($000):** 50923 **Payroll Expense ($000):** 32149
**Personnel:** 276

HI

**Hospital, Medicare Provider Number, Address, Telephone, Approval, Facility, and Physician Codes, Health Care System**

★ American Hospital Association (AHA) membership    ○ Healthcare Facilities Accreditation Program    ⇑ Center for Improvement in Healthcare Quality Accreditation
□ The Joint Commission accreditation    ◇ DNV Healthcare Inc. accreditation    △ Commission on Accreditation of Rehabilitation Facilities (CARF) accreditation

# IDAHO

## AMERICAN FALLS—Power County

★ **POWER COUNTY HOSPITAL DISTRICT (131304)**, 510 Roosevelt Road,
Zip 83211–1362, Mailing Address: P.O. Box 420, Zip 83211–0420;
tel. 208/226–3200, (Nonreporting) **A**9 10 18
Primary Contact: Dallas Clinger, Administrator
COO: Rock Roy, Professional Services Director
CFO: Jeremy Claunch, Chief Financial Officer
CMO: Bret Timmons, D.O., Chief Medical Staff
CIO: Mindy Earl, Health Information Manager
CHR: Norma Hartley, Director Human Resources
CNO: Daniel Kuta, R.N., Director of Nursing
Web address: www.pchd.net
**Control:** Hospital district or authority, Government, nonfederal **Service:** General
Medical and Surgical

Staffed Beds: 10

## ARCO—Butte County

**LOST RIVERS MEDICAL CENTER (131324)**, 551 Highland Drive,
Zip 83213–9771, Mailing Address: P.O. Box 145, Zip 83213–0145;
tel. 208/527–8206, (Nonreporting) **A**9 10 18
Primary Contact: Brad Huerta, Chief Executive Officer and Administrator
CFO: Jon Smith, Chief Financial Officer
CMO: Jeffrey Haskell, M.D., Chief Medical Staff
CHR: Tina Akins, Director Human Resources
CNO: Geri Cammack, R.N., Director of Nursing
Web address: www.lostriversmedical.com
**Control:** Hospital district or authority, Government, nonfederal **Service:** General
Medical and Surgical

Staffed Beds: 43

## BLACKFOOT—Bingham County

⊠ **BINGHAM MEMORIAL HOSPITAL (131325)**, 98 Poplar Street,
Zip 83221–1799; tel. 208/785–4100, (Nonreporting) **A**1 5 9 10 18
Primary Contact: Louis D. Kraml, FACHE, Chief Executive Officer
COO: Dan Cochran, Chief Operating Officer
CFO: Jeff Daniels, Chief Financial Officer
CIO: Robert Weis, Director Information Systems
CHR: Tara Preston, Director Human Resources
CNO: Carolyn Hansen, Chief Nursing Officer
Web address: www.binghammemorial.org
**Control:** Other not–for–profit (including NFP Corporation) **Service:** General
Medical and Surgical

Staffed Beds: 95

**MOUNTAIN RIVER BIRTHING AND SURGERY CENTER (130067)**, 350 North
Meridian Street, Zip 83221–1625; tel. 208/782–0300, (Nonreporting) **A**9 10
Primary Contact: Louis D. Kraml, FACHE, Chief Executive Officer
COO: Dan Cochran, Chief Operating Officer
CFO: Jeff Daniels, Chief Financial Officer
CIO: Robert Weis, Director Information Technology
CHR: Tara Preston, Director Human Resources
CNO: Nathan Buck, R.N., Nursing Manager
Web address: www.binghammemorial.org
**Control:** Corporation, Investor–owned, for–profit **Service:** Obstetrics and
gynecology

Staffed Beds: 8

☐ **STATE HOSPITAL SOUTH (134010)**, 700 East Alice Street, Zip 83221–4925,
Mailing Address: P.O. Box 400, Zip 83221–0400; tel. 208/785–1200,
(Nonreporting) **A**1 10
Primary Contact: Tracey Sessions, Administrator
COO: Greg Horton, Director Support Services
CFO: James Price, Assistant Administrator Finance and Operations
CMO: Kelly Palmer, D.O., Medical Director
CIO: Julie Sutton, Director Performance Improvement
CHR: Sheryl Donnelly, Human Resources Specialist
CNO: Randy Walker, Director Nursing Services
Web address: www.healthandwelfare.idaho.gov
**Control:** State–Government, nonfederal **Service:** Psychiatric

Staffed Beds: 77

## BOISE—Ada County

**BOISE BEHAVIORAL HEALTH HOSPITAL** See Safe Haven Hospital of Treasure
Valley

⊠ **BOISE VETERANS AFFAIRS MEDICAL CENTER**, 500 West Fort Street,
Zip 83702–4598; tel. 208/422–1000, (Total facility includes 28 beds in nursing
home–type unit) **A**1 3 5 9 **F**1 2 3 4 5 8 9 10 12 16 29 30 31 34 35 38 39 40
43 45 46 47 50 53 54 56 57 58 59 60 61 62 63 64 65 66 67 68 70 71 74
75 76 77 78 79 80 81 82 83 84 85 86 87 90 91 92 93 94 96 97 98 100
101 102 103 104 105 106 107 108 111 112 119 120 121 122 123 124 127
128 129 130 132 133 135 143 144 145 146 147 148 **S** Department of
Veterans Affairs, Washington, DC
Primary Contact: David P. Wood, FACHE, Director
CFO: Ron Blanton, Chief Fiscal Services
CMO: Paul Lambert, M.D., Chief of Staff
CHR: Randy Turner, Chief Human Resource Management Services
Web address: www.boise.va.gov/
**Control:** Veterans Affairs, Government, federal **Service:** General Medical and
Surgical

Staffed Beds: 89 Admissions: 3021 Census: 61 Outpatient Visits: 327965
Births: 0 Total Expense ($000): 204000 Payroll Expense ($000): 117000
Personnel: 1160

**IDAHO ELKS REHABILITATION HOSPITAL** See St. Luke's Rehabilitation Hospital

☐ **INTERMOUNTAIN HOSPITAL (134002)**, 303 North Allumbaugh Street,
Zip 83704–9208; tel. 208/377–8400, (Nonreporting) **A**1 9 10 **S** Universal Health
Services, Inc., King of Prussia, PA
Primary Contact: Jeffrey F. Morrell, Chief Executive Officer
CMO: Harry Silsby, M.D., Medical Director
CHR: Angela Billingsley, Director Human Resources
Web address: www.intermountainhospital.com
**Control:** Corporation, Investor–owned, for–profit **Service:** Psychiatric

Staffed Beds: 140

**SAFE HAVEN HOSPITAL OF TREASURE VALLEY (134009)**, 8050 Northview
Street, Zip 83704–7126; tel. 208/327–0504, (Nonreporting) **A**3 9 10 **S** Safe
Haven Health Care, Pocatello, ID
Primary Contact: Scott Proctor, Chief Executive Officer
CMO: David Kent, M.D., Chief Medical Officer
CIO: Debra Alexander, Chief Information Officer
CHR: Kathy Cady, Coordinator Human Resources, Accounts Payable and Payroll
Web address: www.boisepsychhospital.com
**Control:** Corporation, Investor–owned, for–profit **Service:** Psychiatric

Staffed Beds: 22

⊠ △ **SAINT ALPHONSUS REGIONAL MEDICAL CENTER (130007)**, 1055
North Curtis Road, Zip 83706–1309, Mailing Address: 1055 North Curtis Road,
Zip 83706–1309; tel. 208/367–2121 **A**1 2 3 5 7 9 10 **F**3 5 7 8 9 11 12 13 14
15 17 18 20 22 24 26 28 29 30 31 32 33 34 35 36 37 38 39 40 42 43 44
45 48 49 50 52 53 54 55 56 57 58 59 61 64 65 68 70 71 72 74 75 76 77
78 79 81 82 83 84 85 86 87 89 90 91 93 94 96 97 98 99 100 101 102 104
107 108 109 110 111 114 115 116 117 118 119 120 121 123 124 126 127
128 129 130 131 132 135 144 146 147 148 **P**6 8 **S** Trinity Health, Livonia, MI
Primary Contact: Rodney D. Reider, President
CFO: Kenneth Fry, Chief Financial Officer
CMO: Steve Brown, M.D., Chief Quality Officer
CIO: Dwight Pond, TIS Boise
CHR: Teresa Sargent, Vice President Human Resources
CNO: Sherry Parks, R.N., Chief Nursing Officer
Web address: www.saintalphonsus.org
**Control:** Church–operated, Nongovernment, not–for profit **Service:** General
Medical and Surgical

Staffed Beds: 399 Admissions: 16243 Census: 209 Outpatient Visits:
877747 Births: 1619 Total Expense ($000): 500451 Payroll Expense
($000): 199883 Personnel: 2935

☐ **SOUTHWEST IDAHO ADVANCED CARE HOSPITAL (132003)**, 6651 West
Franklin Road, Zip 83709–0914; tel. 208/376–5700, (Nonreporting) **A**1 3 9 10
**S** Ernest Health, Inc., Albuquerque, NM
Primary Contact: Judd Wright, Chief Executive Officer
Web address: www.siach.ernesthealth.com/
**Control:** Corporation, Investor–owned, for–profit **Service:** Long–Term Acute Care
hospital

Staffed Beds: 40

**ID**

*Many Facility Codes have changed. Please refer to the AHA Guide Code Chart.* © 2015 AHA Guide

✠ **ST. LUKE'S REGIONAL MEDICAL CENTER (130006)**, 190 East Bannock Street, Zip 83712–6241; tel. 208/381–2222, (Includes ST. LUKE'S CHILDREN'S HOSPITAL, 190 East Bannock Street, tel. 208/381–2222; ST. LUKE'S MERIDIAN MEDICAL CENTER, 520 South Eagle Road, Meridian, Zip 83642; tel. 208/706–5000) **A**1 2 3 9 10 **F**7 8 11 12 13 15 17 18 19 20 21 22 23 24 25 26 27 28 29 30 31 32 34 35 36 37 40 41 42 46 47 48 49 53 54 56 57 58 59 60 61 62 63 64 68 69 70 71 72 74 75 76 77 78 79 81 82 84 86 87 88 89 107 108 110 111 114 115 116 117 118 119 120 121 124 126 127 129 130 131 132 134 135 136 144 146 147 **P**6 8 **S** St. Luke's Health System, Boise, ID
Primary Contact: Kathy D. Moore, Chief Executive Officer
CFO: Jeff Taylor, Vice President Finance
CMO: Jim Souza, Chief Medical Officer
CIO: Marc Chasin, M.D., Chief Information Officer
CHR: Maureen O'Keeffe, SPHR, CHHR, Vice President and Chief Human Resource Officer
CNO: Cynthia Gearhard, Chief Nursing Officer
Web address: www.stlukesonline.org/boise
**Control:** Other not–for–profit (including NFP Corporation) **Service:** General Medical and Surgical

**Staffed Beds:** 574 **Admissions:** 27621 **Census:** 304 **Outpatient Visits:** 1544012 **Births:** 5433 **Total Expense ($000):** 1174514 **Payroll Expense ($000):** 480539 **Personnel:** 8863

★ △ **ST. LUKE'S REHABILITATION HOSPITAL (133025)**, 600 North Robbins Road, Zip 83702–4565, Mailing Address: P.O. Box 1100, Zip 83701–1100; tel. 208/489–4444, (Nonreporting) **A**5 7 10 **S** St. Luke's Health System, Boise, ID
Primary Contact: Nolan Hoffer, Senior Director
COO: Melissa Honsinger, Chief Operating Officer
CFO: Doug Lewis, Chief Financial Officer
CMO: Lee Kornfield, M.D., Medical Director
CIO: Scott Pyrah, Director Information Systems
CHR: Jim Atkins, Director Employee Services
Web address: www.idahoelksrehab.org
**Control:** Other not–for–profit (including NFP Corporation) **Service:** Rehabilitation

**Staffed Beds:** 31

☐ **TREASURE VALLEY HOSPITAL (130063)**, 8800 West Emerald Street, Zip 83704–8205; tel. 208/373–5000, (Nonreporting) **A**1 3 9 10
Primary Contact: Nick Genna, Administrator
CMO: Jeffrey Hessing, M.D., Medical Director
CHR: Kathleen Phelps, Director Human Resources
Web address: www.treasurevalleyhospital.com
**Control:** Corporation, Investor–owned, for–profit **Service:** General Medical and Surgical

**Staffed Beds:** 9

**VETERANS AFFAIRS MEDICAL CENTER** See Boise Veterans Affairs Medical Center

### BONNERS FERRY—Boundary County

★ ◇ **BOUNDARY COMMUNITY HOSPITAL (131301)**, 6640 Kaniksu Street, Zip 83805–7532; tel. 208/267–3141, (Includes BOUNDARY COUNTY NURSING HOME ), (Total facility includes 28 beds in nursing home–type unit) **A**9 10 18 21 **F**3 11 15 35 40 45 50 57 59 65 75 77 81 85 87 93 107 110 111 114 119 127 128 130 133 143 146 148
Primary Contact: Craig A. Johnson, Chief Executive Officer
CFO: Jordan Leigh, Chief Financial Officer
CHR: Ann Coughlin, Director Human Resources
CNO: Tari Yourzek, Chief Nursing Officer
Web address: www.boundaryhospital.org
**Control:** County–Government, nonfederal **Service:** General Medical and Surgical

**Staffed Beds:** 48 **Admissions:** 180 **Census:** 28 **Outpatient Visits:** 21468 **Births:** 0 **Total Expense ($000):** 12312 **Payroll Expense ($000):** 6628 **Personnel:** 166

### BURLEY—Cassia County

✠ **CASSIA REGIONAL MEDICAL CENTER (131326)**, 1501 Hiland Avenue, Zip 83318–2688; tel. 208/678–4444 **A**1 9 10 18 **F**3 7 8 11 13 15 18 28 29 30 31 34 35 38 40 41 50 57 59 64 68 70 74 75 76 77 78 79 81 82 85 86 93 97 107 108 110 111 114 119 129 130 131 132 146 147 148 **P**6 **S** Intermountain Healthcare, Inc., Salt Lake City, UT
Primary Contact: Rod Barton, Administrator
CFO: Mark Christensen, Director, Finance
CMO: Bernard Boehmer, M.D., Medical Director
CIO: Carie Call, Computer Support
CHR: Keri Perrigot, Manager Human Resources
CNO: Michele Pond–Bell, R.N., Nurse Administrator
Web address: www.cassiaregional.org
**Control:** Other not–for–profit (including NFP Corporation) **Service:** General Medical and Surgical

**Staffed Beds:** 25 **Admissions:** 1578 **Census:** 11 **Outpatient Visits:** 98544 **Births:** 651 **Total Expense ($000):** 44849 **Payroll Expense ($000):** 18861 **Personnel:** 317

### CALDWELL—Canyon County

✠ **WEST VALLEY MEDICAL CENTER (130014)**, 1717 Arlington, Zip 83605–4802; tel. 208/459–4641 **A**1 3 5 9 10 **F**3 8 11 12 13 15 18 20 26 28 29 30 34 35 40 41 44 45 50 51 57 59 60 64 68 69 70 75 76 77 79 81 82 85 87 89 91 92 93 98 100 101 102 103 105 107 108 110 111 114 115 127 129 130 131 132 135 146 147 148 **S** HCA, Nashville, TN
Primary Contact: Elizabeth Hunsicker, Chief Executive Officer
COO: Jennifer Opsut, Interim Chief Operating Officer
CFO: Kate Fowler, Chief Financial Officer
CMO: Richard Augustus, M.D., Chief Medical Officer
CIO: Jason Martinez, Director Information Technology
CHR: Senta Cornelius, Director Human Resources
CNO: Edith E. Irving, R.N., Chief Nursing Officer
Web address: www.westvalleymedctr.com
**Control:** Corporation, Investor–owned, for–profit **Service:** General Medical and Surgical

**Staffed Beds:** 86 **Admissions:** 4709 **Census:** 44 **Outpatient Visits:** 72701 **Births:** 594

### CASCADE—Valley County

★ **CASCADE MEDICAL CENTER (131308)**, 402 Lake Cascade Parkway, Zip 83611–7702, Mailing Address: P.O. Box 1330, Zip 83611–1330; tel. 208/382–4242 **A**9 10 18 **F**11 29 32 34 40 45 53 59 64 65 67 87 91 93 97 102 107 114 127 128 130 131 133 135 147 **P**6
Primary Contact: Virgil Boss, Chief Executive Officer
CFO: Penny Lancaster, Controller
CMO: Mikael Bedell, M.D., Medical Director
CNO: Teri Coombs, R.N., Director Nursing Services
Web address: www.cascademedicalcenter.net
**Control:** Hospital district or authority, Government, nonfederal **Service:** General Medical and Surgical

**Staffed Beds:** 8 **Admissions:** 18 **Census:** 1 **Outpatient Visits:** 7751 **Births:** 0 **Total Expense ($000):** 3287 **Payroll Expense ($000):** 1897 **Personnel:** 29

### COEUR D'ALENE—Kootenai County

★ ◇ **KOOTENAI HEALTH (130049)**, 2003 Kootenai Health Way, Zip 83814–2677; tel. 208/625–4000, (Includes KOOTENAI BEHAVIORAL HEALTH, 2301 North Ironwood Place, Zip 83814–2650; tel. 208/625–4800) **A**2 9 10 19 21 **F**2 3 4 5 6 8 11 13 15 17 18 20 22 24 26 28 29 30 31 32 34 35 37 39 40 41 43 44 45 46 47 48 49 50 51 53 54 56 57 58 59 60 63 64 65 68 70 71 74 75 76 77 78 79 81 82 83 84 85 86 87 89 91 92 93 96 97 98 99 100 101 102 103 104 107 108 110 111 114 115 116 117 118 119 120 121 123 124 126 127 129 130 131 132 134 135 143 144 145 146 148 **P**6
Primary Contact: Jon Ness, Chief Executive Officer
COO: Jeremy Evans, Vice President Operations
CFO: Kimberly Webb, Chief Financial Officer
CMO: Walter Fairfax, M.D., Chief Medical Officer
CHR: Daniel Klocko, Vice President Human Resources
CNO: Joan M. Simon, R.N., Chief Nursing Officer
Web address: www.kh.org
**Control:** Hospital district or authority, Government, nonfederal **Service:** General Medical and Surgical

**Staffed Beds:** 251 **Admissions:** 12996 **Census:** 170 **Outpatient Visits:** 281101 **Births:** 1693 **Total Expense ($000):** 376348 **Payroll Expense ($000):** 168343 **Personnel:** 2083

**ID**

**Hospital, Medicare Provider Number, Address, Telephone, Approval, Facility, and Physician Codes, Health Care System**

★ American Hospital Association (AHA) membership
☐ The Joint Commission accreditation
◇ Healthcare Facilities Accreditation Program
◇ DNV Healthcare Inc. accreditation
⇧ Center for Improvement in Healthcare Quality Accreditation
△ Commission on Accreditation of Rehabilitation Facilities (CARF) accreditation

## COTTONWOOD—Idaho County

★ **ST. MARY'S HOSPITAL (131321)**, Lewiston and North Streets,
Zip 83522–9750, Mailing Address: P.O. Box 137, Zip 83522–0137;
tel. 208/962–3251, (Nonreporting) **A**9 10 18 **S** Essentia Health, Duluth, MN
Primary Contact: Lenne Bonner, Interim President
COO: Sharon J. Moriarty, Chief Operating Officer
CFO: Lenne Bonner, Chief Financial Officer
CMO: Jack Secrest, M.D., Chief Medical Officer
CHR: Debbie Schumacher, Chief Human Resource Officer
Web address: www.smh–cvhc.org/getpage.php?name=index
**Control:** Other not–for–profit (including NFP Corporation) **Service:** General
Medical and Surgical

**Staffed Beds: 28**

## DRIGGS—Teton County

★ **TETON VALLEY HEALTH CARE (131313)**, 120 East Howard Street,
Zip 83422–5112; tel. 208/354–2383, (Nonreporting) **A**9 10 18
Primary Contact: Keith Gnagey, Chief Executive Officer
CFO: Traci Prenot, Chief Financial Officer
CMO: Nathan Levanger, M.D., Chief of Staff
CHR: Dory Harris, Director Human Resource
CNO: Angela Booker, Director of Nursing Services
Web address: www.tvhcare.org
**Control:** County–Government, nonfederal **Service:** General Medical and Surgical

**Staffed Beds: 13**

## EMMETT—Gem County

**VALOR HEALTH (131318)**, 1202 East Locust Street, Zip 83617–2715;
tel. 208/365–3561 **A**9 10 18 **F**3 11 29 31 34 35 40 42 45 57 59 64 76 81
87 107 111 114 119 133 144 146
Primary Contact: Wade C. Johnson, MS, FACHE, Chief Executive Officer
CHR: Susan Vahlberg, Director Employee and Community Relations
Web address: www.wkmh.org
**Control:** County–Government, nonfederal **Service:** General Medical and Surgical

**Staffed Beds: 16 Admissions: 354 Census: 2**

## GOODING—Gooding County

★ **NORTH CANYON MEDICAL CENTER (131302)**, 267 North Canyon Drive,
Zip 83330–5500; tel. 208/934–4433 **A**9 10 18 **F**3 5 11 15 29 33 34 40 41
44 45 47 49 50 53 56 57 59 68 75 81 84 87 90 93 97 107 110 114 119
127 130 133 135 143 148 **S** St. Luke's Health System, Boise, ID
Primary Contact: Tim Powers, Chief Executive Officer
COO: J'Dee Adams, Chief Operating Officer
CFO: Tim Powers, Chief Executive Officer
CMO: Mark Spencer, D.O., Chief of Staff
CIO: Margie McLeod, Director Information Technology
CHR: Sara Otto, Chief Compliance Officer
Web address: www.ncm–c.org
**Control:** Hospital district or authority, Government, nonfederal **Service:** General
Medical and Surgical

**Staffed Beds: 15 Admissions: 447 Census: 4 Outpatient Visits: 24019
Births: 0 Total Expense ($000): 19402 Payroll Expense ($000): 5913
Personnel: 147**

## GRANGEVILLE—Idaho County

★ **SYRINGA HOSPITAL AND CLINICS (131315)**, 607 West Main Street,
Zip 83530–1396; tel. 208/983–1700 **A**9 10 18 **F**7 13 29 30 40 50 59 63 76
81 93 107 119 127 133
Primary Contact: Joseph Cladouhos, Chief Executive Officer
CFO: Betty A. Watson, Chief Financial Officer
CMO: Daniel Griffis, M.D., Chief Medical Officer
CIO: Darla Whitley, Manager Health Information Technology
CHR: Katy Eimers, Human Resources Officer
CNO: Cindy Daly, R.N., Director of Nursing
Web address: www.syringahospital.org
**Control:** Hospital district or authority, Government, nonfederal **Service:** General
Medical and Surgical

**Staffed Beds: 14 Admissions: 380 Census: 4**

## IDAHO FALLS—Bonneville County

⊠ **EASTERN IDAHO REGIONAL MEDICAL CENTER (130018)**, 3100 Channing
Way, Zip 83404–7533, Mailing Address: P.O. Box 2077, Zip 83403–2077;
tel. 208/529–6111, (Nonreporting) **A**1 2 9 10 19 **S** HCA, Nashville, TN
Primary Contact: Douglas Crabtree, Chief Executive Officer
COO: Sandee Moore, Chief Operating Officer
CFO: Jeffrey D. Baiocco, Chief Financial Officer
CMO: Todd Williams, M.D., President Medical Staff
CHR: Wendy Andersen, Director Human Resources
CNO: Kathleen Nelson, R.N., Chief Nursing Officer
Web address: www.eirmc.com
**Control:** Corporation, Investor–owned, for–profit **Service:** General Medical and
Surgical

**Staffed Beds: 309**

**MOUNTAIN VIEW HOSPITAL (130065)**, 2325 Coronado Street,
Zip 83404–7407; tel. 208/557–2700, (Nonreporting) **A**5 9 10
Primary Contact: James Adamson, Chief Executive Officer
COO: Peter Fabrick, Vice President Clinical Operations
CHR: Eilene Horne, Manager Human Resources
Web address: www.mountainviewhospital.org
**Control:** Corporation, Investor–owned, for–profit **Service:** General Medical and
Surgical

**Staffed Beds: 22**

## JEROME—Jerome County

★ **ST. LUKE'S JEROME (131310)**, 709 North Lincoln Street, Zip 83338–1851,
Mailing Address: 709 North Lincoln Avenue, Zip 83338–1851;
tel. 208/324–4301 **A**9 10 18 **F**7 13 15 29 30 32 34 39 40 56 57 59 64 65
68 76 77 79 81 86 87 97 107 111 119 127 133 146 147 **P**6 **S** St. Luke's
Health System, Boise, ID
Primary Contact: James L. Angle, FACHE, Chief Executive Officer
CMO: Elizabeth Sugden, M.D., Chief Medical Officer
CHR: Mark Stevens, Director Human Resources
CNO: Jill Howell, Clinical Director and Chief Nursing Officer
Web address: www.stlukesonline.org/jerome/
**Control:** Other not–for–profit (including NFP Corporation) **Service:** General
Medical and Surgical

**Staffed Beds: 25 Admissions: 436 Census: 8 Outpatient Visits: 45189
Births: 147 Total Expense ($000): 15552 Payroll Expense ($000): 8842
Personnel: 183**

## KELLOGG—Shoshone County

◇ **SHOSHONE MEDICAL CENTER (131314)**, 25 Jacobs Gulch, Zip 83837–2023;
tel. 208/784–1221, (Nonreporting) **A**9 10 18 21
Primary Contact: Jerry Brantz, Chief Executive Officer
CMO: Thomas Heston, M.D., Chief of Staff
CIO: John Wohlman, Manager Information Systems
CHR: Dana Hemphill, Manager Human Resource
CNO: Beth Bates, Chief Nursing Officer
Web address: www.shoshonehealth.com
**Control:** Hospital district or authority, Government, nonfederal **Service:** General
Medical and Surgical

**Staffed Beds: 25**

## KETCHUM—Blaine County

⊠ **ST. LUKE'S WOOD RIVER MEDICAL CENTER (131323)**, 100 Hospital Drive,
Zip 83340, Mailing Address: P.O. Box 100, Zip 83340–0100; tel. 208/727–8800
**A**1 9 10 18 **F**3 7 8 11 13 15 29 30 31 34 35 36 37 39 40 43 45 50 54 57
59 62 64 68 74 75 76 79 81 82 85 86 87 91 93 97 104 107 108 110 111
114 115 119 126 130 131 132 133 134 135 141 143 145 146 147 148 **P**6
8 **S** St. Luke's Health System, Boise, ID
Primary Contact: Cody Langbehn, Administrator
CNO: Suzanne Miller, R.N., Senior Director Patient Care Services and Nursing
Web address: www.slrmc.org
**Control:** Other not–for–profit (including NFP Corporation) **Service:** General
Medical and Surgical

**Staffed Beds: 25 Admissions: 969 Census: 8 Outpatient Visits: 90381
Births: 195 Total Expense ($000): 53388 Payroll Expense ($000): 25596
Personnel: 365**

## LEWISTON—Nez Perce County

⊠ **ST. JOSEPH REGIONAL MEDICAL CENTER (130003)**, 415 Sixth Street,
Zip 83501–2431; tel. 208/743–2511, (Nonreporting) **A**1 2 9 10 **S** Ascension
Health, Saint Louis, MO
Primary Contact: Michael T. Rooney, M.D., Interim President and Chief Executive
Officer
CFO: Thomas Safley, Chief Financial Officer
CMO: Michael T. Rooney, M.D., Chief of Staff
CNO: Joan Agee, Vice President Patient Care Services
Web address: www.sjrmc.org
**Control:** Church–operated, Nongovernment, not–for profit **Service:** General
Medical and Surgical

**Staffed Beds: 119**

## MALAD CITY—Oneida County

**NELL J. REDFIELD MEMORIAL HOSPITAL (131303)**, 150 North 200 West,
Zip 83252–1239, Mailing Address: Box 126, Zip 83252–0126;
tel. 208/766–2231, (Nonreporting) **A**10 18
Primary Contact: John Williams, Administrator and Chief Executive Officer
CFO: Cindy Howard, Director Financial Services
CHR: Kathy Hubbard, Manager Human Resources
Web address: www.oneidahospital.com
**Control:** County–Government, nonfederal **Service:** General Medical and Surgical

**Staffed Beds: 11**

*Many Facility Codes have changed. Please refer to the AHA Guide Code Chart.* © 2015 AHA Guide

**ID**

## MCCALL—Valley County

★ **ST. LUKE'S MCCALL (131312)**, 1000 State Street, Zip 83638–3704;
tel. 208/634–2221 **A**5 9 10 18 **F**3 8 9 11 15 30 32 34 35 36 38 40 45 46 50
57 59 64 68 79 81 85 86 87 93 97 107 115 119 130 132 133 134 135 146
**P**6 8 **S** St. Luke's Health System, Boise, ID
Primary Contact: Michael A. Fenello, Administrator
CFO: Matt Groenig, Vice President Finance
Web address: www.mccallhosp.org
**Control:** Other not–for–profit (including NFP Corporation) **Service:** General
Medical and Surgical

**Staffed Beds:** 15 **Admissions:** 431 **Census:** 3 **Outpatient Visits:** 47851
**Births:** 84 **Total Expense ($000):** 24561 **Payroll Expense ($000):** 13763
**Personnel:** 239

## MERIDIAN—Ada County

**ST. LUKE'S MERIDIAN MEDICAL CENTER** See St. Luke's Regional Medical
Center, Boise

⊞ **VIBRA HOSPITAL OF BOISE (132002)**, 2131 South Bonito Way,
Zip 83642–1659; tel. 877/801–2244, (Nonreporting) **A**1 10 **S** Vibra Healthcare,
Mechanicsburg, PA
Primary Contact: James Elton, Chief Executive Officer
Web address: www.vhboise.com
**Control:** Corporation, Investor–owned, for–profit **Service:** Long–Term Acute Care
hospital

**Staffed Beds:** 60

## MONTPELIER—Bear Lake County

★ **BEAR LAKE MEMORIAL HOSPITAL (131316)**, 164 South Fifth Street,
Zip 83254–1597; tel. 208/847–1630, (Total facility includes 36 beds in nursing
home–type unit) **A**9 10 18 **F**2 3 5 10 11 12 18 34 35 37 39 40 45 50 53 56
57 59 60 62 64 65 68 70 75 79 81 85 86 87 93 97 101 103 104 105 107
114 119 120 126 127 128 129 130 133 135 146 148 **P**6
Primary Contact: Rodney D. Jacobson, Administrator
Web address: www.blmhospital.com
**Control:** County–Government, nonfederal **Service:** General Medical and Surgical

**Staffed Beds:** 57 **Admissions:** 405 **Census:** 37 **Outpatient Visits:** 63810
**Births:** 67 **Total Expense ($000):** 19906 **Payroll Expense ($000):** 9452
**Personnel:** 172

## MOSCOW—Latah County

⊞ **GRITMAN MEDICAL CENTER (131327)**, 700 South Main Street,
Zip 83843–3056; tel. 208/882–4511 **A**1 9 10 18 **F**3 8 11 13 15 19 28 29 34
35 36 37 40 45 46 49 51 53 54 56 57 59 64 70 75 76 77 79 81 82 84 85
86 87 89 93 96 107 108 110 111 115 119 127 129 130 131 132 135 143
146 147 148 **S** QHR, Brentwood, TN
Primary Contact: Kara Besst, President and Chief Executive Officer
CFO: Preston Becker, Chief Financial Officer
CMO: Dustin Worth, M.D., Chief Medical Staff
CIO: Kane Francetich, Chief Information Officer
CHR: Dennis Cockrell, Director Human Resources
CNO: Sheryl M. Washburn, MSN, Chief Nursing Officer
Web address: www.gritman.org
**Control:** Other not–for–profit (including NFP Corporation) **Service:** General
Medical and Surgical

**Staffed Beds:** 25 **Admissions:** 1367 **Census:** 11 **Outpatient Visits:** 62637
**Births:** 343 **Total Expense ($000):** 46397 **Payroll Expense ($000):** 20750
**Personnel:** 350

## MOUNTAIN HOME—Elmore County

⊞ **ST. LUKE'S ELMORE (131311)**, 895 North Sixth East Street, Zip 83647–2207,
Mailing Address: P.O. Box 1270, Zip 83647–1270; tel. 208/587–8401, (Total
facility includes 38 beds in nursing home–type unit) **A**1 9 10 18 **F**3 7 11 13 29
30 34 35 40 45 57 64 75 77 81 107 111 114 119 127 128 129 130 133
146 **P**6 **S** St. Luke's Health System, Boise, ID
Primary Contact: Michael Blauer, Administrator
COO: Betty Van Gheluwe, Chief Operating Officer
CFO: Tricia Senger, Chief Financial Officer
CMO: Karl Olson, M.D., Chief of Staff
CNO: Debbie Plemmons, MSN, Chief Nursing Officer
Web address: www.stlukesonline.org/elmore/
**Control:** Other not–for–profit (including NFP Corporation) **Service:** General
Medical and Surgical

**Staffed Beds:** 63 **Admissions:** 761 **Census:** 25 **Outpatient Visits:** 48723
**Births:** 132 **Total Expense ($000):** 22620 **Payroll Expense ($000):** 10908
**Personnel:** 220

## MOUNTAIN HOME AFB—Elmore County

⊞ **U. S. AIR FORCE CLINIC**, 90 Hope Drive, Building 600, Zip 83648–1057;
tel. 208/828–7610, (Nonreporting) **A**1 9 **S** Department of the Air Force,
Washington, DC
Primary Contact: Lieutenant Colonel Gregory W. Carson, Administrator
CFO: Robert Magnuson, Business Operations Flight Chief
CIO: Richard Broemeling, Information Systems Flight Commander
**Control:** Air Force, Government, federal **Service:** General Medical and Surgical

**Staffed Beds:** 10

## NAMPA—Canyon County

**MERCY MEDICAL CENTER** See Saint Alphonsus Medical Center – Nampa

⊞ **SAINT ALPHONSUS MEDICAL CENTER – NAMPA (130013)**, 1512 12th
Avenue Road, Zip 83686–6008; tel. 208/463–5000 **A**1 9 10 **F**3 11 12 13 15
18 20 22 28 29 30 31 34 35 37 40 41 42 43 44 45 46 47 48 49 50 53 54
55 57 59 64 67 68 69 70 72 73 75 76 77 78 79 80 81 82 85 86 87 89 107
108 110 111 114 115 118 119 126 129 130 132 133 135 141 143 145 146
147 148 **S** Trinity Health, Livonia, MI
Primary Contact: Karl Keeler, Chief Executive Officer
COO: Phil Harrop, Executive Director Operations
CFO: Lannie Checketts, Interim Assistant Chief Financial Officer
CMO: Dustan Hughes, M.D., Vice President Medical Affairs
CIO: Daniel Wright, Director Information Technology
CHR: Stefanie Thiel, Senior Human Resources Business Partner
CNO: Clint L. Child, R.N., Chief Nursing Officer
Web address: www.mercynampa.org
**Control:** Church–operated, Nongovernment, not–for profit **Service:** General
Medical and Surgical

**Staffed Beds:** 142 **Admissions:** 5496 **Census:** 43 **Outpatient Visits:** 87911
**Births:** 973 **Total Expense ($000):** 93305 **Payroll Expense ($000):** 33064
**Personnel:** 611

## OROFINO—Clearwater County

★ **CLEARWATER VALLEY HOSPITAL AND CLINICS (131320)**, 301 Cedar,
Zip 83544–9029; tel. 208/476–4555, (Nonreporting) **A**9 10 18 **S** Essentia
Health, Duluth, MN
Primary Contact: Lenne Bonner, Interim President
COO: Larry Barker, Chief Operating Officer
CFO: Lenne Bonner, Chief Financial Officer
CHR: Debbie Schumacher, Chief Human Resource Officer
Web address: www.smh–cvhc.org
**Control:** Other not–for–profit (including NFP Corporation) **Service:** General
Medical and Surgical

**Staffed Beds:** 23

**STATE HOSPITAL NORTH**, 300 Hospital Drive, Zip 83544–9034;
tel. 208/476–4511, (Nonreporting)
Primary Contact: Todd Hurt, Administrator
CMO: Karla Eisele, M.D., Clinical Director
CIO: James Sarbacher, Chief Information Officer
CHR: Heather Vandenbark, Human Resources Specialist
Web address: www.healthandwelfare.idaho.gov
**Control:** State–Government, nonfederal **Service:** Psychiatric

**Staffed Beds:** 60

## POCATELLO—Bannock County

⊞ **PORTNEUF MEDICAL CENTER (130028)**, 777 Hospital Way,
Zip 83201–5175; tel. 208/239–1000 **A**1 2 3 5 9 10 20 **F**3 7 11 12 13 14 15
17 18 19 20 22 24 28 29 31 34 35 39 40 43 44 45 46 47 48 49 50 56 57
58 59 61 64 65 68 70 71 72 74 75 76 77 78 79 80 81 82 85 86 87 88 89
90 92 93 96 97 98 100 101 102 103 104 107 108 109 110 111 114 115
118 119 120 121 123 124 126 129 130 131 132 143 144 146 147 **P**2
**S** LHP Hospital Group, Plano, TX
Primary Contact: Daniel Ordyna, Chief Executive Officer
COO: Don Wadle, Vice President Clinical and Support Services
CFO: John Abreu, Vice President and Chief Financial Officer
CHR: Don Wadle, Interim Director Human Resources
CNO: Natalie R. Smith, R.N., Vice President Patient Care Services and Chief
Nursing Officer
Web address: www.portmed.org
**Control:** Corporation, Investor–owned, for–profit **Service:** General Medical and
Surgical

**Staffed Beds:** 175 **Admissions:** 8613 **Census:** 94 **Outpatient Visits:** 325066
**Births:** 1542 **Total Expense ($000):** 206659 **Payroll Expense ($000):**
76668 **Personnel:** 1125

ID

**Hospital, Medicare Provider Number, Address, Telephone, Approval, Facility, and Physician Codes, Health Care System**

★ American Hospital Association (AHA) membership  ○ Healthcare Facilities Accreditation Program  ⇑ Center for Improvement in Healthcare Quality Accreditation
□ The Joint Commission accreditation  ◇ DNV Healthcare Inc. accreditation  △ Commission on Accreditation of Rehabilitation Facilities (CARF) accreditation

**SAFE HAVEN HOSPITAL OF POCATELLO (134011)**, 1200 Hospital Way,
Zip 83201–2708; tel. 208/232–2570, (Total facility includes 84 beds in nursing
home–type unit) **A**10 **F**56 98 103 128 130 143 **P**6 **S** Safe Haven Health Care,
Pocatello, ID
Primary Contact: Josiah Dahlstrom, Administrator
Web address: www.safehavenhealthcare.org/safehaven_hospital/index.html
**Control:** Partnership, Investor–owned, for–profit **Service:** Psychiatric

**Staffed Beds: 87 Admissions: 422 Census: 77 Outpatient Visits: 0 Births:**
0

### POST FALLS—Kootenai County

☐ **NORTHERN IDAHO ADVANCED CARE HOSPITAL (132001)**, 600 North Cecil
Road, Zip 83854–6200; tel. 208/262–2800, (Nonreporting) **A**1 9 10 **S** Ernest
Health, Inc., Albuquerque, NM
Primary Contact: Maria Godley, R.N., Chief Executive Officer
Web address: www.niach.ernesthealth.com
**Control:** Corporation, Investor–owned, for–profit **Service:** Long–Term Acute Care
hospital

**Staffed Beds: 40**

☐ **NORTHWEST SPECIALTY HOSPITAL (130066)**, 1593 East Polston Avenue,
Zip 83854–5326; tel. 208/262–2300, (Nonreporting) **A**1 9 10 **S** National
Surgical Healthcare, Chicago, IL
Primary Contact: Vaughn Ward, Chief Executive Officer
CFO: Rick Rasmussen, Chief Financial Officer
CIO: Craig McIntosh, Chief Information Officer
CHR: Gina Schneider, Director Human Resources
CNO: Christi Nance, R.N., Chief Nursing Officer
Web address: www.northwestspecialtyhospital.com
**Control:** Corporation, Investor–owned, for–profit **Service:** Surgical

**Staffed Beds: 34**

### PRESTON—Franklin County

★ **FRANKLIN COUNTY MEDICAL CENTER (131322)**, 44 North First East Street,
Zip 83263–1399; tel. 208/852–0137 **A**9 10 18 **F**2 3 11 13 31 40 45 57 62
63 68 75 76 77 79 81 82 84 85 91 93 104 107 114 119 128 130 131 133
146 **P**1
Primary Contact: Alan Bird, Chief Executive Officer
CFO: Paul Smart, CPA, Chief Financial Officer
CHR: Courtney Dursteler, Chief Human Resources Officer
CNO: Patrica Bowles, R.N., Chief Nursing Officer
Web address: www.fcmc.org
**Control:** County–Government, nonfederal **Service:** General Medical and Surgical

**Staffed Beds: 65 Admissions: 469 Census: 4 Births: 72**

### REXBURG—Madison County

★ ◇ **MADISON MEMORIAL HOSPITAL (130025)**, 450 East Main Street,
Zip 83440–2048, Mailing Address: P.O. Box 310, Zip 83440–0310;
tel. 208/359–6900 **A**9 10 21 **F**3 11 13 29 31 34 35 38 39 40 41 45 54 57
59 60 65 66 68 70 72 75 76 77 78 79 81 82 84 85 86 87 91 93 96 107
108 111 115 118 119 130 146 147 148 **P**8
Primary Contact: Rachel Ann Gonzales, M.D., Chief Executive Officer
COO: Audrey Fletcher, Chief Operating Officer
CFO: Troy Christensen, Chief Financial Officer
CMO: Clay Prince, M.D., Chief Medical Officer
CNO: Robert Kendrick, Chief Nursing Officer
Web address: www.madisonhospital.org
**Control:** County–Government, nonfederal **Service:** General Medical and Surgical

**Staffed Beds: 69 Admissions: 2379 Census: 20 Outpatient Visits: 21782
Births: 1496 Total Expense ($000): 52661 Payroll Expense ($000): 19273
Personnel: 372**

### RUPERT—Minidoka County

★ **MINIDOKA MEMORIAL HOSPITAL (131319)**, 1224 Eighth Street,
Zip 83350–1599; tel. 208/436–0481, (Total facility includes 43 beds in nursing
home–type unit) **A**9 10 18 **F**3 8 11 15 18 29 30 34 35 37 40 45 50 56 57
59 62 63 64 65 68 70 75 77 79 81 83 84 85 86 87 97 107 108 111 114
119 127 128 130 131 132 133 134 143 146 147 148 **P**1 3 5
Primary Contact: Carl Hanson, Administrator
COO: Joel Rogers, Chief Operating Officer
CFO: Jason Gibbons, Chief Financial Officer
CMO: Brian Muir, Chief of Staff
CIO: Nick Martin, Chief Information Officer
CHR: Tammy Hanks, Director Human Resources
CNO: Marcia Drage, R.N., Chief Nursing Officer
Web address: www.minidokamemorial.com
**Control:** County–Government, nonfederal **Service:** General Medical and Surgical

**Staffed Beds: 72 Admissions: 473 Census: 47 Outpatient Visits: 17020
Births: 0 Total Expense ($000): 23252 Payroll Expense ($000): 9935
Personnel: 201**

**MINIDOKA MEMORIAL HOSPITAL AND EXTENDED CARE FACILITY** See
Minidoka Memorial Hospital

### SAINT MARIES—Benewah County

★ **BENEWAH COMMUNITY HOSPITAL (131317)**, 229 South Seventh Street,
Zip 83861–1803; tel. 208/245–5551 **A**9 10 18 **F**13 15 29 30 31 34 35 40 45
56 57 59 64 75 78 79 81 82 84 85 93 97 107 110 111 112 114 119 127
129 131 133 135 146 **P**6
Primary Contact: Jim Broyles, Chief Executive Officer and Chief Nursing Officer
CFO: Lori Stoltz, Chief Financial Officer
CMO: William Wheeler, M.D., Chief of Staff
CHR: Marlana Martin, Director Human Resources
CNO: Mila Russell, Director of Nursing
Web address: www.bchmed.org
**Control:** County–Government, nonfederal **Service:** General Medical and Surgical

**Staffed Beds: 19 Admissions: 284 Census: 2 Outpatient Visits: 14084
Births: 52 Total Expense ($000): 17783 Payroll Expense ($000): 6588
Personnel: 139**

### SALMON—Lemhi County

★ **STEELE MEMORIAL MEDICAL CENTER (131305)**, 203 South Daisy Street,
Zip 83467–4709; tel. 208/756–5600 **A**9 10 18 **F**3 11 13 15 18 28 29 31 34
35 40 45 55 57 59 64 65 66 68 75 76 77 78 79 81 82 85 86 87 90 93 97
104 107 111 115 119 127 129 131 132 133 135 145 146 148 **P**6 **S** QHR,
Brentwood, TN
Primary Contact: Jeff Hill, Chief Executive Officer
COO: Abner King, Chief Operating Officer
CFO: Jim Peterson, Chief Financial Officer
CMO: Richard Natelson, M.D., Chief of Staff
CHR: Libby Brittain, Director Human Resources
CNO: Stephanie Orr, R.N., Chief Nursing Officer
Web address: www.steelemh.org
**Control:** County–Government, nonfederal **Service:** General Medical and Surgical

**Staffed Beds: 18 Admissions: 375 Census: 3 Outpatient Visits: 28233
Births: 36 Total Expense ($000): 18796 Payroll Expense ($000): 7201
Personnel: 137**

### SANDPOINT—Bonner County

★ **BONNER GENERAL HOSPITAL (131328)**, 520 North Third Avenue,
Zip 83864–1507; tel. 208/263–1441 **A**9 10 18 **F**3 11 13 15 17 22 26 28 29
30 34 35 40 45 46 47 48 54 57 59 62 63 64 68 75 76 77 79 81 85 86 87
93 102 107 108 110 111 114 118 119 130 131 132 142 144 146
Primary Contact: Sheryl Rickard, Chief Executive Officer
CIO: Bob Hess, Chief Information Officer
CHR: Brad Waterbury, Director Human Resources
CNO: Linda Rammler, R.N., Chief Nursing Officer
Web address: www.bonnergeneral.org/index.php
**Control:** Other not–for–profit (including NFP Corporation) **Service:** General
Medical and Surgical

**Staffed Beds: 25 Admissions: 1433 Census: 12 Outpatient Visits: 59734
Births: 343 Total Expense ($000): 46406 Payroll Expense ($000): 19434
Personnel: 323**

### SODA SPRINGS—Caribou County

★ **CARIBOU MEMORIAL HOSPITAL AND LIVING CENTER (131309)**, 300 South
Third West, Zip 83276–1598; tel. 208/547–3341, (Total facility includes 30 beds
in nursing home–type unit) **A**9 10 18 **F**70 76 81 128 **P**6
Primary Contact: Jon Smith, Chief Executive Officer
CMO: John K. Franson, M.D., Chief Medical Staff
CIO: Johnathan Inskeep, Chief Information Officer
CHR: Michael D. Peck, Assistant Administrator
CNO: Brenda Bergholm, MSN, Chief Nursing Officer
Web address: www.cmhlc.org/
**Control:** County–Government, nonfederal **Service:** General Medical and Surgical

**Staffed Beds: 55 Admissions: 299 Census: 21 Outpatient Visits: 14829
Births: 34 Total Expense ($000): 13273 Payroll Expense ($000): 7627
Personnel: 153**

### TWIN FALLS—Twin Falls County

⊞ **ST. LUKE'S MAGIC VALLEY MEDICAL CENTER (130002)**, 801 Pole Line
Road West, Zip 83301–5810, Mailing Address: P.O. Box 409, Zip 83303–0409;
tel. 208/814–1000 **A**1 2 3 9 10 **F**3 4 5 7 8 11 13 15 18 20 22 29 30 31 35
40 57 62 63 68 70 72 76 77 78 79 81 85 87 89 90 93 96 98 104 106 107
110 111 114 119 130 146 **P**6 8 **S** St. Luke's Health System, Boise, ID
Primary Contact: James L. Angle, FACHE, Regional Chief Executive Officer
CFO: Joshua Custer, Director Finance
CIO: Melissa Capps, Site Leader Information Technology
CHR: Mark Stevens, Senior Director Human Resources
CNO: Amy Bearden, R.N., Vice President Patient Care Services and Chief Nursing
Officer
Web address: www.stlukesonline.org
**Control:** Other not–for–profit (including NFP Corporation) **Service:** General
Medical and Surgical

**Staffed Beds: 224 Admissions: 9748 Census: 105 Outpatient Visits:
631365 Births: 1704 Total Expense ($000): 286322 Payroll Expense
($000): 96914 Personnel: 2483**

**ID**

**WEISER—Washington County**

★ ◇ **WEISER MEMORIAL HOSPITAL (131307)**, 645 East Fifth Street,
Zip 83672–2202; tel. 208/549–0370, (Nonreporting) **A**9 10 18 21 **S** St. Luke's
Health System, Boise, ID
Primary Contact: Tom Murphy, Chief Executive Officer
CFO: Nate Coburn, Chief Financial Officer
CMO: Bryan L. Drake, D.O., Chief of Staff
CHR: Terri Kautz, Manager Human Resources
CNO: Reuben J. DeKastle, Chief Nursing Officer
Web address: www.weisermemorialhospital.org
**Control:** Hospital district or authority, Government, nonfederal **Service:** General
Medical and Surgical

**Staffed Beds:** 25

ID

**Hospital, Medicare Provider Number, Address, Telephone, Approval, Facility, and Physician Codes, Health Care System**

★ American Hospital Association (AHA) membership    ◯ Healthcare Facilities Accreditation Program    ⇑ Center for Improvement in Healthcare Quality Accreditation
☐ The Joint Commission accreditation    ◇ DNV Healthcare Inc. accreditation    △ Commission on Accreditation of Rehabilitation Facilities (CARF) accreditation

# ILLINOIS

**IL**

### ALEDO—Mercer County

★ **GENESIS MEDICAL CENTER–ALEDO (141304)**, 409 N.W. Ninth Avenue, Zip 61231–1296; tel. 309/582–9100 **A**9 10 18 **F**3 5 11 15 18 29 30 34 35 40 45 50 54 56 57 58 59 64 75 77 79 81 82 85 87 93 94 97 107 108 114 119 127 128 130 131 133 144 146 147 148 **P**6 **S** Genesis Health System, Davenport, IA
Primary Contact: Ted Rogalski, Administrator
CFO: Mark G. Rogers, Chief Financial Officer
CMO: Kristen Wurzburger, M.D., Chief of Staff
CIO: Robert Frieden, Vice President Information Systems
CHR: Megan Clark, Coordinator Human Resources
CNO: Heidi Hess, Chief Nursing Officer
Web address: www.genesishealth.com
**Control:** Other not–for–profit (including NFP Corporation) **Service:** General Medical and Surgical

**Staffed Beds:** 22 **Admissions:** 267 **Census:** 4 **Outpatient Visits:** 18334 **Births:** 0 **Total Expense ($000):** 13055 **Payroll Expense ($000):** 5369 **Personnel:** 98

### ALTON—Madison County

☒ **ALTON MEMORIAL HOSPITAL (140002)**, One Memorial Drive, Zip 62002–6722; tel. 618/463–7311, (Total facility includes 54 beds in nursing home–type unit) **A**1 9 10 **F**3 6 7 11 13 15 18 20 22 29 30 31 34 35 38 39 40 45 46 49 50 56 57 59 64 69 70 74 75 76 77 78 79 81 82 85 86 87 89 92 93 96 98 103 104 107 108 110 111 114 115 116 117 118 119 120 121 123 128 129 130 131 132 146 148 **S** BJC HealthCare, Saint Louis, MO
Primary Contact: David A. Braasch, President
COO: Brad Goacher, Vice President Administration
CFO: Susan Koesterer, Regional Director Finance
CMO: Sebastian Rueckert, M.D., Vice President and Chief Medical Officer
CIO: David Weiss, Vice President Information System
CHR: Bryan Hartwick, Vice President Human Resources
CNO: Debra Turpin, R.N., Vice President Patient Care Services and Chief Nursing Officer
Web address: www.altonmemorialhospital.org
**Control:** Other not–for–profit (including NFP Corporation) **Service:** General Medical and Surgical

**Staffed Beds:** 227 **Admissions:** 7170 **Census:** 133 **Outpatient Visits:** 135441 **Births:** 689 **Total Expense ($000):** 129403 **Payroll Expense ($000):** 46916 **Personnel:** 774

☐ **ALTON MENTAL HEALTH CENTER (144016)**, 4500 College Avenue, Zip 62002–5099; tel. 618/474–3800, (Nonreporting) **A**1 10 **S** Division of Mental Health, Department of Human Services, Springfield, IL
Primary Contact: Brian E. Thomas, Administrator
CFO: Susan Shobe, Director Administration and Support Services
CMO: Claudia Kachigion, M.D., Medical Director
**Control:** State–Government, nonfederal **Service:** Psychiatric

**Staffed Beds:** 165

☒ △ **OSF SAINT ANTHONY'S HEALTH CENTER (140052)**, 1 Saint Anthony's Way, Zip 62002–4579, Mailing Address: PO Box 340, Zip 62002–0340; tel. 618/465–2571, (Includes OSF SAINT CLARE'S HOSPITAL, 915 East Fifth Street, Zip 62002–6434; tel. 618/463–5151), (Total facility includes 30 beds in nursing home–type unit) **A**1 2 7 9 10 **F**2 3 5 10 11 13 15 18 20 22 29 30 31 32 34 35 37 38 39 40 41 44 45 46 47 48 49 50 51 53 56 57 58 59 60 61 62 63 64 65 68 69 70 74 75 76 77 78 79 81 82 84 85 86 87 89 90 91 92 93 95 96 99 100 101 102 103 104 107 108 110 111 114 115 116 117 118 119 120 121 123 128 129 130 131 132 134 135 146 147 148 **P**6 **S** OSF Healthcare System, Peoria, IL
Primary Contact: Ajay Pathak, President
COO: Sister M. Anselma, Chief Operating Officer
CFO: Mike Nelson, Chief Financial Officer
CMO: James Piephoff, Chief Medical Officer
CIO: Justin Patterson, Director Information Technology
CHR: Robyn Grissom, Director Employee Relations
CNO: Deborah L. Birk, Ph.D., Vice President Patient Care Services
Web address: www.osfsaintanthonys.org
**Control:** Church–operated, Nongovernment, not–for profit **Service:** General Medical and Surgical

**Staffed Beds:** 203 **Admissions:** 3687 **Census:** 57 **Outpatient Visits:** 117983 **Births:** 306 **Total Expense ($000):** 77436 **Payroll Expense ($000):** 28147 **Personnel:** 646

### ANNA—Union County

☐ **CHOATE MENTAL HEALTH CENTER (144038)**, 1000 North Main Street, Zip 62906–1699; tel. 618/833–5161, (Nonreporting) **A**1 10 **S** Division of Mental Health, Department of Human Services, Springfield, IL
Primary Contact: Elaine Ray, Administrator
COO: Elaine Ray, Administrator
CMO: John Larcas, M.D., Acting Medical Director
CIO: Cindy Flamm, Manager Quality
CHR: Tammy Tellor, Acting Director Human Resources
**Control:** State–Government, nonfederal **Service:** Psychiatric

**Staffed Beds:** 79

☒ **UNION COUNTY HOSPITAL (141342)**, 517 North Main Street, Zip 62906–1696; tel. 618/833–4511, (Total facility includes 22 beds in nursing home–type unit) **A**1 9 10 18 **F**3 11 15 28 29 30 34 35 40 45 49 50 57 59 64 68 75 77 81 85 87 93 97 107 110 111 114 119 127 130 133 146 148 **P**6 **S** Community Health Systems, Inc., Franklin, TN
Primary Contact: James R. Farris, FACHE, Chief Executive Officer
CFO: Terry Paligo, Chief Financial Officer
CMO: Tamer Aiti, M.D., Chief of Staff
CIO: John Hegger, Director Information Systems
CHR: Tammy Samuels, Director Human Resources
CNO: Melanie Koch, R.N., Chief Nursing Officer
Web address: www.unioncountyhospital.com
**Control:** Corporation, Investor–owned, for–profit **Service:** General Medical and Surgical

**Staffed Beds:** 47 **Admissions:** 500 **Census:** 19 **Outpatient Visits:** 34450 **Births:** 0 **Total Expense ($000):** 20125 **Payroll Expense ($000):** 8432 **Personnel:** 153

### ARLINGTON HEIGHTS—Cook County

☒ **NORTHWEST COMMUNITY HOSPITAL (140252)**, 800 West Central Road, Zip 60005–2392; tel. 847/618–1000 **A**1 2 5 9 10 **F**3 5 8 13 15 17 18 20 22 24 26 28 29 30 31 32 34 35 37 38 39 40 41 43 44 45 46 47 49 50 54 55 56 57 59 61 62 63 64 65 68 70 71 72 73 74 75 76 77 78 79 81 82 84 85 86 87 89 92 93 94 96 98 99 100 101 102 103 104 105 106 107 108 110 111 114 115 116 117 118 119 120 121 123 124 126 129 130 131 132 135 144 145 146 147 148 **P**8
Primary Contact: Stephen Scogna, President and Chief Executive Officer
COO: Michael Hartke, Executive Vice President, Chief Operating Officer
CFO: Marsha Liu, Executive Vice President and Chief Financial Officer
CMO: Eric Benink, M.D., Chief Medical Officer
CIO: Glen Malan, Vice President Information Technology and Chief Information Officer
CHR: Ann M. Patrick, Vice President Human Resources
CNO: Kimberly Nagy, R.N., Executive Vice President, Patient Services and Chief Nursing Officer
Web address: www.nch.org
**Control:** Other not–for–profit (including NFP Corporation) **Service:** General Medical and Surgical

**Staffed Beds:** 386 **Admissions:** 18451 **Census:** 218 **Outpatient Visits:** 346426 **Births:** 2768 **Total Expense ($000):** 419803 **Payroll Expense ($000):** 173338 **Personnel:** 3045

### AURORA—Du Page and Kane Counties

☒ **PRESENCE MERCY MEDICAL CENTER (140174)**, 1325 North Highland Avenue, Zip 60506–1449; tel. 630/859–2222 **A**1 2 9 10 **F**3 5 12 13 15 18 20 22 24 26 28 29 30 31 34 35 36 38 40 43 45 46 49 56 57 59 61 65 68 70 75 76 77 78 79 81 82 85 86 87 93 97 98 99 100 101 102 103 104 105 107 111 114 115 119 125 126 130 132 135 144 146 147 **P**5 **S** Presence Health, Chicago, IL
Primary Contact: Michael L. Brown, Regional President and Chief Executive Officer
COO: Mary Vonderau, Vice President Strategy and Operations
Web address: www.provena.org/mercy/
**Control:** Church–operated, Nongovernment, not–for profit **Service:** General Medical and Surgical

**Staffed Beds:** 170 **Admissions:** 9614 **Census:** 123 **Outpatient Visits:** 271008 **Births:** 422 **Total Expense ($000):** 175548 **Payroll Expense ($000):** 50165 **Personnel:** 853

**PROVENA MERCY MEDICAL CENTER** See Presence Mercy Medical Center

⊠ △ **RUSH–COPLEY MEDICAL CENTER (140029)**, 2000 Ogden Avenue, Zip 60504–7222; tel. 630/978–6200 **A**1 2 3 5 7 9 10 **F**3 7 9 13 15 17 18 19 20 22 24 26 28 29 30 31 32 34 35 36 37 38 39 40 42 43 44 45 46 47 49 50 51 52 53 54 55 56 57 58 59 60 61 62 64 65 66 68 70 72 73 74 75 76 77 78 79 81 82 84 85 86 87 89 90 92 93 96 97 107 108 110 111 114 115 117 118 119 120 121 123 124 130 131 132 134 135 143 144 145 146 147 148 **P**6 **S** Rush University Medical Center, Chicago, IL
Primary Contact: Barry C. Finn, President and Chief Executive Officer
COO: John A. Diederich, Senior Vice President Operations and Chief Operating Officer
CFO: Brenda VanWyhe, Senior Vice President Finance and Chief Financial Officer
CMO: Steve B. Lowenthal, M.D., Senior Vice President Medical Affairs and Chief Medical Officer
CIO: Dennis DeMasie, Vice President Information Systems and Chief Information Officer
CNO: Mary Shilkaitis, Vice President Patient Care and Chief Nursing Officer
Web address: www.rushcopley.com
**Control:** Other not–for–profit (including NFP Corporation) **Service:** General Medical and Surgical

**Staffed Beds:** 210 **Admissions:** 13062 **Census:** 154 **Outpatient Visits:** 216588 **Births:** 3247 **Total Expense ($000):** 285056 **Payroll Expense ($000):** 108732 **Personnel:** 1736

## BARRINGTON—Lake County

★ ◇ **ADVOCATE GOOD SHEPHERD HOSPITAL (140291)**, 450 West Highway 22, Zip 60010–1919; tel. 847/381–0123 **A**2 9 10 21 **F**3 11 12 13 15 17 18 19 20 22 24 26 28 29 30 31 34 35 36 37 40 43 45 46 47 48 49 54 57 59 63 64 65 68 70 74 75 76 77 78 79 81 82 84 87 89 91 92 93 94 97 100 107 110 111 114 115 118 119 121 123 126 129 130 132 135 146 **P**8 **S** Advocate Health Care, Downers Grove, IL
Primary Contact: Karen A. Lambert, President
COO: Michael Ploszek, Vice President Physician Strategy and Clinical Operations
CFO: George Teufel, Vice President Finance
CMO: Barry Rosen, M.D., Vice President Medical Management
CIO: Chuck Malik, Director Information Systems
CHR: Jason Spigner, Vice President Human Resources
CNO: Marianne D. Araujo, R.N., Vice President Nursing and Chief Nurse Executive
Web address: www.advocatehealth.com/gshp/
**Control:** Church–operated, Nongovernment, not–for profit **Service:** General Medical and Surgical

**Staffed Beds:** 176 **Admissions:** 9432 **Census:** 104 **Outpatient Visits:** 242040 **Births:** 1415 **Total Expense ($000):** 225632 **Payroll Expense ($000):** 72922 **Personnel:** 1030

## BELLEVILLE—St. Clair County

⊠ △ **HSHS ST. ELIZABETH'S HOSPITAL (140187)**, 211 South Third Street, Zip 62220–1998; tel. 618/234–2120 **A**1 3 5 7 9 10 **F**3 4 5 11 13 15 18 20 22 24 26 28 29 30 35 39 40 45 46 49 50 53 54 56 57 59 60 64 65 68 70 74 75 76 77 78 79 81 82 85 86 87 90 93 97 98 100 101 102 103 104 105 107 108 111 115 116 117 118 119 121 124 129 130 131 132 135 144 146 147 148 **P**6 8 **S** Hospital Sisters Health System, Springfield, IL
Primary Contact: Shelley Harris, MSN, R.N., Interim Chief Executive Officer
CFO: David Nosacka, Chief Financial Officer
CMO: Shelly Harkins, M.D., Chief Medical Officer
CIO: Leslee Martin, Manager Information Technology
CHR: Jason T. Snow, Director People Services
CNO: Shelley Harris, MSN, Chief Nursing Officer
Web address: www.steliz.org
**Control:** Church–operated, Nongovernment, not–for profit **Service:** General Medical and Surgical

**Staffed Beds:** 260 **Admissions:** 10263 **Census:** 115 **Outpatient Visits:** 171579 **Births:** 949 **Total Expense ($000):** 168798 **Payroll Expense ($000):** 55258 **Personnel:** 1135

★ ○ **MEMORIAL HOSPITAL (140185)**, 4500 Memorial Drive, Zip 62226–5399; tel. 618/233–7750, (Total facility includes 82 beds in nursing home–type unit) **A**3 9 10 11 **F**3 11 13 15 18 20 22 24 26 28 29 30 31 34 37 39 40 45 46 49 53 54 57 59 60 62 64 70 71 74 75 76 77 79 81 82 84 85 86 87 92 93 94 96 107 108 110 111 112 114 115 118 119 126 128 129 130 131 132 135 145 146 147 148 **P**6 8
Primary Contact: Mark J. Turner, President and Chief Executive Officer
COO: Michael T. McManus, Chief Operating Officer
CFO: Amy Thomas, Vice President Finance
CMO: William Casperson, M.D., Vice President Medical Affairs
CIO: Jennifer Meinkoth, Chief Information Officer
CHR: John C. Ziegler, FACHE, Vice President Human Resources
CNO: Nancy R. Weston, R.N., Vice President Nursing Services
Web address: www.memhosp.com
**Control:** Other not–for–profit (including NFP Corporation) **Service:** General Medical and Surgical

**Staffed Beds:** 345 **Admissions:** 16428 **Census:** 239 **Outpatient Visits:** 348620 **Births:** 1488 **Total Expense ($000):** 242243 **Payroll Expense ($000):** 92751 **Personnel:** 2070

## BENTON—Franklin County

★ **FRANKLIN HOSPITAL DISTRICT (141321)**, 201 Bailey Lane, Zip 62812–1969; tel. 618/439–3161 **A**9 10 18 **F**11 15 29 30 34 35 40 45 56 57 59 66 75 77 81 93 97 107 114 119 127 132 133 **P**6
Primary Contact: Hervey E. Davis, Chief Executive Officer
COO: Michael J. Budnick, FACHE, Chief Operating Officer
CMO: Tim Morthland, Chief of Staff
CIO: David Williams, Director Information Technology
CHR: Nancy Seibert, Director Human Resources
CNO: Terri Hermann, R.N., Chief Nursing Officer
Web address: www.franklinhospital.net
**Control:** Hospital district or authority, Government, nonfederal **Service:** General Medical and Surgical

**Staffed Beds:** 25 **Admissions:** 381 **Census:** 3 **Outpatient Visits:** 22505 **Births:** 0 **Total Expense ($000):** 16399 **Payroll Expense ($000):** 7643 **Personnel:** 182

## BERWYN—Cook County

⊠ **MACNEAL HOSPITAL (140054)**, 3249 South Oak Park Avenue, Zip 60402–0715; tel. 708/783–9100 **A**1 2 3 5 8 9 10 13 **F**3 5 11 12 13 15 18 19 20 22 24 26 28 29 30 34 35 37 40 43 45 46 47 48 49 50 54 56 57 58 59 64 65 68 70 73 74 75 76 77 78 79 81 82 85 86 87 89 93 96 97 98 100 101 102 103 104 105 107 108 110 111 113 114 115 116 117 118 119 124 126 130 131 132 134 141 144 146 147 148 **P**5 8 **S** TENET Healthcare Corporation, Dallas, TX
Primary Contact: J. Scott Steiner, Chief Executive Officer
COO: Sharon Oxendale, Chief Operating Officer
CFO: Mary Elizabeth Cleary, Chief Financial Officer
CMO: Charles Bareis, M.D., Medical Director
CIO: Mark Weech, Director of Client Services for Chicago Market
CHR: Richard Dodsworth, Vice President Human Resources
CNO: Kathleen Benjamin, R.N., Chief Nursing Officer
Web address: www.macneal.com
**Control:** Corporation, Investor–owned, for–profit **Service:** General Medical and Surgical

**Staffed Beds:** 371 **Admissions:** 16536 **Census:** 222 **Outpatient Visits:** 212192 **Births:** 1835 **Personnel:** 1726

## BLOOMINGTON—Mclean County

⊠ **OSF ST. JOSEPH MEDICAL CENTER (140162)**, 2200 East Washington Street, Zip 61701–4323; tel. 309/662–3311, (Total facility includes 12 beds in nursing home–type unit) **A**1 2 9 10 **F**3 11 12 13 15 18 20 22 24 28 29 30 31 34 35 37 40 43 45 49 50 51 53 54 57 59 60 61 64 65 68 70 74 75 76 77 78 79 81 82 84 85 86 87 89 92 93 96 97 107 108 110 111 114 115 118 119 127 128 129 130 131 132 135 144 146 147 148 **P**6 **S** OSF Healthcare System, Peoria, IL
Primary Contact: Chad Boore, President
CFO: John R. Zell, Chief Financial Officer
CMO: Paul E. Pedersen, M.D., Vice President and Chief Medical Officer
CHR: Sue A. Herriott, Executive Director Support Services
CNO: Deborah S. Smith, R.N., Vice President, Chief Nursing Officer
Web address: www.osfstjoseph.org
**Control:** Church–operated, Nongovernment, not–for profit **Service:** General Medical and Surgical

**Staffed Beds:** 149 **Admissions:** 6611 **Census:** 72 **Outpatient Visits:** 343602 **Births:** 878 **Total Expense ($000):** 152396 **Payroll Expense ($000):** 54412 **Personnel:** 837

IL

**Hospital, Medicare Provider Number, Address, Telephone, Approval, Facility, and Physician Codes, Health Care System**

★ American Hospital Association (AHA) membership ○ Healthcare Facilities Accreditation Program ⇑ Center for Improvement in Healthcare Quality Accreditation
□ The Joint Commission accreditation ◇ DNV Healthcare Inc. accreditation △ Commission on Accreditation of Rehabilitation Facilities (CARF) accreditation

## BLUE ISLAND—Cook County

✠ **METROSOUTH MEDICAL CENTER (140118)**, 12935 South Gregory Street, Zip 60406–2470; tel. 708/597–2000 **A**1 9 10 **F**3 13 15 18 20 22 24 26 28 29 30 31 34 35 40 43 47 48 49 50 51 53 56 59 60 70 72 74 75 76 78 79 81 82 83 84 85 87 93 96 97 98 102 103 107 108 110 111 114 115 118 119 126 129 130 135 141 142 146 147 148 **S** Community Health Systems, Inc., Franklin, TN
Primary Contact: Aaron R. Hazzard, Interim Chief Executive Officer
CFO: Mei Deng, Chief Financial Officer
CHR: Alanna Barker, Director Human Resources
CNO: Kathleen Hartman, Chief Nursing Officer
Web address: www.metrosouthmedicalcenter.com
**Control:** Corporation, Investor–owned, for–profit **Service:** General Medical and Surgical

**Staffed Beds:** 285 **Admissions:** 8347 **Census:** 90 **Outpatient Visits:** 73906 **Births:** 1438 **Total Expense ($000):** 139528 **Payroll Expense ($000):** 57472 **Personnel:** 796

## BOLINGBROOK—Will County

✠ **ADVENTIST BOLINGBROOK HOSPITAL (140304)**, 500 Remington Boulevard, Zip 60440–4906; tel. 630/312–5000 **A**1 9 10 **F**3 12 13 15 18 20 22 28 29 30 31 34 35 37 40 43 45 46 47 49 50 51 52 54 56 57 58 59 60 61 64 65 68 70 73 74 75 76 78 79 81 82 85 86 87 92 93 96 107 108 110 111 114 115 119 129 130 131 132 145 146 147 148 **P**7 8 **S** Adventist Health System Sunbelt Health Care Corporation, Altamonte Springs, FL
Primary Contact: Rick Mace, Chief Executive Officer
CFO: Mike Murrill, Vice President and Chief Financial Officer
CMO: Richard Carroll, M.D., Chief Medical officer
CIO: John McLendon, Senior Vice President and Chief Information Officer
CHR: Gerald Staley, Director Human Resources
CNO: Jolene Albaugh, R.N., Vice President and Chief Nursing Officer
Web address: www.keepingyouwell.com/abh/
**Control:** Church–operated, Nongovernment, not–for profit **Service:** General Medical and Surgical

**Staffed Beds:** 134 **Admissions:** 5346 **Census:** 50 **Outpatient Visits:** 92325 **Births:** 930 **Total Expense ($000):** 113602 **Payroll Expense ($000):** 33887 **Personnel:** 503

## BREESE—Clinton County

✠ **HSHS ST. JOSEPH'S HOSPITAL (140145)**, 9515 Holy Cross Lane, Zip 62230–3618, Mailing Address: PO Box 99, Zip 62230–0099; tel. 618/526–4511 **A**1 9 10 **F**3 8 11 13 15 18 28 29 30 31 34 35 38 40 43 45 50 53 57 59 62 63 68 70 73 75 76 78 79 81 82 85 87 89 97 107 108 110 111 115 116 117 118 119 127 129 130 131 132 135 144 146 147 **S** Hospital Sisters Health System, Springfield, IL
Primary Contact: Paulette Evans, R.N., MSN, President and Chief Executive Officer
CFO: John Jeffries, Director Finance
CHR: Robert J. Otrembiak, Director of People Services
CNO: Helen Essenpreis, MSN, Chief Nursing Officer
Web address: www.stjoebreese.com
**Control:** Church–operated, Nongovernment, not–for profit **Service:** General Medical and Surgical

**Staffed Beds:** 49 **Admissions:** 1308 **Census:** 9 **Outpatient Visits:** 92556 **Births:** 525 **Total Expense ($000):** 44771 **Payroll Expense ($000):** 17248 **Personnel:** 322

## CANTON—Fulton County

✠ **GRAHAM HOSPITAL (140001)**, 210 West Walnut Street, Zip 61520–2497; tel. 309/647–5240, (Total facility includes 38 beds in nursing home–type unit) **A**1 6 9 10 20 **F**3 11 13 15 26 28 29 30 40 45 50 53 54 57 59 62 63 64 65 67 70 75 76 79 81 82 85 87 89 91 97 107 108 110 111 114 115 119 124 127 128 129 130 131 132 135 143 144 145 146 **P**3
Primary Contact: Robert G. Senneff, FACHE, President and Chief Executive Officer
CFO: Eric Franz, Vice President, Finance and Chief Financial Officer
CHR: Canise A. McComb, Director Human Resources
CNO: Teresa L. McConkey, MSN, Vice President Nursing and Chief Nursing Officer
Web address: www.grahamhospital.org
**Control:** Other not–for–profit (including NFP Corporation) **Service:** General Medical and Surgical

**Staffed Beds:** 87 **Admissions:** 2374 **Census:** 48 **Outpatient Visits:** 185919 **Births:** 241 **Total Expense ($000):** 71768 **Payroll Expense ($000):** 27815 **Personnel:** 592

## CARBONDALE—Jackson County

✠ **MEMORIAL HOSPITAL OF CARBONDALE (140164)**, 405 West Jackson Street, Zip 62901–1467, Mailing Address: P.O. Box 10000, Zip 62902–9000; tel. 618/549–0721 **A**1 2 3 5 9 10 13 19 **F**3 11 13 18 20 22 24 26 28 29 30 31 34 35 40 45 46 48 49 54 56 57 59 64 68 70 72 74 75 76 77 78 79 81 82 83 84 85 86 87 89 107 108 111 114 115 119 120 121 126 130 131 132 135 145 146 147 **P**1 **S** Southern Illinois Hospital Services, Carbondale, IL
Primary Contact: Bart Millstead, Administrator
CFO: Michael Kasser, Vice President Chief Financial Officer and Treasurer
CMO: Marci Moore–Connelly, M.D., Vice President Chief Medical Officer
CIO: David Holland, Vice President Chief Innovation Officer
CHR: Pamela S. Henderson, Vice President Human Resources
CNO: Julie Firman, DNP, R.N., Vice President and Chief Nursing Officer
Web address: www.sih.net
**Control:** Other not–for–profit (including NFP Corporation) **Service:** General Medical and Surgical

**Staffed Beds:** 159 **Admissions:** 10100 **Census:** 96 **Outpatient Visits:** 107947 **Births:** 2007 **Total Expense ($000):** 236204 **Payroll Expense ($000):** 59565 **Personnel:** 1213

## CARLINVILLE—Macoupin County

★ **CARLINVILLE AREA HOSPITAL (141347)**, 20733 North Broad Street, Zip 62626–1499; tel. 217/854–3141 **A**9 10 18 **F**11 15 28 29 34 35 40 45 64 77 79 81 91 93 107 110 115 129 133 148 **P**6 **S** HealthTech Management Services, Brentwood, TN
Primary Contact: Kenneth G. Reid, President and Chief Executive Officer
CFO: Mike Brown, Chief Financial Officer
CMO: Kate Wilkins, M.D., President, Medical Staff
CIO: Jerod Cottingham, Director Information Systems
CHR: Tracy Koster, Director Human Resources
CNO: Sara McPeak, Chief Nursing Officer
Web address: www.cahcare.com
**Control:** Other not–for–profit (including NFP Corporation) **Service:** General Medical and Surgical

**Staffed Beds:** 25 **Admissions:** 451 **Census:** 7 **Outpatient Visits:** 21572 **Births:** 0 **Total Expense ($000):** 19548 **Payroll Expense ($000):** 6961 **Personnel:** 147

## CARROLLTON—Greene County

**THOMAS H. BOYD MEMORIAL HOSPITAL (141300)**, 800 School Street, Zip 62016–1498; tel. 217/942–6946, (Includes REISCH MEMORIAL NURSING HOME ), (Nonreporting) **A**9 10 18
Primary Contact: Deborah Campbell, Administrator
CHR: Lisa Eldridge, Human Resources Officer
**Control:** Other not–for–profit (including NFP Corporation) **Service:** General Medical and Surgical

**Staffed Beds:** 65

## CARTHAGE—Hancock County

☐ **MEMORIAL HOSPITAL (141305)**, 1454 North County Road 2050, Zip 62321–3551, Mailing Address: P.O. Box 160, Zip 62321–0160; tel. 217/357–8500 **A**1 9 10 18 **F**3 11 13 15 28 29 30 34 35 36 40 45 56 57 59 64 70 75 76 81 85 87 103 107 108 110 115 119 125 127 129 130 132 133 144 146
Primary Contact: Ada Bair, Chief Executive Officer
COO: Florine Dixon, Chief Operating Officer
CFO: Teresa Smith, Chief Financial Officer
CIO: Syndi Horn, Director Information Systems
CHR: Dan Smith, Director Human Resources
Web address: www.mhtlc.org
**Control:** Other not–for–profit (including NFP Corporation) **Service:** General Medical and Surgical

**Staffed Beds:** 18 **Admissions:** 585 **Census:** 6 **Outpatient Visits:** 44470 **Births:** 134 **Total Expense ($000):** 21942 **Payroll Expense ($000):** 8712 **Personnel:** 169

## CENTRALIA—Marion County

✠ **ST. MARY'S HOSPITAL (140034)**, 400 North Pleasant Avenue, Zip 62801–3056; tel. 618/436–8000 **A**1 2 9 10 **F**3 5 11 13 15 18 20 26 28 29 30 31 32 34 35 37 38 40 44 45 46 50 54 57 59 61 64 68 70 73 74 75 76 77 78 79 80 81 82 84 85 86 87 89 90 91 92 93 94 98 99 100 101 102 103 104 105 107 108 110 111 114 118 119 120 121 129 130 131 132 135 146 147 148 **P**6 8 **S** SSM Health, Saint Louis, MO
Primary Contact: John R. Sigsbury, President
COO: Mark A. Clark, Vice President Operations
CFO: Deland Evischi, Chief Financial Officer
CMO: Rajendra Shroff, M.D., Administrative Medical Director
CIO: Steve Murphy, Director Information Systems
CHR: Thomas W. Blythe, Vice President Human Resources
CNO: Sherry Dunlay, Chief Nursing Officer
Web address: www.smgsi.com
**Control:** Church–operated, Nongovernment, not–for profit **Service:** General Medical and Surgical

**Staffed Beds:** 113 **Admissions:** 5102 **Census:** 50 **Outpatient Visits:** 206559 **Births:** 371 **Total Expense ($000):** 89598 **Payroll Expense ($000):** 30362 **Personnel:** 787

*Many Facility Codes have changed. Please refer to the AHA Guide Code Chart.* © 2015 AHA Guide

IL

## CENTREVILLE—St. Clair County

☐ **TOUCHETTE REGIONAL HOSPITALS (140077)**, 5900 Bond Avenue, Zip 62207–2326; tel. 618/332–3060 **A**1 9 10 **F**3 11 13 15 18 29 31 40 45 47 50 54 55 62 64 68 70 73 75 76 79 81 85 87 89 92 98 99 101 102 104 105 107 108 110 114 119 125 130 135 143 146 148 **P**6
Primary Contact: Larry W. McCulley, President and Chief Executive Officer
COO: Tom Mikkelson, M.D., Interim Chief Operating Officer
CFO: John Majchrzak, Chief Financial Officer
CMO: Tom Mikkelson, M.D., Vice President Medical Affairs
Web address: www.touchette.org
**Control:** Other not–for–profit (including NFP Corporation) **Service:** General Medical and Surgical

**Staffed Beds:** 109 **Admissions:** 2510 **Census:** 25 **Outpatient Visits:** 55705 **Births:** 270 **Total Expense ($000):** 57407 **Payroll Expense ($000):** 26579 **Personnel:** 472

## CHAMPAIGN—Champaign County

☐ **THE PAVILION (144029)**, 809 West Church Street, Zip 61820–3399; tel. 217/373–1700, (Nonreporting) **A**1 9 10 **S** Universal Health Services, Inc., King of Prussia, PA
Primary Contact: Joseph Sheehy, Chief Executive Officer and Managing Director
CFO: Edith Frasca, Controller and Chief Financial Officer
Web address: www.pavilionhospital.com
**Control:** Corporation, Investor–owned, for–profit **Service:** Psychiatric

**Staffed Beds:** 46

## CHESTER—Randolph County

☐ **CHESTER MENTAL HEALTH CENTER**, Chester Road, Zip 62233–0031, Mailing Address: Box 31, Zip 62233–0031; tel. 618/826–4571, (Nonreporting) **A**1 **S** Division of Mental Health, Department of Human Services, Springfield, IL
Primary Contact: Leah Hammel, Acting Administrator
CFO: Sarah Imhoff, Business Administrator
CMO: Maitra Rupa, M.D., Acting Medical Director
CIO: Anthony Young, Information Services Specialist
CHR: Kim Holsapple, Human Resource Specialist
CNO: Jennifer Klingeman, Director of Nursing
**Control:** State–Government, nonfederal **Service:** Psychiatric

**Staffed Beds:** 245

☐ **MEMORIAL HOSPITAL (141338)**, 1900 State Street, Zip 62233–1116, Mailing Address: P.O. Box 609, Zip 62233–0609; tel. 618/826–4581, (Nonreporting) **A**1 9 10 18
Primary Contact: Brett Bollmann, Administrator
CFO: Gail Miesner, Chief Financial Officer
CMO: Alan Liefer, M.D., President Medical Staff
CIO: Becky Bunselmeyer, Director Information Services
CHR: May Rose, Director Human Resources
Web address: www.mhchester.com
**Control:** Hospital district or authority, Government, nonfederal **Service:** General Medical and Surgical

**Staffed Beds:** 25

## CHICAGO—Cook County

**ADVOCATE BETHANY HOSPITAL** See RML Specialty Hospital

✠ **ADVOCATE ILLINOIS MASONIC MEDICAL CENTER (140182)**, 836 West Wellington Avenue, Zip 60657–5147; tel. 773/975–1600 **A**1 2 3 5 8 9 10 13 **F**3 5 13 15 17 18 19 20 22 24 26 28 29 30 31 32 33 34 35 36 38 40 43 44 45 46 47 48 49 50 53 54 55 56 57 58 59 60 61 64 66 68 70 71 72 73 74 75 76 77 78 79 81 82 84 85 86 87 89 90 92 93 96 97 98 99 100 101 102 103 104 107 108 110 111 115 117 118 119 120 121 123 124 126 129 130 131 132 134 135 141 143 146 147 148 **P**6 8 **S** Advocate Health Care, Downers Grove, IL
Primary Contact: Susan Nordstrom Lopez, President
CFO: Jack Gilbert, Vice President Finance and Support Services
CMO: Robert Zadylak, M.D., Vice President Medical Management
CIO: Margaret Capannari, Director Information Systems
CHR: Katie Bata, Vice President Human Resources
CNO: Donna King, R.N., Vice President Clinical Operations and Chief Nursing Executive
Web address: www.advocatehealth.com/masonic
**Control:** Other not–for–profit (including NFP Corporation) **Service:** General Medical and Surgical

**Staffed Beds:** 315 **Admissions:** 14060 **Census:** 188 **Outpatient Visits:** 177855 **Births:** 2551 **Total Expense ($000):** 327218 **Payroll Expense ($000):** 131538 **Personnel:** 2214

★ ◇ **ADVOCATE TRINITY HOSPITAL (140048)**, 2350 East 93rd Street, Zip 60617; tel. 773/967–2000 **A**9 10 21 **F**1 3 4 13 15 16 17 18 20 22 24 26 28 29 30 31 34 35 40 45 49 50 55 56 57 58 59 60 61 64 65 67 68 70 72 73 74 75 76 77 78 79 80 81 82 87 88 89 90 92 93 98 107 108 110 111 114 115 119 126 128 129 130 132 135 146 148 **P**5 8 **S** Advocate Health Care, Downers Grove, IL
Primary Contact: Michelle Gaskill, R.N., President
CFO: Maureen Morrison, Vice President Financial Services
CMO: Dianna Grant, M.D., Vice President Medical Management
CIO: Bonita Brown–Roberts, Director Information Systems
CHR: Daylashunta Randolph, Senior Vice President Human Resources
CNO: Jacquelyn Whitten, R.N., Chief Nurse Executive and Vice President Nursing
Web address: www.advocatehealth.com/trinity
**Control:** Other not–for–profit (including NFP Corporation) **Service:** General Medical and Surgical

**Staffed Beds:** 188 **Admissions:** 9694 **Census:** 104 **Outpatient Visits:** 76419 **Births:** 1156 **Total Expense ($000):** 154852 **Payroll Expense ($000):** 54537 **Personnel:** 712

✠ **ANN & ROBERT H. LURIE CHILDREN'S HOSPITAL OF CHICAGO (143300)**, 225 East Chicago Avenue, Zip 60611–2991; tel. 312/227–4000 **A**1 2 3 5 8 9 10 **F**3 8 9 11 12 17 18 19 21 23 25 27 29 30 31 32 34 35 36 37 38 39 40 41 43 44 45 46 48 49 50 51 54 55 57 58 59 60 61 63 64 65 68 72 74 75 78 79 81 82 84 85 86 87 88 89 91 92 93 94 96 97 98 99 100 101 102 104 105 107 108 111 113 115 116 117 118 119 124 126 129 130 131 132 134 136 137 138 139 141 142 144 146 148
Primary Contact: Patrick M. Magoon, President and Chief Executive Officer
COO: Gordon B. Bass, Chief Operating Officer
CFO: Paula Noble, Chief Financial Officer and Treasurer
CMO: Michael Kelleher, Chief Medical Officer
CIO: Stan Krok, Chief Information Officer
CHR: Barbara Bowman, Chief Human Resource Officer
Web address: www.luriechildrens.org
**Control:** Other not–for–profit (including NFP Corporation) **Service:** Children's general

**Staffed Beds:** 288 **Admissions:** 13035 **Census:** 205 **Outpatient Visits:** 515164 **Births:** 0 **Total Expense ($000):** 650355 **Payroll Expense ($000):** 268892 **Personnel:** 4002

**BERNARD MITCHELL HOSPITAL** See University of Chicago Medical Center

☐ **CHICAGO LAKESHORE HOSPITAL (144005)**, 4840 North Marine Drive, Zip 60640–4296; tel. 773/878–9700, (Nonreporting) **A**1 3 5 9 10 **S** Signature Healthcare Services, Corona, CA
Primary Contact: Patrick Moallemian, Chief Executive Officer
CFO: Carol Peart, Chief Financial Officer
CMO: Peter Nierman, M.D., Chief Medical Officer
CHR: Johanne Jeanty, Director Human Resources
Web address: www.chicagolakeshorehospital.com
**Control:** Corporation, Investor–owned, for–profit **Service:** Psychiatric

**Staffed Beds:** 115

**CHICAGO LYING–IN HOSPITAL** See University of Chicago Medical Center

☐ **CHICAGO–READ MENTAL HEALTH CENTER (144010)**, 4200 North Oak Park Avenue, Zip 60634–1457; tel. 773/794–4000, (Nonreporting) **A**1 10 **S** Division of Mental Health, Department of Human Services, Springfield, IL
Primary Contact: Thomas Simpatico, M.D., Facility Director and Network System Manager
**Control:** State–Government, nonfederal **Service:** Psychiatric

**Staffed Beds:** 200

**CHILDREN'S MEMORIAL HOSPITAL** See Ann & Robert H. Lurie Children's Hospital of Chicago

✠ **COMMUNITY FIRST MEDICAL CENTER (140251)**, 5645 West Addison Street, Zip 60634–4403; tel. 773/282–7000, (Nonreporting) **A**1 3 9 10
Primary Contact: Dennis FitzMaurice, Interim Chief Executive Officer
COO: Dennis FitzMaurice, Vice President, Professional Services
CFO: Richard Franco, Chief Financial Officer
CMO: David Bordo, M.D., Vice President and Chief Medical Officer
CIO: George Chessum, Senior Vice President and Chief Information Officer
CHR: Ivy McKinley, Regional Human Resources Officer
CNO: Carole Miserendino, MSN, Vice President Patient Care Services and Chief Nursing Officer
Web address: www.cfmedicalcenter.com
**Control:** Church–operated, Nongovernment, not–for profit **Service:** General Medical and Surgical

**Staffed Beds:** 279

**IL**

---

**Hospital, Medicare Provider Number, Address, Telephone, Approval, Facility, and Physician Codes, Health Care System**

★ American Hospital Association (AHA) membership
☐ The Joint Commission accreditation
○ Healthcare Facilities Accreditation Program
◇ DNV Healthcare Inc. accreditation
⇑ Center for Improvement in Healthcare Quality Accreditation
△ Commission on Accreditation of Rehabilitation Facilities (CARF) accreditation

☐ **GARFIELD PARK HOSPITAL (144039)**, 520 North Ridgeway Avenue, Zip 60624–1232; tel. 773/265–3700, (Nonreporting) **A**1 10 **S** Universal Health Services, Inc., King of Prussia, PA
Primary Contact: Len Kirby, Chief Executive Officer
CMO: Tina Mahera, M.D., Chief Medical Officer
CHR: Janice Clark, Manager Human Resources
Web address: www.garfieldparkhospital.com
**Control:** Corporation, Investor–owned, for–profit **Service:** Children's hospital psychiatric

**Staffed Beds:** 88

☐ **HARTGROVE HOSPITAL (144026)**, 5730 West Roosevelt Road, Zip 60644–1580; tel. 773/413–1700, (Nonreporting) **A**1 10 **S** Universal Health Services, Inc., King of Prussia, PA
Primary Contact: Steven Airhart, Chief Executive Officer
CFO: Srbo Nikolic, Chief Financial Officer
CMO: Johnny Williamson, M.D., Chief Medical Officer
CHR: Anthony Rivera, Director Human Resources
CNO: Jody Bhambra, Chief Nursing Officer
Web address: www.hartgrovehospital.com
**Control:** Corporation, Investor–owned, for–profit **Service:** Psychiatric

**Staffed Beds:** 128

★ ○ **HOLY CROSS HOSPITAL (140133)**, 2701 West 68th Street, Zip 60629–1882; tel. 773/884–9000, (Nonreporting) **A**9 10 11 **S** Sinai Health System, Chicago, IL
Primary Contact: Lori Pacura, R.N., MSN, President
COO: Paul M. Teodo, Chief Operating Officer
CMO: Catherine Kallal, M.D., Chief Medical Officer
CIO: Ken Slawkowski, Interim Director Information Systems
CHR: Doris Gutierrez, Director Human Resources
CNO: Katherine Loeb, R.N., Interim Vice President, Patient Care Services
Web address: www.holycrosshospital.org
**Control:** Corporation, Investor–owned, for–profit **Service:** General Medical and Surgical

**Staffed Beds:** 160

☐ **JACKSON PARK HOSPITAL AND MEDICAL CENTER (140177)**, 7531 Stony Island Avenue, Zip 60649–3993; tel. 773/947–7500, (Nonreporting) **A**1 3 9 10
Primary Contact: William Dorsey, M.D., Board Chairman and Chief Executive Officer
COO: Randall Smith, Executive Vice President
CFO: Nelson Vasquez, Vice President Finance
CMO: Bangalore Murthy, M.D., Director Medical Staff
CIO: Thomas Pankow, Chief Information Officer
CHR: Tracey Jones, Director Human Resources
Web address: www.jacksonparkhospital.org
**Control:** Other not–for–profit (including NFP Corporation) **Service:** General Medical and Surgical

**Staffed Beds:** 260

✠ △ **JESSE BROWN VETERANS AFFAIRS MEDICAL CENTER**, 820 South Damen, Zip 60612–3776; tel. 312/569–8387 **A**1 3 5 7 8 **F**2 3 5 8 10 11 12 14 15 17 18 20 22 24 26 28 29 30 31 34 35 38 39 40 44 45 46 47 50 53 54 57 58 59 60 61 62 63 64 65 68 70 71 74 75 77 78 79 80 81 82 84 85 86 87 93 94 97 98 100 101 102 104 105 106 107 111 119 126 127 129 130 132 133 135 143 144 146 147 148 **S** Department of Veterans Affairs, Washington, DC
Primary Contact: Ann R. Brown, FACHE, Director
COO: Michelle Blakely, Associate Director
CFO: Kalpana Mehta, Chief Fiscal Services
CMO: Wendy W. Brown, M.D., Chief of Staff
CIO: Howard Loewenstein, Chief Information Resource Management Services
CHR: Wayne Davis, Manager Human Resources
Web address: www.chicago.va.gov/
**Control:** Veterans Affairs, Government, federal **Service:** General Medical and Surgical

**Staffed Beds:** 198 **Admissions:** 8280 **Census:** 172 **Outpatient Visits:** 922572 **Births:** 0 **Total Expense ($000):** 419898 **Payroll Expense ($000):** 202565 **Personnel:** 2296

✠ **JOHN H. STROGER JR. HOSPITAL OF COOK COUNTY (140124)**, 1969 West Ogden Avenue, Zip 60612–3714; tel. 312/864–6000 **A**1 2 3 5 8 9 10 13 **F**3 5 11 13 15 16 17 18 19 20 22 24 29 30 31 35 36 38 39 40 41 42 43 44 45 46 47 48 49 51 52 54 55 56 58 59 60 61 64 65 68 70 72 74 75 76 77 78 79 81 82 84 85 86 87 88 89 91 92 93 94 97 99 100 101 102 103 104 107 108 110 111 114 115 118 119 121 123 129 130 132 134 135 146 147 148 **P**6 **S** Cook County Health and Hospitals System, Chicago, IL
Primary Contact: John Jay Shannon, M.D., Chief Executive Officer
CFO: John R. Morales, Chief Financial Officer
CMO: Claudia Fegan, M.D., Chief Medical Officer
CIO: Bala Hota, Interim Chief Information Officer
CHR: Paris I. Partee, Associate Administrator and Director Human Resources
CNO: Antoinette Williams, Chief Nursing Officer
Web address: www.cookcountyhealth.net
**Control:** County–Government, nonfederal **Service:** General Medical and Surgical

**Staffed Beds:** 448 **Admissions:** 20608 **Census:** 278 **Outpatient Visits:** 734835 **Births:** 615 **Total Expense ($000):** 1525527 **Payroll Expense ($000):** 429819 **Personnel:** 5431

**JOHNSTON R. BOWMAN HEALTH CENTER** See Rush University Medical Center

**KINDRED CHICAGO LAKESHORE** See Kindred Chicago–Central Hospital

✠ **KINDRED CHICAGO–CENTRAL HOSPITAL (142009)**, 4058 West Melrose Street, Zip 60641–4797; tel. 773/736–7000, (Includes KINDRED CHICAGO LAKESHORE, 6130 North Sheridan Road, Zip 60660; tel. 773/381–1222; Diane Otteman, Chief Executive Officer; KINDRED HOSPITAL CHICAGO NORTH, 2544 West Montrose Avenue, Zip 60618–1589; tel. 773/267–2622; Larry Foster, R.N., MSN, Chief Executive Officer), (Nonreporting) **A**1 9 10 **S** Kindred Healthcare, Louisville, KY
Primary Contact: Bruce Carey, Chief Executive Officer
COO: Joanne Garcia, Chief Operating Officer
CFO: Mary Treacy Shiff, Chief Financial Officer
Web address: www.khchicagocentral.com
**Control:** Corporation, Investor–owned, for–profit **Service:** Long–Term Acute Care hospital

**Staffed Beds:** 187

**KINDRED HOSPITAL CHICAGO NORTH** See Kindred Chicago–Central Hospital

✠ **LA RABIDA CHILDREN'S HOSPITAL (143301)**, 6501 South Promontory Drive, Zip 60649–1003; tel. 773/363–6700 **A**1 3 5 9 10 **F**3 12 19 28 29 32 34 35 38 40 41 50 57 59 64 65 74 75 77 79 82 84 85 86 87 89 91 93 94 96 97 99 100 101 104 130 132 134 143 144 146 148 **P**6
Primary Contact: Brenda J. Wolf, President and Chief Executive Officer
CFO: Mark Renfree, Chief Financial Officer
CMO: David Soglin, Chief Medical Officer
CIO: Sheelah Cabrera, Chief Information Officer
CHR: Frances Lefkow, Director Human Resources
CNO: Aden Henry, R.N., Vice President, Patient Care
Web address: www.larabida.org
**Control:** Other not–for–profit (including NFP Corporation) **Service:** Children's chronic disease

**Staffed Beds:** 49 **Admissions:** 593 **Census:** 18 **Outpatient Visits:** 30432 **Births:** 0 **Total Expense ($000):** 46573 **Payroll Expense ($000):** 22209 **Personnel:** 385

☐ **LORETTO HOSPITAL (140083)**, 645 South Central Avenue, Zip 60644–5059; tel. 773/626–4300 **A**1 10 **F**2 3 4 5 15 18 20 29 30 31 34 35 38 40 44 45 50 54 57 59 60 61 64 65 68 70 74 75 78 79 81 85 86 87 89 92 93 98 102 103 104 105 106 107 108 115 119 130 132 143 146 147 148
Primary Contact: Sonia Mehta, M.D., Chief Executive Officer and Chief Medical Officer
CFO: John Valles, Senior Vice President and Chief Financial Officer
CMO: Sonia Mehta, M.D., Chief Executive Officer and Chief Medical Officer
CIO: Suresh Krishnan, Vice President and Chief Information Officer
CHR: Amy Coleman, Director Human Resources
CNO: James M. Renneker, MSN, Vice President and Chief Nursing Officer
Web address: www.lorettohospital.org
**Control:** Other not–for–profit (including NFP Corporation) **Service:** General Medical and Surgical

**Staffed Beds:** 147 **Admissions:** 4704 **Census:** 69 **Outpatient Visits:** 31582 **Births:** 0 **Total Expense ($000):** 57846 **Payroll Expense ($000):** 28419 **Personnel:** 457

✠ **LOUIS A. WEISS MEMORIAL HOSPITAL (140082)**, 4646 North Marine Drive, Zip 60640–5759; tel. 773/878–8700 **A**1 2 3 5 9 10 **F**3 8 9 15 18 20 22 24 28 29 30 31 34 35 36 37 40 44 45 49 56 57 58 59 64 65 66 68 70 74 75 77 78 79 81 82 85 86 87 90 92 93 96 97 98 100 101 102 103 107 108 110 111 114 118 119 121 126 129 130 131 132 135 141 143 146 147 148 **P**5 6 8 **S** TENET Healthcare Corporation, Dallas, TX
Primary Contact: Anthony Tedeschi, M.D., M.P.H., Chief Executive Officer and Chief Medical Officer
CFO: Jeffrey L. Meigs, Chief Financial Officer
CMO: Anthony Tedeschi, M.D., Chief Executive Officer and Chief Medical Officer
CIO: Thomas Crawford, Chicago Market Chief Information Officer
CHR: Keoni Nader, Director Human Resources
Web address: www.weisshospital.com
**Control:** Corporation, Investor–owned, for–profit **Service:** General Medical and Surgical

**Staffed Beds:** 184 **Admissions:** 5878 **Census:** 90 **Outpatient Visits:** 70329 **Births:** 0 **Total Expense ($000):** 116276 **Payroll Expense ($000):** 48895 **Personnel:** 732

IL

*Many Facility Codes have changed. Please refer to the AHA Guide Code Chart.*

© 2015 AHA Guide

★ ○ **MERCY HOSPITAL AND MEDICAL CENTER (140158)**, 2525 South Michigan Avenue, Zip 60616–2333; tel. 312/567–2000 **A**2 3 5 9 10 11 **F**3 5 12 13 15 17 18 20 22 24 26 28 29 30 31 32 33 34 35 36 40 44 45 46 49 50 51 52 53 54 55 56 57 58 59 61 64 65 66 70 73 74 76 77 78 79 81 82 84 85 86 87 89 90 91 92 93 96 97 98 99 100 101 102 103 104 105 107 108 110 111 114 115 117 118 119 121 123 124 126 129 130 131 132 133 134 135 143 144 145 146 147 148 **P**5 6 **S** Trinity Health, Livonia, MI
Primary Contact: Carol L. Schneider, President and Chief Executive Officer
COO: Richard Cerceo, Executive Vice President and Chief Operating Officer
CFO: Eric Krueger, Chief Financial Officer
CMO: Michael McDonnell, M.D., Chief Medical Officer
CIO: John Romeo, Chief Information Officer
CHR: Nancy L. Hill–Davis, Vice President Human Resources and Risk Management
CNO: Carla Campbell, R.N., Chief Nurse Officer
Web address: www.mercy–chicago.org
**Control:** Other not–for–profit (including NFP Corporation) **Service:** General Medical and Surgical

**Staffed Beds:** 189 **Admissions:** 13983 **Census:** 164 **Outpatient Visits:** 375137 **Births:** 2447 **Total Expense ($000):** 253720 **Payroll Expense ($000):** 98521 **Personnel:** 1536

○ **METHODIST HOSPITAL OF CHICAGO (140197)**, 5025 North Paulina Street, Zip 60640–2772; tel. 773/271–9040, (Nonreporting) **A**9 10 11
Primary Contact: Joseph Chandy, Administrator
CFO: Jim Gregory, Controller
Web address: www.bethanymethodist.org
**Control:** Other not–for–profit (including NFP Corporation) **Service:** General Medical and Surgical

**Staffed Beds:** 189

⊞ **MOUNT SINAI HOSPITAL (140018)**, California Avenue at 15th Street, Zip 60608–1729; tel. 773/542–2000, (Includes SINAI CHILDREN'S HOSPITAL, California Avenue at 15th Street, Zip 60608; tel. 888/287–4624), (Nonreporting) **A**1 2 3 5 8 9 10 **S** Sinai Health System, Chicago, IL
Primary Contact: Loren Chandler, President
CFO: Charles Weis, Chief Financial Officer
CMO: Jack Garon, M.D., Chief Medical Officer
CIO: Richard Duncan, Vice President and Chief Information Officer
CHR: Andrew Wissel, Director Human Resources
Web address: www.sinai.org
**Control:** Other not–for–profit (including NFP Corporation) **Service:** General Medical and Surgical

**Staffed Beds:** 290

⊞ **NORTHWESTERN MEMORIAL HOSPITAL (140281)**, 251 East Huron Street, Zip 60611–2908; tel. 312/926–2000, (Includes PRENTICE WOMEN'S HOSPITAL, 250 East Superior Street, Zip 60611; tel. 312/926–2000; STONE INSTITUTE OF PSYCHIATRY, 320 East Huron Street, Zip 60611; tel. 312/926–2000) **A**1 2 3 5 8 9 10 **F**3 4 5 6 8 9 11 12 13 14 15 17 18 20 22 24 26 28 29 30 31 32 33 34 35 36 37 38 39 40 43 44 45 46 47 48 49 50 51 52 53 54 55 56 57 58 59 60 61 63 64 65 66 68 70 72 73 74 75 76 77 78 79 80 81 82 83 84 85 86 87 92 93 96 97 98 99 100 101 102 103 104 107 108 110 111 114 115 116 117 118 119 120 121 123 124 126 129 130 131 132 134 135 136 137 138 139 140 141 142 143 144 145 146 147 148 **P**5 **S** Northwestern Memorial Healthcare, Chicago, IL
Primary Contact: Dean M. Harrison, President and Chief Executive Officer
CFO: Peter J. McCanna, Executive Vice President Administration and Chief Financial Officer
CMO: Michael G. Ankin, M.D., Vice President Medical Affairs & Chief Medical Officer
CIO: Timothy R. Zoph, Senior Vice President and Chief Information Officer
CHR: Dean Manheimer, Senior Vice President Human Resources
Web address: www.nmh.org
**Control:** Other not–for–profit (including NFP Corporation) **Service:** General Medical and Surgical

**Staffed Beds:** 885 **Admissions:** 47139 **Census:** 655 **Outpatient Visits:** 681798 **Births:** 12497 **Total Expense ($000):** 2015455 **Payroll Expense ($000):** 823874 **Personnel:** 8375

⊞ **NORWEGIAN AMERICAN HOSPITAL (140206)**, 1044 North Francisco Avenue, Zip 60622–2743; tel. 773/292–8200 **A**1 3 5 9 10 **F**5 13 15 18 19 20 22 29 31 32 34 35 36 38 39 40 44 45 46 47 48 49 50 56 57 59 63 64 65 68 70 71 74 75 76 77 78 79 81 82 84 86 87 89 91 92 93 94 96 97 98 100 101 102 103 107 110 111 114 118 119 130 143 146 147 148 **P**8
Primary Contact: Jose R. Sanchez, President and Chief Executive Officer
COO: Abha Agrawal, M.D., Chief Operating Officer and Chief Medical Officer
CFO: Gary M. Krugel, Chief Financial Officer
CMO: Abha Agrawal, M.D., Chief Operating Officer and Chief Medical Officer
CIO: Stephen DePooter, Chief Information Officer
CHR: Marcia Powers, Vice President Human Resources
CNO: Sonia V. Casiano, R.N., Interim Chief Nursing Officer
Web address: www.nahospital.org
**Control:** Other not–for–profit (including NFP Corporation) **Service:** General Medical and Surgical

**Staffed Beds:** 195 **Admissions:** 8197 **Census:** 106 **Outpatient Visits:** 78863 **Births:** 1144 **Total Expense ($000):** 106304 **Payroll Expense ($000):** 47511 **Personnel:** 712

**OUR LADY OF THE RESURRECTION MEDICAL CENTER** See Community First Medical Center

**PRENTICE WOMEN'S HOSPITAL** See Northwestern Memorial Hospital

⊞ △ **PRESENCE RESURRECTION MEDICAL CENTER (140117)**, 7435 West Talcott Avenue, Zip 60631–3746; tel. 773/774–8000 **A**1 2 3 5 7 9 10 13 **F**3 8 11 13 15 18 20 22 24 26 28 29 30 31 34 35 37 38 40 41 45 46 47 49 50 53 57 58 59 60 64 66 68 70 74 75 76 78 79 81 82 83 87 89 90 92 93 96 100 107 108 110 111 114 115 117 118 119 120 121 123 126 130 131 132 133 146 147 148 **S** Presence Health, Chicago, IL
Primary Contact: Lowell W. Johnson, LFACHE, Chief Executive Officer
CFO: Richard Franco, Chief Financial Officer
CMO: David Bordo, M.D., Chief Medical Officer
CHR: Ivy McKinley, Regional Lead Human Resources
CNO: Pam Bell, Vice President Patient Care Services and Chief Nursing Officer
Web address: www.presencehealth.org
**Control:** City–Government, nonfederal **Service:** General Medical and Surgical

**Staffed Beds:** 199 **Admissions:** 12650 **Census:** 180 **Outpatient Visits:** 194404 **Births:** 1014 **Total Expense ($000):** 245444 **Payroll Expense ($000):** 88129 **Personnel:** 1439

⊞ **PRESENCE SAINT JOSEPH HOSPITAL (140224)**, 2900 North Lake Shore Drive, Zip 60657–6274; tel. 773/665–3000 **A**1 2 3 5 9 10 **F**3 4 5 11 12 13 15 18 20 22 24 26 28 29 30 31 32 34 35 36 38 39 40 45 47 48 49 50 53 56 57 58 59 61 64 65 66 70 72 74 75 76 77 78 79 81 82 84 85 86 87 89 90 93 97 98 100 101 102 103 104 107 108 110 111 114 115 118 119 120 121 122 126 128 129 130 131 132 135 145 146 147 148 **S** Presence Health, Chicago, IL
Primary Contact: Roberta Luskin–Hawk, M.D., President and Chief Executive Officer
CFO: Stanley Kazmierczak, Controller
CMO: M. Todd Grendon, M.D., President Medical Staff
CIO: George Chessum, Senior Vice President Information Systems and Chief Information Officer
CHR: Denise Brown, Vice President Human Resources
Web address: www.reshealth.org
**Control:** Church–operated, Nongovernment, not–for profit **Service:** General Medical and Surgical

**Staffed Beds:** 310 **Admissions:** 11960 **Census:** 175 **Outpatient Visits:** 185830 **Births:** 1467 **Total Expense ($000):** 195605 **Payroll Expense ($000):** 75663 **Personnel:** 1268

⊞ **PRESENCE SAINTS MARY & ELIZABETH MEDICAL CENTER (140180)**, 2233 West Division Street, Zip 60622–3086; tel. 312/770–2000, (Includes PRESENCE SAINTS MARY & ELIZABETH MEDICAL CENTER, CLAREMONT AVENUE, 1431 North Claremont Avenue, Zip 60622–1791; tel. 773/278–2000; Martin H. Judd, Regional President and Chief Executive Officer), (Total facility includes 25 beds in nursing home–type unit) **A**1 2 3 5 9 10 **F**3 13 15 18 19 20 22 24 26 28 29 30 31 32 34 35 36 38 40 45 49 50 52 57 58 59 60 64 65 66 68 70 74 75 76 77 78 79 81 82 85 86 87 89 90 91 92 93 94 96 97 98 99 100 101 102 103 107 108 110 111 114 115 119 121 123 126 128 129 130 132 135 143 146 147 148 **P**8 **S** Presence Health, Chicago, IL
Primary Contact: Martin H. Judd, Regional President and Chief Executive Officer
CFO: Bob Cech, Regional Finance Officer
CMO: Laura Concannon, M.D., Regional Chief Medical Officer
CIO: David Lundal, Chief Information Officer
CHR: Melanie Saenz, Regional Human Resources Officer
CNO: Suzanne Lambert, R.N., Regional Chief Nursing Officer and Support Services
Web address: www.presencehealth.org/presence–saints–mary–and–elizabeth–medical–center–chicago
**Control:** Church–operated, Nongovernment, not–for profit **Service:** General Medical and Surgical

**Staffed Beds:** 476 **Admissions:** 18998 **Census:** 278 **Outpatient Visits:** 190317 **Births:** 1354 **Total Expense ($000):** 266480 **Payroll Expense ($000):** 93738 **Personnel:** 1547

IL

---

**Hospital, Medicare Provider Number, Address, Telephone, Approval, Facility, and Physician Codes, Health Care System**

★ American Hospital Association (AHA) membership    ○ Healthcare Facilities Accreditation Program    ⇑ Center for Improvement in Healthcare Quality Accreditation
□ The Joint Commission accreditation    ◇ DNV Healthcare Inc. accreditation    △ Commission on Accreditation of Rehabilitation Facilities (CARF) accreditation

---

⊠ **PROVIDENT HOSPITAL OF COOK COUNTY (140300)**, 500 East 51st Street, Zip 60615–2494; tel. 312/572–2000 **A**1 3 5 9 10 **F**3 8 15 18 29 30 34 35 40 45 50 53 57 59 61 64 66 68 78 81 85 87 92 94 104 107 119 130 132 135 143 146 147 **S** Cook County Health and Hospitals System, Chicago, IL
Primary Contact: John Jay Shannon, M.D., Chief Executive Officer
CFO: Barbara Patterson, Chief Financial Officer
CMO: Aaron Hamb, M.D., Chief Medical Officer
CIO: Donna Hart, Chief Information Officer
Web address: www.ccbhs.org/pages/ProvidentHospitalofCookCounty.htm
**Control:** County–Government, nonfederal **Service:** General Medical and Surgical

**Staffed Beds:** 25 **Admissions:** 1273 **Census:** 14 **Outpatient Visits:** 32411 **Births:** 0 **Total Expense ($000):** 59743 **Payroll Expense ($000):** 34235 **Personnel:** 316

⊠ **REHABILITATION INSTITUTE OF CHICAGO (143026)**, 345 East Superior Street, Zip 60611–2654; tel. 312/238–1000, (Nonreporting) **A**1 3 5 9 10
Primary Contact: Joanne C. Smith, M.D., President and Chief Executive Officer
COO: Peggy Kirk, Senior Vice President Clinical Operations
CFO: Ed Case, Executive Vice President and Chief Financial Officer
CMO: James Sliwa, M.D., Chief Medical Officer
CIO: Tim McKula, Vice President Information Systems and Chief Information Officer
CHR: Lois Huggins, Chief Human Resources Officer and Senior Vice President Human Resources
Web address: www.ric.org
**Control:** Other not–for–profit (including NFP Corporation) **Service:** Rehabilitation

**Staffed Beds:** 182

**RESURRECTION MEDICAL CENTER** See Presence Resurrection Medical Center

★ **RML SPECIALTY HOSPITAL (142012)**, 3435 West Van Buren Street, Zip 60624–3312; tel. 773/826–6300 **F**1 3 18 29 30 31 45 53 58 74 85 107 114 119 130 146 148 **P**6
Primary Contact: James R. Prister, President and Chief Executive Officer
COO: Ken Pawola, Chief Operating Officer
CFO: Tom Pater, Vice President Finance and Chief Financial Officer
CMO: Patrick Fahey, M.D., Chief Medical Director
CIO: Vincent Vitali, Chief Information Officer
CHR: John Landstrom, Vice President Human Resources and Operations
CNO: Marti Edwards, MSN, Chief Nursing Officer
Web address: www.rmlspecialtyhospital.org
**Control:** Other not–for–profit (including NFP Corporation) **Service:** Long–Term Acute Care hospital

**Staffed Beds:** 69 **Admissions:** 593 **Census:** 44 **Outpatient Visits:** 17 **Births:** 0 **Total Expense ($000):** 28104 **Payroll Expense ($000):** 14256 **Personnel:** 265

○ **ROSELAND COMMUNITY HOSPITAL (140068)**, 45 West 111th Street, Zip 60628–4294; tel. 773/995–3000, (Nonreporting) **A**9 10 11
Primary Contact: Timothy Egan, Chief Restructuring Officer and President
CMO: Rogelio Cave, M.D., Medical Director
CIO: William Spence, Director
CNO: Winifred Lewis, R.N., Chief Nursing Officer
Web address: www.roselandhospital.org
**Control:** Other not–for–profit (including NFP Corporation) **Service:** General Medical and Surgical

**Staffed Beds:** 115

⊠ △ **RUSH UNIVERSITY MEDICAL CENTER (140119)**, 1653 West Congress Parkway, Zip 60612–3833; tel. 312/942–5000, (Includes JOHNSTON R. BOWMAN HEALTH CENTER, 700 South Paulina, Zip 60612; tel. 312/942–7000; RUSH CHILDREN'S HOSPITAL, 1653 Wes Congress Parkway, tel. 888/352–7874) **A**1 2 3 5 7 8 9 10 **F**2 3 6 8 9 11 12 13 14 15 17 18 19 20 21 22 23 24 25 26 27 28 29 30 31 32 34 35 36 37 38 39 40 41 43 44 45 46 47 48 49 50 51 52 53 55 56 57 58 59 60 61 62 63 64 65 66 68 70 72 73 74 75 76 77 78 79 81 82 83 84 85 86 87 88 89 90 91 92 93 94 95 96 97 98 99 100 101 102 103 104 105 107 110 111 114 115 117 118 119 120 121 123 124 125 126 129 130 131 132 134 135 136 137 138 139 141 142 145 146 147 148 **P**8 **S** Rush University Medical Center, Chicago, IL
Primary Contact: Larry J. Goodman, M.D., Chief Executive Officer
COO: Peter W. Butler, President and Chief Operating Officer
CFO: John P. Mordach, Senior Vice President and Chief Financial Officer
CMO: David A. Ansell, M.D., Senior Vice President Clinical Affairs and Chief Medical Officer
CIO: Lac Tran, Senior Vice President Information Services
CHR: Mary Ellen Schopp, Senior Vice President Human Resources
CNO: Cynthia Barginere, MSN, Vice President Clinical Nursing and Chief Nursing Officer
Web address: www.rush.edu
**Control:** Other not–for–profit (including NFP Corporation) **Service:** General Medical and Surgical

**Staffed Beds:** 677 **Admissions:** 31515 **Census:** 480 **Outpatient Visits:** 642159 **Births:** 2110 **Total Expense ($000):** 970926 **Payroll Expense ($000):** 299426 **Personnel:** 8337

⊠ **SAINT ANTHONY HOSPITAL (140095)**, 2875 West 19th Street, Zip 60623–3596; tel. 773/484–1000 **A**1 3 9 10 **F**3 13 15 18 19 29 30 31 32 33 34 35 40 41 44 49 50 51 53 54 57 59 60 64 65 68 70 74 75 76 77 78 79 81 82 85 86 87 89 93 96 97 98 100 101 102 104 105 107 108 110 111 115 118 119 130 131 132 143 144 146 147 148 **P**8
Primary Contact: Guy A. Medaglia, President and Chief Executive Officer
CFO: Justin Bynum, Chief Financial Officer
CIO: Mark Jennings, Chief Information Officer
CHR: Malinda Yvonne Carter, Vice President Human Resources
CNO: Jill Stemmerman, R.N., Vice President of Patient Care and Chief Nursing Officer
Web address: www.sahchicago.org
**Control:** Church–operated, Nongovernment, not–for profit **Service:** General Medical and Surgical

**Staffed Beds:** 151 **Admissions:** 6180 **Census:** 75 **Outpatient Visits:** 159592 **Births:** 1820 **Total Expense ($000):** 106019 **Payroll Expense ($000):** 51960 **Personnel:** 825

**SAINT JOSEPH HOSPITAL** See Presence Saint Joseph Hospital

**SAINTS MARY & ELIZABETH MEDICAL CENTER** See Presence Saints Mary & Elizabeth Medical Center

⊠ **SCHWAB REHABILITATION HOSPITAL (143025)**, 1401 South California Avenue, Zip 60608–1858; tel. 773/522–2010 **A**1 3 5 9 10 **F**28 29 35 50 58 60 64 75 77 90 91 92 93 96 119 128 130 131 132 135 143 148 **P**6 **S** Sinai Health System, Chicago, IL
Primary Contact: Karl J. Sandin, M.D., M.P.H., President and Medical Director
CFO: Charles Weis, Chief Financial Officer
CMO: Karl J. Sandin, M.D., President and Medical Director
CHR: Aaron A. Austin, Vice President Human Resources
CNO: Mary A. Gollinger, MS, Director of Nursing
Web address: www.schwabrehab.org
**Control:** Other not–for–profit (including NFP Corporation) **Service:** Rehabilitation

**Staffed Beds:** 21 **Admissions:** 400 **Census:** 13 **Outpatient Visits:** 0 **Births:** 0

☐ **SHRINERS HOSPITALS FOR CHILDREN–CHICAGO (143302)**, 2211 North Oak Park Avenue, Zip 60707–3392; tel. 773/622–5400, (Nonreporting) **A**1 3 5 10 **S** Shriners Hospitals for Children, Tampa, FL
Primary Contact: Mark L. Niederpruem, FACHE, Administrator
CFO: Philip Magid, Director Fiscal Services
CMO: Jeffrey D. Ackman, M.D., Chief of Staff
CHR: James E. Pawlowicz, Director Human Resources
CNO: Terry Wheat, R.N., Director of Patient Care Services
Web address: www.shrinershospitalsforchildren.org/Hospitals/Locations/Chicago.aspx
**Control:** Other not–for–profit (including NFP Corporation) **Service:** Children's orthopedic

**Staffed Beds:** 36

○ **SOUTH SHORE HOSPITAL (140181)**, 8012 South Crandon Avenue, Zip 60617–1124; tel. 773/768–0810, (Nonreporting) **A**10 11
Primary Contact: Timothy Caveney, President
CFO: Scott Spencer, Chief Financial Officer
CMO: James Bob Achebe, M.D., President Medical Staff
CIO: Jim Ritchie, Director Management Information Systems
CHR: Roger Rak, Director Human Resources
CNO: Laura Gonzalez, Interim Chief Nurse Executive
Web address: www.southshorehospital.com
**Control:** Other not–for–profit (including NFP Corporation) **Service:** General Medical and Surgical

**Staffed Beds:** 137

☐ **ST. BERNARD HOSPITAL AND HEALTH CARE CENTER (140103)**, 326 West 64th Street, Zip 60621–3146; tel. 773/962–3900, (Nonreporting) **A**1 9 10
Primary Contact: Charles Holland, President and Chief Executive Officer
COO: Roland Abellera, Chief Quality Officer and Vice President Clinical Operations
CHR: Donna Dertz, Director Human Resources
CNO: Evelyn Jones, R.N., Vice President Nursing Services
Web address: www.stbernardhospital.com
**Control:** Church–operated, Nongovernment, not–for profit **Service:** General Medical and Surgical

**Staffed Beds:** 100

*Many Facility Codes have changed. Please refer to the AHA Guide Code Chart.*   © 2015 AHA Guide

○ **SWEDISH COVENANT HOSPITAL (140114)**, 5145 North California Avenue, Zip 60625–3661; tel. 773/878–8200 **A**2 3 9 10 11 12 13 **F**3 8 13 15 18 19 20 22 24 26 28 29 30 31 32 33 34 35 36 38 40 45 46 47 49 50 53 56 57 58 59 60 62 64 68 70 74 75 76 78 79 81 82 83 84 85 86 87 89 90 92 93 96 97 98 100 101 102 103 105 107 108 110 111 114 115 117 118 119 121 123 124 126 128 129 130 131 132 134 135 143 146 147 148 **P**1 5 7
Primary Contact: Mark Newton, President and Chief Executive Officer
COO: Anthony Guaccio, Senior Vice President & Chief Operating Officer
CFO: Thomas J. Garvey, Senior Vice President Operations and Chief Financial Officer
CMO: Derek J. Kelly, M.D., Vice President Transformation and Chief Medical Information Officer
CIO: Karen Sheehan, Vice President and Chief Information Officer
CHR: Anthony Guaccio, Senior Vice President and Chief Operating Officer
CNO: Mary Shehan, R.N., Senior Vice President and Chief Nursing Officer
Web address: www.schosp.org
**Control:** Church–operated, Nongovernment, not–for profit **Service:** General Medical and Surgical

**Staffed Beds:** 279 **Admissions:** 13423 **Census:** 184 **Outpatient Visits:** 257241 **Births:** 1926 **Total Expense ($000):** 252829 **Payroll Expense ($000):** 99494 **Personnel:** 1878

○ **THOREK MEMORIAL HOSPITAL (140115)**, 850 West Irving Park Road, Zip 60613–3077; tel. 773/525–6780, (Nonreporting) **A**3 9 10 11
Primary Contact: Edward Budd, President and Chief Executive Officer
COO: Peter N. Kamberos, Chief Operating Officer
CMO: Ilona Carlos, M.D., President Medical Staff
CIO: Tony Vavarutsos, Director Information Systems
CHR: Brett Wakefield, Director Human Resources
CNO: Mary McCahill, Chief Nursing Officer
Web address: www.thorek.org
**Control:** Other not–for–profit (including NFP Corporation) **Service:** General Medical and Surgical

**Staffed Beds:** 134

**UNIVERSITY OF CHICAGO COMER CHILDREN'S HOSPITAL** See University of Chicago Medical Center

✠ **UNIVERSITY OF CHICAGO MEDICAL CENTER (140088)**, 5841 South Maryland Avenue, Zip 60637–1447; tel. 773/702–1000, (Includes BERNARD MITCHELL HOSPITAL, 950 East 59th Street, Zip 60637; CHICAGO LYING–IN HOSPITAL, 950 East 59th Street, Zip 60637; tel. 312/684–6100; UNIVERSITY OF CHICAGO COMER CHILDREN'S HOSPITAL, 5721 South Maryland Avenue, Zip 60637; tel. 312/702–6168) **A**1 2 3 5 8 9 10 **F**3 5 6 9 11 12 13 14 15 16 17 18 19 20 21 22 23 24 25 26 27 28 29 30 31 32 34 35 36 37 38 40 41 43 44 45 46 47 48 49 50 51 52 53 54 55 56 57 58 59 60 61 63 64 65 68 70 71 72 73 74 75 76 77 78 79 81 82 83 84 85 86 87 88 89 92 93 97 100 101 102 104 107 108 109 110 111 112 114 115 116 117 118 119 120 121 123 124 126 129 130 131 132 134 135 136 137 138 139 140 141 142 143 144 145 146 147 148 **P**1
Primary Contact: Sharon L. O'Keefe, R.N., President
COO: Jason Keeler, Executive Vice President and Chief Operating Officer
CFO: James Watson, Chief Financial Officer
CMO: Stephen Weber, M.D., Chief Medical Officer
CIO: Eric Yablonka, Vice President and Chief Information Officer
CHR: Robert Hanley, Chief Human Resources Officer
CNO: Debra Albert, MSN, Senior Vice President Patient Care and Chief Nursing Officer
Web address: www.uchospitals.edu
**Control:** Other not–for–profit (including NFP Corporation) **Service:** General Medical and Surgical

**Staffed Beds:** 624 **Admissions:** 26195 **Census:** 457 **Outpatient Visits:** 671067 **Births:** 1586 **Total Expense ($000):** 1378140 **Payroll Expense ($000):** 498230 **Personnel:** 7998

✠ △ **UNIVERSITY OF ILLINOIS HOSPITAL & HEALTH SCIENCES SYSTEM (140150)**, 1740 West Taylor Street, Zip 60612–7232; tel. 312/996–7000 **A**1 2 3 5 7 8 9 10 **F**3 12 13 14 15 17 19 20 21 22 23 24 25 26 27 28 29 30 31 32 34 35 37 38 39 40 41 45 46 47 48 49 50 52 54 55 56 57 58 59 60 61 64 65 66 68 70 72 73 74 75 76 77 78 79 81 82 84 85 86 87 88 89 90 91 92 93 96 97 98 99 100 101 102 103 104 107 108 110 111 114 115 116 117 118 119 120 121 123 124 126 129 130 131 132 134 135 136 138 139 141 142 144 145 146 147 148 **P**4
Primary Contact: Avijit Ghosh, M.D., Chief Executive Officer
COO: David Loffing, Chief Operating Officer
CFO: Jeffrey Rooney, Chief Financial Officer
CMO: Bernard Pygon, M.D., Chief Medical Officer
CIO: Audrius Polikaitis, Chief Information Officer
CHR: Mary Jo Smith, Chief Human Resources Officer
CNO: Jodi S. Joyce, R.N., Interim Chief Nursing Officer
Web address: www.hospital.uillinois.edu/
**Control:** State–Government, nonfederal **Service:** General Medical and Surgical

**Staffed Beds:** 384 **Admissions:** 19082 **Census:** 316 **Outpatient Visits:** 450006 **Births:** 2420 **Total Expense ($000):** 791959 **Payroll Expense ($000):** 295666 **Personnel:** 4186

### CHICAGO HEIGHTS—Cook County

**ST. JAMES HOSPITAL AND HEALTH CENTERS – CHICAGO HEIGHTS CAMPUS** See Franciscan St. James Hospital and Health Centers, Olympia Fields

### CLINTON—De Witt County

**DR. JOHN WARNER HOSPITAL (141303)**, 422 West White Street, Zip 61727–2272; tel. 217/935–9571, (Nonreporting) **A**9 10 18
Primary Contact: Paul Skowron, Chief Executive Officer
CFO: Donna Wisner, Chief Financial Officer
CMO: Brit Williams, M.D., President Medical Staff
CIO: Larry Schleicher, Manager Information Services
CHR: Sarah Gerke, Manager Human Resources
CNO: Heidi Cook, Chief Nursing Officer
Web address: www.djwhospital.org
**Control:** City–Government, nonfederal **Service:** General Medical and Surgical

**Staffed Beds:** 25

### DANVILLE—Vermilion County

✠ **PRESENCE UNITED SAMARITANS MEDICAL CENTER (140093)**, 812 North Logan, Zip 61832–3788; tel. 217/443–5000 **A**1 2 5 9 10 19 **F**3 8 13 15 18 20 29 30 31 34 35 40 57 59 64 68 70 74 75 76 78 79 81 82 85 87 89 102 107 108 110 111 114 115 118 119 120 121 124 126 129 130 132 134 146 147 148 **S** Presence Health, Chicago, IL
Primary Contact: Jared Rogers, M.D., Interim Regional President and Chief Executive Officer
COO: Jennifer Cord, Vice President Operations
CFO: Deborah Schimerowski, Chief Financial Officer
CMO: Carmen Rocco, M.D., Chief Medical Officer
CIO: Paula Keele, Manager Information Systems
CHR: Janet S. Payne, Vice President Human Resources
CNO: Molly Nicholson, R.N., Vice President of Patient Care/Chief Nurse Executive
Web address: www.provena.org/usmc
**Control:** Church–operated, Nongovernment, not–for profit **Service:** General Medical and Surgical

**Staffed Beds:** 117 **Admissions:** 6070 **Census:** 60 **Outpatient Visits:** 203263 **Births:** 586 **Total Expense ($000):** 98475 **Payroll Expense ($000):** 32827 **Personnel:** 594

✠ **VETERANS AFFAIRS ILLIANA HEALTH CARE SYSTEM**, 1900 East Main Street, Zip 61832–5198; tel. 217/554–3000, (Nonreporting) **A**1 3 5 9
**S** Department of Veterans Affairs, Washington, DC
Primary Contact: Diana Carranza, Interim Director
COO: Diana Carranza, Associate Director
CFO: Becky Tissier, Chief Fiscal Service
CMO: Khiem Tran, M.D., Acting Chief of Staff
CIO: Frank D. Jackson, III, Facility Chief Information Officer
CHR: Connie Ohl, Acting Chief Human Resources
Web address: www.danville.va.gov/
**Control:** Veterans Affairs, Government, federal **Service:** General Medical and Surgical

**Staffed Beds:** 221

---

**Hospital, Medicare Provider Number, Address, Telephone, Approval, Facility, and Physician Codes, Health Care System**

★ American Hospital Association (AHA) membership
☐ The Joint Commission accreditation
○ Healthcare Facilities Accreditation Program
◇ DNV Healthcare Inc. accreditation
⇑ Center for Improvement in Healthcare Quality Accreditation
△ Commission on Accreditation of Rehabilitation Facilities (CARF) accreditation

IL

## DECATUR—Macon County

⊠ △ **DECATUR MEMORIAL HOSPITAL (140135)**, 2300 North Edward Street, Zip 62526–4192; tel. 217/876–8121 **A**1 2 3 5 7 9 10 19 **F**3 11 12 13 14 15 17 18 20 22 24 26 28 29 30 31 34 40 45 46 47 48 49 51 53 54 56 57 58 59 60 61 62 63 64 65 69 70 73 74 75 76 77 78 79 81 82 86 87 89 91 92 93 94 96 107 108 110 111 112 114 115 116 117 118 119 120 121 123 126 129 130 131 132 133 143 144 145 146 147 148 **P**8
Primary Contact: Timothy D. Stone, Jr., Executive Vice President and Administrator
CFO: Al Naqvi, Chief Financial Officer
CMO: David Baumberger, Chief Medical Officer
CHR: Kevin Horath, Vice President Human Resources
CNO: Linda L. Fahey, R.N., Vice President and Chief Nurse Executive
Web address: www.dmhcares.org
**Control:** Other not–for–profit (including NFP Corporation) **Service:** General Medical and Surgical

**Staffed Beds:** 188 **Admissions:** 10085 **Census:** 105 **Outpatient Visits:** 279431 **Births:** 958 **Total Expense ($000):** 267240 **Payroll Expense ($000):** 109828 **Personnel:** 1846

⊠ △ **HSHS ST. MARY'S HOSPITAL (140166)**, 1800 East Lake Shore Drive, Zip 62521–3883; tel. 217/464–2966, (Total facility includes 14 beds in nursing home–type unit) **A**1 3 7 9 10 19 **F**2 3 5 11 13 15 18 20 22 28 29 30 31 34 35 40 44 45 50 54 56 57 59 64 66 70 74 75 76 77 78 79 81 82 85 86 87 89 90 92 93 96 98 99 100 101 102 103 104 105 107 108 110 111 114 115 117 119 120 121 123 124 128 129 130 131 132 141 142 146 148 **P**7
**S** Hospital Sisters Health System, Springfield, IL
Primary Contact: Daniel L. Perryman, President and Chief Executive Officer
CMO: Phil Barnell, Chief Medical Officer
CHR: Denise Smith, Director Human Resources
Web address: www.stmarysdecatur.com
**Control:** Church–operated, Nongovernment, not–for profit **Service:** General Medical and Surgical

**Staffed Beds:** 244 **Admissions:** 8151 **Census:** 115 **Outpatient Visits:** 166433 **Births:** 621 **Total Expense ($000):** 127228 **Payroll Expense ($000):** 40030 **Personnel:** 793

## DEKALB—DeKalb County

⊠ **KISHWAUKEE HOSPITAL (140286)**, 1 Kish Hospital Drive, Zip 60115–9602, Mailing Address: P.O. Box 707, Zip 60115–0707; tel. 815/756–1521 **A**1 2 9 10 **F**3 8 11 13 15 18 20 22 26 28 29 30 31 32 34 35 36 37 38 40 43 45 46 48 49 57 58 59 60 64 68 70 71 73 74 75 76 77 78 79 81 82 85 86 87 89 93 96 102 104 107 108 110 111 114 115 117 118 119 129 130 131 132 133 135 143 145 146 147 148 **P**8 **S** Kish Health System, DeKalb, IL
Primary Contact: Brad Copple, President
COO: Brad Copple, President
CFO: Loren Foelske, Vice President Finance
CMO: Michael Kulisz, D.O., Chief Medical Officer
CIO: Heath Bell, Chief Information Officer
CHR: Michele McClelland, Vice President Human Resources
CNO: Pamela Duffy, Vice President Patient Care Services and Chief Nursing Officer
Web address: www.kishhospital.org
**Control:** Other not–for–profit (including NFP Corporation) **Service:** General Medical and Surgical

**Staffed Beds:** 98 **Admissions:** 5340 **Census:** 50 **Outpatient Visits:** 138822 **Births:** 792 **Total Expense ($000):** 156518 **Payroll Expense ($000):** 43413 **Personnel:** 715

## DES PLAINES—Cook County

**HOLY FAMILY MEDICAL CENTER** See Presence Holy Family Medical Center

⊠ **PRESENCE HOLY FAMILY MEDICAL CENTER (142011)**, 100 North River Road, Zip 60016–1255; tel. 847/297–1800 **A**1 9 10 **F**1 3 5 15 18 29 30 34 42 45 110 50 53 54 56 57 59 60 62 63 64 65 66 68 81 82 84 85 87 93 107 109 110 111 118 129 130 135 143 146 147 148 **S** Presence Health, Chicago, IL
Primary Contact: Yolande Wilson–Stubbs, Regional Chief Operating Officer
CFO: Donna Pareti, Business Unit Chief Financial Officer
CMO: David Bordo, M.D., Chief Medical Officer
CIO: David Lundal, Senior Vice President Information Systems and Chief Information Officer
CHR: Ivy McKinley, Director Human Resources
CNO: Carole Miserendino, MSN, Chief Nursing Officer
Web address: www.presencehealth.org
**Control:** Church–operated, Nongovernment, not–for profit **Service:** Long–Term Acute Care hospital

**Staffed Beds:** 128 **Admissions:** 1481 **Census:** 98 **Outpatient Visits:** 32215 **Births:** 0 **Total Expense ($000):** 72988 **Payroll Expense ($000):** 31699 **Personnel:** 606

## DIXON—Lee County

★ **KATHERINE SHAW BETHEA HOSPITAL (140012)**, 403 East First Street, Zip 61021–3187; tel. 815/288–5531 **A**3 5 9 10 **F**3 11 13 15 18 20 22 28 29 30 31 32 34 35 38 39 40 43 44 45 46 47 49 50 54 56 57 59 62 64 65 66 69 70 74 75 76 77 79 81 85 86 87 89 91 92 93 94 96 97 98 100 101 102 103 104 107 108 110 111 115 118 119 127 129 130 131 132 135 144 145 146 147 148 **P**6
Primary Contact: David L. Schreiner, FACHE, President and Chief Executive Officer
COO: Julie D. Mann, Vice President and Chief Administrative Officer
CFO: Anthony Evers, Interim Chief Financial Officer
CMO: A. Timothy Appenheimer, M.D., Vice President and Chief Medical Officer
CHR: Suzanne M. Ravlin, Senior Director Human Resources and Quality
CNO: Linda Clemen, R.N., Vice President and Chief Nursing Officer
Web address: www.ksbhospital.com
**Control:** Other not–for–profit (including NFP Corporation) **Service:** General Medical and Surgical

**Staffed Beds:** 80 **Admissions:** 3089 **Census:** 32 **Outpatient Visits:** 186604 **Births:** 355 **Total Expense ($000):** 128592 **Payroll Expense ($000):** 63500 **Personnel:** 799

## DOWNERS GROVE—Dupage County

★ ◇ **ADVOCATE GOOD SAMARITAN HOSPITAL (140288)**, 3815 Highland Avenue, Zip 60515–1590; tel. 630/275–5900, (Nonreporting) **A**2 3 5 9 10 21 **S** Advocate Health Care, Downers Grove, IL
Primary Contact: David Fox, President
COO: Marjorie A. Maurer, MSN, Vice President Operations, Patient Care Services and Chief Nursing Executive
CFO: Mary Treacy–Shiff, Vice President Finance
CMO: Charles Derus, M.D., Vice President Medical Management
CHR: Elizabeth Calby, Vice President Human Resources
CNO: Sandi Churchill, Vice President Business Development and Operations, Professional Services
Web address: www.advocatehealth.com/gsam
**Control:** Church–operated, Nongovernment, not–for profit **Service:** General Medical and Surgical

**Staffed Beds:** 319

## DU QUOIN—Perry County

⊠ **MARSHALL BROWNING HOSPITAL (141331)**, 900 North Washington Street, Zip 62832–1233, Mailing Address: P.O. Box 192, Zip 62832–0192; tel. 618/542–2146 **A**1 9 10 18 **F**3 11 15 28 29 34 35 40 59 81 85 93 107 108 110 114 119 125 127 129 131 133
Primary Contact: Dan Eaves, Board President and Acting Chief Executive Officer
CFO: Brice Harsy, Chief Financial Officer
CIO: William Ralph Bunton, Supervisor Information Technology
CHR: Sarah J. Dickey, Director Human Resources
CNO: Laurie Kellerman, MSN, Chief Nursing Officer
Web address: www.marshallbrowninghospital.com
**Control:** Other not–for–profit (including NFP Corporation) **Service:** General Medical and Surgical

**Staffed Beds:** 25 **Admissions:** 553 **Census:** 7 **Outpatient Visits:** 28798 **Births:** 0 **Total Expense ($000):** 17118 **Payroll Expense ($000):** 7143 **Personnel:** 141

## EFFINGHAM—Effingham County

⊠ **HSHS ST. ANTHONY'S MEMORIAL HOSPITAL (140032)**, 503 North Maple Street, Zip 62401–2099; tel. 217/342–2121 **A**1 2 3 5 9 10 19 **F**3 11 13 15 18 20 28 29 30 31 32 34 35 40 45 57 59 62 63 64 68 70 75 76 79 81 82 84 85 89 93 107 108 109 110 111 114 119 129 130 132 144 146 147 **S** Hospital Sisters Health System, Springfield, IL
Primary Contact: Theresa Rutherford, R.N., MS, FACHE, President and Chief Executive Officer
CFO: Dave Storm, Director Business Support
Web address: www.stanthonyshospital.org
**Control:** Church–operated, Nongovernment, not–for profit **Service:** General Medical and Surgical

**Staffed Beds:** 133 **Admissions:** 5096 **Census:** 51 **Outpatient Visits:** 243503 **Births:** 708 **Total Expense ($000):** 99093 **Payroll Expense ($000):** 30357 **Personnel:** 545

## ELDORADO—Saline County

**FERRELL HOSPITAL (141324)**, 1201 Pine Street, Zip 62930–1634; tel. 618/273–3361, (Nonreporting) **A**9 10 18
Primary Contact: Alisa Coleman, Chief Executive Officer
CFO: Charles Will, Chief Financial Officer
CIO: Brent Volkert, Director Information Technology
CHR: Caleigh Griffin, Vice President Human Resources
CNO: Lisa Anderson, Vice President Nursing
Web address: www.ferrellhosp.org
**Control:** Other not–for–profit (including NFP Corporation) **Service:** General Medical and Surgical

**Staffed Beds:** 25

*Many Facility Codes have changed. Please refer to the AHA Guide Code Chart.*
© 2015 AHA Guide

IL

## ELGIN—Kane County

★ ◇ **ADVOCATE SHERMAN HOSPITAL (140030)**, 1425 North Randall Road, Zip 60123–2300; tel. 847/742–9800 **A**2 9 10 21 **F**3 11 13 15 18 20 22 24 26 28 29 30 31 34 35 38 40 43 45 46 47 48 49 50 54 55 57 59 64 65 68 70 74 75 76 77 78 79 81 82 85 87 89 92 93 100 102 107 108 110 111 114 115 118 119 120 121 126 129 130 132 135 144 146 147 148 **P**8 **S** Advocate Health Care, Downers Grove, IL
Primary Contact: Linda Deering, MSN, R.N., President
CMO: Bruce Hyman, M.D., Vice President Clinical Performance
CHR: Melissa O'Neill, Vice President Human Resources
CNO: Judith Balcitis, MSN, Vice President, Nursing and Chief Nursing Officer
Web address: www.advocatehealth.com/sherman
**Control:** Other not–for–profit (including NFP Corporation) **Service:** General Medical and Surgical

**Staffed Beds:** 255 **Admissions:** 14623 **Census:** 162 **Outpatient Visits:** 303167 **Births:** 2709 **Total Expense ($000):** 278826 **Payroll Expense ($000):** 98639 **Personnel:** 1496

☐ **ELGIN MENTAL HEALTH CENTER (144037)**, 750 South State Street, Zip 60123–7692; tel. 847/742–1040, (Nonreporting) **A**1 5 10 **S** Division of Mental Health, Department of Human Services, Springfield, IL
Primary Contact: Amparo Lopez, Region Executive Director
CFO: Tajudeen Ibrahim, Interim Business Administrator
CMO: Malini Patel, M.D., Medical Director
CIO: Kelly Callahan, Public Information Officer
CHR: Darek Williams, Director Human Resources
Web address: www.dhs.state.il.us
**Control:** State–Government, nonfederal **Service:** Psychiatric

**Staffed Beds:** 500

☒ △ **PRESENCE SAINT JOSEPH HOSPITAL (140217)**, 77 North Airlite Street, Zip 60123–4912; tel. 847/695–3200 **A**1 2 7 9 10 **F**5 11 12 15 17 18 20 22 24 26 28 29 30 31 34 35 36 37 38 40 43 44 49 50 53 54 56 57 58 59 60 61 62 63 64 65 68 69 70 74 75 77 78 79 81 82 84 85 86 87 90 93 94 96 97 98 99 100 101 102 103 104 105 107 108 111 114 115 117 119 120 121 123 124 126 130 132 134 135 143 145 146 147 148 **P**5 **S** Presence Health, Chicago, IL
Primary Contact: Michael L. Brown, Regional President and Chief Executive Officer
CFO: Kevin Larkin, Regional Chief Financial Officer
CIO: Trevor O'Malley, Site Manager
CHR: Michael O'Rourke, Regional Human Resources Lead
Web address: www.provena.org
**Control:** Other not–for–profit (including NFP Corporation) **Service:** General Medical and Surgical

**Staffed Beds:** 184 **Admissions:** 7148 **Census:** 116 **Outpatient Visits:** 152832 **Births:** 0 **Total Expense ($000):** 134848 **Payroll Expense ($000):** 44072 **Personnel:** 777

**PROVENA SAINT JOSEPH HOSPITAL** See Presence Saint Joseph Hospital

**SHERMAN HOSPITAL** See Advocate Sherman Hospital

## ELK GROVE VILLAGE—Cook County

☒ **ALEXIAN BROTHERS MEDICAL CENTER (140258)**, 800 Biesterfield Road, Zip 60007–3397; tel. 847/437–5500, (Includes ALEXIAN BROTHERS WOMEN & CHILDREN'S HOSPITAL, 1555 Barrington Road, Hoffman Estates, Zip 60169–1019; tel. 847/843–2000; ALEXIAN REHABILITATION HOSPITAL, 935 Beisner Road, Zip 60007; tel. 847/640–5600) **A**1 2 3 5 9 10 **F**3 12 13 15 17 18 20 22 24 26 28 29 30 31 34 35 36 37 39 40 41 43 45 46 47 48 49 50 54 55 56 57 59 62 63 64 70 73 74 75 76 78 79 81 82 84 85 86 87 89 90 91 92 93 95 96 107 108 110 111 113 114 115 116 117 119 120 121 124 126 129 130 132 135 143 145 146 147 148 **P**5 6 **S** Ascension Health, Saint Louis, MO
Primary Contact: John P. Werrbach, Chief Executive Officer
Web address: www.alexian.org
**Control:** Church–operated, Nongovernment, not–for profit **Service:** General Medical and Surgical

**Staffed Beds:** 371 **Admissions:** 17955 **Census:** 266 **Outpatient Visits:** 411656 **Births:** 1952 **Total Expense ($000):** 406580 **Payroll Expense ($000):** 134459 **Personnel:** 2070

## ELMHURST—Dupage County

☒ **ELMHURST MEMORIAL HOSPITAL (140200)**, 155 East Brush Hill Road, Zip 60126–5658; tel. 331/221–1000 **A**1 2 5 9 10 **F**3 5 7 13 15 18 19 20 22 24 26 28 29 30 31 32 34 35 37 38 39 40 41 43 44 45 46 47 48 49 50 54 55 57 58 59 61 63 64 65 70 74 75 76 77 78 79 81 82 84 85 86 87 89 91 92 93 96 97 99 100 101 102 103 104 107 108 109 110 111 114 117 119 120 121 123 126 129 130 131 132 135 144 146 147 148 **P**3 8 **S** Edward–Elmhurst Healthcare, Naperville, IL
Primary Contact: Mary Lou Mastro, President and Chief Executive Officer
COO: Pamela L. Dunley, R.N., Vice President Chief Nursing Officer and Chief Operating Officer
CFO: Jeff Friant Zeisel, Vice President Finance
CMO: Daniel Sullivan, D.O., Chief Medical Officer, Vice President Medical Administration
CIO: Bobbie Byrne, M.D., Vice President Information Systems and Chief Information Officer
CHR: Susan Mitchell, Senior Vice President Human Resources
CNO: Pamela L. Dunley, R.N., Vice President Chief Nursing Officer and Chief Operating Officer
Web address: www.emhc.org
**Control:** Other not–for–profit (including NFP Corporation) **Service:** General Medical and Surgical

**Staffed Beds:** 259 **Admissions:** 13677 **Census:** 157 **Outpatient Visits:** 381214 **Births:** 1859 **Total Expense ($000):** 368743 **Payroll Expense ($000):** 142037 **Personnel:** 2448

## EUREKA—Woodford County

★ ◇ **ADVOCATE EUREKA HOSPITAL (141309)**, 101 South Major Street, Zip 61530–1246; tel. 309/467–2371 **A**9 10 18 21 **F**3 15 28 29 30 31 34 35 39 40 44 45 50 57 59 64 65 67 68 74 75 77 78 79 81 82 85 86 87 89 90 93 107 108 110 111 114 119 128 129 130 132 133 146 **P**8 **S** Advocate Health Care, Downers Grove, IL
Primary Contact: Colleen Kannaday, FACHE, President
CFO: Aron Klein, Vice President of Finance
CMO: Steven K. Jones, M.D., Medical Director
CIO: David Harper, Director, Site Information Systems
CHR: Antonio Coletta, Vice President Human Resources
CNO: Nancy Allen, R.N., Director, Patient Services and Chief Nursing Executive
Web address: www.advocatehealth.com/eureka/
**Control:** Church–operated, Nongovernment, not–for profit **Service:** General Medical and Surgical

**Staffed Beds:** 18 **Admissions:** 317 **Census:** 5 **Outpatient Visits:** 31839 **Births:** 0 **Total Expense ($000):** 14343 **Payroll Expense ($000):** 5567 **Personnel:** 135

**EUREKA COMMUNITY HOSPITAL** See Advocate Eureka Hospital

## EVANSTON—Cook County

☒ **NORTHSHORE UNIVERSITY HEALTH SYSTEM (140010)**, 2650 Ridge Avenue, Zip 60201–1613; tel. 847/570–2000, (Includes NORTHSHORE EVANSTON HOSPITAL, 2650 Ridge Avenue, Zip 60201–1797; tel. 847/570–2000; Douglas M. Silverstein, President; NORTHSHORE GLENBROOK HOSPITAL, 2100 Pfingsten Road, Glenview, Zip 60025; tel. 847/657–5800; NORTHSHORE HIGHLAND PARK HOSPITAL, 718 Glenview Avenue, Highland Park, Zip 60035–2497; tel. 847/432–8000; NORTHSHORE SKOKIE HOSPITAL, 9600 Gross Point Road, Skokie, Zip 60076–1257; tel. 847/677–9600; Kristen Murtos, FACHE, President) **A**1 2 3 5 9 10 **F**3 5 8 9 11 12 13 14 15 18 19 20 22 24 26 28 29 30 31 32 34 35 36 37 38 39 40 43 44 45 46 47 48 49 50 54 55 56 57 58 59 60 61 62 63 64 66 68 70 72 74 75 76 77 78 79 81 82 83 84 85 86 87 88 89 90 92 93 96 97 98 99 100 101 102 103 104 105 107 108 110 111 114 115 116 117 118 119 120 121 123 124 126 129 130 131 132 134 135 136 145 146 147 148 **P**5
Primary Contact: Douglas M. Silverstein, President
COO: J. P. Gallagher, Chief Operating Officer
CFO: Gary Weiss, Chief Financial Officer
CIO: Steven Smith, Chief Information Officer
CHR: Bill Luehrs, Chief Human Resources Officer
CNO: Nancy Semerdjian, R.N., Chief Nursing Officer
Web address: www.northshore.org
**Control:** Other not–for–profit (including NFP Corporation) **Service:** General Medical and Surgical

**Staffed Beds:** 677 **Admissions:** 38070 **Census:** 473 **Outpatient Visits:** 2026913 **Births:** 4739 **Total Expense ($000):** 1346887 **Payroll Expense ($000):** 448096 **Personnel:** 6055

**IL**

---

**Hospital, Medicare Provider Number, Address, Telephone, Approval, Facility, and Physician Codes, Health Care System**

★ American Hospital Association (AHA) membership    ○ Healthcare Facilities Accreditation Program    ⇑ Center for Improvement in Healthcare Quality Accreditation
☐ The Joint Commission accreditation    ◇ DNV Healthcare Inc. accreditation    △ Commission on Accreditation of Rehabilitation Facilities (CARF) accreditation

✠ **PRESENCE SAINT FRANCIS HOSPITAL (140080)**, 355 Ridge Avenue,
Zip 60202–3399; tel. 847/316–4000 **A**1 2 3 5 9 10 **F**3 11 13 15 18 20 22 24
26 28 29 30 31 34 35 38 40 43 45 47 48 49 56 57 58 59 61 64 65 68 70
74 75 76 77 78 79 81 82 84 85 86 87 93 97 107 108 110 111 114 115 118
119 120 121 123 126 130 131 132 135 146 147 148 **S** Presence Health,
Chicago, IL
Primary Contact: Roberta Luskin–Hawk, M.D., Chief Executive Officer
CMO: David DiLoreto, M.D., Executive Vice President and Chief Medical Officer
CIO: George Chessum, Vice President Information Systems
CHR: Paul Skiem, Senior Vice President Human Resources
Web address: www.reshealth.org
**Control:** Church–operated, Nongovernment, not–for profit **Service:** General
Medical and Surgical

| | |
|---|---|
| **Staffed Beds:** 192 **Admissions:** 7963 **Census:** 90 **Outpatient Visits:** 103373 **Births:** 721 **Total Expense ($000):** 145803 **Payroll Expense ($000):** 51241 **Personnel:** 889 | |

**SAINT FRANCIS HOSPITAL** See Presence Saint Francis Hospital

### EVERGREEN PARK—Cook County

☐ **LITTLE COMPANY OF MARY HOSPITAL AND HEALTH CARE CENTERS
(140179)**, 2800 West 95th Street, Zip 60805–2795; tel. 708/422–6200 **A**1 2
9 10 **F**3 5 11 12 13 15 17 18 20 22 26 29 30 31 34 35 36 38 40 41 45 46
47 49 50 54 56 57 59 60 62 63 64 65 71 73 74 75 76 77 78 79 81 82 83
84 85 86 87 89 92 93 94 98 100 101 102 103 104 105 107 108 110 111
114 115 119 120 121 124 126 129 130 131 132 133 135 144 146 147 148
**P**6 7 8 **S** American Province of Little Company of Mary Sisters, Evergreen
Park, IL
Primary Contact: Dennis A. Reilly, President and Chief Executive Officer
COO: Mary Freyer, Chief Operating Officer
CFO: Randy Ruther, Vice President Finance and Chief Financial Officer
CMO: Kent A W Armbruster, M.D., Vice President Medical Affairs
CIO: Darryl Mazzuca, Director Management Information Systems
CHR: Colleen Rohan, Director Human Resources
CNO: Lisa DiMarco, R.N., Vice President Patient Care Service and Chief Nursing
Officer
Web address: www.lcmh.org
**Control:** Other not–for–profit (including NFP Corporation) **Service:** General
Medical and Surgical

| | |
|---|---|
| **Staffed Beds:** 254 **Admissions:** 12882 **Census:** 155 **Outpatient Visits:** 210548 **Births:** 1196 **Total Expense ($000):** 189713 **Payroll Expense ($000):** 85081 **Personnel:** 1502 | |

### FAIRFIELD—Wayne County

✠ **FAIRFIELD MEMORIAL HOSPITAL (141311)**, 303 N.W. 11th Street,
Zip 62837–1203; tel. 618/842–2611, (Total facility includes 30 beds in nursing
home–type unit) **A**1 9 10 18 **F**3 11 15 18 28 31 34 35 38 40 41 45 46 50 56
59 62 64 68 70 75 77 81 82 85 86 87 93 97 104 107 108 110 111 114 119
127 128 130 132 135 146 148 **P**6 **S** Alliant Management Services,
Louisville, KY
Primary Contact: Katherine Bunting, Chief Executive Officer
COO: Dana Shantel Taylor, Director Organizational Development
CFO: Melody Morgan, Chief Financial Officer
CMO: Wesley Thompson, M.D., President Medical Staff
CIO: Brad August, Director Information Systems
CHR: Robert Musoiu, Director Human Resources
CNO: Ann Ignas, R.N., Chief Nurse Executive
Web address: www.fairfieldmemorial.org
**Control:** Other not–for–profit (including NFP Corporation) **Service:** General
Medical and Surgical

| | |
|---|---|
| **Staffed Beds:** 55 **Admissions:** 903 **Census:** 26 **Outpatient Visits:** 55085 **Births:** 0 **Total Expense ($000):** 26122 **Payroll Expense ($000):** 10632 **Personnel:** 233 | |

### FLORA—Clay County

✠ **CLAY COUNTY HOSPITAL (141351)**, 911 Stacy Burk Drive, Zip 62839–3241,
Mailing Address: P.O. Box 280, Zip 62839–0280; tel. 618/662–2131,
(Nonreporting) **A**1 9 10 18 **S** SSM Health, Saint Louis, MO
Primary Contact: Amanda J. Basso, President
COO: Jamie Veach, Chief Operating Officer
CFO: Mike Hobbs, Chief Financial Officer
CMO: Colleen Murphy, M.D., Chief of Staff
CIO: Phil Bute, Manager Information Technology
CHR: Chelsea Musgrave, Director of Human Resources
Web address: www.claycountyhospital.com
**Control:** County–Government, nonfederal **Service:** General Medical and Surgical

| | |
|---|---|
| **Staffed Beds:** 22 | |

### FOREST PARK—Cook County

☐ **RIVEREDGE HOSPITAL (144009)**, 8311 West Roosevelt Road,
Zip 60130–2500; tel. 708/771–7000, (Nonreporting) **A**1 9 10 **S** Universal Health
Services, Inc., King of Prussia, PA
Primary Contact: Carey Carlock, Chief Executive Officer
CFO: Michael E. Nelson, Chief Financial Officer
CMO: Lucyna M. Puszkarska, M.D., Medical Director
CIO: Kyle Heinze, Coordinator Information Technology
CHR: Joseph Baw, Director Human Resources
Web address: www.riveredgehospital.com
**Control:** Corporation, Investor–owned, for–profit **Service:** Psychiatric

| | |
|---|---|
| **Staffed Beds:** 224 | |

### FREEPORT—Stephenson County

★ **FHN MEMORIAL HOSPITAL (140160)**, 1045 West Stephenson Street,
Zip 61032–4899; tel. 815/599–6000 **A**9 10 **F**3 11 13 14 15 18 20 22 28 29
30 31 32 34 38 40 46 47 48 49 50 51 53 57 59 61 63 64 65 68 69 74 75
76 77 78 79 81 82 84 85 86 87 93 97 99 100 101 102 103 104 107 108
109 110 111 114 119 129 130 131 132 135 146 **P**6 8
Primary Contact: Michael R. Perry, M.D., President and Chief Executive Officer
COO: Mark Gridley, FACHE, Executive Vice President and Chief Operating Officer
CFO: Michael Clark, Executive Vice President and Chief Financial Officer
CMO: Robert D. Geller, M.D., Vice President Medical Affairs
CIO: Mike Willams, Chief Information Officer
CHR: Leonard M. Carter, Vice President Human Resources
CNO: Kathryn J. Martinez, Chief Nursing Officer
Web address: www.fhn.org
**Control:** Other not–for–profit (including NFP Corporation) **Service:** General
Medical and Surgical

| | |
|---|---|
| **Staffed Beds:** 100 **Admissions:** 4093 **Census:** 42 **Outpatient Visits:** 107849 **Births:** 392 **Total Expense ($000):** 98188 **Payroll Expense ($000):** 31077 **Personnel:** 490 | |

### GALENA—Jo Daviess County

★ **MIDWEST MEDICAL CENTER (141302)**, One Medical Center Drive,
Zip 61036–1697; tel. 815/777–1340, (Nonreporting) **A**9 10 18
Primary Contact: Tracy Bauer, Chief Executive Officer
COO: Steve Busch, Chief Operating Officer
CMO: Grant Westenfelder, M.D., Chief Medical Officer
CHR: Melissa Conley, Director Human Resources
Web address: www.midwestmedicalcenter.org
**Control:** Corporation, Investor–owned, for–profit **Service:** General Medical and
Surgical

| | |
|---|---|
| **Staffed Beds:** 25 | |

### GALESBURG—Knox County

✠ **GALESBURG COTTAGE HOSPITAL (140040)**, 695 North Kellogg Street,
Zip 61401–2885; tel. 309/343–8131, (Nonreporting) **A**1 10 19 **S** Community
Health Systems, Inc., Franklin, TN
Primary Contact: Barry S. Schneider, Chief Executive Officer
CFO: Rob Gasaway, Chief Financial Officer
CMO: Mark Davis, M.D., President Medical Staff
CIO: Jeremie Kilgore, Director Information Technology
CHR: Karen Russell, Director Human Resources
CNO: Pam Davis, Chief Nursing Officer
Web address: www.cottagehospital.com
**Control:** Other not–for–profit (including NFP Corporation) **Service:** General
Medical and Surgical

| | |
|---|---|
| **Staffed Beds:** 119 | |

✠ **OSF ST. MARY MEDICAL CENTER (140064)**, 3333 North Seminary Street,
Zip 61401–1299; tel. 309/344–3161 **A**1 9 10 **F**3 11 13 15 18 26 28 29 30
31 34 40 41 43 45 49 50 51 53 56 57 59 61 62 63 68 70 74 75 76 77 78
79 81 82 84 85 86 87 89 93 96 97 107 110 111 115 117 119 129 130 132
135 145 146 147 148 **P**6 **S** OSF Healthcare System, Peoria, IL
Primary Contact: Roxanna Crosser, President
COO: Don Shadensack, Vice President Clinical Services
CFO: Curt Lipe, Vice President, Chief Financial Officer
CMO: Mark Meeker, D.O., Medical Staff President
CIO: Becky Lynch, Manager Business Entity Management and Information Systems
CHR: Nichole Hurlbutt, Director Human Resources
CNO: Alice Snyder, Vice President, Chief Nursing Officer
Web address: www.osfstmary.org
**Control:** Church–operated, Nongovernment, not–for profit **Service:** General
Medical and Surgical

| | |
|---|---|
| **Staffed Beds:** 81 **Admissions:** 3017 **Census:** 29 **Outpatient Visits:** 159607 **Births:** 318 **Total Expense ($000):** 73103 **Payroll Expense ($000):** 27730 **Personnel:** 434 | |

*Many Facility Codes have changed. Please refer to the AHA Guide Code Chart.*

© 2015 AHA Guide

IL

## GENESEO—Henry County

⊞ **HAMMOND–HENRY HOSPITAL (141319)**, 600 North College Avenue, Zip 61254–1099; tel. 309/944–4625, (Total facility includes 38 beds in nursing home–type unit) **A**1 9 10 18 **F**3 8 11 13 15 17 18 19 28 29 34 35 40 44 45 50 57 59 62 70 75 76 79 81 82 87 88 89 93 107 111 114 119 128 129 130 131 132 133 144 146 **P**2 **S** HealthTech Management Services, Brentwood, TN
Primary Contact: Florence Spyrow, Interim Chief Executive Officer
CFO: Jodie Criswell, Vice President Fiscal Services
CIO: Heather Henry, Manager Information Systems
CHR: Hazel Butter, Manager Human Resources
CNO: Laura Domino, R.N., Vice President Patient Care Services
Web address: www.hammondhenry.com
**Control:** Hospital district or authority, Government, nonfederal **Service:** General Medical and Surgical

**Staffed Beds:** 61 **Admissions:** 1354 **Census:** 47 **Outpatient Visits:** 98092
**Births:** 211 **Total Expense ($000):** 33518 **Payroll Expense ($000):** 13068
**Personnel:** 260

## GENEVA—Kane County

⊞ **NORTHWESTERN MEDICINE DELNOR HOSPITAL (140211)**, 300 Randall Road, Zip 60134–4200; tel. 630/208–3000 **A**1 2 9 10 **F**3 12 13 15 18 20 22 26 28 29 30 31 32 34 35 36 39 40 43 44 49 50 53 57 59 64 65 69 70 74 75 76 77 78 79 81 82 85 86 87 89 93 94 96 99 100 101 102 104 107 108 110 111 114 115 118 119 120 121 126 129 130 131 132 135 146 147 148 **S** Northwestern Memorial Healthcare, Chicago, IL
Primary Contact: Maureen A. Bryant, FACHE, President
CFO: John Orsini, Executive Vice President and Chief Financial Officer
CMO: Mark Daniels, M.D., Vice President Physician Enterprise
CIO: Daniel F. Kinsella, Executive Vice President Information Technology
CHR: Michael Wukitsch, Executive Vice President Human Resources
Web address: www.cadencehealth.org
**Control:** Other not–for–profit (including NFP Corporation) **Service:** General Medical and Surgical

**Staffed Beds:** 159 **Admissions:** 7635 **Census:** 80 **Outpatient Visits:** 151900
**Births:** 1396 **Total Expense ($000):** 192615 **Payroll Expense ($000):** 61784 **Personnel:** 1735

## GIBSON CITY—Ford County

⊞ **GIBSON AREA HOSPITAL AND HEALTH SERVICES (141317)**, 1120 North Melvin Street, Zip 60936–1477, Mailing Address: P.O. Box 429, Zip 60936–0429; tel. 217/784–4251, (Includes GIBSON COMMUNITY HOSPITAL NURSING HOME ), (Total facility includes 42 beds in nursing home–type unit) **A**1 5 9 10 18 **F**3 7 11 13 15 18 28 29 31 34 35 40 43 44 45 49 50 51 53 55 56 57 59 63 64 65 67 68 69 70 75 76 77 79 81 82 85 87 93 99 100 101 103 104 107 108 110 111 115 119 127 128 129 131 132 133 143 146 147 148 **P**6 7 8 **S** Alliant Management Services, Louisville, KY
Primary Contact: Robert C. Schmitt, II, Chief Executive Officer
COO: Robin Rose, R.N., Chief Operating Officer
CMO: David J. Hagan, M.D., Chief Medical Officer
CIO: Christopher Michael Plaisance, Executive Director of Information Technology
CHR: Ty Royal, Executive Director of Support Services and Human Resources
CNO: Cynthia Philipchuck, R.N., Executive Director of Nursing
Web address: www.gibsonhospital.org
**Control:** Other not–for–profit (including NFP Corporation) **Service:** General Medical and Surgical

**Staffed Beds:** 67 **Admissions:** 1030 **Census:** 44 **Outpatient Visits:** 100191
**Births:** 188 **Total Expense ($000):** 70550 **Payroll Expense ($000):** 32360
**Personnel:** 550

## GLENDALE HEIGHTS—Dupage County

⊞ **AMITA HEALTH ADVENTIST GLENOAKS HOSPITAL (140292)**, 701 Winthrop Avenue, Zip 60139–1403; tel. 630/545–8000 **A**1 9 10 **F**3 11 13 15 17 18 20 22 26 29 30 31 34 35 38 40 43 45 49 57 58 59 61 64 68 70 73 74 75 76 78 79 81 82 85 86 87 92 93 96 97 98 99 100 101 102 103 104 105 107 108 110 111 114 118 119 130 131 132 146 147 148 **P**7 8 **S** Adventist Health System Sunbelt Health Care Corporation, Altamonte Springs, FL
Primary Contact: Bruce C. Christian, Chief Executive Officer
CMO: Richard Carroll, M.D., Chief Medical Officer
CIO: Thomas Schoenig, Regional Chief Information Officer
CHR: Donald Russell, Vice President
CNO: Maria Knecht, R.N., Executive Director of Nursing
Web address: www.adventistglenoaks.com
**Control:** Church–operated, Nongovernment, not–for profit **Service:** General Medical and Surgical

**Staffed Beds:** 120 **Admissions:** 5186 **Census:** 77 **Outpatient Visits:** 35165
**Births:** 451 **Total Expense ($000):** 88708 **Payroll Expense ($000):** 35603
**Personnel:** 526

## GLENVIEW—Cook County

**NORTHSHORE GLENBROOK HOSPITAL** See NorthShore University Health System, Evanston

## GRANITE CITY—Madison County

⊞ **GATEWAY REGIONAL MEDICAL CENTER (140125)**, 2100 Madison Avenue, Zip 62040–4799; tel. 618/798–3000 **A**1 9 10 **F**3 8 11 13 15 18 20 22 24 26 28 29 34 35 40 45 49 50 51 54 59 70 74 75 76 77 79 81 85 87 90 91 92 93 97 98 99 100 101 102 103 107 108 110 111 114 119 126 128 129 130 132 146 147 **P**6 **S** Community Health Systems, Inc., Franklin, TN
Primary Contact: M. Edward Cunningham, Chief Executive Officer
COO: Matthew H. Blevins, Chief Operating Officer
CFO: Ronald Leazer, Chief Financial Officer
CMO: Mike Adams, M.D., Chief Medical Officer
CIO: Dennis Kampwerth, Director Management Information Systems
CHR: Reva S. Weems, Director Human Resources
CNO: Sam R. White, Chief Nursing Officer
Web address: www.gatewayregional.net
**Control:** Corporation, Investor–owned, for–profit **Service:** General Medical and Surgical

**Staffed Beds:** 104 **Admissions:** 6740 **Census:** 99 **Outpatient Visits:** 31782
**Births:** 323 **Total Expense ($000):** 99918 **Payroll Expense ($000):** 31664
**Personnel:** 660

## GREENVILLE—Bond County

★ ○ **GREENVILLE REGIONAL HOSPITAL (140137)**, 200 Healthcare Drive, Zip 62246–1154; tel. 618/664–1230, (Includes FAIR OAKS ), (Total facility includes 108 beds in nursing home–type unit) **A**9 10 11 **F**3 11 13 15 18 28 29 31 34 40 41 45 49 50 56 57 59 76 78 79 81 85 89 93 94 97 98 103 104 107 110 111 115 119 125 127 128 129 130 133 146 **P**6
Primary Contact: Brian Nall, President and Chief Executive Officer
CHR: Vicki Kloeckner, Director Human Resources
CNO: Tammy Lett, R.N., Chief Nursing Officer
Web address: www.greenvilleregionalhospital.com
**Control:** Other not–for–profit (including NFP Corporation) **Service:** General Medical and Surgical

**Staffed Beds:** 150 **Admissions:** 1288 **Census:** 15 **Outpatient Visits:** 38631
**Births:** 273 **Total Expense ($000):** 32912 **Payroll Expense ($000):** 14281
**Personnel:** 292

## HARRISBURG—Saline County

⊞ **HARRISBURG MEDICAL CENTER (140210)**, 100 Drive Warren Tuttle Drive, Zip 62946–2718, Mailing Address: P.O. Box 428, Zip 62946–0428; tel. 618/253–7671 **A**1 9 10 20 **F**3 8 11 15 28 29 30 31 34 40 45 50 56 57 59 61 62 64 75 77 78 81 85 87 89 91 93 97 98 100 101 102 103 104 105 107 108 110 114 118 119 127 129 130 131 133 146
Primary Contact: Rodney Smith, President and Chief Executive Officer
COO: Danny Lampley, Chief Operating Officer
CFO: June Hayes, Chief Financial Officer
CIO: Rick Pyle, Director Information Systems
CHR: Dorene L. Ewell, Director Human Resources and Education
CNO: Cindy Ford, R.N., Chief Nursing Officer
Web address: www.harrisburgmc.com
**Control:** Other not–for–profit (including NFP Corporation) **Service:** General Medical and Surgical

**Staffed Beds:** 76 **Admissions:** 2754 **Census:** 37 **Outpatient Visits:** 74450
**Births:** 0 **Total Expense ($000):** 46241 **Payroll Expense ($000):** 22355
**Personnel:** 317

## HARVARD—Mchenry County

⊞ **MERCY HARVARD HOSPITAL (141335)**, 901 Grant Street, Zip 60033–1898, Mailing Address: P.O. Box 850, Zip 60033–0850; tel. 815/943–5431, (Total facility includes 32 beds in nursing home–type unit) **A**1 9 10 18 **F**3 11 15 28 29 30 35 40 45 46 57 59 64 69 70 75 77 79 81 82 85 87 93 94 96 97 107 108 110 114 119 128 129 130 132 143 146 **P**6 **S** Mercy Health System, Janesville, WI
Primary Contact: Javon R. Bea, Chief Executive Officer
COO: Jennifer Hallatt, Chief Operating Officer
CFO: Shannon Dunphy–Alexander, Director
CMO: Douglas Bryan, President, Medical Staff
CHR: Heather Niles, Director Human Resources Operations
CNO: Caryn Lynn Oleston, Chief Nursing Officer
Web address: www.mercyhealthsystem.org
**Control:** Other not–for–profit (including NFP Corporation) **Service:** General Medical and Surgical

**Staffed Beds:** 45 **Admissions:** 529 **Census:** 27 **Outpatient Visits:** 55617
**Births:** 0 **Total Expense ($000):** 22091 **Payroll Expense ($000):** 8162
**Personnel:** 132

IL

---

**Hospital, Medicare Provider Number, Address, Telephone, Approval, Facility, and Physician Codes, Health Care System**

★ American Hospital Association (AHA) membership
☐ The Joint Commission accreditation
○ Healthcare Facilities Accreditation Program
◇ DNV Healthcare Inc. accreditation
⇑ Center for Improvement in Healthcare Quality Accreditation
△ Commission on Accreditation of Rehabilitation Facilities (CARF) accreditation

## HARVEY—Cook County

★ △ ◇ **INGALLS MEMORIAL HOSPITAL (140191)**, One Ingalls Drive, Zip 60426–3591; tel. 708/333–2300 **A**2 3 5 7 9 10 21 **F**3 5 8 11 13 15 18 20 22 24 26 28 29 30 31 34 35 36 37 40 42 43 45 46 47 49 50 51 54 56 57 58 59 60 62 63 64 68 70 74 75 76 77 78 79 81 82 84 85 86 87 89 90 92 93 94 97 98 99 101 102 103 104 105 107 108 110 111 113 114 115 116 117 118 119 120 121 123 124 129 130 131 132 135 143 144 146 147 148 **P**8
Primary Contact: Kurt E. Johnson, President and Chief Executive Officer
CFO: Andrew Stefo, Senior Vice President Finance and Chief Financial Officer
CHR: Aletha Ross, Vice President Human Resources
Web address: www.ingallshealthsystem.org
**Control:** Other not–for–profit (including NFP Corporation) **Service:** General Medical and Surgical

**Staffed Beds:** 485 **Admissions:** 14405 **Census:** 195 **Outpatient Visits:** 378582 **Births:** 914 **Total Expense ($000):** 282312 **Payroll Expense ($000):** 98274 **Personnel:** 1510

## HAVANA—Mason County

⌧ **MASON DISTRICT HOSPITAL (141313)**, 615 North Promenade Street, Zip 62644–1243, Mailing Address: P.O. Box 530, Zip 62644–0530; tel. 309/543–4431 **A**1 9 10 18 **F**7 8 11 15 18 28 29 30 34 35 40 45 49 50 53 54 56 57 59 62 64 65 68 69 75 79 81 93 97 102 103 107 108 110 114 118 119 127 129 130 131 132 133 143 146 **P**6
Primary Contact: Robert J. Stolba, Chief Executive Officer
COO: Douglas D. Kosier, Chief Operating Officer
CFO: Robert J. Stolba, Chief Financial Officer
CMO: Tad A. Yetter, M.D., President Medical Staff
CIO: Aaron Coots, Information Technology Director
CHR: Anne Davis, Director Human Resources
CNO: Rhonda Hine, R.N., Interim Chief Nursing Executive
Web address: www.masondistricthospital.org
**Control:** Hospital district or authority, Government, nonfederal **Service:** General Medical and Surgical

**Staffed Beds:** 20 **Admissions:** 257 **Census:** 2 **Outpatient Visits:** 22975 **Births:** 0 **Total Expense ($000):** 22111 **Payroll Expense ($000):** 10528 **Personnel:** 215

## HAZEL CREST—Cook County

★ ◇ **ADVOCATE SOUTH SUBURBAN HOSPITAL (140250)**, 17800 South Kedzie Avenue, Zip 60429–0989; tel. 708/799–8000, (Total facility includes 37 beds in nursing home–type unit) **A**2 9 10 21 **F**3 11 13 15 18 20 22 24 26 28 29 30 31 34 35 36 40 45 46 47 49 50 51 53 55 57 59 60 63 64 68 70 75 76 78 79 81 82 85 87 89 107 108 110 111 114 115 118 119 126 128 129 130 132 145 146 147 148 **P**8 **S** Advocate Health Care, Downers Grove, IL
Primary Contact: Richard Heim, President
COO: Karen Clark, MS, Vice President Operations
CFO: Brian Kelly, Vice President Finance
CMO: Richard Multack, D.O., Vice President Medical Management
CIO: Beth Turek, Site Manager Information Systems
CHR: Daylashunta Randolph, Vice President Human Resources
CNO: Sharon A. Otten, Vice President Nursing
Web address: www.advocatehealth.com/ssub/
**Control:** Church–operated, Nongovernment, not–for profit **Service:** General Medical and Surgical

**Staffed Beds:** 280 **Admissions:** 10728 **Census:** 141 **Outpatient Visits:** 141684 **Births:** 1121 **Total Expense ($000):** 205980 **Payroll Expense ($000):** 70669 **Personnel:** 1000

## HERRIN—Williamson County

☐ **HERRIN HOSPITAL (140011)**, 201 South 14th Street, Zip 62948–3631; tel. 618/942–2171 **A**1 5 9 10 **F**3 11 12 18 28 29 30 34 35 40 45 47 49 50 51 54 56 57 59 60 61 64 68 70 74 75 78 79 81 82 84 85 86 87 90 92 93 100 107 108 111 114 115 119 130 131 132 135 143 146 148 **P**1 **S** Southern Illinois Hospital Services, Carbondale, IL
Primary Contact: Terence Farrell, Vice President and Administrator
CFO: Michael Kasser, Chief Financial Officer
CMO: Michelle Jenkins, M.D., President Medical Staff
CIO: David Holland, Chief Information Officer
CHR: Teresa A. Lovellette, Manager Human Resources
Web address: www.sih.net
**Control:** Other not–for–profit (including NFP Corporation) **Service:** General Medical and Surgical

**Staffed Beds:** 114 **Admissions:** 5529 **Census:** 70 **Outpatient Visits:** 133939 **Births:** 0 **Total Expense ($000):** 130928 **Payroll Expense ($000):** 39231 **Personnel:** 876

## HIGHLAND—Madison County

⌧ **HSHS ST. JOSEPH'S HOSPITAL (141336)**, 12866 Troxler Avenue, Zip 62249–1698; tel. 618/654–7421 **A**1 9 10 18 **F**3 8 11 15 26 27 28 29 30 34 35 40 41 44 45 47 49 51 57 59 64 65 68 70 75 79 81 82 84 86 87 93 97 107 108 110 111 114 119 129 130 131 132 133 135 143 146 147 **S** Hospital Sisters Health System, Springfield, IL
Primary Contact: Peggy A. Sebastian, MSN, R.N., President and Chief Executive Officer
CFO: James Johnson, Chief Financial Officer
CMO: A. Greg Miranda, D.O., President Medical Staff
Web address: www.stjosephshighland.com
**Control:** Church–operated, Nongovernment, not–for profit **Service:** General Medical and Surgical

**Staffed Beds:** 25 **Admissions:** 1112 **Census:** 13 **Outpatient Visits:** 52224 **Births:** 0 **Total Expense ($000):** 32603 **Payroll Expense ($000):** 9873 **Personnel:** 214

## HIGHLAND PARK—Lake County

**NORTHSHORE HIGHLAND PARK HOSPITAL** See NorthShore University Health System, Evanston

## HILLSBORO—Montgomery County

⌧ **HILLSBORO AREA HOSPITAL (141332)**, 1200 East Tremont Street, Zip 62049–1900; tel. 217/532–6111 **A**1 9 10 18 **F**3 10 15 28 29 30 34 35 40 56 57 59 64 65 75 77 79 81 85 86 87 89 92 93 94 97 107 110 111 115 125 129 130 131 133 135 146 148 **S** HealthTech Management Services, Brentwood, TN
Primary Contact: Rex H. Brown, President and Chief Executive Officer
CFO: Terri L. Carroll, Vice President Financial Services
CHR: Sharon Clark, Director Human Resources
Web address: www.hillsborohealth.org
**Control:** Other not–for–profit (including NFP Corporation) **Service:** General Medical and Surgical

**Staffed Beds:** 25 **Admissions:** 467 **Census:** 7 **Outpatient Visits:** 20954 **Births:** 0 **Total Expense ($000):** 18429 **Payroll Expense ($000):** 6584 **Personnel:** 168

## HINES—Cook County

⌧ △ **EDWARD HINES, JR. VETERANS AFFAIRS HOSPITAL**, 5000 South Fifth Avenue, Zip 60141–3030, Mailing Address: P.O. Box 5000, Zip 60141–5000; tel. 708/202–8387 **A**1 2 3 5 7 **F**1 3 4 5 6 7 8 9 10 12 13 14 15 17 18 20 22 24 26 28 29 30 31 34 35 36 38 39 40 44 45 46 47 48 49 50 53 56 57 58 59 60 61 63 64 65 66 68 70 71 74 75 77 78 79 80 81 82 83 84 86 87 90 91 92 93 94 96 97 98 100 101 102 103 104 105 106 107 108 109 110 111 112 113 115 116 117 119 120 121 122 123 124 126 127 129 130 131 132 135 143 144 146 147 148 **S** Department of Veterans Affairs, Washington, DC
Primary Contact: Daniel Zomchek, M.D., Acting Director
CFO: Yolanda Martinez, Chief Fiscal Services
CMO: Jack Bulmash, M.D., Chief of Staff
CIO: Robert Tanjuakio, Chief Information Resources Management
CNO: Marianne Locke, R.N., Associate Director Patient Care Services
Web address: www.hines.va.gov/
**Control:** Veterans Affairs, Government, federal **Service:** General Medical and Surgical

**Staffed Beds:** 485 **Admissions:** 10800 **Census:** 507 **Outpatient Visits:** 1085668 **Births:** 0 **Total Expense ($000):** 540000 **Payroll Expense ($000):** 246000 **Personnel:** 3121

☐ **JOHN J. MADDEN MENTAL HEALTH CENTER (144028)**, 1200 South First Avenue, Zip 60141–0800; tel. 708/338–7202 **A**1 3 5 10 **F**98 99 100 101 103 105 130 135 **P**5 **S** Division of Mental Health, Department of Human Services, Springfield, IL
Primary Contact: Edith Newman, Interim Administrator
CFO: Janice Evans, Chief Financial Officer
**Control:** State–Government, nonfederal **Service:** Psychiatric

**Staffed Beds:** 125 **Admissions:** 6574 **Census:** 125 **Outpatient Visits:** 0 **Births:** 0 **Total Expense ($000):** 35732 **Payroll Expense ($000):** 28478 **Personnel:** 299

**VETERANS AFFAIRS EDWARD HINES, JR. HOSPITAL** See Edward Hines, Jr. Veterans Affairs Hospital

IL

## HINSDALE—DuPage County

✠ △ **ADVENTIST HINSDALE HOSPITAL (140122)**, 120 North Oak Street, Zip 60521–3890; tel. 630/856–9000 **A**1 2 3 5 7 9 10 13 **F**3 5 8 11 12 13 14 15 18 20 22 24 26 27 28 29 30 31 34 35 37 38 39 40 43 44 45 47 48 49 52 54 55 56 57 58 59 61 62 63 64 68 70 72 73 74 75 76 78 79 81 82 84 85 86 87 88 89 90 92 93 96 97 98 99 100 101 102 103 104 105 107 108 110 111 114 115 118 119 120 121 123 124 126 129 130 131 132 136 141 146 147 148 **P**7 8 **S** Adventist Health System Sunbelt Health Care Corporation, Altamonte Springs, FL
Primary Contact: Michael Goebel, Vice President and Chief Executive Officer
CFO: Rebecca Mathis, Vice President and Chief Financial Officer
CMO: Gary Lipinski, M.D., Regional Vice President and Chief Medical Officer
CIO: Thomas Schoenig, Chief Information Officer
CHR: Donald Russell, Regional Vice President Human Resources
CNO: Shawn O. Tyrrell, R.N., VP/Chief Nursing Officer
Web address: www.keepingyouwell.com
**Control:** Church–operated, Nongovernment, not–for profit **Service:** General Medical and Surgical

**Staffed Beds:** 291 **Admissions:** 12152 **Census:** 150 **Outpatient Visits:** 283756 **Births:** 2186 **Total Expense ($000):** 286265 **Payroll Expense ($000):** 99320 **Personnel:** 1871

✠ **RML SPECIALTY HOSPITAL (142010)**, 5601 South County Line Road, Zip 60521–4875; tel. 630/286–4000 **A**1 3 5 9 10 **F**1 3 18 29 30 31 45 53 58 74 85 107 114 119 130 146 148 **P**6
Primary Contact: James R. Prister, President and Chief Executive Officer
COO: Ken Pawola, Chief Operating Officer
CFO: Tom Pater, Chief Financial Officer
CMO: Patrick Fahey, M.D., Chief Medical Officer
CIO: Vincent Vitali, Chief Information Officer
CHR: John Landstrom, Director Human Resources
CNO: Marti Edwards, MSN, Chief Nursing Officer
Web address: www.rmlspecialtyhospital.org
**Control:** Other not–for–profit (including NFP Corporation) **Service:** Long–Term Acute Care hospital

**Staffed Beds:** 95 **Admissions:** 909 **Census:** 78 **Outpatient Visits:** 0 **Births:** 0 **Total Expense ($000):** 49920 **Payroll Expense ($000):** 25768 **Personnel:** 392

## HOFFMAN ESTATES—Cook County

✠ **ALEXIAN BROTHERS BEHAVIORAL HEALTH HOSPITAL (144031)**, 1650 Moon Lake Boulevard, Zip 60169–1010; tel. 847/882–1600, (Nonreporting) **A**1 5 9 10 **S** Ascension Health, Saint Louis, MO
Primary Contact: Clayton Ciha, President and Chief Executive Officer
COO: Christopher Novak, Chief Operating Officer
CFO: David Jones, Chief Financial Officer
CMO: Gregory Teas, M.D., Chief Medical Officer
CIO: Sherrie Russell, Vice President and Chief Information Officer
CNO: Christine Quinlan, MS, Chief Nursing Officer
Web address: www.abbhh.org
**Control:** Church–operated, Nongovernment, not–for profit **Service:** Psychiatric

**Staffed Beds:** 141

✠ **ST. ALEXIUS MEDICAL CENTER (140290)**, 1555 Barrington Road, Zip 60169–1019; tel. 847/843–2000 **A**1 2 3 5 9 10 **F**3 12 13 15 18 20 22 26 29 30 31 34 35 36 37 39 40 41 43 45 46 47 48 49 50 54 55 56 57 59 63 64 70 72 73 74 75 76 77 78 79 81 82 84 85 86 87 88 89 93 107 108 110 111 114 115 119 120 121 124 126 130 132 145 146 147 148 **P**5 6 **S** Ascension Health, Saint Louis, MO
Primary Contact: Leonard Wilk, President and Chief Executive Officer
CFO: Sherril Vincent, Vice President Finance/CFO, Alexian Brothers Acute Care Ministries
CMO: Scott Neelsy, M.D., Chief Medical Officer
CIO: Sherrie Russell, Chief Information Officer
CHR: Linda Baker, Director Human Resources
CNO: Chris Budzinsky, R.N., Vice President Nursing/CNO Alexian Brothers Acute Care Ministries
Web address: www.stalexius.org
**Control:** Church–operated, Nongovernment, not–for profit **Service:** General Medical and Surgical

**Staffed Beds:** 280 **Admissions:** 16921 **Census:** 203 **Outpatient Visits:** 228393 **Births:** 3446 **Total Expense ($000):** 284305 **Payroll Expense ($000):** 97399 **Personnel:** 1557

## HOOPESTON—Vermilion County

★ ◇ **CARLE HOOPESTON REGIONAL HEALTH CENTER (141316)**, 701 East Orange Street, Zip 60942–1801; tel. 217/283–5531, (Nonreporting) **A**9 10 18 21 **S** Carle Foundation, Urbana, IL
Primary Contact: Harry Brockus, Chief Executive Officer
CHR: Melodee Bowers, Director Human Resources
Web address: www.carle.org
**Control:** Other not–for–profit (including NFP Corporation) **Service:** General Medical and Surgical

**Staffed Beds:** 100

## HOPEDALE—Tazewell County

**HOPEDALE MEDICAL COMPLEX (141330)**, 107 Tremont Street, Zip 61747–7525; tel. 309/449–3321 **A**9 10 18 **F**10 24 28 29 30 31 32 34 35 36 40 45 49 53 57 59 64 70 81 82 85 93 97 107 109 110 119 125 128 130 131 133 145 146 **P**3
Primary Contact: Alfred N. Rossi, M.D., Chief Executive Officer
COO: Mark F. Rossi, Chief Operating Officer and General Counsel
CHR: Andrea Halley, Director Human Resources
CNO: Timothy Sondag, Senior Nursing Officer
Web address: www.hopedalemc.com
**Control:** Other not–for–profit (including NFP Corporation) **Service:** General Medical and Surgical

**Staffed Beds:** 18 **Admissions:** 458 **Census:** 8 **Outpatient Visits:** 12562 **Births:** 0 **Total Expense ($000):** 22457 **Payroll Expense ($000):** 9354 **Personnel:** 317

## JACKSONVILLE—Morgan County

✠ **PASSAVANT AREA HOSPITAL (140058)**, 1600 West Walnut Street, Zip 62650–1136; tel. 217/245–9541, (Nonreporting) **A**1 9 10 **S** Memorial Health System, Springfield, IL
Primary Contact: Douglas L. Rahn, President and Chief Executive Officer
CFO: David Bolen, Vice President and Chief Financial Officer
CMO: Charles Sheaff, M.D., President Medical Staff
CIO: Janie Cook, Director Information Systems
CHR: Jim Bormann, Director Human Resources
CNO: Karen Daum, R.N., Vice President and Chief Nursing Officer
Web address: www.passavanthospital.com
**Control:** Other not–for–profit (including NFP Corporation) **Service:** General Medical and Surgical

**Staffed Beds:** 108

## JERSEYVILLE—Jersey County

✠ **JERSEY COMMUNITY HOSPITAL (140059)**, 400 Maple Summit Road, Zip 62052–2028, Mailing Address: P.O. Box 426, Zip 62052–0426; tel. 618/498–6402 **A**1 9 10 **F**3 7 11 15 18 28 29 31 32 34 35 36 38 40 41 46 51 53 57 59 64 70 79 81 85 87 94 97 107 111 114 115 117 118 119 129 130 131 132 133 146 147 **P**6
Primary Contact: Jonathan O. Wade, Chief Executive Officer
CFO: Beth King, Chief Financial Officer
CMO: Michael McNear, M.D., Chief Medical Officer
CIO: Bob Bray, Chief Information Officer
CHR: Sharon K. Sanford, Director Human Resources
CNO: Julie Smith, R.N., Director of Nursing
Web address: www.jch.org
**Control:** Hospital district or authority, Government, nonfederal **Service:** General Medical and Surgical

**Staffed Beds:** 46 **Admissions:** 1213 **Census:** 9 **Outpatient Visits:** 43231 **Births:** 94 **Total Expense ($000):** 27611 **Payroll Expense ($000):** 11175 **Personnel:** 226

**IL**

## JOLIET—Will County

✠ △ **PRESENCE SAINT JOSEPH MEDICAL CENTER (140007)**, 333 North Madison Street, Zip 60435–8200; tel. 815/725–7133 **A**1 2 7 9 10 **F**3 5 8 11 12 13 15 17 18 20 22 24 26 28 29 30 31 32 34 35 36 37 38 39 40 41 43 44 45 46 49 50 53 54 56 57 58 59 60 61 64 65 68 70 71 72 74 75 76 77 78 79 80 81 82 84 85 86 87 88 89 90 92 93 96 97 98 99 100 101 102 103 105 107 108 110 111 114 115 118 119 120 121 123 124 126 129 130 131 132 134 135 143 144 145 146 147 **P**8 **S** Presence Health, Chicago, IL
Primary Contact: Kathleen Rhine, Regional President and Chief Executive Officer
CFO: Melony W. Goodhand, Regional Chief Financial Officer
CMO: David R. Franzblau, M.D., Chief Medical Officer
CIO: Russell Soliman, System Manager Client Services and Management Information Services
Web address: www.provena.org/stjoes
**Control:** Church–operated, Nongovernment, not–for profit **Service:** General Medical and Surgical

**Staffed Beds:** 443 **Admissions:** 22728 **Census:** 295 **Outpatient Visits:** 359834 **Births:** 1271 **Total Expense ($000):** 374406 **Payroll Expense ($000):** 127806 **Personnel:** 2005

**PROVENA SAINT JOSEPH MEDICAL CENTER** See Presence Saint Joseph Medical Center

## KANKAKEE—Kankakee County

✠ **PRESENCE ST. MARY'S HOSPITAL (140155)**, 500 West Court Street, Zip 60901–3661; tel. 815/937–2400 **A**1 2 9 10 **F**3 5 11 12 13 15 18 20 22 26 28 29 30 31 32 34 35 36 39 40 43 45 48 49 50 53 54 56 57 58 59 60 61 64 65 68 70 74 75 76 77 78 79 81 82 83 84 85 86 87 89 92 93 97 98 99 100 101 102 103 104 105 106 107 108 110 111 114 115 116 119 129 130 131 132 135 143 146 147 148 **S** Presence Health, Chicago, IL
Primary Contact: Kathleen Rhine, Regional President and Chief Executive Officer
CFO: Melony W. Goodhand, Chief Financial Officer
CMO: Syed Bokhari, M.D., Chief Medical Officer
CIO: Russell Soliman, Director Information Services
CNO: Jacqueline Medland, MS, Regional Chief Nursing Officer
Web address: www.provena.org/stmarys/
**Control:** Church–operated, Nongovernment, not–for profit **Service:** General Medical and Surgical

**Staffed Beds:** 156 **Admissions:** 5493 **Census:** 64 **Outpatient Visits:** 161493 **Births:** 411 **Total Expense ($000):** 118881 **Payroll Expense ($000):** 35991 **Personnel:** 664

**PROVENA ST. MARY'S HOSPITAL** See Presence St. Mary's Hospital

★ ◇ **RIVERSIDE MEDICAL CENTER (140186)**, 350 North Wall Street, Zip 60901–2901; tel. 815/933–1671 **A**2 5 9 10 13 21 **F**3 4 5 6 7 8 9 11 12 13 15 17 18 19 20 22 24 26 28 29 30 31 32 34 35 36 38 39 40 41 43 44 45 46 47 48 49 50 51 54 55 56 57 58 59 61 62 64 65 66 68 70 71 74 75 76 77 78 79 81 82 84 85 86 87 89 90 92 93 96 97 98 99 100 101 102 103 104 105 106 107 108 110 111 114 115 118 119 120 121 123 124 126 127 129 130 131 132 134 135 141 143 144 145 146 147 148 **P**6
Primary Contact: Phillip M. Kambic, President and Chief Executive Officer
COO: David Duda, Senior Vice President and Chief Operating Officer
CFO: Bill Douglas, Senior Vice President and Chief Financial Officer
CMO: John Jurica, M.D., Vice President Medical Affairs
CIO: Kyle Hansen, Corporate Director Information Systems
CHR: Becky Hinrichs, Vice President Human Resources
Web address: www.riversidehealthcare.org
**Control:** Other not–for–profit (including NFP Corporation) **Service:** General Medical and Surgical

**Staffed Beds:** 312 **Admissions:** 9945 **Census:** 137 **Outpatient Visits:** 419192 **Births:** 1012 **Total Expense ($000):** 255033 **Payroll Expense ($000):** 104656 **Personnel:** 1946

## KEWANEE—Henry County

★ **OSF SAINT LUKE MEDICAL CENTER (141325)**, 1051 West South Street, Zip 61443–8354, Mailing Address: P.O. Box 747, Zip 61443–0747; tel. 309/852–7500 **A**9 10 18 **F**3 11 15 29 32 34 35 36 38 40 45 50 57 59 64 65 66 70 75 77 78 79 81 82 85 86 87 92 93 96 97 107 108 110 115 119 127 129 131 132 133 135 146 147 148 **P**6 **S** OSF Healthcare System, Peoria, IL
Primary Contact: Lynn Fulton, President
CFO: John Bowser, Vice President, Chief Financial Officer
CIO: Jeremy Johnson, Director of Information Technology
CHR: Renee A. Salisbury, Director Human Resources
CNO: Jennifer Junis, MSN, Vice President Chief Nursing Officer
Web address: www.osfsaintluke.org
**Control:** Other not–for–profit (including NFP Corporation) **Service:** General Medical and Surgical

**Staffed Beds:** 25 **Admissions:** 535 **Census:** 4 **Outpatient Visits:** 36974 **Births:** 0 **Total Expense ($000):** 27123 **Payroll Expense ($000):** 10195 **Personnel:** 192

## LA GRANGE—Cook County

✠ **ADVENTIST LA GRANGE MEMORIAL HOSPITAL (140065)**, 5101 South Willow Spring Road, Zip 60525–2600; tel. 708/245–9000 **A**1 2 3 5 9 10 13 **F**3 12 13 15 17 18 20 22 24 26 28 29 30 31 34 35 37 39 40 43 44 45 49 50 56 57 58 59 60 61 64 68 70 73 74 75 76 78 79 81 82 85 86 87 93 96 97 100 107 108 110 111 114 115 118 119 120 121 123 126 129 130 131 132 135 146 147 148 **P**7 8 **S** Adventist Health System Sunbelt Health Care Corporation, Altamonte Springs, FL
Primary Contact: Michael Goebel, Vice President and Chief Executive Officer
CFO: Rebecca Mathis, Chief Financial Officer
CMO: Gary Lipinski, M.D., Regional Vice President and Chief Medical Officer
CIO: Thomas Schoenig, Chief Information Officer
CHR: Garry Giertuga, Site Manager Human Resources
CNO: Mary S. Murphy, R.N., Regional Chief Nursing Officer
Web address: www.keepingyouwell.com
**Control:** Church–operated, Nongovernment, not–for profit **Service:** General Medical and Surgical

**Staffed Beds:** 158 **Admissions:** 7732 **Census:** 93 **Outpatient Visits:** 119478 **Births:** 498 **Total Expense ($000):** 165935 **Payroll Expense ($000):** 57494 **Personnel:** 830

## LAKE FOREST—Lake County

**LAKE FOREST HOSPITAL** See Northwestern Lake Forest Hospital

✠ **NORTHWESTERN LAKE FOREST HOSPITAL (140130)**, 660 North Westmoreland Road, Zip 60045–1696; tel. 847/234–5600, (Total facility includes 64 beds in nursing home–type unit) **A**1 2 3 5 9 10 **F**2 3 8 9 11 13 15 18 20 22 26 28 29 30 31 32 34 35 36 38 40 42 43 44 45 46 48 49 50 51 53 54 55 56 57 58 59 62 64 65 70 73 74 75 76 77 78 79 81 82 83 84 85 86 87 89 92 93 96 97 107 108 110 111 114 115 116 117 119 120 121 123 126 128 130 131 132 135 144 146 147 148 **P**5 **S** Northwestern Memorial Healthcare, Chicago, IL
Primary Contact: Thomas J. McAfee, President, North Market
CFO: Matthew J. Flynn, Senior Vice President and Chief Financial Officer
CMO: Michael G. Ankin, M.D., Vice President Medical Affairs & Chief Medical Officer
CNO: Denise Mageski, MSN, Chief Nurse Executive
Web address: www.lfh.org
**Control:** Other not–for–profit (including NFP Corporation) **Service:** General Medical and Surgical

**Staffed Beds:** 181 **Admissions:** 7654 **Census:** 89 **Outpatient Visits:** 188888 **Births:** 1458 **Total Expense ($000):** 268894 **Payroll Expense ($000):** 115099 **Personnel:** 1213

## LAWRENCEVILLE—Lawrence County

**LAWRENCE COUNTY MEMORIAL HOSPITAL (141344)**, 2200 West State Street, Zip 62439–1852; tel. 618/943–1000 **A**9 10 18 **F**3 11 15 28 29 30 40 75 77 81 93 107 114 127 130 133 **S** QHR, Brentwood, TN
Primary Contact: Doug Florkowski, Chief Executive Officer
CFO: Larry Spore, Chief Financial Officer
CIO: Gary Theriac, Director Information Technology
CHR: Kim Alldredge, Director Human Resources
CNO: Rita Garvey, Chief Nursing Officer
Web address: www.lcmhosp.org
**Control:** Other not–for–profit (including NFP Corporation) **Service:** General Medical and Surgical

**Staffed Beds:** 25 **Admissions:** 684 **Census:** 7 **Outpatient Visits:** 31067 **Births:** 0 **Total Expense ($000):** 12686 **Payroll Expense ($000):** 5041 **Personnel:** 128

## LIBERTYVILLE—Lake County

★ ◇ **ADVOCATE CONDELL MEDICAL CENTER (140202)**, 801 South Milwaukee Avenue, Zip 60048–3199; tel. 847/362–2900 **A**2 9 10 21 **F**1 2 3 4 11 12 13 15 16 17 18 19 20 22 24 26 28 29 30 31 32 33 37 39 40 41 43 44 45 46 47 48 49 50 51 53 54 55 56 57 59 60 64 65 67 68 70 72 73 74 75 76 77 78 79 80 81 82 85 86 87 88 89 90 92 93 94 96 98 107 108 110 111 114 115 117 118 119 120 121 123 126 128 129 130 131 132 135 144 145 146 147 148 **P**8 **S** Advocate Health Care, Downers Grove, IL
Primary Contact: Dominica Tallarico, President
CFO: David A. Cartwright, Vice President Finance and Support Services
CMO: Debra Susie–Lattner, M.D., Vice President, Medical Management
CIO: Chuck Malik, Director, Site Information System
CHR: Jason Spigner, Vice President Human Resources
CNO: Mary Hillard, R.N., Vice President Patient Care Services and Clinical Operations, Chief Nursing Executive
Web address: www.advocatehealth.com/condell/
**Control:** Other not–for–profit (including NFP Corporation) **Service:** General Medical and Surgical

**Staffed Beds:** 277 **Admissions:** 16172 **Census:** 179 **Outpatient Visits:** 216477 **Births:** 2236 **Total Expense ($000):** 287167 **Payroll Expense ($000):** 95666 **Personnel:** 1489

**IL**

*Many Facility Codes have changed. Please refer to the AHA Guide Code Chart.* © 2015 AHA Guide

## LINCOLN—Logan County

✠ **ABRAHAM LINCOLN MEMORIAL HOSPITAL (141322)**, 200 Stahlhut Drive,
Zip 62656–5066; tel. 217/732–2161 **A**1 9 10 18 **F**13 15 28 29 30 34 35 40
57 59 64 71 75 76 77 79 81 82 87 93 107 108 110 111 119 129 130 131
132 133 144 146 **P**5 **S** Memorial Health System, Springfield, IL
Primary Contact: Dolan Dalpoas, President and Chief Executive Officer
COO: Kathleen Vipond, Assistant Administrator and Director
CFO: Andrew Costic, Regional Chief Financial Officer
CMO: Richard Bivin, M.D., President Medical Staff
CIO: Keenan Leesman, Director Information Systems
CHR: Michelle Long, Human Resources Business Partner
CNO: Jeanne Dennis, Chief Nursing Officer
Web address: www.almh.org
**Control:** Other not–for–profit (including NFP Corporation) **Service:** General
Medical and Surgical

**Staffed Beds:** 25 **Admissions:** 1092 **Census:** 10 **Outpatient Visits:** 48632
**Births:** 209 **Total Expense ($000):** 38400 **Payroll Expense ($000):** 13658
**Personnel:** 249

## LITCHFIELD—Montgomery County

✠ **HSHS ST. FRANCIS HOSPITAL (141350)**, 1215 Franciscan Drive,
Zip 62056–1799, Mailing Address: P.O. Box 1215, Zip 62056–0999;
tel. 217/324–2191 **A**1 9 10 18 **F**8 11 13 15 18 28 29 30 34 35 40 44 45 46
50 56 57 59 64 68 70 74 75 76 77 79 81 82 85 86 87 92 93 107 111 114
118 119 129 131 132 133 134 135 146 147 **S** Hospital Sisters Health System,
Springfield, IL
Primary Contact: Patricia Fischer, President and Chief Executive Officer
CFO: Patrick Nudo, Finance Director
CNO: John Peipert, R.N., Chief Nursing Officer
Web address: www.stfrancis–litchfield.org
**Control:** Church–operated, Nongovernment, not–for profit **Service:** General
Medical and Surgical

**Staffed Beds:** 25 **Admissions:** 1244 **Census:** 12 **Outpatient Visits:** 47321
**Births:** 255 **Total Expense ($000):** 31263 **Payroll Expense ($000):** 10838
**Personnel:** 208

## MACOMB—Mcdonough County

✠ **MCDONOUGH DISTRICT HOSPITAL (140089)**, 525 East Grant Street,
Zip 61455–3318; tel. 309/833–4101, (Total facility includes 16 beds in nursing
home–type unit) **A**1 9 10 20 **F**2 3 5 7 11 13 15 28 29 31 34 35 38 40 45 47
48 50 51 54 56 57 59 62 63 64 68 70 75 76 77 78 79 81 82 84 85 86 89
91 93 94 96 97 99 100 101 102 104 107 108 110 115 119 124 127 128
129 130 131 132 135 146 148 **P**8
Primary Contact: Kenneth Boyd, Jr., President and Chief Executive Officer
CFO: Linda Dace, Vice President Finance
CMO: Shea Trost, D.O., Chief Medical Officer
CIO: Harlan T. Baker, Department Leader Information Systems
CHR: Sue Dexter, Administrative Department Leader Human Resources
CNO: Wanda Foster, R.N., Vice President Nursing
Web address: www.mdh.org
**Control:** Hospital district or authority, Government, nonfederal **Service:** General
Medical and Surgical

**Staffed Beds:** 64 **Admissions:** 1951 **Census:** 21 **Outpatient Visits:** 191238
**Births:** 265 **Total Expense ($000):** 68882 **Payroll Expense ($000):** 34441
**Personnel:** 500

## MARION—Williamson County

✠ **HEARTLAND REGIONAL MEDICAL CENTER (140184)**, 3333 West DeYoung,
Zip 62959–5884; tel. 618/998–7000, (Nonreporting) **A**1 9 10 **S** Community
Health Systems, Inc., Franklin, TN
Primary Contact: James Flynn, Chief Executive Officer
COO: Kolbe Sheridan, Chief Operating Officer
CFO: Jeff Thomas, Chief Financial Officer
CHR: Sam Hood, Director Human Resources
Web address: www.heartlandregional.com
**Control:** Corporation, Investor–owned, for–profit **Service:** General Medical and
Surgical

**Staffed Beds:** 92

✠ **MARION VETERANS AFFAIRS MEDICAL CENTER**, 2401 West Main Street,
Zip 62959–1188; tel. 618/997–5311, (Nonreporting) **A**1 3 5 **S** Department of
Veterans Affairs, Washington, DC
Primary Contact: Donald Hutson, Director
COO: Frank Kehus, Associate Director for Operations
CFO: Connie McDonald, Chief Financial Officer
CMO: Michael Ladwig, M.D., Chief of Staff
CIO: Clint Bishop, Program Manager
CHR: Tonya L. Searby, Chief Human Resources
CNO: Rose Burke, Associate Director Patient Care Services
Web address: www.marion.va.gov
**Control:** Veterans Affairs, Government, federal **Service:** General Medical and
Surgical

**Staffed Beds:** 225

## MARYVILLE—Madison County

✠ △ **ANDERSON HOSPITAL (140289)**, 6800 State Route 162,
Zip 62062–8500; tel. 618/288–5711 **A**1 7 9 10 **F**3 11 13 15 18 20 22 28 29
30 34 35 40 49 50 57 59 62 70 74 75 76 78 79 81 85 90 93 107 110 111
115 118 119 126 129 130 132 144 146 147 148
Primary Contact: Keith Allen Page, President and Chief Executive Officer
CFO: Michael Marshall, Vice President Finance and Chief Financial Officer
CMO: Christopher Wangard, M.D., President Medical Staff
CIO: Michael Ward, Director Information Services
CHR: Robin Steinmann, Administrative Director Human Resources
CNO: Lisa Klaustermeier, R.N., Chief Nursing Officer
Web address: www.andersonhospital.org
**Control:** Other not–for–profit (including NFP Corporation) **Service:** General
Medical and Surgical

**Staffed Beds:** 154 **Admissions:** 7129 **Census:** 74 **Outpatient Visits:** 176395
**Births:** 1688 **Total Expense ($000):** 113614 **Payroll Expense ($000):**
46478 **Personnel:** 900

## MATTOON—Coles County

✠ **SARAH BUSH LINCOLN HEALTH CENTER (140189)**, 1000 Health Center
Drive, Zip 61938–9253, Mailing Address: P.O. Box 372, Zip 61938–0372;
tel. 217/258–2525 **A**1 9 10 20 **F**3 11 12 18 20 22 28 29 30 31 32 34
35 36 38 39 40 44 47 48 49 50 53 54 56 57 59 61 62 63 64 65 66 68 69
70 71 74 75 76 77 78 79 81 82 84 85 86 87 89 93 97 98 99 100 101 102
103 104 105 107 110 111 114 115 117 119 120 121 123 127 129 130 131
132 134 135 144 145 146 147 148 **P**6
Primary Contact: Timothy A. Ols, FACHE, President and Chief Executive Officer
COO: Dennis Pluard, Vice President Finance and Operations
CFO: Dennis Pluard, Vice President Finance and Operations
CMO: James Hildebrandt, D.O., Vice President Medical Affairs
CIO: Maggie Ratliff, Vice President Information Systems
CHR: Eric Benson, Vice President Human Resources & Wellness
CNO: Mary Lou Wild, Vice President Patient Care Continuum and Chief Nursing
Officer
Web address: www.sarahbush.org
**Control:** Other not–for–profit (including NFP Corporation) **Service:** General
Medical and Surgical

**Staffed Beds:** 118 **Admissions:** 6810 **Census:** 64 **Outpatient Visits:** 462427
**Births:** 827 **Total Expense ($000):** 224384 **Payroll Expense ($000):**
108910 **Personnel:** 1786

## MAYWOOD—Cook County

✠ △ **LOYOLA UNIVERSITY MEDICAL CENTER (140276)**, 2160 South First
Avenue, Zip 60153–3328; tel. 708/216–9000, (Includes RONALD MCDONALD
CHILDREN'S HOSPITAL, 2160 South 1St. Avenue, tel. 888/584–7888) **A**1 2 3 5
7 8 9 10 **F**3 6 7 8 9 11 12 13 14 15 16 17 18 19 20 21 22 23 24 25 26 27
28 29 30 31 32 33 34 35 36 37 38 39 40 41 43 44 45 46 47 48 49 50 51
54 55 56 57 58 59 60 61 62 63 64 65 66 68 70 71 72 73 74 75 76 77 78
79 80 81 82 84 85 86 87 88 90 91 92 93 94 96 97 99 100 101 102 103
104 107 108 110 111 114 115 116 117 118 119 120 121 123 124 126 129
130 131 132 134 135 136 137 138 139 140 141 142 143 144 145 146 147
148 **P**6 **S** Trinity Health, Livonia, MI
Primary Contact: Larry M. Goldberg, President and Chief Executive Officer
CFO: Jay Sial, Chief Financial Officer
CMO: Robert Cherry, M.D., Chief Medical Officer
CIO: Arthur J. Krumrey, Chief Information Officer
CHR: Vicky Piper, Vice President Human Resources
Web address: www.loyolamedicine.org/Medical_Services/index.cfm
**Control:** Other not–for–profit (including NFP Corporation) **Service:** General
Medical and Surgical

**Staffed Beds:** 509 **Admissions:** 22583 **Census:** 370 **Outpatient Visits:**
1403258 **Births:** 995 **Total Expense ($000):** 1086193 **Payroll Expense
($000):** 529264 **Personnel:** 6500

**IL**

---

**Hospital, Medicare Provider Number, Address, Telephone, Approval, Facility, and Physician Codes, Health Care System**

★ American Hospital Association (AHA) membership   ○ Healthcare Facilities Accreditation Program   ⇧ Center for Improvement in Healthcare Quality Accreditation
□ The Joint Commission accreditation   ◇ DNV Healthcare Inc. accreditation   △ Commission on Accreditation of Rehabilitation Facilities (CARF) accreditation

## MCHENRY—Mchenry County

☒ **CENTEGRA HOSPITAL – MCHENRY (140116)**, 4201 Medical Center Drive, Zip 60050–8409; tel. 815/344–5000 **A**1 2 5 9 10 **F**3 4 11 12 13 15 18 20 22 24 26 28 29 30 31 34 35 37 38 39 40 43 44 49 50 51 54 55 57 58 59 62 64 68 69 70 74 75 76 78 79 81 82 85 86 87 90 92 93 96 100 101 102 107 108 110 111 114 115 117 118 119 120 121 123 124 126 129 130 131 132 143 146 147 148 **P**4 5 **S** Centegra Health System, Crystal Lake, IL
Primary Contact: Michael S. Eesley, Chief Executive Officer
COO: Jason Sciarro, President and Chief Operating Officer
CFO: David Tomlinson, Executive Vice President Chief Financial Officer and Chief Information Officer
CMO: Irfan Hafiz, Vice President Medical Affairs
CIO: David Tomlinson, Executive Vice President Chief Financial Officer and Chief Information Officer
CHR: Bernadette S. Szczepanski, Vice President, Human Resources Development
Web address: www.centegra.org
**Control:** Other not–for–profit (including NFP Corporation) **Service:** General Medical and Surgical

**Staffed Beds:** 167 **Admissions:** 9189 **Census:** 108 **Outpatient Visits:** 131280 **Births:** 794 **Total Expense ($000):** 213638 **Payroll Expense ($000):** 86119 **Personnel:** 1019

## MCLEANSBORO—Hamilton County

**HAMILTON MEMORIAL HOSPITAL DISTRICT (141326)**, 611 South Marshall Avenue, Zip 62859–1213, Mailing Address: P.O. Box 429, Mc Leansboro, Zip 62859–0429; tel. 618/643–2361 **A**9 10 18 **F**3 11 15 28 29 40 43 57 81 93 107 108 114 119 127 129 130 133 148
Primary Contact: Gregory F. Sims, Chief Executive Officer
CFO: Kent Mitchell, Chief Financial Officer
CIO: Don Darnell, Chief Information Officer
CNO: Patty Blazier, Chief Nursing Officer
Web address: www.hmhospital.org
**Control:** Hospital district or authority, Government, nonfederal **Service:** General Medical and Surgical

**Staffed Beds:** 25 **Admissions:** 774 **Census:** 8 **Outpatient Visits:** 37989 **Births:** 0 **Total Expense ($000):** 13483 **Payroll Expense ($000):** 5902 **Personnel:** 107

## MELROSE PARK—Cook County

☒ **GOTTLIEB MEMORIAL HOSPITAL (140008)**, 701 West North Avenue, Zip 60160–1612; tel. 708/681–3200 **A**1 3 5 9 10 **F**2 3 11 12 13 15 18 20 22 24 26 28 29 30 31 34 35 36 39 40 43 44 45 47 49 53 54 56 57 59 60 62 63 65 68 70 74 75 76 77 78 79 81 85 86 87 89 92 93 96 97 98 103 107 108 110 111 114 116 117 118 119 128 129 130 131 132 143 144 145 146 147 148 **P**8 **S** Trinity Health, Livonia, MI
Primary Contact: Lori Price, President
COO: Ken Fishbain, Chief Operating Officer
CFO: Ellyn Chin, Vice President Finance
CMO: Gerald Luger, M.D., President Medical Staff
CIO: Maurita Adler, Director Information Services
CHR: Brett Wakefield, Vice President Human Resources
Web address: www.gottliebhospital.org
**Control:** Other not–for–profit (including NFP Corporation) **Service:** General Medical and Surgical

**Staffed Beds:** 205 **Admissions:** 7889 **Census:** 122 **Outpatient Visits:** 179330 **Births:** 989 **Total Expense ($000):** 134552 **Payroll Expense ($000):** 60132 **Personnel:** 1022

★ ○ **WESTLAKE HOSPITAL (140240)**, 1225 Lake Street, Zip 60160–4000; tel. 708/681–3000, (Nonreporting) **A**3 5 9 10 11 **S** TENET Healthcare Corporation, Dallas, TX
Primary Contact: Patrick J. Maloney, Chief Executive Officer
COO: Michael Ditoro, Chief Operating Officer
CFO: Jennifer Lamont, Chief Financial Officer
CMO: Robert Chase, M.D., Chief Medical Officer
CHR: Nancy Gunnell, Chief Human Resource Officer
CNO: Ruth Matthei, R.N., Chief Nursing Officer
Web address: www.westlakehosp.com
**Control:** Corporation, Investor–owned, for–profit **Service:** General Medical and Surgical

**Staffed Beds:** 181

## MENDOTA—Lasalle County

★ **OSF SAINT PAUL MEDICAL CENTER (141310)**, 1401 East 12th Street, Zip 61342–9216; tel. 815/539–7461 **A**9 10 18 **F**3 11 15 28 29 31 34 40 49 57 59 62 65 69 70 77 78 79 81 85 93 107 110 111 115 129 130 133 146 **P**6
Primary Contact: Jennifer Junis, MSN, R.N., President
CFO: Dawn Trompeter, Chief Financial Officer
CMO: Leonardo Lopez, President Medical Staff
CIO: Shawn Soliman, Manager Information Technology
CHR: Kimberly Kennedy, Manager Human Resources
CNO: Heather Bomstad, R.N., Chief Nursing Officer
Web address: www.https://www.osfhealthcare.org/saint–paul
**Control:** Other not–for–profit (including NFP Corporation) **Service:** General Medical and Surgical

**Staffed Beds:** 25 **Admissions:** 883 **Census:** 10 **Outpatient Visits:** 50216 **Births:** 0 **Total Expense ($000):** 35156 **Payroll Expense ($000):** 14513 **Personnel:** 242

## METROPOLIS—Massac County

★ **MASSAC MEMORIAL HOSPITAL (141323)**, 28 Chick Street, Zip 62960–2467, Mailing Address: P.O. Box 850, Zip 62960–0850; tel. 618/524–2176, (Nonreporting) **A**9 10 18
Primary Contact: Tommy Pfitzer, Chief Executive Officer
CFO: Jerry Klein, Interim Chief Financial Officer
CHR: Joel Foster, Director Human Resources
CNO: Janet Hester, R.N., Chief Nurse Executive
Web address: www.massachealth.org
**Control:** Hospital district or authority, Government, nonfederal **Service:** General Medical and Surgical

**Staffed Beds:** 25

## MOLINE—Rock Island County

**UNITYPOINT HEALTH – TRINITY MOLINE** See UnityPoint Health – Trinity Rock Island, Rock Island

## MONMOUTH—Warren County

★ **OSF HOLY FAMILY MEDICAL CENTER (141318)**, 1000 West Harlem Avenue, Zip 61462–1007; tel. 309/734–3141 **A**9 10 18 **F**11 15 28 29 30 34 40 45 46 50 57 59 64 65 68 75 77 81 85 87 93 97 107 110 115 118 119 127 129 130 132 133 135 143 145 146 **P**6 **S** OSF Healthcare System, Peoria, IL
Primary Contact: Patricia A. Luker, President
CFO: Theresa Springer, Chief Financial Officer
CMO: Frank Lasala, M.D., President Medical Staff
CIO: Lew McCann, Director Management Information Systems
CHR: Jenny Jacobs, Director Human Resources
CNO: Shelley Wiborg, MS, Director of Nursing
Web address: www.osfholyfamily.org
**Control:** Church–operated, Nongovernment, not–for profit **Service:** General Medical and Surgical

**Staffed Beds:** 23 **Admissions:** 330 **Census:** 4 **Outpatient Visits:** 73574 **Births:** 0 **Total Expense ($000):** 25305 **Payroll Expense ($000):** 11827 **Personnel:** 170

## MONTICELLO—Piatt County

☒ **KIRBY MEDICAL CENTER (141301)**, 1000 Medical Center Drive, Zip 61856–2116; tel. 217/762–2115, (Nonreporting) **A**1 5 9 10 18
Primary Contact: Steven D. Tenhouse, FACHE, Chief Executive Officer
COO: Mark Fred, R.N., Chief Operating Officer
CFO: Alexander Nazarian, CPA, Chief Financial Officer
CMO: Narain Mandhan, M.D., Chief Medical Officer
CIO: Kyle Willams, Director Information Technology
CHR: Andrew Buffenbarger, Director of Human Resources, Compliance and Risk Management
CNO: Jennifer Moss, MS, Chief Clinical Officer
Web address: www.kirbyhealth.org
**Control:** Other not–for–profit (including NFP Corporation) **Service:** General Medical and Surgical

**Staffed Beds:** 16

*Many Facility Codes have changed. Please refer to the AHA Guide Code Chart.*
© 2015 AHA Guide

## MORRIS—Grundy County

★ ○ **MORRIS HOSPITAL & HEALTHCARE CENTERS (140101)**, 150 West High Street, Zip 60450–1497; tel. 815/942–2932 **A**2 9 10 11 **F**3 11 13 15 18 19 20 22 26 28 29 34 35 40 43 47 49 50 54 57 59 64 66 69 70 74 75 76 77 78 79 81 82 85 86 87 89 93 97 102 107 108 110 111 114 115 118 119 120 121 123 130 132 135 143 144 146 **P**6
Primary Contact: Mark B. Steadham, President and Chief Executive Officer
COO: Patrick O'Connor, Chief Operating Officer
CFO: Dean M. Marketti, Vice President Finance
CIO: Dean M. Marketti, Chief Information Officer
CHR: Erin Murphy–Frobish, Vice President Human Resources
CNO: Kimberly A. Landers, MS, Vice President Patient Care Services
Web address: www.morrishospital.org
**Control:** Other not–for–profit (including NFP Corporation) **Service:** General Medical and Surgical

**Staffed Beds:** 89 **Admissions:** 3972 **Census:** 39 **Outpatient Visits:** 249206 **Births:** 543 **Total Expense ($000):** 124941 **Payroll Expense ($000):** 56192 **Personnel:** 728

## MORRISON—Whiteside County

★ **MORRISON COMMUNITY HOSPITAL (141329)**, 303 North Jackson Street, Zip 61270–3042; tel. 815/772–4003, (Total facility includes 38 beds in nursing home–type unit) **A**9 10 18 **F**3 7 11 15 40 45 59 63 64 65 66 81 93 94 97 99 107 110 119 127 130 133 146 148 **P**6
Primary Contact: Pam Pfister, Chief Executive Officer
COO: Pam Pfister, Chief Executive Officer
CFO: Cami Megli, Controller
CMO: Duncan Dinkha, M.D., Chief of Staff
CIO: Pam Pfister, Chief Executive Officer
CHR: Amber L. Temple, Director Human Resources
Web address: www.morrisonhospital.com
**Control:** Hospital district or authority, Government, nonfederal **Service:** General Medical and Surgical

**Staffed Beds:** 63 **Admissions:** 85 **Census:** 27 **Outpatient Visits:** 14551 **Births:** 0 **Total Expense ($000):** 11648 **Payroll Expense ($000):** 5523 **Personnel:** 134

## MOUNT CARMEL—Wabash County

⊞ **WABASH GENERAL HOSPITAL (141327)**, 1418 College Drive, Zip 62863–2638; tel. 618/262–8621, (Nonreporting) **A**1 9 10 18 **S** Alliant Management Services, Louisville, KY
Primary Contact: Jay Purvis, Administrator and Chief Executive Officer
CFO: Steve McGill, Chief Financial Officer
CMO: Julko Fullop, M.D., Chief of Staff
CIO: Bobby Gage, Director Information Technology
CHR: Bridget Shepard, Director Human Resources
CNO: Tamara Gould, R.N., Director of Nursing
Web address: www.wabashgeneral.com
**Control:** County–Government, nonfederal **Service:** General Medical and Surgical

**Staffed Beds:** 25

## MOUNT VERNON—Jefferson County

⊞ **CROSSROADS COMMUNITY HOSPITAL (140294)**, 8 Doctors Park Road, Zip 62864–6224; tel. 618/244–5500 **A**1 9 10 **F**3 8 11 12 15 18 29 30 34 35 40 45 46 49 50 53 56 57 59 60 64 68 70 74 75 77 79 81 82 85 93 94 95 96 107 110 111 115 119 126 127 129 135 145 146 147 148 **P**1 **S** Community Health Systems, Inc., Franklin, TN
Primary Contact: Finny Mathew, Chief Executive Officer
CFO: Shawn Hartley, Chief Financial Officer
CIO: Chad Black, Director Information Technology
CHR: Jessica Connaway, Director Human Resources
CNO: Tammy Love, Chief Nursing Officer
Web address: www.crossroadshospital.com
**Control:** Corporation, Investor–owned, for–profit **Service:** General Medical and Surgical

**Staffed Beds:** 47 **Admissions:** 1171 **Census:** 13 **Outpatient Visits:** 35451 **Births:** 0 **Total Expense ($000):** 45253 **Payroll Expense ($000):** 16492 **Personnel:** 259

⊞ **GOOD SAMARITAN REGIONAL HEALTH CENTER (140046)**, 1 Good Samaritan Way, Zip 62864–2402; tel. 618/242–4600 **A**1 2 9 10 19 **F**3 4 11 13 15 18 20 22 24 26 28 29 30 31 34 35 38 40 44 45 46 50 51 54 56 57 59 61 64 68 70 73 74 75 76 77 78 79 80 81 82 84 85 86 87 89 90 93 94 107 108 110 111 114 115 119 126 130 131 132 135 144 145 146 147 148 **P**6 8 **S** SSM Health, Saint Louis, MO
Primary Contact: Michael D. Warren, President
COO: Mark A. Clark, Vice President Operations
CFO: Deland Evischi, Regional Chief Financial Officer, Southern Illinois
CMO: Daniel Hoffman, M.D., Administrative Medical Director
CIO: Steve Murphy, FM–East Region IS
CHR: Thomas W. Blythe, System Vice President Human Resources
CNO: Chris Adams, Vice President Patient Care Services
Web address: www.smgsi.com
**Control:** Church–operated, Nongovernment, not–for profit **Service:** General Medical and Surgical

**Staffed Beds:** 134 **Admissions:** 7281 **Census:** 80 **Outpatient Visits:** 175882 **Births:** 1088 **Total Expense ($000):** 149617 **Payroll Expense ($000):** 46317 **Personnel:** 1156

## MURPHYSBORO—Jackson County

★ **ST. JOSEPH MEMORIAL HOSPITAL (141334)**, 2 South Hospital Drive, Zip 62966–3333; tel. 618/684–3156 **A**9 10 18 **F**3 11 18 28 29 30 31 34 35 40 45 56 57 59 64 74 75 77 78 79 81 82 85 86 87 93 107 114 119 129 130 132 133 135 146 148 **P**1 **S** Southern Illinois Hospital Services, Carbondale, IL
Primary Contact: Susan Odle, Administrator
CMO: Emily Hanson, M.D., President, Medical Staff
CIO: David Holland, Vice President Information Services
CHR: Kelly Stevens, Manager Human Resources
CNO: Julie Firman, DNP, R.N., Chief Nursing Officer
Web address: www.sih.net
**Control:** Other not–for–profit (including NFP Corporation) **Service:** General Medical and Surgical

**Staffed Beds:** 25 **Admissions:** 791 **Census:** 12 **Outpatient Visits:** 72500 **Births:** 0 **Total Expense ($000):** 52228 **Payroll Expense ($000):** 13219 **Personnel:** 235

## NAPERVILLE—Dupage County

⊞ **EDWARD HOSPITAL (140231)**, 801 South Washington Street, Zip 60540–7499; tel. 630/527–3000 **A**1 2 9 10 **F**3 7 12 13 15 17 18 19 20 22 24 26 28 29 30 31 32 34 35 37 38 39 40 41 42 43 44 45 46 47 48 49 50 54 55 56 57 58 59 61 63 64 65 68 70 72 73 74 75 76 77 78 79 81 82 84 85 86 87 88 89 91 92 93 96 97 102 107 108 109 110 111 114 115 117 118 119 120 121 123 124 126 129 130 131 132 135 144 146 147 148 **P**1 6 **S** Edward–Elmhurst Healthcare, Naperville, IL
Primary Contact: Pamela M. Davis, System President and Chief Executive Officer
COO: Marianne Spencer, R.N., Vice President Operations and Chief Operating Officer
CFO: Vincent Pryor, System Executive Vice President and Chief Financial Officer
CMO: Brent Smith, M.D., Chief Medical Officer and Vice President Clinical Integration
CIO: Bobbie Byrne, M.D., Vice President Chief Information Officer
CHR: Susan Mitchell, System Executive Vice President Human Resources
CNO: Patti Ludwig–Beymer, Ph.D., Vice President Chief Nursing Officer
Web address: www.edward.org
**Control:** Other not–for–profit (including NFP Corporation) **Service:** General Medical and Surgical

**Staffed Beds:** 311 **Admissions:** 21025 **Census:** 231 **Outpatient Visits:** 528690 **Births:** 3065 **Total Expense ($000):** 509756 **Payroll Expense ($000):** 190620 **Personnel:** 2585

⊞ **LINDEN OAKS HOSPITAL (144035)**, 852 West Street, Zip 60540–6400; tel. 630/305–5500 **A**1 3 5 9 10 **F**4 5 29 34 35 38 56 57 59 64 68 75 87 98 99 100 101 103 104 105 106 130 132 134 **P**1 6 **S** Edward–Elmhurst Healthcare, Naperville, IL
Primary Contact: Gina Sharp, FACHE, President
CFO: Kristen Refness, Chief Financial Officer
CMO: Barry Rabin, M.D., Medical Director
CIO: Hugh Siddiqui, Senior Applications Analyst
CNO: Trish Jones–Bendel, R.N., Chief Nursing Officer
Web address: www.edward.org
**Control:** Other not–for–profit (including NFP Corporation) **Service:** Psychiatric

**Staffed Beds:** 108 **Admissions:** 4530 **Census:** 88 **Outpatient Visits:** 54545 **Births:** 0 **Total Expense ($000):** 40345 **Payroll Expense ($000):** 22242 **Personnel:** 394

IL

**Hospital, Medicare Provider Number, Address, Telephone, Approval, Facility, and Physician Codes, Health Care System**

★ American Hospital Association (AHA) membership
☐ The Joint Commission accreditation
○ Healthcare Facilities Accreditation Program
◇ DNV Healthcare Inc. accreditation
⇧ Center for Improvement in Healthcare Quality Accreditation
△ Commission on Accreditation of Rehabilitation Facilities (CARF) accreditation

**NASHVILLE—Washington County**

✠ **WASHINGTON COUNTY HOSPITAL (141308)**, 705 South Grand Avenue, Zip 62263–1534; tel. 618/327–8236, (Total facility includes 28 beds in nursing home–type unit) **A**1 9 10 18 **F**8 11 15 28 29 31 34 40 49 50 57 59 64 65 78 81 85 93 104 107 114 119 127 129 133 145 146 148 **P**6
Primary Contact: Nancy M. Newby, R.N., Ph.D., FACHE, President and Chief Executive Officer
CFO: Elaine Matzenbacher, Chief Financial Officer
CMO: Alfonso Urdaneta, M.D., President Medical Staff
CIO: Kim Larkin, Chief Information Officer
CHR: David Davenport, Director Human Resources
CNO: Candice Hawley, Chief Nursing Executive
Web address: www.washingtoncountyhospital.org
**Control:** Hospital district or authority, Government, nonfederal **Service:** General Medical and Surgical

**Staffed Beds:** 50 **Admissions:** 269 **Census:** 32 **Outpatient Visits:** 34167 **Births:** 0 **Total Expense ($000):** 13489 **Payroll Expense ($000):** 6251 **Personnel:** 142

**NEW LENOX—Will County**

✠ △ **SILVER CROSS HOSPITAL (140213)**, 1900 Silver Cross Boulevard, Zip 60451–9509; tel. 815/300–1100 **A**1 2 7 9 10 **F**3 5 7 11 12 13 15 18 19 20 22 26 27 28 29 30 31 32 34 35 37 38 40 42 43 44 46 47 48 49 50 54 57 59 60 62 64 68 70 74 75 76 77 78 79 81 82 84 85 89 90 91 92 93 96 98 100 101 102 103 104 105 107 108 110 111 114 115 118 119 120 121 126 129 130 131 132 134 135 146 147 148 **P**5 8
Primary Contact: Paul Pawlak, President and Chief Executive Officer
COO: Mary Bakken, Executive Vice President and Chief Operating Officer
CFO: John Krepps, Senior Vice President Finance
CMO: Christopher Udovich, M.D., Chief of Staff
CIO: Kevin Lane, Vice President Information Systems
CHR: Mark Jepson, Vice President
CNO: Peggy Gricus, R.N., Vice President, Patient Care Services and Chief Nursing Officer
Web address: www.silvercross.org
**Control:** Other not–for–profit (including NFP Corporation) **Service:** General Medical and Surgical

**Staffed Beds:** 289 **Admissions:** 19238 **Census:** 205 **Outpatient Visits:** 238266 **Births:** 2620 **Total Expense ($000):** 244399 **Payroll Expense ($000):** 102282 **Personnel:** 1465

**NORMAL—Mclean County**

★ ◇ **ADVOCATE BROMENN MEDICAL CENTER (140127)**, 1304 Franklin Avenue, Zip 61761–3558, Mailing Address: P.O. Box 2850, Bloomington, Zip 61702–2850; tel. 309/454–1400, (Includes BROMENN REGIONAL MEDICAL CENTER, Virginia and Franklin Streets, Zip 61761, Mailing Address: P.O. Box 2850, Bloomington, Zip 61702–2850; tel. 309/454–1400) **A**2 5 10 13 21 **F**2 3 4 11 12 13 15 17 18 20 22 24 26 28 29 30 31 32 34 35 38 39 40 43 44 45 49 50 51 54 57 59 64 65 66 68 70 74 75 76 77 78 79 81 82 84 85 86 87 89 90 93 96 97 98 100 101 102 103 107 108 110 111 114 115 118 119 126 130 131 132 135 141 146 147 148 **P**8 **S** Advocate Health Care, Downers Grove, IL
Primary Contact: Colleen Kannaday, FACHE, President
CFO: Aron Klein, Vice President Finance
CMO: James Nevin, M.D., Vice President Medical Management
CHR: Antonio Coletta, Vice President Human Resources
CNO: Laurie Round, R.N., Chief Nurse Executive
Web address: www.bromenn.org
**Control:** Church–operated, Nongovernment, not–for profit **Service:** General Medical and Surgical

**Staffed Beds:** 203 **Admissions:** 9151 **Census:** 100 **Outpatient Visits:** 130709 **Births:** 1552 **Total Expense ($000):** 162992 **Payroll Expense ($000):** 54914 **Personnel:** 1034

**ADVOCATE BROMENN REGIONAL MEDICAL CENTER** See Advocate BroMenn Medical Center

**NORTH CHICAGO—Lake County**

✠ **CAPTAIN JAMES A. LOVELL FEDERAL HEALTH CARE CENTER**, 3001 Green Bay Road, Zip 60064–3049; tel. 847/688–1900, (Nonreporting) **A**1 3 5 **S** Department of Veterans Affairs, Washington, DC
Primary Contact: Stephen R. Holt, M.D., Director
CFO: Barbara Meadows, Chief Financial Manager
CMO: Tariq Hassan, M.D., Associate Director of Patient Care
CIO: Jonathan Friedman, Public Affairs Officer
CHR: Amy Sanders, Chief Human Resources
CNO: Sarah Fouse, Associate Director of Patient Services
Web address: www.lovell.fhcc.va.gov
**Control:** Veterans Affairs, Government, federal **Service:** Other specialty

**Staffed Beds:** 103

**NORTHLAKE—Cook County**

✠ **KINDRED HOSPITAL CHICAGO–NORTHLAKE (142008)**, 365 East North Avenue, Zip 60164–2628; tel. 708/345–8100 **A**1 9 10 **F**1 3 29 45 77 80 85 91 107 119 130 148 **S** Kindred Healthcare, Louisville, KY
Primary Contact: Beverly Foster, Chief Executive Officer
COO: Sandra Buckhoy, Chief Clinical Officer
CFO: Jay Schweikart, Chief Financial Officer
CMO: Maher Najjar, M.D., Medical Director
Web address: www.kindrednorthlake.com/
**Control:** Corporation, Investor–owned, for–profit **Service:** Long–Term Acute Care hospital

**Staffed Beds:** 94 **Admissions:** 626 **Census:** 57 **Outpatient Visits:** 0 **Births:** 0 **Total Expense ($000):** 28623 **Payroll Expense ($000):** 10958 **Personnel:** 161

**OAK LAWN—Cook County**

★ △ ◇ **ADVOCATE CHRIST MEDICAL CENTER (140208)**, 4440 West 95th Street, Zip 60453–2699; tel. 708/684–8000, (Includes ADVOCATE HOPE CHILDREN'S HOSPITAL, 4440 West 95th Street, Zip 60453–2600; tel. 708/684–8000) **A**2 3 5 7 8 9 10 13 21 **F**3 5 11 13 15 17 18 19 20 21 22 23 24 25 26 27 28 29 30 31 32 34 35 37 38 39 40 41 43 44 45 46 47 48 49 50 51 52 54 55 56 57 58 59 60 61 62 63 64 65 66 68 69 70 71 72 74 75 76 77 78 79 81 82 84 85 86 87 88 89 90 92 93 96 97 98 99 100 101 102 103 104 105 107 108 109 110 111 114 115 116 117 118 119 120 121 123 124 126 129 130 131 132 134 135 137 138 140 143 145 146 147 148 **P**8 **S** Advocate Health Care, Downers Grove, IL
Primary Contact: Kenneth W. Lukhard, President
COO: Michael Wilkins, Chief Operating Officer
CFO: Robert Pekofske, Vice President Finance
CMO: Robert Stein, M.D., Vice President Medical Management
CIO: Brian Banbury, Director Site Information Systems
Web address: www.advocatehealth.com/christ
**Control:** Other not–for–profit (including NFP Corporation) **Service:** General Medical and Surgical

**Staffed Beds:** 659 **Admissions:** 39804 **Census:** 562 **Outpatient Visits:** 333103 **Births:** 3826 **Total Expense ($000):** 920874 **Payroll Expense ($000):** 321449 **Personnel:** 4712

**OAK PARK—Cook County**

✠ **RUSH OAK PARK HOSPITAL (140063)**, 520 South Maple Avenue, Zip 60304–1097; tel. 708/383–9300, (Total facility includes 18 beds in nursing home–type unit) **A**1 3 5 9 10 **F**3 11 15 18 20 22 29 30 34 35 40 45 47 49 50 56 57 58 59 64 68 70 74 75 77 79 81 82 84 85 87 90 92 93 94 96 100 107 108 110 111 114 115 119 128 130 145 146 148 **P**8 **S** Rush University Medical Center, Chicago, IL
Primary Contact: Bruce M. Elegant, FACHE, President and Chief Executive Officer
COO: Robert S. Spadoni, Vice President of Hospital Operations
CFO: Elvy Yap, Director of Finance
CMO: Michael R. Silver, M.D., Vice President Medical Affairs
CIO: Michael R. Silver, M.D., Chief Information Officer
CHR: Arlene Cruz, Director
CNO: Karen Mayer, R.N., Senior Vice President Patient Care Services
Web address: www.roph.org
**Control:** Other not–for–profit (including NFP Corporation) **Service:** General Medical and Surgical

**Staffed Beds:** 96 **Admissions:** 4581 **Census:** 65 **Outpatient Visits:** 100133 **Births:** 0 **Total Expense ($000):** 102766 **Payroll Expense ($000):** 47234 **Personnel:** 796

✠ **WEST SUBURBAN MEDICAL CENTER (140049)**, 3 Erie Court, Zip 60302–2599; tel. 708/383–6200, (Nonreporting) **A**1 2 3 5 9 10 13 **S** TENET Healthcare Corporation, Dallas, TX
Primary Contact: Patrick J. Maloney, Chief Executive Officer
COO: Joan Ormsby, Vice President
CFO: Gene Smith, Interim Chief Financial Officer
CMO: Robert Chase, M.D., Chief Medical Officer
CHR: Nancy Gunnell, Chief Human Resource Officer
CNO: Roslyn J. Lennon, R.N., Chief Nursing Officer
Web address: www.westsuburbanmc.com/Home.aspx
**Control:** Corporation, Investor–owned, for–profit **Service:** General Medical and Surgical

**Staffed Beds:** 172

**IL**

*Many Facility Codes have changed. Please refer to the AHA Guide Code Chart.*

## OLNEY—Richland County

★ ○ **RICHLAND MEMORIAL HOSPITAL (140147)**, 800 East Locust Street, Zip 62450–2553; tel. 618/395–2131, (Total facility includes 34 beds in nursing home–type unit) **A**9 10 11 **F**3 7 11 13 15 28 29 31 34 35 40 45 57 59 61 62 63 64 68 69 70 75 76 78 79 81 85 87 89 93 97 98 100 102 103 107 108 110 111 115 119 128 129 130 131 132 133 135 143 146 147 **P**6
Primary Contact: David B. Allen, Chief Executive Officer
CFO: Mike Stoverink, Chief Financial Officer
CMO: Robert Nash, M.D., Chief of Staff
CIO: Tim Gillespie, Manager Information Systems
CHR: Jill Van Hyning, Director Human Resources
CNO: Cindy Bailey, R.N., Chief Nursing Officer
Web address: www.richlandmemorial.com
**Control:** Other not–for–profit (including NFP Corporation) **Service:** General Medical and Surgical

**Staffed Beds:** 90 **Admissions:** 2522 **Census:** 31 **Outpatient Visits:** 57114 **Births:** 330 **Total Expense ($000):** 45514 **Payroll Expense ($000):** 21337 **Personnel:** 372

## OLYMPIA FIELDS—Cook County

★ ○ **FRANCISCAN ST. JAMES HOSPITAL AND HEALTH CENTERS (140172)**, 20201 South Crawford Avenue, Zip 60461–1010; tel. 708/747–4000, (Includes ST. JAMES HOSPITAL AND HEALTH CENTERS – CHICAGO HEIGHTS CAMPUS, 1423 Chicago Road, Chicago Heights, Zip 60411–3483; tel. 708/756–1000; ST. JAMES HOSPITALS AND HEALTH CENTERS – OLYMPIA FIELDS CAMPUS, 20201 Crawford Avenue, tel. 708/747–4000) **A**2 9 10 11 12 13 **F**12 13 15 18 20 22 24 26 28 29 30 31 35 40 45 46 49 50 53 57 60 62 63 64 66 68 75 77 78 81 82 84 91 93 97 107 111 114 115 116 117 119 120 121 124 126 129 130 132 135 143 144 146 148 **S** Franciscan Alliance, Mishawaka, IN
Primary Contact: Arnold Kimmel, Chief Executive Officer
CIO: Stephen Maes, Director Information Systems
Web address: www.franciscanalliance.org/hospitals/olympiafields/pages/default.aspx
**Control:** Church–operated, Nongovernment, not–for profit **Service:** General Medical and Surgical

**Staffed Beds:** 329 **Admissions:** 13994 **Census:** 159 **Outpatient Visits:** 165789 **Births:** 939

**ST. JAMES HOSPITAL AND HEALTH CENTERS** See Franciscan St. James Hospital and Health Centers

## OTTAWA—Lasalle County

⊠ **OSF SAINT ELIZABETH MEDICAL CENTER (140110)**, 1100 East Norris Drive, Zip 61350–1687; tel. 815/433–3100 **A**1 9 10 19 **F**3 11 13 15 18 28 29 30 34 35 40 43 45 48 49 53 56 57 59 68 70 75 76 77 79 81 82 84 85 86 87 93 94 98 99 100 101 102 103 104 105 107 108 110 111 115 118 119 130 131 132 135 143 144 146 148 **S** OSF Healthcare System, Peoria, IL
Primary Contact: Kenneth Beutke, President
CFO: Dawn Trompeter, Chief Financial Officer
CMO: Brian S. Rosborough, M.D., Chief Medical Officer
CHR: Robert L. Gibson, Director Employee Relations
CNO: Maeanne Stevens, R.N., Chief Nursing Officer
Web address: www.osfsaintelizabeth.org
**Control:** Church–operated, Nongovernment, not–for profit **Service:** General Medical and Surgical

**Staffed Beds:** 87 **Admissions:** 3261 **Census:** 31 **Outpatient Visits:** 102099 **Births:** 310 **Total Expense ($000):** 66405 **Payroll Expense ($000):** 28262 **Personnel:** 491

## PALOS HEIGHTS—Cook County

⊠ **PALOS COMMUNITY HOSPITAL (140062)**, 12251 South 80th Avenue, Zip 60463–0930; tel. 708/923–4000, (Nonreporting) **A**1 2 9 10
Primary Contact: Terrence Moisan, M.D., Chief Executive Officer
CFO: Hugh Rose, Vice President Fiscal Management
CIO: Peggy Carroll, Chief Information Officer
CHR: Mary Denisienko, Vice President Human Resources
Web address: www.paloscommunityhospital.org
**Control:** Other not–for–profit (including NFP Corporation) **Service:** General Medical and Surgical

**Staffed Beds:** 377

## PANA—Christian County

★ **PANA COMMUNITY HOSPITAL (141341)**, 101 East Ninth Street, Zip 62557–1785; tel. 217/562–2131 **A**9 10 18 **F**3 11 15 28 29 30 31 34 35 40 50 53 56 57 59 62 63 69 75 77 78 81 87 90 93 107 114 124 127 130 131 133 147 148 **P**6
Primary Contact: Trina Casner, President and Chief Executive Officer
CFO: James Moon, Chief Financial Officer
CMO: Alan Frigy, M.D., President Medical Staff
CIO: Dianne Bailey, Chief Information Officer
CHR: Luann Funk, Administrative Assistant and Manager Human Resources
CNO: Vickie Coen, Chief Clinical Officer and Nurse Executive
Web address: www.panahospital.com
**Control:** Other not–for–profit (including NFP Corporation) **Service:** General Medical and Surgical

**Staffed Beds:** 22 **Admissions:** 311 **Census:** 2 **Outpatient Visits:** 46594 **Births:** 0 **Total Expense ($000):** 17772 **Payroll Expense ($000):** 8038 **Personnel:** 145

## PARIS—Edgar County

⊠ **PARIS COMMUNITY HOSPITAL (141320)**, 721 East Court Street, Zip 61944–2460; tel. 217/465–4141 **A**1 9 10 18 **F**3 15 28 29 30 31 34 35 40 45 50 57 59 64 65 67 69 74 75 77 78 79 81 82 85 86 87 89 90 93 107 108 110 111 115 119 127 128 129 130 131 132 133 144 146 148 **P**6 **S** Alliant Management Services, Louisville, KY
Primary Contact: Oliver Smith, President and Chief Executive Officer
CFO: Terry Brinkley, Vice President Finance
CIO: Ed Weeks, Manager Information Services
CNO: Susan Livvix, R.N., Vice President Nursing Services
Web address: www.pariscommunityhospital.com
**Control:** Other not–for–profit (including NFP Corporation) **Service:** General Medical and Surgical

**Staffed Beds:** 25 **Admissions:** 584 **Census:** 6 **Outpatient Visits:** 85050 **Births:** 1 **Total Expense ($000):** 36445 **Payroll Expense ($000):** 16758 **Personnel:** 242

## PARK RIDGE—Cook County

★ △ ◇ **ADVOCATE LUTHERAN GENERAL HOSPITAL (140223)**, 1775 Dempster Street, Zip 60068–1174; tel. 847/723–2210 **A**2 3 5 7 8 9 10 13 21 **F**2 3 5 6 8 9 11 12 13 15 17 18 19 20 21 22 23 24 25 26 27 28 29 30 31 32 34 35 37 38 39 40 41 43 44 45 46 47 48 49 50 53 55 56 57 58 59 60 61 63 64 65 66 68 69 70 72 74 75 76 78 79 80 81 82 84 85 86 87 88 89 90 92 93 94 97 98 99 100 101 102 103 104 105 106 107 108 110 111 112 114 115 116 117 118 119 120 121 123 124 126 129 130 131 132 134 135 136 143 146 147 148 **P**6 8 **S** Advocate Health Care, Downers Grove, IL
Primary Contact: Richard B. Floyd, President
COO: Barbara Weber, Chief Operating Officer
CFO: Jim Kelley, Vice President Finance
CMO: Leo Kelly, M.D., Vice President Medical Management
CIO: Mark Beitzel, Director Information Systems
CHR: Katie Bata, Vice President Human Resources
CNO: Jane Denten, MSN, Vice President Nursing and Chief Nurse Executive
Web address: www.advocatehealth.com/luth/
**Control:** Other not–for–profit (including NFP Corporation) **Service:** General Medical and Surgical

**Staffed Beds:** 625 **Admissions:** 28339 **Census:** 409 **Outpatient Visits:** 311859 **Births:** 4260 **Total Expense ($000):** 646561 **Payroll Expense ($000):** 227924 **Personnel:** 3304

## PEKIN—Tazewell County

⊠ **PEKIN HOSPITAL (140120)**, 600 South 13th Street, Zip 61554–4936; tel. 309/347–1151, (Nonreporting) **A**1 5 9 10 **S** QHR, Brentwood, TN
Primary Contact: Bob J. Haley, Chief Executive Officer
CFO: Steve Hall, Chief Financial Officer
CMO: Kathryn Kramer, M.D., President Medical Staff
CHR: Anne Dierker, Vice President Hospital Services
Web address: www.pekinhospital.org
**Control:** Other not–for–profit (including NFP Corporation) **Service:** General Medical and Surgical

**Staffed Beds:** 125

## PEORIA—Peoria County

**GREATER PEORIA SPECIALTY HOSPITAL** See Kindred Hospital Peoria

IL

---

**Hospital, Medicare Provider Number, Address, Telephone, Approval, Facility, and Physician Codes, Health Care System**

★ American Hospital Association (AHA) membership    ○ Healthcare Facilities Accreditation Program    ⇑ Center for Improvement in Healthcare Quality Accreditation
□ The Joint Commission accreditation    ◇ DNV Healthcare Inc. accreditation    △ Commission on Accreditation of Rehabilitation Facilities (CARF) accreditation

---

⊠ **KINDRED HOSPITAL PEORIA (142013)**, 500 West Romeo B. Garrett Avenue, Zip 61605–2301; tel. 309/680–1500, (Nonreporting) **A**1 9 10 **S** Kindred Healthcare, Louisville, KY
Primary Contact: Ted Paarlberg, Chief Executive Officer
CMO: Michael Peil, M.D., Chief Medical Director
Web address: www.khpeoria.com/
**Control:** Corporation, Investor–owned, for–profit **Service:** Long–Term Acute Care hospital

**Staffed Beds: 50**

**METHODIST MEDICAL CENTER OF ILLINOIS** See UnityPoint Health – Methodist

⊠ △ **OSF SAINT FRANCIS MEDICAL CENTER (140067)**, 530 N.E. Glen Oak Avenue, Zip 61637–0001; tel. 309/655–2000, (Includes CHILDREN'S HOSPITAL OF ILLINOIS, 530 N.E. Glen Oak Avenue, tel. 309/655–7171) **A**1 2 3 5 6 7 8 9 10 19 **F**3 8 9 11 12 13 15 17 18 19 20 21 22 23 24 25 26 27 28 29 30 31 32 34 35 37 38 39 40 41 42 43 44 45 46 47 48 49 50 51 52 54 56 57 58 59 60 64 65 66 67 68 69 70 72 73 74 75 76 77 78 79 80 81 82 83 84 85 86 87 88 89 90 91 92 93 94 96 97 99 100 102 104 105 107 108 110 111 114 115 116 117 118 119 120 121 123 124 126 127 129 130 132 134 138 142 143 144 145 146 147 148 **P**6 **S** OSF Healthcare System, Peoria, IL
Primary Contact: Michael A. Cruz, M.D., President
COO: Susan C. Wozniak, R.N., Senior Vice President and Chief Operating Officer
CFO: Ken Harbaugh, Vice President and Chief Financial Officer
CMO: Tim C. Miller, M.D., Vice President, Chief Medical Officer and Director Academy Affairs
CHR: Lynn J. Gillespie, Vice President Human Resources and Organizational Development
Web address: www.osfsaintfrancis.org
**Control:** Church–operated, Nongovernment, not–for profit **Service:** General Medical and Surgical

**Staffed Beds: 609 Admissions: 31140 Census: 454 Outpatient Visits: 1022960 Births: 2681 Total Expense ($000): 915746 Payroll Expense ($000): 341238 Personnel: 5170**

⊠ **UNITYPOINT HEALTH – METHODIST PROCTOR (140209)**, 221 N.E. Glen Oak Avenue, Zip 61636–4310; tel. 309/672–5522 **A**1 2 3 5 10 13 **F**3 8 9 11 12 13 15 17 18 20 22 24 26 28 29 30 31 32 34 35 36 38 40 43 44 45 46 47 48 49 50 53 54 56 57 58 59 60 62 63 64 68 70 74 75 76 77 78 79 81 82 84 85 86 87 89 90 92 93 96 98 99 100 101 102 103 104 105 107 108 110 111 114 115 116 117 118 119 120 121 126 127 129 130 131 132 134 135 136 143 144 145 146 147 148 **P**8 **S** UnityPoint Health, West Des Moines, IA
Primary Contact: Deborah R. Simon, R.N., President and Chief Executive Officer
COO: Keith Knepp, M.D., Executive Vice President and Chief Operating Officer
CFO: Robert Quin, Vice President Finance and Chief Financial Officer
CMO: Gary Knepp, D.O., Vice President Physician Integration and Chief Medical Officer
CIO: Ryan Walsh, M.D., Chief Medical Information Officer
CHR: Joy Ledbetter, Vice President Employee and Patient Experience and Chief Human Resources Officer
CNO: Jeanine R. Spain, R.N., Vice President Patient and Support Services and Chief Nursing Officer
Web address: www.mymethodist.net
**Control:** Other not–for–profit (including NFP Corporation) **Service:** General Medical and Surgical

**Staffed Beds: 288 Admissions: 13749 Census: 196 Outpatient Visits: 569416 Births: 1762 Total Expense ($000): 364736 Payroll Expense ($000): 143046 Personnel: 2196**

☐ **UNITYPOINT HEALTH–PROCTOR (140013)**, 5409 North Knoxville Avenue, Zip 61614–5069; tel. 309/691–1000, (Total facility includes 20 beds in nursing home–type unit) **A**1 3 5 9 10 **F**3 4 5 11 13 15 18 20 22 24 28 29 30 34 40 45 49 51 53 57 59 62 64 65 70 74 75 76 79 81 85 86 87 89 93 98 103 104 105 107 108 110 111 115 118 119 128 129 130 132 135 145 146 148
Primary Contact: Deborah R. Simon, R.N., President and Chief Executive Officer
CFO: Roger Armstrong, Vice President Finance and Chief Financial Officer
CHR: Linda K. Buck, Vice President Human Resources
Web address: www.proctor.org
**Control:** Other not–for–profit (including NFP Corporation) **Service:** General Medical and Surgical

**Staffed Beds: 174 Admissions: 5122 Census: 73 Outpatient Visits: 65741 Births: 391 Total Expense ($000): 92633 Payroll Expense ($000): 33282 Personnel: 574**

**PERU—Lasalle County**

★ **ILLINOIS VALLEY COMMUNITY HOSPITAL (140234)**, 925 West Street, Zip 61354–2757; tel. 815/223–3300 **A**9 10 **F**2 3 11 13 15 28 29 30 31 34 35 38 40 45 46 47 48 49 50 51 54 57 59 63 64 65 66 68 69 70 74 75 76 77 79 81 82 85 87 93 96 97 104 107 110 111 114 118 119 127 129 130 131 132 133 135 143 144 146 147 148 **P**8
Primary Contact: Tommy Hobbs, Chief Executive Officer
COO: Bobby Smith, Vice President Physician Services and Quality
CFO: Stephen Davis, Chief Financial Officer
CMO: Mark Fernandez, M.D., Chief of Staff and President Medical Staff
CIO: Nancy McDonnell, Manager Information Systems
CHR: Mary Beth Herron, Director of Human Resources
CNO: Wilma Hart–Flynn, Ph.D., Vice President Patient Care Services and Chief Nursing Officer
Web address: www.ivch.org
**Control:** Other not–for–profit (including NFP Corporation) **Service:** General Medical and Surgical

**Staffed Beds: 57 Admissions: 2653 Census: 21 Outpatient Visits: 169738 Births: 500 Total Expense ($000): 79730 Payroll Expense ($000): 28472 Personnel: 521**

**PINCKNEYVILLE—Perry County**

★ **PINCKNEYVILLE COMMUNITY HOSPITAL (141307)**, 101 North Walnut Street, Zip 62274–1099, Mailing Address: PO Box 437, Zip 62274–1099; tel. 618/357–2187 **A**9 10 18 **F**3 15 28 29 31 34 40 43 45 50 53 56 57 65 78 81 85 93 107 108 110 119 127 130 133 148 **P**6
Primary Contact: Randall W. Dauby, CPA, Chief Executive Officer
CFO: Kara Jo Carson, Chief Financial Officer
CIO: Jeff Roberts, Director Information Technology
CHR: Christie Gajewski, Director Human Resources
CNO: Eva Hopp, Chief Nurse Executive
Web address: www.pvillehosp.org/
**Control:** Hospital district or authority, Government, nonfederal **Service:** General Medical and Surgical

**Staffed Beds: 25 Admissions: 499 Census: 7 Outpatient Visits: 40552 Births: 0 Total Expense ($000): 18301 Payroll Expense ($000): 8622 Personnel: 167**

**PITTSFIELD—Pike County**

⊠ **ILLINI COMMUNITY HOSPITAL (141315)**, 640 West Washington Street, Zip 62363–1350; tel. 217/285–2113 **A**1 9 10 18 **F**3 15 18 19 28 29 30 31 34 40 46 50 53 59 64 65 68 70 75 78 81 82 85 87 89 93 97 107 110 115 119 127 129 130 131 133 146
Primary Contact: Kathy Hull, President and Chief Executive Officer
CFO: Alice Coleman, Blessing Corporate Controller
CMO: Bashar Alzein, M.D., President Medical Staff
CHR: Becky Myers, Human Resources Specialist
CNO: Holly A. Jones, Administrative Director Nursing Services
Web address: www.illinihospital.org
**Control:** Other not–for–profit (including NFP Corporation) **Service:** General Medical and Surgical

**Staffed Beds: 21 Admissions: 266 Census: 2 Outpatient Visits: 7037 Births: 0 Total Expense ($000): 19929 Payroll Expense ($000): 7128 Personnel: 157**

**PONTIAC—Livingston County**

⊠ **OSF SAINT JAMES – JOHN W. ALBRECHT MEDICAL CENTER (140161)**, 2500 West Reynolds, Zip 61764–9774; tel. 815/842–2828 **A**1 9 10 20 **F**3 8 11 13 15 18 28 29 30 32 34 35 40 45 50 56 57 59 64 68 70 75 76 77 79 81 82 84 85 86 87 89 90 91 93 96 97 107 110 111 115 117 118 119 127 128 129 130 131 132 133 135 144 146 147 **P**7 **S** OSF Healthcare System, Peoria, IL
Primary Contact: Bradley V. Solberg, FACHE, President
CFO: Paula Corrigan, Vice President and Chief Financial Officer
CMO: John M. Rinker, Chief Medical Officer
CNO: Elizabeth Davidson, R.N., Vice President, Patient Care Services
Web address: www.osfsaintjames.org
**Control:** Church–operated, Nongovernment, not–for profit **Service:** General Medical and Surgical

**Staffed Beds: 42 Admissions: 1218 Census: 10 Outpatient Visits: 181192 Births: 180 Total Expense ($000): 68256 Payroll Expense ($000): 24370 Personnel: 296**

**PRINCETON—Bureau County**

**PERRY MEMORIAL HOSPITAL (141337)**, 530 Park Avenue East, Zip 61356–2598; tel. 815/875–2811, (Nonreporting) **A**9 10 18
Primary Contact: Rex D. Conger, FACHE, President and Chief Executive Officer
CFO: Mike Harrell, Chief Financial Officer
CMO: T. Doran, Chief of Staff
CIO: Karen Behrens, Director Technology Services
Web address: www.perry–memorial.org
**Control:** City–Government, nonfederal **Service:** General Medical and Surgical

**Staffed Beds: 25**

## QUINCY—Adams County

✠ △ **BLESSING HOSPITAL (140015)**, Broadway at 11th Street,
Zip 62305–7005, Mailing Address: P.O. Box 7005, Zip 62305–7005;
tel. 217/223–1200, (Includes BLESSING HOSPITAL, Broadway & 14th Street,
Zip 62301, Mailing Address: P.O. Box 7005, Zip 62305–7005;
tel. 217/223–1200), (Total facility includes 20 beds in nursing home–type unit)
**A**1 2 3 5 7 9 10 13 **F**3 5 8 11 12 13 15 17 18 20 22 24 26 28 29 30 31 32
34 35 40 43 44 48 49 50 53 56 57 58 59 60 61 62 63 64 66 68 70 73 74
75 76 77 78 79 81 82 84 85 86 87 89 90 94 96 98 99 100 101 102 103
104 107 108 110 111 114 115 118 119 120 121 123 124 126 127 128 129
130 131 132 135 144 146 147 148 **P**8
Primary Contact: Maureen A. Kahn, R.N., President and Chief Executive Officer
COO: Tim Moore, Chief Accounting Officer and Vice President Ancillary Services
and Finance
CFO: Patrick M. Gerveler, Vice President Finance and Chief Financial Officer
CMO: George Liesmann, M.D., Chief Medical Officer
CNO: Jill K. Mason, MS, Chief Nursing Officer
Web address: www.blessinghospital.org
**Control:** Other not–for–profit (including NFP Corporation) **Service:** General
Medical and Surgical

**Staffed Beds:** 279 **Admissions:** 13739 **Census:** 166 **Outpatient Visits:**
343018 **Births:** 1122 **Total Expense ($000):** 288381 **Payroll Expense**
**($000):** 109989 **Personnel:** 2051

## RED BUD—Randolph County

✠ **RED BUD REGIONAL HOSPITAL (141348)**, 325 Spring Street,
Zip 62278–1105; tel. 618/282–3831, (Total facility includes 115 beds in nursing
home–type unit) **A**1 9 10 18 **F**1 3 15 29 30 34 35 40 45 50 56 57 59 64 65
68 75 81 87 93 94 95 97 103 104 107 110 111 115 116 117 119 127 129
130 133 135 143 146 147 148 **S** Community Health Systems, Inc., Franklin, TN
Primary Contact: Shane Watson, Chief Executive Officer
CFO: Benjamin Wells, Chief Financial Officer
CMO: Stephanie Skelly, President Medical Staff
CIO: Nick Behnken, Supervisor Information Technology
CHR: Lori Brooks, Director Human Resources
CNO: Linda Harbison, Chief Nursing Officer
Web address: www.redbudregional.com
**Control:** Corporation, Investor–owned, for–profit **Service:** General Medical and
Surgical

**Staffed Beds:** 140 **Admissions:** 909 **Census:** 112 **Outpatient Visits:** 31948
**Births:** 0 **Total Expense ($000):** 29727 **Payroll Expense ($000):** 13782
**Personnel:** 242

## ROBINSON—Crawford County

★ **CRAWFORD MEMORIAL HOSPITAL (141343)**, 1000 North Allen Street,
Zip 62454–1167; tel. 618/544–3131, (Total facility includes 38 beds in nursing
home–type unit) **A**9 10 18 **F**3 11 12 13 15 28 30 31 40 45 53 56 59 62 64 76
77 79 80 81 85 93 107 108 111 119 127 128 129 130 132 133 146 147
**P**6 **S** QHR, Brentwood, TN
Primary Contact: Donald E. Annis, Chief Executive Officer
CFO: Richard Carlson, Chief Financial Officer
CMO: Gregory Kastner, M.D., Chief of Staff
CIO: Tim Richard, IT Coordinator
CHR: Kristi Zane, Chief Human Resources Officer
CNO: Sandra Burtron, MS, Chief Nursing Officer
Web address: www.crawfordmh.org
**Control:** Hospital district or authority, Government, nonfederal **Service:** General
Medical and Surgical

**Staffed Beds:** 63 **Admissions:** 1097 **Census:** 30 **Outpatient Visits:** 50689
**Births:** 171 **Total Expense ($000):** 41720 **Payroll Expense ($000):** 18293
**Personnel:** 316

## ROCHELLE—Ogle County

✠ **ROCHELLE COMMUNITY HOSPITAL (141312)**, 900 North Second Street,
Zip 61068–1764; tel. 815/562–2181 **A**1 9 10 18 **F**3 15 29 30 31 34 35 40
41 50 53 57 59 64 68 70 74 75 77 78 81 82 85 86 87 93 97 107 110 115
130 132 133 135 144 146 **P**6
Primary Contact: Mark Batty, Chief Executive Officer
CFO: Lori Gutierrez, Chief Financial Officer
CMO: Jason Popp, Chief of Medical Staff
CIO: Scott Stewart, Manager Information Services
CHR: Laura Cirone, Manager Human Resources
CNO: Jennifer Montgomery, Chief Nursing Officer
Web address: www.rcha.net
**Control:** Other not–for–profit (including NFP Corporation) **Service:** General
Medical and Surgical

**Staffed Beds:** 16 **Admissions:** 659 **Census:** 6 **Outpatient Visits:** 43397
**Births:** 0 **Total Expense ($000):** 28442 **Payroll Expense ($000):** 9938
**Personnel:** 230

## ROCK ISLAND—Rock Island County

✠ △ **UNITYPOINT HEALTH – TRINITY ROCK ISLAND (140280)**, 2701 17th
Street, Zip 61201–5393; tel. 309/779–5000, (Includes UNITYPOINT HEALTH –
TRINITY MOLINE, 500 John Deere Road, Moline, Zip 61265; tel. 309/779–5000),
(Total facility includes 29 beds in nursing home–type unit) **A**1 2 7 9 10 **F**3 5 11
12 13 15 18 20 22 24 26 28 29 30 31 34 35 37 38 40 43 44 45 46 47 48
49 50 57 58 59 64 70 74 76 78 79 81 82 85 86 87 89 90 93 96 98 99 102
103 104 105 107 108 110 114 115 118 119 120 121 123 126 128 129 130
132 135 146 147 148 **P**8 **S** UnityPoint Health, West Des Moines, IA
Primary Contact: Richard A. Seidler, FACHE, President and Chief Executive Officer
COO: Jay Willsher, Chief Operating Officer
CFO: Greg Pagliuzza, Chief Financial Officer
CMO: Paul McLoone, M.D., Chief Medical Officer
CHR: Cara Fuller, Vice President Human Resources
CNO: Rochelle Marie Tinman, Interim Chief Nurse Executive, Director of
Nursing–Inpatient Services
Web address: www.trinityqc.com
**Control:** Other not–for–profit (including NFP Corporation) **Service:** General
Medical and Surgical

**Staffed Beds:** 345 **Admissions:** 14070 **Census:** 186 **Outpatient Visits:**
282691 **Births:** 1424 **Total Expense ($000):** 279596 **Payroll Expense**
**($000):** 91790 **Personnel:** 2048

## ROCKFORD—Winnebago County

✠ **OSF SAINT ANTHONY MEDICAL CENTER (140233)**, 5666 East State Street,
Zip 61108–2425; tel. 815/226–2000 **A**1 2 3 5 9 10 **F**3 11 12 13 15 16 17 18
20 22 24 26 28 29 30 31 32 34 35 36 37 38 39 40 41 43 44 45 46 49 50
51 53 55 56 57 58 59 64 66 70 73 74 75 76 77 78 79 81 82 84 85 86 87
89 92 93 107 108 110 111 114 115 116 117 118 119 120 121 123 124
129 130 131 132 135 145 146 147 148 **P**6 **S** OSF Healthcare System,
Peoria, IL
Primary Contact: Paula A. Carynski, MS, R.N., President
COO: James Girardy, M.D., Vice President, Chief Surgical Officer
CFO: David Stenerson, Vice President and Chief Financial Officer
CMO: Harneet Bath, M.D., Vice President, Chief Medicine Officer
CIO: Kathy Peterson, Director Information Services
CHR: Karen C. Brown, Vice President Chief Operating Officer
Web address: www.osfhealth.com
**Control:** Church–operated, Nongovernment, not–for profit **Service:** General
Medical and Surgical

**Staffed Beds:** 235 **Admissions:** 10392 **Census:** 129 **Outpatient Visits:**
416344 **Births:** 429 **Total Expense ($000):** 351152 **Payroll Expense**
**($000):** 125740 **Personnel:** 1666

✠ **ROCKFORD MEMORIAL HOSPITAL (140239)**, 2400 North Rockton Avenue,
Zip 61103–3655; tel. 815/971–5000 **A**1 2 3 5 10 **F**3 11 13 18 19 20 22 24
26 27 28 29 30 31 32 34 35 39 40 41 43 44 45 48 49 50 51 54 55 57 59
63 64 65 68 70 71 72 74 75 76 77 78 79 80 81 82 83 84 85 86 87 88 89
91 93 97 98 100 101 102 103 107 108 111 114 115 118 119 121 123 126
129 130 131 132 135 145 146 147 148 **P**6
Primary Contact: Daniel A. Parod, Senior Vice President Hospital and
Administrative Affairs
COO: Daniel A. Parod, Senior Vice President Hospital and Administrative Affairs
CFO: Henry Seybold, Senior Vice President and Chief Financial Officer
CMO: John T. Dorsey, M.D., Vice President Clinical Integration and Population
Health
CIO: Dennis P. L'Heureux, Chief Information Officer
CHR: Heidi Elsbree, Vice President People and Culture
CNO: Susan Schreier, R.N., Chief Nursing Executive
Web address: www.rhsnet.org
**Control:** Other not–for–profit (including NFP Corporation) **Service:** General
Medical and Surgical

**Staffed Beds:** 311 **Admissions:** 13362 **Census:** 184 **Outpatient Visits:**
283629 **Births:** 1504 **Total Expense ($000):** 320499 **Payroll Expense**
**($000):** 108566 **Personnel:** 2101

IL

---

**Hospital, Medicare Provider Number, Address, Telephone, Approval, Facility, and Physician Codes, Health Care System**

★ American Hospital Association (AHA) membership    ○ Healthcare Facilities Accreditation Program    ⇑ Center for Improvement in Healthcare Quality Accreditation
□ The Joint Commission accreditation    ◇ DNV Healthcare Inc. accreditation    △ Commission on Accreditation of Rehabilitation Facilities (CARF) accreditation

✠ **SWEDISHAMERICAN HOSPITAL, A DIVISION OF UW HEALTH (140228)**,
1401 East State Street, Zip 61104–2315; tel. 815/968–4400 **A**1 2 3 5 9 10 **F**3
13 15 17 18 20 22 24 26 28 29 30 31 34 35 36 37 38 39 40 43 44 45 46
49 50 56 57 58 59 61 64 65 68 70 73 74 75 76 77 78 79 81 82 84 85 86
87 89 92 93 98 107 108 110 111 114 115 118 119 129 130 132 135 146
147 148 **P**6
Primary Contact: William R. Gorski, M.D., President and Chief Executive Officer
COO: Don Daniels, Executive Vice President and Chief Operating Officer
CFO: Patti DeWane, Vice President Finance and Treasurer
CMO: Michael Born, M.D., Chief Medical Officer and Chief Quality Officer
CIO: Sheryl Johnson, Chief Information Officer
CHR: Jerry Guinane, Vice President Human Resources
CNO: Ann M. Gantzer, Ph.D., Vice President Patient Services and Chief Nursing
Officer
Web address: www.swedishamerican.org
**Control:** Other not–for–profit (including NFP Corporation) **Service:** General
Medical and Surgical

**Staffed Beds:** 242 **Admissions:** 15381 **Census:** 174 **Outpatient Visits:**
251614 **Births:** 2566 **Total Expense ($000):** 305709 **Payroll Expense
($000):** 113164 **Personnel:** 1931

✠ **VAN MATRE HEALTHSOUTH REHABILITATION HOSPITAL (143028)**, 950
South Mulford Road, Zip 61108–4274; tel. 815/381–8500 **A**1 9 10 **F**28 29 34
57 64 68 74 75 82 86 90 91 93 95 96 130 131 132 148 **P**5 **S** HEALTHSOUTH
Corporation, Birmingham, AL
Primary Contact: Ken Bowman, Chief Executive Officer
CFO: Tim Anderson, Controller
CMO: Scott Craig, M.D., Medical Director
CIO: Angela Bergman, Director Health Information Management
CHR: Dorothy Richardson, Director Human Resources
CNO: Nancy Miller, R.N., Chief Nursing Officer
Web address: www.healthsouth.com
**Control:** Partnership, Investor–owned, for–profit **Service:** Rehabilitation

**Staffed Beds:** 53 **Admissions:** 1394 **Census:** 49 **Outpatient Visits:** 7421
**Births:** 0 **Total Expense ($000):** 18186 **Payroll Expense ($000):** 9707
**Personnel:** 139

### ROSICLARE—Hardin County

★ **HARDIN COUNTY GENERAL HOSPITAL (141328)**, 6 Ferrell Road, Zip 62982,
Mailing Address: PO BOX 2467, Zip 62982–2467; tel. 618/285–6634,
(Nonreporting) **A**9 10 18
Primary Contact: Roby D. Williams, Administrator
CFO: Janie Parker, Chief Financial Officer
CMO: Marcos N. Sunga, M.D., Chief of Staff
CIO: Brian Casteel, Information Technology Technician
CHR: Joyce Shelby, Manager Human Resources
CNO: Courtney Spivey, Chief Nursing Officer
Web address: www.ilhcgh.org
**Control:** Other not–for–profit (including NFP Corporation) **Service:** General
Medical and Surgical

**Staffed Beds:** 25

### RUSHVILLE—Schuyler County

★ **SARAH D. CULBERTSON MEMORIAL HOSPITAL (141333)**, 238 South
Congress Street, Zip 62681–1472; tel. 217/322–4321 **A**9 10 18 **F**11 15 28 29
31 34 40 56 57 59 65 69 75 77 81 85 93 96 97 103 104 107 110 114 119
125 127 129 130 132 133 135 146 148 **P**6
Primary Contact: Lynn E. Stambaugh, R.N., Chief Executive Officer
CFO: Alan Palo, Chief Financial Officer
CMO: S. K. Kanthilal, M.D., President Medical Staff
CIO: Dan Wise, Manager Information Technology
CNO: Lisa M. Downs, R.N., Chief Nursing Officer
Web address: www.cmhospital.com
**Control:** Hospital district or authority, Government, nonfederal **Service:** General
Medical and Surgical

**Staffed Beds:** 22 **Admissions:** 251 **Census:** 4 **Outpatient Visits:** 46719
**Births:** 0 **Total Expense ($000):** 20458 **Payroll Expense ($000):** 7658
**Personnel:** 171

### SALEM—Marion County

★ **SALEM TOWNSHIP HOSPITAL (141345)**, 1201 Ricker Drive, Zip 62881–4263;
tel. 618/548–3194, (Nonreporting) **A**9 10 18
Primary Contact: John E. Kessler, President and Chief Executive Officer
CFO: Teresa Stroud, Chief Financial Officer
CMO: S. Lakshmanan, M.D., Chief of Staff
CIO: Steve Turner, Director Information Technology
CHR: Diane Boswell, Director Human Resources and Marketing
Web address: www.sthcares.org
**Control:** City–County, Government, nonfederal **Service:** General Medical and
Surgical

**Staffed Beds:** 22

### SANDWICH—Dekalb County

✠ **VALLEY WEST HOSPITAL (141340)**, 1302 North Main Street,
Zip 60548–2587; tel. 815/786–8484 **A**1 9 10 18 **F**3 11 13 15 18 28 29 30
31 32 34 35 36 38 40 45 46 49 51 57 58 59 64 68 70 71 75 76 77 78 79
81 82 85 87 89 93 102 104 107 110 115 119 129 130 131 132 135 146
147 **S** Kish Health System, DeKalb, IL
Primary Contact: Brad Copple, President
COO: David R. Proulx, Assistant Vice President Operations
CFO: Loren Foelske, Vice President Finance
CMO: Michael Kulisz, D.O., Chief Medical Officer
CIO: Heath Bell, Chief Information Officer
CHR: Michele McClelland, Vice President Human Resources
CNO: Pamela Duffy, Vice President Patient Services and CNO
Web address: www.kishhealth.org
**Control:** Other not–for–profit (including NFP Corporation) **Service:** General
Medical and Surgical

**Staffed Beds:** 25 **Admissions:** 1022 **Census:** 7 **Outpatient Visits:** 35036
**Births:** 235 **Total Expense ($000):** 40130 **Payroll Expense ($000):** 11725
**Personnel:** 187

### SHELBYVILLE—Shelby County

★ ◇ **SHELBY MEMORIAL HOSPITAL (140019)**, 200 South Cedar Street,
Zip 62565–1838; tel. 217/774–3961 **A**9 10 20 21 **F**3 15 28 29 34 35 40 45
57 59 62 64 77 81 93 97 107 108 110 118 119 127 129 131 132 133
146 **P**5
Primary Contact: Marilyn Sears, President and Chief Executive Officer
CFO: Marilyn Sears, Chief Financial Officer
CMO: Urbano Dauz, M.D., President Medical Staff
CIO: Ian Kuhlman, Manager Information Technology
CHR: Amy Koehler, Director Human Resources
CNO: Regina Calvert, Chief Nursing Executive
Web address: www.mysmh.org
**Control:** Other not–for–profit (including NFP Corporation) **Service:** General
Medical and Surgical

**Staffed Beds:** 30 **Admissions:** 593 **Census:** 5 **Outpatient Visits:** 31968
**Births:** 0 **Total Expense ($000):** 16550 **Payroll Expense ($000):** 6724
**Personnel:** 152

### SILVIS—Rock Island County

✠ **GENESIS MEDICAL CENTER, ILLINI CAMPUS (140275)**, 801 Illini Drive,
Zip 61282–1893; tel. 309/281–4000 **A**1 9 10 **F**3 7 11 13 15 18 20 26 28 29
30 31 34 35 38 40 43 44 46 50 53 54 57 59 63 64 68 70 74 75 76 77 78
79 81 82 84 85 86 87 89 97 107 108 110 111 114 119 129 130 131 132
135 146 147 **P**6 **S** Genesis Health System, Davenport, IA
Primary Contact: Kevin Youmans, Interim President
CFO: Mark G. Rogers, Interim Vice President Finance and Chief Financial Officer
CMO: Peter Metcalf, M.D., President Medical Staff
CIO: Robert Frieden, Vice President Information Systems
CHR: Heidi Kahly–McMahon, Vice President Human Resources
Web address: www.genesishealth.com
**Control:** Other not–for–profit (including NFP Corporation) **Service:** General
Medical and Surgical

**Staffed Beds:** 135 **Admissions:** 4667 **Census:** 32 **Outpatient Visits:** 116774
**Births:** 553 **Total Expense ($000):** 76665 **Payroll Expense ($000):** 23565
**Personnel:** 440

### SPARTA—Randolph County

**SPARTA COMMUNITY HOSPITAL (141349)**, 818 East Broadway Street,
Zip 62286–1820, Mailing Address: P.O. Box 297, Zip 62286–0297;
tel. 618/443–2177 **A**9 10 18 **F**3 11 15 28 34 35 40 41 53 54 57 59 62 64
75 77 81 82 89 93 97 107 111 115 119 127 130 132 133 143 146 147 **P**5
Primary Contact: Joann Emge, Chief Executive Officer
CFO: Paul Mueller, Chief Financial Officer
CMO: Mark Pruess, M.D., Chief Medical Staff
CIO: Susan Gutjahr, Reimbursement Specialist
CHR: Darla Shawgo, Director Human Resources
CNO: Lori Clinton, Chief Nursing Officer
Web address: www.spartahospital.com
**Control:** Hospital district or authority, Government, nonfederal **Service:** General
Medical and Surgical

**Staffed Beds:** 25 **Admissions:** 598 **Census:** 5 **Outpatient Visits:** 37966
**Births:** 0 **Total Expense ($000):** 27485 **Payroll Expense ($000):** 11906
**Personnel:** 243

*Many Facility Codes have changed. Please refer to the AHA Guide Code Chart.* © 2015 AHA Guide

**SPRING VALLEY—Bureau County**

**ST. MARGARET'S HOSPITAL (140143)**, 600 East First Street,
Zip 61362–1512; tel. 815/664–5311 **A**9 10 **F**3 11 13 15 28 29 30 31 32 34
35 38 40 44 45 46 47 49 53 57 58 59 63 70 74 75 76 77 79 81 82 84 85
87 90 93 96 107 108 110 111 115 118 119 129 130 131 132 133 135 143
144 146 147 148 **P**6 8 **S** Sisters of Mary of the Presentation Health System,
Fargo, ND
Primary Contact: Tim Muntz, President and Chief Executive Officer
CFO: Kim D. Santman, Vice President Finance
CIO: John Sabotta, Director Information Systems
CHR: Lisa R. Blackburn, Director Human Resources
CNO: Mary Vega, R.N., Vice President Nursing
Web address: www.aboutsmh.org
**Control:** Church–operated, Nongovernment, not–for profit **Service:** General
Medical and Surgical

**Staffed Beds:** 54 **Admissions:** 1969 **Census:** 19 **Outpatient Visits:** 251471
**Births:** 282 **Total Expense ($000):** 70028 **Payroll Expense ($000):** 30220
**Personnel:** 518

**SPRINGFIELD—Sangamon County**

☐ **ANDREW MCFARLAND MENTAL HEALTH CENTER (144021)**, 901 East
Southwind Road, Zip 62703–5125; tel. 217/786–6994, (Nonreporting) **A**1 3 5
10 **S** Division of Mental Health, Department of Human Services, Springfield, IL
Primary Contact: Karen Schweighart, R.N., MS, Administrator
CFO: Jeff Frey, Business Administrator
CMO: Kasturi Kripakaran, M.D., Medical Director
CIO: Josh Kates, Information Technology Analyst
CNO: Frances Collins, Director of Nursing
**Control:** State–Government, nonfederal **Service:** Psychiatric

**Staffed Beds:** 118

**KINDRED HOSPITAL SPRINGFIELD** See Vibra Hospital of Springfield

☐ **LINCOLN PRAIRIE BEHAVIORAL HEALTH CENTER**, 5230 South Sixth Street,
Zip 62703–5128; tel. 217/585–1180 **A**1 3 5 9 **F**35 38 98 99 100 101 104
105 **P**3 6 **S** Universal Health Services, Inc., King of Prussia, PA
Primary Contact: Mark Littrell, Chief Executive Officer
CFO: Chris Statz, Chief Financial Officer
CMO: Pamela Campbell, M.D., Medical Director
CNO: Renae Hale, Chief Nursing Officer
Web address: www.lincolnprairiebhc.com/
**Control:** Corporation, Investor–owned, for–profit **Service:** Children's hospital
psychiatric

**Staffed Beds:** 97 **Admissions:** 1746 **Census:** 65 **Outpatient Visits:** 7960
**Births:** 0 **Total Expense ($000):** 17543 **Payroll Expense ($000):** 7081
**Personnel:** 200

☒ △ **MEMORIAL MEDICAL CENTER (140148)**, 701 North First Street,
Zip 62781–0001; tel. 217/788–3000 **A**1 2 3 5 7 8 9 10 **F**3 8 11 12 13 14 15
16 17 18 20 22 24 26 28 29 30 31 32 34 35 36 37 40 42 43 44 45 46 47
48 49 50 51 54 57 58 59 60 61 63 64 68 69 70 74 75 76 77 78 79 81 82
84 85 86 87 89 90 92 93 96 97 98 100 101 102 103 104 105 107 108 110
111 114 115 116 117 118 119 120 121 124 126 129 130 131 132 134 135
138 141 142 144 145 146 147 148 **P**3 5 **S** Memorial Health System,
Springfield, IL
Primary Contact: Edgar J. Curtis, FACHE, President and Chief Executive Officer
COO: Charles D. Callahan, Ph.D., Executive Vice President and Chief Operating
Officer
CFO: Robert W. Kay, Senior Vice President and Chief Financial Officer
CMO: Rajesh G. Govindaiah, M.D., Chief Medical Officer
CIO: David B. Graham, M.D., Senior Vice President and Chief Information Officer
CHR: Robert F. Scott, Vice President and Chief Human Resources Officer
CNO: Marsha A. Prater, Ph.D., Senior Vice President and Chief Nursing Officer
Web address: www.memorialmedical.com
**Control:** Other not–for–profit (including NFP Corporation) **Service:** General
Medical and Surgical

**Staffed Beds:** 473 **Admissions:** 23558 **Census:** 316 **Outpatient Visits:**
460018 **Births:** 1635 **Total Expense ($000):** 568963 **Payroll Expense
($000):** 180469 **Personnel:** 3760

☒ **ST. JOHN'S HOSPITAL (140053)**, 800 East Carpenter Street,
Zip 62769–0002; tel. 217/544–6464, (Includes ST. JOHN'S CHILDREN'S
HOSPITAL, 800 East Carpenter Street, Zip 62769; tel. 217/544–6464), (Total
facility includes 37 beds in nursing home–type unit) **A**1 2 3 5 7 8 9 10 **F**3 8 11 12
13 15 17 18 19 20 22 24 26 28 29 30 31 32 34 35 36 37 39 40 43 44 45
46 47 48 49 50 51 53 54 56 57 58 59 60 61 62 63 64 68 70 72 74 75 76
77 78 79 81 82 84 85 86 87 88 89 92 93 94 96 98 100 101 102 103 104
105 107 108 110 111 114 115 116 117 118 119 120 121 122 123 124 126
128 129 130 131 132 135 145 146 147 148 **S** Hospital Sisters Health System,
Springfield, IL
Primary Contact: Charles Lucore, M.D., President and Chief Executive Officer
COO: David R. Olejniczak, Chief Operating Officer
CFO: Patty Allen, St. John's Vice President Finance
CIO: Ryan Leach, Chief Information Officer
CHR: Becky Puclik, Division Chief People Officer
CNO: Sherri Greenwood, Chief Nursing Officer
Web address: www.st–johns.org
**Control:** Other not–for–profit (including NFP Corporation) **Service:** General
Medical and Surgical

**Staffed Beds:** 431 **Admissions:** 19071 **Census:** 284 **Outpatient Visits:**
248087 **Births:** 1837 **Total Expense ($000):** 461838 **Payroll Expense
($000):** 141405 **Personnel:** 2578

☒ **VIBRA HOSPITAL OF SPRINGFIELD (142014)**, 701 North Walnut Street,
Zip 62702–4931; tel. 217/528–1217 **A**1 9 10 **F**1 3 29 148 **P**6 **S** Vibra
Healthcare, Mechanicsburg, PA
Primary Contact: Charles Nordyke, Chief Executive Officer
COO: Mark Dabbs, MSN, Chief Operating Officer
CNO: Cathy Harding, Chief Clinical Officer
Web address: www.222.vhspringfield.com
**Control:** Corporation, Investor–owned, for–profit **Service:** Long–Term Acute Care
hospital

**Staffed Beds:** 30 **Admissions:** 272 **Census:** 20 **Outpatient Visits:** 0 **Births:**
0 **Total Expense ($000):** 11885 **Payroll Expense ($000):** 4809 **Personnel:**
86

**STAUNTON—Macoupin County**

**COMMUNITY MEMORIAL HOSPITAL (141306)**, 400 Caldwell Street,
Zip 62088–1499; tel. 618/635–2200 **A**9 10 18 **F**3 11 15 28 29 31 34 35 40
42 56 57 78 79 81 107 115 130 132 133 146 **P**6
Primary Contact: Susie Campbell, Chief Executive Officer
CFO: Brian Engelke, Chief Financial Officer
CMO: Joshua Poos, M.D., President Medical Staff
CIO: Cheryl Horner, Supervisor Data Processing
CHR: Marilyn Herbeck, Coordinator Human Resources
CNO: Roberta Brown, Chief Nursing Officer
Web address: www.stauntonhospital.org
**Control:** Other not–for–profit (including NFP Corporation) **Service:** General
Medical and Surgical

**Staffed Beds:** 25 **Admissions:** 231 **Census:** 3 **Outpatient Visits:** 23401
**Births:** 0 **Total Expense ($000):** 13986 **Payroll Expense ($000):** 5466
**Personnel:** 128

**STERLING—Whiteside County**

☒ **CGH MEDICAL CENTER (140043)**, 100 East LeFevre Road, Zip 61081–1279;
tel. 815/625–0400 **A**1 9 10 **F**3 7 8 11 13 15 18 20 22 28 29 30 31 34 35 40
45 47 49 50 51 57 59 62 64 68 70 74 78 79 81 85 86 87 93 97 107 108
110 111 114 115 118 119 124 129 130 132 133 135 145 146 148 **P**6
Primary Contact: Paul Steinke, D.O., President and Chief Executive Officer
COO: Cynthia L. Zander, Vice President and Chief Operating Officer
CFO: Ben Schaab, VP Fiscal Services/ Chief Financial Officer
CMO: Keith Martin, M.D., Vice President and Medical Director
CIO: Randy Davis, Vice President and Chief Information Officer
CHR: Shane Brown, Vice President and Chief Human Resources Officer
CNO: Kristie A. Geil, VP, Chief Nursing Officer
Web address: www.cghmc.com
**Control:** City–Government, nonfederal **Service:** General Medical and Surgical

**Staffed Beds:** 99 **Admissions:** 5155 **Census:** 44 **Outpatient Visits:** 364277
**Births:** 557 **Total Expense ($000):** 190362 **Payroll Expense ($000):** 85266
**Personnel:** 1197

IL

**Hospital, Medicare Provider Number, Address, Telephone, Approval, Facility, and Physician Codes, Health Care System**

★ American Hospital Association (AHA) membership   ○ Healthcare Facilities Accreditation Program   ⇑ Center for Improvement in Healthcare Quality Accreditation
☐ The Joint Commission accreditation   ◇ DNV Healthcare Inc. accreditation   △ Commission on Accreditation of Rehabilitation Facilities (CARF) accreditation

## STREAMWOOD—Cook County

☐ **STREAMWOOD BEHAVIORAL HEALTH CENTER (144034)**, 1400 East Irving Park Road, Zip 60107–3203; tel. 630/837–9000 **A**1 9 10 **F**98 99 100 102 104 105 **S** Universal Health Services, Inc., King of Prussia, PA
Primary Contact: Ron Weglarz, Chief Executive Officer and Managing Director
CFO: Patricia Ellison, Chief Financial Officer
CMO: Joseph McNally, M.D., Medical Director
CHR: Joseph Rinke, Director Human Resources
CNO: Olieth Lightbourne, Chief Nursing Officer
Web address: www.streamwoodhospital.com
**Control:** Corporation, Investor–owned, for–profit **Service:** Children's hospital psychiatric

**Staffed Beds:** 178 **Admissions:** 2905 **Census:** 105 **Outpatient Visits:** 25427 **Births:** 0 **Total Expense ($000):** 27185 **Payroll Expense ($000):** 13877 **Personnel:** 282

## STREATOR—Lasalle County

✠ **HSHS ST. MARY'S HOSPITAL (140026)**, 111 Spring Street, Zip 61364–3399; tel. 815/673–2311 **A**1 9 10 **F**3 11 13 15 18 28 29 30 31 34 35 40 41 45 47 50 54 57 59 62 70 75 76 77 78 79 81 82 84 85 87 89 93 107 108 110 111 115 119 130 132 143 146 147 148 **P**8 **S** Hospital Sisters Health System, Springfield, IL
Primary Contact: John T. Flanders, MS, R.N., President and Chief Executive Officer
CFO: Karen S. Clark, Chief Financial Officer
CMO: Maria Granzotti, M.D., Chief Physician Executive, Central Illinois Division
CIO: Georgene Lansford, Director Information Systems
CNO: Diane Genthner, Chief Nursing Officer
Web address: www.stmaryshospital.org
**Control:** Church–operated, Nongovernment, not–for profit **Service:** General Medical and Surgical

**Staffed Beds:** 68 **Admissions:** 1703 **Census:** 17 **Outpatient Visits:** 74464 **Births:** 141 **Total Expense ($000):** 48703 **Payroll Expense ($000):** 14953 **Personnel:** 281

## SYCAMORE—Dekalb County

✠ **KINDRED HOSPITAL–SYCAMORE (142006)**, 225 Edward Street, Zip 60178–2137; tel. 815/895–2144, (Nonreporting) **A**1 10 **S** Kindred Healthcare, Louisville, KY
Primary Contact: Jim Cohick, Chief Executive Officer
CFO: Jay Schweikart, Chief Financial Officer
CMO: Thomas Liske, M.D., Chief Medical Officer
CHR: Eileen Strachan, Coordinator Human Resources
Web address: www.kindredhospitalsyc.com/
**Control:** Corporation, Investor–owned, for–profit **Service:** Long–Term Acute Care hospital

**Staffed Beds:** 69

## TAYLORVILLE—Christian County

✠ **TAYLORVILLE MEMORIAL HOSPITAL (141339)**, 201 East Pleasant Street, Zip 62568–1597; tel. 217/824–3331, (Total facility includes 20 beds in nursing home–type unit) **A**1 3 5 9 10 18 **F**8 15 28 29 30 34 35 40 45 46 50 56 57 59 64 75 77 79 81 87 89 93 103 107 108 110 111 115 119 128 129 130 131 132 133 144 146 **P**5 **S** Memorial Health System, Springfield, IL
Primary Contact: Kimberly L. Bourne, Chief Executive Officer
CFO: Andrew Costic, Regional Chief Financial Officer
CHR: Michelle Long, Regional Human Resource Manager
CNO: Tracy Seaton, Director of Nursing
Web address: www.taylorvillememorial.org
**Control:** Other not–for–profit (including NFP Corporation) **Service:** General Medical and Surgical

**Staffed Beds:** 45 **Admissions:** 1164 **Census:** 11 **Outpatient Visits:** 36971 **Births:** 0 **Total Expense ($000):** 36359 **Payroll Expense ($000):** 14230 **Personnel:** 249

## URBANA—Champaign County

★ △ ◇ **CARLE FOUNDATION HOSPITAL (140091)**, 611 West Park Street, Zip 61801–2595; tel. 217/383–3311 **A**2 3 5 7 9 10 13 21 **F**3 5 7 8 11 12 13 15 17 18 20 22 24 26 28 29 30 31 32 34 35 40 43 44 45 46 47 48 49 50 51 53 56 57 58 59 60 61 62 63 64 65 68 70 72 74 75 76 78 79 80 81 84 85 86 87 89 90 91 93 94 96 107 108 110 111 114 115 116 117 119 126 129 130 131 132 135 145 146 148 **S** Carle Foundation, Urbana, IL
Primary Contact: James C. Leonard, M.D., President and Chief Executive Officer
COO: John Snyder, Executive Vice President and Chief Operating Officer
CFO: Dennis Hesch, Executive Vice President Finance and Chief Financial Officer
CMO: Matthew Gibb, M.D., Executive Vice President and System Chief Medical Officer
CIO: Rick Rinehart, Chief Information Officer
CHR: L. J. Fallon, Executive Vice President, Chief Legal and Human Resources Officer
CNO: Pamela Bigler, R.N., Senior Vice President Chief Nursing Officer
Web address: www.carle.org
**Control:** Other not–for–profit (including NFP Corporation) **Service:** General Medical and Surgical

**Staffed Beds:** 345 **Admissions:** 22191 **Census:** 306 **Outpatient Visits:** 833611 **Births:** 2650 **Total Expense ($000):** 521349 **Payroll Expense ($000):** 150439 **Personnel:** 2860

✠ △ **PRESENCE COVENANT MEDICAL CENTER (140113)**, 1400 West Park Street, Zip 61801–2396; tel. 217/337–2000 **A**1 3 5 7 9 10 **F**3 7 13 15 18 20 22 24 26 28 29 30 31 34 35 38 40 49 57 59 68 70 72 74 75 76 78 79 81 82 85 87 89 90 98 100 101 102 103 107 108 110 111 114 115 119 126 130 132 146 147 148 **S** Presence Health, Chicago, IL
Primary Contact: Jared Rogers, M.D., Interim Regional President and Chief Executive Officer
COO: Jennifer Cord, Assistant Vice President Operations
CFO: Deborah Schimerowski, Vice President Finance and Chief Financial Officer
CMO: Kathleen Collins, M.D., Chief Medical Officer
CIO: Paula Keele, Manager Information Systems
CHR: Janet S. Payne, Vice President Human Resources
CNO: Molly Nicholson, R.N., Chief Nurse Executive
Web address: www.provena.org/covenant
**Control:** Church–operated, Nongovernment, not–for profit **Service:** General Medical and Surgical

**Staffed Beds:** 181 **Admissions:** 7422 **Census:** 83 **Outpatient Visits:** 209304 **Births:** 736 **Total Expense ($000):** 132559 **Payroll Expense ($000):** 38312 **Personnel:** 685

## VANDALIA—Fayette County

✠ **FAYETTE COUNTY HOSPITAL (141346)**, 650 West Taylor Street, Zip 62471–1296; tel. 618/283–1231, (Total facility includes 85 beds in nursing home–type unit) **A**1 9 10 18 **F**3 7 11 15 28 29 30 34 40 45 49 57 59 77 80 81 86 93 107 110 111 112 114 116 117 119 127 128 129 130 132 133 145 146 **P**5 **S** Alliant Management Services, Louisville, KY
Primary Contact: Gregory D. Starnes, Chief Executive Officer
CFO: Pete Fromme, Chief Financial Officer
CMO: Glenn Skow, M.D., Chief of Staff
CIO: Lisa Tessman, Manager Information Technology
CHR: Susan Crawford, Manager Human Resources
CNO: Marci Barth, Chief Nursing Officer
Web address: www.fayettecountyhospital.org
**Control:** Corporation, Investor–owned, for–profit **Service:** General Medical and Surgical

**Staffed Beds:** 110 **Admissions:** 808 **Census:** 64 **Outpatient Visits:** 43212 **Births:** 0 **Total Expense ($000):** 23204 **Payroll Expense ($000):** 8065 **Personnel:** 248

## WATSEKA—Iroquois County

☐ **IROQUOIS MEMORIAL HOSPITAL AND RESIDENT HOME (140167)**, 200 Fairman Avenue, Zip 60970–1644; tel. 815/432–5841, (Nonreporting) **A**1 3 9 10 20
Primary Contact: Charles Bohlmann, Chief Executive Officer
COO: Christopher Curry, Chief Operating Officer
CMO: Philip Zumwalt, M.D., Chief of Staff
CIO: Tim Smith, Director Information Systems
CHR: Jamie Neumann, Director Human Resources
CNO: Leslie Cottrell, R.N., Nurse Lead
Web address: www.iroquoismemorial.com
**Control:** Other not–for–profit (including NFP Corporation) **Service:** General Medical and Surgical

**Staffed Beds:** 68

IL

*Many Facility Codes have changed. Please refer to the AHA Guide Code Chart.* © 2015 AHA Guide

## WAUKEGAN—Lake County

✠ **VISTA MEDICAL CENTER EAST (140084)**, 1324 North Sheridan Road, Zip 60085–2161; tel. 847/360–3000 **A**1 2 3 5 9 10 **F**3 12 13 15 18 20 22 24 26 28 29 30 31 34 35 38 39 40 41 42 43 44 45 46 47 48 49 50 57 59 68 70 73 74 76 78 79 81 82 84 85 87 89 93 100 102 107 108 110 111 114 115 119 126 129 130 132 146 147 148 **S** Community Health Systems, Inc., Franklin, TN
Primary Contact: Barbara J. Martin, R.N., President and Chief Executive Officer
COO: Kim Needham, Assistant Chief Executive Officer
CFO: Kerry Hill, Chief Financial Officer
CMO: Kevin Liebovich, M.D., President Medical Staff
CIO: Cathy Adler–Marks, Director Information Technology
CHR: Michael R. Isaacs, Vice President Human Resources
CNO: Patti Kerkorian, Interim Chief Nursing Officer
Web address: www.vistahealth.com
**Control:** Corporation, Investor–owned, for–profit **Service:** General Medical and Surgical

**Staffed Beds: 190 Admissions: 11269 Census: 123 Outpatient Visits: 132441 Births: 1216 Total Expense ($000): 157815 Payroll Expense ($000): 53133 Personnel: 838**

✠ △ **VISTA MEDICAL CENTER WEST (140033)**, 2615 Washington Street, Zip 60085–4988; tel. 847/249–3900 **A**1 7 9 10 **F**29 30 34 35 38 40 42 43 50 56 59 64 68 77 87 90 96 98 99 101 102 103 104 105 107 119 130 132 135 **S** Community Health Systems, Inc., Franklin, TN
Primary Contact: Barbara J. Martin, R.N., President and Chief Executive Officer
COO: Kim Needham, Assistant Chief Executive Officer
CFO: Kerry Hill, Chief Financial Officer
CMO: Kevin Liebovich, M.D., President Medical Staff
CIO: Cathy Adler–Marks, Director Information Technology
CHR: Michael R. Isaacs, Vice President Human Resources
CNO: Patti Kerkorian, Chief Nursing Officer
Web address: www.vistahealth.com
**Control:** Corporation, Investor–owned, for–profit **Service:** Psychiatric

**Staffed Beds: 67 Admissions: 1713 Census: 35 Outpatient Visits: 24450 Births: 0 Total Expense ($000): 15610 Payroll Expense ($000): 7136 Personnel: 111**

## WHEATON—Du Page County

✠ △ **MARIANJOY REHABILITATION HOSPITAL (143027)**, 26 West 171 Roosevelt Road, Zip 60187–0795, Mailing Address: P.O. Box 795, Zip 60187–0795; tel. 630/909–8000, (Total facility includes 27 beds in nursing home–type unit) **A**1 3 7 9 10 **F**11 29 30 34 35 36 50 56 58 64 68 75 77 82 86 87 90 91 93 96 128 132 143 146 148 **P**6 **S** Wheaton Franciscan Healthcare, Wheaton, IL
Primary Contact: Kathleen C. Yosko, President and Chief Executive Officer
COO: John Brady, Vice President Physician Services and Organizational Planning
CFO: Michael Hedderman, Senior Vice President Finance and Chief Financial Officer
CMO: Noel Rao, M.D., Medical Director
CIO: Robert Sinickas, Director Information Services
CHR: Teresa Chapman, Vice President Human Resources
CNO: Kathleen C. Yosko, President and Chief Executive Officer
Web address: www.marianjoy.org
**Control:** Church–operated, Nongovernment, not–for profit **Service:** Rehabilitation

**Staffed Beds: 128 Admissions: 2948 Census: 114 Outpatient Visits: 46132 Births: 0 Total Expense ($000): 70812 Payroll Expense ($000): 38587 Personnel: 770**

## WINFIELD—DuPage County

✠ **NORTHWESTERN MEDICINE CENTRAL DUPAGE HOSPITAL (140242)**, 25 North Winfield Road, Zip 60190; tel. 630/933–1600, (Includes BEHAVIORAL HEALTH CENTER, 27 West 350 High Lake Road, tel. 630/653–4000) **A**1 2 3 5 9 10 **F**3 4 5 8 12 13 15 17 18 19 20 22 24 26 28 29 30 31 34 35 36 37 39 40 41 42 43 44 45 46 47 48 49 50 54 55 57 58 59 64 68 70 72 73 74 75 76 78 79 81 82 84 85 86 87 88 89 91 92 93 94 96 98 99 100 101 102 103 104 105 106 107 108 110 111 112 114 115 116 117 118 119 120 121 122 123 124 126 129 130 132 135 141 142 144 145 146 147 148 **S** Northwestern Memorial Healthcare, Chicago, IL
Primary Contact: Brian J. Lemon, President
CFO: John Orsini, Executive Vice President and Chief Financial Officer
CMO: Kevin Most, D.O., Vice President Medical Affairs
CIO: Daniel F. Kinsella, Vice President and Chief Information Officer
CHR: Michael Wukitsch, Executive Vice President Human Resources
Web address: www.cdh.org
**Control:** Other not–for–profit (including NFP Corporation) **Service:** General Medical and Surgical

**Staffed Beds: 378 Admissions: 23129 Census: 249 Outpatient Visits: 895614 Births: 3278 Total Expense ($000): 621013 Payroll Expense ($000): 199233 Personnel: 3480**

## WOODSTOCK—Mchenry County

★ **CENTEGRA HOSPITAL – WOODSTOCK (140176)**, 3701 Doty Road, Zip 60098–7509, Mailing Address: P.O. Box 1990, Zip 60098–1990; tel. 815/338–2500, (Total facility includes 25 beds in nursing home–type unit) **A**2 9 10 **F**3 4 5 11 12 13 15 18 28 29 30 31 34 35 37 38 39 40 43 44 47 49 50 51 54 57 58 59 64 68 69 70 74 75 76 78 79 81 82 85 86 87 92 93 98 100 101 102 103 104 105 107 108 110 111 114 118 119 128 129 130 131 132 143 146 147 148 **P**4 5 **S** Centegra Health System, Crystal Lake, IL
Primary Contact: Michael S. Eesley, Chief Executive Officer
COO: Jason Sciarro, President and Chief Operating Officer
CFO: David Tomlinson, Executive Vice President Chief Financial Officer and Chief Information Officer
CMO: Irfan Hafiz, Vice President Medical Affairs
CIO: David Tomlinson, Senior Vice President, Chief Information Officer
CHR: Bernadette S. Szczepanski, Vice President Human Resources Development
Web address: www.centegra.org
**Control:** Other not–for–profit (including NFP Corporation) **Service:** General Medical and Surgical

**Staffed Beds: 135 Admissions: 6756 Census: 84 Outpatient Visits: 97527 Births: 840 Total Expense ($000): 128488 Payroll Expense ($000): 52811 Personnel: 636**

## ZION—Lake County

✠ **MIDWESTERN REGIONAL MEDICAL CENTER (140100)**, 2520 Elisha Avenue, Zip 60099–2587; tel. 847/872–4561 **A**1 2 3 10 **F**3 15 29 30 31 33 35 36 40 45 46 49 50 54 55 57 58 59 60 64 67 70 74 75 77 79 80 81 82 83 84 85 86 87 93 97 102 104 107 108 109 110 111 112 114 115 116 117 119 120 121 122 124 126 129 130 132 135 136 143 144 146 147 148 **P**6 **S** Cancer Treatment Centers of America, Schaumburg, IL
Primary Contact: Scott Jones, President and Chief Executive Officer
COO: Pete Govorchin, Vice President Operations
CFO: Cecilia Taylor, Chief Financial Officer
CMO: Bradford Tan, M.D., Chief Medical Officer
CIO: Jeff Nickerson, Site Manager Information Systems
CHR: Jacqueline DeRousse, Assistant Vice President Talent
CNO: Jacklynn Lesniak, R.N., Vice President Patient Care Services and Chief Nursing Officer
Web address: www.cancercenter.com
**Control:** Corporation, Investor–owned, for–profit **Service:** Cancer

**Staffed Beds: 68 Admissions: 1904 Census: 34 Outpatient Visits: 9970 Births: 0 Personnel: 1245**

---

**Hospital, Medicare Provider Number, Address, Telephone, Approval, Facility, and Physician Codes, Health Care System**

★ American Hospital Association (AHA) membership
□ The Joint Commission accreditation
○ Healthcare Facilities Accreditation Program
◇ DNV Healthcare Inc. accreditation
⇑ Center for Improvement in Healthcare Quality Accreditation
△ Commission on Accreditation of Rehabilitation Facilities (CARF) accreditation

IL

# INDIANA

## ANDERSON—Madison County

☐ **COMMUNITY HOSPITAL OF ANDERSON AND MADISON COUNTY (150113)**, 1515 North Madison Avenue, Zip 46011–3453; tel. 765/298–4242 **A**1 2 9 10 **F**3 6 10 11 13 15 18 20 22 28 29 30 31 32 34 35 40 44 46 49 50 51 54 56 57 58 59 60 61 64 68 70 74 75 76 77 78 79 81 82 85 86 87 89 93 107 108 109 110 111 114 115 119 120 121 122 123 126 129 130 132 135 143 144 146 147 148 **P**6 **S** Community Health Network, Indianapolis, IN
Primary Contact: Beth S. Tharp, R.N., President and Chief Executive Officer
CFO: John B. Harris, Vice President Finance and Chief Financial Officer
CIO: Joey Hobbs, Chief Information Officer
CHR: Michael Harpe, Vice President Human Resources
CNO: Carol Whitesel, Vice President Patient Care Services and Chief Nursing Officer
Web address: www.communityanderson.com
**Control:** Other not–for–profit (including NFP Corporation) **Service:** General Medical and Surgical

**Staffed Beds:** 140 **Admissions:** 5754 **Census:** 58 **Outpatient Visits:** 182706 **Births:** 823 **Total Expense ($000):** 131502 **Payroll Expense ($000):** 56376 **Personnel:** 1028

✠ **ST. VINCENT ANDERSON REGIONAL HOSPITAL (150088)**, 2015 Jackson Street, Zip 46016–4339; tel. 765/649–2511 **A**1 2 9 10 **F**3 4 5 8 11 13 14 15 18 20 22 28 29 30 31 32 34 35 36 38 40 43 44 45 49 50 51 54 58 59 60 61 62 63 64 65 66 68 70 74 75 76 77 78 79 81 82 84 85 86 87 89 90 92 93 94 96 98 99 100 101 102 103 104 105 106 107 108 110 111 114 116 117 118 119 120 121 123 124 129 130 132 134 135 145 146 147 148 **P**6 **S** Ascension Health, Saint Louis, MO
Primary Contact: Thomas J. VanOsdol, President
COO: David Maxwell, Vice President Operations
CFO: Donald L. Apple, Chief Financial Officer
CIO: Robert Pope, Information Technology Director and Ministry Liaison
CHR: Glenn C. Fields, Vice President, Human Resources
CNO: Nancy Pitcock, Vice President Nursing and Chief Nursing Officer
Web address: www.stvincent.org/Saint–Johns/Default.aspx
**Control:** Church–operated, Nongovernment, not–for profit **Service:** General Medical and Surgical

**Staffed Beds:** 141 **Admissions:** 6409 **Census:** 94 **Outpatient Visits:** 238337 **Births:** 493 **Total Expense ($000):** 180082 **Payroll Expense ($000):** 62609 **Personnel:** 881

## ANGOLA—Steuben County

★ **CAMERON MEMORIAL COMMUNITY HOSPITAL (151315)**, 416 East Maumee Street, Zip 46703–2015; tel. 260/665–2141 **A**9 10 18 **F**3 10 11 13 15 28 29 30 34 35 38 45 46 47 48 50 54 57 59 62 63 64 65 68 75 76 77 79 81 83 86 87 93 102 107 108 110 111 114 116 117 119 129 130 132 133 144 146 147
Primary Contact: Connie McCahill, R.N., President and Chief Executive Officer
CFO: Douglas Bomba, Chief Financial Officer
CMO: Thomas Miller, M.D., Chief Medical Officer
CHR: Nancy Covell, Director Human Resources
Web address: www.cameronmch.com
**Control:** Other not–for–profit (including NFP Corporation) **Service:** General Medical and Surgical

**Staffed Beds:** 25 **Admissions:** 1270 **Census:** 11 **Outpatient Visits:** 102937 **Births:** 183 **Total Expense ($000):** 46056 **Payroll Expense ($000):** 16452 **Personnel:** 364

## AUBURN—Dekalb County

★ **DEKALB HEALTH (150045)**, 1316 East Seventh Street, Zip 46706–2515, Mailing Address: P.O. Box 542, Zip 46706–0542; tel. 260/925–4600 **A**9 10 **F**3 7 11 13 15 28 29 32 34 35 36 40 45 53 56 57 59 62 63 64 70 73 75 76 77 79 81 82 84 85 86 87 89 93 100 107 108 110 111 114 115 118 119 129 130 132 135 146 147 148 **P**4 6 8
Primary Contact: Craig Polkow, Chief Executive Officer
CMO: Emilio Vazquez, M.D., Chief Medical Officer
CIO: Ed Hobbs, Director Information Services
CNO: Donna S. Wisemore, Vice President and Chief Nursing Officer
Web address: www.dekalbhealth.com
**Control:** Other not–for–profit (including NFP Corporation) **Service:** General Medical and Surgical

**Staffed Beds:** 52 **Admissions:** 2027 **Census:** 17 **Births:** 489

**NORTHEASTERN CENTER (154050)**, 1850 Wesley Road, Zip 46706–3653; tel. 260/927–0726, (Nonreporting) **A**10
Primary Contact: Jerry Hollister, Chief Executive Officer
Web address: www.necmh.org
**Control:** Other not–for–profit (including NFP Corporation) **Service:** Psychiatric

**Staffed Beds:** 16

## AVON—Hendricks County

**CLARIAN WEST MEDICAL CENTER** See Indiana University Health West Hospital

✠ **INDIANA UNIVERSITY HEALTH WEST HOSPITAL (150158)**, 1111 North Ronald Reagan Parkway, Zip 46123–7085; tel. 317/217–3000 **A**1 2 3 5 9 10 **F**3 13 15 18 22 26 28 29 30 34 35 40 45 47 48 49 50 51 57 59 64 70 73 74 75 76 77 78 79 81 82 85 86 87 89 93 100 107 110 111 113 114 115 119 120 121 129 130 132 135 146 147 148 **S** Indiana University Health, Indianapolis, IN
Primary Contact: Matthew D. Bailey, FACHE, President and Chief Executive Officer
CMO: Andrew Nigh, M.D., Chief of Staff
CHR: Lana Funkhouser, Vice President Human Resources
CNO: Lisa Sparks, R.N., Chief Nursing Officer and Vice President Patient Care Services
Web address: www.iuhealth.org
**Control:** Other not–for–profit (including NFP Corporation) **Service:** General Medical and Surgical

**Staffed Beds:** 127 **Admissions:** 6741 **Census:** 80 **Outpatient Visits:** 197683 **Births:** 1234 **Total Expense ($000):** 136341 **Payroll Expense ($000):** 42968 **Personnel:** 722

## BATESVILLE—Ripley County

✠ **MARGARET MARY HEALTH (151329)**, 321 Mitchell Avenue, Zip 47006–8909, Mailing Address: P.O. Box 226, Zip 47006–0226; tel. 812/934–6624 **A**1 2 9 10 18 **F**3 13 15 28 30 31 34 35 36 39 40 45 46 50 54 56 59 62 63 64 65 70 75 76 77 78 79 81 85 86 87 93 107 108 111 114 118 119 121 123 129 130 131 132 135 144 146 148 **P**1
Primary Contact: Timothy L. Putnam, FACHE, President and Chief Executive Officer
CFO: Brian Daeger, Vice President Financial Services
CMO: Andrew Poltrack, M.D., Chief of Staff
CIO: Trisha Prickel, Director Information Systems
CHR: Kimberly Inscho, Vice President Community Relations and Human Resources
Web address: www.mmhealth.org
**Control:** Other not–for–profit (including NFP Corporation) **Service:** General Medical and Surgical

**Staffed Beds:** 25 **Admissions:** 1600 **Census:** 12 **Outpatient Visits:** 152653 **Births:** 453 **Total Expense ($000):** 73923 **Payroll Expense ($000):** 31588 **Personnel:** 435

## BEDFORD—Lawrence County

**BEDFORD REGIONAL MEDICAL CENTER** See Indiana University Health Bedford Hospital

**DUNN MEMORIAL HOSPITAL** See St. Vincent Dunn Hospital

✠ **INDIANA UNIVERSITY HEALTH BEDFORD HOSPITAL (151328)**, 2900 West 16th Street, Zip 47421–3583; tel. 812/275–1200 **A**1 2 9 10 18 **F**3 7 11 15 18 28 29 30 31 34 35 36 37 38 39 40 41 44 45 46 49 50 53 57 59 64 65 68 70 71 74 75 77 78 79 81 85 86 87 91 92 93 94 97 102 107 108 110 111 115 118 119 129 130 131 132 133 134 135 144 146 **P**6 **S** Indiana University Health, Indianapolis, IN
Primary Contact: Bradford W. Dykes, President and Chief Executive Officer
CFO: Charles L. Shetler, CPA, Chief Financial Officer
CMO: Joanne F. Smart, M.D., Director of Medical Affairs
CNO: Brenda Davis, R.N., Vice President of Patient Services
Web address: www.iuhealth.com
**Control:** Other not–for–profit (including NFP Corporation) **Service:** General Medical and Surgical

**Staffed Beds:** 25 **Admissions:** 1214 **Census:** 14 **Outpatient Visits:** 86323 **Births:** 0 **Total Expense ($000):** 41366 **Payroll Expense ($000):** 16594 **Personnel:** 265

✠ **ST. VINCENT DUNN HOSPITAL (151335)**, 1600 23rd Street, Zip 47421–4704; tel. 812/275–3331, (Nonreporting) **A**1 9 10 18 **S** Ascension Health, Saint Louis, MO
Primary Contact: Matt Balla, Chief Executive Officer
CFO: Crystal Plano, Controller
CMO: Deborah W. Craton, M.D., Chief Medical Officer
CIO: Chad Damon, Contractor
CHR: Darci Medlock, Manager Human Resources
CNO: Michelle Dotts–McCool, Chief Nursing Officer
Web address: www.stvincent.org/St–Vincent–Dunn/Default.aspx
**Control:** Other not–for–profit (including NFP Corporation) **Service:** General Medical and Surgical

**Staffed Beds:** 25

*Many Facility Codes have changed. Please refer to the AHA Guide Code Chart.*   © 2015 AHA Guide

IN

## BLOOMFIELD— County

✠ **MONROE HOSPITAL (150164)**, 5811 East Slick Rock lane, Zip 47424, Mailing Address: 4011 South Monroe Medical Park Boulevard, Bloomington, Zip 47403–8000; tel. 812/825–1111 **A**1 9 10 **F**3 15 18 20 22 29 34 45 46 50 64 65 70 75 79 80 81 85 86 87 91 107 110 111 119 127 146 **S** Prime Healthcare Services, Ontario, CA
Primary Contact: Phillip W. Lowe, Chief Executive Officer
CFO: Janice Wampler, Controller and Chief Information Technology Officer
CMO: Armandeep Singh, Chief Medical Officer
CIO: Janice Wampler, Controller and Chief Information Technology Officer
CHR: Pamela S. Hoffman, Director of Human Resources
CNO: Brenda Cook, Chief Nursing Officer
Web address: www.monroehospital.com
**Control:** Corporation, Investor–owned, for–profit **Service:** General Medical and Surgical

**Staffed Beds:** 32 **Admissions:** 1062 **Census:** 13 **Outpatient Visits:** 34862 **Births:** 0

## BLOOMINGTON—Monroe County

**BLOOMINGTON HOSPITAL** See Indiana University Health Bloomington Hospital

☐ **BLOOMINGTON MEADOWS HOSPITAL (154041)**, 3600 North Prow Road, Zip 47404–1616; tel. 812/331–8000 **A**1 9 10 **F**4 98 99 101 102 104 105 106 **S** Universal Health Services, Inc., King of Prussia, PA
Primary Contact: Jean Scallon, Chief Executive Officer
CFO: Becky T. Nyberg, Chief Financial Officer
CMO: David Gilliam, M.D., Medical Director
CHR: Amanda Shettlesworth, Director Human Resources
CNO: Penny Caswell, Director of Nursing
Web address: www.bloomingtonmeadows.com
**Control:** Corporation, Investor–owned, for–profit **Service:** Psychiatric

**Staffed Beds:** 67 **Admissions:** 1362 **Census:** 53 **Outpatient Visits:** 4818 **Births:** 0 **Total Expense ($000):** 9026 **Payroll Expense ($000):** 5880 **Personnel:** 143

✠ △ **INDIANA UNIVERSITY HEALTH BLOOMINGTON HOSPITAL (150051)**, 601 West Second Street, Zip 47403–2317, Mailing Address: P.O. Box 1149, Zip 47402–1149; tel. 812/336–6821 **A**1 2 7 9 10 19 **F**3 7 8 11 12 13 15 17 18 19 20 22 24 26 28 29 30 31 32 34 35 38 40 45 46 47 48 49 50 53 54 55 57 59 61 62 63 64 65 69 70 72 74 75 76 77 78 79 81 82 84 85 86 87 89 90 92 93 94 97 98 100 101 102 103 104 107 108 111 115 119 120 121 124 126 129 130 131 132 135 143 144 146 147 148 **P**6 **S** Indiana University Health, Indianapolis, IN
Primary Contact: Mark E. Moore, President and Chief Executive Officer
CFO: Mike Craig, Chief Financial Officer
CMO: Ken Marshall, M.D., Chief Medical Officer
CIO: Mark W. McMath, Chief Information Officer
CHR: Steven D. Deckard, Vice President Human Resources
Web address: www.iuhealth.org
**Control:** Other not–for–profit (including NFP Corporation) **Service:** General Medical and Surgical

**Staffed Beds:** 306 **Admissions:** 12165 **Census:** 146 **Outpatient Visits:** 236151 **Births:** 2075 **Total Expense ($000):** 303394 **Payroll Expense ($000):** 114466 **Personnel:** 1932

## BLUFFTON—Wells County

✠ **BLUFFTON REGIONAL MEDICAL CENTER (150075)**, 303 South Main Street, Zip 46714–2503; tel. 260/824–3210, (Total facility includes 13 beds in nursing home–type unit) **A**1 9 10 **F**3 13 15 18 28 29 30 34 35 40 41 45 49 50 57 59 64 70 74 75 76 79 81 82 85 86 87 89 91 93 94 96 97 107 108 110 111 114 119 128 129 130 132 135 146 147 148 **S** Community Health Systems, Inc., Franklin, TN
Primary Contact: Aaron Garofola, Chief Executive Officer
COO: Matt Lehn, Chief Operating Officer
CFO: Donald Lovelace, Chief Financial Officer
CMO: Kay Johnson, M.D., Chief of Staff
CNO: Julie Thompson, Chief Nursing Officer
Web address: www.blufftonregional.com
**Control:** Corporation, Investor–owned, for–profit **Service:** General Medical and Surgical

**Staffed Beds:** 79 **Admissions:** 2031 **Census:** 25 **Outpatient Visits:** 57719 **Births:** 224 **Total Expense ($000):** 34806 **Payroll Expense ($000):** 12827 **Personnel:** 224

## BOONVILLE—Warrick County

✠ **ST. MARY'S WARRICK HOSPITAL (151325)**, 1116 Millis Avenue, Zip 47601–2204; tel. 812/897–4800 **A**1 9 10 18 **F**3 6 11 15 28 29 30 40 45 50 53 56 57 59 64 67 68 79 81 85 87 89 93 98 103 107 111 114 118 119 128 130 132 133 135 146 **S** Ascension Health, Saint Louis, MO
Primary Contact: Kathy J. Hall, Administrator
CFO: Crystal Heaton, Director of Finance
CNO: Karen Waters, Chief Nursing Officer
Web address: www.stmarys.org/warrick
**Control:** Other not–for–profit (including NFP Corporation) **Service:** General Medical and Surgical

**Staffed Beds:** 35 **Admissions:** 740 **Census:** 16 **Outpatient Visits:** 18516 **Births:** 0 **Total Expense ($000):** 14473 **Payroll Expense ($000):** 5632 **Personnel:** 121

## BRAZIL—Clay County

✠ **ST. VINCENT CLAY HOSPITAL (151309)**, 1206 East National Avenue, Zip 47834–2797, Mailing Address: P.O. Box 489, Zip 47834–0489; tel. 812/442–2500 **A**1 9 10 18 **F**3 12 15 18 29 30 34 35 40 45 50 57 59 65 67 68 75 77 79 81 82 85 86 87 107 108 111 114 119 128 130 131 133 135 146 148 **S** Ascension Health, Saint Louis, MO
Primary Contact: Jerry Laue, Administrator
CFO: Wayne Knight, Director Finance
CMO: Craig Johnson, D.O., Medical Director
CHR: Danielle Abrams, Manager Human Resources, Marketing and Executive Assistant
CNO: Sandra Haggart, Chief Nursing Officer
Web address: www.stvincent.org
**Control:** Church–operated, Nongovernment, not–for profit **Service:** General Medical and Surgical

**Staffed Beds:** 25 **Admissions:** 605 **Census:** 7 **Outpatient Visits:** 30997 **Births:** 0 **Total Expense ($000):** 17527 **Payroll Expense ($000):** 5421 **Personnel:** 84

## BREMEN—Marshall County

★ **COMMUNITY HOSPITAL OF BREMEN (151300)**, 1020 High Road, Zip 46506–1093, Mailing Address: P.O. Box 8, Zip 46506–0008; tel. 574/546–2211 **A**9 10 18 **F**3 11 15 29 34 35 40 45 50 57 59 64 69 75 77 79 81 82 85 93 107 110 111 114 119 129 130 132 133 135 146 **P**6
Primary Contact: David Bailey, FACHE, Chief Executive Officer
CFO: Debra Kipfer, Chief Financial Officer
CMO: Jason Marker, M.D., Chief Medical Officer
CIO: Linda Barrett, Vice President of Information Services
CHR: Patricia Board, Vice President Human Resources
CNO: Sue Bettcher, R.N., Vice President of Nursing Services
Web address: www.bremenhospital.com
**Control:** Other not–for–profit (including NFP Corporation) **Service:** General Medical and Surgical

**Staffed Beds:** 24 **Admissions:** 307 **Census:** 2 **Outpatient Visits:** 32861 **Births:** 87 **Total Expense ($000):** 16227 **Payroll Expense ($000):** 5880 **Personnel:** 112

☐ **DOCTORS NEUROMEDICAL HOSPITAL (150180)**, 411 South Whitlock Street, Zip 46506–1626, Mailing Address: P.O. Box 36, Zip 46506–0036; tel. 574/546–3830, (Nonreporting) **A**1 9 10 **S** NeuroPsychiatric Hospitals, Mishawaka, IN
Primary Contact: Alan Fisher, Chief Executive Officer
COO: John M. Day, Chief Operating Officer
CFO: Bernie Hebert, Jr., Chief Financial Officer
CMO: Steven Posar, M.D., Chief of Medicine
CHR: Emyle Kruyer–Collins, Director Human Resources
Web address: www.physicianshospitalsystem.net
**Control:** Partnership, Investor–owned, for–profit **Service:** Rehabilitation

**Staffed Beds:** 20

**DOCTORS NEUROPSYCHIATRIC HOSPITAL AND RESEARCH INSTITUTE (154058)**, 417 South Whitlock Street, Zip 46506–1626; tel. 574/546–0330, (Nonreporting) **A**10 **S** NeuroPsychiatric Hospitals, Mishawaka, IN
Primary Contact: Cameron R. Gilbert, Ph.D., President and Chief Executive Officer
**Control:** Investor–owned, for–profit **Service:** Psychiatric

**Staffed Beds:** 20

## CARMEL—Hamilton County

**CLARIAN NORTH MEDICAL CENTER** See Indiana University Health North Hospital

IN

---

**Hospital, Medicare Provider Number, Address, Telephone, Approval, Facility, and Physician Codes, Health Care System**

★ American Hospital Association (AHA) membership
☐ The Joint Commission accreditation
○ Healthcare Facilities Accreditation Program
◇ DNV Healthcare Inc. accreditation
⇑ Center for Improvement in Healthcare Quality Accreditation
△ Commission on Accreditation of Rehabilitation Facilities (CARF) accreditation

○ **FRANCISCAN ST. FRANCIS HEALTH–CARMEL (150182)**, 12188B North Meridian Street, Zip 46032–4840; tel. 317/705–4500 **A**9 10 11 **F**3 15 29 30 31 35 45 57 59 64 78 79 81 85 94 107 111 115 119 146 **P**7 8 **S** Franciscan Alliance, Mishawaka, IN
Primary Contact: Stephen J. Wheatley, Director of Operations
CFO: Keith A. Lauter, Chief Financial Officer
CMO: Christopher Doehring, M.D., Vice President of Medical Affairs
CIO: Rebecca Merkel, Privacy Officer
CHR: Corey Baute, Vice President of Human Resource
CNO: Susan McRoberts, R.N., Chief Nursing Officer
Web address: www.franciscanalliance.org/hospitals/carmel/Pages/default.aspx
**Control:** Church–operated, Nongovernment, not–for profit **Service:** General Medical and Surgical

| | |
|---|---|
| **Staffed Beds:** 6 **Admissions:** 196 **Census:** 1 **Outpatient Visits:** 2210 **Births:** 0 **Total Expense ($000):** 15354 **Payroll Expense ($000):** 2796 **Personnel:** 33 | |

⊞ **INDIANA UNIVERSITY HEALTH NORTH HOSPITAL (150161)**, 11700 North Meridian Avenue, Zip 46032–4656; tel. 317/688–2000 **A**1 3 5 9 10 **F**3 13 15 18 19 20 22 25 29 30 31 34 35 36 37 40 45 47 49 55 57 59 60 64 68 70 72 74 75 76 78 79 80 81 85 87 88 89 92 93 107 108 110 111 115 119 124 126 129 130 132 135 146 147 148 **S** Indiana University Health, Indianapolis, IN
Primary Contact: Jonathan R. Goble, FACHE, President and Chief Executive Officer
COO: Randall C. Yust, Chief Operating Officer and Chief Financial Officer
CFO: Randall C. Yust, Chief Operating Officer and Chief Financial Officer
CMO: Paul Calkins, M.D., Chief Medical Officer
CIO: Steve Bodenham, Senior Manager Clinical Engineering
CHR: Angela S. Thompson, Vice President Human Resources and Support Services
CNO: Suzanne Del Boccio, MS, Chief Nursing Officer and Vice President Patient Care Services
Web address: www.iuhealth.org
**Control:** Other not–for–profit (including NFP Corporation) **Service:** General Medical and Surgical

| | |
|---|---|
| **Staffed Beds:** 161 **Admissions:** 6535 **Census:** 75 **Outpatient Visits:** 183597 **Births:** 2237 **Total Expense ($000):** 178609 **Payroll Expense ($000):** 50560 **Personnel:** 783 | |

⊞ **ST. VINCENT CARMEL HOSPITAL (150157)**, 13500 North Meridian Street, Zip 46032–1456; tel. 317/582–7000 **A**1 9 10 **F**3 12 13 15 29 30 34 35 36 37 40 44 45 49 50 54 57 58 59 61 64 68 69 70 72 75 76 78 79 80 81 85 87 92 96 107 108 110 111 119 126 130 132 135 146 147 148 **S** Ascension Health, Saint Louis, MO
Primary Contact: Michael D. Chittenden, President
COO: Daniel LaReau, Executive Director Operations and Information
CFO: Robert A. Bates, Executive Director Finance and Chief Financial Officer
CMO: Steven L. Priddy, M.D., Vice President Physician Affairs and Chief Medical Officer
CIO: Daniel LaReau, Executive Director Operations and Information
CHR: Charles Jeffras, Executive Director Human Resources
CNO: Gwynn Perlich, Vice President of Patient Services and Chief Nursing Officer
Web address: www.stvincent.org
**Control:** Church–operated, Nongovernment, not–for profit **Service:** General Medical and Surgical

| | |
|---|---|
| **Staffed Beds:** 121 **Admissions:** 4817 **Census:** 46 **Outpatient Visits:** 101609 **Births:** 1521 **Total Expense ($000):** 109977 **Payroll Expense ($000):** 41673 **Personnel:** 554 | |

### CLARKSVILLE—Clark County

○ **KENTUCKIANA MEDICAL CENTER (150176)**, 4601 Medical Plaza Way, Zip 47129–9204; tel. 812/284–6100, (Nonreporting) **A**9 10 11
Primary Contact: Paul Newsom, Chief Operating Officer
Web address: www.kentuckianamedcen.com/
**Control:** Corporation, Investor–owned, for–profit **Service:** General Medical and Surgical

| | |
|---|---|
| **Staffed Beds:** 40 | |

### CLINTON—Vermillion County

**UNION HOSPITAL CLINTON (151326)**, 801 South Main Street, Zip 47842–2261; tel. 765/832–2451 **A**9 10 18 **F**3 11 15 18 29 30 34 35 40 45 50 57 59 64 65 68 70 75 81 85 86 87 91 93 97 107 108 110 115 119 130 132 133 146 **P**6
Primary Contact: Terri L. Hill, Vice President and Administrator
COO: Scott L. Teffeteller, President and Chief Executive Officer
CFO: Wayne Hutson, Chief Financial Officer
CIO: Kym Pfrank, Vice President Information Systems
CHR: Sally Zuel, Vice President Human Resources
CNO: Rhonda E. Smith, R.N., Chief Nursing Officer
Web address: www.uhhg.org/wcch/index.html
**Control:** Other not–for–profit (including NFP Corporation) **Service:** General Medical and Surgical

| | |
|---|---|
| **Staffed Beds:** 25 **Admissions:** 1101 **Census:** 8 **Outpatient Visits:** 46246 **Births:** 0 **Total Expense ($000):** 22090 **Payroll Expense ($000):** 9616 **Personnel:** 154 | |

### COLUMBIA CITY—Whitley County

⊞ **PARKVIEW WHITLEY HOSPITAL (150101)**, 1260 East State Road 205, Zip 46725–9492; tel. 260/248–9000, (Total facility includes 67 beds in nursing home–type unit) **A**1 9 10 **F**3 5 7 8 13 15 28 29 34 35 38 40 45 50 54 57 59 64 69 70 75 76 79 81 82 85 89 91 93 96 102 107 108 110 111 114 119 125 128 129 132 135 143 144 146 148 **S** Parkview Health, Fort Wayne, IN
Primary Contact: Scott F. Gabriel, President
COO: Scott F. Gabriel, President
CFO: Lisa Peppler, Financial Manager
CMO: Jeffrey Brookes, M.D., Medical Director
CHR: Dianne P. Potter, Manager Human Resources
CNO: Bridget Dolohanty–Johnson, R.N., Vice President Patient Care Services
Web address: www.parkview.com
**Control:** Other not–for–profit (including NFP Corporation) **Service:** General Medical and Surgical

| | |
|---|---|
| **Staffed Beds:** 97 **Admissions:** 1472 **Census:** 61 **Outpatient Visits:** 42601 **Births:** 412 **Total Expense ($000):** 46009 **Payroll Expense ($000):** 14688 **Personnel:** 281 | |

### COLUMBUS—Bartholomew County

★ ○ **COLUMBUS REGIONAL HOSPITAL (150112)**, 2400 East 17th Street, Zip 47201–5360; tel. 812/379–4441 **A**2 9 10 11 19 **F**3 7 11 12 13 15 18 20 22 24 26 28 29 30 31 34 35 38 39 40 45 47 49 50 51 53 57 58 59 64 68 70 73 74 75 76 77 78 79 81 84 85 86 87 89 90 93 98 100 101 102 103 107 108 110 111 114 115 117 118 119 120 121 123 126 129 130 131 132 135 143 146 147 148 **P**3 8
Primary Contact: James Bickel, Chief Executive Officer
CFO: Marlene Weatherwax, Vice President and Chief Financial Officer
CMO: Thomas Sonderman, M.D., Vice President and Chief Medical Officer
CIO: Diana Boyer, Chief Information Officer
CHR: John R. Loya, Vice President Human Resources and Organizational Development
Web address: www.crh.org
**Control:** County–Government, nonfederal **Service:** General Medical and Surgical

| | |
|---|---|
| **Staffed Beds:** 198 **Admissions:** 8806 **Census:** 91 **Outpatient Visits:** 229747 **Births:** 1194 **Total Expense ($000):** 221158 **Payroll Expense ($000):** 68361 **Personnel:** 1481 | |

### CONNERSVILLE—Fayette County

○ **FAYETTE REGIONAL HEALTH SYSTEM (150064)**, 1941 Virginia Avenue, Zip 47331–2833; tel. 765/825–5131, (Nonreporting) **A**9 10 11
Primary Contact: Randall White, Chief Executive Officer
CFO: Debra Michalek, Chief Financial Officer
CMO: Mike Rowe, M.D., Chief of Staff
CIO: Andy Merida, Director Management Information Systems
CHR: Rhonda McPherson, Vice President Human Resources
CNO: Beth A. Wampler, R.N., Chief Nursing Officer
Web address: www.fayetteregional.org
**Control:** Other not–for–profit (including NFP Corporation) **Service:** General Medical and Surgical

| | |
|---|---|
| **Staffed Beds:** 118 | |

### CORYDON—Harrison County

★ **HARRISON COUNTY HOSPITAL (151331)**, 1141 Hospital Drive North W., Zip 47112–1774; tel. 812/738–4251, (Nonreporting) **A**9 10 18
Primary Contact: Steven L. Taylor, Chief Executive Officer
CFO: Jeff Davis, Chief Financial Officer
CIO: Chuck Wiley, Manager Information Systems
CHR: Loren Haverstock, Manager Human Resources
CNO: Ruth Donahue, R.N., Chief Nursing Officer
Web address: www.hchin.org
**Control:** County–Government, nonfederal **Service:** General Medical and Surgical

| | |
|---|---|
| **Staffed Beds:** 25 | |

### CRAWFORDSVILLE—Montgomery County

○ **FRANCISCAN ST. ELIZABETH HEALTH – CRAWFORDSVILLE (150022)**, 1710 Lafayette Road, Zip 47933–1099; tel. 765/362–2800 **A**9 10 11 **F**3 8 15 28 29 30 31 34 39 40 45 50 56 64 68 70 74 78 79 81 82 85 90 93 98 103 107 108 110 111 115 118 119 120 121 123 129 130 132 146 148 **S** Franciscan Alliance, Mishawaka, IN
Primary Contact: Terrance E. Wilson, President and CEO
COO: Terrence Klein, Vice President and Chief Operating Officer
CFO: Keith A. Lauter, Vice President Finance
Web address: www.stclaremedical.org
**Control:** Church–operated, Nongovernment, not–for profit **Service:** General Medical and Surgical

| | |
|---|---|
| **Staffed Beds:** 42 **Admissions:** 1267 **Census:** 15 **Outpatient Visits:** 125704 **Births:** 0 **Total Expense ($000):** 38256 **Payroll Expense ($000):** 9194 **Personnel:** 146 | |

**ST. CLARE MEDICAL CENTER** See Franciscan St. Elizabeth Health – Crawfordsville

**IN**

*Many Facility Codes have changed. Please refer to the AHA Guide Code Chart.* © 2015 AHA Guide

## CROWN POINT—Lake County

○ **FRANCISCAN ST. ANTHONY HEALTH – CROWN POINT (150126)**, 1201 South Main Street, Zip 46307–8483; tel. 219/738–2100, (Nonreporting) **A**2 9 10 11 **S** Franciscan Alliance, Mishawaka, IN
Primary Contact: Barbara M. Anderson, President and Chief Executive Officer
CFO: Marc Golan, Chief Financial Officer
CMO: Daniel McCormick, M.D., Vice President Medical Staff Affairs
CIO: Tim Loosemore, Director
CNO: Carol E. Schuster, R.N., Regional Chief Nursing Officer and Vice President Patient Care Services
Web address: www.franciscanalliance.org
**Control:** Church–operated, Nongovernment, not–for profit **Service:** General Medical and Surgical

| Staffed Beds: 254 |
|---|

**PINNACLE HOSPITAL (150166)**, 9301 Connecticut Drive, Zip 46307–7486; tel. 219/756–2100, (Nonreporting) **A**9 10
Primary Contact: Haroon Naz, Chief Executive Officer
Web address: www.pinnaclehealthcare.net
**Control:** Partnership, Investor–owned, for–profit **Service:** General Medical and Surgical

| Staffed Beds: 18 |
|---|

**ST. ANTHONY MEDICAL CENTER** See Franciscan St. Anthony Health – Crown Point

⊠ **VIBRA HOSPITAL OF NORTHWESTERN INDIANA (152028)**, 9509 Georgia Street, Zip 46307–6518; tel. 219/472–2200 **A**1 10 **F**1 29 75 77 85 86 87 130 148 **S** Vibra Healthcare, Mechanicsburg, PA
Primary Contact: Charles Nordyke, Interim Chief Executive Officer
CFO: Douglas Morris, Chief Financial Officer
CMO: Raja Devanathan, M.D., Chief Medical Officer
CNO: Robert Beard, Chief Clinical Officer
Web address: www.vhnwindiana.com/
**Control:** Corporation, Investor–owned, for–profit **Service:** Long–Term Acute Care hospital

| Staffed Beds: 40 Admissions: 461 Census: 36 Outpatient Visits: 0 Births: 0 Total Expense ($000): 17117 Payroll Expense ($000): 7361 Personnel: 121 |
|---|

## DANVILLE—Hendricks County

★ ○ **HENDRICKS REGIONAL HEALTH (150005)**, 1000 East Main Street, Zip 46122–1948, Mailing Address: P.O. Box 409, Zip 46122–0409; tel. 317/745–4451 **A**2 5 9 10 11 **F**3 8 11 13 15 20 28 29 30 31 32 34 35 40 54 55 56 57 59 60 61 64 66 69 70 73 74 75 76 77 78 79 81 85 86 87 89 93 96 97 107 108 109 110 111 115 117 118 119 120 121 123 129 130 131 132 135 144 146 147 148 **P**6
Primary Contact: Kevin Speer, Chief Executive Officer
CFO: John Komenda, Chief Financial Officer
CMO: John Sparzo, M.D., Vice President Medical Affairs
CIO: Lowell Nicodemus, Director Information Systems
CHR: Gary Lenard, Director Human Resources
Web address: www.hendrickshospital.org
**Control:** County–Government, nonfederal **Service:** General Medical and Surgical

| Staffed Beds: 127 Admissions: 4963 Census: 50 Outpatient Visits: 323585 Births: 1134 Total Expense ($000): 217124 Payroll Expense ($000): 87129 Personnel: 1327 |
|---|

## DECATUR—Adams County

★ **ADAMS MEMORIAL HOSPITAL (151330)**, 1100 Mercer Avenue, Zip 46733–2303, Mailing Address: P.O. Box 151, Zip 46733–0151; tel. 260/724–2145, (Total facility includes 195 beds in nursing home–type unit) **A**9 10 18 **F**3 5 7 10 13 15 29 34 35 38 40 45 47 50 53 57 59 64 65 66 68 70 74 75 76 77 79 81 82 84 85 86 87 92 93 96 97 98 99 100 101 102 103 104 105 106 107 108 110 111 115 119 125 128 129 130 131 132 133 135 143 144 145 146 147 148 **P**6
Primary Contact: JoEllen Eidam, Chief Executive Officer
CFO: Dane Wheeler, Chief Financial Officer
CMO: Mark S. Gresla, M.D., Chief of Staff
CIO: Nick Nelson, Director Support Services
CHR: Alison Kukelhan, Manager Human Resources
Web address: www.adamshospital.com
**Control:** County–Government, nonfederal **Service:** General Medical and Surgical

| Staffed Beds: 233 Admissions: 2393 Census: 186 Outpatient Visits: 97721 Births: 207 Total Expense ($000): 66252 Payroll Expense ($000): 29598 Personnel: 566 |
|---|

## DYER—Lake County

**FRANCISCAN ST. MARGARET HEALTH – DYER** See Franciscan St. Margaret Health – Hammond, Hammond

**SAINT MARGARET MERCY HEALTHCARE CENTERS–SOUTH CAMPUS** See Franciscan St. Margaret Health – Dyer

## EAST CHICAGO—Lake County

⊠ **REGENCY HOSPITAL OF NORTHWEST INDIANA (152024)**, 4321 Fir Street, 4th Floor, Zip 46312–3049; tel. 219/392–7799, (Includes REGENCY HOSPITAL OF PORTER COUNTY, 3630 Willow Creek Road, Portage, Zip 46368; tel. 219/364–3800), (Nonreporting) **A**1 10 **S** Select Medical Corporation, Mechanicsburg, PA
Primary Contact: Cheryl G. Gentry, Chief Executive Officer
Web address: www.regencyhospital.com/company/locations/indiana–northwest–indiana.aspx
**Control:** Corporation, Investor–owned, for–profit **Service:** Long–Term Acute Care hospital

| Staffed Beds: 61 |
|---|

□ △ **ST. CATHERINE HOSPITAL (150008)**, 4321 Fir Street, Zip 46312–3097; tel. 219/392–1700 **A**1 7 9 10 **F**1 3 5 11 13 15 17 18 20 22 24 26 28 29 30 31 34 35 40 46 49 54 57 58 59 60 61 62 64 68 74 75 76 77 78 79 80 81 82 85 86 87 89 92 98 99 100 101 102 103 104 107 108 110 111 112 115 119 129 130 132 135 144 146 147 148 **P**8 **S** Community Healthcare System, Hammond, IN
Primary Contact: JoAnn Birdzell, Chief Executive Officer and Administrator
COO: Craig Bolda, Chief Operating Officer
CFO: Luis Molina, Chief Financial Officer
CMO: John Griep, M.D., Chief Medical Director
CIO: Gary Weiner, Chief Information Officer
CNO: Paula C. Swenson, R.N., Vice President and Chief Nursing Officer
Web address: www.stcatherinehospital.org
**Control:** Other not–for–profit (including NFP Corporation) **Service:** General Medical and Surgical

| Staffed Beds: 189 Admissions: 8331 Census: 103 Outpatient Visits: 140918 Births: 489 Total Expense ($000): 162970 Payroll Expense ($000): 51334 Personnel: 790 |
|---|

## ELKHART—Elkhart County

★ ○ △ **ELKHART GENERAL HEALTHCARE SYSTEM (150018)**, 600 East Boulevard, Zip 46514–2499, Mailing Address: P.O. Box 1329, Zip 46515–1329; tel. 574/294–2621 **A**2 7 9 10 11 **F**3 5 12 13 15 17 18 20 22 24 26 28 29 30 31 34 35 40 45 46 48 49 50 57 59 60 64 68 69 70 72 74 75 76 77 78 79 81 82 84 85 86 87 89 90 91 92 93 98 99 100 102 104 105 107 108 110 111 114 115 118 119 120 121 123 129 130 132 134 135 146 147 148 **P**6 **S** Beacon Health System, South Bend, IN
Primary Contact: Greg Losasso, President
CFO: Jeff Costello, Chief Financial Officer
CMO: William Buckley, M.D., Chief of Staff
CIO: Steve Huffman, Chief Information Officer
CHR: Steven M. Eller, Vice President Human Resources
CNO: Karra Heggen, R.N., Vice President Nursing
Web address: www.egh.org
**Control:** Other not–for–profit (including NFP Corporation) **Service:** General Medical and Surgical

| Staffed Beds: 265 Admissions: 11532 Census: 133 Outpatient Visits: 304787 Births: 1613 Total Expense ($000): 252693 Payroll Expense ($000): 80012 Personnel: 1600 |
|---|

## ELWOOD—Madison County

⊠ **ST. VINCENT MERCY HOSPITAL (151308)**, 1331 South A Street, Zip 46036–1942; tel. 765/552–4600 **A**1 2 9 10 18 **F**3 11 15 28 29 30 31 34 35 40 44 45 50 53 57 59 64 68 74 75 78 79 81 82 85 86 87 89 93 107 108 110 111 114 119 129 130 132 133 135 146 148 **S** Ascension Health, Saint Louis, MO
Primary Contact: Francis G. Albarano, Administrator
CFO: John Arthur, Chief Financial Officer
CMO: Gary Brazel, M.D., Chief Medical Officer
CHR: Ross Brodhead, Manager Human Resources
CNO: Ann C. Yates, R.N., Director Patient Care and Clinical Services
Web address: www.stvincent.org
**Control:** Church–operated, Nongovernment, not–for profit **Service:** General Medical and Surgical

| Staffed Beds: 17 Admissions: 460 Census: 5 Outpatient Visits: 32584 Births: 0 Total Expense ($000): 21053 Payroll Expense ($000): 7394 Personnel: 148 |
|---|

**IN**

| Hospital, Medicare Provider Number, Address, Telephone, Approval, Facility, and Physician Codes, Health Care System |
|---|
| ★ American Hospital Association (AHA) membership   ○ Healthcare Facilities Accreditation Program   ⇑ Center for Improvement in Healthcare Quality Accreditation<br>□ The Joint Commission accreditation   ◇ DNV Healthcare Inc. accreditation   △ Commission on Accreditation of Rehabilitation Facilities (CARF) accreditation |

## EVANSVILLE—Vanderburgh County

★ ○ **DEACONESS HOSPITAL (150082)**, 600 Mary Street, Zip 47710–1658; tel. 812/450–5000, (Includes DEACONESS CROSS POINTE CENTER, 7200 East Indiana Street, Zip 47715; tel. 812/476–7200; Cheryl Rietman, Chief Administrative Officer) **A**2 3 9 10 11 **F**3 5 9 11 12 15 17 18 19 20 22 24 26 29 30 31 32 34 35 36 38 39 40 43 44 45 46 47 48 49 50 53 54 56 57 58 59 60 61 64 65 66 68 70 71 74 75 77 78 79 81 82 84 85 86 87 88 89 92 93 94 96 97 98 99 100 101 102 104 105 107 108 110 111 114 115 116 117 118 119 120 121 123 124 126 129 130 132 134 135 145 146 148 **P**6 8 **S** Deaconess Health System, Evansville, IN
Primary Contact: Shawn W. McCoy, Chief Administrative Officer
CFO: Cheryl A. Wathen, Interim Chief Financial Officer
CMO: James Porter, M.D., Vice President Medical Affairs
CHR: Larry Pile, Director Human Resources
Web address: www.deaconess.com
**Control:** Other not–for–profit (including NFP Corporation) **Service:** General Medical and Surgical

**Staffed Beds:** 484 **Admissions:** 24284 **Census:** 325 **Outpatient Visits:** 590728 **Births:** 0 **Total Expense ($000):** 567061 **Payroll Expense ($000):** 206785 **Personnel:** 3293

**EVANSVILLE PSYCHIATRIC CHILDREN CENTER (15J200)**, 3300 East Morgan Avenue, Zip 47715–2232; tel. 812/477–6436, (Nonreporting) **A**10
Primary Contact: Lottie Cook, Superintendent
COO: Melinda Kendle, Manager Business Office
CMO: Shannon Jones, M.D., Medical Director and Attending Psychiatrist
CIO: David Wirtz, Supervisor Information Technology
CHR: Jennifer Sontz, Director Human Resources
CNO: Elizabeth Angermeier, Director of Nursing
Web address: www.in.gov
**Control:** State–Government, nonfederal **Service:** Children's hospital psychiatric

**Staffed Beds:** 28

☐ **EVANSVILLE STATE HOSPITAL (154056)**, 3400 Lincoln Avenue, Zip 47714–0146; tel. 812/469–6800, (Nonreporting) **A**1 10
Primary Contact: Cathe Fulcher, Superintendent
CFO: Melinda Kendle, Director Fiscal Management
CMO: Melba Briones, M.D., Medical Director
CIO: David Wirtz, Senior LAN Administrator
CHR: Jennifer Sontz, Director Human Resources
**Control:** State–Government, nonfederal **Service:** Psychiatric

**Staffed Beds:** 168

⊠ **HEALTHSOUTH DEACONESS REHABILITATION HOSPITAL (153025)**, 4100 Covert Avenue, Zip 47714–5567, Mailing Address: P.O. Box 5349, Zip 47716–5349; tel. 812/476–9983 **A**1 9 10 **F**28 29 64 68 75 87 90 91 93 94 95 96 130 132 143 148 **S** HEALTHSOUTH Corporation, Birmingham, AL
Primary Contact: Blake Bunner, Chief Executive Officer
CFO: Brandon Stephens, Controller
CMO: Ashok Dhingra, M.D., Executive Medical Director
CIO: Eddie Gomez, Senior Manager Director Information Systems, Environmental Services Laundry
CHR: Darlene Moog, Director Human Resources
CNO: Trish Draeger, Chief Nursing Officer
Web address: www.healthsouthdeaconess.com
**Control:** Corporation, Investor–owned, for–profit **Service:** Rehabilitation

**Staffed Beds:** 85 **Admissions:** 1779 **Census:** 68 **Outpatient Visits:** 6395 **Births:** 0 **Total Expense ($000):** 22190 **Payroll Expense ($000):** 11286 **Personnel:** 240

⊠ **SELECT SPECIALTY HOSPITAL–EVANSVILLE (152014)**, 400 S.E. 4th Street, Zip 47713–1206; tel. 812/421–2500, (Nonreporting) **A**1 10 **S** Select Medical Corporation, Mechanicsburg, PA
Primary Contact: Mike Carney, Chief Executive Officer
Web address: www.selectspecialtyhospitals.com/company/locations/evansville.aspx
**Control:** Corporation, Investor–owned, for–profit **Service:** Long–Term Acute Care hospital

**Staffed Beds:** 60

⊠ △ **ST. MARY'S MEDICAL CENTER OF EVANSVILLE (150100)**, 3700 Washington Avenue, Zip 47714–0541; tel. 812/485–4000 **A**1 2 7 9 10 **F**3 7 8 11 12 13 15 17 18 20 22 24 26 28 29 30 31 32 34 35 36 39 40 42 43 45 46 47 48 49 50 51 53 54 55 56 57 58 59 60 61 64 65 68 70 71 72 73 74 75 76 77 78 79 80 81 82 83 84 85 86 87 88 89 90 92 93 96 98 100 101 102 107 108 110 111 114 115 116 117 118 119 126 129 130 131 132 134 135 143 144 146 147 148 **P**6 **S** Ascension Health, Saint Louis, MO
Primary Contact: Keith Jewell, President
CFO: John Zabrowski, Chief Financial Officer
CMO: Vernon Maas, M.D., Vice President, Medical Affairs
CIO: Jose Diaz, Director Information Systems
CHR: Marty Mattingly, Chief Human Resources Officer
CNO: Darcy Ellison, R.N., Senior Vice President, Chief Nursing Officer and Inpatient Flow
Web address: www.stmarys.org
**Control:** Church–operated, Nongovernment, not–for profit **Service:** General Medical and Surgical

**Staffed Beds:** 436 **Admissions:** 16123 **Census:** 214 **Outpatient Visits:** 346485 **Births:** 1506 **Total Expense ($000):** 391828 **Payroll Expense ($000):** 106654 **Personnel:** 2501

## FISHERS—Hamilton County

⊠ **ST. VINCENT FISHERS HOSPITAL (150181)**, 13861 Olio Road, Zip 46037–3487; tel. 317/415–9000 **A**1 10 **F**3 13 15 29 30 34 35 40 45 46 49 50 53 57 59 60 64 75 76 77 79 81 82 87 91 93 97 107 110 111 114 119 129 130 131 132 146 147 148 **S** Ascension Health, Saint Louis, MO
Primary Contact: Gary Fammartino, Administrator
CMO: Craig Wilson, Chief Medical Officer
Web address: www.stvincent.org
**Control:** Church–operated, Nongovernment, not–for profit **Service:** General Medical and Surgical

**Staffed Beds:** 46 **Admissions:** 852 **Census:** 6 **Outpatient Visits:** 53105 **Births:** 230 **Total Expense ($000):** 42154 **Payroll Expense ($000):** 14845 **Personnel:** 177

## FORT WAYNE—Allen County

⊠ **DUPONT HOSPITAL (150150)**, 2520 East Dupont Road, Zip 46825–1675; tel. 260/416–3000 **A**1 9 10 **F**3 4 13 15 17 20 26 29 30 34 35 40 45 49 51 56 57 59 64 65 67 68 70 72 73 74 75 76 79 81 82 85 86 87 88 89 90 98 107 108 111 112 113 114 115 119 124 128 129 131 132 135 141 145 146 147 148 **P**1 5 **S** Community Health Systems, Inc., Franklin, TN
Primary Contact: Chad Towner, Chief Executive Officer
CFO: Brian Schneider, Chief Financial Officer
CIO: Keith A. Neuman, Chief Information Officer
Web address: www.thedupontdifference.com
**Control:** Partnership, Investor–owned, for–profit **Service:** General Medical and Surgical

**Staffed Beds:** 131 **Admissions:** 4438 **Census:** 49 **Outpatient Visits:** 95113 **Births:** 2179 **Total Expense ($000):** 81617 **Payroll Expense ($000):** 29936 **Personnel:** 494

⊠ **LUTHERAN HOSPITAL OF INDIANA (150017)**, 7950 West Jefferson Boulevard, Zip 46804–4140; tel. 260/435–7001, (Nonreporting) **A**1 2 3 9 10 **S** Community Health Systems, Inc., Franklin, TN
Primary Contact: Brian Bauer, Chief Executive Officer
COO: Erica Wehrmeister, Chief Operating Officer
CFO: Cully Chapman, Chief Financial Officer
CMO: Geoffrey Randolph, M.D., Chief Medical Officer
CIO: Keith A. Neuman, Chief Information Officer
CHR: Maria Kurtz, Director Human Resources
CNO: Diane L. Springer, MS, Chief Nursing Officer
Web address: www.lutheranhospital.com
**Control:** Corporation, Investor–owned, for–profit **Service:** General Medical and Surgical

**Staffed Beds:** 396

⊠ **ORTHOPAEDIC HOSPITAL OF LUTHERAN HEALTH NETWORK (150168)**, 7952 West Jefferson Boulevard, Zip 46804–4140; tel. 260/435–2999 **A**1 9 10 **F**29 34 35 37 64 77 79 80 81 82 93 94 96 111 131 **P**8 **S** Community Health Systems, Inc., Franklin, TN
Primary Contact: Lorie Ailor, Chief Executive Officer
CFO: Amy Hochstetler, Chief Financial Officer
CMO: Kevin Rahn, President Medical Staff
CIO: Keith A. Neuman, Chief Information Officer
CHR: Maria Kurtz, Director Human Resources
CNO: Marci Hamilton, Chief Nursing Officer
Web address: www.theorthohospital.com
**Control:** Corporation, Investor–owned, for–profit **Service:** Orthopedic

**Staffed Beds:** 44 **Admissions:** 2573 **Census:** 17 **Outpatient Visits:** 44909 **Births:** 0 **Total Expense ($000):** 49946 **Payroll Expense ($000):** 12090 **Personnel:** 205

**IN**

*Many Facility Codes have changed. Please refer to the AHA Guide Code Chart.* © 2015 AHA Guide

☒ **PARKVIEW ORTHO HOSPITAL (150167)**, 11130 Parkview Circle Drive, Zip 46845–1735; tel. 260/672–5000 **A**1 9 10 **F**3 8 29 30 34 42 45 50 58 65 68 79 81 82 84 85 86 87 90 91 93 94 96 107 111 119 131 135 141 **S** Parkview Health, Fort Wayne, IN
Primary Contact: Julie Fleck, Chief Operating Officer
Web address: www.parkview.com
**Control:** Corporation, Investor–owned, for–profit **Service:** Orthopedic

> **Staffed Beds:** 37 **Admissions:** 2230 **Census:** 15 **Outpatient Visits:** 6661 **Births:** 0 **Total Expense ($000):** 52251 **Payroll Expense ($000):** 8145 **Personnel:** 246

☒ **PARKVIEW REGIONAL MEDICAL CENTER (150021)**, 11109 Parkview Plaza Drive, Zip 46845–1701; tel. 260/373–4000, (Includes PARKVIEW HOSPITAL RANDALLIA, 2200 Randallia Drive, Zip 46805–4699; tel. 260/373–4000), (Total facility includes 31 beds in nursing home–type unit) **A**1 9 10 **F**3 5 7 11 13 14 15 17 18 20 22 24 26 28 29 30 31 32 34 35 39 40 43 44 45 46 47 48 49 50 51 53 54 55 57 58 59 60 61 62 63 64 65 67 68 69 70 72 74 75 76 78 79 81 82 84 85 86 87 88 89 90 91 92 93 96 98 99 100 101 102 103 104 105 107 108 109 111 114 115 118 119 120 121 123 124 126 128 129 130 131 132 135 141 146 147 148 **S** Parkview Health, Fort Wayne, IN
Primary Contact: Ben Miles, President
Web address: www.parkview.com
**Control:** Other not–for–profit (including NFP Corporation) **Service:** General Medical and Surgical

> **Staffed Beds:** 678 **Admissions:** 33666 **Census:** 479 **Outpatient Visits:** 413774 **Births:** 3073 **Total Expense ($000):** 671655 **Payroll Expense ($000):** 194245 **Personnel:** 3380

☒ △ **REHABILITATION HOSPITAL OF FORT WAYNE (153030)**, 7970 West Jefferson Boulevard, Zip 46804–4140; tel. 260/435–6100 **A**1 7 9 10 **F**29 30 60 69 90 93 96 130 132 146 148 **P**5 **S** Community Health Systems, Inc., Franklin, TN
Primary Contact: Brian Bauer, Chief Executive Officer
COO: Shelley Boxell, R.N., Interim Chief Operating Officer
CFO: Edward Romero, Chief Financial Officer
CMO: Heidi Lang, M.D., Chief Medical Officer
CIO: Keith A. Neuman, Chief Information Officer
CHR: Deborah Giardina, Director Human Resources and Medical Staff Services
CNO: Shelley Boxell, R.N., Chief Nursing Officer
Web address: www.rehabhospital.com
**Control:** Corporation, Investor–owned, for–profit **Service:** Rehabilitation

> **Staffed Beds:** 36 **Admissions:** 485 **Census:** 14 **Outpatient Visits:** 47 **Births:** 0 **Total Expense ($000):** 8819 **Payroll Expense ($000):** 4823 **Personnel:** 82

☒ **SELECT SPECIALTY HOSPITAL–FORT WAYNE (152016)**, 700 Broadway, 7th Floor, Zip 46802–1402; tel. 260/425–3810, (Nonreporting) **A**1 10 **S** Select Medical Corporation, Mechanicsburg, PA
Primary Contact: Teresa R. Detano, M.P.H., Chief Executive Officer
CMO: Yogesh Amin, M.D., Medical Director
CNO: Marielle Lael, R.N., Chief Nursing Officer
Web address: www.fortwayne.selectspecialtyhospitals.com
**Control:** Corporation, Investor–owned, for–profit **Service:** Long–Term Acute Care hospital

> **Staffed Beds:** 32

☒ **ST. JOSEPH HOSPITAL (150047)**, 700 Broadway, Zip 46802–1493; tel. 260/425–3000, (Total facility includes 20 beds in nursing home–type unit) **A**1 3 5 9 10 13 **F**3 4 5 13 15 16 17 18 20 22 24 28 29 30 34 40 45 46 47 49 50 51 53 54 55 56 57 58 59 64 65 68 69 70 72 74 76 77 79 80 81 85 87 92 93 96 98 100 101 102 103 104 105 107 108 110 111 114 115 118 119 128 130 132 142 146 147 148 **P**6 **S** Community Health Systems, Inc., Franklin, TN
Primary Contact: Kenneth Jones, Chief Executive Officer
COO: Jeff Vice, Chief Operating Officer
CFO: Pamela Hess, Chief Financial Officer
CHR: Steve Heggen, Administrative Director Human Resources
Web address: www.stjoehospital.com
**Control:** Corporation, Investor–owned, for–profit **Service:** General Medical and Surgical

> **Staffed Beds:** 182 **Admissions:** 5846 **Census:** 95 **Outpatient Visits:** 101466 **Births:** 408 **Total Expense ($000):** 94659 **Payroll Expense ($000):** 33705

☒ **VETERANS AFFAIRS NORTHERN INDIANA HEALTH CARE SYSTEM**, 2121 Lake Avenue, Zip 46805–5100; tel. 260/426–5431, (Includes VETERANS AFFAIRS NORTHERN INDIANA HEALTH CARE SYSTEM–MARION CAMPUS, 1700 East 38th Street, Marion, Zip 46953–4589; tel. 765/674–3321), (Nonreporting) **A**1 **S** Department of Veterans Affairs, Washington, DC
Primary Contact: Denise M. Deitzen, Director
COO: Helen Rhodes, R.N., Associate Director Operations
CFO: Jay H. Vandermark, Chief Financial Officer
CMO: Ajay Dhawan, M.D., Chief of Staff
CIO: David Troyer, Chief Information Officer
CHR: Brian Flynn, Chief Human Resources Officer
Web address: www.northernindiana.va.gov/
**Control:** Veterans Affairs, Government, federal **Service:** General Medical and Surgical

> **Staffed Beds:** 26

☒ **VIBRA HOSPITAL OF FORT WAYNE (152027)**, 2200 Randallia Drive, Zip 46805–4638; tel. 260/399–2900 **A**1 3 10 **F**1 3 85 148 **S** Vibra Healthcare, Mechanicsburg, PA
Primary Contact: Ryan Cassedy, Chief Executive Officer
Web address: www.vhfortwayne.com
**Control:** Corporation, Investor–owned, for–profit **Service:** Long–Term Acute Care hospital

> **Staffed Beds:** 24 **Admissions:** 256 **Census:** 18 **Outpatient Visits:** 0 **Births:** 0 **Total Expense ($000):** 10645 **Payroll Expense ($000):** 3949 **Personnel:** 41

### FRANKFORT—Clinton County

☒ **ST. VINCENT FRANKFORT HOSPITAL (151316)**, 1300 South Jackson Street, Zip 46041–3394; tel. 765/656–3000 **A**1 9 10 18 **F**3 11 13 15 28 29 30 34 35 40 45 50 57 59 64 65 68 75 76 77 79 81 82 85 86 89 90 93 97 107 111 114 119 130 132 133 135 146 148 **S** Ascension Health, Saint Louis, MO
Primary Contact: Kristi Bledsoe, R.N., Administrator
CMO: Stephen Tharp, M.D., Medical Director
CHR: Krista Wright, Director Human Resources
Web address: www.stvincent.org
**Control:** Church–operated, Nongovernment, not–for profit **Service:** General Medical and Surgical

> **Staffed Beds:** 25 **Admissions:** 836 **Census:** 9 **Outpatient Visits:** 35193 **Births:** 227 **Total Expense ($000):** 22520 **Payroll Expense ($000):** 8020 **Personnel:** 80

### FRANKLIN—Johnson County

★ ○ **JOHNSON MEMORIAL HOSPITAL (150001)**, 1125 West Jefferson Street, Zip 46131–2140, Mailing Address: P.O. Box 549, Zip 46131–0549; tel. 317/736–3300 **A**5 9 10 11 **F**12 13 15 18 20 22 28 29 30 31 34 35 36 40 44 45 49 50 54 57 59 62 64 68 70 74 75 76 77 78 79 81 82 85 87 90 93 97 107 108 110 111 113 114 118 119 129 130 131 132 134 135 144 146 147 148 **P**8
Primary Contact: Larry Heydon, President and Chief Executive Officer
COO: Steve Wohlford, Chief Operating Officer
CFO: Elizabeth A. Hedden, Chief Financial Officer
CMO: John Norris, M.D., Vice President Medical Affairs
CIO: Scott Krodel, Vice President Information Systems
CHR: Judy Ware, Director Human Resources
CNO: Anita M. Keller, R.N., Chief Nursing Officer
Web address: www.johnsonmemorial.org
**Control:** County–Government, nonfederal **Service:** General Medical and Surgical

> **Staffed Beds:** 101 **Admissions:** 2221 **Census:** 24 **Outpatient Visits:** 141211 **Births:** 349 **Total Expense ($000):** 70005 **Payroll Expense ($000):** 33695 **Personnel:** 627

### GARY—Lake County

★ ○ △ **METHODIST HOSPITALS (150002)**, 600 Grant Street, Zip 46402–6099; tel. 219/886–4000, (Includes SOUTHLAKE CAMPUS, 8701 Broadway, Merrillville, Zip 46410; tel. 219/738–5500) **A**2 3 5 7 9 10 11 **F**3 8 11 12 13 15 20 22 24 26 28 29 30 34 35 37 40 43 45 47 48 49 50 51 54 55 57 59 62 64 67 70 72 73 74 75 76 77 78 79 81 82 85 86 87 89 90 93 98 99 100 101 102 103 107 108 110 111 114 115 118 119 120 121 123 124 126 130 132 133 146 147 148 **P**6
Primary Contact: Raymond Grady, FACHE, President and Chief Executive Officer
CMO: Michael Davenport, M.D., Vice President Medical Affairs
CIO: Shaw Collins, Director Information Technology
CHR: Joyce McGlory, Vice President Human Resources
Web address: www.methodisthospitals.org
**Control:** Other not–for–profit (including NFP Corporation) **Service:** General Medical and Surgical

> **Staffed Beds:** 504 **Admissions:** 18095 **Census:** 289 **Outpatient Visits:** 282840 **Births:** 1298 **Total Expense ($000):** 315561 **Payroll Expense ($000):** 137255 **Personnel:** 2013

**IN**

---

**Hospital, Medicare Provider Number, Address, Telephone, Approval, Facility, and Physician Codes, Health Care System**

★ American Hospital Association (AHA) membership  ○ Healthcare Facilities Accreditation Program  ⇑ Center for Improvement in Healthcare Quality Accreditation
□ The Joint Commission accreditation  ◇ DNV Healthcare Inc. accreditation  △ Commission on Accreditation of Rehabilitation Facilities (CARF) accreditation

---

## GOSHEN—Elkhart County

**GOSHEN GENERAL HOSPITAL** See Indiana University Health Goshen Hospital

✠ **INDIANA UNIVERSITY HEALTH GOSHEN HOSPITAL (150026)**, 200 High Park Avenue, Zip 46526–4899, Mailing Address: P.O. Box 139, Zip 46527–0139; tel. 574/533–2141, (Nonreporting) **A**1 2 9 10 **S** Indiana University Health, Indianapolis, IN
Primary Contact: Randal Christophel, President and Chief Executive Officer
COO: Paulette Brown, Chief Operating Officer
CMO: Randall Cammenga, M.D., Vice President Medical Affairs
CIO: Dolph Voelker, Director Information Services
CHR: Alan Weldy, Vice President Human Resources, Compliance and Legal Services
Web address: www.iuhealth.org
**Control:** Other not–for–profit (including NFP Corporation) **Service:** General Medical and Surgical

**Staffed Beds:** 122

**OAKLAWN PSYCHIATRIC CENTER (154031)**, 330 Lakeview Drive, Zip 46528–9365, Mailing Address: P.O. Box 809, Zip 46527–0809; tel. 574/533–1234 **A**9 10 **F**4 5 30 34 54 98 99 100 101 102 103 104 105 106 130 146 **P**6
Primary Contact: Laurie N. Nafziger, President and Chief Executive Officer
CFO: Joseph Barkman, Vice President Financial Services
CMO: Daniel Kinsey, M.D., Medical Director
CIO: Jennifer Glick, Manager Clinical Informatics
CHR: Jill Seifer, Vice President Human Resources
CNO: Elaine G. Miller, Director of Nursing
Web address: www.oaklawn.org
**Control:** Other not–for–profit (including NFP Corporation) **Service:** Psychiatric

**Staffed Beds:** 16 **Admissions:** 804 **Census:** 14 **Outpatient Visits:** 288184 **Births:** 0 **Total Expense ($000):** 46735 **Payroll Expense ($000):** 29046 **Personnel:** 737

## GREENCASTLE—Putnam County

**PUTNAM COUNTY HOSPITAL (151333)**, 1542 Bloomington Street, Zip 46135–2297; tel. 765/653–5121, (Nonreporting) **A**2 9 10 18
Primary Contact: Dennis Weatherford, Chief Executive Officer
CFO: Kevin Fowler, Director Finance
Web address: www.pchosp.org/
**Control:** County–Government, nonfederal **Service:** General Medical and Surgical

**Staffed Beds:** 25

## GREENFIELD—Hancock County

★ ○ **HANCOCK REGIONAL HOSPITAL (150037)**, 801 North State Street, Zip 46140–1270, Mailing Address: P.O. Box 827, Zip 46140–0827; tel. 317/462–5544 **A**9 10 11 **F**3 11 12 13 15 17 18 20 22 28 29 30 31 32 34 35 38 40 44 45 47 48 49 50 53 54 56 57 59 62 63 64 68 69 70 74 75 76 78 79 81 82 84 85 86 87 89 90 92 93 96 98 103 107 108 110 111 114 115 119 127 129 130 132 134 135 146 147 148 **P**2 8
Primary Contact: Steven V. Long, FACHE, President and Chief Executive Officer
COO: Robert Lawrence Matt, Vice President and Chief Operating Officer
CFO: Rick Edwards, Vice President and Chief Financial Officer
CMO: Michael Fletcher, M.D., Vice President and Chief Medical Officer
CIO: Jon Miller, Director Accounting and Information Services
CHR: Laura L. Nichols, Director Human Resources
CNO: Sherry Gehring, R.N., Vice President and Chief Nursing Officer
Web address: www.hancockregional.org
**Control:** County–Government, nonfederal **Service:** General Medical and Surgical

**Staffed Beds:** 76 **Admissions:** 3015 **Census:** 32 **Outpatient Visits:** 146973 **Births:** 378 **Total Expense ($000):** 97974 **Payroll Expense ($000):** 35812 **Personnel:** 638

## GREENSBURG—Decatur County

★ ◇ **DECATUR COUNTY MEMORIAL HOSPITAL (151332)**, 720 North Lincoln Street, Zip 47240–1398; tel. 812/663–4331, (Total facility includes 91 beds in nursing home–type unit) **A**2 9 10 18 21 **F**3 7 11 13 15 18 28 29 31 34 40 45 50 54 57 59 62 64 65 68 69 74 75 76 77 78 79 80 81 82 85 86 87 89 92 93 94 96 97 107 108 110 111 115 118 119 128 129 130 131 132 133 135 145 146 147 148 **P**6
Primary Contact: Linda V. Simmons, President and Chief Executive Officer
COO: Eric Stokes, Vice President of Operations
CFO: Jerry Marks, Vice President Finance
CHR: Amy Lynn Wickens, Executive Director Human Resources
CNO: Diane McKinney, R.N., Vice President Patient Care Service
Web address: www.dcmh.net
**Control:** County–Government, nonfederal **Service:** General Medical and Surgical

**Staffed Beds:** 116 **Admissions:** 1291 **Census:** 34 **Outpatient Visits:** 128764 **Births:** 243 **Total Expense ($000):** 50958 **Payroll Expense ($000):** 22492 **Personnel:** 388

## GREENWOOD—Johnson County

✠ **KINDRED HOSPITAL INDIANAPOLIS SOUTH (152008)**, 607 Greenwood Springs Drive, Zip 46143–6377; tel. 317/888–8155, (Nonreporting) **A**1 10 **S** Kindred Healthcare, Louisville, KY
Primary Contact: Matthew Keppler, Market Chief Executive Officer
CFO: William Brenner, Chief Financial Officer
CMO: Steven Samuels, M.D., Medical Director
CNO: Jennifer Stallings, Chief Clinical Officer
Web address: www.khindysouth.com/
**Control:** Corporation, Investor–owned, for–profit **Service:** Long–Term Acute Care hospital

**Staffed Beds:** 52

☐ **VALLE VISTA HOSPITAL (154024)**, 898 East Main Street, Zip 46143–1400; tel. 317/887–1348, (Nonreporting) **A**1 9 10 **S** Universal Health Services, Inc., King of Prussia, PA
Primary Contact: Sherri R. Jewett, Chief Executive Officer
CFO: Tim Sides, Chief Financial Officer
CMO: Jennifer Comer, M.D., Medical Director
CIO: Karen Hayden, Director Health Information Services, Performance Improvement and Risk Management
CHR: Ismael Santos, Director Human Resources
Web address: www.vallevistahospital.com
**Control:** Corporation, Investor–owned, for–profit **Service:** Psychiatric

**Staffed Beds:** 102

## HAMMOND—Lake County

○ △ **FRANCISCAN ST. MARGARET HEALTH – HAMMOND (150004)**, 5454 Hohman Avenue, Zip 46320–1999; tel. 219/932–2300, (Includes FRANCISCAN ST. MARGARET HEALTH – DYER, 24 Joliet Street, Dyer, Zip 46311–1799; tel. 219/865–2141; Michael J. Stenger, President and Chief Executive Officer; SAINT MARGARET MERCY HEALTHCARE CENTERS–NORTH CAMPUS, 5454 Hohman Avenue, Zip 46320; tel. 219/932–2300), (Nonreporting) **A**2 7 9 10 11 **S** Franciscan Alliance, Mishawaka, IN
Primary Contact: Michael J. Stenger, President and Chief Executive Officer
CFO: Marc Golan, Chief Financial Officer
Web address: www.smmhc.com
**Control:** Church–operated, Nongovernment, not–for profit **Service:** General Medical and Surgical

**Staffed Beds:** 500

✠ **KINDRED HOSPITAL NORTHWEST INDIANA (152012)**, 5454 Hohman Avenue, 5th Floor, Zip 46320–1931; tel. 219/937–9900, (Nonreporting) **A**1 10 **S** Kindred Healthcare, Louisville, KY
Primary Contact: Frank A. Solare, Chief Executive Officer
Web address: www.khnwindiana.com
**Control:** Corporation, Investor–owned, for–profit **Service:** Long–Term Acute Care hospital

**Staffed Beds:** 70

**SAINT MARGARET MERCY HEALTHCARE CENTERS** See Franciscan St. Margaret Health – Hammond

**TRIUMPH HOSPITAL NORTHWEST INDIANA** See Kindred Hospital Northwest Indiana

## HARTFORD CITY—Blackford County

**BLACKFORD COMMUNITY HOSPITAL** See Indiana University Health Blackford Hospital

✠ **INDIANA UNIVERSITY HEALTH BLACKFORD HOSPITAL (151302)**, 410 Pilgrim Boulevard, Zip 47348–1897; tel. 765/348–0300 **A**1 9 10 18 **F**3 11 15 28 29 34 35 40 44 45 57 59 64 75 81 85 87 93 107 110 115 119 130 132 133 135 **S** Indiana University Health, Indianapolis, IN
Primary Contact: Steven J. West, Chief Executive Officer
CFO: Bettie Caldwell, Director Finance
CIO: Steven J. West, Chief Executive Officer
CHR: John Crosbie, Director Support Services
CNO: Kandi Adamson, R.N., Chief Nursing Officer
Web address: www.iuhealth.org/blackford
**Control:** Other not–for–profit (including NFP Corporation) **Service:** General Medical and Surgical

**Staffed Beds:** 15 **Admissions:** 542 **Census:** 7 **Outpatient Visits:** 31930 **Births:** 0 **Total Expense ($000):** 15033 **Payroll Expense ($000):** 5650 **Personnel:** 98

IN

*Many Facility Codes have changed. Please refer to the AHA Guide Code Chart.*

**HOBART—Lake County**

☐ △ **ST. MARY MEDICAL CENTER (150034)**, 1500 South Lake Park Avenue, Zip 46342–6699; tel. 219/942–0551 **A**1 2 7 9 10 **F**3 8 11 12 13 15 18 20 22 24 26 28 29 30 31 34 35 36 38 39 40 45 47 49 50 54 57 58 59 62 64 65 70 74 75 76 77 78 79 80 81 82 85 86 87 89 90 92 93 96 107 108 110 111 114 115 119 120 121 123 126 129 130 131 132 135 144 146 147 148 **P**8 **S** Community Healthcare System, Hammond, IN
Primary Contact: Janice L. Ryba, JD, Chief Executive Officer
CFO: Mary Sudicky, Chief Financial Officer
CIO: Gary Weiner, Vice President Information Technology and Chief Information Officer
CHR: Tony Ferracane, Vice President Human Resources
CNO: Tammie R. Jones, R.N., Chief Nursing Officer
Web address: www.comhs.org
**Control:** Other not–for–profit (including NFP Corporation) **Service:** General Medical and Surgical

**Staffed Beds:** 195 **Admissions:** 10441 **Census:** 149 **Outpatient Visits:** 203290 **Births:** 534 **Total Expense ($000):** 212288 **Payroll Expense ($000):** 61101 **Personnel:** 956

**HUNTINGTON—Huntington County**

✠ **PARKVIEW HUNTINGTON HOSPITAL (150091)**, 2001 Stults Road, Zip 46750–1291; tel. 260/355–3000 **A**1 9 10 **F**3 7 8 13 15 28 29 30 31 32 34 35 36 38 39 40 44 45 46 50 53 56 57 59 64 68 69 70 75 76 77 78 79 81 85 86 87 93 96 97 107 108 111 119 130 131 132 134 135 146 148 **S** Parkview Health, Fort Wayne, IN
Primary Contact: Juli Johnson, R.N., President
CMO: Jeffrey Brooks, M.D., Medical Director
Web address: www.parkview.com
**Control:** Other not–for–profit (including NFP Corporation) **Service:** General Medical and Surgical

**Staffed Beds:** 36 **Admissions:** 1787 **Census:** 15 **Outpatient Visits:** 41201 **Births:** 350 **Total Expense ($000):** 40512 **Payroll Expense ($000):** 12822 **Personnel:** 232

**INDIANAPOLIS—Marion County**

**CLARIAN HEALTH PARTNERS** See Indiana University Health University Hospital

☐ **COMMUNITY HOSPITAL EAST (150074)**, 1500 North Ritter Avenue, Zip 46219–3095; tel. 317/355–1411, (Includes COMMUNITY HEART AND VASCULAR HOSPITAL, 8075 North Shadeland Avenue, Zip 46250–2693; tel. 317/621–8000; Jason Fahrlander, FACHE, President; COMMUNITY WESTVIEW HOSPITAL, 3630 Guion Road, Zip 46222–1699; tel. 317/924–6661; David C. Williams, D.O., President and Chief Executive Officer) **A**1 2 3 5 9 10 **F**3 5 11 13 17 18 20 22 24 26 28 29 30 31 34 35 38 40 44 45 47 49 50 51 53 55 56 57 58 59 60 63 64 65 68 69 70 73 74 75 76 77 78 79 80 81 85 87 91 92 93 96 98 99 100 101 102 103 104 105 106 107 108 109 110 111 114 115 118 119 120 121 123 129 130 132 141 144 146 147 148 **P**8 **S** Community Health Network, Indianapolis, IN
Primary Contact: Robin Ledyard, M.D., M.P.H., President
Web address: www.ecommunity.com/east/
**Control:** Other not–for–profit (including NFP Corporation) **Service:** General Medical and Surgical

**Staffed Beds:** 318 **Admissions:** 15723 **Census:** 185 **Outpatient Visits:** 657758 **Births:** 941 **Total Expense ($000):** 440499 **Payroll Expense ($000):** 165399 **Personnel:** 2624

☐ **COMMUNITY HOSPITAL NORTH (150169)**, 7150 Clearvista Drive, Zip 46256–1695; tel. 317/621–6262 **A**1 3 9 10 **F**3 11 12 13 18 29 30 31 34 35 40 41 45 46 47 48 49 50 52 53 56 57 59 60 61 63 64 65 68 69 70 72 74 75 76 78 79 81 82 84 85 86 87 89 91 92 93 94 96 98 103 107 108 111 115 118 119 126 129 130 131 132 145 146 147 148 **P**8 **S** Community Health Network, Indianapolis, IN
Primary Contact: Jason Fahrlander, FACHE, President
COO: Susan Sandberg, R.N., Chief Operating Officer
CFO: Amy Campbell, Chief Financial Officer
CMO: Wesley Wong, M.D., Acting Vice President Medical and Academic Affairs
CIO: Ron Thieme, Ph.D., Chief Knowledge and Information Officer
CHR: Steve Pearcy, Director Human Resources
Web address: www.ecommunity.com/north
**Control:** Other not–for–profit (including NFP Corporation) **Service:** General Medical and Surgical

**Staffed Beds:** 314 **Admissions:** 16654 **Census:** 207 **Outpatient Visits:** 209981 **Births:** 3869 **Total Expense ($000):** 293099 **Payroll Expense ($000):** 88517 **Personnel:** 1227

☐ **COMMUNITY HOSPITAL SOUTH (150128)**, 1402 East County Line Road South, Zip 46227–0963; tel. 317/887–7000 **A**1 3 9 10 **F**3 11 12 13 15 18 20 22 28 29 30 31 35 37 40 45 46 47 48 49 54 60 64 69 70 73 74 75 76 77 78 79 81 82 84 85 86 89 107 108 110 111 114 115 119 126 129 130 131 135 145 146 147 148 **P**8 **S** Community Health Network, Indianapolis, IN
Primary Contact: Anthony B. Lennen, President
Web address: www.ecommunity.com
**Control:** Other not–for–profit (including NFP Corporation) **Service:** General Medical and Surgical

**Staffed Beds:** 158 **Admissions:** 8595 **Census:** 84 **Outpatient Visits:** 126853 **Births:** 1660 **Total Expense ($000):** 157155 **Payroll Expense ($000):** 45692 **Personnel:** 660

☐ **ESKENAZI HEALTH (150024)**, 720 Eskenazi Avenue, Zip 46202–5166; tel. 317/880–0000 **A**1 3 5 8 9 10 **F**3 5 7 10 13 14 15 16 18 20 22 28 29 30 31 32 34 35 36 38 39 40 43 44 47 48 49 50 53 54 55 56 57 61 62 64 65 66 68 70 71 72 74 75 76 77 78 79 81 82 83 84 85 86 87 93 97 98 99 100 101 102 103 104 105 106 107 110 111 115 119 130 132 134 135 143 144 145 146 147 148
Primary Contact: Lisa E. Harris, M.D., Chief Executive Officer and Medical Director
COO: Parveen Chand, Chief Operating Officer
CFO: Dan Sellers, Chief Financial Officer
CMO: Lisa E. Harris, M.D., Chief Executive Officer
CIO: David Shaw, Vice President Information Systems
CHR: Christia Hicks, Vice President Human Resources
CNO: Lee Ann Blue, MSN, Chief Nursing Officer and Executive Vice President Patient Care Services
Web address: www.eskenazihealth.edu
**Control:** County–Government, nonfederal **Service:** General Medical and Surgical

**Staffed Beds:** 279 **Admissions:** 15200 **Census:** 202 **Outpatient Visits:** 831388 **Births:** 2056 **Total Expense ($000):** 583182 **Payroll Expense ($000):** 216438 **Personnel:** 3786

☐ **FAIRBANKS (150179)**, 8102 Clearvista Parkway, Zip 46256–4698; tel. 317/849–8222 **A**1 3 9 10 **F**4 5 29 30 35 36 75 87 100 105 130 132 135 146 **P**8
Primary Contact: Barb Elliott, Interim President and Chief Executive Officer
CFO: Barb Elliott, Chief Financial Officer
CMO: Dennis Rhyne, M.D., Acting Medical Director
CIO: Randy Walls, Manager Information Services
CHR: Sharon Baker, Director Support Services
CNO: Jennifer M. Horstman, R.N., Chief Nursing Officer and Chief Information Officer
Web address: www.fairbankscd.org
**Control:** Other not–for–profit (including NFP Corporation) **Service:** Alcoholism and other chemical dependency

**Staffed Beds:** 86 **Admissions:** 3347 **Census:** 44 **Outpatient Visits:** 25361 **Births:** 0 **Total Expense ($000):** 20575 **Payroll Expense ($000):** 10589 **Personnel:** 248

○ △ **FRANCISCAN ST. FRANCIS HEALTH – INDIANAPOLIS (150162)**, 8111 South Emerson Avenue, Zip 46237–8601; tel. 317/528–5000 **A**2 3 5 7 9 10 11 **F**8 11 12 13 15 17 18 22 24 28 29 30 31 32 34 35 36 40 46 47 49 50 55 56 57 60 61 62 63 64 65 66 68 70 72 74 75 76 77 78 79 80 81 82 84 85 86 87 89 90 93 97 107 108 109 110 111 113 115 116 117 118 119 120 121 123 124 126 129 130 131 132 135 144 146 147 148 **P**7 8 **S** Franciscan Alliance, Mishawaka, IN
Primary Contact: James Callaghan, III, M.D., President and Chief Executive Officer
CFO: Keith A. Lauter, Regional Chief Financial Officer
CMO: Christopher Doehring, M.D., Vice President Medical Affairs
CIO: Barbara Coulter, Director Information Systems
CHR: Corey Baute, Vice President Human Resources
CNO: Susan McRoberts, R.N., Vice President and Chief Nursing Officer
Web address: www.stfrancishospitals.org
**Control:** Church–operated, Nongovernment, not–for profit **Service:** General Medical and Surgical

**Staffed Beds:** 485 **Admissions:** 18417 **Census:** 239 **Outpatient Visits:** 511594 **Births:** 2221 **Total Expense ($000):** 566346 **Payroll Expense ($000):** 180347 **Personnel:** 2583

○ **INDIANA ORTHOPAEDIC HOSPITAL (150160)**, 8400 Northwest Boulevard, Zip 46278–1381; tel. 317/956–1000, (Nonreporting) **A**3 9 10 11
Primary Contact: Jane Keller, R.N., Chief Executive Officer
COO: Stacie Vance, Vice President Clinical Services
CFO: Anthony Gioia, Chief Financial Officer
CMO: Joseph Randolph, M.D., Chairman Medical Executive Committee
CIO: Paul Frey, Director Information Technology Applications
CHR: Kristy Hensley, Director Human Resources
CNO: Stacie Vance, Chief Nursing Officer and Vice President Clinical Services
Web address: www.orthoindy.com
**Control:** Corporation, Investor–owned, for–profit **Service:** Orthopedic

**Staffed Beds:** 37

**IN**

| Hospital, Medicare Provider Number, Address, Telephone, Approval, Facility, and Physician Codes, Health Care System |
| --- |

★ American Hospital Association (AHA) membership    ◯ Healthcare Facilities Accreditation Program    ⇑ Center for Improvement in Healthcare Quality Accreditation
☐ The Joint Commission accreditation    ◇ DNV Healthcare Inc. accreditation    △ Commission on Accreditation of Rehabilitation Facilities (CARF) accreditation

**INDIANA UNIVERSITY HEALTH METHODIST HOSPITAL** See Indiana University Health University Hospital

✠ **INDIANA UNIVERSITY HEALTH UNIVERSITY HOSPITAL (150056)**, 550 University Boulevard, Zip 46202–5149, Mailing Address: P.O. Box 1367, Zip 46206–1367; tel. 317/944–5000, (Includes INDIANA UNIVERSITY HEALTH METHODIST HOSPITAL, 1701 North Senate Boulevard, Zip 46202, Mailing Address: 1701 North Senate Bouleverd, Zip 46202; tel. 317/962–2000; Herbert Buchanan, President; INDIANA UNIVERSITY HOSPITAL, 550 North University Boulevard, Zip 46202–5262; tel. 317/274–5000; IU HEALTH SAXONY HOSPITAL, 13000 East 136th Street, Fishers, Zip 46037–9478; tel. 317/678–2000; Jonathan R. Goble, FACHE, Chief Executive Officer; RILEY HOSPITAL FOR CHILDREN AT INDIANA UNIVERSITY HEALTH, 702 Barnhill Drive, Zip 46202–5225; tel. 317/274–5000) **A**1 2 3 5 8 9 10 **F**5 6 7 8 9 11 12 13 15 16 17 18 19 20 21 22 23 24 25 26 27 28 29 30 31 32 33 34 35 36 37 38 39 40 41 43 44 45 46 47 48 49 50 51 52 53 54 55 56 57 58 59 60 61 62 63 64 65 68 69 70 71 72 73 74 75 76 77 78 79 80 81 82 83 84 85 86 87 88 89 91 92 93 94 96 97 98 99 100 101 102 103 104 105 106 107 108 109 110 111 112 113 114 115 116 117 118 119 120 121 122 123 124 126 129 130 131 132 134 135 136 137 138 139 140 141 144 145 146 147 148 **S** Indiana University Health, Indianapolis, IN
Primary Contact: Herbert Buchanan, President
COO: Dennis M. Murphy, Chief Operating Officer
CIO: Richard F. Johnson, Senior Vice President and Chief Information Officer
Web address: www.iuhealth.org
**Control:** Other not–for–profit (including NFP Corporation) **Service:** General Medical and Surgical

**Staffed Beds: 1243 Admissions: 50053 Census: 891 Outpatient Visits: 1099625 Births: 3331 Total Expense ($000): 2329936 Payroll Expense ($000): 775024 Personnel: 13479**

**INDIANA UNIVERSITY HOSPITAL** See Indiana University Health University Hospital

✠ **KINDRED HOSPITAL–INDIANAPOLIS (152007)**, 1700 West 10th Street, Zip 46222–3802; tel. 317/636–4400, (Nonreporting) **A**1 10 **S** Kindred Healthcare, Louisville, KY
Primary Contact: Bryan Chatterton, Chief Executive Officer
COO: Angela Lynne Rotert, Chief Clinical Officer
CFO: William Brenner, Chief Financial Officer
CHR: Joe Housh, District Director Human Resources
Web address: www.kindredhospitalindy.com/
**Control:** Corporation, Investor–owned, for–profit **Service:** Long–Term Acute Care hospital

**Staffed Beds: 59**

☐ **LARUE D. CARTER MEMORIAL HOSPITAL (154008)**, 2601 Cold Spring Road, Zip 46222–2273; tel. 317/941–4000, (Nonreporting) **A**1 3 5 10
Primary Contact: Eric Heeter, Superintendent
CFO: Michael Logar, Assistant Superintendent
CMO: Beth Pfau, M.D., Chief Medical Officer
CIO: Denton Gross, Director Information Services
CHR: Rebecca Dutton, Director Human Resources
CNO: Todd Rittman, Director of Nursing
**Control:** State–Government, nonfederal **Service:** Psychiatric

**Staffed Beds: 148**

**METHODIST HOSPITAL** See Indiana University Health Methodist Hospital

☐ **OPTIONS BEHAVIORAL HEALTH SYSTEM (154057)**, 5602 Caito Drive, Zip 46226–1346; tel. 317/544–4340 **A**1 10 **F**98 99 102 103 106 **P**5 **S** Acadia Healthcare Company, Inc., Franklin, TN
Primary Contact: Matthew Love, Chief Executive Officer
Web address: www.optionsbehavioralhealthsystem.com/
**Control:** Corporation, Investor–owned, for–profit **Service:** Psychiatric

**Staffed Beds: 84 Admissions: 1107 Census: 24 Outpatient Visits: 0 Births: 0 Total Expense ($000): 9973 Payroll Expense ($000): 5468 Personnel: 133**

☐ △ **REHABILITATION HOSPITAL OF INDIANA (153028)**, 4141 Shore Drive, Zip 46254–2607; tel. 317/329–2000 **A**1 3 5 7 9 10 **F**1 4 16 17 28 29 30 33 54 58 64 67 70 72 73 75 79 80 86 87 88 89 90 91 92 93 96 98 128 130 131 132 146 148 **P**5 **S** Indiana University Health, Indianapolis, IN
Primary Contact: Daniel B. Woloszyn, Chief Executive Officer
COO: Monte Spence, Chief Operating Officer
CFO: Marjorie Basey, Chief Financial Officer
CMO: Flora Hammond, M.D., Chief Medical Affairs
CIO: Gary Skinner, Director Information Technology
CHR: Joni Brown, Director Human Resources
CNO: Debra Cordes, Chief Nursing Officer
Web address: www.rhin.com
**Control:** Other not–for–profit (including NFP Corporation) **Service:** Rehabilitation

**Staffed Beds: 83 Admissions: 1222 Census: 52 Outpatient Visits: 20464 Births: 0 Total Expense ($000): 35276 Payroll Expense ($000): 17645 Personnel: 364**

✠ △ **RICHARD L. ROUDEBUSH VETERANS AFFAIRS MEDICAL CENTER**, 1481 West Tenth Street, Zip 46202–2884; tel. 317/554–0000 **A**1 2 3 5 7 8 **F**3 5 18 20 22 24 26 28 29 30 31 33 34 35 36 38 39 40 44 45 46 49 50 53 54 56 57 58 59 60 61 62 63 64 65 67 70 74 75 77 78 79 80 81 82 83 84 85 86 87 90 91 92 93 94 96 97 98 100 101 102 103 104 105 107 111 115 117 119 120 121 126 127 129 130 132 135 143 144 146 147 148 **S** Department of Veterans Affairs, Washington, DC
Primary Contact: Ginny L. Creasman, Acting Director
COO: Jeff Nechanicky, Assistant Director
CFO: Paul Pessagno, Chief Financial Officer
CMO: Ken Klotz, M.D., Chief of Staff
CIO: Steve Stoner, Chief Information Officer
Web address: www.indianapolis.va.gov
**Control:** Veterans Affairs, Government, federal **Service:** General Medical and Surgical

**Staffed Beds: 209 Admissions: 8003 Census: 167 Outpatient Visits: 717001 Births: 0 Total Expense ($000): 478520 Payroll Expense ($000): 203158 Personnel: 3042**

**RILEY HOSPITAL FOR CHILDREN** See Riley Hospital for Children at Indiana University Health

**RILEY HOSPITAL FOR CHILDREN AT INDIANA UNIVERSITY HEALTH** See Indiana University Health University Hospital

✠ **SELECT SPECIALTY HOSPITAL–INDIANAPOLIS (152013)**, 8060 Knue Road, Zip 46250–1976; tel. 317/783–8985, (Nonreporting) **A**1 10 **S** Select Medical Corporation, Mechanicsburg, PA
Primary Contact: Rick Ament, Chief Executive Officer
CHR: Kelly Becker, Administrative Coordinator Human Resources
Web address: www.indianapolis.selectspecialtyhospitals.com/
**Control:** Corporation, Investor–owned, for–profit **Service:** Long–Term Acute Care hospital

**Staffed Beds: 45**

**ST. FRANCIS HOSPITAL AND HEALTH CENTERS – SOUTH CAMPUS** See Franciscan St. Francis Health – Indianapolis

✠ **ST. VINCENT HEART CENTER (150153)**, 10580 North Meridian Street, Zip 46290–1028; tel. 317/583–5000 **A**1 9 10 **F**3 18 20 22 24 26 28 29 30 34 35 40 43 45 46 58 59 75 81 85 86 87 111 115 119 129 130 135 148 **P**2 **S** Ascension Health, Saint Louis, MO
Primary Contact: Blake A. Dye, President
COO: Mike Schroyer, Chief Operating Officer
CFO: Becky Jacobson, Vice President Finance
CMO: William Storer, M.D., Medical Director
CIO: Roger Strange, Chief Information Officer
Web address: www.bestheartcare.com/
**Control:** Partnership, Investor–owned, for–profit **Service:** Heart

**Staffed Beds: 107 Admissions: 4378 Census: 50 Outpatient Visits: 10369 Births: 0 Total Expense ($000): 103483 Payroll Expense ($000): 28292 Personnel: 356**

✠ **ST. VINCENT INDIANAPOLIS HOSPITAL (150084)**, 2001 West 86th Street, Zip 46260–1991, Mailing Address: P.O. Box 40970, Zip 46240–0970; tel. 317/338–2345, (Includes PEYTON MANNING CHILDREN'S HOSPITAL, 1707 West 86th Street, Zip 46240, Mailing Address: P.O. Box 40407, Zip 46240; tel. 317/415–5500; Anne Coleman, Administrator; PEYTON MANNING CHILDREN'S HOSPITAL AT ST. VINCENT, 2001 West 86th Street, Zip 46260, Mailing Address: P.O. Box 40970, Zip 46240–0970; tel. 317/415–8111; Anne Coleman, Administrator; ST. VINCENT STRESS CENTER, 8401 Harcourt Road, Zip 46260, Mailing Address: P.O. Box 80160, Zip 46280; tel. 317/338–4600; Sheila Mishler, Chief Executive Officer; ST. VINCENT WOMEN'S HOSPITAL, 8111 Township Line Road, Zip 46260–8043; tel. 317/415–8111; Anne Coleman, Administrator) **A**1 2 3 5 8 9 10 **F**3 4 5 7 8 9 11 13 15 17 18 19 20 21 22 23 24 25 26 27 28 29 30 31 32 34 35 36 37 38 39 40 41 43 44 45 46 47 48 49 50 51 53 54 55 56 57 58 59 61 62 63 64 65 66 68 70 71 72 73 74 75 76 77 78 79 81 82 83 84 85 86 87 88 89 90 91 92 93 94 96 97 98 99 100 101 102 103 104 105 106 107 108 109 110 111 114 115 117 118 119 120 121 124 126 129 130 131 132 134 135 137 138 141 142 143 144 146 147 148 **P**6 **S** Ascension Health, Saint Louis, MO
Primary Contact: Joel Feldman, M.D., President
COO: Darcy Burthay, MSN, Chief Nursing Officer and Chief Operating Officer
CFO: Thomas M. Cook, CPA, Chief Financial Officer
CMO: Daniel LeGrand, M.D., Chief Medical Officer
CIO: Brian Peters, Chief Information Officer
CHR: Marty Du Rall, Executive Director Human Resources
CNO: Mary Myers, R.N., Chief Nursing Officer
Web address: www.stvincent.org
**Control:** Church–operated, Nongovernment, not–for profit **Service:** General Medical and Surgical

**Staffed Beds: 919 Admissions: 35357 Census: 553 Outpatient Visits: 863302 Births: 3618 Total Expense ($000): 988384 Payroll Expense ($000): 344040 Personnel: 4385**

**IN**

*Many Facility Codes have changed. Please refer to the AHA Guide Code Chart.*
© 2015 AHA Guide

☒ **ST. VINCENT SETON SPECIALTY HOSPITAL (152020)**, 8050 Township Line Road, Zip 46260–2478; tel. 317/415–8353 **A**1 9 10 **F**1 29 30 31 35 53 60 68 75 85 114 119 132 146 148 **P**8 **S** Ascension Health, Saint Louis, MO
Primary Contact: Peter H. Alexander, Administrator
COO: Troy T. Reiff, Corporate Director Operations
CFO: David M. Girten, Corporate Director Financial Services
CMO: Ronald Reisman, M.D., Chief Medical Director
CHR: Terry A. Wignall, Director Human Resources
Web address: www.stvincent.org/
**Control:** Other not–for–profit (including NFP Corporation) **Service:** Long–Term Acute Care hospital

**Staffed Beds:** 74 **Admissions:** 631 **Census:** 61 **Outpatient Visits:** 0 **Births:** 0 **Total Expense ($000):** 36911 **Payroll Expense ($000):** 17461 **Personnel:** 281

**WESTVIEW HOSPITAL** See Community Westview Hospital

### JASPER—Dubois County

☒ **MEMORIAL HOSPITAL AND HEALTH CARE CENTER (150115)**, 800 West Ninth Street, Zip 47546–2516; tel. 812/996–2345, (Total facility includes 20 beds in nursing home–type unit) **A**1 2 9 10 19 **F**3 5 7 8 11 12 13 15 18 20 22 24 26 28 29 30 31 34 35 36 40 41 42 45 46 47 48 49 51 54 56 57 59 62 64 66 68 70 74 75 76 77 78 79 81 82 84 85 86 87 89 90 93 97 98 100 101 102 103 104 105 107 108 110 111 112 113 114 115 116 117 118 119 120 121 127 128 129 130 131 132 135 144 146 147 148 **P**6 **S** American Province of Little Company of Mary Sisters, Evergreen Park, IL
Primary Contact: E. Kyle Bennett, President and Chief Executive Officer
CFO: Randall Russell, Vice President and Chief Financial Officer
CMO: Ryan Sherer, M.D., President Medical Staff
CIO: Gary Light, Vice President and Chief Information Officer
CHR: Richard Pea, Director Human Resources
CNO: Tonya Heim, R.N., Vice President Patient Services and Chief Nursing Officer
Web address: www.mhhcc.org
**Control:** Church–operated, Nongovernment, not–for profit **Service:** General Medical and Surgical

**Staffed Beds:** 143 **Admissions:** 6273 **Census:** 74 **Outpatient Visits:** 237945 **Births:** 951 **Total Expense ($000):** 183571 **Payroll Expense ($000):** 77973 **Personnel:** 1099

### JEFFERSONVILLE—Clark County

☒ **CLARK MEMORIAL HOSPITAL (150009)**, 1220 Missouri Avenue, Zip 47130–3743, Mailing Address: P.O. Box 69, Zip 47131–0600; tel. 812/282–6631 **A**1 2 3 5 9 10 **F**3 5 7 8 11 12 13 15 17 18 20 22 26 28 29 30 31 34 35 38 40 45 46 49 50 53 54 56 57 59 64 65 70 74 75 76 77 78 79 81 82 85 86 87 91 92 97 98 100 101 102 103 104 105 107 108 110 111 114 115 119 124 130 132 135 144 145 146 147 148 **P**6
Primary Contact: Martin Padgett, President and Chief Executive Officer
CFO: Kirk Strack, Vice President and Chief Financial Officer
CMO: William Templeton, III, M.D., Medical Director
CIO: Larry Reverman, Director Information Systems
CHR: Scott Hicks, Vice President
CNO: Kathy Neuner, R.N., Chief Nursing Officer
Web address: www.clarkmemorial.org
**Control:** County–Government, nonfederal **Service:** General Medical and Surgical

**Staffed Beds:** 183 **Admissions:** 13547 **Census:** 144 **Outpatient Visits:** 149667 **Births:** 1511 **Total Expense ($000):** 138504 **Payroll Expense ($000):** 56471 **Personnel:** 1388

☐ **WELLSTONE REGIONAL HOSPITAL (154051)**, 2700 Vissing Park Road, Zip 47130–5989; tel. 812/284–8000 **A**1 9 10 **F**4 5 29 33 34 56 59 64 71 74 75 87 98 99 101 102 103 104 105 130 132 135 **P**5 **S** Universal Health Services, Inc., King of Prussia, PA
Primary Contact: Greg Stewart, Chief Executive Officer
CFO: Gracia Winsett, Chief Financial Officer
CMO: Asad Ismail, M.D., Medical Director
CIO: Vickie Sommers, Director Business Office
CHR: Tiffany Smith, Director Human Resources
CNO: Sandy Smithers, Director of Nursing
Web address: www.wellstonehospital.com
**Control:** Corporation, Investor–owned, for–profit **Service:** Psychiatric

**Staffed Beds:** 100 **Admissions:** 3081 **Census:** 68 **Outpatient Visits:** 6831 **Births:** 0 **Total Expense ($000):** 14463 **Payroll Expense ($000):** 8141 **Personnel:** 169

### KENDALLVILLE—Noble County

☒ **PARKVIEW NOBLE HOSPITAL (150146)**, 401 Sawyer Road, Zip 46755–2568; tel. 260/347–8700 **A**1 9 10 **F**3 7 11 13 15 28 29 34 35 40 45 46 47 50 54 57 59 64 70 74 75 76 79 81 82 85 87 93 94 97 107 108 110 111 114 118 119 129 130 132 135 143 145 146 **S** Parkview Health, Fort Wayne, IN
Primary Contact: Gary W. Adkins, Chief Executive Officer
COO: Gary W. Adkins, Chief Executive Officer
CFO: Kem Prince, Manager of Finance
CMO: Gerald Warrener, M.D., Chief Medical Officer
CIO: Ron Double, Chief Information Officer
CHR: Bruce Buttermore, Manager Human Resources
CNO: Catherine Byrd, Vice President Patient Services
Web address: www.parkview.com
**Control:** Other not–for–profit (including NFP Corporation) **Service:** General Medical and Surgical

**Staffed Beds:** 31 **Admissions:** 1698 **Census:** 16 **Outpatient Visits:** 54070 **Births:** 295 **Total Expense ($000):** 40507 **Payroll Expense ($000):** 13192 **Personnel:** 225

### KNOX—Starke County

☒ **INDIANA UNIVERSITY HEALTH STARKE HOSPITAL (150102)**, 102 East Culver Road, Zip 46534–2216, Mailing Address: P.O. Box 339, Zip 46534–0339; tel. 574/772–6231 **A**1 9 10 **F**3 15 18 29 30 32 34 35 38 40 45 46 49 50 53 57 59 65 68 74 75 77 79 81 85 87 93 94 107 108 110 111 114 115 116 117 119 130 132 135 146 147 148 **S** Indiana University Health, Indianapolis, IN
Primary Contact: Craig Felty, Chief Executive Officer
CFO: Rosemarie Heise, Vice President Finance
CMO: A. N. Damodaran, M.D., President Medical Staff
CIO: Ashley Norem, Chief Information Systems
CHR: Doug Jesch, Director Human Resources
Web address: www.iuhealth.org/starke/
**Control:** Other not–for–profit (including NFP Corporation) **Service:** General Medical and Surgical

**Staffed Beds:** 15 **Admissions:** 542 **Census:** 5 **Outpatient Visits:** 24038 **Births:** 0 **Total Expense ($000):** 19918 **Payroll Expense ($000):** 6296 **Personnel:** 118

**STARKE MEMORIAL HOSPITAL** See Indiana University Health Starke Hospital

### KOKOMO—Howard County

☒ **COMMUNITY HOWARD REGIONAL HEALTH (150007)**, 3500 South Lafountain Street, Zip 46902–3803, Mailing Address: P.O. Box 9011, Zip 46904–9011; tel. 765/453–0702 **A**1 2 9 10 **F**3 5 7 8 11 13 15 17 18 20 22 24 26 28 29 30 31 32 34 35 38 40 45 47 48 49 53 54 57 59 61 64 65 67 68 70 71 72 74 75 76 77 78 79 80 81 82 85 86 87 89 92 93 94 96 97 98 99 100 101 102 103 104 105 106 107 108 109 110 111 114 115 116 117 119 120 121 123 129 130 131 132 134 135 141 145 146 147 148 **S** Community Health Network, Indianapolis, IN
Primary Contact: Joseph Hooper, President and Chief Executive Officer
COO: Theodore Brown, Chief Operating Officer
CFO: Theodore Brown, Vice President Financial Services
CIO: Kevin Purvis, Chief Information Officer
CHR: Michael L. Williams, FACHE, Vice President Human Resources
CNO: Melodi Greene, R.N., Chief Nursing Officer
Web address: www.howardregional.org
**Control:** Other not–for–profit (including NFP Corporation) **Service:** General Medical and Surgical

**Staffed Beds:** 162 **Admissions:** 4855 **Census:** 50 **Outpatient Visits:** 112539 **Births:** 499 **Total Expense ($000):** 116179 **Payroll Expense ($000):** 43246 **Personnel:** 1064

☒ **COMMUNITY HOWARD SPECIALTY HOSPITAL (153039)**, 829 North Dixon Road, Zip 46901–7709; tel. 765/452–6700 **A**1 9 10 **F**28 29 30 34 53 54 57 64 68 71 77 90 91 93 94 129 131 132 **S** Community Health Network, Indianapolis, IN
Primary Contact: Michelle L. Russell, Administrator
CFO: Julie Pena, Director Finance
CMO: Brad Vossberg, M.D., Chief Rehabilitation
CNO: Claudia Jean Lowry, R.N., Director of Nursing
Web address: www.communityhoward.org
**Control:** Partnership, Investor–owned, for–profit **Service:** Rehabilitation

**Staffed Beds:** 30 **Admissions:** 536 **Census:** 15 **Outpatient Visits:** 29204 **Births:** 0 **Total Expense ($000):** 11409 **Payroll Expense ($000):** 6392 **Personnel:** 124

**HOWARD REGIONAL HEALTH SYSTEM** See Community Howard Regional Health

**HOWARD REGIONAL HEALTH SYSTEM WEST CAMPUS SPECIALTY HOSPITAL** See Community Howard Specialty Hospital

**IN**

---

**Hospital, Medicare Provider Number, Address, Telephone, Approval, Facility, and Physician Codes, Health Care System**

★ American Hospital Association (AHA) membership  ○ Healthcare Facilities Accreditation Program  ⇑ Center for Improvement in Healthcare Quality Accreditation
☐ The Joint Commission accreditation  ◇ DNV Healthcare Inc. accreditation  △ Commission on Accreditation of Rehabilitation Facilities (CARF) accreditation

⊞ **ST. JOSEPH HOSPITAL & HEALTH CENTER (150010)**, 1907 West Sycamore Street, Zip 46901–4197; tel. 765/452–5611 **A**1 9 10 **F**3 4 5 7 13 15 18 20 28 29 30 31 34 35 36 40 44 45 49 50 51 53 55 57 59 65 66 68 69 70 73 74 75 76 77 78 79 81 85 86 87 89 90 93 96 98 99 100 101 102 103 104 105 107 108 110 111 115 119 120 121 123 129 130 131 132 135 143 145 146 147 148 **P**6 **S** Ascension Health, Saint Louis, MO
Primary Contact: Margaret M. Johnson, Interim President
CFO: Dennis Ressler, Chief Financial Officer
CMO: David L. Williams, M.D., Chief Medical Officer
CIO: Jeffrey Scott, Chief Information Officer
CHR: Cindy Babb, Executive Director Human Resources and Organizational Effectiveness
CNO: Kathleen K. Peoples, R.N., Vice President and Nursing
Web address: www.stvincent.org/stjoseph
**Control:** Church–operated, Nongovernment, not–for profit **Service:** General Medical and Surgical

**Staffed Beds:** 138 **Admissions:** 5189 **Census:** 65 **Outpatient Visits:** 172533 **Births:** 735 **Total Expense ($000):** 108607 **Payroll Expense ($000):** 37126 **Personnel:** 645

## LA PORTE—Laporte County

⊞ **INDIANA UNIVERSITY HEALTH LA PORTE HOSPITAL (150006)**, 1007 Lincolnway, Zip 46350–3201, Mailing Address: P.O. Box 250, Zip 46352–0250; tel. 219/326–1234 **A**1 2 9 10 19 **F**3 8 11 13 15 17 18 20 22 24 26 28 29 30 32 34 35 36 38 39 40 45 46 49 50 51 53 54 56 57 58 59 62 63 64 65 66 68 70 71 74 75 76 77 79 81 85 86 87 89 92 93 96 107 108 110 111 115 118 119 124 126 129 130 131 132 135 144 145 146 147 148 **S** Indiana University Health, Indianapolis, IN
Primary Contact: G. Thor Thordarson, President and Chief Executive Officer
COO: Camie Patterson, Chief Operating Officer and Chief Financial Officer
CFO: Camie Patterson, Chief Operating Officer and Chief Financial Officer
CMO: William J. Houston, M.D., Chief Medical Officer
CIO: Earl Adams, Chief Information Officer
CNO: Pauline Arnold, MSN, Chief Nursing and Quality Officer and Vice President Clinical Operations
Web address: www.iuhealth.org
**Control:** Other not–for–profit (including NFP Corporation) **Service:** General Medical and Surgical

**Staffed Beds:** 129 **Admissions:** 4490 **Census:** 65 **Outpatient Visits:** 89812 **Births:** 594 **Total Expense ($000):** 149906 **Payroll Expense ($000):** 54627 **Personnel:** 1199

**LA PORTE REGIONAL HEALTH SYSTEM** See Indiana University Health La Porte Hospital

## LAFAYETTE—Tippecanoe County

**CLARIAN ARNETT HOSPITAL** See Indiana University Health Arnett Hospital

○ **FRANCISCAN ST. ELIZABETH HEALTH – LAFAYETTE EAST (150109)**, 1701 South Creasy Lane, Zip 47905–4972; tel. 765/502–4000, (Includes FRANCISCAN ST. ELIZABETH HEALTH – LAFAYETTE CENTRAL, 1501 Hartford Street, Zip 47904–2134; tel. 765/423–6011; Terrance E. Wilson, President and CEO) **A**2 5 10 11 **F**3 13 15 17 26 28 29 30 31 34 35 39 40 45 49 50 51 60 62 63 64 68 70 72 74 76 78 79 81 82 84 85 87 89 90 93 98 107 108 110 111 112 114 115 118 119 120 121 123 126 129 130 132 135 146 147 148 **S** Franciscan Alliance, Mishawaka, IN
Primary Contact: Terrance E. Wilson, President and CEO
Web address: www.ste.org
**Control:** Church–operated, Nongovernment, not–for profit **Service:** General Medical and Surgical

**Staffed Beds:** 187 **Admissions:** 10673 **Census:** 115 **Outpatient Visits:** 384021 **Births:** 2049 **Total Expense ($000):** 279860 **Payroll Expense ($000):** 78770 **Personnel:** 1235

★ ○ **INDIANA UNIVERSITY HEALTH ARNETT HOSPITAL (150173)**, 5165 McCarty Lane, Zip 47905–8764, Mailing Address: P.O. Box 5545, Zip 47903–5545; tel. 765/448–8000 **A**2 3 5 9 10 11 **F**3 11 12 13 15 18 20 22 24 26 28 29 30 31 34 35 40 43 45 46 49 50 51 54 57 59 60 61 64 65 68 69 70 72 74 75 76 77 78 79 80 81 82 85 87 89 93 97 107 108 110 111 114 115 116 117 118 119 129 130 131 132 144 146 147 148 **P**6 **S** Indiana University Health, Indianapolis, IN
Primary Contact: Alfonso W. Gatmaitan, Chief Executive Officer
COO: Brian T. Shockney, FACHE, Chief Operating Officer
CFO: Cara Breidster, Chief Financial Officer
CMO: Jim Bien, M.D., Vice President Quality and Patient Safety
CIO: Rusty McGill, System Director Information Technology
CHR: Koreen H. Kyhnell, Vice President Human Resources
Web address: www.iuhealth.org
**Control:** Other not–for–profit (including NFP Corporation) **Service:** General Medical and Surgical

**Staffed Beds:** 191 **Admissions:** 8951 **Census:** 108 **Outpatient Visits:** 78795 **Births:** 1366 **Total Expense ($000):** 338577 **Payroll Expense ($000):** 144892 **Personnel:** 1699

⊞ **LAFAYETTE REGIONAL REHABILITATION HOSPITAL (153042)**, 950 Park East Boulevard, Zip 47905–0792; tel. 765/447–4040, (Nonreporting) **A**1 10 **S** Ernest Health, Inc., Albuquerque, NM
Primary Contact: Michelle Russell, Chief Executive Officer
Web address: www.lrrh.ernesthealth.com
**Control:** Corporation, Investor–owned, for–profit **Service:** Rehabilitation

**Staffed Beds:** 40

**ST. ELIZABETH CENTRAL** See Franciscan St. Elizabeth Health – Lafayette Central

☐ **SYCAMORE SPRINGS HOSPITAL (154059)**, 833 Park East Boulevard, Zip 47905–0785; tel. 765/743–4400 **A**1 9 10 **F**4 5 98 102 103 104 105
Primary Contact: David Fletcher–Janzen, Chief Executive Officer
CFO: Michael Huth, Chief Financial Officer
CMO: Nizar El Khalili, M.D., Medical Director
CHR: Pam Sichts, Director Human Resources
CNO: Brooke Lavignette, Director of Nursing
Web address: www.sycamorespringshealth.com
**Control:** Corporation, Investor–owned, for–profit **Service:** Psychiatric

**Staffed Beds:** 48 **Admissions:** 1419 **Census:** 35 **Outpatient Visits:** 6885 **Births:** 0 **Total Expense ($000):** 8483 **Payroll Expense ($000):** 5069 **Personnel:** 112

## LAGRANGE—Lagrange County

⊞ **PARKVIEW LAGRANGE HOSPITAL (151323)**, 207 North Townline Road, Zip 46761–1325; tel. 260/463–9000 **A**1 9 10 18 **F**3 7 13 15 17 26 29 30 34 35 40 45 50 51 57 59 63 64 70 75 76 79 81 82 83 84 85 86 87 89 90 93 96 107 108 109 110 111 114 118 119 128 129 130 132 133 143 146 148 **S** Parkview Health, Fort Wayne, IN
Primary Contact: Robert T. Myers, President
CFO: Vickie Stanski, Financial Manager
CMO: Jeffrey Brookes, M.D., Chief Medical Officer
CIO: Ron Double, Chief Information Technology Officer
CHR: Bruce Buttermore, Director Human Resources
Web address: www.parkview.com
**Control:** Other not–for–profit (including NFP Corporation) **Service:** General Medical and Surgical

**Staffed Beds:** 25 **Admissions:** 926 **Census:** 9 **Outpatient Visits:** 23794 **Births:** 314 **Total Expense ($000):** 27725 **Payroll Expense ($000):** 8617 **Personnel:** 144

## LAWRENCEBURG—Dearborn County

**COMMUNITY MENTAL HEALTH CENTER (154011)**, 285 Bielby Road, Zip 47025–1055; tel. 812/537–1302, (Nonreporting) **A**9 10
Primary Contact: Tom Talbot, Chief Executive Officer
CFO: Georgii Zhirkin, Chief Financial Officer
CMO: Hasan Bakhtier, M.D., Medical Director
CIO: Skip Hudson, Manager Information Technology
CHR: Kelly Stewart, Director of Human Resources
Web address: www.cmhcinc.org
**Control:** Other not–for–profit (including NFP Corporation) **Service:** Psychiatric

**Staffed Beds:** 14

★ ○ **DEARBORN COUNTY HOSPITAL (150086)**, 600 Wilson Creek Road, Zip 47025–2751; tel. 812/537–1010 **A**9 10 11 **F**3 11 13 15 20 28 30 34 35 37 40 43 44 45 46 47 49 50 57 59 62 63 64 70 75 76 77 79 81 84 85 86 87 92 93 107 108 110 111 114 116 117 118 119 129 130 131 132 146 148 **P**7
Primary Contact: Roger Howard, President and Chief Executive Officer
CFO: Philip A. Meyer, Vice President, Finance
CHR: Claudia Richardt, Vice President, Human Resources, Community Relations and Marketing
CNO: Angela Scudder, R.N., Vice President Patient Care Services
Web address: www.dch.org
**Control:** County–Government, nonfederal **Service:** General Medical and Surgical

**Staffed Beds:** 78 **Admissions:** 4373 **Census:** 43 **Outpatient Visits:** 136361 **Births:** 379 **Total Expense ($000):** 74531 **Payroll Expense ($000):** 31785 **Personnel:** 630

*Many Facility Codes have changed. Please refer to the AHA Guide Code Chart.* © 2015 AHA Guide

**IN**

## LEBANON—Boone County

☒ **WITHAM MEMORIAL HOSPITAL (150104)**, 2605 North Lebanon Street, Zip 46052–1476, Mailing Address: P.O. Box 1200, Zip 46052–3005; tel. 765/485–8000 **A**1 9 10 **F**3 7 13 15 18 20 28 29 30 34 40 42 45 54 56 57 59 64 65 68 69 70 75 76 77 79 81 82 83 85 86 87 93 94 97 98 99 103 107 108 110 111 114 115 118 119 129 130 132 135 141 144 146 147 148 **P**1
Primary Contact: Raymond V. Ingham, Ph.D., President and Chief Executive Officer
COO: Diane Feder, R.N., Senior Vice President and Chief Operating Officer
CFO: George Pogas, CPA, Senior Vice President and Chief Financial Officer
CMO: Anthony Steele, M.D., Chief Medical Officer
CIO: George Pogas, CPA, Senior Vice President and Chief Financial Officer
CHR: Gary A. Deater, Vice President Administration, Human Resources and Risk Management
CNO: Diane Feder, R.N., Senior Vice President and Chief Operating Officer
Web address: www.witham.org
**Control:** County–Government, nonfederal **Service:** General Medical and Surgical

**Staffed Beds:** 52 **Admissions:** 2513 **Census:** 27 **Outpatient Visits:** 125473 **Births:** 476 **Total Expense ($000):** 97407 **Payroll Expense ($000):** 38417 **Personnel:** 563

## LINTON—Greene County

☒ **GREENE COUNTY GENERAL HOSPITAL (151317)**, 1185 North 1000 West, Zip 47441–5282; tel. 812/847–2281 **A**1 9 10 18 **F**1 3 6 10 11 13 15 18 26 29 30 31 34 35 40 41 45 50 57 58 59 62 64 65 66 67 68 70 75 76 77 78 79 81 85 86 87 90 91 93 107 108 110 114 119 125 127 128 130 133 135 146 147 148 **P**6
Primary Contact: Brenda Reetz, FACHE, Chief Executive Officer
CFO: April Settles, Chief Financial Officer
CMO: Frederick R. Ridge, Chief of Staff
CIO: Steve Phillips, Information Officer
CHR: Jean Prather, Director of Human Resources
CNO: Lea Ann Camp, R.N., Chief Nursing Officer
Web address: www.greenecountyhospital.com
**Control:** County–Government, nonfederal **Service:** General Medical and Surgical

**Staffed Beds:** 25 **Admissions:** 822 **Census:** 6 **Outpatient Visits:** 50320 **Births:** 75 **Total Expense ($000):** 29323 **Payroll Expense ($000):** 11962 **Personnel:** 235

## LOGANSPORT—Cass County

**FOUR COUNTY COUNSELING CENTER (154035)**, 1015 Michigan Avenue, Zip 46947–1526; tel. 574/722–5151, (Nonreporting) **A**9 10
Primary Contact: C.J. Davis, Chief Executive Officer/ Executive Director
COO: Carrie Cadwell, M.D., Chief Clinical Officer
CFO: Jason Cadwell, Chief Financial Officer
CMO: John Yarling, M.D., Medical Director
CIO: Becky Mulis, Director of Health Information Management Systems
CHR: Steve Curry, Regional Director Human Resources
CNO: Donna Henry, Vice President of Nursing Services
Web address: www.fourcounty.org
**Control:** Other not–for–profit (including NFP Corporation) **Service:** Psychiatric

**Staffed Beds:** 15

★ ○ **LOGANSPORT MEMORIAL HOSPITAL (150072)**, 1101 Michigan Avenue, Zip 46947–1528, Mailing Address: P.O. Box 7013, Zip 46947–7013; tel. 574/753–7541 **A**9 10 11 20 **F**3 11 13 15 28 29 32 34 35 36 40 44 45 48 49 50 51 57 59 64 65 68 69 70 75 77 78 79 81 85 86 87 93 97 107 108 110 111 114 119 124 129 130 132 133 135 146 147 **P**6
Primary Contact: David J. Ameen, President and Chief Executive Officer
CFO: Julia L. Berndt, Chief Financial Officer
CMO: Charles Montgomery, M.D., Medical Director
CIO: Beth Jump, Chief Information Officer
CHR: Lynda J. Murphy, Vice President Human Resources
Web address: www.logansportmemorial.org
**Control:** County–Government, nonfederal **Service:** General Medical and Surgical

**Staffed Beds:** 83 **Admissions:** 1880 **Census:** 17 **Outpatient Visits:** 98088 **Births:** 535 **Total Expense ($000):** 58733 **Payroll Expense ($000):** 27183 **Personnel:** 508

☐ **LOGANSPORT STATE HOSPITAL**, 1098 South State Road 25, Zip 46947–6723; tel. 574/737–3633, (Nonreporting) **A**1
Primary Contact: Robert Clover, Superintendent and Chief Executive Officer
CFO: Misty Moss, Director Business Administration
CMO: Danny Meadows, M.D., Medical Director
CIO: Joe McIntosh, Director Management Information Systems
CHR: Dianne Renner, Director Human Resources
Web address: www.lshonline.org
**Control:** State–Government, nonfederal **Service:** Psychiatric

**Staffed Beds:** 170

## MADISON—Jefferson County

★ ○ **KING'S DAUGHTERS' HEALTH (150069)**, 1373 East State Road 62, Zip 47250–3357, Mailing Address: P.O. Box 447, Zip 47250–0447; tel. 812/801–0800 **A**2 9 10 11 **F**3 7 8 13 15 18 20 22 28 29 30 31 32 34 35 40 42 45 48 49 50 56 57 59 62 63 64 65 68 70 74 75 76 77 78 79 81 82 84 85 86 91 93 94 97 107 108 110 111 115 119 120 121 123 129 130 131 132 134 135 144 145 146 147 148 **P**6
Primary Contact: Carol Dozier, President and Chief Executive Officer
CFO: Steve Meacham, Vice President Finance
CIO: Linda Darnell, Director Management Information Systems
CHR: Susan Poling, Director Human Resources
CNO: Lisa Morgan, R.N., Vice President Patient Services
Web address: www.kdhhs.org
**Control:** Other not–for–profit (including NFP Corporation) **Service:** General Medical and Surgical

**Staffed Beds:** 77 **Admissions:** 3350 **Census:** 34 **Outpatient Visits:** 193047 **Births:** 486 **Total Expense ($000):** 115895 **Payroll Expense ($000):** 49755 **Personnel:** 817

☐ **MADISON STATE HOSPITAL (154019)**, 711 Green Road, Zip 47250–2199; tel. 812/265–2611, (Nonreporting) **A**1 10
Primary Contact: Peggy Stephens, M.D., Superintendent and Medical Director
COO: Peggy Stephens, M.D., Superintendent and Medical Director
CFO: Carolyn Copeland, Business Administrator
CMO: Peggy Stephens, M.D., Superintendent and Medical Director
CIO: Ric Martin, Information Specialist
Web address: www.in.gov/fssa/msh
**Control:** State–Government, nonfederal **Service:** Psychiatric

**Staffed Beds:** 150

## MARION—Grant County

☐ **GRANT–BLACKFORD MENTAL HEALTH CENTER (154021)**, 505 North Wabash Avenue, Zip 46952–2608; tel. 765/662–3971 **A**1 9 10 **F**4 5 34 35 38 50 54 56 57 64 66 86 87 98 99 100 101 102 103 104 105 106 130 132 134 135 143 146
Primary Contact: Paul Kuczora, Chief Executive Officer
Web address: www.cornerstone.org/
**Control:** Other not–for–profit (including NFP Corporation) **Service:** Psychiatric

**Staffed Beds:** 16 **Admissions:** 483 **Census:** 5 **Outpatient Visits:** 51997 **Births:** 0 **Total Expense ($000):** 10387 **Payroll Expense ($000):** 5414

★ ○ **MARION GENERAL HOSPITAL (150011)**, 441 North Wabash Avenue, Zip 46952–2690; tel. 765/660–6000 **A**2 9 10 11 **F**3 7 8 11 13 15 18 20 22 26 28 29 30 31 34 35 40 41 44 45 50 54 57 58 59 64 66 68 70 74 76 77 78 79 81 82 84 85 86 87 89 90 91 92 93 96 97 107 108 110 111 112 114 115 116 117 118 119 129 130 132 135 145 146 147 148 **P**6
Primary Contact: Paul L. Usher, President and Chief Executive Officer
COO: Bernadine L. Wallace, MSN, Chief Nursing Officer and Chief Operating Officer
CFO: Robyn L. Powell, Chief Financial Officer
CMO: Edward L. Keppler, M.D., Chief Medical Officer
CIO: Emmanuel Ndow, Chief Information Officer
CHR: Karen Jones, Administrative Director Human Resources
Web address: www.mgh.net
**Control:** Other not–for–profit (including NFP Corporation) **Service:** General Medical and Surgical

**Staffed Beds:** 115 **Admissions:** 5151 **Census:** 59 **Outpatient Visits:** 223059 **Births:** 680 **Total Expense ($000):** 150656 **Payroll Expense ($000):** 48785 **Personnel:** 1045

**VETERANS AFFAIRS NORTHERN INDIANA HEALTH CARE SYSTEM–MARION CAMPUS** See Veterans Affairs Northern Indiana Health Care System, Fort Wayne

## MERRILLVILLE—Lake County

**REGIONAL MENTAL HEALTH CENTER (154020)**, 8555 Taft Street, Zip 46410–6123; tel. 219/769–4005, (Nonreporting) **A**9 10
Primary Contact: Robert D. Krumwied, President and Chief Executive Officer
Web address: www.regionalmentalhealth.org/
**Control:** Corporation, Investor–owned, for–profit **Service:** Psychiatric

**Staffed Beds:** 16

**SOUTHLAKE CAMPUS** See Methodist Hospitals, Gary

IN

---

**Hospital, Medicare Provider Number, Address, Telephone, Approval, Facility, and Physician Codes, Health Care System**

★ American Hospital Association (AHA) membership ○ Healthcare Facilities Accreditation Program ⇑ Center for Improvement in Healthcare Quality Accreditation
☐ The Joint Commission accreditation ◇ DNV Healthcare Inc. accreditation △ Commission on Accreditation of Rehabilitation Facilities (CARF) accreditation

## MICHIGAN CITY—Laporte County

○ **FRANCISCAN ST. ANTHONY HEALTH – MICHIGAN CITY (150015)**, 301 West Homer Street, Zip 46360–4358; tel. 219/879–8511, (Nonreporting) **A**2 9 10 11 19 **S** Franciscan Alliance, Mishawaka, IN
Primary Contact: Gene Diamond, Interim President
CFO: Marc Golan, Regional Chief Financial Officer
CIO: Tim Loosemore, Regional Director Information Systems
CHR: John Barrett, Regional Director Human Resources
CNO: Trish Weber, R.N., Vice President Operations and Chief Nursing Officer
Web address: www.franciscanalliance.org
**Control:** Church–operated, Nongovernment, not–for profit **Service:** General Medical and Surgical

Staffed Beds: 171

**SAINT ANTHONY MEMORIAL** See Franciscan St. Anthony Health – Michigan City

## MISHAWAKA—St. Joseph County

⊠ **KINDRED HOSPITAL OF NORTHERN INDIANA (152018)**, 215 West Fourth Street, Suite 200, Zip 46544–1917; tel. 574/252–2000, (Nonreporting) **A**1 10 **S** Kindred Healthcare, Louisville, KY
Primary Contact: Lori Skora, Chief Executive Officer
CFO: Christy Henrich, Controller
CMO: Shaya Mokfi, M.D., Medical Director and President Medical Staff
CHR: Brenda Schweizer, Coordinator Human Resources
CNO: Suzanne M. Morgan, Chief Clinical Officer
Web address: www.khnorthernindiana.com/
**Control:** Corporation, Investor–owned, for–profit **Service:** Long–Term Acute Care hospital

Staffed Beds: 32

○ **RIVERCREST SPECIALTY HOSPITAL (152026)**, 1625 East Jefferson Boulevard, Zip 46545–7103; tel. 574/255–1400, (Nonreporting) **A**10 11 **S** NeuroPsychiatric Hospitals, Mishawaka, IN
Primary Contact: Cameron R. Gilbert, Ph.D., President and Chief Executive Officer
Web address: www.physicianshospitalsystem.net/
**Control:** Partnership, Investor–owned, for–profit **Service:** Long–Term Acute Care hospital

Staffed Beds: 30

⊠ **SAINT JOSEPH REGIONAL MEDICAL CENTER (150012)**, 5215 Holy Cross Parkway, Zip 46545–1469; tel. 574/335–5000 **A**1 2 3 5 9 10 **F**3 11 13 15 17 18 19 20 21 22 23 24 26 28 29 30 31 34 35 36 39 40 45 46 47 48 49 50 52 54 55 57 58 59 60 61 64 66 68 70 71 72 74 75 76 77 78 79 80 81 82 83 84 85 87 89 90 91 92 93 96 97 107 108 110 115 117 118 119 120 121 123 124 126 127 130 131 132 135 146 147 148 **S** Trinity Health, Livonia, MI
Primary Contact: Albert Gutierrez, FACHE, President and Chief Executive Officer
COO: Christopher J. Karam, Chief Operating Officer
CMO: Stephen Anderson, M.D., Chief Medical Officer
CIO: Gary L. Miller, Senior Director Information Systems
CHR: Kurt A. Meyer, Chief Human Resource Officer
CNO: Kenneth C. Hall, R.N., Chief Nursing Officer
Web address: www.sjmed.com
**Control:** Other not–for–profit (including NFP Corporation) **Service:** General Medical and Surgical

Staffed Beds: 294 Admissions: 14138 Census: 172 Outpatient Visits: 158259 Births: 1097 Total Expense ($000): 284047 Payroll Expense ($000): 76400 Personnel: 1339

**TRIUMPH OUR LADY OF PEACE HOSPITAL** See Kindred Hospital of Northern Indiana

○ **UNITY MEDICAL & SURGICAL HOSPITAL (150177)**, 4455 Edison Lakes Parkway, Zip 46545–1442; tel. 574/968–0867, (Nonreporting) **A**9 10 11
Primary Contact: John M. Day, Chief Executive Officer
COO: Donald Allen, Chief Operating Officer
CFO: Matthew M. Sherwood, Chief Financial Officer
CMO: Viraj Patel, M.D., Chief Medical Officer
CIO: Richard Leighton, Financial Application Analyst
CHR: Emyle Kruyer-Collins, Chief Human Resources Officer
CNO: Sylvia K. Coffing, R.N., Chief Nursing and Compliance Officer
Web address: www.umsh.net
**Control:** Partnership, Investor–owned, for–profit **Service:** General Medical and Surgical

Staffed Beds: 15

## MONTICELLO—White County

★ **INDIANA UNIVERSITY HEALTH WHITE MEMORIAL HOSPITAL (151312)**, 720 South Sixth Street, Zip 47960–8182; tel. 574/583–7111 **A**9 10 18 **F**3 11 15 29 30 31 34 35 40 45 50 57 59 64 75 77 78 80 81 85 91 93 107 108 110 111 114 119 129 133 135 146 147 **S** Indiana University Health, Indianapolis, IN
Primary Contact: Jeffrey C. Zeh, President
COO: Mary Minier, Vice President Operations
CMO: Adel Khdour, M.D., Chief Medical Officer
CIO: Michelle Baker, Director Information Systems
CHR: JoEllyn Brockmeyer, Director Human Resources
CNO: Robin S. Smith, Chief Nursing Officer
Web address: www.iuhealth.org/white–memorial
**Control:** Other not–for–profit (including NFP Corporation) **Service:** General Medical and Surgical

Staffed Beds: 25 Admissions: 813 Census: 8 Outpatient Visits: 29758 Births: 70 Total Expense ($000): 23732 Payroll Expense ($000): 7898 Personnel: 145

## MOORESVILLE—Morgan County

○ **FRANCISCAN ST. FRANCIS HEALTH – MOORESVILLE (150057)**, 1201 Hadley Road, Zip 46158–1789; tel. 317/831–1160 **A**3 5 9 10 11 **F**8 12 13 15 29 30 31 35 37 46 47 49 50 57 58 59 64 70 75 76 77 78 79 80 81 87 91 107 108 109 110 111 116 117 119 120 121 123 124 129 130 144 145 146 147 **P**7 8 **S** Franciscan Alliance, Mishawaka, IN
Primary Contact: Peter J. Murphy, Senior Vice President and Chief Operating Officer
CIO: Barbara Coulter, Director Information Systems
CHR: John Ross, Vice President
Web address: www.franciscanalliance.org/hospitals/mooresville/Pages/default.aspx
**Control:** Church–operated, Nongovernment, not–for profit **Service:** General Medical and Surgical

Staffed Beds: 115 Admissions: 2967 Census: 24 Outpatient Visits: 128051 Births: 270 Total Expense ($000): 84413 Payroll Expense ($000): 23856 Personnel: 328

**ST. FRANCIS HOSPITAL–MOORESVILLE** See Franciscan St. Francis Health – Mooresville

## MUNCIE—Delaware County

○ **AMG SPECIALTY HOSPITAL – MUNCIE (152025)**, 2401 West University Avenue, 8th Floor, Zip 47303–3428; tel. 765/751–5253 **A**10 11 **F**1 3 29 85 100 **P**1
Primary Contact: Rodney Midkiff, Chief Executive Officer
CNO: Tina Riegle, R.N., Chief Clinical Officer
Web address: www.amgmuncie.com/
**Control:** Corporation, Investor–owned, for–profit **Service:** Long–Term Acute Care hospital

Staffed Beds: 32 Admissions: 355 Census: 25 Outpatient Visits: 0 Births: 0 Total Expense ($000): 12356 Payroll Expense ($000): 5605

**BALL MEMORIAL HOSPITAL** See Indiana University Health Ball Memorial Hospital

⊠ △ **INDIANA UNIVERSITY HEALTH BALL MEMORIAL HOSPITAL (150089)**, 2401 University Avenue, Zip 47303–3499; tel. 765/747–3111 **A**1 2 3 5 7 8 9 10 19 **F**3 11 12 13 15 17 18 20 22 24 26 27 28 29 30 31 32 34 35 39 40 41 43 45 49 50 51 53 54 56 57 58 59 60 64 65 66 69 70 72 74 75 76 77 78 79 80 81 82 83 84 85 86 87 89 90 91 92 93 94 97 98 99 100 102 107 110 111 114 115 116 117 118 119 120 121 123 124 126 129 130 132 146 147 148 **S** Indiana University Health, Indianapolis, IN
Primary Contact: Michael E. Haley, President and Chief Executive Officer
COO: Jeffrey C. Bird, M.D., Chief Operating Officer and Chief Medical Officer
CFO: Judy Coleman, Chief Financial Officer
CMO: Jeffrey C. Bird, M.D., Chief Operating Officer and Chief Medical Officer
CHR: Ann M. McGuire, Vice President Human Resources
CNO: Carla C. Cox, Chief Nursing Officer
Web address: www.iuhealth.org
**Control:** Other not–for–profit (including NFP Corporation) **Service:** General Medical and Surgical

Staffed Beds: 322 Admissions: 16133 Census: 222 Outpatient Visits: 298510 Births: 1509 Total Expense ($000): 298670 Payroll Expense ($000): 96207 Personnel: 2111

**MERIDIAN HEALTH SERVICES (154053)**, 2401 West University Avenue, Zip 47303–3428; tel. 765/747–3281, (Nonreporting) **A**10
Primary Contact: Hank A. Milius, Chief Executive Officer
CMO: Sarfraz Khan, Medical Director
Web address: www.meridianhs.org
**Control:** Other not–for–profit (including NFP Corporation) **Service:** Psychiatric

Staffed Beds: 20

**RENAISSANCE SPECIALTY HOSPITAL OF CENTRAL INDIANA** See AMG Specialty Hospital – Muncie

IN

*Many Facility Codes have changed. Please refer to the AHA Guide Code Chart.* © 2015 AHA Guide

## MUNSTER—Lake County

☐ **COMMUNITY HOSPITAL (150125)**, 901 Macarthur Boulevard, Zip 46321–2959; tel. 219/836–1600 **A**1 2 9 10 **F**3 8 11 12 13 15 17 18 20 22 24 26 28 29 30 31 34 35 36 38 39 40 45 46 47 49 50 53 54 55 57 58 59 60 62 64 65 70 72 73 74 75 77 78 79 80 81 82 85 86 87 90 92 93 96 107 108 110 111 114 115 116 117 119 120 121 123 124 126 129 130 131 132 135 144 146 147 148 **S** Community Healthcare System, Hammond, IN
Primary Contact: Donald P. Fesko, Chief Executive Officer and Administrator
CFO: Luis Molina, Vice President Finance and Chief Financial Officer
CMO: David Robinson, M.D., President Medical and Dental Staff
CIO: Gary Weiner, Vice President Information Technology, Chief Information Officer
CHR: Debbie Brandt, Director Human Resources
CNO: Ronda McKay, R.N., Vice President Patient Care Services, Chief Nursing Officer
Web address: www.comhs.org
**Control:** Other not–for–profit (including NFP Corporation) **Service:** General Medical and Surgical

**Staffed Beds:** 473 **Admissions:** 19161 **Census:** 290 **Outpatient Visits:** 357599 **Births:** 1878 **Total Expense ($000):** 429837 **Payroll Expense ($000):** 148847 **Personnel:** 2325

○ **FRANCISCAN HEALTHCARE – MUNSTER (150165)**, 701 Superior Avenue, Zip 46321–4037; tel. 219/924–1300, (Nonreporting) **A**9 10 11 **S** Franciscan Alliance, Mishawaka, IN
Primary Contact: Michael J. Stenger, President and Chief Executive Officer
CFO: Harold E. Collins, JD, Chief Financial Officer
CMO: Vijay D. Gupta, M.D., President and Chief Executive Officer
CIO: Steven Krause, Manager Information Technology
Web address: www.franciscanphysicianshospital.org
**Control:** Partnership, Investor–owned, for–profit **Service:** General Medical and Surgical

**Staffed Beds:** 32

## NEW ALBANY—Floyd County

★ ○ **FLOYD MEMORIAL HOSPITAL AND HEALTH SERVICES (150044)**, 1850 State Street, Zip 47150–4997; tel. 812/949–5500, (Total facility includes 266 beds in nursing home–type unit) **A**2 3 5 9 10 11 **F**8 11 12 13 15 17 18 20 22 24 26 28 29 30 31 34 35 40 43 49 50 56 57 59 62 64 70 74 75 76 77 78 79 80 81 82 84 85 86 87 89 93 100 107 108 110 111 114 115 116 117 118 119 120 121 123 128 129 130 131 132 135 144 146 147 148
Primary Contact: Daniel J. Eichenberger, M.D., Interim President and Chief Executive Officer
COO: Mark Truman, Vice President of Operations
CFO: Ted Miller, Chief Financial Officer
CMO: Daniel J. Eichenberger, M.D., Medical Director
CIO: Brian Cox, Director Information Systems
CHR: Mike Ford, Vice President Human Resources
Web address: www.floydmemorial.com
**Control:** County–Government, nonfederal **Service:** General Medical and Surgical

**Staffed Beds:** 477 **Admissions:** 14663 **Census:** 393 **Outpatient Visits:** 539700 **Births:** 1078 **Total Expense ($000):** 304762 **Payroll Expense ($000):** 124321 **Personnel:** 1800

☐ **PHYSICIANS' MEDICAL CENTER (150172)**, 4023 Reas Lane, Zip 47150–2228; tel. 812/206–7660, (Nonreporting) **A**1 9 10
Primary Contact: Dennis Medley, Administrator
COO: Dennis Medley, Chief Executive Officer
CFO: Dennis Medley, Chief Executive Officer
CMO: Perry Cassady, M.D., Medical Director
CIO: Mary Arntz, Manager Business Office and Executive Assistant
CHR: Mary Arntz, Manager Business Office and Executive Assistant
CNO: Rob Jones, Chief Nursing Officer
Web address: www.pmcindiana.com
**Control:** Individual, Investor–owned, for–profit **Service:** General Medical and Surgical

**Staffed Beds:** 12

⊠ △ **SOUTHERN INDIANA REHABILITATION HOSPITAL (153037)**, 3104 Blackiston Boulevard, Zip 47150–9579; tel. 812/941–8300 **A**1 7 9 10 **F**29 34 35 57 59 74 75 77 79 86 87 90 91 130 132 135 143 146 **P**5 **S** Catholic Health Initiatives, Englewood, CO
Primary Contact: Randy L. Napier, President
CFO: Robert Steltenpohl, Vice President
CMO: John C. Shaw, M.D., Medical Director
CHR: Lisa Burris, Director Human Resources
CNO: Suzann Byers, Director of Nursing
Web address: www.sirh.org
**Control:** Other not–for–profit (including NFP Corporation) **Service:** Rehabilitation

**Staffed Beds:** 60 **Admissions:** 1289 **Census:** 41 **Outpatient Visits:** 90328 **Births:** 0 **Total Expense ($000):** 17555 **Payroll Expense ($000):** 9279 **Personnel:** 207

## NEW CASTLE—Henry County

★ ○ **HENRY COUNTY HOSPITAL (150030)**, 1000 North 16th Street, Zip 47362–4319, Mailing Address: P.O. Box 490, Zip 47362–0490; tel. 765/521–0890 **A**9 10 11 **F**3 8 11 13 15 28 29 30 32 34 35 36 37 40 44 45 46 48 53 54 57 59 62 63 64 68 70 75 76 79 81 82 85 87 89 92 93 94 96 97 107 108 110 111 115 118 119 127 129 130 131 132 135 141 144 145 146 **P**6
Primary Contact: Paul Janssen, President and Chief Executive Officer
COO: Brian K. Ring, Chief Operating Officer
CFO: Darin Brown, Vice President Finance
CMO: Wylie McGlothlin, M.D., Chief Medical Officer
CIO: Mike Spencer, Chief Information Officer
CHR: Deanna Malott, Director Human Resources
CNO: Carrie Williams, R.N., Chief Nursing Officer
Web address: www.hcmhcares.org
**Control:** County–Government, nonfederal **Service:** General Medical and Surgical

**Staffed Beds:** 90 **Admissions:** 2124 **Census:** 20 **Outpatient Visits:** 694662 **Births:** 362 **Total Expense ($000):** 86675 **Payroll Expense ($000):** 39774 **Personnel:** 742

## NEWBURGH—Warrick County

☐ **BRENTWOOD MEADOWS (154055)**, 4455 Roslin Road, Zip 47630; tel. 812/858–7200, (Nonreporting) **A**1 9 10
Primary Contact: David C. Bell, Chief Executive Officer
Web address: www.brentwoodmeadows.com
**Control:** Partnership, Investor–owned, for–profit **Service:** Psychiatric

**Staffed Beds:** 48

★ ○ **THE HEART HOSPITAL AT DEACONESS GATEWAY (150175)**, 4007 Gateway Boulevard, Zip 47630–8947; tel. 812/842–4784 **A**9 10 11 **F**3 17 18 20 22 24 26 28 29 30 34 35 57 58 59 60 62 63 64 68 81 83 84 85 86 87 107 108 109 111 114 115 116 117 118 119 130 132 **S** Deaconess Health System, Evansville, IN
Primary Contact: Rebecca Malotte, Executive Director and Chief Nursing Officer
COO: Rebecca Malotte, Executive Director and Chief Nursing Officer
CFO: Tracy Silva, Chief Financial Officer
CMO: Lee Wagmeister, M.D., President Medical Staff
CIO: Lisa Hobgood, Chief Information Officer
CHR: Sarah Bryan, Manager Human Resources
CNO: Rebecca Malotte, Executive Director and Chief Nursing Officer
Web address: www.deaconess.com/
**Control:** Partnership, Investor–owned, for–profit **Service:** Heart

**Staffed Beds:** 24 **Admissions:** 1501 **Census:** 16 **Outpatient Visits:** 6492 **Births:** 0 **Total Expense ($000):** 39951 **Payroll Expense ($000):** 6840 **Personnel:** 124

★ ○ **THE WOMEN'S HOSPITAL (150149)**, 4199 Gateway Boulevard, Zip 47630–8940; tel. 812/842–4200 **A**3 9 10 11 **F**3 13 15 29 30 34 35 36 40 50 53 55 57 59 63 64 65 72 75 76 77 81 84 85 86 87 93 110 119 126 130 132 134 135 147 **P**6 **S** Deaconess Health System, Evansville, IN
Primary Contact: Christina M. Ryan, R.N., Chief Executive Officer
CFO: Tina Cady, Controller
CIO: Jenny Skelton, System Integration Manager
CHR: Jerri Sue Traylor, Director Human Resources and Community and Employee Wellness
CNO: Christina M. Ryan, R.N., Chief Executive Officer and Chief Nursing Officer
Web address: www.deaconess.com
**Control:** Partnership, Investor–owned, for–profit **Service:** Obstetrics and gynecology

**Staffed Beds:** 74 **Admissions:** 3668 **Census:** 46 **Outpatient Visits:** 25752 **Births:** 3108 **Total Expense ($000):** 65958 **Payroll Expense ($000):** 27230 **Personnel:** 467

**IN**

---

**Hospital, Medicare Provider Number, Address, Telephone, Approval, Facility, and Physician Codes, Health Care System**

★ American Hospital Association (AHA) membership  ○ Healthcare Facilities Accreditation Program  ⇑ Center for Improvement in Healthcare Quality Accreditation
☐ The Joint Commission accreditation  ◇ DNV Healthcare Inc. accreditation  △ Commission on Accreditation of Rehabilitation Facilities (CARF) accreditation

**NOBLESVILLE—Hamilton County**

○ △ **RIVERVIEW HOSPITAL (150059)**, 395 Westfield Road, Zip 46060–1425, Mailing Address: P.O. Box 220, Zip 46061–0220; tel. 317/773–0760 **A**2 7 9 10 11 **F**3 8 11 12 13 15 17 18 20 22 24 26 28 29 30 31 34 35 37 38 39 40 45 46 49 50 53 54 56 57 59 60 62 63 64 65 66 68 70 73 74 75 76 77 78 79 81 82 85 86 87 89 90 91 93 94 97 100 102 107 108 110 111 114 115 116 117 118 119 120 121 123 128 129 130 131 132 135 144 146 147 148 **P**2 6
Primary Contact: Patricia K. Fox, President and Chief Executive Officer
COO: Lawrence Christman, Chief Financial Officer and Chief Operating Officer
CFO: Brenda Baker, Chief Financial Officer
CMO: John Paris, M.D., Chief Medical Officer
CIO: Brant Bucciarelli, Chief Information Officer
CHR: Ann Kuzee, Executive Director Human Resources
CNO: Joyce Wood, Vice President Organizational Improvement and Chief Nursing Officer
Web address: www.riverview.org
**Control:** County–Government, nonfederal **Service:** General Medical and Surgical

**Staffed Beds:** 156 **Admissions:** 4626 **Census:** 67 **Outpatient Visits:** 408845 **Births:** 669 **Total Expense ($000):** 164653 **Payroll Expense ($000):** 64716 **Personnel:** 1013

**NORTH VERNON—Jennings County**

✠ **ST. VINCENT JENNINGS HOSPITAL (151303)**, 301 Henry Street, Zip 47265–1097; tel. 812/352–4200 **A**1 9 10 18 **F**3 15 29 30 32 34 35 40 44 45 50 56 57 59 64 65 66 77 79 81 85 97 107 111 115 119 132 133 135 144 146 148 **S** Ascension Health, Saint Louis, MO
Primary Contact: Carl W. Risk, II, Administrator
CFO: Joseph Kubala, Chief Financial Officer
CMO: Jennifer Stanley, M.D., Chief Medical Officer
CHR: Kathryn Johnson, Manager Human Resources, Marketing and Public Relations
CNO: Lori Wise, Chief Nursing Officer and Director of Clinical Services
Web address: www.stvincent.org
**Control:** Other not–for–profit (including NFP Corporation) **Service:** General Medical and Surgical

**Staffed Beds:** 25 **Admissions:** 407 **Census:** 4 **Outpatient Visits:** 29942 **Births:** 0 **Total Expense ($000):** 15528 **Payroll Expense ($000):** 5214 **Personnel:** 80

**PAOLI—Orange County**

**BLOOMINGTON HOSPITAL OF ORANGE COUNTY** See Indiana University Health Paoli Hospital

✠ **INDIANA UNIVERSITY HEALTH PAOLI HOSPITAL (151306)**, 642 West Hospital Road, Zip 47454–9672, Mailing Address: P.O. Box 499, Zip 47454–0499; tel. 812/723–2811 **A**1 9 10 18 **F**3 13 15 29 30 35 40 45 50 57 59 64 76 77 81 84 85 89 93 107 110 111 114 119 129 132 135 146 148 **S** Indiana University Health, Indianapolis, IN
Primary Contact: Larry Bailey, Chief Executive Officer
COO: Sonya Zeller, R.N., Vice President, Chief Operating Officer and Chief Nursing Officer
CMO: Curtis C. Thill, M.D., Medical Staff President
CNO: Sonya Zeller, R.N., Vice President, Chief Operating Officer and Chief Nursing Officer
Web address: www.iuhealth.org/paoli
**Control:** Other not–for–profit (including NFP Corporation) **Service:** General Medical and Surgical

**Staffed Beds:** 24 **Admissions:** 383 **Census:** 2 **Outpatient Visits:** 26040 **Births:** 138 **Total Expense ($000):** 19479 **Payroll Expense ($000):** 8027 **Personnel:** 123

**PERU—Miami County**

✠ **DUKES MEMORIAL HOSPITAL (151318)**, 275 West 12th Street, Zip 46970–1638; tel. 765/472–8000 **A**1 9 10 18 **F**3 7 8 13 15 17 18 28 29 34 35 40 41 50 51 57 59 64 68 69 70 75 76 77 79 81 82 85 87 89 90 93 107 108 110 111 115 118 119 129 130 132 133 135 144 146 147 **P**6 **S** Community Health Systems, Inc., Franklin, TN
Primary Contact: Debra Close, Chief Executive Officer
CFO: Adam Cumbo, Chief Financial Officer
CMO: Neil Stalker, M.D., Chief of Staff
Web address: www.dukesmemorialhosp.com
**Control:** Corporation, Investor–owned, for–profit **Service:** General Medical and Surgical

**Staffed Beds:** 25 **Admissions:** 1078 **Census:** 10 **Outpatient Visits:** 39297 **Births:** 206 **Total Expense ($000):** 34525 **Payroll Expense ($000):** 15580 **Personnel:** 259

**PLYMOUTH—Marshall County**

☐ **MICHIANA BEHAVIORAL HEALTH CENTER (154047)**, 1800 North Oak Drive, Zip 46563–3492; tel. 574/936–3784 **A**1 9 10 **F**98 99 105 106 **S** Universal Health Services, Inc., King of Prussia, PA
Primary Contact: Michael Perry, Chief Executive Officer
CFO: Jeff Calvin, Chief Financial Officer
CMO: Robert Raster, M.D., Medical Director
CIO: Bob Kedalis, Director Business Development
CHR: Becky Nowicki, Director Human Resources
CNO: Brandi Richard, Chief Nursing Officer
Web address: www.michianabhc.com
**Control:** Corporation, Investor–owned, for–profit **Service:** Psychiatric

**Staffed Beds:** 75 **Admissions:** 1503 **Census:** 52 **Outpatient Visits:** 0 **Births:** 0 **Total Expense ($000):** 11568 **Payroll Expense ($000):** 5507 **Personnel:** 130

✠ **SAINT JOSEPH REGIONAL MEDICAL CENTER–PLYMOUTH CAMPUS (150076)**, 1915 Lake Avenue, Zip 46563–9366, Mailing Address: P.O. Box 670, Zip 46563–0670; tel. 574/948–4000 **A**1 9 10 **F**3 13 15 18 20 29 30 31 34 35 40 45 46 50 51 54 57 59 64 65 66 68 70 74 75 76 78 79 81 84 85 87 91 92 93 107 108 110 114 119 120 121 123 124 129 130 132 135 145 146 148 **S** Trinity Health, Livonia, MI
Primary Contact: Loretta Schmidt, President
COO: Tamara Awald, Chief Nursing Officer and Chief Operating Officer
CFO: Janice Dunn, Chief Financial Officer
CMO: Stephen Anderson, M.D., Chief Medical Officer
CIO: Gary L. Miller, Regional Director Information Systems
CHR: Kurt A. Meyer, Chief Human Resources Officer
CNO: Tamara Awald, Chief Nursing Officer and Chief Operating Officer
Web address: www.sjmed.com
**Control:** Other not–for–profit (including NFP Corporation) **Service:** General Medical and Surgical

**Staffed Beds:** 48 **Admissions:** 1767 **Census:** 14 **Outpatient Visits:** 83497 **Births:** 280 **Total Expense ($000):** 42987 **Payroll Expense ($000):** 14384 **Personnel:** 243

**PORTLAND—Jay County**

✠ **JAY COUNTY HOSPITAL (151320)**, 500 West Votaw Street, Zip 47371–1322; tel. 260/726–7131 **A**1 9 10 18 **F**3 8 11 13 15 28 29 30 32 34 35 40 45 50 57 59 68 70 75 76 77 81 85 86 87 103 107 108 110 111 114 119 129 130 132 133 135 146 148 **P**6 **S** Indiana University Health, Indianapolis, IN
Primary Contact: David W. Hyatt, Chief Executive Officer
CFO: Don Michael, Vice President, Chief Financial Officer
CIO: Jeff Horn, Vice President, Information and Support Services
CHR: Jerry Bozell, Vice President, Human Resources
CNO: Lisa Craiger, Vice President, Chief Nursing Officer
Web address: www.jaycountyhospital.com
**Control:** County–Government, nonfederal **Service:** General Medical and Surgical

**Staffed Beds:** 35 **Admissions:** 873 **Census:** 12 **Outpatient Visits:** 94739 **Births:** 80 **Total Expense ($000):** 36430 **Payroll Expense ($000):** 14422 **Personnel:** 272

**PRINCETON—Gibson County**

✠ **GIBSON GENERAL HOSPITAL (151319)**, 1808 Sherman Drive, Zip 47670–1043; tel. 812/385–3401, (Total facility includes 45 beds in nursing home–type unit) **A**1 9 10 18 **F**3 5 11 15 28 29 30 31 34 35 38 40 45 49 50 54 56 57 59 62 64 68 70 75 77 79 81 82 89 93 97 99 100 101 102 103 104 107 110 111 115 119 128 129 130 131 132 133 146 148 **P**6 **S** Alliant Management Services, Louisville, KY
Primary Contact: Emmett C. Schuster, President and Chief Executive Officer
CFO: Ron Harrington, Vice President and Chief Financial Officer
CMO: Bruce Brink, Jr., D.O., Chief of Staff
CIO: Ron Harrington, Chief Financial Officer
CHR: D. Deann Hunt, Director Human Resources
CNO: Lori Phillips, Vice President and Chief Nursing Officer
Web address: www.gibsongeneral.com
**Control:** Other not–for–profit (including NFP Corporation) **Service:** General Medical and Surgical

**Staffed Beds:** 70 **Admissions:** 553 **Census:** 48 **Outpatient Visits:** 33505 **Births:** 0 **Total Expense ($000):** 25339 **Payroll Expense ($000):** 10920 **Personnel:** 304

IN

## RENSSELAER—Jasper County

★ **FRANCISCAN HEALTH RENSSELEAR (151324)**, 1104 East Grace Street, Zip 47978–3296; tel. 219/866–5141 **A**9 10 18 **F**3 11 15 28 29 30 31 34 35 39 40 43 45 47 49 50 51 53 54 57 59 62 63 64 65 68 69 70 74 75 77 78 79 80 81 82 85 86 87 93 96 107 108 110 111 114 115 118 119 127 129 130 131 132 133 135 146 148 **S** Franciscan Alliance, Mishawaka, IN
Primary Contact: Timothy M. Schreeg, President and Chief Executive Officer
CFO: Jeffrey D. Webb, CPA, Chief Financial Officer
CIO: Kirby Reed, Director Information Systems
CHR: Deana Brown, Director Administrative Services
CNO: Stacie Klingler, R.N., Vice President of Patient Services
Web address: www.jchh.com
**Control:** County–Government, nonfederal **Service:** General Medical and Surgical

**Staffed Beds:** 18 **Admissions:** 1100 **Census:** 18 **Outpatient Visits:** 84822 **Births:** 36 **Total Expense ($000):** 36000 **Payroll Expense ($000):** 16132 **Personnel:** 379

## RICHMOND—Wayne County

★ ○ **REID HEALTH (150048)**, 1100 Reid Parkway, Zip 47374–1157; tel. 765/983–3000 **A**2 9 10 11 13 **F**3 11 13 15 18 20 22 24 26 28 29 30 31 32 34 35 40 43 44 45 47 49 50 51 54 55 56 57 59 61 63 64 69 70 74 75 76 77 78 79 81 82 83 84 85 86 87 89 90 91 93 96 97 98 100 101 102 103 104 107 108 110 111 114 115 116 117 118 119 120 121 123 126 127 129 130 131 132 135 144 146 147 148 **P**6 7 8
Primary Contact: Craig C. Kinyon, President
CMO: Thomas Huth, M.D., Vice President Medical Affairs
CIO: Tim Love, Director Information Services
CHR: Scott C. Rauch, Vice President Human Resources
CNO: Kay B. Cartwright, R.N., Vice President and Chief Nursing Officer
Web address: www.reidhealth.org
**Control:** Other not–for–profit (including NFP Corporation) **Service:** General Medical and Surgical

**Staffed Beds:** 217 **Admissions:** 11495 **Census:** 145 **Outpatient Visits:** 306372 **Births:** 656 **Total Expense ($000):** 373862 **Payroll Expense ($000):** 147827 **Personnel:** 2115

☐ **RICHMOND STATE HOSPITAL (154018)**, 498 N.W. 18th Street, Zip 47374–2851; tel. 765/966–0511 **A**1 10 **F**29 30 39 68 75 77 87 98 100 101 103 130 132 135 146 **P**6
Primary Contact: Terry Suttle, Superintendent
CFO: Dave Shelford, Assistant Superintendent
CMO: Donald Graber, M.D., Medical Director
CIO: Robert Boatman, Director Information Technology
CHR: Sarah Witt, Director Human Resources
Web address: www.richmondstatehospital.org
**Control:** State–Government, nonfederal **Service:** Psychiatric

**Staffed Beds:** 213 **Admissions:** 150 **Census:** 198 **Outpatient Visits:** 0 **Births:** 0 **Total Expense ($000):** 39536 **Payroll Expense ($000):** 18164 **Personnel:** 386

## ROCHESTER—Fulton County

★ **WOODLAWN HOSPITAL (151313)**, 1400 East Ninth Street, Zip 46975–8937; tel. 574/223–3141 **A**9 10 18 **F**3 11 13 15 29 30 31 34 40 46 56 57 59 63 65 68 69 75 77 78 79 81 82 93 94 97 107 108 111 115 116 119 129 130 132 133 135 143 146 147 148 **P**6
Primary Contact: John L. Alley, Chief Executive Officer
CFO: Dave Cholger, Chief Financial Officer
CHR: Debra J. Lemasters, Director Human Resources
Web address: www.woodlawnhospital.com
**Control:** County–Government, nonfederal **Service:** General Medical and Surgical

**Staffed Beds:** 25 **Admissions:** 1191 **Census:** 12 **Outpatient Visits:** 51641 **Births:** 199 **Total Expense ($000):** 48934 **Payroll Expense ($000):** 23080

## RUSHVILLE—Rush County

★ **RUSH MEMORIAL HOSPITAL (151304)**, 1300 North Main Street, Zip 46173–1198, Mailing Address: P.O. Box 608, Zip 46173–0608; tel. 765/932–4111 **A**9 10 18 **F**3 7 11 15 18 24 28 29 31 35 36 40 46 51 52 57 59 64 65 74 75 77 78 79 81 85 93 97 107 111 114 117 120 121 122 129 130 131 132 133 135 146 147 148 **P**6
Primary Contact: Bradley Smith, President and Chief Executive Officer
COO: Debbie Jones–Browning, Vice President Operations and Physician Services and Chief Operating Officer
CFO: Karen Meyer, Vice President Finance and Chief Financial Officer
CMO: Daniel Stahl, D.O., Chief of Staff
CIO: Jim Boyer, Vice President Information Technology and Chief Information Officer
CHR: Dennis Fogle, Vice President of Human Resources
CNO: Gretchen Smith, Vice President Nursing and Compliance and Risk
Web address: www.rushmemorial.com
**Control:** County–Government, nonfederal **Service:** General Medical and Surgical

**Staffed Beds:** 25 **Admissions:** 417 **Census:** 4 **Outpatient Visits:** 33141 **Births:** 0 **Total Expense ($000):** 27871 **Payroll Expense ($000):** 12675 **Personnel:** 360

## SALEM—Washington County

⊞ **ST. VINCENT SALEM HOSPITAL (151314)**, 911 North Shelby Street, Zip 47167–1694; tel. 812/883–5881 **A**1 9 10 18 **F**3 11 15 28 29 30 32 34 40 45 47 49 57 59 75 77 79 81 82 85 93 104 107 111 114 119 129 130 132 133 148 **P**6 **S** Ascension Health, Saint Louis, MO
Primary Contact: Dana M. Muntz, Chief Executive Officer
CFO: Joseph Kubala, Director Financial and Support Services
CMO: S. E. Kemker, M.D., President Medical Staff
CIO: Jeremy Long, Manager Information Systems
CHR: Val Potter, Director Human Resources
Web address: www.stvincent.org/St-Vincent-Salem/Default.aspx
**Control:** Other not–for–profit (including NFP Corporation) **Service:** General Medical and Surgical

**Staffed Beds:** 25 **Admissions:** 235 **Census:** 2 **Outpatient Visits:** 29285 **Births:** 0 **Total Expense ($000):** 17027 **Payroll Expense ($000):** 5885 **Personnel:** 117

## SCOTTSBURG—Scott County

⊞ **SCOTT MEMORIAL HOSPITAL (151334)**, 1415 North Gardner Street, Zip 47170, Mailing Address: Box 430, Zip 47170–0430; tel. 812/752–3456, (Nonreporting) **A**1 9 10 18 **S** LifePoint Health, Brentwood, TN
Primary Contact: Michael Everett, Chief Executive Officer
CFO: Angela Doan, Chief Financial Officer
CNO: Dawn Mays, Chief Nursing Officer
Web address: www.scottmemorial.com
**Control:** County–Government, nonfederal **Service:** General Medical and Surgical

**Staffed Beds:** 25

## SEYMOUR—Jackson County

⊞ **SCHNECK MEDICAL CENTER (150065)**, 411 West Tipton Street, Zip 47274–2363, Mailing Address: P.O. Box 2349, Zip 47274–5000; tel. 812/522–2349 **A**1 2 9 10 **F**3 8 12 13 15 18 28 29 30 31 34 35 36 40 45 50 51 56 57 59 60 61 62 63 64 68 69 70 74 75 76 77 78 79 81 82 84 85 86 87 89 93 104 107 110 111 115 116 118 119 120 121 123 124 126 129 130 131 132 133 135 144 146 147 148 **P**8
Primary Contact: Warren Forgey, CPA, FACHE, President and Chief Executive Officer
CFO: Deborah Ridlen, CPA, Vice President Fiscal Services and Chief Financial Officer
CMO: Douglas Towriss, Vice President and Chief Medical Officer
CIO: Craig Rice, Director Information
CHR: Kathy Covert, Vice President Human Resources
CNO: Vicki Johnson–Poynter, MSN, Vice President Nursing Services and Chief Nursing Officer
Web address: www.schneckmed.org
**Control:** County–Government, nonfederal **Service:** General Medical and Surgical

**Staffed Beds:** 93 **Admissions:** 3498 **Census:** 36 **Outpatient Visits:** 195480 **Births:** 804 **Total Expense ($000):** 115056 **Payroll Expense ($000):** 48585 **Personnel:** 756

IN

---

**Hospital, Medicare Provider Number, Address, Telephone, Approval, Facility, and Physician Codes, Health Care System**

★ American Hospital Association (AHA) membership
☐ The Joint Commission accreditation
○ Healthcare Facilities Accreditation Program
◇ DNV Healthcare Inc. accreditation
⇑ Center for Improvement in Healthcare Quality Accreditation
△ Commission on Accreditation of Rehabilitation Facilities (CARF) accreditation

## SHELBYVILLE—Shelby County

★ ○ **MAJOR HOSPITAL (150097)**, 150 West Washington Street, Zip 46176–1236; tel. 317/392–3211 **A**9 10 11 **F**3 12 13 15 28 29 30 31 34 35 40 50 57 59 62 63 64 68 70 73 74 75 76 77 78 79 80 81 82 84 85 89 93 97 107 108 110 111 114 118 119 120 121 123 129 130 131 132 135 144 146 147 148 **P**6
Primary Contact: John M. Horner, President and Chief Executive Officer
CFO: Ralph Mercuri, Vice President and Chief Financial Officer
CMO: Douglas S. Carter, M.D., Vice President and Chief Medical Officer
CIO: Dan Van Gundy, Director of Information Technology Systems and Hardwire
CHR: Nicki Sparling, Manager Human Resources
CNO: Valerie L. Miller, MSN, Director of Nursing
Web address: www.majorhospital.org
**Control:** City–County, Government, nonfederal **Service:** General Medical and Surgical

**Staffed Beds:** 72 **Admissions:** 2784 **Census:** 26 **Outpatient Visits:** 156472 **Births:** 335 **Total Expense ($000):** 83887 **Payroll Expense ($000):** 35517 **Personnel:** 624

## SOUTH BEND—St. Joseph County

⊞ △ **MEMORIAL HOSPITAL OF SOUTH BEND (150058)**, 615 North Michigan Street, Zip 46601–1033; tel. 574/647–1000, (Includes MEMORIAL CHILDREN'S HOSPITAL, 615 North Michigan Street, Zip 46601, Mailing Address: 516 North Michigan Street, Zip 46601; tel. 574/647–1000) **A**1 2 3 7 9 10 **F**3 7 8 9 13 15 17 18 19 20 22 24 26 28 29 30 31 35 36 38 40 43 46 49 50 53 56 59 60 61 64 67 68 70 72 73 74 75 76 77 78 79 81 82 84 85 86 87 88 89 90 92 93 95 98 99 102 103 107 108 110 114 115 116 117 118 119 120 121 123 124 126 129 130 131 132 135 146 147 148 **P**5 8 **S** Beacon Health System, South Bend, IN
Primary Contact: Kreg Gruber, President
CFO: Jeff Costello, Chief Financial Officer
CMO: Cheryl Wibbens, M.D., Vice President Medical Staff Affairs
CIO: Steve Huffman, Chief Information Officer
Web address: www.qualityoflife.org
**Control:** Other not–for–profit (including NFP Corporation) **Service:** General Medical and Surgical

**Staffed Beds:** 445 **Admissions:** 19262 **Census:** 280 **Outpatient Visits:** 192606 **Births:** 2532 **Total Expense ($000):** 408011 **Payroll Expense ($000):** 138415 **Personnel:** 2227

## SULLIVAN—Sullivan County

★ **SULLIVAN COUNTY COMMUNITY HOSPITAL (151327)**, 2200 North Section Street, Zip 47882–7523, Mailing Address: P.O. Box 10, Zip 47882–0010; tel. 812/268–4311 **A**9 10 18 **F**3 8 13 15 28 29 32 34 35 40 44 45 47 48 53 56 57 59 61 62 69 70 75 76 77 78 79 81 86 87 93 97 107 110 111 114 127 129 130 131 133 146 147 148 **P**8 **S** QHR, Brentwood, TN
Primary Contact: Michelle Franklin, Chief Executive Officer
CFO: Scott Andritsch, Chief Financial Officer
CMO: Divyesh Purohit, M.D., Chief of Staff
CIO: Hap Beckes, Director Information Systems
CHR: Denise Hart, Director Human Resources
CNO: Lori Resler, R.N., Chief Nurse
Web address: www.schosp.com
**Control:** County–Government, nonfederal **Service:** General Medical and Surgical

**Staffed Beds:** 25 **Admissions:** 780 **Census:** 6 **Outpatient Visits:** 68471 **Births:** 142 **Total Expense ($000):** 22430 **Payroll Expense ($000):** 10006 **Personnel:** 192

## TELL CITY—Perry County

★ **PERRY COUNTY MEMORIAL HOSPITAL (151322)**, 1 Hospital Road, Zip 47586–2750; tel. 812/547–7011, (Nonreporting) **A**9 10 18 **S** Alliant Management Services, Louisville, KY
Primary Contact: Joseph A. Stuber, President and Chief Executive Officer
COO: Becky Elder, Vice President Clinical Services
CMO: William Marcrum, M.D., Chief of Staff
CIO: Mark Miller, Director Information Systems
CHR: Sheila Gaynor, Director Human Resources
Web address: www.pchospital.org
**Control:** County–Government, nonfederal **Service:** General Medical and Surgical

**Staffed Beds:** 25

## TERRE HAUTE—Vigo County

**HAMILTON CENTER (154009)**, 620 Eighth Avenue, Zip 47804–2744; tel. 812/231–8323 **A**9 10 **F**34 98 101 102 103 104 130 **P**6
Primary Contact: Mel Burks, Chief Executive Officer
COO: Robb Johnson, Director Operations
CFO: Renee Utley, Acting Chief Financial Officer
CMO: Ahsan Mahmood, M.D., Chief Medical Officer
CIO: Hans Eilbracht, Chief Information Officer
CHR: Jan Weber, Chief Human Resources Officer
CNO: Brooke Kempt, Corporate Nursing Director
Web address: www.hamiltoncenter.org
**Control:** Other not–for–profit (including NFP Corporation) **Service:** Psychiatric

**Staffed Beds:** 16 **Admissions:** 693 **Census:** 13 **Outpatient Visits:** 232425 **Births:** 0 **Total Expense ($000):** 29709 **Payroll Expense ($000):** 17074 **Personnel:** 508

□ **HARSHA BEHAVIORAL CENTER (154054)**, 1420 East Crossing Boulevard, Zip 47802–5316; tel. 866/644–8880, (Nonreporting) **A**1 9 10
Primary Contact: Roopam Harshawat, Chief Executive Officer
COO: Holly Near, Chief Administrative Officer
CFO: Holly Near, Chief Administrative Officer
CMO: Paras Harshawat, M.D., Medical Director
CHR: Karen Hunt, Executive Director
CNO: Cindy Dowers, Chief Nursing Officer
Web address: www.harshacenter.com
**Control:** Corporation, Investor–owned, for–profit **Service:** Psychiatric

**Staffed Beds:** 36

⊞ **TERRE HAUTE REGIONAL HOSPITAL (150046)**, 3901 South Seventh Street, Zip 47802–5709; tel. 812/232–0021 **A**1 2 9 10 **F**3 11 13 15 18 20 22 24 26 28 29 31 34 35 37 40 41 45 46 47 49 50 57 59 64 65 70 72 74 76 77 78 79 80 81 82 85 86 89 90 91 92 93 98 101 102 103 107 108 109 110 111 113 115 119 132 135 145 146 147 148 **S** HCA, Nashville, TN
Primary Contact: Mary Ann Conroy, Chief Executive Officer
COO: Tim Prestridge, Chief Operating Officer
CFO: Adam Martin, Chief Financial Officer
CIO: Mike Kuckewich, Director Information Systems
CNO: Angela Ellis, R.N., Chief Nursing Officer
Web address: www.regionalhospital.com
**Control:** Corporation, Investor–owned, for–profit **Service:** General Medical and Surgical

**Staffed Beds:** 208 **Admissions:** 5982 **Census:** 77 **Outpatient Visits:** 44639 **Births:** 414 **Personnel:** 693

★ ○ △ **UNION HOSPITAL (150023)**, 1606 North Seventh Street, Zip 47804–2780; tel. 812/238–7000 **A**2 3 7 9 10 11 19 **F**3 8 13 15 18 20 22 24 26 28 29 30 31 34 35 36 40 45 46 48 49 50 51 53 54 57 59 60 64 68 70 72 73 74 75 76 77 78 79 81 82 85 86 87 89 90 91 92 93 94 95 96 97 100 107 108 110 111 112 114 115 116 117 118 119 120 121 123 126 127 130 131 132 135 144 146 147 148 **P**6
Primary Contact: Steve M. Holman, Chief Executive Officer
CFO: Wayne Hutson, Executive Vice President and Chief Financial Officer
CMO: John Bolinger, M.D., Vice President Medical Affairs
CIO: Kym Pfrank, Senior Vice President and Chief Operating Officer
CNO: Rhonda E. Smith, R.N., Vice President Patient Care Services and Chief Nursing Officer
Web address: www.uhhg.org
**Control:** Other not–for–profit (including NFP Corporation) **Service:** General Medical and Surgical

**Staffed Beds:** 274 **Admissions:** 13829 **Census:** 180 **Outpatient Visits:** 378943 **Births:** 1892 **Total Expense ($000):** 383170 **Payroll Expense ($000):** 126389 **Personnel:** 1783

## TIPTON—Tipton County

⊞ **INDIANA UNIVERSITY HEALTH TIPTON HOSPITAL (151311)**, 1000 South Main Street, Zip 46072–9799; tel. 765/675–8500 **A**1 2 9 10 18 **F**3 8 11 15 18 28 29 30 31 34 35 39 40 45 46 47 48 53 57 59 70 74 75 77 78 79 81 82 85 86 87 93 107 108 110 111 115 119 129 131 132 133 135 146 147 148 **S** Indiana University Health, Indianapolis, IN
Primary Contact: Michael Harlowe, President and Chief Executive Officer
CFO: Randall C. Yust, Chief Financial Officer NCR
CMO: Gaurau Arora, M.D., Chief Medical Officer
CHR: Shelly E. Huff, Manager Human Resources
CNO: Jo Ellen Scott, R.N., Senior Vice President of Patient Care Services and Chief Nursing Officer
Web address: www.iuhealth.org
**Control:** Other not–for–profit (including NFP Corporation) **Service:** General Medical and Surgical

**Staffed Beds:** 25 **Admissions:** 1058 **Census:** 12 **Outpatient Visits:** 42485 **Births:** 0 **Total Expense ($000):** 36289 **Payroll Expense ($000):** 10833 **Personnel:** 196

**TIPTON HOSPITAL** See Indiana University Health Tipton Hospital

## VALPARAISO—Porter County

⊞ **PORTER REGIONAL HOSPITAL (150035)**, 85 East U.S. Highway 6, Zip 46383–8947; tel. 219/983–8300, (Nonreporting) **A**1 5 9 10 **S** Community Health Systems, Inc., Franklin, TN
Primary Contact: Stephen Lunn, Chief Executive Officer
COO: Ashley Dickinson, Chief Operating Officer
CFO: Cheryl A. Harmon, Chief Financial Officer
CMO: Ramireddy K. Tummuru, M.D., Chief Medical Officer
CIO: Robert Richardson, Information Technology Administrator
CHR: Angie Hampton, Director Human Resources
Web address: www.porterhealth.com
**Control:** Corporation, Investor–owned, for–profit **Service:** General Medical and Surgical

**Staffed Beds:** 276

*Many Facility Codes have changed. Please refer to the AHA Guide Code Chart.* © 2015 AHA Guide

**PORTER–STARKE SERVICES (154052)**, 601 Wall Street, Zip 46383–2512;
tel. 219/531–3500 **A**10 **F**5 29 66 68 98 99 101 103 104 **P**6
Primary Contact: Rocco Schiralli, President/Chief Executive Officer
CFO: Mary Idstein, Chief Financial Officer
CMO: Anand Popli, Medical Director
Web address: www.porterstarke.org
**Control:** Other not–for–profit (including NFP Corporation) **Service:** Psychiatric

**Staffed Beds:** 16 **Admissions:** 1069 **Census:** 8 **Outpatient Visits:** 126784
**Births:** 0 **Total Expense ($000):** 15600 **Payroll Expense ($000):** 8908
**Personnel:** 211

## VINCENNES—Knox County

⊠ △ **GOOD SAMARITAN HOSPITAL (150042)**, 520 South Seventh Street,
Zip 47591–1038; tel. 812/882–5220 **A**1 2 7 9 10 19 **F**3 5 8 11 13 15 18 19
20 22 28 29 30 31 32 34 35 38 40 44 45 46 47 48 49 51 53 54 56 57 58
59 60 63 64 65 66 67 68 70 74 75 76 77 78 79 81 84 85 87 89 90 92 93
96 97 98 99 100 101 102 103 104 106 107 108 110 111 115 118 119 120
121 123 127 129 130 131 132 134 135 144 145 146 147 148 **P**6
Primary Contact: Robert D. McLin, President and Chief Executive Officer
CFO: Jerry Stump, Chief Financial Officer
CMO: Charles C. Hedde, M.D., Chief Medical Officer
CIO: Marsha Danielsen, Director Information Systems
CHR: Dean Wagoner, Director Human Resources
CNO: Karen S. Haak, R.N., Chief Nursing Officer
Web address: www.gshvin.org/goodsamaritan
**Control:** County–Government, nonfederal **Service:** General Medical and Surgical

**Staffed Beds:** 191 **Admissions:** 7424 **Census:** 101 **Outpatient Visits:**
493254 **Births:** 520 **Total Expense ($000):** 223849 **Payroll Expense**
**($000):** 103214 **Personnel:** 1607

## WABASH—Wabash County

⊠ **PARKVIEW WABASH COUNTY HOSPITAL (151310)**, 710 North East Street,
Zip 46992–1924, Mailing Address: P.O. Box 548, Zip 46992–0548;
tel. 260/563–3131 **A**1 9 10 18 **F**3 11 15 32 34 35 45 47 50 53 57 58 59 62
63 64 65 68 69 70 75 77 80 81 84 85 86 87 93 97 107 108 111 114 119
124 130 131 132 133 146 147 **S** Parkview Health, Fort Wayne, IN
Primary Contact: Marilyn J. Custer–Mitchell, President
CFO: Jane Bissel, Chief Financial Officer
CMO: Jeff Miller, M.D., Chief of Staff
CIO: David Brinson, Director Information Technology
CHR: Kimberly R. Shininger, Director Human Resources
CNO: Cathy Allyson Wolfe, Chief Nursing Officer
Web address: www.wchospital.com
**Control:** County–Government, nonfederal **Service:** General Medical and Surgical

**Staffed Beds:** 25 **Admissions:** 594 **Census:** 6 **Outpatient Visits:** 46321
**Births:** 0 **Total Expense ($000):** 39514 **Payroll Expense ($000):** 15875
**Personnel:** 229

## WARSAW—Kosciusko County

⊠ **KOSCIUSKO COMMUNITY HOSPITAL (150133)**, 2101 East Dubois Drive,
Zip 46580–3288; tel. 574/267–3200 **A**1 2 9 10 19 **F**3 8 12 13 15 28 29 30
31 32 34 40 43 44 49 50 51 53 57 58 59 64 65 68 70 74 75 76 77 78
79 81 82 85 86 89 90 93 107 108 110 111 114 115 116 117 118 119 120
121 129 130 131 132 144 146 147 148 **P**6 **S** Community Health Systems,
Inc., Franklin, TN
Primary Contact: Kirk M. Ray, Chief Executive Officer
CFO: Douglas J. BeMent, Chief Financial Officer
CMO: Patrick Silveus, M.D., Medical Director
CIO: Tammy Lukens, Director Information
CHR: Joe Jarboe, Director Human Resources
CNO: Kim Finch, Chief Nursing Officer
Web address: www.kch.com
**Control:** Corporation, Investor–owned, for–profit **Service:** General Medical and
Surgical

**Staffed Beds:** 72 **Admissions:** 3487 **Census:** 31 **Outpatient Visits:** 105691
**Births:** 599 **Total Expense ($000):** 67045 **Payroll Expense ($000):** 23428
**Personnel:** 464

★ **OTIS R. BOWEN CENTER FOR HUMAN SERVICES (154014)**, 850 North
Harrison Street, Zip 46580–3163, Mailing Address: 2621 East Jefferson Street,
Zip 46580–3880; tel. 574/267–7169 **A**9 10 **F**4 5 29 34 35 38 50 66 86 87
98 99 100 101 102 103 104 106 127 130 132 134 143 **P**1
Primary Contact: Kurt Carlson, Chief Executive Officer
Web address: www.bowencenter.org
**Control:** Other not–for–profit (including NFP Corporation) **Service:** Psychiatric

**Staffed Beds:** 16 **Admissions:** 1053 **Census:** 9 **Outpatient Visits:** 424419
**Births:** 0 **Total Expense ($000):** 39285 **Payroll Expense ($000):** 24495
**Personnel:** 763

## WASHINGTON—Daviess County

⊠ △ **DAVIESS COMMUNITY HOSPITAL (150061)**, 1314 East Walnut Street,
Zip 47501–2860, Mailing Address: P.O. Box 760, Zip 47501–0760;
tel. 812/254–2760, (Nonreporting) **A**1 7 9 10 **S** QHR, Brentwood, TN
Primary Contact: David Bixler, Chief Executive Officer
CMO: Michael Baker, D.O., Chief of Staff
CIO: Richard Meinhart, Manager Information Systems
CHR: Marilyn Richard, Director Human Resources
Web address: www.dchosp.org
**Control:** County–Government, nonfederal **Service:** General Medical and Surgical

**Staffed Beds:** 48

## WEST LAFAYETTE—Tippecanoe County

★ **RIVER BEND HOSPITAL (154005)**, 2900 North River Road, Zip 47906–3744;
tel. 765/464–0400, (Nonreporting) **A**9 10
Primary Contact: Stephanie Long, President and Chief Executive Officer
COO: Tom Gillian, Chief Operating Officer
CFO: Jeff Nagy, Chief Financial Officer
CMO: Richard Rahdert, M.D., Medical Director
CIO: Craig Anderson, Director Management Information Systems
CHR: Jan Shaw, Director Personnel
CNO: Megan Gibson, Nurse Manager
Web address: www.nchsi.com/riverbendhospital.cfm
**Control:** Other not–for–profit (including NFP Corporation) **Service:** Psychiatric

**Staffed Beds:** 16

**WABASH VALLEY HOSPITAL** See River Bend Hospital

## WILLIAMSPORT—Warren County

⊠ **ST. VINCENT WILLIAMSPORT HOSPITAL (151307)**, 412 North Monroe
Street, Zip 47993–1049; tel. 765/762–4000 **A**1 9 10 18 **F**3 7 15 29 30 34 35
40 45 50 51 57 59 64 75 77 79 81 85 86 87 93 97 107 111 114 119 127
131 132 133 135 143 146 **P**6 **S** Ascension Health, Saint Louis, MO
Primary Contact: Jane Craigin, Chief Executive Officer
CFO: Janet Merritt, Chief Financial Officer
Web address: www.stvincent.org
**Control:** Other not–for–profit (including NFP Corporation) **Service:** General
Medical and Surgical

**Staffed Beds:** 16 **Admissions:** 660 **Census:** 7 **Outpatient Visits:** 68630
**Births:** 0 **Total Expense ($000):** 19616 **Payroll Expense ($000):** 9040
**Personnel:** 150

## WINAMAC—Pulaski County

★ **PULASKI MEMORIAL HOSPITAL (151305)**, 616 East 13th Street,
Zip 46996–1117, Mailing Address: P.O. Box 279, Zip 46996–0279;
tel. 574/946–2100 **A**9 10 18 **F**1 4 11 13 15 18 28 29 30 31 34 35 40 43 45
50 53 57 59 62 63 64 65 67 68 73 75 76 77 78 79 80 81 82 85 86 87 89
90 91 93 96 97 98 103 107 110 114 119 127 128 130 131 132 133 135
146 **P**6
Primary Contact: Thomas Barry, Chief Executive Officer
CFO: Gregg Malott, Chief Financial Officer
CMO: Rex Allman, M.D., President Medical Staff
CIO: Jeff Boer, Director Information Technology
CHR: Mark Fenn, Director Human Resources
CNO: Linda Webb, R.N., Chief Nursing Executive
Web address: www.pmhnet.com
**Control:** County–Government, nonfederal **Service:** General Medical and Surgical

**Staffed Beds:** 25 **Admissions:** 657 **Census:** 7 **Outpatient Visits:** 25279
**Births:** 124 **Total Expense ($000):** 26417 **Payroll Expense ($000):** 12077
**Personnel:** 237

## WINCHESTER—Randolph County

⊠ **ST. VINCENT RANDOLPH HOSPITAL (151301)**, 473 Greenville Avenue,
Zip 47394–9436, Mailing Address: P.O. Box 407, Zip 47394–0407;
tel. 765/584–0004 **A**1 9 10 18 **F**3 11 13 15 28 29 30 31 34 35 40 44 45 50
57 59 64 65 68 75 76 77 79 81 85 86 87 89 93 107 110 111 114 119 129
130 131 132 133 135 146 147 148 **S** Ascension Health, Saint Louis, MO
Primary Contact: Francis G. Albarano, Administrator
CFO: John Arthur, Chief Financial Officer
CMO: Gary Brazel, M.D., Chief Medical Officer
CHR: Richard Ross Brodhead, Director Human Resources
CNO: Carla Fouse, Chief Nursing Officer
Web address: www.stvincent.org
**Control:** Other not–for–profit (including NFP Corporation) **Service:** General
Medical and Surgical

**Staffed Beds:** 16 **Admissions:** 747 **Census:** 6 **Outpatient Visits:** 40742
**Births:** 199 **Total Expense ($000):** 21946 **Payroll Expense ($000):** 8170
**Personnel:** 169

**IN**

---

**Hospital, Medicare Provider Number, Address, Telephone, Approval, Facility, and Physician Codes, Health Care System**

★ American Hospital Association (AHA) membership ○ Healthcare Facilities Accreditation Program ⇧ Center for Improvement in Healthcare Quality Accreditation
☐ The Joint Commission accreditation ◇ DNV Healthcare Inc. accreditation △ Commission on Accreditation of Rehabilitation Facilities (CARF) accreditation

# IOWA

### ALBIA—Monroe County

★ **MONROE COUNTY HOSPITAL AND CLINICS (161342)**, 6580 165th Street,
Zip 52531–8793; tel. 641/932–2134 **A**9 10 18 **F**7 11 15 28 29 31 34 40 50
57 59 63 78 81 85 107 110 114 119 127 130 132 133 **P**6
Primary Contact: Veronica Fuhs, Chief Executive Officer
Web address: www.mchalbia.com
**Control:** County–Government, nonfederal **Service:** General Medical and Surgical

**Staffed Beds:** 25 **Admissions:** 331 **Census:** 5 **Outpatient Visits:** 48805
**Births:** 0 **Total Expense ($000):** 17536 **Payroll Expense ($000):** 7224
**Personnel:** 140

### ALGONA—Kossuth County

★ **KOSSUTH REGIONAL HEALTH CENTER (161353)**, 1515 South Phillips Street,
Zip 50511–3649; tel. 515/295–2451 **A**9 10 18 **F**11 13 15 17 28 29 30 31 32
34 35 36 40 41 43 50 56 57 59 62 63 64 65 67 68 70 75 76 77 78 81 82
84 86 87 89 92 93 97 107 114 119 127 128 129 130 131 132 133 135 146
147 148 **P**8 **S** Trinity Health, Livonia, MI
Primary Contact: Scott A. Curtis, Administrator and Chief Executive Officer
CFO: Jason Feucht, Chief Financial Officer
CMO: Michael Lampe, M.D., Chief of Staff
CIO: Nancy Erickson, Administrator Information Systems
CHR: Paula Seely, Manager Human Resources
CNO: Darlene M. Elbert, R.N., Assistant Administrator and Chief Nursing Officer
Web address: www.krhc.com
**Control:** County–Government, nonfederal **Service:** General Medical and Surgical

**Staffed Beds:** 23 **Admissions:** 682 **Census:** 9 **Outpatient Visits:** 27064
**Births:** 137 **Total Expense ($000):** 29960 **Payroll Expense ($000):** 9892
**Personnel:** 194

### AMES—Story County

⌧ △ **MARY GREELEY MEDICAL CENTER (160030)**, 1111 Duff Avenue,
Zip 50010–5745; tel. 515/239–2011 **A**1 2 7 9 10 19 **F**3 7 8 11 12 13 15 17
18 20 22 26 28 29 30 31 34 35 36 37 38 40 43 45 46 49 50 53 55 56 57
58 59 61 62 63 64 65 68 69 70 72 74 75 76 77 78 79 81 82 84 85 86 89
90 92 93 96 98 99 100 101 102 103 104 107 108 110 111 114 115 118
119 120 121 123 124 126 129 130 131 132 135 146 148
Primary Contact: Brian Dieter, President and Chief Executive Officer
CFO: Gary Botine, Vice President, Chief Financial Officer
CIO: Scott Carlson, Director
CHR: Betsy V. Schoeller, Director Human Resources and Education
Web address: www.mgmc.org
**Control:** City–Government, nonfederal **Service:** General Medical and Surgical

**Staffed Beds:** 183 **Admissions:** 8289 **Census:** 104 **Outpatient Visits:**
167791 **Births:** 1143 **Total Expense ($000):** 161793 **Payroll Expense
($000):** 61432 **Personnel:** 1042

### ANAMOSA—Jones County

★ **UNITYPOINT HEALTH – JONES REGIONAL MEDICAL CENTER (161306)**,
1795 Highway 64 East, Zip 52205–2112; tel. 319/462–6131 **A**9 10 18 **F**3 7
11 12 15 28 29 30 31 34 35 38 40 43 45 50 56 57 59 64 68 71 75 81 82
84 85 87 91 93 96 97 99 100 101 102 103 104 107 110 111 114 118 119
130 132 133 135 145 146 148 **P**4 **S** UnityPoint Health, West Des Moines, IA
Primary Contact: Eric Briesemeister, Chief Executive Officer
CFO: Rachel Von Behren, Director Financial Services
CMO: Victor Salas, M.D., President Medical Staff
CHR: Donna Condry, Director Human Resources
Web address: www.jonesregional.org
**Control:** Other not–for–profit (including NFP Corporation) **Service:** General
Medical and Surgical

**Staffed Beds:** 22 **Admissions:** 633 **Census:** 8 **Outpatient Visits:** 82039
**Births:** 0 **Total Expense ($000):** 19232 **Payroll Expense ($000):** 6869
**Personnel:** 148

### ATLANTIC—Cass County

★ **CASS COUNTY MEMORIAL HOSPITAL (161376)**, 1501 East Tenth Street,
Zip 50022–1997; tel. 712/243–3250 **A**9 10 18 **F**11 13 15 28 29 31 40 57 59
64 69 70 75 76 77 78 81 82 93 97 98 99 101 102 103 104 105 107 108
111 119 124 127 129 130 132 133 135 147 148 **P**8
Primary Contact: Todd R. Hudspeth, FACHE, Chief Executive Officer and President
COO: Alison Bruckner, Chief Operating Officer
CFO: Abbey Stangl, Chief Financial Officer
CMO: Patricia Goodemote, M.D., Chief Medical Officer
CIO: Jeff Osegard, Chief Information Officer
CHR: Denise Coder, Chief Human Resource Officer
Web address: www.casshealth.org
**Control:** County–Government, nonfederal **Service:** General Medical and Surgical

**Staffed Beds:** 29 **Admissions:** 866 **Census:** 11 **Outpatient Visits:** 92157
**Births:** 123 **Total Expense ($000):** 36295 **Payroll Expense ($000):** 13290
**Personnel:** 292

### AUDUBON—Audubon County

**AUDUBON COUNTY MEMORIAL HOSPITAL (161330)**, 515 Pacific Street,
Zip 50025–1056; tel. 712/563–2611 **A**9 10 18 **F**3 11 15 28 31 40 43 45 53
59 64 67 78 79 81 85 90 93 110 119 127 128 133 135
Primary Contact: Thomas G. Smith, Administrator and Chief Executive Officer
CFO: Karen McGuire, Chief Financial Officer
CMO: James Cunnigham, D.O., Chief of Staff
CIO: Kelli Burgin, Director Information Technology
CNO: Holly Kjergaard, Chief Nursing Officer
Web address: www.acmhhosp.org
**Control:** County–Government, nonfederal **Service:** General Medical and Surgical

**Staffed Beds:** 25 **Admissions:** 156 **Census:** 2 **Outpatient Visits:** 15241
**Births:** 0 **Total Expense ($000):** 10906 **Payroll Expense ($000):** 4890
**Personnel:** 89

### BELMOND—Wright County

★ ◇ **IOWA SPECIALTY HOSPITAL–BELMOND (161301)**, 403 First Street S.E.,
Zip 50421–1201; tel. 641/444–3223 **A**9 10 18 21 **F**3 7 11 15 28 29 32 34
35 40 43 45 46 50 53 56 57 59 62 63 64 65 67 68 75 77 79 81 82 85 87
89 92 93 96 97 107 110 111 119 127 128 129 131 133 135 146 148 **P**6
**S** Iowa Specialty Hospitals, Clarion, IA
Primary Contact: Amy McDaniel, Administrator and Chief Executive Officer
CFO: Greg Polzin, Chief Financial Officer
CMO: Charles B. Brindle, M.D., Chief Medical Staff
Web address: www.iowaspecialtyhospital.com
**Control:** City–Government, nonfederal **Service:** General Medical and Surgical

**Staffed Beds:** 22 **Admissions:** 305 **Census:** 4 **Outpatient Visits:** 22814
**Births:** 0 **Total Expense ($000):** 18024 **Payroll Expense ($000):** 3999
**Personnel:** 110

### BETTENDORF—Scott County

⌧ **UNITYPOINT HEALTH – TRINITY BETTENDORF (160104)**, 4500 Utica Ridge
Road, Zip 52722–1626; tel. 563/742–5000 **A**1 9 10 13 **F**3 11 13 15 18 20 22
24 26 29 30 34 35 37 40 44 45 46 48 50 57 59 64 70 73 74 76 79 81 82
85 86 87 93 96 97 102 104 107 108 110 114 119 130 132 135 146 147
148 **P**8 **S** UnityPoint Health, West Des Moines, IA
Primary Contact: Richard A. Seidler, FACHE, President and Chief Executive Officer
COO: Jay Willsher, Chief Operating Officer
CFO: Greg Pagliuzza, Chief Financial Officer
CMO: Paul McLoone, M.D., Chief Medical Officer
CHR: Cara Fuller, Vice President Human Resources
CNO: Jean B. Doerge, MS, Chief Nursing Executive
Web address: www.trinityqc.com
**Control:** Other not–for–profit (including NFP Corporation) **Service:** General
Medical and Surgical

**Staffed Beds:** 82 **Admissions:** 3547 **Census:** 29 **Outpatient Visits:** 39343
**Births:** 796 **Total Expense ($000):** 64641 **Payroll Expense ($000):** 19450
**Personnel:** 285

*Many Facility Codes have changed. Please refer to the AHA Guide Code Chart.*

## BLOOMFIELD—Davis County

★ **DAVIS COUNTY HOSPITAL (161327)**, 509 North Madison Street, Zip 52537–1271; tel. 641/664–2145, (Total facility includes 32 beds in nursing home–type unit) **A**9 10 18 **F**3 7 11 13 15 29 34 35 40 44 45 50 57 59 63 64 65 67 68 69 75 76 79 81 84 85 86 87 97 107 110 111 114 119 130 132 133 146 **P**6
Primary Contact: Kirby Johnson, Chief Executive Officer
CFO: Kendra Warning, Chief Financial Officer
CMO: Robert Floyd, M.D., Chief Medical Staff
CIO: Lynn Sims, Director Information Technology
CHR: Pam Young, Director Human Resources
CNO: Susan Kay Pankey, Chief Nursing Officer
Web address: www.daviscountyhospital.org
**Control:** County–Government, nonfederal **Service:** General Medical and Surgical

**Staffed Beds:** 57 **Admissions:** 339 **Census:** 18 **Outpatient Visits:** 22548 **Births:** 24 **Total Expense ($000):** 22124 **Payroll Expense ($000):** 7685 **Personnel:** 134

## BOONE—Boone County

★ **BOONE COUNTY HOSPITAL (161372)**, 1015 Union Street, Zip 50036–4821; tel. 515/432–3140, (Total facility includes 14 beds in nursing home–type unit) **A**9 10 18 **F**1 2 3 4 7 11 13 15 16 17 28 29 30 31 34 35 40 43 45 50 56 57 59 62 64 65 67 69 70 72 73 75 76 77 78 79 80 81 82 85 86 87 88 89 90 91 93 97 98 107 110 111 114 119 128 131 132 133 134 145 146 147 148 **P**6 **S** QHR, Brentwood, TN
Primary Contact: Joseph S. Smith, Chief Executive Officer
CFO: Joseph Devin, Chief Financial Officer
CMO: Tammara Chance, D.O., Chief of Staff
CIO: Matthew Sabus, Director Information Systems
CHR: Kim Schwartz, Assistant Administrator of Human Resources and Physician Services
Web address: www.boonehospital.com
**Control:** County–Government, nonfederal **Service:** General Medical and Surgical

**Staffed Beds:** 39 **Admissions:** 1346 **Census:** 15 **Outpatient Visits:** 53791 **Births:** 148 **Total Expense ($000):** 42224 **Payroll Expense ($000):** 17288 **Personnel:** 316

## BRITT—Hancock County

★ **HANCOCK COUNTY HEALTH SYSTEM (161307)**, 532 First Street N.W., Zip 50423–1227; tel. 641/843–5000 **A**9 10 18 **F**3 15 28 29 31 34 35 36 40 43 45 46 50 53 56 57 59 62 64 65 75 77 81 82 85 93 97 104 107 110 114 119 129 130 131 132 133 135 146 148 **P**1 **S** Trinity Health, Livonia, MI
Primary Contact: Laura Zwiefel, Interim Chief Executive Officer
CFO: Julie Damm, Chief Financial Officer
CMO: Catherine Butler, M.D., Chief Medical Staff
CIO: Julie Damm, Chief Financial Officer
CHR: Denise Jakoubeck, Director Human Resources
CNO: Laura Zwiefel, Chief Nursing Officer and Assistant Administration
Web address: www.trustchs.com/hancock–county–health–system
**Control:** County–Government, nonfederal **Service:** General Medical and Surgical

**Staffed Beds:** 25 **Admissions:** 482 **Census:** 8 **Outpatient Visits:** 20088 **Births:** 0 **Total Expense ($000):** 19663 **Payroll Expense ($000):** 7165 **Personnel:** 161

## CARROLL—Carroll County

★ **ST. ANTHONY REGIONAL HOSPITAL (160005)**, 311 South Clark Street, Zip 51401–3038, Mailing Address: P.O. Box 628, Zip 51401–0628; tel. 712/792–3581, (Total facility includes 79 beds in nursing home–type unit) **A**9 10 20 **F**6 11 13 15 28 29 30 31 34 35 37 38 39 40 43 44 45 46 50 51 56 57 59 60 61 62 63 64 65 67 68 69 70 74 75 76 77 78 79 81 82 84 85 86 87 89 93 97 98 99 100 101 102 103 104 107 108 110 111 115 118 119 125 126 127 129 130 131 132 133 134 135 145 146 147 148 **P**6
Primary Contact: Edward H. Smith, President and Chief Executive Officer
CFO: John Munson, Vice President and Chief Financial Officer
CMO: Thomas Dulaney, M.D., Chief of Staff
CIO: Randy Eischeid, Director Information Systems
CHR: Anna Fitzpatrick, Director Human Resources
CNO: Karen Timm, R.N., Vice President Patient Services
Web address: www.stanthonyhospital.org
**Control:** Church–operated, Nongovernment, not–for profit **Service:** General Medical and Surgical

**Staffed Beds:** 155 **Admissions:** 2262 **Census:** 106 **Outpatient Visits:** 102323 **Births:** 355 **Total Expense ($000):** 61626 **Payroll Expense ($000):** 26201 **Personnel:** 546

## CEDAR FALLS—Black Hawk County

✠ **SARTORI MEMORIAL HOSPITAL (160040)**, 515 College Street, Zip 50613–2500; tel. 319/268–3000 **A**1 9 10 **F**3 7 8 11 12 15 29 30 35 40 43 44 46 53 57 59 64 68 70 75 77 79 81 91 93 97 98 103 107 110 111 119 130 131 132 146 **P**1 6 **S** Wheaton Franciscan Healthcare, Wheaton, IL
Primary Contact: MaryJo Kavalier, Administrator
CFO: Michele Panicucci, Chief Financial Officer
CHR: Wayne C. Frangesch, Senior Vice President Human Resources
Web address: www.wheatoniowa.org
**Control:** Church–operated, Nongovernment, not–for profit **Service:** General Medical and Surgical

**Staffed Beds:** 50 **Admissions:** 1518 **Census:** 20 **Outpatient Visits:** 42181 **Births:** 0 **Total Expense ($000):** 31601 **Payroll Expense ($000):** 10881 **Personnel:** 182

## CEDAR RAPIDS—Linn County

☐ **CONTINUING CARE HOSPITAL AT ST. LUKE'S (162002)**, 1026 A Avenue N.E., 6th Floor, Zip 52402–5036; tel. 319/369–8142 **A**1 10 **F**1 3 29 30 75 84 85 87 148 **S** CHRISTUS Health, Irving, TX
Primary Contact: Elly Steffen, Chief Executive Officer and Administrator
CNO: Mary Beth Keuter, Director Patient Care
Web address: www.unitypoint.org/cedarrapids/services–continuing–care–hospital.aspx
**Control:** Other not–for–profit (including NFP Corporation) **Service:** Long–Term Acute Care hospital

**Staffed Beds:** 16 **Admissions:** 170 **Census:** 13 **Outpatient Visits:** 0 **Births:** 0 **Total Expense ($000):** 7458 **Payroll Expense ($000):** 2508 **Personnel:** 54

✠ **MERCY MEDICAL CENTER–CEDAR RAPIDS (160079)**, 701 Tenth Street S.E., Zip 52403–1292; tel. 319/398–6011, (Total facility includes 76 beds in nursing home–type unit) **A**1 2 3 5 9 10 **F**3 5 11 12 13 15 22 26 29 30 31 32 34 35 36 38 40 43 44 45 48 49 50 54 55 56 57 59 60 61 62 63 64 65 67 68 70 71 72 74 75 76 77 78 79 81 82 84 85 86 87 88 89 90 91 92 93 94 98 99 100 101 102 103 104 107 108 109 110 114 115 116 117 118 119 120 121 123 124 126 128 130 131 132 135 143 145 146 147 148 **P**2 8
Primary Contact: Timothy L. Charles, President and Chief Executive Officer
CFO: Nathan VanGenderen, Executive Vice President and Chief Financial Officer
CMO: Mark Valliere, M.D., Senior Vice President Medical Affairs and Chief Medical Officer
CIO: Jeff Cash, Senior Vice President and Chief Information Officer
CHR: Doug Jontz, Senior Vice President Human Resources
CNO: Mary Brobst, R.N., Senior Vice President Patient Care Services and Chief Nursing Officer
Web address: www.mercycare.org
**Control:** Church–operated, Nongovernment, not–for profit **Service:** General Medical and Surgical

**Staffed Beds:** 318 **Admissions:** 10833 **Census:** 185 **Outpatient Visits:** 340286 **Births:** 738 **Total Expense ($000):** 274952 **Payroll Expense ($000):** 101376 **Personnel:** 1861

**ST. LUKE'S HOSPITAL** See UnityPoint Health – St. Luke's Hospital

✠ △ **UNITYPOINT HEALTH – ST. LUKE'S HOSPITAL (160045)**, 1026 A Avenue N.E., Zip 52402–3026, Mailing Address: P.O. Box 3026, Zip 52406–3026; tel. 319/369–7211 **A**1 2 3 5 7 9 10 **F**3 5 8 11 12 13 15 17 18 19 20 22 24 26 28 29 30 31 32 34 35 36 37 39 40 43 49 50 54 55 56 57 58 59 60 61 62 63 64 65 66 70 72 74 75 76 77 78 79 81 82 84 85 86 87 88 89 90 91 92 93 95 96 98 99 100 101 103 104 105 107 108 110 111 114 115 118 119 121 126 130 131 132 134 135 145 146 147 148 **P**6 **S** UnityPoint Health, West Des Moines, IA
Primary Contact: Theodore E. Townsend, FACHE, President and Chief Executive Officer
COO: Michelle Niermann, Senior Vice President and Chief Operating Officer
CFO: Milton E. Aunan, II, CPA, Senior Vice President and Chief Financial Officer
CMO: Dustin Arnold, D.O., Chief Medical Officer
CHR: Susan L. Slattery, Director Human Resources
CNO: Mary Ann Osborn, R.N., Senior Vice President and Chief Care Coordinator Officer
Web address: www.unitypoint.org
**Control:** Other not–for–profit (including NFP Corporation) **Service:** General Medical and Surgical

**Staffed Beds:** 346 **Admissions:** 16089 **Census:** 214 **Outpatient Visits:** 539214 **Births:** 2547 **Total Expense ($000):** 312072 **Payroll Expense ($000):** 117217 **Personnel:** 2288

**IA**

---

**Hospital, Medicare Provider Number, Address, Telephone, Approval, Facility, and Physician Codes, Health Care System**

★ American Hospital Association (AHA) membership
☐ The Joint Commission accreditation
○ Healthcare Facilities Accreditation Program
◇ DNV Healthcare Inc. accreditation
⇑ Center for Improvement in Healthcare Quality Accreditation
△ Commission on Accreditation of Rehabilitation Facilities (CARF) accreditation

## CENTERVILLE—Appanoose County

★ **MERCY MEDICAL CENTER–CENTERVILLE (161377)**, 1 St. Joseph's Drive,
Zip 52544–8055; tel. 641/437–4111, (Total facility includes 20 beds in nursing
home–type unit) **A**9 10 18 **F**1 3 4 8 11 13 15 16 17 28 29 30 31 34 40 45 46
50 54 57 59 64 67 70 72 73 75 76 77 78 79 80 81 85 86 87 88 89 90 93
97 98 107 110 111 113 115 117 119 127 128 129 130 132 133 135 **P**6
**S** Catholic Health Initiatives, Englewood, CO
Primary Contact: Clinton J. Christianson, FACHE, President and Chief Executive
Officer
CHR: Tonya Clawson, Manager Human Resources
CNO: Sherri L. Doggett, Vice President Patient Services
Web address: www.mercycenterville.org
**Control:** Church–operated, Nongovernment, not–for profit **Service:** General
Medical and Surgical

**Staffed Beds:** 45 **Admissions:** 779 **Census:** 25 **Outpatient Visits:** 78082
**Births:** 64 **Total Expense ($000):** 23185 **Payroll Expense ($000):** 9055
**Personnel:** 175

## CHARITON—Lucas County

★ **LUCAS COUNTY HEALTH CENTER (161341)**, 1200 North Seventh Street,
Zip 50049–1258; tel. 641/774–3000 **A**9 10 18 **F**3 5 7 8 13 15 28 29 31 34
38 40 43 44 45 47 50 64 66 68 70 75 76 77 81 85 86 87 89 93 97 104
107 115 119 127 128 130 132 133 143 145 146 148
Primary Contact: Daniel B. Minkoff, Interim Chief Executive Officer
CMO: David Marcowitz, M.D., Chief of Staff
CIO: Terri Black, Network Manager
CHR: Lana Kuball, Director Administrative Services
CNO: JoBeth Lawless, Chief Nursing Officer, Nursing Services and Director
Emergency Management Services
Web address: www.lchcia.com
**Control:** County–Government, nonfederal **Service:** General Medical and Surgical

**Staffed Beds:** 25 **Admissions:** 404 **Census:** 3 **Outpatient Visits:** 19311
**Births:** 53 **Total Expense ($000):** 19148 **Payroll Expense ($000):** 9113
**Personnel:** 182

## CHARLES CITY—Floyd County

**FLOYD COUNTY MEDICAL CENTER (161347)**, 800 Eleventh Street,
Zip 50616–3499; tel. 641/228–6830 **A**9 10 18 **F**3 11 13 15 28 29 31 34 35
40 45 48 57 59 64 69 75 79 81 85 86 91 93 97 107 115 119 127 130 132
133 146 148 **S** Mayo Clinic, Rochester, MN
Primary Contact: Bill D. Faust, Administrator
CFO: Ron Timpe, Chief Financial Officer
CHR: Don Nosbisch, Director Human Resources
CNO: Viva Boerschel, Director of Nursing
Web address: www.fcmc.us.com/
**Control:** County–Government, nonfederal **Service:** General Medical and Surgical

**Staffed Beds:** 25 **Admissions:** 813 **Census:** 10 **Outpatient Visits:** 55425
**Births:** 91 **Total Expense ($000):** 23446 **Payroll Expense ($000):** 8536
**Personnel:** 171

## CHEROKEE—Cherokee County

★ **CHEROKEE REGIONAL MEDICAL CENTER (161362)**, 300 Sioux Valley Drive,
Zip 51012–1205; tel. 712/225–5101 **A**9 10 18 **F**7 11 13 15 17 28 29 34 35
40 43 45 53 56 57 59 62 63 64 65 67 68 69 75 76 77 78 81 84 86 87 89
93 96 97 107 111 114 117 119 125 127 128 129 130 131 132 133 135
146 147 148 **P**6
Primary Contact: John M. Comstock, Chief Executive Officer
COO: David Liebsack, Chief Operating Officer
CFO: Joan Bierman, Vice President Finance
CIO: Kevin Naslund, Manager Information Technology
CHR: Theresa Conley, Manager Human Resources
CNO: Christy Syndergaard, Vice President Nursing
Web address: www.cherokeermc.org
**Control:** Other not–for–profit (including NFP Corporation) **Service:** General
Medical and Surgical

**Staffed Beds:** 25 **Admissions:** 811 **Census:** 8 **Outpatient Visits:** 44617
**Births:** 150 **Total Expense ($000):** 20203 **Payroll Expense ($000):** 8590
**Personnel:** 179

☐ **MENTAL HEALTH INSTITUTE (164002)**, 1251 West Cedar Loop,
Zip 51012–1599; tel. 712/225–2594 **A**1 9 10 **F**98 99 100 101 102 104
130 **P**6
Primary Contact: Chris Tosteberg, Superintendent
CFO: Tony Morris, Business Manager
CHR: Mary Ann Hanson, Director Personnel
Web address: www.dhs.state.ia.us
**Control:** State–Government, nonfederal **Service:** Psychiatric

**Staffed Beds:** 36 **Admissions:** 513 **Census:** 27 **Outpatient Visits:** 33 **Births:**
0 **Total Expense ($000):** 16810 **Payroll Expense ($000):** 9468 **Personnel:**
171

## CLARINDA—Page County

★ **CLARINDA REGIONAL HEALTH CENTER (161352)**, 220 Essie Davison Drive,
Zip 51632–2915, Mailing Address: P.O. Box 217, Zip 51632–0217;
tel. 712/542–2176 **A**9 10 18 **F**3 7 11 15 28 29 31 34 36 40 43 50 57 59 64
65 66 69 74 75 77 78 79 81 82 85 86 87 93 97 107 110 111 114 118 119
124 127 128 129 130 133 135 143 146 148 **P**3 6
Primary Contact: Christopher R. Stipe, FACHE, Chief Executive Officer
COO: Elaine Otte, Chief Operating Officer
CFO: Melissa Walter, Chief Financial Officer
CMO: Autumn Morales, Chief Medical Staff Officer
CIO: Richard Morgan–Fine, IT Director
CHR: Tammie Driftmier, PHR, Director Human Resources
CNO: Sherrie L. Laubenthal, R.N., Chief Nursing Officer
Web address: www.clarindahealth.com
**Control:** City–Government, nonfederal **Service:** General Medical and Surgical

**Staffed Beds:** 25 **Admissions:** 464 **Census:** 4 **Outpatient Visits:** 55997
**Births:** 0 **Total Expense ($000):** 26599 **Payroll Expense ($000):** 10727
**Personnel:** 187

**MENTAL HEALTH INSTITUTE (164005)**, 1800 North 16Th Street,
Zip 51632–1101; tel. 712/542–2161, (Total facility includes 20 beds in nursing
home–type unit) **A**9 10 **F**67 98 101 103 130 146 **P**6
Primary Contact: Kristine Weitzell, Superintendent
COO: Kristine Weitzell, Superintendent
CFO: Meredith Baker, Business Manager
CMO: Teresa Rosales, M.D., Clinical Director
CIO: Teresa Barlow, Medical Records Administrator
CHR: Sandy Davison, Personnel Assistant
Web address: www.dhs.state.ia.us/
**Control:** State–Government, nonfederal **Service:** Psychiatric

**Staffed Beds:** 35 **Admissions:** 176 **Census:** 26 **Outpatient Visits:** 0 **Births:**
0 **Total Expense ($000):** 7049 **Payroll Expense ($000):** 5089 **Personnel:**
91

## CLARION—Wright County

★ ◇ **IOWA SPECIALTY HOSPITAL–CLARION (161302)**, 1316 South Main
Street, Zip 50525–2019; tel. 515/532–2811 **A**9 10 18 21 **F**11 13 15 28 29 31
32 34 35 40 43 45 46 50 56 57 59 63 64 65 68 69 75 76 77 79 81 82 85
86 87 92 93 97 107 110 111 114 119 125 127 129 131 132 133 134 135
146 148 **P**6 **S** Iowa Specialty Hospitals, Clarion, IA
Primary Contact: Steven J. Simonin, Chief Executive Officer
COO: Kirk Rier, Chief Operating Officer
CFO: Greg Polzin, Chief Financial Officer
CMO: Dennis Colby, M.D., Chief of Staff
CHR: Holly Martin, Human Resources Leader
CNO: Abby Young, Chief Nursing Officer
Web address: www.iowaspecialtyhospital.com
**Control:** City–Government, nonfederal **Service:** General Medical and Surgical

**Staffed Beds:** 25 **Admissions:** 1174 **Census:** 10 **Outpatient Visits:** 100159
**Births:** 266 **Total Expense ($000):** 49170 **Payroll Expense ($000):** 18465
**Personnel:** 328

## CLINTON—Clinton County

✠ **MERCY MEDICAL CENTER–CLINTON (160080)**, 1410 North Fourth Street,
Zip 52732–2940; tel. 563/244–5555, (Includes MERCY SERVICES FOR AGING,
600 14th Avenue North, Zip 52732; tel. 563/244–3888), (Total facility includes
183 beds in nursing home–type unit) **A**1 9 10 **F**3 11 13 15 18 20 22 28 29 30
31 34 35 36 38 40 44 45 47 49 50 53 56 57 59 60 61 62 63 64 68 70 74
75 76 77 78 79 80 81 82 84 85 87 89 93 98 99 100 101 102 103 107 108
110 115 118 119 121 123 128 129 130 132 146 148 **S** Trinity Health,
Livonia, MI
Primary Contact: Sean J. Williams, President and Chief Executive Officer
CFO: Paul Mangin, Vice President Finance
CHR: Shane Buer, Vice President, Human Resources
CNO: Amy Berentes, R.N., Vice President Patient Care Services
Web address: www.mercyclinton.com
**Control:** Church–operated, Nongovernment, not–for profit **Service:** General
Medical and Surgical

**Staffed Beds:** 290 **Admissions:** 5420 **Census:** 190 **Outpatient Visits:** 75633
**Births:** 441 **Total Expense ($000):** 88998 **Payroll Expense ($000):** 36778
**Personnel:** 821

## CORALVILLE—Johnson County

**IOWA MEDICAL AND CLASSIFICATION CENTER**, 2700 Coral Ridge Avenue,
Zip 52241–4708, Mailing Address: 2700 Coral Rigde Avenue, Zip 52241;
tel. 319/626–2391 **F**29 38 39 59 75 98 101 102 103 105 130 132 143
Primary Contact: Daniel Craig, Warden
Web address: www.oakdaleprison.com/
**Control:** State–Government, nonfederal **Service:** Psychiatric

**Staffed Beds:** 20 **Admissions:** 39 **Census:** 16 **Outpatient Visits:** 0 **Births:** 0
**Total Expense ($000):** 1616 **Personnel:** 26

**IA**

*Many Facility Codes have changed. Please refer to the AHA Guide Code Chart.* © 2015 AHA Guide

## CORNING—Adams County

★ **CHI HEALTH MERCY CORNING (161304)**, 603 Rosary Drive, Zip 50841–1683; tel. 641/322–3121 **A**9 10 18 **F**1 3 4 11 15 16 17 28 30 31 34 40 43 46 50 53 56 57 59 64 67 70 72 73 74 75 77 78 79 80 81 85 88 89 90 97 98 107 110 114 119 127 128 129 130 132 133 135 146 147 148 **P**6 **S** Catholic Health Initiatives, Englewood, CO
Primary Contact: Debra Goldsmith, Chief Executive Officer
CMO: Maen Haddadin, M.D., President Medical Staff
CIO: Kenneth Lawonn, Senior Vice President and Chief Information Officer
CHR: Sandra Lammers, Coordinator Human Resources and Finance
CNO: Jane Carmody, R.N., Vice President and System Chief Nursing Officer
Web address: www.alegent.com
**Control:** Church–operated, Nongovernment, not–for profit **Service:** General Medical and Surgical

**Staffed Beds: 22 Admissions: 204 Census: 3 Outpatient Visits:** 66540 **Births:** 0 **Total Expense ($000):** 16607 **Payroll Expense ($000):** 6627 **Personnel:** 112

## CORYDON—Wayne County

★ **WAYNE COUNTY HOSPITAL (161358)**, 417 South East Street, Zip 50060–1860, Mailing Address: P.O. Box 305, Zip 50060–0305; tel. 641/872–2260 **A**9 10 18 **F**7 13 15 28 29 34 35 40 43 51 56 57 59 60 64 69 70 75 76 77 79 81 85 87 89 91 92 93 97 107 110 114 119 127 130 131 133 148 **P**6
Primary Contact: Daren Relph, Chief Executive Officer
COO: Michael Thomas, Associate Administrator
CFO: Diane Hook, Chief Financial Officer
CMO: Joel Baker, D.O., Chief Medical Officer
CIO: Laurie Ehrich, Chief Communications Officer
CHR: Dave Carlyle, Director Human Resources
CNO: Sheila Mattly, Chief Nursing Officer
Web address: www.waynecountyhospital.org
**Control:** County–Government, nonfederal **Service:** General Medical and Surgical

**Staffed Beds: 25 Admissions: 611 Census: 6 Outpatient Visits:** 24184 **Births:** 140 **Total Expense ($000):** 23980 **Payroll Expense ($000):** 11968 **Personnel:** 212

## COUNCIL BLUFFS—Pottawattamie County

⊠ **CHI HEALTH MERCY COUNCIL BLUFFS (160028)**, 800 Mercy Drive, Zip 51503–3128, Mailing Address: P.O. Box 1C, Zip 51502–3001; tel. 712/328–5000 **A**1 2 9 10 **F**3 5 11 12 13 15 18 20 22 28 29 30 31 34 35 38 39 40 43 44 47 48 49 50 56 57 59 62 64 65 68 70 74 75 76 77 78 79 81 82 84 85 87 89 93 97 98 99 100 101 102 103 104 105 106 107 108 110 111 114 115 119 129 130 132 134 135 143 146 147 148 **P**6 8 **S** Catholic Health Initiatives, Englewood, CO
Primary Contact: Marie E. Knedler, R.N., FACHE, President
CFO: Jeanette Wojtalewicz, Chief Financial Officer
CMO: Joseph Hoagbin, M.D., Chief Quality Officer
CIO: Karun Kapur, Senior Vice President and Chief Information Officer
CHR: Nancy Wallace, Senior Vice President Human Resources
CNO: Jane Carmody, R.N., Vice President and System Chief Nursing Officer
Web address: www.alegent.com/mercy
**Control:** Church–operated, Nongovernment, not–for profit **Service:** General Medical and Surgical

**Staffed Beds: 163 Admissions: 7527 Census: 72 Outpatient Visits:** 84550 **Births:** 617 **Total Expense ($000):** 100057 **Payroll Expense ($000):** 32929 **Personnel:** 642

**JENNIE EDMUNDSON HOSPITAL** See Methodist Jennie Edmundson Hospital

⊠ **METHODIST JENNIE EDMUNDSON HOSPITAL (160047)**, 933 East Pierce Street, Zip 51503–4652, Mailing Address: P.O. Box 2C, Zip 51502–3002; tel. 712/396–6000 **A**1 2 5 9 10 **F**3 11 13 15 18 20 22 26 28 29 30 31 34 35 39 40 43 44 45 47 49 50 57 58 59 61 64 68 70 74 75 76 78 79 81 82 85 86 87 89 92 93 98 100 101 102 103 107 108 110 111 115 118 119 121 123 129 130 131 132 135 143 145 146 147 148 **S** Nebraska Methodist Health System, Inc., Omaha, NE
Primary Contact: Steven P. Baumert, President and Chief Executive Officer
CFO: Linda K. Burt, Corporate Vice President Finance
CMO: Michael A. Romano, M.D., Vice President Medical Affairs
CIO: Steven Zuber, Vice President
CHR: Holly Huerter, Vice President Human Resources
CNO: Peggy Helget, R.N., Vice President Patient Services and Chief Nursing Officer
Web address: www.bestcare.org
**Control:** Other not–for–profit (including NFP Corporation) **Service:** General Medical and Surgical

**Staffed Beds: 114 Admissions: 5305 Census: 58 Outpatient Visits:** 60138 **Births:** 412 **Total Expense ($000):** 88358 **Payroll Expense ($000):** 33740 **Personnel:** 484

## CRESCO—Howard County

★ **REGIONAL HEALTH SERVICES OF HOWARD COUNTY (161328)**, 235 Eighth Avenue West, Zip 52136–1098; tel. 563/547–2101 **A**9 10 18 **F**7 11 13 15 28 29 34 35 36 40 43 44 50 53 57 59 62 63 64 65 68 75 76 77 81 82 85 86 87 93 107 110 114 127 128 130 132 133 146 148 **P**8 **S** Trinity Health, Livonia, MI
Primary Contact: Robin M. Schluter, Chief Executive Officer
CFO: Brenda Moser, Vice President Finance
CMO: Paul Jensen, M.D., Chief of Staff
CIO: Brenda Moser, Chief Information Officer
CHR: Tina Malone, Director Human Resources
CNO: Staci Vrzak, Vice President Patient Care Services
Web address: www.rhshc.com
**Control:** County–Government, nonfederal **Service:** General Medical and Surgical

**Staffed Beds: 20 Admissions: 272 Census: 3 Outpatient Visits:** 21482 **Births:** 47 **Total Expense ($000):** 16267 **Payroll Expense ($000):** 6375 **Personnel:** 148

## CRESTON—Union County

★ **GREATER REGIONAL MEDICAL CENTER (161365)**, 1700 West Townline Street Suite 3, Zip 50801–1099; tel. 641/782–7091 **A**9 10 18 **F**3 7 11 13 15 28 29 31 34 35 40 43 45 50 56 57 59 64 65 66 70 75 76 77 78 79 81 82 84 85 86 93 96 97 107 108 109 110 111 115 119 120 121 122 123 124 125 127 129 130 131 132 133 135 146 148 **P**6 **S** UnityPoint Health, West Des Moines, IA
Primary Contact: Monte Neitzel, Chief Executive Officer
CFO: Matt McCutchan, Chief Financial Officer
CMO: Karen Krogstad, M.D., Chief Medical Officer
CIO: Karla Alford, Chief Information Officer
CHR: Lisa Ross, Human Resources Officer
CNO: Gwen Buck, R.N., Chief Nursing Officer
Web address: www.greaterregional.org
**Control:** County–Government, nonfederal **Service:** General Medical and Surgical

**Staffed Beds: 25 Admissions: 804 Census: 7 Outpatient Visits:** 70750 **Births:** 178 **Total Expense ($000):** 43308 **Payroll Expense ($000):** 17499 **Personnel:** 279

## DAVENPORT—Scott County

⊠ △ **GENESIS MEDICAL CENTER–DAVENPORT (160033)**, 1227 East Rusholme Street, Zip 52803–2498; tel. 563/421–1000, (Includes GENESIS MEDICAL CENTER–EAST CAMPUS, 1227 East Rusholme Street, Zip 52803; tel. 563/421–1000; GENESIS MEDICAL CENTER–WEST CAMPUS, 1401 West Central Park, Zip 52804–1769; tel. 563/421–1000) **A**1 2 3 5 7 9 10 **F**3 7 11 12 13 15 17 18 20 22 24 26 28 29 30 31 34 35 37 38 40 43 44 46 49 50 53 54 57 58 59 63 64 68 70 72 74 75 76 77 78 79 81 82 84 85 86 87 89 90 91 92 93 94 96 97 98 100 102 107 111 114 115 116 118 119 120 121 123 124 126 129 130 131 132 135 146 147 148 **P**6 **S** Genesis Health System, Davenport, IA
Primary Contact: Jordan Voigt, Administrator
CFO: Mark G. Rogers, Interim Vice President Finance and Chief Financial Officer
CMO: Frank Claudy, M.D., Vice President Medical Staff Affairs
CIO: Robert Frieden, Vice President Information Systems
CHR: Heidi Kahly-McMahon, Interim Vice President Human Resources
Web address: www.genesishealth.com
**Control:** Other not–for–profit (including NFP Corporation) **Service:** General Medical and Surgical

**Staffed Beds: 352 Admissions: 18374 Census: 185 Outpatient Visits:** 189429 **Births:** 1988 **Total Expense ($000):** 301038 **Payroll Expense ($000):** 89435 **Personnel:** 1574

⊠ **SELECT SPECIALTY HOSPITAL–QUAD CITIES (162001)**, 1111 West Kimberly Road, Zip 52806–5711; tel. 563/468–2000 **A**1 10 **F**1 3 29 75 77 85 100 119 130 148 **S** Select Medical Corporation, Mechanicsburg, PA
Primary Contact: Connie K. Siffring, Chief Executive Officer
Web address: www.selectmedicalcorp.com
**Control:** Corporation, Investor–owned, for–profit **Service:** Long–Term Acute Care hospital

**Staffed Beds: 48 Admissions: 404 Census: 29 Outpatient Visits:** 0 **Births:** 0 **Total Expense ($000):** 15772 **Payroll Expense ($000):** 6881 **Personnel:** 128

**IA**

## DE WITT—Clinton County

☒ **GENESIS MEDICAL CENTER, DEWITT (161313)**, 1118 11th Street, Zip 52742–1296; tel. 563/659–4200, (Total facility includes 75 beds in nursing home–type unit) **A**1 9 10 18 **F**7 11 15 29 30 31 34 35 38 40 43 44 50 53 57 59 64 74 75 77 78 79 81 85 86 87 97 102 107 110 111 114 119 129 130 131 132 133 135 **P**6 **S** Genesis Health System, Davenport, IA
Primary Contact: Curt Coleman, FACHE, Chief Executive Officer
CMO: Steven Fowler, M.D., President Medical Staff
CHR: Kristin Nicholson, Coordinator Human Resources
CNO: Wanda Haack, MSN, Chief Nursing Officer
Web address: www.genesishealth.com
**Control:** Other not–for–profit (including NFP Corporation) **Service:** General Medical and Surgical

**Staffed Beds:** 86 **Admissions:** 280 **Census:** 77 **Outpatient Visits:** 18280 **Births:** 0 **Total Expense ($000):** 19151 **Payroll Expense ($000):** 7299 **Personnel:** 157

## DECORAH—Winneshiek County

☒ **WINNESHIEK MEDICAL CENTER (161371)**, 901 Montgomery Street, Zip 52101–2325; tel. 563/382–2911 **A**1 9 10 18 **F**3 7 8 11 15 28 29 31 34 35 38 40 43 45 50 56 57 59 61 62 63 64 65 68 69 70 75 76 77 78 79 81 82 86 87 93 94 97 102 104 107 110 111 114 119 128 129 130 131 132 133 135 144 146 147 148 **S** Mayo Clinic, Rochester, MN
Primary Contact: Lisa Radtke, Chief Administrative Officer
COO: David Rooney, Administrator Operaitons
CFO: Lynn Luloff, Chief Financial Officer
CMO: Robert Flinchbaugh, D.O., Chief Medical Officer
CHR: Laurie Bulman, Director Human Resources
CNO: Susan Heitman, Chief Nursing Officer
Web address: www.winmedical.org
**Control:** County–Government, nonfederal **Service:** General Medical and Surgical

**Staffed Beds:** 25 **Admissions:** 1051 **Census:** 11 **Outpatient Visits:** 62874 **Births:** 212 **Total Expense ($000):** 49510 **Payroll Expense ($000):** 17907 **Personnel:** 360

## DENISON—Crawford County

★ **CRAWFORD COUNTY MEMORIAL HOSPITAL (161369)**, 100 Medical Parkway, Zip 51442–2299; tel. 712/265–2500 **A**9 10 18 **F**3 7 8 11 13 15 17 28 29 31 34 35 40 45 50 54 56 57 59 64 65 67 68 70 75 76 77 78 79 81 82 85 87 89 93 97 99 101 107 110 111 114 119 127 128 133 135 148 **P**6
Primary Contact: Bill Bruce, FACHE, Chief Executive Officer
CFO: Rachel Melby, Controller
CIO: Angie Anderson, Director Information Technology
CNO: Diane Arkfeld, R.N., Vice President, Clinical Nursing
Web address: www.ccmhia.com
**Control:** County–Government, nonfederal **Service:** General Medical and Surgical

**Staffed Beds:** 25 **Admissions:** 712 **Census:** 7 **Outpatient Visits:** 40801 **Births:** 172 **Total Expense ($000):** 30386 **Payroll Expense ($000):** 13763 **Personnel:** 228

## DES MOINES—Polk County

☒ **BROADLAWNS MEDICAL CENTER (160101)**, 1801 Hickman Road, Zip 50314–1597; tel. 515/282–2200 **A**1 3 5 9 10 **F**3 5 11 13 15 18 29 30 31 32 34 35 38 39 40 43 44 45 48 50 52 53 56 57 58 59 64 65 66 68 70 74 75 77 78 79 81 82 85 86 87 92 93 94 97 98 99 100 101 102 103 104 105 106 107 111 114 119 129 130 131 132 135 144 146 147 148 **P**6
Primary Contact: Jody J. Jenner, President and Chief Executive Officer
CFO: Al White, CPA, Senior Vice President Business Services
CMO: Vincent Mandracchia, DPM, Chief Medical Officer
CNO: Susan N. Kirstein, R.N., Chief Nursing Officer
Web address: www.broadlawns.org
**Control:** County–Government, nonfederal **Service:** General Medical and Surgical

**Staffed Beds:** 95 **Admissions:** 3295 **Census:** 58 **Outpatient Visits:** 207384 **Births:** 265 **Total Expense ($000):** 123808 **Payroll Expense ($000):** 56816 **Personnel:** 848

**DES MOINES DIVISION** See Veterans Affairs Central Iowa Health Care System

**IOWA LUTHERAN HOSPITAL** See UnityPoint Health–Iowa Lutheran Hospital

☒ △ **MERCY MEDICAL CENTER–DES MOINES (160083)**, 1111 6th Avenue, Zip 50314–2611; tel. 515/247–3121 **A**1 2 3 7 9 10 13 **F**3 4 5 6 7 8 9 10 11 13 15 16 17 18 19 20 21 22 23 24 25 26 27 28 29 30 31 32 34 35 36 38 39 40 41 43 44 46 48 49 50 53 54 55 56 57 58 59 60 61 62 63 64 65 66 68 70 71 72 73 74 75 76 77 78 79 81 82 84 85 86 87 88 89 90 91 92 93 94 96 97 98 99 100 101 102 103 104 105 106 107 108 109 110 111 114 115 116 117 118 119 120 121 123 124 126 129 130 131 132 134 135 138 141 142 143 144 145 146 147 148 **P**6 **S** Catholic Health Initiatives, Englewood, CO
Primary Contact: Robert P. Ritz, FACHE, President
COO: Jacqueline C. Frost–Kunnen, R.N., Senior Vice President Operations
CFO: Michael Wegner, Senior Vice President and Chief Financial Officer
CMO: Tommy Ibrahim, M.D., Chief Physician Officer
CIO: Cristina Thomas, Vice President and Chief Information Officer
CHR: Kevin Elsberry, Senior Vice President Human Resources
CNO: Mary J. Brown, R.N., Vice President and Chief Nursing Officer
Web address: www.mercydesmoines.org
**Control:** Church–operated, Nongovernment, not–for profit **Service:** General Medical and Surgical

**Staffed Beds:** 583 **Admissions:** 28094 **Census:** 414 **Outpatient Visits:** 246816 **Births:** 4800 **Total Expense ($000):** 585896 **Payroll Expense ($000):** 212729 **Personnel:** 3412

☒ **SELECT SPECIALTY HOSPITAL–DES MOINES (160157)**, 1111 6th Avenue, 4th Floor Main, Zip 50314–2610; tel. 515/247–4400, (Nonreporting) **A**1 10 **S** Select Medical Corporation, Mechanicsburg, PA
Primary Contact: Glen Griesheim, Chief Executive Officer
Web address: www.selectspecialtyhospitals.com
**Control:** Corporation, Investor–owned, for–profit **Service:** General Medical and Surgical

**Staffed Beds:** 30

★ △ ◇ **UNITYPOINT HEALTH – IOWA METHODIST MEDICAL CENTER (160082)**, 1200 Pleasant Street, Zip 50309–1406; tel. 515/241–6212, (Includes POWELL CONVALESCENT CENTER, 1200 Pleasant, Zip 50309; RAYMOND BLANK MEMORIAL HOSPITAL FOR CHILDREN, Zip 50308; UNITY POINT HEALTH – JOHN STODDARD CANCER CENTER, 1221 Pleasant Street, Zip 50309–1423; tel. 515/241–6212; UNITYPOINT HEALTH – BLANK CHILDREN'S HOSPITAL, 1200 Pleasant Street, tel. 515/241–5437; UNITYPOINT HEALTH – METHODIST WEST HOSPITAL, 1660 60th Street, West Des Moines, Zip 50266–7700; tel. 515/343–1000; YOUNKER MEMORIAL REHABILITATION CENTER, 1200 Pleasant Road, Zip 50308) **A**2 5 7 8 9 10 21 **F**3 7 8 11 12 13 17 18 20 22 24 26 28 29 30 31 32 33 40 41 43 44 45 46 47 49 50 53 54 55 56 57 58 59 60 61 64 65 68 70 71 72 74 75 76 77 78 79 81 82 84 85 86 87 88 89 90 91 92 93 94 96 97 100 107 108 111 114 115 116 117 118 119 120 121 123 124 126 129 130 131 132 134 135 138 146 147 148 **P**6 **S** UnityPoint Health, West Des Moines, IA
Primary Contact: Eric T. Crowell, President and Chief Executive Officer
COO: Steve R. Stephenson, M.D., Executive Vice President and Chief Operating Officer
CFO: Joe Corfits, Senior Vice President Finance
CMO: Mark Purtle, M.D., Vice President Medical Affairs
CHR: Joyce McDanel, Vice President Human Resources and Education
Web address: www.iowahealth.org
**Control:** Other not–for–profit (including NFP Corporation) **Service:** General Medical and Surgical

**Staffed Beds:** 509 **Admissions:** 24016 **Census:** 337 **Outpatient Visits:** 283057 **Births:** 4229 **Total Expense ($000):** 527923 **Payroll Expense ($000):** 224989 **Personnel:** 3734

★ ◇ **UNITYPOINT HEALTH–IOWA LUTHERAN HOSPITAL (160024)**, 700 East University Avenue, Zip 50316–2392; tel. 515/263–5612, (Total facility includes 16 beds in nursing home–type unit) **A**3 5 9 10 21 **F**3 4 5 8 11 13 15 17 18 20 22 26 28 29 30 34 35 38 39 40 43 44 45 49 50 51 53 56 57 58 59 60 61 64 65 68 70 71 74 75 76 79 81 82 84 85 86 87 91 93 97 98 99 100 101 102 103 104 105 107 108 110 111 114 115 118 119 128 130 132 134 135 146 147 148 **P**6 **S** UnityPoint Health, West Des Moines, IA
Primary Contact: Eric T. Crowell, President and Chief Executive Officer
COO: Eric L. Lothe, Vice President and Administrator
CFO: Joe Corfits, Chief Financial Officer
CMO: Mark Purtle, M.D., Vice President Medical Affairs
CHR: Joyce McDanel, Vice President Human Resources and Education
Web address: www.iowahealth.org
**Control:** Other not–for–profit (including NFP Corporation) **Service:** General Medical and Surgical

**Staffed Beds:** 205 **Admissions:** 7409 **Census:** 117 **Outpatient Visits:** 60008 **Births:** 444 **Total Expense ($000):** 119626 **Payroll Expense ($000):** 50498 **Personnel:** 852

**IA**

✠ △ **VETERANS AFFAIRS CENTRAL IOWA HEALTH CARE SYSTEM**, 3600
30th Street, Zip 50310–5753; tel. 515/699–5999, (Includes DES MOINES
DIVISION, 3600 30th Street, Zip 50310–5774; tel. 515/699–5999; KNOXVILLE
DIVISION, 1515 West Pleasant, Knoxville, Zip 50138–3399; tel. 515/842–3101),
(Total facility includes 140 beds in nursing home–type unit) **A**1 3 5 7 9 **F**2 3 5 8
11 12 18 20 22 28 29 30 31 33 34 35 36 38 39 40 44 45 46 50 53 54
56 57 59 61 62 63 64 65 66 70 71 74 75 77 78 79 80 81 82 83 84 85 86
87 93 94 96 97 98 100 101 102 103 104 105 106 107 108 110 111 112
114 115 116 117 118 119 120 127 128 129 130 132 135 146 147 148
**S** Department of Veterans Affairs, Washington, DC
Primary Contact: Lavonne Liversage, Acting Director
CMO: Fredrick Bahls, M.D., Chief of Staff
CIO: James Danuser, Chief Information Officer
CHR: Sabrina Owen, Human Resources Officer
Web address: www.centraliowa.va.gov/
**Control:** Veterans Affairs, Government, federal **Service:** General Medical and
Surgical

**Staffed Beds:** 256 **Admissions:** 2934 **Census:** 151 **Outpatient Visits:**
339502 **Births:** 0 **Total Expense ($000):** 261815 **Payroll Expense ($000):**
130656 **Personnel:** 1456

### DUBUQUE—Dubuque County

**FINLEY HOSPITAL** See UnityPoint Health – Finley Hospital

✠ △ **MERCY MEDICAL CENTER–DUBUQUE (160069)**, 250 Mercy Drive,
Zip 52001–7360; tel. 563/589–8000, (Total facility includes 40 beds in nursing
home–type unit) **A**1 7 9 10 **F**3 4 5 8 11 15 18 20 22 24 26 28 29 30 31
32 34 35 36 38 39 40 43 44 49 50 51 53 56 57 58 59 61 62 64 65 67 70
72 74 75 76 77 78 79 80 81 85 86 87 89 90 91 93 97 98 99 100 101 102
103 104 107 108 111 114 116 119 126 128 129 130 131 132 134 135 144
146 147 148 **P**8 **S** Trinity Health, Livonia, MI
Primary Contact: Russell M. Knight, President and Chief Executive Officer
CFO: Robert Shafer, Vice President Finance
CIO: Joe Billmeyer, Director, Information Services
CHR: Kathryn Roberts, Director Human Resources
CNO: Kay Takes, R.N., Vice President Patient Care Services and Chief Nursing
Officer
Web address: www.mercydubuque.com
**Control:** Church–operated, Nongovernment, not–for profit **Service:** General
Medical and Surgical

**Staffed Beds:** 235 **Admissions:** 8719 **Census:** 141 **Outpatient Visits:** 42578
**Births:** 918 **Total Expense ($000):** 145450 **Payroll Expense ($000):** 45962
**Personnel:** 1041

✠ △ **UNITYPOINT HEALTH – FINLEY HOSPITAL (160117)**, 350 North
Grandview Avenue, Zip 52001–6392; tel. 563/582–1881 **A**1 7 9 10 **F**3 11 12
13 15 18 20 22 26 28 29 30 31 34 35 39 40 43 44 45 46 48 49 50 53 56
57 59 60 61 62 64 65 69 70 72 74 75 76 77 78 79 81 82 84 85 86 87 90
93 96 97 98 103 107 108 110 111 115 117 118 119 120 121 123 124 126
129 130 131 132 135 144 146 147 148 **P**1 5 **S** UnityPoint Health, West Des
Moines, IA
Primary Contact: David R. Brandon, President and Chief Executive Officer
CFO: Dan Carpenter, Chief Financial Officer
CMO: Bryan Pechous, M.D., Vice President Medical Affairs
CIO: Tim Loeffelholz, Account Executive Information Technology
CHR: Karla Waldbillig, Director Human Resources
CNO: Diana Batchelor, Chief Nursing Officer
Web address: www.unitypoint.org
**Control:** Other not–for–profit (including NFP Corporation) **Service:** General
Medical and Surgical

**Staffed Beds:** 109 **Admissions:** 4712 **Census:** 57 **Outpatient Visits:** 90750
**Births:** 733 **Total Expense ($000):** 99930 **Payroll Expense ($000):** 41959
**Personnel:** 813

### DYERSVILLE—Dubuque County

★ **MERCY MEDICAL CENTER–DYERSVILLE (161378)**, 1111 Third Street S.W.,
Zip 52040–1725; tel. 563/875–7101 **A**9 10 18 **F**11 15 34 35 36 39 40 44 50
56 57 59 64 65 75 79 81 85 86 93 119 130 131 132 133 134 135 146 147
**P**8 **S** Trinity Health, Livonia, MI
Primary Contact: Russell M. Knight, President and Chief Executive Officer
CFO: Robert Shafer, Vice President Finance
Web address: www.mercydubuque.com/mercy–dyersville
**Control:** Church–operated, Nongovernment, not–for profit **Service:** General
Medical and Surgical

**Staffed Beds:** 20 **Admissions:** 79 **Census:** 2 **Outpatient Visits:** 3908 **Births:**
0 **Total Expense ($000):** 4979 **Payroll Expense ($000):** 2293 **Personnel:**
52

### ELKADER—Clayton County

★ **CENTRAL COMMUNITY HOSPITAL (161319)**, 901 Davidson Street N.W.,
Zip 52043–9015; tel. 563/245–7000 **A**9 10 18 **F**7 11 15 28 34 35 40 43 50
56 57 59 64 67 68 75 81 85 87 91 93 107 110 128 130 132 133 134 146
**S** Trinity Health, Livonia, MI
Primary Contact: Frances J. Zichal, Chief Executive Officer
CFO: Patricia Borel, Chief Financial Officer
CIO: Jonathan Holliday, Manager Information Technology
CHR: Angie Gerndt, Human Resources Manager
CNO: Natalie Shea, Chief Nursing Officer
Web address: www.centralcommunityhospital.com
**Control:** Other not–for–profit (including NFP Corporation) **Service:** General
Medical and Surgical

**Staffed Beds:** 25 **Admissions:** 147 **Census:** 2 **Outpatient Visits:** 6526
**Births:** 0 **Total Expense ($000):** 6018 **Payroll Expense ($000):** 2119
**Personnel:** 44

### EMMETSBURG—Palo Alto County

★ **PALO ALTO COUNTY HEALTH SYSTEM (161357)**, 3201 First Street,
Zip 50536–2516; tel. 712/852–5500, (Total facility includes 22 beds in nursing
home–type unit) **A**9 10 18 **F**3 7 11 13 15 28 29 30 31 34 35 40 43 45 46 50
57 59 62 63 64 65 67 68 69 71 75 76 77 79 81 82 85 87 93 107 110 115
119 125 127 130 132 133 135 143 146 **S** Trinity Health, Livonia, MI
Primary Contact: Desiree Einsweiler, Chief Executive Officer
CFO: Renay Hauswirth, Chief Financial Officer
CMO: Paul Matthews, M.D., President of Medical Staff
CIO: Randy Beaver, Chief Information Officer
CHR: Amy Knoup, Director Human Resources
CNO: JoAnn Higgins, Chief Nursing Officer and Assistant Administrator
Web address: www.pachs.com
**Control:** County–Government, nonfederal **Service:** General Medical and Surgical

**Staffed Beds:** 47 **Admissions:** 460 **Census:** 27 **Outpatient Visits:** 22308
**Births:** 112 **Total Expense ($000):** 23648 **Payroll Expense ($000):** 8696
**Personnel:** 180

### ESTHERVILLE—Emmet County

★ **AVERA HOLY FAMILY HOSPITAL (161351)**, 826 North Eighth Street,
Zip 51334–1598; tel. 712/362–2631 **A**9 10 18 **F**3 11 13 15 28 29 30 31 34
35 40 45 59 63 64 68 69 70 75 76 77 78 79 81 85 87 93 107 110 114 119
130 132 133 146 **P**4 **S** Avera Health, Sioux Falls, SD
Primary Contact: Dale Hustedt, Administrator
CFO: Shannon Adams, Chief Financial Officer
CMO: Keith Probst, M.D., Chief of Staff
CHR: Janette Jensen, Manager Human Resources
CNO: Cathi Rae Scharnberg, R.N., Vice President Patient Services
Web address: www.avera–holyfamily.org
**Control:** Church–operated, Nongovernment, not–for profit **Service:** General
Medical and Surgical

**Staffed Beds:** 25 **Admissions:** 804 **Census:** 7 **Outpatient Visits:** 68326
**Births:** 71 **Total Expense ($000):** 23162 **Payroll Expense ($000):** 9787
**Personnel:** 171

### FAIRFIELD—Jefferson County

★ **JEFFERSON COUNTY HEALTH CENTER (161364)**, 2000 South Main,
Zip 52556–9572, Mailing Address: P.O. Box 588, Zip 52556–0010;
tel. 641/472–4111 **A**9 10 18 **F**11 15 28 30 31 34 35 36 40 43 45 50 57 59
67 68 70 75 77 78 79 81 85 89 93 96 102 107 110 115 119 128 129 133
135 143 146 148 **P**5
Primary Contact: Deborah Cardin, R.N., FACHE, MS, Chief Executive Officer
CFO: Larry Peach, Chief Financial Officer
CHR: Nanette Everly, Manager Human Resources and Administrative Assistant
Web address: www.jeffersoncountyhealthcenter.org
**Control:** County–Government, nonfederal **Service:** General Medical and Surgical

**Staffed Beds:** 25 **Admissions:** 876 **Census:** 13 **Outpatient Visits:** 55160
**Births:** 0 **Total Expense ($000):** 29637 **Payroll Expense ($000):** 9554
**Personnel:** 239

**IA**

## FORT DODGE—Webster County

★ ◇ **UNITYPOINT HEALTH – TRINITY REGIONAL MEDICAL CENTER (160016)**, 802 Kenyon Road, Zip 50501–5795; tel. 515/573–3101 **A**2 9 10 21 **F**3 7 8 11 13 15 18 20 22 24 26 28 29 30 31 32 34 35 36 38 40 43 44 45 46 47 49 50 53 54 59 64 68 70 74 75 76 77 78 79 81 82 83 84 86 87 89 92 93 102 107 108 110 111 115 118 119 120 121 123 129 130 131 132 135 145 146 148 **P**6 **S** UnityPoint Health, West Des Moines, IA
Primary Contact: Mike Dewerff, President and Chief Executive Officer
COO: Troy Martens, Chief Operating Officer
CHR: Ted W. Vaughn, Director Human Resources
CNO: Debra Shriver, R.N., Chief Nurse Executive
Web address: www.trmc.org
**Control:** Other not–for–profit (including NFP Corporation) **Service:** General Medical and Surgical

**Staffed Beds:** 106 **Admissions:** 3592 **Census:** 36 **Outpatient Visits:** 97097 **Births:** 516 **Total Expense ($000):** 97199 **Payroll Expense ($000):** 43937 **Personnel:** 645

## FORT MADISON—Lee County

⊞ **FORT MADISON COMMUNITY HOSPITAL (160122)**, 5445 Avenue O, Zip 52627–9611, Mailing Address: P.O. Box 174, Zip 52627–0174; tel. 319/372–6530 **A**1 9 10 **F**3 11 13 15 28 29 31 34 40 43 45 50 51 53 57 59 62 64 67 68 70 74 75 76 77 78 79 81 85 86 87 90 91 93 94 96 97 99 100 101 102 103 104 107 108 110 112 115 117 118 119 128 129 130 131 132 133 143 144 146 147 148 **P**6 **S** QHR, Brentwood, TN
Primary Contact: C. James Platt, Chief Executive Officer
CFO: Bradley J. Kokjohn, Chief Financial Officer
CMO: David Wenger–Keller, M.D., Chief of Staff
CIO: Shane Tapper, Director Management Information Systems
CHR: Vicki Kokjohn, Director Employee Relations
CNO: Shelby Dickens, Director, Patient Care Services
Web address: www.fmchosp.com
**Control:** Other not–for–profit (including NFP Corporation) **Service:** General Medical and Surgical

**Staffed Beds:** 50 **Admissions:** 1716 **Census:** 18 **Outpatient Visits:** 104453 **Births:** 419 **Total Expense ($000):** 55420 **Payroll Expense ($000):** 26257 **Personnel:** 434

## GREENFIELD—Adair County

**ADAIR COUNTY MEMORIAL HOSPITAL (161310)**, 609 S.E. Kent Street, Zip 50849–9454; tel. 641/743–2123 **A**9 10 18 **F**3 7 11 15 18 28 29 31 34 35 36 40 43 45 48 50 57 59 62 64 65 69 70 75 77 79 81 91 93 97 107 108 110 111 114 116 118 119 127 128 129 130 133 **P**6
Primary Contact: Angela Mortoza, Administrator
CFO: Randy Loomis, Chief Financial Officer
CMO: Cassie Rasmussen, M.D., Chief Medical Officer
CIO: Thom Richards, Chief Information Technology
CHR: Angie Frankl, Director Human Resources
CNO: Cindy K. Peeler, R.N., Chief Nursing Officer
Web address: www.adaircountyhealthsystem.org
**Control:** County–Government, nonfederal **Service:** General Medical and Surgical

**Staffed Beds:** 18 **Admissions:** 120 **Census:** 1 **Outpatient Visits:** 10610 **Total Expense ($000):** 11524 **Payroll Expense ($000):** 4293 **Personnel:** 99

## GRINNELL—Poweshiek County

★ **GRINNELL REGIONAL MEDICAL CENTER (160147)**, 210 Fourth Avenue, Zip 50112–1898; tel. 641/236–2300 **A**9 10 **F**3 11 12 13 15 28 29 30 31 32 34 35 36 37 38 40 43 44 45 46 47 50 53 54 56 57 59 61 62 63 64 65 66 70 75 76 77 78 79 81 84 85 86 87 89 93 97 99 100 101 102 103 104 107 110 111 115 118 119 126 127 130 131 132 133 134 135 144 146 147 148 **P**6 7
Primary Contact: Todd C. Linden, President and Chief Executive Officer
CFO: Kyle M. Wilcox, Assistant Vice President Finance
CIO: David L. Ness, Vice President Operations
CHR: Debra S. Nowachek, Director Human Resources
CNO: Doris Rindels, Vice President Operations
Web address: www.grmc.us
**Control:** Other not–for–profit (including NFP Corporation) **Service:** General Medical and Surgical

**Staffed Beds:** 49 **Admissions:** 1305 **Census:** 12 **Outpatient Visits:** 48623 **Births:** 147 **Total Expense ($000):** 45213 **Payroll Expense ($000):** 21036 **Personnel:** 368

## GRUNDY CENTER—Grundy County

★ **GRUNDY COUNTY MEMORIAL HOSPITAL (161303)**, 201 East J Avenue, Zip 50638–2096; tel. 319/824–5421, (Total facility includes 55 beds in nursing home–type unit) **A**9 10 18 **F**15 28 29 34 35 40 43 57 59 63 67 68 75 78 79 81 86 87 93 107 110 111 114 119 128 129 130 131 132 133 135 146 148 **S** UnityPoint Health, West Des Moines, IA
Primary Contact: Jennifer Havens, Director of Nursing and Chief Executive Officer
COO: Ryan Bingman, Director Operations
CFO: Lisa Zinkula, Chief Financial Officer
CMO: Douglas Cooper, M.D., Chief Medical Officer
CIO: Nicholas Betts, Director Information Technology
CHR: Aaron Wedo, Manager, Human Resources
Web address: www.grundycountyhospital.com
**Control:** County–Government, nonfederal **Service:** General Medical and Surgical

**Staffed Beds:** 80 **Admissions:** 324 **Census:** 57 **Outpatient Visits:** 34562 **Births:** 0 **Total Expense ($000):** 18992 **Payroll Expense ($000):** 7758 **Personnel:** 141

## GUTHRIE CENTER—Guthrie County

★ **GUTHRIE COUNTY HOSPITAL (161314)**, 710 North 12th Street, Zip 50115–1544; tel. 641/332–2201 **A**9 10 18 **F**11 15 18 28 29 31 34 35 40 43 45 53 56 57 59 64 69 75 79 81 85 93 107 110 119 128 130 132 133 143 **S** UnityPoint Health, West Des Moines, IA
Primary Contact: Patrick Peters, Chief Executive Officer
CFO: Melinda Alt, Chief Financial Officer
CMO: Steven Bascom, M.D., Chief Medical Officer
CIO: Jeff Cobb, Information Technologist
CHR: Kimberly Myers, Director Human Resources
Web address: www.guthriecountyhospital.org
**Control:** County–Government, nonfederal **Service:** General Medical and Surgical

**Staffed Beds:** 17 **Admissions:** 283 **Census:** 2 **Outpatient Visits:** 40551 **Total Expense ($000):** 14830 **Payroll Expense ($000):** 6312 **Personnel:** 111

## GUTTENBERG—Clayton County

⊞ **GUTTENBERG MUNICIPAL HOSPITAL (161312)**, 200 Main Street, Zip 52052–9108, Mailing Address: P.O. Box 550, Zip 52052–0550; tel. 563/252–1121 **A**1 9 10 18 **F**3 7 8 11 13 15 28 34 35 40 43 45 50 53 57 59 64 68 76 81 82 85 89 93 97 102 107 110 111 114 119 127 128 130 132 133 **P**5 6 **S** UnityPoint Health, West Des Moines, IA
Primary Contact: Kimberley A. Gau, FACHE, Chief Executive Officer
CMO: Michele Sadler, D.O., Chief Medical Staff
CIO: Scott R. Pauls, Director Information Technology
CHR: Leigh Ann Judge, Manager Human Resources
CNO: Kimberley A. Gau, FACHE, Interim Chief Nursing Officer
Web address: www.guttenberghospital.org
**Control:** City–Government, nonfederal **Service:** General Medical and Surgical

**Staffed Beds:** 20 **Admissions:** 307 **Census:** 2 **Outpatient Visits:** 22124 **Births:** 26 **Total Expense ($000):** 13843 **Payroll Expense ($000):** 5620 **Personnel:** 121

## HAMBURG—Fremont County

**GEORGE C GRAPE COMMUNITY HOSPITAL (161324)**, 2959 U.S. Highway 275, Zip 51640–5067; tel. 712/382–1515, (Total facility includes 6 beds in nursing home–type unit) **A**9 10 18 **F**11 15 18 28 31 34 35 40 43 45 50 53 57 59 62 64 65 68 74 75 77 78 79 81 82 85 91 93 107 114 119 128 129 130 131 133 135 148
Primary Contact: Michael O'Neal, Administrator and Chief Executive Officer
CFO: Hilary Christiansen, Chief Financial Officer
CMO: Kelli Woltemath, D.O., Chief Medical Staff
CIO: Craig Wells, Chief Information Officer
CHR: Jackie Wertz, Director Human Resources
CNO: Gloria Mattice, R.N., Director Patient Care
Web address: www.grapehospital.com
**Control:** Other not–for–profit (including NFP Corporation) **Service:** General Medical and Surgical

**Staffed Beds:** 25 **Admissions:** 284 **Census:** 6 **Outpatient Visits:** 19560 **Births:** 0 **Total Expense ($000):** 10133 **Payroll Expense ($000):** 4227 **Personnel:** 92

## HAMPTON—Franklin County

★ **FRANKLIN GENERAL HOSPITAL (161308)**, 1720 Central Avenue East, Suite A., Zip 50441–1867; tel. 641/456–5000, (Total facility includes 52 beds in nursing home–type unit) **A**9 10 18 **F**7 10 11 15 28 30 34 40 43 57 59 63 64 65 67 68 75 77 79 81 82 85 86 89 90 93 107 111 114 119 127 128 129 130 131 132 133 135 146 148 **S** Trinity Health, Livonia, MI
Primary Contact: Kim Price, Chief Executive Officer
CFO: Bonnie Lettow, Chief Financial Officer
CHR: Victoria Kruse, Manager Human Resources
CNO: Ronda Reimer, R.N., Chief Nursing Officer and Assistant Administrator
Web address: www.franklingeneral.com
**Control:** County–Government, nonfederal **Service:** General Medical and Surgical

**Staffed Beds:** 77 **Admissions:** 342 **Census:** 54 **Outpatient Visits:** 17024 **Births:** 0 **Total Expense ($000):** 17526 **Payroll Expense ($000):** 5836 **Personnel:** 133

**IA**

*Many Facility Codes have changed. Please refer to the AHA Guide Code Chart.*   © 2015 AHA Guide

## HARLAN—Shelby County

★ **MYRTUE MEDICAL CENTER (161374)**, 1213 Garfield Avenue, Zip 51537–2057; tel. 712/755–5161 **A**9 10 18 **F**3 11 13 15 28 29 31 32 34 35 38 40 43 45 46 50 53 56 57 59 62 63 64 65 68 75 76 77 78 81 85 87 92 93 97 99 101 102 103 104 107 110 114 119 127 129 130 131 132 133 135 146 148 **P**6 8
Primary Contact: Barry Jacobsen, Chief Executive Officer
CFO: Kristy Hansen, Chief Financial Officer
CMO: David Erlbacher, M.D., Chief of Staff
CIO: David Sirek, Chief Information Officer
CHR: Donna Christensen–Mores, Director Human Resources
CNO: Karen Buman, Chief Nursing Executive
Web address: www.myrtuemedical.org
**Control:** County–Government, nonfederal **Service:** General Medical and Surgical

**Staffed Beds:** 25 **Admissions:** 1046 **Census:** 13 **Outpatient Visits:** 91840 **Births:** 85 **Total Expense ($000):** 34000 **Payroll Expense ($000):** 13732 **Personnel:** 341

## HAWARDEN—Sioux County

★ **HAWARDEN REGIONAL HEALTHCARE (161311)**, 1111 11th Street, Zip 51023–1999; tel. 712/551–3100 **A**9 10 18 **F**11 15 28 29 31 34 35 40 43 53 59 64 67 69 75 77 80 81 89 90 92 93 107 108 114 127 128 132 133 135 148 **P**3 7 **S** Trinity Health, Livonia, MI
Primary Contact: Jayson Pullman, Chief Executive Officer
CFO: Jessica Hughes, Director Finance
CMO: Dale Nystrom, M.D., Chief Medical Officer, Physician
CHR: Maggie Hofer, Human Resources Representative
Web address: www.hawardenregionalhealthcare.com/
**Control:** City–Government, nonfederal **Service:** General Medical and Surgical

**Staffed Beds:** 18 **Admissions:** 172 **Census:** 3 **Outpatient Visits:** 18780 **Births:** 0 **Total Expense ($000):** 7238 **Payroll Expense ($000):** 2877 **Personnel:** 68

## HUMBOLDT—Humboldt County

★ **HUMBOLDT COUNTY MEMORIAL HOSPITAL (161334)**, 1000 North 15th Street, Zip 50548–1008; tel. 515/332–4200, (Total facility includes 28 beds in nursing home–type unit) **A**9 10 18 **F**7 8 10 11 12 14 15 28 29 31 32 34 35 40 41 43 45 47 50 51 59 65 69 75 77 78 79 81 82 85 87 93 102 107 110 111 114 119 125 128 130 133 134 135 **S** UnityPoint Health, West Des Moines, IA
Primary Contact: Michelle Sleiter, Chief Executive Officer
CFO: Betty Etherington, Chief Financial Officer
CHR: Mary Moritz, Administrator Human Resources
Web address: www.humboldthospital.org
**Control:** County–Government, nonfederal **Service:** General Medical and Surgical

**Staffed Beds:** 49 **Admissions:** 359 **Census:** 29 **Outpatient Visits:** 74305 **Births:** 0 **Total Expense ($000):** 14045 **Payroll Expense ($000):** 5803 **Personnel:** 136

## IDA GROVE—Ida County

★ **HORN MEMORIAL HOSPITAL (161354)**, 701 East Second Street, Zip 51445–1699; tel. 712/364–3311 **A**9 10 18 **F**11 15 28 29 34 40 45 57 59 62 63 64 65 66 68 75 77 78 79 81 82 85 89 93 97 107 108 110 111 115 119 127 129 130 131 132 133 135 146 147 148 **P**6
Primary Contact: Christopher Nichols, Chief Executive Officer
CFO: Marcia Fehring, Chief Financial Officer
CIO: Robbie Todd, Director Information Technology
CHR: Lorraine Davis, Vice President Human Resources
CNO: Jo Hayes, Chief Nursing Officer
Web address: www.hornmemorialhospital.org
**Control:** Other not–for–profit (including NFP Corporation) **Service:** General Medical and Surgical

**Staffed Beds:** 25 **Admissions:** 554 **Census:** 8 **Outpatient Visits:** 22790 **Births:** 0 **Total Expense ($000):** 17159 **Payroll Expense ($000):** 7816 **Personnel:** 141

## INDEPENDENCE—Buchanan County

★ **BUCHANAN COUNTY HEALTH CENTER (161335)**, 1600 First Street East, Zip 50644–3155; tel. 319/332–0999, (Total facility includes 39 beds in nursing home–type unit) **A**9 10 18 **F**3 11 15 28 29 32 34 35 40 43 45 50 53 56 57 59 64 65 67 75 77 79 81 82 86 87 91 93 107 110 111 114 119 125 129 130 131 132 133 135 146 148
Primary Contact: Steve Robert Slessor, Chief Executive Officer
CFO: Ben Stevens, Chief Financial Officer
CHR: Shelby Medina, Chief Administrative Officer
CNO: Rachel Goldenstein, R.N., Chief Nursing Officer
Web address: www.bchealth.info
**Control:** County–Government, nonfederal **Service:** General Medical and Surgical

**Staffed Beds:** 58 **Admissions:** 353 **Census:** 40 **Outpatient Visits:** 45818 **Births:** 0 **Total Expense ($000):** 22203 **Payroll Expense ($000):** 8445 **Personnel:** 182

☐ **MENTAL HEALTH INSTITUTE (164003)**, 2277 Iowa Avenue, Zip 50644–9106; tel. 319/334–2583 **A**1 9 10 **F**65 98 99 101 102 106 130 143 146 **P**6
Primary Contact: Bhasker J. Dave, M.D., Superintendent
CFO: Kevin Jimmerson, Business Manager
CMO: Bhasker J. Dave, M.D., Superintendent
Web address: www.dhs.state.ia.us
**Control:** State–Government, nonfederal **Service:** Psychiatric

**Staffed Beds:** 75 **Admissions:** 205 **Census:** 50 **Outpatient Visits:** 28 **Births:** 0 **Total Expense ($000):** 22121 **Payroll Expense ($000):** 12957 **Personnel:** 232

## IOWA CITY—Johnson County

☒ **IOWA CITY VETERANS AFFAIRS HEALTH CARE SYSTEM**, 601 Highway 6 West, Zip 52246–2208; tel. 319/338–0581 **A**1 3 5 8 9 **F**3 5 8 11 12 17 18 20 22 24 29 30 31 34 35 38 39 40 43 44 45 46 47 50 51 54 56 57 58 59 60 61 64 70 74 75 78 79 81 82 83 84 85 86 87 91 92 93 94 97 98 100 101 102 103 104 106 107 108 111 114 115 116 117 118 119 135 138 146 147 148 **P**6 **S** Department of Veterans Affairs, Washington, DC
Primary Contact: Judith Johnson–Mekota, Director
COO: Kevin Kosek, Associate Director Operations
CFO: Jennifer Ruppert, Chief Financial Officer
CMO: Richard A. Charlat, Chief of Staff
CIO: Dwight Schuessler, Chief Information Officer
CHR: Dan Helle, Human Resources Officer
CNO: Dawn Oxley, R.N., Associate Director Patient Care Services and Nurse Executive
Web address: www.iowacity.va.gov/
**Control:** Veterans Affairs, Government, federal **Service:** General Medical and Surgical

**Staffed Beds:** 68 **Admissions:** 3186 **Census:** 47 **Outpatient Visits:** 469089 **Births:** 0 **Total Expense ($000):** 268194 **Payroll Expense ($000):** 112153 **Personnel:** 1803

☒ **MERCY IOWA CITY (160029)**, 500 East Market Street, Zip 52245–2689; tel. 319/339–0300, (Total facility includes 16 beds in nursing home–type unit) **A**1 2 9 10 **F**3 5 8 11 13 15 18 20 22 24 26 28 29 30 31 34 35 38 40 41 43 44 45 47 48 50 56 57 58 59 62 63 64 65 70 72 73 74 75 76 77 78 79 81 82 85 86 87 89 97 98 100 101 102 103 107 108 110 111 114 115 119 126 128 130 132 133 135 144 145 146 148 **P**8
Primary Contact: Ronald R. Reed, President and Chief Executive Officer
CFO: Michael G. Heinrich, Executive Vice President and Chief Financial Officer
CMO: Martin Izakovic, M.D., Vice President Medical Staff Affairs and Chief Medical Officer
CIO: David Fishbaugher, Chief Medical Information
CHR: Dena M. Brockhouse, Director Human Resources
CNO: Cindy L. Penney, R.N., Vice President Nursing
Web address: www.mercyiowacity.org
**Control:** Church–operated, Nongovernment, not–for profit **Service:** General Medical and Surgical

**Staffed Beds:** 234 **Admissions:** 7555 **Census:** 81 **Outpatient Visits:** 320074 **Births:** 1225 **Total Expense ($000):** 142877 **Payroll Expense ($000):** 58920 **Personnel:** 961

**UNIVERSITY HOSPITAL SCHOOL** See Center for Disabilities and Development

**IA**

---

✠ **UNIVERSITY OF IOWA HOSPITALS AND CLINICS (160058)**, 200 Hawkins Drive, Zip 52242–1009; tel. 319/356–1616, (Includes CENTER FOR DISABILITIES AND DEVELOPMENT, 200 Hawkins Drive, Zip 52242; tel. 319/356–1347; CHEMICAL DEPENDENCY CENTER, 200 Hawkins Drive, Zip 52242–1007; tel. 319/384–8765; STATE PSYCHIATRIC HOSPITAL, 200 Hawkins Drive, Zip 52242; tel. 319/356–4658; UNIVERSITY OF IOWA CHILDREN'S HOSPITAL, 200 Hawkins Drive, tel. 888/573–5437) **A**1 2 3 5 8 9 10 **F**3 5 6 7 8 9 11 12 13 14 15 16 17 18 19 20 21 22 23 24 25 26 27 28 29 30 31 32 33 34 35 36 37 38 39 40 41 43 44 45 46 47 48 49 50 51 52 53 54 55 56 57 58 59 60 61 62 63 64 65 66 68 70 72 73 74 75 76 77 78 79 80 81 82 83 84 85 86 87 88 89 90 91 92 93 94 96 97 98 99 100 101 102 103 104 105 107 108 109 110 111 114 115 116 117 118 119 120 121 123 124 126 127 129 130 131 132 135 136 137 138 139 140 141 142 143 144 145 146 147 148 **P**1 7
Primary Contact: Kenneth P. Kates, Chief Executive Officer
COO: Scott Turner, Co–Chief Operating Officer
CFO: Kenneth Fisher, Associate Vice President Finance and Chief Financial Officer
CMO: Theresa Brennan, M.D., Chief Medical Officer
CIO: Lee Carmen, Associate Vice President Health Care Information Systems
CHR: Jana Wessels, Associate Vice President Human Resources
CNO: Kenneth Rempfer, Ph.D., Chief Nursing Officer
Web address: www.uihealthcare.org
**Control:** State–Government, nonfederal **Service:** General Medical and Surgical

**Staffed Beds:** 705 **Admissions:** 30762 **Census:** 536 **Outpatient Visits:** 1164875 **Births:** 2076 **Total Expense ($000):** 1143550 **Payroll Expense ($000):** 415364 **Personnel:** 7419

### IOWA FALLS—Hardin County

★ **HANSEN FAMILY HOSPITAL (161380)**, 920 South Oak, Zip 50126–9506; tel. 641/648–4631 **A**9 10 18 **F**3 11 13 15 28 34 40 43 45 50 53 57 59 64 65 75 76 77 81 82 85 86 87 93 97 100 104 107 110 115 119 133 135 147 **P**6 **S** Trinity Health, Livonia, MI
Primary Contact: Cherelle Montanye–Ireland, Chief Executive Officer
CFO: Mike White, Chief Financial Officer
CMO: George Pfaltzgraff, Chief Medical Officer
CHR: Cheri Geitz, Director Human Resources
CNO: Katie Rieks, Chief Nursing Officer
Web address: www.hansenfamilyhospital.com
**Control:** City–Government, nonfederal **Service:** General Medical and Surgical

**Staffed Beds:** 21 **Admissions:** 633 **Census:** 8 **Outpatient Visits:** 44156 **Births:** 82 **Total Expense ($000):** 24380 **Payroll Expense ($000):** 10440 **Personnel:** 247

### JEFFERSON—Greene County

★ **GREENE COUNTY MEDICAL CENTER (161325)**, 1000 West Lincolnway, Zip 50129–1645; tel. 515/386–2114, (Total facility includes 65 beds in nursing home–type unit) **A**9 10 18 **F**11 13 15 28 29 34 35 36 40 46 56 57 59 62 63 64 65 67 68 75 76 77 79 81 82 85 93 107 110 114 119 125 128 130 131 132 133 147 **P**5 6 **S** UnityPoint Health, West Des Moines, IA
Primary Contact: Carl P. Behne, Administrator and Chief Executive Officer
CFO: Mark A. VanderLinden, Chief Financial Officer
CMO: Jon Van Der Veer, D.O., Vice President Medical Affairs
CIO: Roger Overby, Executive Director Information Systems
CHR: Cathy Krieger, Human Resources Director
CNO: Katie Heldt, Chief Nursing Officer
Web address: www.gcmchealth.com
**Control:** County–Government, nonfederal **Service:** General Medical and Surgical

**Staffed Beds:** 90 **Admissions:** 411 **Census:** 53 **Outpatient Visits:** 25480 **Births:** 49 **Total Expense ($000):** 23765 **Payroll Expense ($000):** 9593 **Personnel:** 246

### KEOKUK—Lee County

✠ **KEOKUK AREA HOSPITAL (160008)**, 1600 Morgan Street, Zip 52632–3456; tel. 319/524–7150 **A**1 9 10 **F**3 11 15 28 29 31 34 35 40 43 45 46 57 59 62 64 68 70 79 81 85 86 87 93 96 107 108 111 114 115 118 119 129 130 131 132 133 146 148 **P**6
Primary Contact: Joseph K. Whiting, FACHE, Interim Chief Executive Officer
CMO: Neville Crenshaw, D.O., Chief of Staff
CIO: Linda Atterberg, Chief Information Officer
CHR: Lora Taylor, Director Human Resources and Compliance Officer
CNO: Vickie White, Director of Nursing
Web address: www.keokukhealthsystems.org
**Control:** Other not–for–profit (including NFP Corporation) **Service:** General Medical and Surgical

**Staffed Beds:** 42 **Admissions:** 1077 **Census:** 10 **Outpatient Visits:** 33053 **Births:** 0 **Total Expense ($000):** 21480 **Payroll Expense ($000):** 8666 **Personnel:** 245

### KEOSAUQUA—Van Buren County

★ **VAN BUREN COUNTY HOSPITAL (161337)**, 304 Franklin Street, Zip 52565–1164; tel. 319/293–3171 **A**9 10 18 **F**3 7 10 11 13 15 28 29 32 34 35 40 43 45 46 50 56 57 59 64 65 70 75 76 77 81 85 86 87 89 93 97 102 107 110 111 114 119 125 127 128 130 132 133 135 146 147 148 **P**6
Primary Contact: Ray Brownsworth, Interim Chief Executive Officer
CFO: Kara McEntee, Chief Financial Officer
CIO: Chris McEntee, Network Specialist
CNO: Kay Gabriel, R.N., Chief Nursing Officer
Web address: www.vbch.org
**Control:** County–Government, nonfederal **Service:** General Medical and Surgical

**Staffed Beds:** 25 **Admissions:** 301 **Census:** 3 **Outpatient Visits:** 11951 **Births:** 52 **Total Expense ($000):** 13665 **Payroll Expense ($000):** 7077 **Personnel:** 146

### KNOXVILLE—Marion County

**KNOXVILLE DIVISION** See Veterans Affairs Central Iowa Health Care System, Des Moines

★ **KNOXVILLE HOSPITAL & CLINICS (161355)**, 1002 South Lincoln Street, Zip 50138–3155; tel. 641/842–2151 **A**9 10 18 **F**3 8 11 13 15 28 29 34 40 43 45 47 48 49 50 54 57 59 64 65 75 76 77 79 81 85 86 93 97 102 107 108 110 111 114 118 119 129 130 132 133 135 146 147 148 **P**6 **S** Catholic Health Initiatives, Englewood, CO
Primary Contact: Kevin Kincaid, Chief Executive Officer
COO: Christine Buttell, Chief Operating Officer
CFO: Maggie Hamilton–Beyer, Chief Financial Officer
CMO: Daniel Rowley, M.D., Chief of Medical Staff
CIO: Thom Richards, Director Information Technology
CHR: Brian Sims, Director Administrative Services
CNO: Mary Jane Applegate, Chief Nursing Officer
Web address: www.knoxvillehospital.org
**Control:** Other not–for–profit (including NFP Corporation) **Service:** General Medical and Surgical

**Staffed Beds:** 25 **Admissions:** 1102 **Census:** 10 **Outpatient Visits:** 61873 **Births:** 52 **Total Expense ($000):** 27129 **Payroll Expense ($000):** 10898 **Personnel:** 239

### LAKE CITY—Calhoun County

★ **STEWART MEMORIAL COMMUNITY HOSPITAL (161350)**, 1301 West Main, Zip 51449–1585; tel. 712/464–3171 **A**9 10 18 **F**11 12 13 15 28 29 30 31 34 40 43 45 59 62 63 64 65 69 70 75 76 77 78 79 81 82 86 93 94 107 110 119 127 130 133 135 147 **P**5 6 **S** UnityPoint Health, West Des Moines, IA
Primary Contact: Heather L. Cain, Chief Executive Officer
CFO: Jim Henkenius, Chief Financial Officer
CHR: Bill Albright, Director Human Resources
Web address: www.stewartmemorial.org
**Control:** Other not–for–profit (including NFP Corporation) **Service:** General Medical and Surgical

**Staffed Beds:** 25 **Admissions:** 637 **Census:** 7 **Outpatient Visits:** 44756 **Births:** 92 **Total Expense ($000):** 31291 **Payroll Expense ($000):** 13104 **Personnel:** 225

### LE MARS—Plymouth County

★ **FLOYD VALLEY HOSPITAL (161368)**, 714 Lincoln Street N.E., Zip 51031–3314; tel. 712/546–7871 **A**9 10 18 **F**3 10 11 13 15 28 29 31 32 34 35 40 43 45 50 53 57 59 62 64 65 67 68 76 78 79 80 81 85 86 87 89 107 110 111 114 119 128 130 132 133 135 146 148 **S** Avera Health, Sioux Falls, SD
Primary Contact: Michael T. Donlin, FACHE, Administrator
CFO: Daryl Friedenbach, Director Fiscal Services
CMO: Sheila Holcomb, M.D., President Medical Staff
CIO: Jason Uhl, Chief Information Officer
CHR: Mary Helen Gibson, Director Human Resources
CNO: Loretta Myers, MS, Director, Patient Care
Web address: www.floydvalleyhospital.org
**Control:** City–Government, nonfederal **Service:** General Medical and Surgical

**Staffed Beds:** 25 **Admissions:** 789 **Census:** 8 **Outpatient Visits:** 52423 **Births:** 97 **Total Expense ($000):** 33916 **Payroll Expense ($000):** 11416 **Personnel:** 254

**IA**

*Many Facility Codes have changed. Please refer to the AHA Guide Code Chart.* © 2015 AHA Guide

## LEON—Decatur County

★ **DECATUR COUNTY HOSPITAL (161340)**, 1405 N.W. Church Street, Zip 50144–1299; tel. 641/446–4871 **A**9 10 18 **F**3 7 11 15 28 29 31 34 40 41 50 57 59 64 68 75 78 79 81 82 85 89 93 107 111 114 119 130 133 146 148
Primary Contact: Suzanne Cooner, R.N., MSN, Chief Executive Officer
CFO: Tara Spidle, Chief Financial Officer
CMO: Larry Richard, M.D., Chief Medical Staff
CIO: Daren Steele, Director of Information
CHR: Jo Beth Smith, Chief Support Services and Human Resources
CNO: Andrea Masters, Chief Nursing Officer
Web address: www.decaturcountyhospital.org
**Control:** County–Government, nonfederal **Service:** General Medical and Surgical

| | |
|---|---|
| **Staffed Beds:** 11 **Admissions:** 330 **Census:** 4 **Outpatient Visits:** 12434 **Births:** 0 **Total Expense ($000):** 11224 **Payroll Expense ($000):** 3609 **Personnel:** 94 | |

## MANCHESTER—Delaware County

★ **REGIONAL MEDICAL CENTER (161343)**, 709 West Main Street, #359, Zip 52057–1526, Mailing Address: P.O. Box 359, Zip 52057–0359; tel. 563/927–3232 **A**9 10 18 **F**3 7 11 13 15 17 28 29 34 35 36 40 43 44 50 53 57 59 61 62 63 64 65 66 68 70 75 76 77 79 81 82 85 86 89 93 94 97 99 104 107 110 111 114 119 126 127 128 129 130 131 132 133 146 148 **P**6
Primary Contact: Lon D. Butikofer, R.N., Ph.D., Chief Executive Officer
CFO: Danette Kramer, Chief Financial Officer
CIO: Amy Mensen, Chief Administrative Officer
CHR: Amy Mensen, Chief Administrative Officer
CNO: Patricia S. Doyle, R.N., Chief Nursing Officer
Web address: www.regmedctr.org
**Control:** County–Government, nonfederal **Service:** General Medical and Surgical

| | |
|---|---|
| **Staffed Beds:** 25 **Admissions:** 1058 **Census:** 10 **Outpatient Visits:** 161487 **Births:** 168 **Total Expense ($000):** 43603 **Payroll Expense ($000):** 20883 **Personnel:** 363 | |

## MANNING—Carroll County

★ **MANNING REGIONAL HEALTHCARE CENTER (161332)**, 1550 6th Street, Zip 51455–1093; tel. 712/655–2072, (Total facility includes 56 beds in nursing home–type unit) **A**9 10 18 **F**3 4 5 11 13 15 31 34 35 38 40 43 45 50 56 57 59 64 68 75 76 81 85 89 92 93 97 107 110 114 119 128 130 132 133 146 148 **P**6
Primary Contact: John O'Brien, Chief Executive Officer
CFO: Amy Monson, Chief Financial Officer
CMO: Douglas McLaws, D.O., Chief Medical Officer
CIO: Kim C. Jahn, Chief Plant Operations and Chief Information Officer
CHR: Shelli Lorenzen, Chief Human Resources Officer
CNO: Amy S. Dawson, Chief Clinical Officer
Web address: www.mrhcia.com
**Control:** Other not–for–profit (including NFP Corporation) **Service:** General Medical and Surgical

| | |
|---|---|
| **Staffed Beds:** 73 **Admissions:** 229 **Census:** 52 **Outpatient Visits:** 7771 **Births:** 18 **Total Expense ($000):** 13729 **Payroll Expense ($000):** 6097 **Personnel:** 176 | |

## MAQUOKETA—Jackson County

⊞ **JACKSON COUNTY REGIONAL HEALTH CENTER (161329)**, 700 West Grove Street, Zip 52060–2163; tel. 563/652–2474 **A**1 9 10 18 **F**3 7 11 15 28 34 40 43 45 53 64 75 81 85 87 93 107 110 114 119 128 129 133 146 148 **S** Genesis Health System, Davenport, IA
Primary Contact: Curt Coleman, FACHE, Administrator
CFO: Donna Roeder, Chief Financial Officer
CHR: Shannon Langenberg, Director Human Resources
Web address: www.jcrhc.org
**Control:** County–Government, nonfederal **Service:** General Medical and Surgical

| | |
|---|---|
| **Staffed Beds:** 25 **Admissions:** 139 **Census:** 3 **Outpatient Visits:** 17705 **Births:** 0 **Total Expense ($000):** 13399 **Payroll Expense ($000):** 4975 **Personnel:** 116 | |

## MARENGO—Iowa County

★ **MARENGO MEMORIAL HOSPITAL, UNITYPOINT HEALTH (161317)**, 300 West May Street, Zip 52301–1261, Mailing Address: P.O. Box 228, Zip 52301–0228; tel. 319/642–5543 **A**9 10 18 **F**3 7 15 28 29 34 35 38 40 43 45 50 59 64 69 75 81 85 96 97 107 110 114 130 133 143 146 **P**5 6 **S** UnityPoint Health, West Des Moines, IA
Primary Contact: Barry Goettsch, FACHE, Chief Executive Officer
COO: Mikaela Gehring, Chief Operating Officer
CFO: Matthew Murphy, Chief Financial Officer
CIO: William Grimm, Director, Information Services
CHR: Lesa Waddell, Director Human Resources
CNO: Teresa Sauerbrei, Chief Nursing Officer
Web address: www.marengohospital.org
**Control:** City–Government, nonfederal **Service:** General Medical and Surgical

| | |
|---|---|
| **Staffed Beds:** 25 **Admissions:** 307 **Census:** 10 **Outpatient Visits:** 25345 **Births:** 0 **Total Expense ($000):** 17148 **Payroll Expense ($000):** 7234 **Personnel:** 149 | |

## MARSHALLTOWN—Marshall County

★ **CENTRAL IOWA HEALTHCARE (160001)**, 3 South Fourth Avenue, Zip 50158–2998; tel. 641/754–5151 **A**9 10 **F**3 7 11 13 15 17 18 20 22 28 30 35 39 40 43 45 50 56 59 62 68 69 70 73 75 76 77 78 79 81 82 85 87 89 93 107 111 114 115 119 124 129 130 131 132 133 146 147 148
Primary Contact: John Hughes, FACHE, President and Chief Executive Officer
CFO: Hilary Dolbee, Chief Financial Officer
CMO: Milt Van Gundy, M.D., President Medical Staff
CHR: Jill Petermeier, Senior Executive Human Resources
Web address: www.marshmed.com/
**Control:** Other not–for–profit (including NFP Corporation) **Service:** General Medical and Surgical

| | |
|---|---|
| **Staffed Beds:** 74 **Admissions:** 2681 **Census:** 24 **Outpatient Visits:** 203410 **Births:** 525 **Total Expense ($000):** 72252 **Payroll Expense ($000):** 32639 **Personnel:** 474 | |

## MASON CITY—Cerro Gordo County

⊞ **MERCY MEDICAL CENTER–NORTH IOWA (160064)**, 1000 Fourth Street S.W., Zip 50401–2800; tel. 641/428–7000 **A**1 2 3 5 9 10 13 **F**3 11 12 13 15 18 20 22 24 26 28 29 30 31 34 35 37 39 40 43 44 45 46 47 48 49 50 54 55 56 57 58 59 60 61 62 63 64 65 68 70 71 72 74 75 76 77 78 79 81 82 84 85 86 87 89 90 91 93 96 97 98 99 100 101 102 103 104 107 108 110 111 113 115 117 118 119 120 121 123 124 125 126 128 129 130 131 132 135 144 145 146 147 148 **P**1 6 **S** Trinity Health, Livonia, MI
Primary Contact: Daniel Varnum, President and Chief Executive Officer
COO: Diane Fischels, Senior Vice President and Chief Operating Officer
CFO: Danette Zook, Chief Financial Officer
CMO: Paul Manternach, M.D., Senior Vice President Physician Integration
CIO: Terry Chartier, Director, Information Systems
CHR: Jackie Luecht, Chief Human Resources Officer
CNO: Kim Chamberlin, Vice President Patient Services and Chief Nursing Officer
Web address: www.mercynorthiowa.com
**Control:** Church–operated, Nongovernment, not–for profit **Service:** General Medical and Surgical

| | |
|---|---|
| **Staffed Beds:** 206 **Admissions:** 11444 **Census:** 127 **Outpatient Visits:** 448067 **Births:** 922 **Total Expense ($000):** 322850 **Payroll Expense ($000):** 131296 **Personnel:** 1886 | |

## MISSOURI VALLEY—Harrison County

★ **CHI HEALTH MISSOURI VALLEY (161309)**, 631 North Eighth Street, Zip 51555–1102; tel. 712/642–2784 **A**9 10 18 **F**1 3 4 16 17 28 34 40 44 45 47 50 54 57 59 62 63 64 65 66 67 68 70 72 73 75 76 80 81 82 83 84 86 87 88 89 90 93 94 97 98 99 100 101 107 110 114 119 127 128 129 133 135 144 146 **P**8 **S** Catholic Health Initiatives, Englewood, CO
Primary Contact: Robert A. Valentine, President
CMO: Daniel Richter, M.D., Chief of Staff
CIO: Ravae Smallwood, IS Coordinator
CHR: Heidi Winters, Business Partner Human Resources
CNO: Darcy Behrendt, R.N., Vice President, Patient Care Services
Web address: www.alegentcreighton.com/community–memorial
**Control:** Other not–for–profit (including NFP Corporation) **Service:** General Medical and Surgical

| | |
|---|---|
| **Staffed Beds:** 16 **Admissions:** 590 **Census:** 5 **Outpatient Visits:** 38528 **Births:** 0 **Total Expense ($000):** 20236 **Payroll Expense ($000):** 10347 **Personnel:** 148 | |

**IA**

---

**Hospital, Medicare Provider Number, Address, Telephone, Approval, Facility, and Physician Codes, Health Care System**

★ American Hospital Association (AHA) membership   ○ Healthcare Facilities Accreditation Program   ⇑ Center for Improvement in Healthcare Quality Accreditation
☐ The Joint Commission accreditation   ◇ DNV Healthcare Inc. accreditation   △ Commission on Accreditation of Rehabilitation Facilities (CARF) accreditation

## MOUNT AYR—Ringgold County

★ **RINGGOLD COUNTY HOSPITAL (161373)**, 504 North Cleveland Street, Zip 50854–2201; tel. 641/464–3226 **A**9 10 18 **F**3 7 15 28 29 31 34 35 38 40 43 56 57 59 64 65 81 93 107 111 114 119 133 148 **P**6
Primary Contact: Gordon W. Winkler, Administrator and Chief Executive Officer
CFO: Teresa Roberts, Chief Financial Officer
CIO: Jan Lyons, Regional Director Health Improvement Management
CHR: Mitzi Hymbaugh, Chief Personnel
Web address: www.rchmtayr.org
**Control:** Hospital district or authority, Government, nonfederal **Service:** General Medical and Surgical

**Staffed Beds:** 16 **Admissions:** 234 **Census:** 3 **Outpatient Visits:** 22276
**Births:** 0 **Total Expense ($000):** 16310 **Payroll Expense ($000):** 5452
**Personnel:** 112

## MOUNT PLEASANT—Henry County

★ **HENRY COUNTY HEALTH CENTER (161356)**, 407 South White Street, Zip 52641–2263; tel. 319/385–3141, (Total facility includes 49 beds in nursing home–type unit) **A**9 10 18 **F**3 7 11 13 15 28 29 31 32 34 35 40 41 43 45 57 59 64 65 67 70 75 76 77 78 79 81 82 85 86 87 89 93 102 107 108 110 115 118 119 128 129 130 131 132 133 135 146 **P**6
Primary Contact: Robb Gardner, Chief Executive Officer
CFO: David Muhs, Chief Financial Officer
CMO: Joel Ryon, M.D., Chief of Staff
CHR: Lynn Humphreys, Director Human Resources
CNO: Jodi Geerts, Chief Nursing Officer
Web address: www.hchc.org
**Control:** County–Government, nonfederal **Service:** General Medical and Surgical

**Staffed Beds:** 74 **Admissions:** 704 **Census:** 52 **Outpatient Visits:** 47387
**Births:** 128 **Total Expense ($000):** 32825 **Payroll Expense ($000):** 13010
**Personnel:** 260

## MUSCATINE—Muscatine County

⊞ **UNITYPOINT HEALTH – TRINITY MUSCATINE (160013)**, 1518 Mulberry Avenue, Zip 52761–3499; tel. 563/264–9100 **A**1 9 10 20 **F**3 5 11 13 15 18 28 31 34 38 40 43 45 50 55 56 57 59 61 64 65 68 69 70 75 76 77 79 81 85 87 89 97 102 107 108 110 111 114 119 124 129 130 131 134 135 147 148 **S** UnityPoint Health, West Des Moines, IA
Primary Contact: James M. Hayes, Chief Executive Officer
CFO: Greg Pagliuzza, Chief Financial Officer
CMO: Manasi Nadkarni, M.D., Vice President Medical Affairs
CIO: Sean Liddell, Manager Regional Service Information Technology
CHR: Karla Blaser, Director Human Resources
CNO: Pam Askew, R.N., Vice President Patient Care Services
Web address: www.unitypoint.org/quadcities/trinity–muscatine.aspx
**Control:** Other not–for–profit (including NFP Corporation) **Service:** General Medical and Surgical

**Staffed Beds:** 48 **Admissions:** 1402 **Census:** 10 **Outpatient Visits:** 84272
**Births:** 371 **Total Expense ($000):** 42147 **Payroll Expense ($000):** 19530
**Personnel:** 262

## NEVADA—Story County

★ **STORY COUNTY MEDICAL CENTER (161333)**, 640 South 19th Street, Zip 50201–2902; tel. 515/382–2111, (Total facility includes 60 beds in nursing home–type unit) **A**9 10 18 **F**3 7 11 28 29 32 34 35 36 40 43 50 53 57 59 64 65 68 75 81 85 87 97 107 114 119 127 130 133 146 148 **P**6 **S** UnityPoint Health, West Des Moines, IA
Primary Contact: Timothy Ahlers, FACHE, Chief Executive Officer
CFO: Jane Ramthun, Chief Financial Officer
CMO: Arthur Check, M.D., Chief Medical Officer
CHR: Jessica Lingo, Human Resource Generalist
CNO: Beth Rehbein, Chief Nursing and Quality Officer
Web address: www.storymedical.org
**Control:** County–Government, nonfederal **Service:** General Medical and Surgical

**Staffed Beds:** 77 **Admissions:** 418 **Census:** 65 **Outpatient Visits:** 22869
**Births:** 0 **Total Expense ($000):** 21285 **Payroll Expense ($000):** 9716
**Personnel:** 222

## NEW HAMPTON—Chickasaw County

★ **MERCY MEDICAL CENTER–NEW HAMPTON (161331)**, 308 North Maple Avenue, Zip 50659–1142; tel. 641/394–4121 **A**9 10 18 **F**3 11 13 15 28 29 34 35 40 43 45 48 56 57 59 64 65 68 74 76 77 79 81 85 93 97 107 110 119 129 131 133 146 148 **P**1 **S** Trinity Health, Livonia, MI
Primary Contact: Aaron Flugum, Chief Executive Officer
CFO: Jennifer Rapenske, Manager Financial Services
CMO: Jack Kline, M.D., Chief of Staff
CIO: Terry Chartier, Director, Information Systems
CHR: Jackie Luecht, Director, Human Resources
CNO: Jody Wright, Interim Chief Nursing Officer
Web address: www.mercynewhampton.com
**Control:** Church–operated, Nongovernment, not–for profit **Service:** General Medical and Surgical

**Staffed Beds:** 18 **Admissions:** 388 **Census:** 4 **Outpatient Visits:** 19313
**Births:** 41 **Total Expense ($000):** 15776 **Payroll Expense ($000):** 5776
**Personnel:** 87

## OELWEIN—Fayette County

★ **MERCY HOSPITAL OF FRANCISCAN SISTERS (161338)**, 201 Eighth Avenue S.E., Zip 50662–2447; tel. 319/283–6000, (Total facility includes 39 beds in nursing home–type unit) **A**9 10 18 **F**7 11 15 29 30 34 35 40 57 59 65 79 81 93 97 107 110 111 119 127 128 130 132 133 146 147 **P**1 **S** Wheaton Franciscan Healthcare, Wheaton, IL
Primary Contact: Terri Derflinger, Administrator
CFO: Timothy Huber, Manager Financial Support
CMO: James A. Lehman, M.D., Vice President Medical Affairs
CNO: Phyllis Doulaveris, MSN, Senior Vice President and Chief Nursing Officer
Web address: www.covhealth.com
**Control:** Church–operated, Nongovernment, not–for profit **Service:** General Medical and Surgical

**Staffed Beds:** 64 **Admissions:** 321 **Census:** 36 **Outpatient Visits:** 24333
**Births:** 0 **Total Expense ($000):** 12134 **Payroll Expense ($000):** 5309
**Personnel:** 95

## ONAWA—Monona County

★ **BURGESS HEALTH CENTER (161359)**, 1600 Diamond Street, Zip 51040–1548; tel. 712/423–2311 **A**9 10 18 **F**3 7 11 13 15 28 29 31 32 34 40 56 57 59 62 63 64 65 70 75 76 77 78 79 81 82 85 93 97 99 100 101 103 104 107 111 114 119 127 130 132 133 135 146 148 **P**6
Primary Contact: Francis G. Tramp, President
CFO: Shawn Gosch, Chief Financial Officer
CMO: John Garred, Sr., M.D., Chief Medical Officer
CIO: Grady Warner, Director of Information Technology
CHR: Erin Brekke, Director Human Resources
CNO: Patty Sandmann, Senior Director of Nursing
Web address: www.burgesshc.org
**Control:** Other not–for–profit (including NFP Corporation) **Service:** General Medical and Surgical

**Staffed Beds:** 25 **Admissions:** 736 **Census:** 8 **Outpatient Visits:** 68868
**Births:** 62 **Total Expense ($000):** 25363 **Payroll Expense ($000):** 11119
**Personnel:** 248

## ORANGE CITY—Sioux County

★ **ORANGE CITY AREA HEALTH SYSTEM (161360)**, 1000 Lincoln Circle S.E., Zip 51041–1862; tel. 712/737–4984, (Total facility includes 83 beds in nursing home–type unit) **A**9 10 18 **F**7 10 11 13 15 18 28 29 31 34 35 40 45 53 56 57 59 60 62 63 64 67 68 69 70 75 76 77 78 79 81 82 85 86 87 89 93 97 107 110 111 114 117 119 120 125 127 130 131 132 133 146 147 148 **P**6 **S** Sanford Health, Sioux Falls, SD
Primary Contact: Martin W. Guthmiller, Chief Executive Officer
COO: Daniel P. McCarty, Chief Operating Officer
CFO: Dina Baas, Director Financial Services
CHR: Shari Baker, Director Human Resources
Web address: www.ochealthsystem.org
**Control:** City–Government, nonfederal **Service:** General Medical and Surgical

**Staffed Beds:** 108 **Admissions:** 974 **Census:** 91 **Outpatient Visits:** 72879
**Births:** 258 **Total Expense ($000):** 41834 **Payroll Expense ($000):** 17561
**Personnel:** 404

## OSAGE—Mitchell County

★ **MITCHELL COUNTY REGIONAL HEALTH CENTER (161323)**, 616 North Eighth Street, Zip 50461–1498; tel. 641/732–6000 **A**9 10 18 **F**7 8 11 15 18 28 29 34 35 40 45 50 57 59 63 64 65 75 81 85 87 91 93 107 110 114 119 127 128 130 132 133 144 146 **P**8 **S** Trinity Health, Livonia, MI
Primary Contact: Shelly Russell, Chief Executive Officer
CFO: Gregory Burkel, Chief Financial Officer
CMO: Jeff Nasstrom, D.O., Chief of Staff
CHR: Jodie Anderson, Director Human Resources
CNO: Shelly Russell, Chief Nursing Officer
Web address: www.mitchellcohospital–clinics.com
**Control:** County–Government, nonfederal **Service:** General Medical and Surgical

**Staffed Beds:** 25 **Admissions:** 366 **Census:** 5 **Outpatient Visits:** 55806
**Births:** 0 **Total Expense ($000):** 18804 **Payroll Expense ($000):** 6649
**Personnel:** 143

## OSCEOLA—Clarke County

★ **CLARKE COUNTY HOSPITAL (161348)**, 800 South Fillmore Street, Zip 50213–1619; tel. 641/342–2184 **A**9 10 18 **F**7 11 15 18 28 29 31 34 35 40 45 50 53 57 59 64 67 68 75 79 81 89 90 93 94 96 107 111 115 116 117 118 119 128 129 130 133 135 148 **S** UnityPoint Health, West Des Moines, IA
Primary Contact: Brian G. Evans, FACHE, Chief Executive Officer
CFO: Michael Thilges, Chief Financial Officer
CMO: George Fotiadis, M.D., Chief of Staff
CIO: Dennis Blazek, Chief Information Officer
CHR: Kate Emanuel, Director Human Resources
Web address: www.clarkehosp.org
**Control:** County–Government, nonfederal **Service:** General Medical and Surgical

**Staffed Beds:** 25 **Admissions:** 284 **Census:** 11 **Outpatient Visits:** 18703
**Births:** 0 **Total Expense ($000):** 18967 **Payroll Expense ($000):** 6665
**Personnel:** 147

**IA**

*Many Facility Codes have changed. Please refer to the AHA Guide Code Chart.*

## OSKALOOSA—Mahaska County

✠ **MAHASKA HEALTH PARTNERSHIP (161379)**, 1229 C Avenue East, Zip 52577–4298; tel. 641/672-3100 **A**1 9 10 18 **F**5 7 11 13 15 28 29 30 31 34 35 40 43 45 47 50 54 56 57 59 62 63 64 68 69 70 75 76 77 78 79 81 84 85 87 93 94 97 98 99 100 101 102 103 104 107 110 111 114 119 129 130 133 135 146 148 **P**6
Primary Contact: Jay Christensen, FACHE, Administrator
COO: Erin Baldwin, M.P.H., Chief Operating Officer
CFO: Jon Davis, Chief Financial Officer
CMO: Matt Whitis, Chief Medical Officer
CHR: Jacky Bresnahan, Director Human Resources
Web address: www.mahaskahealth.com
**Control:** County–Government, nonfederal **Service:** General Medical and Surgical

> **Staffed Beds:** 33 **Admissions:** 1694 **Census:** 19 **Outpatient Visits:** 129293 **Births:** 215 **Total Expense ($000):** 48197 **Payroll Expense ($000):** 27158 **Personnel:** 368

## OTTUMWA—Wapello County

☐ △ **OTTUMWA REGIONAL HEALTH CENTER (160089)**, 1001 Pennsylvania Avenue, Zip 52501–2186; tel. 641/684-2300 **A**1 2 7 9 10 **F**3 6 7 8 10 11 13 15 18 20 22 28 29 30 31 34 35 40 41 43 45 46 47 48 49 51 53 54 56 57 59 60 62 64 73 74 75 76 77 78 79 80 81 82 85 89 90 93 98 103 107 108 110 114 115 118 119 120 121 123 126 127 129 130 131 135 144 146 147 148 **P**6 **S** RegionalCare Hospital Partners, Brentwood, TN
Primary Contact: Philip J. Noel, III, Chief Executive Officer
CFO: Gene Smith, Interim Vice President and Chief Financial Officer
CMO: Brian Quinn, D.O., Chief Medical Officer
CIO: Scott Garrett, Director of IS
CHR: Kelly Gaul–Houser, Director Human Resources
CNO: Barbara Larson, R.N., Vice President and Chief Nursing Officer
Web address: www.ottumwaregionalhealth.com
**Control:** Corporation, Investor–owned, for–profit **Service:** General Medical and Surgical

> **Staffed Beds:** 101 **Admissions:** 3421 **Census:** 41 **Outpatient Visits:** 112599 **Births:** 484 **Total Expense ($000):** 71088 **Payroll Expense ($000):** 22242 **Personnel:** 509

## PELLA—Marion County

✠ **PELLA REGIONAL HEALTH CENTER (161367)**, 404 Jefferson Street, Zip 50219–1257; tel. 641/628-3150, (Total facility includes 15 beds in nursing home–type unit) **A**1 9 10 18 **F**3 11 13 15 18 28 29 30 31 32 34 35 40 43 45 50 51 53 57 59 60 62 63 64 65 66 70 74 75 76 77 78 79 81 82 85 86 87 91 93 94 97 102 107 108 110 111 115 119 126 127 128 129 130 131 132 133 144 146 147 148 **P**6
Primary Contact: Robert D. Kroese, FACHE, Chief Executive Officer
COO: Robert D. Kroese, FACHE, Chief Executive Officer
CFO: Bruce Heifner, Chief Financial Officer
CIO: Tait Smock, Manager Information Systems
CHR: Teri Lickteig, Director Human Resources
CNO: Yvonne M. O'Brien–Evans, MS, Chief of Nursing
Web address: www.pellahealth.org
**Control:** Other not–for–profit (including NFP Corporation) **Service:** General Medical and Surgical

> **Staffed Beds:** 40 **Admissions:** 1638 **Census:** 24 **Outpatient Visits:** 171394 **Births:** 491 **Total Expense ($000):** 50455 **Payroll Expense ($000):** 19471 **Personnel:** 550

## PERRY—Dallas County

★ **DALLAS COUNTY HOSPITAL (161322)**, 610 10th Street, Zip 50220–2221; tel. 515/465-3547 **A**9 10 18 **F**11 15 18 28 29 31 34 35 39 40 41 43 45 47 50 57 59 68 75 77 78 79 81 82 85 89 91 93 107 110 114 119 128 130 132 133 135 146 147 148
Primary Contact: Matt Wille, Chief Executive Officer
CFO: Sandra Christensen, Chief Financial Officer
CMO: Steven Sohn, M.D., President Medical Staff
CHR: Sherry Smith, Manager Human Resources
Web address: www.dallascohospital.org
**Control:** County–Government, nonfederal **Service:** General Medical and Surgical

> **Staffed Beds:** 18 **Admissions:** 242 **Census:** 3 **Outpatient Visits:** 23681 **Births:** 1 **Total Expense ($000):** 20248 **Payroll Expense ($000):** 4296 **Personnel:** 91

## POCAHONTAS—Pocahontas County

★ **POCAHONTAS COMMUNITY HOSPITAL (161305)**, 606 N.W. Seventh Street, Zip 50574–1099; tel. 712/335-3501 **A**9 10 18 **F**1 4 7 11 15 16 17 28 29 31 35 40 43 45 59 62 63 64 67 70 72 73 75 77 78 79 80 81 84 88 89 90 93 107 110 115 119 128 130 132 133 135 146 148 **P**6 **S** UnityPoint Health, West Des Moines, IA
Primary Contact: James D. Roetman, President and Chief Executive Officer
CFO: Lynn Raveling, Chief Financial Officer
CNO: Susie Aden, Director of IP Services
Web address: www.pocahontashospital.org
**Control:** City–Government, nonfederal **Service:** General Medical and Surgical

> **Staffed Beds:** 20 **Admissions:** 218 **Census:** 2 **Outpatient Visits:** 23429 **Births:** 0 **Total Expense ($000):** 10079 **Payroll Expense ($000):** 3343 **Personnel:** 88

## PRIMGHAR—O'brien County

★ **BAUM HARMON MERCY HOSPITAL (161300)**, 255 North Welch Avenue, Zip 51245–7765, Mailing Address: P.O. Box 528, Zip 51245–0528; tel. 712/957-2300 **A**9 10 18 **F**11 15 28 29 30 31 34 35 40 45 53 57 59 64 67 75 77 78 81 89 119 127 128 133 135 **P**6 **S** Trinity Health, Livonia, MI
Primary Contact: Angie Shilling, Chief Executive Officer
CFO: Sue E. McCauley, Director Finance
CMO: Shailesh Desai, M.D., Chief of Staff
Web address: www.baumharmon.org
**Control:** Church–operated, Nongovernment, not–for profit **Service:** General Medical and Surgical

> **Staffed Beds:** 11 **Admissions:** 112 **Census:** 1 **Outpatient Visits:** 21411 **Births:** 0 **Total Expense ($000):** 7385 **Payroll Expense ($000):** 3751 **Personnel:** 64

## RED OAK—Montgomery County

★ **MONTGOMERY COUNTY MEMORIAL HOSPITAL (161363)**, 2301 Eastern Avenue, Zip 51566–1300, Mailing Address: P.O. Box 498, Zip 51566–0498; tel. 712/623-7000 **A**9 10 18 **F**3 11 13 15 28 29 31 34 35 40 44 45 50 53 57 59 62 63 64 68 69 70 71 75 76 77 78 79 81 82 85 86 87 93 107 110 111 114 118 119 128 129 130 133 135 146 147 148
Primary Contact: David E. Abercrombie, Chief Executive Officer
CFO: Rick J. Leinen, Chief Financial Officer
CMO: Warren Hayes, Chief of Staff
CIO: Ron Kloewer, Chief Information Officer
CHR: Shayla Jennings, Human Resources Director
CNO: Diane McGrew, Chief Nurse Executive
Web address: www.mcmh.org
**Control:** County–Government, nonfederal **Service:** General Medical and Surgical

> **Staffed Beds:** 25 **Admissions:** 1011 **Census:** 13 **Outpatient Visits:** 44146 **Births:** 71 **Total Expense ($000):** 29943 **Payroll Expense ($000):** 13312 **Personnel:** 263

## ROCK RAPIDS—Lyon County

**SANFORD MERRILL MEDICAL CENTER** See Sanford Rock Rapids Medical Center

★ **SANFORD ROCK RAPIDS MEDICAL CENTER (161321)**, 801 South Greene Street, Zip 51246–1998; tel. 712/472-2591 **A**9 10 18 **F**11 28 31 34 40 41 45 53 57 59 65 68 75 77 81 87 89 97 107 119 127 130 131 133 135 146 **P**6 **S** Sanford Health, Sioux Falls, SD
Primary Contact: Tammy Loosbrock, Chief Executive Officer
CFO: Stanley Knobloch, Chief Financial Officer
CMO: David Springer, M.D., President Medical Staff
CHR: Holly Anderson, Supervisor Human Resources
CNO: Jack Johnson, Chief Nursing Officer
Web address: www.sanfordmerrill.org
**Control:** Other not–for–profit (including NFP Corporation) **Service:** General Medical and Surgical

> **Staffed Beds:** 14 **Admissions:** 295 **Census:** 3 **Outpatient Visits:** 15993 **Births:** 0 **Total Expense ($000):** 8071 **Payroll Expense ($000):** 3651 **Personnel:** 67

**IA**

---

**Hospital, Medicare Provider Number, Address, Telephone, Approval, Facility, and Physician Codes, Health Care System**

★ American Hospital Association (AHA) membership    ◯ Healthcare Facilities Accreditation Program    ⇑ Center for Improvement in Healthcare Quality Accreditation
☐ The Joint Commission accreditation    ◇ DNV Healthcare Inc. accreditation    △ Commission on Accreditation of Rehabilitation Facilities (CARF) accreditation

**ROCK VALLEY—Sioux County**

★ **HEGG MEMORIAL HEALTH CENTER AVERA (161336)**, 1202 21st Avenue, Zip 51247–1497; tel. 712/476–8000, (Total facility includes 60 beds in nursing home–type unit) **A**9 10 18 **F**3 4 11 13 15 17 28 29 31 34 35 36 40 41 43 45 53 57 59 62 64 65 67 68 70 73 75 76 77 78 79 81 84 85 89 93 97 107 110 111 114 119 128 130 131 132 133 135 144 147 148 **S** Avera Health, Sioux Falls, SD
Primary Contact: Glenn Zevenbergen, Chief Executive Officer
CFO: Kari Timmer, Chief Financial Officer
CMO: Kevin Post, D.O., Chief Medical Officer
CHR: Tammy Faber, Director Human Resources
CNO: Linda VerSteeg, Director of Nursing
Web address: www.hegghc.org
**Control:** Other not–for–profit (including NFP Corporation) **Service:** General Medical and Surgical

**Staffed Beds:** 85 **Admissions:** 286 **Census:** 63 **Outpatient Visits:** 33924
**Births:** 95 **Total Expense ($000):** 17012 **Payroll Expense ($000):** 8618
**Personnel:** 202

**SAC CITY—Sac County**

★ **LORING HOSPITAL (161370)**, 211 Highland Avenue, Zip 50583–2424; tel. 712/662–7105 **A**9 10 18 **F**3 11 15 28 29 30 31 34 35 40 43 45 57 59 62 63 64 68 75 78 79 81 86 91 93 107 110 115 119 125 130 132 133 146 **S** UnityPoint Health, West Des Moines, IA
Primary Contact: James Beck, Interim Chief Executive Officer
CFO: Angie Fischer, Chief Financial Officer
CMO: Les Marczewski, M.D., Chief Medical Officer
CIO: Leah Snyder, Director Health Information Services
CHR: Becky Pontious, Human Resources/Accounting
CNO: Lori Forneris, R.N., Chief Clinical Officer
Web address: www.loringhospital.org
**Control:** Other not–for–profit (including NFP Corporation) **Service:** General Medical and Surgical

**Staffed Beds:** 25 **Admissions:** 460 **Census:** 4 **Outpatient Visits:** 18404
**Births:** 0 **Total Expense ($000):** 12770 **Payroll Expense ($000):** 4321
**Personnel:** 92

**SHELDON—O'brien County**

★ **SANFORD SHELDON MEDICAL CENTER (161381)**, 118 North Seventh Avenue, Zip 51201–1235, Mailing Address: P.O. Box 250, Zip 51201–0250; tel. 712/324–5041, (Total facility includes 70 beds in nursing home–type unit) **A**9 10 18 **F**3 11 13 15 28 29 31 32 34 35 38 40 43 50 53 57 59 62 63 64 65 67 68 74 75 76 77 78 79 81 82 84 86 87 91 93 96 97 99 100 101 102 103 104 107 108 110 111 114 119 127 129 130 131 132 133 135 146 148 **P**6 **S** Sanford Health, Sioux Falls, SD
Primary Contact: Richard E. Nordahl, Chief Executive Officer
CFO: Richard E. Nordahl, Chief Financial Officer
CMO: Scott Lichty, M.D., Physician
CIO: Jason Brown, Director Information Systems
CHR: Dianne Wolthuizen, Director Human Resources
CNO: Joni DeKok, Chief Nursing Officer
Web address: www.sanfordsheldon.org
**Control:** Other not–for–profit (including NFP Corporation) **Service:** General Medical and Surgical

**Staffed Beds:** 95 **Admissions:** 820 **Census:** 67 **Outpatient Visits:** 96503
**Births:** 133 **Total Expense ($000):** 25762 **Payroll Expense ($000):** 11376
**Personnel:** 252

**SHENANDOAH—Page County**

★ **SHENANDOAH MEDICAL CENTER (161366)**, 300 Pershing Avenue, Zip 51601–2355; tel. 712/246–1230, (Total facility includes 50 beds in nursing home–type unit) **A**9 10 18 **F**3 13 15 18 28 29 31 34 36 38 40 41 43 45 50 53 56 57 59 62 63 64 65 67 68 69 70 74 75 76 77 78 79 81 83 84 85 87 89 91 93 104 107 108 110 111 115 117 118 119 127 129 130 131 132 133 135 144 146 147 148 **P**6
Primary Contact: Karen S. Cole, MS, FACHE, Chief Executive Officer
CFO: Matt Sells, CPA, Chief Financial Officer
CMO: Todd Isaacson, M.D., Chief Medical Officer
CIO: Chuck Dougherty, Chief Information Officer
CHR: Keli Royal, Director Human Resources
CNO: Joe Pimentel, Chief Nursing Officer
Web address: www.smchospital.com/
**Control:** Other not–for–profit (including NFP Corporation) **Service:** General Medical and Surgical

**Staffed Beds:** 75 **Admissions:** 634 **Census:** 50 **Outpatient Visits:** 207930
**Births:** 123 **Total Expense ($000):** 31992 **Payroll Expense ($000):** 16168
**Personnel:** 310

**SIBLEY— County**

★ **OSCEOLA COMMUNITY HOSPITAL (161345)**, 600 Ninth Avenue North, Zip 51249–1012, Mailing Address: P.O. Box 258, Zip 51249–0258; tel. 712/754–2574 **A**9 10 18 **F**3 8 9 10 11 13 15 17 18 26 28 29 31 32 34 35 36 40 43 45 46 49 53 56 57 59 61 62 64 65 67 68 70 75 76 77 78 79 81 82 83 84 85 86 87 89 93 107 108 110 114 119 125 128 129 130 131 132 133 135 143 144 145 146 147 148 **P**5 **S** Avera Health, Sioux Falls, SD
Primary Contact: Janet H. Dykstra, Chief Executive Officer
CFO: Jerri Palsrok, Manager Business Office
CMO: Gregory J. Kosters, D.O., Chief Medical Officer
CIO: Sherry McElroy, Director Health Information Management
Web address: www.osceolacommunityhospital.org
**Control:** Other not–for–profit (including NFP Corporation) **Service:** General Medical and Surgical

**Staffed Beds:** 25 **Admissions:** 293 **Census:** 3 **Outpatient Visits:** 20498
**Births:** 19 **Total Expense ($000):** 11579 **Payroll Expense ($000):** 3532
**Personnel:** 88

**SIGOURNEY—Keokuk County**

**KEOKUK COUNTY HEALTH CENTER (161315)**, 23019 Highway 149, Zip 52591–8341; tel. 641/622–2720 **A**9 10 18 **F**1 2 3 7 11 12 28 29 30 34 35 38 40 43 45 46 50 56 57 59 63 64 65 67 75 77 82 84 86 87 90 91 93 97 107 128 130 131 132 133 134 135 144 146 147 148 **P**5
Primary Contact: Matthew Ives, Administrator and Chief Financial Officer
CFO: Matthew Ives, Interim Chief Executive Officer and Chief Financial Officer
Web address: www.kchc.net
**Control:** County–Government, nonfederal **Service:** General Medical and Surgical

**Staffed Beds:** 14 **Admissions:** 169 **Census:** 7 **Outpatient Visits:** 15178
**Births:** 0 **Total Expense ($000):** 9639 **Payroll Expense ($000):** 4445
**Personnel:** 92

**SIOUX CENTER—Sioux County**

★ **SIOUX CENTER HEALTH (161346)**, 1101 9th Street, S.E., Zip 51250–1398; tel. 712/722–8107, (Total facility includes 69 beds in nursing home–type unit) **A**9 10 18 **F**3 8 10 13 15 17 18 28 29 30 31 34 35 40 41 43 45 50 56 57 59 62 63 64 67 68 74 75 76 77 78 79 81 82 84 85 86 87 89 93 96 97 107 110 111 114 119 125 128 130 131 132 133 144 146 147 148 **P**6 **S** Avera Health, Sioux Falls, SD
Primary Contact: Kayleen R. Lee, Chief Executive Officer
CFO: Jackson Schuiteman, Chief Financial Officer
CHR: Theresa Tucker, Human Resources Officer
Web address: www.schospital.org
**Control:** Other not–for–profit (including NFP Corporation) **Service:** General Medical and Surgical

**Staffed Beds:** 90 **Admissions:** 522 **Census:** 71 **Outpatient Visits:** 42859
**Births:** 157 **Total Expense ($000):** 30345 **Payroll Expense ($000):** 13901
**Personnel:** 335

**SIOUX CITY—Woodbury County**

⊞ **MERCY MEDICAL CENTER–SIOUX CITY (160153)**, 801 Fifth Street, Zip 51101–1326, Mailing Address: P.O. Box 3168, Zip 51102–3168; tel. 712/279–2010 **A**1 2 3 5 9 10 **F**3 5 11 13 15 17 18 20 22 24 26 28 29 30 31 32 34 35 36 37 38 40 43 44 45 49 50 55 56 57 59 64 65 68 70 71 74 75 76 77 78 79 81 82 84 85 87 89 90 91 93 96 97 98 100 102 107 108 110 111 115 118 119 124 126 129 130 132 135 144 146 147 148 **P**6 8 **S** Trinity Health, Livonia, MI
Primary Contact: James G. Fitzpatrick, FACHE, Chief Executive Officer
CFO: Hugh DePaulis, Interim Vice President and Chief Financial Officer
CMO: Jerome Pierson, Chief Medical Officer
CIO: Steve Larson, M.D., Director Information Systems
CHR: Julie Anfinson, Director Human Resources
CNO: Tracy Larson, MS, Vice President Patient Care Services and Chief Nursing Officer
Web address: www.mercysiouxcity.com
**Control:** Church–operated, Nongovernment, not–for profit **Service:** General Medical and Surgical

**Staffed Beds:** 192 **Admissions:** 9225 **Census:** 124 **Outpatient Visits:** 233304 **Births:** 273 **Total Expense ($000):** 185969 **Payroll Expense ($000):** 74747 **Personnel:** 1194

**IA**

★ ◇ **UNITYPOINT HEALTH – ST. LUKE'S (160146)**, 2720 Stone Park Boulevard, Zip 51104–3734; tel. 712/279–3500 **A**3 5 9 10 21 **F**3 11 13 15 17 18 20 22 26 28 29 30 31 34 35 39 40 43 45 49 50 51 54 56 57 59 60 64 68 70 72 73 74 75 76 77 78 79 81 82 84 85 86 88 89 90 92 93 96 97 98 102 104 107 108 111 114 118 119 126 129 130 131 132 135 142 143 144 145 146 147 **P**6 **S** UnityPoint Health, West Des Moines, IA
Primary Contact: Lynn Wold, President and Chief Executive Officer
COO: Lynn Wold, Chief Operation Officer
CFO: James Gobell, Chief Financial Officer
CIO: James Gobell, Chief Financial Officer
CHR: Tammy Hartnett, Employee Relations Manager
CNO: Priscilla Stokes, MS, Vice President Patient Care and Hospital Operations
Web address: www.stlukes.org
**Control:** Other not–for–profit (including NFP Corporation) **Service:** General Medical and Surgical

**Staffed Beds:** 146 **Admissions:** 9008 **Census:** 97 **Outpatient Visits:** 84703 **Births:** 2101 **Total Expense ($000):** 145764 **Payroll Expense ($000):** 56417 **Personnel:** 1056

### SPENCER—Clay County

★ **SPENCER HOSPITAL (160112)**, 1200 First Avenue East, Suite 1, Zip 51301–4342; tel. 712/264–6111 **A**9 10 **F**3 7 8 11 13 15 28 29 30 31 34 35 39 40 43 45 50 53 54 56 57 59 60 62 63 64 65 69 70 75 76 77 78 79 81 82 85 86 87 93 96 97 98 103 107 108 109 111 115 118 119 120 121 123 127 129 130 131 132 133 135 146 147 148 **P**5
Primary Contact: William J. Bumgarner, President
CFO: Mark Gaworski, Vice President Finance, Chief Financial Officer
CMO: Jason Hough, Medical Staff President
CIO: Brenda Marie Tiefenthaler, MHA, BSN, R.N., Vice President Patient Care and Informatics
CHR: Stephen Duetsch, Vice President Operations and Support
CNO: Brenda Marie Tiefenthaler, MHA, BSN, R.N., Vice President Patient Care and Informatics
Web address: www.spencerhospital.org
**Control:** City–Government, nonfederal **Service:** General Medical and Surgical

**Staffed Beds:** 74 **Admissions:** 2259 **Census:** 24 **Outpatient Visits:** 116756 **Births:** 285 **Total Expense ($000):** 62362 **Payroll Expense ($000):** 21177 **Personnel:** 438

### SPIRIT LAKE—Dickinson County

★ **LAKES REGIONAL HEALTHCARE (160124)**, 2301 Highway 71 South, Zip 51360–6810, Mailing Address: P.O. Box AB, Zip 51360–0159; tel. 712/336–1230 **A**9 10 **F**3 7 11 13 15 28 29 30 31 34 35 40 41 43 45 50 57 59 62 63 64 65 69 70 75 76 77 78 79 81 85 89 93 97 107 111 114 119 128 129 130 132 133 143 146 148 **P**6 **S** Avera Health, Sioux Falls, SD
Primary Contact: Jason Harrington, FACHE, President and Chief Executive Officer
COO: Connie Lange, R.N., Vice President of Patient Care Services
CFO: Steve Alger, Senior Vice President and Chief Financial Officer
CMO: Steven Vander Leest, Chief of Staff
CIO: Brian McShane, IT Manager
CHR: Sarah Roche, Director Human Resources
CNO: Joni K. Mitchell, Vice President Nursing
Web address: www.lakeshealth.org
**Control:** County–Government, nonfederal **Service:** General Medical and Surgical

**Staffed Beds:** 30 **Admissions:** 1036 **Census:** 10 **Outpatient Visits:** 85379 **Births:** 125 **Total Expense ($000):** 33598 **Payroll Expense ($000):** 10853 **Personnel:** 213

### STORM LAKE—Buena Vista County

✚ **BUENA VISTA REGIONAL MEDICAL CENTER (161375)**, 1525 West Fifth Street, Zip 50588–3027, Mailing Address: P.O. Box 309, Zip 50588–0309; tel. 712/732–4030 **A**1 9 10 18 **F**3 7 8 11 13 15 18 28 29 30 31 34 40 43 45 53 55 56 57 59 63 64 68 70 74 75 76 77 78 79 81 82 84 85 86 87 93 96 98 103 107 108 110 111 115 117 118 119 128 129 130 131 132 133 135 146 147 148 **S** UnityPoint Health, West Des Moines, IA
Primary Contact: Steven Colerick, Chief Executive Officer
CFO: Krista Ketcham, Chief Financial Officer
CMO: Ingrid Franze, Chief Medical Staff
CIO: Brian Granville, Director Information Technology
CHR: Carrie Turnquist, Director Human Resources
CNO: Dawn M. Bach, MS, Chief Clinical Officer
Web address: www.bvrmc.org
**Control:** County–Government, nonfederal **Service:** General Medical and Surgical

**Staffed Beds:** 35 **Admissions:** 1308 **Census:** 19 **Outpatient Visits:** 66496 **Births:** 374 **Total Expense ($000):** 43614 **Payroll Expense ($000):** 17513 **Personnel:** 338

### SUMNER—Bremer County

★ **COMMUNITY MEMORIAL HOSPITAL (161320)**, 909 West First Street, Zip 50674–1203, Mailing Address: P.O. Box 148, Zip 50674–0148; tel. 563/578–3275 **A**9 10 18 **F**3 11 15 28 29 34 40 45 57 59 64 81 85 86 97 107 114 127 128 129 131 133 135 148 **P**5 6 **S** UnityPoint Health, West Des Moines, IA
Primary Contact: Dustin Wright, Chief Executive Officer
CFO: Dawn Everding, Chief Financial Officer
CMO: Jeff Roske, D.O., Chief Medical Staff
CHR: Robin Elliott, Personnel Officer
CNO: Lynne Niemann, Director Nurses and Patient Care
Web address: www.cmhsumner.org
**Control:** Other not–for–profit (including NFP Corporation) **Service:** General Medical and Surgical

**Staffed Beds:** 16 **Admissions:** 216 **Census:** 3 **Outpatient Visits:** 13548 **Births:** 0 **Total Expense ($000):** 12235 **Payroll Expense ($000):** 4428 **Personnel:** 84

### VINTON—Benton County

★ **VIRGINIA GAY HOSPITAL (161349)**, 502 North Ninth Avenue, Zip 52349–2299; tel. 319/472–6200, (Total facility includes 40 beds in nursing home–type unit) **A**9 10 18 **F**3 15 28 29 34 40 43 45 53 59 62 64 75 77 81 85 86 87 96 97 107 111 114 119 125 127 129 130 131 132 133 143 146 **P**6
Primary Contact: Michael J. Riege, Administrator
CFO: Barry Dietsch, Chief Financial Officer
CMO: Brian Meeker, D.O., President Medical Staff
CIO: Sherri Isbell, Chief Information Officer
CHR: Kim Frank, Chief Human Resources Officer
CNO: Tina M. Eden, Director of Nursing
Web address: www.myvgh.org
**Control:** Other not–for–profit (including NFP Corporation) **Service:** General Medical and Surgical

**Staffed Beds:** 65 **Admissions:** 390 **Census:** 41 **Outpatient Visits:** 92959 **Births:** 0 **Total Expense ($000):** 22708 **Payroll Expense ($000):** 11259 **Personnel:** 203

### WASHINGTON—Washington County

★ **WASHINGTON COUNTY HOSPITAL AND CLINICS (161344)**, 400 East Polk Street, Zip 52353–1237, Mailing Address: P.O. Box 909, Zip 52353–0909; tel. 319/653–5481, (Total facility includes 43 beds in nursing home–type unit) **A**9 10 18 **F**3 13 15 28 29 34 40 43 45 55 57 59 64 67 68 69 75 76 77 81 82 84 85 86 93 97 107 110 111 114 119 130 132 133 135 146 147 148 **P**6
Primary Contact: Dennis Hunger, Chief Executive Officer
CFO: Steve Sanders, Chief Financial Officer
CMO: Paul Towner, Chief of Staff
CIO: Makyla Maize, Director Information Services
CHR: Tracy Ousey, Director Human Resources
CNO: Barbara Griswold, Chief Nursing Officer
Web address: www.wchc.org
**Control:** County–Government, nonfederal **Service:** General Medical and Surgical

**Staffed Beds:** 68 **Admissions:** 1208 **Census:** 46 **Outpatient Visits:** 46274 **Births:** 155 **Total Expense ($000):** 26086 **Payroll Expense ($000):** 12047 **Personnel:** 275

### WATERLOO—Black Hawk County

**ALLEN MEMORIAL HOSPITAL** See UnityPoint Health – Allen Hospital

✚ △ **COVENANT MEDICAL CENTER (160067)**, 3421 West Ninth Street, Zip 50702–5401; tel. 319/272–8000, (Includes KIMBALL–RIDGE CENTER, 2101 Kimball Avenue, Zip 50702; tel. 319/291–3131) **A**1 2 3 5 7 9 10 **F**3 4 5 7 11 13 15 18 19 20 22 26 28 29 30 31 33 34 35 40 43 44 46 49 50 51 53 57 58 59 60 61 62 64 68 70 71 72 74 75 76 77 78 79 81 82 89 90 93 97 98 99 100 104 105 107 108 110 111 114 115 116 118 119 120 126 127 129 130 132 143 144 146 147 148 **P**1 6 **S** Wheaton Franciscan Healthcare, Wheaton, IL
Primary Contact: Jack Dusenbery, FACHE, President and Chief Executive Officer
CFO: Michele Panicucci, Senior Vice President and Chief Financial Officer
CMO: James A. Lehman, M.D., Vice President Medical Affairs
CIO: Gregory Smith, Chief Information Officer
CHR: Wayne C. Frangesch, Vice President Human Resources
CNO: Phyllis Doulaveris, MSN, Senior Vice President and Chief Nursing Officer
Web address: www.wheatoniowa.org
**Control:** Church–operated, Nongovernment, not–for profit **Service:** General Medical and Surgical

**Staffed Beds:** 229 **Admissions:** 8701 **Census:** 99 **Outpatient Visits:** 604879 **Births:** 1456 **Total Expense ($000):** 262211 **Payroll Expense ($000):** 118937 **Personnel:** 1751

**IA**

| Hospital, Medicare Provider Number, Address, Telephone, Approval, Facility, and Physician Codes, Health Care System | | |
|---|---|---|
| ★ American Hospital Association (AHA) membership | ○ Healthcare Facilities Accreditation Program | ⇑ Center for Improvement in Healthcare Quality Accreditation |
| □ The Joint Commission accreditation | ◇ DNV Healthcare Inc. accreditation | △ Commission on Accreditation of Rehabilitation Facilities (CARF) accreditation |

⊠ △ **UNITYPOINT HEALTH – ALLEN HOSPITAL (160110)**, 1825 Logan Avenue, Zip 50703–1916; tel. 319/235–3941 **A**1 3 5 7 9 10 **F**3 8 11 13 15 18 20 22 24 26 28 29 30 31 34 35 37 40 43 45 46 48 49 50 51 52 54 56 57 59 63 64 66 68 70 72 74 75 77 78 79 81 82 84 85 86 87 88 90 91 92 93 96 97 98 99 100 101 102 103 104 107 108 110 111 114 115 118 119 126 127 129 130 132 135 146 147 148 **P**6 8 **S** UnityPoint Health, West Des Moines, IA
Primary Contact: Pamela K. Delagardelle, President and Chief Executive Officer
COO: Jennifer Friedly, Chief Operating Officer and Vice President
CFO: Dan Carpenter, Chief Financial Officer
CMO: Timothy Horrigan, M.D., Chief Quality Officer
CIO: Daniel Norman, Regional Service Manager
CHR: Steven Sesterhenn, Vice President
CNO: Mary Hagen, R.N., VP and Chief Nursing Officer
Web address: www.allenhospital.org
**Control:** Other not–for–profit (including NFP Corporation) **Service:** General Medical and Surgical

**Staffed Beds:** 201 **Admissions:** 10087 **Census:** 107 **Outpatient Visits:** 279546 **Births:** 1050 **Total Expense ($000):** 211186 **Payroll Expense ($000):** 70769 **Personnel:** 1316

### WAUKON—Allamakee County

★ **VETERANS MEMORIAL HOSPITAL (161318)**, 40 First Street S.E., Zip 52172–2099; tel. 563/568–3411 **A**9 10 18 **F**7 11 13 15 28 31 34 35 40 45 57 59 62 64 65 75 76 79 81 107 110 119 131 132 133 134 144 146
Primary Contact: Michael D. Myers, R.N., Chief Executive Officer
CFO: Scott Knode, Chief Financial Officer
CHR: Erin Berns, Director Human Resources
Web address: www.vmhospital.com
**Control:** City–Government, nonfederal **Service:** General Medical and Surgical

**Staffed Beds:** 25 **Admissions:** 704 **Census:** 8 **Outpatient Visits:** 44430 **Births:** 148 **Total Expense ($000):** 15141 **Payroll Expense ($000):** 6552 **Personnel:** 146

### WAVERLY—Bremer County

⊠ **WAVERLY HEALTH CENTER (161339)**, 312 Ninth Street S.W., Zip 50677–2999; tel. 319/352–4120 **A**1 9 10 18 **F**3 7 8 11 13 15 28 29 34 35 36 40 43 45 50 57 59 63 64 75 76 77 81 85 86 97 104 107 110 111 114 119 127 130 132 133 134 135 144 146 147 **P**6
Primary Contact: James Atty, Chief Executive Officer
CFO: Lisa Bennett, Chief Financial Officer
CMO: Michael T. Berstler, Chief Medical Officer
CIO: Jerry Tiedt, Director Information Systems
CHR: Angie Tye, Director Human Resources
CNO: Joanne Nathem, MSN, Chief Clinical and Nursing Officer
Web address: www.waverlyhealthcenter.org
**Control:** City–Government, nonfederal **Service:** General Medical and Surgical

**Staffed Beds:** 25 **Admissions:** 893 **Census:** 9 **Outpatient Visits:** 111367 **Births:** 260 **Total Expense ($000):** 50212 **Payroll Expense ($000):** 23310 **Personnel:** 327

### WEBSTER CITY—Hamilton County

**HAMILTON HOSPITAL** See Van Diest Medical Center

★ **VAN DIEST MEDICAL CENTER (161361)**, 2350 Hospital Drive, Zip 50595–6600; tel. 515/832–9400 **A**9 10 18 **F**3 7 11 13 15 28 29 34 35 40 43 45 50 57 59 65 75 80 81 85 93 97 102 107 108 109 110 111 115 119 128 129 132 133 146 148 **P**5 6
Primary Contact: Lori Rathbun, Chief Executive Officer
CFO: Alice Heinrichs, CPA, Chief Financial Officer
CMO: Subhosh Sahai, M.D., Chief of Staff
CIO: Dave Dawson, Director Information Services
CNO: Janet Naset–Payne, R.N., Chief Nursing Officer
Web address: www.vandiestmc.org
**Control:** County–Government, nonfederal **Service:** General Medical and Surgical

**Staffed Beds:** 25 **Admissions:** 1075 **Census:** 12 **Outpatient Visits:** 21207 **Births:** 132 **Total Expense ($000):** 23854 **Payroll Expense ($000):** 8885 **Personnel:** 160

### WEST BURLINGTON—Des Moines County

⊠ △ **GREAT RIVER MEDICAL CENTER (160057)**, 1221 South Gear Avenue, Zip 52655–1681; tel. 319/768–1000, (Total facility includes 165 beds in nursing home–type unit) **A**1 7 9 10 19 **F**3 4 5 7 11 13 15 18 20 22 28 29 30 31 32 34 35 36 38 40 43 48 50 53 57 59 60 62 63 64 67 68 69 70 73 75 76 77 78 79 81 82 84 85 86 87 89 90 91 92 93 96 98 99 100 101 102 103 104 107 108 110 111 114 115 116 117 118 119 121 123 128 129 130 131 132 143 146 147 148 **P**6
Primary Contact: Mark D. Richardson, President and Chief Executive Officer
CFO: Todd J. Sladky, Chief Financial Officer
CMO: John Phillips, Chief of Staff
CIO: Gary Davis, Director Information Systems
CHR: James M. Kammerer, Vice President Support Services
CNO: Teresa Colgan, VP of Nursing
Web address: www.greatrivermedical.org
**Control:** Other not–for–profit (including NFP Corporation) **Service:** General Medical and Surgical

**Staffed Beds:** 378 **Admissions:** 6537 **Census:** 187 **Outpatient Visits:** 261000 **Births:** 569 **Total Expense ($000):** 156917 **Payroll Expense ($000):** 66069 **Personnel:** 1209

### WEST DES MOINES—Polk County

★ **MERCY MEDICAL CENTER – WEST LAKES**, 1755 59th Place, Zip 50266–7737; tel. 515/358–8000 **A**3 9 **F**3 7 11 12 13 15 18 20 22 26 29 30 39 40 41 43 44 50 56 59 61 62 64 65 68 70 75 76 77 78 79 81 85 86 87 93 96 107 108 111 114 118 119 130 132 135 143 146 **P**6 **S** Catholic Health Initiatives, Englewood, CO
Primary Contact: Robert P. Ritz, FACHE, President
COO: Kathy L. Goetz, Administrator
CFO: Michael Wegner, Senior Vice President and Chief Financial Officer
CMO: Tommy Ibrahim, M.D., Chief Physician Office
CIO: Cristina Thomas, Vice President and Chief Information Officer
CHR: Kevin Elsberry, Senior Vice President Human Resources
CNO: Deborah Willyard, R.N., Senior Director Clinical Services
Web address: www.mercywestlakes.org/
**Control:** Church–operated, Nongovernment, not–for profit **Service:** General Medical and Surgical

**Staffed Beds:** 74 **Admissions:** 3935 **Census:** 36 **Outpatient Visits:** 21829 **Births:** 311 **Total Expense ($000):** 47608 **Payroll Expense ($000):** 13561 **Personnel:** 217

### WEST UNION—Fayette County

★ **PALMER LUTHERAN HEALTH CENTER (161316)**, 112 Jefferson Street, Zip 52175–1022; tel. 563/422–3811 **A**9 10 18 **F**3 8 11 13 15 28 29 30 31 34 40 43 56 57 59 62 63 64 65 68 70 76 77 78 79 81 82 85 86 93 96 107 111 114 119 128 129 130 131 132 133 135 144 146 148
Primary Contact: Tanya Tysland, Interim Chief Executive Officer
CFO: Joni Gisleson, Director Finance
CMO: Chaudri Rasool, D.O., Chief of Staff
CIO: Kurt Chicken, Director Support Services
CHR: Cheryl Meyer, Director Human Resources
CNO: Kathy Begalske, Chief Nursing Officer
Web address: www.palmerlutheran.org
**Control:** Other not–for–profit (including NFP Corporation) **Service:** General Medical and Surgical

**Staffed Beds:** 25 **Admissions:** 378 **Census:** 5 **Outpatient Visits:** 67884 **Births:** 91 **Total Expense ($000):** 21864 **Payroll Expense ($000):** 8504 **Personnel:** 166

### WINTERSET—Madison County

★ **MADISON COUNTY HEALTH CARE SYSTEM (161326)**, 300 West Hutchings Street, Zip 50273–2109; tel. 515/462–2373 **A**9 10 18 **F**3 15 18 28 31 35 37 40 43 45 57 59 78 79 81 89 93 97 107 110 114 119 127 128 129 130 131 133 135 146 **P**6 **S** Catholic Health Initiatives, Englewood, CO
Primary Contact: Marcia Hendricks, R.N., FACHE, Chief Executive Officer
COO: Terry E. Simmons, Chief Nursing Officer
CFO: Rebekah Mitchell, Chief Financial Officer
CMO: Amy Kimball, D.O., Chief of Staff
CHR: Jennifer Hannon, Director Human Resources
CNO: Kim Hulbert, R.N., Chief Clinical Officer
Web address: www.madisonhealth.com
**Control:** County–Government, nonfederal **Service:** General Medical and Surgical

**Staffed Beds:** 25 **Admissions:** 369 **Census:** 5 **Outpatient Visits:** 58455 **Births:** 0 **Total Expense ($000):** 17800 **Payroll Expense ($000):** 7150 **Personnel:** 155

**IA**

*Many Facility Codes have changed. Please refer to the AHA Guide Code Chart.* © 2015 AHA Guide

# KANSAS

## ABILENE—Dickinson County

★ **MEMORIAL HEALTH SYSTEM (171381)**, 511 N.E. Tenth Street, Zip 67410–2153; tel. 785/263–2100, (Total facility includes 81 beds in nursing home–type unit) **A**9 10 18 **F**3 13 15 18 28 29 31 34 36 40 45 53 57 59 62 63 64 68 69 71 75 76 77 78 79 81 82 85 87 89 93 98 103 107 108 110 111 115 119 127 128 130 131 132 133 134 135 143 146 148 **P**6
Primary Contact: Mark A. Miller, FACHE, Chief Executive Officer
COO: Bob Brazil, Chief Operating Officer
CFO: Elgin Glanzer, Chief Financial Officer
CMO: W. L. Short, M.D., Chief Medical Officer
CIO: Blaine Cappel, Director Information Systems
CNO: Brenda L. Moffitt, Chief Nursing Officer
Web address: www.mhsks.org
**Control:** Hospital district or authority, Government, nonfederal **Service:** General Medical and Surgical

**Staffed Beds:** 116 **Admissions:** 778 **Census:** 83 **Outpatient Visits:** 25161 **Births:** 44 **Total Expense ($000):** 28720 **Payroll Expense ($000):** 13536 **Personnel:** 244

## ANDOVER—Butler County

**KANSAS MEDICAL CENTER (170197)**, 1124 West 21st Street, Zip 67002–5500; tel. 316/300–4000 **A**9 10 **F**3 17 18 20 22 24 29 30 40 49 51 60 64 68 70 75 77 79 81 82 85 87 93 102 107 108 112 115 119 126 130 131 146 148
Primary Contact: Badr Idbeis, M.D., Chief Executive Officer
COO: Daryl W. Thornton, Chief Operating Officer
CFO: Steven N. Hadley, Chief Financial Officer
CMO: G. Whitney Reader, M.D., Chief Medical Officer
CIO: Mike Buffington, Manager Information Technology
CHR: Norm Nevins, Manager Human Resources
CNO: Janet Kaiser, R.N., Chief Nursing Officer
Web address: www.ksmedcenter.com/
**Control:** Corporation, Investor–owned, for–profit **Service:** General Medical and Surgical

**Staffed Beds:** 58 **Admissions:** 2591 **Census:** 26 **Outpatient Visits:** 9356 **Births:** 0 **Personnel:** 225

## ANTHONY—Harper County

★ **ANTHONY MEDICAL CENTER (171346)**, 1101 East Spring Street, Zip 67003–2122; tel. 620/842–5111 **A**9 10 18 **F**40 48 53 57 64 67 81 93 97 107 119 127 128 133 **P**6
Primary Contact: J. Bryant Anderson, Administrator and Chief Executive Officer
CFO: Lori Allen, Chief Financial Officer
CMO: Sidney Stranathan, D.O., Chief of Staff
CIO: Jim Harbert, Chief Technology Officer
CHR: Kim Barwick, Vice President Human Resources
**Control:** Hospital district or authority, Government, nonfederal **Service:** General Medical and Surgical

**Staffed Beds:** 25 **Admissions:** 268 **Census:** 8 **Outpatient Visits:** 20449 **Births:** 0 **Total Expense ($000):** 8288 **Payroll Expense ($000):** 4046 **Personnel:** 89

## ARKANSAS CITY—Cowley County

★ **SOUTH CENTRAL KANSAS MEDICAL CENTER (170150)**, 6401 Patterson Parkway, Zip 67005–5701, Mailing Address: P.O. Box 1107, Zip 67005–1107; tel. 620/442–2500 **A**9 10 **F**3 11 12 13 15 29 30 34 35 39 40 45 50 52 59 64 68 70 75 76 77 79 81 82 85 87 93 107 108 110 111 115 119 129 132 133 148
Primary Contact: Virgil Watson, Chief Executive Officer
CFO: Holly Beaty, Chief Financial Officer
CMO: Kamran Shahzada, M.D., Chief Medical Staff
CHR: Clayton Pappan, Director Human Resources and Marketing
CNO: Patricia Davis, Chief Nursing Officer
Web address: www.sckrmc.org
**Control:** City–Government, nonfederal **Service:** General Medical and Surgical

**Staffed Beds:** 37 **Admissions:** 959 **Census:** 9 **Outpatient Visits:** 23827 **Births:** 134 **Total Expense ($000):** 18312 **Payroll Expense ($000):** 6830 **Personnel:** 214

## ASHLAND—Clark County

★ **ASHLAND HEALTH CENTER (171304)**, 709 Oak Street, Zip 67831–0188, Mailing Address: P.O. Box 188, Zip 67831–0188; tel. 620/635–2241, (Total facility includes 21 beds in nursing home–type unit) **A**9 10 18 **F**2 30 34 40 53 59 62 64 67 68 85 87 93 107 127 128 133 143 **P**6 **S** Great Plains Health Alliance, Inc., Wichita, KS
Primary Contact: Roger Barnhart, Chief Executive Officer
CFO: Debbie Filson, Chief Financial Officer
CMO: Daniel Shuman, D.O., Chief Medical Officer
CIO: Alan Romans, Director Information Technology
CHR: Debbie Filson, Chief Financial Officer
CNO: Patty Young, R.N., Chief Nursing Officer
Web address: www.ashlandhc.org
**Control:** Hospital district or authority, Government, nonfederal **Service:** General Medical and Surgical

**Staffed Beds:** 45 **Admissions:** 115 **Census:** 25 **Outpatient Visits:** 8688 **Births:** 0 **Total Expense ($000):** 6307 **Payroll Expense ($000):** 3273 **Personnel:** 77

## ATCHISON—Atchison County

★ **ATCHISON HOSPITAL (171382)**, 800 Raven Hill Drive, Zip 66002–9204; tel. 913/367–2131 **A**9 10 18 **F**3 11 13 15 28 29 30 31 34 35 40 45 49 50 57 59 62 63 64 65 68 70 75 76 77 79 81 82 85 87 89 92 93 97 107 108 110 111 114 118 119 127 129 130 131 132 133 135 146 147 148 **P**6
Primary Contact: John L. Jacobson, Chief Executive Officer
CFO: Gary R. Foll, Chief Financial Officer
CMO: Scott Rossow, D.O., Chief of Staff
CIO: Michael Gaul, Manager Information Systems
CHR: Pamela K. Sweger, Director Human Resources
CNO: Sandra Leggett, R.N., Chief Nursing Officer
Web address: www.atchisonhospital.org
**Control:** Other not–for–profit (including NFP Corporation) **Service:** General Medical and Surgical

**Staffed Beds:** 25 **Admissions:** 1058 **Census:** 11 **Outpatient Visits:** 72198 **Births:** 159 **Total Expense ($000):** 36620 **Payroll Expense ($000):** 16432 **Personnel:** 235

## ATWOOD—Rawlins County

★ **RAWLINS COUNTY HEALTH CENTER (171307)**, 707 Grant Street, Zip 67730–1526, Mailing Address: P.O. Box 47, Zip 67730–0047; tel. 785/626–3211 **A**9 10 18 **F**3 28 29 30 34 40 41 45 59 64 65 66 75 81 83 85 87 89 93 97 107 114 125 127 128 130 131 132 133 135 147 148 **P**6 **S** Great Plains Health Alliance, Inc., Wichita, KS
Primary Contact: Sharon K. Cox, FACHE, Chief Executive Officer
COO: Ryan Marvin, Support Services Director
CFO: Heather Prideaux, Chief Financial Officer
CMO: Brewster Kellogg, D.O., Chief Medical Officer
CIO: Destiny Schroeder, Information Systems Director
CHR: Tara Bowles, Employee Relations Director
CNO: Amber Withington, R.N., Chief Nursing Officer
Web address: www.rchc.us
**Control:** County–Government, nonfederal **Service:** General Medical and Surgical

**Staffed Beds:** 24 **Admissions:** 176 **Census:** 3 **Outpatient Visits:** 17870 **Births:** 0 **Total Expense ($000):** 7210 **Payroll Expense ($000):** 3163 **Personnel:** 58

## BELLEVILLE—Republic County

★ **REPUBLIC COUNTY HOSPITAL (171361)**, 2420 G Street, Zip 66935–2400; tel. 785/527–2254, (Total facility includes 38 beds in nursing home–type unit) **A**9 10 18 **F**3 13 15 28 29 30 31 35 39 40 45 56 57 64 67 68 75 76 77 78 79 81 85 86 87 89 93 107 108 114 119 128 130 131 133 **S** Great Plains Health Alliance, Inc., Wichita, KS
Primary Contact: Blaine K. Miller, Administrator
CFO: Barry Bottger, Chief Financial Officer
Web address: www.rphospital.org
**Control:** Other not–for–profit (including NFP Corporation) **Service:** General Medical and Surgical

**Staffed Beds:** 63 **Admissions:** 882 **Census:** 44 **Outpatient Visits:** 14663 **Births:** 57 **Total Expense ($000):** 13713 **Payroll Expense ($000):** 6533 **Personnel:** 153

---

**Hospital, Medicare Provider Number, Address, Telephone, Approval, Facility, and Physician Codes, Health Care System**

★ American Hospital Association (AHA) membership
□ The Joint Commission accreditation
○ Healthcare Facilities Accreditation Program
◇ DNV Healthcare Inc. accreditation
⇑ Center for Improvement in Healthcare Quality Accreditation
△ Commission on Accreditation of Rehabilitation Facilities (CARF) accreditation

**KS**

## BELOIT—Mitchell County

★ **MITCHELL COUNTY HOSPITAL HEALTH SYSTEMS (171375)**, 400 West Eighth, Zip 67420-1605, Mailing Address: P.O. Box 399, Zip 67420-0399; tel. 785/738-2266, (Total facility includes 40 beds in nursing home-type unit) **A**9 10 18 **F**3 11 13 15 28 29 31 34 40 43 45 48 50 56 59 62 63 64 68 69 74 76 77 81 82 84 86 87 93 98 103 106 107 111 114 119 128 129 130 132 133 148
Primary Contact: Jeremy Armstrong, FACHE, Chief Executive Officer
CFO: Eldon Koepke, Chief Financial Officer
CIO: Nate Richards, Director Information Technology
CHR: Phyllis Oetting, Director Human Resources
CNO: Jan Kemmerer, Director of Nursing
Web address: www.mchks.com
**Control:** County-Government, nonfederal **Service:** General Medical and Surgical

**Staffed Beds:** 75 **Admissions:** 1470 **Census:** 63 **Outpatient Visits:** 13191 **Births:** 89 **Total Expense ($000):** 25858 **Payroll Expense ($000):** 11530 **Personnel:** 274

## BURLINGTON—Coffey County

★ **COFFEY COUNTY HOSPITAL (170094)**, 801 North Fourth Street, Zip 66839-2602; tel. 620/364-2121, (Total facility includes 42 beds in nursing home-type unit) **A**9 10 20 **F**3 7 10 11 13 15 17 29 30 31 34 40 45 50 57 59 62 64 65 67 68 70 75 76 77 78 79 81 82 85 87 93 107 110 111 114 119 125 127 128 130 132 133 146 **P**6
Primary Contact: Leonard Hernandez, President and Chief Executive Officer
CFO: Gus Rogers, Chief Financial Officer
CIO: Eric Cole, Director Information Technology
CHR: Theresa Thoele, Director Human Resources
CNO: Melissa Hall, Chief Nursing Officer
Web address: www.coffeyhealth.org
**Control:** County-Government, nonfederal **Service:** General Medical and Surgical

**Staffed Beds:** 78 **Admissions:** 839 **Census:** 32 **Personnel:** 223

## CALDWELL—Sumner County

★ **SUMNER COUNTY HOSPITAL DISTRICT ONE (171329)**, 601 South Osage Street, Zip 67022-1654; tel. 620/845-6492 **A**9 10 18 **F**11 40 57 75 81 93 107 119 133 **P**5
Primary Contact: Thomas Henton, Chief Executive Officer
CFO: Jennifer Marcrum, Chief Financial Officer
CMO: Jim Blunk, D.O., Chief Medical Officer
CIO: Trey Watson, Network Administrator
Web address: www.schd1.com
**Control:** Hospital district or authority, Government, nonfederal **Service:** General Medical and Surgical

**Staffed Beds:** 15 **Admissions:** 149 **Census:** 2 **Outpatient Visits:** 3885 **Births:** 0 **Total Expense ($000):** 4313 **Payroll Expense ($000):** 1647 **Personnel:** 39

## CHANUTE—Neosho County

★ ◇ **NEOSHO MEMORIAL REGIONAL MEDICAL CENTER (171380)**, 629 South Plummer, Zip 66720-1928, Mailing Address: P.O. Box 426, Zip 66720-0426; tel. 620/431-4000 **A**9 10 18 21 **F**3 7 11 13 15 28 29 30 34 40 43 47 48 50 52 53 57 62 63 64 76 77 79 81 82 85 89 93 107 108 110 111 114 119 128 129 130 133 143 146 147 **P**8 **S** QHR, Brentwood, TN
Primary Contact: Dennis Franks, FACHE, Chief Executive Officer
COO: Wendy Brazil, Chief Operating Officer
CFO: Nancy Woodyard, Chief Financial Officer
CMO: Charles Van Houden, M.D., Chief Medical Officer
CIO: Gretchen Keller, Director Health Information
CHR: R. C. Rowan, Director Human Resources
CNO: Jennifer Newton, R.N., Chief Nursing Officer
Web address: www.nmrmc.com
**Control:** County-Government, nonfederal **Service:** General Medical and Surgical

**Staffed Beds:** 25 **Admissions:** 1816 **Census:** 20 **Outpatient Visits:** 38091 **Births:** 332 **Total Expense ($000):** 43522 **Payroll Expense ($000):** 18485 **Personnel:** 321

## CLAY CENTER—Clay County

★ **CLAY COUNTY MEDICAL CENTER (171371)**, 617 Liberty Street, Zip 67432-1564, Mailing Address: P.O. Box 512, Zip 67432-0512; tel. 785/632-2144 **A**9 10 18 **F**13 15 18 19 28 29 30 31 40 45 50 53 55 59 63 64 68 70 74 75 76 77 78 79 81 82 84 85 86 87 93 96 107 108 111 114 119 130 132 133 148
Primary Contact: Austin M. Gillard, Chief Executive Officer
COO: Tyce Young, Nurse Informatist
CFO: James Garbarino, Chief Financial Officer
CIO: Jim Seley, Chief Information Officer
CHR: Cindy Rush, Director Human Resources
CNO: Suzanne Ahlberg, Director of Nursing
Web address: www.ccmcks.org
**Control:** County-Government, nonfederal **Service:** General Medical and Surgical

**Staffed Beds:** 25 **Admissions:** 747 **Census:** 10 **Outpatient Visits:** 44129 **Births:** 59 **Total Expense ($000):** 17502 **Payroll Expense ($000):** 7769 **Personnel:** 174

## COFFEYVILLE—Montgomery County

⊞ **COFFEYVILLE REGIONAL MEDICAL CENTER (170145)**, 1400 West Fourth, Zip 67337-3306; tel. 620/251-1200, (Total facility includes 20 beds in nursing home-type unit) **A**1 2 9 10 **F**3 7 11 13 15 28 29 30 31 34 40 45 46 47 50 57 59 62 64 70 74 75 76 77 78 79 81 82 85 90 93 97 107 108 110 111 112 114 115 117 119 120 121 123 128 130 131 132 135 145 146 147 **P**8
Primary Contact: Mark Woodring, Chief Executive Officer
CFO: Cheryl Batchelor, Chief Financial Officer
CIO: Kris Penco, Director Information Systems
CHR: Becky McCune, Director Human Resources, Community Relations and Education
CNO: Lori Rexwinkle, Chief Nursing Officer
Web address: www.crmcinc.com
**Control:** Other not-for-profit (including NFP Corporation) **Service:** General Medical and Surgical

**Staffed Beds:** 88 **Admissions:** 2126 **Census:** 28 **Outpatient Visits:** 47319 **Births:** 213 **Total Expense ($000):** 38483 **Payroll Expense ($000):** 14949 **Personnel:** 292

## COLBY—Thomas County

★ **CITIZENS MEDICAL CENTER (171362)**, 100 East College Drive, Zip 67701-3799; tel. 785/462-7511, (Total facility includes 62 beds in nursing home-type unit) **A**9 10 18 **F**3 11 13 15 28 30 31 34 40 50 64 67 74 76 77 78 79 81 85 86 87 93 97 107 108 110 111 114 119 127 130 133 146 148 **P**6
Primary Contact: Greg Unruh, Chief Executive Officer
CFO: Patsy Evans, Comptroller
CMO: Kelly Gabel, Chief of Staff
CHR: Margaret Kummer, Chief Human Resource Officer
CNO: Jenny Niblock, Chief Nursing Officer
Web address: www.nwkshealthcare.com
**Control:** Other not-for-profit (including NFP Corporation) **Service:** General Medical and Surgical

**Staffed Beds:** 87 **Admissions:** 711 **Census:** 59 **Outpatient Visits:** 11785 **Births:** 175 **Total Expense ($000):** 26541 **Payroll Expense ($000):** 13228 **Personnel:** 278

## COLDWATER—Comanche County

★ **COMANCHE COUNTY HOSPITAL (171312)**, 202 South Frisco Street, Zip 67029-9101, Mailing Address: HC 65, Box 8A, Zip 67029-9500; tel. 620/582-2144 **A**9 10 18 **F**3 11 30 31 40 43 53 59 61 68 75 78 93 102 107 128 133 **P**6 **S** Great Plains Health Alliance, Inc., Wichita, KS
Primary Contact: Nancy Zimmerman, R.N., Administrator
CFO: Lisa Brooks, Chief Financial Officer
CMO: Daniel Schowengerdt, M.D., Chief of Staff
CIO: LaNell Wagnon, Director Medical Records
CHR: Lisa Brooks, Chief Financial Officer
CNO: Sandra Dobrinski, Director of Nursing
Web address: www.gpha.com
**Control:** County-Government, nonfederal **Service:** General Medical and Surgical

**Staffed Beds:** 12 **Admissions:** 102 **Census:** 2 **Outpatient Visits:** 12581 **Births:** 0 **Total Expense ($000):** 4948 **Payroll Expense ($000):** 2195 **Personnel:** 56

## COLUMBUS—Cherokee County

★ **MERCY MAUDE NORTON HOSPITAL (171308)**, 220 North Pennsylvania Avenue, Zip 66725-1110; tel. 620/429-2545 **A**9 10 18 **F**11 15 40 45 59 77 93 119 133 **S** Mercy Health, Chesterfield, MO
Primary Contact: Cindy Neely, Administrator
Web address: www.mercy.net/newsroom-mercy-maude-norton-hospital-quick-facts
**Control:** Church-operated, Nongovernment, not-for profit **Service:** General Medical and Surgical

**Staffed Beds:** 18 **Admissions:** 90 **Census:** 2 **Outpatient Visits:** 9814 **Births:** 0 **Total Expense ($000):** 5222 **Payroll Expense ($000):** 2383 **Personnel:** 45

## CONCORDIA—Cloud County

★ **CLOUD COUNTY HEALTH CENTER (171349)**, 1100 Highland Drive, Zip 66901-3923; tel. 785/243-1234 **A**9 10 18 **F**3 11 13 15 28 31 34 35 40 41 45 56 57 59 64 65 70 74 75 76 77 79 81 82 85 86 87 89 93 96 97 102 107 108 114 118 119 127 130 133 135 146 148 **P**6
Primary Contact: Don Bates, President and Chief Executive Officer
CFO: Pamela Blochlinger, Acting Vice President Finance
CMO: Justin Poore, D.O., Chief Medical Staff
CIO: Jenny Bergstrom, Project Manager Information Technology
CHR: Dawn Thoman, Vice President Human Resources
CNO: Michelle Metro, Vice President Nursing
Web address: www.cchc.com
**Control:** Other not-for-profit (including NFP Corporation) **Service:** General Medical and Surgical

**Staffed Beds:** 25 **Admissions:** 482 **Census:** 7 **Outpatient Visits:** 24325 **Births:** 22 **Total Expense ($000):** 14684 **Payroll Expense ($000):** 7151 **Personnel:** 154

**KS**

*Many Facility Codes have changed. Please refer to the AHA Guide Code Chart.*

## COUNCIL GROVE—Morris County

★ **MORRIS COUNTY HOSPITAL (171379)**, 600 North Washington Street, Zip 66846–1422; tel. 620/767–6811 **A**9 10 18 **F**7 11 13 15 18 28 31 35 40 45 59 64 65 70 76 77 81 87 93 94 96 107 110 111 130 132 133 146 148 **P**5
Primary Contact: James H. Reagan, Jr., Ph.D., Chief Executive Officer
CFO: Ron Christenson, Chief Financial Officer
CMO: Lora Siegle, M.D., Chief Medical Officer
CIO: Bill Lauer, Chief Information Officer
CHR: Don Zimmerman, Director Human Resources
CNO: Stephanne Wolf, Chief Nursing Officer
Web address: www.mrcohosp.com
**Control:** County–Government, nonfederal **Service:** General Medical and Surgical

**Staffed Beds:** 25 **Admissions:** 410 **Census:** 5 **Outpatient Visits:** 13247 **Births:** 35 **Total Expense ($000):** 8844 **Payroll Expense ($000):** 3154 **Personnel:** 86

## DIGHTON—Lane County

★ **LANE COUNTY HOSPITAL (171303)**, 235 West Vine, Zip 67839–0969, Mailing Address: P.O. Box 969, Zip 67839–0969; tel. 620/397–5321, (Total facility includes 14 beds in nursing home–type unit) **A**9 10 18 **F**30 40 56 67 77 93 97 127 128 131 133 **P**6 **S** Great Plains Health Alliance, Inc., Wichita, KS
Primary Contact: Donna McGowan, Administrator
CFO: Marcia Gabel, Chief Financial Officer
CMO: Paul Chinburg, M.D., Medical Director
CHR: Dina Casey, Human Resources Officer
CNO: Jennifer Whipple, Director Nursing
**Control:** County–Government, nonfederal **Service:** General Medical and Surgical

**Staffed Beds:** 31 **Admissions:** 96 **Census:** 20 **Outpatient Visits:** 12312 **Births:** 0 **Total Expense ($000):** 4873 **Payroll Expense ($000):** 2195 **Personnel:** 48

## DODGE CITY—Ford County

☒ **WESTERN PLAINS MEDICAL COMPLEX (170175)**, 3001 Avenue A, Zip 67801–6508, Mailing Address: P.O. Box 1478, Zip 67801–1478; tel. 620/225–8400 **A**1 3 5 9 10 20 **F**3 8 11 13 15 17 18 20 22 28 29 30 34 35 40 50 51 60 64 70 72 73 74 75 76 77 79 81 85 88 89 90 93 107 108 110 111 115 119 129 130 133 146 **S** LifePoint Health, Brentwood, TN
Primary Contact: Michael R. Burroughs, FACHE, Chief Executive Officer
CFO: Michael Gordian, Chief Financial Officer
CMO: Merrill Conant, M.D., Chief of Staff
CIO: Shawna Culver, Director Information Systems
CHR: Corry Israel, Director Human Resources
CNO: Edna Dunn, Chief Nursing Officer
Web address: www.westernplainsmc.com
**Control:** Corporation, Investor–owned, for–profit **Service:** General Medical and Surgical

**Staffed Beds:** 89 **Admissions:** 2350 **Census:** 22 **Outpatient Visits:** 35505 **Births:** 708 **Personnel:** 235

## EL DORADO—Butler County

☒ **SUSAN B. ALLEN MEMORIAL HOSPITAL (170017)**, 720 West Central Avenue, Zip 67042–2112; tel. 316/321–3300 **A**1 9 10 **F**3 11 13 15 28 30 40 45 59 60 62 68 69 70 76 79 81 85 92 93 96 97 98 103 107 108 110 111 115 119 121 123 130 133 144 146 148
Primary Contact: Patrick A. Auman, Ph.D., Interim President and Chief Executive Officer
COO: David Shaw, Vice President and Chief Operating Officer
CFO: Robin Crawford, Vice President and Chief Financial Officer
CIO: Mark Rooker, Director Information Systems
CHR: D. Gay Kimble, Director Human Resources
CNO: Cecilia B. Goebel, R.N., Vice President and Chief Nursing Officer
Web address: www.sbamh.com
**Control:** Other not–for–profit (including NFP Corporation) **Service:** General Medical and Surgical

**Staffed Beds:** 52 **Admissions:** 1387 **Census:** 13 **Outpatient Visits:** 83050 **Births:** 274 **Total Expense ($000):** 49326 **Payroll Expense ($000):** 20882 **Personnel:** 379

## ELKHART—Morton County

★ **MORTON COUNTY HEALTH SYSTEM (170166)**, 445 Hilltop Street, Zip 67950–0937, Mailing Address: P.O. Box 937, Zip 67950–0937; tel. 620/697–2141, (Total facility includes 80 beds in nursing home–type unit) **A**9 10 20 **F**10 11 18 28 29 34 40 45 54 56 57 59 64 67 68 70 75 81 83 86 87 93 94 96 97 102 105 107 114 119 130 131 132 133 135 143 146 148 **P**6
Primary Contact: Richard Q. Bergling, Interim Chief Executive Officer
CHR: Sonja May, Director Human Resources
Web address: www.mchswecare.com
**Control:** County–Government, nonfederal **Service:** General Medical and Surgical

**Staffed Beds:** 110 **Admissions:** 569 **Census:** 81 **Outpatient Visits:** 28347 **Births:** 0 **Total Expense ($000):** 14143 **Payroll Expense ($000):** 7114 **Personnel:** 264

## ELLINWOOD—Barton County

★ **ELLINWOOD DISTRICT HOSPITAL (171301)**, 605 North Main Street, Zip 67526–1440; tel. 620/564–2548 **A**9 10 18 **F**11 40 64 65 93 107 127 128 133 **P**6 **S** Great Plains Health Alliance, Inc., Wichita, KS
Primary Contact: Kile Magner, Administrator
CFO: Penny Stephenson, Chief Financial Officer
CMO: Christopher Brown, M.D., Chief of Staff
CIO: Becky L. Burns, Manager Health Information Management
CHR: Lindsay Owsley, Manager Human Resources
CNO: Aletha Budig, R.N., Director Nursing
Web address: www.ellinwooddistricthospital.org
**Control:** Other not–for–profit (including NFP Corporation) **Service:** General Medical and Surgical

**Staffed Beds:** 25 **Admissions:** 202 **Census:** 9 **Outpatient Visits:** 13066 **Births:** 0 **Total Expense ($000):** 5971 **Payroll Expense ($000):** 2904 **Personnel:** 64

## ELLSWORTH—Ellsworth County

★ **ELLSWORTH COUNTY MEDICAL CENTER (171327)**, 1604 Aylward Street, Zip 67439–0087, Mailing Address: P.O. Box 87, Zip 67439–0087; tel. 785/472–3111 **A**9 10 18 **F**3 11 28 29 34 35 40 45 47 53 57 59 64 67 77 85 86 87 93 97 107 114 119 127 128 130 133 146 **P**6
Primary Contact: Roger A. Masse, FACHE, Chief Executive Officer
CFO: Preston Sauers, Chief Financial Officer
CIO: Lynette Dick, Director of Support Services
CHR: Christa N. Bohnen, Director Human Resources
CNO: Amanda Thrasher, Director Nursing
Web address: www.ewmed.com
**Control:** County–Government, nonfederal **Service:** General Medical and Surgical

**Staffed Beds:** 20 **Admissions:** 673 **Census:** 8 **Outpatient Visits:** 13378 **Births:** 0 **Total Expense ($000):** 15680 **Payroll Expense ($000):** 7222 **Personnel:** 141

## EMPORIA—Lyon County

★ **NEWMAN REGIONAL HEALTH (171384)**, 1201 West 12th Avenue, Zip 66801–2597; tel. 620/343–6800 **A**9 10 18 20 **F**3 11 13 15 17 18 20 22 26 28 29 31 39 40 41 45 51 53 59 61 63 64 65 68 70 76 77 78 79 81 82 84 85 86 87 89 90 93 96 100 102 107 108 111 114 118 119 129 130 131 132 133 135 144 146 147 148 **P**6
Primary Contact: Robert N. Wright, Chief Executive Officer
CFO: Holly French, Chief Financial Officer
CMO: James Geitz, M.D., Chief of Staff
CHR: Kathy Orear, Director Human Resources
CNO: Julia Pyle, R.N., Chief Nursing Officer
Web address: www.newmanrh.org
**Control:** County–Government, nonfederal **Service:** General Medical and Surgical

**Staffed Beds:** 35 **Admissions:** 2174 **Census:** 20 **Outpatient Visits:** 100566 **Births:** 404 **Total Expense ($000):** 55744 **Payroll Expense ($000):** 24275 **Personnel:** 451

## EUREKA—Greenwood County

**GREENWOOD COUNTY HOSPITAL (171339)**, 100 West 16th Street, Zip 67045–1064; tel. 620/583–7451 **A**9 10 18 **F**3 40 43 53 57 62 81 93 96 107 119 127 128 133 135 146 **P**6
Primary Contact: Nancy J. McKenzie, Chief Executive Officer
CFO: Marian Drake, Chief Financial Officer
CIO: Jason Clark, Director Quality Improvement, Risk Management and Information System
CHR: Janel M. Palmer, Director Human Resources
CNO: Tracy Harrod, Director of Nursing
Web address: www.gwch.org
**Control:** County–Government, nonfederal **Service:** General Medical and Surgical

**Staffed Beds:** 25 **Admissions:** 553 **Census:** 7 **Outpatient Visits:** 19968 **Births:** 0 **Total Expense ($000):** 11607 **Payroll Expense ($000):** 6138 **Personnel:** 113

## FORT SCOTT—Bourbon County

⊠ **MERCY HOSPITAL FORT SCOTT (170058)**, 401 Woodland Hills Boulevard,
Zip 66701–8797; tel. 620/223–2200 **A**1 9 10 **F**3 7 11 13 15 28 29 30 34 35
40 53 57 59 62 63 65 70 72 75 76 77 79 81 82 84 85 90 93 97 107 108
110 111 114 118 119 127 129 130 131 132 133 143 144 145 146 148 **P**6
**S** Mercy Health, Chesterfield, MO
Primary Contact: Reta K. Baker, President
CFO: Shelly Hunter, Chief Financial Officer
CMO: Robert R. Nichols, M.D., Vice President Medical Affairs
CIO: Lori Sturgill, Vice President Business Partnership
CHR: Timothy Murphy, Vice President Human Resources
CNO: Patrick Callanan, Vice President Patient Care Services
Web address: www.mercykansas.com
**Control:** Church–operated, Nongovernment, not–for profit **Service:** General
Medical and Surgical

**Staffed Beds:** 61 **Admissions:** 1717 **Census:** 16 **Outpatient Visits:** 72904
**Births:** 301 **Total Expense ($000):** 34287 **Payroll Expense ($000):** 14686
**Personnel:** 250

## FREDONIA—Wilson County

★ **FREDONIA REGIONAL HOSPITAL (171374)**, 1527 Madison Street,
Zip 66736–1751, Mailing Address: P.O. Box 579, Zip 66736–0579;
tel. 620/378–2121 **A**9 10 18 **F**3 7 11 15 30 40 81 82 85 93 98 103 107 110
114 119 128 133 **S** Great Plains Health Alliance, Inc., Wichita, KS
Primary Contact: John Hart, Chief Executive Officer
CFO: Tracy Row, Manager Business Office
CMO: Jennifer McKenney, M.D., Chief Medical Officer
CIO: Tyler Row, Director Information Technology
CHR: Debbie Marr, Administrative Assistant and Director Human Resources
CNO: Ryan Duft, R.N., Chief Nursing Officer
Web address: www.fredoniaregionalhospital.org
**Control:** City–Government, nonfederal **Service:** General Medical and Surgical

**Staffed Beds:** 34 **Admissions:** 625 **Census:** 11 **Outpatient Visits:** 19870
**Births:** 0 **Total Expense ($000):** 12861 **Payroll Expense ($000):** 4244
**Personnel:** 110

## GALENA—Cherokee County

◇ **PREMIER SURGICAL INSTITUTE (170203)**, 1619 West 7th Street, Zip 66739;
tel. 620/783–1732, (Nonreporting) **A**10 21
Primary Contact: Travis W. Roderick, Chief Executive Officer
Web address: www.premiersurgicalinstitute.com/
**Control:** City–Government, nonfederal **Service:** General Medical and Surgical

**Staffed Beds:** 25

## GARDEN CITY—Finney County

⊠ **ST. CATHERINE HOSPITAL (170023)**, 401 East Spruce Street,
Zip 67846–5679; tel. 620/272–2561 **A**1 9 10 20 **F**3 8 13 15 18 20 22 29 30
31 34 35 40 45 49 51 57 59 60 63 64 65 68 69 70 73 75 77 78 79 81 82
83 84 85 86 87 91 92 93 94 96 97 98 99 100 101 102 103 107 108 109
110 111 112 113 114 115 116 117 118 119 120 121 122 123 124 125 127
129 130 131 132 135 146 147 148 **P**5 6 **S** Catholic Health Initiatives,
Englewood, CO
Primary Contact: Scott J. Taylor, President and Chief Executive Officer
CFO: Amanda Vaughan, Chief Financial Officer
CMO: Matthew C. Byrnes, M.D., Chief Medical Officer
CIO: Lance Kellenbarger, Site Director Information Systems
CHR: Kathy E. Morrison, Executive Director Human Resources
CNO: Margaret Elizabeth Prewitt, Vice President Patient Services and Chief
Nursing Officer
Web address: www.StCatherineHosp.org
**Control:** Church–operated, Nongovernment, not–for profit **Service:** General
Medical and Surgical

**Staffed Beds:** 110 **Admissions:** 3574 **Census:** 37 **Outpatient Visits:** 178033
**Births:** 773 **Total Expense ($000):** 95612 **Payroll Expense ($000):** 36142
**Personnel:** 541

## GARDNER—Johnson County

★ △ **MEADOWBROOK REHABILITATION HOSPITAL (170180)**, 427 West Main
Street, Zip 66030–1183; tel. 913/856–8747, (Total facility includes 42 beds in
nursing home–type unit) **A**7 9 10 **F**34 87 90 91 92 128 130 143 148
Primary Contact: Jon W. Scott, Chief Executive Officer
CFO: Kelly Taul, Business Manager
CMO: David Edalati, M.D., Medical Director
CHR: Carrie Moore, Director Human Resources
CNO: Lisa Perez, R.N., Director Nursing
Web address: www.meadowbrookrehab.com
**Control:** Corporation, Investor–owned, for–profit **Service:** Rehabilitation

**Staffed Beds:** 96 **Admissions:** 530 **Census:** 70 **Outpatient Visits:** 0 **Births:**
0 **Total Expense ($000):** 13819 **Payroll Expense ($000):** 5724 **Personnel:**
156

## GARNETT—Anderson County

★ **ANDERSON COUNTY HOSPITAL (171316)**, 421 South Maple,
Zip 66032–1334, Mailing Address: P.O. Box 309, Zip 66032–0309;
tel. 785/448–3131, (Total facility includes 30 beds in nursing home–type unit) **A**9
10 18 **F**7 8 11 15 29 30 34 35 40 41 43 45 56 57 59 64 65 67 75 79 81 87
91 93 97 107 108 110 114 127 130 133 **P**6 **S** Saint Luke's Health System,
Kansas City, MO
Primary Contact: Dennis A. Hachenberg, FACHE, Chief Executive Officer
CFO: Vicki L. Mills, Chief Financial Officer
CMO: Mackenzie Peterson, M.D., Chief of Staff
CHR: Karen Gillespie, Director Human Resources
CNO: Margo L. Williams, R.N., Chief Nursing Officer
Web address: www.saint–lukes.org
**Control:** Other not–for–profit (including NFP Corporation) **Service:** General
Medical and Surgical

**Staffed Beds:** 40 **Admissions:** 188 **Census:** 31 **Outpatient Visits:** 43616
**Births:** 0 **Total Expense ($000):** 19770 **Payroll Expense ($000):** 8041
**Personnel:** 152

## GIRARD—Crawford County

★ **GIRARD MEDICAL CENTER (171376)**, 302 North Hospital Drive,
Zip 66743–2000; tel. 620/724–8291 **A**9 10 18 **F**3 6 8 11 12 15 29 34 35 40
43 45 47 50 51 53 56 57 59 62 64 65 70 75 77 79 81 87 93 97 98 100
101 102 103 104 105 107 114 119 127 128 130 131 132 133 146 148 **P**6
Primary Contact: Michael E. Payne, Administrator
CFO: Holly Koch, Chief Financial Officer
CIO: Jeff Barnes, Director Information Technology
CHR: Gregory Sullivan, Manager Human Resources
CNO: Joyce Geier, Director Nursing
Web address: www.girardmedicalcenter.com
**Control:** Hospital district or authority, Government, nonfederal **Service:** General
Medical and Surgical

**Staffed Beds:** 35 **Admissions:** 721 **Census:** 14 **Outpatient Visits:** 19979
**Births:** 0 **Total Expense ($000):** 19016 **Payroll Expense ($000):** 9065
**Personnel:** 173

## GOODLAND—Sherman County

★ **GOODLAND REGIONAL MEDICAL CENTER (171370)**, 220 West Second
Street, Zip 67735–1602; tel. 785/890–3625 **A**9 10 18 **F**3 11 13 15 28 31 34
40 45 57 59 60 64 65 67 69 75 76 79 81 82 85 87 89 93 97 107 110 114
119 127 128 130 132 133 148 **P**6
Primary Contact: Donald Lee Wade, Chief Financial Officer
CFO: Donald Lee Wade, Chief Financial Officer
CIO: Christopher Biel, Chief Information Officer
CHR: Linda Taylor, Chief Human Resources Officer
CNO: Lori Gaydusek, Chief Nursing Officer
Web address: www.goodlandregional.com
**Control:** County–Government, nonfederal **Service:** General Medical and Surgical

**Staffed Beds:** 25 **Admissions:** 384 **Census:** 5 **Outpatient Visits:** 42548
**Births:** 63 **Total Expense ($000):** 16819 **Payroll Expense ($000):** 6972
**Personnel:** 155

## GREAT BEND—Barton County

**GREAT BEND REGIONAL HOSPITAL (170191)**, 514 Cleveland Street,
Zip 67530–3562; tel. 620/792–8833 **A**9 10 20 **F**3 13 15 29 30 34 40 45 57
59 64 65 70 75 76 79 81 82 89 107 110 111 114 119 127 130 135
147 148
Primary Contact: Brent Hanson, Chief Executive Officer and HIPAA Security and
Compliance Officer
COO: Adina Gregory, Chief Operating Officer
CFO: Timothy Latimer, Chief Financial Officer
CMO: Randall Hildebrand, M.D., Chief Medical Officer
CHR: Brenda Kaiser, Director Human Resources
CNO: Adina Gregory, Chief Nursing Officer
Web address: www.gbregional.com
**Control:** Partnership, Investor–owned, for–profit **Service:** General Medical and
Surgical

**Staffed Beds:** 33 **Admissions:** 1623 **Census:** 14 **Outpatient Visits:** 37265
**Births:** 311 **Total Expense ($000):** 37130 **Payroll Expense ($000):** 14031
**Personnel:** 327

KS

*Many Facility Codes have changed. Please refer to the AHA Guide Code Chart.* © 2015 AHA Guide

## GREENSBURG—Kiowa County

★ **KIOWA COUNTY MEMORIAL HOSPITAL (171332)**, 721 West Kansas Avenue, Zip 67054–1633; tel. 620/723–3341 **A**9 10 18 **F**3 7 11 40 50 53 59 64 68 107 115 127 128 133 **P**6 **S** Great Plains Health Alliance, Inc., Wichita, KS
Primary Contact: Mary Sweet, Administrator
CFO: Ron Tucker, Business Office Manager
CMO: Nizar Kibar, M.D., Chief Medical Staff
CIO: Jeremy Steven Hoover, Chief Information Officer
CHR: Cathy McFall, Human Resources Manager
CNO: Vanessa Kirk, Director of Nursing
Web address: www.kcmh.net
**Control:** Other not–for–profit (including NFP Corporation) **Service:** General Medical and Surgical

**Staffed Beds:** 15 **Admissions:** 145 **Census:** 4 **Outpatient Visits:** 9919
**Births:** 0 **Total Expense ($000):** 8081 **Payroll Expense ($000):** 3036
**Personnel:** 78

## HANOVER—Washington County

★ **HANOVER HOSPITAL (171365)**, 205 South Hanover, Zip 66945–8924, Mailing Address: P.O. Box 38, Zip 66945–0038; tel. 785/337–2214 **A**9 10 **F**2 7 40 53 67 69 81 133 **P**4
Primary Contact: Roger D. Warren, M.D., Administrator
CFO: Sheryl Adam, Chief Financial Officer
CMO: Roger D. Warren, M.D., Administrator
**Control:** Hospital district or authority, Government, nonfederal **Service:** General Medical and Surgical

**Staffed Beds:** 25 **Admissions:** 126 **Census:** 4 **Outpatient Visits:** 2172
**Births:** 5 **Total Expense ($000):** 3806 **Payroll Expense ($000):** 1941
**Personnel:** 47

## HARPER—Harper County

★ **HARPER HOSPITAL DISTRICT FIVE (171366)**, 700 West 13th Street, Zip 67058–1401; tel. 620/896–7324 **A**9 10 18 **F**3 10 29 34 35 40 43 45 46 50 53 54 57 59 64 65 67 68 75 77 79 81 84 87 90 93 97 107 111 114 119 125 127 128 130 131 133 135 146 147 148 **P**6
Primary Contact: William Widener, Administrator and Chief Executive Officer
CFO: Sandra Owen, Director Fiscal and Accounting
CMO: Ralph Imlay, M.D., Chief of Staff
CIO: Cindi Beadman, Director Medical Records
CHR: Troy Hickman, Director Human Resources
CNO: Karen Aldis, Director of Nursing
Web address: www.hhd5.com
**Control:** Hospital district or authority, Government, nonfederal **Service:** General Medical and Surgical

**Staffed Beds:** 25 **Admissions:** 274 **Census:** 9 **Outpatient Visits:** 36190
**Births:** 0 **Total Expense ($000):** 8706 **Payroll Expense ($000):** 4203
**Personnel:** 104

## HAYS—Ellis County

★ ◇ **HAYS MEDICAL CENTER (170013)**, 2220 Canterbury Drive, Zip 67601–2370, Mailing Address: P.O. Box 8100, Zip 67601–8100; tel. 785/623–5000 **A**3 5 9 10 21 **F**3 11 12 13 15 17 18 20 22 24 26 28 29 30 31 32 34 35 36 37 38 39 40 43 45 46 49 53 55 56 57 59 60 63 64 65 66 68 69 70 71 72 73 74 75 76 77 78 79 80 81 82 84 85 86 87 89 92 93 97 100 101 102 103 104 107 108 110 111 115 118 119 120 121 123 126 127 128 129 130 131 132 135 146 147 148 **P**6
Primary Contact: John H. Jeter, M.D., President and Chief Executive Officer
COO: Bryce A. Young, Chief Operating Officer
CFO: George Harms, Chief Financial Officer
CIO: Scott Rohleder, Chief Information Officer
CHR: Bruce Whittington, Vice President Human Resources
CNO: Terry Siek, MSN, Chief Nursing Officer
Web address: www.haysmed.com
**Control:** Other not–for–profit (including NFP Corporation) **Service:** General Medical and Surgical

**Staffed Beds:** 167 **Admissions:** 6348 **Census:** 67 **Outpatient Visits:** 321155
**Births:** 698 **Total Expense ($000):** 188145 **Payroll Expense ($000):** 80137
**Personnel:** 1202

## HERINGTON—Dickinson County

**HERINGTON MUNICIPAL HOSPITAL (171340)**, 100 East Helen Street, Zip 67449–1606; tel. 785/258–2207 **A**9 10 18 **F**15 28 29 40 45 57 64 77 81 93 97 107 114 115 119 127 133 148
Primary Contact: Michael J. Ryan, Chief Executive Officer
CFO: Alan Meisinger, Chief Financial Officer
CMO: John Mosier, D.O., Chief of Staff
CHR: Nicole Will, Human Resources Officer
CNO: Roni Baker, Director of Nursing
Web address: www.heringtonhospital.org
**Control:** City–Government, nonfederal **Service:** General Medical and Surgical

**Staffed Beds:** 25 **Admissions:** 345 **Census:** 4 **Outpatient Visits:** 13050
**Births:** 0 **Total Expense ($000):** 7569 **Payroll Expense ($000):** 3156
**Personnel:** 73

## HIAWATHA—Brown County

★ **HIAWATHA COMMUNITY HOSPITAL (171341)**, 300 Utah Street, Zip 66434–2314; tel. 785/742–2131 **A**9 10 18 **F**8 13 15 40 45 62 67 69 70 76 81 85 107 114 119 128 130 133 146 **P**6
Primary Contact: John Moore, Administrator
CFO: Jenny Knudson, Controller
CMO: Steffen Shamburg, M.D., Chief of Staff
CIO: Cheryl Wenger, Manager Health Information and Quality Assurance
CHR: Alison Keri, Director Human Resources
CNO: Lisa Thompson, MSN, Director of Nursing
Web address: www.hch–ks.org
**Control:** Other not–for–profit (including NFP Corporation) **Service:** General Medical and Surgical

**Staffed Beds:** 25 **Admissions:** 764 **Census:** 6 **Outpatient Visits:** 27328
**Births:** 84 **Total Expense ($000):** 24580 **Payroll Expense ($000):** 10838
**Personnel:** 205

## HILL CITY—Graham County

★ **GRAHAM COUNTY HOSPITAL (171325)**, 304 West Prout Street, Zip 67642–1435; tel. 785/421–2121 **A**9 10 18 **F**3 11 18 34 40 50 53 57 59 64 65 67 68 69 81 82 84 93 107 127 128 133 148
Primary Contact: Melissa Atkins, CPA, Chief Executive Officer
CHR: Donella Belleau, Director Human Resources
Web address: www.grahamcountyhospital.org
**Control:** County–Government, nonfederal **Service:** General Medical and Surgical

**Staffed Beds:** 20 **Admissions:** 436 **Census:** 5 **Outpatient Visits:** 984 **Births:** 1 **Total Expense ($000):** 8058 **Payroll Expense ($000):** 3990 **Personnel:** 86

## HILLSBORO—Marion County

**HILLSBORO COMMUNITY HOSPITAL (171357)**, 701 South Main Street, Zip 67063–1553; tel. 620/947–3114 **A**9 10 18 **F**3 11 29 30 34 35 40 45 47 50 57 64 65 75 77 81 82 85 86 87 93 107 114 127 130 131 133 146 **P**5 6 **S** Rural Community Hospitals of America, Kansas City, MO
Primary Contact: Marion Regier, Chief Executive Officer
COO: Johna Magnuson, Director Nursing
CIO: Marsha Setzkorn–Meyer, Director Public Relations and Marketing
CHR: Wendy McCarty, Director Human Resources
Web address: www.hchks.com
**Control:** Corporation, Investor–owned, for–profit **Service:** General Medical and Surgical

**Staffed Beds:** 10 **Admissions:** 122 **Census:** 1 **Outpatient Visits:** 6441
**Births:** 0 **Total Expense ($000):** 4925 **Payroll Expense ($000):** 2252
**Personnel:** 40

## HOISINGTON—Barton County

★ **CLARA BARTON HOSPITAL (171333)**, 250 West Ninth Street, Zip 67544–1706; tel. 620/653–2114 **A**9 10 18 **F**11 15 28 40 51 56 57 59 64 77 79 81 85 92 93 97 107 114 119 127 128 133 148 **P**6
Primary Contact: James Blackwell, Chief Executive Officer
CMO: Nathan Knackstedt, D.O., Chief of Staff
CHR: John Moshier, Director Human Resources
CNO: Jane Schepmann, Vice President and Chief Nursing Officer
Web address: www.clarabartonhospital.org
**Control:** Other not–for–profit (including NFP Corporation) **Service:** General Medical and Surgical

**Staffed Beds:** 23 **Admissions:** 500 **Census:** 7 **Outpatient Visits:** 48459
**Births:** 0 **Total Expense ($000):** 18730 **Payroll Expense ($000):** 8986
**Personnel:** 179

---

## HOLTON—Jackson County

★ **HOLTON COMMUNITY HOSPITAL (171319)**, 1110 Columbine Drive, Zip 66436–8824; tel. 785/364–2116 **A**9 10 18 **F**3 7 11 13 15 18 28 29 34 40 43 45 50 59 62 63 64 65 74 75 76 77 79 81 82 87 93 97 107 114 119 127 128 130 131 132 133 135 146 147 148
Primary Contact: Carrie L. Saia, R.N., Chief Executive Officer
CFO: Bart Kenton, Chief Financial Officer
CMO: Malia Warner, Chief Medical Staff
CIO: Holli Peters, Director Health Information Management
CHR: Gretchen Snavely, Director Human Resources
CNO: April Zeller, Director Nursing
Web address: www.holtonhospital.com
**Control:** Other not–for–profit (including NFP Corporation) **Service:** General Medical and Surgical

**Staffed Beds:** 12 **Admissions:** 359 **Census:** 4 **Outpatient Visits:** 56777 **Births:** 47 **Total Expense ($000):** 12292 **Payroll Expense ($000):** 5994 **Personnel:** 140

## HORTON—Brown County

**HORTON COMMUNITY HOSPITAL (171320)**, 240 West 18th Street, Zip 66439–1245; tel. 785/486–2642 **A**9 10 18 **F**7 15 28 29 40 45 46 64 81 93 107 114 119 127 128 133 **P**6 **S** Rural Community Hospitals of America, Kansas City, MO
Primary Contact: James D. Noble, Chief Executive Officer
CFO: Sue Kidd, Chief Financial Officer
CMO: William Buck, Chief of Staff
CHR: Barbara McClain, Human Resources
CNO: Ty Compton, Chief Nursing Officer
Web address: www.horton–hospital.com
**Control:** Corporation, Investor–owned, for–profit **Service:** General Medical and Surgical

**Staffed Beds:** 25 **Admissions:** 363 **Census:** 5 **Outpatient Visits:** 5991 **Births:** 0 **Total Expense ($000):** 6762 **Payroll Expense ($000):** 3501 **Personnel:** 67

## HOXIE—Sheridan County

**SHERIDAN COUNTY HEALTH COMPLEX (171347)**, 826 18th Street, Zip 67740–0167, Mailing Address: P.O. Box 167, Zip 67740–0167; tel. 785/675–3281, (Total facility includes 35 beds in nursing home–type unit) **A**9 10 18 **F**3 10 11 15 29 30 31 34 40 45 49 50 53 56 57 59 67 68 69 81 85 86 93 97 107 115 119 127 130 133 146 147 148
Primary Contact: Niceta Farber, Chief Executive Officer
CFO: Christine Niblock, Chief Financial Officer
CMO: Thomas R. Plumeri, Chief of Staff
CNO: Maria Zimmerman, R.N., Chief Nursing Officer
Web address: www.sheridancountyhospital.com
**Control:** County–Government, nonfederal **Service:** General Medical and Surgical

**Staffed Beds:** 53 **Admissions:** 190 **Census:** 30 **Outpatient Visits:** 5437 **Births:** 0 **Total Expense ($000):** 7591 **Payroll Expense ($000):** 4020 **Personnel:** 96

## HUGOTON—Stevens County

★ **STEVENS COUNTY HOSPITAL (171335)**, 1006 South Jackson Street, Zip 67951–2858, Mailing Address: P.O. Box 10, Zip 67951–0010; tel. 620/544–8511, (Total facility includes 83 beds in nursing home–type unit) **A**9 10 18 **F**3 11 15 28 29 30 40 50 57 67 68 81 93 107 111 119 127 128 130 133 135 146 148
Primary Contact: Linda Stalcup, Chief Executive Officer
CMO: Samer Al–hashmi, M.D., Chief Medical Staff
Web address: www.stevenscountyhospital.com/
**Control:** County–Government, nonfederal **Service:** General Medical and Surgical

**Staffed Beds:** 100 **Admissions:** 221 **Census:** 41 **Outpatient Visits:** 22044 **Births:** 0 **Total Expense ($000):** 11809 **Payroll Expense ($000):** 5341 **Personnel:** 171

## HUTCHINSON—Reno County

✠ △ **HUTCHINSON REGIONAL MEDICAL CENTER (170020)**, 1701 East 23rd Avenue, Zip 67502–1191; tel. 620/665–2000, (Total facility includes 75 beds in nursing home–type unit) **A**1 3 7 9 10 **F**3 7 10 11 13 18 20 22 24 28 29 30 31 40 43 47 48 49 50 51 60 62 63 64 67 68 70 74 75 76 77 78 79 81 82 83 84 85 89 90 93 98 102 103 106 107 108 111 114 115 119 120 121 123 125 126 128 129 130 146 148 **P**6
Primary Contact: Ken Johnson, Interim President and Chief Executive Officer
COO: Ken Johnson, Chief Operating Officer
CFO: Cassie Dolen, Vice President Finance and Chief Financial Officer
CMO: Thomas Smith, M.D., Vice President Medical Affairs
CIO: John Bissell, Chief Information Officer
CHR: Kevin Chiles, Vice President Human Resources
CNO: Julie R. Ward, MSN, Vice President Patient Care Services
Web address: www.hutchregional.com
**Control:** Other not–for–profit (including NFP Corporation) **Service:** General Medical and Surgical

**Staffed Beds:** 230 **Admissions:** 6651 **Census:** 142 **Outpatient Visits:** 124970 **Births:** 636 **Total Expense ($000):** 127984 **Payroll Expense ($000):** 43906 **Personnel:** 847

---

**SUMMIT SURGICAL (170198)**, 1818 East 23rd Avenue, Zip 67502–1106; tel. 620/663–4800 **A**9 10 **F**3 29 45 50 64 79 81 82 85 **P**2
Primary Contact: Ann Hentzen Page, M.D., Chief Executive Officer
COO: Nancy Corwin, Chief Operating Officer
CMO: Ann Hentzen Page, M.D., Medical Director
CNO: Nancy Corwin, Chief Nursing Officer
Web address: www.summitks.com/index_surgical.htm
**Control:** Corporation, Investor–owned, for–profit **Service:** Surgical

**Staffed Beds:** 10 **Admissions:** 252 **Census:** 1 **Outpatient Visits:** 6682 **Births:** 0 **Total Expense ($000):** 3690 **Payroll Expense ($000):** 1069 **Personnel:** 43

## INDEPENDENCE—Montgomery County

✠ **MERCY HOSPITAL INDEPENDENCE (170010)**, 800 West Myrtle Street, Zip 67301–3240, Mailing Address: P.O. Box 388, Zip 67301–0388; tel. 620/331–2200 **A**1 9 10 **F**1 3 4 11 12 13 15 16 17 18 28 30 32 34 35 40 45 50 53 57 59 62 63 65 67 68 70 72 73 76 77 79 80 81 84 88 89 90 91 93 97 98 107 108 110 111 114 118 119 127 128 129 130 131 133 135 143 144 146 **P**3 6 **S** Mercy Health, Chesterfield, MO
Primary Contact: Kim Day, Interim President
CFO: Shelly Hunter, Chief Financial Officer
CMO: Richenda Dawn Herren, M.D., Chief of Staff
CHR: Laura Sanders, Manager Human Resources
Web address: www.mercy.net/independenceks
**Control:** Church–operated, Nongovernment, not–for profit **Service:** General Medical and Surgical

**Staffed Beds:** 40 **Admissions:** 1183 **Census:** 11 **Outpatient Visits:** 48538 **Births:** 227 **Total Expense ($000):** 23293 **Payroll Expense ($000):** 10375 **Personnel:** 187

## IOLA—Allen County

✠ **ALLEN COUNTY REGIONAL HOSPITAL (171373)**, 3066 N. Kentucky Street, Zip 66749–1951, Mailing Address: P.O. Box 540, Zip 66749–0540; tel. 620/365–1000 **A**1 9 10 18 **F**3 11 13 15 29 30 31 34 35 40 49 56 57 59 62 63 64 65 68 70 75 76 77 78 81 82 84 85 86 87 89 93 107 110 114 119 127 129 130 132 133 146 147 148
Primary Contact: Marion A. Thompson, FACHE, Chief Executive Officer
CFO: Larry Peterson, Chief Financial Officer
CMO: Wesley Stone, D.O., Chief of Staff
CHR: Paula Sell, Director Human Resources
CNO: Patty McGuffin, R.N., Chief Nursing Officer
Web address: www.allencountyhospital.com
**Control:** County–Government, nonfederal **Service:** General Medical and Surgical

**Staffed Beds:** 25 **Admissions:** 815 **Census:** 9 **Outpatient Visits:** 20096 **Births:** 83 **Total Expense ($000):** 21756 **Payroll Expense ($000):** 6529 **Personnel:** 138

## JETMORE—Hodgeman County

★ **HODGEMAN COUNTY HEALTH CENTER (171369)**, 809 Bramley Street, Zip 67854–9320, Mailing Address: P.O. Box 310, Zip 67854–0310; tel. 620/357–8361, (Total facility includes 25 beds in nursing home–type unit) **A**10 18 **F**3 40 53 67 81 107 114 125 127 130 133 143 **P**4
Primary Contact: Teresa L. Deuel, Chief Executive Officer
Web address: www.hchonline.org
**Control:** County–Government, nonfederal **Service:** General Medical and Surgical

**Staffed Beds:** 38 **Admissions:** 323 **Census:** 26 **Outpatient Visits:** 35240 **Births:** 0 **Total Expense ($000):** 7260 **Payroll Expense ($000):** 3190 **Personnel:** 81

## JOHNSON—Stanton County

**STANTON COUNTY HOSPITAL (171343)**, 404 North Chestnut Street, Zip 67855–5001, Mailing Address: P.O. Box 779, Zip 67855–0779; tel. 620/492–6250, (Total facility includes 25 beds in nursing home–type unit) **A**9 10 18 **F**3 13 34 35 40 41 45 50 54 56 57 59 64 68 75 76 81 82 86 87 89 93 97 107 114 127 130 131 133 143 **P**6
Primary Contact: Jay Tusten, Chief Executive Officer
CFO: Barbara Anderson, Chief Financial Officer
CMO: Jose Luis Hinojosa, Chief of Staff
CIO: Marco Medina, Chief Information Officer
CHR: Camille Davidson, Director Human Resources
CNO: Marianne Mills, R.N., Chairperson
Web address: www.stantoncountyhospital.com
**Control:** County–Government, nonfederal **Service:** General Medical and Surgical

**Staffed Beds:** 40 **Admissions:** 206 **Census:** 26 **Outpatient Visits:** 16039 **Births:** 17 **Total Expense ($000):** 8911 **Payroll Expense ($000):** 4078 **Personnel:** 95

*Many Facility Codes have changed. Please refer to the AHA Guide Code Chart.* © 2015 AHA Guide

## JUNCTION CITY—Geary County

**GEARY COMMUNITY HOSPITAL (170074)**, 1102 St. Mary's Road,
Zip 66441–4196, Mailing Address: P.O. Box 490, Zip 66441–0490;
tel. 785/238–4131 **A**1 9 10 **F**3 7 8 11 12 13 15 18 19 28 29 30 32 34 35 40
45 48 50 55 56 57 59 61 62 63 64 65 68 70 75 76 77 79 81 85 86 87 97
98 103 107 108 109 110 111 113 114 115 118 119 127 129 130 131 132
133 135 144 145 146 147 148 **P**6
Primary Contact: Joseph Stratton, FACHE, Chief Executive Officer
COO: Alice J. Jensen, Chief Operating Officer
CFO: Darren K. Rumford, Chief Financial Officer
CMO: Anwar Khoury, M.D., Chief of Staff
CIO: Karl DeArmond, Director Information Systems
CHR: Teto E. Henderson, Director Human Resources
CNO: Dawn M. Engel, Chief Nursing Officer
Web address: www.gchks.org
**Control:** County–Government, nonfederal **Service:** General Medical and Surgical

**Staffed Beds:** 58 **Admissions:** 1307 **Census:** 13 **Outpatient Visits:** 24806
**Births:** 332 **Total Expense ($000):** 45182 **Payroll Expense ($000):** 20459
**Personnel:** 392

**IRWIN ARMY COMMUNITY HOSPITAL**, 600 Caisson Hill Road,
Zip 66442–7037; tel. 785/239–7000, (Nonreporting) **A**1 2 3 5 **S** Department of
the Army, Office of the Surgeon General, Falls Church, VA
Primary Contact: Colonel Barry R. Pockrandt, Commander
COO: Lieutenant Colonel Daniel G. Bonnichsen, Deputy Commander for
Administration
CFO: Lieutenant Colonel Daniel G. Bonnichsen, Deputy Commander for
Administration
CMO: Lieutenant Colonel Mark S. Ochoa, M.D., Deputy Commander, Clinical
Services
CIO: David Dougherty, Chief Information Management Officer
CHR: Hope Brunton, Chief Manpower Branch
CNO: Colonel Robert E. Dettmer, Deputy Commander for Health Services
Web address: www.iach.amedd.army.mil
**Control:** Army, Government, federal **Service:** General Medical and Surgical

**Staffed Beds:** 44

## KANSAS CITY—Wyandotte County

**KVC PRAIRIE RIDGE PSYCHIATRIC HOSPITAL**, 4300 Brenner Drive,
Zip 66104–1163; tel. 913/334–0294 **A**1 3 5 **F**32 38 98 99 106
Primary Contact: B. Wayne Sims, President and Chief Executive Officer
COO: Ryan Speier, Vice President Administration
CMO: Vishal Adma, M.D., Medical Director
Web address: www.kvc.org
**Control:** Other not–for–profit (including NFP Corporation) **Service:** Children's
hospital psychiatric

**Staffed Beds:** 100 **Admissions:** 2037 **Census:** 62 **Outpatient Visits:** 0
**Births:** 0 **Total Expense ($000):** 16487 **Payroll Expense ($000):** 6393
**Personnel:** 140

**PROVIDENCE MEDICAL CENTER (170146)**, 8929 Parallel Parkway,
Zip 66112–1689; tel. 913/596–4000 **A**1 9 10 **F**3 13 15 17 18 20 22 24 28
29 30 31 34 35 40 41 44 45 49 56 57 59 64 70 74 75 76 77 78 79 81 82
84 85 87 89 93 97 102 103 107 108 110 111 114 119 120 121 123 124
126 129 130 131 132 135 143 146 147 148 **P**6 **S** Prime Healthcare Services,
Ontario, CA
Primary Contact: Randall G. Nyp, FACHE, Chief Executive Officer
CFO: David Dulny, Chief Financial Officer
CMO: Sabato Sisillo, M.D., Chief Medical Officer
CIO: Charles Soeken, Director Information Technology
CHR: Brenda Farwell, Director Human Resources
CNO: Karen Orr, Chief Nursing Officer
Web address: www.providencekc.com
**Control:** Individual, Investor–owned, for–profit **Service:** General Medical and
Surgical

**Staffed Beds:** 162 **Admissions:** 8888 **Census:** 100 **Outpatient Visits:**
175009 **Births:** 571 **Total Expense ($000):** 146586 **Payroll Expense
($000):** 57555 **Personnel:** 824

**RAINBOW MENTAL HEALTH FACILITY (174010)**, 2205 West 36th Avenue,
Zip 66103–2107; tel. 913/755–7000, (Nonreporting) **A**5 10
Primary Contact: Jerry A. Rea, Ph.D., Interim Superintendent
CFO: Donna Dean, Chief Financial Officer
CMO: Maria Gustilo, M.D., Medical Director
CHR: Marilyn Williamson, Chief Human Resources Officer
Web address: www.srskansas.org/osh/osh–rmhf_main.html
**Control:** State–Government, nonfederal **Service:** Psychiatric

**Staffed Beds:** 36

**SELECT SPECIALTY HOSPITAL–KANSAS CITY (172005)**, 1731 North 90th
Street, Zip 66112–1515; tel. 913/732–5900 **A**1 9 10 **F**1 3 18 29 82 85 91
107 130 148 **P**6 **S** Select Medical Corporation, Mechanicsburg, PA
Primary Contact: Brian Jones, Interim Chief Executive Officer
Web address: www.selectspecialtyhospitals.com
**Control:** Corporation, Investor–owned, for–profit **Service:** Long–Term Acute Care
hospital

**Staffed Beds:** 40 **Admissions:** 443 **Census:** 35 **Outpatient Visits:** 0 **Births:**
0 **Total Expense ($000):** 19421 **Payroll Expense ($000):** 7381 **Personnel:**
129

**THE UNIVERSITY OF KANSAS HOSPITAL (170040)**, 3901 Rainbow Boulevard,
Zip 66160–7200; tel. 913/588–5000, (Includes THE UNIVERSITY OF KANSAS
HOSPITAL – INDIAN CREEK CAMPUS, 10720 Nall Avenue, Overland Park,
Zip 66211–1206; tel. 913/754–5000) **A**1 2 3 5 8 9 10 **F**3 8 11 12 13 15 16
17 18 20 21 22 23 24 25 26 27 28 29 30 31 33 34 35 36 37 38 39 40 41
43 44 45 46 47 48 49 50 51 54 55 56 57 58 59 60 61 63 64 65 68 70 72
74 75 76 77 78 79 80 81 82 83 84 85 86 87 88 89 90 92 93 96 97 98 99
100 101 102 103 104 107 108 110 111 114 115 116 117 118 119 120 121
123 124 126 129 130 131 132 135 136 138 139 141 142 144 145 146 147
148 **P**6
Primary Contact: Bob Page, Chief Executive Officer
COO: Tammy Peterman, R.N., Executive Vice President, Chief Operating Officer
and Chief Nursing Officer
CFO: Bill Marting, Senior Vice President and Chief Financial Officer
CMO: Lou Wetzel, M.D., Chief of Staff
CIO: Chris Hansen, Senior Vice President Ambulatory Services and Chief
Information Officer
CHR: Alisa Ford, Vice President Human Resources
CNO: Tammy Peterman, R.N., Executive Vice President, Chief Operating Officer
and Chief Nursing Officer
Web address: www.kumed.com
**Control:** Hospital district or authority, Government, nonfederal **Service:** General
Medical and Surgical

**Staffed Beds:** 713 **Admissions:** 30109 **Census:** 490 **Outpatient Visits:**
663360 **Births:** 1679 **Total Expense ($000):** 1243341 **Payroll Expense
($000):** 406291 **Personnel:** 6143

## KINGMAN—Kingman County

★ **KINGMAN COMMUNITY HOSPITAL (171378)**, 750 Avenue D. West,
Zip 67068–0376; tel. 620/532–3147 **A**9 10 18 **F**3 11 15 17 18 28 29 31 34
35 40 54 56 57 59 62 64 67 69 70 75 77 78 81 86 87 89 90 93 97 107
114 119 128 130 132 133 145 146 148 **P**6
Primary Contact: Edward E. Riley, Chief Executive Officer and Administrator
CFO: Kent Hudson, Chief Financial Officer
CIO: Jay Gehring, Director Information Systems
CHR: Nancy Stucky, Director Human Resources and Public Relations
CNO: Nita McFarland, Director of Nursing
Web address: www.kchks.com
**Control:** Other not–for–profit (including NFP Corporation) **Service:** General
Medical and Surgical

**Staffed Beds:** 25 **Admissions:** 483 **Census:** 8 **Outpatient Visits:** 23074
**Births:** 0 **Total Expense ($000):** 10221 **Payroll Expense ($000):** 5243
**Personnel:** 118

## KINSLEY—Edwards County

★ **EDWARDS COUNTY HOSPITAL AND HEALTHCARE CENTER (171317)**, 620
West Eighth Street, Zip 67547–2329, Mailing Address: P.O. Box 99,
Zip 67547–0099; tel. 620/659–3621 **A**9 10 18 **F**3 7 11 15 18 19 28 29 30
34 35 39 40 53 56 57 59 64 65 68 75 77 79 81 93 97 98 103 107 110 111
119 127 130 133 146 148
Primary Contact: Jimmie W. Hansel, Ph.D., Chief Executive Officer
CHR: Tammy K. Lampe, Director Human Resources
Web address: www.edwardscohospital.com
**Control:** County–Government, nonfederal **Service:** General Medical and Surgical

**Staffed Beds:** 22 **Admissions:** 427 **Census:** 14 **Outpatient Visits:** 8854
**Births:** 0 **Total Expense ($000):** 8583 **Payroll Expense ($000):** 3211
**Personnel:** 64

---

**Hospital, Medicare Provider Number, Address, Telephone, Approval, Facility, and Physician Codes, Health Care System**

★ American Hospital Association (AHA) membership    ○ Healthcare Facilities Accreditation Program    ⇑ Center for Improvement in Healthcare Quality Accreditation
☐ The Joint Commission accreditation    ◇ DNV Healthcare Inc. accreditation    △ Commission on Accreditation of Rehabilitation Facilities (CARF) accreditation

**KS**

## KIOWA—Barber County

★ **KIOWA DISTRICT HOSPITAL AND MANOR (171331)**, 810 Drumm Street, Zip 67070–1626, Mailing Address: P.O. Box 184, Zip 67070–0184; tel. 620/825–4131, (Total facility includes 29 beds in nursing home–type unit) **A**9 10 18 **F**1 2 4 16 17 29 40 45 56 64 67 70 72 73 76 80 81 85 88 89 90 92 93 97 98 107 111 119 127 128 130 133 **P**6
Primary Contact: Margaret Grisner, Chief Executive Officer
CFO: Robin Lewis, Chief Financial Officer
CMO: Paul Wilhelm, M.D., Chief of Staff
CHR: Tara Girty, Director Human Resources
**Control:** Hospital district or authority, Government, nonfederal **Service:** General Medical and Surgical

**Staffed Beds:** 39 **Admissions:** 176 **Census:** 12 **Outpatient Visits:** 6500 **Births:** 0 **Total Expense ($000):** 4877 **Payroll Expense ($000):** 2214 **Personnel:** 66

## LA CROSSE—Rush County

★ **RUSH COUNTY MEMORIAL HOSPITAL (171342)**, 801 Locust Street, Zip 67548–9673, Mailing Address: P.O. Box 520, Zip 67548–0520; tel. 785/222–2545, (Total facility includes 20 beds in nursing home–type unit) **A**9 10 18 **F**3 40 45 50 53 57 59 63 64 77 81 93 97 107 111 114 119 127 133 **P**6
Primary Contact: Brenda Legleiter, R.N., Chief Executive Officer
CFO: Lorin Haas, Chief Financial Officer
CMO: Oldrich Bubenik, M.D., Chief of Staff
CHR: David Caudill, Director Human Resources
Web address: www.rushcountymemorialhospital.com
**Control:** County–Government, nonfederal **Service:** General Medical and Surgical

**Staffed Beds:** 36 **Admissions:** 173 **Census:** 21 **Outpatient Visits:** 4592 **Births:** 0 **Total Expense ($000):** 5618 **Payroll Expense ($000):** 2540 **Personnel:** 74

## LAKIN—Kearny County

★ **KEARNY COUNTY HOSPITAL (171313)**, 500 Thorpe Street, Zip 67860–9625; tel. 620/355–7111, (Total facility includes 75 beds in nursing home–type unit) **A**9 10 18 **F**2 3 6 10 13 15 28 34 35 40 45 50 56 59 62 64 67 68 69 75 79 81 85 86 93 97 107 119 125 127 128 131 132 133 143 **P**6
Primary Contact: Benjamin Anderson, Chief Executive Officer and Administrator
CFO: ReChelle Kennedy, Chief Financial Officer
CMO: Arlo Reimer, M.D., Chief of Staff
CIO: Scott Good, Manager Information Services
CHR: Donna Winright, Director Human Resources and Senior Services
Web address: www.kearnycountyhospital.com
**Control:** County–Government, nonfederal **Service:** General Medical and Surgical

**Staffed Beds:** 100 **Admissions:** 523 **Census:** 66 **Outpatient Visits:** 42356 **Births:** 200 **Total Expense ($000):** 19530 **Payroll Expense ($000):** 9928 **Personnel:** 225

## LARNED—Pawnee County

☐ **LARNED STATE HOSPITAL (174006)**, 1301 Kansas Highway 264, Zip 67550; tel. 620/285–2131 **A**1 10 **F**30 50 53 57 61 68 75 77 86 87 98 99 101 103 106 130 132 135 143 146
Primary Contact: Thomas Kinlen, Superintendent
COO: Steve Spain, Chief Operating Officer
CMO: Sayed Jehan, M.D., Interim Medical Director
CIO: Sid Smith, Director Information Resources
CHR: Kerri Barnard, Director Human Resources
CNO: Holly Hertel, Director Nursing
Web address: www.larnedstatehospital.org
**Control:** State–Government, nonfederal **Service:** Psychiatric

**Staffed Beds:** 527 **Admissions:** 1368 **Census:** 526 **Outpatient Visits:** 0 **Births:** 0 **Total Expense ($000):** 59262 **Payroll Expense ($000):** 32117 **Personnel:** 743

★ **PAWNEE VALLEY COMMUNITY HOSPITAL (171345)**, 923 Carroll Avenue, Zip 67550–2429; tel. 620/285–3161 **A**9 10 18 **F**3 11 28 29 30 34 40 43 45 46 57 68 77 81 84 85 86 87 91 93 94 102 104 107 111 115 119 127 129 130 131 132 133 135 147 148
Primary Contact: John Hughes, Administrator
COO: Bryce A. Young, Chief Operating Officer
CFO: George Harms, Chief Financial Officer
CMO: David Sanger, M.D., Chief Medical Officer
CHR: Bruce Whittington, Vice President Human Resources
CNO: Paul Henry Carrington, Chief Nursing Officer
Web address: www.pawneevalleyhospital.com
**Control:** County–Government, nonfederal **Service:** General Medical and Surgical

**Staffed Beds:** 25 **Admissions:** 338 **Census:** 7 **Outpatient Visits:** 14919 **Births:** 0 **Total Expense ($000):** 10211 **Payroll Expense ($000):** 4834 **Personnel:** 94

## LAWRENCE—Douglas County

✦ △ **LAWRENCE MEMORIAL HOSPITAL (170137)**, 325 Maine Street, Zip 66044–1360; tel. 785/505–5000, (Total facility includes 12 beds in nursing home–type unit) **A**1 3 5 7 9 10 20 **F**3 11 13 15 18 19 20 22 26 28 29 30 31 34 35 38 39 40 43 44 45 49 50 51 54 55 56 57 59 61 64 65 69 70 74 75 76 77 78 79 81 82 84 85 86 87 89 90 93 94 96 97 100 102 107 110 111 114 115 118 119 120 124 126 128 129 130 131 132 135 146 147 148 **P**6 8
Primary Contact: Eugene W. Meyer, President and Chief Executive Officer
COO: Karen J. Shumate, R.N., Chief Operating Officer
CFO: Joe Pedley, CPA, Vice President and Chief Financial Officer
CIO: Michael Williams, Chief Information Officer
CHR: Carolyn Bowmer
Web address: www.lmh.org
**Control:** City–Government, nonfederal **Service:** General Medical and Surgical

**Staffed Beds:** 152 **Admissions:** 6875 **Census:** 64 **Outpatient Visits:** 166129 **Births:** 1119 **Total Expense ($000):** 179633 **Payroll Expense ($000):** 74332 **Personnel:** 1223

## LEAVENWORTH—Leavenworth County

☐ **SAINT JOHN HOSPITAL (170009)**, 3500 South Fourth Street, Zip 66048–5043; tel. 913/680–6000 **A**1 9 10 **F**3 8 15 18 29 30 34 40 42 44 45 46 54 56 57 59 64 68 70 74 75 77 81 84 85 93 98 103 107 114 119 130 146 147 148 **P**6 **S** Prime Healthcare Services, Ontario, CA
Primary Contact: Randall G. Nyp, FACHE, President and Chief Executive Officer
CFO: David Dulny, Chief Financial Officer
CMO: Sabato Sisillo, M.D., Chief Medical Officer
CIO: Charles Soeken, Director Information Technology
CHR: Brenda Farwell, Director Human Resources
CNO: Jodi Fincher, Vice President Patient Care Services
Web address: www.providence–health.org/sjh
**Control:** Individual, Investor–owned, for–profit **Service:** General Medical and Surgical

**Staffed Beds:** 40 **Admissions:** 1415 **Census:** 23 **Outpatient Visits:** 57459 **Births:** 0 **Total Expense ($000):** 29543 **Payroll Expense ($000):** 11721 **Personnel:** 176

✦ **SAINT LUKE'S CUSHING HOSPITAL (170133)**, 711 Marshall Street, Zip 66048–3235; tel. 913/684–1100 **A**1 9 10 **F**3 11 13 15 28 29 31 34 35 40 45 50 57 59 64 70 74 75 76 77 79 81 82 85 86 87 93 94 100 102 107 108 110 111 114 119 129 130 132 135 146 148 **S** Saint Luke's Health System, Kansas City, MO
Primary Contact: Adele Ducharme, R.N., MSN, Chief Executive Officer
CFO: Julie Murphy, Chief Financial Officer
CMO: Nicholas Brockert, President
CHR: Donna Kunz, Director Human Resources
CNO: Karin Sundblom, Chief Nursing Officer
Web address: www.https://www.saintlukeshealthsystem.org/location/cushing–memorial–hospital
**Control:** Other not–for–profit (including NFP Corporation) **Service:** General Medical and Surgical

**Staffed Beds:** 25 **Admissions:** 1203 **Census:** 11 **Outpatient Visits:** 31680 **Births:** 151 **Total Expense ($000):** 32426 **Payroll Expense ($000):** 11990 **Personnel:** 199

**VETERANS AFFAIRS EASTERN KANSAS HEALTH CARE SYSTEM–DWIGHT D. EISENHOWER VETERANS AFFAIRS MEDICAL CENTER** See Veterans Affairs Eastern Kansas Health Care System, Topeka

## LEAWOOD—Johnson County

☐ **DOCTOR'S HOSPITAL (170194)**, 4901 College Boulevard, Zip 66211–1602; tel. 913/529–1801 **A**1 10 **F**39 79 81 82 111 **P**5
Primary Contact: Phil Harness, Chief Executive Officer
Web address: www.dshospital.net
**Control:** Partnership, Investor–owned, for–profit **Service:** General Medical and Surgical

**Staffed Beds:** 9 **Admissions:** 165 **Census:** 1 **Outpatient Visits:** 12170 **Births:** 0 **Total Expense ($000):** 18982 **Payroll Expense ($000):** 2439 **Personnel:** 45

**KANSAS CITY ORTHOPAEDIC INSTITUTE (170188)**, 3651 College Boulevard, Zip 66211–1910; tel. 913/338–4100 **A**3 5 9 10 **F**29 77 79 81 82 93 111
Primary Contact: Charles E. Rhoades, M.D., Chief Executive Officer
CIO: Jim Leveling, Director Information Technology
CHR: Laura Sinclair, Director Human Resources
Web address: www.kcoi.com
**Control:** Partnership, Investor–owned, for–profit **Service:** Orthopedic

**Staffed Beds:** 9 **Admissions:** 749 **Census:** 5 **Outpatient Visits:** 30407 **Births:** 0 **Personnel:** 112

**KS**

*Many Facility Codes have changed. Please refer to the AHA Guide Code Chart.* © 2015 AHA Guide

## LENEXA—Johnson County

☐ **MINIMALLY INVASIVE SURGERY CENTER (170199)**, 11217 Lakeview Avenue, Zip 66219–1399; tel. 913/322–7401 **A**1 10 **F**18 26 31 45 64 68 70 78 81 82 85 86 107 111 115 119 **P**6
Primary Contact: Parajeet Sabharrwal, Administrator
Web address: www.laplose.com/
**Control:** State–Government, nonfederal **Service:** Surgical

**Staffed Beds:** 9 **Admissions:** 133 **Census:** 1 **Outpatient Visits:** 1450 **Births:** 0 **Personnel:** 24

## LEOTI—Wichita County

★ **WICHITA COUNTY HEALTH CENTER (171306)**, 211 East Earl Street, Zip 67861–9620; tel. 620/375–2233, (Total facility includes 15 beds in nursing home–type unit) **A**9 10 18 **F**2 3 11 29 34 35 40 41 45 50 56 57 59 64 69 75 77 86 87 93 97 102 107 119 127 130 133 135 146 148 **P**6
Primary Contact: Tyson Sterling, Chief Executive Officer
CFO: Janice Campas, Chief Financial Officer
CMO: Jeffrey Alpert, M.D., Medical Director
CHR: Patti Whalen, Manager Human Resources
CNO: Teresa Clark, Director of Nursing
Web address: www.wichitacountyhealthcenter.com
**Control:** County–Government, nonfederal **Service:** General Medical and Surgical

**Staffed Beds:** 40 **Admissions:** 111 **Census:** 15 **Outpatient Visits:** 6178 **Births:** 0 **Total Expense ($000):** 7041 **Payroll Expense ($000):** 3598 **Personnel:** 85

## LIBERAL—Seward County

☐ **SOUTHWEST MEDICAL CENTER (170068)**, 315 West 15th Street, Zip 67901–2455, Mailing Address: Box 1340, Zip 67905–1340; tel. 620/624–1651, (Total facility includes 18 beds in nursing home–type unit) **A**1 9 10 **F**1 3 4 11 13 15 16 17 28 29 34 40 45 48 49 57 59 67 68 70 72 73 75 76 77 79 80 81 85 87 88 89 90 93 96 98 103 104 107 108 110 111 114 118 119 128 129 130 131 145
Primary Contact: William Ermann, President and Chief Executive Officer
COO: Robert Whitaker, Vice President of Operations
CFO: Amber Williams, Vice President and Chief Financial Officer
CHR: Lisa L. Mathes, Human Resources Director
CNO: Jo L. Harrison, Vice President of Patient Care Services
Web address: www.swmedcenter.com
**Control:** County–Government, nonfederal **Service:** General Medical and Surgical

**Staffed Beds:** 101 **Admissions:** 2122 **Census:** 17 **Outpatient Visits:** 45967 **Births:** 762 **Total Expense ($000):** 42144 **Payroll Expense ($000):** 17640 **Personnel:** 364

## LINCOLN—Lincoln County

**LINCOLN COUNTY HOSPITAL (171360)**, 624 North Second Street, Zip 67455–1738, Mailing Address: P.O. Box 406, Zip 67455–0406; tel. 785/524–4403 **A**9 10 18 **F**11 34 40 57 69 107 114 119 127 128 133 **P**6
Primary Contact: Steven L. Granzow, Chief Executive Officer
CFO: Tawnya Seitz, Chief Financial Officer
CNO: Christa Haesemeyer, Chief Nursing Officer
Web address: www.lincolncountyhospital.net
**Control:** County–Government, nonfederal **Service:** General Medical and Surgical

**Staffed Beds:** 14 **Admissions:** 163 **Census:** 2 **Outpatient Visits:** 5427 **Births:** 0 **Total Expense ($000):** 7197 **Payroll Expense ($000):** 2851 **Personnel:** 76

## LINDSBORG—Mcpherson County

★ **LINDSBORG COMMUNITY HOSPITAL (171358)**, 605 West Lincoln Street, Zip 67456–2328; tel. 785/227–3308 **A**9 10 18 **F**3 28 29 40 53 59 62 64 65 67 81 93 97 107 115 119 128 130 133 144 **P**6
Primary Contact: Larry VanDerWege, Administrator
CFO: Laraine Gengler, Chief Financial Officer
CIO: Jeremy Snapp, Director Information Systems
CHR: Brad Malm, Director Human Resources and Education
CNO: Beth Hedberg, R.N., Director Nursing
Web address: www.lindsborghospital.org
**Control:** Other not–for–profit (including NFP Corporation) **Service:** General Medical and Surgical

**Staffed Beds:** 25 **Admissions:** 262 **Census:** 4 **Outpatient Visits:** 18094 **Births:** 0 **Total Expense ($000):** 8010 **Payroll Expense ($000):** 4327 **Personnel:** 89

## LYONS—Rice County

★ **HOSPITAL DISTRICT ONE OF RICE COUNTY (171330)**, 619 South Clark Street, Zip 67554–3003, Mailing Address: P.O. Box 828, Zip 67554–0828; tel. 620/257–5173 **A**9 10 18 **F**1 3 4 10 13 16 17 29 30 34 35 40 43 45 57 67 70 72 73 75 76 77 80 81 88 89 90 93 98 107 125 127 128 130 132 133 143
Primary Contact: George M. Stover, Chief Executive Officer
CFO: Terry Pound, Chief Financial Officer
CMO: Stacy Dashiell, M.D., Chief of Staff
CNO: Judy Hogdson, R.N., Chief Nursing Officer
Web address: www.ricecountyhospital.com
**Control:** Hospital district or authority, Government, nonfederal **Service:** General Medical and Surgical

**Staffed Beds:** 25 **Admissions:** 387 **Census:** 15 **Outpatient Visits:** 14486 **Births:** 83 **Total Expense ($000):** 13697 **Payroll Expense ($000):** 6779 **Personnel:** 128

## MANHATTAN—Riley County

**MANHATTAN SURGICAL (170190)**, 1829 College Avenue, Zip 66502–3381; tel. 785/776–5100 **A**9 10 **F**45 79 81 82
Primary Contact: Scott Chapman, Administrator
Web address: www.manhattansurgical.com
**Control:** Partnership, Investor–owned, for–profit **Service:** Surgical

**Staffed Beds:** 13 **Admissions:** 381 **Census:** 2 **Outpatient Visits:** 9474 **Births:** 0 **Personnel:** 79

★ ○ **VIA CHRISTI HOSPITAL MANHATTAN, INC. (170142)**, 1823 College Avenue, Zip 66502–3346; tel. 785/776–3322 **A**9 10 11 19 **F**3 7 11 12 13 15 18 20 22 28 29 30 31 34 35 37 40 41 44 45 49 50 51 60 67 70 73 76 77 79 81 82 83 84 85 86 87 89 90 93 95 96 102 104 107 108 109 110 111 115 119 126 129 130 132 133 145 146 147 148 **S** Ascension Health, Saint Louis, MO
Primary Contact: John R. Broberg, FACHE, Senior Administrator
CFO: James Fraser, Administrator Finance
CIO: Andy Gagnon, Director Information Technology
CHR: Renee Reed, Director Human Resources
Web address: www.https://www.viachristi.org/manhattan
**Control:** Other not–for–profit (including NFP Corporation) **Service:** General Medical and Surgical

**Staffed Beds:** 100 **Admissions:** 4846 **Census:** 46 **Outpatient Visits:** 89291 **Births:** 1072 **Total Expense ($000):** 70741 **Payroll Expense ($000):** 31708 **Personnel:** 450

## MANKATO—Jewell County

**JEWELL COUNTY HOSPITAL (171309)**, 100 Crestvue Avenue, Zip 66956–2407, Mailing Address: P.O. Box 327, Zip 66956–0327; tel. 785/378–3137 **A**9 10 18 **F**2 3 29 40 50 64 67 75 77 87 93 107 127 128 130 133 148 **P**6
Primary Contact: Doyle L. McKimmy, FACHE, Chief Executive Officer
COO: Eric Borden, Chief Operating Officer and Chief Financial Officer
CFO: Eric Borden, Chief Operating Officer and Chief Financial Officer
Web address: www.jewellcountyhospital.com
**Control:** County–Government, nonfederal **Service:** General Medical and Surgical

**Staffed Beds:** 25 **Admissions:** 88 **Census:** 20 **Outpatient Visits:** 9227 **Births:** 0 **Total Expense ($000):** 4213 **Payroll Expense ($000):** 2177 **Personnel:** 63

## MARION—Marion County

★ **ST. LUKE HOSPITAL AND LIVING CENTER (171356)**, 535 South Freeborn, Zip 66861–1256; tel. 620/382–2177, (Total facility includes 32 beds in nursing home–type unit) **A**9 10 18 **F**3 11 15 28 29 34 40 43 45 56 57 59 62 64 67 68 75 77 81 85 97 102 107 108 110 114 119 127 128 133 135 143 146 147 148 **P**6 **S** QHR, Brentwood, TN
Primary Contact: Jeremy Ensey, Chief Executive Officer
CFO: Bev Reid, Chief Financial Officer
CMO: Don Hodson, M.D., Chief Medical Officer
CIO: Jeff Methvin, Manager Information Technology
CHR: Sharon Zogelman, Director Human Resources
Web address: www.slhmarion.org
**Control:** Hospital district or authority, Government, nonfederal **Service:** General Medical and Surgical

**Staffed Beds:** 37 **Admissions:** 171 **Census:** 32 **Outpatient Visits:** 25068 **Births:** 0 **Total Expense ($000):** 9330 **Payroll Expense ($000):** 4034 **Personnel:** 126

---

**Hospital, Medicare Provider Number, Address, Telephone, Approval, Facility, and Physician Codes, Health Care System**

★ American Hospital Association (AHA) membership
☐ The Joint Commission accreditation
○ Healthcare Facilities Accreditation Program
◇ DNV Healthcare Inc. accreditation
⇑ Center for Improvement in Healthcare Quality Accreditation
△ Commission on Accreditation of Rehabilitation Facilities (CARF) accreditation

**KS**

## MARYSVILLE—Marshall County

★ **COMMUNITY MEMORIAL HEALTHCARE (171363)**, 708 North 18th Street, Zip 66508–1338; tel. 785/562–2311 **A**9 10 18 **F**3 13 15 28 29 30 31 34 35 40 43 45 47 50 57 59 62 64 68 69 75 76 77 78 79 81 85 87 93 94 97 107 108 114 119 127 128 129 130 131 132 133 135 146 147 148 **P**6
Primary Contact: Curtis R. Hawkinson, Chief Executive Officer
CFO: Bev Fiferlick, Chief Financial Officer
CMO: Kenneth Duensing, Chief of Staff
CIO: Colleen Behrens, Director Information Technology
CHR: Jessie Schneider, Director Human Resources
CNO: Diane Luebcke, R.N., Director Nursing
Web address: www.cmhcare.org
**Control:** Other not–for–profit (including NFP Corporation) **Service:** General Medical and Surgical

| | |
|---|---|
| **Staffed Beds:** 25 **Admissions:** 694 **Census:** 9 **Outpatient Visits:** 25523 **Births:** 70 **Total Expense ($000):** 20006 **Payroll Expense ($000):** 9248 **Personnel:** 194 | |

## MEADE—Meade County

★ **MEADE DISTRICT HOSPITAL (171321)**, 510 East Carthage Street, Zip 67864–6401, Mailing Address: P.O. Box 820, Zip 67864–0820; tel. 620/873–2141, (Total facility includes 45 beds in nursing home–type unit) **A**9 10 18 **F**3 15 28 29 34 35 40 45 53 56 57 59 62 64 79 81 82 85 87 93 107 108 114 119 127 128 130 131 133 143 148 **P**6
Primary Contact: Steve Stewart, Administrator
CIO: Matt Bobo, Chief Information Officer
Web address: www.meadehospital.com
**Control:** Hospital district or authority, Government, nonfederal **Service:** General Medical and Surgical

| | |
|---|---|
| **Staffed Beds:** 65 **Admissions:** 255 **Census:** 42 **Outpatient Visits:** 15804 **Births:** 0 **Total Expense ($000):** 13897 **Payroll Expense ($000):** 7105 **Personnel:** 184 | |

## MEDICINE LODGE—Barber County

★ **MEDICINE LODGE MEMORIAL HOSPITAL (171334)**, 710 North Walnut Street, Zip 67104–1019; tel. 620/886–3771 **A**9 10 18 **F**3 7 11 40 44 45 56 64 81 93 107 119 127 128 133 148 **P**6 **S** Great Plains Health Alliance, Inc., Wichita, KS
Primary Contact: Kevin A. White, Administrator
CFO: Thomas G. Lee, Chief Financial Officer
CHR: Johnnie Davis, Director Human Resources
CNO: Kathryn I. Burns, R.N., Director of Nursing
Web address: www.mlmh.net/
**Control:** Hospital district or authority, Government, nonfederal **Service:** General Medical and Surgical

| | |
|---|---|
| **Staffed Beds:** 25 **Admissions:** 232 **Census:** 11 **Outpatient Visits:** 23452 **Births:** 0 **Total Expense ($000):** 9575 **Payroll Expense ($000):** 4502 **Personnel:** 94 | |

## MINNEAPOLIS—Ottawa County

★ **OTTAWA COUNTY HEALTH CENTER (171328)**, 215 East Eighth, Zip 67467–1902, Mailing Address: P.O. Box 290, Zip 67467–0290; tel. 785/392–2122, (Total facility includes 17 beds in nursing home–type unit) **A**9 10 18 **F**10 28 35 40 53 56 62 64 67 85 86 93 128 130 133 143 **S** Great Plains Health Alliance, Inc., Wichita, KS
Primary Contact: Jody Parks, Administrator
CFO: Cheryl Lanoue, Chief Financial Officer
CIO: Linda Wright, Director Information
CNO: Marlene Gawith, Director of Nursing
Web address: www.ottawacountyhealthcenter.com
**Control:** Other not–for–profit (including NFP Corporation) **Service:** General Medical and Surgical

| | |
|---|---|
| **Staffed Beds:** 42 **Admissions:** 189 **Census:** 28 **Outpatient Visits:** 10217 **Births:** 0 **Total Expense ($000):** 5879 **Payroll Expense ($000):** 2671 **Personnel:** 75 | |

## MINNEOLA—Ford County

★ **MINNEOLA DISTRICT HOSPITAL (171368)**, 212 Main Street, Zip 67865–8511, Mailing Address: P.O. Box 127, Zip 67865–0127; tel. 620/885–4264, (Total facility includes 36 beds in nursing home–type unit) **A**9 10 18 **F**13 29 40 45 46 56 57 64 65 67 81 83 93 102 107 127 128 130 133 148 **P**6 **S** Great Plains Health Alliance, Inc., Wichita, KS
Primary Contact: Deborah Bruner, Chief Executive Officer and Administrator
CFO: Marion Blanton, Chief Financial Officer
CMO: Tony Luna, M.D., Chief of Staff
CHR: Vena Harris, Director Human Resources
Web address: www.minneolahealthcare.com
**Control:** Hospital district or authority, Government, nonfederal **Service:** General Medical and Surgical

| | |
|---|---|
| **Staffed Beds:** 54 **Admissions:** 433 **Census:** 39 **Outpatient Visits:** 23653 **Births:** 13 **Total Expense ($000):** 10651 **Payroll Expense ($000):** 5491 **Personnel:** 123 | |

## MOUNDRIDGE—Mcpherson County

★ **MERCY HOSPITAL (170075)**, 218 East Pack Street, Zip 67107–8815, Mailing Address: P.O. Box 180, Zip 67107–0180; tel. 620/345–6391 **A**9 10 **F**4 13 16 17 29 30 40 45 67 70 72 73 76 80 81 88 89 90 93 98 128 130 133
Primary Contact: Doyle K. Johnson, Administrator
CFO: Royce Holdeman, Chief Financial Officer
Web address: www.mercyh.org/
**Control:** Church–operated, Nongovernment, not–for profit **Service:** General Medical and Surgical

| | |
|---|---|
| **Staffed Beds:** 18 **Admissions:** 261 **Census:** 3 **Outpatient Visits:** 7520 **Births:** 28 **Total Expense ($000):** 3242 **Payroll Expense ($000):** 1451 **Personnel:** 35 | |

## NEODESHA—Wilson County

★ **WILSON MEDICAL CENTER (171344)**, 2600 Ottawa Road, Zip 66757–1897, Mailing Address: P.O. Box 360, Zip 66757–0360; tel. 620/325–2611 **A**9 10 18 **F**3 11 15 29 34 35 40 45 53 57 59 64 81 82 85 89 93 107 108 110 114 119 127 128 132 133 148 **S** QHR, Brentwood, TN
Primary Contact: Dennis R. Shelby, Chief Executive Officer
CFO: John Gutschenritter, Chief Financial Officer
CIO: Julie Quanstrom, Director Information Systems
CHR: Laura Dean, Director Human Resources
CNO: Temple Monroe, Director of Nursing Operations
Web address: www.wilsonmedical.org
**Control:** County–Government, nonfederal **Service:** General Medical and Surgical

| | |
|---|---|
| **Staffed Beds:** 15 **Admissions:** 253 **Census:** 5 **Outpatient Visits:** 16896 **Births:** 0 **Total Expense ($000):** 12902 **Payroll Expense ($000):** 5272 **Personnel:** 123 | |

## NESS CITY—Ness County

★ **NESS COUNTY HOSPITAL (171336)**, 312 Custer Street, Zip 67560–1654; tel. 785/798–2291, (Total facility includes 43 beds in nursing home–type unit) **A**9 10 18 **F**3 7 15 40 45 59 62 67 93 111 114 119 125 127 128 133
Primary Contact: Curt Thomas, Administrator
CFO: Debra Frank, Chief Financial Officer
CMQ: Mikhail Imseis, M.D., Chief of Staff
CIO: Vicki Howe, Health Information Management
CHR: Shelly McDonald, Chief Human Resources Officer
CNO: Brenda Dinges, Director of Nursing
Web address: www.nchospital.org
**Control:** Hospital district or authority, Government, nonfederal **Service:** General Medical and Surgical

| | |
|---|---|
| **Staffed Beds:** 63 **Admissions:** 188 **Census:** 38 **Outpatient Visits:** 10257 **Births:** 0 **Total Expense ($000):** 8516 **Payroll Expense ($000):** 3780 **Personnel:** 102 | |

## NEWTON—Harvey County

★ ○ **NEWTON MEDICAL CENTER (170103)**, 600 Medical Center Drive, Zip 67114–8780, Mailing Address: P.O. Box 308, Zip 67114–0308; tel. 316/283–2700 **A**9 10 11 **F**3 8 13 15 20 22 28 29 30 40 45 49 51 59 64 68 70 73 75 76 79 81 85 86 90 103 107 108 110 111 115 118 119 126 130 131 133 146 147 148 **P**6
Primary Contact: Steven G. Kelly, President and Chief Executive Officer
CFO: Todd Kasitz, Vice President Finance
CIO: Mike Cottle, Chief Information Officer
CNO: Vallerie L. Gleason, R.N., Chief Nursing Officer
Web address: www.newtonmedicalcenter.com
**Control:** Other not–for–profit (including NFP Corporation) **Service:** General Medical and Surgical

| | |
|---|---|
| **Staffed Beds:** 103 **Admissions:** 2727 **Census:** 42 **Outpatient Visits:** 54352 **Births:** 509 **Total Expense ($000):** 66524 **Payroll Expense ($000):** 31682 **Personnel:** 619 | |

☐ **PRAIRIE VIEW (174016)**, 1901 East First Street, Zip 67114–5010, Mailing Address: P.O. Box 467, Zip 67114–0467; tel. 316/284–6400, (Nonreporting) **A**1 9 10
Primary Contact: Jessie Kaye, Chief Executive Officer
CFO: Lisa Ramsey, Chief Financial Officer
CMO: Gary Fast, M.D., Medical Director
CHR: Joy Robb, Vice President Human Resources
Web address: www.prairieview.org
**Control:** Other not–for–profit (including NFP Corporation) **Service:** Psychiatric

| | |
|---|---|
| **Staffed Beds:** 38 | |

*Many Facility Codes have changed. Please refer to the AHA Guide Code Chart.* © 2015 AHA Guide

## NORTON—Norton County

★ **NORTON COUNTY HOSPITAL (171348)**, 102 East Holme, Zip 67654–1406, Mailing Address: P.O. Box 250, Zip 67654–0250; tel. 785/877–3351 **A**9 10 18 **F**3 13 15 28 29 30 31 34 35 40 45 50 56 59 64 65 67 69 76 78 79 81 82 86 93 107 110 119 127 128 129 130 131 133 146 148 **P**6
Primary Contact: Ryan Stover, Chief Executive Officer
CHR: Shannan Hempler, Director Human Resources
Web address: www.ntcohosp.com
**Control:** County–Government, nonfederal **Service:** General Medical and Surgical

**Staffed Beds:** 25 **Admissions:** 407 **Census:** 9 **Outpatient Visits:** 65410
**Births:** 71 **Total Expense ($000):** 11595 **Payroll Expense ($000):** 5854
**Personnel:** 127

## OAKLEY—Logan County

**LOGAN COUNTY HOSPITAL (171326)**, 211 Cherry Street, Zip 67748–1201; tel. 785/672–3211, (Total facility includes 42 beds in nursing home–type unit) **A**9 10 18 **F**3 26 27 28 40 45 50 53 64 67 69 81 93 107 127 130 133 143 148 **P**6
Primary Contact: Meldon L. Snow, Chief Executive Officer
COO: Aimee Zimmerman, R.N., Chief Operations Officer
CMO: Celeste Rains, D.O., Chief of Staff
CIO: Terry Grace, Director Information Technology
CHR: Steve Allison, Director Human Resources
CNO: Marcia Kruse, R.N., Director Nursing
Web address: www.logancountyhospital.org
**Control:** County–Government, nonfederal **Service:** General Medical and Surgical

**Staffed Beds:** 59 **Admissions:** 281 **Census:** 40 **Outpatient Visits:** 10945
**Births:** 0 **Total Expense ($000):** 12864 **Payroll Expense ($000):** 7056
**Personnel:** 166

## OBERLIN—Decatur County

**DECATUR HEALTH SYSTEMS (171352)**, 810 West Columbia Street, Zip 67749–2450, Mailing Address: P.O. Box 268, Zip 67749–0268; tel. 785/475–2208, (Total facility includes 37 beds in nursing home–type unit) **A**9 10 18 **F**3 15 29 31 34 35 40 45 53 56 57 64 69 75 78 81 84 85 86 93 107 110 114 127 130 133 135 **P**6
Primary Contact: Johnathan Owens, Chief Executive Officer
CFO: Amanda Fortin, Manager Finance
CMO: Elizabeth Sliter, M.D., Chairman Medical Staff
CIO: Natasha Weishapl, Manager Business Office and Human Resources
CHR: Natasha Weishapl, Manager Business Office and Human Resources
Web address: www.decaturhealthsystems.org
**Control:** City–County, Government, nonfederal **Service:** General Medical and Surgical

**Staffed Beds:** 61 **Admissions:** 217 **Census:** 28 **Outpatient Visits:** 7156
**Births:** 0 **Total Expense ($000):** 7857 **Payroll Expense ($000):** 4215
**Personnel:** 91

## OLATHE—Johnson County

☐ **OLATHE MEDICAL CENTER (170049)**, 20333 West 151st Street, Zip 66061–5350; tel. 913/791–4200 **A**1 2 5 9 10 **F**3 8 11 12 13 15 18 20 22 24 26 28 29 30 31 34 35 39 40 41 45 46 47 48 49 56 57 58 59 61 62 63 64 65 68 70 74 75 76 77 78 79 81 82 84 85 86 87 89 92 93 107 108 110 111 115 116 117 118 119 120 121 129 130 131 132 135 144 145 146 147 148
Primary Contact: Frank H. Devocelle, President and Chief Executive Officer
COO: John Staton, Senior Vice President Operations
CFO: Tierney Lynn Grasser, Senior Vice President and Chief Financial Officer
CMO: James L. Wetzel, M.D., Vice President, Chief Medical Officer
CIO: Randy Rahman, Vice President and Chief Information Officer
CHR: David Klimek, Vice President Human Resources
CNO: Dorothy Carey, Senior Vice President and Chief Nursing Officer
Web address: www.ohsi.com
**Control:** Other not–for–profit (including NFP Corporation) **Service:** General Medical and Surgical

**Staffed Beds:** 235 **Admissions:** 10401 **Census:** 113 **Outpatient Visits:** 311239 **Births:** 1171 **Personnel:** 1415

## ONAGA—Pottawatomie County

★ **COMMUNITY HEALTHCARE SYSTEM (171354)**, 120 West Eighth Street, Zip 66521–9574; tel. 785/889–4272, (Total facility includes 78 beds in nursing home–type unit) **A**9 10 18 **F**2 3 5 6 10 11 12 13 15 29 31 32 34 35 36 40 43 45 50 53 56 57 59 62 64 65 67 74 75 77 78 81 82 84 85 86 87 93 97 99 100 101 102 103 104 105 106 107 110 114 119 125 127 128 130 131 132 133 134 135 143 144 145 146 147 148 **P**6
Primary Contact: Todd Willert, Chief Executive Officer
COO: Marcia S. Walsh, M.P.H., Chief Operating Officer
CFO: Monica Holthaus, Chief Financial Officer
CMO: Marcus Weiser, D.O., Chief of Staff
CIO: Rod Evans, Chief Information Officer
CHR: Terry D. Bernatis, Director Human Resources
CNO: Rosalind Lewis, R.N., Chief Nursing Officer
Web address: www.chcsks.org
**Control:** Other not–for–profit (including NFP Corporation) **Service:** General Medical and Surgical

**Staffed Beds:** 150 **Admissions:** 1015 **Census:** 73 **Outpatient Visits:** 98096
**Births:** 85 **Total Expense ($000):** 29337 **Payroll Expense ($000):** 17419
**Personnel:** 282

## OSAWATOMIE—Miami County

☐ **OSAWATOMIE STATE HOSPITAL (174004)**, 500 State Hospital Drive, Zip 66064–1813, Mailing Address: P.O. Box 500, Zip 66064–0500; tel. 913/755–7000 **A**1 10 **F**30 50 75 86 87 98 101 103 130 132 135 146 **P**6
Primary Contact: Jerry A. Rea, Ph.D., Superintendent
CMO: Maria Gustilo, M.D., Medical Director
CHR: Dezerae Curran, Director Human Resources
Web address: www.srskansas.org/osh/osh–rmhf_info.html
**Control:** State–Government, nonfederal **Service:** Psychiatric

**Staffed Beds:** 206 **Admissions:** 2684 **Census:** 193 **Outpatient Visits:** 0
**Births:** 0 **Total Expense ($000):** 53713 **Payroll Expense ($000):** 15785
**Personnel:** 337

## OSBORNE—Osborne County

★ **OSBORNE COUNTY MEMORIAL HOSPITAL (171364)**, 424 West New Hampshire Street, Zip 67473–2314, Mailing Address: P.O. Box 70, Zip 67473–0070; tel. 785/346–2121 **A**9 10 18 **F**3 11 13 40 45 64 69 76 81 107 119 127 128 133 **P**6 **S** Great Plains Health Alliance, Inc., Wichita, KS
Primary Contact: Kiley Floyd, Administrator
CFO: Linda Murphy, Chief Financial Officer
CMO: Barbara Brown, D.O., Chief of Staff
CIO: Kiley Floyd, Administrator
CNO: Monica Mullender, Director of Nursing
Web address: www.ocmh.org
**Control:** County–Government, nonfederal **Service:** General Medical and Surgical

**Staffed Beds:** 25 **Admissions:** 262 **Census:** 7 **Outpatient Visits:** 9797
**Births:** 14 **Total Expense ($000):** 5967 **Payroll Expense ($000):** 2849
**Personnel:** 52

## OSWEGO—Labette County

**OSWEGO COMMUNITY HOSPITAL (171302)**, 800 Barker Drive, Zip 67356–9014; tel. 620/795–2921 **A**9 10 18 **F**3 9 12 32 34 35 40 57 59 64 65 75 77 90 93 107 127 130 132 133 135 147 148 **P**6 **S** Rural Community Hospitals of America, Kansas City, MO
Primary Contact: Daniel Hiben, Chief Executive Officer
CFO: Christina Schlatter, Chief Financial Officer
CMO: Gordon Kern, M.D., Medical Director
CHR: Christina Schlatter, Chief Financial Officer
Web address: www.oswegocommunityhospital.com
**Control:** Corporation, Investor–owned, for–profit **Service:** General Medical and Surgical

**Staffed Beds:** 12 **Admissions:** 88 **Census:** 4 **Outpatient Visits:** 12387 **Total Expense ($000):** 4815 **Payroll Expense ($000):** 2455 **Personnel:** 46

## OTTAWA—Franklin County

⊞ **RANSOM MEMORIAL HOSPITAL (170014)**, 1301 South Main Street, Zip 66067–3598; tel. 785/229–8200 **A**1 9 10 **F**3 11 13 15 18 28 29 30 32 34 35 38 40 41 44 45 46 47 49 50 53 56 57 59 64 68 70 74 76 77 79 81 82 85 86 91 93 102 107 108 109 110 111 115 116 119 129 130 131 132 145 146 148 **P**6
Primary Contact: Matthew M. Heyn, Chief Executive Officer
CFO: Dean Ohmart, Assistant Administrator and Chief Financial Officer
Web address: www.ransom.org
**Control:** County–Government, nonfederal **Service:** General Medical and Surgical

**Staffed Beds:** 44 **Admissions:** 1319 **Census:** 9 **Outpatient Visits:** 112084
**Births:** 153 **Total Expense ($000):** 34768 **Payroll Expense ($000):** 17999
**Personnel:** 310

---

**Hospital, Medicare Provider Number, Address, Telephone, Approval, Facility, and Physician Codes, Health Care System**

★ American Hospital Association (AHA) membership
☐ The Joint Commission accreditation
○ Healthcare Facilities Accreditation Program
◇ DNV Healthcare Inc. accreditation
⇑ Center for Improvement in Healthcare Quality Accreditation
△ Commission on Accreditation of Rehabilitation Facilities (CARF) accreditation

**KS**

*Many Facility Codes have changed. Please refer to the AHA Guide Code Chart.*

**OVERLAND PARK—Johnson County**

☐ **CHILDREN'S MERCY SOUTH (173300)**, 5808 West 110th Street,
Zip 66211–2504; tel. 913/696–8000 **A**1 9 10 **F**3 9 29 30 32 35 36 40 41 44
48 50 59 62 64 68 75 77 79 81 82 85 87 93 94 100 101 104 107 111 115
119 129 130 131 132 134 144 146 148 **P**6
Primary Contact: Randall L. O'Donnell, Ph.D., President and Chief Executive Officer
CFO: Sandra A J Lawrence, Executive Vice President and Chief Financial Officer
CMO: Charles Roberts, M.D., Medical Director
CIO: Jean Ann Breedlove, Chief Information Officer
CHR: Dan Wright, Vice President Human Resources
Web address: www.childrens–mercy.org
**Control:** Other not–for–profit (including NFP Corporation) **Service:** Children's
General Medical and Surgical

**Staffed Beds: 50 Admissions: 2439 Census: 15 Outpatient Visits:** 119437
**Total Expense ($000):** 100183 **Payroll Expense ($000):** 55004 **Personnel:**
626

**HEARTLAND SPINE & SPECIALTY HOSPITAL** See The University of Kansas
Hospital – Indian Creek Campus

☒ **MENORAH MEDICAL CENTER (170182)**, 5721 West 119th Street,
Zip 66209–3722; tel. 913/498–6000 **A**1 2 3 9 10 **F**3 12 13 15 18 20 22 24
26 28 29 30 31 34 35 38 40 45 46 47 49 55 57 58 59 60 64 65 68 70 72
74 75 76 77 78 79 81 82 85 86 87 90 93 97 102 107 108 110 111 114 115
117 119 121 124 126 129 130 131 132 135 144 145 146 147 148 **S** HCA,
Nashville, TN
Primary Contact: Charles Laird, Chief Executive Officer
COO: Lenetra S. King, Chief Operating Officer
CFO: Deborah Gafford, Chief Financial Officer
CMO: Denise K. Miller, M.D., Chief Medical Officer
CIO: Christina McGinnis, Director Information Technology
CHR: Amy Hunt, Director Human Resources
CNO: Kelly Reno, R.N., Chief Nursing Officer
Web address: www.menorahmedicalcenter.com
**Control:** Corporation, Investor–owned, for–profit **Service:** General Medical and
Surgical

**Staffed Beds: 158 Admissions: 7328 Census: 86 Outpatient Visits:** 65259
**Births:** 865 **Total Expense ($000):** 163421 **Payroll Expense ($000):** 47819
**Personnel:** 664

☒ **OVERLAND PARK REGIONAL MEDICAL CENTER (170176)**, 10500 Quivira
Road, Zip 66215–2306, Mailing Address: P.O. Box 15959, Zip 66215–5959;
tel. 913/541–5000 **A**1 5 9 10 **F**3 13 15 18 20 22 24 26 28 29 30 31 34 35
37 40 42 43 45 49 50 56 61 64 65 67 70 72 73 74 75 76 77 78
79 81 82 83 84 85 86 87 91 92 93 107 108 110 111 114 115 119 126 129
130 131 135 144 145 146 147 148 **S** HCA, Nashville, TN
Primary Contact: Kevin J. Hicks, President and CEO
COO: Jim Beatty, Chief Operating Officer
CFO: Shari Collier, Chief Financial Officer
CMO: George D. Stamos, M.D., Chief Medical Officer
CHR: Connie Miller, Vice President Human Resources
Web address: www.oprmc.com
**Control:** Corporation, Investor–owned, for–profit **Service:** General Medical and
Surgical

**Staffed Beds: 277 Admissions: 10350 Census: 140 Outpatient Visits:**
68129 **Births:** 3321 **Total Expense ($000):** 145665 **Payroll Expense
($000):** 57061 **Personnel:** 924

☐ **PROMISE HOSPITAL OF OVERLAND PARK (172004)**, 6509 West 103rd
Street, Zip 66212–1728; tel. 913/649–3701, (Total facility includes 52 beds in
nursing home–type unit) (Data for 289 days) **A**1 9 10 **F**1 29 60 128 143 **P**5
**S** Promise Healthcare, Boca Raton, FL
Primary Contact: Karen Leverich, Chief Executive Officer
CFO: William Scott, Chief Financial Officer
CHR: Darren Enochs, Director Human Resources
Web address: www.promise–overlandpark.com
**Control:** Corporation, Investor–owned, for–profit **Service:** Long–Term Acute Care
hospital

**Staffed Beds: 104 Admissions: 202 Census: 71 Outpatient Visits:** 0 **Births:**
0 **Total Expense ($000):** 7513 **Payroll Expense ($000):** 5608 **Personnel:**
110

☒ **SAINT LUKE'S SOUTH HOSPITAL (170185)**, 12300 Metcalf Avenue,
Zip 66213–1324; tel. 913/317–7000 **A**1 9 10 **F**3 12 13 15 18 20 22 26 28
29 30 31 34 39 40 45 47 49 54 55 57 58 59 60 64 70 71 72 74 75 76 77
78 79 80 81 82 84 85 86 87 90 92 93 94 96 102 107 108 110 111 114 115
117 118 119 129 130 131 132 141 146 147 148 **S** Saint Luke's Health
System, Kansas City, MO
Primary Contact: Bobby Olm–Shipman, Chief Executive Officer
CFO: Shelby Frigon, Chief Financial Officer
CMO: Bakul Sangani, M.D., President Medical Staff
CIO: Deborah Gash, Chief Information Officer
CHR: Donna Kunz, Manager Human Resources
CNO: Julia Woods, R.N., Vice President and Chief Nursing Officer
Web address: www.saintlukeshealthsystem.org/south
**Control:** Church–operated, Nongovernment, not–for profit **Service:** General
Medical and Surgical

**Staffed Beds: 110 Admissions: 4669 Census: 51 Outpatient Visits:** 80280
**Births:** 477 **Total Expense ($000):** 102816 **Payroll Expense ($000):** 30808
**Personnel:** 422

**PAOLA—Miami County**

☐ **MIAMI COUNTY MEDICAL CENTER (170109)**, 2100 Baptiste Drive,
Zip 66071–1314, Mailing Address: P.O. Box 365, Zip 66071–0365;
tel. 913/294–2327 **A**1 5 9 10 **F**3 11 30 40 43 59 61 64 68 75 77 78 79 81
82 85 87 89 90 93 107 108 110 111 114 119 127 129 130 131 146 148
Primary Contact: Paul W. Luce, R.N., MSN, Vice President Operations
CFO: Cheryl Sharp, Chief Financial Office
CMO: Donald Banks, Chief Medical Officer
CIO: Randy Rahman, Chief Information Officer
CHR: David Klimek, Chief Human Resources Officer
CNO: Paul W. Luce, R.N., Director of Patient Services
Web address: www.olathehealth.org
**Control:** Other not–for–profit (including NFP Corporation) **Service:** General
Medical and Surgical

**Staffed Beds: 18 Admissions: 457 Census: 3 Outpatient Visits:** 30936
**Births:** 0 **Personnel:** 124

**PARSONS—Labette County**

★ ○ **LABETTE HEALTH (170120)**, 1902 South U.S. Highway 59,
Zip 67357–7404; tel. 620/421–4880 **A**9 10 11 **F**3 11 13 15 29 30 34 40 43
50 53 57 59 62 70 75 76 77 79 81 82 86 90 93 97 107 111 114 119 126
127 129 130 131 132 143 144 146 147 148 **P**6
Primary Contact: Brian A. Williams, Chief Executive Officer
CFO: Thomas Macaronas, Chief Financial Officer
CHR: Christina Sykes, Director Human Resources
Web address: www.labettehealth.com
**Control:** County–Government, nonfederal **Service:** General Medical and Surgical

**Staffed Beds: 55 Admissions: 2218 Census: 21 Outpatient Visits:** 72341
**Births:** 217 **Total Expense ($000):** 61253 **Payroll Expense ($000):** 25347
**Personnel:** 468

**PARSONS STATE HOSPITAL AND TRAINING CENTER**, 2601 Gabriel Avenue,
Zip 67357–2341, Mailing Address: P.O. Box 738, Zip 67357–0738;
tel. 620/421–6550 **F**35 39 67 130 146
Primary Contact: Jerry A. Rea, Ph.D., Superintendent
CFO: John Spare, Accountant
CMO: Rema Menon, M.D., Clinical Director
CIO: Ron Malmstrom, Information Research Specialist
CHR: Tim B. Posch, Business Manager and Director Personnel
Web address: www.pshtc.org
**Control:** State–Government, nonfederal **Service:** Intellectual Disabilities

**Staffed Beds: 188 Admissions: 20 Census: 174 Outpatient Visits:** 0 **Births:**
0 **Total Expense ($000):** 27160 **Payroll Expense ($000):** 16637
**Personnel:** 430

**PHILLIPSBURG—Phillips County**

★ **PHILLIPS COUNTY HOSPITAL (171353)**, 1150 State Street, Zip 67661–1743,
Mailing Address: P.O. Box 607, Zip 67661–0607; tel. 785/543–5226 **A**9 10 18
**F**3 11 15 28 30 31 40 45 50 59 64 68 75 77 78 81 86 87 93 107 114 119
127 128 130 132 133 145 146 148 **P**6 **S** Great Plains Health Alliance, Inc.,
Wichita, KS
Primary Contact: David Engel, Chief Executive Officer
CFO: Christi Driggs, Chief Financial Officer
CMO: Ben Stephenson, M.D., Chief of Staff
CIO: Steven Seems, Director of Information Technology
CHR: Peggy Fabin, Director Human Resources
CNO: Vickie Gibbs, Director Nursing
Web address: www.phillipshospital.org
**Control:** Other not–for–profit (including NFP Corporation) **Service:** General
Medical and Surgical

**Staffed Beds: 25 Admissions: 250 Census: 6 Outpatient Visits:** 24406
**Births:** 0 **Total Expense ($000):** 10166 **Payroll Expense ($000):** 4365
**Personnel:** 99

**KS**

*Many Facility Codes have changed. Please refer to the AHA Guide Code Chart.*
© 2015 AHA Guide

## PITTSBURG—Crawford County

✠ **VIA CHRISTI HOSPITAL PITTSBURG (170006)**, 1 Mt. Carmel Way, Zip 66762-7587; tel. 620/231-6100 **A**1 2 9 10 **F**3 5 8 11 12 13 15 18 20 22 26 28 29 30 31 34 35 40 42 43 45 46 47 48 50 51 53 54 56 57 58 59 62 64 68 69 70 75 76 77 78 79 81 82 84 85 86 89 90 93 99 100 101 103 104 107 108 109 110 111 114 115 116 117 118 119 120 121 122 123 126 129 130 131 132 133 135 143 144 145 146 147 148 **P**8 **S** Ascension Health, Saint Louis, MO
Primary Contact: Randall R. Cason, FACHE, Senior Administrator
CFO: Mike Joy, Administrator, Finance
CIO: Missy McDown, Director Information Systems
CHR: Laurie Johnson, Director – Human Resources
CNO: Amy Katherine Renn, Interim Administrator, Patient Care and Nursing
Web address: www.viachristi.org/pittsburg
**Control:** Church-operated, Nongovernment, not-for profit **Service:** General Medical and Surgical

**Staffed Beds:** 120 **Admissions:** 3505 **Census:** 44 **Outpatient Visits:** 105682 **Births:** 566 **Total Expense ($000):** 83025 **Payroll Expense ($000):** 34800 **Personnel:** 613

## PLAINVILLE—Rooks County

★ **ROOKS COUNTY HEALTH CENTER (171311)**, 1210 North Washington Street, Zip 67663-1632, Mailing Address: P.O. Box 389, Zip 67663-0389; tel. 785/434-4553 **A**9 10 18 **F**3 11 13 15 28 29 31 34 35 40 43 45 47 50 57 59 64 67 76 77 81 82 87 93 96 102 107 110 114 119 125 128 130 133 135 143 144 146 147 148
Primary Contact: Michael Sinclair, Chief Executive Officer
COO: William D. Stahl, Chief Operating Officer
CFO: Julie Price, Chief Financial Officer
CMO: Lynn Fisher, M.D., Chief of Staff
CIO: Kathy Ramsay, R.N., Director Communications and Development
CHR: Cindi Knipp, Director Human Resources
Web address: www.rookscountyhealthcenter.com
**Control:** Hospital district or authority, Government, nonfederal **Service:** General Medical and Surgical

**Staffed Beds:** 20 **Admissions:** 449 **Census:** 7 **Outpatient Visits:** 25666 **Births:** 42 **Total Expense ($000):** 13623 **Payroll Expense ($000):** 5637 **Personnel:** 125

## PRATT—Pratt County

★ **PRATT REGIONAL MEDICAL CENTER (170027)**, 200 Commodore Street, Zip 67124-2903; tel. 620/672-7451, (Total facility includes 45 beds in nursing home–type unit) **A**9 10 20 **F**3 11 13 15 30 31 34 40 45 49 56 57 59 61 62 64 68 70 75 76 77 79 81 82 85 86 87 89 90 93 107 108 114 118 119 124 127 128 130 131 133 145 146 147 148 **P**6
Primary Contact: Susan M. Page, President and Chief Executive Officer
CFO: Vincent Scot Wilczek, Vice President and Chief Financial Officer
CIO: Vikki Mader, Director Health Information Services
CHR: Ken Brown, Vice President and Chief Human Resource Officer
CNO: Jack L. Kennedy, Vice President and Chief Nursing Officer
Web address: www.prmc.org
**Control:** Other not-for-profit (including NFP Corporation) **Service:** General Medical and Surgical

**Staffed Beds:** 80 **Admissions:** 1569 **Census:** 52 **Outpatient Visits:** 84883 **Births:** 277 **Total Expense ($000):** 42138 **Payroll Expense ($000):** 20936 **Personnel:** 397

## QUINTER—Gove County

**GOVE COUNTY MEDICAL CENTER (171367)**, 520 West Fifth Street, Zip 67752-0129, Mailing Address: P.O. Box 129, Zip 67752-0129; tel. 785/754-3341, (Total facility includes 43 beds in nursing home–type unit) **A**9 10 18 **F**3 11 13 28 29 31 34 40 45 57 62 67 75 81 86 93 107 119 125 129 133 135 143 148
Primary Contact: Coleen Tummons, Chief Executive Officer
CFO: Alan Waites, Chief Financial Officer
CIO: Brad Mullins, Director Information Technology
CHR: Valerie Schneider, Director Human Resources
CNO: Annie Staats, R.N., Director Nursing
Web address: www.govecountymedicalcenter.org
**Control:** County-Government, nonfederal **Service:** General Medical and Surgical

**Staffed Beds:** 64 **Admissions:** 730 **Census:** 41 **Outpatient Visits:** 9206 **Births:** 63 **Total Expense ($000):** 12780 **Payroll Expense ($000):** 5696 **Personnel:** 159

## RANSOM—Ness County

★ **GRISELL MEMORIAL HOSPITAL DISTRICT ONE (171300)**, 210 South Vermont Avenue, Zip 67572-9525; tel. 785/731-2231, (Total facility includes 34 beds in nursing home–type unit) **A**9 10 18 **F**3 40 56 67 69 85 93 97 127 128 133 **P**6 **S** Great Plains Health Alliance, Inc., Wichita, KS
Primary Contact: David Caudill, Administrator
CFO: Jolene Schuster, Chief Financial Officer
CMO: Allen McLain, M.D., Chief of Staff
CNO: Joni Pfaff, Chief Nursing Officer
Web address: www.grisellmemorialhospital.org
**Control:** Hospital district or authority, Government, nonfederal **Service:** General Medical and Surgical

**Staffed Beds:** 46 **Admissions:** 56 **Census:** 31 **Outpatient Visits:** 8274 **Births:** 0 **Total Expense ($000):** 5235 **Payroll Expense ($000):** 2514 **Personnel:** 59

## RUSSELL—Russell County

★ **RUSSELL REGIONAL HOSPITAL (171350)**, 200 South Main Street, Zip 67665-2920; tel. 785/483-3131, (Total facility includes 22 beds in nursing home–type unit) **A**9 10 18 **F**9 11 15 29 34 40 50 53 57 59 64 65 66 67 69 75 85 87 93 97 107 108 110 115 119 127 130 131 133 135 145 146 147 148 **P**6
Primary Contact: Harold Courtois, Chief Executive Officer
COO: Sharon Collins, Director Human Resources and Chief Operating Officer
CFO: Kevin Kreutzer, Chief Financial Officer
CMO: Earl Merkel, M.D., Chief of Staff
CIO: David Schraeder, Director Information Systems
CHR: Sharon Collins, Director Human Resources and Chief Operating Officer
CNO: Karen Deatherage, Director of Nursing
Web address: www.russellhospital.org
**Control:** Other not-for-profit (including NFP Corporation) **Service:** General Medical and Surgical

**Staffed Beds:** 47 **Admissions:** 407 **Census:** 26 **Outpatient Visits:** 33069 **Births:** 2 **Total Expense ($000):** 13749 **Payroll Expense ($000):** 7099 **Personnel:** 148

## SABETHA—Nemaha County

★ **SABETHA COMMUNITY HOSPITAL (171338)**, 14th and Oregon Streets, Zip 66534-0229, Mailing Address: P.O. Box 229, Zip 66534-0229; tel. 785/284-2121 **A**9 10 18 **F**3 11 13 15 28 34 35 40 45 50 56 57 59 62 63 64 68 75 76 77 79 81 82 84 85 86 93 107 110 114 119 128 130 132 133 146 148 **P**6 **S** Great Plains Health Alliance, Inc., Wichita, KS
Primary Contact: Lora Key, Chief Executive Officer
CFO: Lori Lackey, Chief Financial Officer
CMO: Chris Tramp, Chief of Staff
CIO: Holli Dieckmann, Director Health Information
CHR: Julie K. Holthaus, Director Human Resources
CNO: Stacy Scott, Director Nursing
Web address: www.sabethahospital.com
**Control:** Other not-for-profit (including NFP Corporation) **Service:** General Medical and Surgical

**Staffed Beds:** 25 **Admissions:** 390 **Census:** 6 **Outpatient Visits:** 43545 **Births:** 60 **Total Expense ($000):** 11196 **Payroll Expense ($000):** 5382 **Personnel:** 102

## SAINT FRANCIS—Cheyenne County

★ **CHEYENNE COUNTY HOSPITAL (171310)**, 210 West First Street, Zip 67756-3540, Mailing Address: P.O. Box 547, Zip 67756-0547; tel. 785/332-2104 **A**9 10 18 **F**3 8 11 13 28 29 31 40 57 59 64 65 66 68 76 77 78 81 85 89 93 97 107 119 127 128 133 148 **P**6 **S** Great Plains Health Alliance, Inc., Wichita, KS
Primary Contact: Scott Jenkins, Administrator
CFO: Heidi Tice, Chief Financial Officer
CMO: Mary Beth Miller, M.D., Chief of Staff
CIO: Carol Sloper, Manager Information Technology
CHR: Sara Wilson, Director Human Resources
CNO: Judith Ann Hodgson, Chief Nursing Officer
Web address: www.cheyennecountyhospital.com
**Control:** Other not-for-profit (including NFP Corporation) **Service:** General Medical and Surgical

**Staffed Beds:** 16 **Admissions:** 345 **Census:** 4 **Outpatient Visits:** 21524 **Births:** 7 **Total Expense ($000):** 8897 **Payroll Expense ($000):** 4320 **Personnel:** 79

---

**Hospital, Medicare Provider Number, Address, Telephone, Approval, Facility, and Physician Codes, Health Care System**

★ American Hospital Association (AHA) membership ○ Healthcare Facilities Accreditation Program ⇑ Center for Improvement in Healthcare Quality Accreditation
□ The Joint Commission accreditation ◇ DNV Healthcare Inc. accreditation △ Commission on Accreditation of Rehabilitation Facilities (CARF) accreditation

**KS**

## SALINA—Saline County

★ ○ **SALINA REGIONAL HEALTH CENTER (170012)**, 400 South Santa Fe Avenue, Zip 67401–4198, Mailing Address: P.O. Box 5080, Zip 67402–5080; tel. 785/452–7000, (Includes SALINA REGIONAL HEALTH CENTER– PENN CAMPUS, 139 North Penn Street, Zip 67401, Mailing Address: P.O. Box 5080, Zip 67402–5080; tel. 913/452–7000; SALINA REGIONAL HEALTH CENTER–SANTA FE CAMPUS, 400 South Santa Fe Avenue, Zip 67401, Mailing Address: Box 5080, Zip 67402–5080; tel. 913/452–7000) **A**2 3 5 9 10 11 20 **F**3 13 15 18 19 20 22 24 28 29 30 31 35 40 43 45 46 47 48 49 51 53 54 55 57 59 63 64 65 68 70 71 72 73 74 76 77 78 79 81 85 86 87 89 90 98 99 100 101 102 103 104 105 107 108 110 111 114 115 116 117 118 119 120 121 122 123 126 129 130 143 144 145 146 147 148 **P**6
Primary Contact: Micheal Terry, President and Chief Executive Officer
COO: Joel Phelps, Chief Operating Officer
CFO: Joe Tallon, Vice President Finance
CIO: Larry Barnes, Vice President Information Technology
CHR: David Moody, Vice President Human Resources
Web address: www.srhc.com
**Control:** Other not–for–profit (including NFP Corporation) **Service:** General Medical and Surgical

**Staffed Beds:** 204 **Admissions:** 8827 **Census:** 110 **Outpatient Visits:** 200036 **Births:** 1157 **Total Expense ($000):** 190737 **Payroll Expense ($000):** 84696 **Personnel:** 1511

**SALINA SURGICAL HOSPITAL (170187)**, 401 South Sante Fe, Zip 67401–4143; tel. 785/827–0610 **A**5 9 10 **F**29 45 48 49 51 74 79 81 85 89 131
Primary Contact: LuAnn Puvogel, R.N., Administrator
CFO: Elizabeth Bishop, Manager Business Office
CMO: Michael Johnson, M.D., Medical Director
CIO: Earl Akers, Supervisor Information Technology
CHR: Elizabeth Bishop, Manager Business Office
CNO: Jolene Glavin, R.N., Director Nursing
Web address: www.salinasurgical.com/
**Control:** Partnership, Investor–owned, for–profit **Service:** Surgical

**Staffed Beds:** 16 **Admissions:** 689 **Census:** 5 **Outpatient Visits:** 7568 **Births:** 0 **Total Expense ($000):** 17323 **Payroll Expense ($000):** 5338 **Personnel:** 96

## SATANTA—Haskell County

★ **SATANTA DISTRICT HOSPITAL AND LONG TERM CARE (171324)**, 401 South Cheyenne Street, Zip 67870–0159, Mailing Address: P.O. Box 159, Zip 67870–0159; tel. 620/649–2761, (Total facility includes 4 beds in nursing home–type unit) **A**9 10 18 **F**3 11 40 45 57 64 67 68 75 81 82 87 93 104 107 119 127 128 130 133 **P**4 **S** Great Plains Health Alliance, Inc., Wichita, KS
Primary Contact: Jeremy Clingenpeel, Administrator
CFO: Libby Anderson, Chief Financial Officer
CMO: Virgilio Taduran, M.D., Chief Medical Officer
CIO: Ben Leppke, Chief Information Officer
CHR: Samantha Hett, Manager Human Resources
CNO: Tina Pendergraft, Chief Nursing Officer
Web address: www.satantahospital.org
**Control:** Hospital district or authority, Government, nonfederal **Service:** General Medical and Surgical

**Staffed Beds:** 57 **Admissions:** 201 **Census:** 45 **Outpatient Visits:** 26925 **Births:** 0 **Total Expense ($000):** 12858 **Payroll Expense ($000):** 5686 **Personnel:** 126

## SCOTT CITY—Scott County

★ **SCOTT COUNTY HOSPITAL (171372)**, 201 East Albert Avenue, Zip 67871–1203; tel. 620/872–5811 **A**9 10 18 **F**3 7 13 15 28 29 30 31 35 40 45 46 50 57 59 62 64 68 69 75 76 77 81 82 85 93 107 110 119 127 128 129 130 133 135 148 **P**6
Primary Contact: Mark Burnett, President and Chief Executive Officer
COO: Karma Huck, Chief Operating Officer
CFO: Joe S. Meyer, Chief Financial Officer
CMO: Elizabeth Hineman, M.D., Chief Medical Staff
CHR: Pamela R. Wheeler, Manager Human Resources
Web address: www.scotthospital.net
**Control:** Other not–for–profit (including NFP Corporation) **Service:** General Medical and Surgical

**Staffed Beds:** 22 **Admissions:** 634 **Census:** 9 **Outpatient Visits:** 19318 **Births:** 71 **Total Expense ($000):** 18644 **Payroll Expense ($000):** 9467 **Personnel:** 205

## SEDAN—Chautauqua County

**SEDAN CITY HOSPITAL (171318)**, 300 North Street, Zip 67361–1051, Mailing Address: P.O. Box C, Zip 67361–0427; tel. 620/725–3115 **A**9 10 18 **F**29 34 40 57 64 93 107 128 130 133 148
Primary Contact: Michelle Williams, Administrator
CFO: Jennifer Seever, Regional Chief Financial Officer
CMO: James McDermott, M.D., Chief of Staff
**Control:** City–Government, nonfederal **Service:** General Medical and Surgical

**Staffed Beds:** 25 **Admissions:** 240 **Census:** 3 **Outpatient Visits:** 8125 **Births:** 0 **Total Expense ($000):** 4465 **Payroll Expense ($000):** 1879 **Personnel:** 39

## SENECA—Nemaha County

★ **NEMAHA VALLEY COMMUNITY HOSPITAL (171315)**, 1600 Community Drive, Zip 66538–9739; tel. 785/336–6181 **A**9 10 18 **F**11 12 13 15 28 31 40 56 57 59 64 75 76 77 78 79 81 84 85 89 93 107 114 119 127 129 130 131 132 133 **P**6
Primary Contact: Stan Regehr, President and Chief Executive Officer
CFO: Connie Ingwerson, Chief Financial Officer
CHR: Lynn Hartter, Director Human Resources
CNO: Lynda Cross, R.N., Director of Nurses
Web address: www.nemvch.org
**Control:** Other not–for–profit (including NFP Corporation) **Service:** General Medical and Surgical

**Staffed Beds:** 24 **Admissions:** 205 **Census:** 3 **Outpatient Visits:** 18977 **Births:** 44 **Total Expense ($000):** 11297 **Payroll Expense ($000):** 5387 **Personnel:** 123

## SHAWNEE MISSION—Johnson County

✚ **MID–AMERICA REHABILITATION HOSPITAL (173026)**, 5701 West 110th Street, Zip 66211–2503; tel. 913/491–2400 **A**1 10 **F**29 35 56 64 86 87 90 91 93 95 96 130 132 135 143 148 **S** HEALTHSOUTH Corporation, Birmingham, AL
Primary Contact: Troy DeDecker, FACHE, Chief Executive Officer
CFO: Richard Lane, Chief Financial Officer
CMO: Cielo Dehning, M.D., Medical Director
CHR: Elizabeth Gibson, Director Human Resources
CNO: Amy McKay, Chief Nursing Officer
Web address: www.midamericarehabhospital.com
**Control:** Corporation, Investor–owned, for–profit **Service:** Rehabilitation

**Staffed Beds:** 98 **Admissions:** 2066 **Census:** 71 **Outpatient Visits:** 8629 **Births:** 0 **Total Expense ($000):** 26549 **Payroll Expense ($000):** 13392 **Personnel:** 207

✚ **SHAWNEE MISSION MEDICAL CENTER (170104)**, 9100 West 74th Street, Zip 66204–4004, Mailing Address: Box 2923, Zip 66201–1323; tel. 913/676–2000 **A**1 2 3 5 9 10 **F**3 4 5 8 11 12 13 15 17 18 20 22 24 26 28 29 30 31 32 34 35 36 40 42 45 46 47 48 49 52 53 54 55 56 57 58 59 60 61 62 64 65 70 72 74 75 76 77 78 79 80 81 82 83 84 85 86 87 89 93 96 97 98 100 101 102 103 104 105 107 108 110 111 114 115 117 118 119 120 121 123 124 126 129 130 131 132 135 144 145 146 147 148 **P**6 **S** Adventist Health System Sunbelt Health Care Corporation, Altamonte Springs, FL
Primary Contact: Ken J. Bacon, President and Chief Executive Officer
COO: Trevor Wright, Senior Vice President and Chief Operating Officer
CFO: Karsten Randolph, Executive Vice President and Chief Financial Officer
CMO: Sherri Martin, M.D., President Medical Staff
CIO: Mike Allen, Director Information Services
CHR: Brad Hoffman, Administrative Director Human Resources
CNO: Sheri Hawkins, Chief Nursing Officer
Web address: www.shawneemission.org
**Control:** Church–operated, Nongovernment, not–for profit **Service:** General Medical and Surgical

**Staffed Beds:** 400 **Admissions:** 21530 **Census:** 232 **Outpatient Visits:** 554915 **Births:** 4939 **Total Expense ($000):** 358897 **Payroll Expense ($000):** 146612 **Personnel:** 2511

## SMITH CENTER—Smith County

★ **SMITH COUNTY MEMORIAL HOSPITAL (171377)**, 614 South Main Street, Zip 66967–3001; tel. 785/282–6845, (Total facility includes 28 beds in nursing home–type unit) **A**9 10 18 **F**13 15 28 30 31 34 40 45 53 64 65 67 68 69 75 76 81 85 93 107 114 119 127 128 133 **P**6 **S** Great Plains Health Alliance, Inc., Wichita, KS
Primary Contact: Allen Van Driel, FACHE, Administrator
CFO: Julie Williams, Chief Financial Officer
CIO: Tammy Gaston, Chief Information Officer
CHR: Jody Maxwell, Manager Business Office
CNO: Sarah Ragsdale, R.N., Chief Nursing Officer
Web address: www.gpha.com
**Control:** Other not–for–profit (including NFP Corporation) **Service:** General Medical and Surgical

**Staffed Beds:** 53 **Admissions:** 457 **Census:** 26 **Outpatient Visits:** 24507 **Births:** 28 **Total Expense ($000):** 11329 **Payroll Expense ($000):** 5185 **Personnel:** 110

## STAFFORD—Stafford County

★ **STAFFORD COUNTY HOSPITAL (171323)**, 502 South Buckeye Street, Zip 67578–2035, Mailing Address: P.O. Box 190, Zip 67578–0190; tel. 620/234–5221 **A**9 10 18 **F**3 15 29 35 40 57 59 62 64 67 77 93 107 128 130 133 **P**5
Primary Contact: Todd Taylor, Chief Executive Officer
CFO: MeKinzie Hudson, Chief Financial Officer
Web address: www.staffordcountyhospital.org
**Control:** Hospital district or authority, Government, nonfederal **Service:** General Medical and Surgical

**Staffed Beds:** 25 **Admissions:** 94 **Census:** 5 **Outpatient Visits:** 30677 **Births:** 0 **Total Expense ($000):** 3804 **Payroll Expense ($000):** 1578 **Personnel:** 39

*Many Facility Codes have changed. Please refer to the AHA Guide Code Chart.* © 2015 AHA Guide

## SYRACUSE—Hamilton County

★ **HAMILTON COUNTY HOSPITAL (171322)**, 700 North Huser Street,
Zip 67878–0948, Mailing Address: P.O. Box 948, Zip 67878–0948;
tel. 620/384–7461, (Total facility includes 44 beds in nursing home–type unit) **A**9
10 18 **F**3 18 35 40 41 56 57 59 64 68 81 84 86 93 97 107 111 114 125
127 130 133 **P**6
Primary Contact: Rob Nahmensen, Chief Executive Officer
CMO: John Carey, M.D., Chief Medical Director
CIO: Mark Kleymann, Manager Information Technology
CHR: Angela Talbot, Manager Human Resources
Web address: www.myhch.org
**Control:** County–Government, nonfederal **Service:** General Medical and Surgical

**Staffed Beds: 69 Admissions: 91 Census: 26 Outpatient Visits:** 7652
**Births: 1 Total Expense ($000):** 6529 **Payroll Expense ($000):** 3065
**Personnel:** 93

## TOPEKA—Shawnee County

**KANSAS NEUROLOGICAL INSTITUTE**, 3107 West 21st Street,
Zip 66604–3298; tel. 785/296–5301 **F**29 30 35 39 67 91 97 130 143 146 **P**6
Primary Contact: Brent Widick, Superintendent
CFO: Sara Hoyer, Director Administrative Services
CMO: Mary Gingrich, Director Health Care Services
CIO: Cheryl Fuller, Director Information Resources
CHR: Shawna Mercer, Director Human Resources
Web address: www.kdads.ks.gov/state–hospitals–and–institutions/kansas–
neurological–institute
**Control:** State–Government, nonfederal **Service:** Intellectual Disabilities

**Staffed Beds: 150 Admissions: 4 Census: 145 Outpatient Visits: 0 Births:**
**0 Total Expense ($000):** 27947 **Payroll Expense ($000):** 14931
**Personnel:** 426

⊞ **KANSAS REHABILITATION HOSPITAL (173025)**, 1504 S.W. Eighth Avenue,
Zip 66606–1632; tel. 785/235–6600 **A**1 9 10 **F**29 53 62 64 75 86 90 91 93
95 96 130 132 148 **S** HEALTHSOUTH Corporation, Birmingham, AL
Primary Contact: William J. Overbey, Chief Executive Officer
CMO: Joseph Sankoorikal, M.D., Chief Medical Staff
CHR: Dina Cox, Director Human Resources
CNO: Carol Swanger, Chief Nursing Officer
Web address: www.kansasrehabhospital.com
**Control:** Corporation, Investor–owned, for–profit **Service:** Rehabilitation

**Staffed Beds: 59 Admissions: 1157 Census: 38 Outpatient Visits:** 14118
**Births: 0 Total Expense ($000):** 16061 **Payroll Expense ($000):** 8359
**Personnel:** 155

⊞ **ST. FRANCIS HEALTH (170016)**, 1700 S.W. 7th Street, Zip 66606–1690;
tel. 785/295–8000 **A**1 2 9 10 **F**3 12 13 15 18 20 22 24 26 28 29 30 31 34
35 36 37 38 40 45 48 49 50 51 53 54 56 57 58 59 60 61 62 64 65 70
71 73 74 75 77 78 79 80 81 82 85 86 87 90 92 93 95 96 107 108 110 111
114 115 116 117 118 119 120 121 123 126 130 131 132 135 144 146 147
**P**6 **S** SCL Health, Broomfield, CO
Primary Contact: David P. Setchel, President
CFO: Debra Cartwright, Chief Financial Officer
CMO: Thomas Hamilton, D.O., Chief Medical Officer
CIO: Kevin Mapes, Director Kansas Division System and Technology Service
Center
CHR: Steve Saffa, Director Human Resources
CNO: Scott E. Wells, MSN, Chief Nursing Officer
Web address: www.stfrancistopeka.org
**Control:** Church–operated, Nongovernment, not–for profit **Service:** General
Medical and Surgical

**Staffed Beds: 259 Admissions: 8900 Census: 111 Outpatient Visits:**
245328 **Births: 987 Total Expense ($000):** 202736 **Payroll Expense**
**($000):** 65470 **Personnel:** 1260

⊞ **STORMONT–VAIL HEALTHCARE (170086)**, 1500 S.W. Tenth Avenue,
Zip 66604–1353; tel. 785/354–6000 **A**1 2 5 9 10 **F**3 11 12 13 15 17 18 19
20 22 24 26 28 29 30 31 34 35 37 40 43 44 45 47 49 50 51 55 56 57 58
59 60 61 64 65 68 70 71 72 74 75 76 77 78 79 81 82 84 85 86 87 88 89
91 93 97 98 99 101 102 103 104 105 107 108 110 111 112 114 115 117
119 120 121 123 129 130 131 132 135 143 144 145 146 147 148 **P**6
Primary Contact: Randall Peterson, President and Chief Executive Officer
COO: Janet Stanek, Executive Vice President
CFO: Kevin Han, Vice President and Chief Financial Officer
CMO: Kent Palmberg, M.D., Senior Vice President and Chief Medical Officer
CIO: Judy Corzine, Administrative Director and Chief Information Officer
CHR: Bernard H. Becker, Vice President and Chief Human Resources Officer
CNO: Carol Perry, R.N., Vice President and Chief Nursing Officer
Web address: www.stormontvail.org
**Control:** Other not–for–profit (including NFP Corporation) **Service:** General
Medical and Surgical

**Staffed Beds: 394 Admissions: 20875 Census: 236 Outpatient Visits:**
125728 **Births: 1970 Total Expense ($000):** 514886 **Payroll Expense**
**($000):** 268349 **Personnel:** 3678

⊞ **VETERANS AFFAIRS EASTERN KANSAS HEALTH CARE SYSTEM**, 2200
South West Gage Boulevard, Zip 66622–0002; tel. 785/350–3111, (Includes
VETERANS AFFAIRS EASTERN KANSAS HEALTH CARE SYSTEM–COLMERY–O'NEIL
VETERANS AFFAIRS MEDICAL CENTER, 2200 South West Gage Boulevard,
tel. 785/350–3111; VETERANS AFFAIRS EASTERN KANSAS HEALTH CARE
SYSTEM–DWIGHT D. EISENHOWER VETERANS AFFAIRS MEDICAL CENTER, 4101
South 4th Street Trafficway, Leavenworth, Zip 66048–5055; tel. 913/682–2000),
(Nonreporting) **A**1 3 5 **S** Department of Veterans Affairs, Washington, DC
Primary Contact: Anthony Rudy Klopfer, FACHE, Director
COO: John Moon, Associate Director
CMO: Rajeev Trehan, M.D., Chief of Staff
CIO: Joni Davin, Director Information and Business Management Service Line
Web address: www.topeka.va.gov/
**Control:** Veterans Affairs, Government, federal **Service:** General Medical and
Surgical

**Staffed Beds: 213**

**VETERANS AFFAIRS EASTERN KANSAS HEALTH CARE**
**SYSTEM–COLMERY–O'NEIL VETERANS AFFAIRS MEDICAL CENTER** See
Veterans Affairs Eastern Kansas Health Care System

## TRIBUNE—Greeley County

★ **GREELEY COUNTY HEALTH SERVICES (171359)**, 506 Third Street,
Zip 67879–9684, Mailing Address: P.O. Box 338, Zip 67879–0338;
tel. 620/376–4221, (Total facility includes 32 beds in nursing home–type unit) **A**9
10 18 **F**3 17 28 34 40 45 59 64 65 66 69 81 89 107 127 133 147 **S** QHR,
Brentwood, TN
Primary Contact: Lee Rhodes, Administrator and Chief Executive Officer
CFO: Jennifer Deal, Chief Financial Officer
CMO: Wendel Ellis, D.O., Chief Medical Staff
CIO: Shanon Schneider, Chief Information Officer
CHR: Katelyn Reynolds, Manager Human Resources
CNO: Janie Schmidt, Director of Nursing
Web address: www.mygchs.com
**Control:** Other not–for–profit (including NFP Corporation) **Service:** General
Medical and Surgical

**Staffed Beds: 50 Admissions: 274 Census: 35 Outpatient Visits:** 17894
**Births: 0 Total Expense ($000):** 9614 **Payroll Expense ($000):** 4555
**Personnel:** 117

## ULYSSES—Grant County

★ **BOB WILSON MEMORIAL GRANT COUNTY HOSPITAL (170110)**, 415 North
Main Street, Zip 67880–2133; tel. 620/356–1266 **A**9 10 20 **F**3 11 13 15 29
30 34 35 40 45 50 57 59 64 68 75 76 79 81 82 85 86 87 91 93 96 97 107
119 127 130 133 146 148 **P**6
Primary Contact: Arthur H. Frable, Chief Executive Officer
CFO: Robert Jacobi, Chief Financial Officer
CIO: Chris Moffet, Director Information Services
CHR: Tammy Oxford, Director Human Resources
Web address: www.bwmgch.com
**Control:** County–Government, nonfederal **Service:** General Medical and Surgical

**Staffed Beds: 26 Admissions: 403 Census: 6 Outpatient Visits:** 10116
**Births: 52 Total Expense ($000):** 11887 **Payroll Expense ($000):** 5179
**Personnel:** 121

---

**Hospital, Medicare Provider Number, Address, Telephone, Approval, Facility, and Physician Codes, Health Care System**

| | | |
|---|---|---|
| ★ American Hospital Association (AHA) membership | ○ Healthcare Facilities Accreditation Program | ⇑ Center for Improvement in Healthcare Quality Accreditation |
| ☐ The Joint Commission accreditation | ◇ DNV Healthcare Inc. accreditation | △ Commission on Accreditation of Rehabilitation Facilities (CARF) accreditation |

**KS**

## WAKEENEY—Trego County

★ **TREGO COUNTY–LEMKE MEMORIAL HOSPITAL (171355)**, 320 North 13th Street, Zip 67672–2099; tel. 785/743–2182, (Total facility includes 37 beds in nursing home–type unit) **A**9 10 18 **F**3 8 10 11 15 28 29 34 40 45 53 57 59 62 64 67 69 71 81 86 89 93 107 110 114 127 128 130 133 143 146 148 **P**6 **S** Great Plains Health Alliance, Inc., Wichita, KS
Primary Contact: David Augustine, Chief Executive Officer
CFO: Gail Jensen, Chief Financial Officer
CMO: Gordon Lang, M.D., Chief of Staff
CHR: Cindy Meiar, Human Resources and Payroll Coordinator
CNO: Sandy Purinton, Chief Nursing Officer
Web address: www.tclmh.org
**Control:** County–Government, nonfederal **Service:** General Medical and Surgical

**Staffed Beds:** 62 **Admissions:** 814 **Census:** 52 **Outpatient Visits:** 37446 **Births:** 0 **Total Expense ($000):** 17101 **Payroll Expense ($000):** 7590 **Personnel:** 173

## WAMEGO—Pottawatomie County

★ **WAMEGO HEALTH CENTER (171337)**, 711 Genn Drive, Zip 66547–1179; tel. 785/456–2295 **A**9 10 18 **F**3 11 15 29 32 34 35 40 45 56 59 64 65 75 77 81 93 97 107 114 119 127 130 132 133 142 143 146 147 148 **P**6
Primary Contact: Shannan Flach, Chief Executive Officer
COO: Brian Smith, Director of Operations
CFO: Keith Zachariasen, Chief Financial Officer
CMO: Roland Darey, M.D., Medical Director
CIO: Wes Janzen, Chief Information Officer
CHR: Renee Reed, Director Human Resources
CNO: Tresha Flanary, R.N., Chief Clinical Services Officer
Web address: www.wamegocityhospital.com
**Control:** Other not–for–profit (including NFP Corporation) **Service:** General Medical and Surgical

**Staffed Beds:** 18 **Admissions:** 195 **Census:** 3 **Outpatient Visits:** 23552 **Births:** 0 **Total Expense ($000):** 10432 **Payroll Expense ($000):** 5557 **Personnel:** 89

## WASHINGTON—Washington County

**WASHINGTON COUNTY HOSPITAL (171351)**, 304 East Third Street, Zip 66968–2033; tel. 785/325–2211 **A**9 10 18 **F**2 3 11 13 15 28 29 30 31 35 40 45 53 57 64 67 70 81 85 93 107 114 128 130 133 148
Primary Contact: Roxanne Schottel, Chief Executive Officer
CFO: Linda Rettig, Director Financial Services
CNO: Kelly Otott, R.N., Chief Nursing Officer
Web address: www.washingtoncountyhospital.net
**Control:** County–Government, nonfederal **Service:** General Medical and Surgical

**Staffed Beds:** 25 **Admissions:** 100 **Census:** 6 **Outpatient Visits:** 4715 **Births:** 7 **Total Expense ($000):** 4299 **Payroll Expense ($000):** 1592 **Personnel:** 39

## WELLINGTON—Sumner County

★ **SUMNER REGIONAL MEDICAL CENTER (170039)**, 1323 North A Street, Zip 67152–4350; tel. 620/326–7451, (Total facility includes 9 beds in nursing home–type unit) **A**9 10 **F**10 11 13 15 31 35 40 45 56 59 64 76 77 78 79 81 82 85 98 103 107 108 110 111 119 128 129 130
Primary Contact: Sam Guild, Chief Financial Officer
CFO: Sam Guild, Chief Financial Officer
CHR: Allen Keller, Director Human Resources
CNO: Darlene Cooney, Director Nursing
Web address: www.srmcks.org
**Control:** City–Government, nonfederal **Service:** General Medical and Surgical

**Staffed Beds:** 61 **Admissions:** 578 **Census:** 7 **Outpatient Visits:** 16666 **Births:** 106 **Total Expense ($000):** 18668 **Payroll Expense ($000):** 9778 **Personnel:** 129

## WICHITA—Sedgwick County

☐ **AMG SPECIALTY HOSPITAL–WICHITA (172003)**, 8080 East Pawnee Street, Zip 67207–5475; tel. 316/682–0004 **A**1 10 **F**1 29 30 77 130 148 **P**5 **S** AMG Integrated Healthcare Management, Lafayette, LA
Primary Contact: Robert A. Loepp, Jr., FACHE, Chief Executive Officer
CFO: Myra Dick, Manager Business Office
CIO: Michelle Bradley, Director Health Information Management
CHR: Adrienne Burkholder, Director Human Resources
Web address: www.amgwichita.com/
**Control:** Corporation, Investor–owned, for–profit **Service:** Long–Term Acute Care hospital

**Staffed Beds:** 26 **Admissions:** 267 **Census:** 17 **Outpatient Visits:** 0 **Births:** 0 **Total Expense ($000):** 7756 **Payroll Expense ($000):** 3243 **Personnel:** 94

**KANSAS HEART HOSPITAL (170186)**, 3601 North Webb Road, Zip 67226–8129; tel. 316/630–5000 **A**9 10 **F**3 17 18 20 22 24 26 29 30 64 81 85 86 107 115 119
Primary Contact: Thomas L. Ashcom, M.D., Ph.D., Chief Executive Officer
COO: Joyce Heismeyer, Chief Operating Officer
CFO: Steve Smith, Chief Financial Officer
CHR: Teresa E. Wolfe, Manager Human Resources
CNO: Susan Bradford, Director Nursing
Web address: www.kansasheart.com
**Control:** Corporation, Investor–owned, for–profit **Service:** Heart

**Staffed Beds:** 54 **Admissions:** 1809 **Census:** 22 **Outpatient Visits:** 9052 **Births:** 0 **Personnel:** 185

**KANSAS SPINE AND SPECIALTY HOSPITAL (170196)**, 3333 North Webb Road, Zip 67226–8123; tel. 316/462–5000 **A**9 10 **F**3 29 79 81 82 85 87 107 111 114
Primary Contact: Thomas M. Schmitt, Chief Executive Officer
CFO: Kevin P. Vaughn, Chief Financial Officer
CIO: Michael Knocke, Chief Information Officer
CHR: Jean–Marie Jimeson, Manager Human Resources
Web address: www.ksspine.com
**Control:** Corporation, Investor–owned, for–profit **Service:** General Medical and Surgical

**Staffed Beds:** 36 **Admissions:** 2087 **Census:** 13 **Outpatient Visits:** 6085 **Births:** 0 **Personnel:** 100

**KANSAS SURGERY AND RECOVERY CENTER (170183)**, 2770 North Webb Road, Zip 67226–8112; tel. 316/634–0090 **A**9 10 **F**45 51 64 68 81 85 87 107 111 114 119
Primary Contact: Ely Bartal, M.D., Chief Executive Officer
CFO: Ashley Simon, Chief Financial Officer
CMO: Ely Bartal, M.D., Chief Executive Officer and Medical Director
CIO: Jonathan Wells, Supervisor Information Technology
CNO: Becky Bailey, R.N., Director Nursing
Web address: www.ksrc.org
**Control:** Partnership, Investor–owned, for–profit **Service:** General Medical and Surgical

**Staffed Beds:** 32 **Admissions:** 1428 **Census:** 9 **Outpatient Visits:** 6524 **Births:** 0 **Total Expense ($000):** 22750 **Payroll Expense ($000):** 5917 **Personnel:** 124

⊞ **ROBERT J. DOLE VETERANS AFFAIRS MEDICAL CENTER**, 5500 East Kellogg, Zip 67218–1607; tel. 316/685–2221, (Nonreporting) **A**1 3 5 **S** Department of Veterans Affairs, Washington, DC
Primary Contact: Francisco Vazquez, Director
CFO: Ronald Dreher, Finance Officer
CMO: Kent Murray, M.D., Chief of Staff
CIO: Sharon Williamson, Chief Information Technology
CHR: Nancy Gerstner, Manager Human Resources
Web address: www.wichita.va.gov
**Control:** Veterans Affairs, Government, federal **Service:** General Medical and Surgical

**Staffed Beds:** 41

⊞ **SELECT SPECIALTY HOSPITAL–WICHITA (172007)**, 929 North St. Francis Street, Zip 67214–3821; tel. 316/261–8303 **A**1 10 **F**1 3 12 18 29 50 56 61 75 82 84 85 86 87 130 148 **S** Select Medical Corporation, Mechanicsburg, PA
Primary Contact: Peggy Cliffe, Chief Executive Officer
CHR: Renee Schaffer, Coordinator Human Resources
CNO: Lindsey Cahoj, Chief Nursing Officer
Web address: www.selectspecialtyhospitals.com/company/locations/wichita.aspx
**Control:** Corporation, Investor–owned, for–profit **Service:** Long–Term Acute Care hospital

**Staffed Beds:** 48 **Admissions:** 564 **Census:** 41 **Outpatient Visits:** 0 **Births:** 0 **Total Expense ($000):** 20737 **Payroll Expense ($000):** 7435 **Personnel:** 138

**KS**

*Many Facility Codes have changed. Please refer to the AHA Guide Code Chart.* © 2015 AHA Guide

✠ **VIA CHRISTI HOSPITAL ON ST. FRANCIS (170122)**, 929 North St. Francis Street, Zip 67214–3882; tel. 316/268–5000, (Includes GOOD SHEPHERD CAMPUS, 8901 East Orme, Zip 67207; tel. 316/858–0333; ST. FRANCIS CAMPUS, 929 North St. Francis Street, tel. 316/268–5000; Sherry Hausmann, Senior Administrator; ST. JOSEPH CAMPUS, 3600 East Harry Street, Zip 67218–3713; tel. 316/685–1111; Claudio J. Ferraro, President) **A**1 2 3 5 9 10 13 **F**3 5 7 11 12 13 15 16 17 18 19 20 21 22 23 24 26 27 28 29 30 31 32 34 35 38 40 43 44 45 46 48 49 50 51 54 56 57 58 59 60 61 62 64 68 70 72 74 75 76 77 78 79 80 81 82 84 85 86 87 88 89 92 93 97 98 99 100 101 102 103 104 105 107 108 110 111 114 115 116 117 118 119 120 121 123 124 126 130 131 132 135 136 141 142 143 146 147 148 **P**6 **S** Ascension Health, Saint Louis, MO
Primary Contact: Sherry Hausmann, Senior Administrator
CFO: Jeff Seirer, Interim Chief Financial Officer
CMO: Darrell Youngman, D.O., Chief Medical Officer
CIO: Abdul Bengali, Chief Information Officer
CHR: Judy Espinoza, Chief Human Resources Officer
Web address: www.via–christi.org
**Control:** Church–operated, Nongovernment, not–for profit **Service:** General Medical and Surgical

**Staffed Beds:** 717 **Admissions:** 31346 **Census:** 425 **Outpatient Visits:** 319897 **Births:** 2673 **Total Expense ($000):** 507088 **Payroll Expense ($000):** 207081 **Personnel:** 3142

✠ **VIA CHRISTI HOSPITAL ON ST. TERESA (170200)**, 14800 West St. Teresa, Zip 67235–9602; tel. 316/796–7000 **A**1 9 10 **F**3 8 18 20 22 29 30 34 35 40 45 50 64 68 70 75 78 79 81 85 87 90 94 107 108 111 114 118 119 130 146 147 148 **S** Ascension Health, Saint Louis, MO
Primary Contact: Kevin Strecker, President
Web address: www.via–christi.org/st–teresa
**Control:** Church–operated, Nongovernment, not–for profit **Service:** General Medical and Surgical

**Staffed Beds:** 58 **Admissions:** 1628 **Census:** 20 **Outpatient Visits:** 19162 **Births:** 0 **Total Expense ($000):** 35610 **Payroll Expense ($000):** 11425 **Personnel:** 151

**VIA CHRISTI REGIONAL MEDICAL CENTER** See Via Christi Hospital on St. Francis

✠ **VIA CHRISTI REHABILITATION HOSPITAL (173028)**, 1151 North Rock Road, Zip 67206–1262; tel. 316/634–3400 **A**1 9 10 **F**11 29 30 34 35 44 50 54 57 59 64 77 86 87 90 92 93 94 95 96 119 129 130 131 132 143 146 148 **S** Ascension Health, Saint Louis, MO
Primary Contact: Cindy LaFleur, Senior Administrator
CMO: Kevin Rieg, M.D., President Medical Staff
CNO: Cindy Hagerty, Assistant Chief Nurse Officer and Administrator of Operations
Web address: www.via–christi.org
**Control:** Church–operated, Nongovernment, not–for profit **Service:** Rehabilitation

**Staffed Beds:** 58 **Admissions:** 650 **Census:** 21 **Outpatient Visits:** 102667 **Births:** 0 **Total Expense ($000):** 21740 **Payroll Expense ($000):** 10600 **Personnel:** 190

✠ **WESLEY MEDICAL CENTER (170123)**, 550 North Hillside, Zip 67214–4976; tel. 316/962–2000, (Includes GALICHIA HEART HOSPITAL, 2610 North Woodlawn, Zip 67220; tel. 316/858–2610; Steve Edgar, Chief Executive Officer; THE CHILDREN'S CENTER AT WESLEY, 550 North Hillside Street, Zip 67214–4910) **A**1 3 5 9 10 **F**3 7 11 12 13 15 17 18 19 20 22 24 26 28 29 30 31 34 35 37 39 40 41 42 43 44 45 46 47 48 49 50 51 54 55 56 57 58 59 60 64 65 68 70 72 73 74 76 78 79 81 82 85 86 87 88 89 92 93 94 97 100 102 107 108 110 111 114 115 119 120 121 123 126 129 130 131 132 134 135 146 147 148 **P**6 **S** HCA, Nashville, TN
Primary Contact: Bill Voloch, President and Chief Executive Officer
CFO: Matt Leary, Chief Financial Officer
CMO: Francie H. Ekengren, M.D., Chief Medical Officer
CIO: Jeffrey Schauf, Director Information Systems
CHR: Nikki Freeman, Vice President Human Resources
CNO: Joyce M. Soule, R.N., Chief Nursing Officer
Web address: www.wesleymc.com
**Control:** Corporation, Investor–owned, for–profit **Service:** General Medical and Surgical

**Staffed Beds:** 548 **Admissions:** 26144 **Census:** 337 **Outpatient Visits:** 234959 **Births:** 6049 **Personnel:** 2456

✠ **WESLEY REHABILITATION HOSPITAL (173027)**, 8338 West 13th Street North, Zip 67212–2984; tel. 316/729–9999 **A**1 9 10 **F**29 34 35 62 64 68 90 91 93 95 96 132 148 **S** HEALTHSOUTH Corporation, Birmingham, AL
Primary Contact: James F. Grocholski, FACHE, Chief Executive Officer
CFO: Bob Peck, Chief Financial Officer
CIO: Debbie Patterson, Director Health Information Management
CHR: Betty Shuman, Director Human Resources
CNO: Jessika M. Workman, Chief Nursing Officer
Web address: www.wesleyrehabhospital.com
**Control:** Corporation, Investor–owned, for–profit **Service:** Rehabilitation

**Staffed Beds:** 65 **Admissions:** 1002 **Census:** 36 **Outpatient Visits:** 25875 **Births:** 0 **Total Expense ($000):** 18337 **Payroll Expense ($000):** 8718 **Personnel:** 165

**WICHITA SPECIALTY HOSPITAL** See AMG Specialty Hospital–Wichita

### WINCHESTER—Jefferson County

★ **F. W. HUSTON MEDICAL CENTER (171314)**, 408 Delaware Street, Zip 66097–4003; tel. 913/774–4340, (Total facility includes 38 beds in nursing home–type unit) **A**9 10 18 **F**2 3 10 40 56 57 64 67 69 75 77 93 97 103 104 107 114 128 130 133 143 **P**6 8
Primary Contact: LaMont Cook, Administrator
CFO: Jason Johnson, Controller
CMO: William Greiner, M.D., Chief of Staff
CIO: Jason Johnson, Controller
CHR: Melody Keirns, Manager Human Resources
CNO: Heather R. Aranda, R.N., Chief Nursing Officer
Web address: www.jcmhospital.org
**Control:** Other not–for–profit (including NFP Corporation) **Service:** General Medical and Surgical

**Staffed Beds:** 69 **Admissions:** 70 **Census:** 32 **Outpatient Visits:** 5186 **Births:** 0 **Total Expense ($000):** 4904 **Payroll Expense ($000):** 3244 **Personnel:** 60

**JEFFERSON COUNTY MEMORIAL HOSPITAL** See F. W. Huston Medical Center

### WINFIELD—Cowley County

★ **WILLIAM NEWTON HOSPITAL (171383)**, 1300 East Fifth Street, Zip 67156–2407; tel. 620/221–2300 **A**3 5 9 10 18 **F**3 9 11 13 15 28 29 34 35 39 40 43 45 57 59 62 64 65 70 74 75 76 77 78 79 81 82 85 86 87 93 102 107 108 110 111 114 118 119 121 123 127 129 130 131 132 133 135 146 147 148
Primary Contact: J. Ben Quinton, Administrator
COO: Shona Salzman, Chief Operating Officer
CFO: Debbie Hockenbury, Assistant Administrator and Chief Financial Officer
CMO: Bryan Dennett, M.D., Chief of Staff
CIO: Randy Mayo, Director Information Technology
CHR: Cathy McClurg, Director Human Resources
CNO: Tina Wheeler, R.N., Director Nursing
Web address: www.wnmh.org
**Control:** City–Government, nonfederal **Service:** General Medical and Surgical

**Staffed Beds:** 25 **Admissions:** 1021 **Census:** 10 **Outpatient Visits:** 76447 **Births:** 245 **Total Expense ($000):** 29605 **Payroll Expense ($000):** 13428 **Personnel:** 261

---

**Hospital, Medicare Provider Number, Address, Telephone, Approval, Facility, and Physician Codes, Health Care System**

★ American Hospital Association (AHA) membership
☐ The Joint Commission accreditation
○ Healthcare Facilities Accreditation Program
◇ DNV Healthcare Inc. accreditation
⇑ Center for Improvement in Healthcare Quality Accreditation
△ Commission on Accreditation of Rehabilitation Facilities (CARF) accreditation

**KS**

# KENTUCKY

## ALBANY—Clinton County

**CLINTON COUNTY HOSPITAL (180106)**, 723 Burkesville Road,
Zip 42602–1654; tel. 606/387–6421, (Nonreporting) **A**9 10
Primary Contact: John David Mullins, Jr., Administrator
CHR: Pat Beard, Director Human Resources
Web address: www.clintoncountyhospital.com
**Control:** Other not-for-profit (including NFP Corporation) **Service:** General
Medical and Surgical

Staffed Beds: 42

## ASHLAND—Boyd County

☐ **KING'S DAUGHTERS MEDICAL CENTER (180009)**, 2201 Lexington Avenue,
Zip 41101–2874, Mailing Address: P.O. Box 151, Zip 41105–0151;
tel. 606/408–4000, (Nonreporting) **A**1 2 9 10
Primary Contact: Kristine Whitlatch, President and Chief Executive Officer
COO: Bob Lucas, Vice President Operations
CFO: Paul L. McDowell, Vice President Finance and Chief Financial Officer
CMO: Phil Fioret, M.D., Vice President Medical Affairs
CIO: David Oliver, Director Information Systems
CHR: Larry Higgins, Vice President Human Resources
Web address: www.kdmc.com
**Control:** Other not-for-profit (including NFP Corporation) **Service:** General
Medical and Surgical

Staffed Beds: 616

⊞ **OUR LADY OF BELLEFONTE HOSPITAL (180036)**, St. Christopher Drive,
Zip 41101, Mailing Address: P.O. Box 789, Zip 41105–0789; tel. 606/833–3333
**A**1 2 9 10 12 13 **F**3 4 5 8 11 12 15 18 19 20 28 29 30 31 34 35 37 39 40
44 45 49 50 53 54 55 56 57 58 59 62 64 65 66 69 70 71 74 75 77 78 79
81 82 84 85 86 87 89 93 96 97 98 100 101 102 103 106 107 108 110 111
114 115 118 119 129 130 131 132 135 143 144 145 146 147 148 **P**6 8
**S** Bon Secours Health System, Inc., Marriottsville, MD
Primary Contact: Kevin Halter, Chief Executive Officer
CFO: Joe Buchheit, Chief Financial Officer
CMO: Dan Goulson, M.D., Chief Medical Officer
CIO: Mike Gomez, Site Manager Medical Information Systems
CHR: Judy Daniels, Vice President Human Resources
Web address: www.olbh.com
**Control:** Church-operated, Nongovernment, not-for profit **Service:** General
Medical and Surgical

Staffed Beds: 151 Admissions: 6764 Census: 76 Outpatient Visits: 235937
Births: 0 Total Expense ($000): 137876 Payroll Expense ($000): 43243
Personnel: 1222

## BARBOURVILLE—Knox County

☐ **KNOX COUNTY HOSPITAL (181328)**, 80 Hospital Drive, Zip 40906–7363,
Mailing Address: P.O. Box 10, Zip 40906–0010; tel. 606/546–4175,
(Nonreporting) **A**1 9 10 18 **S** Pacer Health Corporation, Miami Lakes, FL
Primary Contact: Ray B. Canady, Chief Executive Officer and Administrator
CFO: Amanda Ellis, Chief Financial Officer
CMO: Kamran Hasni, M.D., Chief of Medical Staff
CIO: Evan Davis, Director Technology and Environmental Services
CHR: Janet Wilder, Director Human Resources
CNO: Brenda Graham, Chief Nursing Officer
Web address: www.knoxcohospital.com
**Control:** Corporation, Investor-owned, for-profit **Service:** General Medical and
Surgical

Staffed Beds: 25

## BARDSTOWN—Nelson County

⊞ **FLAGET MEMORIAL HOSPITAL (180025)**, 4305 New Shepherdsville Road,
Zip 40004–9019; tel. 502/350–5000, (Total facility includes 40 beds in nursing
home–type unit) **A**1 2 9 10 **F**11 12 13 15 18 28 29 30 31 34 35 37 40 45 49
59 62 63 64 70 76 78 79 81 82 84 85 87 96 107 111 116 117 119 127 128
129 130 132 144 146 147 148 **P**6 **S** Catholic Health Initiatives, Englewood, CO
Primary Contact: Beverly Sue Downs, R.N., MSN, FACHE, President
COO: Norma Goss, R.N., Chief Operating Officer and Chief Nursing Officer
CFO: Mendy Evans, Vice President of Finance
CMO: Sanjiv Mehta, Chief of Staff
CNO: Norma Goss, R.N., Chief Operating Officer and Chief Nursing Officer
Web address: www.flaget.com
**Control:** Other not-for-profit (including NFP Corporation) **Service:** General
Medical and Surgical

Staffed Beds: 52 Admissions: 1953 Census: 52 Outpatient Visits: 72556
Births: 258 Total Expense ($000): 69314 Payroll Expense ($000): 15551
Personnel: 307

## BENTON—Marshall County

⊞ **MARSHALL COUNTY HOSPITAL (181327)**, 615 Old Symsonia Road,
Zip 42025–5042; tel. 270/527–4800 **A**1 9 10 18 **F**3 7 11 15 18 19 28 29 30
34 35 40 57 59 62 77 79 81 85 89 90 93 107 108 119 128 132 133 135 **P**6
Primary Contact: David G. Fuqua, Chief Executive Officer
CFO: Janice Kelley, Chief Financial Officer
CMO: Kim Hall, M.D., Chief of Staff
CIO: Patrick Waters, Director Information Technology
CHR: Jeannie Lee, Director Human Resources
Web address: www.marshallcountyhospital.org
**Control:** Hospital district or authority, Government, nonfederal **Service:** General
Medical and Surgical

Staffed Beds: 25 Admissions: 963 Census: 10 Outpatient Visits: 135573
Births: 0 Total Expense ($000): 18759 Payroll Expense ($000): 7493
Personnel: 215

## BEREA—Madison County

⊞ **SAINT JOSEPH BEREA (181329)**, 305 Estill Street, Zip 40403–1909;
tel. 859/986–3151 **A**1 5 9 10 18 **F**3 29 40 45 70 77 79 81 82 91 97 107
111 114 119 133 **P**4 **S** Catholic Health Initiatives, Englewood, CO
Primary Contact: Eric Gilliam, Chief Executive Officer
CFO: Christy Spitser, Vice President Finance
CMO: Patrick Kelleher, M.D., Chief Medical Staff
CHR: Sandra Turquesa, Human Resources Business Partner
CNO: Leslie Adams, Chief Nursing Executive
Web address: www.kentuckyonehealth.org/berea
**Control:** Church-operated, Nongovernment, not-for profit **Service:** General
Medical and Surgical

Staffed Beds: 25 Admissions: 973 Census: 21 Outpatient Visits: 77799
Births: 0 Total Expense ($000): 27683 Payroll Expense ($000): 9503
Personnel: 157

## BOWLING GREEN—Warren County

☐ **COMMONWEALTH REGIONAL SPECIALTY HOSPITAL (182005)**, 250 Park
Drive, 6th Floor, Zip 42101–1760, Mailing Address: P.O. Box 90010,
Zip 42102–9010; tel. 270/796–6200 **A**1 10 **F**1 3 29 30 34 35 50 57 68 84
85 87 130 135 143 146 148 **P**6 **S** Commonwealth Health Corporation, Bowling
Green, KY
Primary Contact: Christa Atkins, Administrator
CFO: Ronald G. Sowell, Executive Vice President
CMO: Doug Thomson, M.D., Chief Medical Officer
CIO: Jean Cherry, Executive Vice President
CHR: Lynn Williams, Vice President
Web address: www.commonwealthregionalspecialtyhospital.org
**Control:** Other not-for-profit (including NFP Corporation) **Service:** Long-Term
Acute Care hospital

Staffed Beds: 24 Admissions: 227 Census: 17 Outpatient Visits: 0 Births:
0 Personnel: 58

☐ **MEDICAL CENTER AT BOWLING GREEN (180013)**, 250 Park Street,
Zip 42101–1795, Mailing Address: P.O. Box 90010, Zip 42102–9010;
tel. 270/745–1000 **A**1 2 9 10 13 19 **F**1 3 7 12 13 15 17 18 20 22 24 26 28
29 30 31 34 35 37 39 40 46 50 51 56 57 59 60 62 64 68 70 72 74 75 76
78 79 81 82 85 86 87 89 91 93 98 99 100 102 103 104 105 107 108 110
111 114 115 116 117 118 119 120 121 123 124 129 130 132 135 145 146
147 148 **P**6 **S** Commonwealth Health Corporation, Bowling Green, KY
Primary Contact: Connie Smith, Chief Executive Officer
CFO: Ronald G. Sowell, Executive Vice President
CIO: Mark Brookman, Chief Information Officer
CHR: Lynn Williams, Vice President Human Resources
CNO: Betsy Kullman, R.N., Executive Vice President and Chief Nursing Officer
Web address: www.themedicalcenter.org
**Control:** Other not-for-profit (including NFP Corporation) **Service:** General
Medical and Surgical

Staffed Beds: 337 Admissions: 16353 Census: 222 Outpatient Visits:
129162 Births: 2370 Personnel: 1678

☐ **RIVENDELL BEHAVIORAL HEALTH (184017)**, 1035 Porter Pike,
Zip 42103–9581; tel. 270/843–1199, (Nonreporting) **A**1 9 10 **S** Universal Health
Services, Inc., King of Prussia, PA
Primary Contact: Matt Ours, Chief Executive Officer and Managing Director
CFO: Tim Gore, Chief Financial Officer
Web address: www.rivendellbehavioral.com
**Control:** Corporation, Investor-owned, for-profit **Service:** Psychiatric

Staffed Beds: 125

*Many Facility Codes have changed. Please refer to the AHA Guide Code Chart.*
© 2015 AHA Guide

⊠ △ **SOUTHERN KENTUCKY REHABILITATION HOSPITAL (183029)**, 1300 Campbell Lane, Zip 42104–4162; tel. 270/782–6900, (Nonreporting) **A**1 7 9 10 **S** Vibra Healthcare, Mechanicsburg, PA
Primary Contact: Stuart Locke, Chief Executive Officer
COO: Dana Lewis, Director Clinical Services
CMO: Jim Farrage, M.D., Medical Director
CHR: Suzanne Cornett, Director Human Resources
Web address: www.skyrehab.com
**Control:** Corporation, Investor–owned, for–profit **Service:** Rehabilitation

**Staffed Beds:** 60

⊠ **TRISTAR GREENVIEW REGIONAL HOSPITAL (180124)**, 1801 Ashley Circle, Zip 42104–3362; tel. 270/793–1000 **A**1 2 9 10 19 **F**3 8 11 15 18 20 22 29 31 34 35 37 40 45 46 48 49 50 51 57 59 64 65 68 70 74 75 77 78 79 81 82 85 86 87 107 108 110 111 114 118 119 126 128 130 132 133 135 145 146 **S** HCA, Nashville, TN
Primary Contact: Michael Sherrod, Chief Executive Officer
COO: Andrew Bedi, Chief Operating Officer
CFO: Richard Patterson, Chief Financial Officer
CMO: Nagy Morsi, Chief of Staff
CIO: Cyndi Talley, Director Information Systems
CHR: Judy Fulkerson, Director Human Resources
CNO: Anne Leonard, R.N., Chief Nursing Officer
Web address: www.greenviewhospital.com
**Control:** Corporation, Investor–owned, for–profit **Service:** General Medical and Surgical

**Staffed Beds:** 167 **Admissions:** 5056 **Census:** 61 **Outpatient Visits:** 52962 **Births:** 0 **Total Expense ($000):** 91722 **Payroll Expense ($000):** 30558 **Personnel:** 474

### BURKESVILLE—Cumberland County

**CUMBERLAND COUNTY HOSPITAL (181317)**, 299 Glasgow Road, Zip 42717–9696, Mailing Address: P.O. Box 280, Zip 42717–0280; tel. 270/864–2511, (Nonreporting) **A**9 10 18
Primary Contact: Richard Neikirk, Chief Executive Officer
CFO: Rick Capps, Chief Financial Officer
CMO: Christian Konsavage, M.D., Chief of Staff
CHR: Martha Young, Director Human Resources
Web address: www.cchospital.org
**Control:** Other not–for–profit (including NFP Corporation) **Service:** General Medical and Surgical

**Staffed Beds:** 25

### CADIZ—Trigg County

★ **TRIGG COUNTY HOSPITAL (181304)**, 254 Main Street, Zip 42211–9153, Mailing Address: P.O. Box 312, Zip 42211–0312; tel. 270/522–3215 **A**9 10 18 **F**3 7 8 11 15 29 30 34 40 45 50 54 57 59 68 75 77 81 87 93 97 100 101 102 103 104 107 111 114 119 127 130 133 135 143 **P**6
Primary Contact: John Sumner, Chief Executive Officer
CFO: Liz Snodgrass, Chief Financial Officer
CMO: Stuart Harris, M.D., Chief of Staff
CHR: Janet James, Director Human Resources
Web address: www.trigghospital.org
**Control:** County–Government, nonfederal **Service:** General Medical and Surgical

**Staffed Beds:** 25 **Admissions:** 461 **Census:** 7 **Outpatient Visits:** 19521 **Births:** 0 **Total Expense ($000):** 15433 **Payroll Expense ($000):** 6846 **Personnel:** 153

### CAMPBELLSVILLE—Taylor County

⊠ **TAYLOR REGIONAL HOSPITAL (180087)**, 1700 Old Lebanon Road, Zip 42718–9600; tel. 270/465–3561 **A**1 2 9 10 **F**3 8 11 13 15 18 20 28 29 30 31 34 35 39 40 43 45 46 48 49 50 51 54 56 57 59 64 68 70 74 75 76 77 78 79 81 85 86 93 97 107 108 110 111 114 117 119 120 127 129 130 131 132 134 135 141 143 146 147 148 **S** Catholic Health Initiatives, Englewood, CO
Primary Contact: Jane Wheatley, Chief Executive Officer
CFO: Paul Phillips, Chief Financial Officer
CIO: Christopher Michael Gibbs, Director Information Management Systems
CHR: Andrea Settle, Director Human Resources
Web address: www.trhosp.org
**Control:** Hospital district or authority, Government, nonfederal **Service:** General Medical and Surgical

**Staffed Beds:** 90 **Admissions:** 2567 **Census:** 28 **Outpatient Visits:** 91098 **Births:** 345 **Total Expense ($000):** 65584 **Payroll Expense ($000):** 28863 **Personnel:** 591

### CARROLLTON—Carroll County

★ **CARROLL COUNTY MEMORIAL HOSPITAL (181310)**, 309 11th Street, Zip 41008–1400; tel. 502/732–4321 **A**9 10 18 **F**3 11 15 18 28 29 34 40 45 50 56 57 59 74 75 77 78 79 81 82 85 86 93 94 97 107 108 111 114 119 127 128 129 130 133 144 **P**6 **S** Alliant Management Services, Louisville, KY
Primary Contact: Michael A. Kozar, Chief Executive Officer
CMO: Kathy Short, D.O., Family Practice
CHR: Kimberly Adams, Manager Human Resources
CNO: Lisa Penick, R.N., Chief Nursing Officer
Web address: www.ccmhosp.com
**Control:** Hospital district or authority, Government, nonfederal **Service:** General Medical and Surgical

**Staffed Beds:** 25 **Admissions:** 668 **Census:** 6 **Outpatient Visits:** 11086 **Births:** 0

### COLUMBIA—Adair County

⊠ **WESTLAKE REGIONAL HOSPITAL (180149)**, 901 Westlake Drive, Zip 42728–1123, Mailing Address: P.O. Box 1269, Zip 42728–6269; tel. 270/384–4753 **A**1 9 10 **F**4 15 29 38 40 45 57 81 87 93 97 98 100 103 105 107 111 119 127 130 133 147
Primary Contact: Neal Gold, Chief Executive Officer
CFO: David R. Hayes, Chief Financial Officer
CMO: Charles Giles, M.D., President Medical Staff
CHR: Tonya Grant, Director Human Resources
CNO: Gidgett Warren, Director of Nursing
Web address: www.westlakeregionalhospital.com
**Control:** Hospital district or authority, Government, nonfederal **Service:** General Medical and Surgical

**Staffed Beds:** 32 **Admissions:** 790 **Census:** 11 **Outpatient Visits:** 9738 **Births:** 0

### CORBIN—Whitley County

★ ◇ **BAPTIST HEALTH CORBIN (180080)**, 1 Trillium Way, Zip 40701–8420; tel. 606/528–1212 **A**9 10 19 21 **F**1 3 4 5 12 13 15 18 20 22 26 28 29 30 31 32 34 35 38 40 45 47 48 49 51 53 54 57 59 64 68 70 73 78 79 81 84 85 86 87 89 90 93 96 98 99 100 101 102 103 104 105 107 108 110 111 114 115 118 119 126 130 132 133 135 145 146 147 148 **S** Baptist Health, Louisville, KY
Primary Contact: Larry Gray, President
CMO: David Worthy, M.D., Vice President and Chief Medical Officer
CIO: Jeff Thurmond, Vice President Information Systems
CHR: Tim Perry, Executive Director Human Services
CNO: Anthony Powers, Vice President Patient Care Services
Web address: www.baptistregional.com
**Control:** Other not–for–profit (including NFP Corporation) **Service:** General Medical and Surgical

**Staffed Beds:** 273 **Admissions:** 8875 **Census:** 115 **Outpatient Visits:** 134465 **Births:** 859 **Total Expense ($000):** 134377 **Payroll Expense ($000):** 46606 **Personnel:** 1048

◇ **CONTINUECARE HOSPITAL AT BAPTIST HEALTH CORBIN (182006)**, 1 Trillium Way, Lower Level, Zip 40701–8727; tel. 606/523–5150 **A**10 21 **F**1 3 29 30 39 60 130 148 **S** Community Hospital Corporation, Plano, TX
Primary Contact: R. Alan Coppock, FACHE, President
COO: Wilson Weber, Chief Operating Officer
CFO: Kliff Rodgers, Chief Financial Officer
CMO: Steve Morton, M.D., Chief Medical Officer
CIO: Brian Doerr, Chief Information Officer
CHR: Amie Marcum, Human Resources Coordinator
CNO: Della Rains, Chief Nursing Officer
Web address: www.continuecare.org
**Control:** Other not–for–profit (including NFP Corporation) **Service:** Long–Term Acute Care hospital

**Staffed Beds:** 32 **Admissions:** 201 **Census:** 17 **Outpatient Visits:** 0 **Births:** 0 **Total Expense ($000):** 7402 **Payroll Expense ($000):** 2959 **Personnel:** 97

### COVINGTON—Kenton County

**NORTHKEY COMMUNITY CARE (184006)**, 502 Farrell Drive, Zip 41011–3799, Mailing Address: P.O. Box 2680, Zip 41012–2680; tel. 859/578–3200, (Nonreporting) **A**9 10
Primary Contact: Owen Nichols, PsyD, President and Chief Executive Officer
CFO: John Metzger, Controller
Web address: www.northkey.org
**Control:** Other not–for–profit (including NFP Corporation) **Service:** Children's hospital psychiatric

**Staffed Beds:** 25

**ST. ELIZABETH MEDICAL CENTER–NORTH** See St. Elizabeth Covington

---

**Hospital, Medicare Provider Number, Address, Telephone, Approval, Facility, and Physician Codes, Health Care System**

★ American Hospital Association (AHA) membership ○ Healthcare Facilities Accreditation Program ⇑ Center for Improvement in Healthcare Quality Accreditation
□ The Joint Commission accreditation ◇ DNV Healthcare Inc. accreditation △ Commission on Accreditation of Rehabilitation Facilities (CARF) accreditation

**CYNTHIANA—Harrison County**

✠ **HARRISON MEMORIAL HOSPITAL (180079)**, 1210 KY Highway 36E,
Zip 41031–7498; tel. 859/234–2300 **A**1 9 10 **F**3 11 13 15 18 20 28 29 30
31 34 35 36 39 40 44 45 47 49 50 53 57 59 61 64 68 69 70 74 75 76 77
78 79 81 82 85 86 87 89 93 97 107 108 111 115 118 119 129 130 131
132 133 135 146 147 148 **P**6
Primary Contact: Sheila Currans, Chief Executive Officer
CFO: David Mellett, Chief Financial Officer
CIO: Martha Sullivan, Chief Information Officer
CHR: Rebecca Jenkins, Director Human Resources Management
CNO: Wendy Reeder, R.N., Chief Nursing Officer
Web address: www.harrisonmemhosp.com
**Control:** Other not–for–profit (including NFP Corporation) **Service:** General
Medical and Surgical

**Staffed Beds:** 49 **Admissions:** 1300 **Census:** 12 **Outpatient Visits:** 52083
**Births:** 246 **Total Expense ($000):** 35019 **Payroll Expense ($000):** 15572
**Personnel:** 357

**DANVILLE—Boyle County**

✠ **EPHRAIM MCDOWELL REGIONAL MEDICAL CENTER (180048)**, 217 South
Third Street, Zip 40422–1823; tel. 859/239–1000, (Total facility includes 24
beds in nursing home–type unit) **A**1 5 9 10 19 **F**1 3 4 8 10 11 13 15 16 17 18
20 22 28 29 30 31 32 34 35 40 43 45 46 49 51 53 57 59 60 64 65 66
67 70 72 73 74 75 76 77 78 79 80 81 82 84 85 87 88 89 90 93 96 97 98
100 101 102 103 107 108 110 111 114 117 118 119 124 125 127 128 129
130 132 144 146 147 148 **P**5 **S** Ephraim McDowell Health, Danville, KY
Primary Contact: Vicki A. Darnell, R.N., MSN, President and Chief Executive
Officer
COO: Sally M. Davenport, MS, Chief Nursing Officer and Chief Operating Officer
CFO: William R. Snapp, III, Vice President Finance and Chief Financial Officer
CMO: Eric Guerrant, M.D., President Medical Staff
CIO: Angela Allen–Johnson, Director Information Services
CHR: Carl Metz, Vice President Human Resources
CNO: Sally M. Davenport, MS, Chief Nursing Officer and Chief Operating Officer
Web address: www.emrmc.org
**Control:** Other not–for–profit (including NFP Corporation) **Service:** General
Medical and Surgical

**Staffed Beds:** 159 **Admissions:** 6655 **Census:** 92 **Outpatient Visits:** 141003
**Births:** 627 **Total Expense ($000):** 138767 **Payroll Expense ($000):** 46821
**Personnel:** 983

**EDGEWOOD—Kenton County**

✠ **HEALTHSOUTH NORTHERN KENTUCKY REHABILITATION HOSPITAL
(183027)**, 201 Medical Village Drive, Zip 41017–3407; tel. 859/341–2044 **A**1
9 10 **F**28 29 64 79 82 90 93 94 **S** HEALTHSOUTH Corporation, Birmingham, AL
Primary Contact: Richard R. Evens, Chief Executive Officer
CFO: Lisa McGue, Controller
CMO: Neal Moser, M.D., Medical Director
CHR: Bridgette Keith, Director Human Resources
CNO: Terri Ballard, Chief Nursing Officer
Web address: www.healthsouthkentucky.com
**Control:** Corporation, Investor–owned, for–profit **Service:** Rehabilitation

**Staffed Beds:** 40 **Admissions:** 1222 **Census:** 38 **Outpatient Visits:** 3370
**Births:** 0 **Total Expense ($000):** 12877 **Payroll Expense ($000):** 7449
**Personnel:** 134

☐ **ST. ELIZABETH EDGEWOOD (180035)**, 1 Medical Village Drive,
Zip 41017–3403; tel. 859/301–2000, (Includes ST. ELIZABETH COVINGTON,
1500 James Simpson Jr. Way, Covington, Zip 41014–1585; tel. 859/655–8800)
**A**1 2 3 5 9 10 **F**3 5 8 13 14 15 17 18 20 22 24 26 28 29 30 31 34 35 36 38
40 44 45 46 47 48 49 50 51 58 59 60 63 64 68 70 71 72 73 74 75 76
77 78 79 80 81 82 83 84 85 86 87 92 93 97 98 100 103 104 105 107 108
109 110 111 114 115 116 117 118 119 120 121 123 126 129 130 131 132
135 145 146 147 148 **S** St. Elizabeth Healthcare, Edgewood, KY
Primary Contact: Garren Colvin, Chief Executive Officer
CMO: Karl Schmitt, M.D., Chief of Staff
CIO: Alex Rodriguez, Vice President and Chief Information Officer
CHR: Martin Oscadal, Vice President Human Resources
Web address: www.stelizabeth.com
**Control:** Church–operated, Nongovernment, not–for profit **Service:** General
Medical and Surgical

**Staffed Beds:** 499 **Admissions:** 26640 **Census:** 326 **Outpatient Visits:**
922106 **Births:** 4481 **Total Expense ($000):** 591163 **Payroll Expense
($000):** 229661 **Personnel:** 3000

**ST. ELIZABETH HEALTHCARE–EDGEWOOD** See St. Elizabeth Edgewood

**ELIZABETHTOWN—Hardin County**

✠ **HARDIN MEMORIAL HOSPITAL (180012)**, 913 North Dixie Avenue,
Zip 42701–2503; tel. 270/737–1212, (Nonreporting) **A**1 2 5 9 10 19 **S** Baptist
Health, Louisville, KY
Primary Contact: Dennis B. Johnson, President & CEO
COO: Diane Logsdon, Vice President Planning and Development
CFO: John Dempsey, Vice President and Chief Financial Officer
CMO: Stephen Toadvine, M.D., Chief Medical Officer
CIO: Trey Hyberger, Director Information Technology
CHR: Kathy Fetterley, Vice President and Chief Human Resources Officer
CNO: Sharon Wright, R.N., Vice President and Chief Nursing Officer
Web address: www.hmh.net
**Control:** County–Government, nonfederal **Service:** General Medical and Surgical

**Staffed Beds:** 268

✠ **HEALTHSOUTH LAKEVIEW REHABILITATION HOSPITAL (183028)**, 134
Heartland Drive, Zip 42701–2778; tel. 270/769–3100, (Nonreporting) **A**1 10
**S** HEALTHSOUTH Corporation, Birmingham, AL
Primary Contact: Lori Jarboe, Chief Executive Officer
CFO: Scott Hart, Controller
CMO: Toni Abang, M.D., Medical Director
CHR: Janet Morris, Director Human Resources
Web address: www.healthsouthlakeview.com
**Control:** Corporation, Investor–owned, for–profit **Service:** Rehabilitation

**Staffed Beds:** 40

**FLEMINGSBURG—Fleming County**

✠ **FLEMING COUNTY HOSPITAL (180053)**, 55 Foundation Drive,
Zip 41041–9815, Mailing Address: P.O. Box 388, Zip 41041–0388;
tel. 606/849–5000 **A**1 9 10 **F**11 15 28 29 31 34 35 40 45 50 57 59 78 79
81 87 93 107 108 110 111 114 118 119 129 130 133 135 146 **P**6
**S** LifePoint Health, Brentwood, TN
Primary Contact: Michael Clark, Interim Chief Executive Officer
CFO: James McGonnell, Interim Chief Financial Officer
CMO: Glen Womack, M.D., Chief of Staff
CIO: Don Daugherty, Director Information Systems
CHR: Marsha Mitchell, Director Human Resources
CNO: Lynda Skaggs, Chief Nursing Officer
Web address: www.flemingcountyhospital.org
**Control:** Other not–for–profit (including NFP Corporation) **Service:** General
Medical and Surgical

**Staffed Beds:** 52 **Admissions:** 1474 **Census:** 16 **Outpatient Visits:** 26707
**Births:** 0 **Total Expense ($000):** 23047 **Payroll Expense ($000):** 8616
**Personnel:** 200

**FLORENCE—Boone County**

☐ **GATEWAY REHABILITATION HOSPITAL (183030)**, 5940 Merchant Street,
Zip 41042–1158; tel. 859/426–2400, (Nonreporting) **A**1 9 10 **S** Vibra
Healthcare, Mechanicsburg, PA
Primary Contact: Elizabeth Cooley, Chief Executive Officer
CFO: Margaret Cesarez, Chief Financial Officer
CNO: Jenna Wellbrock, Chief Nursing Officer
Web address: www.gatewayflorence.com/
**Control:** Corporation, Investor–owned, for–profit **Service:** Rehabilitation

**Staffed Beds:** 40

☐ **ST. ELIZABETH FLORENCE (180045)**, 4900 Houston Road, Zip 41042–4824;
tel. 859/212–5200 **A**1 9 10 **F**3 11 12 15 20 28 29 30 34 35 39 40 42 44 45
47 48 49 50 55 56 57 59 60 64 70 71 74 75 77 78 79 80 81 82 84 85 86
87 92 93 97 98 100 101 102 107 108 110 111 114 115 118 119 126 128
129 130 132 135 145 146 147 148 **S** St. Elizabeth Healthcare, Edgewood, KY
Primary Contact: Garren Colvin, Chief Executive Officer
COO: Chris Carle, Senior Vice President and Chief Operating Officer
CMO: George Hall, M.D., Vice President Medical Affairs
CIO: Alex Rodriguez, Vice President and Chief Information Officer
CHR: Martin Oscadal, Senior Vice President Human Resources
Web address: www.stelizabeth.com
**Control:** Church–operated, Nongovernment, not–for profit **Service:** General
Medical and Surgical

**Staffed Beds:** 169 **Admissions:** 9719 **Census:** 111 **Outpatient Visits:**
170897 **Births:** 0 **Total Expense ($000):** 114897 **Payroll Expense ($000):**
40309 **Personnel:** 639

**ST. ELIZABETH HEALTHCARE FLORENCE** See St. Elizabeth Florence

**FORT CAMPBELL—Montgomery County**

✠ **COLONEL FLORENCE A. BLANCHFIELD ARMY COMMUNITY HOSPITAL**,
650 Joel Drive, Zip 42223–5318; tel. 270/798–8040, (Nonreporting) **A**1 3 5
**S** Department of the Army, Office of the Surgeon General, Falls Church, VA
Primary Contact: Colonel Paul Cordts, Commander
CMO: Lieutenant Colonel Michael Place, M.D., Deputy Commander Clinical
Services
CHR: Major Travis Burchett, Troop Commander Human Resources
Web address: www.campbell.amedd.army.mil/
**Control:** Army, Government, federal **Service:** General Medical and Surgical

**Staffed Beds:** 66

*Many Facility Codes have changed. Please refer to the AHA Guide Code Chart.*
© 2015 AHA Guide

## FORT KNOX—Hardin County

✠ **IRELAND ARMY COMMUNITY HOSPITAL**, 289 Ireland Avenue, Zip 40121–5111; tel. 502/624–9333, (Nonreporting) **A**1 5 **S** Department of the Army, Office of the Surgeon General, Falls Church, VA
Primary Contact: Colonel Robert Cornes, Commander
Web address: www.iach.knox.amedd.army.mil/
**Control:** Army, Government, federal **Service:** General Medical and Surgical

| Staffed Beds: 33 |

## FORT THOMAS—Campbell County

**CARDINAL HILL SPECIALTY HOSPITAL** See Select Specialty Hospital–Northern Kentucky

✠ **SELECT SPECIALTY HOSPITAL–NORTHERN KENTUCKY (182004)**, 85 North Grand Avenue, Zip 41075–1793; tel. 859/572–3880, (Nonreporting) **A**1 10 **S** Select Medical Corporation, Mechanicsburg, PA
Primary Contact: Victor J. Galfano, FACHE, Chief Executive Officer
Web address: www.selectspecialtyhospitals.com/company/locations/northern–kentucky.aspx
**Control:** Corporation, Investor–owned, for–profit **Service:** Long–Term Acute Care hospital

| Staffed Beds: 33 |

☐ **ST. ELIZABETH FORT THOMAS (180001)**, 85 North Grand Avenue, Zip 41075–1796; tel. 859/572–3100 **A**1 2 9 10 **F**3 4 5 11 15 17 18 20 28 29 30 31 34 35 39 40 44 45 47 48 49 50 51 55 56 57 59 60 61 63 64 70 71 74 75 77 78 79 80 81 82 85 86 87 92 93 97 100 101 102 107 108 110 111 114 115 118 119 120 121 123 126 128 129 130 135 146 147 **S** St. Elizabeth Healthcare, Edgewood, KY
Primary Contact: Garren Colvin, Chief Executive Officer
COO: Thomas Saalfeld, Senior Vice President and Chief Operating Officer
CMO: George Hall, M.D., Vice President Medical Affairs
CIO: Alex Rodriguez, Vice President and Chief Information Officer
CHR: Martin Oscadal, Senior Vice President Human Resources
Web address: www.stelizabeth.com
**Control:** Church–operated, Nongovernment, not–for profit **Service:** General Medical and Surgical

| Staffed Beds: 171 Admissions: 7418 Census: 99 Outpatient Visits: 131143 Births: 0 Total Expense ($000): 101949 Payroll Expense ($000): 37865 Personnel: 570 |

**ST. ELIZABETH HEALTHCARE FORT THOMAS** See St. Elizabeth Fort Thomas

## FRANKFORT—Franklin County

✠ **FRANKFORT REGIONAL MEDICAL CENTER (180127)**, 299 King's Daughters Drive, Zip 40601–4186; tel. 502/875–5240 **A**1 2 3 9 10 19 **F**3 13 15 18 20 22 28 29 30 31 34 40 43 45 49 50 51 57 60 64 68 70 72 74 75 76 77 78 79 81 82 85 87 89 93 107 111 119 124 129 130 133 145 146 147 148 **S** HCA, Nashville, TN
Primary Contact: Chip Peal, Chief Executive Officer
CMO: Willis P. McKee, Jr., M.D., Chief Medical Officer
CIO: Craig Willard, Director Information Technology and Systems
CHR: Bev Young, Director Human Resources
Web address: www.frankfortregional.com
**Control:** Corporation, Investor–owned, for–profit **Service:** Long–Term Acute Care hospital

| Staffed Beds: 103 Admissions: 5103 Census: 56 Outpatient Visits: 89299 Births: 795 Total Expense ($000): 76548 Payroll Expense ($000): 27793 Personnel: 428 |

## FRANKLIN—Simpson County

✠ **MEDICAL CENTER AT FRANKLIN (181318)**, 1100 Brookhaven Road, Zip 42134–2746; tel. 270/598–4800 **A**1 9 10 18 **F**3 15 28 29 30 34 35 40 46 57 59 64 68 75 77 81 86 87 107 108 110 111 114 119 127 130 133 135 146 148 **P**6 **S** Commonwealth Health Corporation, Bowling Green, KY
Primary Contact: Eric Hagan, R.N., Vice President/Administrator
CFO: Ronald G. Sowell, Executive Vice President
CIO: Jean Cherry, Executive Vice President & Chief Information Officer
Web address: www.themedicalcenterfranklin.org
**Control:** Other not–for–profit (including NFP Corporation) **Service:** General Medical and Surgical

| Staffed Beds: 25 Admissions: 1023 Census: 19 Outpatient Visits: 21689 Births: 0 Personnel: 119 |

## GEORGETOWN—Scott County

✠ **GEORGETOWN COMMUNITY HOSPITAL (180101)**, 1140 Lexington Road, Zip 40324–9362; tel. 502/868–1100 **A**1 5 9 10 **F**3 11 12 13 15 18 28 29 30 31 34 35 40 45 46 48 49 50 57 59 60 65 66 70 74 75 76 78 79 81 82 85 87 91 92 93 100 107 108 109 110 111 114 115 116 117 119 124 126 129 130 131 132 133 146 147 **S** LifePoint Health, Brentwood, TN
Primary Contact: William Haugh, Administrator
CFO: Patrick C. Bolander, Chief Financial Officer
CMO: Brian Allen, M.D., President Medical Staff
CHR: Marrianne Slonina, Director Human Resources
Web address: www.georgetowncommunityhospital.com
**Control:** Corporation, Investor–owned, for–profit **Service:** General Medical and Surgical

| Staffed Beds: 58 Admissions: 1990 Census: 17 Outpatient Visits: 64580 Births: 209 Total Expense ($000): 43788 Payroll Expense ($000): 14732 Personnel: 269 |

## GLASGOW—Barren County

☐ **T. J. SAMSON COMMUNITY HOSPITAL (180017)**, 1301 North Race Street, Zip 42141–3483; tel. 270/651–4444, (Nonreporting) **A**1 3 5 9 10 19
Primary Contact: Bud Wethington, Chief Executive Officer
COO: Margie Gentry, Controller
CFO: Steve Fischer, Chief Financial Officer
CMO: Michael Shadowen, M.D., Chief of Staff
CIO: Scott Werkstell, Director Information System
CHR: LaDonna Rogers, Director Human Resources
CNO: Margaret Billingsley, R.N., Chief Nursing Officer
Web address: www.tjsamson.org
**Control:** Other not–for–profit (including NFP Corporation) **Service:** General Medical and Surgical

| Staffed Beds: 196 |

## GREENSBURG—Green County

**JANE TODD CRAWFORD HOSPITAL (181325)**, 202–206 Milby Street, Zip 42743–1100, Mailing Address: P.O. Box 220, Zip 42743–0220; tel. 270/932–4211, (Nonreporting) **A**9 10 18
Primary Contact: Rex A. Tungate, Administrator
CMO: James G. Bland, M.D., Chief of Staff
**Control:** County–Government, nonfederal **Service:** General Medical and Surgical

| Staffed Beds: 45 |

## GREENVILLE—Muhlenberg County

✠ **OWENSBORO HEALTH MUHLENBERG COMMUNITY HOSPITAL (180004)**, 440 Hopkinsville Street, Zip 42345–1172, Mailing Address: P.O. Box 387, Zip 42345–0387; tel. 270/338–8000, (Nonreporting) **A**1 9 10 **S** Alliant Management Services, Louisville, KY
Primary Contact: Ed Heath, Chief Executive Officer
CMO: Vincent P. Genovese, M.D., President Medical Staff
CIO: Alan Trail, Director Information Systems
CHR: Lisa R. Hope, Director Human Resources
CNO: Kathy Mitchell, Chief Nursing Officer
Web address: www.mchky.org
**Control:** Other not–for–profit (including NFP Corporation) **Service:** General Medical and Surgical

| Staffed Beds: 105 |

## HARDINSBURG—Breckinridge County

✠ **BRECKINRIDGE MEMORIAL HOSPITAL (181319)**, 1011 Old Highway 60, Zip 40143–2597; tel. 270/756–7000, (Total facility includes 18 beds in nursing home–type unit) **A**1 5 9 10 18 **F**3 8 15 34 40 45 59 62 67 77 81 86 107 110 127 128 129 130 131 133 143 146 **S** Alliant Management Services, Louisville, KY
Primary Contact: Angela Portman, Chief Executive Officer
CFO: Robert Haralson, Chief Financial Officer
CMO: Robert Chambliss, M.D., Chief Medical Officer
CIO: Virginia D. Bradley, Chief Information Officer
CHR: Clara Cordelia Hall, Chief Human Resources Officer
Web address: www.breckinridgehealth.org/
**Control:** Other not–for–profit (including NFP Corporation) **Service:** General Medical and Surgical

| Staffed Beds: 43 Admissions: 802 Census: 27 Outpatient Visits: 68769 Births: 0 Total Expense ($000): 20414 Payroll Expense ($000): 8450 Personnel: 228 |

---

**Hospital, Medicare Provider Number, Address, Telephone, Approval, Facility, and Physician Codes, Health Care System**

★ American Hospital Association (AHA) membership
☐ The Joint Commission accreditation
◯ Healthcare Facilities Accreditation Program
◇ DNV Healthcare Inc. accreditation
⇑ Center for Improvement in Healthcare Quality Accreditation
△ Commission on Accreditation of Rehabilitation Facilities (CARF) accreditation

## HARLAN—Harlan County

☐ **HARLAN ARH HOSPITAL (180050)**, 81 Ball Park Road, Zip 40831–1792; tel. 606/573–8100 **A**1 9 10 19 **F**3 11 13 15 28 29 30 32 34 35 40 43 50 54 57 59 62 64 70 75 76 77 78 79 81 82 85 86 87 89 93 97 98 102 103 107 108 111 115 118 119 127 129 130 132 146 147 148 **P**6 **S** Appalachian Regional Healthcare, Inc., Lexington, KY
Primary Contact: Donald Fields, Community Chief Executive Officer
CFO: Brad Burkhart, Assistant Administrator
CHR: Sabra Howard, Manager Human Resources
Web address: www.arh.org
**Control:** Other not–for–profit (including NFP Corporation) **Service:** General Medical and Surgical

**Staffed Beds:** 145 **Admissions:** 4042 **Census:** 51 **Outpatient Visits:** 67782 **Births:** 257 **Total Expense ($000):** 55924 **Payroll Expense ($000):** 16410 **Personnel:** 424

## HARRODSBURG—Mercer County

☒ **JAMES B. HAGGIN MEMORIAL HOSPITAL (181302)**, 464 Linden Avenue, Zip 40330–1862; tel. 859/734–5441, (Nonreporting) **A**1 5 9 10 18 **S** Alliant Management Services, Louisville, KY
Primary Contact: Victoria L. Reed, R.N., FACHE, Chief Executive Officer
CFO: Tony Patterson, Chief Financial Officer
Web address: www.hagginhosp.org
**Control:** Other not–for–profit (including NFP Corporation) **Service:** General Medical and Surgical

**Staffed Beds:** 25

## HARTFORD—Ohio County

☒ **OHIO COUNTY HOSPITAL (181323)**, 1211 Main Street, Zip 42347–1619; tel. 270/298–7411, (Nonreporting) **A**1 9 10 18 **S** QHR, Brentwood, TN
Primary Contact: Blaine Pieper, Chief Executive Officer
CFO: John Tichenor, Chief Financial Officer
CMO: Joshua Skibba, Chief Medical Officer
CHR: Sue Wydick, Director Human Resources
CNO: Athena Minor, Chief Nursing Officer
Web address: www.ohiocountyhospital.com
**Control:** Other not–for–profit (including NFP Corporation) **Service:** General Medical and Surgical

**Staffed Beds:** 25

## HAZARD—Perry County

☐ **HAZARD ARH REGIONAL MEDICAL CENTER (180029)**, 100 Medical Center Drive, Zip 41701–9421; tel. 606/439–6600 **A**1 2 3 5 9 10 19 **F**3 11 12 13 15 17 18 20 22 24 26 28 29 30 31 32 34 35 40 43 46 47 48 49 50 54 55 57 59 61 62 64 70 71 73 74 75 76 77 78 79 81 82 85 86 87 89 90 93 97 98 101 102 103 107 108 110 111 115 118 119 120 121 124 127 129 130 132 146 147 148 **P**6 **S** Appalachian Regional Healthcare, Inc., Lexington, KY
Primary Contact: Dan Stone, Senior Community Chief Executive Officer
COO: Donald R. Fields, Senior Community Chief Executive Officer
CMO: J. D. Miller, M.D., Chief Medical Officer
CIO: Jeff Brady, Director Information Systems
CHR: Sheila Cornett, Manager Human Resources
Web address: www.arh.org
**Control:** Other not–for–profit (including NFP Corporation) **Service:** General Medical and Surgical

**Staffed Beds:** 308 **Admissions:** 12263 **Census:** 187 **Outpatient Visits:** 107595 **Births:** 350 **Total Expense ($000):** 145970 **Payroll Expense ($000):** 35064 **Personnel:** 925

## HENDERSON—Henderson County

☐ **METHODIST HOSPITAL (180056)**, 1305 North Elm Street, Zip 42420–2775, Mailing Address: P.O. Box 48, Zip 42419–0048; tel. 270/827–7700 **A**1 9 10 13 **F**3 11 12 13 15 18 20 29 30 31 34 35 36 40 45 46 47 49 50 51 53 57 58 59 64 66 68 70 72 74 75 76 77 78 79 81 82 85 86 87 89 92 93 102 107 108 110 111 114 115 118 119 126 127 129 130 131 132 135 146 147 148 **P**8
Primary Contact: Bruce D. Begley, Executive Director
COO: David B. Park, Chief Operating Officer and General Counsel
CMO: James Fellows, M.D., Chief of Staff
CIO: Jamie Reid, Information Systems Director
CHR: Ty Kahle, Director Human Resources
CNO: Lois Morgan, R.N., Vice President and Chief Nursing Officer
Web address: www.methodisthospital.net
**Control:** Church–operated, Nongovernment, not–for profit **Service:** General Medical and Surgical

**Staffed Beds:** 152 **Admissions:** 4407 **Census:** 55 **Outpatient Visits:** 285414 **Births:** 691 **Total Expense ($000):** 103543 **Payroll Expense ($000):** 38636 **Personnel:** 1118

## HOPKINSVILLE—Christian County

☐ **CUMBERLAND HALL HOSPITAL (184014)**, 270 Walton Way, Zip 42240–6808; tel. 270/886–1919 **A**1 9 10 **F**98 99 100 101 102 103 105 **S** Universal Health Services, Inc., King of Prussia, PA
Primary Contact: James Spruyt, Chief Executive Officer
CFO: Chris Jagoditz, Chief Financial Officer
CMO: Deepak Patel, M.D., Medical Director
CIO: Patricia Gray, Director Health Information Management
CHR: Kelly Hagy, Director Human Resources
CNO: Scott Thomason, Director of Nursing
Web address: www.cumberlandhallhospital.com
**Control:** Corporation, Investor–owned, for–profit **Service:** Psychiatric

**Staffed Beds:** 97 **Admissions:** 1810 **Census:** 60 **Outpatient Visits:** 0 **Births:** 0 **Total Expense ($000):** 10296 **Payroll Expense ($000):** 5092 **Personnel:** 122

☒ **JENNIE STUART MEDICAL CENTER (180051)**, 320 West 18th Street, Zip 42240–1965, Mailing Address: P.O. Box 2400, Zip 42241–2400; tel. 270/887–0100, (Nonreporting) **A**1 3 9 10 **S** QHR, Brentwood, TN
Primary Contact: Eric A. Lee, President and Chief Executive Officer
CMO: Casey Covington, M.D., President Elect, Medical Staff
CIO: Jerry Houston, Director Information Systems
CHR: Austin Moss, Vice President Human Resources
Web address: www.jsmc.org
**Control:** Other not–for–profit (including NFP Corporation) **Service:** General Medical and Surgical

**Staffed Beds:** 139

☐ **WESTERN STATE HOSPITAL (184002)**, Russellville Road, Zip 42240–3017, Mailing Address: P.O. Box 2200, Zip 42241–2200; tel. 270/889–6025 **A**1 10 **F**98 102 103 130 **P**5
Primary Contact: Roger Westfall, Director
CFO: Jessica Cates, Fiscal Manager
CMO: Nayyar Iqbal, M.D., Director Medical Staff
CIO: Valerie Majors, Director Information Services
CHR: James L. Hayes, Director Human Resources
CNO: Jill Thomas, Director of Nursing
Web address: www.westernstatehospital.ky.gov
**Control:** State–Government, nonfederal **Service:** Psychiatric

**Staffed Beds:** 205 **Admissions:** 2064 **Census:** 119 **Outpatient Visits:** 0 **Births:** 0 **Total Expense ($000):** 17272 **Payroll Expense ($000):** 10397

## HORSE CAVE—Hart County

★ **CAVERNA MEMORIAL HOSPITAL (181314)**, 1501 South Dixie Street, Zip 42749–1477; tel. 270/786–2191 **A**9 10 18 **F**3 15 29 34 40 45 57 59 64 70 77 81 85 89 91 103 104 107 110 111 114 119 127 128 133 135 **P**6 **S** Alliant Management Services, Louisville, KY
Primary Contact: Alan B. Alexander, Chief Executive Officer
CFO: Richard Snapp, Chief Financial Officer
CMO: Evelyn Salisbury, M.D., Chief of Staff
CIO: Brad Lowe, Director Information Systems
CHR: Gretchen Nelk, Director Human Resources
CNO: Vanessa Burd, R.N., Chief Nursing Officer
Web address: www.cavernahospital.com
**Control:** Other not–for–profit (including NFP Corporation) **Service:** General Medical and Surgical

**Staffed Beds:** 25 **Admissions:** 290 **Census:** 2 **Outpatient Visits:** 16039 **Births:** 0 **Total Expense ($000):** 9752 **Payroll Expense ($000):** 5386 **Personnel:** 139

## HYDEN—Leslie County

**MARY BRECKINRIDGE ARH HOSPITAL (181316)**, 130 Kate Ireland Drive, Zip 41749–9071, Mailing Address: P.O. Box 447–A, Zip 41749–0717; tel. 606/672–2901 **A**9 10 18 **F**2 3 11 15 29 30 32 34 35 40 41 50 57 59 62 65 68 75 77 81 86 87 92 93 107 110 115 119 130 133 135 146 **P**6 **S** Appalachian Regional Healthcare, Inc., Lexington, KY
Primary Contact: Mallie S. Noble, Administrator
COO: Nathan W. Lee, Chief Executive Officer
CFO: Robert Besten, Chief Financial Officer
CMO: Roy Varghese, M.D., Chief of Staff
CIO: Frank Baker, Chief Information Officer
CHR: Beulah Couch, Director Human Resources
Web address: www.frontiernursing.org
**Control:** Other not–for–profit (including NFP Corporation) **Service:** General Medical and Surgical

**Staffed Beds:** 25 **Admissions:** 834 **Census:** 10 **Outpatient Visits:** 17722 **Births:** 0 **Total Expense ($000):** 11821 **Payroll Expense ($000):** 3572 **Personnel:** 110

*Many Facility Codes have changed. Please refer to the AHA Guide Code Chart.*   © 2015 AHA Guide

## IRVINE—Estill County

★ **MARCUM AND WALLACE MEMORIAL HOSPITAL (181301)**, 60 Mercy Court, Zip 40336–1331; tel. 606/723–2115 **A**9 10 18 **F**3 15 29 30 34 40 43 45 50 57 59 75 81 87 107 110 114 118 119 127 129 133 **S** Mercy Health, Cincinnati, OH
Primary Contact: Susan Starling, President and Chief Executive Officer
CFO: Lori Witt, Site Finance Director
CMO: Maher Kassis, M.D., Chief Medical Staff
CHR: Dana Stepp, Human Resources Officer
CNO: Trena Stocker, Chief Nursing Executive
Web address: www.marcumandwallace.org
**Control:** Church–operated, Nongovernment, not–for profit **Service:** General Medical and Surgical

> Staffed Beds: 25 Admissions: 930 Census: 12 Outpatient Visits: 69253 Births: 0 Total Expense ($000): 17097 Payroll Expense ($000): 7098 Personnel: 142

## JACKSON—Breathitt County

⊞ **KENTUCKY RIVER MEDICAL CENTER (180139)**, 540 Jett Drive, Zip 41339–9622; tel. 606/666–6000, (Nonreporting) **A**1 9 10 20 **S** Community Health Systems, Inc., Franklin, TN
Primary Contact: John Ballard, Ph.D., Chief Executive Officer
CFO: Michael Ackley, Chief Financial Officer
CMO: Eunice Johnson, M.D., Chief Medical Staff
CIO: Diana Tyra, Director Health Information
CHR: Naomi Mitchell, Director Human Resources
Web address: www.kentuckyrivermc.com
**Control:** Corporation, Investor–owned, for–profit **Service:** General Medical and Surgical

> Staffed Beds: 54

## LA GRANGE—Oldham County

★ ○ **BAPTIST HEALTH LA GRANGE (180138)**, 1025 New Moody Lane, Zip 40031–9154; tel. 502/222–5388, (Total facility includes 24 beds in nursing home–type unit) **A**3 5 9 10 11 **F**3 7 11 13 15 18 28 29 30 31 34 35 36 40 43 45 46 49 50 54 56 57 59 64 68 70 74 75 76 77 78 79 81 82 85 86 87 93 97 107 108 110 111 114 119 128 129 130 131 132 133 135 146 147 148 **P**6 **S** Baptist Health, Louisville, KY
Primary Contact: Chris Roty, President
CFO: Jim Morris, Vice President Finance
CMO: Matt McDanald, M.D., Chief Medical Officer
CIO: David Bensema, Chief Information Officer
CHR: Melissa Payton, Manager Human Resources
CNO: Karen Higdon, R.N., Vice President and Chief Nursing Officer
Web address: www.baptisthealthlagrange.com
**Control:** Other not–for–profit (including NFP Corporation) **Service:** General Medical and Surgical

> Staffed Beds: 65 Admissions: 2644 Census: 41 Outpatient Visits: 110399 Births: 488 Total Expense ($000): 67174 Payroll Expense ($000): 22975 Personnel: 374

## LEBANON—Marion County

⊞ **SPRING VIEW HOSPITAL (180024)**, 320 Loretto Road, Zip 40033–1300; tel. 270/692–3161, (Nonreporting) **A**1 9 10 **S** LifePoint Health, Brentwood, TN
Primary Contact: Timothy R. Trottier, Chief Executive Officer
CFO: Denise Thomas, Chief Financial Officer
CIO: Douglas Bland, Manager Information Services
CHR: Ann Dabney, Manager Human Resources
CNO: Linda Hunter, Chief Nursing Officer
Web address: www.springviewhospital.com
**Control:** Corporation, Investor–owned, for–profit **Service:** General Medical and Surgical

> Staffed Beds: 75

## LEITCHFIELD—Grayson County

☐ **TWIN LAKES REGIONAL MEDICAL CENTER (180070)**, 910 Wallace Avenue, Zip 42754–2414; tel. 270/259–9400, (Nonreporting) **A**1 9 10 **S** Alliant Management Services, Louisville, KY
Primary Contact: Wayne Meriwether, Chief Executive Officer
COO: Deneace Clemons, Chief Operating Officer
CFO: Scott Arndell, Chief Financial Officer
CIO: Robbie Lindsey, Chief Information Officer
CHR: Kim Rayls, Director Human Resources
CNO: David Logdson, Chief Nursing Officer
Web address: www.tlrmc.com
**Control:** Other not–for–profit (including NFP Corporation) **Service:** General Medical and Surgical

> Staffed Beds: 75

## LEXINGTON—Fayette County

⊞ **BAPTIST HEALTH LEXINGTON (180103)**, 1740 Nicholasville Road, Zip 40503–1499; tel. 859/260–6100 **A**1 2 3 9 10 **F**3 11 12 13 15 17 18 20 22 24 26 28 29 30 31 34 35 36 40 44 48 49 53 54 55 56 57 58 59 60 62 64 68 70 72 74 75 76 77 78 79 81 84 85 86 87 89 92 93 97 107 108 110 111 114 115 117 118 119 121 124 126 129 130 131 132 135 144 146 147 148 **S** Baptist Health, Louisville, KY
Primary Contact: William G. Sisson, President
COO: Karen S. Hill, R.N., Chief Operating Officer and Chief Nursing Officer
CFO: John Franke, Chief Financial Officer
CMO: James Borders, M.D., Chief Medical Officer
CIO: Lisa Fluty, Director Information Services
CHR: Lynette Walker, R.N., Vice President Human Resources
Web address: www.baptisthealthlexington.com
**Control:** Other not–for–profit (including NFP Corporation) **Service:** General Medical and Surgical

> Staffed Beds: 344 Admissions: 17276 Census: 215 Outpatient Visits: 2962236 Births: 3526 Total Expense ($000): 390372 Payroll Expense ($000): 124004 Personnel: 1726

★ △ **CARDINAL HILL REHABILITATION HOSPITAL (183026)**, 2050 Versailles Road, Zip 40504–1405; tel. 859/254–5701, (Total facility includes 74 beds in nursing home–type unit) **A**3 5 7 9 10 **F**2 3 11 28 29 58 62 64 68 79 87 90 91 93 94 95 96 128 130 143 146
Primary Contact: Gary Payne, Chief Executive Officer
CFO: Marty Lautner, Vice President Finance and Chief Financial Officer
CMO: William Lester, M.D., Vice President Medical Affairs
CIO: LouAnn Hyder, Director Information Integrity Management
CHR: Barry K. Lindeman, Director Human Resources
CNO: Maureen Couture, Chief Nursing Officer and Vice President Nursing
Web address: www.cardinalhill.org
**Control:** Other not–for–profit (including NFP Corporation) **Service:** Rehabilitation

> Staffed Beds: 232 Admissions: 2240 Census: 98 Outpatient Visits: 38100 Births: 0 Total Expense ($000): 60378 Payroll Expense ($000): 29859 Personnel: 597

★ **CONTINUING CARE HOSPITAL (182002)**, 150 North Eagle Creek Drive, 5th Floor, Zip 40509–1805; tel. 859/967–5744 **A**10 **F**1 42 82 84 **S** Catholic Health Initiatives, Englewood, CO
Primary Contact: Tonja Williams, MSN, R.N., President
CMO: Michael Miedler, M.D., Chief Medical Officer
CNO: Regina Masters, R.N., Director of Nursing
**Control:** Church–operated, Nongovernment, not–for profit **Service:** Long–Term Acute Care hospital

> Staffed Beds: 57 Admissions: 458 Census: 112 Outpatient Visits: 0 Births: 0 Total Expense ($000): 16863 Payroll Expense ($000): 5409 Personnel: 102

☐ **EASTERN STATE HOSPITAL (184004)**, 1350 Bull Lea Road, Zip 40511; tel. 859/246–7000 **A**1 3 5 9 10 **F**29 30 35 56 75 77 87 96 97 98 101 103 130 132 135 143 146 **P**6
Primary Contact: John Phillips, Chief Administrative Officer
COO: Susan M. Griffith, Chief Operations Officer
CFO: Tambara Nalle, Chief Financial Officer
CMO: Scott A. Haas, M.D., Chief Medical Officer
CIO: Bud Stone, Director Information Systems
CHR: Jerry Kersey, Director Employee Relations
CNO: Kristan Mowder, Director Administration and Patient Care Services
Web address: www.ukhealthcare.uky.edu/ESH/
**Control:** State–Government, nonfederal **Service:** Psychiatric

> Staffed Beds: 140 Admissions: 2149 Census: 119 Outpatient Visits: 0 Births: 0 Personnel: 347

**FEDERAL MEDICAL CENTER**, 3301 Leestown Road, Zip 40511–8799; tel. 859/255–6812, (Nonreporting)
Primary Contact: Francisco Quintana, Warden
CFO: Mike Kinsel, Controller
CMO: Michael Growse, M.D., Clinical Director
**Control:** Department of Justice, Government, federal **Service:** Hospital unit of an institution (prison hospital, college infirmary, etc.)

> Staffed Beds: 22

---

**Hospital, Medicare Provider Number, Address, Telephone, Approval, Facility, and Physician Codes, Health Care System**

★ American Hospital Association (AHA) membership  ○ Healthcare Facilities Accreditation Program  ⇑ Center for Improvement in Healthcare Quality Accreditation
☐ The Joint Commission accreditation  ◇ DNV Healthcare Inc. accreditation  △ Commission on Accreditation of Rehabilitation Facilities (CARF) accreditation

☒ **LEXINGTON VETERANS AFFAIRS MEDICAL CENTER**, 1101 Veterans Drive, Zip 40502–2235; tel. 859/281–4901, (Nonreporting) **A**1 3 5 **S** Department of Veterans Affairs, Washington, DC
Primary Contact: Emma Metcalf, MSN, R.N., Director
CFO: Patricia Swisshelm, Acting Chief Fiscal Service
CMO: Patricia Breeden, M.D., Chief of Staff
CIO: Jeffrey Sutton, Chief Information Officer
CHR: Laura Faulkner, Chief Human Resource Management Service
CNO: Mary Kelly McCullough, Associate Director Patient Care Services
Web address: www.lexington.va.gov/
**Control:** Veterans Affairs, Government, federal **Service:** General Medical and Surgical

| Staffed Beds: 199 |
|---|

☐ **RIDGE BEHAVIORAL HEALTH SYSTEM (184009)**, 3050 Rio Dosa Drive, Zip 40509–1540; tel. 859/269–2325, (Nonreporting) **A**1 3 5 9 10 **S** Universal Health Services, Inc., King of Prussia, PA
Primary Contact: Nina W. Eisner, Chief Executive Officer and Managing Director
COO: Samantha Castle, Chief Operating Officer
CFO: Richard McDowell, Chief Financial Officer
CMO: Michael Rieser, M.D., Medical Director
CHR: Samantha Castle, Chief Operating Officer
CNO: Georgia Swank, Chief Nursing Officer
Web address: www.ridgebhs.com
**Control:** Corporation, Investor–owned, for–profit **Service:** Psychiatric

| Staffed Beds: 110 |
|---|

☒ **SAINT JOSEPH EAST (180143)**, 150 North Eagle Creek Drive, Zip 40509–1805; tel. 859/967–5000, (Includes WOMEN'S HOSPITAL SAINT JOSEPH EAST, 170 North Eagle Creek Drive, Zip 40509–9087) **A**1 2 5 9 10 **F**3 8 12 13 15 17 18 20 22 24 26 28 29 30 31 40 47 49 50 60 68 70 72 73 74 75 76 77 78 79 81 82 85 86 93 107 108 111 115 118 119 120 121 122 123 126 129 142 146 147 148 **S** Catholic Health Initiatives, Englewood, CO
Primary Contact: Eric Gilliam, President
COO: Christine Mays, R.N., Chief Operating Officer and Chief Nurse Executive
CFO: Melinda S. Evans, Vice President Finance
CIO: Janie Fergus, Director and Chief Information Officer
Web address: www.sjhlex.org
**Control:** Church–operated, Nongovernment, not–for profit **Service:** General Medical and Surgical

| Staffed Beds: 143 Admissions: 8653 Census: 90 Outpatient Visits: 206150 Births: 1672 Total Expense ($000): 146159 Payroll Expense ($000): 42055 Personnel: 746 |
|---|

☒ **SAINT JOSEPH HOSPITAL (180010)**, One St. Joseph Drive, Zip 40504–3754; tel. 859/278–3436 **A**1 3 9 10 **F**1 3 8 11 12 15 17 18 19 20 22 24 25 26 27 28 29 30 31 34 35 37 40 41 42 45 47 49 50 51 54 55 56 57 59 64 65 66 68 70 74 77 78 79 81 82 83 84 85 86 87 92 93 94 97 107 110 111 114 115 116 117 118 119 120 121 123 126 127 129 130 132 135 144 146 147 148 **S** Catholic Health Initiatives, Englewood, CO
Primary Contact: Beverly Sue Downs, R.N., MSN, FACHE, Interim Chief Executive Officer
COO: Christine Mays, R.N., Chief Operating Officer and Chief Nurse Executive
CFO: Melinda S. Evans, Vice President Finance
CIO: Janie Fergus, Director and Chief Information Officer
Web address: www.sjhlex.org
**Control:** Church–operated, Nongovernment, not–for profit **Service:** General Medical and Surgical

| Staffed Beds: 291 Admissions: 14362 Census: 202 Outpatient Visits: 119011 Births: 0 Total Expense ($000): 290166 Payroll Expense ($000): 78714 Personnel: 1269 |
|---|

☒ **SELECT SPECIALTY HOSPITAL–LEXINGTON (182003)**, 310 South Limestone Street, 3rd Floor, Zip 40508–3008; tel. 859/226–7096, (Nonreporting) **A**1 10 **S** Select Medical Corporation, Mechanicsburg, PA
Primary Contact: Mary Lou Guinle, FACHE, Chief Executive Officer
CMO: Fadi Bacha, M.D., Chief Medical Officer
CHR: Tina Kirkland–Rose, Coordinator Human Resources
CNO: Katie Meredith, Chief Nursing Officer
Web address: www.lexington.selectspecialtyhospitals.com/
**Control:** Corporation, Investor–owned, for–profit **Service:** Long–Term Acute Care hospital

| Staffed Beds: 41 |
|---|

☐ **SHRINERS HOSPITALS FOR CHILDREN–LEXINGTON (183300)**, 1900 Richmond Road, Zip 40502–1298; tel. 859/266–2101, (Nonreporting) **A**1 3 5 9 10 **S** Shriners Hospitals for Children, Tampa, FL
Primary Contact: Tony Lewgood, Administrator
CFO: Robert Montgomery, Chief Financial Officer
CMO: Chester Tylkowski, M.D., Chief of Staff
CIO: David Brian, Director Information Services
Web address: www.shrinershospitalsforchildren.org/Hospitals/Locations/Lexington.aspx
**Control:** Other not–for–profit (including NFP Corporation) **Service:** Children's orthopedic

| Staffed Beds: 50 |
|---|

☒ **UNIVERSITY OF KENTUCKY ALBERT B. CHANDLER HOSPITAL (180067)**, 800 Rose Street, Zip 40536–0293; tel. 859/323–5000, (Includes KENTUCKY CHILDREN'S HOSPITAL, N–100 – 800 Rose Street, tel. 859/257–1000; UK HEALTHCARE GOOD SAMARITAN HOSPITAL, 310 South Limestone Street, Zip 40508–3008; tel. 859/226–7000; Michael Karpf, M.D., Executive Vice President of Health Affairs) **A**1 2 3 5 6 7 9 10 12 **F**3 5 6 7 9 11 12 13 15 16 17 18 19 20 21 22 23 24 26 27 28 29 30 31 32 34 35 36 37 38 39 40 41 43 44 45 46 47 48 49 50 52 54 55 56 57 58 59 60 61 64 65 66 68 70 72 73 74 75 76 77 78 79 81 82 84 85 86 87 88 89 92 93 94 95 96 97 98 100 102 104 107 108 110 111 113 114 115 118 119 120 121 123 124 126 130 131 132 134 135 136 137 138 139 140 141 142 145 146 147 148 **P**6
Primary Contact: Michael Karpf, M.D., Executive Vice President of Health Affairs
CHR: Kimberly P. Wilson, Director Human Resources
Web address: www.ukhealthcare.uky.edu
**Control:** State–Government, nonfederal **Service:** General Medical and Surgical

| Staffed Beds: 757 Admissions: 35303 Census: 627 Outpatient Visits: 668855 Births: 1789 Total Expense ($000): 1033681 Payroll Expense ($000): 308780 Personnel: 6192 |
|---|

**UNIVERSITY OF KENTUCKY HOSPITAL** See University of Kentucky Albert B. Chandler Hospital

**LIBERTY—Casey County**

☐ **CASEY COUNTY HOSPITAL (181309)**, 187 Wolford Avenue, Zip 42539–3278; tel. 606/787–6275, (Nonreporting) **A**1 9 10 18
Primary Contact: Rex A. Tungate, Administrator
**Control:** County–Government, nonfederal **Service:** General Medical and Surgical

| Staffed Beds: 24 |
|---|

**LONDON—Laurel County**

☒ **SAINT JOSEPH – LONDON (180011)**, 1001 Saint Joseph Lane, Zip 40741–8345; tel. 606/330–6000 **A**1 9 10 19 **F**3 13 15 17 18 20 22 24 26 28 29 30 31 34 35 40 42 49 50 51 57 59 60 61 64 70 74 76 78 79 81 82 85 87 89 92 93 107 110 111 114 115 119 129 130 131 146 147 **S** Catholic Health Initiatives, Englewood, CO
Primary Contact: Terrence G. Deis, CPA, FACHE, Chief Executive Officer
CFO: Christy Spitser, Vice President Finance and Business Development
CMO: Shelley Stanko, M.D., Chief Medical Officer
CHR: Sandra Turquesa, Senior Human Resources Business Partner
CNO: Lewis Stephen O'Neal, R.N., Chief Nursing Officer
Web address: www.saintjosephhealthsystem.org
**Control:** Church–operated, Nongovernment, not–for profit **Service:** General Medical and Surgical

| Staffed Beds: 114 Admissions: 6496 Census: 73 Outpatient Visits: 156852 Births: 1050 Total Expense ($000): 151849 Payroll Expense ($000): 38759 Personnel: 649 |
|---|

**LOUISA—Lawrence County**

☒ **THREE RIVERS MEDICAL CENTER (180128)**, 2485 Highway 644, Zip 41230–9242, Mailing Address: P.O. Box 769, Zip 41230–0769; tel. 606/638–9451, (Nonreporting) **A**1 9 10 20 **S** Community Health Systems, Inc., Franklin, TN
Primary Contact: Greg Kiser, Chief Executive Officer
CFO: Michael Ackley, Chief Financial Officer
CHR: Pat Hart, Director Human Resources
Web address: www.threeriversmedicalcenter.com
**Control:** Corporation, Investor–owned, for–profit **Service:** General Medical and Surgical

| Staffed Beds: 80 |
|---|

**LOUISVILLE—Jefferson County**

☒ △ **BAPTIST HEALTH LOUISVILLE (180130)**, 4000 Kresge Way, Zip 40207–4676; tel. 502/897–8100 **A**1 2 3 5 7 9 10 **F**3 5 8 11 12 13 15 17 18 20 22 24 26 28 29 30 31 33 34 36 37 38 40 44 45 46 47 48 49 50 51 53 54 56 57 58 59 60 61 62 64 68 70 72 74 75 76 78 79 81 82 83 84 85 86 87 89 90 91 93 97 98 100 101 102 103 104 105 107 108 110 111 114 115 116 117 118 119 120 121 123 124 126 129 130 132 135 145 146 147 148 **S** Baptist Health, Louisville, KY
Primary Contact: David L. Gray, FACHE, President
CFO: Jim Morris, Vice President Finance
CMO: Kenneth Anderson, M.D., Vice President and Chief Medical Officer
CIO: Shari Price, Director Information Services
CNO: Karen Newman, Ed.D., Vice President and Chief Nursing Officer
Web address: www.baptisthealthlouisville.com
**Control:** Other not–for–profit (including NFP Corporation) **Service:** General Medical and Surgical

| Staffed Beds: 488 Admissions: 25810 Census: 354 Outpatient Visits: 330267 Births: 3052 Total Expense ($000): 434488 Payroll Expense ($000): 156912 Personnel: 2893 |
|---|

☐ **CENTRAL STATE HOSPITAL (184015)**, 10510 LaGrange Road, Zip 40223–1228; tel. 502/253–7000 **A**1 3 5 10 **F**29 30 59 75 98 101 102 103 **P**6
Primary Contact: Vital Shah, M.D., Chief Executive Officer ad Chief Medical Officer
CFO: Robert Underhill, Director of Business Services
CMO: Vital Shah, M.D., Chief Executive Officer and Chief Medical Officer
CIO: Steven Puckett, Director Information Technology
CHR: Sonya Wheatley, Human Resources Manager
CNO: Michelle Napier, Director of Nursing
**Control:** State–Government, nonfederal **Service:** Psychiatric

**Staffed Beds:** 112 **Admissions:** 917 **Census:** 55 **Outpatient Visits:** 0 **Births:** 0 **Total Expense ($000):** 28151 **Payroll Expense ($000):** 15581 **Personnel:** 364

★ △ **FRAZIER REHAB INSTITUTE**, 220 Abraham Flexner Way, Zip 40202–1887; tel. 502/582–7400 **A**3 5 7 9 **F**28 29 30 34 35 42 44 50 54 56 57 58 59 60 64 68 74 75 77 78 79 82 84 85 86 87 90 91 93 95 96 100 130 131 132 146 148 **P**6 **S** Catholic Health Initiatives, Englewood, CO
Primary Contact: Randy L. Napier, President
CFO: Robert Steltenpohl, Vice President and Chief Financial Officer
CMO: Darryl Kaelin, M.D., Medical Director
CHR: Lisa Burris, Manager Human Resources
Web address: www.frazierrehab.org
**Control:** Other not–for–profit (including NFP Corporation) **Service:** Rehabilitation

**Staffed Beds:** 79 **Admissions:** 1676 **Census:** 66 **Outpatient Visits:** 81782 **Births:** 0 **Total Expense ($000):** 57221 **Payroll Expense ($000):** 21376 **Personnel:** 419

⊞ **JEWISH HOSPITAL (180040)**, 200 Abraham Flexner Way, Zip 40202–1886; tel. 502/587–4011 **A**1 2 3 5 9 10 **F**1 3 8 11 14 15 18 20 22 24 26 28 29 30 31 34 35 36 37 40 42 43 44 45 46 47 48 49 50 53 54 56 57 58 59 60 61 64 67 68 70 74 75 79 81 84 85 87 92 97 100 107 108 110 111 112 114 115 116 117 118 119 121 123 124 126 130 131 132 135 136 137 138 139 140 141 142 145 146 **P**6 **S** Catholic Health Initiatives, Englewood, CO
Primary Contact: Joseph Gilene, President
CFO: Ronald Farr, Chief Financial Officer
CMO: James P. Ketterhagen, M.D., Senior Vice President and Chief Medical Officer
CIO: Thomas Wittman, Chief Information Officer
CHR: Julie McGregor, Vice President and Chief People Officer
CNO: Cheryl Fugatte, MSN, Vice President and Chief Nursing Officer
Web address: www.jewishhospital.org
**Control:** Other not–for–profit (including NFP Corporation) **Service:** General Medical and Surgical

**Staffed Beds:** 342 **Admissions:** 16914 **Census:** 240 **Outpatient Visits:** 112925 **Births:** 0 **Total Expense ($000):** 380531 **Payroll Expense ($000):** 95274 **Personnel:** 1734

**KINDRED HOSPITAL LOUISVILLE AT JEWISH HOSPITAL** See Kindred Hospital–Louisville

⊞ **KINDRED HOSPITAL–LOUISVILLE (182001)**, 1313 Saint Anthony Place, Zip 40204–1740; tel. 502/587–7001, (Includes KINDRED HOSPITAL LOUISVILLE AT JEWISH HOSPITAL, 200 Abraham Flexner Way, 2nd Floor, Zip 40202; tel. 502/587–3999; David Johnson, Chief Executive Officer), (Nonreporting) **A**1 3 5 10 **S** Kindred Healthcare, Louisville, KY
Primary Contact: Wayne D. Blanchard, Chief Executive Officer
Web address: www.kindredlouisville.com/
**Control:** Corporation, Investor–owned, for–profit **Service:** Long–Term Acute Care hospital

**Staffed Beds:** 164

★ **KOSAIR CHILDREN'S HOSPITAL**, 231 East Chestnut Street, Zip 40202–1821; tel. 502/629–6000 **A**2 3 5 9 **F**3 8 11 19 21 23 25 27 29 30 31 32 34 35 38 39 40 41 42 43 44 45 50 54 58 59 64 65 68 72 74 75 78 79 81 82 84 85 86 87 88 89 92 93 96 98 99 100 101 102 107 108 111 114 115 119 130 131 132 134 136 137 138 146 **S** Norton Healthcare, Louisville, KY
Primary Contact: Thomas D. Kmetz, Division President
Web address: www.kosairchildrens.com/
**Control:** Other not–for–profit (including NFP Corporation) **Service:** Children's general

**Staffed Beds:** 267 **Admissions:** 10573 **Census:** 206 **Outpatient Visits:** 148495 **Births:** 0 **Total Expense ($000):** 304980 **Payroll Expense ($000):** 97349 **Personnel:** 1593

★ **NORTON AUDUBON HOSPITAL**, One Audubon Plaza Drive, Zip 40217–1300, Mailing Address: P.O. Box 17550, Zip 40217–0550; tel. 502/636–7111 **A**2 3 5 9 **F**3 5 11 15 17 18 20 22 24 26 28 29 30 31 34 35 37 40 45 46 47 48 49 50 56 57 59 64 68 70 74 75 78 79 81 82 85 86 87 107 108 110 111 114 115 118 119 129 130 131 132 146 147 **S** Norton Healthcare, Louisville, KY
Primary Contact: Jon Cooper, Chief Administrative Officer
CFO: Jonathan Presser, Vice President Finance and Operations
Web address: www.nortonhealthcare.com/NortonAudubonHospital
**Control:** Other not–for–profit (including NFP Corporation) **Service:** General Medical and Surgical

**Staffed Beds:** 288 **Admissions:** 14124 **Census:** 203 **Outpatient Visits:** 146782 **Births:** 0 **Total Expense ($000):** 221373 **Payroll Expense ($000):** 76782 **Personnel:** 1304

★ **NORTON BROWNSBORO HOSPITAL**, 4960 Norton Healthcare Boulevard, Zip 40241–2831; tel. 502/446–8000 **A**2 9 **F**3 15 18 20 22 29 30 31 34 35 36 37 40 44 45 46 47 48 49 56 57 58 59 64 68 70 74 75 78 79 81 82 85 86 87 92 107 108 110 111 114 115 119 129 130 131 132 146 148 **S** Norton Healthcare, Louisville, KY
Primary Contact: John D. Harryman, Chief Administrative Officer
CFO: Andy Strausbaugh, Vice President Finance and Operations
CMO: Gregory Juhl, M.D., Medical Director
CNO: Regina J. Hymer, DNP, RN, CENP, MSN, Vice President Patient Care Services and Chief Nursing Officer
Web address: www.nortonhealthcare.com/nortonbrownsborohospital
**Control:** Other not–for–profit (including NFP Corporation) **Service:** General Medical and Surgical

**Staffed Beds:** 118 **Admissions:** 7330 **Census:** 75 **Outpatient Visits:** 84999 **Births:** 0 **Total Expense ($000):** 133916 **Payroll Expense ($000):** 40744 **Personnel:** 766

**NORTON HEALTHCARE PAVILION** See Norton Hospital

⊞ **NORTON HOSPITAL (180088)**, 200 East Chestnut Street, Zip 40202–1800, Mailing Address: P.O. Box 35070, Zip 40232–5070; tel. 502/629–8000, (Includes NORTON HEALTHCARE PAVILION, 315 East Broadway, Zip 40202–1703; tel. 502/629–2000) **A**1 2 3 5 9 10 **F**3 11 12 13 15 17 18 20 22 24 26 28 29 30 31 34 35 36 38 39 40 44 45 46 49 50 51 53 55 56 57 59 64 68 70 74 75 76 78 79 81 82 84 85 86 87 92 93 96 98 100 101 102 107 108 110 111 114 115 116 117 118 119 126 130 132 146 147 148 **S** Norton Healthcare, Louisville, KY
Primary Contact: Matthew Ayers, Chief Administrative Officer
CFO: Carl Amorose, Vice President Finance
Web address: www.nortonhealthcare.com/nortonhospital
**Control:** Other not–for–profit (including NFP Corporation) **Service:** General Medical and Surgical

**Staffed Beds:** 379 **Admissions:** 17362 **Census:** 254 **Outpatient Visits:** 100521 **Births:** 3123 **Total Expense ($000):** 316208 **Payroll Expense ($000):** 100048 **Personnel:** 1546

★ **NORTON WOMEN'S AND KOSAIR CHILDREN'S HOSPITAL**, 4001 Dutchmans Lane, Zip 40207–4799; tel. 502/893–1000 **A**2 3 5 9 **F**3 8 11 12 13 15 18 20 29 30 31 34 35 36 40 41 44 45 47 49 50 56 57 59 64 68 70 72 73 74 75 76 78 79 81 82 85 86 87 89 107 108 110 111 114 115 118 119 120 121 123 124 126 130 132 134 135 146 147 **S** Norton Healthcare, Louisville, KY
Primary Contact: Charlotte Ipsan, Chief Administrative Officer
CFO: Mark Kircher, Associate Vice President Finance
CMO: Steven Hester, M.D., Vice President Medical Affairs
CIO: Joseph DeVenuto, Vice President and Chief Information Officer
Web address: www.nortonhealthcare.com/nortonsuburbanhospital
**Control:** Other not–for–profit (including NFP Corporation) **Service:** General Medical and Surgical

**Staffed Beds:** 368 **Admissions:** 13746 **Census:** 171 **Outpatient Visits:** 98260 **Births:** 5531 **Total Expense ($000):** 203669 **Payroll Expense ($000):** 68440 **Personnel:** 1213

★ **OUR LADY OF PEACE**, 2020 Newburg Road, Zip 40205–1879; tel. 502/479–4500 **A**3 5 9 **F**5 29 30 34 35 42 43 53 59 68 98 99 100 101 104 105 106 130 132 143 146 **S** Catholic Health Initiatives, Englewood, CO
Primary Contact: Jennifer Nolan, President
COO: Martha S. Mather, Chief Operating Officer and Vice President
CFO: Beckie Kistler, Director of Finance
CHR: Jan Ostbloom, Human Resources Consultant
CNO: Brad Lincks, R.N., Chief Nursing Officer and Vice President
Web address: www.hopehasaplace.org
**Control:** Other not–for–profit (including NFP Corporation) **Service:** Psychiatric

**Staffed Beds:** 261 **Admissions:** 7868 **Census:** 180 **Outpatient Visits:** 23974 **Births:** 0 **Total Expense ($000):** 54381 **Payroll Expense ($000):** 25214 **Personnel:** 546

---

**Hospital, Medicare Provider Number, Address, Telephone, Approval, Facility, and Physician Codes, Health Care System**

★ American Hospital Association (AHA) membership
☐ The Joint Commission accreditation
○ Healthcare Facilities Accreditation Program
◇ DNV Healthcare Inc. accreditation
⇑ Center for Improvement in Healthcare Quality Accreditation
△ Commission on Accreditation of Rehabilitation Facilities (CARF) accreditation

✠ **ROBLEY REX VETERANS AFFAIRS MEDICAL CENTER**, 800 Zorn Avenue,
Zip 40206–1499; tel. 502/287–4000, (Nonreporting) **A**1 2 3 5 **S** Department of
Veterans Affairs, Washington, DC
Primary Contact: Martin J. Traxler, Chief Executive Officer
CFO: Barbara Roberts, Chief Financial Officer
CMO: Marylee Rothschild, M.D., Chief of Staff
CIO: Augustine Bittner, Chief Information Officer
CHR: Angela Dutton, Chief Human Resources Management Service
Web address: www.louisville.va.gov
**Control:** Veterans Affairs, Government, federal **Service:** General Medical and
Surgical

Staffed Beds: 116

★ **STS. MARY & ELIZABETH HOSPITAL**, 1850 Bluegrass Avenue,
Zip 40215–1199; tel. 502/361–6000 **A**3 5 9 **F**3 8 11 12 15 18 20 22 29 30
31 34 35 40 42 43 44 45 47 49 50 53 54 59 60 64 68 70 74 75 78 79 81
82 84 85 86 87 107 108 110 111 114 115 118 119 129 130 132 135 **P**6
**S** Catholic Health Initiatives, Englewood, CO
Primary Contact: Jennifer Nolan, President
COO: Kenneth Johnson, Vice President
CFO: Elaine Hayes, Controller
CMO: Val Slayton, M.D., Vice President Medical Affairs
CHR: Julie McGregor, Director Human Resources
Web address: www.jhsmh.org
**Control:** Other not-for-profit (including NFP Corporation) **Service:** General
Medical and Surgical

Staffed Beds: 174 Admissions: 9220 Census: 103 Outpatient Visits:
115050 Births: 0 Total Expense ($000): 121875 Payroll Expense ($000):
40344 Personnel: 677

**TEN BROECK DUPONT** See The Brook at Dupont

☐ **THE BROOK AT DUPONT (184007)**, 1405 Browns Lane, Zip 40207–4608;
tel. 502/896–0495, (Nonreporting) **A**1 9 10 **S** Universal Health Services, Inc.,
King of Prussia, PA
Primary Contact: Paul Andrews, Chief Executive Officer
Web address: www.thebrookhospitals.com/
**Control:** Corporation, Investor-owned, for-profit **Service:** Psychiatric

Staffed Beds: 66

☐ **THE BROOK HOSPITAL – KMI (184008)**, 8521 Old LaGrange Road,
Zip 40242–3800; tel. 502/426–6380, (Nonreporting) **A**1 3 5 9 10 **S** Universal
Health Services, Inc., King of Prussia, PA
Primary Contact: Paul Andrews, Chief Executive Officer
COO: Kim Peabody, Chief Operating Officer
CFO: Dennis Collins, Chief Financial Officer
CMO: Timothy Burke, M.D., Medical Director
CIO: Joel Roy, Manager Information Systems
CHR: Christina Taylor, Director Human Resources
Web address: www.thebrookhospitals.com
**Control:** Corporation, Investor-owned, for-profit **Service:** Psychiatric

Staffed Beds: 94

✠ **UNIVERSITY OF LOUISVILLE HOSPITAL (180141)**, 530 South Jackson Street,
Zip 40202–3611; tel. 502/562–3000 **A**1 2 3 5 8 9 10 **F**3 13 15 16 17 18 20
22 24 26 28 29 30 31 34 35 40 43 45 46 47 49 50 51 54 55 57 58 59 60
61 64 65 66 68 70 71 72 73 74 75 76 77 78 79 80 81 82 84 86 91 92 93
94 97 98 100 101 102 103 104 105 106 107 108 109 110 111 112 113
114 115 116 117 118 119 120 121 122 123 124 126 130 132 135 136 146
147 148 **S** Catholic Health Initiatives, Englewood, CO
Primary Contact: Kenneth P. Marshall, President
CMO: Mark P. Pfeifer, M.D., Senior Vice President and Chief Medical Officer
CIO: Troy May, Chief Information Officer
CNO: Mary Jane Adams, R.N., Senior Vice President and Chief Nursing Officer
Web address: www.ulh.org
**Control:** Other not-for-profit (including NFP Corporation) **Service:** General
Medical and Surgical

Staffed Beds: 301 Admissions: 17226 Census: 261 Outpatient Visits:
141747 Births: 1123 Total Expense ($000): 808162 Payroll Expense
($000): 237226 Personnel: 1807

**VETERANS AFFAIRS MEDICAL CENTER–LOUISVILLE** See Robley Rex Veterans
Affairs Medical Center

✠ **BAPTIST HEALTH MADISONVILLE (180093)**, 900 Hospital Drive,
Zip 42431–1694; tel. 270/825–5100, (Total facility includes 20 beds in nursing
home–type unit) **A**1 2 3 5 9 10 **F**3 8 11 13 14 18 20 22 24 26 28 29 30 31
34 35 40 44 49 51 53 55 57 58 59 62 63 68 70 73 76 78 79 81 85 87 88
89 90 93 96 107 108 111 114 117 118 119 120 121 123 128 129 130 131
132 146 148 **S** Baptist Health, Louisville, KY
Primary Contact: Robert L. Ramey, Interim President
CIO: Sheila Bruce, Director Information System
CHR: David Lang, Vice President Human Resources
Web address: www.baptisthealthmadisonville.com
**Control:** Other not-for-profit (including NFP Corporation) **Service:** General
Medical and Surgical

Staffed Beds: 186 Admissions: 8179 Census: 111 Outpatient Visits:
132585 Births: 949 Total Expense ($000): 163760 Payroll Expense
($000): 63897 Personnel: 1284

✠ ○ **MANCHESTER MEMORIAL HOSPITAL (180043)**, 210 Marie Langdon
Drive, Zip 40962–6388; tel. 606/598–5104 **A**1 9 10 11 **F**3 13 15 18 29 30 34
35 40 45 50 57 59 62 65 68 70 71 75 76 77 81 85 86 87 93 97 107 108
110 111 115 119 127 130 135 143 146 147 **S** Adventist Health System
Sunbelt Health Care Corporation, Altamonte Springs, FL
Primary Contact: Erika Skula, President and Chief Executive Officer
COO: Eric E. Lunde, Chief Operating Officer
CFO: Paul Merklin, Vice President Finance and Chief Financial Officer
CHR: Joe Skula, Director Human Resources
CNO: Michael Stimson, Chief Nursing Officer
Web address: www.manchestermemorial.org
**Control:** Church-operated, Nongovernment, not-for profit **Service:** General
Medical and Surgical

Staffed Beds: 63 Admissions: 2280 Census: 18 Outpatient Visits: 49542
Births: 202 Total Expense ($000): 52235 Payroll Expense ($000): 22488
Personnel: 317

☐ **CRITTENDEN COUNTY HOSPITAL (180095)**, 520 West Gum Street,
Zip 42064–1516, Mailing Address: P.O. Box 386, Zip 42064–0386;
tel. 270/965–5281, (Nonreporting) **A**1 9 10 20
Primary Contact: Greg R. McNeil, Chief Executive Officer
COO: Robin Curnel, MSN, Chief Operating Officer and Chief Nursing Officer
CFO: Karen Paris, Controller
CMO: Steven Burkhart, M.D., Chief Medical Officer
CIO: Reese Baker, Director Information Systems
CHR: Jan Gregory, Chief of Human Resources
CNO: Robin Curnel, MSN, Chief Operating Officer and Chief Nursing Officer
Web address: www.crittenden-health.org
**Control:** Other not-for-profit (including NFP Corporation) **Service:** General
Medical and Surgical

Staffed Beds: 48

✠ **SAINT JOSEPH – MARTIN (181305)**, 11203 Main Street, Zip 41649;
tel. 606/285–6400 **A**1 9 10 18 **F**3 15 18 28 35 40 56 81 104 111 114 119
130 **S** Catholic Health Initiatives, Englewood, CO
Primary Contact: Kathy Stumbo, President
CFO: Robert Brock, Vice President Finance
CMO: John Triplett, D.O., President Medical Staff
CIO: Chris Dye, Director Information Systems
Web address: www.saintjosephmartin.org
**Control:** Church-operated, Nongovernment, not-for profit **Service:** General
Medical and Surgical

Staffed Beds: 25 Admissions: 723 Census: 18 Outpatient Visits: 46301
Births: 0 Total Expense ($000): 19103 Payroll Expense ($000): 6408
Personnel: 104

✠ **JACKSON PURCHASE MEDICAL CENTER (180116)**, 1099 Medical Center
Circle, Zip 42066–1159; tel. 270/251–4100 **A**1 9 10 19 **F**3 8 11 12 13 15 18
20 22 28 29 34 37 40 43 45 46 47 48 49 51 57 59 60 64 68 70 74 75 77
79 80 81 85 87 91 93 97 98 103 107 110 111 114 115 117 119 124 127
129 131 132 133 135 144 146 147 148 **S** LifePoint Health, Brentwood, TN
Primary Contact: David Anderson, Chief Executive Officer
CFO: Vicki Parks, Chief Financial Officer
CMO: David Zetter, M.D., Chief of Staff
CIO: Tracy Watt, Director Information Systems
CHR: Tressa B. Hargrove, Director Human Resources
CNO: Julia Grove, Chief Nursing Officer
Web address: www.jacksonpurchase.com
**Control:** Corporation, Investor-owned, for-profit **Service:** General Medical and
Surgical

Staffed Beds: 227 Admissions: 3787 Census: 43 Outpatient Visits: 68425
Births: 362 Total Expense ($000): 56230 Payroll Expense ($000): 23943
Personnel: 413

## MAYSVILLE—Mason County

✠ **MEADOWVIEW REGIONAL MEDICAL CENTER (180019)**, 989 Medical Park Drive, Zip 41056–8750; tel. 606/759–5311, (Nonreporting) **A**1 9 10 **S** LifePoint Health, Brentwood, TN
Primary Contact: Robert Parker, Chief Executive Officer
CFO: Clayton Kolodziejczyk, Chief Financial Officer
CMO: Eric Lohman, M.D., Chief of Staff
CHR: Diana Kennedy, Director Human Resources
Web address: www.meadowviewregional.com
**Control:** Corporation, Investor–owned, for–profit **Service:** General Medical and Surgical

**Staffed Beds:** 101

## MCDOWELL—Floyd County

☐ **MCDOWELL ARH HOSPITAL (181331)**, Route 122, Zip 41647, Mailing Address: P.O. Box 247, Zip 41647–0247; tel. 606/377–3400 **A**1 9 10 18 **F**3 11 15 29 30 34 35 40 43 50 57 59 62 64 65 70 73 75 77 81 82 86 87 89 90 93 97 98 107 111 115 119 127 130 131 133 146 **P**6 **S** Appalachian Regional Healthcare, Inc., Lexington, KY
Primary Contact: Russell Barker, Community Chief Executive Officer
COO: Russell Barker, Community Chief Executive Officer
CFO: Joseph Grossman, Chief Financial Officer
CMO: Mary A. Hall, Chief Medical Staff
CIO: Jeff Brady, Director Information Systems
CHR: Stephanie Owens, Manager Human Resources
Web address: www.arh.org
**Control:** Other not–for–profit (including NFP Corporation) **Service:** General Medical and Surgical

**Staffed Beds:** 25 **Admissions:** 669 **Census:** 7 **Outpatient Visits:** 30125
**Births:** 0 **Total Expense ($000):** 14173 **Payroll Expense ($000):** 5428
**Personnel:** 117

## MIDDLESBORO—Bell County

☐ **MIDDLESBORO ARH HOSPITAL (180020)**, 3600 West Cumberland Avenue, Zip 40965–2614, Mailing Address: P.O. Box 340, Zip 40965–0340; tel. 606/242–1100 **A**1 9 10 **F**3 11 13 15 17 28 29 30 34 35 39 40 50 57 59 62 64 70 75 76 77 79 81 85 86 87 89 93 97 107 108 111 114 118 119 127 130 133 146 147 148 **P**6 **S** Appalachian Regional Healthcare, Inc., Lexington, KY
Primary Contact: Michael Slusher, Community Chief Executive Officer
CFO: Jeremy Hall, Assistant Administrator and Chief Financial Officer
CMO: Maria Hortillosa, M.D., Chief of Staff
CIO: Lisa Dooley, Health Information Officer
CHR: Marina Cawood, Administrative Assistant
CNO: Stacy England, Community Chief Nursing Officer
Web address: www.arh.org/middlesboro
**Control:** Other not–for–profit (including NFP Corporation) **Service:** General Medical and Surgical

**Staffed Beds:** 96 **Admissions:** 2252 **Census:** 25 **Outpatient Visits:** 65049
**Births:** 268 **Total Expense ($000):** 36951 **Payroll Expense ($000):** 10239
**Personnel:** 236

## MONTICELLO—Wayne County

**WAYNE COUNTY HOSPITAL (181321)**, 166 Hospital Street, Zip 42633–2416; tel. 606/348–9343 **A**9 10 18 **F**3 15 29 30 40 47 75 81 107 108 114 119 127 133 135 146 **P**6
Primary Contact: Joseph Murrell, Chief Executive Officer
CFO: Anne Sawyer, Chief Financial Officer
CMO: David Mayer, Chief of Staff
CIO: Angela Burton, Privacy Officer
CHR: Mollie Dick, Coordinator Human Resources
CNO: Lora Elam, R.N., Chief Nursing Officer
Web address: www.waynehospital.org
**Control:** Other not–for–profit (including NFP Corporation) **Service:** General Medical and Surgical

**Staffed Beds:** 25 **Admissions:** 604 **Census:** 10 **Outpatient Visits:** 34289
**Births:** 0 **Total Expense ($000):** 13803 **Payroll Expense ($000):** 5475
**Personnel:** 153

## MOREHEAD—Rowan County

✠ **ST. CLAIRE REGIONAL MEDICAL CENTER (180018)**, 222 Medical Circle, Zip 40351–1179; tel. 606/783–6500, (Total facility includes 10 beds in nursing home–type unit) **A**1 2 3 5 9 10 13 **F**3 5 11 13 15 18 20 22 28 29 30 31 34 35 38 39 40 45 48 49 50 51 54 56 57 58 59 60 61 62 63 64 65 68 70 74 75 76 77 78 79 81 82 84 85 86 87 89 90 93 97 98 99 100 101 102 103 104 107 108 110 111 115 118 119 128 129 130 132 135 146 147 148 **P**6
Primary Contact: Mark J. Neff, FACHE, President and Chief Executive Officer
CFO: G.R. Sonny Jones, Senior Vice President Finance and Chief Financial Officer
CMO: Will L. Melahn, M.D., Vice President Medical Affairs and Chief Medical Officer
CIO: Randy McCleese, Vice President Information Services and Chief Information Officer
CHR: Travis A. Bailey, Vice President Administration
CNO: Lerae Wilson, R.N., Vice President Patient Services and Chief Nursing Officer
Web address: www.st–claire.org
**Control:** Church–operated, Nongovernment, not–for profit **Service:** General Medical and Surgical

**Staffed Beds:** 133 **Admissions:** 5050 **Census:** 59 **Outpatient Visits:** 244488
**Births:** 393 **Total Expense ($000):** 124679 **Payroll Expense ($000):** 61247
**Personnel:** 1121

## MORGANFIELD—Union County

✠ **METHODIST HOSPITAL UNION COUNTY (181306)**, 4604 Highway 60 West, Zip 42437–9570; tel. 270/389–5000 **A**1 9 10 18 **F**3 7 11 15 29 30 34 40 45 57 68 75 77 81 85 87 90 93 107 114 119 128 130 133 135 146
Primary Contact: Patrick Donahue, Vice President and Administrator
CFO: David Massingale, Chief Financial Officer
CMO: Debra Wallace, M.D., Chief of Staff
CNO: Peggy F. Creighton, R.N., Director of Nursing Services
Web address: www.methodisthospitaluc.net
**Control:** Church–operated, Nongovernment, not–for profit **Service:** General Medical and Surgical

**Staffed Beds:** 25 **Admissions:** 590 **Census:** 12 **Outpatient Visits:** 22470
**Births:** 0 **Total Expense ($000):** 13898 **Payroll Expense ($000):** 5715
**Personnel:** 130

## MOUNT STERLING—Montgomery County

✠ **SAINT JOSEPH MOUNT STERLING (180064)**, 225 Falcon Drive, Zip 40353–1158, Mailing Address: P.O. Box 7, Zip 40353–0007; tel. 859/497–5000 **A**1 3 5 9 10 **F**3 13 15 17 28 29 34 35 40 45 46 57 59 64 68 70 74 75 76 77 78 79 81 86 87 93 97 107 114 119 129 130 132 133 135 146 147 148 **S** Catholic Health Initiatives, Englewood, CO
Primary Contact: Benny Nolen, President
CFO: Amanda Kinman, Director of Finance
CMO: Jeff McGinnis, M.D., President Medical Staff
CIO: Jeff Ryder, Director Information Systems
CHR: Annette Saadat, Human Resources Business Partner
CNO: Cinda Fluke, R.N., Chief Nursing Officer
Web address: www.sjhlex.org
**Control:** Church–operated, Nongovernment, not–for profit **Service:** General Medical and Surgical

**Staffed Beds:** 40 **Admissions:** 1945 **Census:** 21 **Outpatient Visits:** 64115
**Births:** 246 **Total Expense ($000):** 46069 **Payroll Expense ($000):** 11771
**Personnel:** 227

## MOUNT VERNON—Rockcastle County

✠ **ROCKCASTLE REGIONAL HOSPITAL AND RESPIRATORY CARE CENTER (180115)**, 145 Newcomb Avenue, Zip 40456–2728, Mailing Address: P.O. Box 1310, Zip 40456–1310; tel. 606/256–2195, (Nonreporting) **A**1 9 10
Primary Contact: Stephen A. Estes, Chief Executive Officer
CFO: Charles Black, Jr., Chief Financial Officer
CMO: Jon A. Arvin, M.D., Chief Medical Officer
CIO: Maleigha Amyx, Chief Information Officer
CHR: Carmen Poynter, Director Human Resources
CNO: Cynthia Burton, R.N., Chief Nursing Officer
Web address: www.rockcastleregional.org
**Control:** Other not–for–profit (including NFP Corporation) **Service:** General Medical and Surgical

**Staffed Beds:** 119

---

**Hospital, Medicare Provider Number, Address, Telephone, Approval, Facility, and Physician Codes, Health Care System**

★ American Hospital Association (AHA) membership
☐ The Joint Commission accreditation
○ Healthcare Facilities Accreditation Program
◇ DNV Healthcare Inc. accreditation
⇑ Center for Improvement in Healthcare Quality Accreditation
△ Commission on Accreditation of Rehabilitation Facilities (CARF) accreditation

**MURRAY—Calloway County**

☒ **MURRAY–CALLOWAY COUNTY HOSPITAL (180027)**, 803 Poplar Street, Zip 42071–2432; tel. 270/762–1100 (Total facility includes 150 beds in nursing home–type unit) **A**1 2 9 10 19 **F**2 3 7 11 12 13 14 15 18 20 28 29 30 31 34 35 40 45 47 49 50 51 53 57 59 62 63 66 68 70 74 75 76 77 78 79 81 82 84 85 87 90 92 93 94 104 107 108 111 114 115 119 121 127 128 129 130 131 132 135 146 147 148 **P**5
Primary Contact: Colonel Jerome Penner, Chief Executive Officer
CFO: Dirk Morgan, Vice President
CIO: Annette Ballard, Director Information Systems
CHR: John R. Wilson, Vice President, Human Resources
CNO: Lisa Ray, R.N., Vice President Patient Care Services
Web address: www.murrayhospital.org
**Control:** City–County, Government, nonfederal **Service:** General Medical and Surgical

**Staffed Beds:** 250 **Admissions:** 4955 **Census:** 205 **Outpatient Visits:** 83818 **Births:** 639

**OWENSBORO—Daviess County**

☒ △ **OWENSBORO HEALTH REGIONAL HOSPITAL (180038)**, 1201 Pleasant Valley Road, Zip 42303; tel. 270/417–2000, (Total facility includes 150 beds in nursing home-type unit) (Includes HEALTHPARK, 1006 Ford Avenue, Zip 42301, Mailing Address: P.O. Box 2839, Zip 42302; tel. 270/688–5433), (Total facility includes 30 beds in nursing home–type unit) **A**1 2 5 7 9 10 **F**3 5 11 12 13 15 17 18 20 22 24 26 28 29 30 31 32 34 35 40 45 46 49 53 54 56 57 58 59 61 62 64 65 66 70 72 74 75 76 77 78 79 81 82 85 86 87 89 90 91 92 93 97 98 100 101 102 103 104 105 107 108 110 111 114 115 116 117 118 119 120 121 123 124 126 127 128 129 130 131 132 135 144 145 146 147 148 **P**6 8
Primary Contact: Philip A. Patterson, President and Chief Executive Officer
COO: Greg Strahan, Chief Operating Officer
CFO: John Hackbarth, CPA, Senior Vice President Finance and Chief Financial Officer
CMO: Wathen Medley, M.D., Chief Medical Officer
CIO: Michael Elley, Chief Information Officer
CHR: Mia Suter, Chief Administration Officer
CNO: Vicki Stogsdill, R.N., Chief Nursing Officer
Web address: www.owensborohealth.org
**Control:** Other not–for–profit (including NFP Corporation) **Service:** General Medical and Surgical

**Staffed Beds:** 356 **Admissions:** 4955 **Census:** 205 **Outpatient Visits:** 593022 **Births:** 1905 **Total Expense ($000):** 410753 **Payroll Expense ($000):** 128364 **Personnel:** 2943

**RIVERVALLEY BEHAVIORAL HEALTH HOSPITAL (184013)**, 1000 Industrial Drive, Zip 42301–8715; tel. 270/689–6500 **A**9 10 **F**29 38 40 59 98 99 100 101 102 104 105 130 **P**6
Primary Contact: Gayle DiCesare, President and Chief Executive Officer
COO: Michelle Parks, Administrator
CFO: J. Michael Mountain, Chief Financial Officer
CMO: David Harmon, D.O., Vice President Medical Services
CIO: Travis Taggart, Director Information Technology
CHR: Cathryn H. Gaddis, Director Human Resources
Web address: www.rvbh.com
**Control:** Other not–for–profit (including NFP Corporation) **Service:** Children's hospital psychiatric

**Staffed Beds:** 80 **Admissions:** 637 **Census:** 14 **Outpatient Visits:** 0 **Births:** 0 **Total Expense ($000):** 4801 **Payroll Expense ($000):** 1884 **Personnel:** 42

**OWENTON—Owen County**

★ **NEW HORIZONS HEALTH SYSTEMS (181312)**, 330 Roland Avenue, Zip 40359–1502; tel. 502/484–3663 **A**9 10 18 **F**8 30 34 35 40 41 57 81 86 93 107 114 115 119 127 128 133 146 **P**5
Primary Contact: Bernard T. Poe, Administrator and Chief Executive Officer
COO: Bernard T. Poe, Administrator and Chief Executive Officer
CMO: Larry C. Johnson, M.D., Medical Director Rural Health Clinic
CIO: Edward Seale, Chief Information Officer
CHR: Kelly Perkins, Director Human Resources
CNO: Eileen Fowler, Clinical Director and Chief Nursing Officer
Web address: www.newhorizonsmedicalcenter.com
**Control:** Corporation, Investor–owned, for–profit **Service:** General Medical and Surgical

**Staffed Beds:** 25 **Admissions:** 272 **Census:** 1 **Outpatient Visits:** 10578 **Births:** 2

**PADUCAH—Mccracken County**

☒ **BAPTIST HEALTH PADUCAH (180104)**, 2501 Kentucky Avenue, Zip 42003–3200; tel. 270/575–2100 **A**1 2 9 10 19 **F**3 11 12 13 15 17 18 20 22 24 28 29 30 31 32 34 35 40 45 46 47 48 50 57 58 59 64 70 71 73 74 75 76 77 78 79 81 82 83 84 85 86 87 91 92 93 96 107 108 109 110 111 112 113 114 115 116 117 118 119 120 121 122 126 128 129 130 131 132 133 135 144 146 147 **S** Baptist Health, Louisville, KY
Primary Contact: William A. Brown, FACHE, President and CEO
COO: Bonnie W. Schrock, FACHE, Chief Operating Officer
CFO: Scott Leckey, Vice President Finance
CMO: Bradley W. Housman, M.D., Chief Medical Officer
CIO: Jay Orazine, Director Information Services
CHR: Kal Keitel, SPHR, Executive Director Human Resources
CNO: Sharon Freyer, Chief Nursing Officer
Web address: www.baptisthealthpaducah.com
**Control:** Other not–for–profit (including NFP Corporation) **Service:** General Medical and Surgical

**Staffed Beds:** 320 **Admissions:** 13404 **Census:** 150 **Outpatient Visits:** 140393 **Births:** 1376 **Total Expense ($000):** 225248 **Payroll Expense ($000):** 66192 **Personnel:** 1194

☒ △ **LOURDES HOSPITAL (180102)**, 1530 Lone Oak Road, Zip 42003–7900, Mailing Address: P.O. Box 7100, Zip 42002–7100; tel. 270/444–2444 **A**1 7 9 10 19 **F**3 7 8 11 13 15 17 18 20 22 24 26 28 29 30 31 34 35 40 45 46 54 57 59 60 62 63 64 68 70 73 74 75 76 77 78 79 81 82 83 84 85 87 90 93 96 97 98 100 101 102 103 104 105 107 108 110 111 114 115 116 118 119 129 130 131 132 135 141 143 146 147 148 **P**3 6 **S** Mercy Health, Cincinnati, OH
Primary Contact: Steven Grinnell, Chief Executive Officer
CFO: Mark Thompson, Vice President Finance and Chief Financial Officer
CHR: Kim Lindsey, Chief Human Resources Officer
Web address: www.lourdes-pad.org
**Control:** Church–operated, Nongovernment, not–for profit **Service:** General Medical and Surgical

**Staffed Beds:** 264 **Admissions:** 10638 **Census:** 130 **Outpatient Visits:** 134594 **Births:** 335 **Total Expense ($000):** 203591 **Payroll Expense ($000):** 76404

**PAINTSVILLE—Johnson County**

☒ **PAUL B. HALL REGIONAL MEDICAL CENTER (180078)**, 625 James S. Trimble Boulevard, Zip 41240–0000; tel. 606/789–3511, (Nonreporting) **A**1 9 10 **S** Community Health Systems, Inc., Franklin, TN
Primary Contact: Deborah Trimble, R.N., Chief Executive Officer
CFO: Pattie Major, Chief Financial Officer
CMO: F. K. Belhasen, M.D., Medical Director
CHR: Carla J. Stapleton, Director Human Resources
Web address: www.pbhrmc.com
**Control:** Corporation, Investor–owned, for–profit **Service:** General Medical and Surgical

**Staffed Beds:** 72

**PARIS—Bourbon County**

☒ **BOURBON COMMUNITY HOSPITAL (180046)**, 9 Linville Drive, Zip 40361–2196; tel. 859/987–3600 **A**1 9 10 **F**3 15 28 29 34 35 38 39 40 44 45 49 50 51 56 57 59 64 68 70 74 75 79 81 86 87 93 98 99 100 101 102 103 107 108 110 111 114 119 129 130 133 146 148 **P**7 **S** LifePoint Health, Brentwood, TN
Primary Contact: Joseph G. Koch, Chief Executive Officer
CFO: Michael Snedegar, Chief Financial Officer
CMO: C. Ray Young, M.D., Chief Medical Officer
CIO: Phil Osborne, Director Information Technology
CHR: Roger K. Davis, Director Human Resources
Web address: www.bourbonhospital.com
**Control:** Corporation, Investor–owned, for–profit **Service:** General Medical and Surgical

**Staffed Beds:** 58 **Admissions:** 2031 **Census:** 26 **Outpatient Visits:** 32760 **Births:** 0 **Personnel:** 152

**PIKEVILLE—Pike County**

☐ **PIKEVILLE MEDICAL CENTER (180044)**, 911 Bypass Road, Zip 41501–1689; tel. 606/218–3500 **A**1 2 9 10 13 **F**3 11 12 13 15 18 20 22 24 26 28 29 30 31 32 34 35 39 40 45 49 50 51 57 59 60 61 62 64 66 68 69 70 72 74 75 76 77 78 79 81 82 84 85 86 87 89 90 93 95 96 97 107 108 110 111 115 116 117 118 119 121 123 124 127 129 130 131 132 135 146 147 148 **P**6
Primary Contact: Walter E. May, President and Chief Executive Officer
COO: Juanita Deskins, Chief Operating Officer
CFO: Michael Hagy, Chief Financial Officer
CIO: Sonja Elder, Director Information Services
CNO: Debra Parsons, Chief Nursing Officer
Web address: www.pikevillehospital.org
**Control:** Other not–for–profit (including NFP Corporation) **Service:** General Medical and Surgical

**Staffed Beds:** 243 **Admissions:** 12588 **Census:** 177 **Outpatient Visits:** 433672 **Births:** 973 **Total Expense ($000):** 368221 **Payroll Expense ($000):** 148788 **Personnel:** 2358

## PINEVILLE—Bell County

○ **PINEVILLE COMMUNITY HOSPITAL ASSOCIATION (180021)**, 850 Riverview Avenue, Zip 40977-1452; tel. 606/337-3051, (Nonreporting) **A**9 10 11
Primary Contact: Stace Holland, Administrator
CFO: Colan Kelly, Chief Financial Officer
CMO: Michael Peterson, M.D., Chief of Staff
CIO: David Hall, Chief Information Officer
CHR: Josh Collett, Director Human Resources
CNO: Dinah Jarvis, Director of Nursing
Web address: www.pinevillehospital.com
**Control:** Other not-for-profit (including NFP Corporation) **Service:** General Medical and Surgical

**Staffed Beds:** 150

## PRESTONSBURG—Floyd County

★ ◇ **HIGHLANDS REGIONAL MEDICAL CENTER (180005)**, 5000 Kentucky Route 321, Zip 41653-1273, Mailing Address: P.O. Box 668, Zip 41653-0668; tel. 606/886-8511 **A**2 5 9 10 19 21 **F**3 11 13 15 18 20 28 29 30 34 35 40 43 53 54 57 59 60 62 65 70 74 75 76 79 81 87 89 91 92 93 98 107 108 110 111 114 115 119 124 127 128 130 131 134 135 146 **P**8
Primary Contact: Harold C. Warman, Jr., FACHE, President and Chief Executive Officer
COO: Chris Hoffman, Chief Operating Officer
CFO: Jack Blackwell, Chief Financial Officer
CIO: Michael Roberts, Chief Information Officer
CHR: Susan Renee' Ellis, R.N., Vice President of Human Resources
CNO: Terresa O. Booher, Vice President of Patient Care Services
Web address: www.hrmc.org
**Control:** Other not-for-profit (including NFP Corporation) **Service:** General Medical and Surgical

**Staffed Beds:** 139 **Admissions:** 3962 **Census:** 37 **Births:** 613

## PRINCETON—Caldwell County

⊠ **CALDWELL MEDICAL CENTER (181322)**, 100 Medical Center Drive, Zip 42445-2430, Mailing Address: P.O. Box 410, Zip 42445-0410; tel. 270/365-0300 **A**1 9 10 18 **F**11 15 28 29 34 35 40 57 59 62 68 77 81 85 107 108 111 118 119 129 133 135 146 **S** QHR, Brentwood, TN
Primary Contact: Charles D. Lovell, Jr., FACHE, President and Chief Executive Officer
CFO: Shane Whittington, Chief Financial Officer
CHR: Rhonda Burns, Director Human Resources
CNO: Douglas James, Chief Nursing Officer
Web address: www.caldwellhosp.org
**Control:** Other not-for-profit (including NFP Corporation) **Service:** General Medical and Surgical

**Staffed Beds:** 25 **Admissions:** 461 **Census:** 4 **Outpatient Visits:** 27445 **Births:** 0 **Total Expense ($000):** 15916 **Payroll Expense ($000):** 4897 **Personnel:** 97

## RADCLIFF—Hardin County

□ **LINCOLN TRAIL BEHAVIORAL HEALTH SYSTEM (184012)**, 3909 South Wilson Road, Zip 40160-8944, Mailing Address: P.O. Box 369, Zip 40159-0369; tel. 270/351-9444, (Nonreporting) **A**1 9 10 **S** Universal Health Services, Inc., King of Prussia, PA
Primary Contact: Charles L. Webb, Jr., Chief Executive Officer
CFO: Debbie Ditto, CPA, Controller
CMO: Muhammad W. Sajid, M.D., Medical Director
CHR: Charlotte C. Davis, Director Human Resources
Web address: www.lincolnbehavioral.com
**Control:** Corporation, Investor-owned, for-profit **Service:** Psychiatric

**Staffed Beds:** 67

## RICHMOND—Madison County

★ ○ **BAPTIST HEALTH RICHMOND (180049)**, 801 Eastern Bypass, Zip 40475-2405, Mailing Address: P.O. Box 1600, Zip 40476-2603; tel. 859/623-3131 **A**9 10 11 19 **F**3 11 13 15 18 20 28 29 30 34 35 40 46 48 49 50 51 57 59 68 70 74 75 76 79 81 84 85 87 91 92 93 97 107 108 110 111 115 118 119 124 129 130 132 146 147 **S** Baptist Health, Louisville, KY
Primary Contact: Todd Jones, President
CMO: Roshan Pais, M.D., Chief of Staff
CIO: Kelly Bonzo, Director
CHR: Joy M. Benedict, Director Human Resources
CNO: Tammy Sullivan, R.N., Chief Nursing Officer
Web address: www.baptisthealthrichmond.com
**Control:** Other not-for-profit (including NFP Corporation) **Service:** General Medical and Surgical

**Staffed Beds:** 69 **Admissions:** 3202 **Census:** 34 **Outpatient Visits:** 88090 **Births:** 754 **Total Expense ($000):** 69054 **Payroll Expense ($000):** 26398 **Personnel:** 564

## RUSSELL SPRINGS—Russell County

★ **RUSSELL COUNTY HOSPITAL (181330)**, 153 Dowell Road, Zip 42642-4579, Mailing Address: P.O. Box 1610, Zip 42642-1610; tel. 270/866-4141 **A**9 10 18 **F**3 11 15 28 29 30 34 40 57 59 70 81 85 91 93 107 111 114 118 119 129 130 133 135 146 148
Primary Contact: Bill Kindred, Chief Executive Officer
CFO: Michael Logan, Chief Financial Officer
CMO: Sam Bradley, M.D., Chief of Staff
CIO: Monte Monsanto, Chief Information Systems
CHR: Jennifer Dykes, Director Human Resources
CNO: Judy Chenoweth, Chief Nursing Officer
Web address: www.russellcohospital.org
**Control:** Hospital district or authority, Government, nonfederal **Service:** General Medical and Surgical

**Staffed Beds:** 25 **Admissions:** 630 **Census:** 6 **Births:** 0

## RUSSELLVILLE—Logan County

⊠ **LOGAN MEMORIAL HOSPITAL (180066)**, 1625 South Nashville Road, Zip 42276-8834, Mailing Address: P.O. Box 10, Zip 42276-0010; tel. 270/726-4011 **A**1 9 10 **F**3 15 28 29 30 34 40 45 50 51 57 59 64 70 75 79 81 87 93 107 110 111 114 119 127 129 130 132 133 146 **S** LifePoint Health, Brentwood, TN
Primary Contact: James Bills, Chief Executive Officer
CFO: Theresa Fite, Chief Financial Officer
CIO: Mike Katz, Director Information Systems
CHR: Courtney Jackson, Director Human Resources
CNO: John Jones, Chief Nursing Officer
Web address: www.loganmemorial.com
**Control:** Corporation, Investor-owned, for-profit **Service:** General Medical and Surgical

**Staffed Beds:** 53 **Admissions:** 1152 **Census:** 14 **Outpatient Visits:** 41264 **Births:** 0

## SALEM—Livingston County

★ **LIVINGSTON HOSPITAL AND HEALTHCARE SERVICES (181320)**, 131 Hospital Drive, Zip 42078-8043; tel. 270/988-2299 **A**9 10 18 **F**11 15 29 30 34 35 40 43 45 46 47 48 56 57 59 68 75 81 85 87 91 93 103 107 110 114 115 119 127 130 133 144 146 **S** Alliant Management Services, Louisville, KY
Primary Contact: Mark A. Edwards, Chief Executive Officer
CMO: William Guyette, M.D., President Medical Staff
CIO: Shannan Landreth, Information Systems
CHR: Carla Wiggins, Director Human Resources
CNO: Joanna Stone, Chief Nursing Officer
Web address: www.lhhs.org
**Control:** Other not-for-profit (including NFP Corporation) **Service:** General Medical and Surgical

**Staffed Beds:** 25 **Admissions:** 813 **Census:** 10 **Outpatient Visits:** 15826 **Total Expense ($000):** 13383 **Payroll Expense ($000):** 5214 **Personnel:** 148

---

**Hospital, Medicare Provider Number, Address, Telephone, Approval, Facility, and Physician Codes, Health Care System**

★ American Hospital Association (AHA) membership
□ The Joint Commission accreditation
○ Healthcare Facilities Accreditation Program
◇ DNV Healthcare Inc. accreditation
⇑ Center for Improvement in Healthcare Quality Accreditation
△ Commission on Accreditation of Rehabilitation Facilities (CARF) accreditation

## SCOTTSVILLE—Allen County

☒ **MEDICAL CENTER AT SCOTTSVILLE (181324)**, 456 Burnley Road,
Zip 42164–6355; tel. 270/622–2800, (Total facility includes 110 beds in nursing
home–type unit) **A**9 10 18 **F**3 15 28 29 30 34 35 40 56 57 59 64 68 71 74 75
79 81 85 86 87 93 97 102 103 104 107 110 111 114 119 127 128 130 132
133 143 146 148 **P**6 **S** Commonwealth Health Corporation, Bowling Green, KY
Primary Contact: Eric Hagan, R.N., Vice President/Administrator
CFO: Ronald G. Sowell, Chief Financial Officer
CIO: Jean Cherry, Chief Information Officer
CHR: Lynn Williams, Vice President Human Resources
Web address: www.themedicalcenterscottsville.org/
**Control:** Other not–for–profit (including NFP Corporation) **Service:** General
Medical and Surgical

**Staffed Beds:** 135 **Admissions:** 646 **Census:** 125 **Outpatient Visits:** 21092
**Births:** 0 **Personnel:** 192

## SHELBYVILLE—Shelby County

☒ **JEWISH HOSPITAL–SHELBYVILLE (180016)**, 727 Hospital Drive,
Zip 40065–1699; tel. 502/647–4000 **A**1 9 10 **F**3 11 15 18 28 29 30 34 35
39 40 43 44 45 46 50 57 59 64 68 70 75 79 81 82 84 85 87 91 93 107
108 110 111 114 119 129 132 135 146 147 148 **P**6 **S** Catholic Health
Initiatives, Englewood, CO
Primary Contact: Barry A. Papania, Interim Administrator
CFO: Erika McGimsey, Controller
CMO: Tony Perez, M.D., President Medical Staff
CHR: Cindy Stewart Rattray, Director Human Resources
Web address: www.jhsmh.org
**Control:** Other not–for–profit (including NFP Corporation) **Service:** General
Medical and Surgical

**Staffed Beds:** 47 **Admissions:** 1586 **Census:** 17 **Outpatient Visits:** 42652
**Births:** 0 **Total Expense ($000):** 33396 **Payroll Expense ($000):** 10114
**Personnel:** 145

## SOMERSET—Pulaski County

☒ **LAKE CUMBERLAND REGIONAL HOSPITAL (180132)**, 305 Langdon Street,
Zip 42503–2750, Mailing Address: P.O. Box 620, Zip 42502–0620;
tel. 606/679–7441, (Total facility includes 12 beds in nursing home–type unit) **A**1
2 9 10 13 **F**3 8 11 12 13 15 17 18 20 22 24 29 30 31 34 39 40 41 45 46
49 50 51 54 56 57 59 64 65 68 70 73 74 75 76 77 78 79 81 82 85 86 87
89 90 91 93 96 97 98 100 102 103 107 108 109 110 111 114 115 119 120
127 128 129 130 131 132 135 144 146 147 148 **S** LifePoint Health,
Brentwood, TN
Primary Contact: Timothy A. Bess, Chief Executive Officer
COO: Rebecca Segal, Chief Operating Officer
CFO: Steve Sloan, Chief Financial Officer
CMO: Michael Citak, M.D., Chief Medical Officer
CIO: Thomas Gilbert, Director Information Technology Services
CHR: James Hughes, Director Human Resources
CNO: Sheryl Glasscock, Chief Nursing Officer
Web address: www.lakecumberlandhospital.com
**Control:** Corporation, Investor–owned, for–profit **Service:** General Medical and
Surgical

**Staffed Beds:** 295 **Admissions:** 11078 **Census:** 147 **Outpatient Visits:**
119309 **Births:** 1234 **Total Expense ($000):** 142008 **Payroll Expense**
**($000):** 53020 **Personnel:** 1260

## SOUTH WILLIAMSON—Pike County

☐ **TUG VALLEY ARH REGIONAL MEDICAL CENTER (180069)**, 260 Hospital
Drive, Zip 41503–4072; tel. 606/237–1710, (Total facility includes 35 beds in
nursing home–type unit) **A**1 9 10 **F**3 11 13 15 29 30 34 35 40 43 50 54 57 59
60 62 64 67 70 74 75 76 77 79 81 82 85 86 87 89 90 93 97 107 108 110
111 115 118 119 127 128 129 130 132 146 147 **P**6 **S** Appalachian Regional
Healthcare, Inc., Lexington, KY
Primary Contact: Timothy A. Hatfield, Community Chief Executive Officer
CMO: J. D. Miller, M.D., Vice President Medical Affairs
CIO: Jeff Brady, Chief Information Officer
Web address: www.arh.org/locations/tug_valley/about_us.aspx
**Control:** Other not–for–profit (including NFP Corporation) **Service:** General
Medical and Surgical

**Staffed Beds:** 141 **Admissions:** 2330 **Census:** 48 **Outpatient Visits:** 47668
**Births:** 76 **Total Expense ($000):** 42239 **Payroll Expense ($000):** 11837
**Personnel:** 275

## STANFORD—Lincoln County

☒ **EPHRAIM MCDOWELL FORT LOGAN HOSPITAL (181315)**, 110 Metker Trail,
Zip 40484–1020; tel. 606/365–4600 **A**1 9 10 18 **F**3 11 13 15 29 30 34 35
40 43 57 59 64 76 81 87 89 107 110 111 119 130 133 135 146 **S** Ephraim
McDowell Health, Danville, KY
Primary Contact: Vicki A. Darnell, R.N., MSN, Chief Executive Officer
CFO: William R. Snapp, III, Vice President and Chief Financial Officer
CMO: James Turpin, Chief of Staff
CIO: Gary Neat, Director Information Systems
CHR: Carl Metz, Vice President
CNO: Ina Louise Glass, Chief Nursing Officer and Vice President and Interim
Administrator
Web address: www.fortloganhospital.org
**Control:** Other not–for–profit (including NFP Corporation) **Service:** General
Medical and Surgical

**Staffed Beds:** 25 **Admissions:** 641 **Census:** 5 **Outpatient Visits:** 32582
**Births:** 330 **Total Expense ($000):** 13648 **Payroll Expense ($000):** 6149
**Personnel:** 135

## TOMPKINSVILLE—Monroe County

☒ **MONROE COUNTY MEDICAL CENTER (180105)**, 529 Capp Harlan Road,
Zip 42167–1840; tel. 270/487–9231 **A**1 9 10 **F**2 3 7 29 34 40 45 57 59 93
107 111 114 119 133 **S** QHR, Brentwood, TN
Primary Contact: Vicky McFall, Chief Executive Officer
CFO: Rickie F. Brown, Chief Financial Officer
CIO: Paul McKiddy, Director Information Technology
CHR: Sue Page, Director Human Resources
Web address: www.mcmccares.com
**Control:** Hospital district or authority, Government, nonfederal **Service:** General
Medical and Surgical

**Staffed Beds:** 49 **Admissions:** 1472 **Census:** 19 **Outpatient Visits:** 8433
**Births:** 0

## VERSAILLES—Woodford County

★ **BLUEGRASS COMMUNITY HOSPITAL (181308)**, 360 Amsden Avenue,
Zip 40383–1286; tel. 859/873–3111 **A**9 10 18 **F**29 40 45 50 59 70 79 81 82
93 107 110 111 119 133 **S** LifePoint Health, Brentwood, TN
Primary Contact: Tommy Haggard, Chief Executive Officer
CFO: Shellie Shouse, Chief Financial Officer
CMO: Michele Welling, M.D., Chief of Staff
CHR: Marcia Carter, Director Human Resources
CNO: Kathy Russell, R.N., Chief Nursing Officer
Web address: www.bluegrasscommunityhospital.com
**Control:** Corporation, Investor–owned, for–profit **Service:** General Medical and
Surgical

**Staffed Beds:** 16 **Admissions:** 328 **Census:** 3 **Outpatient Visits:** 11864
**Births:** 0 **Total Expense ($000):** 15058 **Payroll Expense ($000):** 5232
**Personnel:** 96

## WEST LIBERTY—Morgan County

☐ **MORGAN COUNTY ARH HOSPITAL (181307)**, 476 Liberty Road,
Zip 41472–2049, Mailing Address: P.O. Box 579, Zip 41472–0579;
tel. 606/743–3186 **A**1 9 10 18 **F**11 15 29 30 34 35 40 54 75 82 64 75
82 86 87 93 97 107 114 119 127 129 130 132 133 146 **P**6 **S** Appalachian
Regional Healthcare, Inc., Lexington, KY
Primary Contact: Stephen M. Gavalchik, FACHE, Community Chief Executive
Officer
COO: Paul V. Miles, Chief Operating Officer
CMO: J. D. Miller, M.D., Vice President Medical Affairs
CIO: Jeff Brady, Director Information Systems
CHR: Lisa Redding, Manager Human Resources
Web address: www.arh.org
**Control:** Other not–for–profit (including NFP Corporation) **Service:** General
Medical and Surgical

**Staffed Beds:** 25 **Admissions:** 328 **Census:** 4 **Outpatient Visits:** 22688
**Births:** 0 **Total Expense ($000):** 12315 **Payroll Expense ($000):** 4310
**Personnel:** 97

## WHITESBURG—Letcher County

☐ **WHITESBURG ARH HOSPITAL (180002)**, 240 Hospital Road,
Zip 41858–7627; tel. 606/633–3600 **A**1 9 10 **F**3 11 12 13 15 18 20 24 28
29 30 31 32 34 35 40 43 50 54 57 59 62 64 70 75 76 77 81 82 85 86 87
89 93 97 107 108 110 111 114 118 119 127 129 130 133 146 147 **P**6
**S** Appalachian Regional Healthcare, Inc., Lexington, KY
Primary Contact: Dena C. Sparkman, FACHE, Community Chief Executive Officer
COO: Paul V. Miles, Vice President Administration
CFO: Joseph Grossman, Vice President Fiscal Affairs
CMO: Ricky M. Collins, M.D., Chief of Staff
CIO: Brent Styer, Director Information Technology
CHR: Daniel Fitzpatrick, Director Human Resources
Web address: www.arh.org/whitesburg
**Control:** Other not–for–profit (including NFP Corporation) **Service:** General
Medical and Surgical

**Staffed Beds:** 87 **Admissions:** 3360 **Census:** 35 **Outpatient Visits:** 59697
**Births:** 488 **Total Expense ($000):** 42241 **Payroll Expense ($000):** 11601
**Personnel:** 258

**WILLIAMSTOWN—Grant County**

**ST. ELIZABETH GRANT (181311)**, 238 Barnes Road, Zip 41097–9482;
tel. 859/824–8240 **A**9 10 18 **F**3 11 15 29 30 31 34 35 38 40 44 46 50 57
59 63 64 68 74 75 78 79 84 93 97 107 108 110 111 114 119 129 130 131
132 135 146 148 **S** St. Elizabeth Healthcare, Edgewood, KY
Primary Contact: Garren Colvin, Chief Executive Officer
Web address: www.stelizabeth.com
**Control:** Church–operated, Nongovernment, not–for profit **Service:** General
Medical and Surgical

**Staffed Beds:** 16 **Admissions:** 292 **Census:** 2 **Outpatient Visits:** 51489
**Births:** 0 **Total Expense ($000):** 17873 **Payroll Expense ($000):** 5723
**Personnel:** 86

**ST. ELIZABETH MEDICAL CENTER–GRANT COUNTY** See St. Elizabeth Grant

**WINCHESTER—Clark County**

✶ **CLARK REGIONAL MEDICAL CENTER (180092)**, 175 Hospital Drive,
Zip 40391–9591; tel. 859/745–3500 **A**1 5 9 10 **F**13 15 18 19 29 30 31 34
35 38 40 41 45 46 49 50 51 56 57 59 60 61 64 65 68 70 71 74 75 76 77
78 79 81 82 87 92 93 97 107 108 110 111 115 116 117 119 124 127 128
129 130 133 135 144 146 147 **S** LifePoint Health, Brentwood, TN
Primary Contact: Cherie Sibley, R.N., Chief Executive Officer
CFO: Amber Goodpaster, Chief Financial Officer
CMO: Nicholas Kouns, D.O., Chief of Staff
CHR: Deidre Bradley, Vice President Human Resources
CNO: Barbara Kinder, R.N., Chief Clinical Officer
Web address: www.clarkregional.org
**Control:** Corporation, Investor–owned, for–profit **Service:** General Medical and
Surgical

**Staffed Beds:** 79 **Admissions:** 2834 **Census:** 42 **Outpatient Visits:** 44060
**Births:** 670 **Total Expense ($000):** 47820 **Payroll Expense ($000):** 17017
**Personnel:** 460

---

| **Hospital, Medicare Provider Number, Address, Telephone, Approval, Facility, and Physician Codes, Health Care System** | | |
|---|---|---|
| ★ American Hospital Association (AHA) membership | ○ Healthcare Facilities Accreditation Program | ⇑ Center for Improvement in Healthcare Quality Accreditation |
| □ The Joint Commission accreditation | ◇ DNV Healthcare Inc. accreditation | △ Commission on Accreditation of Rehabilitation Facilities (CARF) accreditation |

## LOUISIANA

**LA**

### ABBEVILLE—Vermilion Parish

☒ **ABBEVILLE GENERAL HOSPITAL (190034)**, 118 North Hospital Drive, Zip 70510–4077, Mailing Address: P.O. Box 580, Zip 70511–0580; tel. 337/893–5466 **A**1 9 10 **F**3 11 13 15 29 30 31 34 40 45 50 54 59 60 64 66 68 70 75 76 79 81 82 85 86 87 89 97 98 103 105 107 108 114 119 127 128 130 133 146 **P**6
Primary Contact: Ray A. Landry, Chief Executive Officer
CFO: Troy Hair, Chief Financial Officer
CIO: Kelly Hair, Director Information Technology
CNO: Denise Noel, Chief Nursing Officer
Web address: www.abbgen.net
**Control:** Hospital district or authority, Government, nonfederal **Service:** General Medical and Surgical

**Staffed Beds:** 60 **Admissions:** 1902 **Census:** 30 **Outpatient Visits:** 88088 **Births:** 197 **Total Expense ($000):** 39296 **Payroll Expense ($000):** 19456 **Personnel:** 364

### ALEXANDRIA—Rapides Parish

◇ **CENTRAL LOUISIANA SURGICAL HOSPITAL (190298)**, 651 North Bolton Avenue, Zip 71301–7449, Mailing Address: P.O. Box 8646, Zip 71306–1646; tel. 318/443–3511 **A**9 10 21 **F**12 39 68 74 79 81 82 85 86 89 90 107 111 119 130
Primary Contact: Louise Barker, R.N., Chief Executive Officer
CFO: Michael Fuselier, FACHE, Chief Financial Officer
CMO: Renick Webb, M.D., Chief Medical Director
CHR: Debbie Norman, Director Human Resources
CNO: Carol Wells, R.N., Chief Nursing Officer
Web address: www.clshospital.com
**Control:** Partnership, Investor–owned, for–profit **Service:** Surgical

**Staffed Beds:** 24 **Admissions:** 1398 **Census:** 10 **Births:** 0

☒ **CHRISTUS DUBUIS HOSPITAL OF ALEXANDRIA (192012)**, 3330 Masonic Drive, 4th Floor, Zip 71301–3841; tel. 318/448–4938 **A**1 10 **F**1 3 29 77 84 85 148 **S** CHRISTUS Health, Irving, TX
Primary Contact: Beth Parsons, R.N., Administrator
CNO: Kimberly Bennett, Director Patient Care
Web address: www.christusdubuis.org/CHRISTUSDubuisHospitalofAlexandriaLA
**Control:** Church–operated, Nongovernment, not–for profit **Service:** Long–Term Acute Care hospital

**Staffed Beds:** 25 **Admissions:** 299 **Census:** 18 **Outpatient Visits:** 0 **Births:** 0

☒ **CHRISTUS ST. FRANCES CABRINI HOSPITAL (190019)**, 3330 Masonic Drive, Zip 71301–3899; tel. 318/487–1122 **A**1 2 9 10 **F**11 12 13 15 18 20 22 24 26 28 29 30 31 34 35 40 45 46 49 54 57 58 59 63 64 70 72 74 76 77 78 79 81 82 84 85 87 89 90 93 96 97 98 103 107 108 109 110 111 114 115 116 117 118 119 120 121 126 129 130 131 132 145 146 147 148 **P**6 **S** CHRISTUS Health, Irving, TX
Primary Contact: Nancy R. Hellyer, R.N., FACHE, Chief Executive Officer
COO: Lisa R. Lauve, R.N., Regional Chief Nursing Executive and Chief Operating Officer
CFO: Debbie White, Chief Financial Officer
CHR: Wendy White, Regional Vice President Human Resources
Web address: www.cabrini.org/
**Control:** Church–operated, Nongovernment, not–for profit **Service:** General Medical and Surgical

**Staffed Beds:** 281 **Admissions:** 12281 **Census:** 143 **Outpatient Visits:** 186625 **Births:** 973 **Total Expense ($000):** 208376 **Payroll Expense ($000):** 65666 **Personnel:** 1327

☐ **COMPASS BEHAVIORAL CENTER OF ALEXANDRIA (194106)**, 6410 Masonic Drve, Zip 71301–2319; tel. 318/442–3163 **A**1 10 **F**29 34 35 38 64 98 100 101 102 103 104 105 130 133 135 **P**5 **S** Compass Health, Crowley, LA
Primary Contact: Phillip Maxwell, Administrator
Web address: www.compasshealthcare.com/site191.php
**Control:** State–Government, nonfederal **Service:** Psychiatric

**Staffed Beds:** 16 **Admissions:** 281 **Census:** 9 **Outpatient Visits:** 0 **Births:** 0

☒ **HEALTHSOUTH REHABILITATION HOSPITAL OF ALEXANDRIA (193031)**, 104 North Third Street, Zip 71301–8581; tel. 318/449–1370, (Nonreporting) **A**1 10 **S** HEALTHSOUTH Corporation, Birmingham, AL
Primary Contact: James W. McClung, Chief Executive Officer
CFO: Linda Wright, Chief Financial Officer
CMO: Vasudeva Dhulipala, M.D., Medical Director
CHR: Suzie Wagner, Director Human Resources
CNO: Karin Jones, Chief Nursing Officer
Web address: www.healthsouthalexandria.com
**Control:** Partnership, Investor–owned, for–profit **Service:** Rehabilitation

**Staffed Beds:** 47

☐ **LONGLEAF HOSPITAL (194022)**, 110 John Eskew Drive, Zip 71303; tel. 318/445–5111, (Nonreporting) **A**9 10 **S** Acadia Healthcare Company, Inc., Franklin, TN
Primary Contact: Cheryl Lachney, Chief Executive Officer
Web address: www.longleafhospital.com/
**Control:** Corporation, Investor–owned, for–profit **Service:** Psychiatric

**Staffed Beds:** 70

☐ **OCEANS BEHAVIORAL HOSPITAL OF ALEXANDRIA (194096)**, 2621 North Bolton Avenue, Zip 71303–4506; tel. 318/448–8473, (Nonreporting) **A**1 9 10 **S** Oceans Healthcare, Lake Charles, LA
Primary Contact: Nicholas D. Guillory, MSN, Interim Administrator
Web address: www.obha.info/
**Control:** Corporation, Investor–owned, for–profit **Service:** Psychiatric

**Staffed Beds:** 24

☒ **RAPIDES REGIONAL MEDICAL CENTER (190026)**, 211 Fourth Street, Zip 71301–8421; tel. 318/473–3000 **A**1 2 3 5 9 10 **F**3 11 13 15 17 18 19 20 22 24 26 28 29 30 31 32 34 35 36 38 40 41 43 44 45 46 47 48 49 50 51 52 54 55 57 59 60 61 64 65 66 68 70 72 74 75 76 77 78 79 81 82 84 85 86 87 88 89 97 107 108 110 111 114 115 118 119 120 121 123 124 129 130 131 132 135 144 146 147 148 **P**1 **S** HCA, Nashville, TN
Primary Contact: Jason E. Cobb, FACHE, Chief Executive Officer
COO: Becky Barnes, Chief Operating Officer
CFO: Randy Rogers, FACHE, Chief Financial Officer
CMO: David Rhodes, M.D., Senior Vice President Medical Affairs and Chief Medical Officer
CHR: Stephen W. Scull, Vice President Ethics and Compliance officer
CNO: Diane Fulton, R.N., Chief Nursing Officer
Web address: www.rapidesregional.com
**Control:** Partnership, Investor–owned, for–profit **Service:** General Medical and Surgical

**Staffed Beds:** 357 **Admissions:** 15945 **Census:** 236 **Outpatient Visits:** 183847 **Births:** 2209 **Total Expense ($000):** 215735 **Payroll Expense ($000):** 79204 **Personnel:** 1362

☐ **RIVERSIDE HOSPITAL OF LOUISIANA (192043)**, 211 Fourth Street, 5th Floor, Zip 71301–8421; tel. 318/767–2900, (Nonreporting) **A**1 10
Primary Contact: Mark J. Rice, Interim Administrator
Web address: www.riversidehospital.net
**Control:** Corporation, Investor–owned, for–profit **Service:** Long–Term Acute Care hospital

**Staffed Beds:** 27

### AMITE—Tangipahoa Parish

★ **HOOD MEMORIAL HOSPITAL (191309)**, 301 West Walnut Street, Zip 70422–2098; tel. 985/748–9485 **A**9 10 18 **F**3 29 35 40 57 59 64 65 86 97 107 108 119 127 133 **P**6
Primary Contact: Edward Dugar, Chief Executive Officer
CFO: Mike Estay, Chief Financial Officer
CMO: Richard Bridges, M.D., Chief of Staff
CIO: David Lowell Teague, Jr., Director Information Technology
CHR: Alicia Chatelain, Director Human Resource
CNO: Fran St. Pierre, Chief Nursing Officer
Web address: www.hoodmemorial.com
**Control:** Hospital district or authority, Government, nonfederal **Service:** General Medical and Surgical

**Staffed Beds:** 25 **Admissions:** 415 **Census:** 8 **Outpatient Visits:** 12094 **Births:** 0 **Total Expense ($000):** 11041 **Payroll Expense ($000):** 4969 **Personnel:** 161

### ARCADIA—Bienville Parish

**BIENVILLE MEDICAL CENTER (191320)**, 1175 Pine Street, Suite 200, Zip 71001–3122; tel. 318/263–4700, (Nonreporting) **A**9 10 18 **S** Allegiance Health Management, Shreveport, LA
Primary Contact: Kirk Lemoine, Chief Operating Officer
**Control:** Other not–for–profit (including NFP Corporation) **Service:** General Medical and Surgical

**Staffed Beds:** 21

*Many Facility Codes have changed. Please refer to the AHA Guide Code Chart.*

## BASTROP—Morehouse Parish

☐ LIBERTY HEALTHCARE SYSTEMS (194083), 4673 Eugene Ware Boulevard, Zip 71220–1425; tel. 318/281–2448 **A**1 9 10 **F**98 99 130 **P**6
Primary Contact: Christine Murphy, MS, Administrator
COO: Jason Spangler, Chief Operating Officer
CFO: Paul Coburn, Chief Financial Officer
CMO: Tommy Dansby, Chief Medical Officer
CHR: Gloria Board, Director Human Resources
CNO: Shelly Hoard, RN, Director of Nursing
Web address: www.libertybh.com/
**Control:** Partnership, Investor–owned, for–profit **Service:** Children's hospital psychiatric

**Staffed Beds:** 60 **Admissions:** 875 **Census:** 20 **Outpatient Visits:** 0 **Births:** 0

★ MOREHOUSE GENERAL HOSPITAL (190116), 323 West Walnut Avenue, Zip 71220–4521, Mailing Address: P.O. Box 1060, Zip 71221–1060; tel. 318/283–3600 **A**3 9 10 **F**3 11 13 15 29 34 39 40 45 50 65 70 76 79 80 81 85 86 102 107 108 110 111 114 118 119 127 133 145 146 147 148 **P**5
Primary Contact: Jim Allbritton, Interim Chief Executive Officer and Chief Financial Officer
CFO: James Allbritton, Chief Financial Officer
CMO: John Coats, M.D., Chief Medical Staff
CIO: B. J. Vail, Director Information Systems
CHR: Debbie Spann, Director Human Resources
CNO: Melinda Jones, R.N., Chief Nursing Officer
Web address: www.mghospital.com
**Control:** Hospital district or authority, Government, nonfederal **Service:** General Medical and Surgical

**Staffed Beds:** 49 **Admissions:** 2110 **Census:** 17 **Outpatient Visits:** 42321 **Births:** 431 **Total Expense ($000):** 27809 **Payroll Expense ($000):** 12858 **Personnel:** 285

STERLINGTON REHABILITATION HOSPITAL (193069), 370 West Hickory Avenue, Zip 71220–4442, Mailing Address: P.O. Box 627, Zip 71221–0627; tel. 318/665–9950 **A**10 **F**29 30 34 35 36 50 54 56 57 59 64 65 66 68 87 90 93 96 99 100 101 103 104 127 130 132 143 148 **P**6
Primary Contact: Cathy Waldrop, Administrator
Web address: www.www.sterlingtonrehab.com
**Control:** Corporation, Investor–owned, for–profit **Service:** Rehabilitation

**Staffed Beds:** 10 **Admissions:** 253 **Census:** 8 **Outpatient Visits:** 1170 **Births:** 0 **Personnel:** 77

## BATON ROUGE—East Baton Rouge Parish

☐ BATON ROUGE BEHAVIORAL HOSPITAL (194107), 4040 North Boulevard, Zip 70806–3829; tel. 225/300–8470, (Nonreporting) **A**1 10
Primary Contact: Larry Godfrey, Administrator
COO: James O'Shea, Chief Operating Officer
CFO: Warren Knight, Chief Financial Officer
CMO: Richard Capiola, M.D., Chief Medical Officer
CNO: Francine Mineau, Chief Nursing Officer
Web address: www.batonrougebehavioral.com
**Control:** Corporation, Investor–owned, for–profit **Service:** Psychiatric

**Staffed Beds:** 15

☐ BATON ROUGE GENERAL MEDICAL CENTER (190065), 8585 Picardy Avenue, Zip 70809–3679; tel. 225/763–4000, (Includes BATON ROUGE GENERAL MEDICAL CENTER–BLUEBONNET, 8585 Picardy Avenue, Mailing Address: P.O. Box 84330, Zip 70884–4330; tel. 225/763–4000; Mark F. Slyter, FACHE, President and Chief Executive Officer) **A**1 2 3 5 6 8 9 10 **F**3 8 11 12 13 15 16 17 18 19 20 22 24 26 28 29 30 31 34 35 38 40 44 45 46 47 49 50 53 54 55 58 59 60 61 64 65 68 70 72 74 75 76 77 79 81 82 84 86 87 88 89 90 93 96 97 98 101 102 103 104 107 108 110 111 114 115 117 118 119 120 121 123 124 126 128 129 130 131 132 135 143 144 146 147 148 **P**4 6
Primary Contact: Mark F. Slyter, FACHE, Chief Executive Officer
COO: Edgardo J. Tenreiro, Executive Vice President and Chief Operating Officer
CFO: Kendall Johnson, Chief Financial Officer
CIO: Bennett Cheramie, Vice President Information Technology
CHR: Paul Douglas, Vice President Human Resources
CNO: Anna Leah Cazes, Chief Nursing Officer
Web address: www.brgeneral.org
**Control:** Other not–for–profit (including NFP Corporation) **Service:** General Medical and Surgical

**Staffed Beds:** 463 **Admissions:** 19410 **Census:** 291 **Outpatient Visits:** 252470 **Births:** 680 **Total Expense ($000):** 369999 **Payroll Expense ($000):** 128730 **Personnel:** 2842

☐ BATON ROUGE REHABILITATION HOSPITAL (193028), 8595 United Plaza Boulevard, Zip 70809–2251; tel. 225/927–0567, (Nonreporting) **A**1 10
Primary Contact: Trisha Guidry, Administrator
CFO: Nicholas Hluchy, Business Analyst, Support Services Manager
CMO: Sundararama R. Vatsavai, M.D., Medical Director
CIO: Roxane Bingham, Director Marketing
CHR: Michelle Smith, Coordinator Human Resources
CNO: Derrick Landreneau, Director of Nursing
Web address: www.brrehab.com
**Control:** Corporation, Investor–owned, for–profit **Service:** Rehabilitation

**Staffed Beds:** 80

BETHESDA REHABILITATION HOSPITAL (193092), 7414 Sumrall Drive, Zip 70812–1240, Mailing Address: 8225 Summa Avenue, Suite B., Zip 70809–3422; tel. 225/767–2034, (Nonreporting) **A**10
Primary Contact: Lionel Murphy, Chief Executive Officer and Administrator
**Control:** Corporation, Investor–owned, for–profit **Service:** Rehabilitation

**Staffed Beds:** 18

HEALTHSOUTH REHABILITATION HOSPITAL OF BATON ROUGE See Baton Rouge Rehabilitation Hospital

OCEANS BEHAVIORAL HOSPITAL OF BATON ROUGE (194086), 11135 Florida Boulevard, Zip 70815–2013; tel. 225/356–7030, (Nonreporting) **A**9 10 **S** Oceans Healthcare, Lake Charles, LA
Primary Contact: Valerie Dalton, R.N., Administrator
Web address: www.obhbr.info/
**Control:** Corporation, Investor–owned, for–profit **Service:** Psychiatric

**Staffed Beds:** 20

✙ OCHSNER MEDICAL CENTER–BATON ROUGE (190202), 17000 Medical Center Drive, Zip 70816–3224; tel. 225/752–2470 **A**1 9 10 **F**3 4 11 12 13 15 18 20 22 24 26 29 30 34 35 38 40 44 45 46 47 48 49 50 51 57 58 59 60 64 68 70 72 75 76 77 78 79 81 82 85 86 87 93 97 98 101 104 107 108 110 111 114 116 117 119 126 129 130 132 135 144 146 147 148 **P**6 **S** Ochsner Health System, New Orleans, LA
Primary Contact: Eric McMillen, Chief Executive Officer
CFO: Stephanie Bushart, Chief Financial Officer
CMO: F. Ralph Dauterive, M.D., Vice President Medical Affairs
CHR: Jan Rivers, Director Human Resources
Web address: www.ochsner.org/page.cfm?id=103
**Control:** Other not–for–profit (including NFP Corporation) **Service:** General Medical and Surgical

**Staffed Beds:** 155 **Admissions:** 6683 **Census:** 68 **Outpatient Visits:** 84477 **Births:** 1215 **Total Expense ($000):** 124164 **Payroll Expense ($000):** 40758 **Personnel:** 602

✙ OUR LADY OF THE LAKE REGIONAL MEDICAL CENTER (190064), 5000 Hennessy Boulevard, Zip 70808–4375; tel. 225/765–6565, (Includes OUR LADY OF THE LAKE CHILDREN'S HOSPITAL, 5000 Hennessy Boulevard, tel. 225/765–8886), (Total facility includes 390 beds in nursing home–type unit) **A**1 2 3 5 8 9 10 **F**3 4 5 8 10 11 12 14 15 17 18 19 20 21 22 24 26 28 29 30 31 34 35 37 38 39 40 41 42 43 46 47 49 50 51 53 54 55 56 57 58 59 60 61 64 66 68 70 71 74 75 77 78 79 81 84 85 86 87 88 89 90 93 94 96 97 98 99 100 101 102 103 104 105 107 108 110 111 114 115 116 117 118 119 126 127 129 130 131 132 133 135 141 142 143 144 146 148 **P**6 **S** Franciscan Missionaries of Our Lady Health System, Inc., Baton Rouge, LA
Primary Contact: K. Scott Wester, FACHE, President and Chief Executive Officer
COO: Terrie Sterling, R.N., Chief Operating Officer
CFO: Jeff Limbocker, Chief Financial Officer
CMO: Richard Vath, M.D., Vice President Medical Affairs
CIO: Vindell Washington, M.D., Vice President Performance Excellence and Technology
CHR: Cora Ford, Vice President Human Resources
CNO: Debbie Ford, R.N., Vice President Patient Care Services
Web address: www.ololrmc.com
**Control:** Church–operated, Nongovernment, not–for profit **Service:** General Medical and Surgical

**Staffed Beds:** 1093 **Admissions:** 33253 **Census:** 762 **Outpatient Visits:** 604260 **Births:** 0 **Total Expense ($000):** 942175 **Payroll Expense ($000):** 341303 **Personnel:** 6105

---

**Hospital, Medicare Provider Number, Address, Telephone, Approval, Facility, and Physician Codes, Health Care System**

★ American Hospital Association (AHA) membership
☐ The Joint Commission accreditation
○ Healthcare Facilities Accreditation Program
◇ DNV Healthcare Inc. accreditation
⇑ Center for Improvement in Healthcare Quality Accreditation
△ Commission on Accreditation of Rehabilitation Facilities (CARF) accreditation

**LA**

☐ **PROMISE HOSPITAL BATON ROUGE – MAIN CAMPUS (192045)**, 5130 Mancuso Lane, Zip 70809–3583; tel. 225/490–9600, (Nonreporting) **A**1 **S** Promise Healthcare, Boca Raton, FL
Primary Contact: Kiley P. Cedotal, Chief Executive Officer
COO: Michael R. Sanders, MS, Chief Operating Officer
CFO: Trina Arceneaux, Assistant Chief Financial Officer
CMO: Subhaker Gummadi, M.D., Chief Medical Staff
CIO: Charmaine T. Mosby, Area Director Health Information Management
CHR: Marilyn Hamilton, Director Human Resources
CNO: Larrie Arceneaux, Chief Clinical Officer
Web address: www.promise–batonrouge.com
**Control:** Corporation, Investor–owned, for–profit **Service:** Long–Term Acute Care hospital

**Staffed Beds:** 54

**PROMISE HOSPITAL OF BATON ROUGE – MID–CITY CAMPUS (192004)**, 3600 Florida Boulevard, 4th Floor, Zip 70806–3842; tel. 225/387–7770, (Nonreporting) **A**10 **S** Promise Healthcare, Boca Raton, FL
Primary Contact: Michael R. Sanders, MS, Administrator and Chief Operating Officer
COO: Michael J. Nolan, Area Chief Operating Officer and Safety
CMO: Subhaker Gummadi, M.D., President Medical Staff
Web address: www.promise–batonrougemidcity.com
**Control:** Corporation, Investor–owned, for–profit **Service:** Long–Term Acute Care hospital

**Staffed Beds:** 57

**PROMISE HOSPITAL OF BATON ROUGE – OCHSNER CAMPUS (192049)**, 17000 Medical Center Drive, 3rd Floor, Zip 70816–3246; tel. 225/236–5440, (Nonreporting) **A**10 **S** Promise Healthcare, Boca Raton, FL
Primary Contact: Michael R. Sanders, MS, Administrator and Chief Operating Officer
COO: Michael J. Nolan, Area Safety Director
CMO: Venkat Banda, M.D., President Medical Staff
CHR: Wendy Cobbs, Director of Human Resources
Web address: www.promise–batonrougeochsner.com
**Control:** Corporation, Investor–owned, for–profit **Service:** Long–Term Acute Care hospital

**Staffed Beds:** 29

**SAGE REHABILITATION HOSPITAL (193078)**, 8000 Summa Avenue, Zip 70809–3423, Mailing Address: P.O. Box 82681, Zip 70884–2681; tel. 225/819–0703, (Total facility includes 15 beds in nursing home–type unit) **A**10 **F**29 54 74 75 77 90 91 93 128 130
Primary Contact: Gayla Bryant, R.N., Administrator
CMO: Christopher Belleau, M.D., Medical Director
CHR: Kathy Ringe, Director Human Resources
CNO: Beth Sibley, Director of Nursing
Web address: www.sage–rehab.org
**Control:** Individual, Investor–owned, for–profit **Service:** Rehabilitation

**Staffed Beds:** 42 **Admissions:** 631 **Census:** 28 **Outpatient Visits:** 0 **Births:** 0 **Personnel:** 156

☐ **SEASIDE HEALTH SYSTEM (194103)**, 4363 Convention Street, Zip 70806–3906; Mailing Address: TX, tel. 225/238–3043, (Nonreporting) **A**1 9 10
Primary Contact: Lawrence Conkerton, Administrator
Web address: www.seasidehc.com
**Control:** Partnership, Investor–owned, for–profit **Service:** Psychiatric

**Staffed Beds:** 24

**SPINE HOSPITAL OF LOUISIANA (FORMALLY THE NEUROMEDICAL CENTER SURGICAL HOSPITAL) (190266)**, 10105 Park Rowe Avenue, Suite 250, Zip 70810–1684; tel. 225/763–9900, (Nonreporting) **A**9 10
Primary Contact: Robert D. Blair, Chief Executive Officer
CFO: Allison Doherty, Chief Financial Officer
CMO: Greg Fautheree, M.D., Medical Director
CIO: Jeremy Deprato, Director Information Technology
CHR: Kimberly Jones, Director Human Resources
Web address: www.theneuromedicalcenter.com
**Control:** Corporation, Investor–owned, for–profit **Service:** Surgical

**Staffed Beds:** 23

☐ **SURGICAL SPECIALTY CENTER OF BATON ROUGE (190251)**, 8080 Bluebonnet Boulevard, Zip 70810–7827; tel. 225/408–8080, (Nonreporting) **A**1 9 10
Primary Contact: Craig P. Hume, Chief Executive Officer
Web address: www.sscbr.com
**Control:** Corporation, Investor–owned, for–profit **Service:** Surgical

**Staffed Beds:** 14

**THE NEUROMEDICAL CENTER REHABILITATION HOSPITAL (193090)**, 10101 Park Rowe Avenue, Suite 500, Zip 70810–1685; tel. 225/906–2999, (Nonreporting) **A**10 **S** AMG Integrated Healthcare Management, Lafayette, LA
Primary Contact: Elizabeth Wilson, Administrator
Web address: www.theneuromedicalcenter.com
**Control:** Corporation, Investor–owned, for–profit **Service:** Rehabilitation

**Staffed Beds:** 23

✖ **WOMAN'S HOSPITAL (190128)**, 100 Woman's Way, Zip 70817–5100, Mailing Address: P.O. Box 95009, Zip 70895–9009; tel. 225/927–1300 **A**1 2 3 5 9 10 **F**3 11 12 13 15 29 31 32 34 35 36 38 45 50 53 54 57 58 59 61 64 65 68 70 71 72 74 75 76 77 78 79 81 84 85 86 87 93 107 110 111 115 119 126 129 130 131 132 134 135 146 147 148 **P**6
Primary Contact: Teri G. Fontenot, FACHE, President and Chief Executive Officer
COO: Stephanie Anderson, Executive Vice President and Chief Operating Officer
CFO: Greg Smith, CPA, Chief Financial Officer
CMO: Susan Puyau, M.D., Medical Director
CIO: Paul Kirk, Vice President
CHR: Donna L. Bodin, Vice President
CNO: Patricia Johnson, R.N., Senior Vice President
Web address: www.womans.org
**Control:** Other not–for–profit (including NFP Corporation) **Service:** Obstetrics and gynecology

**Staffed Beds:** 216 **Admissions:** 12151 **Census:** 139 **Outpatient Visits:** 113683 **Births:** 8802 **Total Expense ($000):** 243775 **Payroll Expense ($000):** 115490 **Personnel:** 1523

**BERNICE—Union Parish**

**REEVES MEMORIAL MEDICAL CENTER (191326)**, 409 First Street, Zip 71222–4001, Mailing Address: P.O. Box 697, Zip 71222–0697; tel. 318/285–9066, (Nonreporting) **A**9 10 18
Primary Contact: David Caston, Chief Executive Officer
COO: Beth Jones, Chief Operating Officer
CFO: Charolette Thompson, Chief Financial Officer
CMO: R. Brian Harris, M.D., Chief of Staff
CIO: Scott Dickson, Director Information Technology
CHR: Robin Adams, Director Human Resources
Web address: www.reevesmemorial.com/
**Control:** Hospital district or authority, Government, nonfederal **Service:** General Medical and Surgical

**Staffed Beds:** 11

**TRI–WARD GENERAL HOSPITAL** See Reeves Memorial Medical Center

**BOGALUSA—Washington Parish**

✖ **OUR LADY OF THE ANGELS HOSPITAL (190312)**, 433 Plaza Street, Zip 70427–3793; tel. 985/730–6700, (Includes BOGALUSA COMMUNITY MEDICAL CENTER, 433 Plaza Street, tel. 985/730–6700) **A**1 3 5 9 10 **F**3 13 15 18 28 29 30 32 34 35 40 45 47 48 49 51 57 59 60 61 64 65 66 68 70 74 75 76 77 79 81 85 89 97 98 99 102 104 107 108 110 111 119 130 135 146 147 148 **S** Franciscan Missionaries of Our Lady Health System, Inc., Baton Rouge, LA
Primary Contact: Rene Ragas, Chief Operating Officer
COO: Rene Ragas, Chief Operating Officer
CFO: Brooke Cummings, Chief Financial Officer
CMO: Hamid Hussain, M.D., Medical Director
CIO: Mike Gilly, Chief Information Officer
CHR: Christi Brown, Director Human Resources
CNO: Mark Kellar, R.N., Interim Chief Nursing Officer
Web address: www.oloah.org
**Control:** Church–operated, Nongovernment, not–for profit **Service:** General Medical and Surgical

**Staffed Beds:** 57 **Admissions:** 2235 **Census:** 26 **Outpatient Visits:** 109335 **Births:** 212 **Total Expense ($000):** 57475 **Payroll Expense ($000):** 20194 **Personnel:** 463

**BOSSIER CITY—Bossier Parish**

☐ **CORNERSTONE HOSPITAL OF BOSSIER CITY (192006)**, 4900 Medical Drive, Zip 71112–4521; tel. 318/747–9500, (Nonreporting) **A**1 10 **S** Cornerstone Healthcare Group, Dallas, TX
Primary Contact: Sheri Burnette, R.N., Chief Executive Officer and Administrator
CFO: Billy Wilcox, Group Controller
CMO: James Jackson, M.D., Chief of Staff
CNO: Tamara Grimm, R.N., Chief Clinical Officer and Chief Nursing Officer
Web address: www.chghospitals.com/
**Control:** Corporation, Investor–owned, for–profit **Service:** Long–Term Acute Care hospital

**Staffed Beds:** 54

◇ **PATHWAY REHABILITATION HOSPITAL (193094)**, 4900 Medical Drive, Zip 71112–4521; tel. 318/841–5555, (Nonreporting) **A**10 21
Primary Contact: James Manning, Administrator
Web address: www.pathrehab.com
**Control:** Corporation, Investor–owned, for–profit **Service:** Rehabilitation

**Staffed Beds:** 24

*Many Facility Codes have changed. Please refer to the AHA Guide Code Chart.* © 2015 AHA Guide

**RED RIVER BEHAVIORAL CENTER (194079)**, 2800 Melrose Avenue, Zip 71111–5870; tel. 318/549–2033 **A**9 10 **F**29 38 56 98 100 101 102 103 135
Primary Contact: Susan Kottenbrook, Chief Executive Officer
Web address: www.redriverbehavioral.com/
**Control:** Partnership, Investor–owned, for–profit **Service:** Psychiatric

**Staffed Beds:** 20 **Admissions:** 338 **Census:** 11 **Outpatient Visits:** 0 **Births:** 0 **Personnel:** 43

**WILLIS–KNIGHTON BOSSIER HEALTH CENTER** See WK Bossier Health Center

✠ △ **WK BOSSIER HEALTH CENTER (190236)**, 2400 Hospital Drive, Zip 71111–2385; tel. 318/212–7000 **A**1 2 7 9 10 **F**3 8 11 12 13 15 18 20 22 28 29 30 34 35 38 40 44 45 46 47 48 49 50 53 54 56 57 59 60 61 64 65 68 74 75 77 78 79 81 82 84 85 86 87 93 96 97 100 101 102 103 107 108 109 110 111 114 115 118 119 126 127 129 130 131 132 135 144 146 147 148 **P**7 **S** Willis–Knighton Health System, Shreveport, LA
Primary Contact: Clifford M. Broussard, FACHE, Administrator
COO: Charles D. Daigle, Chief Operating Officer
CFO: Ramona D. Fryer, Chief Financial Officer
CMO: Charles Powers, M.D., Administrative Medical Director
CIO: Charles Laster, Director Information Management
CHR: Debbie McCall, Director Human Resources
CNO: Sharon Hudnell, R.N., Chief Nursing Officer
Web address: www.wkhs.com/wkb/
**Control:** Other not–for–profit (including NFP Corporation) **Service:** General Medical and Surgical

**Staffed Beds:** 166 **Admissions:** 11436 **Census:** 91 **Outpatient Visits:** 125920 **Births:** 939 **Personnel:** 900

BREAUX BRIDGE—St. Martin Parish

★ **GENESIS BEHAVIORAL HOSPITAL (194089)**, 606 Latiolais Drive, Zip 70517–4231, Mailing Address: PO BOX 159, Zip 70517–0159; tel. 337/442–6084 **A**9 10 **F**98 100 101 102 103 104 105 **P**1
Primary Contact: Will Alredge, Administrator
COO: Gretchen Kaltenbach, R.N., Chief Operating Officer
CFO: Will Alredge, Chief Financial Officer
**Control:** Corporation, Investor–owned, for–profit **Service:** Psychiatric

**Staffed Beds:** 18 **Admissions:** 519 **Census:** 15 **Outpatient Visits:** 16785 **Births:** 0 **Total Expense ($000):** 5648 **Payroll Expense ($000):** 2084 **Personnel:** 75

★ **ST. MARTIN HOSPITAL (191302)**, 210 Champagne Boulevard, Zip 70517–3700, Mailing Address: P.O. Box 357, Zip 70517–0357; tel. 337/332–2178 **A**9 10 18 **F**3 11 15 28 29 34 35 38 40 57 64 75 77 90 93 96 107 108 109 110 111 114 119 128 133 **P**8 **S** Lafayette General Health, Lafayette, LA
Primary Contact: Bryan Laperouse, Interim Administrator
CFO: Shadelle Huval, Director Finance
CHR: Rena B. Mouisset, Director Human Resources and Contract Compliance
Web address: www.stmartinhospital.org
**Control:** Other not–for–profit (including NFP Corporation) **Service:** General Medical and Surgical

**Staffed Beds:** 25 **Admissions:** 356 **Census:** 12 **Outpatient Visits:** 129279 **Births:** 0 **Total Expense ($000):** 15257 **Payroll Expense ($000):** 6227 **Personnel:** 134

BROUSSARD—Lafayette Parish

☐ **OCEANS BEHAVIORAL HOSPITAL OF BROUSSARD (194073)**, 418 Albertson Parkway, Zip 70518–4971; tel. 337/237–6444, (Nonreporting) **A**1 9 10 **S** Oceans Healthcare, Lake Charles, LA
Primary Contact: Amy Dysart–Credeur, Administrator
Web address: www.obhb.info/
**Control:** Corporation, Investor–owned, for–profit **Service:** Psychiatric

**Staffed Beds:** 38

BUNKIE—Avoyelles Parish

**BUNKIE GENERAL HOSPITAL (191311)**, 427 Evergreen Highway, Zip 71322, Mailing Address: P.O. Box 380, Zip 71322–0380; tel. 318/346–6681, (Nonreporting) **A**9 10 18
Primary Contact: Linda F. Deville, Chief Executive Officer
CFO: Frances Deglandon, Chief Financial Officer
CMO: Mohit Srivastava, M.D., Chief of Staff
CIO: Johnny Bergeron, Chief Information Officer
CHR: Tina Louise Juneau, Director Human Resources
CNO: Corey Jeansonne, Chief Nursing Officer
Web address: www.bunkiegeneral.com
**Control:** Hospital district or authority, Government, nonfederal **Service:** General Medical and Surgical

**Staffed Beds:** 18

CAMERON—Cameron Parish

**SOUTH CAMERON MEMORIAL HOSPITAL (190307)**, 5360 West Creole Highway, Zip 70631–5127; tel. 337/542–4111, (Nonreporting) **A**10
Primary Contact: Leslie Trahan, Chief Executive Officer
**Control:** Hospital district or authority, Government, nonfederal **Service:** General Medical and Surgical

**Staffed Beds:** 49

CHALMETTE—Saint Bernard Parish

✠ **ST. BERNARD PARISH HOSPITAL (190308)**, 8000 West Judge Perez Drive, Zip 70043–1668; tel. 504/826–9500 **A**1 10 **F**1 3 4 8 15 16 17 18 20 22 24 29 34 40 45 46 49 53 57 59 67 70 72 73 76 77 79 80 81 88 89 90 91 98 107 108 110 111 114 119 128 129 148
Primary Contact: Charles Lindell, Chief Executive Officer
CFO: Joseph Kemka, Chief Financial Officer
CMO: Paul Verrette, M.D., Chief Medical Officer
CIO: Zane Looney, Chief Information Officer
CHR: Melody M. O'Connell, Director Human Resources
CNO: Jodi Morgan, Chief Nursing Officer
Web address: www.sbph.net
**Control:** Hospital district or authority, Government, nonfederal **Service:** General Medical and Surgical

**Staffed Beds:** 40 **Admissions:** 2323 **Census:** 28 **Outpatient Visits:** 38000 **Births:** 0

CHURCH POINT—Acadia Parish

**ACADIA–ST. LANDRY HOSPITAL (191319)**, 810 South Broadway Street, Zip 70525–4497; tel. 337/684–5435, (Nonreporting) **A**9 10 18
Primary Contact: F. Peter Savoy, III, Chief Executive Officer
CFO: Judy Young, Chief Financial Officer
CMO: Ty Hargroder, M.D., Chief of Staff
CHR: Judy Young, Chief Financial Officer
Web address: www.aslh.org
**Control:** Other not–for–profit (including NFP Corporation) **Service:** General Medical and Surgical

**Staffed Beds:** 25

CLINTON—East Feliciana Parish

**AMG SPECIALTY HOSPITAL–FELICIANA (192041)**, 9725 Grace Lane, Zip 70722–4925; tel. 225/683–1600, (Nonreporting) **A**10 **S** AMG Integrated Healthcare Management, Lafayette, LA
Primary Contact: Michael Sanders, Chief Executive Officer
Web address: www.amgfeliciana.com/
**Control:** Corporation, Investor–owned, for–profit **Service:** Long–Term Acute Care hospital

**Staffed Beds:** 16

COLUMBIA—Caldwell Parish

**CALDWELL MEMORIAL HOSPITAL (190190)**, 411 Main Street, Zip 71418–6704, Mailing Address: P.O. Box 899, Zip 71418–0899; tel. 318/649–6111, (Nonreporting) **A**9 10
Primary Contact: Heather Clark, Chief Executive Officer
COO: Lisa Patrick, Chief Operating Officer
**Control:** Other not–for–profit (including NFP Corporation) **Service:** General Medical and Surgical

**Staffed Beds:** 25

**CITIZENS MEDICAL CENTER (190184)**, 7939 U.S. Highway 165, Zip 71418–1079, Mailing Address: P.O. Box 1079, Zip 71418–1079; tel. 318/649–6106, (Nonreporting) **A**9 10
Primary Contact: Steve Barbo, R.N., Administrator
**Control:** Hospital district or authority, Government, nonfederal **Service:** General Medical and Surgical

**Staffed Beds:** 40

**Hospital, Medicare Provider Number, Address, Telephone, Approval, Facility, and Physician Codes, Health Care System**

★ American Hospital Association (AHA) membership
☐ The Joint Commission accreditation
◯ Healthcare Facilities Accreditation Program
◇ DNV Healthcare Inc. accreditation
⇑ Center for Improvement in Healthcare Quality Accreditation
△ Commission on Accreditation of Rehabilitation Facilities (CARF) accreditation

**LA**

## COUSHATTA—Red River Parish

⊠ **CHRISTUS COUSHATTA HEALTH CARE CENTER (191312)**, 1635 Marvel Street, Zip 71019–9022, Mailing Address: P.O. Box 589, Zip 71019–0589; tel. 318/932–2000 **A**1 9 10 18 **F**3 15 29 30 34 35 39 40 41 50 54 56 57 59 64 65 66 67 68 75 77 78 81 82 91 93 97 103 107 110 115 116 117 119 120 127 128 130 133 135 147 148 **S** CHRISTUS Health, Irving, TX
Primary Contact: Michael Harrington, Administrator
CFO: Scott Merryman, Chief Financial Officer
CMO: Jonathan Weisul, M.D., Vice President Medical Affairs and Chief Medical Officer
CIO: Bruce Honea, Director Information Services
CHR: Donnette Craig, Director Human Resources
Web address: www.christuscoushatta.org
**Control:** Church–operated, Nongovernment, not–for profit **Service:** Hospital unit of an institution (prison hospital, college infirmary, etc.)

**Staffed Beds:** 25 **Admissions:** 1078 **Census:** 13 **Outpatient Visits:** 34065 **Births:** 0 **Total Expense ($000):** 17426 **Payroll Expense ($000):** 5810

**SPECIALTY REHABILITATION HOSPITAL OF COUSHATTA (193080)**, 1110 Ringgold Avenue Suite B., Zip 71019–9073; tel. 318/932–1770, (Nonreporting) **A**10
Primary Contact: Craig Ball, Chief Executive Officer
COO: Charlie Ball, Chief Operating Officer
CFO: Connie Ball, Chief Financial Officer
CMO: Jalal Joudeh, M.D., Chief Medical Officer
CHR: Denise Logan, Director Human Resources
Web address: www.specialtyhealthcare.com
**Control:** Individual, Investor–owned, for–profit **Service:** Rehabilitation

**Staffed Beds:** 12

## COVINGTON—St. Tammany Parish

◇ **FAIRWAY MEDICAL CENTER (190267)**, 67252 Industry Lane, Zip 70433–8704; tel. 985/809–9888, (Nonreporting) **A**9 10 21
Primary Contact: Benjamin Patterson, Chief Executive Officer
CFO: Denise Businelle, Chief Financial Officer
CMO: William Preau, M.D., Medical Director
CIO: Skip Federico, Director Information Systems
CHR: Pam Collins, Director Human Resources
Web address: www.fairwaymedical.com
**Control:** Corporation, Investor–owned, for–profit **Service:** General Medical and Surgical

**Staffed Beds:** 21

⊠ **LAKEVIEW REGIONAL MEDICAL CENTER (190177)**, 95 Judge Tanner Boulevard, Zip 70433–7507; tel. 985/867–3800, (Nonreporting) **A**1 3 9 10 **S** HCA, Nashville, TN
Primary Contact: Bret G. Kolman, CPA, FACHE, Chief Executive Officer
CFO: Carolyn Ridge, Chief Financial Officer
CMO: George Barnes, M.D., Medical Director
CIO: Jinilinn Cass, Director Medical Records
CHR: Lyle Theriot, Director Human Resources
Web address: www.lakeviewregional.com
**Control:** Corporation, Investor–owned, for–profit **Service:** General Medical and Surgical

**Staffed Beds:** 172

**MMO GREENBRIER HOSPITAL (194069)**, 201 Greenbrier Boulevard, Zip 70433–7236; tel. 985/893–2970 **A**9 10 **F**29 35 50 54 56 64 75 98 100 101 102 103 104 105 130
Primary Contact: Trudy Franks, Administrator
CMO: Jason Coe, M.D., Medical Director
Web address: www.mmoinc.com
**Control:** Corporation, Investor–owned, for–profit **Service:** Psychiatric

**Staffed Beds:** 60 **Admissions:** 2030 **Census:** 40 **Outpatient Visits:** 6821 **Births:** 0

**NORTHSHORE SPECIALTY HOSPITAL** See Post Acute Northshore Specialty Hospital

⊠ **POST ACUTE NORTHSHORE SPECIALTY HOSPITAL (192048)**, 20050 Crestwood Boulevard, Zip 70433–5207; tel. 985/875–7525, (Nonreporting) **A**1 10 **S** Post Acute Medical, LLC, Enola, PA
Primary Contact: Stephanie Morvant, Chief Executive Officer
COO: John Bauer, Chief Operating Officer
CFO: Karick Stober, Chief Financial Officer
CMO: Adam Burick, M.D., Chief Medical Officer
CIO: Bryan Munchel, Senior Vice President and Chief Information Officer
CHR: Waynea Finley, Senior Vice President Human Resources
CNO: Marsha Medlin, Senior Vice President of Clinical and Operations
Web address: www.northshoreltach.com
**Control:** Corporation, Investor–owned, for–profit **Service:** Long–Term Acute Care hospital

**Staffed Beds:** 58

⊠ **REGENCY HOSPITAL OF COVINGTON (192051)**, 195 Highland Park Entrance, Zip 70433–7164; tel. 985/867–3977, (Nonreporting) **A**1 10 **S** Select Medical Corporation, Mechanicsburg, PA
Primary Contact: Racheal Z. Fischer, Interim Chief Executive Officer
CMO: Merrill Laurent, M.D., Medical Director
CHR: Deanna Jorgensen, Coordinator Human Resources
CNO: Teri Kessel–Fox, Director Clinical Services
Web address: www.regencyhospital.com
**Control:** Corporation, Investor–owned, for–profit **Service:** Long–Term Acute Care hospital

**Staffed Beds:** 38

⊠ **ST. TAMMANY PARISH HOSPITAL (190045)**, 1202 South Tyler Street, Zip 70433–2330; tel. 985/898–4000 **A**1 2 9 10 **F**3 8 11 12 13 15 17 18 20 22 24 26 28 29 30 31 34 35 37 40 43 45 48 49 50 54 57 59 62 63 64 65 69 70 72 74 75 76 77 78 79 81 82 84 85 86 87 89 90 92 93 96 97 107 108 109 110 111 114 115 119 124 126 129 130 132 135 146 147 148 **P**6
Primary Contact: Patti M. Ellish, FACHE, President and Chief Executive Officer
COO: Sharon A. Toups, Senior Vice President and Chief Operating Officer
CFO: Sandra P. Dipietro, Chief Financial Officer
CMO: Robert Capitelli, M.D., Senior Vice President and Chief Medical Officer
CIO: Craig Doyle, Director and Chief Information Officer
CNO: Kerry K. Milton, R.N., Chief Nursing Officer
Web address: www.stph.org
**Control:** Hospital district or authority, Government, nonfederal **Service:** General Medical and Surgical

**Staffed Beds:** 218 **Admissions:** 10182 **Census:** 124 **Outpatient Visits:** 300066 **Births:** 1719 **Total Expense ($000):** 236459 **Payroll Expense ($000):** 96614 **Personnel:** 1708

## CROWLEY—Acadia Parish

★ **ACADIA GENERAL HOSPITAL (190044)**, 1305 Crowley Rayne Highway, Zip 70526–8202; tel. 337/783–3222, (Nonreporting) **A**9 10 **S** Lafayette General Health, Lafayette, LA
Primary Contact: Heather L. Harper, Chief Executive Officer
CFO: Charmaine R. Vidrine, CPA, Chief Financial Officer
CNO: Caroline Marceaux, R.N., Chief Nursing Officer
Web address: www.acadiageneral.com
**Control:** Other not–for–profit (including NFP Corporation) **Service:** General Medical and Surgical

**Staffed Beds:** 178

★ **COMPASS BEHAVIORAL CENTER OF CROWLEY (194085)**, 1526 North Avenue I., Zip 70526–2434; tel. 337/788–3380, (Nonreporting) **A**9 10 **S** Compass Health, Crowley, LA
Primary Contact: Allison Kidder, Administrator
Web address: www.compasshealthcare.com
**Control:** Corporation, Investor–owned, for–profit **Service:** Psychiatric

**Staffed Beds:** 34

## CUT OFF—Lafourche Parish

★ ◇ **LADY OF THE SEA GENERAL HOSPITAL (191325)**, 200 West 134th Place, Zip 70345–4143; tel. 985/632–6401 **A**9 10 18 21 **F**3 15 29 34 35 40 45 57 59 60 62 65 70 81 85 87 107 108 110 111 114 119 127 130 132 133 146
Primary Contact: Karen S. Collins, R.N., Chief Executive Officer
COO: Lloyd Guidry, Chief Operating Officer
CFO: Jacquelyn Richoux, Chief Financial Officer
CMO: William Crenshaw, M.D., Chief of Staff
CIO: Bennie Smith, Chief Information Officer
CHR: Bennie Smith, Director Human Resources and Risk Management
CNO: Holly Griffin, R.N., Chief Nursing Officer
Web address: www.losgh.org
**Control:** Hospital district or authority, Government, nonfederal **Service:** General Medical and Surgical

**Staffed Beds:** 25 **Admissions:** 778 **Census:** 8 **Outpatient Visits:** 36525 **Births:** 0 **Total Expense ($000):** 29810 **Payroll Expense ($000):** 11866 **Personnel:** 285

*Many Facility Codes have changed. Please refer to the AHA Guide Code Chart.*

**LA**

## DE RIDDER—Beauregard Parish

☒ **BEAUREGARD MEMORIAL HOSPITAL (190050)**, 600 South Pine Street, Zip 70634–4942, Mailing Address: P.O. Box 730, Zip 70634–0730; tel. 337/462–7100 **A**1 9 10 **F**3 11 13 15 18 20 26 28 29 30 31 34 35 39 40 45 46 50 53 57 64 70 75 76 78 79 81 85 89 91 93 96 107 108 110 111 114 119 129 130 133 146 148 **P**6
Primary Contact: Robert M. Charron, Chief Executive Officer
CFO: Darrell L. Kingham, CPA, Vice President Finance
CMO: Andres Guillermo, M.D., President Medical Staff
CIO: Meg Jackson, Director Biomedical and Management Information Systems
CHR: Kelli C. Broocks, Director Human Resources, Public Relations and Physician Recruitment
CNO: Anita Thibodeaux, Chief Nursing Officer
Web address: www.beauregard.org
**Control:** Hospital district or authority, Government, nonfederal **Service:** General Medical and Surgical

**Staffed Beds:** 60 **Admissions:** 2770 **Census:** 29 **Outpatient Visits:** 75102 **Births:** 420 **Total Expense ($000):** 38121 **Payroll Expense ($000):** 17871 **Personnel:** 359

## DELHI—Richland Parish

**RICHLAND PARISH HOSPITAL (191323)**, 407 Cincinnati Street, Zip 71232–3007; tel. 318/878–5171 **A**9 10 18 **F**3 15 18 28 29 34 35 39 40 50 54 56 57 59 64 65 66 71 75 77 81 91 97 103 104 107 111 114 119 127 129 130 132 133 134 135 143 146 148
Primary Contact: Michael W. Carroll, Administrator
CIO: Barbra Hutchison, Director Medical Records
CHR: Patsy Stout, Director Personnel
Web address: www.delhihospital.com
**Control:** Hospital district or authority, Government, nonfederal **Service:** General Medical and Surgical

**Staffed Beds:** 25 **Admissions:** 603 **Census:** 8 **Outpatient Visits:** 43105 **Births:** 0 **Total Expense ($000):** 20573 **Payroll Expense ($000):** 10403 **Personnel:** 202

## DENHAM SPRINGS—Livingston Parish

**AMG SPECIALTY HOSPITAL–DENHAM SPRINGS (192008)**, 8375 Florida Boulevard, Zip 70726–7806; tel. 225/665–2664, (Nonreporting) **A**10 **S** AMG Integrated Healthcare Management, Lafayette, LA
Primary Contact: Karen Crayton, Administrator
CFO: Jessica McGee, Chief Financial Officer
CMO: Durwin Walker, M.D., Chief Medical Officer
CHR: Kim Hernandez, Chief Human Resources Officer
CNO: Sharon Faulkner, Chief Nursing Officer
Web address: www.amgdenham.com/
**Control:** Corporation, Investor–owned, for–profit **Service:** Long–Term Acute Care hospital

**Staffed Beds:** 117

## DEQUINCY—Calcasieu Parish

☐ **DEQUINCY MEMORIAL HOSPITAL (191307)**, 110 West Fourth Street, Zip 70633–3508, Mailing Address: P.O. Box 1166, Zip 70633–1166; tel. 337/786–1200, (Nonreporting) **A**1 9 10 18
Primary Contact: Michael Ashford, Administrator
CFO: Vicky Kelley, Chief Financial Officer
CMO: Jalal Joudeh, M.D., Chief of Staff
Web address: www.dequincyhospital.com
**Control:** City–Government, nonfederal **Service:** General Medical and Surgical

**Staffed Beds:** 19

## DERIDDER—Beauregard Parish

☐ **OCEANS BEHAVIORAL HOSPITAL OF DE RIDDER (194081)**, 1420 Blankenship Drive, Zip 70634–4604; tel. 337/460–9472, (Nonreporting) **A**1 9 10 **S** Oceans Healthcare, Lake Charles, LA
Primary Contact: Sheila Langston, Administrator
Web address: www.obhd.info/
**Control:** Corporation, Investor–owned, for–profit **Service:** Psychiatric

**Staffed Beds:** 20

## DONALDSONVILLE—Ascension Parish

☒ **PREVOST MEMORIAL HOSPITAL (191308)**, 301 Memorial Drive, Zip 70346–4376; tel. 225/473–7931 **A**1 9 10 18 **F**3 11 29 40 57 59 107 110 119 130 133 146
Primary Contact: Vincent A. Cataldo, Administrator
CFO: Jane Arboneaux, Chief Financial Officer
CMO: Marta Robertson, Chief Medical Staff
CHR: Linda Cataldo, Human Resources Secretary
Web address: www.prevosthospital.net
**Control:** Hospital district or authority, Government, nonfederal **Service:** General Medical and Surgical

**Staffed Beds:** 25 **Admissions:** 69 **Census:** 1 **Outpatient Visits:** 21941 **Births:** 0 **Total Expense ($000):** 6467 **Payroll Expense ($000):** 2464 **Personnel:** 54

## FARMERVILLE—Union Parish

**UNION GENERAL HOSPITAL (191301)**, 901 James Avenue, Zip 71241–2234, Mailing Address: P.O. Box 398, Zip 71241–0398; tel. 318/368–9751 **A**9 10 18 **F**15 29 32 35 40 45 56 81 93 104 107 110 114 119 127 128 133 143 **P**6
Primary Contact: Evalyn Ormond, Chief Executive Officer
CFO: William Adcock, Chief Financial Officer
CHR: Sheri Cooper, Director Human Resources
CNO: Darra Jung, Director of Nursing
Web address: www.uniongen.com
**Control:** Other not–for–profit (including NFP Corporation) **Service:** General Medical and Surgical

**Staffed Beds:** 15 **Admissions:** 274 **Census:** 3 **Outpatient Visits:** 31028 **Births:** 0 **Total Expense ($000):** 12084 **Payroll Expense ($000):** 4749 **Personnel:** 105

## FERRIDAY—Concordia Parish

**RIVERLAND MEDICAL CENTER (191318)**, 1700 EE Wallace Boulevard, Zip 71334–0111, Mailing Address: P.O. Box 111, Zip 71334–0111; tel. 318/757–6551 **A**9 10 18 **F**3 15 29 30 34 35 40 45 50 57 59 70 75 77 81 85 86 91 93 104 107 110 115 119 133 146 **P**6
Primary Contact: William H. Rucker, Administrator
CFO: Sam Ellard, Chief Financial Officer
CMO: Carrie Bonomo, M.D., Chief of Staff
CIO: Nekisha Smith, Director Health Information Systems
CHR: Debra Stephens, Director Personnel
CNO: Shelia James, Director of Nursing
Web address: www.riverlandmedical.com/
**Control:** Hospital district or authority, Government, nonfederal **Service:** General Medical and Surgical

**Staffed Beds:** 25 **Admissions:** 837 **Census:** 8 **Outpatient Visits:** 99503 **Births:** 0 **Total Expense ($000):** 15406 **Payroll Expense ($000):** 6663 **Personnel:** 126

## FORT POLK—Vernon Parish

☒ **BAYNE–JONES ARMY COMMUNITY HOSPITAL**, 1585 3rd Street, Zip 71459–5102; tel. 337/531–3928 **A**1 **F**3 7 8 13 15 29 30 32 33 34 35 38 39 40 44 45 46 53 54 57 59 64 65 75 76 77 79 81 85 87 97 99 100 101 104 107 110 111 115 119 130 131 132 134 135 143 146 147 148 **S** Department of the Army, Office of the Surgeon General, Falls Church, VA
Primary Contact: Colonel Carlene Blanding, Commander
COO: Larry R. Patterson, Deputy Commander Administration
CFO: Captain Dustin Mullins, Chief Resource Management
CMO: Colonel Thomas Starkey, M.D., Deputy Commander FDR Clinical Services
CIO: Major William Callahan, Chief Information Management Division
CHR: Captain Dustin Mullins, Chief Human Resources
CNO: Colonel Bridget Little, Deputy Commander Nursing
Web address: www.polk.amedd.army.mil
**Control:** Army, Government, federal **Service:** General Medical and Surgical

**Staffed Beds:** 13 **Admissions:** 1391 **Census:** 10 **Outpatient Visits:** 209921 **Births:** 529 **Total Expense ($000):** 71721 **Personnel:** 908

## FRANKLIN—St. Mary Parish

✠ **FRANKLIN FOUNDATION HOSPITAL (191310)**, 1097 Northwest Boulevard, Zip 70538–3407, Mailing Address: P.O. Box 577, Zip 70538–0577; tel. 337/828–0760 **A**1 9 10 18 **F**3 11 13 15 18 26 28 29 34 40 45 50 57 59 68 70 74 75 76 77 79 81 85 93 107 110 111 114 119 130 133 135 146 147 148 **P**6 **S** QHR, Brentwood, TN
Primary Contact: Craig R. Cudworth, Chief Executive Officer
CFO: Ron Bailey, Chief Financial Officer
CMO: Jesus Chua, M.D., Chief of Staff
CIO: John Spradlin, Information Systems Director
CHR: Elmo Vinas, Director Human Resources
CNO: Jennifer Wise, Chief Nursing Officer
Web address: www.franklinfoundation.org
**Control:** Hospital district or authority, Government, nonfederal **Service:** General Medical and Surgical

**Staffed Beds: 22 Admissions: 811 Census: 11 Outpatient Visits: 25619 Births: 104 Total Expense ($000): 22924 Payroll Expense ($000): 11199 Personnel: 187**

## FRANKLINTON—Washington Parish

☐ **RIVERSIDE MEDICAL CENTER (191313)**, 1900 Main Street, Zip 70438–3688; tel. 985/839–4431, (Nonreporting) **A**1 9 10 18
Primary Contact: Kyle Magee, M.D., Chief Executive Officer
COO: Ben Lott, Vice President of Clinical Services
CFO: Michael J. Magee, Chief Financial Officer
CMO: Chris Foret, M.D., Chief of Staff
CHR: John Seal, Director Human Resources
CNO: Ben Lott, Vice President of Clinical Services
Web address: www.rmchospital.com
**Control:** Hospital district or authority, Government, nonfederal **Service:** General Medical and Surgical

**Staffed Beds: 25**

## GONZALES—Ascension Parish

**SOUTH BATON ROUGE REHABILITATION HOSPITAL** See United Medical Rehabilitation Hospital – Gonzales

✠ **ST. ELIZABETH HOSPITAL (190242)**, 1125 West Highway 30, Zip 70737–5004; tel. 225/647–5000 **A**1 9 10 **F**3 8 11 12 15 18 19 29 30 34 35 40 43 45 46 47 48 49 51 57 59 64 66 70 74 75 79 81 82 84 85 87 92 107 108 110 111 114 115 119 129 130 132 146 **P**6 **S** Franciscan Missionaries of Our Lady Health System, Inc., Baton Rouge, LA
Primary Contact: Robert L. Burgess, President and Chief Executive Officer
COO: Sue Knight, CPA, Chief Operating Officer
CFO: Scott Richard, Vice President Finance and Chief Financial Officer
CMO: Chris Trevino, M.D., Chief Medical Officer
CIO: Shannon Simpson, Director Information Services
CHR: Melissa Miller, Director Human Resources
CNO: Yvonne Pellerin, Chief Nursing Officer
Web address: www.steh.com
**Control:** Church–operated, Nongovernment, not–for profit **Service:** General Medical and Surgical

**Staffed Beds: 46 Admissions: 2311 Census: 27 Outpatient Visits: 255252 Births: 0 Total Expense ($000): 109409 Payroll Expense ($000): 40695 Personnel: 702**

☐ **ST. JAMES BEHAVIORAL HEALTH HOSPITAL (194088)**, 3136 South Saint Landry Road, Zip 70737–5801; tel. 225/647–7524, (Nonreporting) **A**1 10
Primary Contact: Rick Bennett, Administrator
COO: Wendell Smith, Chief Operating Officer
CFO: Rama Kongara, Chief Financial Officer
CMO: Lance Bullock, M.D., Medical Director
CHR: Dessa Frederick, Manager Human Resources
Web address: www.sjbhh.net
**Control:** Corporation, Investor–owned, for–profit **Service:** Psychiatric

**Staffed Beds: 10**

## GREENSBURG—St. Helena Parish

**ST. HELENA PARISH HOSPITAL (191300)**, 16874 Highway 43, Zip 70441–4834; tel. 225/222–6111, (Total facility includes 72 beds in nursing home–type unit) **A**9 10 18 **F**3 7 9 11 14 15 18 28 29 30 31 32 34 35 38 40 41 42 44 53 56 57 58 59 60 63 64 65 68 75 83 84 85 86 87 90 92 93 97 101 102 103 104 107 110 119 129 130 133 135 143 148 **P**4 5 7
Primary Contact: Naveed Awan, FACHE, Chief Executive Officer
CFO: Theresa Brinkhaus, Chief Financial Officer
CMO: Anjanette Varnado, M.D., Chief Medical Officer
CHR: Lorraine L. Ballard, Director Human Resources
Web address: www.sthelenaparishhospital.com
**Control:** Hospital district or authority, Government, nonfederal **Service:** General Medical and Surgical

**Staffed Beds: 75 Admissions: 332 Census: 62 Outpatient Visits: 15231 Births: 0**

## GRETNA—Jefferson Parish

**UNITED MEDICAL HEALTHWEST–NEW ORLEANS (193074)**, 3201 Wall Boulevard, Suite B., Zip 70056–7755; tel. 504/433–5551, (Nonreporting) **A**9 10 **S** United Medical Rehabilitation Hospitals, Gretna, LA
Primary Contact: John E.H. Mills, President and Chief Executive Officer
Web address: www.umrhospital.com/
**Control:** Individual, Investor–owned, for–profit **Service:** Rehabilitation

**Staffed Beds: 15**

## HAMMOND—Tangipahoa Parish

◇ **CYPRESS POINTE SURGICAL HOSPITAL (190303)**, 42570 South Airport Road, Zip 70403–0946; tel. 985/510–6200, (Nonreporting) **A**9 10 21
Primary Contact: Don D. Trexler, Chief Executive Officer
COO: Scot Treitler, Chief Financial Officer and Chief Operating Officer
CFO: Scot Treitler, Chief Financial Officer and Chief Operating Officer
CNO: Denise Fortenberry, Chief Nursing Officer and Chief Compliance Officer
Web address: www.cpsh.org
**Control:** Corporation, Investor–owned, for–profit **Service:** Surgical

**Staffed Beds: 24**

✠ △ **NORTH OAKS MEDICAL CENTER (190015)**, 15790 Paul Vega, MD, Drive, Zip 70403–1436, Mailing Address: P.O. Box 2668, Zip 70404–2668; tel. 985/345–2700 **A**1 7 9 10 19 **F**3 12 13 15 18 20 22 24 26 28 29 30 31 32 34 40 45 49 50 54 56 57 58 59 63 64 68 70 72 73 74 75 76 77 78 79 81 82 84 85 86 87 89 93 94 96 102 107 108 110 111 114 115 118 119 126 129 130 131 132 135 143 144 146 147 148 **P**6 **S** North Oaks Health System, Hammond, LA
Primary Contact: Michele K. Sutton, FACHE, Administrator
CFO: Shirley Hsing, Senior Vice President and Chief Financial Officer
CMO: Robert Peltier, M.D., Senior Vice President and Chief Medical Officer
CIO: Jacob Goodson, Director Information Technology
CHR: Jeff Jarreau, Senior Vice President Human Resources
CNO: Shelly Welch, R.N., Senior Vice President and Chief Nursing Officer
Web address: www.northoaks.org
**Control:** Hospital district or authority, Government, nonfederal **Service:** General Medical and Surgical

**Staffed Beds: 278 Admissions: 10836 Census: 158 Outpatient Visits: 410768 Births: 1391 Total Expense ($000): 276837 Payroll Expense ($000): 141288 Personnel: 2256**

☐ **NORTH OAKS REHABILITATION HOSPITAL (193044)**, 1900 South Morrison Boulevard, Zip 70403–5742; tel. 985/345–2700 **A**1 10 **F**29 56 75 86 87 90 130 132 143 **P**6 **S** North Oaks Health System, Hammond, LA
Primary Contact: Sybil K. Paulson, R.N., Administrator
Web address: www.northoaks.org
**Control:** Hospital district or authority, Government, nonfederal **Service:** Rehabilitation

**Staffed Beds: 27 Admissions: 494 Census: 17 Outpatient Visits: 0 Births: 0 Total Expense ($000): 12351 Payroll Expense ($000): 2260 Personnel: 41**

✠ **POST ACUTE SPECIALTY HOSPITAL OF HAMMOND (192036)**, 42074 Veterans Avenue, Zip 70403–1408; tel. 985/902–8148 **A**1 10 **F**1 29 75 77 148 **P**1 **S** Post Acute Medical, LLC, Enola, PA
Primary Contact: Jerry Elenbaas, Administrator
Web address: www.warmsprings.org/locations/hos/h2/
**Control:** Partnership, Investor–owned, for–profit **Service:** Long–Term Acute Care hospital

**Staffed Beds: 40 Admissions: 343 Census: 25 Outpatient Visits: 0 Births: 0 Total Expense ($000): 12781 Payroll Expense ($000): 4474**

**UNITED MEDICAL REHABILITATION HOSPITAL (193079)**, 15717 Belle Drive, Zip 70403–1439; tel. 985/340–5998, (Includes UNITED MEDICAL REHABILITATION HOSPITAL – GONZALES, 333 East Worthy Road, Gonzales, Zip 70737–4234; tel. 225/450–2231; Bruce Walker, MSN, R.N., Chief Executive Officer), (Nonreporting) **A**10 **S** United Medical Rehabilitation Hospitals, Gretna, LA
Primary Contact: Cyrilla Bonds, Administrator
CFO: Warren Swenson, Chief Financial Officer
CMO: Luis Franco, M.D., Medical Director
CHR: Mark Gros, Director Human Resources
Web address: www.umrhospital.com
**Control:** Corporation, Investor–owned, for–profit **Service:** Rehabilitation

**Staffed Beds: 20**

*Many Facility Codes have changed. Please refer to the AHA Guide Code Chart.*

## HOMER—Claiborne Parish

★ **CLAIBORNE MEMORIAL MEDICAL CENTER (190114)**, 620 East College Street, Zip 71040–3202; tel. 318/927–2024, (Nonreporting) **A**9 10 **S** QHR, Brentwood, TN
Primary Contact: Derrick A. Frazier, Chief Executive Officer
CFO: Robert A. Boullion, Chief Financial Officer
CMO: Mark Haynes, M.D., Chief of Staff
CIO: Landon Dick, Chief Information Officer
CHR: William Colvin, Human Resources Officer
CNO: Ginger S. Smith, Chief Nursing Officer
Web address: www.claibornemedical.com/
**Control:** City–Government, nonfederal **Service:** General Medical and Surgical

**Staffed Beds: 57**

## HOUMA—Terrebonne Parish

**AMG SPECIALTY HOSPITAL–HOUMA (192037)**, 629 Dunn Street, Zip 70360–4707; tel. 985/274–0001 **A**10 **F**1 29 130 **S** AMG Integrated Healthcare Management, Lafayette, LA
Primary Contact: Keith Carruth, Chief Executive Officer
Web address: www.amghouma.com/
**Control:** Corporation, Investor–owned, for–profit **Service:** Long–Term Acute Care hospital

**Staffed Beds: 40 Admissions: 478 Census: 33 Outpatient Visits: 0 Births: 0 Total Expense ($000): 12110 Payroll Expense ($000): 5992**

☐ **COMPASS BEHAVIORAL CENTER OF HOUMA (194109)**, 4701 West Park Avenue, Zip 70364–4426; tel. 985/876–1715, (Nonreporting) **A**1 10 **S** Compass Health, Crowley, LA
Primary Contact: Cheryl Turner, Administrator
Web address: www.compasshealthcare.com/site83.php
**Control:** Corporation, Investor–owned, for–profit **Service:** Psychiatric

**Staffed Beds: 20**

⊠ **LEONARD J. CHABERT MEDICAL CENTER (190183)**, 1978 Industrial Boulevard, Zip 70363–7094; tel. 985/873–2200 **A**1 3 5 9 10 **F**3 4 15 18 20 29 30 31 32 34 35 38 39 40 44 45 46 47 48 49 50 51 55 58 59 61 64 65 66 68 70 74 75 77 78 79 81 82 84 85 86 87 89 91 92 93 94 97 98 100 101 102 107 108 110 111 114 115 119 130 132 146 147 148 **P**1 **S** Ochsner Health System, New Orleans, LA
Primary Contact: Timothy J. Allen, FACHE, Chief Executive Officer
CMO: Michael Garcia, M.D., Medical Director
CIO: Susan Arceneaux, R.N., Coordinator Information Technology
CHR: Bain Manning, Director Human Resources
Web address: www.ochsner.org/locations/leonard_j_chabert_medical_center/
**Control:** County–Government, nonfederal **Service:** General Medical and Surgical

**Staffed Beds: 72 Admissions: 3656 Census: 48 Outpatient Visits: 171155 Births: 0 Total Expense ($000): 80445 Payroll Expense ($000): 21385 Personnel: 634**

**PHYSICIANS ALLIANCE HOSPITAL OF HOUMA** See AMG Specialty Hospital–Houma

**PHYSICIANS MEDICAL CENTER (190241)**, 218 Corporate Drive, Zip 70360–2768; tel. 985/853–1390, (Nonreporting) **A**9 10
Primary Contact: Connie Martin, Chief Executive Officer and Administrator
Web address: www.physicianshouma.com/
**Control:** Partnership, Investor–owned, for–profit **Service:** Surgical

**Staffed Beds: 10**

⊠ △ **TERREBONNE GENERAL MEDICAL CENTER (190008)**, 8166 Main Street, Zip 70360–3498; tel. 985/873–4141, (Total facility includes 8 beds in nursing home–type unit) **A**1 2 7 9 10 **F**8 11 13 14 15 17 18 20 22 24 26 29 30 31 34 35 40 44 49 50 57 58 59 64 65 68 70 72 74 75 76 77 78 79 81 84 85 86 87 89 90 91 92 93 107 108 109 110 111 114 117 118 119 121 123 124 128 130 131 132 134 135 146 147 148 **P**3 5 6
Primary Contact: Phyllis L. Peoples, MSN, R.N., President and Chief Executive Officer
COO: Diane Yeates, Chief Operating Officer
CFO: Dean Verret, Vice President Financial Services
CMO: Robert Gamble, M.D., Chief of Staff
CIO: Jeff Sardella, Director Information Technology
CHR: Mickie Rousseau, Director Human Resources
CNO: Teresita McNabb, R.N., Vice President Nursing Services
Web address: www.tgmc.com
**Control:** Hospital district or authority, Government, nonfederal **Service:** General Medical and Surgical

**Staffed Beds: 231 Admissions: 10161 Census: 135 Outpatient Visits: 115225 Births: 2009 Total Expense ($000): 192600 Payroll Expense ($000): 66026 Personnel: 1271**

## INDEPENDENCE—Tangipahoa Parish

☐ **LALLIE KEMP MEDICAL CENTER (191321)**, 52579 Highway 51 South, Zip 70443–2231; tel. 985/878–9421, (Nonreporting) **A**1 3 5 9 10 18
Primary Contact: Sherre Pack–Hookfin, Administrator
COO: Lisa G. Bruhl, Chief Operating Officer
CFO: Chad Thompson, Chief Financial Officer
CMO: Kathy Willis, M.D., Medical Director
CIO: Charles Tate, Director Information Technology
CHR: Diane Farnham, Acting Director Human Resources
Web address: www.lsuhospitals.org/Hospitals/LK/LK.aspx
**Control:** State–Government, nonfederal **Service:** General Medical and Surgical

**Staffed Beds: 25**

## JACKSON—East Feliciana Parish

☐ **EASTERN LOUISIANA MENTAL HEALTH SYSTEM (194008)**, 4502 Highway 951, Zip 70748–5842, Mailing Address: P.O. Box 498, Zip 70748–0498; tel. 225/634–0100 **A**1 3 10 **F**29 30 35 39 50 59 74 75 87 98 100 101 103 104 130 135 146 **P**6 **S** Louisiana State Hospitals, Baton Rouge, LA
Primary Contact: Hampton P. S. Lea, Acting Chief Executive Officer
CFO: Laura Lott, Administrative Director
CMO: John W. Thompson, M.D., Chief of Staff
CIO: Deborah Brandon, Director Total Quality Management
CHR: Vikki Riggle, Director Human Resources
CNO: Mary Fontenelle, Executive Nurse Director
Web address: www.wwwprd.doa.louisiana.gov
**Control:** State–Government, nonfederal **Service:** Psychiatric

**Staffed Beds: 473 Admissions: 1070 Census: 473 Births: 0 Total Expense ($000): 76026 Payroll Expense ($000): 41588**

**VILLA FELICIANA MEDICAL COMPLEX (190199)**, 5002 Highway 10, Zip 70748–3627, Mailing Address: P.O. Box 438, Zip 70748–0438; tel. 225/634–4017 **A**10 **F**1 3 29 65 67 85 86 90 91 94 106 128 130 132 135 143 148 **P**8
Primary Contact: Mark Anders, Administrator
CFO: Kim Jelks, Fiscal Officer
CMO: John F. Piker, M.D., Medical Director
CIO: Michael James, Information Technology Technical Support Specialist 1
CHR: Sandra Delatte, Director Human Resources
CNO: Linda Williams, Director of Nursing
Web address: www.dhh.state.la.us/
**Control:** State–Government, nonfederal **Service:** Long–Term Acute Care hospital

**Staffed Beds: 307 Admissions: 16 Census: 11 Outpatient Visits: 0 Births: 0 Total Expense ($000): 18234 Payroll Expense ($000): 8575 Personnel: 202**

## JENA—La Salle Parish

★ **LASALLE GENERAL HOSPITAL (190145)**, 187 Ninth Street, Zip 71342–3901, Mailing Address: P.O. Box 2780, Zip 71342–2780; tel. 318/992–9200 **A**9 10 **F**7 11 15 18 29 33 40 45 53 57 59 62 64 71 81 89 93 107 108 110 111 115 119 127 130 133 **P**6
Primary Contact: Lana B. Francis, Interim Chief Executive Officer
CHR: Allyson Fannin, Director Human Resources
CNO: Carolyn Francis, R.N., Director of Nursing
Web address: www.lasallegeneralhospital.com
**Control:** Hospital district or authority, Government, nonfederal **Service:** General Medical and Surgical

**Staffed Beds: 49 Admissions: 545 Census: 6 Outpatient Visits: 30705 Births: 0 Total Expense ($000): 23800 Payroll Expense ($000): 11671 Personnel: 204**

## JENNINGS—Jefferson Davis Parish

☐ **JENNINGS AMERICAN LEGION HOSPITAL (190053)**, 1634 Elton Road, Zip 70546–3614; tel. 337/616–7000 **A**1 9 10 **F**18 20 28 29 40 45 46 70 76 79 81 93 107 108 111 114 119 127 133 147
Primary Contact: Dana D. Williams, Chief Executive Officer
COO: Keith J. Simpson, Chief Operating Officer
CFO: Chris Kohlenberg, Chief Financial Officer
CIO: Gary Courrege, Chief Information Officer
CHR: Ruth Carnes, Manager Human Resources
CNO: Theresa L. Woods, MSN, Chief Nursing Officer
Web address: www.jalh.com
**Control:** Other not–for–profit (including NFP Corporation) **Service:** General Medical and Surgical

**Staffed Beds: 49 Admissions: 3159 Census: 32 Outpatient Visits: 35538 Births: 324 Total Expense ($000): 37737 Payroll Expense ($000): 15420**

---

**Hospital, Medicare Provider Number, Address, Telephone, Approval, Facility, and Physician Codes, Health Care System**

★ American Hospital Association (AHA) membership
☐ The Joint Commission accreditation
○ Healthcare Facilities Accreditation Program
◇ DNV Healthcare Inc. accreditation
⇑ Center for Improvement in Healthcare Quality Accreditation
△ Commission on Accreditation of Rehabilitation Facilities (CARF) accreditation

**LA**

**JENNINGS SENIOR CARE HOSPITAL (194082)**, 1 Hospital Drive, Suite 201, Zip 70546–3641; tel. 337/785–8003, (Nonreporting) **A**9 10
Primary Contact: Kirk Perron, Interim Administrator
**Control:** Corporation, Investor–owned, for–profit **Service:** Psychiatric

**Staffed Beds:** 18

☐ **MMO WESTEND HOSPITAL (194075)**, 1530 Highway 90 West, Zip 70546–4022; tel. 337/616–8122, (Nonreporting) **A**1 9 10
Primary Contact: Jessica Adkinson, Administrator
CMO: Phillip Lafleur, M.D., Medical Director
CHR: Susanna Rodriguez, Director Human Resources
Web address: www.mmoinc.com
**Control:** Corporation, Investor–owned, for–profit **Service:** Psychiatric

**Staffed Beds:** 20

**REHABILITATION HOSPITAL OF JENNINGS (193067)**, 1 Hospital Drive, Suite 101, Zip 70546–3641; tel. 337/821–5353 **A**10 **F**29 30 34 35 56 57 62 65 68 75 77 87 90 91 130 148
Primary Contact: Michael Holland, M.D., Chief Executive Officer
Web address: www.jenningsrehab.com
**Control:** Partnership, Investor–owned, for–profit **Service:** Rehabilitation

**Staffed Beds:** 16 **Admissions:** 267 **Census:** 10 **Outpatient Visits:** 0 **Births:** 0 **Total Expense ($000):** 3904 **Payroll Expense ($000):** 1408 **Personnel:** 41

### JONESBORO—Jackson Parish

★ **JACKSON PARISH HOSPITAL (191317)**, 165 Beech Springs Road, Zip 71251–2059; tel. 318/259–4435, (Nonreporting) **A**9 10 18
Primary Contact: Bobby G. Jordan, Chief Executive Officer
CFO: David Sanders, Chief Financial Officer
CHR: Elizabeth Cheatwood, Human Resource Director and Administrative Assistant
Web address: www.jacksonparishhospital.com
**Control:** Hospital district or authority, Government, nonfederal **Service:** General Medical and Surgical

**Staffed Beds:** 25

### KAPLAN—Vermilion Parish

**ABROM KAPLAN MEMORIAL HOSPITAL (191322)**, 1310 West Seventh Street, Zip 70548–2910; tel. 337/643–8300 **A**9 10 18 **F**34 40 45 57 59 62 77 81 107 108 110 114 119 128 133 **S** Lafayette General Health, Lafayette, LA
Primary Contact: Bryce Quebodeaux, Chief Executive Officer
CFO: Mary Melancon, Chief Financial Officer
CMO: Scott Bergeaux, M.D., Chief Medical Staff
CIO: Bryce Quebodeaux, Chief Information Technology Officer
CHR: Mary Melancon, Chief Financial Officer
CNO: Darnell Kohlenberg, R.N., Director of Nursing
Web address: www.lafayettegeneral.com
**Control:** Hospital district or authority, Government, nonfederal **Service:** General Medical and Surgical

**Staffed Beds:** 35 **Admissions:** 867 **Census:** 13 **Outpatient Visits:** 19000 **Births:** 0

### KENNER—Jefferson Parish

**LOUISIANA EXTENDED CARE HOSPITAL OF KENNER** See Ochsner Extended Care Hospital of Kenner

☐ **OCEANS BEHAVIORAL HOSPITAL OF GREATER NEW ORLEANS (194098)**, 716 Village Road, Zip 70065–2751; tel. 504/464–8895, (Nonreporting) **A**1 9 10 **S** Oceans Healthcare, Lake Charles, LA
Primary Contact: Deborah Spier, Administrator
Web address: www.obhgno.info/
**Control:** Corporation, Investor–owned, for–profit **Service:** Psychiatric

**Staffed Beds:** 30

☐ **OCHSNER EXTENDED CARE HOSPITAL OF KENNER (192015)**, 180 West Esplanade Avenue, 5th Floor, Zip 70065–2467; tel. 504/464–8658, (Nonreporting) **A**1 3 10 **S** LHC Group, Lafayette, LA
Primary Contact: Frederick Nelson, Administrator
Web address: www.lhcgroup.com/
**Control:** Corporation, Investor–owned, for–profit **Service:** Long–Term Acute Care hospital

**Staffed Beds:** 32

✠ **OCHSNER MEDICAL CENTER – KENNER (190274)**, 180 West Esplanade Avenue, Zip 70065–6001; tel. 504/468–8600 **A**1 3 5 9 10 **F**3 4 13 15 17 18 20 22 24 29 30 31 34 35 37 38 40 42 45 46 47 49 50 51 53 54 56 57 58 59 60 61 64 65 66 68 70 72 74 75 76 77 78 79 81 82 84 85 86 87 90 91 93 97 98 102 107 110 111 114 116 117 119 120 129 130 131 132 135 146 147 148 **S** Ochsner Health System, New Orleans, LA
Primary Contact: Stephen Robinson, Chief Executive Officer
COO: Eddy Ramirez, Assistant Vice President Business Development
CFO: Mark Eckert, Vice President Finance
CMO: James Tebbe, M.D., Vice President Medical Affairs
CIO: Dere Krummel, Director Information Systems
Web address: www.ochsner.org/locations/ochsner_health_center_kenner_w_esplanade_ave/
**Control:** Other not–for–profit (including NFP Corporation) **Service:** General Medical and Surgical

**Staffed Beds:** 110 **Admissions:** 5725 **Census:** 59 **Outpatient Visits:** 115622 **Births:** 1337 **Total Expense ($000):** 106069 **Payroll Expense ($000):** 40326 **Personnel:** 689

☐ **ST. THERESA SPECIALTY HOSPITAL (192030)**, 3601 Loyola Drive, Zip 70065–1797; tel. 504/904–7600, (Nonreporting) **A**1 10
Primary Contact: Ethan Thompson, Chief Executive Officer
CFO: Ethan Thompson, Chief Executive Officer
CMO: Ricardo Febry, M.D., Medical Director
CHR: Nicole Wilson, Manager Human Resources
CNO: Collette Jackson, R.N., Director of Clinical Services
Web address: www.stmck.com
**Control:** Corporation, Investor–owned, for–profit **Service:** Long–Term Acute Care hospital

**Staffed Beds:** 73

### KENTWOOD—Tangipahoa Parish

**OCEANS BEHAVIORAL HOSPITAL OF KENTWOOD (194091)**, 921 Avenue G., Zip 70444–2636; tel. 985/229–0717, (Nonreporting) **A**9 10 **S** Oceans Healthcare, Lake Charles, LA
Primary Contact: Gina Isbell, Administrator
Web address: www.obhk.info/
**Control:** Corporation, Investor–owned, for–profit **Service:** Psychiatric

**Staffed Beds:** 18

**SOUTHEAST REGIONAL MEDICAL CENTER (192040)**, 719 Avenue G., Zip 70444–2601; tel. 985/229–9193, (Nonreporting) **A**10
Primary Contact: Lionel Murphy, Chief Executive Officer
**Control:** Corporation, Investor–owned, for–profit **Service:** Long–Term Acute Care hospital

**Staffed Beds:** 14

### KINDER—Allen Parish

★ **ALLEN PARISH HOSPITAL (190133)**, 108 Sixth Avenue, Zip 70648–3187, Mailing Address: P.O. Box 1670, Zip 70648–1670; tel. 337/738–2527 **A**9 10 **F**29 32 34 38 40 50 56 57 59 62 64 65 87 93 98 101 102 107 119 127 130 133 148
Primary Contact: Jackie Reviel, R.N., Chief Executive Officer
COO: Terry Willet, Chief Financial Officer
CFO: Jenny Bono, Chief Financial Officer
CMO: Ejiro Ughouwa, M.D., Chief of Staff
CIO: Bill Marcantel, Chief Information Systems
CHR: Amand Lambert, Director Human Resources
Web address: www.allenparishhospital.com
**Control:** Hospital district or authority, Government, nonfederal **Service:** General Medical and Surgical

**Staffed Beds:** 49 **Admissions:** 682 **Census:** 15 **Outpatient Visits:** 7970 **Births:** 0 **Total Expense ($000):** 9047 **Payroll Expense ($000):** 4627 **Personnel:** 170

### LACOMBE—St. Tammany Parish

**BEACON BEHAVIORAL HEALTHCARE (194102)**, 64026 Highway 434, Suite 300, Zip 70445–5417; tel. 985/882–0226 **A**9 10 **F**98 103 104 130
Primary Contact: Jessika Scallion, Administrator
Web address: www.magnoliabh.com/
**Control:** Corporation, Investor–owned, for–profit **Service:** Psychiatric

**Staffed Beds:** 16 **Admissions:** 383 **Census:** 14 **Outpatient Visits:** 12074 **Births:** 0 **Total Expense ($000):** 5479 **Payroll Expense ($000):** 3060 **Personnel:** 55

☐ **LOUISIANA HEART HOSPITAL (190250)**, 64030 Highway 434, Zip 70445–3456; tel. 985/690–7500 **A**1 3 9 10 **F**3 17 18 20 22 24 26 28 29 34 35 40 45 46 54 55 57 58 59 60 64 65 68 70 74 75 77 79 81 82 85 87 93 97 107 111 119 130 132 135 147 148 **P**6 7
Primary Contact: Roy Wright, FACHE, President and Chief Executive Officer
COO: Glenn L. Craig, Chief Operating Officer
CFO: Suzette Duhe, Chief Financial Officer
CMO: Anthony Morales, M.D., Medical Director
CIO: Jack Fayard, Director Information Technology
CHR: Wendy F. Alexander, Director Human Resources
CNO: Glenda Dobson, Vice President Clinical Services
Web address: www.louisianaheart.com
**Control:** Corporation, Investor–owned, for–profit **Service:** General Medical and Surgical

**Staffed Beds:** 68 **Admissions:** 2897 **Census:** 31 **Outpatient Visits:** 30328 **Births:** 0 **Personnel:** 373

### LAFAYETTE—Lafayette Parish

**ACADIA OPTIMA HOSPITAL (194078)**, 1131 Rue De Belier, Zip 70506–6532; tel. 337/991–0571, (Nonreporting) **A**3 10 **S** Acadia Healthcare Company, Inc., Franklin, TN
Primary Contact: Stephanie Bonin, Administrator
Web address: www.optimaspecialtyhospital.com/
**Control:** Corporation, Investor–owned, for–profit **Service:** General Medical and Surgical

**Staffed Beds:** 24

**ACADIA VERMILION HOSPITAL (194044)**, 2520 North University Avenue, Zip 70507–5306; tel. 337/234–5614, (Nonreporting) **A**9 10 **S** Acadia Healthcare Company, Inc., Franklin, TN
Primary Contact: Eric Kennedy, Chief Executive Officer
CFO: James Todd, Chief Financial Officer
CMO: Bob Winston, M.D., Medical Director
CHR: Claire Rowland, Director Human Resources
Web address: www.acadiavermilion.com
**Control:** Corporation, Investor–owned, for–profit **Service:** Psychiatric

**Staffed Beds:** 54

**AMG SPECIALTY HOSPITAL–LAFAYETTE (192029)**, 310 Youngsville Highway, Zip 70508–4524; tel. 337/839–9880 **A**10 **F**1 3 29 30 34 35 50 56 60 75 77 79 82 84 85 91 119 130 135 143 148 **P**5 **S** AMG Integrated Healthcare Management, Lafayette, LA
Primary Contact: Ben Miller, Chief Executive Officer
CFO: Jessica McGee, Chief Financial Officer
CMO: Maximo LaMarche, M.D., Chief Medical Officer
CHR: Heather Lamarche, Manager Human Resources
CNO: Mary Bollich, Director of Nurses
Web address: www.amglafayette.com
**Control:** Corporation, Investor–owned, for–profit **Service:** Long–Term Acute Care hospital

**Staffed Beds:** 58 **Admissions:** 451 **Census:** 31 **Outpatient Visits:** 0 **Births:** 0 **Total Expense ($000):** 12427 **Payroll Expense ($000):** 5388

✠ **HEART HOSPITAL OF LAFAYETTE (190263)**, 1105 Kaliste Saloom Road, Zip 70508–5705; tel. 337/521–1000 **A**1 9 10 **F**3 17 18 20 22 24 26 28 29 30 34 35 40 46 50 57 59 64 68 74 75 81 85 87 107 108 115 135 **P**5 7 8
Primary Contact: Michelle B. Crain, R.N., MSN, Administrator and Chief Operating Officer
CFO: Rachel Hebert, Chief Financial Officer
CHR: Thomas Duhon, Director Human Resources
Web address: www.hearthospitaloflafayette.com
**Control:** Partnership, Investor–owned, for–profit **Service:** Heart

**Staffed Beds:** 32 **Admissions:** 1437 **Census:** 15 **Outpatient Visits:** 21161 **Births:** 0 **Total Expense ($000):** 34371 **Payroll Expense ($000):** 10432 **Personnel:** 212

**KINDRED HOSPITAL LAFAYETTE** See Post Acute Medical Specialty Hospital of Lafayette

✠ **LAFAYETTE GENERAL MEDICAL CENTER (190002)**, 1214 Coolidge Avenue, Zip 70503–2696, Mailing Address: P.O. Box 52009 OCS, Zip 70505–2009; tel. 337/289–7991, (Includes LAFAYETTE BEHAVIORAL HEALTH, 302 Dulles Drive, Zip 70506–3008; tel. 337/262–4190; Kandy Collins, MSN, Director) **A**1 2 3 5 9 10 **F**3 8 11 12 13 15 18 19 20 21 22 24 26 28 29 30 31 34 35 40 41 45 46 47 48 49 50 53 54 56 57 58 59 64 65 70 72 74 75 76 77 78 79 81 82 85 86 87 89 90 91 92 98 100 107 108 110 111 112 114 115 117 118 119 120 121 123 124 126 130 132 135 146 147 148 **P**8 **S** Lafayette General Health, Lafayette, LA
Primary Contact: Patrick W. Gandy, CPA, Executive Vice President and Chief Executive Officer
CFO: Roger Mattke, Chief Financial Officer
CMO: Angela Mayeux–Hebert, Vice President Medical Affairs
CIO: Edwina Mallery, Assistant Vice President Information Systems
CHR: Sheena Bouquet, Vice President
CNO: Rebecca Benoit, R.N., Chief Nursing Officer
Web address: www.lafayettegeneral.org
**Control:** Other not–for–profit (including NFP Corporation) **Service:** General Medical and Surgical

**Staffed Beds:** 324 **Admissions:** 17435 **Census:** 247 **Outpatient Visits:** 207511 **Births:** 2536 **Total Expense ($000):** 285729 **Payroll Expense ($000):** 99973 **Personnel:** 1687

**LAFAYETTE GENERAL SURGICAL HOSPITAL (190268)**, 1000 West Pinhook Road, Zip 70503–2460; tel. 337/289–8088, (Nonreporting) **A**9 10 **S** Lafayette General Health, Lafayette, LA
Primary Contact: Carrie E. Templeton, FACHE, Chief Executive Officer
CFO: Sandi Hernandez, Controller
CHR: Sheena Bouquet, Vice President
CNO: Susan Woollen, R.N., Director of Nursing
Web address: www.lgsh.us
**Control:** Partnership, Investor–owned, for–profit **Service:** General Medical and Surgical

**Staffed Beds:** 10

**LAFAYETTE PHYSICAL REHABILITATION HOSPITAL (193093)**, 307 Polly Lane, Zip 70508–4960; tel. 337/314–1111, (Nonreporting) **A**10 **S** AMG Integrated Healthcare Management, Lafayette, LA
Primary Contact: Thomas R. Strohe, Chief Executive Officer
Web address: www.lafayettephysicalrehab.com/
**Control:** Corporation, Investor–owned, for–profit **Service:** Rehabilitation

**Staffed Beds:** 32

☐ **LAFAYETTE SURGICAL SPECIALTY HOSPITAL (190259)**, 1101 Kaliste Saloom Road, Zip 70508–5705; tel. 337/769–4100, (Nonreporting) **A**1 9 10 **S** National Surgical Healthcare, Chicago, IL
Primary Contact: Buffy Domingue, Chief Executive Officer
CFO: Stephanie Guidry, Chief Financial Officer
CNO: Selina Guidry, Chief Nursing Officer
Web address: www.lafayettesurgical.com
**Control:** Corporation, Investor–owned, for–profit **Service:** Surgical

**Staffed Beds:** 20

**LONG TERM ACUTE CARE OF ACADIANA** See AMG Specialty Hospital–Lafayette

**LOUISIANA EXTENDED CARE HOSPITAL OF LAFAYETTE (192032)**, 1214 Coolidge Boulevard, Floors 9 & 10, Zip 70503–2621; tel. 337/289–8180, (Includes EUNICE EXTENDED CARE HOSPITAL, 3879 Highway 190, Eunice, Zip 70535; tel. 337/546–0024; Kevin Frank, Administrator; IBERIA EXTENDED CARE HOSPITAL, 2315 East Main Street, 3rd Floor, New Iberia, Zip 70560–4031; tel. 337/289–8190; Kevin Frank, Administrator), (Nonreporting) **A**10 **S** LHC Group, Lafayette, LA
Primary Contact: Kevin Frank, Administrator
Web address: www.lhcgroup.com
**Control:** Other not–for–profit (including NFP Corporation) **Service:** Long–Term Acute Care hospital

**Staffed Beds:** 42

**OPTIMA SPECIALTY HOSPITAL** See Acadia Optima Hospital

---

**Hospital, Medicare Provider Number, Address, Telephone, Approval, Facility, and Physician Codes, Health Care System**

★ American Hospital Association (AHA) membership ☐ The Joint Commission accreditation ◯ Healthcare Facilities Accreditation Program ◇ DNV Healthcare Inc. accreditation ⇑ Center for Improvement in Healthcare Quality Accreditation △ Commission on Accreditation of Rehabilitation Facilities (CARF) accreditation

**LA**

✠ **OUR LADY OF LOURDES REGIONAL MEDICAL CENTER (190102)**, 4801 Ambassador Caffery Parkway, Zip 70508–6917; tel. 337/470–2000 **A**1 2 9 10 **F**3 9 11 12 15 16 18 20 22 24 26 28 29 30 31 32 34 35 38 40 42 43 46 48 49 50 51 53 54 56 57 58 59 60 64 65 66 68 70 71 74 75 77 78 79 81 82 84 85 86 87 90 93 94 96 107 108 110 111 114 115 117 118 119 126 127 129 130 132 134 135 143 144 146 147 148 **P**6 **S** Franciscan Missionaries of Our Lady Health System, Inc., Baton Rouge, LA
Primary Contact: William F. Barrow, II, President and Chief Executive Officer
COO: Donna F. Landry, Chief Operating Officer
CFO: Ronald E. Hogan, Chief Financial Officer
CMO: Andy Blalock, M.D., Physician Executive
CIO: Ryan J. Latiolais, Director Information Systems
CHR: Jennifer Lynch Trahan, Assistant Vice President Human Resources
CNO: Carllene Macmillan, Vice President, Patient Care Services
Web address: www.lourdesrmc.com
**Control:** Church–operated, Nongovernment, not–for profit **Service:** General Medical and Surgical

Staffed Beds: 186 Admissions: 9913 Census: 137 Outpatient Visits: 124076 Births: 0 Total Expense ($000): 195154 Payroll Expense ($000): 56569 Personnel: 1274

◇ **PARK PLACE SURGICAL HOSPITAL (190255)**, 4811 Ambassador Caffery Parkway, Zip 70508–6917; tel. 337/237–8119, (Nonreporting) **A**9 10 21
Primary Contact: Brandon Moore, Administrator and Chief Executive Officer
Web address: www.parkplacesurgery.com/
**Control:** Partnership, Investor–owned, for–profit **Service:** Surgical

Staffed Beds: 10

✠ **POST ACUTE MEDICAL SPECIALTY HOSPITAL OF LAFAYETTE (192033)**, 204 Energy Parkway, Zip 70508–3816; tel. 337/232–1905 **A**1 10 **F**1 3 28 29 30 34 35 50 56 59 67 74 75 77 85 91 143 148 **P**5 **S** Post Acute Medical, LLC, Enola, PA
Primary Contact: Brian Holt, Chief Executive Officer
CFO: Karick Stober, Chief Financial Officer
CMO: Vitalis C. Okechukwu, M.D., President Medical Staff
CHR: Waynea Finley, Senior Vice President Human Resources
CNO: Eileen Turner, Director of Nursing
Web address: www.postacutemedical.com
**Control:** Partnership, Investor–owned, for–profit **Service:** Long–Term Acute Care hospital

Staffed Beds: 50 Admissions: 360 Census: 26 Outpatient Visits: 0 Births: 0 Total Expense ($000): 13361 Payroll Expense ($000): 5369 Personnel: 93

✠ **REGIONAL MEDICAL CENTER OF ACADIANA (190205)**, 2810 Ambassador Caffery Parkway, Zip 70506–5906; tel. 337/981–2949, (Includes WOMEN'S AND CHILDREN'S HOSPITAL, 4600 Ambassador Caffery Parkway, Zip 70508–6923, Mailing Address: P.O. Box 88030, Zip 70598–8030; tel. 337/521–9100; Kathy Bobbs, FACHE, President and Chief Executive Officer) **A**1 9 10 **F**3 13 15 17 18 19 20 22 24 28 29 30 31 34 40 41 45 46 47 48 52 59 60 65 70 72 74 76 77 78 79 81 88 89 90 93 97 107 110 111 114 115 117 119 129 130 131 146 147 148 **S** HCA, Nashville, TN
Primary Contact: Kathy Bobbs, FACHE, President and Chief Executive Officer
COO: Leona Boullion, R.N., Chief Operating Officer
CFO: James Miller, CPA, Chief Financial Officer
CMO: Charles Wyatt, M.D., Chief Medical Officer
CIO: Tony Istre, Director Information Technology Services
CHR: Candice Chopin, Vice President Human Resources
CNO: John Marker, Chief Nursing Officer
Web address: www.medicalcenterofacadiana.com
**Control:** Corporation, Investor–owned, for–profit **Service:** General Medical and Surgical

Staffed Beds: 289 Admissions: 10307 Census: 148 Outpatient Visits: 136934 Births: 3170 Total Expense ($000): 154325 Payroll Expense ($000): 52778 Personnel: 870

☐ **UNIVERSITY HOSPITAL AND CLINICS (190006)**, 2390 West Congress Street, Zip 70506–4298; tel. 337/261–6000, (Nonreporting) **A**1 2 3 5 9 10 **S** Lafayette General Health, Lafayette, LA
Primary Contact: Jared Stark, Chief Executive Officer
COO: Katherine D. Hebert, Chief Operating Officer
CFO: Brian T. Kirk, Vice President Finance
CMO: James B. Falterman, Jr., M.D., Medical Director
CIO: J. Barry Daigle, Manager Information Systems
CNO: Laurence Marie Vincent, Chief Nursing Officer
Web address: www.lafayettegeneral.com
**Control:** Other not–for–profit (including NFP Corporation) **Service:** General Medical and Surgical

Staffed Beds: 105

**LAKE CHARLES—Calcasieu Parish**

**CALCASIEU OAKS GERIATRIC PSYCHIATRIC HOSPITAL (192019)**, 2837 Ernest Street, Zip 70601–8785; tel. 337/439–8111, (Nonreporting) **A**9 10 **S** Pacer Health Corporation, Miami Lakes, FL
Primary Contact: Charles Getwood, Assistant Chief Executive Officer
**Control:** Corporation, Investor–owned, for–profit **Service:** Psychiatric

Staffed Beds: 24

✠ △ **CHRISTUS ST. PATRICK HOSPITAL OF LAKE CHARLES (190027)**, 524 Dr. Michael Debakey Drive, Zip 70601–5799, Mailing Address: P.O. Box 3401, Zip 70602–3401; tel. 337/436–2511 **A**1 2 7 9 10 19 **F**3 11 15 17 18 20 22 24 26 28 29 30 31 32 34 35 38 40 44 45 46 47 48 49 50 56 57 59 61 64 65 70 74 75 78 79 81 84 85 86 87 89 90 93 96 97 98 100 101 102 103 104 105 107 108 110 118 119 120 121 122 123 124 126 130 131 132 134 135 146 147 148 **P**8 **S** CHRISTUS Health, Irving, TX
Primary Contact: Donald H. Lloyd, II, Administrator
COO: Dianne P. Teal, MSN, Vice President Clinical Operations
CMO: David Engleking, M.D., Vice President Medical Affairs
CHR: Wendy White, Assistant Administrator Human Resources
Web address: www.stpatrickhospital.org
**Control:** Church–operated, Nongovernment, not–for profit **Service:** General Medical and Surgical

Staffed Beds: 160 Admissions: 7240 Census: 115 Outpatient Visits: 63582 Births: 0 Total Expense ($000): 138092 Payroll Expense ($000): 36969 Personnel: 686

✠ **LAKE AREA MEDICAL CENTER (190201)**, 4200 Nelson Road, Zip 70605–4118; tel. 337/474–6370 **A**1 9 10 **F**12 13 15 20 22 29 40 45 46 47 48 49 50 57 70 72 75 76 77 79 81 85 89 90 91 93 107 110 114 119 130 132 146 147 148 **S** Community Health Systems, Inc., Franklin, TN
Primary Contact: Bryan S. Bateman, Chief Executive Officer
CFO: Dawn Johnson–Hatcher, Chief Financial Officer
CMO: Floyd Guidry, M.D., Medical Director
CIO: Aaron Cook, Director Information Services
CHR: Charles Buchert, Director Human Resources
CNO: Robbin Odom, R.N., Chief Nursing Officer
Web address: www.women–childrens.com
**Control:** Corporation, Investor–owned, for–profit **Service:** General Medical and Surgical

Staffed Beds: 88 Admissions: 2965 Census: 28 Outpatient Visits: 48814 Births: 1237 Total Expense ($000): 45797 Payroll Expense ($000): 18877 Personnel: 386

✠ **LAKE CHARLES MEMORIAL HOSPITAL (190060)**, 1701 Oak Park Boulevard, Zip 70601–8911; tel. 337/494–3000, (Includes LAKE CHARLES MEMORIAL HOSPITAL FOR WOMEN, 1900 West Gauthier Road, Zip 70605–7170; tel. 337/480–7000; Marilyn McSwain, MSN, R.N., Administrator) **A**1 2 3 5 9 10 19 **F**3 8 11 13 15 17 18 20 22 24 25 26 28 29 30 31 34 37 40 45 49 50 53 54 56 57 58 60 62 64 66 70 71 72 73 74 75 76 77 78 79 81 82 85 86 87 89 90 93 98 99 102 103 107 108 110 111 114 115 119 120 121 123 124 127 129 130 131 132 144 146 147 148 **P**1 6 7
Primary Contact: Larry M. Graham, FACHE, President and Chief Executive Officer
COO: Timothy O. Coffey, Senior Vice President Operations
CFO: Charles P. Whitson, CPA, Senior Vice President Finance
CMO: Kevin Mocklin, M.D., Director Medical Staff
CIO: Belinda Sommers, Chief Information Officer
CHR: Ginger Consigney, Vice President Human Resources
Web address: www.lcmh.com
**Control:** Other not–for–profit (including NFP Corporation) **Service:** General Medical and Surgical

Staffed Beds: 308 Admissions: 12189 Census: 171 Outpatient Visits: 305607 Births: 1804 Total Expense ($000): 248760 Payroll Expense ($000): 79127 Personnel: 2226

**LCMH SPECIALTY HOSPITAL (192019)**, 2837 Ernest Street, Building B., Zip 70601–8785; tel. 337/480–8990 **A**10 **F**1 3 130 148
Primary Contact: Ellen Smith, Administrator
CNO: Harry Dupree, Director of Nursing
Web address: www.lcmh.com/
**Control:** Other not–for–profit (including NFP Corporation) **Service:** Long–Term Acute Care hospital

Staffed Beds: 29 Admissions: 231 Census: 17 Outpatient Visits: 0 Births: 0 Total Expense ($000): 5509 Payroll Expense ($000): 2379 Personnel: 43

**OCEANS BEHAVIORAL HOSPITAL OF LAKE CHARLES (194090)**, 302 West Mcneese Street, Zip 70605–5604; tel. 337/474–7581, (Nonreporting) **A**9 10 **S** Oceans Healthcare, Lake Charles, LA
Primary Contact: Dena Jules, Administrator
Web address: www.obhlc.info/
**Control:** Corporation, Investor–owned, for–profit **Service:** Psychiatric

Staffed Beds: 20

**LAKE PROVIDENCE—East Carroll Parish**

**EAST CARROLL PARISH HOSPITAL (190208)**, 336 North Hood Street, Zip 71254–2140; tel. 318/559–4023, (Nonreporting) **A**9 10
Primary Contact: LaDonna Englerth, Administrator
**Control:** Hospital district or authority, Government, nonfederal **Service:** General Medical and Surgical

Staffed Beds: 11

## LEESVILLE—Vernon Parish

☒ **BYRD REGIONAL HOSPITAL (190164)**, 1020 West Fertitta Boulevard,
Zip 71446–4645; tel. 337/239–9041 **A**1 9 10 **F**3 13 15 18 20 29 34 40 45
47 48 49 50 57 70 76 79 81 89 107 108 110 111 115 119 130 146
**S** Community Health Systems, Inc., Franklin, TN
Primary Contact: Roger C. LeDoux, Chief Executive Officer
CFO: Jared Graves, Chief Financial Officer
CMO: Francis Fraser, M.D., Chief of Staff
CHR: Karolyne Christian, Director Human Resources
CNO: Beth Westerchil, Chief Nursing Officer
Web address: www.byrdregional.com
**Control:** Corporation, Investor–owned, for–profit **Service:** General Medical and
Surgical

**Staffed Beds: 60 Admissions:** 2893 **Census:** 26 **Outpatient Visits:** 31151
**Births:** 249 **Total Expense ($000):** 36676 **Payroll Expense ($000):** 13206
**Personnel:** 267

**DOCTOR'S HOSPITAL OF DEER CREEK (190297)**, 815 South 10th Street,
Zip 71446–4611, Mailing Address: P.O. Box 1391, Zip 71496–1391;
tel. 337/392–5088, (Nonreporting) **A**9 10
Primary Contact: Jeffrey Morrow, Chief Executive Officer
CMO: Gregory D. Lord, M.D., Medical Director
CIO: Kim Smith, Director Business Office
CHR: Annette Hillman, Director Human Resources
CNO: Brenda Willis, Director of Nursing
Web address: www.dhdc.md
**Control:** Corporation, Investor–owned, for–profit **Service:** General Medical and
Surgical

**Staffed Beds: 10**

☐ **LEESVILLE REHABILITATION HOSPITAL (193086)**, 900 South 6th Street,
Zip 71446–4723; tel. 337/392–8118, (Nonreporting) **A**1 10
Primary Contact: Jack M. Causey, Chief Executive Officer
CMO: Gregory D. Lord, M.D., Chief Medical Officer
CHR: Jackie Rubar, Administrative Assistant and Director Human Resources
Web address: www.leesvillerehab.com
**Control:** Corporation, Investor–owned, for–profit **Service:** Rehabilitation

**Staffed Beds: 16**

☐ **TRI PARISH REHABILITATION HOSPITAL (193050)**, 8088 Hawks Road,
Zip 71446–6649; tel. 337/462–8880, (Nonreporting) **A**1 10
Primary Contact: Stephanie Nunez, Interim Chief Executive Officer
Web address: www.triparishrehab.com
**Control:** Corporation, Investor–owned, for–profit **Service:** Rehabilitation

**Staffed Beds: 20**

## LULING—St. Charles Parish

☒ **ST. CHARLES PARISH HOSPITAL (190079)**, 1057 Paul Maillard Road,
Zip 70070–4349, Mailing Address: P.O. Box 87, Zip 70070–0087;
tel. 985/785–6242, (Nonreporting) **A**1 9 10 **S** Ochsner Health System, New
Orleans, LA
Primary Contact: Anthony DiGerolamo, R.N., MSN, Chief Executive Officer
CFO: Peter Torsch, Chief Financial Officer
CMO: Vadakkipalayam N. Devarajan, Chief Medical Staff
CIO: Angela Boudreaux, Director Information Technology
CHR: Karen Ann Judlin, Director Human Resources
CNO: Jean Hill, Chief Nursing Officer and Chief Clinical Officer
Web address: www.ochsner.org/locations/st_charles_parish_hospital/
**Control:** Hospital district or authority, Government, nonfederal **Service:** General
Medical and Surgical

**Staffed Beds: 59**

## LUTCHER—St. James Parish

☒ **ST. JAMES PARISH HOSPITAL (191305)**, 1645 Lutcher Avenue,
Zip 70071–5150; tel. 225/869–5512 **A**1 9 10 18 **F**3 15 29 30 34 35 40 45
50 57 59 64 75 77 80 81 107 110 111 114 119 128 129 132 133 135
Primary Contact: Mary Ellen Pratt, FACHE, Chief Executive Officer
CFO: Tracy L. George, Chief Financial Officer
CIO: Jeremy Martin, Chief Support Services Officer
CHR: Lisa Faucheux, Director Human Resources
CNO: Rhonda Zeringue, R.N., Chief Nursing Officer
Web address: www.sjph.org
**Control:** Hospital district or authority, Government, nonfederal **Service:** General
Medical and Surgical

**Staffed Beds: 25 Admissions:** 519 **Census:** 5 **Outpatient Visits:** 28553
**Births:** 0 **Total Expense ($000):** 23782 **Payroll Expense ($000):** 9061
**Personnel:** 178

## MAMOU—Evangeline Parish

☐ **SAVOY MEDICAL CENTER (190025)**, 801 Poinciana Avenue,
Zip 70554–2298; tel. 337/468–5261, (Nonreporting) **A**1 9 10
Primary Contact: Sherman Fookes, Interim Administrator
COO: Gerald Fuselier, Chief Operating Officer
CMO: Greg Savoy, M.D., Chief Medical Officer
CIO: Daniel Lahaye, Manager
CHR: Annette Thibodeaux, Director Human Resources
Web address: www.savoymedicalcenter.com
**Control:** Corporation, Investor–owned, for–profit **Service:** General Medical and
Surgical

**Staffed Beds: 180**

## MANDEVILLE—St. Tammany Parish

☐ **NORTHLAKE BEHAVIORAL HOSPITAL (194007)**, 23515 Highway 190,
Zip 70448–7334, Mailing Address: P.O. Box 3850, Zip 70470–3850;
tel. 985/626–6300, (Nonreporting) **A**1 3 5 10
Primary Contact: Richard Kramer, Interim Chief Executive Officer
COO: Richard Kramer, Chief Operating Officer
CMO: Girishkumar Shah, M.D., Clinical Director
CIO: Mike Ziemba, Information Technology Project Lead
CHR: Daphne Stewart, Director Human Resources
Web address: www.selh.org
**Control:** State–Government, nonfederal **Service:** Psychiatric

**Staffed Beds: 153**

## MANSFIELD—De Soto Parish

**DE SOTO REGIONAL HEALTH SYSTEM (190118)**, 207 Jefferson Street,
Zip 71052–2603, Mailing Address: P.O. Box 1636, Zip 71052–1636;
tel. 318/871–3100, (Nonreporting) **A**9 10 20 **S** Willis–Knighton Health System,
Shreveport, LA
Primary Contact: Todd Eppler, FACHE, Chief Executive Officer
CMO: Leigh Dillard, M.D., Chief of Staff
CHR: Rhonda Potter, Director Human Resources
CNO: Vernadine Mitchell, R.N., Chief Nursing Officer
Web address: www.desotoregional.com
**Control:** Other not–for–profit (including NFP Corporation) **Service:** General
Medical and Surgical

**Staffed Beds: 12**

## MANY—Sabine Parish

**SABINE MEDICAL CENTER (190218)**, 240 Highland Drive, Zip 71449–3718;
tel. 318/256–5691, (Nonreporting) **A**9 10 20 **S** Allegiance Health Management,
Shreveport, LA
Primary Contact: Chris Beddoe, Chief Executive Officer
COO: Doug Plummer, Chief Operating Officer
CFO: Frances F. Hopkins, Chief Financial Officer
CNO: Karen Ford, Chief Nursing Officer
Web address: www.sabinemedicalcenter.net
**Control:** Individual, Investor–owned, for–profit **Service:** General Medical and
Surgical

**Staffed Beds: 44**

## MARKSVILLE—Avoyelles Parish

☐ **AVOYELLES HOSPITAL (190099)**, 4231 Highway 1192, Zip 71351–4711,
Mailing Address: P.O. Box 249, Zip 71351–0249; tel. 318/253–8611 **A**1 9 10
**F**3 15 29 30 34 40 56 57 64 65 70 75 81 85 86 107 110 114 119 133
135 146
Primary Contact: David M. Mitchel, Chief Executive Officer
CFO: Douglas Lahasky, Chief Financial Officer
CMO: Robert Scott York, M.D., Chief of Staff
CHR: Allison Ferguson, Director Human Resources
CNO: Cindy K. Juneau, Chief Nursing Officer
Web address: www.avoyelleshospital.com
**Control:** Corporation, Investor–owned, for–profit **Service:** General Medical and
Surgical

**Staffed Beds: 35 Admissions:** 1118 **Census:** 12 **Outpatient Visits:** 36605
**Births:** 0 **Total Expense ($000):** 13752 **Payroll Expense ($000):** 6582
**Personnel:** 165

---

**Hospital, Medicare Provider Number, Address, Telephone, Approval, Facility, and Physician Codes, Health Care System**

★ American Hospital Association (AHA) membership    ○ Healthcare Facilities Accreditation Program    ⇑ Center for Improvement in Healthcare Quality Accreditation
☐ The Joint Commission accreditation    ◇ DNV Healthcare Inc. accreditation    △ Commission on Accreditation of Rehabilitation Facilities (CARF) accreditation

**LA**

## MARRERO—Jefferson Parish

**LOUISIANA CONTINUING CARE HOSPITAL (192007)**, 1111 Medical Center Boulevard, Suite S–550, Zip 70072–3151; tel. 504/349–2470, (Nonreporting) **A**10
Primary Contact: James Fritschen, Chief Executive Officer
**Control:** Corporation, Investor–owned, for–profit **Service:** Long–Term Acute Care hospital

**Staffed Beds:** 56

☒ △ **WEST JEFFERSON MEDICAL CENTER (190039)**, 1101 Medical Center Boulevard, Zip 70072–3191; tel. 504/347–5511 **A**1 2 3 5 7 9 10 **F**3 6 7 11 12 13 15 17 18 20 22 24 26 28 29 30 31 34 35 37 38 39 40 41 43 45 46 47 49 50 51 53 56 57 59 61 64 65 68 70 72 74 75 76 78 79 81 82 84 85 86 87 89 90 91 93 96 97 98 100 101 102 104 105 107 108 110 111 114 115 117 118 119 120 121 124 126 127 129 130 132 135 144 146 147 148 **P**6 7
Primary Contact: Nancy R. Cassagne, FACHE, Chief Executive Officer
COO: Angela Greener, Chief Administrative Officer
CMO: Mark Workman, M.D., Chief Medical Officer
CIO: Nicholas Thimis, Chief Information Officer
CHR: Frank Martinez, Vice President Human Resources
Web address: www.wjmc.org
**Control:** Hospital district or authority, Government, nonfederal **Service:** General Medical and Surgical

**Staffed Beds:** 257 **Admissions:** 11390 **Census:** 167 **Outpatient Visits:** 262272 **Births:** 1232 **Total Expense ($000):** 258750 **Payroll Expense ($000):** 95969 **Personnel:** 1609

## METAIRIE—Jefferson Parish

☒ △ **EAST JEFFERSON GENERAL HOSPITAL (190146)**, 4200 Houma Boulevard, Zip 70006–2996; tel. 504/503–4000, (Includes DOCTORS HOSPITAL OF JEFFERSON, 4320 Houma Boulevard, Zip 70006–2973; tel. 504/849–4000) **A**1 2 3 5 7 9 10 **F**3 7 8 11 13 14 15 17 18 20 22 24 26 28 29 30 31 34 35 36 37 40 44 45 46 47 48 49 50 51 53 54 55 56 57 58 59 60 62 64 65 68 70 72 73 74 75 76 77 78 79 81 82 84 85 86 87 89 90 91 92 93 94 96 97 98 102 103 107 108 110 111 114 115 117 118 119 120 121 123 124 126 128 129 130 131 132 135 145 146 147 148 **P**6
Primary Contact: Mark J. Peters, M.D., President and Chief Executive Officer
COO: Judy Brown, Executive Vice President and Chief Operating Officer
CFO: Bruce Naremore, Senior Vice President and Chief Financial Officer
CMO: Raymond P. DeCorte, M.D., Chief Medical Officer
CIO: Steve Baker, Chief Information Officer
CHR: Frank Martinez, Senior Vice President Human Resources
CNO: Ruby Brewer, RN, Senior Vice President and Chief Quality Officer
Web address: www.ejgh.org
**Control:** Hospital district or authority, Government, nonfederal **Service:** General Medical and Surgical

**Staffed Beds:** 424 **Admissions:** 16065 **Census:** 230 **Outpatient Visits:** 225001 **Births:** 1877 **Total Expense ($000):** 339660 **Payroll Expense ($000):** 110992 **Personnel:** 2131

◇ **OMEGA HOSPITAL (190302)**, 2525 Severn Avenue, Zip 70002–5932; tel. 504/832–4200, (Nonreporting) **A**10 21
Primary Contact: Debbie Schenck, Administrator
Web address: www.omega–institute.com
**Control:** Individual, Investor–owned, for–profit **Service:** Surgical

**Staffed Beds:** 10

## MINDEN—Webster Parish

☒ **MINDEN MEDICAL CENTER (190144)**, 1 Medical Plaza, Zip 71055–3330, Mailing Address: P.O. Box 5003, Zip 71058–5003; tel. 318/377–2321 **A**1 9 10 19 **F**11 13 15 18 20 22 29 30 34 40 45 46 56 57 59 62 64 70 75 76 77 79 81 82 87 89 90 93 98 103 107 111 115 119 129 130 132 146 147 148 **S** LifePoint Health, Brentwood, TN
Primary Contact: George E. French, III, FACHE, Chief Executive Officer
CFO: Jim Williams, Chief Financial Officer
CMO: G. Max Stell, M.D., Medical Director
CIO: Mace Morgan, Director Information Systems
CHR: Mary Winget, Director Human Resources
CNO: Donna Carter, MSN, Chief Nursing Officer
Web address: www.mindenmedicalcenter.com
**Control:** Corporation, Investor–owned, for–profit **Service:** General Medical and Surgical

**Staffed Beds:** 161 **Admissions:** 3915 **Census:** 42 **Outpatient Visits:** 42903 **Births:** 756 **Total Expense ($000):** 51639 **Payroll Expense ($000):** 19213 **Personnel:** 464

## MONROE—Ouachita Parish

**BASTROP REHABILITATION HOSPITAL (193058)**, 4310 South Grand Street, Zip 71202–6322; tel. 318/654–8300 **A**10 **F**29 30 35 64 65 67 86 90 91 92 93 97 103 104 127 130 148
Primary Contact: Stephen J. Florentine, Administrator
COO: Tena Paulk, R.N., Program Director and Director Nursing
CMO: James M. Smith, M.D., Medical Director
CIO: Debbie Chunn, Director Medical Records
CHR: Renee Walker, Director Human Resources
**Control:** County–Government, nonfederal **Service:** General Medical and Surgical

**Staffed Beds:** 10 **Admissions:** 251 **Census:** 8 **Outpatient Visits:** 18000 **Births:** 0 **Total Expense ($000):** 7073 **Payroll Expense ($000):** 3489

**E. A. CONWAY MEDICAL CENTER** See University Health Conway

☐ **MONROE SURGICAL HOSPITAL (190245)**, 2408 Broadmoor Boulevard, Zip 71201–2963; tel. 318/410–0002, (Nonreporting) **A**1 3 9 10
Primary Contact: Robyn Hemphill, Interim Chief Executive Officer and Chief Nursing Officer
Web address: www.monroesurgical.com
**Control:** Corporation, Investor–owned, for–profit **Service:** Surgical

**Staffed Beds:** 10

★ ◇ **P & S SURGICAL HOSPITAL (190246)**, 312 Grammont Street Suite 101, Zip 71201–7403; tel. 318/388–4040, (Nonreporting) **A**9 10 21
Primary Contact: Linda S. Holyfield, R.N., MSN, President and Chief Executive Officer
COO: Terri Hicks, Chief Operating Officer and Chief Financial Officer
CFO: Terri Hicks, Chief Operating Officer and Chief Financial Officer
CMO: Lauren Jane Mickey, M.D., Chief of Staff
CIO: Christy Childers, Director Information Technology
CHR: Cheniere Craig, Director Human Resources
CNO: Debbie W. Austin, MSN, Vice President Patient Care Services
Web address: www.pssurgery.com
**Control:** Partnership, Investor–owned, for–profit **Service:** Surgical

**Staffed Beds:** 22

**SPECIALTY HOSPITAL (192016)**, 309 Jackson Street, 7th Floor, Zip 71201–7407, Mailing Address: P.O. Box 1532, Zip 71210–1532; tel. 318/966–7045, (Nonreporting) **A**10 **S** LHC Group, Lafayette, LA
Primary Contact: Cleta Munholland, Administrator
Web address: www.lhcgroup.com
**Control:** Church–operated, Nongovernment, not–for profit **Service:** Long–Term Acute Care hospital

**Staffed Beds:** 32

☒ **ST. FRANCIS MEDICAL CENTER (190125)**, 309 Jackson Street, Zip 71201–7407, Mailing Address: P.O. Box 1901, Zip 71210–1901; tel. 318/966–4000, (Includes ST. FRANCIS NORTH HOSPITAL, 3421 Medical Park Drive, Zip 71203–2399; tel. 318/388–1946; Cindy J. Rogers, FACHE, Administrator) **A**1 2 9 10 **F**3 12 13 15 17 18 19 20 21 22 23 24 26 27 28 29 30 31 32 34 35 37 39 40 44 45 46 49 50 54 55 56 57 59 64 65 68 69 70 72 74 75 76 77 78 79 81 84 85 87 88 89 90 92 93 96 97 98 102 103 104 105 107 108 110 111 114 115 116 117 118 119 124 128 129 130 131 132 134 135 144 146 147 148 **P**8 **S** Franciscan Missionaries of Our Lady Health System, Inc., Baton Rouge, LA
Primary Contact: Kristin Wolkart, President and Chief Executive Officer
CFO: Ronald E. Hogan, Regional Chief Financial Officer
CMO: Robert Seegers, M.D., Vice President Medical Affairs
CHR: James Novak, Vice President, Human Resources
CNO: Kayla Johnson, R.N., Vice President Patient Care Services and Chief Nursing Officer
Web address: www.stfran.com
**Control:** Church–operated, Nongovernment, not–for profit **Service:** General Medical and Surgical

**Staffed Beds:** 343 **Admissions:** 16953 **Census:** 258 **Outpatient Visits:** 206578 **Births:** 1797 **Total Expense ($000):** 268098 **Payroll Expense ($000):** 103508 **Personnel:** 1840

**ST. FRANCIS SPECIALTY HOSPITAL** See Specialty Hospital

*Many Facility Codes have changed. Please refer to the AHA Guide Code Chart.*
© 2015 AHA Guide

□ **UNIVERSITY HEALTH CONWAY (190011)**, 4864 Jackson Street,
Zip 71202–6497, Mailing Address: P.O. Box 1881, Zip 71210–8005;
tel. 318/330–7000 **A**1 3 5 9 10 **F**3 5 8 11 15 18 20 22 24 26 28 29 30 31 32
34 35 38 40 41 45 46 50 54 56 57 59 61 64 65 66 68 70 71 72 74 75 76
77 78 79 81 82 86 87 89 91 92 93 97 98 100 101 102 103 107 111 112
114 119 130 135 143 144 146 147 148 **S** University Health System,
Shreveport, LA
Primary Contact: Larry Donner, Administrator
CFO: Dorothy Whittington, Chief Financial Officer
CMO: Richard Cavell, M.D., Medical Director
CIO: Todd Walters, Director of UHC Information Technology Services
CHR: Rob Hartmann, Assistant Director Human Resources Management
CNO: Patrick King, Director of Nursing
Web address: www.uhsystem.com
**Control:** Other not–for–profit (including NFP Corporation) **Service:** General
Medical and Surgical

**Staffed Beds:** 105 **Admissions:** 5200 **Census:** 60 **Outpatient Visits:** 140000
**Births:** 920 **Total Expense ($000):** 79549 **Payroll Expense ($000):** 30103
**Personnel:** 517

### MORGAN CITY—St. Mary Parish

✠ **TECHE REGIONAL MEDICAL CENTER (190014)**, 1125 Marguerite Street,
Zip 70380–1855, Mailing Address: P.O. Box 2308, Zip 70381–2308;
tel. 985/384–2200 **A**1 9 10 20 **F**3 13 15 18 20 22 29 30 31 34 40 45 50 57
59 60 70 76 79 81 85 89 90 93 98 102 104 105 107 108 110 111 115 119
130 141 146 147 **S** LifePoint Health, Brentwood, TN
Primary Contact: James P. Frazier, III, Chief Executive Officer
COO: Don Knight, Assistant Administrator and Risk Manager
CFO: Michael Mayeux, Chief Financial Officer
CMO: Eric Melancon, Chief of Staff
CIO: Cheryl Lipari, Manager Information Systems
CHR: Timothy Hebert, Director Human Resources
Web address: www.techeregional.com
**Control:** Corporation, Investor–owned, for–profit **Service:** General Medical and
Surgical

**Staffed Beds:** 165 **Admissions:** 3135 **Census:** 39 **Outpatient Visits:** 52634
**Births:** 436 **Total Expense ($000):** 43768 **Payroll Expense ($000):** 14145
**Personnel:** 256

### NAPOLEONVILLE—Assumption Parish

★ **ASSUMPTION COMMUNITY HOSPITAL (191303)**, 135 Highway 402,
Zip 70390–2217; tel. 985/369–3600 **A**9 10 18 **F**32 34 35 40 57 58 59 64 65
90 127 135 **S** Franciscan Missionaries of Our Lady Health System, Inc., Baton
Rouge, LA
Primary Contact: Wayne M. Arboneaux, Chief Executive Officer
CHR: Letonia Pierre, Coordinator Human Resources
CNO: Donna Mullings, Director of Nursing
Web address: www.ololrmc.com
**Control:** Other not–for–profit (including NFP Corporation) **Service:** General
Medical and Surgical

**Staffed Beds:** 6 **Admissions:** 59 **Census:** 1 **Outpatient Visits:** 21516 **Births:**
0 **Total Expense ($000):** 6503 **Payroll Expense ($000):** 2135 **Personnel:**
55

### NATCHITOCHES—Natchitoches Parish

**LOUISIANA EXTENDED CARE HOSPITAL OF NATCHITOCHES (192035)**, 501
Keyser Avenue, Zip 71457–6018; tel. 318/354–2044 **A**10 **F**1 3 28 29 34 38 44
50 57 59 68 74 75 85 86 87 91 97 130 148 **S** LHC Group, Lafayette, LA
Primary Contact: John Rivoire, Administrator
Web address: www.lhcgroup.com
**Control:** Partnership, Investor–owned, for–profit **Service:** Long–Term Acute Care
hospital

**Staffed Beds:** 21 **Admissions:** 215 **Census:** 15 **Outpatient Visits:** 0 **Births:**
0 **Personnel:** 48

✠ **NATCHITOCHES REGIONAL MEDICAL CENTER (190007)**, 501 Keyser
Avenue, Zip 71457–6036, Mailing Address: P.O. Box 2009, Zip 71457–2009;
tel. 318/214–4200, (Nonreporting) **A**1 9 10 20 **S** CHRISTUS Health, Irving, TX
Primary Contact: D. Kirk Soileau, Chief Executive Officer
CFO: Brad McCormick, Chief Financial Officer
CMO: Phyllis Mason, M.D., Chief Medical Officer
CIO: Raymond Bruels, Manager Information Technology
CHR: Ernie Scott, Director Human Resources
CNO: Dawna DeBlieux, Vice President Patient Care Services and Chief Nurse
Executive
Web address: www.natchitocheshospital.org
**Control:** Hospital district or authority, Government, nonfederal **Service:** General
Medical and Surgical

**Staffed Beds:** 208

### NEW IBERIA—Iberia Parish

✠ ○ **DAUTERIVE HOSPITAL (190003)**, 600 North Lewis Street,
Zip 70563–2043; tel. 337/365–7311, (Nonreporting) **A**1 9 10 11 19
Primary Contact: Bradley Mabry, Chief Executive Officer
CMO: Mike Alvarez, M.D., Chief Medical Officer
CIO: Billy Tingle, Chief Information Officer
CNO: Jennifer Wise, Chief Nurse Officer
Web address: www.dauterivehospital.com
**Control:** Corporation, Investor–owned, for–profit **Service:** General Medical and
Surgical

**Staffed Beds:** 103

□ **IBERIA MEDICAL CENTER (190054)**, 2315 East Main Street,
Zip 70560–4031, Mailing Address: P.O. Box 13338, Zip 70562–3338;
tel. 337/364–0441 **A**1 9 10 **F**3 11 13 15 18 20 22 28 29 30 31 34 39 40 45
46 47 48 49 50 57 68 70 72 74 75 76 77 78 79 81 85 89 93 97 107 108
110 115 119 127 130 146 **P**6 **S** HealthTech Management Services,
Brentwood, TN
Primary Contact: Parker A. Templeton, FACHE, Chief Executive Officer
COO: Shane P. Myers, Chief Operating Officer
CFO: Stephanie Kirk, Chief Financial Officer
CMO: Shawn Baquet, Chief of Staff
CIO: Vance Robinson, Chief Information Officer
CHR: Lori Spann, Director Human Resources
CNO: Elizabeth Gondron, R.N., Vice President and Chief Nursing Officer
Web address: www.iberiamedicalcenter.com
**Control:** Hospital district or authority, Government, nonfederal **Service:** General
Medical and Surgical

**Staffed Beds:** 84 **Admissions:** 3801 **Census:** 37 **Outpatient Visits:** 95320
**Births:** 513 **Total Expense ($000):** 60275 **Payroll Expense ($000):** 24510
**Personnel:** 492

□ **IBERIA REHABILITATION HOSPITAL (190304)**, 532 Jefferson Terrace,
Zip 70560–4948; tel. 337/364–6923, (Nonreporting) **A**1 9 10
Primary Contact: Athan Oliver, Administrator and Chief Executive Officer
Web address: www.iberiarehab.net/
**Control:** Partnership, Investor–owned, for–profit **Service:** Rehabilitation

**Staffed Beds:** 24

### NEW ORLEANS—Orleans Parish

□ **BEACON BEHAVIORAL HOSPITAL – NEW ORLEANS (194084)**, 14500 Hayne
Boulevard, Suite 200, Zip 70128–1751; tel. 504/210–0460, (Nonreporting) **A**1
9 10
Primary Contact: Jessika Scallion, Administrator
**Control:** Corporation, Investor–owned, for–profit **Service:** Psychiatric

**Staffed Beds:** 24

□ △ **CHILDREN'S HOSPITAL (193300)**, 200 Henry Clay Avenue,
Zip 70118–5720; tel. 504/899–9511, (Nonreporting) **A**1 2 3 5 7 9 10 **S** LCMC
Health, New Orleans, LA
Primary Contact: Mary R. Perrin, President and Chief Executive Officer
COO: Justin Olsen, Chief Operating Officer
CFO: Courtney Garrett, CPA, Senior Vice President, Chief Financial Officer
CMO: John Heaton, M.D., Senior Vice President and Medical Director
CIO: Tanya Townsend, Senior Vice President, Chief Information Officer (part of
LCMC)
CHR: Wendy L. Willis, Vice President Human Resources
CNO: Diane Michel, Senior Vice President, Chief Nursing Officer
Web address: www.chnola.org
**Control:** Other not–for–profit (including NFP Corporation) **Service:** Children's
general

**Staffed Beds:** 200

□ **COMMUNITY CARE HOSPITAL (194056)**, 1421 General Taylor Street,
Zip 70115–3717; tel. 504/899–2500, (Nonreporting) **A**1 10
Primary Contact: Paul B. Kavanaugh, President and Chief Executive Officer
Web address: www.communitycarehospital.com
**Control:** State–Government, nonfederal **Service:** Psychiatric

**Staffed Beds:** 36

---

**Hospital, Medicare Provider Number, Address, Telephone, Approval, Facility, and Physician Codes, Health Care System**

★ American Hospital Association (AHA) membership    ○ Healthcare Facilities Accreditation Program    ⇧ Center for Improvement in Healthcare Quality Accreditation
□ The Joint Commission accreditation    ◇ DNV Healthcare Inc. accreditation    △ Commission on Accreditation of Rehabilitation Facilities (CARF) accreditation

**LA**

☐ **INTERIM LSU PUBLIC HOSPITAL (190005)**, 2021 Perdido Street, Zip 70112–1396; tel. 504/903–3000 **A**1 2 5 8 9 10 **F**3 8 9 11 12 15 18 20 22 24 26 29 30 31 34 35 39 40 43 45 46 49 50 51 58 61 64 65 66 70 74 75 78 79 81 85 86 87 93 94 97 98 100 102 107 108 110 111 115 116 117 118 119 126 130 135 141 146 147 148 **S** LCMC Health, New Orleans, LA
Primary Contact: Cindy Nuesslein, Chief Executive Officer
COO: Adler Voltaire, Chief Administrative Officer
CFO: Ed Burke, Chief Financial Officer
CMO: Cathi E. Fontenot, M.D., Medical Director
CIO: Mitch Perlin, Chief Information Officer
CHR: Ronald Broadus, Assistant Administrator Human Resources
Web address: www.umcno.org
**Control:** Other not–for–profit (including NFP Corporation) **Service:** General Medical and Surgical

**Staffed Beds:** 390 **Admissions:** 10558 **Census:** 183 **Outpatient Visits:** 301864 **Births:** 0 **Total Expense ($000):** 391135 **Payroll Expense ($000):** 110622 **Personnel:** 1829

✚ **KINDRED HOSPITAL–NEW ORLEANS (192009)**, 3601 Coliseum Street, Zip 70115–3606; tel. 504/899–1555 **A**1 3 9 10 **F**1 3 28 29 30 46 70 75 77 86 87 91 96 98 103 130 135 148 **S** Kindred Healthcare, Louisville, KY
Primary Contact: Jan Turk, Chief Executive Officer
CFO: Laurie Champagne, Controller
Web address: www.kindredhospitalnola.com
**Control:** Corporation, Investor–owned, for–profit **Service:** Long–Term Acute Care hospital

**Staffed Beds:** 80 **Admissions:** 575 **Census:** 43 **Outpatient Visits:** 0 **Births:** 0

**MEDICAL CENTER OF LOUISIANA AT NEW ORLEANS** See Interim LSU Public Hospital

☐ **NEW ORLEANS EAST HOSPITAL (190313)**, 5620 Read Boulevard, Zip 70127–3106, Mailing Address: 5620 Read Boulevard, Zip 70127–3106; tel. 504/592–6600, (Data for 173 days) **A**1 **F**3 11 15 18 20 22 29 30 34 35 38 40 44 45 50 57 59 60 64 68 70 75 77 79 81 85 86 87 89 91 93 97 107 108 110 111 115 118 119 130 146 **P**8 **S** LCMC Health, New Orleans, LA
Primary Contact: Charlotte Parent, R.N., Interim Chief Executive Officer
CFO: Maxwell Owens, FACHE, Chief Financial Officer
CHR: Cindy Mousa, Senior Director Human Resources
CNO: Mary L. Kelly, R.N., Chief Nursing Officer
Web address: www.noehospital.org
**Control:** Hospital district or authority, Government, nonfederal **Service:** General Medical and Surgical

**Staffed Beds:** 34 **Admissions:** 169 **Census:** 3 **Outpatient Visits:** 11833 **Births:** 1 **Total Expense ($000):** 21093 **Payroll Expense ($000):** 6795 **Personnel:** 174

✚ △ **OCHSNER MEDICAL CENTER (190036)**, 1514 Jefferson Highway, Zip 70121–2429; tel. 504/842–3000, (Includes OCHSNER BAPTIST MEDICAL CENTER, 2700 Napoleon Avenue, Zip 70115–6914; tel. 504/899–9311; Dawn Anuszkiewicz, Chief Executive Officer; OCHSNER MEDICAL CENTER – WEST BANK, 2500 Belle Chasse Highway, Gretna, Zip 70056–7127; tel. 504/392–3131; Travis Capers, Chief Executive Officer; OCHSNER MEDICAL CENTER FOR CHILDREN, 1514 Jefferson Highway, tel. 504/842–3000), (Total facility includes 38 beds in nursing home–type unit) **A**1 2 3 5 7 8 9 10 **F**3 4 5 6 7 8 9 11 12 13 14 15 17 18 19 20 21 22 23 24 25 26 27 28 29 30 31 32 34 35 36 37 38 40 41 43 44 45 46 47 48 49 50 51 54 55 56 57 58 59 60 61 63 64 65 68 70 72 73 74 75 76 77 78 79 80 81 82 84 85 86 87 88 89 90 91 92 93 94 96 97 98 99 100 101 102 103 104 105 107 108 110 111 114 115 116 117 118 119 120 121 123 124 126 128 129 130 131 132 134 135 136 137 138 139 140 141 142 145 146 147 148 **P**6 **S** Ochsner Health System, New Orleans, LA
Primary Contact: Robert K. Wolterman, Chief Executive Officer
CFO: Scott J. Posecai, Executive Vice President and Chief Financial Officer
CMO: Patrick J. Quinlan, M.D., Chief Executive Officer
CIO: Lynn Witherspoon, Vice President and Chief Information Officer
CHR: Joan Mollohan, Vice President Human Resources
Web address: www.ochsner.org
**Control:** Other not–for–profit (including NFP Corporation) **Service:** General Medical and Surgical

**Staffed Beds:** 789 **Admissions:** 38058 **Census:** 584 **Outpatient Visits:** 438768 **Births:** 3690 **Total Expense ($000):** 1076486 **Payroll Expense ($000):** 371483 **Personnel:** 8049

**PSYCHIATRIC PAVILION NEW ORLEANS** See Beacon Behavioral Hospital – New Orleans

☐ **RIVER OAKS HOSPITAL (194031)**, 1525 River Oaks Road West, Zip 70123–2162; tel. 504/734–1740, (Includes RIVER OAKS CHILD AND ADOLESCENT HOSPITAL, 1525 River Oaks Road West, tel. 504/734–1740) **A**1 3 9 10 **F**4 5 98 99 102 105 130 **S** Universal Health Services, Inc., King of Prussia, PA
Primary Contact: Evelyn Nolting, Chief Executive Officer and Managing Director
CFO: Kyle Meguess, Chief Financial Officer
CMO: Lincoln Paine, M.D., Medical Director
CIO: Vincent Chatelain, Director Business Development
CHR: Wanda Hoffmann, Director Human Resources
CNO: Michelle Wells, Director of Nursing
Web address: www.riveroakshospital.com
**Control:** Corporation, Investor–owned, for–profit **Service:** Psychiatric

**Staffed Beds:** 126 **Admissions:** 3500 **Census:** 79 **Outpatient Visits:** 0 **Births:** 0 **Total Expense ($000):** 15756 **Payroll Expense ($000):** 7519 **Personnel:** 160

**SEASIDE BEHAVIORAL CENTER (194100)**, 4201 Woodland Drive, Zip 70131–7339; tel. 504/393–4223, (Nonreporting) **A**3 9 10
Primary Contact: Mary L. Matamoros, R.N., Chief Executive Officer
**Control:** Partnership, Investor–owned, for–profit **Service:** Psychiatric

**Staffed Beds:** 24

☐ **ST. CATHERINE MEMORIAL HOSPITAL (192023)**, 14500 Hayne Boulevard, Zip 70128–1751; tel. 504/210–3000, (Nonreporting) **A**1 10
Primary Contact: Lexis Landry Nunez, Chief Executive Officer
Web address: www.stcatherine–hospital.com
**Control:** Corporation, Investor–owned, for–profit **Service:** Long–Term Acute Care hospital

**Staffed Beds:** 21

◇ **ST. CHARLES SURGICAL HOSPITAL (190300)**, 1717 Saint Charles Avenue, Zip 70130–5223; tel. 504/529–6600, (Nonreporting) **A**10 21
Primary Contact: Cheri Saltaformaggio, Chief Executive Officer
Web address: www.scsh.com
**Control:** Corporation, Investor–owned, for–profit **Service:** Surgical

**Staffed Beds:** 39

✚ △ **TOURO INFIRMARY (190046)**, 1401 Foucher Street, Zip 70115–3593; tel. 504/897–7011, (Includes TOURO REHABILITATION CENTER, 1401 Foucher Street, Zip 70115–3515; tel. 504/897–8560; Susan E. Andrews, Chief Executive Officer), (Total facility includes 240 beds in nursing home–type unit) **A**1 2 3 5 7 9 10 **F**3 8 10 11 13 15 18 20 22 24 28 29 30 31 34 35 36 37 39 40 43 44 45 50 53 54 55 57 59 60 61 62 63 64 68 70 72 74 75 76 77 78 79 81 83 84 85 86 87 90 93 96 97 107 108 109 110 111 114 115 116 117 118 119 120 121 123 124 125 126 128 130 131 132 135 143 146 147 148 **P**8 **S** LCMC Health, New Orleans, LA
Primary Contact: Susan E. Andrews, Chief Executive Officer
COO: Susan Pitoscia, MSN, Chief Operating Officer
CFO: Cynthia Polt, Chief Financial Officer
CIO: Jeff Lott, Director Information Services
CHR: Chad Courrege, Vice President Human Resources
CNO: Penny A. Menge, MSN, Chief Nursing Officer and Vice President Patient Care Services
Web address: www.touro.com
**Control:** Other not–for–profit (including NFP Corporation) **Service:** General Medical and Surgical

**Staffed Beds:** 539 **Admissions:** 11413 **Census:** 196 **Outpatient Visits:** 307959 **Births:** 3349 **Total Expense ($000):** 238537 **Payroll Expense ($000):** 92052 **Personnel:** 1596

✚ **TULANE MEDICAL CENTER (190176)**, 1415 Tulane Avenue, Zip 70112–2600; tel. 504/988–5263, (Includes TULANE–LAKESIDE HOSPITAL, 4700 South I. 10 Service Road West, Metairie, Zip 70001–1269; tel. 504/780–4200) **A**1 2 3 5 8 9 10 **F**3 13 15 17 18 19 20 21 22 23 24 25 26 27 28 29 30 31 34 40 41 45 46 47 48 49 50 52 55 58 60 61 64 65 68 70 74 77 78 79 81 82 85 87 88 90 91 92 93 97 99 100 101 102 104 107 108 110 111 114 115 118 119 120 121 122 123 124 126 129 130 131 132 136 138 139 141 142 146 147 **P**4 5 **S** HCA, Nashville, TN
Primary Contact: William Lunn, M.D., Chief Executive Officer
COO: Jennifer Eslinger, Chief Operating Officer
CFO: Todd LaCaze, Chief Financial Officer
CMO: John Pigott, M.D., Chief Medical Officer
CIO: Sue Rachuig, Director Information Services
CHR: Leah Grau, Director Human Resources
CNO: Danita S. Sullivan, R.N., Chief Nursing Officer
Web address: www.tuhc.com
**Control:** Corporation, Investor–owned, for–profit **Service:** General Medical and Surgical

**Staffed Beds:** 362 **Admissions:** 13368 **Census:** 185 **Outpatient Visits:** 341713 **Births:** 2162 **Total Expense ($000):** 353932 **Payroll Expense ($000):** 108224

*Many Facility Codes have changed. Please refer to the AHA Guide Code Chart.* © 2015 AHA Guide

**LA**

**UNIVERSITY CAMPUS**, 2000 Canal Street, Zip 70112–1396, Mailing Address: 2021 Perdido Street, Zip 70112–1396; tel. 504/588–3000, (Nonreporting) **A**3 **S** LCMC Health, New Orleans, LA
Primary Contact: Cindy Nuesslein, Interim Chief Executive Officer
Web address: www.umcno.org
**Control:** Other not–for–profit (including NFP Corporation) **Service:** General Medical and Surgical

Staffed Beds: 272

---

**NEW ROADS—Pointe Coupee Parish**

★ **POINTE COUPEE GENERAL HOSPITAL (191316)**, 2202 False River Drive, Zip 70760–2614; tel. 225/638–6331 **A**9 10 18 **F**29 40 45 77 81 87 93 107 111 125 133 **P**5
Primary Contact: Chad E. Olinde, CPA, Administrator and Chief Executive Officer
CFO: John Cazayoux, Chief Financial Officer
CMO: Carol Smothers, M.D., Chief of Staff
CIO: Anthony Sauro, Chief Information Officer
CHR: Lisa Patterson, Director Human Resources
CNO: Valerie S. Jarreau, RN, Chief Nursing Officer
Web address: www.pcgh.org
**Control:** Hospital district or authority, Government, nonfederal **Service:** General Medical and Surgical

Staffed Beds: 25 Admissions: 466 Census: 7 Outpatient Visits: 21266 Births: 0 Total Expense ($000): 16210 Payroll Expense ($000): 6957 Personnel: 160

---

**OAK GROVE—West Carroll Parish**

**WEST CARROLL MEMORIAL HOSPITAL (190081)**, 706 Ross Street, Zip 71263–9798; tel. 318/428–3237, (Nonreporting) **A**9 10
Primary Contact: R. Randall Morris, Administrator
**Control:** Other not–for–profit (including NFP Corporation) **Service:** General Medical and Surgical

Staffed Beds: 21

---

**OAKDALE—Allen Parish**

☐ **OAKDALE COMMUNITY HOSPITAL (190106)**, 130 North Hospital Drive, Zip 71463–3035, Mailing Address: P.O. Box 629, Zip 71463–0629; tel. 318/335–3700, (Nonreporting) **A**1 9 10
Primary Contact: Calvin Green, Chief Executive Officer
CMO: Tommy Davis, M.D., Chief of Staff
CIO: Melissa Welch, Director Health Information Management
CHR: Becky Johnson, Director Human Resources
CNO: Annette Wyble Hatsfelt, Chief Nursing Officer
Web address: www.oakdalecommunityhospital.com/
**Control:** Partnership, Investor–owned, for–profit **Service:** General Medical and Surgical

Staffed Beds: 27

---

**OLLA—Caldwell Parish**

**HARDTNER MEDICAL CENTER (191315)**, 1102 North Pine Road, Zip 71465–4804; tel. 318/495–3131 **A**9 10 18 **F**7 29 34 35 39 40 45 46 50 56 57 59 64 79 81 92 93 98 103 104 107 111 115 119 127 130 133 148 **P**4
Primary Contact: Paul G. Mathews, CPA, Administrator
CIO: Sarah Thompson, Director Health Information Management
CNO: Cherry B. Salter, Director of Nursing
Web address: www.hardtnermedical.com
**Control:** Hospital district or authority, Government, nonfederal **Service:** General Medical and Surgical

Staffed Beds: 35 Admissions: 1260 Census: 18 Outpatient Visits: 19092 Births: 0 Total Expense ($000): 25773 Payroll Expense ($000): 11024

---

**OPELOUSAS—St. Landry Parish**

☐ **OCEANS BEHAVIORAL HOSPITAL OF OPELOUSAS (194095)**, 1310 Heather Drive, Zip 70570–7714; tel. 337/948–8820, (Nonreporting) **A**1 9 10 **S** Oceans Healthcare, Lake Charles, LA
Primary Contact: Theresa Fontenot, Executive Director
Web address: www.obho.info/
**Control:** Corporation, Investor–owned, for–profit **Service:** Psychiatric

Staffed Beds: 20

---

⊞ **OPELOUSAS GENERAL HEALTH SYSTEM (190017)**, 539 East Prudhomme Street, Zip 70570–6499, Mailing Address: P.O. Box 1389, Zip 70571–1389; tel. 337/948–3011, (Includes OPELOUSAS GENERAL HEALTH SYSTEM–SOUTH CAMPUS, 3983 I–49 South Service Road, Zip 70570–8975; tel. 337/948–2100) **A**1 2 9 10 19 **F**3 13 15 18 20 22 28 29 31 34 37 40 44 45 48 49 50 53 57 60 65 68 70 73 76 77 78 79 80 81 85 87 89 90 91 93 96 97 98 102 103 104 105 107 108 110 111 112 114 115 116 117 119 121 126 129 130 131 132 146 147 148 **P**6
Primary Contact: Kenneth Cochran, President and Chief Executive Officer
COO: Bob Hardy, Chief Operating Officer
CFO: James B. Juneau, Chief Financial Officer
CMO: Richard Harmon, Chief of Staff
CIO: Jared Lormand, Vice President Information Technology
CHR: Suzanne F. Kidder, Director Human Resources
CNO: Karen Gremillion, R.N., Chief Nursing Officer
Web address: www.opelousasgeneral.com
**Control:** Hospital district or authority, Government, nonfederal **Service:** General Medical and Surgical

Staffed Beds: 224 Admissions: 7077 Census: 82 Outpatient Visits: 141170 Births: 1120 Total Expense ($000): 129270 Payroll Expense ($000): 48441 Personnel: 889

---

**ST. LANDRY EXTENDED CARE HOSPITAL (192034)**, 3983 1–49 South Service Road, 2nd Floor, Zip 70570; tel. 337/948–2251, (Nonreporting) **A**10 **S** LHC Group, Lafayette, LA
Primary Contact: Biff David, R.N., Administrator
Web address: www.lhcgroup.com
**Control:** Corporation, Investor–owned, for–profit **Service:** Long–Term Acute Care hospital

Staffed Beds: 41

---

**PINEVILLE—Rapides Parish**

⊞ **ALEXANDRIA VETERANS AFFAIRS HEALTH CARE SYSTEM**, 2495 Shreveport Highway, 71 N., Zip 71360–4044, Mailing Address: P.O. Box 69004, Alexandria, Zip 71306–9004; tel. 318/473–0010, (Nonreporting) **A**1 2 3 5 **S** Department of Veterans Affairs, Washington, DC
Primary Contact: Peter P. Henry, FACHE, Interim Director
CFO: Bianca A. Obey, Chief Financial Officer
CMO: Robert Bernard, M.D., Chief of Staff
CIO: Robin McBryde, Chief Information Officer
CHR: Alex Love, Acting Manager Human Resources
CNO: Amy Lesniewski, Associate Director Patient Care Services
Web address: www.alexandria.va.gov/
**Control:** Veterans Affairs, Government, federal **Service:** General Medical and Surgical

Staffed Beds: 143

---

☐ **CENTRAL LOUISIANA STATE HOSPITAL (194025)**, 242 West Shamrock Avenue, Zip 71360–6439, Mailing Address: P.O. Box 5031, Zip 71361–5031; tel. 318/484–6200, (Nonreporting) **A**1 10 **S** Louisiana State Hospitals, Baton Rouge, LA
Primary Contact: Ronald G. Williams, Administrator
COO: Paul Benoit, Associate Administrator
CFO: Tina Darbonne, Chief Financial Officer
CMO: L. Lee Tynes, Jr., M.D., Medical Director
CIO: William Haynes, Director Information Technology
CHR: Tom Crout, MS, Director Human Resources
Web address: www.dhh.louisiana.gov/index.cfm/directory/detail/217
**Control:** State–Government, nonfederal **Service:** Psychiatric

Staffed Beds: 128

---

**VETERANS AFFAIRS MEDICAL CENTER – ALEXANDRIA** See Alexandria Veterans Affairs Health Care System

---

**PLAQUEMINE—Iberville Parish**

**MMO REHABILITATION AND WELLNESS CENTER (193070)**, 59213 Riverwest Drive, Zip 70764–6552; tel. 225/687–8100, (Nonreporting) **A**10
Primary Contact: Bridget Suire, Acting Administrator
Web address: www.mmoinc.com
**Control:** Other not–for–profit (including NFP Corporation) **Service:** Rehabilitation

Staffed Beds: 8

---

| Hospital, Medicare Provider Number, Address, Telephone, Approval, Facility, and Physician Codes, Health Care System | | |
|---|---|---|
| ★ American Hospital Association (AHA) membership | ○ Healthcare Facilities Accreditation Program | ⇑ Center for Improvement in Healthcare Quality Accreditation |
| ☐ The Joint Commission accreditation | ◇ DNV Healthcare Inc. accreditation | △ Commission on Accreditation of Rehabilitation Facilities (CARF) accreditation |

*Many Facility Codes have changed. Please refer to the AHA Guide Code Chart.*

**LA**

## RACELAND—Lafourche Parish

⊠ **OCHSNER ST. ANNE GENERAL HOSPITAL (191324)**, 4608 Highway 1,
Zip 70394–2623; tel. 985/537–6841 **A**1 9 10 18 **F**3 4 5 13 15 17 18 29 30
34 35 40 45 57 59 63 65 70 72 74 75 76 79 81 85 86 87 88 89 98 99 100
101 102 103 104 107 108 110 111 114 118 119 127 130 133 135 146 147
**S** Ochsner Health System, New Orleans, LA
Primary Contact: Timothy J. Allen, FACHE, Chief Executive Officer
COO: Jonathan Carothers, Chief Operating Officer
CHR: Ann Ritchie, Director Human Resources
CNO: Allyson Dill Vedros, R.N., Chief Nursing Officer
Web address: www.ochsnerstanne.org
**Control:** Other not–for–profit (including NFP Corporation) **Service:** General
Medical and Surgical

> **Staffed Beds:** 35 **Admissions:** 1636 **Census:** 17 **Outpatient Visits:** 52985
> **Births:** 300 **Total Expense ($000):** 33205 **Payroll Expense ($000):** 13687
> **Personnel:** 326

## RAYNE—Acadia Parish

☐ **PHOENIX BEHAVIORAL HOSPITAL (194097)**, 2021 Crowley Rayne Highway,
Zip 70578–4027; tel. 337/788–0091, (Nonreporting) **A**1 9 10
Primary Contact: Joseph Tidwell, Administrator
**Control:** Corporation, Investor–owned, for–profit **Service:** Psychiatric

> **Staffed Beds:** 18

## RAYVILLE—Richland Parish

**RICHARDSON MEDICAL CENTER (190151)**, 254 Highway 3048 Christian
Drive, Zip 71269–0388, Mailing Address: P.O. Box 388, Zip 71269–0388;
tel. 318/728–4181, (Nonreporting) **A**9 10
Primary Contact: James W. Barrett, Jr., Chief Executive Officer
CFO: Mallory Gulley Wells, Chief Financial Officer
CMO: David Thompson, M.D., Chief of Staff
CHR: Rita Brown, Director Human Resources
Web address: www.richardsonmed.org
**Control:** Hospital district or authority, Government, nonfederal **Service:** General
Medical and Surgical

> **Staffed Beds:** 38

## RUSTON—Lincoln Parish

**ALLEGIANCE HEALTH CENTER OF RUSTON (194087)**, 1401 Ezell Street,
Zip 71270–7218; tel. 318/255–8085, (Nonreporting) **A**9 10 **S** Allegiance Health
Management, Shreveport, LA
Primary Contact: Donna K. Thompson, Chief Executive Officer
Web address: www.ahmgt.com
**Control:** Corporation, Investor–owned, for–profit **Service:** Psychiatric

> **Staffed Beds:** 14

**LIBERTY HEALTHCARE SYSTEMS** See Serenity Springs Specialty Hospital

⊠ **LIFECARE SPECIALTY HOSPITAL OF NORTH LOUISIANA (192022)**, 1401
Ezell Street, Zip 71270–7218; tel. 318/251–3126, (Nonreporting) **A**1 10
**S** LifeCare Management Services, Plano, TX
Primary Contact: Brent Martin, Administrator
Web address: www.lifecare–hospitals.com/hospital.php?id=19
**Control:** Corporation, Investor–owned, for–profit **Service:** Long–Term Acute Care
hospital

> **Staffed Beds:** 70

⊠ **NORTHERN LOUISIANA MEDICAL CENTER (190086)**, 401 East Vaughn
Avenue, Zip 71270–5950; tel. 318/254–2100, (Includes GREEN CLINIC
SURGICAL HOSPITAL, 1118 Farmerville Street, Zip 71270–5914;
tel. 318/232–7700; Chad Conner, Administrator), (Nonreporting) **A**1 9 10 19
**S** Community Health Systems, Inc., Franklin, TN
Primary Contact: Brady Dubois, Chief Executive Officer
CFO: Frank Malek, Chief Financial Officer
CMO: Derek McClusky, M.D., Chief of Staff
CIO: Heather Nolan, Director Information Services
CHR: Tonya Duggan, Director Human Resources
Web address: www.northernlouisianamedicalcenter.com
**Control:** Other not–for–profit (including NFP Corporation) **Service:** General
Medical and Surgical

> **Staffed Beds:** 104

**SERENITY SPRINGS SPECIALTY HOSPITAL (194074)**, 1495 Frazier Road,
Zip 71270–1632; tel. 318/202–3860, (Nonreporting) **A**9 10
Primary Contact: Adrian Williams, Chief Executive Officer
Web address: www.serenityhospital.com
**Control:** Corporation, Investor–owned, for–profit **Service:** Psychiatric

> **Staffed Beds:** 18

## SAINT FRANCISVILLE—West Feliciana Parish

⊠ **WEST FELICIANA PARISH HOSPITAL (191306)**, 5266 Commerce Street,
Zip 70775, Mailing Address: P.O. Box 368, Zip 70775–0368;
tel. 225/635–3811, (Nonreporting) **A**1 9 10 18
Primary Contact: Lee Chastant, M.D., Chief Executive Officer
CFO: Linda Harvey, Chief Financial Officer
CHR: Neta F. Leake, Administrative Assistant Human Resources
Web address: www.wfph.org
**Control:** Hospital district or authority, Government, nonfederal **Service:** General
Medical and Surgical

> **Staffed Beds:** 22

## SHREVEPORT—Caddo Parish

☐ **BRENTWOOD HOSPITAL (194020)**, 1006 Highland Avenue, Zip 71101–4103;
tel. 318/678–7500 **A**1 9 10 **F**3 4 5 50 54 56 98 99 100 101 102 103 104
105 **P**6 **S** Universal Health Services, Inc., King of Prussia, PA
Primary Contact: William Weaver, Chief Executive Officer
COO: Charles Lee, Director Clinical Operations
CFO: Kae Bell, Chief Financial Officer
CMO: Colonel Daniel Feeney, M.D., Medical Director
CHR: Talicia Johnson, Director Human Resources
CNO: Carey Ouzts, Director of Nursing
Web address: www.brentwoodbehavioral.com
**Control:** Corporation, Investor–owned, for–profit **Service:** Psychiatric

> **Staffed Beds:** 172 **Admissions:** 5600 **Census:** 142 **Outpatient Visits:** 2500
> **Births:** 0 **Total Expense ($000):** 23742 **Payroll Expense ($000):** 12470
> **Personnel:** 328

⊠ **CHRISTUS HEALTH SHREVEPORT–BOSSIER (190041)**, 1453 East Bert Koun
Industrial Loop, Zip 71105–6800; tel. 318/681–5000, (Includes CHRISTUS
HIGHLAND MEDICAL CENTER, 1453 East Bert Kouns Industrial Loop,
Zip 71105–6050; tel. 318/681–5000) **A**1 2 3 5 9 10 **F**3 11 12 13 15 17 18
20 22 24 26 29 30 31 32 34 35 40 43 45 46 47 48 49 50 53 54 55 56 57
58 59 61 64 70 72 73 74 75 77 78 79 81 82 84 85 86 87 90 93 96 97 102
107 108 110 111 114 115 119 120 121 123 124 126 130 131 132 134 135
146 147 148 **S** CHRISTUS Health, Irving, TX
Primary Contact: Isaac Palmer, Chief Executive Officer
COO: Billy Porter, Vice President Clinical Operations
CFO: Scott Merryman, Chief Financial Officer
CMO: Marisa Johnson, M.D., Vice President Medical Affairs
CIO: Mary Merryman, Regional Director Information Management
CHR: Wendy White, Vice President Human Resources
CNO: Charlotte Knoll, R.N., Chief Nursing Executive
Web address: www.christushealthsb.org
**Control:** Church–operated, Nongovernment, not–for profit **Service:** General
Medical and Surgical

> **Staffed Beds:** 196 **Admissions:** 6340 **Census:** 101 **Outpatient Visits:**
> 124082 **Births:** 1374 **Total Expense ($000):** 172428 **Payroll Expense**
> **($000):** 53366 **Personnel:** 816

⊠ **LIFECARE HOSPITALS OF SHREVEPORT (192011)**, 9320 Linwood Avenue,
Zip 71106–7003; tel. 318/688–8504, (Includes LIFECARE HOSPITALS OF
SHREVEPORT–WILLIS KNIGHTON, 8001 Youree Drive, Zip 71115–2302; Keith
Cox, Chief Executive Officer and Administrator; LIFECARE HOSPITALS OF SOUTH
SHREVEPORT–WILLIS KNIGHTON NORTH, 2550 Kings Highway, Zip 71103–3922;
Keith Cox, Chief Executive Officer and Administrator), (Nonreporting) **A**1 9 10
**S** LifeCare Management Services, Plano, TX
Primary Contact: Keith Cox, Administrator
Web address: www.lifecare–hospitals.com
**Control:** Corporation, Investor–owned, for–profit **Service:** Long–Term Acute Care
hospital

> **Staffed Beds:** 119

⊠ **OVERTON BROOKS VETERANS AFFAIRS MEDICAL CENTER**, 510 East
Stoner Avenue, Zip 71101–4295; tel. 318/221–8411, (Nonreporting) **A**1 2 3 5
**S** Department of Veterans Affairs, Washington, DC
Primary Contact: Toby T. Mathew, Medical Center Director
CFO: Kim Lane, Chief Fiscal Service
CIO: Janey Taylor, Chief Information and Technology
CHR: Michael L. Palmier, Chief Human Resources Management
Web address: www.shreveport.va.gov/
**Control:** Veterans Affairs, Government, federal **Service:** General Medical and
Surgical

> **Staffed Beds:** 100

**PHYSICIANS BEHAVIORAL HOSPITAL (194094)**, 2025 Desoto Street,
Zip 71103–4717; tel. 318/550–0520, (Nonreporting) **A**9 10
Primary Contact: Allison Cooper, Administrator
**Control:** Corporation, Investor–owned, for–profit **Service:** Psychiatric

> **Staffed Beds:** 12

*Many Facility Codes have changed. Please refer to the AHA Guide Code Chart.* © 2015 AHA Guide

☐ **PROMISE HOSPITAL OF LOUISIANA – SHREVEPORT CAMPUS (192010)**, 1800 Irving Place, Zip 71101–4608; tel. 318/425–4096, (Includes PROMISE HOSPITAL OF LOUISIANA – BOSSIER CITY CAMPUS, 2525 Viking Drive, Bossier City, Zip 71111–2103; tel. 318/841–2525), (Nonreporting) **A**1 9 10 **S** Promise Healthcare, Boca Raton, FL
Primary Contact: Rick Stockton, Chief Executive Officer
Web address: www.promise–shreveport.com
**Control:** Corporation, Investor–owned, for–profit **Service:** Long–Term Acute Care hospital

Staffed Beds: 146

**PROMISE SPECIALTY HOSPITAL OF SHREVEPORT** See Promise Hospital of Louisiana – Shreveport Campus

☐ **SHRINERS HOSPITALS FOR CHILDREN–SHREVEPORT (193301)**, 3100 Samford Avenue, Zip 71103–4289; tel. 318/222–5704 **A**1 3 5 9 10 **F**34 50 59 64 68 79 81 85 93 94 119 130 131 146 **S** Shriners Hospitals for Children, Tampa, FL
Primary Contact: Garry Kim Green, FACHE, Administrator
CFO: Randy Tabor, Director Fiscal Services
CMO: John A. Fox, Interim Chief of Staff
CIO: Kim Crockett, Director Management Information Systems
CHR: Rena Arbuthnot, Director Human Resources
CNO: Gail Rains, R.N., Director Patient Care Services
Web address: www.shrinershospitalsforchildren.org/Hospitals/Locations/Shreveport.aspx
**Control:** Other not–for–profit (including NFP Corporation) **Service:** Children's orthopedic

Staffed Beds: 45 Admissions: 343 Census: 3 Outpatient Visits: 14714
Births: 0 Personnel: 190

**SPECIALISTS HOSPITAL – SHREVEPORT (190278)**, 1500 Line Avenue, Zip 71101–4639; tel. 318/213–3800, (Nonreporting) **A**9 10
Primary Contact: Kandi Moore, Administrator
Web address: www.specialistshospitalshreveport.com/
**Control:** Corporation, Investor–owned, for–profit **Service:** General Medical and Surgical

Staffed Beds: 15

**UNIVERSITY HEALTH SHREVEPORT (190098)**, 1501 Kings Highway, Zip 71103–4228, Mailing Address: P.O. Box 33932, Zip 71130–3932; tel. 318/675–5000, (Includes CHILDREN'S HOSPITAL OF SHREVEPORT, 1501 Kings Highway, Mailing Address: PO Box 33932, Zip 71130–3932; tel. 318/675–5000), (Nonreporting) **A**2 3 5 9 10 **S** University Health System, Shreveport, LA
Primary Contact: Roderick L. Williams, M.P.H., President
COO: Betty Johnson, Associate Administrator
CFO: Harold White, Vice Chancellor
CMO: Kevin Sittig, M.D., Senior Associate Dean and Chief Medical Officer
CIO: Marcus Hobgood, Director Information Services
CHR: David Fuqua, Director Human Resources Management
Web address: www.lsuhscshreveport.edu
**Control:** State–Government, nonfederal **Service:** General Medical and Surgical

Staffed Beds: 459

★ △ **WILLIS–KNIGHTON MEDICAL CENTER (190111)**, 2600 Greenwood Road, Zip 71103–3908, Mailing Address: P.O. Box 32600, Zip 71130–2600; tel. 318/212–4600, (Includes WILLIS–KNIGHTON PIERREMONT HEALTH CENTER, 8001 Youree Drive, Zip 71115; tel. 318/212–3000; WILLIS–KNIGHTON SOUTH – THE CENTER FOR WOMEN'S HEALTH, 2510 Bert Kouns Industrial Loop, Zip 71118; tel. 318/212–5000; Keri Elrod, Administrator) **A**1 2 3 5 7 9 10 **F**3 4 5 7 8 12 17 20 22 24 28 29 30 31 35 40 45 46 52 53 54 57 59 62 63 64 65 68 70 72 74 75 76 77 78 81 84 87 88 89 90 91 93 97 98 107 111 114 115 116 117 119 120 121 122 126 128 130 132 138 139 143 **P**7 **S** Willis–Knighton Health System, Shreveport, LA
Primary Contact: James K. Elrod, FACHE, Chief Executive Officer
COO: Charles D. Daigle, Senior Vice President and Chief Operating Officer
CMO: Dan Moller, M.D., Chief Medical Officer
CHR: Jaf Fielder, Vice President and Administrator
CNO: Debbie D. Olds, R.N., Director of Nursing
Web address: www.wkhs.com
**Control:** Other not–for–profit (including NFP Corporation) **Service:** General Medical and Surgical

Staffed Beds: 720 Admissions: 39840 Census: 472 Outpatient Visits: 384193 Births: 2490 Personnel: 4373

**AMG SPECIALTY HOSPITAL–SLIDELL (192046)**, 1400 Lindberg Drive, Zip 70458–8056; tel. 985/326–0440, (Nonreporting) **A**10 **S** AMG Integrated Healthcare Management, Lafayette, LA
Primary Contact: Timothy Burke, Chief Executive Officer
COO: Gene Smith, Senior Vice President Operations
CFO: Jessica McGee, Chief Financial Officer
CMO: Marie Mahoney, M.D., Chief Medical Officer
CHR: Kim Hernandez, Director Human Resources
Web address: www.amgslidell.com/
**Control:** Partnership, Investor–owned, for–profit **Service:** Long–Term Acute Care hospital

Staffed Beds: 40

**NORTHSHORE REGIONAL MEDICAL CENTER** See Ochsner Medical Center – North Shore

✠ **OCHSNER MEDICAL CENTER – NORTH SHORE (190204)**, 100 Medical Center Drive, Zip 70461–5520; tel. 985/649–7070 **A**1 9 10 **F**3 4 13 15 17 18 20 22 24 26 29 30 31 34 35 38 40 41 43 44 45 46 49 50 51 57 59 61 64 68 70 72 74 75 76 77 78 79 81 84 85 86 87 88 89 90 91 93 95 96 97 98 102 107 108 110 111 114 116 117 118 119 129 130 132 135 146 147 148 **S** Ochsner Health System, New Orleans, LA
Primary Contact: Bradley R. Goodson, Chief Executive Officer
CFO: Forrest Whichard, Chief Financial Officer
CMO: James Newcomb, M.D., Vice President Medical
CHR: Terri Joseph–Taylor, Chief Human Resource Manager
CNO: Cheryl Woods, Chief Nursing Officer
Web address: www.ochsner.org/locations/northshore
**Control:** Other not–for–profit (including NFP Corporation) **Service:** General Medical and Surgical

Staffed Beds: 110 Admissions: 4396 Census: 60 Outpatient Visits: 69600
Births: 56 Total Expense ($000): 86405 Payroll Expense ($000): 34529
Personnel: 612

✠ **SLIDELL MEMORIAL HOSPITAL (190040)**, 1001 Gause Boulevard, Zip 70458–2987; tel. 985/280–2200 **A**1 2 3 5 9 10 **F**3 11 13 15 18 20 22 24 26 28 29 30 31 32 34 35 40 45 47 49 54 56 57 59 62 64 65 70 72 75 76 78 79 81 82 85 86 87 89 90 91 93 96 97 102 107 108 110 111 114 115 116 117 118 119 120 121 124 129 130 132 135 **P**6
Primary Contact: John William Davis, Chief Executive Officer
COO: Bruce Clement, Chief Operating Officer
CFO: Sandy Badinger, Chief Financial Officer
CMO: James Griffee, M.D., Chief Medical Officer
CHR: Jeanne M. Stachovsky, Director Human Resources
CNO: Lynn Strain, R.N., Chief Nursing Officer
Web address: www.slidellmemorial.org
**Control:** Hospital district or authority, Government, nonfederal **Service:** General Medical and Surgical

Staffed Beds: 168 Admissions: 7030 Census: 83 Outpatient Visits: 119071
Births: 1298 Total Expense ($000): 139711 Payroll Expense ($000): 59069 Personnel: 1086

☐ **SOUTHERN SURGICAL HOSPITAL (190270)**, 1700 Lindberg Drive, Zip 70458–8062; tel. 985/641–0600 **A**1 9 10 **F**3 8 12 29 45 57 59 60 70 79 81 82 107 111 114 119 130 131 132 **P**5
Primary Contact: Michael J. Pisciotta, Chief Executive Officer
CFO: Michael J. Maurin, Chief Financial Officer
CMO: J. Gosey, M.D., Medical Director
CIO: Buddy Graves, Chief Information Officer
CHR: Lorrie Alfred, Director Human Resources
Web address: www.sshla.com/
**Control:** Partnership, Investor–owned, for–profit **Service:** Surgical

Staffed Beds: 37 Admissions: 1047 Census: 12 Outpatient Visits: 5200
Births: 0 Total Expense ($000): 28000

**STERLING SURGICAL HOSPITAL (190256)**, 989 Robert Boulevard, Zip 70458–2009; tel. 985/690–8200, (Nonreporting) **A**9 10
Primary Contact: Christopher W. Daniel, Administrator
Web address: www.sterlingsurgical.net/
**Control:** Corporation, Investor–owned, for–profit **Service:** Other specialty

Staffed Beds: 10

| Hospital, Medicare Provider Number, Address, Telephone, Approval, Facility, and Physician Codes, Health Care System |
| --- |

★ American Hospital Association (AHA) membership    ○ Healthcare Facilities Accreditation Program    ⇑ Center for Improvement in Healthcare Quality Accreditation
☐ The Joint Commission accreditation    ◇ DNV Healthcare Inc. accreditation    △ Commission on Accreditation of Rehabilitation Facilities (CARF) accreditation

**LA**

## SPRINGHILL—Webster Parish

☐ **SPRINGHILL MEDICAL CENTER (190088)**, 2001 Doctors Drive, Zip 71075–4526, Mailing Address: P.O. Box 920, Zip 71075–0920; tel. 318/539–1000 **A**1 9 10 **F**3 15 18 26 29 30 32 34 35 40 45 47 48 49 50 51 54 57 59 64 65 66 68 70 75 79 81 85 86 87 93 98 103 107 108 110 111 114 119 127 129 130 131 133 135 146 148 **P**6 **S** Willis–Knighton Health System, Shreveport, LA
Primary Contact: Vince Sedminik, Chief Executive Officer
CFO: Layla Chase, Chief Financial Officer
CMO: Jerry W. Sessions, M.D., Chief Medical Staff
CIO: Brian Griffin, Director Information Services
CHR: Ashley Ortego, Director Human Resources and Marketing
CNO: Dana Jones, R.N., Chief Nursing Officer
Web address: www.smccare.com
**Control:** Other not–for–profit (including NFP Corporation) **Service:** General Medical and Surgical

**Staffed Beds: 58 Admissions: 1117 Census: 15 Births: 0**

## SULPHUR—Calcasieu Parish

⊠ **CORNERSTONE HOSPITAL OF SOUTHWEST LOUISIANA (192013)**, 703 Cypress Street, Zip 70663–5053; tel. 337/310–6000, (Nonreporting) **A**1 10 **S** Cornerstone Healthcare Group, Dallas, TX
Primary Contact: David Smith, President
CFO: Amy Bryant, Chief Financial Officer
Web address: www.chghospitals.com/sulphur/
**Control:** Partnership, Investor–owned, for–profit **Service:** Long–Term Acute Care hospital

**Staffed Beds: 30**

☐ **WEST CALCASIEU CAMERON HOSPITAL (190013)**, 701 Cypress Street, Zip 70663–5000, Mailing Address: P.O. Box 2509, Zip 70664–2509; tel. 337/527–7034, (Nonreporting) **A**1 9 10
Primary Contact: Janie Fruge, R.N., MSN, Chief Executive Officer
CFO: Jobie James, FACHE, Chief Financial Officer
CIO: Trey Rion, Chief Information Officer
CHR: Christi Kingsley, Director Human Resources
CNO: Brenda Quesnel, R.N., Vice President of Patient Care and Chief Nursing Officer
Web address: www.wcch.com
**Control:** Hospital district or authority, Government, nonfederal **Service:** General Medical and Surgical

**Staffed Beds: 79**

## TALLULAH—Madison Parish

**MADISON PARISH HOSPITAL (191314)**, 900 Johnson Street, Zip 71282–4537; tel. 318/574–2374, (Nonreporting) **A**9 10 18
Primary Contact: Ted Topolewski, Chief Executive Officer
CFO: W. Robert Laurents, CPA, Chief Financial Officer
CIO: Charles Whitaker, Director Information Technology
CHR: Chasity Whitaker, Administrative Assistant
Web address: www.madisonparishhospital.com
**Control:** Other not–for–profit (including NFP Corporation) **Service:** General Medical and Surgical

**Staffed Beds: 25**

## THIBODAUX—Lafourche Parish

⊠ △ **THIBODAUX REGIONAL MEDICAL CENTER (190004)**, 602 North Acadia Road, Zip 70301–4847, Mailing Address: P.O. Box 1118, Zip 70302–1118; tel. 985/447–5500 **A**1 2 7 9 10 **F**3 8 11 12 13 15 18 19 20 22 24 28 29 30 31 32 34 39 40 46 49 57 59 62 64 70 73 74 75 76 77 78 79 81 82 85 86 87 90 92 93 96 97 98 103 104 105 107 108 110 111 115 116 117 119 120 121 123 124 126 127 129 130 131 132 135 146 147 148
Primary Contact: Greg K. Stock, Chief Executive Officer
COO: Scott Flowers, Vice President Professional Services
CFO: Steve C. Gaubert, Chief Financial Officer
CMO: Allen Vander, M.D., Chief Medical Staff
CIO: Bernie Clement, Chief Information Officer
CHR: Eric Degravelle, Director Human Resources
Web address: www.thibodaux.com
**Control:** Hospital district or authority, Government, nonfederal **Service:** General Medical and Surgical

**Staffed Beds: 154 Admissions: 7729 Census: 83 Outpatient Visits: 162306 Births: 1099 Total Expense ($000): 150700 Payroll Expense ($000): 62026 Personnel: 903**

## VIDALIA—Concordia Parish

☐ **PROMISE HOSPITAL OF MISS LOU (192028)**, 209 Front Street, Zip 71373–2837; tel. 318/336–6500, (Nonreporting) **A**1 10 **S** Promise Healthcare, Boca Raton, FL
Primary Contact: Benny Costello, Chief Executive Officer
COO: Howard B. Koslow, President and Chief Executive Officer
CFO: James Hopwood, Chief Financial Officer
CMO: Randy Tillman, M.D., Chief Medical Staff
CIO: Robert Greene, Director Information Technology
CHR: Roxan Houghton, Director Human Resources
CNO: Regetta Woods, Chief Nursing Officer and Chief Clinical Officer
Web address: www.promise–misslou.com
**Control:** Corporation, Investor–owned, for–profit **Service:** Long–Term Acute Care hospital

**Staffed Beds: 40**

## VILLE PLATTE—Evangeline Parish

⊞ **MERCY REGIONAL MEDICAL CENTER (190167)**, 800 East Main Street, Zip 70586–4618; tel. 337/363–5684, (Includes ACADIAN MEDICAL CENTER, 3501 Highway 190, Eunice, Zip 70535–5129; tel. 337/580–7500; Scott M. Smith, Chief Executive Officer), (Nonreporting) **A**1 9 10 **S** LifePoint Health, Brentwood, TN
Primary Contact: Scott M. Smith, Chief Executive Officer
COO: John Whiteside, Chief Operating Officer
CFO: Micheal Fontenot, Chief Financial Officer
CMO: Zebediah Stearns, M.D., Chief of Staff
CIO: Courtney Bieber, Director Information Systems
CHR: Cody Ardoin, Director Human Resources
CNO: Sandy Morein, Chief Nursing Officer
Web address: www.mercyregionalmedicalcenter.com
**Control:** Corporation, Investor–owned, for–profit **Service:** General Medical and Surgical

**Staffed Beds: 109**

## VIVIAN—Caddo Parish

**NORTH CADDO MEDICAL CENTER (191304)**, 1000 South Spruce Street, Zip 71082–3232, Mailing Address: P.O. Box 792, Zip 71082–0792; tel. 318/375–3235, (Nonreporting) **A**3 5 9 10 18
Primary Contact: David C. Jones, Administrator
CFO: Carol Reisz, Chief Financial Officer
CMO: John H. Haynes, Jr., M.D., Chief of Medical Staff
CIO: Allyson Allums, Director Medical Records
CHR: Lanell Audirsch, Administrative Assistant
Web address: www.northcaddomedicalcenter.com
**Control:** Hospital district or authority, Government, nonfederal **Service:** General Medical and Surgical

**Staffed Beds: 27**

## WEST MONROE—Ouachita Parish

☐ **CORNERSTONE HOSPITAL–WEST MONROE (192031)**, 6198 Cypress Street, Zip 71291–9010; tel. 318/396–5600, (Nonreporting) **A**1 10 **S** Cornerstone Healthcare Group, Dallas, TX
Primary Contact: Chris Simpson, Chief Executive Officer
COO: Jay Quintana, Vice President Operations
CFO: Kurt Schultz, Chief Financial Officer
CMO: Khaled Shafici, M.D., President Medical Staff
CIO: Adam Davis, Chief Information Officer
CHR: Dan Perkins, Corporate Director Human Resources
Web address: www.chghospitals.com/chwm.html
**Control:** Corporation, Investor–owned, for–profit **Service:** Long–Term Acute Care hospital

**Staffed Beds: 40**

◇ **GLENWOOD REGIONAL MEDICAL CENTER (190160)**, 503 McMillan Road, Zip 71291–5327; tel. 318/329–4200 **A**2 9 10 21 **F**3 8 11 12 13 15 17 18 20 22 24 28 29 30 31 34 35 37 38 40 45 46 47 48 49 50 51 54 55 56 57 58 59 60 61 64 65 68 70 71 72 74 75 76 78 79 81 85 86 87 89 90 91 92 93 96 98 99 100 101 102 103 104 105 107 108 110 111 113 114 115 119 126 128 129 130 134 144 145 146 147 148 **P**8 **S** IASIS Healthcare, Franklin, TN
Primary Contact: Matthew S. Roberts, Chief Executive Officer
COO: Larry D. Walker, Chief Operating Officer
CFO: John DeSantis, Chief Financial Officer
CMO: Ron Hammett, M.D., Chief of Staff
CIO: Ronnie Maxwell, Director Information Systems
CHR: Jan Walker, Director Human Resources
CNO: Jeremy Tinnerello, R.N., Chief Nursing Officer
Web address: www.grmc.com
**Control:** Corporation, Investor–owned, for–profit **Service:** General Medical and Surgical

**Staffed Beds: 268 Admissions: 12272 Census: 175 Outpatient Visits: 58990 Births: 929 Total Expense ($000): 127206 Payroll Expense ($000): 47143 Personnel: 900**

*Many Facility Codes have changed. Please refer to the AHA Guide Code Chart.* © 2015 AHA Guide

◇ **LOUISIANA EXTENDED CARE HOSPITAL WEST MONROE (192055)**, 503 McMillan Road, 3rd Floor, Zip 71291–5327; tel. 318/329–4378, (Nonreporting) **A**10 **S** LHC Group, Lafayette, LA
Primary Contact: Cleta Munholland, Administrator
**Control:** Corporation, Investor–owned, for–profit **Service:** Long–Term Acute Care hospital

**Staffed Beds: 18**

◇ **OUACHITA COMMUNITY HOSPITAL (190261)**, 1275 Glenwood Drive, Zip 71291–5539; tel. 318/322–1339 **A**9 10 21 **F**3 12 34 35 37 45 56 57 65 75 79 81 82 85 132 135 **S** IASIS Healthcare, Franklin, TN
Primary Contact: Robert L. Colvin, Administrator
CFO: John DeSantis, Chief Financial Officer
CMO: H. Jerrel Fontenot, M.D., Medical Director
CNO: Brenda Wallace, R.N., Chief Nursing Officer
Web address: www.ouachitacommunityhospital.com
**Control:** Partnership, Investor–owned, for–profit **Service:** Surgical

**Staffed Beds: 10 Admissions: 94 Census: 1 Outpatient Visits: 2161 Births: 0 Personnel: 30**

### WINNFIELD—Winn Parish

□ **SPECIALTY HOSPITAL OF WINNFIELD (192052)**, 915 First Street, Zip 71483–2945; tel. 318/648–0212, (Nonreporting) **A**1 10
Primary Contact: Chuck Jurek, Interim Administrator and Chief Operating Officer
CFO: Chuck Jurek, Business Office Manager
CIO: Shamada Venzant, Manager Health Information
**Control:** Corporation, Investor–owned, for–profit **Service:** Long–Term Acute Care hospital

**Staffed Beds: 20**

**WINN PARISH MEDICAL CENTER (190090)**, 301 West Boundary Street, Zip 71483–3427, Mailing Address: P.O. Box 152, Zip 71483–0152; tel. 318/648–3000, (Nonreporting) **A**9 10
Primary Contact: Patricia Flowers, Chief Executive Officer
CFO: Suzette Fatula, Chief Financial Officer
CMO: Ricky Hendrix, M.D., Chief of Staff
CHR: Ashley S. Files, Director Human Resources and Public Relations and Marketing
CNO: Toby Wise, Chief Nursing Officer
Web address: www.winnparishmedical.com
**Control:** Partnership, Investor–owned, for–profit **Service:** General Medical and Surgical

**Staffed Beds: 60**

### WINNSBORO—Franklin Parish

★ **FRANKLIN MEDICAL CENTER (190140)**, 2106 Loop Road, Zip 71295–3344, Mailing Address: P.O. Box 1300, Zip 71295–1300; tel. 318/435–9411, (Nonreporting) **A**3 9 10
Primary Contact: Blake Kramer, Chief Executive Officer
CMO: Jay Busby, M.D., President Medical Staff
CIO: Judy Ogden, Director Information Technology
Web address: www.fmc–cares.com
**Control:** Hospital district or authority, Government, nonfederal **Service:** General Medical and Surgical

**Staffed Beds: 43**

### ZACHARY—East Baton Rouge Parish

✦ **LANE REGIONAL MEDICAL CENTER (190020)**, 6300 Main Street, Zip 70791–4037; tel. 225/658–4000, (Total facility includes 38 beds in nursing home–type unit) **A**1 9 10 **F**3 11 13 15 18 20 22 26 29 34 35 36 39 40 45 46 48 50 54 56 57 59 62 64 67 70 73 75 76 77 79 80 81 85 87 90 93 107 108 110 111 114 115 119 128 130 146 148 **P**6
Primary Contact: Randall M. Olson, Chief Executive Officer
CFO: Mark Anderson, Chief Financial Officer
CMO: Brad Smith, M.D., Chief Medical Staff
CIO: Scarlet Collier, Chief Information Officer
CHR: David Beck, Chief Operating Officer and Director Human Resources
CNO: Staci Sullivan, MSN, Chief Nursing Officer
Web address: www.lanermc.org
**Control:** Hospital district or authority, Government, nonfederal **Service:** General Medical and Surgical

**Staffed Beds: 179 Admissions: 4489 Census: 93 Outpatient Visits: 97086 Births: 564 Total Expense ($000): 77865 Payroll Expense ($000): 32722 Personnel: 684**

---

**Hospital, Medicare Provider Number, Address, Telephone, Approval, Facility, and Physician Codes, Health Care System**

| | |
|---|---|
| ★ American Hospital Association (AHA) membership | ○ Healthcare Facilities Accreditation Program |
| □ The Joint Commission accreditation | ◇ DNV Healthcare Inc. accreditation |
| ⇑ Center for Improvement in Healthcare Quality Accreditation | △ Commission on Accreditation of Rehabilitation Facilities (CARF) accreditation |

## MAINE

### AUGUSTA—Kennebec County

☒ **MAINE VETERANS AFFAIRS MEDICAL CENTER**, 1 VA Center, Zip 04330–6719; tel. 207/623–8411, (Nonreporting) **A**1 3 **S** Department of Veterans Affairs, Washington, DC
Primary Contact: Ryan S. Lilly, Director
CFO: Daniel Howard, Chief Financial Officer
CMO: Timothy J. Richardson, M.D., Chief of Staff
CIO: Richard McNaughton, Chief Information Management Service
CHR: Christine Miller, Chief Human Resources Management Services
Web address: www.maine.va.gov/
**Control:** Veterans Affairs, Government, federal **Service:** General Medical and Surgical

**Staffed Beds:** 181

☒ **MAINEGENERAL MEDICAL CENTER (200039)**, 35 Medical Center Parkway, Zip 04330; tel. 207/626–1000, (Includes MAINEGENERAL MEDICAL CENTER–AUGUSTA CAMPUS, 6 East Chestnut Street, Zip 04330–9988; tel. 207/626–1000; Chuck Hays, President and Chief Executive Officer) **A**1 2 10 19 **F**3 4 5 8 11 12 13 15 17 18 20 28 29 30 31 34 35 36 40 42 44 45 46 47 49 50 51 54 56 57 58 59 63 64 65 66 70 74 75 76 77 78 79 81 82 84 85 86 87 89 90 93 94 96 97 98 99 100 101 102 103 104 105 107 108 110 114 115 116 117 118 119 120 121 123 124 126 129 130 131 132 135 143 144 145 146 147 148 **P**6 8
Primary Contact: Chuck Hays, President and Chief Executive Officer
COO: Paul Stein, Chief Operating Officer
CFO: Terry Brann, Chief Financial Officer
CMO: Steve Diaz, M.D., Chief Medical Officer
CIO: Daniel Burgess, Chief Information Officer
CHR: Rebecca Lamey, Vice President Human Resources
CNO: Jen Riggs, Chief Nurse Officer
Web address: www.mainegeneral.org
**Control:** Other not–for–profit (including NFP Corporation) **Service:** General Medical and Surgical

**Staffed Beds:** 192 **Admissions:** 10335 **Census:** 154 **Outpatient Visits:** 1698219 **Births:** 967 **Total Expense ($000):** 412587 **Payroll Expense ($000):** 174632 **Personnel:** 3514

**MAINEGENERAL MEDICAL CENTER–AUGUSTA CAMPUS** See MaineGeneral Medical Center

☐ **RIVERVIEW PSYCHIATRIC CENTER (204007)**, 250 Arsenal Street, Zip 04330–5742; tel. 207/624–3900, (Nonreporting) **A**1 10
Primary Contact: Robert J. Harper, Superintendent
COO: David Lovejoy, Chief Operations Officer
CFO: Samantha Kavanaugh, Chief Financial Officer
CMO: Brendan Kirby, M.D., Medical Director
CHR: Aimee Rice, Human Resources Manager
CNO: Roland Pushard, Director of Nursing
Web address: www.state.me.us/dhhs/riverview
**Control:** State–Government, nonfederal **Service:** Psychiatric

**Staffed Beds:** 92

**VETERANS AFFAIRS MEDICAL CENTER** See Maine Veterans Affairs Medical Center

### BANGOR—Penobscot County

☐ **DOROTHEA DIX PSYCHIATRIC CENTER (204004)**, 656 State Street, Zip 04401–5609, Mailing Address: P.O. Box 926, Zip 04402–0926; tel. 207/941–4000, (Nonreporting) **A**1 10
Primary Contact: Sharon Sprague, Superintendent
CMO: Michelle Gardner, M.D., Clinical Director
CHR: Ruth Mullaney, Personnel Officer
CNO: Janet Babcock, Director of Nursing
Web address: www.maine.gov/dhhs/ddpc/index.shtml
**Control:** State–Government, nonfederal **Service:** Psychiatric

**Staffed Beds:** 60

☒ **EASTERN MAINE MEDICAL CENTER (200033)**, 489 State Street, Zip 04401–6674, Mailing Address: P.O. Box 404, Zip 04402–0404; tel. 207/973–7000, (Includes ROSS SKILLED NURSING FACILITY ) **A**1 2 3 5 9 10 13 **F**3 11 12 13 15 17 18 19 20 22 24 26 28 29 30 31 34 36 37 39 40 43 44 45 46 47 48 49 50 51 53 54 55 57 58 59 61 64 70 72 74 75 76 77 78 79 81 82 84 85 86 87 88 89 90 92 93 94 96 97 102 107 108 110 111 114 115 117 118 119 120 121 123 124 126 129 130 131 132 144 145 146 147 148 **P**6 **S** Eastern Maine Healthcare Systems, Brewer, ME
Primary Contact: Deborah Carey Johnson, R.N., President and Chief Executive Officer
CMO: James Raczek, M.D., Sr. Vice President of Operations and Chief Medical Officer
CIO: Catherine Bruno, FACHE, Chief Information Officer
CHR: Greg Howat, Vice President Human Resources
CNO: Jodi Galli, Chief Nursing Officer
Web address: www.emh.org
**Control:** Other not–for–profit (including NFP Corporation) **Service:** General Medical and Surgical

**Staffed Beds:** 361 **Admissions:** 19407 **Census:** 285 **Outpatient Visits:** 454502 **Births:** 1642 **Total Expense ($000):** 652245 **Payroll Expense ($000):** 271623 **Personnel:** 3544

☒ **ST. JOSEPH HOSPITAL (200001)**, 360 Broadway, Zip 04401–3979, Mailing Address: P.O. Box 403, Zip 04402–0403; tel. 207/262–1000, (Nonreporting) **A**1 9 10 **S** Covenant Health, Tewksbury, MA
Primary Contact: Mary Prybylo, President and Chief Executive Officer
CFO: Michael A. Hendrix, Jr., Chief Financial Officer
CMO: William Wood, M.D., Vice President Medical Affairs
CHR: Paige A. Hagerstrom, Director Human Resources
CNO: Dianne Swandal, R.N., Vice President Patient Care
Web address: www.sjhhealth.com
**Control:** Church–operated, Nongovernment, not–for profit **Service:** General Medical and Surgical

**Staffed Beds:** 84

☒ **THE ACADIA HOSPITAL (204006)**, 268 Stillwater Avenue, Zip 04401–3945, Mailing Address: P.O. Box 422, Zip 04402–0422; tel. 207/973–6100 **A**1 10 **F**5 29 30 50 57 66 68 75 77 82 87 98 99 100 101 103 104 105 130 132 **P**6 **S** Eastern Maine Healthcare Systems, Brewer, ME
Primary Contact: Daniel B. Coffey, President and Chief Executive Officer
CFO: Marie Suitter, Chief Financial Officer
CMO: Anthony Ng, M.D., Vice President and Chief Medical Officer
CIO: Jeanne Paradis, Director Information Services
CHR: Paul Bolin, Vice President Human Resources
CNO: Wayne Steller, Vice President Chief Nursing Officer
Web address: www.acadiahospital.org
**Control:** Other not–for–profit (including NFP Corporation) **Service:** Psychiatric

**Staffed Beds:** 68 **Admissions:** 1498 **Census:** 55 **Outpatient Visits:** 82610 **Births:** 0 **Total Expense ($000):** 48563 **Payroll Expense ($000):** 24990 **Personnel:** 457

### BAR HARBOR—Hancock County

★ **MOUNT DESERT ISLAND HOSPITAL (201304)**, 10 Wayman Lane, Zip 04609–1625, Mailing Address: P.O. Box 8, Zip 04609–0008; tel. 207/288–5081 **A**5 9 10 18 **F**3 5 6 10 11 13 15 28 29 31 34 35 36 39 40 50 54 56 57 59 64 65 70 74 75 76 77 78 79 81 82 84 85 87 91 92 93 97 99 100 101 104 107 108 111 114 119 125 127 130 131 132 133 135 145 146 147 **P**6 7
Primary Contact: Arthur J. Blank, President and Chief Executive Officer
CFO: Christina Harding, Vice President Finance
CMO: Stuart Davidson, President Medical Staff
CIO: Bruce Donlin, Director Information Services
CHR: Joanne Harris, Director Human Resources
CNO: Karen Mueller, R.N., Chief Nursing Officer
Web address: www.mdihospital.org
**Control:** Other not–for–profit (including NFP Corporation) **Service:** General Medical and Surgical

**Staffed Beds:** 25 **Admissions:** 979 **Census:** 8 **Outpatient Visits:** 188285 **Births:** 152 **Total Expense ($000):** 50393 **Payroll Expense ($000):** 23800 **Personnel:** 365

*Many Facility Codes have changed. Please refer to the AHA Guide Code Chart.*

© 2015 AHA Guide

## BELFAST—Waldo County

**WALDO COUNTY GENERAL HOSPITAL (201312)**, 118 Northport Avenue, Zip 04915–6072, Mailing Address: P.O. Box 287, Zip 04915–0287; tel. 207/338–2500 **A**9 10 18 **F**3 11 13 15 16 18 19 28 29 30 31 34 35 39 40 45 46 51 57 59 62 63 64 65 70 74 75 76 78 79 81 83 85 93 97 107 108 110 111 114 117 118 119 127 129 130 132 133 135 145 146 147 148 **P**8 **S** MaineHealth, Portland, ME
Primary Contact: Mark A. Biscone, Chief Executive Officer
COO: Dan Bennett, Director Operations
CFO: Linda Drinkwater, Chief Financial Officer
CMO: Kent Clark, M.D., Chief Medical Affairs and Quality
CIO: David Felton, Manager Information Systems
CHR: Karen Littlefield, Manager Human Resources
CNO: Heather Iorio Quesnel, Director of Nursing
Web address: www.wcgh.org
**Control:** Other not–for–profit (including NFP Corporation) **Service:** General Medical and Surgical

**Staffed Beds:** 25 **Admissions:** 1438 **Census:** 14 **Outpatient Visits:** 132532 **Births:** 156 **Total Expense ($000):** 74731 **Payroll Expense ($000):** 36775 **Personnel:** 624

## BIDDEFORD—York County

⊞ **SOUTHERN MAINE HEALTH CARE – BIDDEFORD MEDICAL CENTER (200019)**, One Medical Center Drvie, Zip 04005–9496, Mailing Address: P.O. Box 626, Zip 04005–0626; tel. 207/283–7000, (Includes SOUTHERN MAINE HEALTH CARE – BIDDEFORD MEDICAL CENTER, One Medical Center Drvie, Mailing Address: P.O. Box 626, Zip 04005–0626; tel. 207/283–7000; Edward J. McGeachey, President and Chief Executive Officer; SOUTHERN MAINE HEALTH CARE – SANFORD MEDICAL CENTER, 25 June Street, Sanford, Zip 04073–2645; tel. 207/324–4310; Edward J. McGeachey, President and Chief Executive Officer), (Total facility includes 112 beds in nursing home–type unit) **A**1 2 10 **F**2 3 5 6 10 11 12 13 15 18 20 26 28 29 30 34 35 36 38 40 44 45 46 47 48 50 51 53 54 58 59 64 65 66 67 70 74 75 76 77 79 81 82 84 85 87 89 93 97 98 100 102 105 107 108 110 111 114 115 118 119 128 129 130 131 132 135 144 146 147 148
Primary Contact: Edward J. McGeachey, President and Chief Executive Officer
COO: Patricia Aprile, Chief Operating Officer
CFO: Norman Belair, Senior Vice President and Chief Financial Officer
CMO: Michael Albaum, M.D., Senior Vice President and Chief Medical Officer
CIO: Ralph Johnson, Interim Chief Information Officer
CHR: Yvonne McAllister, Senior Director Human Resources
CNO: Patricia M. Camire, MS, Senior Vice President Clinical Services and Chief Nursing Officer
Web address: www.smhc.org
**Control:** Other not–for–profit (including NFP Corporation) **Service:** General Medical and Surgical

**Staffed Beds:** 254 **Admissions:** 7921 **Census:** 187 **Outpatient Visits:** 719759 **Births:** 645 **Total Expense ($000):** 252878 **Payroll Expense ($000):** 122791 **Personnel:** 1663

## BLUE HILL—Hancock County

★ **BLUE HILL MEMORIAL HOSPITAL (201300)**, 57 Water Street, Zip 04614–5231; tel. 207/374–3400 **A**9 10 18 **F**8 15 18 28 29 31 32 34 35 40 41 43 44 45 50 51 57 59 64 65 66 75 78 79 80 81 82 85 86 87 91 93 96 97 107 110 119 130 132 133 135 146 147 148 **S** Eastern Maine Healthcare Systems, Brewer, ME
Primary Contact: John Ronan, President and Chief Executive Officer
CFO: Wendy Jones, Interim Chief Financial Officer
CHR: David Wheaton, Director Human Resources
CNO: Kathy Lirakis, R.N., Chief Nursing Officer
Web address: www.bhmh.org
**Control:** Other not–for–profit (including NFP Corporation) **Service:** General Medical and Surgical

**Staffed Beds:** 23 **Admissions:** 430 **Census:** 4 **Outpatient Visits:** 176017 **Births:** 0 **Total Expense ($000):** 35140 **Payroll Expense ($000):** 16345 **Personnel:** 259

## BRIDGTON—Cumberland County

★ **BRIDGTON HOSPITAL (201310)**, 10 Hospital Drive, Zip 04009–1148; tel. 207/647–6000 **A**3 9 10 18 **F**3 7 8 11 13 15 18 29 30 31 34 35 40 43 44 45 50 57 59 64 65 67 68 75 76 77 78 79 80 81 85 87 90 91 93 94 96 97 107 108 110 111 114 119 128 130 131 132 133 135 143 144 146 148 **P**6 8
Primary Contact: R. David Frum, President
COO: John A. Ludwig, R.N., Vice President Operations
CFO: Philip Morissette, Chief Financial Officer
CMO: Alan Verrill, M.D., President Medical Staff
CHR: Kirk Miklavic, Director Human Resources
Web address: www.bridgtonhospital.org
**Control:** Other not–for–profit (including NFP Corporation) **Service:** General Medical and Surgical

**Staffed Beds:** 25 **Admissions:** 1012 **Census:** 13 **Outpatient Visits:** 96379 **Births:** 114 **Total Expense ($000):** 44561 **Payroll Expense ($000):** 18049 **Personnel:** 273

## BRUNSWICK—Cumberland County

⊞ **MID COAST HOSPITAL (200021)**, 123 Medical Center Drive, Zip 04011–2652; tel. 207/373–6000 **A**1 2 5 10 **F**3 5 11 12 13 15 18 20 28 29 30 31 32 34 35 36 40 41 44 45 46 47 48 49 51 53 54 57 58 59 61 64 66 68 70 74 75 76 77 78 79 81 82 84 85 86 87 89 92 93 97 98 103 105 107 108 110 111 115 118 119 129 130 131 132 134 135 144 146 147 148 **P**6
Primary Contact: Lois N. Skillings, R.N., MSN, President and Chief Executive Officer
COO: Philip A. Ortolani, Vice President Operations
CFO: Robert N. McCue, Vice President Finance
CMO: Scott Mills, M.D., Vice President Medical Staff Administration and Chief Medical Officer
CIO: Gale Stoy, Manager Information Systems
CHR: Coleen M. Farrell, Vice President Human Resources
CNO: Deborah MacLeod, MS, Vice President Nursing and Patient Care Services
Web address: www.midcoasthealth.com
**Control:** Other not–for–profit (including NFP Corporation) **Service:** General Medical and Surgical

**Staffed Beds:** 92 **Admissions:** 4518 **Census:** 53 **Outpatient Visits:** 187377 **Births:** 663 **Total Expense ($000):** 132769 **Payroll Expense ($000):** 62745 **Personnel:** 887

## CALAIS—Washington County

★ **CALAIS REGIONAL HOSPITAL (201305)**, 24 Hospital Lane, Zip 04619–1398; tel. 207/454–7521 **A**9 10 18 **F**3 11 13 15 28 29 31 32 34 35 36 40 42 45 46 50 57 59 62 64 65 68 70 75 76 77 79 81 85 89 90 93 97 107 108 110 111 114 119 127 128 129 130 132 133 146 147 148 **S** QHR, Brentwood, TN
Primary Contact: Bert Whitaker, Interim Chief Executive Officer
CFO: Nancy Glidden, Chief Financial Officer
CMO: David Feiner, M.D., Chief Staff
CIO: Dee Dee Travis, Director Community Relations
CHR: Kristi K. Saunders, Director and Compliance Officer
CNO: Cheryl Zwingman–Bagley, R.N., Chief Nursing Officer
Web address: www.calaishospital.com
**Control:** Other not–for–profit (including NFP Corporation) **Service:** General Medical and Surgical

**Staffed Beds:** 25 **Admissions:** 698 **Census:** 12 **Outpatient Visits:** 37618 **Births:** 67 **Total Expense ($000):** 32480 **Payroll Expense ($000):** 14624 **Personnel:** 240

## CARIBOU—Aroostook County

⊞ **CARY MEDICAL CENTER (200031)**, 163 Van Buren Road, Suite 1, Zip 04736–3567; tel. 207/498–3111, (Total facility includes 9 beds in nursing home–type unit) **A**1 9 10 **F**3 8 11 13 15 28 29 31 32 34 35 36 38 40 43 44 51 53 54 56 57 59 61 64 67 68 70 75 76 77 78 79 81 82 84 85 86 87 89 90 93 97 107 108 111 115 118 119 121 130 131 132 135 144 146 147 148 **S** QHR, Brentwood, TN
Primary Contact: Kris A. Doody, R.N., Chief Executive Officer
COO: Shawn Anderson, Chief Operating Officer
CFO: Galen Dickinson, Chief Financial Officer
CMO: Regen Gallagher, M.D., Chief Medical Officer
CIO: Dave Silsbee, Chief Information Officer
CHR: Paula A. Parent, R.N., Director Human Resources and Nursing Administration
Web address: www.carymedicalcenter.org
**Control:** City–Government, nonfederal **Service:** General Medical and Surgical

**Staffed Beds:** 49 **Admissions:** 1957 **Census:** 31 **Outpatient Visits:** 75222 **Births:** 214 **Total Expense ($000):** 50913 **Payroll Expense ($000):** 20176 **Personnel:** 434

---

**Hospital, Medicare Provider Number, Address, Telephone, Approval, Facility, and Physician Codes, Health Care System**

★ American Hospital Association (AHA) membership
☐ The Joint Commission accreditation
○ Healthcare Facilities Accreditation Program
◇ DNV Healthcare Inc. accreditation
⇑ Center for Improvement in Healthcare Quality Accreditation
△ Commission on Accreditation of Rehabilitation Facilities (CARF) accreditation

**ME**

### DAMARISCOTTA—Lincoln County

★ **LINCOLNHEALTH (201302)**, 35 Miles Street, Zip 04543–4047;
tel. 207/563–1234, (Includes LINCOLNHEALTH MILES CAMPUS, 35 Miles Street,
tel. 207/563–1234; James W. Donovan, President and Chief Executive Officer;
LINCOLNHEALTH ST. ANDREWS CAMPUS, 6 St. Andrews Lane, Boothbay Harbor,
Zip 04538–1732, Mailing Address: P.O. Box 417, Zip 04538–0417;
tel. 207/633–2121), (Total facility includes 54 beds in nursing home–type unit)
**A**9 10 **F**3 11 13 15 29 30 32 34 35 40 43 44 45 50 57 59 64 65 67 70 75
76 79 81 85 86 87 93 96 97 107 108 110 111 114 118 119 127 128 130
132 133 135 144 146 147 148 **P**6 **S** MaineHealth, Portland, ME
Primary Contact: James W. Donovan, President and Chief Executive Officer
COO: Cynthia Wade, RN, BSN, R.N., Executive Vice President and Chief Operating
Officer
CFO: Wayne Printy, Chief Financial Officer and Senior Vice President Finance
CMO: Mark Fourre, Senior Vice President and Chief Medical Officer
CIO: David Felton, Regional Chief Information Officer
CHR: Thomas R. Girard, Vice President Human Resources
CNO: Christine Anderson, Chief Nursing Officer and Vice President of Patient Care
Services
Web address: www.lchcare.org
**Control:** Other not–for–profit (including NFP Corporation) **Service:** General
Medical and Surgical

**Staffed Beds:** 79 **Admissions:** 1855 **Census:** 69 **Outpatient Visits:** 104009
**Births:** 138 **Total Expense ($000):** 71174 **Payroll Expense ($000):** 21176
**Personnel:** 492

### DOVER–FOXCROFT—Piscataquis County

★ **MAYO REGIONAL HOSPITAL (201309)**, 897 West Main Street,
Zip 04426–1099; tel. 207/564–8401 **A**9 10 18 **F**3 5 7 8 11 15 18 28 29
30 31 34 35 38 40 45 50 57 59 64 65 70 71 75 76 77 78 79 81 85 86 87
93 96 97 99 104 107 110 111 114 119 127 128 129 130 132 133 135 146
147 148
Primary Contact: Marie E. Vienneau, FACHE, President and Chief Executive Officer
CFO: Nancy Glidden, Chief Financial Officer and Vice President Finance
CMO: Challa Reddy, M.D., President Medical Staff
CHR: James R. Godley, Vice President of Human Resources
CNO: Denise Scuderi, Vice President Patient Care Services
Web address: www.mayohospital.com
**Control:** Hospital district or authority, Government, nonfederal **Service:** General
Medical and Surgical

**Staffed Beds:** 25 **Admissions:** 1160 **Census:** 11 **Outpatient Visits:** 122838
**Births:** 124 **Total Expense ($000):** 47577 **Payroll Expense ($000):** 25332
**Personnel:** 449

### ELLSWORTH—Hancock County

⊞ **MAINE COAST MEMORIAL HOSPITAL (200050)**, 50 Union Street,
Zip 04605–1599; tel. 207/664–5311, (Nonreporting) **A**1 9 10
Primary Contact: Charles D. Therrien, Chief Executive Officer
CFO: Chris Frauenhofer, Chief Financial Officer
CMO: Sheena Whittaker, M.D., President Medical Staff
CIO: Scott Burtchell, Director Information Systems
CHR: Rosemary C. Loring, Vice President Human Resources
CNO: Ardelle Bigos, R.N., Chief Nursing Officer and Vice President Patient Care
Services
Web address: www.mainehospital.org
**Control:** Other not–for–profit (including NFP Corporation) **Service:** General
Medical and Surgical

**Staffed Beds:** 48

### FARMINGTON—Franklin County

⊞ **FRANKLIN MEMORIAL HOSPITAL (200037)**, 111 Franklin Health Commons,
Zip 04938–6144; tel. 207/778–6031 **A**1 5 9 10 20 **F**3 5 7 8 11 13 15 28 29
30 31 32 34 35 36 40 41 45 46 50 51 54 56 59 61 64 65 70 75 76 77 78
79 81 82 83 84 85 86 87 89 93 97 99 104 107 108 110 111 115 118 119
129 130 131 132 133 135 146 147 148
Primary Contact: Rebecca L. Arsenault, R.N., MS, President and Chief Executive
Officer
COO: Gerald Cayer, Executive Vice President and Chief Operating Officer
CFO: Wayne Bennett, Chief Financial Officer
CMO: Michael Rowland, M.D., Vice President Medical Affairs
CIO: Ralph Johnson, Chief Information Officer
CHR: Joline Hart, Vice President Human Resources
Web address: www.fchn.org
**Control:** Other not–for–profit (including NFP Corporation) **Service:** General
Medical and Surgical

**Staffed Beds:** 48 **Admissions:** 2093 **Census:** 20 **Outpatient Visits:** 110884
**Births:** 311 **Total Expense ($000):** 77501 **Payroll Expense ($000):** 38914

### FORT FAIRFIELD—Aroostook County

**COMMUNITY GENERAL HEALTH CENTER** See The Aroostook Medical Center,
Presque Isle

### FORT KENT—Aroostook County

⊞ **NORTHERN MAINE MEDICAL CENTER (200052)**, 194 East Main Street,
Zip 04743–1497; tel. 207/834–3155, (Total facility includes 45 beds in nursing
home–type unit) **A**1 10 20 **F**13 15 28 29 31 34 40 45 54 57 59 62 64 67 68
70 75 76 77 78 79 81 82 86 87 89 98 99 100 101 102 103 104 107 108
111 115 119 127 128 130 131 132 133 135 146 147 **P**6
Primary Contact: Peter Sirois, Chief Executive Officer
CFO: Cindy Daigle, Chief Financial Officer
CMO: Michael Sullivan, M.D., Chief Medical Officer
CIO: Adam Landry, Coordinator Computer Systems
CHR: Robin Damboise, Director Human Resources
CNO: Alain Bois, R.N., Director of Nursing
Web address: www.nmmc.org
**Control:** Other not–for–profit (including NFP Corporation) **Service:** General
Medical and Surgical

**Staffed Beds:** 81 **Admissions:** 1188 **Census:** 58 **Outpatient Visits:** 53519
**Births:** 66 **Total Expense ($000):** 45105 **Payroll Expense ($000):** 24770
**Personnel:** 406

### GREENVILLE—Piscataquis County

★ **CHARLES A. DEAN MEMORIAL HOSPITAL (201301)**, 364 Pritham Avenue,
Zip 04441–1395, Mailing Address: P.O. Box 1129, Zip 04441–1129;
tel. 207/695–5200, (Nonreporting) **A**10 18 **S** Eastern Maine Healthcare Systems,
Brewer, ME
Primary Contact: Geno Murray, President and Chief Executive Officer
CFO: Edward Olivier, Chief Financial Officer
CMO: Darin Peck, M.D., Chief of Staff
Web address: www.cadean.org
**Control:** Other not–for–profit (including NFP Corporation) **Service:** General
Medical and Surgical

**Staffed Beds:** 36

### HOULTON—Aroostook County

★ **HOULTON REGIONAL HOSPITAL (201308)**, 20 Hartford Street,
Zip 04730–1891; tel. 207/532–9471 **A**9 10 18 **F**1 3 4 11 13 15 16 17 28 29
30 34 40 43 45 46 50 59 65 67 70 72 73 75 76 79 80 81 83 84 85 86 87
88 89 90 93 97 98 107 108 110 111 114 118 119 127 128 130 132 133
135 146 148
Primary Contact: Thomas J. Moakler, Chief Executive Officer
CHR: Vicky Moody, Director Human Resources
Web address: www.houlton.net/hrh
**Control:** Other not–for–profit (including NFP Corporation) **Service:** General
Medical and Surgical

**Staffed Beds:** 25 **Admissions:** 1206 **Census:** 16 **Outpatient Visits:** 100100
**Births:** 156 **Total Expense ($000):** 45354 **Payroll Expense ($000):** 20772
**Personnel:** 348

### LEWISTON—Androscoggin County

⊞ △ **CENTRAL MAINE MEDICAL CENTER (200024)**, 300 Main Street,
Zip 04240–7027; tel. 207/795–0111 **A**1 2 3 5 7 9 10 13 **F**3 11 12 13 15 18
19 20 22 24 26 28 29 30 31 32 34 35 36 40 41 43 44 45 46 47 48 49 50
51 52 53 55 56 57 58 59 61 64 65 66 67 68 70 71 73 74 75 76 77 78 79
81 82 84 85 86 87 89 90 91 92 93 97 100 101 102 104 107 108 110 114
115 118 119 120 121 123 124 129 130 131 132 135 143 146 147 148 **P**8
Primary Contact: Tina Legere, President
CFO: Philip Morissette, Chief Financial Officer
CMO: David Lauver, M.D., Chief Division Hospital Based Care
CIO: Denis Tanguay, Chief Information Officer
CHR: Kirk Miklavic, Director, Human Resources
CNO: Sharron Sieleman, R.N., VP, Nursing
Web address: www.cmmc.org
**Control:** Other not–for–profit (including NFP Corporation) **Service:** General
Medical and Surgical

**Staffed Beds:** 190 **Admissions:** 10222 **Census:** 114 **Outpatient Visits:**
740898 **Births:** 679 **Total Expense ($000):** 323835 **Payroll Expense
($000):** 137821 **Personnel:** 1825

*Many Facility Codes have changed. Please refer to the AHA Guide Code Chart.*
© 2015 AHA Guide

**ST. MARY'S REGIONAL MEDICAL CENTER (200034)**, 318 Sabattus Street, Zip 04240–5553, Mailing Address: P.O. Box 291, Zip 04243–0291; tel. 207/777–8100 **A**1 2 5 10 **F**3 4 5 7 12 13 15 17 18 20 22 28 29 30 31 34 35 36 37 38 39 40 44 45 49 50 54 56 57 59 61 64 65 66 68 70 74 75 77 78 79 80 81 82 84 85 86 87 89 93 97 98 99 100 101 102 103 104 105 107 108 110 111 114 115 116 117 118 119 127 129 130 131 132 134 135 143 144 146 147 148 **P**1 6 **S** Covenant Health, Tewksbury, MA
Primary Contact: Christopher Chekouras, President and Chief Executive Officer
COO: Susan Keiler, Chief Operating Officer
CFO: Carolyn Kasabian, Chief Financial Officer
CMO: Ira Shapiro, M.D., Chief Medical Officer
CIO: Rene Dumont, Vice President Strategic Growth
CHR: Nicole Morin–Scribner, Director Human Resources
CNO: Karen Clark, Vice President Patient Care Services
Web address: www.stmarysmaine.com
**Control:** Other not–for–profit (including NFP Corporation) **Service:** General Medical and Surgical

**Staffed Beds:** 171 **Admissions:** 5998 **Census:** 82 **Outpatient Visits:** 315042 **Births:** 604 **Total Expense ($000):** 149574 **Payroll Expense ($000):** 72673 **Personnel:** 1264

**LINCOLN—Penobscot County**

★ **PENOBSCOT VALLEY HOSPITAL (201303)**, 7 Transalpine Road, Zip 04457–4222, Mailing Address: P.O. Box 368, Zip 04457–0368; tel. 207/794–3321, (Nonreporting) **A**10 18 **S** QHR, Brentwood, TN
Primary Contact: Gary R. Poquette, FACHE, Chief Executive Officer
CFO: Ann Marie Rush, Chief Financial Officer
CHR: Sarah Loman, Director Human Resources
Web address: www.pvhme.org
**Control:** Other not–for–profit (including NFP Corporation) **Service:** General Medical and Surgical

**Staffed Beds:** 25

**MACHIAS—Washington County**

★ **DOWN EAST COMMUNITY HOSPITAL (201311)**, 11 Hospital Drive, Zip 04654–3325; tel. 207/255–3356, (Total facility includes 28 beds in nursing home–type unit) **A**9 10 18 **F**3 13 15 28 29 34 35 40 43 56 57 59 64 65 75 76 77 79 81 82 83 84 85 89 93 97 107 108 110 111 119 127 128 129 130 133 146 147
Primary Contact: Dennis Welsh, Chief Executive Officer
CFO: Lynnette Parr, Chief Financial Officer
CMO: Rodney Sparks, M.D., Chief Staff
CIO: Lynnette Parr, Chief Financial Officer
CHR: Ernestine O. Reisman, Vice President Human Resources
CNO: Charleen Ryan, Vice President Nursing Services
Web address: www.dech.org
**Control:** Other not–for–profit (including NFP Corporation) **Service:** General Medical and Surgical

**Staffed Beds:** 53 **Admissions:** 856 **Census:** 33 **Outpatient Visits:** 29629 **Births:** 132 **Total Expense ($000):** 37731 **Payroll Expense ($000):** 18457 **Personnel:** 272

**MARS HILL—Aroostook County**

**AROOSTOOK HEALTH CENTER** See The Aroostook Medical Center, Presque Isle

**MILLINOCKET—Penobscot County**

★ **MILLINOCKET REGIONAL HOSPITAL (201307)**, 200 Somerset Street, Zip 04462–1298; tel. 207/723–5161, (Nonreporting) **A**9 10 18
Primary Contact: Robert Peterson, Chief Executive Officer
CFO: Catherine LeMay, Vice President Finance
CMO: Daniel Herbert, M.D., Medical Administrative Officer
CHR: Lisa Arsenault, Vice President Human Resources and Compliance
CNO: Jason Fugleberg, R.N., Vice President Patient Services and Chief Nursing Officer
Web address: www.mrhme.org
**Control:** Other not–for–profit (including NFP Corporation) **Service:** General Medical and Surgical

**Staffed Beds:** 25

**NORWAY—Oxford County**

★ **STEPHENS MEMORIAL HOSPITAL (201315)**, 181 Main Street, Zip 04268–5664; tel. 207/743–5933 **A**5 9 10 18 **F**3 7 13 15 28 29 30 31 34 35 40 43 45 57 59 61 64 65 68 75 76 78 79 80 81 85 89 93 96 97 102 107 108 110 111 115 119 127 130 132 146 148 **S** MaineHealth, Portland, ME
Primary Contact: Timothy A. Churchill, President
CMO: James Eshleman, D.O., President Medical Staff
CHR: Roberta Metivier, Vice President Human Resources and Administrator, Western Main Nursing Home
Web address: www.wmhcc.com
**Control:** Other not–for–profit (including NFP Corporation) **Service:** General Medical and Surgical

**Staffed Beds:** 25 **Admissions:** 1309 **Census:** 12 **Outpatient Visits:** 101990 **Births:** 144 **Total Expense ($000):** 52980 **Payroll Expense ($000):** 24384 **Personnel:** 401

**PITTSFIELD—Somerset County**

**SEBASTICOOK VALLEY HEALTH (201313)**, 447 North Main Street, Zip 04967–3707; tel. 207/487–4000, (Nonreporting) **A**1 9 10 18 **S** Eastern Maine Healthcare Systems, Brewer, ME
Primary Contact: Terri Vieira, President and Chief Executive Officer
COO: Michael Peterson, Chief Operating Officer
CFO: Randal Clark, Vice President Finance
CMO: Robert Schlager, M.D., Chief Medical Officer
CIO: Michael Peterson, Chief Operating Officer
CHR: Tammy Hatch, Manager
Web address: www.sebasticookvalleyhealth.org
**Control:** Other not–for–profit (including NFP Corporation) **Service:** General Medical and Surgical

**Staffed Beds:** 25

**PORTLAND—Cumberland County**

**MAINE MEDICAL CENTER (200009)**, 22 Bramhall Street, Zip 04102–3175; tel. 207/662–0111, (Includes BARBARA BUSH CHILDREN'S HOSPITAL, 22 Bramhall Street, Zip 04102–3134; tel. 207/662–0111; Richard W. Petersen, President and Chief Executive Officer; MAINE MEDICAL CENTER, BRIGHTON CAMPUS, 335 Brighton Avenue, Zip 04102–9735, Mailing Address: P.O. Box 9735, Zip 04102–9735; tel. 207/879–8000; Richard W. Petersen, President and Chief Executive Officer) **A**1 2 3 5 8 10 **F**3 5 6 8 11 12 13 15 17 18 19 20 21 22 23 24 25 26 27 28 29 30 31 32 34 35 36 38 40 41 42 43 44 45 46 47 48 49 50 51 54 55 56 57 58 59 60 61 64 65 66 68 70 72 73 74 75 76 78 79 80 81 82 84 85 86 87 88 89 91 92 97 98 99 100 101 102 103 104 105 107 108 110 111 115 116 117 118 119 120 121 123 124 126 129 130 131 132 134 135 138 141 144 146 147 148 **P**6 8 **S** MaineHealth, Portland, ME
Primary Contact: Richard W. Petersen, President and Chief Executive Officer
COO: Jeff Sanders, Senior Vice President, Chief Operating Officer
CFO: Lou Inzana, Senior Vice President and Chief Financial Officer
CMO: Peter Bates, M.D., Vice President Medical Affairs and Chief Medical Officer
CIO: Andy Crowder, Senior Vice President, Chief Information Officer
CHR: Judith M. West, Senior Vice President Human Resources and Chief Human Resources Officer
CNO: Marjorie Wiggins, Senior Vice President, Chief Nursing Officer
Web address: www.mmc.org
**Control:** Other not–for–profit (including NFP Corporation) **Service:** General Medical and Surgical

**Staffed Beds:** 637 **Admissions:** 27049 **Census:** 396 **Outpatient Visits:** 534292 **Births:** 1981 **Total Expense ($000):** 912352 **Payroll Expense ($000):** 374289 **Personnel:** 5720

**MERCY HOSPITAL OF PORTLAND (200008)**, 144 State Street, Zip 04101–3795; tel. 207/879–3000 **A**1 2 3 10 **F**3 4 5 11 13 15 18 20 26 29 30 31 34 35 36 40 44 45 48 49 50 51 54 55 56 57 58 59 61 64 68 70 72 74 75 76 77 78 79 81 82 84 86 87 93 96 97 100 102 107 108 110 111 114 115 117 119 130 132 135 143 144 146 147 148 **P**6 **S** Eastern Maine Healthcare Systems, Brewer, ME
Primary Contact: Eileen F. Skinner, FACHE, President and Chief Executive Officer
COO: Robert Nutter, Chief Operating Officer, Vice President of Human Resources and Support Services
CFO: Michael Hachey, Senior Vice President and Chief Financial Officer
CMO: Scott Rusk, M.D., Vice President Medical Administration
CIO: Craig Dreher, Chief Information Officer
CHR: Elizabeth B. Christensen, Director Human Resources
CNO: Bette Neville, R.N., Vice President and Chief Nursing Officer
Web address: www.mercyhospital.org
**Control:** Other not–for–profit (including NFP Corporation) **Service:** General Medical and Surgical

**Staffed Beds:** 148 **Admissions:** 6824 **Census:** 63 **Outpatient Visits:** 458584 **Births:** 838 **Total Expense ($000):** 221075 **Payroll Expense ($000):** 99824 **Personnel:** 1225

---

**Hospital, Medicare Provider Number, Address, Telephone, Approval, Facility, and Physician Codes, Health Care System**

★ American Hospital Association (AHA) membership
□ The Joint Commission accreditation
○ Healthcare Facilities Accreditation Program
◇ DNV Healthcare Inc. accreditation
⇑ Center for Improvement in Healthcare Quality Accreditation
△ Commission on Accreditation of Rehabilitation Facilities (CARF) accreditation

⊠ **NEW ENGLAND REHABILITATION HOSPITAL OF PORTLAND (203025)**, 335 Brighton Avenue, Zip 04102–2363; tel. 207/775–4000 **A**1 3 10 **F**29 34 35 75 79 82 90 93 95 96 131 132 135 146 **S** HEALTHSOUTH Corporation, Birmingham, AL
Primary Contact: Jeanine Chesley, Chief Executive Officer
CFO: James Paladino, Controller
CMO: Thomas Morrione, Medical Director
CHR: Mary Cote, Director Human Resources
CNO: Elizabeth Glidden, Chief Nursing Officer
Web address: www.nerhp.org
**Control:** Partnership, Investor–owned, for–profit **Service:** Rehabilitation

**Staffed Beds: 90 Admissions: 1896 Census: 74 Outpatient Visits:** 12354 **Births:** 0 **Total Expense ($000):** 23543 **Payroll Expense ($000):** 14169 **Personnel:** 227

**PRESQUE ISLE—Aroostook County**

⊠ **THE AROOSTOOK MEDICAL CENTER (200018)**, 140 Academy Street, Zip 04769–3171, Mailing Address: P.O. Box 151, Zip 04769–0151; tel. 207/768–4000, (Includes AROOSTOOK HEALTH CENTER, 15 Highland Avenue, Mars Hill, Zip 04758; tel. 207/768–4900; ARTHUR R. GOULD MEMORIAL HOSPITAL, 140 Academy Street, Zip 04769, Mailing Address: P.O. Box 151, Zip 04769; tel. 207/768–4000; COMMUNITY GENERAL HEALTH CENTER, 3 Green Street, Fort Fairfield, Zip 04742; tel. 207/768–4700), (Total facility includes 64 beds in nursing home–type unit) **A**1 10 **F**3 7 8 12 13 15 18 20 28 29 30 31 32 34 35 36 38 39 40 43 45 46 50 51 52 53 54 56 57 59 60 61 64 65 67 68 69 70 74 75 76 77 78 79 80 81 82 85 86 87 89 90 91 92 93 96 97 99 104 107 108 110 114 115 118 119 121 123 128 129 130 131 132 134 135 143 146 147 148 **P**6 **S** Eastern Maine Healthcare Systems, Brewer, ME
Primary Contact: Sylvia Getman, President and Chief Executive Officer
COO: Jay Reynolds, M.D., Chief Medical Officer and Chief Clinical Officer
CFO: C. Bruce Sandstrom, Vice President and Chief Financial Officer
CMO: Jay Reynolds, M.D., Chief Medical Officer and Chief Clinical Officer
CIO: Kyle Johnson, Chief Information Officer
CHR: Joseph Siddiqui, Vice President Human Resources
CNO: Roland Eugene Joy, Jr., Vice President and Chief Nursing Officer
Web address: www.tamc.org
**Control:** Other not–for–profit (including NFP Corporation) **Service:** General Medical and Surgical

**Staffed Beds: 122 Admissions: 2073 Census: 82 Outpatient Visits:** 180243 **Births:** 185 **Total Expense ($000):** 109133 **Payroll Expense ($000):** 56928 **Personnel:** 895

**ROCKPORT—Knox County**

⊠ **PEN BAY MEDICAL CENTER (200063)**, 6 Glen Cove Drive, Zip 04856–4240; tel. 207/921–8000, (Total facility includes 84 beds in nursing home–type unit) **A**1 2 5 10 20 **F**3 4 5 6 13 15 17 18 28 29 30 31 32 34 35 40 43 45 51 58 59 61 64 65 67 70 74 75 76 77 78 79 81 82 83 85 86 87 89 93 97 98 100 107 110 111 114 118 119 128 129 130 131 132 134 135 144 146 147 148 **P**1 **S** MaineHealth, Portland, ME
Primary Contact: Mark A. Biscone, Chief Executive Officer
COO: Eric Waters, Vice President Operations
CFO: Maura Kelly, Vice President Fiscal Services
CMO: Dana L. Goldsmith, M.D., Vice President Medical Affairs
CIO: Brooks Betts, Director Information Systems and Chief Information Officer
CHR: Thomas R. Girard, Vice President Human Resources
Web address: www.penbayhealthcare.org
**Control:** Other not–for–profit (including NFP Corporation) **Service:** General Medical and Surgical

**Staffed Beds: 165 Admissions: 3617 Census: 128 Outpatient Visits:** 140132 **Births:** 300 **Total Expense ($000):** 126471 **Payroll Expense ($000):** 59436 **Personnel:** 879

**PENOBSCOT BAY MEDICAL CENTER** See Pen Bay Medical Center

**RUMFORD—Oxford County**

★ **RUMFORD HOSPITAL (201306)**, 420 Franklin Street, Zip 04276–2145; tel. 207/369–1000 **A**9 10 18 **F**3 8 11 13 15 18 28 29 30 31 34 35 40 43 44 45 50 57 59 64 65 67 68 70 75 76 77 78 79 81 85 87 89 90 91 93 94 96 97 107 110 114 119 127 128 130 132 133 135 143 146 148 **P**6 8
Primary Contact: R. David Frum, President
CNO: Becky Hall, R.N., Director Nursing
Web address: www.rumfordhospital.org
**Control:** Other not–for–profit (including NFP Corporation) **Service:** General Medical and Surgical

**Staffed Beds: 21 Admissions: 1097 Census: 14 Outpatient Visits:** 78336 **Births:** 91 **Total Expense ($000):** 35591 **Payroll Expense ($000):** 14120 **Personnel:** 241

**SKOWHEGAN—Somerset County**

★ **REDINGTON–FAIRVIEW GENERAL HOSPITAL (201314)**, 46 Fairview Avenue, Zip 04976, Mailing Address: P.O. Box 468, Zip 04976–0468; tel. 207/474–5121 **A**5 9 10 18 **F**3 7 11 13 15 18 28 29 30 31 34 35 40 45 47 50 53 57 59 65 68 70 74 75 76 77 78 79 81 82 85 92 93 97 107 108 110 114 115 118 119 130 131 132 134 135 146 147 **P**6
Primary Contact: Richard Willett, Chief Executive Officer
CFO: Elmer H. Doucette, Chief Financial Officer
CMO: Michael Lambke, M.D., Medical Director
CHR: Lisa G. Landry, Human Resources Director
CNO: Sherry L. Rogers, MS, Chief Nursing Officer
Web address: www.rfgh.net
**Control:** Other not–for–profit (including NFP Corporation) **Service:** General Medical and Surgical

**Staffed Beds: 25 Admissions: 1546 Census: 14 Outpatient Visits:** 78731 **Births:** 164 **Total Expense ($000):** 74982 **Payroll Expense ($000):** 37824 **Personnel:** 525

**WATERVILLE—Kennebec County**

★ ○ **INLAND HOSPITAL (200041)**, 200 Kennedy Memorial Drive, Zip 04901–4595; tel. 207/861–3000, (Nonreporting) **A**9 10 11 **S** Eastern Maine Healthcare Systems, Brewer, ME
Primary Contact: John Dalton, President and Chief Executive Officer
COO: Daniel Booth, Vice President Operations and Chief Human Resources Officer
CFO: Dean Bither, Chief Financial Officer
CMO: Michael Palumbo, D.O., Vice President Medical Affairs and Chief Education
CIO: Kevin Dieterich, Director Information Services
CHR: Daniel Booth, Vice President Operations
Web address: www.inlandhospital.org
**Control:** Other not–for–profit (including NFP Corporation) **Service:** General Medical and Surgical

**Staffed Beds: 46**

**WESTBROOK—Cumberland County**

⊠ **SPRING HARBOR HOSPITAL (204005)**, 123 Andover Road, Zip 04092–3850; tel. 207/761–2200, (Nonreporting) **A**1 10 **S** MaineHealth, Portland, ME
Primary Contact: Mary Jane Krebs, Chief Executive Officer
CFO: Michael Abbatiello, Chief Financial Officer
CMO: Girard Robinson, M.D., Senior Vice President Medical and Clinical Affairs
CIO: Susan Moulton, Interim Director Health Information Management
CHR: Timothy McNulty, Director Human Resources
Web address: www.springharbor.org
**Control:** Other not–for–profit (including NFP Corporation) **Service:** Psychiatric

**Staffed Beds: 88**

**YORK—York County**

★ **YORK HOSPITAL (200020)**, 15 Hospital Drive, Zip 03909–1099; tel. 207/363–4321, (Nonreporting) **A**2 9 10
Primary Contact: Jud Knox, President
COO: Stephen Pelletier, Leader Guest Services
CFO: Robin LaBonte, Leader Financial Care
CMO: Lawrence Petrovich, M.D., Chief Medical Officer
CIO: Robin LaBonte, Leader Financial Care
CHR: Olivia Chayer, Lead Human Resources
CNO: Gregory A. Bird, R.N., Interim Chief Nursing Officer
Web address: www.yorkhospital.com
**Control:** Other not–for–profit (including NFP Corporation) **Service:** General Medical and Surgical

**Staffed Beds: 79**

*Many Facility Codes have changed. Please refer to the AHA Guide Code Chart.* © 2015 AHA Guide

# MARYLAND

## ANNAPOLIS—Anne Arundel County

☒ **ANNE ARUNDEL MEDICAL CENTER (210023)**, 2001 Medical Parkway, Zip 21401–3019; tel. 443/481–1000, (Total facility includes 40 beds in nursing home–type unit) **A**1 2 3 5 9 10 **F**3 4 5 6 9 11 12 13 14 15 18 20 22 26 28 29 30 31 32 34 35 36 37 38 39 40 41 44 45 46 49 50 51 53 54 55 56 57 58 59 60 61 63 64 65 66 68 70 71 72 74 75 76 77 78 79 81 82 83 84 85 86 87 89 91 92 93 94 96 97 100 101 102 103 105 107 108 110 111 114 115 116 117 118 119 120 121 123 124 126 129 130 131 132 134 135 144 145 146 147 148 **P**1 6 7
Primary Contact: Victoria Bayless, President and Chief Executive Officer
COO: Sherry Perkins, Ph.D., Chief Operating Officer and Chief Nursing Officer
CFO: Robert Reilly, Vice President and Chief Financial Officer
CMO: Mitchell Schwartz, M.D., Chief Medical Officer
CIO: Barbara Baldwin, Chief Information Officer
CHR: Julie McGovern, Vice President Human Resources
Web address: www.aahs.org
**Control:** Other not–for–profit (including NFP Corporation) **Service:** General Medical and Surgical

**Staffed Beds:** 455 **Admissions:** 26395 **Census:** 290 **Outpatient Visits:** 482164 **Births:** 5379 **Total Expense ($000):** 489470 **Payroll Expense ($000):** 185160 **Personnel:** 3413

## BALTIMORE—Baltimore City County

☒ **BON SECOURS BALTIMORE HEALTH SYSTEM (210013)**, 2000 West Baltimore Street, Zip 21223–1558; tel. 410/362–3000, (Nonreporting) **A**1 9 10 **S** Bon Secours Health System, Inc., Marriottsville, MD
Primary Contact: Samuel Lee Ross, M.D., MS, Chief Executive Officer
CFO: Richard Jones, Chief Financial Officer
CMO: Sidney Mir, M.D., Vice President Medical Affairs and Chief Medical Officer
CIO: Sanjay Purushotham, Executive Director Information Systems
CNO: Lesia Douglas, R.N., Vice President Patient Care Services and Chief Nurse Executive
Web address: www.bonsecoursbaltimore.com
**Control:** Church–operated, Nongovernment, not–for profit **Service:** General Medical and Surgical

**Staffed Beds:** 93

**FRANKLIN SQUARE HOSPITAL CENTER** See MedStar Franklin Square Medical Center

**GOOD SAMARITAN HOSPITAL OF MARYLAND** See MedStar Good Samaritan Hospital

☒ **GREATER BALTIMORE MEDICAL CENTER (210044)**, 6701 North Charles Street, Zip 21204–6892; tel. 443/849–2000, (Total facility includes 25 beds in nursing home–type unit) **A**1 2 3 5 9 10 **F**3 8 11 12 13 18 20 22 26 29 30 31 34 35 40 41 44 45 46 47 48 49 50 51 55 56 57 58 59 60 61 63 66 68 70 72 74 75 76 77 78 79 81 82 83 84 85 86 87 89 92 96 102 107 108 114 115 119 120 121 123 124 126 128 129 130 132 135 136 142 145 146 147 148 **P**4
Primary Contact: John B. Chessare, M.D., M.P.H., FACHE, President and Chief Executive Officer
COO: Keith R. Poisson, Executive Vice President and Chief Operating Officer
CFO: Eric L. Melchior, Executive Vice President and Chief Financial Officer
CMO: John R. Saunders, M.D., Senior Vice President Medical Affairs and Chief Medical Officer
CHR: Deloris Simpson–Tuggle, Vice President Human Resources and Organizational Development and Chief Human Resources Officer
CNO: Jody Porter, R.N., Senior Vice President Patient Care Services and Chief Nursing Officer
Web address: www.gbmc.org
**Control:** Other not–for–profit (including NFP Corporation) **Service:** General Medical and Surgical

**Staffed Beds:** 310 **Admissions:** 16562 **Census:** 174 **Outpatient Visits:** 127583 **Births:** 3893 **Total Expense ($000):** 381697 **Payroll Expense ($000):** 183931 **Personnel:** 3289

**HARBOR HOSPITAL** See MedStar Harbor Hospital

☒ **JOHNS HOPKINS BAYVIEW MEDICAL CENTER (210029)**, 4940 Eastern Avenue, Zip 21224–2780; tel. 410/550–0100, (Total facility includes 67 beds in nursing home–type unit) **A**1 2 3 5 8 9 10 **F**2 3 4 5 6 8 9 11 12 13 15 16 17 18 20 22 26 28 29 30 31 32 34 35 36 38 40 41 43 44 45 46 47 48 49 50 51 54 55 56 57 58 59 60 61 64 65 66 68 70 71 72 74 75 76 77 78 79 80 81 82 84 85 86 87 89 90 91 92 93 94 97 98 99 100 101 102 103 104 105 107 110 111 114 115 116 117 118 119 120 126 129 130 131 132 134 135 141 143 146 147 148 **S** Johns Hopkins Health System, Baltimore, MD
Primary Contact: Richard G. Bennett, M.D., President
COO: Charlie Reuland, Sc.D., Executive Vice President and Chief Operating Officer
CFO: Carl H. Francioli, Vice President Finance
CIO: Sandy Reckert, Director Communications and Public Affairs
CHR: Craig R. Brodian, Vice President Human Resources
Web address: www.hopkinsbayview.org
**Control:** Other not–for–profit (including NFP Corporation) **Service:** General Medical and Surgical

**Staffed Beds:** 428 **Admissions:** 20323 **Census:** 338 **Outpatient Visits:** 440400 **Births:** 1303 **Total Expense ($000):** 426697 **Payroll Expense ($000):** 147430 **Personnel:** 3041

☒ △ **JOHNS HOPKINS HOSPITAL (210009)**, 733 North Broadway MRB 104, Zip 21205–1832; tel. 410/955–5000, (Includes JOHNS HOPKINS CHILDREN'S CENTER, 600 North Wolfe Street, Zip 21287–0005; tel. 410/955–5000) **A**1 2 3 5 7 8 9 10 **F**3 5 6 7 8 9 11 13 14 15 16 17 18 19 20 21 22 23 24 25 26 27 28 29 30 31 32 34 35 36 38 39 40 41 43 44 45 46 47 48 49 50 51 52 54 55 56 57 58 59 60 61 63 64 65 66 68 70 72 74 75 76 77 78 79 80 81 82 83 84 85 86 87 88 89 90 92 93 94 96 97 98 99 100 101 102 103 104 105 107 108 110 111 112 114 115 116 117 118 119 120 121 123 124 126 129 130 131 132 134 135 136 137 138 139 140 141 142 143 145 146 147 148 **S** Johns Hopkins Health System, Baltimore, MD
Primary Contact: Ronald R. Peterson, President
COO: Judy A. Reitz, Sc.D., Executive Vice President and Chief Operating Officer
CFO: Ronald J. Werthman, Senior Vice President Finance, Chief Financial Officer and Treasurer
CMO: Redonda G. Miller, M.D., Vice President Medical Affairs
CIO: Stephanie L. Reel, Senior Vice President Information Services
CHR: Bonnie Windsor, Senior Vice President Human Resources
CNO: Karen B. Haller, Ph.D., Vice President Nursing and Patient Care Services
Web address: www.hopkinsmedicine.org
**Control:** Other not–for–profit (including NFP Corporation) **Service:** General Medical and Surgical

**Staffed Beds:** 998 **Admissions:** 48203 **Census:** 835 **Outpatient Visits:** 595655 **Births:** 2054 **Total Expense ($000):** 1928280 **Payroll Expense ($000):** 557674 **Personnel:** 9781

☐ △ **KENNEDY KRIEGER INSTITUTE (213301)**, 707 North Broadway, Zip 21205–1890; tel. 443/923–9200, (Nonreporting) **A**1 3 5 7 9 10
Primary Contact: Gary W. Goldstein, M.D., President and Chief Executive Officer
COO: James M. Anders, Jr., Administrator and Chief Operating Officer
CFO: Michael J. Neuman, Vice President Finance
CMO: Michael V. Johnston, M.D., Chief Medical Officer and Senior Vice President Medical Programs
CIO: Kenneth Davis, Assistant Vice President Information Systems
CHR: Michael Loughran, Vice President Human Resources
Web address: www.kennedykrieger.org
**Control:** Other not–for–profit (including NFP Corporation) **Service:** Children's other specialty

**Staffed Beds:** 70

☐ △ **LEVINDALE HEBREW GERIATRIC CENTER AND HOSPITAL (210064)**, 2434 West Belvedere Avenue, Zip 21215–5267; tel. 410/601–2400, (Nonreporting) **A**1 7 9 10 **S** LifeBridge Health, Baltimore, MD
Primary Contact: Barry Eisenberg, FACHE, Chief Operating Officer and Executive Director
CMO: Susan M. Levy, M.D., Vice President Medical Affairs
CIO: Tressa Springmann, Vice President and Chief Information Officer
CHR: Cheryl T. Boyer, Vice President Human Resources
CNO: Candy Hamner, Vice President and Chief Nursing Officer
Web address: www.sinai–balt.com
**Control:** Other not–for–profit (including NFP Corporation) **Service:** Long–Term Acute Care hospital

**Staffed Beds:** 481

**MD**

✠ **MEDSTAR FRANKLIN SQUARE MEDICAL CENTER (210015)**, 9000 Franklin Square Drive, Zip 21237–3901; tel. 443/777–7000 **A**1 2 3 5 8 9 10 **F**3 5 11 12 13 14 15 18 20 22 26 28 29 30 31 32 34 35 36 37 38 39 40 41 44 45 46 47 48 49 50 51 55 56 57 58 59 60 61 64 65 66 68 70 71 72 74 75 76 77 78 79 81 82 85 86 87 89 92 93 94 97 98 99 100 101 102 103 104 107 108 109 110 111 115 118 119 126 129 130 131 132 134 135 145 146 147 148 **P**6 **S** MedStar Health, Columbia, MD
Primary Contact: Samuel E. Moskowitz, President
CFO: Robert P. Lally, Jr., Vice President Finance
CMO: Tony Sclama, M.D., Vice President Medical Affairs
CIO: Stephen Mannion, Assistant Vice President Information Systems Customer Service
CHR: Karen Robertson–Keck, Vice President Human Resources
CNO: Lawrence F. Strassner III, Ph.D., Senior Vice President Operations and Chief Nursing Officer
Web address: www.medstarfranklin.org
**Control:** Other not–for–profit (including NFP Corporation) **Service:** General Medical and Surgical

**Staffed Beds:** 401 **Admissions:** 21784 **Census:** 266 **Outpatient Visits:** 475985 **Births:** 2836 **Total Expense ($000):** 468648 **Payroll Expense ($000):** 210741 **Personnel:** 3031

✠ △ **MEDSTAR GOOD SAMARITAN HOSPITAL (210056)**, 5601 Loch Raven Boulevard, Zip 21239–2995; tel. 443/444–8000, (Total facility includes 30 beds in nursing home–type unit) **A**1 2 3 5 7 9 10 **F**3 6 9 11 14 15 17 18 20 26 28 29 30 31 34 35 36 37 38 40 43 44 45 50 51 53 55 56 57 58 59 60 61 64 65 66 68 70 74 75 77 78 79 80 81 82 84 85 86 87 90 91 93 96 97 99 100 101 102 103 104 107 108 110 111 114 118 119 121 124 128 129 130 131 132 135 146 148 **P**6 **S** MedStar Health, Columbia, MD
Primary Contact: Bradley Chambers, President and Chief Executive Officer
CFO: Deana Stout, Vice President Financial Services
Web address: www.goodsam–md.org
**Control:** Other not–for–profit (including NFP Corporation) **Service:** General Medical and Surgical

**Staffed Beds:** 287 **Admissions:** 12409 **Census:** 188 **Outpatient Visits:** 157885 **Births:** 0 **Total Expense ($000):** 309041 **Payroll Expense ($000):** 124719 **Personnel:** 1797

✠ **MEDSTAR HARBOR HOSPITAL (210034)**, 3001 South Hanover Street, Zip 21225–1290; tel. 410/350–3200 **A**1 2 3 5 9 10 **F**3 9 11 13 14 15 18 20 26 29 30 31 34 35 36 40 43 44 45 46 48 49 50 51 53 55 56 57 58 59 60 61 64 65 66 68 70 72 74 75 76 77 78 79 81 82 84 85 86 87 89 92 93 94 97 102 103 107 108 110 111 114 119 120 121 129 130 131 132 135 146 147 **P**6 **S** MedStar Health, Columbia, MD
Primary Contact: Dennis W. Pullin, FACHE, President
COO: Jill Donaldson, Vice President Operations
CFO: David R. Pitman, Vice President Finance
CMO: Allan Birenberg, Vice President Medical Affairs
CIO: Cynthia Tanebaum, Director Information Services
CHR: Karen Evelius, Director Human Resources
CNO: Lenora Addison, Vice President Patient Care and Nursing
Web address: www.harborhospital.org
**Control:** Other not–for–profit (including NFP Corporation) **Service:** General Medical and Surgical

**Staffed Beds:** 150 **Admissions:** 7591 **Census:** 83 **Outpatient Visits:** 179404 **Births:** 1379 **Total Expense ($000):** 189326 **Payroll Expense ($000):** 78466 **Personnel:** 1073

✠ △ **MEDSTAR UNION MEMORIAL HOSPITAL (210024)**, 201 East University Parkway, Zip 21218–2895; tel. 410/554–2000 **A**1 2 3 5 7 9 10 **F**3 5 8 9 11 14 15 17 18 20 22 24 26 28 29 30 31 34 35 37 38 39 40 41 43 44 45 46 47 48 49 50 51 52 53 54 55 56 59 60 61 63 64 65 66 69 74 75 77 78 79 80 81 82 84 85 86 87 89 90 91 92 93 94 96 97 98 100 101 102 103 104 105 107 108 110 111 114 115 118 119 120 121 123 129 130 131 132 135 142 146 148 **S** MedStar Health, Columbia, MD
Primary Contact: Bradley Chambers, President
COO: Neil MacDonald, Vice President Operations
CFO: Deana Stout, Vice President Finance
CMO: Stuart Bell, M.D., Vice President Medical Affairs
CIO: Janet Decker, Assistant Vice President
CHR: Linda Layman, Director Human Resources
CNO: Sharon A. Bottcher, R.N., Vice President Patient Care Services
Web address: www.medstarunionmemorial.org
**Control:** Other not–for–profit (including NFP Corporation) **Service:** General Medical and Surgical

**Staffed Beds:** 231 **Admissions:** 12811 **Census:** 155 **Outpatient Visits:** 150938 **Births:** 0 **Total Expense ($000):** 406993 **Payroll Expense ($000):** 158589 **Personnel:** 2183

✠ **MERCY MEDICAL CENTER (210008)**, 301 St. Paul Place, Zip 21202–2165; tel. 410/332–9000 **A**1 2 3 9 10 **F**3 4 8 11 13 14 15 17 18 20 29 30 31 34 35 36 37 39 40 41 44 45 46 47 48 49 50 51 55 57 58 59 64 65 66 68 70 72 74 75 76 77 78 79 81 82 85 86 87 89 92 93 94 100 102 107 108 110 111 114 115 116 117 118 119 120 121 123 124 126 128 129 130 131 132 135 141 142 143 144 145 146 147 148 **P**6
Primary Contact: Thomas R. Mullen, President and Chief Executive Officer
COO: Susan D. Finlayson, R.N., Senior Vice President of Operations
CFO: Justin Deibel, Senior Vice President and Chief Financial Officer
CMO: Scott A. Spier, M.D., Senior Vice President Medical Affairs
CIO: Kathleen Perry, Senior Vice President and Chief Information Officer
CHR: Tammy Janus, Senior Vice President Human Resources
CNO: Kim Bushnell, R.N., Chief Nursing Officer
Web address: www.mdmercy.com
**Control:** Church–operated, Nongovernment, not–for profit **Service:** General Medical and Surgical

**Staffed Beds:** 280 **Admissions:** 15946 **Census:** 184 **Outpatient Visits:** 286770 **Births:** 2963 **Total Expense ($000):** 444053 **Payroll Expense ($000):** 158737 **Personnel:** 3424

✠ △ **MT. WASHINGTON PEDIATRIC HOSPITAL (213300)**, 1708 West Rogers Avenue, Zip 21209–4545; tel. 410/578–8600, (Nonreporting) **A**1 3 5 7 9 10 **S** University of Maryland Medical System, Baltimore, MD
Primary Contact: Sheldon J. Stein, President and Chief Executive Officer
CFO: Mary Miller, Vice President Finance and Business Development
CMO: Richard Katz, M.D., Vice President Medical Affairs
CIO: Tim Brady, Director Information Systems
CHR: Thomas J. Ellis, Vice President Human Resources
Web address: www.mwph.org
**Control:** Other not–for–profit (including NFP Corporation) **Service:** Children's other specialty

**Staffed Beds:** 61

✠ **SAINT AGNES HOSPITAL (210011)**, 900 Caton Avenue, Zip 21229–5201; tel. 410/368–6000 **A**1 2 3 5 9 10 **F**3 8 11 12 13 14 15 17 18 20 22 26 28 29 30 31 32 34 35 40 41 44 46 49 50 53 54 55 56 57 58 59 60 61 64 65 68 70 72 74 75 76 77 78 79 81 82 84 85 86 87 88 89 92 93 96 97 100 107 108 110 111 114 115 117 118 119 120 121 123 124 126 129 130 131 132 134 135 144 146 147 148 **P**6 **S** Ascension Health, Saint Louis, MO
Primary Contact: Bonnie Phipps, President and Chief Executive Officer
CFO: Scott Furniss, Senior Vice President and Chief Financial Officer
CMO: Adrian Long, M.D., Executive Vice President and Chief Medical Officer
CIO: William Greskovich, Chief Information Officer
CHR: James Bobbitt, Vice President Human Resources
CNO: Yolanda Copeland, R.N., Senior Vice President and Chief Nursing Officer
Web address: www.stagnes.org
**Control:** Church–operated, Nongovernment, not–for profit **Service:** General Medical and Surgical

**Staffed Beds:** 367 **Admissions:** 17685 **Census:** 200 **Outpatient Visits:** 451232 **Births:** 1925 **Total Expense ($000):** 388965 **Payroll Expense ($000):** 193071 **Personnel:** 2479

☐ **SHEPPARD PRATT HEALTH SYSTEM (214000)**, 6501 North Charles Street, Zip 21204–6819, Mailing Address: P.O. Box 6815, Zip 21285–6815; tel. 410/938–3000 **A**1 3 5 9 10 **F**10 30 35 38 56 58 64 75 87 98 99 101 103 104 105 106 130 132 143 144 146
Primary Contact: Steven S. Sharfstein, M.D., President and Chief Executive Officer
COO: Bonnie B. Katz, Vice President, Business Development and Support Operations
CFO: Gerald Noll, Vice President and Chief Financial Officer
CMO: Robert Roca, M.D., Vice President Medical Affairs
CIO: Greg Merkle, Director Information Systems
CHR: Cathy Doughty, Vice President Human Resources
CNO: Ernestine Y. Cosby, Vice President Clinical Services and Chief Nursing Officer
Web address: www.sheppardpratt.org
**Control:** Other not–for–profit (including NFP Corporation) **Service:** Psychiatric

**Staffed Beds:** 333 **Admissions:** 9203 **Census:** 291 **Outpatient Visits:** 53490 **Births:** 0 **Total Expense ($000):** 193845 **Payroll Expense ($000):** 103045 **Personnel:** 2133

*Many Facility Codes have changed. Please refer to the AHA Guide Code Chart.*   © 2015 AHA Guide

✠ △ **SINAI HOSPITAL OF BALTIMORE (210012)**, 2401 West Belvedere Avenue, Zip 21215–5271; tel. 410/601–9000 **A**1 2 3 5 7 9 10 **F**3 5 6 8 9 11 12 13 15 17 18 19 20 22 24 26 28 29 30 31 32 34 35 36 38 39 40 41 43 44 45 46 47 48 49 50 55 56 57 58 59 60 61 64 65 66 68 70 72 73 74 75 76 77 78 79 80 81 82 83 84 85 86 87 88 89 90 92 93 94 95 96 97 98 99 100 101 102 103 104 105 107 108 110 111 113 114 115 116 117 118 119 120 121 123 124 126 129 130 131 132 134 135 143 146 147 **P**6
Primary Contact: Amy Perry, President
CFO: David Krajewski, Senior Vice President and Chief Financial Officer
CMO: Daniel C. Silverman, M.D., Vice President and Chief Medical Officer
CIO: Karen Barker, Vice President and Chief Information Officer
CHR: Cheryl T. Boyer, Vice President Human Resources
CNO: Diane Johnson, R.N., Vice President Patient Care Services and Chief Nursing Officer
Web address: www.lifebridgehealth.org
**Control:** Other not–for–profit (including NFP Corporation) **Service:** General Medical and Surgical

**Staffed Beds:** 471 **Admissions:** 24549 **Census:** 334 **Outpatient Visits:** 197375 **Births:** 2151 **Total Expense ($000):** 675091 **Payroll Expense ($000):** 295439 **Personnel:** 3957

☐ **SPRING GROVE HOSPITAL CENTER (214018)**, 55 Wade Avenue, Zip 21228–4663; tel. 410/402–6000, (Nonreporting) **A**1 3 5 9 10
Primary Contact: David S. Helsel, M.D., Chief Executive Officer
CFO: Edward Swartz, Chief Financial Officer
CMO: Kelly Phillips, M.D., Clinical Director and Chief Staff
Web address: www.springgrove.com
**Control:** State–Government, nonfederal **Service:** Psychiatric

**Staffed Beds:** 425

**UNION MEMORIAL HOSPITAL** See MedStar Union Memorial Hospital

✠ **UNIVERSITY OF MARYLAND MEDICAL CENTER (210002)**, 22 South Greene Street, Zip 21201–1595; tel. 410/328–8667, (Includes UNIVERSITY OF MARYLAND HOSPITAL FOR CHILDREN, 22 South Greene Street, Zip 21201–1544; tel. 800/492–5538) **A**1 2 3 5 8 9 10 **F**3 5 6 7 9 11 12 13 14 15 17 18 19 20 21 22 23 24 25 26 27 28 29 30 31 32 34 35 36 38 39 40 41 43 44 45 46 47 48 49 50 51 52 54 55 56 57 58 59 60 61 64 65 66 68 70 71 72 73 74 75 76 77 78 79 80 81 82 84 85 86 87 88 89 92 93 94 97 98 99 100 101 102 103 104 105 106 107 108 109 110 111 114 115 116 117 118 119 120 121 123 124 126 129 130 131 132 134 135 136 137 138 139 140 141 142 143 144 145 146 147 148 **P**6 **S** University of Maryland Medical System, Baltimore, MD
Primary Contact: Jeffrey A. Rivest, FACHE, President and Chief Executive Officer
CFO: Keith D. Persinger, Senior Vice President Finance and Chief Financial Officer
CMO: Jonathan Gottlieb, M.D., Senior Vice President and Chief Medical Officer
CIO: Jon P. Burns, Chief Information Officer
CHR: R. Keith Allen, Senior Vice President Human Resources
CNO: Lisa Rowen, R.N., Senior Vice President and Chief Nursing Officer
Web address: www.umm.edu
**Control:** Other not–for–profit (including NFP Corporation) **Service:** General Medical and Surgical

**Staffed Beds:** 725 **Admissions:** 32464 **Census:** 613 **Outpatient Visits:** 272094 **Births:** 1726 **Total Expense ($000):** 1293058 **Payroll Expense ($000):** 518792 **Personnel:** 10494

✠ **UNIVERSITY OF MARYLAND MEDICAL CENTER MIDTOWN CAMPUS (210038)**, 827 Linden Avenue, Zip 21201–4606; tel. 410/225–8000 **A**1 3 5 9 10 **F**1 5 11 15 18 20 29 30 31 34 35 40 44 45 49 50 56 57 59 60 61 64 65 66 68 70 74 75 77 78 79 81 82 84 85 87 91 93 94 96 97 98 100 101 102 103 104 106 107 108 111 114 115 118 119 129 143 148 **S** University of Maryland Medical System, Baltimore, MD
Primary Contact: John W. Ashworth, Interim President and Chief Executive Officer
COO: Donald Ray, Vice President Operations
CFO: Craig Fleischmann, Vice President Finance
CMO: W. Eugene Egerton, M.D., Chief Medical Officer
CIO: Jon P. Burns, Senior Vice President and Chief Information Officer
CHR: Paula Henderson, Vice President Human Resources
CNO: Lisa Rowen, R.N., Chief Nursing Officer
Web address: www.ummidtown.org/
**Control:** Other not–for–profit (including NFP Corporation) **Service:** General Medical and Surgical

**Staffed Beds:** 220 **Admissions:** 6178 **Census:** 128 **Outpatient Visits:** 123870 **Births:** 0 **Total Expense ($000):** 178869 **Payroll Expense ($000):** 72441 **Personnel:** 1402

✠ △ **UNIVERSITY OF MARYLAND REHABILITATION & ORTHOPAEDIC INSTITUTE (210058)**, 2200 Kernan Drive, Zip 21207–6697; tel. 410/448–2500 **A**1 3 5 7 9 10 **F**1 8 29 34 35 36 39 68 70 74 79 81 82 90 91 93 94 95 96 107 115 120 130 131 132 148 **S** University of Maryland Medical System, Baltimore, MD
Primary Contact: Cynthia Kelleher, M.P.H., President and Chief Executive Officer
CFO: W. Walter Augustin, III, CPA, Vice President Financial Services and Chief Financial Officer
CMO: John P. Straumanis, M.D., Vice President Medical Affairs and Chief Medical Officer
CIO: Linda Hines, Vice President Information Technology and Information Systems
CHR: Paula Henderson, Vice President Human Resources
CNO: Cheryl D. Lee, R.N., Vice President of Patient Care Services and Chief Nursing Officer
Web address: www.umrehabortho.org
**Control:** Other not–for–profit (including NFP Corporation) **Service:** Rehabilitation

**Staffed Beds:** 144 **Admissions:** 3602 **Census:** 115 **Outpatient Visits:** 27569 **Births:** 0 **Total Expense ($000):** 102736 **Payroll Expense ($000):** 42275 **Personnel:** 613

✠ △ **VETERANS AFFAIRS MARYLAND HEALTH CARE SYSTEM–BALTIMORE DIVISION**, 10 North Greene Street, Zip 21201–1524; tel. 410/605–7001, (Includes VETERANS AFFAIRS MARYLAND HEALTH CARE SYSTEM–PERRY POINT DIVISION, Circle Drive, Perry Point, Zip 21902; tel. 410/642–2411; Dennis H. Smith, Director), (Nonreporting) **A**1 2 3 5 7 8 9 **S** Department of Veterans Affairs, Washington, DC
Primary Contact: Adam M. Robinson, Acting Director
CFO: Major Tom Scheffler, Chief Fiscal Officer
CMO: Dorothy Snow, M.D., Chief of Staff
CIO: Sharon Zielinski, Chief Information Resource Officer
CHR: Jeff Craig, Chief Human Resource Management
Web address: www.maryland.va.gov/
**Control:** Veterans Affairs, Government, federal **Service:** General Medical and Surgical

**Staffed Beds:** 727

**BEL AIR—Harford County**

✠ **UNIVERSITY OF MARYLAND UPPER CHESAPEAKE MEDICAL CENTER (210049)**, 500 Upper Chesapeake Drive, Zip 21014–4324; tel. 443/643–1000, (Data for 182 days) **A**1 2 3 9 10 **F**3 11 15 18 20 22 26 28 29 30 31 34 35 36 38 40 41 42 45 46 49 50 51 54 57 59 60 64 65 68 70 71 74 75 76 77 78 79 81 82 84 85 86 87 89 92 93 96 107 108 110 111 114 115 118 119 120 121 124 130 131 132 143 146 147 **S** University of Maryland Medical System, Baltimore, MD
Primary Contact: Lyle Ernest Sheldon, FACHE, President and Chief Executive Officer
CFO: Joseph E. Hoffman, III, Executive Vice President and Chief Financial Officer
CMO: Peggy Vaughan, M.D., Senior Vice President Medical Affairs
CIO: Rick Casteel, Vice President Management Information Systems and Chief Information Officer
CHR: Toni M. Shivery, Vice President Human Resources
Web address: www.uchs.org
**Control:** Other not–for–profit (including NFP Corporation) **Service:** General Medical and Surgical

**Staffed Beds:** 162 **Admissions:** 5940 **Census:** 132 **Outpatient Visits:** 96810 **Births:** 606 **Total Expense ($000):** 120872 **Payroll Expense ($000):** 44480 **Personnel:** 1468

**BERLIN—Worcester County**

✠ **ATLANTIC GENERAL HOSPITAL (210061)**, 9733 Healthway Drive, Zip 21811–1155; tel. 410/641–1100, (Nonreporting) **A**1 9 10
Primary Contact: Michael A. Franklin, FACHE, President and Chief Executive Officer
COO: Kim Justice, Vice President Planning and Operations
CFO: Cheryl Nottingham, Chief Financial Officer
CMO: Stephen F. Waters, M.D., Medical Director
CIO: Andrew Fowler, Vice President Information Services
CHR: Jim Brannon, Vice President Human Resources
CNO: Colleen Wareing, Vice President Patient Care Services
Web address: www.atlanticgeneral.org
**Control:** Other not–for–profit (including NFP Corporation) **Service:** General Medical and Surgical

**Staffed Beds:** 58

MD

---

**Hospital, Medicare Provider Number, Address, Telephone, Approval, Facility, and Physician Codes, Health Care System**

★ American Hospital Association (AHA) membership
☐ The Joint Commission accreditation
○ Healthcare Facilities Accreditation Program
◇ DNV Healthcare Inc. accreditation
⇧ Center for Improvement in Healthcare Quality Accreditation
△ Commission on Accreditation of Rehabilitation Facilities (CARF) accreditation

**MD**

## BETHESDA—Montgomery County

✠ **NATIONAL INSTITUTES OF HEALTH CLINICAL CENTER**, (Biomedical Research), 9000 Rockville Pike, Building 10, Room 6–2551, Zip 20892–1504; tel. 301/496–4000, (Includes CHILDREN'S INN AT NIH, 7 West Drive, Zip 20814–1509; tel. 301/496–5672) **A**1 3 5 8 **F**3 4 5 14 20 22 26 30 31 36 39 45 53 55 58 59 60 61 64 65 68 70 74 75 77 78 79 81 82 84 85 86 87 89 91 92 93 94 95 96 98 99 100 101 104 105 107 108 111 112 114 115 116 117 118 119 120 121 124 126 129 130 132 135 136 141 142 145 146 148 **S** U. S. Indian Health Service, Rockville, MD
Primary Contact: John I. Gallin, M.D., Director
COO: Maureen E. Gormley, R.N., Chief Operating Officer
CFO: Maria Joyce, Chief Financial Officer
CMO: David K. Henderson, M.D., Deputy Director Clinical Care
CIO: Jon W. McKeeby, Chief Information Officer
CHR: Bonnie Tuma, Human Resources Team Lead
CNO: Clare Hastings, R.N., Chief Nurse Officer
Web address: www.clinicalcenter.nih.gov
**Control:** Public Health Service, Government, federal **Service:** Other specialty

**Staffed Beds:** 146 **Admissions:** 5615 **Census:** 132 **Outpatient Visits:** 99410
**Births:** 0 **Total Expense ($000):** 407339 **Payroll Expense ($000):** 170628
**Personnel:** 1939

**NATIONAL NAVAL MEDICAL CENTER** See Walter Reed National Military Medical Center

✠ **SUBURBAN HOSPITAL (210022)**, 8600 Old Georgetown Road, Zip 20814–1497; tel. 301/896–3100 **A**1 2 3 5 9 10 **F**3 5 8 11 15 17 18 20 22 24 26 28 29 30 31 34 35 36 37 38 39 40 41 43 44 45 46 50 51 56 57 58 59 60 64 70 71 74 75 77 78 79 81 82 84 85 87 92 93 98 99 100 101 102 103 104 105 107 108 110 111 115 118 119 120 121 123 126 129 130 132 135 146 148 **P**6 **S** Johns Hopkins Health System, Baltimore, MD
Primary Contact: Gene E. Green, M.D., President
COO: Joseph Linstrom, Vice President Operations
CFO: Marty Basso, Senior Vice President Finance
CMO: Robert Rothstein, M.D., Vice President Medical Affairs
CIO: Jason Cole, Senior Director, Management Information Systems
CNO: Jacky Schultz, R.N., Chief Nurse Officer
Web address: www.suburbanhospital.org
**Control:** Other not–for–profit (including NFP Corporation) **Service:** General Medical and Surgical

**Staffed Beds:** 235 **Admissions:** 13209 **Census:** 158 **Outpatient Visits:** 110793 **Births:** 0 **Total Expense ($000):** 262968 **Payroll Expense ($000):** 92331 **Personnel:** 1506

✠ **WALTER REED NATIONAL MILITARY MEDICAL CENTER**, 8901 Wisconsin Avenue, Zip 20889–5600; tel. 301/295–4611 **A**1 2 3 5 **F**3 5 7 8 9 10 13 14 15 17 18 19 20 21 22 23 24 26 27 28 29 30 31 32 33 34 35 36 37 38 39 40 41 43 45 46 47 48 49 50 51 52 53 55 56 57 58 59 60 61 64 65 68 70 72 73 74 75 76 77 78 79 80 81 82 84 85 86 87 88 89 90 91 92 93 94 95 96 97 98 99 100 101 102 103 104 105 106 107 108 109 110 111 113 115 116 117 118 119 120 121 123 124 126 129 130 131 132 133 135 136 138 141 142 143 144 145 146 147 148 **S** Bureau of Medicine and Surgery, Department of the Navy, Washington, DC
Primary Contact: Brigadier General Jeffrey B. Clark, Director
CFO: Commander Joseph Pickel, Director Resource Management
CIO: Commander Cayetano Thornton, Chief Information Officer
CHR: Captain Jaime Carroll, Department Head
Web address: www.wrnmmc.capmed.mil/SitePages/home.aspx
**Control:** Navy, Government, federal **Service:** General Medical and Surgical

**Staffed Beds:** 247 **Admissions:** 13351 **Census:** 166 **Outpatient Visits:** 1027939 **Births:** 1490 **Total Expense ($000):** 881521 **Payroll Expense ($000):** 421461 **Personnel:** 6724

## CAMBRIDGE—Dorchester County

☐ **EASTERN SHORE HOSPITAL CENTER (214002)**, 5262 Woods Road, Zip 21613–3796, Mailing Address: P.O. Box 800, Zip 21613–0800; tel. 410/221–2300, (Nonreporting) **A**1 9 10
Primary Contact: Randy L. Bradford, Chief Executive Officer
COO: William Webb, Assistant Superintendent
CFO: William Webb, Assistant Superintendent
CMO: Evangeline Garcia, M.D., Clinical Director
CHR: Cassandra Stanley, Director Personnel
CNO: Lisa Hines, Director Nursing
Web address: www.dhmh.state.md.us/eshc
**Control:** State–Government, nonfederal **Service:** Psychiatric

**Staffed Beds:** 76

✠ **UNIVERSITY OF MARYLAND SHORE MEDICAL CENTER AT DORCHESTER**, 300 Byrn Street, Zip 21613–1908; tel. 410/228–5511 **A**1 9 **F**3 11 15 18 20 29 30 31 34 35 40 43 44 45 50 57 59 62 64 68 70 74 75 77 78 81 82 84 85 86 87 91 93 98 99 100 101 102 103 104 105 107 108 110 111 113 118 119 129 130 132 146 **P**3 5 **S** University of Maryland Medical System, Baltimore, MD
Primary Contact: Kenneth D. Kozel, FACHE, President and Chief Executive Officer
COO: Jim Ross, Senior Vice President and Interim Chief Operating Officer
CFO: Joanne A. Hahey, Senior Vice President and Chief Financial Officer
CMO: William Huffner, M.D., Vice President Medical Affairs
CIO: Elizabeth Fish, Chief Information Officer
CHR: Susan Coe, Regional Vice President Human Resources
Web address: www.shorehealth.org
**Control:** Other not–for–profit (including NFP Corporation) **Service:** General Medical and Surgical

**Staffed Beds:** 41 **Admissions:** 2408 **Census:** 29 **Outpatient Visits:** 51268
**Births:** 0 **Total Expense ($000):** 41089 **Payroll Expense ($000):** 18112
**Personnel:** 251

## CHESTERTOWN—Kent County

**CHESTER RIVER HOSPITAL CENTER** See University of Maryland Shore Medical Center at Chestertown

✠ **UNIVERSITY OF MARYLAND SHORE MEDICAL CENTER AT CHESTERTOWN (210030)**, 100 Brown Street, Zip 21620–1499; tel. 410/778–3300 **A**1 9 10 **F**3 11 15 18 28 29 30 31 34 35 39 40 41 42 45 46 47 50 53 55 56 57 59 60 62 63 64 65 68 70 75 78 79 81 82 84 85 87 89 97 102 107 110 111 115 119 128 129 130 132 143 146 147 **S** University of Maryland Medical System, Baltimore, MD
Primary Contact: Kenneth D. Kozel, FACHE, President and Chief Executive Officer
CFO: Joanne A. Hahey, Vice President Finance and Chief Financial Officer
CMO: William Huffner, M.D., Chief Medical Officer
CIO: Elizabeth Fish, Senior Director Site Executive and Information Technology
CHR: Susan Coe, Vice President Human Resources
CNO: Christopher J. Parker, R.N., Senior Vice President Patient Care Services and Chief Nursing Officer
Web address: www.umms.org/hospitals/shore–health–system.htm
**Control:** Other not–for–profit (including NFP Corporation) **Service:** General Medical and Surgical

**Staffed Beds:** 41 **Admissions:** 1880 **Census:** 22 **Outpatient Visits:** 45578
**Births:** 0 **Total Expense ($000):** 47393 **Payroll Expense ($000):** 17382
**Personnel:** 393

## CHEVERLY—Prince George's County

**GLADYS SPELLMAN SPECIALTY HOSPITAL AND NURSING CENTER**, 2900 Mercy Lane, Zip 20785–1157; tel. 301/618–2010, (Nonreporting)
Primary Contact: Stewart R. Seitz, Chief Executive Officer
CFO: Ketty Taboado, Chief Financial Officer
CMO: Paul A. Devore, M.D., Medical Director
CIO: Dennis Lilik, Chief Information Officer
CHR: Michael Jacobs, Vice President Human Resources
Web address: www.dimensionshealth.org
**Control:** Corporation, Investor–owned, for–profit **Service:** Chronic disease

**Staffed Beds:** 30

☐ **PRINCE GEORGE'S HOSPITAL CENTER (210003)**, 3001 Hospital Drive, Zip 20785–1189; tel. 301/618–2000 **A**1 3 5 9 10 **F**3 11 13 15 17 18 20 22 24 26 28 29 31 34 35 38 40 42 43 45 46 47 48 49 50 54 55 56 57 59 60 61 63 64 65 66 68 69 70 72 74 75 76 77 78 79 81 82 84 85 86 87 89 92 93 97 98 100 101 102 103 104 105 107 108 110 111 114 115 118 119 130 131 132 134 135 142 144 146 148 **P**6 **S** Dimensions Healthcare System, Cheverly, MD
Primary Contact: K. Singh Taneja, Chief Operating Officer
CMO: David Goldman, M.D., Vice President Medical Affairs and Education
CIO: Dennis Lilik, Chief Information Officer
CHR: Michael Jacobs, Vice President Human Resources
Web address: www.princegeorgeshospital.org
**Control:** Other not–for–profit (including NFP Corporation) **Service:** General Medical and Surgical

**Staffed Beds:** 158 **Admissions:** 11437 **Census:** 168 **Births:** 1982

*Many Facility Codes have changed. Please refer to the AHA Guide Code Chart.*  © 2015 AHA Guide

## CLINTON—Prince George's County

✠ **MEDSTAR SOUTHERN MARYLAND HOSPITAL CENTER (210062)**, 7503 Surratts Road, Zip 20735–3358; tel. 301/868–8000, (Total facility includes 24 beds in nursing home–type unit) **A**1 2 9 10 **F**3 11 12 13 15 17 18 20 22 26 28 29 30 31 32 34 35 36 37 39 40 43 44 45 46 47 48 49 50 57 59 64 65 68 70 73 74 75 76 77 78 79 80 81 82 85 86 87 89 91 92 93 96 98 100 101 102 103 105 107 108 114 115 118 119 128 129 130 135 145 146 147 148 **S** MedStar Health, Columbia, MD
Primary Contact: Christine R. Wray, President and Chief Executive Officer
CFO: Charles R. Stewart, Vice President Business, Finance and Corporate Compliance
CMO: J. Andrew Sumner, M.D., Vice President Medical Affairs
CIO: Lou Mavromatis, Vice President Data Processing
CHR: Paul Zeller, Vice President Human Resources
Web address: www.smhhealth.org
**Control:** Other not–for–profit (including NFP Corporation) **Service:** General Medical and Surgical

**Staffed Beds:** 275 **Admissions:** 13029 **Census:** 148 **Outpatient Visits:** 107122 **Births:** 1623 **Total Expense ($000):** 219467 **Payroll Expense ($000):** 90727 **Personnel:** 1308

**SOUTHERN MARYLAND HOSPITAL CENTER** See MedStar Southern Maryland Hospital Center

## COLUMBIA—Howard County

✠ **HOWARD COUNTY GENERAL HOSPITAL (210048)**, 5755 Cedar Lane, Zip 21044–2999; tel. 410/740–7890 **A**1 2 5 9 10 **F**3 8 11 13 15 18 20 22 26 28 29 30 31 32 34 35 36 39 40 41 44 45 46 47 49 50 53 56 57 58 59 60 61 64 65 68 70 72 74 75 76 77 78 79 81 82 84 85 86 87 89 91 92 93 96 98 100 101 102 103 107 108 110 111 115 119 129 130 131 132 134 135 146 147 148 **S** Johns Hopkins Health System, Baltimore, MD
Primary Contact: Steven C. Snelgrove, President
COO: Jay H. Blackman, Senior Vice President and Chief Operating Officer
CFO: James Young, Senior Vice President Finance and Chief Financial Officer
CIO: Rick Edwards, Director Information Systems
CHR: Dorothy Brillantes, Senior Vice President Human Resources
Web address: www.hcgh.org
**Control:** Other not–for–profit (including NFP Corporation) **Service:** General Medical and Surgical

**Staffed Beds:** 256 **Admissions:** 16720 **Census:** 202 **Outpatient Visits:** 138057 **Births:** 3550 **Total Expense ($000):** 229546 **Payroll Expense ($000):** 85945 **Personnel:** 1433

## CRISFIELD—Somerset County

☐ **MCCREADY FOUNDATION (210045)**, 201 Hall Highway, Zip 21817–1299; tel. 410/968–1200, (Nonreporting) **A**1 9 10
Primary Contact: Joy A. Strand, Chief Executive Officer
CFO: Gary W. Broadwater, Chief Financial Officer
Web address: www.mccreadyfoundation.org
**Control:** Other not–for–profit (including NFP Corporation) **Service:** General Medical and Surgical

**Staffed Beds:** 89

## CUMBERLAND—Allegany County

☐ **THOMAS B. FINAN CENTER (214012)**, 10102 Country Club Road S.E., Zip 21502–8339, Mailing Address: P.O. Box 1722, Zip 21501–1722; tel. 301/777–2405, (Nonreporting) **A**1 9 10
Primary Contact: Judith Hott, Chief Executive Officer
COO: John Cullen, Assistant Superintendent
CFO: Craig Alexander, Fiscal Specialist
CMO: David Millis, M.D., Clinical Director
CHR: Chris Loney, Director Personnel
CNO: Gayle Walter, Director of Nursing
Web address: www.dhmh.state.md.us
**Control:** State–Government, nonfederal **Service:** Psychiatric

**Staffed Beds:** 80

✠ △ **WESTERN MARYLAND REGIONAL MEDICAL CENTER (210027)**, 12500 Willowbrook Road S.E., Zip 21502–6393, Mailing Address: P.O. Box 539, Zip 21501–0539; tel. 240/964–7000, (Total facility includes 88 beds in nursing home–type unit) **A**1 2 7 9 10 20 **F**3 5 11 13 14 15 17 18 20 22 24 26 28 29 30 31 32 34 35 40 43 44 45 49 50 51 53 54 56 57 58 59 60 62 63 64 66 68 70 73 74 75 76 77 78 79 80 81 82 85 86 87 89 90 93 94 96 97 98 100 102 103 104 107 108 111 114 115 116 117 118 119 120 121 124 128 129 130 132 134 135 144 145 146 148 **P**6
Primary Contact: Barry P. Ronan, President and Chief Executive Officer
COO: Nancy D. Adams, R.N., Senior Vice President Chief Operating Officer and Chief Nurse Executive
CFO: Kimberly S. Repac, Senior Vice President and Chief Financial Officer
CMO: Gerald Goldstein, M.D., Senior Vice President and Chief Medical Officer
CIO: William Byers, Chief Technology Officer
CHR: Christopher Bumbaugh, Corporate Director, Human Resources
CNO: Nancy D. Adams, R.N., Senior Vice President Chief Operating Officer and Chief Nurse Executive
Web address: www.wmhs.com
**Control:** Other not–for–profit (including NFP Corporation) **Service:** General Medical and Surgical

**Staffed Beds:** 321 **Admissions:** 11879 **Census:** 229 **Outpatient Visits:** 538853 **Births:** 1018 **Total Expense ($000):** 282309 **Payroll Expense ($000):** 104975 **Personnel:** 1701

## EAST NEW MARKET—Dorchester County

**WARWICK MANOR BEHAVIORAL HEALTH**, 3680 Warwick Road, Zip 21631–1420; tel. 410/943–8108, (Nonreporting)
Primary Contact: L. Wesley Fuhrman, President and Chief Executive Officer
Web address: www.warwickmanor.org/
**Control:** Corporation, Investor–owned, for–profit **Service:** Alcoholism and other chemical dependency

**Staffed Beds:** 42

## EASTON—Talbot County

✠ △ **UNIVERSITY OF MARYLAND SHORE MEDICAL CENTER AT EASTON (210037)**, 219 South Washington Street, Zip 21601–2996; tel. 410/822–1000 **A**1 2 7 9 10 **F**3 8 11 13 15 18 20 22 28 29 30 31 34 35 36 37 39 40 42 43 44 45 49 51 54 57 58 59 60 62 63 64 65 70 74 76 78 79 81 82 83 84 85 86 89 90 91 93 100 102 107 108 111 114 116 117 118 119 120 121 123 124 126 129 130 132 144 147 148 **P**3 5 **S** University of Maryland Medical System, Baltimore, MD
Primary Contact: Kenneth D. Kozel, FACHE, President and Chief Executive Officer
COO: Jim Ross, Senior Vice President and Interim Chief Operating Officer
CFO: Joanne A. Hahey, Senior Vice President and Chief Financial Officer
CMO: William Huffner, M.D., Chief Medical Officer
CIO: Elizabeth Fish, Chief Information Officer
CHR: Susan Coe, Regional Vice President Human Resources
CNO: Christopher J. Parker, R.N., Chief Nursing Officer
Web address: www.shorehealth.org
**Control:** Other not–for–profit (including NFP Corporation) **Service:** General Medical and Surgical

**Staffed Beds:** 132 **Admissions:** 7940 **Census:** 90 **Outpatient Visits:** 391646 **Births:** 1126 **Total Expense ($000):** 168202 **Payroll Expense ($000):** 62263 **Personnel:** 1186

## ELKTON—Cecil County

✠ **UNION HOSPITAL (210032)**, 106 Bow Street, Zip 21921–5596; tel. 410/398–4000 **A**1 2 3 5 9 10 **F**2 3 11 13 15 18 26 29 30 31 34 35 40 44 45 46 49 50 51 54 57 59 61 63 64 69 70 74 75 76 77 78 79 81 82 84 85 86 87 89 92 97 98 100 102 104 105 107 108 110 111 114 118 119 129 130 131 132 135 146 147 148 **P**6
Primary Contact: Kenneth S. Lewis, M.D., JD, President and Chief Executive Officer
COO: David N. Gipson, Senior Vice President and Chief Clinical Operations Officer
CFO: Laurie Beyer, Senior Vice President and Chief Financial Officer
CMO: Cydney Teal, M.D., Vice President Medical Affairs
CIO: Anne Lara, Chief Information Officer
CHR: Terrence Lovell, Vice President Human Resources
CNO: Katie Boston, Senior Vice President Patient Care Services
Web address: www.uhcc.com
**Control:** Other not–for–profit (including NFP Corporation) **Service:** General Medical and Surgical

**Staffed Beds:** 118 **Admissions:** 5051 **Census:** 55 **Outpatient Visits:** 144944 **Births:** 667 **Total Expense ($000):** 146636 **Payroll Expense ($000):** 65791 **Personnel:** 961

---

**Hospital, Medicare Provider Number, Address, Telephone, Approval, Facility, and Physician Codes, Health Care System**

★ American Hospital Association (AHA) membership
☐ The Joint Commission accreditation
○ Healthcare Facilities Accreditation Program
◇ DNV Healthcare Inc. accreditation
⇧ Center for Improvement in Healthcare Quality Accreditation
△ Commission on Accreditation of Rehabilitation Facilities (CARF) accreditation

**MD**

## FREDERICK—Frederick County

☒ **FREDERICK MEMORIAL HOSPITAL (210005)**, 400 West Seventh Street, Zip 21701–4593; tel. 240/566–3300, (Nonreporting) **A**1 2 5 9 10
Primary Contact: Thomas A. Kleinhanzl, President and Chief Executive Officer
COO: John R. Verbus, Senior Vice President and Chief Operating Officer
CFO: Michelle K. Mahan, Senior Vice President and Chief Financial Officer
CMO: Manuel Casiano, M.D., Senior Vice President Medical Affairs
CIO: David Quirke, Vice President Information Services
CNO: Cheryl Cioffi, R.N., Senior Vice President Patient Care Services and Chief Nursing Officer
Web address: www.fmh.org
**Control:** Other not–for–profit (including NFP Corporation) **Service:** General Medical and Surgical

**Staffed Beds:** 295

## GERMANTOWN—Montgomery County

★ **HOLY CROSS GERMANTOWN HOSPITAL**, 19801 Observation Drive, Zip 20876–4070; tel. 301/754–7000, (Nonreporting) **S** Trinity Health, Livonia, MI
Primary Contact: Doug Ryder, President
Web address: www.holycrosshealth.org/germantown
**Control:** Other not–for–profit (including NFP Corporation) **Service:** General Medical and Surgical

**Staffed Beds:** 93

## GLEN BURNIE—Anne Arundel County

☒ **UNIVERSITY OF MARYLAND BALTIMORE WASHINGTON MEDICAL CENTER (210043)**, 301 Hospital Drive, Zip 21061–5899; tel. 410/787–4000 **A**1 2 3 5 9 10 **F**3 8 11 13 14 18 20 22 26 28 29 30 31 34 35 40 41 43 44 45 46 48 49 50 54 55 56 57 58 59 60 64 65 68 70 74 75 76 77 78 79 81 82 84 85 87 89 93 98 100 102 105 107 108 111 114 115 118 119 120 121 123 126 129 130 131 132 135 146 147 148 **P**6 **S** University of Maryland Medical System, Baltimore, MD
Primary Contact: Karen E. Olscamp, President and Chief Executive Officer
COO: Kathleen McCollum, Senior Vice President, Clinical Integration and Chief Operating Officer
CFO: Al Pietsch, CPA, Senior Vice President and Chief Financial Officer
CMO: Lawrence Linder, M.D., Senior Vice President and Chief Medical Officer
CHR: Kathy Poehler, Vice President, Human Resources
CNO: Catherine Whitaker, R.N., Vice President and Chief Nursing Officer
Web address: www.bwmc.umms.org
**Control:** Other not–for–profit (including NFP Corporation) **Service:** General Medical and Surgical

**Staffed Beds:** 323 **Admissions:** 18632 **Census:** 218 **Outpatient Visits:** 139770 **Births:** 812 **Total Expense ($000):** 322702 **Payroll Expense ($000):** 130249 **Personnel:** 2284

## HAGERSTOWN—Washington County

☐ **BROOK LANE HEALTH SERVICES (214003)**, 13121 Brook Lane Drive, Zip 21742–1435, Mailing Address: P.O. Box 1945, Zip 21742–1945; tel. 301/733–0330 **A**1 9 10 **F**5 26 27 30 56 68 98 99 100 101 103 104 105 130 143 146 **P**4 6
Primary Contact: R. Lynn Rushing, Chief Executive Officer
CFO: Floyd Klauka, Chief Financial Officer
CMO: David Gonzalez, M.D., Medical Director
CIO: Sharon Gladfelter, Health Information Manager
CHR: Nicole Twigg, Director Human Resources
CNO: Jason Allen, Director Patient Care Services
Web address: www.brooklane.org
**Control:** Other not–for–profit (including NFP Corporation) **Service:** Psychiatric

**Staffed Beds:** 41 **Admissions:** 1665 **Census:** 34 **Outpatient Visits:** 72694 **Births:** 0 **Total Expense ($000):** 23046 **Payroll Expense ($000):** 14288 **Personnel:** 318

☒ △ **MERITUS MEDICAL CENTER (210001)**, 11116 Medical Campus Road, Zip 21742–6710; tel. 301/790–8000 **A**1 2 7 9 10 **F**3 5 11 12 13 15 17 18 20 22 26 28 29 30 31 34 35 38 40 43 44 49 51 52 54 56 57 58 59 60 61 62 64 65 70 74 75 76 77 78 79 81 82 83 84 85 86 87 89 90 93 94 96 97 98 99 100 101 102 103 104 105 107 108 111 114 115 118 119 120 121 123 130 131 132 135 143 144 145 146 147 148 **P**6 8
Primary Contact: Joseph P. Ross, President and Chief Executive Officer
COO: Jesus Cepero, Ph.D., Chief Operating Officer and Chief Nursing Officer
CFO: Thomas T. Chan, Chief Financial Officer
CMO: Heather Lorenzo, M.D., Vice President and Chief Medical Officer
CHR: Christopher Bumbaugh, Executive Human Resources
CNO: Jesus Cepero, Ph.D., Chief Operating Officer and Chief Nursing Officer
Web address: www.meritushealth.com
**Control:** Other not–for–profit (including NFP Corporation) **Service:** General Medical and Surgical

**Staffed Beds:** 257 **Admissions:** 16542 **Census:** 173 **Outpatient Visits:** 190825 **Births:** 1996 **Total Expense ($000):** 292347 **Payroll Expense ($000):** 106981 **Personnel:** 1739

**WASHINGTON COUNTY HEALTH SYSTEM** See Meritus Medical Center

☐ △ **WESTERN MARYLAND HOSPITAL CENTER (212002)**, 1500 Pennsylvania Avenue, Zip 21742–3194; tel. 301/745–4200, (Nonreporting) **A**1 7 9 10
Primary Contact: Gerard Walsh, Chief Executive Officer
COO: David Davis, Chief Operating Officer
CFO: Kelly Edmonds, Chief Financial Officer
CMO: Monica Stallworth, M.D., Chief of Staff
CIO: Ron Keplinger, Chief Information Officer
CHR: David Davis, Chief Operating Officer
Web address: www.wmhc.us
**Control:** State–Government, nonfederal **Service:** Long–Term Acute Care hospital

**Staffed Beds:** 120

## HAVRE DE GRACE—Harford County

☒ **UNIVERSITY OF MARYLAND HARFORD MEMORIAL HOSPITAL (210006)**, 501 South Union Avenue, Zip 21078–3493; tel. 443/843–5000, (Data for 182 days) **A**1 2 9 10 **F**3 11 12 15 29 30 31 34 35 36 38 40 42 46 49 50 51 57 59 60 64 65 66 68 70 71 74 75 77 78 79 81 82 84 85 86 87 92 93 96 98 102 103 104 107 108 110 111 114 115 118 119 129 130 131 132 135 146 148 **S** University of Maryland Medical System, Baltimore, MD
Primary Contact: Lyle Ernest Sheldon, FACHE, President and Chief Executive Officer
CFO: Joseph E. Hoffman, III, Executive Vice President and Chief Financial Officer
CMO: Peggy Vaughan, M.D., Senior Vice President Medical Affairs
CIO: Rick Casteel, Vice President Management Information Systems and Chief Information Officer
CHR: Toni M. Shivery, Vice President Human Resources
Web address: www.uchs.org
**Control:** Other not–for–profit (including NFP Corporation) **Service:** General Medical and Surgical

**Staffed Beds:** 79 **Admissions:** 2351 **Census:** 66 **Outpatient Visits:** 43742 **Births:** 0 **Total Expense ($000):** 40864 **Payroll Expense ($000):** 19071 **Personnel:** 675

## JESSUP—Howard County

☐ **CLIFTON T. PERKINS HOSPITAL CENTER**, 8450 Dorsey Run Road, Zip 20794–9486; tel. 410/724–3000 **A**1 3 5 **F**3 11 29 39 75 98 106 143 146
Primary Contact: Thomas D. Lewis, Acting Chief Executive Officer
COO: Steve Mason, Assistant Superintendent and Chief Operating Officer
CFO: George Parnel, Chief Financial Officer
CMO: Muhammed Ajanah, M.D., Clinical Director
CIO: Chanda Hamilton, Chief Information Officer
CHR: Beverly Stacie, Director Human Resources
Web address: www.dhmh.state.md.us/perkins/
**Control:** State–Government, nonfederal **Service:** Psychiatric

**Staffed Beds:** 250 **Admissions:** 94 **Census:** 243 **Outpatient Visits:** 0 **Births:** 0 **Total Expense ($000):** 60954 **Payroll Expense ($000):** 36049 **Personnel:** 571

## LA PLATA—Charles County

☒ **UNIVERSITY OF MARYLAND CHARLES REGIONAL MEDICAL CENTER (210035)**, 5 Garrett Avenue, Zip 20646–5960, Mailing Address: P.O. Box 1070, Zip 20646–1070; tel. 301/609–4000 **A**1 2 9 10 **F**3 11 13 15 18 28 29 30 31 34 35 36 38 40 44 45 50 51 56 57 59 60 61 64 70 74 76 77 78 79 81 82 85 86 87 89 91 92 93 96 107 108 110 111 114 115 118 119 129 130 132 135 145 146 147 148 **S** University of Maryland Medical System, Baltimore, MD
Primary Contact: Noel A. Cervino, President and Chief Executive Officer
CFO: Erik Boas, Vice President Finance
CMO: Sanjeeb Mishra, M.D., Chief of Staff
CHR: Stacey M. Cook, MS, Director Human Resources
Web address: www.charlesregional.org
**Control:** Other not–for–profit (including NFP Corporation) **Service:** General Medical and Surgical

**Staffed Beds:** 121 **Admissions:** 7580 **Census:** 81 **Outpatient Visits:** 70780 **Births:** 852 **Total Expense ($000):** 109466 **Payroll Expense ($000):** 46248 **Personnel:** 785

## LANHAM—Prince George's County

☒ **DOCTORS COMMUNITY HOSPITAL (210051)**, 8118 Good Luck Road, Zip 20706–3574; tel. 301/552–8118 **A**1 9 10 **F**3 8 12 15 18 20 26 28 29 30 31 34 35 40 45 49 50 51 53 57 59 64 70 75 77 78 79 81 82 84 85 86 87 90 93 107 108 111 114 115 119 126 130 131 132 135 146 **P**6
Primary Contact: Philip B. Down, Chief Executive Officer
COO: Paul Grenaldo, Executive Vice President and Chief Operating Officer
CFO: Camille Bash, Chief Financial Officer
CMO: Gabriel Jaffe, M.D., Vice President Medical Affairs
CIO: Alan Johnson, Chief Information Officer
CHR: Paul Hagens, Vice President Human Resources
Web address: www.dchweb.org
**Control:** Other not–for–profit (including NFP Corporation) **Service:** General Medical and Surgical

**Staffed Beds:** 183 **Admissions:** 9709 **Census:** 124 **Outpatient Visits:** 61989 **Births:** 0 **Total Expense ($000):** 176796 **Payroll Expense ($000):** 77218 **Personnel:** 1233

*Many Facility Codes have changed. Please refer to the AHA Guide Code Chart.*   © 2015 AHA Guide

## LAUREL—Prince George's County

☐ △ **LAUREL REGIONAL HOSPITAL (210055)**, 7300 Van Dusen Road, Zip 20707–9463; tel. 301/725–4300, (Nonreporting) **A**1 7 9 10 **S** Dimensions Healthcare System, Cheverly, MD
Primary Contact: John Spearman, President and Chief Operating Officer
COO: John Spearman, Interim Chief Operating Officer
CFO: Lisa Goodlett, Senior Vice President and Chief Financial Officer
CMO: Trudy Hall, M.D., Vice President Medical Affairs
CIO: David Peterson, Chief Information Officer
CHR: John Peeples, Senior Vice President Human Resources
CNO: June Meyer, MSN, Vice President Chief Nursing Officer
Web address: www.laurelregionalhospital.org
**Control:** Other not–for–profit (including NFP Corporation) **Service:** General Medical and Surgical

**Staffed Beds:** 166

## LEONARDTOWN—St. Mary's County

✶ **MEDSTAR ST. MARY'S HOSPITAL (210028)**, 25500 Point Lookout Road, Zip 20650–2015, Mailing Address: P.O. Box 527, Zip 20650–0527; tel. 301/475–6001 **A**1 2 9 10 **F**3 11 13 15 18 28 29 30 31 32 34 35 36 39 40 44 45 48 50 51 53 54 56 57 59 60 63 64 65 66 68 70 71 74 75 76 77 78 79 81 82 84 85 86 87 89 93 98 100 101 102 103 104 105 107 108 110 111 114 115 118 119 129 130 132 134 135 144 146 147 148 **S** MedStar Health, Columbia, MD
Primary Contact: Christine R. Wray, President
COO: Stephen T. Michaels, M.D., Chief Operating Officer and Chief Medical Officer
CFO: Richard Braam, Vice President Finance
CMO: Conor F. Lundergan, M.D., Chief of Medical Staff
CIO: Donald Sirk, Director Information Systems
CHR: Evelyn Campos–Diaz, Director Human Resources
CNO: Mary Lou Watson, MS, Vice President Nursing
Web address: www.medstarstmarys.org
**Control:** Other not–for–profit (including NFP Corporation) **Service:** General Medical and Surgical

**Staffed Beds:** 89 **Admissions:** 6681 **Census:** 59 **Outpatient Visits:** 236101 **Births:** 1176 **Total Expense ($000):** 131819 **Payroll Expense ($000):** 59529 **Personnel:** 1000

## OAKLAND—Garrett County

✶ **GARRETT COUNTY MEMORIAL HOSPITAL (210017)**, 251 North Fourth Street, Zip 21550–1375; tel. 301/533–4000, (Total facility includes 10 beds in nursing home–type unit) **A**1 9 10 **F**3 11 13 28 30 32 34 35 38 40 45 50 53 56 57 59 64 65 70 75 76 79 81 85 87 89 102 107 108 114 118 119 128 130 135 141 146 148 **P**6
Primary Contact: Mark Boucot, President and Chief Executive Officer
CFO: Tracy Lipscomb, Vice President Financial Services and Chief Financial Officer
CMO: Marjorie Fridkin, M.D., Chief Medical Officer
CIO: Stephen Peterson, Vice President Chief Information Officer
CHR: Annette Livengood, Vice President Human Resources
CNO: Kendra Thayer, Vice President Clinical and Support Services and Chief Nursing Officer
Web address: www.https://www.gcmh.com
**Control:** Other not–for–profit (including NFP Corporation) **Service:** General Medical and Surgical

**Staffed Beds:** 59 **Admissions:** 1884 **Census:** 18 **Outpatient Visits:** 69383 **Births:** 263 **Total Expense ($000):** 39577 **Payroll Expense ($000):** 16496 **Personnel:** 321

## OLNEY—Montgomery County

✶ **MEDSTAR MONTGOMERY MEDICAL CENTER (210018)**, 18101 Prince Philip Drive, Zip 20832–1512; tel. 301/774–8882 **A**1 2 3 9 10 **F**3 5 11 12 13 18 20 26 28 29 30 31 34 35 37 38 40 41 45 46 48 49 50 51 53 55 56 57 59 65 68 70 74 75 76 77 78 79 80 81 82 84 85 86 87 89 92 93 98 99 100 102 103 104 105 107 108 111 114 115 118 119 120 121 126 129 130 132 134 135 146 **S** MedStar Health, Columbia, MD
Primary Contact: Peter W. Monge, President
CFO: David A. Havrilla, Chief Financial Officer
CMO: Frederick Finelli, M.D., Vice President Medical Affairs
CIO: Chistiane Brown, Assistant Vice President
CHR: Kevin Mell, Vice President Operations
CNO: Connie Stone, R.N., Chief Nursing Officer
Web address: www.medstarmontgomery.org
**Control:** Other not–for–profit (including NFP Corporation) **Service:** General Medical and Surgical

**Staffed Beds:** 149 **Admissions:** 8230 **Census:** 85 **Outpatient Visits:** 80429 **Births:** 810 **Total Expense ($000):** 141656 **Payroll Expense ($000):** 56818 **Personnel:** 800

## OXEN HILL—Prince George's County

✶ **FORT WASHINGTON MEDICAL CENTER (210060)**, 174 Waterfront Street, Suite 225, tel. 301/292–7000, (Nonreporting) **A**1 9 10
Primary Contact: Reginald Jones, Interim President and Chief Executive Officer
CFO: Joseph B. Tucker, Senior Vice President and Chief Financial Officer
CMO: Elias Debbas, M.D., President Medical Staff
CIO: Fred Ashby, Director Information Technology
CHR: Alexander Morris, Corporate Director Human Resources
CNO: Marjorie Quint–Bouzid, Chief Nursing Officer and Vice President Patient Care Services
Web address: www.fortwashingtonmc.org
**Control:** Other not–for–profit (including NFP Corporation) **Service:** General Medical and Surgical

**Staffed Beds:** 37

## PERRY POINT—Cecil County

**VETERANS AFFAIRS MARYLAND HEALTH CARE SYSTEM–PERRY POINT DIVISION** See Veterans Affairs Maryland Health Care System–Baltimore Division, Baltimore

## PRINCE FREDERICK—Calvert County

✶ **CALVERT MEMORIAL HOSPITAL (210039)**, 100 Hospital Road, Zip 20678–4017; tel. 410/535–4000, (Total facility includes 18 beds in nursing home–type unit) **A**1 9 10 **F**3 11 13 14 20 26 28 29 30 31 32 34 35 36 38 40 41 45 49 54 56 57 59 61 64 65 68 70 74 75 76 77 78 79 81 82 84 85 86 87 89 93 94 96 98 99 100 101 102 104 105 107 108 111 112 114 115 119 127 129 130 132 134 135 144 146 147 148 **P**4
Primary Contact: Dean Teague, Chief Executive Officer
CFO: Robert Kertis, Vice President Finance
CMO: Barbara Estes, M.D., Chief of Staff
CIO: Ed Grogan, Vice President Information Services and Chief Information Officer
CHR: Anthony M. Bladen, Vice President Human Resources
CNO: Diane Couchman, Vice President Patient Care Services and Chief Nursing Executive
Web address: www.calverthospital.com
**Control:** Other not–for–profit (including NFP Corporation) **Service:** General Medical and Surgical

**Staffed Beds:** 130 **Admissions:** 6077 **Census:** 72 **Outpatient Visits:** 134085 **Births:** 784 **Total Expense ($000):** 119799 **Payroll Expense ($000):** 51062 **Personnel:** 985

## RANDALLSTOWN—Baltimore County

☐ **NORTHWEST HOSPITAL (210040)**, 5401 Old Court Road, Zip 21133–5185; tel. 410/521–2200, (Nonreporting) **A**1 2 3 9 10 **S** LifeBridge Health, Baltimore, MD
Primary Contact: Brian M. White, President
CFO: Nancy Kane, Assistant Vice President Finance LifeBridge Health
CMO: Ronald L. Ginsberg, M.D., Vice President Medical Affairs
CIO: Tressa Springmann, Vice President and Chief Information Officer
CHR: Valerie Brandenburg, Director Human Resources
CNO: Susan L. Jalbert, R.N., Vice President Patient Care Services and Chief Nursing Officer
Web address: www.lifebridgehealth.org
**Control:** Other not–for–profit (including NFP Corporation) **Service:** General Medical and Surgical

**Staffed Beds:** 244

## ROCKVILLE—Montgomery County

☐ **ADVENTIST BEHAVIORAL HEALTH ROCKVILLE (214013)**, 14901 Broschart Road, Zip 20850–3318; tel. 301/251–4500 **A**1 9 10 **F**5 29 30 34 35 38 50 56 98 99 100 101 102 103 104 105 106 130 132 135 **P**6 8 **S** Adventist HealthCare, Gaithersburg, MD
Primary Contact: Kevin Young, FACHE, President
CFO: Randy Reimer, Chief Financial Officer
CMO: Peter H. Levine, M.D., Executive Medical Director Behavioral Health Services
CIO: Kathleen Dyer, Vice President and Chief Information Officer
CHR: Mary Cloutier, Director Human Resources
Web address: www.adventistbehavioralhealth.com
**Control:** Other not–for–profit (including NFP Corporation) **Service:** Psychiatric

**Staffed Beds:** 220 **Admissions:** 3032 **Census:** 108 **Outpatient Visits:** 19270 **Births:** 0 **Total Expense ($000):** 34954 **Payroll Expense ($000):** 18601 **Personnel:** 81

---

**Hospital, Medicare Provider Number, Address, Telephone, Approval, Facility, and Physician Codes, Health Care System**

★ American Hospital Association (AHA) membership
☐ The Joint Commission accreditation
○ Healthcare Facilities Accreditation Program
◇ DNV Healthcare Inc. accreditation
⇑ Center for Improvement in Healthcare Quality Accreditation
△ Commission on Accreditation of Rehabilitation Facilities (CARF) accreditation

**MD**

☐ △ **ADVENTIST REHABILITATION HOSPITAL OF MARYLAND (213029),** 9909 Medical Center Drive, Zip 20850–6361; tel. 240/864–6000, (Nonreporting) **A**1 7 9 10 **S** Adventist HealthCare, Gaithersburg, MD
Primary Contact: Brent Reitz, President
COO: Jason Makaroff, Chief Operating Officer and Associate Vice President
CFO: Jim Litsinger, Chief Financial Officer
CMO: Terrence P. Sheehan, M.D., Medical Director
CHR: Carrie Hibbard, Human Resource Business Partner
CNO: Valerie Summerlin, R.N., Chief Nursing Officer
Web address: www.adventistrehab.com
**Control:** Other not–for–profit (including NFP Corporation) **Service:** Rehabilitation

| Staffed Beds: 77 |
| --- |

**POTOMAC RIDGE BEHAVIORAL HEALTH** See Adventist Behavioral Health Rockville

☐ **SHADY GROVE ADVENTIST HOSPITAL (210057),** 9901 Medical Center Drive, Zip 20850–3395; tel. 240/826–6000 **A**1 2 3 9 10 **F**3 12 13 15 18 20 22 26 28 29 30 31 39 40 41 42 45 48 50 51 53 55 57 60 61 64 66 68 70 72 74 75 76 77 78 79 81 82 84 85 87 89 102 107 108 110 111 114 115 116 117 119 120 121 126 129 130 146 148 **S** Adventist HealthCare, Gaithersburg, MD
Primary Contact: John Sackett, President
COO: Eunmee Shim, R.N., Vice President Operations
CFO: Daniel Cochran, Vice President and Chief Financial Officer
CMO: Kevin Smothess, M.D., Vice President Chief Medical Officer
CIO: christopher Ghion, Vice President and Chief Information Officer
CNO: Skip Margot, Vice President Patient Care Services and Chief Nurse Executive
Web address: www.adventisthealthcare.com
**Control:** Church–operated, Nongovernment, not–for profit **Service:** General Medical and Surgical

| Staffed Beds: 331 Admissions: 19502 Census: 214 Outpatient Visits: 98926 Births: 4907 Total Expense ($000): 326374 Payroll Expense ($000): 120896 Personnel: 1582 |
| --- |

**SALISBURY—Wicomico County**

✠ **DEER'S HEAD HOSPITAL CENTER (212003),** 351 Deer's Head Hospital Road, Zip 21801–3201, Mailing Address: PO Box 2018, Zip 21802–2018; tel. 410/543–4000, (Total facility includes 61 beds in nursing home–type unit) **A**1 9 10 **F**1 3 11 28 29 30 44 50 56 57 59 60 61 65 68 75 77 82 84 85 86 87 90 91 93 94 96 128 130 132 135 146 148 **P**6
Primary Contact: Mary Beth Waide, R.N., MS, JD, Chief Executive Officer
COO: Michael Dollinger, Chief Operating Officer and Assistant Superintendent
CFO: Kenneth Waller, Fiscal Administrator
CMO: Michael P. Buchness, M.D., Director Medical
CIO: Mac Beattie, Computer Network Specialist
CHR: Luanne G. Dashield, Personnel Administrator
CNO: Tess Iten, Director of Nursing and Chief Nursing Officer
Web address: www.deershead.org
**Control:** State–Government, nonfederal **Service:** Chronic disease

| Staffed Beds: 73 Admissions: 141 Census: 57 Outpatient Visits: 10900 Births: 0 Total Expense ($000): 22899 Payroll Expense ($000): 10067 Personnel: 246 |
| --- |

✠ △ **HEALTHSOUTH CHESAPEAKE REHABILITATION HOSPITAL (213028),** 220 Tilghman Road, Zip 21804–1921; tel. 410/546–4600, (Nonreporting) **A**1 7 9 10 **S** HEALTHSOUTH Corporation, Birmingham, AL
Primary Contact: Steven Walas, Chief Executive Officer
CFO: Karen Rounsley, Controller
CHR: Belinda Thompson, Coordinator Human Resources
CNO: Belle Goslee, Chief Nursing Officer
Web address: www.healthsouthchesapeake.com
**Control:** Corporation, Investor–owned, for–profit **Service:** Rehabilitation

| Staffed Beds: 54 |
| --- |

✠ **PENINSULA REGIONAL MEDICAL CENTER (210019),** 100 East Carroll Street, Zip 21801–5422; tel. 410/546–6400 **A**1 2 9 10 **F**3 11 12 13 15 17 18 20 22 24 26 28 29 30 31 32 34 35 40 43 45 46 47 48 49 50 51 53 54 57 58 59 60 61 62 64 68 70 71 73 74 75 76 77 78 79 81 82 84 85 86 87 89 93 97 98 100 102 104 105 107 108 110 111 114 115 118 119 120 121 123 124 126 130 132 143 144 145 146 147 148 **P**5 8
Primary Contact: Margaret Naleppa, Ph.D., President and Chief Executive Officer
COO: Cindy Lunsford, Executive Vice President and Chief Operating Officer
CFO: Bruce Ritchie, Vice President of Finance and Chief Financial Officer
CMO: Charles B. Silvia, M.D., Chief Medical Officer and Vice President Medical Affairs
CIO: Raymond Adkins, Chief Information Officer
CHR: Scott Peterson, Vice President of People and Organizational Development
CNO: Karen C. Poisker, MSN, Vice President Patient Care Services and Chief Nursing Officer
Web address: www.peninsula.org
**Control:** Other not–for–profit (including NFP Corporation) **Service:** General Medical and Surgical

| Staffed Beds: 298 Admissions: 17464 Census: 203 Outpatient Visits: 546152 Births: 1905 Total Expense ($000): 373900 Payroll Expense ($000): 150202 Personnel: 2326 |
| --- |

**SILVER SPRING—Montgomery County**

✠ **HOLY CROSS HOSPITAL (210004),** 1500 Forest Glen Road, Zip 20910–1487; tel. 301/754–7000 **A**1 2 3 5 8 9 10 **F**2 3 11 12 13 15 17 18 19 20 22 26 29 30 31 32 34 35 36 37 39 40 41 45 46 49 50 54 56 57 58 59 60 64 66 68 70 72 74 75 76 77 78 79 81 82 84 85 86 87 89 93 97 100 107 108 110 111 114 115 119 120 121 123 124 126 129 130 131 132 134 144 146 147 **S** Trinity Health, Livonia, MI
Primary Contact: Judith Rogers, R.N., Ph.D., President and Chief Executive Officer
CFO: Anne Gillis, Chief Financial Officer
CMO: Blair Eig, M.D., Senior Vice President Medical Affairs
CIO: Matthew Trimmer, Director Information Services
CHR: J. Manuel Ocasio, Vice President Human Resources
CNO: Celia Guarino, R.N., Vice President and Chief Nursing Officer
Web address: www.holycrosshealth.org
**Control:** Church–operated, Nongovernment, not–for profit **Service:** General Medical and Surgical

| Staffed Beds: 425 Admissions: 27509 Census: 326 Outpatient Visits: 173907 Births: 8239 Total Expense ($000): 390903 Payroll Expense ($000): 169087 Personnel: 3436 |
| --- |

**SAINT LUKE INSTITUTE,** 8901 New Hampshire Avenue, Zip 20903–3611; tel. 301/445–7970, (Nonreporting)
Primary Contact: David Songy, President and Chief Executive Officer
COO: Sister Danile Lynch, Chief Operating Officer
Web address: www.sli.org
**Control:** Other not–for–profit (including NFP Corporation) **Service:** Psychiatric

| Staffed Beds: 24 |
| --- |

**SYKESVILLE—Carroll County**

☐ **SPRINGFIELD HOSPITAL CENTER (214004),** 6655 Sykesville Road, Zip 21784–7966; tel. 410/970–7000 **A**1 3 9 10 **F**11 30 35 39 44 50 53 56 57 68 75 77 86 87 98 101 103 130 132 135 146 **P**6
Primary Contact: Paula A. Langmead, Chief Executive Officer
COO: Daniel Triplett, Acting Chief Operating Officer
CFO: Keith Hardesty, Chief Financial Officer
CMO: Kim Bright, M.D., Clinical Director
CIO: Denise Maskell, Chief Information Officer
CNO: Gloria Merek, Director of Nursing
Web address: www.dhmh.state.md.us/springfield
**Control:** State–Government, nonfederal **Service:** Psychiatric

| Staffed Beds: 228 Admissions: 305 Census: 225 Outpatient Visits: 0 Births: 0 Total Expense ($000): 71250 Payroll Expense ($000): 41624 Personnel: 687 |
| --- |

**TAKOMA PARK—Montgomery County**

☐ △ **WASHINGTON ADVENTIST HOSPITAL (210016),** 7600 Carroll Avenue, Zip 20912–6392; tel. 301/891–7600, (Nonreporting) **A**1 2 3 5 7 9 10 **S** Adventist HealthCare, Gaithersburg, MD
Primary Contact: Erik Wangsness, President
Web address: www.adventisthealthcare.com
**Control:** Other not–for–profit (including NFP Corporation) **Service:** General Medical and Surgical

| Staffed Beds: 252 |
| --- |

**TOWSON—Baltimore County**

✠ **UNIVERSITY OF MARYLAND ST. JOSEPH MEDICAL CENTER (210063),** 7601 Osler Drive, Zip 21204–7582; tel. 410/337–1000 **A**1 2 3 9 10 **F**3 11 12 13 15 17 18 20 22 24 26 28 29 30 31 34 35 36 37 40 41 44 45 46 47 48 49 50 54 56 57 58 59 60 61 64 65 66 68 70 71 72 74 75 76 77 78 79 81 82 84 85 86 87 89 91 92 93 97 98 99 100 101 102 103 104 105 107 108 110 114 115 118 119 120 121 122 123 124 126 129 130 131 132 134 135 144 146 147 148 **P**6 **S** University of Maryland Medical System, Baltimore, MD
Primary Contact: Mohan Suntha, M.D., President and Chief Executive Officer
COO: Craig Carmichael, Vice President, Operations
CMO: Gail Cunningham, Interim Chief Medical Officer
CIO: Sean Shuffield, Regional Chief Information Officer
CNO: Pamela Jamieson, Vice President Patient Care Services and Chief Nursing Officer
Web address: www.sjmcmd.org
**Control:** Other not–for–profit (including NFP Corporation) **Service:** General Medical and Surgical

| Staffed Beds: 314 Admissions: 15740 Census: 173 Outpatient Visits: 106775 Births: 2024 Total Expense ($000): 392163 Payroll Expense ($000): 155585 Personnel: 1624 |
| --- |

*Many Facility Codes have changed. Please refer to the AHA Guide Code Chart.* © 2015 AHA Guide

**WESTMINSTER—Carroll County**

✠ **CARROLL HOSPITAL CENTER (210033)**, 200 Memorial Avenue,
Zip 21157–5799; tel. 410/848–3000 **A**1 2 9 10 **F**3 5 11 13 15 18 19 20 22
26 28 29 30 31 32 34 35 36 37 38 39 40 44 45 46 49 50 51 54 55 56 57
58 59 62 63 64 68 70 74 75 76 77 78 79 81 82 83 84 85 86 87 89 93 94
98 99 100 101 102 103 104 105 107 108 109 111 114 115 118 119 120
121 126 129 130 131 132 134 135 145 146 147 148 **P**6 8 **S** LifeBridge
Health, Baltimore, MD
Primary Contact: Leslie Simmons, R.N., FACHE, R.N., President and Chief
Executive Officer
CFO: Kevin Kelbly, Senior Vice President Finance and Corporate Fiscal Affairs
CMO: Mark Olszyk, M.D., Vice President Medical Affairs and Chief Medical Officer
CIO: Jennifer Moore, Interim Chief Information Officer
CHR: Tracey Ellison, Vice President Human Resources
CNO: Stephanie Reid, R.N., Vice President of Quality and Chief Nursing Officer
Web address: www.carrollhospitalcenter.org
**Control:** Other not–for–profit (including NFP Corporation) **Service:** General
Medical and Surgical

**Staffed Beds:** 151 **Admissions:** 11217 **Census:** 103 **Outpatient Visits:**
165275 **Births:** 1088 **Total Expense ($000):** 279381 **Payroll Expense
($000):** 123169 **Personnel:** 1488

---

**Hospital, Medicare Provider Number, Address, Telephone, Approval, Facility, and Physician Codes, Health Care System**

★ American Hospital Association (AHA) membership
☐ The Joint Commission accreditation
◯ Healthcare Facilities Accreditation Program
◇ DNV Healthcare Inc. accreditation
⇑ Center for Improvement in Healthcare Quality Accreditation
△ Commission on Accreditation of Rehabilitation Facilities (CARF) accreditation

---

# MASSACHUSETTS

## ATHOL—Worcester County

☐ **ATHOL MEMORIAL HOSPITAL (221303)**, 2033 Main Street, Zip 01331–3598; tel. 978/249–3511 **A**1 9 10 18 **F**3 15 18 29 30 31 34 35 40 50 57 59 64 65 68 75 77 78 79 81 82 84 85 86 87 97 107 110 111 114 119 130 132 133 135 146
Primary Contact: Winfield S. Brown, FACHE, President and Chief Executive Officer
COO: Michael Grimmer, Chief Operating Officer
CFO: Robert Crosby, Chief Financial Officer
CMO: Mohsen Noreldin, M.D., President Medical Staff
CIO: Carol Roosa, Vice President Information Services and Chief Information Officer
CNO: Lucille Songer, Chief Nursing Officer
Web address: www.atholhospital.org
**Control:** Other not–for–profit (including NFP Corporation) **Service:** General Medical and Surgical

**Staffed Beds:** 25 **Admissions:** 575 **Census:** 9 **Outpatient Visits:** 38489 **Births:** 0 **Total Expense ($000):** 21425 **Payroll Expense ($000):** 7980

## ATTLEBORO—Bristol County

☐ **ARBOUR–FULLER HOSPITAL (224021)**, 200 May Street, Zip 02703–5520; tel. 508/761–8500, (Nonreporting) **A**1 9 10 **S** Universal Health Services, Inc., King of Prussia, PA
Primary Contact: Kevin Burchill, Chief Executive Officer
CFO: James Rollins, Chief Financial Officer
CMO: Aminadav Zakai, M.D., Medical Director
CHR: Brian Jenkins, Director Human Resources
Web address: www.arbourhealth.com
**Control:** Corporation, Investor–owned, for–profit **Service:** Psychiatric

**Staffed Beds:** 46

✠ **STURDY MEMORIAL HOSPITAL (220008)**, 211 Park Street, Zip 02703–3137, Mailing Address: PO Box 2963, Zip 02703–0963; tel. 508/222–5200 **A**1 2 5 9 10 **F**3 8 13 15 18 20 28 29 30 31 32 34 35 36 39 40 44 45 46 49 50 56 57 58 59 61 64 70 74 75 76 77 78 79 81 82 85 86 87 89 93 97 100 107 108 109 110 111 115 118 119 129 130 131 132 134 144 146 147 148 **P**5 6
Primary Contact: Bruce S. Auerbach, M.D., President and Chief Executive Officer
CFO: Joseph Casey, Chief Financial Officer
CMO: Daniel Pietro, M.D., Medical Director
CHR: Cheryl Barrows, Vice President Human Resources
CNO: Marita Prater, MS, Vice President Patient Care Services
Web address: www.sturdymemorial.org
**Control:** Other not–for–profit (including NFP Corporation) **Service:** General Medical and Surgical

**Staffed Beds:** 128 **Admissions:** 5948 **Census:** 69 **Outpatient Visits:** 219232 **Births:** 737 **Total Expense ($000):** 148738 **Payroll Expense ($000):** 78987 **Personnel:** 993

## AYER—Middlesex County

☐ **NASHOBA VALLEY MEDICAL CENTER (220098)**, 200 Groton Road, Zip 01432–3300; tel. 978/784–9000, (Nonreporting) **A**1 9 10 **S** Steward Health Care System, LLC, Boston, MA
Primary Contact: Salvatore Perla, President
CFO: Ben Moll, Assistant Chief Financial Officer
CMO: Michael Older, M.D., President Medical Staff
Web address: www.nashobamed.com
**Control:** Corporation, Investor–owned, for–profit **Service:** General Medical and Surgical

**Staffed Beds:** 42

## BEDFORD—Middlesex County

✠ **BEDFORD VETERANS AFFAIRS MEDICAL CENTER, EDITH NOURSE ROGERS MEMORIAL VETERANS HOSPITAL**, 200 Springs Road, Zip 01730–1198; tel. 781/687–2000, (Nonreporting) **A**1 3 5 **S** Department of Veterans Affairs, Washington, DC
Primary Contact: Christine Croteau, MBA, Director
COO: Mark Fontaine–Westhart, Associate Director
CFO: Edward Koetting, Chief Financial Officer
CMO: Dan Berlowitz, M.D., Acting Chief of Staff
CHR: Robert Colpitts, Chief Human Resource Service
CNO: Mary Ann Petrillo, R.N., Acting Associate Director Nursing and Patient Clinical Services
Web address: www.bedford.va.gov
**Control:** Veterans Affairs, Government, federal **Service:** Psychiatric

**Staffed Beds:** 147

## BELMONT—Middlesex County

✠ **MCLEAN HOSPITAL (224007)**, 115 Mill Street, Zip 02478–1064; tel. 617/855–2000 **A**1 3 5 9 10 **F**4 5 29 50 53 56 58 64 68 77 86 98 99 100 101 103 104 105 106 111 119 130 132 134 146 **P**6 **S** Partners HealthCare System, Inc., Boston, MA
Primary Contact: Scott L. Rauch, M.D., President
COO: Michele L. Gougeon, Executive Vice President and Chief Operating Officer
CFO: David A. Lagasse, Senior Vice President Fiscal Affairs
CMO: Joseph Gold, M.D., Chief Medical Officer
CIO: Andrew Laband, Chief Information Officer
CNO: Linda Flaherty, R.N., Senior Vice President, Patient Care Services
Web address: www.mclean.harvard.edu
**Control:** Other not–for–profit (including NFP Corporation) **Service:** Psychiatric

**Staffed Beds:** 177 **Admissions:** 5767 **Census:** 159 **Outpatient Visits:** 115501 **Births:** 0 **Total Expense ($000):** 183123 **Payroll Expense ($000):** 78269 **Personnel:** 1591

## BEVERLY—Essex County

✠ **BEVERLY HOSPITAL (220033)**, 85 Herrick Street, Zip 01915–1777; tel. 978/922–3000, (Includes ADDISON GILBERT HOSPITAL, 298 Washington Street, Gloucester, Zip 01930–4887; tel. 978/283–4000) **A**1 2 3 5 9 10 **F**3 5 8 11 12 13 15 18 20 22 26 28 29 30 31 32 34 35 40 42 43 44 45 46 47 48 49 50 51 53 54 55 56 57 59 60 61 63 64 65 68 70 73 74 75 76 77 78 79 81 82 83 84 85 86 87 89 91 92 93 96 97 98 100 102 103 104 105 107 108 110 111 114 115 119 130 131 132 134 135 141 142 145 146 147 148 **P**1 5 6 **S** Lahey Health, Burlington, MA
Primary Contact: Philip M. Cormier, Chief Executive Officer
COO: Pauline Pike, Chief Operating Officer
CFO: Gary P. Marlow, Chief Financial Officer
CMO: Peter H. Short, M.D., Senior Vice President Medical Affairs
CIO: Robert Laramie, Chief Information Officer
CHR: Althea C. Lyons, Vice President Human Resources and Development
Web address: www.beverlyhospital.org
**Control:** Other not–for–profit (including NFP Corporation) **Service:** General Medical and Surgical

**Staffed Beds:** 320 **Admissions:** 19554 **Census:** 254 **Outpatient Visits:** 165792 **Births:** 2372 **Total Expense ($000):** 317312 **Payroll Expense ($000):** 148336

## BOSTON—Suffolk County

☐ **ARBOUR HOSPITAL (224013)**, 49 Robinwood Avenue, Zip 02130–2156; tel. 617/522–4400, (Nonreporting) **A**1 9 10 **S** Universal Health Services, Inc., King of Prussia, PA
Primary Contact: Laura Ames, Chief Executive Officer
Web address: www.arbourhealth.com
**Control:** Other not–for–profit (including NFP Corporation) **Service:** Psychiatric

**Staffed Beds:** 118

✠ **BETH ISRAEL DEACONESS MEDICAL CENTER (220086)**, 330 Brookline Avenue, Zip 02215–5491; tel. 617/667–7000, (Includes BETH ISRAEL DEACONESS HOSPITAL–NEEDHAM CAMPUS, 148 Chestnut Street, Needham, Zip 02492; tel. 781/453–3000; John M. Fogarty, President and Chief Executive Officer) **A**1 2 3 5 8 9 10 **F**3 6 9 11 12 13 14 15 17 18 20 22 24 26 28 29 30 31 34 35 36 37 38 40 43 44 45 46 47 48 49 50 51 52 53 54 55 56 57 58 59 60 61 63 64 65 66 68 70 71 72 73 74 75 76 77 78 79 81 82 84 85 86 87 91 92 93 94 97 98 100 101 102 103 104 107 108 109 110 111 112 113 114 115 116 117 118 119 120 121 123 124 126 129 130 131 132 135 136 138 139 141 142 143 144 145 146 147 148 **P**8
Primary Contact: Kevin Tabb, M.D., President and Chief Executive Officer
COO: Nancy A. Formella, R.N., Chief Operating Officer
CFO: Steven P. Fischer, Chief Financial Officer
CIO: John Halamka, M.D., Chief Information Officer
CHR: Judi Bieber, Senior Vice President Human Resources
CNO: Marsha L. Maurer, R.N., Chief Nursing Officer Patient Care Services
Web address: www.bidmc.harvard.edu
**Control:** Other not–for–profit (including NFP Corporation) **Service:** General Medical and Surgical

**Staffed Beds:** 649 **Admissions:** 33634 **Census:** 612 **Outpatient Visits:** 629407 **Births:** 5000 **Total Expense ($000):** 1385322 **Payroll Expense ($000):** 558715 **Personnel:** 7743

*Many Facility Codes have changed. Please refer to the AHA Guide Code Chart.*    © 2015 AHA Guide

☐ **BOSTON CHILDREN'S HOSPITAL (223302)**, 300 Longwood Avenue, Zip 02115–5737; tel. 617/355–6000 **A**1 3 5 8 9 10 **F**3 5 8 11 12 14 18 19 20 21 22 23 24 25 26 27 28 29 30 31 32 34 35 36 37 38 39 40 41 43 44 45 46 48 49 50 51 54 55 57 58 59 60 61 62 63 64 65 67 68 72 74 75 77 78 79 80 81 82 83 84 85 86 87 88 89 92 93 94 97 98 99 100 101 102 104 107 108 109 111 112 113 114 115 116 117 118 119 120 121 123 124 126 129 130 131 132 134 135 136 137 138 139 140 141 142 143 144 146 147 148 **P**3 5
Primary Contact: Sandra L. Fenwick, M.P.H., President and Chief Executive Officer
COO: Kevin B. Churchwell, M.D., Chief Operating Officer and Executive Vice President Health Affairs
CFO: Douglas M. Vanderslice, Senior Vice President and Chief Financial Officer
CIO: Daniel Nigrin, M.D., Vice President Information Services and Chief Information Officer
CHR: Inez Stewart, Vice President
Web address: www.childrenshospital.org/
**Control:** Other not–for–profit (including NFP Corporation) **Service:** Children's general

**Staffed Beds:** 395 **Admissions:** 15077 **Census:** 304 **Outpatient Visits:** 658711 **Births:** 0 **Total Expense ($000):** 1329785 **Payroll Expense ($000):** 471573 **Personnel:** 8866

✠ **BOSTON MEDICAL CENTER (220031)**, 1 Boston Medical Center Place, Zip 02118–2908; tel. 617/638–8000 **A**1 2 3 5 8 9 10 **F**3 5 8 14 15 17 18 20 22 24 26 28 29 30 31 32 34 35 36 38 40 41 43 44 45 46 47 48 49 50 51 54 55 56 57 58 59 61 64 65 66 68 70 72 73 74 75 76 77 78 79 81 82 84 85 86 87 88 89 93 97 99 100 101 102 103 104 107 108 110 111 114 116 117 118 119 120 121 123 124 126 129 130 131 132 134 135 136 138 142 143 144 145 146 147 148 **P**7
Primary Contact: Kate Walsh, MPH, President and Chief Executive Officer
CFO: Ronald E. Bartlett, Chief Financial Officer
CMO: Ravin Davidoff, M.D., Chief Medical Officer
CHR: Stephanie Lovell, Vice President and General Counsel
Web address: www.bmc.org
**Control:** Other not–for–profit (including NFP Corporation) **Service:** General Medical and Surgical

**Staffed Beds:** 460 **Admissions:** 23763 **Census:** 330 **Outpatient Visits:** 1066635 **Births:** 2568 **Total Expense ($000):** 1049088 **Payroll Expense ($000):** 400433 **Personnel:** 5335

✠ **BRIGHAM AND WOMEN'S FAULKNER HOSPITAL (220119)**, 1153 Centre Street, Zip 02130–3446; tel. 617/983–7000 **A**1 3 5 8 9 10 **F**3 5 11 15 17 18 28 29 30 32 34 35 40 41 43 44 45 46 47 49 50 51 57 58 59 64 65 68 70 74 75 77 79 81 82 84 85 86 87 93 94 96 98 100 102 103 104 105 107 108 110 111 114 115 119 126 129 130 131 132 135 145 146 147 **S** Partners HealthCare System, Inc., Boston, MA
Primary Contact: Michael Gustafson, M.D., President
CFO: Vincent McDermott, Vice President, Finance and Real Estate
CMO: Margaret M. Duggan, M.D., Chief Medical Officer
CIO: Catherine Schroeder, Deputy Chief Information Officer
CHR: Laura Barnett, Executive Director, Human Resources
CNO: Judy M. Hayes, R.N., Vice President Nursing and Chief Nursing Officer
Web address: www.brighamandwomensfaulkner.org/index.asp
**Control:** Other not–for–profit (including NFP Corporation) **Service:** General Medical and Surgical

**Staffed Beds:** 117 **Admissions:** 7627 **Census:** 94 **Outpatient Visits:** 187957 **Births:** 0 **Total Expense ($000):** 196579 **Payroll Expense ($000):** 87138 **Personnel:** 931

✠ **BRIGHAM AND WOMEN'S HOSPITAL (220110)**, 75 Francis Street, Zip 02115–6110; tel. 617/732–5500 **A**1 2 3 5 8 9 10 **F**3 5 6 8 9 11 12 13 14 15 16 17 18 20 22 24 26 28 29 30 31 32 33 34 35 36 37 38 39 40 43 44 45 46 47 48 49 50 51 52 54 55 56 57 58 59 60 61 64 65 66 68 70 71 72 74 75 76 77 78 79 81 82 83 84 85 86 87 92 93 97 99 100 101 102 103 104 105 107 108 110 111 112 114 115 116 117 118 119 120 121 123 124 126 129 130 131 132 133 134 135 136 137 138 140 141 142 143 144 145 146 147 148 **P**6 **S** Partners HealthCare System, Inc., Boston, MA
Primary Contact: Elizabeth Nabel, M.D., President
COO: Mairead Hickey, Ph.D., Executive Vice President and Chief Operating Officer
CFO: Michael Reney, Chief Financial Officer
CMO: Stanley Ashley, M.D., Chief Medical Officer
CIO: William C. Johnston, Interim Vice President, Information System
CHR: Julie Celano, Vice President Human Resources
CNO: Jacqueline G. Somerville, R.N., Senior Vice President for Patient Care Services and Chief Nursing Officer
Web address: www.brighamandwomens.org
**Control:** Other not–for–profit (including NFP Corporation) **Service:** General Medical and Surgical

**Staffed Beds:** 757 **Admissions:** 40240 **Census:** 689 **Outpatient Visits:** 798368 **Births:** 6794 **Total Expense ($000):** 2364302 **Payroll Expense ($000):** 713414 **Personnel:** 13303

☐ **CARNEY HOSPITAL (220017)**, 2100 Dorchester Avenue, Zip 02124–5615; tel. 617/296–4000, (Nonreporting) **A**1 2 3 5 9 10 **S** Steward Health Care System, LLC, Boston, MA
Primary Contact: Walter J. Ramos, ESQ, President and Chief Executive Officer
COO: Christian Stroucken, Chief Operating Officer
CFO: David McGrail, Vice President Finance
CMO: Alexander White, Vice President Medical Affairs
CHR: Mary Orlandi, Manager Human Resources
Web address: www.carneyhospital.org
**Control:** Corporation, Investor–owned, for–profit **Service:** General Medical and Surgical

**Staffed Beds:** 81

✠ **DANA–FARBER CANCER INSTITUTE (220162)**, 450 Brookline Avenue, Zip 02215–5418; tel. 617/632–3000 **A**1 2 3 5 9 10 **F**3 11 15 29 30 31 32 34 35 36 44 50 54 55 57 58 59 64 65 66 68 71 75 77 78 82 83 84 85 86 87 99 100 101 104 107 108 110 111 114 115 117 118 119 120 121 123 124 130 132 134 135 136 146 147 148 **P**6
Primary Contact: Edward J. Benz, Jr., M.D., President and Chief Executive Officer
COO: Dorothy E. Puhy, Executive VP and Chief Operating Officer
CMO: Lawrence N. Shulman, M.D., Senior Vice President Medical Affairs and Chief Medical Officer
CIO: Jeffrey R. Kessler, Vice President Information Services
CHR: Emily Barclay, Vice President Human Resources
Web address: www.dana–farber.org
**Control:** Other not–for–profit (including NFP Corporation) **Service:** General Medical and Surgical

**Staffed Beds:** 30 **Admissions:** 1121 **Census:** 25 **Outpatient Visits:** 364049 **Births:** 0 **Total Expense ($000):** 1056094 **Payroll Expense ($000):** 322379 **Personnel:** 4098

**DR. SOLOMON CARTER FULLER MENTAL HEALTH CENTER (224040)**, 85 East Newton Street, Zip 02118–2340; tel. 617/626–8700, (Nonreporting) **A**3 5 10
Primary Contact: Mary–Louise White, M.D., Chief Executive Officer
**Control:** Other not–for–profit (including NFP Corporation) **Service:** Psychiatric

**Staffed Beds:** 32

✠ **FRANCISCAN HOSPITAL FOR CHILDREN (223300)**, 30 Warren Street, Zip 02135–3680; tel. 617/254–3800 **A**1 3 9 10 **F**8 29 32 38 39 62 64 68 74 75 81 86 89 90 91 93 97 98 100 104 105 106 130 132 **P**5
Primary Contact: John D. Nash, FACHE, President and Chief Executive Officer
COO: Donna Polselli, Chief Operating Officer
CFO: Alex Denucci, Chief Financial Officer
CMO: Jane E. O'Brien, M.D., Medical Director
CIO: Sean McKeon, Director, Information Technology
CHR: Nancy Murphy, Vice President, Human Resources
CNO: Mary Lou Kelleher, R.N., Vice President, Nursing
Web address: www.franciscanhospital.org
**Control:** Other not–for–profit (including NFP Corporation) **Service:** Children's rehabilitation

**Staffed Beds:** 112 **Admissions:** 785 **Census:** 59 **Outpatient Visits:** 28530 **Births:** 0 **Total Expense ($000):** 57151 **Payroll Expense ($000):** 29317 **Personnel:** 553

★ △ **HEBREW REHABILITATION CENTER (222007)**, 1200 Centre Street, Zip 02131–1097; tel. 617/363–8000, (Total facility includes 50 beds in nursing home–type unit) **A**7 10 **F**1 2 6 18 29 30 35 39 50 58 59 60 64 65 68 69 75 77 82 83 84 93 97 100 103 104 119 128 130 132 143 146 148 **P**6
Primary Contact: Mary K. Moscato, FACHE, President
COO: Gregory P. Toot, Chief Operating Officer
CFO: Lise Paul, Vice President Reimbursement and Network Planning
CMO: Helen Chen, M.D., Chief Medical Officer
CIO: Peter X. Ingram, Chief Information Officer
CHR: Deborah Lemmerman, Vice President, Human Resources
CNO: Tammy B. Retalic, R.N., Chief Nursing Officer
Web address: www.hebrewseniorlife.org
**Control:** Other not–for–profit (including NFP Corporation) **Service:** Long–Term Acute Care hospital

**Staffed Beds:** 725 **Admissions:** 1475 **Census:** 669 **Outpatient Visits:** 35450 **Births:** 0 **Total Expense ($000):** 124677 **Payroll Expense ($000):** 74420 **Personnel:** 834

**MA**

---

**Hospital, Medicare Provider Number, Address, Telephone, Approval, Facility, and Physician Codes, Health Care System**

★ American Hospital Association (AHA) membership
☐ The Joint Commission accreditation
○ Healthcare Facilities Accreditation Program
◇ DNV Healthcare Inc. accreditation
⇧ Center for Improvement in Healthcare Quality Accreditation
△ Commission on Accreditation of Rehabilitation Facilities (CARF) accreditation

**MA**

☐ **MASSACHUSETTS EYE AND EAR INFIRMARY (220075)**, 243 Charles Street, Zip 02114–3002; tel. 617/523–7900 **A**1 3 5 9 10 **F**3 7 8 11 29 30 31 34 35 36 40 41 44 50 54 55 56 57 58 59 64 65 66 68 74 75 77 78 81 82 85 86 87 89 107 111 114 119 130 132 141 143 144 146 148 **P**6
Primary Contact: John R. Fernandez, President and Chief Executive Officer
CFO: CarolAnn Williams, Chief Financial Officer
CIO: Leo Hill, Chief Information Officer
CHR: Martha Pyle Farrell, Vice President Human Resources and General Counsel
Web address: www.masseyeandear.org
**Control:** Other not–for–profit (including NFP Corporation) **Service:** Eye, ear, nose, and throat

**Staffed Beds:** 41 **Admissions:** 1325 **Census:** 13 **Outpatient Visits:** 362938 **Births:** 0 **Total Expense ($000):** 227816 **Payroll Expense ($000):** 66577 **Personnel:** 1749

☒ **MASSACHUSETTS GENERAL HOSPITAL (220071)**, 55 Fruit Street, Zip 02114–2696; tel. 617/726–2000, (Includes MASSGENERAL HOSPITAL FOR CHILDREN, 55 Fruit Street, Zip 02114–2621; tel. 888/644–3248) **A**1 3 5 8 9 10 **F**3 5 6 8 9 11 12 13 14 15 16 17 18 19 20 21 22 24 25 26 27 28 29 30 31 32 33 34 35 36 37 38 39 40 41 43 44 45 46 47 48 49 50 51 52 53 54 55 56 57 58 59 60 61 62 63 64 65 66 68 70 72 74 75 76 77 78 79 81 82 84 85 86 87 88 89 91 92 93 94 96 97 98 99 100 101 102 103 104 107 108 110 111 112 113 114 115 116 117 118 119 120 121 122 123 124 126 129 130 131 132 134 135 136 137 138 139 140 141 142 143 144 145 146 147 148 **P**6 7 **S** Partners HealthCare System, Inc., Boston, MA
Primary Contact: Peter L. Slavin, M.D., President
CFO: Sally Mason Boemer, Senior Vice President Finance
CMO: Britain Nicholson, M.D., Chief Medical Officer
CIO: Keith Jennings, Chief Information Officer
CHR: Jeff Davis, Senior Vice President Human Resources
CNO: Jeanette R. Ives Erickson, MS, Senior Vice President Patient Care and Chief Nurse
Web address: www.massgeneral.org
**Control:** Other not–for–profit (including NFP Corporation) **Service:** General Medical and Surgical

**Staffed Beds:** 999 **Admissions:** 49482 **Census:** 813 **Outpatient Visits:** 944104 **Births:** 3950 **Total Expense ($000):** 3113947 **Payroll Expense ($000):** 995223 **Personnel:** 16999

☒ **NEW ENGLAND BAPTIST HOSPITAL (220088)**, 125 Parker Hill Avenue, Zip 02120–2847; tel. 617/754–5800 **A**1 3 5 9 10 **F**3 8 9 14 18 20 29 30 34 35 36 37 44 45 50 51 53 54 57 58 59 60 64 65 66 68 70 74 75 77 79 81 82 85 86 87 91 92 93 96 97 100 107 108 111 119 130 131 132 141 143 144 146 148 **P**6
Primary Contact: Trish Hannon, FACHE, President and Chief Executive Officer
CFO: Thomas Gheringhelli, Chief Financial Officer
CIO: Maureen Mulkerrin, R.N., Chief Information Officer, Vice President Innovation and Technology
CHR: Linda Thompson, Vice President Human Resources
CNO: Mary Sullivan Smith, R.N., Vice President Clinical Operations and Chief Nursing Officer
Web address: www.nebh.org
**Control:** Other not–for–profit (including NFP Corporation) **Service:** Orthopedic

**Staffed Beds:** 118 **Admissions:** 8193 **Census:** 71 **Outpatient Visits:** 130398 **Births:** 0 **Total Expense ($000):** 233650 **Payroll Expense ($000):** 83824 **Personnel:** 867

☐ **SHRINERS HOSPITALS FOR CHILDREN–BOSTON (223304)**, (Pediatric Burns, Orthopaedics, Cleft Lip & Palate), 51 Blossom Street, Zip 02114–2601; tel. 617/722–3000 **A**1 3 5 10 **F**3 16 29 30 34 35 57 64 68 75 77 79 81 85 86 87 93 99 104 130 132 141 143 146 148 **S** Shriners Hospitals for Children, Tampa, FL
Primary Contact: John Patrick O'Neill, FACHE, Administrator
CFO: Maria Chung, CPA, Director Fiscal Services
CMO: Matthias B. Donelan, M.D., Chief of Staff
CIO: Mary Dolan, Regional Director Information Services and HIPAA Security Official
CHR: John Donlin, Regional Director Human Resources – Boston, Erie, and Springfield
Web address: www.shrinershospitalsforchildren.org/Hospitals/Locations/Boston
**Control:** Other not–for–profit (including NFP Corporation) **Service:** Children's other specialty

**Staffed Beds:** 18 **Admissions:** 283 **Census:** 7 **Outpatient Visits:** 5719 **Births:** 0 **Total Expense ($000):** 34311 **Payroll Expense ($000):** 14486 **Personnel:** 190

☒ **TUFTS MEDICAL CENTER (220116)**, 800 Washington Street, Zip 02111–1552; tel. 617/636–5000 **A**1 2 3 5 8 9 10 **F**3 12 13 14 15 17 18 19 20 21 22 23 24 25 26 27 28 29 30 31 32 34 35 39 40 41 43 44 45 47 49 50 51 52 55 56 57 58 59 61 64 65 68 70 71 72 74 75 76 77 78 79 81 82 84 85 86 87 88 89 93 97 98 99 100 102 104 107 108 111 114 115 116 117 118 119 120 121 123 124 126 129 130 131 132 134 135 136 137 138 143 146 147 148 **P**5
Primary Contact: Michael Wagner, M.D., President and Chief Executive Officer
CFO: C. Okey Agba, Senior Vice President, Chief Financial Officer and Treasurer
CMO: David Fairchild, M.D., Chief Medical Officer
CIO: William Shickolovich, Chief Information Officer
CNO: Therese M. Hudson–Jinks, R.N., Chief Nursing Officer
Web address: www.tuftsmedicalcenter.org
**Control:** Other not–for–profit (including NFP Corporation) **Service:** General Medical and Surgical

**Staffed Beds:** 268 **Admissions:** 16940 **Census:** 254 **Outpatient Visits:** 408288 **Births:** 1139 **Total Expense ($000):** 636133 **Payroll Expense ($000):** 252427 **Personnel:** 3527

★ △ **VETERANS AFFAIRS BOSTON HEALTHCARE SYSTEM**, 1400 VFW Parkway, Zip 02132–4927; tel. 617/323–7700, (Nonreporting) **A**3 5 7 8 **S** Department of Veterans Affairs, Washington, DC
Primary Contact: Vincent Ng, Director
CFO: Joe Costa, Chief Financial Officer
CMO: Brian Hoffman, M.D., Chief Medical Services
CIO: David M. Goodman, Ph.D., Chief Information Officer
CHR: William Warfield, Chief Human Resources Management
Web address: www.boston.va.gov/
**Control:** Veterans Affairs, Government, federal **Service:** General Medical and Surgical

**Staffed Beds:** 361

**BRADFORD—Essex County**

☒ **WHITTIER REHABILITATION HOSPITAL (222047)**, 145 Ward Hill Avenue, Zip 01835–6928; tel. 978/372–8000, (Nonreporting) **A**1 10 **S** Whittier Health Network, Haverhill, MA
Primary Contact: Alfred J. Arcidi, M.D., Senior Vice President
Web address: www.whittierhealth.com
**Control:** Partnership, Investor–owned, for–profit **Service:** Long–Term Acute Care hospital

**Staffed Beds:** 60

**BRAINTREE—Norfolk County**

☐ **BRAINTREE REHABILITATION HOSPITAL (223027)**, 250 Pond Street, Zip 02184–5351; tel. 781/348–2500 **A**1 3 5 10 **F**29 34 35 54 57 59 64 74 75 77 78 79 86 87 90 91 92 93 101 108 119 130 131 132 146 **P**5 **S** Five Star Quality Care, Newton, MA
Primary Contact: Randy Doherty, CPA, Chief Executive Officer
CMO: Arthur Williams, M.D., Medical Director
CHR: Cathryn Wigman, Director Human Resources
CNO: Jinia Drinkwater, R.N., Director Patient Care Services
Web address: www.braintreerehabhospital.com
**Control:** Corporation, Investor–owned, for–profit **Service:** Rehabilitation

**Staffed Beds:** 187 **Admissions:** 2541 **Census:** 85 **Outpatient Visits:** 91137 **Births:** 0 **Total Expense ($000):** 45614 **Payroll Expense ($000):** 23525 **Personnel:** 305

**BRIDGEWATER—Plymouth County**

**BRIDGEWATER STATE HOSPITAL**, 20 Administration Road, Zip 02324–3201; tel. 508/279–4521, (Nonreporting) **A**3 5
Primary Contact: Kenneth W. Nelson, Superintendent
CFO: Diane Wholley, Director Fiscal Services
**Control:** State–Government, nonfederal **Service:** Psychiatric

**Staffed Beds:** 350

**BRIGHTON—Suffolk County**

**CARITAS ST. ELIZABETH'S MEDICAL CENTER** See St. Elizabeth's Medical Center

☒ **KINDRED HOSPITAL–BOSTON (222045)**, 1515 Commonwealth Avenue, Zip 02135–3617; tel. 617/254–1100, (Nonreporting) **A**1 10 **S** Kindred Healthcare, Louisville, KY
Primary Contact: Susan Downey, R.N., MS, Chief Executive Officer
CFO: Lawrence J. Toye, Chief Financial Officer
CMO: Mark Rohrer, M.D., Chief Medical Officer
Web address: www.kindredbos.com/
**Control:** Corporation, Investor–owned, for–profit **Service:** Long–Term Acute Care hospital

**Staffed Beds:** 59

*Many Facility Codes have changed. Please refer to the AHA Guide Code Chart.* © 2015 AHA Guide

☐ **ST. ELIZABETH'S MEDICAL CENTER (220036)**, 736 Cambridge Street, Zip 02135–2997; tel. 617/789–3000, (Nonreporting) **A**1 2 3 5 8 9 10 **S** Steward Health Care System, LLC, Boston, MA
Primary Contact: Roger Mitty, Interim Chief Executive Officer
CFO: Jeffrey P. Dion, Vice President Finance
CIO: Joseph Schmitt, Chief Information Officer
CHR: Claudia Henderson, Chief Human Resources
Web address: www.stewardhealth.org/St_Elizabeths
**Control:** Corporation, Investor–owned, for–profit **Service:** General Medical and Surgical

**Staffed Beds:** 338

### BROCKTON—Plymouth County

**CARITAS GOOD SAMARITAN MEDICAL CENTER** See Good Samaritan Medical Center

☐ **GOOD SAMARITAN MEDICAL CENTER (220111)**, 235 North Pearl Street, Zip 02301–1794; tel. 508/427–3000, (Includes GOOD SAMARITAN MEDICAL CENTER – CUSHING CAMPUS, 235 North Pearl Street, Zip 02401–1794; tel. 508/427–3000), (Nonreporting) **A**1 2 3 5 9 10 **S** Steward Health Care System, LLC, Boston, MA
Primary Contact: John A. Jurczyk, FACHE, Interim President
COO: Donna Rubinate, R.N., Chief Operating Officer
CFO: Thomas Whalen, Vice President Finance
CMO: Scott Stewart, M.D., Vice President Medical Management
CIO: Lori Caswell, Director Information Technology
CHR: David J. Cronin, Regional Vice President Human Resources
Web address: www.stewardhealth.org/Good–Samaritan
**Control:** Corporation, Investor–owned, for–profit **Service:** General Medical and Surgical

**Staffed Beds:** 190

⊞ **SIGNATURE HEALTHCARE BROCKTON HOSPITAL (220052)**, 680 Centre Street, Zip 02302–3395; tel. 508/941–7000, (Total facility includes 29 beds in nursing home–type unit) **A**1 2 3 6 9 10 **F**3 11 12 13 15 17 18 20 22 24 28 29 30 31 32 34 35 38 40 45 46 47 48 49 50 51 52 54 55 56 57 59 60 61 64 65 66 68 70 73 74 75 76 77 78 79 81 82 84 85 87 89 93 97 98 100 101 102 103 104 105 107 108 110 111 114 115 116 117 118 119 120 121 123 128 131 132 135 143 144 146 147 148 **P**6 8
Primary Contact: Kim Norton Hollon, FACHE, President and Chief Executive Officer
CFO: James Papadakos, Chief Financial Officer
CMO: Vera De Palo, M.D., Chief Medical Officer
CIO: Marc Delacroix, Chief Information Officer
CHR: David Fisher, Vice President Human Resources
CNO: Kim Walsh, Chief Nursing Officer
Web address: www.signature–healthcare.org
**Control:** Other not–for–profit (including NFP Corporation) **Service:** General Medical and Surgical

**Staffed Beds:** 245 **Admissions:** 11467 **Census:** 137 **Outpatient Visits:** 380807 **Births:** 1017 **Total Expense ($000):** 218783 **Payroll Expense ($000):** 99807 **Personnel:** 1351

★ **VETERANS AFFAIRS BOSTON HEALTHCARE SYSTEM BROCKTON DIVISION**, 940 Belmont Street, Zip 02301–5596; tel. 508/583–4500, (Includes VETERANS AFFAIRS MEDICAL CENTER WEST ROXBURY DIVISION, 1400 VFW Parkway, West Roxbury, Zip 02132, Mailing Address: 1400 VVF Parkway, West Roxbury, Boston, Zip 02132; tel. 617/323–7700; William H. Kelleher, Director), (Nonreporting) **A**3 5 8 **S** Department of Veterans Affairs, Washington, DC
Primary Contact: Vincent Ng, Interim Director
CFO: Joe Costa, Acting Chief Fiscal Officer
Web address: www.boston.va.gov/
**Control:** Veterans Affairs, Government, federal **Service:** General Medical and Surgical

**Staffed Beds:** 375

### BROOKLINE—Norfolk County

☐ **ARBOUR H. R. I. HOSPITAL (224018)**, 227 Babcock Street, Zip 02446–6799; tel. 617/731–3200, (Nonreporting) **A**1 9 10 **S** Universal Health Services, Inc., King of Prussia, PA
Primary Contact: William Zella, Chief Executive Officer
CFO: James Rollins, Chief Financial Officer
CMO: Anthony Raynes, M.D., Psychiatrist in Chief
CHR: Kris Munson, Director Human Resources
Web address: www.arbourhealth.com
**Control:** Corporation, Investor–owned, for–profit **Service:** Psychiatric

**Staffed Beds:** 68

**BOURNEWOOD HEALTH SYSTEMS (224022)**, 300 South Street, Zip 02467–3658; tel. 617/469–0300 **A**3 5 9 10 **F**4 5 98 99 104 105 130 132 **P**1
Primary Contact: Philip A. Mason, Chief Executive Officer
CFO: Michael Gale, Chief Financial Officer
CMO: Carmel Heinsohn, M.D., Medical Director
CHR: Paula Berardi, Manager Human Resources
Web address: www.bournewood.com
**Control:** Corporation, Investor–owned, for–profit **Service:** Psychiatric

**Staffed Beds:** 90 **Admissions:** 3725 **Census:** 85 **Outpatient Visits:** 9850 **Births:** 0 **Total Expense ($000):** 23148 **Payroll Expense ($000):** 13668 **Personnel:** 189

### BURLINGTON—Middlesex County

⊞ **LAHEY HOSPITAL & MEDICAL CENTER, BURLINGTON (220171)**, 41 Mall Road, Zip 01805–0001; tel. 781/744–5100, (Includes LAHEY MEDICAL CENTER, PEABODY, 1 Essex Center Drive, Peabody, Zip 01960–2901; tel. 978/538–4000) **A**1 2 3 5 8 9 10 **F**3 5 6 8 9 11 12 14 15 17 18 20 22 24 26 28 29 30 31 34 35 36 37 38 40 43 44 45 46 47 48 49 50 51 53 54 55 56 57 58 59 60 61 64 65 68 70 74 75 77 78 79 81 82 84 85 86 87 91 92 93 94 96 97 100 101 102 103 104 107 108 110 111 114 115 116 117 118 119 120 121 123 124 126 129 130 131 132 135 136 138 139 141 142 143 144 145 146 147 148 **P**6 **S** Lahey Health, Burlington, MA
Primary Contact: Joanne Conroy, M.D., Chief Executive Officer
COO: Richard R. Bias, Chief Operating Officer
CFO: Timothy P. O'Connor, Executive Vice President and Chief Financial Officer
CMO: Andrew Villanueva, M.D., Interim Chief Medical Officer
CIO: Bruce Metz, Ph.D., Senior Vice President and Chief Information Officer
CHR: Elizabeth P. Conrad, Senior Vice President and Chief Human Resource Officer
CNO: Lisa Colombo, R.N., Senior Vice President and Chief Nursing Officer
Web address: www.lahey.org
**Control:** Other not–for–profit (including NFP Corporation) **Service:** General Medical and Surgical

**Staffed Beds:** 345 **Admissions:** 20981 **Census:** 282 **Outpatient Visits:** 938404 **Births:** 0 **Total Expense ($000):** 755152 **Payroll Expense ($000):** 272909 **Personnel:** 5787

### CAMBRIDGE—Middlesex County

⊞ **CAMBRIDGE HEALTH ALLIANCE (220011)**, 1493 Cambridge Street, Zip 02139–1099; tel. 617/665–1000, (Includes CAMBRIDGE HOSPITAL, 1493 Cambridge Street, tel. 617/498–1000; SOMERVILLE HOSPITAL, 230 Highland Avenue, Somerville, Zip 02143; tel. 617/666–4400; WHIDDEN MEMORIAL HOSPITAL, 103 Garland Street, Everett, Zip 02149–5095; tel. 617/389–6270) **A**1 2 3 5 8 9 10 **F**4 5 11 13 15 29 30 34 35 36 38 39 40 44 45 46 47 48 49 50 56 57 58 59 61 64 65 66 68 70 75 76 77 78 79 81 82 86 87 93 97 98 99 100 101 102 103 104 107 108 110 111 114 115 119 129 130 131 132 134 135 143 146 147 148 **P**6
Primary Contact: Patrick R. Wardell, Chief Executive Officer
CFO: Jill I. Batty, Chief Financial Officer
CMO: Assaad Sayah, M.D., Chief Medical Officer
CIO: Judith S. Klickstein, Chief Information Officer
CHR: Joy U. Curtis, Senior Vice President Human Resources
CNO: Elizabeth Cadigan, R.N., Senior Vice President Patient Care Services and Chief Nursing Officer
Web address: www.challiance.org
**Control:** Hospital district or authority, Government, nonfederal **Service:** General Medical and Surgical

**Staffed Beds:** 190 **Admissions:** 10996 **Census:** 160 **Outpatient Visits:** 660135 **Births:** 1202 **Total Expense ($000):** 556157 **Payroll Expense ($000):** 302572 **Personnel:** 3296

⊞ **MOUNT AUBURN HOSPITAL (220002)**, 330 Mount Auburn Street, Zip 02138–5597; tel. 617/492–3500 **A**1 2 3 5 8 9 10 **F**3 5 11 12 13 14 15 17 18 20 22 24 26 28 29 30 31 34 35 37 40 45 49 50 51 52 55 56 57 58 59 60 61 62 64 65 68 70 73 74 75 76 77 78 79 81 82 86 87 93 97 98 100 101 102 103 104 107 108 110 111 114 115 117 118 119 120 121 123 124 126 129 130 131 132 135 144 145 146 147 **P**5 6 7
Primary Contact: Jeanette G. Clough, President and Chief Executive Officer
COO: Nicholas T. Dileso, R.N., Chief Operating Officer
CFO: William Sullivan, Chief Financial Officer
CIO: Bob Todd, Director Information Systems
CHR: Tom Fabiano, Director Human Resources
CNO: Deborah Baker, Vice President, Patient Care Services
Web address: www.mountauburnhospital.org
**Control:** Other not–for–profit (including NFP Corporation) **Service:** General Medical and Surgical

**Staffed Beds:** 195 **Admissions:** 11365 **Census:** 142 **Outpatient Visits:** 169798 **Births:** 2776 **Total Expense ($000):** 301408 **Payroll Expense ($000):** 142035 **Personnel:** 2294

**SPAULDING HOSPITAL CAMBRIDGE** See Spaulding Hospital for Continuing Medical Care Cambridge

**MA**

---

**Hospital, Medicare Provider Number, Address, Telephone, Approval, Facility, and Physician Codes, Health Care System**

★ American Hospital Association (AHA) membership
☐ The Joint Commission accreditation
○ Healthcare Facilities Accreditation Program
◇ DNV Healthcare Inc. accreditation
⇑ Center for Improvement in Healthcare Quality Accreditation
△ Commission on Accreditation of Rehabilitation Facilities (CARF) accreditation

**MA**

⊠ **SPAULDING HOSPITAL FOR CONTINUING MEDICAL CARE CAMBRIDGE (222000)**, 1575 Cambridge Street, Zip 02138–4308; tel. 617/876–4344, (Nonreporting) **A**1 10 **S** Partners HealthCare System, Inc., Boston, MA
Primary Contact: Maureen Banks, R.N., FACHE, President
COO: Timothy Lynch, Vice President Operations
CFO: Mary Shaughnessy, Vice President Finance
CMO: Jonathon Schwartz, M.D., Medical Director and Chief Medical Officer
CIO: John Campbell, Director Information Systems
CHR: Jack Carroll, Senior Director Human Resources
CNO: Joanne Fucile, R.N., Vice President Operations and Director of Nursing
Web address: www.spauldingnetwork.org
**Control:** Other not–for–profit (including NFP Corporation) **Service:** Long–Term Acute Care hospital

**Staffed Beds:** 180

### CANTON—Norfolk County

⊠ **MASSACHUSETTS HOSPITAL SCHOOL (222025)**, 3 Randolph Street, Zip 02021–2351; tel. 781/828–2440, (Nonreporting) **A**1 10 **S** Massachusetts Department of Public Health, Boston, MA
Primary Contact: Brian V. Devin, Chief Executive Officer
CFO: Sharon Porter, Chief Financial Officer
CMO: Aruna Sachdev, M.D., Medical Director
CIO: Robert Lima, Director Information Systems
CHR: Trish Scully, Manager Employment Services
Web address: www.mhsf.us/
**Control:** State–Government, nonfederal **Service:** Children's Long–Term Acute Care

**Staffed Beds:** 80

### CHARLESTOWN—Suffolk County

⊠ △ **SPAULDING REHABILITATION HOSPITAL (223034)**, 300 First Avenue, Zip 02129–3109; tel. 617/573–7000 **A**1 3 5 7 10 **F**3 7 29 30 34 35 36 39 50 54 57 58 60 64 68 74 75 77 82 85 86 87 90 91 92 93 94 95 96 100 104 119 129 130 131 132 143 146 148 **S** Partners HealthCare System, Inc., Boston, MA
Primary Contact: David E. Storto, President
COO: Maureen Banks, R.N., Chief Operating Officer
CFO: Mary Shaughnessy, Vice President Finance
CMO: Ross Zafonte, D.O., Chief, Physical Medicine and Rehabilitation and Vice President Medical Affairs, Research and Education
CIO: John Campbell, Director Management Information Systems
CHR: Russell Averna, Director Human Resources
Web address: www.spauldingrehab.org
**Control:** Other not–for–profit (including NFP Corporation) **Service:** Rehabilitation

**Staffed Beds:** 132 **Admissions:** 2254 **Census:** 125 **Outpatient Visits:** 179680 **Births:** 0 **Total Expense ($000):** 129232 **Payroll Expense ($000):** 57828 **Personnel:** 1125

### CLINTON—Worcester County

★ ◇ **CLINTON HOSPITAL (220058)**, 201 Highland Street, Zip 01510–1096; tel. 978/368–3000, (Nonreporting) **A**3 5 9 10 21 **S** UMass Memorial Health Care, Inc., Worcester, MA
Primary Contact: Sheila Daly, R.N., MS, President and Chief Executive Officer
CFO: Steven McCue, Chief Financial Officer
CHR: Martha Chiarchiaro, Vice President Human Resources
CNO: Charlene Elie, Vice President Patient Care Services
Web address: www.clintonhospital.org
**Control:** Other not–for–profit (including NFP Corporation) **Service:** General Medical and Surgical

**Staffed Beds:** 41

### CONCORD—Middlesex County

⊠ **EMERSON HOSPITAL (220084)**, 133 Old Road to Nine Acre Corner, Zip 01742–9120; tel. 978/369–1400 **A**1 5 9 10 **F**3 7 8 11 12 13 14 15 17 18 28 29 30 31 32 34 35 36 37 38 40 45 48 49 50 51 54 57 59 60 62 64 65 68 70 72 73 74 75 76 77 78 79 81 85 86 87 89 93 98 100 101 102 103 104 105 107 110 111 114 115 119 121 128 129 130 131 132 141 145 146 148 **P**5 8
Primary Contact: Christine C. Schuster, R.N., President and Chief Executive Officer
CFO: Michael Hachey, Senior Vice President and Chief Financial Officer
CMO: C. Gregory Martin, M.D., Chief Medical Officer
CIO: John O. Wilhelm, Jr., Senior Vice President and Chief Financial Officer
CHR: Eric Stastny, Vice President Human Resources
CNO: Joyce Welsh, R.N., Vice President of Clinical Services and Chief Nursing Officer
Web address: www.emersonhospital.org
**Control:** Other not–for–profit (including NFP Corporation) **Service:** General Medical and Surgical

**Staffed Beds:** 170 **Admissions:** 7551 **Census:** 101 **Outpatient Visits:** 249344 **Births:** 1175 **Total Expense ($000):** 189032 **Payroll Expense ($000):** 86030 **Personnel:** 1121

### EAST SANDWICH—Barnstable County

⊠ △ **SPAULDING REHABILITATION HOSPITAL CAPE COD (223032)**, 311 Service Road, Zip 02537–1370; tel. 508/833–4000 **A**1 7 10 **F**3 28 29 30 32 34 35 36 50 56 60 64 74 75 79 82 90 91 92 93 94 96 130 131 132 146 147 148 **P**4 6 **S** Partners HealthCare System, Inc., Boston, MA
Primary Contact: Maureen Banks, R.N., FACHE, President
COO: Stephanie Nadolny, Vice President of Hospital Operations
CFO: Mary Shaughnessy, Vice President Finance
CMO: David Lowell, M.D., Chief Medical Officer
CIO: John Campbell, Chief Information Officer
CHR: Russell Averna, Vice President of Human Resources
CNO: Adrienne Sarnecki, R.N., Chief Nursing Officer
Web address: www.spauldingrehab.org
**Control:** State–Government, nonfederal **Service:** Rehabilitation

**Staffed Beds:** 60 **Admissions:** 1151 **Census:** 43 **Outpatient Visits:** 104604 **Births:** 0 **Total Expense ($000):** 36149 **Payroll Expense ($000):** 19818 **Personnel:** 319

### EVERETT—Middlesex County

**WHIDDEN MEMORIAL HOSPITAL** See Cambridge Health Alliance, Cambridge

### FALL RIVER—Bristol County

**CHARLTON MEMORIAL HOSPITAL** See Southcoast Hospitals Group

☐ **DR. J. CORRIGAN MENTAL HEALTH CENTER (224028)**, 49 Hillside Street, Zip 02720–5266; tel. 508/235–7200, (Nonreporting) **A**1 10 **S** Massachusetts Department of Mental Health, Boston, MA
Primary Contact: Roberta H. Guez, Director
**Control:** State–Government, nonfederal **Service:** Psychiatric

**Staffed Beds:** 16

☐ **SAINT ANNE'S HOSPITAL (220020)**, 795 Middle Street, Zip 02721–1798; tel. 508/674–5741, (Nonreporting) **A**1 2 9 10 **S** Steward Health Care System, LLC, Boston, MA
Primary Contact: Craig A. Jesiolowski, FACHE, President
CFO: Michael Bushell, Vice President Finance, Business Development and Support Services
CMO: Harvey Kowaloff, M.D., Vice President Medical Affairs
CHR: Lisa Berry, Director
CNO: Carole Billington, R.N., Vice President Patient Care Services
Web address: www.saintanneshospital.org
**Control:** Corporation, Investor–owned, for–profit **Service:** General Medical and Surgical

**Staffed Beds:** 160

⊠ **SOUTHCOAST HOSPITALS GROUP (220074)**, 363 Highland Avenue, Zip 02720–3703; tel. 508/679–3131, (Includes CHARLTON MEMORIAL HOSPITAL, 363 Highland Avenue, tel. 508/679–3131; ST. LUKE'S HOSPITAL, 101 Page Street, New Bedford, Zip 02740; tel. 508/997–1515; TOBEY HOSPITAL, 43 High Street, Wareham, Zip 02571; tel. 508/295–0880) **A**1 2 9 10 **F**3 8 11 12 13 14 15 17 18 20 22 24 26 28 29 30 31 34 35 37 40 41 44 45 46 47 48 49 50 51 54 56 57 58 59 60 61 64 65 68 70 71 73 74 75 76 77 78 79 81 82 83 84 85 86 87 89 90 91 92 93 95 96 98 100 101 102 103 107 108 110 111 114 115 116 117 118 119 120 121 123 124 126 130 131 132 134 135 144 146 147 148 **P**5 6
Primary Contact: Keith A. Hovan, R.N., President and Chief Executive Officer
COO: Linda Bodenmann, Chief Operating Officer
CFO: Gary F. Conner, Chief Financial Officer
CMO: Robert Caldas, D.O., Chief Medical Officer
CIO: Joan McFaul, Senior Vice President and Chief Information Officer
CHR: David DeJesus, Senior Vice President Human Resources
Web address: www.southcoast.org
**Control:** Other not–for–profit (including NFP Corporation) **Service:** General Medical and Surgical

**Staffed Beds:** 593 **Admissions:** 35300 **Census:** 453 **Outpatient Visits:** 902111 **Births:** 3415 **Total Expense ($000):** 688496 **Payroll Expense ($000):** 311910 **Personnel:** 4134

### FALMOUTH—Barnstable County

⊠ **FALMOUTH HOSPITAL (220135)**, 100 Ter Heun Drive, Zip 02540–2599; tel. 508/548–5300 **A**1 2 9 10 **F**3 8 11 13 15 18 20 28 29 30 34 35 36 38 40 45 50 53 54 57 59 61 64 65 68 70 74 75 76 77 79 81 82 85 86 87 89 93 96 102 107 108 110 111 115 118 119 129 130 131 132 135 143 144 146 147 148 **P**6 8 **S** Cape Cod Healthcare, Inc., Hyannis, MA
Primary Contact: Michael K. Lauf, President and Chief Executive Officer
COO: Jeff Dykens, CPA, Chief Operating Officer
CFO: Michael Connors, Senior Vice President and Chief Financial Officer
CMO: Alex Heard, Chief Medical Officer
CIO: Jeanne M. Fallon, Chief Information Officer
CHR: Emily Schorer, Vice President, Human Resources
CNO: Lori Jewett, Vice President of Nursing
Web address: www.capecodhealth.org
**Control:** Other not–for–profit (including NFP Corporation) **Service:** General Medical and Surgical

**Staffed Beds:** 95 **Admissions:** 5878 **Census:** 66 **Outpatient Visits:** 140139 **Births:** 435 **Total Expense ($000):** 143293 **Payroll Expense ($000):** 63098 **Personnel:** 531

## FRAMINGHAM—Middlesex County

✠ **METROWEST MEDICAL CENTER (220175)**, 115 Lincoln Street,
Zip 01702–6342; tel. 508/383–1000, (Includes FRAMINGHAM UNION HOSPITAL,
115 Lincoln Street, Zip 01702; tel. 508/383–1000; LEONARD MORSE HOSPITAL,
67 Union Street, Natick, Zip 01760; tel. 508/650–7000) **A**1 2 3 5 9 10 **F**3 5 12
13 14 15 18 20 22 26 28 29 30 31 32 34 35 36 40 44 45 49 50 54 56 57
59 61 62 63 64 65 68 70 72 74 75 76 77 78 79 81 82 85 86 87 89 93 97
98 99 100 102 103 104 105 107 108 110 114 115 118 119 120 121 129
130 131 132 134 135 143 144 146 147 148 **S** TENET Healthcare Corporation,
Dallas, TX
Primary Contact: Barbara J. Doyle, R.N., MS, Chief Executive Officer
CHR: Rebecca Heffernan, Director Human Resources
CNO: Donna T. Gemme, R.N., Chief Nursing Officer
Web address: www.mwmc.com
**Control:** Corporation, Investor–owned, for–profit **Service:** General Medical and
Surgical

**Staffed Beds:** 148 **Admissions:** 11171 **Census:** 142 **Outpatient Visits:**
369388 **Births:** 804 **Total Expense ($000):** 246146 **Payroll Expense**
**($000):** 117937 **Personnel:** 1837

## GARDNER—Worcester County

☐ **HEYWOOD HOSPITAL (220095)**, 242 Green Street, Zip 01440–1373;
tel. 978/632–3420 **A**1 3 5 9 10 **F**3 11 15 18 28 29 30 31 34 40 50 53 57
59 64 65 68 70 75 76 77 78 79 81 82 84 85 86 87 89 92 96 98 99 100
101 102 103 104 105 107 110 111 114 115 116 117 118 119 129 130 132
134 135 146
Primary Contact: Winfield S. Brown, FACHE, President and Chief Executive Officer
CFO: Robert Crosby, Senior Vice President and Chief Financial Officer
CHR: Thomas Cady, Vice President Human Resources
Web address: www.heywood.org
**Control:** Other not–for–profit (including NFP Corporation) **Service:** General
Medical and Surgical

**Staffed Beds:** 93 **Admissions:** 5003 **Census:** 67 **Outpatient Visits:** 76261
**Births:** 412 **Total Expense ($000):** 99802 **Payroll Expense ($000):** 43311

## GLOUCESTER—Essex County

**ADDISON GILBERT HOSPITAL** See Beverly Hospital, Beverly

## GREAT BARRINGTON—Berkshire County

✠ **FAIRVIEW HOSPITAL (221302)**, 29 Lewis Avenue, Zip 01230–1713;
tel. 413/528–0790 **A**1 9 10 18 **F**3 11 13 15 18 29 30 34 35 40 45 46 49 50
54 57 59 64 65 68 70 75 77 79 81 85 86 87 92 93 94 107 108 110 114
119 130 131 132 133 135 146 147 148 **P**6 **S** Berkshire Health Systems, Inc.,
Pittsfield, MA
Primary Contact: Eugene A. Dellea, President
COO: Doreen M. Sylvia–Hutchinson, Vice President Operations and Chief Nurse
Executive
CFO: Anthony Rinaldi, Executive Vice President
CMO: Brian Burke, M.D., President Medical Staff
CHR: Laura Farkas, Director Human Resources
Web address: www.bhs1.org/body_fh.cfm?id=39
**Control:** Other not–for–profit (including NFP Corporation) **Service:** General
Medical and Surgical

**Staffed Beds:** 24 **Admissions:** 761 **Census:** 8 **Outpatient Visits:** 75190
**Births:** 140 **Total Expense ($000):** 45551 **Payroll Expense ($000):** 21468
**Personnel:** 215

## GREENFIELD—Franklin County

✠ **BAYSTATE FRANKLIN MEDICAL CENTER (220016)**, 164 High Street,
Zip 01301–2613; tel. 413/773–0211 **A**1 3 9 10 **F**3 11 12 13 14 15 18 24 28
29 30 31 34 35 36 40 45 46 47 48 50 51 55 57 59 64 68 70 74 75 76 77
78 79 81 82 85 86 87 89 93 98 100 101 105 107 108 110 111 115 118
119 129 130 131 132 146 147 148 **S** Baystate Health, Inc., Springfield, MA
Primary Contact: Thomas Higgins, M.D., Interim President and Chief Executive
Officer
COO: Gina Campbell, R.N., Chief Operating Officer
CFO: Andrea Nathanson, Director Finance
CMO: Thomas Higgins, M.D., Chief Medical Officer
CHR: Kerry Damon, Director Human Resources
CNO: Leesa–Lee Keith, R.N., Chief Nursing Officer
Web address: www.baystatehealth.com/fmc
**Control:** Other not–for–profit (including NFP Corporation) **Service:** General
Medical and Surgical

**Staffed Beds:** 90 **Admissions:** 4022 **Census:** 46 **Outpatient Visits:** 106842
**Births:** 497 **Total Expense ($000):** 81455 **Payroll Expense ($000):** 33276
**Personnel:** 436

## HAVERHILL—Essex County

**BALDPATE HOSPITAL (224033)**, 83 Baldpate Road, Zip 01833–2303;
tel. 978/352–2131, (Nonreporting) **A**9 10
Primary Contact: Lucille M. Batal, Administrator
Web address: www.baldpateh.com
**Control:** Corporation, Investor–owned, for–profit **Service:** Psychiatric

**Staffed Beds:** 59

**WHITTIER PAVILION (224039)**, 76 Summer Street, Zip 01830–5814;
tel. 978/373–8222 **A**9 10 **F**77 98 103 104 **S** Whittier Health Network,
Haverhill, MA
Primary Contact: Alfred L. Arcidi, M.D., Chief Executive Officer
Web address: www.whittierhealth.com
**Control:** Individual, Investor–owned, for–profit **Service:** Psychiatric

**Staffed Beds:** 65 **Admissions:** 1924 **Census:** 53 **Outpatient Visits:** 2495
**Births:** 0

## HOLYOKE—Hampden County

☐ **HOLYOKE MEDICAL CENTER (220024)**, 575 Beech Street, Zip 01040–2223;
tel. 413/534–2500 **A**1 2 5 9 10 **F**3 5 9 11 13 14 15 17 18 28 29 31 34 35
38 40 44 45 46 49 50 57 59 64 65 68 70 74 75 76 77 78 79 81 82 85 86
87 89 91 92 93 96 98 100 101 102 104 105 107 108 110 111 114 118 119
124 129 130 132 135 143 145 146 147 148 **P**8
Primary Contact: Spiros Hatiras, FACHE, President and Chief Executive Officer
CFO: Antonio Correia, Chief Financial Officer
CMO: Karen Ferroni, M.D., Medical Director
CIO: Carl Cameron, Director Information Systems
CHR: Mary Kelleher, Vice President Human Resources
Web address: www.holyokehealth.com
**Control:** Other not–for–profit (including NFP Corporation) **Service:** General
Medical and Surgical

**Staffed Beds:** 198 **Admissions:** 5610 **Census:** 66 **Outpatient Visits:** 274733
**Births:** 420 **Total Expense ($000):** 116803 **Payroll Expense ($000):** 63465

## HYANNIS—Barnstable County

✠ **CAPE COD HOSPITAL (220012)**, 27 Park Street, Zip 02601–5230;
tel. 508/771–1800 **A**1 2 5 9 10 20 **F**3 11 13 14 15 17 18 20 22 24 26 28 29
30 31 34 35 37 38 40 45 49 50 51 54 57 61 64 65 68 70 74 75 76 77 78
79 81 82 85 86 87 89 93 97 98 99 100 101 102 103 104 105 107 108 110
111 114 115 119 120 121 123 124 126 130 131 132 143 144 146 147 **P**6
8 **S** Cape Cod Healthcare, Inc., Hyannis, MA
Primary Contact: Michael K. Lauf, President and Chief Executive Officer
COO: Kevin Mulroy, D.O., Chief Operating Officer and Chief Quality Officer
CFO: Michael Connors, Senior Vice President and Chief Financial Officer
CMO: Donald Guadagnoli, M.D., Chief Medical Officer
CIO: Jeanne M. Fallon, Senior Vice President and Chief Information Officer
CHR: Emily Schorer, Senior Vice President Human Resources
CNO: Judith Quinn, Vice President Patient Care Services
Web address: www.capecodhealth.org
**Control:** Other not–for–profit (including NFP Corporation) **Service:** General
Medical and Surgical

**Staffed Beds:** 259 **Admissions:** 15132 **Census:** 177 **Outpatient Visits:**
591991 **Births:** 785 **Total Expense ($000):** 421767 **Payroll Expense**
**($000):** 157920 **Personnel:** 1467

## JAMAICA PLAIN—Suffolk County

☐ **LEMUEL SHATTUCK HOSPITAL (222006)**, 170 Morton Street,
Zip 02130–3735; tel. 617/522–8110 **A**1 3 5 10 **F**3 5 8 15 18 29 30 31 39 45
50 58 59 60 61 64 65 68 70 74 75 77 78 79 81 87 90 93 94 97 98 103
104 106 107 108 110 114 115 118 119 130 132 135 146 148 **P**6
**S** Massachusetts Department of Public Health, Boston, MA
Primary Contact: Rosette Martinez, Acting Chief Executive Officer
CFO: Mike Donovan, Chief Financial Officer
CMO: Kenneth Freedman, M.D., Chief Medical Officer
CIO: Kathryn Noonan, Director Information Management
CHR: Jill Sampson, Director Human Resources
Web address: www.mass.gov/shattuckhospital
**Control:** State–Government, nonfederal **Service:** General Medical and Surgical

**Staffed Beds:** 260 **Admissions:** 1545 **Census:** 229 **Outpatient Visits:** 25269
**Births:** 0 **Total Expense ($000):** 90001 **Payroll Expense ($000):** 57016
**Personnel:** 766

**MA**

---

**Hospital, Medicare Provider Number, Address, Telephone, Approval, Facility, and Physician Codes, Health Care System**

★ American Hospital Association (AHA) membership  ◯ Healthcare Facilities Accreditation Program  ⇑ Center for Improvement in Healthcare Quality Accreditation
☐ The Joint Commission accreditation  ◇ DNV Healthcare Inc. accreditation  △ Commission on Accreditation of Rehabilitation Facilities (CARF) accreditation

---

**LAWRENCE—Essex County**

✠ **LAWRENCE GENERAL HOSPITAL (220010)**, 1 General Street,
Zip 01841–2961, Mailing Address: P.O. Box 189, Zip 01842–0389;
tel. 978/683–4000 **A**1 2 3 5 7 9 10 **F**7 11 12 13 15 16 17 20 22 28 29 30 34
35 40 41 43 45 46 49 50 51 57 59 60 65 68 70 73 74 75 76 77 78 79 81
84 85 87 88 89 100 107 108 110 114 115 119 129 130 132 135 144 146
147 148 **P**5 6 8
Primary Contact: Dianne J. Anderson, MS, R.N., President and Chief Executive
Officer
COO: Denise S. Palumbo, MSN, Executive Vice President and Chief Operating
Officer
CFO: Deborah J. Wilson, Senior Vice President and Chief Financial Officer
CMO: Neil S. Meehan, D.O., Chief Medical Officer and Chief Medical Information
Officer
CIO: Jeffrey L. Brown, Director Information Systems
CHR: Cynthia Phelan, Vice President Human Resources
Web address: www.lawrencegeneral.org
**Control:** Other not–for–profit (including NFP Corporation) **Service:** General
Medical and Surgical

> **Staffed Beds:** 189 **Admissions:** 11179 **Census:** 118 **Outpatient Visits:**
> 222322 **Births:** 1538 **Total Expense ($000):** 220672 **Payroll Expense
> ($000):** 109029 **Personnel:** 1093

**LEEDS—Hampshire County**

✠ **VETERANS AFFAIRS CENTRAL WESTERN MASSACHUSETTS HEALTHCARE
SYSTEM**, 421 North Main Street, Zip 01053–9764; tel. 413/582–3000,
(Nonreporting) **A**1 5 **S** Department of Veterans Affairs, Washington, DC
Primary Contact: John P. Collins, Medical Center Director
COO: Joyce Fredrick, Associate Director
CFO: Andrew McMahon, Chief Fiscal Officer
CMO: Neil Nusbaum, M.D., Chief of Staff
CIO: Michael Marley, Chief Information Officer
CHR: Pablo Feliciano, Manager Human Resources
Web address: www.centralwesternmass.va.gov/
**Control:** Veterans Affairs, Government, federal **Service:** Psychiatric

> **Staffed Beds:** 101

**LEOMINSTER—Worcester County**

✠ **HEALTHALLIANCE HOSPITALS (220001)**, 60 Hospital Road, Zip 01453–2205;
tel. 978/466–2000 **A**1 2 3 5 9 10 **F**3 15 28 29 30 31 34 35 36 40 45 46 47
49 50 51 55 59 60 62 63 64 68 70 74 75 76 77 78 79 81 82 84 85 89 92
93 97 107 108 110 114 115 119 130 135 144 146 **P**6 **S** UMass Memorial
Health Care, Inc., Worcester, MA
Primary Contact: Deborah K. Weymouth, FACHE, President and Chief Executive
Officer
CFO: John Bronhard, Interim Chief Financial Officer
CMO: Daniel H. O'Leary, M.D., Chief Medical Officer
CIO: Christopher Walden, Vice President and Chief Information Officer
CHR: Cynthia Ring, Vice President Human Resources and Patient Experience
CNO: Paul MacKinnon, MS, Senior Vice President Patient Care Services and Chief
Nursing Officer
Web address: www.healthalliance.com
**Control:** Other not–for–profit (including NFP Corporation) **Service:** General
Medical and Surgical

> **Staffed Beds:** 97 **Admissions:** 6210 **Census:** 70 **Outpatient Visits:** 245806
> **Births:** 910 **Total Expense ($000):** 158679 **Payroll Expense ($000):** 65976
> **Personnel:** 835

**LOWELL—Middlesex County**

✠ **LOWELL GENERAL HOSPITAL (220063)**, 295 Varnum Avenue,
Zip 01854–2134; tel. 978/937–6000, (Includes LOWELL GENERAL HOSPITAL,
SAINTS CAMPUS, 1 Hospital Drive, Zip 01852–1311; tel. 978/458–1411;
Stephen J. Guimond, President and Chief Executive Officer) **A**1 2 3 5 9 10 **F**1 3
4 8 11 12 13 15 16 17 18 20 22 26 28 29 30 31 32 34 35 36 38 40 41 43
44 45 49 50 51 54 55 56 57 58 59 60 61 62 63 64 65 66 67 68 70 72 73
74 75 76 77 78 79 80 81 82 84 85 86 87 88 89 90 93 97 98 107 108 110
114 115 118 119 120 121 123 124 126 128 129 130 131 132 134 135 144
146 147 **P**5 6 8
Primary Contact: Normand E. Deschene, FACHE, Chief Executive Officer
COO: Amy J. Hoey, R.N., Executive Vice President and Chief Operating Officer
CFO: Susan Green, Senior Vice President Finance, Chief Financial Officer
CMO: David Pickul, M.D., Chief Medical Officer, Circle Health
CIO: Brian Sandager, Chief Information Officer
CHR: Sabrina M. Granville, Senior Vice President and Chief Human Resources
Officer
CNO: Cecelia Lynch, R.N., Vice President Patient Care Services and Chief Nursing
Officer
Web address: www.lowellgeneral.org
**Control:** Other not–for–profit (including NFP Corporation) **Service:** General
Medical and Surgical

> **Staffed Beds:** 305 **Admissions:** 19565 **Census:** 213 **Outpatient Visits:**
> 528339 **Births:** 2323 **Total Expense ($000):** 409225 **Payroll Expense
> ($000):** 160769 **Personnel:** 2386

**SAINTS MEDICAL CENTER** See Lowell General Hospital, Saints Campus

**LUDLOW—Hampden County**

✠ **HEALTHSOUTH REHABILITATION HOSPITAL OF WESTERN
MASSACHUSETTS (223030)**, 222 State Street, Zip 01056–3437;
tel. 413/308–3300, (Nonreporting) **A**1 10 **S** HEALTHSOUTH Corporation,
Birmingham, AL
Primary Contact: Victoria Healy, Chief Executive Officer
CFO: John Flaherty, Chief Financial Officer
CMO: Adnan Dahdul, M.D., Medical Director
CHR: Mary Mazza, Director Human Resources
CNO: Deborah Cabanas, R.N., Chief Nursing Officer
Web address: www.healthsouthrehab.org
**Control:** Corporation, Investor–owned, for–profit **Service:** Rehabilitation

> **Staffed Beds:** 53

**LYNN—Essex County**

**UNION CAMPUS** See North Shore Medical Center, Salem

**UNION HOSPITAL** See Union Campus

**MARLBOROUGH—Bristol County**

✠ **UMASS MEMORIAL–MARLBOROUGH HOSPITAL (220049)**, 157 Union Street,
Zip 01752–1297; tel. 508/481–5000 **A**1 3 5 9 10 **F**3 11 15 18 24 28 29 30
31 34 35 40 49 50 53 57 68 70 75 77 78 79 81 82 85 93 98 100 101 105
107 114 119 132 146 147 **S** UMass Memorial Health Care, Inc., Worcester, MA
Primary Contact: Steven P. Roach, FACHE, President and Chief Executive Officer
COO: John Kelly, Chief Nursing Officer and Chief Operating Officer
CFO: Steven McCue, Chief Financial Officer
CHR: Francis Meringolo, Vice President Human Resources
CNO: John Kelly, Chief Nursing Officer and Chief Operating Officer
Web address: www.marlboroughhospital.org
**Control:** Other not–for–profit (including NFP Corporation) **Service:** General
Medical and Surgical

> **Staffed Beds:** 67 **Admissions:** 3748 **Census:** 43 **Outpatient Visits:** 25933
> **Births:** 0 **Total Expense ($000):** 78455 **Payroll Expense ($000):** 29531
> **Personnel:** 390

**MEDFORD—Middlesex County**

**LAWRENCE MEMORIAL HOSPITAL OF MEDFORD** See Hallmark Health
System, Melrose

**MELROSE—Middlesex County**

✠ **HALLMARK HEALTH SYSTEM (220070)**, 585 Lebanon Street,
Zip 02176–3225; tel. 781/979–3000, (Includes LAWRENCE MEMORIAL
HOSPITAL OF MEDFORD, 170 Governors Avenue, Medford, Zip 02155–1643;
tel. 781/306–6000; MELROSE–WAKEFIELD HOSPITAL, 585 Lebanon Street,
Zip 02176; tel. 781/979–3000; Michael V. Sack, FACHE, Chief Executive Officer)
**A**1 2 3 10 **F**2 3 11 12 13 15 18 20 22 26 28 29 30 31 34 35 38 40 41 45
46 47 49 50 51 54 55 56 57 58 59 60 61 62 63 64 65 68 70 72 74 75 76
77 78 79 81 82 84 85 86 87 93 97 98 100 101 102 103 104 107 108 110
111 114 115 116 117 118 119 120 121 123 124 130 131 132 135 144 146
147 148 **P**5 6
Primary Contact: Alan G. Macdonald, President and Chief Executive Officer
COO: William J. Doherty, M.D., Executive Vice President and Chief Operating
Officer
CFO: James A. Nania, System Vice President and Chief Financial Officer
CMO: Steven Sbardella, M.D., Chief Medical Officer
CIO: Carol Ann Dresser, Vice President Information Services and Chief Information
Officer
CHR: David P. Ryan, Vice President Human Resources
Web address: www.hallmarkhealth.org
**Control:** Other not–for–profit (including NFP Corporation) **Service:** General
Medical and Surgical

> **Staffed Beds:** 250 **Admissions:** 10817 **Census:** 158 **Outpatient Visits:**
> 556954 **Births:** 977 **Total Expense ($000):** 251080 **Payroll Expense
> ($000):** 127189 **Personnel:** 1328

**METHUEN—Essex County**

☐ **HOLY FAMILY HOSPITAL (220080)**, 70 East Street, Zip 01844–4597;
tel. 978/687–0151, (Includes HOLY FAMILY HOPSITAL AT MERRIMACK VALLEY,
140 Lincoln Avenue, Haverhill, Zip 01830–6798; tel. 978/374–2000; Michael F.
Collins, Chief Executive Officer), (Nonreporting) **A**1 2 9 10 **S** Steward Health Care
System, LLC, Boston, MA
Primary Contact: Joseph Roach, Chief Executive Officer
COO: Martha M. McDrury, R.N., Chief Operating Officer and Chief Nursing Officer
CFO: Kevin Kilday, Vice President Finance
CHR: Patricia Gauron, Director Human Resources
CNO: Martha M. McDrury, R.N., Chief Operating Officer and Chief Nursing Officer
Web address: www.stewardhealth.org/Holy–Family–Hospital
**Control:** Corporation, Investor–owned, for–profit **Service:** General Medical and
Surgical

> **Staffed Beds:** 329

MA

## MILFORD—Worcester County

✠ **MILFORD REGIONAL MEDICAL CENTER (220090)**, 14 Prospect Street, Zip 01757–3003; tel. 508/473–1190, (Includes WHITINSVILLE MEDICAL CENTER, 18 Granite Street, Whitinsville, Zip 01588; tel. 508/234–6311) **A**1 2 3 5 9 10 **F**3 11 12 13 15 18 20 28 29 30 31 32 34 35 40 41 47 49 50 51 52 57 59 64 65 68 70 74 75 76 77 79 80 81 82 83 84 85 86 87 89 93 107 108 110 114 115 118 119 124 126 130 131 132 134 135 146 147 148 **P**6
Primary Contact: Francis M. Saba, Chief Executive Officer
COO: Peggy Novick, Vice President, Clinical Support and Outpatient Services
CFO: Jeanne Lynskey, Vice President and Chief Financial Officer
CMO: Mary Czymbor, Chief Medical Officer
CIO: Nicole Heim, Chief Information Officer
CHR: Linda Greason, Vice President Human Resources
CNO: Nancy Tomaso, Vice President, Patient Care Services
Web address: www.milfordregional.org
**Control:** Other not–for–profit (including NFP Corporation) **Service:** General Medical and Surgical

**Staffed Beds:** 145 **Admissions:** 7277 **Census:** 72 **Outpatient Visits:** 372440 **Births:** 954 **Total Expense ($000):** 181003 **Payroll Expense ($000):** 83466 **Personnel:** 1572

## MILTON—Norfolk County

☐ **BETH ISRAEL DEACONESS HOSPITAL–MILTON (220108)**, 199 Reedsdale Road, Zip 02186–3926; tel. 617/696–4600 **A**1 9 10 **F**12 15 17 18 26 29 30 31 34 35 40 50 51 56 57 59 64 68 70 74 75 77 79 81 82 85 87 93 107 108 110 111 114 119 126 129 130 131 132 146 148
Primary Contact: Peter J. Healy, Chief Executive Officer
CIO: Jean Fernandez, Chief Information Officer
CHR: Kathleen Harrington, Vice President Human Resources
Web address: www.miltonhospital.org
**Control:** Other not–for–profit (including NFP Corporation) **Service:** General Medical and Surgical

**Staffed Beds:** 88 **Admissions:** 6107 **Census:** 56 **Outpatient Visits:** 121637 **Births:** 0 **Total Expense ($000):** 82046 **Payroll Expense ($000):** 34142 **Personnel:** 408

## NANTUCKET—Nantucket County

✠ **NANTUCKET COTTAGE HOSPITAL (220177)**, 57 Prospect Street, Zip 02554–2799; tel. 508/825–8100 **A**1 9 10 **F**13 15 28 29 31 35 40 45 50 57 59 60 64 68 70 75 76 77 78 79 81 82 84 85 86 87 89 93 100 102 107 110 111 115 119 130 132 133 147 148 **P**5 **S** Partners HealthCare System, Inc., Boston, MA
Primary Contact: Margot Hartmann, M.D., Ph.D., President and Chief Executive Officer
COO: Jim Kelly, Chief Operating Officer
CFO: David J. Burke, Director Finance and Chief Financial Officer
CMO: Jock Lawrason, M.D., Chief Medical Officer
CIO: Terry Hughes, Director Information Systems
CHR: Susan Partridge, Director Human Resources
CNO: Bonnie J. Kester, R.N., Vice President Patient Care Services and Chief Nursing Officer
Web address: www.nantuckethospital.org
**Control:** Other not–for–profit (including NFP Corporation) **Service:** General Medical and Surgical

**Staffed Beds:** 19 **Admissions:** 748 **Census:** 5 **Outpatient Visits:** 32610 **Births:** 124 **Total Expense ($000):** 38451 **Payroll Expense ($000):** 17407 **Personnel:** 206

## NATICK—Middlesex County

**LEONARD MORSE HOSPITAL** See MetroWest Medical Center, Framingham

## NEEDHAM—Norfolk County

**BETH ISRAEL DEACONESS HOSPITAL–NEEDHAM CAMPUS** See Beth Israel Deaconess Medical Center, Boston

## NEW BEDFORD—Bristol County

✠ **NEW BEDFORD REHABILITATION HOSPITAL (222043)**, 4499 Acushnet Avenue, Zip 02745–4707; tel. 508/995–6900 **A**1 10 **F**1 12 18 28 29 50 56 57 64 74 75 77 79 87 93 94 96 101 103 104 130 135 146 148 **P**6 **S** Vibra Healthcare, Mechanicsburg, PA
Primary Contact: Edward B. Leary, Chief Executive Officer
CFO: Cheryl Perry, Chief Financial Officer
CMO: Albert Loerinc, M.D., Medical Director
CHR: Ilene Mirabella, Director Human Resources
CNO: Emmanuel Berthil, Chief Clinical Officer
Web address: www.newbedfordrehab.com
**Control:** Corporation, Investor–owned, for–profit **Service:** Long–Term Acute Care hospital

**Staffed Beds:** 90 **Admissions:** 637 **Census:** 73 **Outpatient Visits:** 3834 **Births:** 0 **Total Expense ($000):** 25029 **Payroll Expense ($000):** 13688 **Personnel:** 192

**ST. LUKE'S HOSPITAL** See Southcoast Hospitals Group, Fall River

## NEWBURYPORT—Essex County

✠ **ANNA JAQUES HOSPITAL (220029)**, 25 Highland Avenue, Zip 01950–3894; tel. 978/463–1000 **A**1 9 10 **F**3 13 14 15 18 20 26 28 29 31 34 40 43 45 46 50 64 65 70 75 76 77 78 79 80 81 82 85 89 93 98 102 105 107 108 110 111 115 116 117 118 119 129 130 135 146 148 **P**5 8
Primary Contact: Mark L. Goldstein, President and Chief Executive Officer
CMO: Gail Fayre, M.D., Medical Director
CIO: Robert Buchanan, Chief Information Officer
CHR: Stephen Salvo, Vice President Human Resources
CNO: Richard Maki, R.N., Vice President Nursing and Chief Nursing Officer
Web address: www.ajh.org
**Control:** Other not–for–profit (including NFP Corporation) **Service:** General Medical and Surgical

**Staffed Beds:** 123 **Admissions:** 6884 **Census:** 85 **Outpatient Visits:** 254156 **Births:** 740 **Total Expense ($000):** 111242 **Payroll Expense ($000):** 53388 **Personnel:** 694

## NEWTON LOWER FALLS—Middlesex County

✠ **NEWTON–WELLESLEY HOSPITAL (220101)**, 2014 Washington Street, Zip 02462–1699; tel. 617/243–6000, (Includes MASSGENERAL FOR CHILDREN AT NEWTON–WELLESLEY HOSPITAL, 2000 Washington Street, Newton, Zip 02462–1650; tel. 617/243–6585) **A**1 2 3 5 9 10 **F**3 8 11 12 13 15 18 26 28 29 30 31 34 35 36 38 40 41 44 45 46 47 48 49 50 51 52 53 54 55 56 57 58 59 60 61 64 65 68 70 74 75 76 77 78 79 81 82 84 85 86 87 89 93 94 97 98 99 100 101 102 107 108 110 111 113 114 115 116 117 118 119 129 130 131 132 135 143 144 146 147 148 **P**1 6 **S** Partners HealthCare System, Inc., Boston, MA
Primary Contact: Kerry Watson, President
COO: Ellen Moloney, Chief Operating Officer
CFO: Jeffrey P. Dion, Vice President Finance and Chief Financial Officer
CMO: Leslie Selbovitz, M.D., Senior Vice President Medical Affairs
CIO: Beth Downie, Chief Information Officer
CHR: Beth Taylor, Vice President, Human Resources
CNO: Karen A. Conley, R.N., Chief Nursing Officer and Senior Vice President Patient Care Services
Web address: www.nwh.org
**Control:** Other not–for–profit (including NFP Corporation) **Service:** General Medical and Surgical

**Staffed Beds:** 252 **Admissions:** 15775 **Census:** 181 **Outpatient Visits:** 621378 **Births:** 4316 **Total Expense ($000):** 408714 **Payroll Expense ($000):** 189028 **Personnel:** 2461

## NORTHAMPTON—Hampshire County

✠ **COOLEY DICKINSON HOSPITAL (220015)**, 30 Locust Street, Zip 01060–2093, Mailing Address: P.O. Box 5001, Zip 01061–5001; tel. 413/582–2000 **A**1 2 9 10 **F**3 11 13 14 15 18 20 26 28 29 30 31 34 35 36 38 39 40 49 50 51 54 55 56 57 59 60 61 64 68 70 74 75 76 78 79 81 82 85 86 87 89 93 96 98 100 102 107 108 110 111 114 115 119 120 121 123 126 130 131 132 134 135 144 146 147 148 **P**8 **S** Partners HealthCare System, Inc., Boston, MA
Primary Contact: Joanne Marqusee, President and Chief Executive Officer
CFO: Laurie Lamoureux, Director of Finance
CMO: Mark Novotny, M.D., Chief Medical Officer
CIO: Lee Martinez, Chief Information Officer
CHR: Lori A. Kerwood, Director Human Resources
Web address: www.cooley-dickinson.org
**Control:** Other not–for–profit (including NFP Corporation) **Service:** General Medical and Surgical

**Staffed Beds:** 93 **Admissions:** 6350 **Census:** 75 **Outpatient Visits:** 222098 **Births:** 756 **Total Expense ($000):** 153536 **Payroll Expense ($000):** 70820 **Personnel:** 856

**MA**

---

**Hospital, Medicare Provider Number, Address, Telephone, Approval, Facility, and Physician Codes, Health Care System**

★ American Hospital Association (AHA) membership
☐ The Joint Commission accreditation
○ Healthcare Facilities Accreditation Program
◇ DNV Healthcare Inc. accreditation
⇑ Center for Improvement in Healthcare Quality Accreditation
△ Commission on Accreditation of Rehabilitation Facilities (CARF) accreditation

**MA**

## NORWOOD—Norfolk County

☐ **NORWOOD HOSPITAL (220126)**, 800 Washington Street, Zip 02062–3487; tel. 781/769–4000, (Nonreporting) **A**1 2 9 10 **S** Steward Health Care System, LLC, Boston, MA
Primary Contact: Kimberly S. Bassett, R.N., Interim President
COO: William P. Fleming, Chief Operating Officer
CFO: Mark Johnson, Chief Financial Officer
CHR: Kimberly Brosnan, Director Human Resources
CNO: Mary Kinneman, R.N., Chief Nursing Officer, Vice President Patient Care Services
Web address: www.stewardhealth.org/Norwood–Hospital
**Control:** Corporation, Investor–owned, for–profit **Service:** General Medical and Surgical

**Staffed Beds:** 188

## OAK BLUFFS—Dukes County

☒ **MARTHA'S VINEYARD HOSPITAL (221300)**, One Hospital Road, Zip 02557, Mailing Address: P.O. Box 1477, Zip 02557–1477; tel. 508/693–0410 **A**1 9 10 18 **F**3 8 13 15 28 29 30 31 39 40 45 50 57 60 70 75 76 78 79 81 82 85 86 89 93 97 107 110 111 115 119 130 133 135 146 147 **P**6 **S** Partners HealthCare System, Inc., Boston, MA
Primary Contact: Timothy J. Walsh, Chief Executive Officer
CFO: Edward Olivier, Chief Financial Officer
CMO: Pieter Pil, M.D., Chief Medical Staff
CHR: Ken Chisholm, Director Human Resources
CNO: Carol A. Bardwell, R.N., Chief Nurse Executive
Web address: www.marthasvineyardhospital.org
**Control:** Other not–for–profit (including NFP Corporation) **Service:** General Medical and Surgical

**Staffed Beds:** 25 **Admissions:** 1519 **Census:** 19 **Outpatient Visits:** 54522 **Births:** 124 **Total Expense ($000):** 68027 **Payroll Expense ($000):** 32060 **Personnel:** 314

## PALMER—Hampden County

☒ **BAYSTATE WING HOSPITAL (220030)**, 40 Wright Street, Zip 01069–1138; tel. 413/283–7651 **A**1 5 9 10 **F**3 5 11 15 18 29 30 31 33 34 36 37 40 45 49 50 51 56 57 59 61 62 63 64 65 68 70 74 75 76 77 78 79 81 85 89 92 93 97 98 99 100 101 103 104 107 108 110 115 118 119 129 130 131 132 146 147 148 **P**6 **S** Baystate Health, Inc., Springfield, MA
Primary Contact: Charles E. Cavagnaro, III, M.D., President and Chief Executive Officer
CFO: Keary T. Allicon, Vice President Finance and Chief Financial Officer
CMO: David L. Maguire, M.D., Vice President Medical Affairs
CIO: Kenneth Riley, Director Information Systems
CHR: Thomas Guilfoil, Director Human Resources
Web address: www.baystatewinghospital.org/
**Control:** Other not–for–profit (including NFP Corporation) **Service:** General Medical and Surgical

**Staffed Beds:** 74 **Admissions:** 3056 **Census:** 46 **Outpatient Visits:** 229021 **Births:** 0 **Total Expense ($000):** 87487 **Payroll Expense ($000):** 40947 **Personnel:** 721

## PEABODY—Essex County

☒ **KINDRED HOSPITAL BOSTON–NORTH SHORE (222044)**, 15 King Street, Zip 01960–4379; tel. 978/531–2900, (Nonreporting) **A**1 10 **S** Kindred Healthcare, Louisville, KY
Primary Contact: Amber Hester, Chief Executive Officer
COO: Beth Cullum, Chief Operating Officer
CFO: Amber Tatum, Controller
CMO: M. Akbarian, M.D., Medical Director
CHR: Jan Pray, Coordinator Payroll and Benefits
CNO: Michelle Mastin, Chief Clinical Officer
Web address: www.kindredbns.com
**Control:** Corporation, Investor–owned, for–profit **Service:** Long–Term Acute Care hospital

**Staffed Beds:** 50

## PEMBROKE—Plymouth County

**PEMBROKE HOSPITAL**, 199 Oak Street, Zip 02359–1953; tel. 781/829–7000, (Nonreporting) **A**9 **S** Universal Health Services, Inc., King of Prussia, PA
Primary Contact: Thomas P. Hickey, Chief Executive Officer and Managing Director
CFO: Diane Airosus, Chief Financial Officer
CMO: Gary Jacobson, M.D., Chief Medical Officer
Web address: www.arbourhealth.com/organizations/pembroke–hospital/
**Control:** Partnership, Investor–owned, for–profit **Service:** Psychiatric

**Staffed Beds:** 80

## PITTSFIELD—Berkshire County

☒ **BERKSHIRE MEDICAL CENTER (220046)**, 725 North Street, Zip 01201–4124; tel. 413/447–2000, (Includes HILLCREST HOSPITAL, 165 Tor Court, Zip 01201–3099, Mailing Address: Box 1155, Zip 01202–1155; tel. 413/443–4761) **A**1 2 3 5 8 9 10 12 13 **F**3 4 8 12 13 14 15 17 18 20 26 28 29 30 31 32 34 35 38 39 40 42 43 44 48 49 50 51 53 54 55 56 57 58 59 60 61 62 63 64 65 68 70 71 74 75 76 77 78 79 81 82 84 85 86 87 89 90 92 93 94 96 98 99 100 101 102 103 104 105 107 108 110 111 112 114 115 116 117 118 119 120 121 122 123 124 126 129 130 131 132 134 135 145 146 147 148 **P**6 **S** Berkshire Health Systems, Inc., Pittsfield, MA
Primary Contact: David E. Phelps, President and Chief Executive Officer
COO: Diane Kelly, R.N., Chief Operating Officer
CFO: Darlene Rodowicz, Chief Financial Officer
CMO: Robert Cella, M.D., Vice President Medical Affairs
CIO: William Young, Chief Information Officer
CHR: Arthur D. Milano, Vice President Human Resources
CNO: Brenda E. Cadorette, R.N., Chief Nursing Officer
Web address: www.bhs1.org/body_bmc.cfm?id=43
**Control:** Other not–for–profit (including NFP Corporation) **Service:** General Medical and Surgical

**Staffed Beds:** 274 **Admissions:** 13203 **Census:** 163 **Outpatient Visits:** 540391 **Births:** 763 **Total Expense ($000):** 360189 **Payroll Expense ($000):** 172246 **Personnel:** 2249

## PLYMOUTH—Plymouth County

☒ **BETH ISRAEL DEACONESS HOSPITAL PLYMOUTH (220060)**, 275 Sandwich Street, Zip 02360–2196; tel. 508/746–2000 **A**1 2 5 9 10 **F**3 13 15 17 18 20 28 29 30 31 34 35 36 37 40 44 45 51 57 58 59 61 64 68 70 74 75 76 77 78 79 81 82 85 86 87 89 93 96 98 100 102 103 104 107 108 109 110 111 115 117 118 119 120 121 123 126 129 130 131 132 134 135 143 146 147 148 **P**6
Primary Contact: Peter J. Holden, President and Chief Executive Officer
COO: James E. Fanale, M.D., Senior Vice President System Development
CFO: Jason Radzevich, Vice President Finance
CIO: Ronald Rutherford, Chief Information Officer
CNO: Donna Doherty, R.N., Vice President of Nursing and Chief Nursing Officer
Web address: www.bidplymouth.org
**Control:** Other not–for–profit (including NFP Corporation) **Service:** General Medical and Surgical

**Staffed Beds:** 155 **Admissions:** 7624 **Census:** 98 **Outpatient Visits:** 258321 **Births:** 683 **Total Expense ($000):** 191494 **Payroll Expense ($000):** 79972 **Personnel:** 917

## POCASSET—Barnstable County

☐ **CAPE COD & ISLAND COMMUNITY MENTAL HEALTH CENTER (224031)**, 830 County Road, Zip 02559–2110; tel. 508/564–9600, (Nonreporting) **A**1 10
Primary Contact: Steven Jochim, Administrator
**Control:** Other not–for–profit (including NFP Corporation) **Service:** Psychiatric

**Staffed Beds:** 24

## ROCHDALE—Worcester County

**VIBRA HOSPITAL OF WESTERN MASSACHUSETTS–CENTRAL CAMPUS** See Vibra Hospital of Western Massachusetts, Springfield

## SALEM—Essex County

**NORTH SHORE CHILDREN'S HOSPITAL** See MassGeneral for Children at North Shore Medical Center

☒ **NORTH SHORE MEDICAL CENTER (220035)**, 81 Highland Avenue, Zip 01970–2714; tel. 978/741–1200, (Includes MASSGENERAL FOR CHILDREN AT NORTH SHORE MEDICAL CENTER, 57 Highland Avenue, Zip 01970–6508; tel. 978/745–2100; SALEM CAMPUS, 81 Highland Avenue, Zip 01970; tel. 978/741–1200; UNION CAMPUS, 500 Lynnfield Street, Lynn, Zip 01904–1487; tel. 781/581–9200) **A**1 3 5 9 10 **F**5 12 13 15 17 18 20 22 24 26 28 29 30 31 32 34 35 36 38 40 41 43 45 46 49 50 51 55 57 59 61 63 64 68 70 73 74 75 76 77 78 79 81 82 84 85 86 87 89 93 98 99 100 101 102 103 104 105 107 108 111 114 116 118 119 121 123 129 130 131 132 135 143 146 147 148 **P**6 8 **S** Partners HealthCare System, Inc., Boston, MA
Primary Contact: Robert G. Norton, President
CFO: Sally Mason Boemer, Chief Financial Officer
CMO: Mitchell S. Rein, M.D., Chief Medical Officer
CIO: Fran X. Hinckley, Chief Information Officer
CHR: Arthur Bowes, Senior Vice President Human Resources
Web address: www.nsmc.partners.org
**Control:** Other not–for–profit (including NFP Corporation) **Service:** General Medical and Surgical

**Staffed Beds:** 406 **Admissions:** 17185 **Census:** 239 **Outpatient Visits:** 663225 **Births:** 1272 **Total Expense ($000):** 435216 **Payroll Expense ($000):** 197370 **Personnel:** 2386

**SALEM HOSPITAL** See Salem Campus

⊠ **SPAULDING HOSPITAL FOR CONTINUING MEDICAL CARE NORTH SHORE (222026)**, 1 Dove Avenue, Zip 01970–2999; tel. 978/825–8900, (Nonreporting) **A**1 10 **S** Partners HealthCare System, Inc., Boston, MA
Primary Contact: Maureen Banks, R.N., FACHE, President
CFO: Virginia Mirisola, Fiscal Director
CIO: Robert Sawyer, Senior Project Specialist
CHR: Colleen M. Moran, Director Human Resources
Web address: www.shaughnessy–kaplan.org
**Control:** Other not–for–profit (including NFP Corporation) **Service:** Long–Term Acute Care hospital

**Staffed Beds:** 160

---

### SOMERVILLE—Middlesex County

**SOMERVILLE HOSPITAL** See Cambridge Health Alliance, Cambridge

---

### SOUTH WEYMOUTH—Norfolk County

⊠ **SOUTH SHORE HOSPITAL (220100)**, 55 Fogg Road, Zip 02190–2432; tel. 781/624–8000 **A**1 2 3 5 9 10 **F**3 7 11 13 15 17 18 20 22 24 26 28 29 30 31 32 34 35 36 37 40 41 43 44 45 46 49 50 51 53 54 55 57 58 59 60 62 63 64 65 68 70 72 73 74 75 76 78 79 81 82 84 85 86 87 89 91 92 93 96 107 108 110 111 114 115 118 119 124 126 129 130 132 134 135 143 146 147 148 **P**1
Primary Contact: Joseph Cahill, President and Chief Operating Officer
COO: Joseph Cahill, Executive Vice President and Chief Operating Officer
CFO: Michael Cullen, Senior Vice President and Chief Financial Officer
CMO: John Stevenson, M.D., Senior Vice President and Chief Medical Officer
CIO: Del Dixon, Chief Information Officer
CHR: Robert Wheeler, Vice President Human Resources
Web address: www.southshorehospital.org
**Control:** Other not–for–profit (including NFP Corporation) **Service:** General Medical and Surgical

**Staffed Beds:** 362 **Admissions:** 22226 **Census:** 247 **Outpatient Visits:** 591306 **Births:** 3520 **Total Expense ($000):** 478526 **Payroll Expense ($000):** 237333 **Personnel:** 3182

---

### SOUTHBRIDGE—Worcester County

☐ **HARRINGTON MEMORIAL HOSPITAL (220019)**, 100 South Street, Zip 01550–4051; tel. 508/765–9771 **A**1 5 10 **F**3 5 8 11 13 15 17 18 19 28 29 30 31 32 34 35 38 39 40 42 45 48 49 50 51 54 57 59 61 64 65 68 70 71 74 75 76 77 78 79 81 82 85 86 87 89 92 93 94 96 98 99 100 101 102 103 104 105 107 108 110 111 114 115 117 118 119 129 130 131 132 134 135 145 146 147 148 **P**6 8
Primary Contact: Edward H. Moore, President and Chief Executive Officer
COO: Douglas Crapser, Executive Vice President
CFO: Thomas Sullivan, Vice President Fiscal Services
CMO: Arthur Russo, M.D., Director Medical Affairs
CIO: Harry Lemieux, Chief Information Officer
CHR: Christopher Canniff, Executive Director, Human Resources
CNO: Thomas W. Hijeck, R.N., Vice President Nursing Services and Chief Nursing Officer
Web address: www.harringtonhospital.org
**Control:** Other not–for–profit (including NFP Corporation) **Service:** General Medical and Surgical

**Staffed Beds:** 114 **Admissions:** 3921 **Census:** 44 **Outpatient Visits:** 336123 **Births:** 280 **Total Expense ($000):** 113602 **Payroll Expense ($000):** 54869 **Personnel:** 652

---

### SPRINGFIELD—Hampden County

⊠ **BAYSTATE MEDICAL CENTER (220077)**, 759 Chestnut Street, Zip 01199–0001; tel. 413/794–0000, (Includes BAYSTATE CHILDREN'S HOSPITAL, 759 Chestnut Street, Zip 01199–1001; tel. 413/794–0000; Mark A. Keroack, M.D., President and Chief Executive Officer, Baystate Health) **A**1 3 5 8 9 10 **F**3 8 12 13 14 15 17 18 19 20 22 24 26 28 29 30 31 32 34 35 38 40 41 43 44 45 46 47 48 49 50 51 52 53 54 55 56 57 58 59 60 61 64 65 66 68 70 72 74 75 76 77 78 79 80 81 82 84 85 86 87 88 89 91 92 93 97 98 99 100 101 102 103 104 105 107 108 110 111 114 115 118 119 120 121 123 124 126 129 130 131 132 135 138 143 145 146 147 148 **P**8 **S** Baystate Health, Inc., Springfield, MA
Primary Contact: Mark A. Keroack, M.D., MPH, President and Chief Executive Officer
COO: Nancy Shendell–Falik, R.N., Senior Vice President, Chief Operating Officer and Chief Nursing Officer
CFO: Dennis Chalke, Senior Vice President, Finance and Community Hospitals, Chief Financial Officer and Treasurer
CMO: John Schreiber, M.D., President and Chief Physician Executive
CIO: Joel L. Vengco, MS, Vice President, Chief Information Officer
CHR: Paula C. Squires, Senior Vice President, Chief Human Resources Officer
CNO: Nancy Shendell–Falik, R.N., Senior Vice President, Chief Operating Officer and Chief Nursing Officer
Web address: www.baystatehealth.org/bmc
**Control:** Other not–for–profit (including NFP Corporation) **Service:** General Medical and Surgical

**Staffed Beds:** 710 **Admissions:** 36310 **Census:** 513 **Outpatient Visits:** 787282 **Births:** 4079 **Total Expense ($000):** 979786 **Payroll Expense ($000):** 381312 **Personnel:** 7102

**KINDRED HOSPITAL PARK VIEW** See Vibra Hospital of Western Massachusetts

⊠ △ **MERCY MEDICAL CENTER (220066)**, 271 Carew Street, Zip 01104–2398, Mailing Address: P.O. Box 9012, Zip 01102–9012; tel. 413/748–9000 **A**1 2 7 9 10 **F**3 4 7 8 12 13 14 15 18 20 26 29 30 31 34 35 38 40 44 45 46 47 48 49 50 51 55 56 57 58 59 61 64 68 70 74 75 76 77 78 79 81 82 83 84 85 86 87 89 90 91 92 93 96 98 99 100 101 102 103 104 105 106 107 108 110 111 113 114 115 116 117 118 119 120 121 123 124 126 130 131 132 134 135 143 146 147 148 **P**6 **S** Trinity Health, Livonia, MI
Primary Contact: Daniel P. Moen, President and Chief Executive Officer
COO: Scott A. Wolf, D.O., Senior Vice President, Medical Affairs, Chief Medical Officer and Chief Operating Officer
CFO: Thomas W. Robert, Senior Vice President of Finance and Chief Financial Officer
CMO: Scott A. Wolf, D.O., Senior Vice President, Medical Affairs, Chief Medical Officer and Chief Operating Officer
CIO: Joan Methe, Chief Information Officer
CHR: Leonard F. Pansa, Senior Vice President Human Resources and Administrative Services
CNO: Sharon Adams, R.N., Senior Vice President Patient Care Services and Chief Quality Officer
Web address: www.mercycares.com
**Control:** Other not–for–profit (including NFP Corporation) **Service:** General Medical and Surgical

**Staffed Beds:** 336 **Admissions:** 15533 **Census:** 228 **Outpatient Visits:** 505209 **Births:** 1329 **Total Expense ($000):** 233622 **Payroll Expense ($000):** 94570

☐ **SHRINERS HOSPITALS FOR CHILDREN–SPRINGFIELD (223303)**, 516 Carew Street, Zip 01104–2396; tel. 413/787–2000 **A**1 3 5 10 **F**3 29 32 34 35 55 58 59 64 66 68 71 74 75 77 79 81 85 86 89 91 92 93 94 95 96 119 130 134 143 146 **P**1 6 **S** Shriners Hospitals for Children, Tampa, FL
Primary Contact: H. Lee Kirk, Jr., FACHE, Administrator
CFO: Richard Fulkerson, Director Fiscal Services
CMO: David M. Drvaric, M.D., Chief of Staff
CIO: Mary Dolan, Director Information Services
CHR: John Donlin, Director Human Resources
CNO: Diane Brunelle, MSN, Director Patient Care Services and Chief Nursing Officer
Web address: www.shrinershospitalsforchildren.org/Hospitals/Locations/Springfield.aspx
**Control:** Other not–for–profit (including NFP Corporation) **Service:** Children's orthopedic

**Staffed Beds:** 20 **Admissions:** 118 **Census:** 1 **Outpatient Visits:** 12900 **Births:** 0 **Total Expense ($000):** 19071 **Payroll Expense ($000):** 8627 **Personnel:** 138

---

**MA**

✠ **VIBRA HOSPITAL OF WESTERN MASSACHUSETTS (222046)**, 1400 State Street, Zip 01109–2550; tel. 413/726–6700, (Includes VIBRA HOSPITAL OF WESTERN MASSACHUSETTS–CENTRAL CAMPUS, 111 Huntoon Memorial Highway, Rochdale, Zip 01542; tel. 508/892–6000; Scott MacLean, Administrator), (Nonreporting) **A**1 10 **S** Vibra Healthcare, Mechanicsburg, PA
Primary Contact: Daniel Mitchell, Chief Executive Officer
CFO: Anna Dyrkacz, Chief Financial Officer
CHR: Donna Ciarefella, Director Human Resources
Web address: www.vhwmass.com
**Control:** Corporation, Investor–owned, for–profit **Service:** Long–Term Acute Care hospital

**Staffed Beds:** 202

**STOCKBRIDGE—Berkshire County**

✠ **AUSTEN RIGGS CENTER**, 25 Main Street, Zip 01262, Mailing Address: P.O. Box 962, Zip 01262–0962; tel. 413/298–5511 **A**1 3 5 **F**98 105 106 130
Primary Contact: Andrew Gerber, M.D., Ph.D., Medical Director and Chief Executive Officer
CFO: Chauncey Collins, Director Operations and Finance
CIO: Ave Schwartz, Chief Information Officer
CHR: Bertha Mary Connelley, Director Human Resources
CNO: Jane Bloom, Ph.D., Chief Nursing Officer
Web address: www.austenriggs.org
**Control:** Other not–for–profit (including NFP Corporation) **Service:** Psychiatric

**Staffed Beds:** 74 **Admissions:** 62 **Census:** 61 **Outpatient Visits:** 0 **Births:** 0 **Total Expense ($000):** 16396 **Payroll Expense ($000):** 9011 **Personnel:** 146

**STOUGHTON—Norfolk County**

✠ **KINDRED HOSPITAL NORTHEAST–STOUGHTON (222002)**, 909 Sumner Street, 1st Floor, Zip 02072–3396; tel. 781/297–8200 **A**1 10 **F**1 3 29 60 68 85 87 98 100 119 130 143 148 **S** Kindred Healthcare, Louisville, KY
Primary Contact: Robert A. Gundersen, Market Chief Executive Officer
Web address: www.khstoughton.com
**Control:** Individual, Investor–owned, for–profit **Service:** Long–Term Acute Care hospital

**Staffed Beds:** 111 **Admissions:** 764 **Census:** 92 **Outpatient Visits:** 1251 **Births:** 0 **Total Expense ($000):** 37909 **Payroll Expense ($000):** 16373 **Personnel:** 251

☐ **NEW ENGLAND SINAI HOSPITAL AND REHABILITATION CENTER (222027)**, 150 York Street, Zip 02072–1881; tel. 781/344–0600, (Nonreporting) **A**1 3 5 10 **S** Steward Health Care System, LLC, Boston, MA
Primary Contact: Judith C. Waterston, R.N., MS, President and Chief Executive Officer
CFO: Victoria Lobban, Vice President Finance
CMO: Lawrence S. Hotes, M.D., Chief Medical Officer
CIO: Michael West, Manager Systems Account
CHR: Julie Burke, Director Human Resources
CNO: Mary Beth Urquhart, Vice President Patient Care Services and Director of Quality
Web address: www.newenglandsinai.org
**Control:** Other not–for–profit (including NFP Corporation) **Service:** Long–Term Acute Care hospital

**Staffed Beds:** 212

**TAUNTON—Bristol County**

☐ **MORTON HOSPITAL AND MEDICAL CENTER (220073)**, 88 Washington Street, Zip 02780–2465; tel. 508/828–7000, (Nonreporting) **A**1 2 9 10 **S** Steward Health Care System, LLC, Boston, MA
Primary Contact: Kimberly S. Bassett, R.N., President
COO: Donna Maher, R.N., Chief Operating Officer
CFO: Carmen Acker, Chief Financial Officer
CMO: Kelly Hoye, M.D., Vice President Medical Affairs
CNO: Jane Metzger, Ph.D., Chief Nursing Officer
Web address: www.mortonhospital.org
**Control:** Other not–for–profit (including NFP Corporation) **Service:** General Medical and Surgical

**Staffed Beds:** 153

☐ **TAUNTON STATE HOSPITAL (224001)**, 60 Hodges Avenue Extension, Zip 02780–3034, Mailing Address: PO Box 4007, Zip 02780–0997; tel. 508/977–3000 **A**1 10 **F**30 50 53 68 98 130 **S** Massachusetts Department of Mental Health, Boston, MA
Primary Contact: Joyce O. Connor, Chief Operating Officer
CHR: Trish Scully, Director Human Resources
**Control:** State–Government, nonfederal **Service:** Psychiatric

**Staffed Beds:** 45 **Admissions:** 42 **Census:** 43 **Outpatient Visits:** 0 **Births:** 0

**TEWKSBURY—Middlesex County**

☐ **TEWKSBURY HOSPITAL (222003)**, 365 East Street, Zip 01876–1998; tel. 978/851–7321, (Nonreporting) **A**1 3 10 **S** Massachusetts Department of Public Health, Boston, MA
Primary Contact: Debra Tosti, Chief Executive Officer
COO: Betsy L. Schwechheimer, Chief Operating Officer
CFO: Maureen DiPalma, Chief Financial Officer
CMO: James DeVita, M.D., Chief Medical Officer
CNO: Janice E. Bishop, R.N., Chief Nursing Officer
Web address: www.mass.gov
**Control:** State–Government, nonfederal **Service:** Long–Term Acute Care hospital

**Staffed Beds:** 381

**WALTHAM—Middlesex County**

☐ **WALDEN PSYCHIATRIC CARE (224038)**, 9 Hope Avenue, Zip 02453–2741; tel. 781/647–6700 **A**1 9 10 **F**98 99 **P**6
Primary Contact: Stuart Koman, Ph.D., President and Chief Executive Officer
COO: Paula Vass, Vice President Clinical Operations
CFO: Lawrence Behan, Vice President Administration and Finance, Chief Financial Officer
CMO: James Greenblatt, M.D., Chief Medical Officer, Vice President Medical Clinical Services
CIO: Lawrence Behan, Vice President Administration and Finance, Chief Financial Officer
CHR: Carol Pender, Assistant Vice President Human Resources
CNO: Stephen Reider, R.N., Director of Nursing, Assistant Vice President Patient Care Services
Web address: www.waldenbehavioralcare.com/
**Control:** Partnership, Investor–owned, for–profit **Service:** Psychiatric

**Staffed Beds:** 45 **Admissions:** 1651 **Census:** 45 **Outpatient Visits:** 16503 **Births:** 0 **Total Expense ($000):** 9509 **Payroll Expense ($000):** 5624 **Personnel:** 219

**WARE—Hampshire County**

✠ **BAYSTATE MARY LANE HOSPITAL (220050)**, 85 South Street, Zip 01082–1697; tel. 413/967–6211 **A**1 9 10 **F**15 29 34 35 40 45 50 54 57 59 64 70 75 77 79 81 82 89 92 93 97 107 108 110 114 119 129 130 132 146 **S** Baystate Health, Inc., Springfield, MA
Primary Contact: Charles E. Cavagnaro, III, M.D., President
COO: Mohammed Shafeeq Ahmed, M.D., Chief Operating Officer and Chief Medical Officer
CFO: Curtis Davis, Director Finance
CMO: Mohammed Shafeeq Ahmed, M.D., Chief Operating Officer and Chief Medical Officer
CIO: Joel L. Vengco, MS, Vice President and Chief Information Officer, Baystate Health
CHR: Donna Arsenault, Director Human Resources
CNO: Lisa Beaudry, M.P.H., Director, Patient Care
Web address: www.baystatehealth.com
**Control:** Other not–for–profit (including NFP Corporation) **Service:** General Medical and Surgical

**Staffed Beds:** 25 **Admissions:** 983 **Census:** 8 **Outpatient Visits:** 69625 **Births:** 0 **Total Expense ($000):** 27585 **Payroll Expense ($000):** 11584

**WAREHAM—Plymouth County**

**TOBEY HOSPITAL** See Southcoast Hospitals Group, Fall River

**WEST ROXBURY—Suffolk County**

**VETERANS AFFAIRS MEDICAL CENTER WEST ROXBURY DIVISION** See Veterans Affairs Boston Healthcare System Brockton Division, Brockton

**WESTBOROUGH—Worcester County**

☐ **WHITTIER REHABILITATION HOSPITAL (222048)**, 150 Flanders Road, Zip 01581–1017; tel. 508/871–2000, (Nonreporting) **A**1 10 **S** Whittier Health Network, Haverhill, MA
Primary Contact: Alfred J. Arcidi, M.D., Senior Vice President
Web address: www.whittierhealth.com
**Control:** Partnership, Investor–owned, for–profit **Service:** Long–Term Acute Care hospital

**Staffed Beds:** 74

**WESTFIELD—Hampden County**

✠ **BAYSTATE NOBLE HOSPITAL (220065)**, 115 West Silver Street, Zip 01085–3628; tel. 413/568–2811, (Nonreporting) **A**1 2 5 9 10 **S** Baystate Health, Inc., Springfield, MA
Primary Contact: Ronald Bryant, President
CFO: John Shaver, Chief Financial Officer
CMO: Stanley Strzempko, M.D., Vice President Medical Affairs and Chief Medical Officer
CIO: Steven Cummings, Chief Operating Officer and Chief Information Officer
CHR: Joanne Ollson, Vice President Human Resources
Web address: www.baystatehealth.org/locations/noble–hospital
**Control:** Other not–for–profit (including NFP Corporation) **Service:** General Medical and Surgical

**Staffed Beds:** 97

*Many Facility Codes have changed. Please refer to the AHA Guide Code Chart.*

☐ **WESTERN MASSACHUSETTS HOSPITAL (222023)**, 91 East Mountain Road, Zip 01085–1801; tel. 413/562–4131, (Nonreporting) **A**1 10 **S** Massachusetts Department of Public Health, Boston, MA
Primary Contact: Valenda M. Liptak, Chief Executive Officer
CMO: Chabilal Neergheen, M.D., Medical Director
CHR: James E. Duggan, Director Human Resources
Web address: www.mass.gov/eohhs/gov/departments/dph/programs/western–massachusetts–hospital.html
**Control:** State–Government, nonfederal **Service:** Long–Term Acute Care hospital

Staffed Beds: 70

---

**WESTWOOD—Norfolk County**

☐ **WESTWOOD LODGE HOSPITAL (224023)**, 45 Clapboardtree Street, Zip 02090–2903; tel. 781/762–7764, (Nonreporting) **A**1 5 9 10 **S** Universal Health Services, Inc., King of Prussia, PA
Primary Contact: Gregory Brownstein, Chief Executive Officer
CFO: Charles Denno, Chief Financial Officer
Web address: www.arbourhealth.com
**Control:** Corporation, Investor–owned, for–profit **Service:** Psychiatric

Staffed Beds: 130

---

**WHITINSVILLE—Worcester County**

**WHITINSVILLE MEDICAL CENTER** See Milford Regional Medical Center, Milford

---

**WINCHESTER—Middlesex County**

⊞ **WINCHESTER HOSPITAL (220105)**, 41 Highland Avenue, Zip 01890–1496; tel. 781/729–9000 **A**1 2 3 5 9 10 **F**3 8 12 13 15 18 26 28 29 30 31 32 34 35 36 38 40 41 44 45 46 49 50 51 54 55 56 57 59 62 64 68 70 73 74 75 76 77 78 79 81 82 85 86 87 89 92 93 107 108 110 114 115 118 119 120 121 126 129 130 131 132 135 144 145 146 147 148 **S** Lahey Health, Burlington, MA
Primary Contact: Dale M. Lodge, Chief Executive Officer
CFO: Matthew Woods, Vice President Finance
CMO: Richard Iseke, M.D., Vice President Medical Affairs
CHR: Alex Barker, Vice President Human Resources and Compliance and Privacy Officer
CNO: Kathy Schuler, R.N., Vice President of Patient Care Services
Web address: www.winchesterhospital.org
**Control:** Other not–for–profit (including NFP Corporation) **Service:** General Medical and Surgical

Staffed Beds: 198 Admissions: 10506 Census: 117 Outpatient Visits: 554591 Births: 1867 Total Expense ($000): 263135 Payroll Expense ($000): 124834 Personnel: 1768

---

**WOBURN—Middlesex County**

☐ **NEW ENGLAND REHABILITATION HOSPITAL (223026)**, Two Rehabilitation Way, Zip 01801–6098; tel. 781/935–5050 **A**1 3 10 **F**29 90 91 93 95 96 130 132 143 146 148 **S** Five Star Quality Care, Newton, MA
Primary Contact: Abraham Sims, Chief Executive Officer
CFO: Lester Felege, Controller
CMO: A. Deniz Ozel, M.D., Medical Director
CHR: Annamarie Cronin, Director Human Resources
Web address: www.newenglandrehab.com
**Control:** Corporation, Investor–owned, for–profit **Service:** Rehabilitation

Staffed Beds: 210 Admissions: 2549 Census: 84 Outpatient Visits: 36301 Births: 0 Total Expense ($000): 40475 Payroll Expense ($000): 19353 Personnel: 318

---

**WORCESTER—Worcester County**

**ADCARE HOSPITAL OF WORCESTER (220062)**, 107 Lincoln Street, Zip 01605–2499; tel. 508/799–9000, (Nonreporting) **A**3 5 9 10
Primary Contact: David W. Hillis, Chairman and Chief Executive Officer
COO: Jeffrey W. Hillis, Chief Operating Officer
CFO: Christine Judycki–Crepeault, Chief Financial Officer
CMO: Ronald F. Pike, M.D., Medical Director
CHR: Joan L. Bertrand, Vice President Human Resources
CNO: Judith Richards, Director of Nursing
Web address: www.adcare.com
**Control:** Other not–for–profit (including NFP Corporation) **Service:** Alcoholism and other chemical dependency

Staffed Beds: 114

---

⊞ **FAIRLAWN REHABILITATION HOSPITAL (223029)**, 189 May Street, Zip 01602–4339; tel. 508/791–6351 **A**1 3 5 10 **F**3 28 29 34 35 56 57 59 64 74 75 77 79 82 86 87 90 91 93 95 96 130 132 135 146 148 **P**8 **S** HEALTHSOUTH Corporation, Birmingham, AL
Primary Contact: R. David Richer, Chief Executive Officer
CFO: John Flaherty, Controller
CMO: Peter Bagley, M.D., Medical Director
CIO: Crystal Anson, Director Health Information
CHR: Rosalie Lawless, Director Human Resources
CNO: Judith Chuli, R.N., Chief Nursing Officer
Web address: www.fairlawnrehab.org
**Control:** Corporation, Investor–owned, for–profit **Service:** Rehabilitation

Staffed Beds: 110 Admissions: 2476 Census: 88 Outpatient Visits: 10919 Births: 0 Total Expense ($000): 31264 Payroll Expense ($000): 17517 Personnel: 339

---

⊞ **SAINT VINCENT HOSPITAL (220176)**, 123 Summer Street, Zip 01608–1216; tel. 508/363–5000 **A**1 2 3 5 9 10 **F**3 8 12 13 15 17 18 20 22 24 26 28 29 30 31 35 38 40 45 46 47 48 49 50 57 59 60 64 68 70 74 75 76 77 78 79 81 82 84 85 86 87 89 92 93 97 98 100 101 102 107 108 110 111 114 115 116 117 118 119 120 121 123 124 126 129 130 131 132 135 146 147 148 **P**5 **S** TENET Healthcare Corporation, Dallas, TX
Primary Contact: Steven MacLauchlan, President and CEO
COO: Deborah Bitsoli, Chief Operating Officer
CFO: Peter D'Elia, Chief Financial Officer
CMO: Douglas Waite, M.D., Chief Medical Officer
CHR: Jan Peters, Vice President Human Resources
CNO: Lisa Zapatka, R.N., Chief Nursing Officer
Web address: www.stvincenthospital.com
**Control:** Corporation, Investor–owned, for–profit **Service:** General Medical and Surgical

Staffed Beds: 283 Admissions: 17500 Census: 194 Outpatient Visits: 259281 Births: 2024 Total Expense ($000): 366840 Payroll Expense ($000): 150963 Personnel: 1420

---

⊞ **UMASS MEMORIAL MEDICAL CENTER (220163)**, 119 Belmont Street, Zip 01605–2982; tel. 508/334–1000, (Includes HAHNEMANN CAMPUS, 281 Lincoln Street, Zip 01605; tel. 508/334–1000; MEMORIAL CAMPUS, 119 Belmont Street, Zip 01605; tel. 508/334–1000; UMASS MEMORIAL CHILDREN'S MEDICAL CENTER, 55 Lake Avenue North, Zip 01655–0002; tel. 508/334–1000; UNIVERSITY CAMPUS, 55 Lake Avenue North, Zip 01655–0002; tel. 508/334–1000) **A**1 2 3 5 8 9 10 **F**3 5 7 8 9 12 13 14 15 16 17 18 19 20 22 24 25 26 29 30 31 32 34 38 40 41 43 45 46 47 48 49 50 51 52 55 56 58 59 60 61 64 65 68 70 72 73 74 75 76 78 79 81 82 84 85 87 88 89 92 93 97 98 99 100 101 102 103 104 105 107 108 110 114 115 118 119 120 121 123 124 126 127 130 131 132 134 135 136 138 139 142 144 145 146 147 148 **S** UMass Memorial Health Care, Inc., Worcester, MA
Primary Contact: Patrick L. Muldoon, FACHE, President and CEO
COO: Andrew Sussman, M.D., Chief Operating Officer
CFO: Therese Day, Chief Financial Officer
CMO: Stephen E. Tosi, M.D., Chief Medical Officer
CIO: George Brenkle, Chief Information Officer
Web address: www.umassmemorial.org
**Control:** Other not–for–profit (including NFP Corporation) **Service:** General Medical and Surgical

Staffed Beds: 807 Admissions: 36690 Census: 543 Outpatient Visits: 1002657 Births: 4002 Total Expense ($000): 1493653 Payroll Expense ($000): 501742 Personnel: 7033

---

☐ **WORCESTER RECOVERY CENTER AND HOSPITAL (224032)**, 305 Belmont Street, Zip 01604–1695; tel. 508/368–3300, (Nonreporting) **A**1 3 5 10 **S** Massachusetts Department of Mental Health, Boston, MA
Primary Contact: Anthony Riccitelli, Chief Operating Officer
COO: Anthony Riccitelli, Chief Operating Officer
CIO: Ron Medciros, Director Applied Information Technology
**Control:** State–Government, nonfederal **Service:** Psychiatric

Staffed Beds: 126

---

**MA**

# MICHIGAN

MI

### ADRIAN—Lenawee County

★ ○ **PROMEDICA BIXBY HOSPITAL (230005)**, 818 Riverside Avenue, Zip 49221–1446; tel. 517/265–0900 **A**2 9 10 11 **F**3 11 13 15 18 28 30 34 35 40 45 46 50 51 55 57 59 64 68 70 74 75 76 77 78 79 81 82 85 91 92 93 100 102 104 107 108 111 114 116 117 118 119 120 121 126 130 131 132 135 143 145 146 148 **P**6 8 **S** ProMedica Health System, Toledo, OH
Primary Contact: Julie Yaroch, D.O., President
CFO: Bernie Nawrocki, Administrative Director Finance
CIO: Stephanie Sonnenberg, Director Information Technology
CHR: Cathy J. Davis, Director Human Resources
CNO: Kathryn M. Greenlee, R.N., Vice President, Clinical Services/CNO
Web address: www.promedica.org
**Control:** Other not–for–profit (including NFP Corporation) **Service:** General Medical and Surgical

**Staffed Beds:** 66 **Admissions:** 3669 **Census:** 35 **Outpatient Visits:** 130867 **Births:** 713 **Total Expense ($000):** 73180 **Payroll Expense ($000):** 24992 **Personnel:** 445

### ALLEGAN—Allegan County

★ ◇ **ALLEGAN GENERAL HOSPITAL (231328)**, 555 Linn Street, Zip 49010–1524; tel. 269/673–8424 **A**9 10 18 21 **F**3 12 15 28 29 31 34 35 40 45 47 48 50 57 59 62 70 75 77 78 79 81 82 85 86 87 96 99 100 101 104 107 108 110 114 119 127 129 130 131 132 135 146 147 **S** QHR, Brentwood, TN
Primary Contact: Gerald J. Barbini, President and Chief Executive Officer
CFO: Richard Harning, Vice President Finance and Chief Financial Officer
CMO: Nabil Nouna, M.D., Chief of Staff
CIO: David Federinko, Chief Information Officer
CHR: Denise A. Eberth, Chief Human Resources Officer
CNO: Kathy Chapman, Chief Clinical Officer and Vice President of Patient Services
Web address: www.aghosp.org
**Control:** Other not–for–profit (including NFP Corporation) **Service:** General Medical and Surgical

**Staffed Beds:** 25 **Admissions:** 852 **Census:** 8 **Outpatient Visits:** 86308 **Births:** 0 **Total Expense ($000):** 46302 **Payroll Expense ($000):** 18100 **Personnel:** 279

### ALMA—Gratiot County

**GRATIOT MEDICAL CENTER** See MidMichigan Medical Center–Gratiot

⊞ △ **MIDMICHIGAN MEDICAL CENTER–GRATIOT (230030)**, 300 East Warwick Drive, Zip 48801–1014; tel. 989/463–1101 **A**1 5 7 9 10 18 **F**3 11 12 13 15 18 20 28 29 31 32 34 35 40 50 51 56 57 59 61 64 65 66 68 70 74 75 76 77 78 79 81 82 85 86 87 89 90 92 93 96 98 100 101 102 103 105 107 108 110 111 115 117 118 119 127 129 130 132 135 144 146 148 **S** MidMichigan Health, Midland, MI
Primary Contact: Mark A. Santamaria, President
CFO: Jeff Provenzano, Vice President and Chief Financial Officer
Web address: www.midmichigan.org/gratiot
**Control:** Other not–for–profit (including NFP Corporation) **Service:** General Medical and Surgical

**Staffed Beds:** 79 **Admissions:** 4300 **Census:** 54 **Outpatient Visits:** 130911 **Births:** 544 **Total Expense ($000):** 95438 **Payroll Expense ($000):** 29143 **Personnel:** 516

### ALPENA—Alpena County

⊞ **ALPENA REGIONAL MEDICAL CENTER (230036)**, 1501 West Chisholm Street, Zip 49707–1401; tel. 989/356–7390 **A**1 2 9 10 **F**3 11 13 15 20 26 28 29 31 34 35 40 44 45 46 47 48 49 50 59 62 64 65 70 71 73 74 75 76 77 78 79 81 82 85 86 87 90 92 93 96 97 98 99 100 101 102 103 104 106 107 108 110 111 114 115 118 119 129 130 131 132 135 146 147 148 **P**6
Primary Contact: Karmon T. Bjella, Chief Executive Officer
COO: Charles H. Sherwin, Vice President of Business Development and Clinical Services
CFO: George J. Smart, Vice President Finance and Information Technology
CMO: Richard Bates, Vice President of Medical Affairs
CHR: Diane Shields, Chief Human Resources Officer
CNO: Charles H. Sherwin, Chief Nursing Officer
Web address: www.alpenaregionalmedicalcenter.org
**Control:** County–Government, nonfederal **Service:** General Medical and Surgical

**Staffed Beds:** 125 **Admissions:** 4957 **Census:** 59 **Outpatient Visits:** 209311 **Births:** 391 **Total Expense ($000):** 122626 **Payroll Expense ($000):** 49001 **Personnel:** 864

### ANN ARBOR—Washtenaw County

⊞ **UNIVERSITY OF MICHIGAN HOSPITALS AND HEALTH CENTERS (230046)**, 1500 East Medical Center Drive, Zip 48109; tel. 734/936–4000, (Includes C. S. MOTT CHILDREN'S HOSPITAL, 1540 East Hospital Drive, Zip 48109–5475; tel. 734/936–4000; Paul A. King, Executive Director) **A**1 2 3 5 8 9 10 **F**3 5 6 8 9 11 12 13 15 16 17 18 19 20 21 22 23 24 25 26 27 28 29 30 31 32 34 35 36 37 38 39 40 41 43 44 45 46 47 48 49 50 51 52 53 54 55 56 57 58 59 60 61 62 64 65 66 68 69 70 72 74 75 76 77 78 79 80 81 82 84 85 86 87 88 89 90 91 92 93 94 95 97 98 99 100 101 102 103 104 107 108 110 111 112 114 115 116 117 118 119 120 121 123 124 126 127 129 130 131 132 134 135 136 137 138 139 140 141 142 145 146 147 148 **P**6
Primary Contact: Tony Denton, JD, Acting Chief Executive Officer and Chief Operating Officer
COO: Tony Denton, JD, Chief Operating Officer
CFO: Paul Castillo, Chief Financial Officer
CMO: Jeffrey Desmond, M.D., Interim Chief Medical Officer
CIO: Sue Schade, Chief Information Officer
CHR: Joseph Fournier, Chief Human Resources Officer
Web address: www.med.umich.edu
**Control:** Other not–for–profit (including NFP Corporation) **Service:** General Medical and Surgical

**Staffed Beds:** 962 **Admissions:** 47988 **Census:** 794 **Outpatient Visits:** 2128965 **Births:** 4506 **Total Expense ($000):** 2495990 **Payroll Expense ($000):** 966493 **Personnel:** 14933

⊞ **VETERANS AFFAIRS ANN ARBOR HEALTHCARE SYSTEM**, 2215 Fuller Road, Zip 48105–2399; tel. 734/769–7100, (Total facility includes 40 beds in nursing home–type unit) **A**1 2 3 5 8 9 **F**3 5 12 18 20 22 24 26 28 29 30 31 34 35 36 38 39 40 45 46 48 49 50 54 56 57 58 59 60 61 62 63 64 65 68 70 71 74 75 77 78 79 81 82 83 84 85 86 87 91 92 93 94 96 97 98 100 101 102 103 104 105 107 108 111 114 115 116 117 118 119 121 123 126 128 129 130 132 135 143 144 146 147 148 **P**6 **S** Department of Veterans Affairs, Washington, DC
Primary Contact: Robert P. McDivitt, FACHE, Director
COO: Himanshu Singh, M.D., Associate Director
CFO: Joel Wallinga, Chief Financial Officer
CMO: Eric Young, M.D., Chief of Staff
CIO: Rob Whitehurst, Chief, Office of Information and Technology
CHR: Stephanie Hunter, Chief Human Resources Officer
CNO: Stacey Breedveld, R.N., Associate Director for Patient Care
Web address: www.annarbor.va.gov
**Control:** Veterans Affairs, Government, federal **Service:** General Medical and Surgical

**Staffed Beds:** 109 **Admissions:** 6296 **Census:** 88 **Outpatient Visits:** 602200 **Births:** 0 **Total Expense ($000):** 430203 **Payroll Expense ($000):** 175668 **Personnel:** 3086

### AUBURN HILLS—Oakland County

☐ **HAVENWYCK HOSPITAL (234023)**, 1525 University Drive, Zip 48326–2673; tel. 248/373–9200 **A**1 9 10 **F**98 99 102 103 105 106 130 **P**8 **S** Universal Health Services, Inc., King of Prussia, PA
Primary Contact: Diane Henneman, Chief Executive Officer
CFO: David Kunkle, Chief Financial Officer
CMO: Hani Mekhael, M.D., Chief Staff
CHR: Amy Giannosa, Director Human Resources
CNO: Mitzi Sawicki, Director of Nursing
Web address: www.havenwyckhospital.com
**Control:** Corporation, Investor–owned, for–profit **Service:** Psychiatric

**Staffed Beds:** 235 **Admissions:** 6609 **Census:** 196 **Outpatient Visits:** 4756 **Births:** 0 **Total Expense ($000):** 43323 **Payroll Expense ($000):** 16084 **Personnel:** 377

### BAD AXE—Huron County

**HURON MEDICAL CENTER (230118)**, 1100 South Van Dyke Road, Zip 48413–9615; tel. 989/269–9521 **A**5 9 10 20 **F**3 11 13 14 15 18 20 28 29 31 32 34 35 40 45 53 56 57 59 64 70 74 75 76 77 78 79 81 82 85 90 93 97 107 108 114 119 126 127 130 132 134 135 144 146 148 **P**6
Primary Contact: Jeffery Longbrake, President and Chief Executive Officer
CFO: Kristen Hedley, Controller
CMO: Christopher Gong, M.D., Chief Staff
CHR: Nancy Bouck, Director Human Resources
CNO: Carrie Franzel, Chief Nursing Officer
Web address: www.huronmedicalcenter.org
**Control:** Other not–for–profit (including NFP Corporation) **Service:** General Medical and Surgical

**Staffed Beds:** 35 **Admissions:** 1674 **Census:** 14 **Outpatient Visits:** 52977 **Births:** 382 **Total Expense ($000):** 44677 **Payroll Expense ($000):** 18044 **Personnel:** 354

*Many Facility Codes have changed. Please refer to the AHA Guide Code Chart.* © 2015 AHA Guide

**MI**

## BATTLE CREEK—Calhoun County

⊠ **BATTLE CREEK VETERANS AFFAIRS MEDICAL CENTER**, 5500 Armstrong Road, Zip 49037–7314; tel. 269/966–5600, (Total facility includes 75 beds in nursing home–type unit) **A**1 5 9 **F**3 4 5 7 12 18 29 30 34 35 36 38 39 50 53 54 56 57 58 59 61 62 63 64 65 68 74 75 77 82 83 84 86 87 91 92 93 94 96 97 98 100 101 102 103 104 106 107 108 111 114 119 127 128 130 132 135 143 144 146 147 148 **S** Department of Veterans Affairs, Washington, DC
Primary Contact: Mary Beth Skupien, Director
COO: Edward G. Dornoff, Associate Director
CFO: James M. Rupert, Chief Fiscal Services
CMO: Wilfredo Rodriguez, M.D., Chief of Staff
CIO: Scott Hershberger, Acting Chief Information Management Services
CHR: Palma Simkins, Chief Human Resources Management Services
CNO: Kay Bower, Associate Director for Patient Care Services
Web address: www.battlecreek.va.gov/
**Control:** Veterans Affairs, Government, federal **Service:** Psychiatric

**Staffed Beds:** 242 **Admissions:** 2349 **Census:** 214 **Outpatient Visits:** 501397 **Births:** 0 **Personnel:** 1431

⊠ **BRONSON BATTLE CREEK (230075)**, 300 North Avenue, Zip 49017–3307; tel. 269/245–8000, (Includes FIELDSTONE CENTER, 165 North Washington Avenue, Zip 49037; tel. 269/245–8570; MAIN CAMPUS, 300 North Avenue, Zip 49017; tel. 616/966–8000) **A**1 2 9 10 **F**3 4 5 6 9 11 13 15 18 20 26 28 29 30 31 34 35 38 40 43 44 45 49 50 51 54 55 56 57 58 59 60 62 64 65 66 68 70 71 74 75 76 77 78 79 81 82 84 85 86 87 91 92 93 97 98 100 101 102 103 104 107 108 110 111 114 115 116 117 118 119 120 121 123 124 126 129 130 131 132 135 143 144 146 147 148 **P**8 **S** Bronson Healthcare Group, Inc., Kalamazoo, MI
Primary Contact: Frank J. Sardone, President and Chief Executive Officer
COO: James E. Mckernan, Chief Operating Officer
CFO: Mary Meitz, Senior Vice President and Chief Financial Officer
CMO: Daniel Stewart, M.D., Vice President Medical Affairs
CHR: John Hayden, Senior Vice President and Human Resources Officer
CNO: Susan Watson, MSN, Vice President
Web address: www.bronsonhealth.com
**Control:** Other not–for–profit (including NFP Corporation) **Service:** General Medical and Surgical

**Staffed Beds:** 198 **Admissions:** 9358 **Census:** 114 **Outpatient Visits:** 809203 **Births:** 808 **Total Expense ($000):** 208837 **Payroll Expense ($000):** 98743 **Personnel:** 1990

⊠ **SELECT SPECIALTY HOSPITAL–BATTLE CREEK (232035)**, 300 North Avenue, Zip 49017–3307; tel. 269/245–4675, (Nonreporting) **A**1 9 10 **S** Select Medical Corporation, Mechanicsburg, PA
Primary Contact: Salvatore Iweimrin, R.N., Chief Executive Officer
Web address: www.battlecreek.selectspecialtyhospitals.com/
**Control:** Corporation, Investor–owned, for–profit **Service:** Long–Term Acute Care hospital

**Staffed Beds:** 25

**VETERANS AFFAIRS MEDICAL CENTER** See Battle Creek Veterans Affairs Medical Center

## BAY CITY—Bay County

☐ △ **MCLAREN BAY REGION (230041)**, 1900 Columbus Avenue, Zip 48708–6831; tel. 989/894–3000, (Includes BAY REGIONAL MEDICAL CENTER–WEST CAMPUS, 3250 East Midland Road, Zip 48706; tel. 989/667–6750) **A**1 2 5 7 9 10 12 13 **F**3 7 11 13 17 18 20 22 24 26 28 29 30 31 32 34 35 36 38 40 44 45 46 47 48 49 50 57 58 59 64 65 68 70 73 74 75 76 78 79 81 82 85 86 87 89 90 92 93 96 97 98 100 102 103 107 108 110 111 114 115 119 120 121 123 124 129 130 131 132 135 141 143 146 147 148 **P**6 **S** McLaren Health Care Corporation, Flint, MI
Primary Contact: Clarence Sevillian, President and Chief Executive Officer
CFO: Damon Sorensen, Chief Financial Officer
CMO: Jay Summer, M.D., Vice President Corporate Medical Affairs
CIO: Ronald Strachan, Chief Information Officer
CHR: Carolyn Potter, Vice President Human Resources
CNO: Ellen E. Talbott, R.N., Vice President Patient Care Services
Web address: www.bayregional.org
**Control:** Other not–for–profit (including NFP Corporation) **Service:** General Medical and Surgical

**Staffed Beds:** 338 **Admissions:** 14821 **Census:** 196 **Outpatient Visits:** 304523 **Births:** 868 **Total Expense ($000):** 269588 **Payroll Expense ($000):** 122269 **Personnel:** 1834

○ **MCLAREN BAY SPECIAL CARE (232020)**, 3250 East Midland Road, Suite 1, Zip 48706–2835; tel. 989/667–6802 **A**9 10 11 **F**1 3 29 31 79 87 96 148 **S** McLaren Health Care Corporation, Flint, MI
Primary Contact: Cheryl A. Burzynski, President
CFO: Damon Sorensen, Chief Financial Officer
CMO: Janet Sutton, M.D., Medical Director
CIO: Greg Jacobs, Manager
CHR: Carolyn Potter, Vice President Human Resources
Web address: www.bayspecialcare.org
**Control:** Other not–for–profit (including NFP Corporation) **Service:** Long–Term Acute Care hospital

**Staffed Beds:** 26 **Admissions:** 354 **Census:** 25 **Outpatient Visits:** 0 **Births:** 0 **Total Expense ($000):** 8824 **Payroll Expense ($000):** 4173 **Personnel:** 66

## BIG RAPIDS—Mecosta County

⊠ **SPECTRUM HEALTH BIG RAPIDS HOSPITAL (230093)**, 605 Oak Street, Zip 49307–2099; tel. 231/796–8691 **A**1 5 9 10 20 **F**3 8 13 15 17 28 29 34 35 40 45 53 59 62 63 64 65 70 75 76 77 79 81 85 86 87 89 90 91 93 96 97 107 108 110 111 115 119 124 127 129 130 132 135 146 147 148 **P**1 **S** Spectrum Health, Grand Rapids, MI
Primary Contact: Mary Kay VanDriel, President
COO: Catherine Rybicki, Vice President Physician Services and Chief Operating Officer
CFO: Thomas Khoerl, Vice President Finance
CIO: Patrick Whiteside, Manager Information Services
CHR: Ricky Green, Senior Human Resources Business Partner
CNO: Netty S. Cove, R.N., Vice President Patient Services and Chief Nursing Officer
Web address: www.mcmcbr.com
**Control:** Other not–for–profit (including NFP Corporation) **Service:** General Medical and Surgical

**Staffed Beds:** 53 **Admissions:** 2060 **Census:** 17 **Outpatient Visits:** 130512 **Births:** 591 **Total Expense ($000):** 62466 **Payroll Expense ($000):** 26815 **Personnel:** 480

## BRIGHTON—Livingston County

★ **BRIGHTON CENTER FOR RECOVERY (230279)**, 12851 Grand River Road, Zip 48116–8506; tel. 810/227–1211 **A**10 **F**4 5 35 68 75 104 132 **P**3 6 8 **S** Ascension Health, Saint Louis, MO
Primary Contact: Raymond Waller, Director
COO: Raymond Waller, Director
CFO: Michael J. Felczak, Jr., Finance Manager
CMO: Jeffrey Berger, M.D., Chief Medical Officer
CIO: Frank Sanzone, Manager Information Technology
CHR: Marney Daugherty, Worklife Services Consultant
CNO: Barbara Shaw, Chief Nursing Officer
Web address: www.brightonrecovery.org
**Control:** Other not–for–profit (including NFP Corporation) **Service:** Alcoholism and other chemical dependency

**Staffed Beds:** 99 **Admissions:** 4010 **Census:** 92 **Outpatient Visits:** 16416 **Births:** 0 **Total Expense ($000):** 15201 **Payroll Expense ($000):** 7578 **Personnel:** 141

## CADILLAC—Wexford County

⊠ **MUNSON HEALTHCARE CADILLAC HOSPITAL (230081)**, 400 Hobart Street, Zip 49601–2389; tel. 231/876–7200 **A**1 9 10 20 **F**3 11 13 28 29 30 31 34 35 40 44 45 50 51 59 64 68 70 76 77 78 79 81 85 87 89 91 93 97 107 108 111 114 115 116 119 127 129 130 132 146 **P**6 8 **S** Munson Healthcare, Traverse City, MI
Primary Contact: Tonya Smith, President and Chief Executive Officer
CFO: Kristin Ellis, Vice President Finance
CMO: James Whelan, Chief Medical Officer
CIO: Randi Terry, Site Director Management Information Systems
CHR: Mary Rosser, Director Human Resources
Web address: www.mercyhealthcadillac.com/welcome–cadillac
**Control:** Church–operated, Nongovernment, not–for profit **Service:** General Medical and Surgical

**Staffed Beds:** 65 **Admissions:** 3557 **Census:** 32 **Outpatient Visits:** 125731 **Births:** 352 **Total Expense ($000):** 75260 **Payroll Expense ($000):** 27628 **Personnel:** 496

**MI**

## CARO—Tuscola County

☐ **CARO CENTER (234025)**, 2000 Chambers Road, Zip 48723–9296; tel. 989/673–3191, (Nonreporting) **A**1 9 10
Primary Contact: Rose Laskowski, R.N., Director
COO: Rose Laskowski, R.N., Director
CFO: Mary Jo Drzewiecki–Burger, Administrative Manager
CMO: William Clark, M.D., Chief Clinical Affairs
CIO: Michele Wills, Registered Health Information Administrator
CHR: Barbara Frank, Human Resource Specialist
**Control:** State–Government, nonfederal **Service:** Psychiatric

Staffed Beds: 193

★ **CARO COMMUNITY HOSPITAL (231329)**, 401 North Hooper Street, Zip 48723–1476, Mailing Address: P.O. Box 435, Zip 48723–0435; tel. 989/673–3141 **A**5 9 10 18 **F**3 11 15 29 34 35 40 45 50 57 59 65 75 81 82 85 87 92 93 97 107 108 110 115 119 129 130 131 135 **P**6
Primary Contact: Marc Augsburger, R.N., President and Chief Executive Officer
CFO: Ron Srebinski, Chief Financial Officer
CHR: Allyson Joyce, Vice President Human Resources
CNO: Kelly Whittaker, Vice President Nursing
Web address: www.cch–mi.org
**Control:** Other not–for–profit (including NFP Corporation) **Service:** General Medical and Surgical

Staffed Beds: 25 Admissions: 163 Census: 1 Outpatient Visits: 30439
Births: 0 Total Expense ($000): 12145 Payroll Expense ($000): 5088
Personnel: 115

## CARSON CITY—Montcalm County

★ ○ **SPARROW CARSON HOSPITAL (230208)**, 406 East Elm Street, Zip 48811–9693, Mailing Address: P.O. Box 879, Zip 48811–0879; tel. 989/584–3131, (Nonreporting) **A**3 5 9 10 11 19 **S** Sparrow Health System, Lansing, MI
Primary Contact: Matthew J. Thompson, Chief Executive Officer
CFO: Richard Reid, Vice President Chief Finance Officer
CMO: Robert Seals, D.O., Medical Director
CIO: Richard Terry, Vice President & Chief Information Officer
CHR: Georgette Russell, Vice President of Talent & Organizational Effectiveness
Web address: www.carsoncityhospital.com
**Control:** Other not–for–profit (including NFP Corporation) **Service:** General Medical and Surgical

Staffed Beds: 62

## CASS CITY—Tuscola County

★ **HILLS & DALES GENERAL HOSPITAL (231316)**, 4675 Hill Street, Zip 48726–1099; tel. 989/872–2121 **A**5 9 10 18 **F**3 11 15 29 30 31 32 34 35 40 46 53 56 57 59 61 64 68 74 75 77 79 81 85 86 87 93 97 107 108 109 110 115 118 119 127 129 130 131 132 135 144 146 147 148 **P**6
Primary Contact: Jean Anthony, R.N., President and Chief Executive Officer
CFO: Kenneth Baranski, Chief Financial Officer
CMO: Donald Robbins, Jr., M.D., Chief Staff
CHR: Tom Bardwell, Vice President Human Resources
CNO: Jennifer TerBush, Director of Nursing
Web address: www.hdghmi.org
**Control:** Other not–for–profit (including NFP Corporation) **Service:** General Medical and Surgical

Staffed Beds: 25 Admissions: 479 Census: 4 Outpatient Visits: 64121
Births: 0 Total Expense ($000): 27245 Payroll Expense ($000): 12431
Personnel: 226

## CHARLEVOIX—Charlevoix County

✠ **CHARLEVOIX AREA HOSPITAL (231322)**, 14700 Lake Shore Drive, Zip 49720–1999; tel. 231/547–4024 **A**1 5 9 10 18 **F**11 13 15 28 31 32 34 35 40 50 57 59 75 77 78 79 81 82 93 107 108 111 115 119 129 130 131 132 133 135 144 146 **P**6
Primary Contact: Lyn Jenks, Chief Executive Officer
COO: Christine Wilhelm, Chief Operating Officer
CFO: Robert Zimmerman, Vice President Financial Services
CMO: Craig Boss, M.D., Chief Medical Officer
CIO: David Priest, Director Information Systems
CHR: Patty Fitzgerald, Staff Services
CNO: Bernadette Green Cole, R.N., Chief Nursing Officer
Web address: www.cah.org
**Control:** Other not–for–profit (including NFP Corporation) **Service:** General Medical and Surgical

Staffed Beds: 25 Admissions: 1022 Census: 8 Outpatient Visits: 20871
Births: 206 Total Expense ($000): 40591 Payroll Expense ($000): 17977
Personnel: 308

## CHARLOTTE—Eaton County

✠ **HAYES GREEN BEACH MEMORIAL HOSPITAL (231327)**, 321 East Harris Street, Zip 48813–1629; tel. 517/543–1050 **A**1 9 10 18 **F**3 7 11 15 18 26 28 29 34 35 36 40 45 46 50 53 57 59 62 64 65 68 69 75 77 79 81 82 85 87 89 92 93 97 107 108 110 111 114 118 119 129 130 131 132 135 143 144 146 148 **P**6 **S** QHR, Brentwood, TN
Primary Contact: Matthew Rush, President and Chief Executive Officer
CFO: Kim Capps, Chief Financial Officer
CMO: Hugh Lindsey, M.D., Chief Medical Officer
CIO: Kevin Neugent, Chief Information Officer
CHR: Jennifer C. Bucienski, Vice President Human Resources
CNO: Maureen Hillary, Chief Nursing Officer
Web address: www.hgbhealth.com
**Control:** Other not–for–profit (including NFP Corporation) **Service:** General Medical and Surgical

Staffed Beds: 25 Admissions: 675 Census: 6 Outpatient Visits: 148167
Births: 0 Total Expense ($000): 48553 Payroll Expense ($000): 20437
Personnel: 387

## CHELSEA—Washtenaw County

✠ **ST. JOSEPH MERCY CHELSEA (230259)**, 775 South Main Street, Zip 48118–1383; tel. 734/593–6000 **A**1 3 5 9 10 **F**3 5 8 9 11 15 28 29 30 31 34 35 36 40 45 51 56 59 62 64 65 68 70 75 77 78 79 81 82 84 85 86 87 90 91 93 97 98 99 100 101 102 104 107 110 111 114 115 119 129 130 131 132 134 135 146 147 148 **P**6 **S** Trinity Health, Livonia, MI
Primary Contact: Nancy Kay Graebner, President and Chief Executive Officer
CFO: Barb Fielder, Vice President Finance
CMO: Randall T. Forsch, M.D., Chief Medical Officer
CHR: Jeremy Stephens, Vice President and Chief Human Resources Officer
CNO: Kathy M. Brubaker, R.N., Vice President and Chief Nursing Officer
Web address: www.cch.org
**Control:** Other not–for–profit (including NFP Corporation) **Service:** General Medical and Surgical

Staffed Beds: 113 Admissions: 5055 Census: 47 Outpatient Visits: 272989
Births: 0 Total Expense ($000): 119456 Payroll Expense ($000): 51353
Personnel: 716

## CLARE—Clare County

✠ **MIDMICHIGAN MEDICAL CENTER–CLARE (230180)**, 703 North McEwan Street, Zip 48617–1440; tel. 989/802–5000 **A**1 5 9 10 **F**3 11 15 18 20 28 29 30 34 35 40 45 50 53 57 58 59 61 64 75 77 79 80 81 85 87 91 93 97 107 108 110 111 115 118 119 127 129 130 132 135 144 146 **S** MidMichigan Health, Midland, MI
Primary Contact: Raymond Stover, President and Chief Executive Officer
CFO: Jeff Provenzano, Vice President and Chief Financial Officer
CMO: David Bremer, D.O., Chief of Staff
CIO: Michael Larson, Vice President Chief Information Officer
CNO: Glenn King, R.N., Vice President, Chief Nursing Officer
Web address: www.midmichigan.org
**Control:** Other not–for–profit (including NFP Corporation) **Service:** General Medical and Surgical

Staffed Beds: 49 Admissions: 1172 Census: 10 Outpatient Visits: 103020
Births: 0 Total Expense ($000): 43579 Payroll Expense ($000): 14272
Personnel: 233

## CLINTON TOWNSHIP—Macomb County

✠ **HENRY FORD MACOMB HOSPITALS (230047)**, 15855 19 Mile Road, Zip 48038–6324; tel. 586/263–2300, (Includes HENRY FORD MACOMB HOSPITAL – MOUNT CLEMENS CAMPUS, 215 North Avenue, Mount Clemens, Zip 48043; tel. 586/466–9300; ST. JOSEPH'S MERCY HOSPITAL–WEST, 15855 19 Mile Road, Zip 48038; tel. 586/263–2707; ST. JOSEPH'S MERCY–NORTH, 80650 North Van Dyke, Romeo, Zip 48065; tel. 810/798–3551) **A**1 2 3 9 10 13 **F**3 7 11 12 13 15 18 19 20 22 24 26 28 29 30 31 32 34 35 36 38 40 41 43 44 45 46 47 49 50 51 54 56 57 58 59 60 61 64 65 66 68 69 70 73 74 75 76 77 78 79 80 81 82 84 85 86 87 89 90 92 93 96 97 98 99 100 101 102 103 104 107 108 110 111 114 115 116 117 118 119 120 121 123 124 126 129 130 131 132 134 144 146 147 148 **P**6 8 **S** Henry Ford Health System, Detroit, MI
Primary Contact: Barbara Rossmann, R.N., President and Chief Executive Officer
COO: Gary Beaulac, Chief Operating Officer
CFO: Terry Goodbalian, Vice President Finance and Chief Financial Officer
CMO: Charles Kelly, D.O., Vice President Medical Affairs and Chief Medical Officer
CHR: Joel Gibson, Vice President Human Resources
Web address: www.henryfordmacomb.com
**Control:** Other not–for–profit (including NFP Corporation) **Service:** General Medical and Surgical

Staffed Beds: 420 Admissions: 20721 Census: 285 Outpatient Visits: 560833 Births: 1742 Total Expense ($000): 396098 Payroll Expense ($000): 161440 Personnel: 2625

*Many Facility Codes have changed. Please refer to the AHA Guide Code Chart.*
© 2015 AHA Guide

**COLDWATER—Branch County**

✠ **COMMUNITY HEALTH CENTER OF BRANCH COUNTY (230022)**, 274 East Chicago Street, Zip 49036–2041; tel. 517/279–5400 **A**1 9 10 13 19 **F**3 8 11 12 13 15 28 29 30 31 34 37 40 43 45 57 59 61 62 63 64 65 70 74 75 76 78 79 81 84 85 87 89 91 92 93 96 97 98 100 101 102 103 104 107 108 110 111 115 118 119 127 129 130 132 146 148 **P**6 8
Primary Contact: Randy DeGroot, President and Chief Executive Officer
COO: Mary R. Rose, R.N., Chief Clinical Officer
CFO: Amy Crouch, Chief Financial Officer
CMO: Joudat Daoud, M.D., Chief of Staff
CIO: Joel Lederman, Director Information Systems
CHR: Amy Jensen, Director Human Resources
Web address: www.chcbc.com
**Control:** County–Government, nonfederal **Service:** General Medical and Surgical

**Staffed Beds:** 87 **Admissions:** 3436 **Census:** 37 **Outpatient Visits:** 133252 **Births:** 290 **Total Expense ($000):** 65933 **Payroll Expense ($000):** 28132 **Personnel:** 453

**COMMERCE TOWNSHIP—Oakland County**

✠ **DMC HURON VALLEY–SINAI HOSPITAL (230277)**, 1 William Carls Drive, Zip 48382–2201; tel. 248/937–3300 **A**1 3 5 9 10 **F**3 4 11 12 13 15 16 17 18 20 22 26 28 29 30 31 34 35 37 39 40 43 44 45 46 47 48 49 50 51 53 57 58 59 60 61 64 65 68 70 72 73 74 75 76 77 78 79 80 81 82 84 85 86 87 88 89 90 93 98 107 108 110 111 114 115 117 118 119 121 123 124 126 129 130 132 135 141 146 147 148 **P**1 6 **S** TENET Healthcare Corporation, Dallas, TX
Primary Contact: Karen Fordham, President
CFO: William Lantzy, Vice President Finance
CMO: Marc Bocknek, D.O., Vice President Medical Affairs
CHR: Ayanna Weber, Director Human Resources
CNO: Cathy Grant, R.N., Associate Vice President, Patient Services
Web address: www.hvsh.org
**Control:** Corporation, Investor–owned, for–profit **Service:** General Medical and Surgical

**Staffed Beds:** 145 **Admissions:** 8870 **Census:** 92 **Outpatient Visits:** 91977 **Births:** 1194 **Total Expense ($000):** 169147 **Payroll Expense ($000):** 58029 **Personnel:** 936

**DEARBORN—Wayne County**

✠ **BEAUMONT HOSPITAL–DEARBORN (230020)**, 18101 Oakwood Boulevard, Zip 48124–4089, Mailing Address: P.O. Box 2500, Zip 48123–2500; tel. 313/593–7000 **A**1 2 3 5 8 9 10 **F**3 11 12 13 15 17 18 20 22 24 26 28 29 30 31 32 34 35 37 38 39 40 43 44 47 49 50 52 55 56 57 58 59 60 61 64 65 68 70 72 73 74 75 76 77 78 79 80 81 82 84 85 86 87 89 92 93 96 97 100 102 107 108 110 111 114 115 118 119 123 124 126 130 131 132 135 146 147 148 **P**8 **S** Beaumont Health, Royal Oak, MI
Primary Contact: Kelly C. Smith, Division President
COO: Kimberlie McAllister, Chief Administrative Officer
CFO: Matt LeGault, Chief Financial Administrator
CMO: Malcolm S. Henoch, M.D., Chief Medical Officer
CIO: Paula Smith, Leader Information Services and Chief Information Officer
CHR: Sherry Huffman, Administrator Human Resources
CNO: Mary Ellen Kochis, Administrator Nursing Operations
Web address: www.oakwood.org
**Control:** Other not–for–profit (including NFP Corporation) **Service:** General Medical and Surgical

**Staffed Beds:** 521 **Admissions:** 30675 **Census:** 427 **Outpatient Visits:** 179558 **Births:** 4047 **Total Expense ($000):** 592771 **Payroll Expense ($000):** 221702 **Personnel:** 3089

**DECKERVILLE—Sanilac County**

**DECKERVILLE COMMUNITY HOSPITAL (231311)**, 3559 Pine Street, Zip 48427–7703, Mailing Address: P.O. Box 126, Zip 48427–0126; tel. 810/376–2835, (Nonreporting) **A**9 10 18
Primary Contact: David West, Administrator
COO: David West, Administrator
CFO: Valerie Bryant, Chief Financial Officer
CMO: Bassam Afaneh, M.D., Chief of Staff
Web address: www.deckervillehosp.org
**Control:** Other not–for–profit (including NFP Corporation) **Service:** General Medical and Surgical

**Staffed Beds:** 15

**DETROIT—Wayne County**

**BCA STONECREST HOSPITAL** See Stonecrest Center

✠ △ **CHILDREN'S HOSPITAL OF MICHIGAN (233300)**, 3901 Beaubien Street, Zip 48201–2119; tel. 313/745–5437 **A**1 3 5 7 9 10 **F**3 7 11 16 17 18 19 20 21 22 23 24 25 26 27 29 30 31 32 34 35 38 39 40 41 43 44 45 48 49 50 51 54 55 57 58 59 60 61 64 65 66 68 72 74 75 77 78 79 80 81 82 84 85 86 87 88 89 90 91 92 93 94 95 96 97 99 100 107 108 111 114 115 116 117 119 120 121 123 124 129 130 131 132 134 136 137 138 139 141 142 144 146 148 **P**1 6 **S** TENET Healthcare Corporation, Dallas, TX
Primary Contact: Larry M. Gold, Chief Executive Officer
CMO: Rudolph Valentini, M.D., Chief Medical Officer
CHR: Walter Tetteh, Director Human Resources
CNO: Claudine N. Hoppen, MSN, Interim Chief Nursing Officer
Web address: www.chmkids.org
**Control:** Corporation, Investor–owned, for–profit **Service:** Children's general

**Staffed Beds:** 222 **Admissions:** 10862 **Census:** 144 **Outpatient Visits:** 301203 **Births:** 0 **Total Expense ($000):** 343110 **Payroll Expense ($000):** 126201 **Personnel:** 2038

✠ **DETROIT RECEIVING HOSPITAL/UNIVERSITY HEALTH CENTER (230273)**, 4201 Saint Antoine Street, Zip 48201–2153; tel. 313/745–3000 **A**1 3 5 9 10 **F**3 16 17 18 29 30 34 35 38 40 43 44 49 50 56 57 58 59 61 64 65 66 68 70 74 75 77 79 81 82 84 85 86 87 93 97 98 100 102 103 104 107 114 115 119 129 130 131 132 134 135 141 144 146 148 **P**1 6 **S** TENET Healthcare Corporation, Dallas, TX
Primary Contact: Iris Taylor, Ph.D., R.N., President
CFO: Gloria Larkins, Vice President Finance
CMO: Safwan Badr, M.D., Executive Vice President and Chief Medical Officer
CIO: Michael LeRoy, Senior Vice President and Chief Information Officer
CHR: Paulette Griffin, Vice President Human Resources
Web address: www.dmc.org
**Control:** Corporation, Investor–owned, for–profit **Service:** General Medical and Surgical

**Staffed Beds:** 210 **Admissions:** 13557 **Census:** 194 **Outpatient Visits:** 146686 **Births:** 0 **Total Expense ($000):** 263300 **Payroll Expense ($000):** 91286 **Personnel:** 1538

✠ **DMC HARPER UNIVERSITY HOSPITAL (230104)**, 3990 John R Street, Zip 48201–2018; tel. 313/745–8040 **A**1 3 5 9 10 **F**3 8 9 11 12 13 15 17 18 20 22 24 26 28 29 30 34 35 39 40 43 44 45 46 47 48 49 50 51 52 54 55 56 57 58 59 60 61 64 65 66 68 70 72 73 74 75 76 77 78 79 80 81 82 83 84 85 86 87 93 97 100 107 108 111 118 119 126 128 130 131 132 134 135 136 138 141 146 147 148 **P**1 6 **S** TENET Healthcare Corporation, Dallas, TX
Primary Contact: Reginald J. Eadie, M.D., Chief Executive Officer
COO: Valerie Gibson, Chief Operating Officer
CFO: Tina Wood, Chief Financial Officer
CMO: Patricia Wilkerson–Uddyback, M.D., Chief Medical Officer
CIO: Michael LeRoy, Senior Vice President and Chief Information Officer
CHR: Deloris Hunt, Corporate Vice President Human Resources
CNO: Christine Bowen, R.N., Chief Nursing Officer
Web address: www.harperhospital.org
**Control:** Corporation, Investor–owned, for–profit **Service:** General Medical and Surgical

**Staffed Beds:** 412 **Admissions:** 20146 **Census:** 262 **Outpatient Visits:** 215474 **Births:** 4397 **Total Expense ($000):** 477693 **Payroll Expense ($000):** 162658 **Personnel:** 2721

**HARPER UNIVERSITY HOSPITAL** See DMC Harper University Hospital

✠ **HENRY FORD HOSPITAL (230053)**, 2799 West Grand Boulevard, Zip 48202–2608; tel. 313/916–2600 **A**1 2 3 5 8 9 10 **F**3 4 5 6 8 9 11 12 13 15 17 18 20 22 24 26 28 29 30 31 32 33 34 35 36 38 40 41 42 43 44 45 46 47 48 49 50 51 52 53 54 55 56 57 58 59 60 61 62 63 64 65 66 68 70 71 72 73 74 75 76 77 78 79 80 81 82 83 84 85 86 87 91 92 93 96 97 99 100 101 102 103 104 105 107 108 110 111 112 113 114 115 116 117 118 119 120 121 123 124 126 129 130 131 132 134 135 136 137 138 139 140 141 142 144 145 146 147 148 **P**6 **S** Henry Ford Health System, Detroit, MI
Primary Contact: John Popovich, M.D., President and Chief Executive Officer
COO: Veronica Hall, R.N., Chief Operating Officer
CFO: Joseph Schmitt, III, Senior Vice President Finance and Chief Financial Officer
CIO: Mary Alice Annecharico, Chief Information Officer
CHR: Kathy Oswald, Senior Vice President and Chief Human Resources Officer
CNO: Gwen Gnam, R.N., Chief Nursing Officer
Web address: www.henryfordhealth.org
**Control:** Other not–for–profit (including NFP Corporation) **Service:** General Medical and Surgical

**Staffed Beds:** 673 **Admissions:** 33802 **Census:** 510 **Outpatient Visits:** 2756834 **Births:** 2514 **Total Expense ($000):** 1628788 **Payroll Expense ($000):** 812383 **Personnel:** 11149

MI

---

**Hospital, Medicare Provider Number, Address, Telephone, Approval, Facility, and Physician Codes, Health Care System**

★ American Hospital Association (AHA) membership
☐ The Joint Commission accreditation
○ Healthcare Facilities Accreditation Program
◇ DNV Healthcare Inc. accreditation
⇑ Center for Improvement in Healthcare Quality Accreditation
△ Commission on Accreditation of Rehabilitation Facilities (CARF) accreditation

⊠ △ **JOHN D. DINGELL VETERANS AFFAIRS MEDICAL CENTER**, 4646 John R Street, Zip 48201–1932; tel. 313/576–1000, (Total facility includes 109 beds in nursing home–type unit) **A**1 2 3 5 7 9 **F**3 5 8 9 11 12 18 20 26 28 29 30 31 34 35 36 38 39 40 44 45 49 50 54 55 57 58 59 60 61 62 63 64 65 66 67 68 70 74 75 77 78 79 81 82 83 84 85 86 87 90 93 94 97 98 100 101 102 103 104 105 107 108 111 114 115 118 119 121 123 126 127 128 129 130 132 135 143 144 145 146 147 148 **P**6 **S** Department of Veterans Affairs, Washington, DC
Primary Contact: Pamela J. Reeves, M.D., Director
COO: Annette Walker, Associate Director
CFO: Sherry Kilgore, Chief Financial Management Service
CMO: Scott Gruber, M.D., Chief of Staff
CIO: Jonathan Small, Chief Operations Information and Technology
CHR: Kathleen Osinski, Chief Human Resources Service
CNO: Belina Brown–Tezera, MSN, Associate Director Patient Care Services
Web address: www.detroit.va.gov/
**Control:** Veterans Affairs, Government, federal **Service:** General Medical and Surgical

**Staffed Beds:** 157 **Admissions:** 4922 **Census:** 157 **Outpatient Visits:** 504157 **Births:** 0 **Total Expense ($000):** 342524 **Payroll Expense ($000):** 200612 **Personnel:** 1637

□ **KARMANOS CANCER CENTER (230297)**, 4100 John R Street, Zip 48201–2013; tel. 313/576–8670 **A**1 2 3 5 9 10 **F**3 14 15 29 30 31 34 35 36 39 44 50 54 55 57 58 59 64 65 68 70 74 75 78 79 81 82 83 84 85 86 87 100 107 108 110 111 113 114 115 119 120 121 123 124 126 130 132 135 136 146 147 148 **P**6
Primary Contact: Gerold Bepler, M.D., Ph.D., President and Chief Executive Officer
CFO: Brian Gamble, Chief Financial Officer
CMO: George Yoo, M.D., Chief Medical Officer
CIO: Scott McCarter, Chief Information Officer
CHR: David Jansen, Vice President Human Resources
Web address: www.karmanos.org
**Control:** Other not–for–profit (including NFP Corporation) **Service:** Cancer

**Staffed Beds:** 86 **Admissions:** 3681 **Census:** 71 **Outpatient Visits:** 144144 **Births:** 0 **Total Expense ($000):** 230444 **Payroll Expense ($000):** 60458 **Personnel:** 1063

⊠ **KINDRED HOSPITAL DETROIT (232027)**, 4777 East Outer Drive, Zip 48234–3241; tel. 313/369–5800, (Nonreporting) **A**1 9 10 **S** Kindred Healthcare, Louisville, KY
Primary Contact: Mary Hoskins, Chief Executive Officer
CFO: Clayton Kubacki, Interim Controller
CMO: Kevin Potts, M.D., Medical Director
CHR: Angela Moncrief–Wells, Coordinator Human Resources
Web address: www.kindreddetroit.com/
**Control:** Corporation, Investor–owned, for–profit **Service:** Long–Term Acute Care hospital

**Staffed Beds:** 77

⊠ △ **REHABILITATION INSTITUTE OF MICHIGAN (233027)**, 261 Mack Avenue, Zip 48201–2495; tel. 313/745–1203 **A**1 3 5 7 9 10 **F**3 29 30 34 35 44 53 58 59 64 68 86 87 90 91 92 93 94 95 96 119 130 131 132 134 146 148 **P**1 6 **S** TENET Healthcare Corporation, Dallas, TX
Primary Contact: William H. Restum, Ph.D., President
COO: Patty Jobbitt, Vice President Operations
CFO: Kevin Smith, Vice President Finance and Support Services
CMO: Ali Bitar, M.D., Vice President Medical Affairs
CHR: Walter Tetteh, Director Human Resources
CNO: Julia Libcke, R.N., VP Patient Care Services
Web address: www.rimrehab.org
**Control:** Corporation, Investor–owned, for–profit **Service:** Rehabilitation

**Staffed Beds:** 69 **Admissions:** 1358 **Census:** 59 **Outpatient Visits:** 226868 **Births:** 0 **Total Expense ($000):** 83020 **Payroll Expense ($000):** 46272 **Personnel:** 732

⊠ **SELECT SPECIALTY HOSPITAL–NORTHWEST DETROIT (232032)**, 6071 West Outer Drive, Zip 48235–2624; tel. 313/966–4747, (Nonreporting) **A**1 9 10 **S** Select Medical Corporation, Mechanicsburg, PA
Primary Contact: Marilouise Riska, Chief Executive Officer
Web address: www.selectspecialtyhospitals.com/company/locations/northwestdetroit.aspx
**Control:** Corporation, Investor–owned, for–profit **Service:** Long–Term Acute Care hospital

**Staffed Beds:** 36

⊠ **SINAI–GRACE HOSPITAL (230024)**, 6071 West Outer Drive, Zip 48235–2679; tel. 313/966–3300 **A**1 3 5 9 10 12 13 **F**3 5 8 11 13 15 18 20 22 24 26 28 29 30 31 32 34 35 38 39 40 43 44 45 49 50 51 54 55 57 58 59 60 61 64 65 68 70 72 74 75 76 77 78 79 80 81 82 84 85 86 87 90 93 96 97 98 100 102 104 107 108 110 111 114 115 117 118 119 120 121 123 126 129 130 132 134 135 141 144 146 147 148 **P**1 6 **S** TENET Healthcare Corporation, Dallas, TX
Primary Contact: Paula R. Autry, FACHE, Chief Executive Officer
COO: London Quicci, Chief Operating Officer
CFO: Michael Prusatis, Vice President Finance
CMO: Matthew Griffin, M.D., Vice President Medical Affairs
CHR: Paulette Griffin, Director Human Resources
Web address: www.sinaigrace.org
**Control:** Corporation, Investor–owned, for–profit **Service:** General Medical and Surgical

**Staffed Beds:** 304 **Admissions:** 20242 **Census:** 275 **Outpatient Visits:** 212801 **Births:** 1453 **Total Expense ($000):** 340074 **Payroll Expense ($000):** 128651 **Personnel:** 2073

⊠ **ST. JOHN HOSPITAL AND MEDICAL CENTER (230165)**, 22101 Moross Road, Zip 48236–2148; tel. 313/343–4000 **A**1 2 3 5 8 9 10 **F**3 8 9 11 12 13 14 15 17 18 20 22 24 26 28 29 30 31 32 34 35 36 37 38 39 40 41 42 43 44 45 46 47 48 49 50 54 55 56 57 58 59 60 61 63 64 65 66 68 70 72 74 75 76 77 78 79 80 81 82 84 85 86 87 88 89 90 91 92 93 95 96 97 98 100 101 102 103 107 108 110 111 114 115 116 117 118 119 120 121 123 124 126 130 131 132 135 138 141 143 144 146 147 148 **P**3 6 8 **S** Ascension Health, Saint Louis, MO
Primary Contact: Robert E. Hoban, Chief Executive Officer
COO: Brant Russell, R.N., Chief Operating Officer
CFO: Tomasine Marx, Chief Financial Officer
CMO: Kevin Grady, M.D., Chief Medical Officer
CIO: Ralph Tenney, Chief Information Officer
CHR: Joanne E. Tuscany, Director Human Resources
CNO: Maryann Barnes, MS, Vice President and Chief Nursing Officer East Region
Web address: www.stjohn.org
**Control:** Church–operated, Nongovernment, not–for profit **Service:** General Medical and Surgical

**Staffed Beds:** 635 **Admissions:** 29730 **Census:** 405 **Outpatient Visits:** 887250 **Births:** 3161 **Total Expense ($000):** 705798 **Payroll Expense ($000):** 254692 **Personnel:** 3682

□ **STONECREST CENTER (234038)**, 15000 Gratiot Avenue, Zip 48205–1973; tel. 313/245–0600, (Nonreporting) **A**1 9 10 **S** Acadia Healthcare Company, Inc., Franklin, TN
Primary Contact: Steve Savage, Chief Executive Officer
Web address: www.stonecrestcenter.com
**Control:** Corporation, Investor–owned, for–profit **Service:** Psychiatric

**Staffed Beds:** 81

**TRIUMPH HOSPITAL DETROIT** See Kindred Hospital Detroit

**DOWAGIAC—Cass County**

⊠ **BORGESS–LEE MEMORIAL HOSPITAL (231315)**, 420 West High Street, Zip 49047–1943; tel. 269/782–8681 **A**1 9 10 18 **F**3 11 15 18 29 30 31 34 35 40 41 50 54 57 59 64 65 68 70 75 77 78 79 81 85 86 87 93 97 100 104 107 108 114 119 127 128 130 132 133 135 146 148 **P**6 **S** Ascension Health, Saint Louis, MO
Primary Contact: John E. Ryder, Chief Operating Officer
COO: John E. Ryder, Chief Operating Officer
CFO: Ken Holst, Chief Financial Officer
CMO: Robert Hill, M.D., Chief Medical Officer
CHR: Pete Krueger, Director Human Resources
CNO: James Nemeth, R.N., Chief Nursing Officer
Web address: www.borgess.com
**Control:** Church–operated, Nongovernment, not–for profit **Service:** General Medical and Surgical

**Staffed Beds:** 25 **Admissions:** 518 **Census:** 4 **Outpatient Visits:** 90771 **Births:** 0 **Total Expense ($000):** 25496 **Payroll Expense ($000):** 13433 **Personnel:** 170

**EAST CHINA—St. Clair County**

⊠ **ST. JOHN RIVER DISTRICT HOSPITAL (230241)**, 4100 River Road, Zip 48054–2909; tel. 810/329–7111 **A**1 3 9 10 **F**3 7 11 13 15 18 20 29 30 31 34 35 36 40 43 44 45 49 50 56 57 59 60 63 64 65 68 70 74 75 76 77 79 81 82 84 85 87 89 92 93 97 102 107 108 110 111 115 116 117 119 129 130 132 146 147 **S** Ascension Health, Saint Louis, MO
Primary Contact: Frank W. Poma, President
CMO: H. Lee Bacheldor, D.O., Medical Director
CHR: Dawn Beindit, Director Work Life Services
CNO: Joyce Kasperski, Director Nursing
Web address: www.stjohn.org
**Control:** Church–operated, Nongovernment, not–for profit **Service:** General Medical and Surgical

**Staffed Beds:** 68 **Admissions:** 1691 **Census:** 16 **Outpatient Visits:** 58354 **Births:** 275 **Total Expense ($000):** 38564 **Payroll Expense ($000):** 17343 **Personnel:** 416

*Many Facility Codes have changed. Please refer to the AHA Guide Code Chart.*   © 2015 AHA Guide

MI

## EATON RAPIDS—Eaton County

★ ◇ **EATON RAPIDS MEDICAL CENTER (231324)**, 1500 South Main Street, Zip 48827–1952, Mailing Address: P.O. Box 130, Zip 48827–0130; tel. 517/663–2671 **A**9 10 18 21 **F**3 15 29 34 35 40 41 45 46 50 53 56 57 59 64 65 66 68 75 77 81 85 86 91 93 97 107 115 117 119 127 129 130 131 132 133 146 147 148
Primary Contact: Timothy Johnson, President and Chief Executive Officer
CFO: Shari Glynn, Vice President Finance and Chief Financial Officer
CMO: Ashok K. Gupta, M.D., Chief of Staff
CIO: Mark Rodge, Director Information Systems
CHR: Laurie Field, Director Human Resources
Web address: www.eatonrapidsmedicalcenter.org
**Control:** Other not–for–profit (including NFP Corporation) **Service:** General Medical and Surgical

**Staffed Beds: 20 Admissions: 382 Census: 3 Outpatient Visits:** 54577
**Births: 0 Total Expense ($000):** 20659 **Payroll Expense ($000):** 9671
**Personnel:** 196

## ESCANABA—Delta County

⊠ **OSF ST. FRANCIS HOSPITAL AND MEDICAL GROUP (231337)**, 3401 Ludington Street, Zip 49829–1377; tel. 906/786–3311 **A**1 9 10 18 **F**3 11 13 15 18 28 29 30 34 35 40 45 46 56 57 59 62 63 64 65 66 68 70 74 75 76 77 78 79 81 83 84 85 86 92 93 96 97 107 108 110 111 115 119 127 129 130 131 132 133 144 145 146 147 148 **P**6 **S** OSF Healthcare System, Peoria, IL
Primary Contact: David Lord, President
COO: Kelly Jefferson, Vice President, Operations
CFO: Fred Wagner, Chief Financial Officer
CMO: Mark Povich, D.O., Medical Director
CIO: Mark Irving, Manager Management Information Systems
CHR: Elizabeth Zorza, Assistant Administrator
CNO: Joy Hopkins, Vice President Patient Care Services
Web address: www.osfstfrancis.org
**Control:** Church–operated, Nongovernment, not–for profit **Service:** General Medical and Surgical

**Staffed Beds: 25 Admissions: 1713 Census: 13 Outpatient Visits:** 119257
**Births: 302 Total Expense ($000):** 71234 **Payroll Expense ($000):** 28393
**Personnel:** 394

## FARMINGTON HILLS—Oakland County

★ ○ **BEAUMONT HOSPITAL – FARMINGTON HILLS (230151)**, 28050 Grand River Avenue, Zip 48336–5933; tel. 248/471–8000 **A**2 3 9 10 11 12 13 **F**3 8 9 11 12 13 15 17 18 20 22 26 28 29 30 31 32 34 35 36 38 39 40 41 43 44 45 46 47 48 49 50 51 54 56 57 58 59 60 61 63 64 65 68 70 74 75 76 77 78 79 80 81 82 83 84 85 86 87 89 90 92 93 94 96 97 98 100 101 102 103 107 108 110 111 114 115 118 119 120 121 123 124 126 129 130 131 132 134 135 144 146 147 148 **P**1 4 5 6 **S** Beaumont Health, Royal Oak, MI
Primary Contact: Paul E. LaCasse, D.O., M.P.H., President and Chief Executive Officer
COO: David Marcellino, Corporate Executive Vice President and Chief Administrative Officer
CFO: Regina Doxtader, Corporate Vice President and Chief Financial Officer
CMO: David Walters, D.O., Vice President and Chief Clinical Officer
CIO: Brian McPherson, Chief Information Officer
CHR: Barbara Palmer, Corporate Vice President Human Resources
CNO: Marge Hasler, R.N., Vice President Patient Care Services and Chief Nursing Officer
Web address: www.botsford.org
**Control:** Other not–for–profit (including NFP Corporation) **Service:** General Medical and Surgical

**Staffed Beds: 310 Admissions: 14819 Census: 197 Outpatient Visits:** 433428 **Births: 807 Total Expense ($000):** 280820 **Payroll Expense ($000):** 138529 **Personnel:** 2121

## FERNDALE—Oakland County

⊠ **HENRY FORD KINGSWOOD HOSPITAL (234011)**, 10300 West Eight Mile Road, Zip 48220–2100; tel. 248/398–3200 **A**1 9 10 **F**4 29 30 32 34 35 44 50 56 57 59 68 75 77 80 82 86 87 98 99 101 103 130 134 135 **P**6 **S** Henry Ford Health System, Detroit, MI
Primary Contact: DoreeAnn V. Espiritu, M.D., Interim Chair, Behavioral Health Services
CFO: Tony Gaglio, Chief Financial Officer
CMO: Robert Lagrou, D.O., Medical Director
CNO: Cheryl Taylor, R.N., Director of Nursing
Web address: www.henryford.com
**Control:** Other not–for–profit (including NFP Corporation) **Service:** Psychiatric

**Staffed Beds: 80 Admissions: 3918 Census: 64 Outpatient Visits:** 0 **Births:** 0 **Total Expense ($000):** 20150 **Payroll Expense ($000):** 12267 **Personnel:** 205

## FLINT—Genesee County

⊠ **HURLEY MEDICAL CENTER (230132)**, One Hurley Plaza, Zip 48503–5993; tel. 810/262–6887, (Includes HURLEY CHILDREN'S HOSPITAL, 1 Hurley Plaza, Zip 48503–5902) **A**1 2 3 5 8 9 10 **F**3 5 11 12 13 15 16 17 18 19 20 22 26 28 29 30 31 32 35 39 40 41 43 45 46 49 50 52 54 55 56 57 61 64 66 70 72 74 75 76 77 78 79 80 81 82 84 85 86 87 88 89 90 93 96 97 98 100 101 102 103 104 107 108 110 111 114 115 118 119 120 121 123 124 126 129 130 131 132 135 141 143 144 146 147 148
Primary Contact: Melany Gavulic, President & Chief Executive Officer
COO: Melany Gavulic, Senior Vice President Operations & COO
CFO: Cass Wisniewski, Interim Chief Financial Officer
CMO: Michael Jaggi, D.O., Vice President and Chief Medical Officer
CIO: Gary Townsend, Chief Information Officer
CHR: Beth Brophy, Interim VP for Human Resources
CNO: Teresa Bourque, Sr. Administrator for Nursing/Chief Nurse
Web address: www.hurleymc.com
**Control:** City–Government, nonfederal **Service:** General Medical and Surgical

**Staffed Beds: 418 Admissions: 17767 Census: 263 Outpatient Visits:** 431372 **Births: 2769 Total Expense ($000):** 367823 **Payroll Expense ($000):** 160732 **Personnel:** 2420

☐ **MCLAREN FLINT (230141)**, 401 South Ballenger Highway, Zip 48532–3685; tel. 810/342–2000 **A**1 2 3 5 8 9 10 **F**3 5 8 11 12 13 15 17 18 20 22 24 26 28 29 30 31 32 34 35 36 38 39 40 43 44 45 46 49 50 52 53 54 55 56 57 58 59 60 61 64 68 70 74 75 76 77 78 79 81 82 84 85 86 87 89 90 91 93 96 97 98 99 100 101 102 103 104 105 107 108 111 114 115 118 119 120 121 123 124 126 129 130 131 132 135 141 144 146 147 148 **P**6 7 **S** McLaren Health Care Corporation, Flint, MI
Primary Contact: Donald C. Kooy, President and Chief Executive Officer
COO: Brent Wheeler, Vice President Ancillary and Support Services
CFO: Rick Wyles, Chief Financial Officer
CMO: Jason White, M.D., Vice President of Medical Affairs
CIO: Ronald Strachan, Chief Information Officer
CHR: Rachelle Hulett, Vice President Human Resources
CNO: Diane Kallas, Vice President of Nursing Services
Web address: www.mclarenregional.org
**Control:** Other not–for–profit (including NFP Corporation) **Service:** General Medical and Surgical

**Staffed Beds: 336 Admissions: 20531 Census: 266 Outpatient Visits:** 375311 **Births: 499 Total Expense ($000):** 406706 **Payroll Expense ($000):** 181381 **Personnel:** 2269

⊠ **SELECT SPECIALTY HOSPITAL–FLINT (232012)**, 401 South Ballenger Highway, 5th Floor Central, Zip 48532–3638; tel. 810/342–4500, (Nonreporting) **A**1 9 10 **S** Select Medical Corporation, Mechanicsburg, PA
Primary Contact: Patricia Adams, Chief Executive Officer
CMO: Jitendra P. Katneni, M.D., Medical Director
CHR: Gayle Barthel, Coordinator Human Resources
CNO: Kathleen Gallardo, Chief Nursing Officer
Web address: www.selectspecialtyhospitals.com/company/locations/flint.aspx
**Control:** Corporation, Investor–owned, for–profit **Service:** Long–Term Acute Care hospital

**Staffed Beds: 26**

## FRANKFORT—Benzie County

★ **PAUL OLIVER MEMORIAL HOSPITAL (231300)**, 224 Park Avenue, Zip 49635–9658; tel. 231/352–2200, (Total facility includes 39 beds in nursing home–type unit) **A**9 10 18 **F**11 15 28 30 34 35 40 45 46 50 53 57 59 60 64 70 72 75 77 81 86 87 93 107 110 111 115 119 129 130 132 133 143 146 148 **S** Munson Healthcare, Traverse City, MI
Primary Contact: Peter Marinoff, President
CMO: George Ryckman, D.O., Chief of Staff
CHR: Julie Banktson, Manager Human Resources
Web address: www.munsonhealthcare.org
**Control:** Other not–for–profit (including NFP Corporation) **Service:** General Medical and Surgical

**Staffed Beds: 47 Admissions: 108 Census: 36 Outpatient Visits:** 43163
**Births: 0 Total Expense ($000):** 15071 **Payroll Expense ($000):** 5036
**Personnel:** 126

**MI**

---

**Hospital, Medicare Provider Number, Address, Telephone, Approval, Facility, and Physician Codes, Health Care System**

★ American Hospital Association (AHA) membership
☐ The Joint Commission accreditation
○ Healthcare Facilities Accreditation Program
◇ DNV Healthcare Inc. accreditation
⇑ Center for Improvement in Healthcare Quality Accreditation
△ Commission on Accreditation of Rehabilitation Facilities (CARF) accreditation

**MI**

## FREMONT—Newaygo County

⊠ **SPECTRUM HEALTH GERBER MEMORIAL (230106)**, 212 South Sullivan Avenue, Zip 49412–1548; tel. 231/924–3300 **A**1 3 9 10 **F**3 11 13 15 28 29 31 32 34 35 36 40 43 45 50 53 59 62 64 68 70 75 76 77 78 79 81 86 87 93 96 107 108 110 111 115 118 119 127 129 130 131 132 135 146 147 **S** Spectrum Health, Grand Rapids, MI
Primary Contact: Randall Stasik, President and Chief Executive Officer
COO: Janice Stone, Vice President Clinical Integration
CFO: Deidre Weller, Vice President, Finance
CMO: Kevin Gerth, M.D., Chief of Staff
CIO: Shane Meeks, Manager Technology Information Systems
CHR: Christine Schurkamp, Senior Human Resources Business Partner
Web address: www.spectrumhealth.org
**Control:** Other not–for–profit (including NFP Corporation) **Service:** General Medical and Surgical

**Staffed Beds:** 40 **Admissions:** 2089 **Census:** 15 **Outpatient Visits:** 117288 **Births:** 457 **Total Expense ($000):** 66411 **Payroll Expense ($000):** 25456 **Personnel:** 484

## GARDEN CITY—Wayne County

★ ○ **GARDEN CITY HOSPITAL (230244)**, 6245 Inkster Road, Zip 48135–4001; tel. 734/421–3300 **A**9 10 11 12 13 **F**3 4 11 13 15 17 18 20 22 26 28 29 31 34 35 36 40 43 44 45 46 47 48 49 50 58 65 68 70 71 74 75 76 77 78 79 80 81 82 85 87 89 90 91 92 93 96 97 107 110 111 112 114 115 119 129 130 131 132 135 143 146 148 **P**5 6 **S** Prime Healthcare Services, Ontario, CA
Primary Contact: Saju George, Chief Executive Officer
CFO: Timothy Jodway, Chief Financial Officer
CIO: William Moncrief, Director Information Systems
CHR: Jolene L. Jacobs, Director of Human Resources
CNO: Karla Zarb, Chief Nursing Officer
Web address: www.gch.org
**Control:** Corporation, Investor–owned, for–profit **Service:** General Medical and Surgical

**Staffed Beds:** 170 **Admissions:** 9091 **Census:** 106 **Outpatient Visits:** 151492 **Births:** 748 **Total Expense ($000):** 138012 **Payroll Expense ($000):** 50455 **Personnel:** 993

## GAYLORD—Otsego County

⊠ **OTSEGO MEMORIAL HOSPITAL (230133)**, 825 North Center Avenue, Zip 49735–1592; tel. 989/731–2100, (Includes MCREYNOLDS HALL ), (Total facility includes 34 beds in nursing home–type unit) **A**1 5 9 10 20 **F**3 13 15 28 29 31 32 34 35 36 37 40 43 44 45 46 49 50 51 54 56 57 59 64 65 70 74 75 76 77 78 79 81 82 85 86 87 93 96 97 104 107 108 110 111 115 118 119 124 127 128 130 131 132 134 135 144 146 147 148 **P**6
Primary Contact: Thomas R. Lemon, Chief Executive Officer
CFO: Robert Courtois, Vice President Finance
CMO: Kevin Smith, D.O., Chief of Staff
CIO: Timothy Hella, Chief Information Officer
CHR: Terra Deming, Director Human Resources
CNO: Diane Fisher, R.N., VP, Patient Care Services
Web address: www.myomh.org
**Control:** Other not–for–profit (including NFP Corporation) **Service:** General Medical and Surgical

**Staffed Beds:** 80 **Admissions:** 1996 **Census:** 48 **Outpatient Visits:** 231572 **Births:** 327 **Total Expense ($000):** 78829 **Payroll Expense ($000):** 39687 **Personnel:** 662

## GLADWIN—Gladwin County

⊠ **MIDMICHIGAN MEDICAL CENTER–GLADWIN (231325)**, 515 Quarter Street, Zip 48624–1959; tel. 989/426–9286 **A**1 5 9 10 18 **F**3 11 15 18 28 29 30 31 34 35 40 45 53 57 59 64 75 77 81 85 86 93 97 107 108 110 111 114 118 119 127 129 130 132 135 143 144 146 **S** MidMichigan Health, Midland, MI
Primary Contact: Raymond Stover, President and Chief Executive Officer
CFO: Jeff Provenzano, Vice President and Chief Financial Officer
CMO: Cheryl Loubert, M.D., Chief Medical Staff
CIO: Dan Waltz, Vice President and Chief Information Officer
CNO: Glenn King, R.N., Vice President and Chief Nursing Officer
Web address: www.midmichigan.org
**Control:** Other not–for–profit (including NFP Corporation) **Service:** General Medical and Surgical

**Staffed Beds:** 25 **Admissions:** 638 **Census:** 5 **Outpatient Visits:** 53235 **Births:** 0 **Total Expense ($000):** 25497 **Payroll Expense ($000):** 7877 **Personnel:** 233

## GRAND BLANC—Genesee County

⊠ △ **GENESYS REGIONAL MEDICAL CENTER (230197)**, One Genesys Parkway, Zip 48439–8066; tel. 810/606–5000 **A**1 3 5 7 9 10 12 13 **F**3 11 13 17 18 20 22 24 26 28 29 30 31 32 34 35 40 41 43 44 45 46 47 48 49 50 51 54 57 58 60 61 63 64 68 70 73 74 75 76 77 78 79 81 82 84 85 86 87 89 90 92 93 96 97 102 107 108 111 114 115 117 118 119 126 129 130 132 135 144 145 146 147 148 **P**1 6 **S** Ascension Health, Saint Louis, MO
Primary Contact: Elizabeth Aderholdt, President and Chief Executive Officer
COO: Christopher Palazzolo, Senior Vice President and Chief Operating Officer
CFO: Nancy Haywood, Chief Financial Officer
CMO: James C. Bonnette, M.D., Chief Clinical Officer
CIO: Daniel Stross, Chief Information Officer
CNO: Julie A. Gorczyca, R.N., Chief Nursing Officer
Web address: www.genesys.org
**Control:** Church–operated, Nongovernment, not–for profit **Service:** General Medical and Surgical

**Staffed Beds:** 410 **Admissions:** 20937 **Census:** 282 **Outpatient Visits:** 579264 **Births:** 2103 **Total Expense ($000):** 405375 **Payroll Expense ($000):** 181389 **Personnel:** 2710

## GRAND HAVEN—Ottawa County

★ ◇ **NORTH OTTAWA COMMUNITY HOSPITAL (230174)**, 1309 Sheldon Road, Zip 49417–2488; tel. 616/842–3600 **A**9 10 21 **F**3 7 11 12 13 15 29 30 34 35 40 43 45 50 51 57 59 61 62 63 64 65 68 69 70 74 75 79 81 83 84 86 87 97 107 108 115 119 126 128 129 130 131 132 135 143 144 145 146 147 148 **P**6
Primary Contact: Shelleye Yaklin, President and Chief Executive Officer
CFO: Donald J. Longpre, Vice President Finance and Chief Financial Officer
CMO: Haney Assaad, Vice President Medical Affairs
CIO: Joe Abbott, Director Information Systems
CHR: Carla Wallis, Director Human Resources
CNO: Cindy Van Kampen, Chief Nursing Officer
Web address: www.noch.org
**Control:** Other not–for–profit (including NFP Corporation) **Service:** General Medical and Surgical

**Staffed Beds:** 57 **Admissions:** 1754 **Census:** 14 **Outpatient Visits:** 109427 **Births:** 368 **Total Expense ($000):** 64261 **Payroll Expense ($000):** 24570 **Personnel:** 525

## GRAND RAPIDS—Kent County

□ **FOREST VIEW PSYCHIATRIC HOSPITAL (234030)**, 1055 Medical Park Drive S.E., Zip 49546–3607; tel. 616/942–9610 **A**1 9 10 **F**87 98 99 100 101 102 103 104 105 130 132 **S** Universal Health Services, Inc., King of Prussia, PA
Primary Contact: Andrew Hotaling, Chief Executive Officer
CFO: Andre Pierre, Chief Financial Officer
CMO: James VanHaren, M.D., Medical Director
CHR: Mike Henderson, Director Human Resources
CNO: Jo ell Harris, Director of Nursing
Web address: www.forestviewhospital.com
**Control:** Corporation, Investor–owned, for–profit **Service:** Psychiatric

**Staffed Beds:** 82 **Admissions:** 2642 **Census:** 72 **Outpatient Visits:** 10346 **Births:** 0 **Total Expense ($000):** 16618 **Payroll Expense ($000):** 7820 **Personnel:** 142

⊠ **GREAT LAKES SPECIALTY HOSPITAL–GRAND RAPIDS (232026)**, 200 S.E. Jefferson Avenue, 5th Floor, Zip 49503–4502; tel. 616/965–8650, (Nonreporting) **A**1 9 10 **S** Select Medical Corporation, Mechanicsburg, PA
Primary Contact: Jevne Conover, Chief Executive Officer
CMO: Mark J. Ivey, M.D., Medical Director
CNO: Tracie Peterson, R.N., Chief Nursing Officer
Web address: www.selectmedicalcorp.com
**Control:** Corporation, Investor–owned, for–profit **Service:** Long–Term Acute Care hospital

**Staffed Beds:** 20

**LIFECARE HOSPITALS OF WESTERN MICHIGAN** See Great Lakes Specialty Hospital–Grand Rapids

⊠ △ **MARY FREE BED REHABILITATION HOSPITAL (233026)**, 235 Wealthy Street S.E., Zip 49503–5247; tel. 616/840–8000 **A**1 3 5 7 9 10 **F**30 34 54 56 58 64 68 75 77 78 79 82 86 90 91 92 93 94 95 96 100 104 119 130 131 132 143 146 **P**6
Primary Contact: Kent Riddle, Chief Executive Officer
COO: Jim Wilson, Chief Operating Officer
CFO: Randall DeNeff, Vice President Finance
CMO: John Butzer, M.D., Medical Director
CIO: Jeff Burns, Manager of Information Technology
CNO: Linda Page, Chief Nursing Officer
Web address: www.maryfreebed.com
**Control:** Other not–for–profit (including NFP Corporation) **Service:** Rehabilitation

**Staffed Beds:** 80 **Admissions:** 1243 **Census:** 68 **Outpatient Visits:** 86574 **Births:** 0 **Total Expense ($000):** 53008 **Payroll Expense ($000):** 39413 **Personnel:** 910

*Many Facility Codes have changed. Please refer to the AHA Guide Code Chart.*  © 2015 AHA Guide

✠ **MERCY HEALTH SAINT MARY'S (230059)**, 200 Jefferson Avenue S.E.,
Zip 49503–4598; tel. 616/685–5000, (Includes MERCY HEALTH ROCKFORD,
6050 Northland Drive N.E., Rockford, Zip 49341–9244; tel. 616/685–7950) **A**1
2 3 5 9 10 **F**3 6 13 15 18 20 22 26 28 29 30 34 35 36 37 40 42 43 44 45
46 48 49 50 54 55 56 57 58 59 61 64 65 66 68 70 72 74 75 76 77 78 79
80 81 82 83 84 85 86 87 97 98 100 102 105 107 108 110 111 114 115
116 117 118 119 120 121 123 124 126 129 130 132 135 138 144 146 148
**P**6 8 **S** Trinity Health, Livonia, MI
Primary Contact: Bill Manns, President
COO: Randall J. Wagner, Chief Operating Officer
CFO: Steve Eavenson, Vice President Finance
CMO: Rolland Mambourg, M.D., Vice President Medical Affairs
CIO: Jim Keller, Site Director Information Services
CHR: Thomas L. Karel, Vice President Organization and Talent Effectiveness
CNO: Elizabeth A. Murphy, R.N., Vice President for Patient Care Services
Web address: www.mercyhealthsaintmarys.org
**Control:** Church–operated, Nongovernment, not–for profit **Service:** General
Medical and Surgical

**Staffed Beds:** 334 **Admissions:** 19098 **Census:** 257 **Outpatient Visits:**
997650 **Births:** 1967 **Total Expense ($000):** 454239 **Payroll Expense
($000):** 144741 **Personnel:** 2987

✠ **PINE REST CHRISTIAN MENTAL HEALTH SERVICES (234006)**, 300 68th
Street S.E., Zip 49548–6927, Mailing Address: P.O. Box 165, Zip 49501–0165;
tel. 616/455–5000 **A**1 5 9 10 13 **F**4 5 6 29 30 32 34 35 38 55 56 58 59 66
68 75 77 82 86 87 98 99 100 101 102 103 104 105 106 130 132 134 135
146 **P**6
Primary Contact: Mark C. Eastburg, Ph.D., President and Chief Executive Officer
COO: Robert Nykamp, Vice President and Chief Operating Officer
CFO: Paul H. Karsten, Vice President Finance and Chief Financial Officer
CMO: Alan Armstrong, M.D., Chief Medical Officer
Web address: www.pinerest.org
**Control:** Other not–for–profit (including NFP Corporation) **Service:** Psychiatric

**Staffed Beds:** 451 **Admissions:** 5908 **Census:** 159 **Outpatient Visits:**
295201 **Births:** 0 **Total Expense ($000):** 118200 **Payroll Expense ($000):**
66000 **Personnel:** 1305

✠ **SPECTRUM HEALTH – BUTTERWORTH HOSPITAL (230038)**, 100 Michigan
Street N.E., Zip 49503–2560; tel. 616/774–7444, (Includes HELEN DEVOS
CHILDREN'S HOSPITAL, 100 Michigan Street N.E., tel. 616/391–9000; Robert
Connors, M.D., President, HDVCH; SPECTRUM HEALTH, 100 Michigan Street
N.E., Zip 49503–2551; tel. 616/391–1774; Christina Freese–Decker, President,
Spectrum Health Hospital Group; SPECTRUM HEALTH – BLODGETT CAMPUS,
1840 Wealthy Street S.E., Zip 49506–2921; tel. 616/774–7444; Paul Bonis,
President, Blodgett Hospital) **A**1 2 3 5 9 10 **F**3 8 9 11 12 13 15 16 17 18 19
20 21 22 23 24 25 26 27 28 29 30 31 32 34 35 40 41 43 44 45
46 47 48 49 50 51 52 54 55 56 57 58 59 60 61 64 65 66 68 70 71 72 73
74 75 76 77 78 79 80 81 82 84 85 86 87 88 89 90 93 96 99 100 101 102
107 108 110 111 112 113 114 115 116 117 118 119 120 121 123 124 126
130 131 132 134 135 136 137 138 140 145 146 147 148 **P**6 8 **S** Spectrum
Health, Grand Rapids, MI
Primary Contact: Christina Freese–Decker, President, Spectrum Health Hospital
Group
COO: Gwen L. Sandefur, Chief Operating Officer
CFO: Doug Welday, Vice President Finance
CMO: Ralph Rogers, M.D., Vice President Medical Affairs and Chief Medical Officer
CIO: Michael Rosencrance, Vice President Information Services
CHR: David Beach, Vice President Human Resources
CNO: Shawn Ulreich, R.N., Vice President Clinical Operations and Chief Nursing
Executive
Web address: www.spectrumhealth.org
**Control:** Other not–for–profit (including NFP Corporation) **Service:** General
Medical and Surgical

**Staffed Beds:** 1102 **Admissions:** 54768 **Census:** 722 **Outpatient Visits:**
1339164 **Births:** 7461 **Total Expense ($000):** 1593873 **Payroll Expense
($000):** 451408 **Personnel:** 6490

✠ △ **SPECTRUM HEALTH SPECIAL CARE HOSPITAL (232029)**, 750 Fuller
Avenue N.E., Zip 49503–1995; tel. 616/486–3000, (Nonreporting) **A**1 7 9 10
**S** Spectrum Health, Grand Rapids, MI
Primary Contact: Jennifer Groeneweg, R.N., Interim Chief Executive Officer and
Chief Nurse Executive
COO: Linda Joel, Vice President Operations
CFO: Larry Oberst, Vice President Finance
CMO: Peter Sholler, M.D., Medical Director
CIO: Mary Nader, Director Information Technology
CHR: Mark Pakkala, Director Human Resources
CNO: Jennifer Groeneweg, R.N., Director of Nursing
Web address: www.spectrum–health.org
**Control:** Other not–for–profit (including NFP Corporation) **Service:** Long–Term
Acute Care hospital

**Staffed Beds:** 36

---

## GRAYLING—Crawford County

✠ **MUNSON HEALTHCARE GRAYLING HOSPITAL (230058)**, 1100 East
Michigan Avenue, Zip 49738–1312; tel. 989/348–5461, (Total facility includes
39 beds in nursing home–type unit) **A**1 5 9 10 20 **F**3 11 13 15 28 29 30 32 34
35 36 38 40 44 45 50 51 54 56 57 58 59 64 65 66 70 75 76 77 78 79 81
85 86 87 93 97 107 108 111 115 119 127 129 130 131 135 146 147 148
**P**6 8 **S** Munson Healthcare, Traverse City, MI
Primary Contact: Stephanie J. Riemer–Matuzak, Chief Executive Officer
COO: Kirsten Korth–White, Vice President Physician Network and Ambulatory
Service
CFO: Lori Shively, Vice President of Finance
CMO: Vince Schultz, M.D., Chief Medical Officer
CHR: Kirsten Korth–White, Vice President Physician Network and Ambulatory
Services
CNO: Carla Gardner, Director of Nursing
Web address: www.mercygrayling.munsonhealthcare.org/
**Control:** Other not–for–profit (including NFP Corporation) **Service:** General
Medical and Surgical

**Staffed Beds:** 94 **Admissions:** 3239 **Census:** 59 **Outpatient Visits:** 151027
**Births:** 323 **Total Expense ($000):** 75415 **Payroll Expense ($000):** 30720
**Personnel:** 427

## GREENVILLE—Montcalm County

✠ **SPECTRUM HEALTH UNITED HOSPITAL (230035)**, 615 South Bower Street,
Zip 48838–2614; tel. 616/754–4691, (Includes SPECTRUM HEALTH KELSEY
HOSPITAL, 418 Washington Avenue, Lakeview, Zip 48850; tel. 989/352–7211),
(Total facility includes 70 beds in nursing home–type unit) **A**1 9 10 **F**3 8 11 13
15 18 29 30 31 32 34 35 40 43 44 45 46 50 54 57 59 64 65 66 70 71
75 76 77 78 79 81 85 86 87 89 93 96 97 107 108 110 111 115 119 124
127 128 129 130 132 133 134 135 143 146 147 148 **P**6 **S** Spectrum Health,
Grand Rapids, MI
Primary Contact: Brian Brasser, President
COO: Priscilla Mahar, Chief Clinical Officer
CFO: Ryan K. Johnson, Vice President Finance
CMO: Kevin O'Connor, D.O., President Medical Staff
CIO: David Dutmers, Manager Technology Information System
CHR: Mary Fenske, Human Resource Business Partner
CNO: Andrea M. Leslie, MSN, Chief Nursing Officer
Web address: www.spectrumhealth.org/
**Control:** Other not–for–profit (including NFP Corporation) **Service:** General
Medical and Surgical

**Staffed Beds:** 116 **Admissions:** 2938 **Census:** 91 **Outpatient Visits:** 172436
**Births:** 464 **Total Expense ($000):** 83517 **Payroll Expense ($000):** 32738
**Personnel:** 654

## GROSSE POINTE—Wayne County

✠ **BEAUMONT HOSPITAL GROSSE POINTE (230089)**, 468 Cadieux Road,
Zip 48230–1507; tel. 313/473–1000 **A**1 2 3 5 9 10 **F**3 6 11 12 13 14 15 18
20 22 26 28 29 30 31 32 34 35 36 39 40 43 44 45 46 47 48 49 50 51 53
54 55 56 57 58 59 61 62 63 64 65 66 68 69 70 71 74 75 76 77 78 79
80 81 82 84 85 86 87 89 91 92 93 94 96 97 100 107 108 110 111 114 115
116 117 118 119 126 129 130 131 132 134 135 145 146 147 148 **P**6
**S** Beaumont Health, Royal Oak, MI
Primary Contact: Richard P. Swaine, President
COO: Chris Stesney–Ridenour, Vice President Operations
CFO: Nickolas A. Vitale, Senior Vice President and Chief Financial Officer
CMO: Donna Hoban, M.D., Senior Vice President and Physician–in–Chief
CIO: Subra Sripada, Senior Vice President and Chief Information Officer
CHR: Jay T. Holden, Vice President, Human Resources
CNO: Phyllis Reynolds, R.N., VP, Nursing
Web address: www.beaumont.edu/grosse–pointe–hospital–campus
**Control:** Other not–for–profit (including NFP Corporation) **Service:** General
Medical and Surgical

**Staffed Beds:** 250 **Admissions:** 11147 **Census:** 126 **Outpatient Visits:**
288835 **Births:** 808 **Total Expense ($000):** 165542 **Payroll Expense
($000):** 53477 **Personnel:** 1129

✠ **SELECT SPECIALTY HOSPITAL–GROSSE POINTE (232038)**, 468 Cadieux
Road, 3 North East, Zip 48230–1507; tel. 313/473–6131, (Nonreporting) **A**1 9
10 **S** Select Medical Corporation, Mechanicsburg, PA
Primary Contact: Miriam Deemer, Chief Executive Officer
Web address: www.grossepointe.selectspecialtyhospitals.com/
**Control:** Corporation, Investor–owned, for–profit **Service:** Long–Term Acute Care
hospital

**Staffed Beds:** 30

---

**Hospital, Medicare Provider Number, Address, Telephone, Approval, Facility, and Physician Codes, Health Care System**

★ American Hospital Association (AHA) membership    ○ Healthcare Facilities Accreditation Program    ⇑ Center for Improvement in Healthcare Quality Accreditation
□ The Joint Commission accreditation    ◇ DNV Healthcare Inc. accreditation    △ Commission on Accreditation of Rehabilitation Facilities (CARF) accreditation

## HANCOCK—Houghton County

☒ **UP HEALTH SYSTEM–PORTAGE (230108)**, 500 Campus Drive,
Zip 49930–1569; tel. 906/483–1000, (Total facility includes 60 beds in nursing
home–type unit) **A**1 5 9 10 20 **F**3 8 11 13 15 28 29 30 31 32 34 35 40 43 50
53 56 57 59 60 62 63 64 65 67 68 70 75 76 77 78 79 81 84 85 86 87 89
90 93 94 97 107 108 110 111 115 119 129 130 131 132 133 144 145 146
148 **P**6 **S** LifePoint Health, Brentwood, TN
Primary Contact: Jeff Lang, President
CFO: Steve Bishop, Chief Financial Officer
CMO: Mary Beth Hines, D.O., Chief Medical Officer
CIO: John Steenport, Director Information Technology
CHR: Robbyn Lucier, Director Human Resources
Web address: www.portagehealth.org
**Control:** Corporation, Investor–owned, for–profit **Service:** General Medical and
Surgical

**Staffed Beds:** 96 **Admissions:** 1499 **Census:** 72 **Outpatient Visits:** 133036
**Births:** 311 **Total Expense ($000):** 52780 **Payroll Expense ($000):** 18331
**Personnel:** 577

## HARBOR BEACH—Huron County

**HARBOR BEACH COMMUNITY HOSPITAL (231313)**, 210 South First Street,
Zip 48441–1236; tel. 989/479–3201, (Nonreporting) **A**5 9 10 18
Primary Contact: Paul Clabuesch, President and Chief Executive Officer
CFO: Jill Wehner, Vice President Financial Services
CMO: Richard Lloyd, D.O., Chief of Staff
CIO: Tami Nickrand, Director Information Technology
CHR: Tina Osantoski, Director Human Resources
CNO: Deb Geiger, Executive Director of Acute Care
Web address: www.hbch.org
**Control:** Other not–for–profit (including NFP Corporation) **Service:** General
Medical and Surgical

**Staffed Beds:** 54

## HASTINGS—Barry County

☒ **SPECTRUM HEALTH PENNOCK (230040)**, 1009 West Green Street,
Zip 49058–1710; tel. 269/945–3451 **A**1 9 10 **F**3 11 13 15 29 30 32 34 35
36 39 40 44 45 50 53 54 56 57 59 62 63 64 65 68 70 74 75 76 77 79 81
82 84 85 86 87 89 91 92 93 96 97 107 108 110 111 115 119 125 126 130
131 132 135 144 146 147 148 **P**6 8 **S** Spectrum Health, Grand Rapids,
MI
Primary Contact: Sheryl Lewis Blake, FACHE, President
COO: Carla Wilson–Neil, FACHE, Chief Operating Officer
CFO: Connie Downs, CPA, Vice President, Finance and Chief Financial Officer
CMO: Douglas Smendik, M.D., Chief Medical Officer
CIO: Teri VanTongeren, Director Information Services
CHR: Sherri Thrasher, Executive Director Human Resources
CNO: Steve Marzolf, R.N., Vice President Patient Care Services
Web address: www.pennockhealth.com
**Control:** Other not–for–profit (including NFP Corporation) **Service:** General
Medical and Surgical

**Staffed Beds:** 58 **Admissions:** 2356 **Census:** 24 **Outpatient Visits:** 411704
**Births:** 319 **Total Expense ($000):** 62972 **Payroll Expense ($000):** 29675
**Personnel:** 487

## HILLSDALE—Hillsdale County

★ ○ **HILLSDALE COMMUNITY HEALTH CENTER (230037)**, 168 South Howell
Street, Zip 49242–2081; tel. 517/437–4451, (Total facility includes 39 beds in
nursing home–type unit) **A**9 10 11 12 13 19 **F**3 11 12 13 15 28 29 31 34 35
38 40 45 48 50 59 62 70 74 75 76 78 79 81 82 87 93 97 98 102 107 110
111 115 119 127 128 130 131 132 135 146 147 148 **P**6 8
Primary Contact: Duke Anderson, President and Chief Executive Officer
CFO: Valerie Fetters, Chief Financial Officer
CMO: Dan McCance, D.O., Chief of Staff
CIO: Sheila Puffenberger, Manager Information Technology
CHR: Stacy Mellon, Manager Human Resource
CNO: Julie Walters, Chief Nursing Officer
Web address: www.hchc.com
**Control:** Other not–for–profit (including NFP Corporation) **Service:** General
Medical and Surgical

**Staffed Beds:** 104 **Admissions:** 2992 **Census:** 48 **Outpatient Visits:** 104342
**Births:** 370 **Total Expense ($000):** 57845 **Payroll Expense ($000):** 21672
**Personnel:** 392

## HOLLAND—Ottawa County

★ ◇ **HOLLAND HOSPITAL (230072)**, 602 Michigan Avenue, Zip 49423–4999;
tel. 616/392–5141, (Nonreporting) **A**9 10 21
Primary Contact: Dale Sowders, President and Chief Executive Officer
CFO: Terry L. Steele, Vice President Finance and Chief Financial Officer
CMO: William Vandervliet, M.D., Vice President Medical Affairs
CIO: Randy J. Paruch, Director, Information Systems
CHR: Michael Matthews, Vice President Human Resources
CNO: Patti J. VanDort, MSN, Vice President Nursing/Chief Nursing Officer
Web address: www.hollandhospital.org
**Control:** Other not–for–profit (including NFP Corporation) **Service:** General
Medical and Surgical

**Staffed Beds:** 130

## HOWELL—Livingston County

☒ **ST. JOSEPH MERCY LIVINGSTON HOSPITAL (230069)**, 620 Byron Road,
Zip 48843–1093; tel. 517/545–6000 **A**1 3 5 9 10 13 **F**3 5 8 11 15 18 28 29
30 31 34 35 40 41 42 45 51 54 56 57 59 62 63 64 65 66 68 70 74 75 77
78 79 81 82 83 84 85 86 87 93 97 100 104 107 108 110 111 114 115 119
120 130 131 132 134 135 141 145 146 147 148 **P**1 **S** Trinity Health,
Livonia, MI
Primary Contact: Robert F. Casalou, President and Chief Executive Officer
COO: Robin Damschroder, Chief Operating Officer
CFO: Kathy O'Connor, Vice President Finance and Controller
CMO: Mark Baumeier, M.D., Chief of Staff
CIO: Frank Rademacher, Director, Information Systems
CHR: Tonia Schemer, Interim Chief Human Resources
CNO: Joyce Young, Ph.D., Vice President, Patient Services and Chief Nursing
Officer
Web address: www.stjoeslivingston.org/livingston
**Control:** Church–operated, Nongovernment, not–for profit **Service:** General
Medical and Surgical

**Staffed Beds:** 42 **Admissions:** 2949 **Census:** 25 **Outpatient Visits:** 276452
**Births:** 0 **Total Expense ($000):** 104166 **Payroll Expense ($000):** 35396
**Personnel:** 552

## IONIA—Ionia County

☒ **SPARROW IONIA HOSPITAL (231331)**, 3565 South State Road,
Zip 48846–1870, Mailing Address: Box 1001, Zip 48846–6001;
tel. 616/523–1400 **A**1 9 10 18 **F**3 12 15 29 31 34 35 40 45 50 54 57 59 64
65 68 70 74 75 77 78 79 81 85 89 93 107 108 110 115 119 127 129 130
131 146 148 **P**6 **S** Sparrow Health System, Lansing, MI
Primary Contact: William Roeser, President and Chief Executive Officer
COO: Kevin A. Price, Vice President and Chief Operating Officer
CFO: Mark Brisboe, VP and Chief Financial Officer
CMO: Amy Jentz, M.D., Chief of Staff
CIO: Bob Neal, Information Technology
CHR: Debbie Olsen, Human Resource Partner
Web address: www.sparrow.org/sparrowionia
**Control:** Other not–for–profit (including NFP Corporation) **Service:** General
Medical and Surgical

**Staffed Beds:** 25 **Admissions:** 458 **Census:** 3 **Outpatient Visits:** 44096
**Births:** 0 **Total Expense ($000):** 34637 **Payroll Expense ($000):** 13515
**Personnel:** 232

## IRON MOUNTAIN—Dickinson County

☒ **DICKINSON COUNTY HEALTHCARE SYSTEM (230055)**, 1721 South
Stephenson Avenue, Zip 49801–3637; tel. 906/774–1313 **A**1 9 10 20 **F**3 11 13
15 18 28 29 31 34 35 40 45 46 50 51 53 57 59 61 62 64 70 74 75 76 77
78 79 80 81 85 86 87 89 91 92 93 96 107 108 110 111 114 115 119 120
121 123 127 129 130 131 132 133 135 145 146 148 **P**6
Primary Contact: John Schon, Administrator and Chief Executive Officer
COO: Jeff Gussert, Director Operations
CFO: Eileen Sparpana, Director Finance
CMO: Don Kube, M.D., Chief of Staff
CIO: Dean Decremer, Chief Information Officer
CHR: Paula Swartout, HR Manager
Web address: www.dchs.org
**Control:** County–Government, nonfederal **Service:** General Medical and Surgical

**Staffed Beds:** 96 **Admissions:** 3322 **Census:** 32 **Outpatient Visits:** 255982
**Births:** 433 **Total Expense ($000):** 92431 **Payroll Expense ($000):** 40446
**Personnel:** 628

☒ **OSCAR G. JOHNSON VETERANS AFFAIRS MEDICAL CENTER**, 325 East H
Street, Zip 49801–4792; tel. 906/774–3300, (Nonreporting) **A**1 9 **S** Department
of Veterans Affairs, Washington, DC
Primary Contact: Andrea Collins, Acting Director
Web address: www.ironmountain.va.gov/
**Control:** Veterans Affairs, Government, federal **Service:** General Medical and
Surgical

**Staffed Beds:** 17

**VETERANS AFFAIRS MEDICAL CENTER** See Oscar G. Johnson Veterans Affairs
Medical Center

*Many Facility Codes have changed. Please refer to the AHA Guide Code Chart.* © 2015 AHA Guide

**IRON RIVER—Iron County**

✠ **ASPIRUS IRON RIVER HOSPITALS AND CLINICS (231318)**, 1400 West Ice Lake Road, Zip 49935–9526; tel. 906/265–6121 **A**1 9 10 18 **F**7 11 15 28 29 31 32 33 34 35 40 43 50 54 56 57 59 60 62 63 64 70 75 77 78 79 81 86 87 89 93 97 104 107 111 115 119 128 130 131 132 133 135 144 145 146 147 148 **S** Aspirus, Inc., Wausau, WI
Primary Contact: Connie L. Koutouzos, R.N., MSN, Chief Executive Officer and President
CFO: Glenn E. Dobson, Chief Financial Officer
CMO: Nasseem Rizkalla, M.D., Chief Medical Officer
CIO: Matthew Welch, Chief Clinical Information Officer and Director of Pharmacy
CHR: Carol Bastianello, Director Employee Services
CNO: Nancy Lynn Ponozzo, Chief Nursing Officer
Web address: www.northstarhs.org
**Control:** Other not–for–profit (including NFP Corporation) **Service:** General Medical and Surgical

**Staffed Beds:** 12 **Admissions:** 811 **Census:** 8 **Outpatient Visits:** 57685 **Births:** 0 **Total Expense ($000):** 38165 **Payroll Expense ($000):** 14807 **Personnel:** 245

**IRONWOOD—Gogebic County**

✠ **ASPIRUS GRAND VIEW (231333)**, N10561 Grand View Lane, Zip 49938–9622; tel. 906/932–2525 **A**1 9 10 18 **F**3 11 13 15 17 28 29 31 34 35 40 50 56 57 59 62 64 65 70 75 76 77 78 79 81 85 89 93 97 107 110 115 119 127 129 130 132 133 135 144 146 147 **P**6 **S** Aspirus, Inc., Wausau, WI
Primary Contact: Paula L. Chermside, Chief Operating Officer
COO: Paula L. Chermside, Chief Operating Officer
CFO: Charmaine Chiantello, Chief Financial Officer
CMO: Chris Pogliano, M.D., Chief Medical Staff
CIO: Ron Eyer, Manager Information Services
CHR: Keri Van Epern, Manager Human Resources
CNO: Grace Tousignant, R.N., Chief Nursing Officer
Web address: www.aspirusgrandview.org
**Control:** Other not–for–profit (including NFP Corporation) **Service:** General Medical and Surgical

**Staffed Beds:** 25 **Admissions:** 1046 **Census:** 12 **Outpatient Visits:** 62241 **Births:** 133 **Total Expense ($000):** 33265 **Payroll Expense ($000):** 13136 **Personnel:** 216

**ISHPEMING—Marquette County**

★ **UP HEALTH SYSTEM–BELL (231321)**, 901 Lakeshore Drive, Zip 49849–1367; tel. 906/486–4431 **A**9 10 18 **F**3 7 11 13 15 29 30 34 40 50 51 53 57 59 65 68 70 75 76 77 79 81 82 85 87 92 93 96 97 107 108 110 119 129 133 135 144 146 147 **P**6 **S** LifePoint Health, Brentwood, TN
Primary Contact: Mitchell D. Leckelt, Chief Executive Officer
CFO: Teresa J. Perry, Chief Financial Officer
CMO: Douglas LaBelle, M.D., Chief Medical Officer
CIO: Jeffrey Wagner, Supervisor Information Systems
CHR: Tami Ketchem, Human Resource Director
CNO: Sandra McGovern, Chief Nursing Officer
Web address: www.bellhospital.org
**Control:** Corporation, Investor–owned, for–profit **Service:** General Medical and Surgical

**Staffed Beds:** 25 **Admissions:** 902 **Census:** 7 **Outpatient Visits:** 60603 **Births:** 279 **Total Expense ($000):** 35563 **Payroll Expense ($000):** 13339 **Personnel:** 198

**JACKSON—Jackson County**

✠ **ALLEGIANCE HEALTH (230092)**, 205 North East Avenue, Zip 49201–1753; tel. 517/788–4800, (Total facility includes 20 beds in nursing home–type unit) **A**1 2 3 5 9 10 12 13 **F**3 4 5 9 11 12 13 15 17 18 20 22 24 26 28 29 30 31 33 34 35 38 40 44 45 46 47 48 49 50 51 53 54 56 57 58 59 61 62 63 64 65 68 69 70 73 74 75 76 77 78 79 81 82 84 85 87 89 92 93 96 98 99 100 101 102 103 104 105 106 107 108 110 111 114 115 119 121 123 126 128 129 130 131 132 135 146 147 148 **P**6
Primary Contact: Georgia R. Fojtasek, R.N., Ed.D., President and Chief Executive Officer
COO: Karen Chaprnka, Senior Vice President and Chief Operating Officer
CFO: Jeanne' Wickens, Senior Vice President Finance and Strategy and Chief Financial Officer
CMO: Ray King, M.D., Senior Vice President and Chief Medical Officer
CIO: Aaron Wootton, Vice President Health Information Systems
CNO: Ondrea Bates, Senior Vice President Patient Care Continuum and Chief Nursing Officer
Web address: www.allegiancehealth.org
**Control:** Other not–for–profit (including NFP Corporation) **Service:** General Medical and Surgical

**Staffed Beds:** 302 **Admissions:** 17376 **Census:** 202 **Outpatient Visits:** 487047 **Births:** 1684 **Total Expense ($000):** 468110 **Payroll Expense ($000):** 211138 **Personnel:** 3348

✠ **CARELINK OF JACKSON (232036)**, 110 North Elm Avenue, Zip 49202–3595; tel. 517/787–1440 **A**1 9 10 **F**1 3 29 30 31 50 57 60 77 85 87 130 146 148
Primary Contact: J. Mark Fall, Chief Executive Officer
COO: Charlotte Hyatt, MSN, Chief Operating Officer and Chief Nursing Officer
CFO: Dale L. Friesen, Chief Financial Officer
CMO: Robert Albertson, M.D., Chief Medical Officer
CNO: Charlotte Hyatt, MSN, Chief Operating Officer and Chief Nursing Officer
Web address: www.carelinkofjackson.org
**Control:** Other not–for–profit (including NFP Corporation) **Service:** Long–Term Acute Care hospital

**Staffed Beds:** 44 **Admissions:** 461 **Census:** 33 **Outpatient Visits:** 0 **Births:** 0 **Total Expense ($000):** 15872 **Payroll Expense ($000):** 5801 **Personnel:** 110

**DUANE L. WATERS HOSPITAL**, 3857 Cooper Street, Zip 49201–7521; tel. 517/780–5600, (Nonreporting)
Primary Contact: Carol Griffes, Administrator
**Control:** State–Government, nonfederal **Service:** Hospital unit of an institution (prison hospital, college infimary, etc.)

**Staffed Beds:** 150

**KALAMAZOO—Kalamazoo County**

✠ △ **BORGESS MEDICAL CENTER (230117)**, 1521 Gull Road, Zip 49048–1640; tel. 269/226–7000 **A**1 3 5 7 9 10 12 13 **F**3 7 8 9 11 12 13 15 17 18 20 22 24 28 29 30 31 32 33 34 35 36 37 38 39 40 43 44 45 46 49 50 53 54 56 57 58 59 60 61 64 68 70 74 75 76 77 78 79 81 82 84 85 86 87 90 91 92 93 94 96 97 98 99 100 101 102 103 104 105 107 108 110 114 115 118 119 126 129 130 131 132 135 144 146 147 148 **P**3 6 8 **S** Ascension Health, Saint Louis, MO
Primary Contact: Kathlene A. Young, MS, FACHE, Chief Executive Officer
COO: Mark Anthony, Executive Vice President and Chief Operating Officer
CFO: Richard Felbinger, Senior Vice President and Chief Financial Officer
CMO: Robert Hill, M.D., Vice President Medical Staff Affairs
CIO: Donna Roach, Chief Information Officer
CHR: Laura Lentenbrink, Vice President, Human Resources
CNO: Lois J. Van Donselaar, R.N., Vice President & Chief Nursing Officer
Web address: www.borgess.com
**Control:** Church–operated, Nongovernment, not–for profit **Service:** General Medical and Surgical

**Staffed Beds:** 366 **Admissions:** 15115 **Census:** 243 **Outpatient Visits:** 503484 **Births:** 1003 **Total Expense ($000):** 376022 **Payroll Expense ($000):** 155655 **Personnel:** 2138

✠ **BRONSON METHODIST HOSPITAL (230017)**, 601 John Street, Zip 49007–5346; tel. 269/341–6000, (Includes BRONSON VICKSBURG HOSPITAL, 13326 North Boulevard, Vicksburg, Zip 49097–1099; tel. 269/649–2321; Frank J. Sardone, President and Chief Executive Officer; CHILDREN'S HOSPITAL AT BRONSON, 601 John Street, Zip 49007–5341; tel. 269/341–7654) **A**1 3 5 9 10 12 13 **F**3 9 11 12 13 15 16 17 18 19 20 22 24 26 28 29 30 31 32 34 35 37 39 40 41 42 43 44 45 46 47 49 50 51 55 56 57 58 59 60 61 62 64 65 66 68 70 71 72 74 75 76 77 78 79 80 81 82 83 84 85 86 87 88 89 92 93 97 102 107 108 110 111 114 115 117 118 119 126 129 130 131 132 134 135 141 144 145 146 147 148 **P**6 **S** Bronson Healthcare Group, Inc., Kalamazoo, MI
Primary Contact: Frank J. Sardone, President and Chief Executive Officer
COO: Kenneth L. Taft, Executive Vice President and Chief Operating Officer
CFO: Mary Meitz, Vice President Finance
CMO: Scott Larson, M.D., Vice President Medical Affairs and Chief Medical Officer
CHR: John Hayden, Vice President and Chief Human Resources Officer
CNO: Denise Neely, R.N., Vice President and Chief Nursing Officer
Web address: www.bronsonhealth.com
**Control:** Other not–for–profit (including NFP Corporation) **Service:** General Medical and Surgical

**Staffed Beds:** 410 **Admissions:** 21667 **Census:** 277 **Outpatient Visits:** 639865 **Births:** 3563 **Total Expense ($000):** 584295 **Payroll Expense ($000):** 274471 **Personnel:** 4312

☐ **KALAMAZOO PSYCHIATRIC HOSPITAL (234026)**, 1312 Oakland Drive, Zip 49008–1205; tel. 269/337–3000 **A**1 9 10 12 13 **F**3 39 50 53 56 65 74 75 77 86 87 97 98 101 103 130 132 135 143 146 148 **P**6
Primary Contact: Jill A. Krause, Director
CMO: Anil R. Patel, M.D., Medical Services Director
CIO: Brian Bayer, Information Technology Site Leader
CHR: Holly Hiday, Director Human Resources
CNO: Tedi Beckett, Director of Nursing
**Control:** State–Government, nonfederal **Service:** Psychiatric

**Staffed Beds:** 203 **Admissions:** 286 **Census:** 154 **Outpatient Visits:** 0 **Births:** 0 **Personnel:** 499

MI

---

**Hospital, Medicare Provider Number, Address, Telephone, Approval, Facility, and Physician Codes, Health Care System**

★ American Hospital Association (AHA) membership
☐ The Joint Commission accreditation
○ Healthcare Facilities Accreditation Program
◇ DNV Healthcare Inc. accreditation
⇑ Center for Improvement in Healthcare Quality Accreditation
△ Commission on Accreditation of Rehabilitation Facilities (CARF) accreditation

## KALKASKA—Kalkaska County

★ **KALKASKA MEMORIAL HEALTH CENTER (231301)**, 419 South Coral Street, Zip 49646–2503; tel. 231/258–7500, (Total facility includes 84 beds in nursing home–type unit) **A**9 10 18 **F**2 10 15 28 34 35 40 44 45 50 53 56 57 59 60 64 65 66 79 81 84 87 93 97 107 110 111 115 119 127 128 129 130 132 134 143 144 146 147 148 **S** Munson Healthcare, Traverse City, MI
Primary Contact: Kevin L. Rogols, FACHE, Administrator
CMO: Jeremy Holmes, D.O., Chief of Staff
CHR: Kimberly Babcock, Administrative Director of Operations
CNO: Christine Bissonette, R.N., Service Line Director for Acute Services
Web address: www.munsonhealthcare.org
**Control:** Hospital district or authority, Government, nonfederal **Service:** General Medical and Surgical

**Staffed Beds:** 92 **Admissions:** 123 **Census:** 81 **Outpatient Visits:** 64400 **Births:** 0 **Total Expense ($000):** 28619 **Payroll Expense ($000):** 11401 **Personnel:** 252

## L'ANSE—L'Anse County

☐ **BARAGA COUNTY MEMORIAL HOSPITAL (231307)**, 18341 U.S. Highway 41, Zip 49946–8024; tel. 906/524–3300 **A**1 9 10 18 **F**3 5 11 15 28 31 34 40 45 53 57 59 62 63 64 74 77 78 79 81 82 84 85 89 93 107 108 110 114 118 119 127 130 132 133 146 **P**6
Primary Contact: Margie Hale, R.N., MSN, Chief Operating Officer
COO: Margie Hale, R.N., Interim Chief Operating Officer and Chief Nursing Officer
CFO: Gail Jestila–Peltola, Chief Financial Officer
CMO: Promilia Timothy, Chief of Staff
CIO: Taylor Makela, Director Information Technology
CHR: Janelle E. Beehler, Human Resource Manager
CNO: Margie Hale, R.N., Director of Nursing
Web address: www.bcmh.org
**Control:** County–Government, nonfederal **Service:** General Medical and Surgical

**Staffed Beds:** 15 **Admissions:** 536 **Census:** 7 **Outpatient Visits:** 23952 **Births:** 0 **Total Expense ($000):** 22624 **Payroll Expense ($000):** 8216 **Personnel:** 128

## LAKEVIEW—Montcalm County

**SPECTRUM HEALTH KELSEY HOSPITAL** See Spectrum Health United Hospital, Greenville

## LANSING—Ingham County

○ **MCLAREN GREATER LANSING (230167)**, 401 West Greenlawn Avenue, Zip 48910–2819; tel. 517/975–6000, (Includes INGHAM REGIONAL MEDICAL CENTER, GREENLAWN CAMPUS, 401 West Greenlawn Avenue, tel. 517/334–2121; MCLAREN ORTHOPEDIC HOSPITAL, 2727 South Pennsylvania Avenue, Zip 48910–3490; tel. 517/975–6000; Rick Wright, President and Chief Executive Officer) **A**2 3 5 9 10 11 13 **F**3 8 11 13 15 17 18 20 22 24 26 28 29 30 31 34 35 37 40 44 45 47 49 50 56 57 58 59 60 61 63 64 65 66 70 74 75 76 77 78 79 80 81 82 84 85 86 87 89 90 93 97 98 100 101 102 103 104 107 108 110 111 114 115 119 120 121 124 126 129 130 131 132 135 146 147 148 **P**8 **S** McLaren Health Care Corporation, Flint, MI
Primary Contact: Rick Wright, President and Chief Executive Officer
COO: Thomas Mee, R.N., Chief Operating Officer
CFO: Dale Thompson, Chief Financial Officer
CMO: Linda Peterson, M.D., Vice President Medical Affairs
CHR: Floyd Chasse, Vice President Human Resources
Web address: www.irmc.org
**Control:** Other not–for–profit (including NFP Corporation) **Service:** General Medical and Surgical

**Staffed Beds:** 321 **Admissions:** 12162 **Census:** 135 **Outpatient Visits:** 365523 **Births:** 1206 **Total Expense ($000):** 289568 **Payroll Expense ($000):** 110601 **Personnel:** 1826

✖ ○ △ **SPARROW HOSPITAL (230230)**, 1215 East Michigan Avenue, Zip 48912–1811; tel. 517/364–1000, (Includes SPARROW CHILDREN'S CENTER, 1215 East Michigan Avenue, tel. 517/364–1000) **A**1 2 3 5 7 9 10 11 12 13 **F**3 4 5 11 12 13 15 17 18 20 22 24 26 28 29 30 31 34 35 36 38 40 41 43 44 45 46 49 50 51 54 55 56 57 58 59 60 63 64 65 66 67 68 70 72 74 75 76 77 78 79 81 82 84 85 86 87 88 89 90 91 92 93 94 96 97 98 99 100 101 102 103 104 105 107 108 109 110 114 115 116 117 118 119 120 121 123 124 126 128 129 130 131 132 135 144 146 147 148 **P**1 6 **S** Sparrow Health System, Lansing, MI
Primary Contact: Dennis A. Swan, JD, FACHE, President and Chief Executive Officer
COO: Joseph Ruth, Executive Vice President and Chief Operating Officer
CFO: Paula Reichle, Senior Vice President and Chief Operating Officer
CMO: Brian D. Schroeder, M.D., Senior Vice President and Chief Medical Officer
CIO: Thomas Bres, Senior Vice President and Chief Administrative Officer
CHR: Paul Sturgis, Vice President and Chief Human Resources Officer
CNO: Mary Lou Wesley, R.N., Senior Vice President and Chief Nursing Officer
Web address: www.sparrow.org
**Control:** Other not–for–profit (including NFP Corporation) **Service:** General Medical and Surgical

**Staffed Beds:** 655 **Admissions:** 34290 **Census:** 447 **Outpatient Visits:** 398998 **Births:** 4286 **Total Expense ($000):** 797510 **Payroll Expense ($000):** 376059 **Personnel:** 5089

★ ○ **SPARROW SPECIALTY HOSPITAL (232037)**, 8 West Sparrow Hospital Tower, Zip 48912; tel. 517/364–4840 **A**9 10 11 **F**1 3 29 30 36 60 68 85 100 101 119 130 148 **S** Sparrow Health System, Lansing, MI
Primary Contact: Kira Carter–Robertson, FACHE, President and Chief Executive Officer
CFO: David Przybylski, Controller
CMO: Paul Entler, D.O., Medical Director
CHR: Paul Sturgis, Chief Human Resource Officer
CNO: Tina Gross, Chief Nursing Officer
Web address: www.sparrowspecialty.org
**Control:** Other not–for–profit (including NFP Corporation) **Service:** Long–Term Acute Care hospital

**Staffed Beds:** 36 **Admissions:** 308 **Census:** 24 **Outpatient Visits:** 0 **Births:** 0 **Total Expense ($000):** 12155 **Payroll Expense ($000):** 5869 **Personnel:** 118

## LAPEER—Lapeer County

○ **MCLAREN LAPEER REGION (230193)**, 1375 North Main Street, Zip 48446–1350; tel. 810/667–5500, (Total facility includes 19 beds in nursing home–type unit) **A**2 9 10 11 **F**3 11 13 15 18 20 28 29 30 31 34 40 43 45 46 49 50 51 54 56 57 59 61 64 68 70 74 75 76 77 78 79 81 82 83 85 86 87 92 93 97 98 102 107 108 111 114 115 119 128 129 130 131 132 135 143 144 146 148 **S** McLaren Health Care Corporation, Flint, MI
Primary Contact: Barton Buxton, Ed.D., President and Chief Executive Officer
COO: Thomas Mee, R.N., Vice President Operations
CFO: Mary Beth Callahan, Chief Financial Officer
CMO: Gary Salem, M.D., Vice President Medical Affairs
CIO: Gayle Consiglio, Chief Information Officer
CHR: Amy Dorr, Vice President Human Resources
Web address: www.lapeerregional.org
**Control:** Other not–for–profit (including NFP Corporation) **Service:** General Medical and Surgical

**Staffed Beds:** 159 **Admissions:** 7145 **Census:** 90 **Outpatient Visits:** 137574 **Births:** 342 **Total Expense ($000):** 107620 **Payroll Expense ($000):** 48595 **Personnel:** 590

## LAURIUM—Houghton County

✖ **ASPIRUS KEWEENAW HOSPITAL (231319)**, 205 Osceola Street, Zip 49913–2134; tel. 906/337–6500 **A**1 9 10 18 **F**3 7 11 13 15 17 18 28 29 30 31 34 35 36 40 45 52 53 56 57 59 61 62 63 64 65 70 75 76 77 78 79 81 85 87 89 92 93 97 107 108 110 111 115 118 119 127 129 130 131 132 133 135 145 146 147 148 **P**6 **S** Aspirus, Inc., Wausau, WI
Primary Contact: Michael Hauswirth, Chief Operating Officer
COO: Michael Hauswirth, Chief Operating Officer
CFO: Shane Jacques, Regional Chief Financial Officer – U.P.
CMO: Elizabeth Benyi, D.O., Chief of Staff
CIO: Dave Olsson, Director of Marketing
CHR: Chad Rowe, Human Resource Director
CNO: Grace Tousignant, R.N., Chief Nursing Officer
Web address: www.aspiruskeweenaw.org
**Control:** Other not–for–profit (including NFP Corporation) **Service:** General Medical and Surgical

**Staffed Beds:** 25 **Admissions:** 922 **Census:** 9 **Outpatient Visits:** 40039 **Births:** 91 **Total Expense ($000):** 39002 **Payroll Expense ($000):** 18524 **Personnel:** 336

## LINCOLN PARK—Wayne County

✖ **VIBRA HOSPITAL OF SOUTHEASTERN MICHIGAN, LLC (232019)**, 26400 West Outer Drive, Zip 48146–2088; tel. 313/386–2000, (Nonreporting) **A**1 9 10 **S** Vibra Healthcare, Mechanicsburg, PA
Primary Contact: Denise Wayne, Chief Executive Officer
COO: Cindy Brassinger, Chief Operating Officer
CFO: Douglas Morris, Chief Financial Officer
CHR: Karen D. Gray, Director Human Resources
Web address: www.vhsemichigan.com/
**Control:** Corporation, Investor–owned, for–profit **Service:** Long–Term Acute Care hospital

**Staffed Beds:** 220

*Many Facility Codes have changed. Please refer to the AHA Guide Code Chart.*   © 2015 AHA Guide

## LIVONIA—Wayne County

⊞ **ST. MARY MERCY HOSPITAL (230002)**, 36475 Five Mile Road,
Zip 48154–1988; tel. 734/655–4800 **A**1 2 3 9 10 12 13 15 18
20 22 26 28 29 30 31 34 35 36 38 40 45 46 47 49 50 51 56 57 58 59 63
64 68 70 74 75 76 78 79 81 84 85 87 90 93 97 98 100 101 102 103 104
107 108 110 111 114 115 116 117 118 119 120 121 126 128 129 130 131
132 135 143 145 146 147 148 **P**6 **S** Trinity Health, Livonia, MI
Primary Contact: David A. Spivey, President and Chief Executive Officer
COO: Shannon Striebich, Chief Operating Officer
CFO: Mike Samyn, Vice President, Finance and Chief Financial Officer
CIO: Janet Yim, Director Information Services
CHR: Kenneth Antczak, Vice President Human Resources
Web address: www.stmarymercy.org
**Control:** Church–operated, Nongovernment, not–for profit **Service:** General
Medical and Surgical

**Staffed Beds:** 301 **Admissions:** 17220 **Census:** 205 **Outpatient Visits:**
209689 **Births:** 895 **Total Expense ($000):** 248259 **Payroll Expense**
**($000):** 102944 **Personnel:** 1417

## LUDINGTON—Mason County

★ ◇ **SPECTRUM HEALTH LUDINGTON HOSPITAL (230110)**, One Atkinson
Drive, Zip 49431–1906; tel. 231/843–2591 **A**9 10 20 21 **F**3 8 11 13 15 17 28
29 31 34 35 40 45 49 51 54 57 59 62 68 75 76 77 78 79 81 82 85 89 92
93 98 100 102 103 107 108 110 111 114 115 118 119 129 130 131 132
135 146 147 148 **S** Spectrum Health, Grand Rapids, MI
Primary Contact: Mark Vipperman, President
CFO: Kerri Nelson, Chief Financial Officer
CMO: Steve Strbich, D.O., Chief of Staff
CIO: Jeremy Vronko, Manager, Information Services
CHR: Jill Vasquez, Manager Human Resources
CNO: Helen Johnson, R.N., Vice President Patient Services
Web address: www.mmcwm.com
**Control:** Other not–for–profit (including NFP Corporation) **Service:** General
Medical and Surgical

**Staffed Beds:** 52 **Admissions:** 2472 **Census:** 26 **Outpatient Visits:** 96069
**Births:** 339

## MANISTEE—Manistee County

**WEST SHORE MEDICAL CENTER (231335)**, 1465 East Parkdale Avenue,
Zip 49660–9709; tel. 231/398–1100 **A**3 9 10 **F**3 7 11 13 15 28 29 30 32 34
35 39 40 46 50 51 53 54 57 59 74 75 76 77 79 81 85 86 93 97 107 108
110 111 115 118 119 127 129 132 135 146 147 148 **P**6
Primary Contact: James Barker, Chief Executive Officer
COO: Donn J. Lemmer, Chief Financial Officer and Chief Operating Officer
CFO: Donn J. Lemmer, Chief Financial Officer and Chief Operating Officer
CMO: Marion Fuller, Chief of Staff
CHR: Kim Weckesser, Director Human Resources
CNO: Thomas Kane, R.N., Vice President Patient Services and Chief Nursing
Officer
Web address: www.westshoremedcenter.org
**Control:** County–Government, nonfederal **Service:** General Medical and Surgical

**Staffed Beds:** 25 **Admissions:** 1538 **Census:** 14 **Outpatient Visits:** 91355
**Births:** 173 **Total Expense ($000):** 56913 **Payroll Expense ($000):** 23312
**Personnel:** 305

## MANISTIQUE—Schoolcraft County

★ **SCHOOLCRAFT MEMORIAL HOSPITAL (231303)**, 7870W U.S. Highway 2,
Zip 49854–8992; tel. 906/341–3200 **A**9 10 18 **F**3 11 15 28 29 30 31 32 34
35 40 41 44 45 50 53 56 57 59 62 63 64 65 66 70 75 77 78 79 81 82 84
85 93 97 107 108 110 114 118 119 127 129 130 132 133 144 146 147
148 **P**6
Primary Contact: Tanya Hoar, Chief Executive Officer and Chief Financial Officer
CFO: Tanya Hoar, Chief Executive Officer and Chief Financial Officer
CMO: David Schoenow, M.D., Chief Medical Officer
CIO: Kent La Croix, Supervisor Information Technology
CHR: Gina Lindquist, Director Human Resources
CNO: Cindy Olli, R.N., Chief Nursing Officer
Web address: www.scmh.org
**Control:** County–Government, nonfederal **Service:** General Medical and Surgical

**Staffed Beds:** 12 **Admissions:** 394 **Census:** 5 **Outpatient Visits:** 36479
**Births:** 0 **Total Expense ($000):** 27069 **Payroll Expense ($000):** 12873
**Personnel:** 191

## MARLETTE—Sanilac County

**MARLETTE REGIONAL HOSPITAL (231330)**, 2770 Main Street,
Zip 48453–1141, Mailing Address: P.O. Box 307, Zip 48453–0307;
tel. 989/635–4000, (Nonreporting) **A**5 9 10 18
Primary Contact: Daniel Babcock, Chief Executive Officer
CFO: James L. Singles, Chief Financial Officer
CMO: Daniel Kulick, M.D., Chief of Staff
CIO: Paul Gugel, Manager Information Technology
CHR: Connie Kennedy, Director Human Resources
CNO: Hilda Hebberd, R.N., Senior Director Clinical Services
Web address: www.marletteregionalhospital.org
**Control:** Other not–for–profit (including NFP Corporation) **Service:** General
Medical and Surgical

**Staffed Beds:** 74

## MARQUETTE—Marquette County

⊞ **UP HEALTH SYSTEM–MARQUETTE (230054)**, 580 West College Avenue,
Zip 49855–2736; tel. 906/228–9440 **A**1 2 3 5 9 10 13 **F**3 4 5 7 8 11 12 13
14 15 17 18 20 22 24 26 28 29 30 31 32 34 35 37 38 40 43 45 46 48 49
50 51 53 55 56 57 58 59 60 62 63 64 65 68 70 72 74 75 76 77 78 79 81
82 85 86 87 89 90 93 94 98 99 100 101 102 103 104 107 108 110 111
114 115 116 117 118 119 120 121 122 123 124 127 129 130 131 132 135
143 145 146 147 148 **P**6 **S** Duke LifePoint Healthcare, Brentwood, TN
Primary Contact: James Bogan, FACHE, Interim Chief Executive Officer
COO: Jeff Perry, Chief Operating Officer
CFO: Steve Embree, Chief Financial Officer
CMO: Tom Noren, M.D., Chief Medical Officer
CIO: Doug Stacy, Director Information Technology
CHR: Ruth Solinski, Senior Director Human Resources
CNO: Dagmar Raica, R.N., Chief Nursing Officer
Web address: www.mgh.org
**Control:** Corporation, Investor–owned, for–profit **Service:** General Medical and
Surgical

**Staffed Beds:** 268 **Admissions:** 9720 **Census:** 127 **Outpatient Visits:**
208836 **Births:** 649 **Total Expense ($000):** 319618 **Payroll Expense**
**($000):** 125701 **Personnel:** 1875

## MARSHALL—Calhoun County

★ ◇ **OAKLAWN HOSPITAL (230217)**, 200 North Madison Street,
Zip 49068–1199; tel. 269/781–4271, (Nonreporting) **A**9 10 21
Primary Contact: Ginger Williams, M.D., FACHE, President and Chief Executive
Officer
COO: Sharon L. Thomas–Boyd, Chief Support and Ancillary Services Officer
CFO: Gregg M. Beeg, FACHE, Chief Financial Officer
CIO: Natalie Spivak, Director Information Services
CHR: Jan Sinclair, Chief Personnel Officer
Web address: www.oaklawnhospital.org
**Control:** Other not–for–profit (including NFP Corporation) **Service:** General
Medical and Surgical

**Staffed Beds:** 78

## MIDLAND—Midland County

⊞ **MIDMICHIGAN MEDICAL CENTER–MIDLAND (230222)**, 4000 Wellness Drive,
Zip 48670–2000; tel. 989/839–3000, (Nonreporting) **A**1 2 3 5 9 10
**S** MidMichigan Health, Midland, MI
Primary Contact: Gregory H. Rogers, President
CFO: Scott D. Currie, Vice President and Chief Financial Officer
CMO: Margueritte Kuhn, M.D., Vice President Medical Affairs
CIO: C. Harlan Goodrich, Vice President and Chief Information Officer
CNO: Jan Penney, R.N., Vice President and Chief Nursing Officer
Web address: www.midmichigan.org
**Control:** Other not–for–profit (including NFP Corporation) **Service:** General
Medical and Surgical

**Staffed Beds:** 265

---

**Hospital, Medicare Provider Number, Address, Telephone, Approval, Facility, and Physician Codes, Health Care System**

★ American Hospital Association (AHA) membership  ◯ Healthcare Facilities Accreditation Program  ⇑ Center for Improvement in Healthcare Quality Accreditation
☐ The Joint Commission accreditation  ◇ DNV Healthcare Inc. accreditation  △ Commission on Accreditation of Rehabilitation Facilities (CARF) accreditation

## MONROE—Monroe County

⊞ **PROMEDICA MONROE REGIONAL HOSPITAL (230099)**, 718 North Macomb Street, Zip 48162–7815; tel. 734/240–8400, (Total facility includes 69 beds in nursing home–type unit) **A**1 2 9 10 13 **F**3 5 8 11 13 15 18 20 28 29 30 34 35 38 40 41 44 45 46 49 50 51 54 56 57 59 62 63 64 65 66 69 70 71 74 75 76 77 79 81 84 85 86 87 89 92 93 97 98 99 100 101 102 103 104 107 108 109 110 111 113 114 115 116 117 118 119 126 129 130 131 132 135 145 146 147 148 **P**6 **S** ProMedica Health System, Toledo, OH
Primary Contact: Annette S. Phillips, President and Chief Executive Officer
CFO: Thomas Schilling, Chief Financial Officer and Senior Vice President Finance
CMO: Gary L. Moorman, D.O., Chief Medical Officer and Senior Vice President Medical Affairs
CIO: Bruce Kelly, Chief Information Officer
CHR: Aline Lafferty, Vice President Human Resources
CNO: Pamela A. Urbanski, R.N., Chief Nursing Officer, Senior Vice President, Patient Care Services
Web address: www.mercymemorial.org
**Control:** Other not–for–profit (including NFP Corporation) **Service:** General Medical and Surgical

**Staffed Beds:** 179 **Admissions:** 9061 **Census:** 97 **Outpatient Visits:** 165947 **Births:** 786 **Total Expense ($000):** 157006 **Payroll Expense ($000):** 67562 **Personnel:** 1215

## MOUNT CLEMENS—Macomb County

**HENRY FORD MACOMB HOSPITAL – MOUNT CLEMENS CAMPUS** See Henry Ford Macomb Hospitals, Clinton Township

○ **MCLAREN MACOMB (230227)**, 1000 Harrington Boulevard, Zip 48043–2992; tel. 586/493–8000 **A**2 9 10 11 12 13 **F**3 7 8 12 13 14 15 18 20 22 24 26 28 29 30 31 34 35 37 40 42 43 45 46 47 48 49 50 51 58 59 62 63 65 68 71 74 75 76 77 78 79 80 81 82 83 84 85 87 89 92 93 97 100 102 107 108 110 111 112 114 115 116 117 118 119 120 121 123 124 126 129 130 131 132 135 145 146 147 148 **P**8 **S** McLaren Health Care Corporation, Flint, MI
Primary Contact: Thomas M. Brisse, President and Chief Executive Officer
COO: Sue Durst, R.N., Vice President Plant Operations
CMO: Michael K. Smith, D.O., Vice President Medical Affairs
Web address: www.mclaren.org/macomb/macomb.aspx
**Control:** Other not–for–profit (including NFP Corporation) **Service:** General Medical and Surgical

**Staffed Beds:** 288 **Admissions:** 14235 **Census:** 158 **Outpatient Visits:** 154931 **Births:** 1001 **Total Expense ($000):** 286398 **Payroll Expense ($000):** 122673 **Personnel:** 1743

⊞ **SELECT SPECIALTY HOSPITAL–MACOMB COUNTY (232023)**, 215 North Avenue, Zip 48043–1700; tel. 586/307–9000, (Nonreporting) **A**1 9 10 12 13 **S** Select Medical Corporation, Mechanicsburg, PA
Primary Contact: Jon P. O'Malley, Chief Executive Officer
CFO: Sharon Ryan, Regional Controller
CMO: Arsenio V. Deleon, M.D., Chief Medical Officer
CHR: Katelyn Andre, Human Resource Coordinator
CNO: Lydia Alaszewski, Chief Nursing Officer
Web address: www.macomb.selectspecialtyhospitals.com/
**Control:** Corporation, Investor–owned, for–profit **Service:** Long–Term Acute Care hospital

**Staffed Beds:** 36

## MOUNT PLEASANT—Isabella County

○ **MCLAREN CENTRAL MICHIGAN (230080)**, 1221 South Drive, Zip 48858–3257; tel. 989/772–6700 **A**2 5 9 10 11 19 **F**3 12 13 15 18 20 22 26 28 29 30 31 34 35 40 44 45 48 49 50 51 54 57 59 62 64 65 68 70 74 75 77 78 79 81 82 85 86 87 89 96 97 107 108 110 111 114 117 118 119 120 121 123 124 129 130 131 132 144 145 146 147 148 **S** McLaren Health Care Corporation, Flint, MI
Primary Contact: William P. Lawrence, President and Chief Executive Officer
CFO: Gregg Beeg, Chief Financial Officer
CMO: Ashok Vashishta, M.D., Vice President Medical Affairs
CIO: Nicolette Zalud, Customer Site Manager
CHR: Carolyn Potter, Vice President Human Resources
CNO: Sheri Myers, Vice President Patient Care Services
Web address: www.cmch.org
**Control:** Other not–for–profit (including NFP Corporation) **Service:** General Medical and Surgical

**Staffed Beds:** 78 **Admissions:** 3527 **Census:** 27 **Outpatient Visits:** 159452 **Births:** 546 **Total Expense ($000):** 82382 **Payroll Expense ($000):** 35576 **Personnel:** 515

## MUNISING—Alger County

**MUNISING MEMORIAL HOSPITAL (231308)**, 1500 Sand Point Road, Zip 49862–1406; tel. 906/387–4110, (Nonreporting) **A**9 10 18
Primary Contact: Kevin P. Calhoun, Chief Executive Officer
CFO: Barb Trombley, Director Financial Services
CMO: Christine Krueger, M.D., Chief of Staff
CHR: Melissa Hall, Human Resources
CNO: Andrea Wills, R.N., Chief Nursing Executive
Web address: www.munisingmemorial.org
**Control:** Other not–for–profit (including NFP Corporation) **Service:** General Medical and Surgical

**Staffed Beds:** 25

## MUSKEGON—Muskegon County

⊞ **GREAT LAKES SPECIALTY HOSPITAL–MUSKEGON (232021)**, 1700 Clinton Street, 3 South, Zip 49442–5502; tel. 231/728–5811, (Nonreporting) **A**1 9 10 **S** Select Medical Corporation, Mechanicsburg, PA
Primary Contact: Sharon Purkis, Chief Executive Officer
Web address: www.greatlakesspecialtyhospital.com
**Control:** Corporation, Investor–owned, for–profit **Service:** Long–Term Acute Care hospital

**Staffed Beds:** 31

⊞ **MERCY HEALTH HACKLEY CAMPUS (230066)**, 1700 Clinton Street, Zip 49442–5502, Mailing Address: P.O. Box 3302, Zip 49443–3302; tel. 231/726–3511 **A**1 2 9 10 13 **F**3 7 11 12 13 15 26 29 30 35 40 45 49 50 51 53 54 57 59 61 64 68 70 74 76 77 79 81 82 84 85 87 89 90 91 93 96 97 98 99 100 101 102 103 104 105 106 107 108 109 111 114 115 116 117 118 119 127 144 146 147 148 **P**6 7 8 **S** Trinity Health, Livonia, MI
Primary Contact: Greg Loomis, President
CFO: Gary Allore, Chief Financial Officer
CMO: F. Remington Sprague, M.D., Chief Medical Officer
CIO: William Stefl, Director Information Systems
CNO: Kimberly Maguire, R.N., Chief Nursing Officer
Web address: www.mercyhealthmuskegon.com
**Control:** Other not–for–profit (including NFP Corporation) **Service:** General Medical and Surgical

**Staffed Beds:** 213 **Admissions:** 8267 **Census:** 98 **Outpatient Visits:** 258895 **Births:** 1977 **Total Expense ($000):** 165863 **Payroll Expense ($000):** 58600 **Personnel:** 1044

⊞ **MERCY HEALTH, MERCY CAMPUS (230004)**, 1500 East Sherman Boulevard, Zip 49444–1849; tel. 231/672–2000, (Includes MERCY HEALTH, GENERAL CAMPUS, 1700 Oak Avenue, Zip 49442; tel. 231/672–3311; Greg Loomis, Interim President and Chief Operating Officer) **A**1 2 9 10 12 13 **F**3 7 11 12 15 18 20 22 24 26 28 29 30 31 34 35 40 44 50 51 53 54 56 57 58 59 64 68 70 74 75 77 78 79 81 82 84 85 86 87 91 93 97 107 108 111 114 115 116 117 118 119 120 121 122 123 124 129 130 131 132 135 144 146 147 148 **P**6 7 8 **S** Trinity Health, Livonia, MI
Primary Contact: Greg Loomis, President
CFO: Gary Allore, Chief Financial Officer
CMO: F. Remington Sprague, M.D., Chief Medical Officer
CIO: William Stefl, Director Information Systems
CNO: Kimberly Maguire, R.N., Chief Nursing Officer
Web address: www.mercyhealth.com
**Control:** Other not–for–profit (including NFP Corporation) **Service:** General Medical and Surgical

**Staffed Beds:** 188 **Admissions:** 8781 **Census:** 99 **Outpatient Visits:** 670097 **Births:** 0 **Total Expense ($000):** 289283 **Payroll Expense ($000):** 132139 **Personnel:** 2026

**SELECT SPECIALTY HOSPITAL–WESTERN MICHIGAN** See Great Lakes Specialty Hospital–Muskegon

## NEW BALTIMORE—Macomb County

**HARBOR OAKS HOSPITAL (234021)**, 35031 23 Mile Road, Zip 48047–3649; tel. 586/725–5777, (Nonreporting) **A**9 10 **S** Acadia Healthcare Company, Inc., Franklin, TN
Primary Contact: Sari Abromovich, Chief Executive Officer
CFO: Michael Ferguson, Chief Financial Officer
CMO: James D. Adamo, M.D., Medical Director
CHR: Zena Ridley, Director Human Resources
CNO: Leeann Duncan, Director Patient Care Services
Web address: www.harboroaks.com
**Control:** Corporation, Investor–owned, for–profit **Service:** Psychiatric

**Staffed Beds:** 45

MI

## NEWBERRY—Luce County

★ ◇ **HELEN NEWBERRY JOY HOSPITAL (231304)**, 502 West Harrie Street, Zip 49868–1209; tel. 906/293–9200, (Includes HELEN NEWBERRY JOY HOSPITAL ANNEX ), (Total facility includes 37 beds in nursing home–type unit) **A**9 10 18 21 **F**15 18 28 29 30 31 32 34 35 36 38 40 44 45 53 57 59 63 64 65 75 78 81 85 86 87 93 97 107 108 111 114 118 119 127 128 129 130 131 132 133 134 135 143 144 146 148 **P**6
Primary Contact: Scott Pillion, Chief Executive Officer
CMO: Raghu Rao, M.D., Chief of Staff
CIO: Michelle Sears, Director Information Systems
CHR: Roger Bergh, Director Human Resources
Web address: www.hnjh.org
**Control:** County–Government, nonfederal **Service:** General Medical and Surgical

**Staffed Beds:** 62 **Admissions:** 597 **Census:** 54 **Outpatient Visits:** 29538 **Births:** 0 **Total Expense ($000):** 33931 **Payroll Expense ($000):** 15439 **Personnel:** 320

## NORTHVILLE—Wayne County

☐ **HAWTHORN CENTER**, 18471 Haggerty Road, Zip 48168–9575; tel. 248/735–6771, (Nonreporting) **A**1 3 9
Primary Contact: Roy Kelly, Facility Director
CIO: Robert W. Bailey, Chief Information Officer
Web address: www.https://www.michigan.gov
**Control:** State–Government, nonfederal **Service:** Children's hospital psychiatric

**Staffed Beds:** 69

## NOVI—Oakland County

**PROVIDENCE – PROVIDENCE PARK HOSPITAL, NOVI CAMPUS** See Providence – Providence Park Hospital, Southfield Campus, Southfield

## ONTONAGON—Ontonagon County

⊞ **ASPIRUS ONTONAGON HOSPITAL (231309)**, 601 South Seventh Street, Zip 49953–1459; tel. 906/884–8000, (Total facility includes 46 beds in nursing home–type unit) **A**1 9 10 18 **F**3 6 15 28 29 31 34 40 41 45 53 56 59 64 65 69 75 78 79 81 85 87 93 97 107 110 119 128 131 132 133 **P**6 **S** Aspirus, Inc., Wausau, WI
Primary Contact: Michael Hauswirth, Chief Operating Officer
COO: Michael Hauswirth, Chief Operating Officer
CMO: Richard Chaltry, M.D., Director Medical Staff
CHR: Gina Linna, Manager Human Resources
CNO: Deanna Wilson, VP Patient Care Services/Site Manager
Web address: www.aspirus–ontonagon.org
**Control:** Other not–for–profit (including NFP Corporation) **Service:** General Medical and Surgical

**Staffed Beds:** 64 **Admissions:** 231 **Census:** 47 **Outpatient Visits:** 17357 **Births:** 0 **Total Expense ($000):** 13890 **Payroll Expense ($000):** 5472 **Personnel:** 86

## OWOSSO—Shiawassee County

⊞ **MEMORIAL HEALTHCARE (230121)**, 826 West King Street, Zip 48867–2120; tel. 989/723–5211, (Total facility includes 32 beds in nursing home–type unit) **A**1 2 5 9 10 **F**11 13 15 28 29 30 31 32 34 35 36 38 40 45 50 51 56 57 59 62 63 64 65 69 70 74 75 76 77 78 79 81 82 85 87 89 93 97 98 100 101 102 107 108 110 111 115 119 127 128 129 130 131 132 143 144 146 147 148 **P**6 7
Primary Contact: Brian Long, FACHE, President and Chief Executive Officer
CFO: Brian Long, FACHE, President and Chief Executive Officer
CMO: Wael Salman, M.D., Vice President Medical Affairs
CIO: Frank Fear, Vice President Ancillary Services and Chief Information Officer
CHR: Ruthann Liagre, Vice President Human Resources
CNO: Dawn Blackwell, R.N., VP, Patient Care Services
Web address: www.memorialhealthcare.org
**Control:** Other not–for–profit (including NFP Corporation) **Service:** General Medical and Surgical

**Staffed Beds:** 149 **Admissions:** 3769 **Census:** 81 **Outpatient Visits:** 383558 **Births:** 485 **Total Expense ($000):** 111019 **Payroll Expense ($000):** 52764 **Personnel:** 945

## PAW PAW—Van Buren County

⊞ **BRONSON LAKEVIEW HOSPITAL (231332)**, 408 Hazen Street, Zip 49079–1019, Mailing Address: P.O. Box 209, Zip 49079–0209; tel. 269/657–3141 **A**1 10 18 **F**3 6 11 15 29 30 34 35 40 44 50 56 57 59 64 65 66 68 74 75 77 79 81 82 85 86 87 93 97 98 100 101 102 103 107 110 114 127 129 130 132 146 147 148 **P**6 **S** Bronson Healthcare Group, Inc., Kalamazoo, MI
Primary Contact: Kirk Richardson, Chief Operating Officer
COO: Kirk Richardson, Vice President Chief Operating Officer Chief Nursing Officer
CMO: Matthew Dommer, M.D., Chief Medical Officer
CHR: John Hayden, Senior Vice President and Chief Human Resources Officer
CNO: Kirk Richardson, Vice President Chief Operating Officer Chief Nursing Officer
Web address: www.bronsonhealth.com/lakeview
**Control:** Other not–for–profit (including NFP Corporation) **Service:** General Medical and Surgical

**Staffed Beds:** 35 **Admissions:** 1067 **Census:** 13 **Outpatient Visits:** 92745 **Births:** 0 **Total Expense ($000):** 33835 **Payroll Expense ($000):** 12792 **Personnel:** 448

## PETOSKEY—Emmet County

☐ **MCLAREN NORTHERN MICHIGAN (230105)**, 416 Connable Avenue, Zip 49770–2297; tel. 231/487–4000 **A**1 2 5 9 10 **F**3 12 13 15 17 18 20 22 24 26 28 29 30 31 32 34 35 36 38 40 42 44 45 48 49 50 51 53 57 58 59 60 64 68 70 74 75 76 77 78 79 81 82 85 86 87 89 90 91 93 94 96 107 108 110 111 114 115 119 120 121 123 124 129 130 132 135 146 148 **S** McLaren Health Care Corporation, Flint, MI
Primary Contact: David M. Zechman, FACHE, President and Chief Executive Officer
COO: Mary–Anne D. Ponti, R.N., Chief Operating Officer
CFO: David Bellamy, Chief Financial Officer
CMO: Kirk Lufkin, M.D., VPMA
CIO: David Bellamy, Chief Financial Officer
CHR: Gene Kaminski, Vice President Human Resources
CNO: Jennifer Woods, R.N., Chief Nursing Officer
Web address: www.northernhealth.org
**Control:** Other not–for–profit (including NFP Corporation) **Service:** General Medical and Surgical

**Staffed Beds:** 188 **Admissions:** 9954 **Census:** 106 **Outpatient Visits:** 213745 **Births:** 647 **Total Expense ($000):** 201211 **Payroll Expense ($000):** 74393 **Personnel:** 1269

## PIGEON—Huron County

⊞ **SCHEURER HOSPITAL (231310)**, 170 North Caseville Road, Zip 48755–9781; tel. 989/453–3223, (Total facility includes 19 beds in nursing home–type unit) **A**1 5 9 10 18 **F**3 7 10 11 15 28 29 30 31 34 36 40 44 45 50 53 54 56 57 59 64 68 69 75 77 78 79 81 85 86 87 91 93 97 107 108 110 114 119 125 127 130 131 132 133 143 144 146 **P**6
Primary Contact: Dwight Gascho, President and Chief Executive Officer
CFO: Terry Lutz, Chief Financial Officer
CMO: Scott Reiter, D.O., Chief of Staff
CIO: Suzanne LeMaire, Manager Health Information Management Services and Corporate Compliance Officer
CHR: Gregory S. Foy, Human Resources System Leader
Web address: www.scheurer.org
**Control:** Other not–for–profit (including NFP Corporation) **Service:** General Medical and Surgical

**Staffed Beds:** 44 **Admissions:** 677 **Census:** 28 **Outpatient Visits:** 43736 **Births:** 0 **Total Expense ($000):** 36670 **Payroll Expense ($000):** 17062 **Personnel:** 340

## PLAINWELL—Allegan County

⊞ **BORGESS–PIPP HOSPITAL (232034)**, 411 Naomi Street, Zip 49080–1222; tel. 269/685–6811, (Nonreporting) **A**1 9 10 **S** Ascension Health, Saint Louis, MO
Primary Contact: John E. Ryder, Administrator and Chief Operating Officer
Web address: www.borgess.com
**Control:** Other not–for–profit (including NFP Corporation) **Service:** Long–Term Acute Care hospital

**Staffed Beds:** 43

---

**Hospital, Medicare Provider Number, Address, Telephone, Approval, Facility, and Physician Codes, Health Care System**

★ American Hospital Association (AHA) membership ◯ Healthcare Facilities Accreditation Program ⇑ Center for Improvement in Healthcare Quality Accreditation
☐ The Joint Commission accreditation ◇ DNV Healthcare Inc. accreditation △ Commission on Accreditation of Rehabilitation Facilities (CARF) accreditation

**MI**

## PONTIAC—Oakland County

☐ **DOCTORS' HOSPITAL OF MICHIGAN (230013)**, 461 West Huron Street, Zip 48341–1601; tel. 248/857–7200, (Nonreporting) **A**1 3 9 10
Primary Contact: Robert Barrow, Chief Executive Officer
COO: Dennis Franks, Vice President Operations
CFO: Dennis Franks, Interim Chief Financial Officer
CMO: Ray Breitenbach, M.D., Chief of Staff
CIO: Albert Sinisi, Director Information Systems
Web address: www.dhofm.com
**Control:** Other not–for–profit (including NFP Corporation) **Service:** General Medical and Surgical

**Staffed Beds:** 106

☐ ○ **MCLAREN OAKLAND (230207)**, 50 North Perry Street, Zip 48342–2253; tel. 248/338–5000, (Total facility includes 120 beds in nursing home–type unit) **A**1 2 9 10 11 12 13 **F**3 4 7 8 11 12 14 15 18 20 24 26 28 29 30 31 32 33 34 35 36 40 42 43 44 45 50 53 54 57 59 62 63 64 65 66 68 70 74 75 77 78 79 81 82 90 92 93 94 98 103 107 108 111 114 118 119 124 128 130 131 132 135 136 137 138 139 140 141 142 143 144 146 148 **P**4 8 **S** McLaren Health Care Corporation, Flint, MI
Primary Contact: Chad M. Grant, President and Chief Executive Officer
CFO: Fred Korte, Chief Financial Officer
CMO: Steven Calkin, D.O., Vice President Medical Affairs
CIO: Darin Boka, Chief Information Officer
CHR: Dwan Cosby, Manager Human Resources
CNO: Michele Carey, Vice President Patient Care and Chief Nursing Officer
Web address: www.pohmedical.org
**Control:** Other not–for–profit (including NFP Corporation) **Service:** General Medical and Surgical

**Staffed Beds:** 269 **Admissions:** 5401 **Census:** 192 **Outpatient Visits:** 160451 **Births:** 0 **Total Expense ($000):** 160284 **Payroll Expense ($000):** 66892 **Personnel:** 1188

☒ **SELECT SPECIALTY HOSPITAL–PONTIAC (232030)**, 44405 Woodward Avenue, 8th Floor, Zip 48341–5023; tel. 248/452–5252, (Nonreporting) **A**1 9 10 **S** Select Medical Corporation, Mechanicsburg, PA
Primary Contact: Peggy Kingston, Chief Executive Officer
CMO: Fadi Salloum, M.D., Medical Director
CNO: Cathy Boyd, Chief Nursing Officer
Web address: www.selectspecialtyhospitals.com/company/locations/pontiac.aspx
**Control:** Corporation, Investor–owned, for–profit **Service:** Long–Term Acute Care hospital

**Staffed Beds:** 30

☒ **ST. JOSEPH MERCY OAKLAND (230029)**, 44405 Woodward Avenue, Zip 48341–5023; tel. 248/858–3000 **A**1 2 3 5 9 10 13 **F**3 8 11 12 13 15 17 18 20 22 24 26 28 29 30 31 34 35 36 39 40 41 43 44 45 46 50 53 54 55 56 57 58 59 61 64 65 66 68 70 72 74 75 76 77 78 79 81 82 84 85 86 87 89 90 93 94 96 97 98 100 103 105 107 108 110 111 114 115 119 126 129 130 131 132 135 144 146 147 148 **P**5 6 **S** Trinity Health, Livonia, MI
Primary Contact: Jack Weiner, Ph.D., President and Chief Executive Officer
COO: Shannon Striebich, Chief Operating Officer
CFO: Michael Gusho, Chief Financial Officer
CMO: Michael Smith, M.D., Vice President Medical Affairs
CIO: Robert Jones, Director Management Information Systems
CHR: Ane McNeil, Vice President Human Resources
CNO: Ann McDonald–Upton, Chief Nursing Officer
Web address: www.stjoesoakland.com
**Control:** Church–operated, Nongovernment, not–for profit **Service:** General Medical and Surgical

**Staffed Beds:** 443 **Admissions:** 19097 **Census:** 256 **Outpatient Visits:** 357831 **Births:** 1949 **Total Expense ($000):** 386666 **Payroll Expense ($000):** 145395 **Personnel:** 2395

## PORT HURON—St. Clair County

☒ ○ **MCLAREN PORT HURON (230216)**, 1221 Pine Grove Avenue, Zip 48060–3511; tel. 810/987–5000, (Nonreporting) **A**1 2 9 10 11 **S** McLaren Health Care Corporation, Flint, MI
Primary Contact: Thomas D. DeFauw, FACHE, President and Chief Executive Officer
CFO: John Liston, Chief Financial Officer
CMO: Michael W. Tawney, D.O., Vice President Medical Affairs
CHR: Doris A. Seidl, Vice President Human Resources
CNO: Jennifer Montgomery, R.N., Vice President, Nursing
Web address: www.porthuronhospital.org
**Control:** Other not–for–profit (including NFP Corporation) **Service:** General Medical and Surgical

**Staffed Beds:** 186

☒ **ST. JOSEPH MERCY PORT HURON (230031)**, 2601 Electric Avenue, Zip 48060–6518; tel. 810/985–1500 **A**1 2 9 10 **F**3 11 12 15 18 20 29 30 31 34 35 37 40 45 49 50 54 56 57 58 59 61 64 66 70 74 75 77 78 79 81 82 85 86 87 90 91 93 96 97 107 108 110 114 118 119 120 121 123 126 130 131 132 135 146 147 148 **P**6 8 **S** Prime Healthcare Services, Ontario, CA
Primary Contact: Rebekah Smith, R.N., President and Chief Executive Officer
COO: Janet Herbert, Vice President Operations and Chief Nursing Officer
CFO: Chris Fulks, Vice President Finance
CMO: Robert Camara, M.D., Chief Medical Officer
CIO: Peggy Assessor, Director Information Services
CNO: Janet Herbert, Vice President Operations and Chief Nursing Officer
Web address: www.mymercy.us
**Control:** Church–operated, Nongovernment, not–for profit **Service:** General Medical and Surgical

**Staffed Beds:** 119 **Admissions:** 3496 **Census:** 44 **Outpatient Visits:** 116439 **Births:** 0 **Total Expense ($000):** 80021 **Payroll Expense ($000):** 30062 **Personnel:** 613

## REED CITY—Osceola County

☒ **SPECTRUM HEALTH REED CITY HOSPITAL (231323)**, 300 North Patterson Road, Zip 49677–8041, Mailing Address: P.O. Box 75, Zip 49677–0075; tel. 231/832–3271, (Total facility includes 50 beds in nursing home–type unit) **A**1 5 9 10 18 **F**3 8 15 29 31 34 35 40 45 53 54 57 59 64 65 70 75 77 78 79 81 84 85 86 87 93 96 97 107 108 110 111 115 119 120 121 123 124 127 128 129 130 131 133 146 147 **P**6 **S** Spectrum Health, Grand Rapids, MI
Primary Contact: Mary Kay VanDriel, President
COO: Cathy Rybicki, Chief Operating Officer
CFO: Thomas Knoerl, Vice President Finance
CMO: Thomas Campana, M.D., Chief of Staff
CIO: Brandi Johnson, Site Manager Technology Information Systems
CHR: Kris Miller, Senior Human Resources Business Partner
CNO: Scott Lombard, Acting Chief Nursing Officer
Web address: www.reedcity.spectrum–health.org
**Control:** Other not–for–profit (including NFP Corporation) **Service:** General Medical and Surgical

**Staffed Beds:** 75 **Admissions:** 862 **Census:** 58 **Outpatient Visits:** 335492 **Births:** 0 **Total Expense ($000):** 52014 **Payroll Expense ($000):** 18107 **Personnel:** 350

## ROCHESTER—Oakland County

☐ △ **CRITTENTON HOSPITAL MEDICAL CENTER (230254)**, 1101 West University Drive, Zip 48307–1831; tel. 248/652–5000, (Nonreporting) **A**1 3 5 7 9 10
Primary Contact: Roy A. Powell, President and Chief Executive Officer
COO: Gregory A. Partamian, Chief Operating Officer
CFO: Donna Kopinski, Chief Financial Officer
CMO: Frank Sottile, M.D., Chief Medical Officer
CIO: Tom Ventameglia, Director Information Systems
Web address: www.crittenton.com
**Control:** Other not–for–profit (including NFP Corporation) **Service:** General Medical and Surgical

**Staffed Beds:** 254

## ROMEO—Macomb County

**ST. JOSEPH'S MERCY–NORTH** See Henry Ford Macomb Hospitals, Clinton Township

## ROYAL OAK—Oakland County

☒ **BEAUMONT HOSPITAL – ROYAL OAK (230130)**, 3601 West Thirteen Mile Road, Zip 48073–6712; tel. 248/898–5000, (Includes BEAUMONT CHILDREN'S HOSPITAL, 3601 West 13 Mile Road, tel. 248/898–5000) **A**1 2 3 5 8 9 10 **F**3 5 6 8 11 12 13 15 17 18 19 20 22 24 26 27 28 29 30 31 32 34 35 36 37 38 39 40 41 43 44 45 46 47 48 49 50 51 54 55 56 57 58 59 60 61 62 63 64 65 66 68 70 71 72 74 75 76 77 78 79 80 81 82 83 84 85 86 87 88 89 90 91 92 93 94 95 96 97 98 99 100 101 102 103 104 105 107 108 109 110 111 114 115 116 117 118 119 120 121 123 124 126 129 130 131 132 134 135 138 139 141 142 143 144 145 146 147 148 **P**6 **S** Beaumont Health, Royal Oak, MI
Primary Contact: Shane Cerone, President
CFO: Nickolas A. Vitale, Executive Vice President and Chief Financial Officer
CMO: David Wood, M.D., Executive Vice President and Chief Medical Officer
CIO: Subra Sripada, Senior Vice President and Chief Information Officer
CHR: Jay T. Holden, Senior Vice President Chief Human Resources Officer
CNO: Maureen Bowman, Vice President of Nursing and Chief Nursing Officer
Web address: www.beaumont.edu/royal–oak–hospital–campus
**Control:** Other not–for–profit (including NFP Corporation) **Service:** General Medical and Surgical

**Staffed Beds:** 1070 **Admissions:** 58539 **Census:** 835 **Outpatient Visits:** 1283189 **Births:** 5259 **Total Expense ($000):** 1125415 **Payroll Expense ($000):** 364404 **Personnel:** 8018

*Many Facility Codes have changed. Please refer to the AHA Guide Code Chart.*   © 2015 AHA Guide

## SAGINAW—Saginaw County

✠ **ALEDA E. LUTZ VETERANS AFFAIRS MEDICAL CENTER**, 1500 Weiss Street, Zip 48602–5298; tel. 989/497–2500, (Total facility includes 81 beds in nursing home–type unit) **A**1 3 9 **F**3 5 8 11 12 15 18 29 30 31 34 35 36 38 39 44 45 50 53 54 56 57 58 59 61 63 64 68 74 75 77 78 81 82 83 84 85 86 87 93 94 97 100 101 102 103 104 107 108 119 127 128 130 131 132 133 135 136 137 138 139 140 141 142 143 144 146 147 148 **P**6 **S** Department of Veterans Affairs, Washington, DC
Primary Contact: Peggy W. Kearns, MS, FACHE, Medical Center Director
COO: Stephanie Young, Associate Director
CFO: Jeff Drew, Fiscal Officer
CMO: Gregory Movsesian, M.D., Acting Chief of Staff
CIO: Angie Schmus, Chief Information Technology
CHR: Thomas Stredney, Chief Human Resources Management Service
CNO: Penny Holland, Associate Director for Patient Care Services
Web address: www.saginaw.va.gov/
**Control:** Veterans Affairs, Government, federal **Service:** General Medical and Surgical

**Staffed Beds:** 89 **Admissions:** 861 **Census:** 43 **Outpatient Visits:** 379457 **Births:** 0 **Total Expense ($000):** 183969 **Payroll Expense ($000):** 74343 **Personnel:** 1070

★ ○ △ **COVENANT HEALTHCARE (230070)**, 1447 North Harrison Street, Zip 48602–4727; tel. 989/583–0000, (Includes COVENANT MEDICAL CENTER–COOPER, 700 Cooper Avenue, Zip 48602–5399; tel. 517/583–0000; COVENANT MEDICAL CENTER–HARRISON, 1447 North Harrison Street, Zip 48602–4785; tel. 517/583–0000), (Total facility includes 20 beds in nursing home–type unit) **A**2 3 5 7 9 10 11 **F**3 8 11 12 13 15 17 18 19 20 22 24 25 26 27 28 29 30 31 35 36 40 41 42 43 45 46 47 48 49 50 54 57 58 59 60 61 62 63 64 65 70 72 74 75 76 77 78 79 81 82 83 84 86 87 88 89 90 91 92 93 94 97 107 108 110 111 113 114 115 118 119 120 121 123 124 126 128 129 130 131 132 135 143 144 146 147 148 **P**7 8
Primary Contact: Edward Bruff, President and Chief Executive Officer
COO: Daniel M. George, Executive Vice President, Operations
CFO: Kevin Albosta, Vice President, Chief Financial Officer
CMO: John Kosanovich, M.D., Vice President Covenant Healthcare and Chief Executive Officer Covenant Medical Group
CHR: Kevin Birchmeier, Director Human Resources
CNO: Carol Stoll, Vice President Patient Services and Chief Nursing Officer
Web address: www.covenanthealthcare.com
**Control:** Other not–for–profit (including NFP Corporation) **Service:** General Medical and Surgical

**Staffed Beds:** 532 **Admissions:** 25789 **Census:** 368 **Births:** 3018 **Total Expense ($000):** 498290 **Payroll Expense ($000):** 215074

☐ **HEALTHSOURCE SAGINAW, INC. (230275)**, 3340 Hospital Road, Zip 48603–9622, Mailing Address: P.O. Box 6280, Zip 48608–6280; tel. 989/790–7700, (Nonreporting) **A**1 5 9 10
Primary Contact: Lisa Lapham, President and Chief Executive Officer
CMO: Daniel Duffy, D.O., Chief Medical Director
CIO: Randall Sanborn, Director Information Technology
CNO: Susan Graham, R.N., Nurse Executive
Web address: www.healthsourcesaginaw.org
**Control:** Other not–for–profit (including NFP Corporation) **Service:** Psychiatric

**Staffed Beds:** 319

✠ **SELECT SPECIALTY HOSPITAL–SAGINAW (232033)**, 1447 North Harrison Street, 8th Floor, Zip 48602–4785; tel. 989/583–4235, (Nonreporting) **A**1 9 10 **S** Select Medical Corporation, Mechanicsburg, PA
Primary Contact: Matthew Cannon, Chief Executive Officer
Web address: www.selectspecialtyhospitals.com/company/locations/saginaw.aspx
**Control:** Corporation, Investor–owned, for–profit **Service:** Long–Term Acute Care hospital

**Staffed Beds:** 32

✠ **ST. MARY'S OF MICHIGAN (230077)**, 800 South Washington Avenue, Zip 48601–2594; tel. 989/907–8000 **A**1 2 3 5 9 10 **F**2 3 11 12 15 17 18 20 22 24 26 28 29 30 31 34 35 40 42 43 44 45 49 50 54 57 58 59 64 66 68 70 74 77 78 79 80 81 82 84 85 86 87 92 93 96 97 100 102 107 108 110 111 114 115 118 119 120 121 123 124 126 129 130 132 146 **P**6 8
**S** Ascension Health, Saint Louis, MO
Primary Contact: Elizabeth Aderholdt, President and Chief Executive Officer
CFO: Nancy Haywood, Chief Financial Officer
CMO: Raghu Sarvepalli, M.D., Vice President of Medical Affairs
CIO: Alex Veletsos, Chief Information Officer
CHR: Paula Coffee, Director Human Resources
CNO: Bernie Jore, Chief Nursing Officer
Web address: www.stmarysofmichigan.org
**Control:** Church–operated, Nongovernment, not–for profit **Service:** General Medical and Surgical

**Staffed Beds:** 236 **Admissions:** 9807 **Census:** 136 **Outpatient Visits:** 206892 **Births:** 0 **Total Expense ($000):** 245374 **Payroll Expense ($000):** 97976 **Personnel:** 1434

## SAINT IGNACE—Mackinac County

★ **MACKINAC STRAITS HEALTH SYSTEM, INC. (231306)**, 1140 North State Street, Zip 49781–1048; tel. 906/643–8585, (Total facility includes 48 beds in nursing home–type unit) **A**9 10 18 **F**15 18 28 29 31 32 40 42 43 53 54 56 59 60 64 65 74 75 77 78 91 93 97 107 110 111 114 119 127 128 130 133 135 144 146 147
Primary Contact: Rodney M. Nelson, Chief Executive Officer
CFO: Jason Anderson, Chief Financial Officer
CMO: Carl Hawkins, M.D., Chief of Staff
CHR: Karen Cheeseman, Executive Vice President
CNO: Wendy Frush, R.N., Nursing Executive
Web address: www.mshosp.org
**Control:** Other not–for–profit (including NFP Corporation) **Service:** General Medical and Surgical

**Staffed Beds:** 63 **Admissions:** 331 **Census:** 49 **Outpatient Visits:** 35038 **Births:** 0 **Total Expense ($000):** 34330 **Payroll Expense ($000):** 12425 **Personnel:** 189

## SAINT JOHNS—Clinton County

✠ **SPARROW CLINTON HOSPITAL (231326)**, 805 South Oakland Street, Zip 48879–2253; tel. 989/227–3400 **A**1 9 10 18 **F**3 8 11 15 18 19 31 32 34 35 40 45 50 53 57 59 64 68 70 75 77 78 79 81 85 93 107 108 110 111 114 119 129 130 131 133 145 146 148 **P**6 **S** Sparrow Health System, Lansing, MI
Primary Contact: Edward Bruun, President and Chief Executive Officer
COO: Kevin A. Price, Vice President and Chief Operating Officer
CFO: Mark Brisboe, VP and Chief Financial Officer
CMO: Christopher Beal, M.D., Chief of Staff
CNO: Beth Ann Daugherty, R.N., Vice President Care Services and Chief Nursing Executive
Web address: www.sparrowclinton.org
**Control:** Other not–for–profit (including NFP Corporation) **Service:** General Medical and Surgical

**Staffed Beds:** 25 **Admissions:** 672 **Census:** 5 **Outpatient Visits:** 57789 **Births:** 0 **Total Expense ($000):** 37617 **Payroll Expense ($000):** 14490 **Personnel:** 209

## SAINT JOSEPH—Berrien County

☐ **LAKELAND MEDICAL CENTER, ST. JOSEPH (230021)**, 1234 Napier Avenue, Zip 49085–2158; tel. 269/983–8300, (Includes LAKELAND HOSPITAL, NILES, 31 North Saint Joseph Avenue, Niles, Zip 49120; tel. 269/683–5510; Debra Johnson, R.N., Chief Administrator), (Nonreporting) **A**1 2 9 10 13 **S** Lakeland Health, Saint Joseph, MI
Primary Contact: Loren Hamel, M.D., President and Chief Executive Officer
CFO: Timothy Calhoun, Vice President Finance and Chief Financial Officer
CMO: Stephen Hempel, M.D., President Medical Staff
CIO: Emily Gallay, Vice President and Chief Information Officer
CHR: Gerard Guinane, Vice President Human Resources and Diversity Management
Web address: www.lakelandhealth.org
**Control:** Other not–for–profit (including NFP Corporation) **Service:** General Medical and Surgical

**Staffed Beds:** 250

**MI**

## SALINE—Washtenaw County

☐ **CENTER FOR FORENSIC PSYCHIATRY (234041)**, 8303 Platt Road,
Zip 48176–9773, Mailing Address: P.O. Box 2060, Ann Arbor, Zip 48106–2060;
tel. 734/429–2531, (Nonreporting) **A**1 10
Primary Contact: Carol E. Holden, M.D., Director
Web address: www.michigan.gov
**Control:** County–Government, nonfederal **Service:** Psychiatric

**Staffed Beds:** 210

## SANDUSKY—Sanilac County

**MCKENZIE HEALTH SYSTEM (231314)**, 120 North Delaware Street,
Zip 48471–1087; tel. 810/648–3770, (Nonreporting) **A**9 10 18
Primary Contact: Steve Barnett, MS, President and Chief Executive Officer
COO: Janet Herbert, R.N., Chief Operating Officer
CFO: Amy Ruedisueli, Vice President of Finance
CMO: Michael Merkler, Chief of Staff
CHR: Carrie Krampits, Director Human Resources
CNO: Patricia Schafsnitz, Director of Nursing Services
Web address: www.mckenziehealth.org
**Control:** Other not–for–profit (including NFP Corporation) **Service:** General
Medical and Surgical

**Staffed Beds:** 25

## SAULT SAINTE MARIE—Chippewa County

★ ◇ **WAR MEMORIAL HOSPITAL (230239)**, 500 Osborn Boulevard,
Zip 49783–1884; tel. 906/635–4460, (Total facility includes 51 beds in nursing
home–type unit) **A**5 9 10 20 21 **F**3 11 12 13 15 18 28 29 30 31 34 35 36 38
40 43 44 45 50 51 53 54 56 57 59 60 61 64 65 66 68 70 74 75 76 77 79
81 82 85 87 92 93 96 97 98 100 101 103 104 107 108 110 111 115 119
127 128 129 130 131 132 133 135 143 144 146 147 148 **P**6
Primary Contact: David B. Jahn, President and Chief Executive Officer
COO: Marla Bunker, Vice President Nursing and Chief Operating Officer
CFO: Kevin Kalchik, Chief Financial Officer
CMO: Paula Rechner, Chief Medical Officer
CIO: Steve Pietrangelo, Director Information Services
CHR: Susan Sliger, Director Human Resources
CNO: Marla Bunker, Vice President of Nursing and Operations
Web address: www.warmemorialhospital.org
**Control:** Other not–for–profit (including NFP Corporation) **Service:** General
Medical and Surgical

**Staffed Beds:** 133 **Admissions:** 3144 **Census:** 85 **Outpatient Visits:** 145418
**Births:** 378 **Total Expense ($000):** 92543 **Payroll Expense ($000):** 39828
**Personnel:** 760

## SHELBY—Oceana County

⊠ **MERCY HEALTH, LAKESHORE CAMPUS (231320)**, 72 South State Street,
Zip 49455–1299; tel. 231/861–2156 **A**1 9 10 18 **F**3 11 15 29 30 34 35 40
50 57 59 68 81 83 84 85 87 89 97 107 111 115 119 127 129 131 132 146
**S** Trinity Health, Livonia, MI
Primary Contact: Jay Bryan, President and Chief Executive Officer
CFO: Mark Gross, Senior Business Director Finance
Web address: www.mercyhealthmuskegon.com
**Control:** Other not–for–profit (including NFP Corporation) **Service:** General
Medical and Surgical

**Staffed Beds:** 24 **Admissions:** 331 **Census:** 3 **Outpatient Visits:** 21896
**Births:** 0 **Total Expense ($000):** 20706 **Payroll Expense ($000):** 10172
**Personnel:** 183

## SHERIDAN—Montcalm County

★ **SHERIDAN COMMUNITY HOSPITAL (231312)**, 301 North Main Street,
Zip 48884–9235, Mailing Address: P.O. Box 279, Zip 48884–0279;
tel. 989/291–3261 **A**5 9 10 18 **F**3 15 18 34 40 45 50 54 57 59 64 65 66 77
79 81 85 93 97 107 115 119 127 129 132 133 146 **P**5
Primary Contact: Randolph K. Flechsig, Administrator
COO: Steve Scott, Chief Operating Officer
CFO: Randolph K. Flechsig, Administrator
CMO: Maria Charlotte Alvarez, M.D., Chief of Staff
CIO: David Bussler, Chief Information Officer
CHR: Sharon Bowers, R.N., Manager of Community, Public and Employee
Relations
CNO: Kim Christensen, Interim Chief Nursing Executive
Web address: www.sheridanhospital.com
**Control:** Other not–for–profit (including NFP Corporation) **Service:** General
Medical and Surgical

**Staffed Beds:** 22 **Admissions:** 246 **Census:** 3 **Outpatient Visits:** 24927
**Births:** 0 **Total Expense ($000):** 14980 **Payroll Expense ($000):** 7418
**Personnel:** 181

## SOUTH HAVEN—Van Buren County

**SOUTH HAVEN COMMUNITY HOSPITAL** See South Haven Health System

⊠ **SOUTH HAVEN HEALTH SYSTEM (230085)**, 955 South Bailey Avenue,
Zip 49090–6743; tel. 269/637–5271 **A**1 9 10 **F**3 11 15 28 29 30 31 34 35
36 40 41 45 46 50 53 54 57 59 62 64 65 68 75 77 78 79 81 82 85 87 89
91 93 96 97 107 108 110 114 115 119 127 129 130 131 132 135 144 146
147 **P**4
Primary Contact: Joanne Urbanski, President and Chief Executive Officer
CFO: Mark Gross, Executive Vice President and Chief Financial Officer
CMO: Allan Caudill, M.D., Chief of Staff
CIO: Dennis Sorenson, Supervisor Information Technology
CHR: Kim Wise, Director Human Resources
CNO: Donna Cassidy, Chief Nursing Executive
Web address: www.sh–hs.org
**Control:** Hospital district or authority, Government, nonfederal **Service:** General
Medical and Surgical

**Staffed Beds:** 82 **Admissions:** 1112 **Census:** 7 **Outpatient Visits:** 127060
**Births:** 312 **Total Expense ($000):** 42831 **Payroll Expense ($000):** 19928
**Personnel:** 312

## SOUTHFIELD—Oakland County

★ ○ **OAKLAND REGIONAL HOSPITAL (230301)**, 22401 Foster Winter Drive,
Zip 48075–3724; tel. 248/423–5100, (Total facility includes 26 beds in nursing
home–type unit) **A**9 10 11 **F**45 79 81 82 85 87 90 93 111 115 128 130
Primary Contact: Amelia Jones, Chief Operating Officer and Acting Chief Executive
Officer
COO: Amelia Jones, Chief Operating Officer
CMO: John Jack Ryan, M.D., Chief Medical Officer
CIO: William Moncrief, ORH IT Client Executive
CHR: Gordon Meyer, Director Human Resources
Web address: www.oaklandregionalhospital.com
**Control:** Corporation, Investor–owned, for–profit **Service:** General Medical and
Surgical

**Staffed Beds:** 71 **Admissions:** 676 **Census:** 26 **Outpatient Visits:** 5215
**Births:** 0 **Total Expense ($000):** 27101 **Payroll Expense ($000):** 6759
**Personnel:** 130

⊞ **PROVIDENCE – PROVIDENCE PARK HOSPITAL, SOUTHFIELD CAMPUS
(230019)**, 16001 West Nine Mile Road, Zip 48075–4818, Mailing Address: P.O.
Box 2043, Zip 48037–2043; tel. 248/424–3000, (Includes PROVIDENCE –
PROVIDENCE PARK HOSPITAL, NOVI CAMPUS, 47601 Grand River Avebue, Novi,
Zip 48374–1233; tel. 248/465–4100; Peter Karadjoff, President) **A**1 2 3 5 9 10
**F**3 5 8 9 11 12 13 15 17 18 20 22 24 26 28 29 30 31 34 35 36 38 39 40
44 45 46 47 48 49 50 51 54 55 56 57 58 59 60 61 63 64 65 66 68 70 72
74 75 76 77 78 79 80 81 82 84 85 86 87 89 90 92 93 97 98 99 100 101
102 103 104 105 107 108 110 111 114 115 116 117 118 119 120 121 123
124 126 129 130 131 132 135 141 143 146 147 148 **S** Ascension Health,
Saint Louis, MO
Primary Contact: Michael Wiemann, M.D., President
CFO: Douglas Winner, Chief Financial Officer
CHR: Sue Gronbach, Director Human Resources
Web address: www.providence–stjohnhealth.org
**Control:** Church–operated, Nongovernment, not–for profit **Service:** General
Medical and Surgical

**Staffed Beds:** 577 **Admissions:** 34245 **Census:** 410 **Outpatient Visits:**
305587 **Births:** 4248 **Total Expense ($000):** 607787 **Payroll Expense
($000):** 234797 **Personnel:** 3658

⊞ **STRAITH HOSPITAL FOR SPECIAL SURGERY (230071)**, 23901 Lahser Road,
Zip 48033–6035; tel. 248/357–3360 **A**1 9 10 **F**29 64 65 81 91 130 141
148 **P**5
Primary Contact: H. Roger Jones, Chief Executive Officer
COO: Jan Rys, Chief Operating Officer
CFO: Bradley Bescoe, Chief Financial Officer
Web address: www.straith.org/
**Control:** Other not–for–profit (including NFP Corporation) **Service:** General
Medical and Surgical

**Staffed Beds:** 24 **Admissions:** 672 **Census:** 15 **Outpatient Visits:** 1238
**Births:** 0 **Total Expense ($000):** 10650 **Payroll Expense ($000):** 4607
**Personnel:** 95

## STANDISH—Arenac County

⊞ **ST. MARY'S OF MICHIGAN STANDISH HOSPITAL (231305)**, 805 West Cedar
Street, Zip 48658–9526; tel. 989/846–4521, (Nonreporting) **A**1 5 9 10 18
**S** Ascension Health, Saint Louis, MO
Primary Contact: Elizabeth Aderholdt, President and Chief Executive Officer
CFO: Tony Doud, Controller
CMO: Jaya Sankaran, M.D., Chief of Staff
CIO: Tammy Copes, Director Information Systems
CHR: Renee Reetz, Director Human Resources
Web address: www.stmarysofmichigan.org/standish
**Control:** Other not–for–profit (including NFP Corporation) **Service:** General
Medical and Surgical

**Staffed Beds:** 64

## STURGIS—St. Joseph County

★ ◇ **STURGIS HOSPITAL (230096)**, 916 Myrtle Street, Zip 49091–2326; tel. 269/651–7824 **A**9 10 21 **F**3 11 13 15 28 29 30 31 34 35 40 45 46 49 50 57 59 62 63 64 65 68 70 75 76 77 78 79 81 82 85 87 89 93 97 102 107 108 110 115 118 119 127 129 130 132 144 146 147 148 **P**6 **S** QHR, Brentwood, TN
Primary Contact: Robert J. LaBarge, President and Chief Executive Officer
CFO: Robert J. Morin, Vice President Finance and Chief Financial Officer
CMO: Bharat Vakharia, M.D., President Medical Staff
CIO: Rita Denison, Director of Information Systems
CHR: Mary Kay Schultz, Director Human Resources
CNO: Charlotte J. Pavilanis, R.N., Vice President of Clinical Services and Chief Nursing Officer
Web address: www.sturgishospital.com
**Control:** Other not–for–profit (including NFP Corporation) **Service:** General Medical and Surgical

**Staffed Beds:** 49 **Admissions:** 1512 **Census:** 12 **Outpatient Visits:** 89902 **Births:** 400 **Total Expense ($000):** 45787 **Payroll Expense ($000):** 20556 **Personnel:** 272

## TAWAS CITY—Iosco County

⊞ **ST. JOSEPH HEALTH SYSTEM (230100)**, 200 Hemlock Street, Zip 48763–9237, Mailing Address: P.O. Box 659, Zip 48764–0659; tel. 989/362–3411, (Nonreporting) **A**1 9 10 20 **S** Ascension Health, Saint Louis, MO
Primary Contact: Ann M. Balfour, R.N., President
CFO: Linda Stancill, Vice President and Chief Financial Officer
CHR: Nancy Bodenner, Director Human Resources
Web address: www.sjhsys.org
**Control:** Other not–for–profit (including NFP Corporation) **Service:** General Medical and Surgical

**Staffed Beds:** 20

## TAYLOR—Wayne County

⊞ **BEAUMONT HOSPITAL – TAYLOR (230270)**, 10000 Telegraph Road, Zip 48180–3330; tel. 313/295–5000 **A**1 3 5 9 10 **F**3 11 15 29 30 34 35 37 38 39 40 44 46 49 50 56 57 59 60 61 64 65 68 70 74 75 78 79 81 82 84 85 86 87 90 92 93 96 98 100 101 102 103 105 107 108 111 114 118 119 130 131 132 135 146 148 **P**8 **S** Beaumont Health, Royal Oak, MI
Primary Contact: Lee Ann Odom, Division President
CFO: Mark Deming, Controller
CMO: Vijay Khanna, M.D., Chief of Staff
CIO: Paula Smith, Chief Information Officer
CHR: Sherry Huffman, Administrator Human Resources
Web address: www.oakwood.org
**Control:** Other not–for–profit (including NFP Corporation) **Service:** General Medical and Surgical

**Staffed Beds:** 135 **Admissions:** 8059 **Census:** 135 **Outpatient Visits:** 68095 **Births:** 0 **Total Expense ($000):** 134618 **Payroll Expense ($000):** 54706 **Personnel:** 947

## TECUMSEH—Lenawee County

★ **PROMEDICA HERRICK HOSPITAL (231334)**, 500 East Pottawatamie Street, Zip 49286–2018; tel. 517/424–3000, (Total facility includes 25 beds in nursing home–type unit) **A**9 10 18 **F**3 11 15 29 30 40 43 45 46 53 64 68 70 74 75 77 79 81 85 91 92 93 98 100 101 102 104 107 108 110 114 119 124 128 129 130 132 135 145 146 147 **P**6 8 **S** ProMedica Health System, Toledo, OH
Primary Contact: Julie Yaroch, D.O., President
CFO: Bernie Nawrocki, Administrative Director Finance
CIO: Stephanie Sonnenberg, Director Information Technology
CHR: Cathy J. Davis, Director Human Resources
CNO: Kathryn M. Greenlee, R.N., Vice President, Clinical Services/CNO
Web address: www.promedica.org
**Control:** Other not–for–profit (including NFP Corporation) **Service:** General Medical and Surgical

**Staffed Beds:** 60 **Admissions:** 1423 **Census:** 33 **Outpatient Visits:** 41963 **Births:** 0 **Total Expense ($000):** 34348 **Payroll Expense ($000):** 11084 **Personnel:** 174

## THREE RIVERS—St. Joseph County

★ ○ △ **THREE RIVERS HEALTH (230015)**, 701 South Health Parkway, Zip 49093–8352; tel. 269/278–1145, (Nonreporting) **A**7 9 10 11 **S** QHR, Brentwood, TN
Primary Contact: William B. Russell, Chief Executive Officer
COO: Laurie Herbert, Vice President Operations
CFO: Steve Andrews, Chief Financial Officer
CIO: Dave Parks, Chief Information Officer
Web address: www.threerivershealth.org
**Control:** Hospital district or authority, Government, nonfederal **Service:** General Medical and Surgical

**Staffed Beds:** 35

## TRAVERSE CITY—Grand Traverse County

⊞ **MUNSON MEDICAL CENTER (230097)**, 1105 Sixth Street, Zip 49684–2386; tel. 231/935–5000 **A**1 2 3 5 9 10 12 13 **F**3 4 5 6 11 12 13 15 17 18 20 22 24 26 28 29 30 31 32 34 35 36 38 39 40 43 44 45 46 47 48 49 50 53 54 55 56 57 58 59 60 61 62 63 64 65 68 70 71 72 74 75 76 77 78 79 81 82 84 85 86 87 89 90 92 93 94 96 97 98 100 101 102 103 104 105 107 108 110 111 115 116 117 118 119 120 121 123 124 126 129 130 131 132 134 135 141 142 143 144 145 146 147 148 **P**6 **S** Munson Healthcare, Traverse City, MI
Primary Contact: Alfred E. Pilong, Jr., President
COO: Derk Pronger, Chief Operating Officer
CFO: Mark A. Helper, Vice President, Chief Financial Officer
CMO: David S. McGreaham, M.D., Vice President Medical Affairs and Chief Medical Officer
CIO: Christopher J. Podges, Chief Information Officer and Vice President Outpatient and Retail Services
CHR: Sue Peters, Vice President Human Resources
CNO: James Fischer, R.N., Vice President Patient Care Services/Chief Nursing Officer
Web address: www.munsonhealthcare.org
**Control:** Other not–for–profit (including NFP Corporation) **Service:** General Medical and Surgical

**Staffed Beds:** 391 **Admissions:** 20815 **Census:** 273 **Outpatient Visits:** 501328 **Births:** 1950 **Total Expense ($000):** 490702 **Payroll Expense ($000):** 193318 **Personnel:** 2881

## TRENTON—Wayne County

⊞ **BEAUMONT HOSPITAL – TRENTON (230176)**, 5450 Fort Street, Zip 48183–4625; tel. 734/671–3800 **A**1 3 9 10 12 13 **F**3 8 11 13 15 17 18 20 22 26 28 29 30 31 34 35 38 39 40 43 44 46 47 49 50 56 57 59 60 61 64 65 68 70 74 75 76 78 79 80 81 82 85 86 87 92 93 96 100 102 107 108 110 111 115 118 119 130 131 132 135 146 147 148 **P**8 **S** Beaumont Health, Royal Oak, MI
Primary Contact: Edith M. Hughes, R.N., President
COO: David J. Campbell, Executive Vice President Operations Systems Strategy and Growth
CFO: Paul Lauzau, Controller
CMO: Iqbal Nasir, M.D., Chief of Staff
CIO: Paula Smith, Vice President Information Services and Chief Information Officer
CHR: Juliet Hafford, Director Human Resources
Web address: www.oakwood.org
**Control:** Other not–for–profit (including NFP Corporation) **Service:** General Medical and Surgical

**Staffed Beds:** 173 **Admissions:** 9218 **Census:** 98 **Outpatient Visits:** 67373 **Births:** 614 **Total Expense ($000):** 144337 **Payroll Expense ($000):** 51542 **Personnel:** 688

## TROY—Oakland County

⊞ **BEAUMONT HOSPITAL – TROY (230269)**, 44201 Dequindre Road, Zip 48085–1117; tel. 248/964–5000 **A**1 2 3 5 9 10 13 **F**3 8 11 12 13 14 15 17 18 20 22 24 26 27 28 29 30 31 32 34 35 36 39 40 41 44 45 46 47 48 49 50 51 53 54 55 56 57 58 59 60 61 64 65 66 68 70 71 72 74 75 76 77 78 79 80 81 82 84 85 86 87 89 90 91 92 93 94 96 97 100 102 103 107 108 109 110 111 114 115 117 118 119 120 121 123 124 126 129 130 131 132 135 141 142 143 145 146 147 148 **P**6 **S** Beaumont Health, Royal Oak, MI
Primary Contact: Nancy Susick, MSN, President
CFO: Mark Leonard, Vice President Finance
CMO: Roger Howard, M.D., Senior Vice President and Medical Director
CIO: Subra Sripada, Senior Vice President and Chief Information Officer
CHR: Lisa Ouelette, Director Human Resources
Web address: www.beaumont.edu/troy–hospital–campus
**Control:** Other not–for–profit (including NFP Corporation) **Service:** General Medical and Surgical

**Staffed Beds:** 458 **Admissions:** 33759 **Census:** 378 **Outpatient Visits:** 914122 **Births:** 3626 **Total Expense ($000):** 507382 **Payroll Expense ($000):** 161273 **Personnel:** 3260

---

**Hospital, Medicare Provider Number, Address, Telephone, Approval, Facility, and Physician Codes, Health Care System**

★ American Hospital Association (AHA) membership    ○ Healthcare Facilities Accreditation Program    ⇑ Center for Improvement in Healthcare Quality Accreditation
□ The Joint Commission accreditation    ◇ DNV Healthcare Inc. accreditation    △ Commission on Accreditation of Rehabilitation Facilities (CARF) accreditation

**MI**

### VICKSBURG—Kalamazoo County

**BRONSON VICKSBURG HOSPITAL** See Bronson Methodist Hospital, Kalamazoo

### WARREN—Macomb County

☐ **BEHAVIORAL CENTER OF MICHIGAN (234042)**, 4050 East 12 Mile Road, Zip 48092–2534; tel. 586/261–2266, (Nonreporting) **A**1 9 10
Primary Contact: Ryan Gunabalan, Chief Executive Officer
COO: Efren Lusterio, Director of Nursing
CFO: Mark Corey, Chief Financial Officer
CMO: Eleanor Medina, M.D., Chief Medical Officer
CIO: Kashmira Khade, Coordinator Non–Clinical Services
CHR: Erin R. Youngblood, Chief Human Resources Officer
Web address: www.behavioralcenter.com
**Control:** Corporation, Investor–owned, for–profit **Service:** Psychiatric

Staffed Beds: 42

☐ **SOUTHEAST MICHIGAN SURGICAL HOSPITAL (230264)**, 21230 Dequindre, Zip 48091–2287; tel. 586/427–1000, (Nonreporting) **A**1 9 10 **S** National Surgical Healthcare, Chicago, IL
Primary Contact: Yvonne Kughn, Chief Executive Officer
CMO: Benjamin Paolucci, D.O., Chief of Staff
CHR: Dawn Meiers, Coordinator Medical Staff and Personnel Services
Web address: www.nshinc.com
**Control:** Corporation, Investor–owned, for–profit **Service:** Surgical

Staffed Beds: 13

☒ **ST. JOHN MACOMB–OAKLAND HOSPITAL (230195)**, 11800 East 12 Mile Road, Zip 48093–3472; tel. 586/573–5000, (Includes ST. JOHN MACOMB–OAKLAND HOSPITAL, MADISON HEIGHTS CAMPUS, 27351 Dequindre, Madison Heights, Zip 48071–3487; tel. 248/967–7000; ST. JOHN MACOMB–OAKLAND HOSPITAL, WARREN CAMPUS, 11800 East Twelve Mile Road, tel. 586/573–5000) **A**1 2 3 9 10 12 13 **F**3 11 12 13 15 17 18 20 22 24 26 28 29 30 31 34 35 36 38 39 40 44 45 46 47 48 49 50 51 56 57 58 59 60 61 63 64 65 68 70 74 75 76 77 78 79 80 81 82 84 85 86 87 90 91 92 93 95 96 97 98 100 101 102 103 105 107 108 110 111 114 115 116 117 118 119 121 123 126 129 130 131 132 135 141 143 146 147 148 **P**3 6 8 **S** Ascension Health, Saint Louis, MO
Primary Contact: Terry Hamilton, President
CFO: Tomasine Marx, Chief Financial Officer
CMO: Gary L. Berg, D.O., Chief Medical Officer
CIO: Ralph Tenney, Chief Information Officer
CHR: Joanne E. Tuscany, Director Worklife Services
CNO: Maryann Barnes, MS, Chief Nursing Officer
Web address: www.stjohnprovidence.org/macomb–oakland/
**Control:** Church–operated, Nongovernment, not–for profit **Service:** General Medical and Surgical

Staffed Beds: 522 Admissions: 26234 Census: 368 Outpatient Visits: 432290 Births: 1072 Total Expense ($000): 368484 Payroll Expense ($000): 150904 Personnel: 2174

### WATERVLIET—Berrien County

**COMMUNITY HOSPITAL** See Lakeland Hospital, Watervliet

☐ △ **LAKELAND HOSPITAL, WATERVLIET (230078)**, 400 Medical Park Drive, Zip 49098–9225; tel. 269/463–3111 **A**1 7 9 10 **F**3 11 29 30 34 35 38 40 45 50 54 57 59 64 68 75 77 79 81 85 86 87 90 93 97 107 119 127 130 131 132 135 144 146 **S** Lakeland Health, Saint Joseph, MI
Primary Contact: Ray Cruse, Chief Executive Officer
CFO: Timothy Calhoun, Vice President Finance, Chief Financial Officer
CIO: Norma Tirado, Vice President, Human Resources and Health Information Technology
CHR: Norma Tirado, Vice President, Human Resources and Health Information Technology
CNO: Connie Harmon, Director of Nursing
**Control:** Other not–for–profit (including NFP Corporation) **Service:** General Medical and Surgical

Staffed Beds: 38 Admissions: 844 Census: 11 Outpatient Visits: 72867 Births: 0 Total Expense ($000): 33780 Payroll Expense ($000): 15027 Personnel: 254

### WAYNE—Wayne County

☒ **BEAUMONT HOSPITAL – WAYNE (230142)**, 33155 Annapolis Street, Zip 48184–2405; tel. 734/467–4000 **A**1 3 9 10 **F**3 11 13 15 18 20 22 26 28 29 30 31 34 35 38 40 43 44 47 49 50 57 59 60 61 64 65 68 70 74 75 76 78 79 80 81 82 84 85 86 87 89 91 92 93 96 100 102 107 108 111 114 115 118 119 130 131 132 135 146 147 148 **P**8 **S** Beaumont Health, Royal Oak, MI
Primary Contact: Eric W. Widner, Division President
CFO: Jay Bonnell, Controller
CMO: Ashok Jain, M.D., Chief of Staff
CIO: Paula Smith, Senior Vice President Chief Information Officer
CHR: Robert L. James, Director Human Resources
CNO: Diane L. Hartley, R.N., Director of Patient Care Services
Web address: www.oakwood.org
**Control:** Other not–for–profit (including NFP Corporation) **Service:** General Medical and Surgical

Staffed Beds: 198 Admissions: 8459 Census: 87 Outpatient Visits: 90259 Births: 1060 Total Expense ($000): 143596 Payroll Expense ($000): 61252 Personnel: 864

### WEST BLOOMFIELD—Oakland County

★ ◇ **HENRY FORD WEST BLOOMFIELD HOSPITAL (230302)**, 6777 West Maple Road, Zip 48322–3013; tel. 248/661–4100 **A**2 9 10 21 **F**3 4 5 6 11 12 13 15 18 20 22 26 28 29 30 31 32 34 35 36 38 39 40 41 44 45 46 49 50 51 53 55 56 57 58 59 60 61 62 63 64 65 68 70 73 74 75 76 77 78 79 80 81 82 84 85 86 87 89 91 92 93 97 98 100 102 103 107 108 110 111 114 115 116 117 118 119 120 121 123 124 126 130 131 132 135 146 147 148 **P**6 **S** Henry Ford Health System, Detroit, MI
Primary Contact: Lynn M. Torossian, President and Chief Executive Officer
CFO: Terry Goodbalian, Regional Chief Financial Officer
Web address: www.henryford.com
**Control:** Other not–for–profit (including NFP Corporation) **Service:** General Medical and Surgical

Staffed Beds: 191 Admissions: 13555 Census: 145 Outpatient Visits: 294283 Births: 2004 Total Expense ($000): 244673 Payroll Expense ($000): 93785 Personnel: 1834

### WEST BRANCH—Ogemaw County

★ ◯ **WEST BRANCH REGIONAL MEDICAL CENTER (230095)**, 2463 South M–30, Zip 48661–1199; tel. 989/345–3660 **A**5 9 10 11 20 **F**3 11 15 17 20 28 29 30 34 35 40 50 57 59 63 64 75 77 79 81 84 93 107 111 114 115 117 119 130 146 148 **P**6
Primary Contact: Robert McGrail, Interim Chief Executive Officer
CFO: Robert McGrail, Chief Financial Officer
CMO: Patrick Morse, M.D., President Medical Staff
CHR: Kent Allen, Director Human Resources
CNO: Lanette Lumbardo, MS, Chief Nursing Officer
Web address: www.wbrmc.com
**Control:** City–Government, nonfederal **Service:** General Medical and Surgical

Staffed Beds: 88 Admissions: 2103 Census: 23 Outpatient Visits: 67042 Births: 0 Total Expense ($000): 39712 Payroll Expense ($000): 13071 Personnel: 299

### WESTLAND—Wayne County

☐ **WALTER P. REUTHER PSYCHIATRIC HOSPITAL (234035)**, 30901 Palmer Road, Zip 48186–5389; tel. 734/367–8400, (Nonreporting) **A**1 9 10
Primary Contact: Richard T. Young, FACHE, Director
CMO: H. Bandla, M.D., Chief Clinical Affairs
CHR: Deborah Moore, Director Human Resources
CNO: E. McDade, R.N.
Web address: www.mhweb.org/wayne/reuther.htm
**Control:** State–Government, nonfederal **Service:** Psychiatric

Staffed Beds: 239

### WYANDOTTE—Wayne County

★ △ ◇ **HENRY FORD WYANDOTTE HOSPITAL (230146)**, 2333 Biddle Avenue, Zip 48192–4668; tel. 734/246–6000 **A**3 7 9 10 12 13 21 **F**3 4 5 6 8 11 12 13 15 17 18 20 22 26 28 29 30 31 32 34 35 36 38 40 41 42 43 44 45 46 47 49 50 51 54 56 57 58 59 60 61 62 63 64 65 66 68 70 73 74 75 76 77 78 79 80 81 82 84 85 86 87 89 90 92 93 94 96 97 98 100 101 102 103 107 108 110 111 114 115 116 117 118 119 126 129 130 131 132 135 144 146 147 148 **P**6 **S** Henry Ford Health System, Detroit, MI
Primary Contact: Denise Brooks–Williams, President and Chief Executive Officer
CFO: Terry Goodbalian, Vice President, Finance and Chief Financial Officer
CMO: Dennis R. Lemanski, D.O., Senior Vice President Medical Affairs and Medical Education/CMO
CIO: Mary Alice Annecharico, Senior VP and CIO, Henry Ford Health System
CNO: Josephine Sclafani Wahl, R.N., VP, Patient Care Services & CNO
Web address: www.henryfordhealth.org
**Control:** Other not–for–profit (including NFP Corporation) **Service:** General Medical and Surgical

Staffed Beds: 353 Admissions: 15342 Census: 229 Outpatient Visits: 390105 Births: 1591 Total Expense ($000): 270256 Payroll Expense ($000): 116057 Personnel: 2013

☒ **SELECT SPECIALTY HOSPITAL–DOWNRIVER (232031)**, 2333 Biddle Avenue, 8th Floor, Zip 48192–4668; tel. 734/246–5500, (Nonreporting) **A**1 9 10 **S** Select Medical Corporation, Mechanicsburg, PA
Primary Contact: Douglas R. Dascenzo, MSN, R.N., Chief Executive Officer
CMO: Roderick Boyer, M.D., Medical Director
CHR: Barb Wierzbicki, Manager Human Resources
Web address: www.downriver.selectspecialtyhospitals.com/
**Control:** Corporation, Investor–owned, for–profit **Service:** Long–Term Acute Care hospital

Staffed Beds: 35

## WYOMING—Kent County

★ ○ **METRO HEALTH HOSPITAL (230236)**, 5900 Byron Center Avenue S.W.,
Zip 49519–9606, Mailing Address: P.O. Box 916, Zip 49509–0916;
tel. 616/252–7200 **A**3 5 9 10 11 12 13 **F**3 12 13 15 18 20 22 26 29 30 31
34 35 40 44 45 48 49 50 54 57 58 59 64 65 66 70 71 74 75 76 77 78 79
80 81 82 85 86 87 92 94 97 107 108 110 111 114 115 119 126 129 130
131 132 135 146 147 148 **P**8
Primary Contact: Michael D. Faas, President and Chief Executive Officer
CFO: Kris Kurtz, Controller
CIO: William Lewkowski, Executive Vice President Information Services and Chief
Information Officer
Web address: www.metrohealth.net
**Control:** Other not–for–profit (including NFP Corporation) **Service:** General
Medical and Surgical

**Staffed Beds:** 208 **Admissions:** 9299 **Census:** 129 **Outpatient Visits:**
405977 **Births:** 1928 **Total Expense ($000):** 276922 **Payroll Expense
($000):** 95282 **Personnel:** 2011

## YPSILANTI—Washtenaw County

☐ **FOREST HEALTH MEDICAL CENTER (230144)**, 135 South Prospect Street,
Zip 48198–7914; tel. 734/547–4700 **A**1 9 10 **F**12 30 46 64 74 75 79 81 82
85 111 119 130 132
Primary Contact: Trevor J. Dyksterhouse, President
COO: Andrea Walrath, Chief Operating Officer
CFO: David Althoen, Director Financial Planning and Analysis
CMO: Jason Adams, M.D., Medical Staff President
CIO: Andrea Walrath, Chief Operating Officer
CHR: Amy Mohr, Coordinator Human Resources
Web address: www.fhmc–mi.com
**Control:** Corporation, Investor–owned, for–profit **Service:** General Medical and
Surgical

**Staffed Beds:** 24 **Admissions:** 919 **Census:** 5 **Outpatient Visits:** 9230
**Births:** 0 **Personnel:** 51

☒ **SELECT SPECIALTY HOSPITAL–ANN ARBOR (232024)**, 5301 East Huron
River Drive, 5th Floor, Zip 48197–1051; tel. 734/712–0111, (Nonreporting) **A**1 9
10 **S** Select Medical Corporation, Mechanicsburg, PA
Primary Contact: John F. O'Malley, FACHE, Chief Executive Officer
CMO: Hamid Halimi, M.D., Medical Director
CHR: Leah Warshaw, Coordinator Human Resources
CNO: Tim Varney, R.N., Chief Nursing Officer
Web address: www.selectspecialtyhospitals.com/company/locations/annarbor.
aspx
**Control:** Corporation, Investor–owned, for–profit **Service:** Long–Term Acute Care
hospital

**Staffed Beds:** 36

★ **ST. JOSEPH MERCY ANN ARBOR (230156)**, 5301 Mcauley Drive,
Zip 48197–1051, Mailing Address: P.O. Box 995, Ann Arbor, Zip 48106–0995;
tel. 734/712–3456 **A**2 3 5 8 10 **F**3 4 5 6 8 9 11 12 13 15 17 18 19 20 22 24
26 28 29 30 31 32 34 35 36 37 38 40 41 42 43 44 45 46 50 51 53 54 56
57 58 59 61 62 63 64 65 66 67 68 70 71 72 73 74 75 76 77 78 79 80 81
82 83 84 85 86 87 89 90 91 92 93 94 97 98 99 100 101 102 103 104 105
107 108 109 110 111 114 115 117 118 119 120 121 123 124 125 126 128
129 130 131 132 134 135 141 143 144 145 146 147 **P**1 **S** Trinity Health,
Livonia, MI
Primary Contact: Robert F. Casalou, President and Chief Executive Officer
COO: Robin Damschroder, Chief Operating Officer
CFO: Kathy O'Connor, Vice President Finance
CIO: Frank Rademacher, Senior Director Information Systems
CNO: Joyce Young, Ph.D., Vice President, Patient Services and Chief Nursing
Officer
Web address: www.sjmercyhealth.org
**Control:** Church–operated, Nongovernment, not–for profit **Service:** General
Medical and Surgical

**Staffed Beds:** 481 **Admissions:** 31300 **Census:** 381 **Outpatient Visits:**
1114431 **Births:** 3483 **Total Expense ($000):** 718045 **Payroll Expense
($000):** 262679 **Personnel:** 5427

## ZEELAND—Ottawa County

☒ **SPECTRUM HEALTH ZEELAND COMMUNITY HOSPITAL (230003)**, 8333
Felch Street, Zip 49464–2608; tel. 616/772–4644 **A**1 9 10 **F**3 12 13 15 18 29
32 34 35 39 40 45 50 56 57 59 64 65 68 69 70 74 75 76 78 79 81 85 87
89 91 92 93 97 107 108 110 111 115 119 129 130 132 135 144 146
**S** Spectrum Health, Grand Rapids, MI
Primary Contact: Ron Lewis, President
CFO: Ryan J. Powers, Vice President Finance
CMO: Ruel R. Lirio, M.D., Clinical Physician Advisor
CIO: Imran Syed, Manager Technology Information Services
CHR: Jennifer F. Becksvoort, Senior Human Resource Business Partner
CNO: Jane Czerew, Vice President Clinical Services and Quality
Web address: www.spectrumhealth.org/zeeland
**Control:** Other not–for–profit (including NFP Corporation) **Service:** General
Medical and Surgical

**Staffed Beds:** 50 **Admissions:** 2261 **Census:** 17 **Outpatient Visits:** 87025
**Births:** 473 **Total Expense ($000):** 43374 **Payroll Expense ($000):** 15093
**Personnel:** 308

**ZEELAND COMMUNITY HOSPITAL** See Spectrum Health Zeeland Community
Hospital

# MINNESOTA

### ADA—Norman County

**BRIDGES MEDICAL CENTER** See Essentia Health Ada

★ **ESSENTIA HEALTH ADA (241313)**, 201 9th Street West, Zip 56510–1279;
tel. 218/784–5000, (Nonreporting) **A**9 10 18 **S** Essentia Health, Duluth, MN
Primary Contact: Ryan Hill, Chief Executive Officer
CMO: Jeff Peterson, M.D., Chief of Staff
CHR: Shayla Hennenberg, Director Human Resources
Web address: www.essentiahealth.org
**Control:** Other not–for–profit (including NFP Corporation) **Service:** General
Medical and Surgical

| Staffed Beds: 14 |
|---|

### AITKIN—Crow Wing County

✉ **RIVERWOOD HEALTHCARE CENTER (241305)**, 200 Bunker Hill Drive,
Zip 56431–1865; tel. 218/927–2121 **A**1 2 9 10 18 **F**3 8 11 13 15 28 29 31
32 34 35 40 43 45 54 56 57 59 64 65 70 75 76 77 78 79 81 82 86 87 93
97 104 107 110 111 114 119 127 129 130 131 132 133 135 144 145 146
147 148 **P**6
Primary Contact: Chad D. Cooper, Chief Executive Officer
CMO: Mark Heggem, M.D., Chief Medical Officer
CIO: Daryl Kallevig, Chief Information Officer
CHR: Cindi Hills, Director Human Resources
CNO: Kristine Layne, R.N., Chief Nursing Officer
Web address: www.riverwoodhealthcare.org
**Control:** Other not–for–profit (including NFP Corporation) **Service:** General
Medical and Surgical

| Staffed Beds: 25 Admissions: 1069 Census: 11 Outpatient Visits: 71321 |
|---|
| Births: 54 Total Expense ($000): 53021 Payroll Expense ($000): 20460 |
| Personnel: 322 |

### ALBANY—Stearns County

★ **CHI ALBANY AREA HEALTH (241331)**, 300 Third Avenue, Zip 56307–9363;
tel. 320/845–2121 **A**9 10 18 **F**29 30 34 35 40 45 50 59 64 65 77 79 81 87
93 107 114 119 127 128 130 132 133 135 146 **P**6 **S** Catholic Health
Initiatives, Englewood, CO
Primary Contact: Tressa Schmidt, Administrator
CFO: Steve Smith, Chief Financial Officer
CMO: Aaron Gersch, M.D., Chief of Staff
CHR: Bernie Cekalla, Manager Human Resources
CNO: Diane Roerick, Interim Chief Nursing Executive
Web address: www.albanyareahospital.com
**Control:** Church–operated, Nongovernment, not–for profit **Service:** General
Medical and Surgical

| Staffed Beds: 17 Admissions: 224 Census: 2 Outpatient Visits: 6897 |
|---|
| Births: 18 Total Expense ($000): 8837 Payroll Expense ($000): 2655 |
| Personnel: 56 |

### ALBERT LEA—Freeborn County

☐ **MAYO CLINIC HEALTH SYSTEM IN ALBERT LEA (240043)**, 404 West
Fountain Street, Zip 56007–2473; tel. 507/373–2384, (Nonreporting) **A**1 3 5 9
10 **S** Mayo Clinic, Rochester, MN
Primary Contact: Mark Ciota, M.D., Chief Executive Officer
CFO: Sheri Dankert, Chief Financial Officer
CMO: John Grzybowski, M.D., Medical Director
CHR: Monica Fleegel, Director Human Resources
CNO: Lori Routh, R.N., Nurse Administrator
Web address: www.almedcenter.org
**Control:** Other not–for–profit (including NFP Corporation) **Service:** General
Medical and Surgical

| Staffed Beds: 129 |
|---|

### ALEXANDRIA—Sherburne County

☐ **COMMUNITY BEHAVIORAL HEALTH HOSPITAL – ALEXANDRIA (244012)**,
1610 8th Avenue East, Zip 56308–2472; tel. 320/335–6201, (Nonreporting) **A**1
10 **S** Minnesota Department of Human Services, Saint Paul, MN
Primary Contact: Jennifer Westrum, Administrator
CFO: Shirley Jacobson, Chief Financial Officer
Web address: www.health.state.mn.us
**Control:** State–Government, nonfederal **Service:** Psychiatric

| Staffed Beds: 16 |
|---|

★ ○ **DOUGLAS COUNTY HOSPITAL (240030)**, 111 17th Avenue East,
Zip 56308–3798; tel. 320/762–1511 **A**2 9 10 11 **F**3 8 11 13 15 28 29 30 31
32 34 35 36 40 43 45 50 57 61 64 65 68 69 70 76 77 78 79 81 82 85 86
87 89 91 93 97 107 108 111 115 117 118 119 129 130 131 132 135 144
146 **P**6
Primary Contact: Carl P. Vaagenes, Chief Executive Officer
CFO: Nate Meyer, Director Finance
CHR: Shelly Gompf, Director Human Resources
Web address: www.dchospital.com
**Control:** County–Government, nonfederal **Service:** General Medical and Surgical

| Staffed Beds: 99 Admissions: 3126 Census: 35 Outpatient Visits: 62836 |
|---|
| Births: 626 Personnel: 621 |

### ANNANDALE—Wright County

☐ **COMMUNITY BEHAVIORAL HEALTH HOSPITAL – ANNANDALE (244011)**,
400 Annandale Boulevard, Zip 55302–3141; tel. 651/259–3850, (Nonreporting)
**A**1 10 **S** Minnesota Department of Human Services, Saint Paul, MN
Primary Contact: Pamela R. Bajari, R.N., Interim Administrator
CMO: Shabeer A. Ahmed, M.D., Clinical Director
CNO: Lennetta M. Reynolds, Administrative Supervisor
Web address: www.health.state.mn.us
**Control:** State–Government, nonfederal **Service:** Psychiatric

| Staffed Beds: 16 |
|---|

### ANOKA—Anoka County

☐ **ANOKA–METROPOLITAN REGIONAL TREATMENT CENTER (244002)**, 3301
Seventh Avenue, Zip 55303–4516; tel. 651/431–5000, (Nonreporting) **A**1 10
**S** Minnesota Department of Human Services, Saint Paul, MN
Primary Contact: Tina Sneen, Administrator
Web address: www.health.state.mn.us
**Control:** State–Government, nonfederal **Service:** Psychiatric

| Staffed Beds: 200 |
|---|

### APPLETON—Swift County

★ **APPLETON AREA HEALTH SERVICES (241341)**, 30 South Behl Street,
Zip 56208–1699; tel. 320/289–2422, (Nonreporting) **A**9 10 18
Primary Contact: Jeffrey A. Cook, Chief Executive Officer
CFO: Anne Kells, Interim Chief Financial Officer
Web address: www.appletonareahealth.com
**Control:** City–Government, nonfederal **Service:** General Medical and Surgical

| Staffed Beds: 68 |
|---|

### ARLINGTON—Sibley County

★ ◇ **RIDGEVIEW SIBLEY MEDICAL CENTER (241311)**, 601 West Chandler
Street, Zip 55307–2127; tel. 507/964–2271 **A**9 10 18 21 **F**3 8 11 15 18 28
29 31 34 35 40 41 43 44 45 50 57 59 62 64 65 68 77 78 79 81 89 93 97
107 114 115 118 119 127 128 130 133 144 146 **S** Ridgeview Medical Center,
Waconia, MN
Primary Contact: Todd Sandberg, Chief Executive Officer and Administrator
CFO: Darla Anderson, Chief Financial Officer
CMO: Ehtaisham Mohammed, M.D., Chief Medical Officer
CIO: Chris Bulau, Manager Information Technology
CHR: Sara Christiansen, Interim Director Human Resources
CNO: Sandy Domeier, Director Patient Care Services
Web address: www.sibleymedical.org
**Control:** Other not–for–profit (including NFP Corporation) **Service:** General
Medical and Surgical

| Staffed Beds: 16 Admissions: 182 Census: 3 Outpatient Visits: 9686 |
|---|
| Births: 0 Total Expense ($000): 11961 Payroll Expense ($000): 6114 |
| Personnel: 110 |

## AURORA—St. Louis County

★ **ESSENTIA HEALTH NORTHERN PINES MEDICAL CENTER (241340)**, 5211 Highway 110, Zip 55705–1599; tel. 218/229–2211, (Total facility includes 50 beds in nursing home–type unit) **A**9 10 18 **F**28 29 34 38 40 50 56 59 65 75 77 79 81 82 87 91 93 97 99 100 101 102 103 104 107 128 130 133 **P**6 **S** Essentia Health, Duluth, MN
Primary Contact: Laura Ackman, Chief Operating Officer and Administrator
CFO: Kevin Boren, Chief Financial Officer
CMO: Michelle Oman, D.O., Chief Medical Officer
CHR: Kim Carlson, Director Human Resources
CNO: Cindy Loe, R.N., Director of Nursing
Web address: www.essentiahealth.org/NorthernPines/FindaClinic/Essentia–HealthNorthern–Pines–36.aspx
**Control:** Other not–for–profit (including NFP Corporation) **Service:** General Medical and Surgical

**Staffed Beds:** 58 **Admissions:** 162 **Census:** 50 **Outpatient Visits:** 18929 **Births:** 0 **Total Expense ($000):** 15477 **Payroll Expense ($000):** 7540 **Personnel:** 131

**WHITE COMMUNITY HOSPITAL** See Essentia Health Northern Pines Medical Center

## AUSTIN—Mower County

**MAYO CLINIC HEALTH SYSTEM–ALBERT LEA AND AUSTIN (240117)**, 1000 First Drive N.W., Zip 55912–2904; tel. 507/433–7351, (Nonreporting) **A**3 5 9 **S** Mayo Clinic, Rochester, MN
Primary Contact: Mark Ciota, M.D., Chief Executive Officer
CFO: Sheri Dankert, Vice President Finance
CMO: Cynthia Dube, M.D., Medical Director
CIO: Tammy Kritzer, Vice President Clinic Operations
CHR: Rodney Nording, Vice President Organizational Support
CNO: Lori Routh, R.N., Nurse Administrator
Web address: www.austinmedicalcenter.org
**Control:** Other not–for–profit (including NFP Corporation) **Service:** General Medical and Surgical

**Staffed Beds:** 82

## BAGLEY—Clearwater County

★ **SANFORD BAGLEY MEDICAL CENTER (241328)**, 203 Fourth Street N.W., Zip 56621–8307; tel. 218/694–6501 **A**9 10 18 **F**3 7 15 28 34 40 45 53 59 65 75 77 79 81 87 89 93 97 104 107 114 119 127 128 133 143 **P**6 **S** Sanford Health, Sioux Falls, SD
Primary Contact: Sammi Davidson, Administrative Director
CMO: Andre Spence, Chief Medical Staff
CNO: Marsha Leintz, Patient Care Manager
Web address: www.sanfordhealth.org
**Control:** Other not–for–profit (including NFP Corporation) **Service:** General Medical and Surgical

**Staffed Beds:** 25 **Admissions:** 121 **Census:** 1 **Outpatient Visits:** 13885 **Births:** 0 **Total Expense ($000):** 9952 **Payroll Expense ($000):** 4305 **Personnel:** 59

## BAUDETTE—Lake Of The Woods County

★ **CHI LAKEWOOD HEALTH (241301)**, 600 Main Avenue South, Zip 56623–2855; tel. 218/634–2120, (Nonreporting) **A**9 10 18 **S** Catholic Health Initiatives, Englewood, CO
Primary Contact: Benjamin Koppelman, Interim President
CFO: Jay Ross, Vice President of Finance
CIO: Dan Leadbetter, Information Technology Systems Site Lead
CHR: Lois Slick, Director Human Resources
Web address: www.lakewoodhealthcenter.org
**Control:** Church–operated, Nongovernment, not–for profit **Service:** General Medical and Surgical

**Staffed Beds:** 55

## BAXTER—Crow Wing County

☐ **COMMUNITY BEHAVIORAL HEALTH HOSPITAL – BAXTER (244015)**, 14241 Grand Oaks Drive, Zip 56425–8749; tel. 218/316–3101, (Nonreporting) **A**1 10 **S** Minnesota Department of Human Services, Saint Paul, MN
Primary Contact: Richard G. Slieter, Jr., Administrator
**Control:** State–Government, nonfederal **Service:** Psychiatric

**Staffed Beds:** 16

## BEMIDJI—Beltrami County

☐ **COMMUNITY BEHAVIORAL HEALTH HOSPITAL – BEMIDJI (244014)**, 800 Bemidji Avenue North, Zip 56601–3054; tel. 218/308–2400, (Nonreporting) **A**1 10 **S** Minnesota Department of Human Services, Saint Paul, MN
Primary Contact: Larry A. Laudon, Administrator
**Control:** State–Government, nonfederal **Service:** Psychiatric

**Staffed Beds:** 16

**NORTH COUNTRY REGIONAL HOSPITAL** See Sanford Bemidji Medical Center

★ **SANFORD BEMIDJI MEDICAL CENTER (240100)**, 1300 Anne Street N.W., Zip 56601–5103; tel. 218/751–5430, (Total facility includes 78 beds in nursing home–type unit) **A**2 9 10 **F**3 7 8 10 11 13 14 15 18 20 22 28 29 30 31 34 35 40 43 44 45 46 49 50 51 53 54 55 56 57 58 59 60 62 63 64 65 68 70 74 75 76 77 78 79 81 82 85 86 87 90 93 96 97 103 104 107 108 110 111 114 115 117 119 120 121 123 124 125 126 127 128 129 130 131 132 133 135 141 142 144 145 146 148 **P**6 **S** Sanford Health, Sioux Falls, SD
Primary Contact: Dan Olson, President
CFO: Craig Boyer, Vice President Finance
CMO: Daniel DeKrey, M.D., Chief of Staff
CIO: Dan Moffatt, Chief Information Officer
Web address: www.nchs.com
**Control:** Other not–for–profit (including NFP Corporation) **Service:** General Medical and Surgical

**Staffed Beds:** 196 **Admissions:** 6117 **Census:** 143 **Outpatient Visits:** 233008 **Births:** 955 **Total Expense ($000):** 131629 **Payroll Expense ($000):** 51012 **Personnel:** 630

## BENSON—Swift County

★ **SWIFT COUNTY–BENSON HOSPITAL (241365)**, 1815 Wisconsin Avenue, Zip 56215–1653; tel. 320/843–1311, (Nonreporting) **A**9 10 18
Primary Contact: Kurt Waldbillig, Chief Executive Officer
CFO: Jayne Thielke, Chief Financial Officer
CMO: Richard Horecka, Chief Medical Officer
CIO: Jayne Thielke, Chief Financial Officer
CHR: Naomi Sands, Administrative Assistant and Manager Human Resources
Web address: www.scbh.org
**Control:** Hospital district or authority, Government, nonfederal **Service:** General Medical and Surgical

**Staffed Beds:** 18

## BIGFORK—Itasca County

★ **BIGFORK VALLEY HOSPITAL (241316)**, 258 Pine Tree Drive, Zip 56628, Mailing Address: P.O. Box 258, Zip 56628–0258; tel. 218/743–3177, (Total facility includes 40 beds in nursing home–type unit) **A**9 10 18 **F**2 3 8 10 11 15 28 29 31 33 34 35 40 45 53 56 57 59 62 64 77 79 80 81 82 85 89 92 93 97 110 119 125 128 130 132 133 143 146 148
Primary Contact: Aaron Saude, Chief Executive Officer
CFO: Christine Lokken, Manager of Finance
CMO: Edwin Anderson, M.D., Chief of Staff and Chief Medical Officer
CIO: Sally Sedgwick, Manager Public Relations and Marketing
CHR: Jennifer Drotts, Manager Human Resources
CNO: Nancy Probst, R.N., Chief Nursing Officer
Web address: www.bigforkvalley.org
**Control:** Hospital district or authority, Government, nonfederal **Service:** General Medical and Surgical

**Staffed Beds:** 60 **Admissions:** 800 **Census:** 41 **Outpatient Visits:** 19734 **Total Expense ($000):** 22731 **Payroll Expense ($000):** 8008 **Personnel:** 176

## BLUE EARTH—Faribault County

⊡ **UNITED HOSPITAL DISTRICT (241369)**, 515 South Moore Street, Zip 56013–2158, Mailing Address: P.O. Box 160, Zip 56013–0160; tel. 507/526–3273 **A**1 9 10 18 **F**3 4 5 7 8 11 13 15 17 28 29 30 31 34 35 40 45 46 47 48 50 53 56 57 59 62 63 64 65 68 69 70 75 76 77 79 81 82 85 86 89 91 93 96 97 107 110 111 114 115 119 128 129 130 132 133 134 135 144 146 148 **P**6
Primary Contact: Richard M. Ash, Chief Executive Officer
CFO: Larry Lee, Chief Financial Officer
Web address: www.uhd.org
**Control:** Hospital district or authority, Government, nonfederal **Service:** General Medical and Surgical

**Staffed Beds:** 25 **Admissions:** 800 **Census:** 20 **Outpatient Visits:** 53120 **Births:** 78

---

**Hospital, Medicare Provider Number, Address, Telephone, Approval, Facility, and Physician Codes, Health Care System**

★ American Hospital Association (AHA) membership    ◯ Healthcare Facilities Accreditation Program    ⇑ Center for Improvement in Healthcare Quality Accreditation
☐ The Joint Commission accreditation    ◇ DNV Healthcare Inc. accreditation    △ Commission on Accreditation of Rehabilitation Facilities (CARF) accreditation

MN

## BRAINERD—Crow Wing County

☒ **ESSENTIA HEALTH ST. JOSEPH'S MEDICAL CENTER (240075)**, 523 North Third Street, Zip 56401–3098; tel. 218/829–2861 **A**1 2 9 10 **F**3 4 5 11 13 15 18 20 22 26 28 29 30 31 34 35 40 43 45 48 49 50 51 54 57 58 59 64 65 68 70 74 75 76 77 78 79 80 81 85 86 87 89 92 93 94 95 96 98 100 101 102 104 105 107 108 110 111 115 118 119 120 124 126 127 129 130 131 132 144 146 147 148 **P**2 **S** Essentia Health, Duluth, MN
Primary Contact: Adam Rees, President
COO: Mike Larson, Chief Operating Officer
CFO: Dave Pilot, Chief Financial Officer
CMO: Peter Henry, M.D., Chief Medical Officer
CIO: Pam Marlatt, Business Systems Director
CHR: Sarah Carlson, Director Human Resources
CNO: Patricia DeLong, Chief Nursing Officer
Web address: www.essentiahealth.org
**Control:** Church–operated, Nongovernment, not–for profit **Service:** General Medical and Surgical

**Staffed Beds:** 162 **Admissions:** 5285 **Census:** 55 **Outpatient Visits:** 114242 **Births:** 455 **Total Expense ($000):** 170400 **Payroll Expense ($000):** 74981 **Personnel:** 971

**ST. JOSEPH'S MEDICAL CENTER** See Essentia Health St. Joseph's Medical Center

## BRECKENRIDGE—Wilkin County

★ **CHI ST. FRANCIS HEALTH (241377)**, 2400 St. Francis Drive, Zip 56520–1025; tel. 218/643–3000, (Total facility includes 80 beds in nursing home–type unit) **A**5 9 10 18 **F**3 5 8 11 13 15 28 29 30 34 35 38 40 43 45 46 50 56 57 59 64 65 75 79 81 87 93 96 97 99 100 101 103 104 107 110 111 115 119 125 127 128 129 130 131 132 133 146 **P**6 **S** Catholic Health Initiatives, Englewood, CO
Primary Contact: David A. Nelson, President
CFO: Becky Thompson, Chief Financial Officer
CHR: Gail Grant, Director Human Resources
Web address: www.sfcare.org
**Control:** Church–operated, Nongovernment, not–for profit **Service:** General Medical and Surgical

**Staffed Beds:** 105 **Admissions:** 901 **Census:** 96 **Outpatient Visits:** 18952 **Births:** 149 **Total Expense ($000):** 30734 **Payroll Expense ($000):** 11484 **Personnel:** 274

## BUFFALO—Wright County

☒ **BUFFALO HOSPITAL (240076)**, 303 Catlin Street, Zip 55313–1947; tel. 763/682–1212 **A**1 9 10 **F**3 11 13 15 18 28 29 30 31 32 34 35 36 40 43 44 45 50 53 57 59 64 75 76 77 78 79 80 81 85 86 87 89 93 107 110 111 114 118 119 129 130 131 132 135 146 148 **S** Allina Health, Minneapolis, MN
Primary Contact: Jennifer Myster, President
COO: Laura Jenkins, Director Operations Finance and Business Development
CFO: Sandra Matrella, Manager Finance
CMO: Corey Martin, M.D., Director Medical Affairs
CIO: Lois Nevinski, Manager Information Services
CHR: Nikki Mills, Director Human Resources and Operations
CNO: Gretchen A. Frederick, R.N., Director Patient Care Services
Web address: www.buffalohospital.org
**Control:** Other not–for–profit (including NFP Corporation) **Service:** General Medical and Surgical

**Staffed Beds:** 44 **Admissions:** 2263 **Census:** 15 **Outpatient Visits:** 75500 **Births:** 680 **Total Expense ($000):** 62882 **Payroll Expense ($000):** 25238 **Personnel:** 326

## BURNSVILLE—Dakota County

☒ **FAIRVIEW RIDGES HOSPITAL (240207)**, 201 East Nicollet Boulevard, Zip 55337–5799; tel. 952/892–2000 **A**1 2 3 5 9 10 **F**3 13 15 18 19 20 22 28 29 30 31 34 35 40 41 43 44 45 46 49 50 52 55 57 59 60 64 65 68 70 72 74 75 76 77 78 79 81 82 84 85 87 89 93 100 107 108 110 111 114 115 118 119 126 130 132 146 148 **P**6 **S** Fairview Health Services, Minneapolis, MN
Primary Contact: Patrick Belland, President and Chief Executive Officer
COO: Brian A. Knapp, Vice President Operations
CFO: Alan Lem, Vice President Finance
CMO: Lizbeth Thomas, M.D., Vice President Medical Affairs
CHR: Mary Kaphings, Director Human Resources
Web address: www.fairview.org
**Control:** Other not–for–profit (including NFP Corporation) **Service:** General Medical and Surgical

**Staffed Beds:** 157 **Admissions:** 10915 **Census:** 109 **Outpatient Visits:** 109711 **Births:** 2518 **Total Expense ($000):** 185242 **Payroll Expense ($000):** 88975 **Personnel:** 967

## CAMBRIDGE—Isanti County

☒ **CAMBRIDGE MEDICAL CENTER (240020)**, 701 South Dellwood Street, Zip 55008–1920; tel. 763/689–7700 **A**1 2 9 10 **F**3 4 5 11 13 14 15 18 28 29 30 31 32 34 35 38 40 43 45 50 55 56 57 59 61 64 65 69 70 74 75 76 77 78 79 81 82 85 86 87 89 93 97 98 99 100 101 102 103 104 107 108 111 114 119 125 129 130 131 132 134 135 144 145 146 147 148 **P**5 6 **S** Allina Health, Minneapolis, MN
Primary Contact: Gary Shaw, President
CFO: Nancy Treacy, Director Finance
CHR: Diane Rasmussen, Director Human Resources
CNO: Sherri Abrahamson–Baty, Director Patient Care Services
Web address: www.allina.com/ahs/cambridge.nsf
**Control:** Other not–for–profit (including NFP Corporation) **Service:** General Medical and Surgical

**Staffed Beds:** 78 **Admissions:** 3320 **Census:** 36 **Outpatient Visits:** 93064 **Births:** 426 **Total Expense ($000):** 74914 **Payroll Expense ($000):** 30472 **Personnel:** 654

## CANBY—Yellow Medicine County

★ **SANFORD CANBY MEDICAL CENTER (241347)**, 112 St. Olaf Avenue South, Zip 56220–1433; tel. 507/223–7277, (Includes SENIOR HAVEN CONVALESCENT NURSING CENTER ), (Total facility includes 68 beds in nursing home–type unit) **A**9 10 18 **F**3 7 10 11 13 15 28 29 31 34 35 39 40 45 46 53 56 59 60 62 64 65 70 71 75 79 81 85 89 92 93 107 110 119 127 128 130 132 133 135 144 **P**6 **S** Sanford Health, Sioux Falls, SD
Primary Contact: Lori Sisk, R.N., Chief Executive Officer
CFO: Allison Nelson, Chief Financial Officer
CMO: Maritza Lopez, M.D., Chief of Staff
CIO: Cheryl L. Ferguson, Associate Administrator
Web address: www.sanfordcanby.org
**Control:** Other not–for–profit (including NFP Corporation) **Service:** General Medical and Surgical

**Staffed Beds:** 93 **Admissions:** 375 **Census:** 62 **Outpatient Visits:** 29742 **Births:** 7 **Total Expense ($000):** 20873 **Payroll Expense ($000):** 10029 **Personnel:** 191

## CANNON FALLS—Goodhue County

☐ **MAYO CLINIC HEALTH SYSTEM IN CANNON FALLS (241346)**, 1116 West Mill Street, Zip 55009–1898; tel. 507/263–4221, (Nonreporting) **A**1 9 10 18 **S** Mayo Clinic, Rochester, MN
Primary Contact: Thomas J. Witt, M.D., President and Chief Executive Officer
COO: Glenn Christian, Administrator
CFO: Edward A. Tusa, Chief Financial Officer
CMO: Tarlochan Turna, M.D., Medical Director
CHR: Mary Garlets, Director Human Resources
Web address: www.mayoclinichealthsystem.org/locations/cannon–falls
**Control:** Hospital district or authority, Government, nonfederal **Service:** General Medical and Surgical

**Staffed Beds:** 21

## CASS LAKE—Cass County

★ **U. S. PUBLIC HEALTH SERVICE INDIAN HOSPITAL (241358)**, 7th Street & Grant Utley Avenue N.W., Zip 56633, Mailing Address: Rural Route 3, Box 211, Zip 56633; tel. 218/335–3200, (Nonreporting) **A**5 9 10 18 **S** U. S. Indian Health Service, Rockville, MD
Primary Contact: Norine Smith, Chief Executive Officer
CMO: Antonio Guimaraes, M.D., Clinical Director
CHR: Terrance Lascano, Administrative Officer
CNO: Roberta A. Williams, Director of Nursing
Web address: www.ihs.gov
**Control:** PHS, Indian Service, Government, federal **Service:** General Medical and Surgical

**Staffed Beds:** 13

## CLOQUET—Carlton County

★ **COMMUNITY MEMORIAL HOSPITAL (241364)**, 512 Skyline Boulevard, Zip 55720–1199; tel. 218/879–4641, (Nonreporting) **A**9 10 18
Primary Contact: Rick Breuer, Chief Executive Officer and Administrator
CFO: Brad Anderson, Chief Financial Officer
CIO: Sam Jacobson, Director Management Information Systems
Web address: www.cloquethospital.com
**Control:** Other not–for–profit (including NFP Corporation) **Service:** General Medical and Surgical

**Staffed Beds:** 113

*Many Facility Codes have changed. Please refer to the AHA Guide Code Chart.*

## COOK—St. Louis County

★ **COOK HOSPITAL AND CONVALESCENT NURSING CARE UNIT (241312)**, 10 Fifth Street S.E., Zip 55723–9745; tel. 218/666–5945, (Total facility includes 28 beds in nursing home–type unit) **A**9 10 18 **F**2 3 11 15 28 29 35 40 43 50 53 56 57 64 77 81 93 96 107 110 111 119 128 130 133 148
Primary Contact: Teresa Debevec, Chief Executive Officer
CFO: Kaylee S. Hoard, Chief Financial Officer
Web address: www.cookhospital.org
**Control:** Hospital district or authority, Government, nonfederal **Service:** General Medical and Surgical

| | |
|---|---|
| **Staffed Beds:** 42 **Admissions:** 239 **Census:** 30 **Outpatient Visits:** 15582 **Births:** 0 **Total Expense ($000):** 12351 **Payroll Expense ($000):** 5260 **Personnel:** 105 | |

## COON RAPIDS—Anoka County

✠ **MERCY HOSPITAL (240115)**, 4050 Coon Rapids Boulevard, Zip 55433–2586; tel. 763/236–6000 **A**1 2 3 5 9 10 **F**3 8 11 17 18 20 22 24 26 28 29 30 31 34 35 36 37 38 40 43 45 46 49 53 55 59 63 64 65 68 69 70 74 75 76 77 78 79 81 82 85 87 89 93 97 98 99 100 101 102 103 104 105 107 108 111 115 119 126 130 132 135 146 147 148 **P**4 5 6 **S** Allina Health, Minneapolis, MN
Primary Contact: Sara J. Criger, President
COO: Brandi Lunneborg, Vice President Operations
CFO: Gerald Pietz, Vice President Finance
CMO: Ryan Else, M.D., Vice President Medical Affairs
CIO: Susan Heichert, Chief Information Officer
CHR: Nancy Watson, Director Human Resources
CNO: MariBeth Olson, R.N., Vice President Patient Care Services
Web address: www.allinamercy.org
**Control:** Other not–for–profit (including NFP Corporation) **Service:** General Medical and Surgical

| | |
|---|---|
| **Staffed Beds:** 255 **Admissions:** 19067 **Census:** 195 **Outpatient Visits:** 143247 **Births:** 1879 **Total Expense ($000):** 375941 **Payroll Expense ($000):** 134785 **Personnel:** 1414 | |

## CROOKSTON—Polk County

✠ **RIVERVIEW HEALTH (241320)**, 323 South Minnesota Street, Zip 56716–1601; tel. 218/281–9200, (Nonreporting) **A**1 5 9 10 18
Primary Contact: Carrie Michalski, President and Chief Executive Officer
COO: Chris Bruggeman, Chief Operating Officer
CFO: Betty Arvidson, Chief Financial Officer
CMO: Colin Fennell, M.D., Chief Medical Officer
CIO: Jason King, Chief Information Officer
CHR: Jean Tate, Vice President Human Resources
CNO: April Grunhovd, Chief Nursing Officer
Web address: www.riverviewhealth.org
**Control:** Other not–for–profit (including NFP Corporation) **Service:** General Medical and Surgical

| | |
|---|---|
| **Staffed Beds:** 52 | |

## CROSBY—Crow Wing County

✠ **CUYUNA REGIONAL MEDICAL CENTER (241353)**, 320 East Main Street, Zip 56441–1690; tel. 218/546–7000, (Total facility includes 117 beds in nursing home–type unit) **A**1 2 3 5 9 10 18 **F**3 7 12 13 15 18 28 29 31 34 35 40 43 45 46 47 48 49 50 51 56 57 59 62 63 64 65 68 70 75 76 77 78 79 81 82 84 85 86 87 91 92 93 94 97 99 100 101 103 104 107 110 111 115 116 117 118 119 124 127 128 130 131 132 133 143 144 146 147 148 **P**6
Primary Contact: John H. Solheim, Chief Executive Officer
COO: Amy Hart, Chief Operating Officer
CFO: Kyle Bauer, Chief Financial Officer
CMO: Robert Westin, M.D., Chief Medical Officer
CHR: Caity Eggen, Chief Human Resource Officer
CNO: Renee Steffin, Chief Nursing Officer
Web address: www.cuyunamed.org
**Control:** Hospital district or authority, Government, nonfederal **Service:** General Medical and Surgical

| | |
|---|---|
| **Staffed Beds:** 142 **Admissions:** 2630 **Census:** 125 **Outpatient Visits:** 132941 **Births:** 255 **Total Expense ($000):** 96715 **Payroll Expense ($000):** 36366 **Personnel:** 595 | |

## DAWSON—Lac Qui Parle County

**JOHNSON MEMORIAL HEALTH SERVICES (241314)**, 1282 Walnut Street, Zip 56232–2333; tel. 320/769–4323, (Total facility includes 56 beds in nursing home–type unit) **A**9 10 18 **F**3 7 8 10 11 12 15 28 31 32 34 40 41 43 45 50 56 57 62 64 65 68 69 70 71 75 77 78 79 81 82 84 89 93 97 107 110 111 119 127 128 129 130 133 135 145 146 148 **P**6
Primary Contact: Kathy Johnson, Chief Executive Officer and Administrator
CFO: Crystal Bothun, Chief Financial Officer
CMO: Ayaz Virji, M.D., Chief of Staff
CIO: Derrick Ochsendorf, Manager Information Technology and Systems
CHR: Ellen Alberg, Director Human Resources
CNO: Lori Andreas, Director Patient Care Services
Web address: www.jmhsmn.org
**Control:** Hospital district or authority, Government, nonfederal **Service:** General Medical and Surgical

| | |
|---|---|
| **Staffed Beds:** 78 **Admissions:** 243 **Census:** 56 **Outpatient Visits:** 10207 **Births:** 1 **Total Expense ($000):** 14241 **Payroll Expense ($000):** 7397 **Personnel:** 148 | |

## DEER RIVER—Itasca County

★ **ESSENTIA HEALTH–DEER RIVER (241360)**, 115 10th Avenue N.E., Zip 56636–8795; tel. 218/246–2900, (Total facility includes 32 beds in nursing home–type unit) **A**9 10 18 **F**2 3 7 11 12 13 15 28 29 31 34 35 40 45 46 50 56 57 59 62 64 65 70 71 74 75 76 77 79 81 82 85 91 92 93 96 97 107 108 110 115 118 119 125 128 130 131 133 135 143 146 147 148 **P**6 **S** Essentia Health, Duluth, MN
Primary Contact: Marsha Green, Chief Executive Officer
CMO: David Goodall, M.D., Chief Medical Staff
CHR: Brittany Mohler, Director Human Resources
Web address: www.essentiahealth.org
**Control:** Other not–for–profit (including NFP Corporation) **Service:** General Medical and Surgical

| | |
|---|---|
| **Staffed Beds:** 52 **Admissions:** 438 **Census:** 32 **Outpatient Visits:** 22383 **Births:** 87 **Total Expense ($000):** 27251 **Payroll Expense ($000):** 12774 **Personnel:** 235 | |

## DETROIT LAKES—Becker County

✠ **ESSENTIA HEALTH ST. MARY'S – DETROIT LAKES (240101)**, 1027 Washington Avenue, Zip 56501–3409; tel. 218/847–5611, (Total facility includes 96 beds in nursing home–type unit) **A**1 5 9 10 20 **F**7 10 11 13 15 18 28 29 30 31 40 41 43 45 56 57 59 62 64 65 70 75 76 77 79 81 89 93 97 104 107 110 111 119 125 128 130 131 132 135 144 146 147 148 **S** Essentia Health, Duluth, MN
Primary Contact: Peter Jacobson, President
CFO: Ryan Hill, Chief Financial Officer
CMO: Rich Vetter, M.D., Associate Chief
CIO: Ken Gilles, Associate Chief Information Officer
CHR: Diane Sundrud, Human Resource Service Partner
CNO: Kay Larson, R.N., Chief Nursing Officer
Web address: www.essentiahealth.org
**Control:** Other not–for–profit (including NFP Corporation) **Service:** General Medical and Surgical

| | |
|---|---|
| **Staffed Beds:** 131 **Admissions:** 2404 **Census:** 106 **Outpatient Visits:** 14228 **Births:** 509 **Total Expense ($000):** 78299 **Payroll Expense ($000):** 35897 **Personnel:** 494 | |

**ST. MARY'S INNOVIS HEALTH** See Essentia Health St. Mary's – Detroit Lakes

## DULUTH—St. Louis County

✠ △ **ESSENTIA HEALTH DULUTH (240019)**, 502 East Second Street, Zip 55805–1982; tel. 218/727–8762 **A**1 3 5 7 9 10 **F**3 5 11 12 15 16 29 30 31 32 34 35 49 50 51 52 54 55 56 57 59 60 64 65 70 74 75 77 78 79 81 82 84 85 86 87 90 92 93 94 96 97 98 99 100 101 103 104 105 107 108 110 111 114 115 116 117 118 119 120 121 123 124 129 130 131 132 134 135 141 144 146 147 148 **P**6 **S** Essentia Health, Duluth, MN
Primary Contact: James Garvey, Administrator
CFO: Kevin Boren, Chief Financial Officer
CMO: Hugh Renier, M.D., Vice President Medical Affairs
CIO: Dennis Dassenko, Chief Information Officer
CHR: Diane Davidson, Senior Vice President Human Resources
CNO: Sandee Carlson, Director of Nursing
Web address: www.smdcmedicalcenter.org
**Control:** Other not–for–profit (including NFP Corporation) **Service:** General Medical and Surgical

| | |
|---|---|
| **Staffed Beds:** 154 **Admissions:** 3632 **Census:** 73 **Outpatient Visits:** 37550 **Births:** 7 **Total Expense ($000):** 362193 **Payroll Expense ($000):** 188675 **Personnel:** 2148 | |

MN

---

**Hospital, Medicare Provider Number, Address, Telephone, Approval, Facility, and Physician Codes, Health Care System**

★ American Hospital Association (AHA) membership
☐ The Joint Commission accreditation
○ Healthcare Facilities Accreditation Program
◇ DNV Healthcare Inc. accreditation
⇑ Center for Improvement in Healthcare Quality Accreditation
△ Commission on Accreditation of Rehabilitation Facilities (CARF) accreditation

⊞ **ESSENTIA HEALTH ST. MARY'S MEDICAL CENTER (240002)**, 407 East Third Street, Zip 55805–1984; tel. 218/786–4000, (Includes ST. MARY'S CHILDREN'S HOSPITAL, 407 East Third Street, Zip 55805–1950; tel. 218/786–5437) **A**1 2 3 5 9 10 **F**3 11 12 13 17 18 20 22 24 26 28 29 30 34 35 37 38 40 41 43 45 46 47 48 49 50 57 59 63 65 67 70 72 74 76 78 79 81 83 84 85 86 87 88 89 102 107 108 111 115 119 126 129 130 132 135 141 146 **P**6 **S** Essentia Health, Duluth, MN
Primary Contact: James Garvey, Executive Vice President, Operations and Administrator
CMO: Hugh Renier, M.D., Vice President Medical Affairs
CIO: Tess Jettergren, Director Clinical Informatics
CHR: Glen Porter, Vice President Human Resources
Web address: www.essentiahealth.org/StMarysMedicalCenter/FindaClinic/Essentia–HealthSt–Marys–Medical–Center–46.aspx
**Control:** Other not–for–profit (including NFP Corporation) **Service:** General Medical and Surgical

**Staffed Beds:** 306 **Admissions:** 17454 **Census:** 221 **Outpatient Visits:** 105195 **Births:** 1223 **Total Expense ($000):** 332898 **Payroll Expense ($000):** 146617 **Personnel:** 2086

**SMDC MEDICAL CENTER** See Essentia Health Duluth

⊞ △ **ST. LUKE'S HOSPITAL (240047)**, 915 East First Street, Zip 55805–2193; tel. 218/249–5555 **A**1 2 3 7 9 10 **F**3 8 9 11 12 13 15 17 18 20 22 24 26 28 29 30 31 34 35 39 40 43 46 47 48 49 51 53 54 57 58 59 60 61 62 63 64 65 70 74 75 76 77 78 79 81 82 83 84 85 86 87 90 92 93 97 98 100 102 104 107 108 110 114 115 117 118 119 120 121 123 124 126 129 130 131 132 144 145 146 148 **P**6
Primary Contact: John Strange, President and Chief Executive Officer
CFO: Eric Lohn, Vice President and Chief Financial Officer
CMO: Gary Peterson, M.D., Vice President Medical Affairs and Medical Director
CIO: Clark Averill, Director Information Technology
CHR: Marla Halvorson, Director Human Resources
CNO: Susan Hamel, Chief Nursing Officer
Web address: www.slhduluth.com
**Control:** Other not–for–profit (including NFP Corporation) **Service:** General Medical and Surgical

**Staffed Beds:** 267 **Admissions:** 10066 **Census:** 132 **Outpatient Visits:** 144138 **Births:** 779 **Total Expense ($000):** 367524 **Payroll Expense ($000):** 174828 **Personnel:** 1882

**ST. MARY'S MEDICAL CENTER** See Essentia Health St. Mary's Medical Center

### EDINA—Hennepin County

⊞ **FAIRVIEW SOUTHDALE HOSPITAL (240078)**, 6401 France Avenue South, Zip 55435–2199; tel. 952/924–5000 **A**1 2 3 5 9 10 **F**3 5 8 11 12 13 15 17 18 20 22 24 26 28 29 30 31 34 35 38 39 40 43 45 46 49 50 51 55 56 57 59 60 64 65 68 70 72 74 75 76 77 78 79 81 82 83 84 85 87 93 94 96 98 100 102 107 108 110 111 114 115 117 118 119 121 124 126 129 130 131 132 134 135 146 147 148 **P**6 **S** Fairview Health Services, Minneapolis, MN
Primary Contact: Bradley Beard, Regional President
CFO: Alan Lem, Vice President Finance
CHR: Michelle LeDell, Director Human Resources
Web address: www.fairview.org
**Control:** Other not–for–profit (including NFP Corporation) **Service:** General Medical and Surgical

**Staffed Beds:** 338 **Admissions:** 17906 **Census:** 201 **Outpatient Visits:** 127684 **Births:** 3073 **Total Expense ($000):** 383420 **Payroll Expense ($000):** 154368 **Personnel:** 1624

### ELBOW LAKE—Grant County

**ELEAH MEDICAL CENTER** See Prairie Ridge Hospital and Health Services

★ **PRAIRIE RIDGE HOSPITAL AND HEALTH SERVICES (241379)**, 1411 Highway 79 E., Zip 56531–4611; tel. 218/685–4461 **A**9 10 18 **F**7 15 28 31 40 43 45 46 47 48 59 64 79 81 93 107 119 133 148 **P**5
Primary Contact: Thomas Kooiman, Chief Executive Officer
CFO: Loraine Martineau, Chief Financial Officer
CMO: David Bjork, M.D., Chief Medical Officer
CNO: Manda Westrom, Director of Nursing
Web address: www.prairiehealth.org/
**Control:** Other not–for–profit (including NFP Corporation) **Service:** General Medical and Surgical

**Staffed Beds:** 10 **Admissions:** 167 **Census:** 2 **Outpatient Visits:** 21401 **Births:** 0 **Total Expense ($000):** 16050 **Payroll Expense ($000):** 4228 **Personnel:** 106

### ELY—St. Louis County

★ **ELY–BLOOMENSON COMMUNITY HOSPITAL (241318)**, 328 West Conan Street, Zip 55731–1198; tel. 218/365–3271 **A**9 10 18 **F**3 13 15 28 31 40 45 53 62 64 76 81 107 110 119 130 133 148 **P**6
Primary Contact: John Fossum, Chief Executive Officer
CFO: Scott Kellerman, Chief Financial Officer
CHR: Rochelle Sjoberg, Director Human Resources
CNO: Becky Gaulke, Chief Nursing Officer
Web address: www.ebch.org
**Control:** Other not–for–profit (including NFP Corporation) **Service:** General Medical and Surgical

**Staffed Beds:** 25 **Admissions:** 319 **Census:** 3 **Outpatient Visits:** 8171 **Births:** 19 **Total Expense ($000):** 16093 **Payroll Expense ($000):** 5266 **Personnel:** 96

### FAIRMONT—Martin County

⊞ **MAYO CLINIC HEALTH SYSTEM IN FAIRMONT (240166)**, 800 Medical Center Drive, Zip 56031–4575; tel. 507/238–8100, (Includes LUTZ WING CONVALESCENT AND NURSING CARE UNIT ), (Total facility includes 40 beds in nursing home–type unit) **A**1 9 10 20 **F**3 9 11 12 13 14 15 17 18 28 29 30 31 34 36 40 43 56 57 59 64 65 68 74 75 76 77 78 79 81 82 84 85 86 87 92 93 97 99 100 101 103 104 107 108 110 111 115 118 119 128 129 130 132 133 144 146 **P**6 **S** Mayo Clinic, Rochester, MN
Primary Contact: Robert Bartingale, Administrator
COO: Gayle B. Hansen, R.N., Chief Operating Officer
CFO: Brian Suter, Chief Financial Officer
CMO: Rufus Rodriguez, M.D., Medical Director
Web address: www.fairmontmedicalcenter.org
**Control:** Other not–for–profit (including NFP Corporation) **Service:** General Medical and Surgical

**Staffed Beds:** 96 **Admissions:** 2149 **Census:** 49 **Outpatient Visits:** 146524 **Births:** 243 **Personnel:** 392

### FARIBAULT—Rice County

★ **DISTRICT ONE HOSPITAL (240071)**, 200 State Avenue, Zip 55021–6345; tel. 507/334–6451, (Nonreporting) **A**9 10 **S** Allina Health, Minneapolis, MN
Primary Contact: Stephen J. Pribyl, FACHE, Chief Executive Officer
COO: Joan Boysen, Chief Operating Officer
CFO: Rick Miller, Chief Financial Officer
CMO: Brant Barr, M.D., Chief Medical Officer
CIO: Glenn Gregersen, Director Information Technology
CHR: Lucy G. Dupree, Director Human Resources
CNO: Lynette Dickson, Director Clinical Operations and Director of Nursing
Web address: www.districtonehospital.com
**Control:** Hospital district or authority, Government, nonfederal **Service:** General Medical and Surgical

**Staffed Beds:** 42

### FERGUS FALLS—Otter Tail County

☐ **COMMUNITY BEHAVIORAL HEALTH HOSPITAL – FERGUS FALLS (244013)**, 1801 West Alcott Avenue, Zip 56537–2661, Mailing Address: P.O. Box 478, Zip 56538–0478; tel. 218/332–5001, (Nonreporting) **A**1 9 10 **S** Minnesota Department of Human Services, Saint Paul, MN
Primary Contact: Brenda Schleske, Interim Administrator
**Control:** State–Government, nonfederal **Service:** Psychiatric

**Staffed Beds:** 16

⊞ △ **LAKE REGION HEALTHCARE (240052)**, 712 South Cascade Street, Zip 56537–2900, Mailing Address: P.O. Box 728, Zip 56538–0728; tel. 218/736–8000 **A**1 7 9 10 20 **F**3 10 11 13 15 17 18 26 28 29 30 31 32 34 35 36 40 43 44 45 50 51 53 54 56 57 58 59 61 64 65 70 74 75 76 77 78 79 81 82 84 85 86 87 89 90 92 93 94 96 97 98 100 101 102 103 104 107 108 110 111 115 118 119 120 121 123 130 131 132 135 144 146 147 148
Primary Contact: Larry A. Schulz, Chief Executive Officer
CFO: Brett Longtin, Chief Financial Officer
CMO: Greg Smith, Chief Medical Officer
CIO: Wade A. Jyrkas, Director Computer Information Systems
CHR: Patti Fandrich, Human Resources Operations Director
CNO: Lucia E. Anderson, Senior Vice President Operations and Chief Nurse Executive
Web address: www.lrhc.org
**Control:** Other not–for–profit (including NFP Corporation) **Service:** General Medical and Surgical

**Staffed Beds:** 108 **Admissions:** 2692 **Census:** 29 **Outpatient Visits:** 53914 **Births:** 358 **Total Expense ($000):** 112082 **Payroll Expense ($000):** 36733 **Personnel:** 723

*Many Facility Codes have changed. Please refer to the AHA Guide Code Chart.*

MN

## FOSSTON—Polk County

★ **ESSENTIA HEALTH FOSSTON (241357)**, 900 Hilligoss Boulevard S.E., Zip 56542–1599; tel. 218/435–1133, (Total facility includes 50 beds in nursing home–type unit) **A**9 10 18 **F**3 7 10 11 13 15 28 29 31 34 35 40 43 44 50 56 57 59 62 63 64 65 68 69 70 75 76 77 78 79 80 81 82 84 85 87 93 97 99 104 107 110 114 127 128 129 130 131 132 133 135 145 146 148 **P**6 **S** Essentia Health, Duluth, MN
Primary Contact: Kevin Gish, Administrator and Vice President
CFO: Kim Bodensteiner, Chief Financial Officer
CHR: Diane Sundrud, Director Human Resources
Web address: www.essentiahealth.org
**Control:** Other not–for–profit (including NFP Corporation) **Service:** General Medical and Surgical

**Staffed Beds:** 75 **Admissions:** 577 **Census:** 51 **Outpatient Visits:** 45335 **Births:** 67 **Total Expense ($000):** 24179 **Payroll Expense ($000):** 11788 **Personnel:** 177

**FIRST CARE MEDICAL SERVICES** See Essentia Health Fosston

## FRIDLEY—Anoka County

☒ **UNITY HOSPITAL (240132)**, 550 Osborne Road N.E., Zip 55432–2799; tel. 763/236–5000 **A**1 2 5 9 10 **F**3 4 5 11 12 13 18 20 22 24 26 28 29 30 31 34 35 40 43 45 50 53 55 56 57 59 64 65 69 70 73 75 76 77 78 79 81 82 85 86 87 93 96 98 99 100 101 102 103 104 107 108 111 114 115 119 126 130 132 135 145 146 147 148 **S** Allina Health, Minneapolis, MN
Primary Contact: Helen J. Strike, R.N., President
CFO: Gerald Pietz, Vice President Finance
CMO: Paul Kettler, M.D., Vice President Medical Affairs
CIO: Susan Heichert, Chief Information Officer
CHR: Kenneth E. Auer, Director Human Resources
CNO: Mari J. Holt, R.N., Vice President Patient Care Services
Web address: www.allina.com
**Control:** Other not–for–profit (including NFP Corporation) **Service:** General Medical and Surgical

**Staffed Beds:** 176 **Admissions:** 11418 **Census:** 120 **Outpatient Visits:** 91231 **Births:** 1130 **Total Expense ($000):** 187257 **Payroll Expense ($000):** 74566 **Personnel:** 839

## GLENCOE—Mcleod County

★ **GLENCOE REGIONAL HEALTH SERVICES (241355)**, 1805 Hennepin Avenue North, Zip 55336–1416; tel. 320/864–3121, (Total facility includes 110 beds in nursing home–type unit) **A**9 10 18 **F**11 13 15 28 29 31 34 40 43 48 56 64 68 75 76 77 78 81 86 87 89 93 97 107 110 111 114 119 125 128 130 132 133 135 146 **P**6 **S** HealthPartners, Bloomington, MN
Primary Contact: Jon D. Braband, FACHE, President and Chief Executive Officer
CFO: John C. Doidge, Vice President Finance
CMO: John H. Bergseng, D.O., Vice President Medical Affairs
CIO: Ryan Lake, Director Medical Imaging and Information Technology
CHR: Jill Hatlestad, Vice President Human Resources and Marketing
CNO: Patricia Henderson, R.N., Vice President Nursing and Clinical Services
Web address: www.grhsonline.org
**Control:** Other not–for–profit (including NFP Corporation) **Service:** General Medical and Surgical

**Staffed Beds:** 135 **Admissions:** 909 **Census:** 107 **Outpatient Visits:** 25500 **Births:** 165 **Total Expense ($000):** 48924 **Payroll Expense ($000):** 23101 **Personnel:** 362

## GLENWOOD—Pope County

★ **GLACIAL RIDGE HEALTH SYSTEM (241376)**, 10 Fourth Avenue S.E., Zip 56334–1898; tel. 320/634–4521 **A**9 10 18 **F**7 11 12 13 15 17 28 31 34 35 40 41 43 53 59 62 63 64 75 76 79 81 93 107 110 111 114 119 127 130 133 146 148 **P**6
Primary Contact: Kirk A. Stensrud, Chief Executive Officer
CFO: Kyle Chase, Chief Financial Officer
CMO: Robert Montenegro, M.D., Chief of Staff
CIO: Heidi Engle, Manager Information Technology
CHR: Gordon Paulson, Manager Personnel
CNO: Lynn Flesner, Director of Nursing
Web address: www.glacialridge.org
**Control:** Hospital district or authority, Government, nonfederal **Service:** General Medical and Surgical

**Staffed Beds:** 19 **Admissions:** 616 **Census:** 5 **Outpatient Visits:** 14957 **Births:** 69 **Total Expense ($000):** 26296 **Payroll Expense ($000):** 12643 **Personnel:** 192

## GOLDEN VALLEY—Hennepin County

☒ **REGENCY HOSPITAL OF MINNEAPOLIS (242005)**, 1300 Hidden Lakes Parkway, Zip 55422–4286; tel. 763/588–2750, (Nonreporting) **A**1 10 **S** Select Medical Corporation, Mechanicsburg, PA
Primary Contact: Marshall E. Smith, Chief Executive Officer
CMO: Alaka Nagaraj, M.D., Medical Director
CNO: Caren Gaytko, Chief Nursing Officer
Web address: www.regencyhospital.com
**Control:** Corporation, Investor–owned, for–profit **Service:** Long–Term Acute Care hospital

**Staffed Beds:** 92

## GRACEVILLE—Big Stone County

★ **ESSENTIA HEALTH–GRACEVILLE (241321)**, 115 West Second Street, Zip 56240–4845, Mailing Address: P.O. Box 157, Zip 56240–0157; tel. 320/748–7223, (Total facility includes 45 beds in nursing home–type unit) **A**9 10 18 **F**10 11 12 15 18 28 30 34 35 40 41 45 47 50 57 59 62 64 65 75 77 79 81 82 84 91 92 93 97 107 108 110 111 114 117 118 119 127 128 129 132 133 135 **S** Essentia Health, Duluth, MN
Primary Contact: John Campion, Administrator
CFO: John Campion, Interim Chief Financial Officer
CMO: Arthur Van Vranken, M.D., Chief Medical Officer
CIO: Brad Tostenson, Chief Information Officer
CHR: Jenny Lee, Human Resources Generalist
CNO: Jill Johnsrud, Director of Nursing
Web address: www.essentiahealth.org/HolyTrinityHospital/FindaClinic/Essentia–HealthHoly–Trinity–Hospital–96.aspx
**Control:** Other not–for–profit (including NFP Corporation) **Service:** General Medical and Surgical

**Staffed Beds:** 60 **Admissions:** 106 **Census:** 42 **Outpatient Visits:** 7120 **Births:** 0 **Personnel:** 97

**GRACEVILLE HEALTH CENTER** See Essentia Health–Graceville

## GRAND MARAIS—Cook County

★ **COOK COUNTY NORTH SHORE HOSPITAL (241317)**, 515 5th Avenue West, Zip 55604–3017; tel. 218/387–3040, (Total facility includes 37 beds in nursing home–type unit) **A**9 10 18 **F**3 7 11 13 15 28 31 40 45 50 56 59 62 64 75 76 77 84 85 89 93 107 110 111 114 119 128 130 133 148
Primary Contact: Kimber L. Wraalstad, FACHE, Administrator
CFO: Vera Schumann, Director of Finance and Controller
CMO: Milan Schmidt, Medical Director
CIO: Greg Johnson, Chief Information Officer
CHR: Shelly Starkey, Human Resources Coordinator
CNO: Bridget Sobieck, Director of Nursing
Web address: www.nshorehospital.com
**Control:** Hospital district or authority, Government, nonfederal **Service:** General Medical and Surgical

**Staffed Beds:** 53 **Admissions:** 216 **Census:** 34 **Outpatient Visits:** 11417 **Births:** 11 **Total Expense ($000):** 13885 **Payroll Expense ($000):** 5942 **Personnel:** 111

## GRAND RAPIDS—Itasca County

☒ **GRAND ITASCA CLINIC AND HOSPITAL (240064)**, 1601 Golf Course Road, Zip 55744–8648; tel. 218/326–5000 **A**1 9 10 20 **F**3 11 12 13 15 17 28 29 31 33 35 36 38 40 43 44 45 50 53 56 59 61 62 64 65 75 76 77 78 79 81 82 85 86 87 93 96 97 107 108 110 111 115 118 119 129 130 131 132 135 141 146 147 148 **P**6
Primary Contact: Michael Youso, Chief Executive Officer
CFO: Sarah S. Gustafson, Vice President of Finance
CHR: Julie Schmidt, Director Human Resources
CNO: Sue Skinner, Vice President of Patient Care Services
Web address: www.granditasca.org
**Control:** Other not–for–profit (including NFP Corporation) **Service:** General Medical and Surgical

**Staffed Beds:** 31 **Admissions:** 1701 **Census:** 13 **Outpatient Visits:** 211740 **Births:** 328 **Total Expense ($000):** 78473 **Payroll Expense ($000):** 38905 **Personnel:** 526

MN

---

**Hospital, Medicare Provider Number, Address, Telephone, Approval, Facility, and Physician Codes, Health Care System**

★ American Hospital Association (AHA) membership  ◯ Healthcare Facilities Accreditation Program  ⇑ Center for Improvement in Healthcare Quality Accreditation
☐ The Joint Commission accreditation  ◇ DNV Healthcare Inc. accreditation  △ Commission on Accreditation of Rehabilitation Facilities (CARF) accreditation

**MN**

## GRANITE FALLS—Yellow Medicine County

★ **GRANITE FALLS MUNICIPAL HOSPITAL AND MANOR (241343)**, 345 Tenth Avenue, Zip 56241–1499; tel. 320/564–3111, (Total facility includes 57 beds in nursing home–type unit) **A**9 10 18 **F**3 7 13 15 28 31 40 41 43 45 62 71 76 77 79 81 85 89 93 107 118 128 130 133 148
Primary Contact: George Gerlach, Chief Executive Officer and Administrator
CFO: Val Hoffman, Chief Financial Officer
CIO: Kris Wilke, Manager Health Information
CHR: Sue Tollefson, Coordinator Payroll Personnel
CNO: Patty Massman, Director of Nursing
Web address: www.granitefallshealthcare.com
**Control:** City–Government, nonfederal **Service:** General Medical and Surgical

**Staffed Beds:** 82 **Admissions:** 450 **Census:** 47 **Outpatient Visits:** 15216
**Births:** 27

## HALLOCK—Kittson County

★ **KITTSON MEMORIAL HEALTHCARE CENTER (241336)**, 1010 South Birch Street, Zip 56728–4215, Mailing Address: P.O. Box 700, Zip 56728–0700; tel. 218/843–3612, (Total facility includes 60 beds in nursing home–type unit) **A**9 10 18 **F**7 10 11 15 28 34 35 40 45 50 53 54 59 62 63 65 68 93 107 127 128 130 133 143 148
Primary Contact: Cindy Urbaniak, Chief Executive Officer
CFO: Todd Christensen, Chief Financial Officer
CMO: Thomas Lohstreter, M.D., Chief of Staff
CIO: Holly Knutson, Manager Information Technology
CHR: Carlene Cole, Manager Human Resources
CNO: Tawnya Sorenson, Director of Nursing
Web address: www.kmhc.net
**Control:** Other not–for–profit (including NFP Corporation) **Service:** General Medical and Surgical

**Staffed Beds:** 75 **Admissions:** 162 **Census:** 67 **Outpatient Visits:** 1085
**Births:** 0 **Total Expense ($000):** 10622 **Payroll Expense ($000):** 5055
**Personnel:** 161

## HASTINGS—Dakota County

⊠ **REGINA HOSPITAL (240059)**, 1175 Nininger Road, Zip 55033–1098; tel. 651/480–4100 **A**1 9 10 **F**3 8 11 13 15 28 29 30 34 35 40 43 45 46 50 57 59 68 70 75 77 79 81 83 87 93 98 103 107 110 111 114 118 119 129 130 132 145 146 148 **S** Allina Health, Minneapolis, MN
Primary Contact: Thomas R. Thompson, Chief Executive Officer
CFO: Andy Rolling, Director of Finance
CMO: James Noreen, M.D., Chief Medical Officer
CHR: Robert P. Verchota, Vice President Support Services
CNO: Karen S. Strauman, R.N., Vice President Patient Care Services
Web address: www.reginamedical.org
**Control:** Other not–for–profit (including NFP Corporation) **Service:** General Medical and Surgical

**Staffed Beds:** 55 **Admissions:** 1914 **Census:** 22 **Outpatient Visits:** 47018
**Births:** 315 **Total Expense ($000):** 47228 **Payroll Expense ($000):** 19265
**Personnel:** 271

## HENDRICKS—Lincoln County

★ **HENDRICKS COMMUNITY HOSPITAL ASSOCIATION (241339)**, 503 East Lincoln Street, Zip 56136–9598, Mailing Address: P.O. Box 106, Zip 56136–0106; tel. 507/275–3134, (Total facility includes 55 beds in nursing home–type unit) **A**9 10 18 **F**2 3 7 10 11 15 17 28 29 31 34 35 40 59 62 63 70 81 93 125 127 128 130 132 133 146 148
Primary Contact: Jeffrey Gollaher, Chief Executive Officer
CMO: Tabb McCluskey, M.D., Chief Medical Officer
CHR: Lynn R. Olson, Director Human Resources
Web address: www.hendrickshosp.org
**Control:** Other not–for–profit (including NFP Corporation) **Service:** General Medical and Surgical

**Staffed Beds:** 70 **Admissions:** 187 **Census:** 56 **Outpatient Visits:** 10979
**Births:** 0 **Total Expense ($000):** 12701 **Payroll Expense ($000):** 6519
**Personnel:** 120

## HIBBING—St. Louis County

⊠ **RANGE REGIONAL HEALTH SERVICES (240040)**, 750 East 34th Street, Zip 55746–4600; tel. 218/262–4881 **A**1 2 9 10 **F**3 6 11 13 15 18 28 29 30 31 33 34 35 40 43 45 53 57 59 62 63 64 65 70 75 76 77 78 79 81 82 84 85 87 91 92 93 96 97 98 102 104 107 108 110 111 115 116 117 119 120 121 129 130 132 135 143 144 146 147 148 **P**6 **S** Fairview Health Services, Minneapolis, MN
Primary Contact: Debra K. Boardman, FACHE, President and Chief Executive Officer
COO: Patrick Sharp, Senior Vice President and Chief Operating Officer
CFO: Tom Fink, Vice President Regional Finance Officer
CMO: Susan Rudberg, M.D., Chief Medical Officer
CIO: Jessica Valento, Director Information Systems
CHR: Mitch Vincent, Vice President Organizational Support
CNO: Connie Harle, Senior Vice President and Chief Nursing Officer
Web address: www.range.fairview.org
**Control:** Other not–for–profit (including NFP Corporation) **Service:** General Medical and Surgical

**Staffed Beds:** 53 **Admissions:** 2714 **Census:** 31 **Outpatient Visits:** 159484
**Births:** 398 **Total Expense ($000):** 106079 **Payroll Expense ($000):** 53934
**Personnel:** 748

## HUTCHINSON—Mcleod County

⊠ **HUTCHINSON HEALTH (240187)**, 1095 Highway 15 South, Zip 55350–3182; tel. 320/234–5000 **A**1 9 10 20 **F**3 5 11 13 15 18 26 28 29 31 34 35 36 38 40 43 45 56 57 59 62 65 69 70 75 76 77 78 79 81 82 85 86 87 93 97 98 99 100 101 103 104 107 110 111 115 119 127 129 130 131 132 144 146 147 148 **P**6 **S** Allina Health, Minneapolis, MN
Primary Contact: Steven Mulder, M.D., President and Chief Executive Officer
COO: Glen Kegley, Chief Operating Officer
CFO: Pamela Larson, Division Director Financial Services
CMO: Brian Pollman, Chief Medical Officer
CIO: Jim Lyons, Chief Clinic Officer
CHR: Rebecca Streich, Manager Human Resources and Education Manager
CNO: Mary Kay Henze, Chief Nursing Officer
Web address: www.hutchhealth.com
**Control:** Other not–for–profit (including NFP Corporation) **Service:** General Medical and Surgical

**Staffed Beds:** 57 **Admissions:** 2228 **Census:** 22 **Outpatient Visits:** 216884
**Births:** 279 **Total Expense ($000):** 83750 **Payroll Expense ($000):** 29692
**Personnel:** 451

## INTERNATIONAL FALLS—Koochiching County

⊠ **RAINY LAKE MEDICAL CENTER (241322)**, 1400 Highway 71, Zip 56649–2189; tel. 218/283–4481, (Nonreporting) **A**1 9 10 18
Primary Contact: Daniel Odegaard, FACHE, Chief Executive Officer
CFO: Melissa Marcotte, Chief Financial Officer
CIO: Michael Blesi, Director Information Technology
CNO: Donita Ettestad, R.N., Chief Nursing Officer
Web address: www.rainylakemedical.com
**Control:** Other not–for–profit (including NFP Corporation) **Service:** General Medical and Surgical

**Staffed Beds:** 25

## JACKSON—Jackson County

★ **SANFORD JACKSON MEDICAL CENTER (241315)**, 1430 North Highway, Zip 56143–1093; tel. 507/847–2420, (Nonreporting) **A**9 10 18 **S** Sanford Health, Sioux Falls, SD
Primary Contact: Mary J. Ruyter, Chief Executive Officer
CFO: Gail Eike, Chief Financial Officer
CMO: Sister Marie Paul Lockerd, M.D., Chief Medical Officer
CNO: Dawn Schnell, Chief Nursing Officer
Web address: www.sanfordjackson.org
**Control:** Other not–for–profit (including NFP Corporation) **Service:** General Medical and Surgical

**Staffed Beds:** 16

## LAKE CITY—Goodhue County

☐ **MAYO CLINIC HEALTH SYSTEM IN LAKE CITY (241338)**, 500 West Grant Street, Zip 55041–1143; tel. 651/345–3321, (Nonreporting) **A**1 9 10 18 **S** Mayo Clinic, Rochester, MN
Primary Contact: Susan M. Stiene, R.N., MS, Interim Chief Administrative Officer
CFO: David Biren, Chief Financial Officer
CMO: Dennis Spano, M.D., Medical Director
CHR: Jacqueline Ryan, Director Human Resources
Web address: www.lakecitymedicalcenter.org
**Control:** Other not–for–profit (including NFP Corporation) **Service:** General Medical and Surgical

**Staffed Beds:** 108

*Many Facility Codes have changed. Please refer to the AHA Guide Code Chart.* © 2015 AHA Guide

## LE SUEUR—Le Sueur County

★ **MINNESOTA VALLEY HEALTH CENTER (241375)**, 621 South Fourth Street, Zip 56058–2298; tel. 507/665–3375, (Includes GARDENVIEW NURSING HOME ), (Nonreporting) **A**9 10 18 **S** Essentia Health, Duluth, MN
Primary Contact: Pam Williams, Chief Executive Officer
CFO: Patricia Schlegel, Executive Director Finance
CMO: Carolyn Stelter, M.D., Chief of Staff
CHR: Bonnie Barnhardt, Executive Director Human Resources
CNO: Kim Lewis, R.N., Director of Nursing Hospital
Web address: www.mvhc.org
**Control:** Other not–for–profit (including NFP Corporation) **Service:** General Medical and Surgical

| Staffed Beds: 64 |
| --- |

## LITCHFIELD—Meeker County

★ **MEEKER MEMORIAL HOSPITAL (241366)**, 612 South Sibley Avenue, Zip 55355–3398; tel. 320/693–3242 **A**9 10 18 **F**11 13 15 28 29 31 34 40 43 45 57 59 70 75 76 77 78 81 93 107 110 111 114 119 130 133 146 148
Primary Contact: Kyle R. Rasmussen, Chief Executive Officer
CFO: Stephen Plaisance, Chief Financial Officer
CMO: Tim Peterson, M.D., Chief of Staff
CIO: Troy Bruning, Director Information Technology
CHR: Cindi Twardy, Manager Human Resources
CNO: Ann Lien, R.N., Chief Nursing Officer
Web address: www.meekermemorial.com
**Control:** County–Government, nonfederal **Service:** General Medical and Surgical

| Staffed Beds: 39 Admissions: 1027 Census: 15 Outpatient Visits: 33166 Births: 139 Total Expense ($000): 28108 Payroll Expense ($000): 10294 Personnel: 153 |
| --- |

## LITTLE FALLS—Morrison County

⊞ **CHI ST. GABRIEL'S HEALTH (241370)**, 815 Second Street S.E., Zip 56345–3596; tel. 320/632–5441 **A**1 9 10 18 **F**3 11 13 15 26 28 29 30 31 34 40 43 45 57 59 62 63 64 65 68 70 75 76 77 79 81 84 85 86 87 93 107 108 110 111 115 119 127 128 130 131 132 133 146 **P**6 **S** Catholic Health Initiatives, Englewood, CO
Primary Contact: Lee Boyles, President
CFO: Steve Smith, Assistant Vice President Finance
CMO: Susan Okoniewski, M.D., Chief of Staff
Web address: www.stgabriels.com
**Control:** Church–operated, Nongovernment, not–for profit **Service:** General Medical and Surgical

| Staffed Beds: 25 Admissions: 1344 Census: 10 Outpatient Visits: 42656 Births: 205 Total Expense ($000): 46248 Payroll Expense ($000): 12734 Personnel: 272 |
| --- |

## LONG PRAIRIE—Todd County

★ **CENTRACARE HEALTH–LONG PRAIRIE (241326)**, 20 Ninth Street S.E., Zip 56347–1404; tel. 320/732–2141, (Nonreporting) **A**5 9 10 18 **S** CentraCare Health, Saint Cloud, MN
Primary Contact: Daniel J. Swenson, FACHE, Administrator and Chief Executive Officer
CFO: Larry Knutson, Director Finance
CMO: Rene Eldidy, M.D., Chief of Staff
Web address: www.centracare.com
**Control:** Other not–for–profit (including NFP Corporation) **Service:** General Medical and Surgical

| Staffed Beds: 20 |
| --- |

**LONG PRAIRIE MEMORIAL HOSPITAL AND HOME** See CentraCare Health–Long Prairie

## LUVERNE—Rock County

★ **SANFORD LUVERNE MEDICAL CENTER (241371)**, 1600 North Kniss Avenue, Zip 56156–1067; tel. 507/283–2321 **A**9 10 18 **F**3 4 5 7 8 11 13 15 18 19 28 29 31 32 34 35 40 43 45 56 57 59 63 64 65 67 74 75 76 77 78 79 81 82 83 84 85 86 87 90 93 96 97 107 111 114 118 119 128 129 131 132 133 135 146 147 148 **P**6 **S** Sanford Health, Sioux Falls, SD
Primary Contact: Tammy Loosbrock, Chief Executive Officer
COO: Nancy E. Drenth, Director Ancillary Services
CFO: Stanley Knobloch, Chief Financial Officer
CMO: Stephen Chesley, Chief of Staff
CNO: Nyla H. Sandbulte, R.N., Chief Nursing Officer
Web address: www.sanfordluverne.org
**Control:** Other not–for–profit (including NFP Corporation) **Service:** General Medical and Surgical

| Staffed Beds: 25 Admissions: 493 Census: 6 Outpatient Visits: 31125 Births: 93 Total Expense ($000): 21548 Payroll Expense ($000): 8718 Personnel: 145 |
| --- |

## MADELIA—Watonwan County

⊞ **MADELIA COMMUNITY HOSPITAL (241323)**, 121 Drew Avenue S.E., Zip 56062–1899; tel. 507/642–3255 **A**1 3 5 9 10 18 **F**3 11 13 15 34 35 40 57 59 62 64 68 69 75 76 77 81 84 85 86 93 102 107 110 114 128 130 132 133 144 145
Primary Contact: Candace Fenske, Chief Executive Officer
CFO: Donna M. Klinkner, Chief Financial Officer
CMO: Todd Gavin, Chief Medical Officer
CIO: Valerie Juhl, Director of Health
CHR: Donna M. Klinkner, Chief Financial Officer
CNO: Deidre Hruby, Director of Patient Care
Web address: www.mchospital.org
**Control:** Other not–for–profit (including NFP Corporation) **Service:** General Medical and Surgical

| Staffed Beds: 21 Admissions: 168 Census: 3 Outpatient Visits: 3915 Births: 0 Total Expense ($000): 10275 Payroll Expense ($000): 3757 Personnel: 71 |
| --- |

## MADISON—Lac Qui Parle County

★ **MADISON HOSPITAL (241372)**, 900 Second Avenue, Zip 56256–1006; tel. 320/598–7556 **A**9 10 18 **F**10 11 15 28 29 30 34 40 43 57 59 62 64 65 76 77 78 79 81 82 84 89 93 97 107 110 111 119 127 130 132 133 145 147 **P**5
Primary Contact: Allen Anderson, Interim Chief Executive Officer
CFO: Carol Borgerson, Business Office Manager and Chief Financial Officer
CIO: Jerry Harberts, Information Technologist
CHR: Allen Anderson, Director Human Resources
Web address: www.madisonlutheranhome.com
**Control:** Other not–for–profit (including NFP Corporation) **Service:** General Medical and Surgical

| Staffed Beds: 12 Admissions: 209 Census: 2 Outpatient Visits: 12469 Births: 2 Total Expense ($000): 10084 Payroll Expense ($000): 3556 Personnel: 62 |
| --- |

## MAHNOMEN—Mahnomen County

★ **MAHNOMEN HEALTH CENTER (241300)**, 414 West Jefferson Avenue, Zip 56557–4912, Mailing Address: P.O. Box 396, Zip 56557–0396; tel. 218/935–2511, (Nonreporting) **A**9 10 18 **S** Sanford Health, Sioux Falls, SD
Primary Contact: Susan K. Klassen, Chief Executive Officer
CFO: Mary Pazdernik, Chief Financial Officer
CMO: Anju Gurung, M.D., Chief Medical Officer
CHR: Kristi Stall, Chief Human Resources Officer
Web address: www.mahnomenhealthcenter.com
**Control:** City–County, Government, nonfederal **Service:** General Medical and Surgical

| Staffed Beds: 68 |
| --- |

## MANKATO—Blue Earth County

⊞ **MAYO CLINIC HEALTH SYSTEM IN MANKATO (240093)**, 1025 Marsh Street, Zip 56001–4752; tel. 507/625–4031 **A**1 3 5 9 10 13 **F**3 11 12 13 15 18 20 22 26 27 28 29 30 31 33 34 35 36 38 39 40 41 43 45 49 53 54 56 57 58 59 60 61 63 64 65 66 68 70 73 74 75 77 78 79 81 82 83 84 85 86 87 91 92 93 97 98 99 100 102 103 104 107 108 110 111 114 115 116 118 119 120 121 123 126 127 129 130 132 135 144 146 147 148 **P**6 **S** Mayo Clinic, Rochester, MN
Primary Contact: Gregory Kutcher, M.D., President and Chief Executive Officer
CFO: James Tarasovitch, Chief Financial Officer
CMO: Susan Pearson, M.D., Chief Medical Officer
CIO: Sarah Daniels, Vice President, Information Technology
CHR: Beth Dittbenner, Regional Director, Human Resources
Web address: www.isj–mhs.org
**Control:** Other not–for–profit (including NFP Corporation) **Service:** General Medical and Surgical

| Staffed Beds: 166 Admissions: 9985 Census: 105 Outpatient Visits: 284748 Births: 1497 Personnel: 1871 |
| --- |

MN

---

**Hospital, Medicare Provider Number, Address, Telephone, Approval, Facility, and Physician Codes, Health Care System**

★ American Hospital Association (AHA) membership
☐ The Joint Commission accreditation
○ Healthcare Facilities Accreditation Program
◇ DNV Healthcare Inc. accreditation
⇑ Center for Improvement in Healthcare Quality Accreditation
△ Commission on Accreditation of Rehabilitation Facilities (CARF) accreditation

---

## MAPLE GROVE—Hennepin County

✠ ◇ **MAPLE GROVE HOSPITAL (240214)**, 9875 Hospital Drive, Zip 55369–4648; tel. 763/581–1000 **A**1 9 10 21 **F**3 13 15 18 29 30 40 43 45 60 68 70 73 76 77 79 81 84 85 89 100 102 107 108 111 115 118 119 130 146 148 **P**8 **S** North Memorial Health Care, Robbinsdale, MN
Primary Contact: Andrew S. Cochrane, Chief Executive Officer
COO: Colleen Nadeau, Vice President Patient Care Operations
CFO: Robert Geiman, Senior Financial Analyst
CMO: Pamela Doorenbos, Medical Director, Medical Affairs
CHR: Rebecca A. Thiesfeld Rauen, Director Human Resources
CNO: Faith Zwirchitz, Director Nursing and Professional Practice
Web address: www.maplegrovehospital.org
**Control:** Other not–for–profit (including NFP Corporation) **Service:** General Medical and Surgical

**Staffed Beds: 108 Admissions: 8376 Census: 62 Outpatient Visits:** 180037 **Births: 4319 Total Expense ($000): 136085 Payroll Expense ($000):** 45195 **Personnel: 650**

## MAPLEWOOD—Ramsey County

✠ **ST. JOHN'S HOSPITAL (240210)**, 1575 Beam Avenue, Zip 55109–1126; tel. 651/232–7000 **A**1 2 3 5 10 **F**3 13 15 28 29 30 31 34 35 36 37 38 40 43 44 49 50 54 55 57 59 61 63 64 68 70 72 74 75 76 77 78 79 81 85 86 87 89 93 96 97 100 102 104 107 108 110 111 114 115 116 117 118 119 121 123 126 130 131 132 146 147 148 **P**8 **S** HealthEast Care System, Saint Paul, MN
Primary Contact: Scott L. North, FACHE, Senior Vice President and President, Acute Care Hospitals
COO: Paul Torgerson, Senior Vice President Chief Administrative Officer and General Counsel
CFO: Douglas Davenport, Senior Vice President and Chief Financial Officer
CMO: Stephen J. Kolar, M.D., Vice President Medical Affairs
CIO: Joanne Sundquist, Chief Information Officer
CHR: Dawn Kessler, Senior Vice President Human Resources
CNO: Debra J. Hurd, R.N., Vice President Nursing Acute Care
Web address: www.stjohnshospital–mn.org
**Control:** Other not–for–profit (including NFP Corporation) **Service:** General Medical and Surgical

**Staffed Beds: 192 Admissions: 12572 Census: 113 Outpatient Visits:** 111655 **Births: 2473 Total Expense ($000): 235807 Payroll Expense ($000):** 84017 **Personnel: 973**

## MARSHALL—Lyon County

★ **AVERA MARSHALL REGIONAL MEDICAL CENTER (241359)**, 300 South Bruce Street, Zip 56258–3900; tel. 507/532–9661, (Total facility includes 76 beds in nursing home–type unit) **A**9 10 18 **F**1 2 11 12 13 15 28 29 30 31 40 43 45 46 50 54 59 62 63 64 70 75 76 77 78 79 81 82 84 89 90 93 97 98 102 104 107 110 111 115 119 129 130 132 133 144 146 148 **P**6 **S** Avera Health, Sioux Falls, SD
Primary Contact: Mary B. Maertens, FACHE, President and Chief Executive Officer
CFO: Sharon Williams, Vice President Finance and Information Technology
CMO: Edward Woiske, M.D., Chief Medical Officer
CIO: Sharon Williams, Vice President Finance and Information Technology
CHR: Sonya Kayser, Human Resources Officer
CNO: Dodie Derynck, Chief Nursing Officer
Web address: www.averamarshall.org
**Control:** Other not–for–profit (including NFP Corporation) **Service:** General Medical and Surgical

**Staffed Beds: 111 Admissions: 2597 Census: 95 Outpatient Visits:** 95615 **Births: 532 Total Expense ($000): 62160 Payroll Expense ($000): 27177 Personnel: 348**

## MELROSE—Stearns County

★ **CENTRACARE HEALTH–MELROSE (241330)**, 525 Main Street West, Zip 56352–1043; tel. 320/256–4231, (Total facility includes 75 beds in nursing home–type unit) **A**9 10 18 **F**2 6 7 10 13 15 28 30 34 35 40 46 56 57 59 75 76 77 78 79 81 82 85 89 93 99 102 103 107 110 114 119 121 122 125 127 128 129 130 132 133 146 148 **S** CentraCare Health, Saint Cloud, MN
Primary Contact: Gerry Gilbertson, FACHE, Administrator
COO: Gerry Gilbertson, FACHE, Administrator
CFO: Adam Paulson, Director Finance
CMO: Dante Beretta, M.D., Chief of Staff
CIO: Janet Kruzel, Business Office Manager
CHR: Joyce Chan, Chief Human Resources Officer
CNO: Keri Wimmer, R.N., Patient Care Director
Web address: www.centracare.com
**Control:** Other not–for–profit (including NFP Corporation) **Service:** General Medical and Surgical

**Staffed Beds: 93 Admissions: 597 Census: 79 Total Expense ($000):** 24418 **Payroll Expense ($000): 11262**

## MINNEAPOLIS—Hennepin County

✠ ◇ **ABBOTT NORTHWESTERN HOSPITAL (240057)**, 800 East 28th Street, Zip 55407–3799; tel. 612/863–4000, (Includes SISTER KENNY REHABILITATION INSTITUTE, 810 East 27th Street, Zip 55407; tel. 612/874–4000), (Total facility includes 44 beds in nursing home–type unit) **A**1 2 3 5 9 10 21 **F**3 8 9 12 13 15 17 18 19 20 22 24 26 28 29 30 31 34 35 36 37 38 39 40 41 42 43 44 45 46 47 48 49 50 51 52 53 54 55 56 57 58 59 60 61 63 64 65 66 68 70 71 74 75 76 77 78 79 81 82 83 84 85 86 87 90 91 92 93 94 95 96 97 98 99 100 101 102 103 104 105 107 108 109 110 111 112 113 114 115 116 117 118 119 120 121 123 124 126 128 129 130 131 132 135 136 137 138 141 143 144 145 146 147 148 **P**6 **S** Allina Health, Minneapolis, MN
Primary Contact: Ben Bache–Wiig, M.D., President
CFO: Brian Weinreis, Vice President Operations and Finance
CMO: Penny Ann Wheeler, M.D., President and Chief Medical Officer
CIO: Susan Heichert, Senior Vice President and Chief Information Officer
CHR: Margaret Butler, Vice President Human Resources
CNO: Terry J. Graner, R.N., Vice President Patient Care
Web address: www.abbottnorthwestern.com
**Control:** Other not–for–profit (including NFP Corporation) **Service:** General Medical and Surgical

**Staffed Beds: 674 Admissions: 37046 Census: 488 Outpatient Visits:** 406195 **Births: 5357 Total Expense ($000): 1020125 Payroll Expense ($000): 415483 Personnel: 4161**

✠ **CHILDREN'S HOSPITALS AND CLINICS OF MINNESOTA (243302)**, 2525 Chicago Avenue South, Zip 55404–4518; tel. 612/813–6100, (Includes CHILDREN'S HOSPITALS AND CLINICS OF MINNESOTA, 345 North Smith Avenue, Saint Paul, Zip 55102–2346; tel. 651/220–6000; Robert Bonar, Jr., Chief Executive Officer) **A**1 3 5 9 10 **F**3 8 9 17 18 19 20 21 22 23 24 25 26 27 28 29 30 31 32 34 35 36 38 39 40 43 50 51 54 55 57 58 59 61 62 63 64 65 68 71 72 73 74 75 77 78 79 80 81 82 84 85 86 87 88 89 91 93 97 99 100 101 102 104 107 108 111 115 119 129 130 131 132 134 135 136 143 145 146 148 **P**6 8
Primary Contact: Robert Bonar, Jr., Chief Executive Officer
COO: David S. Overman, President and Chief Operating Officer
CFO: K. Alec Mahmood, Chief Financial Officer
CMO: Phillip M. Kibort, M.D., Vice President Medical Affairs and Chief Medical Officer
CIO: Jeffrey D. Young, Chief Information Officer
CHR: Samantha Hanson, Chief Human Resources Officer
CNO: Roxanne Fernandes, R.N., Chief Nursing Officer
Web address: www.childrensmn.org
**Control:** Other not–for–profit (including NFP Corporation) **Service:** Children's general

**Staffed Beds: 385 Admissions: 14516 Census: 280 Outpatient Visits:** 437518 **Births: 0 Total Expense ($000): 706166 Payroll Expense ($000):** 329139 **Personnel: 3710**

**FAIRVIEW RIVERSIDE HOSPITAL** See University of Minnesota Medical Center, Fairview

☐ △ **HENNEPIN COUNTY MEDICAL CENTER (240004)**, 701 Park Avenue South, Zip 55415–1829; tel. 612/873–3000, (Includes HCMC DEPARTMENT OF PEDIATRICS, 701 Park Avenue, Zip 55415–1623; tel. 612/873–2064) **A**1 2 3 5 7 8 9 10 **F**3 5 7 12 13 15 16 18 20 22 24 26 28 29 30 31 32 33 34 35 36 38 39 40 41 43 44 45 46 48 49 50 51 53 54 55 56 57 58 59 60 61 64 65 66 68 70 72 74 75 76 77 78 79 81 82 84 85 86 87 88 89 90 92 93 94 96 97 98 99 100 101 102 103 104 105 107 108 110 111 112 114 115 117 118 119 120 121 129 130 131 132 134 135 138 141 144 145 146 147 148 **P**6
Primary Contact: Jon Pryor, M.D., Chief Executive Officer
CFO: Larry Kryzaniak, Chief Financial Officer
CMO: Michael Belzer, M.D., Medical Director
CIO: Nancy Garrett, Chief Analytics and Information Technology Officer
CHR: Walter Chesley, Vice President Human Resources
CNO: Kathy R. Wilde, R.N., Chief Nursing Officer
Web address: www.hcmc.org
**Control:** County–Government, nonfederal **Service:** General Medical and Surgical

**Staffed Beds: 449 Admissions: 21628 Census: 336 Outpatient Visits:** 664357 **Births: 2183 Total Expense ($000): 800364 Payroll Expense ($000): 444938 Personnel: 4890**

✠ △ **MINNEAPOLIS VETERANS AFFAIRS HEALTH CARE SYSTEM**, One Veterans Drive, Zip 55417–2399; tel. 612/725–2000, (Nonreporting) **A**1 2 3 5 7 8 **S** Department of Veterans Affairs, Washington, DC
Primary Contact: Patrick J. Kelly, FACHE, Director
COO: Kurt Thielen, Manager Business Office
CFO: LeAnn Stomberg, Chief Financial Officer
CMO: Kent Crossley, M.D., Acting Chief of Staff
CIO: Karl Reid, Chief Information Officer
CHR: Kevin Upham, Chief Human Resources Officer
CNO: Helen Pearlman, Nurse Executive
Web address: www.minneapolis.va.gov
**Control:** Veterans Affairs, Government, federal **Service:** General Medical and Surgical

**Staffed Beds: 279**

*Many Facility Codes have changed. Please refer to the AHA Guide Code Chart.* © 2015 AHA Guide

**MN**

☒ **PHILLIPS EYE INSTITUTE (240196)**, 2215 Park Avenue, Zip 55404–3756; tel. 612/775–8800 **A**1 9 10 **F**81 **S** Allina Health, Minneapolis, MN
Primary Contact: Daniel S. Conrad, M.D., President
CFO: Chris Verdon, Director Finance
CMO: Emmett Carpel, M.D., Medical Director and Chief of Staff
CNO: Margaret Watry, Director of Patient Care Services and Nurse Executive
Web address: www.allinahealth.org/ahs/pei.nsf/
**Control:** Other not–for–profit (including NFP Corporation) **Service:** Eye, ear, nose, and throat

**Staffed Beds:** 8 **Admissions:** 6 **Census:** 1 **Outpatient Visits:** 15050 **Births:** 0 **Total Expense ($000):** 31149 **Payroll Expense ($000):** 9806 **Personnel:** 118

☐ **SHRINERS HOSPITALS FOR CHILDREN–TWIN CITIES (243303)**, 2025 East River Parkway, Zip 55414–3696; tel. 612/596–6100, (Nonreporting) **A**1 3 5 10 **S** Shriners Hospitals for Children, Tampa, FL
Primary Contact: Charles C. Lobeck, Administrator
CMO: Kenneth Guidera, M.D., Chief of Staff
CHR: Karen Frigen, Director Human Resources
Web address: www.shrinershospitalsforchildren.org/Hospitals/Locations/twincities.aspx
**Control:** Other not–for–profit (including NFP Corporation) **Service:** Children's orthopedic

**Staffed Beds:** 40

**SISTER KENNY REHABILITATION INSTITUTE** See Abbott Northwestern Hospital

**ST. MARY'S HOSPITAL AND REHABILITATION CENTER** See University of Minnesota Medical Center, Fairview

**UNIVERSITY OF MINNESOTA HOSPITAL AND CLINIC** See University of Minnesota Medical Center, Fairview

☒ **UNIVERSITY OF MINNESOTA MEDICAL CENTER, FAIRVIEW (240080)**, 2450 Riverside Avenue, Zip 55454–1400; tel. 612/672–6000, (Includes FAIRVIEW RIVERSIDE HOSPITAL, 2312 South Sixth Street, Zip 55454; tel. 612/371–6300; ST. MARY'S HOSPITAL AND REHABILITATION CENTER, 2414 South Seventh Street, Zip 55454; tel. 612/338–2229; UNIVERSITY OF MINNESOTA HOSPITAL AND CLINIC, 420 S.E. Delaware Street, Zip 55455–0392; tel. 612/626–3000; UNIVERSITY OF MINNESOTA MASONIC CHILDREN'S HOSPITAL, 420 Delaware Street, S.E., Zip 55455–0341; tel. 888/543–7866), (Total facility includes 36 beds in nursing home–type unit) **A**1 3 5 8 9 10 **F**2 3 4 5 6 8 9 11 12 13 15 17 18 19 20 21 22 23 24 25 26 27 28 29 30 31 32 33 34 35 36 37 38 39 40 41 43 44 45 46 47 48 49 50 51 52 54 55 56 57 58 59 60 61 64 65 66 68 70 71 72 74 75 76 77 78 79 80 81 82 84 85 86 87 88 89 90 91 92 93 96 97 98 99 100 101 102 103 104 105 106 107 108 109 110 111 112 113 114 115 116 117 118 119 120 121 123 124 126 128 129 130 131 132 134 135 136 137 138 139 140 141 142 145 146 147 148 **P**5 **S** Fairview Health Services, Minneapolis, MN
Primary Contact: Carolyn Wilson, R.N., President
CFO: John Doherty, Vice President Finance
CMO: Barbara Gold, M.D., Chief Medical Officer
CHR: Don Moschkau, Senior Director Human Resources
CNO: Laura Reed, Chief Nursing Officer
Web address: www.fairview.org
**Control:** Other not–for–profit (including NFP Corporation) **Service:** General Medical and Surgical

**Staffed Beds:** 839 **Admissions:** 34717 **Census:** 612 **Outpatient Visits:** 777363 **Births:** 2331 **Total Expense ($000):** 1312589 **Payroll Expense ($000):** 473772 **Personnel:** 7658

**VETERANS AFFAIRS MEDICAL CENTER** See Minneapolis Veterans Affairs Health Care System

**MONTEVIDEO—Chippewa County**

★ **CHIPPEWA COUNTY–MONTEVIDEO HOSPITAL (241325)**, 824 North 11th Street, Zip 56265–1683; tel. 320/269–8877, (Nonreporting) **A**9 10 18
Primary Contact: Mark E. Paulson, Chief Executive Officer
CFO: Darlene Boike, Chief Financial Officer
CIO: Jeff Plemel, Director Health Information
CHR: Vonnie Erickson, Human Resource Generalist
CNO: Linda M. Nelson, R.N., Director of Nursing Services
Web address: www.montevideomedical.com
**Control:** City–County, Government, nonfederal **Service:** General Medical and Surgical

**Staffed Beds:** 25

**MONTICELLO—Wright County**

☒ **CENTRACARE HEALTH–MONTICELLO (241362)**, 1013 Hart Boulevard, Zip 55362–8230; tel. 763/295–2945, (Nonreporting) **A**1 3 9 10 18 **S** CentraCare Health, Saint Cloud, MN
Primary Contact: Mary Ellen Wells, FACHE, Administrator
CFO: Nancy Friesen, Chief Financial Officer
CMO: Mark Dietz, Chief Medical Officer
CIO: Ruth Kremer, Director Information Services
CHR: Kathy Voss, Director Human Resources
CNO: Euretta Sorenson, R.N., Chief Nursing Officer
Web address: www.newrivermedical.com
**Control:** Hospital district or authority, Government, nonfederal **Service:** General Medical and Surgical

**Staffed Beds:** 110

**MOOSE LAKE—Carlton County**

★ **MERCY HOSPITAL (241350)**, 4572 County Road 61, Zip 55767–9405; tel. 218/485–4481 **A**9 10 18 **F**3 7 8 11 13 15 28 29 31 34 35 40 41 43 45 46 53 57 59 62 64 68 70 75 76 77 79 81 85 86 87 89 93 107 111 114 119 130 131 132 133 135 143 144 146 148 **P**5
Primary Contact: Michael Delfs, Chief Executive Officer
CHR: Sonya Towle, Director Human Resources
CNO: Donita Korpela, R.N., Director of Patient Care Services
Web address: www.mercymooselake.org
**Control:** Hospital district or authority, Government, nonfederal **Service:** General Medical and Surgical

**Staffed Beds:** 25 **Admissions:** 753 **Census:** 8 **Outpatient Visits:** 17082 **Births:** 121 **Total Expense ($000):** 31330 **Payroll Expense ($000):** 13936 **Personnel:** 205

**MORA—Kanabec County**

☒ **FIRSTLIGHT HEALTH SYSTEM (241367)**, 301 South Highway 65 South, Zip 55051–1899; tel. 320/679–1212 **A**1 9 10 18 **F**3 7 11 12 13 15 28 30 31 34 35 40 43 51 53 57 59 70 75 76 77 78 79 81 84 85 87 93 94 107 110 111 115 118 119 127 130 131 132 133 135 146 148
Primary Contact: Randy Ulseth, Chief Executive Officer
COO: Sandy Zutz–Wiczek, Chief Operating Officer
CFO: Gordy Forbort, Chief Financial Officer
CIO: Becky Gallik, Information Systems Manager
CHR: Kim Carlson, Senior Vice President Human Resources
CNO: Diane Bankers, Director of Nursing
Web address: www.firstlighthealthsystem.org
**Control:** County–Government, nonfederal **Service:** General Medical and Surgical

**Staffed Beds:** 25 **Admissions:** 1165 **Census:** 8 **Outpatient Visits:** 32658 **Births:** 141 **Total Expense ($000):** 55329 **Payroll Expense ($000):** 19617 **Personnel:** 344

**MORRIS—Stevens County**

★ **STEVENS COMMUNITY MEDICAL CENTER (241363)**, 400 East First Street, Zip 56267–1408, Mailing Address: P.O. Box 660, Zip 56267–0660; tel. 320/589–1313 **A**9 10 18 **F**3 11 13 15 28 29 31 34 35 40 44 45 50 57 59 64 70 76 77 79 81 85 86 87 89 97 107 111 114 119 131 132 133 135 145 146 148 **P**6
Primary Contact: John Rau, President and Chief Executive Officer
CFO: Kerrie Erickson, Vice President of Finance
CIO: Kerrie Erickson, Vice President of Finance
CHR: Karla Larson, Director Human Resources
Web address: www.scmcinc.org
**Control:** Other not–for–profit (including NFP Corporation) **Service:** General Medical and Surgical

**Staffed Beds:** 25 **Admissions:** 860 **Census:** 8 **Outpatient Visits:** 77543 **Births:** 108 **Total Expense ($000):** 34457 **Payroll Expense ($000):** 16623 **Personnel:** 239

**NEW PRAGUE—Scott County**

☒ **MAYO CLINIC HEALTH SYSTEM IN NEW PRAGUE (241361)**, 301 Second Street N.E., Zip 56071–1799; tel. 952/758–4431 **A**1 9 10 18 **F**8 11 13 15 28 29 30 31 34 35 36 39 40 43 46 53 57 59 63 64 68 74 75 77 78 79 81 82 85 87 93 97 107 108 111 114 117 119 125 129 130 131 132 133 135 146 147 **P**6 **S** Mayo Clinic, Rochester, MN
Primary Contact: Mary J. Klimp, FACHE, Administrator
CMO: Marty Herrmann, M.D., Medical Director
Web address: www.mayoclinichealthsystem.org/locations/new-prague
**Control:** Other not–for–profit (including NFP Corporation) **Service:** General Medical and Surgical

**Staffed Beds:** 25 **Admissions:** 824 **Census:** 10 **Outpatient Visits:** 43304 **Births:** 152 **Personnel:** 158

MN

**Hospital, Medicare Provider Number, Address, Telephone, Approval, Facility, and Physician Codes, Health Care System**

★ American Hospital Association (AHA) membership ☐ The Joint Commission accreditation ○ Healthcare Facilities Accreditation Program ◇ DNV Healthcare Inc. accreditation ⇑ Center for Improvement in Healthcare Quality Accreditation △ Commission on Accreditation of Rehabilitation Facilities (CARF) accreditation

**NEW ULM—Brown County**

✠ **NEW ULM MEDICAL CENTER (241378)**, 1324 Fifth Street North,
Zip 56073–1553; tel. 507/217–5000 **A**1 9 10 18 **F**3 4 5 11 13 15 28 29 31
32 34 35 36 40 43 45 55 56 57 59 64 65 68 70 75 76 77 78 79 81 82 85
87 93 94 97 98 99 100 101 102 103 104 107 108 111 114 119 129 130
131 132 135 144 146 148 **S** Allina Health, Minneapolis, MN
Primary Contact: Toby Freier, President
CFO: Steve Schneider, Manager Behavioral Services and Director Operations
CMO: Daniel Holmberg, M.D., Director of Medical Affairs
CHR: Anne Makepeace, Director Human Resources
CNO: Jennifer Brehmer, Director of Patient Care
Web address: www.newulmmedicalcenter.com
**Control:** Other not–for–profit (including NFP Corporation) **Service:** General
Medical and Surgical

**Staffed Beds:** 45 **Admissions:** 2315 **Census:** 19 **Outpatient Visits:** 119624
**Births:** 311 **Total Expense ($000):** 75347 **Payroll Expense ($000):** 25074
**Personnel:** 424

**NORTHFIELD—Dakota County**

★ **NORTHFIELD HOSPITAL (240014)**, 2000 North Avenue, Zip 55057–1498;
tel. 507/646–1000, (Includes LONG TERM CARE CENTER ), (Total facility includes
40 beds in nursing home–type unit) **A**9 10 **F**3 7 11 15 30 31 40 43 59 62 63
64 68 69 70 75 76 77 78 79 81 85 87 89 93 107 110 111 115 119 128 129
130 131 132 133 144 146 **P**6
Primary Contact: Steve Underdahl, Chief Executive Officer
COO: Jerry Ehn, Chief Operating Officer
CFO: Timothy L. Gronseth, Vice President and Chief Financial Officer
CMO: Jeff Meland, M.D., Vice President, Chief Medical Officer
CHR: Vicki Stevens, Human Resources Executive
CNO: Tammy A. Hayes, R.N., Chief Nurse Executive and Long Term Care
Administrator
Web address: www.northfieldhospital.org
**Control:** City–Government, nonfederal **Service:** General Medical and Surgical

**Staffed Beds:** 77 **Admissions:** 1753 **Census:** 51 **Outpatient Visits:** 124468
**Births:** 515 **Total Expense ($000):** 83383 **Payroll Expense ($000):** 33752
**Personnel:** 481

**OLIVIA—Renville County**

★ **RC HOSPITAL AND CLINICS (241306)**, 611 East Fairview Avenue,
Zip 56277–4213; tel. 320/523–1261, (Nonreporting) **A**9 10 18
Primary Contact: Nathan Blad, Chief Executive Officer
CFO: Nathan Blad, Chief Financial Officer
CIO: Cherry Weigel, Director Health Information Management
Web address: www.rchospital.com
**Control:** County–Government, nonfederal **Service:** General Medical and Surgical

**Staffed Beds:** 25

**ONAMIA—Mille Lacs County**

★ **MILLE LACS HEALTH SYSTEM (241356)**, 200 North Elm Street,
Zip 56359–7901; tel. 320/532–3154, (Total facility includes 57 beds in nursing
home–type unit) **A**9 10 18 **F**7 11 15 28 29 31 33 34 40 43 45 50 59 62 63 64
75 77 81 85 93 98 103 107 110 114 115 127 129 130 132 133 135 144 **P**6
Primary Contact: Bill Nelson, Chief Executive Officer
COO: Kim Kucera, Chief Operating Officer
CFO: John Unzen, Chief Financial Officer
CMO: Thomas H. Bracken, M.D., Vice President Medical Affairs
Web address: www.mlhealth.org
**Control:** Other not–for–profit (including NFP Corporation) **Service:** General
Medical and Surgical

**Staffed Beds:** 85 **Admissions:** 989 **Census:** 67 **Outpatient Visits:** 24690
**Births:** 2 **Total Expense ($000):** 36514 **Payroll Expense ($000):** 18116
**Personnel:** 328

**ORTONVILLE—Big Stone County**

★ **ORTONVILLE AREA HEALTH SERVICES (241342)**, 450 Eastvold Avenue,
Zip 56278–1133; tel. 320/839–2502, (Nonreporting) **A**5 9 10 18 **S** Sanford
Health, Sioux Falls, SD
Primary Contact: Kevin Benson, Interim Chief Executive Officer
CFO: Kevin Benson, Chief Financial Officer
CMO: Stacy Longnecker, Chief of Staff
CIO: Barbara Voecks, Chief Information Officer
CHR: Kim McCrea, Chief Human Resources Officer
CNO: Jennifer Wiik, Chief Nursing Officer
Web address: www.oahs.us
**Control:** City–Government, nonfederal **Service:** General Medical and Surgical

**Staffed Beds:** 89

**OWATONNA—Steele County**

✠ **OWATONNA HOSPITAL (240069)**, 2250 N.W. 26th Street, Zip 55060–5503;
tel. 507/451–3850 **A**1 9 10 **F**11 13 28 29 34 35 40 57 76 77 79 80 81 89
93 98 100 101 102 103 107 108 119 129 130 131 145 **S** Allina Health,
Minneapolis, MN
Primary Contact: David L. Albrecht, President
COO: Mark T. Gillen, Director of Operations
CFO: Mark T. Gillen, Director Finance and Operations
CHR: Sarah Stumme, Director Human Resources
CNO: Anne Draeger, Chief Nursing Officer
Web address: www.owatonnahospital.com
**Control:** Other not–for–profit (including NFP Corporation) **Service:** General
Medical and Surgical

**Staffed Beds:** 43 **Admissions:** 2613 **Census:** 26 **Outpatient Visits:** 36954
**Births:** 567 **Total Expense ($000):** 47424 **Payroll Expense ($000):** 17424
**Personnel:** 219

**PARK RAPIDS—Hubbard County**

✠ **CHI ST. JOSEPH'S HEALTH (241380)**, 600 Pleasant Avenue,
Zip 56470–1431; tel. 218/732–3311 **A**1 5 9 10 18 **F**3 11 12 13 15 28 29 30
32 34 35 39 40 43 45 47 50 57 59 63 64 65 70 75 76 77 79 81 82 84 85
93 107 108 110 115 118 129 130 131 132 133 134 146 **S** Catholic Health
Initiatives, Englewood, CO
Primary Contact: Benjamin Koppelman, President
CFO: Jay Ross, Chief Financial Officer
CMO: Darryl Beehler, D.O., Chief of Staff
CHR: John Tormanen, Director Mission and Human Resources
CNO: Deb Haagenson, R.N., Vice President of Patient Care
Web address: www.sjahs.org
**Control:** Church–operated, Nongovernment, not–for profit **Service:** General
Medical and Surgical

**Staffed Beds:** 25 **Admissions:** 1385 **Census:** 15 **Outpatient Visits:** 43229
**Births:** 141 **Total Expense ($000):** 44209 **Payroll Expense ($000):** 16310
**Personnel:** 229

**PAYNESVILLE—Stearns County**

★ **CENTRACARE HEALTH–PAYNESVILLE (241349)**, 200 West 1st Street,
Zip 56362–1496; tel. 320/243–3767, (Total facility includes 52 beds in nursing
home–type unit) (Data for 273 days) **A**9 10 18 **F**7 10 11 13 15 17 28 31 34 40
43 45 56 57 64 76 81 85 93 107 110 111 115 119 125 127 128 130 133
145 146 148 **S** CentraCare Health, Saint Cloud, MN
Primary Contact: Dennis C. Miley, Administrator
CFO: Gregg Redfield, Director Finance
CMO: Timothy Malling, M.D., Chief of Staff
CHR: Paulette Hagen, Human Resources and Administrative Services Director
CNO: Rachel A. Walz, Director Patient Care
Web address: www.centracare.com
**Control:** Other not–for–profit (including NFP Corporation) **Service:** General
Medical and Surgical

**Staffed Beds:** 82 **Admissions:** 339 **Census:** 57 **Outpatient Visits:** 25668
**Births:** 61 **Total Expense ($000):** 26755 **Payroll Expense ($000):** 12820
**Personnel:** 144

**PERHAM—Otter Tail County**

✠ **PERHAM HEALTH (241373)**, 1000 Coney Street West, Zip 56573–1108;
tel. 218/347–4500, (Total facility includes 96 beds in nursing home–type unit) **A**1
9 10 18 **F**3 7 10 11 13 15 28 29 30 33 34 35 36 40 43 45 56 57 59 62 64
69 75 76 77 79 81 85 86 89 93 97 104 107 110 111 115 119 125 128 129
130 131 132 133 144 146 147 148 **S** Sanford Health, Sioux Falls, SD
Primary Contact: Chuck Hofius, Chief Executive Officer
CFO: Brad D. Wurgler, Chief Financial Officer
CMO: Tim Studer, President Medical Staff
CIO: Jim Rieber, Director Information Systems
CNO: Bonnie Johnson, R.N., Vice President of Patient Services
Web address: www.perhamhealth.org
**Control:** Hospital district or authority, Government, nonfederal **Service:** General
Medical and Surgical

**Staffed Beds:** 121 **Admissions:** 786 **Census:** 105 **Outpatient Visits:** 271355
**Births:** 153 **Total Expense ($000):** 43981 **Payroll Expense ($000):** 19737
**Personnel:** 252

**PIPESTONE—Pipestone County**

★ **PIPESTONE COUNTY MEDICAL CENTER AVERA (241374)**, 916 4th Avenue
S.W., Zip 56164–1890; tel. 507/825–5811 **A**9 10 18 **F**8 13 15 28 29 31 34
35 40 45 46 47 48 50 53 56 57 59 62 63 64 65 68 75 77 79 81 82 85 93
97 107 110 111 115 119 130 131 132 133 135 146 148 **P**6 **S** Avera Health,
Sioux Falls, SD
Primary Contact: Bradley D. Burris, Chief Executive Officer
CFO: Dave Keeler, Chief Financial Officer
CHR: Judy Raschke, Director Human Resources
CNO: Jessica Smidt, R.N., Director of Nursing
Web address: www.pcmchealth.org
**Control:** County–Government, nonfederal **Service:** General Medical and Surgical

**Staffed Beds:** 25 **Admissions:** 443 **Census:** 4 **Outpatient Visits:** 32435
**Births:** 70 **Total Expense ($000):** 23502 **Payroll Expense ($000):** 8298
**Personnel:** 190

**MN**

## PRINCETON—Sherburne County

⊞ **FAIRVIEW NORTHLAND MEDICAL CENTER (240141)**, 911 Northland Drive, Zip 55371–2173; tel. 763/389–1313 **A**1 5 9 10 **F**3 11 13 15 18 19 26 28 29 30 31 32 33 34 35 36 40 43 45 46 50 57 59 64 70 75 76 77 78 79 81 85 86 87 89 91 93 94 100 107 110 111 114 115 119 129 130 131 132 146 147 148 **P**6 **S** Fairview Health Services, Minneapolis, MN
Primary Contact: John W. Herman, Chief Executive Officer
CFO: Kim Ericson, Vice President Finance
CMO: Greg Schoen, M.D., Regional Medical Director
Web address: www.northland.fairview.org
**Control:** Other not–for–profit (including NFP Corporation) **Service:** General Medical and Surgical

**Staffed Beds:** 37 **Admissions:** 1751 **Census:** 13 **Outpatient Visits:** 55935 **Births:** 426 **Payroll Expense ($000):** 25695 **Personnel:** 284

## RED LAKE—Beltrami County

☐ **RED LAKE INDIAN HEALTH SERVICE HOSPITAL (240206)**, 24760 Hospital Drive, Zip 56671, Mailing Address: P.O. Box 497, Zip 56671–0497; tel. 218/679–3912, (Nonreporting) **A**1 9 10 **S** U. S. Indian Health Service, Rockville, MD
Primary Contact: Louis P. Erdrich, Interim Chief Executive Officer
CMO: Paul Ditmanson, M.D., Clinical Director
CNO: Mary Ann Cook, R.N., Director of Nursing
Web address: www.rlnnredlakehospital.com/
**Control:** PHS, Indian Service, Government, federal **Service:** General Medical and Surgical

**Staffed Beds:** 19

## RED WING—Goodhue County

⊞ **MAYO CLINIC HEALTH SYSTEM IN RED WING (240018)**, 701 Hewitt Boulevard, Zip 55066–2848, Mailing Address: P.O. Box 95, Zip 55066–0095; tel. 651/267–5000, (Nonreporting) **A**1 9 10 **S** Mayo Clinic, Rochester, MN
Primary Contact: Thomas J. Witt, M.D., President and Chief Executive Officer
CMO: Jack Alexander, M.D., Chief Medical Officer
CHR: Kim Trittin, Manager Human Resources
Web address: www.mayoclinichealthsystem.org/locations/red–wing
**Control:** Other not–for–profit (including NFP Corporation) **Service:** General Medical and Surgical

**Staffed Beds:** 134

## REDWOOD FALLS—Redwood County

★ **REDWOOD AREA HOSPITAL (241351)**, 100 Fallwood Road, Zip 56283–1828; tel. 507/637–4500 **A**9 10 18 **F**2 3 11 13 15 29 31 34 35 40 45 46 57 59 62 63 75 77 79 81 84 93 107 111 115 119 129 130 131 133 146 148
Primary Contact: Bryan Lydick, Chief Executive Officer
CFO: Thomas Richard, Director Budget and Revenue Cycle
CIO: Tom Balko, Manager Information Systems
CHR: Jody Rindfleisch, Manager Human Resources
CNO: Dawn Allen, R.N., Chief Clinical Officer
Web address: www.redwoodareahospital.org
**Control:** City–Government, nonfederal **Service:** General Medical and Surgical

**Staffed Beds:** 25 **Admissions:** 537 **Census:** 5 **Outpatient Visits:** 21189 **Births:** 73 **Total Expense ($000):** 21919 **Payroll Expense ($000):** 8212 **Personnel:** 131

## ROBBINSDALE—Hennepin County

★ △ ◇ **NORTH MEMORIAL MEDICAL CENTER (240001)**, 3300 Oakdale Avenue North, Zip 55422–2926; tel. 763/520–5200 **A**2 3 5 7 9 10 21 **F**3 7 11 12 13 15 17 18 20 22 24 26 28 29 30 31 32 34 35 38 40 43 44 45 46 49 50 53 54 55 56 57 58 59 60 62 63 64 68 70 72 73 74 75 76 77 78 79 81 82 84 85 86 87 89 90 91 92 93 96 97 98 100 102 103 104 105 107 108 110 111 113 114 115 117 118 119 124 126 129 130 132 133 135 143 144 146 147 148 **P**6 8 **S** North Memorial Health Care, Robbinsdale, MN
Primary Contact: Jeff Wicklander, President
COO: Laura Latt, Vice President of Operations
CFO: Todd Ostendorf, Chief Financial Officer
CMO: J. Kevin Croston, M.D., Chief Medical Officer
CIO: Patrick Taffe, Vice President Information Services
CHR: David Abrams, Vice President Human Resources
CNO: Kelly Lynn White, Vice President of Patient Care and Chief Nursing Officer
Web address: www.northmemorial.com
**Control:** Other not–for–profit (including NFP Corporation) **Service:** General Medical and Surgical

**Staffed Beds:** 355 **Admissions:** 18155 **Census:** 212 **Outpatient Visits:** 646233 **Births:** 923 **Total Expense ($000):** 657608 **Payroll Expense ($000):** 312732 **Personnel:** 2613

## ROCHESTER—Olmsted County

☐ **COMMUNITY BEHAVIORAL HEALTH HOSPITAL – ROCHESTER (244017)**, 251 Wood Lake Drive S.E., Zip 55904–5530; tel. 507/206–2561, (Nonreporting) **A**1 9 10 **S** Minnesota Department of Human Services, Saint Paul, MN
Primary Contact: Stephanie Juhl, Administrator
CFO: Shirley Jacobson, Chief Financial Officer
CMO: Peter S. Millen, Chief Medical Officer MHSATS
CIO: Thomas Baden, Jr., Chief Information Officer
CHR: Connie Jones, Director Human Resources
CNO: Pamela R. Bajari, R.N., Nurse Executive MHSATS
Web address: www.health.state.mn.us
**Control:** State–Government, nonfederal **Service:** Psychiatric

**Staffed Beds:** 16

⊞ △ **MAYO CLINIC HOSPITAL – ROCHESTER (240010)**, 1216 Second Street S.W., Zip 55902–1906; tel. 507/255–5123, (Includes MAYO CLINIC – SAINT MARYS HOSPITAL, 1216 Second Street S.W., Zip 55902–1970; tel. 507/255–5123; ROCHESTER METHODIST HOSPITAL, 201 West Center Street, Zip 55902–3084; tel. 507/266–7890) **A**1 2 3 5 7 9 10 20 **F**3 4 5 6 8 9 11 12 13 14 15 17 18 19 20 21 22 23 24 25 26 27 28 29 30 33 34 35 36 37 38 39 40 41 43 44 45 46 47 48 49 50 51 52 53 54 55 56 57 58 59 60 61 63 64 65 66 68 70 72 73 74 75 76 77 78 79 80 81 82 83 84 85 86 87 88 89 90 91 92 93 94 95 96 97 98 99 100 101 102 103 104 105 106 107 108 110 111 112 114 115 116 117 118 119 124 126 130 132 134 135 136 137 138 139 140 141 142 143 144 146 148 **P**6 **S** Mayo Clinic, Rochester, MN
Primary Contact: F. Kenneth Ackerman, Chair, Hospital Operations
COO: Jeffrey W. Bolton, Chief Administrative Officer
CFO: Kedrick D. Adkins, Chief Financial Officer
CMO: Amy W. Williams, M.D., Chief Medical Officer
CIO: Christopher Ross, Chief Information Technology Officer
CHR: Jill M. Ragsdale, Chief Human Resources Officer
CNO: Pamela O. Johnson, MS, Chief Nursing Officer
Web address: www.mayoclinic.org
**Control:** Other not–for–profit (including NFP Corporation) **Service:** General Medical and Surgical

**Staffed Beds:** 1243 **Admissions:** 54010 **Census:** 822 **Outpatient Visits:** 278812 **Births:** 2525 **Personnel:** 28144

★ ◇ **OLMSTED MEDICAL CENTER (240006)**, 1650 Fourth Street S.E., Zip 55904–4717, Mailing Address: 210 Ninth Street S.E., Zip 55904–6756; tel. 507/288–3443 **A**9 10 21 **F**3 11 12 13 15 18 26 28 29 30 34 40 44 45 46 50 51 53 54 57 58 59 64 65 68 74 75 76 77 79 80 81 82 84 85 86 87 92 93 97 99 100 102 104 107 108 110 111 115 119 129 130 131 132 135 146 147 148 **P**6
Primary Contact: Tim W. Weir, Chief Executive Officer
CFO: Kevin A. Higgins, Chief Financial Officer
CIO: Susan M. Schuett, Chief Information Officer
CHR: Tom Hunsberger, Director Human Resources
CNO: Susan Klenner, Chief Nursing Officer and Vice President of Hospital Operations
Web address: www.olmmed.org
**Control:** Other not–for–profit (including NFP Corporation) **Service:** General Medical and Surgical

**Staffed Beds:** 42 **Admissions:** 1754 **Census:** 12 **Outpatient Visits:** 351949 **Births:** 873 **Total Expense ($000):** 168574 **Payroll Expense ($000):** 85215 **Personnel:** 796

## SAINT CLOUD—Stearns County

⊞ △ **ST. CLOUD HOSPITAL (240036)**, 1406 Sixth Avenue North, Zip 56303–1901; tel. 320/251–2700 **A**1 2 3 5 7 9 10 20 **F**3 5 11 12 13 14 15 17 18 19 20 22 24 26 27 28 29 30 31 32 34 35 36 37 38 39 40 43 44 45 46 47 48 49 50 51 54 56 57 58 59 60 61 62 63 64 66 68 69 70 72 74 75 76 77 78 79 80 81 82 84 85 86 87 88 89 90 92 93 94 96 97 98 99 100 101 102 103 104 105 106 107 108 110 111 115 117 118 119 120 121 123 126 129 130 131 132 134 135 141 145 146 147 148 **P**6 **S** CentraCare Health, Saint Cloud, MN
Primary Contact: Craig J. Broman, FACHE, President
COO: Linda A. Chmielewski, R.N., Vice President Operations
CFO: Greg Klugherz, Vice President Corporate Services and Chief Financial Officer
CMO: Mark Matthias, M.D., Vice President of Medical Affairs
CIO: Amy Porwoll, Vice President of Information Systems
CHR: Duane Rasmusson, Vice President Human Resources
CNO: Linda A. Chmielewski, R.N., Vice President Operations
Web address: www.centracare.com
**Control:** Other not–for–profit (including NFP Corporation) **Service:** General Medical and Surgical

**Staffed Beds:** 482 **Admissions:** 25548 **Census:** 305 **Outpatient Visits:** 473231 **Births:** 2551 **Total Expense ($000):** 643165 **Payroll Expense ($000):** 270369 **Personnel:** 4629

**MN**

---

**Hospital, Medicare Provider Number, Address, Telephone, Approval, Facility, and Physician Codes, Health Care System**

★ American Hospital Association (AHA) membership  ○ Healthcare Facilities Accreditation Program  ⇑ Center for Improvement in Healthcare Quality Accreditation
☐ The Joint Commission accreditation  ◇ DNV Healthcare Inc. accreditation  △ Commission on Accreditation of Rehabilitation Facilities (CARF) accreditation

**MN**

☒ **ST. CLOUD VETERANS AFFAIRS HEALTH CARE SYSTEM**, 4801 Veterans Drive, Zip 56303–2099; tel. 320/252–1670, (Total facility includes 225 beds in nursing home–type unit) **A**1 **F**2 3 4 5 6 8 9 11 12 15 18 29 30 31 34 35 36 38 39 44 45 47 50 53 54 56 57 58 59 61 63 64 65 68 74 75 77 78 79 81 82 83 84 85 86 87 91 92 93 94 97 98 100 102 103 104 105 106 107 111 115 119 128 130 132 135 143 144 146 147 148 **S** Department of Veterans Affairs, Washington, DC
Primary Contact: Barry I. Bahl, Director
COO: Barry I. Bahl, Director
CFO: Joseph Schmitz, Chief Financial Officer
CMO: Susan Markstrom, M.D., Chief of Staff
CIO: Denise Hanson, Information Technology Specialist
CHR: Lisa Rosendahl, Director Human Resources
CNO: Meri Hauge, R.N., Associate Director of Patient Care Services and Nurse Executive
Web address: www.stcloud.va.gov
**Control:** Veterans Affairs, Government, federal **Service:** General Medical and Surgical

**Staffed Beds:** 388 **Admissions:** 2455 **Census:** 346 **Outpatient Visits:** 397527 **Births:** 0 **Total Expense ($000):** 232508 **Payroll Expense ($000):** 111939 **Personnel:** 1573

**VETERANS AFFAIRS MEDICAL CENTER** See St. Cloud Veterans Affairs Health Care System

### SAINT JAMES—Watonwan County

☐ **MAYO CLINIC HEALTH SYSTEM IN SAINT JAMES (241333)**, 1101 Moulton and Parsons Drive, Zip 56081–5550; tel. 507/375–3261 **A**1 9 10 18 **F**3 15 18 28 34 35 40 43 53 57 59 64 75 81 86 87 97 107 110 114 119 128 129 130 132 133 144 146 148 **P**6 **S** Mayo Clinic, Rochester, MN
Primary Contact: Ryan J. Smith, Administrator
COO: Richard Grace, Chief Administrative Officer
CFO: James Tarasovich, Chief Financial Officer
CMO: Jennifer Langbehn, Medical Director
CIO: Thomas Borowski, Chief Information Officer
CHR: Gayle B. Hansen, R.N., Chief Integration Officer
CNO: Mark Fratzke, R.N., Chief Nursing Officer and Chief Operating Officer
Web address: www.mayoclinichealthsystem.org/locations/st-james
**Control:** Other not–for–profit (including NFP Corporation) **Service:** General Medical and Surgical

**Staffed Beds:** 13 **Admissions:** 243 **Census:** 5 **Outpatient Visits:** 40484 **Births:** 0 **Personnel:** 58

### SAINT LOUIS PARK—Hennepin County

☐ **PARK NICOLLET METHODIST HOSPITAL (240053)**, 6500 Excelsior Boulevard, Zip 55426–4702; Mailing Address: Minneapolis, tel. 952/993–5000 **A**1 2 3 5 9 10 **F**3 8 12 13 15 18 20 22 24 26 28 29 30 31 33 34 35 36 40 43 45 46 47 49 51 52 53 55 56 58 59 60 61 62 63 64 65 67 68 70 73 74 75 76 77 78 79 81 82 83 84 85 86 87 89 90 92 93 94 96 97 99 100 102 104 106 107 108 109 110 111 115 116 117 118 119 120 121 123 124 126 129 130 131 132 144 146 147 148 **S** HealthPartners, Bloomington, MN
Primary Contact: David Abelson, M.D., President and Chief Executive Officer
COO: Michael Kaupa, Executive Vice President and Chief Operating Officer
CFO: Sheila McMillan, Chief Financial Officer
CMO: Steven Connelly, M.D., Chief Medical Officer
CIO: Julie Flaschenriem, Chief Information Officer
CHR: Paul Dominski, Vice President Human Resources
CNO: Roxanna L. Gapstur, Ph.D., Chief Nursing Officer
Web address: www.parknicollet.com
**Control:** Other not–for–profit (including NFP Corporation) **Service:** General Medical and Surgical

**Staffed Beds:** 411 **Admissions:** 25194 **Census:** 217 **Outpatient Visits:** 58091 **Births:** 2992 **Total Expense ($000):** 397827 **Payroll Expense ($000):** 181525

### SAINT PAUL—Ramsey County

☒ **BETHESDA HOSPITAL (242004)**, 559 Capitol Boulevard, Zip 55103–2101; tel. 651/232–2000 **A**1 3 5 9 10 **F**1 3 6 11 29 30 38 44 45 50 53 56 60 61 64 68 74 75 77 79 85 86 87 91 93 100 101 103 104 105 107 111 114 119 130 132 146 **P**8 **S** HealthEast Care System, Saint Paul, MN
Primary Contact: Catherine Barr, Senior Vice President and President, Bethesda Hospital
CFO: Lea Jilek, Director Finance
CMO: Stephen J. Kolar, M.D., Vice President Medical Affairs
CIO: Mac McClurkan, Chief Information Officer
Web address: www.healtheast.org
**Control:** Other not–for–profit (including NFP Corporation) **Service:** Long–Term Acute Care hospital

**Staffed Beds:** 126 **Admissions:** 1173 **Census:** 91 **Outpatient Visits:** 0 **Births:** 0 **Total Expense ($000):** 76002 **Payroll Expense ($000):** 33012 **Personnel:** 414

☒ △ **GILLETTE CHILDREN'S SPECIALTY HEALTHCARE (243300)**, (Pediatric Specialty Hospital), 200 University Avenue East, Zip 55101–2507; tel. 651/291–2848 **A**1 3 5 7 9 10 **F**3 29 30 35 36 39 43 50 54 64 68 71 74 79 81 82 84 85 88 89 90 91 92 93 94 107 111 115 119 129 130 146 **P**6
Primary Contact: Barbara Walczyk–Joers, President and Chief Executive Officer
COO: Kathryn Wardrop, Vice President Strategy and Operations
CFO: James Haddican, Chief Financial Officer, Vice President Finance
CMO: Steven Koop, M.D., Medical Director
CIO: Timothy Getsay, Chief Information Officer, Vice President of Performance & Information Mgmt
CHR: Kit Brady, Vice President Human Resources
CNO: Karen Brill, R.N., Chief Nursing Officer, Vice President Care
Web address: www.gillettechildrens.org
**Control:** Other not–for–profit (including NFP Corporation) **Service:** Children's other specialty

**Staffed Beds:** 60 **Admissions:** 2446 **Census:** 34 **Outpatient Visits:** 152356 **Births:** 0 **Total Expense ($000):** 206469 **Payroll Expense ($000):** 99557 **Personnel:** 1116

☐ △ **REGIONS HOSPITAL (240106)**, 640 Jackson Street, Zip 55101–2595; tel. 651/254–3456 **A**1 2 3 5 7 8 9 10 **F**3 4 5 7 8 13 15 16 17 18 20 22 24 26 28 29 30 31 34 35 36 38 40 42 43 45 46 47 48 49 50 51 53 54 55 56 57 58 59 60 64 65 68 70 71 72 74 75 76 77 78 79 81 82 84 85 86 87 88 90 92 93 96 98 100 101 102 103 104 105 106 107 108 109 110 111 112 114 115 116 117 119 120 121 122 124 126 128 129 130 131 132 135 143 146 147 148 **S** HealthPartners, Bloomington, MN
Primary Contact: Megan Remark, Chief Executive Officer
CFO: Heidi Conrad, Vice President and Chief Financial Officer
CMO: Charles Fazio, Chief Health Officer and Medical Director Health Plan
CIO: Kim LaReau, Vice President and Chief Information Officer
CHR: Kim Egan, Executive Director Human Resources
CNO: Chris Boese, Vice President and Chief Nursing Officer
Web address: www.regionshospital.com
**Control:** Other not–for–profit (including NFP Corporation) **Service:** General Medical and Surgical

**Staffed Beds:** 451 **Admissions:** 25744 **Census:** 338 **Outpatient Visits:** 270733 **Births:** 2465 **Total Expense ($000):** 650812 **Payroll Expense ($000):** 310957 **Personnel:** 2918

☒ **ST. JOSEPH'S HOSPITAL (240063)**, 45 West 10th Street, Zip 55102–1053; tel. 651/232–3000 **A**1 2 3 5 9 10 **F**3 4 5 11 12 13 15 17 18 20 22 24 26 28 29 30 31 34 35 36 37 38 40 43 45 46 49 53 56 57 59 61 63 64 70 74 75 76 77 78 79 81 85 86 87 92 93 96 97 98 100 101 102 104 105 107 108 111 114 115 119 120 121 124 130 132 146 **P**8 **S** HealthEast Care System, Saint Paul, MN
Primary Contact: Scott L. North, FACHE, Senior Vice President and President, Acute Care Hospitals
COO: Brian Gager, Vice President, Acute Care Operations
CFO: Douglas Davenport, Senior Vice President and Chief Financial Officer
CMO: Stephen J. Kolar, M.D., Senior Vice President – Chief Medical Officer
CIO: Joanne Sunquist, Information System, Senior Vice President and Chief Information Officer
CHR: Dawn Kessler, Senior Vice President Human Resources
CNO: Debra J. Hurd, R.N., Vice President Nursing
Web address: www.healtheast.org
**Control:** Other not–for–profit (including NFP Corporation) **Service:** General Medical and Surgical

**Staffed Beds:** 234 **Admissions:** 11370 **Census:** 157 **Outpatient Visits:** 47977 **Births:** 986 **Total Expense ($000):** 255634 **Payroll Expense ($000):** 93533 **Personnel:** 1202

☒ △ ◇ **UNITED HOSPITAL (240038)**, 333 North Smith Avenue, Zip 55102–2389; tel. 651/241–8000 **A**1 2 3 5 7 9 10 21 **F**3 8 12 13 15 18 20 22 24 26 28 29 30 31 34 35 36 37 40 43 46 49 53 56 58 60 61 64 65 70 74 75 76 77 78 79 81 82 85 87 90 91 92 93 97 98 100 101 102 103 104 105 107 108 110 111 112 113 114 115 118 119 120 121 123 124 126 129 130 132 146 148 **P**6 **S** Allina Health, Minneapolis, MN
Primary Contact: Thomas O'Connor, President
CFO: John Bien, Vice President Finance
CMO: Alison Peterson, Vice President Medical Affairs
CIO: Susan Heichert, Senior Vice President
CHR: James McGlade, Director Human Resources
CNO: Mandy Richards, R.N., Vice President Patient Care
Web address: www.allina.com
**Control:** Other not–for–profit (including NFP Corporation) **Service:** General Medical and Surgical

**Staffed Beds:** 364 **Admissions:** 22158 **Census:** 254 **Outpatient Visits:** 169233 **Births:** 3313 **Total Expense ($000):** 443712 **Payroll Expense ($000):** 168899 **Personnel:** 2265

### SAINT PETER—Nicollet County

☐ **COMMUNITY BEHAVIORAL HEALTH HOSPITAL – ST. PETER (244010)**, 2000 Klein Street, Zip 56082–5800; tel. 507/933–5001, (Nonreporting) **A**1 10 **S** Minnesota Department of Human Services, Saint Paul, MN
Primary Contact: Christopher Schiffer, Administrator
CFO: Shirley Jacobson, Chief Financial Officer
Web address: www.health.state.mn.us
**Control:** State–Government, nonfederal **Service:** Psychiatric

**Staffed Beds:** 16

*Many Facility Codes have changed. Please refer to the AHA Guide Code Chart.*   © 2015 AHA Guide

★ ◇ **RIVER'S EDGE HOSPITAL AND CLINIC (241334)**, 1900 North Sunrise Drive, Zip 56082–5376; tel. 507/931–2200, (Nonreporting) **A**9 10 18 21
Primary Contact: George A. Rohrich, FACHE, Chief Executive Officer
CFO: Ann Lauer, Director Finance
CMO: Michael Sparacino, M.D., Chief Medical Staff
CIO: Kevin Schaefer, Manager Information Services
CNO: Paula Meskan, Director of Nursing
Web address: www.riversedgehealth.org
**Control:** City–Government, nonfederal **Service:** General Medical and Surgical

Staffed Beds: 17

### SANDSTONE—Pine County

★ **ESSENTIA HEALTH SANDSTONE (241309)**, 109 Court Avenue South, Zip 55072–5120; tel. 320/245–2212, (Total facility includes 45 beds in nursing home–type unit) **A**9 10 18 **F**7 11 12 15 28 29 30 34 35 40 45 59 64 65 75 77 80 81 85 87 91 92 93 107 110 114 128 130 132 133 135 143 144 148 **P**5 6 **S** Essentia Health, Duluth, MN
Primary Contact: Michael D. Hedrix, Administrator and President
CMO: Sarah Aldredge, M.D., Chief Medical Officer
Web address: www.pinemedicalcenter.org
**Control:** Hospital district or authority, Government, nonfederal **Service:** General Medical and Surgical

Staffed Beds: 56 Admissions: 241 Census: 48 Outpatient Visits: 17513
Births: 3 Total Expense ($000): 17614 Payroll Expense ($000): 8618
Personnel: 168

### SAUK CENTRE—Stearns County

★ **CENTRACARE HEALTH–SAUK CENTRE (241368)**, 425 North Elm Street, Zip 56378–1010; tel. 320/352–2221, (Nonreporting) **A**5 9 10 18 **S** CentraCare Health, Saint Cloud, MN
Primary Contact: Delano Christianson, Administrator
CFO: Delano Christianson, Administrator
Web address: www.centracare.com/hospitals/sauk_centre/index.html
**Control:** City–Government, nonfederal **Service:** General Medical and Surgical

Staffed Beds: 85

### SHAKOPEE—Scott County

✠ **ST. FRANCIS REGIONAL MEDICAL CENTER (240104)**, 1455 St. Francis Avenue, Zip 55379–3380; tel. 952/428–3000 **A**1 2 5 9 10 **F**3 12 15 28 29 30 31 34 35 36 38 40 41 43 45 46 50 51 53 57 58 59 64 68 75 77 78 79 80 81 82 84 86 87 93 107 108 110 111 115 117 118 119 120 124 129 130 131 132 144 146 147 148 **S** Allina Health, Minneapolis, MN
Primary Contact: Mike McMahan, Chief Executive Officer
CFO: Cynthia Vincent, Vice President Finance
CMO: Brian Prokosch, M.D., Vice President Medical Affairs
CIO: Joe Delveaux, Manager Information Services
CHR: Ann Glaves, Vice President Human Resources
CNO: Debora Ryan, R.N., Vice President Patient Care
Web address: www.stfrancis-shakopee.com
**Control:** Other not–for–profit (including NFP Corporation) **Service:** General Medical and Surgical

Staffed Beds: 86 Admissions: 5376 Census: 40 Outpatient Visits: 111733
Births: 1285 Total Expense ($000): 115869 Payroll Expense ($000): 41732 Personnel: 503

### SLAYTON—Murray County

★ **MURRAY COUNTY MEDICAL CENTER (241319)**, 2042 Juniper Avenue, Zip 56172–1017; tel. 507/836–6111, (Nonreporting) **A**9 10 18 **S** Sanford Health, Sioux Falls, SD
Primary Contact: Dennis Goebel, Chief Executive Officer
CFO: Renee Logan, Chief Financial Officer
CMO: Joyce Tarbet, M.D., Chief Medical Officer
CIO: Justin Keller, Chief Information Officer
CHR: Nancy Andert, Director Human Resources
CNO: Lorrie Mortensen, R.N., Chief Patient Services
Web address: www.murraycountymed.org
**Control:** County–Government, nonfederal **Service:** General Medical and Surgical

Staffed Beds: 18

### SLEEPY EYE—Brown County

**SLEEPY EYE MEDICAL CENTER (241327)**, 400 Fourth Avenue N.W., Zip 56085–1109, Mailing Address: P.O. Box 323, Zip 56085–0323; tel. 507/794–3571 **A**9 10 18 **F**13 15 28 34 40 43 45 59 68 77 81 91 93 107 114 119 127 129 130 133 **P**6
Primary Contact: Kevin Sellheim, Administrator
CHR: Connie Dahlberg, Director Business and Employee
CNO: Karee Schmiesing, Director of Nursing
Web address: www.semedicalcenter.org
**Control:** City–Government, nonfederal **Service:** General Medical and Surgical

Staffed Beds: 16 Admissions: 347 Census: 3 Outpatient Visits: 11107
Births: 30 Total Expense ($000): 11264 Payroll Expense ($000): 5110
Personnel: 90

### SPRINGFIELD—Brown County

☐ **MAYO CLINIC HEALTH SYSTEM IN SPRINGFIELD (241352)**, 625 North Jackson Avenue, Zip 56087–1714, Mailing Address: P.O. Box 146, Zip 56087–0146; tel. 507/723–6201 **A**1 9 10 18 **F**3 15 28 32 34 40 45 57 59 65 75 81 85 89 93 97 107 110 114 128 133 146 148 **P**6 **S** Mayo Clinic, Rochester, MN
Primary Contact: Scott D. Thoreson, FACHE, Administrator
CFO: James Tarasovich, Chief Financial Officer
CMO: Jennifer White, Chief of Staff
Web address: www.mayoclinichealthsystem.org
**Control:** Other not–for–profit (including NFP Corporation) **Service:** General Medical and Surgical

Staffed Beds: 23 Admissions: 213 Census: 3 Outpatient Visits: 15070
Births: 0 Personnel: 57

### STAPLES—Todd County

**LAKEWOOD HEALTH SYSTEM (241329)**, 49725 County 83, Zip 56479–5280; tel. 218/894–1515, (Total facility includes 100 beds in nursing home–type unit) **A**9 10 18 **F**3 6 7 8 10 11 12 13 15 28 29 30 31 34 35 36 39 40 43 50 52 53 56 57 59 62 63 64 65 68 75 77 78 79 81 82 84 85 86 87 93 97 98 99 100 101 102 103 104 105 107 110 114 119 125 127 128 129 130 131 132 133 135 143 146 147 148 **P**7
Primary Contact: Tim Rice, President and Chief Executive Officer
CFO: Jim Dregney, Chief Financial Officer
CMO: John Halfen, M.D., Medical Director
CHR: Janet Jacobson, Director Human Resources
CNO: Teresa Fisher, Chief Nursing Officer
Web address: www.lakewoodhealthsystem.com
**Control:** Other not–for–profit (including NFP Corporation) **Service:** General Medical and Surgical

Staffed Beds: 135 Admissions: 1867 Census: 116 Outpatient Visits: 209109 Births: 460 Total Expense ($000): 90030 Payroll Expense ($000): 33934 Personnel: 675

### STILLWATER—Washington County

✠ **LAKEVIEW HOSPITAL (240066)**, 927 Churchill Street West, Zip 55082–6605; tel. 651/439–5330 **A**1 3 5 9 10 **F**3 7 8 11 13 15 18 26 28 29 30 31 34 35 40 43 45 50 62 63 64 68 70 75 77 78 79 81 84 85 87 91 92 93 96 107 108 110 111 115 118 119 129 130 132 135 141 146 147 148 **P**6 **S** HealthPartners, Bloomington, MN
Primary Contact: Theodore Wegleitner, Chief Executive Officer
CFO: Douglas E. Johnson, Chief Financial Officer
CMO: Thomas Anderson, Vice President Medical Affairs
CIO: Emad Awwad, Director Care Delivery Sites Information Systems and Technology
CHR: Angy Duchesneau, Senior Director Human Resources
CNO: Jo Sittlow, Vice President Patient Care and Chief Nursing Officer
Web address: www.lakeview.org
**Control:** Other not–for–profit (including NFP Corporation) **Service:** General Medical and Surgical

Staffed Beds: 54 Admissions: 3705 Census: 28 Outpatient Visits: 61439
Births: 560 Total Expense ($000): 89408 Payroll Expense ($000): 91695

### THIEF RIVER FALLS—Pennington County

**MERITCARE THIEF RIVER FALLS NORTHWEST MEDICAL CENTER** See Sanford Thief River Falls Medical Center

**MN**

---

**Hospital, Medicare Provider Number, Address, Telephone, Approval, Facility, and Physician Codes, Health Care System**

★ American Hospital Association (AHA) membership ◇ Healthcare Facilities Accreditation Program ⇧ Center for Improvement in Healthcare Quality Accreditation
☐ The Joint Commission accreditation ◇ DNV Healthcare Inc. accreditation △ Commission on Accreditation of Rehabilitation Facilities (CARF) accreditation

★ **SANFORD THIEF RIVER FALLS MEDICAL CENTER (241381)**, 120 LaBree Avenue South, Zip 56701–2840; tel. 218/681–4240 **A**9 10 18 **F**3 5 11 13 15 28 29 31 33 34 35 38 39 40 43 45 50 53 64 65 68 70 74 75 76 78 79 81 82 85 87 93 94 98 99 100 101 102 104 106 107 110 111 115 119 129 130 131 132 133 135 144 146 147 148 **P**6 **S** Sanford Health, Sioux Falls, SD
Primary Contact: Brian J. Carlson, FACHE, Chief Executive Officer
COO: Rob Lovejoy, Chief Operating Officer
CFO: Casey R. Johnson, Chief Financial Officer
CMO: Janell Hudson, M.D., Chief Clinical Officer
CHR: Rob Lovejoy, Chief Operating Officer
Web address: www.sanfordhealth.org
**Control:** Other not–for–profit (including NFP Corporation) **Service:** General Medical and Surgical

**Staffed Beds:** 35 **Admissions:** 1713 **Census:** 17 **Outpatient Visits:** 59111 **Births:** 288 **Total Expense ($000):** 63976 **Payroll Expense ($000):** 23411 **Personnel:** 566

### TRACY—Lyon County

★ **SANFORD TRACY MEDICAL CENTER (241303)**, 251 Fifth Street East, Zip 56175–1536; tel. 507/629–3200 **A**9 10 18 **F**3 28 29 31 32 34 40 41 42 43 45 50 56 57 59 62 64 65 68 77 81 85 87 89 91 93 97 107 108 111 114 125 127 129 130 131 132 133 135 143 **S** Sanford Health, Sioux Falls, SD
Primary Contact: Stacy Barstad, Chief Executive Officer
CMO: Muhammad Ali, M.D., Chief Medical Officer
CIO: Janet Theisen, Chief Information Officer
CHR: Becky Foster, Manager Human Resources
CNO: Jeri Schons, R.N., Chief Nursing Officer
Web address: www.sanfordtracy.org
**Control:** Other not–for–profit (including NFP Corporation) **Service:** General Medical and Surgical

**Staffed Beds:** 25 **Admissions:** 147 **Census:** 1 **Outpatient Visits:** 17551 **Births:** 0 **Total Expense ($000):** 10228 **Payroll Expense ($000):** 4718 **Personnel:** 89

### TWO HARBORS—Lake County

**LAKE VIEW MEMORIAL HOSPITAL (241308)**, 325 11th Avenue, Zip 55616–1360; tel. 218/834–7300 **A**9 10 18 **F**15 28 35 40 43 53 59 63 64 75 77 81 82 84 93 111 115 119 130 133 144 148
Primary Contact: Greg Ruberg, Administrator
CFO: Eric Lohn, Chief Financial Officer
Web address: www.lvmhospital.com
**Control:** Other not–for–profit (including NFP Corporation) **Service:** General Medical and Surgical

**Staffed Beds:** 17 **Admissions:** 252 **Census:** 7 **Outpatient Visits:** 32026 **Births:** 0 **Total Expense ($000):** 14292 **Payroll Expense ($000):** 5524 **Personnel:** 93

### TYLER—Lincoln County

**TYLER HEALTHCARE CENTER AVERA (241348)**, 240 Willow Street, Zip 56178–1166; tel. 507/247–5521, (Nonreporting) **A**9 10 18 **S** Avera Health, Sioux Falls, SD
Primary Contact: Dale K. Kruger, Chief Executive Officer and Chief Financial Officer
CFO: Dale K. Kruger, Chief Executive Officer and Chief Financial Officer
Web address: www.www1.avera.org/amck/regionalfacilities/tyler/index.aspx
**Control:** Other not–for–profit (including NFP Corporation) **Service:** General Medical and Surgical

**Staffed Beds:** 25

### VIRGINIA—St. Louis County

✠ △ **ESSENTIA HEALTH–VIRGINIA (240084)**, 901 Ninth Street North, Zip 55792–2398; tel. 218/741–3340, (Total facility includes 90 beds in nursing home–type unit) **A**1 7 9 10 **F**3 11 13 15 17 18 28 29 30 31 34 35 40 41 43 45 47 48 56 59 63 64 65 70 75 76 79 80 81 84 85 87 89 90 96 97 107 108 110 111 115 119 124 128 129 130 132 135 146 147 148 **P**6 **S** Essentia Health, Duluth, MN
Primary Contact: Daniel Milbridge, Administrator and Chief Operating Officer
CFO: Steven Feltman, CPA, Chief Financial Officer
CMO: Michelle Oman, D.O., Chief Medical Officer
CNO: Michelle M. Fleming, Chief Nursing Officer
Web address: www.essentiahealth.org
**Control:** Other not–for–profit (including NFP Corporation) **Service:** General Medical and Surgical

**Staffed Beds:** 150 **Admissions:** 2004 **Census:** 94 **Outpatient Visits:** 41317 **Births:** 249 **Total Expense ($000):** 79209 **Payroll Expense ($000):** 37096 **Personnel:** 518

### WABASHA—Wabasha County

★ **SAINT ELIZABETH'S MEDICAL CENTER (241335)**, 1200 Grant Boulevard West, Zip 55981–1042; tel. 651/565–4531, (Total facility includes 146 beds in nursing home–type unit) **A**9 10 18 **F**2 6 10 11 12 13 15 28 29 30 34 35 40 43 45 46 49 50 53 56 59 62 65 75 76 77 81 85 93 94 107 110 114 119 125 128 130 133 143 145 146 148 **S** Ascension Health, Saint Louis, MO
Primary Contact: Thomas Crowley, President and Chief Executive Officer
CFO: John Wolfe, Chief Financial Officer
CMO: Brian E. Kelly, M.D., President Medical Staff
CHR: Jim Root, Vice President Human Resources
CNO: Kathy Lueders, R.N., Director of Nursing–Acute Care
Web address: www.stelizabethswabasha.org
**Control:** Church–operated, Nongovernment, not–for profit **Service:** General Medical and Surgical

**Staffed Beds:** 166 **Admissions:** 552 **Census:** 139 **Outpatient Visits:** 22577 **Births:** 61 **Total Expense ($000):** 24814 **Payroll Expense ($000):** 12036 **Personnel:** 265

### WACONIA—Carver County

★ ◇ **RIDGEVIEW MEDICAL CENTER (240056)**, 500 South Maple Street, Zip 55387–1791; tel. 952/442–2191, (Nonreporting) **A**2 9 10 21 **S** Ridgeview Medical Center, Waconia, MN
Primary Contact: Robert Stevens, President and Chief Executive Officer
CFO: Gordon Gablenz, Vice President Finance
CIO: Tamara Korbel, Director Management Information Systems
CHR: Sarah M. Hastings, Executive Director
Web address: www.ridgeviewmedical.org
**Control:** Other not–for–profit (including NFP Corporation) **Service:** General Medical and Surgical

**Staffed Beds:** 102

### WADENA—Wadena County

✠ **TRI–COUNTY HOSPITAL (241354)**, 415 Jefferson Street North, Zip 56482–1297; tel. 218/631–3510 **A**1 9 10 18 **F**3 7 11 13 15 17 28 31 34 35 40 50 54 57 59 64 65 70 75 76 77 81 85 86 87 89 93 99 104 107 110 111 114 115 118 119 127 129 130 131 132 133 135 146 147 148 **P**6
Primary Contact: Joel Beiswenger, Chief Executive Officer
CFO: Kim Aagard, Chief Financial Officer
CMO: John Pate, M.D., Chief Medical Officer
CIO: Bill Blaha, Manager Information Technology
CHR: Bryan Pederson, Human Resources Manager
CNO: Kathy Kleen, Chief Nursing Officer
Web address: www.tchc.org
**Control:** Other not–for–profit (including NFP Corporation) **Service:** General Medical and Surgical

**Staffed Beds:** 25 **Admissions:** 1127 **Census:** 8 **Outpatient Visits:** 110680 **Births:** 184 **Total Expense ($000):** 52871 **Payroll Expense ($000):** 21767 **Personnel:** 400

### WARREN—Marshall County

★ **NORTH VALLEY HEALTH CENTER (241337)**, 300 West Good Samaritan Drive, Zip 56762; tel. 218/745–4211, (Nonreporting) **A**9 10 18
Primary Contact: Brian G. Neubauer, Chief Executive Officer
CFO: Mitchell Kotrba, Chief Financial Officer
CNO: Sara Marie Kazmierczak, R.N., Director of Nursing
Web address: www.northvalleyhealth.org
**Control:** Other not–for–profit (including NFP Corporation) **Service:** General Medical and Surgical

**Staffed Beds:** 20

### WASECA—Waseca County

☐ **MAYO CLINIC HEALTH SYSTEM IN WASECA (241345)**, 501 North State Street, Zip 56093–2811; tel. 507/835–1210 **A**1 3 5 9 10 18 **F**3 8 11 15 18 28 29 30 31 32 34 35 40 45 50 53 56 57 59 63 64 65 74 75 77 79 81 82 87 90 93 97 103 104 107 110 111 114 119 128 130 131 132 133 143 144 146 147 148 **P**6 **S** Mayo Clinic, Rochester, MN
Primary Contact: Thomas Borowski, Administrator
CMO: Daniel Stahl, M.D., Medical Director
Web address: www.mayoclinichealthsystem.org
**Control:** Other not–for–profit (including NFP Corporation) **Service:** General Medical and Surgical

**Staffed Beds:** 25 **Admissions:** 260 **Census:** 6 **Outpatient Visits:** 47565 **Births:** 0 **Personnel:** 92

## WESTBROOK—Cottonwood County

★ **SANFORD WESTBROOK MEDICAL CENTER (241302)**, 920 Bell Avenue, Zip 56183–9669, Mailing Address: P.O. Box 188, Zip 56183–0188; tel. 507/274–6121 **A**9 10 18 **F**3 29 31 34 35 40 42 43 56 57 59 62 64 65 68 71 75 77 81 85 86 87 89 91 93 97 99 100 101 102 103 104 107 108 114 125 127 130 131 132 133 135 143 **P**6 **S** Sanford Health, Sioux Falls, SD
Primary Contact: Stacy Barstad, Chief Executive Officer
COO: Gordon Kopperud, Director Operations
CIO: Janet Theisen, Chief Information Officer
CHR: Becky Foster, Manager Human Resources
Web address: www.sanfordwestbrook.org
**Control:** Other not–for–profit (including NFP Corporation) **Service:** General Medical and Surgical

**Staffed Beds: 6 Admissions: 92 Census: 1 Outpatient Visits: 10290 Births:** 0 **Total Expense ($000):** 6225 **Payroll Expense ($000):** 2346 **Personnel:** 35

## WHEATON—Traverse County

★ **SANFORD WHEATON MEDICAL CENTER (241304)**, 401 12th Street North, Zip 56296–1099; tel. 320/563–8226 **A**9 10 18 **F**3 7 11 15 18 28 29 30 34 40 43 45 57 59 64 65 81 86 97 107 110 114 119 127 128 132 133 **P**6 **S** Sanford Health, Sioux Falls, SD
Primary Contact: JoAnn M. Foltz, R.N., Chief Executive Officer
CFO: Shane Ayres, Chief Financial Officer
CHR: Brenda Petersen, Human Resources
CNO: Chelsie Falk, Chief Nursing Officer
Web address: www.sanfordhealth.org
**Control:** Other not–for–profit (including NFP Corporation) **Service:** General Medical and Surgical

**Staffed Beds: 15 Admissions: 88 Census: 1 Outpatient Visits: 13730 Births: 0 Total Expense ($000):** 7639 **Payroll Expense ($000):** 2728 **Personnel:** 55

## WILLMAR—Kandiyohi County

☐ **CHILD AND ADOLESCENT BEHAVIORAL HEALTH SERVICES (244005)**, 1701 Technology Drive Northeast, Zip 56201–2275; tel. 320/231–5421, (Nonreporting) **A**1 10
Primary contact: Pamela Peters, Administrator
Web address: www.dhs.state.mn.us
**Control:** County–Government, nonfederal **Service:** Psychiatric

**Staffed Beds: 16**

⊞ **RICE MEMORIAL HOSPITAL (240088)**, 301 Becker Avenue S.W., Zip 56201–3395; tel. 320/235–4543, (Total facility includes 78 beds in nursing home–type unit) **A**1 2 9 10 **F**7 11 12 13 28 29 30 34 35 39 40 43 45 47 48 49 50 57 59 60 63 64 65 68 70 73 75 76 77 78 79 81 82 85 86 87 89 90 93 98 100 101 102 103 104 105 107 108 111 115 118 119 121 128 130 132 143 146 147 148
Primary Contact: Michael Schramm, Chief Executive Officer
CFO: Bill Fenske, Chief Financial Officer
CMO: Kenneth Flowe, M.D., Chief Medical Officer
CIO: Teri Beyer, Chief Information Officer, Quality
CNO: Wendy Ulferts, R.N., Chief Nursing Officer
Web address: www.ricehospital.com
**Control:** City–Government, nonfederal **Service:** General Medical and Surgical

**Staffed Beds: 188 Admissions: 3735 Census: 101 Outpatient Visits: 66299 Births:** 785 **Total Expense ($000):** 99166 **Payroll Expense ($000):** 42539 **Personnel:** 530

## WINDOM—Cottonwood County

★ **WINDOM AREA HOSPITAL (241332)**, 2150 Hospital Drive, Zip 56101–0339, Mailing Address: P.O. Box 339, Zip 56101–0339; tel. 507/831–2400 **A**9 10 18 **F**11 13 15 28 31 34 35 40 45 53 57 59 76 77 81 93 107 115 119 130 133 148 **S** Sanford Health, Sioux Falls, SD
Primary Contact: Geraldine F. Burmeister, FACHE, Chief Executive Officer
CFO: Kim Armstrong, Chief Financial Officer
CIO: Lori Ling, Information Technician
CHR: Emily Masters, Director Human Resources and Marketing
CNO: Kari Witte, Director Patient Care
Web address: www.windomareahospital.com
**Control:** City–Government, nonfederal **Service:** General Medical and Surgical

**Staffed Beds: 25 Admissions: 351 Census: 4 Outpatient Visits: 27453 Births:** 108 **Total Expense ($000):** 14361 **Payroll Expense ($000):** 5774 **Personnel:** 100

## WINONA—Winona County

★ **WINONA HEALTH (240044)**, 855 Mankato Avenue, Zip 55987–4868, Mailing Address: P.O. Box 5600, Zip 55987–0600; tel. 507/454–3650 **A**2 9 10 20 **F**11 13 15 28 29 30 31 32 34 35 48 49 50 53 56 57 59 60 61 70 74 75 76 77 78 79 81 82 84 85 86 87 93 96 97 98 99 100 101 102 103 104 107 108 110 111 115 118 119 127 129 130 131 132 135 144 146 147 148
Primary Contact: Rachelle H. Schultz, President and Chief Executive Officer
CFO: Jan Brosnahan, Chief Financial Officer
CMO: Dan Parker, M.D., Chief of Staff
CIO: Polly Peterson, Information Technology Director
CHR: Ashley Anderson, Manager Human Resources
Web address: www.winonahealth.org
**Control:** Other not–for–profit (including NFP Corporation) **Service:** General Medical and Surgical

**Staffed Beds: 53 Admissions: 2134 Census: 23 Outpatient Visits: 221602 Births:** 342 **Total Expense ($000):** 112893 **Payroll Expense ($000):** 48429 **Personnel:** 922

## WOODBURY—Washington County

⊞ **WOODWINDS HEALTH CAMPUS (240213)**, 1925 Woodwinds Drive, Zip 55125–4445; tel. 651/232–0228 **A**1 3 5 9 10 **F**3 13 15 28 29 30 31 34 35 36 37 38 40 43 44 49 50 57 59 61 63 64 68 70 74 75 76 77 78 79 81 85 86 87 93 96 97 100 102 104 106 107 108 111 115 119 121 130 132 146 **P**8 **S** HealthEast Care System, Saint Paul, MN
Primary Contact: Scott L. North, FACHE, Senior Vice President and President, Acute Care Hospitals
COO: Brian Gager, Vice President of Operations, Acute Care Hospitals
CFO: Douglas Davenport, Senior Vice President and Chief Financial Officer
CMO: Stephen J. Kolar, M.D., Senior Vice President and Chief Medical Officer
CIO: Joanne Sunquist, Chief Information Officer
CHR: Julie Garrison, System Director Human Resources Operations
CNO: Debra J. Hurd, R.N., Vice President of Nursing, Acute Care Hospitals
Web address: www.woodwinds.org
**Control:** Other not–for–profit (including NFP Corporation) **Service:** General Medical and Surgical

**Staffed Beds: 86 Admissions: 7321 Census: 54 Outpatient Visits: 56816 Births:** 1647 **Total Expense ($000):** 122799 **Payroll Expense ($000):** 43656 **Personnel:** 510

## WORTHINGTON—Nobles County

**SANFORD REGIONAL HOSPITAL WORTHINGTON** See Sanford Worthington Medical Center

★ **SANFORD WORTHINGTON MEDICAL CENTER (240022)**, 1018 Sixth Avenue, Zip 56187–2202, Mailing Address: P.O. Box 997, Zip 56187–0997; tel. 507/372–2941 **A**9 10 20 **F**3 11 13 15 18 19 26 27 28 31 34 35 40 43 45 50 57 59 60 62 64 68 69 70 75 76 78 79 81 85 86 93 97 107 110 111 114 116 119 120 121 126 129 130 131 132 133 135 144 146 147 148 **S** Sanford Health, Sioux Falls, SD
Primary Contact: Michael Hammer, Chief Executive Officer
CFO: Linda Wagner, Chief Financial Officer
CMO: Charles Dike, M.D., Chief of Staff
CIO: Brad Klassen, Information Technology Coordinator
CNO: Jennifer Weg, R.N., Chief Nursing Officer
Web address: www.sanfordhealth.org
**Control:** Other not–for–profit (including NFP Corporation) **Service:** General Medical and Surgical

**Staffed Beds: 48 Admissions: 1244 Census: 9 Outpatient Visits: 66962 Births:** 399 **Total Expense ($000):** 33541 **Payroll Expense ($000):** 13558 **Personnel:** 208

## WYOMING—Chisago County

⊞ **FAIRVIEW LAKES HEALTH SERVICES (240050)**, 5200 Fairview Boulevard, Zip 55092–8013; tel. 651/982–7000 **A**1 9 10 **F**3 11 13 15 18 26 28 29 30 32 34 35 36 40 43 45 51 57 59 62 63 64 65 68 70 75 76 77 79 81 85 87 93 96 107 110 111 114 115 119 129 130 131 132 134 144 146 147 148 **P**6 **S** Fairview Health Services, Minneapolis, MN
Primary Contact: John W. Herman, Chief Executive Officer
CFO: Kim Ericson, Vice President Finance
CMO: David Milbrandt, M.D., Vice President Medical Affairs
CNO: Margaret J. Swanson, Chief Nursing Officer
Web address: www.fairview.org/
**Control:** Other not–for–profit (including NFP Corporation) **Service:** General Medical and Surgical

**Staffed Beds: 49 Admissions: 3046 Census: 24 Outpatient Visits: 91187 Births:** 698 **Personnel:** 407

**MN**

# MISSISSIPPI

### ABERDEEN—Monroe County

★ ◇ **PIONEER COMMUNITY HOSPITAL OF ABERDEEN (251302)**, 400 South Chestnut Street, Zip 39730–3335, Mailing Address: P.O. Box 548, Zip 39730–0548; tel. 662/369–2455 **A**9 10 18 21 **F**3 8 10 11 29 35 40 41 43 45 50 53 70 75 77 81 85 86 89 90 93 96 97 98 103 106 107 112 115 119 125 127 128 130 131 133 135 143 146 **S** Pioneer Health Services, Magee, MS
Primary Contact: Christopher Chandler, Chief Executive Officer
CFO: Julie Gieger, Chief Financial Officer
CMO: Kevin Hayes, M.D., Chief of Staff
CHR: Lee Rob, Director Human Resources
Web address: www.pchaberdeen.com
**Control:** Corporation, Investor–owned, for–profit **Service:** General Medical and Surgical

**Staffed Beds:** 35 **Admissions:** 473 **Census:** 15 **Outpatient Visits:** 4020 **Births:** 0 **Personnel:** 179

### ACKERMAN—Choctaw County

⊠ **CHOCTAW REGIONAL MEDICAL CENTER (251334)**, 311 West Cherry Street, Zip 39735–8708; tel. 662/285–6235 **A**1 9 10 18 **F**29 40 43 77 87 89 90 93 107 119 127 130 133
Primary Contact: Jamie Rodgers, Interim Chief Executive Officer
**Control:** Corporation, Investor–owned, for–profit **Service:** General Medical and Surgical

**Staffed Beds:** 15 **Admissions:** 178 **Census:** 5 **Outpatient Visits:** 13866 **Births:** 0 **Personnel:** 100

### AMORY—Monroe County

⊠ **MERIT HEALTH GILMORE MEMORIAL(250025)**, 1105 Earl Frye Boulevard, Zip 38821–5500, Mailing Address: P.O. Box 459, Zip 38821–0459; tel. 662/256–7111 **A**1 9 10 **F**3 13 15 17 18 29 32 34 35 40 41 43 45 49 50 53 55 57 59 64 65 68 70 72 73 75 76 77 81 85 86 87 88 89 90 107 108 110 111 114 115 119 126 130 135 146 147 **P**8 **S** Community Health Systems, Inc., Franklin, TN
Primary Contact: J. Allen Tyra, Chief Executive
COO: Carol Upton, Regional Area Practice Manager
CFO: Bert Pickard, Chief Financial Officer
CMO: William Rogers, Chief Medical Officer
CIO: Jeff Wideman, Director Information Systems
CHR: Angie L. Weaver, Director Human Resources
Web address: www.gilmorehealth.com
**Control:** Corporation, Investor–owned, for–profit **Service:** General Medical and Surgical

**Staffed Beds:** 95 **Admissions:** 2941 **Census:** 33 **Outpatient Visits:** 47957 **Births:** 559 **Total Expense ($000):** 37228 **Payroll Expense ($000):** 11650 **Personnel:** 223

### BATESVILLE—Panola County

★ **MERIT HEALTH BATESVILLE (250128)**, 303 Medical Center Drive, Zip 38606–8608; tel. 662/563–5611 **A**9 10 **F**4 5 13 15 29 35 40 43 56 70 76 81 87 89 97 98 100 101 102 103 107 108 119 127 130 132 146 147 **P**1 **S** Community Health Systems, Inc., Franklin, TN
Primary Contact: Travis Sisson, Interim Chief Executive Officer
COO: Vince Brummett, Director Administrative Services
CMO: Michael R. Hovens, M.D., Chief Medical Officer
CIO: Will Morris, Director Information Technology
CHR: Arthur A. Wasek, Director Human Resources
Web address: www.trilakesmc.com
**Control:** Corporation, Investor–owned, for–profit **Service:** General Medical and Surgical

**Staffed Beds:** 112 **Admissions:** 2966 **Census:** 41 **Outpatient Visits:** 20575 **Births:** 227 **Personnel:** 296

### BAY SAINT LOUIS—Hancock County

⊠ **HANCOCK MEDICAL CENTER (250162)**, 149 Drinkwater Boulevard, Zip 39520–1658, Mailing Address: 149 Drinkwater Road, Zip 39520–1658; tel. 228/467–8600 **A**1 10 **F**3 13 15 17 18 28 29 30 34 35 39 40 43 45 51 54 57 59 64 65 70 75 76 77 79 81 82 85 86 87 89 90 93 97 107 108 110 111 114 115 118 119 127 130 131 135 144 146 147 **S** Ochsner Health System, New Orleans, LA
Primary Contact: Alan Hodges, Chief Executive Officer
CFO: Thomas Ramsey, Chief Financial Officer
CIO: Wes Griffith, Director Information Technology
CHR: Cathy Benvenutti, Human Resource Director
CNO: Virginia Kenny, Interim Chief Nursing Officer
Web address: www.hmc.org
**Control:** County–Government, nonfederal **Service:** General Medical and Surgical

**Staffed Beds:** 102 **Admissions:** 1923 **Census:** 18 **Outpatient Visits:** 45138 **Births:** 239 **Total Expense ($000):** 37770 **Payroll Expense ($000):** 16645 **Personnel:** 280

### BAY SPRINGS—Jasper County

★ **JASPER GENERAL HOSPITAL (250018)**, 15 A South Sixth Street, Zip 39422–9738, Mailing Address: P.O. Box 527, Zip 39422–0527; tel. 601/764–2101, (Includes JASPER COUNTY NURSING HOME ), (Total facility includes 110 beds in nursing home–type unit) **A**9 10 **F**10 55 59 62 64 108 128 130 133
Primary Contact: M. Kenneth Posey, FACHE, Administrator
CFO: Steve Green, Comptroller
CMO: A. K. Lay, Jr., M.D., Chief Medical Officer
CHR: Beth Gable, Administrative Assistant
CNO: Becky Ulmer, R.N., Director of Nursing
**Control:** County–Government, nonfederal **Service:** General Medical and Surgical

**Staffed Beds:** 126 **Admissions:** 166 **Census:** 99 **Outpatient Visits:** 0 **Births:** 0 **Personnel:** 47

### BILOXI—Harrison County

⊠ **MERIT HEALTH BILOXI (250007)**, 150 Reynoir Street, Zip 39530–4199, Mailing Address: P.O. Box 128, Zip 39533–0128; tel. 228/432–1571 **A**1 9 10 **F**3 8 11 12 13 15 17 18 20 22 26 29 31 34 35 37 40 43 45 46 47 48 49 50 54 59 61 64 65 68 70 73 74 75 76 77 78 79 81 82 85 86 87 89 90 92 93 94 97 98 100 102 103 104 105 106 107 108 110 111 112 114 115 118 119 120 121 122 123 126 130 135 143 146 147 148 **P**8 **S** Community Health Systems, Inc., Franklin, TN
Primary Contact: Monte J. Bostwick, Chief Executive Officer
COO: Tonda V. Haigler, Chief Operating Officer
CFO: Mark Wack, Chief Financial Officer
CMO: George Loukatos, M.D., President Medical Staff Affairs
CIO: George Bickel, Director, Information Systems
CHR: Brion Stanford, Director Human Resources
CNO: Mary Franklin, R.N., Chief Nursing Officer
Web address: www.merithealthbiloxi.com
**Control:** Corporation, Investor–owned, for–profit **Service:** General Medical and Surgical

**Staffed Beds:** 198 **Admissions:** 6918 **Census:** 95 **Outpatient Visits:** 102191 **Births:** 828 **Personnel:** 692

⊠ **VETERANS AFFAIRS GULF COAST VETERANS HEALTH CARE SYSTEM**, 400 Veterans Avenue, Zip 39531–2410; tel. 228/523–5000, (Nonreporting) **A**1 3 5 **S** Department of Veterans Affairs, Washington, DC
Primary Contact: Anthony L. Dawson, FACHE, Director
COO: Alexander Murray, Interim Associate Director
CFO: John D. Williams, Jr., Chief Financial Officer
CMO: Kenneth B. Simon, M.D., Chief of Staff
CIO: David D. Wagner, Chief Information Management Service
CHR: Andrew Roberts, Interim Chief Human Resources Officer
CNO: Deatosha D. Haynes, Interim Associates Director for Patient
Web address: www.biloxi.va.gov/
**Control:** Veterans Affairs, Government, federal **Service:** General Medical and Surgical

**Staffed Beds:** 392

MS

## BOONEVILLE—Prentiss County

☒ **BAPTIST MEMORIAL HOSPITAL–BOONEVILLE (250044)**, 100 Hospital Street, Zip 38829–3359; tel. 662/720–5000 **A**1 9 10 **F**3 12 15 17 18 28 29 30 40 43 57 59 68 70 75 81 85 87 89 90 93 98 103 107 108 111 118 119 130 132 133 146 **P**3 **S** Baptist Memorial Health Care Corporation, Memphis, TN
Primary Contact: James Grantham, Administrator and Chief Executive Officer
CFO: Donavan Leonard, Chief Financial Officer
CMO: Nathan Baldwin, M.D., President Medical Staff
CIO: Linda Chaffin, Director Medical Review
CHR: Shannon Bolen, Director Human Resources
Web address: www.bmhcc.org/booneville
**Control:** Other not–for–profit (including NFP Corporation) **Service:** General Medical and Surgical

**Staffed Beds:** 66 **Admissions:** 1587 **Census:** 32 **Outpatient Visits:** 29994 **Births:** 0 **Total Expense ($000):** 22250 **Payroll Expense ($000):** 8823 **Personnel:** 187

## BRANDON—Rankin County

☒ **MERIT HEALTH RANKIN (250096)**, 350 Crossgates Boulevard, Zip 39042–2698; tel. 601/825–2811 **A**1 5 9 10 **F**3 6 15 17 29 30 34 40 43 45 50 57 59 64 70 78 79 81 85 87 90 93 97 98 103 106 107 108 109 110 111 112 114 119 129 130 146 **P**8 **S** Community Health Systems, Inc., Franklin, TN
Primary Contact: Jon–Paul Croom, Chief Executive Officer
CFO: Christy Wilson, Chief Financial Officer
CMO: Edward Rigdon, M.D., Chief Medical Officer
CIO: Heather Holmes, Director Health Information Systems
CHR: Joy M. Hutson, Director Human Resources
CNO: Jacqueline C. Sullins, R.N., Chief Nursing Officer
Web address: www.crossgatesriveroaks.com
**Control:** Corporation, Investor–owned, for–profit **Service:** General Medical and Surgical

**Staffed Beds:** 134 **Admissions:** 2262 **Census:** 40 **Outpatient Visits:** 53279 **Births:** 0 **Total Expense ($000):** 39590 **Payroll Expense ($000):** 14571 **Personnel:** 287

## BROOKHAVEN—Lincoln County

★ ◇ **KING'S DAUGHTERS MEDICAL CENTER (250057)**, 427 Highway 51 North, Zip 39601–2350, Mailing Address: P.O. Box 948, Zip 39602–0948; tel. 601/833–6011 **A**9 10 20 21 **F**3 7 11 13 15 17 29 30 34 35 40 41 43 45 53 54 57 59 64 65 68 70 73 74 75 76 77 79 80 81 82 88 89 93 94 96 97 107 108 111 114 115 118 119 126 130 131 132 135 143 146 147 **S** QHR, Brentwood, TN
Primary Contact: Alvin Hoover, FACHE, Chief Executive Officer
COO: Tom Hood, Chief Operating Officer
CFO: Randy B. Pirtle, Chief Financial Officer
CMO: Richard Rushing, Chief of Staff
CIO: Carl Smith, Director Information Systems
CHR: Celine Craig, Director Human Resources
CNO: Cheri Walker, R.N., Chief Nursing Officer
Web address: www.kdmc.org
**Control:** Other not–for–profit (including NFP Corporation) **Service:** General Medical and Surgical

**Staffed Beds:** 122 **Admissions:** 2843 **Census:** 33 **Outpatient Visits:** 81568 **Births:** 651 **Total Expense ($000):** 76085 **Payroll Expense ($000):** 31523 **Personnel:** 580

## CALHOUN CITY—Calhoun County

★ **CALHOUN HEALTH SERVICES (251331)**, 140 Burke–Calhoun City Road, Zip 38916–9690; tel. 662/628–6611, (Total facility includes 120 beds in nursing home–type unit) **A**9 10 18 **F**7 40 43 64 68 70 81 87 89 98 103 107 114 119 128 130 133 **S** North Mississippi Health Services, Inc., Tupelo, MS
Primary Contact: James P. Franklin, Administrator
CFO: Kenneth Conley, Controller
CMO: Bruce Longest, M.D., President Medical Staff
Web address: www.nmhs.net/calhoun_city
**Control:** City–County, Government, nonfederal **Service:** General Medical and Surgical

**Staffed Beds:** 150 **Admissions:** 482 **Census:** 108 **Outpatient Visits:** 4461 **Births:** 0 **Total Expense ($000):** 17187 **Payroll Expense ($000):** 7873 **Personnel:** 275

## CANTON—Madison County

☒ **MERIT HEALTH MADISON (250038)**, Highway 16 East, Zip 39046–8823, Mailing Address: P.O. Box 1607, Zip 39046–1607; tel. 601/859–1331 **A**1 9 10 **F**13 15 29 35 40 43 70 73 76 81 87 107 108 119 130 146 **S** Community Health Systems, Inc., Franklin, TN
Primary Contact: Britton Phelps, Chief Executive Officer
CMO: Robert Tatum, M.D., Chief of Staff
CIO: Michelle Hughes, Director Health Information Management
CHR: Jackie Williams, Director Human Resources
Web address: www.madisonriveroaks.com
**Control:** Partnership, Investor–owned, for–profit **Service:** General Medical and Surgical

**Staffed Beds:** 44 **Admissions:** 1645 **Census:** 14 **Outpatient Visits:** 38763 **Births:** 394 **Personnel:** 238

## CARTHAGE—Leake County

★ **BAPTIST MEDICAL CENTER LEAKE (251315)**, 310 Ellis Street, Zip 39051–3809, Mailing Address: P.O. Box 909, Zip 39051–0909; tel. 601/267–1100, (Total facility includes 44 beds in nursing home–type unit) **A**9 10 18 **F**15 29 40 43 70 81 87 107 119 127 130 133 **P**6 **S** Baptist Health Systems, Jackson, MS
Primary Contact: Daryl W. Weaver, Interim Chief Executive Officer
COO: C. Gerald Cotton, Interim Chief Operating Officer
CFO: David Jackson, Chief Financial Officer
CMO: Doug Perry, M.D., Chief of Staff
Web address: www.mbhs.com/locations/baptist–medical–center–leake/
**Control:** Other not–for–profit (including NFP Corporation) **Service:** General Medical and Surgical

**Staffed Beds:** 69 **Admissions:** 776 **Census:** 55 **Outpatient Visits:** 20159 **Births:** 1 **Personnel:** 189

## CENTREVILLE—Wilkinson County

☒ **FIELD MEMORIAL COMMUNITY HOSPITAL (251309)**, 270 West Main Street, Zip 39631, Mailing Address: P.O. Box 639, Zip 39631–0639; tel. 601/645–5221 **A**1 9 10 18 **F**15 18 29 30 34 39 40 43 45 57 59 61 64 75 77 79 81 89 90 93 107 114 118 127 130 133 135 **P**6
Primary Contact: Chad Netterville, Administrator
CFO: Bryan N. Stevens, Chief Financial Officer
CIO: Locke Wheeles, Information Technology Manager
CHR: Dana McNabb, Human Resources Manager
CNO: Robin Walker, Chief Nursing Officer
Web address: www.fmch.org
**Control:** County–Government, nonfederal **Service:** General Medical and Surgical

**Staffed Beds:** 25 **Admissions:** 686 **Census:** 11 **Outpatient Visits:** 14279 **Births:** 0 **Personnel:** 145

## CHARLESTON—Tallahatchie County

**TALLAHATCHIE GENERAL HOSPITAL (251304)**, 201 South Market, Zip 38921–2236, Mailing Address: P.O. Box 230, Zip 38921–0240; tel. 662/647–5535, (Total facility includes 98 beds in nursing home–type unit) **A**9 10 18 **F**29 34 40 42 53 57 64 70 86 87 93 107 114 127 128 130 133 135 143 **P**6
Primary Contact: Jim Blackwood, Chief Executive Officer
CFO: Sammie Bell, Jr., Chief Financial Officer
**Control:** County–Government, nonfederal **Service:** General Medical and Surgical

**Staffed Beds:** 116 **Admissions:** 429 **Census:** 102 **Outpatient Visits:** 3498 **Births:** 0 **Personnel:** 330

## CLARKSDALE—Coahoma County

☒ **MERIT HEALTH NORTHWEST MISSISSIPPI (250042)**, 1970 Hospital Drive, Zip 38614–7202, Mailing Address: P.O. Box 1218, Zip 38614–1218; tel. 662/627–3211 **A**1 9 10 19 **F**3 13 15 17 18 20 22 28 29 30 31 34 35 40 43 46 49 50 53 57 59 64 65 70 73 74 76 79 80 81 85 87 89 92 93 107 108 110 111 114 115 119 126 130 131 132 **P**8 **S** Community Health Systems, Inc., Franklin, TN
Primary Contact: Joel Southern, R.N., MSN, Chief Executive Officer
CFO: Justin Stroud, Chief Financial Officer
CMO: Maha Wasef, M.D., Chief of Staff
CIO: Patricia Keenum, Health Information Management Systems Officer
CHR: Brandy Andrews, Director Human Resources
CNO: Clifton Smith, R.N., Interim Chief Nursing Executive
Web address: www.northwestregional.com
**Control:** Corporation, Investor–owned, for–profit **Service:** General Medical and Surgical

**Staffed Beds:** 181 **Admissions:** 3937 **Census:** 45 **Outpatient Visits:** 55668 **Births:** 689 **Total Expense ($000):** 62348 **Payroll Expense ($000):** 27168 **Personnel:** 385

**MS**

---

**Hospital, Medicare Provider Number, Address, Telephone, Approval, Facility, and Physician Codes, Health Care System**

★ American Hospital Association (AHA) membership
☐ The Joint Commission accreditation
◯ Healthcare Facilities Accreditation Program
◇ DNV Healthcare Inc. accreditation
⇑ Center for Improvement in Healthcare Quality Accreditation
△ Commission on Accreditation of Rehabilitation Facilities (CARF) accreditation

## CLEVELAND—Bolivar County

☒ **BOLIVAR MEDICAL CENTER (250093)**, 901 East Sunflower Road, Zip 38732–2833, Mailing Address: P.O. Box 1380, Zip 38732–1380; tel. 662/846–0061, (Total facility includes 35 beds in nursing home–type unit) **A**1 9 10 20 **F**3 11 13 15 17 18 26 29 30 34 35 39 40 41 43 45 46 56 57 59 60 70 73 76 79 81 82 85 87 88 89 93 94 96 103 107 108 109 110 111 112 115 116 118 119 120 130 132 133 146 **S** LifePoint Health, Brentwood, TN
Primary Contact: Robert L. Marshall, Jr., FACHE, Chief Executive Officer
CFO: Chad Miller, Chief Financial Officer
CMO: Michael Portner, M.D., Chief Medical Staff
CIO: Dusty Griffith, Director Information Systems
CHR: David Kent, Director Human Resources
Web address: www.bolivarmedical.com
**Control:** Corporation, Investor–owned, for–profit **Service:** General Medical and Surgical

**Staffed Beds:** 127 **Admissions:** 3405 **Census:** 72 **Outpatient Visits:** 49748 **Births:** 422 **Personnel:** 364

## COLLINS—Covington County

★ ◇ **COVINGTON COUNTY HOSPITAL (251325)**, Gerald McRaney Street, Zip 39428–3899, Mailing Address: P.O. Box 1149, Zip 39428–1149; tel. 601/765–6711, (Total facility includes 60 beds in nursing home–type unit) **A**9 10 18 21 **F**3 7 34 40 41 43 45 50 54 57 59 64 65 66 68 70 81 89 93 94 103 107 114 119 127 128 133 135 144 146 147
Primary Contact: Woody White, Chief Executive Officer
CFO: Kirstie Evans, Chief Financial Officer
CMO: Word Johnston, Medical Director
CIO: Ransom Jones, Information Technology Director
CHR: Beverly K. Ponder, Executive Assistant and Human Resources Coordinator
CNO: Martha Lynn Scott, Chief Patient Care Officer
Web address: www.covingtoncountyhospital.com
**Control:** County–Government, nonfederal **Service:** General Medical and Surgical

**Staffed Beds:** 94 **Admissions:** 754 **Census:** 74 **Outpatient Visits:** 25287 **Births:** 0 **Total Expense ($000):** 23489 **Payroll Expense ($000):** 10913 **Personnel:** 268

## COLUMBIA—Marion County

**MARION GENERAL HOSPITAL (250085)**, 1560 Sumrall Road, Zip 39429–2654, Mailing Address: P.O. Box 630, Zip 39429–0630; tel. 601/736–6303 **A**9 10 **F**29 35 39 40 43 61 70 75 81 87 89 90 93 97 107 108 111 118 119 130 133 144 146
Primary Contact: Bryan K. Maxie, Administrator
CMO: Mark Stevens, M.D., Chief Medical Staff
CIO: Donny Bracey, Director Information Services
CNO: Patricia Reid, Director of Nursing
**Control:** County–Government, nonfederal **Service:** General Medical and Surgical

**Staffed Beds:** 49 **Admissions:** 1212 **Census:** 24 **Outpatient Visits:** 29818 **Births:** 0 **Personnel:** 136

## COLUMBUS—Lowndes County

☒ **BAPTIST MEMORIAL HOSPITAL–GOLDEN TRIANGLE (250100)**, 2520 Fifth Street North, Zip 39705–2095, Mailing Address: P.O. Box 1307, Zip 39703–1307; tel. 662/244–1000 **A**1 9 10 19 **F**3 4 5 7 11 13 15 17 18 20 22 26 28 29 30 31 34 38 39 40 43 49 51 55 57 59 61 64 65 70 73 75 76 77 78 79 80 81 84 85 87 88 89 93 96 98 100 102 104 105 106 107 108 110 111 114 115 116 117 118 119 120 121 123 126 130 132 134 135 146 147 **S** Baptist Memorial Health Care Corporation, Memphis, TN
Primary Contact: Paul Cade, Administrator and Chief Executive Officer
CFO: David Webb, Chief Financial Officer
CMO: John E. Reed, M.D., Medical Director
CIO: Sheila Bardwell, Director Information Systems
CHR: Bob McCallister, Director Human Resources
CNO: Mary Ellen Sumrall, Chief Nursing Officer
Web address: www.baptistonline.org/golden–triangle/
**Control:** Other not–for–profit (including NFP Corporation) **Service:** General Medical and Surgical

**Staffed Beds:** 236 **Admissions:** 8615 **Census:** 104 **Outpatient Visits:** 110252 **Births:** 919 **Total Expense ($000):** 148033 **Payroll Expense ($000):** 46426 **Personnel:** 905

## CORINTH—Alcorn County

☐ **MAGNOLIA REGIONAL HEALTH CENTER (250009)**, 611 Alcorn Drive, Zip 38834–9321; tel. 662/293–1000 **A**1 9 10 13 19 **F**13 15 17 29 35 39 40 43 51 53 62 63 70 75 76 77 78 81 82 86 87 89 93 98 100 101 102 103 107 108 111 116 118 119 127 130 131 132 143 146 147 **P**7 8
Primary Contact: Ronny Humes, President and Chief Executive Officer
COO: Angela Nowlin, R.N., Senior VP, Operations
CFO: Jeff Taylor, Senior Vice President Finance
CMO: Felton Combest, M.D., Vice President Medical Affairs
CIO: David Parker, VP Information Technology
CHR: Regenia Brown, Vice President Human Resources
CNO: Pam B. Wallis, MSN, RN–B, MSN, Vice President Nursing Services
Web address: www.mrhc.org
**Control:** City–County, Government, nonfederal **Service:** General Medical and Surgical

**Staffed Beds:** 200 **Admissions:** 7485 **Census:** 92 **Outpatient Visits:** 143445 **Births:** 594 **Personnel:** 1189

## DE KALB—Kemper County

★ **JOHN C. STENNIS MEMORIAL HOSPITAL (251335)**, 14365 Highway 16 West, Zip 39328–7974; tel. 769/486–1000 **A**9 10 18 **F**29 40 43 70 75 107 119 127 133 **P**6 **S** Rush Health Systems, Meridian, MS
Primary Contact: Michael Nester, Administrator
Web address: www.johncstennismemorialhospital.com/jcsmh/
**Control:** Other not–for–profit (including NFP Corporation) **Service:** General Medical and Surgical

**Staffed Beds:** 25 **Admissions:** 326 **Census:** 7 **Outpatient Visits:** 6325 **Births:** 1 **Personnel:** 167

## EUPORA—Webster County

☒ **NORTH MISSISSIPPI MEDICAL CENTER–EUPORA (250020)**, 70 Medical Plaza, Zip 39744–4018; tel. 662/258–6221, (Total facility includes 35 beds in nursing home–type unit) **A**1 9 10 **F**29 35 40 43 53 70 86 87 89 107 111 119 127 128 130 133 146 **S** North Mississippi Health Services, Inc., Tupelo, MS
Primary Contact: Wes Sigler, Administrator
CFO: Adonna Mitchell, Director Fiscal Services
CMO: Christy Vowell, D.O., Chief of Staff
CIO: Helen Reed, Director Health Information
CHR: Dorothy Castle, Director Human Resources
Web address: www.nmhs.net/eupora
**Control:** Other not–for–profit (including NFP Corporation) **Service:** General Medical and Surgical

**Staffed Beds:** 73 **Admissions:** 1379 **Census:** 55 **Outpatient Visits:** 15908 **Births:** 0 **Personnel:** 190

## FAYETTE—Jefferson County

★ **JEFFERSON COUNTY HOSPITAL (250060)**, 870 South Main Street, Zip 39069–5695, Mailing Address: P.O. Box 577, Zip 39069–0577; tel. 601/786–3401 **A**9 10 **F**3 40 42 70 106 130
Primary Contact: Wanda C. Fleming, Chief Executive Officer
CMO: Khar Omolara, M.D., Chief Medical Staff
CHR: Patricia Selmon, Director Public Relations and Chief Human Resources
**Control:** County–Government, nonfederal **Service:** General Medical and Surgical

**Staffed Beds:** 30 **Admissions:** 606 **Census:** 17 **Births:** 0 **Personnel:** 97

## FLOWOOD—Rankin County

☒ **MERIT HEALTH RIVER OAKS (250138)**, 1030 River Oaks Drive, Zip 39232–9553, Mailing Address: P.O. Box 5100, Jackson, Zip 39296–5100; tel. 601/932–1030 **A**1 3 10 **F**13 15 29 35 39 45 43 51 70 72 73 76 81 82 87 89 93 111 130 146 147 **P**8 **S** Community Health Systems, Inc., Franklin, TN
Primary Contact: L. Dwayne Blaylock, Chief Executive Officer
COO: Heather Sistrunk, R.N., Chief Operating Officer
CFO: Brad Sinclair, Chief Financial Officer
CIO: Pat Jones, Director Information Systems
CHR: Warren Weed, Director Human Resources
CNO: Sherry P. Cook, R.N., Chief Nursing Executive
Web address: www.riveroakshosp.com
**Control:** Corporation, Investor–owned, for–profit **Service:** General Medical and Surgical

**Staffed Beds:** 158 **Admissions:** 4764 **Census:** 48 **Outpatient Visits:** 55825 **Births:** 1619 **Personnel:** 540

☒ **MERIT HEALTH WOMAN'S HOSPITAL (250136)**, 1026 North Flowood Drive, Zip 39232–9532, Mailing Address: P.O. Box 4546, Jackson, Zip 39296–4546; tel. 601/932–1000 **A**1 10 **F**13 15 35 39 70 72 73 76 81 108 130 147 **S** Community Health Systems, Inc., Franklin, TN
Primary Contact: Sherry J. Pitts, Chief Executive Officer
CFO: Jeff Bedford, Executive Vice President and Chief Financial Officer
CMO: Edra Kimmel, M.D., Chief of Staff
CHR: Warren Weed, Director Associate Relations
Web address: www.womanshospitalms.com
**Control:** Corporation, Investor–owned, for–profit **Service:** Obstetrics and gynecology

**Staffed Beds:** 60 **Admissions:** 1720 **Census:** 15 **Outpatient Visits:** 11592 **Births:** 1248 **Personnel:** 178

**MS**

*Many Facility Codes have changed. Please refer to the AHA Guide Code Chart.*    © 2015 AHA Guide

## FOREST—Scott County

★ ◇ **LACKEY MEMORIAL HOSPITAL (251300)**, 330 Broad Street, Zip 39074–3508, Mailing Address: P.O. Box 428, Zip 39074–0428; tel. 601/469–4151, (Total facility includes 20 beds in nursing home–type unit) **A**9 10 18 21 **F**3 8 11 15 18 29 34 35 38 40 41 43 45 50 54 55 56 57 59 64 65 66 68 70 81 89 92 98 106 107 108 110 111 114 119 127 128 130 133 143 **P**5 6 **S** Pioneer Health Services, Magee, MS
Primary Contact: Steve Widener, Interim Chief Executive Officer
CFO: Julie Gieger, Chief Financial Officer
CMO: John Paul Lee, M.D., Chief of Staff
CIO: Eddie Pope, Chief Information Officer
CHR: Donn Paul, Chief Human Resources
Web address: www.lackeymemorialhospital.com
**Control:** Other not–for–profit (including NFP Corporation) **Service:** General Medical and Surgical

**Staffed Beds:** 55 **Admissions:** 1537 **Census:** 48 **Outpatient Visits:** 22020 **Births:** 0 **Total Expense ($000):** 25059 **Payroll Expense ($000):** 9060 **Personnel:** 150

## GREENVILLE—Washington County

◇ **ALLEGIANCE SPECIALTY HOSPITAL OF GREENVILLE (252013)**, 300 South Washington Avenue, 3rd Floor, Zip 38701–4719; tel. 662/332–7344 **A**10 21 **F**17 29 70 87 130 **S** Allegiance Health Management, Shreveport, LA
Primary Contact: Vernail Herzog, Chief Executive Officer
CMO: Parvez Karim, M.D., Chief Medical Officer
CIO: Sharon Scott, Health Information Director
CHR: Sharon Taylor, Human Resources Director
CNO: John Read, Chief Nursing Officer
Web address: www.ahmgt.com
**Control:** Corporation, Investor–owned, for–profit **Service:** Long–Term Acute Care hospital

**Staffed Beds:** 39 **Admissions:** 375 **Census:** 27 **Outpatient Visits:** 0 **Births:** 0 **Personnel:** 101

★ **DELTA REGIONAL MEDICAL CENTER (250082)**, 1400 East Union Street, Zip 38704–5247; tel. 662/378–3783, (Includes THE KING'S DAUGHTERS HOSPITAL, 300 Washington Avenue, Zip 38701–3614, Mailing Address: P.O. Box 1857, Zip 38702–1857; tel. 662/378–2020) **A**9 10 19 **F**1 3 4 11 13 15 17 18 20 22 28 29 30 31 34 35 38 39 40 43 45 46 50 51 55 57 59 62 63 64 65 66 68 70 72 73 75 76 77 78 79 81 84 85 89 90 93 94 96 97 98 103 104 107 108 109 110 111 114 115 116 118 119 127 129 130 131 132 135 144 146 147 148 **P**6 8
Primary Contact: Scott Christensen, Chief Executive Officer
CFO: C. Thomas Moore, Chief Financial Officer
CIO: Jennifer Parker, Director Information Systems
CHR: Chrissy Nicholson, Vice President Human Resources
CNO: Amy Walker, Chief Nursing Officer
Web address: www.deltaregional.com
**Control:** County–Government, nonfederal **Service:** General Medical and Surgical

**Staffed Beds:** 217 **Admissions:** 7632 **Census:** 114 **Outpatient Visits:** 88413 **Births:** 795 **Total Expense ($000):** 112368 **Payroll Expense ($000):** 50225 **Personnel:** 866

## GREENWOOD—Leflore County

**AMG SPECIALTY HOSPITAL–GREENWOOD (252010)**, 1401 River Road Floor 2, Zip 38930–4030; tel. 662/459–2681 **A**9 10 **F**1 3 18 34 50 59 130 **S** AMG Integrated Healthcare Management, Lafayette, LA
Primary Contact: Jennifer Wallace, Chief Executive Officer
CMO: Gutti Rao, M.D., Medical Director
CNO: Brenda Small, Chief Clinical Officer
Web address: www.amggreenwood.com/
**Control:** Partnership, Investor–owned, for–profit **Service:** Long–Term Acute Care hospital

**Staffed Beds:** 40 **Admissions:** 389 **Census:** 27 **Outpatient Visits:** 0 **Births:** 0 **Personnel:** 77

☐ △ **GREENWOOD LEFLORE HOSPITAL (250099)**, 1401 River Road, Zip 38930–4030, Mailing Address: Drawer 1410, Zip 38935–1410; tel. 662/459–7000 **A**1 7 9 10 19 **F**3 8 13 15 17 18 20 29 31 32 33 35 39 40 43 45 53 56 57 59 61 68 70 74 75 76 79 81 82 85 86 87 89 90 93 94 96 98 103 107 108 110 111 114 117 118 119 127 128 129 130 132 145 146 147 148 **P**6 8
Primary Contact: James H. Jackson, Jr., Executive Director
COO: Dodie McElmurray, Chief Operating Officer
CFO: Dawne Holmes, Chief Financial Officer
CMO: Daneca Donna DiPaolo, Chief of Staff
CIO: Mark S. Hutson, Chief Information Officer
CHR: Key Britt, Associate Director
CNO: Rebecca Edwards, Chief Nursing Officer
Web address: www.glh.org
**Control:** City–County, Government, nonfederal **Service:** General Medical and Surgical

**Staffed Beds:** 220 **Admissions:** 6542 **Census:** 83 **Outpatient Visits:** 142937 **Births:** 580 **Personnel:** 887

## GRENADA—Grenada County

★ ◇ **UNIVERSITY OF MISSISSIPPI MEDICAL CENTER GRENADA (250015)**, 960 Avent Drive, Zip 38901–5230; tel. 662/227–7000 **A**9 10 20 21 **F**3 7 8 11 13 15 17 29 30 32 34 35 39 40 43 53 56 57 59 60 62 64 65 70 73 76 77 79 80 81 82 85 87 89 90 93 94 96 97 103 107 108 110 111 115 118 119 127 128 130 143 146 147 **P**6 **S** University Hospitals and Health System, Jackson, MS
Primary Contact: David G. Putt, FACHE, Chief Executive Officer
COO: Molly B. Brown, Chief Operating Officer
CFO: Scott Whittemore, Chief Financial Officer
CIO: Sarah Longest, Chief Information Officer
CHR: Claudette Hathcock, Administrative Director Human Resources
CNO: Carla Stanley, Chief Nursing Officer
Web address: www.glmc.net
**Control:** State–Government, nonfederal **Service:** General Medical and Surgical

**Staffed Beds:** 107 **Admissions:** 2594 **Census:** 28 **Outpatient Visits:** 49650 **Births:** 443 **Total Expense ($000):** 43435 **Payroll Expense ($000):** 18533 **Personnel:** 392

## GULFPORT—Harrison County

⊞ **GARDEN PARK MEDICAL CENTER (250123)**, 15200 Community Road, Zip 39503–3085, Mailing Address: P.O. Box 1240, Zip 39502–1240; tel. 228/575–7000 **A**1 9 10 **F**3 12 13 15 18 19 29 34 35 40 41 45 46 49 57 59 70 74 76 79 81 85 86 87 89 90 97 98 103 107 108 110 111 112 114 115 116 118 119 126 130 132 146 147 **S** HCA, Nashville, TN
Primary Contact: Brenda M. Waltz, FACHE, Chief Executive Officer
COO: Daphne David, Chief Operating Officer
CFO: Regina Ramazani, Chief Financial Officer
CMO: T. Paul Mace, Chief Medical Officer
CIO: Chris Oubre, Information Technology Director
CHR: Michael Pocchiari, Director Human Resources
CNO: Cheryl Thompson, Chief Nursing Officer
Web address: www.gpmedical.com
**Control:** Corporation, Investor–owned, for–profit **Service:** General Medical and Surgical

**Staffed Beds:** 130 **Admissions:** 4050 **Census:** 48 **Outpatient Visits:** 67546 **Births:** 839 **Total Expense ($000):** 71532 **Payroll Expense ($000):** 24544 **Personnel:** 446

⊞ △ **MEMORIAL HOSPITAL AT GULFPORT (250019)**, 4500 13th Street, Zip 39501–2569, Mailing Address: P.O. Box 1810, Zip 39502–1810; tel. 228/867–4000, (Includes MEMORIAL BEHAVIORAL HEALTH, 11150 Highway 49 North, Zip 39503–4110; tel. 228/831–1700; Michael A. Zieman, Administrator) **A**1 2 3 7 9 10 **F**3 4 8 11 13 15 17 18 20 22 26 28 29 30 31 34 35 40 43 44 45 46 48 49 50 51 53 54 57 59 64 65 68 70 71 72 73 74 76 77 78 79 80 81 84 85 87 89 90 92 93 95 96 98 99 100 101 102 104 105 107 108 110 111 114 115 116 117 118 119 120 121 124 126 130 132 135 145 146 **P**3 8
Primary Contact: Gary G. Marchand, President and Chief Executive Officer
COO: Kent Nicaud, Chief Operating Officer
CFO: Jeffrey T. Steiner, Vice President Finance
CIO: Gene Thomas, Vice President, Information Systems, Chief Information Officer
CHR: Cathy Wood, Vice President, Human Resources
CNO: Jennifer Dumal, R.N., Chief Operating Officer of Clinical and Chief Nursing Officer
Web address: www.gulfportmemorial.com
**Control:** City–County, Government, nonfederal **Service:** General Medical and Surgical

**Staffed Beds:** 445 **Admissions:** 15620 **Census:** 230 **Outpatient Visits:** 433396 **Births:** 1308 **Total Expense ($000):** 411713 **Payroll Expense ($000):** 187895 **Personnel:** 2712

**MS**

---

**Hospital, Medicare Provider Number, Address, Telephone, Approval, Facility, and Physician Codes, Health Care System**

★ American Hospital Association (AHA) membership
☐ The Joint Commission accreditation
◯ Healthcare Facilities Accreditation Program
◇ DNV Healthcare Inc. accreditation
⇑ Center for Improvement in Healthcare Quality Accreditation
△ Commission on Accreditation of Rehabilitation Facilities (CARF) accreditation

⊞ **SELECT SPECIALTY HOSPITAL–GULFPORT (252005)**, 1520 Broad Avenue, Suite 300, Zip 39501–3601; tel. 228/575–7500 **A**1 10 **F**29 70 82 87 90 130 **S** Select Medical Corporation, Mechanicsburg, PA
Primary Contact: John O'Keefe, Chief Executive Officer
Web address: www.selectspecialtyhospitals.com/company/locations/gulfcoast.aspx
**Control:** Corporation, Investor–owned, for–profit **Service:** Long–Term Acute Care hospital

**Staffed Beds:** 61 **Admissions:** 422 **Census:** 33 **Outpatient Visits:** 0 **Births:** 0 **Personnel:** 139

### HATTIESBURG—Forrest County

★ △ ◇ **FORREST GENERAL HOSPITAL (250078)**, 6051 U.S. Highway 49, Zip 39401–7200, Mailing Address: P.O. Box 16389, Zip 39404–6389; tel. 601/288–7000 **A**2 3 5 7 9 10 19 21 **F**3 4 5 8 12 13 15 17 18 20 22 26 28 29 30 31 34 35 37 40 43 45 46 47 48 49 53 57 58 59 60 62 63 64 68 70 72 73 75 76 77 78 79 81 85 86 87 89 90 91 92 93 95 96 98 99 100 102 103 104 106 107 108 111 114 115 118 119 120 121 123 124 126 128 130 131 132 135 146 147
Primary Contact: Evan S. Dillard, M.P.H., FACHE, President and Chief Executive Officer
COO: Douglas A. Jones, Chief Operating Officer
CFO: Andy Woodard, Chief Financial Officer
CMO: Steven E. Farrell, M.D., Chief Medical Officer
CHR: Troy Daniel, Chief Human Resources Officer
CNO: Micah Rehm, Chief Nursing Officer
Web address: www.forrestgeneral.com
**Control:** County–Government, nonfederal **Service:** General Medical and Surgical

**Staffed Beds:** 512 **Admissions:** 25935 **Census:** 328 **Outpatient Visits:** 137898 **Births:** 2387 **Total Expense ($000):** 375107 **Payroll Expense ($000):** 136967 **Personnel:** 2725

⊞ **MERIT HEALTH WESLEY (250094)**, 5001 Hardy Street, Zip 39402–1308, Mailing Address: P.O. Box 16509, Zip 39404–6509; tel. 601/268–8000 **A**1 9 10 19 **F**3 8 11 12 13 15 17 18 20 22 24 26 28 29 30 32 34 35 37 39 40 41 45 46 49 53 54 57 58 59 60 61 64 65 70 71 72 73 74 75 76 77 78 79 81 82 85 87 89 90 91 93 96 97 107 108 110 111 114 115 117 118 119 126 129 130 132 135 146 148 **P**6 7 **S** Community Health Systems, Inc., Franklin, TN
Primary Contact: Michael Neuendorf, Chief Executive Officer
CFO: Randy Humphrey, Chief Financial Officer
CMO: William Reno, III, M.D., President Medical Staff
CHR: Terry Trigg, Director Human Resources
Web address: www.wesley.com
**Control:** Corporation, Investor–owned, for–profit **Service:** General Medical and Surgical

**Staffed Beds:** 211 **Admissions:** 7018 **Census:** 98 **Outpatient Visits:** 84768 **Births:** 1271 **Personnel:** 1017

⊞ **REGENCY HOSPITAL OF HATTIESBURG (252009)**, 6051 U.S. Highway 495, 5th Floor, Zip 39401–6031; tel. 601/288–8510 **A**1 10 **F**40 70 **S** Select Medical Corporation, Mechanicsburg, PA
Primary Contact: Rachael Fisher, Chief Executive Officer
CMO: Ralph Kahler, M.D., Medical Director
CHR: Jared Burns, Coordinator Human Resources
Web address: www.regencyhospital.com/hattiesburg
**Control:** Corporation, Investor–owned, for–profit **Service:** Long–Term Acute Care hospital

**Staffed Beds:** 33 **Admissions:** 397 **Census:** 30 **Outpatient Visits:** 0 **Births:** 0 **Personnel:** 145

### HAZLEHURST—Copiah County

★ **HARDY WILSON MEMORIAL HOSPITAL (251327)**, 233 Magnolia Street, Zip 39083–2228, Mailing Address: P.O. Box 889, Zip 39083–0889; tel. 601/894–4541 **A**9 10 18 **F**15 35 39 40 43 56 70 75 81 90 93 98 103 107 111 119 130 133
Primary Contact: William Giles, Interim Chief Executive Officer
Web address: www.hardywilsonhospital.com
**Control:** County–Government, nonfederal **Service:** General Medical and Surgical

**Staffed Beds:** 25 **Admissions:** 728 **Census:** 19 **Outpatient Visits:** 8898 **Births:** 0 **Personnel:** 131

### HOLLY SPRINGS—Marshall County

**ALLIANCE HEALTHCARE SYSTEM (250012)**, 1430 Highway 4 East, Zip 38635–2140, Mailing Address: P.O. Box 6000, Zip 38634–6000; tel. 662/252–1212 **A**9 10 20 **F**15 29 35 40 43 70 75 81 87 89 98 103 104 119 130 132 133 143
Primary Contact: Perry E. Williams, Sr., Administrator and Chief Executive Officer
COO: Cecelia Bost, Chief Operating Officer
CFO: William F. Magee, Chief Financial Officer
CMO: Subbu Rayudu, M.D., Chief of Staff
CIO: Saul Mbenga, Manager Information Technology
CHR: Judy Eggers, Manager Human Resources
Web address: www.alliancehealth.us
**Control:** Corporation, Investor–owned, for–profit **Service:** General Medical and Surgical

**Staffed Beds:** 40 **Admissions:** 553 **Census:** 10 **Outpatient Visits:** 7013 **Births:** 0 **Personnel:** 94

### HOUSTON—Chickasaw County

**TRACE REGIONAL HOSPITAL (250017)**, Highway 8 East, Zip 38851–9396, Mailing Address: P.O. Box 626, Zip 38851–0626; tel. 662/456–3700 **A**9 10 **F**15 61 70 75 82 89 93 98 101 102 103 107 111 119 127 128 133 146 **P**6 **S** Sunlink Health Systems, Atlanta, GA
Primary Contact: Gary L. Staten, Chief Executive Officer
CFO: Pamela W. Cook, Chief Financial Officer
CMO: Bill Brohawn, Chief of Staff
CHR: Sherry Craig, Director Human Resources
CNO: Marianne Johnson, Chief Nursing Officer
Web address: www.traceregional.com
**Control:** Corporation, Investor–owned, for–profit **Service:** General Medical and Surgical

**Staffed Beds:** 84 **Admissions:** 730 **Census:** 12 **Outpatient Visits:** 18578 **Births:** 0 **Personnel:** 211

### INDIANOLA—Sunflower County

★ **SOUTH SUNFLOWER COUNTY HOSPITAL (250095)**, 121 East Baker Street, Zip 38751–2498; tel. 662/887–5235 **A**9 10 20 **F**13 15 17 40 43 70 76 81 107 111 119 127 130 **P**8
Primary Contact: Courtney Phillips, Chief Executive Officer
COO: Barbara Prichard, Assistant Administrator
CFO: Meredith Taylor, Comptroller
CMO: Wade Dowell, M.D., Chief of Staff
CIO: Julie Sterling, Manager Information System
**Control:** County–Government, nonfederal **Service:** General Medical and Surgical

**Staffed Beds:** 49 **Admissions:** 1076 **Census:** 10 **Outpatient Visits:** 10644 **Births:** 186 **Personnel:** 94

### IUKA—Tishomingo County

⊞ **TISHOMINGO HEALTH SERVICES (250002)**, 1777 Curtis Drive, Zip 38852–1001, Mailing Address: P.O. Box 860, Zip 38852–0860; tel. 662/423–6051 **A**1 9 10 **F**17 29 35 40 43 53 70 75 82 86 87 89 90 93 107 108 111 119 130 132 133 134 **S** North Mississippi Health Services, Inc., Tupelo, MS
Primary Contact: Fred A. Truesdale, Jr., Administrator
CFO: Betty Moore, Business Manager
CMO: Margaret Glynn, M.D., Chief Medical Officer
CIO: Fred A. Truesdale, Jr., Administrator
CHR: Jane Chamblee, Manager Human Resources
Web address: www.nmhs.net
**Control:** Other not–for–profit (including NFP Corporation) **Service:** General Medical and Surgical

**Staffed Beds:** 48 **Admissions:** 734 **Census:** 9 **Outpatient Visits:** 21750 **Births:** 0 **Personnel:** 145

### JACKSON—Hinds County

☐ **BRENTWOOD BEHAVIORAL HEALTHCARE OF MISSISSIPPI (254007)**, 3531 East Lakeland Drive, Zip 39232–8839; tel. 601/936–2024 **A**1 10 **F**35 98 99 101 102 104 105 130 132 134 **S** Universal Health Services, Inc., King of Prussia, PA
Primary Contact: Michael J. Carney, Chief Executive Officer
Web address: www.brentwoodjackson.com
**Control:** Corporation, Investor–owned, for–profit **Service:** Psychiatric

**Staffed Beds:** 105 **Admissions:** 2763 **Census:** 73 **Outpatient Visits:** 0 **Births:** 0 **Personnel:** 220

MS

✠ **MERIT HEALTH CENTRAL (250072)**, 1850 Chadwick Drive, Zip 39204–3479, Mailing Address: P.O. Box 59001, Zip 39284–9001; tel. 601/376–1000 **A**1 2 3 9 10 **F**13 15 16 17 29 35 40 43 51 61 70 72 73 75 76 77 78 80 81 86 87 90 93 97 98 100 102 107 108 111 116 118 119 130 146 147 **P**8 **S** Community Health Systems, Inc., Franklin, TN
Primary Contact: Linda Dolan, Chief Executive Officer
CFO: Scott Whittemore, Chief Financial Officer
CIO: John Simpson, Director Information Systems
CHR: Mark B. Cook, Director Human Resources
CNO: Lorie N. Ramsey, MSN, Chief Nursing Executive
Web address: www.centralmississippimedicalcenter.com
**Control:** Corporation, Investor–owned, for–profit **Service:** General Medical and Surgical

**Staffed Beds:** 217 **Admissions:** 6480 **Census:** 77 **Outpatient Visits:** 117034 **Births:** 926 **Personnel:** 789

✠ **G.V. (SONNY) MONTGOMERY VETERANS AFFAIRS MEDICAL CENTER**, 1500 East Woodrow Wilson Drive, Zip 39216–5199; tel. 601/362–4471, (Nonreporting) **A**1 2 3 5 **S** Department of Veterans Affairs, Washington, DC
Primary Contact: Joe Battle, Director
COO: Jed Fillingim, Acting Chief Operating Officer and Associate Director
CFO: Joy Willis, Acting Chief Fiscal Service
CMO: Kent Kirchner, M.D., Chief of Staff
CIO: Robert Wolak, Chief Information Resource Management Service
CHR: Sam Evans, Chief Human Resources Management
Web address: www.jackson.va.gov/
**Control:** Veterans Affairs, Government, federal **Service:** General Medical and Surgical

**Staffed Beds:** 323

✠ △ **METHODIST REHABILITATION CENTER (250152)**, 1350 Woodrow Wilson Drive, Zip 39216–5198; tel. 601/981–2611, (Total facility includes 60 beds in nursing home–type unit) **A**1 3 5 7 9 10 **F**8 29 30 34 35 50 57 58 59 70 77 81 82 86 87 90 91 92 93 94 96 119 130 132 143 146
Primary Contact: Mark A. Adams, President and Chief Executive Officer
COO: Joseph M. Morette, Executive Vice President
CFO: Gary Armstrong, Executive Vice President
CIO: Gary Armstrong, Executive Vice President
CHR: Steve Hope, Vice President Corporate Services
Web address: www.methodistrehab.org
**Control:** Other not–for–profit (including NFP Corporation) **Service:** Rehabilitation

**Staffed Beds:** 184 **Admissions:** 1060 **Census:** 105 **Outpatient Visits:** 45188 **Births:** 0 **Total Expense ($000):** 50563 **Payroll Expense ($000):** 27894 **Personnel:** 482

✠ **MISSISSIPPI BAPTIST MEDICAL CENTER (250102)**, 1225 North State Street, Zip 39202–2064; tel. 601/968–1000 **A**1 2 3 5 9 10 **F**3 4 5 8 11 12 13 15 17 18 19 20 22 24 26 27 28 29 30 31 34 35 36 39 40 43 44 45 46 47 48 49 50 51 52 54 55 57 59 60 61 64 65 68 70 71 72 73 74 75 76 78 79 80 81 82 85 86 89 90 91 92 93 94 98 100 103 107 108 109 110 111 113 114 115 116 117 118 119 126 130 132 144 145 146 147 **S** Baptist Health Systems, Jackson, MS
Primary Contact: Chris Anderson, Chief Executive Officer
CFO: Russell W. York, Chief Financial Officer
CMO: Eric A. McVey, M.D., Vice President and Chief Medical Officer
CIO: Steve M. Stanic, Vice President and Chief Information Officer
CHR: Lee Ann Foreman, Vice President Human Resources
CNO: Bobbie K. Ware, R.N., Vice President/Patient Care/Chief Nursing Officer
Web address: www.mbhs.org
**Control:** Other not–for–profit (including NFP Corporation) **Service:** General Medical and Surgical

**Staffed Beds:** 554 **Admissions:** 20918 **Census:** 294 **Outpatient Visits:** 176458 **Births:** 1392 **Personnel:** 2816

✠ **MISSISSIPPI HOSPITAL FOR RESTORATIVE CARE (252003)**, 1225 North State Street, Zip 39202–2097, Mailing Address: P.O. Box 23695, Zip 39225–3695; tel. 601/968–1000 **A**1 10 **F**3 29 39 56 61 70 80 82 85 130 **P**7 **S** Baptist Health Systems, Jackson, MS
Primary Contact: Bobbie K. Ware, R.N., FACHE, Chief Executive Officer and Chief Nursing Officer
CFO: Russell W. York, Vice President and Chief Financial Officer
CMO: Holland M. Addison, M.D., Medical Director
CIO: Steve M. Stanic, Vice President and Chief Information Officer
CHR: Lee Ann Foreman, Vice President Human Resources
Web address: www.mbhs.org
**Control:** Other not–for–profit (including NFP Corporation) **Service:** Long–Term Acute Care hospital

**Staffed Beds:** 20 **Admissions:** 198 **Census:** 18 **Outpatient Visits:** 0 **Births:** 0 **Total Expense ($000):** 11127 **Payroll Expense ($000):** 3854 **Personnel:** 65

✠ **REGENCY HOSPITAL OF JACKSON (252012)**, 969 Lakeland Drive, 6th Floor, Zip 39216–4643; tel. 601/364–6200 **A**1 10 **F**70 130 **S** Select Medical Corporation, Mechanicsburg, PA
Primary Contact: R. Shannon Canard, Chief Executive Officer
Web address: www.regencyhospital.com
**Control:** Corporation, Investor–owned, for–profit **Service:** Long–Term Acute Care hospital

**Staffed Beds:** 36 **Admissions:** 432 **Census:** 31 **Outpatient Visits:** 0 **Births:** 0 **Personnel:** 77

✠ **SELECT SPECIALTY HOSPITAL–JACKSON (252007)**, 5903 Ridgewood Road, Suite 100, Zip 39211–3700; tel. 601/899–3800 **A**1 10 **F**107 119 **P**7 **S** Select Medical Corporation, Mechanicsburg, PA
Primary Contact: Chandler Ewing, Chief Executive Officer
CFO: Melissa Smith, Controller
CIO: Jacqueline Barnes, Manager Health Information
CHR: Vicki Watson, Manager Human Resources
Web address: www.selectspecialtyhospitals.com/company/locations/jackson.aspx
**Control:** Corporation, Investor–owned, for–profit **Service:** Long–Term Acute Care hospital

**Staffed Beds:** 53 **Admissions:** 658 **Census:** 47 **Outpatient Visits:** 0 **Births:** 0 **Personnel:** 212

✠ **ST. DOMINIC–JACKSON MEMORIAL HOSPITAL (250048)**, 969 Lakeland Drive, Zip 39216–4606; tel. 601/200–2000 **A**1 2 3 5 9 10 **F**3 4 11 12 13 15 17 18 20 22 24 26 28 29 30 31 34 35 36 37 38 39 40 43 46 47 49 50 51 53 57 58 60 61 64 65 68 70 72 73 74 75 76 77 78 79 80 81 82 84 85 86 89 90 92 93 96 97 98 100 101 102 103 106 107 108 109 110 111 114 115 116 117 118 119 120 121 123 124 126 129 130 131 147 148 **P**8
Primary Contact: Lester K. Diamond, President
CFO: Matt Fisher, Vice President Finance
CMO: Lawrence Riddles, M.D., Executive Vice President Medical Affairs and Quality
CIO: Keith Van Camp, Vice President Information Services
CHR: Lorraine Washington, Vice President Human Resources
CNO: Theresa Horne, MS, Vice President Patient Care Services
Web address: www.stdom.com
**Control:** Other not–for–profit (including NFP Corporation) **Service:** General Medical and Surgical

**Staffed Beds:** 502 **Admissions:** 36093 **Census:** 392 **Outpatient Visits:** 177942 **Births:** 1737 **Total Expense ($000):** 414827 **Payroll Expense ($000):** 170408 **Personnel:** 2718

✠ △ **UNIVERSITY OF MISSISSIPPI MEDICAL CENTER (250001)**, 2500 North State Street, Zip 39216–4505; tel. 601/984–1000, (Includes BLAIR E. BATSON HOSPITAL FOR CHILDREN, 2500 North State State Room W019, Zip 39216–4500; tel. 601/984–1000; CHILDREN'S HEALTHCARE OF MISSISSIPPI, 2500 North State Street, Zip 39216–4500) **A**1 2 3 5 7 8 9 10 13 **F**3 6 7 8 11 12 13 15 17 18 19 20 21 22 23 24 25 26 29 30 31 32 34 35 37 39 40 41 43 44 45 46 47 48 49 50 52 53 54 55 56 57 58 59 60 61 64 65 66 68 70 71 72 73 74 75 76 77 78 79 80 81 84 85 86 87 88 89 90 92 93 94 96 97 98 99 100 101 102 103 104 107 108 110 111 112 114 115 116 117 118 119 120 121 123 124 126 127 129 130 131 132 134 135 136 137 138 139 141 142 143 144 146 147 148 **P**6 **S** University Hospitals and Health System, Jackson, MS
Primary Contact: Kevin S. Cook, Chief Executive Officer
CFO: Dan Janicak, Chief Financial Officer
CMO: William H. Cleland, M.D., Chief Medical Officer
CHR: Michael Estes, Director Human Resources
Web address: www.umc.edu
**Control:** State–Government, nonfederal **Service:** General Medical and Surgical

**Staffed Beds:** 684 **Admissions:** 27854 **Census:** 504 **Outpatient Visits:** 209262 **Births:** 2129 **Total Expense ($000):** 729320 **Payroll Expense ($000):** 259751 **Personnel:** 4664

**KEESLER AFB—Harrison County**

✠ **U. S. AIR FORCE MEDICAL CENTER KEESLER**, 301 Fisher Street, Room 1A132, Zip 39534–2519; tel. 228/376–2550, (Nonreporting) **A**1 2 3 5 **S** Department of the Air Force, Washington, DC
Primary Contact: Colonel Thomas Harrell, M.D., Commander
COO: Brigadier General James Dougherty, Commander
CFO: Major Brenda Yi, Director Medical Resource Management and Chief Financial Officer
CMO: Colonel James Gasque, M.D., Chief Hospital Services
CIO: Major Samuel Silverthorne, Chief Information Officer
CHR: Major Brenda Yi, Director Medical Resource Management and Chief Financial Officer
Web address: www.keesler.af.mil
**Control:** Air Force, Government, federal **Service:** General Medical and Surgical

**Staffed Beds:** 56

**MS**

---

**Hospital, Medicare Provider Number, Address, Telephone, Approval, Facility, and Physician Codes, Health Care System**

★ American Hospital Association (AHA) membership
☐ The Joint Commission accreditation
○ Healthcare Facilities Accreditation Program
◇ DNV Healthcare Inc. accreditation
⇧ Center for Improvement in Healthcare Quality Accreditation
△ Commission on Accreditation of Rehabilitation Facilities (CARF) accreditation

---

**KOSCIUSKO—Attala County**

★ ◇ **BAPTIST MEDICAL CENTER ATTALA (251336)**, 220 Highway 12 West, Zip 39090–3208, Mailing Address: P.O. Box 887, Zip 39090–0887; tel. 662/289–4311 **A**9 10 18 21 **F**15 17 29 35 40 43 56 63 70 81 89 90 93 107 108 116 118 119 130 133 **S** Baptist Health Systems, Jackson, MS
Primary Contact: John Dawson, Chief Executive Officer
CFO: Josh Harmond, Chief Financial Officer
CHR: Linnie Pearson, Coordinator Human Resources and Benefits
CNO: Allison Schuler, R.N., Chief Nursing Officer
Web address: www.montfortjones.com
**Control:** County–Government, nonfederal **Service:** General Medical and Surgical

**Staffed Beds:** 25 **Admissions:** 969 **Census:** 13 **Outpatient Visits:** 19503 **Births:** 0 **Personnel:** 120

**LAUREL—Jones County**

★ ◇ **SOUTH CENTRAL REGIONAL MEDICAL CENTER (250058)**, 1220 Jefferson Street, Zip 39440–4374, Mailing Address: P.O. Box 607, Zip 39441–0607; tel. 601/426–4000, (Total facility includes 252 beds in nursing home–type unit) **A**9 10 21 **F**4 13 15 17 29 35 40 43 51 53 62 63 70 73 75 76 77 78 81 86 87 89 90 93 100 102 104 105 108 111 118 119 127 128 130 131 132 134 143 144 146 147 **P**6
Primary Contact: G. Douglas Higginbotham, President and Chief Executive Officer
CFO: Tom Canizaro, Vice President and Chief Financial Officer
CMO: James Holston, M.D., Vice President and Chief Quality Officer
CIO: Dell Blakeney, Vice President and Chief Information Officer
CHR: Janet Staples, Vice President Human Resources
CNO: Beth W. Endom, R.N., Vice President and Chief Nursing Officer
Web address: www.scrmc.com
**Control:** County–Government, nonfederal **Service:** General Medical and Surgical

**Staffed Beds:** 402 **Admissions:** 7701 **Census:** 329 **Outpatient Visits:** 81190 **Births:** 855 **Personnel:** 1566

**LEAKESVILLE—Greene County**

**GREENE COUNTY HOSPITAL (251329)**, 1017 Jackson Avenue, Zip 39451–9105; tel. 601/394–4139 **A**9 10 18 **F**40 43 70 107 128 133
Primary Contact: Deborah Berry, Director of Operations
CFO: Debbie Brannan, Chief Financial Officer
CMO: Larry Henderson, M.D., Medical Director
CHR: Carla Shows, Payroll Clerk
Web address: www.georeregional.com
**Control:** County–Government, nonfederal **Service:** General Medical and Surgical

**Staffed Beds:** 7 **Admissions:** 61 **Census:** 2 **Outpatient Visits:** 2850 **Births:** 0 **Personnel:** 49

**LEXINGTON—Holmes County**

⌧ **UNIVERSITY OF MISSISSIPPI MEDICAL CENTER HOLMES COUNTY (251319)**, 239 Bowling Green Road, Zip 39095–5167; tel. 601/496–5200 **A**1 9 10 18 **F**3 11 15 29 34 40 43 45 50 56 57 59 64 70 86 87 89 93 107 108 114 118 119 127 130 133 146 **P**6 **S** University Hospitals and Health System, Jackson, MS
Primary Contact: David G. Putt, FACHE, Chief Executive Officer
COO: Paige Lawrence, Assistant Administrator
CFO: Scott Whittemore, Chief Financial Officer
CMO: Mark Smothers, M.D., Chief Medical Officer
CIO: Sammuel Townsend, LAN Administrator
CHR: Claudette Hathcock, Human Resources Director
Web address: www.ummchealth.com/holmes/
**Control:** State–Government, nonfederal **Service:** General Medical and Surgical

**Staffed Beds:** 25 **Admissions:** 367 **Census:** 8 **Outpatient Visits:** 13045 **Births:** 0 **Total Expense ($000):** 12182 **Payroll Expense ($000):** 6363 **Personnel:** 105

**LOUISVILLE—Winston County**

**WINSTON MEDICAL CENTER (250027)**, 562 East Main Street, Zip 39339–2742, Mailing Address: P.O. Box 967, Zip 39339–0967; tel. 662/773–6211 **A**9 10 20 **F**29 34 35 40 43 57 59 65 70 81 89 93 103 107 110 114 119 127 128 130 133 146
Primary Contact: Paul S. Black, Interim Administrator
Web address: www.winstonmedical.org
**Control:** Other not–for–profit (including NFP Corporation) **Service:** General Medical and Surgical

**Staffed Beds:** 41 **Admissions:** 646 **Census:** 17 **Outpatient Visits:** 15518 **Births:** 0 **Personnel:** 96

**LUCEDALE—Jackson County**

**GEORGE REGIONAL HOSPITAL (250036)**, 859 Winter Street, Zip 39452–6603, Mailing Address: P.O. Box 607, Zip 39452–0607; tel. 601/947–3161 **A**9 10 20 **F**3 11 13 15 17 18 29 30 34 35 40 43 45 47 48 49 53 54 57 59 65 68 70 76 81 86 87 93 107 108 111 119 127 129 130 133 135 146 148 **P**8
Primary Contact: Greg Havard, Administrator
CFO: Debbie Brannan, Chief Financial Officer
CMO: Seth Scott, M.D., Chief of Staff
CHR: Carla Shows, Payroll Clerk
Web address: www.georgeregional.com
**Control:** County–Government, nonfederal **Service:** General Medical and Surgical

**Staffed Beds:** 48 **Admissions:** 1266 **Census:** 13 **Outpatient Visits:** 44418 **Births:** 206 **Personnel:** 273

**MACON—Noxubee County**

**NOXUBEE GENERAL HOSPITAL (251307)**, 606 North Jefferson Street, Zip 39341–2242, Mailing Address: P.O. Box 480, Zip 39341–0480; tel. 662/726–4231, (Total facility includes 60 beds in nursing home–type unit) **A**9 10 18 **F**40 43 70 89 107 127 128 130 133
Primary Contact: Danny H. McKay, Administrator
Web address: www.noxubeecountyms.com/quality–of–life–noxubee–mississipp/health–care–noxubee–mississippi/
**Control:** County–Government, nonfederal **Service:** General Medical and Surgical

**Staffed Beds:** 85 **Admissions:** 878 **Census:** 73 **Outpatient Visits:** 4718 **Births:** 0 **Personnel:** 179

**MAGEE—Simpson County**

★ **MAGEE GENERAL HOSPITAL (250124)**, 300 Third Avenue S.E., Zip 39111–3698; tel. 601/849–5070 **A**9 10 **F**13 15 29 35 40 43 70 76 81 89 107 108 111 119 130 133 146
Primary Contact: Amy Tolliver, Administrator
CMO: Kelli Smith, M.D., Chief of Staff
CIO: Kirby Craft, Chief Information Officer
CHR: Steve Beckham, Director Human Resources
CNO: Cindy McIntyre, R.N., Administrative Director Clinical Services
Web address: www.mghosp.org
**Control:** Other not–for–profit (including NFP Corporation) **Service:** General Medical and Surgical

**Staffed Beds:** 64 **Admissions:** 1284 **Census:** 21 **Outpatient Visits:** 40378 **Births:** 254 **Personnel:** 287

**MAGNOLIA—Pike County**

**BEACHAM MEMORIAL HOSPITAL (250049)**, 205 North Cherry Street, Zip 39652–2819, Mailing Address: P.O. Box 351, Zip 39652–0351; tel. 601/783–2351 **A**9 10 **F**35 70 107 127 130 133 146
Primary Contact: Gene Amons, Administrator and Chief Executive Officer
CMO: Lucius Lampton, M.D., Medical Director
CHR: Jackie McKenzie, Director Administrative Services
Web address: www.beachammemhos.com
**Control:** Other not–for–profit (including NFP Corporation) **Service:** General Medical and Surgical

**Staffed Beds:** 37 **Admissions:** 569 **Census:** 10 **Outpatient Visits:** 0 **Births:** 0 **Personnel:** 42

**MARKS—Quitman County**

**QUITMAN COUNTY HOSPITAL (251314)**, 340 Getwell Drive, Zip 38646–9785; tel. 662/326–8031 **A**9 10 18 **F**40 43 70 89 90 103 107 119 133
Primary Contact: Jeff Geraci, Administrator
CFO: Jane Moore, Director, Fiscal Services
CMO: James E. Warrington, Sr., M.D., Chief of Staff
CHR: Sandra Biffle, Personnel Clerk
CNO: Dana Hall, Director of Nursing
**Control:** Corporation, Investor–owned, for–profit **Service:** General Medical and Surgical

**Staffed Beds:** 33 **Admissions:** 446 **Census:** 10 **Outpatient Visits:** 8918 **Births:** 0 **Personnel:** 121

*Many Facility Codes have changed. Please refer to the AHA Guide Code Chart.* © 2015 AHA Guide

## MCCOMB—Pike County

★ ◇ **SOUTHWEST MISSISSIPPI REGIONAL MEDICAL CENTER (250097)**, 215 Marion Avenue, Zip 39648–2705, Mailing Address: P.O. Box 1307, Zip 39649–1307; tel. 601/249–5500 **A**9 10 19 21 **F**3 8 11 12 13 15 17 18 20 22 24 26 28 29 30 31 34 35 37 39 40 41 43 44 45 47 48 49 50 53 55 57 59 64 65 70 72 73 74 75 76 77 78 79 81 85 86 87 89 92 93 107 108 109 110 111 115 118 119 120 121 126 127 129 130 131 132 135 145 146 148 **P**6 **S** Southwest Health Systems, Mccomb, MS
Primary Contact: Norman M. Price, FACHE, Chief Executive Officer
COO: Richard Williams, Chief Operating Officer
CFO: Charla Rowley, Chief Financial Officer
CMO: Kevin Richardson, M.D., Chief of Staff
CIO: Mike Moak, Chief Information Officer
CHR: Don Haskins, Administrative Director Human Resources
CNO: Katie McKinley, Assistant Administrator/Nursing
Web address: www.smrmc.com
**Control:** Hospital district or authority, Government, nonfederal **Service:** General Medical and Surgical

**Staffed Beds:** 143 **Admissions:** 6206 **Census:** 75 **Outpatient Visits:** 100822 **Births:** 803 **Personnel:** 964

## MEADVILLE—Franklin County

**FRANKLIN COUNTY MEMORIAL HOSPITAL (251330)**, 40 Union Church Road, Zip 39653–8336, Mailing Address: P.O. Box 636, Zip 39653–0636; tel. 601/384–5801 **A**9 10 18 **F**29 35 40 43 56 70 86 89 93 98 103 107 119 127 130 133 143 148 **P**3 6
Primary Contact: Mike Boleware, Administrator
Web address: www.fcmh.net
**Control:** County–Government, nonfederal **Service:** General Medical and Surgical

**Staffed Beds:** 25 **Admissions:** 396 **Census:** 18 **Outpatient Visits:** 2771 **Births:** 0 **Personnel:** 193

## MENDENHALL—Simpson County

**SIMPSON GENERAL HOSPITAL (251317)**, 1842 Simpson Highway 149, Zip 39114–3438; tel. 601/847–2221 **A**9 10 18 **F**35 40 56 70 81 86 87 90 98 103 107 119 127 130 132 133 134 146 **P**1 5
Primary Contact: Randall Neely, Chief Executive Officer
COO: Al Gary, COO
CFO: Al Gary, COO
CMO: Chip Holbrook, M.D., Chief of Staff
CIO: David Welch, Director Information Technology
CHR: Randall Neely, CEO
CNO: Sharon Burnham, Director of Nursing
Web address: www.simpsongeneralhospital.com
**Control:** Other not–for–profit (including NFP Corporation) **Service:** General Medical and Surgical

**Staffed Beds:** 35 **Admissions:** 755 **Census:** 17 **Outpatient Visits:** 10519 **Births:** 0 **Personnel:** 156

## MERIDIAN—Lauderdale County

☐ **ALLIANCE HEALTH CENTER (250151)**, 5000 Highway 39 North, Zip 39301–1021; tel. 601/483–6211 **A**1 9 10 **F**4 32 34 35 36 38 54 57 59 64 70 71 86 87 98 99 101 102 103 106 135 **P**6 **S** Universal Health Services, Inc., King of Prussia, PA
Primary Contact: James Miller, Interim Chief Executive Officer
CFO: Robert Jackson, Chief Financial Officer
CMO: Terry Jordan, M.D., Chief of Staff
CIO: Brenda Smith, Director Financial Services
CHR: Shrea Johnson, Director Human Resources
Web address: www.alliancehealthcenter.com
**Control:** Corporation, Investor–owned, for–profit **Service:** Psychiatric

**Staffed Beds:** 134 **Admissions:** 3099 **Census:** 78 **Outpatient Visits:** 0 **Births:** 0 **Total Expense ($000):** 22002 **Payroll Expense ($000):** 10930 **Personnel:** 304

⊠ **ANDERSON REGIONAL MEDICAL CENTER (250104)**, 2124 14th Street, Zip 39301–4040; tel. 601/553–6000 **A**1 2 9 10 19 **F**3 13 15 17 18 20 22 24 28 30 31 34 35 39 40 43 45 48 49 50 53 57 59 65 68 70 72 73 74 75 76 77 78 79 80 81 84 85 86 87 88 89 90 93 94 98 107 108 110 111 114 115 116 117 118 119 120 121 123 126 127 129 130 131 132 135 146 **P**7 8
Primary Contact: John G. Anderson, Chief Executive Officer
CFO: Keith Heartsill, Vice President of Finance
CMO: Scot Bell, Chief Medical Officer
CHR: Sharon Futch, Interim Vice President Human Resources
CNO: Matt Edwards, Vice President Nursing Services and Chief Nursing Officer
Web address: www.andersonregional.org
**Control:** Other not–for–profit (including NFP Corporation) **Service:** General Medical and Surgical

**Staffed Beds:** 260 **Admissions:** 10743 **Census:** 142 **Outpatient Visits:** 106394 **Births:** 1330 **Total Expense ($000):** 148507 **Payroll Expense ($000):** 56348 **Personnel:** 1431

☐ △ **ANDERSON REGIONAL MEDICAL CENTER–SOUTH CAMPUS (250081)**, 1102 Constitution Avenue, Zip 39301–4001; tel. 601/703–5000 **A**1 7 9 10 **F**3 4 18 29 34 35 50 57 59 60 61 64 68 70 74 75 81 82 84 86 87 90 97 98 103 106 107 114 115 117 119 127 130 132 133 135 144 146 **P**7 8
Primary Contact: John G. Anderson, Vice President, Administrator
CFO: Keith Heartsill, Vice President Finance
CMO: Bradley Boone, M.D., Chief Medical Staff
CIO: Steve Taylor, Chief Information Officer
CHR: Sharon Futch, Interim Vice President Human Resources
CNO: Betty Cryer, Chief Nursing Officer
Web address: www.andersonregional.org
**Control:** Other not–for–profit (including NFP Corporation) **Service:** General Medical and Surgical

**Staffed Beds:** 69 **Admissions:** 988 **Census:** 36 **Outpatient Visits:** 33373 **Births:** 0 **Total Expense ($000):** 30380 **Payroll Expense ($000):** 10712 **Personnel:** 216

☐ **EAST MISSISSIPPI STATE HOSPITAL**, 1818 College Drive, Zip 39307, Mailing Address: Box 4128, West Station, Zip 39304–4128; tel. 601/482–6186 **A**1 **F**4 29 56 87 98 99 101 103 128 130 146 **S** Mississippi State Department of Mental Health, Jackson, MS
Primary Contact: Charles Carlisle, Director
CFO: Geri Doggett, Director Business
CMO: Gloria Gomez, M.D., Medical Director
CIO: Scotty Taylor, Information Technology Director
CHR: Shearmaine Calaway, Director Human Resources
CNO: Diane Nobles, Nurse Executive
Web address: www.emsh.state.ms.us
**Control:** State–Government, nonfederal **Service:** Psychiatric

**Staffed Beds:** 181 **Admissions:** 960 **Census:** 151 **Outpatient Visits:** 0 **Births:** 0 **Total Expense ($000):** 56646 **Payroll Expense ($000):** 28665 **Personnel:** 677

⊠ **REGENCY HOSPITAL OF MERIDIAN (252006)**, 1102 Constitution Avenue, 2nd Floor, Zip 39301–4001; tel. 601/484–7900 **A**1 10 **F**40 70 **S** Select Medical Corporation, Mechanicsburg, PA
Primary Contact: Clifton Quinn, Chief Executive Officer
Web address: www.regencyhospital.com
**Control:** Corporation, Investor–owned, for–profit **Service:** Long–Term Acute Care hospital

**Staffed Beds:** 40 **Admissions:** 380 **Census:** 28 **Outpatient Visits:** 0 **Births:** 0 **Personnel:** 117

**RILEY HOSPITAL** See Anderson Regional Medical Center–South Campus

★ ◇ **RUSH FOUNDATION HOSPITAL (250069)**, 1314 19th Avenue, Zip 39301–4195; tel. 601/483–0011 **A**9 10 19 21 **F**13 15 17 29 35 39 40 43 70 72 73 76 77 81 82 86 87 89 90 93 97 107 108 118 119 131 146 **P**3 8 **S** Rush Health Systems, Meridian, MS
Primary Contact: Chuck A. Reece, President and Chief Executive Officer
COO: Morris A. Reece, President and Chief Operating Officer
CMO: W. Scot Bell, M.D., Chief Medical Officer
CIO: Angela Sherrill, Corporate Director Information System
CHR: Donnie Smith, Director Human Resources
Web address: www.rushhealthsystems.org/rfh/
**Control:** Other not–for–profit (including NFP Corporation) **Service:** General Medical and Surgical

**Staffed Beds:** 182 **Admissions:** 6859 **Census:** 87 **Outpatient Visits:** 24546 **Births:** 976 **Personnel:** 845

MS

★ **SPECIALTY HOSPITAL OF MERIDIAN (252004)**, 1314 19th Avenue, Zip 39301–4116; tel. 601/703–4211 **A**9 10 **F**3 18 20 22 30 31 34 57 59 65 68 70 74 78 79 85 87 94 96 127 133 135 144 **P**7 **S** Rush Health Systems, Meridian, MS
Primary Contact: Elizabeth C. Mitchell, Vice President and Administrator
CFO: Lexie Fuller, Controller
CMO: Richmond Alexander, M.D., President Medical Staff
CIO: Angela Sherrill, Corporate Director Information System
CHR: Donnie Smith, Director of Human Resources
CNO: Kawanda Johnson, Director of Nursing
Web address: www.specialtyhospitalofmeridian.com/shm/
**Control:** Other not–for–profit (including NFP Corporation) **Service:** Long–Term Acute Care hospital

**Staffed Beds:** 49 **Admissions:** 619 **Census:** 47 **Outpatient Visits:** 0 **Births:** 0 **Personnel:** 143

**MONTICELLO—Lawrence County**

**LAWRENCE COUNTY HOSPITAL (251305)**, Highway 84 East, Zip 39654–0788, Mailing Address: P.O. Box 788, Zip 39654–0788; tel. 601/587–4051 **A**9 10 18 **F**3 39 40 43 45 70 87 107 114 127 133 **S** Southwest Health Systems, Mccomb, MS
Primary Contact: Semmes Ross, Jr., Administrator
CFO: Jennifer Moak, Business Office Manager
Web address: www.smrmc.com
**Control:** County–Government, nonfederal **Service:** General Medical and Surgical

**Staffed Beds:** 25 **Admissions:** 493 **Census:** 7 **Outpatient Visits:** 7897 **Births:** 0 **Total Expense ($000):** 9782 **Payroll Expense ($000):** 4032 **Personnel:** 104

**MORTON—Scott County**

★ **SCOTT REGIONAL HOSPITAL (251323)**, 317 Highway 13 South, Zip 39117–3353, Mailing Address: P.O. Box 259, Zip 39117–0259; tel. 601/732–6301 **A**9 10 18 **F**3 30 35 40 43 55 57 70 77 81 89 93 107 111 112 114 119 127 130 133 **S** Rush Health Systems, Meridian, MS
Primary Contact: Michael R. Edwards, Administrator
CFO: Paul S. Black, Chief Financial Officer
CHR: Amy Sugg, Director Human Resources
Web address: www.scottregional.org/srh/
**Control:** Other not–for–profit (including NFP Corporation) **Service:** General Medical and Surgical

**Staffed Beds:** 25 **Admissions:** 563 **Census:** 8 **Outpatient Visits:** 10151 **Births:** 0 **Personnel:** 143

**NATCHEZ—Adams County**

⊞ **NATCHEZ COMMUNITY HOSPITAL (250122)**, 129 Jefferson Davis Boulevard, Zip 39120–5100, Mailing Address: P.O. Box 1203, Zip 39121–1203; tel. 601/445–6200 **A**1 9 10 **F**13 17 29 35 40 43 51 60 61 70 73 76 78 81 82 87 89 93 107 108 119 130 146 **P**6 8 **S** Community Health Systems, Inc., Franklin, TN
Primary Contact: Eric Robinson, Chief Executive Officer
Web address: www.natchezcommunityhospital.com/default.aspx
**Control:** Partnership, Investor–owned, for–profit **Service:** General Medical and Surgical

**Staffed Beds:** 101 **Admissions:** 3306 **Census:** 40 **Outpatient Visits:** 42762 **Births:** 514 **Personnel:** 259

⊞ △ **MERIT HEALTH NATCHEZ (250084)**, 54 Seargent S Prentiss Drive, Zip 39120–4726; tel. 601/443–2100 **A**1 7 9 10 **F**13 15 17 29 35 40 43 60 70 73 75 76 77 78 81 82 86 87 88 89 90 93 103 107 108 111 116 118 119 130 131 132 134 146 147 **P**5 **S** Community Health Systems, Inc., Franklin, TN
Primary Contact: Eric Robinson, Chief Executive Officer
CFO: Charles Mack, Vice President Finance and Chief Financial Officer
CMO: Leslie England, Chief of Staff
CIO: Leslie Makoro, Director Information management Systems
CHR: Jean E. Juchnowicz, Director Human Resources
Web address: www.natchezregional.com
**Control:** Corporation, Investor–owned, for–profit **Service:** General Medical and Surgical

**Staffed Beds:** 155 **Admissions:** 2486 **Census:** 35 **Outpatient Visits:** 29172 **Births:** 422 **Personnel:** 337

**NEW ALBANY—Union County**

⊞ **BAPTIST MEMORIAL HOSPITAL–UNION COUNTY (250006)**, 200 Highway 30 West, Zip 38652–3112; tel. 662/538–7631 **A**1 9 10 **F**13 15 17 29 35 39 40 51 70 75 76 77 81 86 87 89 90 93 107 108 111 118 119 130 132 133 146 147 **S** Baptist Memorial Health Care Corporation, Memphis, TN
Primary Contact: Walter Grace, Chief Executive Officer and Administrator
CFO: Kim High, Chief Financial Officer
CMO: Justin Lohmeier, M.D., Chief of Staff
CIO: Missy Coltharp, Director
CHR: Lori Goode, Director Human Resources
CNO: Randy White, Chief Nursing Officer
Web address: www.baptistonline.org/union–county/
**Control:** Other not–for–profit (including NFP Corporation) **Service:** General Medical and Surgical

**Staffed Beds:** 153 **Admissions:** 3663 **Census:** 32 **Outpatient Visits:** 47734 **Births:** 1061 **Total Expense ($000):** 49098 **Payroll Expense ($000):** 17712 **Personnel:** 321

**NEWTON—Newton County**

**NEWTON REGIONAL HOSPITAL** See Pioneer Community Hospital of Newton

★ ◇ **PIONEER COMMUNITY HOSPITAL OF NEWTON (251332)**, 9421 Eastside Drive, Zip 39345–8063; tel. 601/683–2031 **A**9 10 18 21 **F**29 35 39 40 43 53 70 81 89 90 98 103 107 119 127 130 133 146 **P**6 **S** Pioneer Health Services, Magee, MS
Primary Contact: Mark Norman, Administrator
CFO: Julie Gieger, Chief Financial Officer
CMO: Sohaib Arair, M.D., Chairman of Medical Staff
CIO: Jack York, Chief Information Officer
CHR: Dominica Johnson, Executive Administrative Assistant and Executive Assistant Human Resources and Payroll
CNO: Christie Malbrough, Director of Nursing
Web address: www.pchnewton.com
**Control:** Corporation, Investor–owned, for–profit **Service:** General Medical and Surgical

**Staffed Beds:** 30 **Admissions:** 801 **Census:** 16 **Outpatient Visits:** 12473 **Births:** 0 **Personnel:** 148

**OCEAN SPRINGS—Jackson County**

**OCEAN SPRINGS HOSPITAL** See Singing River Health System, Pascagoula

**OLIVE BRANCH—Desoto County**

☐ **METHODIST OLIVE BRANCH HOSPITAL (250167)**, 4250 Bethel Road, Zip 38654–8737; tel. 662/932–9000 **A**1 10 **F**4 13 15 17 29 35 40 60 62 63 70 72 73 76 77 78 81 82 86 87 88 89 90 93 107 108 111 118 119 130 132 138 144 146 147 **P**8 **S** Methodist Le Bonheur Healthcare, Memphis, TN
Primary Contact: David G. Baytos, Chief Executive Officer
CFO: Larry Fogarty, Chief Financial Officer
CHR: Robin Mathis, Director of Human Resources
CNO: Annelise Jensen, Chief Nursing Officer
Web address: www.methodisthealth.org/olivebranch
**Control:** Corporation, Investor–owned, for–profit **Service:** General Medical and Surgical

**Staffed Beds:** 44 **Admissions:** 1465 **Census:** 16 **Outpatient Visits:** 114570 **Births:** 185 **Personnel:** 230

☐ **PARKWOOD BEHAVIORAL HEALTH SYSTEM (254005)**, 8135 Goodman Road, Zip 38654–2103; tel. 662/895–4900, (Total facility includes 40 beds in nursing home–type unit) **A**1 9 10 **F**4 5 29 34 35 54 57 64 71 75 82 86 87 98 99 100 101 102 103 104 105 106 130 135 **S** Universal Health Services, Inc., King of Prussia, PA
Primary Contact: Coleby Wright, Chief Executive Officer
CFO: David Denegri, Chief Financial Officer
CMO: Paul King, M.D., Medical Director
CNO: Alicia Plunkett, Director of Nursing
Web address: www.parkwoodbhs.com
**Control:** Corporation, Investor–owned, for–profit **Service:** Psychiatric

**Staffed Beds:** 148 **Admissions:** 2769 **Census:** 104 **Outpatient Visits:** 0 **Births:** 0 **Personnel:** 272

*Many Facility Codes have changed. Please refer to the AHA Guide Code Chart.* © 2015 AHA Guide

**OXFORD—Lafayette County**

⊠ △ **BAPTIST MEMORIAL HOSPITAL–NORTH MISSISSIPPI (250034)**, 2301 South Lamar Boulevard, Zip 38655–5373, Mailing Address: P.O. Box 946, Zip 38655–6002; tel. 662/232–8100 **A**1 2 7 9 10 19 **F**7 11 12 13 15 17 18 20 22 26 28 29 30 31 34 35 40 43 47 48 49 50 53 57 59 64 68 70 73 74 76 78 79 81 84 85 86 87 89 90 93 96 107 108 110 111 114 115 116 117 118 119 126 130 131 132 146 147 **S** Baptist Memorial Health Care Corporation, Memphis, TN
Primary Contact: William C. Henning, Administrator and Chief Executive Officer
CFO: Dana Williams, Chief Financial Officer
CMO: Dennis P. Morgan, Chief of Staff
CIO: Linda Britt, Director Information Systems
CHR: Debbie Swan, Director Human Resources
CNO: Mark Ottens, Chief Nursing Officer
Web address: www.baptistonline.org/north–mississippi/
**Control:** Other not–for–profit (including NFP Corporation) **Service:** General Medical and Surgical

**Staffed Beds:** 217 **Admissions:** 7788 **Census:** 97 **Outpatient Visits:** 78320 **Births:** 925 **Personnel:** 717

**PASCAGOULA—Jackson County**

⊠ △ **SINGING RIVER HEALTH SYSTEM (250040)**, 2809 Denny Avenue, Zip 39581–5301; tel. 228/809–5000, (Includes OCEAN SPRINGS HOSPITAL, 3109 Bienville Boulevard, Ocean Springs, Zip 39564–4361; tel. 228/818–1111; Heath Thompson, R.N., Administrator; SINGING RIVER HOSPITAL, 2809 Denny Avenue, tel. 228/809–5000; Davis Walton, Administrator) **A**1 2 7 9 10 **F**3 11 13 15 17 18 19 20 21 22 24 26 28 29 30 31 38 39 40 41 43 44 45 47 48 49 53 54 61 64 70 72 73 74 76 78 80 81 82 83 84 85 86 87 88 89 90 92 94 95 96 98 99 100 101 102 103 104 106 107 108 110 111 114 115 118 119 120 121 123 124 126 127 129 130 135 144 145 146 148
Primary Contact: Kevin Holland, Chief Executive Officer
COO: Larry D. Shoemaker, M.D., Chief Operating Officer
CFO: Lee Bond, Chief Financial Officer
CMO: Randy Roth, Interim Chief Medical Officer
CHR: Craig Summerlin, Chief Human Resources Officer
CNO: Judy Powers, Chief Nursing Officer
Web address: www.mysrhs.com
**Control:** County–Government, nonfederal **Service:** General Medical and Surgical

**Staffed Beds:** 376 **Admissions:** 16661 **Census:** 206 **Outpatient Visits:** 402845 **Births:** 1461 **Total Expense ($000):** 374103 **Payroll Expense ($000):** 143388 **Personnel:** 2143

**PHILADELPHIA—Neshoba County**

☐ **CHOCTAW HEALTH CENTER (250127)**, 210 Hospital Circle, Zip 39350–6781; tel. 601/656–2211, (Nonreporting) **A**1 9 10
Primary Contact: Tina Scott, Acting Health Director
CFO: Myrna Hancock, Director Financial Services
CMO: Juantina Johnson, Chief of Staff
CIO: Raymond Willis, IT Manager
CHR: Anna Denson, Human Resources Specialist
CNO: Regina Isaac, Director of Nursing
Web address: www.choctaw.org
**Control:** PHS, Indian Service, Government, federal **Service:** General Medical and Surgical

**Staffed Beds:** 35

**NESHOBA COUNTY GENERAL HOSPITAL (250043)**, 1001 Holland Avenue, Zip 39350–2161, Mailing Address: P.O. Box 648, Zip 39350–0648; tel. 601/663–1200, (Total facility includes 160 beds in nursing home–type unit) **A**9 10 20 **F**3 7 11 15 29 32 34 40 43 45 46 57 59 64 65 70 81 82 89 90 93 103 107 108 111 114 118 119 127 128 132 133 143 144
Primary Contact: Lee McCall, Jr., Chief Executive Officer
CFO: Scott McNair, Chief Financial Officer
CMO: Julia Riley, M.D., Medical Director
CHR: Hedda Stewart, Director Human Resources
CNO: Scott Breazeale, Chief Nursing Officer
Web address: www.neshobageneral.com
**Control:** County–Government, nonfederal **Service:** General Medical and Surgical

**Staffed Beds:** 208 **Admissions:** 1745 **Census:** 176 **Births:** 0 **Personnel:** 432

**PICAYUNE—Pearl River County**

**HIGHLAND COMMUNITY HOSPITAL (250117)**, 130 Highland Parkway, Zip 39466–5574, Mailing Address: P.O. Box 909, Zip 39466–0909; tel. 601/358–9400 **A**9 10 **F**13 15 29 40 43 70 75 76 81 86 87 89 93 103 107 108 111 119 130 146 147
Primary Contact: Mark Stockstill, R.N., Administrator
CMO: Robert Lopez, Chief Medical Officer
CHR: Cynthia Render–Leach, Director Human Resources
CNO: Melissa Wise, Chief Nursing Officer
Web address: www.highlandch.com
**Control:** County–Government, nonfederal **Service:** General Medical and Surgical

**Staffed Beds:** 60 **Admissions:** 1869 **Census:** 18 **Outpatient Visits:** 46666 **Births:** 314 **Personnel:** 299

**PONTOTOC—Pontotoc County**

⊠ **NORTH MISSISSIPPI MEDICAL CENTER–PONTOTOC (251308)**, 176 South Main Street, Zip 38863–3311, Mailing Address: P.O. Box 790, Zip 38863–0790; tel. 662/488–7640, (Total facility includes 44 beds in nursing home–type unit) **A**1 9 10 18 **F**35 40 43 70 82 86 87 107 119 128 130 133 146 **S** North Mississippi Health Services, Inc., Tupelo, MS
Primary Contact: Leslia Carter, Administrator
CFO: M. Denise Heard, Director Business Services
CHR: P. Marie Barnes, Director, Human Resources
CNO: Cathy Waldrop, Director, Hospital Nursing Services
Web address: www.nmhs.net
**Control:** Other not–for–profit (including NFP Corporation) **Service:** General Medical and Surgical

**Staffed Beds:** 69 **Admissions:** 396 **Census:** 53 **Outpatient Visits:** 14698 **Births:** 0 **Personnel:** 151

**POPLARVILLE—Pearl River County**

**PEARL RIVER COUNTY HOSPITAL (251333)**, 305 West Moody Street, Zip 39470–7338, Mailing Address: P.O. Box 392, Zip 39470–0392; tel. 601/795–4543, (Total facility includes 126 beds in nursing home–type unit) **A**9 10 18 **F**35 40 43 70 93 103 107 119 127 128 130 133 143 146
Primary Contact: Steve Vaughan, Chief Executive Officer
CNO: Lisa Brown, Director of Nursing
**Control:** County–Government, nonfederal **Service:** General Medical and Surgical

**Staffed Beds:** 150 **Admissions:** 198 **Census:** 101 **Outpatient Visits:** 5931 **Births:** 0 **Personnel:** 402

**PORT GIBSON—Claiborne County**

**CLAIBORNE COUNTY MEDICAL CENTER (251320)**, 123 McComb Avenue, Zip 39150–2915, Mailing Address: P.O. Box 1004, Zip 39150–1004; tel. 601/437–5141 **A**9 10 18 **F**15 29 40 43 53 62 63 69 70 75 77 89 98 103 107 119 130 133
Primary Contact: Linda Dunigan, Chief Executive Officer
CFO: Linda Caho–Mooney, Chief Financial Officer
CIO: Ada Ratliff, Chief Information Officer
**Control:** County–Government, nonfederal **Service:** General Medical and Surgical

**Staffed Beds:** 32 **Admissions:** 1014 **Census:** 15 **Outpatient Visits:** 6382 **Births:** 0 **Personnel:** 88

**PRENTISS—Jefferson Davis County**

**JEFFERSON DAVIS COMMUNITY HOSPITAL (251326)**, 1102 Rose Street, Zip 39474–5200, Mailing Address: P.O. Box 1288, Zip 39474–1288; tel. 601/792–4276, (Total facility includes 60 beds in nursing home–type unit) **A**9 10 18 **F**3 35 40 43 53 56 57 64 65 66 70 86 87 89 93 98 103 107 111 119 127 128 130 132 133
Primary Contact: Jimmy Graves, Interim Chief Executive Officer
CHR: Diane Daughdrill, Director Human Resources
Web address: www.jdchospital.com
**Control:** County–Government, nonfederal **Service:** General Medical and Surgical

**Staffed Beds:** 95 **Admissions:** 438 **Census:** 61 **Outpatient Visits:** 11667 **Births:** 0 **Total Expense ($000):** 14200 **Payroll Expense ($000):** 4518 **Personnel:** 132

**MS**

---

**Hospital, Medicare Provider Number, Address, Telephone, Approval, Facility, and Physician Codes, Health Care System**

★ American Hospital Association (AHA) membership
☐ The Joint Commission accreditation
○ Healthcare Facilities Accreditation Program
◇ DNV Healthcare Inc. accreditation
⇑ Center for Improvement in Healthcare Quality Accreditation
△ Commission on Accreditation of Rehabilitation Facilities (CARF) accreditation

**MS**

### PURVIS—Lamar County

☐ **SOUTH MISSISSIPPI STATE HOSPITAL (254008)**, 823 Highway 589,
Zip 39475–4194; tel. 601/794–0100 **A**1 10 **F**3 98 106 130 146 **S** Mississippi
State Department of Mental Health, Jackson, MS
Primary Contact: Clint Ashley, Director
CFO: Andy Tucker, Chief Financial Officer
CMO: Allen Harris, M.D., Clinical Director
CIO: Sabrina Young, Administrative Support Director
CHR: Kelly Reid, Human Resources Director
CNO: Pam Brinson, Nurse Executive
Web address: www.smsh.state.ms.us
**Control:** State–Government, nonfederal **Service:** Psychiatric

**Staffed Beds:** 50 **Admissions:** 632 **Census:** 45 **Outpatient Visits:** 0 **Births:**
0 **Personnel:** 104

### QUITMAN—Clarke County

★ **H. C. WATKINS MEMORIAL HOSPITAL (251316)**, 605 South Archusa Avenue,
Zip 39355–2331; tel. 601/776–6925 **A**9 10 18 **F**29 40 43 70 81 89 107 127
130 133 **S** Rush Health Systems, Meridian, MS
Primary Contact: Clinton Eaves, Administrator
CFO: Paul S. Black, Controller
CMO: O. Wayne Byrd, M.D., Chief of Staff
CIO: Melinda Smith, Chief Information Systems
CHR: Leigh Moore, Administrative Assistant Human Resources
Web address: www.watkinsmemorialhospital.com/hcwmh/
**Control:** Other not–for–profit (including NFP Corporation) **Service:** General
Medical and Surgical

**Staffed Beds:** 25 **Admissions:** 488 **Census:** 15 **Outpatient Visits:** 6056
**Births:** 0 **Personnel:** 175

### RALEIGH—Smith County

**PATIENTS CHOICE MEDICAL CENTER OF SMITH COUNTY (250163)**, 347
Magnolia Drive, Zip 39153–6011; tel. 601/782–9997 **A**10 **F**70 98 103 108
130 **P**6
Primary Contact: Tim Cockrell, Chief Executive Officer
**Control:** Corporation, Investor–owned, for–profit **Service:** General Medical and
Surgical

**Staffed Beds:** 10 **Admissions:** 139 **Census:** 5 **Outpatient Visits:** 2703
**Births:** 0 **Personnel:** 26

### RICHTON—Perry County

**PERRY COUNTY GENERAL HOSPITAL (251306)**, 206 Bay Avenue,
Zip 39476–2941; tel. 601/788–6316 **A**9 10 18 **F**3 34 40 41 43 57 59 64 65
70 107 115 119 127 133 146
Primary Contact: David Paris, Chief Executive Officer
Web address: www.pcghospital.com/
**Control:** Partnership, Investor–owned, for–profit **Service:** General Medical and
Surgical

**Staffed Beds:** 22 **Admissions:** 282 **Census:** 6 **Births:** 0 **Personnel:** 57

### RIPLEY—Tippah County

★ **TIPPAH COUNTY HOSPITAL (250010)**, 1005 City Avenue North,
Zip 38663–1414, Mailing Address: P.O. Box 499, Zip 38663–0499;
tel. 662/837–9221, (Total facility includes 40 beds in nursing home–type unit) **A**9
10 20 **F**29 40 43 53 70 81 89 90 93 107 119 128 130 131 133
Primary Contact: Bob Jones, Interim CEO
CFO: Mark Richey, Chief Financial Officer
CMO: Charles M. Elliott, M.D., Chief of Staff
CHR: Tony Bell, Manager Personnel
Web address: www.tippahcounty.ripley.ms/hospital.html
**Control:** County–Government, nonfederal **Service:** General Medical and Surgical

**Staffed Beds:** 69 **Admissions:** 464 **Census:** 43 **Outpatient Visits:** 13976
**Births:** 0 **Personnel:** 167

### ROLLING FORK—Sharkey County

**SHARKEY–ISSAQUENA COMMUNITY HOSPITAL (250079)**, 108 South Fourth
Street, Zip 39159–5146, Mailing Address: P.O. Box 339, Zip 39159–0339;
tel. 662/873–4395 **A**9 10 **F**40 53 56 70 89 107 111 119 133
Primary Contact: Jerry Keever, Administrator
**Control:** County–Government, nonfederal **Service:** General Medical and Surgical

**Staffed Beds:** 29 **Admissions:** 553 **Census:** 9 **Births:** 0 **Personnel:** 73

### RULEVILLE—Sunflower County

★ **NORTH SUNFLOWER MEDICAL CENTER (251318)**, 840 North Oak Avenue,
Zip 38771–3227, Mailing Address: P.O. Box 369, Zip 38771–0369;
tel. 662/756–2711, (Total facility includes 60 beds in nursing–type unit) **A**9
10 18 **F**3 8 15 29 30 32 34 35 40 42 43 44 45 50 53 56 57 59 62 63 64 65
68 70 74 77 79 81 82 84 87 90 93 97 103 107 110 115 119 127 128 130
132 133 134 143 147 **P**6
Primary Contact: Sam Miller, Chief Executive Officer
COO: Rodney Clark, Chief Operating Officer
CFO: Nickie Moore, Chief Financial Officer
CMO: Bennie B. Wright, M.D., Chief of Staff
CIO: Roger Goss, Director, Information Services
CHR: Robbie Taylor, Director Human Resources
CNO: Lisa Miller, R.N., Director of Nursing
Web address: www.northsunflower.com
**Control:** County–Government, nonfederal **Service:** General Medical and Surgical

**Staffed Beds:** 95 **Admissions:** 1293 **Census:** 80 **Outpatient Visits:** 40989
**Births:** 0 **Total Expense ($000):** 57397 **Payroll Expense ($000):** 19923
**Personnel:** 318

### SENATOBIA—Tate County

☐ **NORTH OAK REGIONAL MEDICAL CENTER (250126)**, 401 Getwell Drive,
Zip 38668–2213, Mailing Address: P.O. Box 648, Zip 38668–0648;
tel. 662/562–3100 **A**1 9 10 **F**40 43 56 70 86 98 103 107 119 130 132
Primary Contact: Sonja Graham, Chief Executive Officer
CHR: Vickie Barksdale, Manager Human Resources
Web address: www.normc.org
**Control:** Corporation, Investor–owned, for–profit **Service:** General Medical and
Surgical

**Staffed Beds:** 53 **Admissions:** 917 **Census:** 13 **Outpatient Visits:** 11450
**Births:** 0 **Personnel:** 111

### SOUTHAVEN—Desoto County

⊠ △ **BAPTIST MEMORIAL HOSPITAL–DESOTO (250141)**, 7601 Southcrest
Parkway, Zip 38671–4742; tel. 662/772–4000 **A**1 3 7 9 10 **F**3 8 11 13 15 17
18 20 22 26 28 29 30 31 35 39 40 43 44 45 46 47 48 49 50 57 59 60 61
68 70 73 74 75 76 77 78 79 80 81 82 84 85 86 87 90 93 96 107 108 109
110 111 114 115 116 117 118 119 120 121 123 124 126 130 131 132 135
143 144 146 147 **S** Baptist Memorial Health Care Corporation, Memphis, TN
Primary Contact: James Huffman, Chief Executive Officer and Administrator
CFO: Joe McWherter, Chief Financial Officer
CMO: Joann Wood, M.D., Chief Medical Officer
CHR: Walter Banks, Director Human Resources
Web address: www.baptistonline.org/desoto/
**Control:** Other not–for–profit (including NFP Corporation) **Service:** General
Medical and Surgical

**Staffed Beds:** 242 **Admissions:** 15179 **Census:** 203 **Outpatient Visits:**
98625 **Births:** 1743 **Personnel:** 1282

### STARKVILLE—Oktibbeha County

★ ◇ **OCH REGIONAL MEDICAL CENTER (250050)**, 400 Hospital Road,
Zip 39759–2163, Mailing Address: P.O. Box 1506, Zip 39760–1506;
tel. 662/323–4320 **A**9 10 21 **F**3 7 11 13 15 17 28 29 32 34 39 40 41 43
45 47 48 51 53 57 59 61 64 65 70 73 74 75 76 77 79 81 82 85 87 88 89
90 93 97 98 107 108 110 111 114 115 118 119 126 130 131 132 133 135
146 147 **P**6
Primary Contact: Richard G. Hilton, Administrator and Chief Executive Officer
COO: Mike Andrews, Associate Administrator and Chief Operating Officer
CFO: Susan Russell, Chief Financial Officer
CIO: Chamath Wijewardane, Director Information Technology
CHR: Mike Andrews, Associate Administrator and Chief Operating Officer
CNO: Martha Fulcher, MSN, Chief Nursing Officer
Web address: www.och.org
**Control:** County–Government, nonfederal **Service:** General Medical and Surgical

**Staffed Beds:** 96 **Admissions:** 2350 **Census:** 25 **Outpatient Visits:** 230078
**Births:** 939 **Total Expense ($000):** 66825 **Payroll Expense ($000):** 32023
**Personnel:** 577

### TUPELO—Lee County

⊠ △ **NORTH MISSISSIPPI MEDICAL CENTER – TUPELO (250004)**, 830 South
Gloster Street, Zip 38801–4934; tel. 662/377–3000, (Total facility includes 107
beds in nursing home–type unit) **A**1 **F**3 4 5 7 9 10 19 **F**3 4 5 7 11 12 13 15 17
18 19 20 22 24 26 28 29 30 31 32 34 35 37 38 40 41 43 44 46 47 48 49
50 51 53 56 57 58 59 61 62 63 64 66 68 70 71 72 73 74 75 76 77 78 79
80 81 83 84 85 86 87 88 89 90 91 92 93 96 97 98 100 101 103 104 106
107 108 109 110 111 112 113 114 115 116 117 118 119 120 121 122 123
124 126 128 129 130 131 132 134 135 146 147 148 **S** North Mississippi
Health Services, Inc., Tupelo, MS
Primary Contact: David C. Wilson, Chief Executive Officer
CFO: Joseph A. Reppert, Executive Vice President and Chief Financial Officer
CHR: Rodger Brown, Vice President Human Resources
Web address: www.nmhs.net
**Control:** Other not–for–profit (including NFP Corporation) **Service:** General
Medical and Surgical

**Staffed Beds:** 747 **Admissions:** 24615 **Census:** 495 **Outpatient Visits:**
232142 **Births:** 2136 **Personnel:** 3976

*Many Facility Codes have changed. Please refer to the AHA Guide Code Chart.*

☐ **NORTH MISSISSIPPI STATE HOSPITAL (254009)**, 1937 Briar Ridge Road, Zip 38804–5963; tel. 662/690–4200 **A**1 10 **F**29 87 98 101 130 143 146 **S** Mississippi State Department of Mental Health, Jackson, MS
Primary Contact: Paul A. Callens, Ph.D., Director
CFO: Joe Rials, Director Fiscal Services
CMO: Ken Lippincott, M.D., Chief of Staff
CIO: James Wilhite, Director Systems Information
Web address: www.nmsh.state.ms.us
**Control:** State–Government, nonfederal **Service:** Psychiatric

**Staffed Beds:** 50 **Admissions:** 479 **Census:** 43 **Outpatient Visits:** 0 **Births:** 0 **Personnel:** 116

**TYLERTOWN—Walthall County**

★ **WALTHALL COUNTY GENERAL HOSPITAL (251324)**, 100 Hospital Drive, Zip 39667–2099; tel. 601/876–2122 **A**9 10 18 **F**40 43 70 81 89 93 107 119 127 130 133 146
Primary Contact: Bryan K. Maxie, Administrator
Web address: www.walthallhospitalms.org
**Control:** County–Government, nonfederal **Service:** General Medical and Surgical

**Staffed Beds:** 25 **Admissions:** 381 **Census:** 5 **Outpatient Visits:** 13415 **Births:** 0 **Personnel:** 97

**UNION—Newton County**

★ **LAIRD HOSPITAL (251322)**, 25117 Highway 15, Zip 39365–9099; tel. 601/774–8214 **A**9 10 18 **F**15 29 35 40 43 70 81 87 89 93 107 119 130 132 133 146 **S** Rush Health Systems, Meridian, MS
Primary Contact: Thomas G. Bartlett, III, Administrator
COO: Morris A. Reece, EVP/COO
CFO: Jennifer Flint, Chief Financial Officer
CMO: John Mutziger, M.D., Chief Medical Officer
CIO: Angela Sherrill, Chief Information Officer
CHR: Donnie Smith, Chief Human Resources Officer
CNO: Pam Rigdon, Director Nursing
Web address: www.lairdhospital.com/lh/
**Control:** Other not–for–profit (including NFP Corporation) **Service:** General Medical and Surgical

**Staffed Beds:** 25 **Admissions:** 550 **Census:** 10 **Outpatient Visits:** 13106 **Births:** 0 **Personnel:** 275

**VICKSBURG—Warren County**

**PROMISE HOSPITAL OF VICKSBURG (252008)**, 1111 North Frontage Road, 2nd Floor, Zip 39180–5102; tel. 601/619–3526 **A**10 **F**70 90 **S** Promise Healthcare, Boca Raton, FL
Primary Contact: Michael Harrell, Chief Executive Officer
COO: Dawn Posey, Chief Operating Officer
CFO: Christopher A. Stegall, Regional Chief Financial Officer and Chief Operating Officer
CMO: Daniel Edney, M.D., Chief of Staff
CIO: Barbara Whiting, Director Health Information Management
CHR: Debbie Carson, Director Human Resources
Web address: www.promise–vicksburg.com
**Control:** Corporation, Investor–owned, for–profit **Service:** Long–Term Acute Care hospital

**Staffed Beds:** 33 **Admissions:** 379 **Census:** 27 **Outpatient Visits:** 0 **Births:** 0 **Personnel:** 111

⊞ **MERIT HEALTH RIVER REGION (250031)**, 2100 Highway 61 North, Zip 39183–8211, Mailing Address: P.O. Box 590, Zip 39181–0590; tel. 601/883–5000, (Includes RIVER REGION WEST CAMPUS, 1111 North Frontage Road, Zip 39180–5102; tel. 601/883–5000) **A**1 9 10 **F**3 4 7 13 15 17 18 20 22 24 26 29 30 35 38 39 40 43 45 47 49 50 51 56 60 64 65 70 73 75 76 77 78 79 81 82 85 87 89 90 93 97 98 100 101 102 103 108 110 111 114 115 118 119 126 127 130 131 132 135 146 147 **S** Community Health Systems, Inc., Franklin, TN
Primary Contact: Gregory Pearson, Chief Executive Officer
CFO: John Milazzo, Chief Financial Officer
CMO: W. Briggs Hopson, M.D., Clinical Medical Director
CIO: J. B. White, Director Information Systems
CHR: Hal Harrington, Vice President Human Resources
Web address: www.riverregion.com
**Control:** Corporation, Investor–owned, for–profit **Service:** General Medical and Surgical

**Staffed Beds:** 317 **Admissions:** 8352 **Census:** 133 **Outpatient Visits:** 128357 **Births:** 688 **Personnel:** 882

**WATER VALLEY—Yalobusha County**

★ **YALOBUSHA GENERAL HOSPITAL (250061)**, 630 South Main, Zip 38965–3468, Mailing Address: P.O. Box 728, Zip 38965–0728; tel. 662/473–1411, (Total facility includes 122 beds in nursing home–type unit) **A**9 10 **F**2 3 7 15 29 30 32 33 59 64 65 70 107 110 115 119 127 128 130 133 143 146 **P**3 6
Primary Contact: Terry Varner, Administrator
COO: Ashlee Langdon, Controller
CHR: Katie Rotenberry–Baggett, Administrative Assistant and Human Resources
Web address: www.yalobushageneral.com/
**Control:** County–Government, nonfederal **Service:** General Medical and Surgical

**Staffed Beds:** 148 **Admissions:** 521 **Census:** 130 **Outpatient Visits:** 0 **Births:** 0 **Total Expense ($000):** 20124 **Payroll Expense ($000):** 12414 **Personnel:** 261

**WAYNESBORO—Wayne County**

☐ **WAYNE GENERAL HOSPITAL (250077)**, 950 Matthew Drive, Zip 39367–2590, Mailing Address: P.O. Box 1249, Zip 39367–1249; tel. 601/735–5151 **A**1 9 10 20 **F**13 15 35 39 40 43 53 61 62 63 70 75 76 81 86 88 89 90 93 107 108 111 119 127 130 132 133 146
Primary Contact: Kathy Waddell, Administrator
Web address: www.waynegeneralhospital.org
**Control:** County–Government, nonfederal **Service:** General Medical and Surgical

**Staffed Beds:** 80 **Admissions:** 1849 **Census:** 28 **Outpatient Visits:** 31990 **Births:** 208 **Personnel:** 351

**WEST POINT—Clay County**

⊞ **NORTH MISSISSIPPI MEDICAL CENTER–WEST POINT (250067)**, 835 Medical Center Drive, Zip 39773–9320; tel. 662/495–2300 **A**1 9 10 **F**3 7 8 11 13 15 17 28 29 30 31 32 34 35 40 42 43 45 48 53 57 59 64 65 70 73 75 76 78 79 80 81 85 86 87 89 90 97 107 108 109 110 114 119 120 130 132 133 135 143 145 146 147 **P**4 **S** North Mississippi Health Services, Inc., Tupelo, MS
Primary Contact: Barry L. Keel, Chief Executive Officer
CFO: Kay Lawler, Business Office Manager
CMO: B. Keith Watson, M.D., Chief Medical Staff
CIO: Stacie Griggs, MIS Analyst
CHR: Brenda Johnson, Director Human Resources
CNO: Jane Windle, R.N., Director of Nurses
Web address: www.nmhs.net/westpoint
**Control:** Other not–for–profit (including NFP Corporation) **Service:** General Medical and Surgical

**Staffed Beds:** 60 **Admissions:** 1869 **Census:** 22 **Outpatient Visits:** 44600 **Births:** 323 **Total Expense ($000):** 28603 **Payroll Expense ($000):** 13667 **Personnel:** 252

**WHITFIELD—Rankin County**

⊞ **MISSISSIPPI STATE HOSPITAL (254010)**, 3550 Highway 468 West, Zip 39193–5529, Mailing Address: P.O. Box 157–A, Zip 39193–0157; tel. 601/351–8000, (Includes WHITFIELD MEDICAL SURGICAL HOSPITAL, Oak Circle, Zip 39193; tel. 601/351–8023), (Total facility includes 423 beds in nursing home–type unit) **A**1 3 9 10 **F**3 4 29 39 70 75 87 98 99 100 101 102 103 104 106 107 119 128 130 143 **P**1 **S** Mississippi State Department of Mental Health, Jackson, MS
Primary Contact: James G. Chastain, FACHE, Director
COO: Kelly R. Breland, CPA, Director Support Services
CFO: Alicia Harris, Director Fiscal Services
CMO: Duncan Stone, D.D.S., Chief Medical Staff
CIO: Bart Uharriet, Director Information Services
CHR: Katie Storr, Director of Human Resources
CNO: Jackie Yates, R.N., Nurse Executive
Web address: www.msh.state.ms.us
**Control:** State–Government, nonfederal **Service:** Psychiatric

**Staffed Beds:** 899 **Admissions:** 2608 **Census:** 696 **Outpatient Visits:** 3209 **Births:** 0 **Personnel:** 1330

**WIGGINS—Stone County**

**STONE COUNTY HOSPITAL (251303)**, 1434 East Central Avenue, Zip 39577–9602; tel. 601/928–6600 **A**9 10 18 **F**3 7 29 34 40 43 46 57 59 64 70 77 79 81 89 90 97 107 111 112 114 115 119 127 130 133 135 **P**6
Primary Contact: Julie Cain, Administrator
Web address: www.schospital.net/
**Control:** Corporation, Investor–owned, for–profit **Service:** General Medical and Surgical

**Staffed Beds:** 25 **Admissions:** 530 **Census:** 17 **Births:** 0 **Total Expense ($000):** 20333 **Payroll Expense ($000):** 7377 **Personnel:** 176

**MS**

---

**Hospital, Medicare Provider Number, Address, Telephone, Approval, Facility, and Physician Codes, Health Care System**

★ American Hospital Association (AHA) membership   ○ Healthcare Facilities Accreditation Program   ⇑ Center for Improvement in Healthcare Quality Accreditation
☐ The Joint Commission accreditation   ◇ DNV Healthcare Inc. accreditation   △ Commission on Accreditation of Rehabilitation Facilities (CARF) accreditation

## WINONA—Montgomery County

**TYLER HOLMES MEMORIAL HOSPITAL (251312)**, 409 Tyler Holmes Drive,
Zip 38967–1599; tel. 662/283–4114 **A**9 10 18 **F**3 11 34 35 40 41 43 50 51
57 59 70 87 107 111 114 119 130 133 135 **P**8
Primary Contact: Rosamond M. Tyler, Administrator
CFO: Cori Bailey, Accountant
CHR: Becky Corley, Director Human Resources
**Control:** County–Government, nonfederal **Service:** General Medical and Surgical

> **Staffed Beds:** 25 **Admissions:** 557 **Census:** 10 **Outpatient Visits:** 12591
> **Births:** 0 **Total Expense ($000):** 13032 **Payroll Expense ($000):** 6548
> **Personnel:** 140

## YAZOO CITY—Yazoo County

★ **BAPTIST MEDICAL CENTER YAZOO (251313)**, 823 Grand Avenue,
Zip 39194–3233; tel. 662/746–2261 **A**9 10 18 **F**8 11 15 29 30 40 53 54 56
70 81 89 93 97 107 110 111 114 119 133 **S** Baptist Health Systems,
Jackson, MS
Primary Contact: Sean Johnson, Chief Executive Officer
COO: Marsha Jones, R.N., Director Nursing
CFO: James L. Miller, Chief Financial Officer
CMO: Marion Sigrest, M.D., Chief of Staff
CIO: Benton D. Estes, Materials Management
CHR: Stephanie Washington, Director Community Relations and Human Resources
CNO: Marsha Jones, R.N., Director of Nursing
Web address: www.kdhyazoo.com
**Control:** Other not–for–profit (including NFP Corporation) **Service:** General
Medical and Surgical

> **Staffed Beds:** 25 **Admissions:** 804 **Census:** 11 **Outpatient Visits:** 15789
> **Births:** 1 **Personnel:** 279

**MS**

*Many Facility Codes have changed. Please refer to the AHA Guide Code Chart.* © 2015 AHA Guide

# MISSOURI

### ALBANY—Gentry County

★ **NORTHWEST MEDICAL CENTER (261328)**, 705 North College Street, Zip 64402–1433; tel. 660/726–3941 **A**9 10 18 **F**3 11 15 18 28 29 34 35 40 44 45 50 56 57 59 62 64 65 68 74 75 77 79 81 85 86 87 90 93 97 104 107 108 110 111 114 118 119 127 128 130 131 133 135 148 **P**6
Primary Contact: Jon D. Doolittle, President and Chief Executive Officer
COO: Nate Blackford, Chief Operating Officer
CFO: Tina Gillespie, Vice President and Chief Financial Officer
CMO: Angelia Martin, M.D., Chief of Staff
CIO: James Crouch, Vice President Technical Services
CHR: Vickie Cline, Director Human Resources
CNO: Miranda Floyd, R.N., Chief Nursing Officer
Web address: www.northwestmedicalcenter.org
**Control:** Other not–for–profit (including NFP Corporation) **Service:** General Medical and Surgical

**Staffed Beds:** 25 **Admissions:** 346 **Census:** 6 **Outpatient Visits:** 47659 **Births:** 0 **Total Expense ($000):** 16680 **Payroll Expense ($000):** 7765 **Personnel:** 160

### APPLETON CITY—St. Clair County

★ **ELLETT MEMORIAL HOSPITAL (261301)**, 610 North Ohio Avenue, Zip 64724–1609, Mailing Address: P.O. Box 6, Zip 64724–0006; tel. 660/476–2111, (Data for 212 days) **A**9 10 18 **F**3 7 11 18 34 40 45 50 57 59 77 79 81 97 107 111 114 119 127 128 129 130 133 143 **P**6
Primary Contact: Tom Hollis, Chief Executive Officer
CMO: Richard R. Dailey, D.O., President Medical Staff
CIO: John Stamp, Director Information Services
CNO: Cathy Menninga, R.N., Chief Nursing Officer
Web address: www.ellettmemorial.com
**Control:** Hospital district or authority, Government, nonfederal **Service:** General Medical and Surgical

**Staffed Beds:** 12 **Admissions:** 119 **Census:** 4 **Outpatient Visits:** 5980 **Births:** 0 **Total Expense ($000):** 4714 **Payroll Expense ($000):** 2049 **Personnel:** 75

### AURORA—Lawrence County

⊞ **MERCY HOSPITAL AURORA (261316)**, 500 Porter Street, Zip 65605–2365; tel. 417/678–2122 **A**1 9 10 18 **F**3 11 13 15 28 29 30 34 35 40 41 45 50 57 59 64 65 75 76 77 81 85 86 87 89 92 93 94 96 107 108 110 111 114 119 129 132 133 135 148 **P**6 **S** Mercy Health, Chesterfield, MO
Primary Contact: Douglas M. Stroemel, President
CFO: Sherry Clouse Day, CPA, Vice President Finance and Regional Chief Financial Officer
CMO: Christie Hurt, M.D., Chief of Staff and Medical Director
CHR: George Roden, Vice President Human Resources
CNO: Nicki Gamet, R.N., Vice President and Chief Nursing Officer
Web address: www.stjohns.com/aboutus/aurora.aspx
**Control:** Church–operated, Nongovernment, not–for profit **Service:** General Medical and Surgical

**Staffed Beds:** 25 **Admissions:** 680 **Census:** 6 **Outpatient Visits:** 30474 **Births:** 218 **Total Expense ($000):** 18374 **Payroll Expense ($000):** 8046 **Personnel:** 148

### BELTON—Cass County

⊞ **BELTON REGIONAL MEDICAL CENTER (260214)**, 17065 South 71 Highway, Zip 64012–4631; tel. 816/348–1200 **A**1 2 9 10 **F**3 15 18 20 29 30 31 34 35 37 40 43 45 57 59 65 68 70 74 75 77 78 79 81 82 85 87 90 93 107 108 110 111 118 119 129 130 131 132 146 **P**5 **S** HCA, Nashville, TN
Primary Contact: Todd Krass, Chief Executive Officer
CFO: Susan Shreeve, Chief Financial Officer
CMO: Douglas Bradley, M.D., Chief Medical Officer
CIO: Sarah Richardson, Director Information Systems
CHR: Yvonne Brewington, Director Human Resources
CNO: Karen Lee, MSN, Chief Nursing Officer
Web address: www.beltonregionalmedicalcenter.com
**Control:** Corporation, Investor–owned, for–profit **Service:** General Medical and Surgical

**Staffed Beds:** 46 **Admissions:** 2465 **Census:** 25 **Outpatient Visits:** 105798 **Births:** 0 **Total Expense ($000):** 49289 **Payroll Expense ($000):** 15662 **Personnel:** 201

**RESEARCH BELTON HOSPITAL** See Belton Regional Medical Center

### BETHANY—Harrison County

★ **HARRISON COUNTY COMMUNITY HOSPITAL (261312)**, 2600 Miller Street, Zip 64424–2701, Mailing Address: P.O. Box 428, Zip 64424–0428; tel. 660/425–2211 **A**9 10 18 **F**3 11 15 18 28 29 34 40 44 45 46 50 53 54 57 59 62 64 65 66 67 75 77 79 81 82 87 89 90 93 96 97 98 102 103 104 107 108 110 111 114 119 127 128 129 130 131 133 143 144 145 146 148 **P**5
Primary Contact: Kelly Pottorff, Chief Executive Officer
CFO: Lee Ann Miles, Chief Financial Officer
CIO: Will Holt, Director Information Technology
CHR: Cathie Chalfant, Director Human Resources
CNO: Crystal Hicks, R.N., Chief Nursing Officer
Web address: www.hcchospital.org
**Control:** Hospital district or authority, Government, nonfederal **Service:** General Medical and Surgical

**Staffed Beds:** 19 **Admissions:** 377 **Census:** 6 **Outpatient Visits:** 49123 **Births:** 0 **Total Expense ($000):** 21149 **Payroll Expense ($000):** 9650 **Personnel:** 203

### BLUE SPRINGS—Jackson County

⊞ **ST. MARY'S MEDICAL CENTER (260193)**, 201 West R. D. Mize Road, Zip 64014–2518; tel. 816/228–5900 **A**1 9 10 13 **F**3 8 12 15 17 18 20 22 28 29 30 34 35 40 49 50 53 56 57 58 59 60 64 68 70 74 75 77 78 79 81 82 84 85 86 87 90 93 96 107 108 110 111 115 118 119 121 123 129 130 132 135 143 146 148 **S** Prime Healthcare Services, Ontario, CA
Primary Contact: Debra Ohnoutka, Chief Executive Officer
CFO: Steven R. Cleary, Vice President Finance
CMO: Stephens Stoops, M.D., Chief Medical Officer
Web address: www.carondelethealth.org
**Control:** Church–operated, Nongovernment, not–for profit **Service:** General Medical and Surgical

**Staffed Beds:** 90 **Admissions:** 4096 **Census:** 48 **Outpatient Visits:** 73056 **Births:** 0 **Total Expense ($000):** 69826 **Payroll Expense ($000):** 24217 **Personnel:** 423

### BOLIVAR—Polk County

⊞ **CITIZENS MEMORIAL HOSPITAL (260195)**, 1500 North Oakland Avenue, Zip 65613–3011; tel. 417/326–6000 **A**1 9 10 20 **F**3 7 11 13 15 18 20 22 26 28 29 31 34 35 36 40 43 44 50 51 54 56 57 59 62 64 66 70 74 75 76 77 78 79 80 81 82 84 85 86 87 89 90 93 94 96 97 98 100 102 103 104 107 108 110 111 115 117 119 124 127 128 129 130 131 132 133 135 146 147 148 **P**6
Primary Contact: Donald J. Babb, Chief Executive Officer
COO: Jeff Miller, Chief Operating Officer
CFO: Gary D. Fullbright, Comptroller
CMO: Michael Misko, M.D., Chief Medical Officer
CIO: Denni McColm, Chief Information Officer
CHR: Jeremy MacLaughlin, Director Human Resources
CNO: Lesa Stock, R.N., Chief Clinical Officer
Web address: www.citizensmemorial.com
**Control:** Hospital district or authority, Government, nonfederal **Service:** General Medical and Surgical

**Staffed Beds:** 72 **Admissions:** 3132 **Census:** 30 **Outpatient Visits:** 298064 **Births:** 522 **Total Expense ($000):** 116269 **Payroll Expense ($000):** 53047 **Personnel:** 852

### BONNE TERRE—St. Francois County

★ **PARKLAND HEALTH CENTER–BONNE TERRE (261315)**, 7245 Raider Road, Zip 63628–3767; tel. 573/358–1400 **A**9 10 18 **F**3 11 29 30 31 34 35 40 50 53 57 59 64 65 75 77 78 86 90 93 107 129 130 135 146 **S** BJC HealthCare, Saint Louis, MO
Primary Contact: Christinia Jepsen, R.N., Administrator
CFO: Cheri L. Goldsmith, Director Financial Services
CHR: Sheri Graham, Director Human Resources and Administrative Services
CNO: Jeanne Boyer, R.N., Director of Nurses
Web address: www.parklandhealthcenter.org
**Control:** Other not–for–profit (including NFP Corporation) **Service:** General Medical and Surgical

**Staffed Beds:** 3 **Admissions:** 10 **Census:** 1 **Outpatient Visits:** 21617 **Births:** 0 **Personnel:** 49

**MO**

---

**Hospital, Medicare Provider Number, Address, Telephone, Approval, Facility, and Physician Codes, Health Care System**

★ American Hospital Association (AHA) membership  ○ Healthcare Facilities Accreditation Program  ⇑ Center for Improvement in Healthcare Quality Accreditation
☐ The Joint Commission accreditation  ◇ DNV Healthcare Inc. accreditation  △ Commission on Accreditation of Rehabilitation Facilities (CARF) accreditation

**MO**

## BOONVILLE—Cooper County

★ **COOPER COUNTY MEMORIAL HOSPITAL (260004)**, 17651 B Highway,
Zip 65233–2839, Mailing Address: P.O. Box 88, Zip 65233–0088;
tel. 660/882–7461, (Total facility includes 14 beds in nursing home–type unit) **A**9
10 20 **F**3 7 11 28 29 34 35 40 45 53 57 59 62 64 67 68 75 79 81 85 89 93
94 107 111 114 119 127 128 130 131 132 133 135 146 148 **S** Rural
Community Hospitals of America, Kansas City, MO
Primary Contact: Danielle Gearhart, Chief Executive Officer
CFO: Patricia Nowlin, Director Accounting
CMO: Mona Brownfield, M.D., Chief Medical Staff
CIO: Bill Fletcher, Director Information Technology
CHR: Patricia Nowlin, Director Human Resources
CNO: Nancy Fredrich, R.N., Chief Clinical Officer
Web address: www.coopercmh.org
**Control:** County–Government, nonfederal **Service:** General Medical and Surgical

**Staffed Beds:** 32 **Admissions:** 319 **Census:** 11 **Outpatient Visits:** 36593
**Births:** 0 **Total Expense ($000):** 12795 **Payroll Expense ($000):** 5001
**Personnel:** 105

## BRANSON—Taney County

⊠ △ **COX MEDICAL CENTER BRANSON (260094)**, 251 Skaggs Road,
Zip 65616–2031, Mailing Address: P.O. Box 650, Zip 65615–0650;
tel. 417/335–7000 **A**1 7 9 10 **F**3 8 13 15 17 18 20 22 26 28 29 31 32 34 35
40 41 44 45 46 47 50 51 53 56 57 59 60 61 62 63 64 65 66 68 70 74 75
76 77 78 79 80 81 82 84 85 86 87 89 90 93 97 98 100 103 106 107 108
110 111 114 117 118 119 121 123 127 129 130 131 132 135 143 144 146
147 148 **P**3 6 8 **S** CoxHealth, Springfield, MO
Primary Contact: William K. Mahoney, President and Chief Executive Officer
CFO: David Strong, Chief Financial Officer/Vice President Finance
CHR: Carol Murrow, Vice President Business Development
Web address: www.skaggs.net
**Control:** Other not–for–profit (including NFP Corporation) **Service:** General
Medical and Surgical

**Staffed Beds:** 119 **Admissions:** 5857 **Census:** 68 **Outpatient Visits:** 238436
**Births:** 575 **Total Expense ($000):** 150710 **Payroll Expense ($000):** 55702
**Personnel:** 1101

## BRIDGETON—St. Louis County

⊠ **SSM DEPAUL HEALTH CENTER (260104)**, 12303 De Paul Drive,
Zip 63044–2512; tel. 314/344–6000, (Total facility includes 52 beds in nursing
home–type unit) **A**1 2 5 9 10 **F**3 5 11 12 13 15 17 18 20 22 24 28 29 30 31
34 35 36 38 40 43 44 49 50 51 53 55 56 57 59 60 61 64 68 70 73 74 75
76 78 79 81 82 84 85 86 87 89 98 99 100 101 102 103 104 105 107 108
111 114 115 117 119 120 121 124 126 128 130 132 135 143 144 146 147
148 **P**6 8 **S** SSM Health, Saint Louis, MO
Primary Contact: Sean Hogan, President
COO: Tina Garrison, Vice President Operations
CFO: Hal Holder, Director Finance
CMO: John Moore, M.D., Vice President Medical Affairs
CIO: Scott Feldmann, Director Information Technology
CHR: Gloria Reed, Leader Human Resources
CNO: Kathleen Bonser, R.N., Vice President Nursing and Chief Nursing Officer
Web address: www.ssmdepaul.com
**Control:** Church–operated, Nongovernment, not–for profit **Service:** General
Medical and Surgical

**Staffed Beds:** 474 **Admissions:** 23119 **Census:** 343 **Outpatient Visits:**
228763 **Births:** 1156 **Total Expense ($000):** 336641 **Payroll Expense
($000):** 105351 **Personnel:** 1751

## BROOKFIELD—Linn County

**GENERAL JOHN J. PERSHING MEMORIAL HOSPITAL (261307)**, 130 East
Lockling Avenue, Zip 64628–2337, Mailing Address: P.O. Box 408,
Zip 64628–0408; tel. 660/258–2222 **A**9 10 18 **F**11 15 28 29 36 40 44 57 59
64 75 81 87 89 93 97 107 111 114 119 127 130 133 146 **P**6
Primary Contact: Phil Hamilton, R.N., Chief Executive Officer
CFO: Gary R. Tandy, Chief Financial Officer
CMO: B. K. Knowles, D.O., Chief of Staff
CIO: Elaine Sutton, Chief Information Officer
CHR: Amy Sayre, Director Human Resources
Web address: www.pershinghealthsystem.com
**Control:** Other not–for–profit (including NFP Corporation) **Service:** General
Medical and Surgical

**Staffed Beds:** 25 **Admissions:** 763 **Census:** 8 **Outpatient Visits:** 61207
**Births:** 0 **Total Expense ($000):** 16988 **Payroll Expense ($000):** 6704
**Personnel:** 153

## BUTLER—Bates County

★ **BATES COUNTY MEMORIAL HOSPITAL (260034)**, 615 West Nursery Street,
Zip 64730–1840, Mailing Address: P.O. Box 370, Zip 64730–0370;
tel. 660/200–7000 **A**9 10 20 **F**3 7 11 15 28 29 30 31 34 40 50 57 59 64 68
70 77 78 79 81 87 90 93 107 108 109 110 111 115 118 119 127 129 130
132 133 143 **P**5 6
Primary Contact: Edward J. Hannon, Chief Executive Officer
CFO: Terri Floyd, Chief Financial Officer
CMO: William F. Joyce, Chief of Staff
CIO: Marcia Cook, Director Information Technology
CHR: Melinda R. Jackson, Director Human Resources
CNO: Rebecca Tarver, Chief Nursing Officer
Web address: www.bcmhospital.com
**Control:** County–Government, nonfederal **Service:** General Medical and Surgical

**Staffed Beds:** 49 **Admissions:** 813 **Census:** 11 **Outpatient Visits:** 70975
**Births:** 0 **Total Expense ($000):** 34267 **Payroll Expense ($000):** 12877
**Personnel:** 233

## CAMERON—Clinton County

**CAMERON REGIONAL MEDICAL CENTER (260057)**, 1600 East Evergreen,
Zip 64429–2400, Mailing Address: P.O. Box 557, Zip 64429–0557;
tel. 816/632–2101 **A**3 5 9 10 **F**3 11 12 13 15 28 29 30 31 34 35 39 40 46
47 49 56 57 59 61 62 63 64 67 70 74 75 76 77 78 79 81 82 84 85 86 87
89 90 98 100 104 107 110 111 115 119 128 129 130 131 133 143 146
147 148 **P**6
Primary Contact: Joseph F. Abrutz, Jr., Administrator
CFO: Rosa Patti, Chief Financial Officer
CIO: Bill Walser, Coordinator Technology
CHR: Pat Bestgen, Manager Human Resources
Web address: www.cameronregional.org
**Control:** Other not–for–profit (including NFP Corporation) **Service:** General
Medical and Surgical

**Staffed Beds:** 58 **Admissions:** 1948 **Census:** 32 **Outpatient Visits:** 312689
**Births:** 140 **Total Expense ($000):** 49965 **Payroll Expense ($000):** 21653
**Personnel:** 360

## CAPE GIRARDEAU—Cape Girardeau County

☐ **LANDMARK HOSPITAL OF CAPE GIRARDEAU (262015)**, 3255 Independence
Street, Zip 63701–4914; tel. 573/335–1091, (Nonreporting) **A**1 9 10
**S** Landmark Hospitals, Cape Girardeau, MO
Primary Contact: Rodney Brown, Chief Executive Officer
COO: Michael L. Norman, Executive Vice President and Chief Operating Officer
CFO: Richard H. Hogan, CPA, Chief Financial Officer
CMO: William Fritsch, M.D., Medical Director
CIO: Renee Hesselrode, Director Health Information Management
CHR: Angela Kisner, Director Human Resources and Coordinator Medical Staff
Web address: www.landmarkhospitals.com
**Control:** Partnership, Investor–owned, for–profit **Service:** Long–Term Acute Care
hospital

**Staffed Beds:** 30

⊠ **SAINT FRANCIS MEDICAL CENTER (260183)**, 211 St. Francis Drive,
Zip 63703–5049; tel. 573/331–3000 **A**1 2 9 10 19 **F**3 9 11 12 13 15 17 18
20 22 24 26 28 29 30 31 32 34 35 39 40 43 44 45 46 47 48 49 50 53 54
56 57 58 59 60 61 62 64 65 68 70 72 73 74 75 76 77 78 79 80 81 82 83
84 85 86 87 89 90 91 92 93 96 97 107 108 110 111 114 115 117 118 119
120 121 123 124 126 129 130 131 132 135 141 142 143 144 145 146 147
148 **P**6
Primary Contact: Steven C. Bjelich, President and Chief Executive Officer
COO: Maryann Reese, R.N., Chief Operating Officer
CFO: Tony Balsano, Vice President Finance
CMO: James Schell, M.D., Vice President Medical Affairs
CIO: Edward E. Duryee, Director Information Systems
CHR: Teri Kreitzer, Director Human Resources
CNO: Jeannie Fadler, R.N., Vice President Patient Care Services
Web address: www.sfmc.net
**Control:** Church–operated, Nongovernment, not–for profit **Service:** General
Medical and Surgical

**Staffed Beds:** 277 **Admissions:** 11284 **Census:** 159 **Outpatient Visits:**
399108 **Births:** 985 **Total Expense ($000):** 394104 **Payroll Expense
($000):** 156555 **Personnel:** 2203

*Many Facility Codes have changed. Please refer to the AHA Guide Code Chart.*

✠ **SOUTHEAST HOSPITAL (260110)**, 1701 Lacey Street, Zip 63701–5230; tel. 573/334–4822 **A**1 9 10 19 **F**3 11 13 15 17 18 20 22 24 26 28 29 30 31 32 34 35 40 45 46 49 50 51 53 54 57 58 59 60 61 62 63 64 65 70 72 73 74 75 76 77 78 79 80 81 82 85 86 87 88 89 90 92 93 96 97 98 100 102 107 108 110 111 115 117 119 120 121 123 124 126 127 129 130 131 132 146 147 148 **P**6 **S** SoutheastHEALTH, Cape Girardeau, MO
Primary Contact: Kenneth Bateman, CPA, Chief Executive Officer
COO: Sylvia Moore, Vice President and Chief Operating Officer
CFO: Bruce Fairbanks, Vice President and Chief Financial Officer
CMO: Matt Shoemaker, D.O., Vice President and Chief Medical Officer
CIO: Mike Dozier, Chief Information Officer
CHR: Lincoln Scott, Vice President Human Resources
CNO: Judy Aslin, MSN, Vice President and Chief Nursing Officer
Web address: www.sehealth.org/
**Control:** Other not–for–profit (including NFP Corporation) **Service:** General Medical and Surgical

**Staffed Beds: 221 Admissions: 9649 Census: 111 Outpatient Visits: 326491 Births: 1015 Total Expense ($000): 328750 Payroll Expense ($000): 122878 Personnel: 2211**

### CARROLLTON—Carroll County

★ **CARROLL COUNTY MEMORIAL HOSPITAL (261332)**, 1502 North Jefferson Street, Zip 64633–1948; tel. 660/542–1695 **A**9 10 **F**3 11 15 28 29 30 34 35 38 40 45 50 53 56 57 59 62 63 64 65 75 77 79 86 87 90 91 92 93 96 98 103 104 107 108 110 111 114 117 119 125 127 129 130 131 132 133 143 146 148 **P**6
Primary Contact: Jeff A. Tindle, Chief Executive Officer
COO: Marty Rucker, Construction/Plant Operations
CFO: Amy Ireland, Chief Financial Officer
CMO: Timothy Reid, M.D., Chief Medical Staff
CIO: Bill Bollinger, Chief Information Officer
CHR: Michael Schubach, Director Human Resources
CNO: Jeanne Rector, Chief Nursing Officer
Web address: www.carrollcountyhospital.org
**Control:** Other not–for–profit (including NFP Corporation) **Service:** General Medical and Surgical

**Staffed Beds: 25 Admissions: 315 Census: 4 Outpatient Visits: 53280 Births: 0 Total Expense ($000): 15802 Payroll Expense ($000): 6213 Personnel: 161**

### CARTHAGE—Jasper County

★ **MERCY HOSPITAL CARTHAGE (260228)**, 3125 Drive Russell Smith Way, Zip 64836–7402; tel. 417/358–8121 **A**9 10 18 **F**3 11 15 28 29 30 34 35 40 45 50 53 57 59 62 64 67 68 69 70 75 76 79 81 89 90 98 104 107 111 114 119 127 129 130 131 132 133 135 146 147 **P**6 **S** Mercy Health, Chesterfield, MO
Primary Contact: Robert Watson, JD, Administrator
CFO: Douglas Culver, Chief Financial Officer
CIO: Cheryl Lease–Homeyer, Lead Information Technology Business Partner
CHR: Colette St. Peter, Senior Manager Human Resources
Web address: www.mercy.net
**Control:** Church–operated, Nongovernment, not–for profit **Service:** General Medical and Surgical

**Staffed Beds: 49 Admissions: 1302 Census: 12 Outpatient Visits: 99525 Births: 321 Total Expense ($000): 53478 Payroll Expense ($000): 16390 Personnel: 277**

### CASSVILLE—Barry County

✠ **MERCY HOSPITAL CASSVILLE (261317)**, 94 Main Street, Zip 65625–1610; tel. 417/847–6000 **A**1 9 10 18 **F**3 11 15 28 29 30 34 40 41 45 50 53 57 59 64 65 75 77 81 85 86 87 89 92 93 94 96 103 107 110 111 114 119 132 133 135 148 **P**6 **S** Mercy Health, Chesterfield, MO
Primary Contact: Douglas M. Stroemel, President
CFO: Sherry Clouse Day, CPA, Chief Financial Officer
CMO: Jamie Zengotita, M.D., Chief Medical Staff
CHR: George Roden, Vice President Human Resources
CNO: Nicki Gamet, R.N., Chief Nursing Officer
Web address: www.mercy.net/northwestarar/practice/mercy–hospital–cassville
**Control:** Church–operated, Nongovernment, not–for profit **Service:** General Medical and Surgical

**Staffed Beds: 18 Admissions: 326 Census: 3 Outpatient Visits: 28102 Births: 0 Total Expense ($000): 14440 Payroll Expense ($000): 6520 Personnel: 107**

### CHESTERFIELD—St. Louis County

☐ △ **MERCY REHABILITATION HOSPITAL (263029)**, 14561 North Outer Forty Road, Zip 63017; tel. 314/881–4000 **A**1 7 9 10 **F**16 29 30 75 90 91 130 132 143 148 **S** Kindred Healthcare, Louisville, KY
Primary Contact: Donna M. Flannery, Chief Executive Officer
CMO: Siresha Samudrala, M.D., Medical Director
Web address: www.stjohnsmercyrehab.com
**Control:** Partnership, Investor–owned, for–profit **Service:** Rehabilitation

**Staffed Beds: 90 Admissions: 1527 Census: 56 Outpatient Visits: 0 Births: 0 Total Expense ($000): 25078 Payroll Expense ($000): 11030 Personnel: 238**

✠ **ST. LUKE'S HOSPITAL (260179)**, 232 South Woods Mill Road, Zip 63017–3417; tel. 314/434–1500, (Total facility includes 140 beds in nursing home–type unit) **A**1 2 3 9 10 **F**3 10 11 13 15 17 18 20 22 24 26 28 29 30 31 32 34 35 36 39 40 41 42 44 45 46 48 49 50 52 53 54 55 56 57 58 59 60 61 62 63 64 65 66 68 69 70 71 73 74 75 76 77 78 79 81 82 83 84 85 86 87 89 90 93 97 107 108 110 111 114 115 117 118 119 120 121 123 124 126 128 129 130 131 132 135 144 145 146 147 148 **P**6 8
Primary Contact: Christine Candio, President and Chief Executive Officer
COO: Donald L. Miller, FACHE, Vice President, Operations
CFO: Scott Johnson, Vice President Finance
CIO: William Meyers, Chief Information Officer
CHR: Janette Taaffe, Vice President, Human Resource
CNO: Diane Ray, R.N., Vice President and Chief Nursing Officer Patient Services
Web address: www.stlukes–stl.com
**Control:** Church–operated, Nongovernment, not–for profit **Service:** General Medical and Surgical

**Staffed Beds: 501 Admissions: 15217 Census: 287 Outpatient Visits: 922894 Births: 1829 Total Expense ($000): 457679 Payroll Expense ($000): 203122 Personnel: 3099**

✠ **ST. LUKE'S REHABILITATION HOSPITAL (263030)**, 14709 Olive Boulevard, Zip 63017–2221; tel. 314/317–5700 **A**1 9 10 **F**12 28 29 34 75 79 90 96 100 119 130 132 **P**8 **S** Kindred Healthcare, Louisville, KY
Primary Contact: Christopher Baechle, Chief Executive Officer
Web address: www.khrehabstluke.com
**Control:** Partnership, Investor–owned, for–profit **Service:** Rehabilitation

**Staffed Beds: 35 Admissions: 693 Census: 23 Outpatient Visits: 0 Births: 0 Total Expense ($000): 9050 Payroll Expense ($000): 4667 Personnel: 85**

### CHILLICOTHE—Livingston County

✠ **HEDRICK MEDICAL CENTER (261321)**, 2799 North Washington Street, Zip 64601–2902; tel. 660/646–1480 **A**1 9 10 18 **F**3 11 13 15 18 28 29 30 31 34 35 39 40 41 43 44 45 50 56 68 69 70 74 75 76 77 78 79 81 82 85 86 87 89 90 92 93 96 97 99 100 102 104 107 108 110 111 115 118 119 127 128 129 130 131 133 146 147 148 **P**6 **S** Saint Luke's Health System, Kansas City, MO
Primary Contact: Steven M. Schieber, Interim Chief Executive Officer
CHR: Lisa Hecker, Director Human Resources
CNO: Catherine Hamilton, Chief Nursing Officer
Web address: www.saintlukeskc.org
**Control:** Other not–for–profit (including NFP Corporation) **Service:** General Medical and Surgical

**Staffed Beds: 25 Admissions: 1090 Census: 13 Outpatient Visits: 99428 Births: 219 Total Expense ($000): 39177 Payroll Expense ($000): 15560 Personnel: 270**

### CLINTON—Henry County

✠ **GOLDEN VALLEY MEMORIAL HEALTHCARE (260175)**, 1600 North Second Street, Zip 64735–1192; tel. 660/885–5511 **A**1 9 10 **F**3 7 11 13 15 17 18 28 29 30 31 33 34 35 40 45 47 48 49 53 57 59 61 62 64 68 70 74 75 76 77 78 79 81 85 86 87 90 93 96 107 108 111 115 118 119 127 128 129 130 131 132 133 143 146 147 148
Primary Contact: Randy S. Wertz, Chief Executive Officer
COO: Craig Thompson, Chief Operating Officer
CFO: Tammy R. Nadler, Chief Financial Officer
CIO: Mike Gaul, Director Information Technology
CHR: Greg Shannon, Director Human Resources
CNO: Mark David Mattes, R.N., Assistant Administrator/Patient Care Services
Web address: www.gvmh.org
**Control:** Hospital district or authority, Government, nonfederal **Service:** General Medical and Surgical

**Staffed Beds: 56 Admissions: 2654 Census: 23 Outpatient Visits: 247117 Births: 349 Total Expense ($000): 73040 Payroll Expense ($000): 35172 Personnel: 621**

**MO**

---

**Hospital, Medicare Provider Number, Address, Telephone, Approval, Facility, and Physician Codes, Health Care System**

★ American Hospital Association (AHA) membership
☐ The Joint Commission accreditation
○ Healthcare Facilities Accreditation Program
◇ DNV Healthcare Inc. accreditation
⇑ Center for Improvement in Healthcare Quality Accreditation
△ Commission on Accreditation of Rehabilitation Facilities (CARF) accreditation

## COLUMBIA—Boone County

✠ **BOONE HOSPITAL CENTER (260068)**, 1600 East Broadway, Zip 65201–5844; tel. 573/815–8000 **A**1 2 3 5 9 10 **F**3 7 11 12 13 15 17 18 20 22 24 26 28 29 30 31 34 35 36 40 45 46 47 48 49 50 51 53 56 57 59 60 61 64 65 68 70 71 72 73 74 75 76 77 78 79 80 81 82 84 85 86 87 89 90 93 96 107 108 110 111 114 115 117 118 119 126 129 130 131 132 135 145 146 147 148 **S** BJC HealthCare, Saint Louis, MO
Primary Contact: James J. Sinek, FACHE, President
CFO: Randy Morrow, Vice President and Chief Operating Officer
CMO: Jerry Kennett, M.D., Chief Medical Officer
CHR: Michelle Zvanut, Vice President Human Resources
Web address: www.boone.org
**Control:** Other not–for–profit (including NFP Corporation) **Service:** General Medical and Surgical

**Staffed Beds:** 304 **Admissions:** 14973 **Census:** 180 **Outpatient Visits:** 178478 **Births:** 2202 **Total Expense ($000):** 294875 **Payroll Expense ($000):** 78611 **Personnel:** 1514

**ELLIS FISCHEL CANCER CENTER** See University of Missouri Hospitals and Clinics

✠ **HARRY S. TRUMAN MEMORIAL VETERANS HOSPITAL**, 800 Hospital Drive, Zip 65201–5275; tel. 573/814–6000, (Total facility includes 41 beds in nursing home–type unit) **A**1 3 5 **F**3 4 5 17 18 20 22 24 28 29 30 31 34 35 39 40 44 49 54 56 58 59 61 62 63 64 67 70 74 75 78 79 81 82 84 85 86 87 90 92 93 94 97 98 100 101 102 103 104 105 106 107 108 111 115 118 119 127 128 129 130 132 135 146 147 **P**6 **S** Department of Veterans Affairs, Washington, DC
Primary Contact: Wade Vlosich, Director
COO: Robert G. Ritter, Associate Director
CFO: Deborah Henderson, Acting Chief Financial Officer
CMO: Lana Zerrer, M.D., Chief of Staff
CIO: Donna Krause, Chief Information Officer
CHR: Jimmy Powell, Manager Human Resources
Web address: www.columbiamo.va.gov
**Control:** Veterans Affairs, Government, federal **Service:** General Medical and Surgical

**Staffed Beds:** 123 **Admissions:** 3690 **Census:** 90 **Outpatient Visits:** 649902 **Births:** 0 **Total Expense ($000):** 299444 **Payroll Expense ($000):** 101074 **Personnel:** 1387

✠ **HOWARD A. RUSK REHABILITATION CENTER (263027)**, 315 Business Loop 70 West, Zip 65203–3248; tel. 573/817–2703 **A**1 3 5 9 10 **F**29 34 58 68 75 90 91 94 95 96 132 143 148 **S** HEALTHSOUTH Corporation, Birmingham, AL
Primary Contact: Larry Meeker, Chief Executive Officer
CFO: Jeff Reese, Chief Financial Officer
CMO: Gregory Worsowicz, M.D., Medical Director
CHR: Robin Prater, Director Human Resources
CNO: Lori Mann, R.N., Chief Nursing Officer
Web address: www.ruskrehab.com
**Control:** Partnership, Investor–owned, for–profit **Service:** Rehabilitation

**Staffed Beds:** 60 **Admissions:** 1059 **Census:** 45 **Outpatient Visits:** 0 **Births:** 0 **Total Expense ($000):** 20691 **Payroll Expense ($000):** 8179 **Personnel:** 156

⇑ **LANDMARK HOSPITAL OF COLUMBIA (262020)**, 604 Old 63 North, Zip 65201–6308; tel. 573/499–6600, (Nonreporting) **A**3 5 9 10 22 **S** Landmark Hospitals, Cape Girardeau, MO
Primary Contact: Mindy S. Moore, Chief Executive Officer
Web address: www.landmarkhospitals.com
**Control:** Partnership, Investor–owned, for–profit **Service:** Long–Term Acute Care hospital

**Staffed Beds:** 42

✠ **UNIVERSITY OF MISSOURI HOSPITALS AND CLINICS (260141)**, One Hospital Drive, Zip 65212–0001; tel. 573/882–4141, (Includes ELLIS FISCHEL CANCER CENTER, 115 Business Loop 70 West, Zip 65203; tel. 573/882–5460; WOMEN'S AND CHILDREN'S HOSPITAL, 404 Keene Street, Zip 65201–6626; tel. 573/875–9000; Keri Simon, Executive Director) **A**1 2 3 5 8 9 10 **F**3 4 7 9 11 12 13 15 16 17 18 19 20 22 24 26 28 29 30 31 32 34 35 37 38 39 40 41 42 43 44 45 46 47 48 49 50 51 52 53 54 55 56 57 58 59 60 61 64 65 66 68 70 71 72 73 74 75 76 77 78 79 81 82 83 84 85 86 87 88 89 92 93 97 98 99 100 101 102 103 104 107 108 110 111 114 115 117 118 119 120 121 123 124 126 129 130 131 132 134 135 138 141 142 143 144 146 147 148 **P**1 6 **S** University of Missouri Health Care, Columbia, MO
Primary Contact: Mitchell L. Wasden, Ed.D., Chief Executive Officer and Chief Operating Officer
CFO: Kevin Necas, Chief Financial Officer
CMO: Stevan Whitt, M.D., Chief Medical Officer
CHR: Sue Kopfle, Chief Human Resources Officer
CNO: Deborah Pasch, Chief Nurse Executive
Web address: www.muhealth.org
**Control:** State–Government, nonfederal **Service:** General Medical and Surgical

**Staffed Beds:** 477 **Admissions:** 24568 **Census:** 328 **Outpatient Visits:** 811234 **Births:** 1869 **Total Expense ($000):** 692597 **Payroll Expense ($000):** 218165 **Personnel:** 4511

## CRYSTAL CITY—Jefferson County

★ ○ △ **MERCY HOSPITAL JEFFERSON (260023)**, Highway 61 South, Zip 63019, Mailing Address: P.O. Box 350, Zip 63019–0350; tel. 636/933–1000 **A**7 9 10 11 **F**3 4 5 7 8 11 12 13 15 18 20 22 24 26 28 29 30 34 35 40 44 45 49 50 51 53 54 57 59 62 63 64 68 70 74 75 76 77 79 81 82 84 85 86 87 89 90 92 93 94 96 97 98 100 101 102 103 104 107 110 111 114 115 116 117 118 119 129 130 131 132 135 143 144 146 147 148 **P**6 **S** Mercy Health, Chesterfield, MO
Primary Contact: Eric Ammons, President
CMO: Mark Briete, M.D., Vice President Medical Affairs
CIO: Jan Poneta, Director Information Services
CHR: Saundra G. Turner, Director Human Resources
Web address: www.mercy.net/crystalcitymo
**Control:** Other not–for–profit (including NFP Corporation) **Service:** General Medical and Surgical

**Staffed Beds:** 213 **Admissions:** 12686 **Census:** 120 **Outpatient Visits:** 156179 **Births:** 423 **Total Expense ($000):** 130419 **Payroll Expense ($000):** 53049 **Personnel:** 1069

## DEXTER—Stoddard County

**SOUTHEAST HEALTH CENTER OF STODDARD COUNTY (260160)**, 1200 North One Mile Road, Zip 63841–1000; tel. 573/624–5566 **A**9 10 **F**3 11 15 28 29 31 34 39 40 45 59 62 65 70 75 77 78 81 85 89 90 93 97 107 108 111 115 118 119 127 130 133 146 **P**6 **S** SoutheastHEALTH, Cape Girardeau, MO
Primary Contact: Adam Bracks, Chief Executive Officer
CHR: Judy Bowling, Director Human Resources
Web address: www.sehealth.org
**Control:** Other not–for–profit (including NFP Corporation) **Service:** General Medical and Surgical

**Staffed Beds:** 16 **Admissions:** 801 **Census:** 7 **Outpatient Visits:** 116761 **Births:** 0 **Total Expense ($000):** 29604 **Payroll Expense ($000):** 10214 **Personnel:** 165

## DONIPHAN—Ripley County

★ **SOUTHEAST HEALTH CENTER OF RIPLEY COUNTY (260080)**, 109 Plum Street, Zip 63935–1299; tel. 573/996–2141 **A**9 10 **F**3 29 34 40 57 59 62 64 65 93 107 111 115 119 127 130 **P**6 **S** SoutheastHEALTH, Cape Girardeau, MO
Primary Contact: Cheryl Barton, R.N., Chief Executive Officer
CFO: Rickie Maples, Interim Chief Financial Officer
CMO: Ureej Mansoor, M.D., Chief of Staff
CIO: Riley March, Manager Information Technology
CHR: Peggy Teasdale, Director Human Resources
Web address: www.sehealth.org/southeast–health–center–of–ripley–county/SoutheastHEALTH.aspx?nd=41
**Control:** Other not–for–profit (including NFP Corporation) **Service:** General Medical and Surgical

**Staffed Beds:** 8 **Admissions:** 240 **Census:** 2 **Outpatient Visits:** 46423 **Births:** 0 **Total Expense ($000):** 10162 **Payroll Expense ($000):** 4526 **Personnel:** 96

## EL DORADO SPRINGS—Cedar County

**CEDAR COUNTY MEMORIAL HOSPITAL (261323)**, 1401 South Park Street, Zip 64744–2037; tel. 417/876–2511 **A**9 10 18 **F**11 15 18 28 29 30 34 35 40 45 53 56 57 59 62 64 65 68 74 77 81 85 87 89 90 93 102 103 107 110 111 114 119 127 129 130 133 146 147 148 **P**6
Primary Contact: Jana Witt, Chief Executive Officer
CFO: Carla Gilbert, Director Finance
CMO: Rick Casey, M.D., Chief Medical Staff
CIO: Lois Willmore, Supervisor Health Information Management
CHR: Diana Pyle, Director Human Resources and Executive Assistant to Chief Executive Officer
CNO: Dixie Flynn, Chief Nursing Officer
Web address: www.cedarcountyhospital.org
**Control:** County–Government, nonfederal **Service:** General Medical and Surgical

**Staffed Beds:** 25 **Admissions:** 448 **Census:** 11 **Outpatient Visits:** 33213 **Births:** 0 **Total Expense ($000):** 11623 **Payroll Expense ($000):** 4250 **Personnel:** 108

## ELLINGTON— County

**SOUTHEAST HEALTH CENTER OF REYNOLDS COUNTY (250229)**, 100 Highway 21 South, Zip 63638, Mailing Address: Rural Route 4, Box 4269, Zip 63638–9409; tel. 573/663–2511 **A**9 10 **F**3 29 34 40 57 59 64 65 107 111 114 119 127 129 130 **P**6 **S** SoutheastHEALTH, Cape Girardeau, MO
Primary Contact: Cheryl Barton, RN, Chief Executive Officer
COO: Steve Myers, Assistant Administrator
CFO: Katie Caudel, Controller
CIO: Thomas Barker, Director Information
**Control:** Other not–for–profit (including NFP Corporation) **Service:** General Medical and Surgical

**Staffed Beds:** 8 **Admissions:** 139 **Census:** 1 **Outpatient Visits:** 17803 **Births:** 0 **Total Expense ($000):** 6808 **Payroll Expense ($000):** 2843 **Personnel:** 56

**MO**

*Many Facility Codes have changed. Please refer to the AHA Guide Code Chart.* © 2015 AHA Guide

## EXCELSIOR SPRINGS—Clay County

★ **EXCELSIOR SPRINGS HOSPITAL (261322)**, 1700 Rainbow Boulevard, Zip 64024–1190; tel. 816/630–6081, (Total facility includes 80 beds in nursing home–type unit) **A**9 10 18 **F**3 10 11 15 18 29 30 31 32 34 35 39 40 45 49 56 57 59 62 63 64 67 68 70 75 77 78 79 81 82 84 85 86 89 90 93 102 107 108 110 111 114 116 117 118 119 125 128 129 130 133 143 146 147
Primary Contact: Sally S. Nance, Chief Executive Officer
CFO: Dennis Hartman, Chief Financial Officer
CMO: Manoch Kuangparichat, M.D., President Medical Staff
CIO: Alicia Harrison, Data Management Officer
CHR: Joni Schwan, Director Human Resources
Web address: www.esmc.org
**Control:** City–Government, nonfederal **Service:** General Medical and Surgical

**Staffed Beds:** 105 **Admissions:** 474 **Census:** 74 **Outpatient Visits:** 28533 **Births:** 0 **Total Expense ($000):** 25527 **Payroll Expense ($000):** 10684 **Personnel:** 229

## FAIRFAX—Atchison County

**COMMUNITY HOSPITAL ASSOCIATION** See Community Hospital–Fairfax

★ **COMMUNITY HOSPITAL–FAIRFAX (261303)**, 26136 U.S. Highway 59, Zip 64446–9105, Mailing Address: P.O. Box 107, Zip 64446–0107; tel. 660/686–2211 **A**9 10 18 **F**3 11 13 15 28 29 30 34 40 45 57 59 62 64 67 79 79 81 85 87 89 90 93 97 107 110 114 117 119 128 130 132 133
Primary Contact: Roger W. Steinkruger, Chief Executive Officer
CFO: Suzanne Southard, Director Finance
CIO: Chris Hedlund, Director Information Systems
CHR: Amber Durr, Director Human Resources
Web address: www.fairfaxmed.com
**Control:** Other not–for–profit (including NFP Corporation) **Service:** General Medical and Surgical

**Staffed Beds:** 18 **Admissions:** 433 **Census:** 5 **Outpatient Visits:** 14951 **Births:** 36 **Total Expense ($000):** 11934 **Payroll Expense ($000):** 4101 **Personnel:** 94

## FARMINGTON—St. Francois County

⊞ **PARKLAND HEALTH CENTER – LIBERTY STREET (260163)**, 1101 West Liberty Street, Zip 63640–1921; tel. 573/756–6451 **A**1 9 10 **F**3 11 13 15 28 29 30 34 35 40 45 46 49 50 53 57 59 60 64 65 68 69 70 75 76 77 79 81 85 86 87 89 93 98 103 107 108 111 115 118 119 130 132 135 143 146 147 148 **S** BJC HealthCare, Saint Louis, MO
Primary Contact: Thomas P. Karl, President
COO: Steven R. Marler, Assistant Administrator
CFO: Cheri L. Goldsmith, Director Financial Services
CMO: Jamesy Smith, D.O., Chief of Staff
CHR: Sheri Graham, Director Human Resources and Administrative Services
CNO: Barbara Berrong, R.N., Chief Nursing Officer
Web address: www.parklandhealthcenter.org
**Control:** Other not–for–profit (including NFP Corporation) **Service:** General Medical and Surgical

**Staffed Beds:** 103 **Admissions:** 3026 **Census:** 28 **Outpatient Visits:** 84838 **Births:** 376 **Total Expense ($000):** 73141 **Payroll Expense ($000):** 26471 **Personnel:** 386

★ ○ **PARKLAND HEALTH CENTER – WEBER ROAD (260116)**, 1212 Weber Road, Zip 63640–3325; tel. 573/756–4581 **A**9 10 11 19 **F**3 11 15 18 28 29 30 34 40 45 50 57 59 60 62 64 68 70 76 77 79 81 85 89 90 93 98 100 102 103 107 111 114 119 127 129 130 132 133 146 147 **S** BJC HealthCare, Saint Louis, MO
Primary Contact: Christie Westrich, Administrator
CFO: Cheri L. Goldsmith, Director, Financial Services
CMO: Jamesy Smith, D.O., President, Medical Staff
CHR: Sheri Graham, Administrative Director Human Resources and Volunteer Services Associate Ethics and Compliance Officer
CNO: Teri Ragsdale, Chief Nursing Officer
Web address: www.parklandhealthcenter.org
**Control:** Corporation, Investor–owned, for–profit **Service:** General Medical and Surgical

**Staffed Beds:** 127 **Admissions:** 3000 **Census:** 33 **Outpatient Visits:** 74470 **Births:** 378 **Total Expense ($000):** 48550 **Payroll Expense ($000):** 19990 **Personnel:** 378

☐ **SOUTHEAST MISSOURI MENTAL HEALTH CENTER (264005)**, 1010 West Columbia Street, Zip 63640–2997; tel. 573/218–6792 **A**1 10 **F**4 11 30 39 53 65 75 77 86 87 97 98 101 103 106 130 132 135 143 146
Primary Contact: Julie Inman, Regional Executive Officer
CMO: Jay Englehart, M.D., Medical Director
CHR: Mark Remspecher, Director Human Resources
Web address: www.dmh.missouri.gov/southeast/
**Control:** State–Government, nonfederal **Service:** Psychiatric

**Staffed Beds:** 323 **Admissions:** 50 **Census:** 292 **Outpatient Visits:** 0 **Births:** 0 **Total Expense ($000):** 54941 **Payroll Expense ($000):** 30991 **Personnel:** 882

## FENTON—St. Louis County

⊞ **SSM ST. CLARE HEALTH CENTER (260081)**, 1015 Bowles Avenue, Zip 63026–2394; tel. 636/496–2000 **A**1 9 10 **F**3 11 13 15 17 18 20 22 24 28 29 30 31 32 34 35 40 44 45 49 50 51 53 56 57 59 61 64 70 73 74 75 76 78 79 81 82 84 85 86 87 89 100 102 103 107 108 110 111 114 115 117 118 119 130 132 135 143 146 147 148 **P**6 8 **S** SSM Health, Saint Louis, MO
Primary Contact: Ellis Hawkins, President
COO: Lee Bernstein, Regional Executive Vice President and Chief Operating Officer
CFO: Hal Holder, Regional Chief Financial Officer–Hospital Operations
CMO: Timothy J. Pratt, M.D., Vice President Medical Affairs and Chief Medical Officer
CIO: Mike Paasch, Vice President, Regional Chief Information Officer
CHR: Renee Roach, System Vice President, Human Resources
CNO: Wayne Laramie, Vice President Nursing
Web address: www.ssmstclare.com
**Control:** Church–operated, Nongovernment, not–for profit **Service:** General Medical and Surgical

**Staffed Beds:** 184 **Admissions:** 9782 **Census:** 104 **Outpatient Visits:** 107796 **Births:** 1208 **Total Expense ($000):** 164678 **Payroll Expense ($000):** 48992 **Personnel:** 797

## FORT LEONARD WOOD—Pulaski County

⊞ **GENERAL LEONARD WOOD ARMY COMMUNITY HOSPITAL**, 126 Missouri Avenue, Zip 65473–8952; tel. 573/596–0414 **A**1 3 **F**3 4 5 7 8 12 13 14 15 29 30 32 33 34 35 36 38 39 40 45 49 54 55 56 57 59 61 64 65 68 70 74 75 76 77 79 81 85 86 87 89 90 93 97 98 99 100 101 102 103 104 107 108 109 110 111 114 115 118 119 130 131 135 144 147 **S** Department of the Army, Office of the Surgeon General, Falls Church, VA
Primary Contact: Colonel Peter Nielsen, M.D., Commander
CFO: Major Michael Hogan, Chief Resource Management
CMO: Lieutenant Colonel John Lowery, M.D., Deputy Commander Clinical Services
CHR: Major Sandra Roper, Chief Human Resources
Web address: www.glwach.amedd.army.mil/
**Control:** Army, Government, federal **Service:** General Medical and Surgical

**Staffed Beds:** 42 **Admissions:** 2296 **Census:** 18 **Outpatient Visits:** 334983 **Births:** 534 **Total Expense ($000):** 115409 **Payroll Expense ($000):** 52651 **Personnel:** 795

## FREDERICKTOWN—Madison County

**MADISON MEDICAL CENTER (261302)**, 611 West Main Street, Zip 63645–1111; tel. 573/783–3341, (Total facility includes 80 beds in nursing home–type unit) **A**9 10 18 **F**6 11 15 18 28 31 35 40 45 59 62 64 67 70 74 77 78 79 81 85 87 103 107 111 119 127 128 130 133 146
Primary Contact: Lisa Twidwell, Administrator
CMO: P. A. George, M.D., Chief of Staff
CHR: Jennifer Penuel, Director Human Resources
Web address: www.madisonmedicalcenter.net
**Control:** County–Government, nonfederal **Service:** General Medical and Surgical

**Staffed Beds:** 97 **Admissions:** 360 **Census:** 79 **Outpatient Visits:** 51362 **Births:** 0 **Total Expense ($000):** 18334 **Payroll Expense ($000):** 9262 **Personnel:** 259

**MO**

---

**Hospital, Medicare Provider Number, Address, Telephone, Approval, Facility, and Physician Codes, Health Care System**

★ American Hospital Association (AHA) membership
☐ The Joint Commission accreditation
○ Healthcare Facilities Accreditation Program
◇ DNV Healthcare Inc. accreditation
⇑ Center for Improvement in Healthcare Quality Accreditation
△ Commission on Accreditation of Rehabilitation Facilities (CARF) accreditation

## FULTON—Callaway County

☐ **FULTON MEDICAL CENTER (260209)**, 10 South Hospital Drive,
Zip 65251–2510; tel. 573/642–3376 **A**1 3 5 9 10 **F**3 11 15 29 34 35 40 45
50 57 59 67 68 81 85 89 90 93 97 98 103 107 108 111 114 119 127 128
130 133 **P**6 **S** University of Missouri Health Care, Columbia, MO
Primary Contact: Mike Powell, Chief Executive Officer
COO: Chuck Baker, R.N., Chief Operating Officer and Chief Nursing Officer
CHR: Martie Jeney, Director Human Resources
CNO: Chuck Baker, R.N., Chief Operating Officer and Chief Nursing Officer
Web address: www.mycallaway.org
**Control:** Corporation, Investor–owned, for–profit **Service:** General Medical and
Surgical

**Staffed Beds:** 37 **Admissions:** 550 **Census:** 16 **Outpatient Visits:** 34247
**Births:** 0 **Total Expense ($000):** 15823 **Payroll Expense ($000):** 5697
**Personnel:** 155

☐ **FULTON STATE HOSPITAL (264004)**, 600 East Fifth Street, Zip 65251–1753;
tel. 573/592–4100 **A**1 3 5 10 **F**3 4 11 29 30 39 44 50 53 56 57 58 59 65 75
77 82 86 87 98 100 101 102 103 130 132 135 143 146 **P**6
Primary Contact: Robert Reitz, Ph.D., Chief Executive Officer
COO: Marty Ann Martin–Forman, Chief Operating Officer
CFO: Forrest Bud H. Smith, Jr., Chief Financial Officer
CMO: Sanjiv Sethi, M.D., Medical Director
CIO: Thomas Gillespie, Chief Information Officer
CHR: Lori Hollinger, Manager Human Resources
CNO: Sherry Lee, Chief Nurse Executive
Web address: www.dmh.missouri.gov/fulton
**Control:** State–Government, nonfederal **Service:** Psychiatric

**Staffed Beds:** 376 **Admissions:** 135 **Census:** 342 **Outpatient Visits:** 0
**Births:** 0 **Total Expense ($000):** 90643 **Payroll Expense ($000):** 46907
**Personnel:** 1193

## HANNIBAL—Marion County

☒ **HANNIBAL REGIONAL HOSPITAL (260025)**, 6000 Hospital Drive,
Zip 63401–6887, Mailing Address: P.O. Box 551, Zip 63401–0551;
tel. 573/248–1300 **A**1 2 9 10 **F**3 13 15 18 20 22 26 28 31 34 40 45 47 49
51 57 59 60 62 64 68 70 74 75 76 78 79 81 82 85 86 87 89 92 107 108
110 111 114 115 117 118 119 120 121 123 124 129 130 132 135 148 **P**1
Primary Contact: Lynn W. Olson, President and Chief Executive Officer
CFO: Roger J. Dix, Vice President Finance
CMO: Bryson McHardy, M.D., President Medical Staff
CIO: Jeff W. Evans, Vice President Information and Technology
CHR: Susan R. Wathen, Vice President Human Resources
Web address: www.hrhonline.org
**Control:** Other not–for–profit (including NFP Corporation) **Service:** General
Medical and Surgical

**Staffed Beds:** 91 **Admissions:** 4459 **Census:** 44 **Outpatient Visits:** 131867
**Births:** 605 **Total Expense ($000):** 115741 **Payroll Expense ($000):** 50454
**Personnel:** 786

## HARRISONVILLE—Cass County

☒ **CASS REGIONAL MEDICAL CENTER (261324)**, 2800 East Rock Haven Road,
Zip 64701–4411; tel. 816/380–3474 **A**1 9 10 18 **F**3 8 11 12 15 18 28 29 30
31 32 34 35 37 39 40 43 45 46 48 50 54 56 57 59 64 65 66 70 74 75 77
78 79 80 81 82 84 85 86 87 92 93 96 97 98 107 110 111 114 115 119 127
129 130 131 132 133 135 146 147 **P**6
Primary Contact: John Christopher Lang, Chief Executive Officer
CFO: Brent Probasco, Chief Financial Officer
CIO: Lester Vohs, Manager Information Systems
CHR: Carla Wallen, Manager Human Resources
CNO: Twila Buckner, Chief Nursing Officer
Web address: www.cassregional.org
**Control:** County–Government, nonfederal **Service:** General Medical and Surgical

**Staffed Beds:** 35 **Admissions:** 1469 **Census:** 18 **Outpatient Visits:** 102332
**Births:** 0 **Total Expense ($000):** 59052 **Payroll Expense ($000):** 21450
**Personnel:** 376

## HAYTI—Pemiscot County

**PEMISCOT MEMORIAL HEALTH SYSTEM (260070)**, 946 East Road,
Zip 63851–1245, Mailing Address: P.O. Box 489, Zip 63851–0489;
tel. 573/359–1372, (Total facility includes 66 beds in nursing home–type unit) **A**9
10 **F**3 7 11 13 15 17 28 29 30 34 39 40 50 57 59 64 67 68 70 75 76 79 81
82 85 87 89 90 93 97 98 99 103 104 107 111 119 127 128 130 133 143
144 146 147 148 **P**6
Primary Contact: Kerry L. Noble, Chief Executive Officer
CHR: Jackie Powell, Director Human Resources
Web address: www.pemiscot.org/
**Control:** County–Government, nonfederal **Service:** General Medical and Surgical

**Staffed Beds:** 167 **Admissions:** 3403 **Census:** 74 **Outpatient Visits:** 88144
**Births:** 23 **Total Expense ($000):** 35159 **Payroll Expense ($000):** 16798
**Personnel:** 470

## HERMANN—Gasconade County

★ **HERMANN AREA DISTRICT HOSPITAL (261314)**, 509 West 18th Street,
Zip 65041–1547, Mailing Address: P.O. Box 470, Zip 65041–0470;
tel. 573/486–2191 **A**9 10 18 **F**3 11 15 18 28 29 34 35 40 41 44 45 53 56
57 59 62 64 67 69 71 75 77 78 81 85 86 87 89 90 93 96 97 104 107 111
114 119 128 143 146 **P**6
Primary Contact: Dan McKinney, Administrator
COO: Matt Siebert, Assistant Administrator Ancillary Services
CFO: Michele Fehlings, Controller
CMO: Michael Rothermich, M.D., Chief of Staff
CIO: Chris Gooch, Information Technology Director
CHR: Gabrielle Gleeson, Human Resources
CNO: Sue Daller, R.N., Assistant Administrator Nursing
Web address: www.hadh.org
**Control:** Hospital district or authority, Government, nonfederal **Service:** General
Medical and Surgical

**Staffed Beds:** 24 **Admissions:** 439 **Census:** 10 **Outpatient Visits:** 59008
**Births:** 0 **Total Expense ($000):** 18082 **Payroll Expense ($000):** 7878
**Personnel:** 177

## HOUSTON—Texas County

**TEXAS COUNTY MEMORIAL HOSPITAL (260024)**, 1333 South Sam Houston
Boulevard, Zip 65483–2046; tel. 417/967–3311 **A**9 10 20 **F**3 7 13 15 28 29
34 40 45 57 59 62 63 64 70 76 81 85 86 87 89 93 97 107 110 111 115
119 127 128 129 130 133 143 148 **P**6
Primary Contact: Wesley E. Murray, Chief Executive Officer
CFO: Linda Pamperien, Chief Financial Officer
CMO: Charles Mueller, M.D., Chief of Staff
CHR: Anita Kuhn, Controller
Web address: www.tcmh.org
**Control:** County–Government, nonfederal **Service:** General Medical and Surgical

**Staffed Beds:** 47 **Admissions:** 1587 **Census:** 17 **Outpatient Visits:** 103860
**Births:** 234 **Total Expense ($000):** 29748 **Payroll Expense ($000):** 14877
**Personnel:** 336

## INDEPENDENCE—Jackson County

☒ **CENTERPOINT MEDICAL CENTER (260095)**, 19600 East 39th Street,
Zip 64057–2301; tel. 816/698–7000 **A**1 2 9 10 **F**3 8 13 15 17 18 20 22 24
26 28 29 30 31 34 35 38 40 43 49 50 54 55 56 57 59 60 64 68 70 72 73
74 75 76 77 78 79 80 81 82 84 85 86 87 92 93 107 108 110 111 114 115
116 117 118 119 126 129 130 131 132 144 145 146 147 148 **S** HCA,
Nashville, TN
Primary Contact: David R. Williams, Chief Executive Officer
COO: Phil Buttell, Chief Operating Officer
CFO: James H. Brown, Chief Financial Officer
CMO: Christopher Sullivan, M.D., Chief Medical Officer
CIO: Carl Sifers, Director Information Technology and System Services
CHR: Kyla Stoltz, Vice President Human Resources
CNO: Lynn Barrett, Chief Nursing Officer
Web address: www.centerpointmedical.com
**Control:** Corporation, Investor–owned, for–profit **Service:** General Medical and
Surgical

**Staffed Beds:** 221 **Admissions:** 15413 **Census:** 173 **Outpatient Visits:**
147686 **Births:** 1477 **Total Expense ($000):** 224645 **Payroll Expense
($000):** 71523 **Personnel:** 1254

## JEFFERSON CITY—Cole County

☒ **CAPITAL REGION MEDICAL CENTER (260047)**, 1125 Madison Street,
Zip 65101–5200, Mailing Address: P.O. Box 1128, Zip 65102–1128;
tel. 573/632–5000 **A**1 3 5 9 10 12 13 **F**3 5 11 13 15 17 18 20 22 24 26 28
29 30 31 32 34 35 36 38 40 45 48 51 53 54 56 57 58 59 61 62 64
65 66 70 73 74 75 76 77 78 79 80 81 85 87 89 90 92 93 94 97 99 100
102 104 107 108 110 111 115 118 119 120 121 123 129 130 131 132 135
144 146 147 **P**2 6 **S** University of Missouri Health Care, Columbia, MO
Primary Contact: Gaspare Calvaruso, President
COO: Janet Weckenborg, FACHE, Vice President Operations
CFO: Tom Luebbering, Vice President Finance
CMO: Thomas Hetherington, M.D., Chief of Staff
CIO: Jason Cecil, Chief Information Officer
CHR: Robert Mazur, Vice President Human Resources
CNO: Lynne Voskamp, R.N., Vice President of Nursing
Web address: www.crmc.org
**Control:** Other not–for–profit (including NFP Corporation) **Service:** General
Medical and Surgical

**Staffed Beds:** 114 **Admissions:** 5447 **Census:** 56 **Outpatient Visits:** 427995
**Births:** 900 **Total Expense ($000):** 157291 **Payroll Expense ($000):** 69401
**Personnel:** 1209

**MO**

**SSM HEALTH ST. MARY'S HOSPITAL – JEFFERSON CITY (260011)**, 2505 Mission Drive, Zip 65109; tel. 573/681–3000 **A**1 9 10 19 **F**3 4 5 11 13 15 17 18 20 22 24 28 29 30 31 34 40 45 47 48 49 50 51 54 57 59 60 64 70 73 74 75 76 77 78 79 81 85 86 87 89 93 96 98 100 101 102 104 107 108 110 111 115 118 119 120 121 123 124 127 129 130 131 132 135 141 144 146 147 148 **P**6 **S** SSM Health, Saint Louis, MO
Primary Contact: R. Brent VanConia, President
CFO: James Stratton, Vice President Finance
CMO: Stephen Stewart, M.D., Vice President Medical Affairs
CHR: Susan Mankoski, Vice President Human Resources
CNO: Alice M. Chatley, R.N., Vice President Acute Care Services
Web address: www.lethealingbegin.com
**Control:** Church–operated, Nongovernment, not–for profit **Service:** General Medical and Surgical

> **Staffed Beds:** 152 **Admissions:** 6874 **Census:** 78 **Outpatient Visits:** 189709 **Births:** 704 **Total Expense ($000):** 142247 **Payroll Expense ($000):** 45251 **Personnel:** 871

## JOPLIN—Newton County

★ ○ **FREEMAN HOSPITAL WEST (260137)**, 1102 West 32nd Street, Zip 64804–3503; tel. 417/347–1111, (Includes FREEMAN HOSPITAL EAST, 932 East 34th Street, Zip 64804–3999; tel. 417/623–4640) **A**9 10 11 13 **F**3 8 11 13 15 17 18 20 22 24 26 28 29 30 31 34 35 40 42 43 44 45 47 48 49 50 54 56 57 58 59 60 61 62 64 65 68 70 72 73 74 75 76 77 78 79 81 82 84 85 86 87 89 90 93 96 97 98 100 102 103 107 108 110 111 114 115 117 119 124 129 130 131 132 144 145 146 147 148 **P**1 6 **S** Freeman Health System, Joplin, MO
Primary Contact: Paula F. Baker, President and Chief Executive Officer
COO: Richard D. Schooler, M.D., Executive Vice President and Chief Operating Officer
CFO: Steve W. Graddy, Chief Financial Officer
CMO: Richard D. Schooler, M.D., Chief Medical Officer
CIO: Sue Annesser, Chief Information Officer
CHR: Mary Frerer, Chief Human Resources Officer
CNO: Jeffrey Carrier, R.N., Chief Clinical Officer
Web address: www.freemanhealth.com
**Control:** Other not–for–profit (including NFP Corporation) **Service:** General Medical and Surgical

> **Staffed Beds:** 396 **Admissions:** 17830 **Census:** 275 **Outpatient Visits:** 752912 **Births:** 2272 **Total Expense ($000):** 443674 **Payroll Expense ($000):** 204683 **Personnel:** 3090

◇ **LANDMARK HOSPITAL OF JOPLIN (262016)**, 2040 West 32nd Street, Zip 64804–3512; tel. 417/627–1300, (Nonreporting) **A**9 10 21 **S** Landmark Hospitals, Cape Girardeau, MO
Primary Contact: Kevin J. Clement, Chief Executive Officer
CMO: Jack Rhoads, M.D., Medical Director
CHR: Janice Nordstrom, Director Human Resources
CNO: Stephanie Slater–Nesuold, Director of Nursing
Web address: www.landmarkhospitals.com
**Control:** Partnership, Investor–owned, for–profit **Service:** Long–Term Acute Care hospital

> **Staffed Beds:** 30

⊞ **MERCY HOSPITAL JOPLIN (260001)**, 100 Mercy Way, Zip 64804–1626; tel. 417/781–2727, (Includes ST. JOHN'S REHABILITATION CENTER, 2727 McClelland Boulevard, Zip 64804; tel. 417/659–6716) **A**1 2 10 13 **F**3 4 5 7 11 13 15 17 18 20 22 24 26 28 29 30 31 34 35 37 38 39 40 44 45 46 49 50 54 57 58 59 60 61 62 63 64 65 66 68 70 74 75 76 77 78 79 81 82 85 86 87 93 94 97 98 99 100 101 102 103 104 105 106 107 108 110 111 114 115 117 118 119 126 127 129 130 131 132 134 135 144 146 147 148 **P**6 **S** Mercy Health, Chesterfield, MO
Primary Contact: Gary W. Pulsipher, President and Chief Executive Officer
COO: Michele Stewart, R.N., Chief Operating Officer
CFO: Shelly Hunter, Chief Financial Officer
CHR: Timothy Murphy, Vice President Human Resources
CNO: Dennis Manley, R.N., Chief Nursing Officer
Web address: www.mercy.net/joplinmo
**Control:** Church–operated, Nongovernment, not–for profit **Service:** General Medical and Surgical

> **Staffed Beds:** 179 **Admissions:** 7533 **Census:** 96 **Outpatient Visits:** 131594 **Births:** 503 **Total Expense ($000):** 170668 **Payroll Expense ($000):** 50805 **Personnel:** 950

## KANSAS CITY—Jackson County

☐ **CENTER FOR BEHAVIORAL MEDICINE (264008)**, 1000 East 24th Street, Zip 64108–2776; tel. 816/512–7000 **A**1 3 5 10 **F**4 29 35 36 38 50 53 86 87 98
Primary Contact: Denise Norbury, Chief Executive Officer
COO: Jeanette Simmons, Chief Operating Officer
CFO: Randy Riley, Chief Financial Officer
CMO: Nashaat Boutros, M.D., Clinical Director
CIO: Robert Curren, Director Information Technology
CHR: Silva Ward, Director Human Resources
CNO: John Tucker, Chief Nursing Executive
Web address: www.dmhonline.dmh.state.mo.us
**Control:** State–Government, nonfederal **Service:** Psychiatric

> **Staffed Beds:** 133 **Admissions:** 76 **Census:** 120 **Outpatient Visits:** 0 **Births:** 0 **Total Expense ($000):** 22380 **Payroll Expense ($000):** 13193 **Personnel:** 357

⊞ **CHILDREN'S MERCY HOSPITALS AND CLINICS (263302)**, 2401 Gillham Road, Zip 64108–4619; tel. 816/234–3000 **A**1 2 3 5 8 9 10 **F**3 7 8 9 11 12 16 19 20 21 22 23 24 25 26 27 29 30 31 32 34 35 36 39 40 41 43 44 48 50 54 55 57 58 59 60 61 62 64 65 68 72 73 74 75 77 78 79 81 82 84 85 86 87 88 89 90 91 92 93 94 96 97 100 101 104 107 108 111 115 117 118 119 130 131 132 134 136 138 139 141 142 144 146 148 **P**6
Primary Contact: Randall L. O'Donnell, Ph.D., President and Chief Executive Officer
COO: Jo W. Stueve, Executive Vice President and Co–Chief Operating Officer
CFO: Sandra A J Lawrence, Executive Vice President and Chief Financial Officer
CMO: Charles Roberts, M.D., Executive Vice President and Executive Medical Director
CIO: Jean Ann Breedlove, Chief Information Officer
CNO: Cheri Hunt, R.N., Vice President Patient Care Services and Chief Nursing Officer
Web address: www.childrensmercy.org
**Control:** Other not–for–profit (including NFP Corporation) **Service:** Children's general

> **Staffed Beds:** 301 **Admissions:** 11210 **Census:** 211 **Outpatient Visits:** 368358 **Births:** 111 **Total Expense ($000):** 856013 **Payroll Expense ($000):** 418084 **Personnel:** 5526

⊞ **CRITTENTON CHILDREN'S CENTER (264018)**, 10918 Elm Avenue, Zip 64134–4108; tel. 816/765–6600 **A**1 10 **F**5 29 30 32 34 35 68 75 77 86 87 98 99 100 101 102 104 106 130 132 146 **P**6 **S** Saint Luke's Health System, Kansas City, MO
Primary Contact: Janine Hron, Chief Executive Officer
CFO: Willard Staron, Chief Financial Officer
CMO: Eileen Duggan, M.D., Medical Director
CIO: Deborah Gash, Vice President and Chief Information Officer
CHR: Terri Neal, Director Human Resources
CNO: Belva Giesing, Chief Nursing Officer
Web address: www.crittentonkc.org
**Control:** Other not–for–profit (including NFP Corporation) **Service:** Children's hospital psychiatric

> **Staffed Beds:** 46 **Admissions:** 2189 **Census:** 39 **Outpatient Visits:** 12568 **Births:** 0 **Total Expense ($000):** 26822 **Payroll Expense ($000):** 15303 **Personnel:** 298

⊞ **KANSAS CITY VETERANS AFFAIRS MEDICAL CENTER**, 4801 East Linwood Boulevard, Zip 64128–2226; tel. 816/861–4700, (Nonreporting) **A**1 2 3 5 **S** Department of Veterans Affairs, Washington, DC
Primary Contact: Kevin Inkley, Acting Medical Center Director
CFO: Bryan Bieri, Manager Finance
CMO: Ahmad Batrash, Chief of Staff
CIO: Eddie Johnson, Chief Information Technology Officer
CHR: Kathi Nippert, Acting Chief Human Resources Officer
CNO: Patricia Ten Haaf, R.N., Associate Director of Patient Care Services
Web address: www.kansascity.va.gov/
**Control:** Veterans Affairs, Government, federal **Service:** General Medical and Surgical

> **Staffed Beds:** 157

⊞ **KINDRED HOSPITAL KANSAS CITY (262011)**, 8701 Troost Avenue, Zip 64131–2767; tel. 816/995–2000 **A**1 9 10 **F**1 18 29 56 60 70 75 82 85 87 100 107 130 148 **S** Kindred Healthcare, Louisville, KY
Primary Contact: Alexander Gill, Chief Executive Officer
CFO: Brett Stevenson, Controller
CNO: Patricia J. Dixon, R.N., Chief Clinical Officer
Web address: www.kindredhospitalkc.com
**Control:** Corporation, Investor–owned, for–profit **Service:** Long–Term Acute Care hospital

> **Staffed Beds:** 130 **Admissions:** 618 **Census:** 53 **Outpatient Visits:** 0 **Births:** 0 **Total Expense ($000):** 31857 **Payroll Expense ($000):** 10020 **Personnel:** 180

**MO**

---

**Hospital, Medicare Provider Number, Address, Telephone, Approval, Facility, and Physician Codes, Health Care System**

★ American Hospital Association (AHA) membership  ○ Healthcare Facilities Accreditation Program  ⇧ Center for Improvement in Healthcare Quality Accreditation
☐ The Joint Commission accreditation  ◇ DNV Healthcare Inc. accreditation  △ Commission on Accreditation of Rehabilitation Facilities (CARF) accreditation

**KINDRED HOSPITAL NORTHLAND (262018)**, 500 Northwest 68th Street, Zip 64118–2455; tel. 816/420–6300 **A**1 9 10 **F**1 3 16 18 28 29 30 60 68 77 80 82 84 85 90 100 119 130 135 142 148 **S** Kindred Healthcare, Louisville, KY
Primary Contact: H. Frank Schneider, Chief Executive Officer
CFO: Austin Walker, Accounting Manager
CMO: Sean R. Muldoon, M.D., Senior Vice President and Chief Medical Officer–Kindred Healthcare, Hospital Division
CNO: Julie Duben, Chief Clinical Officer
Web address: www.khnorthland.com
**Control:** Corporation, Investor–owned, for–profit **Service:** Long–Term Acute Care hospital

**Staffed Beds: 35 Admissions: 419 Census: 31 Outpatient Visits: 0 Births: 0 Total Expense ($000): 17771 Payroll Expense ($000): 6476 Personnel: 109**

**NORTHLAND LTAC HOSPITAL** See Kindred Hospital Northland

**RESEARCH MEDICAL CENTER (260027)**, 2316 East Meyer Boulevard, Zip 64132–1136; tel. 816/276–4000, (Includes RESEARCH PSYCHIATRIC CENTER, 2323 East 63rd Street, Zip 64130–3462; tel. 816/444–8161; Lisa St. Aubyn, Chief Executive Officer) **A**1 2 3 5 9 10 13 **F**3 4 5 8 11 13 15 16 17 18 20 22 24 26 28 29 30 31 34 35 38 39 40 42 43 44 45 46 47 49 50 52 53 54 55 57 58 59 60 61 64 68 70 72 73 74 75 76 77 78 79 81 82 84 85 86 87 90 91 93 94 96 97 98 99 100 101 102 103 104 105 107 108 110 111 112 114 115 116 118 119 120 121 122 124 126 129 130 131 132 134 135 138 142 143 146 147 148 **S** HCA, Nashville, TN
Primary Contact: Jacqueline DeSouza, Chief Executive Officer
COO: Eric Becker, Chief Operating Officer
CFO: Susan Shreeve, Chief Financial Officer
CMO: James Bower, M.D., Chief Medical Officer
CIO: Shawn Kegley, Director Information Services
CHR: Charlotte O'Neal, Vice President Human Resources
Web address: www.researchmedicalcenter.com
**Control:** Corporation, Investor–owned, for–profit **Service:** General Medical and Surgical

**Staffed Beds: 450 Admissions: 19071 Census: 298 Outpatient Visits: 163510 Births: 1165 Total Expense ($000): 373977 Payroll Expense ($000): 112114 Personnel: 1776**

**SAINT LUKE'S HOSPITAL OF KANSAS CITY (260138)**, 4401 Wornall Road, Zip 64111–3220; tel. 816/932–3800 **A**1 2 3 5 8 9 10 **F**3 6 9 11 12 13 15 17 18 20 22 24 25 26 28 29 30 31 32 34 35 36 37 38 39 40 43 44 45 46 47 48 49 50 55 56 57 58 59 60 61 64 65 66 68 70 71 72 73 74 75 76 77 78 79 80 81 82 84 85 86 87 89 90 91 92 93 94 95 96 97 100 101 102 103 104 107 108 110 111 114 115 116 117 118 119 120 121 123 124 126 129 130 131 132 134 135 137 138 139 141 146 147 148 **P**6 **S** Saint Luke's Health System, Kansas City, MO
Primary Contact: Jani L. Johnson, R.N., MSN, Chief Executive Officer
COO: Brad Simmons, Chief Operating Officer
CFO: Amy Nachtigal, Chief Financial Officer
CMO: Peter Holt, M.D., Director Medical Affairs
CIO: Deborah Gash, Chief Information Officer
CHR: Doris Rogers, Vice President Human Resources
CNO: Debra Wilson, Vice President and Chief Nursing Officer
Web address: www.saint–lukes.org
**Control:** Church–operated, Nongovernment, not–for profit **Service:** General Medical and Surgical

**Staffed Beds: 431 Admissions: 18558 Census: 294 Outpatient Visits: 388202 Births: 2224 Total Expense ($000): 575305 Payroll Expense ($000): 156450 Personnel: 2547**

**SAINT LUKE'S NORTH HOSPITAL – BARRY ROAD (260062)**, 5830 N.W. Barry Road, Zip 64154–2778; tel. 816/891–6000, (Includes SAINT LUKE'S NORTH HOSPITAL–SMITHVILLE CAMPUS, 601 South 169 Highway, Smithville, Zip 64089–9317; tel. 816/532–3700; Matthew Wenzel, Chief Executive Officer) **A**1 9 10 **F**3 11 13 15 18 20 22 26 28 29 30 31 34 35 36 38 40 44 45 49 50 53 57 59 60 64 65 69 70 73 74 75 76 77 78 79 80 81 82 84 85 86 87 89 90 92 93 96 98 99 100 101 102 103 104 105 107 108 110 111 114 115 116 117 118 119 129 130 131 132 135 141 143 146 147 148 **S** Saint Luke's Health System, Kansas City, MO
Primary Contact: Matthew Wenzel, President and Chief Executive Officer
CFO: Julie Murphy, Chief Financial Officer
CMO: Leonardo J. Lozada, M.D., Chief Physician Executive
CIO: LaDonna Seger, Director Information Services
CHR: Donna Kunz, Director Human Resources
CNO: Jeffrey Eye, R.N., Chief Nursing Officer
Web address: www.saint–lukes.org
**Control:** Church–operated, Nongovernment, not–for profit **Service:** General Medical and Surgical

**Staffed Beds: 142 Admissions: 7245 Census: 83 Outpatient Visits: 86642 Births: 855 Total Expense ($000): 116255 Payroll Expense ($000): 37763 Personnel: 631**

**SELECT SPECIALTY HOSPITAL–WESTERN MISSOURI (262014)**, 2316 East Meyer Boulevard, 3 West, Zip 64132–1136; tel. 816/276–3300 **A**1 9 10 **F**1 3 29 **S** Select Medical Corporation, Mechanicsburg, PA
Primary Contact: Jeffrey Alexander, Chief Executive Officer
Web address: www.selectspecialtyhospitals.com/company/locations/ westernmissouri.aspx
**Control:** Corporation, Investor–owned, for–profit **Service:** Long–Term Acute Care hospital

**Staffed Beds: 34 Admissions: 336 Census: 25 Outpatient Visits: 0 Births: 0 Total Expense ($000): 13194 Payroll Expense ($000): 5470 Personnel: 98**

**SIGNATURE PSYCHIATRIC HOSPITAL (264030)**, 2900 Clay Edwards Drive, Zip 64116–3235; tel. 816/691–5101 **F**34 59 98 101 102 103 104 105 130 132
Primary Contact: Dennis Anderson, Administrator and Director of Nursing
COO: Susan Mathis, R.N., Chief Operating Officer and Chief Nurse Executive
CFO: Tariq F. Malik, CPA, Chief Financial Officer
CMO: Todd Hill, D.O., Medical Director
CIO: Mike Solom, Director Information Technology
CHR: Sheila Shipley, Human Resources Educator
CNO: Dennis Anderson, Administrator and Director of Nursing
Web address: www.signaturepsychiatrichospitalkc.com
**Control:** Corporation, Investor–owned, for–profit **Service:** Psychiatric

**Staffed Beds: 24 Admissions: 802 Census: 12 Outpatient Visits: 92 Births: 0 Total Expense ($000): 4380 Payroll Expense ($000): 2480 Personnel: 43**

**ST. JOSEPH MEDICAL CENTER (260085)**, 1000 Carondelet Drive, Zip 64114–4673; tel. 816/942–4400 **A**1 2 9 10 **F**3 11 13 15 17 18 20 22 24 26 28 29 30 31 34 35 36 40 45 47 49 50 51 56 57 59 60 64 68 70 71 72 74 75 76 77 78 79 80 81 82 84 85 87 90 96 107 108 110 111 114 115 116 118 119 129 130 132 135 146 147 148 **S** Prime Healthcare Services, Ontario, CA
Primary Contact: Robert J. Erickson, Chief Executive Officer
CFO: Debra Cartwright, Chief Financial Officer
CMO: Tommy Ko, M.D., Chief Medical Officer
CIO: Cheryl Johnson, Regional Chief Information Officer
CHR: Donna Sumner, Director, Human Resources and Organizational Development
CNO: Greg Simpson, Chief Nursing Officer
Web address: www.carondelethealth.org
**Control:** Other not–for–profit (including NFP Corporation) **Service:** General Medical and Surgical

**Staffed Beds: 187 Admissions: 8978 Census: 116 Outpatient Visits: 99467 Births: 988 Total Expense ($000): 152242 Payroll Expense ($000): 49745 Personnel: 1053**

**TRUMAN MEDICAL CENTER–HOSPITAL HILL (260048)**, 2301 Holmes Street, Zip 64108–2640; tel. 816/404–1000 **A**1 2 3 5 8 9 10 13 **F**3 4 5 11 12 13 15 17 18 20 22 26 28 29 30 31 34 35 36 38 39 40 41 43 44 45 46 48 49 50 52 53 55 57 58 59 61 64 65 66 68 70 71 72 74 75 76 77 78 79 81 82 84 85 86 87 90 93 94 97 98 99 100 101 102 103 104 107 108 110 111 114 115 119 129 130 131 132 134 135 143 146 147 148 **P**5 6 **S** Truman Medical Centers, Kansas City, MO
Primary Contact: Charlie Shields, President and Chief Executive Officer
CFO: Allen Johnson, Chief Financial Officer
CMO: Mark Steele, M.D., Chief Medical Officer
CIO: Mitzi Cardenas, Chief Information Officer
CHR: Marcos DeLeon, Vice President Community Engagement
CNO: Lynette Wheeler, MSN, Chief Nursing Officer
Web address: www.trumed.org
**Control:** Other not–for–profit (including NFP Corporation) **Service:** General Medical and Surgical

**Staffed Beds: 232 Admissions: 14237 Census: 186 Outpatient Visits: 534689 Births: 1901 Total Expense ($000): 348160 Payroll Expense ($000): 146998 Personnel: 2715**

**TRUMAN MEDICAL CENTER–LAKEWOOD (260102)**, 7900 Lee's Summit Road, Zip 64139–1236; tel. 816/404–7000, (Total facility includes 188 beds in nursing home–type unit) **A**1 3 5 9 10 **F**3 4 5 6 11 13 15 29 30 32 34 36 38 39 40 41 44 45 50 53 54 56 57 64 65 66 67 68 70 71 72 74 75 76 77 78 79 81 85 86 87 89 90 92 93 94 96 97 98 99 100 101 102 103 104 107 112 114 119 126 128 129 130 131 132 134 135 143 146 147 **P**5 6 **S** Truman Medical Centers, Kansas City, MO
Primary Contact: Charlie Shields, President and Chief Executive Officer
COO: Amy Peters, R.N., Interim Chief Operating Officer
CFO: Allen Johnson, Chief Financial Officer
CMO: Mark Steele, M.D., Chief Medical Officer
CIO: Mitzi Cardenas, Chief Information Officer
CHR: Marcos DeLeon, Vice President Community Engagement
CNO: Lynette Wheeler, MSN, Chief Nursing Officer
Web address: www.trumed.org
**Control:** Other not–for–profit (including NFP Corporation) **Service:** General Medical and Surgical

**Staffed Beds: 296 Admissions: 4540 Census: 229 Outpatient Visits: 487223 Births: 1582 Total Expense ($000): 132455 Payroll Expense ($000): 58729 Personnel: 864**

MO

✉ **TWO RIVERS BEHAVIORAL HEALTH SYSTEM (264017)**, 5121 Raytown Road, Zip 64133–2141; tel. 816/382–6300 **A**1 10 **F**4 5 29 30 34 35 38 75 86 87 98 99 101 102 103 104 105 130 132 134 143 **P**6 **S** Universal Health Services, Inc., King of Prussia, PA
Primary Contact: Cara Macaleer, Chief Executive Officer/Managing Director
CFO: Michael Delaney, Chief Financial Officer
CMO: Shahbaz Khan, M.D., Medical Director
CHR: Diane Peoples, Director Human Resources
CNO: Rebecca Dvorak, Chief Nursing Officer
Web address: www.tworivershospital.com
**Control:** Corporation, Investor–owned, for–profit **Service:** Psychiatric

**Staffed Beds:** 105 **Admissions:** 3156 **Census:** 52 **Outpatient Visits:** 4101
**Births:** 0 **Total Expense ($000):** 16906 **Payroll Expense ($000):** 7694
**Personnel:** 167

**VETERANS AFFAIRS MEDICAL CENTER** See Kansas City Veterans Affairs Medical Center

### KENNETT—Dunklin County

✉ **TWIN RIVERS REGIONAL MEDICAL CENTER (260015)**, 1301 First Street, Zip 63857–2508, Mailing Address: P.O. Box 728, Zip 63857–0728; tel. 573/888–4522 **A**1 9 10 **F**3 11 13 15 18 29 30 31 35 40 50 56 57 59 60 64 68 70 75 76 78 79 81 85 89 90 98 99 100 101 102 103 104 107 108 110 111 114 115 117 119 127 129 130 135 147 148 **S** Community Health Systems, Inc., Franklin, TN
Primary Contact: Gerald Faircloth, FACHE
CFO: Michelle Beachman, Chief Financial Officer
CHR: Mark Niemeier, Director Human Resources
Web address: www.twinriversregional.com
**Control:** Corporation, Investor–owned, for–profit **Service:** General Medical and Surgical

**Staffed Beds:** 100 **Admissions:** 3338 **Census:** 33 **Outpatient Visits:** 88610
**Births:** 435 **Total Expense ($000):** 46140 **Payroll Expense ($000):** 15049
**Personnel:** 317

### KIRKSVILLE—Adair County

★ ○ **NORTHEAST REGIONAL MEDICAL CENTER (260022)**, 315 South Osteopathy, Zip 63501–6401, Mailing Address: P.O. Box C8502, Zip 63501–8599; tel. 660/785–1000 **A**9 10 11 12 13 **F**3 12 13 15 18 20 24 28 29 30 34 35 39 40 43 45 46 49 50 51 53 57 59 60 62 64 68 70 74 75 76 77 79 81 82 85 86 87 89 90 93 107 108 110 111 114 115 119 127 129 130 131 132 133 135 146 147 148 **S** Community Health Systems, Inc., Franklin, TN
Primary Contact: Ranee C. Brayton, R.N., MSN, Chief Executive Officer
CFO: Tammy Cobb, Chief Financial Officer
CMO: Brent Speak, Chief of Staff
CIO: Chad Tatro, Supervisor Information Systems
CHR: Jim Bergman, Director Human Resources
CNO: Cindy Carter, Chief Nursing Officer
Web address: www.nermc.com
**Control:** Corporation, Investor–owned, for–profit **Service:** General Medical and Surgical

**Staffed Beds:** 115 **Admissions:** 2730 **Census:** 31 **Outpatient Visits:** 68880
**Births:** 507 **Total Expense ($000):** 55064 **Payroll Expense ($000):** 18527
**Personnel:** 463

### LAKE SAINT LOUIS—St. Charles County

✉ **SSM ST. JOSEPH HOSPITAL WEST (260200)**, 100 Medical Plaza, Zip 63367–1366; tel. 636/625–5200 **A**1 2 9 10 **F**3 11 13 15 17 20 22 28 29 30 31 34 35 36 38 40 41 43 44 49 50 51 53 55 56 57 59 60 61 64 68 70 73 74 75 76 78 79 81 82 84 85 86 87 89 102 107 108 110 111 114 118 119 129 130 132 134 135 145 146 147 148 **P**6 8 **S** SSM Health, Saint Louis, MO
Primary Contact: Lisle Wescott, President
CFO: Hal Holder, Director Finance
CMO: Michael Handler, M.D., Vice President Medical Administration
CIO: Sharon Gardner, Manager Information Systems
CHR: Sheila Shortt, R.N., Human Resources Consultant
CNO: Janet K. Pestle, R.N., Vice President Nursing and Chief Nursing Officer
Web address: www.ssmstjoseph.com
**Control:** Church–operated, Nongovernment, not–for profit **Service:** General Medical and Surgical

**Staffed Beds:** 119 **Admissions:** 9149 **Census:** 88 **Outpatient Visits:** 136998
**Births:** 1149 **Total Expense ($000):** 132399 **Payroll Expense ($000):** 46282 **Personnel:** 717

### LAMAR—Barton County

**BARTON COUNTY MEMORIAL HOSPITAL (261325)**, 29 N.W. First Lane, Zip 64759–8105; tel. 417/681–5100 **A**9 10 18 **F**3 11 15 18 28 30 34 35 36 40 44 45 50 57 59 64 65 68 74 75 77 79 81 84 85 86 87 89 90 92 93 97 107 108 110 111 114 119 127 128 129 130 132 133 135 143 146 148
Primary Contact: Wendy Duvall, Chief Executive Officer
CIO: Brad Butler, Network Administrator
CHR: Sheila Boice, Director Human Resources
CNO: Marlys Buckner, Chief Nursing Officer
Web address: www.bcmh.net
**Control:** County–Government, nonfederal **Service:** General Medical and Surgical

**Staffed Beds:** 25 **Admissions:** 1040 **Census:** 12 **Outpatient Visits:** 47696
**Births:** 0 **Total Expense ($000):** 19812 **Payroll Expense ($000):** 8084
**Personnel:** 185

### LEBANON—Laclede County

✉ **MERCY HOSPITAL LEBANON (260059)**, 100 Hospital Drive, Zip 65536–9210; tel. 417/533–6100 **A**1 9 10 20 **F**3 11 13 15 28 29 30 31 35 36 37 40 50 53 57 59 64 65 68 70 71 74 75 76 77 78 79 81 82 83 85 86 87 89 90 93 94 102 107 108 110 111 114 119 129 130 131 132 133 135 144 146 147 148 **P**6 **S** Mercy Health, Chesterfield, MO
Primary Contact: David R. Steinmann, Administrator
CFO: Douglas M. Hoban, Vice President and Chief Financial Officer
CNO: Judy O'Connor–Snyder, Chief Nursing Officer
Web address: www.mercy.net/practice/mercy–hospital–lebanon
**Control:** Church–operated, Nongovernment, not–for profit **Service:** General Medical and Surgical

**Staffed Beds:** 58 **Admissions:** 2567 **Census:** 20 **Outpatient Visits:** 140127
**Births:** 479 **Total Expense ($000):** 74558 **Payroll Expense ($000):** 26695
**Personnel:** 493

### LEE'S SUMMIT—Jackson County

✉ **LEE'S SUMMIT MEDICAL CENTER (260190)**, 2100 S.E. Blue Parkway, Zip 64063–1007; tel. 816/282–5000 **A**1 9 10 **F**3 15 18 20 22 28 29 30 31 34 40 43 49 57 59 60 64 65 68 69 70 74 75 77 78 79 81 82 84 85 87 93 107 108 110 111 115 119 126 129 130 131 132 145 146 148 **S** HCA, Nashville, TN
Primary Contact: Matt Sogard, Chief Executive Officer
CFO: John Heurtin, Chief Financial Officer
CIO: Andrew Beechy, Manager Information Technology Systems
CHR: Linda Duncan, Director Human Resources
Web address: www.leessummitmedicalcenter.com
**Control:** Corporation, Investor–owned, for–profit **Service:** General Medical and Surgical

**Staffed Beds:** 64 **Admissions:** 3602 **Census:** 34 **Outpatient Visits:** 91474
**Births:** 0 **Total Expense ($000):** 73249 **Payroll Expense ($000):** 31222
**Personnel:** 345

✉ **SAINT LUKE'S EAST HOSPITAL (260216)**, 100 N.E. Saint Luke's Boulevard, Zip 64086–6000; tel. 816/347–5000 **A**1 9 10 **F**3 13 15 18 20 22 26 28 29 30 31 34 35 38 40 43 44 45 46 49 50 56 57 58 59 60 65 70 71 72 73 74 75 76 77 78 79 80 81 82 84 85 86 87 92 93 94 96 100 107 108 110 111 114 115 117 118 119 120 121 126 129 130 131 132 135 145 146 147 148 **S** Saint Luke's Health System, Kansas City, MO
Primary Contact: Ronald L. Baker, Chief Executive Officer
CFO: Joseph P. Stasi, Chief Financial Officer
CHR: John Clabaugh, Director Human Resources
CNO: Gloria Solis, R.N., Chief Operating Officer and Chief Nursing Officer
Web address: www.saintlukeskc.org
**Control:** Church–operated, Nongovernment, not–for profit **Service:** General Medical and Surgical

**Staffed Beds:** 161 **Admissions:** 9350 **Census:** 96 **Outpatient Visits:** 114322
**Births:** 1964 **Total Expense ($000):** 159300 **Payroll Expense ($000):** 47647 **Personnel:** 781

**MO**

---

**LEXINGTON—Lafayette County**

✠ **LAFAYETTE REGIONAL HEALTH CENTER (261320)**, 1500 State Street,
Zip 64067–1107; tel. 660/259–2203 **A**1 9 10 18 **F**11 15 29 31 40 64 68 70
75 78 79 81 85 93 107 110 111 114 116 119 127 129 130 133 147 148 **P**6
**S** HCA, Nashville, TN
Primary Contact: Darrel Box, Chief Executive Officer
COO: Daniel Astleford, Vice President Operations
CFO: Teri James, Chief Financial Officer
CIO: Keith Richcreek, Manager Technical Services
CHR: Stephen Davidson, Director Human Resources
CNO: Kim Leakey, R.N., Chief Nursing Officer
Web address: www.lafayetteregionalhealthcenter.com
**Control:** Corporation, Investor–owned, for–profit **Service:** General Medical and
Surgical

**Staffed Beds:** 25 **Admissions:** 1158 **Census:** 11 **Outpatient Visits:** 73038
**Births:** 0 **Total Expense ($000):** 28128 **Payroll Expense ($000):** 10789
**Personnel:** 203

**LIBERTY—Clay County**

✠ **LIBERTY HOSPITAL (260177)**, 2525 Glenn Hendren Drive, Zip 64068–9600,
Mailing Address: P.O. Box 1002, Zip 64069–1002; tel. 816/781–7200 **A**1 2 9
10 **F**3 9 11 13 15 18 20 22 24 28 29 30 31 34 35 40 43 44 45 47 49 59 62
63 64 68 69 70 73 74 75 76 77 78 79 80 81 82 84 85 86 87 89 92 93 97
102 107 108 110 111 114 115 118 119 126 129 130 132 143 146 148
Primary Contact: David Feess, President and Chief Executive Officer
CFO: Dan Williams, Vice President Finance and Support
CMO: Robert Haas, M.D., Chief Medical Officer
CIO: Paul Klehn, Chief Information Technology Officer
CHR: Nancy E. Cattell, Vice President Human Resources
CNO: Shirley Heintz, R.N., Vice President Patient Care
Web address: www.Libertyhospital.org
**Control:** Hospital district or authority, Government, nonfederal **Service:** General
Medical and Surgical

**Staffed Beds:** 228 **Admissions:** 9561 **Census:** 102 **Outpatient Visits:**
259075 **Births:** 1094 **Total Expense ($000):** 180156 **Payroll Expense
($000):** 78065 **Personnel:** 1149

**LOUISIANA—Pike County**

✠ **PIKE COUNTY MEMORIAL HOSPITAL (261333)**, 2305 Georgia Street,
Zip 63353–2559; tel. 573/754–5531 **A**1 9 10 18 **F**3 7 11 15 18 28 29 30 34
35 40 45 50 53 54 56 57 59 64 65 68 74 75 77 79 81 85 86 87 89 90 93
97 100 107 110 114 127 130 131 132 133 147 148
Primary Contact: Justin Selle, Chief Executive Officer
CFO: Ann Tran, Chief Financial Officer
CIO: Jeremy Gruen, Director Information Systems
CHR: Connie Bair, Human Resources Assistant
Web address: www.pcmh–mo.org
**Control:** County–Government, nonfederal **Service:** General Medical and Surgical

**Staffed Beds:** 25 **Admissions:** 506 **Census:** 5 **Outpatient Visits:** 37792
**Births:** 0 **Total Expense ($000):** 15235 **Payroll Expense ($000):** 6871
**Personnel:** 149

**MACON—Macon County**

★ **SAMARITAN MEMORIAL HOSPITAL (261313)**, 1205 North Missouri Street,
Zip 63552–2095; tel. 660/385–8700 **A**9 10 18 **F**3 7 8 11 15 18 28 29 31 34
35 40 45 46 53 56 57 59 63 64 65 68 71 75 78 79 81 82 84 85 86 87 89
90 93 94 107 111 115 119 127 128 129 130 131 133 143 146 148 **P**5
Primary Contact: Bernard A. Orman, Jr., Administrator
CFO: Susan Spencer, Chief Financial Officer
CHR: Suzanne Britt, Director Human Resources
Web address: www.samaritanhospital.net
**Control:** County–Government, nonfederal **Service:** General Medical and Surgical

**Staffed Beds:** 25 **Admissions:** 733 **Census:** 12 **Outpatient Visits:** 62087
**Births:** 0 **Total Expense ($000):** 24547 **Payroll Expense ($000):** 9126
**Personnel:** 196

**MARSHALL—Saline County**

★ **FITZGIBBON HOSPITAL (260142)**, 2305 South 65 Highway, Zip 65340–0250,
Mailing Address: P.O. Box 250, Zip 65340–0250; tel. 660/886–7431 **A**5 9 10
20 **F**3 11 13 15 30 31 34 35 40 45 50 57 59 62 63 64 68 70 74 75 76 77
78 79 81 82 85 87 89 90 93 98 103 104 107 110 111 115 118 119 120
121 127 128 129 130 131 132 133 135 143 146 147 148
Primary Contact: Darin L. Haug, D.O., President and Chief Executive Officer
COO: Angy Littrell, Chief Financial Officer and Chief Operating Officer
CFO: Angy Littrell, Chief Financial Officer and Chief Operating Officer
CIO: Tom Jones, Chief Information Officer
CHR: Jessica Henderson, Employee Relations Specialist
CNO: Lynne Ott, MSN, Vice President Patient Care Services and Chief Nursing
Officer
Web address: www.fitzgibbon.org
**Control:** Other not–for–profit (including NFP Corporation) **Service:** General
Medical and Surgical

**Staffed Beds:** 52 **Admissions:** 2012 **Census:** 18 **Outpatient Visits:** 96586
**Births:** 243 **Total Expense ($000):** 46310 **Payroll Expense ($000):** 21026
**Personnel:** 449

**MARYLAND HEIGHTS—St. Louis County**

★ **RANKEN JORDAN PEDIATRIC BRIDGE HOSPITAL (263303)**, 11365 Dorsett
Road, Zip 63043–3411; tel. 314/872–6400 **A**9 10 **F**1 3 12 29 30 32 34 35 38
44 50 68 82 86 87 89 90 91 92 93 94 96 98 99 104 130 132 146 148 **P**6
Primary Contact: Laureen K. Tanner, R.N., MSN, FACHE, President and Chief
Executive Officer
COO: Brett Moorehouse, FACHE, Vice President and Chief Operating Officer
CFO: Jean Bardwell, Vice President and Chief Financial Officer
CMO: Nicholas Holekamp, M.D., Chief Medical Officer
CIO: Jean Bardwell, Vice President and Chief Financial Officer
CHR: Thomas M. Irvin, Administrator Human Resources
CNO: Laureen K. Tanner, R.N., President and Chief Executive Officer
Web address: www.rankenjordan.org
**Control:** Other not–for–profit (including NFP Corporation) **Service:** Children's
rehabilitation

**Staffed Beds:** 34 **Admissions:** 293 **Census:** 28 **Outpatient Visits:** 9910
**Births:** 0 **Total Expense ($000):** 28338 **Payroll Expense ($000):** 14560
**Personnel:** 314

**MARYVILLE—Nodaway County**

✠ **SSM HEALTH ST. FRANCIS HOSPITAL – MARYVILLE (260050)**, 2016 South
Main Street, Zip 64468–2655; tel. 660/562–2600 **A**1 9 10 20 **F**3 11 13 15 28
29 30 34 35 38 40 45 57 59 64 65 68 70 73 75 76 77 79 81 82 84 85 86 89
90 93 96 97 98 102 103 104 107 108 110 111 114 118 119 127 128 130
131 132 133 135 **P**6 **S** SSM Health, Saint Louis, MO
Primary Contact: Michael A. Baumgartner, President
COO: Frank Grispino, Vice President Operations
CFO: Jocelyn Skidmore, Director Finance
CMO: Lisa DiStefano, M.D., President Medical Staff
CIO: Dave Lewis, Director Information Services
CHR: Melissa McClurg, Human Resources Leader
CNO: Debbie Hoffman, Vice President Patient Services
Web address: www.ssmhealthstfrancis.com
**Control:** Church–operated, Nongovernment, not–for profit **Service:** General
Medical and Surgical

**Staffed Beds:** 56 **Admissions:** 1646 **Census:** 17 **Outpatient Visits:** 134440
**Births:** 309 **Total Expense ($000):** 60029 **Payroll Expense ($000):** 25765
**Personnel:** 382

**MEMPHIS—Scotland County**

★ **SCOTLAND COUNTY HOSPITAL (261310)**, 450 Sigler Avenue,
Zip 63555–1726, Mailing Address: 450 East Sigler Avenue, Zip 63555–1726;
tel. 660/465–8511 **A**9 10 18 **F**3 7 8 9 11 13 15 18 28 29 30 31 32 33 34 35
39 40 45 46 47 48 50 56 57 59 64 65 67 70 75 76 77 78 79 81 82 85 86
87 89 90 93 97 107 119 127 128 130 131 132 135 146 147 148 **P**6
Primary Contact: Randy Tobler, M.D., Chief Executive Officer
CFO: Sheryl Templeton, Chief Financial Officer
CMO: Randy Tobler, M.D., Chief Medical Officer
CIO: Ken McMinn, Director Information Technology
CHR: Missy Smith, Coordinator Human Resources
CNO: Carla Cook, Director of Nursing
Web address: www.scotlandcountyhospital.com
**Control:** Hospital district or authority, Government, nonfederal **Service:** General
Medical and Surgical

**Staffed Beds:** 25 **Admissions:** 1008 **Census:** 11 **Outpatient Visits:** 87264
**Births:** 133 **Total Expense ($000):** 19720 **Payroll Expense ($000):** 10195
**Personnel:** 179

**SCOTLAND COUNTY MEMORIAL HOSPITAL** See Scotland County Hospital

**MEXICO—Audrain County**

✠ **SSM HEALTH ST. MARY'S HOSPITAL – AUDRAIN (260064)**, 620 East
Monroe Street, Zip 65265–2919; tel. 573/582–5000 **A**1 2 9 10 **F**3 11 13 15
18 20 22 26 28 29 30 31 34 40 45 54 57 59 64 65 70 73 74 75 76 77 78
79 81 82 85 86 87 89 90 93 107 108 110 111 114 118 119 123 127 129
130 131 132 146 147 **P**6 **S** SSM Health, Saint Louis, MO
Primary Contact: R. Brent VanConia, Acting President
COO: Kari Wilson, R.N., Vice President Clinical Services, Chief Operating Officer
and Chief Nursing Officer
CFO: James Stratton, Regional Vice President Finance
CMO: Joseph Corrado, M.D., Chief of Staff
CIO: Dawn Evans, Manager Information Technology
CHR: Christy Smiley, Director Human Resources
CNO: Kari Wilson, R.N., Vice President Clinical Services, Chief Operating Officer
and Chief Nursing Officer
Web address: www.audrainmedicalcenter.com
**Control:** Church–operated, Nongovernment, not–for profit **Service:** General
Medical and Surgical

**Staffed Beds:** 49 **Admissions:** 1863 **Census:** 16 **Outpatient Visits:** 140087
**Births:** 229 **Total Expense ($000):** 56955 **Payroll Expense ($000):** 21036
**Personnel:** 391

MO

*Many Facility Codes have changed. Please refer to the AHA Guide Code Chart.*   © 2015 AHA Guide

## MILAN—Sullivan County

★ **SULLIVAN COUNTY MEMORIAL HOSPITAL (261306)**, 630 West Third Street, Zip 63556–1076; tel. 660/265–4212, (Total facility includes 14 beds in nursing home–type unit) **A**9 10 18 **F**28 29 34 40 50 53 57 59 64 67 68 77 79 87 97 107 111 114 119 127 128 130 133 147 148 **P**5
Primary Contact: Jerry Dover, Chief Executive Officer
COO: Amy J. Michael, Chief Operating Officer
CMO: Dale Essmyer, M.D., Chief of Staff
CIO: Vern Johnson, Director Information Technology
CHR: Billie Ryals, Director Human Resources
CNO: Carol Fordyce, Director Patient Care Services
Web address: www.scmhospital.org
**Control:** County–Government, nonfederal **Service:** General Medical and Surgical

**Staffed Beds:** 39 **Admissions:** 213 **Census:** 21 **Outpatient Visits:** 14984 **Births:** 0 **Total Expense ($000):** 7364 **Payroll Expense ($000):** 3157 **Personnel:** 76

## MOBERLY—Randolph County

⊞ **MOBERLY REGIONAL MEDICAL CENTER (260074)**, 1515 Union Avenue, Zip 65270–9449; tel. 660/263–8400 **A**1 9 10 20 **F**3 18 20 22 26 28 29 30 34 35 38 39 40 44 45 46 49 50 53 56 57 59 64 65 70 74 75 77 79 81 85 86 87 89 93 97 98 100 103 107 108 110 111 114 118 119 127 129 130 131 132 135 146 147 148 **P**5 **S** Community Health Systems, Inc., Franklin, TN
Primary Contact: Leslie Paul Luke, Interim Chief Executive Officer
CFO: Tracey Matheis, Chief Financial Officer
CMO: Philip Stitzer, D.O., Chief Medical Officer
CIO: Doris Whelan, Chief Information Officer
CHR: Tim Clark, Director Human Resources
Web address: www.moberlyhospital.com
**Control:** Corporation, Investor–owned, for–profit **Service:** General Medical and Surgical

**Staffed Beds:** 94 **Admissions:** 1657 **Census:** 20 **Outpatient Visits:** 57316 **Births:** 52 **Total Expense ($000):** 49920 **Payroll Expense ($000):** 14704 **Personnel:** 214

## MONETT—Barry County

☐ **COX MONETT (261329)**, 801 North Lincoln Avenue, Zip 65708–1641; tel. 417/235–3144 **A**1 9 10 18 **F**3 11 13 15 28 29 31 32 34 35 40 45 50 56 57 59 64 76 77 81 85 89 90 93 107 111 114 119 127 128 129 130 131 133 135 146 147 **P**6 **S** CoxHealth, Springfield, MO
Primary Contact: Darren Bass, President
CFO: Josh Powell, Facility Controller
CMO: Frank Romero, M.D., Vice President Medical Affairs and Chief Medical Officer
CHR: Debra Isenmann, Human Resources Generalist
CNO: Bev Eli, Chief Nursing Officer
Web address: www.coxhealth.com
**Control:** Other not–for–profit (including NFP Corporation) **Service:** General Medical and Surgical

**Staffed Beds:** 25 **Admissions:** 715 **Census:** 7 **Outpatient Visits:** 59167 **Births:** 264 **Total Expense ($000):** 28928 **Payroll Expense ($000):** 13621 **Personnel:** 223

## MOUNTAIN VIEW—Howell County

⊞ **MERCY ST. FRANCIS HOSPITAL (261335)**, 100 West Highway 60, Zip 65548–7125; tel. 417/934–7000 **A**1 9 10 18 **F**3 11 15 28 29 30 34 40 45 50 57 59 64 65 75 77 81 85 89 90 93 107 110 111 114 119 129 131 132 133 148 **P**6 **S** Mercy Health, Chesterfield, MO
Primary Contact: David R. Steinmann, Administrator
CFO: Sherry Clouse Day, CPA, Chief Financial Officer
CMO: Barry Spoon, M.D., Chief of Staff
CHR: Tracy Smith, Director Human Resources
Web address: www.stjohns.com/aboutus/stfrancis.aspx
**Control:** Church–operated, Nongovernment, not–for profit **Service:** General Medical and Surgical

**Staffed Beds:** 20 **Admissions:** 444 **Census:** 6 **Outpatient Visits:** 23984 **Births:** 0 **Total Expense ($000):** 15229 **Payroll Expense ($000):** 6793 **Personnel:** 106

## NEOSHO—Newton County

★ **FREEMAN NEOSHO HOSPITAL (261331)**, 113 West Hickory Street, Zip 64850–1705; tel. 417/455–4352 **A**9 10 18 **F**3 11 15 28 29 30 34 35 40 44 45 47 56 57 59 64 68 70 75 77 79 81 84 85 86 87 90 93 97 107 110 111 113 119 130 131 132 133 146 147 148 **P**1 3 6 **S** Freeman Health System, Joplin, MO
Primary Contact: Paula F. Baker, President and Chief Executive Officer
CFO: Steve W. Graddy, Chief Financial Officer
CMO: Rodney McFarland, M.D., Medical Director
CIO: Sue Annesser, Director Information Systems
CHR: Mary Frerer, Chief Human Resources Officer
Web address: www.freemanhealth.com
**Control:** Other not–for–profit (including NFP Corporation) **Service:** General Medical and Surgical

**Staffed Beds:** 25 **Admissions:** 976 **Census:** 12 **Outpatient Visits:** 50550 **Births:** 0 **Total Expense ($000):** 21548 **Payroll Expense ($000):** 9187 **Personnel:** 196

## NEVADA—Vernon County

☐ **HEARTLAND BEHAVIORAL HEALTH SERVICES**, 1500 West Ashland Street, Zip 64772–1710; tel. 417/667–2666 **A**1 **F**98 99 101 102 106 **P**6 **S** Universal Health Services, Inc., King of Prussia, PA
Primary Contact: Alyson Wysong–Harder, Chief Executive Officer
CFO: Bryan Bishop, Chief Financial Officer
CMO: Ahmad Tarar, M.D., Medical Director
CHR: Carri Compton–Ogle, Administrative Officer
CNO: Nathan Taylor, Director of Nursing
Web address: www.heartlandbehavioral.com
**Control:** Corporation, Investor–owned, for–profit **Service:** Psychiatric

**Staffed Beds:** 69 **Admissions:** 1498 **Census:** 44 **Outpatient Visits:** 0 **Births:** 0 **Total Expense ($000):** 13518 **Payroll Expense ($000):** 7500 **Personnel:** 158

⊞ **NEVADA REGIONAL MEDICAL CENTER (260061)**, 800 South Ash Street, Zip 64772–3223; tel. 417/667–3355 **A**1 9 10 **F**3 11 13 15 26 27 28 29 30 31 32 34 35 39 40 41 45 50 54 57 59 62 63 64 65 66 70 74 75 76 77 78 79 81 82 83 84 85 86 87 89 90 91 93 94 96 98 101 102 103 104 107 110 111 114 119 127 129 130 131 132 133 135 143 144 146 147 148 **S** QHR, Brentwood, TN
Primary Contact: Kevin Leeper, Chief Executive Officer
CFO: Greg Shaw, Chief Financial Officer
CMO: Sean Gravely, D.O., Chief of Staff
CIO: Chris Crist, Director Information Technology
CHR: Heather Brockmeyer, Human Resource Administrative Officer
CNO: Cory Vokoun, Chief Nursing Officer
Web address: www.nrmchealth.com
**Control:** City–Government, nonfederal **Service:** General Medical and Surgical

**Staffed Beds:** 71 **Admissions:** 2310 **Census:** 26 **Outpatient Visits:** 55122 **Births:** 323 **Total Expense ($000):** 38346 **Payroll Expense ($000):** 14426 **Personnel:** 215

## NORTH KANSAS CITY—Clay County

⊞ **NORTH KANSAS CITY HOSPITAL (260096)**, 2800 Clay Edwards Drive, Zip 64116–3220; tel. 816/691–2000 **A**1 2 3 5 9 10 **F**3 11 12 13 15 17 18 20 22 24 26 28 29 30 31 34 35 37 38 39 40 43 44 45 46 47 48 49 50 53 54 57 58 59 62 63 64 70 72 74 75 76 77 78 79 80 81 82 83 84 85 86 87 89 90 93 96 107 108 110 111 114 115 117 118 119 120 121 123 124 126 129 130 132 135 146 147
Primary Contact: Peggy Schmitt, President and Chief Executive Officer
COO: Jody Abbott, Senior Vice President and Chief Operating Officer
CFO: Jim McNey, Senior Vice President Finance and Chief Financial Officer
CMO: Gary L. Carter, M.D., Vice President and Chief Medical Officer
CIO: Paul Foelsch, Vice President and Chief Information Technology Officer
CHR: Beverly Johnson, Vice President Human Resources
CNO: Sarah G. Oakley, Vice President Nursing
Web address: www.nkch.org
**Control:** City–Government, nonfederal **Service:** General Medical and Surgical

**Staffed Beds:** 415 **Admissions:** 20000 **Census:** 250 **Outpatient Visits:** 268751 **Births:** 1263 **Total Expense ($000):** 396407 **Payroll Expense ($000):** 141494 **Personnel:** 2349

**MO**

---

**Hospital, Medicare Provider Number, Address, Telephone, Approval, Facility, and Physician Codes, Health Care System**

★ American Hospital Association (AHA) membership  ○ Healthcare Facilities Accreditation Program  ⇧ Center for Improvement in Healthcare Quality Accreditation
☐ The Joint Commission accreditation  ◇ DNV Healthcare Inc. accreditation  △ Commission on Accreditation of Rehabilitation Facilities (CARF) accreditation

**MO**

## O'FALLON—St. Charles County

✠ **PROGRESS WEST HOSPITAL (260219)**, Two Progress Point Parkway, Zip 63368–2208; tel. 636/344–1000 **A**1 9 10 **F**3 13 15 18 20 22 29 30 34 40 41 45 49 51 57 59 60 70 76 79 81 85 87 89 107 108 110 111 115 118 119 130 135 146 148 **S** BJC HealthCare, Saint Louis, MO
Primary Contact: Larry A. Tracy, Jr., FACHE, President
CFO: Glen Schwaegel, Chief Financial Officer
CMO: Dane Glueck, M.D., Chief of Staff
CHR: Michael J. Miller, Director Human Resources
CNO: Jill Skyles, R.N., Vice President Patient Care Services and Chief Nurse Executive
Web address: www.progresswest.org
**Control:** Other not–for–profit (including NFP Corporation) **Service:** General Medical and Surgical

**Staffed Beds:** 44 **Admissions:** 3168 **Census:** 29 **Outpatient Visits:** 47282 **Births:** 641 **Total Expense ($000):** 65231 **Payroll Expense ($000):** 22687 **Personnel:** 298

## OSAGE BEACH—Camden County

✠ **LAKE REGIONAL HEALTH SYSTEM (260186)**, 54 Hospital Drive, Zip 65065–3050; tel. 573/348–8000, (Total facility includes 16 beds in nursing home–type unit) **A**1 2 9 10 **F**3 11 12 13 15 18 20 22 24 28 29 30 31 32 34 35 38 39 40 43 44 45 48 49 50 51 53 57 59 60 62 64 65 68 70 74 75 76 77 78 79 81 82 84 85 86 87 93 96 107 108 111 114 115 118 119 120 121 123 127 128 129 130 131 132 135 144 145 146 148 **P**6
Primary Contact: Michael E. Henze, Chief Executive Officer
COO: Kevin G. McRoberts, FACHE, Senior Vice President of Operations
CFO: David Halsell, Senior Vice President and Chief Financial Officer
CMO: Robert Hyatt, M.D., Senior Vice President Medical Affairs
CIO: Scott Poest, Chief Information Officer
CHR: Tom Williams, Vice President Human Resources
CNO: Janice L. Dungan, Senior Vice President Clinical Services
Web address: www.lakeregional.com
**Control:** Other not–for–profit (including NFP Corporation) **Service:** General Medical and Surgical

**Staffed Beds:** 116 **Admissions:** 4955 **Census:** 60 **Outpatient Visits:** 304009 **Births:** 562 **Total Expense ($000):** 166137 **Payroll Expense ($000):** 67042 **Personnel:** 1097

☐ **OSAGE BEACH CENTER FOR COGNITIVE DISORDERS**, 840 Passover Road, Zip 65065; tel. 855/690–3146, (Nonreporting) **A**1
Primary Contact: David Garvin, Chief Executive Officer
Web address: www.osagebeachccd.com
**Control:** Corporation, Investor–owned, for–profit **Service:** Psychiatric

**Staffed Beds:** 14

## PERRYVILLE—Perry County

✠ **PERRY COUNTY MEMORIAL HOSPITAL (261311)**, 434 North West Street, Zip 63775–1398; tel. 573/547–2536 **A**1 9 10 18 **F**3 7 8 11 13 15 28 29 30 31 34 35 40 44 48 51 53 54 56 57 59 62 64 66 68 75 76 77 78 79 81 85 87 89 90 92 93 97 99 100 101 102 103 104 107 111 114 117 119 129 130 131 132 133 135 143 144 145 147 148
Primary Contact: Patrick E. Carron, FACHE, President and Chief Executive Officer
COO: Lee Clinton, FACHE, Vice President Operations
CFO: Randall Wolf, Vice President Finance
CMO: Michael Steele, M.D., Chief of Staff
CIO: Ron Heuring, Director Information Systems
CHR: Christopher Wibbenmeyer, Director Human Resources
Web address: www.pchmo.org
**Control:** Other not–for–profit (including NFP Corporation) **Service:** General Medical and Surgical

**Staffed Beds:** 25 **Admissions:** 950 **Census:** 11 **Outpatient Visits:** 50163 **Births:** 150 **Total Expense ($000):** 31719 **Payroll Expense ($000):** 12037 **Personnel:** 320

## PILOT KNOB—Iron County

**IRON COUNTY MEDICAL CENTER (261336)**, 301 North Highway 21, Zip 63663–0548; Mailing Address: P.O. Box 548, Zip 63663–0548; tel. 573/546–1260 **A**9 10 18 **F**3 11 15 18 34 35 40 45 57 59 64 66 79 82 93 96 97 104 107 111 114 119 127 129 130 133 145 148 **P**6
Primary Contact: Terry Nichols, Chief Executive Officer
COO: Cyndi Basler, Chief Operating Officer
CFO: Justin Lattimore, Chief Financial Officer
CNO: Cindy Finley, Chief Nursing Officer
Web address: www.ironhospital.com
**Control:** Hospital district or authority, Government, nonfederal **Service:** General Medical and Surgical

**Staffed Beds:** 15 **Admissions:** 233 **Census:** 4 **Outpatient Visits:** 18374 **Births:** 0 **Total Expense ($000):** 9592 **Payroll Expense ($000):** 3826 **Personnel:** 121

## POPLAR BLUFF—Butler County

✠ **BLACK RIVER MEDICAL CENTER (560227)**, 217 Physicians Park Drive, Zip 63901–3956, Mailing Address: 219 Physicians Park Drive, Zip 63901–3956; tel. 573/727–9080 **A**1 9 10 **F**3 15 29 34 40 45 57 59 64 65 81 86 107 108 110 111 115 118 119 135
Primary Contact: Christy Shawan, Chief Executive Officer
CFO: Phillip Crocker, Accounting Specialist
CMO: Christopher Pinderski, M.D., Medical Director of Emergency Room
CIO: James Hall, Information Technology Support
CHR: Angie Bolin, Executive Administrative Assistant and Human Resources Manager
CNO: E. Kay Fox, Director of Nursing
Web address: www.blackrivermed.com
**Control:** Other not–for–profit (including NFP Corporation) **Service:** General Medical and Surgical

**Staffed Beds:** 3 **Admissions:** 197 **Census:** 2 **Outpatient Visits:** 7963 **Births:** 0 **Total Expense ($000):** 12752 **Payroll Expense ($000):** 4086 **Personnel:** 95

✠ **JOHN J. PERSHING VETERANS AFFAIRS MEDICAL CENTER**, 1500 North Westwood Boulevard, Zip 63901–3318; tel. 573/686–4151, (Total facility includes 40 beds in nursing home–type unit) **A**1 **F**3 5 11 15 29 30 33 34 36 38 39 40 45 53 54 56 59 62 63 64 65 75 77 79 81 83 84 86 87 90 93 94 97 100 104 107 111 114 119 127 128 129 130 135 143 144 146 147 **S** Department of Veterans Affairs, Washington, DC
Primary Contact: Michael Moore, Ph.D., Acting Medical Center Director
COO: Seth Barlage, Associate Medical Center Director
CFO: Kristy Siebert, Manager Finance
CMO: Vijayachandran Nair, M.D., Chief of Staff
CIO: Janice Vernon, Supervisory Information Technology Specialist
CHR: Genise Denton, Manager Human Resources
CNO: Elizabeth A. Smith, Director of Nursing
Web address: www.poplarbluff.va.gov
**Control:** Veterans Affairs, Government, federal **Service:** General Medical and Surgical

**Staffed Beds:** 58 **Admissions:** 912 **Census:** 32 **Outpatient Visits:** 125901 **Births:** 0 **Total Expense ($000):** 120437 **Payroll Expense ($000):** 43579 **Personnel:** 320

✠ **POPLAR BLUFF REGIONAL MEDICAL CENTER (260119)**, 3100 Oak Grove Road, Zip 63901, Mailing Address: P.O. Box 88, Zip 63902–0088; tel. 573/776–2000, (Includes POPLAR BLUFF REGIONAL MEDICAL CENTER–SOUTH CAMPUS, 621 Pine Boulevard, tel. 573/785–7721) **A**1 2 9 10 **F**3 11 13 15 17 18 20 22 24 28 29 30 31 35 40 43 45 46 49 50 51 53 54 57 59 60 64 65 68 70 74 75 76 77 78 79 80 81 82 85 87 89 90 93 98 102 107 108 111 114 117 118 119 121 126 127 130 131 132 146 148 **P**5
**S** Community Health Systems, Inc., Franklin, TN
Primary Contact: Kenneth James, Chief Executive Officer
CFO: Steve Dorris, Chief Financial Officer
CMO: Steve Pu, D.O., Chief Medical Officer
CIO: Gary Dollins, Director Management Information Systems
CHR: Denise Rushin, Director Human Resources
CNO: Melissa A. Samuelson, R.N., Chief Nurse Executive
Web address: www.poplarbluffregional.com
**Control:** Individual, Investor–owned, for–profit **Service:** General Medical and Surgical

**Staffed Beds:** 241 **Admissions:** 10809 **Census:** 120 **Outpatient Visits:** 103943 **Births:** 1404 **Total Expense ($000):** 148485 **Payroll Expense ($000):** 38499 **Personnel:** 923

## POTOSI—Washington County

★ **WASHINGTON COUNTY MEMORIAL HOSPITAL (261308)**, 300 Health Way, Zip 63664–1420; tel. 573/438–5451 **A**9 10 18 **F**3 11 15 28 29 33 34 35 40 45 57 59 64 65 74 75 77 79 81 87 90 93 97 98 104 106 107 108 110 111 114 119 127 129 130 133 144 145 146 147 148 **P**6
Primary Contact: Kenneth Marx, Chief Executive Officer
CFO: Steve Weiss, Chief Financial Officer
CMO: James Weber, D.O., Chief of Staff
CIO: Jim Smith, Director Information Systems
CHR: Christy Aubuchon, Director Personnel
CNO: Beverly Williams, R.N., Chief Nursing Officer
Web address: www.wcmhosp.org
**Control:** County–Government, nonfederal **Service:** General Medical and Surgical

**Staffed Beds:** 25 **Admissions:** 875 **Census:** 10 **Outpatient Visits:** 98633 **Births:** 0 **Total Expense ($000):** 28216 **Payroll Expense ($000):** 12666 **Personnel:** 254

*Many Facility Codes have changed. Please refer to the AHA Guide Code Chart.* © 2015 AHA Guide

### RICHMOND—Ray County

★ **RAY COUNTY MEMORIAL HOSPITAL (261327)**, 904 Wollard Boulevard, Zip 64085–2229; tel. 816/470–5432 **A9** 10 18 **F3** 11 15 29 31 40 45 62 64 68 74 75 78 79 81 82 85 87 93 107 108 110 111 115 117 119 130 133 146
Primary Contact: Earl N. Sheehy, Administrator
CFO: Donald Harr, Controller
CHR: Donna Strain, Director Human Resources
Web address: www.raycountyhospital.com
**Control:** County–Government, nonfederal **Service:** General Medical and Surgical

**Staffed Beds:** 25 **Admissions:** 822 **Census:** 9 **Outpatient Visits:** 17315
**Births:** 0 **Total Expense ($000):** 20133 **Payroll Expense ($000):** 9102
**Personnel:** 209

### RICHMOND HEIGHTS—St. Louis County

⊠ △ **SSM SELECT REHABILITATION HOSPITAL (263031)**, 1027 Bellevue Avenue, 3rd Floor, Zip 63117–1851, Mailing Address: 1027 Bellevue Avenue, Zip 63117–1851; tel. 314/768–5300, (Includes SSM SELECT REHABILITATION HOSPITAL, 12380 De Paul Drive, Bridgeton, Zip 63044–2511; tel. 314/447–9700; Timothy Wadman, Chief Executive Officer), (Nonreporting) **A1** 7 10 **S** Select Medical Corporation, Mechanicsburg, PA
Primary Contact: Timothy Wadman, Chief Executive Officer
Web address: www.ssm–select.com
**Control:** Partnership, Investor–owned, for–profit **Service:** Rehabilitation

**Staffed Beds:** 95

### ROLLA—Phelps County

⊠ △ **PHELPS COUNTY REGIONAL MEDICAL CENTER (260017)**, 1000 West Tenth Street, Zip 65401–2905; tel. 573/458–8899, (Total facility includes 20 beds in nursing home–type unit) **A1** 2 7 9 10 **F3** 7 8 11 13 15 18 20 22 26 28 29 30 31 34 35 39 40 45 47 49 50 51 56 57 59 60 62 63 68 70 73 74 75 76 77 78 79 81 82 84 85 86 87 89 90 93 96 98 100 101 102 103 104 107 108 110 111 114 115 117 118 119 120 121 127 128 129 130 131 132 135 143 144 146 147 148 **P6**
Primary Contact: John R. Denbo, Chief Executive Officer
CFO: Edward Clayton, Chief Financial Officer
CMO: Donald James, D.O., Chief Medical Officer
CIO: Jeff McKune, Director Information Technology
CHR: Frank A. Lazzaro, III, Chief Human Resources Officer
CNO: Keri S. Brookshire–Heavin, Chief Nurse Executive
Web address: www.pcrmc.com
**Control:** County–Government, nonfederal **Service:** General Medical and Surgical

**Staffed Beds:** 161 **Admissions:** 6132 **Census:** 81 **Outpatient Visits:** 456039
**Births:** 853 **Total Expense ($000):** 192156 **Payroll Expense ($000):** 85264
**Personnel:** 1443

### SAINT CHARLES—St. Charles County

⊠ **CENTERPOINTE HOSPITAL (264012)**, 4801 Weldon Spring Parkway, Zip 63304–9101; tel. 636/441–7300 **A1** 9 10 **F4** 5 34 35 38 44 54 59 80 87 98 99 100 101 102 103 104 105 106 130 132 143
Primary Contact: Azfar Malik, M.D., Chief Executive Officer and Chief Medical Officer
COO: Susan Mathis, R.N., Chief Operating Officer and Chief Nurse Executive
CFO: Tariq F. Malik, CPA, Acting Chief Financial Officer
CMO: Azfar Malik, M.D., Chief Executive Officer and Chief Medical Officer
CIO: Jennifer Bourn, Director Health Information Services, Performance Improvement and Medical Staff Services
CHR: Kelli White, Manager Human Resources
CNO: Susan Mathis, R.N., Chief Operating Officer and Chief Nurse Executive
Web address: www.centerpointehospital.com
**Control:** Corporation, Investor–owned, for–profit **Service:** Psychiatric

**Staffed Beds:** 151 **Admissions:** 4852 **Census:** 100 **Outpatient Visits:** 67515
**Births:** 0 **Total Expense ($000):** 43039 **Payroll Expense ($000):** 19939
**Personnel:** 379

⊠ **SELECT SPECIALTY HOSPITAL–ST. LOUIS (262013)**, 300 First Capitol Drive, Unit 1, Zip 63301–2844; tel. 636/947–5010 **A1** 9 10 **F1** 29 74 75 148 **S** Select Medical Corporation, Mechanicsburg, PA
Primary Contact: Patrice L. Komoroski, Ph.D., R.N., Chief Executive Officer
Web address: www.selectspecialtyhospitals.com/company/locations/stlouis.aspx
**Control:** Corporation, Investor–owned, for–profit **Service:** Long–Term Acute Care hospital

**Staffed Beds:** 33 **Admissions:** 355 **Census:** 29 **Outpatient Visits:** 0 **Births:** 0 **Total Expense ($000):** 16773 **Payroll Expense ($000):** 6708 **Personnel:** 111

⊠ **SSM ST. JOSEPH HEALTH CENTER (260005)**, 300 First Capitol Drive, Zip 63301–2844; tel. 636/947–5000, (Includes SSM ST. JOSEPH HEALTH CENTER – WENTZVILLE, 500 Medical Drive, Wentzville, Zip 63385–3421; tel. 636/327–1000) **A1** 2 9 10 **F3** 4 11 13 15 17 18 20 22 24 26 28 29 30 31 34 35 38 40 41 42 43 44 45 46 49 50 53 54 55 56 57 58 59 60 64 68 70 73 74 75 76 78 79 81 82 84 85 86 87 90 96 97 98 99 100 101 102 103 104 105 107 108 110 111 114 115 118 119 120 121 129 130 132 135 144 146 147 148 **P6** 8 **S** SSM Health, Saint Louis, MO
Primary Contact: Michael E. Bowers, President
COO: Lee Bernstein, Regional Executive Vice President and Chief Operating Officer
CFO: Karen Rewerts, System Vice President Finance
CIO: Margaret Feilner, Director Information Services
CHR: Debbie G. Walkenhorst, System Vice President Talent Management
Web address: www.ssmstjoseph.com
**Control:** Church–operated, Nongovernment, not–for profit **Service:** General Medical and Surgical

**Staffed Beds:** 331 **Admissions:** 14401 **Census:** 199 **Outpatient Visits:** 168106 **Births:** 733 **Total Expense ($000):** 209299 **Payroll Expense ($000):** 72069 **Personnel:** 1136

### SAINT JOSEPH—Buchanan County

★ **LONG–TERM ACUTE CARE HOSPITAL, MOSAIC LIFE CARE AT ST. JOSEPH (262019)**, 5325 Faraon Street, Zip 64506–3488; tel. 816/271–6000 **A9** 10 **F1** 3 29 85 130 148
Primary Contact: Dana Anderson, Interim Administrator
Web address: www.https://www.mymosaiclifecare.org/General/Long–Term– Acute–Care–Hospital/
**Control:** Other not–for–profit (including NFP Corporation) **Service:** Long–Term Acute Care hospital

**Staffed Beds:** 41 **Admissions:** 251 **Census:** 23 **Outpatient Visits:** 0 **Births:** 0 **Total Expense ($000):** 13205 **Payroll Expense ($000):** 3759 **Personnel:** 68

⊠ **MOSAIC LIFE CARE AT ST. JOSEPH (260006)**, 5325 Faraon Street, Zip 64506–3488; tel. 816/271–6000 **A1** 2 9 10 20 **F3** 8 9 11 12 13 15 17 18 20 22 24 26 28 29 30 31 32 33 34 35 36 37 40 43 45 46 48 49 50 53 54 57 58 59 62 63 64 65 66 70 71 74 75 76 77 78 79 80 81 82 84 85 86 87 89 92 93 94 96 97 98 100 102 103 104 107 108 110 111 114 115 118 119 120 121 123 126 129 130 131 134 135 143 144 146 147 148 **P6**
Primary Contact: Samuel Mark Laney, M.D., President and Chief Executive Officer
COO: Curt Kretzinger, Chief Operating Officer
CFO: John P. Wilson, Chief Financial Officer
CIO: Joe Boyce, M.D., Chief Technology Officer and Chief Medical Information Officer
CHR: Michael Pulido, Chief Administrative Officer
CNO: Carolyn Paden, Associate Administrator Surgical Services
Web address: www.https://www.mymosaiclifecare.org/Main/Location/st–joseph– mo/mosaic–life–care–at–st.–joseph/
**Control:** Other not–for–profit (including NFP Corporation) **Service:** General Medical and Surgical

**Staffed Beds:** 352 **Admissions:** 16283 **Census:** 191 **Outpatient Visits:** 916535 **Births:** 1637 **Total Expense ($000):** 535262 **Payroll Expense ($000):** 243986 **Personnel:** 3159

☐ **NORTHWEST MISSOURI PSYCHIATRIC REHABILITATION CENTER (264007)**, 3505 Frederick Avenue, Zip 64506–2914; tel. 816/387–2300 **A1** 10 **F4** 29 30 34 58 59 65 68 75 77 86 87 97 98 101 102 103 130 132 135 143 146 **P6**
Primary Contact: Denise Norbury, Regional Executive Officer
COO: Mary Attebury, Chief Operating Officer
CFO: Randy Riley, Fiscal and Administrative Manager
CMO: James B. Reynolds, M.D., Medical Director
CIO: Robert Curren, Western Region Chief Information Technology Officer
CHR: Mary Blakey Gorman, Director Human Resources
CNO: Pam Nold, Chief Nurse Executive
Web address: www.dmh.mo.gov/nmprc/index.htm
**Control:** State–Government, nonfederal **Service:** Psychiatric

**Staffed Beds:** 108 **Admissions:** 59 **Census:** 107 **Outpatient Visits:** 0 **Births:** 0 **Total Expense ($000):** 21295 **Payroll Expense ($000):** 11910 **Personnel:** 327

**MO**

---

**Hospital, Medicare Provider Number, Address, Telephone, Approval, Facility, and Physician Codes, Health Care System**

★ American Hospital Association (AHA) membership
☐ The Joint Commission accreditation
○ Healthcare Facilities Accreditation Program
◇ DNV Healthcare Inc. accreditation
⇑ Center for Improvement in Healthcare Quality Accreditation
△ Commission on Accreditation of Rehabilitation Facilities (CARF) accreditation

**SAINT LOUIS—St. Louis City County**

✠ **BARNES–JEWISH HOSPITAL (260032)**, 1 Barnes–Jewish Hospital Plaza, Zip 63110–1003; tel. 314/747–3000, (Includes BARNES–JEWISH HOSPITAL PSYCHIATRIC SUPPORT CENTER, 5355 Delmar Boulevard, Zip 63112–3146; tel. 314/273–0040; John M. Eiler, President), (Total facility includes 120 beds in nursing home–type unit) **A**1 2 3 5 8 9 10 **F**3 4 8 9 11 12 13 14 15 16 17 18 20 22 24 26 28 29 30 31 34 35 36 37 38 39 40 43 44 45 46 47 48 49 50 51 52 53 54 55 56 57 58 59 60 61 63 64 65 66 68 70 71 73 74 75 76 77 78 79 80 81 82 84 85 86 87 89 90 91 92 93 94 95 96 97 98 100 101 102 103 104 105 107 108 109 110 111 112 114 115 116 117 118 119 120 121 122 123 124 126 128 129 130 131 132 134 135 136 137 138 139 140 141 142 143 144 145 146 147 148 **P**6 **S** BJC HealthCare, Saint Louis, MO
Primary Contact: Douglas W. Cannon, President
CFO: Mark Krieger, Vice President and Chief Financial Officer
CMO: John Lynch, M.D., Vice President and Chief Medical Officer
CIO: Jerry Vuchak, Vice President Information Systems
CHR: John Beatty, Vice President Human Resources
CNO: Coreen Vlodarchyk, R.N., Vice President, Patient Care Services and Chief Nursing Officer
Web address: www.barnesjewish.org
**Control:** Other not–for–profit (including NFP Corporation) **Service:** General Medical and Surgical

**Staffed Beds:** 1323 **Admissions:** 54494 **Census:** 927 **Outpatient Visits:** 745994 **Births:** 3239 **Total Expense ($000):** 1775171 **Payroll Expense ($000):** 537984 **Personnel:** 9879

✠ **BARNES–JEWISH WEST COUNTY HOSPITAL (260162)**, 12634 Olive Boulevard, Zip 63141–6337; tel. 314/996–8000 **A**1 3 5 9 10 **F**3 12 15 18 29 34 35 40 45 46 47 49 50 51 57 59 60 64 65 70 74 75 77 78 79 81 82 85 90 93 107 110 111 114 115 117 119 120 121 126 129 130 131 142 145 146 148 **S** BJC HealthCare, Saint Louis, MO
Primary Contact: Doug Black, President
CFO: Diane M. Glen, Assistant Administrator
CMO: Sam B. Bhayani, M.D., Chief Medical Officer
CIO: Jerry Vuchak, Vice President Information Systems
CNO: Yoany Finetti, R.N., Chief Nursing Officer
Web address: www.barnesjewishwestcounty.org
**Control:** Other not–for–profit (including NFP Corporation) **Service:** General Medical and Surgical

**Staffed Beds:** 77 **Admissions:** 2863 **Census:** 21 **Outpatient Visits:** 120175 **Births:** 0 **Total Expense ($000):** 99959 **Payroll Expense ($000):** 30445 **Personnel:** 407

✠ **CHRISTIAN HOSPITAL (260180)**, 11133 Dunn Road, Zip 63136–6119; tel. 314/653–5000 **A**1 2 9 10 **F**3 4 5 7 8 11 15 17 18 20 22 24 26 28 29 30 31 34 35 40 42 45 46 47 49 50 51 53 56 57 58 59 60 63 64 65 68 69 70 74 75 77 78 79 80 81 82 83 84 85 86 87 90 92 93 94 96 98 100 101 102 103 104 105 107 108 109 110 111 112 113 114 115 116 117 118 119 120 121 123 126 129 130 132 135 146 147 148 **P**6 **S** BJC HealthCare, Saint Louis, MO
Primary Contact: Ronald B. McMullen, President
CMO: Sebastian Rueckert, M.D., Chief Medical Officer
CIO: Michael Kelly, Vice President
CHR: Bryan Hartwick, Vice President Human Resources
CNO: Jennifer Cordia, Vice President and Chief Nursing Executive
Web address: www.christianhospital.org
**Control:** Other not–for–profit (including NFP Corporation) **Service:** General Medical and Surgical

**Staffed Beds:** 252 **Admissions:** 14101 **Census:** 208 **Outpatient Visits:** 277296 **Births:** 0 **Total Expense ($000):** 330714 **Payroll Expense ($000):** 104046 **Personnel:** 1775

✠ **DES PERES HOSPITAL (260176)**, 2345 Dougherty Ferry Road, Zip 63122–3313; tel. 314/966–9100 **A**1 3 5 9 10 12 13 **F**3 12 15 17 18 20 22 24 26 29 30 31 34 35 36 40 44 48 49 50 56 57 58 59 60 64 68 69 70 75 77 79 81 82 85 86 87 93 107 110 111 114 119 126 130 132 135 143 146 148 **S** TENET Healthcare Corporation, Dallas, TX
Primary Contact: John A. Grah, JD, FACHE, Chief Executive Officer
COO: Alex Lovshin, Chief Operating Officer
CFO: Rhonda Rogers, Chief Financial Officer
CMO: Karen Webb, M.D., Chief Medical Officer
CIO: Kay Hannon, Director Information Systems
CHR: Kathaleen Clutts, Chief Human Resources Officer
CNO: Mary Ann Hampton, R.N., Chief Nursing Officer
Web address: www.despereshospital.com
**Control:** Corporation, Investor–owned, for–profit **Service:** General Medical and Surgical

**Staffed Beds:** 143 **Admissions:** 5118 **Census:** 53 **Outpatient Visits:** 33261 **Births:** 0 **Total Expense ($000):** 116855 **Payroll Expense ($000):** 33914 **Personnel:** 551

☐ **HAWTHORN CHILDREN PSYCHIATRIC HOSPITAL (264028)**, 1901 Pennsylvania, Zip 63133–1325; tel. 314/512–7800 **A**1 3 10 **F**98 99 106 **P**6
Primary Contact: Laurent D. Javois, Regional Executive Officer
COO: Marcia F. Ford, Chief Operating Officer
CFO: James D. Martin, Chief Financial Officer
CMO: Joshua Calhoun, M.D., Medical Director
CHR: Donna Harris–Brekel, Director Human Resources
CNO: Melody Patterson, Chief Nurse Executive
Web address: www.dmh.missouri.gov/hcph/
**Control:** State–Government, nonfederal **Service:** Children's hospital psychiatric

**Staffed Beds:** 52 **Admissions:** 114 **Census:** 37 **Outpatient Visits:** 0 **Births:** 0 **Total Expense ($000):** 14560 **Payroll Expense ($000):** 8268 **Personnel:** 208

✠ **KINDRED HOSPITAL–ST. LOUIS (262010)**, 4930 Lindell Boulevard, Zip 63108–1510; tel. 314/361–8700, (Includes KINDRED HOSPITAL ST. LOUIS–ST. ANTHONY'S, 10018 Kennerly Road, 3rd Floor, Zip 63128; tel. 314/525–8100; Len McDade, Chief Executive Officer), (Nonreporting) **A**1 9 10 **S** Kindred Healthcare, Louisville, KY
Primary Contact: Stephanie Bridges, Chief Executive Officer
COO: Dakota Redd, R.N., Chief Clinical Officer
CFO: Maureen Roach, Senior Chief Financial Officer
CMO: Michael Holtzman, M.D., Medical Director
CIO: Thomas C. Christman, Director Plant Operations
CHR: Cindy Sander, Coordinator Human Resources
Web address: www.kindredstlouis.com/
**Control:** Corporation, Investor–owned, for–profit **Service:** Long–Term Acute Care hospital

**Staffed Beds:** 98

✠ **KINDRED HOSPITAL–ST. LOUIS AT MERCY (260230)**, 615 South New Ballas Road, 7th Floor, Zip 63141–8221; tel. 314/567–4326 **A**1 9 10 **F**3 77 80 85 130 148 **S** Kindred Healthcare, Louisville, KY
Primary Contact: Robert S. Adcock, Chief Executive Officer
CFO: Paul Veillon, CPA, Chief Financial Officer
CMO: Rekha Lakshmanan, M.D., Medical Director
Web address: www.kindredstlouismercy.com
**Control:** Corporation, Investor–owned, for–profit **Service:** Long–Term Acute Care hospital

**Staffed Beds:** 54 **Admissions:** 306 **Census:** 22 **Outpatient Visits:** 0 **Births:** 0 **Total Expense ($000):** 13240 **Payroll Expense ($000):** 4775 **Personnel:** 73

**MERCY CONTINUING CARE HOSPITAL** See Kindred Hospital–St. Louis at Mercy

✠ **MERCY HOSPITAL ST. LOUIS (260020)**, 615 South New Ballas Road, Zip 63141–8277; tel. 314/569–6000, (Includes MERCY CHILDREN'S HOSPITAL ST. LOUIS, 615 South New Ballas Road, Zip 63141–8221; tel. 314/251–6000), (Total facility includes 120 beds in nursing home–type unit) **A**1 2 3 5 8 9 10 **F**1 3 4 5 8 11 12 13 14 15 16 17 18 19 20 22 24 25 26 27 28 29 30 31 32 33 34 35 36 38 39 40 41 43 45 46 47 48 49 50 51 52 53 54 55 56 57 58 59 60 61 64 66 67 68 69 70 71 72 73 74 75 76 77 78 79 80 81 82 84 85 86 87 88 89 90 92 93 94 96 97 98 99 100 101 102 103 104 105 106 107 108 110 111 114 115 116 117 118 119 120 121 123 124 126 128 129 130 131 132 134 135 143 144 146 147 148 **P**6 8 **S** Mercy Health, Chesterfield, MO
Primary Contact: Jeffrey A. Johnston, President
COO: Eric J. Eoloff, Chief Operating Officer
CFO: Cheryl Matejka, Chief Financial Officer
CMO: Paul Hintze, M.D., Vice President Medical Affairs
CIO: Eugene Roth, Vice President Information Services
CHR: Rocky Ruello, Vice President Human Resources
Web address: www.mercy.net/stlouismo
**Control:** Other not–for–profit (including NFP Corporation) **Service:** General Medical and Surgical

**Staffed Beds:** 979 **Admissions:** 40584 **Census:** 598 **Outpatient Visits:** 943253 **Births:** 8413 **Total Expense ($000):** 787613 **Payroll Expense ($000):** 293145 **Personnel:** 4779

☐ **METROPOLITAN ST. LOUIS PSYCHIATRIC CENTER (264025)**, 5351 Delmar, Zip 63112–3198; tel. 314/877–0500, (Nonreporting) **A**1 3 10
Primary Contact: Laurent D. Javois, Regional Executive Officer
COO: Michael Anderson, Ph.D., Chief Operating Officer
CFO: James D. Martin, Chief Financial Officer
CMO: Roy Wilson, M.D., Medical Director
CHR: Donna Harris–Brekel, Director Human Resources
CNO: Ebony Fisher, Chief Nurse Executive
Web address: www.dmh.missouri.gov/mpc
**Control:** State–Government, nonfederal **Service:** Psychiatric

**Staffed Beds:** 50

*Many Facility Codes have changed. Please refer to the AHA Guide Code Chart.* © 2015 AHA Guide

MO

✠ **MISSOURI BAPTIST MEDICAL CENTER (260108)**, 3015 North Ballas Road, Zip 63131–2329; tel. 314/996–5000 **A**1 2 3 5 9 10 **F**3 11 13 14 15 17 18 20 22 24 26 29 30 31 32 34 35 36 40 41 45 46 48 49 50 51 54 55 56 57 58 59 60 64 65 68 70 72 74 75 76 77 78 79 81 82 83 84 85 86 87 89 90 91 92 93 94 96 97 102 107 108 110 111 114 115 116 117 118 119 120 121 123 124 126 130 131 132 135 145 146 147 148 **P**6 **S** BJC HealthCare, Saint Louis, MO
Primary Contact: John Antes, President
CFO: Augusto A. Noronha, Vice President Finance and Chief Financial Officer
CMO: Mitchell Botney, M.D., Vice President Medical Affairs and Chief Medical Officer
CIO: Derrick Marcum, Director Information Systems
CHR: Sandra G. Young, Vice President Human Resources
CNO: Tim Mislan, MS, Vice President and Chief Nurse Executive
Web address: www.missouribaptist.org
**Control:** Other not–for–profit (including NFP Corporation) **Service:** General Medical and Surgical

**Staffed Beds:** 448 **Admissions:** 22307 **Census:** 248 **Outpatient Visits:** 339153 **Births:** 4076 **Total Expense ($000):** 478047 **Payroll Expense ($000):** 159218 **Personnel:** 2281

☐ **SHRINERS HOSPITALS FOR CHILDREN–ST. LOUIS (263304)**, 4400 Clayton Avenue, Zip 63110–1624; tel. 314/432–3600 **A**1 3 5 9 10 **F**3 29 58 64 74 75 79 81 85 86 87 89 93 94 130 131 146 148 **S** Shriners Hospitals for Children, Tampa, FL
Primary Contact: John Gloss, FACHE, Administrator
CFO: Sandra K. Lawson, Interim Director Fiscal Services
CMO: Perry L. Schoenecker, M.D., Chief of Staff
CIO: Jeanne Hall, Director Information Systems
CHR: Mark Venable, Interim Director Human Resources
Web address: www.shrinershospitalsforchildren.org/Hospitals/Locations/Stlouis.aspx
**Control:** Other not–for–profit (including NFP Corporation) **Service:** Children's orthopedic

**Staffed Beds:** 42 **Admissions:** 366 **Census:** 5 **Outpatient Visits:** 9805 **Births:** 0 **Total Expense ($000):** 28759 **Payroll Expense ($000):** 11086 **Personnel:** 199

★ **SSM CARDINAL GLENNON CHILDREN'S MEDICAL CENTER (269807)**, 1465 South Grand Boulevard, Zip 63104–1095; tel. 314/577–5600 **A**3 5 9 10 **F**3 11 19 21 23 25 27 29 30 31 32 34 36 44 45 46 47 48 49 50 51 54 55 57 59 60 61 64 66 68 72 73 74 75 77 78 79 80 81 82 84 85 86 87 88 89 90 93 94 97 99 100 101 102 104 107 111 114 115 119 127 129 130 131 132 134 136 137 138 139 141 142 146 148 **P**6 8 **S** SSM Health, Saint Louis, MO
Primary Contact: Damon R. Harbison, MBA, Interim Chief Executive Officer
CFO: Karen Rewerts, System Vice President of Finance
CMO: John Peter, M.D., Vice President Medical Affairs
CIO: Michael Paasch, Regional Vice President and Chief Information Officer
CHR: Debbie G. Walkenhorst, Network Vice President
Web address: www.cardinalglennon.com
**Control:** Church–operated, Nongovernment, not–for profit **Service:** Children's general

**Staffed Beds:** 176 **Admissions:** 7819 **Census:** 131 **Outpatient Visits:** 204438 **Births:** 0 **Total Expense ($000):** 289601 **Payroll Expense ($000):** 87206 **Personnel:** 1470

✠ **SSM HEALTH SAINT LOUIS UNIVERSITY HOSPITAL (260105)**, 3635 Vista at Grand Boulevard, Zip 63110–0250, Mailing Address: P.O. Box 15250, Zip 63110–0250; tel. 314/577–8000 **A**1 2 3 5 8 9 10 **F**3 4 6 7 8 9 11 14 15 17 18 20 22 24 26 28 29 30 34 39 40 43 44 45 46 47 48 49 50 51 55 56 57 58 59 60 61 63 64 65 66 68 70 74 75 77 78 79 81 82 84 85 86 87 90 91 92 93 94 96 97 98 100 101 102 103 104 107 108 110 111 112 113 114 115 116 117 118 119 120 121 123 124 126 129 130 131 132 135 136 138 139 141 142 146 147 148 **P**1 **S** SSM Health, Saint Louis, MO
Primary Contact: Kathleen R. Becker, MPH, JD, President
COO: Robert William Hoefer, FACHE, Chief Operating Officer
CFO: Raymond Alvey, Chief Financial Officer
CMO: Nirav Patel, M.D., Interim Chief Medical Officer
CIO: Patrick Brennan, Director Information System Technology
CHR: Vera W. Daniel, Chief Human Resources Officer
CNO: Russell Schroeder, Chief Nursing Officer
Web address: www.sluhospital.com
**Control:** Corporation, Investor–owned, for–profit **Service:** General Medical and Surgical

**Staffed Beds:** 356 **Admissions:** 16406 **Census:** 256 **Outpatient Visits:** 144653 **Births:** 0 **Total Expense ($000):** 434215 **Payroll Expense ($000):** 89760 **Personnel:** 1400

★ **SSM ST. MARY'S HEALTH CENTER (260091)**, 6420 Clayton Road, Zip 63117–1811; tel. 314/768–8000 **A**2 5 9 **F**3 4 13 15 17 18 20 22 24 26 28 29 30 31 34 35 37 38 40 44 45 46 49 50 51 52 55 56 57 58 59 60 61 64 66 70 72 73 74 75 76 78 79 81 82 84 85 86 87 97 98 100 101 102 103 104 105 107 108 110 111 114 115 119 120 121 129 130 132 135 143 144 146 147 148 **P**6 8 **S** SSM Health, Saint Louis, MO
Primary Contact: Candice Jennings, FACHE, President
CFO: Karen Rewerts, System Vice President of Finance
CMO: Stephen Kelly, M.D., Chief Medical Officer
CIO: Michael Paasch, Regional Chief Information Officer
CNO: Patti Kelley, MSN, Chief Nursing Officer
Web address: www.stmarys–stlouis.com
**Control:** Church–operated, Nongovernment, not–for profit **Service:** General Medical and Surgical

**Staffed Beds:** 381 **Admissions:** 18554 **Census:** 263 **Outpatient Visits:** 211902 **Births:** 3386 **Total Expense ($000):** 304429 **Payroll Expense ($000):** 101652 **Personnel:** 1649

☐ **ST. ALEXIUS HOSPITAL – BROADWAY CAMPUS (260210)**, 3933 South Broadway, Zip 63118–4601; tel. 314/865–7000, (Includes SOUTHPOINTE HOSPITAL, 2639 Miami Street, Zip 63118–3929; tel. 314/772–1456; ST. ALEXIUS HOSPITAL – FOREST PARK CAMPUS, 6150 Oakland Avenue, Zip 63139–3215; tel. 314/768–3000; Michael J. Motte, Chief Executive Officer) **A**1 5 6 9 10 **F**3 12 15 20 29 30 35 38 39 40 56 57 59 60 68 70 74 77 78 79 81 86 87 98 101 102 103 104 107 108 110 111 118 119 130 143 146 148 **P**6 **S** Success Healthcare, Boca Raton, FL
Primary Contact: Michael J. Motte, Chief Executive Officer
CFO: Matthew Brandt, Chief Financial Officer
Web address: www.stalexiushospital.com
**Control:** Corporation, Investor–owned, for–profit **Service:** General Medical and Surgical

**Staffed Beds:** 189 **Admissions:** 4233 **Census:** 99 **Outpatient Visits:** 29776 **Births:** 0 **Total Expense ($000):** 54355 **Payroll Expense ($000):** 30823 **Personnel:** 674

✠ △ **ST. ANTHONY'S MEDICAL CENTER (260077)**, 10010 Kennerly Road, Zip 63128–2106; tel. 314/525–1000 **A**1 2 3 7 9 10 **F**3 4 5 8 11 12 13 15 17 18 20 22 24 26 28 29 30 31 34 35 36 38 40 41 43 47 48 49 50 51 53 54 56 57 58 59 60 61 62 63 64 65 68 69 70 73 74 75 76 77 78 79 80 81 82 84 85 86 87 89 90 91 92 93 94 95 96 97 98 99 100 101 102 103 104 105 107 108 110 111 114 115 118 119 120 121 122 123 124 126 129 130 131 132 143 144 146 147 148 **P**6
Primary Contact: David Sindelar, Chief Executive Officer
COO: Christopher Bowe, M.D., Chief Operating Officer
CFO: Kenneth Venuto, Chief Financial Officer
CMO: David Morton, M.D., Chief Medical Officer
CIO: Jim Weldon, Chief Information Officer
CNO: Beverly Bokovitz, R.N., Chief Nursing Officer
Web address: www.stanthonysmedcenter.com
**Control:** Other not–for–profit (including NFP Corporation) **Service:** General Medical and Surgical

**Staffed Beds:** 579 **Admissions:** 27712 **Census:** 336 **Outpatient Visits:** 655654 **Births:** 1309 **Total Expense ($000):** 441592 **Payroll Expense ($000):** 206473 **Personnel:** 3208

**ST. JOHN'S MERCY CHILDREN'S HOSPITAL** See Mercy Children's Hospital St. Louis

**ST. JOHN'S MERCY MEDICAL CENTER** See Mercy Hospital St. Louis

✠ △ **ST. LOUIS CHILDREN'S HOSPITAL (263301)**, One Children's Place, Zip 63110–1002; tel. 314/454–6000 **A**1 3 5 7 8 9 10 **F**3 5 7 11 16 17 19 20 21 22 23 25 26 27 29 30 31 32 34 35 38 39 40 41 42 43 44 45 46 47 48 49 50 54 57 58 59 60 61 62 63 64 65 68 71 72 74 75 77 78 79 81 82 83 84 85 86 87 88 89 90 92 93 96 99 100 101 102 104 107 108 109 111 112 114 115 119 129 130 131 132 134 135 136 137 138 139 140 141 142 143 144 145 146 148 **S** BJC HealthCare, Saint Louis, MO
Primary Contact: Joan Magruder, President
CFO: Michele McKee, Vice President and Chief Financial Officer
CMO: F. Sessions Cole, M.D., Chief Medical Officer
Web address: www.stlouischildrens.org
**Control:** Other not–for–profit (including NFP Corporation) **Service:** Children's general

**Staffed Beds:** 264 **Admissions:** 10417 **Census:** 180 **Outpatient Visits:** 161937 **Births:** 0 **Total Expense ($000):** 540564 **Payroll Expense ($000):** 170599 **Personnel:** 2566

**MO**

---

**Hospital, Medicare Provider Number, Address, Telephone, Approval, Facility, and Physician Codes, Health Care System**

★ American Hospital Association (AHA) membership   ◯ Healthcare Facilities Accreditation Program   ⇑ Center for Improvement in Healthcare Quality Accreditation
☐ The Joint Commission accreditation   ◇ DNV Healthcare Inc. accreditation   △ Commission on Accreditation of Rehabilitation Facilities (CARF) accreditation

☐ **ST. LOUIS PSYCHIATRIC REHABILITATION CENTER (264010)**, 5300 Arsenal Street, Zip 63139–1463; tel. 314/877–6501 **A**1 10 **F**11 30 39 65 68 75 86 87 98 100 101 106 130 143 146
Primary Contact: Laurent D. Javois, Chief Executive Officer
COO: Felix T. Vincenz, Ph.D., Chief Operating Officer
CFO: James D. Martin, Chief Financial Officer
CMO: Roy Wilson, M.D., Medical Director
CHR: Donna Harris–Brekel, Director Human Resources
CNO: Terra Buzzanga, Chief Nurse Executive
Web address: www.dmh.missouri.gov
**Control:** State–Government, nonfederal **Service:** Psychiatric

**Staffed Beds:** 180 **Admissions:** 31 **Census:** 180 **Outpatient Visits:** 0 **Births:** 0 **Total Expense ($000):** 35752 **Payroll Expense ($000):** 17847
**Personnel:** 515

☒ △ **THE REHABILITATION INSTITUTE OF ST. LOUIS (263028)**, 4455 Duncan Avenue, Zip 63110–1111; tel. 314/658–3800 **A**1 7 9 10 **F**29 44 56 58 64 68 74 75 79 82 87 90 91 93 94 100 130 132 143 146 148 **S** HEALTHSOUTH Corporation, Birmingham, AL
Primary Contact: Tara Diebling, Chief Executive Officer
CFO: Tara Diebling, Chief Executive Officer
CMO: David Carr, M.D., Physician Medical Director
CHR: Heather Savage, Director Human Resources
CNO: Angelina Sherman, R.N., Chief Nursing Officer
Web address: www.rehabinstitutestl.com
**Control:** Partnership, Investor–owned, for–profit **Service:** Rehabilitation

**Staffed Beds:** 96 **Admissions:** 2000 **Census:** 81 **Outpatient Visits:** 37321 **Births:** 0 **Total Expense ($000):** 36643 **Payroll Expense ($000):** 18231
**Personnel:** 301

☒ △ **VETERANS AFFAIRS ST. LOUIS HEALTH CARE SYSTEM**, 915 North Grand, Zip 63106–1621; tel. 314/652–4100, (Nonreporting) **A**1 3 5 7 **S** Department of Veterans Affairs, Washington, DC
Primary Contact: Patricia Ten Haaf, R.N., MSN, Ph.D., Acting Director
COO: Keith D. Repko, Associate Medical Center Director
CFO: Karen Westerheide, Chief Financial Officer
CIO: Steve Warmbold, Director Information Management Service Line
CHR: Marie Lewis, Human Resources Liaison
CNO: Richard Holt, R.N., Associate Director Patient Care Services
Web address: www.stlouis.va.gov/
**Control:** Veterans Affairs, Government, federal **Service:** General Medical and Surgical

**Staffed Beds:** 356

### SAINT PETERS—St. Charles County

☒ **BARNES–JEWISH ST. PETERS HOSPITAL (260191)**, 10 Hospital Drive, Zip 63376–1659; tel. 636/916–9000 **A**1 3 5 9 10 **F**3 8 11 15 18 20 22 28 29 30 31 34 35 44 45 49 51 57 59 64 70 75 77 78 79 81 85 86 90 93 107 108 110 111 114 115 118 119 120 121 123 129 130 132 135 146 147 148 **S** BJC HealthCare, Saint Louis, MO
Primary Contact: Larry A. Tracy, Jr., FACHE, President
CFO: Glen Schwaegel, Vice President and Chief Financial Officer
CMO: Feliipe Orellana, Chief Medical Officer
CIO: Cindy Gross, Director of Finance
CHR: Michael J. Miller, Director Human Resources
CNO: Jill Skyles, R.N., Vice President Patient Care Services and Chief Nurse Executive
Web address: www.bjsph.org/
**Control:** Other not–for–profit (including NFP Corporation) **Service:** General Medical and Surgical

**Staffed Beds:** 101 **Admissions:** 5108 **Census:** 61 **Outpatient Visits:** 86425 **Births:** 130 **Total Expense ($000):** 113653 **Payroll Expense ($000):** 37793
**Personnel:** 526

### SALEM—Dent County

★ **SALEM MEMORIAL DISTRICT HOSPITAL (261318)**, Highway 72 North, Zip 65560–0774; Mailing Address: P.O. Box 774, Zip 65560–0774; tel. 573/729–6626, (Total facility includes 18 beds in nursing home–type unit) **A**9 10 18 **F**3 7 11 29 30 34 40 59 60 62 67 75 81 85 87 89 107 115 119 127 128 130 133 135 146
Primary Contact: Dennis P. Pryor, Administrator
CFO: Becky Cunningham, Controller
CMO: John Demorlis, M.D., Chief Medical Staff
CHR: Jodie Gorman, Director Human Resources
Web address: www.smdh.net
**Control:** Hospital district or authority, Government, nonfederal **Service:** General Medical and Surgical

**Staffed Beds:** 43 **Admissions:** 674 **Census:** 25 **Outpatient Visits:** 35355 **Births:** 0 **Total Expense ($000):** 17997 **Payroll Expense ($000):** 7713
**Personnel:** 172

### SEDALIA—Pettis County

☒ **BOTHWELL REGIONAL HEALTH CENTER (260009)**, 601 East 14th Street, Zip 65301–5972, Mailing Address: P.O. Box 1706, Zip 65302–1706; tel. 660/826–8833, (Total facility includes 10 beds in nursing home–type unit) **A**1 9 10 **F**3 9 11 12 13 14 15 18 20 22 28 29 30 31 34 35 39 40 51 54 56 57 59 60 62 64 65 68 70 73 74 75 76 77 78 79 80 81 82 84 85 86 87 89 92 93 107 108 110 111 114 115 116 117 118 119 120 121 123 124 127 128 129 130 131 132 135 146 147 148
Primary Contact: John M. Dawes, FACHE, Chief Executive Officer
COO: Mark I. Hirshberg, Chief Operating Officer
CFO: James A. Robertson, Jr., Chief Financial Officer
CIO: Tom Fairfax, Director Information Systems
CHR: Deb Clemmer, Vice President Human Resources
CNO: Regina W. Crow, R.N., Chief Nursing Officer
Web address: www.brhc.org
**Control:** City–Government, nonfederal **Service:** General Medical and Surgical

**Staffed Beds:** 137 **Admissions:** 4883 **Census:** 55 **Outpatient Visits:** 117575 **Births:** 514 **Total Expense ($000):** 100437 **Payroll Expense ($000):** 38698
**Personnel:** 677

### SIKESTON—Scott County

☐ **MISSOURI DELTA MEDICAL CENTER (260113)**, 1008 North Main Street, Zip 63801–5044; tel. 573/471–1600 **A**1 9 10 **F**3 11 13 15 18 28 29 30 31 32 34 35 39 40 44 50 51 53 54 56 57 59 60 62 64 68 70 74 75 76 77 78 79 81 82 84 85 86 87 89 90 93 97 98 103 107 108 109 110 111 115 116 117 118 119 127 129 130 131 132 144 146 147 148 **P**6
Primary Contact: Jason Schrumpf, President
CFO: Greg Carda, Vice President Finance
Web address: www.missouridelta.com
**Control:** Other not–for–profit (including NFP Corporation) **Service:** General Medical and Surgical

**Staffed Beds:** 110 **Admissions:** 3950 **Census:** 56 **Outpatient Visits:** 228004 **Births:** 429 **Total Expense ($000):** 88805 **Payroll Expense ($000):** 41469
**Personnel:** 806

### SPRINGFIELD—Greene County

☒ **COX MEDICAL CENTERS (260040)**, 1423 North Jefferson Street, Zip 65802–1988; tel. 417/269–3000, (Includes COX MEDICAL CENTER NORTH, 1423 North Jefferson Avenue, Zip 65802; tel. 417/269–3000; COX MEDICAL CENTER SOUTH, 3801 South National Avenue, Zip 65807; tel. 417/269–6000) **A**1 2 3 5 9 10 **F**3 4 5 7 11 12 13 15 17 18 19 20 22 24 26 28 29 30 31 32 34 35 38 39 40 42 43 44 45 46 47 48 49 50 51 52 53 54 55 56 57 58 59 60 61 62 64 65 68 69 70 71 72 74 75 76 77 78 79 80 81 82 84 85 86 87 88 89 90 92 93 94 95 96 97 98 99 100 101 102 103 104 107 108 110 111 114 115 117 118 119 120 121 124 126 127 128 129 130 131 132 134 135 143 144 146 147 148 **P**3 6 **S** CoxHealth, Springfield, MO
Primary Contact: Steven D. Edwards, President and Chief Executive Officer
CFO: Jacob McWay, Senior Vice President and Chief Financial Officer
CMO: Frank Romero, M.D., Chief Medical Officer
CIO: Bruce Robison, Vice President and Chief Information Officer
CHR: John Hursh, Vice President Human Resources
CNO: Karen Kramer, R.N., Vice President and System Chief Nursing Officer
Web address: www.coxhealth.com
**Control:** Other not–for–profit (including NFP Corporation) **Service:** General Medical and Surgical

**Staffed Beds:** 660 **Admissions:** 32989 **Census:** 435 **Outpatient Visits:** 1384539 **Births:** 3244 **Total Expense ($000):** 934940 **Payroll Expense ($000):** 327136 **Personnel:** 6370

☐ **LAKELAND BEHAVIORAL HEALTH SYSTEM (264024)**, 440 South Market Street, Zip 65806–2026; tel. 417/865–5581 **A**1 10 **F**98 130 **S** Acadia Healthcare Company, Inc., Franklin, TN
Primary Contact: Nathan Duncan, Chief Executive Officer
COO: Randy Fox, Director Performance Improvement and Risk Management
CFO: Rick Crump, Chief Financial Officer
CMO: Richard Aiken, M.D., Medical Director
CIO: Brad Strothkamp, Chief Information Systems
CHR: Dave England, Director Human Resources
Web address: www.lakeland–hospital.com
**Control:** Corporation, Investor–owned, for–profit **Service:** Psychiatric

**Staffed Beds:** 122 **Admissions:** 2234 **Census:** 91 **Outpatient Visits:** 0 **Births:** 0 **Total Expense ($000):** 20537 **Payroll Expense ($000):** 12214
**Personnel:** 340

**MO**

*Many Facility Codes have changed. Please refer to the AHA Guide Code Chart.*          © 2015 AHA Guide

✠ **MERCY HOSPITAL SPRINGFIELD (260065)**, 1235 East Cherokee Street, Zip 65804–2263; tel. 417/820–2000, (Includes MERCY CHILDREN'S HOSPITAL SPRINGFIELD, 1235 East Cherokee Street, Zip 65804–2203; tel. 417/820–2000; MERCY ORTHOPEDIC HOSPITAL SPRINGFIELD, 3050 East Riverbluff Boulevard, Ozark, Zip 65721; tel. 417/820–5611; Robert Steele, M.D., President), (Total facility includes 25 beds in nursing home–type unit) **A**1 2 3 5 9 10 **F**3 5 6 7 8 9 11 12 13 14 15 16 17 18 19 20 21 22 24 25 26 28 29 30 31 32 34 35 36 37 38 39 40 43 44 45 46 47 48 49 51 54 55 56 57 58 59 60 61 62 63 64 65 66 67 68 70 71 72 73 74 75 76 77 78 79 81 82 84 85 86 87 88 89 90 91 92 93 94 96 97 98 99 100 101 102 103 104 107 108 110 111 114 115 116 117 118 119 120 121 123 124 126 127 128 129 130 131 132 134 135 143 144 145 146 147 148 **P**6 8 **S** Mercy Health, Chesterfield, MO
Primary Contact: Dr. Alan Scarrow, MD, President
COO: Jay Guffey, Senior Vice President and Chief Operating Officer
CFO: Scott Reynolds, Vice President Finance
CMO: Allan Allphin, M.D., Chief of Staff
CIO: Lori Sturgill, Vice President Business Partnership
CHR: Tanya Maricn, Interim Vice President Human Resources
CNO: Lisa Person, MSN, Vice President and Chief Nursing Officer
Web address: www.mercy.net/springfieldmo
**Control:** Church–operated, Nongovernment, not–for profit **Service:** General Medical and Surgical

**Staffed Beds:** 628 **Admissions:** 37214 **Census:** 441 **Outpatient Visits:** 624944 **Births:** 3176 **Total Expense ($000):** 897350 **Payroll Expense ($000):** 259183 **Personnel:** 8032

☐ **MERCY REHABILITATION HOSPITAL SPRINGFIELD (263032)**, 5904 South Southwood Road, Zip 65804–5234; tel. 417/227–9000 **A**1 10 **F**29 30 75 90 130 132 146 **S** Kindred Healthcare, Louisville, KY
Primary Contact: Jerry Wise, Chief Executive Officer
CFO: Melissa Campbell, Controller
CMO: Hollis Bell, M.D., Medical Director
CHR: Sarah Eiffert, Director Human Resources
CNO: Jennifer Friedline, R.N., Director of Nursing
Web address: www.mercy.net
**Control:** Corporation, Investor–owned, for–profit **Service:** Rehabilitation

**Staffed Beds:** 60 **Admissions:** 487 **Census:** 16 **Outpatient Visits:** 0 **Births:** 0 **Total Expense ($000):** 8644 **Payroll Expense ($000):** 3599 **Personnel:** 98

○ **OZARKS COMMUNITY HOSPITAL (260207)**, 2828 North National, Zip 65803–4306; tel. 417/837–4000 **A**9 10 11 **F**3 29 40 45 50 54 65 68 74 77 79 81 82 85 86 87 89 90 93 97 100 104 107 108 111 114 119 127 129 130 143 147 148 **P**6
Primary Contact: Paul Taylor, Chief Executive Officer
CFO: Misty Hampshire, Chief Financial Officer
Web address: www.ochonline.com
**Control:** Corporation, Investor–owned, for–profit **Service:** General Medical and Surgical

**Staffed Beds:** 7 **Admissions:** 472 **Census:** 7 **Outpatient Visits:** 200170 **Births:** 0 **Total Expense ($000):** 52103 **Payroll Expense ($000):** 14277 **Personnel:** 507

✠ **SELECT SPECIALTY HOSPITAL–SPRINGFIELD (262017)**, 1630 East Primrose Street, Zip 65804–7929; tel. 417/885–4700, (Nonreporting) **A**1 10 **S** Select Medical Corporation, Mechanicsburg, PA
Primary Contact: Mark S. Brodeur, FACHE, Chief Executive Officer
CHR: Tonya Eddington, Coordinator Human Resources
Web address: www.selectspecialtyhospitals.com/company/locations/springfield.aspx
**Control:** Corporation, Investor–owned, for–profit **Service:** Long–Term Acute Care hospital

**Staffed Beds:** 44

**STE. GENEVIEVE—Ste. Genevieve County**

★ **STE. GENEVIEVE COUNTY MEMORIAL HOSPITAL (261330)**, 800 Suite Genevieve Drive, Zip 63670–1434; tel. 573/883–2751 **A**10 18 **F**2 3 11 13 15 18 28 29 31 34 35 39 40 50 53 56 57 59 62 64 65 68 75 76 77 78 79 81 82 85 86 87 89 92 93 107 110 111 115 119 124 127 129 130 131 132 133 135 146 147 148 **P**6
Primary Contact: Thomas Keim, Chief Executive Officer
CFO: Susan Eckenfels, Chief Financial Officer
CMO: Joseph Sharlow, M.D., Chief of Staff
CHR: Sarah Jo Kelley, Director Human Resources
CNO: Rita Brumfield, R.N., Chief Nursing Officer
Web address: www.stegenevievehospital.org
**Control:** County–Government, nonfederal **Service:** General Medical and Surgical

**Staffed Beds:** 25 **Admissions:** 1094 **Census:** 11 **Outpatient Visits:** 103913 **Births:** 131 **Total Expense ($000):** 38064 **Payroll Expense ($000):** 15613 **Personnel:** 308

**SULLIVAN—Crawford County**

★ **MISSOURI BAPTIST SULLIVAN HOSPITAL (261337)**, 751 Sappington Bridge Road, Zip 63080–2354; tel. 573/468–4186 **A**9 10 18 **F**3 4 7 11 13 15 28 29 30 31 34 35 40 53 56 57 59 63 64 65 70 75 76 77 78 79 81 82 83 84 85 86 87 89 90 93 97 98 102 103 104 107 111 115 119 127 129 130 131 132 133 146 **S** BJC HealthCare, Saint Louis, MO
Primary Contact: Tony Schwarm, President
CFO: Kim Lubbring, Director Financial Services
CMO: Thomas Jackson, M.D., Chief of Staff
CHR: Kathleen Reed, Manager Human Resources
CNO: Carmen J. Bartolotta, Chief Nursing Officer
Web address: www.missouribaptistsullivan.org
**Control:** Other not–for–profit (including NFP Corporation) **Service:** General Medical and Surgical

**Staffed Beds:** 35 **Admissions:** 1754 **Census:** 21 **Outpatient Visits:** 94825 **Births:** 261 **Total Expense ($000):** 45142 **Payroll Expense ($000):** 16924 **Personnel:** 329

**SWEET SPRINGS—Saline County**

**I-70 COMMUNITY HOSPITAL (261334)**, 105 Hospital Drive, Zip 65351–2229; tel. 660/335–4700 **A**9 10 18 **F**3 29 34 35 40 45 59 64 65 68 75 81 83 85 87 89 90 93 102 107 111 114 119 127 128 133 143 148 **S** Rural Community Hospitals of America, Kansas City, MO
Primary Contact: Jeff Bloemker, Chief Executive Officer
CFO: Scott Tongate, Chief Financial Officer
CMO: Deborah Herrmann, M.D., Chief of Staff
CIO: Diane Swift, Director Medical Records
CHR: Diane Steinkuhler, Administrative Assistant Human Resources
CNO: Geri Fuhrman, Chief Nursing Officer
Web address: www.i70medcenter.com
**Control:** Corporation, Investor–owned, for–profit **Service:** General Medical and Surgical

**Staffed Beds:** 15 **Admissions:** 128 **Census:** 3 **Outpatient Visits:** 13751 **Births:** 0 **Total Expense ($000):** 8603 **Payroll Expense ($000):** 3584 **Personnel:** 61

**TRENTON—Grundy County**

★ **WRIGHT MEMORIAL HOSPITAL (261309)**, 191 Iowa Boulevard, Zip 64683–8343; tel. 660/358–5700 **A**9 10 18 **F**3 11 13 15 28 29 30 31 34 35 40 45 50 57 59 64 68 75 76 77 78 79 81 82 84 85 87 89 90 93 102 104 107 108 111 115 119 127 129 130 133 146 148 **P**6 **S** Saint Luke's Health System, Kansas City, MO
Primary Contact: Gary W. Jordan, FACHE, Chief Executive Officer
CFO: Leslie Reed, Chief Financial Officer
CMO: Gerald C. Zabielski, M.D., Chief Medical Staff
CHR: Jenny Donovan, Director Human Resources
Web address: www.saintlukeshealthsystem.org
**Control:** Other not–for–profit (including NFP Corporation) **Service:** General Medical and Surgical

**Staffed Beds:** 25 **Admissions:** 677 **Census:** 8 **Outpatient Visits:** 63502 **Births:** 224 **Total Expense ($000):** 26067 **Payroll Expense ($000):** 9330 **Personnel:** 167

**TROY—Lincoln County**

✠ **MERCY HOSPITAL LINCOLN (261319)**, 1000 East Cherry Street, Zip 63379–1513; tel. 636/528–8551 **A**1 9 10 18 **F**3 11 15 17 18 28 29 30 34 35 40 44 45 50 51 57 59 62 64 65 68 70 75 77 79 81 85 86 87 89 90 93 104 107 110 111 113 114 119 127 129 130 131 132 133 135 144 146 148 **P**6 **S** Mercy Health, Chesterfield, MO
Primary Contact: Anthony Rothermich, Administrator
CFO: Mark Thorn, FACHE, Executive Director, Finance
CIO: Travis Boyd, Manager, Information Technology
CHR: Mary Kay Kunza, Manager Human Resources
CNO: Breanne Griffin, R.N., Executive Director, Nursing
Web address: www.mercy.net
**Control:** County–Government, nonfederal **Service:** General Medical and Surgical

**Staffed Beds:** 25 **Admissions:** 1031 **Census:** 12 **Outpatient Visits:** 78625 **Births:** 0 **Total Expense ($000):** 37616 **Payroll Expense ($000):** 16330 **Personnel:** 252

**MO**

---

**Hospital, Medicare Provider Number, Address, Telephone, Approval, Facility, and Physician Codes, Health Care System**

★ American Hospital Association (AHA) membership   ○ Healthcare Facilities Accreditation Program   ⇑ Center for Improvement in Healthcare Quality Accreditation
☐ The Joint Commission accreditation   ◇ DNV Healthcare Inc. accreditation   △ Commission on Accreditation of Rehabilitation Facilities (CARF) accreditation

## UNIONVILLE—Putnam County

**PUTNAM COUNTY MEMORIAL HOSPITAL (261305)**, 1926 Oak Street, Zip 63565–1180, Mailing Address: P.O. Box 389, Zip 63565–0389; tel. 660/947–2411 **A**9 10 18 **F**3 11 15 18 28 29 34 35 40 45 50 51 57 59 64 65 75 77 81 85 87 89 90 93 97 98 104 105 107 111 114 119 127 128 129 130 133 135 143 **P**5
Primary Contact: Cindy Cummings, Chief Executive Officer
COO: Jerry Cummings, Chief Operating Officer
CFO: Doug Wismer, Chief Financial Officer
CMO: Dawn Ann Fairley, M.D., Chief of Staff
CHR: Debbie Douglas, Director Human Resources
CNO: Gayle Pickens, Chief Nursing Officer
Web address: www.pcmhosp.com
**Control:** County–Government, nonfederal **Service:** General Medical and Surgical

**Staffed Beds:** 25 **Admissions:** 211 **Census:** 9 **Outpatient Visits:** 14500 **Births:** 0 **Total Expense ($000):** 14035 **Payroll Expense ($000):** 5264 **Personnel:** 138

## WARRENSBURG—Johnson County

⊞ **WESTERN MISSOURI MEDICAL CENTER (260097)**, 403 Burkarth Road, Zip 64093–3101; tel. 660/747–2500 **A**1 9 10 20 **F**3 8 11 12 13 15 17 18 28 29 30 31 32 34 35 40 45 47 57 59 61 64 65 68 70 75 76 77 78 79 81 82 85 89 90 93 102 107 108 110 111 115 118 119 127 129 130 131 132 133 135 146 147 148 **P**6
Primary Contact: Darinda Reberry, MSN, RN, NEBC, Interim Chief Executive Officer
COO: Michael L. Gasparini, Vice President Clinical Services and Chief Operating Officer
CFO: Terri Bradley, CPA, Vice President Financial Services and Chief Financial Officer
CIO: Bill Ladd, Director Information Services
CHR: Dennis Long, Director Human Resources
CNO: Darinda Reberry, Chief Nursing Officer
Web address: www.wmmc.com
**Control:** County–Government, nonfederal **Service:** General Medical and Surgical

**Staffed Beds:** 72 **Admissions:** 2771 **Census:** 23 **Outpatient Visits:** 118016 **Births:** 744 **Total Expense ($000):** 71276 **Payroll Expense ($000):** 25598 **Personnel:** 453

## WASHINGTON—Franklin County

⊞ **MERCY HOSPITAL WASHINGTON (260052)**, 901 East Fifth Street, Zip 63090–3127; tel. 636/239–8000 **A**1 9 10 **F**3 8 11 12 13 14 15 17 18 20 22 28 29 30 31 32 34 35 39 40 43 44 48 49 50 51 52 53 57 59 61 64 66 68 69 70 73 75 76 77 78 79 80 81 82 84 85 87 89 90 93 94 96 97 100 101 104 107 108 110 111 114 116 117 118 119 120 121 127 129 130 131 132 134 135 143 144 146 147 148 **P**6 8 **S** Mercy Health, Chesterfield, MO
Primary Contact: Terri L. McLain, FACHE, President
COO: Joan Frost, R.N., Chief Operating Officer
CFO: Cheryl Matejka, Chief Financial Officer
CMO: Thomas Riechers, M.D., Chief Medical Staff
CIO: Michael McCreary, Chief of Services
CHR: Barbara Grayson, Vice President Human Resources
CNO: Stacy Blankenship, Chief Nursing Officer
Web address: www.mercy.net
**Control:** Other not–for–profit (including NFP Corporation) **Service:** General Medical and Surgical

**Staffed Beds:** 166 **Admissions:** 6191 **Census:** 55 **Outpatient Visits:** 293163 **Births:** 846 **Total Expense ($000):** 138760 **Payroll Expense ($000):** 52163 **Personnel:** 741

## WENTZVILLE—St. Charles County

**SSM ST. JOSEPH HEALTH CENTER – WENTZVILLE** See SSM St. Joseph Health Center, Saint Charles

## WEST PLAINS—Howell County

⊞ **OZARKS MEDICAL CENTER (260078)**, 1100 Kentucky Avenue, Zip 65775–2029, Mailing Address: P.O. Box 1100, Zip 65775–1100; tel. 417/256–9111 **A**1 9 10 **F**2 3 5 11 13 15 17 18 20 22 24 28 29 30 31 34 38 40 44 45 49 50 57 59 61 62 63 64 68 70 74 75 76 77 78 79 81 82 84 85 86 87 89 90 91 93 94 98 99 100 101 102 103 104 107 108 110 111 115 118 119 120 121 127 129 130 131 132 135 144 145 146 147 148 **P**8
Primary Contact: Thomas Keller, President and Chief Executive Officer
COO: Jeanne M. Looper, Chief Operating Officer
CFO: Kim Thompson, Vice President and Chief Financial Officer
CMO: Walter R. Holloway, Chief Medical Officer
CIO: John Wilcox, Chief Information Officer
CHR: Connie Schott, Vice President, Human Resources
CNO: Marcia Robson, R.N., Chief Nursing Officer
Web address: www.ozarksmedicalcenter.com
**Control:** Other not–for–profit (including NFP Corporation) **Service:** General Medical and Surgical

**Staffed Beds:** 103 **Admissions:** 5595 **Census:** 54 **Outpatient Visits:** 581369 **Births:** 637 **Total Expense ($000):** 126844 **Payroll Expense ($000):** 60378 **Personnel:** 1026

## WINDSOR—Henry County

☐ **ROYAL OAKS HOSPITAL (264020)**, 307 North Main, Zip 65360–1449; tel. 660/647–2182 **A**1 3 5 10 **F**75 98 99 100 101 102 103 **P**6
Primary Contact: Alan W. Greiman, Chief Executive Officer and President
CFO: Dave Turner, Chief Financial Officer
CMO: Syed Arshad Husain, M.D., Executive Vice President and Chief Medical Officer
CIO: Richard Colvert, Chief Information Officer
CHR: Diane Coletta, Director Human Resources
CNO: Erin Allee, R.N., Director of Nursing
Web address: www.royal–oaks–hospital.org
**Control:** Other not–for–profit (including NFP Corporation) **Service:** Psychiatric

**Staffed Beds:** 41 **Admissions:** 1198 **Census:** 25 **Outpatient Visits:** 0 **Births:** 0 **Total Expense ($000):** 11866 **Payroll Expense ($000):** 6203 **Personnel:** 151

*Many Facility Codes have changed. Please refer to the AHA Guide Code Chart.* © 2015 AHA Guide

# MONTANA

## ANACONDA—Deer Lodge County

★ **COMMUNITY HOSPITAL OF ANACONDA (271335)**, 401 West Pennsylvania Street, Zip 59711; tel. 406/563–8500, (Total facility includes 62 beds in nursing home–type unit) **A**9 10 18 **F**1 3 6 8 11 13 15 29 30 31 34 40 43 45 50 57 59 62 63 64 75 77 79 81 82 87 93 107 111 114 119 128 130 133 135 143 144 146 148 **P**6 **S** Providence Health & Services, Renton, WA
Primary Contact: Steve McNeece, Chief Executive Officer
COO: Laura Austin, Chief Financial Officer and Chief Operating Officer
CFO: Laura Austin, Chief Financial Officer and Chief Operating Officer
CMO: Shawna Baker, M.D., Chief of Staff
CIO: Laura Austin, Chief Financial Officer and Chief Operating Officer
CHR: Meg Hickey–Boynton, Director Human Resources and Marketing
CNO: Jamie Johnson, R.N., Vice President Nursing
Web address: www.communityhospitalofanaconda.org
**Control:** Other not–for–profit (including NFP Corporation) **Service:** General Medical and Surgical

**Staffed Beds: 87 Admissions:** 1000 **Census:** 70 **Outpatient Visits:** 53588 **Births:** 78 **Total Expense ($000):** 38378 **Payroll Expense ($000):** 18440 **Personnel:** 326

## BAKER—Fallon County

**FALLON MEDICAL COMPLEX (271301)**, 202 South 4th Street West, Zip 59313–9156, Mailing Address: P.O. Box 820, Zip 59313–0820; tel. 406/778–3331, (Total facility includes 15 beds in nursing home–type unit) **A**9 10 18 **F**11 15 28 32 34 36 40 56 57 59 62 64 65 68 69 75 93 97 107 110 114 119 127 128 130 133 146 148 **P**6
Primary Contact: David Espeland, Chief Executive Officer
CFO: Selena Nelson, Chief Financial Officer
CMO: Darryl Espeland, D.O., Chief Medical Staff
CIO: Susan Stevens, Information Technology Specialist
CHR: Theresa Weimer, Director Personnel
CNO: Susan Lunde, R.N., Director of Nursing
Web address: www.fallonmedical.org
**Control:** Other not–for–profit (including NFP Corporation) **Service:** General Medical and Surgical

**Staffed Beds: 40 Admissions:** 149 **Census:** 29 **Outpatient Visits:** 18956 **Births:** 0 **Total Expense ($000):** 9052 **Payroll Expense ($000):** 4581 **Personnel:** 96

## BIG SANDY—Chouteau County

★ **BIG SANDY MEDICAL CENTER (271311)**, 166 Montana Avenue East, Zip 59520–8474, Mailing Address: P.O. Box 530, Zip 59520–0530; tel. 406/378–2188, (Total facility includes 22 beds in nursing home–type unit) **A**9 10 18 **F**40 64 93 127 128 133
Primary Contact: Leah Grubb, Chief Executive Officer
CFO: Nora Grubb, Chief Financial Officer
Web address: www.bsmc.org
**Control:** Other not–for–profit (including NFP Corporation) **Service:** General Medical and Surgical

**Staffed Beds: 30 Admissions:** 47 **Census:** 19 **Outpatient Visits:** 3361 **Births:** 0 **Total Expense ($000):** 3128 **Payroll Expense ($000):** 1806 **Personnel:** 34

## BIG TIMBER—Sweet Grass County

★ **PIONEER MEDICAL CENTER (271313)**, 301 West Seventh Avenue, Zip 59011–7893, Mailing Address: P.O. Box 1228, Zip 59011–1228; tel. 406/932–4603, (Total facility includes 25 beds in nursing home–type unit) **A**9 10 18 **F**2 7 10 29 34 35 40 41 45 57 59 63 64 65 69 75 77 93 97 107 114 127 128 130 131 132 133 **P**3 6
Primary Contact: Erik Wood, Chief Executive Officer
CFO: Kyle Gee, Chief Financial Officer
CMO: Benjamin P. Bullington, M.D., Chief of Staff
CHR: Miki Gregorich, Director Human Resources
CNO: Randi Pike, Director of Nursing
Web address: www.pmcmt.org/
**Control:** County–Government, nonfederal **Service:** General Medical and Surgical

**Staffed Beds: 50 Admissions:** 164 **Census:** 27 **Outpatient Visits:** 11402 **Births:** 0 **Total Expense ($000):** 7161 **Payroll Expense ($000):** 2738 **Personnel:** 83

## BILLINGS—Yellowstone County

☐ **ADVANCED CARE HOSPITAL OF MONTANA (272001)**, 3528 Gabel Road, Zip 59102–7307; tel. 406/373–8000, (Nonreporting) **A**1 9 10 **S** Ernest Health, Inc., Albuquerque, NM
Primary Contact: Diana Parker, Chief Executive Officer
Web address: www.achm.ernesthealth.com
**Control:** Corporation, Investor–owned, for–profit **Service:** Long–Term Acute Care hospital

**Staffed Beds: 40**

✠ **BILLINGS CLINIC (270004)**, 2800 10th Avenue North, Zip 59101–0703, Mailing Address: P.O. Box 37000, Zip 59107–7000; tel. 406/657–7000, (Total facility includes 125 beds in nursing home–type unit) **A**1 2 9 10 19 **F**3 7 8 9 10 11 12 13 15 17 18 19 20 22 24 26 27 28 29 30 31 32 34 35 36 38 40 43 44 45 46 48 49 50 51 52 54 55 56 57 58 59 60 61 62 63 64 65 66 68 70 71 72 74 75 76 77 78 79 81 82 84 85 86 87 91 92 93 97 98 99 100 101 102 103 104 105 107 108 110 111 114 115 116 117 118 119 120 121 124 126 128 129 130 131 132 134 135 143 144 146 147 148 **P**6
Primary Contact: Nicholas Wolter, M.D., Chief Executive Officer
CFO: Connie F. Prewitt, Chief Financial Officer
CMO: Randall K. Gibb, M.D., Chief Medical Officer
CIO: Chris E. Stevens, Chief Information Officer
CHR: Karla Stauffer, Executive Director People Resources
CNO: Lu Byrd, R.N., Vice President Hospital Operations and Chief Nursing Officer
Web address: www.billingsclinic.com
**Control:** Other not–for–profit (including NFP Corporation) **Service:** General Medical and Surgical

**Staffed Beds: 393 Admissions:** 14953 **Census:** 299 **Outpatient Visits:** 940380 **Births:** 1383 **Total Expense ($000):** 519674 **Payroll Expense ($000):** 256469 **Personnel:** 3350

✠ △ **ST. VINCENT HEALTHCARE (270049)**, 1233 North 30th Street, Zip 59101–0165, Mailing Address: P.O. Box 35200, Zip 59107–5200; tel. 406/237–7000 **A**1 2 7 9 10 **F**3 8 11 12 13 15 18 19 20 22 24 26 28 29 30 31 32 34 35 36 37 38 39 40 43 44 46 47 49 50 51 56 57 59 60 61 64 68 70 71 72 74 75 77 78 79 81 82 84 85 86 87 88 90 92 93 97 99 100 101 103 104 107 108 111 114 115 116 117 118 119 120 121 123 124 126 129 130 131 132 134 135 143 144 145 146 147 148 **P**6 **S** SCL Health, Broomfield, CO
Primary Contact: Steve Loveless, President and Chief Executive Officer
CMO: Michael Schweitzer, M.D., Chief Medical Officer
CIO: Al Rooney, Director Information Systems
Web address: www.svh-mt.org
**Control:** Church–operated, Nongovernment, not–for profit **Service:** General Medical and Surgical

**Staffed Beds: 221 Admissions:** 11402 **Census:** 143 **Outpatient Visits:** 168675 **Births:** 1526 **Total Expense ($000):** 305494 **Payroll Expense ($000):** 95884 **Personnel:** 1659

## BOZEMAN—Gallatin County

✠ **BOZEMAN DEACONESS HOSPITAL (270057)**, 915 Highland Boulevard, Zip 59715–6902; tel. 406/585–5000, (Nonreporting) **A**1 2 9 10 20
Primary Contact: Kevin M. Pitzer, President and Chief Executive Officer
Web address: www.bozemandeaconess.org
**Control:** Other not–for–profit (including NFP Corporation) **Service:** General Medical and Surgical

**Staffed Beds: 70**

**MT**

---

**Hospital, Medicare Provider Number, Address, Telephone, Approval, Facility, and Physician Codes, Health Care System**

★ American Hospital Association (AHA) membership  ○ Healthcare Facilities Accreditation Program  ⇑ Center for Improvement in Healthcare Quality Accreditation
☐ The Joint Commission accreditation  ◇ DNV Healthcare Inc. accreditation  △ Commission on Accreditation of Rehabilitation Facilities (CARF) accreditation

## BUTTE—Silver Bow County

✠ **ST. JAMES HEALTHCARE (270017)**, 400 South Clark Street,
Zip 59701–2328; tel. 406/723–2500 **A**1 9 10 **F**3 11 13 15 18 20 22 26 28
29 30 31 34 35 40 43 45 47 48 49 50 51 54 56 57 59 64 65 68 70 72 74
75 76 77 78 79 81 82 85 86 87 89 92 93 97 107 108 110 111 114 115 116
117 118 119 120 121 123 126 127 130 131 132 135 145 146 147 148
**S** SCL Health, Broomfield, CO
Primary Contact: Charles T. Wright, President and Chief Executive Officer
CFO: Jay Doyle, Chief Financial Officer
CMO: Dennis Salisbury, M.D., Vice President for Medical Affairs
CHR: Trisha Palmer, Director
CNO: Shannon S. Holland, R.N., Vice President of Patient Care Service
Web address: www.stjameshealthcare.org
**Control:** Other not–for–profit (including NFP Corporation) **Service:** General
Medical and Surgical

**Staffed Beds:** 67 **Admissions:** 3674 **Census:** 41 **Outpatient Visits:** 61246
**Births:** 456 **Total Expense ($000):** 94766 **Payroll Expense ($000):** 33527
**Personnel:** 490

## CHESTER—Liberty County

**LIBERTY MEDICAL CENTER (271334)**, 315 West Madison Avenue, Zip 59522,
Mailing Address: P.O. Box 705, Zip 59522–0705; tel. 406/759–5181 **A**9 10 18
**F**2 3 10 11 34 35 40 43 45 56 57 59 64 67 81 86 87 93 97 107 114 119
127 128 130 133 **P**6
Primary Contact: Derek Daly, Chief Executive Officer
CFO: Shari Dolan, Chief Financial Officer
CMO: Anna Earl, M.D., Chief of Staff
CHR: Bev Halter, Director Human Resources and Payroll
CNO: Shirley Morkrid, Chief Nursing Officer
Web address: www.lchnh.org
**Control:** Other not–for–profit (including NFP Corporation) **Service:** General
Medical and Surgical

**Staffed Beds:** 25 **Admissions:** 34 **Census:** 1 **Outpatient Visits:** 9124 **Births:**
0 **Total Expense ($000):** 6031 **Payroll Expense ($000):** 3249 **Personnel:**
73

## CHOTEAU—Teton County

★ **TETON MEDICAL CENTER (271307)**, 915 4th Street North West,
Zip 59422–9123; tel. 406/466–5763, (Total facility includes 30 beds in nursing
home–type unit) **A**9 10 18 **F**2 3 34 35 40 41 43 53 54 56 57 59 63 64 68 77
87 93 107 127 128 130 131 133 143 146 **P**6
Primary Contact: Louie King, Chief Executive Officer
Web address: www.tetonmedicalcenter.net
**Control:** Hospital district or authority, Government, nonfederal **Service:** General
Medical and Surgical

**Staffed Beds:** 46 **Admissions:** 193 **Census:** 23 **Outpatient Visits:** 7729
**Births:** 0 **Total Expense ($000):** 6809 **Payroll Expense ($000):** 3897
**Personnel:** 80

## CIRCLE—McCone County

★ **MCCONE COUNTY HEALTH CENTER (271305)**, 605 Sullivan Avenue,
Zip 59215, Mailing Address: P.O. Box 48, Zip 59215–0048; tel. 406/485–3381
**A**9 10 18 **F**2 3 11 34 40 41 42 58 65 69 86 87 93 133 135 143 146
Primary Contact: Nancy Rosaaen, Chief Executive Officer
CFO: Nancy Rosaaen, Chief Executive Officer
CHR: Jacque Gardner, Administrative Assistant, Clinic Manager, Co–Chief Financial
Officer and Chief Human Resources
Web address: www.mcconehealth.org/
**Control:** County–Government, nonfederal **Service:** General Medical and Surgical

**Staffed Beds:** 25 **Admissions:** 59 **Census:** 23 **Outpatient Visits:** 3146
**Births:** 0 **Total Expense ($000):** 3237 **Payroll Expense ($000):** 1730
**Personnel:** 41

## COLUMBUS—Stillwater County

★ **STILLWATER COMMUNITY HOSPITAL (271330)**, 44 West Fourth Avenue
North, Zip 59019–0959, Mailing Address: P.O. Box 959, Zip 59019–0959;
tel. 406/322–5316, (Nonreporting) **A**9 10 18
Primary Contact: Tim Russell, Administrator
Web address: www.billingsclinic.com
**Control:** Other not–for–profit (including NFP Corporation) **Service:** General
Medical and Surgical

**Staffed Beds:** 23

## CONRAD—Pondera County

**PONDERA MEDICAL CENTER (271324)**, 805 Sunset Boulevard,
Zip 59425–1717, Mailing Address: P.O. Box 758, Zip 59425–0758;
tel. 406/271–3211, (Total facility includes 59 beds in nursing home–type unit) **A**9
10 18 **F**3 6 7 11 13 15 28 29 34 35 40 43 53 57 59 62 63 65 66 77 81 87
91 93 97 102 107 119 128 130 133 144 146 148 **P**6
Primary Contact: Bill O'Leary, Chief Executive Officer
CFO: Randy Nightengale, Chief Financial Officer
CMO: Jay Taylor, M.D., Chief of Staff
CIO: Sean Kavanagh, Supervisor Information Technology and Information Systems
CHR: Patrick Johnson, Director Human Resources
Web address: www.ponderamedical.com
**Control:** Other not–for–profit (including NFP Corporation) **Service:** General
Medical and Surgical

**Staffed Beds:** 79 **Admissions:** 119 **Census:** 51 **Outpatient Visits:** 7162
**Births:** 0 **Total Expense ($000):** 12271 **Payroll Expense ($000):** 6501
**Personnel:** 191

## CROW AGENCY—Big Horn County

**CROW/NORTHERN CHEYENNE HOSPITAL (271339)**, 10110 South 7650
East, Zip 59022–0009, Mailing Address: P.O. Box 9, Zip 59022–0009;
tel. 406/638–2626, (Nonreporting) **A**10 18 **S** U. S. Indian Health Service,
Rockville, MD
Primary Contact: Gary Wabaunsee, Chief Executive Officer
CMO: Jim Upchurch, M.D., Chief Medical Officer
CIO: Melanie Falls Down, Site Manager
Web address: www.ihs.gov/facilitiesservices/areaoffices/billings/crow/index.asp
**Control:** Public Health Service, Government, federal **Service:** General Medical
and Surgical

**Staffed Beds:** 24

## CULBERTSON—Roosevelt County

★ **ROOSEVELT MEDICAL CENTER (271308)**, 818 Second Avenue East,
Zip 59218, Mailing Address: P.O. Box 419, Zip 59218–0419; tel. 406/787–6401
**A**9 10 18 **F**2 3 7 11 15 34 35 40 43 50 56 57 59 65 69 93 97 119 127 128
130 133 143 146 **P**6
Primary Contact: Audrey Stromberg, Administrator
CFO: Jennifer Kessner, Financial Director
CMO: Don Helland, M.D., Chief Medical Officer
CIO: Brian Fordyce, Director Information Technology
CHR: Elizabeth Raaum, Manger Business Office
Web address: www.roosmem.org
**Control:** Other not–for–profit (including NFP Corporation) **Service:** General
Medical and Surgical

**Staffed Beds:** 25 **Admissions:** 55 **Census:** 21 **Outpatient Visits:** 8542
**Births:** 0 **Total Expense ($000):** 5164 **Payroll Expense ($000):** 2729
**Personnel:** 58

## CUT BANK—Glacier County

**NORTHERN ROCKIES MEDICAL CENTER (271337)**, 802 Second Street S.E.,
Zip 59427–3329; tel. 406/873–2251, (Nonreporting) **A**9 10 18
Primary Contact: Cherie Taylor, Chief Executive Officer
CFO: Treasure Berkram, Chief Financial Officer
CMO: Adron Medley, M.D., Chief Medical Staff
CHR: Kandie Lemieux, Administrative Assistant and Director Human Resources
Web address: www.nmrcinc.org
**Control:** Other not–for–profit (including NFP Corporation) **Service:** General
Medical and Surgical

**Staffed Beds:** 13

## DEER LODGE—Powell County

**DEER LODGE MEDICAL CENTER (271314)**, 1100 Hollenbeck Lane,
Zip 59722–2317; tel. 406/846–2212, (Nonreporting) **A**9 10 18
Primary Contact: Tony Pfaff, Chief Executive Officer
CFO: Jaena Richards, Chief Financial Officer
CMO: Michelle Corbin, M.D., Chief of Staff
CIO: Chris Foster, Director Health Information Management
Web address: www.dlmed.org/
**Control:** Other not–for–profit (including NFP Corporation) **Service:** General
Medical and Surgical

**Staffed Beds:** 16

**MT**

*Many Facility Codes have changed. Please refer to the AHA Guide Code Chart.* © 2015 AHA Guide

## DILLON—Beaverhead County

★ **BARRETT HOSPITAL & HEALTHCARE (271318)**, 600 State Highway 91 South, Zip 59725–7379; tel. 406/683–3000 **A**5 9 10 18 **F**3 13 15 28 31 34 40 45 50 57 59 62 63 64 65 69 75 77 79 81 84 85 87 93 96 97 107 110 111 115 119 130 133 144 146 **P**6 **S** HealthTech Management Services, Brentwood, TN
Primary Contact: Ken Westman, Chief Executive Officer
CFO: Dick Achter, Chief Financial Officer
CMO: Carol Kennedy, Chief Clinical Officer
CIO: Dick Achter, Chief Financial Officer
CHR: Geoff Roach, Director Human Resources
Web address: www.barretthospital.org
**Control:** Hospital district or authority, Government, nonfederal **Service:** General Medical and Surgical

**Staffed Beds:** 18 **Admissions:** 587 **Census:** 6 **Outpatient Visits:** 31621
**Births:** 75 **Total Expense ($000):** 31286 **Payroll Expense ($000):** 14063
**Personnel:** 217

## EKALAKA—Carter County

**DAHL MEMORIAL HEALTHCARE ASSOCIATION (271302)**, 215 Sandy Street, Zip 59324, Mailing Address: P.O. Box 46, Zip 59324–0046; tel. 406/775–8730, (Total facility includes 23 beds in nursing home–type unit) **A**9 10 18 **F**2 7 40 41 57 59 65 69 127 128 130 131 133 135 143 146 148 **P**6
Primary Contact: Nadine Elmore, Chief Executive Officer
CFO: Nadine Elmore, Chief Executive Officer
CMO: Darryl Espeland, D.O., Medical Director
CIO: Davie Ann Barrere, Coordinator Information Technology
CHR: Melissa Matthews, Director Human Resources
CNO: Patricia Rogers, Director of Nursing
Web address: www.dahlmemorial.com
**Control:** Other not–for–profit (including NFP Corporation) **Service:** General Medical and Surgical

**Staffed Beds:** 31 **Admissions:** 30 **Census:** 16 **Outpatient Visits:** 2863
**Births:** 0 **Total Expense ($000):** 2524 **Payroll Expense ($000):** 1243
**Personnel:** 34

## ENNIS—Madison County

**MADISON VALLEY MEDICAL CENTER (271329)**, 305 North Main Street, Zip 59729–8001; tel. 406/682–4222 **A**9 10 18 **F**3 8 11 28 29 32 34 35 36 38 40 41 43 45 46 50 53 56 57 59 64 65 66 71 75 77 81 87 92 93 94 97 107 114 119 127 128 130 131 132 133 135 148 **P**6
Primary Contact: John Bishop, Chief Executive Officer and Chief Financial Officer
CFO: John Bishop, Chief Executive Officer and Chief Financial Officer
CMO: Cindy Sharp, M.D., Chief Medical Officer
CIO: Bo Nix, Chief Information Officer
Web address: www.mvmedcenter.org
**Control:** Other not–for–profit (including NFP Corporation) **Service:** General Medical and Surgical

**Staffed Beds:** 10 **Admissions:** 119 **Census:** 2 **Outpatient Visits:** 12075
**Births:** 0 **Total Expense ($000):** 5871 **Payroll Expense ($000):** 2273
**Personnel:** 48

## FORSYTH—Rosebud County

★ **ROSEBUD HEALTH CARE CENTER (271327)**, 383 North 17th Avenue, Zip 59327–0268, Mailing Address: P.O. Box 268, Zip 59327–0268; tel. 406/346–2161, (Nonreporting) **A**9 10 18
Primary Contact: Ryan Tooke, Chief Executive Officer
CMO: William Anderson, M.D., Medical Director
CHR: Karla Allies, Director Human Resources
Web address: www.rosebudhealthcare.com/
**Control:** Other not–for–profit (including NFP Corporation) **Service:** General Medical and Surgical

**Staffed Beds:** 55

## FORT BENTON—Chouteau County

**MISSOURI RIVER MEDICAL CENTER (271304)**, 1501 St. Charles Street, Zip 59442–0249, Mailing Address: P.O. Box 249, Zip 59442–0249; tel. 406/622–3331, (Total facility includes 41 beds in nursing home–type unit) **A**9 10 18 **F**2 3 40 41 50 57 59 63 64 67 84 89 93 107 114 119 127 128 130 131 133 135 143 146 148 **P**6 **S** Benefis Health System, Great Falls, MT
Primary Contact: Louie King, President, Harry Bold Nursing Home Administrator
CMO: Jace Bird, M.D., Chief Medical Officer
CIO: Bryan Cartwright, Chief Information Technology Officer
CHR: Carolyn Johnsrud, Manager Human Resources
CNO: Janice Woodhouse, Director of Nursing
Web address: www.mrmcfb.org
**Control:** Hospital district or authority, Government, nonfederal **Service:** Long–Term Acute Care hospital

**Staffed Beds:** 52 **Admissions:** 106 **Census:** 33 **Outpatient Visits:** 5618
**Births:** 0 **Total Expense ($000):** 5853 **Payroll Expense ($000):** 3043
**Personnel:** 66

## FORT HARRISON—Lewis And Clark County

☒ **VETERANS AFFAIRS MONTANA HEALTH CARE SYSTEM**, 3687 Veterans Drive, Zip 59636–9703, Mailing Address: P.O. Box 1500, Zip 59636–1500; tel. 406/442–6410, (Total facility includes 30 beds in nursing home–type unit) **A**1 **F**3 4 5 7 8 28 29 30 31 33 35 36 38 39 40 44 45 50 51 53 54 55 56 59 63 64 65 66 70 71 74 75 77 78 79 81 82 83 84 85 87 91 92 93 94 97 98 100 101 102 103 104 105 106 107 108 111 115 116 117 118 119 127 129 130 132 135 143 144 146 147 148 **P**6 **S** Department of Veterans Affairs, Washington, DC
Primary Contact: John Ginnity, Interim Director
CFO: Brian Gustafson, Chief Financial Officer
CMO: Kurt Werner, M.D., Chief of Staff
CIO: Paul Gauthier, Chief Information Resources Management
CHR: Aggie Hamilton, Chief Human Resources
Web address: www.montana.va.gov/
**Control:** Veterans Affairs, Government, federal **Service:** General Medical and Surgical

**Staffed Beds:** 94 **Admissions:** 2043 **Census:** 37 **Outpatient Visits:** 475054
**Births:** 0 **Total Expense ($000):** 286084 **Payroll Expense ($000):** 86957
**Personnel:** 1240

## GLASGOW—Valley County

☒ **FRANCES MAHON DEACONESS HOSPITAL (271316)**, 621 Third Street South, Zip 59230–2699; tel. 406/228–3500 **A**1 9 10 18 **F**3 7 11 13 15 28 29 30 31 34 35 40 42 43 53 56 57 59 61 64 70 75 76 78 79 81 82 86 87 89 93 100 102 105 107 108 110 111 114 118 119 127 128 130 131 133 135 145 146 **P**6 7
Primary Contact: Randall G. Holom, Chief Executive Officer
COO: Ellen Guttenberg, Chief Operating Officer
CFO: Cami Kalinski, Director Financial Services
CMO: Gordon Bell, M.D., Chief of Staff
CIO: David L. Nixdorf, Director Support Services
CHR: Charam Orth, Director Human Resources
CNO: Brenda Koessl, R.N., Director of Nursing Services
Web address: www.fmdh.org
**Control:** Other not–for–profit (including NFP Corporation) **Service:** General Medical and Surgical

**Staffed Beds:** 25 **Admissions:** 565 **Census:** 5 **Outpatient Visits:** 33382
**Births:** 130 **Total Expense ($000):** 20127 **Payroll Expense ($000):** 9549
**Personnel:** 171

## GLENDIVE—Dawson County

★ **GLENDIVE MEDICAL CENTER (271332)**, 202 Prospect Drive, Zip 59330–1999; tel. 406/345–3306, (Total facility includes 71 beds in nursing home–type unit) **A**9 10 18 **F**3 10 11 15 28 29 30 31 35 38 40 41 43 50 56 57 59 61 62 63 64 67 69 70 75 76 77 78 79 81 82 87 89 93 94 98 102 103 104 107 108 111 115 119 127 128 130 131 132 133 143 144 146 147 148 **P**6 7 8
Primary Contact: Parker Powell, Chief Executive Officer
CFO: Barbara Markham, Chief Financial Officer
CMO: Joseph M. Leal, Jr., M.D., Chief of Staff
CIO: Barbara Markham, Chief Financial Officer
CHR: Joetta J. Pearcy, Director, Human Resources
Web address: www.gmc.org
**Control:** Other not–for–profit (including NFP Corporation) **Service:** General Medical and Surgical

**Staffed Beds:** 96 **Admissions:** 836 **Census:** 62 **Outpatient Visits:** 24665
**Births:** 103 **Total Expense ($000):** 28077 **Payroll Expense ($000):** 13016
**Personnel:** 245

**MT**

---

**Hospital, Medicare Provider Number, Address, Telephone, Approval, Facility, and Physician Codes, Health Care System**

★ American Hospital Association (AHA) membership
□ The Joint Commission accreditation
○ Healthcare Facilities Accreditation Program
◇ DNV Healthcare Inc. accreditation
⇑ Center for Improvement in Healthcare Quality Accreditation
△ Commission on Accreditation of Rehabilitation Facilities (CARF) accreditation

## GREAT FALLS—Cascade County

△ **BENEFIS HOSPITALS (270012)**, 1101 26th Street South, Zip 59405–5104; tel. 406/455–5000, (Includes BENEFIS HEALTH CARE–EAST CAMPUS, 1101 26th Street, Zip 59405; tel. 406/761–1200; BENEFIS HEALTH CARE–WEST CAMPUS, 500 15th Avenue South, Zip 59405, Mailing Address: P.O. Box 5013, Zip 59403–5013; tel. 406/727–3333), (Total facility includes 146 beds in nursing home–type unit) **A**2 7 9 10 20 **F**3 4 5 6 8 10 11 12 13 15 18 20 22 24 26 28 29 30 31 34 35 37 38 40 43 45 48 49 50 53 54 55 56 57 58 59 61 62 63 64 65 70 71 72 73 74 75 76 77 78 79 80 81 82 83 84 85 86 87 88 89 90 92 93 96 97 98 100 101 102 103 104 105 107 108 110 111 113 114 115 119 120 121 123 124 126 127 128 129 130 131 132 133 134 135 136 141 143 144 145 146 147 148 **P**6 8 **S** Benefis Health System, Great Falls, MT
Primary Contact: John H. Goodnow, Chief Executive Officer
CFO: Forrest Ehlinger, System Chief Financial Officer
CMO: Gregory Tierney, M.D., Office of the Chief Medical Officer, Lead
CIO: Sam Norton, System Chief Information Officer
CHR: Ann Graff, Vice President System Human Resources
Web address: www.benefis.org
**Control:** Other not–for–profit (including NFP Corporation) **Service:** General Medical and Surgical

**Staffed Beds: 441 Admissions: 13490 Census: 294 Outpatient Visits:** 438873 **Births:** 1542 **Total Expense ($000):** 354921 **Payroll Expense ($000):** 152248 **Personnel:** 2352

**GREAT FALLS CLINIC MEDICAL CENTER (270086)**, 1411 9th Street South, Zip 59405–4507; tel. 406/216–8000, (Nonreporting) **A**9 10
Primary Contact: David B. Rowe, Chief Executive Officer
COO: Vicki Newmiller, Chief Operating Officer
CFO: Cheryl Cornwell, Chief Financial Officer
CMO: Nicholas Bonfilio, M.D., Chief of Staff
Web address: www.greatfallsclinicmedicalcenter.com
**Control:** Corporation, Investor–owned, for–profit **Service:** Surgical

**Staffed Beds: 20**

## HAMILTON—Ravalli County

★ **MARCUS DALY MEMORIAL HOSPITAL (271340)**, 1200 Westwood Drive, Zip 59840–2345; tel. 406/363–2211 **A**9 10 18 **F**3 7 8 11 13 15 17 28 29 30 34 35 40 45 50 57 59 62 63 64 65 70 74 75 76 77 79 81 83 84 89 93 97 102 105 107 110 111 115 119 127 128 129 130 131 132 133 144 145 146 148
Primary Contact: John M. Bartos, Chief Executive Officer
CFO: Donja Erdman, Chief Financial Officer
CMO: John Moreland, M.D., Chief Medical Officer
CIO: Cheryl Dohlzel, Director Information Technology
CHR: Debbie M. Morris, Director Human Resources
CNO: Susan Hill, R.N., Director of Nursing
Web address: www.mdmh.org
**Control:** Other not–for–profit (including NFP Corporation) **Service:** General Medical and Surgical

**Staffed Beds: 31 Admissions: 1961 Census: 14 Outpatient Visits:** 38860 **Births:** 149 **Total Expense ($000):** 50713 **Payroll Expense ($000):** 27419 **Personnel:** 446

## HARDIN—Big Horn County

★ **BIG HORN COUNTY MEMORIAL HOSPITAL (271338)**, 17 North Miles Avenue, Zip 59034–2323; tel. 406/665–2310, (Total facility includes 36 beds in nursing home–type unit) **A**9 10 18 **F**10 11 13 15 40 43 50 57 59 64 65 68 75 76 77 81 85 86 87 93 107 110 111 114 119 125 128 130 132 133 143 146
Primary Contact: Kristi Gatrell, Chief Executive Officer
CFO: Roxie Cain, Chief Financial Officer
Web address: www.bighornhospital.org
**Control:** Other not–for–profit (including NFP Corporation) **Service:** General Medical and Surgical

**Staffed Beds: 61 Admissions: 358 Census: 41 Outpatient Visits:** 7884 **Births:** 35 **Total Expense ($000):** 13482 **Payroll Expense ($000):** 7375 **Personnel:** 163

## HARLEM—Blaine County

**FORT BELKNAP U. S. PUBLIC HEALTH SERVICE INDIAN HOSPITAL (271315)**, 669 Agency Main Street, Zip 59526–9455; tel. 406/353–3100, (Nonreporting) **A**10 18 **S** U. S. Indian Health Service, Rockville, MD
Primary Contact: Steve Fox, Chief Executive Officer
CMO: Ethel L. Moore, M.D., Director of Medical Affairs
CIO: Mikki Grant, Chief Information Officer
CHR: Charlotte Lamebull, Administrative Officer
CNO: Diana Hunter, Director of Nursing
Web address: www.ihs.gov
**Control:** PHS, Indian Service, Government, federal **Service:** General Medical and Surgical

**Staffed Beds: 6**

## HARLOWTON—Wheatland County

★ **WHEATLAND MEMORIAL HEALTHCARE (271321)**, 530 Third Street North West, Zip 59036, Mailing Address: P.O. Box 287, Zip 59036–0287; tel. 406/632–4351, (Nonreporting) **A**9 10 18
Primary Contact: Mike Zwicker, Chief Executive Officer
CFO: Doug Lewis, Chief Financial Officer
CMO: Kathy Jutila, M.D., Chief of Staff
CIO: Ray Hetherington, Network Administrator
CHR: Peggy Hiner, Director Human Resources
CNO: Lauri Ann Cooney, Director Nursing
Web address: www.wheatlandmemorial.org
**Control:** Other not–for–profit (including NFP Corporation) **Service:** General Medical and Surgical

**Staffed Beds: 25**

## HAVRE—Hill County

★ **NORTHERN MONTANA HOSPITAL (270032)**, 30 13th Street, Zip 59501–5222, Mailing Address: P.O. Box 1231, Zip 59501–1231; tel. 406/265–2211, (Total facility includes 115 beds in nursing home–type unit) **A**9 10 20 **F**10 11 13 15 28 29 34 35 36 38 40 50 53 56 57 59 60 63 64 68 70 75 76 77 79 81 82 84 85 89 93 97 99 101 102 103 104 105 107 108 110 111 115 118 119 127 128 129 130 132 133 135 146 148 **P**6
Primary Contact: David Henry, President and Chief Executive Officer
COO: Julia Mariani, Vice President Business Operations
CFO: Kim Lucke, Vice President Finance
CHR: Bonnie O'Neill, Vice President Employee Services
CNO: Maggie C. Conklin, Interim Vice President, Patient Care Services
Web address: www.nmhcare.org
**Control:** Other not–for–profit (including NFP Corporation) **Service:** General Medical and Surgical

**Staffed Beds: 142 Admissions: 1624 Census: 117 Outpatient Visits:** 89580 **Births:** 388 **Total Expense ($000):** 52722 **Payroll Expense ($000):** 28303 **Personnel:** 499

## HELENA—Lewis And Clark County

⊞ **SHODAIR CHILDREN'S HOSPITAL (274004)**, 2755 Colonial Drive, Zip 59601–4926, Mailing Address: P.O. Box 5539, Zip 59604–5539; tel. 406/444–7500 **A**1 9 10 **F**55 98 99 101 104 106 130 **P**6
Primary Contact: John P. Casey, Administrator
COO: John P. Casey, Administrator
CFO: Ron Wiens, Chief Financial Officer
CMO: Abe Elias, M.D., President Medical Staff
CIO: Judy Jackson, Director Health Information Management and Privacy Officer
Web address: www.shodair.org
**Control:** Other not–for–profit (including NFP Corporation) **Service:** Children's hospital psychiatric

**Staffed Beds: 84 Admissions: 1021 Census: 71 Outpatient Visits:** 3003 **Births:** 0 **Total Expense ($000):** 22629 **Payroll Expense ($000):** 13261 **Personnel:** 235

⊞ **ST. PETER'S HOSPITAL (270003)**, 2475 Broadway, Zip 59601–4928; tel. 406/442–2480 **A**1 2 9 10 20 **F**3 7 11 13 15 18 20 22 28 29 30 31 34 35 40 45 46 49 50 51 54 56 57 59 60 62 63 64 65 70 74 75 76 78 79 81 82 84 85 87 89 92 93 98 100 102 103 107 108 110 111 114 115 116 117 119 120 121 122 129 130 132 133 135 144 146 147 148 **P**6
Primary Contact: Nate Olson, Chief Executive Officer
CFO: John Green, Vice President Finance
CIO: Tammy K. Buyok, Vice President Support Services
CHR: Thomas Gregg, Vice President Human Resources
Web address: www.stpetes.org
**Control:** Other not–for–profit (including NFP Corporation) **Service:** General Medical and Surgical

**Staffed Beds: 123 Admissions: 5686 Census: 74 Outpatient Visits:** 169996 **Births:** 784 **Total Expense ($000):** 168461 **Payroll Expense ($000):** 69233 **Personnel:** 1000

## JORDAN—Garfield County

**GARFIELD COUNTY HEALTH CENTER (271310)**, 332 Leavitt Avenue, Zip 59337, Mailing Address: P.O. Box 389, Zip 59337–0389; tel. 406/557–2500, (Nonreporting) **A**9 10 18
Primary Contact: Hanz Arnston, R.N., Chief Executive Officer
CFO: Charlotte Herbold, Manager Business Officer
CMO: David M. Kidder, D.O., Chief Medical Officer
CIO: Charlotte Herbold, Manager Business Officer
CHR: Hanz Arnston, R.N., Chief Executive Officer
CNO: Sarah Nordlund, Director of Nursing
**Control:** County–Government, nonfederal **Service:** General Medical and Surgical

**Staffed Beds: 24**

## KALISPELL—Flathead County

**HEALTHCENTER NORTHWEST** See The HealthCenter

**MT**

★ △ **KALISPELL REGIONAL MEDICAL CENTER (270051)**, 310 Sunnyview Lane, Zip 59901–3129; tel. 406/752–5111, (Includes PATHWAYS TREATMENT CENTER, 200 Heritage Way, Zip 59901; tel. 406/756–3950) **A**2 3 5 7 9 10 **F**3 4 5 8 13 15 18 20 22 24 26 28 29 30 31 35 36 40 43 45 46 49 50 56 57 58 59 62 63 64 68 70 72 74 75 76 77 78 79 81 84 85 86 87 90 98 99 100 101 102 103 104 105 107 108 114 115 118 119 120 121 123 126 129 130 131 132 143 144 145 146 147 148 **P**6
Primary Contact: Velinda Stevens, President
COO: Ted W. Hirsch, Senior Executive Director
CFO: Charles T. Pearce, Chief Financial and Information Officer
CHR: Deb Wilson, Director Human Resources
Web address: www.krmc.org
**Control:** Other not–for–profit (including NFP Corporation) **Service:** General Medical and Surgical

**Staffed Beds:** 163 **Admissions:** 7403 **Census:** 96 **Outpatient Visits:** 183972 **Births:** 688 **Total Expense ($000):** 243084 **Payroll Expense ($000):** 112741 **Personnel:** 2390

★ **THE HEALTHCENTER (270087)**, 320 Sunnyview Lane, Zip 59901–3129; tel. 406/751–7550 **A**9 10 **F**3 8 15 31 36 39 64 68 74 78 79 81 82 85 87 100 107 110 111 114 115 117 119 126 147 **P**2
Primary Contact: Tate J. Kreitinger, Chief Executive Officer
CFO: Charles T. Pearce, Chief Financial and Information Officer
CIO: Charles T. Pearce, Chief Financial and Information Officer
CHR: Susan Stevens, Director Human Resources
CNO: Victoria Johnson, R.N., Nursing Director of Surgical and Medical Services
Web address: www.krmc.org
**Control:** Corporation, Investor–owned, for–profit **Service:** General Medical and Surgical

**Staffed Beds:** 30 **Admissions:** 580 **Census:** 4 **Outpatient Visits:** 39209 **Births:** 0 **Total Expense ($000):** 34189 **Payroll Expense ($000):** 7372 **Personnel:** 144

### LEWISTOWN—Fergus County

★ **CENTRAL MONTANA MEDICAL CENTER (271345)**, 408 Wendell Avenue, Zip 59457–2261; tel. 406/535–7711, (Total facility includes 65 beds in nursing home–type unit) **A**9 10 18 **F**3 7 11 13 15 28 29 31 34 35 40 43 45 50 53 57 59 62 63 64 65 75 76 77 81 84 85 86 87 89 91 92 93 94 97 107 108 110 111 115 119 128 129 130 131 132 133 146 148 **P**6 **S** QHR, Brentwood, TN
Primary Contact: Christopher Noland, Interim Chief Executive Officer
CFO: Alan Aldrich, Chief Financial Officer
CHR: Torie A. Lynch, Manager Human Resources
CNO: Delilah Duffy, Interim Chief Nurse Officer
Web address: www.cmmccares.com
**Control:** Other not–for–profit (including NFP Corporation) **Service:** General Medical and Surgical

**Staffed Beds:** 90 **Admissions:** 764 **Census:** 52 **Outpatient Visits:** 51802 **Births:** 85 **Total Expense ($000):** 27993 **Payroll Expense ($000):** 15150 **Personnel:** 308

### LIBBY—Lincoln County

★ **CABINET PEAKS MEDICAL CENTER (271320)**, 209 Health Park Drive, Zip 59923–2130; tel. 406/283–7000 **A**5 9 10 18 **F**3 11 13 15 17 28 29 30 31 34 35 40 45 56 57 59 64 68 70 75 76 77 79 81 82 84 85 86 87 89 91 93 97 102 107 110 111 114 119 128 129 130 131 132 133 135 144 146 147 148 **P**6
Primary Contact: Bruce Whitfield, CPA, Chief Executive Officer and Chief Financial Officer
CFO: Bruce Whitfield, CPA, Chief Executive Officer and Chief Financial Officer
CMO: Jay Maloney, M.D., Chief of Staff
Web address: www.sjlh.com
**Control:** Other not–for–profit (including NFP Corporation) **Service:** General Medical and Surgical

**Staffed Beds:** 25 **Admissions:** 681 **Census:** 7 **Outpatient Visits:** 36254 **Births:** 116 **Total Expense ($000):** 27858 **Payroll Expense ($000):** 13371 **Personnel:** 201

### LIVINGSTON—Park County

★ **LIVINGSTON HEALTHCARE (271317)**, 504 South 13th Street, Zip 59047–3727; tel. 406/222–3541 **A**5 9 10 18 **F**13 15 17 28 29 34 35 36 40 43 45 50 57 59 62 63 64 65 66 67 68 70 75 76 77 78 79 81 82 85 86 87 89 93 102 107 108 110 111 114 119 124 128 129 130 131 133 135 **P**3
Primary Contact: Bren Lowe, Chief Executive Officer
CFO: Ryan Speas, Director Finance
CMO: D. Scott Coleman, Medical Director
CIO: Jody Duran, Manager Information Systems
CHR: Vicki Axtell, Director Human Resources
CNO: Lori Koby, R.N., Director of Nursing
Web address: www.livingstonhealthcare.org
**Control:** Other not–for–profit (including NFP Corporation) **Service:** General Medical and Surgical

**Staffed Beds:** 25 **Admissions:** 987 **Census:** 10 **Outpatient Visits:** 32450 **Births:** 98 **Total Expense ($000):** 28982 **Payroll Expense ($000):** 15090 **Personnel:** 277

### MALTA—Phillips County

★ **PHILLIPS COUNTY HOSPITAL (271312)**, 417 South Fourth East, Zip 59538–8825, Mailing Address: P.O. Box 640, Zip 59538–0640; tel. 406/654–1100 **A**9 10 18 **F**3 29 31 34 40 41 43 50 56 57 59 62 66 84 90 93 107 114 127 129 132 133 **P**4
Primary Contact: Ward C. VanWichen, Chief Executive Officer
CFO: Stephanie Denham, Chief Financial Officer and Human Resources Officer
CMO: Ed Medina, M.D., Medical Director
CHR: Stephanie Denham, Chief Financial Officer and Human Resources Officer
CNO: Lonna Crowder, Director of Nursing
Web address: www.pchospital.us/
**Control:** Other not–for–profit (including NFP Corporation) **Service:** General Medical and Surgical

**Staffed Beds:** 6 **Admissions:** 183 **Census:** 2 **Outpatient Visits:** 6011 **Births:** 0 **Total Expense ($000):** 5355 **Payroll Expense ($000):** 2774 **Personnel:** 67

### MILES CITY—Custer County

⊞ **HOLY ROSARY HEALTHCARE (271347)**, 2600 Wilson Street, Zip 59301–5094; tel. 406/233–2600, (Total facility includes 65 beds in nursing home–type unit) **A**1 9 10 18 **F**3 13 15 28 29 30 31 32 34 35 40 48 56 57 59 63 64 65 68 70 75 76 77 78 79 81 84 85 89 93 94 97 99 100 101 103 104 107 108 110 111 115 119 124 127 129 130 131 133 143 144 146 147 148 **P**6 **S** SCL Health, Broomfield, CO
Primary Contact: Paul Lewis, Chief Executive Officer
CFO: Travis Scheving, Chief Financial Officer
CMO: Michael Bush, M.D., Chief Medical Officer
CHR: Cathy Rodenbaugh, Director Human Resources
CNO: Lisa Sanford, VP Patient Care/CNO
Web address: www.holyrosaryhealthcare.org
**Control:** Church–operated, Nongovernment, not–for profit **Service:** General Medical and Surgical

**Staffed Beds:** 90 **Admissions:** 1294 **Census:** 62 **Outpatient Visits:** 29798 **Births:** 287 **Total Expense ($000):** 31968 **Payroll Expense ($000):** 12737 **Personnel:** 191

### MISSOULA—Missoula County

⊞ △ **COMMUNITY MEDICAL CENTER (270023)**, 2827 Fort Missoula Road, Zip 59804–7408; tel. 406/728–4100 **A**1 3 5 7 9 10 19 **F**2 3 11 13 17 18 20 22 26 28 29 30 31 34 35 37 40 43 45 46 47 48 49 51 54 57 59 64 65 68 70 72 73 74 75 76 78 79 81 82 83 84 85 87 88 89 90 91 92 93 94 96 97 107 108 110 115 116 117 118 119 120 121 126 130 132 134 135 143 144 145 146 147 148 **P**6 7
Primary Contact: Dean French, M.D., Interim Chief Executive Officer
COO: Devin Huntley, Vice President Operations
CFO: David Richhart, Vice President Fiscal Services
CMO: David Lechner, M.D., Chief Medical Officer and Vice President Innovation
CIO: Stan Moser, Vice President Information Systems
CNO: Jan Perry, R.N., Vice President Patient Care Services
Web address: www.communitymed.org
**Control:** Other not–for–profit (including NFP Corporation) **Service:** General Medical and Surgical

**Staffed Beds:** 135 **Admissions:** 4628 **Census:** 59 **Outpatient Visits:** 139766 **Births:** 1497 **Total Expense ($000):** 158368 **Payroll Expense ($000):** 64063 **Personnel:** 956

**MT**

---

**Hospital, Medicare Provider Number, Address, Telephone, Approval, Facility, and Physician Codes, Health Care System**

★ American Hospital Association (AHA) membership   ○ Healthcare Facilities Accreditation Program   ⇑ Center for Improvement in Healthcare Quality Accreditation
☐ The Joint Commission accreditation   ◇ DNV Healthcare Inc. accreditation   △ Commission on Accreditation of Rehabilitation Facilities (CARF) accreditation

✠ △ **ST. PATRICK HOSPITAL (270014)**, 500 West Broadway,
Zip 59802–4096, Mailing Address: P.O. Box 4587, Zip 59806–4587;
tel. 406/543–7271 **A**1 2 3 5 7 9 10 19 **F**3 5 8 11 12 15 18 20 22 24 26 28
29 30 31 34 35 38 40 43 45 49 50 53 57 58 59 61 64 65 68 70 74 75 77
78 79 81 82 84 85 86 88 89 90 92 93 96 97 98 99 100 101 102 103 104
105 107 108 110 111 113 114 115 116 117 118 119 120 121 123 124 126
127 129 130 131 132 135 141 146 147 148 **P**4 6 7 **S** Providence Health &
Services, Renton, WA
Primary Contact: Jeff Fee, Chief Executive Officer
CFO: Kirk Bodlovic, Regional Chief Financial Officer
CHR: Karyn Trainor, Director Human Resources
CNO: Joyce Dombrouski, R.N., Regional Chief Nursing Officer
Web address: www.saintpatrick.org
**Control:** Church–operated, Nongovernment, not–for profit **Service:** General
Medical and Surgical

**Staffed Beds:** 193 **Admissions:** 8870 **Census:** 118 **Outpatient Visits:**
265222 **Births:** 0 **Total Expense ($000):** 189535 **Payroll Expense ($000):**
61375 **Personnel:** 1335

### PHILIPSBURG—Granite County

**GRANITE COUNTY MEDICAL CENTER (271303)**, 310 Sansome Street,
Zip 59858–0729, Mailing Address: P.O. Box 729, Zip 59858–0729;
tel. 406/859–3271, (Nonreporting) **A**9 10 18
Primary Contact: Pamela Olsen, Interim Chief Executive Officer
CFO: Susan Ossello, Chief Financial Officer
CMO: John Moore, M.D., Medical Director
Web address: www.gcmedcenter.org/
**Control:** County–Government, nonfederal **Service:** General Medical and Surgical

**Staffed Beds:** 9

### PLAINS—Sanders County

★ **CLARK FORK VALLEY HOSPITAL (271323)**, 10 Kruger Road, Zip 59859,
Mailing Address: P.O. Box 768, Zip 59859–0768; tel. 406/826–4800, (Total
facility includes 28 beds in nursing home–type unit) **A**9 10 18 **F**3 11 13 15 28
29 30 32 34 35 36 40 43 44 45 50 57 58 59 62 63 64 65 68 70 74 75 76
77 81 82 83 84 85 89 93 97 107 110 114 118 119 127 128 130 132 133
135 143 146 147 148 **P**3 6
Primary Contact: Gregory S. Hanson, M.D., Chief Executive Officer
CFO: Carla Neiman, Chief Financial Officer
CMO: Ronald Black, M.D., Chief of Staff
CIO: Carla Neiman, Chief Financial Officer
CHR: Barry Fowler, Director Human and System Resources
Web address: www.cfvh.org
**Control:** Other not–for–profit (including NFP Corporation) **Service:** General
Medical and Surgical

**Staffed Beds:** 44 **Admissions:** 340 **Census:** 24 **Outpatient Visits:** 25274
**Births:** 42 **Total Expense ($000):** 16367 **Payroll Expense ($000):** 7512
**Personnel:** 120

### PLENTYWOOD—Sheridan County

**SHERIDAN MEMORIAL HOSPITAL (271322)**, 440 West Laurel Avenue,
Zip 59254–1596; tel. 406/765–3700, (Total facility includes 78 beds in nursing
home–type unit) **A**9 10 18 **F**3 7 11 13 15 17 35 40 50 57 59 63 67 75 76 77
81 87 89 93 107 110 114 119 127 128 130 132 133 145 146
Primary Contact: Gregory L. Maurer, Chief Executive Officer
CIO: Troy McClymont, Chief Information Technology Officer
Web address: www.sheridanmemorial.net/
**Control:** Other not–for–profit (including NFP Corporation) **Service:** General
Medical and Surgical

**Staffed Beds:** 97 **Admissions:** 303 **Census:** 55 **Outpatient Visits:** 10886
**Births:** 0 **Total Expense ($000):** 12197 **Payroll Expense ($000):** 5840
**Personnel:** 126

### POLSON—Lake County

✠ **PROVIDENCE ST. JOSEPH MEDICAL CENTER (271343)**, 6 Thirteenth Avenue
East, Zip 59860–5315, Mailing Address: P.O. Box 1010, Zip 59860–1010;
tel. 406/883–5377 **A**1 9 10 18 **F**3 10 13 15 28 29 30 34 35 40 43 46 50 57
59 64 68 75 77 79 81 82 84 85 87 93 97 100 102 107 110 111 114 119
125 127 129 130 131 133 146 147 148 **P**6 **S** Providence Health & Services,
Renton, WA
Primary Contact: James R. Kiser, II, Chief Executive Officer
COO: Colleen Nielsen, Director Operations
CFO: Kirk Bodlovic, Vice President and Chief Financial Officer
CMO: Kelly Bagnell, M.D., Chief of Staff
Web address: www.saintjoes.org
**Control:** Church–operated, Nongovernment, not–for profit **Service:** General
Medical and Surgical

**Staffed Beds:** 22 **Admissions:** 673 **Census:** 6 **Outpatient Visits:** 73486
**Births:** 140 **Total Expense ($000):** 22765 **Payroll Expense ($000):** 12644
**Personnel:** 196

### POPLAR—Roosevelt County

★ **POPLAR COMMUNITY HOSPITAL (271300)**, H and Court Avenue, Zip 59255,
Mailing Address: P.O. Box 38, Zip 59255–0038; tel. 406/768–3452 **A**9 10 18
**F**3 7 40 43 50 57 59 73 78 87 99 100 101 102 103 104 107 110 119 130
133 143 147 **P**3 6
Primary Contact: Margaret B. Norgaard, Chief Executive Officer
CHR: Annie Block, Director Human Resources
Web address: www.nemhs.net
**Control:** Other not–for–profit (including NFP Corporation) **Service:** General
Medical and Surgical

**Staffed Beds:** 20 **Admissions:** 72 **Census:** 8 **Outpatient Visits:** 7677 **Births:**
0 **Total Expense ($000):** 9257 **Payroll Expense ($000):** 4556 **Personnel:**
71

### RED LODGE—Carbon County

★ **BEARTOOTH BILLINGS CLINIC (271326)**, 2525 North Broadway Avenue,
Zip 59068–9222, Mailing Address: P.O. Box 590, Zip 59068–0590;
tel. 406/446–2345 **A**9 10 18 **F**3 11 15 18 28 29 34 35 40 43 44 45 50 56
57 59 62 63 64 65 68 75 77 81 84 85 86 87 91 93 94 96 97 107 110 114
119 130 131 133 135 146 147 148 **P**6
Primary Contact: Deborah Agnew, M.D., Chief Executive Officer
CFO: Kyle Gee, Chief Financial Officer
CMO: William George, M.D., Chief of Staff
CHR: Katie Nordstrom, Director Human Resources
CNO: Bridgett Chartier, Director of Nursing
Web address: www.beartoothbillingsclinic.org
**Control:** Other not–for–profit (including NFP Corporation) **Service:** General
Medical and Surgical

**Staffed Beds:** 10 **Admissions:** 216 **Census:** 2 **Outpatient Visits:** 54015
**Births:** 0 **Total Expense ($000):** 12673 **Payroll Expense ($000):** 4029
**Personnel:** 100

### RONAN—Lake County

★ **ST. LUKE COMMUNITY HEALTHCARE (271325)**, 107 Sixth Avenue S.W.,
Zip 59864–2634; tel. 406/676–4441, (Total facility includes 75 beds in nursing
home–type unit) **A**9 10 18 **F**2 13 15 28 29 34 40 43 45 53 54 56 57 59 61 64
65 68 75 76 79 81 85 93 97 107 108 110 111 115 119 127 128 129 130
131 132 133 135 144 145 147 **P**5 6
Primary Contact: Steve J. Todd, Chief Executive Officer
CFO: Paul Soukup, Chief Financial Officer
CMO: Hikmat A. Maaliki, M.D., Chief of Staff
CHR: Theresa Jones, Manager Human Resources
CNO: Leah Emerson, Director of Nursing
Web address: www.stlukehealthcare.org
**Control:** Other not–for–profit (including NFP Corporation) **Service:** General
Medical and Surgical

**Staffed Beds:** 100 **Admissions:** 1011 **Census:** 59 **Outpatient Visits:** 70573
**Births:** 163 **Total Expense ($000):** 36684 **Payroll Expense ($000):** 17536
**Personnel:** 308

### ROUNDUP—Musselshell County

★ **ROUNDUP MEMORIAL HEALTHCARE (271346)**, 1202 Third Street West,
Zip 59072–1816, Mailing Address: P.O. Box 40, Zip 59072–0040;
tel. 406/323–2301, (Nonreporting) **A**9 10 18
Primary Contact: Bradley Howell, Chief Executive Officer
CFO: Kyle Gee, Regional Vice President Financial Operations
CMO: Mark Ward, M.D., Chief of Staff
CHR: Michelle Clement, Executive Assistant/Human Resources Director
CNO: Emily Shoup, Director Nursing Services
Web address: www.rmhmt.org/
**Control:** Other not–for–profit (including NFP Corporation) **Service:** General
Medical and Surgical

**Staffed Beds:** 25

### SAINT MARY—Glacier County

**U. S. PUBLIC HEALTH SERVICE BLACKFEET COMMUNITY HOSPITAL
(270074)**, 760 New Hospital Circle, Zip 59417–0760, Mailing Address: P.O. Box
760, Browning, Zip 59417–0760; tel. 406/338–6100, (Nonreporting) **A**5 10 **S** U.
S. Indian Health Service, Rockville, MD
Primary Contact: Merlin Gilham, Chief Executive Officer
Web address: www.ihs.gov
**Control:** PHS, Indian Service, Government, federal **Service:** General Medical and
Surgical

**Staffed Beds:** 25

**MT**

*Many Facility Codes have changed. Please refer to the AHA Guide Code Chart.* © 2015 AHA Guide

## SCOBEY—Daniels County

**DANIELS MEMORIAL HEALTHCARE CENTER (271342)**, 105 Fifth Avenue East, Zip 59263, Mailing Address: P.O. Box 400, Zip 59263–0400; tel. 406/487–2296, (Total facility includes 30 beds in nursing home–type unit) **A**9 10 18 **F**2 11 29 31 34 35 40 43 50 56 57 59 64 65 67 69 75 77 85 86 87 91 93 97 102 103 107 114 127 130 131 132 133 143 146 148 **P**6
Primary Contact: David Hubbard, Chief Executive Officer
CMO: Don Sawdey, M.D., Medical Director
CHR: Edith Huda, Director Human Resources
CNO: Kathy Ware, Director of Nursing
Web address: www.danielsmemorialhealthcare.org
**Control:** Hospital district or authority, Government, nonfederal **Service:** General Medical and Surgical

**Staffed Beds:** 54 **Admissions:** 76 **Census:** 35 **Outpatient Visits:** 7146 **Births:** 0 **Total Expense ($000):** 7169 **Payroll Expense ($000):** 3636 **Personnel:** 94

## SHELBY—Toole County

★ **MARIAS MEDICAL CENTER (271328)**, 640 Park Drive, Zip 59474–1663, Mailing Address: P.O. Box 915, Zip 59474–0915; tel. 406/434–3200, (Total facility includes 63 beds in nursing home–type unit) **A**9 10 18 **F**3 7 10 11 13 15 17 34 40 43 45 56 57 59 63 64 70 75 76 77 78 79 81 82 85 89 91 93 102 107 110 111 115 119 125 128 129 130 133
Primary Contact: William Hartley, FACHE, Interim Chief Executive Officer
CFO: Melissa Ostberg, Chief Financial Officer
CMO: Melanie Hardy, D.O., Chief of Staff
CIO: Jayce Yarn, Director Information Technology
CHR: Cindy Lamb, Director Human Resources
CNO: Tamra Fender, Chief Nursing Officer
Web address: www.mmcmt.org
**Control:** County–Government, nonfederal **Service:** General Medical and Surgical

**Staffed Beds:** 88 **Admissions:** 129 **Census:** 16 **Outpatient Visits:** 11503 **Births:** 28 **Total Expense ($000):** 14624 **Payroll Expense ($000):** 6104 **Personnel:** 119

## SHERIDAN—Madison County

★ **RUBY VALLEY HOSPITAL (271319)**, 220 East Crofoot Street, Zip 59749–7714, Mailing Address: P.O. Box 336, Zip 59749–0336; tel. 406/842–5453 **A**9 10 18 **F**2 11 28 29 34 35 38 40 56 57 59 64 65 66 75 82 86 90 91 93 97 107 114 119 127 128 130 133 135 147 148 **P**6
Primary Contact: John H. Semington, Chief Executive Officer
CFO: Dennis Holschbach, Chief Financial Officer and Director Human Resources
CMO: Roman Hendrickson, M.D., Medical Director
CHR: Dennis Holschbach, Chief Financial Officer and Director Human Resources
CNO: Ted Woirhaye, R.N., Director of Nursing
Web address: www.rubyvalleyhospital.com/
**Control:** Hospital district or authority, Government, nonfederal **Service:** General Medical and Surgical

**Staffed Beds:** 8 **Admissions:** 116 **Census:** 2 **Outpatient Visits:** 4500 **Births:** 0 **Total Expense ($000):** 4990 **Payroll Expense ($000):** 3086 **Personnel:** 43

## SIDNEY—Richland County

★ **SIDNEY HEALTH CENTER (271344)**, 216 14th Avenue S.W., Zip 59270–3586; tel. 406/488–2100, (Total facility includes 56 beds in nursing home–type unit) **A**9 10 18 **F**2 3 13 15 17 28 30 31 34 35 40 41 45 50 56 57 59 62 63 64 68 70 75 76 78 79 81 82 84 85 86 87 89 93 96 107 108 110 111 115 119 120 121 122 123 128 129 130 133 135 144 145 146 147 148 **P**6
Primary Contact: Richard Haraldson, Chief Executive Officer
CFO: Tina Montgomery, Chief Financial Officer
CMO: Rajohn Karanjai, M.D., Chief Medical Officer
CIO: Brian Fay, Director Information Systems
CHR: Lisa Aisenbrey, Administrator Human Resources and Support Services
Web address: www.sidneyhealth.org
**Control:** Other not–for–profit (including NFP Corporation) **Service:** General Medical and Surgical

**Staffed Beds:** 81 **Admissions:** 1069 **Census:** 60 **Outpatient Visits:** 33030 **Births:** 154 **Total Expense ($000):** 52026 **Payroll Expense ($000):** 20309 **Personnel:** 333

## SUPERIOR—Mineral County

★ **MINERAL COMMUNITY HOSPITAL (271331)**, 1208 6th Avenue East, Zip 59872–9618, Mailing Address: P.O. Box 66, Zip 59872–0066; tel. 406/822–4841 **A**9 10 18 **F**10 29 31 40 45 57 69 75 77 81 93 107 110 114 119 133 143
Primary Contact: Ronald M. Gleason, Chief Executive Officer
CFO: Cliff Case, Chief Financial Officer
CMO: Roger Pafford, M.D., Medical Director
CHR: Stacy Conrow–Ververis, Director Human Resources
CNO: Jenifer Mitchell, R.N., Director of Nursing Services
Web address: www.mineralcommunityhospital.com/
**Control:** Other not–for–profit (including NFP Corporation) **Service:** General Medical and Surgical

**Staffed Beds:** 25 **Admissions:** 164 **Census:** 16 **Outpatient Visits:** 5669 **Births:** 0 **Total Expense ($000):** 6372 **Payroll Expense ($000):** 3138 **Personnel:** 68

## TERRY—Prairie County

**PRAIRIE COMMUNITY HEALTH CENTER** See Prairie Community Hospital

★ **PRAIRIE COMMUNITY HOSPITAL (271309)**, 312 South Adams Avenue, Zip 59349–0156, Mailing Address: P.O. Box 156, Zip 59349–0156; tel. 406/635–5511 **A**9 10 18 **F**1 2 3 32 34 40 41 43 57 59 64 65 67 69 75 87 90 127 128 133 135 146 147 148 **P**6
Primary Contact: Candyce Payne, Chief Executive Officer
CFO: Laurie Chandler, Financial Officer
CIO: Laurie Chandler, Chairman
CNO: Susan Morgan, Director of Nursing Services
Web address: www.prairiecommunityhospital.org/
**Control:** Hospital district or authority, Government, nonfederal **Service:** General Medical and Surgical

**Staffed Beds:** 22 **Admissions:** 59 **Census:** 17 **Outpatient Visits:** 2648 **Births:** 0 **Total Expense ($000):** 2274 **Payroll Expense ($000):** 965 **Personnel:** 32

## TOWNSEND—Broadwater County

**BROADWATER HEALTH CENTER (271333)**, 110 North Oak Street, Zip 59644–2306; tel. 406/266–3186 **A**9 10 18 **F**3 7 9 15 29 32 34 40 41 43 50 53 54 55 57 59 64 66 67 71 75 77 79 87 91 93 97 107 111 130 131 133 135 143 144 146 147 148 **P**6
Primary Contact: Kyle Hopstad, Chief Executive Officer
CFO: Jennifer Clowes, Chief Financial Officer
CMO: Kathleen Trapp, M.D., Medical Director
CHR: April Campbell, Director Human Resources
CNO: Fran Wright, Director of Nursing
Web address: www.broadwaterhealthcenter.com
**Control:** Other not–for–profit (including NFP Corporation) **Service:** Long–Term Acute Care hospital

**Staffed Beds:** 25 **Admissions:** 85 **Census:** 1 **Outpatient Visits:** 1570 **Births:** 0 **Total Expense ($000):** 5453 **Payroll Expense ($000):** 2746 **Personnel:** 129

## WARM SPRINGS—Deer Lodge County

**MONTANA STATE HOSPITAL (274086)**, 300 Garnet Way, Zip 59756–0300, Mailing Address: P.O. Box 300, Zip 59756–0300; tel. 406/693–7000 **A**10 **F**29 38 39 50 59 66 68 74 75 77 89 97 98 100 103 106 119 130 132 135 **P**6
Primary Contact: John W. Glueckert, Administrator
CFO: Tracey Thun, Director Business and Support Services
CMO: Thomas Gray, M.D., Medical Director
CIO: Melinda Bridgewater, Director, Information Services
CHR: Todd Thun, Director Human Resources
CNO: Dave Olson, Director of Nursing
Web address: www.msh.mt.gov
**Control:** State–Government, nonfederal **Service:** Psychiatric

**Staffed Beds:** 208 **Admissions:** 625 **Census:** 187 **Outpatient Visits:** 0 **Births:** 0 **Total Expense ($000):** 34327 **Payroll Expense ($000):** 18537 **Personnel:** 428

## WHITE SULPHUR SPRINGS—Meagher County

**MOUNTAINVIEW MEDICAL CENTER (271306)**, 16 West Main Street, Zip 59645–9036, Mailing Address: P.O. Box Q, Zip 59645–0817; tel. 406/547–3321 **A**9 10 18 **F**1 3 11 34 35 40 56 57 59 64 65 67 82 90 93 97 107 114 119 127 128 133 **P**3
Primary Contact: Rob Brandt, Chief Executive Officer
Web address: www.mvmc.org
**Control:** Other not–for–profit (including NFP Corporation) **Service:** General Medical and Surgical

**Staffed Beds:** 21 **Admissions:** 60 **Census:** 1 **Outpatient Visits:** 3800 **Births:** 0

MT

---

**Hospital, Medicare Provider Number, Address, Telephone, Approval, Facility, and Physician Codes, Health Care System**

★ American Hospital Association (AHA) membership
□ The Joint Commission accreditation
○ Healthcare Facilities Accreditation Program
◇ DNV Healthcare Inc. accreditation
⇑ Center for Improvement in Healthcare Quality Accreditation
△ Commission on Accreditation of Rehabilitation Facilities (CARF) accreditation

## WHITEFISH—Flathead County

★ **NORTH VALLEY HOSPITAL (271336)**, 1600 Hospital Way, Zip 59937–7849;
tel. 406/863–3500 **A**9 10 18 **F**3 11 13 15 29 30 31 34 35 37 40 43 45 50
51 54 56 57 59 64 68 70 75 79 81 85 86 87 97 100 102 103 104 107 110
111 114 119 126 127 129 130 131 132 133 135 144 146 148 **P**6 **S** QHR,
Brentwood, TN
Primary Contact: Jason A. Spring, FACHE, Chief Executive Officer
COO: Christina Bogers, Chief Clinical Officer
CFO: Arebi Garsa, Interim Chief Financial Officer
CMO: Ronald Miller, M.D., Chief Medical Officer
CIO: Michael Barnes, Chief Information Officer
CHR: Joseph Schmier, Interim Director Human Resources
Web address: www.nvhosp.org
**Control:** Other not–for–profit (including NFP Corporation) **Service:** General
Medical and Surgical

**Staffed Beds:** 25 **Admissions:** 1549 **Census:** 13 **Outpatient Visits:** 62202
**Births:** 488 **Total Expense ($000):** 47492 **Payroll Expense ($000):** 16898
**Personnel:** 282

## WOLF POINT—Roosevelt County

★ **TRINITY HOSPITAL (271341)**, 315 Knapp Street, Zip 59201–1826;
tel. 406/653–6500, (Total facility includes 60 beds in nursing home–type unit) **A**9
10 18 **F**3 6 7 8 13 15 29 31 32 34 40 43 45 50 56 57 59 64 70 75 76 78
81 92 110 119 120 125 127 128 130 133 143 145 **P**5
Primary Contact: Margaret B. Norgaard, Chief Executive Officer
Web address: www.nemhs.net
**Control:** Other not–for–profit (including NFP Corporation) **Service:** General
Medical and Surgical

**Staffed Beds:** 82 **Admissions:** 444 **Census:** 59 **Outpatient Visits:** 14177
**Births:** 170 **Total Expense ($000):** 20339 **Payroll Expense ($000):** 10011
**Personnel:** 180

*Many Facility Codes have changed. Please refer to the AHA Guide Code Chart.*

# NEBRASKA

## AINSWORTH—Brown County

**BROWN COUNTY HOSPITAL (281325)**, 945 East Zero Street,
Zip 69210–1547; tel. 402/387–2800, (Nonreporting) **A**9 10 18
Primary Contact: Shannon Sorensen, Chief Executive Officer
CFO: Lisa Wood, Chief Financial Officer
CMO: Melvin Campbell, M.D., Medical Staff Chairman
CIO: Mike Depko, Director Information Technology
CHR: Lisa Fischer, Director Human Resources
CNO: Matt Lentz, R.N., Director of Patient Services
Web address: www.browncountyhospital.org
**Control:** County–Government, nonfederal **Service:** General Medical and Surgical

**Staffed Beds:** 18

## ALBION—Boone County

★ **BOONE COUNTY HEALTH CENTER (281334)**, 723 West Fairview Street,
Zip 68620–1725, Mailing Address: P.O. Box 151, Zip 68620–0151;
tel. 402/395–2191 **A**5 9 10 18 **F**3 11 13 15 28 29 31 34 35 38 40 45 50 57
59 62 64 65 76 77 78 79 81 82 85 86 87 93 104 107 108 111 115 116 119
127 128 129 130 131 132 133 134 135 145 146 148 **P**6
Primary Contact: Victor N. Lee, FACHE, President and Chief Executive Officer
CFO: Tanya Sharp, Vice President of Fiscal Services and Chief Financial Officer
CMO: Lynette Kramer, M.D., Chief Medical Officer
CIO: Larry Zoucha, Chief Information Officer
CHR: Jennifer Beierman, Director Human Resources
CNO: Cindy Lesiak, Vice President Patient Care Services and Director of Nursing
Web address: www.boonecohealth.org
**Control:** County–Government, nonfederal **Service:** General Medical and Surgical

**Staffed Beds:** 25 **Admissions:** 777 **Census:** 8 **Outpatient Visits:** 79000
**Births:** 100

## ALLIANCE—Box Butte County

⊞ **BOX BUTTE GENERAL HOSPITAL (281360)**, 2101 Box Butte Avenue,
Zip 69301–4445, Mailing Address: P.O. Box 810, Zip 69301–0810;
tel. 308/762–6660 **A**1 9 10 18 **F**3 5 11 13 15 28 29 32 34 35 36 38 40 43
47 48 50 53 57 59 60 64 68 69 75 77 78 79 81 82 85 86 87 92 93 97 100
101 104 107 108 111 114 116 118 119 127 129 130 131 132 133 134 135
146 148
Primary Contact: Dan Griess, FACHE, Chief Executive Officer
COO: Lori Mazanec, Chief Operating Officer
CFO: Tracy E. Jatczak, CPA, Chief Financial Officer
CNO: Carolyn Jones, R.N., Chief Nursing Officer
Web address: www.bbgh.org
**Control:** County–Government, nonfederal **Service:** General Medical and Surgical

**Staffed Beds:** 25 **Admissions:** 810 **Census:** 8 **Outpatient Visits:** 33084
**Births:** 80 **Total Expense ($000):** 31480 **Payroll Expense ($000):** 13047
**Personnel:** 233

## ALMA—Harlan County

★ **HARLAN COUNTY HEALTH SYSTEM (281300)**, 717 North Brown Street,
Zip 68920–2132, Mailing Address: P.O. Box 836, Zip 68920–0836;
tel. 308/928–2151 **A**9 10 18 **F**1 3 4 11 15 16 17 29 30 31 40 45 46 50 64
67 70 72 73 80 81 85 86 88 89 90 93 98 107 110 114 119 127 128 130
132 133 135 146 147 **P**6 **S** Great Plains Health Alliance, Inc., Wichita, KS
Primary Contact: Manuela Wolf, R.N., Chief Executive Officer
CFO: Sue Lans, Comptroller
CMO: Michele Durr, M.D., Chief of Medical Staff
CIO: Michael Andrews, Coordinator Information Systems
CHR: Ana York, Coordinator Human Resources and Benefits
CNO: Katherine Fleischmann, Director of Nursing
Web address: www.harlancountyhealth.com
**Control:** County–Government, nonfederal **Service:** General Medical and Surgical

**Staffed Beds:** 19 **Admissions:** 107 **Census:** 3 **Outpatient Visits:** 18138
**Births:** 0 **Total Expense ($000):** 8067 **Payroll Expense ($000):** 3237
**Personnel:** 56

## ATKINSON—Holt County

**WEST HOLT MEMORIAL HOSPITAL (281343)**, 406 West Neely Street,
Zip 68713–4801; tel. 402/925–2811, (Nonreporting) **A**9 10 18 **S** Faith Regional
Health Services, Norfolk, NE
Primary Contact: Bradley D. Pfeifer, Chief Executive Officer
CFO: Karen Nollette, Chief Financial Officer
CMO: John Tubbs, M.D., Chief of Staff
CIO: Mark Johnson, Chief Information Officer
CHR: Margaret Linse, Administrative Secretary and Director Human Resources
CNO: Tana ONeill, R.N., Chief Nursing Officer
Web address: www.westholtmed.org
**Control:** Other not–for–profit (including NFP Corporation) **Service:** General
Medical and Surgical

**Staffed Beds:** 18

## AUBURN—Nemaha County

★ ◇ **NEMAHA COUNTY HOSPITAL (281324)**, 2022 13th Street,
Zip 68305–1799; tel. 402/274–4366 **A**9 10 18 21 **F**1 3 4 7 12 15 16 17 28
29 30 31 34 35 40 43 62 64 67 68 70 72 73 74 75 77 78 79 80 81 82 85
87 88 89 90 93 94 98 104 107 110 111 114 117 119 128 129 131 133 135
141 147 148
Primary Contact: Marty Fattig, Chief Executive Officer
COO: Kermit Moore, R.N., Chief Operating Officer and Chief Nursing Officer
CFO: Stacy Taylor, Chief Financial Officer
CHR: Susan Shupp, Chief Human Resources Officer
Web address: www.nchnet.org
**Control:** County–Government, nonfederal **Service:** General Medical and Surgical

**Staffed Beds:** 20 **Admissions:** 209 **Census:** 3 **Outpatient Visits:** 19085
**Births:** 0 **Total Expense ($000):** 11588 **Payroll Expense ($000):** 4701
**Personnel:** 84

## AURORA—Hamilton County

★ **MEMORIAL COMMUNITY HEALTH (281320)**, 1423 Seventh Street,
Zip 68818–1197; tel. 402/694–3171, (Nonreporting) **A**9 10 18
Primary Contact: Diane R. Keller, Chief Executive Officer
CFO: Phil Fendt, Chief Financial Officer
CMO: Jeff Muilenburg, Chief of Staff
CIO: Brad Tiede, Director Information Systems
CHR: Laura Teichmeier, Director of Human Resources
CNO: Lindy Mosel, Director of Nursing
Web address: www.memorialcommunityhealth.org
**Control:** Other not–for–profit (including NFP Corporation) **Service:** General
Medical and Surgical

**Staffed Beds:** 74

**MEMORIAL HOSPITAL** See Memorial Community Health

## BASSETT—Rock County

**ROCK COUNTY HOSPITAL (281333)**, 102 East South Street,
Zip 68714–5508; tel. 402/684–3366, (Total facility includes 30 beds in nursing
home–type unit) **A**9 10 18 **F**7 11 15 28 40 53 57 81 84 107 110 127 128 133
Primary Contact: Stacey A. Knox, Administrator
CMO: John Tubbs, M.D., Chief of Staff
CHR: Jackie Carpenter, Office Manager
CIO: Cal Adler, Director of Information Technology
CNO: Connie Olson, R.N., Director of Nursing
Web address: www.rockcountyhospital.com
**Control:** County–Government, nonfederal **Service:** General Medical and Surgical

**Staffed Beds:** 54 **Admissions:** 174 **Census:** 25 **Outpatient Visits:** 6082
**Births:** 0 **Total Expense ($000):** 6063 **Payroll Expense ($000):** 2818
**Personnel:** 73

**NE**

---

**Hospital, Medicare Provider Number, Address, Telephone, Approval, Facility, and Physician Codes, Health Care System**

★ American Hospital Association (AHA) membership
☐ The Joint Commission accreditation
○ Healthcare Facilities Accreditation Program
◇ DNV Healthcare Inc. accreditation
⇑ Center for Improvement in Healthcare Quality Accreditation
△ Commission on Accreditation of Rehabilitation Facilities (CARF) accreditation

## BEATRICE—Gage County

☒ **BEATRICE COMMUNITY HOSPITAL AND HEALTH CENTER (281364)**, 4800 Hospital Parkway, Zip 68310–6906, Mailing Address: P.O. Box 278, Zip 68310–0278; tel. 402/228–3344 **A**1 9 10 18 **F**3 13 15 28 29 31 34 35 40 45 57 62 63 64 65 68 69 70 75 76 78 79 81 82 85 87 93 107 108 110 111 114 118 119 127 129 130 131 132 133 135 146 147
Primary Contact: Dr. John Findley, Interim Chief Executive Officer
CFO: Alan W. Streeter, Chief Financial Officer
CMO: John T Findley, M.D., Chief Medical Officer
CHR: Kathryn G. Humble, Chief Human Resources Officer
CNO: Julie L. Jones, R.N., Chief Nursing Officer
Web address: www.beatricecommunityhospital.com
**Control:** Other not-for-profit (including NFP Corporation) **Service:** General Medical and Surgical

**Staffed Beds:** 25 **Admissions:** 1054 **Census:** 11 **Outpatient Visits:** 189551 **Births:** 197 **Total Expense ($000):** 62131 **Payroll Expense ($000):** 27662 **Personnel:** 437

## BELLEVUE—Sarpy County

**MADONNA REHABILITATION SPECIALTY HOSPITAL (280136)**, 2500 Bellevue Medical Center Drive, Fourth Floor, Zip 68123–1591; tel. 402/401–3000, (Nonreporting)
Primary Contact: Deborah Istas, Chief Operating Officer
Web address: www.madonna.org
**Control:** Other not-for-profit (including NFP Corporation) **Service:** General Medical and Surgical

**Staffed Beds:** 32

☐ **NEBRASKA MEDICINE – BELLEVUE (280132)**, 2500 Bellevue Medical Center Drive, Zip 68123–1591; tel. 402/763–3000, (Nonreporting) **A**1 3 5 9 10
Primary Contact: Rosanna D. Morris, R.N., Interim Chief Executive Officer
COO: Paulette Davidson, FACHE, Chief Experience Officer
CFO: Stephanie Daubert, Chief Financial Officer
CMO: Marlin G. Stahl, M.D., Chief Medical Officer
CIO: Mark Weiss, Executive Director Enterprise Technology Services
CHR: Paulette Davidson, FACHE, Chief Experience Officer
CNO: Lisa Walters, R.N., Director of Nursing
Web address: www.bellevuemed.com
**Control:** Partnership, Investor–owned, for–profit **Service:** General Medical and Surgical

**Staffed Beds:** 55

## BENKELMAN—Dundy County

★ **DUNDY COUNTY HOSPITAL (281340)**, 1313 North Cheyenne Street, Zip 69021–3074, Mailing Address: P.O. Box 626, Zip 69021–0626; tel. 308/423–2204 **A**9 10 18 **F**3 15 28 29 31 32 40 43 44 45 50 54 56 57 59 64 65 66 75 86 87 89 91 93 97 107 110 127 134 **P**1 3 5 6 8
Primary Contact: Rita A. Jones, Chief Executive Officer
COO: Wendy Elkins, Director Operations
CFO: Renee Fink, CPA, Chief Financial Officer
CMO: Jose Garcia, M.D., Chief Medical Staff
CIO: David Craw, Coordinator Information Technology
CHR: Sandy Noffsinger, Executive Assistant, Risk Manager and Director Marketing
CNO: Laken Vrbas, R.N., Director of Nursing
Web address: www.bwtelcom.net/dch
**Control:** County–Government, nonfederal **Service:** General Medical and Surgical

**Staffed Beds:** 14 **Admissions:** 108 **Census:** 1 **Outpatient Visits:** 30877 **Births:** 0

## BLAIR—Washington County

★ **MEMORIAL COMMUNITY HOSPITAL AND HEALTH SYSTEM (281359)**, 810 North 22nd Street, Zip 68008–1199, Mailing Address: P.O. Box 250, Zip 68008–0250; tel. 402/426–2182, (Nonreporting) **A**9 10 18
Primary Contact: Robert C. Copple, FACHE, President and CEO
CMO: Bradley Sawtelle, M.D., President Medical Staff
CHR: Kristine Nielsen, Manager Human Resources
CNO: Laura Stawniak, R.N., Chief Nursing Executive
Web address: www.mchhs.org
**Control:** Other not-for-profit (including NFP Corporation) **Service:** General Medical and Surgical

**Staffed Beds:** 25

## BRIDGEPORT—Morrill County

**MORRILL COUNTY COMMUNITY HOSPITAL (281318)**, 1313 S Street, Zip 69336–0579; tel. 308/262–1616 **A**9 10 18 **F**7 28 34 35 36 40 41 43 45 46 47 56 57 59 62 65 66 69 75 77 79 81 93 97 114 119 127 130 133 **P**6
Primary Contact: Robin Stuart, Chief Executive Officer
COO: Robin Stuart, Chief Operating Officer
CFO: Connie Christensen, Chief Financial Officer
CMO: John Post, M.D., Medical Director
CIO: Lori Shengle, Director Information Technology
CHR: Rhea Basa, Director Human Resources
CNO: Sylvia Marie Lichius, R.N., Chief Nursing Officer
Web address: www.morrillcountyhospital.org
**Control:** County–Government, nonfederal **Service:** General Medical and Surgical

**Staffed Beds:** 20 **Admissions:** 94 **Census:** 1 **Outpatient Visits:** 25912 **Births:** 0 **Total Expense ($000):** 8675 **Payroll Expense ($000):** 4122 **Personnel:** 101

## BROKEN BOW—Custer County

**JENNIE M. MELHAM MEMORIAL MEDICAL CENTER (281365)**, 145 Memorial Drive, Zip 68822–1378, Mailing Address: P.O. Box 250, Zip 68822–0250; tel. 308/872–4100, (Nonreporting) **A**9 10 18
Primary Contact: Michael J. Steckler, President and Chief Executive Officer
CFO: Tim Schuckman, Chief Financial Officer
CIO: Tim Schuckman, Chief Financial Officer
CNO: Shelly Amsberry, Director of Nursing
Web address: www.brokenbow-ne.com/community/healthcare/melham.htm
**Control:** Other not-for-profit (including NFP Corporation) **Service:** General Medical and Surgical

**Staffed Beds:** 83

## CALLAWAY—Custer County

★ **CALLAWAY DISTRICT HOSPITAL (281335)**, 211 East Kimball, Zip 68825–2589, Mailing Address: P.O. Box 100, Zip 68825–0100; tel. 308/836–2228, (Nonreporting) **A**9 10 18
Primary Contact: Marvin Neth, Chief Executive Officer
CHR: Carol Koch, Manager Human Resources
Web address: www.callawayhospital.org
**Control:** Hospital district or authority, Government, nonfederal **Service:** General Medical and Surgical

**Staffed Beds:** 12

## CAMBRIDGE—Furnas County

★ **TRI VALLEY HEALTH SYSTEM (281348)**, 1305 West Highway 6 and 34, Zip 69022–0488, Mailing Address: P.O. Box 488, Zip 69022–0488; tel. 308/697–3329, (Total facility includes 32 beds in nursing home–type unit) **A**9 10 18 **F**3 8 10 11 13 15 28 29 30 31 32 34 35 40 41 43 45 46 53 56 57 59 64 65 67 68 69 71 75 77 78 79 81 82 86 87 91 93 107 110 115 116 119 125 127 128 129 130 131 132 133 135 143 145 146 147 148 **P**6
**S** HealthTech Management Services, Brentwood, TN
Primary Contact: Deborah L. Herzberg, R.N., MS, FACHE, Chief Executive Officer
CFO: Diana Rippe, Chief Financial Officer
CMO: Shelly Kasper–Cope, M.D., Chief of Staff
CIO: Ciprian Galarneau, Director Information Systems
CHR: Tammy Claussen, Human Resources Executive
CNO: Shawn Cole, Chief Clinical Officer
Web address: www.trivalleyhealth.com
**Control:** Other not-for-profit (including NFP Corporation) **Service:** General Medical and Surgical

**Staffed Beds:** 48 **Admissions:** 459 **Census:** 28 **Outpatient Visits:** 8818 **Births:** 48

## CENTRAL CITY—Merrick County

★ **LITZENBERG MEMORIAL COUNTY HOSPITAL (281328)**, 1715 26th Street, Zip 68826–9620; tel. 308/946–3015, (Nonreporting) **A**9 10 18
Primary Contact: Julie Murray, Chief Executive Officer
CHR: Shauna Graham, Director of Professional Services Human Resources, Marketing Foundation
Web address: www.lmchealth.com
**Control:** County–Government, nonfederal **Service:** General Medical and Surgical

**Staffed Beds:** 65

**NE**

*Many Facility Codes have changed. Please refer to the AHA Guide Code Chart.* © 2015 AHA Guide

## CHADRON—Dawes County

★ **CHADRON COMMUNITY HOSPITAL AND HEALTH SERVICES (281341)**, 825 Centennial Drive, Zip 69337–9400; tel. 308/432–5586, (Nonreporting) **A**3 9 10 18
Primary Contact: Harold L. Krueger, Jr., Chief Executive Officer
COO: Anna Turman, Chief Operating Officer
CFO: Russ Bohnenkamp, Chief Financial Officer
CMO: Jerry McLain, M.D., Chief of Staff
CIO: Anna Turman, Chief Information Officer
CHR: Ellen Krueger, Director Human Resources
CNO: Cheryl Cassiday, R.N., Director of Nursing
Web address: www.chadronhospital.com
**Control:** Other not–for–profit (including NFP Corporation) **Service:** General Medical and Surgical

**Staffed Beds:** 25

## COLUMBUS—Platte County

⊠ **COLUMBUS COMMUNITY HOSPITAL (280111)**, 4600 38th Street, Zip 68601–1664, Mailing Address: P.O. Box 1800, Zip 68602–1800; tel. 402/564–7118, (Nonreporting) **A**1 9 10 20
Primary Contact: Michael T. Hansen, FACHE, President and Chief Executive Officer
COO: James P. Goulet, Vice President Operations
CFO: J. Joseph Barbaglia, Vice President Financial Services
CMO: Mark Howerter, M.D., President Medical Staff
CIO: Cheryl Tira, Director Information Systems
CHR: Scott E. Messersmith, Director Human Resources
CNO: Linda K. Walline, R.N., Vice President Nursing
Web address: www.columbushosp.org
**Control:** Other not–for–profit (including NFP Corporation) **Service:** General Medical and Surgical

**Staffed Beds:** 51

## COZAD—Dawson County

★ **COZAD COMMUNITY HOSPITAL (281327)**, 300 East 12th Street, Zip 69130–1505, Mailing Address: P.O. Box 108, Zip 69130–0108; tel. 308/784–2261 **A**9 10 18 **F**3 10 13 15 28 30 31 34 35 40 43 50 53 56 57 59 62 63 70 75 76 77 81 82 84 86 93 94 97 107 110 114 119 127 128 129 130 131 132 133 135 146 148 **P**6
Primary Contact: Lyle E. Davis, Administrator
Web address: www.cozadhealthcare.com
**Control:** Hospital district or authority, Government, nonfederal **Service:** General Medical and Surgical

**Staffed Beds:** 21 **Admissions:** 376 **Census:** 4 **Outpatient Visits:** 8717 **Births:** 40 **Total Expense ($000):** 12639 **Payroll Expense ($000):** 6208 **Personnel:** 121

## CREIGHTON—Knox County

★ **AVERA CREIGHTON HOSPITAL (281331)**, 1503 Main Street, Zip 68729–3007, Mailing Address: P.O. Box 186, Zip 68729–0186; tel. 402/358–5700, (Total facility includes 47 beds in nursing home–type unit) **A**9 10 18 **F**8 15 18 28 29 30 40 43 44 45 46 53 54 59 62 63 64 65 68 77 81 82 87 93 107 110 114 119 127 128 129 130 131 133 143 148 **S** Avera Health, Sioux Falls, SD
Primary Contact: Jennifer Poppen, Chief Executive Officer
CFO: Gregory Beckmann, Finance Controller
CHR: Jane E. Miller, Director Human Resources
CNO: Jean M. Henes, MSN, RN–B, R.N., Director of Nursing
Web address: www.avera.org/creighton/
**Control:** Other not–for–profit (including NFP Corporation) **Service:** General Medical and Surgical

**Staffed Beds:** 63 **Admissions:** 230 **Census:** 43 **Outpatient Visits:** 11457 **Births:** 0 **Total Expense ($000):** 10377 **Payroll Expense ($000):** 4856

## CRETE—Saline County

★ **CRETE AREA MEDICAL CENTER (281354)**, 2910 Betten Drive, Zip 68333–3084, Mailing Address: P.O. Box 220, Zip 68333–0220; tel. 402/826–2102, (Nonreporting) **A**9 10 18 **S** Bryan Health, Lincoln, NE
Primary Contact: Rebekah Mussman, Chief Executive Officer
CFO: Kate Watson, Interim Chief Financial Officer
CMO: Jason Hesser, M.D., Chief of Staff
CIO: Drew Kotil, Director Information Technology
CHR: Bobbie Wilson, Director Human Resources
CNO: Jayne Van Asperen, Acting Director of Nursing
Web address: www.creteareamedicalcenter.com
**Control:** Other not–for–profit (including NFP Corporation) **Service:** General Medical and Surgical

**Staffed Beds:** 24

## DAVID CITY—Butler County

★ **BUTLER COUNTY HEALTH CARE CENTER (281332)**, 372 South Ninth Street, Zip 68632–2116; tel. 402/367–1200, (Nonreporting) **A**5 9 10 18
Primary Contact: Donald T. Naiberk, Administrator
CFO: Jodi Prochaska, Chief Financial Officer
CMO: Victor Thoendel, M.D., Chief Medical Officer
CIO: Cindy Neesen, Director of Information Technology
CHR: Andra Vandenberg, Director Human Resources
CNO: Sue M. Birkel, R.N., Director of Nursing
Web address: www.bchccnet.org
**Control:** County–Government, nonfederal **Service:** General Medical and Surgical

**Staffed Beds:** 20

## ELKHORN—Douglas County

**METHODIST WOMEN'S HOSPITAL** See Nebraska Methodist Hospital, Omaha

## FAIRBURY—Jefferson County

★ **JEFFERSON COMMUNITY HEALTH CENTER (281319)**, 2200 H Street, Zip 68352–1119, Mailing Address: P.O. Box 277, Zip 68352–0277; tel. 402/729–3351, (Total facility includes 40 beds in nursing home–type unit) **A**9 10 18 **F**2 3 13 15 28 29 30 31 34 35 40 45 50 53 57 59 62 64 75 77 78 79 81 85 86 87 93 107 110 114 119 128 130 131 132 133 135 146
Primary Contact: Chad Jurgens, Chief Executive Officer
CFO: Chance Klasek, CPA, Chief Financial Officer
CIO: Dennis Ahl, Director Information Technology
CHR: Sandra A. Bauer, Director Human Resources
Web address: www.jchc.us
**Control:** Other not–for–profit (including NFP Corporation) **Service:** General Medical and Surgical

**Staffed Beds:** 65 **Admissions:** 418 **Census:** 40 **Outpatient Visits:** 25898 **Births:** 27 **Total Expense ($000):** 15974 **Payroll Expense ($000):** 6895 **Personnel:** 168

## FALLS CITY—Richardson County

★ **COMMUNITY MEDICAL CENTER (281352)**, 3307 Barada Street, Zip 68355–2470, Mailing Address: P.O. Box 399, Zip 68355–0399; tel. 402/245–2428 **A**9 10 18 **F**3 13 15 28 31 34 35 40 43 45 59 75 78 81 85 93 97 107 111 119 127 130 133 135 **P**6
Primary Contact: Ryan C. Larsen, FACHE, Chief Executive Officer
CFO: Scott Sawyer, Chief Financial Officer
CMO: David E. Borg, Chief of Medical Staff
CIO: Joe Buckminster, Manager Information Technology
CHR: Shannon Weinmann, Human Resources Manager
CNO: Ivy Campbell, Director of Nursing
Web address: www.cmcfc.org
**Control:** Other not–for–profit (including NFP Corporation) **Service:** General Medical and Surgical

**Staffed Beds:** 24 **Admissions:** 810 **Census:** 9 **Outpatient Visits:** 49210 **Births:** 66 **Total Expense ($000):** 21889 **Payroll Expense ($000):** 7384 **Personnel:** 169

## FRANKLIN—Franklin County

★ **FRANKLIN COUNTY MEMORIAL HOSPITAL (281311)**, 1406 Q Street, Zip 68939–0315, Mailing Address: P.O. Box 315, Zip 68939–0315; tel. 308/425–6221, (Nonreporting) **A**9 10 18
Primary Contact: Theresa Rizzo, Administrator
CFO: Linda Bush, Director of Finance
CMO: Linda Mazour, M.D., President
CNO: Julie Bydalek, Director of Nursing
Web address: www.fcmh.com
**Control:** County–Government, nonfederal **Service:** General Medical and Surgical

**Staffed Beds:** 10

## FREMONT—Dodge County

☐ **FREMONT HEALTH (280077)**, 450 East 23rd Street, Zip 68025–2387; tel. 402/721–1610, (Total facility includes 112 beds in nursing home–type unit) **A**1 9 10 20 **F**3 8 11 13 15 17 18 20 22 26 28 29 30 31 34 35 37 40 45 56 57 59 62 63 64 68 70 72 74 75 76 77 78 79 81 85 86 87 89 93 99 100 103 104 107 108 110 111 114 119 120 121 123 124 126 128 129 130 131 132 135 143 146
Primary Contact: Patrick M. Booth, FACHE, Chief Executive Officer
CFO: Michael Sindelar, Vice President and Chief Financial Officer
CIO: Matt Sakalosky, Director Information Services and Chief Information Officer
CHR: Bethany Childers, Director Human Resources
CNO: Peggy S. Kennedy, R.N., Vice President and Chief Nurse Executive
Web address: www.fremonthealth.com
**Control:** County–Government, nonfederal **Service:** General Medical and Surgical

**Staffed Beds:** 202 **Admissions:** 3815 **Census:** 118 **Outpatient Visits:** 67824 **Births:** 355 **Total Expense ($000):** 88220 **Payroll Expense ($000):** 35982

---

**Hospital, Medicare Provider Number, Address, Telephone, Approval, Facility, and Physician Codes, Health Care System**

★ American Hospital Association (AHA) membership
☐ The Joint Commission accreditation
○ Healthcare Facilities Accreditation Program
◇ DNV Healthcare Inc. accreditation
⇑ Center for Improvement in Healthcare Quality Accreditation
△ Commission on Accreditation of Rehabilitation Facilities (CARF) accreditation

---

NE

**FRIEND—Saline County**

**WARREN MEMORIAL HOSPITAL (281330)**, 905 Second Street,
Zip 68359–1133; tel. 402/947–2541, (Nonreporting) **A**9 10 18
Primary Contact: Christopher R. Bjornberg, Chief Executive Officer
CFO: James Houlihan, Chief Financial Officer
CMO: Roger Meyer, M.D., Chief of Staff
CIO: Matt Scott, Chief Information Officer
CHR: Stacy Kirchhoff, Coordinator Human Resources
CNO: Melinda Johanna Kentfield, Chief Nursing Officer
Web address: www.wmhospital.com
**Control:** City–Government, nonfederal **Service:** General Medical and Surgical

Staffed Beds: 63

**GENEVA—Fillmore County**

**FILLMORE COUNTY HOSPITAL (281301)**, 1900 F Street, Zip 68361–1325,
Mailing Address: P.O. Box 193, Zip 68361–0193; tel. 402/759–3167,
(Nonreporting) **A**9 10 18
Primary Contact: Paul Utemark, Chief Executive Officer
COO: Debbie Domann, Director of Operations
CFO: Jeanne Ackland, Director of Finance
CMO: Jason Bespalec, M.D., Chief of Staff
CIO: Tyler Gewecke, Information Technology Technician
CHR: Abby Tuberville, Human Resource Manager
Web address: www.fhsofgeneva.org
**Control:** County–Government, nonfederal **Service:** General Medical and Surgical

Staffed Beds: 25

**GENOA—Nance County**

**GENOA MEDICAL FACILITIES (281312)**, 706 Ewing Avenue, Zip 68640–3035,
Mailing Address: P.O. Box 310, Zip 68640–0310; tel. 402/993–2283,
(Nonreporting) **A**9 10 18
Primary Contact: Amanda Roebuck, Interim Chief Executive Officer
CFO: Jennifer Wieck, Director Financial Services
CMO: Brian Buhlke, M.D., Medical Director
CHR: Angie Sutton, Manager Human Resources
CNO: Amanda Roebuck, Director Patient Care Services
Web address: www.genoamedical.org/
**Control:** City–County, Government, nonfederal **Service:** General Medical and Surgical

Staffed Beds: 58

**GORDON—Sheridan County**

★ **GORDON MEMORIAL HOSPITAL (281358)**, 300 East Eighth Street,
Zip 69343–1123; tel. 308/282–0401, (Nonreporting) **A**9 10 18
Primary Contact: Julie Schnell, Interim Chief Executive Officer
CFO: Heidi Cushing, Director Finance
CMO: Christopher P. Costa, M.D., Chief of Staff
CIO: Ray Waldron, Director Information Technology
CHR: Lisa Woodcock, MBA, PHR, SHRM–CD, Director Human Resources
CNO: Glenda Capler, Interim Director of Nursing
Web address: www.gordonmemorial.org
**Control:** Hospital district or authority, Government, nonfederal **Service:** General Medical and Surgical

Staffed Beds: 25

**GOTHENBURG—Dawson County**

★ **GOTHENBURG MEMORIAL HOSPITAL (281313)**, 910 20th Street,
Zip 69138–1237, Mailing Address: P.O. Box 469, Zip 69138–0469;
tel. 308/537–3661, (Nonreporting) **A**9 10 18
Primary Contact: Mick Brant, FACHE, Chief Executive Officer
CFO: Taci Bartlett, Chief Financial Officer
CMO: Carol Shackleton, Medical Director
CIO: Tinna Therrien, Chief Information Officer and Director Clinical Infomatics
CHR: Marsha Engel, Director Human Resources
CNO: Carolyn Evenson, R.N., Chief Nursing Officer
Web address: www.ghospital.org
**Control:** Hospital district or authority, Government, nonfederal **Service:** General Medical and Surgical

Staffed Beds: 12

**GRAND ISLAND—Hall County**

⊠ **CHI HEALTH SAINT FRANCIS (280023)**, 2620 West Faidley Avenue,
Zip 68803–4297, Mailing Address: P.O. Box 9804, Zip 68802–9804;
tel. 308/384–4600, (Includes ST. FRANCIS MEDICAL PLAZA, 2116 West Faidley
Avenue, Zip 68803, Mailing Address: P.O. Box 9804, Zip 68802;
tel. 308/384–4600), (Total facility includes 34 beds in nursing home–type unit)
**A**1 2 3 5 9 10 19 **F**3 5 11 12 13 15 17 18 19 20 22 28 30 31 34 35 40 43
45 47 50 51 53 59 60 62 63 64 65 68 70 72 74 75 76 77 78 79 81 82 84
85 89 90 91 97 104 105 110 120 121 123 128 129 130 132 135 145 146
148 **S** Catholic Health Initiatives, Englewood, CO
Primary Contact: Daniel P. McElligott, FACHE, President
CFO: Lisa Webb, Vice President Operational Finance
CMO: Shu–Ming Wang, MD, Vice President Medical Affairs
CHR: Nancy Wallace, Vice President Human Resources, CHI Health
CNO: Beth Bartlett, MSN, Vice President Nursing
Web address: www.saintfrancisgi.org
**Control:** Church–operated, Nongovernment, not–for profit **Service:** General Medical and Surgical

Staffed Beds: 192 Admissions: 7718 Census: 93 Outpatient Visits: 95262
Births: 1088 Total Expense ($000): 142814 Payroll Expense ($000): 38890 Personnel: 862

**GRANT—Perkins County**

★ **PERKINS COUNTY HEALTH SERVICES (281356)**, 900 Lincoln Avenue,
Zip 69140–3095; tel. 308/352–7200, (Includes GOLDEN OURS CONVALESCENT
HOME ), (Nonreporting) **A**9 10 18
Primary Contact: James LeBrun, Chief Executive Officer
CFO: Derick Lorentz, Interim Chief Financial Officer
CMO: Ruth Demmel, M.D., Chief Medical Officer
CIO: Jennifer Baumgartner, Chief Information Officer
CHR: Julie Bevard, Director Human Resources
CNO: Dana McArtor, R.N., Director of Nursing
Web address: www.pchsgrant.com
**Control:** Hospital district or authority, Government, nonfederal **Service:** General Medical and Surgical

Staffed Beds: 20

**HASTINGS—Adams County**

⊠ **MARY LANNING HEALTHCARE (280032)**, 715 North St. Joseph Avenue,
Zip 68901–4497; tel. 402/463–4521, (Nonreporting) **A**1 2 9 10
Primary Contact: Eric A. Barber, FACHE, President and Chief Executive Officer
COO: Mark Callahan, Chief Operating Officer
CFO: Shawn A. Nordby, Chief Financial Officer
CMO: Michael Skoch, M.D., Chief Medical Officer
CIO: Lisa Nonneman, Interim Director Information Technology Services
CHR: Bruce E. Cutright, MS, Vice President Human Resources
CNO: Ronda S. Ehly, R.N., Chief Nursing Officer
Web address: www.marylanning.org
**Control:** Other not–for–profit (including NFP Corporation) **Service:** General Medical and Surgical

Staffed Beds: 148

**HEBRON—Thayer County**

★ **THAYER COUNTY HEALTH SERVICES (281304)**, 120 Park Avenue,
Zip 68370–2019, Mailing Address: P.O. Box 49, Zip 68370–0049;
tel. 402/768–6041 **A**9 10 18 **F**1 3 4 7 11 13 15 16 17 18 19 26 27 28 29 30
31 32 34 35 38 40 43 45 46 47 48 49 50 53 54 56 57 59 62 64 65 67 68
69 70 72 73 74 75 76 77 79 80 81 85 86 87 88 90 91 92 93 97 98 107
110 115 117 119 127 128 129 130 131 132 133 135 **P**3 4 6
Primary Contact: Michael G. Burcham, Sr., FACHE, Chief Executive Officer
CFO: Cameron Meyer, Chief Financial Officer
CMO: Bryan Hubl, M.D., Chief of Staff
CIO: Dan Engle, Chief Information Officer
CHR: Tamara Francik, Human Resources Generalist
CNO: Jamie Koch, R.N., Director of Nursing
Web address: www.thayercountyhealth.com
**Control:** State–Government, nonfederal **Service:** General Medical and Surgical

Staffed Beds: 19 Admissions: 380 Census: 4 Outpatient Visits: 24933
Births: 41 Total Expense ($000): 17633 Payroll Expense ($000): 7897

**HENDERSON—York County**

**HENDERSON HEALTH CARE SERVICES (281308)**, 1621 Front Street,
Zip 68371–8902; tel. 402/723–4512, (Nonreporting) **A**9 10 18
Primary Contact: Cheryl Brown, Administrator
CMO: James M. Ohrt, M.D., Director Medical Staff
CHR: Lynette Friesen, Manager Human Resources
Web address: www.hendersonhealthcare.org/getpage.php?name=message
**Control:** Other not–for–profit (including NFP Corporation) **Service:** General Medical and Surgical

Staffed Beds: 56

**NE**

## HOLDREGE—Phelps County

★ ◇ **PHELPS MEMORIAL HEALTH CENTER (281362)**, 1215 Tibbals Street, Zip 68949–1255; tel. 308/995–2211, (Nonreporting) **A**9 10 18 21 **S** QHR, Brentwood, TN
Primary Contact: Mark Harrel, Chief Executive Officer
CFO: Loren D. Schroder, Chief Financial Officer
CMO: Stuart Embury, M.D., Chief Medical Officer
CIO: Leora Smith, Information System and Health Information Management Team Leader
CHR: Cindy Jackson, Director Human Resources
Web address: www.phelpsmemorial.com
**Control:** Other not–for–profit (including NFP Corporation) **Service:** General Medical and Surgical

**Staffed Beds:** 25

## IMPERIAL—Chase County

**CHASE COUNTY COMMUNITY HOSPITAL (281351)**, 600 West 12th Street, Zip 69033–3130, Mailing Address: P.O. Box 819, Zip 69033–0819; tel. 308/882–7111 **A**9 10 18 **F**11 13 15 28 29 30 31 34 35 40 41 42 43 45 57 59 64 75 81 91 93 107 110 114 127 133 **P**6
Primary Contact: Stephen Lewis, Chief Executive Officer
CFO: Stephen Lewis, Chief Financial Officer
CMO: Jonathan Richman, M.D., Chief of Staff
CIO: Jen Harris, Director Health Information Management
CHR: Julie Sharp, Supervisor Human Resources
CNO: Kathy Geier, Director of Nursing
Web address: www.chasecountyhospital.com
**Control:** County–Government, nonfederal **Service:** General Medical and Surgical

**Staffed Beds:** 22 **Admissions:** 136 **Census:** 2 **Outpatient Visits:** 11861 **Births:** 20 **Total Expense ($000):** 10137 **Payroll Expense ($000):** 4296 **Personnel:** 83

## KEARNEY—Buffalo County

⊞ **CHI HEALTH GOOD SAMARITAN (280009)**, 10 East 31st Street, Zip 68847–2926, Mailing Address: P.O. Box 1990, Zip 68848–1990; tel. 308/865–7100, (Includes RICHARD H. YOUNG BEHAVIORAL HEALTH CENTER, 1755 Prairie View Place, Zip 68848, Mailing Address: P.O. Box 1750, Zip 68848–1705; tel. 308/865–2000; Michelle Hansen, Interim Director), (Total facility includes 16 beds in nursing home–type unit) **A**1 2 3 5 9 10 **F**7 9 12 13 15 18 20 22 24 28 29 30 31 34 35 37 40 43 44 45 46 48 49 50 51 53 57 58 59 60 64 68 69 70 71 72 74 75 76 77 78 79 81 82 83 84 85 86 87 89 90 92 93 98 99 101 102 103 104 107 108 110 111 114 115 116 117 118 119 120 121 123 124 126 128 129 130 132 134 135 146 148 **S** Catholic Health Initiatives, Englewood, CO
Primary Contact: Michael H. Schnieders, FACHE, President
CFO: Lisa Webb, Vice President for Operational Finance
CMO: Dennis Edwards, M.D., Vice President Medical Affairs
CIO: Katie Gartner, Director Health Information Management
CNO: Carol R. Wahl, R.N., Vice President Patient Care Services
Web address: www.gshs.org
**Control:** Church–operated, Nongovernment, not–for profit **Service:** General Medical and Surgical

**Staffed Beds:** 233 **Admissions:** 10025 **Census:** 135 **Outpatient Visits:** 70074 **Births:** 1072 **Total Expense ($000):** 190779 **Payroll Expense ($000):** 58655 **Personnel:** 1063

**GOOD SAMARITAN HEALTH SYSTEMS** See CHI Health Good Samaritan

★ ◯ **KEARNEY REGIONAL MEDICAL CENTER (280134)**, 804 22nd Avenue, Zip 68845–2206; tel. 855/404–5762, (Nonreporting) **A**10 11
Primary Contact: Larry Speicher, Chief Executive Officer
CFO: Steve Regier, Chief Financial Officer
CIO: Travis Gregg, Director Support Services
CHR: Steve Beck, MS, Manager Human Resources
CNO: Adrienne Carney, R.N., Director Nursing and Surgical Services
Web address: www.kearneyregional.com
**Control:** Investor–owned, for–profit **Service:** General Medical and Surgical

**Staffed Beds:** 44

## KIMBALL—Kimball County

★ **KIMBALL HEALTH SERVICES (281305)**, 505 South Burg Street, Zip 69145–1398; tel. 308/235–1952, (Nonreporting) **A**9 10 18
Primary Contact: Ken Hunter, R.N., Chief Executive Officer
CFO: Melissa Prante, Chief Financial Officer
CMO: James Plate, M.D., Chief of Staff
CIO: Charles Walker, Director Information Technology
CHR: James R. Imler, Director Human Resources
CNO: Richard Harriger, Director of Emergency Services
Web address: www.kimballhealth.org
**Control:** County–Government, nonfederal **Service:** General Medical and Surgical

**Staffed Beds:** 10

## LEXINGTON—Dawson County

★ ◇ **LEXINGTON REGIONAL HEALTH CENTER (281361)**, 1201 North Erie Street, Zip 68850–1560, Mailing Address: P.O. Box 980, Zip 68850–0980; tel. 308/324–5651, (Nonreporting) **A**5 9 10 18 21
Primary Contact: Leslie Marsh, ACHE, Chief Executive Officer
COO: Jim Hain, Chief Operating Officer
CFO: Wade Eschenbrenner, Chief Financial Officer
CMO: Francisca Acosta–Carlson, M.D., Chief of Staff
CIO: Robb Hanna, Executive Director Information Technology
CHR: Jill Denker, Executive Director Human Resources
CNO: Dana Steiner, R.N., Executive Director of Nursing Services
Web address: www.lexingtonregional.org
**Control:** Hospital district or authority, Government, nonfederal **Service:** General Medical and Surgical

**Staffed Beds:** 25

## LINCOLN—Lancaster County

⊞ △ **BRYAN MEDICAL CENTER (280003)**, 1600 South 48th Street, Zip 68506–1299; tel. 402/489–0200, (Includes BRYAN MEDICAL CENTER–EAST, 1600 South 48th Street, tel. 402/489–0200; BRYAN MEDICAL CENTER–WEST, 2300 South 16th Street, Zip 68502–3781; tel. 402/475–1011) **A**1 2 7 9 10 **F**3 4 5 8 12 13 15 17 18 19 20 22 24 26 28 29 30 31 34 35 37 38 39 40 43 45 46 47 48 49 50 54 56 57 58 59 61 64 68 70 71 72 74 75 76 77 78 79 81 82 85 86 87 89 90 92 93 96 98 99 101 102 103 104 105 107 108 110 111 112 114 115 116 117 118 119 120 123 124 126 129 130 131 132 135 145 146 147 148 **S** Bryan Health, Lincoln, NE
Primary Contact: John T. Woodrich, ACHE, President and Chief Operating Officer
CFO: Russell Gronewold, Chief Financial Officer
CMO: John Trapp, Vice President Medical Affairs
CIO: George Carr, Chief Information Officer
CHR: Jan Garvin, Vice President Human Resources
CNO: Lisa M. Vail, R.N., Chief Nursing Officer and Vice President of Patient Care Services
Web address: www.bryanhealth.com
**Control:** Other not–for–profit (including NFP Corporation) **Service:** General Medical and Surgical

**Staffed Beds:** 328 **Admissions:** 22722 **Census:** 287 **Outpatient Visits:** 231392 **Births:** 2988 **Total Expense ($000):** 437924 **Payroll Expense ($000):** 151031 **Personnel:** 2720

★ **CHI HEALTH NEBRASKA HEART (280128)**, 7500 South 91st Street, Zip 68526–9437; tel. 402/327–2700, (Nonreporting) **A**9 10 **S** Catholic Health Initiatives, Englewood, CO
Primary Contact: Dan Schonlau, Interim President
CFO: Dan Schonlau, Chief Financial Officer and Vice President of Finance
CMO: Peter Dionisopoulos, Chief Medical Officer
CNO: Jackie Mendoza, Chief Nursing Officer
Web address: www.CHIhealthNebraskaHeart.com
**Control:** Other not–for–profit (including NFP Corporation) **Service:** Heart

**Staffed Beds:** 52

⊞ **CHI HEALTH ST ELIZABETH (280020)**, 555 South 70th Street, Zip 68510–2494; tel. 402/219–8000, (Nonreporting) **A**1 2 3 5 9 10 **S** Catholic Health Initiatives, Englewood, CO
Primary Contact: Kim S. Moore, FACHE, President
CFO: Dan Schonlau, Chief Financial Officer and Vice President of Finance
CMO: Michael Ferris, M.D., Chief Medical Officer
CIO: Richard Bohaty, Director Information Technology
CHR: Nancy Wallace, Senior Vice President, Chief Human Resources Officer
CNO: Elizabeth A. Raetz, R.N., Vice President Nursing and Chief Nursing Officer
Web address: www.saintelizabethonline.com
**Control:** Other not–for–profit (including NFP Corporation) **Service:** General Medical and Surgical

**Staffed Beds:** 260

**LINCOLN DIVISION** See Veterans Affairs Nebraska–Western Iowa Health Care System – Lincoln

**NE**

---

**Hospital, Medicare Provider Number, Address, Telephone, Approval, Facility, and Physician Codes, Health Care System**

★ American Hospital Association (AHA) membership
☐ The Joint Commission accreditation
◯ Healthcare Facilities Accreditation Program
◇ DNV Healthcare Inc. accreditation
⇑ Center for Improvement in Healthcare Quality Accreditation
△ Commission on Accreditation of Rehabilitation Facilities (CARF) accreditation

☐ **LINCOLN REGIONAL CENTER (284003)**, West Prospector Place and South Folsom, Zip 68522–2299, Mailing Address: P.O. Box 94949, Zip 68509–4949; tel. 402/479–5207, (Nonreporting) **A**1 9 10
Primary Contact: William R. Gibson, Chief Executive Officer
COO: Stacey Werth–Sweeney, Facility Operating Officer
CFO: Randy Willey, Business Manager
CMO: Vijay Dewan, M.D., Clinical Director
CHR: Scott Rasmussen, Director Human Resources
Web address: www.hhs.state.ne.us/beh/rc
**Control:** State–Government, nonfederal **Service:** Psychiatric

**Staffed Beds: 224**

**LINCOLN SURGICAL HOSPITAL (280127)**, 1710 South 70th Street, Suite 200, Zip 68506–1677; tel. 402/484–9090, (Nonreporting) **A**9 10
Primary Contact: Robb Linafelter, Chief Executive Officer
Web address: www.lincolnsurgery.com
**Control:** Corporation, Investor–owned, for–profit **Service:** Other specialty

**Staffed Beds: 7**

**MADONNA REHABILITATION HOSPITAL (282000)**, 5401 South Street, Zip 68506–2150; tel. 402/413–3000, (Nonreporting)
Primary Contact: Marsha Lommel, FACHE, President and Chief Executive Officer
Web address: www.madonna.org/
**Control:** Other not–for–profit (including NFP Corporation) **Service:** Long–Term Acute Care hospital

**Staffed Beds: 300**

△ **MADONNA REHABILITATION HOSPITAL (283025)**, 5401 South Street, Zip 68506–2134; tel. 402/489–7102, (Nonreporting) **A**7 9 10
Primary Contact: Marsha Lommel, FACHE, President and Chief Executive Officer
COO: Paul Dongilli, Jr., Ph.D., Executive Vice President and Chief Operating Officer
CFO: Victor J. Witkowicz, Senior Vice President and Chief Financial Officer
CMO: Thomas Stadler, M.D., Vice President Medical Affairs and Chief Medical Officer
CIO: David Rolfe, Chief Information Officer
CHR: Lou Ann Manske, Director Human Resources
Web address: www.madonna.org
**Control:** Other not–for–profit (including NFP Corporation) **Service:** Rehabilitation

**Staffed Beds: 300**

**NEBRASKA PENAL AND CORRECTIONAL HOSPITAL**, 14th And Pioneer Streets, Zip 68501, Mailing Address: P.O. Box 94661, Zip 94661; tel. 402/471–3161, (Nonreporting)
Primary Contact: Randy T. Kohl, M.D., Deputy Director, Health Services
Web address: www.corrections.nebraska.gov
**Control:** State–Government, nonfederal **Service:** Hospital unit of an institution (prison hospital, college infimary, etc.)

**Staffed Beds: 12**

⊠ **SELECT SPECIALTY HOSPITAL – LINCOLN (282002)**, 2300 South 16th Street, 7th Floor, Zip 68502–3704; tel. 402/483–8444, (Nonreporting) **A**1 10 **S** Select Medical Corporation, Mechanicsburg, PA
Primary Contact: Scott Butterfield, Chief Executive Officer
**Control:** Corporation, Investor–owned, for–profit **Service:** General Medical and Surgical

**Staffed Beds: 24**

★ **VETERANS AFFAIRS NEBRASKA–WESTERN IOWA HEALTH CARE SYSTEM – LINCOLN**, 600 South 70th Street, Zip 68510–2493; tel. 402/489–3802, (Includes LINCOLN DIVISION, 600 South 70th Street, tel. 402/489–3802), (Nonreporting) **A**9 **S** Department of Veterans Affairs, Washington, DC
Primary Contact: Don Burman, Director
CIO: David Daiker, Chief Information Resource Management
CHR: Dave Peters, Chief Human Resources Officer
Web address: www.nebraska.va.gov/
**Control:** Veterans Affairs, Government, federal **Service:** General Medical and Surgical

**Staffed Beds: 162**

**NIOBRARA VALLEY HOSPITAL (281303)**, 401 South Fifth Street, Zip 68746–0118, Mailing Address: P.O. Box 118, Zip 68746–0118; tel. 402/569–2451, (Nonreporting) **A**9 10 18 **S** Faith Regional Health Services, Norfolk, NE
Primary Contact: Kelly Kalkowski, Chief Executive Officer
CFO: Martha Nelson, Chief Financial Officer
Web address: www.nvhcares.org
**Control:** Other not–for–profit (including NFP Corporation) **Service:** General Medical and Surgical

**Staffed Beds: 20**

✠ **COMMUNITY HOSPITAL (281363)**, 1301 East H Street, Zip 69001–1328, Mailing Address: P.O. Box 1328, Zip 69001–1328; tel. 308/344–2650, (Nonreporting) **A**1 9 10 18
Primary Contact: James P. Ulrich, Jr., FACHE, President and Chief Executive Officer
CFO: Troy Bruntz, Vice President Finance and Chief Financial Officer
CMO: Jason Blomstedt, Chief of Staff
CIO: Lori Beeby, Director Information Systems
CHR: Leanne R. Miller, Director Human Resources
CNO: Janelle Kircher, R.N., Vice President Patient Care Services and Chief Nursing Officer
Web address: www.chmccook.org
**Control:** Other not–for–profit (including NFP Corporation) **Service:** General Medical and Surgical

**Staffed Beds: 25**

★ **KEARNEY COUNTY HEALTH SERVICES (281306)**, 727 East First Street, Zip 68959–1705; tel. 308/832–3400, (Total facility includes 34 beds in nursing home–type unit) **A**9 10 18 **F**10 15 28 34 40 41 43 45 59 64 65 67 81 97 99 103 104 107 110 114 119 127 128 130 133 145 146 147 148
Primary Contact: Fred J. Meis, Chief Executive Officer
CFO: Kayla Rhynalds, Interim Chief Financial Officer
CMO: Douglas Althouse, Chief Medical Staff
CHR: Rebecca L. Cooke, Director Human Resources
CNO: Mary Bunger, R.N., Director Nursing Services
Web address: www.kchs.org
**Control:** County–Government, nonfederal **Service:** General Medical and Surgical

**Staffed Beds: 44 Admissions: 101 Census: 30 Outpatient Visits: 7417 Births: 0 Total Expense ($000): 9755 Payroll Expense ($000): 4586 Personnel: 113**

★ **CHI HEALTH ST. MARY'S (281342)**, 1301 Grundman Boulevard, Zip 68410; tel. 402/873–3321 **A**9 10 18 **F**3 13 15 17 28 31 35 40 45 64 67 68 69 70 75 76 78 79 81 82 85 87 89 97 107 110 111 114 118 119 128 129 132 133 135 148 **S** Catholic Health Initiatives, Englewood, CO
Primary Contact: Daniel J. Kelly, ACHE, President
CFO: Tim H. Schnack, Vice President Operations Finance
CMO: Jonathan Stelling, M.D., Vice President Medical Affairs
CNO: Brenda Jean Sebek, R.N., Vice President Patient Care Services
Web address: www.chihealthstmarys.com
**Control:** Church–operated, Nongovernment, not–for profit **Service:** General Medical and Surgical

**Staffed Beds: 18 Admissions: 415 Census: 4 Outpatient Visits: 38552 Births: 114 Total Expense ($000): 20887 Payroll Expense ($000): 8271 Personnel: 140**

★ **ANTELOPE MEMORIAL HOSPITAL (281326)**, 102 West Ninth Street, Zip 68756–1114, Mailing Address: P.O. Box 229, Zip 68756–0229; tel. 402/887–4151 **A**9 10 18 **F**7 8 13 15 28 35 36 40 41 53 56 57 59 62 63 64 68 75 76 77 79 81 89 93 107 119 127 128 130 131 133 147 **P**6
Primary Contact: Jack W. Green, Administrator
CFO: Martha Nelson, Chief Financial Officer
CMO: Troy Dawson, M.D., President Medical Staff
CIO: Kevin Trease, Chief Information Officer
CHR: Mary A. Schwager, Director Human Resources
CNO: Merry Sprout, R.N., Chief Nursing Officer
Web address: www.amhne.org/
**Control:** Other not–for–profit (including NFP Corporation) **Service:** General Medical and Surgical

**Staffed Beds: 25 Admissions: 332 Census: 6 Outpatient Visits: 20529 Births: 21 Total Expense ($000): 14060 Payroll Expense ($000): 5898 Personnel: 121**

*Many Facility Codes have changed. Please refer to the AHA Guide Code Chart.* © 2015 AHA Guide

## NORFOLK—Madison County

✠ **FAITH REGIONAL HEALTH SERVICES (280125)**, 2700 West Norfolk Avenue, Zip 68701–4438, Mailing Address: P.O. Box 869, Zip 68702–0869; tel. 402/644–7201, (Includes EAST CAMPUS, 1500 Koenigstein Avenue, Zip 68701; tel. 402/371–3402; WEST CAMPUS, 2700 Norfolk Avenue, Zip 68701, Mailing Address: P.O. Box 869, Zip 68702–0869; tel. 402/371–4880), (Total facility includes 83 beds in nursing home–type unit) **A**1 2 3 5 9 10 20 **F**3 10 11 13 15 18 20 22 24 26 28 29 30 31 34 35 38 40 43 44 45 46 50 53 54 57 58 59 60 62 63 64 65 67 68 70 71 72 73 74 75 76 77 78 79 81 82 84 85 86 87 89 90 91 92 93 98 100 101 102 104 107 108 110 111 114 115 119 120 128 129 130 131 132 135 146 147 148 **P**6 7 8 **S** Faith Regional Health Services, Norfolk, NE
Primary Contact: Mark D. Klosterman, FACHE, President and Chief Executive Officer
CFO: Johnathan Wilker, Vice President Finance and Chief Financial Officer
CMO: Dean O. French, M.D., Chief of Staff
CIO: Brian Sterud, Chief Information Officer
CHR: Janet Pinkelman, Director Human Resources
Web address: www.frhs.org
**Control:** Other not–for–profit (including NFP Corporation) **Service:** General Medical and Surgical

**Staffed Beds:** 146 **Admissions:** 4905 **Census:** 145 **Outpatient Visits:** 81698 **Births:** 830 **Total Expense ($000):** 144139 **Payroll Expense ($000):** 46077 **Personnel:** 969

## NORTH PLATTE—Lincoln County

✠ **GREAT PLAINS HEALTH (280065)**, 601 West Leota Street, Zip 69101–6598, Mailing Address: P.O. Box 1167, Zip 69103–1167; tel. 308/696–8000 **A**1 2 3 5 9 10 **F**3 8 12 13 15 18 20 22 28 29 30 31 34 35 40 43 45 48 50 51 57 59 60 62 63 68 70 73 74 75 76 78 79 81 82 84 85 89 93 98 99 102 103 104 105 107 108 110 111 115 116 117 119 120 121 122 124 129 130 131 132 135 145 146 147 148 **P**8
Primary Contact: Melvin McNea, Chief Executive Officer
CFO: Krystal Claymore, Chief Financial Officer
CIO: Jim Saul, Chief Information Officer
CHR: Jayne Johnson, Director of Human Resources
CNO: Tadd Greenfield, Chief Nursing Officer
Web address: www.gprmc.com
**Control:** Other not–for–profit (including NFP Corporation) **Service:** General Medical and Surgical

**Staffed Beds:** 101 **Admissions:** 5203 **Census:** 55 **Outpatient Visits:** 259208 **Births:** 471 **Total Expense ($000):** 127346 **Payroll Expense ($000):** 51094 **Personnel:** 912

## O'NEILL—Holt County

★ **AVERA ST. ANTHONY'S HOSPITAL (281329)**, 300 North Second Street, Zip 68763–1514, Mailing Address: P.O. Box 270, Oneill, Zip 68763–0270; tel. 402/336–2611 **A**5 9 10 18 **F**3 8 13 15 18 28 29 30 31 32 34 35 38 40 43 44 45 46 48 57 59 60 62 64 65 68 74 75 76 77 78 79 81 82 84 86 87 90 91 93 94 96 97 100 101 107 108 110 111 112 114 119 120 124 127 128 129 130 131 133 135 143 146 148 **P**1 6 **S** Avera Health, Sioux Falls, SD
Primary Contact: Ronald J. Cork, President and Chief Executive Officer
CFO: Michael Garman, Chief Financial Officer
CIO: Michael Garman, Chief Financial Officer
CHR: Kathryn Benson, Human Resource and Marketing Partner
Web address: www.avera.org/st-anthonys
**Control:** Church–operated, Nongovernment, not–for profit **Service:** General Medical and Surgical

**Staffed Beds:** 25 **Admissions:** 761 **Census:** 8 **Outpatient Visits:** 46332 **Births:** 152 **Total Expense ($000):** 32978 **Payroll Expense ($000):** 13353 **Personnel:** 207

## OAKLAND—Burt County

★ **OAKLAND MERCY HOSPITAL (281321)**, 601 East Second Street, Zip 68045–1499; tel. 402/685–5601 **A**9 10 18 **F**11 15 18 20 22 24 26 28 29 30 31 34 35 40 43 44 50 57 59 75 81 93 97 107 108 110 114 119 127 128 132 133 148 **P**6 **S** Trinity Health, Livonia, MI
Primary Contact: John W. Werner, Chief Executive Officer
COO: John W. Werner, Chief Executive Officer
CFO: Terri Mentink, Chief Financial Officer
CMO: Tracie Martin, M.D., Chief Medical Officer
CNO: Paula Rathbun, Director of Nursing
Web address: www.oaklandhospital.org
**Control:** Church–operated, Nongovernment, not–for profit **Service:** General Medical and Surgical

**Staffed Beds:** 18 **Admissions:** 165 **Census:** 2 **Outpatient Visits:** 5108 **Births:** 0 **Total Expense ($000):** 5838 **Payroll Expense ($000):** 2991 **Personnel:** 40

## OGALLALA—Keith County

★ **OGALLALA COMMUNITY HOSPITAL (281355)**, 2601 North Spruce Street, Zip 69153–2465; tel. 308/284–4011 **A**9 10 18 **F**3 13 15 29 31 34 36 40 43 56 59 64 65 75 78 79 81 85 93 107 119 130 131 133 134 147 **S** Banner Health, Phoenix, AZ
Primary Contact: Aileen Chandler, Interim Chief Executive Officer
CFO: Dena Klockman, Chief Financial Officer
CMO: Kurt Johnson, M.D., Chief of Staff
CHR: Cynda Eklund, Interim Chief Human Resources Officer
CNO: Aileen Chandler, Director of Nursing
Web address: www.bannerhealth.com/Locations/Nebraska/Ogallala+Community+Hospital
**Control:** Other not–for–profit (including NFP Corporation) **Service:** General Medical and Surgical

**Staffed Beds:** 18 **Admissions:** 509 **Census:** 4 **Outpatient Visits:** 20991 **Births:** 83 **Total Expense ($000):** 14257 **Payroll Expense ($000):** 5543 **Personnel:** 109

## OMAHA—Douglas County

☐ **BOYS TOWN NATIONAL RESEARCH HOSPITAL (283300)**, 555 North 30th Street, Zip 68131–2198; tel. 402/498–6511 **A**1 3 5 9 10 **F**3 34 35 58 65 68 79 81 86 87 89 97 99 104 106 107 108 111 119 129 130 131 **P**6
Primary Contact: John K. Arch, FACHE, Director
CFO: Leigh Jean Koinzan, Director Finance
CMO: Edward Kolb, M.D., Medical Director
CIO: Ann Ducey, Chief Information Officer
CHR: Michael Gell, Director Human Resources
CNO: Patricia Allgeier, R.N., Chief Nursing Officer
Web address: www.boystownhospital.org
**Control:** Other not–for–profit (including NFP Corporation) **Service:** Children's general

**Staffed Beds:** 131 **Admissions:** 210 **Census:** 2 **Outpatient Visits:** 202858 **Births:** 0 **Total Expense ($000):** 96506 **Payroll Expense ($000):** 42551 **Personnel:** 831

✠ **CHI HEALTH BERGAN MERCY (280060)**, 7500 Mercy Road, Zip 68124–2319; tel. 402/398–6060, (Includes LASTING HOPE RECOVERY CENTER, 415 South 25th Avenue, Zip 68131; tel. 402/717–5300; Robin Conyers, Administrator) **A**1 2 3 5 9 10 **F**3 8 11 13 15 17 18 20 22 24 26 28 29 30 31 32 34 35 37 38 40 43 44 45 46 47 48 49 50 51 53 54 55 56 57 58 59 60 61 62 63 64 65 68 70 72 74 75 76 77 78 79 80 81 82 83 84 85 86 87 89 92 93 97 98 100 105 107 108 109 110 111 114 115 116 117 118 119 120 121 123 124 126 127 130 131 132 133 134 143 144 145 146 147 148 **P**6 8 **S** Catholic Health Initiatives, Englewood, CO
Primary Contact: Marie E. Knedler, R.N., FACHE, President
COO: Chris Evans, Vice President Operations
CFO: Tim H. Schnack, Vice President Financial Services
CMO: Kevin Reagan, M.D., Chief Medical Officer
CIO: Karun Kapur, Chief Information Officer
CHR: Nancy Wallace, Vice President Human Resources
CNO: Jane Carmody, R.N., Vice President and System Chief Nursing Officer
Web address: www.alegent.com/bergan
**Control:** Church–operated, Nongovernment, not–for profit **Service:** General Medical and Surgical

**Staffed Beds:** 336 **Admissions:** 12766 **Census:** 156 **Outpatient Visits:** 116359 **Births:** 3532 **Total Expense ($000):** 235332 **Payroll Expense ($000):** 76780 **Personnel:** 1321

✠ **CHI HEALTH CREIGHTON UNIVERSITY MEDICAL CENTER (280030)**, 601 North 30th Street, Zip 68131–2197; tel. 402/449–4000, (Nonreporting) **A**1 3 5 9 10 **S** Catholic Health Initiatives, Englewood, CO
Primary Contact: Kevin J. Nokels, FACHE, President
COO: Todd Defreece, Vice President Operations
CFO: Tim H. Schnack, Chief Financial Officer
CMO: Devin Fox, M.D., Chief Medical Officer
CIO: Ellen Deao, Director Information Services
CHR: Rebecca Ruetsch, Human Resource Partner
CNO: Cary Reimers, Chief Nurse Executive
Web address: www.alegentcreighton.com
**Control:** Other not–for–profit (including NFP Corporation) **Service:** General Medical and Surgical

**Staffed Beds:** 223

**NE**

---

**Hospital, Medicare Provider Number, Address, Telephone, Approval, Facility, and Physician Codes, Health Care System**

★ American Hospital Association (AHA) membership
☐ The Joint Commission accreditation
◯ Healthcare Facilities Accreditation Program
◇ DNV Healthcare Inc. accreditation
⇑ Center for Improvement in Healthcare Quality Accreditation
△ Commission on Accreditation of Rehabilitation Facilities (CARF) accreditation

⊞ △ **CHI HEALTH IMMANUEL (280081)**, 6901 North 72nd Street, Zip 68122–1799; tel. 402/572–2121, (Total facility includes 165 beds in nursing home–type unit) **A**1 2 3 5 7 9 10 **F**3 4 5 6 11 12 13 15 17 18 20 22 26 28 29 30 31 32 34 35 36 37 38 40 43 44 45 49 50 51 53 55 56 57 59 62 63 64 68 70 72 73 74 75 76 77 78 79 80 81 82 83 84 85 86 87 88 89 90 91 92 93 96 97 98 99 100 101 102 103 104 105 106 107 108 109 110 111 114 115 117 118 119 120 121 123 124 126 128 129 130 131 132 134 136 142 146 147 148 **P**6 8 **S** Catholic Health Initiatives, Englewood, CO
Primary Contact: Ann Schumacher, R.N., MSN, FACHE, President
CFO: Tim H. Schnack, Chief Financial Officer
CMO: Joseph Hoagbin, M.D., Chief Medical Officer
CHR: Nancy Wallace, Vice President Human Resources
CNO: Jane Carmody, R.N., Chief Nursing Officer
Web address: www.alegent.com/immanuel
**Control:** Church–operated, Nongovernment, not–for profit **Service:** General Medical and Surgical

**Staffed Beds:** 289 **Admissions:** 9586 **Census:** 152 **Outpatient Visits:** 123471 **Births:** 587 **Total Expense ($000):** 177900 **Payroll Expense ($000):** 58002 **Personnel:** 1065

⊞ **CHI HEALTH LAKESIDE (280130)**, 16901 Lakeside Hills Court, Zip 68130–2318; tel. 402/717–8000 **A**1 2 3 5 7 9 10 **F**3 8 12 13 15 17 18 20 22 26 28 29 30 31 32 34 35 36 38 40 44 45 46 49 53 54 55 56 59 60 63 64 68 70 72 73 74 75 76 77 78 79 81 82 83 84 85 86 93 94 97 99 100 102 103 104 107 108 110 111 114 115 118 119 120 121 122 123 124 126 129 130 131 132 134 143 146 147 148 **P**6 8 **S** Catholic Health Initiatives, Englewood, CO
Primary Contact: Cindy Alloway, President
COO: Joan E. Neuhaus, Senior Vice President Chief Operating Officer
CFO: Tyler DeJong, Senior Director of Finance
CMO: Patricia Murdock–Langan, M.D., Chief Medical Officer
CIO: Karun Kapur, Regional Chief Information Officer
CHR: Nancy Wallace, Senior Vice President, Chief Human Resource Officer
CNO: Jane Carmody, R.N., Chief Nursing Officer
Web address: www.CHIhealth.com
**Control:** Church–operated, Nongovernment, not–for profit **Service:** General Medical and Surgical

**Staffed Beds:** 135 **Admissions:** 7041 **Census:** 72 **Outpatient Visits:** 101976 **Births:** 1010 **Total Expense ($000):** 124361 **Payroll Expense ($000):** 36545 **Personnel:** 435

⊞ **CHILDREN'S HOSPITAL AND MEDICAL CENTER (283301)**, 8200 Dodge Street, Zip 68114–4113; tel. 402/955–5400 **A**1 3 5 9 10 **F**3 7 11 12 13 19 21 23 25 27 29 30 31 32 34 35 40 41 43 45 48 49 54 55 59 62 64 68 72 74 75 77 78 79 81 82 84 85 87 88 89 92 93 99 104 107 108 111 115 119 126 129 130 131 132 137 143 144 145 146 148 **P**6
Primary Contact: Gary A. Perkins, FACHE, President and Chief Executive Officer
COO: Kathy L. English, R.N., Executive Vice President and Chief Operating Officer
CFO: Amy Hatcher, Chief Financial Officer
CMO: Carl H. Gumbiner, M.D., Senior Vice President Medical Affairs and Chief Medical Officer
CIO: Mark Stastny, Vice President and Chief Information Officer
CHR: Suzanne Nocita, Interim Vice President Human Resources
CNO: Debra Arnow, R.N., VP Patient Care & Chief Nursing Officer
Web address: www.childrensomaha.org
**Control:** Other not–for–profit (including NFP Corporation) **Service:** Children's General Medical and Surgical

**Staffed Beds:** 126 **Admissions:** 4929 **Census:** 91 **Outpatient Visits:** 317214 **Births:** 7 **Total Expense ($000):** 293537 **Payroll Expense ($000):** 123480 **Personnel:** 2406

★ ○ **DOUGLAS COUNTY COMMUNITY MENTAL HEALTH CENTER (284009)**, 4102 Woolworth Avenue, Zip 68105–1899; tel. 402/444–7000, (Nonreporting) **A**3 5 9 10 11
Primary Contact: Sherry L. Glasnapp, Director
CFO: DeDe Will, Director Finance
CMO: Sidney A. Kauzlarich, M.D., Medical Director
CIO: Dianne Wallace, County Information Manager
CHR: Lee A. Lazure, Director Civil Service Commission
CNO: Marti Christensen, Director of Psychiatric Nursing
Web address: www.co.douglas.ne.us
**Control:** County–Government, nonfederal **Service:** Psychiatric

**Staffed Beds:** 18

**MIDWEST SURGICAL HOSPITAL (280131)**, 7915 Farnam Drive, Zip 68114–4504; tel. 402/399–1900, (Nonreporting) **A**3 9 10
Primary Contact: Charles Livingston, Chief Executive Officer
Web address: www.mwsurgicalhospital.com
**Control:** Corporation, Investor–owned, for–profit **Service:** Surgical

**Staffed Beds:** 19

⊞ **NEBRASKA MEDICINE – NEBRASKA MEDICAL CENTER (280013)**, 987400 Nebraska Medical Center, Zip 68198–7400; tel. 402/552–2000 **A**1 2 3 5 8 9 10 **F**3 6 9 11 12 13 15 16 17 18 20 22 26 28 29 30 31 34 35 36 37 38 40 41 43 44 45 46 47 48 49 50 53 54 57 58 59 61 64 65 68 70 72 74 76 77 78 79 80 81 82 84 85 86 87 88 89 91 92 93 94 96 97 98 101 107 108 110 111 113 114 115 116 117 118 119 120 121 123 124 126 129 130 131 132 135 136 137 138 139 141 142 145 146 147 148 **P**5 8
Primary Contact: Rosanna D. Morris, R.N., Interim Chief Executive Officer
COO: Dennis Bierle, Chief Operating Officer
CFO: Stephanie Daubert, Chief Financial Officer
CMO: Harris Frankel, M.D., Interim Chief Medical Officer
CIO: Michael A. Ash, Chief Transformation Officer
CHR: Frank Venuto, Chief Human Capital Officer
CNO: Suzanne Langan Nuss, M.D., Chief Nursing Officer
Web address: www.nebraskamed.com
**Control:** Other not–for–profit (including NFP Corporation) **Service:** General Medical and Surgical

**Staffed Beds:** 525 **Admissions:** 22458 **Census:** 370 **Outpatient Visits:** 433710 **Births:** 1807 **Total Expense ($000):** 747129 **Payroll Expense ($000):** 251734 **Personnel:** 4266

⊞ △ **NEBRASKA METHODIST HOSPITAL (280040)**, 8303 Dodge Street, Zip 68114–4199; tel. 402/354–4000, (Includes METHODIST WOMEN'S HOSPITAL, 707 North 190th Plaza, Elkhorn, Zip 68022–3974; tel. 402/815–4000; Susan Korth, M.P.H., Ph.D., Vice President and Chief Operating Officer) **A**1 2 3 5 7 9 10 **F**3 8 11 12 13 15 17 18 20 22 24 26 28 29 30 31 34 35 40 45 46 47 48 49 50 51 52 53 54 55 56 57 58 59 62 63 64 65 66 68 70 72 74 75 76 77 78 79 81 82 83 84 85 86 87 90 91 92 93 96 100 101 104 107 108 110 111 114 115 117 118 119 120 121 123 124 126 129 130 132 135 136 141 143 146 147 148 **S** Nebraska Methodist Health System, Inc., Omaha, NE
Primary Contact: Stephen L. Goeser, FACHE, President and Chief Executive Officer
CFO: Linda K. Burt, Corporate Vice President Finance
CMO: William Shiffermiller, M.D., Vice President Medical Affairs
CHR: Holly Huerter, Vice President Human Resources
CNO: Teri Tipton, MSN, Chief Nursing Officer and Vice President Patient Care Services
Web address: www.bestcare.org
**Control:** Other not–for–profit (including NFP Corporation) **Service:** General Medical and Surgical

**Staffed Beds:** 368 **Admissions:** 17070 **Census:** 242 **Outpatient Visits:** 131798 **Births:** 4461 **Total Expense ($000):** 411350 **Payroll Expense ($000):** 151813 **Personnel:** 2172

☐ **NEBRASKA ORTHOPAEDIC HOSPITAL (280129)**, 2808 South 143rd Plaza, Zip 68144–5611; tel. 402/609–1600 **A**1 3 5 9 10 **F**3 9 29 34 35 37 39 40 44 50 57 58 59 64 77 79 81 82 85 86 87 93 94 96 107 111 131 141 142 **P**6
Primary Contact: Levi Scheppers, Chief Executive Officer
COO: Mark E. Longacre, FACHE, Chief Operating Officer
CFO: Anna McCaslin, Chief Financial Officer
CMO: Ian Crabb, M.D., Chief Medical Officer
CIO: Tim Pugsley, Chief Information Officer
CHR: Lori L. Thompson, Manager Human Resources
CNO: Nancy Laughlin, R.N., Chief Nursing Officer
Web address: www.neorthohospital.com
**Control:** Partnership, Investor–owned, for–profit **Service:** Orthopedic

**Staffed Beds:** 24 **Admissions:** 1639 **Census:** 11 **Outpatient Visits:** 62296 **Births:** 0 **Total Expense ($000):** 64305 **Payroll Expense ($000):** 18849 **Personnel:** 307

⊞ **NEBRASKA SPINE HOSPITAL (280133)**, 6901 North 72nd Street, Suite 20300, Zip 68122–1755, Mailing Address: 6901 North 72nd Street, Zip 68122–1709; tel. 402/572–3000, (Nonreporting) **A**1 9 10 **S** Catholic Health Initiatives, Englewood, CO
Primary Contact: Cory Kruger, Interim Chief Executive Officer
Web address: www.nebraskaspinehospital.com
**Control:** Partnership, Investor–owned, for–profit **Service:** Orthopedic

**Staffed Beds:** 34

⊞ **SELECT SPECIALTY HOSPITAL–OMAHA (282001)**, 1870 South 75th Street, Zip 68124–1700; tel. 402/361–5700, (Nonreporting) **A**1 9 10 **S** Select Medical Corporation, Mechanicsburg, PA
Primary Contact: Thomas N. Theroult, ACHE, Chief Executive Officer
COO: Joel White, Chief Operating Officer
CMO: Guillermo Huerta, M.D., Chief Medical Officer
CHR: Gwen Cox, Human Resources Coordinator
CNO: Brenda O'Gorman, R.N., Interim Chief Nursing Officer
Web address: www.selectspecialtyhospitals.com/company/locations/omahacentral.aspx
**Control:** Corporation, Investor–owned, for–profit **Service:** Long–Term Acute Care hospital

**Staffed Beds:** 52

*Many Facility Codes have changed. Please refer to the AHA Guide Code Chart.* © 2015 AHA Guide

NE

✠ **VETERANS AFFAIRS NEBRASKA–WESTERN IOWA HEALTH CARE SYSTEM**, 4101 Woolworth Avenue, Zip 68105–1873; tel. 402/346–8800, (Total facility includes 38 beds in nursing home–type unit) **A**1 2 3 5 8 9 **F**3 4 5 8 9 12 18 20 22 29 30 31 34 35 36 38 39 40 45 46 47 48 49 50 51 53 54 56 57 58 59 60 61 63 64 65 70 71 74 75 77 78 79 81 82 83 84 85 86 87 91 92 93 94 95 96 97 98 100 101 102 103 104 105 106 107 111 115 117 118 119 127 128 129 130 132 135 143 144 145 146 147 148 **S** Department of Veterans Affairs, Washington, DC
Primary Contact: Don Burman, Director
COO: Denise Harrison, Associate Director
CFO: Kirk Kay, Chief Financial Officer
CMO: Grace Stringfellow, M.D., Chief of Staff
CIO: Jennifer Rosenbalm, Manager Business Office
CHR: Cheryl M. DeWispelare, Chief Human Resources Officer
CNO: Eileen M. Kingston, R.N., Nurse Executive, Associate Director Patient Care
Web address: www.nebraska.va.gov/
**Control:** Veterans Affairs, Government, federal **Service:** General Medical and Surgical

**Staffed Beds:** 137 **Admissions:** 5152 **Census:** 95 **Outpatient Visits:** 551362 **Births:** 0 **Total Expense ($000):** 401879 **Payroll Expense ($000):** 152834 **Personnel:** 1986

### ORD—Valley County

★ **VALLEY COUNTY HEALTH SYSTEM (281353)**, 2707 L. Street, Zip 68862–1275; tel. 308/728–4200, (Total facility includes 40 beds in nursing home–type unit) **A**9 10 18 **F**1 40 43 67 74 75 77 78 79 81 82 84 87 90 93 94 97 107 111 115 119 127 128 129 133 143 148
Primary Contact: Ashley Woodward, Interim Chief Executive Officer
CFO: Ashley Woodward, Director Financial Services
CMO: Jennifer Bengston, M.D., Chief Medical Officer
CIO: Shane Molacek, Chief Information Officer
CHR: Danielle Proskocil, Director Human Resources
Web address: www.valleycountyhospital.org
**Control:** County–Government, nonfederal **Service:** General Medical and Surgical

**Staffed Beds:** 56 **Admissions:** 459 **Census:** 36 **Outpatient Visits:** 28376 **Births:** 0 **Total Expense ($000):** 22850 **Payroll Expense ($000):** 9279 **Personnel:** 200

### OSCEOLA—Polk County

**ANNIE JEFFREY MEMORIAL COUNTY HEALTH CENTER (281314)**, 531 Beebe Street, Zip 68651–5537, Mailing Address: P.O. Box 428, Zip 68651–0428; tel. 402/747–2031, (Nonreporting) **A**9 10 18
Primary Contact: Joseph W. Lohrman, ACHE, Chief Executive Officer
CFO: Joseph W. Lohrman, ACHE, Chief Executive Officer
CMO: David Jameson, M.D., Chief of Staff
CIO: Frank Vrba, Chief Information Officer
CHR: Sue Leif, R.N., Director Human Resources
Web address: www.ajhc.org
**Control:** County–Government, nonfederal **Service:** General Medical and Surgical

**Staffed Beds:** 21

### OSHKOSH—Garden County

**REGIONAL WEST GARDEN COUNTY (281310)**, 1100 West Second Street, Zip 69154–6152; tel. 308/772–3283, (Nonreporting) **A**9 10 18
Primary Contact: Chad Thompson, Interim Chief Executive Officer
CFO: Jennifer Moffat, Staff Accountant
CMO: Harold Keenan, M.D., Chief Medical Officer
CIO: DeeDee Dunlap, Information Officer
CHR: Ricca Sanford, Director Human Resources
CNO: Darlene Schaeffer, Chief Nursing Officer
Web address: www.gchealth.org
**Control:** County–Government, nonfederal **Service:** General Medical and Surgical

**Staffed Beds:** 50

### OSMOND—Pierce County

★ **OSMOND GENERAL HOSPITAL (281347)**, 402 North Maple Street, Zip 68765–5726, Mailing Address: P.O. Box 429, Zip 68765–0429; tel. 402/748–3393 **A**9 10 18 **F**3 28 34 40 57 59 64 69 81 107 133 143 **P**5 6
Primary Contact: Lon Knievel, Chief Executive Officer
CFO: Jodi Aschoff, Chief Financial Officer
CMO: David Mwebe, M.D., Chief of Staff
Web address: www.osmondhospital.com
**Control:** Other not–for–profit (including NFP Corporation) **Service:** General Medical and Surgical

**Staffed Beds:** 21 **Admissions:** 129 **Census:** 1 **Outpatient Visits:** 4395 **Births:** 0 **Total Expense ($000):** 7458 **Payroll Expense ($000):** 3367 **Personnel:** 67

### PAPILLION—Sarpy County

✠ **CHI HEALTH MIDLANDS (280105)**, 11111 South 84th Street, Zip 68046–4122; tel. 402/593–3000 **A**1 2 9 10 **F**3 11 13 15 17 18 20 22 26 28 29 30 34 35 36 38 40 42 43 44 45 46 49 50 51 53 56 57 59 60 61 62 63 64 65 68 70 76 77 79 81 84 85 86 87 93 97 107 110 111 114 115 117 118 119 129 130 131 132 135 143 146 147 **P**6 8 **S** Catholic Health Initiatives, Englewood, CO
Primary Contact: Cindy Alloway, President
COO: Joan E. Neuhaus, Senior Vice President, Chief Operating Officer
CFO: Tyler DeJong, Senior Director of Finance
CMO: Patricia Murdock–Langan, M.D., Chief Medical Officer
CIO: Karun Kapur, Regional Chief Information Officer
CHR: Nancy Wallace, Senior Vice President, Chief Human Resource Officer
CNO: Jane Carmody, R.N., Chief Nursing Officer
Web address: www.CHIhealth.com
**Control:** Church–operated, Nongovernment, not–for profit **Service:** General Medical and Surgical

**Staffed Beds:** 50 **Admissions:** 1745 **Census:** 18 **Outpatient Visits:** 43967 **Births:** 88 **Total Expense ($000):** 49058 **Payroll Expense ($000):** 14804 **Personnel:** 250

### PAWNEE CITY—Pawnee County

★ **PAWNEE COUNTY MEMORIAL HOSPITAL AND RURAL HEALTH CLINIC (281302)**, 600 I Street, Zip 68420–3001, Mailing Address: P.O. Box 433, Zip 68420–0433; tel. 402/852–2231, (Nonreporting) **A**9 10 18
Primary Contact: Gary Bieganski, Interim Chief Executive Officer
CHR: Jennifer Bartels, Director Human Resources
CNO: Eulala Mitchell, Interim Director of Nursing
Web address: www.pawneehospital.com
**Control:** County–Government, nonfederal **Service:** General Medical and Surgical

**Staffed Beds:** 11

### PENDER—Thurston County

★ **PENDER COMMUNITY HOSPITAL (281349)**, 100 Hospital Drive, Zip 68047–0100, Mailing Address: P.O. Box 100, Zip 68047–0100; tel. 402/385–3083, (Nonreporting) **A**9 10 18 **S** Trinity Health, Livonia, MI
Primary Contact: Melissa Kelly, Administrator
COO: Melissa Kelly, Chief Operating Officer
CFO: Melissa Kelly, Chief Financial Officer
CMO: Matt Timm, M.D., Medical Director
CIO: Teresa Heise, Coordinator Management Information Systems
CHR: Nancy Suhr, Manager Human Resources
CNO: Katie Peterson, R.N., Chief Nursing Officer
Web address: www.pendercommunityhospital.com
**Control:** Hospital district or authority, Government, nonfederal **Service:** General Medical and Surgical

**Staffed Beds:** 67

### PLAINVIEW—Pierce County

★ **CHI HEALTH PLAINVIEW (281346)**, 704 North Third Street, Zip 68769–2047, Mailing Address: P.O. Box 489, Zip 68769–0489; tel. 402/582–4245, (Nonreporting) **A**9 10 18 **S** Catholic Health Initiatives, Englewood, CO
Primary Contact: Richard B. Gamel, President, Regional Hospital
CFO: Tim H. Schnack, Chief Financial Officer
CMO: Steve Peterson, M.D., Chief of Staff
CHR: Diane Blair, Human Resources and Admissions
CNO: Debra K. Rutledge, R.N., Vice President Nursing Services
Web address: www.alegentcreighton.com/plainview–hospital
**Control:** Church–operated, Nongovernment, not–for profit **Service:** General Medical and Surgical

**Staffed Beds:** 16

### RED CLOUD—Webster County

**WEBSTER COUNTY COMMUNITY HOSPITAL (281316)**, Sixth Avenue and Franklin Street, Zip 68970–0465, Mailing Address: P.O. Box 465, Zip 68970–0465; tel. 402/746–5600 **A**9 10 18 **F**3 15 18 28 29 30 32 34 35 40 41 45 50 56 57 59 64 65 68 70 75 77 78 79 81 82 83 84 90 91 93 94 96 97 107 110 111 112 118 119 127 128 129 130 133 145 146
Primary Contact: Luke Poore, Administrator
CFO: Marcia Olson, Business Office Manager
CMO: Amy Springer, Medical Director
CIO: Eileen Berry, Manager Information Technology
CHR: Marcia Olson, Business Office Manager
CNO: Candace Peters, R.N., Director of Nursing
Web address: www.websterhospital.org
**Control:** County–Government, nonfederal **Service:** General Medical and Surgical

**Staffed Beds:** 13 **Admissions:** 127 **Census:** 2 **Outpatient Visits:** 774 **Births:** 0 **Total Expense ($000):** 4751 **Payroll Expense ($000):** 2968 **Personnel:** 48

---

**Hospital, Medicare Provider Number, Address, Telephone, Approval, Facility, and Physician Codes, Health Care System**

★ American Hospital Association (AHA) membership    ○ Healthcare Facilities Accreditation Program    ⇑ Center for Improvement in Healthcare Quality Accreditation
□ The Joint Commission accreditation    ◇ DNV Healthcare Inc. accreditation    △ Commission on Accreditation of Rehabilitation Facilities (CARF) accreditation

**NE**

**SAINT PAUL—Howard County**

**HOWARD COUNTY COMMUNITY HOSPITAL** See Howard County Medical Center

★ **HOWARD COUNTY MEDICAL CENTER (281338)**, 1113 Sherman Street, Zip 68873–1546, Mailing Address: P.O. Box 406, Zip 68873–0406; tel. 308/754–4421, (Nonreporting) **A**9 10 18
Primary Contact: Arlan D. Johnson, ACHE, Chief Executive Officer
COO: Jillyn Klein, Chief Operating Officer
CFO: Morgan Meyer, Chief Financial Officer
CMO: Angela Brennan, M.D., Chief of Staff
CIO: Kari Pierson, Manager
CHR: Leslie Smith, Director Human Resources
CNO: Janelle Morgan, Interim Director of Nursing
Web address: www.hcmc.us.com
**Control:** County–Government, nonfederal **Service:** General Medical and Surgical

Staffed Beds: 25

**SCHUYLER—Colfax County**

★ **CHI HEALTH SCHUYLER (281323)**, 104 West 17th Street, Zip 68661–1304; tel. 402/352–2441, (Nonreporting) **A**9 10 18 **S** Catholic Health Initiatives, Englewood, CO
Primary Contact: Connie Peters, R.N., President
CFO: Tim H. Schnack, Chief Financial Officer
CIO: Kenneth Lawonn, Senior Vice President and Chief Information Officer
CHR: Nancy Wallace, Vice President Human Resources
CNO: Jane Carmody, R.N., Vice President and System Chief Nursing Officer
Web address: www.alegent.org
**Control:** Church–operated, Nongovernment, not–for profit **Service:** General Medical and Surgical

Staffed Beds: 25

**SCOTTSBLUFF—Scotts Bluff County**

✉ △ **REGIONAL WEST MEDICAL CENTER (280061)**, 4021 Avenue B, Zip 69361–4695; tel. 308/635–3711, (Nonreporting) **A**1 2 3 5 7 9 10
Primary Contact: John Mentgen, FACHE, President and Chief Executive Officer
CFO: Jim Strong, MBA, Chief Financial Officer
CMO: Jon Morgan, M.D., Chief Medical Officer
CIO: Steve Mathews, Vice President and Chief Information Officer
CHR: Bradford L. Evans, Director Human Resources
CNO: Shirley Knodel, R.N., Chief Nursing Officer
Web address: www.rwhs.org
**Control:** Other not–for–profit (including NFP Corporation) **Service:** General Medical and Surgical

Staffed Beds: 145

**SEWARD—Seward County**

★ **MEMORIAL HEALTH CARE SYSTEMS (281339)**, 300 North Columbia Avenue, Zip 68434–2228; tel. 402/643–2971, (Nonreporting) **A**9 10 18
Primary Contact: Roger J. Reamer, Chief Executive Officer
CFO: Jim Strong, MBA, Chief Financial Officer
CMO: Tricia Sams, M.D., Medical Director
CIO: Carol Carlson, Director Community Relations
CHR: Core Mann, Director of Human Resources
Web address: www.mhcs.us
**Control:** Other not–for–profit (including NFP Corporation) **Service:** General Medical and Surgical

Staffed Beds: 25

**SIDNEY—Cheyenne County**

★ **SIDNEY REGIONAL MEDICAL CENTER (281357)**, 645 Osage Street, Zip 69162–1799; tel. 308/254–5825, (Total facility includes 63 beds in nursing home–type unit) **A**3 5 9 10 18 **F**8 10 11 13 15 18 19 28 29 30 31 34 35 40 41 45 49 50 56 57 59 62 63 64 65 68 70 75 76 77 79 81 82 84 85 89 92 93 97 107 108 110 111 114 119 127 128 129 130 131 132 133 135 146 148 **P**6
Primary Contact: Jason Petik, ACHE, Chief Executive Officer
CMO: Mandy Shaw, M.D., Chief of Staff
CIO: Jennifer Brockhaus, Chief Information Officer
CHR: Catherine T. Arterburn, R.N., Vice President Human Resources
CNO: Julie A. Slagle, R.N., Vice President Patient Care Services
Web address: www.sidneyrmc.com
**Control:** Other not–for–profit (including NFP Corporation) **Service:** General Medical and Surgical

Staffed Beds: 93 Admissions: 839 Census: 74 Outpatient Visits: 30445 Births: 83 Total Expense ($000): 38282 Payroll Expense ($000): 16609 Personnel: 345

**SUPERIOR—Nuckolls County**

★ **BRODSTONE MEMORIAL HOSPITAL (281315)**, 520 East Tenth Street, Zip 68978–1225, Mailing Address: P.O. Box 187, Zip 68978–0187; tel. 402/879–3281 **A**9 10 18 **F**3 8 11 13 15 17 28 29 30 31 34 35 40 41 57 59 62 65 66 67 70 74 75 76 77 79 81 82 85 86 87 89 93 97 107 110 111 114 119 127 128 129 130 131 132 133 135 146 148
Primary Contact: John E. Keelan, Administrator and Chief Executive Officer
COO: Dena C. Alvarez, R.N., COO & Chief Compliance Officer
CFO: Sandy Borden, Chief Financial Officer
CMO: Timothy Blecha, M.D., Medical Director
CIO: Tim Hiatt, Chief Information Officer
CHR: Jeremy Littrell, Director Human Resources
CNO: Kori Field, Director of Nursing
Web address: www.brodstonehospital.org
**Control:** Other not–for–profit (including NFP Corporation) **Service:** General Medical and Surgical

Staffed Beds: 25 Admissions: 405 Census: 3 Outpatient Visits: 16462 Births: 35 Total Expense ($000): 20173 Payroll Expense ($000): 8172 Personnel: 159

**SYRACUSE—Otoe County**

★ **COMMUNITY MEMORIAL HOSPITAL (281309)**, 1579 Midland Street, Zip 68446–9732, Mailing Address: P.O. Box N., Zip 68446–0518; tel. 402/269–2011 **A**9 10 18 **F**1 3 11 15 28 29 40 43 45 53 59 62 64 67 79 81 85 89 90 93 107 110 119 127 128 133
Primary Contact: Michael Harvey, FACHE, President and Chief Executive Officer
COO: Julie Werner, Chief Operating Officer
CFO: Karrie Beach, Vice President of Finance
CMO: Zak Tempelmeyer, M.D., Chief Medical Staff
CIO: Matthew Steinblock, Systems Administrator
CHR: Nancy Brack, Vice President of Human Resources
CNO: Pat Howell, Chief Nursing Officer
Web address: www.syracusecmh.org
**Control:** Hospital district or authority, Government, nonfederal **Service:** General Medical and Surgical

Staffed Beds: 10 Admissions: 131 Census: 2 Outpatient Visits: 12866 Births: 0 Total Expense ($000): 12667 Payroll Expense ($000): 5710 Personnel: 99

**TECUMSEH—Johnson County**

★ **JOHNSON COUNTY HOSPITAL (281350)**, 202 High Street, Zip 68450–2443, Mailing Address: P.O. Box 599, Zip 68450–0599; tel. 402/335–3361, (Nonreporting) **A**9 10 18
Primary Contact: Diane Newman, FACHE, Administrator
COO: Diane Newman, FACHE, Administrator
CFO: Emily Ideus, Manager Business Office
CMO: Keith Shuey, M.D., Chief Medical Staff
CIO: Fred Pooch, Supervisor Information Technology
CHR: Susan Hessheimer, Director Human Resources
CNO: Matthew Snyder, R.N., Director of Nursing
Web address: www.jchosp.com
**Control:** County–Government, nonfederal **Service:** General Medical and Surgical

Staffed Beds: 25

**VALENTINE—Cherry County**

★ **CHERRY COUNTY HOSPITAL (281344)**, 510 North Green Street, Zip 69201–1932, Mailing Address: P.O. Box 410, Zip 69201–0410; tel. 402/376–2525, (Nonreporting) **A**9 10 18
Primary Contact: Brent A. Peterson, Administrator
CFO: Peggy Snell, Chief Finance Officer
**Control:** County–Government, nonfederal **Service:** General Medical and Surgical

Staffed Beds: 25

**WAHOO—Saunders County**

★ **SAUNDERS MEDICAL CENTER (281307)**, 1760 County Road J., Zip 68066–4152; tel. 402/443–4191, (Nonreporting) **A**9 10 18 **S** Bryan Health, Lincoln, NE
Primary Contact: Tyler Toline, FACHE, Interim Chief Executive Officer
CFO: Chase Manstedt, Chief Financial Officer
CMO: Leo L. Meduna, M.D., Chief Medical Officer
CIO: Carrie Stephens, Director of Information Technology and Support Services
CHR: Karen Leise, Coordinator Human Resources
CNO: LaLah Landers, BSN, RN, Director of Nursing
Web address: www.saundersmedicalcenter.com
**Control:** County–Government, nonfederal **Service:** General Medical and Surgical

Staffed Beds: 87

**NE**

*Many Facility Codes have changed. Please refer to the AHA Guide Code Chart.* © 2015 AHA Guide

## WAYNE—Wayne County

★ **PROVIDENCE MEDICAL CENTER (281345)**, 1200 Providence Road,
Zip 68787–1299; tel. 402/375–3800 **A**9 10 18 **F**3 7 13 15 28 29 30 31 34
35 36 40 50 53 57 59 62 63 64 68 75 76 81 84 85 93 107 110 111 114
119 128 130 132 133 135
Primary Contact: Jim Frank, CPA, Chief Executive Officer
CFO: Kim Hixson, Vice President of Financial Officer and Chief Financial Officer
CHR: Jacqueline Ann Backer, Vice President of Human Resources
CNO: Laura Gamble, Vice President of Clinical Services
COO: Kris Giese, Chief Operating Officer
Web address: www.providencemedical.com
**Control:** Other not–for–profit (including NFP Corporation) **Service:** General
Medical and Surgical

> **Staffed Beds:** 25 **Admissions:** 498 **Census:** 6 **Outpatient Visits:** 14292
> **Births:** 64 **Total Expense ($000):** 17793 **Payroll Expense ($000):** 8061
> **Personnel:** 164

## WEST POINT—Cuming County

★ **ST. FRANCIS MEMORIAL HOSPITAL (281322)**, 430 North Monitor Street,
Zip 68788–1555; tel. 402/372–2404, (Total facility includes 63 beds in nursing
home–type unit) **A**9 10 18 **F**3 6 11 13 15 28 29 30 31 34 35 40 43 45 50 53
57 59 62 63 64 68 75 76 77 78 79 81 82 85 86 90 92 93 94 98 99 100
103 107 111 114 119 127 128 129 130 131 132 133 135 146 147 148 **P**6
**S** Franciscan Sisters of Christian Charity Sponsored Ministries, Inc.,
Manitowoc, WI
Primary Contact: Jerry Wordekemper, President and Chief Executive Officer
CFO: Dennis Dinslage, Vice President Finance and Chief Financial Officer
CMO: Brian Hass, M.D., Chief of Staff
CIO: Jean Meiergerd, Chief Information Officer
CHR: Terri Ridder, Director Human Resources
CNO: Carol Kampschnieder, Vice President Clinical and Regulatory Services
Web address: www.fcswp.org
**Control:** Church–operated, Nongovernment, not–for profit **Service:** General
Medical and Surgical

> **Staffed Beds:** 92 **Admissions:** 628 **Census:** 64 **Outpatient Visits:** 69087
> **Births:** 77 **Total Expense ($000):** 31594 **Payroll Expense ($000):** 13819
> **Personnel:** 226

## WINNEBAGO—Thurston County

☐ ◇ **U. S. PUBLIC HEALTH SERVICE INDIAN HOSPITAL (280119)**, Highway
7577, Zip 68071; tel. 402/878–2231, (Nonreporting) **A**1 9 10 21 **S** U. S. Indian
Health Service, Rockville, MD
Primary Contact: Patricia Medina, Service Unit Director
CFO: Audrey Parker, Budget Analyst
Web address: www.ihs.gov
**Control:** PHS, Indian Service, Government, federal **Service:** General Medical and
Surgical

> **Staffed Beds:** 30

## YORK—York County

★ **YORK GENERAL HOSPITAL (281336)**, 2222 North Lincoln Avenue,
Zip 68467–1095; tel. 402/362–6671, (Total facility includes 129 beds in nursing
home–type unit) **A**9 10 18 **F**3 10 11 12 13 15 28 29 31 34 35 40 45 53 56 57
59 60 62 64 68 70 75 76 77 78 79 81 82 85 86 87 89 93 96 107 108 110
111 115 117 118 119 125 128 129 130 131 132 133 145 146 148
Primary Contact: Charles K. Schulz, ACHE, Chief Executive Officer
CFO: Bob McQuistan, Vice President Finance
CMO: Ye Ye, Chief of Staff
CIO: Chris Kraft, Director Information Systems
CHR: Cathy Norquest, Director Human Resources
CNO: Jenny Obermier, VP, Director of Nursing
Web address: www.yorkgeneral.org
**Control:** Other not–for–profit (including NFP Corporation) **Service:** General
Medical and Surgical

> **Staffed Beds:** 154 **Admissions:** 940 **Census:** 124 **Births:** 106 **Total
> Expense ($000):** 37825 **Payroll Expense ($000):** 18048 **Personnel:** 366

NE

---

**Hospital, Medicare Provider Number, Address, Telephone, Approval, Facility, and Physician Codes, Health Care System**

★ American Hospital Association (AHA) membership    ◯ Healthcare Facilities Accreditation Program    ⇑ Center for Improvement in Healthcare Quality Accreditation
☐ The Joint Commission accreditation    ◇ DNV Healthcare Inc. accreditation    △ Commission on Accreditation of Rehabilitation Facilities (CARF) accreditation

# NEVADA

## BATTLE MOUNTAIN—Lander County

**BATTLE MOUNTAIN GENERAL HOSPITAL (291303)**, 535 South Humboldt Street, Zip 89820–1988; tel. 775/635–2550, (Nonreporting) **A**9 10 18
Primary Contact: Kelley Price, Administrator and Chief Executive Officer
CFO: Cindy Fagg, Fiscal Officer
CMO: Mark S. Meyers, M.D., Chief of Staff
CIO: Terry Dunn, Director Information Technology
CHR: Lori Sherbondy, Director Human Resources
CNO: Kelley Price, R.N., Chief Nursing Officer
Web address: www.bmgh.org
**Control:** Hospital district or authority, Government, nonfederal **Service:** General Medical and Surgical

**Staffed Beds:** 7

## BOULDER CITY—Clark County

**BOULDER CITY HOSPITAL (291309)**, 901 Adams Boulevard, Zip 89005–2213; tel. 702/293–4111, (Nonreporting) **A**9 10 18
Primary Contact: Thomas Maher, Chief Executive Officer and Administrator
COO: Rae Cummings, Chief Operating Officer
CFO: Douglas Lewis, Chief Financial Officer
CMO: Derek Meeks, D.O., Chief of Staff
CIO: Scott Brooks, Information Technology
CHR: Belinda McGraw, Director Human Resources
CNO: Andre Pastian, R.N., Chief Nursing Officer
Web address: www.bouldercityhospital.org
**Control:** Other not–for–profit (including NFP Corporation) **Service:** General Medical and Surgical

**Staffed Beds:** 25

## CALIENTE—Lincoln County

**GROVER C. DILS MEDICAL CENTER (291312)**, 700 North Spring Street, Zip 89008, Mailing Address: P.O. Box 1010, Zip 89008–1010; tel. 775/726–3171, (Nonreporting) **A**9 10 18
Primary Contact: Jason Bleak, Administrator and Chief Executive Officer
COO: Jason Bleak, Administrator and Chief Executive Officer
CFO: Sherlyn Fackrell, Finance Controller
CMO: R. William Katschke, Jr., M.D., Medical Director
CHR: Rozanne Mangum, Administrative Assistant and Director Human Resources
Web address: www.gcdmc.org
**Control:** Other not–for–profit (including NFP Corporation) **Service:** Other specialty

**Staffed Beds:** 20

## CARSON CITY—Carson City County

**CARSON TAHOE CONTINUING CARE HOSPITAL (292008)**, 775 Fleischmann Way, 2nd Floor, Zip 89703–2995; tel. 775/445–7795, (Nonreporting) **A**9 10
Primary Contact: Kelly Wilcher, Chief Executive Officer
CFO: Ann Beck, Vice President and Chief Financial Officer
CMO: Jose Aguirre, M.D., Medical Director
CHR: Angie Rodriguez, Human Resource Manager
CNO: Stu Talley, Chief Nursing Officer
Web address: www.carsontahoe.com
**Control:** Other not–for–profit (including NFP Corporation) **Service:** Long–Term Acute Care hospital

**Staffed Beds:** 29

⊞ ⇑ **CARSON TAHOE HEALTH (290019)**, 1600 Medical Parkway, Zip 89703–4625, Mailing Address: P.O. Box 2168, Zip 89702–2168; tel. 775/445–8672 **A**1 2 5 9 10 22 **F**3 4 5 8 11 13 15 17 18 20 22 24 28 29 30 31 34 35 40 42 45 47 49 50 54 56 59 64 65 68 70 73 74 75 76 77 78 79 81 82 85 86 87 89 90 93 96 98 99 100 101 102 103 104 105 107 108 110 111 115 116 117 118 119 130 132 135 144 146 147 148
Primary Contact: Edward L. Epperson, Chief Executive Officer
CFO: Ann Beck, Vice President Finance
CMO: Jeffrey Sanders, M.D., Chief of Staff
CHR: Jim Lewandowski, Interim Director of Human Resources
CNO: Anna Anders, Vice President and Chief Nursing Officer
Web address: www.carsontahoe.com
**Control:** Other not–for–profit (including NFP Corporation) **Service:** General Medical and Surgical

**Staffed Beds:** 190 **Admissions:** 10860 **Census:** 134 **Outpatient Visits:** 219066 **Births:** 910 **Total Expense ($000):** 200240 **Payroll Expense ($000):** 66895 **Personnel:** 988

## SIERRA SURGERY HOSPITAL (290051)

☐ **SIERRA SURGERY HOSPITAL (290051)**, 1400 Medical Parkway, Zip 89703–4624; tel. 775/883–1700, (Nonreporting) **A**1 3 9 10
Primary Contact: Ken Doran, Interim Chief Executive Officer
CFO: Sheryl Hayden, Chief Financial Officer
Web address: www.sierrasurgery.com
**Control:** Partnership, Investor–owned, for–profit **Service:** Surgical

**Staffed Beds:** 15

## ELKO—Elko County

⊞ **NORTHEASTERN NEVADA REGIONAL HOSPITAL (290008)**, 2001 Errecart Boulevard, Zip 89801–8333; tel. 775/738–5151 **A**1 6 9 10 20 **F**3 8 11 13 15 20 28 29 30 31 34 40 41 45 46 49 50 51 57 59 60 68 70 75 76 79 81 82 85 89 93 102 107 108 111 114 115 119 129 **S** LifePoint Health, Brentwood, TN
Primary Contact: Richard L. Palagi, Chief Executive Officer
CFO: Grant Trollope, Chief Financial Officer
CIO: Jeff Morgan, Director Information Systems
CHR: Laura Elliott, Director Human Resources
CNO: Dona E. Townsend, Chief Nursing Officer
Web address: www.nnrhospital.com
**Control:** Corporation, Investor–owned, for–profit **Service:** General Medical and Surgical

**Staffed Beds:** 50 **Admissions:** 2929 **Census:** 24 **Outpatient Visits:** 56563 **Births:** 649 **Total Expense ($000):** 45517 **Payroll Expense ($000):** 17574 **Personnel:** 267

## ELY—White Pine County

⊞ **WILLIAM BEE RIRIE HOSPITAL (291302)**, 1500 Avenue H, Zip 89301–2699; tel. 775/289–3001 **A**1 9 10 18 **F**8 13 15 29 31 32 35 40 44 45 50 57 59 64 65 66 68 75 76 77 79 81 82 85 86 87 102 104 107 108 110 111 114 119 127 129 130 135 **P**6
Primary Contact: Matthew Walker, Chief Executive Officer and Administrator
CMO: G. N. Christensen, M.D., Chief Medical Officer
CIO: Destin Brandis, Chief Information Officer
CHR: Vicki Pereace, Manager Human Resources
Web address: www.elynevadahospital.org
**Control:** Hospital district or authority, Government, nonfederal **Service:** General Medical and Surgical

**Staffed Beds:** 15 **Admissions:** 405 **Census:** 3 **Outpatient Visits:** 26934 **Births:** 78 **Total Expense ($000):** 27074 **Payroll Expense ($000):** 13677 **Personnel:** 97

## FALLON—Churchill County

⊞ **BANNER CHURCHILL COMMUNITY HOSPITAL (290006)**, 801 East Williams Avenue, Zip 89406–3052; tel. 775/423–3151 **A**1 9 10 20 **F**3 7 11 13 15 29 30 31 34 35 40 45 47 50 57 59 64 65 68 70 75 76 78 79 81 85 86 87 93 107 108 110 111 115 118 119 130 146 **S** Banner Health, Phoenix, AZ
Primary Contact: Hoyt Skabelund, Chief Executive Officer
CFO: Steven Fraker, Chief Financial Officer
CMO: Tedd McDonald, M.D., Chief Medical Officer
CHR: Darlene Hanefeld, Chief Human Resources Officer
CNO: Robert H. Carnahan, II, Chief Nursing Officer
Web address: www.bannerhealth.com/churchill
**Control:** Other not–for–profit (including NFP Corporation) **Service:** General Medical and Surgical

**Staffed Beds:** 40 **Admissions:** 1734 **Census:** 17 **Births:** 403 **Total Expense ($000):** 36296 **Payroll Expense ($000):** 15007 **Personnel:** 257

## GARDNERVILLE—Douglas County

★ **CARSON VALLEY MEDICAL CENTER (291306)**, 1107 Highway 395, Zip 89410; tel. 775/782–1500 **A**3 9 10 18 **F**3 8 11 15 29 31 34 35 40 45 50 53 54 56 57 59 64 65 68 70 75 77 78 79 81 85 86 87 91 93 102 103 104 107 108 110 115 119 127 129 130 131 132 133 135 144 146 148 **P**6
Primary Contact: Susan Davila, Chief Executive Officer and Administrator
COO: Linda Lilleboe, R.N., Director Operations
CFO: Julie Howes, Director Finance
CMO: Evan Easley, M.D., Chief Medical Officer
CIO: Brian Gould, Director Information System
CHR: Lisa Tremaine, Manager Human Resources
CNO: Christy Raynes, R.N., Director Clinical Services
Web address: www.carsonvalleymedicalcenter.com
**Control:** Other not–for–profit (including NFP Corporation) **Service:** General Medical and Surgical

**Staffed Beds:** 23 **Admissions:** 827 **Census:** 7 **Outpatient Visits:** 132344 **Births:** 0 **Total Expense ($000):** 41466 **Payroll Expense ($000):** 15596 **Personnel:** 279

*Many Facility Codes have changed. Please refer to the AHA Guide Code Chart.*

NV

## HAWTHORNE—Mineral County

**MOUNT GRANT GENERAL HOSPITAL (291300)**, First and A Street,
Zip 89415, Mailing Address: P.O. Box 1510, Zip 89415–1510;
tel. 775/945–2461, (Nonreporting) **A**9 10 18
Primary Contact: Richard Munger, Administrator
Web address: www.mtgrantgenhospital.org/
**Control:** Other not–for–profit (including NFP Corporation) **Service:** General
Medical and Surgical

**Staffed Beds:** 11

## HENDERSON—Clark County

**HEALTHSOUTH REHABILITATION HOSPITAL – HENDERSON (293032)**,
10301 Jeffreys Street, Zip 89052–3922; tel. 702/939–9400, (Nonreporting) **A**1
10 **S** HEALTHSOUTH Corporation, Birmingham, AL
Primary Contact: Samantha Billig, Chief Executive Officer
CFO: Robert Bollard, Chief Financial Officer
Web address: www.hendersonrehabhospital.com
**Control:** Corporation, Investor–owned, for–profit **Service:** Rehabilitation

**Staffed Beds:** 90

**SEVEN HILLS HOSPITAL (294012)**, 3021 West Horizon Ridge Parkway,
Zip 89052–3990; tel. 702/646–5000 **A**9 10 **F**4 5 29 34 38 56 64 98 99 101
103 104 105 130 132 135 143 148 **P**8 **S** Acadia Healthcare Company, Inc.,
Franklin, TN
Primary Contact: Robert L. Turner, Ph.D., Chief Executive Officer
CFO: MiRhee Chun, Chief Financial Officer
CMO: Keith Breiland, M.D., Medical Director
CIO: Greg Schultz, Director Health Information Management
CNO: Christopher Monteros, Director of Nursing
Web address: www.sevenhillsbi.com
**Control:** Corporation, Investor–owned, for–profit **Service:** Psychiatric

**Staffed Beds:** 94 **Admissions:** 3851 **Census:** 74 **Outpatient Visits:** 3658
**Births:** 0 **Total Expense ($000):** 14260 **Payroll Expense ($000):** 7768

**ST. ROSE DOMINICAN HOSPITALS – ROSE DE LIMA CAMPUS (290012)**,
102 East Lake Mead Parkway, Zip 89015–5524; tel. 702/616–5000 **A**1 9 10 **F**3
8 12 15 18 20 29 30 31 32 34 35 38 40 43 44 45 49 50 57 59 62 63 64 65
68 70 74 75 77 78 79 81 82 84 85 86 87 90 93 95 96 102 107 108 111
114 119 130 131 132 135 143 146 147 148 **S** Dignity Health, San
Francisco, CA
Primary Contact: Teressa Conley, President and Chief Executive Officer
COO: Teressa Conley, Vice President and Chief Operating Officer
CFO: Kevin Walters, Chief Financial Officer
CMO: Stephen K. Jones, M.D., Vice President Medical Staff Affairs
Web address: www.strosehospitals.org
**Control:** Church–operated, Nongovernment, not–for profit **Service:** General
Medical and Surgical

**Staffed Beds:** 109 **Admissions:** 5632 **Census:** 83 **Outpatient Visits:** 43341
**Births:** 0 **Total Expense ($000):** 134171 **Payroll Expense ($000):** 61168
**Personnel:** 686

**ST. ROSE DOMINICAN HOSPITALS – SIENA CAMPUS (290045)**, 3001 St.
Rose Parkway, Zip 89052; tel. 702/616–5000 **A**1 3 5 7 8 13 15 18 19
20 22 24 26 28 29 30 31 32 34 35 38 40 41 43 44 45 46 50 51 57 59 62
63 64 68 70 72 74 75 76 77 78 79 81 82 83 84 85 86 87 88 89 93 102
107 108 110 111 114 115 119 126 130 131 132 135 146 147 148 **S** Dignity
Health, San Francisco, CA
Primary Contact: Brian G. Brannman, President and Chief Executive Officer
COO: Teressa Conley, Chief Operating Officer
CFO: Melissa Walker, Chief Financial Officer
CMO: Robert Pretzlaff, M.D., Chief Medical Officer
CIO: Russ Patterson, Director Information Technology
CHR: Linda Gerstenberger, Vice President Human Resources
Web address: www.strosehospitals.com
**Control:** Church–operated, Nongovernment, not–for profit **Service:** General
Medical and Surgical

**Staffed Beds:** 230 **Admissions:** 15567 **Census:** 182 **Outpatient Visits:**
79294 **Births:** 3168 **Total Expense ($000):** 317204 **Payroll Expense
($000):** 132778 **Personnel:** 1588

## INCLINE VILLAGE—Washoe County

★ **INCLINE VILLAGE COMMUNITY HOSPITAL (291301)**, 880 Alder Avenue,
Zip 89451–8335; tel. 775/833–4100, (Nonreporting) **A**3 5 9 10 18 **S** Tahoe
Forest Health System, Truckee, CA
Primary Contact: Judy Newland, R.N., Chief Nursing Officer
CFO: Crystal Betts, Chief Financial Officer
CIO: Mark Griffiths, Director Management Information Systems
CHR: Jayne O'Flanagan, Director Human Resources
Web address: www.tfhd.com
**Control:** Hospital district or authority, Government, nonfederal **Service:** General
Medical and Surgical

**Staffed Beds:** 6

## LAS VEGAS—Clark County

**AMG SPECIALTY HOSPITAL – LAS VEGAS (292007)**, 4015 South McLeod
Drive, Zip 89121–4305; tel. 702/433–2200 **A**9 10 **F**1 29 30 85 130 148 **P**5
**S** AMG Integrated Healthcare Management, Lafayette, LA
Primary Contact: William (Bill) Fox, Chief Executive Officer
CFO: Ruth Knutson, Chief Financial Officer
CMO: Anthony Pollard, D.O., Chief Medical Officer
CNO: Arlene Harper, R.N., Chief Nursing Officer
Web address: www.amgihm.com/locations/#map_top
**Control:** Partnership, Investor–owned, for–profit **Service:** Long–Term Acute Care
hospital

**Staffed Beds:** 24 **Admissions:** 163 **Census:** 14 **Births:** 0

☐ **CENTENNIAL HILLS HOSPITAL MEDICAL CENTER (290054)**, 6900 North
Durango Drive, Zip 89149–4409; tel. 702/835–9700, (Nonreporting) **A**1 9 10
**S** Universal Health Services, Inc., King of Prussia, PA
Primary Contact: Sajit Pullarkat, Chief Executive Officer and Managing Director
Web address: www.centennialhillshospital.com
**Control:** Corporation, Investor–owned, for–profit **Service:** General Medical and
Surgical

**Staffed Beds:** 165

**COMPLEX CARE HOSPITAL AT TENAYA (292006)**, 2500 North Tenaya,
Zip 89128–0482; tel. 702/562–2021, (Nonreporting) **A**1 9 10 **S** LifeCare
Management Services, Plano, TX
Primary Contact: Michael R. Shaw, Chief Executive Officer
COO: Paul D'Ambrosio, Chief Operating Officer
CFO: Anna Rich, Chief Financial Officer
CMO: C. Dean Milne, D.O., Medical Director
CIO: Lynn Tunson, Manager Medical Records
CHR: Belinda McGraw, Director Human Resources
CNO: Robin Wolf, Chief Nursing Officer
Web address: www.lifecare–hospitals.com
**Control:** Corporation, Investor–owned, for–profit **Service:** Long–Term Acute Care
hospital

**Staffed Beds:** 70

☐ **DESERT SPRINGS HOSPITAL MEDICAL CENTER (290022)**, 2075 East
Flamingo Road, Zip 89119–5121; tel. 702/733–8800, (Nonreporting) **A**1 9 10
**S** Universal Health Services, Inc., King of Prussia, PA
Primary Contact: Samuel Kaufman, Chief Executive Officer and Managing Director
CMO: Adel R. Shehata, M.D., Medical Director
CIO: Tom Schoenig, System Director Information Services
CHR: Shirley A. Shadwick, Administrator Human Resources
Web address: www.desertspringshospital.com
**Control:** Corporation, Investor–owned, for–profit **Service:** General Medical and
Surgical

**Staffed Beds:** 346

**DESERT WILLOW TREATMENT CENTER**, 6171 West Charleston Boulevard,
Zip 89146–1126; tel. 702/486–8900 **A**3 5 **F**29 98 99 106 **P**6
Primary Contact: Linda Santangelo, Ph.D., Director
**Control:** State–Government, nonfederal **Service:** Psychiatric

**Staffed Beds:** 58 **Admissions:** 354 **Census:** 43 **Outpatient Visits:** 0 **Births:**
0 **Total Expense ($000):** 8974 **Personnel:** 117

**HARMON MEDICAL AND REHABILITATION HOSPITAL (290042)**, 2170 East
Harmon Avenue, Zip 89119–7840; tel. 702/794–0100, (Nonreporting) **A**10
**S** Fundamental Long Term Care Holdings, LLC, Sparks Glencoe, MD
Primary Contact: Bonnie Essex Hillegass, Chief Executive Officer
**Control:** Corporation, Investor–owned, for–profit **Service:** Rehabilitation

**Staffed Beds:** 118

NV

---

**Hospital, Medicare Provider Number, Address, Telephone, Approval, Facility, and Physician Codes, Health Care System**

★ American Hospital Association (AHA) membership    ○ Healthcare Facilities Accreditation Program    ⇑ Center for Improvement in Healthcare Quality Accreditation
☐ The Joint Commission accreditation    ◇ DNV Healthcare Inc. accreditation    △ Commission on Accreditation of Rehabilitation Facilities (CARF) accreditation

---

✠ **HEALTHSOUTH DESERT CANYON REHABILITATION HOSPITAL (293033)**,
9175 West Oquendo Road, Zip 89148–1234; tel. 702/252–7342 **A**1 10 **F**3 29
77 78 79 90 91 93 132 **S** HEALTHSOUTH Corporation, Birmingham, AL
Primary Contact: Andrea Davis, Chief Executive Officer
CMO: Bevins Chue, M.D., Medical Director
CNO: Timothy Murphy, R.N., Chief Nursing Officer
Web address: www.healthsouthdesertcanyon.com
**Control:** Corporation, Investor–owned, for–profit **Service:** Rehabilitation

**Staffed Beds: 50 Admissions: 1278 Census: 44 Births: 0**

✠ **HEALTHSOUTH REHABILITATION HOSPITAL–LAS VEGAS (293026)**, 1250
South Valley View Boulevard, Zip 89102–1861; tel. 702/877–8898,
(Nonreporting) **A**1 10 **S** HEALTHSOUTH Corporation, Birmingham, AL
Primary Contact: Michael Ward, Chief Executive Officer
CFO: Daniel Lai, Controller
CMO: John D. Reneau, Medical Director
CHR: Debra Tafoya, Director Human Resources
CNO: Susan Ramirez, Chief Nursing Officer
Web address: www.healthsouthlasvegas.com
**Control:** Corporation, Investor–owned, for–profit **Service:** Rehabilitation

**Staffed Beds: 79**

☐ **HORIZON SPECIALTY HOSPITAL (292003)**, 640 Desert Lane,
Zip 89106–4207; tel. 702/382–3155, (Nonreporting) **A**1 9 10 **S** Fundamental
Long Term Care Holdings, LLC, Sparks Glencoe, MD
Primary Contact: William Fox, Chief Executive Officer and Administrator
CFO: Darnell Bennett, Director Finance
CMO: Syed Rahman, M.D., Chief of Staff
CIO: Azena Ansi, Manager Health Information Management
CHR: Melvin Layugan, Director Human Resources
Web address: www.horizonspecialtyhosp.com/
**Control:** Corporation, Investor–owned, for–profit **Service:** Long–Term Acute Care
hospital

**Staffed Beds: 49**

**KINDRED HOSPITAL LAS VEGAS, DESERT SPRINGS CAMPUS** See Kindred
Hospital Las Vegas–Sahara

✠ **KINDRED HOSPITAL LAS VEGAS–SAHARA (292002)**, 5110 West Sahara
Avenue, Zip 89146–3406; tel. 702/871–1418, (Includes KINDRED HOSPITAL LAS
VEGAS, DESERT SPRINGS CAMPUS, 2075 East Flamingo Road, Suite 114,
Zip 89119; tel. 702/894–5728; KINDRED HOSPITAL–FLAMINGO, 2250 East
Flamingo Road, Zip 89119; tel. 702/871–1418), (Nonreporting) **A**1 9 10
**S** Kindred Healthcare, Louisville, KY
Primary Contact: Doug McCoy, Chief Executive Officer
CFO: William Lysaght, Chief Financial Officer
CMO: Paul Stewart, M.D., Medical Director
CHR: Jim Sturgeon, Area Director Human Resources
Web address: www.kindredhospitalvs.com/
**Control:** Corporation, Investor–owned, for–profit **Service:** Long–Term Acute Care
hospital

**Staffed Beds: 238**

☐ **MONTEVISTA HOSPITAL (294009)**, 5900 West Rochelle Avenue,
Zip 89103–3327; tel. 702/364–1111, (Nonreporting) **A**1 9 10 **S** Strategic
Behavioral Health, LLC, Memphis, TN
Primary Contact: Richard Failla, Chief Executive Officer
CMO: William Bauer, M.D., Medical Director
CHR: Carol Nelson, Director Human Resources
Web address: www.montevistahospital.com
**Control:** Corporation, Investor–owned, for–profit **Service:** Psychiatric

**Staffed Beds: 90**

✠ **MOUNTAINVIEW HOSPITAL (290039)**, 3100 North Tenaya Way,
Zip 89128–0436; tel. 702/255–5000 **A**1 3 5 9 10 **F**3 11 12 13 15 18 20 22
24 26 28 29 31 34 35 40 45 46 47 48 49 50 70 74 75 77 78 79 81 90 91
93 107 108 111 112 114 115 116 117 119 126 130 146 147 148 **P**1 **S** HCA,
Nashville, TN
Primary Contact: Chris Mowan, Chief Executive Officer
CFO: Lana Arad, Chief Financial Officer
CMO: Jack Collier, M.D., Chief of Staff
CHR: Robert Nettles, Director Human Resources
CNO: Natalie Ransom, Chief Nursing Officer
Web address: www.mountainview–hospital.com
**Control:** Corporation, Investor–owned, for–profit **Service:** General Medical and
Surgical

**Staffed Beds: 340 Admissions: 19184 Census: 271**

☐ **RED ROCK BEHAVIORAL HOSPITAL (294008)**, 5975 West Twain Avenue,
Zip 89103–1237; tel. 702/214–8099 **A**1 9 10 **F**98 102 103 **P**5 **S** Strategic
Behavioral Health, LLC, Memphis, TN
Primary Contact: Toby Davis, Chief Executive Officer
Web address: www.redrockhospital.com
**Control:** Corporation, Investor–owned, for–profit **Service:** Psychiatric

**Staffed Beds: 21 Admissions: 434 Census: 17 Outpatient Visits: 0 Births:**
**0**

✠ **SOUTHERN HILLS HOSPITAL AND MEDICAL CENTER (290047)**, 9300 West
Sunset Road, Zip 89148–4844; tel. 702/880–2100, (Nonreporting) **A**1 9 10
**S** HCA, Nashville, TN
Primary Contact: Adam Rudd, Interim Chief Executive Officer
CFO: Jennifer Le, Chief Financial Officer
CMO: Eric Ramos, M.D., Division Chief Medical Officer
CIO: Joe Grandiosi, Director Information Technology
CHR: Brian Wood, Director Human Resources
CNO: Maura Wright, Chief Nursing Officer
Web address: www.southernhillshospital.com
**Control:** Corporation, Investor–owned, for–profit **Service:** General Medical and
Surgical

**Staffed Beds: 134**

☐ **SOUTHERN NEVADA ADULT MENTAL HEALTH SERVICES (294002)**, 6161
West Charleston Boulevard, Zip 89146–1126; tel. 702/486–6000, (Nonreporting)
**A**1 3 5 10
Primary Contact: Chelsea Szklany, Hospital Administrator
Web address: www.mhds.state.nv.us
**Control:** State–Government, nonfederal **Service:** Psychiatric

**Staffed Beds: 293**

☐ **SPRING MOUNTAIN SAHARA (294010)**, 5460 West Sahara, Zip 89146–3307;
tel. 702/216–8900 **A**1 9 10 **F**29 56 64 98 103 104 130 **S** Universal Health
Services, Inc., King of Prussia, PA
Primary Contact: Darryl S. Dubroca, Chief Executive Officer and Managing
Director
Web address: www.springmountainsahara.com
**Control:** Corporation, Investor–owned, for–profit **Service:** Psychiatric

**Staffed Beds: 30 Admissions: 779 Census: 22 Outpatient Visits: 1280**
**Births: 0 Total Expense ($000): 5763 Payroll Expense ($000): 2690**
**Personnel: 56**

✠ **SPRING MOUNTAIN TREATMENT CENTER (294011)**, 7000 West Spring
Mountain Road, Zip 89117–3816; tel. 702/873–2400 **A**1 9 10 **F**29 98 99 105
130 **S** Universal Health Services, Inc., King of Prussia, PA
Primary Contact: Darryl S. Dubroca, Chief Executive Officer and Managing
Director
Web address: www.springmountaintreatmentcenter.com/
**Control:** Corporation, Investor–owned, for–profit **Service:** Psychiatric

**Staffed Beds: 82 Admissions: 3241 Census: 65 Outpatient Visits: 2369**
**Births: 0 Total Expense ($000): 16090 Payroll Expense ($000): 7101**
**Personnel: 150**

☐ **SPRING VALLEY HOSPITAL MEDICAL CENTER (290046)**, 5400 South
Rainbow Boulevard, Zip 89118–1859; tel. 702/853–3000, (Nonreporting) **A**1 3 9
10 **S** Universal Health Services, Inc., King of Prussia, PA
Primary Contact: Leonard Freehof, Chief Executive Officer and Managing Director
COO: Matthew Wheelus, Chief Operating Officer
CFO: Carl Caley, Chief Financial Officer
CMO: S. Daniel, M.D., Chief Medical Officer
CHR: Angelique Ford, Administrator Human Resources
CNO: Margaret Covelli, R.N., Chief Nursing Officer
Web address: www.springvalleyhospital.com
**Control:** Corporation, Investor–owned, for–profit **Service:** General Medical and
Surgical

**Staffed Beds: 169**

✠ **ST. ROSE DOMINICAN HOSPITALS – SAN MARTIN CAMPUS (290053)**,
8280 West Warm Springs Road, Zip 89113–3612; tel. 702/492–8000 **A**1 9 10
**F**3 8 13 15 18 19 20 22 24 26 28 29 30 31 32 34 35 38 40 43 44 45 47 49
50 57 59 62 63 64 68 70 73 74 75 76 77 78 79 80 81 82 84 85 86 87 93
95 102 107 108 110 111 114 119 126 130 131 132 135 146 147 148
**S** Dignity Health, San Francisco, CA
Primary Contact: Lawrence Barnard, President and Chief Executive Officer
CFO: Melissa Walker, Chief Financial Officer
CMO: Robert Pretzlaff, M.D., Chief Medical Officer
CIO: Roy Hagerman, Site Manager Information Technology
CHR: Linda Gerstenberger, Vice President Human Resources
Web address: www.strosehospitals.org
**Control:** Church–operated, Nongovernment, not–for profit **Service:** General
Medical and Surgical

**Staffed Beds: 147 Admissions: 6442 Census: 78 Outpatient Visits: 35241**
**Births: 934 Total Expense ($000): 161673 Payroll Expense ($000): 60310**
**Personnel: 643**

☐ **SUMMERLIN HOSPITAL MEDICAL CENTER (290041)**, 657 Town Center
Drive, Zip 89144–6367; tel. 702/233–7000, (Nonreporting) **A**1 9 10 **S** Universal
Health Services, Inc., King of Prussia, PA
Primary Contact: Robert S. Freymuller, Chief Executive Officer
Web address: www.summerlinhospital.com
**Control:** Corporation, Investor–owned, for–profit **Service:** General Medical and
Surgical

**Staffed Beds: 148**

**NV**

⊞ △ **SUNRISE HOSPITAL AND MEDICAL CENTER (290003)**, 3186 Maryland Parkway, Zip 89109–2306, Mailing Address: P.O. Box 98530, Zip 89193; tel. 702/731–8000, (Includes SUNRISE CHILDREN'S HOSPITAL ) **A**1 2 3 5 7 9 10 **F**3 11 12 13 15 17 18 19 20 21 22 23 24 25 26 27 28 29 30 31 32 34 35 39 40 41 43 45 46 49 50 51 57 58 59 60 61 64 65 68 70 72 74 75 76 77 78 79 81 82 84 85 87 88 89 90 91 92 96 107 108 110 111 114 115 116 117 118 119 124 126 130 132 135 142 146 147 148 **S** HCA, Nashville, TN
Primary Contact: Todd Sklamberg, President
CFO: Daniel Perritt, Chief Financial Officer
CMO: Katherine Keeley, M.D., Chief of Staff
CIO: Alan Burt, Director Information Services
CNO: Lori J. Brown, MSN, Chief Nursing Officer
Web address: www.sunrisehospital.com
**Control:** Corporation, Investor–owned, for–profit **Service:** General Medical and Surgical

**Staffed Beds:** 664 **Admissions:** 30384 **Census:** 491 **Outpatient Visits:** 165547 **Births:** 4821 **Total Expense ($000):** 490662 **Payroll Expense ($000):** 205111 **Personnel:** 2586

⊞ **UNIVERSITY MEDICAL CENTER (290007)**, 1800 West Charleston Boulevard, Zip 89102–2386; tel. 702/383–2000, (Includes CHILDREN'S HOSPITAL OF NEVADA AT UMC, 1800 West Charleston Boulevard, Zip 89102–2329; tel. 702/383–2000), (Nonreporting) **A**1 2 3 5 9 10
Primary Contact: Mason VanHouweling, Chief Executive Officer
COO: Kurt Houser, Chief Operating Officer
CFO: Stephanie Merrill, Chief Financial Officer
CMO: Joan Brookhyser, M.D., Medical Center Director and Chief Executive Officer
CIO: Ernie McKinley, Chief Information Officer
CHR: John Espinoza, Chief Human Resources Officer
CNO: Debra Fox, Chief Nursing Officer
Web address: www.umcsn.com
**Control:** County–Government, nonfederal **Service:** General Medical and Surgical

**Staffed Beds:** 541

☐ **VALLEY HOSPITAL MEDICAL CENTER (290021)**, 620 Shadow Lane, Zip 89106–4119; tel. 702/388–4000, (Nonreporting) **A**1 3 9 10 **S** Universal Health Services, Inc., King of Prussia, PA
Primary Contact: Elaine Glaser, Chief Executive Officer, Managing Director
CFO: Betsy A. Sponsler, Chief Financial Officer
CMO: Dost Wattoo, M.D., Chief of Staff
CIO: Tom Schoenig, Regional Director Information Services
CHR: Dana Thorne, Administrator Human Resources
Web address: www.valleyhospital.net
**Control:** Corporation, Investor–owned, for–profit **Service:** General Medical and Surgical

**Staffed Beds:** 365

★ **PERSHING GENERAL HOSPITAL (291304)**, 855 Sixth Street, Zip 89419, Mailing Address: P.O. Box 661, Zip 89419–0661; tel. 775/273–2621, (Nonreporting) **A**9 10 18
Primary Contact: Patty Bianchi, Chief Executive Officer
CFO: Marjorie Skinner, Director Finance
CMO: Yousri Gadallah, M.D., Chief Medical Officer
CIO: Jim Weeldreyer, Manager Information Technology
CHR: Cynthia Hixenbaugh, Director Human Resources
Web address: www.pershinghospital.org
**Control:** Hospital district or authority, Government, nonfederal **Service:** General Medical and Surgical

**Staffed Beds:** 38

⊞ **MESA VIEW REGIONAL HOSPITAL (291307)**, 1299 Bertha Howe Avenue, Zip 89027–7500; tel. 702/346–8040 **A**1 9 10 18 **F**3 11 13 15 29 30 34 35 40 45 46 51 56 57 59 64 70 75 76 77 79 81 85 87 107 108 110 111 114 119 130 132 133 135 146 147 148 **P**7 **S** Community Health Systems, Inc., Franklin, TN
Primary Contact: Patricia Holden, Chief Executive Officer
CFO: Eric S. Hardy, Chief Financial Officer
Web address: www.mesaviewhospital.com
**Control:** Corporation, Investor–owned, for–profit **Service:** General Medical and Surgical

**Staffed Beds:** 25 **Admissions:** 750 **Census:** 6 **Outpatient Visits:** 23712 **Births:** 114 **Total Expense ($000):** 22126 **Payroll Expense ($000):** 9500 **Personnel:** 172

⊞ **MIKE O'CALLAGHAN FEDERAL HOSPITAL**, 4700 Las Vegas Boulevard North, Suite 2419, Zip 89191–6600; tel. 702/653–2000, (Nonreporting) **A**1 3 5 **S** Department of the Air Force, Washington, DC
Primary Contact: Colonel Christian Benjamin, USAF, MC, Commander
COO: Colonel Linnes L. Chester, USAF, Administrator
CFO: Major Kari Turkal–Barrett, Flight Commander Resource Management Officer
CMO: Lieutenant Colonel Markham Brown, M.D., Chief Medical Staff
CIO: Major Kevin Seeley, Chief Information Officer
Web address: www.lasvegas.va.gov/
**Control:** Air Force, Government, federal **Service:** General Medical and Surgical

**Staffed Beds:** 46

★ ◇ **NORTH VISTA HOSPITAL (290005)**, 1409 East Lake Mead Boulevard, Zip 89030–7197; tel. 702/649–7711, (Nonreporting) **A**9 10 21 **S** IASIS Healthcare, Franklin, TN
Primary Contact: Vincenzo Variale, Chief Executive Officer
CFO: George Wiley, Chief Financial Officer
CIO: Edward Zaparzynski, Director Information Services
CHR: Shari Olson, Human Resources Manager
CNO: Joanna Young, R.N., Chief Nursing Officer
Web address: www.northvistahospital.com
**Control:** Corporation, Investor–owned, for–profit **Service:** General Medical and Surgical

**Staffed Beds:** 198

⊞ **VETERANS AFFAIRS SOUTHERN NEVADA HEALTHCARE SYSTEM**, 6900 North Pecos Road, tel. 702/791–9000, (Nonreporting) **A**1 5 **S** Department of Veterans Affairs, Washington, DC
Primary Contact: Isabel Duff, MS, Director
CFO: Richard O. Hays, Chief Fiscal Service
CMO: Ramanujam Komanduri, M.D., Chief of Staff
Web address: www.lasvegas.va.gov/
**Control:** Veterans Affairs, Government, federal **Service:** General Medical and Surgical

**Staffed Beds:** 58

★ **DESERT VIEW HOSPITAL (291311)**, 360 South Lola Lane, Zip 89048–0884; tel. 775/751–7500 **A**9 10 18 **F**3 15 18 29 34 40 45 57 59 65 77 79 81 86 107 111 119 133 135 148 **P**6 **S** Rural Health Group, Nephi, UT
Primary Contact: Kelly H. Adams, Chief Executive Officer
CFO: Ryan Eggleston, Chief Financial Officer
CMO: Fredric Siegel, M.D., Chief of Staff
CHR: Lisa Doty, Manager Human Resources
CNO: Markeeta Araujo, Chief Nursing Officer
Web address: www.desertviewhospital.com
**Control:** Corporation, Investor–owned, for–profit **Service:** General Medical and Surgical

**Staffed Beds:** 25 **Admissions:** 1728 **Census:** 13 **Births:** 0

**DESERT VIEW REGIONAL MEDICAL CENTER** See Desert View Hospital

⊞ **RENOWN REGIONAL MEDICAL CENTER (290001)**, 1155 Mill Street, Zip 89502–1576; tel. 775/982–4100, (Includes RENOWN CHILDREN'S HOSPITAL, 1155 Mill Street, tel. 775/982–5437) **A**1 2 3 5 9 10 **F**3 5 11 13 15 17 18 19 20 21 22 23 24 25 26 27 28 29 30 31 32 34 35 40 41 43 45 49 54 56 57 58 59 61 62 64 65 66 68 70 72 73 74 75 76 77 78 79 80 81 84 85 86 87 88 89 92 99 100 101 102 103 104 105 107 108 111 114 115 118 119 120 121 123 124 126 130 131 132 135 146 148 **S** Renown Health, Reno, NV
Primary Contact: Erik Olson, Chief Executive Officer
COO: Sy Johnson, Executive Vice President, Chief Operating Officer
CFO: Sam King, Chief Financial Officer
CMO: Charles Johnson, M.D., Chief of Staff
CIO: Charles Scully, Chief Information Officer
CHR: Michelle Sanchez–Bickley, Vice President Human Resources
Web address: www.renown.org
**Control:** Other not–for–profit (including NFP Corporation) **Service:** General Medical and Surgical

**Staffed Beds:** 643 **Admissions:** 27021 **Census:** 374 **Outpatient Visits:** 445334 **Births:** 4146 **Total Expense ($000):** 483403 **Payroll Expense ($000):** 155990 **Personnel:** 3023

NV

---

**Hospital, Medicare Provider Number, Address, Telephone, Approval, Facility, and Physician Codes, Health Care System**

★ American Hospital Association (AHA) membership
☐ The Joint Commission accreditation
○ Healthcare Facilities Accreditation Program
◇ DNV Healthcare Inc. accreditation
⇑ Center for Improvement in Healthcare Quality Accreditation
△ Commission on Accreditation of Rehabilitation Facilities (CARF) accreditation

★ △ **RENOWN REHABILITATION HOSPITAL**, 1495 Mill Street,
Zip 89502–1479; tel. 775/982–3500 **A**3 5 7 **F**29 54 77 82 90 93 95 96 143
148 **S** Renown Health, Reno, NV
Primary Contact: Erik Olson, Chief Executive Officer
CFO: Dawn Ahner, Chief Financial Officer
CIO: Ronald Fuschillo, Chief Information Officer
CHR: Michelle Sanchez–Bickley, Vice President Human Resources
CNO: Melodie Osborn, Chief Nursing Officer
Web address: www.renown.org
**Control:** Other not–for–profit (including NFP Corporation) **Service:** Rehabilitation

**Staffed Beds: 62 Admissions: 899 Census: 37 Outpatient Visits:** 19924
**Births: 0 Total Expense ($000):** 20341 **Payroll Expense ($000):** 10083
**Personnel:** 288

⊠ **RENOWN SOUTH MEADOWS MEDICAL CENTER (290049)**, 10101 Double R
Boulevard, Zip 89521–5931; tel. 775/982–7000 **A**1 3 5 9 10 **F**8 10 12 29 30
35 39 40 46 49 68 70 74 75 79 81 82 84 85 87 93 97 107 108 111 119
125 130 131 146 **S** Renown Health, Reno, NV
Primary Contact: Mark Behl, Chief Executive Officer
COO: Sy Johnson, Executive Vice President, Chief Operating Officer
CFO: Gina Nelson, Chief Financial Officer
CMO: Dennis Rochier, Chief Medical Officer
CIO: Ronald Fuschillo, Chief Information Officer
CHR: Michelle Sanchez–Bickley, Vice President Human Resources
CNO: Melodie Osborn, Chief Nursing Officer
Web address: www.renown.org
**Control:** Other not–for–profit (including NFP Corporation) **Service:** General
Medical and Surgical

**Staffed Beds: 76 Admissions: 2913 Census: 24 Outpatient Visits:** 64331
**Births: 0 Total Expense ($000):** 60759 **Payroll Expense ($000):** 21723
**Personnel:** 641

☐ **SAINT MARY'S REGIONAL MEDICAL CENTER (290009)**, 235 West Sixth
Street, Zip 89503–4548; tel. 775/770–3000, (Nonreporting) **A**1 2 3 5 9 10
**S** Prime Healthcare Services, Ontario, CA
Primary Contact: Helen Lidholm, Chief Executive Officer
CFO: John R. Deakyne, Chief Financial Officer
CIO: Cindy Mullins, Director Information Technology
CHR: David Milovich, Vice President Human Resources
Web address: www.saintmarysreno.org
**Control:** Corporation, Investor–owned, for–profit **Service:** General Medical and
Surgical

**Staffed Beds:** 272

⊠ **VETERANS AFFAIRS SIERRA NEVADA HEALTH CARE SYSTEM**, 975 Kirman
Avenue, Zip 89502–0993; tel. 775/786–7200 **A**1 3 5 **F**1 5 18 20 22 29 30
31 34 35 36 38 39 40 44 45 46 47 49 50 54 56 57 58 59 60 61 62 63 64
65 66 68 70 74 75 77 78 79 81 82 83 84 85 86 87 91 92 93 94 96 97 98
100 101 102 103 104 107 111 114 115 119 127 129 130 132 135 143 144
146 147 148 **P**6 **S** Department of Veterans Affairs, Washington, DC
Primary Contact: Lisa M. Howard, Acting Director
COO: Lisa M. Howard, Associate Director
CFO: Kelly Manson, Chief Financial Officer
CMO: Steven Brilliant, M.D., Chief of Staff
CIO: Jack Smith, Acting Chief Information Resources Management Service
CHR: Debbie Jenkins, Chief Human Resources Management Service
CNO: Rachel Crossley, R.N., Chief Patient Care Services
Web address: www.reno.va.gov/
**Control:** Veterans Affairs, Government, federal **Service:** General Medical and
Surgical

**Staffed Beds: 124 Admissions: 3657 Census: 95 Outpatient Visits:** 429550
**Births: 0 Total Expense ($000):** 248000 **Payroll Expense ($000):** 131600
**Personnel:** 1360

☐ **WEST HILLS HOSPITAL (294003)**, 1240 East Ninth Street, Zip 89512–2964;
tel. 775/323–0478, (Nonreporting) **A**1 9 10 **S** Universal Health Services, Inc.,
King of Prussia, PA
Primary Contact: Allison Zednicek, Chief Executive Officer
CMO: Philip Rich, M.D., Chief Medical Officer
CHR: Don Gay, Director Human Resources
Web address: www.westhillshospital.net
**Control:** Corporation, Investor–owned, for–profit **Service:** Psychiatric

**Staffed Beds:** 190

**WILLOW SPRINGS CENTER**, 690 Edison Way, Zip 89502–4135;
tel. 775/858–3303 **A**3 5 **F**98 99 104 106
Primary Contact: Duane Runyan, Chief Executive Officer and Managing Director
CFO: Joe Bradick, Chief Financial Officer
CMO: Dana Arlien, M.D., Chief Medical Officer
CNO: Sam McCord, Chief Nursing Officer
Web address: www.willowspringscenter.com
**Control:** Corporation, Investor–owned, for–profit **Service:** Children's hospital
psychiatric

**Staffed Beds: 116 Admissions: 420 Census: 98 Outpatient Visits:** 9533
**Births: 0 Total Expense ($000):** 15340 **Payroll Expense ($000):** 8548
**Personnel:** 158

**SPARKS—Washoe County**

☐ **NORTHERN NEVADA ADULT MENTAL HEALTH SERVICES (294000)**, 480
Galletti Way, Zip 89431–5564; tel. 775/688–2001 **A**1 3 5 9 10 **F**29 50 98 103
104 130
Primary Contact: Cody Phinney, Administrator
CFO: Elizabeth O'Brien, Chief Financial Officer
CIO: Lois Repass, Quality Assurance Specialist and Coordinator Performance
Improvement
Web address: www.mhds.state.nv.us/
**Control:** State–Government, nonfederal **Service:** Psychiatric

**Staffed Beds: 30 Admissions: 2270 Census: 16 Outpatient Visits:** 88513
**Births: 0 Total Expense ($000):** 18576 **Payroll Expense ($000):** 12469
**Personnel:** 244

☐ **NORTHERN NEVADA MEDICAL CENTER (290032)**, 2375 East Prater Way,
Zip 89434–9641; tel. 775/331–7000, (Nonreporting) **A**1 9 10 **S** Universal Health
Services, Inc., King of Prussia, PA
Primary Contact: Alan C. Olive, Chief Executive Officer
COO: Tiffany Meert, Chief Operating Officer
CFO: Ryan Heit, Chief Financial Officer
CHR: Patricia Downs, Director Human Resources
Web address: www.nnmc.com
**Control:** Corporation, Investor–owned, for–profit **Service:** General Medical and
Surgical

**Staffed Beds:** 108

⊠ **TAHOE PACIFIC HOSPITALS (292004)**, 2375 East Prater Way, Zip 89434;
tel. 775/355–5600, (Includes TAHOE PACIFIC HOSPITALS – WEST, 235 West
Sixth Street, 5th Floor, Reno, Zip 89503–4548) **A**1 9 10 **F**1 3 29 35 75 148 **P**8
**S** LifeCare Management Services, Plano, TX
Primary Contact: Derrick Glum, Chief Executive Officer
COO: Theresa Fegan, R.N., Chief Clinical Officer
CFO: Nena Swenson, Financial Manager
CMO: T. Brian Callister, M.D., Chief Medical Officer
CIO: Kaylene Reeves, Director
CHR: Nelson Coy, Director Human Resources
Web address: www.lifecare–hospitals.com
**Control:** Corporation, Investor–owned, for–profit **Service:** Long–Term Acute Care
hospital

**Staffed Beds: 60 Admissions: 441 Census: 35 Outpatient Visits: 0 Births:**
0 **Total Expense ($000):** 21999 **Payroll Expense ($000):** 9877 **Personnel:**
166

**WINNEMUCCA—Humboldt County**

★ **HUMBOLDT GENERAL HOSPITAL (291308)**, 118 East Haskell Street,
Zip 89445–3299; tel. 775/623–5222, (Nonreporting) **A**3 9 10 18
Primary Contact: James G. Parrish, FACHE, Chief Executive Officer
COO: Craig Prest, Director Operation Services
CFO: Sandi Lehman, Chief Financial Officer
CMO: B. Leonard Perkinson, M.D., Chief of Staff
CHR: Rose Marie Green, Director Human Resources
CNO: Darlene Bryan, R.N., Chief Nursing Officer
Web address: www.hghospital.org
**Control:** Hospital district or authority, Government, nonfederal **Service:** General
Medical and Surgical

**Staffed Beds:** 52

**YERINGTON—Lyon County**

**SOUTH LYON MEDICAL CENTER (290002)**, 213 South Whitacre,
Zip 89447–2561, Mailing Address: P.O. Box 940, Zip 89447–0940;
tel. 775/463–2301 **A**9 10 20 **F**15 29 30 34 35 40 50 54 57 59 60 64 65 68
87 91 93 97 107 114 115 119 127 130 133 146 148
Primary Contact: Toni A. Inserra, Interim Administrator
Web address: www.southlyonmedicalcenter.org
**Control:** Other not–for–profit (including NFP Corporation) **Service:** General
Medical and Surgical

**Staffed Beds: 14 Admissions: 118 Census: 1 Births: 3**

**NV**

*Many Facility Codes have changed. Please refer to the AHA Guide Code Chart.*

# NEW HAMPSHIRE

## BERLIN—Coos County

**ANDROSCOGGIN VALLEY HOSPITAL (301310)**, 59 Page Hill Road,
Zip 03570–3531; tel. 603/752–2200 **A**10 18 **F**3 8 11 12 13 15 17 28 29 30
34 40 41 43 45 47 57 59 61 64 67 70 74 75 76 77 79 81 82 85 89 92 93
102 107 108 110 114 119 128 129 130 131 132 133 146 147 **P**6
Primary Contact: Russell G. Keene, Chief Executive Officer
CFO: Jeremy Roberge, Director Reimbursement
CMO: Keith M. Shute, M.D., Senior Vice President Medical Affairs and Clinical
Services
CIO: Linda M. Laperle, Vice President Administrative Services
CHR: James A. Wheeler, Vice President Human Relations and Community
Development
Web address: www.avhnh.org
**Control:** Other not–for–profit (including NFP Corporation) **Service:** General
Medical and Surgical

**Staffed Beds:** 25 **Admissions:** 1107 **Census:** 15 **Outpatient Visits:** 66952
**Births:** 102 **Total Expense ($000):** 52728 **Payroll Expense ($000):** 23349
**Personnel:** 295

## CLAREMONT—Sullivan County

☒ **VALLEY REGIONAL HOSPITAL (301308)**, 243 Elm Street, Zip 03743–4921;
tel. 603/542–7771 **A**1 9 10 18 **F**2 3 11 14 15 28 29 34 35 38 40 43 45 49
50 51 54 57 59 62 63 64 68 70 74 75 77 79 81 84 85 87 93 97 104 107
108 110 114 118 119 130 132 133 135 146 147 148 **P**6
Primary Contact: Peter J. Wright, FACHE, Chief Executive Officer
COO: Tim Clark, RN, Chief Operating Officer
CFO: Jean Shaw, Chief Financial Officer
CMO: Oliver Herfort, M.D., Chief Medical Officer
CIO: Patricia Witthaus, Director Information Services
CHR: Shelly Bragg, Director Human Resources
CNO: Lynne Gagnon, Chief Nursing Officer
Web address: www.vrh.org
**Control:** Other not–for–profit (including NFP Corporation) **Service:** General
Medical and Surgical

**Staffed Beds:** 25 **Admissions:** 697 **Census:** 11 **Outpatient Visits:** 65570
**Births:** 0 **Total Expense ($000):** 40290 **Payroll Expense ($000):** 16482
**Personnel:** 292

## COLEBROOK—Coos County

**UPPER CONNECTICUT VALLEY HOSPITAL (301300)**, 181 Corliss Lane,
Zip 03576–3207; tel. 603/237–4971 **A**9 10 18 **F**3 15 29 30 31 34 35 40 43
45 50 56 57 59 64 67 68 75 78 81 85 93 102 107 110 114 119 128 130
133 134 135 146 147 148 **P**6
Primary Contact: Peter L. Gosline, Chief Administrative Officer
CFO: Celeste Pitts, Chief Financial Officer
CMO: Nicole Paier–Mullan, M.D., Medical Director
CIO: Heather Leighton, Director, Revenue Cycle and Privacy Officer
CHR: Heidi L. Saari, Director, Human Resources
CNO: Laurie Cotnoir, Director Nursing and Quality
Web address: www.ucvh.org
**Control:** Other not–for–profit (including NFP Corporation) **Service:** General
Medical and Surgical

**Staffed Beds:** 16 **Admissions:** 311 **Census:** 4 **Outpatient Visits:** 17790
**Total Expense ($000):** 14655 **Payroll Expense ($000):** 6362 **Personnel:** 95

## CONCORD—Merrimack County

★ ◇ **CONCORD HOSPITAL (300001)**, 250 Pleasant Street, Zip 03301–2598;
tel. 603/225–2711 **A**2 3 5 9 10 21 **F**3 8 12 13 14 15 17 18 20 22 24 26 28
29 30 31 33 34 35 36 37 38 39 40 42 43 44 46 49 50 51 53 54 55 56 57
58 59 61 64 65 66 68 69 70 71 74 75 76 77 78 79 80 81 82 83 84 85 86
87 89 93 97 98 99 100 101 102 103 104 105 107 108 110 111 114 115
118 119 120 121 123 126 129 130 131 132 134 135 144 145 146 147
148 **P**6
Primary Contact: Robert P. Steigmeyer, President and Chief Executive Officer
COO: Timothy P. Jones, Chief Operating Officer
CFO: Bruce R. Burns, Chief Financial Officer
CMO: David F. Green, M.D., Chief Medical Officer
CIO: Deane Morrison, Chief Information Officer
CHR: Robin A. Moore, Vice President Human Resources
CNO: Diane Wood–Allen, MS, Chief Nursing Officer
Web address: www.concordhospital.org
**Control:** Other not–for–profit (including NFP Corporation) **Service:** General
Medical and Surgical

**Staffed Beds:** 237 **Admissions:** 11779 **Census:** 147 **Outpatient Visits:**
715138 **Births:** 1231 **Total Expense ($000):** 386223 **Payroll Expense
($000):** 185543 **Personnel:** 2998

☒ **HEALTHSOUTH REHABILITATION HOSPITAL (303027)**, 254 Pleasant Street,
Zip 03301–2508; tel. 603/226–9800 **A**1 10 **F**29 34 35 64 74 79 90 91 93 95
96 130 132 **S** HEALTHSOUTH Corporation, Birmingham, AL
Primary Contact: Catherine Devaney, Chief Executive Officer
CFO: Diana Lachapelle, Controller
CMO: Muhammad Salmanullah, Chief Medical Director
CHR: Myra Nixon, Director Human Resources
CNO: Joseph Adamski, Chief Nursing Officer
Web address: www.healthsouthrehabconcordnh.com
**Control:** Corporation, Investor–owned, for–profit **Service:** Rehabilitation

**Staffed Beds:** 50 **Admissions:** 940 **Census:** 34 **Outpatient Visits:** 4929
**Births:** 0 **Total Expense ($000):** 16172 **Payroll Expense ($000):** 7192
**Personnel:** 127

☐ **NEW HAMPSHIRE HOSPITAL (304000)**, 36 Clinton Street, Zip 03301–2359;
tel. 603/271–5300 **A**1 3 10 **F**3 29 30 39 56 57 61 68 74 75 86 87 91 98 99
101 103 130 135 146 **P**4 6
Primary Contact: Robert J. MacLeod, Chief Executive Officer
CFO: Jamie Dall, Chief Financial Officer
CMO: David G. Folks, M.D., Chief Medical Officer
CIO: David Levesque, Director, Information Systems
CHR: Mark Bussiere, Administrator Human Resources
CNO: Roberta A. Vitale–Nolen, Administrator, Patient Care Services
Web address: www.dhhs.state.nh.us./dhhs/default.htm
**Control:** State–Government, nonfederal **Service:** Psychiatric

**Staffed Beds:** 158 **Admissions:** 2070 **Census:** 159 **Outpatient Visits:** 0
**Births:** 0 **Total Expense ($000):** 54004 **Payroll Expense ($000):** 28124
**Personnel:** 509

## DERRY—Rockingham County

☒ **PARKLAND MEDICAL CENTER (300017)**, One Parkland Drive,
Zip 03038–2750; tel. 603/432–1500, (Nonreporting) **A**1 2 9 10 **S** HCA,
Nashville, TN
Primary Contact: Chris Accashian, Chief Executive Officer
COO: Jeff Scionti, Chief Operating Officer
CFO: Jacob Wisemann, Chief Financial Officer
CMO: Edward Yourtee, M.D., Chief Medical Officer
CIO: Brad George, Director Information Systems
CHR: Molly Lahti, Director Human Resources
CNO: Eileen Keefe, Chief Nursing Officer
Web address: www.parklandmedicalcenter.com
**Control:** Corporation, Investor–owned, for–profit **Service:** General Medical and
Surgical

**Staffed Beds:** 82

---

**Hospital, Medicare Provider Number, Address, Telephone, Approval, Facility, and Physician Codes, Health Care System**

★ American Hospital Association (AHA) membership    ◯ Healthcare Facilities Accreditation Program    ⇑ Center for Improvement in Healthcare Quality Accreditation
☐ The Joint Commission accreditation    ◇ DNV Healthcare Inc. accreditation    △ Commission on Accreditation of Rehabilitation Facilities (CARF) accreditation

## DOVER—Strafford County

✠ **WENTWORTH–DOUGLASS HOSPITAL (300018)**, 789 Central Avenue, Zip 03820; tel. 603/742–5252 **A**1 2 9 10 **F**3 8 13 17 18 19 20 22 26 28 29 30 31 32 34 35 36 39 40 41 42 43 44 45 46 47 48 49 50 54 55 57 58 59 61 62 63 64 65 68 70 73 74 75 76 77 78 79 81 82 84 85 86 87 89 92 93 94 96 97 100 101 104 107 108 110 111 114 115 118 119 120 121 123 124 126 129 130 131 132 134 135 143 144 145 146 147 148 **P**6 8
Primary Contact: Gregory J. Walker, Chief Executive Officer
COO: Daniel N. Dunn, Vice President Operations
CFO: Peter Walcek, Vice President Finance
CMO: Paul Cass, D.O., Chief Medical & Clinical Integration Officer
CIO: Jeffrey Pollock, Chief Information Officer
CHR: Erin Flanigan, Vice President Human Resources
CNO: Sheila Woolley, R.N., Vice President, Patient Care Services
Web address: www.wdhospital.com
**Control:** Other not–for–profit (including NFP Corporation) **Service:** General Medical and Surgical

> **Staffed Beds:** 125 **Admissions:** 6037 **Census:** 73 **Outpatient Visits:** 275212 **Births:** 1116 **Total Expense ($000):** 230013 **Payroll Expense ($000):** 90343 **Personnel:** 1467

## EXETER—Rockingham County

★ ◇ **EXETER HOSPITAL (300023)**, 5 Alumni Drive, Zip 03833–2128; tel. 603/778–7311 **A**2 9 10 21 **F**3 8 13 14 15 18 20 22 26 28 29 30 31 32 34 35 36 37 38 40 44 45 46 47 48 49 50 51 52 54 55 57 58 59 64 70 74 75 76 77 78 79 80 81 84 85 86 87 89 93 107 108 110 111 114 118 119 120 121 123 124 129 130 131 132 135 143 144 145 146 147 148
Primary Contact: Kevin J. Callahan, President and Chief Executive Officer
CFO: Kevin J. O'Leary, Senior Vice President and Chief Financial Officer
CMO: Richard Hollister, President of Medical Staff
CIO: David Briden, Chief Information Officer
CHR: Christopher M. Callahan, Vice President Human Resources
CNO: Susan Burns–Tisdale, Senior Vice President Clinical Operations, Interim CNO
Web address: www.ehr.org
**Control:** Other not–for–profit (including NFP Corporation) **Service:** General Medical and Surgical

> **Staffed Beds:** 99 **Admissions:** 4988 **Census:** 57 **Outpatient Visits:** 170813 **Births:** 662 **Total Expense ($000):** 174558 **Payroll Expense ($000):** 67176 **Personnel:** 1185

## FRANKLIN—Merrimack County

★ **FRANKLIN REGIONAL HOSPITAL (301306)**, 15 Aiken Avenue, Zip 03235–1299; tel. 603/934–2060 **A**10 18 **F**3 11 15 18 29 30 34 35 36 39 40 44 45 46 47 48 49 50 57 58 59 61 64 65 66 68 70 74 75 77 78 79 81 82 83 84 85 86 87 93 97 98 100 101 102 103 107 119 127 128 130 131 132 133 135 146 147 148 **P**4 6 **S** LRGHealthcare, Laconia, NH
Primary Contact: Seth Warren, Interim Chief Executive Officer
CMO: Peter Doane, M.D., Chief Medical Officer
CIO: Kevin Irish, Chief Information Officer
CHR: Cass Walker, Senior Director Administrative Services
Web address: www.lrgh.org
**Control:** Other not–for–profit (including NFP Corporation) **Service:** General Medical and Surgical

> **Staffed Beds:** 35 **Admissions:** 1099 **Census:** 22 **Outpatient Visits:** 48250 **Births:** 0 **Total Expense ($000):** 41104 **Payroll Expense ($000):** 20678 **Personnel:** 210

## GREENFIELD—Hillsborough County

**CROTCHED MOUNTAIN REHABILITATION CENTER**, 1 Verney Drive, Zip 03047–5000; tel. 603/547–3311, (Nonreporting)
Primary Contact: Donald L. Shumway, Chief Executive Officer
COO: Michael Redmond, Senior Vice President and Chief Operating Officer
CFO: Thomas Zubricki, Vice President Finance, Chief Financial Officer
CMO: W. Carl Cooley, M.D., Chief Medical Officer
CIO: Jerry Hunter, Vice President, Information Technology
CHR: Lorrie Rudis, Vice President, Human Resources
Web address: www.cmf.org
**Control:** Other not–for–profit (including NFP Corporation) **Service:** Rehabilitation

> **Staffed Beds:** 181

## HAMPSTEAD—Rockingham County

☐ **HAMPSTEAD HOSPITAL (304001)**, 218 East Road, Zip 03841–2305; tel. 603/329–5311, (Nonreporting) **A**1 10
Primary Contact: Phillip J. Kubiak, President
COO: Cynthia A. Gove, Chief Operating Officer
CFO: Cherie Clough–Berry, Vice President, Finance
CMO: Michael Knight, M.D., Medical Director
CIO: Sandra J. Lucia, Director Health Information and Corporate Compliance Officer
CHR: Lisa M. Ryan, Coordinator Human Resources
CNO: Julie D'Apollo, R.N., Director of Nursing
Web address: www.hampsteadhospital.com
**Control:** Corporation, Investor–owned, for–profit **Service:** Psychiatric

> **Staffed Beds:** 60

## KEENE—Cheshire County

✠ **CHESHIRE MEDICAL CENTER (300019)**, 580 Court Street, Zip 03431–1718; tel. 603/354–5400, (Nonreporting) **A**1 2 3 9 10
Primary Contact: Seth Warren, President and Chief Executive Officer
CFO: Robert K. Cochrane, Interim Vice President, Finance
CMO: Don Caruso, M.D., Chief Medical Officer
CIO: Peter Malloy, Chief Information Officer
CHR: Julie Green, Vice President Human Resources
CNO: Cynthia Coughlin, MS, Chief Nursing Officer
Web address: www.cheshire–med.com
**Control:** Other not–for–profit (including NFP Corporation) **Service:** General Medical and Surgical

> **Staffed Beds:** 140

## LACONIA—Belknap County

★ **LAKES REGION GENERAL HOSPITAL (300005)**, 80 Highland Street, Zip 03246–3298; tel. 603/524–3211 **A**10 **F**3 8 11 12 13 15 18 28 29 30 31 32 34 35 36 37 39 40 43 44 45 46 47 48 49 50 53 54 56 57 58 59 60 61 64 65 66 68 70 74 75 76 77 78 79 81 82 83 84 85 86 87 93 97 98 99 100 101 102 103 107 108 114 118 119 129 130 131 132 133 135 144 146 147 148 **P**4 6 **S** LRGHealthcare, Laconia, NH
Primary Contact: Seth Warren, Interim Chief Executive Officer
CFO: Henry D. Lipman, Senior Vice President, Financial Strategy and External Relations
CMO: Peter Doane, M.D., Chief Medical Officer
CIO: Kevin Irish, Chief Information Officer
CHR: Cass Walker, Senior Director, Administrative Services
Web address: www.lrgh.org
**Control:** Other not–for–profit (including NFP Corporation) **Service:** General Medical and Surgical

> **Staffed Beds:** 88 **Admissions:** 4735 **Census:** 68 **Outpatient Visits:** 215624 **Births:** 356 **Total Expense ($000):** 178241 **Payroll Expense ($000):** 83722 **Personnel:** 973

## LANCASTER—Coos County

★ **WEEKS MEDICAL CENTER (301303)**, 173 Middle Street, Zip 03584–3508; tel. 603/788–4911 **A**9 10 18 **F**3 11 15 18 28 29 31 32 34 35 36 40 45 50 51 56 57 59 61 62 63 64 65 66 68 70 75 77 78 79 81 85 87 91 92 93 94 97 100 104 107 108 110 111 114 116 117 118 119 127 130 131 132 133 134 135 146 147 148 **P**6
Primary Contact: Scott W. Howe, Chief Executive Officer
CMO: Lars Nielson, M.D., Chief Medical Officer
CIO: Darrell Bodnar, Director Information
CHR: Linda Rexford, Director Human Resources
CNO: Donna Walker, Chief Nurse Executive
Web address: www.weeksmedical.org
**Control:** Other not–for–profit (including NFP Corporation) **Service:** General Medical and Surgical

> **Staffed Beds:** 25 **Admissions:** 864 **Census:** 10 **Outpatient Visits:** 79289 **Births:** 0 **Total Expense ($000):** 40327 **Payroll Expense ($000):** 22209 **Personnel:** 291

## LEBANON—Grafton County

★ **ALICE PECK DAY MEMORIAL HOSPITAL (301305)**, 10 Alice Peck Day Drive, Zip 03766–2650; tel. 603/448–3121 **A**9 10 18 **F**3 11 13 15 29 34 35 36 37 39 40 41 42 45 47 50 51 54 56 57 59 63 64 65 66 67 75 76 77 79 81 82 83 84 85 93 97 107 110 113 114 115 116 117 119 128 129 130 131 133 135 145 146 147 148 **P**5 6
Primary Contact: Susan E. Mooney, M.D., MS, President and Chief Executive Officer
COO: J. Todd Miller, Vice President and Chief Operating Officer
CFO: Evalie M. Crosby, CPA, Vice President Finance and Chief Financial Officer
CMO: Randy Lea, M.D., Vice President and Chief Medical Officer
CIO: Kristin Kneisel, Interim Director, Information Services
CHR: Brenda Blair, Vice President Human Resources
CNO: Beverley A. Rankin, R.N., Vice President & Chief Nursing Officer
Web address: www.alicepeckday.org
**Control:** Other not–for–profit (including NFP Corporation) **Service:** General Medical and Surgical

> **Staffed Beds:** 25 **Admissions:** 1123 **Census:** 13 **Outpatient Visits:** 93313 **Births:** 293 **Total Expense ($000):** 54924 **Payroll Expense ($000):** 30552 **Personnel:** 379

**NH**

**DARTMOUTH–HITCHCOCK MEDICAL CENTER (300003)**, One Medical Center Drive, Zip 03756–0001; tel. 603/650–5000, (Includes CHILDREN'S HOSPITAL AT DARTMOUTH, One Medical Center Drive, Zip 03756; tel. 603/650–5000) **A**1 3 5 8 9 10 **F**3 5 6 7 8 9 11 12 13 14 15 17 18 19 20 21 22 23 24 25 26 27 28 29 30 31 32 34 35 36 37 38 39 40 41 43 44 45 46 47 48 49 50 51 52 53 54 55 56 57 58 59 60 61 63 64 65 66 68 70 71 72 74 75 76 77 78 79 80 81 82 84 85 86 87 88 89 91 92 93 94 96 97 98 99 100 101 102 103 104 105 107 108 110 111 112 114 115 116 117 118 119 120 121 123 124 126 129 130 131 132 134 135 136 138 141 142 143 145 146 147 148 **P**6
Primary Contact: James Weinstein, D.O., MS, President and Chief Executive Officer
COO: Daniel Jantzen, Senior Vice President and Chief Operating Officer
CFO: Robin F. Kilfeather–Mackey, Chief Financial Officer
CMO: Edward J. Merrens, M.D., Medical Director
CIO: Terrence Carroll, Ph.D., Vice President, Information Services
CHR: John S. Malanowski, Chief Human Resources Officer
CNO: Gay L. Landstrom, Ph.D., Chief Nursing Officer
Web address: www.hitchcock.org
**Control:** Other not–for–profit (including NFP Corporation) **Service:** General Medical and Surgical

**Staffed Beds:** 417 **Admissions:** 19234 **Census:** 304 **Outpatient Visits:** 862640 **Births:** 1115 **Total Expense ($000):** 1056717 **Payroll Expense ($000):** 497070 **Personnel:** 6014

### LITTLETON—Grafton County

**LITTLETON REGIONAL HOSPITAL (301302)**, 600 Saint Johnsbury Road, Zip 03561–3442; tel. 603/444–9000 **A**9 10 18 **F**3 11 13 15 18 26 28 29 31 32 34 35 36 38 40 43 44 45 50 56 57 59 64 65 67 70 74 75 76 77 78 79 81 84 85 86 87 89 90 92 93 96 97 100 104 107 108 110 111 115 118 119 127 128 129 130 131 133 143 146 147 148 **P**6
Primary Contact: Danielle Ocker, Director
CFO: Robert L. Fotter, Chief Financial Officer
CIO: Scott Vachon, Director Information Technology
CHR: Georgene Novak, Director Human Resources
CNO: Linda Gilmore, Chief Nursing Officer/Chief Administrative Officer
Web address: www.littletonhospital.org
**Control:** Other not–for–profit (including NFP Corporation) **Service:** General Medical and Surgical

**Staffed Beds:** 25 **Admissions:** 1463 **Census:** 14 **Outpatient Visits:** 54505 **Births:** 327 **Total Expense ($000):** 82955 **Payroll Expense ($000):** 34658 **Personnel:** 377

### MANCHESTER—Hillsborough County

**CATHOLIC MEDICAL CENTER (300034)**, 100 McGregor Street, Zip 03102–3770; tel. 603/668–3545 **A**1 2 3 10 **F**3 9 11 12 13 15 18 20 22 24 26 28 29 30 31 32 34 35 36 37 38 39 40 41 43 44 46 47 48 49 50 53 57 58 59 60 61 63 64 65 66 70 71 73 74 75 76 77 78 79 80 81 82 84 85 86 87 90 93 96 100 102 104 105 107 108 110 111 114 115 118 119 124 126 129 130 131 132 134 135 143 144 146 147 148 **P**6
Primary Contact: Joseph Pepe, M.D., President and Chief Executive Officer
COO: Alexander J. Walker, Executive Vice President Operations and Strategic Development
CFO: Edward L. Dudley, III, Executive Vice President and Chief Financial Officer
CMO: William H. Goodman, Vice President Medical Affairs, Chief Medical Officer
CIO: Thomas Della Flora, Vice President and Chief Information Officer
CHR: Merryll Rosenfeld, Vice President, Human Resources
CNO: Robert A. Duhaime, R.N., Senior Vice President Clinical Operations and Chief Nursing Officer
Web address: www.catholicmedicalcenter.org
**Control:** Other not–for–profit (including NFP Corporation) **Service:** General Medical and Surgical

**Staffed Beds:** 240 **Admissions:** 10204 **Census:** 141 **Outpatient Visits:** 165930 **Births:** 967 **Total Expense ($000):** 286715 **Payroll Expense ($000):** 123813 **Personnel:** 1475

**ELLIOT HOSPITAL (300012)**, One Elliot Way, Zip 03103–3502; tel. 603/669–5300 **A**1 2 3 9 10 **F**3 8 9 12 13 15 18 20 22 26 28 29 30 31 32 34 35 36 37 38 39 40 41 42 43 44 45 46 47 48 49 50 51 53 54 55 56 57 59 64 65 68 70 72 74 75 77 78 79 81 82 83 84 85 86 87 88 89 91 97 98 99 100 101 102 103 107 108 110 111 114 115 118 119 120 121 123 124 126 129 130 131 132 134 135 144 146 147 148 **P**6
Primary Contact: James L. Woodward, President and Chief Executive Officer
COO: Rick Phelps, M.D., President and Chief Operating Officer
CFO: Richard Elwell, Senior Vice President and Chief Financial Officer
CMO: Greg Baxter, M.D., Senior Vice President Medical Affairs and Chief Medical Officer
CIO: Denise Purington, Vice President and Chief Information Officer
CHR: Catherine Bardier, Vice President, Human Resources
CNO: Joni Spring, R.N., Vice President Patient Care Services and Chief Nursing Officer
Web address: www.elliothospital.org
**Control:** Other not–for–profit (including NFP Corporation) **Service:** General Medical and Surgical

**Staffed Beds:** 266 **Admissions:** 12458 **Census:** 164 **Outpatient Visits:** 508833 **Births:** 2039 **Total Expense ($000):** 340885 **Payroll Expense ($000):** 123684 **Personnel:** 2959

**MANCHESTER VETERANS AFFAIRS MEDICAL CENTER**, 718 Smyth Road, Zip 03104–4098; tel. 603/624–4366, (Nonreporting) **A**5 **S** Department of Veterans Affairs, Washington, DC
Primary Contact: Tammy A. Krueger, Acting Director
COO: Richard T. Rose, Associate Director
CFO: Frank Ryan, Chief Financial Officer
CMO: Andrew Breuder, M.D., Chief of Staff
CIO: John Foote, Chief Information Officer
CHR: Mary Ellen Kenney, Chief Human Services
Web address: www.manchester.va.gov/
**Control:** Veterans Affairs, Government, federal **Service:** Rehabilitation

**Staffed Beds:** 90

**VETERANS AFFAIRS MEDICAL CENTER** See Manchester Veterans Affairs Medical Center

### NASHUA—Hillsborough County

**SOUTHERN NEW HAMPSHIRE MEDICAL CENTER (300020)**, 8 Prospect Street, Zip 03060–3925, Mailing Address: P.O. Box 2014, Zip 03061–2014; tel. 603/577–2000, (Nonreporting) **A**2 3 5 9 10 21
Primary Contact: Thomas E. Wilhelmsen, Jr., President and Chief Executive Officer
COO: Tate Curti, Senior Vice President and Chief Operating Officer
CFO: Michael S. Rose, Senior Vice President Finance and Chief Financial Officer
CMO: Stephanie Wolf–Rosenblum, M.D., Chief Medical Officer
CIO: Andrew Watt, M.D., Vice President, Chief Information Officer and Chief Medical Information Officer
CHR: Linda Rossi, Vice President Human Relations
CNO: Colette Tilton, Vice President and Chief Nursing Officer
Web address: www.snhhs.org
**Control:** Other not–for–profit (including NFP Corporation) **Service:** General Medical and Surgical

**Staffed Beds:** 183

**ST. JOSEPH HOSPITAL (300011)**, 172 Kinsley Street, Zip 03060–3648; tel. 603/882–3000 **A**2 7 10 21 **F**3 4 11 12 13 15 18 20 22 28 29 30 31 32 34 35 36 37 40 43 44 45 46 49 50 51 54 55 56 57 59 61 62 63 64 65 68 70 74 75 76 77 78 79 81 82 83 84 85 86 87 89 90 91 93 94 97 98 102 107 108 110 111 114 115 116 117 119 126 129 130 131 132 135 144 146 147 148 **P**6 8 **S** Covenant Health, Tewksbury, MA
Primary Contact: Richard Boehler, M.D., President and Chief Executive Officer
COO: Pam Duchene, R.N., Vice President Patient Care Services
CFO: Richard Plamondon, Vice President Finance and Chief Financial Officer
CIO: Keith A. Choinka, Vice President Information Systems and Chief Information Officer
CHR: Jacqueline Woolley, Vice President Human Resources
Web address: www.stjosephhospital.com
**Control:** Church–operated, Nongovernment, not–for profit **Service:** General Medical and Surgical

**Staffed Beds:** 126 **Admissions:** 5495 **Census:** 70 **Outpatient Visits:** 188982 **Births:** 516 **Total Expense ($000):** 158001 **Payroll Expense ($000):** 65646 **Personnel:** 879

NH

**Hospital, Medicare Provider Number, Address, Telephone, Approval, Facility, and Physician Codes, Health Care System**

★ American Hospital Association (AHA) membership  ○ Healthcare Facilities Accreditation Program  ⇧ Center for Improvement in Healthcare Quality Accreditation
□ The Joint Commission accreditation  ◇ DNV Healthcare Inc. accreditation  △ Commission on Accreditation of Rehabilitation Facilities (CARF) accreditation

## NEW LONDON—Merrimack County

★ **NEW LONDON HOSPITAL (301304)**, 273 County Road, Zip 03257–5736; tel. 603/526–2911, (Total facility includes 58 beds in nursing home–type unit) (Data for 273 days) **A**3 9 10 18 **F**3 7 11 15 18 29 30 31 32 34 40 41 45 50 51 54 56 57 59 64 67 70 74 75 77 78 79 81 82 84 85 87 89 93 94 97 99 100 102 104 107 110 111 114 119 127 128 130 131 133 134 146 147 148 **P**6
Primary Contact: Bruce King, President and Chief Executive Officer
CFO: Donald Griffin, CPA, Chief Financial Officer
CMO: James M. Murphy, M.D., Chief Medical Officer Regional Development and Outpatient Services
CIO: David Foss, Chief Information Officer
CHR: Shari Bostwick, Director Human Resources
CNO: Sally K. Patton, R.N., Chief Nursing Officer
Web address: www.newlondonhospital.org
**Control:** Other not–for–profit (including NFP Corporation) **Service:** General Medical and Surgical

**Staffed Beds:** 83 **Admissions:** 949 **Census:** 71 **Outpatient Visits:** 104098 **Births:** 0 **Total Expense ($000):** 44636 **Payroll Expense ($000):** 21107 **Personnel:** 424

## NORTH CONWAY—Carroll County

★ **MEMORIAL HOSPITAL (301307)**, 3073 White Mountain Highway, Zip 03860–7101; tel. 603/356–5461, (Total facility includes 45 beds in nursing home–type unit) **A**9 10 18 **F**3 11 13 15 28 29 30 31 34 35 36 40 43 45 50 51 57 59 64 67 68 70 75 76 77 78 79 81 82 84 85 86 87 90 94 96 97 105 107 110 115 119 128 129 130 131 132 133 144 146 147 **P**6 **S** MaineHealth, Portland, ME
Primary Contact: Scott McKinnon, President and Chief Executive Officer
CFO: Diane Maheux, Vice President Finance
CMO: Ray Rabideau, M.D., Senior Vice President and Chief Medical Officer
CIO: Curtis Kerbs, Vice President Information Services
CHR: Margaret Phillips, Director Human Resources
CNO: Ethnee Garner, R.N., Vice President Nursing Services
Web address: www.memorialhospitalnh.org
**Control:** Other not–for–profit (including NFP Corporation) **Service:** General Medical and Surgical

**Staffed Beds:** 70 **Admissions:** 1598 **Census:** 54 **Outpatient Visits:** 56371 **Births:** 228 **Total Expense ($000):** 64083 **Payroll Expense ($000):** 28616 **Personnel:** 439

## PETERBOROUGH—Hillsborough County

★ **MONADNOCK COMMUNITY HOSPITAL (301309)**, 452 Old Street Road, Zip 03458–1295; tel. 603/924–7191 **A**5 9 10 18 **F**3 11 13 15 28 29 30 34 35 36 40 41 44 45 50 53 57 59 64 65 70 74 75 76 77 78 79 81 82 85 86 89 91 92 93 97 99 100 101 102 103 104 107 108 110 118 119 124 127 130 131 132 133 134 135 146 147 148 **P**6
Primary Contact: Cynthia McGuire, Chief Executive Officer
CFO: Richard Scheinblum, Chief Financial Officer
CIO: Nancy Barisano, Chief Information Officer
CHR: John Sansone, Director Human Resources
CNO: Vicki Loughery, R.N., Chief Nursing Officer
Web address: www.monadnockhospital.org
**Control:** Other not–for–profit (including NFP Corporation) **Service:** General Medical and Surgical

**Staffed Beds:** 25 **Admissions:** 1422 **Census:** 14 **Outpatient Visits:** 76468 **Births:** 276 **Total Expense ($000):** 74489 **Payroll Expense ($000):** 32701 **Personnel:** 478

## PLYMOUTH—Grafton County

★ **SPEARE MEMORIAL HOSPITAL (301311)**, 16 Hospital Road, Zip 03264–1199; tel. 603/536–1120 **A**9 10 18 **F**3 13 15 28 29 30 31 32 34 35 39 40 45 53 54 57 59 64 70 75 76 77 78 79 81 84 85 93 94 97 107 110 111 113 114 119 127 129 130 131 132 133 146 147 148 **P**8
Primary Contact: Michelle McEwen, President and Chief Executive Officer
CFO: Thomas Lenkowski, Chief Financial Officer
CMO: Joseph Ebner, M.D., Chief Medical Officer
CIO: Michael Cosgrave, Director, Information System
CHR: Laurie Bolognani, Human Resources Officer
CNO: Kristine Hering, R.N., Chief Nursing Officer
Web address: www.spearehospital.com
**Control:** Other not–for–profit (including NFP Corporation) **Service:** General Medical and Surgical

**Staffed Beds:** 25 **Admissions:** 1287 **Census:** 14 **Outpatient Visits:** 36522 **Births:** 332 **Total Expense ($000):** 50890 **Payroll Expense ($000):** 22845 **Personnel:** 381

## PORTSMOUTH—Rockingham County

☒ **PORTSMOUTH REGIONAL HOSPITAL (300029)**, 333 Borthwick Avenue, Zip 03801–7128; tel. 603/436–5110, (Nonreporting) **A**1 2 9 10 **S** HCA, Nashville, TN
Primary Contact: Dean Carucci, Interim Chief Executive Officer
COO: Stuart Hemming, Chief Operating Officer
CFO: Richard Senger, Chief Financial Officer
CMO: Tim Pike, M.D., Chief Medical Officer
CIO: Ed Sovetskhy, Director Information Services
CHR: Jackie Brayton, Vice President Human Resources
Web address: www.portsmouthhospital.com
**Control:** Corporation, Investor–owned, for–profit **Service:** General Medical and Surgical

**Staffed Beds:** 165

## ROCHESTER—Strafford County

★ **FRISBIE MEMORIAL HOSPITAL (300014)**, 11 Whitehall Road, Zip 03867–3297; tel. 603/332–5211 **A**9 10 **F**3 7 11 13 17 18 20 21 28 29 31 32 34 35 40 45 46 49 50 56 57 59 64 68 70 75 77 78 79 81 82 83 86 87 93 97 98 103 104 105 107 111 115 117 118 119 129 130 132 135 146 147 **P**5 8
Primary Contact: John A. Marzinzik, President and Chief Executive Officer
CMO: Susan Gaire, M.D., President Medical Staff
CHR: Carol Themelis, Vice President Human Resources
Web address: www.frisbiehospital.com
**Control:** Other not–for–profit (including NFP Corporation) **Service:** General Medical and Surgical

**Staffed Beds:** 82 **Admissions:** 3246 **Census:** 40 **Outpatient Visits:** 127429 **Births:** 348 **Total Expense ($000):** 127061 **Payroll Expense ($000):** 55280 **Personnel:** 767

## SALEM—Rockingham County

☐ △ **NORTHEAST REHABILITATION HOSPITAL (303026)**, 70 Butler Street, Zip 03079–3925; tel. 603/893–2900, (Nonreporting) **A**1 7 10
Primary Contact: John F. Prochilo, Chief Executive Officer and Administrator
COO: Robert Kotsonis, Chief Operating Officer
CFO: Charles Champagne, Chief Financial Officer
CMO: A. Deniz Ozel, M.D., Chief Medical Director
CIO: Deana Fassio, Director
CHR: Thomas A. Prince, Vice President Human Resources
CNO: Helene Thibodeau, R.N., Vice President Patient Care Services
Web address: www.northeastrehab.com
**Control:** Corporation, Investor–owned, for–profit **Service:** Rehabilitation

**Staffed Beds:** 135

## WOLFEBORO—Carroll County

★ **HUGGINS HOSPITAL (301312)**, 240 South Main Street, Zip 03894–4455, Mailing Address: P.O. Box 912, Zip 03894–0912; tel. 603/569–7500, (Nonreporting) **A**9 10 18
Primary Contact: Michael Connelly, President
CFO: Jeremy Roberge, Chief Financial Officer
CMO: John Boornazian, M.D., Chief Medical Officer
CIO: Pam McGovern, Director Technology
CHR: Laura Stauss, Director of Human Resources
Web address: www.hugginshospital.org
**Control:** Other not–for–profit (including NFP Corporation) **Service:** General Medical and Surgical

**Staffed Beds:** 25

## WOODSVILLE—Grafton County

★ **COTTAGE HOSPITAL (301301)**, 90 Swiftwater Road, Zip 03785–1421, Mailing Address: P.O. Box 2001, Zip 03785–2001; tel. 603/747–9000 **A**9 10 18 **F**3 11 13 15 18 28 29 30 31 34 35 40 43 46 49 50 54 64 65 67 68 70 74 75 76 77 78 79 81 82 84 85 87 89 93 97 107 111 114 119 127 128 130 132 133 135 146 147 148
Primary Contact: Maria Ryan, Ph.D., Chief Executive Officer
COO: Lori Hughes, R.N., Chief Nursing Officer, Vice President Operations and Patient Care Services
CFO: Steven L. Plant, Chief Financial Officer
CIO: Rick Fredrick, Director Information Technology
CNO: Lori Hughes, R.N., Chief Nursing Officer, Vice President Operations & Patient Care Services
Web address: www.cottagehospital.org
**Control:** Other not–for–profit (including NFP Corporation) **Service:** General Medical and Surgical

**Staffed Beds:** 25 **Admissions:** 616 **Census:** 7 **Outpatient Visits:** 39500 **Births:** 73 **Total Expense ($000):** 28841 **Payroll Expense ($000):** 12570 **Personnel:** 211

*Many Facility Codes have changed. Please refer to the AHA Guide Code Chart.* © 2015 AHA Guide

# NEW JERSEY

## ATLANTIC CITY—Atlantic County

★ ◇ **ACUITY SPECIALTY HOSPITAL OF NEW JERSEY (312023)**, 1925 Pacific Avenue, 7th Floor, Zip 08401–6713; tel. 609/441–2122, (Nonreporting) **A**10 21 **S** AcuityHealthcare, LP, Charlotte, NC
Primary Contact: Monica Titus, President and Chief Executive Officer
CFO: Cheryl Lambert, Chief Financial Officer
CHR: Maria Ciro, Director Human Resources
CNO: Kathleen Kerstetter, R.N., Chief Clinical Officer
Web address: www.acuityhealthcare.net
**Control:** Corporation, Investor–owned, for–profit **Service:** Long–Term Acute Care hospital

**Staffed Beds:** 30

⊞ **ATLANTICARE REGIONAL MEDICAL CENTER (310064)**, 1925 Pacific Avenue, Zip 08401–6713; tel. 609/441–8994, (Includes ATLANTICARE REGIONAL MEDICAL CENTER–MAINLAND DIVISION, Jimmie Leeds Road, Pomona, Zip 08240; tel. 609/652–1000) **A**1 2 3 9 10 13 **F**3 7 11 12 13 15 17 18 20 22 24 26 29 30 31 34 35 36 37 38 40 41 42 43 45 46 47 48 49 50 54 57 58 59 60 61 64 66 68 70 71 72 73 74 75 76 78 79 81 82 83 84 85 86 87 89 93 97 98 99 100 102 103 104 105 106 107 108 110 111 114 115 116 117 118 119 120 121 123 124 126 130 132 135 143 146 147 148 **P**6 **S** AtlantiCare, Egg Harbor Township, NJ
Primary Contact: Lori Herndon, R.N., President and Chief Executive Officer
COO: Lori Herndon, R.N., President and Chief Executive Officer
CFO: Walter Greiner, Chief Financial Officer
CMO: Marilouise Vendetti, M.D., Chief Medical Officer
CIO: Christopher A. Scanzera, Vice President and Chief Information Officer
CHR: Richard Lovering, Corporate Vice President Human Resources and Organizational Development
CNO: Robyn Begley, R.N., Chief Nursing Officer
Web address: www.atlanticare.org
**Control:** Other not–for–profit (including NFP Corporation) **Service:** General Medical and Surgical

**Staffed Beds:** 540 **Admissions:** 29750 **Census:** 378 **Outpatient Visits:** 316521 **Births:** 2202 **Total Expense ($000):** 646205 **Payroll Expense ($000):** 269284 **Personnel:** 3128

## BAYONNE—Hudson County

⊞ **BAYONNE MEDICAL CENTER (310025)**, 29th Street & Avenue E., Zip 07002–4699; tel. 201/858–5000 **A**1 2 6 9 10 **F**3 15 18 20 22 29 31 34 35 40 45 46 49 50 54 57 58 59 60 64 65 66 68 70 71 74 75 77 78 79 81 82 84 85 86 87 90 91 92 94 97 98 99 100 101 103 107 108 110 111 114 116 117 119 129 130 132 146 147 148 **P**6 7 **S** CarePoint Health, Jersey City, NJ
Primary Contact: Paul E. Minnick, R.N., MSN, Chief Operating Officer
COO: Paul E. Minnick, R.N., Chief Operating Officer
CIO: Don Lutz, Chief Information Officer
CHR: Jennifer Dobin, Vice President Human Resources
Web address: www.bayonnemedicalcenter.org/
**Control:** Corporation, Investor–owned, for–profit **Service:** General Medical and Surgical

**Staffed Beds:** 178 **Admissions:** 6480 **Census:** 99 **Births:** 0

## BELLE MEAD—Somerset County

⊞ **CARRIER CLINIC (314012)**, 252 County Route 601, Zip 08502–0147, Mailing Address: P.O. Box 147, Zip 08502–0147; tel. 908/281–1000 **A**1 3 5 9 10 **F**4 5 98 99 100 101 102 103 **P**6
Primary Contact: Donald J. Parker, President and Chief Executive Officer
CFO: Randolph Jacobson, Chief Financial Officer
CMO: David Buch, M.D., Chief Medical Officer
CIO: Peter Schwartz, Manager Information Services
CHR: Trish Toole, Vice President Administrative Services
CNO: Carol Kosztyo, R.N., Vice President, Patient Care Services
Web address: www.carrierclinic.org
**Control:** Other not–for–profit (including NFP Corporation) **Service:** Psychiatric

**Staffed Beds:** 278 **Admissions:** 5986 **Census:** 229 **Outpatient Visits:** 1005 **Births:** 0 **Total Expense ($000):** 64717 **Payroll Expense ($000):** 40435 **Personnel:** 623

**EAST MOUNTAIN HOSPITAL (314026)**, 252 County Route 601, Zip 08502; tel. 908/281–1500, (Nonreporting) **A**10
Primary Contact: Michael Voorhees, MS, Executive Director
CFO: Randolph Jacobson, Chief Financial Officer
CMO: Bohdan Cehelyk, M.D., Chief Medical Officer
CIO: Peter Schwartz, Director Information Systems
CHR: Patricia Toole, Vice President Human Resources
CNO: Deborah Charette, Director of Nursing
Web address: www.eastmountainhospital.com
**Control:** Corporation, Investor–owned, for–profit **Service:** Psychiatric

**Staffed Beds:** 16

## BELLEVILLE—Essex County

⊞ **CLARA MAASS MEDICAL CENTER (310009)**, One Clara Maass Drive, Zip 07109–3557; tel. 973/450–2000 **A**1 2 3 5 9 10 **F**3 4 8 11 12 13 15 16 18 19 20 22 28 29 30 31 34 35 38 40 41 44 45 47 49 50 51 54 55 56 57 58 59 60 61 63 64 65 66 67 68 70 72 73 74 75 76 77 78 79 81 82 83 84 85 86 87 88 89 90 91 92 93 94 98 101 102 103 107 108 110 111 114 115 116 117 118 119 120 121 123 124 126 128 129 130 131 132 143 144 146 147 148 **S** Barnabas Health, West Orange, NJ
Primary Contact: Mary Ellen Clyne, Ph.D., MSN, R.N., President and Chief Executive Officer
CFO: Nik Alexiades, Chief Financial Officer
CMO: Frank Mazzarella, M.D., Chief Medical Officer
CIO: Michael McTigue, Chief Information Officer
CHR: Jim Rolek, Chief Human Resources Officer
CNO: Lea Rodriguez, Chief Nursing Officer
Web address: www.barnabashealth.org/hospitals/clara_maass/index.html
**Control:** Other not–for–profit (including NFP Corporation) **Service:** General Medical and Surgical

**Staffed Beds:** 469 **Admissions:** 15693 **Census:** 215 **Outpatient Visits:** 129228 **Births:** 1434 **Total Expense ($000):** 248857 **Payroll Expense ($000):** 103454 **Personnel:** 1314

## BERKELEY HEIGHTS—Union County

**CORNERSTONE BEHAVIORAL HEALTH HOSPITAL OF UNION COUNTY**, 40 Watchung Way, Zip 07922–2618; tel. 908/771–5700
Primary Contact: Michael Flemming, Adminstrator
**Control:** County-Government, nonfederal **Service:** Psychiatric

**Staffed Beds:** 44

★ **RUNNELLS CENTER FOR REHABILITATION AND HEALTHCARE (314027)**, 40 Watchung Way, Zip 07922–2618; tel. 908/771–5700, (Nonreporting) **A**9 10
Primary Contact: Joseph Sharp, Administrator
CFO: Michael Drummond, Chief Financial Officer
CMO: Raymond Lanza, D.O., Medical Director
CHR: Greg Hardoby, Director Personnel
CNO: Patricia Spina, R.N., Director of Nursing
Web address: www.ucnj.org/runnells
**Control:** Corporation, investor–owned, for–profit **Service:** Other specialty

**Staffed Beds:** 344

## BOONTON TOWNSHIP—Morris County

**SAINT CLARE'S HOSPITAL/BOONTON TOWNSHIP** See Saint Clare's Health System, Denville

## BRICK—Ocean County

☐ **SHORE REHABILITATION INSTITUTE (313033)**, 425 Jack Martin Boulevard, Zip 08724–7732; tel. 732/836–4500 **A**1 10 **F**29 56 57 90 91 93 94 96
Primary Contact: Amit Mohan, Executive Director
CFO: Richard C. Smith, Senior Vice President Finance
CMO: Lisa M. Luciano, D.O., Medical Director
CNO: Maria Clohsey, Director of Nursing
Web address: www.shorerehabilitationinstitute.com
**Control:** Other not–for–profit (including NFP Corporation) **Service:** Rehabilitation

**Staffed Beds:** 40 **Admissions:** 1017 **Census:** 33 **Outpatient Visits:** 3000 **Births:** 0

NJ

---

**Hospital, Medicare Provider Number, Address, Telephone, Approval, Facility, and Physician Codes, Health Care System**

★ American Hospital Association (AHA) membership
☐ The Joint Commission accreditation
◯ Healthcare Facilities Accreditation Program
◇ DNV Healthcare Inc. accreditation
⇑ Center for Improvement in Healthcare Quality Accreditation
△ Commission on Accreditation of Rehabilitation Facilities (CARF) accreditation

## BRICK TOWNSHIP—Ocean County

⊠ **OCEAN MEDICAL CENTER (310052)**, 425 Jack Martin Boulevard,
Zip 08724–7732; tel. 732/840–2200 **A**1 2 9 10 **F**3 11 12 13 15 17 18 20 22
28 29 30 31 32 34 35 36 38 39 40 41 42 43 44 45 46 47 48 49 50 53 54
55 56 57 58 59 60 63 64 65 66 68 70 71 73 74 75 76 77 78 79 80 81 82
84 85 86 87 91 92 93 94 96 97 100 101 102 103 107 108 110 111 114
115 116 117 118 119 120 121 123 126 129 130 131 132 134 135 144 146
147 148 **P**6 7 **S** Meridian Health, Neptune, NJ
Primary Contact: Dean Q. Lin, FACHE, President
COO: Regina Foley, R.N., Vice President Nursing and Operations
CFO: Robert Palermo, Vice President Finance
CMO: James Clarke, M.D., Vice President Medical Affairs and Clinical
Effectiveness
CIO: Rebecca Weber, Senior Vice President and Chief Information Officer
CHR: Sherrie String, Senior Vice President Human Resources
Web address: www.meridianhealth.com
**Control:** Other not–for–profit (including NFP Corporation) **Service:** General
Medical and Surgical

**Staffed Beds:** 271 **Admissions:** 13208 **Census:** 181 **Outpatient Visits:**
163271 **Births:** 951 **Total Expense ($000):** 235226 **Payroll Expense**
**($000):** 101526 **Personnel:** 1334

## BRIDGETON—Cumberland County

**BRIDGETON HEALTH CENTER** See Inspira Medical Center–Vineland, Vineland

## BROWNS MILLS—Burlington County

☐ **DEBORAH HEART AND LUNG CENTER (310031)**, 200 Trenton Road,
Zip 08015–1705; tel. 609/893–6611, (Nonreporting) **A**1 3 5 9 10 13
Primary Contact: Joseph Chirichella, President and Chief Executive Officer
COO: Joseph Manni, Vice President Operations Chief Operating Officer
CFO: R. Grant Leidy, Vice President Finance
CMO: Lynn McGrath, M.D., Vice President Medical Affairs
CHR: James Carlino, Vice President Human Resources
CNO: Rita Zenna, R.N., Vice President Patient Care Services
Web address: www.deborah.org
**Control:** Other not–for–profit (including NFP Corporation) **Service:** Other specialty

**Staffed Beds:** 89

## CAMDEN—Camden County

⊠ **COOPER UNIVERSITY HEALTH CARE (310014)**, 618 Benson Street,
Zip 08103–1489, Mailing Address: One Cooper Plaza, Zip 08103–1489;
tel. 856/342–2000, (Includes CHILDEN'S REGIONAL HOSPITAL AT COOPER,
Three Cooper Plaza, Zip 08103; tel. 800/826–6737) **A**1 2 3 5 8 9 10 13 **F**3 8
11 12 13 15 17 18 19 20 22 24 26 29 30 31 32 34 35 36 37 39 40 41 42
43 44 45 46 47 48 49 50 51 52 54 55 56 57 58 59 60 61 64 65 66 68 70
72 73 74 75 76 78 79 80 81 82 84 85 86 87 88 89 92 93 96 97 98 99 100
101 102 103 104 107 108 109 110 111 114 115 117 118 119 120 121 123
124 126 129 130 131 132 135 144 146 147 148 **P**6
Primary Contact: Adrienne Kirby, Ph.D., FACHE, President and Chief Executive
Officer
CFO: Douglas E. Shirley, Senior Executive Vice President and Chief Financial
Officer
CMO: Anthony J. Mazzarelli, M.D., Senior Executive Vice President Chief Physician
Executive and Chief Medical Officer
CIO: Stephanie Conners, Senior Executive Vice President Chief Operating Officer
and Chief Nursing Officer
CHR: Douglas H. Allen, Senior Vice President Human Resources
Web address: www.cooperhealth.org
**Control:** Other not–for–profit (including NFP Corporation) **Service:** General
Medical and Surgical

**Staffed Beds:** 518 **Admissions:** 26137 **Census:** 378 **Outpatient Visits:**
307014 **Births:** 2158 **Total Expense ($000):** 677779 **Payroll Expense**
**($000):** 249703 **Personnel:** 4758

⊠ △ **OUR LADY OF LOURDES MEDICAL CENTER (310029)**, 1600 Haddon
Avenue, Zip 08103–3117; tel. 856/757–3500 **A**1 2 3 6 7 9 10 **F**3 7 11 12 13
15 17 18 20 22 24 26 28 29 30 31 32 34 35 36 37 38 40 44 46 47 49 50
55 56 57 58 59 60 61 64 65 66 68 70 72 73 74 75 76 78 79 81 82 84 85
86 87 89 90 95 96 100 107 108 110 111 114 115 118 119 126 130 132
134 135 138 139 142 146 147 148 **P**6 8 **S** Trinity Health, Livonia, MI
Primary Contact: Alexander J. Hatala, FACHE, President and Chief Executive
Officer
COO: Mark Nessel, Chief Operating Officer
CFO: Michael Hammond, Chief Financial Officer
CMO: Alan R. Pope, M.D., Chief Medical Officer
CIO: Maureen Hetu, Chief Information Officer
CHR: Jennifer L. Moughan, Chief Human Resources Officer
CNO: Audrey Jadczak, R.N., Vice President Chief Nursing Officer
Web address: www.lourdesnet.org
**Control:** Other not–for–profit (including NFP Corporation) **Service:** General
Medical and Surgical

**Staffed Beds:** 350 **Admissions:** 12930 **Census:** 179 **Outpatient Visits:**
134641 **Births:** 1040 **Total Expense ($000):** 274859 **Payroll Expense**
**($000):** 98704 **Personnel:** 1468

## CAPE MAY COURT HOUSE—Cape May County

⊠ **CAPE REGIONAL MEDICAL CENTER (310011)**, Two Stone Harbor Boulevard,
Zip 08210–9990; tel. 609/463–2000 **A**1 2 9 10 **F**3 8 11 13 15 18 20 28 29
30 31 34 35 40 44 45 46 49 50 53 57 59 64 70 74 75 76 77 78 79 81 82
84 85 86 87 89 91 93 97 107 111 114 118 119 120 121 123 130 132 135
143 146 148
Primary Contact: Joanne Carrocino, FACHE, President and Chief Executive Officer
CFO: Mark Gill, Vice President Finance and Chief Financial Officer
CMO: Andrea C.S. McCoy, M.D., Chief Medical Officer
CIO: Richard Wheatley, Chief Information Officer
CHR: Byron Hunter, Vice President Human Resources
CNO: Deborah Baehser, Vice President Patient Care Services
Web address: www.caperegional.com
**Control:** Other not–for–profit (including NFP Corporation) **Service:** General
Medical and Surgical

**Staffed Beds:** 149 **Admissions:** 6842 **Census:** 74 **Outpatient Visits:** 181018
**Births:** 471 **Total Expense ($000):** 110047 **Payroll Expense ($000):** 48279
**Personnel:** 771

## CEDAR GROVE—Essex County

☐ **ESSEX COUNTY HOSPITAL CENTER (314020)**, 204 Grove Avenue,
Zip 07009–1436; tel. 973/571–2800, (Nonreporting) **A**1 10
Primary Contact: Frank J. Del Gaudio, Administrator
CFO: Ian Finnell, Business Manager
CMO: Robert Stern, M.D., Medical Director
CIO: Anthony C. Greco, Compliance Officer
CHR: Mary Ann Root, Supervisor Personnel
Web address: www.essexcountynj.org
**Control:** County–Government, nonfederal **Service:** Psychiatric

**Staffed Beds:** 180

## CHERRY HILL—Camden County

⊠ ○ **KENNEDY HEALTH SYSTEM (310086)**, 2201 Chapel Avenue West,
Zip 08002–2048; tel. 856/488–6500, (Includes KENNEDY UNIVERSITY HOSPITAL
– STRATFORD, 18 East Laurel Road, Stratford, Zip 08084; tel. 609/346–6000;
KENNEDY UNIVERSITY HOSPITAL – WASHINGTON TOWNSHIP, 435
Hurffville–Cross Keys Road, Turnersville, Zip 08012; tel. 609/582–2500) **A**1 2 10
11 12 **F**3 5 7 8 11 12 13 15 18 20 22 29 30 31 32 34 35 38 39 40 41 44
46 49 50 54 55 56 57 59 60 61 62 64 65 66 68 70 72 73 74 75 76 77 78
79 81 82 84 85 86 87 89 93 97 98 99 100 101 102 103 104 105 107 108
110 111 114 115 117 118 119 120 121 123 126 129 130 131 132 134 143
146 147 148
Primary Contact: Joseph W. Devine, FACHE, President and Chief Executive Officer
CFO: Gary G. Terrinoni, Chief Financial Officer and Executive Vice President
Administration
CMO: David Condoluci, M.D., Senior Vice President and Chief Medical Officer
CIO: Thomas Balcavage, Vice President Information Systems and Chief Information
Officer Technology
CHR: Anneliese McMenamin, Vice President Human Resources
CNO: Helene M. Burns, MSN, Chief Nursing Executive
Web address: www.kennedyhealth.org
**Control:** Other not–for–profit (including NFP Corporation) **Service:** General
Medical and Surgical

**Staffed Beds:** 540 **Admissions:** 26093 **Census:** 339 **Outpatient Visits:**
390000 **Births:** 1000 **Total Expense ($000):** 464232 **Payroll Expense**
**($000):** 195164

**KENNEDY MEMORIAL HOSPITALS–UNIVERSITY MEDICAL CENTER** See
Kennedy Health System

## CHESTER—Morris County

**KESSLER INSTITUTE FOR REHABILITATION** See Kessler Institute for
Rehabilitation, West Orange

## DENVILLE—Morris County

⊠ **SAINT CLARE'S HEALTH SYSTEM (310050)**, 25 Pocono Road,
Zip 07834–2954; tel. 973/625–6000, (Includes SAINT CLARE'S HEALTH CENTER
AT SUSSEX, 20 Walnut Street, Sussex, Zip 07461; tel. 973/702–2200; SAINT
CLARE'S HOSPITAL/BOONTON TOWNSHIP, 130 Powerville Road, Boonton
Township, Zip 07005; tel. 973/316–1800; SAINT CLARE'S HOSPITAL/DENVILLE,
25 Pocono Road, Zip 07834; tel. 973/625–6000; SAINT CLARE'S
HOSPITAL/DOVER, 400 West Blackwell Street, Dover, Zip 07801–3311;
tel. 973/989–3000) **A**1 2 9 10 **F**1 3 4 5 7 11 13 15 18 20 22 26 28 29 30 31
34 35 36 38 40 41 42 44 45 46 47 48 49 50 51 54 56 57 59 62 64 65 66
68 70 71 73 74 75 76 77 78 79 81 82 85 86 87 89 92 93 97 98 99 100
101 102 103 104 105 106 107 108 109 110 111 112 114 116 117 118 119
120 121 123 125 126 129 130 132 134 135 146 147 **P**5 **S** Catholic Health
Initiatives, Englewood, CO
Primary Contact: Jonathan Timmis, Interim President and Chief Executive Officer
COO: Joe Nolan, Chief Operating Officer
CFO: Dianne Halford, Chief Financial Officer
CMO: Alma Ratcliffe, M.D., Executive Vice President Medical Staff and Business
Development
CIO: Tero Caamano, Director Information Technology
CHR: Kay Bryant, Executive Director Human Resources
CNO: Debbie Regen, MS, Vice President and Chief Nursing Officer
Web address: www.saintclares.org
**Control:** Church–operated, Nongovernment, not–for profit **Service:** General
Medical and Surgical

**Staffed Beds:** 412 **Admissions:** 14241 **Census:** 177 **Outpatient Visits:**
177431 **Births:** 1188 **Total Expense ($000):** 282451 **Payroll Expense
($000):** 123389 **Personnel:** 1755

**SAINT CLARE'S HOSPITAL/DENVILLE** See Saint Clare's Health System

## DOVER—Morris County

⊠ **KINDRED HOSPITAL–NEW JERSEY MORRIS COUNTY (312020)**, 400 West
Blackwell Street, Zip 07801–2525; tel. 973/537–3818, (Includes KINDRED
HOSPITAL NEW JERSEY – RAHWAY, 865 Stone Street, Rahway, Zip 07065;
tel. 732/453–2950; KINDRED HOSPITAL NEW JERSEY – WAYNE, 224 Hamburg
Turnpike, Wayne, Zip 07470; tel. 973/636–7200; Alice M. O'Connor, R.N.,
Administrator), (Nonreporting) **A**1 10 **S** Kindred Healthcare, Louisville, KY
Primary Contact: Jonathan Cohee, Chief Executive Officer
CFO: Rishab Punjabi, Chief Financial Officer
CHR: Neil Rosner, Area Director Human Resources
Web address: www.khmorriscounty.com/
**Control:** Corporation, Investor–owned, for–profit **Service:** Long–Term Acute Care
hospital

**Staffed Beds:** 117

## EAST ORANGE—Essex County

⊠ **EAST ORANGE GENERAL HOSPITAL (310083)**, 300 Central Avenue,
Zip 07018–2897; tel. 973/672–8400, (Nonreporting) **A**1 9 10
Primary Contact: Martin A. Bieber, Interim President and Chief Executive Officer
CFO: Al Aboud, Chief Financial Officer
CMO: Valentine Burroughs, M.D., Chief Medical Officer
CIO: Thomas Ciccarelli, Chief Information Officer
CHR: Chester Banks, Director Human Resources
Web address: www.evh.org
**Control:** Other not–for–profit (including NFP Corporation) **Service:** General
Medical and Surgical

**Staffed Beds:** 190

⊠ **VETERANS AFFAIRS NEW JERSEY HEALTH CARE SYSTEM**, 385 Tremont
Avenue, Zip 07018–1095; tel. 973/676–1000, (Includes EAST ORANGE DIVISION,
385 Tremont Avenue, tel. 973/676–1000; LYONS DIVISION, 151 Knollcroft Road,
Lyons, Zip 07939–9998; tel. 908/647–0180) **A**1 2 3 5 **F**4 5 11 15 18 20 24
29 30 31 33 34 35 38 39 40 45 46 50 53 54 56 57 58 59 60 61 62 64 68
70 71 74 75 77 78 79 81 82 83 84 85 86 87 91 92 93 94 96 97 98 100
101 102 103 104 105 106 107 111 114 119 121 123 128 129 130 132 133
135 143 146 147 148 **P**6 **S** Department of Veterans Affairs, Washington, DC
Primary Contact: Kenneth H. Mizrach, Director
COO: Kenneth H. Mizrach, Director
CFO: Tyrone Taylor, Chief Financial Officer
CMO: Steven L. Lieberman, M.D., Chief of Staff
CIO: Kamesha Scarlett, Chief Information Resource Management
CHR: Nancy Hamilton, Chief Human and Learning Resources
CNO: Patrick J. Troy, R.N., Associate Director Patient Care Services
Web address: www.newjersey.va.gov/
**Control:** Veterans Affairs, Government, federal **Service:** General Medical and
Surgical

**Staffed Beds:** 439 **Admissions:** 4270 **Census:** 433 **Outpatient Visits:**
709523 **Births:** 0 **Total Expense ($000):** 534653 **Payroll Expense ($000):**
249550 **Personnel:** 1549

## EDISON—Middlesex County

★ △ **JFK JOHNSON REHABILITATION INSTITUTE**, 65 James Street,
Zip 08818; tel. 732/321–7050 **A**7 **F**3 9 28 29 30 35 36 50 53 54 64 82 90
91 92 93 94 96 130 131 132 143 **P**6 **S** JFK Health System, Edison, NJ
Primary Contact: Anthony Cuzzola, Vice President Administrator
Web address: www.njrehab.org
**Control:** Other not–for–profit (including NFP Corporation) **Service:** Rehabilitation

**Staffed Beds:** 94 **Admissions:** 2005 **Census:** 73 **Outpatient Visits:** 94187
**Births:** 0 **Total Expense ($000):** 65759 **Payroll Expense ($000):** 42944
**Personnel:** 669

⊠ **JFK MEDICAL CENTER (310108)**, 65 James Street, Zip 08818;
tel. 732/321–7000 **A**1 2 3 6 9 10 **F**3 5 6 7 8 9 11 12 13 14 15 18 20 22 29
30 31 32 34 35 39 40 41 42 44 45 50 51 53 54 56 57 58 59 60 63 64 65
66 67 70 73 74 75 76 77 78 79 81 82 83 84 86 87 89 90 97 100 101 102
103 104 107 108 110 111 113 114 115 116 117 118 119 120 121 122 123
128 129 130 131 132 134 135 143 145 146 147 148 **P**4 5 6 7 **S** JFK Health
System, Edison, NJ
Primary Contact: Raymond F. Fredericks, President and CEO
COO: Scott Gebhard, Executive VP and Chief Operating Officer
CFO: Richard C. Smith, Senior Vice President and Chief Financial Officer
CMO: William F. Oser, M.D., Senior Vice President and Chief Medical Officer
CIO: Indranil Ganguly, Vice President and Chief Information Officer
CHR: Shirley Higgins Bowers, Senior Vice President Human Resources
CNO: James Lindquist, R.N., Chief Nursing Officer
Web address: www.jfkmc.org
**Control:** Other not–for–profit (including NFP Corporation) **Service:** General
Medical and Surgical

**Staffed Beds:** 334 **Admissions:** 17776 **Census:** 237 **Outpatient Visits:**
174696 **Births:** 2331 **Total Expense ($000):** 379722 **Payroll Expense
($000):** 184872

## ELIZABETH—Union County

⊠ **TRINITAS REGIONAL MEDICAL CENTER (310027)**, 225 Williamson Street,
Zip 07202–3625; tel. 908/994–5000, (Includes TRINITAS HOSPITAL, 925 East
Jersey Street, Zip 07201; tel. 908/994–5000; TRINITAS REGIONAL MEDICAL
CENTER – NEW POINT CAMPUS, 655 East Jersey Street, Zip 07206;
tel. 908/994–5000), (Total facility includes 124 beds in nursing home–type unit)
**A**1 2 3 5 6 9 10 13 **F**3 5 7 8 11 12 13 15 17 18 20 22 28 29 30 31 32 34
35 36 38 40 44 45 46 48 49 51 53 54 56 59 60 61 64 65 66 68 70 73 74
75 76 77 78 79 81 82 84 85 86 87 91 93 97 98 99 100 101 102 103 104
105 106 107 108 110 111 114 118 119 120 121 123 124 126 128 129 130
132 134 135 141 143 146 147 **P**6
Primary Contact: Gary S. Horan, FACHE, President and Chief Executive Officer
CFO: Karen Lumpp, Senior Vice President and Chief Financial Officer
CMO: William McHugh, M.D., Medical Director and Chief Medical Officer
CIO: Judy Comitto, Vice President Information Services and Chief Information
Officer
CHR: Glenn Nacion, Vice President Human Resources
CNO: Mary McTigue, Vice President Patient Care Services and Chief Nursing
Officer
Web address: www.trinitasrmc.com
**Control:** Other not–for–profit (including NFP Corporation) **Service:** General
Medical and Surgical

**Staffed Beds:** 458 **Admissions:** 15611 **Census:** 398 **Outpatient Visits:**
452050 **Births:** 2203 **Total Expense ($000):** 293268 **Payroll Expense
($000):** 134644 **Personnel:** 2305

## ELMER—Salem County

★ ◇ **INSPIRA MEDICAL CENTER–ELMER (310069)**, 501 West Front Street,
Zip 08318–2101; tel. 856/363–1000 **A**9 10 21 **F**3 8 11 12 13 15 18 20 28
29 30 34 38 40 44 50 57 59 64 68 70 74 75 76 77 78 79 81 82 85 86 87
89 93 107 108 110 111 119 130 131 132 134 146 147 148 **S** Inspira Health
Network, Mullica Hill, NJ
Primary Contact: John A. DiAngelo, President and Chief Executive Officer
COO: David Yhlen, Chief Operating Officer
CFO: Thomas Baldosaro, Chief Financial Officer
CMO: Steven C. Linn, M.D., Chief Medical Officer
CIO: Thomas Pacek, Vice President Information Systems and Chief Information
Officer
CHR: Erich Florentine, Chief People Officer
CNO: Elizabeth Sheridan, Chief Operating Officer and Chief Nursing Executive
Web address: www.inspirahealthnetwork.org/?id=5281&sid=1
**Control:** Other not–for–profit (including NFP Corporation) **Service:** General
Medical and Surgical

**Staffed Beds:** 88 **Admissions:** 3532 **Census:** 37 **Outpatient Visits:** 71481
**Births:** 338 **Total Expense ($000):** 57086 **Payroll Expense ($000):** 25574
**Personnel:** 286

**NJ**

---

**Hospital, Medicare Provider Number, Address, Telephone, Approval, Facility, and Physician Codes, Health Care System**

★ American Hospital Association (AHA) membership  ◯ Healthcare Facilities Accreditation Program  ⇑ Center for Improvement in Healthcare Quality Accreditation
☐ The Joint Commission accreditation  ◇ DNV Healthcare Inc. accreditation  △ Commission on Accreditation of Rehabilitation Facilities (CARF) accreditation

**ENGLEWOOD—Bergen County**

✠ **ENGLEWOOD HOSPITAL AND MEDICAL CENTER (310045)**, 350 Engle Street, Zip 07631–1898; tel. 201/894–3000 **A**1 2 3 5 9 10 **F**7 8 12 13 15 17 18 19 20 21 22 24 26 28 29 30 31 34 35 36 38 40 45 46 49 50 51 54 55 56 57 58 59 60 64 70 72 73 74 75 76 77 78 79 81 82 83 84 85 86 87 89 91 92 93 94 98 99 100 101 102 103 104 105 106 107 108 109 110 111 112 114 115 116 117 118 119 120 121 124 126 129 130 143 145 146 148 **P**6
Primary Contact: Warren Geller, President and Chief Executive Officer
CFO: Anthony T. Orlando, Senior Vice President Finance
CMO: Michael Harris, M.D., Chief Medical Officer
CIO: Dihitri Cruz, Vice President, Information Technology
CHR: Patricia Wilson, Senior Vice President, Human Resources
CNO: Kathy Kaminsky, RN, Chief Quality Officer and Interim Chief Nursing Officer
Web address: www.englewoodhospital.com
**Control:** Other not–for–profit (including NFP Corporation) **Service:** General Medical and Surgical

**Staffed Beds:** 275 **Admissions:** 14925 **Census:** 199 **Outpatient Visits:** 789758 **Births:** 2058 **Total Expense ($000):** 425016 **Payroll Expense ($000):** 135219 **Personnel:** 2188

**FLEMINGTON—Hunterdon County**

✠ **HUNTERDON MEDICAL CENTER (310005)**, 2100 Wescott Drive, Zip 08822–4604; tel. 908/788–6100 **A**1 2 3 5 9 10 13 **F**3 4 5 8 11 12 13 14 15 18 20 22 27 28 29 30 31 32 34 35 38 40 45 46 47 48 49 53 54 56 57 58 59 60 61 62 64 65 68 70 71 74 75 76 77 78 79 81 82 83 84 85 86 87 89 91 92 93 94 97 98 99 100 101 102 103 104 105 106 107 108 110 114 115 118 119 121 123 126 127 129 130 131 132 134 135 146 147 148
Primary Contact: Robert P. Wise, FACHE, President and Chief Executive Officer
COO: Lawrence N. Grand, Executive Vice President and Chief Operating Officer
CFO: Gail Kosyla, Chief Financial Officer
CMO: George Roksvaag, M.D., Chief Medical Officer
CIO: Glenn Mamary, Chief Information Officer
CHR: Violet Kocsis, Chief Human Resources Officer
CNO: Patricia Steingall, R.N., Vice President, Patient Care Services
Web address: www.hunterdonhealthcare.org
**Control:** Other not–for–profit (including NFP Corporation) **Service:** General Medical and Surgical

**Staffed Beds:** 186 **Admissions:** 8346 **Census:** 105 **Outpatient Visits:** 644935 **Births:** 910 **Total Expense ($000):** 258784 **Payroll Expense ($000):** 125973 **Personnel:** 1827

**FREEHOLD—Monmouth County**

✠ **CENTRASTATE HEALTHCARE SYSTEM (310111)**, 901 West Main Street, Zip 07728–2549; tel. 732/431–2000 **A**1 2 3 5 9 10 **F**3 11 12 13 15 16 18 19 20 28 29 30 31 32 34 35 36 37 38 40 41 45 46 49 56 57 58 59 61 64 65 66 70 73 74 75 76 77 78 79 81 82 84 86 87 89 92 93 97 98 100 101 102 107 108 110 114 118 119 120 121 123 124 126 129 130 131 132 134 135 144 146 147 148 **P**1 6
Primary Contact: John Gribbin, FACHE, President and Chief Executive Officer
COO: Thomas W. Scott, Senior Vice President and Chief Operating Officer
CFO: John Dellocono, Senior Vice President and Chief Financial Officer
CMO: Jack H. Dworkin, M.D., Vice President Medical Affairs and Chief Medical Officer
CIO: John Ulett, Vice President and Chief Information Officer
CHR: Fran Keane, Vice President Human Resources
CNO: Linda W. Geisler, R.N., Vice President Patient Services
Web address: www.centrastate.com
**Control:** Other not–for–profit (including NFP Corporation) **Service:** General Medical and Surgical

**Staffed Beds:** 283 **Admissions:** 13744 **Census:** 161 **Outpatient Visits:** 256602 **Births:** 1402 **Total Expense ($000):** 239694 **Payroll Expense ($000):** 103574 **Personnel:** 1444

**HACKENSACK—Bergen County**

✠ **HACKENSACK UNIVERSITY MEDICAL CENTER (310001)**, 30 Prospect Avenue, Zip 07601–1914; tel. 201/996–2000, (Includes THE JOSEPH M. SANZARI CHILDREN'S HOSPITAL, 30 Prospect Avenue, tel. 201/996–2000) **A**1 2 3 5 8 9 10 **F**2 3 4 5 6 7 8 9 10 11 12 13 14 15 16 17 18 19 20 22 24 26 27 28 29 30 31 32 33 34 35 36 37 38 39 40 41 42 43 44 45 46 47 48 49 50 51 52 53 54 55 56 57 58 59 60 61 64 65 66 68 69 70 71 72 73 74 75 76 77 78 79 80 81 82 84 85 86 87 88 89 90 91 92 93 94 96 97 98 99 100 101 102 103 104 107 108 109 110 111 112 113 114 115 116 117 118 119 120 121 123 124 126 129 130 131 132 134 135 136 138 141 142 143 144 145 146 147 148 **P**1 5 6 **S** Hackensack University Health Network, Hackensack, NJ
Primary Contact: Robert C. Garrett, FACHE, President and Chief Executive Officer
CFO: Robert Glenning, Executive Vice President Finance and Chief Financial Officer
CMO: Peter A. Gross, M.D., Senior Vice President and Chief Medical Officer
CHR: Nancy R. Corcoran, Senior Vice President Human Resources and Quality Service
Web address: www.hackensackumc.org
**Control:** Other not–for–profit (including NFP Corporation) **Service:** General Medical and Surgical

**Staffed Beds:** 710 **Admissions:** 69457 **Census:** 614 **Outpatient Visits:** 2743449 **Births:** 6297 **Total Expense ($000):** 1437910 **Payroll Expense ($000):** 642468 **Personnel:** 7292

**HACKETTSTOWN—Warren County**

☐ **HACKETTSTOWN REGIONAL MEDICAL CENTER (310115)**, 651 Willow Grove Street, Zip 07840–1799; tel. 908/852–5100, (Nonreporting) **A**1 9 10 **S** Adventist HealthCare, Gaithersburg, MD
Primary Contact: Jason C. Coe, President and Chief Executive Officer
COO: Stella Visaggio, Chief Operating Officer
CFO: Robert Peterson, Chief Financial Officer
CMO: Kenneth Janowski, M.D., Chief Medical Officer
CIO: Dorothy Cox, Manager Information Systems
CHR: Jeanne Jepson, Director Human Resources
CNO: Linda Ambacher, Interim Chief Nursing Officer
Web address: www.hrmcnj.org
**Control:** Church–operated, Nongovernment, not–for profit **Service:** General Medical and Surgical

**Staffed Beds:** 111

**HAMILTON—Mercer County**

✠ **ROBERT WOOD JOHNSON UNIVERSITY HOSPITAL AT HAMILTON (310110)**, One Hamilton Health Place, Zip 08690–3599; tel. 609/586–7900 **A**1 2 3 5 9 10 **F**3 8 9 11 12 13 15 17 18 22 26 28 29 30 31 32 34 35 36 37 39 40 41 44 46 47 48 49 50 51 53 54 55 56 57 58 59 60 61 63 64 65 66 68 69 70 71 73 74 75 76 77 78 79 81 82 84 85 86 87 92 93 96 97 100 102 103 107 108 110 111 114 115 116 117 118 119 120 121 123 124 126 129 130 131 132 134 135 143 144 145 146 147 148 **P**6 **S** Robert Wood Johnson Health System & Network, New Brunswick, NJ
Primary Contact: Richard Freeman, President and Chief Executive Officer
COO: Barbara H. Smith, Senior Vice President & Chief Operating Officer
CFO: James M. Maher, Senior Vice President and Chief Financial Officer
CMO: Ronald Ryder, D.O., President of the Medical Staff
CNO: Lisa Breza, R.N., Vice President and Chief Nursing Officer
Web address: www.rwjhamilton.org
**Control:** Other not–for–profit (including NFP Corporation) **Service:** General Medical and Surgical

**Staffed Beds:** 213 **Admissions:** 10054 **Census:** 126 **Outpatient Visits:** 127863 **Births:** 948 **Total Expense ($000):** 193615 **Payroll Expense ($000):** 77395 **Personnel:** 1092

**HAMMONTON—Camden County**

☐ **ANCORA PSYCHIATRIC HOSPITAL (314005)**, 301 Spring Garden Road, Zip 08037–9699; tel. 609/561–1700 **A**1 10 **F**30 39 56 68 75 87 97 98 130 135 143 146 **P**6 **S** Division of Mental Health and Addiction Services, Department of Human Services, State of New Jersey, Trenton, NJ
Primary Contact: John Lubitsky, Chief Executive Officer
CFO: John Holmes, Business Manager
CMO: David Roat, D.O., Medical Director
CIO: Charlene Ruberti, Director Information Technology Development
CHR: Alfred Filipini, Manager Human Resources
CNO: Catherine Jones, Chief Nursing Officer
Web address: www.state.nj.us/humanservices/dmhs/oshm/aph/
**Control:** State–Government, nonfederal **Service:** Psychiatric

**Staffed Beds:** 500 **Admissions:** 748 **Census:** 517 **Outpatient Visits:** 0 **Births:** 0 **Total Expense ($000):** 166439 **Payroll Expense ($000):** 85541 **Personnel:** 1658

**HOBOKEN—Hudson County**

✠ **HOBOKEN UNIVERSITY MEDICAL CENTER (310040)**, 308 Willow Avenue, Zip 07030–3889; tel. 201/418–1000, (Nonreporting) **A**1 3 5 9 10 **S** CarePoint Health, Jersey City, NJ
Primary Contact: Ann P. Logan, R.N., Ph.D., Chief Operating Officer
COO: Ann P. Logan, R.N., Chief Operating Officer
CFO: Vincent Riccitelli, Vice President Finance
CMO: Meika Roberson, M.D., Chief Medical Officer
CIO: Joel Taylor, Chief Information Officer
CHR: Roberto Gonzalez, Executive Director Human Resources
CNO: Neena S. Philip, R.N., Assistant Vice President Nursing
Web address: www.hobokenumc.com
**Control:** Corporation, Investor–owned, for–profit **Service:** General Medical and Surgical

**Staffed Beds:** 333

*Many Facility Codes have changed. Please refer to the AHA Guide Code Chart.* © 2015 AHA Guide

**NJ**

## HOLMDEL—Monmouth County

☒ **BAYSHORE COMMUNITY HOSPITAL (310112)**, 727 North Beers Street, Zip 07733–1598; tel. 732/739–5900 **A**1 2 9 10 **F**3 11 12 15 18 20 22 28 29 30 31 32 34 35 36 38 39 40 41 43 44 45 46 49 50 51 54 55 56 57 58 59 60 63 64 65 66 68 69 70 71 74 75 77 78 79 80 81 82 84 85 86 87 91 92 93 94 96 97 100 101 102 103 107 108 110 111 114 116 117 118 119 129 130 131 132 134 135 146 147 148 **P**6 7 **S** Meridian Health, Neptune, NJ
Primary Contact: Timothy J. Hogan, FACHE, Regional President
COO: Anthony V. Cava, Chief Operating Officer
CFO: Joseph M. Lemaire, Executive Vice President Finance and Partner Company Operations
CMO: Ian Leber, M.D., Chief Medical Officer
CIO: Rebecca Weber, Senior Vice President and Chief Information Officer
CHR: Sherrie String, Senior Vice President Human Resources
CNO: Linda Walsh, R.N., Vice President Chief Nursing Executive
Web address: www.bchs.com
**Control:** Other not–for–profit (including NFP Corporation) **Service:** General Medical and Surgical

**Staffed Beds:** 152 **Admissions:** 6803 **Census:** 97 **Outpatient Visits:** 81615 **Births:** 0 **Total Expense ($000):** 119939 **Payroll Expense ($000):** 51740 **Personnel:** 774

## JERSEY CITY—Hudson County

☒ **CHRIST HOSPITAL (310016)**, 176 Palisade Avenue, Zip 07306–1196, Mailing Address: 176 Palisades Avenue, Zip 07306–1196; tel. 201/795–8200, (Nonreporting) **A**1 3 6 9 10 12 13 **S** CarePoint Health, Jersey City, NJ
Primary Contact: Marie Theresa Duffy, Chief Operating Officer
COO: Marie Theresa Duffy, Chief Operating Officer
CFO: Patrick Ryan, Chief Financial Officer
CMO: William Holubek, M.D., Chief Medical Officer
CHR: Josiane Deroncerey, Director Human Resources
Web address: www.christhospital.org
**Control:** Other not–for–profit (including NFP Corporation) **Service:** General Medical and Surgical

**Staffed Beds:** 376

★ ◇ **JERSEY CITY MEDICAL CENTER (310074)**, 355 Grand Street, Zip 07302–4321; tel. 201/915–2000 **A**3 5 9 10 13 21 **F**3 5 7 11 12 13 15 17 18 20 22 24 26 29 30 31 34 35 38 39 40 41 43 45 46 47 48 49 50 54 55 56 57 59 60 61 64 65 66 68 70 71 72 73 74 75 76 77 78 79 81 82 84 85 87 89 91 92 93 96 97 98 99 100 101 102 104 105 106 107 108 110 111 112 114 115 119 130 132 135 143 146 148 **P**6 **S** Barnabas Health, West Orange, NJ
Primary Contact: Joseph F. Scott, FACHE, President and Chief Executive Officer
CFO: Paul R. Goldberg, Chief Financial Officer
CMO: Kenneth Garay, M.D., Chief Medical Officer
CIO: Stephen Li, Vice President Management Information Systems
CHR: Mary Cataudella, Corporate Director Human Resources
Web address: www.barnabashealth.org/Jersey–City–Medical–Center.aspx
**Control:** Other not–for–profit (including NFP Corporation) **Service:** General Medical and Surgical

**Staffed Beds:** 316 **Admissions:** 15905 **Census:** 236 **Outpatient Visits:** 250380 **Births:** 2058 **Total Expense ($000):** 362049 **Payroll Expense ($000):** 144141 **Personnel:** 2245

## LAKEWOOD—Ocean County

☒ **MONMOUTH MEDICAL CENTER, SOUTHERN CAMPUS (310084)**, 600 River Avenue, Zip 08701–5237; tel. 732/363–1900 **A**1 2 9 10 **F**3 11 15 18 20 28 29 30 31 32 34 35 36 38 40 41 43 44 50 54 56 57 58 59 60 61 64 68 70 74 75 77 78 79 81 82 84 86 87 93 96 98 100 101 102 103 104 105 107 108 111 114 117 119 130 131 132 133 134 146 147 148 **S** Barnabas Health, West Orange, NJ
Primary Contact: Frank J. Vozos, M.D., FACS, President and Chief Executive Officer
CFO: David McClung, Chief Financial Officer
CMO: Todd Phillips, M.D., Chief Medical Officer
CIO: Ray Duarte, Director, Information Technology and Services
CHR: Michele Schweers, Vice President and Chief Human Resources Officer
CNO: Judy Colorado, R.N., Chief Nursing Officer
Web address: www.barnabashealth.org/hospitals/monmouth–medical–center–southern–campus.aspx
**Control:** Other not–for–profit (including NFP Corporation) **Service:** General Medical and Surgical

**Staffed Beds:** 116 **Admissions:** 6302 **Census:** 103 **Outpatient Visits:** 88866 **Births:** 182 **Total Expense ($000):** 112773 **Payroll Expense ($000):** 47023 **Personnel:** 468

☐ **SPECIALTY HOSPITAL OF CENTRAL JERSEY (312017)**, 600 River Avenue, 4 West, Zip 08701–5237; tel. 732/942–3588, (Nonreporting) **A**1 10
Primary Contact: Violeta Peters, R.N., Chief Executive Officer
CFO: Kristin Prentiss, Chief Financial Officer
CMO: Howard Lebowitz, M.D., Chief Medical Officer
CHR: Mary Pat Napolitano, Director Human Resources
CNO: Judy Boccellato, R.N., Chief Nursing Officer
Web address: www.acutecarehs.com
**Control:** Corporation, Investor–owned, for–profit **Service:** Long–Term Acute Care hospital

**Staffed Beds:** 50

## LAWRENCEVILLE—Mercer County

☒ **ST. LAWRENCE REHABILITATION CENTER (313027)**, 2381 Lawrenceville Road, Zip 08648–2025; tel. 609/896–9500, (Nonreporting) **A**1 10
Primary Contact: Darlene S. Hanley, R.N., FACHE, President and Chief Executive Officer
COO: Shirley Pukala, R.N., Assistant Administrator Operations
CFO: Thomas W. Boyle, Chief Financial Officer
CMO: Kevin McGuigan, M.D., Medical Director
CIO: Joseph Castronuevo, Director Information Management
CHR: John Levi, Director Human Resources
CNO: Janet Machulsky, RN, BSN, Director of Nursing
Web address: www.slrc.org
**Control:** Church-operated, Nongovernment, not–for profit **Service:** Rehabilitation

**Staffed Beds:** 109

## LIVINGSTON—Essex County

☒ **SAINT BARNABAS MEDICAL CENTER (310076)**, 94 Old Short Hills Road, Zip 07039–5672; tel. 973/322–5000 **A**1 2 3 5 8 9 10 13 **F**3 8 11 12 13 16 17 18 19 20 22 24 26 28 29 30 31 33 34 35 36 38 39 40 41 44 45 46 47 48 49 50 54 55 56 57 58 59 60 61 62 63 64 65 66 68 69 70 71 72 73 74 75 76 77 78 79 81 82 84 85 86 87 88 89 91 92 93 94 96 97 100 102 107 108 111 114 115 118 119 120 121 123 124 126 129 130 132 134 135 138 141 142 146 147 148 **P**7 **S** Barnabas Health, West Orange, NJ
Primary Contact: Stephen P. Zieniewicz, FACHE, President and Chief Executive Officer
COO: Patrick Ahearn, Chief Operating Officer and Senior Vice President
CFO: Richard Davis, Chief Financial Officer
CMO: Gregory Rokosz, D.O., Senior Vice President Medical and Academic Affairs
CIO: Michael McTigue, Chief Information Officer
CHR: Arnold D. Manzo, Vice President Human Resources
CNO: Jennifer A. O'Neill, R.N., Vice President Patient Care Services
Web address: www.barnabashealth.org/hospitals/saint_barnabas/index.html
**Control:** Other not–for–profit (including NFP Corporation) **Service:** General Medical and Surgical

**Staffed Beds:** 523 **Admissions:** 32853 **Census:** 400 **Outpatient Visits:** 233334 **Births:** 5770 **Total Expense ($000):** 645151 **Payroll Expense ($000):** 228062 **Personnel:** 3101

## LONG BRANCH—Monmouth County

☒ **MONMOUTH MEDICAL CENTER, LONG BRANCH CAMPUS (310075)**, 300 Second Avenue, Zip 07740–6303; tel. 732/222–5200, (Includes CHILDREN'S HOSPITAL AT MONMOUTH MEDICAL CENTER, 300 Second Avenue, tel. 732/222–5200) **A**1 2 3 5 8 9 10 **F**3 5 8 9 11 12 13 14 15 17 18 19 20 22 28 29 30 31 32 34 35 36 37 38 40 41 45 46 47 48 49 50 51 52 53 54 55 56 57 58 59 60 61 63 64 65 66 68 70 72 73 74 75 76 77 78 79 81 82 83 84 85 86 87 88 89 97 98 99 100 101 102 103 104 105 106 107 108 109 110 111 112 114 115 117 119 120 121 123 124 126 129 130 131 132 133 134 135 143 144 145 146 147 148 **P**7 **S** Barnabas Health, West Orange, NJ
Primary Contact: Frank J. Vozos, M.D., FACS, President and Chief Executive Officer
COO: Bill Arnold, Chief Operating Officer
CFO: David McClung, Chief Financial Officer
CMO: Eric Burkett, M.D., Vice President Medical Affairs
CIO: Chris Butler, Chief Information Officer
CHR: Richard Kiernan, Vice President Human Resources
CNO: Diann Johnston, R.N., Vice President of Patient Care Services
Web address: www.barnabashealth.org/hospitals/monmouth_medical/index.html
**Control:** Other not–for–profit (including NFP Corporation) **Service:** General Medical and Surgical

**Staffed Beds:** 294 **Admissions:** 17239 **Census:** 219 **Outpatient Visits:** 243730 **Births:** 4988 **Total Expense ($000):** 350758 **Payroll Expense ($000):** 133160 **Personnel:** 1872

## LYONS—Somerset County

**LYONS DIVISION** See Veterans Affairs New Jersey Health Care System, East Orange

**NJ**

---

**Hospital, Medicare Provider Number, Address, Telephone, Approval, Facility, and Physician Codes, Health Care System**

★ American Hospital Association (AHA) membership
☐ The Joint Commission accreditation
○ Healthcare Facilities Accreditation Program
◇ DNV Healthcare Inc. accreditation
⇑ Center for Improvement in Healthcare Quality Accreditation
△ Commission on Accreditation of Rehabilitation Facilities (CARF) accreditation

## MANAHAWKIN—Ocean County

☒ **SOUTHERN OCEAN MEDICAL CENTER (310113)**, 1140 Route 72 West, Zip 08050–2499; tel. 609/597–6011, (Total facility includes 20 beds in nursing home–type unit) **A**1 2 9 10 **F**3 11 12 13 15 18 20 28 29 30 31 32 34 35 36 39 40 41 43 44 45 46 48 49 50 51 54 55 56 57 58 59 60 63 64 65 66 68 70 71 74 75 76 77 78 79 80 81 82 84 85 86 87 91 92 93 94 96 97 100 101 102 103 107 108 110 111 114 115 116 117 118 119 128 129 130 131 132 134 135 146 147 148 **P**6 7 **S** Meridian Health, Neptune, NJ
Primary Contact: Joseph P. Coyle, President and Chief Executive Officer
COO: Kim Frazee, R.N., Vice President Physician and Business Development
CFO: Joseph M. Lemaire, Executive Vice President
CMO: Theodore Zaleski, M.D., Vice President Clinical Effectiveness
CIO: Rebecca Weber, Senior Vice President and Chief Information Officer
CHR: Susan Tillman–Taylor, Manager Human Resources
CNO: Donna Ciufo, R.N., Vice President and Chief Nurse Executive
Web address: www.soch.com
**Control:** Other not–for–profit (including NFP Corporation) **Service:** General Medical and Surgical

**Staffed Beds:** 139 **Admissions:** 6572 **Census:** 88 **Outpatient Visits:** 99783 **Births:** 366 **Total Expense ($000):** 130245 **Payroll Expense ($000):** 51652 **Personnel:** 709

## MARLTON—Burlington County

☒ △ **MARLTON REHABILITATION HOSPITAL (313032)**, 92 Brick Road, Zip 08053–2177; tel. 856/988–8778 **A**1 7 10 **F**34 50 57 59 64 68 75 77 85 86 87 90 91 92 93 94 96 130 132 148 **P**8 **S** Vibra Healthcare, Mechanicsburg, PA
Primary Contact: Phyllis J. Schlichtmann, Chief Executive Officer
CFO: Stuart Moss, Chief Financial Officer
CMO: Kenneth Wu, M.D., Medical Director
CHR: Joanne Cernava, Director Human Resources
CNO: Chris Kreeley, Director Nursing
Web address: www.marltonrehab.com
**Control:** Corporation, Investor–owned, for–profit **Service:** Rehabilitation

**Staffed Beds:** 61 **Admissions:** 1822 **Census:** 57 **Outpatient Visits:** 14218 **Births:** 0 **Total Expense ($000):** 24214 **Payroll Expense ($000):** 11652 **Personnel:** 163

☒ **VIRTUA MARLTON**, 90 Brick Road, Zip 08053–2177; tel. 856/355–6000 **A**1 2 3 5 9 **F**3 20 22 26 29 31 40 45 46 47 49 56 60 64 68 70 75 78 79 81 82 84 85 87 91 92 107 108 111 114 115 118 119 130 141 146 **S** Virtua Health, Marlton, NJ
Primary Contact: Matthew Zuino, Senior Vice President
CFO: Robert Segin, Executive Vice President & Chief Financial Officer
CMO: John Matsinger, D.O., Chief Medical Officer
CIO: Thomas Gordon, Chief Information Officer
CHR: Rhonda R. Jordan, Chief Human Resources Officer
CNO: Tracy Carlino, R.N., Chief Nursing Officer
Web address: www.virtua.org
**Control:** Other not–for–profit (including NFP Corporation) **Service:** General Medical and Surgical

**Staffed Beds:** 192 **Admissions:** 8811 **Census:** 122 **Outpatient Visits:** 45481 **Births:** 0 **Total Expense ($000):** 203668 **Payroll Expense ($000):** 56571 **Personnel:** 683

☐ **WEISMAN CHILDREN'S REHABILITATION HOSPITAL (313302)**, 92 Brick Road 3rd Floor, Zip 08053–2177; tel. 856/489–4520, (Nonreporting) **A**1 10
Primary Contact: Michael Rosiak, Chief Operating Officer
COO: Michael Rosiak, Chief Operating Officer
CMO: Connie Domingo, M.D., Medical Director
CIO: Darren Pedersen, Coordinator Information Technology
CHR: Jill Koerner, Manager Employee Relations
CNO: Daniel William Pfeffer, Chief Nurse Executive
Web address: www.weismanchildrens.com
**Control:** Corporation, Investor–owned, for–profit **Service:** Children's rehabilitation

**Staffed Beds:** 24

## MONTCLAIR—Essex County

☒ **HACKENSACK UNIVERSITY MEDICAL CENTER MOUNTAINSIDE (310054)**, 1 Bay Avenue, Zip 07042–4898; tel. 973/429–6000 **A**1 2 3 5 6 9 10 **F**3 8 12 13 14 15 18 20 22 26 28 29 30 31 34 35 38 39 40 42 43 44 45 46 48 49 50 51 52 53 54 55 56 57 59 60 66 67 68 70 73 74 75 76 77 78 79 81 82 84 85 86 87 91 93 94 97 98 102 103 104 105 107 108 109 110 111 114 115 116 117 118 119 120 121 123 124 126 128 129 130 131 132 134 135 144 145 146 147 148 **P**5 **S** LHP Hospital Group, Plano, TX
Primary Contact: John A. Fromhold, FACHE, Chief Executive Officer
CFO: Anthony M. Esposito, Jr., CPA, Vice President Chief Financial Officer
CMO: Theresa Soroko, M.D., Chief Medical Officer
CIO: Robert Gates, Director Information Technology
CHR: Fran Corridon, Vice President Human Resources and Shared Services
CNO: Bonnie Michaels, R.N., Vice President and Chief Nursing Officer
Web address: www.mountainsidenow.com
**Control:** Partnership, Investor–owned, for–profit **Service:** General Medical and Surgical

**Staffed Beds:** 218 **Admissions:** 10051 **Census:** 127 **Outpatient Visits:** 101745 **Births:** 1229 **Total Expense ($000):** 201146 **Payroll Expense ($000):** 84248 **Personnel:** 1286

## MORRIS PLAINS—Morris County

☐ **GREYSTONE PARK PSYCHIATRIC HOSPITAL (314016)**, 59 Koch Avenue, Zip 07950–4400; tel. 973/538–1800, (Nonreporting) **A**1 3 5 10 **S** Division of Mental Health and Addiction Services, Department of Human Services, State of New Jersey, Trenton, NJ
Primary Contact: Janet J. Monroe, R.N., Chief Executive Officer
COO: Ross Friedman, Chief Operating Officer
CFO: Jack Frey, Acting Business Manager
CMO: Cherry Monroy–Miller, M.D., Acting Medical Director
CIO: David Saleem, Director Information Technology
CHR: James Frey, Jr., Acting Manager Human Resources
CNO: Doreen Sperber–Weiss, Ph.D., Chief Nursing Officer
Web address: www.state.nj.us/humanservices/dmhs/oshm/gpph/
**Control:** State–Government, nonfederal **Service:** Psychiatric

**Staffed Beds:** 506

## MORRISTOWN—Morris County

☒ **MORRISTOWN MEDICAL CENTER (310015)**, 100 Madison Avenue, Zip 07960–6136; tel. 973/971–5000, (Includes REHABILITATION INSTITUTE AT THE MOUNT KEMBLE DIVISION ; GORYEB CHILDREN'S HOSPITAL, 100 Madison Avenue, tel. 800/247–9580), (Total facility includes 40 beds in nursing home–type unit) **A**1 2 3 5 8 9 10 13 **F**3 5 6 7 8 9 11 12 13 14 15 17 18 19 20 22 24 26 28 29 30 31 32 33 34 35 36 37 38 39 40 43 44 45 46 47 48 49 50 51 52 53 54 55 56 57 58 59 60 61 62 63 64 65 66 68 69 70 71 72 73 74 75 76 77 78 79 81 82 83 84 85 86 87 88 89 90 91 92 93 94 95 96 97 98 99 100 101 102 103 104 105 107 108 110 111 114 115 116 117 118 119 120 121 123 126 128 129 130 131 132 134 135 141 143 144 145 146 147 148 **P**2 3 5 6 **S** Atlantic Health System, Morristown, NJ
Primary Contact: Trish O'Keefe, R.N., Ph.D., MSN, Interim President
COO: Deborah Visconi, Director, Hospital Operations
CFO: Kevin Lenahan, Vice President Finance and Chief Financial Officer
CMO: Jan Schwarz–Miller, M.D., Vice President Quality and Chief Medical Officer
CIO: Linda Reed, Vice President and Chief Information Officer
CHR: Andrew L. Kovach, Vice President Human Resources and Chief Administrative Officer
CNO: Trish O'Keefe, R.N., Chief Nursing Officer and Chief Experience Officer
Web address: www.atlantichealth.org/Morristown/
**Control:** Other not–for–profit (including NFP Corporation) **Service:** General Medical and Surgical

**Staffed Beds:** 678 **Admissions:** 36786 **Census:** 558 **Outpatient Visits:** 419118 **Births:** 4317 **Total Expense ($000):** 1031356 **Payroll Expense ($000):** 428427 **Personnel:** 6167

## MOUNT HOLLY—Burlington County

☒ **VIRTUA MEMORIAL (310057)**, 175 Madison Avenue, Zip 08060–2099; tel. 609/267–0700 **A**1 3 5 9 10 **F**3 11 12 13 15 18 20 22 28 29 30 31 40 41 45 46 48 49 56 60 70 73 74 75 76 77 78 79 81 85 86 87 89 92 93 98 102 105 107 108 110 111 114 115 118 119 120 121 123 126 129 130 143 146 147 **S** Virtua Health, Marlton, NJ
Primary Contact: Matthew Zuino, Senior Vice President Hospital Services
CFO: Robert Segin, Chief Financial Officer
CMO: James P. Dwyer, D.O., Executive Vice President and Chief Medical Officer
CHR: E. D. Dunn, Vice President Human Resources
Web address: www.virtua.org
**Control:** Other not–for–profit (including NFP Corporation) **Service:** General Medical and Surgical

**Staffed Beds:** 334 **Admissions:** 17913 **Census:** 229 **Outpatient Visits:** 186471 **Births:** 2421 **Total Expense ($000):** 285451 **Payroll Expense ($000):** 92907 **Personnel:** 1290

**VIRTUA MEMORIAL HOSPITAL BURLINGTON COUNTY** See Virtua Memorial

## NEPTUNE—Monmouth County

☒ **JERSEY SHORE UNIVERSITY MEDICAL CENTER (310073)**, 1945 Route 33, Zip 07754–0397; tel. 732/775–5500, (Includes K. HOVNANIAN CHILDREN'S HOSPITAL, 1945 State Route 33, Zip 07753–4859; tel. 800/560–9990) **A**1 2 3 5 8 9 10 13 **F**3 5 11 12 13 17 18 19 20 22 24 26 28 29 30 31 32 34 35 36 38 39 40 41 43 44 45 46 47 48 49 50 51 54 55 56 57 58 59 60 61 63 64 66 68 70 71 72 73 74 75 76 77 78 79 80 81 82 84 85 86 87 88 89 91 92 93 94 96 97 98 99 100 101 102 103 104 105 107 108 111 114 115 116 117 118 119 120 121 123 126 129 130 131 132 134 135 145 146 147 148 **P**6 7 **S** Meridian Health, Neptune, NJ
Primary Contact: Kenneth N. Sable, M.D., President
COO: Robert H. Adams, Vice President Operations
CFO: John Gantner, Executive Vice President Finance and Partner Company Operations
CMO: David Kountz, M.D., Senior Vice President Medical Affairs
CIO: Rebecca Weber, Senior Vice President and Chief Information Officer
Web address: www.meridianhealth.com
**Control:** Other not–for–profit (including NFP Corporation) **Service:** General Medical and Surgical

**Staffed Beds:** 544 **Admissions:** 24892 **Census:** 367 **Outpatient Visits:** 208862 **Births:** 1897 **Total Expense ($000):** 575636 **Payroll Expense ($000):** 222884 **Personnel:** 2934

*Many Facility Codes have changed. Please refer to the AHA Guide Code Chart.* © 2015 AHA Guide

**NJ**

**NEW BRUNSWICK—Middlesex County**

☐ **CHILDREN'S SPECIALIZED HOSPITAL–PSE&G (313300)**, 200 Somerset Street, Zip 08901–1942; tel. 732/258–7000, (Includes CHILDREN'S SPECIALIZED HOSPITAL, 150 New Providence Road, Mountainside, Zip 07092; tel. 732/258–7134), (Total facility includes 72 beds in nursing home–type unit) **A**1 3 5 10 **F**29 32 35 54 64 65 74 75 77 79 90 91 93 94 97 99 104 130 146 **S** Robert Wood Johnson Health System & Network, New Brunswick, NJ
Primary Contact: Amy B. Mansue, President and Chief Executive Officer
COO: Warren E. Moore, Executive Vice President and Chief Operating Officer
CFO: Joseph J. Dobosh, Jr., Vice President and Chief Financial Officer
CMO: Christopher Haines, M.D., Medical Director
CIO: Chuck Chianese, Chief Information Officer
CHR: William Dwyer, Vice President Human Resources
CNO: Bonnie Baloga–Altieri, Ph.D., Chief Nursing Officer
Web address: www.childrens–specialized.org
**Control:** Other not–for–profit (including NFP Corporation) **Service:** Children's rehabilitation

**Staffed Beds:** 140 **Admissions:** 565 **Census:** 123 **Outpatient Visits:** 178618 **Births:** 0 **Total Expense ($000):** 123016 **Payroll Expense ($000):** 70263 **Personnel:** 987

✠ **ROBERT WOOD JOHNSON UNIVERSITY HOSPITAL (310038)**, 1 Robert Wood Johnson Place, Zip 08901–1928; tel. 732/828–3000, (Includes BRISTOL–MYERS SQUIBB CHILDREN'S HOSPITAL, One Robert Wood Johnson Place, Zip 08901, Mailing Address: P.O. Box 2601, Zip 08903–2601; tel. 732/828–3000; ROBERT WOOD JOHNSON UNIVERSITY HOSPITAL SOMERSET, 110 Rehill Avenue, Somerville, Zip 08876–2598; tel. 908/685–2200; Michael A. Antoniades, Executive Vice President) **A**1 2 3 5 8 9 10 **F**3 6 7 8 9 11 12 13 14 15 17 18 19 20 22 24 26 28 29 30 31 32 34 35 36 37 38 39 40 41 43 44 45 46 47 48 49 50 51 52 53 54 55 56 57 58 59 60 61 62 63 64 65 66 68 70 71 72 73 74 75 76 77 78 79 81 82 83 84 85 86 87 88 89 91 92 93 94 96 97 99 100 102 104 107 108 109 110 111 112 113 114 115 116 117 118 119 120 121 123 124 126 129 130 131 132 134 135 136 137 138 141 142 143 146 147 148 **P**3 6 7 **S** Robert Wood Johnson Health System & Network, New Brunswick, NJ
Primary Contact: Stephen K. Jones, FACHE, President and Chief Executive Officer
COO: Michael A. Antoniades, Executive Vice President and Chief Operating Officer
CFO: Brian M. Reilly, Chief Financial Officer
CMO: Joshua M. Bershad, M.D., Senior Vice President Medical Affairs and Chief Medical Officer
CIO: Robert G. Irwin, Vice President Information Systems
CHR: Martin S. Everhart, Senior Vice President Human Resources
CNO: Lori Colineri, MSN, Senior Vice President Nursing and Chief Nursing Officer
Web address: www.rwjuh.edu
**Control:** Other not–for–profit (including NFP Corporation) **Service:** General Medical and Surgical

**Staffed Beds:** 610 **Admissions:** 32650 **Census:** 532 **Outpatient Visits:** 248827 **Births:** 2493 **Total Expense ($000):** 874578 **Payroll Expense ($000):** 326530 **Personnel:** 4489

✠ **SAINT PETER'S UNIVERSITY HOSPITAL (310070)**, 254 Easton Avenue, Zip 08901–1780; tel. 732/745–8600, (Includes THE CHILDREN'S HOSPITAL AT SAINT PETER'S UNIVERSITY, 254 Easton Avenue, Zip 08901–1766; tel. 732/565–5437) **A**1 2 3 5 8 9 10 **F**2 3 11 12 13 15 17 18 19 20 21 22 26 27 28 29 30 31 32 34 35 37 38 39 40 41 44 45 46 49 50 51 56 57 58 59 60 61 64 65 66 68 70 71 72 73 74 75 76 77 78 79 81 82 83 84 85 86 87 88 89 91 92 93 94 95 96 97 100 102 105 107 108 110 111 113 114 115 118 119 120 121 123 126 129 130 131 132 135 143 144 145 146 147 148 **P**3 6
Primary Contact: Ronald C. Rak, JD, Chief Executive Officer
CFO: Garrick J. Stoldt, Vice President and Chief Financial Officer
CMO: Anthony Passannante, Jr., M.D., Vice President, Chief Medical Officer and Co–Chief Quality Officer
CIO: Frank DiSanzo, Vice President and Chief Information Officer and Chief Strategy Officer
CHR: Susan Ballestero, Vice President and Chief Human Resources Officer
CNO: Elizabeth Wise, R.N., Chief Nursing Officer and Vice President, Patient Care Services
Web address: www.saintpetersuh.com
**Control:** Church–operated, Nongovernment, not–for profit **Service:** General Medical and Surgical

**Staffed Beds:** 348 **Admissions:** 18138 **Census:** 227 **Outpatient Visits:** 390517 **Births:** 5579 **Total Expense ($000):** 403669 **Payroll Expense ($000):** 191640 **Personnel:** 2660

**NEWARK—Essex County**

◇ **COLUMBUS HOSPITAL LTACH (312024)**, 495 North Thirteenth Street, Zip 07107–1317; tel. 973/587–7777, (Nonreporting) **A**10 21
Primary Contact: Richard Lipsky, M.D., Chief Executive Officer
Web address: www.columbusltach.org
**Control:** Corporation, Investor–owned, for–profit **Service:** Long–Term Acute Care hospital

**Staffed Beds:** 66

✠ **NEWARK BETH ISRAEL MEDICAL CENTER (310002)**, 201 Lyons Avenue, Zip 07112–2027; tel. 973/926–7000, (Includes CHILDREN'S HOSPITAL OF NEW JERSEY, 201 Lyons Avenue, tel. 973/926–7000; John A. Brennan, M.D., M.P.H., President and Chief Executive Officer) **A**1 2 3 5 8 9 10 12 13 **F**3 15 17 18 19 20 21 22 23 24 25 26 27 28 29 30 31 32 34 35 38 39 40 41 44 45 46 47 48 49 50 51 53 55 56 57 58 59 60 61 63 64 65 66 68 70 71 72 73 74 75 76 77 78 79 81 84 85 86 87 88 89 92 93 94 97 98 99 100 101 102 103 104 105 107 108 109 110 111 114 115 117 118 119 120 121 123 126 129 130 131 132 137 140 141 143 145 146 147 148 **P**8 **S** Barnabas Health, West Orange, NJ
Primary Contact: John A. Brennan, M.D., M.P.H., President and Chief Executive Officer
COO: Darrell K. Terry, Sr., Senior Vice President Operations
CFO: Douglas A. Zehner, Chief Financial Officer
CMO: Jeremias Murillo, M.D., Chief Medical Officer
CHR: Zach Lipner, Vice President Human Resources
CNO: Mary Fuhro, Chief Nursing Officer
Web address: www.barnabashealth.org/hospitals/newark_beth_israel/index.html
**Control:** Other not–for–profit (including NFP Corporation) **Service:** General Medical and Surgical

**Staffed Beds:** 355 **Admissions:** 19986 **Census:** 359 **Outpatient Visits:** 324263 **Births:** 3267 **Total Expense ($000):** 559779 **Payroll Expense ($000):** 244973 **Personnel:** 2950

✠ **SAINT MICHAEL'S MEDICAL CENTER (310096)**, 111 Central Avenue, Zip 07102–1909; tel. 973/877–5350 **A**1 2 3 5 9 10 12 13 **F**3 5 12 15 17 18 20 22 24 26 29 30 31 34 35 37 40 45 47 49 50 57 58 59 61 64 66 68 70 71 74 77 78 79 81 85 87 97 98 100 107 108 110 111 114 115 119 121 123 126 130 132 143 146 147 148 **S** Trinity Health, Livonia, MI
Primary Contact: David A. Ricci, President and Chief Executive Officer
COO: Dennis Pettigrew, Chief Operating Officer
CFO: Dennis Pettigrew, Chief Financial Officer
CMO: Joseph DePasquale, M.D., Interim Chief Medical Officer
CIO: Tom Addington, Chief Information Officer
CHR: Dennis Sparks, Vice President Human Resources
CNO: Johanna Magner, Interim Chief Nursing Officer
Web address: www.smmcnj.org
**Control:** Church–operated, Nongovernment, not–for profit **Service:** General Medical and Surgical

**Staffed Beds:** 147 **Admissions:** 7938 **Census:** 110 **Outpatient Visits:** 102257 **Births:** 0 **Total Expense ($000):** 212457 **Payroll Expense ($000):** 78217 **Personnel:** 1175

✠ **UNIVERSITY HOSPITAL (310119)**, 150 Bergen Street, Zip 07103–2496; tel. 973/972–4300 **A**1 2 3 5 8 9 10 **F**3 7 8 11 15 17 18 20 22 24 26 28 29 30 31 32 34 35 37 38 39 40 41 43 44 45 46 47 48 49 50 54 55 57 58 59 60 61 64 65 66 68 70 71 72 73 74 75 76 77 78 79 80 81 82 84 85 86 87 88 89 92 93 96 97 98 100 102 107 108 110 111 114 118 119 120 121 123 124 126 130 131 132 134 135 139 141 142 145 146 147 148
Primary Contact: Nancy Hamstra, Interim President and Chief Executive Officer
CFO: Thomas M. Daly, Chief Financial Officer
CMO: Suzanne Atkin, M.D., Chief of Staff and Associate Dean Clinical Affairs
CIO: Richard Tunnell, Director Information Systems Technology and Health Management Information Systems
CHR: Gerard Garcia, Acting Vice President Human Resources
Web address: www.uhnj.org
**Control:** State–Government, nonfederal **Service:** General Medical and Surgical

**Staffed Beds:** 300 **Admissions:** 14017 **Census:** 232 **Outpatient Visits:** 265057 **Births:** 1637 **Total Expense ($000):** 615941 **Payroll Expense ($000):** 294745 **Personnel:** 3438

**NJ**

**Hospital, Medicare Provider Number, Address, Telephone, Approval, Facility, and Physician Codes, Health Care System**
★ American Hospital Association (AHA) membership   ◯ Healthcare Facilities Accreditation Program   ⇈ Center for Improvement in Healthcare Quality Accreditation
☐ The Joint Commission accreditation   ◇ DNV Healthcare Inc. accreditation   △ Commission on Accreditation of Rehabilitation Facilities (CARF) accreditation

## NEWTON—Sussex County

⊞ **NEWTON MEDICAL CENTER (310028)**, 175 High Street, Zip 07860–1004; tel. 973/383–2121 **A**1 2 9 10 **F**3 5 6 8 9 11 12 13 14 15 18 19 20 26 28 29 30 31 32 34 35 37 38 39 40 41 44 45 46 47 48 49 50 53 54 55 56 57 58 59 60 61 62 64 65 66 68 69 70 71 73 74 75 76 77 78 79 81 82 83 84 85 86 87 91 92 93 94 95 96 97 98 99 100 101 102 103 104 105 106 107 108 110 111 114 118 119 129 130 131 132 134 135 143 144 145 146 147 148 **P**6 **S** Atlantic Health System, Morristown, NJ
Primary Contact: Joseph DiPaolo, FACHE, President
CFO: Kevin Lenahan, Director Corporate Accounting, Budgets, Grants and Reimbursements
CMO: David Lazarus, M.D., Medical Director Clinical Affairs
CIO: Linda Reed, Vice President Information Systems and Chief Information Officer
CHR: Andrew L. Kovach, Vice President Human Resources and Chief Administrative Officer
Web address: www.atlantichealth.org/newton/
**Control:** Other not–for–profit (including NFP Corporation) **Service:** General Medical and Surgical

**Staffed Beds:** 148 **Admissions:** 7371 **Census:** 96 **Outpatient Visits:** 106542 **Births:** 472 **Total Expense ($000):** 147470 **Payroll Expense ($000):** 70237 **Personnel:** 917

## NORTH BERGEN—Hudson County

⊞ **PALISADES MEDICAL CENTER (310003)**, 7600 River Road, Zip 07047–6217; tel. 201/854–5000 **A**1 3 5 10 12 13 **F**3 7 8 11 12 13 15 18 20 28 29 30 34 35 38 40 43 45 49 50 56 57 68 70 73 74 75 76 77 78 79 81 82 84 85 86 87 89 92 93 102 104 107 110 111 114 115 119 129 130 132 143 145 146 147 148
Primary Contact: Bruce J. Markowitz, President and Chief Executive Officer
COO: David J. Berkowitz, Vice President and Chief Operating Officer
CFO: John Calandriello, Vice President and Chief Financial Officer
CMO: Suresh Raina, Vice President Medical Staff and Chief Medical Officer
CIO: Albert Porco, Director Management Information Systems
CHR: Donna Cahill, Vice President Human Resources
CNO: Ruben D. Fernandez, R.N., Vice President and Chief Nursing Officer
Web address: www.palisadesmedical.org
**Control:** Other not–for–profit (including NFP Corporation) **Service:** General Medical and Surgical

**Staffed Beds:** 169 **Admissions:** 9772 **Census:** 117 **Outpatient Visits:** 92309 **Births:** 1430 **Total Expense ($000):** 146910 **Payroll Expense ($000):** 68868 **Personnel:** 859

## OLD BRIDGE—Middlesex County

**OLD BRIDGE DIVISION** See Raritan Bay Medical Center, Perth Amboy

## PARAMUS—Bergen County

☐ **BERGEN REGIONAL MEDICAL CENTER (310058)**, 230 East Ridgewood Avenue, Zip 07652–4142; tel. 201/967–4000, (Nonreporting) **A**1 3 10
Primary Contact: Susan Mendelowitz, R.N., FACHE, President, Administrator and Chief Operating Officer
COO: Susan Mendelowitz, R.N., Executive Vice President and Chief Operating Officer
CFO: Connie Magdangal, Executive Vice President and Chief Financial Officer
CMO: Robert M. Harris, M.D., President Medical and Dental Staff
CIO: Ronald Li, Vice President Management Information Systems
CHR: Guy Mennonna, Senior Vice President Human Resources
Web address: www.bergenregional.com
**Control:** County–Government, nonfederal **Service:** Psychiatric

**Staffed Beds:** 432

## PASSAIC—Passaic County

☐ **ST. MARY'S GENERAL HOSPITAL (310006)**, 350 Boulevard, Zip 07055–2840; tel. 973/365–4300, (Nonreporting) **A**1 9 10 **S** Prime Healthcare Services, Ontario, CA
Primary Contact: Edward Condit, President and Chief Executive Officer
CFO: Nicholas Lanza, Controller
CMO: Ronald Poblete, M.D., President Medical and Dental Staff
CHR: Cathy Lynch–Kilic, Vice President Human Resources
Web address: www.smh–passaic.org
**Control:** Other not–for–profit (including NFP Corporation) **Service:** General Medical and Surgical

**Staffed Beds:** 221

## PATERSON—Passaic County

★ ◇ **ST. JOSEPH'S REGIONAL MEDICAL CENTER (310019)**, 703 Main Street, Zip 07503–2691; tel. 973/754–2000, (Includes ST. JOSEPH'S CHILDREN'S HOSPITAL, 703 Main Street, Zip 07503–2621; tel. 973/754–2500; Kevin J. Slavin, FACHE, President and Chief Executive Officer; ST. JOSEPH'S WAYNE HOSPITAL, 224 Hamburg Turnpike, Wayne, Zip 07470–2100; tel. 973/942–6900; Daniel B. Kline, Administrator), (Total facility includes 151 beds in nursing home–type unit) **A**2 3 5 9 10 13 21 **F**3 5 7 8 11 12 13 14 15 17 18 19 20 21 22 23 24 25 26 27 28 29 30 31 32 34 35 37 38 39 40 41 43 44 45 46 47 48 49 50 54 55 56 57 58 59 60 61 62 63 64 65 66 68 70 71 72 73 74 75 77 78 79 81 82 83 84 85 86 87 88 89 90 92 93 94 96 97 98 99 100 101 102 103 104 105 107 108 109 110 111 112 114 115 116 117 118 119 120 121 123 126 129 130 131 132 133 134 135 143 144 145 146 147 148 **P**3 5 6
Primary Contact: Kevin J. Slavin, FACHE, President and Chief Executive Officer
COO: Gloria A. Kunze, R.N., Interim Chief Operating Officer
CFO: David Alexander, Chief Financial Officer
CMO: James Labagnara, M.D., Vice President Medical Affairs
CIO: Jane Tsui–Wu, Vice President and Chief Information Officer
CHR: John P. Bruno, Vice President Human Resources
CNO: Maria Brennan, R.N., Vice President and Chief Nursing Officer
Web address: www.stjosephshealth.org
**Control:** Church–operated, Nongovernment, not–for profit **Service:** General Medical and Surgical

**Staffed Beds:** 700 **Admissions:** 34873 **Census:** 481 **Outpatient Visits:** 394040 **Births:** 3370 **Total Expense ($000):** 702198 **Payroll Expense ($000):** 330842 **Personnel:** 3688

## PEAPACK—Somerset County

☐ **MATHENY MEDICAL AND EDUCATIONAL CENTER (312014)**, 65 Highland Avenue, Zip 07977, Mailing Address: P.O. Box 339, Zip 07977–0339; tel. 908/234–0011, (Nonreporting) **A**1 5 10
Primary Contact: Kendell R. Sprott, M.D., JD, Chief Executive Officer
COO: Christopher King, Director Operations and Administrative Services
CFO: Wayne Guberman, Director Finance
CMO: Gary E. Eddey, M.D., Medical Director
CIO: Ron Daniel, Manager Information Systems
CHR: Nancy Petrillo, Director Human Resources
Web address: www.matheny.org
**Control:** Other not–for–profit (including NFP Corporation) **Service:** Long–Term Acute Care hospital

**Staffed Beds:** 102

## PENNINGTON—Mercer County

⊞ **CAPITAL HEALTH MEDICAL CENTER–HOPEWELL (310044)**, 1 Capital Way, Zip 08534–2520; tel. 609/303–4000 **A**1 2 5 9 10 **F**3 7 8 11 12 13 15 18 19 20 22 29 30 31 32 34 35 36 39 40 41 44 45 46 47 48 49 50 51 52 54 55 57 58 59 60 61 64 65 66 68 70 73 74 75 76 78 79 81 82 84 85 86 87 89 90 93 94 96 97 107 108 109 110 111 112 114 115 117 118 119 120 121 123 124 126 130 132 135 143 144 145 146 147 148 **P**6 **S** Capital Health, Trenton, NJ
Primary Contact: Al Maghazehe, Ph.D., FACHE, President and Chief Executive Officer
COO: Larry DiSanto, Executive Vice President and Chief Operating Officer
CFO: Shane Fleming, Chief Financial Officer
CMO: Robert Remstein, D.O., Vice President Medical Affairs
CIO: Eugene Grochala, Vice President Information Systems
CHR: J. Scott Clemmensen, Vice President Human Resources and Leadership Enhancement
CNO: Eileen M. Horton, Vice President Patient Services and Chief Nursing Officer
Web address: www.capitalhealth.org
**Control:** Other not–for–profit (including NFP Corporation) **Service:** General Medical and Surgical

**Staffed Beds:** 197 **Admissions:** 14163 **Census:** 160 **Outpatient Visits:** 138354 **Births:** 2614 **Personnel:** 1416

## PERTH AMBOY—Middlesex County

☐ **CARE ONE AT RARITAN BAY MEDICAL CENTER (312018)**, 530 New Brunswick Avenue, Zip 08861–3654; tel. 732/324–6090, (Nonreporting) **A**1 10
Primary Contact: Sharon Bready, R.N., Chief Executive Officer
CFO: Richard Burguillos, Chief Financial Officer
Web address: www.care-one.com
**Control:** Corporation, Investor–owned, for–profit **Service:** Long–Term Acute Care hospital

**Staffed Beds:** 30

*Many Facility Codes have changed. Please refer to the AHA Guide Code Chart.* © 2015 AHA Guide

✠ **RARITAN BAY MEDICAL CENTER (310039)**, 530 New Brunswick Avenue, Zip 08861–3654; tel. 732/442–3700, (Includes OLD BRIDGE DIVISION, One Hospital Plaza, Old Bridge, Zip 08857; tel. 732/360–1000; PERTH AMBOY DIVISION, 530 New Brunswick Avenue, Zip 08861–3685; tel. 732/442–3700) **A**1 3 5 9 10 **F**5 7 9 11 12 13 15 18 20 22 26 29 30 31 34 35 36 38 39 40 45 46 49 50 51 54 56 57 59 60 61 64 65 66 68 70 74 75 76 77 78 79 81 82 87 89 92 93 94 97 98 100 101 102 103 104 107 108 110 111 114 115 117 119 129 130 132 143 146 147 148 **P**6
Primary Contact: Michael R. D'Agnes, FACHE, President and Chief Executive Officer
COO: Vincent Costantino, Vice President Operations and Human Resources
CFO: Thomas Shanahan, Chief Financial Officer and Senior Vice President
CMO: Michael Ciencewicki, M.D., Vice President Medical Affairs
CHR: Vincent Costantino, Vice President Operations and Human Resources
Web address: www.rbmc.org
**Control:** Other not–for–profit (including NFP Corporation) **Service:** General Medical and Surgical

**Staffed Beds:** 277 **Admissions:** 12337 **Census:** 169 **Outpatient Visits:** 140887 **Births:** 1238 **Total Expense ($000):** 225949 **Payroll Expense ($000):** 106300 **Personnel:** 1675

---

### PHILLIPSBURG—Warren County

☐ **ST. LUKE'S HOSPITAL – WARREN CAMPUS (310060)**, 185 Roseberry Street, Zip 08865–1690; tel. 908/859–6700 **A**1 2 3 5 9 10 13 **F**2 3 8 11 15 18 20 28 29 30 31 34 35 39 40 45 48 49 53 56 59 61 64 65 66 68 70 74 75 77 78 79 81 82 85 86 87 91 92 93 97 98 100 102 103 104 106 107 108 110 111 114 118 119 124 129 130 131 132 134 146 147 148 **S** St. Luke's University Health Network, Bethlehem, PA
Primary Contact: Scott R. Wolfe, CPA, President
COO: Alice Wilson, FACHE, Vice President Administration
CMO: Edward Gilkey, M.D., Vice President Medical Affairs
CHR: Morgan G. Mahl, Director Human Resources
CNO: Gail Newton, R.N., Vice President Patient Care Services
Web address: www.slhn.org
**Control:** Other not–for–profit (including NFP Corporation) **Service:** General Medical and Surgical

**Staffed Beds:** 140 **Admissions:** 4276 **Census:** 55 **Outpatient Visits:** 114326 **Births:** 0 **Total Expense ($000):** 98382 **Payroll Expense ($000):** 42481 **Personnel:** 527

---

### PISCATAWAY—Middlesex County

**UNIVERSITY BEHAVIORAL HEALTHCARE (314011)**, 671 Hoes Lane West, Zip 08854–8021; tel. 732/235–5900, (Nonreporting) **A**3 5 9 10
Primary Contact: Christopher O. Kosseff, President and Chief Executive Officer
COO: Rosemarie Rosati, Chief Operating Officer
CFO: Alan Weinkrantz, Chief Financial Officer, Finance
CMO: Theresa Miskimen, M.D., Vice President Medical Services
CIO: Adam Levinson, Associate Director, Information Services
CNO: Michele A. Miller, R.N., Vice President, Acute and Nursing Services
Web address: www.ubhc.rutgers.edu
**Control:** State–Government, nonfederal **Service:** Psychiatric

**Staffed Beds:** 48

---

### PLAINSBORO—Middlesex County

**UNIVERSITY MEDICAL CENTER AT PRINCETON** See University Medical Center of Princeton at Plainsboro

✠ **UNIVERSITY MEDICAL CENTER OF PRINCETON AT PLAINSBORO (310010)**, One Plainsboro Road, Zip 08536–1913; tel. 609/853–7100, (Includes ACUTE GENERAL HOSPITAL, MERWICK UNIT–EXTENDED CARE AND REHABILITATION, PRINCETON HOUSE UNIT–COMMUNITY MENTAL HEALTH AND SUBSTANCE ABUSE ) **A**1 2 3 5 9 10 **F**3 4 5 8 11 12 13 14 15 18 19 20 22 26 28 29 30 31 32 34 35 36 38 39 40 41 45 46 47 48 49 50 51 53 54 55 56 57 58 59 60 61 62 63 64 65 66 68 70 73 74 75 76 77 78 79 81 82 84 85 86 87 89 90 91 92 93 96 97 98 99 100 101 102 103 104 105 107 108 110 111 114 115 116 117 118 119 120 121 123 124 126 129 130 131 132 134 135 143 145 146 147 148 **P**6
Primary Contact: Barry S. Rabner, President and Chief Executive Officer
COO: James Demetriades, Vice President, Operations
CFO: Glenn Zirbser, Chief Financial Officer
CMO: Donald Denny, M.D., Senior Vice President, Medical Affairs
CIO: Anne Searle, Chief Information Officer
CHR: Marcia M. Telthorster, M.Ed, CCP, Vice President Human Resources
CNO: Barbara Christiano, Vice President, Patient Care Services and Chief Nursing Officer
Web address: www.princetonhcs.org
**Control:** Other not–for–profit (including NFP Corporation) **Service:** General Medical and Surgical

**Staffed Beds:** 369 **Admissions:** 17045 **Census:** 253 **Outpatient Visits:** 460809 **Births:** 2189 **Total Expense ($000):** 379389 **Payroll Expense ($000):** 139716 **Personnel:** 2943

---

### POMONA—Atlantic County

**ATLANTICARE REGIONAL MEDICAL CENTER–MAINLAND DIVISION** See AtlantiCare Regional Medical Center, Atlantic City

✠ △ **BACHARACH INSTITUTE FOR REHABILITATION (313030)**, 61 West Jimmie Leeds Road, Zip 08240–9102, Mailing Address: P.O. Box 723, Zip 08240–0723; tel. 609/652–7000, (Nonreporting) **A**1 7 10
Primary Contact: Richard J. Kathrins, Ph.D, President and Chief Executive Officer
CFO: Jeanne Vuksta, Chief Financial Officer
CMO: Craig Anmuth, M.D., Medical Director
CIO: Jeff Rees, Director Information Systems
CHR: Diane Croshaw, Vice President Human Resources
Web address: www.bacharach.org
**Control:** Other not–for–profit (including NFP Corporation) **Service:** Rehabilitation

**Staffed Beds:** 80

---

### POMPTON PLAINS—Morris County

✠ **CHILTON MEDICAL CENTER (310017)**, 97 West Parkway, Zip 07444–1696; tel. 973/831–5000 **A**1 2 9 10 **F**3 7 11 12 13 15 18 20 22 24 26 28 29 30 31 32 34 35 38 40 41 44 45 47 49 50 54 57 59 60 62 63 64 65 66 70 73 74 75 76 77 78 79 81 82 85 86 87 89 93 97 102 107 108 109 110 111 114 115 118 119 121 123 126 129 130 131 132 135 143 146 147 148 **P**3 6
**S** Atlantic Health System, Morristown, NJ
Primary Contact: Alan Lieber, Interim President and Chief
COO: Thomas Scott, Chief Operating Officer
CFO: Michael Richetti, Chief Financial Officer
CMO: Charles Ross, M.D., Vice President Medical Affairs
CIO: Karen S. Smith, Director Information Services
CHR: Julia McGovern, Vice President Human Resources
Web address: www.chiltonmemorial.org
**Control:** Other not–for–profit (including NFP Corporation) **Service:** General Medical and Surgical

**Staffed Beds:** 199 **Admissions:** 10286 **Census:** 140 **Outpatient Visits:** 157129 **Births:** 766 **Total Expense ($000):** 173447 **Payroll Expense ($000):** 83975 **Personnel:** 1031

---

### RAHWAY—Union County

**KINDRED HOSPITAL NEW JERSEY – RAHWAY** See Kindred Hospital–New Jersey Morris County, Dover

✠ **ROBERT WOOD JOHNSON UNIVERSITY HOSPITAL RAHWAY (310024)**, 865 Stone Street, Zip 07065–2797; tel. 732/381–4200, (Total facility includes 24 beds in nursing home–type unit) **A**1 10 **F**3 11 15 17 20 29 30 31 34 35 38 40 46 47 49 50 53 56 57 59 64 65 68 70 74 75 77 78 79 81 82 86 87 93 97 100 101 102 107 108 111 117 118 119 128 129 130 132 134 143 144 146 147 148 **S** Robert Wood Johnson Health System & Network, New Brunswick, NJ
Primary Contact: Kirk C. Tice, President and Chief Executive Officer
CFO: Peter Bihuniak, Vice President Finance
CMO: Juan Baez, M.D., President Medical Staff
CIO: Denine Izzi, Site Manager Information Systems
CHR: Barbara M. Mullery, Vice President Administration
CNO: Ann Marie Shears, Vice President Patient Care Services
Web address: www.rwjuhr.com
**Control:** Other not–for–profit (including NFP Corporation) **Service:** General Medical and Surgical

**Staffed Beds:** 147 **Admissions:** 5919 **Census:** 88 **Outpatient Visits:** 62822 **Births:** 0 **Total Expense ($000):** 102426 **Payroll Expense ($000):** 43451 **Personnel:** 716

**NJ**

---

## RED BANK—Monmouth County

☒ △ **RIVERVIEW MEDICAL CENTER (310034)**, 1 Riverview Plaza,
Zip 07701–1864; tel. 732/741–2700 **A**1 2 7 9 10 **F**3 5 11 13 15 18 20 22 28
29 30 31 32 34 35 36 37 38 39 40 41 43 44 45 46 49 50 51 54 55 56 57
58 59 60 61 63 64 65 66 68 70 71 73 74 75 76 77 78 79 80 81 82 84 85
86 87 90 91 92 93 94 96 97 98 99 100 101 102 103 104 105 107 108 110
111 114 115 116 117 118 119 120 121 123 124 126 129 130 131 132 134
135 146 147 148 **P**6 7 **S** Meridian Health, Neptune, NJ
Primary Contact: Timothy J. Hogan, FACHE, Regional President
COO: Kelly O'Brien, Chief Operating Officer
CFO: Joseph Lemaire, Executive Vice President Finance
CMO: Joseph Reichman, M.D., Vice President Medical Affairs and Clinical
Effectiveness
CIO: Rebecca Weber, Senior Vice President Information Technology
CHR: Sherrie String, Senior Vice President Human Resources
CNO: Kathy McKean, M.P.H., Vice President, Chief Nursing Executive
Web address: www.riverviewmedicalcenter.com
**Control:** Other not–for–profit (including NFP Corporation) **Service:** General
Medical and Surgical

**Staffed Beds:** 301 **Admissions:** 11933 **Census:** 177 **Outpatient Visits:**
135953 **Births:** 1291 **Total Expense ($000):** 229390 **Payroll Expense
($000):** 97735 **Personnel:** 1261

## RIDGEWOOD—Bergen County

☒ **VALLEY HOSPITAL (310012)**, 223 North Van Dien Avenue, Zip 07450–2726;
tel. 201/447–8000 **A**1 2 3 5 9 10 **F**3 8 11 12 13 15 17 18 19 20 22 24 26
28 29 30 31 32 34 35 36 37 38 40 41 45 46 47 48 49 50 51 52 53 54 55
56 57 58 59 60 61 64 65 66 68 69 70 72 73 74 75 76 77 78 79 80 81 83
84 85 86 87 88 89 91 92 93 94 96 97 100 101 102 103 107 108 109 110
111 112 114 115 116 118 119 120 121 123 124 126 129 130 131 132 134
135 143 145 146 147 148 **P**6
Primary Contact: Audrey Meyers, FACHE, President and Chief Executive Officer
COO: Peter Diestel, Senior Vice President and Chief Operating Officer
CFO: Richard Keenan, Senior Vice President Finance and Chief Financial Officer
CMO: Joseph Yallowitz, Vice President Medical Affairs
CIO: Eric R. Carey, Vice President Information Systems and Chief Information
Officer
CHR: Jose Balderrama, Vice President Human Resources
CNO: Ann Marie Leichman, R.N., Vice President Patient Care Services and Chief
Nursing Officer
Web address: www.valleyhealth.com
**Control:** Other not–for–profit (including NFP Corporation) **Service:** General
Medical and Surgical

**Staffed Beds:** 446 **Admissions:** 28674 **Census:** 322 **Outpatient Visits:**
287188 **Births:** 3424 **Total Expense ($000):** 562033 **Payroll Expense
($000):** 236172 **Personnel:** 3137

## ROCHELLE PARK—Bergen County

☒ **SELECT SPECIALTY HOSPITAL–NORTHEAST NEW JERSEY (312019)**, 96
Parkway, Zip 07662–4200; tel. 201/221–2358, (Nonreporting) **A**1 10 **S** Select
Medical Corporation, Mechanicsburg, PA
Primary Contact: Barbara E. Hannan, MS, R.N., Chief Executive Officer
Web address: www.selectspecialtyhospitals.com/company/locations/
northeastnewjersey.aspx
**Control:** Corporation, Investor–owned, for–profit **Service:** Long–Term Acute Care
hospital

**Staffed Beds:** 62

## SADDLE BROOK—Bergen County

**KESSLER INSTITUTE FOR REHABILITATION** See Kessler Institute for
Rehabilitation, West Orange

## SALEM—Salem County

☒ **MEMORIAL HOSPITAL OF SALEM COUNTY (310091)**, 310 Woodstown Road,
Zip 08079–2080; tel. 856/935–1000 **A**1 9 10 **F**3 12 14 15 18 28 29 30 40
45 46 47 49 50 51 54 56 60 62 63 64 70 74 75 77 79 81 82 85 87 89 93
97 100 107 108 110 111 114 116 119 129 130 132 135 146 148
**S** Community Health Systems, Inc., Franklin, TN
Primary Contact: Ryan Jensen, Chief Executive Officer
CFO: Donald Bevers, Chief Financial Officer
CIO: Brian McCarthy, Director Information Systems
Web address: www.salemhospitalnj.org
**Control:** Corporation, Investor–owned, for–profit **Service:** General Medical and
Surgical

**Staffed Beds:** 110 **Admissions:** 3384 **Census:** 34 **Outpatient Visits:** 44690
**Births:** 0 **Total Expense ($000):** 60243 **Payroll Expense ($000):** 19004
**Personnel:** 342

## SECAUCUS—Hudson County

**LIBERTYHEALTH–MEADOWLANDS HOSPITAL MEDICAL CENTER** See
Meadowlands Hospital Medical Center

◇ **MEADOWLANDS HOSPITAL MEDICAL CENTER (310118)**, 55 Meadowlands
Parkway, Zip 07094–2977; tel. 201/392–3100, (Nonreporting) **A**9 10 12 13 21
Primary Contact: Felicia Karsos, R.N., President and Chief Executive Officer
COO: Lynn McVey, Chief Operating Officer
CMO: Michael Sciarra, M.D., Chief Medical Officer
CHR: Elizabeth Garrity, Director Human Resources
CNO: Felicia Karsos, R.N., Chief Nursing Officer
Web address: www.meadowlandshospital.org
**Control:** Partnership, Investor–owned, for–profit **Service:** General Medical and
Surgical

**Staffed Beds:** 230

## SOMERS POINT—Atlantic County

☒ **SHORE MEDICAL CENTER (310047)**, 100 Medical Center Way, Zip 08244;
tel. 609/653–3500, (Nonreporting) **A**1 2 9 10
Primary Contact: Ronald W. Johnson, FACHE, President and Chief Executive
Officer
COO: Linda S. Kenwood, R.N., Chief Nursing Officer and Chief Operating Officer
CFO: James T. Foley, CPA, Vice President and Chief Financial Officer
CMO: Jeanne M. Rowe, M.D., Chief Medical Officer
CIO: Fred Banner, Chief Information Officer
CHR: Alan L. Beatty, Vice President Human Resources
CNO: Linda S. Kenwood, R.N., Chief Nursing Officer and Chief Operating Officer
Web address: www.shoremedicalcenter.org
**Control:** Other not–for–profit (including NFP Corporation) **Service:** General
Medical and Surgical

**Staffed Beds:** 198

## STRATFORD—Camden County

**KENNEDY UNIVERSITY HOSPITAL – STRATFORD** See Kennedy Health System,
Cherry Hill

## SUMMIT—Union County

☒ **OVERLOOK MEDICAL CENTER (310051)**, 99 Beauvoir Avenue,
Zip 07901–3533; tel. 908/522–2000 **A**1 2 3 5 8 9 10 13 **F**3 5 6 7 8 9 11 12
13 14 15 17 18 19 20 22 28 29 30 31 32 34 35 36 37 38 39 40 41 42 44
45 46 47 48 49 50 51 52 53 54 55 56 57 58 59 60 61 62 63 64 65 66 68
69 70 71 72 73 74 75 76 77 78 79 81 82 83 84 85 86 87 89 91 92 93 94
95 96 97 98 99 100 101 102 103 104 105 107 108 110 111 113 114 115
116 117 118 119 120 121 123 124 126 129 130 131 132 134 135 143 144
145 146 147 148 **P**3 5 6 **S** Atlantic Health System, Morristown, NJ
Primary Contact: Alan R. Lieber, President
CFO: Kevin Lenahan, Vice President Finance and Chief Financial Officer
CMO: John R. Audett, M.D., Medical Director Clinical Affairs
CIO: Linda Reed, Vice President and Chief Information Officer
CHR: Andrew L. Kovach, Vice President Human Resources and Chief
Administrative Officer
CNO: Mary Patricia Sullivan, R.N., Chief Nursing Officer
Web address: www.atlantichealth.org/Overlook
**Control:** Other not–for–profit (including NFP Corporation) **Service:** General
Medical and Surgical

**Staffed Beds:** 461 **Admissions:** 22177 **Census:** 292 **Outpatient Visits:**
269644 **Births:** 2390 **Total Expense ($000):** 599283 **Payroll Expense
($000):** 280032 **Personnel:** 3774

☐ **SUMMIT OAKS HOSPITAL (314001)**, 19 Prospect Street, Zip 07901–2530;
tel. 908/522–7000, (Nonreporting) **A**1 9 10 **S** Universal Health Services, Inc.,
King of Prussia, PA
Primary Contact: Oana Radu, Chief Executive Officer
Web address: www.summitoakshospital.com/
**Control:** Corporation, Investor–owned, for–profit **Service:** Psychiatric

**Staffed Beds:** 90

## SUSSEX—Sussex County

**SAINT CLARE'S HEALTH CENTER AT SUSSEX** See Saint Clare's Health
System, Denville

## TEANECK—Bergen County

**HOLY NAME HOSPITAL** See Holy Name Medical Center

**NJ**

✠ **HOLY NAME MEDICAL CENTER (310008)**, 718 Teaneck Road,
Zip 07666–4281; tel. 201/833–3000 **A**1 2 5 6 9 10 **F**2 3 7 8 11 12 13 15 18
19 20 22 28 29 30 31 32 34 35 36 37 38 39 40 41 44 45 46 47 48 49 50
51 53 54 55 56 57 58 59 60 62 63 64 65 66 68 70 71 73 74 75 76 77 78
79 80 81 82 83 84 85 86 87 89 90 91 92 93 94 96 97 98 100 101 102 103
107 108 110 111 114 115 116 117 118 119 120 121 123 124 126 129 130
131 132 133 135 143 144 145 146 147 148 **P**3 4 6 7
Primary Contact: Michael Maron, President and Chief Executive Officer
CFO: Ryan Kennedy, Chief Financial Officer
CMO: Adam D. Jarrett, M.D., Executive Vice President and Chief Medical Officer
CIO: Michael Skvarenina, Assistant Vice President Information Systems
CHR: April Rodgers, Vice President, Human Resources
CNO: Sheryl A. Slonim, Executive Vice President and Chief Nursing Officer
Web address: www.holyname.org
**Control:** Other not–for–profit (including NFP Corporation) **Service:** General
Medical and Surgical

**Staffed Beds:** 318 **Admissions:** 18975 **Census:** 214 **Outpatient Visits:**
346981 **Births:** 1210 **Total Expense ($000):** 296868 **Payroll Expense
($000):** 132646 **Personnel:** 2347

---

**TINTON FALLS—Monmouth County**

★ **REHABILITATION HOSPITAL OF TINTON FALLS (313035)**, 2 Centre Plaza,
Zip 07724–9744; tel. 732/460–5320 **A**10 **F**29 64 68 74 75 82 90 93 94 95
96 100 119 148 **S** HEALTHSOUTH Corporation, Birmingham, AL
Primary Contact: Linda A. Savino, MS, Chief Executive Officer
CFO: Lynne Traister, Controller
CMO: Todd Cooperman, M.D., Medical Director
CHR: Anita Saum, Director Human Resources
Web address: www.rehabnj.com
**Control:** Corporation, Investor–owned, for–profit **Service:** Rehabilitation

**Staffed Beds:** 60 **Admissions:** 1434 **Census:** 50 **Outpatient Visits:** 9259
**Births:** 0 **Total Expense ($000):** 18469 **Payroll Expense ($000):** 11071
**Personnel:** 225

---

**TOMS RIVER—Ocean County**

✠ **BARNABAS HEALTH BEHAVIORAL HEALTH CENTER (314022)**, 1691
Highway 9, Zip 08754; tel. 732/914–1688, (Nonreporting) **A**1 9 10 **S** Barnabas
Health, West Orange, NJ
Primary Contact: Joe Hicks, President and Chief Executive Officer
Web address: www.barnabashealth.org/hospitals/psychiatric/index.html
**Control:** Other not–for–profit (including NFP Corporation) **Service:** Psychiatric

**Staffed Beds:** 40

✠ **COMMUNITY MEDICAL CENTER (310041)**, 99 Route 37 West,
Zip 08755–6423; tel. 732/557–8051, (Total facility includes 25 beds in nursing
home–type unit) **A**1 2 3 9 10 **F**3 11 13 15 17 18 20 22 28 29 30 31 32 34 35
36 38 40 41 43 44 46 47 48 49 50 54 55 56 57 58 59 60 61 62 63 64 68
69 70 73 74 75 76 77 78 79 81 82 84 85 86 87 89 92 93 96 100 102 107
108 109 110 111 114 115 118 119 120 121 123 124 126 128 129 130 131
132 133 134 143 146 147 148 **P**6 **S** Barnabas Health, West Orange, NJ
Primary Contact: Michael Mimoso, FACHE, Interim Chief Executive Officer
COO: Frank Gelormini, Chief Operating Officer
CFO: Mark Ostrander, Vice President Financial Services
CMO: John Crisanti, M.D., Vice President Medical Affairs
CIO: Shawn Fitzsimmons, Director Information Technology Services
CHR: Mary Deno, Vice President Human Resources
CNO: Fern Papalia, Vice President, Patient Care Services
Web address: www.barnabashealth.org/hospitals/community_medical/index.html
**Control:** Other not–for–profit (including NFP Corporation) **Service:** General
Medical and Surgical

**Staffed Beds:** 431 **Admissions:** 22658 **Census:** 291 **Outpatient Visits:**
249025 **Births:** 2204 **Total Expense ($000):** 324995 **Payroll Expense
($000):** 122571 **Personnel:** 1998

✠ **HEALTHSOUTH REHABILITATION HOSPITAL OF TOMS RIVER (313029)**, 14
Hospital Drive, Zip 08755–6470; tel. 732/244–3100, (Nonreporting) **A**1 10
**S** HEALTHSOUTH Corporation, Birmingham, AL
Primary Contact: Patricia Ostaszewski, MS, Chief Executive Officer
COO: Patricia Ostaszewski, MS, Chief Executive Officer
CFO: Janet Turso, Controller
CMO: Carol Sonatore, D.O., Medical Director
CIO: Coleen Rossi, Director Quality Services
CHR: Lori Munyan, Director, Human Resources
CNO: Susan Castor, Chief Nursing Officer
Web address: www.rehabnjtomsriver.com/
**Control:** Corporation, Investor–owned, for–profit **Service:** Rehabilitation

**Staffed Beds:** 92

**SAINT BARNABAS BEHAVIORAL HEALTH CENTER** See Barnabas Health
Behavioral Health Center

---

**TRENTON—Mercer County**

✠ **CAPITAL HEALTH REGIONAL MEDICAL CENTER (310092)**, 750 Brunswick
Avenue, Zip 08638–4143; tel. 609/394–6000 **A**1 3 5 6 9 10 **F**3 7 11 13 15 18
29 30 34 40 43 44 45 46 47 48 50 54 57 58 59 60 61 64 65 66 68 70 72
73 74 75 76 77 78 79 81 82 84 85 87 89 93 96 97 98 99 100 101 102 105
107 108 109 111 114 115 118 119 129 130 132 135 143 144 145 146 147
148 **S** Capital Health, Trenton, NJ
Primary Contact: Al Maghazehe, Ph.D., FACHE, President and Chief Executive
Officer
COO: Larry DiSanto, Executive Vice President and Chief Operating Officer
CFO: Shane Fleming, Chief Financial Officer
CMO: Steve Lowenthal, M.D., Vice President Medical Affairs
CIO: Eugene Grochala, Vice President Information Systems
CHR: J. Scott Clemmensen, Vice President Human Resources and Leadership
Enhancement
CNO: Eileen M. Horton, Vice President, Patient Services/Chief Nursing Officer
Web address: www.capitalhealth.org
**Control:** Other not–for–profit (including NFP Corporation) **Service:** General
Medical and Surgical

**Staffed Beds:** 222 **Admissions:** 10640 **Census:** 166 **Outpatient Visits:**
161112 **Births:** 246 **Personnel:** 1449

✠ **ST. FRANCIS MEDICAL CENTER (310021)**, 601 Hamilton Avenue,
Zip 08629–1986; tel. 609/599–5000 **A**1 2 3 6 9 10 **F**2 3 11 12 15 17 18 20
22 24 26 29 30 31 34 35 40 45 46 48 49 50 56 57 58 59 60 61 64 65
66 69 70 71 74 75 78 79 81 82 84 85 86 87 92 93 97 98 99 100 101 102
103 104 105 107 108 110 111 114 115 118 119 121 123 124 129 130 132
135 143 144 146 147 148 **P**5 6 **S** Trinity Health, Livonia, MI
Primary Contact: Vincent Costantino, Chief Administrative Officer
CFO: Mark Kelly, Vice President Finance
CMO: C. James Romano, M.D., Chief Medical Officer
CIO: Richard Dowgun, Chief Information Officer
CHR: Laura James, Director Human Resources
CNO: Mary Anne Suttles, Chief Nursing Officer
Web address: www.stfrancismedical.com
**Control:** Church–operated, Nongovernment, not–for profit **Service:** General
Medical and Surgical

**Staffed Beds:** 163 **Admissions:** 5402 **Census:** 76 **Outpatient Visits:** 93424
**Births:** 0 **Total Expense ($000):** 125950 **Payroll Expense ($000):** 43204
**Personnel:** 910

☐ **TRENTON PSYCHIATRIC HOSPITAL (314013)**, Route 29 and Sullivan Way,
Zip 08628–3425, Mailing Address: P.O. Box 7500, West Trenton,
Zip 08628–0500; tel. 609/633–1500, (Nonreporting) **A**1 3 10 **S** Division of
Mental Health and Addiction Services, Department of Human Services, State of
New Jersey, Trenton, NJ
Primary Contact: Teresa A. McQuaide, Chief Executive Officer
COO: Christopher Morrison, Deputy Chief Executive Officer
CFO: Joseph Canale, Business Manager
CMO: Lawrence Rossi, M.D., Clinical Director
CIO: Scott Eustace, Director Health Information Technology
CHR: Marybeth Longo, Manager Human Resources
CNO: Colleen Birkhofer, Chief Nursing Officer
Web address: www.state.nj.us/humanservices/dmhs/oshm/tph/
**Control:** State–Government, nonfederal **Service:** Psychiatric

**Staffed Beds:** 430

---

**TURNERSVILLE—Camden County**

**KENNEDY UNIVERSITY HOSPITAL – WASHINGTON TOWNSHIP** See Kennedy
Health System, Cherry Hill

---

**VINELAND—Cumberland County**

✠ **HEALTHSOUTH REHABILITATION HOSPITAL OF VINELAND (313036)**, 1237
West Sherman Avenue, Zip 08360–6920; tel. 856/696–7100 **A**1 10 **F**29 30 34
59 90 103 130 132 148 **S** HEALTHSOUTH Corporation, Birmingham, AL
Primary Contact: Tammy Feuer, Chief Executive Officer
CMO: Eugenio Rocksmith, M.D., Medical Director
CHR: Dawn Pearson, Director Human Resources
Web address: www.healthsouthvineland.com
**Control:** Corporation, Investor–owned, for–profit **Service:** Rehabilitation

**Staffed Beds:** 41 **Admissions:** 965 **Census:** 36 **Outpatient Visits:** 0 **Births:**
0 **Total Expense ($000):** 12335 **Payroll Expense ($000):** 7585 **Personnel:**
130

**NJ**

---

**Hospital, Medicare Provider Number, Address, Telephone, Approval, Facility, and Physician Codes, Health Care System**

★ American Hospital Association (AHA) membership    ◯ Healthcare Facilities Accreditation Program    ⇑ Center for Improvement in Healthcare Quality Accreditation
☐ The Joint Commission accreditation    ◇ DNV Healthcare Inc. accreditation    △ Commission on Accreditation of Rehabilitation Facilities (CARF) accreditation

---

★ ◇ **INSPIRA MEDICAL CENTER–VINELAND (310032)**, 1505 West Sherman Avenue, Zip 08360–6912; tel. 856/641–8000, (Includes BRIDGETON HEALTH CENTER, 333 Irving Avenue, Bridgeton, Zip 08302–2100; tel. 856/575–4500) **A**2 3 9 10 12 13 21 **F**3 8 11 12 13 15 17 18 20 28 29 30 34 35 37 38 40 41 42 43 44 50 54 57 59 60 64 68 70 72 73 74 75 76 77 78 79 81 82 85 86 87 89 93 98 99 100 101 102 103 104 105 107 108 110 111 114 115 118 119 120 121 123 126 130 131 132 134 144 146 147 148 **P**6 **S** Inspira Health Network, Mullica Hill, NJ
Primary Contact: John A. DiAngelo, President and Chief Executive Officer
COO: Elizabeth Sheridan, Chief Operating Officer and Chief Nursing Executive
CFO: Thomas Baldosaro, Chief Financial Officer
CMO: Steven C. Linn, M.D., Chief Medical Officer
CIO: Thomas Pacek, Vice President Information Systems and Chief Information Officer
CHR: Erich Florentine, Chief People Officer
CNO: Elizabeth Sheridan, Chief Operating Officer and Chief Nursing Executive
Web address: www.inspirahealthnetwork.org/?id=5280&sid=1
**Control:** Other not–for–profit (including NFP Corporation) **Service:** General Medical and Surgical

**Staffed Beds:** 335 **Admissions:** 18104 **Census:** 236 **Outpatient Visits:** 329971 **Births:** 2077 **Total Expense ($000):** 333700 **Payroll Expense ($000):** 136824 **Personnel:** 1500

### VOORHEES—Camden County

✠ **VIRTUA VOORHEES (310022)**, 100 Bowman Drive, Zip 08043–9612; tel. 856/325–3000, (Includes VOORHEES PEDIATRIC FACILITY, 1304 Laurel Oak Road, Zip 08043–4310; tel. 888/873–5437) **A**1 3 5 10 **F**3 11 13 29 30 31 34 35 40 41 45 46 48 49 50 55 58 59 64 66 68 70 72 73 74 75 76 78 79 81 82 86 87 88 89 90 92 93 107 108 111 115 116 117 119 126 129 130 143 145 146 147 **S** Virtua Health, Marlton, NJ
Primary Contact: Matthew Zuino, Senior Vice President
COO: Michael S. Kotzen, Vice President and Chief Operating Officer
CFO: Robert Rosvold, Director Finance
CMO: James P. Dwyer, D.O., Executive Vice President and Chief Medical Officer
CIO: Alfred Campanella, Chief Information Officer
Web address: www.virtua.org
**Control:** Other not–for–profit (including NFP Corporation) **Service:** General Medical and Surgical

**Staffed Beds:** 398 **Admissions:** 22839 **Census:** 273 **Outpatient Visits:** 257117 **Births:** 4864 **Total Expense ($000):** 405270 **Payroll Expense ($000):** 130586 **Personnel:** 1824

### WAYNE—Passaic County

**KINDRED HOSPITAL NEW JERSEY – WAYNE** See Kindred Hospital–New Jersey Morris County, Dover

### WEST ORANGE—Essex County

✠ △ **KESSLER INSTITUTE FOR REHABILITATION (313025)**, 1199 Pleasant Valley Way, Zip 07052–1424; tel. 973/731–3600, (Includes KESSLER INSTITUTE FOR REHABILITATION, 201 Pleasant Hill Road, Chester, Zip 07930–2141; tel. 973/252–6300; Sue Kida, Chief Executive Officer; KESSLER INSTITUTE FOR REHABILITATION, 300 Market Street, Saddle Brook, Zip 07663–5309; tel. 201/368–6000; Philip J. Driscoll, Jr., Chief Executive Officer; KESSLER INSTITUTE FOR REHABILITATION, 1199 Pleasant Valley Way, tel. 973/731–3600; Bonnie Evans, Chief Executive Officer) **A**1 3 5 7 10 **F**29 53 54 64 77 82 90 91 92 93 94 95 96 119 130 131 132 146 148 **P**6 **S** Select Medical Corporation, Mechanicsburg, PA
Primary Contact: Robert Brehm, President
CMO: Bruce M. Gans, M.D., Executive Vice President and Chief Medical Officer
CHR: Ken Caldera, Director Human Resources
Web address: www.kessler–rehab.com
**Control:** Corporation, Investor–owned, for–profit **Service:** Rehabilitation

**Staffed Beds:** 336 **Admissions:** 6908 **Census:** 295 **Outpatient Visits:** 138558 **Births:** 0

**KESSLER INSTITUTE FOR REHABILITATION** See Kessler Institute for Rehabilitation

### WESTAMPTON—Burlington County

☐ **HAMPTON BEHAVIORAL HEALTH CENTER (314021)**, 650 Rancocas Road, Zip 08060–5613; tel. 609/267–7000 **A**1 9 10 **F**30 35 98 99 100 102 103 104 105 130 132 143 **P**6 **S** Universal Health Services, Inc., King of Prussia, PA
Primary Contact: Craig Hilton, Chief Executive Officer
COO: Joanne Wijaya, Chief Operating Officer
CMO: Charles Trigiani, D.O., Medical Director
CHR: Lori DeCelis, Director Human Resources
CNO: Kathleena Cohen, Director of Nursing
Web address: www.hamptonhospital.com
**Control:** Corporation, Investor–owned, for–profit **Service:** Psychiatric

**Staffed Beds:** 110 **Admissions:** 2544 **Census:** 103 **Outpatient Visits:** 19084 **Births:** 0 **Total Expense ($000):** 21771 **Payroll Expense ($000):** 14457 **Personnel:** 265

### WESTWOOD—Bergen County

✠ **HACKENSACK UNIVERSITY MEDICAL CENTER AT PASCACK VALLEY (310130)**, 250 Old Hook Road, Zip 07675–3123; tel. 201/383–1035 **A**1 **F**3 12 13 15 18 20 28 29 30 34 35 40 44 45 46 47 49 50 70 72 74 76 77 78 79 81 82 85 87 93 107 108 110 111 115 119 129 130 135 146 147 **S** LHP Hospital Group, Plano, TX
Primary Contact: Emily L. Holliman, Chief Executive Officer
COO: Colleen Smorra, Assistant Administrator
CFO: Jason Pritchard, Chief Financial Officer
CMO: George Lin, M.D., Physician Advisor
CIO: Anthony Teri, Director Information Technology
CHR: Theodora Carter, Administrative Director Human Resources
CNO: Susan Giordano, R.N., Chief Nursing Officer
Web address: www.hackensackumcpv.com/
**Control:** Partnership, Investor–owned, for–profit **Service:** General Medical and Surgical

**Staffed Beds:** 128 **Admissions:** 3009 **Census:** 38 **Outpatient Visits:** 19640 **Births:** 306 **Total Expense ($000):** 79536 **Payroll Expense ($000):** 27870 **Personnel:** 518

### WILLINGBORO—Burlington County

✠ **LOURDES MEDICAL CENTER OF BURLINGTON COUNTY (310061)**, 218–A Sunset Road, Zip 08046–1162; tel. 609/835–2900 **A**1 2 9 10 **F**3 7 11 12 15 17 18 29 30 31 34 35 36 38 40 42 44 45 46 47 49 50 55 56 57 59 60 61 64 66 68 70 74 75 78 79 81 82 85 86 87 93 98 100 107 108 109 110 111 114 118 119 129 130 132 135 146 147 148 **P**8 **S** Trinity Health, Livonia, MI
Primary Contact: Mark Nessel, Executive Vice President and Chief Operating Officer
CFO: Michael Hammond, Chief Financial Officer
CMO: Alan R. Pope, M.D., Vice President, Medical Affairs
CIO: Mike Elfert, Director Information Services
CHR: Richard P. Kropp, Vice President Human Resources
CNO: Audrey Jadczak, R.N., Vice President/Chief Nursing Officer
Web address: www.lourdesnet.org
**Control:** Other not–for–profit (including NFP Corporation) **Service:** General Medical and Surgical

**Staffed Beds:** 169 **Admissions:** 6655 **Census:** 90 **Outpatient Visits:** 113171 **Births:** 0 **Total Expense ($000):** 109907 **Payroll Expense ($000):** 42929 **Personnel:** 527

✠ **LOURDES SPECIALTY HOSPITAL OF SOUTHERN NEW JERSEY (312022)**, 220 Sunset Road, Zip 08046–1110; tel. 609/835–3650 **A**1 10 **F**1 3 29 60 75 77 85 87 91 100 107 111 119 130 132 148 **S** AcuityHealthcare, LP, Charlotte, NC
Primary Contact: Cheri Cowperthwait, R.N., Chief Executive Officer
CFO: James Weinstein, Chief Financial Officer
CHR: Lisa M. Sinnott, Director Human Resources
CNO: Kim Fetterolf, R.N., Chief Clinical Officer
Web address: www.lshnj.com
**Control:** Hospital district or authority, Government, nonfederal **Service:** Long–Term Acute Care hospital

**Staffed Beds:** 69 **Admissions:** 519 **Census:** 43 **Outpatient Visits:** 0 **Births:** 0 **Total Expense ($000):** 30297 **Payroll Expense ($000):** 14024 **Personnel:** 195

### WOODBURY—Gloucester County

★ ◇ **INSPIRA MEDICAL CENTER–WOODBURY (310081)**, 509 North Broad Street, Zip 08096–1697; tel. 856/845–0100 **A**3 5 9 10 21 **F**3 5 11 13 15 17 18 20 22 26 28 29 30 31 34 35 38 40 41 45 46 47 48 49 50 56 57 58 59 62 64 66 67 70 73 74 75 77 78 79 81 85 86 87 91 92 93 96 97 98 99 100 101 102 104 105 107 109 110 114 115 119 129 130 131 132 133 135 146 147 148 **P**6 **S** Inspira Health Network, Mullica Hill, NJ
Primary Contact: Eileen K. Cardile, R.N., MS, Executive Vice President, Inspira Health Network and President and Chief Executive Officer, Inspira
COO: Patrick B. Nolan, Chief Operating Officer
CIO: Robert Mizia, Director Information Systems and Chief Information Officer
CHR: Robert Manestrina, Vice President Human Resources
CNO: Gina Mumolie, Senior Vice President and Chief Nurse Executive
Web address: www.inspirahealthnetwork.org/?id=5282&sid=1
**Control:** Other not–for–profit (including NFP Corporation) **Service:** General Medical and Surgical

**Staffed Beds:** 256 **Admissions:** 10658 **Census:** 141 **Outpatient Visits:** 137419 **Births:** 875 **Total Expense ($000):** 175134 **Payroll Expense ($000):** 81308 **Personnel:** 1222

**NJ**

⊞ **CHRISTIAN HEALTH CARE CENTER (314019)**, 301 Sicomac Avenue, Zip 07481–2194; tel. 201/848–5200, (Total facility includes 184 beds in nursing home–type unit) **A**1 9 10 **F**2 6 10 29 30 34 35 50 56 57 59 63 64 69 83 86 87 90 96 98 99 101 103 104 105 125 128 130 132 143 146 148 **P**6
Primary Contact: Douglas A. Struyk, CPA, President and Chief Executive Officer
COO: Denise Ratcliffe, Executive Vice President and Chief Operating Officer
CFO: Kevin Stagg, Executive Vice President Finance and Chief Financial Officer
CMO: Howard Gilman, M.D., Medical Executive
CIO: Jennifer D'Angelo, Assistant Vice President Information Services
CHR: Bob Zierold, Senior Vice President Human Resources
CNO: Marianne Guerriero, Nurse Executive
Web address: www.chccnj.org
**Control:** Other not–for–profit (including NFP Corporation) **Service:** Psychiatric

**Staffed Beds:** 530 **Admissions:** 2124 **Census:** 500 **Outpatient Visits:** 51278
**Births:** 0 **Total Expense ($000):** 73466 **Payroll Expense ($000):** 43182
**Personnel:** 710

NJ

# NEW MEXICO

## ACOMA— County

☐ **ACOMA–CANONCITO–LAGUNA HOSPITAL (320070)**, 80B Veterans Boulevard, Zip 87034, Mailing Address: P.O. Box 130, San Fidel, Zip 87049–0130; tel. 505/552–5300, (Nonreporting) **A**1 10 **S** U. S. Indian Health Service, Rockville, MD
Primary Contact: William Thorne, Jr., Chief Executive Officer
Web address: www.ihs.gov/albuquerque/index.cfm?module=dsp_abq_acoma_canoncito_laguna
**Control:** PHS, Indian Service, Government, federal **Service:** General Medical and Surgical

**Staffed Beds:** 25

## ALAMOGORDO—Otero County

★ ◇ **GERALD CHAMPION REGIONAL MEDICAL CENTER (320004)**, 2669 North Scenic Drive, Zip 88310–8799; tel. 575/439–6100 **A**3 9 10 20 21 **F**3 8 11 13 18 29 30 31 34 35 38 40 43 45 50 51 56 57 58 59 60 64 70 76 77 78 79 81 85 86 87 90 92 96 97 98 100 101 102 103 104 107 108 111 114 115 119 129 130 132 133 145 146 147 148 **P**8
Primary Contact: Robert J. Heckert, Jr., Chief Executive Officer
CFO: Morgan Hay, Chief Financial Officer
CMO: Arthur Austin, M.D., Vice President Medical Affairs
CIO: Ana Castro, Director Information Services and Clinical Information Services
CHR: Karen O'Brien, Director Human Resources
CNO: Catherine A. Rhyne, M.P.H., Chief Nursing Officer
Web address: www.gcrmc.org
**Control:** Other not–for–profit (including NFP Corporation) **Service:** General Medical and Surgical

**Staffed Beds:** 99 **Admissions:** 3571 **Census:** 40 **Outpatient Visits:** 97755 **Births:** 490 **Total Expense ($000):** 106507 **Payroll Expense ($000):** 36164 **Personnel:** 574

## ALBUQUERQUE—Bernalillo County

☐ **AMG SPECIALTY HOSPITAL–ALBUQUERQUE (322003)**, 235 Elm Street N.E., Zip 87102–3672; tel. 505/842–5550, (Nonreporting) **A**1 9 10 **S** AMG Integrated Healthcare Management, Lafayette, LA
Primary Contact: Elizabeth Rees, Chief Executive Officer
CFO: Julie Lenzo, Director Business Office
CMO: Jeffrey Ross, M.D., Medical Director
CHR: Robin Stendel–Freels, Coordinator Human Resources
Web address: www.amgalbuquerque.com/
**Control:** Partnership, Investor–owned, for–profit **Service:** Long–Term Acute Care hospital

**Staffed Beds:** 24

☐ **HAVEN BEHAVIORAL SENIOR CARE OF ALBUQUERQUE (324013)**, 5400 Gibson Boulevard S.E., 4th Floor, Zip 87108–4729; tel. 505/254–4500, (Nonreporting) **A**1 10
Primary Contact: Ambrozino Storr, Chief Executive Officer
Web address: www.havenbehavioral.com
**Control:** Corporation, Investor–owned, for–profit **Service:** Psychiatric

**Staffed Beds:** 32

⊠ **HEALTHSOUTH REHABILITATION HOSPITAL (323027)**, 7000 Jefferson Street N.E., Zip 87109–4313; tel. 505/344–9478 **A**1 9 10 **F**28 29 34 35 56 57 59 60 62 64 74 75 77 79 90 91 93 94 95 96 130 132 143 148 **S** HEALTHSOUTH Corporation, Birmingham, AL
Primary Contact: Byron Aten, Interim Chief Executive Officer
CFO: Byron Aten, Controller
CMO: Angela Walker, M.D., Medical Director
CHR: Kristen Hernandez, Director Human Resources
CNO: Veronica Gadomski, R.N., Chief Nursing Officer
Web address: www.healthsouthnewmexico.com
**Control:** Corporation, Investor–owned, for–profit **Service:** Rehabilitation

**Staffed Beds:** 87 **Admissions:** 1744 **Census:** 64 **Outpatient Visits:** 8022 **Births:** 0 **Total Expense ($000):** 21636 **Payroll Expense ($000):** 11606 **Personnel:** 229

⊠ **KINDRED HOSPITAL–ALBUQUERQUE (322002)**, 700 High Street N.E., Zip 87102–2565; tel. 505/242–4444 **A**1 9 10 **F**1 3 16 29 30 67 70 75 80 90 91 98 107 130 135 148 **S** Kindred Healthcare, Louisville, KY
Primary Contact: Bud Schawl, Chief Executive Officer
CFO: Margaret Wantland, Chief Financial Officer
CMO: Jeffrey Dorf, M.D., Medical Director
CHR: Donald Whitney, Director Human Resources
CNO: Gary Gum, R.N., Chief Nursing Officer
Web address: www.kindredalbuquerque.com/
**Control:** Corporation, Investor–owned, for–profit **Service:** General Medical and Surgical

**Staffed Beds:** 61 **Admissions:** 504 **Census:** 42 **Births:** 0

★ ◇ **LOVELACE MEDICAL CENTER (320009)**, 601 Martin Luther King Avenue N.E., Zip 87102–3619; tel. 505/727–8000, (Includes HEART HOSPITAL OF NEW MEXICO, 504 Elm Street, Zip 87102; tel. 505/724–2000; Ronald C. Winger, President), (Nonreporting) **A**3 5 9 10 21 **S** Ardent Health Services, Nashville, TN
Primary Contact: Troy Greer, Chief Executive Officer
CMO: Jean D. Remillard, M.D., Chief Medical Officer/Chief Quality Officer
CHR: Helen V. Nielsen, Director Human Resources
CNO: Laurie S. Bigham, R.N., Chief Nursing Officer
Web address: www.lovelace.com/albuquerque–hospital/lovelace–medical–center#.UDZ1laDhf48
**Control:** Corporation, Investor–owned, for–profit **Service:** General Medical and Surgical

**Staffed Beds:** 263

★ △ **LOVELACE REHABILITATION HOSPITAL (323028)**, 505 Elm Street N.E., Zip 87102–2500; tel. 505/727–4700 **A**3 5 7 9 10 **F**3 29 30 90 143 148 **S** Ardent Health Services, Nashville, TN
Primary Contact: Derrick Jones, Chief Executive Officer
CFO: Andrea Solin, Chief Financial Officer
CHR: Helen V. Nielsen, Director Human Resources
CNO: Cynthia Rankin, Chief Nursing Officer
Web address: www.lovelace.com
**Control:** Corporation, Investor–owned, for–profit **Service:** Rehabilitation

**Staffed Beds:** 52 **Admissions:** 1083 **Census:** 41

★ ◇ **LOVELACE WESTSIDE HOSPITAL (320074)**, 10501 Golf Course Road N.W., Zip 87114–5000, Mailing Address: P.O. Box 25555, Zip 87125–0555; tel. 505/727–2000 **A**3 5 9 10 21 **F**3 12 13 15 29 30 34 39 40 41 49 51 57 59 68 70 75 79 81 85 93 107 110 111 115 119 130 133 135 146 148 **S** Ardent Health Services, Nashville, TN
Primary Contact: Farron Sneed, FACHE, Chief Executive Officer
COO: Karrie Brazaski, R.N., Chief Operating Officer and Chief Nursing Officer
Web address: www.lovelace.com/albuquerque–hospital/lovelace–westside–hospital#.UDZ1t6Dhf48
**Control:** Corporation, Investor–owned, for–profit **Service:** General Medical and Surgical

**Staffed Beds:** 80 **Admissions:** 2433 **Census:** 21 **Outpatient Visits:** 31318 **Births:** 247 **Total Expense ($000):** 48550 **Payroll Expense ($000):** 16722 **Personnel:** 289

★ ◇ **LOVELACE WOMEN'S HOSPITAL (320017)**, 4701 Montgomery Boulevard N.E., Zip 87109–1251, Mailing Address: P.O. Box 25555, Zip 87125–0555; tel. 505/727–7800 **A**3 5 9 10 21 **F**8 11 13 15 29 34 35 40 43 46 49 57 59 64 70 72 73 76 78 79 81 85 89 91 93 107 108 110 111 114 115 116 117 119 126 130 132 146 147 **S** Ardent Health Services, Nashville, TN
Primary Contact: Sheri Milone, Chief Executive Officer and Administrator
COO: Janelle Raborn, Chief Operating Officer
CFO: Joseph Sereno, Chief Financial Officer
CHR: Carol Shelton, Director Human Resources
CNO: Jane Ritter, R.N., Chief Nursing Officer
Web address: www.lovelace.com/albuquerque–hospital/lovelace–womens–hospital#.UDZ17KDhf48
**Control:** Corporation, Investor–owned, for–profit **Service:** General Medical and Surgical

**Staffed Beds:** 78 **Admissions:** 9208 **Census:** 85 **Outpatient Visits:** 134247 **Births:** 3225

⊠ △ **NEW MEXICO VETERANS AFFAIRS HEALTH CARE SYSTEM – RAYMOND G. MURPHY MEDICAL CENTER**, (acute inpt; outpt; residential; psych), 1501 San Pedro S.E., Zip 87108–5153; tel. 505/265–1711 **A**1 2 3 5 7 8 **F**3 4 5 8 12 15 17 18 20 22 24 26 28 29 30 31 34 35 38 39 40 44 45 46 47 48 49 50 54 56 57 58 59 60 61 62 63 65 68 70 74 75 77 78 79 80 81 82 83 84 85 86 87 90 91 92 93 94 96 97 98 100 101 102 103 104 105 106 107 110 111 112 113 119 126 129 130 132 135 143 144 146 147 148 **S** Department of Veterans Affairs, Washington, DC
Primary Contact: Andrew Welch, Director
CFO: Michael McNeill, Chief Financial Management
CMO: Meghan Gerety, M.D., Chief of Staff
CIO: Ronald Ferrell, Chief Information Officer
CHR: Melvin Hooker, Chief Human Resources
Web address: www.albuquerque.va.gov/
**Control:** Veterans Affairs, Government, federal **Service:** General Medical and Surgical

**Staffed Beds:** 203 **Admissions:** 4618 **Census:** 66 **Outpatient Visits:** 660000 **Births:** 0 **Personnel:** 2546

*Many Facility Codes have changed. Please refer to the AHA Guide Code Chart.* © 2015 AHA Guide

NM

⊠ **PRESBYTERIAN HOSPITAL (320021)**, 1100 Central Avenue S.E., Zip 87106–4934, Mailing Address: P.O. Box 26666, Zip 87125–6666; tel. 505/841–1234, (Includes PRESBYTERIAN RUST MEDICAL CENTER, 2400 Unser Boulevard S.E., Rio Rancho, Zip 87124–4740; tel. 505/253–7878; Jeff McBee, Administrator) **A**1 2 3 5 9 10 **F**3 7 8 11 13 14 17 18 19 20 21 22 23 24 25 26 27 29 30 31 35 38 40 44 45 46 47 48 49 51 53 57 59 60 68 70 72 74 75 76 77 78 79 81 84 85 86 87 88 89 92 93 96 100 101 107 108 111 113 114 115 118 119 124 126 130 131 132 138 142 144 145 146 147 148 **P**6 **S** Presbyterian Healthcare Services, Albuquerque, NM
Primary Contact: Sandra C. Podley, Administrator
COO: Paul Briggs, Executive Vice President and Chief Operating Officer
CFO: Dale Maxwell, Executive Vice President and Chief Financial Officer
CMO: Jayne McCormick, M.D., Chief Medical Officer CDS
CIO: Lee Marley, VP/Information Services Chief Application Officer
CHR: Lee Patchell, Lead Human Resources Business Partner
CNO: Ann L. Wright, R.N., Assistant Central Delivery System CNO
Web address: www.phs.org
**Control:** Other not–for–profit (including NFP Corporation) **Service:** General Medical and Surgical

**Staffed Beds:** 409 **Admissions:** 27749 **Census:** 369 **Outpatient Visits:** 1625273 **Births:** 3490 **Total Expense ($000):** 826795 **Payroll Expense ($000):** 362436 **Personnel:** 4109

★ **PRESBYTERIAN KASEMAN HOSPITAL (320079)**, 8300 Constitution Avenue N.E., Zip 87110–7624, Mailing Address: P.O. Box 26666, Zip 87125–6666; tel. 505/291–2000 **A**9 **F**3 5 29 30 31 40 50 53 56 63 64 65 68 75 78 79 81 82 84 86 87 93 97 98 99 100 101 102 103 104 105 107 108 111 114 117 118 119 120 121 123 128 129 130 132 146 148 **P**6 **S** Presbyterian Healthcare Services, Albuquerque, NM
Primary Contact: Doyle Boykin, R.N., MSN, Administrator
COO: Paul Briggs, Executive VP/Chief Operating Officer
CFO: Dale Maxwell, Senior VP Chief Financial Officer
CMO: Jayne McCormick, M.D., Chief Medical Officer CDS
CIO: Lee Marley, VP/Information Services Chief Application Officer
CHR: Cindy McGill, Senior Vice President Human Resources
Web address: www.phs.org
**Control:** Other not–for–profit (including NFP Corporation) **Service:** Surgical

**Staffed Beds:** 90 **Admissions:** 4780 **Census:** 104 **Outpatient Visits:** 124712 **Births:** 0 **Total Expense ($000):** 95691 **Payroll Expense ($000):** 34989 **Personnel:** 540

**TURQUOISE LODGE HOSPITAL**, 5901 Zuni Road S.E., Zip 87108–3073; tel. 505/841–8978, (Nonreporting)
Primary Contact: Shauna Hartley, Hospital Administrator
CFO: Juliette Aragon, Finance Director
CIO: Eric Gurule, Chief Information Officer
CHR: Mario Lechuga, Director Human Resources
CNO: Debra Jane Green, R.N., Director of Nursing
Web address: www.health.state.nm.us
**Control:** State–Government, nonfederal **Service:** Alcoholism and other chemical dependency

**Staffed Beds:** 34

⊠ **UNIVERSITY OF NEW MEXICO HOSPITALS (320001)**, 2211 Lomas Boulevard N.E., Zip 87106–2745; tel. 505/272–2111, (Includes CARRIE TINGLEY HOSPITAL, 1127 University Boulevard N.E., Zip 87102–1715; tel. 505/272–5200; Crystal E. Frantz, MSN, R.N., Executive Director; MENTAL HEALTH CENTER, 2600 Marble N.E., Zip 87131–2600; tel. 505/272–2800; UNIVERSITY OF NEW MEXICO CHILDREN'S PSYCHIATRIC HOSPITAL, 1001 Yale Boulevard N.E., Zip 87131–3830; tel. 505/272–2890; UNM CHILDREN'S HOSPITAL, 2211 Lomas Boulevard, N.E., tel. 505/272–2111) **A**1 2 3 5 8 9 10 **F**3 9 11 13 15 16 18 19 20 22 24 25 26 29 30 31 32 34 35 38 40 41 43 44 45 46 47 48 49 50 51 54 56 57 59 60 61 63 64 65 68 70 72 73 74 75 76 77 78 79 81 82 83 84 85 86 87 88 89 90 92 93 94 95 96 97 107 108 109 110 111 114 115 116 117 118 119 121 123 126 129 130 131 132 135 136 138 144 146 147 148 **S** University of New Mexico Hospitals, Albuquerque, NM
Primary Contact: Stephen W. McKernan, Chief Executive Officer
COO: Paul F. Herzog, Chief Operating Officer
CFO: Ella Watt, Chief Financial Officer
CMO: Robert Katz, M.D., Vice President Clinical Affairs
CIO: Ron Margolis, Chief Information Officer
CHR: Jim Pendergast, Administrator Human Resources
Web address: www.unm.edu
**Control:** State–Government, nonfederal **Service:** General Medical and Surgical

**Staffed Beds:** 537 **Admissions:** 28653 **Census:** 409 **Outpatient Visits:** 625947 **Births:** 3161 **Total Expense ($000):** 848626 **Payroll Expense ($000):** 321430 **Personnel:** 5566

★ **ARTESIA GENERAL HOSPITAL (320030)**, 702 North 13th Street, Zip 88210–1199; tel. 575/748–3333 **A**9 10 20 **F**3 11 15 18 29 30 34 40 45 46 47 48 50 51 56 59 64 65 68 75 79 81 85 92 93 98 101 103 104 107 108 110 111 115 119 124 127 128 130 131 133 135
Primary Contact: Kenneth W. Randall, Chief Executive Officer
CFO: Carl Hollingsworth, Chief Financial Officer
CMO: Joe Salgado, M.D., Chief of Staff
CHR: Bruce Hinshaw, Director Human Resources
CNO: Wendi Hulett, Chief Nursing Officer
Web address: www.artesiageneral.com
**Control:** Other not–for–profit (including NFP Corporation) **Service:** General Medical and Surgical

**Staffed Beds:** 30 **Admissions:** 816 **Census:** 11 **Outpatient Visits:** 69681 **Births:** 0 **Total Expense ($000):** 44040 **Payroll Expense ($000):** 20698 **Personnel:** 270

⊠ **CARLSBAD MEDICAL CENTER (320063)**, 2430 West Pierce Street, Zip 88220–3597; tel. 575/887–4100, (Nonreporting) **A**1 9 10 **S** Community Health Systems, Inc., Franklin, TN
Primary Contact: Cathy Hibbs, Chief Executive Officer
CFO: Craig Morse, Chief Financial Officer
CIO: Thomas Motejzik, Director Information Systems
CHR: Michael L. Turner, Director Human Resources
CNO: Connie Shofner, Chief Nursing Officer
Web address: www.carlsbadmedicalcenter.com
**Control:** Corporation, Investor–owned, for–profit **Service:** General Medical and Surgical

**Staffed Beds:** 127

★ **UNION COUNTY GENERAL HOSPITAL (321304)**, 300 Wilson Street, Zip 88415–3304, Mailing Address: P.O. Box 489, Zip 88415–0489; tel. 575/374–2585 **A**9 10 18 **F**3 11 13 29 31 35 40 45 50 57 59 62 64 65 68 70 76 77 81 82 85 87 89 93 97 102 107 114 119 129 130 133 144 145 148
Primary Contact: Jerry Wiesner, Interim Chief Executive Officer
CFO: Alexander B. Altman, III, Chief Financial Officer
CMO: Daniel Radunsky, M.D., Medical Staff President
CIO: David Hall, Chief Information Officer
CHR: Jill Swagerty, Director Human Resources
CNO: Stacye Bradley, R.N., Chief Nursing Officer
Web address: www.unioncountygeneral.com/
**Control:** Other not–for–profit (including NFP Corporation) **Service:** General Medical and Surgical

**Staffed Beds:** 21 **Admissions:** 321 **Census:** 3

⊠ **PLAINS REGIONAL MEDICAL CENTER (320022)**, 2100 Martin Luther King Boulevard, Zip 88101–9412, Mailing Address: P.O. Box 1688, Zip 88102–1688; tel. 575/769–2141 **A**1 9 10 **F**3 8 11 13 15 20 28 29 30 31 35 39 40 45 47 48 50 51 53 54 57 58 61 62 63 64 65 68 69 70 75 76 77 78 79 81 84 85 87 89 93 97 107 108 110 111 112 114 115 116 119 120 121 123 129 130 135 146 147 148 **P**6 **S** Presbyterian Healthcare Services, Albuquerque, NM
Primary Contact: Vincent B. DiFranco, Chief Executive Officer
CMO: Brian Willmon, M.D., Medical Director
CHR: Cindy Duncan, Manager Human Resources
CNO: Terri A. Marney, R.N., Director of Nursing
Web address: www.phs.org
**Control:** Other not–for–profit (including NFP Corporation) **Service:** General Medical and Surgical

**Staffed Beds:** 50 **Admissions:** 4641 **Census:** 38 **Births:** 1234 **Total Expense ($000):** 83154 **Payroll Expense ($000):** 29681 **Personnel:** 461

**NM**

## CROWNPOINT—McKinley County

★ **U. S. PUBLIC HEALTH SERVICE INDIAN HOSPITAL (320062)**, Route 9 and State Road 371, Zip 87313, Mailing Address: P.O. Box 358, Zip 87313–0358; tel. 505/786–5291, (Nonreporting) **A**10 **S** U. S. Indian Health Service, Rockville, MD
Primary Contact: Anslem Roanhorse, Chief Executive Officer
CFO: Darlene Kirk, Manager Finance
CMO: John Johnson, M.D., Clinical Director
CIO: Jimmy Burbank, Chief Information Officer
CHR: Christina Bitsilly, Human Resource Specialist
CNO: Alex Daniels, Chief Nurse Executive
Web address: www.ihs.gov
**Control:** PHS, Indian Service, Government, federal **Service:** General Medical and Surgical

**Staffed Beds:** 12

## DEMING—Luna County

✠ **MIMBRES MEMORIAL HOSPITAL (321309)**, 900 West Ash Street, Zip 88030–4098, Mailing Address: P.O. Box 710, Zip 88031–0710; tel. 575/546–5800, (Total facility includes 52 beds in nursing home–type unit) **A**1 9 10 18 **F**3 11 13 15 29 40 45 50 57 64 68 70 75 76 79 81 85 89 93 108 110 114 119 128 132 143 146 **S** Community Health Systems, Inc., Franklin, TN
Primary Contact: Steve Westenhofer, Chief Executive Officer
CFO: Trisha Smith, Chief Financial Officer
CHR: Johanna Gramer, Director Human Resources
CNO: Joy Harrell, R.N., Chief Nursing Officer
Web address: www.mimbresmemorial.com
**Control:** Corporation, Investor–owned, for–profit **Service:** General Medical and Surgical

**Staffed Beds:** 75 **Admissions:** 1907 **Census:** 47 **Outpatient Visits:** 49487 **Births:** 274 **Personnel:** 197

## ESPANOLA—Rio Arriba County

✠ **PRESBYTERIAN ESPANOLA HOSPITAL (320011)**, 1010 Spruce Street, Zip 87532–2746; tel. 505/753–7111 **A**1 9 10 20 **F**3 7 8 13 15 29 32 34 35 40 45 50 53 57 59 62 70 75 76 79 81 85 93 107 108 110 114 115 118 119 129 146 **P**6 **S** Presbyterian Healthcare Services, Albuquerque, NM
Primary Contact: Brenda Romero, Administrator
CFO: Lupe Lucero, Manager Business Office
CMO: Fernando Bayardo, M.D., Chief Medical Officer
CHR: Julie Mackenzie, Manager Human Resources
CNO: Sharon Redman, Director Patient Care Services
Web address: www.phs.org
**Control:** Other not–for–profit (including NFP Corporation) **Service:** General Medical and Surgical

**Staffed Beds:** 42 **Admissions:** 2398 **Census:** 24 **Outpatient Visits:** 124512 **Births:** 265 **Total Expense ($000):** 58454 **Payroll Expense ($000):** 26884 **Personnel:** 299

## FARMINGTON—San Juan County

✠ ◇ **SAN JUAN REGIONAL MEDICAL CENTER (320005)**, 801 West Maple Street, Zip 87401–5630; tel. 505/609–2000, (Includes SAN JUAN REGIONAL MEDICAL CENTER REHABILITATION HOSPITAL, 525 South Schwartz, Zip 87401; tel. 505/609–2625) **A**1 2 9 10 21 **F**3 7 8 11 13 15 18 20 22 26 28 29 30 31 32 34 35 39 40 42 43 47 48 49 50 53 54 57 59 60 64 65 68 70 74 75 76 78 79 81 82 85 86 87 89 90 93 96 97 98 99 100 102 107 108 111 112 114 115 118 119 121 130 132 135 143 144 146 148 **P**5 6
Primary Contact: Rick D. Wallace, FACHE, President and Chief Executive Officer
COO: John Buffington, Chief Operating Officer
CFO: J. Michael Philips, Chief Strategy Officer
CMO: Melanie Yeats, M.D., Vice President Medical Affairs
CIO: Sheri Rawlings, Chief Information Officer
CHR: Elizabeth Volkerding, Director Workforce Excellence
CNO: Suzanne E. Smith, R.N., Chief Nursing Officer
Web address: www.sanjuanregional.com
**Control:** Other not–for–profit (including NFP Corporation) **Service:** General Medical and Surgical

**Staffed Beds:** 198 **Admissions:** 9815 **Census:** 121 **Outpatient Visits:** 698186 **Births:** 1293 **Total Expense ($000):** 250389 **Payroll Expense ($000):** 116696 **Personnel:** 1661

## GALLUP—McKinley County

✠ **GALLUP INDIAN MEDICAL CENTER (320061)**, 516 East Nizhoni Boulevard, Zip 87301–5748, Mailing Address: P.O. Box 1337, Zip 87305–1337; tel. 505/722–1000 **A**1 5 10 **F**5 8 13 15 18 29 34 39 40 43 50 59 61 64 65 66 70 74 76 79 81 83 84 85 89 99 100 107 115 119 130 144 147 148 **S** U. S. Indian Health Service, Rockville, MD
Primary Contact: Vida J. Khow, Chief Executive Officer
CFO: Agnes Kee, Financial Manager
CMO: Douglas G. Peter, M.D., Chief Medical Officer
CIO: Adrian C. Haven, Site Manager
CHR: Karen Lee, Director Human Resources
CNO: Selva Thompson, R.N., Chief Nurse Executive
Web address: www.ihs.gov/navajo/index.cfm?module=nao_hcc_gallup
**Control:** PHS, Indian Service, Government, federal **Service:** General Medical and Surgical

**Staffed Beds:** 84 **Admissions:** 3872 **Census:** 39

✠ **REHOBOTH MCKINLEY CHRISTIAN HEALTH CARE SERVICES (320038)**, 1901 Red Rock Drive, Zip 87301–5683; tel. 505/863–7000 **A**1 5 9 10 20 **F**3 11 13 15 28 29 30 32 34 35 40 45 50 57 59 62 63 64 65 68 70 75 76 77 79 81 84 85 86 87 89 93 104 107 108 110 111 115 119 129 130 132 133 135 **P**6
Primary Contact: David Conejo, Chief Executive Officer
COO: William Kiefer, Chief Operating Officer
CFO: John McMullin, Chief Financial Officer
CMO: Samuel MacBride, M.D., Chief Medical Officer
CIO: David Odom, Chief Information Officer
CHR: Susan Macias, Chief Human Resources Officer
CNO: William Kiefer, Chief Nursing Officer
Web address: www.rmch.org
**Control:** Other not–for–profit (including NFP Corporation) **Service:** General Medical and Surgical

**Staffed Beds:** 60 **Admissions:** 2010 **Census:** 17 **Outpatient Visits:** 103517 **Births:** 382 **Total Expense ($000):** 51430 **Payroll Expense ($000):** 21933 **Personnel:** 450

## GRANTS—Cibola County

✠ **CIBOLA GENERAL HOSPITAL (321308)**, 1016 East Roosevelt Avenue, Zip 87020–2118; tel. 505/287–4446 **A**1 9 10 18 **F**3 13 15 29 30 34 40 45 46 50 56 57 59 64 65 66 68 70 75 76 77 81 85 93 97 107 110 115 119 129 130 133 135 147 148 **S** QHR, Brentwood, TN
Primary Contact: Bob Phillips, Interim Chief Executive Officer
CFO: Jeff Rimel, Chief Financial Officer
CMO: Janice Shipley, M.D., Chief Medical Officer
CIO: Rick Smith, Director Information Services
CHR: Sheila Cox, Director Human Resources
CNO: Glenna Losito, R.N., Chief Nursing Officer
Web address: www.cibolahospital.com
**Control:** Other not–for–profit (including NFP Corporation) **Service:** General Medical and Surgical

**Staffed Beds:** 25 **Admissions:** 913 **Census:** 8 **Outpatient Visits:** 14500 **Births:** 230 **Total Expense ($000):** 24660 **Payroll Expense ($000):** 11071

## HOBBS—Lea County

✠ **LEA REGIONAL MEDICAL CENTER (320065)**, 5419 North Lovington Highway, Zip 88240–9125, Mailing Address: P.O. Box 3000, Zip 88241–9501; tel. 575/492–5000, (Nonreporting) **A**1 9 10 **S** Community Health Systems, Inc., Franklin, TN
Primary Contact: Timothy Thornell, FACHE, Chief Executive Officer
CFO: Jorge Latibeaudiere, Chief Financial Officer
CMO: Jesus Fonseca, M.D., Chief of Staff
CIO: Terry Purcell, Director Information Services
CHR: Lisa D. Thompson, Director Human Resources
CNO: Patrick A. Dunn, R.N., Chief Nursing Officer
Web address: www.learegionalmedical.com
**Control:** Corporation, Investor–owned, for–profit **Service:** General Medical and Surgical

**Staffed Beds:** 214

## LAS CRUCES—Dona Ana County

☐ **ADVANCED CARE HOSPITAL OF SOUTHERN NEW MEXICO (322004)**, 4451 East Lohman Avenue, Zip 88011–8267; tel. 575/521–6600, (Nonreporting) **A**1 9 10 **S** Ernest Health, Inc., Albuquerque, NM
Primary Contact: Claudia Saiz, Chief Operating Officer
Web address: www.achsnm.ernesthealth.com
**Control:** Corporation, Investor–owned, for–profit **Service:** Long–Term Acute Care hospital

**Staffed Beds:** 40

**NM**

*Many Facility Codes have changed. Please refer to the AHA Guide Code Chart.*

✠ **MEMORIAL MEDICAL CENTER (320018)**, 2450 South Telshor Boulevard, Zip 88011–5076; tel. 575/522–8641 **A**1 2 3 9 10 13 **F**3 8 11 13 15 17 18 20 22 24 26 28 29 30 31 35 39 40 44 45 49 50 51 54 57 59 60 61 62 64 65 68 70 72 74 75 76 78 79 81 85 89 93 97 98 102 103 107 108 111 114 115 118 119 121 122 123 124 130 132 135 147 148 **S** LifePoint Health, Brentwood, TN
Primary Contact: John Harris, Chief Executive Officer
COO: Steven T. Ruwoldt, Chief Operating Officer
CFO: Raymond Grenier, Chief Financial Officer
CMO: Bruce San Filippo, M.D., Chief Medical Officer
CHR: Laura Pierce, Director Human Resources
CNO: Ann Debooy, R.N., Chief Nursing Officer
Web address: www.mmclc.org
**Control:** Corporation, Investor–owned, for–profit **Service:** General Medical and Surgical

| | |
|---|---|
| **Staffed Beds:** 224 **Admissions:** 10395 **Census:** 114 **Outpatient Visits:** 164057 **Births:** 1065 | |

✠ **MESILLA VALLEY HOSPITAL (324010)**, 3751 Del Rey Boulevard, Zip 88012–8526; tel. 575/382–3500 **A**1 9 10 **F**87 98 99 100 101 103 106 **S** Universal Health Services, Inc., King of Prussia, PA
Primary Contact: Robert Mansfield, Chief Executive Officer
CFO: Dana McRimmon, Chief Financial Officer
CMO: Ernest Flores, M.D., Chief of Staff and Medical Director
CIO: Rebecca Mumpower, Director Marketing
CHR: Linda Moya, Director Human Resources
CNO: Veronica Hughes, Chief Nursing Officer
Web address: www.mesillavalleyhospital.com
**Control:** Corporation, Investor–owned, for–profit **Service:** Psychiatric

| | |
|---|---|
| **Staffed Beds:** 120 **Admissions:** 2341 **Census:** 84 **Outpatient Visits:** 0 **Births:** 0 **Total Expense ($000):** 18209 **Payroll Expense ($000):** 7434 **Personnel:** 208 | |

✠ **MOUNTAINVIEW REGIONAL MEDICAL CENTER (320085)**, 4311 East Lohman Avenue, Zip 88011–8255; tel. 575/556–7600, (Nonreporting) **A**1 9 10 **S** Community Health Systems, Inc., Franklin, TN
Primary Contact: Denten Park, Chief Executive Officer
CFO: Nathan Crabdree, Chief Financial Officer
CIO: Donald Harlow, Director of Information Services
CHR: Timothy C. Egan, Director, Human Resources
CNO: Gayle Nash, R.N., Chief Nursing Officer
Web address: www.mountainviewregional.com
**Control:** Corporation, Investor–owned, for–profit **Service:** General Medical and Surgical

| | |
|---|---|
| **Staffed Beds:** 142 | |

✠ **REHABILITATION HOSPITAL OF SOUTHERN NEW MEXICO (323032)**, 4441 East Lohman Avenue, Zip 88011–8267; tel. 575/521–6400, (Nonreporting) **A**1 9 10 **S** Ernest Health, Inc., Albuquerque, NM
Primary Contact: Sabrina Martin, Chief Executive Officer
COO: Sabrina Martin, Chief Operating Officer
CFO: Elizabeth Striplin, Chief Financial Officer
CMO: Kimberly Encapera, M.D., Medical Director
CIO: Ricky Molina, Director Marketing and Business Development
CHR: Yolanda Mendoza, Director Human Resources
CNO: Carole Carson, Director of Nursing Operations
Web address: www.rhsnm.ernesthealth.com
**Control:** Corporation, Investor–owned, for–profit **Service:** Rehabilitation

| | |
|---|---|
| **Staffed Beds:** 40 | |

### LAS VEGAS—San Miguel County

✠ **ALTA VISTA REGIONAL HOSPITAL (320003)**, 104 Legion Drive, Zip 87701–4804; tel. 505/426–3500, (Nonreporting) **A**1 9 10 20 **S** Community Health Systems, Inc., Franklin, TN
Primary Contact: R. Chris Wolf, Chief Executive Officer
CMO: Nancy Wright, M.D., Chief Medical Staff
CIO: Laird Thornton, Director Information Systems
CHR: Michael Freeman, Director Human Resources
CNO: Rhonda Clark, Interim Chief Nursing Officer
Web address: www.altavistaregionalhospital.com
**Control:** Corporation, Investor–owned, for–profit **Service:** General Medical and Surgical

| | |
|---|---|
| **Staffed Beds:** 54 | |

☐ **NEW MEXICO BEHAVIORAL HEALTH INSTITUTE AT LAS VEGAS**, 3695 Hot Springs Boulevard, Zip 87701–9549; tel. 505/454–2100, (Nonreporting) **A**1 9
Primary Contact: Steve Martinez, Executive Director and Administrator
CFO: Albino Martinez, Director Finance and Budget
Web address: www.health.state.nm.us
**Control:** State–Government, nonfederal **Service:** Psychiatric

| | |
|---|---|
| **Staffed Beds:** 257 | |

### LOS ALAMOS—Los Alamos County

✠ **LOS ALAMOS MEDICAL CENTER (320033)**, 3917 West Road, Zip 87544–2293; tel. 505/661–9500 **A**1 9 10 20 **F**3 8 11 13 15 28 29 30 31 34 35 40 41 45 50 52 55 57 59 64 65 68 70 73 75 76 78 81 82 85 87 89 90 92 93 107 108 110 111 114 115 116 117 118 119 124 130 146 147 148 **P**8 **S** LifePoint Health, Brentwood, TN
Primary Contact: Feliciano Jiron, Chief Executive Officer
CFO: Steve Weingart, Chief Financial Officer
CMO: Barbara Van Eeckhout, M.D., Chief of Staff
CIO: Kevin Vigil, Director Information Systems
CHR: Jacqueline Carroll, Director Human Resources
CNO: Tracie Stratton, Chief Nursing Officer
Web address: www.losalamosmedicalcenter.com
**Control:** Corporation, Investor–owned, for–profit **Service:** General Medical and Surgical

| | |
|---|---|
| **Staffed Beds:** 29 **Admissions:** 1222 **Census:** 7 **Outpatient Visits:** 62216 **Births:** 244 **Total Expense ($000):** 38521 **Payroll Expense ($000):** 13905 **Personnel:** 262 | |

### LOVINGTON—Lea County

★ ◇ **NOR–LEA GENERAL HOSPITAL (321305)**, 1600 North Main Avenue, Zip 88260–2871; tel. 575/396–6611 **A**9 10 18 21 **F**3 9 15 18 26 28 29 30 31 32 34 35 39 40 43 45 46 49 50 51 54 57 59 64 65 66 68 74 75 78 81 89 92 93 97 100 101 102 103 104 107 108 110 111 115 119 127 129 130 132 133 135 147 148 **P**6
Primary Contact: David B. Shaw, Chief Executive Officer and Administrator
COO: Dan Hamilton, Director Inpatient Services
CFO: Allyson Roberts, CPA, Chief Financial Officer
CMO: Ronald Hopkins, D.O., Chief of Staff
CIO: Brent Kelley, Director Information Technology
CHR: David Camp, Director Human Resources
CNO: Cyndie Cribbs, Director of Nursing
Web address: www.norlea.org/
**Control:** Hospital district or authority, Government, nonfederal **Service:** General Medical and Surgical

| | |
|---|---|
| **Staffed Beds:** 25 **Admissions:** 585 **Census:** 4 **Outpatient Visits:** 174967 **Births:** 0 **Total Expense ($000):** 50765 **Payroll Expense ($000):** 20109 **Personnel:** 340 | |

### MESCALERO—Otero County

☐ **MESCALERO PUBLIC HEALTH SERVICE INDIAN HOSPITAL (320058)**, 318 Abalone Loop, Zip 88340, Mailing Address: Box 210, Zip 88340–0210; tel. 505/671–4441, (Nonreporting) **A**1 9 10 **S** U. S. Indian Health Service, Rockville, MD
Primary Contact: Dorlynn Simmons, Chief Executive Officer
CFO: Rainey Enjady, Administrative Officer
CIO: Kathy Murphy, Site Manager
Web address: www.ihs.gov
**Control:** Public Health Service, Government, federal **Service:** General Medical and Surgical

| | |
|---|---|
| **Staffed Beds:** 13 | |

### PORTALES—Roosevelt County

◇ **ROOSEVELT GENERAL HOSPITAL (320084)**, 42121 U.S. Highway 70, Zip 88130, Mailing Address: P.O. Box 868, Zip 88130–0868; tel. 575/359–1800, (Nonreporting) **A**9 10 21
Primary Contact: Larry E. Leaming, Ph.D., FACHE, Chief Executive Officer
CFO: Eva Steven, Chief Financial Officer
CMO: Les Donaldson, M.D., Chief of Staff
CHR: Cindy Duncan, Director Human Resources
Web address: www.myrgh.org
**Control:** Hospital district or authority, Government, nonfederal **Service:** General Medical and Surgical

| | |
|---|---|
| **Staffed Beds:** 22 | |

### RATON—Colfax County

★ **MINERS' COLFAX MEDICAL CENTER (321307)**, 200 Hospital Drive, Zip 87740–2099; tel. 575/445–7700, (Includes MINERS' HOSPITAL OF NEW MEXICO, Hospital Drive, Zip 87740, Mailing Address: Box 1067, Zip 87740; tel. 505/445–2741), (Nonreporting) **A**9 10 18
Primary Contact: Shawn Lerch, Chief Executive Officer
CFO: Albino Martinez, Director Budget and Finance
CIO: Richard Laner, Jr., Manager Information Systems
CHR: Jamie Johnson, Director Human Resources
Web address: www.minershosp.com
**Control:** County–Government, nonfederal **Service:** General Medical and Surgical

| | |
|---|---|
| **Staffed Beds:** 33 | |

**NM**

| | | |
|---|---|---|
| **Hospital, Medicare Provider Number, Address, Telephone, Approval, Facility, and Physician Codes, Health Care System** | | |
| ★ American Hospital Association (AHA) membership | ○ Healthcare Facilities Accreditation Program | ⇑ Center for Improvement in Healthcare Quality Accreditation |
| ☐ The Joint Commission accreditation | ◇ DNV Healthcare Inc. accreditation | △ Commission on Accreditation of Rehabilitation Facilities (CARF) accreditation |

**RIO RANCHO—Sandoval County**

◇ **UNM SANDOVAL REGIONAL MEDICAL CENTER (320089)**, 3001 Broadmoor Boulevard N.E., Zip 87144–2100; tel. 505/994–7000 **A**3 5 9 10 21 **F**3 7 15 29 30 35 40 43 45 46 47 48 49 50 70 79 80 81 85 86 87 93 97 98 103 107 108 110 111 114 115 119 126 129 130 143 146 147 **P**8 **S** University of New Mexico Hospitals, Albuquerque, NM
Primary Contact: Jamie A. Silva–Steele, R.N., President and Chief Executive Officer
CFO: Darlene Fernandez, Chief Financial Officer
CMO: J. Anthony Ogburn, M.D., Chief Medical Officer
CIO: Matthew Braun, Executive Director Information Systems
CHR: Correen Bales, Executive Director Human Resources
CNO: Pamela Demarest, R.N., Chief Nursing Officer
Web address: www.hospitals.unm.edu/
**Control:** Other not–for–profit (including NFP Corporation) **Service:** General Medical and Surgical

**Staffed Beds:** 72 **Admissions:** 2733 **Census:** 33 **Outpatient Visits:** 44168 **Births:** 0 **Total Expense ($000):** 67054 **Payroll Expense ($000):** 21767 **Personnel:** 408

**ROSWELL—Chaves County**

✖ **EASTERN NEW MEXICO MEDICAL CENTER (320006)**, 405 West Country Club Road, Zip 88201–5209; tel. 575/622–8170, (Nonreporting) **A**1 3 9 10 19 **S** Community Health Systems, Inc., Franklin, TN
Primary Contact: Maridel Acosta–Cruz, Chief Executive Officer
COO: Warren Yehl, Chief Operating Officer
CFO: Leanne Hacker, Chief Financial Officer
CMO: Richard Pinon, Chief Medical Officer
CIO: Deepak Surl, Chief Information Officer
CHR: Sheila Nunez, Director Human Resources
CNO: Kathy Williams, Chief Nursing Officer
Web address: www.enmmc.com
**Control:** Corporation, Investor–owned, for–profit **Service:** General Medical and Surgical

**Staffed Beds:** 149

★ **LOVELACE REGIONAL HOSPITAL – ROSWELL (320086)**, 117 East 19th Street, Zip 88201–5151; tel. 575/627–7000 **A**9 10 **F**3 13 18 29 34 40 42 45 57 59 70 79 81 82 85 91 93 107 111 119 130 146 147 **P**6 7 **S** Ardent Health Services, Nashville, TN
Primary Contact: Dawn M. Tschabrun, R.N., Chief Executive Officer
CNO: Kristin Trotter, Chief Nursing Officer
Web address: www.lovelace.com
**Control:** Corporation, Investor–owned, for–profit **Service:** General Medical and Surgical

**Staffed Beds:** 26 **Admissions:** 2087 **Census:** 15 **Outpatient Visits:** 50657 **Births:** 929 **Total Expense ($000):** 33854 **Payroll Expense ($000):** 10505 **Personnel:** 189

☐ **NEW MEXICO REHABILITATION CENTER (323026)**, 72 Gail Harris Street, Zip 88203–8116; tel. 575/347–3400, (Includes PECOS VALLEY LODGE, 31 Gail Harris Avenue, Zip 88201; tel. 505/347–5491), (Nonreporting) **A**1 10
Primary Contact: Bradley McGrath, Administrator
CFO: Janie Davies, Chief Financial Officer
CMO: Stephen Dorman, M.D., Chief Medical Officer
CIO: Dennis Hoefs, Manager Information Technology
CHR: Teresa Casarez, Director Human Resources
**Control:** State–Government, nonfederal **Service:** Rehabilitation

**Staffed Beds:** 41

**RUIDOSO—Lincoln County**

✖ **LINCOLN COUNTY MEDICAL CENTER (321306)**, 211 Sudderth Drive, Zip 88345–6043, Mailing Address: P.O. Box 8000, Zip 88355–8000; tel. 575/257–8200 **A**1 9 10 18 **F**7 11 13 15 29 30 35 39 40 45 46 53 56 57 59 64 68 70 76 77 78 81 85 87 91 93 103 107 110 111 115 119 132 135 144 146 148 **P**6 **S** Presbyterian Healthcare Services, Albuquerque, NM
Primary Contact: Alfred Santos, Administrator
CFO: Dudley McCauley, Controller
CMO: Gary Jackson, D.O., Medical Director
CHR: Susanne Johnston, Manager Human Resources
Web address: www.phs.org
**Control:** Other not–for–profit (including NFP Corporation) **Service:** General Medical and Surgical

**Staffed Beds:** 25 **Admissions:** 1446 **Census:** 11 **Outpatient Visits:** 73733 **Births:** 336 **Total Expense ($000):** 37107 **Payroll Expense ($000):** 16598 **Personnel:** 229

**SANTA FE—Santa Fe County**

✖ △ **CHRISTUS ST. VINCENT REGIONAL MEDICAL CENTER (320002)**, 455 St. Michael's Drive, Zip 87505–7663, Mailing Address: P.O. Box 2107, Zip 87504–2107; tel. 505/983–3361, (Includes CHRISTUS ST. VINCENT PHYSICIANS MEDICAL CENTER, 2990 Rodeo Park Drive East, Zip 87505; tel. 505/428–5400; J. Alex Valdez, JD, President and Chief Executive Officer) **A**1 2 3 7 9 10 20 **F**3 8 12 13 15 17 18 19 20 21 22 24 26 28 29 30 31 32 34 35 36 37 38 39 40 41 43 45 46 47 48 49 50 51 53 54 56 57 64 65 66 68 70 73 74 75 76 77 78 79 81 82 83 84 85 86 87 88 89 90 91 92 93 97 98 100 101 102 103 104 107 108 109 110 111 112 113 114 115 116 117 118 119 120 121 122 124 126 129 130 131 132 135 143 144 146 147 148 **S** CHRISTUS Health, Irving, TX
Primary Contact: Bruce J. Tassin, President and Chief Executive Officer
COO: Jason Adams, Chief Operating Officer
CFO: Bob Moon, Chief Financial Officer
CMO: John C. Beeson, M.D., Chief Medical Officer
CIO: Ron Dekeyzer, Regional Director Information Systems
CHR: Pearl Mohnkern, Vice President and Director Human Resources
Web address: www.stvin.org
**Control:** Other not–for–profit (including NFP Corporation) **Service:** General Medical and Surgical

**Staffed Beds:** 268 **Admissions:** 12240 **Census:** 140 **Births:** 1062

☐ **PHS SANTA FE INDIAN HOSPITAL (320057)**, 1700 Cerrillos Road, Zip 87505–3554; tel. 505/988–9821, (Nonreporting) **A**1 5 9 10 **S** U. S. Indian Health Service, Rockville, MD
Primary Contact: Robert J. Lyon, Chief Executive Officer
CMO: Bret Smoker, M.D., Clinical Director
CIO: Vernita Jones, Site Manager
**Control:** Public Health Service, Government, federal **Service:** General Medical and Surgical

**Staffed Beds:** 39

**SANTA ROSA—Guadalupe County**

★ **GUADALUPE COUNTY HOSPITAL (320067)**, 117 Camino de Vida, Zip 88435–2267; tel. 575/472–3417 **A**9 10 20 **F**3 29 34 35 40 50 57 59 64 65 81 82 87 107 114 119 130 132 148 **P**5
Primary Contact: Christina Campos, Administrator
CFO: Bret Goebel, Finance Officer
CMO: Randal Brown, M.D., Chief of Staff
CIO: Emilio Campos, Manager Information Technology
CHR: Colleen Gallegos, Director Human Resources
CNO: Mandelyn Cordova, R.N., Director of Nurses
Web address: www.gchnm.org
**Control:** County–Government, nonfederal **Service:** General Medical and Surgical

**Staffed Beds:** 10 **Admissions:** 204 **Census:** 2 **Outpatient Visits:** 6033 **Births:** 2 **Total Expense ($000):** 7580 **Payroll Expense ($000):** 1662 **Personnel:** 41

**SANTA TERESA—Dona Ana County**

☐ **PEAK BEHAVIORAL HEALTH SERVICES (324012)**, 5065 McNutt Road, Zip 88008–9442; tel. 575/589–3000, (Nonreporting) **A**1 9 10 **S** Strategic Behavioral Health, LLC, Memphis, TN
Primary Contact: Lyle Reese–Gardner, Interim Chief Executive Officer
COO: Doug Ginn, Executive Vice President Operations
CFO: Espie Herrara, Chief Financial Officer
CHR: Norma Oaxaca, Director Human Resources
Web address: www.peakbehavioral.com/
**Control:** Corporation, Investor–owned, for–profit **Service:** Psychiatric

**Staffed Beds:** 36

**SHIPROCK—San Juan County**

✖ **NORTHERN NAVAJO MEDICAL CENTER (320059)**, Highway 491 North, Zip 87420–0160, Mailing Address: P.O. Box 160, Zip 87420–0160; tel. 505/368–6001, (Nonreporting) **A**1 5 10 **S** U. S. Indian Health Service, Rockville, MD
Primary Contact: Fannessa Comer, Chief Executive Officer
CFO: Shawn Morgan, Acting Finance Officer
CMO: George C. Baacke, II, M.D., Acting Clinical Director
CIO: Roland Chapman, Chief Information Officer
CHR: Gloria Redhorse–Charley, Director Human Resources
CNO: Lavenia Diswood, R.N., Chief Nurse Executive
Web address: www.ihs.gov/
**Control:** Public Health Service, Government, federal **Service:** General Medical and Surgical

**Staffed Beds:** 62

*Many Facility Codes have changed. Please refer to the AHA Guide Code Chart.* © 2015 AHA Guide

## SILVER CITY—Grant County

✠ **GILA REGIONAL MEDICAL CENTER (320016)**, 1313 East 32nd Street,
Zip 88061–7251; tel. 575/538–4000 **A**1 3 9 10 20 **F**3 7 11 13 15 30 31 35
37 40 41 45 50 51 53 57 59 62 63 64 70 73 75 76 78 79 81 85 87 89 93
98 102 103 107 108 111 115 119 120 121 123 129 130 132 148 **P**5
Primary Contact: Brian Cunningham, Interim Chief Executive Officer
CFO: Craig Stewart, Chief Financial Officer
CIO: David Furnas, Chief Information Officer
CHR: Barbara Barela, Director Human Resources
CNO: Patricia Sheyka, Chief Nursing Officer
Web address: www.grmc.org
**Control:** County–Government, nonfederal **Service:** General Medical and Surgical

**Staffed Beds:** 68 **Admissions:** 3182 **Census:** 27 **Births:** 380

## SOCORRO—Socorro County

✠ **SOCORRO GENERAL HOSPITAL (321301)**, 1202 Highway 60 West,
Zip 87801–3914, Mailing Address: P.O. Box 1009, Zip 87801–1009;
tel. 505/835–1140 **A**1 9 10 18 **F**3 8 11 13 15 29 30 34 35 40 45 57 59 62
63 64 68 75 77 81 83 85 91 93 100 103 107 114 130 132 133 134 135
147 **P**6 **S** Presbyterian Healthcare Services, Albuquerque, NM
Primary Contact: Veronica Pound, R.N., Administrator
CFO: Scott Shannon, Director Finance
CMO: Darla Bejnar, M.D., Chief Medical Officer
CHR: Pam Miller–Balfour, Director Human Resources
CNO: Veronica Pound, R.N., Interim Administrator and Director of Patient Care
Web address: www.phs.org
**Control:** Other not–for–profit (including NFP Corporation) **Service:** General Medical and Surgical

**Staffed Beds:** 14 **Admissions:** 625 **Census:** 5 **Births:** 169 **Total Expense ($000):** 25800 **Payroll Expense ($000):** 12792 **Personnel:** 172

## TAOS—Taos County

★ ◇ **HOLY CROSS HOSPITAL (320013)**, 1397 Weimer Road,
Zip 87571–6253; tel. 575/758–8883 **A**3 9 10 20 21 **F**11 13 15 18 29 30 34
35 36 40 43 45 46 50 59 64 68 70 75 79 81 82 86 87 89 93 107 110 114
115 118 119 127 130 132 145 146 147 148 **P**8 **S** QHR, Brentwood, TN
Primary Contact: William D. Patten, Jr., Chief Executive Officer
CFO: Steve Rozenboom, Chief Financial Officer
CHR: Brian Chew, Human Resources Officer
CNO: Mary Anna Abeyta, R.N., Chief Nursing/Clinical Services Officer
Web address: www.taoshospital.org
**Control:** Other not–for–profit (including NFP Corporation) **Service:** General Medical and Surgical

**Staffed Beds:** 29 **Admissions:** 1706 **Census:** 16 **Outpatient Visits:** 70010
**Births:** 247 **Total Expense ($000):** 49519 **Payroll Expense ($000):** 20934
**Personnel:** 339

## TRUTH OR CONSEQUENCES—Sierra County

★ **SIERRA VISTA HOSPITAL (321300)**, 800 East Ninth Avenue, Zip 87901–1961;
tel. 575/894–2111 **A**9 10 18 **F**7 11 15 16 30 34 40 54 57 59 65 67 93 99
102 104 107 110 127 128 130 133 **P**6
Primary Contact: Michael P. Zimmerman, Chief Executive Officer
CFO: Bret Gobel, Chief Financial Officer
CMO: James F. Malcolmson, M.D., Chief of Staff
CIO: Dan Morrell, Manager Information Systems
CHR: Mindee Holguin, Manager Human Resources
CNO: Palmer Greene, R.N., Chief Nursing Officer
Web address: www.svhnm.org
**Control:** City–County, Government, nonfederal **Service:** General Medical and Surgical

**Staffed Beds:** 15 **Admissions:** 554 **Census:** 4

## TUCUMCARI—Quay County

★ **DR. DAN C. TRIGG MEMORIAL HOSPITAL (321302)**, 301 East Miel De Luna
Avenue, Zip 88401–3810, Mailing Address: P.O. Box 608, Zip 88401–0608;
tel. 575/461–7000 **A**9 10 18 **F**3 11 15 29 35 38 40 45 59 62 63 64 65 68
81 85 87 97 104 107 110 114 119 127 130 133 135 146 148 **P**6
**S** Presbyterian Healthcare Services, Albuquerque, NM
Primary Contact: Lance C. Labine, Administrator
CMO: Darrell Willis, M.D., Chief of Staff
CNO: Vickie Gutierrez, Director of Patient Care
Web address: www.phs.org
**Control:** Other not–for–profit (including NFP Corporation) **Service:** General Medical and Surgical

**Staffed Beds:** 10 **Admissions:** 328 **Census:** 3 **Outpatient Visits:** 29583
**Births:** 0 **Total Expense ($000):** 14368 **Payroll Expense ($000):** 5330
**Personnel:** 85

## ZUNI—McKinley County

☐ **U. S. PUBLIC HEALTH SERVICE INDIAN HOSPITAL (320060)**, Route 301
North B. Street, Zip 87327, Mailing Address: P.O. Box 467, Zip 87327–0467;
tel. 505/782–4431, (Nonreporting) **A**1 9 10 **S** U. S. Indian Health Service,
Rockville, MD
Primary Contact: Jean Othole, Chief Executive Officer
CFO: Clyde Yatsattie, Administrative Officer
CMO: David Kessler, M.D., Clinical Director
CHR: Cynthia Tsalate, Human Resource Specialist
Web address: www.ihs.gov
**Control:** PHS, Indian Service, Government, federal **Service:** General Medical and Surgical

**Staffed Beds:** 32

**NM**

# NEW YORK

## ALBANY—Albany County

⊞ **ALBANY MEDICAL CENTER (330013)**, 43 New Scotland Avenue,
Zip 12208–3478; tel. 518/262–3125, (Includes ALBANY MEDICAL CENTER
SOUTH–CLINICAL CAMPUS, 25 Hackett Boulevard, Zip 12208–3499;
tel. 518/242–1200; Timothy W. Duffy, General Director) **A**1 2 3 5 8 9 10 19 **F**3
6 7 8 11 12 13 15 17 18 19 20 21 22 23 24 25 26 27 28 29 30 31 32 34
35 36 38 39 40 41 43 44 45 46 47 49 50 51 52 53 54 55 56 57 58 59 60
61 64 65 68 70 72 73 74 75 76 77 78 79 81 82 85 86 87 88 89 90 92 93
96 98 100 102 103 104 105 107 108 109 110 111 114 115 116 117 118
119 120 121 123 124 126 130 131 132 135 138 142 145 146 148
Primary Contact: James J. Barba, President and Chief Executive Officer
COO: Bernadette R. Pedlow, Senior Vice President Business and Chief Operating
Officer
CFO: William C. Hasselbarth, Chief Financial Officer
CMO: Dennis McKenna, M.D., Interim Vice President Medical Affairs
CIO: George Hickman, Executive Vice President and Chief Information Officer
CHR: Catherine Halakan, Senior Vice President
Web address: www.amc.edu
**Control:** Other not–for–profit (including NFP Corporation) **Service:** General
Medical and Surgical

**Staffed Beds: 704 Admissions: 33514 Census: 573 Outpatient Visits:**
351330 **Births: 2099 Total Expense ($000): 797680 Payroll Expense**
**($000): 258518 Personnel: 5601**

★ **ALBANY MEMORIAL HOSPITAL (330003)**, 600 Northern Boulevard,
Zip 12204–1083; tel. 518/471–3221 **A**5 9 10 **F**8 15 29 30 31 40 45 46 49
50 57 59 60 63 68 70 77 81 84 85 87 93 107 111 119 130 146 147 148
**S** Trinity Health, Livonia, MI
Primary Contact: Ann Errichetti, M.D., Chief Executive Officer
CFO: Lori Santos, Vice President Finance
CMO: Robert Cella, M.D., Chief Medical Officer
CIO: Jonathan Goldberg, Chief Information Officer
CHR: Judy Gray, Vice President Human Resources
Web address: www.nehealth.com
**Control:** Other not–for–profit (including NFP Corporation) **Service:** General
Medical and Surgical

**Staffed Beds: 74 Admissions: 3206 Census: 49 Births: 0 Total Expense**
**($000): 86982 Payroll Expense ($000): 37033 Personnel: 674**

⊞ **ALBANY STRATTON VETERANS AFFAIRS MEDICAL CENTER**, 113 Holland
Avenue, Zip 12208–3473; tel. 518/626–5000, (Total facility includes 50 beds in
nursing home–type unit) **A**1 2 3 5 8 9 **F**2 3 4 5 12 15 17 18 20 22 28 29 30
31 34 35 39 40 45 46 47 49 50 54 55 56 57 58 59 60 61 62 63 64 65 68
70 74 75 77 78 79 81 82 83 84 85 86 87 91 92 93 94 97 98 100 102 103
104 105 106 107 108 109 110 111 115 116 117 118 119 120 121 122 126
127 128 129 130 132 135 143 146 147 148 **S** Department of Veterans Affairs,
Washington, DC
Primary Contact: Linda W. Weiss, MS, FACHE, Director
CFO: Gerard Scorzelli, Chief Financial Officer
CMO: Lourdes Irizarry, M.D., Chief of Staff
CIO: Ron Diaz, Manager Operations
CHR: Kenneth Kio, Manager Human Resources
CNO: Deborah Spath, R.N., Associate Director Patient and Nurses Services
Web address: www.albany.va.gov/
**Control:** Veterans Affairs, Government, federal **Service:** General Medical and
Surgical

**Staffed Beds: 149 Admissions: 2991 Census: 91 Outpatient Visits:** 340645
**Births: 0 Total Expense ($000): 236451 Payroll Expense ($000): 138899**
**Personnel: 1361**

☐ **CAPITAL DISTRICT PSYCHIATRIC CENTER (334046)**, 75 New Scotland
Avenue, Zip 12208–3474; tel. 518/447–9611, (Nonreporting) **A**1 3 5 10 **S** New
York State Office of Mental Health, Albany, NY
Primary Contact: William Dickson, Acting Executive Director
CMO: Beatrice Kovasznay, M.D., Clinical Director
Web address: www.omh.ny.gov/omhweb/facilities/cdpc/facility.htm
**Control:** State–Government, nonfederal **Service:** Psychiatric

**Staffed Beds: 200**

⊞ **ST. PETER'S HOSPITAL (330057)**, 315 South Manning Boulevard,
Zip 12208–1789; tel. 518/525–1550 **A**1 2 3 5 9 10 19 **F**4 5 8 11 12 13 15
17 18 19 20 21 22 23 24 26 27 28 29 30 31 34 35 36 37 38 39 40 45 46
47 48 49 50 51 53 54 56 57 59 60 61 62 63 64 65 66 68 69 70 71 72 73
74 75 77 78 79 81 82 84 85 86 87 92 93 97 107 108 109 110 111 114 115
116 117 118 119 120 121 123 124 126 129 130 132 133 135 143 145 146
147 148 **P**6 **S** Trinity Health, Livonia, MI
Primary Contact: Ann Errichetti, M.D., Chief Executive Officer
CFO: Lori Santos, Chief Financial Officer
CMO: Robert Cella, M.D., Chief Medical Officer
CIO: Jonathan Goldberg, Chief Information Officer
CHR: Judy Gray, Vice President Human Resources
CNO: Jane O'Rourke, R.N., Chief Nursing Officer, Vice President Operations
Web address: www.sphcs.org
**Control:** Church–operated, Nongovernment, not–for profit **Service:** General
Medical and Surgical

**Staffed Beds: 442 Admissions: 26771 Census: 362**

## ALEXANDRIA BAY—Jefferson County

★ **RIVER HOSPITAL (331309)**, 4 Fuller Street, Zip 13607–1316;
tel. 315/482–2511 **A**9 10 18 **F**3 11 15 18 29 34 35 40 45 50 57 59 64 68
81 84 87 93 97 104 105 107 114 119 130 133 135 147
Primary Contact: Ben Moore, III, President and Chief Executive Officer
COO: William Connor, Assistant Administrator and Director Human Resources
CFO: Traci Mintonye, Chief Financial Officer
CMO: Prasad Yitta, M.D., Medical Director
CIO: John Smithers, Network Specialist
CHR: William Connor, Assistant Administrator and Director Human Resources
CNO: Ann Narrow, Director of Nursing
Web address: www.riverhospital.org
**Control:** Other not–for–profit (including NFP Corporation) **Service:** General
Medical and Surgical

**Staffed Beds: 11 Admissions: 125 Census: 5 Outpatient Visits: 52939**
**Births: 0 Total Expense ($000): 18786 Payroll Expense ($000): 10333**
**Personnel: 169**

## AMITYVILLE—Suffolk County

☐ **BRUNSWICK PSYCH CENTER (334026)**, 81 Louden Avenue,
Zip 11701–2736; tel. 631/789–7421, (Nonreporting) **A**1 10
Primary Contact: Amarjit Singh, President and Chief Executive Officer
**Control:** Corporation, Investor–owned, for–profit **Service:** Psychiatric

**Staffed Beds: 50**

☐ **SOUTH OAKS HOSPITAL (334027)**, 400 Sunrise Highway, Zip 11701–2508;
tel. 631/264–4000 **A**1 6 9 10 **F**4 5 50 53 68 98 99 100 **P**5 6 **S** North
Shore–Long Island Jewish Health System, Great Neck, NY
Primary Contact: Patricia Porter, Executive Director
CMO: Tina Walch, M.D., Medical Director
CHR: Pam Duffy, Vice President Human Resources
Web address: www.longislandhome.org
**Control:** Other not–for–profit (including NFP Corporation) **Service:** Psychiatric

**Staffed Beds: 260 Admissions: 5099 Census: 132 Outpatient Visits: 88987**
**Births: 0 Total Expense ($000): 56295 Payroll Expense ($000): 33700**
**Personnel: 631**

## AMSTERDAM—Montgomery County

**ST. MARY'S HEALTHCARE** See St. Mary's Healthcare

⊞ **ST. MARY'S HEALTHCARE (330047)**, 427 Guy Park Avenue, Zip 12010–1054;
tel. 518/842–1900, (Includes ST. MARY'S HEALTHCARE, 427 Guy Park Avenue,
tel. 518/842–1900), (Total facility includes 160 beds in nursing home–type unit)
**A**1 9 10 **F**2 3 4 5 8 11 13 15 17 28 29 30 31 34 35 36 38 40 45 46 49 50
51 54 56 57 59 60 61 65 66 68 70 71 74 75 76 77 78 79 81 84 85 86 87
90 93 94 96 97 98 99 100 101 102 103 104 105 106 107 108 110 111 115
118 119 126 127 128 130 131 132 135 144 145 146 147 **S** Ascension
Health, Saint Louis, MO
Primary Contact: Victor Giulianelli, FACHE, President and Chief Executive Officer
COO: Scott Bruce, Vice President Operations
CFO: Rick Henze, Vice President, Finance
CMO: William Mayer, M.D., Vice President Medical Staff Services
CIO: James DeGroff, Vice President Technology and Network Services
CHR: Albert Turo, Vice President Human Resources
Web address: www.smha.org
**Control:** Other not–for–profit (including NFP Corporation) **Service:** General
Medical and Surgical

**Staffed Beds: 290 Admissions: 6393 Census: 254 Outpatient Visits:**
401469 **Births: 504 Total Expense ($000): 145599 Payroll Expense**
**($000): 76912 Personnel: 1373**

**NY**

*Many Facility Codes have changed. Please refer to the AHA Guide Code Chart.* © 2015 AHA Guide

## AUBURN—Cayuga County

✠ **AUBURN COMMUNITY HOSPITAL (330235)**, 17 Lansing Street,
Zip 13021–1943; tel. 315/255–7011, (Total facility includes 80 beds in nursing
home–type unit) **A**1 9 10 20 **F**1 3 12 13 15 26 28 29 30 31 34 35 40 45 49
50 51 53 54 55 57 59 64 70 76 78 79 81 82 85 89 98 103 107 108 110
111 114 119 124 129 130 132 135 144 146 147
Primary Contact: Scott A. Berlucchi, FACHE, President and Chief Executive Officer
COO: Thomas Filiak, Vice President Administration
CFO: Jason Lesch, Chief Financial Officer
CMO: John A. Riccio, M.D., Chief Medical Officer
CIO: Chris Ryan, Chief Information Officer
CNO: Tammy Sunderlin, Director of Nursing
Web address: www.auburnhospital.org
**Control:** Other not–for–profit (including NFP Corporation) **Service:** General
Medical and Surgical

**Staffed Beds:** 179 **Admissions:** 4546 **Census:** 136 **Outpatient Visits:**
144494 **Births:** 404 **Total Expense ($000):** 110780 **Payroll Expense**
**($000):** 51082 **Personnel:** 773

## BATAVIA—Genesee County

✠ **UNITED MEMORIAL MEDICAL CENTER (330073)**, 127 North Street,
Zip 14020–1631; tel. 585/343–6030, (Includes UNITED MEMORIAL MEDICAL
CENTER–BANK STREET, 127 North Street, Zip 14020–2260;
tel. 716/343–3131; UNITED MEMORIAL MEDICAL CENTER–NORTH STREET, 16
Banks Street, Zip 14020–1697; tel. 585/343–6030) **A**1 9 10 13 **F**3 4 8 13 15
17 18 28 29 30 31 34 35 40 43 49 50 54 57 59 64 65 68 70 75 76 77 78
79 81 82 84 85 86 87 89 93 97 107 111 114 115 119 127 129 130 131
132 135 144 146 147 148 **S** Rochester Regional Health, Rochester, NY
Primary Contact: Daniel P. Ireland, FACHE, President
CFO: Robert Chiavetta, Vice President Finance
CMO: Michael Merrill, M.D., Interim Vice President Medical Affairs
CIO: Kurt Calman, Chief Information Officer
CHR: Sonja Gonyea, Director Human Resources
CNO: Mary Beth Bowen, R.N., Vice President Nursing and Chief Nursing Officer
Web address: www.ummc.org
**Control:** Other not–for–profit (including NFP Corporation) **Service:** General
Medical and Surgical

**Staffed Beds:** 131 **Admissions:** 3780 **Census:** 54 **Outpatient Visits:** 219959
**Births:** 642 **Total Expense ($000):** 82231 **Payroll Expense ($000):** 34595
**Personnel:** 691

★ **VETERANS AFFAIRS WESTERN NEW YORK HEALTHCARE**
**SYSTEM–BATAVIA DIVISION**, 222 Richmond Avenue, Zip 14020–1288;
tel. 585/297–1000, (Nonreporting) **A**5 9 **S** Department of Veterans Affairs,
Washington, DC
Primary Contact: Brian G. Stiller, Director Medical Center
Web address: www.buffalo.va.gov/batavia.asp
**Control:** Veterans Affairs, Government, federal **Service:** General Medical and
Surgical

**Staffed Beds:** 128

## BATH—Steuben County

✠ **BATH VETERANS AFFAIRS MEDICAL CENTER**, 76 Veterans Avenue,
Zip 14810–0842; tel. 607/664–4000, (Nonreporting) **A**1 **S** Department of
Veterans Affairs, Washington, DC
Primary Contact: Michael J. Swartz, FACHE, Medical Center Director
COO: David Krueger, Associate Director
CFO: Jill Haynes, Financial Coach
CMO: Felipe Diaz, M.D., Chief of Staff
CIO: Karen Clancy, Manager Information Systems Operations
CHR: Susan DeSalvo, Manager Human Resources
Web address: www.bath.va.gov
**Control:** Veterans Affairs, Government, federal **Service:** General Medical and
Surgical

**Staffed Beds:** 371

◇ **IRA DAVENPORT MEMORIAL HOSPITAL (330144)**, 7571 State Route 54,
Zip 14810–9590; tel. 607/776–8500, (Nonreporting) **A**9 10 21 **S** Arnot Health,
Elmira, NY
Primary Contact: James B. Watson, President and Chief Operating Officer
COO: James B. Watson, President and Chief Operating Officer
CFO: Ronald J. Kintz, Chief Financial Officer
CMO: Dennis O'Connor, M.D., Medical Director
CIO: Gregg Martin, Chief Information Officer
CHR: Brian K. Forrest, Director Human Resources
CNO: Linda Donley, Vice President Operations
Web address: www.arnothealth.org
**Control:** Other not–for–profit (including NFP Corporation) **Service:** General
Medical and Surgical

**Staffed Beds:** 184

## BAY SHORE—Suffolk County

✠ △ **SOUTHSIDE HOSPITAL (330043)**, 301 East Main Street,
Zip 11706–8458; tel. 631/968–3000 **A**1 2 3 5 7 9 10 **F**3 11 13 15 17 18 20
22 24 26 28 29 30 31 32 34 35 36 38 40 41 43 44 45 46 49 50 54 55 56
57 58 59 60 61 62 63 64 65 66 68 70 73 74 75 76 77 78 79 81 82 84 85
86 87 89 90 93 96 97 98 100 101 102 103 107 108 110 111 114 115 118
119 120 121 123 126 129 130 131 132 135 146 147 148 **P**5 6 **S** North
Shore–Long Island Jewish Health System, Great Neck, NY
Primary Contact: Donna Moravick, R.N., MSN, Executive Director
CFO: Robert Power, Associate Executive Director Finance
CMO: Jay Enden, M.D., Medical Director
CIO: Lowney Mincy, Director Information Services
CHR: Anne J. Barrett, Associate Executive Director Human Resources
Web address: www.southsidehospital.org
**Control:** Other not–for–profit (including NFP Corporation) **Service:** General
Medical and Surgical

**Staffed Beds:** 300 **Admissions:** 18315 **Census:** 266 **Outpatient Visits:**
153720 **Births:** 2645 **Total Expense ($000):** 448789 **Payroll Expense**
**($000):** 227055 **Personnel:** 2274

## BELLEROSE—Queens County, See New York City

## BETHPAGE—Nassau County

□ **ST. JOSEPH HOSPITAL (330332)**, 4295 Hempstead Turnpike,
Zip 11714–5769; tel. 516/579–6000 **A**1 9 10 **F**3 8 15 17 18 29 30 34 35 39
40 45 46 49 50 51 56 57 59 60 64 65 68 69 70 74 75 79 81 85 86 87 93
107 108 110 111 114 119 129 130 131 132 135 141 146 148 **S** Catholic
Health Services of Long Island, Rockville Centre, NY
Primary Contact: Drew Pallas, Executive Vice President and Chief Administrative
Officer
CFO: John Morahan, Vice President Finance
CMO: Howard Sussman, M.D., Chief Medical Officer
CHR: Peter Chiacchiaro, Vice President Human Resources
CNO: Barbara Gibbons, Vice President Patient Care Services
Web address: www.stjosephhospitalny.org
**Control:** Other not–for–profit (including NFP Corporation) **Service:** General
Medical and Surgical

**Staffed Beds:** 128 **Admissions:** 6092 **Census:** 93 **Outpatient Visits:** 45892
**Births:** 0 **Total Expense ($000):** 110373 **Payroll Expense ($000):** 47515
**Personnel:** 685

## BINGHAMTON—Broome County

**BINGHAMTON GENERAL HOSPITAL** See United Health Services
Hospitals–Binghamton

□ **GREATER BINGHAMTON HEALTH CENTER (334012)**, 425 Robinson Street,
Zip 13904–1735; tel. 607/724–1391 **A**1 10 **F**29 30 50 54 56 58 65 66 71 75
77 86 98 99 100 101 103 104 105 106 130 132 135 143 146 **P**1 **S** New
York State Office of Mental Health, Albany, NY
Primary Contact: Mark Stephany, Executive Director
CFO: Cherry Randall, Business Officer
CHR: Renee O'Brien, Director Human Resources
Web address: www.omh.ny.gov/omhweb/facilities/bipc/facility.htm
**Control:** State–Government, nonfederal **Service:** Psychiatric

**Staffed Beds:** 101 **Admissions:** 386 **Census:** 104 **Outpatient Visits:** 19823
**Births:** 0 **Total Expense ($000):** 51678 **Payroll Expense ($000):** 23168
**Personnel:** 367

✠ **OUR LADY OF LOURDES MEMORIAL HOSPITAL, INC. (330011)**, 169
Riverside Drive, Zip 13905–4246; tel. 607/798–5111 **A**1 2 9 10 13 **F**3 11 12
13 15 18 19 28 29 30 31 32 34 35 36 39 40 44 45 46 47 49 50 51 53 54
56 57 59 60 62 63 64 65 66 68 70 71 74 75 76 77 78 79 81 84 85 86 87
89 93 97 99 100 101 103 104 107 108 110 111 114 115 118 119 120 121
123 124 126 127 129 130 131 132 134 135 143 144 145 146 147 148 **P**6
**S** Ascension Health, Saint Louis, MO
Primary Contact: Kathryn Connerton, Chief Executive Officer
COO: Linda Miller, R.N., Senior Vice President Operations and Chief Nursing
Officer
CFO: Gregg Hayton, Vice President Finance and Chief Financial Officer
CMO: Lisa Harris, M.D., Senior Vice President Medical Affairs
CIO: Thomas Ellerson, Chief Information Officer
CHR: Mary Hughs, Chief Human Resources Officer
CNO: Linda Miller, R.N., Senior Vice President Operations and Chief Nursing
Officer
Web address: www.lourdes.com
**Control:** Church–operated, Nongovernment, not–for profit **Service:** General
Medical and Surgical

**Staffed Beds:** 154 **Admissions:** 9841 **Census:** 116 **Outpatient Visits:**
1510035 **Births:** 1211 **Total Expense ($000):** 279592 **Payroll Expense**
**($000):** 120312 **Personnel:** 1711

**NY**

---

**Hospital, Medicare Provider Number, Address, Telephone, Approval, Facility, and Physician Codes, Health Care System**

★ American Hospital Association (AHA) membership    ◇ Healthcare Facilities Accreditation Program    ⇑ Center for Improvement in Healthcare Quality Accreditation
□ The Joint Commission accreditation    ◇ DNV Healthcare Inc. accreditation    △ Commission on Accreditation of Rehabilitation Facilities (CARF) accreditation

**UNITED HEALTH SERVICES HOSPITALS–BINGHAMTON (330394)**, 10–42 Mitchell Avenue, Zip 13903–1678; tel. 607/763–6000, (Includes BINGHAMTON GENERAL HOSPITAL, 10–42 Mitchell Avenue, Zip 13903; tel. 607/762–2200; WILSON MEMORIAL REGIONAL MEDICAL CENTER, 33–57 Harrison Street, Johnson City, Zip 13790; tel. 607/763–6000) **A**8 9 10 13 **F**1 3 4 5 8 11 12 13 15 17 18 20 22 24 26 28 29 30 31 32 33 34 35 38 39 40 43 45 46 49 50 51 54 56 57 58 59 61 64 65 68 70 72 74 75 76 77 78 79 81 82 84 85 86 87 89 90 92 93 96 97 98 99 100 101 102 103 104 105 107 108 110 114 115 118 119 120 121 123 124 127 129 130 131 132 135 144 145 146 147 148 **P**3 **S** United Health Services, Binghamton, NY
Primary Contact: Matthew J. Salanger, President and Chief Executive Officer
COO: John Carrigg, Executive Vice President and Chief Operating Officer
CFO: David MacDougall, Chief Financial Officer
CMO: Rajesh J. Dave', M.D., Executive Vice President and Chief Medical Officer
CHR: Michael McNally, Vice President Human Resources
CNO: E. Kay Boland, R.N., Vice President and Chief Nursing Officer
Web address: www.uhs.net
**Control:** Other not–for–profit (including NFP Corporation) **Service:** General Medical and Surgical

**Staffed Beds:** 465 **Admissions:** 16901 **Census:** 288 **Outpatient Visits:** 952166 **Births:** 1415 **Total Expense ($000):** 523804 **Payroll Expense ($000):** 194774 **Personnel:** 3704

### BRENTWOOD—Suffolk County

☐ **PILGRIM PSYCHIATRIC CENTER (334013)**, 998 Crooked Hill Road, Zip 11717–1019; tel. 631/761–3500, (Nonreporting) **A**1 5 10 **S** New York State Office of Mental Health, Albany, NY
Primary Contact: Kathy O'Keefe, Executive Director
CFO: Florence Corwin, Director for Administration
CMO: Inderjit Singh, M.D., Clinical Director
CIO: Douglas Cargonara, Ph.D., Chief Information Officer
CHR: Florence Corwin, Director Administration
Web address: www.omh.ny.gov/omhweb/facilities/pgpc/facility.htm
**Control:** State–Government, nonfederal **Service:** Psychiatric

**Staffed Beds:** 569

### BRONX—Bronx County, See New York City

### BRONXVILLE—Westchester County

☒ **NEW YORK–PRESBYTERIAN/LAWRENCE HOSPITAL (330061)**, 55 Palmer Avenue, Zip 10708–3403; tel. 914/787–1000 **A**1 2 5 9 10 **F**3 7 11 12 13 15 18 20 22 26 28 29 30 31 34 35 36 40 41 45 46 47 49 50 51 55 57 59 60 62 63 64 65 68 69 70 72 74 75 76 77 78 79 81 82 84 85 87 89 91 92 93 94 107 108 110 111 114 115 118 119 126 129 130 131 132 135 141 146 147 148 **S** New York Presbyterian Healthcare System, New York, NY
Primary Contact: Michael Fossina, President and Chief Executive Officer
COO: James Y. Lee, Executive Vice President and Chief Operating Officer
CFO: Murray Askinazi, Senior Vice President and Chief Financial Officer
CMO: Werner Roeder, M.D., Vice President Medical Affairs
CHR: Tom Mastroianni, Vice President Human Resources
CNO: Rose Ann O'Hare, R.N., Senior Vice President Patient Services
Web address: www.lawrencehealth.org
**Control:** Other not–for–profit (including NFP Corporation) **Service:** General Medical and Surgical

**Staffed Beds:** 187 **Admissions:** 10369 **Census:** 137 **Outpatient Visits:** 170057 **Births:** 1456 **Total Expense ($000):** 202622 **Payroll Expense ($000):** 88527 **Personnel:** 1099

### BROOKLYN—Kings County, See New York City

### BUFFALO—Erie County

**BRYLIN HOSPITALS (334022)**, 1263 Delaware Avenue, Zip 14209–2402; tel. 716/886–8200 **A**9 10 **F**5 54 98 99 103 104
Primary Contact: Eric D. Pleskow, President and Chief Executive Officer
CFO: E. Paul Hettich, Chief Financial Officer
CMO: Maria Cartagena, M.D., Chief Medical Officer
CIO: Pawel Wieczorek, Director Information Technology
CHR: Jacquelyn Bixler, Vice President Human Resources
Web address: www.brylin.com
**Control:** Corporation, Investor–owned, for–profit **Service:** Psychiatric

**Staffed Beds:** 88 **Admissions:** 1294 **Census:** 40 **Births:** 0

☐ **BUFFALO PSYCHIATRIC CENTER (334052)**, 400 Forest Avenue, Zip 14213–1298; tel. 716/885–2261, (Nonreporting) **A**1 3 5 10 **S** New York State Office of Mental Health, Albany, NY
Primary Contact: Thomas Dodson, Executive Director
COO: Celia Spacone, M.D., Director Operations
CFO: Pamela Esposito, Director Administration
CMO: Jeffery Grace, M.D., Clinical Director
CIO: Anne Buchheit, Coordinator Mental Health Local Information Systems
CHR: Charles Siewert, Director Human Resources
CNO: Susan Fallis, Chief Nursing Officer
Web address: www.omh.ny.gov
**Control:** State–Government, nonfederal **Service:** Psychiatric

**Staffed Beds:** 240

☒ **ERIE COUNTY MEDICAL CENTER (330219)**, 462 Grider Street, Zip 14215–3098; tel. 716/898–3000, (Total facility includes 390 beds in nursing home–type unit) **A**1 3 5 9 10 **F**3 4 5 8 12 15 16 17 18 20 22 24 26 27 29 30 31 33 34 35 38 39 40 43 45 50 53 54 56 57 58 59 60 61 62 63 64 65 66 67 68 70 71 74 75 77 78 79 81 82 83 84 85 87 90 91 93 94 96 97 98 99 100 101 102 103 104 105 107 110 111 115 119 128 130 131 132 138 146 148 **P**4 5 6 7
Primary Contact: Richard C. Cleland, FACHE, President and Chief Operating Officer and Interim Chief Executive Officer
COO: Richard C. Cleland, FACHE, President and Chief Operating Officer and Interim Chief Executive Officer
CFO: Michael Sammarco, M.D., Chief Financial Officer
CMO: Brian Murray, M.D., Medical Director
CIO: Leslie Feidt, Chief Information Officer
CHR: Kathleen O'Hara, Vice President Human Resources
CNO: Karen Ziemianski, R.N., Senior Vice President Nursing
Web address: www.ecmc.edu
**Control:** Hospital district or authority, Government, nonfederal **Service:** General Medical and Surgical

**Staffed Beds:** 876 **Admissions:** 18398 **Census:** 775 **Outpatient Visits:** 449792 **Births:** 0 **Total Expense ($000):** 513747 **Payroll Expense ($000):** 183473 **Personnel:** 2737

△ ◇ **KALEIDA HEALTH (330005)**, 100 High Street, Zip 14203–1154; tel. 716/859–5600, (Includes DE GRAFF MEMORIAL HOSPITAL, 445 Tremont Street, North Tonawanda, Zip 14120–0750, Mailing Address: P.O. Box 0750, Zip 14120–0750; tel. 716/694–4500; Tamara Owen, President; MILLARD FILLMORE SUBURBAN HOSPITAL, 1540 Maple Road, Williamsville, Zip 14221; tel. 716/688–3100; WOMEN AND CHILDREN'S HOSPITAL, 219 Bryant Street, Zip 14222–2099; tel. 716/878–7000; Cheryl Klass, President), (Total facility includes 380 beds in nursing home–type unit) **A**3 5 7 10 21 **F**1 2 3 6 8 9 11 12 13 15 17 18 19 20 21 22 24 26 27 28 29 30 31 32 34 35 36 37 38 39 40 41 43 44 45 46 47 48 49 50 51 54 55 56 57 58 59 60 61 62 63 64 65 66 67 68 70 71 72 73 74 75 76 77 78 79 80 81 82 83 84 85 86 87 88 89 90 91 92 93 94 96 97 99 100 101 102 103 104 105 107 108 109 110 111 114 115 118 119 120 124 126 128 130 131 132 134 135 136 143 146 147 148 **P**2 4 5 6
Primary Contact: Jody Lomeo, Chief Executive Officer
CFO: Joseph Kessler, Executive Vice President and Chief Financial Officer
CMO: Margaret Paroski, M.D., Executive Vice President and Chief Medical Officer
CIO: Francis Meyer, Vice President Information Systems Technology
Web address: www.kaleidahealth.org
**Control:** Other not–for–profit (including NFP Corporation) **Service:** General Medical and Surgical

**Staffed Beds:** 1368 **Admissions:** 48233 **Census:** 1073 **Outpatient Visits:** 660775 **Births:** 5430 **Total Expense ($000):** 1131336 **Payroll Expense ($000):** 468655 **Personnel:** 7342

☒ **MERCY HOSPITAL (330279)**, 565 Abbott Road, Zip 14220–2095; tel. 716/826–7000, (Total facility includes 84 beds in nursing home–type unit) **A**1 3 5 9 10 **F**3 5 8 13 15 17 18 20 22 24 26 29 30 32 34 35 39 40 42 45 48 49 54 57 59 60 64 65 66 70 72 74 75 76 78 79 81 83 84 85 86 87 89 90 92 93 94 96 97 107 108 110 111 114 115 118 119 126 128 130 131 132 146 147 **P**5 6 **S** Catholic Health System, Buffalo, NY
Primary Contact: Charles J. Urlaub, President and Chief Executive Officer
COO: John J. Herman, Chief Operating Officer
CFO: James H. Dunlop, Jr., CPA, Senior Vice President Finance and Chief Financial Officer
CMO: Timothy Gabryel, M.D., Vice President Medical Affairs and Medical Director
CIO: Michael Galang, M.D., Chief Information Officer
CHR: Joseph A. Scrivo, Jr., Director Human Resources
CNO: Kathleen Guarino, R.N., Vice President Patient Care Services
Web address: www.chsbuffalo.org
**Control:** Church–operated, Nongovernment, not–for profit **Service:** General Medical and Surgical

**Staffed Beds:** 438 **Admissions:** 19009 **Census:** 350 **Outpatient Visits:** 333064 **Births:** 2420 **Total Expense ($000):** 369091 **Payroll Expense ($000):** 154972 **Personnel:** 1941

☐ **ROSWELL PARK CANCER INSTITUTE (330354)**, Elm and Carlton Streets, Zip 14263–0001; tel. 716/845–2300 **A**1 2 3 5 8 9 10 **F**3 8 14 15 18 29 30 31 32 34 35 38 39 44 45 46 47 49 50 55 56 57 58 59 64 65 66 67 70 74 75 77 78 81 82 84 85 86 87 89 90 93 94 96 97 98 100 104 107 108 110 111 112 114 115 116 118 119 120 121 123 124 126 130 132 135 136 141 145 146 147 148 **P**6
Primary Contact: Candace Johnson, Ph.D., President and Chief Executive Officer
COO: Joyce M. Yasko, Ph.D., Chief Operating Officer
CFO: Gregory McDonald, Vice President Finance and Chief Financial Officer
CMO: Anthony Picone, M.D., Medical Director
CIO: Kerry Kerlin, Vice President Information Technology
CNO: Maureen Kelly, R.N., Chief Nursing Officer
Web address: www.roswellpark.org
**Control:** Hospital district or authority, Government, nonfederal **Service:** Cancer

**Staffed Beds:** 133 **Admissions:** 4688 **Census:** 105 **Outpatient Visits:** 199960 **Births:** 0 **Total Expense ($000):** 643262 **Payroll Expense ($000):** 234907 **Personnel:** 3416

NY

⊞ **SISTERS OF CHARITY HOSPITAL OF BUFFALO (330078)**, 2157 Main Street, Zip 14214–2692; tel. 716/862–1000, (Total facility includes 80 beds in nursing home–type unit) **A**1 2 3 5 9 10 12 13 **F**2 3 5 8 12 13 15 17 18 28 29 30 31 32 34 35 39 40 45 47 49 52 54 57 59 60 62 64 65 66 68 70 71 72 73 74 75 76 77 78 79 81 82 84 85 86 87 90 92 93 94 96 97 107 108 110 111 114 115 118 119 128 129 130 131 132 146 147 148 **P**5 6 **S** Catholic Health System, Buffalo, NY
Primary Contact: Peter U. Bergmann, President and Chief Executive Officer
COO: Matthew Hamp, Chief Operating Officer
CFO: James H. Dunlop, Jr., CPA, Chief Financial Officer
CMO: Nady Shehata, M.D., Vice President Medical Affairs
CIO: Michael Galang, M.D., Chief Information Officer
CHR: David DeLorenzo, Senior Director Human Resources
CNO: Mary E. Dillon, MS, Vice President Patient Care Services
Web address: www.chsbuffalo.org
**Control:** Church–operated, Nongovernment, not–for profit **Service:** General Medical and Surgical

**Staffed Beds:** 467 **Admissions:** 16318 **Census:** 303 **Outpatient Visits:** 711163 **Births:** 3556 **Total Expense ($000):** 318120 **Payroll Expense ($000):** 142919 **Personnel:** 2054

⊞ **VETERANS AFFAIRS WESTERN NEW YORK HEALTHCARE SYSTEM–BUFFALO DIVISION**, 3495 Bailey Avenue, Zip 14215–1129; tel. 716/834–9200, (Nonreporting) **A**1 2 3 5 8 9 **S** Department of Veterans Affairs, Washington, DC
Primary Contact: Brian G. Stiller, Director Medical Center
CFO: Susan Gage, Financial Manager
CMO: Ali El–Solh, M.D., Interim Chief of Staff
CIO: Margaret Senker, Chief Information Officer
Web address: www.buffalo.va.gov/index.asp
**Control:** Veterans Affairs, Government, federal **Service:** General Medical and Surgical

**Staffed Beds:** 113

**WOMEN AND CHILDREN'S HOSPITAL** See KALEIDA Health

**CALLICOON—Sullivan County**

**GROVER M. HERMANN HOSPITAL (331303)**, 8881 Route 97, Zip 12723; tel. 845/887–5530 **A**9 10 18 **F**2 8 11 13 15 18 28 29 30 31 34 35 38 40 51 54 56 57 59 65 68 78 79 81 85 86 87 93 97 102 103 107 111 114 119 127 130 132 133 146 147 148 **S** Greater Hudson Valley Health System, Middletown, NY
Primary Contact: Rolland Bojo, R.N., Administrator
Web address: www.crmcny.org
**Control:** Other not–for–profit (including NFP Corporation) **Service:** General Medical and Surgical

**Staffed Beds:** 25 **Admissions:** 121 **Census:** 3

**CANANDAIGUA—Ontario County**

★ **CANANDAIGUA VETERANS AFFAIRS MEDICAL CENTER**, 400 Fort Hill Avenue, Zip 14424–1159; tel. 585/394–2000, (Nonreporting) **A**3 5 **S** Department of Veterans Affairs, Washington, DC
Primary Contact: Michael Schwartz, Medical Center Director
CMO: Robert Babcock, M.D., Chief of Staff
CIO: Patricia Simon, Manager Information Systems
Web address: www.canandaigua.va.gov/
**Control:** Veterans Affairs, Government, federal **Service:** Psychiatric

**Staffed Beds:** 196

⊞ **F. F. THOMPSON HOSPITAL (330074)**, 350 Parrish Street, Zip 14424–1731; tel. 585/396–6000, (Total facility includes 188 beds in nursing home–type unit) **A**1 9 10 **F**3 11 13 15 18 28 29 30 32 34 35 40 45 49 54 57 59 64 70 75 76 77 79 81 85 89 93 96 97 107 108 110 111 115 118 119 126 128 129 130 131 132 135 144 145 146 147 148 **S** University of Rochester Medical Center, Rochester, NY
Primary Contact: Michael Stapleton, President and Chief Executive Officer
COO: Kurt Koczent, Executive Vice President and Chief Operating Officer
CFO: Mark Prunoske, Chief Financial Officer and Senior Vice President Finance
CMO: David Baum, M.D., Senior Vice President Medical Services
CIO: Mark Halladay, Director Information Services
CHR: Jennifer DeVault, Vice President Associate Services
CNO: Hazel Robertshaw, R.N., Chief Nursing Officer, Vice President Patient Services
Web address: www.thompsonhealth.com
**Control:** Other not–for–profit (including NFP Corporation) **Service:** General Medical and Surgical

**Staffed Beds:** 251 **Admissions:** 6034 **Census:** 240

**THOMPSON HEALTH** See F. F. Thompson Hospital

**CARMEL—Putnam County**

**ARMS ACRES**, 75 Seminary Hill Road, Zip 10512–1921; tel. 845/225–3400, (Nonreporting) **A**9
Primary Contact: Patrice Wallace–Moore, Chief Executive Officer and Executive Director
CFO: Jason Burczeuski, Controller
CMO: Fred Hesse, M.D., Medical Director
CIO: Dolores Watson, Director Health Information Management
CHR: Kim Halpin, Director Human Resources
CNO: Barbara Klein, R.N., Director of Nursing
Web address: www.armsacres.com
**Control:** Corporation, Investor–owned, for–profit **Service:** Alcoholism and other chemical dependency

**Staffed Beds:** 146

☐ **PUTNAM HOSPITAL CENTER (330273)**, 670 Stoneleigh Avenue, Zip 10512–3997; tel. 845/279–5711 **A**1 2 9 10 **F**3 8 12 13 15 18 28 29 30 31 34 35 37 38 40 41 45 46 49 55 56 57 59 61 64 65 68 70 74 75 76 77 78 79 81 82 83 84 85 87 92 93 94 97 98 100 102 103 104 105 107 108 110 111 114 118 119 120 121 126 129 130 131 132 143 146 148 **S** Health Quest Systems, Inc., LaGrangeville, NY
Primary Contact: James Caldas, President
COO: Maureen Zipparo, Chief Operating Officer
CFO: Anthony Mirdita, Chief Financial Officer
CMO: Ronald Tatelbaum, M.D., Interim Vice President Medical Affairs
CIO: Robert Diamond, Vice President and Chief Information Officer
CHR: Joan L. Calabrese, Director Human Resources
Web address: www.health–quest.org
**Control:** Other not–for–profit (including NFP Corporation) **Service:** General Medical and Surgical

**Staffed Beds:** 164 **Admissions:** 6290 **Census:** 76 **Outpatient Visits:** 203559 **Births:** 401 **Total Expense ($000):** 147202 **Payroll Expense ($000):** 47969

**CARTHAGE—Jefferson County**

⊞ **CARTHAGE AREA HOSPITAL (331318)**, 1001 West Street, Zip 13619–9703; tel. 315/493–1000 **A**1 9 10 18 20 **F**5 8 10 11 13 15 29 30 34 35 39 40 44 45 50 54 57 59 64 65 66 68 75 77 79 81 84 85 87 93 99 100 101 104 107 110 111 115 119 129 130 131 132 133 141 142 145 147 **P**3 6
Primary Contact: Richard Duvall, Chief Executive Officer
CFO: Donald Schnackel, Chief Financial Officer
CMO: Mirza Ashraf, M.D., Medical Director
CIO: Joe Virkler, Chief Information Officer
CHR: Cathy Siedlecki, Director Human Resources
CNO: Susan Kellogg, Administrator Patient Care Services
Web address: www.carthagehospital.com
**Control:** Other not–for–profit (including NFP Corporation) **Service:** General Medical and Surgical

**Staffed Beds:** 55 **Admissions:** 690 **Census:** 5 **Outpatient Visits:** 117277 **Births:** 291

**CATSKILL—Greene County**

**KAATERSKILL CARE** See Columbia Memorial Hospital, Hudson

**CLIFTON SPRINGS—Ontario County**

★ ◇ **CLIFTON SPRINGS HOSPITAL AND CLINIC (330265)**, 2 Coulter Road, Zip 14432–1189; tel. 315/462–9561, (Total facility includes 108 beds in nursing home–type unit) **A**6 9 10 21 **F**4 5 11 15 28 29 30 31 34 35 36 38 40 45 48 49 50 51 57 59 60 64 65 68 70 75 77 78 79 81 82 87 93 97 98 100 102 104 107 110 111 115 116 117 119 124 128 130 132 146 148 **P**5 6 **S** Rochester Regional Health, Rochester, NY
Primary Contact: Dustin Riccio, M.D., President
CFO: Sharon Kelley, Chief Financial Officer
CIO: Eric Jansen, Director Information Systems
CHR: Kathy Babb, Manager Human Resources
CNO: Donna P. Smith, R.N., Vice President Chief Operating Officer and Chief Nursing Officer
Web address: www.cliftonspringshospital.org
**Control:** Other not–for–profit (including NFP Corporation) **Service:** General Medical and Surgical

**Staffed Beds:** 214 **Admissions:** 2701 **Census:** 151 **Outpatient Visits:** 75200 **Births:** 0 **Total Expense ($000):** 53298 **Payroll Expense ($000):** 25494 **Personnel:** 541

**NY**

## COBLESKILL—Schoharie County

✠ **COBLESKILL REGIONAL HOSPITAL (330268)**, 178 Grandview Drive, Zip 12043–5144; tel. 518/254–3456, (Nonreporting) **A**1 9 10 20 **S** Bassett Healthcare Network, Cooperstown, NY
Primary Contact: Eric H. Stein, FACHE, President and Chief Executive Officer
CFO: Leanna Jensen, Vice President Finance and Chief Financial Officer
CMO: Roy Korn, M.D., Medical Director
CIO: Bridgette West, Director Patient Access Services
CHR: Christine Pirri, Senior Director Human Resources
CNO: Susan Oakes Ferrucci, MS, Vice President Patient Services and Chief Nursing Officer
Web address: www.cobleskillhospital.org
**Control:** Other not–for–profit (including NFP Corporation) **Service:** General Medical and Surgical

**Staffed Beds:** 40

## COOPERSTOWN—Otsego County

✠ **BASSETT MEDICAL CENTER (330136)**, One Atwell Road, Zip 13326–1394; tel. 607/547–3100 **A**1 2 3 5 8 9 10 **F**3 8 11 12 13 15 18 20 22 24 26 28 29 30 31 32 34 35 38 39 40 43 44 45 48 49 50 51 54 56 57 58 59 60 61 64 65 68 70 71 74 75 76 77 78 79 81 82 84 85 86 87 92 93 94 97 98 99 100 101 102 103 104 107 108 109 110 111 114 115 116 117 118 119 120 121 123 124 126 129 130 131 132 134 135 141 142 143 144 146 147 148 **P**6 **S** Bassett Healthcare Network, Cooperstown, NY
Primary Contact: Vance Brown, M.D., President and Chief Executive Officer
CFO: Michael A. Tengeres, Corporate Vice President and Chief Financial Officer
CMO: William W. LeCates, M.D., Medical Director
CIO: Scott C. Groom, Vice President Information Services and Chief Information Officer
CHR: Sara Z. Albright, Vice President Human Resources
CNO: Judi Brendle, Vice President Clinical Support and Chief Nursing Officer
Web address: www.bassett.org
**Control:** Other not–for–profit (including NFP Corporation) **Service:** General Medical and Surgical

**Staffed Beds:** 152 **Admissions:** 8780 **Census:** 126 **Outpatient Visits:** 687234 **Births:** 868 **Total Expense ($000):** 450328 **Payroll Expense ($000):** 238260 **Personnel:** 3235

## CORNING—Steuben County

✠ **CORNING HOSPITAL (330277)**, One Guthrie Drive, Zip 14830–3696; tel. 607/937–7200 **A**1 9 10 **F**3 8 11 13 15 28 29 31 32 34 35 37 38 40 44 45 49 50 53 57 59 64 70 75 77 78 79 81 82 87 92 93 100 107 108 110 111 115 119 120 121 124 129 130 131 132 135 145 146 147 148 **S** Guthrie Clinic, Sayre, PA
Primary Contact: Garrett W. Hoover, FACHE, Senior Vice President, President and Chief Operating Officer
CFO: Francis M. Macafee, Vice President Finance and Chief Financial Officer
CMO: Chris Wentzel, M.D., Interim Medical Director
CHR: Laura Manning, Administrative Director
CNO: Debra Raupers, MSN, Chief Nursing Officer
Web address: www.corninghospital.com
**Control:** Other not–for–profit (including NFP Corporation) **Service:** General Medical and Surgical

**Staffed Beds:** 82 **Admissions:** 3837 **Census:** 39 **Outpatient Visits:** 126129 **Births:** 409 **Total Expense ($000):** 72292 **Payroll Expense ($000):** 26837 **Personnel:** 554

## CORNWALL—Orange County

**ST. LUKE'S CORNWALL HOSPITAL – CORNWALL CAMPUS** See St. Luke's Cornwall Hospital, Newburgh

## CORTLAND—Cortland County

✠ **CORTLAND REGIONAL MEDICAL CENTER (330175)**, 134 Homer Avenue, Zip 13045–1206; tel. 607/756–3500, (Total facility includes 82 beds in nursing home–type unit) **A**1 9 10 20 **F**2 8 11 13 15 18 28 29 30 31 34 35 40 45 49 50 54 56 57 59 62 64 70 75 76 77 78 79 81 82 85 86 87 91 93 96 98 100 102 107 108 110 111 114 115 118 119 128 130 131 132 133 135 144 146 147 148 **P**6
Primary Contact: Mark Webster, President and Chief Executive Officer
COO: David A. Kobis, Vice President Operations and Chief Operating Officer
CFO: Denise Wrinn, Vice President Finance and Chief Financial Officer
CMO: Roger Scott, D.O., Vice President Medical Affairs and Chief Medical Officer
CIO: Robert J. Duthe, Director Information Systems and Chief Information Officer
CHR: Bonita N. Lindberg, Director Human Resources
CNO: Mary Wright, Vice President Nursing Services and Chief Nursing Officer
Web address: www.cortlandregional.org
**Control:** Other not–for–profit (including NFP Corporation) **Service:** General Medical and Surgical

**Staffed Beds:** 194 **Admissions:** 3927 **Census:** 136 **Outpatient Visits:** 133783 **Births:** 428 **Total Expense ($000):** 81344 **Payroll Expense ($000):** 36128 **Personnel:** 698

## CORTLANDT MANOR—Westchester County

☐ **NEW YORK–PRESBYTERIAN/HUDSON VALLEY HOSPITAL (330267)**, 1980 Crompond Road, Zip 10567–4182; tel. 914/737–9000 **A**1 9 10 **F**3 7 8 9 11 12 13 15 18 28 29 30 31 34 35 37 40 45 46 47 53 57 59 67 70 72 74 75 76 77 78 79 81 82 85 86 87 89 93 107 108 110 111 115 119 121 130 131 132 135 145 146 147 148 **S** New York Presbyterian Healthcare System, New York, NY
Primary Contact: John C. Federspiel, President and Chief Executive Officer
COO: Deborah Neuendorf, Vice President Administration
CFO: Mark Webster, Vice President Finance
CMO: William Higgins, M.D., Vice President Medical Affairs
CIO: Bud Sorbello, Director Management Information Systems
CHR: Jeane L. Costella, Vice President
CNO: Kathleen Webster, R.N., Vice President Patient Services
Web address: www.hvhc.org
**Control:** Other not–for–profit (including NFP Corporation) **Service:** General Medical and Surgical

**Staffed Beds:** 128 **Admissions:** 7633 **Census:** 95

## CUBA—Allegany County

**CUBA MEMORIAL HOSPITAL (331301)**, 140 West Main Street, Zip 14727–1398; tel. 585/968–2000, (Nonreporting) **A**9 10 18
Primary Contact: Andrew Boser, Chief Executive Officer
CFO: Jack Ormond, Chief Financial Officer
Web address: www.cubamemorialhospital.com
**Control:** Other not–for–profit (including NFP Corporation) **Service:** General Medical and Surgical

**Staffed Beds:** 81

## DANSVILLE—Livingston County

✠ **NICHOLAS H. NOYES MEMORIAL HOSPITAL (330238)**, 111 Clara Barton Street, Zip 14437–9503; tel. 585/335–6001 **A**1 9 10 **F**3 8 11 13 15 29 30 31 32 34 35 38 40 45 47 49 50 53 54 57 59 60 64 70 75 76 77 78 79 81 82 83 84 85 87 93 99 100 103 104 107 108 110 114 119 127 130 131 132 133 135 144 146 **P**5
Primary Contact: Amy Pollard, R.N., President and Chief Executive Officer
CFO: Jay T. Maslyn, Chief Financial Officer
CMO: Douglas Mayhle, M.D., Medical Director
CIO: John Dorak, Chief Information Officer
CNO: Tamara West, R.N., Vice President Patient Care
Web address: www.noyes–health.org
**Control:** Other not–for–profit (including NFP Corporation) **Service:** General Medical and Surgical

**Staffed Beds:** 67 **Admissions:** 1720 **Census:** 23 **Outpatient Visits:** 171551 **Births:** 315 **Total Expense ($000):** 49192 **Payroll Expense ($000):** 20312 **Personnel:** 417

## DELHI—Delaware County

✠ **O'CONNOR HOSPITAL (331305)**, 460 Andes Road, State Route 28, Zip 13753–7407; tel. 607/746–0300 **A**1 9 10 18 **F**15 29 34 35 40 45 46 50 56 57 59 64 65 75 77 79 81 85 86 87 91 92 93 96 107 110 111 119 130 131 132 133 135 147 **S** Bassett Healthcare Network, Cooperstown, NY
Primary Contact: Carlton Rule, M.D., Chief Executive Officer
CFO: Sue E. Andrews, Chief Financial Officer
CMO: Alberto Gaitan, M.D., Medical Director
CHR: Barbara Green, Director Human Resources
CNO: Debra Neale, R.N., Chief Nursing Officer
Web address: www.bassett.org
**Control:** Other not–for–profit (including NFP Corporation) **Service:** General Medical and Surgical

**Staffed Beds:** 16 **Admissions:** 286 **Census:** 6 **Outpatient Visits:** 30664 **Births:** 0 **Total Expense ($000):** 20976 **Payroll Expense ($000):** 6987 **Personnel:** 155

## DIX HILLS—Suffolk County

☐ **SAGAMORE CHILDREN'S PSYCHIATRIC CENTER**, 197 Half Hollow Road, Zip 11746–5861; tel. 631/370–1700, (Nonreporting) **A**1 **S** New York State Office of Mental Health, Albany, NY
Primary Contact: Kathy O'Keefe, Interim Executive Director
COO: Cathy Stein, Chief Inpatient Services
CFO: Jane Alexander, Director Facility Administrative Services
CIO: Bryan Doherty, Management Information Technology Services I
CHR: Nancy Angell, Associate Administrator Personnel
CNO: Sandra King, Chief Nursing Officer
Web address: www.omh.ny.gov
**Control:** State–Government, nonfederal **Service:** Children's hospital psychiatric

**Staffed Beds:** 69

*Many Facility Codes have changed. Please refer to the AHA Guide Code Chart.* © 2015 AHA Guide

**NY**

## DUNKIRK—Chautauqua County

◇ **BROOKS MEMORIAL HOSPITAL (330229)**, 529 Central Avenue,
Zip 14048–2599; tel. 716/366–1111, (Nonreporting) **A**9 10 21
Primary Contact: J. Gary Rhodes, FACHE, Interim President and Chief Executive
Officer
CFO: Ralph Webdale, Vice President Finance
CIO: Kathy Kucharski, Director Management Information Systems
CHR: Joan VanDette, Vice President Human Resources
Web address: www.brookshospital.org
**Control:** Other not–for–profit (including NFP Corporation) **Service:** General
Medical and Surgical

**Staffed Beds:** 65

## EAST MEADOW—Nassau County

✠ **NASSAU UNIVERSITY MEDICAL CENTER (330027)**, 2201 Hempstead
Turnpike, Zip 11554–1859; tel. 516/572–0123, (Nonreporting) **A**1 3 5 9 10
12 13
Primary Contact: Victor Politi, M.D., President and Chief Executive Officer
COO: Harold E. McDonald, Deputy Executive Director and Senior Vice President
Administration
CFO: John P. Maher, Executive Vice President and Chief Financial Officer
CMO: Victor Scarmato, M.D., Acting Medical Director
CIO: Farooq Ajmal, Vice President and Chief Information Officer
CHR: Maureen Roarty, Executive Vice President Human Resources
CNO: Kathy Skarka, MSN, Executive Vice President Patient Care Services
Web address: www.nuhealth.net
**Control:** Hospital district or authority, Government, nonfederal **Service:** General
Medical and Surgical

**Staffed Beds:** 481

## ELIZABETHTOWN—Essex County

✠ **THE UNIVERSITY OF VERMONT HEALTH NETWORK ELIZABETHTOWN
COMMUNITY HOSPITAL (331302)**, Park Street, Zip 12932–0277, Mailing
Address: P.O. Box 277, Zip 12932–0277; tel. 518/873–6377 **A**1 9 10 18 **F**3 7
11 12 15 28 29 30 31 32 34 35 40 44 45 46 53 54 57 59 64 65 68 75 77
78 81 86 87 90 91 93 97 107 110 115 119 127 130 133 145 146 147 **P**6
Primary Contact: Rodney C. Boula, Administrator and Chief Executive Officer
COO: Matthew Nolan, Director Facilities and Operations
CFO: Alan Chardavoyne, Controller
CMO: Rob DeMuro, M.D., President Medical Staff
CHR: Michelle Meachem, Director Human Resources
Web address: www.ech.org
**Control:** Other not–for–profit (including NFP Corporation) **Service:** General
Medical and Surgical

**Staffed Beds:** 25 **Admissions:** 473 **Census:** 12 **Outpatient Visits:** 38286
**Births:** 0 **Total Expense ($000):** 21801 **Payroll Expense ($000):** 11743
**Personnel:** 150

## ELLENVILLE—Ulster County

★ **ELLENVILLE REGIONAL HOSPITAL (331310)**, 10 Healthy Way,
Zip 12428–5612; tel. 845/647–6400 **A**9 10 18 **F**3 15 28 29 30 34 35 40 45
46 50 57 59 68 81 85 87 93 107 108 110 111 114 116 119 132 133 146
147 148
Primary Contact: Steven L. Kelley, President and Chief Executive Officer
CFO: Patricia Gavis, Chief Financial Officer
CMO: Walter Sperling, M.D., Medical Director
CHR: Deborah Briggs, Vice President Human Resources, Marketing, Volunteer
Services and Community Relations
CNO: Ann Marie Kelly, Chief Nursing Officer
Web address: www.ellenvilleregional.org
**Control:** Other not–for–profit (including NFP Corporation) **Service:** General
Medical and Surgical

**Staffed Beds:** 25 **Admissions:** 498 **Census:** 4 **Outpatient Visits:** 30464
**Births:** 0

## ELMHURST—Queens County, See New York City

## ELMIRA—Chemung County

★ ◇ **ARNOT OGDEN MEDICAL CENTER (330090)**, 600 Roe Avenue,
Zip 14905–1629; tel. 607/737–4100 **A**2 6 9 10 12 13 21 **F**11 12 15 17 18
20 22 24 26 28 29 30 31 35 40 45 46 48 49 50 51 53 56 57 59 60 61
65 68 70 72 73 74 75 76 77 78 79 81 87 89 91 93 97 100 103 106 107
110 111 115 116 119 129 130 131 132 135 143 146 147 148 **S** Arnot
Health, Elmira, NY
Primary Contact: H. Fred Farley, R.N., Ph.D., FACHE, President and Chief
Operating Officer
CFO: Ronald J. Kintz, Vice President and Treasurer
CMO: William Huffner, M.D., Vice President Medical Affairs
CIO: Gregg Martin, Manager Management Information Systems
CHR: Brian K. Forrest, Director Human Resources
CNO: Mary M. Vosburgh, R.N., Vice President Nursing and Chief Nursing Officer
Web address: www.aomc.org
**Control:** Other not–for–profit (including NFP Corporation) **Service:** General
Medical and Surgical

**Staffed Beds:** 176 **Admissions:** 11522 **Census:** 151 **Outpatient Visits:**
338095 **Births:** 1414 **Total Expense ($000):** 349872 **Payroll Expense
($000):** 174728

☐ **ELMIRA PSYCHIATRIC CENTER (334045)**, 100 Washington Street,
Zip 14901–2898; tel. 607/737–4739 **A**1 10 **F**29 30 35 39 54 64 71 98 99
101 104 106 **P**6 **S** New York State Office of Mental Health, Albany, NY
Primary Contact: Mark Stephany, Executive Director
COO: Karen Patterson, Deputy Director Operations
CFO: J. Paul Bedzyk, Deputy Director Administration
CMO: Kurt Hahn, M.D., Acting Clinical Director
CIO: Jeremy Newcomer, Director Information Services
CHR: Patricia Santulli, Director Human Resources
CNO: Pam Seeley, Chief Nursing Officer
Web address: www.omh.ny.gov/omhweb/facilities/elpc/facility.htm
**Control:** State–Government, nonfederal **Service:** Psychiatric

**Staffed Beds:** 100 **Admissions:** 295 **Census:** 91 **Outpatient Visits:** 47548
**Births:** 0

◇ **ST. JOSEPH'S HOSPITAL (330108)**, 555 St. Joseph's Boulevard,
Zip 14901–3223; tel. 607/733–6541, (Includes TWIN TIERS REHABILITATION
CENTER ), (Nonreporting) **A**9 10 21 **S** Arnot Health, Elmira, NY
Primary Contact: H. Fred Farley, R.N., Ph.D., FACHE, President and Chief
Operating Officer
COO: H. Fred Farley, R.N., President and Chief Operating Officer
CFO: Ronald J. Kintz, Senior Vice President Finance and Chief Financial Officer
CMO: William Huffner, M.D., Chief Medical Officer and Senior Vice President
Medical Affairs
CIO: Gregg Martin, Chief Information Officer
CHR: Brian K. Forrest, Vice President Human Resources
CNO: Mary M. Vosburgh, R.N., Vice President Nursing and Chief Nursing Officer
Web address: www.stjosephs.org
**Control:** Other not–for–profit (including NFP Corporation) **Service:** General
Medical and Surgical

**Staffed Beds:** 212

## ENDICOTT—Broome County

**UHS WALK–IN – ENDICOTT** See United Health Services Hospitals–Binghamton,
Binghamton

## FAR ROCKAWAY—Queens County, See New York City

## FLUSHING—Queens County, See New York City

## FOREST HILLS—Queens County, See New York City

## FRESH MEADOWS—Queens County

**CORNERSTONE OF MEDICAL ARTS CENTER HOSPITAL**, 159–05 Union
Turnpike, Zip 11366–1950; tel. 212/755–0200, (Nonreporting) **A**9
Primary Contact: Norman J. Sokolow, Chairman and Chief Executive Officer
COO: Thomas C. Puzo, President and Chief Operating Officer
CFO: Jeff OniFather, Chief Financial Officer
CMO: Sami Kaddouri, M.D., Medical Director
CHR: Gloria Burtch, Director Human Resources
Web address: www.cornerstoneny.com
**Control:** Corporation, Investor–owned, for–profit **Service:** Alcoholism and other
chemical dependency

**Staffed Beds:** 162

**NY**

---

**Hospital, Medicare Provider Number, Address, Telephone, Approval, Facility, and Physician Codes, Health Care System**

★ American Hospital Association (AHA) membership    ○ Healthcare Facilities Accreditation Program    ⇑ Center for Improvement in Healthcare Quality Accreditation
☐ The Joint Commission accreditation    ◇ DNV Healthcare Inc. accreditation    △ Commission on Accreditation of Rehabilitation Facilities (CARF) accreditation

## GENEVA—Ontario County

✠ **GENEVA GENERAL HOSPITAL (330058)**, 196 North Street, Zip 14456–1694; tel. 315/787–4000 **A**1 3 6 9 10 **F**3 8 11 13 15 17 18 28 29 30 31 32 34 35 40 45 50 54 57 59 60 61 64 66 69 70 74 75 76 77 79 81 85 86 87 90 92 93 96 97 107 108 110 111 115 118 119 129 130 131 132 135 146 147 **P**6 **S** Finger Lakes Health, Geneva, NY
Primary Contact: Jose Acevedo, M.D., President and Chief Executive Officer
COO: James Hiserodt, Senior Vice President Operations
CFO: Pamela Johnson, Treasurer and Chief Financial Officer
CMO: Jason Feinberg, M.D., Vice President Medical Affairs and Chief Medical Officer
CIO: John Oates, Director Information Systems
CHR: Patrick R. Boyle, Vice President Human Resources
CNO: Eileen Gage, R.N., Vice President Nursing
Web address: www.flhealth.org
**Control:** Other not–for–profit (including NFP Corporation) **Service:** General Medical and Surgical

**Staffed Beds:** 132 **Admissions:** 3659 **Census:** 52 **Outpatient Visits:** 440120 **Births:** 0 **Total Expense ($000):** 94298 **Payroll Expense ($000):** 45045 **Personnel:** 786

## GLEN COVE—Nassau County

✠ **GLEN COVE HOSPITAL (330181)**, 101 St. Andrews Lane, Zip 11542–2254; tel. 516/674–7300 **A**1 2 3 5 9 10 **F**3 8 9 11 14 15 17 18 28 29 30 31 32 33 34 35 36 38 39 40 43 45 46 47 48 49 50 54 55 56 57 58 59 60 61 63 64 65 66 68 69 70 74 75 77 78 79 81 82 84 85 86 87 90 91 92 93 94 96 97 100 102 103 104 107 108 110 111 115 118 119 122 121 130 131 132 135 143 146 147 **P**5 6 **S** North Shore–Long Island Jewish Health System, Great Neck, NY
Primary Contact: Susan Kwiatek, R.N., Executive Director
COO: Michele Frankel, Associate Executive Director Finance
CFO: Michele Frankel, Associate Executive Director Finance
CMO: Barbara Barnett, M.D., Medical Director
CHR: Thomas Salvo, Associate Executive Director Human Resources
CNO: Cathy Sheerin, R.N., Director Patient Care Services
Web address: www.northshorelij.com
**Control:** Other not–for–profit (including NFP Corporation) **Service:** General Medical and Surgical

**Staffed Beds:** 140 **Admissions:** 4499 **Census:** 86 **Outpatient Visits:** 74435 **Births:** 0 **Total Expense ($000):** 135098 **Payroll Expense ($000):** 74268 **Personnel:** 678

## GLEN OAKS—Queens County, See New York City

## GLENS FALLS—Warren County

✠ **GLENS FALLS HOSPITAL (330191)**, 100 Park Street, Zip 12801–4413; tel. 518/926–1000 **A**1 2 5 9 10 **F**3 5 8 11 13 15 17 18 20 22 26 28 29 30 31 32 34 35 40 43 44 45 46 47 49 50 53 54 57 59 60 64 68 70 71 73 74 75 76 77 78 79 81 82 84 85 86 87 89 90 92 93 96 97 98 99 100 102 103 104 105 107 108 110 114 115 118 119 120 121 123 124 126 127 129 130 132 135 144 145 146 147 148 **P**6
Primary Contact: Dianne Shugrue, President and Chief Executive Officer
COO: Mark Holtz, Senior Vice President Operations and Chief Operating Officer
CFO: Mitchell Amado, Senior Vice President Finance and Chief Financial Officer
CMO: Robert W. Pringle, M.D., Vice President Medical Affairs and Chief Medical Officer
CIO: John Kelleher, Vice President Information Technology and Chief Information Officer
CHR: Kyle Brock, Vice President Human Resources
CNO: Donna Kirker NEA–BC, R.N., Vice President Patient Services and Chief Nursing Officer
Web address: www.glensfallshospital.org
**Control:** Other not–for–profit (including NFP Corporation) **Service:** General Medical and Surgical

**Staffed Beds:** 317 **Admissions:** 12736 **Census:** 186 **Outpatient Visits:** 731264 **Births:** 1268 **Total Expense ($000):** 304923 **Payroll Expense ($000):** 141847 **Personnel:** 2169

## GLENVILLE—Schenectady County

**CONIFER PARK**, 79 Glenridge Road, Zip 12302–4523; tel. 518/399–6446, (Nonreporting) **A**9
Primary Contact: Jeanne Gluchowski, Executive Director
COO: Jeanne Gluchowski, Executive Director
CFO: Jason Burczeuski, Controller
CMO: John Melbourne, M.D., Medical Director
CIO: Amy Kentera, Chief Information Officer
CHR: Maureen Fowler, Director Human Resources
Web address: www.libertymgt.com
**Control:** Corporation, Investor–owned, for–profit **Service:** Alcoholism and other chemical dependency

**Staffed Beds:** 225

## GLOVERSVILLE—Fulton County

★ ◇ **NATHAN LITTAUER HOSPITAL AND NURSING HOME (330276)**, 99 East State Street, Zip 12078–1203; tel. 518/725–8621, (Total facility includes 84 beds in nursing home–type unit) **A**5 9 10 21 **F**3 8 11 13 15 18 28 29 30 31 32 34 35 36 37 40 45 50 53 54 57 59 61 64 65 70 74 75 76 77 78 79 81 82 85 86 87 89 93 97 107 108 110 115 118 119 128 130 131 132 135 145 146 147 **P**6
Primary Contact: Laurence E. Kelly, President and Chief Executive Officer
CFO: Michael Ostrander, Chief Financial Officer
CMO: Frederick Goldberg, M.D., Vice President Medical Affairs and Chief Medical Officer
CIO: Martin Brown, Vice President Information Services and Chief Information Officer
CHR: Lana Wydra, Vice President Human Resources
CNO: Stephanie Fishel, Vice President Patient Care Services and Chief Nursing Officer
Web address: www.nlh.org
**Control:** Other not–for–profit (including NFP Corporation) **Service:** General Medical and Surgical

**Staffed Beds:** 158 **Admissions:** 2846 **Census:** 112 **Outpatient Visits:** 244924 **Births:** 352 **Total Expense ($000):** 91227 **Payroll Expense ($000):** 45839 **Personnel:** 791

## GOUVERNEUR—St. Lawrence County

★ ◇ **GOUVERNEUR HOSPITAL (331315)**, 77 West Barney Street, Zip 13642–1040; tel. 315/287–1000 **A**9 10 18 21 **F**3 8 11 15 29 34 40 45 57 59 64 75 81 85 87 89 93 107 108 111 114 119 129 130 133 **P**6 **S** St. Lawrence Health System, Potsdam, NY
Primary Contact: Marlinda L. LaValley, Chief Executive Officer
CFO: Richard T. Lang, Chief Financial Officer
CMO: George Dodds, M.D., Medical Director
CHR: Suzan McDermott, Director, Human Resources
CNO: Jennifer Shaver, Director of Nursing
Web address: www.gvnhospital.org
**Control:** Other not–for–profit (including NFP Corporation) **Service:** General Medical and Surgical

**Staffed Beds:** 25 **Admissions:** 485 **Census:** 6 **Outpatient Visits:** 49734 **Births:** 0 **Total Expense ($000):** 16186 **Payroll Expense ($000):** 7086 **Personnel:** 148

## GREENPORT—Suffolk County

✠ **EASTERN LONG ISLAND HOSPITAL (330088)**, 201 Manor Place, Zip 11944–1298; tel. 631/477–1000 **A**1 9 10 **F**3 4 17 18 28 29 34 40 45 47 49 53 56 59 64 65 68 70 74 78 79 81 82 85 93 97 98 100 102 103 106 107 110 111 119 130 132 135 146
Primary Contact: Paul J. Connor, III, President and Chief Executive Officer
CFO: Robert A. Ragona, Vice President Finance
CMO: Lloyd Simon, M.D., Medical Director
CIO: Dan Scotto, Director Data Processing
CHR: Frank Dumont, Director Human Resources
CNO: D. Patricia Pispisa, Vice President Patient Care Services
Web address: www.elih.org
**Control:** Other not–for–profit (including NFP Corporation) **Service:** General Medical and Surgical

**Staffed Beds:** 90 **Admissions:** 2695 **Census:** 50 **Outpatient Visits:** 43351 **Births:** 0 **Total Expense ($000):** 47708 **Payroll Expense ($000):** 21414 **Personnel:** 313

## HAMILTON—Madison County

✠ **COMMUNITY MEMORIAL HOSPITAL (331316)**, 150 Broad Street, Zip 13346–9518; tel. 315/824–1100, (Total facility includes 40 beds in nursing home–type unit) **A**1 9 10 **F**3 11 18 29 40 45 53 56 57 64 70 74 79 81 85 89 93 97 107 108 110 111 119 127 128 130 135 144 146
Primary Contact: Sean Fadale, President and Chief Executive Officer
CFO: Christopher W. Graham, Chief Financial Officer
CMO: Michael S. Jastremski, M.D., Vice President Medical Affairs and Director Emergency Services
CHR: Cynthia Sternard, Director Human Resources
CNO: Denise Hummer, R.N., Vice President Administrative Services
Web address: www.communitymemorial.org
**Control:** Other not–for–profit (including NFP Corporation) **Service:** General Medical and Surgical

**Staffed Beds:** 76 **Admissions:** 1704 **Census:** 44 **Births:** 0

**NY**

*Many Facility Codes have changed. Please refer to the AHA Guide Code Chart.* © 2015 AHA Guide

## HARRIS—Sullivan County

☒ **CATSKILL REGIONAL MEDICAL CENTER (330386)**, 68 Harris Bushville Road, Zip 12742–5030, Mailing Address: P.O. Box 800, Zip 12742–0800; tel. 845/794–3300, (Total facility includes 64 beds in nursing home–type unit) **A**1 9 10 **F**2 3 8 11 13 15 17 18 28 29 30 31 34 35 38 40 42 45 51 54 56 57 59 65 68 70 76 78 79 81 85 86 87 89 93 96 97 98 102 103 107 111 115 119 127 128 130 132 133 146 147 148 **S** Greater Hudson Valley Health System, Middletown, NY
Primary Contact: Gerard Galarneau, M.D., Chief Executive Officer and Chief Medical Officer
CFO: Frank Hemeon, Interim Chief Financial Officer
CMO: Gerard Galarneau, M.D., Chief Executive Officer and Chief Medical Officer
CIO: John Lynch, Vice President Chief Information Officer
CNO: Rolland Bojo, R.N., Chief Nursing Officer, Administrator Patient Care and Services
Web address: www.crmcny.org
**Control:** Other not–for–profit (including NFP Corporation) **Service:** General Medical and Surgical

**Staffed Beds:** 184 **Admissions:** 3853 **Census:** 118 **Outpatient Visits:** 98372 **Births:** 430 **Total Expense ($000):** 88292 **Payroll Expense ($000):** 37956 **Personnel:** 557

## HOLLISWOOD—Queens County, See New York City

## HORNELL—Steuben County

☒ **ST. JAMES MERCY HEALTH SYSTEM (330151)**, 411 Canisteo Street, Zip 14843–2197; tel. 607/324–8000, (Nonreporting) **A**1 9 10 20 **S** Trinity Health, Livonia, MI
Primary Contact: Jennifer Sullivan, President and Chief Executive Officer
CFO: Stan Konopko, Chief Financial Officer
CMO: John Carroll, M.D., Chief Medical Officer
CIO: Jason Soles, Manager Information Systems
CHR: Jennifer Spike, Director Human Resources
CNO: Kathleen Brodbeck, MSN, RN–B, Chief Nursing Officer
Web address: www.stjamesmercy.org
**Control:** Other not–for–profit (including NFP Corporation) **Service:** General Medical and Surgical

**Staffed Beds:** 222

## HUDSON—Columbia County

★ **COLUMBIA MEMORIAL HOSPITAL (330094)**, 71 Prospect Avenue, Zip 12534–2907; tel. 518/828–7601, (Includes KAATERSKILL CARE, 161 Jefferson Heights, Catskill, Zip 12414; tel. 518/943–6363), (Nonreporting) **A**9 10 19
Primary Contact: Jay P. Cahalan, Chief Executive Officer
COO: Karen Tassey, FACHE, Chief Operating Officer
CFO: Vincent Dingman, III, Chief Financial Officer
CMO: Lawrence Perl, M.D., Chief Medical Officer
CHR: Patricia Finnegan, Vice President
Web address: www.columbiamemorialhealth.org
**Control:** Other not–for–profit (including NFP Corporation) **Service:** General Medical and Surgical

**Staffed Beds:** 218

## HUNTINGTON—Suffolk County

☒ **HUNTINGTON HOSPITAL (330045)**, 270 Park Avenue, Zip 11743–2799; tel. 631/351–2200 **A**1 2 3 9 10 **F**3 8 11 12 13 15 17 18 20 22 26 29 30 31 34 35 36 38 40 41 43 44 45 49 50 51 53 54 55 56 57 58 59 60 63 64 65 66 68 69 70 73 74 75 76 78 79 81 82 84 85 86 87 89 91 93 97 98 100 101 102 103 107 108 110 111 114 115 118 119 126 130 132 135 146 147 148 **P**5 6 **S** North Shore–Long Island Jewish Health System, Great Neck, NY
Primary Contact: Gerard Brogan, Jr., M.D., Executive Director
CFO: Michael Fagan, Chief Financial Officer
CMO: Michael Grosso, M.D., Senior Vice President Medical Affairs
CIO: Linda Fischer, Director Information Services
CHR: Donna Cice, Vice President Human Resources
CNO: Susan Knoepffler, R.N., Vice President Nursing
Web address: www.hunthosp.org
**Control:** Other not–for–profit (including NFP Corporation) **Service:** General Medical and Surgical

**Staffed Beds:** 290 **Admissions:** 14438 **Census:** 198 **Outpatient Visits:** 120420 **Births:** 1443 **Total Expense ($000):** 336830 **Payroll Expense ($000):** 173980 **Personnel:** 1660

## IRVING—Chautauqua County

◇ **TLC HEALTH NETWORK – LAKE SHORE HOSPITAL**, 845 Route 5 and 20, Zip 14081–9716; tel. 716/951–7000, (Nonreporting) **A**9 21
Primary Contact: John P. Galati, Chief Executive Officer
CFO: John Eichner, Vice President Finance
CMO: James Wild, M.D., Medical Director
CIO: Raymond Manning, Director Information Technology
CHR: Shannon Bobseine, Manager Human Resources
CNO: Patricia Dole, Vice President Patient Care Services
Web address: www.tlchealth.org
**Control:** Other not–for–profit (including NFP Corporation) **Service:** General Medical and Surgical

**Staffed Beds:** 200

## ITHACA—Tompkins County

☒ **CAYUGA MEDICAL CENTER AT ITHACA (330307)**, 101 Dates Drive, Zip 14850–1342; tel. 607/274–4011 **A**1 2 5 9 10 **F**3 8 12 13 15 18 20 22 28 29 30 31 34 35 38 40 41 45 48 49 50 51 54 57 59 61 64 68 70 72 74 75 77 78 79 81 82 84 85 86 87 90 92 93 98 99 100 101 102 103 107 108 110 111 114 115 116 117 118 119 121 129 130 131 132 133 135 144 145 146 147 148 **P**6
Primary Contact: John Rudd, President and Chief Executive Officer
CFO: John Collett, Vice President and Chief Financial Officer
CMO: David M. Evelyn, M.D., Vice President Medical Affairs
CIO: Brett Mello, Chief Information Officer
CHR: Alan Pedersen, Vice President Human Resources
CNO: Susan Nohelty, R.N., Vice President Patient Services
Web address: www.cayugamed.org
**Control:** Other not–for–profit (including NFP Corporation) **Service:** General Medical and Surgical

**Staffed Beds:** 193 **Admissions:** 6443 **Census:** 83 **Outpatient Visits:** 230639 **Births:** 894 **Total Expense ($000):** 173621 **Payroll Expense ($000):** 63342 **Personnel:** 1046

## JACKSON HEIGHTS—Queens County, See New York City

## JAMAICA—Queens County, See New York City

## JAMESTOWN—Chautauqua County

☒ **WOMAN'S CHRISTIAN ASSOCIATION HOSPITAL (330239)**, 207 Foote Avenue, Zip 14701–7077, Mailing Address: P.O. Box 840, Zip 14702–0840; tel. 716/487–0141 **A**1 2 9 10 **F**3 4 5 8 11 13 15 18 19 20 28 29 31 32 34 35 40 45 46 57 59 64 68 69 70 74 75 76 77 78 79 81 82 83 84 85 86 87 89 90 92 93 94 96 98 99 100 101 102 103 104 107 108 110 111 117 119 121 126 129 130 131 132 135 141 146 147 148
Primary Contact: Betsy T. Wright, President and Chief Executive Officer
CMO: Marlene Garone, M.D., Vice President Medical Affairs and Medical Director
CIO: Keith Robison, Chief Information Officer
CHR: Karen Bohall, Director Human Resources
Web address: www.wcahospital.org
**Control:** Other not–for–profit (including NFP Corporation) **Service:** General Medical and Surgical

**Staffed Beds:** 197 **Admissions:** 6425 **Census:** 90 **Outpatient Visits:** 274136 **Births:** 699 **Total Expense ($000):** 101742 **Payroll Expense ($000):** 40315 **Personnel:** 891

## JOHNSON CITY—Broome County

**WILSON MEMORIAL REGIONAL MEDICAL CENTER** See United Health Services Hospitals–Binghamton, Binghamton

## KATONAH—Westchester County

☒ **FOUR WINDS HOSPITAL (334002)**, 800 Cross River Road, Zip 10536–3549; tel. 914/763–8151, (Nonreporting) **A**1 9 10
Primary Contact: Martin A. Buccolo, Ph.D., Chief Executive Officer
COO: Moira Morrissey, Chief Operating Officer and General Counsel
CFO: Barry S. Weinstein, Chief Financial Officer
CMO: Jonathan Bauman, M.D., Chief Medical Officer
CIO: Barry S. Weinstein, Chief Financial Officer
CHR: Susan Cusano, Director Human Resources
Web address: www.fourwindshospital.com
**Control:** Partnership, Investor–owned, for–profit **Service:** Psychiatric

**Staffed Beds:** 181

**NY**

---

**Hospital, Medicare Provider Number, Address, Telephone, Approval, Facility, and Physician Codes, Health Care System**

★ American Hospital Association (AHA) membership
☐ The Joint Commission accreditation
○ Healthcare Facilities Accreditation Program
◇ DNV Healthcare Inc. accreditation
⇑ Center for Improvement in Healthcare Quality Accreditation
△ Commission on Accreditation of Rehabilitation Facilities (CARF) accreditation

## KENMORE—Erie County

✠ **KENMORE MERCY HOSPITAL (330102)**, 2950 Elmwood Avenue, Zip 14217–1390; tel. 716/447–6100, (Total facility includes 160 beds in nursing home–type unit) **A**1 9 10 **F**3 15 17 18 29 30 31 32 34 35 39 40 45 49 54 57 59 60 64 65 66 68 70 74 75 78 79 81 84 85 86 87 90 92 93 94 96 97 107 108 110 111 114 115 118 119 126 128 129 130 131 132 146 **P**5 6 **S** Catholic Health System, Buffalo, NY
Primary Contact: James M. Millard, President and Chief Executive Officer
COO: Walter Ludwig, Chief Operating Officer
CFO: James H. Dunlop, Jr., CPA, Executive Vice President and Chief Financial Officer
CMO: James Fitzpatrick, M.D., Vice President Medical Affairs
CHR: Laura Cianflone, Director Human Resources
CNO: Cheryl Hayes, Vice President Patient Care Services
Web address: www.chsbuffalo.org
**Control:** Church–operated, Nongovernment, not–for profit **Service:** General Medical and Surgical

**Staffed Beds:** 288 **Admissions:** 8863 **Census:** 243 **Outpatient Visits:** 131664 **Births:** 0 **Total Expense ($000):** 154372 **Payroll Expense ($000):** 67236 **Personnel:** 1008

## KINGSTON—Ulster County

**BENEDICTINE HOSPITAL** See Health Alliance Hospital – Mary's Avenue Campus

★ ◇ **HEALTH ALLIANCE HOSPITAL – BROADWAY CAMPUS (330004)**, 396 Broadway, Zip 12401–4692; tel. 845/331–3131 **A**6 9 10 19 21 **F**3 8 11 13 15 18 20 28 29 30 34 35 36 40 45 49 50 54 56 57 59 60 63 64 68 70 74 75 76 77 79 81 82 83 84 85 86 87 92 93 102 107 108 111 114 115 119 130 131 132 135 146 147 148 **S** HealthAlliance of the Hudson Valley, Kingston, NY
Primary Contact: David Scarpino, President and Chief Executive Officer
COO: Robert Seidman, Chief Operating Officer
CFO: Steven J. Haas, Chief Financial Officer
CMO: Frank Ehrlich, M.D., Chief Medical Officer
CIO: John Finch, Vice President Information Services
CHR: Greg M. Howard, Director Human Resource
Web address: www.hahv.org
**Control:** Other not–for–profit (including NFP Corporation) **Service:** General Medical and Surgical

**Staffed Beds:** 150 **Admissions:** 7471 **Census:** 98 **Outpatient Visits:** 86965 **Births:** 349 **Total Expense ($000):** 109150 **Payroll Expense ($000):** 43121 **Personnel:** 801

◇ **HEALTH ALLIANCE HOSPITAL – MARY'S AVENUE CAMPUS (330224)**, 105 Marys Avenue, Zip 12401–5894; tel. 845/338–2500 **A**2 9 10 19 21 **F**3 4 8 11 15 18 20 29 30 31 34 35 36 45 49 50 54 56 57 59 63 64 66 68 70 74 75 78 79 81 82 83 84 85 86 87 90 98 105 107 108 110 114 119 120 121 123 129 130 131 132 146 147 148 **P**7 **S** HealthAlliance of the Hudson Valley, Kingston, NY
Primary Contact: David Scarpino, President and Chief Executive Officer
COO: Robert Seidman, Chief Operating Officer
CFO: Steven J. Haas, Chief Financial Officer
CMO: Frank Ehrlich, M.D., Chief Medical Officer
CIO: John Finch, Chief Information and Community Officer
CHR: Greg M. Howard, Vice President Human Resources
Web address: www.hahv.org
**Control:** Other not–for–profit (including NFP Corporation) **Service:** General Medical and Surgical

**Staffed Beds:** 120 **Admissions:** 3404 **Census:** 68 **Outpatient Visits:** 31927 **Births:** 0 **Total Expense ($000):** 61664 **Payroll Expense ($000):** 22222 **Personnel:** 544

**KINGSTON HOSPITAL** See Health Alliance Hospital – Broadway Campus

## LEWISTON—Niagara County

✠ **MOUNT ST. MARY'S HOSPITAL AND HEALTH CENTER (330188)**, 5300 Military Road, Zip 14092–1903; tel. 716/297–4800, (Total facility includes 250 beds in nursing home–type unit) **A**1 9 10 **F**1 3 4 11 13 15 16 17 18 28 29 30 34 35 40 41 42 49 50 51 54 56 57 59 60 64 65 66 67 68 70 72 73 74 75 76 77 79 80 81 82 84 85 87 88 89 90 92 93 97 98 107 108 110 111 114 115 119 128 130 132 135 143 146 147 148 **P**5 **S** Ascension Health, Saint Louis, MO
Primary Contact: Gary C. Tucker, President and Chief Executive Officer
CFO: Stephen Franko, Vice President Finance and Chief Financial Officer
CMO: Domenic F. Falsetti, M.D., Chief of Staff and Medical Director
CHR: Deborah J. Serafin, Vice President Human Resources
CNO: Barbara A. Bucci, R.N., Vice President Patient Care and Chief Nursing Officer
Web address: www.msmh.org
**Control:** Church–operated, Nongovernment, not–for profit **Service:** General Medical and Surgical

**Staffed Beds:** 377 **Admissions:** 6967 **Census:** 321 **Outpatient Visits:** 154848 **Births:** 308 **Total Expense ($000):** 115801 **Payroll Expense ($000):** 57134 **Personnel:** 677

## LITTLE FALLS—Herkimer County

★ **LITTLE FALLS HOSPITAL (331311)**, 140 Burwell Street, Zip 13365–1725; tel. 315/823–1000, (Nonreporting) **A**9 10 18 **S** Bassett Healthcare Network, Cooperstown, NY
Primary Contact: Michael L. Ogden, President and Chief Executive Officer
CFO: James Vielkind, Chief Financial Officer
CMO: Mark Winther, M.D., Medical Director
CIO: Duane Merry, Chief Information Officer
CHR: Marlene Little, Senior Director
CNO: Heidi Camardello, Vice President Patient Care Services and Chief Nursing Officer
Web address: www.lfhny.org
**Control:** Other not–for–profit (including NFP Corporation) **Service:** General Medical and Surgical

**Staffed Beds:** 59

## LITTLE NECK—Queens County, See New York City

## LOCKPORT—Niagara County

★ **EASTERN NIAGARA HOSPITAL (330163)**, 521 East Avenue, Zip 14094–3299; tel. 716/514–5700, (Includes EASTERN NIAGARA HOSPITAL LOCKPORT, 521 East Avenue, tel. 716/514–5700; EASTERN NIAGARA HOSPITAL NEWFANE, 2600 William Street, Newfane, Zip 14108–1093; tel. 716/778–5111) **A**9 10 **F**3 4 13 15 18 19 28 29 30 31 34 40 42 45 46 47 48 49 54 57 59 60 63 65 68 70 74 75 76 77 79 81 82 83 84 85 87 89 93 94 98 99 100 102 107 108 110 111 115 118 119 126 130 132 135 144 146 147 148
Primary Contact: Clare A. Haar, Chief Executive Officer
COO: David J. Di Bacco, Chief Operating Officer
CFO: Michael F. Ickowski, Chief Financial Officer
CMO: Bruce J. Cusenz, M.D., Medical Director
CHR: Joseph Farrauto, Director Human Resources
CNO: Mary Beth Campo, MS, Director of Nursing
Web address: www.enhs.org
**Control:** Other not–for–profit (including NFP Corporation) **Service:** General Medical and Surgical

**Staffed Beds:** 125 **Admissions:** 4157 **Census:** 58 **Outpatient Visits:** 836389 **Births:** 364 **Total Expense ($000):** 65488 **Payroll Expense ($000):** 29626 **Personnel:** 673

## LONG ISLAND CITY—Queens County, See New York City

## LOWVILLE—Lewis County

✠ **LEWIS COUNTY GENERAL HOSPITAL (331317)**, 7785 North State Street, Zip 13367–1297; tel. 315/376–5200, (Total facility includes 160 beds in nursing home–type unit) **A**1 9 10 18 **F**2 3 6 8 11 15 29 30 34 40 45 50 54 56 57 59 62 63 70 75 76 77 78 79 81 82 84 85 86 87 91 93 96 97 107 108 110 111 115 119 124 127 129 130 131 132 133 143 146 147 148 **P**6 8
Primary Contact: Eric Burch, Chief Executive Officer
CFO: Jeffrey Hellinger, Interim Chief Financial Officer
CMO: Catherine Williams, M.D., Medical Director
CIO: Rob Uttendorfsky, Director Information Management
CHR: James Swords, Director Human Resources
CNO: Jennifer Shaver, Director of Nursing
Web address: www.lcgh.net
**Control:** County–Government, nonfederal **Service:** General Medical and Surgical

**Staffed Beds:** 185 **Admissions:** 1530 **Census:** 170 **Outpatient Visits:** 125955 **Births:** 294 **Total Expense ($000):** 71896 **Payroll Expense ($000):** 26500 **Personnel:** 579

## MALONE—Franklin County

✠ **ALICE HYDE MEDICAL CENTER (330084)**, 133 Park Street, Zip 12953–1243, Mailing Address: P.O. Box 729, Zip 12953–0729; tel. 518/483–3000, (Total facility includes 75 beds in nursing home–type unit) **A**1 9 10 20 **F**3 11 13 15 17 18 28 29 31 34 35 36 39 40 45 50 57 59 64 68 70 75 76 77 78 79 81 82 84 85 86 87 90 93 97 107 108 110 111 115 117 119 121 127 128 129 130 131 132 135 143 144 146 148 **P**6
Primary Contact: Douglas F. DiVello, President and Chief Executive Officer
COO: Matthew Jones, Senior Director Support Services and Facilities
CFO: Sean Curtin, Chief Financial Officer
CMO: William Latreille, M.D., Chief Medical Officer
CIO: Darrin Goodrow, Chief Information Officer
CHR: Emily Campbell, Senior Director Human Resources
CNO: Julie Marshall, Chief Nursing Officer
Web address: www.alicehyde.com
**Control:** Other not–for–profit (including NFP Corporation) **Service:** General Medical and Surgical

**Staffed Beds:** 135 **Admissions:** 2210 **Census:** 95 **Outpatient Visits:** 158508 **Births:** 252 **Total Expense ($000):** 70641 **Payroll Expense ($000):** 34713 **Personnel:** 505

## MANHASSET—Nassau County

**MANHASSET AMBULATORY CARE PAVILION** See Long Island Jewish Medical Center, New Hyde Park

**NY**

*Many Facility Codes have changed. Please refer to the AHA Guide Code Chart.* © 2015 AHA Guide

✠ **NORTH SHORE UNIVERSITY HOSPITAL (330106)**, 300 Community Drive, Zip 11030–3816; tel. 516/562–0100 **A**1 2 3 5 8 9 10 **F**3 6 7 8 9 11 12 13 14 15 17 18 19 20 21 22 23 24 26 28 29 30 31 32 34 35 36 37 38 39 40 41 43 44 45 46 47 48 49 50 51 52 53 54 55 56 57 58 59 60 61 62 63 64 65 66 68 69 70 71 72 73 74 75 76 77 78 79 80 81 82 83 84 85 86 87 91 92 93 94 97 98 99 100 101 102 103 104 107 108 109 110 111 112 114 115 116 117 118 119 120 121 123 124 126 129 130 131 132 134 135 136 138 141 142 143 144 145 146 147 148 **P**5 6 **S** North Shore–Long Island Jewish Health System, Great Neck, NY
Primary Contact: Alessandro Bellucci, M.D., Executive Director
CFO: Frank Rizzo, Chief Financial Officer, Central Region
CMO: Michael Gitman, M.D., Medical Director
CIO: Nympha Meindel, R.N., Chief Information Officer
CHR: Debra Bierman, Associate Executive Director Human Resources
CNO: Kerri Scanlon, MSN, Chief Nursing Officer
Web address: www.northshorelij.com
**Control:** Other not–for–profit (including NFP Corporation) **Service:** General Medical and Surgical

**Staffed Beds:** 764 **Admissions:** 45207 **Census:** 703 **Outpatient Visits:** 824496 **Births:** 6655 **Total Expense ($000):** 1703976 **Payroll Expense ($000):** 894207 **Personnel:** 9759

**MANHATTAN—New York County, See New York City**

**MARCY—Oneida County**

☐ **CENTRAL NEW YORK PSYCHIATRIC CENTER**, 9005 Old River Road, Zip 13403–3000, Mailing Address: P.O. Box 300, Zip 13403–0300; tel. 315/765–3600, (Nonreporting) **A**1 **S** New York State Office of Mental Health, Albany, NY
Primary Contact: Maureen Bosco, Executive Director
Web address: www.omh.ny.gov
**Control:** State–Government, nonfederal **Service:** Psychiatric

**Staffed Beds:** 226

**MARGARETVILLE—Delaware County**

◇ **MARGARETVILLE HOSPITAL (331304)**, 42084 State Highway 28, Zip 12455–2820; tel. 845/586–2631, (Nonreporting) **A**9 10 18 21 **S** HealthAlliance of the Hudson Valley, Kingston, NY
Primary Contact: Sandra A. Horan, Executive Director
CHR: Linda Mead, Director Human Resources
Web address: www.margaretvillehospital.org
**Control:** Other not–for–profit (including NFP Corporation) **Service:** General Medical and Surgical

**Staffed Beds:** 15

**MASSENA—St. Lawrence County**

✠ **MASSENA MEMORIAL HOSPITAL (330223)**, One Hospital Drive, Zip 13662–1097; tel. 315/764–1711, (Nonreporting) **A**1 9 10 20
Primary Contact: Robert G. Wolleben, Chief Executive Officer
CFO: Patrick M. Facteau, Chief Financial Officer
CMO: Nimesh Desai, M.D., Medical Director
CIO: Jana Grose, Chief Information Officer
CHR: Jonnie Dorothy, Senior Director Human Resources
Web address: www.massenahospital.org
**Control:** City–Government, nonfederal **Service:** General Medical and Surgical

**Staffed Beds:** 50

**MEDINA—Orleans County**

★ △ ◇ **MEDINA MEMORIAL HOSPITAL (331319)**, 200 Ohio Street, Zip 14103–1095; tel. 585/798–2000, (Total facility includes 30 beds in nursing home–type unit) **A**7 9 10 21 **F**3 11 15 18 24 26 29 34 35 40 45 46 50 51 53 54 57 59 60 62 64 68 70 75 77 79 81 85 86 87 89 90 91 92 93 96 97 107 108 110 111 115 118 119 128 129 130 132 135 144 146 148
Primary Contact: Wendy Jacobson, Interim President and Chief Executive Officer
COO: Wendy Jacobson, Chief Operating Officer and Chief Nursing Officer
CFO: David Britton, Interim Chief Financial Officer
CMO: Joseph Misiti, M.D., President Medical Staff
CHR: Mary Williams, Director Human Resources
CNO: Wendy Jacobson, Chief Operating Officer and Chief Nursing Officer
Web address: www.medinamemorial.org
**Control:** Other not–for–profit (including NFP Corporation) **Service:** General Medical and Surgical

**Staffed Beds:** 100 **Admissions:** 1555 **Census:** 28 **Births:** 0 **Total Expense ($000):** 31424 **Payroll Expense ($000):** 14720 **Personnel:** 323

**MIDDLETOWN—Orange County**

✠ △ **ORANGE REGIONAL MEDICAL CENTER (330126)**, 707 East Main Street, Zip 10940–2650; tel. 845/333–1000 **A**1 2 7 9 10 12 13 **F**3 5 8 11 12 13 15 17 18 19 20 22 26 28 29 30 31 34 35 40 49 51 54 55 57 59 60 64 68 70 72 74 75 76 77 78 79 81 82 83 84 85 86 87 89 90 93 96 98 99 100 101 102 103 104 105 107 108 110 111 114 115 117 118 119 120 121 123 124 126 129 130 132 135 144 146 147 148 **S** Greater Hudson Valley Health System, Middletown, NY
Primary Contact: Scott Batulis, President and Chief Executive Officer
COO: Timothy P. Selz, Vice President
CFO: Mitch Amodo, Vice President and Chief Financial Officer
CMO: James Oxley, D.O., Vice President Medical Affairs
CIO: Shafiq Rab, Chief Information Officer
CHR: Deborah Carr, Vice President Human Resources
Web address: www.ormc.org
**Control:** Other not–for–profit (including NFP Corporation) **Service:** General Medical and Surgical

**Staffed Beds:** 301 **Admissions:** 21002 **Census:** 283 **Births:** 1523

**MINEOLA—Nassau County**

✠ **WINTHROP–UNIVERSITY HOSPITAL (330167)**, 259 First Street, Zip 11501–3957; tel. 516/663–0333, (Includes CHILDREN'S MEDICAL CENTER, 259 First Street, tel. 516/663–0333) **A**1 2 3 5 8 9 10 **F**3 5 6 8 9 11 12 13 14 15 17 18 19 20 22 24 26 28 29 30 31 32 34 35 37 38 39 40 41 43 44 45 46 47 48 49 50 51 53 54 55 56 57 58 59 60 61 62 63 64 65 66 68 69 70 71 72 73 74 75 76 77 78 79 81 82 84 85 86 87 88 89 92 93 94 97 100 103 107 108 110 111 113 114 115 116 117 118 119 120 121 123 124 126 129 130 131 132 134 135 141 142 144 145 146 147 148 **P**5 6 7 8
Primary Contact: John F. Collins, President and Chief Executive Officer
COO: Garry Schwall, Chief Operating Officer
CFO: Palmira Cataliotti, Senior Vice President, Chief Financial Officer and Treasurer
CMO: Michael Ammazzalorso, M.D., Chief Medical Officer
CIO: Nicholas Casabona, Chief Information Officer
CHR: Stacey Pfeffer, Senior Vice President Human Resources
CNO: Valerie Terzano, MS, Chief Nursing Officer, Senior Vice President Nursing
Web address: www.winthrop.org
**Control:** Other not–for–profit (including NFP Corporation) **Service:** General Medical and Surgical

**Staffed Beds:** 511 **Admissions:** 30818 **Census:** 449 **Outpatient Visits:** 382716 **Births:** 4858 **Total Expense ($000):** 1142861 **Payroll Expense ($000):** 585854 **Personnel:** 6948

**MONTOUR FALLS—Schuyler County**

✠ **SCHUYLER HOSPITAL (331313)**, 220 Steuben Street, Zip 14865–9709; tel. 607/535–7121, (Total facility includes 120 beds in nursing home unit) **A**1 9 10 18 **F**3 11 12 14 15 18 29 30 34 35 40 45 57 59 64 70 75 77 81 82 85 87 91 92 93 94 97 107 110 111 114 119 128 129 130 131 133 135 146 148 **P**6
Primary Contact: Andrew R. Manzer, President and Chief Executive Officer
CMO: Michael Eisman, M.D., Medical Director
CHR: Troy Preston, Director Human Resources
Web address: www.schuylerhospital.org
**Control:** Other not–for–profit (including NFP Corporation) **Service:** General Medical and Surgical

**Staffed Beds:** 145 **Admissions:** 1063 **Census:** 126 **Outpatient Visits:** 44040 **Births:** 0 **Total Expense ($000):** 31506 **Payroll Expense ($000):** 16792 **Personnel:** 323

**NY**

**MONTROSE—Westchester County**

☒ **VETERANS AFFAIRS HUDSON VALLEY HEALTH CARE SYSTEM**, 2094 Albany Post Road, Zip 10548–1454, Mailing Address: P.O. Box 100, Zip 10548–0100; tel. 914/737–4400, (Includes VETERAN AFFAIRS HUDSON VALLEY HEALTH CARE SYSTEM–CASTLE POINT CAMPUS, 41 Castle Point Road, Wappingers, Zip 12590; tel. 914/831–2000; VETERANS AFFAIRS HUDSON VALLEY HEALTH CARE SYSTEM–MONTROSE CAMPUS, 2094 Albany Post Road, Zip 10548; tel. 914/737–4400), (Total facility includes 180 beds in nursing home–type unit) **A**1 3 5 9 **F**1 4 5 29 30 31 34 35 38 39 53 54 56 57 59 61 63 64 65 66 68 71 75 77 78 81 82 83 84 86 87 91 93 94 97 98 100 101 102 103 104 107 111 112 115 117 119 120 127 130 132 133 143 144 145 146 147 148 **P**6 **S** Department of Veterans Affairs, Washington, DC
Primary Contact: Margaret B. Caplan, Director
COO: John M. Grady, Associate Director
CFO: John Walsh, Chief Fiscal Services
CMO: Joanne J. Malina, M.D., Chief of Staff
CIO: Thomas Rooney, Chief Information Resource Management
CHR: Dardanella Russell, Chief Human Resources Management Service
Web address: www.hudsonvalley.va.gov/
**Control:** Veterans Affairs, Government, federal **Service:** Psychiatric

**Staffed Beds:** 403 **Admissions:** 1586 **Census:** 270 **Outpatient Visits:** 389749 **Births:** 0 **Total Expense ($000):** 242194 **Payroll Expense ($000):** 122721 **Personnel:** 1521

**MOUNT KISCO—Westchester County**

☒ **NORTHERN WESTCHESTER HOSPITAL (330162)**, 400 East Main Street, Zip 10549–3477; tel. 914/666–1200 **A**1 2 9 10 **F**3 8 12 13 15 17 18 19 28 29 30 31 32 34 35 36 37 40 43 46 47 48 49 50 51 54 55 56 57 59 60 61 64 65 68 70 72 73 74 75 76 78 79 81 82 84 85 86 87 89 91 92 93 97 98 99 100 101 102 103 107 108 109 110 111 114 115 118 119 120 121 123 124 126 129 130 131 132 135 146 147 148
Primary Contact: Joel Seligman, President and Chief Executive Officer
CFO: John Partenza, Vice President and Treasurer
CMO: Marla Koroly, M.D., Chief Medical Officer and Senior Vice President Medical Affairs
CIO: Sue Prince, Director Information Systems
CHR: Kerry Flynn Barrett, Vice President Human Resources
CNO: Lauraine Szekely, R.N., Senior Vice President, Patient Care
Web address: www.nwhc.net
**Control:** Other not–for–profit (including NFP Corporation) **Service:** General Medical and Surgical

**Staffed Beds:** 208 **Admissions:** 8656 **Census:** 111 **Outpatient Visits:** 147409 **Births:** 1622 **Total Expense ($000):** 235791 **Payroll Expense ($000):** 95091 **Personnel:** 1313

**MOUNT VERNON—Westchester County**

☐ **MONTEFIORE MOUNT VERNON (330086)**, 12 North Seventh Avenue, Zip 10550–2098; tel. 914/664–8000 **A**1 3 5 9 10 **F**3 14 15 18 29 30 31 34 35 40 45 50 59 60 61 64 65 66 68 74 75 77 78 79 81 84 85 86 87 92 93 98 100 102 107 110 111 114 119 130 146 147 **P**5 **S** Montefiore Health System, Bronx, NY
Primary Contact: Susan Green–Lorenzen, Senior Vice President Operations
CFO: Albert M. Farina, Chief Financial Officer
CMO: Gary Ishkanian, M.D., Vice President Medical Affairs
CIO: Barbara Cooke, Director Health Information Systems
CHR: Dennis H. Ashley, Vice President Human Resources
Web address: www.montefiorehealthsystem.org/landing.cfm?id=17
**Control:** Other not–for–profit (including NFP Corporation) **Service:** General Medical and Surgical

**Staffed Beds:** 83 **Admissions:** 3315 **Census:** 65 **Outpatient Visits:** 142802 **Births:** 0 **Total Expense ($000):** 79366 **Payroll Expense ($000):** 37154 **Personnel:** 542

**NEW HAMPTON—Orange County**

☐ **MID–HUDSON FORENSIC PSYCHIATRIC CENTER (334061)**, Route 17M, Zip 10958, Mailing Address: P.O. Box 158, Zip 10958–0158; tel. 845/374–8700 **A**1 10 **F**39 68 77 87 98 106 130 **S** New York State Office of Mental Health, Albany, NY
Primary Contact: Joseph Freebern, Executive Director
Web address: www.omh.ny.gov
**Control:** State–Government, nonfederal **Service:** Psychiatric

**Staffed Beds:** 169 **Admissions:** 289 **Census:** 177 **Births:** 0 **Total Expense ($000):** 91296 **Payroll Expense ($000):** 45892 **Personnel:** 49

**NEW HYDE PARK—Queens County, See New York City**

**NEW ROCHELLE—Westchester County**

☒ **MONTEFIORE NEW ROCHELLE (330184)**, 16 Guion Place, Zip 10801–5502; tel. 914/632–5000, (Total facility includes 150 beds in nursing home–type unit) **A**1 2 3 5 6 9 10 **F**2 3 8 11 12 13 15 18 28 29 30 31 32 35 37 40 43 45 50 55 61 64 65 66 68 70 73 74 76 77 78 79 81 82 84 85 87 89 90 92 93 97 100 107 108 110 114 119 128 129 130 132 146 **P**5 **S** Montefiore Health System, Bronx, NY
Primary Contact: Anthony Alfano, Vice President Executive Director
COO: John P. Mamangakis, Senior Vice President
CFO: Albert M. Farina, Senior Vice President and Chief Financial Officer
CMO: Richard Barone, M.D., Medical Director
CIO: Barbara Cooke, Director Health Information Systems
CHR: Dennis H. Ashley, Vice President Human Resources
CNO: Pamela M. Dupuis, R.N., Senior Vice President Patient Care Services
Web address: www.montefiorehealthsystem.org
**Control:** Other not–for–profit (including NFP Corporation) **Service:** General Medical and Surgical

**Staffed Beds:** 253 **Admissions:** 7545 **Census:** 220 **Outpatient Visits:** 104994 **Births:** 1025 **Total Expense ($000):** 190574 **Payroll Expense ($000):** 89096 **Personnel:** 1304

**NEW YORK (Includes all hospitals located within the five boroughs)**
    **BRONX** - Bronx County (Mailing Address - Bronx)
    **BROOKLYN** - Kings County (Mailing Address - Brooklyn)
    **MANHATTAN** - New York County (Mailing Address - New York)
    **QUEENS** - Queens County (Mailing Addresses - Bellerose, Elmhurst, Far Rockaway, Flushing, Forest Hills, Glen Oaks, Holliswood, Jackson Heights, Jamaica, Little Neck, Long Island City, New Hyde Park, and Queens Village)
    **RICHMOND VALLEY** - Richmond County (Mailing Address - Staten Island)

☒ **BELLEVUE HOSPITAL CENTER (330204)**, 462 First Avenue, Zip 10016–9198; tel. 212/562–4141 **A**1 3 5 9 10 **F**3 4 5 8 11 12 13 15 17 18 19 20 22 24 26 28 29 30 31 34 35 36 38 39 40 41 43 44 45 46 48 49 50 52 55 56 57 58 59 60 61 64 65 66 68 70 71 72 73 74 75 76 77 78 79 81 82 84 85 86 87 88 89 90 91 92 93 94 96 97 98 99 100 101 102 103 104 105 107 108 110 111 114 115 118 119 130 132 134 135 141 143 144 146 147 148 **S** New York City Health and Hospitals Corporation, New York, NY
Primary Contact: Steven Alexander, Executive Director
COO: William Hicks, Chief Operating Officer
CFO: Jay Weinmann, Chief Financial Officer
CMO: Nate Link, M.D., Medical Director
CIO: Tonguc Yaman, Deputy Chief Information Officer
CHR: Howard Kritz, Director Human Resources
CNO: Kim K. Mendez, Ed.D., Chief Nurse Officer
Web address: www.nyc.gov/bellevue
**Control:** City–Government, nonfederal **Service:** General Medical and Surgical

**Staffed Beds:** 827 **Admissions:** 28478 **Census:** 645 **Outpatient Visits:** 611773 **Births:** 1394 **Total Expense ($000):** 842137 **Payroll Expense ($000):** 308143 **Personnel:** 4578

**BETH ISRAEL MEDICAL CENTER** See Mount Sinai Beth Israel

**BETH ISRAEL MEDICAL CENTER–KINGS HIGHWAY DIVISION** See Mount Sinai Beth Israel Brooklyn

☐ **BRONX PSYCHIATRIC CENTER (334053)**, 1500 Waters Place, Bronx, Zip 10461–2796; tel. 718/931–0600, (Nonreporting) **A**1 3 5 10 **S** New York State Office of Mental Health, Albany, NY
Primary Contact: Pamela Turner, Executive Director
CFO: Robert Erway, Director for Administration
Web address: www.omh.ny.gov
**Control:** State–Government, nonfederal **Service:** Psychiatric

**Staffed Beds:** 450

☒ **BRONX–LEBANON HOSPITAL CENTER HEALTH CARE SYSTEM (330009)**, 1276 Fulton Avenue, Bronx, Zip 10456–3499; tel. 718/590–1800, (Includes BRONX–LEBANON SPECIAL CARE CENTER, 1265 Fulton Avenue, Zip 10465; tel. 718/579–7000; CONCOURSE DIVISION, 1650 Grand Concourse, Zip 10457; tel. 718/590–1800; FULTON DIVISION, 1276 Fulton Avenue, Zip 10456; tel. 718/590–1800; HIGHBRIDGE WOODYCREST CENTER, 936 Woodycrest Avenue, Zip 10452; tel. 718/293–3200), (Total facility includes 330 beds in nursing home–type unit) **A**1 3 5 9 10 **F**2 3 4 5 8 9 11 12 13 15 17 18 19 20 22 26 28 29 30 31 32 34 35 37 38 39 40 41 44 45 46 47 48 49 50 51 52 54 55 56 57 58 59 60 61 64 65 66 68 70 71 72 73 74 75 76 77 78 79 80 81 82 83 84 85 86 87 88 89 91 92 93 94 96 97 98 99 100 101 102 103 104 105 106 107 108 109 110 111 113 114 115 118 119 123 126 128 129 130 131 132 133 134 135 144 145 146 147 148 **P**6
Primary Contact: Miguel A. Fuentes, Jr., President and Chief Executive Officer
COO: Steven Anderman, Chief Operating Officer
CFO: Victor DeMarco, Chief Financial Officer
CMO: Milton A. Gumbs, M.D., Vice President and Medical Director
CIO: Ivan Durbak, Chief Information Officer
CHR: Selena Griffin–Mahon, Assistant Vice President Human Resources
Web address: www.bronxcare.org
**Control:** Other not–for–profit (including NFP Corporation) **Service:** General Medical and Surgical

**Staffed Beds:** 972 **Admissions:** 29926 **Census:** 763 **Outpatient Visits:** 1141692 **Births:** 2213 **Total Expense ($000):** 757443 **Payroll Expense ($000):** 370974 **Personnel:** 4305

*Many Facility Codes have changed. Please refer to the AHA Guide Code Chart.*

NY

☐ **BROOKDALE HOSPITAL MEDICAL CENTER (330233)**, One Brookdale Plaza, Brooklyn, Zip 11212–3139; tel. 718/240–5000, (Nonreporting) **A**1 3 5 9 10
Primary Contact: Mark Toney, President and Chief Executive Officer
CFO: James Porter, Chief Financial Officer
CMO: Estevan Garcia, M.D., Chief Medical Officer
CIO: David Reitzel, Chief Information Officer
CHR: Margaret M. Brubaker, Senior Vice President Human Resources
CNO: Suzanne Pennacchio, Senior Vice President Patient Care Services
Web address: www.brookdalehospital.org
**Control:** Other not-for-profit (including NFP Corporation) **Service:** General Medical and Surgical

**Staffed Beds: 790**

☐ **BROOKLYN HOSPITAL CENTER (330056)**, 121 DeKalb Avenue, Brooklyn, Zip 11201–5425; tel. 718/250–8000 **A**1 3 5 8 9 10 **F**3 4 8 12 13 14 15 17 18 20 29 30 31 32 34 35 38 39 40 49 50 51 54 56 57 59 60 61 62 64 65 66 68 70 72 74 75 76 77 78 79 80 81 82 83 84 85 86 87 88 89 90 97 100 102 104 107 108 110 111 114 115 118 119 120 121 123 124 129 130 131 132 135 143 144 146 147 148
Primary Contact: Jonathan M. Weld, Interim President and Chief Executive Officer
COO: Wayne Allen, Acting Chief Operating Officer
CFO: Joseph Guarracino, Senior Vice President and Chief Financial Officer
CIO: Irene Farrelly, Vice President and Chief Information Officer
CHR: Ira Warm, Senior Vice President Human Resources
Web address: www.tbh.org
**Control:** Church-operated, Nongovernment, not-for profit **Service:** General Medical and Surgical

**Staffed Beds: 332 Admissions: 16629 Census: 261 Outpatient Visits:** 329253 **Total Expense ($000):** 394945 **Payroll Expense ($000):** 212362 **Personnel:** 3355

⊠ **CALVARY HOSPITAL (332006)**, 1740 Eastchester Road, Bronx, Zip 10461–2392; tel. 718/863–6900 **A**1 3 5 9 10 **F**1 29 30 35 39 62 63 64 68 74 78 82 84 87 119 121 130 132 134 146 148 **P**6
Primary Contact: Frank A. Calamari, President and Chief Executive Officer
COO: Richard J. Kutilek, Chief Operating Officer
CFO: Andrew Greco, Chief Financial Officer
CMO: Michael J. Brescia, M.D., Executive Medical Director
CIO: Patrick Martin, Director Information Systems
CHR: Michael T. Troncone, Chief Human Resources Officer
CNO: Margaret Pelkowski, R.N., Vice President Patient Care Services
Web address: www.calvaryhospital.org
**Control:** Church-operated, Nongovernment, not-for profit **Service:** Long-Term Acute Care hospital

**Staffed Beds: 225 Admissions: 2899 Census: 209 Outpatient Visits:** 107520 **Births: 0 Total Expense ($000):** 113186 **Payroll Expense ($000):** 60259 **Personnel:** 879

**COLER–GOLDWATER SPECIALTY HOSPITAL AND NURSING FACILITY** See Henry J. Carter Specialty Hospital and Nursing Facility

**CONCOURSE DIVISION** See Bronx–Lebanon Hospital Center Health Care System, Bronx

⊠ **CONEY ISLAND HOSPITAL (330196)**, 2601 Ocean Parkway, Brooklyn, Zip 11235–7795; tel. 718/616–3000 **A**1 3 5 9 10 12 13 **F**3 4 5 8 9 11 13 15 17 18 19 20 28 29 30 31 32 34 35 38 39 40 41 45 46 49 50 51 54 55 56 57 58 59 60 61 64 65 66 68 70 71 73 74 75 76 77 78 79 81 82 83 84 85 87 89 90 91 93 94 96 97 98 99 100 102 103 104 106 107 108 110 111 114 115 118 119 129 130 132 135 143 146 147 148 **S** New York City Health and Hospitals Corporation, New York, NY
Primary Contact: Arthur Wagner, Senior Vice President and Executive Director
COO: Vito Bucculato, Chief Operating Officer
CFO: Paul Pandolfini, Chief Financial Officer
CMO: John Maese, M.D., Chief Medical Officer
CIO: Robert Kee, Chief Information Officer
CHR: Rodney Parker, Senior Associate Executive Director
CNO: Terry Mancher, R.N., Chief Nurse Executive
Web address: www.nyc.gov/html/hhc/html/facilities/coneyisland.shtml
**Control:** City-Government, nonfederal **Service:** General Medical and Surgical

**Staffed Beds: 371 Admissions: 14494 Census: 283 Outpatient Visits:** 319352 **Births: 1051 Total Expense ($000):** 429244 **Payroll Expense ($000):** 173463 **Personnel:** 3043

☐ **CREEDMOOR PSYCHIATRIC CENTER (334004)**, 79–25 Winchester Boulevard, Jamaica, Zip 11427–2128; tel. 718/264–3600, (Nonreporting) **A**1 10 **S** New York State Office of Mental Health, Albany, NY
Primary Contact: Ann Marie Barbarotta, Executive Director
CFO: Viodelda Ho–Shing, Deputy Director Administration
CIO: Ed Yunusov, Chief Information Officer
CHR: Adrienne Jones, Director Human Resources
CNO: Marie S. Jean–Louis, R.N., Chief Nursing Officer
Web address: www.omh.ny.gov
**Control:** State-Government, nonfederal **Service:** Psychiatric

**Staffed Beds: 380**

⊠ **ELMHURST HOSPITAL CENTER (330128)**, 79–01 Broadway, Elmhurst, Zip 11373–1329; tel. 718/334–4000 **A**1 2 3 5 9 10 **F**3 5 8 9 13 14 15 17 18 20 22 26 29 30 31 32 34 35 38 40 41 43 45 49 50 51 53 55 56 57 59 60 61 64 68 70 72 73 74 75 76 77 78 79 81 82 83 84 85 86 87 89 90 92 93 97 98 99 100 101 102 103 104 105 107 108 110 111 115 119 121 126 130 131 132 134 135 143 146 147 **P**6 **S** New York City Health and Hospitals Corporation, New York, NY
Primary Contact: Chris D. Constantino, Senior Vice President and Executive Director
COO: Wayne Zimmermann, Chief Operating Officer
CFO: Alina Moran, Chief Financial Officer
CMO: Jasmin Moshirpur, M.D., Dean and Medical Director
CIO: Vincent Smith, Chief Information Officer
CHR: Jeannith Michelen, Associate Executive Director
CNO: Joann Bernadette Gull, Chief Nursing Officer
Web address: www.nyc.gov/html/hhc/ehc/html/home/home.shtml
**Control:** City-Government, nonfederal **Service:** General Medical and Surgical

**Staffed Beds: 532 Admissions: 22118 Census: 439 Outpatient Visits:** 644916 **Births: 3154 Total Expense ($000):** 624481 **Payroll Expense ($000):** 234425 **Personnel:** 3162

⊠ **FLUSHING HOSPITAL MEDICAL CENTER (330193)**, 4500 Parsons Boulevard, Flushing, Zip 11355–2205; tel. 718/670–5000 **A**1 3 5 9 10 **F**3 4 5 7 8 11 12 13 15 17 18 29 30 31 32 34 35 36 39 40 41 45 50 56 57 59 60 61 63 64 65 68 70 71 72 73 74 75 77 78 79 81 82 84 85 87 91 92 93 97 98 100 101 102 103 104 107 110 111 114 119 128 130 132 135 146 147 148 **P**5 7 **S** MediSys Health Network, Jamaica, NY
Primary Contact: Bruce J. Flanz, President and Chief Executive Officer
COO: Robert V. Levine, Executive Vice President and Chief Operating Officer
CFO: Mounir F. Doss, Executive Vice President and Chief Financial Officer
CMO: Siamack Nemazie, M.D., Medical Director, Patient Safety Officer
CIO: Tony Gatto, Director Management Information Systems
CHR: Sheila Garvey, Vice President Human Resources
Web address: www.flushinghospital.org
**Control:** Other not-for-profit (including NFP Corporation) **Service:** General Medical and Surgical

**Staffed Beds: 299 Admissions: 14576 Census: 222 Outpatient Visits:** 152241 **Births: 2734 Total Expense ($000):** 296963 **Payroll Expense ($000):** 117168 **Personnel:** 1700

⊠ **FOREST HILLS HOSPITAL (330353)**, 102–01 66th Road, Forest Hills, Zip 11375–2029; tel. 718/830–4000 **A**1 2 3 9 10 **F**3 8 12 13 15 19 23 29 30 31 34 35 37 38 40 43 45 46 49 50 51 52 55 57 58 59 60 63 64 65 66 68 70 73 74 75 76 77 78 79 81 82 84 85 86 87 97 100 107 111 115 119 130 132 135 143 146 147 148 **P**5 6 **S** North Shore–Long Island Jewish Health System, Great Neck, NY
Primary Contact: Susan Browning, Executive Director
COO: Mark J. Solazzo, Senior Vice President and Chief Operating Officer
CFO: Robert S. Shapiro, Senior Vice President and Chief Financial Officer
CMO: Lawrence Smith, M.D., Senior Vice President and Chief Medical Officer
CIO: John Bosco, Vice President and Chief Information Officer
Web address: www.northshorelij.com
**Control:** Other not-for-profit (including NFP Corporation) **Service:** General Medical and Surgical

**Staffed Beds: 235 Admissions: 16029 Census: 208 Outpatient Visits:** 75695 **Births: 1931 Total Expense ($000):** 241820 **Payroll Expense ($000):** 120701 **Personnel:** 1265

**FULTON DIVISION** See Bronx–Lebanon Hospital Center Health Care System, Bronx

**GOLDWATER MEMORIAL HOSPITAL** See Henry J. Carter Specialty Hospital and Nursing Facility

☐ **GRACIE SQUARE HOSPITAL (334048)**, 420 East 76th Street, Zip 10021–3396; tel. 212/988–4400, (Nonreporting) **A**1 9 10
Primary Contact: David Wyman, President and Chief Executive Officer
Web address: www.nygsh.org
**Control:** Other not-for-profit (including NFP Corporation) **Service:** Psychiatric

**Staffed Beds: 157**

⊠ △ **HARLEM HOSPITAL CENTER (330240)**, 506 Lenox Avenue, Zip 10037–1802; tel. 212/939–1000, (Includes HARLEM GENERAL CARE UNIT AND HARLEM PSYCHIATRIC UNIT ) **A**1 3 5 7 9 10 **F**3 4 5 8 11 12 13 15 16 17 18 19 20 29 30 32 34 35 38 39 40 41 43 44 45 46 47 48 49 50 52 53 55 57 58 59 60 61 64 69 70 71 72 73 74 75 76 77 79 81 82 84 85 86 87 88 89 90 93 94 97 98 99 100 101 102 103 104 107 108 110 111 114 115 116 117 118 119 130 134 135 141 146 147 148 **S** New York City Health and Hospitals Corporation, New York, NY
Primary Contact: Denise C. Soares, R.N., Executive Director
Web address: www.nyc.gov/html/hhc/harlem
**Control:** City-Government, nonfederal **Service:** General Medical and Surgical

**Staffed Beds: 279 Admissions: 11350 Census: 186 Outpatient Visits:** 313039 **Births: 998 Total Expense ($000):** 429896 **Payroll Expense ($000):** 149496 **Personnel:** 2061

**NY**

---

**HENRY J. CARTER SPECIALTY HOSPITAL AND NURSING FACILITY (332008)**, 1752 Park Avenue, Zip 10035; tel. 646/686–0000, (Includes COLER MEMORIAL HOSPITAL, Roosevelt Island, Zip 10044; tel. 212/848–6000; GOLDWATER MEMORIAL HOSPITAL, Franklin D. Roosevelt Island, Zip 10044; tel. 212/318–8000), (Nonreporting) **A**1 3 10 **F**1 3 11 28 29 30 39 56 58 68 74 75 77 79 84 85 87 100 103 104 114 119 128 130 132 135 146 148 **S** New York City Health and Hospitals Corporation, New York, NY
Primary Contact: Robert K. Hughes, Executive Director
CFO: Gloria Ranghelli, Deputy Chief Financial Officer
CMO: Yolanda Bruno, M.D., Medical Director
CHR: Howard Kritz, Director
Web address: www.coler–goldwater.org
**Control:** City–Government, nonfederal **Service:** Long–Term Acute Care hospital

**Staffed Beds:** 386 **Total Expense ($000):** 181342 **Payroll Expense ($000):** 60662 **Admissions:** 679 **Census:** 313 **Outpatient Visits:** 0 **Births:** 0 **Personnel:** 857

**HOSPITAL FOR SPECIAL SURGERY (330270)**, 535 East 70th Street, Zip 10021–4898; tel. 212/606–1000 **A**1 3 5 8 9 10 **F**3 8 9 29 30 32 33 34 35 36 37 38 43 44 50 53 54 55 57 58 59 64 66 68 70 74 75 77 79 80 81 82 84 85 86 87 89 92 93 94 97 100 107 109 111 114 115 116 117 118 119 121 123 126 130 131 132 134 141 142 146 147 148 **P**8
Primary Contact: Louis A. Shapiro, President and Chief Executive Officer
COO: Lisa Goldstein, Executive Vice President and Chief Operating Officer
CFO: Stacey Malakoff, Executive Vice President and Chief Financial Officer
CMO: Todd Albert, M.D., Surgeon–in–Chief and Medical Director
CIO: Jamie Nelson, Vice President and Chief Information Officer
CHR: Bruce Slawitsky, Vice President Human Resources
CNO: Stephanie J. Goldberg, MSN, Senior Vice President and Chief Nursing Officer
Web address: www.hss.edu
**Control:** Other not–for–profit (including NFP Corporation) **Service:** Orthopedic

**Staffed Beds:** 199 **Admissions:** 14986 **Census:** 150 **Outpatient Visits:** 393571 **Births:** 0 **Total Expense ($000):** 844441 **Payroll Expense ($000):** 358290 **Personnel:** 3909

**INTERFAITH MEDICAL CENTER (330397)**, 1545 Atlantic Avenue, Brooklyn, Zip 11213–1122; tel. 718/613–4000, (Nonreporting) **A**1 3 5 9 10
Primary Contact: Patrick Sullivan, Interim President and Chief Executive Officer
CMO: Jochanan Weisenfreund, M.D., Senior Vice President Academic and Medical Affairs
CIO: Mark Lederman, Chief Information Officer
CHR: Venra Mathurin, Vice President Human Resources
Web address: www.interfaithmedical.com
**Control:** Other not–for–profit (including NFP Corporation) **Service:** General Medical and Surgical

**Staffed Beds:** 277

**JACK D WEILER HOSPITAL OF ALBERT EINSTEIN COLLEGE OF MEDICINE**
See Montefiore Medical Center, Bronx

**JACOBI MEDICAL CENTER (330127)**, 1400 Pelham Parkway South, Bronx, Zip 10461–1197; tel. 718/918–5000 **A**1 3 5 9 10 **F**3 4 5 8 11 12 13 15 16 17 18 20 26 29 30 31 32 34 35 38 39 40 41 43 44 45 46 47 50 51 56 57 58 59 60 61 62 64 65 66 70 72 73 74 75 76 77 78 79 80 81 82 84 85 87 88 89 90 92 93 94 96 97 98 99 100 101 102 103 104 107 108 110 111 117 119 130 131 132 134 135 144 146 147 148 **P**6 **S** New York City Health and Hospitals Corporation, New York, NY
Primary Contact: Chris Fugazy, Acting Executive Director
COO: Christopher Fugazy, Chief Operating Officer
CFO: Kathy Garramone, Chief Financial Officer
CMO: John McNelis, M.D., Acting Medical Director
CIO: Diane Carr, Chief Information Officer
CHR: Dolores Leite, Chief Human Resource Executive
CNO: Ellen O'Connor, Chief Nursing Officer
Web address: www.nyc.gov/html/hhc/jacobi/home.html
**Control:** City–Government, nonfederal **Service:** General Medical and Surgical

**Staffed Beds:** 457 **Admissions:** 19751 **Census:** 353 **Outpatient Visits:** 437063 **Births:** 2668 **Total Expense ($000):** 692613 **Payroll Expense ($000):** 265373 **Personnel:** 3452

**JAMAICA HOSPITAL MEDICAL CENTER (330014)**, 8900 Van Wyck Expressway, Jamaica, Zip 11418–2832; tel. 718/206–6000, (Total facility includes 224 beds in nursing home–type unit) **A**1 3 5 9 10 13 **F**1 3 7 11 13 15 17 18 19 20 22 26 29 30 31 32 34 35 36 38 39 40 41 43 44 45 49 50 52 53 54 55 56 57 58 59 60 61 62 64 65 66 68 70 71 72 73 74 75 76 77 78 79 80 81 82 83 84 85 86 87 89 90 92 93 94 96 97 98 100 101 102 103 104 107 108 110 111 114 115 118 119 128 129 130 131 132 134 135 143 144 146 147 **P**5 7 8 **S** MediSys Health Network, Jamaica, NY
Primary Contact: Bruce J. Flanz, President and Chief Executive Officer
COO: William Lynch, Executive Vice President and Chief Operating Officer
CFO: Mounir F. Doss, Executive Vice President and Chief Financial Officer
CMO: Antonietta Morisco, M.D., Medical Director, Chairman Anesthesiology
CIO: Sami Boshut, Chief Information Officer
CHR: Sheila Garvey, Vice President Human Resources
CNO: Kathleen Scher, R.N., Chief Nursing Officer
Web address: www.Jamaicahospital.org
**Control:** Other not–for–profit (including NFP Corporation) **Service:** General Medical and Surgical

**Staffed Beds:** 650 **Admissions:** 21826 **Census:** 554 **Outpatient Visits:** 397303 **Births:** 2417 **Total Expense ($000):** 641461 **Payroll Expense ($000):** 239142 **Personnel:** 3295

△ **JAMES J. PETERS VETERANS AFFAIRS MEDICAL CENTER**, 130 West Kingsbridge Road, Bronx, Zip 10468–3904; tel. 718/584–9000, (Total facility includes 80 beds in nursing home–type unit) **A**1 2 3 5 7 8 **F**3 8 9 11 12 18 29 30 31 33 34 35 36 38 39 40 43 44 45 46 47 48 49 50 51 53 54 56 57 58 59 60 61 62 63 64 65 66 68 70 71 74 75 77 78 79 80 81 82 83 84 85 86 87 90 91 92 93 94 95 96 97 98 100 101 102 103 104 107 108 109 111 113 114 115 118 119 120 121 122 123 126 129 130 131 132 135 143 146 147 148 **S** Department of Veterans Affairs, Washington, DC
Primary Contact: Erik Langhoff, M.D., Ph.D., Director
CFO: Gregory Angelo, Chief Fiscal Program
CMO: Clive Rosendorff, M.D., Chief Medical Program
CIO: Linda Bund, Chief Information Officer and Director Education
CHR: Peter Tinker, Chief Human Resources Officer
CNO: Kathleen Capitulo, Ph.D., Chief Nurse Executive
Web address: www.bronx.va.gov/
**Control:** Veterans Affairs, Government, federal **Service:** General Medical and Surgical

**Staffed Beds:** 325 **Admissions:** 3841 **Census:** 74 **Outpatient Visits:** 352698 **Births:** 0 **Total Expense ($000):** 278154 **Payroll Expense ($000):** 132941

**KINGS COUNTY HOSPITAL CENTER (330202)**, 451 Clarkson Avenue, Brooklyn, Zip 11203–2097; tel. 718/245–3131 **A**1 2 3 5 9 10 **F**3 4 5 8 9 11 12 13 15 17 18 19 20 24 26 28 29 30 31 32 34 35 38 39 40 41 43 46 47 49 50 51 52 53 56 57 58 59 60 61 64 65 68 70 71 72 73 74 75 76 77 78 79 81 82 83 84 85 86 87 88 89 90 91 92 93 94 97 98 99 100 101 102 103 104 105 106 107 108 110 111 114 115 116 119 120 121 123 129 130 131 132 134 135 143 144 145 146 147 148 **P**6 **S** New York City Health and Hospitals Corporation, New York, NY
Primary Contact: Ernest Baptiste, Executive Director
COO: Robert R. Miller, II, Chief Operating Officer
CFO: Julian John, Chief Financial Officer
CMO: Ghassan Jamaleddine, M.D., Medical Director
CIO: Dino Civan, Chief Information Officer
CHR: Michelle Emmons, Associate Executive Director
CNO: Opal Sinclair–Chung, R.N., Chief Nursing Officer, Deputy Executive Director
Web address: www.nyc.gov/html/hhc/kchc/html/home/home.shtml
**Control:** City–Government, nonfederal **Service:** General Medical and Surgical

**Staffed Beds:** 599 **Admissions:** 22390 **Census:** 530 **Outpatient Visits:** 704228 **Births:** 2262 **Total Expense ($000):** 811615 **Personnel:** 4932

**KINGSBORO PSYCHIATRIC CENTER (334063)**, 681 Clarkson Avenue, Brooklyn, Zip 11203–2125; tel. 718/221–7395, (Nonreporting) **A**1 3 5 10 **S** New York State Office of Mental Health, Albany, NY
Primary Contact: Deborah Parchment, Executive Director
CFO: Yinusa Awolowo, Business Officer
CMO: Jeffery Lucey, M.D., Clinical Director
CIO: George Gavora, Director Program Evaluation
CHR: Vera Thompson, Director Human Resources
CNO: Deborah Denigris, Chief Nursing Officer
Web address: www.omh.ny.gov/omhweb/facilities/kbpc/facility/htm
**Control:** State–Government, nonfederal **Service:** Psychiatric

**Staffed Beds:** 290

NY

*Many Facility Codes have changed. Please refer to the AHA Guide Code Chart.* © 2015 AHA Guide

☐ △ **KINGSBROOK JEWISH MEDICAL CENTER (330201)**, 585 Schenectady Avenue, Brooklyn, Zip 11203–1891; tel. 718/604–5000, (Total facility includes 466 beds in nursing home–type unit) **A**1 3 5 7 9 10 **F**3 8 15 17 18 28 29 30 31 34 35 39 40 45 46 48 49 50 54 56 57 59 60 61 64 65 68 70 74 75 77 78 79 80 81 82 84 85 87 90 91 92 93 94 96 97 98 100 101 103 104 107 108 110 111 115 119 128 130 131 135 143 146 147 148
Primary Contact: Linda Brady, M.D., President and Chief Executive Officer
COO: Robert Dubicki, Executive Vice President and Chief Operating Officer
CFO: John Schmitt, Senior Vice President and Chief Financial Officer
CMO: Sibte Burney, M.D., Senior Vice President Medical Affairs and Chief Medical Officer
CIO: Daniel Morreale, Vice President and Chief Information Officer
CHR: John McKeon, Vice President Human Resources
CNO: Jane Lederer, R.N., Vice President and Chief Nursing Officer
Web address: www.kingsbrook.org
**Control:** Other not–for–profit (including NFP Corporation) **Service:** General Medical and Surgical

**Staffed Beds:** 748 **Admissions:** 9436 **Census:** 622 **Outpatient Visits:** 136624 **Births:** 0 **Personnel:** 1891

☒ **LENOX HILL HOSPITAL (330119)**, 100 East 77th Street, Zip 10075–1850; tel. 212/434–2000, (Includes MANHATTAN EYE, EAR AND THROAT HOSPITAL, 210 East 64th Street, Zip 10021–9885; tel. 212/838–9200; Philip P. Rosenthal, Executive Director) **A**1 3 5 8 9 10 **F**3 7 8 9 11 12 13 14 15 17 18 20 22 24 26 29 30 31 32 34 35 36 37 38 39 40 42 43 44 45 46 47 48 49 50 51 52 54 55 56 57 58 59 60 61 62 63 64 65 66 68 70 72 74 75 76 77 78 79 81 82 84 85 86 87 89 91 92 93 94 97 98 99 100 101 102 103 104 107 108 110 111 115 116 117 118 119 120 121 123 124 126 130 131 132 135 141 143 146 147 148 **P**5 6 **S** North Shore–Long Island Jewish Health System, Great Neck, NY
Primary Contact: Dennis Connors, Executive Director
CMO: Marc L. Napp, M.D., Vice President Medical Affairs
CIO: Beth Dituro, Divisional Chief Information Officer
Web address: www.lenoxhillhospital.org
**Control:** Other not–for–profit (including NFP Corporation) **Service:** General Medical and Surgical

**Staffed Beds:** 441 **Admissions:** 28699 **Census:** 373 **Outpatient Visits:** 208459 **Births:** 4239 **Total Expense ($000):** 915751 **Payroll Expense ($000):** 448435 **Personnel:** 3951

☒ **LINCOLN MEDICAL AND MENTAL HEALTH CENTER (330080)**, 234 East 149th Street, Bronx, Zip 10451–5504; tel. 718/579–5700 **A**1 2 3 5 9 10 **F**3 5 8 11 13 15 18 19 29 30 31 32 34 35 38 39 40 41 43 45 50 55 56 57 58 59 60 61 64 65 66 68 70 71 72 73 74 75 76 77 78 79 81 82 83 86 87 88 89 93 97 98 99 100 101 102 103 104 107 108 110 111 114 115 119 121 123 130 132 134 135 143 144 146 147 148 **P**4 **S** New York City Health and Hospitals Corporation, New York, NY
Primary Contact: Milton Nunez, Executive Director
CFO: Caswell Samms, Network Chief Financial Officer
CMO: Melissa Schori, M.D., Medical Director
CIO: Maricar Barrameda, Chief Information Officer
CHR: Jeannith Michelen, Senior Associate Executive Director
Web address: www.nyc.gov/html/hhc/lincoln/
**Control:** City–Government, nonfederal **Service:** General Medical and Surgical

**Staffed Beds:** 355 **Admissions:** 20998 **Census:** 264 **Outpatient Visits:** 556761 **Births:** 2275 **Total Expense ($000):** 556267 **Payroll Expense ($000):** 208259 **Personnel:** 3202

☒ **LONG ISLAND JEWISH MEDICAL CENTER (330195)**, 270–05 76th Avenue, New Hyde Park, Zip 11040–1496; tel. 718/470–7000, (Includes MANHASSET AMBULATORY CARE PAVILION, 1554 Northern Boulevard, Manhasset, Zip 11030; tel. 516/365–2070; STEVEN AND ALEXANDRA COHEN CHILDREN'S MEDICAL CENTER OF NEW YORK, 270–05 76th Avenue, Zip 11040; tel. 718/470–3000; ZUCKER HILLSIDE HOSPITAL, 75–59 263rd Street, Glen Oaks, Zip 11004; tel. 718/470–8000) **A**1 2 3 5 8 9 10 13 **F**2 3 5 6 7 8 9 11 12 13 14 15 17 18 19 20 21 22 23 24 25 26 27 28 29 30 31 32 34 35 38 39 40 41 43 44 45 46 47 48 49 50 51 52 53 54 55 56 57 58 59 60 61 62 63 64 65 66 68 70 72 73 74 75 76 77 78 79 80 81 82 84 85 86 87 88 89 92 93 97 98 99 100 101 102 103 104 105 106 107 108 109 110 111 114 115 116 117 118 119 120 121 123 124 126 129 130 131 132 134 135 136 141 142 143 144 145 146 147 148 **P**5 6 **S** North Shore–Long Island Jewish Health System, Great Neck, NY
Primary Contact: Michael Goldberg, Executive Director
CIO: Ty Knox, Chief Information Officer
CHR: Ronald W. Stone, Regional Chief Human Resource Officer
Web address: www.lij.edu
**Control:** Other not–for–profit (including NFP Corporation) **Service:** General Medical and Surgical

**Staffed Beds:** 900 **Admissions:** 51936 **Census:** 839 **Outpatient Visits:** 766753 **Births:** 7660 **Total Expense ($000):** 1673598 **Payroll Expense ($000):** 835770 **Personnel:** 9132

☒ **MAIMONIDES MEDICAL CENTER (330194)**, 4802 Tenth Avenue, Brooklyn, Zip 11219–2916; tel. 718/283–6000, (Includes MAIMONIDES INFANTS AND CHILDREN'S HOSPITAL OF BROOKLYN, 4802 Tenth Avenue, tel. 718/283–6000) **A**1 2 3 5 8 9 10 12 13 **F**2 3 7 8 9 11 12 13 14 15 17 18 19 20 22 24 26 28 29 30 31 32 34 35 38 39 40 41 44 45 46 47 48 49 50 51 52 54 55 56 57 58 59 60 61 64 65 66 68 70 72 73 74 75 76 77 78 79 81 82 84 85 86 87 88 89 91 92 93 96 97 98 99 100 101 102 103 104 107 108 110 111 114 115 117 118 119 120 121 123 124 126 129 130 131 132 135 145 146 147 148 **P**5 6
Primary Contact: Pamela S. Brier, President and Chief Executive Officer
COO: Mark McDougle, Executive Vice President and Chief Operating Officer
CFO: Robert Naldi, Chief Financial Officer
CMO: Samuel Kopel, M.D., Medical Director
CIO: Walter Fahey, Chief Information Officer
Web address: www.maimonidesmed.org/
**Control:** Other not–for–profit (including NFP Corporation) **Service:** General Medical and Surgical

**Staffed Beds:** 575 **Admissions:** 34771 **Census:** 547 **Outpatient Visits:** 490728 **Births:** 7817 **Total Expense ($000):** 1058091 **Payroll Expense ($000):** 534695 **Personnel:** 5660

☐ **MANHATTAN PSYCHIATRIC CENTER–WARD'S ISLAND (334054)**, 600 East 125th Street, Zip 10035–6000; tel. 646/672–6767, (Nonreporting) **A**1 3 5 10 **S** New York State Office of Mental Health, Albany, NY
Primary Contact: Vinny Miccoli, Executive Director
Web address: www.omh.ny.gov
**Control:** State–Government, nonfederal **Service:** Psychiatric

**Staffed Beds:** 745

☒ **MEMORIAL SLOAN–KETTERING CANCER CENTER (330154)**, 1275 York Avenue, Zip 10065–6007; tel. 212/639–2000 **A**1 2 3 5 8 9 10 **F**3 11 14 15 29 31 32 34 35 36 37 39 44 45 46 47 48 49 50 54 55 56 57 58 59 60 61 64 66 68 70 74 75 77 78 79 81 82 84 85 86 87 88 89 92 93 94 96 99 100 103 104 107 108 110 111 112 114 115 117 118 119 120 121 123 124 126 130 132 135 136 142 143 144 145 146 147 148 **P**6
Primary Contact: Craig B. Thompson, M.D., President and Chief Executive Officer
COO: John R. Gunn, Executive Vice President and Chief Operating Officer
CFO: Michael Gutnick, Senior Vice President Finance
CMO: Jose Baselga, M.D., Physician–in–Chief
CIO: Patricia Skarulis, Vice President Information Systems
CHR: Kerry Besset, Senior Vice President Human Resources
CNO: Elizabeth Nelkin McCormick, MSN, Chief Nursing Officer
Web address: www.mskcc.org
**Control:** Other not–for–profit (including NFP Corporation) **Service:** Cancer

**Staffed Beds:** 478 **Admissions:** 22144 **Census:** 402 **Outpatient Visits:** 1433378 **Births:** 0 **Total Expense ($000):** 2593466 **Payroll Expense ($000):** 996281 **Personnel:** 13459

☒ **METROPOLITAN HOSPITAL CENTER (330199)**, 1901 First Avenue, Zip 10029–7404; tel. 212/423–6262, (Includes METROPOLITAN GENERAL CARE UNIT, METROPOLITAN DRUG DETOXIFICATION AND METROPOLITAN PSYCHIATRIC UNIT ) **A**1 3 5 9 10 **F**3 4 8 9 11 13 15 17 18 28 29 30 31 32 34 35 38 39 40 41 43 45 46 49 50 51 55 56 57 58 59 60 61 64 65 66 68 70 72 73 74 75 76 77 78 79 81 82 84 85 87 89 90 92 93 96 97 98 99 100 101 102 103 104 107 108 110 111 114 118 119 130 131 132 133 134 135 144 146 147 148 **S** New York City Health and Hospitals Corporation, New York, NY
Primary Contact: Anthony Rajkumar, Executive Director
COO: Elizabeth Guzman, Chief Operating Officer
CFO: Tracy V. Green, Chief Financial Officer
CMO: John T. Pellicone, M.D., Chief Medical Officer
CIO: Tonguc Yaman, Chief Information Officer
CHR: April Alexander, Director Human Resources
CNO: Lillian Diaz, R.N., Chief Nursing Officer
Web address: www.nyc.gov/html/hhc/mhc/html/home/home.shtml
**Control:** City–Government, nonfederal **Service:** General Medical and Surgical

**Staffed Beds:** 317 **Admissions:** 12867 **Census:** 212 **Outpatient Visits:** 401312 **Births:** 1109 **Total Expense ($000):** 343907 **Payroll Expense ($000):** 136791 **Personnel:** 1921

**NY**

---

| **Hospital, Medicare Provider Number, Address, Telephone, Approval, Facility, and Physician Codes, Health Care System** |

★ American Hospital Association (AHA) membership  ◯ Healthcare Facilities Accreditation Program  ⇑ Center for Improvement in Healthcare Quality Accreditation
☐ The Joint Commission accreditation  ◇ DNV Healthcare Inc. accreditation  △ Commission on Accreditation of Rehabilitation Facilities (CARF) accreditation

✠ **MONTEFIORE MEDICAL CENTER (330059)**, 111 East 210th Street, Bronx, Zip 10467–2401; tel. 718/920–4321, (Includes CHILDREN'S HOSPITAL OF MONTEFIORE, 3415 Bainbridge Avenue, Zip 10467–2403; tel. 718/741–2426; JACK D WEILER HOSPITAL OF ALBERT EINSTEIN COLLEGE OF MEDICINE, 1825 Eastchester Road, Zip 10461–2373; tel. 718/904–2000; MONTEFIORE MEDICAL CENTER – NORTH DIVISION, 600 East 233rd Street, Zip 10466–2697; tel. 718/920–9000) **A**1 2 3 5 8 9 10 **F**3 5 6 7 8 9 11 12 13 14 15 17 18 19 20 21 22 23 24 25 26 27 28 29 30 31 32 34 35 36 37 38 39 40 41 42 44 45 46 47 48 49 50 51 52 53 54 55 56 57 58 59 60 61 62 63 64 65 66 68 70 71 72 73 74 75 77 78 79 80 81 82 83 84 85 86 87 88 90 91 92 93 94 96 97 98 99 100 101 102 103 104 105 107 108 109 110 111 112 113 114 115 116 117 118 119 120 121 123 124 126 129 130 131 132 134 135 136 137 138 139 141 142 143 144 145 146 147 148 **P**5 6 **S** Montefiore Health System, Bronx, NY
Primary Contact: Steven M. Safyer, M.D., President and Chief Executive Officer
COO: Robert B. Conaty, Executive Vice President Operations
CFO: Joel A. Perlman, Executive Vice President Finance
CMO: Gary Kalkut, M.D., Senior Vice President and Chief Medical Officer
CIO: Jack Wolf, Vice President Information Systems
Web address: www.montefiore.org
**Control:** Other not–for–profit (including NFP Corporation) **Service:** General Medical and Surgical

**Staffed Beds:** 1512 **Admissions:** 84938 **Census:** 1356 **Outpatient Visits:** 1607093 **Births:** 5981 **Total Expense ($000):** 3481398 **Payroll Expense ($000):** 1573133 **Personnel:** 19242

**MORGAN STANLEY CHILDREN'S HOSPITAL OF NEW YORK–PRESBYTERIAN** See New York–Presbyterian Hospital

✠ **MOUNT SINAI BETH ISRAEL (330169)**, First Avenue and 16th Street, Zip 10003–3803; tel. 212/420–2000, (Includes MOUNT SINAI BETH ISRAEL BROOKLYN, 3201 Kings Highway, Brooklyn, Zip 11234; tel. 718/252–3000; Lin H. Mo, M.P.H., President), (Total facility includes 28 beds in nursing home–type unit) **A**1 2 3 5 6 8 9 10 **F**3 4 5 7 8 9 11 13 14 15 17 18 19 20 22 24 26 28 29 30 31 32 33 34 35 36 38 39 40 41 43 44 45 46 47 48 49 50 51 52 53 54 55 56 57 58 59 60 61 62 63 64 65 66 68 70 72 74 75 76 77 78 79 80 81 82 83 84 85 86 87 88 89 90 92 93 94 96 97 98 99 100 101 102 103 104 107 108 110 111 114 115 117 118 119 120 121 123 126 128 129 130 131 132 134 135 141 143 144 145 146 147 148 **P**5 **S** Mount Sinai Health System, New York, NY
Primary Contact: Susan Somerville, R.N., President
COO: Kevin Molloy, Senior Vice President and Chief Operating Officer
CFO: Donald Scanlon, Chief Corporate Services, Mount Sinai Health System
CMO: Jeremy Boal, M.D., Executive Vice President and Chief Medical Officer
CIO: Kumar Chatani, Senior Vice President and Chief Information Officer Mount Sinai Health System
CHR: Jane Maksoud, R.N., Senior Vice President Human Resources and Labor Relations, Mount Sinai Health System
CNO: Mary Walsh, R.N., Vice President Patient Care Services and Chief Nursing Officer
Web address: www.bethisraelny.org
**Control:** Other not–for–profit (including NFP Corporation) **Service:** General Medical and Surgical

**Staffed Beds:** 989 **Admissions:** 47399 **Census:** 706 **Outpatient Visits:** 564031 **Births:** 3845 **Total Expense ($000):** 1411476 **Payroll Expense ($000):** 686760 **Personnel:** 7973

✠ △ **MOUNT SINAI HOSPITAL (330024)**, One Gustave L. Levy Place, Zip 10029–6574; tel. 212/241–6500, (Includes KRAVIS CHILDREN'S HOSPITAL, One Gustave L. Levy Pl, Zip 10029, Mailing Address: PO Box 1153, Zip 10002–0916; tel. 800/637–4624; MOUNT SINAI QUEENS, 25–10 30th Avenue, Long Island City, Zip 11102–2448; tel. 718/932–1000; Caryn A. Schwab, Executive Director) **A**1 2 3 5 7 8 9 10 **F**3 4 6 7 8 9 11 12 13 14 15 17 18 19 20 21 22 23 24 25 26 27 28 29 30 31 32 34 35 36 37 38 39 40 41 42 43 44 45 46 47 48 49 50 51 52 54 55 56 57 58 59 60 61 62 63 64 65 66 68 70 71 72 73 74 75 76 77 78 79 80 81 82 83 84 85 86 87 88 89 90 91 92 93 94 95 96 97 98 99 100 101 102 103 104 105 107 108 110 111 114 115 116 117 118 119 120 121 123 124 126 129 130 131 132 134 135 136 137 138 139 141 142 143 144 145 146 147 148 **P**5 6 **S** Mount Sinai Health System, New York, NY
Primary Contact: David L. Reich, M.D., President
COO: David L. Reich, M.D., President and Chief Operating Officer
CFO: Donald Scanlon, Chief Financial Officer
CMO: Vicki LoPachin, M.D., Chief Medical Officer
CIO: Kumar Chatani, Senior Vice President and Chief Information Officer Mount Sinai Health System
CHR: Jane Maksoud, R.N., Senior Vice President Human Resources and Labor Relations
Web address: www.mountsinai.org
**Control:** Other not–for–profit (including NFP Corporation) **Service:** General Medical and Surgical

**Staffed Beds:** 1183 **Admissions:** 60462 **Census:** 999 **Outpatient Visits:** 820435 **Births:** 7127 **Total Expense ($000):** 1941757 **Payroll Expense ($000):** 737767 **Personnel:** 9212

**MOUNT SINAI ROOSEVELT HOSPITAL** See Mount Sinai St. Luke's – Roosevelt

✠ **MOUNT SINAI ST. LUKE'S – ROOSEVELT (330046)**, 1111 Amsterdam Avenue, Zip 10025–1716; tel. 212/523–4000, (Includes MOUNT SINAI ROOSEVELT HOSPITAL, 1000 Tenth Avenue, Zip 10019; tel. 212/523–4000; Evan Flatow, M.D., President) **A**1 3 5 8 9 10 **F**3 4 5 7 8 11 12 13 14 15 17 18 20 22 24 26 29 30 31 32 34 35 38 39 40 41 43 44 46 49 50 51 52 54 55 56 57 58 59 60 61 62 63 64 65 66 68 70 72 74 75 76 77 78 79 81 82 84 85 86 87 90 92 93 94 96 97 98 99 100 101 102 103 104 107 108 110 111 114 115 119 120 121 123 124 126 130 131 132 134 135 143 144 145 146 147 148 **P**5 **S** Mount Sinai Health System, New York, NY
Primary Contact: Arthur A. Gianelli, M.P.H., President
COO: Kevin Molloy, Senior Vice President and Chief Operating Officer
CFO: Donald Scanlon, Chief Corporate Services, Mount Sinai Health System
CMO: Jeremy Boal, M.D., Executive Vice President and Chief Medical Officer
CIO: Kumar Chatani, Chief Information Officer, Mount Sinai Health System
CHR: Jane Maksoud, R.N., Senior Vice President Human Resources and Labor Relations, Mount Sinai Health System
CNO: Mary Walsh, R.N., Vice President Patient Care Services and Chief Nursing Officer
Web address: www.stlukeshospitalnyc.org
**Control:** Other not–for–profit (including NFP Corporation) **Service:** General Medical and Surgical

**Staffed Beds:** 685 **Admissions:** 37106 **Census:** 570 **Outpatient Visits:** 563255 **Births:** 6148 **Total Expense ($000):** 1199085 **Payroll Expense ($000):** 579069 **Personnel:** 5703

☐ **NEW YORK CITY CHILDREN'S CENTER**, 74–03 Commonwealth Boulevard, Jamaica, Zip 11426–1890; tel. 718/264–4506, (Includes BRONX CHILDREN'S PSYCHIATRIC CENTER, 1000 Waters Place, Bronx, Zip 10461–2799; tel. 718/239–3600; BROOKLYN CHILDREN'S PSYCHIATRIC CENTER, 1819 Bergen Street, Brooklyn, Zip 11233–4513; tel. 718/221–4500), (Nonreporting) **A**1 **S** New York State Office of Mental Health, Albany, NY
Primary Contact: Anita Daniels, Executive Director
CMO: David M. Rube, M.D., Clinical Director
CIO: Ed Yunusov, Coordinator Facility Information Center
Web address: www.omh.ny.gov/omhweb/facilities/nyccc/
**Control:** State–Government, nonfederal **Service:** Children's hospital psychiatric

**Staffed Beds:** 84

☐ **NEW YORK COMMUNITY HOSPITAL (330019)**, 2525 Kings Highway, Brooklyn, Zip 11229–1705; tel. 718/692–5300, (Nonreporting) **A**1 5 9 10
Primary Contact: Barry Stern, President and Chief Executive Officer
COO: Una E. Morrissey, R.N., Senior Vice President Chief Operating Officer and Chief Nursing Officer
CFO: Leonardo Tamburello, Divisional Chief Financial Officer
CMO: Herbert Rader, M.D., Advisor for Medical Affairs
CIO: Edward B. Stolyar, D.O., Director Management Information Systems
CHR: Steve Meyers, Director Human Resources
CNO: Una E. Morrissey, R.N., Senior Vice President Chief Operating Officer and Chief Nursing Officer
Web address: www.nych.com
**Control:** Other not–for–profit (including NFP Corporation) **Service:** General Medical and Surgical

**Staffed Beds:** 134

✠ **NEW YORK EYE AND EAR INFIRMARY OF MOUNT SINAI (330100)**, 310 East 14th Street, Zip 10003–4201; tel. 212/979–4000 **A**1 3 5 9 10 **F**3 8 11 29 30 32 34 35 44 50 54 57 58 59 64 66 68 74 81 82 85 86 87 91 92 93 94 97 107 114 119 129 130 132 142 146 **S** Mount Sinai Health System, New York, NY
Primary Contact: James Tsai, M.D., President
COO: Allan Fine, Chief Operating Officer
CFO: Donald Scanlon, Chief Corporate Services, Mount Sinai Health System
CMO: Jeremy Boal, M.D., Executive Vice President and Chief Medical Officer
CIO: Kumar Chatani, Chief Information Officer, Mount Sinai Health System
CHR: Jane Maksoud, R.N., Senior Vice President Human Resources and Labor Relations, Mount Sinai Health System
CNO: Sonja Tennaro, Ed.D., Senior Vice President Clinical Operations
Web address: www.nyee.edu
**Control:** Other not–for–profit (including NFP Corporation) **Service:** Eye, ear, nose, and throat

**Staffed Beds:** 32 **Admissions:** 489 **Census:** 3 **Outpatient Visits:** 209981 **Births:** 0 **Total Expense ($000):** 117423 **Payroll Expense ($000):** 81052 **Personnel:** 970

**NY**

☒ **NEW YORK METHODIST HOSPITAL (330236)**, 506 Sixth Street, Brooklyn, Zip 11215–3609; tel. 718/780–3000 **A**1 2 3 5 8 9 10 **F**3 6 8 9 11 12 13 15 17 18 19 20 22 24 26 29 30 31 32 33 34 35 36 39 40 41 43 44 45 46 47 48 49 50 51 52 54 55 56 57 58 59 60 61 64 65 66 68 70 72 73 74 75 76 77 78 79 81 82 83 84 85 87 88 89 90 91 92 93 95 96 97 98 99 102 103 104 107 108 109 110 111 114 118 119 126 129 130 131 132 135 144 145 146 147 148 **P**4 5 6 7
Primary Contact: Mark J. Mundy, President and Chief Executive Officer
CFO: Michael Fagan, Senior Vice President Finance
CMO: Steven Silber, M.D., Senior Vice President Medical Affairs
CIO: Rick Plisko, Director information Systems
CHR: Dennis Buchanan, Vice President Human Resources
CNO: Rebecca L. Flood, R.N., Senior Vice President Nursing
Web address: www.nym.org
**Control:** Other not–for–profit (including NFP Corporation) **Service:** General Medical and Surgical

**Staffed Beds:** 591 **Admissions:** 36313 **Census:** 544 **Outpatient Visits:** 515538 **Births:** 5738 **Total Expense ($000):** 805398 **Payroll Expense ($000):** 306615 **Personnel:** 3943

☐ **NEW YORK STATE PSYCHIATRIC INSTITUTE (334009)**, 1051 Riverside Drive, Zip 10032–1007; tel. 212/543–5000, (Nonreporting) **A**1 3 5 10 **S** New York State Office of Mental Health, Albany, NY
Primary Contact: Jeffrey A. Lieberman, M.D., Executive Director
COO: Janelle Dierkens, Chief Administration Officer
CFO: Jonathan Segal, Chief Financial Officer
CMO: David Lowenthal, M.D., Clinical Director
CIO: Joseph Grun, Chief Information Officer
CHR: Rebecca Dechabert, Acting Director Personnel
Web address: www.nyspi.org
**Control:** State–Government, nonfederal **Service:** Psychiatric

**Staffed Beds:** 58

☒ △ **NEW YORK–PRESBYTERIAN HOSPITAL (330101)**, 525 East 68th Street, Zip 10065–4870; tel. 212/746–5454, (Includes MORGAN STANLEY CHILDREN'S HOSPITAL OF NEW YORK–PRESBYTERIAN, 3959 Broadway, Zip 10032–3784; tel. 212/305–2500; NEW YORK PRESBYTERIAN LOWER MANHATTAN HOSPITAL, 170 William Street, Zip 10038–2649; tel. 212/312–5000; Robert E. Kelly, M.D., President; NEW YORK–PRESBYTERIAN HOSPITAL, WESTCHESTER DIVISION, 21 Bloomingdale Road, White Plains, Zip 10605; tel. 914/682–9100; NEW YORK–PRESBYTERIAN HOSPITAL/WEILL CORNELL MEDICAL CENTER, 525 East 68th Street, Zip 10021–4885; tel. 212/746–5454; NEW YORK–PRESBYTERIAN/COLUMBIA UNIVERSITY MEDICAL CENTER, 161 Fort Washington Avenue, Zip 10032; tel. 212/305–2500; PAYNE WHITNEY PSYCHIATRIC CLINIC, 525 East 68th Street, Zip 10021; tel. 212/746–3800; PHYLLIS AND DAVID KOMANSKY CENTER FOR CHILDREN'S HEALTH, 525 East 68th Street, Zip 10021; tel. 212/746–5454; THE ALLEN PAVILION, 5141 Broadway, Zip 10032; tel. 212/932–5000) **A**1 2 3 5 7 8 9 10 **F**3 4 5 6 7 8 9 11 12 13 14 15 16 17 18 19 20 21 22 23 24 25 26 27 28 29 30 31 32 34 35 36 37 38 39 40 41 43 44 45 46 47 48 49 50 51 52 53 54 55 56 57 58 59 60 61 62 63 64 65 66 69 70 71 72 73 74 75 76 77 78 79 80 81 82 83 84 85 86 87 88 89 90 91 92 93 94 95 96 97 98 99 100 101 102 103 104 105 107 108 110 111 114 115 116 117 118 119 120 121 123 124 126 129 130 131 132 134 135 136 137 138 139 140 141 142 143 144 145 146 147 148 **S** New York Presbyterian Healthcare System, New York, NY
Primary Contact: Steven J. Corwin, M.D., Chief Executive Officer
CFO: Phyllis R. Lantos, Executive Vice President, Corporate Chief Financial Officer and Treasurer
CMO: Laura Forese, M.D., Senior Vice President and Chief Medical Officer
CIO: Aurelia Boyer, Senior Vice President and Chief Information Officer
CHR: G. Thomas Ferguson, Senior Vice President and Chief Human Resources Officer
Web address: www.nyp.org
**Control:** Other not–for–profit (including NFP Corporation) **Service:** General Medical and Surgical

**Staffed Beds:** 2328 **Admissions:** 110409 **Census:** 1959 **Outpatient Visits:** 2043190 **Births:** 14318 **Total Expense ($000):** 4243713 **Payroll Expense ($000):** 2032991 **Personnel:** 20834

☐ **NEW YORK–PRESBYTERIAN/QUEENS (330055)**, 56–45 Main Street, Flushing, Zip 11355–5045; tel. 718/670–1231 **A**1 2 3 5 9 10 **F**1 3 4 5 6 7 8 9 12 13 14 15 16 17 18 19 20 21 22 23 24 25 26 27 28 29 30 31 33 34 35 36 37 38 39 40 41 42 43 44 45 46 47 48 49 50 51 53 54 55 56 57 58 59 60 61 62 63 64 65 66 67 68 70 71 72 73 74 75 76 77 78 79 80 81 82 83 84 85 86 87 88 89 90 91 92 93 95 96 97 98 107 108 109 110 111 112 113 114 115 118 119 120 121 122 123 124 125 126 127 128 130 131 132 133 134 135 143 144 145 146 147 148 **P**4 **S** New York Presbyterian Healthcare System, New York, NY
Primary Contact: Stephen S. Mills, President and Chief Executive Officer
COO: John E. Sciortino, Senior Vice President and Chief Operating Officer
CFO: Kevin J. Ward, Vice President and Chief Financial Officer
CMO: Stephen Rimar, M.D., Senior Vice President Medical Affairs
CIO: Thomas Kemp, Chief Information Officer
CHR: Lorraine Orlando, Vice President Human Resources
Web address: www.nyhq.org
**Control:** Other not–for–profit (including NFP Corporation) **Service:** General Medical and Surgical

**Staffed Beds:** 559 **Admissions:** 27132 **Census:** 401 **Outpatient Visits:** 516623 **Births:** 4619 **Total Expense ($000):** 680647 **Payroll Expense ($000):** 328405 **Personnel:** 4020

☒ **NORTH CENTRAL BRONX HOSPITAL (330385)**, 3424 Kossuth Avenue, Bronx, Zip 10467–2489; tel. 718/519–3500 **A**1 3 5 9 10 **F**3 5 8 11 12 13 15 18 28 29 30 32 34 35 38 39 40 41 43 44 45 46 48 50 51 55 56 57 58 59 60 61 64 65 66 68 70 72 73 74 75 76 77 78 79 80 81 82 84 85 87 92 93 94 96 97 98 99 100 101 102 103 104 105 107 108 110 111 115 119 130 131 132 135 144 146 147 148 **P**6 **S** New York City Health and Hospitals Corporation, New York, NY
Primary Contact: Gregory Calliste, PhD, Acting Executive Director
COO: Sheldon McLeod, Chief Operating Officer
CFO: Kathy Garramone, Chief Financial Officer
CMO: Joseph Skarzynski, M.D., Medical Director
CIO: Diane Carr, Chief Information Officer
CHR: Dolores Leite, Chief Human Resource Executive
CNO: Elizabeth Gerdts, Chief Nursing Officer
Web address: www.nyc.gov/html/hhc/ncbh/html/home/home.shtml
**Control:** City–Government, nonfederal **Service:** General Medical and Surgical

**Staffed Beds:** 207 **Admissions:** 5293 **Census:** 105 **Outpatient Visits:** 205122 **Births:** 158 **Total Expense ($000):** 184839 **Payroll Expense ($000):** 69330 **Personnel:** 1164

**NYU HOSPITAL FOR JOINT DISEASES** See NYU Langone Medical Center's Hospital for Joint Diseases

☒ △ **NYU LANGONE MEDICAL CENTER (330214)**, 550 First Avenue, Zip 10016–6402; tel. 212/263–7300, (Includes NYU CHILDREN'S HOSPITAL, 545 First Avenue, Zip 10016–6401; tel. 212/263–7300; NYU LANGONE MEDICAL CENTER'S HOSPITAL FOR JOINT DISEASES, 301 East 17th Street, Zip 10003–3890; tel. 212/598–6000; David A. Dibner, FACHE, Senior Vice President Hospital Operations and Musculoskeletal Strategic Area; RUSK INSTITUTE, 400 East 34th Street, Zip 10016) **A**1 2 3 5 7 8 9 10 **F**3 5 6 8 9 11 12 13 14 15 17 18 19 20 21 22 23 24 25 26 27 28 29 30 31 32 33 34 35 36 37 38 39 40 41 43 44 45 46 47 48 49 50 52 53 54 55 56 57 58 59 60 61 63 64 65 66 68 70 72 73 74 75 76 77 78 79 81 82 84 85 86 87 88 89 90 91 92 93 95 96 97 98 99 100 101 102 103 104 107 108 110 111 113 114 115 116 117 118 119 120 121 123 124 126 129 130 131 132 134 135 136 138 139 141 142 144 145 146 147 148 **P**5 6 **S** NYU Langone Health System, New York, NY
Primary Contact: Robert I. Grossman, M.D., Chief Executive Officer
COO: Bernard Birnbaum, M.D., Senior Vice President, Vice Dean and Chief Hospital Operations
CFO: Michael Burke, Senior Vice President and Corporate Chief Financial Officer
CMO: Robert Press, M.D., Chief Medical Officer
CIO: Nader Mherabi, Senior Vice President and Vice Dean, Chief Information Officer
CHR: Nancy Sanchez, Senior Vice President and Vice Dean Human Resources
CNO: Kimberly S. Glassman, Ph.D., Chief Nursing Officer
Web address: www.nyumedicalcenter.org
**Control:** Other not–for–profit (including NFP Corporation) **Service:** General Medical and Surgical

**Staffed Beds:** 718 **Admissions:** 32260 **Census:** 457 **Outpatient Visits:** 903544 **Births:** 5355 **Total Expense ($000):** 2149264 **Payroll Expense ($000):** 736018 **Personnel:** 9655

**NY**

---

**Hospital, Medicare Provider Number, Address, Telephone, Approval, Facility, and Physician Codes, Health Care System**

★ American Hospital Association (AHA) membership    ○ Healthcare Facilities Accreditation Program    ⇑ Center for Improvement in Healthcare Quality Accreditation
☐ The Joint Commission accreditation    ◇ DNV Healthcare Inc. accreditation    △ Commission on Accreditation of Rehabilitation Facilities (CARF) accreditation

✠ **NYU LUTHERAN (330306)**, 150 55th Street, Brooklyn, Zip 11220–2559; tel. 718/630–7000 **A**1 3 5 9 10 **F**3 7 8 11 12 13 14 15 17 18 19 20 22 29 30 31 32 34 35 36 38 39 40 41 43 44 45 49 50 51 52 54 55 56 57 58 59 60 61 64 65 66 68 70 72 73 74 75 76 77 78 79 81 82 84 85 86 87 89 90 91 92 93 94 96 97 98 100 101 102 103 104 107 108 110 111 114 115 118 119 121 123 124 130 131 132 134 135 146 147 148 **P**6 **S** NYU Langone Health System, New York, NY
Primary Contact: Wendy Z. Goldstein, Chief Executive Officer
COO: Claudia Caine, President and Chief Operating Officer
CFO: Richard Langfelder, Executive Vice President and Chief Financial Officer
CIO: Steve Art, Senior Vice President and Chief Information Officer
CHR: Frank Scheets, Senior Vice President
Web address: www.lmcmc.com
**Control:** Other not–for–profit (including NFP Corporation) **Service:** General Medical and Surgical

**Staffed Beds:** 400 **Admissions:** 23044 **Census:** 338 **Outpatient Visits:** 723480 **Births:** 3901 **Total Expense ($000):** 611121 **Payroll Expense ($000):** 291108

**PAYNE WHITNEY PSYCHIATRIC CLINIC** See New York–Presbyterian Hospital

**QUEENS CHILDREN'S PSYCHIATRIC CENTER** See New York City Children's Center

✠ **QUEENS HOSPITAL CENTER (330231)**, 82–68 164th Street, Jamaica, Zip 11432–1104; tel. 718/883–3000 **A**1 2 3 5 9 10 **F**3 5 8 11 13 14 15 18 29 30 31 32 34 35 38 39 40 43 45 50 53 54 56 57 59 61 64 68 70 72 73 76 77 78 79 81 83 84 85 87 90 93 97 98 99 100 102 103 104 105 107 111 115 116 119 121 129 130 134 135 146 147 **P**6 **S** New York City Health and Hospitals Corporation, New York, NY
Primary Contact: Julius Wool, Executive Director
COO: Robert Rossdale, Deputy Executive Director
CFO: Brian Stacey, Chief Financial Officer
CMO: Jasmin Moshirpur, M.D., Chief Medical Officer
CIO: Vincent Smith, Chief Information Officer
CHR: Jeannith Michelen, Senior Associate Executive Director
CNO: Joan Gabriele, Deputy Executive Director
Web address: www.nyc.gov/html/hhc/qhc/html/home/home.shtml
**Control:** City–Government, nonfederal **Service:** General Medical and Surgical

**Staffed Beds:** 281 **Admissions:** 12632 **Census:** 235 **Outpatient Visits:** 415221 **Births:** 1654 **Total Expense ($000):** 410558 **Payroll Expense ($000):** 142937 **Personnel:** 1810

✠ **RICHMOND UNIVERSITY MEDICAL CENTER (330028)**, 355 Bard Avenue, Staten Island, Zip 10310–1664; tel. 718/818–1234 **A**1 2 3 5 9 10 **F**3 4 5 7 8 11 13 14 15 17 18 19 20 26 29 30 31 32 34 35 38 40 41 43 45 47 49 50 51 55 56 57 58 59 61 64 65 66 68 70 71 72 73 74 75 76 77 78 79 80 81 82 84 85 86 87 88 89 91 92 93 94 97 98 99 100 101 102 103 104 107 108 109 110 111 114 115 119 126 130 131 132 135 143 144 146 147 148
Primary Contact: Daniel J. Messina, Ph.D., FACHE, President and Chief Executive Officer
CMO: Edward Arsura, M.D., Chief Medical Officer
CHR: Patricia Caldari, Vice President
Web address: www.rumcsi.org
**Control:** Other not–for–profit (including NFP Corporation) **Service:** General Medical and Surgical

**Staffed Beds:** 374 **Admissions:** 15283 **Census:** 248 **Outpatient Visits:** 234735 **Births:** 2943 **Total Expense ($000):** 295718 **Payroll Expense ($000):** 145745 **Personnel:** 1798

☐ **ROCKEFELLER UNIVERSITY HOSPITAL (330387)**, 1230 York Avenue, Zip 10065–6399; tel. 212/327–8000, (Nonreporting) **A**1 10
Primary Contact: James G. Krueger, M.D., Ph.D., Chief Executive Officer
CMO: Barbara O'Sullivan, M.D., Medical Director
Web address: www.rucares.org
**Control:** Other not–for–profit (including NFP Corporation) **Service:** Other specialty

**Staffed Beds:** 40

**ROOSEVELT HOSPITAL** See Mount Sinai Roosevelt Hospital

☐ **SOUTH BEACH PSYCHIATRIC CENTER (334043)**, 777 Seaview Avenue, Staten Island, Zip 10305–3409; tel. 718/667–2300, (Nonreporting) **A**1 3 10 **S** New York State Office of Mental Health, Albany, NY
Primary Contact: Rosanne Gaylor, M.D., Acting Executive Director
CHR: George Bouquio, Director Human Resources
Web address: www.omh.ny.gov/omhweb/facilities/sbpc/facility.htm
**Control:** State–Government, nonfederal **Service:** Psychiatric

**Staffed Beds:** 340

☒ **ST. BARNABAS HOSPITAL (330399)**, 183rd Street & Third Avenue, Bronx, Zip 10457–9998; tel. 718/960–9000, (Total facility includes 199 beds in nursing home–type unit) **A**1 3 5 9 10 12 13 **F**2 3 4 5 6 7 8 9 11 13 15 18 19 20 22 26 28 29 30 31 32 34 35 36 38 39 40 41 43 44 45 46 47 49 50 51 54 55 56 57 58 59 60 61 64 65 66 68 70 71 72 74 75 76 77 78 79 81 82 83 84 85 86 87 89 91 92 93 94 97 98 99 100 101 102 103 104 107 108 109 110 111 114 115 117 119 128 129 130 131 132 134 135 143 146 147 148 **P**6
Primary Contact: Scott Cooper, M.D., Chief Executive Officer
COO: Len Walsh, Executive Vice President and Chief Operating Officer
CFO: Todd Gorlewski, Senior Vice President and Chief Financial Officer
CMO: David A. Perlstein, M.D., Chief Medical Officer
CIO: Jitendra Barmecha, M.D., Senior Vice President and Chief Information Officer
CHR: Marc Wolf, Assistant Vice President Human Resources
CNO: Denise Richardson, R.N., Senior Vice President and Chief Nursing Officer
Web address: www.sbhny.org
**Control:** Other not–for–profit (including NFP Corporation) **Service:** General Medical and Surgical

**Staffed Beds:** 660 **Admissions:** 16579 **Census:** 414 **Outpatient Visits:** 562242 **Births:** 1062 **Total Expense ($000):** 369479 **Payroll Expense ($000):** 159872 **Personnel:** 2196

☐ **ST. JOHN'S EPISCOPAL HOSPITAL–SOUTH SHORE (330395)**, 327 Beach 19th Street, Far Rockaway, Zip 11691–4423; tel. 718/869–7000, (Nonreporting) **A**1 3 5 9 10 12 13
Primary Contact: Richard L. Brown, Interim Chief Executive Officer
COO: Patrick L. Sullivan, Chief Operating Officer
CFO: Kathleen Garcia, Controller
CMO: Raymond Pastore, M.D., Chief Medical Officer
CIO: Michael J. Piro, Chief Information Officer
CHR: Roger Franco, Director Human Resources
Web address: www.ehs.org
**Control:** Church–operated, Nongovernment, not–for profit **Service:** General Medical and Surgical

**Staffed Beds:** 251

☒ △ **STATEN ISLAND UNIVERSITY HOSPITAL (330160)**, 475 Seaview Avenue, Staten Island, Zip 10305–3436; tel. 718/226–9000 **A**1 2 3 5 7 8 9 10 **F**3 4 5 7 8 11 13 14 15 16 17 18 19 20 22 24 26 28 29 30 31 32 34 35 36 38 39 40 41 43 44 45 46 48 49 50 51 52 54 55 56 57 58 59 60 61 63 64 65 66 68 70 72 73 74 75 76 77 78 79 81 82 83 84 85 86 87 88 89 90 91 92 93 94 96 97 98 100 101 102 103 104 105 107 108 110 111 114 115 116 117 118 119 120 121 123 124 126 129 130 132 134 135 145 146 147 148 **P**5 6 **S** North Shore–Long Island Jewish Health System, Great Neck, NY
Primary Contact: Donna Proske, MS, R.N., Executive Director
CFO: Thomas Reca, Sr., Senior Vice President Finance and Chief Financial Officer
CMO: Mark Jarrett, M.D., Chief Medical Officer
CIO: Kathy Kania, Chief Information Officer
CHR: Margaret DiAlto, Vice President Human Resources
CNO: Dian I. Johnson, MSN, Chief Nurse Executive
Web address: www.siuh.edu
**Control:** Other not–for–profit (including NFP Corporation) **Service:** General Medical and Surgical

**Staffed Beds:** 663 **Admissions:** 40474 **Census:** 583 **Outpatient Visits:** 935509 **Births:** 2997 **Total Expense ($000):** 786188 **Payroll Expense ($000):** 355062 **Personnel:** 4821

**STEVEN AND ALEXANDRA COHEN CHILDREN'S MEDICAL CENTER OF NEW YORK** See Long Island Jewish Medical Center, New Hyde Park

☒ **SUNY DOWNSTATE MEDICAL CENTER UNIVERSITY HOSPITAL (330350)**, 445 Lenox Road, Brooklyn, Zip 11203–2017; tel. 718/270–1000, (Includes THE CHILDREN'S HOSPITAL AT SUNY DOWNSTATE, 450 Clarkson Avenue, Zip 11203–2012; tel. 718/270–1625; UNIVERSITY HOSPITAL OF BROOKLYN AT LONG ISLAND COLLEGE HOSPITAL, 339 Hicks Street, Zip 11201–5509; tel. 718/780–1000; George P. Caralis, Interim Chief Executive Officer), (Nonreporting) **A**1 2 3 5 8 9 10
Primary Contact: John F. Williams, Jr., M.D., Ed.D., M.P.H., President
COO: David Conley, Chief Administrative Officer
CFO: Gerry Dantis, Assistant Vice President Finance
CMO: Michael Lucchesi, M.D., Interim Chief Medical Officer
CIO: Ernest P. Weber, Jr., Interim Chief Information Officer
CHR: Hendrina Goeloe–Alston, Assistant Vice President Personnel
Web address: www.downstate.edu
**Control:** State–Government, nonfederal **Service:** General Medical and Surgical

**Staffed Beds:** 697

**TERENCE CARDINAL COOKE HEALTH CARE CENTER (332022)**, 1249 Fifth Avenue, Zip 10029–4413; tel. 212/360–1000, (Nonreporting) **A**10
Primary Contact: Mitch Marsh, Interim Executive Director
COO: Neil Pollack, Senior Administrator
CFO: Ann Marie Covone, Senior Vice President and Chief Financial Officer
CMO: Anthony Lechich, M.D., Chief Medical Officer
CIO: Mitze Amoroso, Chief Information Officer
CHR: Hugo A. Pizarro, Vice President Human Resources
CNO: Monica McGibbon, Chief Nursing Officer
Web address: www.tcchcc.org/
**Control:** Church–operated, Nongovernment, not–for profit **Service:** Long–Term Acute Care hospital

**Staffed Beds:** 28

**THE ALLEN PAVILION** See New York–Presbyterian Hospital

*Many Facility Codes have changed. Please refer to the AHA Guide Code Chart.* © 2015 AHA Guide

**NY**

**VETERANS AFFAIRS MEDICAL CENTER** See James J. Peters Veterans Affairs Medical Center

⊠ **VETERANS AFFAIRS NEW YORK HARBOR HEALTHCARE SYSTEM**, 800 Poly Place, Brooklyn, Zip 11209–7104; tel. 718/630–3500, (Includes VETERANS AFFAIRS NEW YORK HARBOR HEALTHCARE SYSTEM – MANHATTAN CAMPUS, 423 East 23rd Street, New York, Zip 10010–5050; tel. 212/686–7500), (Total facility includes 179 beds in nursing home–type unit) **A**1 2 3 5 **F**2 3 4 5 7 8 9 12 15 17 18 20 22 24 26 28 29 30 31 33 34 35 38 39 40 44 45 46 48 49 50 53 54 56 57 58 59 60 61 62 63 64 65 68 70 74 75 77 78 79 80 81 82 83 84 85 86 87 90 92 93 94 95 96 97 98 100 101 102 103 104 105 106 107 108 110 111 114 115 118 119 120 121 123 124 128 129 130 131 132 135 143 146 147 148 **P**6 **S** Department of Veterans Affairs, Washington, DC
Primary Contact: Martina A. Parauda, Director
CFO: Daniel Downey, Chief Fiscal Service
CIO: Maria Schay, Chief Information Officer
Web address: www.nyharbor.va.gov
**Control:** Veterans Affairs, Government, federal **Service:** General Medical and Surgical

**Staffed Beds:** 522 **Admissions:** 8262 **Census:** 358 **Outpatient Visits:** 451425 **Births:** 0 **Total Expense ($000):** 704234 **Payroll Expense ($000):** 317103 **Personnel:** 3825

⊠ **WOODHULL MEDICAL AND MENTAL HEALTH CENTER (330396)**, 760 Broadway, Brooklyn, Zip 11206–5383; tel. 718/963–8000 **A**1 3 5 9 10 **F**3 4 5 8 11 13 15 29 30 31 34 35 38 39 40 41 43 45 46 48 49 53 54 55 56 57 58 59 60 61 64 65 66 68 70 71 72 73 74 75 76 77 78 79 81 82 83 84 85 86 87 89 93 94 97 98 99 100 101 102 103 104 107 111 119 130 132 135 143 146 147 **P**6 **S** New York City Health and Hospitals Corporation, New York, NY
Primary Contact: George M. Proctor, Senior Vice President and Executive Director
COO: Eve Borzon, R.N., Chief Operating Officer
CFO: Rick Walker, Network, Chief Financial Officer
CMO: Edward Fishkin, M.D., Medical Director
CIO: Cynthia Bianchi, Chief Information Officer
CHR: Irma Suarez, Network Deputy Executive Director
CNO: Angela Imelda Edwards, R.N., Chief Nurse Executive
Web address: www.nyc.gov/html/hhc
**Control:** City–County, Government, nonfederal **Service:** General Medical and Surgical

**Staffed Beds:** 323 **Admissions:** 13090 **Census:** 253 **Outpatient Visits:** 504928 **Births:** 1936 **Total Expense ($000):** 460902 **Payroll Expense ($000):** 163214 **Personnel:** 2183

☐ **WYCKOFF HEIGHTS MEDICAL CENTER (330221)**, 374 Stockholm Street, Brooklyn, Zip 11237–4006; tel. 718/963–7272 **A**1 3 5 9 10 12 13 **F**3 7 8 9 13 14 15 17 18 19 20 26 29 30 31 32 34 35 38 39 40 41 44 45 46 50 54 56 57 59 61 64 65 68 70 72 73 74 75 76 77 78 79 81 82 85 86 87 89 90 92 93 94 97 102 107 108 109 110 111 114 115 118 119 120 121 123 124 130 132 134 135 143 146 147 148
Primary Contact: Ramon J. Rodriguez, President and Chief Executive Officer
COO: David Rock, Executive Vice President and Chief Operating Officer
CFO: Frank A. Vutrano, Chief Financial Officer
CMO: Gustavo Del Toro, M.D., Chief Medical Officer
CIO: Jebashini Jesurasa, Vice President, Chief Information Technology Officer
CHR: Margaret E. Cornelius, Vice President Human Resources
CNO: Catherine A. Gallogly–Simon, R.N., Chief Nursing Officer
Web address: www.wyckoffhospital.org
**Control:** Other not–for–profit (including NFP Corporation) **Service:** General Medical and Surgical

**Staffed Beds:** 276 **Admissions:** 13687 **Census:** 178 **Outpatient Visits:** 215450 **Births:** 1406 **Total Expense ($000):** 291320 **Payroll Expense ($000):** 122959 **Personnel:** 1740

**ZUCKER HILLSIDE HOSPITAL** See Long Island Jewish Medical Center, New Hyde Park

⊠ **NEWARK–WAYNE COMMUNITY HOSPITAL (330030)**, 1200 Driving Park Avenue, Zip 14513–1057, Mailing Address: P.O. Box 111, Zip 14513–0111; tel. 315/332–2022, (Total facility includes 180 beds in nursing home unit) **A**1 9 10 **F**2 3 6 8 11 13 15 28 29 30 34 35 38 40 44 50 54 55 56 57 59 61 64 68 70 74 75 77 79 80 81 85 86 87 90 93 97 98 100 102 103 107 110 111 114 118 119 126 128 130 131 132 135 143 146 147 148 **P**5 7 **S** Rochester Regional Health, Rochester, NY
Primary Contact: Dustin Riccio, M.D., Regional President Operations
CFO: Tom Crilly, Executive Vice President, Chief Financial Officer
CMO: Robert Mayo, M.D., Executive Vice President, Chief Medical Officer
CIO: John Glynn, Executive Vice President, Chief Information Officer
CHR: Janine Schue, Executive Vice President, Chief Human Resources Officer
CNO: Debbie Stamps, Vice President, Chief Nursing Officer
Web address: www.rochesterregional.org
**Control:** Other not–for–profit (including NFP Corporation) **Service:** General Medical and Surgical

**Staffed Beds:** 280 **Admissions:** 6090 **Census:** 229 **Outpatient Visits:** 160283 **Births:** 771 **Total Expense ($000):** 93286 **Payroll Expense ($000):** 42618 **Personnel:** 757

⊠ **ST. LUKE'S CORNWALL HOSPITAL (330264)**, 70 Dubois Street, Zip 12550–4851; tel. 845/561–4400, (Includes ST. LUKE'S CORNWALL HOSPITAL – CORNWALL CAMPUS, 19 Laurel Avenue, Cornwall, Zip 12518–1499; tel. 845/534–7711; ST. LUKE'S CORNWALL HOSPITAL – NEWBURGH CAMPUS, 70 Dubois Street, Zip 12550–4898; tel. 845/561–4400) **A**1 2 9 10 **F**3 11 13 15 18 20 22 26 29 31 34 35 37 40 42 46 49 51 54 57 59 60 61 64 70 72 74 75 76 77 78 79 81 82 84 85 86 87 89 93 100 102 107 108 110 114 115 118 119 120 121 123 124 126 129 130 131 132 146 147
Primary Contact: Joan Cusack–McGuirk, Interim President and Chief Executive Officer
CFO: Thomas Gibney, Senior Vice President and Chief Financial Officer
CMO: Christine Jelalian, M.D., Medical Director
CIO: Cletis Earle, Vice President and Chief Information Officer
CHR: Glenn Courounis, Vice President People and Patient Experience
CNO: Joan Cusack–McGuirk, Senior Vice President and Chief Nursing Officer
Web address: www.stlukescornwallhospital.org
**Control:** Other not–for–profit (including NFP Corporation) **Service:** General Medical and Surgical

**Staffed Beds:** 128 **Admissions:** 10404 **Census:** 127 **Outpatient Visits:** 158195 **Births:** 833 **Total Expense ($000):** 175025 **Payroll Expense ($000):** 66203 **Personnel:** 887

○ **NIAGARA FALLS MEMORIAL MEDICAL CENTER (330065)**, 621 Tenth Street, Zip 14301–1813, Mailing Address: P.O. Box 708, Zip 14302–0708; tel. 716/278–4000, (Nonreporting) **A**3 5 9 10 11 13
Primary Contact: Joseph A. Ruffolo, President and Chief Executive Officer
CMO: Fatma Patel, M.D., Vice President Medical Affairs
CIO: Diane Martin–Pratt, Director Information Systems
Web address: www.nfmmc.org
**Control:** Other not–for–profit (including NFP Corporation) **Service:** General Medical and Surgical

**Staffed Beds:** 288

**DE GRAFF MEMORIAL HOSPITAL** See KALEIDA Health, Buffalo

⊠ △ **NORTHPORT VETERANS AFFAIRS MEDICAL CENTER**, 79 Middleville Road, Zip 11768–2200; tel. 631/261–4400, (Total facility includes 170 beds in nursing home–type unit) **A**1 2 3 5 7 8 **F**3 5 8 17 20 29 30 31 33 34 35 36 38 39 40 44 45 46 47 49 50 51 53 54 56 57 58 59 60 61 62 63 64 65 68 70 71 74 75 77 78 79 81 82 83 84 85 86 87 90 91 92 93 94 95 96 97 98 100 101 102 103 104 105 106 107 108 111 114 116 117 118 119 120 121 122 123 127 128 129 130 132 133 135 144 146 147 148 **S** Department of Veterans Affairs, Washington, DC
Primary Contact: Philip C. Moschitta, Director
COO: Maria Favale, FACHE, Associate Director
CFO: Mary Pat Hessman, Chief Fiscal
CMO: Edward Mack, M.D., Chief of Staff
CIO: Robert Ziskin, Chief Information Officer
CHR: Wilmino Sainbert, Chief Human Resources Management Service
Web address: www.northport.va.gov/index.asp
**Control:** Veterans Affairs, Government, federal **Service:** General Medical and Surgical

**Staffed Beds:** 502 **Admissions:** 3840 **Census:** 247 **Outpatient Visits:** 575850 **Births:** 0 **Personnel:** 1781

NY

## NORWICH—Chenango County

★ ○ **CHENANGO MEMORIAL HOSPITAL (330033)**, 179 North Broad Street, Zip 13815–1097; tel. 607/337–4111, (Total facility includes 80 beds in nursing home–type unit) **A**9 10 11 **F**3 8 11 13 15 17 18 29 32 34 35 38 39 40 45 47 50 54 56 57 59 61 64 65 68 70 75 76 77 79 81 82 85 86 87 89 93 97 107 108 110 111 115 119 127 128 130 132 133 146 147 148 **P**6 **S** United Health Services, Binghamton, NY
Primary Contact: Drake M. Lamen, M.D., President and Chief Executive Officer
COO: Christina A. Kisacky, Vice President, Operations
CFO: Robert R. McCarthy, Vice President Finance and Chief Financial Officer
CMO: Drake M. Lamen, M.D., President and Chief Executive Officer, Chief Medical Officer
CIO: Richard Stone, Manager, Technical Services
CHR: Anne L. English, Director Human Resources
CNO: David Finney, R.N., Vice President Nursing
Web address: www.uhs.net/cmh
**Control:** Other not–for–profit (including NFP Corporation) **Service:** General Medical and Surgical

**Staffed Beds:** 138 **Admissions:** 1609 **Census:** 89 **Outpatient Visits:** 254344 **Births:** 310 **Total Expense ($000):** 65840 **Payroll Expense ($000):** 19713 **Personnel:** 416

## NYACK—Rockland County

☐ **NYACK HOSPITAL (330104)**, 160 North Midland Avenue, Zip 10960–1998; tel. 845/348–2000 **A**1 2 5 9 10 **F**4 5 8 11 14 15 17 29 30 31 34 40 43 45 46 62 70 73 75 76 77 78 79 81 82 83 84 85 86 87 89 93 98 99 102 103 107 108 111 118 119 129 130 135 146 148
Primary Contact: Mark Geller, M.D., President and Chief Executive Officer
CFO: John Burke, Chief Financial Officer
CMO: Michael E. Rader, M.D., Vice President and Medical Director
CIO: John Volanto, Vice President and Chief Operating Officer
CHR: Mary K. Shinick, Vice President Human Resources
CNO: Celeste Ann Bethon, MS, Chief Nursing Officer
Web address: www.nyackhospital.org
**Control:** Other not–for–profit (including NFP Corporation) **Service:** General Medical and Surgical

**Staffed Beds:** 245 **Admissions:** 11820 **Census:** 158 **Outpatient Visits:** 174155 **Births:** 1751 **Total Expense ($000):** 221558 **Payroll Expense ($000):** 92856

## OCEANSIDE—Nassau County

⌧ **SOUTH NASSAU COMMUNITIES HOSPITAL (330198)**, One Healthy Way, Zip 11572–1551; tel. 516/632–3000 **A**1 2 3 5 9 10 12 13 **F**3 5 11 12 13 15 17 18 20 22 26 28 29 30 31 34 35 37 38 40 43 44 45 46 47 49 50 54 55 56 57 58 59 60 62 64 66 68 69 70 73 74 75 76 77 78 79 81 82 83 84 85 87 89 91 92 93 97 98 99 100 102 103 104 105 107 108 109 110 111 114 115 118 119 120 121 123 124 126 128 129 130 131 132 135 144 145 146 148 **P**8
Primary Contact: Richard J. Murphy, President and Chief Executive Officer
CFO: Mark A. Bogen, Senior Vice President and Chief Financial Officer
CMO: Adhi Sharma, M.D., Chief Medical Officer
CIO: John Mertz, Chief Information Officer
CHR: Paul Giordano, Vice President Human Resources
CNO: Sue Penque, R.N., Senior Vice President and Chief Nursing Officer
Web address: www.southnassau.org
**Control:** Other not–for–profit (including NFP Corporation) **Service:** General Medical and Surgical

**Staffed Beds:** 378 **Admissions:** 19539 **Census:** 294 **Outpatient Visits:** 348204 **Births:** 1957 **Total Expense ($000):** 426967 **Payroll Expense ($000):** 212506 **Personnel:** 2605

## OGDENSBURG—St. Lawrence County

★ ◇ **CLAXTON–HEPBURN MEDICAL CENTER (330211)**, 214 King Street, Zip 13669–1142; tel. 315/393–3600 **A**2 9 10 20 21 **F**3 11 13 15 28 29 30 31 34 35 36 38 40 44 45 50 51 53 54 56 57 59 60 61 64 70 74 75 76 77 78 79 81 82 85 86 87 90 91 92 93 94 96 97 98 100 101 102 103 104 107 108 110 111 115 118 119 121 123 129 130 131 132 133 135 145 146 147 148 **P**6 7
Primary Contact: Nathan Howell, President and Chief Executive Officer
COO: Vicki Perrine, FACHE, Chief Operating Officer
CFO: Kelley Tiernan, Chief Financial Officer
CMO: Gary Hart, M.D., Chief Medical Officer
CIO: James Flood, Director Information Systems
CHR: Lou–Ann McNally, Director Human Resources
CNO: David Ferris, Chief Nursing Officer and Vice President Patient Care Services
Web address: www.claxtonhepburn.org
**Control:** Other not–for–profit (including NFP Corporation) **Service:** General Medical and Surgical

**Staffed Beds:** 97 **Admissions:** 2918 **Census:** 52 **Outpatient Visits:** 163237 **Births:** 196 **Total Expense ($000):** 96327 **Payroll Expense ($000):** 43228 **Personnel:** 606

☐ **ST. LAWRENCE PSYCHIATRIC CENTER (334003)**, 1 Chimney Point Drive, Zip 13669–2291; tel. 315/541–2001, (Nonreporting) **A**1 9 10 **S** New York State Office of Mental Health, Albany, NY
Primary Contact: Timothy Farrell, Executive Director
CMO: Harishankar Sanghi, M.D., Clinical Director
CHR: Rosie Turnbull, Director Human Resources
Web address: www.omh.ny.gov/omhweb/facilities/slpc/facility.htm
**Control:** State–Government, nonfederal **Service:** Psychiatric

**Staffed Beds:** 146

## OLEAN—Cattaraugus County

⌧ **OLEAN GENERAL HOSPITAL (330103)**, 515 Main Street, Zip 14760–1513; tel. 716/373–2600 **A**1 3 5 9 10 19 **F**3 8 11 13 15 17 18 20 22 28 29 30 31 34 35 38 39 40 45 46 47 48 49 50 51 53 54 57 58 59 60 61 62 64 65 70 71 74 75 76 77 78 79 81 82 83 84 85 86 87 89 92 93 94 97 98 100 101 102 103 107 108 109 110 111 115 116 117 118 119 120 121 123 127 129 130 131 132 133 134 135 143 144 145 146 147 148 **P**6 **S** Upper Allegheny Health System, Olean, NY
Primary Contact: Timothy J. Finan, FACHE, President and Chief Executive Officer
CFO: Richard G. Braun, Jr., CPA, Senior Vice President and Chief Financial Officer
CMO: William Mills, M.D., Senior Vice President Quality and Professional Affairs
CIO: Jason Yaworsky, Senior Vice President Information Systems and Chief Information Officer
CHR: Timothy M. McNamara, Senior Vice President Human Resources
CNO: Jeff S. Zewe, R.N., Vice President Patient Care Services and Chief Nursing Officer
Web address: www.ogh.org
**Control:** Other not–for–profit (including NFP Corporation) **Service:** General Medical and Surgical

**Staffed Beds:** 186 **Admissions:** 5901 **Census:** 81 **Outpatient Visits:** 214616 **Births:** 768 **Total Expense ($000):** 108278 **Payroll Expense ($000):** 42584 **Personnel:** 843

## ONEIDA—Madison County

⌧ **ONEIDA HEALTHCARE (330115)**, 321 Genesee Street, Zip 13421–2611; tel. 315/363–6000, (Total facility includes 160 beds in nursing home–type unit) **A**1 9 10 **F**3 11 13 15 18 29 34 40 45 49 50 54 57 59 64 65 68 70 74 75 77 79 81 85 86 87 92 93 97 107 108 111 115 117 118 119 126 128 129 130 135 146 **P**6
Primary Contact: Gene Morreale, President and Chief Executive Officer
COO: Mary Parry, Vice President Operations and Chief Operating Officer
CFO: John D. Milligan, Vice President Finance and Chief Financial Officer
CMO: Dan J. Vick, M.D., Vice President of Medical Affairs and Chief Medical Officer
CIO: Mary McGuirl, Director Information Systems
CHR: Michael Fifield, Vice President Human Resources
CNO: Janis Kohlbrenner, R.N., Vice President Clinical Services and Chief Nursing Officer
Web address: www.oneidahealthcare.org
**Control:** Other not–for–profit (including NFP Corporation) **Service:** General Medical and Surgical

**Staffed Beds:** 211 **Admissions:** 3188 **Census:** 179 **Outpatient Visits:** 173806 **Births:** 463 **Total Expense ($000):** 90035 **Payroll Expense ($000):** 40743 **Personnel:** 690

## ONEONTA—Otsego County

★ ◇ **AURELIA OSBORN FOX MEMORIAL HOSPITAL (330085)**, 1 Norton Avenue, Zip 13820–2629; tel. 607/432–2000, (Total facility includes 131 beds in nursing home–type unit) **A**9 10 21 **F**2 3 11 13 15 26 28 29 30 34 35 39 40 45 46 47 48 51 53 54 56 57 59 64 65 68 75 76 77 81 85 86 87 93 96 97 104 107 108 110 111 115 118 119 120 121 123 128 129 130 146 147 **P**6 **S** Bassett Healthcare Network, Cooperstown, NY
Primary Contact: John R. Remillard, President
CFO: Mark J. Wright, Vice President Finance
CMO: Benjamin Friedell, Vice President Medical Affairs
CHR: Jennie Gliha, Vice President Human Resources and Clinical Services
CNO: Robbin Scobie, Vice President Nursing
Web address: www.bassett.org/ao–fox–hospital/
**Control:** Other not–for–profit (including NFP Corporation) **Service:** General Medical and Surgical

**Staffed Beds:** 191 **Admissions:** 2661 **Census:** 159 **Outpatient Visits:** 187012 **Births:** 271 **Total Expense ($000):** 82882 **Payroll Expense ($000):** 34126 **Personnel:** 611

## ORANGEBURG—Rockland County

☐ **ROCKLAND CHILDREN'S PSYCHIATRIC CENTER**, 599 Convent Road, Zip 10962–1162; tel. 845/359–7400, (Nonreporting) **A**1 3 5 **S** New York State Office of Mental Health, Albany, NY
Primary Contact: Christopher Tavella, Acting Executive Director
COO: Kenneth Perrotte, Director Operations
CFO: Peter Gorey, Administrative Coordinator
CMO: Sadhana Sardana, M.D., Clinical Director
CIO: Mary Pivonka, Director Quality Management
Web address: www.omh.ny.gov/
**Control:** State–Government, nonfederal **Service:** Children's hospital psychiatric

**Staffed Beds:** 54

*Many Facility Codes have changed. Please refer to the AHA Guide Code Chart.*      © 2015 AHA Guide

☐ **ROCKLAND PSYCHIATRIC CENTER (334015)**, 140 Old Orangeburg Road, Zip 10962–1157; tel. 845/359–1000, (Nonreporting) **A**1 3 5 10 **S** New York State Office of Mental Health, Albany, NY
Primary Contact: Christopher Tavella, Executive Director
Web address: www.omh.ny.gov/
**Control:** State–Government, nonfederal **Service:** Psychiatric

**Staffed Beds: 525**

### OSSINING—Westchester County

**OSSINING CORRECTIONAL FACILITIES HOSPITAL**, 354 Hunter Street, Zip 10562–5498; tel. 914/941–0108, (Nonreporting)
Primary Contact: John Perilli, M.D., Health Services Director
**Control:** State–Government, nonfederal **Service:** Hospital unit of an institution (prison hospital, college infimary, etc.)

**Staffed Beds: 25**

### OSWEGO—Oswego County

⊞ **OSWEGO HOSPITAL (330218)**, 110 West Sixth Street, Zip 13126–2507; tel. 315/349–5511 **A**1 9 10 20 **F**3 11 13 15 17 18 29 34 37 38 40 41 45 49 50 54 57 59 70 74 75 77 79 81 85 86 87 93 98 99 100 101 102 104 107 108 110 111 114 115 118 119 130 131 132 135 144 146 **P**6
Primary Contact: Charles Gijanto, President and Chief Executive Officer
CFO: Eric Campbell, Chief Financial Officer
CMO: Renato Mandanas, M.D., Chief Medical Officer
CIO: Barry W. Ryle, Chief Information Officer
CHR: Linda Daley, Vice President Human Resources
CNO: Valerie Favata, R.N., Chief Nursing Officer
Web address: www.oswegohealth.org
**Control:** Other not–for–profit (including NFP Corporation) **Service:** General Medical and Surgical

**Staffed Beds: 107 Admissions: 4565 Census: 68 Outpatient Visits: 334297 Births: 538 Total Expense ($000): 105759 Payroll Expense ($000): 51618 Personnel: 883**

### PATCHOGUE—Suffolk County

★ ◇ **BROOKHAVEN MEMORIAL HOSPITAL MEDICAL CENTER (330141)**, 101 Hospital Road, Zip 11772–4897; tel. 631/714–2941, (Nonreporting) **A**9 10 12 13 21
Primary Contact: Richard T. Margulis, President and Chief Executive Officer
COO: Ron Stephenson, Chief Operating Officer
CFO: Brenda Farrell, Vice President Finance
CMO: Nejat Zeyneloglu, Vice President and Chief Quality Medical Officer
CIO: Kevin Conroy, Vice President and Chief Information Officer
CHR: Susan C. Hever, Director Human Resources
Web address: www.bmhmc.org
**Control:** Other not–for–profit (including NFP Corporation) **Service:** General Medical and Surgical

**Staffed Beds: 242**

### PENN YAN—Yates County

**SOLDIERS AND SAILORS MEMORIAL HOSPITAL OF YATES COUNTY (331314)**, 418 North Main Street, Zip 14527–1085; tel. 315/531–2000 **A**9 10 18 **F**2 3 11 15 18 28 29 34 35 38 40 45 54 56 57 59 64 65 66 68 70 75 81 87 93 97 98 100 101 102 103 104 107 110 114 119 128 130 132 133 135 146 147 **P**6 **S** Finger Lakes Health, Geneva, NY
Primary Contact: Jose Acevedo, M.D., President and Chief Executive Officer
COO: Frank Korich, Vice President and Site Administrator
CFO: Pamela Johnson, Treasurer and Chief Financial Officer
CMO: Jason Feinberg, M.D., Vice President Medical Affairs and Chief Medical Officer
CIO: John Oates, Director Information Systems
CHR: Patrick R. Boyle, Vice President Human Resources
CNO: Eileen Gage, R.N., Vice President Nursing
Web address: www.flhealth.org
**Control:** Other not–for–profit (including NFP Corporation) **Service:** General Medical and Surgical

**Staffed Beds: 186 Admissions: 938 Census: 152 Outpatient Visits: 155391 Births: 0 Total Expense ($000): 29031 Payroll Expense ($000): 15566 Personnel: 351**

### PLAINVIEW—Nassau County

⊞ **PLAINVIEW HOSPITAL (330331)**, 888 Old Country Road, Zip 11803–4978; tel. 516/719–3000 **A**1 2 9 10 12 13 **F**3 8 9 15 17 18 29 30 31 34 35 36 38 40 43 44 45 46 49 50 51 57 58 59 60 63 64 65 68 69 70 71 74 75 78 79 81 84 85 86 87 97 100 101 102 107 108 110 111 114 115 119 130 132 135 146 148 **P**5 6 **S** North Shore–Long Island Jewish Health System, Great Neck, NY
Primary Contact: Michael Fener, Executive Director
CMO: Alan Mensch, M.D., Senior Vice President Medical Affairs
CIO: Nicholas O'Connor, Vice President and Chief Information Officer
Web address: www.northshorelij.com
**Control:** Other not–for–profit (including NFP Corporation) **Service:** General Medical and Surgical

**Staffed Beds: 189 Admissions: 8746 Census: 120 Outpatient Visits: 57776 Births: 0 Total Expense ($000): 189096 Payroll Expense ($000): 96317 Personnel: 1011**

### PLATTSBURGH—Clinton County

⊞ **THE UNIVERSITY OF VERMONT HEALTH NETWORK–CHAMPLAIN VALLEY PHYSICIANS HOSPITAL (330250)**, 75 Beekman Street, Zip 12901–1438; tel. 518/561–2000, (Total facility includes 96 beds in nursing home–type unit) **A**1 2 6 9 10 **F**3 7 8 11 13 14 15 18 20 22 26 28 29 30 31 34 35 36 38 39 40 41 43 45 46 49 50 53 56 58 59 64 68 70 76 77 78 79 81 83 84 85 87 89 93 94 96 98 99 102 107 108 110 111 114 115 116 117 118 119 120 121 123 126 128 130 132 143 144 145 146 147 148 **P**6
Primary Contact: Stephens M. Mundy, President and Chief Executive Officer
COO: Debra Donahue, Senior Vice President and Chief Operating Officer
CFO: Joyce Rafferty, Vice President Finance
CMO: Kent Hall, M.D., Vice President and Chief Medical Officer
CIO: Wouter Rietsema, M.D., Chief Quality and Information Officer
CHR: Michelle Lebeau, Vice President Human Resources
CNO: Debra Donahue, Senior Vice President and Chief Operating Officer
Web address: www.cvph.org
**Control:** Other not–for–profit (including NFP Corporation) **Service:** General Medical and Surgical

**Staffed Beds: 289 Admissions: 9297 Census: 242 Outpatient Visits: 360949 Births: 871 Total Expense ($000): 293326 Payroll Expense ($000): 141228 Personnel: 1842**

### POMONA—Rockland County

☐ **SUMMIT PARK HOSPITAL AND NURSING CARE CENTER (332014)**, (57 bed LTACH & 321 bed nursing home), 50 Sanatorium Road, Building A., Zip 10970–3555; tel. 845/364–2700, (Total facility includes 251 beds in nursing home–type unit) **A**1 9 10 **F**1 3 6 11 29 30 34 35 38 44 50 53 54 57 59 60 65 66 75 77 82 86 87 90 91 92 128 130 132 143 146
Primary Contact: Donna M. Pauldine, Deputy Commissioner
COO: Donna M. Pauldine, Deputy Commissioner
CFO: William Renc, Chief Fiscal Officer
CMO: Karen Castley, Medical Director
CHR: Theresa Sullivan, Director Human Resources
Web address: www.co.rockland.ny.us
**Control:** County–Government, nonfederal **Service:** Long–Term Acute Care hospital

**Staffed Beds: 308 Admissions: 617 Census: 233 Outpatient Visits: 0 Births: 0**

### PORT JEFFERSON—Suffolk County

⊞ **JOHN T. MATHER MEMORIAL HOSPITAL (330185)**, 75 North Country Road, Zip 11777–2190; tel. 631/473–1320 **A**1 2 3 9 10 **F**5 8 11 12 14 15 17 18 29 34 35 36 37 38 40 44 46 49 51 55 56 57 59 60 64 65 69 70 75 77 78 79 81 82 85 86 87 93 98 99 100 102 103 104 105 107 108 110 111 114 115 118 119 120 126 129 130 132 146 147 148
Primary Contact: Kenneth D. Roberts, President
COO: Kevin J. Murray, Senior Vice President
CFO: Joseph Wisnoski, Vice President Finance and Chief Financial Officer
CMO: Joan Faro, M.D., Chief Medical Officer
CIO: Thomas Heiman, Vice President Information Services and Chief Information Officer
CHR: Diane Marotta, Vice President Human Resources
CNO: Marie Mulligan, R.N., Vice President Nursing
Web address: www.matherhospital.com
**Control:** Other not–for–profit (including NFP Corporation) **Service:** General Medical and Surgical

**Staffed Beds: 248 Admissions: 11567 Census: 191 Outpatient Visits: 161513 Births: 0 Total Expense ($000): 284167 Payroll Expense ($000): 137613 Personnel: 1967**

**NY**

---

**Hospital, Medicare Provider Number, Address, Telephone, Approval, Facility, and Physician Codes, Health Care System**

★ American Hospital Association (AHA) membership
☐ The Joint Commission accreditation
○ Healthcare Facilities Accreditation Program
◇ DNV Healthcare Inc. accreditation
⇑ Center for Improvement in Healthcare Quality Accreditation
△ Commission on Accreditation of Rehabilitation Facilities (CARF) accreditation

☐ △ **ST. CHARLES HOSPITAL (330246)**, 200 Belle Terre Road,
Zip 11777–1928; tel. 631/474–6000 **A**1 2 3 7 9 10 **F**3 4 12 13 15 17 18 28
29 30 31 34 35 37 39 40 41 45 46 49 50 56 57 59 61 64 65 66 69 70 72
73 74 75 76 78 79 81 82 83 84 86 87 89 90 92 93 96 97 102 107 108 110
111 115 118 119 126 129 130 131 132 135 143 145 146 147 148
**S** Catholic Health Services of Long Island, Rockville Centre, NY
Primary Contact: James O'Connor, Executive Vice President and Chief
Administrative Officer
COO: Ronald Weingartner, Vice President Administration
CFO: Kathleen Vasil, Vice President Finance
CMO: Michael Sauter, M.D., Chief Medical Officer
CIO: Felix Pabon–Ramirez, Chief Information Officer
CNO: Nicolette Fiore–Lopez, R.N., Chief Nursing Officer
Web address: www.stcharleshospital.chsli.org
**Control:** Church–operated, Nongovernment, not–for profit **Service:** General
Medical and Surgical

> **Staffed Beds:** 231 **Admissions:** 8919 **Census:** 169 **Outpatient Visits:**
> 148341 **Births:** 1444 **Total Expense ($000):** 192198 **Payroll Expense**
> **($000):** 99226 **Personnel:** 1133

### PORT JERVIS—Orange County

☒ **BON SECOURS COMMUNITY HOSPITAL (330135)**, 160 East Main Street,
Zip 12771–2245, Mailing Address: P.O. Box 1014, Zip 12771–0268;
tel. 845/858–7000, (Nonreporting) **A**1 9 10 **S** Bon Secours Health System, Inc.,
Marriottsville, MD
Primary Contact: Jeff Reilly, Senior Vice President Operations
COO: Gaynor Rosenstein, Vice President Operations
CMO: Jeffrey Auerbach, D.O., Medical Director
CHR: Kim Hirkaler, Director Human Resources
Web address: www.bonsecourscommunityhosp.org
**Control:** Church–operated, Nongovernment, not–for profit **Service:** General
Medical and Surgical

> **Staffed Beds:** 187

### POTSDAM—St. Lawrence County

★ ◇ **CANTON–POTSDAM HOSPITAL (330197)**, 50 Leroy Street,
Zip 13676–1799; tel. 315/265–3300, (Nonreporting) **A**9 10 20 21 **S** St.
Lawrence Health System, Potsdam, NY
Primary Contact: David B. Acker, FACHE, President and CEO
COO: Linda Summers, Chief Operating Officer
CFO: Richard Jacobs, Vice President Finance and Chief Financial Officer
CMO: Robert T. Rogers, II, M.D., Medical Director
CIO: Jorge C. Grillo, Chief Information Officer
CHR: Darlene Lewis, Vice President Human Resources
CNO: Susan M. Hodgson, R.N., Vice President Patient Care Services and Chief
Nursing Officer
Web address: www.cphospital.org
**Control:** Other not–for–profit (including NFP Corporation) **Service:** General
Medical and Surgical

> **Staffed Beds:** 94

### POUGHKEEPSIE—Dutchess County

☐ **VASSAR BROTHERS MEDICAL CENTER (330023)**, 45 Reade Place,
Zip 12601–3947; tel. 845/454–8500 **A**1 2 9 10 **F**3 8 11 12 13 15 17 18 20
22 24 26 28 29 30 31 34 35 36 37 40 44 45 46 47 48 49 50 51 54 55 57
58 59 60 68 70 72 73 74 75 76 77 78 79 81 82 84 85 86 87 89 92 93 97
99 100 107 108 109 110 111 114 115 118 119 120 121 123 124 126 129
130 131 132 135 146 147 148 **S** Health Quest Systems, Inc., LaGrangeville, NY
Primary Contact: Robert Friedberg, President
CFO: Katherine Bacher, Interim Senior Vice President and Chief Financial Officer
CMO: Ronald Tatelbaum, M.D., Chief Medical Officer – Health Quest
CIO: Robert Diamond, Chief Information Officer
CHR: Jeffrey McDonough, Vice President Human Resources
CNO: Loretta Bogolin, MSN, Chief Nursing Officer and Vice President Care
Services
Web address: www.health–quest.org
**Control:** Other not–for–profit (including NFP Corporation) **Service:** General
Medical and Surgical

> **Staffed Beds:** 365 **Admissions:** 17998 **Census:** 248 **Outpatient Visits:**
> 247065 **Births:** 2237 **Total Expense ($000):** 416631 **Payroll Expense**
> **($000):** 123492 **Personnel:** 1685

### QUEENS—Queens County, See New York City

### QUEENS VILLAGE—Queens County, See New York City

### RHINEBECK—Dutchess County

☐ △ **NORTHERN DUTCHESS HOSPITAL (330049)**, 6511 Springbrook Avenue,
Zip 12572–3709, Mailing Address: P.O. Box 5002, Zip 12572–5002;
tel. 845/876–3001 **A**1 7 9 10 **F**3 11 13 15 18 28 29 34 35 36 37 40 45 50
53 56 64 68 70 74 75 76 77 78 79 81 82 84 85 87 90 93 100 107 108 110
111 114 115 118 119 129 130 132 146 147 148 **S** Health Quest Systems,
Inc., LaGrangeville, NY
Primary Contact: Denise George, R.N., President
CFO: Alan Mossoff, Chief Financial Officer
CMO: John Sabia, M.D., Vice President Medical Affairs
CIO: Robert Diamond, Senior Vice President and Chief Information Officer
CHR: Eileen Miller, Director Human Resources
CNO: Pamela Rhodes, R.N., Vice President Patient Services and Chief Nursing
Officer
Web address: www.health–quest.org/home_nd.cfm?id=9
**Control:** Other not–for–profit (including NFP Corporation) **Service:** General
Medical and Surgical

> **Staffed Beds:** 68 **Admissions:** 3760 **Census:** 43 **Births:** 918 **Total Expense**
> **($000):** 74165 **Payroll Expense ($000):** 24960 **Personnel:** 334

### RICHMOND VALLEY—Richmond County, See New York City

### RIVERHEAD—Suffolk County

☒ **PECONIC BAY MEDICAL CENTER (330107)**, 1300 Roanoke Avenue,
Zip 11901–2031; tel. 631/548–6000 **A**1 3 9 10 12 13 **F**7 11 12 13 15 24 29
30 31 34 40 45 46 47 49 50 54 57 59 60 61 62 64 68 70 74 75 76 77
78 79 80 81 82 83 84 85 86 87 93 96 97 107 108 110 111 115 118 119
126 130 131 132 143 146 147 148 **P**7 **S** North Shore–Long Island Jewish
Health System, Great Neck, NY
Primary Contact: Andrew J. Mitchell, President and Chief Executive Officer
COO: Ronald McManus, Senior Vice President Clinical Services and Business
Entities
CFO: Michael O'Donnell, Chief Financial Officer
CMO: Richard Kubiak, M.D., Vice President Medical Affairs
CIO: Arthur Crowe, Director Information Systems
CHR: Monica Chestnut–Rauls, Vice President Human Resources
CNO: Gerard Zunno, R.N., Vice President Patient Care Services
Web address: www.pbmchealth.org
**Control:** Other not–for–profit (including NFP Corporation) **Service:** General
Medical and Surgical

> **Staffed Beds:** 94 **Admissions:** 6707 **Census:** 79 **Outpatient Visits:** 101177
> **Births:** 353 **Personnel:** 896

### ROCHESTER—Monroe County

☒ **HIGHLAND HOSPITAL OF ROCHESTER (330164)**, 1000 South Avenue,
Zip 14620–2733; tel. 585/473–2200 **A**1 3 5 9 10 19 **F**3 8 12 13 15 18 24 29
30 31 34 35 37 39 40 44 45 46 47 48 49 50 54 56 57 58 59 63 64 65 66
68 70 74 75 76 78 79 81 82 83 84 85 87 91 97 100 107 108 110 111 114
115 118 119 120 121 123 124 126 130 131 132 134 135 141 145 146 147
148 **P**5 6 **S** University of Rochester Medical Center, Rochester, NY
Primary Contact: Steven I. Goldstein, President and Chief Executive Officer
COO: Cindy Becker, Vice President and Chief Operating Officer
CFO: Adam Anolik, Chief Financial Officer
CMO: Raymond Mayewski, M.D., Chief Medical Officer
CIO: D. Jerome Powell, M.D., Chief Information Officer
CHR: Kathleen Gallucci, Chief Human Resources
CNO: Tommye Hinton, R.N., Chief Nursing Officer
Web address: www.stronghealth.com
**Control:** Hospital district or authority, Government, nonfederal **Service:** General
Medical and Surgical

> **Staffed Beds:** 261 **Admissions:** 15910 **Census:** 198 **Outpatient Visits:**
> 265120 **Births:** 2939 **Total Expense ($000):** 299152 **Payroll Expense**
> **($000):** 142780 **Personnel:** 2117

☒ **ROCHESTER GENERAL HOSPITAL (330125)**, 1425 Portland Avenue,
Zip 14621–3099; tel. 585/922–4000 **A**1 2 3 5 6 9 10 **F**3 5 8 9 11 12 13 14
15 17 18 20 22 24 26 28 29 30 31 32 34 35 36 38 39 40 41 44 47 49 50
51 53 54 55 56 57 58 59 60 61 63 64 65 66 68 70 73 74 75 76 77 78 79
80 81 82 84 85 86 87 89 90 92 93 96 97 98 99 100 101 102 103 104 107
108 110 111 114 115 116 117 118 119 120 121 123 124 126 130 131 132
134 135 145 146 147 148 **P**5 7 **S** Rochester Regional Health, Rochester, NY
Primary Contact: Douglas Stewart, PsyD, President
CMO: Robert Mayo, M.D., Chief Medical Officer
CHR: Janine Schue, Senior Vice President Human Resources
CNO: Cheryl Sheridan, R.N., Senior Vice President Patient Care Services
Web address: www.rochestergeneral.org
**Control:** Other not–for–profit (including NFP Corporation) **Service:** General
Medical and Surgical

> **Staffed Beds:** 520 **Admissions:** 29395 **Census:** 459 **Outpatient Visits:**
> 1538470 **Births:** 2272 **Total Expense ($000):** 837711 **Payroll Expense**
> **($000):** 378341 **Personnel:** 5872

**NY**

☐ **ROCHESTER PSYCHIATRIC CENTER (334020)**, 1111 Elmwood Avenue, Zip 14620–3005; tel. 585/241–1200, (Nonreporting) **A**1 3 5 10 **S** New York State Office of Mental Health, Albany, NY
Primary Contact: Elizabeth Suhre, Executive Director
COO: Joseph Coffey, Director Facility Administration
CFO: Rosanne Minnis, Business Officer
CMO: Laurence Guttmacher, M.D., Clinical Director
CIO: Lori Hintz, Coordinator Information Systems
CHR: Colomba Misseritti, Director Human Resources
CNO: Christopher Kirisits, Chief Nursing Officer
Web address: www.omh.ny.gov/omhweb/facilities/ropc/facility.htm
**Control:** State–Government, nonfederal **Service:** Psychiatric

> **Staffed Beds:** 180

⊠ △ **STRONG MEMORIAL HOSPITAL OF THE UNIVERSITY OF ROCHESTER (330285)**, 601 Elmwood Avenue, Zip 14642–0002; tel. 585/275–2100, (Includes GOLISANO CHILDREN'S HOSPITAL, 601 Elmwood Avenue, Zip 14610; tel. 585/275–2182) **A**1 2 3 5 7 8 9 10 19 **F**3 5 6 8 9 11 12 13 14 15 16 17 18 19 20 21 22 23 24 25 26 27 28 29 30 31 32 33 34 35 38 39 40 41 42 43 44 45 46 47 48 49 50 51 52 53 54 55 56 57 58 59 61 63 64 65 66 68 70 71 72 73 74 75 76 77 78 79 81 82 83 84 85 86 87 88 89 90 91 92 93 94 96 97 98 99 100 101 102 103 104 105 107 108 110 111 114 115 116 117 118 119 120 121 123 124 126 129 130 131 132 134 135 136 137 138 139 141 142 143 144 146 147 148 **P**6 **S** University of Rochester Medical Center, Rochester, NY
Primary Contact: Steven I. Goldstein, President and Chief Executive Officer
COO: Kathleen M. Parrinello, Ph.D., Chief Operating Officer
CFO: Leonard J. Shute, Chief Financial Officer
CMO: Raymond Mayewski, M.D., Chief Medical Officer
CIO: D. Jerome Powell, M.D., Chief Information Officer
CHR: Charles J. Murphy, Associate Vice President Human Resources
Web address: www.urmc.rochester.edu
**Control:** Other not–for–profit (including NFP Corporation) **Service:** General Medical and Surgical

> **Staffed Beds:** 815 **Admissions:** 36790 **Census:** 747 **Outpatient Visits:** 1396910 **Births:** 3103 **Total Expense ($000):** 1291943 **Payroll Expense ($000):** 519397 **Personnel:** 9483

⊠ **UNITY HOSPITAL (330226)**, 1555 Long Pond Road, Zip 14626–4182; tel. 585/723–7000, (Total facility includes 120 beds in nursing home–type unit) **A**1 2 3 5 9 10 **F**3 4 5 13 15 18 20 22 26 28 29 30 31 33 34 35 38 39 40 44 45 46 47 48 49 50 52 55 56 57 59 60 61 63 64 65 66 67 70 71 73 74 75 76 77 78 79 81 82 84 85 86 87 90 91 92 93 96 97 98 100 102 104 107 108 118 119 126 128 129 130 131 132 134 141 144 146 147 148 **P**6 **S** Rochester Regional Health, Rochester, NY
Primary Contact: Douglas Stewart, PsyD, President
COO: Stewart C. Putnam, Executive Vice President and Chief Operating Officer
CFO: Tom Crilly, Executive Vice President and Chief Financial Officer
CMO: James Haley, M.D., Senior Vice President and Chief Medical Officer
CIO: John Glynn, Senior Vice President and Chief Information Officer
CHR: Maryalice Keller, Vice President Brand and Talent Management
CNO: Jane McCormack, R.N., Vice President, Chief Nursing Officer and Nursing and Patient Care Services
Web address: www.unityhealth.org
**Control:** Other not–for–profit (including NFP Corporation) **Service:** General Medical and Surgical

> **Staffed Beds:** 487 **Admissions:** 15816 **Census:** 372 **Outpatient Visits:** 1119913 **Births:** 1600 **Total Expense ($000):** 424137 **Payroll Expense ($000):** 210266 **Personnel:** 3515

**ROCKVILLE CENTRE—Nassau County**

☐ **MERCY MEDICAL CENTER (330259)**, 1000 North Village Avenue, Zip 11570–1000; tel. 516/705–2525 **A**1 2 3 9 10 13 **F**3 8 12 13 15 20 26 29 30 31 34 35 37 38 40 41 43 45 46 48 49 50 51 56 57 58 59 60 64 65 66 68 70 72 74 75 76 77 78 79 81 82 84 85 87 90 92 93 94 96 97 98 100 102 103 104 105 107 108 110 111 115 116 117 119 130 131 132 135 141 142 143 146 147 148 **P**5 **S** Catholic Health Services of Long Island, Rockville Centre, NY
Primary Contact: Aaron Glatt, M.D., Executive Vice President and Chief Administrative Officer
COO: Ronald Steimel, Vice President Administration and Chief Operating Officer
CFO: William C. Armstrong, Senior Vice President and Chief Financial Officer
CMO: John Reilly, M.D., Vice President Medical Affairs and Chief Medical Officer
CIO: Marcy Dunn, Vice President Information Services and Chief Information Officer
CHR: Allison Cianciotto Croyle, Vice President of Human Resources
CNO: Beth Vlahavas, R.N., Vice President Patient Care Services and Chief Nursing Officer
Web address: www.mercymedicalcenter.chsli.org
**Control:** Church–operated, Nongovernment, not–for profit **Service:** General Medical and Surgical

> **Staffed Beds:** 191 **Admissions:** 9871 **Census:** 177 **Outpatient Visits:** 100201 **Births:** 1063 **Total Expense ($000):** 198767 **Payroll Expense ($000):** 90614 **Personnel:** 1121

**ROME—Oneida County**

★ ○ **ROME MEMORIAL HOSPITAL (330215)**, 1500 North James Street, Zip 13440–2844; tel. 315/338–7000, (Total facility includes 82 beds in nursing home–type unit) **A**9 10 11 **F**3 5 8 13 15 18 26 27 29 30 31 34 35 37 40 46 49 56 57 59 61 64 65 66 70 74 75 76 77 78 79 80 81 84 85 86 87 89 93 97 98 101 102 103 106 107 108 110 111 115 118 119 120 121 123 128 129 130 131 132 135 146 147 148 **P**6
Primary Contact: Darlene A. Burns, MS, R.N., Interim Chief Executive Officer
CFO: Dewey R. Rowlands, Vice President and Chief Financial Officer
CMO: Ankur Desai, Interim Chief Medical officer
CIO: Bruce Peterson, Chief Information Officer
CHR: Regina Chambers, Vice President Human Resource
CNO: Durinda Durr, Vice President Clinical Services and Chief Nursing Officer
Web address: www.romehospital.org
**Control:** Other not–for–profit (including NFP Corporation) **Service:** General Medical and Surgical

> **Staffed Beds:** 203 **Admissions:** 3859 **Census:** 122 **Outpatient Visits:** 159117 **Births:** 541 **Total Expense ($000):** 78936 **Payroll Expense ($000):** 36750 **Personnel:** 668

**ROSLYN—Nassau County**

⊠ **ST. FRANCIS HOSPITAL (330182)**, 100 Port Washington Boulevard, Zip 11576–1353; tel. 516/562–6000 **A**1 3 9 10 **F**3 7 11 12 15 17 18 19 20 21 22 23 24 26 27 28 29 30 31 34 35 36 37 38 39 40 43 44 45 46 47 49 50 53 54 55 56 57 58 59 60 61 62 63 64 65 66 68 70 71 74 75 77 78 79 81 82 83 84 85 86 87 93 94 97 100 102 107 108 109 110 111 114 115 116 117 118 119 124 126 130 131 132 135 141 145 146 147 148 **P**6 8 **S** Catholic Health Services of Long Island, Rockville Centre, NY
Primary Contact: Ruth Hennessey, Executive Vice President and Chief Administrative Officer
CFO: William C. Armstrong, Vice President and Chief Financial Officer
CMO: Jack Soterakis, M.D., Executive Vice President Medical Affairs
CIO: Marcy Dunn, Vice President Information Services and Chief Information Officer
CHR: Barbara Fierro, Director, Human Resources
CNO: Ann S. Cella, R.N., Senior Vice President, Patient Care Services
Web address: www.stfrancisheartcenter.com/index.html
**Control:** Church–operated, Nongovernment, not–for profit **Service:** General Medical and Surgical

> **Staffed Beds:** 306 **Admissions:** 15695 **Census:** 270 **Outpatient Visits:** 192639 **Births:** 0 **Total Expense ($000):** 565234 **Payroll Expense ($000):** 266005 **Personnel:** 2838

**NY**

---

**Hospital, Medicare Provider Number, Address, Telephone, Approval, Facility, and Physician Codes, Health Care System**

★ American Hospital Association (AHA) membership   ○ Healthcare Facilities Accreditation Program   ⇑ Center for Improvement in Healthcare Quality Accreditation
☐ The Joint Commission accreditation   ◇ DNV Healthcare Inc. accreditation   △ Commission on Accreditation of Rehabilitation Facilities (CARF) accreditation

---

## SARANAC LAKE—Franklin County

★ ○ **ADIRONDACK MEDICAL CENTER (330079)**, 2233 State Route 86, Zip 12983–5644, Mailing Address: P.O. Box 471, Zip 12983–0471; tel. 518/891–4141, (Total facility includes 140 beds in nursing home–type unit) **A**9 10 11 **F**3 8 9 12 13 15 18 28 29 30 31 34 35 37 38 39 40 41 42 43 45 46 49 50 53 54 56 57 59 60 64 70 71 74 75 76 77 78 79 81 82 84 85 86 89 90 92 93 94 97 98 102 103 104 107 108 110 111 114 116 119 127 128 129 130 131 132 135 146 147 148 **P**6 **S** HealthTech Management Services, Brentwood, TN
Primary Contact: Chandler M. Ralph, President and Chief Executive Officer
COO: Patti Hammond, Chief Operating Officer
CFO: Tristan Glanville, Chief Financial Officer
CMO: John Broderick, M.D., Chief Medical Officer
CHR: Michael D. Lee, Chief Human Resources Officer
CNO: Linda McClarigan, R.N., Chief Nursing Officer
Web address: www.adirondackhealth.org
**Control:** Other not–for–profit (including NFP Corporation) **Service:** General Medical and Surgical

**Staffed Beds:** 200 **Admissions:** 2435 **Census:** 156 **Outpatient Visits:** 130329 **Births:** 143 **Total Expense ($000):** 95849 **Payroll Expense ($000):** 44368 **Personnel:** 742

## SARATOGA SPRINGS—Saratoga County

☐ **FOUR WINDS HOSPITAL (334049)**, 30 Crescent Avenue, Zip 12866–5142; tel. 518/584–3600, (Nonreporting) **A**1 9 10
Primary Contact: Samuel A. Bastien, IV, Ph.D., Chief Executive Officer
CFO: Juanita Wheeler–Moore, Director Financial Services
CMO: Kevin P. Martin, M.D., Chief Medical Officer
CIO: Susan Snowdon, Director Information Technology
CHR: Susan M. Kirchner, Director Human Resources
CNO: James Colamaria, Director of Nursing
Web address: www.fourwindshospital.com
**Control:** Corporation, Investor–owned, for–profit **Service:** Children's hospital psychiatric

**Staffed Beds:** 83

⊞ **SARATOGA HOSPITAL (330222)**, 211 Church Street, Zip 12866–1003; tel. 518/587–3222, (Nonreporting) **A**1 2 5 9 10
Primary Contact: Angelo G. Calbone, President and Chief Executive Officer
CFO: Gary Foster, Vice President and Chief Financial Officer
CMO: Richard Falivena, D.O., Vice President and Chief Medical Officer
CIO: John Mangona, Vice President, Chief Information Officer and Compliance Officer
CHR: Jeffrey M. Methven, Vice President Ambulatory Services and Chief Human Resources Officer
CNO: Mary Jo LaPosta, Ph.D., Senior Vice President Patient Care and Organizational Excellence
Web address: www.saratogacare.org
**Control:** Other not–for–profit (including NFP Corporation) **Service:** General Medical and Surgical

**Staffed Beds:** 207

## SCHENECTADY—Schenectady County

⊞ **ELLIS HOSPITAL (330153)**, 1101 Nott Street, Zip 12308–2425; tel. 518/243–4000, (Includes BELLEVUE WOMAN'S CARE CENTER, 2210 Troy Road, Zip 12309–4797; tel. 518/346–9400; ELLIS HOSPITAL HEALTH CENTER, 600 McClellan Street, Zip 12304–1090; tel. 518/382–2000), (Nonreporting) **A**1 3 5 6 9 10 13
Primary Contact: James W. Connolly, President and Chief Executive Officer
COO: Paul A. Milton, Executive Vice President and Chief Operating Officer
CFO: Daniel Rinaldi, Chief Financial Officer
CMO: David Liebers, M.D., Chief Medical Officer and Vice President Medical Affairs
CIO: David Snyder, Chief Information Officer and Vice President Information Technology
CHR: Joseph Giansante, Vice President Human Resources
CNO: Kathleen A. Hale, MS, Vice President and Chief Nursing Officer
Web address: www.ellismedicine.org
**Control:** Other not–for–profit (including NFP Corporation) **Service:** General Medical and Surgical

**Staffed Beds:** 431

**ELLIS HOSPITAL HEALTH CENTER** See Ellis Hospital

**ELLIS HOSPITAL MCCLELLAN CAMPUS** See Ellis Hospital Health Center

⊞ △ **SUNNYVIEW REHABILITATION HOSPITAL (330406)**, 1270 Belmont Avenue, Zip 12308–2104; tel. 518/382–4500 **A**1 3 5 7 9 10 **F**3 28 29 53 56 57 59 64 74 79 90 93 94 95 119 130 132 135 **P**5 **S** Trinity Health, Livonia, MI
Primary Contact: Edward Eisenman, Chief Executive Officer
CFO: Kristin Signor, Director Finance
CMO: Lynne T. Nicolson, M.D., Medical Director
CIO: Patrick Clark, Manager Information Technology
CHR: Meghan Glowa, Director Human Resources
Web address: www.sunnyview.org
**Control:** Other not–for–profit (including NFP Corporation) **Service:** Rehabilitation

**Staffed Beds:** 115 **Admissions:** 2379 **Census:** 89 **Outpatient Visits:** 72474 **Births:** 0 **Total Expense ($000):** 47822 **Payroll Expense ($000):** 27710 **Personnel:** 542

## SLEEPY HOLLOW—Westchester County

⊞ **PHELPS MEMORIAL HOSPITAL CENTER (330261)**, 701 North Broadway, Zip 10591–1020; tel. 914/366–3000, (Nonreporting) **A**1 2 3 5 9 10
Primary Contact: Daniel Blum, President
CFO: Vincent DeSantis, Vice President Finance
CHR: Jussi Maijala, Vice President, Human Resources
CNO: Mary McDermott, Vice President Nursing
Web address: www.phelpshospital.org
**Control:** Other not–for–profit (including NFP Corporation) **Service:** General Medical and Surgical

**Staffed Beds:** 238

## SMITHTOWN—Suffolk County

☐ **ST. CATHERINE OF SIENA MEDICAL CENTER (330401)**, 50 Route 25–A, Zip 11787–1348; tel. 631/862–3000, (Nonreporting) **A**1 9 10 **S** Catholic Health Services of Long Island, Rockville Centre, NY
Primary Contact: Dennis Verzi, Executive Vice President and Chief Administrative Officer
CFO: Dan Macksood, Regional Vice President and Chief Financial Officer
CHR: Danielle A. Robbins, Vice President Human Resources
Web address: www.stcatherinemedicalcenter.org
**Control:** Church–operated, Nongovernment, not–for profit **Service:** General Medical and Surgical

**Staffed Beds:** 503

## SOUTHAMPTON—Suffolk County

⊞ **SOUTHAMPTON HOSPITAL (330340)**, 240 Meeting House Lane, Zip 11968–5090; tel. 631/726–8200 **A**1 3 9 10 12 13 **F**3 12 13 15 18 28 29 30 31 34 35 36 37 39 40 44 45 46 47 49 51 53 54 55 56 57 59 60 61 63 65 68 70 74 75 76 77 78 79 81 82 84 85 87 89 93 107 108 110 111 115 119 130 131 132 135 145 146 147 148 **P**6
Primary Contact: Robert S. Chaloner, President and Chief Executive Officer
COO: Frederic Weinbaum, M.D., Executive Vice President Operations and Chief Medical Officer
CFO: Chris Schulteis, Vice President/Chief Financial Officer
CMO: Frederic Weinbaum, M.D., Executive Vice President Operations and Chief Medical Officer
CIO: Jim Maul, Chief Information Officer and Director Information Services
CNO: Patricia Darcey, R.N., Vice President/Chief Nursing Officer
Web address: www.southamptonhospital.org
**Control:** Other not–for–profit (including NFP Corporation) **Service:** General Medical and Surgical

**Staffed Beds:** 80 **Admissions:** 5393 **Census:** 57 **Outpatient Visits:** 775033 **Births:** 646 **Total Expense ($000):** 135618 **Payroll Expense ($000):** 61674 **Personnel:** 833

## SPRINGVILLE—Erie County

**BERTRAND CHAFFEE HOSPITAL (330111)**, 224 East Main Street, Zip 14141–1497; tel. 716/592–2871, (Nonreporting) **A**9 10
Primary Contact: Nils Gunnersen, Administrator
CMO: J. Matthew Baker, M.D., President Medical Staff
CHR: Mary Beth Brown, Director Human Resources
Web address: www.chaffeehospitalandhome.com
**Control:** Other not–for–profit (including NFP Corporation) **Service:** General Medical and Surgical

**Staffed Beds:** 24

## STAR LAKE—St. Lawrence County

★ **CLIFTON–FINE HOSPITAL (331307)**, 1014 Oswegatchie Trail, Zip 13690–3143; tel. 315/848–3351, (Nonreporting) **A**9 10 18
Primary Contact: Robert L. Seamon, Chief Executive Officer
CFO: Nancy Russell, Chief Financial Officer
CMO: David Welch, M.D., Medical Director
CIO: Devin Rice, Director Information Systems
CNO: Michelle Bristol, Director of Nursing
Web address: www.cliftonfinehospital.org
**Control:** Other not–for–profit (including NFP Corporation) **Service:** General Medical and Surgical

**Staffed Beds:** 20

**NY**

**STATEN ISLAND—Richmond County, See New York City**

**STONY BROOK—Suffolk County**

⊞ **STONY BROOK UNIVERSITY MEDICAL CENTER (330393)**, State University of New York, Zip 11794–8410; tel. 631/444–1077, (Includes STONY BROOK CHILDREN'S HOSPITAL, 100 Nicolls Road, Zip 11794–0001; tel. 631/444–4000) **A**1 2 3 5 8 9 10 **F**3 6 7 8 9 10 11 12 13 14 15 16 17 18 19 20 22 24 26 28 29 30 31 32 34 35 36 38 39 40 41 43 44 45 46 47 48 49 50 51 52 53 54 55 56 57 58 59 60 61 64 65 66 68 70 72 73 74 75 76 77 78 79 81 82 84 85 86 87 88 89 91 92 93 96 97 98 99 100 101 102 103 104 105 107 108 110 111 114 115 116 117 118 119 120 121 122 123 124 126 129 130 131 132 134 135 136 138 141 143 145 146 147 148 **P**1 6
Primary Contact: L. Reuven Pasternak, M.D., M.P.H., Vice President for Health System and Chief Executive Officer
COO: Carol Gomes, FACHE, Chief Operating Officer
CFO: Gary E. Bie, CPA, Chief Financial Officer
CMO: Joseph H. Laver, M.D., Chief Medical Officer
CIO: Jim Murry, Chief Information Officer
CHR: Luis de Onis, Interim Chief Human Resources Officer
CNO: Mary Ann T. Donohue, Ph.D., Chief Patient Care Services Officer
Web address: www.stonybrookmedicalcenter.org
**Control:** State–Government, nonfederal **Service:** General Medical and Surgical

**Staffed Beds:** 603 **Admissions:** 33012 **Census:** 513 **Outpatient Visits:** 351661 **Births:** 3295 **Total Expense ($000):** 1029588 **Payroll Expense ($000):** 446341 **Personnel:** 5319

**SUFFERN—Rockland County**

⊞ **GOOD SAMARITAN HOSPITAL (330158)**, 255 Lafayette Avenue, Zip 10901–4869; tel. 845/368–5000, (Nonreporting) **A**1 2 9 10 **S** Bon Secours Health System, Inc., Marriottsville, MD
Primary Contact: Mary Leahy, M.D., Chief Executive Officer
COO: Gerry Durney, Chief Operating Officer
CFO: Melinda Hancock, Interim Chief Financial Officer
CMO: Rodney W. Williams, M.D., Vice President Medical Affairs
CIO: Deborah K. Marshall, Vice President Public Relations
CHR: Pamela Tarulli, Senior Vice President Human Resources
Web address: www.goodsamhosp.org
**Control:** Church–operated, Nongovernment, not–for profit **Service:** General Medical and Surgical

**Staffed Beds:** 308

**SYOSSET—Nassau County**

★ **SYOSSET HOSPITAL**, 221 Jericho Turnpike, Zip 11791–4515; tel. 516/496–6500 **A**3 9 **F**3 12 15 18 29 30 31 34 35 36 40 43 44 45 50 57 58 59 60 62 63 64 65 68 70 74 78 79 81 82 84 85 87 97 98 100 101 102 107 108 114 119 126 130 132 135 146 **P**5 6 **S** North Shore–Long Island Jewish Health System, Great Neck, NY
Primary Contact: Michael Fener, Executive Director
COO: Mark J. Solazzo, Regional Chief Operating Officer
CFO: Richard Reilly, Deputy Executive Director
CMO: Randolph DiLorenzo, M.D., Medical Director
CHR: Andrew S. Goldberg, Associate Executive Director
Web address: www.northshorelij.com
**Control:** Other not–for–profit (including NFP Corporation) **Service:** General Medical and Surgical

**Staffed Beds:** 75 **Admissions:** 3677 **Census:** 54 **Outpatient Visits:** 56118 **Births:** 0 **Total Expense ($000):** 162072 **Payroll Expense ($000):** 84215 **Personnel:** 725

**SYRACUSE—Onondaga County**

**COMMUNITY–GENERAL HOSPITAL OF GREATER SYRACUSE** See Upstate University Hospital at Community General

★ ◇ **CROUSE HOSPITAL (330203)**, 736 Irving Avenue, Zip 13210–1690; tel. 315/470–7111 **A**3 5 6 9 10 21 **F**3 4 5 8 11 12 13 15 18 19 20 21 22 23 26 27 29 31 34 35 36 37 40 49 50 53 59 60 70 72 74 75 76 77 78 79 81 84 86 87 89 93 96 107 108 110 112 114 115 116 117 118 119 126 129 130 131 132 135 144 145 146 147 148
Primary Contact: Kimberly Boynton, President and Chief Executive Officer
COO: Jeffrey E. Tetrault, Director Facilities and Construction
CFO: Kelli Harris, Chief Financial Officer
CMO: Ronald Stahl, M.D., Chief Medical Officer
CIO: Kim Rose, Director Information Technology
CHR: John Bergemann, Director Human Resources
CNO: Ann Sedore, Ph.D., Chief Nursing Officer
Web address: www.crouse.org
**Control:** Other not–for–profit (including NFP Corporation) **Service:** General Medical and Surgical

**Staffed Beds:** 501 **Admissions:** 20248 **Census:** 315 **Outpatient Visits:** 370714 **Births:** 3944 **Total Expense ($000):** 373599 **Payroll Expense ($000):** 158797 **Personnel:** 2109

☐ **RICHARD H. HUTCHINGS PSYCHIATRIC CENTER (334001)**, 620 Madison Street, Zip 13210–2319; tel. 315/426–3632, (Nonreporting) **A**1 3 5 10 **S** New York State Office of Mental Health, Albany, NY
Primary Contact: Colleen A. Sawyer, R.N., MSN, Executive Director
COO: David Peppel, Director Operations
CFO: Robert Stapleton, Director Administration
CMO: Mark Cattalani, M.D., Clinical Director
CIO: Neil Nemi, Administrator Facility Information Center
CHR: Katherine Herron, Director Human Resources
Web address: www.omh.ny.gov
**Control:** State–Government, nonfederal **Service:** Psychiatric

**Staffed Beds:** 131

★ ◇ **ST. JOSEPH'S HOSPITAL HEALTH CENTER (330140)**, 301 Prospect Avenue, Zip 13203–1807; tel. 315/448–5111 **A**3 5 9 10 21 **F**2 3 5 8 11 12 13 14 15 18 20 22 24 26 28 29 30 31 34 35 38 39 40 45 46 47 48 49 50 53 54 57 58 59 60 62 64 66 68 70 71 72 73 74 75 76 77 78 79 81 82 83 84 87 92 93 94 97 98 99 100 101 102 104 106 107 108 110 114 115 118 119 126 129 130 131 132 135 144 145 146 147 148 **S** Trinity Health, Livonia, MI
Primary Contact: Kathryn H. Ruscitto, President
COO: Mary W. Brown, Senior Vice President Operations
CFO: Meredith Price, Vice President Fiscal Services and Chief Financial Officer
CMO: Sandra Sulik, M.D., Vice President Medical Affairs
CIO: Charles Fennell, Vice President Information Management
CHR: Sallie Biittner, Vice President Human Resources
CNO: AnneMarie Czyz, R.N., Vice President for Clinical and Educational Services
Web address: www.sjhsyr.org
**Control:** Other not–for–profit (including NFP Corporation) **Service:** General Medical and Surgical

**Staffed Beds:** 431 **Admissions:** 26269 **Census:** 385 **Outpatient Visits:** 618218 **Births:** 1989 **Total Expense ($000):** 581464 **Payroll Expense ($000):** 242758 **Personnel:** 3286

⊞ △ **SYRACUSE VETERANS AFFAIRS MEDICAL CENTER**, 800 Irving Avenue, Zip 13210–2716; tel. 315/425–4400, (Nonreporting) **A**1 3 5 7 8 **S** Department of Veterans Affairs, Washington, DC
Primary Contact: James Cody, Director
CFO: Elisabeth Kittell, Chief Financial Officer
CMO: William Marx, M.D., Chief of Staff
CIO: Dennis Wells, Chief Information Officer
CHR: Mark Antinelli, Manager Human Resources
CNO: Colene O'Neill, Associate Director Patient Nursing Services
Web address: www.syracuse.va.gov/
**Control:** Veterans Affairs, Government, federal **Service:** General Medical and Surgical

**Staffed Beds:** 235

★ ◇ **UPSTATE UNIVERSITY HOSPITAL (330241)**, 750 East Adams Street, Zip 13210–2342; tel. 315/464–5540, (Includes GOLISANO CHILDREN'S HOSPITAL, 750 East Adams Street, tel. 315/464–4570; UPSTATE UNIVERSITY HOSPITAL AT COMMUNITY GENERAL, 4900 Broad Road, Zip 13215–2293; tel. 315/492–5011) **A**2 8 9 10 21 **F**3 6 9 12 13 15 16 17 18 19 20 21 22 23 24 25 26 27 28 29 30 31 34 35 36 37 38 39 40 41 43 44 45 46 47 48 49 50 51 52 53 54 55 56 57 58 59 61 64 65 66 70 74 76 78 79 81 82 84 85 86 87 88 89 90 92 93 95 96 97 98 99 100 101 102 104 107 108 109 110 111 112 114 115 118 119 120 121 123 124 126 128 129 130 131 132 135 136 138 141 142 145 146 147 148 **P**4
Primary Contact: John B. McCabe, M.D., Chief Executive Officer
CFO: Stuart M. Wright, CPA, Chief Financial Officer
CMO: Anthony Weiss, M.D., Medical Director
CIO: Terry Wagner, Chief Information Officer
CHR: Eric Frost, Associate Vice President Human Resources
CNO: Nancy E. Page, MS, Interim Chief Nursing Officer
Web address: www.upstate.edu/hospital
**Control:** State–Government, nonfederal **Service:** General Medical and Surgical

**Staffed Beds:** 608 **Admissions:** 27596 **Census:** 473 **Outpatient Visits:** 620253 **Births:** 1157 **Total Expense ($000):** 849341 **Payroll Expense ($000):** 301413 **Personnel:** 4776

**VETERANS AFFAIRS MEDICAL CENTER** See Syracuse Veterans Affairs Medical Center

**TICONDEROGA—Essex County**

★ **MOSES LUDINGTON HOSPITAL (331306)**, 1019 Wicker Street,
Zip 12883–1097; tel. 518/585–2831 **A**9 10 18 **F**11 15 39 40 53 57 63 64 68
78 79 81 93 107 110 114 119 130 131 132 133
Primary Contact: Rodney C. Boula, Interim Chief Executive Officer
CMO: Glen Chapman, M.D., Medical Director
CHR: Tamara Evens, Director Human Resources
Web address: www.interlakeshealth.com
**Control:** Other not–for–profit (including NFP Corporation) **Service:** General
Medical and Surgical

Staffed Beds: 15 **Admissions:** 139 **Census:** 1 **Outpatient Visits:** 15725
**Births:** 1 **Total Expense ($000):** 11804 **Payroll Expense ($000):** 5134
**Personnel:** 114

**TROY—Rensselaer County**

★ **SAMARITAN HOSPITAL (330180)**, 2215 Burdett Avenue, Zip 12180–2475;
tel. 518/271–3300, (Nonreporting) **A**9 10 **S** Trinity Health, Livonia, MI
Primary Contact: Norman E. Dascher, Jr., Chief Executive Officer
CFO: Daniel A. Kochie, CPA, Chief Financial Officer
CMO: Daniel C. Silverman, M.D., Chief Medical Officer, Acute Care Troy
CIO: Karen LeBlanc, Director, Applications
CNO: Jacqueline Priore, Chief Nursing Officer
Web address: www.nehealth.com
**Control:** Other not–for–profit (including NFP Corporation) **Service:** General
Medical and Surgical

Staffed Beds: 212

★ **ST. MARY'S HOSPITAL (330232)**, 1300 Massachusetts Avenue,
Zip 12180–1695; tel. 518/268–5000, (Includes SETON HEALTH SYSTEM–ST.
MARY'S HOSPITAL, 1300 Massachusetts Avenue, Zip 12180;
tel. 518/272–5000), (Nonreporting) **A**9 10 **S** Trinity Health, Livonia, MI
Primary Contact: Norman E. Dascher, Jr., Chief Executive Officer
CFO: Daniel A. Kochie, CPA, Chief Financial Officer
CMO: Daniel C. Silverman, M.D., Chief Medical Officer
CIO: Jonathan Goldberg, Vice President and Chief Information Officer
CHR: Barbara McCandless, Vice President Human Resources
CNO: Carol Crucetti, R.N., Chief Nursing Officer
Web address: www.setonhealth.org
**Control:** Church–operated, Nongovernment, not–for profit **Service:** General
Medical and Surgical

Staffed Beds: 173

**UTICA—Oneida County**

★ △ ◇ **FAXTON–ST. LUKE'S HEALTHCARE (330044)**, 1656 Champlin
Avenue, Zip 13502–4830, Mailing Address: P.O. Box 479, Zip 13503–0479;
tel. 315/624–6000, (Includes FAXTON CAMPUS, 1676 Sunset Avenue,
Zip 13502–5475; tel. 315/624–6200; ST. LUKE'S CAMPUS, Zip 13413;
tel. 315/624–6000) **A**2 3 7 9 10 21 **F**2 3 11 12 13 15 17 18 20 22 26 28 29
30 31 34 35 36 39 40 45 46 47 48 50 51 53 54 56 57 58 59 60 62 64
66 68 70 73 74 75 76 77 78 79 80 81 84 85 86 87 89 90 92 93 97 98 104
107 108 110 114 115 116 117 118 119 120 121 123 124 130 131 132 135
141 143 144 146 147 148 **P**6
Primary Contact: Scott H. Perra, President and Chief Executive Officer
CFO: Louis Aiello, Senior Vice President and Chief Financial Officer
CMO: Michael F. Trevisani, M.D., Senior Vice President and Chief Medical Officer
CHR: Anthony Scibelli, Senior Vice President Human Resources, Post Acute and
Support Services
CNO: Patricia A. Roach, R.N., Senior Vice President and Chief Nursing Officer
Web address: www.mvnhealth.com
**Control:** Other not–for–profit (including NFP Corporation) **Service:** General
Medical and Surgical

Staffed Beds: 370 **Admissions:** 14045 **Census:** 197 **Outpatient Visits:**
454912 **Births:** 1960 **Total Expense ($000):** 276884 **Payroll Expense
($000):** 126416 **Personnel:** 1445

□ **MOHAWK VALLEY PSYCHIATRIC CENTER (334021)**, 1400 Noyes Street,
Zip 13502–3854; tel. 315/738–3800, (Nonreporting) **A**1 10 **S** New York State
Office of Mental Health, Albany, NY
Primary Contact: Colleen A. Sawyer, R.N., MSN, Executive Director
Web address: www.omh.ny.gov/omhweb/facilities/mvpc/facility.htm
**Control:** State–Government, nonfederal **Service:** Psychiatric

Staffed Beds: 614

★ ◇ **ST. ELIZABETH MEDICAL CENTER (330245)**, 2209 Genesee Street,
Zip 13501–5999; tel. 315/798–8100 **A**3 6 9 10 13 21 **F**3 11 15 17 18 20 22
24 26 29 30 31 34 36 37 40 43 45 50 57 58 59 61 62 66 68 70 74 75 77
78 79 80 81 84 85 87 89 92 93 97 98 102 107 108 110 114 115 119 127
129 130 131 132 135 141 146 147 148 **P**6 **S** Sisters of Saint Francis,
Syracuse, NY
Primary Contact: Scott H. Perra, Chief Executive Officer
COO: Robert Scholefield, Chief Operating Officer
CFO: Louis Aiello, Chief Financial Officer
CMO: Albert D'Accurzio, M.D., Medical Director
CIO: Robert Gillette, Chief Information Officer
CHR: Patrick Buckley, Vice President Human Resources
CNO: Varinya Sheppard, R.N., Chief Nursing Officer
Web address: www.stemc.org
**Control:** Church–operated, Nongovernment, not–for profit **Service:** General
Medical and Surgical

Staffed Beds: 181 **Admissions:** 11019 **Census:** 147 **Outpatient Visits:**
480969 **Births:** 0 **Total Expense ($000):** 205044 **Payroll Expense ($000):**
97911 **Personnel:** 1683

**ST. LUKE'S CAMPUS** See Faxton–St. Luke's Healthcare

**VALHALLA—Westchester County**

✠ **BLYTHEDALE CHILDREN'S HOSPITAL (333301)**, 95 Bradhurst Avenue,
Zip 10595–1697; tel. 914/592–7555, (Nonreporting) **A**1 6 9 10
Primary Contact: Larry L. Levine, President and Chief Executive Officer
COO: Maureen Desimone, Chief Operating Officer
CFO: John Canning, Chief Financial Officer
CMO: Joelle Mast, Ph.D., Chief Medical Officer
CHR: Ronald Gallo, Director Human Resources
Web address: www.blythedale.org
**Control:** Other not–for–profit (including NFP Corporation) **Service:** Children's
rehabilitation

Staffed Beds: 92

◇ **WESTCHESTER MEDICAL CENTER (330234)**, 100 Woods Road,
Zip 10595–1530; tel. 914/493–7000, (Includes MARIA FARERI CHILDREN'S
HOSPITAL, 100 Woods Road, Zip 10595–1652; tel. 866/962–7337; MIDHUDSON
REGIONAL HOSPITAL OF WESTCHESTER MEDICAL CENTER, 241 North Road,
Poughkeepsie, Zip 12601–1154; tel. 845/483–5000; Paul S. Hochenberg,
Executive Director) **A**2 3 5 8 9 10 21 **F**3 4 5 8 12 13 14 15 16 17 18 19 20
21 22 23 24 25 26 27 28 29 30 31 32 34 35 36 37 38 39 40 41 43 44 45
46 47 48 49 50 51 52 54 55 56 57 58 59 60 61 62 64 65 66 68 70 71 72
73 74 75 76 77 78 79 80 81 82 84 85 86 87 88 89 90 91 92 93 94 97 98
99 100 101 102 103 104 107 108 110 111 114 115 116 117 118 119 120
121 123 124 126 129 130 131 132 134 135 136 137 138 139 141 142 145
146 147 148 **P**6
Primary Contact: Michael D. Israel, President and Chief Executive Officer
COO: Gary F. Brudnicki, Senior Executive Vice President, Chief Operating Officer
and Chief Financial Officer
CFO: Gary F. Brudnicki, Senior Executive Vice President, Chief Operating Officer
and Chief Financial Officer
CMO: Renee Garrick, M.D., Director, Executive Medical
CIO: John Moustakakis, Senior Vice President Information Systems and Chief
Information Officer
CHR: Paul S. Hochenberg, Senior Vice President Human Resources
CNO: Patricia A. Wrobbel, Senior Vice President and Chief Nurse Executive
Web address: www.worldclassmedicine.com
**Control:** Hospital district or authority, Government, nonfederal **Service:** General
Medical and Surgical

Staffed Beds: 895 **Admissions:** 24973 **Census:** 608 **Outpatient Visits:**
108800 **Births:** 892 **Total Expense ($000):** 973405 **Payroll Expense
($000):** 284800 **Personnel:** 4464

**VALLEY STREAM—Nassau County**

✠ **FRANKLIN HOSPITAL (330372)**, 900 Franklin Avenue, Zip 11580–2190;
tel. 516/256–6000, (Total facility includes 120 beds in nursing home–type unit)
**A**1 2 3 9 10 **F**2 3 8 11 12 17 18 26 29 30 31 34 35 40 43 45 49 50 56 57
58 59 60 62 63 64 65 68 70 74 75 77 78 79 81 82 83 84 85 86 87 92 94
97 98 100 102 103 107 108 111 114 118 119 128 130 132 135 143 146
148 **P**5 6 **S** North Shore–Long Island Jewish Health System, Great Neck, NY
Primary Contact: Catherine Hottendorf, R.N., MS, Executive Director
COO: Mark J. Solazzo, Executive Vice President and Chief Operating Officer
CFO: John Udisky, Associate Executive Director Finance
CMO: Joseph Marino, M.D., Medical Director
CIO: John Bosco, Chief Information Officer
CHR: Karina Norr-McPhillips, Associate Executive Director Human Resources
CNO: Ralph Jay Civello, RN, MSN, Associate Executive Director Patient Care
Services
Web address: www.northshorelij.com
**Control:** Other not–for–profit (including NFP Corporation) **Service:** General
Medical and Surgical

Staffed Beds: 330 **Admissions:** 10607 **Census:** 240 **Outpatient Visits:**
71314 **Births:** 0 **Total Expense ($000):** 196750 **Payroll Expense ($000):**
97569 **Personnel:** 1095

*Many Facility Codes have changed. Please refer to the AHA Guide Code Chart.*   © 2015 AHA Guide

## WALTON—Delaware County

**DELAWARE VALLEY HOSPITAL (331312)**, 1 Titus Place, Zip 13856–1498; tel. 607/865–2100 **A**9 10 18 **F**3 4 5 11 15 18 28 29 34 35 40 45 50 57 59 64 75 77 81 85 87 89 93 97 107 110 114 119 130 133 146 147 148 **S** United Health Services, Binghamton, NY
Primary Contact: Paul Summers, President and Chief Executive Officer
CFO: Paul Summers, Chief Financial Officer
CMO: John Giannone, M.D., Chief Medical Officer
CIO: James Armstrong, Manager Information Technology
CHR: Paul Summers, Chief Human Resources Officer
CNO: Victoria Conkling, Vice President Patient Care Services and Chief Nursing Officer
Web address: www.uhs.net
**Control:** Other not–for–profit (including NFP Corporation) **Service:** General Medical and Surgical

**Staffed Beds:** 25 **Admissions:** 602 **Census:** 11 **Outpatient Visits:** 106338 **Births:** 0 **Total Expense ($000):** 17042 **Payroll Expense ($000):** 6736 **Personnel:** 155

## WAPPINGERS—Dutchess County

**VETERAN AFFAIRS HUDSON VALLEY HEALTH CARE SYSTEM–CASTLE POINT CAMPUS** See Veterans Affairs Hudson Valley Health Care System, Montrose

## WARSAW—Wyoming County

☐ **WYOMING COUNTY COMMUNITY HOSPITAL (330008)**, 400 North Main Street, Zip 14569–1025; tel. 585/786–8940, (Nonreporting) **A**1 9 10 20
Primary Contact: Donald T. Eichenauer, Chief Executive Officer
COO: Michael Corcimiglia, Chief Operating Officer
CMO: Scott Treutlein, M.D., Medical Director
CIO: Jane Beechler, Director Healthcare Information Systems
CHR: Denise M. Morley, Director Human Resources
CNO: Dawn James, Director of Nursing
Web address: www.wcchs.net
**Control:** County–Government, nonfederal **Service:** General Medical and Surgical

**Staffed Beds:** 75

## WARWICK—Orange County

✠ **ST. ANTHONY COMMUNITY HOSPITAL (330205)**, 15 Maple Avenue, Zip 10990–1028; tel. 845/986–2276, (Nonreporting) **A**1 9 10 **S** Bon Secours Health System, Inc., Marriottsville, MD
Primary Contact: Jeff Reilly, Senior Vice President Operations
Web address: www.stanthonycommunityhosp.org
**Control:** Church–operated, Nongovernment, not–for profit **Service:** General Medical and Surgical

**Staffed Beds:** 73

## WATERTOWN—Jefferson County

✠ **SAMARITAN MEDICAL CENTER (330157)**, 830 Washington Street, Zip 13601–4034; tel. 315/785–4000 **A**1 9 10 12 13 20 **F**3 5 8 13 15 18 20 29 30 31 35 40 49 51 57 60 64 68 70 73 74 75 76 77 78 79 81 82 87 89 90 93 97 98 99 100 102 103 104 107 108 111 114 116 119 120 121 126 127 129 130 135 146 147 148 **P**6
Primary Contact: Thomas H. Carman, President and Chief Executive Officer
CFO: Sean Mills, Chief Financial Officer
CMO: Mario Victoria, M.D., Vice President, Medical Affairs
CIO: M. Andrew Short, Vice President Information Services
CHR: Thomas Shatraw, Director Human Resources
CNO: Brian O'Hearn, Vice President Patient Care Services and Chief Nursing Officer
Web address: www.samaritanhealth.com
**Control:** Other not–for–profit (including NFP Corporation) **Service:** General Medical and Surgical

**Staffed Beds:** 208 **Admissions:** 8998 **Census:** 132 **Outpatient Visits:** 266826 **Births:** 1783 **Total Expense ($000):** 190273 **Payroll Expense ($000):** 86522 **Personnel:** 1332

## WELLSVILLE—Allegany County

✠ **JONES MEMORIAL HOSPITAL (330096)**, 191 North Main Street, Zip 14895–1150, Mailing Address: P.O. Box 72, Zip 14895–0072; tel. 585/593–1100 **A**1 9 10 20 **F**3 8 11 13 15 17 28 29 30 31 34 35 36 40 43 57 59 61 64 68 70 75 76 77 78 79 81 82 85 89 93 97 107 110 114 119 129 131 132 133 146 147
Primary Contact: Eva Benedict, R.N., President and Chief Executive Officer
CFO: Tracy Gates, Chief Financial Officer
CMO: Frank Edwards, M.D., Medical Director
CIO: Tracy Gates, Chief Financial Officer
CHR: Brenda Sobeck, Director of Human Resources
CNO: Donna Bliven, Vice President Patient Care Services and Chief Nursing Officer
Web address: www.jmhny.org
**Control:** Other not–for–profit (including NFP Corporation) **Service:** General Medical and Surgical

**Staffed Beds:** 33 **Admissions:** 1678 **Census:** 19 **Outpatient Visits:** 145427 **Births:** 350 **Total Expense ($000):** 35740 **Payroll Expense ($000):** 17109 **Personnel:** 329

## WEST HAVERSTRAW—Rockland County

☐ △ **HELEN HAYES HOSPITAL (330405)**, Route 9W, Zip 10993–1127; tel. 845/786–4000, (Nonreporting) **A**1 5 7 10
Primary Contact: Edmund Coletti, Chief Executive Officer
COO: Kathleen Martucci, Chief Operating Officer
CFO: Lori A. Meszler, Chief Financial Officer
CIO: Virgil Ennis, Chief Information Officer
CHR: Patrick J. Ryan, Chief Human Resources Officer
Web address: www.helenhayeshospital.org
**Control:** State–Government, nonfederal **Service:** Rehabilitation

**Staffed Beds:** 155

## WEST ISLIP—Suffolk County

✠ **GOOD SAMARITAN HOSPITAL MEDICAL CENTER (330286)**, 1000 Montauk Highway, Zip 11795–4927; tel. 631/376–3000, (Total facility includes 100 beds in nursing home–type unit) **A**1 2 3 5 9 10 12 13 **F**3 8 11 12 13 15 17 18 19 20 22 24 26 28 29 30 31 32 34 35 40 41 43 44 49 50 54 55 56 57 58 59 60 61 62 64 66 68 70 72 73 74 75 76 77 78 79 81 82 83 84 85 87 88 89 91 93 94 97 100 107 108 110 111 114 115 116 117 118 119 120 121 123 124 126 128 129 130 132 135 141 146 147 **P**1 5 6 7 8 **S** Catholic Health Services of Long Island, Rockville Centre, NY
Primary Contact: Nancy B. Simmons, Executive Vice President and Chief Administrative Officer
CFO: Dan Macksood, Regional Senior Vice President and Chief Financial Officer
CMO: Jerome Weiner, M.D., Senior Vice President Medical Affairs
CIO: Marcy Dunn, Vice President Information Services and Chief Information Officer
CHR: Lori Spina, Vice President Human Resources
CNO: Jeanne Dzurenko, R.N., Chief Nursing Officer and Senior Vice President Patient Care
Web address: www.good–samaritan–hospital.org
**Control:** Church–operated, Nongovernment, not–for profit **Service:** General Medical and Surgical

**Staffed Beds:** 531 **Admissions:** 24545 **Census:** 444 **Outpatient Visits:** 299924 **Births:** 2697 **Total Expense ($000):** 584664 **Payroll Expense ($000):** 245203 **Personnel:** 3097

## WEST POINT—Orange County

✠ **KELLER ARMY COMMUNITY HOSPITAL**, 900 Washington Road, Zip 10996–1197, Mailing Address: U.S. Military Academy, Building 900, Zip 10996–1197; tel. 845/938–5169 **A**1 3 5 **F**3 13 15 29 30 32 34 35 36 38 40 44 45 50 54 57 59 64 65 68 75 76 77 79 81 85 86 87 97 99 100 101 102 104 107 110 111 115 131 132 135 141 146 **P**6 **S** Department of the Army, Office of the Surgeon General, Falls Church, VA
Primary Contact: Colonel Felicia Pehrson, M.D., Commanding Officer
CFO: Russell DeVries, Chief Business Operations
CIO: Patrick McGuinness, Chief Information Management
CHR: Margaret Greco, Chief Human Resources
Web address: www.kach.amedd.army.mil/
**Control:** Army, Government, federal **Service:** General Medical and Surgical

**Staffed Beds:** 20 **Admissions:** 813 **Census:** 4 **Outpatient Visits:** 126254 **Births:** 142 **Personnel:** 547

NY

---

**Hospital, Medicare Provider Number, Address, Telephone, Approval, Facility, and Physician Codes, Health Care System**

★ American Hospital Association (AHA) membership
☐ The Joint Commission accreditation
○ Healthcare Facilities Accreditation Program
◇ DNV Healthcare Inc. accreditation
⇑ Center for Improvement in Healthcare Quality Accreditation
△ Commission on Accreditation of Rehabilitation Facilities (CARF) accreditation

## WEST SENECA—Erie County

☐ **WESTERN NEW YORK CHILDREN'S PSYCHIATRIC CENTER**, 1010 East and West Road, Zip 14224–3602; tel. 716/677–7000, (Nonreporting) **A**1 3 5 **S** New York State Office of Mental Health, Albany, NY
Primary Contact: Kathe Hayes, Executive Director
COO: David Privett, Deputy Director
CMO: Patrick Stein, M.D., Clinical Director
CIO: Dan Hrubiak, Associate Computer Program Analyst
CHR: Charles Siewert, Director Human Resources
Web address: www.omh.ny.gov
**Control:** State–Government, nonfederal **Service:** Children's hospital psychiatric

Staffed Beds: 46

## WESTFIELD—Chautauqua County

★ **WESTFIELD MEMORIAL HOSPITAL (330166)**, 189 East Main Street, Zip 14787–1195; tel. 716/326–4921 **A**9 10 **F**3 8 11 14 15 18 34 40 45 57 59 68 75 79 81 86 87 93 107 108 110 119 129 135 147 148 **P**3 **S** Allegheny Health Network, Pittsburgh, PA
Primary Contact: Scott Whalen, Ph.D., FACHE, President and Chief Executive Officer
COO: Patricia Ballman, Director
CFO: Tina Gowen, System Controller
CMO: Russell Elwell, M.D., Medical Director
CIO: Cindy Harper, Manager Patient Data
Web address: www.wmhinc.org
**Control:** Other not–for–profit (including NFP Corporation) **Service:** General Medical and Surgical

Staffed Beds: 4 Admissions: 19 Census: 1

## WHITE PLAINS—Westchester County

☒ △ **BURKE REHABILITATION HOSPITAL (330404)**, 785 Mamaroneck Avenue, Zip 10605–2523; tel. 914/597–2500 **A**1 3 5 7 10 **F**11 28 29 30 34 35 39 44 50 53 54 57 58 64 75 77 79 86 87 90 91 93 94 95 96 100 130 131 132 146 148
Primary Contact: Mary Beth Walsh, M.D., Chief Executive Officer
COO: Brian M. Swift, Senior Administrator Plant Operations
CFO: John Stewart, Director Finance
CMO: Mary Beth Walsh, M.D., Chief Executive Officer
CIO: Cathy Dwyer, Senior Administrator Information Systems
CHR: Annette Bucci, Senior Administrator Human Resources
CNO: Marie Spencer, Chief Nursing Officer and Senior Administrator
Web address: www.burke.org
**Control:** Other not–for–profit (including NFP Corporation) **Service:** Rehabilitation

Staffed Beds: 150 Admissions: 2688 Census: 107 Outpatient Visits: 98626 Births: 0 Total Expense ($000): 72074 Payroll Expense ($000): 41489 Personnel: 601

**NEW YORK–PRESBYTERIAN HOSPITAL, WESTCHESTER DIVISION** See New York–Presbyterian Hospital, New York

☒ **WHITE PLAINS HOSPITAL CENTER (330304)**, 41 East Post Road, Zip 10601–4699; tel. 914/681–0600 **A**1 2 3 5 9 10 **F**3 11 12 13 14 15 17 18 20 22 26 29 30 31 32 34 35 36 40 41 44 45 46 47 49 50 51 54 55 56 57 58 59 60 61 63 64 65 66 68 70 72 73 74 75 77 78 79 81 82 84 85 86 87 92 93 97 99 101 104 107 108 110 111 115 116 117 118 119 120 121 122 123 126 129 130 131 132 135 145 146 147 148 **P**5 6
Primary Contact: Susan Fox, President
COO: Edward F. Leonard, Executive Vice President and Chief Operating Officer
CFO: David Ho, Senior Vice President and Chief Financial Officer
CMO: Michael Palumbo, M.D., Executive Vice President and Medical Director
CIO: Elizabeth King, Director
CHR: John Sanchez, Vice President Human Resources
CNO: Leigh McMahon, MS, Senior Vice President Patient Care Services and Chief Nursing Officer
Web address: www.wphospital.org
**Control:** Other not–for–profit (including NFP Corporation) **Service:** General Medical and Surgical

Staffed Beds: 292 Admissions: 14500 Census: 184 Outpatient Visits: 160000 Births: 1800 Total Expense ($000): 406187 Payroll Expense ($000): 188817 Personnel: 2185

## WILLIAMSVILLE—Erie County

**MILLARD FILLMORE SUBURBAN HOSPITAL** See KALEIDA Health, Buffalo

## YONKERS—Westchester County

**ANDRUS PAVILION** See St. John's Riverside Hospital

☐ **ST. JOHN'S RIVERSIDE HOSPITAL (330208)**, 967 North Broadway, Zip 10701–1399; tel. 914/964–4444, (Includes ANDRUS PAVILION, 967 North Broadway, tel. 914/964–4444; ST. JOHN'S RIVERSIDE HOSPITAL – PARK CARE PAVILION, Two Park Avenue, Zip 10703–3497; tel. 914/964–7300; ST. JOHN'S RIVERSIDE HOSPITAL – DOBBS FERRY PAVILION, 128 Ashford Avenue, Dobbs Ferry, Zip 10522–1896; tel. 914/693–0700) **A**1 2 3 6 9 10 **F**3 4 5 8 11 12 13 15 17 18 29 30 31 34 35 36 37 40 41 45 48 49 50 57 59 60 61 68 70 73 76 77 78 79 81 82 84 85 86 87 92 93 107 108 110 111 113 114 115 118 119 123 124 126 128 129 130 132 135 143 146 147 148 **P**7
Primary Contact: Ronald J. Corti, President and Chief Executive Officer
COO: Lynn M. Nelson, R.N., Chief Nursing Officer and Chief Operating Officer
CFO: Dennis M. Keane, Vice President Finance and Chief Financial Officer
CMO: Paul Antonecchia, M.D., Vice President Medical Affairs and Chief Medical Officer
CIO: Peter Weidner, Director Information Technology
CHR: Marc Leff, Vice President Human Resources
CNO: Lynn M. Nelson, R.N., Chief Nursing Officer and Chief Operating Officer
Web address: www.riversidehealth.org
**Control:** Other not–for–profit (including NFP Corporation) **Service:** General Medical and Surgical

Staffed Beds: 378 Admissions: 18816 Census: 257 Outpatient Visits: 221050 Births: 1432 Total Expense ($000): 244382 Payroll Expense ($000): 111669 Personnel: 1963

☒ **ST. JOSEPH'S MEDICAL CENTER (330006)**, 127 South Broadway, Zip 10701–4006; tel. 914/378–7000, (Total facility includes 200 beds in nursing home–type unit) **A**1 3 5 9 10 **F**2 3 4 5 8 11 15 18 29 30 31 34 35 38 39 40 45 47 48 49 54 56 57 58 59 60 61 62 64 68 70 74 75 77 78 79 81 82 85 87 89 93 94 97 98 99 100 101 102 103 104 105 106 107 108 110 111 115 118 119 128 130 132 134 135 143 144 146 **P**5 8
Primary Contact: Michael J. Spicer, President and Chief Executive Officer
COO: Frances Casola, Senior Vice President Operations
CFO: James J. Curcuruto, Senior Vice President Finance
CMO: James Neuendorf, M.D., Medical Director
CIO: Deborah Di Bernardo, Chief Information Officer
CHR: Dean Civitello, Vice President Human Resources, Public Relations and Development
CNO: Margaret M. Cusumano, R.N., Vice President Patient Care Services and Chief Nursing Officer
Web address: www.saintjosephs.org
**Control:** Other not–for–profit (including NFP Corporation) **Service:** General Medical and Surgical

Staffed Beds: 477 Admissions: 9026 Census: 433 Outpatient Visits: 1338858 Total Expense ($000): 244579 Payroll Expense ($000): 113473 Personnel: 1562

*Many Facility Codes have changed. Please refer to the AHA Guide Code Chart.* © 2015 AHA Guide

# NORTH CAROLINA

## AHOSKIE—Hertford County

☒ **VIDANT ROANOKE–CHOWAN HOSPITAL (340099)**, 500 South Academy Street, Zip 27910–3261, Mailing Address: P.O. Box 1385, Zip 27910–1385; tel. 252/209–3000 **A**1 9 10 20 **F**3 11 13 15 28 29 30 31 34 35 40 43 44 45 53 56 57 59 64 68 70 75 76 77 78 79 81 82 85 86 87 89 92 98 100 101 102 103 107 108 110 111 114 119 121 123 129 130 132 146 148 **S** Vidant Health, Greenville, NC
Primary Contact: Susan S. Lassiter, FACHE, President and Chief Executive Officer
CFO: Jon Graham, Chief Financial Officer
CMO: Jeff Severa, D.O., Chief of Staff
CHR: Debbie Sisler, Director Human Resources
CNO: Susan Mitchell, Vice President Patient Care Services
Web address: www.vidanthealth.com
**Control:** Other not–for–profit (including NFP Corporation) **Service:** General Medical and Surgical

**Staffed Beds:** 70 **Admissions:** 4279 **Census:** 53 **Outpatient Visits:** 65334 **Births:** 356 **Total Expense ($000):** 68566 **Payroll Expense ($000):** 26224 **Personnel:** 625

## ALBEMARLE—Stanly County

☒ **STANLY REGIONAL MEDICAL CENTER (340119)**, 301 Yadkin Street, Zip 28001–3441, Mailing Address: P.O. Box 1489, Zip 28002–1489; tel. 704/984–4000 **A**1 2 9 10 **F**3 11 12 13 15 20 28 29 30 31 34 35 39 40 45 49 57 59 60 61 62 63 64 68 70 74 75 76 77 78 79 81 82 85 86 89 93 98 100 101 102 103 107 108 110 111 114 115 119 123 129 130 131 132 146 148 **S** Carolinas Healthcare System, Charlotte, NC
Primary Contact: Alfred P. Taylor, President and Chief Executive Officer
COO: Brian Freeman, Vice President of Operations
CFO: Nick Samilo, Vice President Fiscal Services and Chief Financial Officer
CMO: Paul D'Amico, M.D., Chief of Staff
CIO: Brian Freeman, Vice President of Operations
CNO: Judy Doran, R.N., Vice President of Hospital Services and Chief Nurse Executive
Web address: www.stanly.org
**Control:** Hospital district or authority, Government, nonfederal **Service:** General Medical and Surgical

**Staffed Beds:** 94 **Admissions:** 4062 **Census:** 42 **Outpatient Visits:** 80958 **Births:** 704 **Total Expense ($000):** 100769 **Payroll Expense ($000):** 31886 **Personnel:** 619

## ASHEBORO—Randolph County

☒ **RANDOLPH HOSPITAL (340123)**, 364 White Oak Street, Zip 27203–5400, Mailing Address: P.O. Box 1048, Zip 27204–1048; tel. 336/625–5151 **A**1 2 9 10 **F**3 8 13 15 18 28 29 30 31 34 35 37 40 45 48 49 50 53 56 57 58 59 61 62 64 68 70 74 75 76 77 78 79 80 81 83 84 85 86 87 89 91 92 93 94 96 97 107 109 110 111 114 115 119 120 121 123 130 131 132 143 146 **P**6
Primary Contact: Steven E. Eblin, Chief Executive Officer / President
CMO: Charles West, M.D., Chief Medical Officer
CIO: Angela Burgess, Chief Information Officer
Web address: www.randolphhospital.org
**Control:** Other not–for–profit (including NFP Corporation) **Service:** General Medical and Surgical

**Staffed Beds:** 101 **Admissions:** 5293 **Census:** 54 **Outpatient Visits:** 131090 **Births:** 728 **Total Expense ($000):** 97565 **Payroll Expense ($000):** 40878 **Personnel:** 947

## ASHEVILLE—Buncombe County

★ **ASHEVILLE SPECIALTY HOSPITAL (342017)**, 428 Biltmore Avenue, 4th Floor, Zip 28801–4502; tel. 828/213–5400 **A**3 10 **F**1 3 29 30 36 77 85 91 148 **S** Mission Health System, Asheville, NC
Primary Contact: Robert C. Desotelle, President and Chief Executive Officer
COO: Michelle Stillman, Director of Care Management
CMO: Joseph Aiello, M.D., Chief of Staff
CIO: Dorothy L. Porter, Director of Compliance/Risk/Quality
CHR: Jennifer Calloway, Human Resources Coordinator
CNO: Wanda Miller, R.N., Director of Clinical Services
Web address: www.missionhospitals.org/acute–care
**Control:** Partnership, Investor–owned, for–profit **Service:** Long–Term Acute Care hospital

**Staffed Beds:** 32 **Admissions:** 351 **Census:** 27 **Outpatient Visits:** 0 **Births:** 0 **Total Expense ($000):** 13578 **Payroll Expense ($000):** 5989 **Personnel:** 97

☒ △ **CAREPARTNERS HEALTH SERVICES (343025)**, 68 Sweeten Creek Road, Zip 28803–2318, Mailing Address: P.O. Box 15025, Zip 28813–0025; tel. 828/277–4800, (Nonreporting) **A**1 7 9 10
Primary Contact: Tracy Buchanan, Chief Executive Officer / President
CFO: Gregg Dixon, CPA, Chief Financial Officer
CMO: Michael Parmer, Chief Medical Officer
CIO: Jennifer Scott, Director of Informatics
CHR: Katy Pless, Director of Human Resources
CNO: Cathleen Adams, Chief Nursing Officer
Web address: www.carepartners.org
**Control:** Other not–for–profit (including NFP Corporation) **Service:** Rehabilitation

**Staffed Beds:** 80

☒ **CHARLES GEORGE VETERANS AFFAIRS MEDICAL CENTER**, 1100 Tunnel Road, Zip 28805–2087; tel. 828/298–7911, (Total facility includes 85 beds in nursing home–type unit) **A**1 3 5 **F**3 4 5 12 18 20 22 24 26 28 29 30 31 34 35 36 38 39 40 45 49 50 56 57 58 59 61 62 63 64 65 68 70 74 75 77 78 79 81 82 83 84 85 86 87 91 92 93 94 97 98 100 101 102 103 104 107 108 111 114 115 119 128 130 132 135 145 146 147 148 **S** Department of Veterans Affairs, Washington, DC
Primary Contact: Cynthia Breyfogle, FACHE, Director
CFO: Margaret Wilkes, Chief Fiscal Officer
CMO: Webster Carl Bazemore, M.D., Interim Chief of Staff
CIO: Carla McLendon, Director Information Resource Management Services
CHR: James Sitlinger, Chief Human Resources Management
CNO: David Przestrzelski, Associate Director, Patient Care Services and Chief Nursing Executive
Web address: www.asheville.va.gov/
**Control:** Veterans Affairs, Government, federal **Service:** General Medical and Surgical

**Staffed Beds:** 257 **Admissions:** 5105 **Census:** 144 **Outpatient Visits:** 428792 **Births:** 0 **Total Expense ($000):** 299812 **Payroll Expense ($000):** 137205 **Personnel:** 1716

☒ **MISSION HOSPITAL (340002)**, 509 Biltmore Avenue, Zip 28801–4690; tel. 828/213–1111, (Includes MEMORIAL MISSION HOSPITAL, 509 Biltmore Avenue, tel. 828/255–4000; MISSION CHILDREN'S HOSPITAL, 509 Biltmore Avenue, Zip 28801–4601; tel. 828/213–1740; ST. JOSEPH'S HOSPITAL, 428 Biltmore Avenue, Zip 28801–9839; tel. 828/255–3100) **A**1 2 3 5 9 10 **F**3 7 8 11 12 13 15 17 18 19 20 22 24 26 28 29 30 31 32 34 35 36 37 39 40 43 44 45 46 47 48 49 50 51 53 54 55 56 57 58 59 60 61 64 65 68 70 71 72 73 74 75 76 77 78 79 80 81 82 84 85 86 87 88 89 91 92 93 95 96 97 98 99 100 101 102 103 104 105 107 108 110 111 114 115 116 117 118 119 120 121 123 124 126 129 130 131 132 134 135 141 142 143 146 147 148 **P**1 **S** Mission Health System, Asheville, NC
Primary Contact: Jill Hoggard Green, R.N., Ph.D., President
COO: Brian W. Aston, Chief Operating Officer
CFO: Charles F. Ayscue, Senior Vice President Finance and Chief Financial Officer
CMO: William Hathaway, M.D., Chief Medical Officer
CIO: D. Arlo Jennings, Ph.D., Chief Information Officer
CHR: Maria Roloff, Vice President Human Resources
Web address: www.missionhospitals.org
**Control:** Other not–for–profit (including NFP Corporation) **Service:** General Medical and Surgical

**Staffed Beds:** 763 **Admissions:** 42326 **Census:** 547 **Outpatient Visits:** 507604 **Births:** 3916 **Total Expense ($000):** 916636 **Payroll Expense ($000):** 282171 **Personnel:** 6000

## BLACK MOUNTAIN—Buncombe County

**JULIAN F. KEITH ALCOHOL AND DRUG ABUSE TREATMENT CENTER (344023)**, 201 Tabernacle Road, Zip 28711–2599; tel. 828/669–3400, (Nonreporting) **A**10
Primary Contact: W. Douglas Baker, Director
CFO: Jackie Maurer, Fiscal Officer
CMO: Anthony Burnett, M.D., Medical Director
CHR: Faye Hamlin, Manager Human Resources
Web address: www.jfkadatc.net
**Control:** State–Government, nonfederal **Service:** Alcoholism and other chemical dependency

**Staffed Beds:** 80

---

**Hospital, Medicare Provider Number, Address, Telephone, Approval, Facility, and Physician Codes, Health Care System**

★ American Hospital Association (AHA) membership
□ The Joint Commission accreditation
○ Healthcare Facilities Accreditation Program
◇ DNV Healthcare Inc. accreditation
⇧ Center for Improvement in Healthcare Quality Accreditation
△ Commission on Accreditation of Rehabilitation Facilities (CARF) accreditation

**NC**

## BOLIVIA—Brunswick County

✠ **NOVANT HEALTH BRUNSWICK MEDICAL CENTER (340158)**, 240 Hospital Drive N.E., Zip 28422–8346; tel. 910/721–1000 **A**1 9 10 **F**3 11 13 15 18 26 28 29 30 34 35 40 45 46 57 59 64 70 75 76 80 81 87 93 96 102 107 108 110 111 114 118 119 126 130 135 146 147 148 **S** Novant Health, Winston Salem, NC
Primary Contact: Shelbourn Stevens, President
CFO: Joan Thomas, Chief Financial Officer
CMO: Robert Hassler, M.D., Director Medical Affairs
CIO: Pamela Parrish, Director Information Systems
Web address: www.brunswicknovant.org
**Control:** Other not–for–profit (including NFP Corporation) **Service:** General Medical and Surgical

**Staffed Beds:** 52 **Admissions:** 4441 **Census:** 44 **Outpatient Visits:** 104372 **Births:** 495 **Total Expense ($000):** 79813 **Payroll Expense ($000):** 23152 **Personnel:** 452

## BOONE—Watauga County

✠ **WATAUGA MEDICAL CENTER (340051)**, 336 Deerfield Road, Zip 28607–5008, Mailing Address: P.O. Box 2600, Zip 28607–2600; tel. 828/262–4100 **A**1 2 9 10 **F**3 5 13 15 17 18 20 22 26 28 29 30 31 32 34 35 38 40 44 45 46 47 48 49 50 53 54 57 59 64 70 73 75 76 77 78 81 82 84 85 86 87 91 92 93 96 107 108 110 111 114 115 118 119 120 121 122 123 124 129 130 131 132 135 144 145 146 147 148 **P**6 **S** Appalachian Regional Healthcare System, Boone, NC
Primary Contact: Richard G. Sparks, Chief Executive Officer
CFO: Kevin B. May, Chief Financial Officer
CMO: Herman A. Godwin, Jr., M.D., Senior Vice President and Medical Director
CIO: Mike Quinto, Chief Information Officer
CHR: Amy Crabbe, Senior Vice President Human Resources
Web address: www.https://apprhs.org/contact–us
**Control:** Other not–for–profit (including NFP Corporation) **Service:** General Medical and Surgical

**Staffed Beds:** 99 **Admissions:** 3860 **Census:** 37 **Outpatient Visits:** 121983 **Births:** 515 **Total Expense ($000):** 112949 **Payroll Expense ($000):** 36449 **Personnel:** 531

## BREVARD—Transylvania County

✠ **TRANSYLVANIA REGIONAL HOSPITAL (341319)**, 260 Hospital Drive, Zip 28712–3378; tel. 828/884–9111, (Total facility includes 10 beds in nursing home–type unit) **A**1 9 10 18 **F**2 3 11 13 15 28 29 30 31 34 35 36 40 45 49 53 56 57 59 62 63 64 65 70 76 77 78 79 80 81 82 85 97 107 110 111 114 119 128 130 131 132 133 146 **P**6 **S** Mission Health System, Asheville, NC
Primary Contact: Catherine Landis, R.N., President and Chief Nursing Officer
CFO: Marc Nakagawa, Regional Director Finance
CMO: Mark Lemel, Chief of Staff
CIO: Ed Coye, Director Information Technology
CHR: Mark L. Emory, Director Human Resources
CNO: Catherine Landis, R.N., President and Chief Nursing Officer
Web address: www.trhospital.org
**Control:** Other not–for–profit (including NFP Corporation) **Service:** General Medical and Surgical

**Staffed Beds:** 52 **Admissions:** 1709 **Census:** 17 **Outpatient Visits:** 101886 **Births:** 132 **Total Expense ($000):** 61876 **Payroll Expense ($000):** 27137 **Personnel:** 379

## BRYSON CITY—Swain County

★ **SWAIN COMMUNITY HOSPITAL (341305)**, 45 Plateau Street, Zip 28713–4200; tel. 828/488–2155 **A**9 10 18 **F**8 11 15 29 30 35 40 44 57 59 62 63 68 75 77 81 82 84 85 91 93 103 107 119 130 133 146 148 **S** Duke LifePoint Healthcare, Brentwood, TN
Primary Contact: Steve Heatherly, Chief Executive Officer
CMO: David Zimmerman, M.D., Chief of Staff
Web address: www.westcare.org
**Control:** Corporation, Investor–owned, for–profit **Service:** General Medical and Surgical

**Staffed Beds:** 25 **Admissions:** 466 **Census:** 4 **Outpatient Visits:** 29344 **Births:** 0 **Total Expense ($000):** 11316 **Payroll Expense ($000):** 4747 **Personnel:** 90

## BURGAW—Pender County

✠ **PENDER MEMORIAL HOSPITAL (341307)**, 507 East Freemont Street, Zip 28425–5131; tel. 910/259–5451, (Total facility includes 43 beds in nursing home–type unit) **A**1 9 10 18 **F**3 11 15 29 34 40 45 54 57 59 62 64 68 81 85 86 87 93 96 107 110 114 119 128 129 130 133 135 143 146 148 **S** New Hanover Regional Medical Center, Wilmington, NC
Primary Contact: Ruth Glaser, President
CFO: Morrison Hall, Chief Financial Officer
CMO: Heather Davis, M.D., Chief of Staff
CIO: Ashley Hernandez, Chief Information Technology Officer
CHR: Lori McKoy, Business Partner
CNO: Cynthia Faulkner, R.N., Chief Nursing Executive
Web address: www.pendermemorial.org
**Control:** County–Government, nonfederal **Service:** General Medical and Surgical

**Staffed Beds:** 68 **Admissions:** 761 **Census:** 45 **Outpatient Visits:** 23741 **Births:** 2 **Total Expense ($000):** 19228 **Payroll Expense ($000):** 6845 **Personnel:** 172

## BURLINGTON—Alamance County

✠ **ALAMANCE REGIONAL MEDICAL CENTER (340070)**, 1240 Huffman Mill Road, Zip 27215–8700, Mailing Address: P.O. Box 202, Zip 27216–0202; tel. 336/538–7000 **A**1 2 9 10 **F**3 8 9 12 13 15 18 20 22 24 26 28 29 30 31 32 34 35 36 38 39 40 44 45 46 47 49 50 53 54 56 57 58 59 60 64 66 68 70 73 74 75 76 77 78 79 81 82 84 85 86 87 89 91 93 94 96 97 98 100 101 102 103 107 108 110 111 114 117 118 119 120 121 123 126 130 131 132 135 144 145 146 147 148 **P**6 **S** Carolinas Healthcare System, Charlotte, NC
Primary Contact: Preston W. Hammock, President and Chief Executive Officer
COO: Preston W. Hammock, President and Chief Operating Officer
CFO: Rex Street, Senior Vice President and Chief Financial Officer
CMO: Andrew Lamb, M.D., Chief of Staff
CIO: Terri Andrews, Director Information Technology
CNO: Theresa M. Brodrick, R.N., Chief Nursing Officer
Web address: www.armc.com
**Control:** Other not–for–profit (including NFP Corporation) **Service:** General Medical and Surgical

**Staffed Beds:** 218 **Admissions:** 9878 **Census:** 128 **Outpatient Visits:** 116779 **Births:** 1305 **Total Expense ($000):** 242938 **Payroll Expense ($000):** 83291 **Personnel:** 1345

## BUTNER—Granville County

☐ **CENTRAL REGIONAL HOSPITAL (344004)**, 300 Veazey Road, Zip 27509–1668; tel. 919/764–2000 **A**1 3 5 10 **F**3 30 39 74 75 98 99 103 106 119 130 143 146 **P**6
Primary Contact: Michael Hennike, Chief Executive Officer
COO: Cliff Hood, Chief Operating Officer
CFO: Steve Bruno, Manager Business
CMO: Stephen Oxley, M.D., Chief Medical Officer
CIO: Joe Thurber, Director Information Technology
CHR: Debbie Thomas, Director Human Resources
CNO: Amanda Dorgan, Chief Nursing Officer
**Control:** State–Government, nonfederal **Service:** Psychiatric

**Staffed Beds:** 382 **Admissions:** 1261 **Census:** 368 **Outpatient Visits:** 0 **Births:** 0 **Total Expense ($000):** 159389 **Payroll Expense ($000):** 92035 **Personnel:** 1857

## CAMP LEJEUNE—Onslow County

✠ **NAVAL HOSPITAL CAMP LEJEUNE**, 100 Brewster Boulevard, Zip 28547–2538, Mailing Address: P.O. Box 10100, Zip 28547–0100; tel. 910/450–4300, (Nonreporting) **A**1 3 5 **S** Bureau of Medicine and Surgery, Department of the Navy, Washington, DC
Primary Contact: Captain Rick Freedman, Commanding Officer
Web address: www.med.navy.mil/sites/nhcl/Pages/default.aspx
**Control:** Navy, Government, federal **Service:** General Medical and Surgical

**Staffed Beds:** 117

## CARY—Wake County

✠ **WAKEMED CARY HOSPITAL (340173)**, 1900 Kildaire Farm Road, Zip 27518–6616; tel. 919/350–2300 **A**1 9 10 **F**3 7 12 13 15 18 20 24 28 29 30 31 35 40 42 44 45 46 48 49 50 54 61 64 68 70 73 74 75 76 77 79 81 82 85 86 92 107 110 111 114 115 118 119 126 128 129 130 132 146 147 **P**6 **S** WakeMed Health & Hospitals, Raleigh, NC
Primary Contact: Donald R. Gintzig, President and Chief Executive Officer
COO: Thomas Gettinger, Chief Operating Officer and Executive Vice President
CFO: Michael D. DeVaughn, Executive Vice President and Chief Financial Officer
CMO: West Lawson, M.D., Chief Medical Officer
CIO: Denton Arledge, Vice President and Chief Information Officer
CHR: Jeanene R. Martin, M.P.H., Senior Vice President Human Resources
CNO: Cindy Boily, MSN, Senior Vice President and Chief Nursing Officer
Web address: www.wakemed.org
**Control:** Other not–for–profit (including NFP Corporation) **Service:** General Medical and Surgical

**Staffed Beds:** 192 **Admissions:** 9851 **Census:** 114 **Outpatient Visits:** 247142 **Births:** 2205 **Total Expense ($000):** 158972 **Payroll Expense ($000):** 58031 **Personnel:** 1015

NC

*Many Facility Codes have changed. Please refer to the AHA Guide Code Chart.* © 2015 AHA Guide

## CHAPEL HILL—Orange County

☒ △ **UNIVERSITY OF NORTH CAROLINA HOSPITALS (340061)**, 101 Manning Drive, Zip 27514–4220; tel. 919/966–4131, (Includes NORTH CAROLINA CHILDREN'S AND WOMEN'S HOSPITAL ; N.C. WOMEN'S HOSPITAL, 101 Manning Drive, tel. 919/966–4131; NORTH CAROLINA CHILDREN'S HOSPITAL, 101 Manning Drive, tel. 919/966–4131; NORTH CAROLINA NEUROSCIENCES HOSPITAL, University Campus, Zip 27514; tel. 919/966–1141; UNC LINEBERGER COMPREHENSIVE CANCER CENTER, 450 West Drive, Zip 27599–5020; tel. 919/966–3036) **A**1 2 3 5 7 8 9 10 **F**3 4 5 7 8 9 11 12 13 14 15 16 17 18 19 20 21 22 23 24 25 26 27 28 29 30 31 32 34 35 36 38 39 40 41 43 44 45 46 47 48 49 50 52 53 54 55 56 57 58 59 60 61 62 63 64 65 66 68 70 72 73 74 75 76 77 78 79 80 81 82 84 85 86 87 88 89 90 91 92 93 96 97 98 99 100 101 102 103 104 105 106 107 108 110 111 114 115 116 117 118 119 120 121 123 124 126 129 130 131 132 134 135 136 137 138 139 140 141 142 143 144 145 146 147 148 **S** UNC Health Care, Chapel Hill, NC
Primary Contact: Gary L. Park, President
COO: Brian Goldstein, M.D., Executive Vice President and Chief Operating Officer
CFO: Christopher Ellington, Executive Vice President and Chief Financial Officer
CMO: Tony Lindsey, M.D., Chief of Staff
CIO: Tracy Parham, MSN
CHR: William Rotella, Vice President Human Resources
CNO: Mary Crabtree Tonges, Ph.D., Senior Vice President and Chief Nursing Officer
Web address: www.unchealthcare.org
**Control:** State–Government, nonfederal **Service:** General Medical and Surgical

**Staffed Beds:** 830 **Admissions:** 37196 **Census:** 705 **Outpatient Visits:** 952338 **Births:** 3575 **Total Expense ($000):** 1190334 **Payroll Expense ($000):** 509429 **Personnel:** 8957

## CHARLOTTE—Mecklenburg County

☒ **CAROLINAS CONTINUECARE HOSPITAL AT PINEVILLE (342015)**, 10648 Park Road, Zip 28210; tel. 704/667–8050 **A**1 5 10 **F**1 18 29 34 35 59 65 68 74 75 77 79 82 84 85 130 146 148 **S** Community Hospital Corporation, Plano, TX
Primary Contact: Daniel C. Dunmyer, Chief Executive Officer
CFO: Joanne Tyo, Chief Financial Officer
CMO: Joseph Lang, M.D., Chief of Staff
CHR: Doug Gallagher, Director Human Resources
CNO: Teshia Davis, Chief Clinical Officer
Web address: www.cshnc.com
**Control:** Other not–for–profit (including NFP Corporation) **Service:** Long–Term Acute Care hospital

**Staffed Beds:** 40 **Admissions:** 500 **Census:** 33 **Outpatient Visits:** 0 **Births:** 0 **Total Expense ($000):** 20699 **Payroll Expense ($000):** 8607 **Personnel:** 152

☒ **CAROLINAS HEALTHCARE SYSTEM PINEVILLE (340098)**, 10628 Park Road, Zip 28210–8407; tel. 704/543–2000 **A**1 2 3 9 10 **F**3 13 17 18 20 22 24 26 28 29 30 40 42 45 49 50 64 70 72 73 74 75 76 77 79 81 82 84 86 87 90 91 92 93 100 107 111 112 114 115 119 126 129 130 132 146 147 148 **S** Carolinas Healthcare System, Charlotte, NC
Primary Contact: Christopher R. Hummer, President
Web address: www.carolinashealthcare.org/pineville
**Control:** Hospital district or authority, Government, nonfederal **Service:** General Medical and Surgical

**Staffed Beds:** 229 **Admissions:** 14583 **Census:** 178 **Outpatient Visits:** 155575 **Births:** 2213 **Total Expense ($000):** 258951 **Payroll Expense ($000):** 87854 **Personnel:** 1326

☒ △ **CAROLINAS MEDICAL CENTER (340113)**, 1000 Blythe Boulevard, Zip 28203–5871, Mailing Address: P.O. Box 32861, Zip 28232–2861; tel. 704/355–2000, (Includes CAROLINAS MEDICAL CENTER–MERCY, 2001 Vail Avenue, Zip 28207–1289; tel. 704/304–5000; Scott Jones, Vice President and Facility Executive; LEVINE CHILDREN'S HOSPITAL, 1000 Blythe Boulevard, Zip 28203; tel. 704/381–2000) **A**1 2 3 5 6 7 8 9 10 **F**3 4 5 7 8 12 13 15 17 18 19 20 21 22 23 24 25 26 27 28 29 30 31 32 34 35 36 37 38 39 40 41 42 43 44 45 46 47 48 49 50 52 54 55 56 57 58 59 60 61 62 64 65 66 68 70 71 72 73 74 75 76 77 78 79 80 81 82 83 84 85 86 87 88 89 90 93 96 97 98 99 100 101 102 103 104 105 107 109 111 114 115 116 117 118 119 120 121 123 124 126 129 130 131 132 134 135 136 137 138 139 141 142 143 145 146 147 148 **P**6 **S** Carolinas Healthcare System, Charlotte, NC
Primary Contact: Spencer Lilly, President
CFO: Greg A. Gombar, Chief Financial Officer
CMO: Roger A. Ray, M.D., Executive Vice President and Chief Medical Officer
CIO: Craig D. Richardville, Senior Vice President and Chief Information Officer
CHR: Debra Plousha–Moore, Senior Vice President Human Resources
Web address: www.carolinashealthcare.org/cmc
**Control:** Hospital district or authority, Government, nonfederal **Service:** General Medical and Surgical

**Staffed Beds:** 1132 **Admissions:** 62460 **Census:** 892 **Outpatient Visits:** 926603 **Births:** 6605 **Total Expense ($000):** 1862602 **Payroll Expense ($000):** 521695 **Personnel:** 12184

☒ **CAROLINAS MEDICAL CENTER–UNIVERSITY (340166)**, 8800 North Tryon Street, Zip 28262–3300, Mailing Address: P.O. Box 560727, Zip 28256–0727; tel. 704/863–6000 **A**1 2 9 10 **F**3 8 13 15 18 20 26 29 30 31 34 40 42 43 44 45 46 49 50 51 57 59 60 64 65 68 70 72 74 75 76 78 79 81 82 84 85 86 87 93 107 111 114 115 118 119 126 129 130 145 146 148 **S** Carolinas Healthcare System, Charlotte, NC
Primary Contact: William H. Leonard, President
CFO: Greg A. Gombar, Chief Financial Officer
CIO: John Knox, Senior Vice President and Chief Information Officer
Web address: www.carolinashealthcare.org/university
**Control:** Hospital district or authority, Government, nonfederal **Service:** General Medical and Surgical

**Staffed Beds:** 94 **Admissions:** 6079 **Census:** 60 **Outpatient Visits:** 147633 **Births:** 1501 **Total Expense ($000):** 140823 **Payroll Expense ($000):** 47569 **Personnel:** 709

☒ △ **CAROLINAS REHABILITATION (343026)**, 1100 Blythe Boulevard, Zip 28203–5864; tel. 704/355–4300 **A**1 7 9 10 **F**3 11 29 30 31 64 74 77 79 82 90 91 93 95 129 130 131 132 146 **P**1 **S** Carolinas Healthcare System, Charlotte, NC
Primary Contact: Robert G. Larrison, Jr., President
CFO: William Hopkins, Director Finance
CMO: William Bockenek, M.D., Chief Medical Officer
CIO: Craig D. Richardville, Chief Information Officer
CHR: Deonca Leach, Director, Human Resources
CNO: Susan Chase, Vice President
Web address: www.carolinashealthcare.org/rehabilitation
**Control:** Other not–for–profit (including NFP Corporation) **Service:** Rehabilitation

**Staffed Beds:** 157 **Admissions:** 2655 **Census:** 121 **Outpatient Visits:** 80057 **Births:** 0 **Total Expense ($000):** 86261 **Payroll Expense ($000):** 37310 **Personnel:** 720

★ **NOVANT HEALTH CHARLOTTE ORTHOPAEDIC HOSPITAL (340153)**, 1901 Randolph Road, Zip 28207–1195; tel. 704/316–2000, (Total facility includes 16 beds in nursing home–type unit) **A**9 10 **F**3 11 29 30 37 44 50 51 64 68 75 79 81 82 86 87 107 111 118 119 128 130 131 132 146 **S** Novant Health, Winston Salem, NC
Primary Contact: Jason Bernd, Vice President
CFO: Tammy Geist, Chief Financial Officer
CIO: Shelia Cook, Director Information Systems
CNO: Maurice Wilson, Director of Nursing
Web address: www.novanthealth.org
**Control:** Other not–for–profit (including NFP Corporation) **Service:** Orthopedic

**Staffed Beds:** 33 **Admissions:** 3344 **Census:** 30 **Outpatient Visits:** 20635 **Births:** 0 **Total Expense ($000):** 85296 **Payroll Expense ($000):** 20351 **Personnel:** 316

---

**Hospital, Medicare Provider Number, Address, Telephone, Approval, Facility, and Physician Codes, Health Care System**

★ American Hospital Association (AHA) membership
☐ The Joint Commission accreditation
◯ Healthcare Facilities Accreditation Program
◇ DNV Healthcare Inc. accreditation
⇑ Center for Improvement in Healthcare Quality Accreditation
△ Commission on Accreditation of Rehabilitation Facilities (CARF) accreditation

**NC**

✠ **NOVANT HEALTH PRESBYTERIAN MEDICAL CENTER (340053)**, 200 Hawthorne Lane, Zip 28204–2528, Mailing Address: P.O. Box 33549, Zip 28233–3549; tel. 704/384–4000, (Includes PRESBYTERIAN HEMBY CHILDREN'S HOSPITAL, 200 Hawthorne Lane, Zip 28204–2515; tel. 704/384–5134) **A**1 2 3 9 10 **F**3 5 7 8 11 12 13 15 17 18 19 20 22 24 26 28 29 30 31 32 34 35 36 38 40 41 45 46 47 48 49 53 54 55 56 57 58 59 60 61 63 64 65 67 68 70 71 72 73 74 75 76 77 78 79 81 82 84 85 86 87 88 89 91 92 93 98 99 100 101 102 103 104 105 107 108 111 112 113 114 115 116 117 118 119 120 121 124 126 129 130 132 135 142 143 145 146 147 148 **P**6 **S** Novant Health, Winston Salem, NC
Primary Contact: Paula Vincent, MSN, President and Chief Operating Officer
CFO: Melissa Masterton, Vice President
CMO: Thomas Zweng, M.D., Executive Vice President Medical Affairs
CIO: David B. Garrett, Senior Vice President Information Technology
CHR: Janet Smith–Hill, Senior Vice President Human Resources
CNO: Michael Vaccaro, Chief Nursing Officer
Web address: www.novanthealth.org
**Control:** Other not–for–profit (including NFP Corporation) **Service:** General Medical and Surgical

**Staffed Beds:** 416 **Admissions:** 29884 **Census:** 405 **Outpatient Visits:** 399398 **Births:** 5061 **Total Expense ($000):** 557574 **Payroll Expense ($000):** 174883 **Personnel:** 3259

**PRESBYTERIAN HOSPITAL** See Novant Health Presbyterian Medical Center

**PRESBYTERIAN–ORTHOPAEDIC HOSPITAL** See Novant Health Charlotte Orthopaedic Hospital

**STRATEGIC BEHAVIORAL HEALTH – CHARLOTTE**, 1715 Sharon Road West, Zip 28210–5663; tel. 704/944–0650, (Nonreporting) **S** Strategic Behavioral Health, LLC, Memphis, TN
Primary Contact: Mercy Estevez, Chief Executive Officer
Web address: www.sbccharlotte.com/
**Control:** Investor–owned, for–profit **Service:** Children's hospital psychiatric

**Staffed Beds:** 60

### CHEROKEE—Swain County

✠ **CHEROKEE INDIAN HOSPITAL (340156)**, 1 Hospital Road, Zip 28719; tel. 828/497–9163 **A**1 10 **F**5 15 32 36 39 40 50 54 59 63 64 65 66 68 75 77 79 82 86 93 97 99 104 107 110 111 114 119 127 130 131 132 135 **P**6
Primary Contact: Casey Cooper, Chief Executive Officer
COO: Beth Greene, Chief Operating Officer
CFO: Chrissy Arch, Chief Financial Officer
CMO: Michael E. Toedt, M.D., Director Clinical Services
CIO: Anthony Taylor, Manager Information Technology
**Control:** PHS, Indian Service, Government, federal **Service:** General Medical and Surgical

**Staffed Beds:** 15 **Admissions:** 590 **Census:** 9 **Outpatient Visits:** 40727 **Births:** 0 **Total Expense ($000):** 46548 **Payroll Expense ($000):** 21926 **Personnel:** 382

### CLINTON—Sampson County

✠ **SAMPSON REGIONAL MEDICAL CENTER (340024)**, 607 Beaman Street, Zip 28328–2697, Mailing Address: P.O. Box 260, Zip 28329–0260; tel. 910/592–8511 **A**1 9 10 12 13 **F**3 13 14 15 29 34 35 40 41 45 50 53 54 57 59 62 64 65 68 70 75 76 77 79 81 82 85 86 89 96 97 107 110 111 114 115 119 129 130 132 133 144 146 148 **P**6
Primary Contact: Shawn Howerton, M.D., Chief Executive Officer and President, Medical Staff
COO: Geraldine H. Shipp, Director of Risk Management
CFO: Jerry Heinzman, Senior Vice President and Chief Financial Officer
CMO: Shawn Howerton, M.D., Chief Executive Officer and President, Medical Staff
CIO: Kelly Lucas, Chief Information Officer
CHR: Michael W. Gilpin, Vice President Human Resources
CNO: Allison H. Taylor, R.N., Chief Nursing Officer and Vice President Clinical Services
Web address: www.sampsonrmc.org
**Control:** County–Government, nonfederal **Service:** General Medical and Surgical

**Staffed Beds:** 105 **Admissions:** 3370 **Census:** 40 **Outpatient Visits:** 73158 **Births:** 471 **Total Expense ($000):** 57706 **Payroll Expense ($000):** 24274 **Personnel:** 506

### CLYDE—Haywood County

✠ **HAYWOOD REGIONAL MEDICAL CENTER (340184)**, 262 Leroy George Drive, Zip 28721–7430; tel. 828/456–7311 **A**1 9 10 **F**3 11 13 15 18 20 28 29 30 31 34 35 38 40 44 45 46 50 51 53 54 57 59 62 63 64 65 68 70 71 74 75 76 77 78 79 81 82 84 85 86 87 93 98 100 101 102 107 108 111 114 118 119 129 130 131 132 144 146 147 148 **P**8 **S** Duke LifePoint Healthcare, Brentwood, TN
Primary Contact: Phillip L. Wright, FACHE, Chief Executive Officer
COO: Teresa Reynolds, Chief Operating Officer
CFO: Rose Coyne, Interim CFO
CMO: Tyson Smith, M.D., Chief Medical Officer
CIO: Greg Copen, Chief Information Officer
CHR: Janet Millsaps, Vice President Human Resources
Web address: www.haymed.org
**Control:** Corporation, Investor–owned, for–profit **Service:** General Medical and Surgical

**Staffed Beds:** 146 **Admissions:** 4736 **Census:** 49 **Outpatient Visits:** 236996 **Births:** 283 **Total Expense ($000):** 108549 **Payroll Expense ($000):** 45839 **Personnel:** 760

### COLUMBUS—Polk County

✠ **ST. LUKE'S HOSPITAL (341322)**, 101 Hospital Drive, Zip 28722–6418; tel. 828/894–3311 **A**1 9 10 18 **F**3 11 15 29 30 34 35 40 45 56 57 59 64 70 75 77 79 81 85 87 91 93 98 103 104 107 108 114 119 130 133 135 146 **P**6 **S** Carolinas Healthcare System, Charlotte, NC
Primary Contact: Kenneth A. Shull, FACHE, Chief Executive Officer
CFO: Elizabeth Presnell, Assistant Vice President of Finance
CMO: James Holleman, M.D., Chief of Staff
CIO: Nick Whichard, Chief Information Officer
CHR: Amy Norville, Vice President Support Services
CNO: Cathy Moore, Chief Nursing Officer
Web address: www.saintlukeshospital.com
**Control:** Other not–for–profit (including NFP Corporation) **Service:** General Medical and Surgical

**Staffed Beds:** 35 **Admissions:** 1549 **Census:** 22 **Outpatient Visits:** 22408 **Births:** 0 **Total Expense ($000):** 27953 **Payroll Expense ($000):** 11499 **Personnel:** 270

### CONCORD—Cabarrus County

✠ **CAROLINAS HEALTHCARE SYSTEM NORTHEAST (340001)**, 920 Church Street North, Zip 28025–2983; tel. 704/403–3000 **A**1 2 9 10 **F**3 5 8 9 11 12 13 15 17 18 20 22 24 26 28 29 30 32 34 36 37 38 40 42 43 44 45 46 49 50 51 53 55 56 57 58 59 60 61 64 65 68 70 71 72 73 74 75 76 78 79 81 82 84 85 86 87 88 89 93 97 98 99 100 102 103 104 105 107 108 111 114 115 116 117 118 119 121 123 124 126 129 130 131 132 135 145 146 147 148 **P**6 **S** Carolinas Healthcare System, Charlotte, NC
Primary Contact: Phyllis A. Wingate, FACHE, President
COO: Bill Hubbard, Vice President, Operations
CFO: Rodney Ball, Vice President Finance
CMO: Dan Hagler, M.D., Vice President and Chief Medical Officer
CIO: Lisa Sykes, Manager, Information Services
CHR: Lesley Chambless, Assistant Vice President Workforce Relations
CNO: Kate Grew, MSN, Vice President/Chief Nurse Executive
Web address: www.carolinashealthcare.org/northeast
**Control:** Hospital district or authority, Government, nonfederal **Service:** General Medical and Surgical

**Staffed Beds:** 455 **Admissions:** 22274 **Census:** 261 **Outpatient Visits:** 361423 **Births:** 2724 **Total Expense ($000):** 429343 **Payroll Expense ($000):** 147685 **Personnel:** 2518

### DANBURY—Stokes County

★ ◇ **PIONEER COMMUNITY HOSPITAL OF STOKES (341317)**, 1570 Highway 8 and 89 North, Zip 27016, Mailing Address: P.O. Box 10, Zip 27016–0010; tel. 336/593–2831, (Nonreporting) **A**9 10 18 21 **S** Pioneer Health Services, Magee, MS
Primary Contact: Pamela P. Tillman, R.N., Chief Executive Officer
COO: Tim Fontaine, Chief Operating Officer
CFO: Julie Gieger, Chief Financial Officer
CMO: Samuel C. Newsome, M.D., Chief of Staff
CIO: Jack York, Chief Information Officer
CHR: Lashaunda Lash, Manager Human Resources
CNO: Jane Pantano, R.N., Chief Nursing Officer
Web address: www.pchstokes.com
**Control:** Corporation, Investor–owned, for–profit **Service:** General Medical and Surgical

**Staffed Beds:** 25

**NC**

*Many Facility Codes have changed. Please refer to the AHA Guide Code Chart.*

## DUNN—Harnett County

☐ **HARNETT HEALTH SYSTEM (340071)**, 800 Tilghman Drive, Zip 28334–5599, Mailing Address: P.O. Box 1706, Zip 28335–1706; tel. 910/892–1000, (Includes CENTRAL HARTNETT HOSPITAL, 215 Brightwater Drive, Lillington, Zip 27546; tel. 910/892–1000) **A**1 9 10 12 13 **F**3 11 13 15 18 28 29 30 34 35 39 40 45 50 56 57 59 70 73 75 76 77 79 81 85 86 87 89 92 93 96 102 107 108 110 111 114 118 119 129 130 135 146 148 **S** Cape Fear Valley Health System, Fayetteville, NC
Primary Contact: Dan Weatherly, Chief Executive Officer
COO: Kenneth E. Bryan, FACHE, President and Chief Executive Officer
CFO: Lynn Lambert, Chief Financial Officer
CIO: Tim Krieger, Director Information Systems
CHR: Sondra Davis, Vice President Human Resources & System Development
CNO: Vicki Allen, R.N., Vice President Patient Care Services and Chief Nursing Officer
Web address: www.myharnetthealth.org/
**Control:** Other not–for–profit (including NFP Corporation) **Service:** General Medical and Surgical

**Staffed Beds:** 96 **Admissions:** 6773 **Census:** 72 **Outpatient Visits:** 120513 **Births:** 663 **Total Expense ($000):** 109877 **Payroll Expense ($000):** 48058 **Personnel:** 975

## DURHAM—Durham County

✠ **DUKE REGIONAL HOSPITAL (340155)**, 3643 North Roxboro Road, Zip 27704–2763; tel. 919/470–4000 **A**1 3 5 6 9 10 **F**3 8 11 12 13 15 17 18 20 22 24 26 29 30 31 34 35 40 44 45 48 50 51 57 58 59 60 64 66 68 70 73 74 75 76 77 78 79 80 81 82 84 85 86 87 90 96 98 100 102 107 108 110 111 115 118 119 120 121 123 124 126 130 131 132 146 147 148 **P**6 **S** Duke University Health System, Durham, NC
Primary Contact: Kathleen B. Galbraith, President
CFO: Jonathan B. Hoy, Chief Financial Officer
CMO: Barbara Griffith, M.D., Chief Medical Officer
CIO: Terry Mears, Director Information Systems
CHR: Richard J. Walsh, Ph.D., Chief Human Resources Officer
CNO: Victoria K. Orto, R.N., Chief Nursing and Patient Care Services Officer
Web address: www.dukeregional.org/
**Control:** Other not–for–profit (including NFP Corporation) **Service:** General Medical and Surgical

**Staffed Beds:** 210 **Admissions:** 15392 **Census:** 210 **Outpatient Visits:** 108362 **Births:** 2294 **Total Expense ($000):** 266376 **Payroll Expense ($000):** 124048 **Personnel:** 1902

✠ **DUKE UNIVERSITY HOSPITAL (340030)**, 2301 Erwin Road, Zip 27705–4699, Mailing Address: P.O. Box 3708, Zip 27710–3708; tel. 919/684–8111, (Includes DUKE CHILDREN'S HOSPITAL & HEALTH CENTER, 2301 Erwin Road, Zip 27710–0001, Mailing Address: PO Box 3708, Zip 27702; tel. 919/684–8111) **A**1 2 3 5 8 9 10 **F**3 5 6 7 8 9 11 12 13 15 17 18 19 20 21 22 23 24 25 26 27 28 29 30 31 32 34 35 36 37 39 40 41 43 44 45 46 47 48 49 50 52 53 54 55 56 57 58 59 60 62 63 64 65 66 69 70 72 73 74 75 76 77 78 79 80 81 82 84 85 86 87 88 89 91 92 93 94 95 96 97 98 99 100 101 102 103 104 107 108 110 111 112 114 115 116 117 118 119 120 121 123 124 126 127 129 130 131 132 134 135 136 137 138 139 140 141 142 145 146 147 148 **P**1 **S** Duke University Health System, Durham, NC
Primary Contact: Kevin W. Sowers, R.N., MSN, President
CFO: Sabrina Olsen, Chief Financial Officer
CMO: Lisa C. Pickett, M.D., Chief Medical Officer
CIO: Jeffrey Ferranti, M.D., Chief Information Officer
CHR: Deborah Page, Chief Human Resources Officer
CNO: Mary Ann Fuchs, R.N., Vice President Patient Care and System Chief Nurse Executive
Web address: www.dukehealth.org
**Control:** Other not–for–profit (including NFP Corporation) **Service:** General Medical and Surgical

**Staffed Beds:** 919 **Admissions:** 39535 **Census:** 716 **Outpatient Visits:** 1026501 **Births:** 3103 **Total Expense ($000):** 1921093 **Payroll Expense ($000):** 650238 **Personnel:** 10239

**DURHAM REGIONAL HOSPITAL** See Duke Regional Hospital

✠ **DURHAM VETERANS AFFAIRS MEDICAL CENTER**, 508 Fulton Street, Zip 27705–3897; tel. 919/286–0411, (Nonreporting) **A**1 3 5 8 **S** Department of Veterans Affairs, Washington, DC
Primary Contact: DeAnne Seekins, Director
COO: Sara Haigh, Associate Director
CFO: David Kuboushek, Chief, Fiscal Service
CMO: John D. Shelburne, M.D., Chief of Staff
CIO: Toby Dickerson, Chief Information Resources Management Services
CHR: Jerry Freeman, Chief, Human Resources Management Services
CNO: Gregory S. Eagerton, Ph.D., Nurse Executive
Web address: www.durham.va.gov/
**Control:** Veterans Affairs, Government, federal **Service:** General Medical and Surgical

**Staffed Beds:** 265

☐ **NORTH CAROLINA SPECIALTY HOSPITAL (340049)**, 3916 Ben Franklin Boulevard, Zip 27704–2383, Mailing Address: PO Box 15819, Zip 27704–2383; tel. 919/956–9300 **A**1 9 10 **F**3 51 64 79 81 82 85 86 87 107 119 126 130 131 148 **S** National Surgical Healthcare, Chicago, IL
Primary Contact: Randi L. Shults, Chief Executive Officer
CFO: Bill Wilson, Chief Financial Officer
CMO: Thomas Dimmig, M.D., Medical Director
CHR: Maggie Glenn, Director Human Resources
CNO: John Medlin, Chief Nursing Officer
Web address: www.ncspecialty.com
**Control:** Partnership, Investor–owned, for–profit **Service:** General Medical and Surgical

**Staffed Beds:** 18 **Admissions:** 1680 **Census:** 11 **Outpatient Visits:** 9152 **Births:** 0 **Total Expense ($000):** 34973 **Payroll Expense ($000):** 10555 **Personnel:** 188

✠ **SELECT SPECIALTY HOSPITAL–DURHAM (342018)**, 3643 North Roxboro Road, 6th Floor, Zip 27704–2702; tel. 919/470–9137, (Nonreporting) **A**1 10 **S** Select Medical Corporation, Mechanicsburg, PA
Primary Contact: Theresa Hunkins, R.N., Chief Executive Officer
Web address: www.selectspecialtyhospitals.com/company/locations/durham.aspx
**Control:** Corporation, Investor–owned, for–profit **Service:** Long–Term Acute Care hospital

**Staffed Beds:** 30

## EDEN—Rockingham County

★ ◇ **MOREHEAD MEMORIAL HOSPITAL (340060)**, 117 East King's Highway, Zip 27288–5201; tel. 336/623–9711, (Total facility includes 121 beds in nursing home–type unit) **A**2 9 10 21 **F**3 11 13 15 18 26 29 30 34 35 45 47 48 49 50 57 59 64 68 70 74 75 76 77 79 81 82 85 87 89 90 93 97 107 108 110 111 114 118 119 122 123 128 129 130 132 135 143 144 146 147 148
Primary Contact: Howard N. Ainsley, Chief Executive Officer
CFO: Robert G. Hetrick, Vice President Finance and Chief Financial Officer
CHR: Tom Stevens, Director Personnel
Web address: www.morehead.org
**Control:** Other not–for–profit (including NFP Corporation) **Service:** General Medical and Surgical

**Staffed Beds:** 188 **Admissions:** 3765 **Census:** 139 **Outpatient Visits:** 169545 **Births:** 521 **Total Expense ($000):** 87521 **Payroll Expense ($000):** 39115 **Personnel:** 620

## EDENTON—Chowan County

✠ **VIDANT CHOWAN HOSPITAL (341318)**, 211 Virginia Road, Zip 27932–9668, Mailing Address: PO Box 629, Zip 27932–0629; tel. 252/482–8451 **A**1 3 9 10 18 **F**3 11 13 15 18 29 30 31 34 35 40 45 46 56 57 59 64 70 74 75 76 77 78 79 81 82 85 89 93 107 108 110 111 114 119 130 132 146 147 **S** Vidant Health, Greenville, NC
Primary Contact: Jeffery Dial, President
CFO: Brian Harvill, Vice President Financial Services
CMO: William Hope, IV, M.D., Chief of Medical Staff
CIO: Carl Grooms, Infrastructure Support Specialist
CHR: Debbie Swicegood, Director Human Resources
CNO: Cindy Coker, M.P.H., Vice President, Patient Care Services
Web address: www.vidanthealth.com
**Control:** Other not–for–profit (including NFP Corporation) **Service:** General Medical and Surgical

**Staffed Beds:** 19 **Admissions:** 1382 **Census:** 13 **Outpatient Visits:** 37347 **Births:** 289 **Total Expense ($000):** 44172 **Payroll Expense ($000):** 17366 **Personnel:** 329

## ELIZABETH CITY—Pasquotank County

✠ **SENTARA ALBEMARLE MEDICAL CENTER (340109)**, 1144 North Road Street, Zip 27909–3473, Mailing Address: P.O. Box 1587, Zip 27906–1587; tel. 252/335–0531 **A**1 9 10 **F**3 13 15 17 18 20 28 29 30 31 34 35 39 40 45 53 57 59 64 68 70 74 75 76 77 78 79 81 84 85 86 87 92 93 94 107 111 115 118 119 121 126 129 130 131 132 146 147 148 **S** Sentara Healthcare, Norfolk, VA
Primary Contact: Coleen F. Santa Ana, Chief Executive Officer
COO: Jan King Robinson, Vice President, Operations
CFO: Craig Lewis, Interim Chief Financial Officer
CMO: Daniel S. Terryberry, M.D., Vice President of Medical Affairs
CIO: Steve Clark, Chief Information Officer
CHR: Brenda Rosecrans, Executive Director Human Resources
CNO: Kathy Lawrence, Interim Vice President of Patient Care Services
Web address: www.albemarlehealth.org
**Control:** Other not–for–profit (including NFP Corporation) **Service:** General Medical and Surgical

**Staffed Beds:** 83 **Admissions:** 5240 **Census:** 58 **Outpatient Visits:** 145605 **Births:** 642 **Total Expense ($000):** 101603 **Payroll Expense ($000):** 35267 **Personnel:** 744

---

**Hospital, Medicare Provider Number, Address, Telephone, Approval, Facility, and Physician Codes, Health Care System**

★ American Hospital Association (AHA) membership
☐ The Joint Commission accreditation
○ Healthcare Facilities Accreditation Program
◇ DNV Healthcare Inc. accreditation
⇑ Center for Improvement in Healthcare Quality Accreditation
△ Commission on Accreditation of Rehabilitation Facilities (CARF) accreditation

**NC**

## ELIZABETHTOWN—Bladen County

**BLADEN COUNTY HOSPITAL** See Cape Fear Valley – Bladen County Hospital

☒ **CAPE FEAR VALLEY – BLADEN COUNTY HOSPITAL (341315)**, 501 South Poplar Street, Zip 28337–9375, Mailing Address: P.O. Box 398, Zip 28337–0398; tel. 910/862–5100 **A**1 9 10 18 **F**3 11 13 14 15 28 29 30 34 35 40 45 50 54 59 64 68 70 76 77 81 90 91 93 97 107 114 119 129 133 135 144 146 147 **P**6 **S** Cape Fear Valley Health System, Fayetteville, NC
Primary Contact: Lisa Byrd, Interim President
CFO: Sandra Williams, Chief Financial Officer
CMO: Pearly Graham Hoskins, M.D., President Medical Staff
CIO: Craig Kellum, Director Management Information Systems
CHR: Ginger Parks, Director Human Resources
Web address: www.bchn.org
**Control:** Other not–for–profit (including NFP Corporation) **Service:** General Medical and Surgical

**Staffed Beds:** 25 **Admissions:** 991 **Census:** 9 **Outpatient Visits:** 39444
**Births:** 207 **Total Expense ($000):** 34512 **Payroll Expense ($000):** 19345

## ELKIN—Surry County

☒ **HUGH CHATHAM MEMORIAL HOSPITAL (340097)**, 180 Parkwood Drive, Zip 28621–2430, Mailing Address: P.O. Box 560, Zip 28621–0560; tel. 336/527–7000, (Total facility includes 127 beds in nursing home–type unit) **A**1 9 10 **F**3 11 13 15 28 29 30 34 40 45 49 53 57 59 62 64 70 76 79 81 85 87 91 93 96 97 100 107 108 110 111 114 118 119 120 121 125 127 128 130 131 132 133 135 144 146 148 **P**6 **S** Alliant Management Services, Louisville, KY
Primary Contact: Paul Hammes, Chief Executive Officer
COO: Mary Blackburn, Vice President Operations and Chief Practice Officer
CFO: Donald E. Trippel, Chief Financial Officer
CMO: Dominick Carbone, M.D., Chief of Staff
CIO: Lee Powe, Director Management Information Systems
CHR: Kathy Poteate, Interim Director Human Resources
CNO: Paula Moore, R.N., Chief Clinical Officer
Web address: www.hughchatham.org
**Control:** Other not–for–profit (including NFP Corporation) **Service:** General Medical and Surgical

**Staffed Beds:** 208 **Admissions:** 4317 **Census:** 84 **Outpatient Visits:** 61413
**Births:** 540 **Total Expense ($000):** 64236 **Payroll Expense ($000):** 22098
**Personnel:** 606

## FAYETTEVILLE—Cumberland County

☒ △ **CAPE FEAR VALLEY MEDICAL CENTER (340028)**, 1638 Owen Drive, Zip 28304–3431, Mailing Address: P.O. Box 2000, Zip 28302–2000; tel. 910/615–4000, (Includes SOUTHEASTERN REGIONAL REHABILITATION CENTER ; BEHAVIORAL HEALTH CARE OF CAPE FEAR VALLEY HEALTH SYSTEM, 3425 Melrose Road, Zip 28304–1695; tel. 910/609–3000; CAPE FEAR VALLEY REHABILITATION CENTER, 1638 Owen Drive, Zip 28304; tel. 910/609–4000) **A**1 2 3 5 7 9 10 **F**3 4 5 7 12 13 18 20 22 24 26 28 29 30 31 34 35 38 39 40 41 43 44 46 49 53 54 56 57 59 61 64 65 68 70 72 73 74 75 76 77 78 79 81 82 84 86 87 88 89 90 91 92 93 96 97 98 99 100 101 102 103 104 106 107 108 109 110 111 114 115 116 117 118 119 120 121 122 123 124 126 127 129 130 132 135 143 144 146 147 148 **P**6 **S** Cape Fear Valley Health System, Fayetteville, NC
Primary Contact: Michael Nagowski, Chief Executive Officer
CFO: Sandra Williams, Chief Financial Officer
CMO: Christopher T. Aul, M.D., Chief Medical Officer
CIO: Phillip E. Wood, Jr., Chief Information Officer
CHR: William B. Pryor, Senior Vice President, Human Resources
CNO: Jana S. Stonestreet, R.N., Chief Nursing Officer
Web address: www.capefearvalley.com
**Control:** Other not–for–profit (including NFP Corporation) **Service:** General Medical and Surgical

**Staffed Beds:** 592 **Admissions:** 29954 **Census:** 508 **Outpatient Visits:** 621875 **Births:** 4619 **Total Expense ($000):** 628207 **Payroll Expense ($000):** 295976 **Personnel:** 4521

☒ **FAYETTEVILLE VETERANS AFFAIRS MEDICAL CENTER**, 2300 Ramsey Street, Zip 28301–3899; tel. 910/488–2120, (Nonreporting) **A**1 3 5 **S** Department of Veterans Affairs, Washington, DC
Primary Contact: Elizabeth Goolsby, Director
COO: James Galkowski, Associate Director for Operations
CFO: Patrick Bullard, Chief Financial Officer
CMO: Greg Antoine, M.D., Chief of Staff
CIO: Kenneth Williams, Chief Information Officer
CHR: Joseph Whaley, Chief, Human Resources Management Service
CNO: Joyce Alexander–Hines, R.N., Associate Director, Patient Care Services
Web address: www.fayettevillenc.va.gov
**Control:** Veterans Affairs, Government, federal **Service:** General Medical and Surgical

**Staffed Beds:** 58

☐ **HIGHSMITH–RAINEY SPECIALTY HOSPITAL (342014)**, 150 Robeson Street, Zip 28301–5570; tel. 910/615–1000 **A**1 9 10 **F**1 11 29 30 35 39 50 51 56 58 68 70 81 82 107 114 119 130 132 144 146 148 **P**5 **S** Cape Fear Valley Health System, Fayetteville, NC
Primary Contact: Kevin Jackson, On Site Administrator
Web address: www.capefearvalley.com
**Control:** Other not–for–profit (including NFP Corporation) **Service:** Long–Term Acute Care hospital

**Staffed Beds:** 66 **Admissions:** 310 **Census:** 51 **Outpatient Visits:** 2094
**Births:** 0 **Total Expense ($000):** 33724 **Payroll Expense ($000):** 19648
**Personnel:** 325

**VETERANS AFFAIRS MEDICAL CENTER** See Fayetteville Veterans Affairs Medical Center

## FORT BRAGG—Cumberland County

☒ **WOMACK ARMY MEDICAL CENTER**, Normandy Drive, Zip 28307–5000; tel. 910/907–6000, (Nonreporting) **A**1 3 5 **S** Department of the Army, Office of the Surgeon General, Falls Church, VA
Primary Contact: Colonel Ronald Stephens, Commander
Web address: www.wamc.amedd.army.mil/
**Control:** Army, Government, federal **Service:** General Medical and Surgical

**Staffed Beds:** 156

## FRANKLIN—Macon County

☒ **ANGEL MEDICAL CENTER (341326)**, 120 Riverview Street, Zip 28734–2612, Mailing Address: P.O. Box 1209, Zip 28744–0569; tel. 828/524–8411, (Nonreporting) **A**1 9 10 18 **S** Mission Health System, Asheville, NC
Primary Contact: James B. Bross, President
COO: Martin Wadewitz, Chief Operations Officer/ Vice President, Operations
CFO: George Kimbro, Vice President Finance
CIO: Ed Coye, Director Information Technology Mission Health System Hospitals
CHR: Teresa Mallonee, Director Human Resources
CNO: Sheila C. Price, R.N., Chief Nursing Officer/Vice President of Nursing
Web address: www.angelmed.org
**Control:** Hospital district or authority, Government, nonfederal **Service:** General Medical and Surgical

**Staffed Beds:** 25

## GARNER—Wake County

☐ **STRATEGIC BEHAVIORAL HEALTH – RALEIGH (344028)**, 3200 Waterfield Drive, Zip 27529–7727; tel. 919/573–4163, (Nonreporting) **A**1 10 **S** Strategic Behavioral Health, LLC, Memphis, TN
Primary Contact: Robert Eklofe, Chief Executive Officer
CMO: Karen Miles, M.D., Medical Director
CHR: Christina Meeker, Director Human Resources
CNO: Shawanna Royal, R.N., Director Nursing
Web address: www.sbcraleigh.com/
**Control:** Investor–owned, for–profit **Service:** Children's hospital psychiatric

**Staffed Beds:** 50

## GASTONIA—Gaston County

☒ **CAROMONT REGIONAL MEDICAL CENTER (340032)**, 2525 Court Drive, Zip 28054–2140, Mailing Address: P.O. Box 1747, Zip 28053–1747; tel. 704/834–2000 **A**1 2 9 10 **F**3 13 15 17 18 20 22 24 26 28 29 30 31 34 35 40 43 44 45 49 50 53 54 55 57 58 59 60 64 68 70 71 72 73 74 75 76 78 79 81 82 84 87 89 91 92 93 94 96 98 99 100 101 102 107 110 111 114 115 116 117 118 119 120 121 123 124 126 129 130 132 135 146 147 148
Primary Contact: Douglas R. Luckett, President and Chief Executive Officer
COO: Kathleen Besson, Executive Vice President and Chief Operating Officer
CFO: David O'Connor, Executive Vice President and Chief Financial Officer
CMO: Todd Davis, M.D., Vice President Medical Affairs, Patient Safety Officer
CIO: Mike Johnson, Vice President, Chief Information Officer
CHR: Elizabeth McCraw, Vice President, Human Resources
CNO: Bonnie H. Faust, R.N., Vice President Chief Nursing Officer
Web address: www.caromont.org
**Control:** Other not–for–profit (including NFP Corporation) **Service:** General Medical and Surgical

**Staffed Beds:** 423 **Admissions:** 20573 **Census:** 250 **Outpatient Visits:** 346527 **Births:** 2159 **Total Expense ($000):** 340559 **Payroll Expense ($000):** 138543 **Personnel:** 2572

**GASTON MEMORIAL HOSPITAL** See CaroMont Regional Medical Center

*Many Facility Codes have changed. Please refer to the AHA Guide Code Chart.* © 2015 AHA Guide

## GOLDSBORO—Wayne County

☐ **CHERRY HOSPITAL (344026)**, 201 Stevens Mill Road, Zip 27530–1057; tel. 919/731–3200 **A**1 3 10 **F**30 39 98 99 103 108 130 143 146
Primary Contact: J. Luckey Welsh, Jr., Chief Executive Officer
CFO: Susie Sherrod Sanders, Budget Officer
CMO: Jim Mayo, M.D., Clinical Director
CIO: Mike Letchworth, Manager Information Systems
CHR: Carol Thornton, Director Human Resources
CNO: Cherie Custer, Chief Nursing Officer
Web address: www.cherryhospital.org
**Control:** State–Government, nonfederal **Service:** Psychiatric

**Staffed Beds:** 197 **Admissions:** 836 **Census:** 175 **Outpatient Visits:** 671 **Births:** 0 **Total Expense ($000):** 78269 **Payroll Expense ($000):** 45432 **Personnel:** 948

✠ **WAYNE MEMORIAL HOSPITAL (340010)**, 2700 Wayne Memorial Drive, Zip 27534–9494, Mailing Address: P.O. Box 8001, Zip 27533–8001; tel. 919/736–1110 **A**1 3 9 10 **F**3 8 13 15 18 20 22 28 29 30 31 34 35 39 40 47 49 50 57 58 59 60 64 65 68 70 71 73 74 76 77 78 79 80 81 85 86 89 92 93 96 98 100 101 102 103 107 108 110 111 114 118 119 126 129 130 132 134 135 142 143 145 146 147 148 **P**6
Primary Contact: J. William Paugh, FACHE, President and Chief Executive Officer
COO: Thomas A. Bradshaw, Vice President Operations
CFO: Rebecca W. Craig, Vice President and Chief Financial Officer
CIO: Lori Cole, Director Information Technology
CHR: Richard K. Rogers, FACHE, Vice President Human Resources
CNO: Shirley S. Harkey, R.N., Vice President, Patient Services
Web address: www.waynehealth.org
**Control:** Other not–for–profit (including NFP Corporation) **Service:** General Medical and Surgical

**Staffed Beds:** 274 **Admissions:** 10660 **Census:** 137 **Outpatient Visits:** 203741 **Births:** 1471 **Total Expense ($000):** 201525 **Payroll Expense ($000):** 81278 **Personnel:** 1556

## GREENSBORO—Guilford County

✠ **KINDRED HOSPITAL–GREENSBORO (342012)**, 2401 Southside Boulevard, Zip 27406–3311; tel. 336/271–2800, (Nonreporting) **A**1 9 10 **S** Kindred Healthcare, Louisville, KY
Primary Contact: Christopher Haynes, Chief Executive Officer
CMO: Percy E. Jones, M.D., Chief of Staff
CIO: Little Shuford, Manager Medical Information
CHR: Michele Roberts, Hospital Recruiter
Web address: www.khgreensboro.com
**Control:** Corporation, Investor–owned, for–profit **Service:** Long–Term Acute Care hospital

**Staffed Beds:** 124

✠ △ **MOSES H. CONE MEMORIAL HOSPITAL (340091)**, 1200 North Elm Street, Zip 27401–1020; tel. 336/832–7000, (Includes ANNIE PENN HOSPITAL, 618 South Main Street, Reidsville, Zip 27320–5094; tel. 336/951–4000; Mickey Foster, President; BEHAVIORAL HEALTH CENTER, 700 Walter Reed Drive, Zip 27403–1129; tel. 336/832–9600; Debbie Green, R.N., MSN, President; MOSES H. CONE MEMORIAL HOSPITAL, 1200 North Elm Street, Zip 27401; tel. 336/832–7000; Judith A. Schanel, R.N., MSN, FACHE, President; WESLEY LONG COMMUNITY HOSPITAL, 501 North Elam Avenue, Zip 27403; tel. 336/832–1000; Paul A. Jeffrey, President; WOMEN'S HOSPITAL OF GREENSBORO, 801 Green Valley Road, Zip 27408; tel. 336/832–6500), (Total facility includes 92 beds in nursing home–type unit) **A**1 2 3 5 7 9 10 **F**3 5 7 8 11 12 13 15 17 18 19 20 22 24 26 28 29 30 31 32 34 35 36 37 39 40 41 42 43 44 45 46 47 49 50 54 55 56 57 58 59 60 61 63 64 66 68 70 72 74 75 76 77 78 79 80 81 82 83 84 85 86 87 88 89 90 92 93 95 96 97 98 99 100 101 102 103 104 107 108 110 111 114 115 117 118 119 120 121 123 124 126 128 129 130 131 132 134 135 144 145 146 147 148 **P**8
**S** Carolinas Healthcare System, Charlotte, NC
Primary Contact: Mickey Foster, President
COO: Terry Akin, President and Chief Operating Officer
CFO: Jeffrey Jones, Chief Financial Officer
CMO: William Bowman, M.D., Vice President Medical Affairs
CIO: Steve Horsley, Vice President and Chief Information Officer
CHR: Noel F. Burt, Ph.D., Chief Human Resources Officer
CNO: Theresa M. Brodrick, R.N., Executive Vice President and Chief Nursing Officer
Web address: www.conehealth.com/locations/moses-cone-hospital/
**Control:** Other not–for–profit (including NFP Corporation) **Service:** General Medical and Surgical

**Staffed Beds:** 1007 **Admissions:** 44256 **Census:** 647 **Outpatient Visits:** 804872 **Births:** 6026 **Total Expense ($000):** 1083049 **Payroll Expense ($000):** 380369 **Personnel:** 7916

✠ **SELECT SPECIALTY HOSPITAL–GREENSBORO (342020)**, 1200 North Elm Street, 5th Floor, Zip 27401–1004; tel. 336/832–8571, (Nonreporting) **A**1 10 **S** Select Medical Corporation, Mechanicsburg, PA
Primary Contact: Deana Knight, Chief Executive Officer
CHR: Karen Tracey, Chief Human Resources
CNO: Robin Clark, Chief Nursing Officer
Web address: www.selectspecialtyhospitals.com/company/locations/greensboro.aspx
**Control:** Corporation, Investor–owned, for–profit **Service:** Long–Term Acute Care hospital

**Staffed Beds:** 30

## GREENVILLE—Pitt County

**PITT COUNTY MEMORIAL HOSPITAL** See Vidant Medical Center

✠ △ **VIDANT MEDICAL CENTER (340040)**, 2100 Stantonsburg Road, Zip 27834–2818, Mailing Address: P.O. Box 6028, Zip 27835–6028; tel. 252/847–4100, (Includes JAMES AND CONNIE MAYNARD CHILDREN'S HOSPITAL, 2101 Stantonsburg Road, Zip 27834–2817; tel. 252/847–5712; UNIVERSITY HEALTH SYSTEMS CHILDREN'S HOSPITAL, 2100 Stantonsburg Road, Mailing Address: PO Box 6028, Zip 27835–6028; tel. 252/847–4100) **A**1 2 3 5 7 8 9 10 **F**3 7 12 13 14 17 18 19 20 21 22 23 24 25 26 27 28 29 30 31 34 35 38 40 41 42 43 44 45 46 47 48 49 50 51 52 55 56 57 58 59 60 61 64 65 68 70 72 73 74 75 76 77 78 79 80 81 82 83 84 85 86 87 88 89 90 92 93 94 95 96 97 98 100 101 102 103 104 107 108 111 114 115 116 117 118 119 124 126 129 130 131 132 134 135 138 139 143 145 146 147 148 **P**6 **S** Vidant Health, Greenville, NC
Primary Contact: Brian Floyd, President Emeritus
CFO: David S. Hughes, Chief Financial Officer
CMO: Paul Shackelford, M.D., Chief Medical Officer
CIO: Donnette Herring, Chief Information Officer
CHR: Tyree Walker, Chief Human Resources Officer
CNO: Linda D. Hofler, Ph.D., Senior Vice President, Nurse Executive
Web address: www.https://www.vidanthealth.com/
**Control:** Other not–for–profit (including NFP Corporation) **Service:** General Medical and Surgical

**Staffed Beds:** 909 **Admissions:** 38685 **Census:** 703 **Outpatient Visits:** 293659 **Births:** 3552 **Total Expense ($000):** 999890 **Payroll Expense ($000):** 356178 **Personnel:** 6269

**WALTER B. JONES ALCOHOL AND DRUG ABUSE TREATMENT CENTER (344024)**, 2577 West Fifth Street, Zip 27834–7813; tel. 252/830–3426, (Nonreporting) **A**10
Primary Contact: Ben Gregory, Director
CFO: Jo Ann Whitfield, Business Officer
CMO: Sonya Longest, M.D., Clinical Director
CNO: Cecelia Karas, Director of Nursing
Web address: www.ncdhhs.gov
**Control:** State–Government, nonfederal **Service:** Alcoholism and other chemical dependency

**Staffed Beds:** 80

## HAMLET—Richmond County

✠ **SANDHILLS REGIONAL MEDICAL CENTER (340106)**, 1000 West Hamlet Avenue, Zip 28345–4522, Mailing Address: P.O. Box 1109, Zip 28345–1109; tel. 910/205–8000 **A**1 9 10 **F**3 8 15 18 29 34 35 40 45 49 57 59 64 68 70 75 79 81 82 87 98 102 103 106 107 108 111 114 118 119 130 135 146 **P**6 **S** Community Health Systems, Inc., Franklin, TN
Primary Contact: David Clay, Chief Executive Officer
CFO: Patrick Sloan, Chief Financial Officer
CMO: Charlita Mangrum, M.D., Chief of Staff
CIO: Regina Yingling, Supervisor
CHR: Della Connor, Director Human Resource
CNO: Brenda Ewing, Chief Nursing Officer
Web address: www.sandhillsregional.com
**Control:** Corporation, Investor–owned, for–profit **Service:** General Medical and Surgical

**Staffed Beds:** 64 **Admissions:** 1994 **Census:** 24 **Outpatient Visits:** 13794 **Births:** 0 **Total Expense ($000):** 26009 **Payroll Expense ($000):** 8141 **Personnel:** 157

---

**Hospital, Medicare Provider Number, Address, Telephone, Approval, Facility, and Physician Codes, Health Care System**

★ American Hospital Association (AHA) membership   ○ Healthcare Facilities Accreditation Program   ⇑ Center for Improvement in Healthcare Quality Accreditation
☐ The Joint Commission accreditation   ◇ DNV Healthcare Inc. accreditation   △ Commission on Accreditation of Rehabilitation Facilities (CARF) accreditation

**NC**

## HENDERSON—Vance County

✠ △ **MARIA PARHAM MEDICAL CENTER (340132)**, 566 Ruin Creek Road, Zip 27536–2927; tel. 252/438–4143 **A**1 2 3 7 9 10 **F**3 11 13 15 18 20 28 29 30 31 34 35 39 40 44 45 46 48 49 50 54 57 59 60 62 64 68 70 74 75 76 77 78 79 80 81 82 85 86 87 90 91 92 93 94 96 97 107 108 110 111 114 118 119 120 121 123 129 130 131 132 135 146 147 148 **P**6 **S** Duke LifePoint Healthcare, Brentwood, TN
Primary Contact: Brian Sinotte, Chief Executive Officer
COO: Tim Harclerode, Chief Operating Officer
CFO: Jim Chatman, Chief Financial Officer
CIO: Randy Williams, Director Management Information Systems
CHR: Tonya A. Jones, Vice President Human Resources
Web address: www.mariaparham.com
**Control:** Partnership, Investor–owned, for–profit **Service:** General Medical and Surgical

**Staffed Beds:** 102 **Admissions:** 5118 **Census:** 63 **Outpatient Visits:** 129766 **Births:** 626 **Total Expense ($000):** 86478 **Payroll Expense ($000):** 29853 **Personnel:** 864

## HENDERSONVILLE—Henderson County

★ ◇ **MARGARET R. PARDEE MEMORIAL HOSPITAL (340017)**, 800 North Justice Street, Zip 28791–3410; tel. 828/696–1000 **A**2 3 9 10 21 **F**3 4 5 11 13 15 18 22 28 29 30 31 34 35 36 38 39 40 44 45 46 47 48 49 50 56 57 58 59 62 63 65 68 69 70 74 75 76 77 78 79 81 82 85 86 87 89 93 94 97 98 100 101 102 103 104 107 108 110 111 114 115 118 119 121 123 129 130 131 132 135 143 144 146 147 148 **P**6 **S** UNC Health Care, Chapel Hill, NC
Primary Contact: James M. Kirby, II, President and Chief Executive Officer
CFO: Alan House, Chief Financial Officer
CMO: Robert Kiskaddon, M.D., Chief Medical Officer
CHR: Hope Reynolds, Executive Director Human Resources and Support Services
CNO: Denise Lucas, R.N., Vice President Clinical Services and Chief Nursing Officer
Web address: www.pardeehospital.org
**Control:** County–Government, nonfederal **Service:** General Medical and Surgical

**Staffed Beds:** 138 **Admissions:** 6801 **Census:** 73 **Outpatient Visits:** 231215 **Births:** 298 **Total Expense ($000):** 152704 **Payroll Expense ($000):** 58542 **Personnel:** 994

✠ ○ **PARK RIDGE HEALTH (340023)**, 100 Hospital Drive, Zip 28792–5272; tel. 828/684–8501 **A**1 2 9 10 11 19 **F**3 11 13 15 18 28 29 30 31 32 34 35 40 43 45 46 47 48 49 50 56 57 59 62 65 68 70 71 74 75 76 77 78 79 80 81 82 85 87 93 94 97 98 101 102 103 104 105 107 108 110 111 114 115 119 129 130 131 132 135 142 146 147 148 **P**6 **S** Adventist Health System Sunbelt Health Care Corporation, Altamonte Springs, FL
Primary Contact: Jimm Bunch, President and Chief Executive Officer
CFO: Wendi Barber, Vice President Finance and Chief Financial Officer
CMO: Carlo Mainardi, M.D., Vice President Medical Affairs and Chief Medical Officer
CIO: Lee Strickland, Regional Director Information Technology
CNO: Craig Lindsey, R.N., Vice President Clinical Services/Chief Nursing Officer
Web address: www.parkridgehealth.org
**Control:** Other not–for–profit (including NFP Corporation) **Service:** General Medical and Surgical

**Staffed Beds:** 95 **Admissions:** 4160 **Census:** 53 **Outpatient Visits:** 539094 **Births:** 563 **Total Expense ($000):** 149469 **Payroll Expense ($000):** 62770 **Personnel:** 1141

## HICKORY—Catawba County

✠ △ **CATAWBA VALLEY MEDICAL CENTER (340143)**, 810 Fairgrove Church Road S.E., Zip 28602–9643; tel. 828/326–3000 **A**1 2 5 7 9 10 **F**3 5 11 12 13 15 18 20 22 26 28 29 30 31 33 34 35 39 40 44 45 49 50 54 56 57 58 59 61 64 65 68 70 71 73 74 75 76 77 78 79 81 84 85 86 87 89 90 91 92 93 96 97 98 100 101 102 103 104 107 108 109 110 111 114 115 117 118 119 120 121 122 123 124 126 129 130 131 132 135 143 144 145 146 147 148
Primary Contact: J. Anthony Rose, President and Chief Executive Officer
COO: Edward L. Beard, R.N., Chief Operating Officer and Chief Nursing Officer
CFO: David J. Boone, Senior Vice President, Finance
CIO: Jerry Reardon, Director Information Systems
CHR: Phyllis Johnston, Vice President
CNO: Edward L. Beard, R.N., Chief Operating Officer and Chief Nursing Officer
Web address: www.catawbavalleymc.org
**Control:** County–Government, nonfederal **Service:** General Medical and Surgical

**Staffed Beds:** 239 **Admissions:** 9916 **Census:** 129 **Outpatient Visits:** 202709 **Births:** 1933 **Total Expense ($000):** 208345 **Payroll Expense ($000):** 87958 **Personnel:** 1339

✠ **FRYE REGIONAL MEDICAL CENTER (340116)**, 420 North Center Street, Zip 28601–5049; tel. 828/322–6070, (Includes FRYE REGIONAL MEDICAL CENTER–SOUTH CAMPUS, One Third Avenue N.W., Zip 28601, Mailing Address: P.O. Box 369, Zip 28603; tel. 704/315–5777) **A**1 2 9 10 **F**3 11 12 13 15 17 18 20 22 24 26 28 29 30 31 34 35 37 40 44 45 46 49 54 57 59 64 70 72 74 75 76 77 78 79 81 82 85 86 87 89 90 93 96 98 101 103 107 108 110 111 114 115 118 119 126 128 130 131 132 144 146 147 148 **P**6 **S** TENET Healthcare Corporation, Dallas, TX
Primary Contact: Philip Shaw, Interim Chief Executive Officer
COO: Rich Ellis, Chief Operating Officer
CMO: Frank C. Smeeks, M.D., Chief Medical Officer
CHR: Liz Elich, Vice President Human Resources
Web address: www.fryemedctr.com
**Control:** Corporation, Investor–owned, for–profit **Service:** General Medical and Surgical

**Staffed Beds:** 279 **Admissions:** 10762 **Census:** 160 **Outpatient Visits:** 133347 **Births:** 392 **Personnel:** 1185

## HIGH POINT—Guilford County

✠ △ **HIGH POINT REGIONAL HEALTH SYSTEM (340004)**, 601 North Elm Street, Zip 27262–4398, Mailing Address: P.O. Box HP–5, Zip 27261–1899; tel. 336/878–6000, (Data for 273 days) **A**1 2 7 9 10 **F**3 4 5 7 8 11 12 13 15 17 18 20 22 24 26 28 29 30 31 34 35 38 39 40 44 45 47 48 49 50 51 52 53 54 55 57 58 59 60 61 62 64 66 68 70 71 73 74 75 76 77 78 79 80 81 82 84 85 86 87 90 91 92 93 96 97 98 100 101 102 103 104 105 107 108 110 111 114 115 116 117 118 119 120 121 123 124 126 129 130 131 132 135 144 145 146 147 148 **P**6 **S** UNC Health Care, Chapel Hill, NC
Primary Contact: Ernest L. Bovio, Jr., Chief Executive Officer
COO: Gregory W. Taylor, M.D., Vice President and Chief Operating Officer
CFO: Kimberly Crews, Vice President Finance and Chief Financial Officer
CMO: L. Dale Williams, M.D., Vice President and Chief Medical Director
CIO: Nancy Waters, Interim Chief Information Officer
CHR: Katherine Burns, Vice President Human Resources
CNO: Tammi Erving–Mengel, Vice President, Chief Nursing Officer
Web address: www.highpointregional.com
**Control:** Other not–for–profit (including NFP Corporation) **Service:** General Medical and Surgical

**Staffed Beds:** 335 **Admissions:** 12050 **Census:** 195 **Outpatient Visits:** 205597 **Births:** 1087 **Total Expense ($000):** 172781 **Payroll Expense ($000):** 63267 **Personnel:** 1687

## HIGHLANDS—Macon County

✠ **HIGHLANDS–CASHIERS HOSPITAL (341316)**, 190 Hospital Drive, Zip 28741–7600, Mailing Address: P.O. Drawer 190, Zip 28741–0190; tel. 828/526–1200, (Total facility includes 80 beds in nursing home–type unit) **A**1 9 10 18 **F**3 11 15 28 29 30 34 35 40 45 46 47 48 53 56 57 59 64 65 74 75 77 79 81 91 97 107 108 110 111 113 119 128 130 133 146 **S** Mission Health System, Asheville, NC
Primary Contact: Jackie Ring, President and Chief Nursing Officer
COO: Frank Leslie, Vice President Operations
CFO: Michael E. Daiken, Chief Financial Officer
CHR: Teresa Malloonee, Director Human Resources
CNO: Kathy Crist, Director of Patient Care Services
Web address: www.hchospital.org
**Control:** Other not–for–profit (including NFP Corporation) **Service:** General Medical and Surgical

**Staffed Beds:** 104 **Admissions:** 468 **Census:** 66 **Outpatient Visits:** 29604 **Births:** 0 **Total Expense ($000):** 21417 **Payroll Expense ($000):** 9519 **Personnel:** 241

## HUNTERSVILLE—Mecklenburg County

✠ **NOVANT HEALTH HUNTERSVILLE MEDICAL CENTER (340183)**, 10030 Gilead Road, Zip 28078–7545, Mailing Address: P.O. Box 3508, Zip 28070–3508; tel. 704/316–4000 **A**1 2 9 10 13 **F**8 11 12 13 15 18 26 28 29 30 31 34 35 40 45 50 53 55 56 57 59 64 67 68 70 74 75 76 77 78 79 81 82 85 86 87 88 89 93 96 100 102 107 108 110 111 114 115 118 119 120 126 129 130 132 135 146 147 **S** Novant Health, Winston Salem, NC
Primary Contact: Mike Riley, President
CFO: Jason Yanni, Senior Financial Analyst
CMO: David Cook, M.D., Chief Medical Officer
CIO: Richard B. McKnight, Senior Vice President and Chief Information Officer
CHR: Tracy Craig, Director Human Resources
Web address: www.novanthealth.org
**Control:** Other not–for–profit (including NFP Corporation) **Service:** General Medical and Surgical

**Staffed Beds:** 78 **Admissions:** 6581 **Census:** 67 **Outpatient Visits:** 127085 **Births:** 1189 **Total Expense ($000):** 112777 **Payroll Expense ($000):** 34948 **Personnel:** 832

**NC**

*Many Facility Codes have changed. Please refer to the AHA Guide Code Chart.* © 2015 AHA Guide

## JACKSONVILLE—Onslow County

☐ **BRYNN MARR HOSPITAL (344016)**, 192 Village Drive, Zip 28546–7299; tel. 910/577–1400, (Nonreporting) **A**1 10 **S** Universal Health Services, Inc., King of Prussia, PA
Primary Contact: Jay Kortemeyer, Chief Executive Officer
CFO: David Warmerdam, Chief Financial Officer
CMO: Ashraf Mikhail, M.D., Medical Director
CIO: Amy Black, Risk Manager/PI Director
CHR: Jennifer Gier, Director Human Resources
CNO: Sheila Maraan, Director of Nursing
Web address: www.brynnmarr.org
**Control:** Corporation, Investor–owned, for–profit **Service:** Psychiatric

| **Staffed Beds:** 99 |
| --- |

✠ **ONSLOW MEMORIAL HOSPITAL (340042)**, 317 Western Boulevard, Zip 28546–6379, Mailing Address: P.O. Box 1358, Zip 28541–1358; tel. 910/577–2345 **A**1 2 9 10 20 **F**3 8 11 13 15 19 20 28 29 34 35 40 45 46 47 48 49 54 57 59 60 64 68 70 72 73 75 77 79 81 82 84 85 86 87 89 93 96 107 108 110 111 117 118 119 126 129 131 132 135 146 147 148 **P**8
Primary Contact: Ed Piper, Ph.D., President and Chief Executive Officer
CFO: Roy Smith, Chief Financial Officer
CMO: Elizabeth D'Angelo, M.D., Chief of Staff
CIO: Christina Feak, Chief Information Officer
CHR: Sue Kegley, Director Human Resources
CNO: Crystal Hayden, MSN, Chief Nursing Officer
Web address: www.onslow.org
**Control:** Hospital district or authority, Government, nonfederal **Service:** General Medical and Surgical

| **Staffed Beds:** 125 **Admissions:** 7220 **Census:** 81 **Outpatient Visits:** 139857 **Births:** 1904 **Total Expense ($000):** 133690 **Payroll Expense ($000):** 50984 **Personnel:** 922 |
| --- |

## JEFFERSON—Ashe County

✠ **ASHE MEMORIAL HOSPITAL (341325)**, 200 Hospital Avenue, Zip 28640–9244; tel. 336/846–7101 **A**1 9 10 18 **F**3 11 13 15 28 30 34 35 40 45 48 53 57 59 64 75 76 79 80 81 85 86 89 93 102 107 108 110 111 114 118 119 127 130 132 133 135 141 142 146 147 **S** Novant Health, Winston Salem, NC
Primary Contact: Laura Lambeth, Chief Executive Officer
COO: Joe Thore, Chief Operating Officer
CFO: Charles Wright, Chief Financial Officer
CMO: David Factor, M.D., Chief of Staff
CIO: William Baldwin, Chief Information Officer
CHR: Sherry Cox, Chief Human Resources Officer
CNO: Sara Houser, Chief Nursing Officer
Web address: www.ashememorial.org
**Control:** Other not–for–profit (including NFP Corporation) **Service:** General Medical and Surgical

| **Staffed Beds:** 25 **Admissions:** 1401 **Census:** 14 **Outpatient Visits:** 51179 **Births:** 113 **Total Expense ($000):** 26026 **Payroll Expense ($000):** 11791 **Personnel:** 256 |
| --- |

## KENANSVILLE—Duplin County

✠ **VIDANT DUPLIN HOSPITAL (340120)**, 401 North Main Street, Zip 28349–8801, Mailing Address: P.O. Box 278, Zip 28349–0278; tel. 910/296–0941 **A**1 9 10 **F**3 11 13 15 18 19 29 30 34 35 39 40 45 56 57 59 68 70 75 76 77 79 81 91 93 99 101 102 103 107 108 110 111 115 119 129 130 131 135 146 147 **S** Vidant Health, Greenville, NC
Primary Contact: Jay Briley, President
CFO: Lucinda Crawford, Vice President Financial Services
CMO: Danny Pate, M.D., Chief Medical Staff
CIO: Lucinda Crawford, Vice President Financial Services
CHR: Pansy Chase, Director Human Resources
CNO: Sue O. Taylor, Vice President Nursing
Web address: www.vidanthealth.com
**Control:** Other not–for–profit (including NFP Corporation) **Service:** General Medical and Surgical

| **Staffed Beds:** 48 **Admissions:** 3234 **Census:** 43 **Outpatient Visits:** 43252 **Births:** 470 **Total Expense ($000):** 43072 **Payroll Expense ($000):** 17368 **Personnel:** 395 |
| --- |

## KINGS MOUNTAIN—Cleveland County

**CAROLINAS CONTINUECARE HOSPITAL AT KINGS MOUNTAIN (342019)**, 706 West King Street, 2nd Floor, Zip 28086–2708, Mailing Address: P.O. Box 159, Zip 28086–0159; tel. 980/487–5520, (Nonreporting) **S** Community Hospital Corporation, Plano, TX
Primary Contact: Denise R. Murray, Chief Executive Officer
Web address: www.continuecare.org/kings–mountain/
**Control:** Other not–for–profit (including NFP Corporation) **Service:** Long–Term Acute Care hospital

| **Staffed Beds:** 28 |
| --- |

✠ **KINGS MOUNTAIN HOSPITAL (340037)**, 706 West King Street, Zip 28086–2708; tel. 980/487–5000 **A**1 9 10 **F**3 4 15 29 30 34 40 45 49 59 70 79 81 82 85 93 98 107 110 111 115 119 130 133 146 148 **S** Carolinas Healthcare System, Charlotte, NC
Primary Contact: Brian Gwyn, President and Chief Executive Officer
COO: Sheri Deshazo, Chief Operating Officer
CFO: Terry Edwards, Controller
CHR: Debra Kale, Director Human Resources
Web address: www.clevelandregional.org/kings–mountain–hospital.html
**Control:** Hospital district or authority, Government, nonfederal **Service:** General Medical and Surgical

| **Staffed Beds:** 59 **Admissions:** 2612 **Census:** 33 **Outpatient Visits:** 50551 **Births:** 0 **Total Expense ($000):** 34693 **Payroll Expense ($000):** 14239 **Personnel:** 263 |
| --- |

## KINSTON—Lenoir County

☐ **LENOIR MEMORIAL HOSPITAL (340027)**, 100 Airport Road, Zip 28501–1634, Mailing Address: P.O. Box 1678, Zip 28503–1678; tel. 252/522–7000 **A**1 9 10 **F**3 8 11 13 18 20 22 28 29 30 31 34 35 38 40 43 45 47 48 49 50 53 56 57 59 60 61 64 65 68 70 75 76 77 78 79 81 82 85 86 87 89 90 93 102 107 108 111 114 115 118 119 120 121 129 130 132 134 135 143 145 146 148
Primary Contact: Gary E. Black, President and Chief Executive Officer
CFO: Sarah Mayo, Vice President Financial and Information Services
CMO: Alan Kirollos, M.D., President Medical Staff
CIO: Karl Vanderstouw, Vice President Management Information Systems
CHR: Jim Dobbins, Vice President Human Resources
CNO: Laurel Molloy, Vice President Nursing Services
Web address: www.lenoirmemorial.org
**Control:** Other not–for–profit (including NFP Corporation) **Service:** General Medical and Surgical

| **Staffed Beds:** 155 **Admissions:** 5194 **Census:** 74 **Outpatient Visits:** 84242 **Births:** 436 **Total Expense ($000):** 98292 **Payroll Expense ($000):** 42573 **Personnel:** 802 |
| --- |

## LAURINBURG—Scotland County

✠ **SCOTLAND HEALTH CARE SYSTEM (340008)**, 500 Lauchwood Drive, Zip 28352–5599; tel. 910/291–7000 **A**1 2 3 9 10 **F**3 11 13 15 18 28 29 31 34 37 40 45 54 57 59 64 66 70 71 73 74 75 76 77 78 79 81 85 86 87 89 90 92 93 96 97 107 110 111 114 115 119 120 121 123 127 130 132 135 143 144 145 146 147 148 **S** Carolinas Healthcare System, Charlotte, NC
Primary Contact: Gregory C. Wood, President and Chief Executive Officer
CFO: Matthew Pracht, Vice President Finance
CMO: Cheryl Davis, M.D., Chief Medical Officer
CIO: Gary Liuzzo, Director Information Systems
CHR: Ann Locklear, Vice President, Human Resources
CNO: Camille Utter, R.N., Chief Nursing Officer
Web address: www.scotlandhealth.org
**Control:** Other not–for–profit (including NFP Corporation) **Service:** General Medical and Surgical

| **Staffed Beds:** 102 **Admissions:** 5014 **Census:** 53 **Outpatient Visits:** 206515 **Births:** 685 **Total Expense ($000):** 102764 **Payroll Expense ($000):** 36175 **Personnel:** 735 |
| --- |

## LELAND—Brunswick County

☐ **STRATEGIC BEHAVIORAL HEALTH – WILMINGTON (344030)**, 2050 Mercantile Drive, Zip 28451–4053; tel. 910/371–2500, (Nonreporting) **A**1 10 **S** Strategic Behavioral Health, LLC, Memphis, TN
Primary Contact: Daniel Kern, Chief Executive Officer
CHR: Kelly Pace, Director Human Resource
CNO: Brooke Cook, Director of Nursing
Web address: www.sbcwilmington.com/
**Control:** Investor–owned, for–profit **Service:** Children's hospital psychiatric

| **Staffed Beds:** 92 |
| --- |

---

**Hospital, Medicare Provider Number, Address, Telephone, Approval, Facility, and Physician Codes, Health Care System**

★ American Hospital Association (AHA) membership    ◯ Healthcare Facilities Accreditation Program    ⇑ Center for Improvement in Healthcare Quality Accreditation
☐ The Joint Commission accreditation    ◇ DNV Healthcare Inc. accreditation    △ Commission on Accreditation of Rehabilitation Facilities (CARF) accreditation

**NC**

## LENOIR—Caldwell County

✠ **CALDWELL MEMORIAL HOSPITAL (340041)**, 321 Mulberry Street S.W., Zip 28645–5720, Mailing Address: P.O. Box 1890, Zip 28645–1890; tel. 828/757–5100 **A**1 2 9 10 **F**3 8 11 13 15 18 20 22 29 31 34 35 37 40 45 46 48 49 50 53 54 55 57 59 64 65 70 75 76 77 78 79 81 82 85 86 87 93 97 107 108 109 110 111 114 115 120 121 122 123 129 132 135 144 145 146 147 148 **P**6 **S** UNC Health Care, Chapel Hill, NC
Primary Contact: Laura J. Easton, R.N., President and Chief Executive Officer
COO: Rebecca Smith, Chief Operating Officer and Vice President
CFO: Stephen Rinaldi, Vice President Finance and Chief Financial Officer
CMO: David Masters, M.D., Chief of Staff
CIO: Daniel Thelen, Director Information Systems
CHR: Rebecca Smith, Vice President and Chief Operating Officer
Web address: www.caldwellmemorial.org
**Control:** Other not–for–profit (including NFP Corporation) **Service:** General Medical and Surgical

**Staffed Beds:** 76 **Admissions:** 3373 **Census:** 48 **Outpatient Visits:** 81436 **Births:** 424 **Total Expense ($000):** 110054 **Payroll Expense ($000):** 43577 **Personnel:** 901

## LEXINGTON—Davidson County

**LEXINGTON MEMORIAL HOSPITAL** See Wake Forest Baptist Health–Lexington Medical Center

✠ **WAKE FOREST BAPTIST HEALTH–LEXINGTON MEDICAL CENTER (340096)**, 250 Hospital Drive, Zip 27292–6728, Mailing Address: P.O. Box 1817, Zip 27293–1817; tel. 336/248–5161 **A**1 3 9 10 **F**3 13 15 18 28 29 30 31 34 35 40 45 46 50 57 59 61 64 65 70 74 75 76 78 79 80 81 82 85 87 89 91 92 93 97 102 107 108 110 111 115 119 121 123 129 130 131 146 147 148 **P**6 **S** Wake Forest Baptist Health, Winston–Salem, NC
Primary Contact: William B. James, FACHE, Chief Executive Officer
CFO: Danny Squires, Vice President and Chief Financial Officer
CMO: Gordon Kammire, M.D., Chief of Staff
CIO: Kevin Buchanan, Chief Information Officer
Web address: www.lexingtonmemorial.com
**Control:** Other not–for–profit (including NFP Corporation) **Service:** General Medical and Surgical

**Staffed Beds:** 76 **Admissions:** 3300 **Census:** 27 **Outpatient Visits:** 109319 **Births:** 639 **Total Expense ($000):** 61198 **Payroll Expense ($000):** 24610 **Personnel:** 563

## LINCOLNTON—Lincoln County

✠ **CAROLINAS HEALTHCARE SYSTEM LINCOLN (340145)**, 433 McAlister Road, Zip 28092–4147, Mailing Address: PO Box 677, Zip 28093–0677; tel. 980/212–2000 **A**1 9 10 **F**3 8 11 13 15 18 28 29 30 31 34 40 44 45 50 51 57 59 64 68 70 73 74 75 76 77 78 79 81 82 84 85 87 91 93 94 96 107 108 111 114 115 118 119 129 130 131 132 135 146 148 **S** Carolinas Healthcare System, Charlotte, NC
Primary Contact: Peter W. Acker, President and Chief Executive Officer
COO: Teresa C. Watson, Vice President Administration
CFO: Jarrett L. Morris, Controller
CMO: Vineet Goel, Chief Medical Officer
CIO: Jarrett L. Morris, Controller and Chief Information Officer
CHR: Lesley Chambless, Assistant Vice President Human Resources
CNO: Elaine S. Haynes, R.N., Vice President Patient Services and Chief Nursing Executive
Web address: www.carolinashealthcare.org/lincoln
**Control:** Hospital district or authority, Government, nonfederal **Service:** General Medical and Surgical

**Staffed Beds:** 101 **Admissions:** 4469 **Census:** 47 **Outpatient Visits:** 94916 **Births:** 460 **Total Expense ($000):** 93414 **Payroll Expense ($000):** 30243 **Personnel:** 513

## LINVILLE—Avery County

✠ **CHARLES A. CANNON MEMORIAL HOSPITAL (341323)**, 434 Hospital Drive, Zip 28646, Mailing Address: P.O. Box 767, Zip 28646–0767; tel. 828/737–7000 **A**1 9 10 18 **F**3 11 13 15 18 28 29 30 31 38 40 64 68 70 76 77 81 85 91 93 98 100 102 104 107 110 115 119 130 133 135 146 **S** Appalachian Regional Healthcare System, Boone, NC
Primary Contact: Carmen Lacey, MSN, R.N., President
CFO: Kevin B. May, System Director Finance
CMO: Thomas M. Haizlip, Jr., M.D., Chief of Staff
CIO: Nathan White, Chief Information Officer
CHR: Amy Crabbe, Vice President People Services
CNO: Carmen Lacey, MSN, President and Director of Patient Care Services
Web address: www.https://locations/cannon–memorial–hospital
**Control:** Other not–for–profit (including NFP Corporation) **Service:** General Medical and Surgical

**Staffed Beds:** 35 **Admissions:** 1838 **Census:** 20 **Outpatient Visits:** 25625 **Births:** 93 **Total Expense ($000):** 23348 **Payroll Expense ($000):** 9510 **Personnel:** 181

## LOUISBURG—Franklin County

✠ **NOVANT HEALTH FRANKLIN MEDICAL CENTER (340036)**, 100 Hospital Drive, Zip 27549–2256, Mailing Address: P.O. Box 609, Zip 27549–0609; tel. 919/497–8401 **A**1 9 10 **F**3 11 12 15 18 30 34 40 44 45 50 56 57 59 67 70 74 75 79 80 81 82 85 86 90 98 103 107 108 110 111 114 118 119 128 129 130 146 **S** Novant Health, Winston Salem, NC
Primary Contact: Jody Morris, President and Chief Operating Officer
CIO: Mark Elliott, Manager Information Systems
CHR: Joanna Holder, Director Human Resources
CNO: Lilly Wing, Chief Nursing Officer
Web address: www.https://www.novanthealth.org/franklin–medical–center.aspx
**Control:** Other not–for–profit (including NFP Corporation) **Service:** General Medical and Surgical

**Staffed Beds:** 17 **Admissions:** 1089 **Census:** 15 **Outpatient Visits:** 35790 **Births:** 0 **Total Expense ($000):** 29555 **Payroll Expense ($000):** 11539 **Personnel:** 145

## LUMBERTON—Robeson County

✠ **SOUTHEASTERN HEALTH (340050)**, 300 West 27th Street, Zip 28358–3075, Mailing Address: P.O. Box 1408, Zip 28359–1408; tel. 910/671–5000, (Total facility includes 115 beds in nursing home–type unit) **A**1 2 9 10 12 13 **F**3 5 7 8 9 12 13 15 17 18 20 22 24 28 29 30 31 34 35 37 40 45 48 49 50 53 54 57 59 60 61 62 63 64 67 68 70 71 72 73 74 75 76 77 78 79 80 81 82 83 84 85 87 89 92 93 98 102 103 107 108 111 112 113 114 115 116 118 119 120 121 126 127 128 129 130 131 132 135 143 144 146 147 148 **P**6
Primary Contact: Joann Anderson, President and Chief Executive Officer
CFO: C. Thomas Johnson, III, Vice President Finance and Chief Financial Officer
CMO: Barry Williamson, President Medical Staff
CIO: Eric Harper, Chief Information Officer
CHR: Susan Hayes, Director Human Resources
CNO: Renae Taylor, Chief Nursing Officer
Web address: www.srmc.org
**Control:** Other not–for–profit (including NFP Corporation) **Service:** General Medical and Surgical

**Staffed Beds:** 356 **Admissions:** 15057 **Census:** 295 **Outpatient Visits:** 488291 **Births:** 1456

## MARION—Mcdowell County

✠ **MCDOWELL HOSPITAL (340087)**, 430 Rankin Drive, Zip 28752–6568, Mailing Address: P.O. Box 730, Zip 28752–0730; tel. 828/659–5000 **A**1 9 10 **F**3 13 15 28 29 30 31 34 35 39 40 45 54 57 59 64 65 70 76 77 78 79 81 82 85 90 91 93 97 107 108 110 111 114 119 127 129 130 131 132 133 135 144 146 147 148 **S** Mission Health System, Asheville, NC
Primary Contact: Carol C. Wolfenbarger, R.N., MSN, FACHE, President and Chief Executive Officer
CFO: Clint Stewart, Regional Director of Finance East
CMO: Rex Henderson, M.D., Chief of Staff
CIO: Pam Belvins, Director Information Technology Member Hospitals Mission
CHR: Susan Parille, Director Human Resources Affiliate Mission Health System
CNO: Kathy Hefner, Chief Nursing Officer
Web address: www.mcdhospital.org
**Control:** Other not–for–profit (including NFP Corporation) **Service:** General Medical and Surgical

**Staffed Beds:** 49 **Admissions:** 2169 **Census:** 20 **Outpatient Visits:** 117239 **Births:** 204 **Total Expense ($000):** 50766 **Payroll Expense ($000):** 15617 **Personnel:** 367

## MATTHEWS—Mecklenburg County

✠ **NOVANT HEALTH MATTHEWS MEDICAL CENTER (340171)**, 1500 Matthews Township Parkway, Zip 28105–4656, Mailing Address: P.O. Box 3310, Zip 28106–3310; tel. 704/384–6500 **A**1 2 9 10 **F**3 11 12 13 15 18 20 22 29 30 31 34 35 36 40 45 49 56 57 59 64 67 68 70 73 75 76 77 78 79 81 82 84 85 86 87 92 93 107 108 110 111 114 115 118 119 126 129 130 132 145 146 147 148 **S** Novant Health, Winston Salem, NC
Primary Contact: Roland R. Bibeau, FACHE, President
COO: Amy Vance, Executive Vice President and Chief Operating Officer
CFO: Greg Klein, Senior Director Finance
CMO: Thomas Zweng, M.D., Senior Vice President Medical Affairs
CIO: David B. Garrett, Chief Information Officer
CHR: Susan Kennedy, Manager Human Resources
Web address: www.presbyterian.org
**Control:** Other not–for–profit (including NFP Corporation) **Service:** General Medical and Surgical

**Staffed Beds:** 102 **Admissions:** 9395 **Census:** 99 **Outpatient Visits:** 180127 **Births:** 2087 **Total Expense ($000):** 141314 **Payroll Expense ($000):** 45947 **Personnel:** 1033

NC

*Many Facility Codes have changed. Please refer to the AHA Guide Code Chart.* © 2015 AHA Guide

## MOCKSVILLE—Davie County

★ **WAKE FOREST BAPTIST HEALTH–DAVIE MEDICAL CENTER (341313)**, 223 Hospital Street, Zip 27028–2038, Mailing Address: 329 NC Highway 801 North, Bermuda Run, Zip 27006; tel. 336/998–1300 **A**9 10 **F**3 15 28 29 30 34 35 40 42 50 57 59 64 77 81 85 93 107 115 119 130 133 146 **S** Wake Forest Baptist Health, Winston–Salem, NC
Primary Contact: Chad J. Brown, M.P.H., President
CFO: Danny Squires, Chief Financial Officer
CMO: Bret Nicks, M.D., Chief Medical Officer and Chief of Staff
CIO: Dee Emon, R.N., Vice President and Chief Information Officer
CHR: Danielle Wright, Director Human Resources
CNO: Susan T. Bachmeier, R.N., Chief Nursing Officer
Web address: www.wakehealth.edu/Davie–Medical–Center
**Control:** Other not–for–profit (including NFP Corporation) **Service:** General Medical and Surgical

**Staffed Beds:** 25 **Admissions:** 157 **Census:** 9 **Outpatient Visits:** 18547 **Births:** 0 **Total Expense ($000):** 21552 **Payroll Expense ($000):** 7466 **Personnel:** 196

## MONROE—Union County

✠ **CAROLINAS HEALTHCARE SYSTEM UNION (340130)**, 600 Hospital Drive, Zip 28112–6000, Mailing Address: P.O. Box 5003, Zip 28111–5003; tel. 980/993–3100, (Total facility includes 70 beds in nursing home–type unit) **A**1 2 3 9 10 **F**3 4 5 8 11 13 18 20 26 28 29 30 31 34 35 39 40 42 45 49 53 56 57 59 64 66 67 70 73 74 75 76 77 78 79 81 82 85 86 87 89 93 107 108 111 114 115 118 119 120 121 123 128 129 130 132 135 146 147 148 **S** Carolinas Healthcare System, Charlotte, NC
Primary Contact: Michael Lutes, President
COO: Dave Anderson, FACHE, Vice President Administration
CFO: John G. Moore, Vice President and Chief Financial Officer
CMO: Craig M. Slater, M.D., Chief Medical Officer
CIO: Lisa Sykes, Director Information Services
CHR: Rhonda McFarland, Director Human Resources
CNO: Denise White, MSN, Chief Nurse Executive
Web address: www.carolinashealthcare.org/union
**Control:** Hospital district or authority, Government, nonfederal **Service:** General Medical and Surgical

**Staffed Beds:** 247 **Admissions:** 8524 **Census:** 148 **Outpatient Visits:** 153319 **Births:** 1093 **Total Expense ($000):** 171492 **Payroll Expense ($000):** 58259 **Personnel:** 1009

## MOORESVILLE—Iredell County

✠ **LAKE NORMAN REGIONAL MEDICAL CENTER (340129)**, 171 Fairview Road, Zip 28117–9500, Mailing Address: P.O. Box 3250, Zip 28117–3250; tel. 704/660–4000, (Nonreporting) **A**1 2 9 10 19 **S** Community Health Systems, Inc., Franklin, TN
Primary Contact: Stephen L. Midkiff, Chief Executive Officer
COO: Matthew Banks, Chief Operating Officer
CFO: Marcus Conley, Chief Financial Officer
CHR: Stephanie Williams, Market Director Human Resources
CNO: Marie Marks, Chief Nursing Officer
Web address: www.lnrmc.com
**Control:** Corporation, Investor–owned, for–profit **Service:** General Medical and Surgical

**Staffed Beds:** 123

## MOREHEAD CITY—Carteret County

✠ **CARTERET HEALTH CARE (340142)**, 3500 Arendell Street, Zip 28557–2901, Mailing Address: P.O. Box 1619, Zip 28557–1619; tel. 252/499–6000 **A**1 2 9 10 **F**3 7 11 12 13 15 18 28 29 30 31 34 35 37 40 45 46 54 57 59 62 63 64 65 68 70 74 75 76 77 78 79 81 82 84 85 86 87 89 91 93 97 107 108 110 111 114 115 118 119 120 121 123 129 130 132 135 143 145 146 148
Primary Contact: Richard A. Brvenik, FACHE, President
CFO: Joanie King, Chief Financial Officer
CIO: Kyle Marek, Manager Information Services
CHR: Elizabeth Beswick, Vice President Human Resources and Public Relations
Web address: www.carterethealth.org
**Control:** County–Government, nonfederal **Service:** General Medical and Surgical

**Staffed Beds:** 104 **Admissions:** 5552 **Census:** 69 **Outpatient Visits:** 136886 **Births:** 768 **Total Expense ($000):** 119674 **Payroll Expense ($000):** 50503 **Personnel:** 910

## MORGANTON—Burke County

✠ **BLUE RIDGE HEALTHCARE HOSPITALS (340075)**, 2201 South Sterling Street, Zip 28655–4058; tel. 828/580–5000, (Includes GRACE HOSPITAL, 2201 South Sterling Street, tel. 828/580–5000; VALDESE GENERAL HOSPITAL, 720 Malcolm Boulevard, Valdese, Zip 28690–2872, Mailing Address: P.O. Box 700, Zip 28690–0700; tel. 828/874–2251) **A**1 2 9 10 12 13 **F**3 13 15 18 20 22 28 29 30 31 34 35 40 44 45 50 53 57 59 60 64 68 69 70 71 72 76 77 78 81 82 86 93 96 97 98 105 107 108 110 111 114 115 119 131 146 147 148 **S** Carolinas Healthcare System, Charlotte, NC
Primary Contact: Kathy C. Bailey, Ph.D., FACHE, President and Chief Executive Officer
CFO: Robert G. Fritts, Chief Financial Officer and Senior Vice President
CMO: Joe Mazzola, D.O., Senior Vice President Medical Affairs and Chief Medical Officer
CHR: Thomas Eure, Vice President Administration
CNO: Susan E. Brown, R.N., Sr. Vice President, Chief Nursing Officer
**Control:** Other not–for–profit (including NFP Corporation) **Service:** General Medical and Surgical

**Staffed Beds:** 149 **Admissions:** 8454 **Census:** 93 **Outpatient Visits:** 161175 **Births:** 875 **Total Expense ($000):** 183350 **Payroll Expense ($000):** 60712 **Personnel:** 1198

☐ **BROUGHTON HOSPITAL (344025)**, 1000 South Sterling Street, Zip 28655–3999; tel. 828/433–2111 **A**1 5 10 **F**3 30 39 53 56 59 65 75 77 86 87 91 92 98 99 100 101 102 103 130 132 135 146
Primary Contact: Vivian Streater, Co–Acting Chief Executive Officer
CFO: Bea Tullis, Chief Financial Officer and Budget Officer
CMO: George Krebs, M.D., Chief Medical Officer
CIO: Darin Kiracofe, Director Information Resource Management
CHR: Jean Buchanan, Director Human Resources
CNO: Vivian Streater, Chief Nursing Officer and Co–Acting Chief Executive Officer
Web address: www.ncdhhs.gov/dsohf/broughton
**Control:** State–Government, nonfederal **Service:** Psychiatric

**Staffed Beds:** 297 **Admissions:** 738 **Census:** 256 **Outpatient Visits:** 0 **Births:** 0 **Total Expense ($000):** 87928 **Payroll Expense ($000):** 53383 **Personnel:** 1208

## MOUNT AIRY—Surry County

✠ **NORTHERN HOSPITAL OF SURRY COUNTY (340003)**, 830 Rockford Street, Zip 27030–5365, Mailing Address: P.O. Box 1101, Zip 27030–1101; tel. 336/719–7000, (Total facility includes 33 beds in nursing home–type unit) **A**1 9 10 **F**1 3 4 13 15 16 17 18 29 30 31 34 35 40 45 50 51 56 57 59 64 65 67 70 72 73 75 76 77 79 80 81 82 85 86 87 88 89 90 98 102 107 108 110 111 114 115 116 118 119 128 129 130 131 132 133 145 146 147 **P**6 **S** QHR, Brentwood, TN
Primary Contact: Ned Hill, President and Chief Executive Officer
COO: Mike Leonard, Vice President Operations and Imaging Director
CFO: Andrea Hickling, Vice President Finance and Chief Finance Officer
CMO: Dennis Clemens, Chief of Staff
CIO: Rodney Bond, Director Information Technology
CHR: Julia Nelson, Vice President Human Resources
CNO: Robin Hodgin, R.N., Vice President Patient Services and Chief Nursing Officer
Web address: www.northernhospital.com
**Control:** Hospital district or authority, Government, nonfederal **Service:** General Medical and Surgical

**Staffed Beds:** 108 **Admissions:** 3703 **Census:** 66 **Outpatient Visits:** 111109 **Births:** 374 **Total Expense ($000):** 78064 **Payroll Expense ($000):** 30795 **Personnel:** 575

## MURPHY—Cherokee County

✠ **MURPHY MEDICAL CENTER (340160)**, 3990 U.S. Highway 64 East Alt, Zip 28906–7917; tel. 828/837–8161, (Total facility includes 134 beds in nursing home–type unit) **A**1 9 10 **F**3 6 11 13 15 28 29 30 31 34 35 40 45 49 50 53 54 57 59 62 63 64 67 70 76 77 78 79 81 93 107 108 110 111 115 119 128 130 131 135 144 146 147 148 **P**6 **S** Carolinas Healthcare System, Charlotte, NC
Primary Contact: Michael Stevenson, Chief Executive Officer
COO: Toni Lovingood, Chief Operating Officer
CFO: Steve Gilgen, Chief Financial Officer
CMO: Jeffrey H. Martin, M.D., Chief of Staff
CIO: Connie Stalcup, Manager Information Systems
CHR: Russ Paine, Human Resources Officer
CNO: Teresa Bowleg, R.N., Chief Nursing Officer
Web address: www.murphymedical.org
**Control:** Other not–for–profit (including NFP Corporation) **Service:** General Medical and Surgical

**Staffed Beds:** 191 **Admissions:** 2410 **Census:** 126 **Outpatient Visits:** 32926 **Births:** 128 **Total Expense ($000):** 56294 **Payroll Expense ($000):** 25085 **Personnel:** 403

---

**Hospital, Medicare Provider Number, Address, Telephone, Approval, Facility, and Physician Codes, Health Care System**

★ American Hospital Association (AHA) membership
☐ The Joint Commission accreditation
○ Healthcare Facilities Accreditation Program
◇ DNV Healthcare Inc. accreditation
⇑ Center for Improvement in Healthcare Quality Accreditation
△ Commission on Accreditation of Rehabilitation Facilities (CARF) accreditation

NC

## NAGS HEAD—Dare County

✠ **THE OUTER BANKS HOSPITAL (341324)**, 4800 South Croatan Highway, Zip 27959–9704; tel. 252/449–4511 **A**1 9 10 18 **F**3 13 15 29 30 31 34 35 40 45 50 51 54 57 59 64 65 68 71 75 76 77 78 79 81 82 84 85 87 93 100 107 108 109 110 111 115 118 119 120 121 122 129 130 133 135 141 144 146 147 **P**5 **S** Vidant Health, Greenville, NC
Primary Contact: Ronald A. Sloan, FACHE, President
CFO: Todd Warlitner, Vice President Business Operations
CMO: Roger Lever, M.D., President Medical Staff
CHR: Mary Kelley, Director Human Resources
CNO: Judy Bruno, R.N., Vice President, Clinical Operations
Web address: www.theouterbankshospital.com
**Control:** Other not–for–profit (including NFP Corporation) **Service:** General Medical and Surgical

**Staffed Beds: 21 Admissions: 1007 Census: 7 Outpatient Visits:** 42032 **Births: 355 Total Expense ($000):** 47399 **Payroll Expense ($000):** 15995 **Personnel:** 262

## NEW BERN—Craven County

✠ △ **CAROLINAEAST HEALTH SYSTEM (340131)**, 2000 Neuse Boulevard, Zip 28560–3499, Mailing Address: P.O. Box 12157, Zip 28561–2157; tel. 252/633–8111 **A**1 2 7 9 10 **F**3 7 8 11 13 15 17 18 20 22 24 26 28 29 30 31 34 35 40 42 45 47 48 49 54 57 59 61 62 64 67 70 74 75 76 77 78 79 81 85 87 89 90 91 92 93 94 96 98 100 101 102 103 104 105 107 108 110 111 113 114 115 116 117 118 119 120 121 123 126 129 130 132 135 143 146 147 148 **P**6
Primary Contact: G. Raymond Leggett, III, President and Chief Executive Officer
CFO: Tammy M. Sherron, Vice President Finance
CMO: Ronald B. May, M.D., Vice President Medical Affairs
CIO: Ronald B. May, M.D., Vice President Medical Affairs
CHR: Bruce A. Martin, Vice President Human Resources
CNO: Rosanne Leahy, Vice President Nursing Services
Web address: www.carolinaeasthealth.com
**Control:** Hospital district or authority, Government, nonfederal **Service:** General Medical and Surgical

**Staffed Beds: 350 Admissions: 12165 Census: 161 Outpatient Visits:** 164659 **Births: 1190 Total Expense ($000):** 232052 **Payroll Expense ($000):** 87761 **Personnel:** 1666

## NORTH WILKESBORO—Wilkes County

✠ **WILKES REGIONAL MEDICAL CENTER (340064)**, 1370 West D Street, Zip 28659–3506, Mailing Address: P.O. Box 609, Zip 28659–0609; tel. 336/651–8100, (Total facility includes 10 beds in nursing home–type unit) **A**1 9 10 **F**3 8 11 13 15 18 29 30 34 35 40 45 57 59 60 64 67 68 70 74 76 77 79 81 82 85 87 92 93 107 108 110 111 114 115 119 124 128 130 146 **S** Carolinas Healthcare System, Charlotte, NC
Primary Contact: J. Gene Faile, Chief Executive Officer and President
CFO: Barry Wald, Chief Financial Officer
CMO: Richard Barber, M.D., Chief Medical Officer
CIO: William Hofman, Manager Information Technology
CHR: Vanya Baker, Director
CNO: Sandy Sheppard, Vice President Patient Services
Web address: www.wilkesregional.com/
**Control:** City–Government, nonfederal **Service:** General Medical and Surgical

**Staffed Beds: 91 Admissions: 4125 Census: 47 Outpatient Visits:** 105577 **Births: 486 Total Expense ($000):** 68544 **Payroll Expense ($000):** 26141 **Personnel:** 583

## OXFORD—Granville County

✠ **GRANVILLE HEALTH SYSTEM (340127)**, 1010 College Street, Zip 27565–2507, Mailing Address: P.O. Box 947, Zip 27565–0947; tel. 919/690–3000, (Total facility includes 80 beds in nursing home–type unit) **A**1 3 9 10 **F**2 3 7 11 13 15 18 19 29 30 31 34 35 38 39 40 45 50 54 55 56 57 59 64 66 70 75 76 77 78 79 81 82 85 86 93 99 100 101 103 104 107 108 110 111 118 119 124 127 128 129 130 132 133 143 144 146 147 148 **P**3 6 8
Primary Contact: L. Lee Isley, Ph.D., FACHE, Chief Executive Officer
COO: Cristina Rigsbee Carroll, Chief Operating Officer
CFO: Jeffery Armstrong, CPA, Chief Financial Officer
CMO: Michael Mahan, M.D., Chief Medical Staff
CIO: Geoff Tanthorey, Director Information Systems
CHR: Scott Thomas, Administrative Director Human Resources and Communications
CNO: Bill Hughes, Chief Nursing Officer
Web address: www.ghshospital.org
**Control:** County–Government, nonfederal **Service:** General Medical and Surgical

**Staffed Beds: 142 Admissions: 2638 Census: 91 Outpatient Visits:** 55699 **Births: 368 Total Expense ($000):** 59754 **Payroll Expense ($000):** 25721 **Personnel:** 504

## PINEHURST—Moore County

✠ △ **FIRSTHEALTH MOORE REGIONAL HOSPITAL (340115)**, 155 Memorial Drive, Zip 28374–8710, Mailing Address: P.O. Box 3000, Zip 28374–3000; tel. 910/715–1000 **A**1 2 7 9 10 13 19 **F**3 4 5 11 12 13 15 17 18 20 22 24 26 28 29 30 31 34 35 40 44 45 46 47 48 49 50 51 53 54 55 56 57 58 59 60 64 65 68 70 72 74 75 76 77 78 79 81 82 86 87 89 90 93 96 98 99 100 101 102 103 104 105 107 108 111 114 115 118 119 120 121 124 126 129 130 132 134 135 143 146 147 148 **S** FirstHealth of the Carolinas, Pinehurst, NC
Primary Contact: David J. Kilarski, Chief Executive Officer
COO: Brian Canfield, Chief Operating Officer
CFO: Lynn S. DeJaco, Chief Financial Officer
CMO: John F. Krahnert, M.D., Chief Medical Officer
CIO: David B. Dillehunt, Chief Information Officer
CHR: Daniel F. Biediger, Vice President Human Resources
CNO: Karen Robeano, R.N., Chief Nursing Officer and Vice President Patient Care Services
Web address: www.firsthealth.org
**Control:** Other not–for–profit (including NFP Corporation) **Service:** General Medical and Surgical

**Staffed Beds: 371 Admissions: 21565 Census: 259 Outpatient Visits:** 195155 **Births: 1706 Total Expense ($000):** 356274 **Payroll Expense ($000):** 132746 **Personnel:** 3108

## PLYMOUTH—Washington County

◇ **WASHINGTON COUNTY HOSPITAL (341314)**, 958 U.S. Highway 64 East, Zip 27962–9591; tel. 252/793–4135, (Nonreporting) **A**9 10 18 21 **S** Rural Community Hospitals of America, Kansas City, MO
Primary Contact: Cameron Highsmith, Chief Executive Officer
CFO: Al Arrowood, Chief Financial Officer
CMO: Robert Venable, M.D., Chief Medical Staff
CIO: Christina Craft, Director Information Systems
CNO: Kimberly Manning, Chief Nursing Officer
**Control:** County–Government, nonfederal **Service:** General Medical and Surgical

**Staffed Beds: 25**

## RALEIGH—Wake County

**CENTRAL PRISON HOSPITAL**, 1300 Western Boulevard, Zip 27606–2148; tel. 919/743–2440, (Nonreporting)
Primary Contact: Dean Doering, Chief Executive Officer
CMO: Olushola Metiko, M.D., Medical Director
CHR: Bruce McKinney, Business Officer, Administrative Services
CNO: Cindy J. McLean, R.N., Director of Nursing
Web address: www.https://www.ncdps.gov/index2.cfm?a= 000003,002240,002381,002252
**Control:** State–Government, nonfederal **Service:** Hospital unit of an institution (prison hospital, college infirmary, etc.)

**Staffed Beds: 230**

✠ **DUKE RALEIGH HOSPITAL (340073)**, 3400 Wake Forest Road, Zip 27609–7373; tel. 919/954–3000 **A**1 2 3 9 10 **F**3 11 12 15 18 20 22 26 28 29 30 31 34 35 36 39 40 44 45 46 47 49 50 51 53 54 55 57 58 59 60 64 68 70 74 75 77 78 79 80 81 82 84 85 87 92 93 94 96 100 101 102 103 104 107 108 110 111 115 117 118 119 120 121 123 126 129 130 131 132 146 148 **P**8 **S** Duke University Health System, Durham, NC
Primary Contact: David Zaas, M.D., Chief Executive Officer
CMO: Ted Kunstling, M.D., Chief Medical Officer
CIO: Janis Curtis, Interim Director Information Technology
CHR: Donald K. Barnes, Chief Human Resources Officer
Web address: www.dukehealthraleigh.org
**Control:** Other not–for–profit (including NFP Corporation) **Service:** General Medical and Surgical

**Staffed Beds: 148 Admissions: 7791 Census: 92 Outpatient Visits:** 145651 **Births: 0 Total Expense ($000):** 267581 **Payroll Expense ($000):** 78174 **Personnel:** 1356

☐ **HOLLY HILL HOSPITAL (344014)**, 3019 Falstaff Road, Zip 27610–1812; tel. 919/250–7000 **A**1 10 **F**4 29 38 56 68 98 99 103 105 **S** Universal Health Services, Inc., King of Prussia, PA
Primary Contact: Michael S. McDonald, Jr., Chief Executive Officer
CFO: Ron Howard, Chief Financial Officer
CMO: Thomas Cornwall, M.D., Medical Director
CHR: Ebuni McFall–Roberts, Director Human Resources
CNO: Michael Hartley, MS, Chief Nursing Officer
Web address: www.hollyhillhospital.com
**Control:** Corporation, Investor–owned, for–profit **Service:** Psychiatric

**Staffed Beds: 205 Admissions: 6659 Census: 165 Outpatient Visits:** 4929 **Births: 0 Total Expense ($000):** 35350 **Payroll Expense ($000):** 15977 **Personnel:** 375

*Many Facility Codes have changed. Please refer to the AHA Guide Code Chart.*   © 2015 AHA Guide

**LARRY B. ZIEVERINK, SR. ALCOHOLISM TREATMENT CENTER**, 3000 Falstaff Road, Zip 27610–1897; tel. 919/250–1500, (Nonreporting)
Primary Contact: Martin D. Woodward, Director Acute Care Services
COO: Martin D. Woodward, Director Acute Care Services
CFO: Paul Gross, Human Services and Finance Officer
CMO: Enrique Lopez, M.D., Medical Director
CIO: Wil A. Glenn, Director Communications
Web address: www.wakegov.com/county/family/atc
**Control:** County–Government, nonfederal **Service:** Alcoholism and other chemical dependency

Staffed Beds: 34

☒ **REX HEALTHCARE (340114)**, 4420 Lake Boone Trail, Zip 27607–6599; tel. 919/784–3100, (Total facility includes 227 beds in nursing home–type unit) **A**1 2 3 5 9 10 **F**3 7 8 11 12 13 14 15 17 18 20 22 24 26 28 29 30 31 34 35 36 40 44 45 46 47 48 49 50 53 54 56 57 58 59 60 62 64 65 66 68 70 71 73 74 75 76 77 78 79 81 82 84 85 86 87 89 92 93 96 97 100 102 107 108 110 111 114 115 116 117 118 119 120 121 123 126 128 129 130 131 132 135 142 143 144 145 146 147 148 **P**6 **S** UNC Health Care, Chapel Hill, NC
Primary Contact: Steve W. Burriss, Interim President
COO: Steve W. Burriss, Chief Operating Officer
CFO: Erick Hawkins, Chief Financial Officer
CMO: Linda H. Butler, M.D., Chief Medical Officer
CIO: Michelle Gray, Vice President and Regional Chief Information Officer
CHR: Sylvia D. Hackett, Vice President Human Resources
CNO: Colonel Joel Ray, MSN, Vice President and Chief Nursing Officer
Web address: www.rexhealth.com
**Control:** Other not–for–profit (including NFP Corporation) **Service:** General Medical and Surgical

Staffed Beds: 660 Admissions: 26850 Census: 509 Outpatient Visits: 633421 Births: 5658 Total Expense ($000): 735312 Payroll Expense ($000): 332846 Personnel: 4842

☒ △ **WAKEMED RALEIGH CAMPUS (340069)**, 3000 New Bern Avenue, Zip 27610–1295; tel. 919/350–8000 **A**1 3 5 7 9 10 **F**3 7 8 12 13 15 17 18 20 22 24 26 28 29 30 31 32 34 35 37 38 40 41 42 43 44 45 46 48 49 50 53 54 56 57 58 59 60 61 62 64 65 66 68 70 71 72 73 74 75 77 78 79 80 81 85 86 87 88 89 90 92 93 95 96 97 107 110 111 114 115 118 119 126 128 130 131 132 135 143 144 146 147 148 **P**6 **S** WakeMed Health & Hospitals, Raleigh, NC
Primary Contact: Donald R. Gintzig, President and Chief Executive Officer
COO: Thomas Gettinger, Executive Vice President and Chief Operating Officer
CFO: Michael D. DeVaughn, Senior Vice President Finance and Chief Financial Officer
CMO: West Lawson, M.D., Chief Medical Officer
CIO: Denton Arledge, Vice President and Chief Information Officer
CHR: Jeanene R. Martin, M.P.H., Senior Vice President Human Resources
Web address: www.wakemed.org
**Control:** Other not–for–profit (including NFP Corporation) **Service:** General Medical and Surgical

Staffed Beds: 704 Admissions: 32722 Census: 507 Outpatient Visits: 1280768 Births: 5264 Total Expense ($000): 878008 Payroll Expense ($000): 445467 Personnel: 6047

**REIDSVILLE—Rockingham County**

**ANNIE PENN HOSPITAL** See Moses H. Cone Memorial Hospital, Greensboro

**ROANOKE RAPIDS—Halifax County**

☒ **HALIFAX REGIONAL MEDICAL CENTER (340151)**, 250 Smith Church Road, Zip 27870–4914, Mailing Address: P.O. Box 1089, Zip 27870–1089; tel. 252/535–8011 **A**1 9 10 20 **F**3 11 13 15 18 29 31 34 35 38 39 40 45 50 57 59 60 64 65 68 70 75 76 77 78 79 81 85 86 87 91 93 97 98 99 100 101 102 103 106 107 108 110 111 114 119 124 127 129 130 132 146 148 **S** Novant Health, Winston Salem, NC
Primary Contact: William Mahone, President and Chief Executive Officer
CFO: Sherry Jensen, Chief Financial Officer
CIO: Robert Gordon, Manager Information Systems
CHR: Thomas Mastroianni, Administrative Director of Human Resources
CNO: Karen Daniels, MSN, Chief Nursing Officer
Web address: www.halifaxmedicalcenter.org
**Control:** Other not–for–profit (including NFP Corporation) **Service:** General Medical and Surgical

Staffed Beds: 142 Admissions: 4688 Census: 53 Outpatient Visits: 74445 Births: 621 Total Expense ($000): 79716 Payroll Expense ($000): 31667 Personnel: 715

**ROCKINGHAM—Richmond County**

★ **FIRSTHEALTH RICHMOND MEMORIAL HOSPITAL (340035)**, 925 Long Drive, Zip 28379–4835; tel. 910/417–3000, (Nonreporting) **A**9 **S** FirstHealth of the Carolinas, Pinehurst, NC
Primary Contact: John J. Jackson, President
COO: Allison G. Duckworth, R.N., Chief Operating Officer and Chief Nursing Officer
CFO: John D. Price, Chief Financial Officer
CMO: Matthew Vreeland, M.D., Chief Medical Officer
Web address: www.firsthealth.org
**Control:** Other not–for–profit (including NFP Corporation) **Service:** General Medical and Surgical

Staffed Beds: 91

**ROCKY MOUNT—Nash County**

☒ **LIFECARE HOSPITALS OF NORTH CAROLINA (342013)**, 1051 Noell Lane, Zip 27804–1761; tel. 252/451–2300 **A**1 10 **F**1 3 29 30 50 65 74 75 77 82 83 84 85 86 87 100 130 135 148 **P**8 **S** LifeCare Management Services, Plano, TX
Primary Contact: Robyn Perkerson, R.N., Administrator
COO: Robyn Perkerson, R.N., Administrator
CMO: Daniel Crocker, M.D., Chief Medical Officer
CHR: Vicky Goode, Director Human Resources
CNO: Brandee Chappell, Director of Nursing
Web address: www.lifecare–hospitals.com
**Control:** Corporation, Investor–owned, for–profit **Service:** Long–Term Acute Care hospital

Staffed Beds: 41 Admissions: 513 Census: 40 Outpatient Visits: 0 Births: 0 Total Expense ($000): 19372 Payroll Expense ($000): 8673 Personnel: 153

☒ **NASH HEALTH CARE SYSTEMS (340147)**, 2460 Curtis Ellis Drive, Zip 27804–2237; tel. 252/443–8000 **A**1 2 9 10 **F**3 4 11 12 13 15 18 20 22 28 29 30 31 34 35 38 40 41 44 45 48 49 50 54 55 57 59 60 63 64 70 73 74 75 76 77 78 79 80 81 82 84 85 86 87 89 90 93 94 96 98 100 101 102 103 104 107 108 110 111 114 115 117 118 119 120 121 123 125 126 129 130 131 132 135 146 147 148 **P**6 **S** UNC Health Care, Chapel Hill, NC
Primary Contact: Larry H. Chewning, III, President and Chief Executive Officer
COO: Brad Weisner, Executive Vice President and Chief Operating Officer
CFO: Al Hooks, Senior Vice President and Chief Financial Officer
CMO: David R. Gorby, M.D., Vice President Quality and Patient Safety
CIO: David Hinkle, Senior Vice President and Chief Information Officer
CHR: Cam Blalock, Senior Vice President Corporate Services
CNO: Leslie Hall, R.N., Senior Vice President–Chief Nursing Officer
Web address: www.nhcs.org
**Control:** Hospital district or authority, Government, nonfederal **Service:** General Medical and Surgical

Staffed Beds: 303 Admissions: 12372 Census: 177 Outpatient Visits: 180236 Births: 1026 Total Expense ($000): 224749 Payroll Expense ($000): 93476 Personnel: 1542

**ROXBORO—Person County**

☒ **PERSON MEMORIAL HOSPITAL (340159)**, 615 Ridge Road, Zip 27573–4629; tel. 336/599–2121, (Total facility includes 60 beds in nursing home–type unit) **A**1 9 10 **F**3 11 15 18 28 29 34 40 45 57 59 64 70 75 77 79 81 85 87 93 96 97 107 108 110 114 119 128 130 132 146 **P**6 **S** Duke LifePoint Healthcare, Brentwood, TN
Primary Contact: Beemal A. Shah, Chief Executive Officer
CFO: Jessi Ayers, Chief Financial Officer
CIO: Rhonda M. Elliott, Director Information Technology and Meaningful Use
CHR: Mary Barksdale, Director Human Resources
CNO: Lynn Peoples, Interim Chief Nursing Officer
Web address: www.personhospital.com
**Control:** Partnership, Investor–owned, for–profit **Service:** General Medical and Surgical

Staffed Beds: 106 Admissions: 1715 Census: 64 Outpatient Visits: 39979 Births: 0 Total Expense ($000): 29342 Payroll Expense ($000): 10433 Personnel: 259

## RUTHERFORDTON—Rutherford County

✠ **RUTHERFORD REGIONAL HEALTH SYSTEM (340013)**, 288 South Ridgecrest Avenue, Zip 28139–2838; tel. 828/286–5000, (Data for 214 days) **A**1 2 9 10 19 **F**3 11 13 15 18 20 28 29 30 31 34 35 40 45 48 49 50 57 59 62 64 70 74 75 76 77 78 79 81 82 85 86 87 89 93 97 98 100 101 102 104 106 107 108 110 111 114 115 118 119 130 131 132 135 146 147 **S** Duke LifePoint Healthcare, Brentwood, TN
Primary Contact: Cindy D. Buck, Chief Executive Officer
COO: John Domansky, Vice President Operations
CFO: Jeff Rush, Chief Financial Officer
CIO: Tommy Finley, Chief Information Officer
CHR: Robin B. Callas, R.N., Vice President Human Resources
Web address: www.rutherfordhosp.org
**Control:** Partnership, Investor–owned, for–profit **Service:** General Medical and Surgical

**Staffed Beds:** 112 **Admissions:** 2988 **Census:** 55 **Outpatient Visits:** 90072 **Births:** 281 **Total Expense ($000):** 49662 **Payroll Expense ($000):** 21107 **Personnel:** 686

## SALISBURY—Rowan County

✠ **NOVANT HEALTH ROWAN MEDICAL CENTER (340015)**, 612 Mocksville Avenue, Zip 28144–2799; tel. 704/210–5000 **A**1 2 9 10 19 **F**3 6 8 11 12 13 15 17 18 20 22 26 28 29 30 31 32 34 35 37 39 40 44 45 49 50 51 53 54 56 57 59 60 61 63 64 68 70 71 73 74 75 76 77 78 79 81 84 85 86 87 90 91 92 93 94 96 98 100 102 103 107 108 110 111 114 115 116 117 118 119 120 121 123 126 130 131 132 135 146 147 148 **S** Novant Health, Winston Salem, NC
Primary Contact: Dari Caldwell, R.N., Ph.D., FACHE, President and Chief Operating Officer
COO: Dari Caldwell, R.N., President and Chief Operating Officer
CMO: Thomas F. Trahey, M.D., Vice President Medical Affairs
CNO: Cora Greene, Chief Nursing Officer
Web address: www.https://www.novanthealth.org/rowan–medical–center.aspx
**Control:** Other not–for–profit (including NFP Corporation) **Service:** General Medical and Surgical

**Staffed Beds:** 148 **Admissions:** 9836 **Census:** 135 **Outpatient Visits:** 114813 **Births:** 746 **Total Expense ($000):** 172991 **Payroll Expense ($000):** 57606 **Personnel:** 1313

**VETERANS AFFAIRS MEDICAL CENTER** See W. G. (Bill) Heffner Veterans Affairs Medical Center

✠ **W. G. (BILL) HEFFNER VETERANS AFFAIRS MEDICAL CENTER**, 1601 Brenner Avenue, Zip 28144–2559; tel. 704/638–9000, (Nonreporting) **A**1 3 5 **S** Department of Veterans Affairs, Washington, DC
Primary Contact: Kaye Green, FACHE, Director
CFO: Steve Patil, Chief Financial Officer
CIO: Deborah Gunn, Chief Information Officer
CHR: Sandra Fischer, Director Human Resources
Web address: www.salisbury.va.gov
**Control:** Veterans Affairs, Government, federal **Service:** Psychiatric

**Staffed Beds:** 171

## SANFORD—Lee County

✠ **CENTRAL CAROLINA HOSPITAL (340020)**, 1135 Carthage Street, Zip 27330–4162; tel. 919/774–2100, (Nonreporting) **A**1 9 10 **S** TENET Healthcare Corporation, Dallas, TX
Primary Contact: David E. Loving, Chief Executive Officer
CFO: Ronald Groteluschen, Chief Financial Officer
CIO: Jimmy Whitaker, Director Information Systems
CHR: Joseph F. Eastman, Director Human Resources
CNO: Tracy Temple, Chief Nursing Officer
Web address: www.centralcarolinahosp.com
**Control:** Corporation, Investor–owned, for–profit **Service:** General Medical and Surgical

**Staffed Beds:** 116

## SCOTLAND NECK—Halifax County

★ **OUR COMMUNITY HOSPITAL (341302)**, 921 Junior High Road, Zip 27874–0405, Mailing Address: Box 405, Zip 27874–0405; tel. 252/826–4144, (Nonreporting) **A**9 10 18
Primary Contact: Thomas K. Majure, Administrator
CFO: Sarah Diversi, Chief Financial Officer
CMO: Cornelius Artis, M.D., Chief Medical Officer
CIO: Dana Mobley, Chief Information Officer
CNO: Claudia Giddings, R.N., Chief Nursing Officer
Web address: www.och–bltc.org
**Control:** Other not–for–profit (including NFP Corporation) **Service:** General Medical and Surgical

**Staffed Beds:** 75

## SHELBY—Cleveland County

✠ **CLEVELAND REGIONAL MEDICAL CENTER (340021)**, 201 East Grover Street, Zip 28150–3917; tel. 980/487–3000, (Total facility includes 120 beds in nursing home–type unit) **A**1 2 9 10 19 **F**3 8 13 15 18 20 28 29 30 31 32 34 35 39 40 43 45 47 48 49 50 51 56 57 59 64 65 67 70 74 75 76 77 78 79 80 81 85 86 87 89 93 102 107 108 110 111 114 115 119 121 123 126 128 130 131 132 135 143 145 146 147 148 **S** Carolinas Healthcare System, Charlotte, NC
Primary Contact: Brian Gwyn, President and Chief Executive Officer
COO: Brian Gwyn, President Chief Operating Officer
CFO: Christine M. Martin, Vice President and Chief Financial Officer
CMO: Charles M. Tomlinson, M.D., Chief Medical Officer
CIO: Craig D. Richardville, Chief Information Officer
CHR: Debra Kale, Vice President Human Resources
CNO: Veronica Poole–Adams, R.N., Vice President, Chief Operating Officer and Chief Nursing Executive
Web address: www.clevelandregional.org
**Control:** Hospital district or authority, Government, nonfederal **Service:** General Medical and Surgical

**Staffed Beds:** 293 **Admissions:** 7813 **Census:** 198 **Outpatient Visits:** 136169 **Births:** 1065 **Total Expense ($000):** 156902 **Payroll Expense ($000):** 59765 **Personnel:** 1028

## SILER CITY—Chatham County

✠ **CHATHAM HOSPITAL (341311)**, 475 Progress Boulevard, Zip 27344–6787, Mailing Address: P.O. Box 649, Zip 27344–0649; tel. 919/799–4000 **A**1 9 10 18 **F**3 15 18 28 29 30 34 35 40 45 57 59 68 70 75 77 81 85 92 93 107 110 111 114 119 130 133 135 **S** UNC Health Care, Chapel Hill, NC
Primary Contact: Robert A. Enders, Jr., President
CFO: David Paugh, Chief Financial Officer
CMO: Cody Deen, Chief of Medical Staff
CIO: Janice Fraley, IT Entity Director – Information Services Division
CHR: Jodie Sartor Solow, Director Human Resources
CNO: Tammy Needham, Chief Nursing Officer
Web address: www.chathamhospital.org
**Control:** Other not–for–profit (including NFP Corporation) **Service:** General Medical and Surgical

**Staffed Beds:** 25 **Admissions:** 740 **Census:** 11 **Outpatient Visits:** 36768 **Births:** 6 **Total Expense ($000):** 29153 **Payroll Expense ($000):** 9209 **Personnel:** 188

## SMITHFIELD—Johnston County

✠ **JOHNSTON HEALTH (340090)**, 509 North Bright Leaf Boulevard, Zip 27577–4407, Mailing Address: P.O. Box 1376, Zip 27577–1376; tel. 919/934–8171 **A**1 9 10 **F**3 8 11 13 15 17 18 20 26 28 29 30 31 32 34 35 40 42 45 49 50 52 53 54 56 57 59 61 62 63 64 66 68 70 73 74 75 76 79 81 82 85 86 87 89 92 93 97 98 100 107 108 110 111 114 115 119 120 121 125 126 130 132 144 146 147 148 **P**6 **S** UNC Health Care, Chapel Hill, NC
Primary Contact: Charles W. Elliott, Jr., Chief Executive Officer
COO: Ruth Marler, Chief Nursing Officer and Chief Operating Officer
CFO: Edward A. Klein, Chief Financial Officer
CMO: Donald Pocock, M.D., Vice President Medical Affairs
CIO: Teresa Chappell, Chief Information Officer
CHR: Timothy A. Hays, Vice President Human Resources
CNO: Ruth Marler, Chief Nursing Officer and Chief Operating Officer
Web address: www.johnstonhealth.org
**Control:** Hospital district or authority, Government, nonfederal **Service:** General Medical and Surgical

**Staffed Beds:** 145 **Admissions:** 8836 **Census:** 103 **Outpatient Visits:** 152215 **Births:** 1467 **Total Expense ($000):** 160626 **Payroll Expense ($000):** 64883 **Personnel:** 1208

## SOUTHPORT—Brunswick County

✠ **J. ARTHUR DOSHER MEMORIAL HOSPITAL (341327)**, 924 North Howe Street, Zip 28461–3099; tel. 910/457–3800, (Total facility includes 57 beds in nursing home–type unit) **A**1 9 10 18 **F**3 15 28 30 34 35 40 45 47 50 54 57 59 64 68 75 77 79 81 91 93 97 107 110 111 114 118 119 127 128 129 130 131 132 133 144 146 148 **P**6
Primary Contact: Thomas R. Siemers, Chief Executive Officer
CFO: Don Porter, Senior Vice President and Chief Financial Officer
CMO: Brad L. Hilaman, M.D., Chief of Staff
CIO: Susan Shomaker, Director Information Management Systems
CHR: Pat Aderhold, Director Human Resources
CNO: Carol Northup, R.N., Chief Nursing Officer
Web address: www.dosher.org
**Control:** Other not–for–profit (including NFP Corporation) **Service:** General Medical and Surgical

**Staffed Beds:** 89 **Admissions:** 1025 **Census:** 51 **Outpatient Visits:** 59896 **Births:** 0 **Total Expense ($000):** 36096 **Payroll Expense ($000):** 14681 **Personnel:** 291

**NC**

*Many Facility Codes have changed. Please refer to the AHA Guide Code Chart.* © 2015 AHA Guide

## SPARTA—Alleghany County

✠ **ALLEGHANY MEMORIAL HOSPITAL (341320)**, 233 Doctors Street,
Zip 28675–9247; tel. 336/372–5511 **A**1 9 10 18 **F**3 15 18 28 29 30 34 35
40 43 45 59 64 67 77 78 79 81 82 87 90 93 97 107 111 114 119 129 130
131 133 135 146 **S** Alliant Management Services, Louisville, KY
Primary Contact: Brent R. Lammers, Chief Executive Officer
CFO: Brett Liverman, Chief Financial Officer
CMO: Tammy Thone, M.D., Chief Medical Staff
CIO: Darlene Keith, Chief Information Systems
CNO: Wendy Orton, Chief Nursing Officer
Web address: www.amhsparta.org
**Control:** Other not–for–profit (including NFP Corporation) **Service:** General
Medical and Surgical

> **Staffed Beds:** 25 **Admissions:** 509 **Census:** 6 **Outpatient Visits:** 27449
> **Births:** 0 **Total Expense ($000):** 11935 **Payroll Expense ($000):** 5139
> **Personnel:** 148

## SPRUCE PINE—Mitchell County

✠ **BLUE RIDGE REGIONAL HOSPITAL (340011)**, 125 Hospital Drive,
Zip 28777–3035, Mailing Address: P.O. Drawer 9, Zip 28777–0009;
tel. 828/765–4201, (Includes BLUE RIDGE MEDICAL CENTER – YANCEY
CAMPUS, 800 Medical Campus Drive, Burnsville, Zip 28714–9010;
tel. 828/682–0200; Will Wantland, Director) **A**1 9 10 **F**3 13 15 17 28 29 30 31
32 34 35 39 40 43 45 46 50 53 54 57 59 64 66 70 75 76 77 78 79 81 82
85 87 90 93 96 97 107 108 111 114 118 119 127 128 129 130 131 132
133 135 146 147 148 **P**6 **S** Mission Health System, Asheville, NC
Primary Contact: Rebecca W. Carter, MSN, R.N., FACHE, Chief Executive Officer
and Chief Nursing Officer
CFO: Clint Stewart, Chief Financial Officer
CMO: Jennifer Larson, M.D., Chief of Staff
CIO: Pam Blevins, R.N., Director, Clinical Informatics
CHR: Susan Parille, Director Human Resources
CNO: Rebecca W. Carter, MSN, Chief Executive Officer and Chief Nursing Officer
Web address: www.spchospital.org
**Control:** Other not–for–profit (including NFP Corporation) **Service:** General
Medical and Surgical

> **Staffed Beds:** 42 **Admissions:** 1710 **Census:** 15 **Outpatient Visits:** 129017
> **Births:** 156 **Total Expense ($000):** 39904 **Payroll Expense ($000):** 17546
> **Personnel:** 279

## STATESVILLE—Iredell County

✠ **DAVIS REGIONAL MEDICAL CENTER (340144)**, 218 Old Mocksville Road,
Zip 28625–1930, Mailing Address: P.O. Box 1823, Zip 28687–1823;
tel. 704/873–0281, (Nonreporting) **A**1 9 10 19 **S** Community Health Systems,
Inc., Franklin, TN
Primary Contact: William Chad French, Chief Executive Officer
CFO: Hugh Tobin, Chief Financial Officer
CMO: John Allan, Chief of Staff
CIO: Janie Stikeleather, Director Marketing and Community Relations
CHR: Christine McKenzie, Director Human Resources
CNO: Janice S. Martin, R.N., Chief Nursing Officer
Web address: www.davisregional.com
**Control:** Corporation, Investor–owned, for–profit **Service:** General Medical and
Surgical

> **Staffed Beds:** 131

✠ **IREDELL MEMORIAL HOSPITAL (340039)**, 557 Brookdale Drive,
Zip 28677–4107, Mailing Address: P.O. Box 1828, Zip 28687–1828;
tel. 704/873–5661, (Total facility includes 48 beds in nursing home–type unit) **A**1
2 9 10 **F**3 11 13 15 17 18 20 22 28 29 30 31 32 34 35 40 41 45 47 49 50
56 57 58 59 60 62 64 68 70 74 75 76 77 78 79 81 82 85 86 87 89 93 97
107 108 111 114 115 117 118 119 120 121 123 128 129 130 132 135 146
147 148 **P**6
Primary Contact: Ed Rush, President and Chief Executive Officer
COO: John Snow, Vice President Ancillary and Support Services
CFO: Skip Smith, Vice President Finance
CMO: Carla Pence, President Medical Staff
CIO: Kyle Smith, Director Information Systems
CHR: John Green, Vice President Professional Services and Facility Planning
CNO: Becky Quate, R.N., Vice President Nursing and Patient Care Services
Web address: www.iredellhealth.org
**Control:** Other not–for–profit (including NFP Corporation) **Service:** General
Medical and Surgical

> **Staffed Beds:** 203 **Admissions:** 7975 **Census:** 119 **Outpatient Visits:**
> 117555 **Births:** 772 **Total Expense ($000):** 130321 **Payroll Expense**
> **($000):** 56356 **Personnel:** 974

## SYLVA—Jackson County

✠ **HARRIS REGIONAL HOSPITAL (340016)**, 68 Hospital Road, Zip 28779–2722;
tel. 828/586–7000 **A**1 9 10 **F**3 7 8 11 13 15 28 29 30 31 34 35 40 46 50 54
62 63 64 68 70 72 75 76 77 78 79 81 82 84 85 86 87 89 93 107 108 110
111 114 119 120 121 129 130 131 135 143 144 146 147 148 **S** Duke
LifePoint Healthcare, Brentwood, TN
Primary Contact: Steve Heatherly, Chief Executive Officer
CHR: Janet Millsaps, Chief Human Resources Officer
Web address: www.westcare.org
**Control:** Corporation, Investor–owned, for–profit **Service:** General Medical and
Surgical

> **Staffed Beds:** 86 **Admissions:** 3630 **Census:** 35 **Outpatient Visits:** 203131
> **Births:** 594 **Total Expense ($000):** 92272 **Payroll Expense ($000):** 41496
> **Personnel:** 682

## TARBORO—Edgecombe County

✠ △ **VIDANT EDGECOMBE HOSPITAL (340107)**, 111 Hospital Drive,
Zip 27886–2011; tel. 252/641–7700 **A**1 2 3 7 9 10 **F**3 11 12 13 15 18 28 29
30 31 40 45 50 57 59 70 73 75 78 79 81 82 85 87 90 92 93 96 107 110
111 119 127 130 131 132 135 145 146 **S** Vidant Health, Greenville, NC
Primary Contact: Wendell H. Baker, Jr., President
CFO: Charles Alford, Vice President Financial Services
CMO: Barry Bunn, M.D., Chief of Staff
CHR: Kadie Moore, Director Human Resources
CNO: Patrick Heins, Vice President Patient Care Services
Web address: www.https://www.vidanthealth.com/edgecombe/default.aspx
**Control:** Other not–for–profit (including NFP Corporation) **Service:** General
Medical and Surgical

> **Staffed Beds:** 59 **Admissions:** 3604 **Census:** 42 **Outpatient Visits:** 68001
> **Births:** 407 **Total Expense ($000):** 67725 **Payroll Expense ($000):** 24338
> **Personnel:** 485

## THOMASVILLE—Davidson County

✠ ◇ **NOVANT HEALTH THOMASVILLE MEDICAL CENTER (340085)**, 207 Old
Lexington Road, Zip 27360–3428, Mailing Address: P.O. Box 789,
Zip 27361–0789; tel. 336/472–2000 **A**1 3 9 10 21 **F**8 13 15 18 20 28 29 30
34 35 40 45 47 48 50 56 57 59 64 70 74 75 76 77 78 79 81 82 83 84 85
86 87 91 93 98 103 104 107 108 111 114 117 118 119 124 129 130
131 132 135 144 146 147 148 **S** Novant Health, Winston Salem, NC
Primary Contact: Kathie A. Johnson, R.N., MS, Ph.D., Chief Executive Officer
CNO: Christina Grabus, R.N., Chief Nursing Officer
Web address: www.thomasvillemedicalcenter.org
**Control:** Other not–for–profit (including NFP Corporation) **Service:** General
Medical and Surgical

> **Staffed Beds:** 75 **Admissions:** 4023 **Census:** 67 **Outpatient Visits:** 113716
> **Births:** 643 **Total Expense ($000):** 76007 **Payroll Expense ($000):** 27538
> **Personnel:** 544

## TROY—Montgomery County

✠ **FIRSTHEALTH MONTGOMERY MEMORIAL HOSPITAL (341303)**, 520 Allen
Street, Zip 27371–2802; tel. 910/571–5000 **A**1 9 10 18 **F**3 11 15 29 30 40
45 59 64 81 85 87 93 97 107 110 114 119 127 129 133 146 **S** FirstHealth of
the Carolinas, Pinehurst, NC
Primary Contact: Beth Walker, R.N., President
CFO: Bryan Hawkins, Controller
CHR: Tina H. Thompson, Coordinator Human Resources
CNO: Pam Gaddy, Director, Patient Care Services and Chief Nursing Officer
Web address: www.firsthealth.org
**Control:** Other not–for–profit (including NFP Corporation) **Service:** General
Medical and Surgical

> **Staffed Beds:** 25 **Admissions:** 292 **Census:** 2 **Outpatient Visits:** 19984
> **Births:** 0 **Total Expense ($000):** 11830 **Payroll Expense ($000):** 5643
> **Personnel:** 102

---

**Hospital, Medicare Provider Number, Address, Telephone, Approval, Facility, and Physician Codes, Health Care System**

★ American Hospital Association (AHA) membership  ○ Healthcare Facilities Accreditation Program  ⇑ Center for Improvement in Healthcare Quality Accreditation
□ The Joint Commission accreditation  ◇ DNV Healthcare Inc. accreditation  △ Commission on Accreditation of Rehabilitation Facilities (CARF) accreditation

**NC**

### WADESBORO—Anson County

⊞ **CAROLINAS HEALTHCARE SYSTEM ANSON (340084)**, 2301 U.S Highway 74 West, Zip 28170; tel. 704/994–4500 **A**1 9 10 **F**11 15 28 29 34 35 40 57 59 62 64 65 71 77 81 86 87 93 97 107 110 114 119 130 132 135 145 146 **S** Carolinas Healthcare System, Charlotte, NC
Primary Contact: Michael Lutes, President
CFO: Jeff Griffin, Assistant Vice President Finance
CMO: Edward Blasko, Chief of Staff
CIO: Lisa Sykes, IS/Communications Director
CHR: Rhonda McFarland, Director Human Resources
CNO: Denise White, MSN, Chief Nurse Executive
Web address: www.carolinashealthcare.org/anson
**Control:** Hospital district or authority, Government, nonfederal **Service:** General Medical and Surgical

> **Staffed Beds:** 15 **Admissions:** 234 **Census:** 2 **Outpatient Visits:** 22690 **Births:** 0 **Total Expense ($000):** 23559 **Payroll Expense ($000):** 8548 **Personnel:** 106

### WASHINGTON—Beaufort County

**BEAUFORT COUNTY HOSPITAL** See Vidant Beaufort Hospital

⊞ **VIDANT BEAUFORT HOSPITAL (340186)**, 628 East 12th Street, Zip 27889–3409; tel. 252/975–4100 **A**1 9 10 **F**3 5 7 9 13 15 26 27 28 29 30 31 34 35 36 38 40 49 53 57 59 64 65 69 70 75 76 77 78 79 81 82 85 86 87 93 97 98 99 100 101 102 104 107 108 109 111 115 118 119 129 130 132 135 143 144 145 146 **S** Vidant Health, Greenville, NC
Primary Contact: Harvey Case, President
CFO: Charles Alford, Vice President Finance
CMO: Fred Teixeira, M.D., Chief of Staff
CIO: Amy Boyd, Information Systems Manager
CHR: Penny Coltrain, Director Human Resources
CNO: Lou Montana–Rhodes, Vice President of Patient Care Services
Web address: www.vidanthealth.com
**Control:** Hospital district or authority, Government, nonfederal **Service:** General Medical and Surgical

> **Staffed Beds:** 43 **Admissions:** 3314 **Census:** 41 **Outpatient Visits:** 51302 **Births:** 352 **Total Expense ($000):** 60740 **Payroll Expense ($000):** 20815 **Personnel:** 477

### WHITEVILLE—Columbus County

⊞ **COLUMBUS REGIONAL HEALTHCARE SYSTEM (340068)**, 500 Jefferson Street, Zip 28472–3634; tel. 910/642–8011, (Nonreporting) **A**1 9 10 19 **S** Carolinas Healthcare System, Charlotte, NC
Primary Contact: Carla Hollis, President and Chief Executive Officer
CFO: Carl Biber, Chief Financial Officer
CIO: Lisa Ward, Director Management Information Systems
CHR: Andrea West, MS, Vice President of Human Resources
CNO: Terry Beasley, R.N., Chief Nursing Officer
Web address: www.crhealthcare.org/
**Control:** Hospital district or authority, Government, nonfederal **Service:** General Medical and Surgical

> **Staffed Beds:** 103

### WILLIAMSTON—Martin County

⊞ **MARTIN GENERAL HOSPITAL (340133)**, 310 South McCaskey Road, Zip 27892–2150, Mailing Address: P.O. Box 1128, Zip 27892–1128; tel. 252/809–6300, (Nonreporting) **A**1 9 10 **S** Community Health Systems, Inc., Franklin, TN
Primary Contact: Taffy J. Arias, Chief Executive Officer
CFO: John Jacobson, Chief Financial Officer
CIO: James Griffin, Manager Information Systems
CHR: Rebecca Edwards, Director Human Resources
CNO: Greg Hornick, Chief Nursing Officer
Web address: www.martingeneral.com
**Control:** Corporation, Investor–owned, for–profit **Service:** General Medical and Surgical

> **Staffed Beds:** 49

### WILMINGTON—New Hanover County

⊞ △ **NEW HANOVER REGIONAL MEDICAL CENTER (340141)**, 2131 South 17th Street, Zip 28401–7483, Mailing Address: P.O. Box 9000, Zip 28402–9000; tel. 910/343–7000, (Includes CAPE FEAR HOSPITAL, 5301 Wrightsville Avenue, Zip 28403–6599; tel. 910/452–8100) **A**1 2 3 5 7 9 10 12 13 20 **F**3 7 8 11 12 13 15 17 18 20 22 24 26 28 29 30 31 34 35 36 37 39 40 43 44 45 46 47 48 49 50 53 54 56 57 58 59 60 61 64 65 66 68 70 72 73 74 75 76 77 78 79 80 81 82 84 85 86 87 88 89 90 92 93 94 96 97 98 100 101 102 103 107 108 110 111 114 115 117 118 119 121 123 126 130 131 132 135 144 146 147 148 **S** New Hanover Regional Medical Center, Wilmington, NC
Primary Contact: John K. Barto, Jr., President and Chief Executive Officer
COO: John H. Gizdic, Chief Operating Officer
CFO: Edwin J. Ollie, Executive Vice President and Chief Financial Officer
CMO: Sam Spicer, M.D., Vice President Medical Affairs
CIO: Avery Cloud, Vice President and Chief Information Officer
CHR: Keith A. Strawn, Vice President Human Resources
CNO: Mary Ellen Bonczek, R.N., Chief Nursing Executive
Web address: www.nhrmc.org
**Control:** County–Government, nonfederal **Service:** General Medical and Surgical

> **Staffed Beds:** 692 **Admissions:** 38597 **Census:** 519 **Outpatient Visits:** 351752 **Births:** 4117 **Total Expense ($000):** 706622 **Payroll Expense ($000):** 272385 **Personnel:** 4445

**WILMINGTON TREATMENT CENTER (340168)**, 2520 Troy Drive, Zip 28401–7643; tel. 910/762–2727 **A**10 **F**4 5 29 54 64 82 132 135 **P**6 **S** CRC Health Group, Inc., Cupertino, CA
Primary Contact: Robert Pitts, Executive Director
COO: Paige Bottom, Director Operations
CFO: Virginia Powell, Director Finance
CMO: Patrick Martin, M.D., Medical Director
Web address: www.wilmtreatment.com
**Control:** Corporation, Investor–owned, for–profit **Service:** Alcoholism and other chemical dependency

> **Staffed Beds:** 44 **Admissions:** 1100 **Census:** 19 **Outpatient Visits:** 36650 **Births:** 0 **Total Expense ($000):** 13500 **Payroll Expense ($000):** 5000 **Personnel:** 132

### WILSON—Wilson County

**TRIANGLE EAST NURSING CARE CENTER** See WilMed Nursing Care Center

⊞ **WILSON MEDICAL CENTER (340126)**, 1705 Tarboro Street, S.W., Zip 27893–3428; tel. 252/399–8040, (Nonreporting) **A**1 2 9 10 19 **S** Duke LifePoint Healthcare, Brentwood, TN
Primary Contact: William E. Caldwell, Jr., Chief Executive Officer
COO: Bert Beard, Chief Operating Officer
CMO: Rick Guarino, M.D., Vice President Medical Affairs
CIO: Brian Dietrick, Director Information Systems
CHR: Denise O'Hara, Vice President Human Resources
Web address: www.wilmed.org
**Control:** Other not–for–profit (including NFP Corporation) **Service:** General Medical and Surgical

> **Staffed Beds:** 294

### WINDSOR—Bertie County

⊞ **VIDANT BERTIE HOSPITAL (341304)**, 1403 South King Street, Zip 27983–9666, Mailing Address: P.O. Box 40, Zip 27983–0040; tel. 252/794–6600 **A**1 9 10 18 **F**3 15 29 30 34 35 40 45 57 59 64 77 78 79 81 82 93 94 97 107 110 114 119 127 132 135 146 **S** Vidant Health, Greenville, NC
Primary Contact: Jeffery Dial, President
CFO: Brian Harvill, Vice President Financial Services
CMO: William Ballance, M.D., Chief of Medical Staff
CIO: Brian White, Director Strategic Planning
CHR: Debbie Swicegood, Director Human Resources
CNO: Silvia B. Rose, R.N., Director Patient Care Services
Web address: www.vidanthealth.com
**Control:** Other not–for–profit (including NFP Corporation) **Service:** General Medical and Surgical

> **Staffed Beds:** 6 **Admissions:** 427 **Census:** 4 **Outpatient Visits:** 24157 **Births:** 0 **Total Expense ($000):** 20060 **Payroll Expense ($000):** 6461 **Personnel:** 110

### WINSTON SALEM—Forsyth County

**BRENNER CHILDREN'S HOSPITAL & HEALTH SERVICES** See Wake Forest Baptist Medical Center, Winston–Salem

### WINSTON-SALEM—Forsyth County

**MEDICAL PARK HOSPITAL** See Novant Health Medical Park Hospital

**NC**

☒ △ **NOVANT HEALTH FORSYTH MEDICAL CENTER (340014)**, 3333 Silas Creek Parkway, Zip 27103–3090; tel. 336/718–5000, (Includes KERNERSVILLE MEDICAL CENTER, 2911750 Kernersville Medical Parkway, Kernersville, Zip 27284–2932, Mailing Address: 1750 Kernersville Medical Parkway, Zip 27284–2932; tel. 336/564–4000; Joanne Allen, R.N., President) **A**1 2 3 5 7 9 10 **F**3 4 5 7 8 9 10 12 13 14 15 17 18 20 22 24 26 28 29 30 31 32 34 35 37 38 40 42 44 45 46 49 50 53 54 56 57 58 59 60 61 64 65 66 67 68 70 71 72 74 75 76 77 78 79 80 81 82 83 84 85 86 87 89 90 93 98 100 101 102 103 104 105 107 108 109 111 112 114 115 116 117 118 119 120 121 123 124 126 128 129 130 131 132 135 143 146 147 148 **P**6 **S** Novant Health, Winston Salem, NC
Primary Contact: Sean M. Sanz, Chief Executive Officer
CMO: Elms Allen, M.D., Senior Vice President Medical Affairs
CIO: David B. Garrett, Chief Information Officer
CHR: Janet Smith–Hill, Senior Vice President Human Resources
Web address: www.forsythmedicalcenter.org
**Control:** Other not–for–profit (including NFP Corporation) **Service:** General Medical and Surgical

**Staffed Beds:** 689 **Admissions:** 42780 **Census:** 652 **Outpatient Visits:** 407488 **Births:** 6261 **Total Expense ($000):** 750427 **Payroll Expense ($000):** 247125 **Personnel:** 4751

☒ **NOVANT HEALTH MEDICAL PARK HOSPITAL (340148)**, 1950 South Hawthorne Road, Zip 27103–3993; tel. 336/718–0600 **A**1 2 9 10 **F**3 29 35 39 64 68 74 78 79 81 82 85 89 126 130 131 146 **S** Novant Health, Winston Salem, NC
Primary Contact: Chad Setliff, Chief Executive Officer
CMO: Elms Allen, M.D., Senior Vice President Medical Affairs
CHR: Vasilia Perimenis, Vice President Human Resources
Web address: www.novanthealth.org
**Control:** Other not–for–profit (including NFP Corporation) **Service:** General Medical and Surgical

**Staffed Beds:** 16 **Admissions:** 864 **Census:** 9 **Outpatient Visits:** 35948 **Births:** 0 **Total Expense ($000):** 48700 **Payroll Expense ($000):** 11697 **Personnel:** 216

☐ **OLD VINEYARD BEHAVIORAL HEALTH SERVICES (344007)**, 3637 Old Vineyard Road, Zip 27104–4842; tel. 336/794–3550 **A**1 10 **F**29 50 75 87 98 99 101 102 103 104 105 130 **S** Universal Health Services, Inc., King of Prussia, PA
Primary Contact: Kevin Patton, Chief Executive Officer
CFO: Ernest C. Priddy, III, Chief Financial Officer
CMO: Raj Thotakura, M.D., Medical Director
CHR: Jackie Pennino, Director Human Resources
CNO: Carol Fisher, Director of Nursing
Web address: www.oldvineyardbhs.com
**Control:** Corporation, Investor–owned, for–profit **Service:** Psychiatric

**Staffed Beds:** 104 **Admissions:** 4035 **Census:** 96 **Outpatient Visits:** 3338 **Births:** 0 **Total Expense ($000):** 19059 **Payroll Expense ($000):** 9582 **Personnel:** 166

☒ **SELECT SPECIALTY HOSPITAL–WINSTON–SALEM (342016)**, 3333 Silas Creek Parkway, 6th Floor, Zip 27103–3013; tel. 336/718–6300, (Nonreporting) **A**1 10 **S** Select Medical Corporation, Mechanicsburg, PA
Primary Contact: Leslie Deane, Chief Executive Officer
CHR: Sherry Meacham, Coordinator Human Resources
Web address: www.selectspecialtyhospitals.com/company/locations/winston–salem.aspx
**Control:** Corporation, Investor–owned, for–profit **Service:** Long–Term Acute Care hospital

**Staffed Beds:** 42

☒ △ **WAKE FOREST BAPTIST MEDICAL CENTER (340047)**, Medical Center Boulevard, Zip 27157–0001; tel. 336/716–2011, (Includes BRENNER CHILDREN'S HOSPITAL & HEALTH SERVICES, Medical Center Boulevard, Winston Salem, Zip 27157, Mailing Address: One Medical Center Boulevard, Zip 27157; tel. 336/716–2255) **A**1 2 3 5 7 8 9 10 **F**3 5 6 7 8 9 11 12 15 16 17 18 19 20 21 22 23 24 25 26 27 28 29 30 31 32 34 35 36 37 38 39 40 41 43 44 45 46 47 48 49 50 52 53 54 55 56 57 58 59 60 61 62 64 65 66 67 68 70 71 72 73 74 75 77 78 79 80 81 82 83 84 85 86 87 88 89 90 92 93 96 97 98 99 100 101 102 103 104 107 108 110 111 113 114 115 116 117 118 119 120 121 122 123 124 126 129 130 131 132 133 134 135 136 137 138 141 142 143 144 145 146 147 148 **P**6 7 **S** Wake Forest Baptist Health, Winston–Salem, NC
Primary Contact: John D. McConnell, M.D., Chief Executive Officer
CMO: Russell M. Howerton, M.D., Chief Medical Officer
CIO: Chad Eckes, Vice President Information Services and Chief Information Officer
CHR: Cheryl Locke, Vice President and Chief Human Resource Officer
Web address: www.wakehealth.edu
**Control:** Other not–for–profit (including NFP Corporation) **Service:** General Medical and Surgical

**Staffed Beds:** 831 **Admissions:** 36259 **Census:** 653 **Outpatient Visits:** 843702 **Births:** 2 **Total Expense ($000):** 1166130 **Payroll Expense ($000):** 487926 **Personnel:** 7850

---

# NORTH DAKOTA

## ASHLEY—Mcintosh County

★ **ASHLEY MEDICAL CENTER (351322)**, 612 North Center Avenue,
Zip 58413–7013, Mailing Address: P.O. Box 450, Zip 58413–0450;
tel. 701/288–3433, (Nonreporting) **A**9 10 18
Primary Contact: Jerry Lepp, Chief Executive Officer
CMO: Udom Tinsa, M.D., Medical Director
Web address: www.amctoday.org
**Control:** Other not–for–profit (including NFP Corporation) **Service:** General
Medical and Surgical

| Staffed Beds: 64 |
|---|

## BELCOURT—Rolette County

☐ ◇ **INDIAN HEALTH SERVICE – QUENTIN N. BURDICK MEMORIAL HEALTH
CARE FACILITY (350063)**, 1300 Hospital Loop, Zip 58316, Mailing Address:
P.O. Box 160, Zip 58316–0160; tel. 701/477–6111 **A**1 3 5 10 21 **F**3 29 34 38
39 40 41 45 48 50 54 56 57 59 61 62 64 65 75 76 77 81 82 83 85 86 87
89 93 96 97 99 100 101 102 103 104 107 108 110 114 119 130 132 135
143 144 145 146 147 148 **S** U. S. Indian Health Service, Rockville, MD
Primary Contact: Shelly Harris, Chief Executive Officer
CFO: Deland Davis, Chief Financial Officer
CMO: Vernon Azure, Clinical Director
CIO: Chance Wilkie, Information Technology Specialist
CHR: Donna Belgarde, Human Resources Specialist
CNO: Lynelle Hunt, Director of Nursing
Web address: www.ihs.gov
**Control:** PHS, Indian Service, Government, federal **Service:** General Medical and
Surgical

| Staffed Beds: 27 Admissions: 385 Census: 5 Outpatient Visits: 172139 |
|---|
| Births: 305 Total Expense ($000): 46352 Payroll Expense ($000): 19363 |
| Personnel: 290 |

## BISMARCK—Burleigh County

⊞ △ **CHI ST. ALEXIUS HEALTH (350002)**, 900 East Broadway,
Zip 58501–4586, Mailing Address: P.O. Box 5510, Zip 58506–5510;
tel. 701/530–7000, (Total facility includes 19 beds in nursing home–type unit) **A**1
2 3 5 7 9 10 **F**3 8 9 11 12 13 15 17 18 19 20 21 22 23 24 25 26 28 29 30
32 34 35 38 40 43 49 53 56 57 58 59 60 62 63 64 68 70 72 74 75 76 77
78 79 81 82 85 86 87 88 89 90 91 92 93 94 95 97 98 99 100 101 102 103
104 105 106 107 110 111 114 117 119 128 129 130 131 132 135 146 147
148 **P**8 **S** Catholic Health Initiatives, Englewood, CO
Primary Contact: Kurt Schley, Market Chief Executive Officer
CFO: Susan Sisk, Chief Financial Officer
CMO: Shiraz Hyder, M.D., Director Medical Affairs
CIO: Todd Bortke, Director Information Systems
CHR: Tom Gregg, Vice President Human Resources
CNO: Rosanne Schmidt, R.N., Chief Nursing Officer
Web address: www.st.alexius.org
**Control:** Church–operated, Nongovernment, not–for profit **Service:** General
Medical and Surgical

| Staffed Beds: 271 Admissions: 10721 Census: 130 Outpatient Visits: |
|---|
| 259509 Births: 1540 Total Expense ($000): 267953 Payroll Expense |
| ($000): 129870 Personnel: 2167 |

⊞ △ **SANFORD BISMARCK (350015)**, 300 North Seventh Street,
Zip 58501–4439, Mailing Address: P.O. Box 5525, Zip 58506–5525;
tel. 701/323–6000 **A**1 2 3 5 7 9 10 19 **F**3 7 9 11 12 13 15 17 18 20 22 24
26 28 29 30 31 32 33 34 35 36 37 38 40 43 44 45 48 49 50 51 52 53 54
56 57 58 59 60 61 62 63 64 65 68 69 70 72 73 74 76 77 78 79 81 82 85
86 87 88 89 90 91 92 93 96 97 98 99 100 101 102 103 104 105 107 108
110 111 114 115 116 117 118 119 126 128 129 130 131 132 135 138 144
146 147 148 **P**6 **S** Sanford Health, Sioux Falls, SD
Primary Contact: Craig Lambrecht, M.D., President
COO: Al Hurley, Clinic Chief Operating Officer
CFO: Kirk Cristy, Chief Financial Officer
CMO: Chris Meeker, M.D., Chief Medical Officer
CHR: Scott D. Boehm, Executive Vice President Human Resources and Facilities
CNO: Jan Kamphuis, Ph.D., Executive Vice President and Chief Nurse Executive
Web address: www.bismarck.sanfordhealth.org/
**Control:** Other not–for–profit (including NFP Corporation) **Service:** General
Medical and Surgical

| Staffed Beds: 208 Admissions: 11012 Census: 133 Outpatient Visits: |
|---|
| 150605 Births: 1044 Total Expense ($000): 387721 Payroll Expense |
| ($000): 72481 Personnel: 2861 |

**SANFORD HEALTH** See Sanford Bismarck

## BOTTINEAU—Bottineau County

**ST. ANDREW'S HEALTH CENTER (351307)**, 316 Ohmer Street,
Zip 58318–1045; tel. 701/228–9300 **A**5 9 10 18 **F**3 15 28 29 30 34 35 40
43 57 59 79 81 93 107 108 110 125 127 130 132 133 143 144 146 **P**5
**S** Sisters of Mary of the Presentation Health System, Fargo, ND
Primary Contact: Jodi Atkinson, President and Chief Executive Officer
CFO: Sean Rinkenberger, Chief Financial Officer
CMO: Jessica Skjolden, M.D., Chief of Staff
CIO: Jeff Ofstedal, Director Information Technology
CHR: Brenda Arneson, Administrative Assistant
CNO: Karla Spence, Director of Nursing
Web address: www.standrewshealth.com
**Control:** Church–operated, Nongovernment, not–for profit **Service:** General
Medical and Surgical

| Staffed Beds: 25 Admissions: 173 Census: 20 Outpatient Visits: 8000 |
|---|
| Births: 0 Total Expense ($000): 7939 Payroll Expense ($000): 3277 |
| Personnel: 93 |

## BOWMAN—Bowman County

**SOUTHWEST HEALTHCARE SERVICES (351313)**, 802 2nd Street Northwest,
Zip 58623–4483, Mailing Address: P.O. Drawer C, Zip 58623;
tel. 701/523–5265, (Total facility includes 40 beds in nursing home–type unit) **A**9
10 18 **F**3 6 7 10 11 12 15 28 29 30 34 35 36 40 43 45 50 56 57 59 62 64
65 77 79 81 82 87 93 97 107 110 111 119 125 127 128 129 130 131 132
133 **P**6
Primary Contact: Becky Hansen, Chief Executive Officer
CFO: Becky Hansen, Chief Financial Officer
Web address: www.swhealthcare.net
**Control:** Other not–for–profit (including NFP Corporation) **Service:** General
Medical and Surgical

| Staffed Beds: 55 Admissions: 79 Census: 39 Outpatient Visits: 10000 |
|---|
| Births: 0 Total Expense ($000): 12664 Payroll Expense ($000): 7106 |
| Personnel: 151 |

## CANDO—Towner County

★ **TOWNER COUNTY MEDICAL CENTER (351331)**, State Highway 281 North,
Zip 58324, Mailing Address: P.O. Box 688, Zip 58324–0688;
tel. 701/968–4411, (Nonreporting) **A**5 9 10 18
Primary Contact: Ivan Mitchell, Chief Executive Officer
CFO: Tammy Larson, Chief Financial Officer
CMO: Russ Petty, M.D., Chief of Staff
CIO: David Fite, Director Information Technology
CHR: Pat Klingenberg, Director Human Resources
Web address: www.tcmedcenter.org
**Control:** Other not–for–profit (including NFP Corporation) **Service:** General
Medical and Surgical

| Staffed Beds: 20 |
|---|

## CARRINGTON—Foster County

★ **CARRINGTON HEALTH CENTER (351318)**, 800 North Fourth Street,
Zip 58421–1217, Mailing Address: P.O. Box 461, Zip 58421–0461;
tel. 701/652–3141, (Nonreporting) **A**5 9 10 18 **S** Catholic Health Initiatives,
Englewood, CO
Primary Contact: Mariann Doeling, R.N., President
COO: Brenda Rask, Vice President Operations
CFO: Cyndee Thormodson, Chief Financial Officer
CIO: Keith Stauffer, Regional Chief Information Officer
CHR: Lesley Erlandson, Human Resources
CNO: Jodi Lynn Hovdenes, Vice President of Patient Care
Web address: www.carringtonhealthcenter.org
**Control:** Church–operated, Nongovernment, not–for profit **Service:** General
Medical and Surgical

| Staffed Beds: 49 |
|---|

## CAVALIER—Pembina County

★ **PEMBINA COUNTY MEMORIAL HOSPITAL AND WEDGEWOOD MANOR
(351319)**, 301 Mountain Street East, Zip 58220–4015, Mailing Address: P.O.
Box 380, Zip 58220–0380; tel. 701/265–8461, (Total facility includes 50 beds
in nursing home–type unit) **A**5 9 10 18 **F**2 3 28 29 31 40 42 43 45 56 59 65
68 78 81 82 84 87 93 97 107 114 119 127 128 130 131 132 133 135
146 **P**5
Primary Contact: Everett A. Butler, Interim Chief Executive Officer
CMO: K. S. Sumra, M.D., Chief of Staff
CIO: Robert Heidt, Director Information Systems
Web address: www.cavalierhospital.com
**Control:** Other not–for–profit (including NFP Corporation) **Service:** General
Medical and Surgical

**Staffed Beds:** 74 **Admissions:** 334 **Census:** 41 **Outpatient Visits:** 18994
**Births:** 0 **Total Expense ($000):** 11386 **Payroll Expense ($000):** 4979
**Personnel:** 135

## COOPERSTOWN—Griggs County

**COOPERSTOWN MEDICAL CENTER (351306)**, 1200 Roberts Avenue,
Zip 58425–7101; tel. 701/797–2221, (Nonreporting) **A**9 10 18
Primary Contact: Nikki Johnson, Interim Chief Executive Officer
CMO: Jeffrey Peterson, M.D., Medical Director
CHR: Pamela VenHuizen, Chief Human Resources Officer
Web address: www.coopermc.com
**Control:** Other not–for–profit (including NFP Corporation) **Service:** General
Medical and Surgical

**Staffed Beds:** 10

## CROSBY—Divide County

**ST. LUKE'S MEDICAL CENTER (351325)**, 702 First Street Southwest,
Zip 58730–3329, Mailing Address: P.O. Box 10, Zip 58730–0010;
tel. 701/965–6384, (Total facility includes 15 beds in nursing home–type unit) **A**9
10 18 **F**1 35 40 59 81 128 133 **P**6
Primary Contact: Cody Barnhart, Chief Executive Officer
Web address: www.dcstlukes.org/
**Control:** Other not–for–profit (including NFP Corporation) **Service:** Other specialty

**Staffed Beds:** 15 **Admissions:** 257 **Census:** 3 **Outpatient Visits:** 1357
**Births:** 0 **Personnel:** 76

## DEVILS LAKE—Ramsey County

⊞ **CHI MERCY HOSPITAL (351333)**, 1031 Seventh Street N.E.,
Zip 58301–2798; tel. 701/662–2131 **A**1 5 9 10 18 **F**3 11 13 28 29 30 34 35
40 43 45 50 57 70 75 76 81 87 93 107 108 111 114 119 130 133 146 148
**S** Catholic Health Initiatives, Englewood, CO
Primary Contact: Andrew Lankowicz, President
CFO: Cyndee Thormodson, Assistant Vice President Finance
CHR: Bonnie Mattern, Director Human Resources
CNO: Sarah Aliff, Vice President Patient Care Service and Chief Nursing Officer
Web address: www.mercyhospitaldl.com
**Control:** Other not–for–profit (including NFP Corporation) **Service:** General
Medical and Surgical

**Staffed Beds:** 25 **Admissions:** 798 **Census:** 12 **Outpatient Visits:** 18779
**Births:** 324 **Total Expense ($000):** 22042 **Payroll Expense ($000):** 8945
**Personnel:** 127

## DICKINSON—Stark County

⊞ **ST. JOSEPH'S HOSPITAL AND HEALTH CENTER (351336)**, 30 Seventh
Street West, Zip 58601–4399; tel. 701/456–4000 **A**1 5 9 10 18 **F**3 8 11 13 15
28 29 30 34 35 40 53 57 59 64 70 75 76 79 81 84 85 86 87 89 97 107
108 111 114 119 127 129 130 132 133 146 **S** Catholic Health Initiatives,
Englewood, CO
Primary Contact: Reed Reyman, President
CFO: Stephanie Franken, Vice President Operational Finance
CHR: Denise Lutz, Chief Human Resources Officer
CNO: DeeAnna Opstedahl, Vice President Patient Care Services
Web address: www.stjoeshospital.org
**Control:** Church–operated, Nongovernment, not–for profit **Service:** General
Medical and Surgical

**Staffed Beds:** 25 **Admissions:** 1693 **Census:** 12 **Outpatient Visits:** 46556
**Births:** 556 **Total Expense ($000):** 55460 **Payroll Expense ($000):** 24677
**Personnel:** 292

## ELGIN—Grant County

**JACOBSON MEMORIAL HOSPITAL CARE CENTER (351314)**, 601 East Street
North, Zip 58533–7105, Mailing Address: P.O. Box 367, Zip 58533–0367;
tel. 701/584–2792 **A**9 10 18 **F**1 28 34 40 41 43 56 59 71 90 93 97 102 107
119 127 130 131 133 146 148
Primary Contact: Theo Stoller, Chief Executive Officer
CFO: Scott Ostenson, Chief Financial Officer
CMO: Deepak Goyal, M.D., Chief of Staff
CHR: Rynae Golke, Director Human Resources
CNO: Connie Gustafson, Director of Nursing
Web address: www.jacobsonhospital.org
**Control:** Other not–for–profit (including NFP Corporation) **Service:** Long–Term
Acute Care hospital

**Staffed Beds:** 25 **Admissions:** 192 **Census:** 22 **Outpatient Visits:** 8194
**Births:** 0 **Total Expense ($000):** 6068 **Payroll Expense ($000):** 2185
**Personnel:** 65

## FARGO—Cass County

⊞ **ESSENTIA HEALTH FARGO (350070)**, 3000 32nd Avenue South,
Zip 58103–6132; tel. 701/364–8000, (Nonreporting) **A**1 2 5 9 10 **S** Essentia
Health, Duluth, MN
Primary Contact: Timothy Sayler, Chief Operating Officer
COO: Timothy Sayler, Chief Operating Officer
CFO: Dennis Fuhrman, Vice President Finance
CMO: Michael Briggs, M.D., Chief Medical Officer
CIO: Ken Gilles, Chief Information Officer
CHR: Keith Wahlund, Vice President Human Resources
Web address: www.essentiahealth.com
**Control:** Other not–for–profit (including NFP Corporation) **Service:** General
Medical and Surgical

**Staffed Beds:** 94

⊞ **FARGO VETERANS AFFAIRS HEALTH CARE SYSTEM**, 2101 Elm Street North,
Zip 58102–2498; tel. 701/232–3241, (Nonreporting) **A**1 2 3 5 **S** Department of
Veterans Affairs, Washington, DC
Primary Contact: Lavonne Liversage, Director
COO: Dale DeKrey, MS, Associate Director Operations and Resources
CFO: Roger Sayler, Finance Officer
CMO: J. Brian Hancock, M.D., Chief of Staff
CIO: Raymond Nelson, Acting Chief Information Resource Management
CHR: Jason Wells, Chief Human Resources Management Service
CNO: Julie Bruhn, R.N., Associate Director Patient Care and Nurse Executive
Web address: www.fargo.va.gov/
**Control:** Veterans Affairs, Government, federal **Service:** General Medical and
Surgical

**Staffed Beds:** 42

**INNOVIS HEALTH** See Essentia Health Fargo

**KINDRED HOSPITAL FARGO** See Vibra Hospital of Fargo

**MERITCARE MEDICAL CENTER** See Sanford Medical Center Fargo

⊞ **PRAIRIE ST. JOHN'S (354004)**, 510 4th Street South, Zip 58103–1914;
tel. 701/476–7200 **A**1 9 10 **F**4 5 29 34 35 40 41 50 57 87 98 99 100 101
102 103 104 105 106 **P**6 **S** Universal Health Services, Inc., King of Prussia, PA
Primary Contact: Jeff Herman, Chief Executive Officer
COO: Jennifer Faul, Chief Operating Officer
CFO: Tom Eide, Chief Financial Officer
CMO: Eduardo Meza, M.D., Medical Director
CHR: Michelle A. Parkinson, Director Human Resources
CNO: Jacki Toppen, Director of Nursing
Web address: www.prairie–stjohns.com
**Control:** Corporation, Investor–owned, for–profit **Service:** Psychiatric

**Staffed Beds:** 94 **Admissions:** 3436 **Census:** 71 **Outpatient Visits:** 31320
**Births:** 0 **Total Expense ($000):** 27245 **Payroll Expense ($000):** 17378
**Personnel:** 326

✠ △ **SANFORD MEDICAL CENTER FARGO (350011)**, 801 Broadway North, Zip 58122–3641; tel. 701/234–2000, (Includes SANFORD SOUTH UNIVERSITY, 1720 South University Drive, Zip 58103–4994; tel. 701/234–2000; Paul F. Richard, President) **A**1 2 3 5 7 8 9 10 19 **F**3 7 8 9 11 12 13 15 17 18 19 20 21 22 23 24 25 26 27 28 29 30 31 32 33 34 35 36 37 38 39 40 43 44 45 46 47 48 49 50 51 52 53 54 55 56 57 58 59 60 61 62 63 64 65 68 70 71 72 73 74 75 76 78 79 80 81 82 83 84 85 86 87 88 89 90 91 92 93 94 96 97 98 99 100 101 102 103 104 105 107 111 112 114 115 116 117 118 119 120 121 123 124 126 129 130 131 132 135 138 141 142 143 144 145 146 147 148 **P**6 **S** Sanford Health, Sioux Falls, SD
Primary Contact: Paul F. Richard, President
COO: Ellen Cooke, Chief Operating Officer
CFO: Tiffany Lawrence, Chief Financial Officer
CMO: James Volk, M.D., Chief Medical Officer
CIO: Arlyn Broekhuis, Chief Information Officer
CHR: Ann Christenson, Executive Vice President Human Resources and Support Services
CNO: Roberta Young, Chief Nurse Executive
Web address: www.sanfordhealth.org
**Control:** Other not–for–profit (including NFP Corporation) **Service:** General Medical and Surgical

**Staffed Beds:** 486 **Admissions:** 24845 **Census:** 325 **Outpatient Visits:** 422966 **Births:** 2551 **Total Expense ($000):** 814333 **Payroll Expense ($000):** 211822 **Personnel:** 3653

**VETERANS AFFAIRS HEALTH CARE SYSTEM** See Fargo Veterans Affairs Health Care System

✠ **VIBRA HOSPITAL OF FARGO (352004)**, 1720 University Drive South, Zip 58103–4940; tel. 701/241–9099, (Nonreporting) **A**1 9 10 **S** Vibra Healthcare, Mechanicsburg, PA
Primary Contact: Custer Huseby, Chief Executive Officer
Web address: www.vhfargo.com
**Control:** Corporation, Investor–owned, for–profit **Service:** Long–Term Acute Care hospital

**Staffed Beds:** 31

### FORT YATES—Sioux County

**STANDING ROCK SERVICE UNIT, FORT YATES HOSPITAL, INDIAN HEALTH SERVICE, DHHS (350064)**, 10 North River Road, Zip 58538, Mailing Address: P.O. Box J, Zip 58538; tel. 701/854–3831, (Nonreporting) **A**5 9 10 **S** U. S. Indian Health Service, Rockville, MD
Primary Contact: Jana Gipp, Chief Executive Officer
CFO: Anna McLaughlin, Acting Financial Management Officer
CMO: Sara Jumping Eagle, Clinical Director
CNO: Joelle Keepseagle, Director of Nursing
Web address: www.ihs.gov
**Control:** PHS, Indian Service, Government, federal **Service:** General Medical and Surgical

**Staffed Beds:** 14

### GARRISON—McLean County

★ **GARRISON MEMORIAL HOSPITAL (351303)**, 407 Third Avenue S.E., Zip 58540–7235; tel. 701/463–2275, (Nonreporting) **A**5 9 10 18 **S** Catholic Health Initiatives, Englewood, CO
Primary Contact: Tod Graeber, Administrator
CMO: Vern Harchenko, M.D., Chief of Staff
CNO: Beth Hetletved, Director of Nurses
Web address: www.garrisonmh.com
**Control:** Other not–for–profit (including NFP Corporation) **Service:** General Medical and Surgical

**Staffed Beds:** 50

### GRAFTON—Walsh County

★ **UNITY MEDICAL CENTER (351320)**, 164 West 13th Street, Zip 58237–1896; tel. 701/352–1620, (Nonreporting) **A**5 9 10 18
Primary Contact: Alan O'Neil, Chief Executive Officer
CFO: Rachel Ray, Chief Financial Officer
Web address: www.unitymedcenter.com
**Control:** Other not–for–profit (including NFP Corporation) **Service:** General Medical and Surgical

**Staffed Beds:** 14

### GRAND FORKS—Grand Forks County

✠ △ **ALTRU HEALTH SYSTEM (350019)**, 1200 South Columbia Road, Zip 58201–4036, Mailing Address: P.O. Box 6002, Zip 58206–6002; tel. 701/780–5000, (Includes ALTRU HOSPITAL, 1200 South Columbia Road, Zip 58201; tel. 701/780–5000; ALTRU REHABILITATION CENTER, 1300 South Columbia Road, Zip 58201; tel. 701/780–2311) **A**1 2 3 5 7 9 10 20 **F**3 5 7 8 10 11 12 13 14 15 18 20 22 24 26 28 29 30 31 32 33 34 35 36 37 38 40 43 44 45 48 49 50 52 53 55 56 57 58 59 60 61 62 63 64 65 68 69 70 71 72 74 75 76 77 78 79 81 82 83 84 85 86 87 90 91 92 93 94 96 97 98 99 100 101 102 103 104 105 107 108 110 111 114 117 119 121 123 124 125 129 130 131 132 135 143 144 145 146 147 148 **P**6
Primary Contact: David R. Molmen, Chief Executive Officer
COO: Brad Wehe, Chief Operating Officer
CFO: Dwight Thompson, Chief Financial Officer
CMO: Eric Lunn, M.D., Chief Medical Executive
CIO: Mark Waind, Administrative Director Information Services
CHR: Kellee J. Fisk, Chief People Resources Executive
CNO: Margaret M. Reed, R.N., Chief Nursing Executive
Web address: www.altru.org
**Control:** Other not–for–profit (including NFP Corporation) **Service:** General Medical and Surgical

**Staffed Beds:** 288 **Admissions:** 12630 **Census:** 168 **Outpatient Visits:** 776135 **Births:** 1816 **Total Expense ($000):** 471516 **Payroll Expense ($000):** 246447 **Personnel:** 3221

◇ **RICHARD P. STADTER PSYCHIATRIC CENTER (354005)**, 1451 44th Avenue South Unit A., Zip 58201–3434; tel. 701/772–2500, (Nonreporting) **A**9 10 21
Primary Contact: Bonnie Peterson, Chief Executive Officer
CFO: Michelle Currie, Chief Financial Officer
CMO: Thomas Peterson, M.D., President
CHR: Amanda Altendorf, Chief Human Resources and Quality Management
Web address: www.stadtercenter.com
**Control:** Corporation, Investor–owned, for–profit **Service:** Psychiatric

**Staffed Beds:** 71

### HARVEY—Wells County

★ **ST. ALOISIUS MEDICAL CENTER (351327)**, 325 East Brewster Street, Zip 58341–1653; tel. 701/324–4651, (Total facility includes 95 beds in nursing home–type unit) **A**5 9 10 18 **F**15 28 30 40 45 53 56 57 59 77 81 85 93 107 110 114 125 128 130 131 132 133 146 147 **S** Sisters of Mary of the Presentation Health System, Fargo, ND
Primary Contact: Sandra Teubner, Interim Chief Executive Officer
CFO: Sandra Teubner, Chief Financial Officer
Web address: www.staloisius.com
**Control:** Church–operated, Nongovernment, not–for profit **Service:** General Medical and Surgical

**Staffed Beds:** 120 **Admissions:** 361 **Census:** 80 **Outpatient Visits:** 6874 **Births:** 0 **Total Expense ($000):** 12347 **Payroll Expense ($000):** 6033 **Personnel:** 203

### HAZEN—Mercer County

★ **SAKAKAWEA MEDICAL CENTER (351310)**, 510 Eighth Avenue N.E., Zip 58545–4637; tel. 701/748–2225, (Nonreporting) **A**5 9 10 18
Primary Contact: Darrold Bertsch, Chief Executive Officer
CFO: Renae Snyder, Chief Financial Officer
CHR: Laurie Miller, Administrative Assistant
CNO: Marcie Schulz, Director Patient Care
Web address: www.sakmedcenter.com
**Control:** Other not–for–profit (including NFP Corporation) **Service:** General Medical and Surgical

**Staffed Beds:** 18

### HETTINGER—Adams County

**WEST RIVER REGIONAL MEDICAL CENTER (351330)**, 1000 Highway 12, Zip 58639–7530; tel. 701/567–4561, (Nonreporting) **A**3 5 9 10 18
Primary Contact: James K. Long, CPA, Administrator and Chief Executive Officer
CFO: Nathan Stadheim, Chief Financial Officer
CMO: Josh Ronum, Chief of Staff
CIO: Julia Gochenour, Manager Information Systems
CHR: Tera Fried, Manager Human Resources
CNO: Barbara Stadheim, Chief Nursing Officer
Web address: www.wrhs.com
**Control:** Other not–for–profit (including NFP Corporation) **Service:** General Medical and Surgical

**Staffed Beds:** 25

*Many Facility Codes have changed. Please refer to the AHA Guide Code Chart.*
© 2015 AHA Guide

## HILLSBORO—Traill County

★ **SANFORD HILLSBORO MEDICAL CENTER (351329)**, 12 Third Street S.E., Zip 58045–4840, Mailing Address: P.O. Box 609, Zip 58045–0609; tel. 701/636–3200, (Total facility includes 36 beds in nursing home–type unit) **A**5 9 10 18 **F**7 10 11 34 35 40 64 65 68 75 93 97 103 125 128 130 131 133 143 146 148 **P**6 **S** Sanford Health, Sioux Falls, SD
Primary Contact: Jac McTaggart, Chief Executive Officer
CFO: Scott Awalt, Chief Financial Officer
CMO: Charles J. Breen, M.D., Medical Director
CHR: Jenny Jacobson, Manager Human Resources
Web address: www.hillsboromedicalcenter.com
**Control:** Other not–for–profit (including NFP Corporation) **Service:** General Medical and Surgical

**Staffed Beds:** 52 **Admissions:** 202 **Census:** 41 **Outpatient Visits:** 13326 **Births:** 0 **Total Expense ($000):** 8521 **Payroll Expense ($000):** 3613 **Personnel:** 87

## JAMESTOWN—Stutsman County

✠ **JAMESTOWN REGIONAL MEDICAL CENTER (351335)**, 2422 20th Street S.W., Zip 58401–6201; tel. 701/252–1050 **A**1 5 10 18 **F**1 3 4 11 13 15 16 17 28 29 31 34 35 40 43 45 50 53 57 59 62 63 64 67 70 72 73 75 76 77 79 80 81 82 84 85 86 87 88 89 90 93 98 107 108 110 111 115 118 119 128 130 131 132 133 135 146 148
Primary Contact: K. C. DeBoer, President and Chief Executive Officer
COO: Ricki Ramlo, Chief Operating Officer and Vice President Operations
CFO: Brandon Vaughan, Chief Financial Officer and Vice President Finance
CMO: Derek Brickner, President Medical Staff
CIO: Jeff Gunkel, Chief Information Officer
CHR: Ricki Ramlo, Vice President Human Resources
CNO: Trisha Jungels, Chief Nursing Officer and Vice President Clinical Services
Web address: www.jamestownhospital.com
**Control:** Other not–for–profit (including NFP Corporation) **Service:** General Medical and Surgical

**Staffed Beds:** 25 **Admissions:** 1220 **Census:** 10 **Outpatient Visits:** 26045 **Births:** 359 **Total Expense ($000):** 39623 **Payroll Expense ($000):** 16052 **Personnel:** 276

☐ **NORTH DAKOTA STATE HOSPITAL (354003)**, 2605 Circle Drive S.E., Zip 58401–6905; tel. 701/253–3964, (Nonreporting) **A**1 5 9 10
Primary Contact: Rosalie Etherington, Superintendent and Chief Executive Officer
COO: Ken Schulz, Chief Operating Officer
CMO: Eduardo Yabut, M.D., Medical Director
CIO: Amy Shape, Information Technology
CHR: Lyle Grove, Human Resources Director
CNO: Leah Schulz, Director of Nursing
Web address: www.nd.gov/
**Control:** State–Government, nonfederal **Service:** Psychiatric

**Staffed Beds:** 140

## KENMARE—Ward County

★ **KENMARE COMMUNITY HOSPITAL (351305)**, 317 First Avenue N.W., Zip 58746–7104, Mailing Address: P.O. Box 697, Zip 58746–0697; tel. 701/385–4296 **A**9 10 18 **F**34 40 53 57 59 78 80 93 127 133 143
Primary Contact: Margaret Shawn Smothers, Administrator
COO: Bev Heninger, Director of Nursing
CFO: Dennis Empey, Chief Financial Officer
CMO: Buki Oni, M.D., Chief Medical Officer
CIO: David Wanner, Director Information Technology
CHR: Ranae Ehlke, Administrative Secretary and Coordinator Risk Management and Human Resources
CNO: Bev Heninger, Director of Nursing
Web address: www.kenmarend.net/hospital.htm
**Control:** Other not–for–profit (including NFP Corporation) **Service:** General Medical and Surgical

**Staffed Beds:** 25 **Admissions:** 43 **Census:** 19 **Outpatient Visits:** 4462 **Births:** 1 **Total Expense ($000):** 4595 **Payroll Expense ($000):** 3078 **Personnel:** 69

## LANGDON—Cavalier County

★ **CAVALIER COUNTY MEMORIAL HOSPITAL (351323)**, 909 Second Street, Zip 58249–2407; tel. 701/256–6100 **A**5 9 10 18 **F**1 3 4 7 8 9 12 15 16 17 18 19 28 29 30 34 35 40 45 50 56 57 59 64 65 66 67 68 70 72 73 75 77 78 79 80 81 82 86 87 88 89 90 93 96 97 98 99 100 101 102 103 104 107 110 127 128 129 130 131 132 133 143 144 147 148 **P**6
Primary Contact: Lawrence Blue, Administrator and Chief Executive Officer
COO: Lawrence Blue, Administrator and Chief Executive Officer
CFO: Julie Feil, Accountant
CMO: Suresh Patel, M.D., Chief Medical Officer
CIO: Mary Jane Domres, Director Materials Management and Administrator Information Technology
CHR: Andrea Jacobson, Human Resource Officer
Web address: www.cavaliercountyhospital.com
**Control:** Other not–for–profit (including NFP Corporation) **Service:** General Medical and Surgical

**Staffed Beds:** 20 **Admissions:** 350 **Census:** 3 **Outpatient Visits:** 11200 **Births:** 0 **Total Expense ($000):** 7845 **Payroll Expense ($000):** 3007 **Personnel:** 50

## LINTON—Emmons County

**LINTON HOSPITAL (351328)**, 518 North Broadway, Zip 58552–7308, Mailing Address: P.O. Box 850, Zip 58552–0850; tel. 701/254–4511, (Nonreporting) **A**5 9 10 18
Primary Contact: Robert O. Black, Chief Executive Officer
CMO: John Knecht, Chief Medical Staff
CHR: Sue Meidinger, Manager Business Office
Web address: www.lintonhospital.com
**Control:** Other not–for–profit (including NFP Corporation) **Service:** General Medical and Surgical

**Staffed Beds:** 14

## LISBON—Ransom County

★ **CHI LISBON HEALTH (351311)**, 905 Main Street, Zip 58054–4334, Mailing Address: P.O. Box 353, Zip 58054–0353; tel. 701/683–5241 **A**5 9 10 18 **F**3 15 28 29 30 31 34 40 56 57 64 67 78 85 87 89 119 128 130 133 147 **S** Catholic Health Initiatives, Englewood, CO
Primary Contact: Peggy Reinke, R.N., Administrator
COO: Sheri Heinisch, Compliance Officer
CFO: Amber Stowman, Controller
CHR: Janet Froemke, Human Resources Officer
Web address: www.lisbonhospital.com
**Control:** Church–operated, Nongovernment, not–for profit **Service:** General Medical and Surgical

**Staffed Beds:** 18 **Admissions:** 298 **Census:** 5 **Outpatient Visits:** 11135 **Births:** 0 **Total Expense ($000):** 11170 **Payroll Expense ($000):** 3934

## MANDAN—Morton County

**TRIUMPH HOSPITAL – CENTRAL DAKOTAS** See Vibra Hospital of Central Dakotas

✠ **VIBRA HOSPITAL OF CENTRAL DAKOTAS (352005)**, 1000 18th Street N.W., Zip 58554–1612; tel. 701/667–2000, (Nonreporting) **A**1 9 10 **S** Vibra Healthcare, Mechanicsburg, PA
Primary Contact: Glynda Troyo-Sauviac, Chief Executive Officer
Web address: www.vhcentraldakotas.com
**Control:** Corporation, Investor–owned, for–profit **Service:** Long–Term Acute Care hospital

**Staffed Beds:** 41

## MAYVILLE—Traill County

**MERITCARE MAYVILLE UNION HOSPITAL** See Sanford Mayville Medical Center

★ **SANFORD MAYVILLE MEDICAL CENTER (351309)**, 42 Sixth Avenue S.E., Zip 58257–1598; tel. 701/786–3800 **A**5 9 10 18 **F**7 40 43 45 50 65 77 81 93 97 107 119 128 129 130 133 **P**6 **S** Sanford Health, Sioux Falls, SD
Primary Contact: Roger Baier, Chief Executive Officer
CFO: Shauna Slabik, Chief Financial Officer
CMO: Jane Ostlig, Chief Medical Officer
Web address: www.unionhospital.com
**Control:** Other not–for–profit (including NFP Corporation) **Service:** General Medical and Surgical

**Staffed Beds:** 18 **Admissions:** 233 **Census:** 4 **Outpatient Visits:** 20064 **Births:** 1 **Total Expense ($000):** 8400 **Payroll Expense ($000):** 2871 **Personnel:** 60

---

**Hospital, Medicare Provider Number, Address, Telephone, Approval, Facility, and Physician Codes, Health Care System**

★ American Hospital Association (AHA) membership
☐ The Joint Commission accreditation
○ Healthcare Facilities Accreditation Program
◇ DNV Healthcare Inc. accreditation
⇑ Center for Improvement in Healthcare Quality Accreditation
△ Commission on Accreditation of Rehabilitation Facilities (CARF) accreditation

## MCVILLE—Nelson County

**NELSON COUNTY HEALTH SYSTEM (351308)**, 200 Main Street, Zip 58254, Mailing Address: P.O. Box 367, Zip 58254–0367; tel. 701/322–4328, (Nonreporting) **A**9 10 18
Primary Contact: Bruce D. Bowersox, Chief Executive Officer
CFO: Steve Forde, Chief Financial Officer
CMO: Erling Martinson, M.D., Medical Director
Web address: www.nelsoncountyhealthsystem.org
**Control:** Other not–for–profit (including NFP Corporation) **Service:** General Medical and Surgical

Staffed Beds: 58

## MINOT—Ward County

☒ △ **TRINITY HEALTH (350006)**, One Burdick Expressway West, Zip 58701–4406, Mailing Address: P.O. Box 5020, Zip 58702–5020; tel. 701/857–5766, (Includes TRINITY HOSPITAL–ST. JOSEPH'S, 407 3rd Street S.E., Zip 58702–5001; tel. 701/857–2000), (Total facility includes 230 beds in nursing home–type unit) **A**1 2 3 5 7 9 10 19 **F**3 4 5 7 8 11 13 14 15 17 18 20 22 24 28 29 30 31 34 35 36 38 40 43 44 45 46 49 50 54 55 56 57 58 59 60 62 63 64 65 68 70 72 73 74 75 76 77 78 79 80 81 82 85 86 87 89 90 91 92 93 94 96 97 98 99 100 101 102 103 104 105 107 108 110 111 114 115 116 117 118 119 120 121 123 124 126 127 128 129 130 131 132 133 143 144 146 147 148 **P**8
Primary Contact: John M. Kutch, President
CFO: Dennis Empey, Chief Financial Officer
CIO: David Wanner, Chief Information Officer
CHR: Paul Simonson, Vice President
Web address: www.trinityhealth.org
**Control:** Other not–for–profit (including NFP Corporation) **Service:** General Medical and Surgical

Staffed Beds: 630 Admissions: 10025 Census: 330 Outpatient Visits: 198670 Births: 1679 Total Expense ($000): 384829 Payroll Expense ($000): 186517 Personnel: 1527

## NORTHWOOD—Grand Forks County

★ **NORTHWOOD DEACONESS HEALTH CENTER (351312)**, 4 North Park Street, Zip 58267–4102, Mailing Address: P.O. Box 190, Zip 58267–0190; tel. 701/587–6060, (Nonreporting) **A**5 9 10 18 **S** Sanford Health, Sioux Falls, SD
Primary Contact: Pete Antonson, Chief Executive Officer
CMO: Jon Berg, M.D., Chief of Staff
CIO: Chad Peterson, Chief Information Officer
Web address: www.ndhc.net
**Control:** Church–operated, Nongovernment, not–for profit **Service:** General Medical and Surgical

Staffed Beds: 73

## OAKES—Dickey County

★ **CHI OAKES HOSPITAL (351315)**, 1200 North Seventh Street, Zip 58474–2502; tel. 701/742–3291 **A**5 9 10 18 **F**28 29 31 40 81 82 85 107 119 127 133 **S** Catholic Health Initiatives, Englewood, CO
Primary Contact: Becki Thompson, President
CMO: Katie O'Brien–Paradis, M.D., Chief Medical Officer
CHR: Julie Entzminger, Manager Human Resources
CNO: Kimberly A. Ketterling, Vice President of Nursing
Web address: www.oakeshospital.com
**Control:** Other not–for–profit (including NFP Corporation) **Service:** General Medical and Surgical

Staffed Beds: 20 Admissions: 364 Census: 5 Outpatient Visits: 11146 Births: 0 Total Expense ($000): 11251 Payroll Expense ($000): 3880

## PARK RIVER—Walsh County

★ **FIRST CARE HEALTH CENTER (351326)**, 115 Vivian Street, Zip 58270–4540, Mailing Address: PO Box I., Zip 58270–0708; tel. 701/284–7500 **A**5 9 10 18 **F**11 15 28 29 30 31 34 35 40 45 50 59 64 65 68 77 81 93 104 107 110 111 114 119 127 130 133 135 **P**6
Primary Contact: Louise Dryburgh, Chief Executive Officer
CFO: Layne Ensrude, Chief Financial Officer
CMO: Joel Johnson, M.D., Chief Medical Staff
CNO: Lori Seim, R.N., Director Nursing Services
Web address: www.firstcarehc.com
**Control:** Other not–for–profit (including NFP Corporation) **Service:** General Medical and Surgical

Staffed Beds: 14 Admissions: 341 Census: 7 Outpatient Visits: 29801 Births: 0 Total Expense ($000): 9718 Payroll Expense ($000): 3494 Personnel: 74

## ROLLA—Rolette County

**PRESENTATION MEDICAL CENTER (351316)**, 213 Second Avenue N.E., Zip 58367–7153, Mailing Address: P.O. Box 759, Zip 58367–0759; tel. 701/477–3161 **A**5 9 10 18 **F**1 4 11 15 16 17 18 28 29 30 31 34 40 41 43 45 57 59 63 64 66 67 70 72 73 80 81 88 89 90 93 97 98 107 110 114 115 119 127 128 129 133 135 146 **P**6 **S** Sisters of Mary of the Presentation Health System, Fargo, ND
Primary Contact: Mark Kerr, Chief Executive Officer
CFO: Paula Wilkie, Chief Financial Officer
CMO: Roy Cordy, M.D., President Medical Staff
CHR: Tara Okerson, Director Human Resources
Web address: www.pmc–rolla.com
**Control:** Church–operated, Nongovernment, not–for profit **Service:** General Medical and Surgical

Staffed Beds: 25 Admissions: 286 Census: 7 Outpatient Visits: 7954 Births: 0 Total Expense ($000): 8775 Payroll Expense ($000): 3544 Personnel: 77

## RUGBY—Pierce County

★ **HEART OF AMERICA MEDICAL CENTER (351332)**, 800 Main Avenue South, Zip 58368–2198; tel. 701/776–5261, (Nonreporting) **A**5 9 10 18
Primary Contact: Jeff Lingerfelt, Chief Executive Officer
CFO: Bonnie Kuehnemund, Comptroller
CIO: Jeremy Schonebery, Director Information Technology
Web address: www.hamc.com
**Control:** Other not–for–profit (including NFP Corporation) **Service:** General Medical and Surgical

Staffed Beds: 20

## STANLEY—Mountrail County

★ **MOUNTRAIL COUNTY MEDICAL CENTER (351301)**, 615 6th Street S.E., Zip 58784–4444, Mailing Address: P.O. Box 399, Zip 58784–0399; tel. 701/628–2424, (Nonreporting) **A**9 10 18
Primary Contact: Michael Hall, Interim Chief Executive Officer
CFO: Susan Weston, CPA, Chief Financial Officer
CMO: Marla Longmuir, M.D., Chief Medical Officer
CIO: Kathy Janssen, Director Medical Records
CHR: Alisha McMahon, Director Human Resources
CNO: Belinda Moen, R.N., Interim Director of Nursing
Web address: www.stanleyhealth.org
**Control:** Other not–for–profit (including NFP Corporation) **Service:** General Medical and Surgical

Staffed Beds: 11

## TIOGA—Williams County

★ **TIOGA MEDICAL CENTER (351300)**, 810 North Welo Street, Zip 58852–7157, Mailing Address: P.O. Box 159, Zip 58852–0159; tel. 701/664–3305, (Nonreporting) **A**3 5 9 10 18
Primary Contact: Randall K. Pederson, Chief Executive Officer
CMO: Swami P. Gade, M.D., Medical Director
CHR: Mary Ann Holm, Office Clerk
Web address: www.tiogahealth.org
**Control:** Other not–for–profit (including NFP Corporation) **Service:** General Medical and Surgical

Staffed Beds: 55

## TURTLE LAKE—McLean County

★ **COMMUNITY MEMORIAL HOSPITAL (351304)**, 220 Fifth Avenue, Zip 58575–4005, Mailing Address: P.O. Box 280, Zip 58575–0280; tel. 701/448–2331, (Nonreporting) **A**9 10 18 **S** Catholic Health Initiatives, Englewood, CO
Primary Contact: Tod Graeber, Administrator
CFO: Janet Kurle, Chief Financial Officer
CNO: Jason Landenberger, Director of Nursing
Web address: www.wrtc.com/cullum/hospital
**Control:** Church–operated, Nongovernment, not–for profit **Service:** General Medical and Surgical

Staffed Beds: 25

## VALLEY CITY—Barnes County

★ **CHI MERCY HEALTH (351324)**, 570 Chautauqua Boulevard, Zip 58072–3199; tel. 701/845–6400, (Nonreporting) **A**9 10 18 **S** Catholic Health Initiatives, Englewood, CO
Primary Contact: Keith E. Heuser, President
COO: Camille Settelmeyer, Assistant Administrator Clinical Services
CFO: Beth Smith, Controller
CHR: Lesley Erlandson, Human Resources Generalist
Web address: www.mercyhospitalvalleycity.org
**Control:** Church–operated, Nongovernment, not–for profit **Service:** General Medical and Surgical

Staffed Beds: 19

**WATFORD CITY—Mckenzie County**

★ **MCKENZIE COUNTY HEALTHCARE SYSTEM (351302)**, 516 North Main Street, Zip 58854–7310; tel. 701/842–3000 **A**9 10 18 **F**3 11 28 29 34 40 43 50 57 59 64 67 81 85 93 94 97 107 119 127 128 129 131 133 146
Primary Contact: Daniel R. Kelly, Chief Executive Officer
COO: Michael Curtis, Chief Administrative Officer
CFO: Kenneth Cox, Interim Chief Financial Officer
CMO: Gary Ramage, M.D., Chief Medical Officer
CIO: Karn Pederson, Manager Health Information Management
CHR: Amy Gonzales, Director of Human Resources
CNO: Cheryl Faulkner, Director of Nursing
Web address: www.mckenziehealth.com
**Control:** Other not–for–profit (including NFP Corporation) **Service:** General Medical and Surgical

**Staffed Beds:** 24 **Admissions:** 73 **Census:** 1 **Outpatient Visits:** 15865 **Births:** 0 **Total Expense ($000):** 14699 **Payroll Expense ($000):** 4878 **Personnel:** 134

**WILLISTON—Williams County**

⊞ **MERCY MEDICAL CENTER (351334)**, 1301 15th Avenue West, Zip 58801–3896; tel. 701/774–7400 **A**1 3 9 10 18 **F**3 13 15 28 29 30 31 34 35 40 45 47 50 51 56 59 64 65 70 75 76 77 78 79 81 82 85 87 93 97 102 107 108 110 111 114 118 119 120 121 123 124 129 130 132 133 135 141 142 143 146 147 148 **S** Catholic Health Initiatives, Englewood, CO
Primary Contact: Matthew Grimshaw, President
CMO: Brett Vibeto, M.D., Chief of Staff
CIO: Jeff Rust, Information Technology Systems Site Manager
CHR: Dan Bjerknes, Director Human Resources
CNO: Lori Hahn, Vice President Nursing Services
Web address: www.mercy–williston.org
**Control:** Church–operated, Nongovernment, not–for profit **Service:** General Medical and Surgical

**Staffed Beds:** 25 **Admissions:** 1625 **Census:** 12 **Outpatient Visits:** 68750 **Births:** 750 **Total Expense ($000):** 59394 **Payroll Expense ($000):** 31050 **Personnel:** 474

**WISHEK—Mcintosh County**

★ **WISHEK COMMUNITY HOSPITAL AND CLINICS (351321)**, 1007 Fourth Avenue South, Zip 58495–7527, Mailing Address: P.O. Box 647, Zip 58495–0647; tel. 701/452–2326 **A**5 9 10 18 **F**3 7 11 15 17 18 28 29 30 32 34 35 36 40 42 44 50 53 56 57 59 60 64 65 68 75 81 83 87 91 92 93 97 107 114 127 128 130 131 133 143 146 147 **P**3 6
Primary Contact: Beverly Vilhauer, Chief Executive Officer
CFO: Beverly Vilhauer, Chief Financial Officer
CMO: Joseph Thirumalareddy, M.D., Chief of Staff
CIO: Kari Buchholz, Director Health Information Management
CHR: Shar Bauer, Executive Secretary
Web address: www.wishekhospital.com
**Control:** Other not–for–profit (including NFP Corporation) **Service:** General Medical and Surgical

**Staffed Beds:** 17 **Admissions:** 286 **Census:** 3 **Outpatient Visits:** 10682 **Births:** 0 **Total Expense ($000):** 6704 **Payroll Expense ($000):** 2670 **Personnel:** 74

---

**Hospital, Medicare Provider Number, Address, Telephone, Approval, Facility, and Physician Codes, Health Care System**

★ American Hospital Association (AHA) membership ◯ Healthcare Facilities Accreditation Program ⇑ Center for Improvement in Healthcare Quality Accreditation
☐ The Joint Commission accreditation ◇ DNV Healthcare Inc. accreditation △ Commission on Accreditation of Rehabilitation Facilities (CARF) accreditation

## OHIO

**OH**

### AKRON—Summit County

⊠ **AKRON CHILDREN'S HOSPITAL (363303)**, One Perkins Square,
Zip 44308–1063; tel. 330/543–1000 **A**1 2 3 5 8 9 10 13 **F**3 7 11 16 18 19
20 21 22 23 25 26 27 29 30 31 32 33 34 35 36 38 39 40 41 42 44 48 50
54 55 57 58 59 60 61 62 63 64 65 66 68 72 73 74 75 77 78 79 80 81 82
84 85 86 87 88 89 91 92 93 94 96 97 98 99 100 101 102 104 105 107 108
111 112 114 115 116 117 118 119 129 130 131 132 134 135 136 141 143
144 146 148 **P**6
Primary Contact: William H. Considine, President
COO: Grace Wakulchik, R.N., Chief Operating Officer
CFO: Michael Trainer, Chief Financial Officer
CMO: Robert McGregor, M.D., Chief Medical Officer
CIO: Tom Ogg, Vice President Information Services and Chief Information Officer
CHR: Walt Schwoeble, Vice President Human Resources
CNO: Lisa Aurilio, R.N., Vice President Patient Services and Chief Nursing Officer
Web address: www.akronchildrens.org
**Control:** Other not–for–profit (including NFP Corporation) **Service:** Children's
general

**Staffed Beds: 414 Admissions: 10130 Census: 201 Outpatient Visits:**
845979 **Births:** 0 **Total Expense ($000):** 615567 **Payroll Expense ($000):**
312919 **Personnel:** 4248

⊠ **AKRON GENERAL MEDICAL CENTER (360027)**, 1 Akron General Avenue,
Zip 44307–2433; tel. 330/344–6000 **A**1 2 3 5 8 9 10 **F**3 5 8 11 12 13 14 15
17 18 20 22 24 26 28 29 30 31 34 35 36 38 39 40 42 43 44 45 46 47 48
49 50 51 52 53 54 55 56 57 58 59 60 61 64 65 66 68 70 71 72 74 75 76
78 79 81 82 84 85 86 87 91 92 93 94 96 97 98 100 101 102 103 104 105
107 108 110 111 112 114 115 118 119 120 121 123 124 126 129 130 131
132 134 135 144 145 146 147 148 **P**6 8 **S** Akron General Health System,
Akron, OH
Primary Contact: Alan Papa, President
CFO: Dave Frigo, Vice President Financial Planning and Treasury
CMO: David Peter, M.D., Senior Vice President Medical Affairs and Chief Medical
Director
CIO: David Fiser, Vice President and Chief Information Officer
CHR: Don Corpora, Executive Vice President and Chief Human Resources Officer
CNO: Cherie M. Guster, R.N., Senior Vice President and Chief Nursing Officer
Web address: www.akrongeneral.org
**Control:** Other not–for–profit (including NFP Corporation) **Service:** General
Medical and Surgical

**Staffed Beds: 407 Admissions: 21971 Census: 274 Outpatient Visits:**
588333 **Births:** 2919 **Total Expense ($000):** 458414 **Payroll Expense**
**($000):** 183039 **Personnel:** 2516

⊠ **SELECT SPECIALTY HOSPITAL–AKRON (362027)**, 200 East Market Street,
Zip 44308–2015; tel. 330/761–7500, (Nonreporting) **A**1 10 **S** Select Medical
Corporation, Mechanicsburg, PA
Primary Contact: Sonda Burns, Chief Executive Officer
Web address: www.selectspecialtyhospitals.com/company/locations/akron.aspx
**Control:** Corporation, Investor–owned, for–profit **Service:** Long–Term Acute Care
hospital

**Staffed Beds:** 60

⊠ **SUMMA AKRON CITY HOSPITAL (360020)**, 525 East Market Street,
Zip 44304–1619; tel. 330/375–3000, (Includes SUMMA AKRON CITY HOSPITAL,
525 East Market Street, Zip 44309–2090, Mailing Address: P.O. Box 2090,
Zip 44309–2090; tel. 330/375–3000; SUMMA SAINT THOMAS HOSPITAL, 444
North Main Street, Zip 44310; tel. 330/375–3000) **A**1 2 3 5 8 9 10 13 **F**3 4 5
6 8 11 12 13 15 17 18 20 22 24 26 28 29 30 31 33 34 35 36 37 38 39 40
41 42 43 44 45 46 49 50 51 53 54 55 56 57 59 61 62 63 64 65
66 68 70 71 73 74 75 76 77 78 79 80 81 82 83 84 85 86 87 92 93 96 97
98 100 101 102 103 104 105 107 108 109 110 111 114 115 116 117 118
119 120 121 123 124 126 129 130 131 132 133 135 144 146 147 148 **P**6
8 **S** Summa Health System, Akron, OH
Primary Contact: Thomas Malone, M.D., President and Chief Executive Officer
COO: Robert Harrigan, President, Summa Hospitals
CMO: Erik N. Steele, D.O., Senior Vice President and Chief Medical Officer
CIO: Greg Kall, Chief Information Officer
CHR: Kyle Klawitter, Vice President Human Resources
Web address: www.summahealth.org
**Control:** Other not–for–profit (including NFP Corporation) **Service:** General
Medical and Surgical

**Staffed Beds: 436 Admissions: 29398 Census: 363 Outpatient Visits:**
404229 **Births:** 3388 **Total Expense ($000):** 715561 **Payroll Expense**
**($000):** 202787 **Personnel:** 3896

**SUMMA AKRON CITY HOSPITAL** See Summa Akron City Hospital

**SUMMA HEALTH SYSTEM** See Summa Akron City Hospital

☐ △ **SUMMA REHAB HOSPITAL (363035)**, 29 North Adams Street,
Zip 44304–1641; tel. 330/572–7300, (Nonreporting) **A**1 7 10 **S** Summa Health
System, Akron, OH
Primary Contact: Cheryl Henthorn, Chief Executive Officer
Web address: www.summarehabhospital.com/
**Control:** Corporation, Investor–owned, for–profit **Service:** Rehabilitation

**Staffed Beds:** 60

**SUMMA SAINT THOMAS HOSPITAL** See Summa Akron City Hospital

### ALLIANCE—Stark County

○ **ALLIANCE COMMUNITY HOSPITAL (360131)**, 200 East State Street,
Zip 44601–4936; tel. 330/596–6000, (Total facility includes 78 beds in nursing
home–type unit) **A**2 5 9 10 11 **F**3 8 11 13 15 28 29 30 31 34 35 44 45 49
50 51 56 57 59 60 62 63 64 68 69 70 74 75 76 77 79 81 82 85 86 87 90
93 96 98 103 107 108 110 111 115 118 119 128 129 130 132 135 143
146 147 148 **P**5 7 8
Primary Contact: Stanley W. Jonas, Chief Executive Officer
COO: Dale W. Wells, Chief Financial and Operating Officer
CFO: Dale W. Wells, Chief Financial and Operating Officer
CMO: Ashraf Ahmed, M.D., Senior Vice President Physician and Hospital Services
CIO: David W. Shroades, Vice President Technology Services
CHR: Nicole L. Russ, Director Colleague Relations
CNO: Amy Antonacci, MSN, Vice President Nursing Services
Web address: www.achosp.org
**Control:** Other not–for–profit (including NFP Corporation) **Service:** General
Medical and Surgical

**Staffed Beds: 202 Admissions: 3409 Census: 103 Outpatient Visits:**
162285 **Births:** 391 **Total Expense ($000):** 88758 **Payroll Expense ($000):**
38610 **Personnel:** 777

### AMHERST—Lorain County

☐ **SPECIALTY HOSPITAL OF LORAIN (362025)**, 254 Cleveland Avenue,
Zip 44001–1620; tel. 440/988–6260, (Nonreporting) **A**1 10
Primary Contact: Julia M. Meeks, Chief Operating Officer
**Control:** Other not–for–profit (including NFP Corporation) **Service:** Long–Term
Acute Care hospital

**Staffed Beds:** 30

### ARCHBOLD—Fulton County

**ARCHBOLD HOSPITAL** See Community Hospitals and Wellness Centers, Bryan

### ASHLAND—Ashland County

⊠ **SAMARITAN REGIONAL HEALTH SYSTEM (360002)**, 1025 Center Street,
Zip 44805–4011; tel. 419/289–0491, (Nonreporting) **A**1 5 9 10
Primary Contact: Danny L. Boggs, President and Chief Executive Officer
CFO: Mary Griest, Vice President Finance and Chief Financial Officer
CMO: Philip Myers, M.D., Vice President Medical Affairs
CIO: Kathleen Metcalf, Chief Information Officer
CHR: Alyce Legg, Vice President Human Resources
CNO: Karin Schwan, Chief Nursing Officer, Vice President Patient Care Services
Web address: www.samaritanhospital.org
**Control:** Other not–for–profit (including NFP Corporation) **Service:** General
Medical and Surgical

**Staffed Beds:** 55

### ASHTABULA—Ashtabula County

☐ **ASHTABULA COUNTY MEDICAL CENTER (360125)**, 2420 Lake Avenue,
Zip 44004–4954; tel. 440/997–2262, (Total facility includes 15 beds in nursing
home–type unit) **A**1 5 9 10 20 **F**3 11 13 15 18 19 20 26 28 29 30 31 34 35
38 40 44 45 49 50 51 53 54 57 59 61 62 63 64 68 70 74 75 76 77 78 79
81 82 83 84 85 86 87 89 92 93 97 98 100 102 103 104 105 107 108 110
111 114 116 117 118 119 128 129 130 131 132 135 143 144 146 147 148
**P**4 6 8
Primary Contact: Michael J. Habowski, President and Chief Executive Officer
COO: Lewis Hutchison, Vice President Operations and Quality
CFO: Donald L. Kepner, Chief Financial Officer
CMO: Jude Cauwenberg, M.D., Chief of Staff
CIO: Jared Swiger, Director Information Systems
CHR: Jonathan Forbes, Director Human Resources
CNO: Ken Frame, Chief Nursing Officer
Web address: www.acmchealth.org
**Control:** Other not–for–profit (including NFP Corporation) **Service:** General
Medical and Surgical

**Staffed Beds: 151 Admissions: 5741 Census: 72 Outpatient Visits:** 226827
**Births:** 397 **Total Expense ($000):** 108675 **Payroll Expense ($000):** 50059
**Personnel:** 739

## ATHENS—Athens County

☐ **APPALACHIAN BEHAVIORAL HEALTHCARE (364015)**, 100 Hospital Drive, Zip 45701–2301; tel. 740/594–5000, (Nonreporting) **A**1 10 **S** Ohio Department of Mental Health, Columbus, OH
Primary Contact: Jane E. Krason, R.N., Chief Executive Officer
CMO: Mark F. McGee, M.D., Chief Clinical Officer
CHR: Amy Grover, Director
Web address: www.mh.state.oh.us
**Control:** State–Government, nonfederal **Service:** Psychiatric

| Staffed Beds: 224 |
|---|

⌧ **O'BLENESS MEMORIAL HOSPITAL (360014)**, 55 Hospital Drive, Zip 45701–2302; tel. 740/593–5551 **A**1 9 10 12 13 **F**3 13 15 18 20 28 31 34 40 51 57 59 64 65 70 75 76 78 79 80 81 82 85 87 93 94 97 107 108 110 111 115 118 119 130 131 135 146 147 148 **P**6 **S** OhioHealth, Columbus, OH
Primary Contact: Mark R. Seckinger, President
CFO: Robert Melaragno, Vice President Finance
CIO: Kristine Barr, Vice President Communication Services
CHR: Sandie Leasure, Senior Vice President Human Resources
CNO: Sandy Wood, MSN, Vice President Patient Services and Chief Nursing Officer
Web address: www.obleness.org
**Control:** Other not–for–profit (including NFP Corporation) **Service:** General Medical and Surgical

| Staffed Beds: 64 Admissions: 2725 Census: 22 Outpatient Visits: 77182 Births: 687 Total Expense ($000): 73490 Payroll Expense ($000): 22645 Personnel: 472 |
|---|

## BARBERTON—Summit County

⌧ **SUMMA BARBERTON CITIZENS HOSPITAL (360019)**, 155 Fifth Street N.E., Zip 44203–3332; tel. 330/615–3000 **A**1 2 3 5 9 10 **F**3 8 13 14 15 17 18 20 22 24 26 28 29 30 31 34 35 40 46 47 48 49 50 51 56 57 58 59 60 61 63 68 70 74 76 77 78 79 81 82 83 84 85 86 87 93 97 98 100 102 103 104 105 107 108 110 111 113 114 116 117 118 119 129 130 131 132 135 146 147 148 **P**6 8 **S** Summa Health System, Akron, OH
Primary Contact: Jason Niehaus, Senior Vice President Operations and Administrator
CFO: Charles Alderson, Chief Financial Officer
CMO: Jeffrey Morris, M.D., Medical Director
CIO: David Lynch, Regional Director Information Systems
CHR: Donald V. Argiro, Vice President, Human Resources
CNO: Kathy Jobe, R.N., Chief Nursing Officer and Vice President Patient Care Services
Web address: www.summahealth.org/locations/hospitals/barberton
**Control:** Other not–for–profit (including NFP Corporation) **Service:** General Medical and Surgical

| Staffed Beds: 192 Admissions: 8564 Census: 103 Outpatient Visits: 95477 Births: 617 Total Expense ($000): 162433 Payroll Expense ($000): 56678 Personnel: 956 |
|---|

## BARNESVILLE—Belmont County

⌧ **BARNESVILLE HOSPITAL (361321)**, 639 West Main Street, Zip 43713–1039, Mailing Address: P.O. Box 309, Zip 43713–0309; tel. 740/425–3941 **A**1 9 10 18 **F**3 11 15 17 28 29 30 32 34 35 39 40 41 45 50 57 59 64 65 69 70 74 75 77 78 79 81 85 86 87 89 90 91 93 107 108 114 119 128 129 130 132 133 135 145 146 **P**6
Primary Contact: David D. Phillips, Chief Executive Officer and Administrator
CFO: Willie Cooper–Lohr, Chief Financial Officer
CMO: David J. Hilliard, D.O., Chief of Staff
CIO: Tiffany Gramby, Senior Director Information Management and Privacy Officer
CHR: Beth K. Brill, Senior Director Human Resources
CNO: Cynthia Touvelle, R.N., Senior Director Care Management and Chief Nursing Officer
Web address: www.barnesvillehospital.com
**Control:** Other not–for–profit (including NFP Corporation) **Service:** General Medical and Surgical

| Staffed Beds: 25 Admissions: 932 Census: 10 Outpatient Visits: 33432 Births: 0 Total Expense ($000): 20595 Payroll Expense ($000): 7978 Personnel: 182 |
|---|

## BATAVIA—Clermont County

⌧ **MERCY HEALTH – CLERMONT HOSPITAL (360236)**, 3000 Hospital Drive, Zip 45103–1921; tel. 513/732–8200, (Nonreporting) **A**1 2 3 9 10 **S** Mercy Health, Cincinnati, OH
Primary Contact: Jeff Graham, Market Leader and President
CFO: Philip Wheeler, Director Finance
CMO: Parma Hariharan, M.D., Chief of Staff
CHR: Angie Ferrell, Director Human Resources
CNO: Gayle Heintzelman, R.N., Site Administrator and Chief Nursing Officer
Web address: www.e–mercy.com
**Control:** Church–operated, Nongovernment, not–for profit **Service:** General Medical and Surgical

| Staffed Beds: 119 |
|---|

## BEACHWOOD—Cuyahoga County

⌧ **UNIVERSITY HOSPITALS AHUJA MEDICAL CENTER (360359)**, 3999 Richmond Road, Zip 44122–6046; tel. 216/593–5500 **A**1 3 9 10 **F**3 5 15 18 20 22 24 26 28 29 30 34 35 36 40 41 42 43 45 46 47 48 49 50 51 56 57 59 60 61 65 68 70 74 75 77 79 80 81 82 85 87 91 107 108 109 110 111 115 119 126 130 144 145 146 148 **S** University Hospitals, Cleveland, OH
Primary Contact: Susan V. Juris, President
Web address: www.uhhospitals.org/ahuja/tabid/7051/uhahujamedicalcenter.aspx
**Control:** Other not–for–profit (including NFP Corporation) **Service:** General Medical and Surgical

| Staffed Beds: 144 Admissions: 8758 Census: 96 Outpatient Visits: 177437 Births: 0 Total Expense ($000): 146449 Payroll Expense ($000): 47081 Personnel: 872 |
|---|

## BEAVERCREEK—Greene County County

★ ◯ **SOIN MEDICAL CENTER (360360)**, 3535 Pentagon Boulevard, Zip 45431–1705; tel. 937/702–4000 **A**9 10 11 **F**3 11 13 18 20 22 29 30 31 34 35 38 39 40 43 44 45 46 48 49 50 51 53 56 57 59 61 64 70 73 74 75 76 77 78 79 81 82 85 86 87 102 107 108 111 114 115 116 117 118 119 126 130 132 135 146 148 **S** Kettering Health Network, Dayton, OH
Primary Contact: Terry M. Burns, Administrator, Senior Vice President of KHN
COO: Ron D. Connovich, Chief Financial Officer and Chief Operating Officer
CFO: Ron D. Connovich, Chief Financial Officer and Chief Operating Officer
CMO: David Small, M.D., Chief Medical Officer
CIO: Andy Lehman, Vice President Information Systems
CNO: Belinda Mallett, R.N., Vice President, Patient Care and Clinical Services
Web address: www.khnetwork.org/soin
**Control:** Church–operated, Nongovernment, not–for profit **Service:** General Medical and Surgical

| Staffed Beds: 102 Admissions: 4874 Census: 47 Outpatient Visits: 57756 Births: 424 Total Expense ($000): 115546 Payroll Expense ($000): 40160 Personnel: 619 |
|---|

## BELLAIRE—Belmont County

☐ **BELMONT COMMUNITY HOSPITAL (360153)**, 4697 Harrison Street, Zip 43906–1338, Mailing Address: P.O. Box 653, Zip 43906–0653; tel. 740/671–1200, (Nonreporting) **A**1 9 10
Primary Contact: John DeBlasis, Vice President
CFO: James B. Murdy, Chief Financial Officer
CMO: C. N. Patel, M.D., Chief of Staff
CHR: Serge Gentile, Director Human Resources
Web address: www.wheelinghospital.org/facilities/bch/
**Control:** Other not–for–profit (including NFP Corporation) **Service:** General Medical and Surgical

| Staffed Beds: 66 |
|---|

## BELLEFONTAINE—Logan County

★ ◇ **MARY RUTAN HOSPITAL (360197)**, 205 Palmer Avenue, Zip 43311–2281; tel. 937/592–4015 **A**3 5 9 10 20 21 **F**3 11 13 14 15 18 20 28 29 30 31 32 34 40 50 54 57 59 64 66 68 70 75 76 77 78 79 81 82 85 86 87 89 107 108 110 111 115 119 129 130 132 133 135 146 147
Primary Contact: Mandy C. Goble, President and Chief Executive Officer
CFO: Steven Brown, Vice President Fiscal Affairs
CMO: Grant Varian, M.D., Medical Director
CIO: Robert Reynolds, Director Information Systems
CHR: Vickie L. Crumley, Vice President Human Resources
CNO: Frank Gliha, Vice President of Patient Care
Web address: www.maryrutan.org
**Control:** Other not–for–profit (including NFP Corporation) **Service:** General Medical and Surgical

| Staffed Beds: 100 Admissions: 1647 Census: 14 Outpatient Visits: 96706 Births: 341 Total Expense ($000): 85317 Payroll Expense ($000): 32592 Personnel: 541 |
|---|

---

**Hospital, Medicare Provider Number, Address, Telephone, Approval, Facility, and Physician Codes, Health Care System**

★ American Hospital Association (AHA) membership
☐ The Joint Commission accreditation
◯ Healthcare Facilities Accreditation Program
◇ DNV Healthcare Inc. accreditation
⇑ Center for Improvement in Healthcare Quality Accreditation
△ Commission on Accreditation of Rehabilitation Facilities (CARF) accreditation

**OH**

## BELLEVUE—Sandusky County

✠ **BELLEVUE HOSPITAL (360107)**, 1400 West Main Street, Zip 44811–9088, Mailing Address: P.O. Box 8004, Zip 44811–8004; tel. 419/483–4040 **A**1 5 9 10 **F**13 15 28 29 30 31 34 35 40 41 46 50 53 56 57 59 61 62 68 70 74 75 77 79 81 82 85 93 107 110 111 114 118 119 127 129 130 131 132 133 135 143 144 146 **P**8
Primary Contact: Michael Winthrop, President
CFO: Timothy Buit, Executive Vice President and Chief Financial Officer
CMO: Donald Smith, President Medical Staff
CIO: Kim Stults, Director, Information Systems
CHR: Lisa M. Sartain, Vice President, Human Resources
CNO: Sara Brokaw, Vice President Patient Care Services
Web address: www.bellevuehospital.com
**Control:** Other not–for–profit (including NFP Corporation) **Service:** General Medical and Surgical

> Staffed Beds: 50 Admissions: 1538 Census: 12 Outpatient Visits: 80438 Births: 376 Total Expense ($000): 43221 Payroll Expense ($000): 16364 Personnel: 345

## BLUFFTON—Allen County

★ **BLUFFTON HOSPITAL (361322)**, 139 Garau Street, Zip 45817–1027; tel. 419/358–9010 **A**9 10 18 **F**11 13 15 18 29 40 45 54 57 59 63 64 70 76 77 81 82 83 84 91 93 107 110 114 119 127 130 135 146 148 **S** Blanchard Valley Health System, Findlay, OH
Primary Contact: Christine Keller, Chief Administrative Officer
CFO: David Cytlak, Vice President Finance
CMO: William H. Kose, M.D., Vice President Quality and Medical Affairs
CIO: David Cytlak, Vice President Finance
CHR: Ryan Fisher, Director Human Resources
CNO: Barbara J. Pasztor, R.N., Vice President Nursing and Patient Care Services
Web address: www.bvhealthsystem.org/
**Control:** Other not–for–profit (including NFP Corporation) **Service:** General Medical and Surgical

> Staffed Beds: 25 Admissions: 318 Census: 2 Outpatient Visits: 37017 Births: 241 Total Expense ($000): 12814 Payroll Expense ($000): 8303 Personnel: 116

## BOARDMAN—Mahoning County

**MAHONING VALLEY HOSPITAL** See Vibra Hospital of Mahoning Valley

✠ **SELECT SPECIALTY HOSPITAL – YOUNGSTOWN (360363)**, 8401 Market Street, 7 South, Zip 44512–6725; tel. 330/729–1750, (Nonreporting) **A**1 10 **S** Select Medical Corporation, Mechanicsburg, PA
Primary Contact: Sharon Noro, Interim Chief Executive Officer
**Control:** Corporation, Investor–owned, for–profit **Service:** Long–Term Acute Care hospital

> Staffed Beds: 56

✠ **ST. ELIZABETH BOARDMAN HEALTH CENTER (360276)**, 8401 Market Street, Zip 44512–6777; tel. 330/729–2929 **A**1 9 10 13 **F**3 8 11 13 15 18 29 30 31 34 40 45 46 47 49 50 59 60 68 70 74 75 76 77 78 79 81 84 87 93 94 107 108 110 111 114 115 117 118 119 120 121 123 129 130 146 147 148 **P**6 **S** Mercy Health, Cincinnati, OH
Primary Contact: Eugenia Aubel, President
CFO: Matt Love, Senior Vice President Finance
CMO: Nicholas Kreatsoulas, M.D., Vice President Medical Affairs and Chief Quality Officer
CIO: Maureen Kordupel, Director Relationship Manager
CHR: Scott Dimmick, Senior Vice President Human Resources
CNO: Lori DeNiro, Senior Director Nursing
Web address: www.ehealthconnection.com/regions/youngstown/content/show_facility.asp?facility_id=190
**Control:** Church–operated, Nongovernment, not–for profit **Service:** General Medical and Surgical

> Staffed Beds: 169 Admissions: 10668 Census: 119 Outpatient Visits: 103013 Births: 1756 Total Expense ($000): 116445 Payroll Expense ($000): 37276 Personnel: 925

✠ **VIBRA HOSPITAL OF MAHONING VALLEY (362023)**, 8049 South Avenue, Zip 44512–6154; tel. 330/726–5000, (Includes VIBRA HOSPITAL OF MAHONING VALLEY–TRUMBULL CAMPUS, 1350 East Market Street, 9th Floor, Warren, Zip 44483–6608; tel. 330/675–5591; Mary Lou Sankovich, R.N., MSN, Chief Executive Officer) **A**1 10 **F**1 3 29 130 148 **S** Vibra Healthcare, Mechanicsburg, PA
Primary Contact: Mary Lou Sankovich, R.N., MSN, Chief Executive Officer
CMO: Lawrence Goldstein, M.D., Chief Medical Officer
CNO: Mary Jane Larmon, Chief Clinical Officer
Web address: www.vhmvalley.com
**Control:** Corporation, Investor–owned, for–profit **Service:** Long–Term Acute Care hospital

> Staffed Beds: 42 Admissions: 744 Census: 35 Outpatient Visits: 0 Births: 0 Total Expense ($000): 16216 Payroll Expense ($000): 6208 Personnel: 115

## BOWLING GREEN—Wood County

✠ **WOOD COUNTY HOSPITAL (360029)**, 950 West Wooster Street, Zip 43402–2603; tel. 419/354–8900 **A**1 3 5 9 10 **F**3 11 12 13 15 17 18 28 29 30 31 32 34 35 40 44 45 46 50 57 59 64 65 68 69 70 74 75 76 77 78 79 81 82 85 87 89 93 107 108 110 111 114 115 118 119 120 121 123 124 129 130 131 132 135 144 146 147 148 **P**6 8
Primary Contact: Stanley R. Korducki, President
CFO: Karol Bortel, Vice President Financial Services
CMO: Shawn Stansbery, M.D., Chief of Staff
CIO: Joanne White, Chief Information Officer
CHR: Michael Ford, Vice President Patient Services
CNO: Sandra Beidelschies, MSN, Vice President Patient Services
Web address: www.woodcountyhospital.org
**Control:** Other not–for–profit (including NFP Corporation) **Service:** General Medical and Surgical

> Staffed Beds: 102 Admissions: 3097 Census: 26 Outpatient Visits: 99973 Births: 346 Total Expense ($000): 80770 Payroll Expense ($000): 29719 Personnel: 610

## BRYAN—Williams County

☐ **COMMUNITY HOSPITALS AND WELLNESS CENTERS (360121)**, 433 West High Street, Zip 43506–1679; tel. 419/636–1131, (Includes ARCHBOLD HOSPITAL, 121 Westfield Drive, Archbold, Zip 43502; tel. 419/445–4415; BRYAN HOSPITAL, 433 West High Street, Zip 43506; tel. 419/636–1131; MONTPELIER HOSPITAL, 909 East Snyder Avenue, Montpelier, Zip 43543; tel. 419/485–3154), (Nonreporting) **A**1 2 5 9 10
Primary Contact: Philip L. Ennen, Vice President and Chief Executive Officer
CFO: Leroy P. Feather, Vice President Finance
CIO: Greg Slattery, Vice President Information
CHR: Mary Ann Potts, Director Personnel
Web address: www.chwcchospital.com
**Control:** Other not–for–profit (including NFP Corporation) **Service:** General Medical and Surgical

> Staffed Beds: 113

## BUCYRUS—Crawford County

★ ◇ **BUCYRUS COMMUNITY HOSPITAL (361316)**, 629 North Sandusky Avenue, Zip 44820–1821; tel. 419/562–4677, (Nonreporting) **A**5 9 10 18 21 **S** Avita Health System, Galion, OH
Primary Contact: Jerome Morasko, Chief Executive Officer
COO: Andy Daniels, Chief Operating Officer
CMO: Michael A. Johnson, M.D., Chief of Staff
CIO: Joann Riedlinger, Vice President Nursing and Manager Information Systems
CHR: Jeanne Perkins, Vice President Nursing and Interim Manager Human Resources
Web address: www.bchonline.org
**Control:** Other not–for–profit (including NFP Corporation) **Service:** General Medical and Surgical

> Staffed Beds: 25

## CADIZ—Harrison County

✠ **HARRISON COMMUNITY HOSPITAL (361311)**, 951 East Market Street, Zip 43907–9799; tel. 740/942–4631 **A**1 9 10 18 **F**7 11 15 18 28 29 30 31 34 35 40 45 47 50 51 53 57 59 62 64 65 68 75 77 78 79 81 82 85 86 87 93 97 107 108 110 111 114 119 129 130 132 133 135 143 146 147 148
Primary Contact: Clifford K. Harmon, Chief Executive Officer
CMO: Siripurapu Prasad, Chief of Staff
CIO: Will Combs, Director Information Technology
CHR: Peter Giordano, Senior Director Human Resources
CNO: Janis Olinski, R.N., Vice President Clinical Services
Web address: www.harrisoncommunity.com
**Control:** Other not–for–profit (including NFP Corporation) **Service:** General Medical and Surgical

> Staffed Beds: 25 Admissions: 391 Census: 5 Outpatient Visits: 38207 Births: 0 Total Expense ($000): 16726 Payroll Expense ($000): 6603 Personnel: 154

*Many Facility Codes have changed. Please refer to the AHA Guide Code Chart.*     © 2015 AHA Guide

## CAMBRIDGE—Guernsey County

**SOUTHEASTERN OHIO REGIONAL MEDICAL CENTER (360203)**, 1341 North Clark Street, Zip 43725–9614, Mailing Address: P.O. Box 610, Zip 43725–0610; tel. 740/439–8000 **A**1 2 9 10 20 **F**3 7 11 13 15 18 20 28 29 30 31 32 34 35 40 43 46 48 49 51 57 59 60 62 63 64 65 66 70 75 77 78 79 81 82 83 84 85 86 87 91 93 96 97 107 108 110 111 114 116 118 119 129 130 131 132 135 144 146 147 148 **P**6 8
Primary Contact: Raymond M. Chorey, President and Chief Executive Officer
CFO: Timothy R. Evancho, Chief Financial Officer
CMO: E. Edwin Conaway, M.D., Vice President Medical Affairs and Chief Medical Officer
CIO: Kevin Ludwigsen, Chief Information Officer
CHR: Steven Michael Brooks, Vice President Human Resources
CNO: Angela S. Long, Vice President Clinical Services and Chief Nursing Officer
Web address: www.seormc.org
**Control:** Other not–for–profit (including NFP Corporation) **Service:** General Medical and Surgical

**Staffed Beds: 95 Admissions: 3564 Census: 31 Outpatient Visits:** 137184
**Births: 418 Total Expense ($000): 82179 Payroll Expense ($000):** 29540
**Personnel: 641**

## CANAL WINCHESTER—Fairfield County

**DILEY RIDGE MEDICAL CENTER (360358)**, 7911 Diley Road, Zip 43110–9653; tel. 614/838–7911 **A**1 9 10 **F**3 15 29 30 35 40 50 54 64 68 85 87 107 110 111 114 119 130 147
Primary Contact: Jodi Wilson, President and Chief Operating Officer
COO: Jodi Wilson, President and Chief Operating Officer
Web address: www.dileyridgemedicalcenter.com
**Control:** Other not–for–profit (including NFP Corporation) **Service:** General Medical and Surgical

**Staffed Beds: 10 Admissions: 11 Census: 1 Outpatient Visits:** 51837
**Births: 0 Total Expense ($000): 12492 Payroll Expense ($000):** 4224
**Personnel: 82**

## CANTON—Stark County

**AULTMAN HOSPITAL (360084)**, 2600 Sixth Street S.W., Zip 44710–1702; tel. 330/452–9911, (Includes AULTMAN HOSPITAL PEDIATRIC SERVICES, 2600 Sixth Street, S.W., tel. 330/363–5455), (Total facility includes 60 beds in nursing home–type unit) **A**1 2 3 5 7 10 **F**3 7 8 11 12 13 14 15 17 18 20 22 24 26 28 29 30 31 34 35 39 40 43 44 45 48 49 50 51 53 54 55 56 57 58 59 60 61 62 63 64 68 70 71 72 74 75 76 77 78 79 81 82 83 84 85 86 87 89 90 93 96 97 98 102 103 104 105 106 107 108 109 110 111 114 117 118 119 120 121 123 127 128 129 130 131 132 133 134 135 143 144 145 146 147 148 **P**6 7 **S** Aultman Health Foundation, Canton, OH
Primary Contact: Edward J. Roth, III, President and Chief Executive Officer
CFO: Mark Wright, Vice President
CMO: Allison Oprandi, M.D., Chief Medical Officer
CIO: Liz Getz, Chief Information Officer
CHR: Sue Olivera, Vice President
CNO: Anne Gunther, DNP, R.N., Chief Nursing Officer
Web address: www.aultman.com
**Control:** Other not–for–profit (including NFP Corporation) **Service:** General Medical and Surgical

**Staffed Beds: 542 Admissions: 23837 Census: 363 Outpatient Visits:** 450912 **Births: 2619 Total Expense ($000): 430831 Payroll Expense ($000): 175845 Personnel: 3500**

**AULTMAN SPECIALTY HOSPITAL (362032)**, 2600 Sixth Street, S.W., Zip 44710–1702; tel. 330/363–4000, (Nonreporting) **A**1 10 **S** Aultman Health Foundation, Canton, OH
Primary Contact: Terry Regula, Chief Executive Officer
CFO: Mark Wright, Chief Financial Officer
CMO: George Kefalas, Chief Medical Officer
Web address: www.aultman.org
**Control:** Other not–for–profit (including NFP Corporation) **Service:** Long–Term Acute Care hospital

**Staffed Beds: 30**

**MERCY MEDICAL CENTER (360070)**, 1320 Mercy Drive N.W., Zip 44708–2641; tel. 330/489–1000 **A**1 2 3 5 7 9 10 **F**3 11 13 15 17 18 20 22 24 26 28 29 30 31 34 35 39 40 43 44 46 48 49 50 51 53 54 57 58 59 60 61 62 63 64 66 68 70 72 74 75 76 77 78 79 80 81 82 84 85 86 87 89 90 91 92 93 96 97 107 108 110 111 114 115 116 117 118 120 121 123 124 126 129 130 131 132 135 144 146 147 148 **P**6 7 **S** Sisters of Charity Health System, Cleveland, OH
Primary Contact: Thomas E. Cecconi, President and Chief Executive Officer
COO: David D. Cemate, FACHE, Senior Vice President and Chief Operating Officer
CFO: David K. Stewart, Chief Financial Officer
CMO: David Gormsen, D.O., Chief Medical Officer
CIO: Trevor Clere, Director Information Technology
CHR: Patti Bresnahan, Director Human Resources
CNO: Barbara Yingling, R.N., Vice President Patient Care Services and Chief Nursing Officer
Web address: www.cantonmercy.org
**Control:** Other not–for–profit (including NFP Corporation) **Service:** General Medical and Surgical

**Staffed Beds: 322 Admissions: 14711 Census: 191 Outpatient Visits:** 633813 **Births: 1721 Total Expense ($000): 297563 Payroll Expense ($000): 121136 Personnel: 2076**

**SELECT SPECIALTY HOSPITAL–CANTON (362016)**, 1320 Mercy Drive N.W., 6th Floor, Zip 44708–2614; tel. 330/489–8189, (Nonreporting) **A**1 10 **S** Select Medical Corporation, Mechanicsburg, PA
Primary Contact: Dawne Wheeler, Chief Executive Officer
Web address: www.selectspecialtyhospitals.com/company/locations/canton.aspx
**Control:** Corporation, Investor–owned, for–profit **Service:** Long–Term Acute Care hospital

**Staffed Beds: 30**

## CHARDON—Geauga County

**HEATHERHILL CARE COMMUNITIES (362014)**, 12340 Bass Lake Road, Zip 44024–8327; tel. 440/285–4040, (Nonreporting) **A**1 10
Primary Contact: Jim Homa, Chief Executive Officer
COO: Lisa Deering, Administrator
CFO: Valerie Love, Manager Business Office
CMO: Beejadi Makunda, M.D., Chief Medical Officer
CHR: Pam McCall, Director Human Resources
CNO: Alice Harvey, Director of Nursing
Web address: www.heatherhill.com
**Control:** Other not–for–profit (including NFP Corporation) **Service:** Long–Term Acute Care hospital

**Staffed Beds: 214**

**UNIVERSITY HOSPITALS GEAUGA MEDICAL CENTER (360192)**, 13207 Ravenna Road, Zip 44024–7032; tel. 440/269–6000 **A**1 2 3 9 10 **F**3 8 11 12 13 14 15 18 20 22 26 28 29 30 31 32 34 35 36 37 38 39 40 41 43 44 47 49 50 51 54 56 57 58 59 60 62 64 65 68 70 74 75 76 77 78 79 81 82 85 86 87 91 92 93 96 97 98 100 101 102 103 107 108 110 111 114 115 116 117 118 119 120 121 123 124 129 130 131 132 134 135 143 146 147 148 **S** University Hospitals, Cleveland, OH
Primary Contact: M. Steven Jones, President
COO: M. Steven Jones, President
CFO: Paul Amantea, Director Finance
CMO: David Kosnosky, M.D., Chief Medical Officer
CIO: Lou Ciraldo, Information Services Representative
CHR: Danialle Lynce, Manager Human Resources
CNO: Peggy A. Kuhar, R.N., Chief Nursing Officer
Web address: www.uhhospitals.org/geauga/
**Control:** Other not–for–profit (including NFP Corporation) **Service:** General Medical and Surgical

**Staffed Beds: 126 Admissions: 8999 Census: 89 Outpatient Visits:** 121437 **Births: 1112 Total Expense ($000): 117601 Payroll Expense ($000): 39031 Personnel: 698**

---

**Hospital, Medicare Provider Number, Address, Telephone, Approval, Facility, and Physician Codes, Health Care System**

★ American Hospital Association (AHA) membership
□ The Joint Commission accreditation
○ Healthcare Facilities Accreditation Program
◇ DNV Healthcare Inc. accreditation
⇑ Center for Improvement in Healthcare Quality Accreditation
△ Commission on Accreditation of Rehabilitation Facilities (CARF) accreditation

**OH**

---

### CHILLICOTHE—Ross County

☒ **ADENA MEDICAL CENTER (360159)**, 272 Hospital Road, Zip 45601–9031; tel. 740/779–7500 **A**1 2 5 9 10 12 13 19 **F**3 5 8 13 15 17 18 20 22 24 26 28 29 30 31 32 34 35 38 40 41 45 46 48 49 50 54 57 59 62 63 64 70 74 75 76 77 78 79 81 82 83 84 85 87 89 90 91 93 96 97 98 99 100 101 102 103 104 107 108 114 115 119 120 121 123 126 129 130 131 132 133 135 144 146 147 148 **P**6 **S** Adena Health System, Chillicothe, OH
Primary Contact: Mark H. Shuter, President and Chief Executive Officer
CFO: Robert Rosenberger, Chief Financial Officer
CMO: John Fortney, M.D., Chief Medical Officer
CIO: Linn Weimer, Chief Information Officer
CHR: Eric Perdue, Chief Human Resource Officer
CNO: Judith Henson, R.N., Chief Nursing Officer
Web address: www.adena.org
**Control:** Other not–for–profit (including NFP Corporation) **Service:** General Medical and Surgical

| |
|---|
| **Staffed Beds:** 209 **Admissions:** 10371 **Census:** 112 **Outpatient Visits:** 696161 **Births:** 1029 **Total Expense ($000):** 422297 **Payroll Expense ($000):** 197721 **Personnel:** 2428 |

☒ **CHILLICOTHE VETERANS AFFAIRS MEDICAL CENTER**, 17273 State Route 104, Zip 45601–9718; tel. 740/773–1141, (Total facility includes 162 beds in nursing home–type unit) **A**1 3 4 5 6 9 11 18 29 30 33 34 35 36 38 39 45 46 54 56 59 61 62 63 64 67 71 74 75 79 82 83 84 86 87 92 93 94 97 98 100 102 103 104 105 106 107 111 114 115 119 128 129 130 132 135 144 146 147 148 **P**6 **S** Department of Veterans Affairs, Washington, DC
Primary Contact: Wendy J. Hepker, FACHE, Director
COO: Keith Sullivan, Associate Director
CFO: Rick Deckard, Chief Fiscal Service
CMO: Deborah Meesig, M.D., Chief of Staff
CIO: William Gawler, Chief Information Officer
CHR: Angela Young, Human Resources Officer
Web address: www.chillicothe.va.gov/
**Control:** Veterans Affairs, Government, federal **Service:** Psychiatric

| |
|---|
| **Staffed Beds:** 303 **Admissions:** 3657 **Census:** 253 **Outpatient Visits:** 335257 **Births:** 0 |

**VETERANS AFFAIRS MEDICAL CENTER** See Chillicothe Veterans Affairs Medical Center

---

### CINCINNATI—Hamilton County

☒ **BETHESDA NORTH HOSPITAL (360179)**, 10500 Montgomery Road, Zip 45242–4402; tel. 513/865–1111, (Includes BETHESDA BUTLER HOSPITAL, 3125 Hamilton Mason Road, Hamilton, Zip 45011–5307; tel. 513/894–8888; Chuck Brown, Administrator) **A**1 3 5 9 10 **F**3 5 8 9 11 12 13 15 17 18 20 22 24 26 28 29 30 31 34 35 36 37 38 39 40 41 42 43 44 45 46 47 48 49 50 53 54 55 56 57 58 59 61 63 64 65 66 68 70 71 73 74 75 76 77 78 79 81 82 84 85 86 87 90 91 92 93 94 96 97 99 100 101 102 103 104 107 108 110 111 114 115 116 117 118 119 120 121 123 124 126 129 130 131 132 134 135 141 143 144 145 146 147 148 **P**1 6
Primary Contact: Barbara Boyne, Executive Director, Operations
COO: Jenny Oliphant, Executive Vice President and Chief Operating Officer
CFO: Michael Crofton, Senior Vice President and Chief Financial Officer
CMO: Georges Feghali, M.D., Senior Vice President Quality and Chief Medical Officer
CIO: Rick Moore, Chief Information Officer
CHR: Walter L. McLarty, Chief Human Resources Officer
CNO: Mary Irvin, R.N., Senior Vice President and Chief Nursing Officer
Web address: www.trihealth.com
**Control:** Other not–for–profit (including NFP Corporation) **Service:** General Medical and Surgical

| |
|---|
| **Staffed Beds:** 342 **Admissions:** 21954 **Census:** 256 **Outpatient Visits:** 285813 **Births:** 4177 **Total Expense ($000):** 429995 **Payroll Expense ($000):** 151459 **Personnel:** 3259 |

**BRIDGEWELL HOSPITAL OF CINCINNATI (364046)**, 5500 Verulam Avenue, Zip 45213–2418; tel. 513/531–6444, (Nonreporting) **A**10
Primary Contact: Glenna Coffey, R.N., Chief Operating Officer
CNO: Doug Eppley, Director of Nursing
Web address: www.bridgewellhospitals.com
**Control:** Corporation, Investor–owned, for–profit **Service:** Psychiatric

| |
|---|
| **Staffed Beds:** 48 |

---

☐ △ **CHRIST HOSPITAL (360163)**, 2139 Auburn Avenue, Zip 45219–2906; tel. 513/585–2000 **A**1 2 3 5 7 9 10 **F**1 3 6 8 9 11 12 13 15 17 18 20 22 24 26 28 29 30 31 34 35 36 37 38 39 40 44 45 46 47 48 49 50 51 53 54 55 56 57 58 59 60 61 64 65 66 68 70 73 74 75 76 77 78 79 80 81 82 83 84 85 86 87 90 92 93 94 96 97 98 99 100 101 102 103 104 107 108 109 110 111 114 115 116 117 118 119 120 121 123 124 126 129 130 131 132 135 136 138 141 143 144 145 146 147 148 **P**6
Primary Contact: Michael Keating, President and Chief Executive Officer
COO: Victor DiPilla, Vice President and Chief Business Development Officer
CFO: Chris Bergman, Chief Financial Officer
CMO: Bernard B. Gawne, M.D., Vice President and Chief Medical Officer
CIO: Alex Vaillancourt, Chief Information Officer
CHR: Rick Tolson, Chief Administrative Officer and Chief Human Resources Officer
CNO: Deborah Marie Hayes, R.N., Chief Hospital Officer and Chief Nursing Officer
Web address: www.thechristhospital.com
**Control:** Other not–for–profit (including NFP Corporation) **Service:** General Medical and Surgical

| |
|---|
| **Staffed Beds:** 529 **Admissions:** 23722 **Census:** 297 **Outpatient Visits:** 471240 **Births:** 3170 **Total Expense ($000):** 584767 **Payroll Expense ($000):** 209929 **Personnel:** 3282 |

☒ △ **CINCINNATI CHILDREN'S HOSPITAL MEDICAL CENTER (363300)**, 3333 Burnet Avenue MLC 8006, Zip 45229–3039, Mailing Address: 3333 Burnet Avenue, Zip 45229–3039; tel. 513/636–4200, (Includes DIVISION OF ADOLESCENT MEDICINE, CINCINNATI CENTER FOR DEVELOPMENTAL DISORDERS, AND CONVALESCENT HOSPITAL FOR CHILDREN ; CHILDREN'S HOSPITAL, Elland and Bethesda Avenues, Zip 45229) **A**1 2 3 5 7 8 9 10 **F**3 7 9 11 12 17 18 19 20 21 22 23 24 25 26 27 28 29 30 31 32 34 35 36 37 38 39 40 41 42 43 44 46 48 49 50 51 54 55 57 58 59 60 61 62 63 64 65 66 68 72 74 75 76 77 78 79 81 82 84 85 86 87 88 89 90 91 92 93 94 95 96 97 98 99 100 101 102 104 105 106 107 108 111 112 113 114 115 116 117 118 119 126 129 130 131 132 134 135 136 137 138 139 140 141 142 144 146 148 **P**1
Primary Contact: Michael Fisher, President and Chief Executive Officer
CFO: Scott J. Hamlin, Chief Financial Officer
CIO: Marianne Speight, Vice President Information System and Chief Information Officer
Web address: www.cincinnatichildrens.org
**Control:** Other not–for–profit (including NFP Corporation) **Service:** Children's general

| |
|---|
| **Staffed Beds:** 584 **Admissions:** 18167 **Census:** 390 **Outpatient Visits:** 1173713 **Births:** 19 **Total Expense ($000):** 1947840 **Payroll Expense ($000):** 985876 **Personnel:** 15038 |

☒ **CINCINNATI VETERANS AFFAIRS MEDICAL CENTER**, 3200 Vine Street, Zip 45220–2288; tel. 513/475–6300, (Total facility includes 64 beds in nursing home–type unit) **A**1 2 3 5 **F**1 3 4 5 8 15 17 18 20 22 26 28 29 30 31 33 34 35 36 37 38 39 40 44 45 46 47 48 50 51 53 54 55 56 57 58 59 60 61 62 63 64 65 68 70 71 74 75 77 78 79 81 82 83 84 85 86 87 91 92 93 94 97 98 100 101 102 103 104 105 106 107 108 111 114 115 116 117 119 126 127 129 130 131 132 135 143 144 145 146 147 148 **S** Department of Veterans Affairs, Washington, DC
Primary Contact: John Gennaro, FACHE, Director
COO: David Ninneman, Associate Director
CFO: Sandra Selvidge, Chief Fiscal Service
CIO: Vique Caro, Chief Information Officer
CHR: Sandra Stenger, Acting Chief Human Resources
CNO: Katheryn Cook, R.N., Nurse Executive
Web address: www.cincinnati.va.gov/
**Control:** Veterans Affairs, Government, federal **Service:** General Medical and Surgical

| |
|---|
| **Staffed Beds:** 268 **Admissions:** 6869 **Census:** 86 **Outpatient Visits:** 604425 **Births:** 0 **Total Expense ($000):** 393712 **Payroll Expense ($000):** 172109 **Personnel:** 2120 |

☒ **DANIEL DRAKE CENTER FOR POST ACUTE CARE (362004)**, 151 West Galbraith Road, Zip 45216–1015; tel. 513/418–2500, (Nonreporting) **A**1 3 5 10 **S** UC Health, Cincinnati, OH
Primary Contact: Amy Schroyer, Vice President Administration and Senior Site Executive
CFO: Duane Pifko, Interim Director Financial Services
Web address: www.uchealth.com/danieldrakecenter/
**Control:** Other not–for–profit (including NFP Corporation) **Service:** Long–Term Acute Care hospital

| |
|---|
| **Staffed Beds:** 202 |

*Many Facility Codes have changed. Please refer to the AHA Guide Code Chart.* © 2015 AHA Guide

**OH**

✠ △ **GOOD SAMARITAN HOSPITAL (360134)**, 375 Dixmyth Avenue, Zip 45220–2489; tel. 513/862–1400 **A**1 2 3 5 6 7 8 9 10 **F**3 5 6 9 11 12 13 15 17 18 20 22 24 26 28 29 30 31 34 35 36 37 38 39 40 41 42 44 45 46 47 48 49 50 53 54 55 56 57 58 59 61 63 64 65 66 68 70 71 72 74 75 77 78 79 81 82 84 85 86 87 90 91 92 93 94 96 97 98 99 100 101 102 103 104 105 107 108 110 111 114 115 116 117 118 119 120 121 123 124 126 129 130 131 132 134 135 141 143 144 145 146 147 148 **P**1 6 **S** Catholic Health Initiatives, Englewood, CO
Primary Contact: Jamie Easterling, Executive Director, Operations
COO: Gerald P. Oliphant, Executive Vice President and Chief Operating Officer
CFO: Michael Crofton, Chief Financial Officer
CMO: Georges Feghali, M.D., Senior Vice President Quality and Chief Medical Officer
CIO: Rick Moore, Chief Information Officer
CHR: Walter L. McLarty, Chief Human Resources Officer
Web address: www.trihealth.com
**Control:** Church–operated, Nongovernment, not–for profit **Service:** General Medical and Surgical

**Staffed Beds: 472 Admissions: 23469 Census: 322 Outpatient Visits: 253581 Births: 5995 Total Expense ($000): 490768 Payroll Expense ($000): 172768 Personnel: 3093**

✠ **HEALTHSOUTH REHABILITATION HOSPITAL AT DRAKE (363034)**, 151 West Galbraith Road, Zip 45216–1015; tel. 513/418–5600 **A**1 6 9 10 **F**29 31 34 35 56 74 90 91 92 130 148 **S** HEALTHSOUTH Corporation, Birmingham, AL
Primary Contact: Brad Kennedy, Chief Executive Officer
CFO: Scott Corder, Controller
CMO: Mark Goddard, M.D., Medical Director
CHR: Jason Sparks, Director, Human Resources
CNO: Kathy McNally, Chief Nursing Officer
Web address: www.healthsouthatdrake.com
**Control:** Corporation, Investor–owned, for–profit **Service:** Rehabilitation

**Staffed Beds: 60 Admissions: 1138 Census: 46 Outpatient Visits: 0 Births: 0 Total Expense ($000): 14886 Payroll Expense ($000): 7943 Personnel: 72**

✠ **MERCY HEALTH – ANDERSON HOSPITAL (360001)**, 7500 State Road, Zip 45255–2492; tel. 513/624–4500, (Nonreporting) **A**1 2 3 9 10 **S** Mercy Health, Cincinnati, OH
Primary Contact: Jeff Graham, Market Leader and President
COO: Katherine Edrington, R.N., Administrator
CFO: Patrick A. Kowalski, Chief Financial Officer
CMO: Leonard M. Randolph, Jr., M.D., Senior Vice President and Chief Medical Officer
CIO: Matt Eversole, Regional Vice President Information Services
CHR: Angie Ferrell, Director Human Resources
Web address: www.e–mercy.com
**Control:** Church–operated, Nongovernment, not–for profit **Service:** General Medical and Surgical

**Staffed Beds: 188**

✠ **MERCY HEALTH – WEST HOSPITAL (360234)**, 3300 Mercy Health Boulevard, Zip 45211; tel. 513/215–5000, (Nonreporting) **A**1 2 9 10 **S** Mercy Health, Cincinnati, OH
Primary Contact: Michael R. Stephens, Market Leader and President
COO: Michael Kramer, Chief Operating Officer
CHR: Liz Freedman, Director Human Resources
CNO: Stephanie Meade, R.N., Chief Nursing Officer
Web address: www.e–mercy.com/west–hospital
**Control:** Church–operated, Nongovernment, not–for profit **Service:** General Medical and Surgical

**Staffed Beds: 250**

✠ **SELECT SPECIALTY HOSPITAL – CINCINNATI NORTH (362034)**, 10500 Montgomery Road, Zip 45242–4402; tel. 513/865–5300, (Nonreporting) **A**1 10 **S** Select Medical Corporation, Mechanicsburg, PA
Primary Contact: Susan Glen, Chief Executive Officer
CMO: Sunil Dama, M.D., Medical Director
CHR: Elizabeth M. Wilson, Coordinator Human Resources
Web address: www.cincinnatinorth.selectspecialtyhospitals.com/
**Control:** Corporation, Investor–owned, for–profit **Service:** Long–Term Acute Care hospital

**Staffed Beds: 41**

✠ **SELECT SPECIALTY HOSPITAL–CINCINNATI (362019)**, 375 Dixmyth Avenue, 15th Floor, Zip 45220–2475; tel. 513/872–4444, (Nonreporting) **A**1 9 10 **S** Select Medical Corporation, Mechanicsburg, PA
Primary Contact: Curtis Ohashi, Chief Executive Officer
CMO: Brian Boster, M.D., Medical Director
CNO: Bobbi Schmidt, Chief Nursing Officer
Web address: www.selectspecialtyhospitals.com/company/locations/cincinnati.aspx
**Control:** Corporation, Investor–owned, for–profit **Service:** Long–Term Acute Care hospital

**Staffed Beds: 36**

☐ **SHRINERS HOSPITALS FOR CHILDREN–CINCINNATI BURNS HOSPITAL (363308)**, 3229 Burnet Avenue, Zip 45229–3095; tel. 513/872–6000, (Nonreporting) **A**1 6 10 **S** Shriners Hospitals for Children, Tampa, FL
Primary Contact: Mark D. Shugarman, Administrator
CFO: Susan Harris, Director Fiscal Services
CMO: Petra Warner, Interim Chief of Staff
CIO: David Brian, Chief Information Officer
CHR: Debra A. Felder, Director Human Resources
Web address: www.shrinershospitalsforchildren.org/Hospitals/Locations/Cincinnati.aspx
**Control:** Other not–for–profit (including NFP Corporation) **Service:** Children's other specialty

**Staffed Beds: 30**

✠ **SUMMIT BEHAVIORAL HEALTHCARE (364035)**, 1101 Summit Road, Zip 45237–2652; tel. 513/948–3600, (Nonreporting) **A**1 10 **S** Ohio Department of Mental Health, Columbus, OH
Primary Contact: Elizabeth Banks, Chief Executive Officer
COO: Steven Burns, Director Fiscal Services
CFO: Steven Burns, Director Fiscal Services
CMO: Patrick McCullough, M.D., Chief Medical Services
CIO: Eric Bradley, Director Computer Information Services
CHR: Bobbie Carrelli, Director Human Resources
CNO: Kathy A. Smith, MSN, Nurse Executive
Web address: www.mh.state.oh.us/
**Control:** State–Government, nonfederal **Service:** Psychiatric

**Staffed Beds: 291**

✠ **THE JEWISH HOSPITAL – MERCY HEALTH (360016)**, 4777 East Galbraith Road, Zip 45236–2725; tel. 513/686–3000, (Nonreporting) **A**1 2 3 5 9 10 **S** Mercy Health, Cincinnati, OH
Primary Contact: Patricia Davis–Hagens, R.N., Market Leader and President
COO: Jack Hill, Chief Operating Officer and Administrator
Web address: www.jewishhospitalcincinnati.com/
**Control:** Other not–for–profit (including NFP Corporation) **Service:** General Medical and Surgical

**Staffed Beds: 209**

☐ **TRIHEALTH EVENDALE HOSPITAL (360362)**, 3155 Glendale Milford Road, Zip 45241–3134; tel. 513/454–2222 **A**1 2 9 10 **F**3 8 29 34 35 44 46 50 57 59 64 68 70 75 79 81 82 85 86 87 107 111 115 119 130 131 143 146 **P**1 6
Primary Contact: Kelvin Hanger, Chief Executive Officer
CFO: Michael Crofton, Chief Financial Officer
Web address: www.evendalemedical.com
**Control:** Other not–for–profit (including NFP Corporation) **Service:** Surgical

**Staffed Beds: 20 Admissions: 665 Census: 3 Outpatient Visits: 25272 Births: 0 Total Expense ($000): 37363 Payroll Expense ($000): 11531 Personnel: 168**

---

**Hospital, Medicare Provider Number, Address, Telephone, Approval, Facility, and Physician Codes, Health Care System**

★ American Hospital Association (AHA) membership    ○ Healthcare Facilities Accreditation Program    ⇑ Center for Improvement in Healthcare Quality Accreditation
☐ The Joint Commission accreditation    ◇ DNV Healthcare Inc. accreditation    △ Commission on Accreditation of Rehabilitation Facilities (CARF) accreditation

✠ **UNIVERSITY OF CINCINNATI MEDICAL CENTER (360003)**, 234 Goodman Street, Zip 45219–2316; tel. 513/584–1000 **A**1 2 3 5 8 10 **F**3 6 7 9 11 12 13 15 16 17 18 20 22 24 26 28 29 30 31 34 35 36 37 38 39 40 43 44 45 46 47 48 49 50 51 52 53 54 55 56 57 58 59 60 61 63 64 66 68 70 71 72 73 74 75 76 77 78 79 80 81 84 85 86 87 92 93 97 98 100 101 102 103 104 107 108 110 111 112 114 115 116 117 118 119 120 121 123 124 126 129 130 131 132 134 135 136 138 139 141 142 145 146 147 148 **P**5 6 **S** UC Health, Cincinnati, OH
Primary Contact: Lee Ann Liska, President and Chief Executive Officer
COO: Nancy Barone, Vice President and Executive Director Operations and Strategic Planning
CFO: Matthew Nealon, Vice President, Chief Financial Officer
CMO: Bill Hurford, Chief Medical Officer
CIO: Jay Brown, Vice President and Chief Information Officer
CHR: Clarence Pauley, Senior Vice President and Chief Human Resources Officer
CNO: Jennifer Jackson, R.N., Vice President and Chief Nursing Officer
Web address: www.uchealth.com/university–of–cincinnati–medical–center/
**Control:** Other not–for–profit (including NFP Corporation) **Service:** General Medical and Surgical

**Staffed Beds:** 605 **Admissions:** 28063 **Census:** 428 **Outpatient Visits:** 383913 **Births:** 2499 **Total Expense ($000):** 772949 **Payroll Expense ($000):** 249800 **Personnel:** 4438

**VETERANS AFFAIRS MEDICAL CENTER** See Cincinnati Veterans Affairs Medical Center

### CIRCLEVILLE—Pickaway County

✠ **BERGER HEALTH SYSTEM (360170)**, 600 North Pickaway Street, Zip 43113–1447; tel. 740/474–2126 **A**1 5 9 10 **F**3 13 15 17 18 20 28 29 30 31 34 35 40 45 46 50 54 56 57 59 63 64 65 66 75 76 79 81 85 87 93 96 107 108 110 111 115 119 124 129 130 131 132 135 146 147 148
Primary Contact: Timothy D. Colburn, President and Chief Executive Officer
CFO: Richard Filler, Chief Financial Officer
CMO: Brett Call, D.O., Chief of Staff
CIO: Andy Chileski, Chief Information Officer and Vice President Facilities
CHR: Suzanne Welker, Chief Human Resources Officer and Vice President Marketing Strategy
CNO: Brenda M. Strittmatter, Patient Services Officer
Web address: www.bergerhealth.com
**Control:** City–County, Government, nonfederal **Service:** General Medical and Surgical

**Staffed Beds:** 56 **Admissions:** 2006 **Census:** 19 **Outpatient Visits:** 98845 **Births:** 369 **Total Expense ($000):** 65994 **Payroll Expense ($000):** 22034 **Personnel:** 415

### CLEVELAND—Cuyahoga County

**CLEVELAND CAMPUS** See Northcoast Behavioral Healthcare System, Northfield

✠ **CLEVELAND CLINIC (360180)**, 9500 Euclid Avenue, Zip 44195–5108; tel. 216/444–2200, (Includes CLEVELAND CLINIC CHILDREN'S HOSPITAL, 9500 Euclid Avenue, Zip 44103; tel. 800/223–2273) **A**1 3 5 8 9 10 **F**3 6 7 8 9 12 13 14 15 17 18 19 20 21 22 23 24 25 26 27 28 29 30 31 32 33 34 35 36 37 38 39 40 42 44 45 46 47 48 49 50 51 52 53 54 55 56 57 58 59 60 61 62 63 64 65 66 68 70 71 72 73 74 75 76 77 78 79 80 81 82 83 84 85 86 87 88 89 90 91 92 93 94 96 97 100 101 103 104 107 108 109 110 111 112 113 114 115 116 117 118 119 120 121 123 124 126 129 130 131 132 134 135 136 137 138 139 140 141 142 143 144 145 146 147 148 **P**6 **S** Cleveland Clinic Health System, Cleveland, OH
Primary Contact: Delos Cosgrove, M.D., President and Chief Executive Officer
CFO: Steven Glass, Chief Financial Officer
CMO: Joseph Hahn, M.D., Chief of Staff
CIO: C. Martin Harris, M.D., Chief Information Officer
CHR: Joseph Cabral, Chief Human Resources Officer
CNO: Katherine Hancock, R.N., Executive Chief Nursing Officer
Web address: www.clevelandclinic.org
**Control:** Other not–for–profit (including NFP Corporation) **Service:** General Medical and Surgical

**Staffed Beds:** 1278 **Admissions:** 53722 **Census:** 983 **Outpatient Visits:** 5482310 **Births:** 106 **Total Expense ($000):** 4530463 **Payroll Expense ($000):** 2315213 **Personnel:** 27172

✠ △ **CLEVELAND CLINIC CHILDREN'S HOSPITAL FOR REHABILITATION (363304)**, 2801 Martin Luther King Jr. Drive, Zip 44104–3865; tel. 216/448–6400 **A**1 3 7 9 10 **F**28 29 30 32 34 35 36 44 50 57 60 68 74 75 79 80 82 86 89 90 91 93 94 96 99 100 130 131 132 143 146 148 **S** Cleveland Clinic Health System, Cleveland, OH
Primary Contact: Michael J. McHugh, M.D., Medical Director
COO: Alec G. Kulik, Administrator
CFO: Debra Nyikes, Director Finance and Chief Financial Officer
CMO: Roberta Bauer, M.D., Acting Chair Medical Staff
CIO: C. Martin Harris, M.D., Chief Information Officer
CHR: Jan Hlahol, Manager Human Resources
Web address: www.my.clevelandclinic.org/childrens–hospital/default.aspx
**Control:** Other not–for–profit (including NFP Corporation) **Service:** Children's rehabilitation

**Staffed Beds:** 25 **Admissions:** 209 **Census:** 17 **Outpatient Visits:** 73748 **Births:** 0 **Total Expense ($000):** 37735 **Payroll Expense ($000):** 21372 **Personnel:** 363

✠ **FAIRVIEW HOSPITAL (360077)**, 18101 Lorain Avenue, Zip 44111–5656; tel. 216/476–7000 **A**1 2 3 5 9 10 13 **F**3 8 11 12 13 15 17 18 19 20 22 24 26 28 29 30 31 32 34 35 40 41 43 45 46 47 49 50 51 53 55 57 58 59 60 64 65 66 68 69 70 71 72 74 75 76 78 79 81 82 85 86 87 89 92 93 97 98 99 100 107 108 110 111 114 115 117 118 119 120 121 123 124 126 130 131 132 135 143 145 146 147 148 **S** Cleveland Clinic Health System, Cleveland, OH
Primary Contact: Neil Smith, D.O., President
COO: John C. Mills, Senior Vice President Operations
CFO: Ankit Chhabra, Director Finance
CMO: Brent Burkey, M.D., Chief Medical Officer
CIO: C. Martin Harris, M.D., Chief Information Officer
CHR: Ann Beatty, Director Human Resources
CNO: Deborah C. Small, R.N., Vice President Patient Care Services and Chief Nursing Officer
Web address: www.fairviewhospital.org
**Control:** Other not–for–profit (including NFP Corporation) **Service:** General Medical and Surgical

**Staffed Beds:** 426 **Admissions:** 21056 **Census:** 248 **Outpatient Visits:** 251971 **Births:** 4658 **Total Expense ($000):** 337253 **Payroll Expense ($000):** 123452 **Personnel:** 1997

☐ **GRACE HOSPITAL (362015)**, 2307 West 14th Street, Zip 44113–3698; tel. 216/687–1500, (Nonreporting) **A**1 10
Primary Contact: Rajive Khanna, Chief Executive Officer
COO: Rajive Khanna, Chief Executive Officer
CFO: Michelle Hennis, Administrative Director Financial Services
CMO: John Nickels, M.D., President Medical Staff
CNO: Barbara Moran, R.N., Director Patient Care Services and Chief Nursing Officer
Web address: www.gracehospital.org
**Control:** Other not–for–profit (including NFP Corporation) **Service:** Long–Term Acute Care hospital

**Staffed Beds:** 87

**HANNA HOUSE SKILLED NURSING FACILITY** See University Hospitals Case Medical Center

✠ **HILLCREST HOSPITAL (360230)**, 6780 Mayfield Road, Zip 44124–2203; tel. 440/312–4500 **A**1 2 3 9 10 **F**3 11 12 13 15 17 18 20 22 24 26 28 29 30 31 34 35 36 37 38 40 41 43 46 49 50 51 53 55 57 59 60 64 65 68 69 70 72 74 75 76 77 78 79 81 82 84 85 86 89 93 97 100 107 108 110 111 114 115 116 117 118 119 120 121 126 129 130 131 132 135 143 145 146 147 148 **S** Cleveland Clinic Health System, Cleveland, OH
Primary Contact: Brian J. Harte, M.D., President
Web address: www.hillcresthospital.org
**Control:** Other not–for–profit (including NFP Corporation) **Service:** General Medical and Surgical

**Staffed Beds:** 438 **Admissions:** 22353 **Census:** 298 **Outpatient Visits:** 241316 **Births:** 4354 **Total Expense ($000):** 347935 **Payroll Expense ($000):** 122370 **Personnel:** 2073

★ **KINDRED HOSPITAL CLEVELAND–GATEWAY (362026)**, 2351 East 22nd Street, 7th Floor, Zip 44115–3111; tel. 216/363–2671, (Includes KINDRED HOSPITAL OF CLEVELAND, 11900 Fairhill Road, Zip 44120–1062; tel. 216/983–8030; Steve Jakubcanin, Executive Director), (Nonreporting) **A**3 10 **S** Kindred Healthcare, Louisville, KY
Primary Contact: Prentice Lipsey, Chief Executive Officer
Web address: www.kindredgateway.com
**Control:** Corporation, Investor–owned, for–profit **Service:** Long–Term Acute Care hospital

**Staffed Beds:** 153

**KINDRED HOSPITAL OF CLEVELAND** See Kindred Hospital Cleveland–Gateway

✠ △ **LOUIS STOKES CLEVELAND VETERANS AFFAIRS MEDICAL CENTER**, 10701 East Boulevard, Zip 44106–1702; tel. 216/791–3800, (Nonreporting) **A**1 2 3 5 7 8 **S** Department of Veterans Affairs, Washington, DC
Primary Contact: Susan Fuehrer, Director
COO: John F. Merkle, Deputy Director
CFO: Michael Pappas, Chief Fiscal Service Officer
CMO: Murray Altose, M.D., Chief of Staff
CIO: Steve Gaj, Facility Chief Information Officer
CHR: Charles Franks, Chief Human Resources
CNO: Innette Mary Sarduy, M.P.H., Associate Director Patient Care Services and Nurse Executive
Web address: www.cleveland.va.gov/
**Control:** Veterans Affairs, Government, federal **Service:** General Medical and Surgical

**Staffed Beds:** 585

*Many Facility Codes have changed. Please refer to the AHA Guide Code Chart.* © 2015 AHA Guide

☒ **LUTHERAN HOSPITAL (360087)**, 1730 West 25th Street, Zip 44113–3170; tel. 216/696–4300 **A**1 3 9 10 **F**3 4 5 15 29 30 34 35 37 40 50 56 57 58 59 60 64 65 70 74 75 77 79 81 82 85 86 87 93 98 99 103 104 105 107 111 114 119 129 130 131 132 135 143 146 148 **S** Cleveland Clinic Health System, Cleveland, OH
Primary Contact: Donald Malone, M.D., President
COO: Kris Bennett, Chief Operating Officer
CFO: Don Urbancsik, Director Finance
CMO: Ronald Golovan, M.D., Vice President Medical Operations
CIO: C. Martin Harris, M.D., Chief Information Officer
CHR: Ron Robinson, Business Partner
CNO: Denise Minor, R.N., Chief Nursing Officer
Web address: www.lutheranhospital.org
**Control:** Other not–for–profit (including NFP Corporation) **Service:** General Medical and Surgical

**Staffed Beds:** 198 **Admissions:** 7924 **Census:** 99 **Outpatient Visits:** 58951 **Births:** 0 **Total Expense ($000):** 90450 **Payroll Expense ($000):** 36601 **Personnel:** 580

☒ △ **METROHEALTH MEDICAL CENTER (360059)**, 2500 MetroHealth Drive, Zip 44109–1998; tel. 216/778–7800, (Total facility includes 143 beds in nursing home–type unit) **A**1 2 3 5 7 8 9 10 13 **F**3 5 6 7 8 9 11 12 13 15 16 17 18 19 20 22 24 26 27 28 29 30 31 32 34 35 36 38 39 40 43 44 45 46 47 48 49 50 51 52 53 54 55 56 57 58 59 60 61 63 64 65 66 68 70 73 74 75 76 77 78 79 80 81 82 83 84 85 86 87 88 89 90 91 92 93 94 95 96 97 98 99 100 101 102 103 104 105 107 108 110 111 114 115 116 117 118 119 120 121 123 124 126 128 129 130 131 132 133 134 135 143 144 146 147 148 **P**6
Primary Contact: Akram Boutros, M.D., FACHE, President and Chief Executive Officer
COO: Daniel Lewis, Executive Vice President and Chief Operating Officer
CFO: Craig Richmond, Senior Vice President and Chief Financial Officer
CMO: Alfred Connors, M.D., Executive Vice President and Chief Quality Officer and Interim Chief Medical Officer
CIO: Don Reichert, Vice President Associate Chief Information Officer
CHR: Debbie Warman, Vice President Human Resources
CNO: Mavis Bechtle, MSN, Senior Vice President and Chief Nursing Officer
Web address: www.metrohealth.org
**Control:** County–Government, nonfederal **Service:** General Medical and Surgical

**Staffed Beds:** 742 **Admissions:** 25471 **Census:** 500 **Outpatient Visits:** 1149400 **Births:** 2920 **Total Expense ($000):** 869665 **Payroll Expense ($000):** 483341 **Personnel:** 5815

**RAINBOW BABIES AND CHILDREN'S HOSPITAL** See University Hospitals Case Medical Center

☐ **ST. VINCENT CHARITY MEDICAL CENTER (360037)**, 2351 East 22nd Street, Zip 44115–3111; tel. 216/861–6200 **A**1 2 3 5 9 10 **F**3 4 5 8 12 15 17 18 20 22 24 28 29 30 31 33 34 35 37 39 40 45 50 54 56 57 59 60 61 62 64 65 66 68 70 74 75 77 78 79 81 82 84 85 86 87 93 97 98 100 102 103 107 108 110 111 114 115 118 119 129 130 131 144 146 148 **P**4 **S** Sisters of Charity Health System, Cleveland, OH
Primary Contact: David F. Perse, M.D., President and Chief Executive Officer
COO: Joan Ross, Senior Vice President and Chief Operating Officer
CFO: John Rusnaczyk, Senior Vice President and Chief Financial Officer
CMO: Joseph A. Sopko, M.D., Chief Medical Officer
CIO: Robin Stursa, Chief Information Officer
CHR: Ted Monczewski, Vice President Human Resources
CNO: Beverly Lozar, Chief Nursing Executive
Web address: www.stvincentcharity.com/
**Control:** Other not–for–profit (including NFP Corporation) **Service:** General Medical and Surgical

**Staffed Beds:** 199 **Admissions:** 7765 **Census:** 107 **Outpatient Visits:** 139911 **Births:** 0 **Total Expense ($000):** 150425 **Payroll Expense ($000):** 58699 **Personnel:** 1078

☒ **UH REGIONAL HOSPITALS (360075)**, 27100 Chardon Road, Zip 44143–1116; tel. 440/585–6500, (Includes UNIVERSITY HOSPITALS BEDFORD MEDICAL CENTER, 44 Blaine Avenue, Zip 44146–2709; tel. 440/735–3900; UNIVERSITY HOSPITALS RICHMOND MEDICAL CENTER, 27100 Chardon Road, tel. 440/585–6500) **A**1 8 14 15 20 29 30 40 43 44 49 50 57 59 60 65 66 68 69 70 75 77 79 81 82 86 87 89 93 96 97 107 108 109 110 111 114 116 117 118 119 128 129 130 132 133 135 143 146 147 148 **S** University Hospitals, Cleveland, OH
Primary Contact: Robert G. David, President
CFO: Scott Platz, Director Finance
CMO: Rosemary Leeming, M.D., Chief Medical Officer
CHR: Stephanie W. Neonakis, Manager Human Resources
CNO: Michelle Giltner, Interim Chief Nursing Officer
Web address: www.uhhospitals.org
**Control:** Other not–for–profit (including NFP Corporation) **Service:** General Medical and Surgical

**Staffed Beds:** 101 **Admissions:** 4687 **Census:** 54 **Outpatient Visits:** 164943 **Births:** 0 **Total Expense ($000):** 103120 **Payroll Expense ($000):** 38886 **Personnel:** 749

☒ **UNIVERSITY HOSPITALS CASE MEDICAL CENTER (360137)**, 11100 Euclid Avenue, Zip 44106–1716; tel. 216/844–1000, (Includes ALFRED AND NORMA LERNER TOWER, BOLWELL HEALTH CENTER, HANNA PAVILION, LAKESIDE HOSPITAL, SAMUEL MATHER PAVILION ; HANNA HOUSE SKILLED NURSING FACILITY, 11100 Euclid Avenue, Zip 44106; RAINBOW BABIES AND CHILDREN'S HOSPITAL, 2101 Adelbert Road, Zip 44106–2624; tel. 216/844–3911; Patricia DePompei, President; UNIVERSITY MACDONALD WOMEN'S HOSPITAL, 2101 Adelbert Road, Zip 44106–2624; tel. 216/844–3911; Patricia DePompei, President), (Total facility includes 38 beds in nursing home–type unit) **A**1 2 3 5 8 9 10 **F**3 5 6 8 9 11 12 13 14 15 17 18 19 20 21 22 23 24 25 26 27 28 29 30 31 32 34 35 36 37 38 39 40 41 42 43 44 45 46 47 48 49 50 51 52 53 54 55 56 57 58 59 60 61 62 63 64 65 66 68 70 71 72 73 74 75 76 77 78 79 80 81 82 83 84 85 86 87 88 89 91 92 93 94 96 97 98 99 100 101 102 103 104 105 107 108 109 110 111 112 114 115 116 117 118 119 120 121 123 124 126 128 129 130 131 132 133 134 135 136 137 138 139 140 141 142 143 144 145 146 147 148 **P**6 7 **S** University Hospitals, Cleveland, OH
Primary Contact: Fred C. Rothstein, M.D., President
COO: Ron Dziedzicki, R.N., Chief Operating Officer
CFO: Sonia Salvino, Vice President Finance
CMO: Michael Anderson, M.D., Chief Medical Officer
CIO: John V. Foley, Chief Information Officer
CHR: Julie Chester, Vice President Human Resources
CNO: Catherine S. Koppelman, MSN, Chief Nursing Officer
Web address: www.UHhospitals.org
**Control:** Other not–for–profit (including NFP Corporation) **Service:** General Medical and Surgical

**Staffed Beds:** 790 **Admissions:** 42653 **Census:** 651 **Outpatient Visits:** 468025 **Births:** 4226 **Total Expense ($000):** 1203463 **Payroll Expense ($000):** 422404 **Personnel:** 7907

**VETERANS AFFAIRS MEDICAL CENTER** See Louis Stokes Cleveland Veterans Affairs Medical Center

**COLDWATER—Mercer County**

☒ **MERCER HEALTH (360058)**, 800 West Main Street, Zip 45828–1698; tel. 419/678–2341 **A**1 9 10 **F**3 7 11 12 13 15 18 28 29 30 31 34 35 40 44 45 47 50 51 54 57 59 61 62 64 65 70 75 76 77 78 79 81 82 85 87 92 93 94 97 107 108 110 111 114 118 119 130 131 132 133 134 135 143 144 145 146 147 148 **P**3
Primary Contact: Lisa R. Klenke, R.N., Chief Executive Officer and Chief Nursing Officer
CFO: George Boyles, Senior Vice President of Finance and Chief Financial Officer
CMO: James Reichert, Chief Medical Officer
CIO: DeWayne Marsee, Director of Information Systems and Chief Information Officer
CHR: Ed Sweetnich, Vice President of Human Resources
Web address: www.mercer–health.com
**Control:** Hospital district or authority, Government, nonfederal **Service:** General Medical and Surgical

**Staffed Beds:** 60 **Admissions:** 1876 **Census:** 12 **Outpatient Visits:** 136046 **Births:** 356 **Total Expense ($000):** 44924 **Payroll Expense ($000):** 15950 **Personnel:** 397

**COLUMBUS—Franklin County**

☒ **JAMES CANCER HOSPITAL AND SOLOVE RESEARCH INSTITUTE (360242)**, 300 West Tenth Avenue, Zip 43210–1280; tel. 614/293–3300 **A**1 2 3 5 8 9 10 **F**3 15 29 30 31 32 34 35 36 37 38 39 44 46 47 48 49 50 52 54 55 57 58 59 61 62 64 66 68 70 71 74 75 77 78 79 81 82 84 85 86 87 93 97 100 107 108 110 111 112 114 115 116 117 118 119 120 121 123 124 126 130 132 134 135 136 141 143 144 145 146 147 148 **P**6 **S** Ohio State University Health System, Columbus, OH
Primary Contact: Michael Caligiuri, Chief Executive Officer
COO: Dennis J. Smith, Chief Operating Officer
CFO: Bell Julian, Associate Executive Director and Chief Financial Officer
CIO: Twyla Pohar, Manager Computer Systems
CHR: Jill Hannah, Director Human Resources
Web address: www.jamesline.com
**Control:** State–Government, nonfederal **Service:** Cancer

**Staffed Beds:** 236 **Admissions:** 11262 **Census:** 214 **Outpatient Visits:** 336695 **Births:** 0 **Total Expense ($000):** 655268 **Payroll Expense ($000):** 157055 **Personnel:** 2993

---

**Hospital, Medicare Provider Number, Address, Telephone, Approval, Facility, and Physician Codes, Health Care System**

★ American Hospital Association (AHA) membership
☐ The Joint Commission accreditation
○ Healthcare Facilities Accreditation Program
◇ DNV Healthcare Inc. accreditation
⇑ Center for Improvement in Healthcare Quality Accreditation
△ Commission on Accreditation of Rehabilitation Facilities (CARF) accreditation

**OH**

☒ △ **MOUNT CARMEL (360035)**, 793 West State Street, Zip 43222–1551; tel. 614/234–5000, (Includes MOUNT CARMEL EAST HOSPITAL, 6001 East Broad Street, Zip 43213; tel. 614/234–6000; Brinsley Lewis, FACHE, President; MOUNT CARMEL WEST HOSPITAL, 793 West State Street, Zip 43222; tel. 614/234–5000) **A**1 2 3 5 7 9 10 **F**3 11 12 13 15 17 18 20 22 24 26 28 29 30 31 34 35 37 40 42 43 44 45 46 47 48 49 50 51 54 55 57 58 59 61 63 64 65 66 68 70 72 74 75 76 77 78 79 81 82 83 84 85 86 87 90 92 96 97 98 100 101 102 103 104 107 108 109 110 111 114 115 116 117 118 119 120 121 123 124 126 130 131 132 144 145 146 147 148 **P**6 8 **S** Trinity Health, Livonia, MI
Primary Contact: Sean McKibben, President and Chief Operating Officer
COO: Mary R. Trimmer, Interim Chief Operating Officer
CFO: Keith T. Coleman, Chief Financial Officer
Web address: www.mountcarmelhealth.com
**Control:** Church–operated, Nongovernment, not–for profit **Service:** General Medical and Surgical

**Staffed Beds: 747 Admissions: 38168 Census: 465 Outpatient Visits:** 365224 **Births: 3750 Total Expense ($000): 643614 Payroll Expense ($000): 220317 Personnel: 4182**

☒ △ **NATIONWIDE CHILDREN'S HOSPITAL (363305)**, 700 Children's Drive, Zip 43205–2664; tel. 614/722–2000 **A**1 3 5 7 9 10 **F**3 7 8 12 16 17 18 19 20 21 22 23 24 25 26 27 28 29 30 31 32 34 35 36 38 39 40 41 43 44 45 47 48 50 51 53 54 55 57 58 59 60 61 62 63 64 65 66 68 71 72 74 75 77 78 79 81 82 83 84 85 86 87 88 89 90 92 93 94 96 97 98 99 100 101 102 104 105 107 108 111 112 114 115 116 117 118 119 126 127 129 130 131 132 133 134 135 136 137 138 140 141 143 144 145 146 148 **P**8
Primary Contact: Steve Allen, M.D., Chief Executive Officer
COO: Rick Miller, President and Chief Operating Officer
CFO: Tim Robinson, Executive Vice President, Chief Financial and Administrative Officer and Treasurer
CMO: Richard Brilli, M.D., Chief Medical Officer
CIO: Denise Zabawski, Vice President Information Services and Chief Information Officer
Web address: www.nationwidechildrens.org
**Control:** Other not–for–profit (including NFP Corporation) **Service:** Children's general

**Staffed Beds: 604 Admissions: 17980 Census: 359 Outpatient Visits:** 1116771 **Births: 0 Total Expense ($000): 933928 Payroll Expense ($000): 429099 Personnel: 7408**

☐ **OHIO HOSPITAL FOR PSYCHIATRY (364041)**, 880 Greenlawn Avenue, Zip 43223–2616; tel. 614/449–9664, (Nonreporting) **A**1 9 10 **S** Acadia Healthcare Company, Inc., Franklin, TN
Primary Contact: Stanley Frank, Chief Executive Officer
COO: Shannon Robbins, Chief Operating Officer
CFO: Steve Snyder, Chief Financial Officer
CMO: Richard Nockowitz, M.D., Medical Director
CNO: Jayne Zink, Director of Nursing
Web address: www.ohiohospitalforpsychiatry.com/
**Control:** Corporation, Investor–owned, for–profit **Service:** Children's hospital psychiatric

**Staffed Beds: 78**

☒ △ **OHIO STATE UNIVERSITY WEXNER MEDICAL CENTER (360085)**, 370 West 9th Avenue, Zip 43210–1238; tel. 614/293–8000, (Includes OHIO STATE UNIVERSITY HOSPITALS EAST, 1492 East Broad Street, Zip 43205–1546; tel. 614/257–3000) **A**1 3 5 7 8 10 **F**3 4 5 6 8 9 11 12 13 15 16 17 18 20 22 24 26 28 29 30 31 33 34 35 36 37 38 39 40 43 44 45 46 47 48 49 50 51 52 53 54 55 56 57 58 59 60 61 62 64 65 66 68 70 72 73 74 75 76 77 78 79 80 81 82 84 85 86 87 90 91 92 93 94 95 96 97 98 99 100 101 102 103 104 105 107 108 110 111 112 113 114 115 118 119 126 129 130 131 132 134 135 137 138 139 140 141 142 143 144 145 146 147 148 **P**6 **S** Ohio State University Health System, Columbus, OH
Primary Contact: Sheldon Retchin, M.D., Chief Executive Officer
COO: Peter E. Geier, Chief Operating Officer
CMO: Andrew Thomas, M.D., Chief Medical Officer
CIO: Phyllis Teater, Chief Information Officer
CHR: Kim Shumate, Human Resources Director
CNO: Mary G. Nash, Ph.D., Chief Nursing Officer
Web address: www.medicalcenter.osu.edu
**Control:** State–Government, nonfederal **Service:** General Medical and Surgical

**Staffed Beds: 962 Admissions: 45762 Census: 754 Outpatient Visits:** 1256824 **Births: 4861 Total Expense ($000): 1364256 Payroll Expense ($000): 415296 Personnel: 9877**

☒ ○ **OHIOHEALTH DOCTORS HOSPITAL (360152)**, 5100 West Broad Street, Zip 43228–1607; tel. 614/544–1000 **A**1 2 3 5 9 10 11 12 13 15 17 18 20 22 24 26 28 29 30 34 35 36 40 45 46 47 48 49 50 57 58 59 64 65 66 68 70 72 74 75 76 78 79 81 85 87 92 93 97 100 107 109 110 111 114 115 116 117 119 120 121 123 126 130 131 134 135 145 146 147 148 **P**1 3 5 **S** OhioHealth, Columbus, OH
Primary Contact: Michael L. Reichfield, President
CFO: Troy Hammett, Vice President and Chief Financial Officer
CMO: Dean Colwell, D.O., Vice President Medical Affairs
CIO: Michael Krouse, Chief Information Officer
CHR: David Sullivan, Director Human Resources
Web address: www.ohiohealth.com
**Control:** Church–operated, Nongovernment, not–for profit **Service:** General Medical and Surgical

**Staffed Beds: 243 Admissions: 8381 Census: 88 Outpatient Visits: 232890 Births: 946 Total Expense ($000): 235226 Payroll Expense ($000): 113706 Personnel: 1052**

☒ **OHIOHEALTH GRANT MEDICAL CENTER (360017)**, 111 South Grant Avenue, Zip 43215–1898; tel. 614/566–9000 **A**1 2 3 5 8 9 10 **F**3 7 8 9 11 13 15 17 18 20 22 24 26 28 29 30 31 34 35 36 37 40 42 43 45 46 47 48 50 53 54 56 57 58 59 60 61 64 66 67 68 70 72 74 75 76 78 79 81 82 83 84 85 86 87 97 100 102 107 108 109 110 111 114 115 116 117 119 120 121 123 124 126 129 130 131 132 135 143 144 146 147 148 **P**1 3 5 **S** OhioHealth, Columbus, OH
Primary Contact: Michael Lawson, President and Chief Operating Officer
COO: Michael Lawson, President and Chief Operating Officer
CMO: Greg Morrison, M.D., Vice President Medical Affairs
CIO: Michael Krouse, Chief Information Officer
CHR: Linda Simpson, Vice President Human Resources
Web address: www.ohiohealth.com
**Control:** Church–operated, Nongovernment, not–for profit **Service:** General Medical and Surgical

**Staffed Beds: 427 Admissions: 19821 Census: 241 Outpatient Visits:** 596965 **Births: 2556 Total Expense ($000): 586815 Payroll Expense ($000): 250237 Personnel: 2359**

☒ **OHIOHEALTH REHABILITATION HOSPITAL (363037)**, 1087 Dennison Avenue, 4th Floor, Zip 43201–3201; tel. 614/484–9600 **A**1 10 **F**3 90 96 107 119 **S** Select Medical Corporation, Mechanicsburg, PA
Primary Contact: Eric Yap, Chief Executive Officer
CFO: Ted Bolcavage, Vice President Division Controller, Inpatient
CMO: Jonathan Pedrick, M.D., Medical Director
CHR: Matt Bernosky, Manager Human Resources
CNO: Graydon Todd Auckerman, Chief Nursing Officer
Web address: www.ohiohealth–rehab.com
**Control:** Partnership, Investor–owned, for–profit **Service:** Rehabilitation

**Staffed Beds: 43 Admissions: 897 Census: 33 Outpatient Visits: 0 Births: 0**

☒ **OHIOHEALTH RIVERSIDE METHODIST HOSPITAL (360006)**, 3535 Olentangy River Road, Zip 43214–3998; tel. 614/566–5000 **A**1 2 3 5 8 9 10 **F**3 7 8 11 12 13 14 15 17 18 20 21 22 24 26 28 29 30 31 33 34 35 36 37 38 39 40 43 44 45 46 47 48 49 50 51 53 54 55 56 57 58 59 60 61 62 63 64 65 66 68 69 70 71 72 74 75 76 77 78 79 80 81 82 83 84 85 86 87 90 91 92 93 94 96 97 98 100 102 103 104 105 107 108 110 111 114 115 116 117 118 119 120 121 123 124 126 129 130 132 135 143 144 145 146 147 148 **P**1 3 5 **S** OhioHealth, Columbus, OH
Primary Contact: Brian Jepson, President
COO: Elizabeth Brill, M.D., Chief Operating Officer
CFO: Peter Bury, Vice President Finance
CMO: Thomas Harmon, M.D., Vice President Medical Affairs
CIO: Michael Krouse, Chief Information Officer
CHR: Shereen Solaiman, Vice President Human Resources
CNO: Lisa Gossett, MSN, Chief Nursing Officer
Web address: www.ohiohealth.com
**Control:** Church–operated, Nongovernment, not–for profit **Service:** General Medical and Surgical

**Staffed Beds: 756 Admissions: 43318 Census: 505 Outpatient Visits:** 799449 **Births: 6334 Total Expense ($000): 880532 Payroll Expense ($000): 358733 Personnel: 4690**

☒ **REGENCY HOSPITAL OF COLUMBUS (362037)**, 1430 South High Street, Zip 43207–1045; tel. 614/456–0300, (Includes SELECT SPECIALTY HOSPITAL – COLUMBUS EAST, 1492 East Broad Street, 6th Floor, Zip 43205–1546; tel. 614/685–1703; Lisa J. Pettrey, MSN, R.N., Interim Chief Executive Officer), (Nonreporting) **A**1 10 **S** Select Medical Corporation, Mechanicsburg, PA
Primary Contact: Lisa J. Pettrey, MSN, R.N., Chief Executive Officer
Web address: www.regencyhospital.com/
**Control:** Corporation, Investor–owned, for–profit **Service:** Long–Term Acute Care hospital

**Staffed Beds: 43**

*Many Facility Codes have changed. Please refer to the AHA Guide Code Chart.* © 2015 AHA Guide

☒ **SELECT SPECIALTY HOSPITAL–COLUMBUS (362022)**, 1087 Dennison Avenue, Zip 43201–3201; tel. 614/458–9000, (Includes SELECT SPECIALTY HOSPITAL–COLUMBUS, MOUNT CARMEL CAMPUS, 793 West State Street, Zip 43222–1551; tel. 614/234–0950), (Nonreporting) **A**1 10 **S** Select Medical Corporation, Mechanicsburg, PA
Primary Contact: Patrick Tuer, Chief Executive Officer
CMO: Victoria Ruff, M.D., Medical Director
CHR: Charles Pankowski, Manager Human Resources
Web address: www.selectspecialtyhospitals.com/company/locations/columbus.aspx
**Control:** Corporation, Investor–owned, for–profit **Service:** Long–Term Acute Care hospital

Staffed Beds: 186

**SELECT SPECIALTY HOSPITAL–COLUMBUS, MOUNT CARMEL CAMPUS** See Select Specialty Hospital–Columbus

☒ **TWIN VALLEY BEHAVIORAL HEALTHCARE (364007)**, 2200 West Broad Street, Zip 43223–1297; tel. 614/752–0333, (Nonreporting) **A**1 10 **S** Ohio Department of Mental Health, Columbus, OH
Primary Contact: Veronica Lofton, Acting Chief Executive Officer
COO: David Blahnik, Chief Operating Officer
CFO: Tracy Gladen, Chief Financial Officer
CMO: R. Alan Freeland, M.D., Chief Clinical Officer
CIO: Missy McGarvey, Chief Information Officer
CHR: Marcia McKeen, Director Human Resources
CNO: Michael Breakwell, R.N., Nurse Executive
Web address: www.mh.state.oh.us/ibhs/bhos/tvbh.html
**Control:** State–Government, nonfederal **Service:** Psychiatric

Staffed Beds: 248

**CONCORD TOWNSHIP—Lake County**

☒ **LAKE HEALTH (360098)**, 7590 Auburn Road, Zip 44077–9176; tel. 440/354–1641, (Includes TRIPOINT MEDICAL CENTER, 7950 Auburn Road, Painesville, Zip 44077; Cynthia Moore–Hardy, FACHE, President and Chief Executive Officer) **A**1 9 10 **F**3 5 11 12 13 15 17 18 20 22 24 26 28 29 30 34 35 36 40 42 44 45 49 50 51 53 54 56 57 58 59 60 62 63 64 65 68 70 75 76 77 79 81 82 84 85 86 87 90 93 97 98 103 107 108 110 111 112 113 114 115 116 117 119 120 121 122 123 124 126 129 130 131 132 133 135 143 144 146 147 148 **P**1
Primary Contact: Cynthia Moore–Hardy, FACHE, President and Chief Executive Officer
CFO: Michael Kittoe, Chief Financial Officer
CMO: John Baniewicz, M.D., Chief Medical Officer
CIO: Gerald Peters, Vice President Information Technologies and Chief Information Officer
CHR: Craig J. Ghidotti, Vice President Human Resources
CNO: Mary L. Ogrinc, R.N., Chief Nursing Officer, Senior Vice President Patient Care Services
Web address: www.lakehealth.org
**Control:** Other not–for–profit (including NFP Corporation) **Service:** General Medical and Surgical

Staffed Beds: 350 Admissions: 16341 Census: 190 Outpatient Visits: 677784 Births: 1810 Total Expense ($000): 315762 Payroll Expense ($000): 112878 Personnel: 2218

**CONNEAUT—Ashtabula County**

☒ **UNIVERSITY HOSPITALS CONNEAUT MEDICAL CENTER (361308)**, 158 West Main Road, Zip 44030–2039; tel. 440/593–1131 **A**1 9 10 18 **F**3 7 11 15 18 28 29 34 35 37 40 45 56 57 59 64 68 70 75 77 78 79 81 82 85 86 87 93 107 110 111 114 119 130 132 133 135 143 146 147 148 **S** University Hospitals, Cleveland, OH
Primary Contact: M. Steven Jones, President
COO: Richard Trice, Director Operations
CFO: Michael McGrath, Manager Finance
CMO: Gary Huston, D.O., Chief Medical Officer
CIO: Cheryl Vibbard, Manager Health Information Services
CHR: Barbara Gurto, Manager Human Resources
CNO: Karen McNeil, Chief Nursing Officer
Web address: www.uhhospitals.org
**Control:** Other not–for–profit (including NFP Corporation) **Service:** General Medical and Surgical

Staffed Beds: 25 Admissions: 572 Census: 6 Outpatient Visits: 47780 Births: 0 Total Expense ($000): 26186 Payroll Expense ($000): 9234 Personnel: 169

**COSHOCTON—Coshocton County**

☐ **COSHOCTON COUNTY MEMORIAL HOSPITAL (360109)**, 1460 Orange Street, Zip 43812–2229, Mailing Address: P.O. Box 1330, Zip 43812–6330; tel. 740/622–6411, (Nonreporting) **A**1 5 9 10 20
Primary Contact: Lorri Wildi, Interim Chief Executive Officer
CFO: Robin Nichols, Chief Financial Officer
CMO: Tammy S. Alverson, M.D., Chief of Staff
CIO: Seth Peterson, Director Information Services
CHR: Rick Davis, Chief Operating Officer and Support Services
Web address: www.ccmh.com
**Control:** Other not–for–profit (including NFP Corporation) **Service:** General Medical and Surgical

Staffed Beds: 109

**CUYAHOGA FALLS—Summit County**

**CUYAHOGA FALLS GENERAL HOSPITAL** See Summa Western Reserve Hospital

☒ △ **EDWIN SHAW REHAB (360241)**, 330 Broadway Street East, Zip 44221–3312; tel. 330/436–0910, (Nonreporting) **A**1 5 7 9 10 **S** Akron General Health System, Akron, OH
Primary Contact: Lynne Blinco, Associate Vice President
CFO: Debbie Gorbach, Vice President and Treasurer
CMO: Anthony Hayek, D.O., Medical Director
CHR: Heather Saus, Human Resource Generalist
Web address: www.edwinshaw.com
**Control:** County–Government, nonfederal **Service:** Rehabilitation

Staffed Beds: 38

○ **SUMMA WESTERN RESERVE HOSPITAL (360150)**, 1900 23rd Street, Zip 44223–1499; tel. 330/971–7000 **A**9 10 11 12 13 **F**3 8 11 18 20 26 29 30 31 32 33 34 35 36 38 40 44 45 47 49 50 51 54 57 59 60 63 64 65 66 68 70 74 75 77 78 79 81 82 84 85 86 87 92 93 94 96 97 100 107 108 111 114 115 119 129 130 132 135 144 146 148 **P**6 8 **S** Summa Health System, Akron, OH
Primary Contact: Robert Kent, D.O., President and Chief Executive Officer
CFO: Jill Hiner, Vice President and Chief Financial Officer
CMO: Charles Feunning, M.D., President Medical Staff
CHR: Heather Milicevic, Director Human Resources
Web address: www.westernreservehospital.org
**Control:** Partnership, Investor–owned, for–profit **Service:** General Medical and Surgical

Staffed Beds: 65 Admissions: 3424 Census: 39 Outpatient Visits: 122169 Births: 0 Total Expense ($000): 101808 Payroll Expense ($000): 34419 Personnel: 755

**DAYTON—Montgomery County**

☐ **ACCESS HOSPITAL DAYTON (364050)**, 2611 Wayne Avenue, Zip 45420–1833; tel. 937/256–7802, (Nonreporting) **A**1 10
Primary Contact: Belinda Stevens, Chief Executive Officer
Web address: www.accesshospital.com/
**Control:** Corporation, Investor–owned, for–profit **Service:** Psychiatric

Staffed Beds: 28

☐ **CHILDREN'S MEDICAL CENTER (363306)**, One Children's Plaza, Zip 45404–1815; tel. 937/641–3000, (Nonreporting) **A**1 2 3 5 9 10
Primary Contact: Deborah A. Feldman, President and Chief Executive Officer
COO: Matthew P. Graybill, Chief Operating Officer
CFO: David T. Miller, Vice President and Chief Financial Officer
CMO: Adam Mezoff, M.D., Vice President and Chief Medical Officer
CIO: Beth Fredette, Chief Information Officer
Web address: www.childrensdayton.org
**Control:** Other not–for–profit (including NFP Corporation) **Service:** Children's general

Staffed Beds: 133

☐ **DAYTON REHABILITATION INSTITUTE (363033)**, One Elizabeth Place, Zip 45417–3445; tel. 937/424–8200 **A**1 10 **F**3 29 90 96 130 148 **S** Reliant Healthcare Partners, Richardson, TX
Primary Contact: Randy J. Kitchen, Chief Executive Officer
Web address: www.reliantdayton.com
**Control:** Partnership, Investor–owned, for–profit **Service:** Rehabilitation

Staffed Beds: 50 Admissions: 595 Census: 20 Outpatient Visits: 0 Births: 0 Total Expense ($000): 7597 Payroll Expense ($000): 3511 Personnel: 61

---

**Hospital, Medicare Provider Number, Address, Telephone, Approval, Facility, and Physician Codes, Health Care System**

★ American Hospital Association (AHA) membership
☐ The Joint Commission accreditation
○ Healthcare Facilities Accreditation Program
◇ DNV Healthcare Inc. accreditation
⇑ Center for Improvement in Healthcare Quality Accreditation
△ Commission on Accreditation of Rehabilitation Facilities (CARF) accreditation

**OH**

✠ △ **DAYTON VETERANS AFFAIRS MEDICAL CENTER**, 4100 West Third Street, Zip 45428–9000; tel. 937/268–6511, (Nonreporting) **A**1 2 3 5 7 8 **S** Department of Veterans Affairs, Washington, DC
Primary Contact: Glenn A. Costie, FACHE, Director
COO: Mark Murdock, Associate Director
CFO: Shannon Rappach, Chief Fiscal Services
CMO: James Hardy, D.O., Chief of Staff
CIO: Susan Sherer, Chief Information Resource Management
CHR: Rolanda Watkins, Chief Human Resources Management Service
CNO: Anna Jones Monnett, MS, Associate Director Patient Care Services
Web address: www.dayton.va.gov/
**Control:** Veterans Affairs, Government, federal **Service:** General Medical and Surgical

| Staffed Beds: 460 |
| --- |

✠ **GOOD SAMARITAN HOSPITAL (360052)**, 2222 Philadelphia Drive, Zip 45406–1813; tel. 937/734–2612 **A**1 2 3 5 9 10 **F**3 11 13 15 17 18 20 22 24 26 28 29 30 31 36 37 39 40 42 44 45 46 49 50 53 54 56 58 60 61 64 66 70 73 74 75 76 77 78 79 80 81 82 83 85 86 87 92 93 97 100 101 102 107 108 110 111 114 115 118 119 126 129 130 131 132 145 146 148 **P**6 **S** Premier Health, Dayton, OH
Primary Contact: Eloise Broner, President and Chief Executive Officer
COO: Mary E. Garman, R.N., Chief Operating Officer and Chief Nursing Officer
CMO: Daniel L. Schoulties, M.D., Vice President Medical Affairs
CHR: Barbara A. Johnson, Vice President Human Resources
CNO: Mary E. Garman, R.N., Chief Nursing Officer and Chief Operating Officer
Web address: www.goodsamdayton.com
**Control:** Church–operated, Nongovernment, not–for profit **Service:** General Medical and Surgical

| Staffed Beds: 346 Admissions: 13175 Census: 161 Outpatient Visits: 168633 Births: 987 Total Expense ($000): 328355 Payroll Expense ($000): 123293 Personnel: 2080 |
| --- |

★ ○ **GRANDVIEW MEDICAL CENTER (360133)**, 405 West Grand Avenue, Zip 45405–4796; tel. 937/723–3200, (Includes SOUTHVIEW MEDICAL CENTER, 1997 Miamisburg–Centerville Road, Zip 45459–3800; tel. 937/439–6000; Rebecca Lewis, Senior Vice President, Administrator) **A**2 3 9 10 11 12 **F**3 11 12 13 15 18 20 22 24 28 29 30 31 34 35 36 38 39 40 42 43 44 45 47 48 49 50 51 53 54 56 57 58 59 60 61 64 65 66 68 70 73 74 75 76 77 78 79 81 82 85 86 87 93 96 97 98 100 101 102 103 104 105 107 108 110 111 114 115 116 117 118 119 120 121 123 124 129 130 131 132 135 141 144 145 146 147 148 **S** Kettering Health Network, Dayton, OH
Primary Contact: Russell J. Wetherell, Senior Vice President, Administrator
CFO: Luis Chanaga, Chief Financial Officer
CMO: Paul Martin, Chief Medical Officer
CIO: Andy Lehman, Senior Vice President Technology and Analytics
CHR: Keith Jenkins, Director, Human Resources
CNO: Ronda Brandstater, Vice President Patient Care
Web address: www.ketteringhealth.org/grandview/
**Control:** Church–operated, Nongovernment, not–for profit **Service:** General Medical and Surgical

| Staffed Beds: 278 Admissions: 11335 Census: 147 Outpatient Visits: 334422 Births: 1674 Total Expense ($000): 386181 Payroll Expense ($000): 145385 Personnel: 1525 |
| --- |

☐ **HAVEN BEHAVIORAL SENIOR CARE OF DAYTON (364048)**, One Elizabeth Place, 4th Floor Southwest Tower, Zip 45417–3445; tel. 937/234–0100, (Nonreporting) **A**1 10 **S** Haven Behavioral Healthcare, Nashville, TN
Primary Contact: Keith Kuhn, Chief Executive Officer
CMO: Amita Patel, M.D., Medical Director
CNO: Cheryl Meyer, MSN, Director of Nursing
Web address: www.havenbehavioraldayton.com/
**Control:** Corporation, Investor–owned, for–profit **Service:** Psychiatric

| Staffed Beds: 32 |
| --- |

✠ **KINDRED HOSPITAL–DAYTON (362033)**, 707 South Edwin C. Moses Boulevard, Zip 45417–3462; tel. 937/222–5963, (Nonreporting) **A**1 10 **S** Kindred Healthcare, Louisville, KY
Primary Contact: Lynn Schoen, Chief Executive Officer
CMO: Felipe Rubio, M.D., Medical Director
Web address: www.khdayton.com
**Control:** Corporation, Investor–owned, for–profit **Service:** Long–Term Acute Care hospital

| Staffed Beds: 67 |
| --- |

✠ △ **MIAMI VALLEY HOSPITAL (360051)**, One Wyoming Street, Zip 45409–2793; tel. 937/208–8000, (Includes MIAMI VALLEY HOSPITAL SOUTH, 2400 Miami Valley Drive, Centerville, Zip 45459–4774; tel. 937/438–2400) **A**1 2 3 5 7 9 10 **F**3 5 7 12 13 15 16 17 18 20 22 24 26 28 29 30 31 34 35 37 39 40 42 43 44 45 46 47 48 49 50 53 54 55 56 57 58 59 60 61 64 68 70 72 73 74 75 76 77 78 79 81 82 84 85 86 87 90 91 92 93 96 98 100 101 102 103 104 107 108 110 111 114 115 117 118 119 120 121 123 125 129 130 131 132 134 135 136 141 143 145 146 147 148 **P**6 **S** Premier Health, Dayton, OH
Primary Contact: Mark S. Shaker, President and Chief Executive Officer
COO: Mikki Clancy, Chief Operating Officer
CFO: Thomas M. Duncan, Executive Vice President and Chief Financial Officer
CMO: Mark Williams, M.D., Vice President and Chief Medical Officer
CIO: Gary Ginter, System Vice President and Chief Information Officer
CHR: Barbara A. Johnson, Vice President Human Resources
CNO: Jolyn M. Angus, R.N., Chief Nursing Officer
Web address: www.miamivalleyhospital.org
**Control:** Other not–for–profit (including NFP Corporation) **Service:** General Medical and Surgical

| Staffed Beds: 870 Admissions: 37020 Census: 484 Outpatient Visits: 320658 Births: 5031 Total Expense ($000): 757095 Payroll Expense ($000): 280909 Personnel: 5300 |
| --- |

**SOUTHVIEW MEDICAL CENTER** See Grandview Medical Center

☐ **THE MEDICAL CENTER AT ELIZABETH PLACE (360274)**, One Elizabeth Place, Zip 45417–3445; tel. 937/660–3100, (Nonreporting) **A**1 9 10
Primary Contact: Alexander M. Rintoul, Chief Executive Officer
Web address: www.regentsurgicalhealth.com/Partner+Centers/Medical+Center+at+Elizabeth+Place
**Control:** Partnership, Investor–owned, for–profit **Service:** General Medical and Surgical

| Staffed Beds: 26 |
| --- |

**VETERANS AFFAIRS MEDICAL CENTER** See Dayton Veterans Affairs Medical Center

**DEFIANCE—Defiance County**

✠ **MERCY HOSPITAL OF DEFIANCE (360270)**, 1404 East Second Street, Zip 43512–2440; tel. 419/782–8444, (Nonreporting) **A**1 10 **S** Mercy Health, Cincinnati, OH
Primary Contact: Chad Peter, President
COO: Kerry Knuth, Chief Operating Officer
CFO: James Puffenberger, Vice President and Chief Financial Officer
CMO: Jeffrey Pruitt, M.D., Chief of Staff
CHR: Susan Pscodna, Director Human Resources
CNO: Sonya Selhorst, R.N., Administrator and Chief Nursing Officer
Web address: www.ehealthconnection.com/regions/toledo/
**Control:** Partnership, Investor–owned, for–profit **Service:** General Medical and Surgical

| Staffed Beds: 23 |
| --- |

✠ **PROMEDICA DEFIANCE REGIONAL HOSPITAL (361328)**, 1200 Ralston Avenue, Zip 43512–1396; tel. 419/783–6955 **A**1 5 9 10 18 **F**3 11 13 15 18 20 28 31 32 34 40 43 57 59 64 66 68 70 75 76 77 78 79 81 82 85 86 87 93 98 100 101 102 103 104 105 107 108 110 111 114 118 119 129 130 132 135 144 146 147 148 **S** ProMedica Health System, Toledo, OH
Primary Contact: Julie Yaroch, D.O., Interim President
CFO: Ken Swint, Director Finance
CMO: Stanislaw Dajczak, M.D., Chief of Staff
CIO: Patricia Swint, Director Information Management Systems
CHR: Carrie Miller, Director Human Resources
Web address: www.promedica.org
**Control:** Other not–for–profit (including NFP Corporation) **Service:** General Medical and Surgical

| Staffed Beds: 35 Admissions: 2231 Census: 17 Outpatient Visits: 88210 Births: 621 Total Expense ($000): 50859 Payroll Expense ($000): 14350 Personnel: 135 |
| --- |

**DELAWARE—Delaware County**

✠ **OHIOHEALTH GRADY MEMORIAL HOSPITAL (360210)**, 561 West Central Avenue, Zip 43015–1410; tel. 740/615–1000 **A**1 2 9 10 **F**3 13 15 18 20 26 28 29 30 31 34 35 40 45 46 48 50 54 57 58 59 60 63 64 66 68 70 75 76 77 78 79 81 82 85 86 87 92 93 96 97 102 107 108 109 110 111 114 119 124 129 130 131 132 134 135 146 147 148 **P**1 3 5 **S** OhioHealth, Columbus, OH
Primary Contact: Steve Bunyard, President
COO: Anna Hensley, Chief Operating Officer
CFO: David Hensel, Director Financial Operations
CMO: Barbara Evert, M.D., Vice President Medical Affairs
CIO: Michael Krouse, Chief Information Officer Information Services
CHR: Victoria L. Matlack, Director and Human Resources Business Partner
CNO: Elizabeth Anne Biegler, R.N., Chief Nursing Officer
Web address: www.ohiohealth.com
**Control:** Church–operated, Nongovernment, not–for profit **Service:** General Medical and Surgical

| Staffed Beds: 61 Admissions: 2681 Census: 27 Outpatient Visits: 109166 Births: 254 Total Expense ($000): 73294 Payroll Expense ($000): 31813 Personnel: 378 |
| --- |

**OH**

## DENNISON—Tuscarawas County

☐ **TEN LAKES CENTER (364042)**, 819 North First Street, 3rd Floor, Zip 44621–1003; tel. 740/922–7499 **A**1 9 10 **F**2 98 102 103 105 130 **P**6 **S** Acadia Healthcare Company, Inc., Franklin, TN
Primary Contact: Debra C. Gardner, R.N., MSN, Administrator
Web address: www.tenlakescenter.com/
**Control:** Corporation, Investor–owned, for–profit **Service:** Psychiatric

Staffed Beds: 16 Admissions: 335 Census: 13 Outpatient Visits: 3860
Births: 0 Total Expense ($000): 3631 Payroll Expense ($000): 1755
Personnel: 43

✖ **TRINITY HOSPITAL TWIN CITY (361302)**, 819 North First Street, Zip 44621–1098; tel. 740/922–2800 **A**1 9 10 18 **F**11 15 18 19 28 29 30 34 35 40 45 50 57 59 64 70 75 77 81 85 86 87 89 93 97 107 114 119 127 128 129 130 132 133 146 147 148 **P**4 **S** Catholic Health Initiatives, Englewood, CO
Primary Contact: Joseph J. Mitchell, President
CMO: Tim McKnight, M.D., Chief of Staff
CHR: Bianca Love, Assistant Administrator Human Resources
CNO: Teresa Gagliardi, R.N., Chief Nursing Officer
Web address: www.trinitytwincity.org
**Control:** Church–operated, Nongovernment, not–for profit **Service:** General Medical and Surgical

Staffed Beds: 13 Admissions: 323 Census: 3 Outpatient Visits: 29187
Births: 0 Total Expense ($000): 22122 Payroll Expense ($000): 10266
Personnel: 218

## DOVER—Tuscarawas County

★ ◇ **UNION HOSPITAL (360010)**, 659 Boulevard, Zip 44622–2077; tel. 330/343–3311 **A**9 10 19 21 **F**3 8 11 13 15 18 28 29 34 35 40 42 50 53 54 57 59 62 64 70 74 75 76 77 79 80 81 82 85 86 89 90 91 93 107 108 110 111 115 119 124 129 130 131 132 135 144 146 148 **P**6
Primary Contact: Bruce James, Chief Executive Officer
CFO: Eugene A. Thorn, III, Vice President Finance and Chief Financial Officer
CMO: Todd Meyerhoefer, M.D., Vice President Medical Affairs
CIO: David Baumgardner, Director Information Management
CHR: Darwin K. Smith, Vice President Human Resources
CNO: Diana Boyd, Vice President Nursing
Web address: www.unionhospital.org
**Control:** Other not–for–profit (including NFP Corporation) **Service:** General Medical and Surgical

Staffed Beds: 149 Admissions: 5196 Census: 54 Outpatient Visits: 250787
Births: 693 Total Expense ($000): 108144 Payroll Expense ($000): 46028
Personnel: 1007

## DUBLIN—Franklin County

☐ **DUBLIN SPRINGS (364049)**, 7625 Hospital Drive, Zip 43016–9649; tel. 614/717–1800 **A**1 10 **F**4 5 64 98 101 103 104 105 130 132 **P**5
Primary Contact: Garry W. Hoyes, Chief Executive Officer
CFO: Alexis Barbour, Director Finance
CMO: Mark Blair, M.D., Medical Director
CHR: Tam Wisler, Director Human Resources
CNO: Rolaine Weeks, R.N., Director of Nursing
Web address: www.dublinsprings.com/
**Control:** Corporation, Investor–owned, for–profit **Service:** Psychiatric

Staffed Beds: 72 Admissions: 2727 Census: 63 Outpatient Visits: 26736
Births: 0 Total Expense ($000): 14025 Payroll Expense ($000): 7865
Personnel: 185

✖ **OHIOHEALTH DUBLIN METHODIST HOSPITAL (360348)**, 7500 Hospital Drive, Zip 43016–8518; tel. 614/544–8000 **A**1 9 10 **F**3 13 15 18 20 22 29 30 34 40 45 46 57 59 62 68 70 76 77 79 81 82 85 87 97 107 110 111 115 119 126 129 130 131 132 135 144 146 147 148 **P**1 3 5 **S** OhioHealth, Columbus, OH
Primary Contact: Steve Bunyard, President
CMO: Barbara Evert, M.D., Vice President Medical Affairs
CIO: Michael Krouse, Senior Vice President Chief Information Officer
CHR: Victoria L. Matlack, Director and Human Resources Business Partner
CNO: Elizabeth Anne Biegler, R.N., Chief Nursing Officer
Web address: www.ohiohealth.com
**Control:** Church–operated, Nongovernment, not–for profit **Service:** General Medical and Surgical

Staffed Beds: 100 Admissions: 5642 Census: 41 Outpatient Visits: 106674
Births: 1993 Total Expense ($000): 122075 Payroll Expense ($000): 47830 Personnel: 556

## EAST LIVERPOOL—Columbiana County

✖ **EAST LIVERPOOL CITY HOSPITAL (360096)**, 425 West Fifth Street, Zip 43920–2498; tel. 330/385–7200 **A**1 9 10 13 **F**3 11 15 18 28 29 30 31 34 35 39 40 41 44 50 51 53 54 56 57 59 60 64 65 66 70 75 77 78 79 81 85 86 87 93 97 98 100 101 102 103 107 110 111 115 118 119 130 131 132 135 146 147 148 **P**6
Primary Contact: Kenneth Cochran, R.N., FACHE, President and Chief Executive Officer
CFO: Kyle Johnson, Vice President Finance
CMO: Steve LaTulippe, President Medical Staff
CIO: Frank Mader, Director Information Services
CHR: Teri Pasco, Director Human Resources
CNO: Stacie Call, R.N., Vice President Patient Care and Chief Nursing Officer
Web address: www.elch.org
**Control:** Other not–for–profit (including NFP Corporation) **Service:** General Medical and Surgical

Staffed Beds: 120 Admissions: 4183 Census: 45 Outpatient Visits: 108011
Births: 168 Total Expense ($000): 62454 Payroll Expense ($000): 19934
Personnel: 365

## ELYRIA—Lorain County

✖ **UNIVERSITY HOSPITALS ELYRIA MEDICAL CENTER (360145)**, 630 East River Street, Zip 44035–5902; tel. 440/329–7500 **A**1 2 9 10 13 **F**3 8 11 12 13 15 17 18 20 22 24 26 28 29 30 31 34 35 37 40 42 50 53 54 57 59 62 64 68 70 73 74 75 76 77 78 79 81 82 85 86 87 89 92 93 94 98 107 108 110 111 114 115 118 119 126 129 130 131 135 146 148 **P**6 7 8 **S** University Hospitals, Cleveland, OH
Primary Contact: Donald S. Sheldon, M.D., President and Chief Executive Officer
CFO: David A. Cook, Vice President and Chief Financial Officer
CMO: Douglas McDonald, M.D., Vice President Medical Affairs
CIO: Char Wray, Vice President Chief Clinical Operations and Chief Information Officer
CHR: Daniel Miller, Vice President Human Resources
CNO: Jill Cooksey, Vice President Chief Nursing Officer
Web address: www.emh–healthcare.org
**Control:** Other not–for–profit (including NFP Corporation) **Service:** General Medical and Surgical

Staffed Beds: 237 Admissions: 11280 Census: 137 Outpatient Visits: 273169 Births: 864 Total Expense ($000): 191098 Payroll Expense ($000): 72826 Personnel: 1496

## EUCLID—Cuyahoga County

✖ △ **EUCLID HOSPITAL (360082)**, 18901 Lake Shore Boulevard, Zip 44119–1090; tel. 216/531–9000, (Total facility includes 40 beds in nursing home–type unit) **A**1 3 7 10 **F**3 15 17 18 26 28 29 30 34 35 39 40 45 47 50 51 56 57 59 60 64 70 74 75 77 79 81 82 85 87 90 91 93 94 96 98 100 102 103 107 108 111 114 118 119 128 130 131 146 148 **S** Cleveland Clinic Health System, Cleveland, OH
Primary Contact: Napierkowski, M.D., President
COO: Rich Lea, Vice President Operations
CFO: Don Urbancsik, Director Finance
CMO: Andrew Brobbey, M.D., Chief of Staff
CHR: Gloria Donnelly, Director Human Resources
CNO: Dawn A. Bailey, R.N., Vice President Nursing and Chief Nursing Officer
Web address: www.euclidhospital.org
**Control:** Other not–for–profit (including NFP Corporation) **Service:** General Medical and Surgical

Staffed Beds: 219 Admissions: 7043 Census: 128 Outpatient Visits: 95359
Births: 0 Total Expense ($000): 109299 Payroll Expense ($000): 44442
Personnel: 659

## FAIRFIELD—Butler County

✖ △ **MERCY HEALTH – FAIRFIELD HOSPITAL (360056)**, 3000 Mack Road, Zip 45014–5335; tel. 513/870–7000, (Nonreporting) **A**1 2 3 7 9 10 **S** Mercy Health, Cincinnati, OH
Primary Contact: Thomas S. Urban, Market Leader and President
CFO: Robin Yon, Site Finance Director
CMO: John Kennedy, M.D., Vice President Medical Affairs
CIO: Yousuf Ahmad, Divisional Senior Vice President and Chief Network Transformation Officer
CHR: Maggie Lund, Divisional Senior Vice President Human Resources
Web address: www.e–mercy.com
**Control:** Church–operated, Nongovernment, not–for profit **Service:** General Medical and Surgical

Staffed Beds: 229

---

**Hospital, Medicare Provider Number, Address, Telephone, Approval, Facility, and Physician Codes, Health Care System**

★ American Hospital Association (AHA) membership
☐ The Joint Commission accreditation
◯ Healthcare Facilities Accreditation Program
◇ DNV Healthcare Inc. accreditation
⇑ Center for Improvement in Healthcare Quality Accreditation
△ Commission on Accreditation of Rehabilitation Facilities (CARF) accreditation

**OH**

## FINDLAY—Hancock County

✠ **BLANCHARD VALLEY HOSPITAL (360095)**, 1900 South Main Street, Zip 45840–1214; tel. 419/423–4500, (Includes BLANCHARD VALLEY HOSPITAL, 1900 South Main Street, Zip 45840; tel. 419/423–4500) **A**1 2 3 5 9 10 19 **F**3 7 8 11 13 15 17 18 20 22 24 26 28 29 30 31 34 35 40 41 42 43 45 48 49 50 58 59 60 64 65 70 73 74 76 77 78 79 81 82 83 84 85 86 87 91 93 96 97 98 103 107 108 110 111 114 115 118 119 120 121 124 126 129 130 131 132 134 135 146 147 148 **P**5 **S** Blanchard Valley Health System, Findlay, OH
Primary Contact: Scott C. Malaney, President and Chief Executive Officer
CFO: David Cytlak, Chief Financial Officer
CMO: William H. Kose, M.D., Chief Quality Officer
CIO: Jamie Sorg, Chief Information Officer and Information Security Officer
CHR: Ryan Fisher, Director of Human Resources
CNO: Barbara J. Pasztor, R.N., Vice President Patient Care Services and Chief Nursing Officer
Web address: www.bvhealthsystem.org
**Control:** Other not–for–profit (including NFP Corporation) **Service:** General Medical and Surgical

**Staffed Beds:** 159 **Admissions:** 7303 **Census:** 68 **Outpatient Visits:** 216418 **Births:** 1356 **Total Expense ($000):** 140183 **Payroll Expense ($000):** 73439 **Personnel:** 1318

## FOSTORIA—Hancock County

✠ **PROMEDICA FOSTORIA COMMUNITY HOSPITAL (361318)**, 501 Van Buren Street, Zip 44830–1534, Mailing Address: P.O. Box 907, Zip 44830–0907; tel. 419/435–7734 **A**1 5 9 10 18 **F**3 11 15 28 31 32 34 35 40 45 46 55 57 59 60 62 64 66 68 70 75 78 79 81 82 85 86 87 89 93 94 96 97 107 108 110 111 115 117 118 119 128 129 130 131 132 133 135 144 146 **P**7 **S** ProMedica Health System, Toledo, OH
Primary Contact: Holly L. Bristoll, President
COO: Tom Borer, Vice President Operations
CFO: Ken Swint, Vice President Finance and Chief Financial Officer
CMO: Terrence Fondessy, M.D., Vice President Medical Affairs
CIO: Rose Ann Laureto, Chief Information Officer
CNO: Paula Grieb, R.N., Chief Nursing Officer
Web address: www.promedica.org
**Control:** Other not–for–profit (including NFP Corporation) **Service:** General Medical and Surgical

**Staffed Beds:** 25 **Admissions:** 799 **Census:** 7 **Outpatient Visits:** 56703 **Births:** 0 **Total Expense ($000):** 36126 **Payroll Expense ($000):** 8676 **Personnel:** 165

## FREMONT—Sandusky County

✠ **MEMORIAL HOSPITAL (360156)**, 715 South Taft Avenue, Zip 43420–3237; tel. 419/332–7321 **A**1 9 10 **F**3 7 11 13 15 18 19 28 29 30 34 35 38 40 44 45 46 47 48 50 51 53 56 57 59 61 64 65 68 69 70 74 75 77 79 80 81 82 84 85 86 87 91 92 93 96 97 99 100 101 103 104 107 108 110 111 114 115 119 129 130 131 132 135 141 142 143 146 147 148 **P**1 6
Primary Contact: Pamela Jensen, FACHE, President
CFO: David Brewer, Chief Financial Officer
CIO: Dustin Hufford, Chief Information Officer
CHR: Warrenette Parthemore, Director Human Resources
Web address: www.promedica.org
**Control:** Other not–for–profit (including NFP Corporation) **Service:** General Medical and Surgical

**Staffed Beds:** 49 **Admissions:** 1397 **Census:** 13 **Outpatient Visits:** 92460 **Births:** 306 **Total Expense ($000):** 66337 **Payroll Expense ($000):** 25354 **Personnel:** 403

## GAHANNA—Franklin County

**THE WOODS AT PARKSIDE (360247)**, 349 Olde Ridenour Road, Zip 43230–2528; tel. 614/471–2552, (Nonreporting) **A**10
Primary Contact: Harry Nguyen, Medical Director
Web address: www.thewoodsatparkside.com
**Control:** Partnership, Investor–owned, for–profit **Service:** Alcoholism and other chemical dependency

**Staffed Beds:** 50

## GALION—Crawford County

★ ◇ **AVITA GALION HOSPITAL (361325)**, 269 Portland Way South, Zip 44833–2399; tel. 419/468–4841, (Nonreporting) **A**9 10 18 21 **S** Avita Health System, Galion, OH
Primary Contact: Jerome Morasko, President and Chief Executive Officer
CIO: Andy Daniels, Vice President Non–Clinical Operations and Information Systems
CHR: Traci L. Oswald, Vice President Human Resources
Web address: www.avitahs.org
**Control:** Other not–for–profit (including NFP Corporation) **Service:** General Medical and Surgical

**Staffed Beds:** 35

## GALLIPOLIS—Gallia County

☐ △ **HOLZER MEDICAL CENTER (360054)**, 100 Jackson Pike, Zip 45631–1563; tel. 740/446–5000, (Nonreporting) **A**1 2 3 5 7 9 10 13 19
Primary Contact: Dr. Christopher Meyer, DO, Chief Executive Officer
CFO: Kenneth G. Payne, Chief Financial Officer
CMO: John Viall, M.D., Vice President Medical Affairs
CIO: John Allen, Chief Information Officer
CHR: Lisa B. Halley, Vice President Human Resources
Web address: www.holzer.org
**Control:** Other not–for–profit (including NFP Corporation) **Service:** General Medical and Surgical

**Staffed Beds:** 181

## GARFIELD HEIGHTS—Cuyahoga County

✠ **MARYMOUNT HOSPITAL (360143)**, 12300 McCracken Road, Zip 44125–2975; tel. 216/581–0500 **A**1 2 3 10 **F**3 7 8 11 15 18 28 29 30 31 34 35 38 39 40 42 44 50 51 53 54 56 57 59 60 62 63 64 65 68 70 74 75 77 78 79 81 82 85 86 87 92 93 96 97 98 100 102 103 104 107 108 110 111 114 116 118 119 124 129 130 131 132 135 143 146 147 148 **S** Cleveland Clinic Health System, Cleveland, OH
Primary Contact: Richard Parker, M.D., President
COO: Mark Nussbaum, Vice President Operations
CFO: Mike Stilgenbauer, Director Finance
CMO: Douglas Kohler, M.D., Vice President Medical Operations
CIO: Ralph A. Cagna, Director Information Technology Operations, Cleveland Clinic Health System South Market
CHR: Judith Santora, Human Resources Business Partner
CNO: Barbara Zinner, Chief Nursing Officer
Web address: www.marymount.org
**Control:** Other not–for–profit (including NFP Corporation) **Service:** General Medical and Surgical

**Staffed Beds:** 284 **Admissions:** 9331 **Census:** 139 **Outpatient Visits:** 124739 **Births:** 0 **Total Expense ($000):** 150412 **Payroll Expense ($000):** 53090 **Personnel:** 909

## GENEVA—Ashtabula County

✠ **UNIVERSITY HOSPITALS GENEVA MEDICAL CENTER (361307)**, 870 West Main Street, Zip 44041–1295; tel. 440/466–1141 **A**1 9 10 18 **F**3 7 11 15 18 29 34 35 40 46 51 59 64 68 70 75 77 78 79 81 82 86 87 93 107 110 111 114 119 129 130 132 133 135 143 146 147 **S** University Hospitals, Cleveland, OH
Primary Contact: M. Steven Jones, President
COO: Richard Trice, Director Operations
CFO: Michael McGrath, Manager Finance
CMO: Amitabh Goel, M.D., Chief Medical Officer
CIO: Cheryl Vibbard, Manager Health Information Systems
CHR: Barbara Gurto, Manager Human Resources
CNO: Karen McNeil, Chief Nursing Officer
Web address: www.uhhs.com
**Control:** Other not–for–profit (including NFP Corporation) **Service:** General Medical and Surgical

**Staffed Beds:** 25 **Admissions:** 1166 **Census:** 14 **Outpatient Visits:** 69910 **Births:** 0 **Total Expense ($000):** 33254 **Payroll Expense ($000):** 11897 **Personnel:** 226

## GREEN SPRINGS—Sandusky County

☐ **ELMWOOD HEALTHCARE CENTER AT THE SPRINGS (362007)**, 401 North Broadway, Zip 44836–9653; tel. 419/639–2626, (Nonreporting) **A**1 10
Primary Contact: Kathy Hunt, Chief Executive Officer
CFO: Douglas Morris, Chief Financial Officer
CMO: John Yuhas, D.O., Medical Director
CHR: Joan E. Schmidt, Director Human Resources
Web address: www.sfhcc.org
**Control:** Church–operated, Nongovernment, not–for profit **Service:** Long–Term Acute Care hospital

**Staffed Beds:** 186

## GREENFIELD—Highland County

☐ △ ◇ **ADENA GREENFIELD MEDICAL CENTER (361304)**, 550 Mirabeau Street, Zip 45123–1617; tel. 937/981–9400, (Nonreporting) **A**1 7 9 10 18 21 **S** Adena Health System, Chillicothe, OH
Primary Contact: Kathy Dye, Interim Administrator
CFO: Ralph W. Sorrell, Sr., Chief Financial Officer
CIO: Marcus Bost, Director Information Services and Chief Information Officer
CHR: Brandt Lippert, Vice President Human Resources
Web address: www.adena.org
**Control:** Other not–for–profit (including NFP Corporation) **Service:** General Medical and Surgical

**Staffed Beds:** 25

*Many Facility Codes have changed. Please refer to the AHA Guide Code Chart.*

## GREENVILLE—Darke County

★ ○ **WAYNE HOSPITAL (360044)**, 835 Sweitzer Street, Zip 45331–1077; tel. 937/548–1141 **A**2 9 10 11 **F**3 8 11 13 15 28 29 30 31 34 35 39 40 41 45 57 59 64 65 70 75 76 78 79 81 82 84 85 86 89 93 107 108 110 111 114 118 119 129 130 131 132 135 141 146 147 148 **P**1
Primary Contact: Wayne G. Deschambeau, President and Chief Executive Officer
COO: Jeffrey R. Subler, Vice President Support Services
CFO: Dennis Lockard, Vice President Fiscal Services and Chief Financial Officer
CMO: Tom Brown, M.D., President Medical Staff
CIO: Shelton Monger, Director Information Technology
CHR: Peggy Schwartz, Vice President Human Resources
CNO: Kimberlee Freeman, R.N., Vice President Patient Care Services and Chief Nursing Officer
Web address: www.waynehealthcare.org
**Control:** Other not–for–profit (including NFP Corporation) **Service:** General Medical and Surgical

**Staffed Beds:** 63 **Admissions:** 2046 **Census:** 18 **Outpatient Visits:** 76076 **Births:** 339 **Total Expense ($000):** 50898 **Payroll Expense ($000):** 17146 **Personnel:** 335

## HAMILTON—Butler County

★ ○ **FORT HAMILTON HOSPITAL (360132)**, 630 Eaton Avenue, Zip 45013–2770; tel. 513/867–2000 **A**2 9 10 11 **F**3 11 13 15 18 20 22 24 28 29 30 31 34 35 40 45 46 49 50 53 54 59 60 64 68 70 73 74 75 76 78 79 81 82 85 86 87 93 98 99 100 105 107 108 110 111 114 115 116 117 119 120 121 124 129 130 131 135 144 146 147 148 **S** Kettering Health Network, Dayton, OH
Primary Contact: Mark T. Smith, JD, CPA, President
CFO: Michael Mewhirter, Vice President Finance and Operations
CMO: Marcus Romanello, Chief Medical Officer
CIO: Andy Lehman, Senior Vice President Technology and Analytics
CHR: Joseph Geigle, Director Human Resources
CNO: Brenda Kuhn, Ph.D., Chief Nursing Officer
Web address: www.khnetwork.org/forthamilton
**Control:** Church–operated, Nongovernment, not–for profit **Service:** General Medical and Surgical

**Staffed Beds:** 166 **Admissions:** 7998 **Census:** 92 **Outpatient Visits:** 109030 **Births:** 628 **Total Expense ($000):** 131203 **Payroll Expense ($000):** 57153 **Personnel:** 822

## HICKSVILLE—Defiance County

☐ **COMMUNITY MEMORIAL HOSPITAL (361301)**, 208 North Columbus Street, Zip 43526–1299; tel. 419/542–6692, (Nonreporting) **A**1 9 10 18
Primary Contact: Michelle Waggoner, Chief Executive Officer
CNO: Jane Zachrich, Chief Nursing Officer
Web address: www.cmhosp.com
**Control:** Hospital district or authority, Government, nonfederal **Service:** General Medical and Surgical

**Staffed Beds:** 25

## HILLSBORO—Highland County

⊞ **HIGHLAND DISTRICT HOSPITAL (361332)**, 1275 North High Street, Zip 45133–8273; tel. 937/393–6100 **A**1 9 10 18 **F**3 11 13 15 29 30 31 34 35 40 45 47 49 50 57 59 62 64 74 76 77 78 79 81 85 86 87 92 93 94 96 98 103 107 111 118 119 127 130 131 132 133 135 146 148 **P**3
Primary Contact: James E. Baer, FACHE, President and Chief Executive Officer
CFO: Randal P. Lennartz, Vice President Finance
CMO: Ron Zile, M.D., Chief of Staff
CIO: Tim Bogard, Manager Information Technology
CHR: Melanie Wymer, Director Human Resources
CNO: Timothy Parry, R.N., Vice President Nursing
Web address: www.hdh.org
**Control:** Hospital district or authority, Government, nonfederal **Service:** General Medical and Surgical

**Staffed Beds:** 25 **Admissions:** 1937 **Census:** 18 **Outpatient Visits:** 78750 **Births:** 292 **Total Expense ($000):** 35882 **Payroll Expense ($000):** 14126 **Personnel:** 317

## JACKSON—Jackson County

☐ **HOLZER MEDICAL CENTER – JACKSON (361320)**, 500 Burlington Road, Zip 45640–9360; tel. 740/288–4625, (Nonreporting) **A**1 9 10 18
Primary Contact: Dr. Christopher Meyer, DO, Chief Executive Officer
CFO: Kevin Yeager, Vice President Fiscal Services
CMO: Nimal Dutla, M.D., Chief Medical Staff
CHR: Sandy Carlisle, Manager Human Resources
Web address: www.holzer.org
**Control:** Other not–for–profit (including NFP Corporation) **Service:** General Medical and Surgical

**Staffed Beds:** 24

## KENTON—Hardin County

⊞ **OHIOHEALTH HARDIN MEMORIAL HOSPITAL (361315)**, 921 East Franklin Street, Zip 43326–2099; tel. 419/673–0761 **A**1 9 10 18 **F**11 15 29 30 34 40 45 57 59 61 75 77 78 79 81 86 87 93 97 102 107 108 110 111 114 116 119 129 130 131 132 133 146 147 **S** OhioHealth, Columbus, OH
Primary Contact: Ron Snyder, Interim President and Chief Executive Officer
CFO: Ron Snyder, Chief Financial Officer
Web address: www.hardinmemorial.org
**Control:** Other not–for–profit (including NFP Corporation) **Service:** General Medical and Surgical

**Staffed Beds:** 25 **Admissions:** 716 **Census:** 8 **Outpatient Visits:** 59065 **Births:** 0 **Total Expense ($000):** 20390 **Payroll Expense ($000):** 8826 **Personnel:** 184

## KETTERING—Montgomery County

★ ○ △ **KETTERING MEDICAL CENTER (360079)**, 3535 Southern Boulevard, Zip 45429–1221; tel. 937/298–4331 **A**2 3 5 7 8 10 11 **F**3 11 13 15 17 18 20 22 24 26 28 29 30 31 34 35 37 38 39 40 43 44 45 46 47 48 49 50 51 52 53 54 55 56 57 58 59 61 64 65 66 68 70 71 72 74 75 76 77 78 79 81 82 84 85 86 87 90 92 93 96 97 102 107 108 110 111 114 115 116 117 118 119 120 121 123 124 126 129 130 131 132 135 141 145 146 147 148 **S** Kettering Health Network, Dayton, OH
Primary Contact: Roy G. Chew, Ph.D., President
CFO: Steven Chavez, Vice President Finance and Operations
CMO: Robert T. Smith, M.D., Chief Medical Officer
CIO: Andy Lehman, Senior Vice President Technology and Analytics
CHR: Derek Morgan, Vice President Human Resources
CNO: Brenda Kuhn, Ph.D., Chief Nursing Officer
Web address: www.ketteringhealth.org/kettering
**Control:** Church–operated, Nongovernment, not–for profit **Service:** General Medical and Surgical

**Staffed Beds:** 388 **Admissions:** 20085 **Census:** 251 **Outpatient Visits:** 267425 **Births:** 2545 **Total Expense ($000):** 583537 **Payroll Expense ($000):** 230227 **Personnel:** 2686

## LAKEWOOD—Cuyahoga County

⊞ **LAKEWOOD HOSPITAL (360212)**, 14519 Detroit Avenue, Zip 44107–4383; tel. 216/521–4200, (Total facility includes 25 beds in nursing home–type unit) **A**1 2 9 10 **F**3 6 11 13 15 20 22 26 28 29 30 34 35 40 45 46 49 50 56 57 59 60 64 65 68 70 74 75 76 77 79 81 85 86 87 90 93 98 100 101 102 103 107 108 111 119 128 130 132 134 146 148 **S** Cleveland Clinic Health System, Cleveland, OH
Primary Contact: Shannan Ritchie, Interim President
COO: Shannan Ritchie, Chief Operating Officer
CFO: Ankit Chhabra, Director Finance
CMO: William Riebel, M.D., Vice President Medical Operations
CIO: C. Martin Harris, M.D., Chief Information Officer
CHR: Sheree Laborie, Director Human Resources
CNO: Mary R. Sauer, R.N., Chief Nursing Officer
Web address: www.lakewoodhospital.org
**Control:** Other not–for–profit (including NFP Corporation) **Service:** General Medical and Surgical

**Staffed Beds:** 243 **Admissions:** 7764 **Census:** 123 **Outpatient Visits:** 148687 **Births:** 666 **Total Expense ($000):** 124522 **Payroll Expense ($000):** 48338 **Personnel:** 754

## LANCASTER—Fairfield County

⊞ △ **FAIRFIELD MEDICAL CENTER (360072)**, 401 North Ewing Street, Zip 43130–3371; tel. 740/687–8000 **A**1 2 3 5 7 9 10 13 **F**3 8 11 12 13 15 18 20 22 24 26 28 29 30 31 34 35 38 40 42 44 45 48 49 50 53 54 57 59 64 70 74 75 76 77 78 79 81 82 83 84 85 87 89 93 96 97 98 102 104 107 108 110 111 114 115 118 119 129 130 131 132 135 145 146 147 148
Primary Contact: John R. Janoso, Chief Executive Officer
COO: Howard Sniderman, Chief Operating Officer
CFO: Sky Gettys, Chief Financial Officer
CMO: Steve Cox, M.D., Chief Medical Officer
CIO: Jean Robertson, M.D., Chief Information Officer
CHR: Debra L. Palmer, MS, Chief Human Resources Officer and Corporate Compliance Officer
CNO: Cynthia Pearsall, Chief Nursing Officer
Web address: www.fmchealth.org
**Control:** Other not–for–profit (including NFP Corporation) **Service:** General Medical and Surgical

**Staffed Beds:** 222 **Admissions:** 9488 **Census:** 96 **Outpatient Visits:** 261912 **Births:** 1069 **Total Expense ($000):** 217727 **Payroll Expense ($000):** 84724 **Personnel:** 1780

---

**Hospital, Medicare Provider Number, Address, Telephone, Approval, Facility, and Physician Codes, Health Care System**

★ American Hospital Association (AHA) membership     ○ Healthcare Facilities Accreditation Program     ⇑ Center for Improvement in Healthcare Quality Accreditation
☐ The Joint Commission accreditation     ◇ DNV Healthcare Inc. accreditation     △ Commission on Accreditation of Rehabilitation Facilities (CARF) accreditation

**OH**

## LIMA—Allen County

☒ **INSTITUTE FOR ORTHOPAEDIC SURGERY (360263)**, 801 Medical Drive, Suite B., Zip 45804–4030; tel. 419/224–7586, (Nonreporting) **A**1 9 10 **S** Mercy Health, Cincinnati, OH
Primary Contact: Mark McDonald, M.D., President and Chief Executive Officer
CMO: Mark McDonald, M.D., President and Chief Executive Officer
CHR: Pat Farmer, Coordinator Human Resources and Safety Officer
Web address: www.ioshospital.com
**Control:** Partnership, Investor–owned, for–profit **Service:** Orthopedic

| Staffed Beds: 3 |
| --- |

☒ **KINDRED HOSPITAL LIMA (362020)**, 730 West Market Street, 6th Floor, Zip 45801–4602; tel. 419/224–1888, (Nonreporting) **A**1 10 **S** Kindred Healthcare, Louisville, KY
Primary Contact: Susan Krinke, Chief Executive Officer
Web address: www.khlima.com
**Control:** Corporation, Investor–owned, for–profit **Service:** Long–Term Acute Care hospital

| Staffed Beds: 26 |
| --- |

☒ △ **LIMA MEMORIAL HEALTH SYSTEM (360009)**, 1001 Bellefontaine Avenue, Zip 45804–2899; tel. 419/228–3335, (Total facility includes 17 beds in nursing home–type unit) **A**1 2 7 9 10 **F**3 11 13 15 17 18 20 22 24 28 29 30 31 34 35 36 40 41 43 45 46 47 48 49 50 51 54 57 59 60 62 63 64 65 68 70 73 74 75 76 77 78 79 81 82 84 85 86 89 90 93 96 107 108 110 111 114 115 118 119 121 126 130 131 132 135 146 147 148 **P**8
Primary Contact: Michael D. Swick, President and Chief Executive Officer
COO: Robert Armstrong, Senior Vice President and Chief Operating Officer
CFO: Stacey Deitering, Administrative Director of Finance
CMO: Kha H. Tran, M.D., Vice President Medical Affairs
CIO: Cheryl Homan, Administrative Director
CHR: Adam Cozad, Director Human Resources
CNO: Ann–Marie J. Pohl, R.N., Vice President and Chief Nursing Officer
Web address: www.limamemorial.org
**Control:** Other not–for–profit (including NFP Corporation) **Service:** General Medical and Surgical

| Staffed Beds: 217 Admissions: 6427 Census: 80 Outpatient Visits: 266223 |
| --- |
| Births: 680 Total Expense ($000): 155599 Payroll Expense ($000): 54038 |
| Personnel: 1004 |

**OAKWOOD CORRECTIONAL FACILITY**, 3200 North West Street, Zip 45801–2000; tel. 419/225–8052, (Nonreporting)
Primary Contact: Ed Sheldon, Warden and Chief Executive Officer
CFO: Thomas Ferry, Business Administrator
CHR: Glenda Turner, Director Personnel
Web address: www.drc.state.oh.us/public/ocf.htm
**Control:** State–Government, nonfederal **Service:** Psychiatric

| Staffed Beds: 61 |
| --- |

☒ △ **ST. RITA'S MEDICAL CENTER (360066)**, 730 West Market Street, Zip 45801–4602; tel. 419/227–3361 **A**1 2 7 9 10 **F**3 4 5 8 9 11 12 13 15 17 18 20 22 24 26 28 29 30 31 32 34 35 36 39 40 42 43 45 46 47 49 50 53 54 56 57 58 59 60 61 62 63 64 66 68 70 72 73 74 75 77 78 79 81 82 84 85 86 87 90 92 93 96 98 102 103 104 105 107 108 110 111 112 114 115 116 117 118 119 120 121 123 124 126 128 129 130 131 132 135 144 146 147 148 **P**6 8 **S** Mercy Health, Cincinnati, OH
Primary Contact: Robert O. Baxter, President and Chief Executive Officer
COO: Brian Smith, Executive Vice President and Chief Operating Officer
CMO: Herbert Schumm, M.D., Vice President Medical Affairs
CHR: Will Cason, Vice President Human Resources
Web address: www.stritas.org
**Control:** Church–operated, Nongovernment, not–for profit **Service:** General Medical and Surgical

| Staffed Beds: 415 Admissions: 17984 Census: 221 Outpatient Visits: 475057 Births: 1513 Total Expense ($000): 325988 Payroll Expense ($000): 94590 Personnel: 2049 |
| --- |

**TRIUMPH HOSPITAL LIMA** See Kindred Hospital Lima

## LODI—Medina County

☒ **LODI COMMUNITY HOSPITAL (361303)**, 225 Elyria Street, Zip 44254–1096; tel. 330/948–1222 **A**1 9 10 18 **F**3 11 15 18 26 28 29 30 34 35 40 45 51 57 59 64 65 75 77 81 82 91 93 96 97 107 114 119 129 130 132 133 135 146 147 **P**6 **S** Akron General Health System, Akron, OH
Primary Contact: Alan Papa, President and Chief Operating Officer
COO: Dana Kocsis, R.N., Vice President Nursing and Operations
CFO: Dave Frigo, Director Finance and Controller
CMO: David Peter, M.D., Senior Vice President Medical Affairs and Chief Medical Officer
CIO: Robb Baldauf, Coordinator Information Systems
CHR: Lynn Moraca, Director Human Resources
Web address: www.lodihospital.org
**Control:** Other not–for–profit (including NFP Corporation) **Service:** General Medical and Surgical

| Staffed Beds: 20 Admissions: 319 Census: 6 Outpatient Visits: 35269 |
| --- |
| Births: 0 Total Expense ($000): 13889 Payroll Expense ($000): 6150 |
| Personnel: 101 |

## LOGAN—Hocking County

☒ **HOCKING VALLEY COMMUNITY HOSPITAL (361330)**, 601 State Route 664 North, Zip 43138–8541, Mailing Address: P.O. Box 966, Zip 43138–0966; tel. 740/380–8000 **A**1 9 10 18 **F**3 8 11 15 28 29 31 34 40 56 57 59 64 70 75 77 78 79 81 82 85 86 87 93 98 103 107 111 114 118 119 129 130 133 135 144 146 147 148 **P**1
Primary Contact: Julie Stuck, R.N., Chief Executive Officer
CFO: Julie E. Grow, Chief Financial Officer
CMO: Duane Mast, M.D., Medical Director
CIO: John Burgess, Director Information Services
CHR: Robert F. Schmidt, Director Human Resources
CNO: Janelle Hicks, R.N., Vice President Patient Services
Web address: www.hvch.org
**Control:** County–Government, nonfederal **Service:** General Medical and Surgical

| Staffed Beds: 35 Admissions: 1232 Census: 20 Outpatient Visits: 72252 |
| --- |
| Births: 0 Total Expense ($000): 34412 Payroll Expense ($000): 13238 |
| Personnel: 296 |

## LONDON—Madison County

☒ **MADISON HEALTH (360189)**, 210 North Main Street, Zip 43140–1115; tel. 740/845–7000 **A**1 9 10 **F**3 11 13 15 18 29 31 40 45 50 53 64 68 70 75 76 77 78 79 81 82 85 87 89 93 97 107 108 110 111 114 118 119 129 130 131 132 135 146 147
Primary Contact: Dana E. Engle, Chief Executive Officer
CFO: Michael Browning, Chief Financial Officer
CMO: Mark Coate, M.D., Chief of Staff
CIO: Dennis Vogt, Director Information Technology
CHR: Becky Rozell, Chief Human Resources Officer
CNO: Jennifer Piccione, Chief Nursing and Clinical Services Officer
Web address: www.madison–health.com
**Control:** Other not–for–profit (including NFP Corporation) **Service:** General Medical and Surgical

| Staffed Beds: 55 Admissions: 1163 Census: 13 Outpatient Visits: 37176 |
| --- |
| Births: 237 Total Expense ($000): 34467 Payroll Expense ($000): 12732 |
| Personnel: 261 |

## LORAIN—Lorain County

☒ △ **MERCY REGIONAL MEDICAL CENTER (360172)**, 3700 Kolbe Road, Zip 44053–1697; tel. 440/960–4000 **A**1 2 7 9 10 **F**8 11 13 15 18 20 22 24 26 28 29 30 31 32 34 35 36 38 39 40 41 46 50 53 54 56 57 58 59 61 62 63 64 65 66 68 70 74 75 76 77 78 79 81 82 84 85 86 87 90 93 96 97 98 100 101 102 103 104 105 107 111 114 115 116 119 120 121 129 130 131 132 135 143 146 147 148 **P**8 **S** Mercy Health, Cincinnati, OH
Primary Contact: Edwin M. Oley, President and Chief Executive Officer
COO: Robert Tonkinson, Chief Operating Officer and Chief Financial Officer
CFO: Robert Tonkinson, Chief Operating Officer and Chief Financial Officer
CMO: Sam El–Dalati, M.D., Chief Medical Officer
CHR: JC Fischer, Director Human Resources
CNO: Catherine Walsh, Interim Nursing Executive
Web address: www.community–health–partners.com
**Control:** Church–operated, Nongovernment, not–for profit **Service:** General Medical and Surgical

| Staffed Beds: 259 Admissions: 12381 Census: 154 Outpatient Visits: 350578 Births: 854 Total Expense ($000): 192995 Payroll Expense ($000): 69223 Personnel: 1525 |
| --- |

## MANSFIELD—Richland County

☒ **KINDRED HOSPITAL OF CENTRAL OHIO (362021)**, 335 Glessner Avenue, 5th Floor, Zip 44903–2269; tel. 419/526–0777, (Nonreporting) **A**1 10 **S** Kindred Healthcare, Louisville, KY
Primary Contact: Pamela A. Edson, Chief Executive Officer
Web address: www.khcentralohio.com/
**Control:** Corporation, Investor–owned, for–profit **Service:** Long–Term Acute Care hospital

| Staffed Beds: 33 |
| --- |

**MEDCENTRAL – MANSFIELD HOSPITAL** See OhioHealth MedCentral Mansfield Hospital

*Many Facility Codes have changed. Please refer to the AHA Guide Code Chart.*   © 2015 AHA Guide

⊠ **OHIOHEALTH MEDCENTRAL MANSFIELD HOSPITAL (360118)**, 335 Glessner Avenue, Zip 44903–2265; tel. 419/526–8000, (Includes MANSFIELD HOSPITAL, 335 Glessner Avenue, tel. 419/526–8000) **A**1 2 5 9 10 **F**3 5 8 11 13 15 17 18 20 22 24 26 28 29 30 31 32 34 35 38 39 40 43 44 45 46 47 48 49 50 51 53 54 55 56 57 58 59 61 62 63 64 65 68 70 73 74 75 76 77 78 79 81 82 83 84 85 86 87 89 90 92 93 96 98 99 100 101 102 103 104 105 107 108 110 111 114 116 117 118 119 120 121 122 123 124 129 130 131 132 133 135 144 146 147 148 **P**3 **S** OhioHealth, Columbus, OH
Primary Contact: Jean Halpin, President
CFO: Michael Bichimer, Acting Vice President of Finance
CMO: Terry Weston, M.D., Vice President Physician Services
CIO: Cindy Sheets, Vice President Information Systems and Chief Information Officer
CHR: Beth Hildreth, Vice President Human Resources
CNO: Pam Crawford, R.N., Vice President of Nursing and Chief Nursing Officer
Web address: www.medcentral.org
**Control:** Other not–for–profit (including NFP Corporation) **Service:** General Medical and Surgical

**Staffed Beds: 232 Admissions: 10278 Census: 129 Outpatient Visits: 259778 Births: 935 Personnel: 1725**

### MARIETTA—Washington County

★ ○ △ **MARIETTA MEMORIAL HOSPITAL (360147)**, 401 Matthew Street, Zip 45750–1699; tel. 740/374–1400, (Nonreporting) **A**2 5 7 9 10 11 13
Primary Contact: J. Scott Cantley, President and Chief Executive Officer
CFO: Eric L. Young, Vice President Finance and Chief Financial Officer
CMO: Matthew Macatol, M.D., President Medical Staff
CIO: Andy Altenburger, Chief Information Officer
CHR: Dee Ann Gehlauf, Senior Vice President Business and Organization Development
Web address: www.mhsystem.org
**Control:** Other not–for–profit (including NFP Corporation) **Service:** General Medical and Surgical

**Staffed Beds: 152**

★ **SELBY GENERAL HOSPITAL (361319)**, 1106 Colegate Drive, Zip 45750–1323; tel. 740/568–2000 **A**9 10 18 **F**3 29 40 41 45 69 74 79 81 82 85 87 89 93 104 107 111 114 116 119 130 133 135 **P**5
Primary Contact: Stephen Smith, President
CFO: Eric L. Young, Chief Financial Officer
CMO: David Spears, D.O., Chief of Staff
CHR: Tricia A. Engfehr, Chief Human Resources
CNO: Misti Spencer, Director Inpatient Services
Web address: www.selbygeneral.org
**Control:** Other not–for–profit (including NFP Corporation) **Service:** General Medical and Surgical

**Staffed Beds: 25 Admissions: 972 Census: 9 Outpatient Visits: 28426 Births: 0 Total Expense ($000): 27456 Payroll Expense ($000): 9962 Personnel: 146**

### MARION—Marion County

⊠ **OHIOHEALTH MARION GENERAL HOSPITAL (360011)**, 1000 McKinley Park Drive, Zip 43302–6397; tel. 740/383–8400, (Nonreporting) **A**1 2 9 10 19 **S** OhioHealth, Columbus, OH
Primary Contact: Bruce P. Hagen, President
CMO: Julie Tome, M.D., Vice President North Central Region Medical Affairs
CIO: Chris King, Director Information Services
CHR: Gianna Ferrarotti, Director Human Resources North Region
Web address: www.ohiohealth.com/mariongeneral
**Control:** Other not–for–profit (including NFP Corporation) **Service:** General Medical and Surgical

**Staffed Beds: 204**

### MARTINS FERRY—Belmont County

☐ **EAST OHIO REGIONAL HOSPITAL (360080)**, 90 North Fourth Street, Zip 43935–1648; tel. 740/633–1100, (Total facility includes 50 beds in nursing home–type unit) **A**1 9 10 **F**3 11 13 15 20 28 29 30 31 34 35 37 40 43 44 45 53 57 59 64 68 70 74 75 76 77 79 81 82 85 87 89 107 108 110 111 114 115 118 119 128 129 130 131 132 133 135 146 148 **P**6 **S** Ohio Valley Health Services and Education Corporation, Wheeling, WV
Primary Contact: Michael J. Caruso, President and Chief Executive Officer
COO: Bernie Albertini, Chief Administrative Officer
CFO: Lisa M. Simon, Senior Vice President Chief Financial Officer
CIO: Lisa M. Simon, Senior Vice President Chief Financial Officer
CHR: Robert Wright, Senior Human Resource Advisor
CNO: Christine Kerwood, Chief Nursing Officer
Web address: www.ovmc–eorh.com
**Control:** Other not–for–profit (including NFP Corporation) **Service:** General Medical and Surgical

**Staffed Beds: 139 Admissions: 3252 Census: 69 Outpatient Visits: 137721 Births: 287 Total Expense ($000): 67261 Payroll Expense ($000): 23350 Personnel: 510**

### MARYSVILLE—Union County

★ ◇ **MEMORIAL HEALTH (360092)**, 500 London Avenue, Zip 43040–1594; tel. 937/644–6115 **A**5 9 10 21 **F**3 11 13 15 18 20 22 28 29 30 31 32 34 35 40 45 48 49 50 51 53 57 59 62 66 68 69 74 75 76 77 78 79 80 82 84 85 87 92 93 94 107 108 110 111 114 115 118 119 129 130 131 132 135 144 145 146 **P**6
Primary Contact: Olas A. Hubbs, III, FACHE, President and Chief Executive Officer
COO: Laurie A. Whittington, Chief Operating Officer
CFO: Jeffrey Ehlers, Chief Financial Officer
CMO: Matthew Hazelrigg, M.D., President Medical Staff
CIO: Carl Zani, Chief Technology Director
CHR: Larry C. Schleeter, Chief Human Resources Officer
CNO: Robin Slattman, Chief Nursing Officer
Web address: www.memorialhosp.org
**Control:** County–Government, nonfederal **Service:** General Medical and Surgical

**Staffed Beds: 74 Admissions: 1994 Census: 16 Outpatient Visits: 125046 Births: 616 Total Expense ($000): 79689 Payroll Expense ($000): 32380 Personnel: 486**

### MASON—Warren County

⊠ **LINDNER CENTER OF HOPE (364044)**, 4075 Old Western Row Road, Zip 45040–3104; tel. 513/536–0311, (Nonreporting) **A**1 9 10
Primary Contact: Paul Keck, M.D., President and Chief Executive Officer
COO: Brian Owens, Chief Operating Officer
CFO: David McAdams, Chief Financial Officer
CIO: Cliff McClintick, Chief Information Officer
CHR: Debbie A. Strawser, Director Human Resources
Web address: www.lindnercenterofhope.org
**Control:** Other not–for–profit (including NFP Corporation) **Service:** Psychiatric

**Staffed Beds: 48**

### MASSILLON—Stark County

★ ○ △ **AFFINITY MEDICAL CENTER (360151)**, 875 Eighth Street N.E., Zip 44646–8503, Mailing Address: P.O. Box 4805, Zip 44648–0805; tel. 330/832–8761, (Nonreporting) **A**7 9 10 11 12 13 **S** Community Health Systems, Inc., Franklin, TN
Primary Contact: Ronald L. Bierman, Chief Executive Officer
CFO: James Hutchinson, CPA, Chief Financial Officer
Web address: www.affinitymedicalcenter.com
**Control:** Corporation, Investor–owned, for–profit **Service:** General Medical and Surgical

**Staffed Beds: 112**

☐ **HEARTLAND BEHAVIORAL HEALTHCARE (364031)**, 3000 Erie Stree South, Zip 44646–7993, Mailing Address: 3000 Erie Street South, Zip 44646–7976; tel. 330/833–3135, (Nonreporting) **A**1 5 10 **S** Ohio Department of Mental Health, Columbus, OH
Primary Contact: Jeffrey Sims, Chief Executive Officer
CFO: Patricia Eddleman, Fiscal Officer
CMO: Steven Thomson, M.D., Medical Director
CIO: Robert Hobart, Director Management Information Systems
CHR: Jerald Wilhite, Administrator Human Resources
Web address: www.mh.state.oh.us/ibhs/bhos/hoh.html
**Control:** State–Government, nonfederal **Service:** Psychiatric

**Staffed Beds: 130**

---

**Hospital, Medicare Provider Number, Address, Telephone, Approval, Facility, and Physician Codes, Health Care System**

★ American Hospital Association (AHA) membership    ○ Healthcare Facilities Accreditation Program    ⇑ Center for Improvement in Healthcare Quality Accreditation
☐ The Joint Commission accreditation    ◇ DNV Healthcare Inc. accreditation    △ Commission on Accreditation of Rehabilitation Facilities (CARF) accreditation

**OH**

## MAUMEE—Lucas County

☐ **ARROWHEAD BEHAVIORAL HEALTH HOSPITAL (364036)**, 1725 Timber Line Road, Zip 43537–4015; tel. 419/891–9333, (Nonreporting) **A**1 9 10 **S** Universal Health Services, Inc., King of Prussia, PA
Primary Contact: Joseph Denicola, Chief Executive Officer and Managing Director
CFO: Allison Duncan, Chief Financial Officer
CMO: Kenneth Adler, M.D., Medical Director
CIO: Peggy Montgomery, Director Medical Records
CHR: Dawn Bosworth, Director Human Resources
CNO: Anita Zych, Director of Nursing
Web address: www.arrowheadbehavioral.com
**Control:** Corporation, Investor–owned, for–profit **Service:** Other specialty

**Staffed Beds:** 42

★ ◇ **PROMEDICA ST. LUKE'S HOSPITAL (360090)**, 5901 Monclova Road, Zip 43537–1899; tel. 419/893–5911 **A**2 3 5 9 10 21 **F**3 8 11 13 15 17 18 20 22 24 26 28 29 30 31 34 35 40 45 46 48 49 56 57 59 64 65 68 70 74 76 77 78 79 81 82 85 86 87 89 92 93 100 107 108 111 114 115 118 119 126 129 130 132 143 145 146 147 148 **S** ProMedica Health System, Toledo, OH
Primary Contact: Daniel L. Wakeman, President
COO: Daniel Schwanke, Chief Operating Officer
CMO: Stephen Bazeley, M.D., Vice President Medical Affairs
CIO: Patricia Swint, Director Information Technology
CHR: Connie Sessler, Director Human Resources
CNO: Jill A. Trosin, R.N., Vice President Patient Care Services, Chief Nursing Officer
Web address: www.stlukeshospital.com
**Control:** Other not–for–profit (including NFP Corporation) **Service:** General Medical and Surgical

**Staffed Beds:** 172 **Admissions:** 11296 **Census:** 115 **Outpatient Visits:** 200480 **Births:** 869 **Total Expense ($000):** 162164 **Payroll Expense ($000):** 56019

## MEDINA—Medina County

⊞ **MEDINA HOSPITAL (360091)**, 1000 East Washington Street, Zip 44256–2170; tel. 330/725–1000 **A**1 2 5 9 10 **F**3 7 13 15 18 20 28 29 30 31 34 35 40 47 49 50 57 59 60 64 70 74 75 76 77 78 79 81 82 85 86 93 96 107 111 114 117 119 129 130 131 132 133 135 146 147 148 **S** Cleveland Clinic Health System, Cleveland, OH
Primary Contact: Thomas Tulisiak, M.D., President
COO: Vicky Snyder, Chief Operating Officer and Chief Financial Officer
CFO: Vicky Snyder, Chief Operating Officer and Chief Financial Officer
CMO: Rick Shewbridge, M.D., Vice President Medical Operations
CIO: David Ingram, Director Management Information Systems
CHR: Tracie Curtis, Vice President Human Resources
CNO: Mary Kennedy, R.N., Chief Nursing Officer
Web address: www.medinahospital.org
**Control:** Other not–for–profit (including NFP Corporation) **Service:** General Medical and Surgical

**Staffed Beds:** 136 **Admissions:** 6039 **Census:** 65 **Outpatient Visits:** 94882 **Births:** 903 **Total Expense ($000):** 101890 **Payroll Expense ($000):** 37543 **Personnel:** 586

## MIAMISBURG—Montgomery County

⊞ **LIFECARE HOSPITAL OF DAYTON (362028)**, 4000 Miamisburg–Centerville Road, Zip 45342–7615; tel. 937/384–8300, (Nonreporting) **A**1 9 10 **S** LifeCare Management Services, Plano, TX
Primary Contact: William Bryant, Chief Executive Officer
CMO: Richard Gregg, M.D., Medical Director
CHR: Pam Fannin, Coordinator Human Resources
Web address: www.lifecare–hospitals.com
**Control:** Corporation, Investor–owned, for–profit **Service:** Long–Term Acute Care hospital

**Staffed Beds:** 44

★ ○ **SYCAMORE MEDICAL CENTER (360239)**, 4000 Miamisburg–Centerville Road, Zip 45342–7615; tel. 937/866–0551 **A**9 10 11 **F**3 11 12 15 18 20 28 29 30 31 34 35 36 38 39 40 44 45 47 48 49 50 53 54 56 57 58 59 60 61 64 65 66 68 70 74 75 77 78 79 81 82 84 85 86 87 93 97 98 99 100 101 102 103 104 105 107 108 110 111 114 115 118 119 129 130 131 132 134 135 141 145 146 148 **S** Kettering Health Network, Dayton, OH
Primary Contact: Walter Sackett, President
CFO: Steven Chavez, Vice President Finance and Operations
CMO: Robert T. Smith, M.D., Chief Medical Officer
CIO: Andy Lehman, Senior Vice President Technology and Analytics
CHR: Derek Morgan, Vice President Human Resources
CNO: Brenda Kuhn, Ph.D., Chief Nursing Officer
Web address: www.khnetwork.org/sycamore
**Control:** Church–operated, Nongovernment, not–for profit **Service:** General Medical and Surgical

**Staffed Beds:** 172 **Admissions:** 7930 **Census:** 88 **Outpatient Visits:** 125650 **Births:** 0 **Total Expense ($000):** 142015 **Payroll Expense ($000):** 58629 **Personnel:** 629

## MIDDLE POINT—Van Wert County

☐ **RIDGEVIEW BEHAVIORAL HOSPITAL (364047)**, 17872 Lincoln Highway, Zip 45863–9700; tel. 419/968–2950, (Nonreporting) **A**1 10
Primary Contact: Pat Tracy, Administrator
Web address: www.ridgeviewhospital.net/
**Control:** Corporation, Investor–owned, for–profit **Service:** Psychiatric

**Staffed Beds:** 40

## MIDDLEBURG HEIGHTS—Cuyahoga County

☐ **SOUTHWEST GENERAL HEALTH CENTER (360155)**, 18697 Bagley Road, Zip 44130–3497; tel. 440/816–8000 **A**1 2 3 5 10 **F**3 5 7 11 13 15 18 20 22 24 26 28 29 30 31 32 34 35 36 37 38 39 40 42 43 44 45 49 50 51 53 54 56 57 59 60 62 63 64 65 66 68 70 74 75 76 77 78 79 81 82 84 85 86 87 90 92 93 94 98 99 100 101 102 103 104 105 107 108 110 111 114 115 118 119 120 121 123 126 128 129 130 131 132 134 135 143 144 146 147 148 **P**6
Primary Contact: Thomas A. Selden, FACHE, President and Chief Executive Officer
COO: Bradley W. Rauh, Vice President, Chief Operating Officer
CFO: Mary Ann Freas, Senior Vice President and Chief Financial Officer
CMO: Marilyn McNamara, M.D., Vice President Medical Affairs
CIO: Teresa Rini Barber, Vice President Support Services
CHR: Judy Murphy, Vice President Human Resources
CNO: Martha F. Bauschka, R.N., Vice President and Chief Nursing Officer
Web address: www.swgeneral.com
**Control:** Other not–for–profit (including NFP Corporation) **Service:** General Medical and Surgical

**Staffed Beds:** 310 **Admissions:** 16092 **Census:** 209 **Outpatient Visits:** 441535 **Births:** 1051 **Total Expense ($000):** 286500 **Payroll Expense ($000):** 109107 **Personnel:** 2083

## MIDDLETOWN—Warren County

☐ △ **ATRIUM MEDICAL CENTER (360076)**, One Medical Center Drive, Zip 45005–1066; tel. 513/424–2111 **A**1 2 3 7 9 10 **F**3 8 13 15 17 18 20 22 24 26 28 29 30 31 34 35 39 40 41 43 44 45 46 47 48 49 50 54 56 57 59 60 61 64 68 70 73 74 75 76 77 78 79 80 81 82 84 85 86 87 90 91 92 93 94 96 98 100 101 102 103 107 108 110 111 114 115 116 117 118 119 126 130 131 132 135 145 146 147 148 **S** Premier Health, Dayton, OH
Primary Contact: Carol Turner, President and Chief Executive Officer
CFO: Scott Shelton, Chief Financial Officer
CMO: Jeff Hoffman, M.D., Chief Medical Officer
CHR: Ted Ripperger, Administrative Director Human Resources
CNO: Marquita Turner, Chief Nursing Officer
Web address: www.atriummedcenter.org
**Control:** Other not–for–profit (including NFP Corporation) **Service:** General Medical and Surgical

**Staffed Beds:** 302 **Admissions:** 8937 **Census:** 111 **Outpatient Visits:** 59490 **Births:** 852 **Total Expense ($000):** 209858 **Payroll Expense ($000):** 79669 **Personnel:** 1312

## MILLERSBURG—Holmes County

⇑ **POMERENE HOSPITAL (360148)**, 981 Wooster Road, Zip 44654–1094; tel. 330/763–2001 **A**9 10 22 **F**3 11 13 15 18 29 30 34 35 40 45 50 53 55 57 59 68 70 75 76 79 81 85 86 87 89 93 107 108 110 114 119 127 130 131 132 135 144 146 **P**7
Primary Contact: Tony Snyder, Administrator and Chief Executive Officer
CFO: Jason Justus, Vice President Finance and Chief Financial Officer
CMO: Yasser Omran, M.D., President Medical Staff
CIO: Mark Jacobs, Director Information Services
CHR: Kim Croft, R.N., Executive Director Human Resources
CNO: Nicole Kolacz, Vice President Patient Services
Web address: www.pomerenehospital.org
**Control:** County–Government, nonfederal **Service:** General Medical and Surgical

**Staffed Beds:** 41 **Admissions:** 1442 **Census:** 13 **Outpatient Visits:** 40067 **Births:** 542 **Total Expense ($000):** 27410 **Payroll Expense ($000):** 11367 **Personnel:** 209

## MONTPELIER—Williams County

**COMMUNITY HOSPITALS AND WELLNESS CENTERS–MONTPELIER (361327)**, 909 East Snyder Avenue, Zip 43543–1251; tel. 419/385–3154, (Nonreporting) **A**9 10 18
Primary Contact: Philip L. Ennen, President and Chief Executive Officer
Web address: www.chwchospital.com
**Control:** Corporation, Investor–owned, for–profit **Service:** General Medical and Surgical

**Staffed Beds:** 35

**MONTPELIER HOSPITAL** See Community Hospitals and Wellness Centers, Bryan

*Many Facility Codes have changed. Please refer to the AHA Guide Code Chart.*
© 2015 AHA Guide

**OH**

## MOUNT GILEAD—Morrow County

☒ **MORROW COUNTY HOSPITAL (361313)**, 651 West Marion Road,
Zip 43338–1027; tel. 419/946–5015, (Nonreporting) **A**1 5 9 10 18
**S** OhioHealth, Columbus, OH
Primary Contact: Chad J. Miller, President and Chief Executive Officer
CFO: Joe Schueler, Chief Financial Officer
Web address: www.morrowcountyhospital.com
**Control:** County–Government, nonfederal **Service:** General Medical and Surgical

| Staffed Beds: 22 |
| --- |

## MOUNT VERNON—Knox County

☒ **KNOX COMMUNITY HOSPITAL (360040)**, 1330 Coshocton Road,
Zip 43050–1495; tel. 740/393–9000 **A**1 2 9 10 20 **F**3 5 11 13 15 18 20 22
26 28 29 30 31 32 34 35 36 40 44 45 50 51 53 57 59 64 69 70 75 76 77
78 79 81 82 83 84 85 86 87 93 96 97 107 108 110 111 114 115 116 117
118 119 120 121 129 130 131 132 134 144 146 147 **P**6 **S** QHR,
Brentwood, TN
Primary Contact: Bruce D. White, Chief Executive Officer
COO: Bruce M. Behner, Chief Operating Officer
CFO: Michael Ambrosiani, Chief Financial Officer
CMO: Jeffrey Northup, D.O., Chief Medical Officer
CIO: Kwi Holland, Vice President Information Services
CHR: Lisa Bragg, Vice President Human Resources
CNO: James Middleton, MSN, Chief Nursing Officer
Web address: www.knoxcommhosp.org
**Control:** Other not–for–profit (including NFP Corporation) **Service:** General Medical and Surgical

| Staffed Beds: 61 Admissions: 2951 Census: 24 Outpatient Visits: 143472 Births: 340 Total Expense ($000): 122603 Payroll Expense ($000): 52795 Personnel: 791 |
| --- |

## NAPOLEON—Henry County

★ ◇ **HENRY COUNTY HOSPITAL (361309)**, 1600 East Riverview Avenue,
Zip 43545–9399; tel. 419/592–4015 **A**5 9 10 18 21 **F**3 5 11 13 15 18 29 30
31 34 35 36 40 45 50 53 57 59 64 65 68 70 75 76 77 78 79 81 82 85 86
87 93 99 100 101 104 107 108 110 114 119 130 132 133 135 146
Primary Contact: Kimberly Hupp Bordenkircher, Chief Executive Officer
CFO: Diane Walther, Controller
CIO: Jeff Pompos, Manager Information Technology
CHR: Jennifer A. Fisher, Manager Human Resources
CNO: Patricia Frank, Chief Nursing Officer
Web address: www.henrycountyhospital.org
**Control:** Other not–for–profit (including NFP Corporation) **Service:** General Medical and Surgical

| Staffed Beds: 25 Admissions: 856 Census: 11 Outpatient Visits: 65046 Births: 106 Total Expense ($000): 26818 Payroll Expense ($000): 10796 Personnel: 212 |
| --- |

## NEW ALBANY—Franklin County

☒ **MOUNT CARMEL NEW ALBANY SURGICAL HOSPITAL (360266)**, 7333
Smith's Mill Road, Zip 43054–9291; tel. 614/775–6600 **A**1 9 10 **F**3 29 34 35
44 57 58 59 64 65 68 74 75 79 81 85 86 87 107 111 114 119 146 **P**6 8
**S** Trinity Health, Livonia, MI
Primary Contact: Diane Doucette, MBA, RN, President
Web address: www.mountcarmelhealth.com
**Control:** Church–operated, Nongovernment, not–for profit **Service:** Surgical

| Staffed Beds: 60 Admissions: 4460 Census: 22 Outpatient Visits: 13668 Births: 0 Total Expense ($000): 84221 Payroll Expense ($000): 13413 Personnel: 230 |
| --- |

## NEWARK—Licking County

☐ **LICKING MEMORIAL HOSPITAL (360218)**, 1320 West Main Street,
Zip 43055–3699; tel. 740/348–4000 **A**1 2 9 10 **F**3 4 5 13 15 18 20 22 26 28
29 30 31 32 34 35 40 41 45 48 49 50 53 57 59 62 64 65 68 70 74 75 76
77 78 79 81 82 84 85 86 87 89 90 92 93 97 98 100 101 102 104 105 106
107 108 110 111 114 115 118 119 130 132 135 144 146 147 148 **P**6
Primary Contact: Robert A. Montagnese, President and Chief Executive Officer
CFO: Cindy Webster, Vice President Financial Services
CMO: Craig Cairns, M.D., Vice President Medical Affairs
CIO: Sallie Arnett, Vice President Information Systems
CHR: Anne Peterson, Vice President Human Resources and Support Services
Web address: www.lmhealth.org
**Control:** Other not–for–profit (including NFP Corporation) **Service:** General Medical and Surgical

| Staffed Beds: 199 Admissions: 8018 Census: 75 Outpatient Visits: 319939 Births: 1137 Total Expense ($000): 151086 Payroll Expense ($000): 62832 Personnel: 1329 |
| --- |

## NORTHFIELD—Summit County

☐ **NORTHCOAST BEHAVIORAL HEALTHCARE SYSTEM (364011)**, 1756
Sagamore Road, Zip 44067–1086; tel. 330/467–7131, (Includes CLEVELAND
CAMPUS, 1708 Southpoint Drive, Cleveland, Zip 44109–1999;
tel. 216/787–0500; NORTHFIELD CAMPUS, 1756 Sagamore Road, Zip 44067,
Mailing Address: P.O. Box 305, Zip 44067–0305; tel. 330/467–7131; TOLEDO
CAMPUS, 930 South Detroit Avenue, Toledo, Zip 43614–2701;
tel. 419/381–1881) **A**1 3 10 **F**30 53 65 75 77 82 98 106 130 135 146 **S** Ohio
Department of Mental Health, Columbus, OH
Primary Contact: Douglas W. Kern, Chief Executive Officer
CFO: Jeff Comfort, Vice President Administration
CIO: Karl Donenwirth, Vice President Information Services
Web address: www.mha.ohio.gov
**Control:** State–Government, nonfederal **Service:** Psychiatric

| Staffed Beds: 260 Admissions: 2000 Census: 225 Outpatient Visits: 0 Births: 0 Total Expense ($000): 46623 Payroll Expense ($000): 25678 Personnel: 419 |
| --- |

## NORWALK—Huron County

★ ○ **FISHER–TITUS MEDICAL CENTER (360065)**, 272 Benedict Avenue,
Zip 44857–2374; tel. 419/668–8101, (Total facility includes 69 beds in nursing
home–type unit) **A**2 5 9 10 11 19 **F**3 10 11 13 15 18 20 28 29 31 34 35 36
39 40 43 45 49 50 51 54 56 57 58 59 62 64 68 70 74 75 76 77 78 79 81
82 85 86 87 92 93 94 96 97 107 108 110 111 115 118 119 126 128 129
130 131 132 135 143 146 147 148 **P**2 6 7
Primary Contact: Lorna Strayer, President and Chief Executive Officer
COO: Lorna Strayer, Executive Vice President
CFO: Duane L. Woods, Jr., Chief Financial Officer
CMO: Shankar Kurra, M.D., Senior Vice President Medical Affairs
CIO: John Britton, Vice President Information Services
CHR: Phillip Annarino, Vice President Human Resources
CNO: Suzanne Inglis, MSN, Senior Vice President Nursing Services
Web address: www.fisher–titus.org
**Control:** Other not–for–profit (including NFP Corporation) **Service:** General Medical and Surgical

| Staffed Beds: 147 Admissions: 3944 Census: 98 Outpatient Visits: 162334 Births: 645 Total Expense ($000): 108287 Payroll Expense ($000): 45716 Personnel: 793 |
| --- |

## OBERLIN—Lorain County

☒ **MERCY ALLEN HOSPITAL (361306)**, 200 West Lorain Street,
Zip 44074–1077; tel. 440/775–1211, (Nonreporting) **A**1 9 10 18 **S** Mercy
Health, Cincinnati, OH
Primary Contact: Joe Sober, President
COO: Robert Tonkinson, Chief Operating Officer and Chief Financial Officer
CFO: Robert Tonkinson, Chief Operating Officer and Chief Financial Officer
CMO: Vamsee Amirneni, M.D., Chief of Staff
CNO: Catherine Walsh, Interim Chief Nursing Officer
Web address: www.mercyonline.org/mercy_allen_hospital.aspx
**Control:** Other not–for–profit (including NFP Corporation) **Service:** General Medical and Surgical

| Staffed Beds: 25 |
| --- |

## OREGON—Lucas County

☒ △ **MERCY ST. CHARLES HOSPITAL (360081)**, 2600 Navarre Avenue,
Zip 43616–3297; tel. 419/696–7200 **A**1 2 3 7 9 10 **F**3 11 13 15 18 28 29 30
31 34 35 40 43 44 46 48 49 51 56 57 59 60 64 66 68 70 74 75 76 77 78
79 81 82 85 86 87 90 92 93 97 98 100 102 103 107 108 110 111 114 115
118 119 120 121 123 129 130 132 135 146 147 148 **P**8 **S** Mercy Health,
Cincinnati, OH
Primary Contact: Jeffrey Dempsey, President and Chief Executive Officer
COO: Jeffrey Dempsey, President and Chief Executive Officer
CFO: Jim Puffenberger, Senior Vice President Northern Region and Chief Financial
Officer
CMO: Norbert Stockort, M.D., Chief of Staff
CIO: Brian Sterns, Director Information Systems Services
CHR: Gary George, Regional Vice President Human Resources
CNO: Craig Slbers, Vice President Patient Care and Chief Nursing Officer
Web address: www.mercyweb.org
**Control:** Church–operated, Nongovernment, not–for profit **Service:** General Medical and Surgical

| Staffed Beds: 265 Admissions: 8930 Census: 136 Outpatient Visits: 132045 Births: 453 Personnel: 881 |
| --- |

---

### Hospital, Medicare Provider Number, Address, Telephone, Approval, Facility, and Physician Codes, Health Care System

★ American Hospital Association (AHA) membership ○ Healthcare Facilities Accreditation Program ⇑ Center for Improvement in Healthcare Quality Accreditation
☐ The Joint Commission accreditation ◇ DNV Healthcare Inc. accreditation △ Commission on Accreditation of Rehabilitation Facilities (CARF) accreditation

**OH**

✠ **PROMEDICA BAY PARK HOSPITAL (360259)**, 2801 Bay Park Drive, Zip 43616–4920; tel. 419/690–7900 **A**1 9 10 **F**3 11 13 15 18 29 30 34 40 49 50 54 57 58 59 64 68 70 75 76 77 78 79 81 82 85 86 87 92 93 97 107 108 110 111 114 118 119 124 126 129 130 131 132 135 146 147 148 **S** ProMedica Health System, Toledo, OH
Primary Contact: Holly L. Bristol, President
COO: Darrell Wachowiak, Associate Vice President Operations
CFO: Scott Fought, Vice President Finance
CMO: David Lindstrom, M.D., Vice President Medical Affairs
CIO: Rose Ann Laureto, Corporate Vice President Information Resources
CHR: Kara Zimmerly, Manager Human Resources
CNO: Paula Grieb, R.N., Vice President Patient Care Service and Chief Nursing Officer
Web address: www.promedica.org
**Control:** Other not–for–profit (including NFP Corporation) **Service:** General Medical and Surgical

**Staffed Beds:** 77 **Admissions:** 3092 **Census:** 35 **Outpatient Visits:** 98714 **Births:** 564 **Total Expense ($000):** 72230 **Payroll Expense ($000):** 22864 **Personnel:** 412

**ST. CHARLES MERCY HOSPITAL** See Mercy St. Charles Hospital

**ORRVILLE—Wayne County**

✠ **AULTMAN ORRVILLE HOSPITAL (361323)**, 832 South Main Street, Zip 44667–2208; tel. 330/682–3010 **A**1 9 10 18 **F**3 8 11 13 14 15 28 29 30 34 35 40 45 50 51 53 55 57 59 68 70 75 77 79 81 82 85 86 87 93 108 110 111 115 118 119 129 130 131 132 133 135 143 146 147 **S** Aultman Health Foundation, Canton, OH
Primary Contact: Marchelle Suppan, DPM, President and Chief Executive Officer
COO: Judy Erb, Vice President Patient Care Services and Chief Nursing Officer
CFO: Matthew A. Stewart, Vice President Finance and Chief Financial Officer
CIO: Terry Andrews, Manager Information Technology
CHR: Jennifer Kessel, Director Human Resources
CNO: Judy Erb, Vice President Patient Services and Chief Nursing Officer
Web address: www.aultmanorrville.org
**Control:** Other not–for–profit (including NFP Corporation) **Service:** General Medical and Surgical

**Staffed Beds:** 25 **Admissions:** 785 **Census:** 5 **Outpatient Visits:** 37155 **Births:** 388 **Total Expense ($000):** 21760 **Payroll Expense ($000):** 8780 **Personnel:** 159

**OXFORD—Butler County**

★ ○ **MCCULLOUGH–HYDE MEMORIAL HOSPITAL/TRIHEALTH (360046)**, 110 North Poplar Street, Zip 45056–1292; tel. 513/523–2111, (Nonreporting) **A**9 10 11
Primary Contact: Bryan D. Hehemann, President and Chief Executive Officer
CFO: John R. Clements, Chief Financial Officer
CMO: Amy Spivey, Chief Medical Officer
CIO: Kathy Dickman, Director Information Technology
CHR: Sharon Hancock, Chief Human Resources Officer
CNO: Pamela Collins, Vice President Chief Patient Services Officer
Web address: www.mhmh.org
**Control:** Other not–for–profit (including NFP Corporation) **Service:** General Medical and Surgical

**Staffed Beds:** 45

**PARMA—Cuyahoga County**

✠ △ **UNIVERSITY HOSPITALS PARMA MEDICAL CENTER (360041)**, 7007 Powers Boulevard, Zip 44129–5495; tel. 440/743–3000, (Total facility includes 11 beds in nursing home–type unit) **A**1 2 7 10 13 **F**2 3 10 11 12 13 15 17 18 20 22 24 26 28 29 30 31 34 35 36 40 44 45 49 50 51 53 55 56 57 58 59 62 63 64 65 68 69 70 71 74 75 77 78 79 81 82 85 86 87 90 93 96 98 100 101 103 107 108 111 114 115 116 117 118 119 120 121 126 128 130 131 132 135 143 146 147 148 **P**6 **S** University Hospitals, Cleveland, OH
Primary Contact: Nancy Tinsley, President and Chief Executive Officer
COO: David Cook, Chief Operating Officer
CHR: Daniel Miller, Vice President Human Resources
CNO: Sharon Thomas, Vice President and Chief Nursing Officer
Web address: www.parmahospital.org
**Control:** Other not–for–profit (including NFP Corporation) **Service:** General Medical and Surgical

**Staffed Beds:** 255 **Admissions:** 11667 **Census:** 145 **Outpatient Visits:** 249518 **Births:** 435 **Total Expense ($000):** 169318 **Payroll Expense ($000):** 69089 **Personnel:** 1328

**PAULDING—Paulding County**

☐ **PAULDING COUNTY HOSPITAL (361300)**, 1035 West Wayne Street, Zip 45879–1544; tel. 419/399–4080, (Nonreporting) **A**1 9 10 18
Primary Contact: Randy Ruge, Chief Executive Officer
COO: Randy Ruge, Chief Operating Officer
CFO: Rob Goshia, Chief Financial Officer
CMO: Wendell J. Spangler, M.D., Chief of Staff
CIO: Dan Kaufman, Director Information Services
CHR: Melanie Rittenour, Director Human Resources
Web address: www.pauldingcountyhospital.com
**Control:** County–Government, nonfederal **Service:** General Medical and Surgical

**Staffed Beds:** 25

**PORT CLINTON—Ottawa County**

✠ **MAGRUDER MEMORIAL HOSPITAL (361314)**, 615 Fulton Street, Zip 43452–2001; tel. 419/734–3131 **A**1 5 9 10 18 **F**3 11 15 18 28 29 31 34 35 40 44 45 46 48 50 53 57 59 64 65 70 74 75 78 79 81 82 85 86 87 89 93 107 108 110 115 118 119 129 130 131 132 133 135 146 147 148 **P**6 8
Primary Contact: J. Todd Almendinger, President and Chief Executive Officer
COO: Nick Marsico, Vice President and Chief Operating Officer
CFO: Ronald Weiner, Vice President Finance and Chief Financial Officer
CMO: Barry Cover, M.D., Medical Director
CIO: Charles Dellick, Director Information Technology
CHR: Jason Kraus, Director Human Resources
Web address: www.magruderhospital.com
**Control:** Other not–for–profit (including NFP Corporation) **Service:** General Medical and Surgical

**Staffed Beds:** 25 **Admissions:** 730 **Census:** 6 **Outpatient Visits:** 88905 **Births:** 0 **Total Expense ($000):** 49586 **Payroll Expense ($000):** 19776 **Personnel:** 355

**PORTSMOUTH—Scioto County**

✠ △ **SOUTHERN OHIO MEDICAL CENTER (360008)**, 1805 27th Street, Zip 45662–2640; tel. 740/356–5000 **A**1 2 5 7 9 10 13 **F**3 11 13 15 17 18 20 22 24 26 28 29 30 31 34 35 37 38 40 41 44 45 46 49 50 53 54 57 59 62 63 64 65 68 70 74 75 76 77 78 79 81 84 85 86 87 89 90 92 97 98 100 102 103 104 107 108 109 110 111 114 115 116 117 118 119 120 121 122 123 124 129 130 131 132 135 144 145 146 **P**3
Primary Contact: Randal M. Arnett, President and Chief Executive Officer
CFO: Dean Wray, Vice President Finance
CMO: Kendall Stewart, M.D., Chief Medical Officer
CIO: Brent Richard, Administrative Director Information Systems
CHR: Vicki Noel, Vice President Human Resources
CNO: Claudia L. Burchett, R.N., Vice President of Patient Services
Web address: www.somc.org
**Control:** Other not–for–profit (including NFP Corporation) **Service:** General Medical and Surgical

**Staffed Beds:** 247 **Admissions:** 11666 **Census:** 159 **Outpatient Visits:** 309868 **Births:** 1244 **Total Expense ($000):** 254102 **Payroll Expense ($000):** 96843 **Personnel:** 2048

**PROCTORVILLE—Lawrence County**

☐ **THREE GABLES SURGERY CENTER (360261)**, 5897 County Road 107, Zip 45669–8852, Mailing Address: P.O. Box 490, Zip 45669–0490; tel. 740/886–9911, (Nonreporting) **A**1 9 10
Primary Contact: Tony Aluise, Chief Executive Officer
Web address: www.threegablessurgery.com
**Control:** Partnership, Investor–owned, for–profit **Service:** Surgical

**Staffed Beds:** 8

**RAVENNA—Portage County**

✠ **UH ROBINSON MEDICAL CENTER (360078)**, 6847 North Chestnut Street, Zip 44266–3929, Mailing Address: P.O. Box 1204, Zip 44266–1204; tel. 330/297–0811, (Nonreporting) **A**1 2 3 5 9 10 **S** University Hospitals, Cleveland, OH
Primary Contact: Stephen Colecchi, President and Chief Executive Officer
CFO: Carl Ebner, Vice President Finance
CMO: Stephen Francis, M.D., Vice President Medical Affairs
CIO: David Baldwin, Chief Information Officer
CHR: Neil Everett, Vice President Human Resources
CNO: Linda Breedlove, Vice President of Patient Care Services and Chief Nursing Officer
Web address: www.robinsonmemorial.org
**Control:** Other not–for–profit (including NFP Corporation) **Service:** General Medical and Surgical

**Staffed Beds:** 141

*Many Facility Codes have changed. Please refer to the AHA Guide Code Chart.*
© 2015 AHA Guide

**OH**

## ROCK CREEK—Ashtabula County

**GLENBEIGH HOSPITAL AND OUTPATIENT CENTERS (360245)**, 2863 Route 45, Zip 44084, Mailing Address: P.O. Box 298, Zip 44084–0298; tel. 440/563–3400 **A**9 10 **F**4 5 29 30 34 36 53 54 57 75 86 87 100 130 132 135 **P**5
Primary Contact: Patricia Weston–Hall, Chief Executive Officer
CFO: Phil Pawlowski, Chief Financial Officer
CIO: Linda Advey, Manager Information Systems
CHR: Shirley Deary, Director Human Resources
Web address: www.glenbeigh.com
**Control:** Other not–for–profit (including NFP Corporation) **Service:** Alcoholism and other chemical dependency

**Staffed Beds:** 114 **Admissions:** 3071 **Census:** 72 **Outpatient Visits:** 95076 **Births:** 0 **Total Expense ($000):** 19655 **Payroll Expense ($000):** 9719 **Personnel:** 248

## SAINT MARYS—Auglaize County

◇ **JOINT TOWNSHIP DISTRICT MEMORIAL HOSPITAL (360032)**, 200 St. Clair Street, Zip 45885–2400; tel. 419/394–3335, (Total facility includes 13 beds in nursing home–type unit) **A**9 10 21 **F**3 7 8 11 12 13 15 28 29 30 32 34 35 36 40 41 43 45 47 51 53 57 59 62 63 64 70 74 75 76 77 79 81 82 83 84 85 87 90 93 107 108 110 115 119 128 129 130 131 132 143 144 146 147 148
Primary Contact: Kevin W. Harlan, President
CFO: Jeffrey W. Vossler, Chief Financial Officer
CIO: Joshua Miller, Director Information Systems
CHR: Art Swain, Vice President Support Services
CNO: Debra McKee, R.N., Chief Nursing Officer
Web address: www.grandlakehealth.org
**Control:** Other not–for–profit (including NFP Corporation) **Service:** General Medical and Surgical

**Staffed Beds:** 53 **Admissions:** 1675 **Census:** 13 **Outpatient Visits:** 72484 **Births:** 276 **Total Expense ($000):** 60350 **Payroll Expense ($000):** 17952 **Personnel:** 473

## SALEM—Columbiana County

⊠ **SALEM REGIONAL MEDICAL CENTER (360185)**, 1995 East State Street, Zip 44460–2423; tel. 330/332–1551, (Total facility includes 15 beds in nursing home–type unit) **A**1 5 9 10 **F**3 8 13 15 18 29 30 31 34 35 40 45 48 49 51 54 57 59 64 70 74 75 76 77 78 79 81 82 85 86 87 93 100 104 105 107 108 109 110 111 114 115 116 117 118 119 128 129 130 132 144 145 146 148 **P**6
Primary Contact: Anita Hackstedde, M.D., President and Chief Executive Officer
COO: Keith Meredith, Chief Operating Officer
CFO: Mike Giangardella, Vice President Finance and Administration
CMO: Anita Hackstedde, M.D., Vice President Medical Affairs
CIO: Mark L'Italien, Director Information Services
CHR: Barb Hirst, Vice President Human Resources and Chief Nursing Officer
CNO: Barb Hirst, Vice President Human Resources and Chief Nursing Officer
Web address: www.salemregional.com
**Control:** Other not–for–profit (including NFP Corporation) **Service:** General Medical and Surgical

**Staffed Beds:** 116 **Admissions:** 4757 **Census:** 59 **Outpatient Visits:** 127356 **Births:** 470 **Total Expense ($000):** 97660 **Payroll Expense ($000):** 37957 **Personnel:** 781

## SANDUSKY—Erie County

◯ **FIRELANDS REGIONAL HEALTH SYSTEM (360025)**, 1111 Hayes Avenue, Zip 44870–3323; tel. 419/557–7400, (Includes FIRELANDS REGIONAL MEDICAL CENTER – MAIN CAMPUS, 1111 Hayes Avenue, Zip 44870; tel. 419/557–7400; FIRELANDS REGIONAL MEDICAL CENTER SOUTH CAMPUS, 1912 Hayes Avenue, Zip 44870–4736; tel. 419/557–7000), (Nonreporting) **A**2 9 10 11 12 13 19
Primary Contact: Martin Tursky, President and Chief Executive Officer
CFO: Daniel J. Moncher, Vice President and Chief Financial Officer
CMO: Brenda Violette, M.D., Director Medical Staff
CIO: Robert Ayres, Director Information Systems
CHR: James Sennish, Vice President Human Resources
Web address: www.firelands.com
**Control:** Other not–for–profit (including NFP Corporation) **Service:** General Medical and Surgical

**Staffed Beds:** 221

## SEAMAN—Adams County

⊠ **ADAMS COUNTY REGIONAL MEDICAL CENTER (361326)**, 230 Medical Center Drive, Zip 45679–8002; tel. 937/386–3400 **A**1 9 10 18 **F**3 15 28 29 30 31 34 40 45 49 50 53 57 59 62 64 65 75 77 78 79 81 85 86 93 107 110 111 115 116 119 129 130 131 132 133 148
Primary Contact: Roland D. Gee, Interim Chief Executive Officer
CFO: Pete Dagenbach, Chief Financial Officer
CHR: Heather Hoop, Human Resources Generalist
CNO: Sharon Ashley, MSN, Chief Nursing Officer
Web address: www.acrmc.com
**Control:** County–Government, nonfederal **Service:** General Medical and Surgical

**Staffed Beds:** 25 **Admissions:** 837 **Census:** 8 **Outpatient Visits:** 53371 **Births:** 0 **Total Expense ($000):** 23830 **Payroll Expense ($000):** 8693 **Personnel:** 236

## SHELBY—Richland County

★ **OHIOHEALTH MEDCENTRAL SHELBY HOSPITAL (361324)**, 199 West Main Street, Zip 44875–1490; tel. 419/342–5015 **A**9 10 18 **F**3 11 13 15 18 29 30 31 34 35 40 57 59 64 68 69 70 75 76 78 79 81 93 107 110 114 119 130 133 146 **S** OhioHealth, Columbus, OH
Primary Contact: Jean Halpin, President
CNO: Trish DelGreco, Director of Nursing
Web address: www.medcentral.org/body.cfm?id=153
**Control:** Other not–for–profit (including NFP Corporation) **Service:** General Medical and Surgical

**Staffed Beds:** 25 **Admissions:** 1268 **Census:** 12 **Outpatient Visits:** 33177 **Births:** 207 **Personnel:** 156

## SIDNEY—Shelby County

★ ◯ **WILSON MEMORIAL HOSPITAL (360013)**, 915 West Michigan Street, Zip 45365–2491; tel. 937/498–2311 **A**9 10 11 **F**3 11 13 15 20 28 29 30 34 40 45 49 56 57 59 62 63 64 68 70 75 76 77 79 81 82 85 86 87 89 93 97 98 103 107 108 111 115 118 119 129 130 131 132 135 144 146 147 **P**6
Primary Contact: Mark J. Dooley, Chief Executive Officer
COO: Craig Lannoye, Vice President Operations
CFO: Julie Covault, Vice President Finance
CMO: Robert J. McDevitt, M.D., Chief of Staff
CIO: Larry Meyers, Chief Information Officer
CHR: John R. Eve, Vice President Human Resources
CNO: Linda Maurer, Vice President Patient Care Services
Web address: www.wilsonhospital.com
**Control:** Other not–for–profit (including NFP Corporation) **Service:** General Medical and Surgical

**Staffed Beds:** 71 **Admissions:** 2656 **Census:** 30 **Outpatient Visits:** 186000 **Births:** 822 **Total Expense ($000):** 70794 **Payroll Expense ($000):** 26061 **Personnel:** 613

## SPRINGFIELD—Clark County

☐ **MENTAL HEALTH SERVICES FOR CLARK AND MADISON COUNTIES (364040)**, 474 North Yellow Springs Street, Zip 45504–2463; tel. 937/399–9500, (Nonreporting) **A**1 9 10
Primary Contact: Curt Gillespie, Chief Executive Officer
Web address: www.mhscc.org
**Control:** County–Government, nonfederal **Service:** Psychiatric

**Staffed Beds:** 16

☐ **OHIO VALLEY SURGICAL HOSPITAL (360355)**, 100 West Main Street, Zip 45502–1312; tel. 937/521–3900, (Nonreporting) **A**1 9 10
Primary Contact: Steve Eisentrager, President
CFO: Amanda martin, Manager Human Resources
CMO: Thales Pavlatos, Medical Director
CIO: Jonathan Bisdorf, Director Information Technology
CNO: Beth Lizza, Chief Nursing Officer
Web address: www.ovsurgical.com/
**Control:** Partnership, Investor–owned, for–profit **Service:** Surgical

**Staffed Beds:** 24

---

**Hospital, Medicare Provider Number, Address, Telephone, Approval, Facility, and Physician Codes, Health Care System**

★ American Hospital Association (AHA) membership
☐ The Joint Commission accreditation
◯ Healthcare Facilities Accreditation Program
◇ DNV Healthcare Inc. accreditation
⇑ Center for Improvement in Healthcare Quality Accreditation
△ Commission on Accreditation of Rehabilitation Facilities (CARF) accreditation

**OH**

✠ **SPRINGFIELD REGIONAL MEDICAL CENTER (360086)**, 100 Medical Center Drive, Zip 45504–2687; tel. 937/523–1000 **A**1 2 9 10 **F**3 5 8 11 13 15 17 18 20 22 24 26 28 29 30 31 34 35 37 40 45 49 51 53 59 61 63 64 68 70 74 75 76 77 78 79 81 82 83 84 85 86 87 89 90 93 107 108 110 111 114 115 118 119 120 121 126 129 130 131 132 135 146 147 148 **P**6 **S** Mercy Health, Cincinnati, OH
Primary Contact: Paul C. Hiltz, FACHE, Market President and Chief Executive Officer
COO: Gary Hagens, Chief Operating Officer and Chief Medical Officer
CFO: William J. Kusnierz, Vice President and Chief Financial Officer
CMO: Gary Hagens, Chief Operating Officer and Chief Medical Officer
CIO: Denise Craven, Director Information Systems Relationship Management
CHR: Steven E. Kile, Director Human Resources
CNO: Sherry Nelson, JD, Chief Nursing Officer
Web address: www.community–mercy.org
**Control:** Church–operated, Nongovernment, not–for profit **Service:** General Medical and Surgical

**Staffed Beds: 259 Admissions: 14203 Census: 167 Outpatient Visits:** 297717 **Births: 1226 Total Expense ($000): 209377 Payroll Expense ($000): 63897 Personnel: 1382**

### STEUBENVILLE—Jefferson County

✠ **ACUITY SPECIALTY HOSPITALS OHIO VALLEY (362035)**, 380 Summit Avenue, 3rd Floor, Zip 43952–2667; tel. 740/283–7600, (Includes ACUITY SPECIALTY HOSPITALS OHIO VALLEY AT BELMONT, 4697 Harrison Street, Bellaire, Zip 43906–1338; tel. 740/671–2086), (Nonreporting) **A**1 9 10 **S** AcuityHealthcare, LP, Charlotte, NC
Primary Contact: Judy K. Weaver, MS, Chief Executive Officer
Web address: www.acuityhealthcare.net
**Control:** Corporation, Investor–owned, for–profit **Service:** Long–Term Acute Care hospital

**Staffed Beds: 40**

**LIFE LINE HOSPITAL (362039)**, 200 School Street, Zip 43953–9610; tel. 740/346–2600, (Nonreporting) **A**10
Primary Contact: Patricia Cross, Chief Executive Officer
Web address: www.llhospital.com
**Control:** Partnership, Investor–owned, for–profit **Service:** Long–Term Acute Care hospital

**Staffed Beds: 30**

✠ **TRINITY HEALTH SYSTEM (360211)**, 380 Summit Avenue, Zip 43952–2699; tel. 740/283–7000, (Includes TRINITY MEDICAL CENTER EAST, 380 Summit Avenue, tel. 740/283–7000; TRINITY MEDICAL CENTER WEST, 4000 Johnson Road, Zip 43952–2393; tel. 740/264–8000) **A**1 2 6 9 10 **F**3 4 5 12 13 15 17 18 20 22 24 26 28 29 30 31 32 33 34 35 38 40 45 46 47 49 51 54 56 57 59 62 64 65 70 74 75 76 77 78 79 81 85 86 87 89 90 92 93 94 96 97 98 99 100 101 102 103 104 105 107 108 110 111 114 115 117 118 119 120 121 123 126 128 129 130 131 132 135 144 146 147 148 **P**6 **S** Catholic Health Initiatives, Englewood, CO
Primary Contact: Fred B. Brower, President and Chief Executive Officer
COO: JoAnn M. Mulrooney, R.N., Chief Operating Officer
CFO: Dave Werkin, Vice President Finance and Chief Financial Officer
CMO: Gray Goncz, Vice President of Medical Affairs
CIO: Tom Kiger, Director Information Systems
CHR: Lewis C. Musso, Vice President Human Resources
Web address: www.trinityhealth.com
**Control:** Other not–for–profit (including NFP Corporation) **Service:** General Medical and Surgical

**Staffed Beds: 312 Admissions: 10800 Census: 179 Outpatient Visits:** 272653 **Births: 593 Total Expense ($000): 214555 Payroll Expense ($000): 78229 Personnel: 1564**

### SYLVANIA—Lucas County

✠ △ **PROMEDICA FLOWER HOSPITAL (360074)**, 5200 Harroun Road, Zip 43560–2196; tel. 419/824–1444 **A**1 2 3 5 7 9 10 **F**3 9 11 12 13 15 18 20 22 24 28 29 30 31 34 36 38 40 47 48 49 50 54 57 58 59 60 64 65 67 68 70 75 76 77 78 79 81 82 84 85 86 87 90 91 92 93 94 96 97 98 100 101 102 103 107 108 109 110 111 114 116 117 118 119 120 121 123 124 126 129 130 131 132 146 147 **S** ProMedica Health System, Toledo, OH
Primary Contact: Neeraj Kanwal, M.D., President
CFO: Alan Sattler, Chief Financial Officer
CMO: John Evanoff, M.D., Vice President Medical Affairs
CIO: Rose Ann Laureto, Chief Information Officer
CHR: Karen Strauss, Chief Human Resources Officer
CNO: Maurine Weis, Vice President Nursing and Chief Nursing Officer
Web address: www.promedica.org
**Control:** Other not–for–profit (including NFP Corporation) **Service:** General Medical and Surgical

**Staffed Beds: 273 Admissions: 10682 Census: 157 Outpatient Visits:** 192926 **Births: 962 Total Expense ($000): 211068 Payroll Expense ($000): 66487 Personnel: 1210**

✠ **REGENCY HOSPITAL OF TOLEDO (362036)**, 5220 Alexis Road, Zip 43560–2504; tel. 419/318–5700, (Nonreporting) **A**1 3 5 10 **S** Select Medical Corporation, Mechanicsburg, PA
Primary Contact: Matt Cannon, Chief Executive Officer
Web address: www.regencyhospital.com
**Control:** Corporation, Investor–owned, for–profit **Service:** Long–Term Acute Care hospital

**Staffed Beds: 45**

### TIFFIN—Seneca County

✠ **MERCY TIFFIN HOSPITAL (360089)**, 45 St. Lawrence Drive, Zip 44883–8310; tel. 419/455–7000 **A**1 2 9 10 **F**3 12 13 15 18 19 20 28 29 30 31 34 35 36 40 46 49 50 51 56 57 59 62 64 66 68 70 74 75 76 77 78 79 81 82 83 84 85 86 87 89 93 97 107 108 110 111 115 118 119 129 130 132 133 134 135 145 146 147 148 **S** Mercy Health, Cincinnati, OH
Primary Contact: B. Lynn Detterman, President
CMO: Christopher Sears, M.D., President Medical Staff
Web address: www.mercyweb.org
**Control:** Church–operated, Nongovernment, not–for profit **Service:** General Medical and Surgical

**Staffed Beds: 51 Admissions: 1835 Census: 19 Outpatient Visits: 77380 Births: 274 Total Expense ($000): 51124 Payroll Expense ($000): 12863 Personnel: 304**

### TOLEDO—Lucas County

☐ **ADVANCED SPECIALTY HOSPITAL OF TOLEDO (362038)**, 1015 Garden Lake Parkway, Zip 43614–2779; tel. 419/381–0037, (Nonreporting) **A**1 3 10
Primary Contact: Kim Burkholder–McNutt, Chief Executive Officer
CFO: Troy Holmes, Director Finance
CMO: B. Sarroui, M.D., Chief of Staff
CHR: Tina Hacker, Director Human Resources
CNO: Jennifer Olivier, Chief Clinical Officer
Web address: www.advancedspecialtyhospitals.com
**Control:** Corporation, Investor–owned, for–profit **Service:** Long–Term Acute Care hospital

**Staffed Beds: 25**

✠ **MERCY ST. ANNE HOSPITAL (360262)**, 3404 West Sylvania Avenue, Zip 43623–4467; tel. 419/407–2663 **A**1 2 9 10 **F**3 15 17 18 20 22 24 29 30 31 34 35 36 38 40 45 56 57 59 64 65 67 68 70 74 75 78 79 81 82 84 85 86 87 92 107 108 110 111 115 118 119 120 121 123 126 129 130 132 135 146 147 **P**8 **S** Mercy Health, Cincinnati, OH
Primary Contact: Bradley J. Bertke, President
CFO: Robert Moon, Chief Financial Officer
CMO: Herbert Stockard, M.D., Chief Medical Officer
CIO: Rebecca S. Sykes, Chief Information Officer
CHR: Gary George, Regional Vice President Human Resources
CNO: Pamela Kadlick, Vice President Nursing
Web address: www.mercyweb.org
**Control:** Church–operated, Nongovernment, not–for profit **Service:** General Medical and Surgical

**Staffed Beds: 96 Admissions: 4498 Census: 48 Outpatient Visits: 186494 Births: 0 Personnel: 715**

✠ **MERCY ST. VINCENT MEDICAL CENTER (360112)**, 2213 Cherry Street, Zip 43608–2691; tel. 419/251–3232, (Includes MERCY CHILDREN'S HOSPITAL, 2213 Cherry Street, Zip 419/251–8000) **A**1 2 3 5 9 10 12 13 **F**3 7 8 11 12 13 15 16 17 18 19 20 21 22 23 24 25 26 29 30 31 32 34 35 37 38 39 40 41 42 43 44 45 46 48 49 50 51 53 54 55 56 57 58 59 60 61 64 65 66 67 68 70 72 73 74 75 76 77 78 79 81 82 83 84 85 86 87 88 89 92 93 97 98 107 108 110 111 114 115 118 119 126 129 130 131 132 134 135 146 147 148 **P**8 **S** Mercy Health, Cincinnati, OH
Primary Contact: Kerry Tirman, President
COO: Kerry Tirman, President and Chief Operating Officer
CMO: Thomas Welch, M.D., Chief Medical Officer
CHR: Gary George, Senior Vice President Human Resources
CNO: Barbara Martin, Chief Nursing Officer
Web address: www.mercyweb.org
**Control:** Church–operated, Nongovernment, not–for profit **Service:** General Medical and Surgical

**Staffed Beds: 409 Admissions: 17193 Census: 212 Outpatient Visits:** 228372 **Births: 1332 Personnel: 2625**

☐ **NORTHWEST OHIO PSYCHIATRIC HOSPITAL (364014)**, 930 Detroit Avenue, Zip 43614–2701; tel. 419/381–1881, (Nonreporting) **A**1 3 10 **S** Ohio Department of Mental Health, Columbus, OH
Primary Contact: Mychail Scheramic, M.D., Chief Executive Officer
CMO: Thomas Osinowo, M.D., Chief Clinical Officer
CIO: Michael Carter, Administrator Information Technology
CHR: Lois Mason–Williams, Director of Human Resources
CNO: Deb Duris, Director of Nursing
Web address: www.mh.state.oh.us/
**Control:** State–Government, nonfederal **Service:** Psychiatric

**Staffed Beds: 114**

*Many Facility Codes have changed. Please refer to the AHA Guide Code Chart.* © 2015 AHA Guide

PROMEDICA TOLEDO HOSPITAL (360068), 2142 North Cove Boulevard, Zip 43606–3896; tel. 419/291–4000, (Includes PROMEDICA WILDWOOD ORTHOPAEDIC AND SPINE HOSPITAL, 2901 North Reynolds Road, Zip 43615; tel. 419/578–7700; Holly L. Bristoll, President; TOLEDO CHILDREN'S HOSPITAL, 2142 North Cove Boulevard, Zip 43606), (Total facility includes 25 beds in nursing home–type unit) A1 2 3 5 9 10 13 F3 7 8 11 12 13 15 17 18 19 20 22 24 26 29 30 31 32 34 36 38 39 40 41 43 48 49 50 51 53 54 55 57 58 59 60 64 65 67 68 70 72 74 75 76 77 78 79 81 82 84 85 86 87 88 89 91 92 93 94 96 97 98 99 100 101 102 104 105 107 108 111 114 115 118 119 126 128 130 131 132 134 135 143 144 146 147 148 S ProMedica Health System, Toledo, OH
Primary Contact: Arturo Polizzi, President
CMO: Khurram Kamran, M.D., Vice President Medical Affairs
CIO: Rose Ann Laureto, Chief Information Officer
CHR: Arturo Polizzi, Chief Human Resources Officer
Web address: www.promedica.org
Control: Other not–for–profit (including NFP Corporation) Service: General Medical and Surgical

Staffed Beds: 649 Admissions: 31637 Census: 447 Outpatient Visits: 740737 Births: 3689 Total Expense ($000): 753083 Payroll Expense ($000): 230206 Personnel: 4337

△ THE UNIVERSITY OF TOLEDO MEDICAL CENTER (360048), 3000 Arlington Avenue, Zip 43614–2595; tel. 419/383–4000 A1 2 3 5 7 8 9 10 F3 8 11 15 17 18 20 22 24 26 28 29 30 31 32 34 35 36 37 38 39 40 43 44 45 46 47 48 49 50 51 53 54 55 56 57 58 59 60 61 64 65 68 70 74 75 77 78 79 81 82 84 85 86 87 90 91 92 93 94 96 97 98 99 100 101 102 104 105 107 108 110 111 114 115 116 117 118 119 120 121 123 124 126 129 130 131 132 134 135 138 146 147 148
Primary Contact: David Morlock, Chief Executive Officer
COO: Carl Sirio, M.D., Professor, Vice President Medical Affairs, Associate Dean for Clinical Affairs, Chief Medical Information Officer
CFO: David Morlock, Chief Executive Officer, Executive Vice President Finance and Administration
CMO: Carl Sirio, M.D., Chief Operating and Clinical Officer
CIO: Godfrey Ovwigho, Vice President Information Technology and Chief Information Officer
CHR: Jovita Thomas–Williams, Associate Vice President Human Resources
CNO: Daniel Barbee, Vice President Clinical Affairs
Web address: www.utoledo.edu
Control: State–Government, nonfederal Service: General Medical and Surgical

Staffed Beds: 249 Admissions: 10826 Census: 162 Outpatient Visits: 279730 Births: 0 Total Expense ($000): 270584 Payroll Expense ($000): 106030 Personnel: 2247

TOLEDO CAMPUS See Northcoast Behavioral Healthcare System, Northfield

### TROY—Miami County

□ △ UPPER VALLEY MEDICAL CENTER (360174), 3130 North County Road 25A, Zip 45373–1309; tel. 937/440–4000, (Includes DETTMER HOSPITAL, 3130 North Dixie Highway, Zip 45373–1039; tel. 937/440–7500), (Nonreporting) A1 2 5 7 9 10 S Premier Health, Dayton, OH
Primary Contact: Thomas Parker, Chief Executive Officer
CFO: Tim Snider, Senior Vice President and Chief Financial Officer
CMO: Dan Bailey, M.D., Vice President Medical Affairs and Chief Medical Officer
CIO: William Watercutter, Director Management Information System
CHR: Tracy Moser, Director Human Resources
Web address: www.uvmc.com
Control: Other not–for–profit (including NFP Corporation) Service: General Medical and Surgical

Staffed Beds: 168

### UPPER SANDUSKY—Wyandot County

★ WYANDOT MEMORIAL HOSPITAL (361329), 885 North Sandusky Avenue, Zip 43351–1098; tel. 419/294–4991 A9 10 18 F3 11 15 28 29 30 31 34 35 40 45 53 57 59 64 65 74 75 76 77 78 79 81 82 85 86 87 89 92 93 97 107 108 110 111 115 117 118 119 124 129 130 132 133 135 146 148 P6
Primary Contact: Joseph A. D'Ettorre, Chief Executive Officer
COO: Ty Shaull, Chief Operating Officer
CFO: Alan H. Yeates, Vice President Fiscal Services
CHR: Vickie Underwood, Director Human Resources
CNO: Marty Gray, R.N., Director of Nursing
Web address: www.wyandotmemorial.org
Control: Hospital district or authority, Government, nonfederal Service: General Medical and Surgical

Staffed Beds: 25 Admissions: 1022 Census: 13 Outpatient Visits: 61321 Births: 162 Total Expense ($000): 38503 Payroll Expense ($000): 12274 Personnel: 213

### URBANA—Champaign County

★ MERCY MEMORIAL HOSPITAL (361312), 904 Scioto Street, Zip 43078–2200; tel. 937/653–5231 A9 10 18 F3 5 8 11 15 28 29 30 34 35 40 45 50 59 63 64 70 75 77 79 81 84 85 90 107 108 110 111 114 119 130 133 135 146 148 P6 S Mercy Health, Cincinnati, OH
Primary Contact: Paul Hiltz, President and Chief Executive Officer
Web address: www.health–partners.org
Control: Church–operated, Nongovernment, not–for profit Service: General Medical and Surgical

Staffed Beds: 25 Admissions: 978 Census: 9 Outpatient Visits: 84480 Births: 0 Total Expense ($000): 22713 Payroll Expense ($000): 7705 Personnel: 134

### VAN WERT—Van Wert County

VAN WERT COUNTY HOSPITAL (360071), 1250 South Washington Street, Zip 45891–2599; tel. 419/238–2390 A1 5 9 10 F8 13 15 28 29 34 35 40 48 50 53 54 57 59 62 64 70 76 77 79 81 85 87 89 91 93 107 108 113 119 127 129 130 135 146 P7 8
Primary Contact: Mark J. Minick, President and Chief Executive Officer
CFO: Michael T. Holliday, Vice President Fiscal and Administrative Services
CMO: Jennifer Hohman, M.D., President Medical Staff
CIO: Brett Taylor, M.D., Manager Information
CHR: Joyce Pothast, Vice President Human and Environmental Services
CNO: Shelia Kay Brokenshire, Vice President of Nursing
Web address: www.vanwerthospital.org
Control: Other not–for–profit (including NFP Corporation) Service: General Medical and Surgical

Staffed Beds: 69 Admissions: 985 Census: 9 Outpatient Visits: 124684 Births: 151 Total Expense ($000): 36539 Payroll Expense ($000): 11128 Personnel: 266

### WARREN—Trumbull County

△ HILLSIDE REHABILITATION HOSPITAL (363026), 8747 Squires Lane N.E., Zip 44484–1649; tel. 330/841–3700, (Nonreporting) A1 5 7 9 10 S Community Health Systems, Inc., Franklin, TN
Primary Contact: Ian Cooper, Chief Executive Officer
CMO: Cynthia DiMauro, M.D., Medical Director
CIO: Timothy Roe, Chief Information Officer
CHR: Lisa Johnson, Vice President Human Resources
Web address: www.valleycarehealth.net
Control: Corporation, Investor–owned, for–profit Service: Rehabilitation

Staffed Beds: 65

SELECT SPECIALTY HOSPITAL–YOUNGSTOWN, BOARDMAN CAMPUS See Select Specialty Hospital–Youngstown, Youngstown

ST. JOSEPH HEALTH CENTER (360161), 667 Eastland Avenue S.E., Zip 44484–4531; tel. 330/841–4000 A1 2 9 10 13 F3 5 8 11 12 13 15 28 29 30 31 34 35 40 42 43 44 45 46 49 50 51 53 54 56 57 59 61 64 66 68 70 75 76 77 78 79 81 82 83 84 85 86 87 89 93 97 107 108 111 114 115 116 118 119 120 121 123 126 129 130 132 135 143 144 146 147 148 P6 S Mercy Health, Cincinnati, OH
Primary Contact: Kathy Cook, R.N., MSN, President
COO: Robert W. Shroder, President and Chief Executive Officer
CFO: Donald E. Kline, Senior Vice President Finance
CMO: Nicholas Kreatsoulas, M.D., Vice President Medical Affairs
Web address: www.hmpartners.org
Control: Church–operated, Nongovernment, not–for profit Service: General Medical and Surgical

Staffed Beds: 136 Admissions: 8060 Census: 93 Outpatient Visits: 178838 Births: 827 Total Expense ($000): 134080 Payroll Expense ($000): 40199 Personnel: 606

TRUMBULL MEMORIAL HOSPITAL (360055), 1350 East Market Street, Zip 44483–6628; tel. 330/841–9011, (Nonreporting) A1 2 5 9 10 S Community Health Systems, Inc., Franklin, TN
Primary Contact: John Walsh, Chief Executive Officer
COO: Jay De Los Reyes, Chief Operating Officer
CFO: Anthony Seminaro, Chief Financial Officer
CMO: Thomas L. James, M.D., Chief Medical Officer
CIO: Barry Fitts, Chief Information Officer
CHR: Robert Sincich, Vice President Human Resources
CNO: Melissa Bennett, Chief Nursing Officer
Web address: www.vchs.net
Control: Corporation, Investor–owned, for–profit Service: General Medical and Surgical

Staffed Beds: 292

---

**Hospital, Medicare Provider Number, Address, Telephone, Approval, Facility, and Physician Codes, Health Care System**

★ American Hospital Association (AHA) membership  ○ Healthcare Facilities Accreditation Program  ⇑ Center for Improvement in Healthcare Quality Accreditation
□ The Joint Commission accreditation  ◇ DNV Healthcare Inc. accreditation  △ Commission on Accreditation of Rehabilitation Facilities (CARF) accreditation

**OH**

### WARRENSVILLE HEIGHTS—Cuyahoga County

✠ **REGENCY HOSPITAL CLEVELAND EAST (362029)**, 4200 Interchange Corporate Center Road, Zip 44128–5631; tel. 216/910–3800, (Includes REGENCY HOSPITAL OF CLEVELAND – WEST, 6990 Engle Road, Middleburg Heights, Zip 44130–3420; tel. 440/202–4200; Timothy Rolsen, Chief Executive Officer), (Nonreporting) **A**1 10 **S** Select Medical Corporation, Mechanicsburg, PA
Primary Contact: Thomas Knoske, Chief Executive Officer
Web address: www.regencyhospital.com/
**Control:** Corporation, Investor–owned, for–profit **Service:** Long–Term Acute Care hospital

> **Staffed Beds:** 132

✠ **SOUTH POINTE HOSPITAL (360144)**, 20000 Harvard Road, Zip 44122–6805; tel. 216/491–6000 **A**1 2 9 10 12 13 **F**15 18 28 29 30 31 34 35 36 38 39 40 42 44 50 51 54 56 57 58 59 60 61 64 65 66 68 70 74 75 77 78 79 81 82 84 85 86 87 92 93 97 100 102 107 108 110 111 114 117 119 130 131 132 135 143 144 146 148 **S** Cleveland Clinic Health System, Cleveland, OH
Primary Contact: Robert S. Juhasz, D.O., President
COO: Andrea Jacobs, Chief Operating Officer
CFO: Lindsay Bird, Director Finance
CMO: Arun Gupta, M.D., Vice President Medical Affairs
CIO: Ralph A. Cagna, Director Information Technology
CHR: Doris A. Zajec, Director Human Resources
Web address: www.southpointehospital.org
**Control:** Other not–for–profit (including NFP Corporation) **Service:** General Medical and Surgical

> **Staffed Beds:** 176 **Admissions:** 6771 **Census:** 88 **Outpatient Visits:** 120916 **Births:** 0 **Total Expense ($000):** 119321 **Payroll Expense ($000):** 46864 **Personnel:** 793

### WASHINGTON COURT HOUSE—Fayette County

✠ **FAYETTE COUNTY MEMORIAL HOSPITAL (361331)**, 1430 Columbus Avenue, Zip 43160–1791; tel. 740/335–1210 **A**1 9 10 18 **F**3 7 8 11 15 18 29 30 34 35 40 45 50 57 59 64 70 75 79 81 82 87 93 96 97 107 108 110 114 119 127 128 129 130 131 132 133 135 144 146 148 **P**4 **S** Trinity Health, Livonia, MI
Primary Contact: John DesMarais, M.D., President and Chief Executive Officer
COO: Lenora Fitton, D.O., Chief of Staff
CFO: Thomas McDermott, Vice President Finance
CIO: Bruce Denen, Manager Data Processing
CHR: Earlene Christensen, Director Human Resources
CNO: Beverly Hughes, R.N., Vice President Nursing
Web address: www.fcmh.org
**Control:** County–Government, nonfederal **Service:** General Medical and Surgical

> **Staffed Beds:** 25 **Admissions:** 846 **Census:** 10 **Outpatient Visits:** 20259 **Births:** 0 **Total Expense ($000):** 43698 **Payroll Expense ($000):** 21667 **Personnel:** 361

### WAUSEON—Fulton County

✠ **FULTON COUNTY HEALTH CENTER (361333)**, 725 South Shoop Avenue, Zip 43567–1701; tel. 419/335–2015, (Total facility includes 71 beds in nursing home–type unit) **A**1 2 5 9 10 18 **F**3 8 11 13 15 18 20 26 28 29 31 34 40 53 57 59 67 69 70 75 76 77 78 79 81 87 89 93 98 101 102 103 104 105 107 108 111 115 118 119 128 129 130 131 132 135 146 148
Primary Contact: Patti Finn, Chief Executive Officer
COO: Patti Finn, Chief Executive Officer
CFO: Darrell Topmiller, Director Finance
CIO: Larry Hefflinger, Director Information Systems
CHR: Kristy Snyder, Director Human Resources
CNO: Jo Short, Director of Nursing
Web address: www.fultoncountyhealthcenter.org
**Control:** Other not–for–profit (including NFP Corporation) **Service:** General Medical and Surgical

> **Staffed Beds:** 106 **Admissions:** 1632 **Census:** 78 **Outpatient Visits:** 173608 **Births:** 276 **Total Expense ($000):** 58277 **Payroll Expense ($000):** 22640 **Personnel:** 641

### WAVERLY—Pike County

□ **ADENA PIKE MEDICAL CENTER (361334)**, 100 Dawn Lane, Zip 45690–9138; tel. 740/947–2186 **A**9 10 18 **F**3 11 18 29 30 34 35 40 41 45 50 54 57 59 79 81 93 97 107 108 114 118 119 130 133 135 146 **P**6 **S** Adena Health System, Chillicothe, OH
Primary Contact: David M. Zanni, Associate Administrator
COO: Tina Perko, Vice President Operations
CFO: Sharon Novak, CPA, Vice President Finance
CHR: Berna Brock, Vice President Human Resources
Web address: www.pikecommunityhospital.org
**Control:** Church–operated, Nongovernment, not–for profit **Service:** General Medical and Surgical

> **Staffed Beds:** 21 **Admissions:** 581 **Census:** 7 **Outpatient Visits:** 35944 **Births:** 0

### WEST CHESTER—Butler County

□ **BECKETT SPRINGS (364051)**, 8614 Shepherd Farm Drive, Zip 45069; tel. 513/942–9500, (Nonreporting) **A**1 10
Primary Contact: Phil Sheridan, Chief Executive Officer
Web address: www.springstone.com/hospitals.stmhl
**Control:** Corporation, Investor–owned, for–profit **Service:** Psychiatric

> **Staffed Beds:** 48

✠ **WEST CHESTER HOSPITAL (360354)**, 7700 University Drive, Zip 45069–2505; tel. 513/298–3000, (Includes WEST CHESTER HOSPITAL SURGICAL CENTER, 7750 University Court, Zip 45069; tel. 513/475–8300) **A**1 3 10 **F**3 9 12 15 18 20 22 26 29 30 31 34 35 37 38 40 43 44 45 46 47 48 49 50 51 54 57 58 59 60 61 63 64 68 70 71 74 75 77 78 79 80 81 84 85 86 87 92 107 108 110 111 114 115 119 126 129 130 131 132 135 141 145 146 147 148 **P**6 **S** UC Health, Cincinnati, OH
Primary Contact: Kevin Joseph, M.D., Chief Executive Officer
COO: Tom G. Daskalakis, Chief Operating Officer
CFO: Karen Shadowens, Director Finance and Chief Financial Officer
CMO: Kevin Joseph, M.D., Chief Medical Officer
CIO: Jay Brown, Senior Vice President, Chief Information Officer
CHR: Jack Talbot, Director, Human Resources
CNO: Patrick Baker, R.N., Vice President, Chief Nursing Officer
Web address: www.uchealth.com/westchesterhospital
**Control:** Other not–for–profit (including NFP Corporation) **Service:** General Medical and Surgical

> **Staffed Beds:** 181 **Admissions:** 8595 **Census:** 95 **Outpatient Visits:** 159073 **Births:** 2 **Total Expense ($000):** 159877 **Payroll Expense ($000):** 46734 **Personnel:** 1026

### WESTERVILLE—Franklin County

✠ **MOUNT CARMEL ST. ANN'S (360012)**, 500 South Cleveland Avenue, Zip 43081–8998; tel. 614/898–4000 **A**1 2 3 5 9 10 **F**3 11 13 15 18 20 22 24 26 28 29 30 31 34 35 37 40 44 45 47 48 49 50 51 54 55 57 58 59 61 63 64 65 66 68 70 74 75 76 77 78 79 81 83 84 85 86 87 93 97 100 101 102 107 108 109 110 111 114 115 116 118 119 120 121 123 124 126 130 131 132 145 146 147 148 **P**6 8 **S** Trinity Health, Livonia, MI
Primary Contact: Roger Spoelman, Interim President and Chief Executive Officer
Web address: www.mountcarmelhealth.com
**Control:** Church–operated, Nongovernment, not–for profit **Service:** General Medical and Surgical

> **Staffed Beds:** 281 **Admissions:** 20749 **Census:** 164 **Outpatient Visits:** 174677 **Births:** 4461 **Total Expense ($000):** 249571 **Payroll Expense ($000):** 87410 **Personnel:** 1543

### WESTLAKE—Cuyahoga County

□ **ST. JOHN MEDICAL CENTER (360123)**, 29000 Center Ridge Road, Zip 44145–5293; tel. 440/835–8000 **A**1 2 3 9 10 12 13 **F**3 8 13 15 17 18 20 22 24 26 28 29 30 31 34 35 39 40 43 44 45 46 47 49 50 51 54 56 57 59 64 65 68 70 71 74 75 76 78 79 80 81 82 84 85 86 87 89 92 93 100 107 108 110 111 114 115 119 130 132 143 144 146 147 148 **P**4 **S** Sisters of Charity Health System, Cleveland, OH
Primary Contact: William A. Young, Jr., President and Chief Executive Officer
CFO: Allen R. Tracy, Senior Vice President and Chief Financial Officer
CMO: Michael Dobrovich, M.D., Chief Medical Officer
CIO: James H. Carroll, Chief Information Officer
CHR: Gary Lazroff, Vice President Human Resources
Web address: www.sjws.net
**Control:** Other not–for–profit (including NFP Corporation) **Service:** General Medical and Surgical

> **Staffed Beds:** 191 **Admissions:** 10599 **Census:** 102 **Outpatient Visits:** 142802 **Births:** 818 **Total Expense ($000):** 141416 **Payroll Expense ($000):** 56815 **Personnel:** 1050

**ST. JOHN WEST SHORE HOSPITAL** See St. John Medical Center

### WILLARD—Huron County

✠ **MERCY WILLARD HOSPITAL (361310)**, 1100 Neal Zick Road, Zip 44890–9287; tel. 419/964–5000 **A**1 9 10 18 **F**3 5 7 15 18 28 29 30 31 34 35 40 46 57 59 68 70 74 75 77 78 79 81 84 85 87 89 93 107 111 114 119 129 130 131 132 133 135 143 145 146 147 **S** Mercy Health, Cincinnati, OH
Primary Contact: B. Lynn Detterman, President and Chief Executive Officer
CFO: Cindy Dennison, Senior Director Rural Division
CMO: Bill Back, M.D., Chief of Staff
CHR: Diana Olson, Chief Human Resources Officer
CNO: Pamela Napier, R.N., Chief Nursing Officer
Web address: www.mercyweb.org
**Control:** Church–operated, Nongovernment, not–for profit **Service:** General Medical and Surgical

> **Staffed Beds:** 20 **Admissions:** 591 **Census:** 8 **Outpatient Visits:** 40026 **Births:** 0 **Total Expense ($000):** 24363 **Payroll Expense ($000):** 7031 **Personnel:** 153

## WILLOUGHBY—Lake County

☐ **WINDSOR–LAURELWOOD CENTER FOR BEHAVIORAL MEDICINE (364029)**, 35900 Euclid Avenue, Zip 44094–4648; tel. 440/953–3000 **A**1 9 10 **F**4 5 54 64 98 99 100 101 103 104 105 130 132 143 **P**5 6 **S** Universal Health Services, Inc., King of Prussia, PA
Primary Contact: Ric McAllister, Chief Executive Officer
COO: Brenda Bailey, Assistant Administrator
CFO: Robin Stough, Chief Financial Officer
CMO: Leonard Barley, M.D., Chief Medical Officer
CIO: Cory Wheatcraft, Information Technology and Purchasing Officer
CHR: Pam Connell, Manager Human Resources
CNO: Debra Schaefer, Chief Nursing Officer
Web address: www.windsorlaurelwood.com
**Control:** Corporation, Investor–owned, for–profit **Service:** Psychiatric

> **Staffed Beds:** 159 **Admissions:** 4778 **Census:** 127 **Outpatient Visits:** 10864
> **Births:** 0 **Total Expense ($000):** 30603 **Payroll Expense ($000):** 12021
> **Personnel:** 227

## WILMINGTON—Clinton County

☐ **CLINTON MEMORIAL HOSPITAL (360175)**, 610 West Main Street, Zip 45177–2125; tel. 937/382–6611, (Nonreporting) **A**1 2 3 5 9 10 **S** RegionalCare Hospital Partners, Brentwood, TN
Primary Contact: Gregory A. Nielsen, FACHE, Chief Executive Officer
CFO: Bradley Boggus, Chief Financial Officer
CIO: Ray Doherty, Director Information Technology
CHR: Jan Blair, Director Human Resources
CNO: Sheila Martin, Chief Nursing Officer
Web address: www.cmhregional.com
**Control:** Corporation, Investor–owned, for–profit **Service:** General Medical and Surgical

> **Staffed Beds:** 102

## WOOSTER—Wayne County

☐ △ **WOOSTER COMMUNITY HOSPITAL (360036)**, 1761 Beall Avenue, Zip 44691–2342; tel. 330/263–8100, (Nonreporting) **A**1 2 5 7 9 10 19 **S** QHR, Brentwood, TN
Primary Contact: William E. Sheron, Chief Executive Officer
Web address: www.woosterhospital.org
**Control:** City–Government, nonfederal **Service:** General Medical and Surgical

> **Staffed Beds:** 152

## WRIGHT–PATTERSON AFB—Greene County

✠ **WRIGHT PATTERSON MEDICAL CENTER**, 4881 Sugar Maple Drive, Zip 45433–5529; tel. 937/257–9144 **A**1 2 3 5 **F**3 4 5 7 8 11 12 13 14 15 18 19 20 21 29 30 31 32 33 34 35 36 38 39 40 41 43 45 48 49 50 52 53 55 56 57 58 59 60 61 64 65 68 70 74 75 76 77 78 79 81 86 87 90 93 97 98 99 100 101 102 103 104 107 108 109 110 111 114 115 116 117 119 120 121 123 124 129 130 132 134 135 144 146 147 **S** Department of the Air Force, Washington, DC
Primary Contact: Colonel Brent J. Erickson, Administrator
COO: Colonel Brent J. Erickson, Administrator
CFO: Major Kelly Lesnick, Resource Manager Flight Commander
CMO: Gregory Sweitzer, Chief Medical Officer
CIO: John Beighle, Flight Chief Medical Information Systems
CHR: Hubert Chatman, Chief Civilian Personnel
CNO: Colonel Daniel Gerke, Chief Nursing Officer
Web address: www.wpafb.af.mil/units/wpmc/
**Control:** Air Force, Government, federal **Service:** General Medical and Surgical

> **Staffed Beds:** 62 **Admissions:** 3531 **Census:** 21 **Outpatient Visits:** 302644
> **Births:** 409 **Total Expense ($000):** 144526 **Payroll Expense ($000):**
> 144526 **Personnel:** 1740

## XENIA—Greene County

★ ○ **GREENE MEMORIAL HOSPITAL (360026)**, 1141 North Monroe Drive, Zip 45385–1600; tel. 937/352–2000 **A**2 3 5 9 10 11 **F**3 11 15 18 28 29 30 31 34 35 38 40 43 44 45 46 48 50 51 53 54 56 57 59 61 64 70 74 75 77 78 79 81 82 85 86 87 91 93 96 102 107 108 110 111 114 119 129 130 135 146 148 **S** Kettering Health Network, Dayton, OH
Primary Contact: Terry M. Burns, President
CFO: Ron D. Connovich, Chief Financial Officer
CMO: David Small, M.D., Chief Medical Officer
CIO: Andy Lehman, Senior Vice President Technology & Analytics
CHR: Jeff Jones, Director Human Resources
CNO: Brenda Kuhn, Ph.D., Chief Nursing Officer
Web address: www.ketteringhealth.org/greene
**Control:** Church–operated, Nongovernment, not–for profit **Service:** General Medical and Surgical

> **Staffed Beds:** 49 **Admissions:** 2097 **Census:** 21 **Outpatient Visits:** 98768
> **Births:** 0 **Total Expense ($000):** 64798 **Payroll Expense ($000):** 24924
> **Personnel:** 340

## YOUNGSTOWN—Trumbull County

☐ **BELMONT PINES HOSPITAL (364038)**, 615 Churchill–Hubbard Road, Zip 44505–1379; tel. 330/759–2700 **A**1 9 10 **F**1 4 16 17 29 30 38 50 59 64 67 70 72 73 76 80 87 88 89 90 98 99 101 102 104 105 106 128 130 **P**6 **S** Universal Health Services, Inc., King of Prussia, PA
Primary Contact: Lisa Cocca, Chief Executive Officer
CFO: Robin Stough, Chief Financial Officer
CMO: Phillip Maiden, M.D., Medical Director
Web address: www.belmontpines.com
**Control:** Corporation, Investor–owned, for–profit **Service:** Children's hospital psychiatric

> **Staffed Beds:** 96 **Admissions:** 1995 **Census:** 27 **Outpatient Visits:** 0 **Births:** 0

✚ **NORTHSIDE MEDICAL CENTER (360141)**, 500 Gypsy Lane, Zip 44504–1315; tel. 330/884–1000, (Includes NORTHSIDE MEDICAL CENTER, 500 Gypsy Lane, Zip 44501–0240; tel. 330/747–1444), (Nonreporting) **A**1 2 3 5 9 10 **S** Community Health Systems, Inc., Franklin, TN
Primary Contact: W. Trent Crable, Chief Executive Officer
CMO: Jay Osborne, M.D., Senior Vice President Medical Affairs
CHR: Lavern H. Carrera, Senior Vice President Human Resources
Web address: www.northsidemedicalcenter.net
**Control:** Corporation, Investor–owned, for–profit **Service:** General Medical and Surgical

> **Staffed Beds:** 373

**NORTHSIDE MEDICAL CENTER** See Northside Medical Center

✚ **SELECT SPECIALTY HOSPITAL–YOUNGSTOWN (262024)**, 1044 Belmont Avenue, Zip 44504–1006; tel. 330/480–2349, (Includes SELECT SPECIALTY HOSPITAL–YOUNGSTOWN, BOARDMAN CAMPUS, 667 Eastland Avenue S.E., Warren, Zip 44484–4503; tel. 330/729–1700), (Nonreporting) **A**1 10 **S** Select Medical Corporation, Mechanicsburg, PA
Primary Contact: Sharon Noro, Chief Executive Officer
Web address: www.selectspecialtyhospitals.com/company/locations/youngstown.aspx
**Control:** Corporation, Investor–owned, for–profit **Service:** Long–Term Acute Care hospital

> **Staffed Beds:** 51

✚ △ **ST. ELIZABETH HEALTH CENTER (360064)**, 1044 Belmont Avenue, Zip 44504–1096, Mailing Address: P.O. Box 1790, Zip 44501–1790; tel. 330/746–7211 **A**1 2 3 5 7 9 10 **F**1 3 7 8 11 12 14 15 17 18 20 22 24 26 28 29 30 31 34 35 39 40 42 43 44 45 46 47 49 50 51 53 54 56 57 58 59 60 61 64 66 68 70 71 74 75 77 78 79 81 82 84 85 86 87 88 89 90 92 93 96 97 98 100 101 102 103 107 108 110 111 114 115 117 118 119 120 121 123 124 126 129 130 131 132 135 143 146 147 148 **P**6 **S** Mercy Health, Cincinnati, OH
Primary Contact: Robert W. Shroder, President and Chief Executive Officer
COO: Donald E. Koenig, Jr., Executive Vice President and Chief Operating Officer
CFO: Matt Love, Senior Vice President Finance
CMO: Nicholas Kreatsoulas, M.D., Senior Vice President and Chief Medical Officer and Chief Quality Officer
CIO: Maureen Kordupel, Director Relationship Manager
CHR: Scott Dimmick, Senior Vice President Human Resources
CNO: Catherine L. Tolbert, R.N., Senior Vice President Nursing and Clinical Services and Chief Nurse Executive
Web address: www.mercy.com
**Control:** Church–operated, Nongovernment, not–for profit **Service:** General Medical and Surgical

> **Staffed Beds:** 362 **Admissions:** 17304 **Census:** 243 **Outpatient Visits:** 275940 **Births:** 477 **Total Expense ($000):** 292333 **Payroll Expense ($000):** 90575 **Personnel:** 1572

---

**Hospital, Medicare Provider Number, Address, Telephone, Approval, Facility, and Physician Codes, Health Care System**

★ American Hospital Association (AHA) membership
☐ The Joint Commission accreditation
○ Healthcare Facilities Accreditation Program
◇ DNV Healthcare Inc. accreditation
⇑ Center for Improvement in Healthcare Quality Accreditation
△ Commission on Accreditation of Rehabilitation Facilities (CARF) accreditation

☐ **SURGICAL HOSPITAL AT SOUTHWOODS (360352)**, 7630 Southern Boulevard, Zip 44512–5633; tel. 330/729–8000, (Nonreporting) **A**1 3 9 10
Primary Contact: Ed Muransky, Owner
Web address: www.surgeryatsouthwoods.com/
**Control:** Individual, Investor–owned, for–profit **Service:** Surgical

**Staffed Beds:** 12

---

**ZANESVILLE—Muskingum County**

★ ○ △ **GENESIS HEALTHCARE SYSTEM (360039)**, 2951 Maple Avenue, Zip 43701–1406; tel. 740/454–5000, (Includes BETHESDA HOSPITAL, 2951 Maple Avenue, Zip 43701–1465; tel. 614/454–4000; GOOD SAMARITAN MEDICAL AND REHABILITATION CENTER, 800 Forest Avenue, Zip 43701–2881; tel. 614/454–5000) **A**2 5 7 9 10 11 **F**3 5 8 9 11 13 15 17 18 20 22 24 26 28 29 30 31 32 34 35 36 40 43 44 45 46 47 48 50 51 54 57 58 59 60 63 64 65 68 70 73 74 75 76 77 78 79 80 81 82 84 85 86 87 89 90 91 92 93 94 96 98 99 100 101 102 103 104 105 107 108 109 110 111 114 115 116 117 118 119 120 121 123 124 126 129 130 131 132 135 144 146 147 148 **P**6 8 **S** Franciscan Sisters of Christian Charity Sponsored Ministries, Inc., Manitowoc, WI
Primary Contact: Matthew J. Perry, President and Chief Executive Officer
COO: Richard S. Helsper, Chief Operating Officer
CFO: Paul Masterson, Chief Financial Officer
CMO: Dan Scheerer, M.D., Chief Medical Officer
CIO: Edmund J. Romito, Chief Information Officer
CHR: Dianna LeVeck, Chief Human Resources Officer
CNO: Abby Nguyen, R.N., Chief Nursing Officer
Web address: www.genesishcs.org
**Control:** Other not–for–profit (including NFP Corporation) **Service:** General Medical and Surgical

**Staffed Beds:** 298 **Admissions:** 14828 **Census:** 166 **Outpatient Visits:** 399935 **Births:** 1532 **Total Expense ($000):** 314184 **Payroll Expense ($000):** 117474 **Personnel:** 2692

✼ **SELECT SPECIALTY HOSPITAL OF SOUTHEAST OHIO (362031)**, 800 Forest Avenue, 6th Floor, Zip 43701–2882; tel. 740/588–7888, (Nonreporting) **A**1 10 **S** Select Medical Corporation, Mechanicsburg, PA
Primary Contact: Linda Supplee, Chief Executive Officer
CMO: Armand Bermudez, M.D., Medical Director
CHR: Jacqueline Nezbeth, Human Resources Officer
CNO: Taryn Vierling, Chief Nursing Officer
Web address: www.selectspecialtyhospitals.com/company/locations/zanesville.aspx
**Control:** Corporation, Investor–owned, for–profit **Service:** Long–Term Acute Care hospital

**Staffed Beds:** 35

*Many Facility Codes have changed. Please refer to the AHA Guide Code Chart.*    © 2015 AHA Guide

# OKLAHOMA

## ADA—Pontotoc County

⊠ **CHICKASAW NATION MEDICAL CENTER (370180)**, 1921 Stonecipher Drive, Zip 74820–3439; tel. 580/436–3980 **A**1 10 **F**3 5 7 8 13 15 18 29 30 34 38 39 40 43 45 50 53 54 57 58 59 60 61 64 65 66 68 69 70 75 76 79 81 82 85 86 87 89 91 92 93 97 99 100 104 107 110 111 115 119 127 130 132 135 143 144 146 147 148
Primary Contact: Judy Goforth Parker, Ph.D., Secretary of Health
CFO: Marty Wafford, Executive Officer of Support and Programs
CMO: Richard McClain, M.D., Chief Medical Officer
CIO: Desiree Traylor, Chief Information Officer
CHR: Jalinda Kelley, Secretary of Interior Services
CNO: Jerod Waters, Chief Nursing Officer
Web address: www.chickasaw.net
**Control:** PHS, Indian Service, Government, federal **Service:** General Medical and Surgical

**Staffed Beds:** 72 **Admissions:** 3782 **Census:** 31 **Outpatient Visits:** 574887 **Births:** 765 **Total Expense ($000):** 171252 **Payroll Expense ($000):** 70740 **Personnel:** 566

⊠ **MERCY HOSPITAL ADA (370020)**, 430 North Monte Vista, Zip 74820–4610; tel. 580/332–2323 **A**1 2 9 10 **F**3 7 11 13 15 18 29 30 31 34 35 40 41 43 45 49 59 64 69 70 72 75 76 77 78 79 81 85 87 89 90 93 98 100 101 102 103 104 107 108 110 111 114 116 119 120 121 124 127 129 130 131 132 133 146 147 148 **P**6 **S** Mercy Health, Chesterfield, MO
Primary Contact: Lori Wightman, R.N., MSN, FACHE, Chief Executive Officer
COO: Daniel J. Coats, Vice President Operations
CFO: Mary Garber, Vice President Finance
CMO: Imtiaz Ahmed, Chief of Staff
CHR: Katrina Godfrey, Director Human Resources
CNO: Karen Sweeney, MSN, Vice President, Chief Nursing Officer
Web address: www.mercy.net/ada
**Control:** Church–operated, Nongovernment, not–for profit **Service:** General Medical and Surgical

**Staffed Beds:** 156 **Admissions:** 4484 **Census:** 56 **Outpatient Visits:** 76013 **Births:** 498 **Total Expense ($000):** 66312 **Payroll Expense ($000):** 29033 **Personnel:** 538

☐ **ROLLING HILLS HOSPITAL (374016)**, 1000 Rolling Hills Lane, Zip 74820–9415; tel. 580/436–3600 **A**1 9 10 **F**98 103 104 **S** Acadia Healthcare Company, Inc., Franklin, TN
Primary Contact: Selena Stockley, Chief Executive Officer
CMO: Robert Morton, M.D., Medical Director
CIO: Sherry Barnes, Director Health Information and Quality Management
CHR: Timothy Blackwell, Manager Human Resources
Web address: www.rollinghillshospital.com
**Control:** Corporation, Investor–owned, for–profit **Service:** Psychiatric

**Staffed Beds:** 44 **Admissions:** 1355 **Census:** 54

## ALTUS—Jackson County

⊠ **JACKSON COUNTY MEMORIAL HOSPITAL (370022)**, 1200 East Pecan Street, Zip 73521–6192, Mailing Address: P.O. Box 8190, Zip 73522–8190; tel. 580/379–5000 **A**1 3 5 9 10 **F**3 10 11 13 15 29 30 34 35 40 43 45 49 56 57 59 62 63 64 65 68 70 75 76 77 79 81 85 86 87 93 100 101 103 104 107 110 111 114 119 129 130 132 133 135 145 146 147 148 **P**6
Primary Contact: Steve L. Hartgraves, President and Chief Executive Officer
COO: Jim King, Executive Vice President and Chief Operating Officer
CFO: Nancy Davidson, Senior Vice President and Chief Financial Officer
CMO: Gregory D. Pickett, M.D., Chief of Staff
CIO: Dena Daniel, Director Information Systems
CHR: Richard Pope, Vice President Human Resources
CNO: Kay Bolding, R.N., Vice President Patient Care Services and Chief Nursing Officer
Web address: www.jcmh.com
**Control:** Hospital district or authority, Government, nonfederal **Service:** General Medical and Surgical

**Staffed Beds:** 69 **Admissions:** 3091 **Census:** 31 **Outpatient Visits:** 146178 **Births:** 444 **Total Expense ($000):** 66775 **Payroll Expense ($000):** 32699 **Personnel:** 632

## ALVA—Woods County

**SHARE MEDICAL CENTER (370080)**, 800 Share Drive, Zip 73717–3618, Mailing Address: P.O. Box 727, Zip 73717–0727; tel. 580/327–2800, (Total facility includes 65 beds in nursing home–type unit) **A**9 10 20 **F**3 15 29 30 34 40 45 57 59 63 64 65 67 69 81 85 87 93 97 100 104 107 110 119 129 130 133 146 148
Primary Contact: Kandice K. Allen, R.N., Chief Executive Officer
CFO: Kevin O'Brien, Chief Financial Officer
CMO: Elizabeth Kinzic, M.D., Chief of Staff
CIO: Alan Vaughan, Director Information Technology
CHR: Mary Herold, Director Human Resources
CNO: Regina Wilson, R.N., Director of Nursing
Web address: www.smcok.com
**Control:** Hospital district or authority, Government, nonfederal **Service:** General Medical and Surgical

**Staffed Beds:** 90 **Admissions:** 216 **Census:** 54 **Outpatient Visits:** 21056 **Births:** 0 **Total Expense ($000):** 11590 **Payroll Expense ($000):** 5435 **Personnel:** 160

## ANADARKO—Caddo County

**PHYSICIANS' HOSPITAL IN ANADARKO (371314)**, 1002 Central Boulevard East, Zip 73005–4496; tel. 405/247–2551 **A**9 10 18 **F**3 8 11 29 30 35 40 41 45 47 57 64 65 77 81 82 85 89 90 93 107 114 128 130 133 146 **S** Southern Plains Medical Group, Oklahoma City, OK
Primary Contact: Drew Flowers, Interim Administrator
Web address: www.anadarkohospital.com
**Control:** Other not–for–profit (including NFP Corporation) **Service:** General Medical and Surgical

**Staffed Beds:** 25 **Admissions:** 214 **Census:** 2 **Outpatient Visits:** 27823 **Births:** 0

## ANTLERS—Pushmataha County

**PUSHMATAHA HOSPITAL & HOME HEALTH (370083)**, 510 East Main Street, Zip 74523–3262, Mailing Address: P.O. Box 518, Zip 74523–0518; tel. 580/298–3341 **A**9 10 **F**3 8 11 34 39 40 45 57 59 64 65 81 107 119 128 133
Primary Contact: Paul Reano, Chief Executive Officer
COO: Nick Rowland, Chief Operating Officer
CFO: Rory Ward, Chief Financial Officer
CMO: G. Wayne Flatt, D.O., Chief Medical Director
CHR: Paula Schalski, Director Human Resources
CNO: Marla Barnes, Director of Nursing
Web address: www.pushhospital.com
**Control:** City–County, Government, nonfederal **Service:** General Medical and Surgical

**Staffed Beds:** 25 **Admissions:** 646 **Census:** 6 **Outpatient Visits:** 5197 **Births:** 0 **Total Expense ($000):** 7159 **Payroll Expense ($000):** 2541 **Personnel:** 71

## ARDMORE—Carter County

⊠ **MERCY HOSPITAL ARDMORE (370047)**, 1011 14th Avenue N.W., Zip 73401–1828; tel. 580/223–5400 **A**1 9 10 **F**3 8 11 13 15 18 20 22 28 29 30 31 34 40 41 43 45 47 49 57 59 62 64 70 74 76 78 79 81 82 83 84 85 87 89 90 91 93 98 103 107 108 110 111 114 117 118 119 120 121 123 126 129 130 146 148 **P**6 **S** Mercy Health, Chesterfield, MO
Primary Contact: Daryle Voss, FACHE, President
CFO: Karen Hendren, Vice President of Finance and Operations
CMO: Pam Kimbrough, M.D., Vice President Medical Affairs
CHR: Melinda Sharum, Director of Human Resources
CNO: Debra Pender, R.N., Vice President of Nursing
Web address: www.mercyok.net
**Control:** Church–operated, Nongovernment, not–for profit **Service:** General Medical and Surgical

**Staffed Beds:** 190 **Admissions:** 7615 **Census:** 89 **Outpatient Visits:** 132423 **Births:** 897 **Total Expense ($000):** 122792 **Payroll Expense ($000):** 38184 **Personnel:** 715

---

**Hospital, Medicare Provider Number, Address, Telephone, Approval, Facility, and Physician Codes, Health Care System**

★ American Hospital Association (AHA) membership
☐ The Joint Commission accreditation
◯ Healthcare Facilities Accreditation Program
◇ DNV Healthcare Inc. accreditation
⇑ Center for Improvement in Healthcare Quality Accreditation
△ Commission on Accreditation of Rehabilitation Facilities (CARF) accreditation

## ATOKA—Atoka County

★ **ATOKA COUNTY MEDICAL CENTER (371300)**, 1200 West Liberty Road, Zip 74525–1621; tel. 580/889–3333 **A**9 10 18 **F**3 34 40 45 46 53 56 57 59 64 81 85 103 104 107 114 119 133 146
Primary Contact: Paul Reano, Chief Executive Officer
CFO: Rory Ward, Chief Financial Officer
CMO: Ted Rowland, Chief of Medical Staff
CIO: Owetha Wilson, Chief Information Officer
CHR: Paula Schalski, Director Human Resources
CNO: Beverly Pickett, R.N., Chief Nursing Officer
Web address: www.atokamedicalcenter.org
**Control:** Hospital district or authority, Government, nonfederal **Service:** General Medical and Surgical

**Staffed Beds:** 25 **Admissions:** 848 **Census:** 8 **Outpatient Visits:** 12421 **Births:** 1 **Total Expense ($000):** 11652 **Payroll Expense ($000):** 3094 **Personnel:** 93

## BARTLESVILLE—Washington County

★ ◇ **JANE PHILLIPS MEDICAL CENTER (370018)**, 3500 East Frank Phillips Boulevard, Zip 74006–2411; tel. 918/333–7200 **A**3 5 9 10 21 **F**3 8 11 13 15 17 18 20 22 24 28 29 30 31 34 35 40 43 46 49 50 51 53 57 58 59 60 61 62 64 68 74 75 76 77 78 79 81 82 84 85 86 87 90 92 93 96 98 102 103 107 111 114 115 116 117 118 119 121 123 127 129 130 131 135 143 145 146 147 148 **P**4 **S** Ascension Health, Saint Louis, MO
Primary Contact: Mike Moore, President and Chief Operating Officer
CFO: James Brasel, Chief Financial Officer
CMO: Paul McQuillen, M.D., Chief Medical Officer
CIO: Rob Poole, Director
CHR: Jennifer Workman, Director Human Resources
Web address: www.jpmc.org
**Control:** Church–operated, Nongovernment, not–for profit **Service:** General Medical and Surgical

**Staffed Beds:** 119 **Admissions:** 4907 **Census:** 48 **Outpatient Visits:** 87037 **Births:** 652 **Total Expense ($000):** 99733 **Payroll Expense ($000):** 38390 **Personnel:** 684

## BEAVER—Beaver County

**BEAVER COUNTY MEMORIAL HOSPITAL (371322)**, 212 East Eighth Street, Zip 73932, Mailing Address: P.O. Box 640, Zip 73932–0640; tel. 580/625–4551, (Nonreporting) **A**9 10 18
Primary Contact: Alissa Schlessman, Administrator
CMO: Gary Mathews, M.D., Medical Doctor
CHR: Karla Leisher, Business Office Manager
CNO: Stacey Perry, Director of Nursing
Web address: www.beavercountyhospitalauthority.com
**Control:** Hospital district or authority, Government, nonfederal **Service:** General Medical and Surgical

**Staffed Beds:** 24

## BETHANY—Oklahoma County

△ **THE CHILDREN'S CENTER REHABILITATION HOSPITAL (373302)**, 6800 N.W. 39th Expressway, Zip 73008–2513; tel. 405/789–6711 **A**5 7 9 10 **F**1 29 30 35 39 53 59 68 74 75 79 84 87 90 91 93 96 107 130 146 148 **P**6
Primary Contact: Albert Gray, Chief Executive Officer
Web address: www.tccokc.org
**Control:** Other not–for–profit (including NFP Corporation) **Service:** Children's general

**Staffed Beds:** 120 **Admissions:** 231 **Census:** 102 **Outpatient Visits:** 8435 **Births:** 0 **Total Expense ($000):** 30706 **Payroll Expense ($000):** 19155 **Personnel:** 442

## BLACKWELL—Kay County

⊞ **ALLIANCEHEALTH BLACKWELL (370030)**, 710 South 13th Street, Zip 74631–3700; tel. 580/363–2311 **A**1 9 10 **F**3 15 29 30 34 40 57 59 62 64 65 79 81 107 108 111 119 128 129 130 133 146 **P**5 6 **S** Community Health Systems, Inc., Franklin, TN
Primary Contact: Andrew Wachtel, Chief Executive Officer
CFO: Sheryl Schmidtberger, Chief Financial Officer
CMO: Samuel Hague, M.D., Chief of Staff
CHR: Karen Ware, Director Human Resources
Web address: www.integris-health.com
**Control:** Corporation, Investor–owned, for–profit **Service:** General Medical and Surgical

**Staffed Beds:** 49 **Admissions:** 558 **Census:** 7 **Outpatient Visits:** 13013 **Births:** 0 **Total Expense ($000):** 9584 **Payroll Expense ($000):** 3263 **Personnel:** 70

## BOISE CITY—Cimarron County

**CIMARRON MEMORIAL HOSPITAL (371307)**, 100 South Ellis Street, Zip 73933, Mailing Address: P.O. Box 1059, Zip 73933–1059; tel. 580/544–2501 **A**9 10 18 **F**3 15 29 32 34 40 41 50 57 59 64 65 68 75 85 93 97 107 117 119 127 130 131 133 148 **P**1
Primary Contact: Tim Beard, Chief Executive Officer
CFO: John Dolan, Chief Financial Officer
CIO: Tim Beard, Director, Information Technology
CNO: Barbara Carter, Chief Nursing Officer
Web address: www.cimarronmemorialhospital.org
**Control:** County–Government, nonfederal **Service:** General Medical and Surgical

**Staffed Beds:** 25 **Admissions:** 175 **Census:** 3 **Outpatient Visits:** 319 **Births:** 0

## BRISTOW—Creek County

**BRISTOW MEDICAL CENTER (370041)**, 700 West 7th Avenue, Suite 6, Zip 74010–2302; tel. 918/367–2215, (Nonreporting) **A**9 10
Primary Contact: Jan Winter–Clark, Chief Executive Officer
CFO: Robin Van Vickle, Chief Financial Officer
Web address: www.bristowmedcenter.com
**Control:** Corporation, Investor–owned, for–profit **Service:** General Medical and Surgical

**Staffed Beds:** 30

## BROKEN ARROW—Tulsa County

★ ◇ **ST. JOHN BROKEN ARROW (370235)**, 1000 West Boise Circle, Zip 74012–4900; tel. 918/994–8100 **A**9 10 21 **F**3 8 11 14 15 18 29 30 34 35 37 40 43 45 50 57 59 64 65 68 74 79 81 84 85 87 93 94 107 108 110 111 114 115 119 130 132 135 143 146 **P**1 5 **S** Ascension Health, Saint Louis, MO
Primary Contact: David L. Phillips, Chief Executive Officer
CFO: Michael R. Nevins, Chief Financial Officer
CMO: Todd Hoffman, M.D., Medical Director
CNO: Dwan Borens, Director of Nursing
Web address: www.stjohnbrokenarrow.com
**Control:** Church–operated, Nongovernment, not–for profit **Service:** General Medical and Surgical

**Staffed Beds:** 44 **Admissions:** 2608 **Census:** 17 **Outpatient Visits:** 85347 **Births:** 0 **Total Expense ($000):** 50860 **Payroll Expense ($000):** 12420 **Personnel:** 237

## BUFFALO—Harper County

★ **HARPER COUNTY COMMUNITY HOSPITAL (371324)**, Highway 64 North, Zip 73834, Mailing Address: P.O. Box 60, Zip 73834–0060; tel. 580/735–2555 **A**9 10 18 **F**40 68 69 75 93 97 107 128 133 135 **P**6
Primary Contact: Georganna Buss, Chief Executive Officer
COO: Pam Dodd, Chief Operating Officer
CFO: Lisa Oakley, Chief Financial Officer
CNO: Melissa Madrid, R.N., Chief Nursing Officer
Web address: www.hcchospital.com/
**Control:** County–Government, nonfederal **Service:** General Medical and Surgical

**Staffed Beds:** 16 **Admissions:** 153 **Census:** 2 **Births:** 0

## CARNEGIE—Caddo County

**CARNEGIE TRI–COUNTY MUNICIPAL HOSPITAL (371334)**, 102 North Broadway, Zip 73015, Mailing Address: P.O. Box 97, Zip 73015–0097; tel. 580/654–1050, (Nonreporting) **A**9 10 18
Primary Contact: Bart Daugherty, Interim Administratorr
**Control:** City–Government, nonfederal **Service:** General Medical and Surgical

**Staffed Beds:** 19

## CHEYENNE—Roger Mills County

★ **ROGER MILLS MEMORIAL HOSPITAL (371303)**, Fifth and L. L Males Avenue, Zip 73628; tel. 580/497–3336 **A**9 10 18 **F**3 7 34 40 57 59 64 65 93 107 115 133
Primary Contact: Cynthia Duncan, Chief Executive Officer
Web address: www.rogermillsmemorialhospital.com/
**Control:** Hospital district or authority, Government, nonfederal **Service:** General Medical and Surgical

**Staffed Beds:** 15 **Admissions:** 39 **Census:** 1 **Outpatient Visits:** 3035 **Births:** 0 **Total Expense ($000):** 4325 **Payroll Expense ($000):** 2359 **Personnel:** 50

*Many Facility Codes have changed. Please refer to the AHA Guide Code Chart.* © 2015 AHA Guide

## CHICKASHA—Grady County

★ **GRADY MEMORIAL HOSPITAL (370054)**, 2220 West Iowa Avenue,
Zip 73018–2738; tel. 405/224–2300 **A**9 10 **F**3 8 11 13 15 17 29 30 34 35
40 43 45 57 59 60 65 68 69 70 73 76 79 81 82 85 87 89 91 92 93 107
110 111 114 115 119 127 128 129 130 131 132 133 144 146 147 148 **P**6
Primary Contact: Warren K. Spellman, Chief Executive Officer
CFO: Linda Hart, Vice President Finance
CMO: Thomas Essex, M.D., Chief of Staff
CIO: Sylvia Ho, Director Health Information Systems
CHR: Rebel Rutledge, Director Human Resources
CNO: Cathy Groseclose, Vice President Patient Care Serivces
Web address: www.gradymem.org
**Control:** Hospital district or authority, Government, nonfederal **Service:** General
Medical and Surgical

**Staffed Beds:** 52 **Admissions:** 1673 **Census:** 16 **Outpatient Visits:** 76190
**Births:** 302 **Total Expense ($000):** 41891 **Payroll Expense ($000):** 20775
**Personnel:** 341

## CLAREMORE—Rogers County

☐ **CLAREMORE INDIAN HOSPITAL (370173)**, 101 South Moore Avenue,
Zip 74017–5091; tel. 918/342–6200, (Nonreporting) **A**1 10 **S** U. S. Indian Health
Service, Rockville, MD
Primary Contact: George Valliere, Chief Executive Officer
CFO: LaLana Spears, Supervisor Accounting
CIO: David Ponder, Information Technology Officer
CHR: Quinn Proctor, Director Human Resources
CNO: Tamara Wampler, Chief Nursing Executive
Web address: www.ihs.gov
**Control:** PHS, Indian Service, Government, federal **Service:** General Medical and
Surgical

**Staffed Beds:** 44

★ ◇ **HILLCREST HOSPITAL CLAREMORE (370039)**, 1202 North Muskogee
Place, Zip 74017–3036; tel. 918/341–2556 **A**9 10 21 **F**3 11 13 15 18 20 22
26 28 29 30 34 35 37 40 45 49 51 59 64 70 74 76 77 79 81 82 85 86 87
93 98 103 107 108 110 111 119 126 129 130 131 133 135 145 146 147
148 **P**6 **S** Ardent Health Services, Nashville, TN
Primary Contact: David Chaussard, Chief Executive Officer
CFO: Brandon Bullard, Chief Financial Officer
CIO: Celeste Rodden, Chief Information Officer
CHR: Pat Goad, Director Human Resources
CNO: Randy Walker, Chief Nursing Officer
Web address: www.hillcrestclaremore.com
**Control:** Corporation, Investor–owned, for–profit **Service:** General Medical and
Surgical

**Staffed Beds:** 67 **Admissions:** 3057 **Census:** 32 **Outpatient Visits:** 40254
**Births:** 663 **Total Expense ($000):** 37918 **Payroll Expense ($000):** 15193
**Personnel:** 295

## CLEVELAND—Pawnee County

★ **CLEVELAND AREA HOSPITAL (371320)**, 1401 West Pawnee Street,
Zip 74020–3019; tel. 918/358–2501 **A**9 10 18 **F**5 11 15 29 34 35 38 40 45
50 53 57 59 64 77 81 85 87 93 100 101 102 103 107 110 114 119 128
130 133 147 148
Primary Contact: Edred Benton, Chief Exeutive Officer and Chief Operating Officer
COO: Edred Benton, Chief Executive Officer and Chief Operating Officer
CMO: Jason Sims, M.D., Chief Medical Officer
CHR: Sherry Brown, Director Human Resources
Web address: www.clevelandareahospital.com
**Control:** Hospital district or authority, Government, nonfederal **Service:** General
Medical and Surgical

**Staffed Beds:** 14 **Admissions:** 194 **Census:** 4 **Outpatient Visits:** 5093
**Births:** 0 **Personnel:** 82

## CLINTON—Custer County

⊞ **ALLIANCEHEALTH CLINTON (370029)**, 100 North 30th Street,
Zip 73601–3117, Mailing Address: P.O. Box 1569, Zip 73601–1569;
tel. 580/323–2363 **A**1 9 10 **F**3 11 13 29 30 31 34 35 40 45 59 62 63 68 70
75 76 77 78 81 90 93 107 108 111 119 121 123 129 130 131 133 146 147
148 **P**6 **S** Community Health Systems, Inc., Franklin, TN
Primary Contact: Cameron Lewis, Chief Executive Officer
CFO: Jay Johnson, Chief Financial Officer
CHR: Julie Graumann, Director
Web address: www.alliancehealthclinton.com
**Control:** Corporation, Investor–owned, for–profit **Service:** General Medical and
Surgical

**Staffed Beds:** 49 **Admissions:** 1391 **Census:** 13

## COALGATE—Coal County

★ **COAL COUNTY GENERAL HOSPITAL (371319)**, 6 North Covington Street,
Zip 74538–2002, Mailing Address: P.O. Box 326, Zip 74538–0326;
tel. 580/927–2327, (Nonreporting) **A**10 18
Primary Contact: Billy Johnson, Chief Executive Officer
CFO: Diane Downard, Chief Financial Officer
CMO: R.J Helton, D.O., Chief of Staff
CIO: Matt Balliett, Chief Information Officer
CHR: Cyndie Martin, Director
CNO: Farra Ybarra, R.N., Chief Nursing Officer
Web address: www.hillcrest.com
**Control:** Other not–for–profit (including NFP Corporation) **Service:** General
Medical and Surgical

**Staffed Beds:** 20

## CORDELL—Washita County

★ **CORDELL MEMORIAL HOSPITAL (371325)**, 1220 North Glenn English Street,
Zip 73632–2010; tel. 580/832–3339 **A**9 10 18 **F**7 40 57 59 65 107 133
Primary Contact: Landon Hise, Chief Executive Officer
CFO: Sue Kelley, Chief Financial Officer
**Control:** City–Government, nonfederal **Service:** General Medical and Surgical

**Staffed Beds:** 25 **Admissions:** 206 **Census:** 3 **Outpatient Visits:** 4984
**Births:** 0

## CUSHING—Payne County

★ **HILLCREST HOSPITAL CUSHING (370099)**, 1027 East Cherry Street,
Zip 74023–4101, Mailing Address: P.O. Box 1409, Zip 74023–1409;
tel. 918/225–2915 **A**9 10 **F**11 13 15 18 29 30 31 34 35 40 43 44 45 46 50
51 56 57 59 64 65 66 68 70 71 75 78 81 82 86 87 93 94 97 98 100 101
102 103 106 107 110 111 114 115 119 129 130 143 145 146 147 148
**S** Ardent Health Services, Nashville, TN
Primary Contact: Kevin Hawk, Chief Executive Officer
CFO: Joseph Mendoza, Chief Financial Officer
CHR: Jennifer Strope, Manager Human Resources
CNO: Tina Petersen, Chief Nursing Officer
Web address: www.hillcrestcushing.com/
**Control:** Corporation, Investor–owned, for–profit **Service:** General Medical and
Surgical

**Staffed Beds:** 95 **Admissions:** 1827 **Census:** 22 **Outpatient Visits:** 18744
**Births:** 167 **Total Expense ($000):** 24310 **Payroll Expense ($000):** 8724
**Personnel:** 167

## DRUMRIGHT—Creek County

**DRUMRIGHT REGIONAL HOSPITAL (371331)**, 610 West Bypass,
Zip 74030–5957; tel. 918/382–2300, (Nonreporting) **A**9 10 18 **S** Rural
Community Hospitals of America, Kansas City, MO
Primary Contact: William Holland, Chief Executive Officer
CFO: Mark Conrath, Chief Financial Officer
Web address: www.drumrighthospital.com/
**Control:** Corporation, Investor–owned, for–profit **Service:** General Medical and
Surgical

**Staffed Beds:** 15

## DUNCAN—Stephens County

⊞ △ **DUNCAN REGIONAL HOSPITAL (370023)**, 1407 North Whisenant Drive,
Zip 73533–1650, Mailing Address: P.O. Box 2000, Zip 73534–2000;
tel. 580/252–5300, (Total facility includes 16 beds in nursing home–type unit) **A**1
5 7 9 10 20 **F**3 11 13 15 18 28 29 30 34 35 40 43 45 50 57 59 62 63 64
70 75 76 77 79 81 85 86 87 90 93 96 98 103 104 107 108 110 111 114
115 119 128 129 130 131 132 141 142 143 145 146 147 148 **P**6
Primary Contact: Jay R. Johnson, FACHE, President and Chief Executive Officer
CFO: Douglas R. Volinski, Vice President and Chief Financial Officer
CIO: Roger Neal, Vice President and Chief Information Officer
CHR: Mark Rhoades, Vice President and Chief Human Resources Officer
CNO: Cindy Rauh, R.N., Vice President and Chief Nursing Officer
Web address: www.duncanregional.com
**Control:** Other not–for–profit (including NFP Corporation) **Service:** General
Medical and Surgical

**Staffed Beds:** 117 **Admissions:** 4015 **Census:** 51 **Outpatient Visits:** 144290
**Births:** 573 **Total Expense ($000):** 87701 **Payroll Expense ($000):** 39101
**Personnel:** 825

---

**Hospital, Medicare Provider Number, Address, Telephone, Approval, Facility, and Physician Codes, Health Care System**

★ American Hospital Association (AHA) membership    ○ Healthcare Facilities Accreditation Program    ⇑ Center for Improvement in Healthcare Quality Accreditation
☐ The Joint Commission accreditation    ◇ DNV Healthcare Inc. accreditation    △ Commission on Accreditation of Rehabilitation Facilities (CARF) accreditation

OK

### DURANT—Bryan County

✠ **ALLIANCEHEALTH DURANT (370014)**, 1800 University Boulevard,
Zip 74701–3006, Mailing Address: P.O. Box 1207, Zip 74702–1207;
tel. 580/924–3080 **A**1 5 9 10 13 19 **F**3 11 12 13 15 17 18 20 28 29 39 40
43 45 51 59 70 74 75 76 79 80 81 85 86 89 107 108 110 111 115 118 119
126 129 130 135 145 146 147 148 **P**8 **S** Community Health Systems, Inc.,
Franklin, TN
Primary Contact: Jeff Tarrant, Chief Executive Officer
CFO: Cindy Rios, Chief Financial Officer
CMO: Kevin Gordon, M.D., Chief of Staff
CIO: Katy Stinson, Director Information Services
Web address: www.mymcso.com
**Control:** Corporation, Investor–owned, for–profit **Service:** General Medical and
Surgical

**Staffed Beds:** 148 **Admissions:** 5408 **Census:** 54 **Outpatient Visits:** 56930
**Births:** 987 **Personnel:** 382

### EDMOND—Oklahoma County

☐ **AMG SPECIALTY HOSPITAL–EDMOND (372005)**, 1100 East Ninth Street,
Zip 73034–5755; tel. 405/341–8150, (Nonreporting) **A**1 9 10 **S** AMG Integrated
Healthcare Management, Lafayette, LA
Primary Contact: Michael E. Gerten, Chief Executive Officer
CFO: Rowena Davidson, Manager Business Office
CMO: Brian Levy, M.D., Medical Director
CHR: Pam Grimes, Director Human Resources
Web address: www.amgedmond.com/
**Control:** Corporation, Investor–owned, for–profit **Service:** Long–Term Acute Care
hospital

**Staffed Beds:** 37

**EDMOND MEDICAL CENTER** See OU Medical Center Edmond

✠ **INTEGRIS HEALTH EDMOND (370236)**, 4801 Integris Parkway,
Zip 73034–8864; tel. 405/657–3000 **A**1 9 10 **F**3 8 13 15 18 20 22 29 30 34
35 40 42 43 46 49 50 59 60 68 70 76 79 81 82 85 87 93 102 107 110 111
119 130 132 135 146 **P**6 7 **S** INTEGRIS Health, Oklahoma City, OK
Primary Contact: Avilla Williams, MS, President
CNO: Angela K. Kamermayer, MS, Chief Nursing Officer
Web address: www.integrisok.com/edmond
**Control:** Other not–for–profit (including NFP Corporation) **Service:** General
Medical and Surgical

**Staffed Beds:** 40 **Admissions:** 1681 **Census:** 15 **Outpatient Visits:** 27852
**Births:** 454 **Total Expense ($000):** 35409 **Payroll Expense ($000):** 12417
**Personnel:** 269

**OU MEDICAL CENTER EDMOND** See OU Medical Center, Oklahoma City

★ **SUMMIT MEDICAL CENTER (370225)**, 1800 South Renaissance Boulevard,
Zip 73013–3023; tel. 405/359–2400 **A**9 10 **F**3 12 29 40 41 45 54 64 70 75
79 81 82 85 89 107 111 119 127 129 148
Primary Contact: Curtis Summers, Chief Executive Officer
Web address: www.summitmedcenter.com/
**Control:** Individual, Investor–owned, for–profit **Service:** General Medical and
Surgical

**Staffed Beds:** 15 **Admissions:** 233 **Census:** 1 **Outpatient Visits:** 20132
**Births:** 0

### EL RENO—Canadian County

★ **MERCY HOSPITAL EL RENO (370011)**, 2115 Parkview Drive,
Zip 73036–2199, Mailing Address: P.O. Box 129, Zip 73036–0129;
tel. 405/262–2640 **A**9 10 **F**3 7 8 11 29 30 34 35 40 41 43 45 46 50 57 59
62 63 64 65 68 74 75 77 79 81 82 85 91 93 107 111 119 130 132 135 146
**S** Mercy Health, Chesterfield, MO
Primary Contact: Doug Danker, Administrator
CMO: Michael Dean Sullivan, M.D., Chief of Staff
CIO: Karen Heldreth, Director Data Processing
CHR: Wendy Ward, Director Human Resources
Web address: www.mercyok.net
**Control:** Church–operated, Nongovernment, not–for profit **Service:** General
Medical and Surgical

**Staffed Beds:** 48 **Admissions:** 533 **Census:** 5 **Outpatient Visits:** 25093
**Births:** 0 **Total Expense ($000):** 12170 **Payroll Expense ($000):** 6413
**Personnel:** 111

**PARKVIEW HOSPITAL** See Mercy Hospital El Reno

### ELK CITY—Beckham County

✠ **GREAT PLAINS REGIONAL MEDICAL CENTER (370019)**, 1801 West Third
Street, Zip 73644–5145, Mailing Address: P.O. Box 2339, Zip 73648–2339;
tel. 580/225–2511 **A**1 3 9 10 **F**3 11 13 15 18 20 22 26 29 30 31 34 35 40
43 47 50 51 56 57 59 62 64 68 70 75 76 77 78 79 81 82 85 87 89 91 93
96 98 100 101 102 103 107 108 110 111 115 118 119 120 121 123 129
130 131 132 133 135 146 147 148
Primary Contact: Corey Lively, Chief Executive Officer
COO: Misty Carter, Director Human Resources and Chief Operating Officer
CFO: Monica Scott, Chief Financial Officer
CIO: Terry Davis, Chief Information Officer
CHR: Misty Carter, Director Human Resources
CNO: Laura Kurzendoerfer, R.N., Chief Nursing Officer
Web address: www.gprmc-ok.com
**Control:** Other not–for–profit (including NFP Corporation) **Service:** General
Medical and Surgical

**Staffed Beds:** 46 **Admissions:** 1753 **Census:** 19 **Outpatient Visits:** 53853
**Births:** 417 **Total Expense ($000):** 45055 **Payroll Expense ($000):** 16058
**Personnel:** 375

### ENID—Garfield County

**INTEGRIS BASS BEHAVIORAL HEALTH SYSTEM** See Integris Bass
Meadowlake

✠ **INTEGRIS BASS BAPTIST HEALTH CENTER (370016)**, 600 South Monroe
Street, Zip 73701–7211, Mailing Address: P.O. Box 3168, Zip 73702–3168;
tel. 580/233–2300 **A**1 9 10 13 19 **F**3 11 13 15 17 18 20 22 24 28 29 30 31
35 40 43 45 49 57 62 68 70 74 75 76 77 78 79 81 85 98 99 103 107 108
111 114 117 118 119 120 121 127 128 129 132 144 146 147 148
**S** INTEGRIS Health, Oklahoma City, OK
Primary Contact: Edward Herrman, R.N., FACHE, President
CFO: Duane Miller, Chief Financial Officer
CNO: Cynthia Leathers, R.N., Chief Nursing Officer
Web address: www.integris–health.com
**Control:** Other not–for–profit (including NFP Corporation) **Service:** General
Medical and Surgical

**Staffed Beds:** 167 **Admissions:** 4656 **Census:** 86 **Outpatient Visits:** 64367
**Total Expense ($000):** 108728 **Payroll Expense ($000):** 50692 **Personnel:**
617

☐ **INTEGRIS BASS PAVILION (372016)**, 401 South Third Street,
Zip 73701–5737; tel. 580/249–4260 **A**1 9 10 **F**1 11 29 30 40 43 68 75 77
82 85 93 132 146 148
Primary Contact: Edward Herrman, R.N., FACHE, President
CFO: Duane Miller, Chief Financial Officer
CHR: Stacy Froese, Regional Director Human Resources
CNO: Cynthia Leathers, R.N., Chief Nursing Officer
Web address: www.integris–health.com/integris/en–us/locations/bass–enid
**Control:** Other not–for–profit (including NFP Corporation) **Service:** Long–Term
Acute Care hospital

**Staffed Beds:** 24 **Admissions:** 165 **Census:** 11 **Outpatient Visits:** 0 **Births:**
0 **Total Expense ($000):** 6230 **Payroll Expense ($000):** 3473 **Personnel:**
58

☐ △ **ST. MARY'S REGIONAL MEDICAL CENTER (370026)**, 305 South Fifth
Street, Zip 73701–5899, Mailing Address: P.O. Box 232, Zip 73702–0232;
tel. 580/233–6100 **A**1 7 9 10 **F**3 11 13 15 17 18 20 22 26 28 29 30 31 34
35 39 40 43 45 51 53 54 57 59 60 64 68 69 70 73 74 75 76 77 78 79 80
81 82 85 86 87 89 90 91 92 93 96 100 107 108 110 111 114 115 118 119
129 130 131 132 135 146 147 **P**6 **S** Universal Health Services, Inc., King of
Prussia, PA
Primary Contact: Stanley D. Tatum, FACHE, Chief Executive Officer
COO: Krista Roberts, Chief Operating Officer
CFO: David Jamin, Chief Financial Officer
CMO: Tim Teske, D.O., Chief of Staff
CIO: Tracy Andersen, Chief Information Officer
CHR: Linda Hoag, Director Human Resources
CNO: Douglas W. Coffey, R.N., Chief Nursing Officer
Web address: www.stmarysregional.com
**Control:** Corporation, Investor–owned, for–profit **Service:** General Medical and
Surgical

**Staffed Beds:** 149 **Admissions:** 4404 **Census:** 58 **Outpatient Visits:** 67012
**Births:** 365 **Total Expense ($000):** 73835 **Payroll Expense ($000):** 28693
**Personnel:** 448

### EUFAULA—Mcintosh County

**EPIC MEDICAL CENTER (370169)**, 1 Hospital Drive, Zip 74432–4010, Mailing
Address: P.O. Box 629, Zip 74432–0629; tel. 918/689–2535 **A**9 10 **F**40 45
Primary Contact: Vicki Schaff, Chief Operating Officer
COO: Vicki Schaff, Chief Operating Officer
CHR: Sondra Edwards, Human Resources Supervisor
CNO: Kelly Teal, Chief Nursing Officer
Web address: www.epichealthcare.net
**Control:** Corporation, Investor–owned, for–profit **Service:** General Medical and
Surgical

**Staffed Beds:** 33 **Admissions:** 135 **Census:** 1 **Outpatient Visits:** 9427
**Births:** 0 **Total Expense ($000):** 3652 **Payroll Expense ($000):** 1889
**Personnel:** 46

*Many Facility Codes have changed. Please refer to the AHA Guide Code Chart.* © 2015 AHA Guide

## FAIRFAX—Osage County

**FAIRFAX COMMUNITY HOSPITAL (371318)**, 40 Hospital Road, Zip 74637–5084; tel. 918/642–3291 **A**9 10 18 **F**3 29 40 45 57 77 81 90 93 107 117 128 129 133 **S** Rural Community Hospitals of America, Kansas City, MO
Primary Contact: Tina Steele, Chief Executive Officer and Chief Financial Officer
COO: Linda Thompson, Chief Operating Officer
CFO: Tina Steele, Chief Executive Officer and Chief Financial Officer
CMO: Arman Janloo, M.D., Chief Medical Staff
CIO: Lisa Drymon, Manager
CHR: Sharon Binkley, Director Human Resources
**Control:** Corporation, Investor–owned, for–profit **Service:** General Medical and Surgical

**Staffed Beds:** 15 **Admissions:** 169 **Census:** 3 **Outpatient Visits:** 6059
**Births:** 0 **Total Expense ($000):** 5679 **Payroll Expense ($000):** 2765
**Personnel:** 46

**FAIRFAX MEMORIAL HOSPITAL** See Fairfax Community Hospital

## FAIRVIEW—Major County

**FAIRVIEW REGIONAL MEDICAL CENTER (371329)**, 523 East State Road, Zip 73737–1453, Mailing Address: P.O. Box 548, Zip 73737–0548; tel. 580/227–3721 **A**9 10 18 **F**3 28 34 40 43 45 57 59 64 65 69 75 77 81 82 84 85 91 93 107 114 127 128 131 133 135 146 **P**5 6
Primary Contact: Roger Knak, Administrator
CFO: Christie Schakelaar, Chief Financial Officer
CMO: Solomon Ali, M.D., Chief of Staff
CIO: Bob Maynard, Chief Information Officer
CNO: Tamara Eitzen, Chief Nursing Officer
Web address: www.fairviewregionalmedicalcenter.com
**Control:** Hospital district or authority, Government, nonfederal **Service:** General Medical and Surgical

**Staffed Beds:** 25 **Admissions:** 174 **Census:** 2 **Outpatient Visits:** 10194
**Births:** 0 **Total Expense ($000):** 5838 **Payroll Expense ($000):** 3003
**Personnel:** 64

## FORT SILL—Comanche County

☒ **REYNOLDS ARMY COMMUNITY HOSPITAL**, 4301 Wilson Street, Zip 73503–4472; tel. 580/558–3000, (Nonreporting) **A**1 3 5 **S** Department of the Army, Office of the Surgeon General, Falls Church, VA
Primary Contact: Colonel Noel J. Cardenas, FACHE, Commander and Chief Executive Officer
COO: Lieutenant Jennifer R. House, Chief Operations and Readiness
CFO: Lieutenant Colonel David Rollins, Chief Resource Management Division
CMO: Lieutenant Colonel Timothy Switaj, Deputy Commander for Clinical Services
CIO: Russell Seymour, Chief Information Management Division
CHR: Jacqueline V. Jones, Chief Civilian Personnel Branch
CNO: Lieutenant Colonel Richard A. Behr, Deputy Commander for Health Services
Web address: www.rach.sill.amedd.army.mil
**Control:** Army, Government, federal **Service:** General Medical and Surgical

**Staffed Beds:** 24

## FORT SUPPLY— County

**NORTHWEST CENTER FOR BEHAVIORAL HEALTH (374001)**, 1 Mi East Highway 270, Zip 73841; tel. 580/766–2311 **A**10 **F**98 104 106 130 135 **P**6 **S** Oklahoma Department of Mental Health and Substance Abuse Services, Oklahoma City, OK
Primary Contact: Trudy Hoffman, Executive Director
Web address: www.ncbhok.org/
**Control:** State–Government, nonfederal **Service:** Psychiatric

**Staffed Beds:** 28 **Admissions:** 735 **Census:** 25 **Outpatient Visits:** 43557
**Births:** 0 **Total Expense ($000):** 13665 **Payroll Expense ($000):** 6777
**Personnel:** 171

## FREDERICK—Tillman County

★ **MEMORIAL HOSPITAL AND PHYSICIAN GROUP (370051)**, 319 East Josephine Avenue, Zip 73542–2220; tel. 580/335–7565, (Total facility includes 30 beds in nursing home–type unit) **A**9 10 20 **F**11 29 40 59 62 64 67 89 93 107 119 133 **P**5 6
Primary Contact: Richard Coleman, Interim Administrator
Web address: www.frederickhospital.com
**Control:** Hospital district or authority, Government, nonfederal **Service:** General Medical and Surgical

**Staffed Beds:** 55 **Admissions:** 312 **Census:** 29 **Outpatient Visits:** 9370
**Births:** 0

## GROVE—Delaware County

☒ **INTEGRIS GROVE HOSPITAL (370113)**, 1001 East 18th Street, Zip 74344–2907; tel. 918/786–2243 **A**1 9 10 20 **F**3 7 11 13 15 18 20 22 29 30 34 35 40 54 57 59 62 64 70 77 79 81 85 93 107 110 111 114 119 125 129 146 147 **S** INTEGRIS Health, Oklahoma City, OK
Primary Contact: Tim Bowen, President
COO: Bennett Geister, Vice President Operations
CFO: Valerie Reeves, Chief Financial Officer
CMO: James Rutter, M.D., Chief of Staff
CHR: Stacy Froese, Regional Director Human Resources
CNO: Angela Bidleman, R.N., Chief Nursing Officer
Web address: www.integris–health.com
**Control:** Other not–for–profit (including NFP Corporation) **Service:** General Medical and Surgical

**Staffed Beds:** 58 **Admissions:** 2176 **Census:** 19 **Outpatient Visits:** 49178
**Births:** 289 **Total Expense ($000):** 53081 **Payroll Expense ($000):** 20402
**Personnel:** 226

## GUTHRIE—Logan County

★ **MERCY HOSPITAL LOGAN COUNTY (371317)**, 200 South Academy Road, Zip 73044–8727, Mailing Address: P.O. Box 1017, Zip 73044–1017; tel. 405/282–6700 **A**9 10 18 **F**3 15 29 30 34 40 41 43 45 49 50 57 59 68 74 75 77 79 81 85 91 93 97 99 102 107 108 110 111 114 119 127 129 130 131 133 144 146 148 **P**6 **S** Mercy Health, Chesterfield, MO
Primary Contact: Joshua Tucker, Administrator
CMO: Jignesh Veragiwala, Chief of Staff
CHR: Mary Jo Messelt, Senior Human Resources Manager
CNO: Kim Williams, R.N., Director of Nursing
Web address: www.mercy.net
**Control:** Church–operated, Nongovernment, not–for profit **Service:** General Medical and Surgical

**Staffed Beds:** 25 **Admissions:** 795 **Census:** 10 **Outpatient Visits:** 66981
**Births:** 0 **Total Expense ($000):** 18858 **Payroll Expense ($000):** 10114
**Personnel:** 134

## GUYMON—Texas County

★ **MEMORIAL HOSPITAL OF TEXAS COUNTY (370138)**, 520 Medical Drive, Zip 73942–4438; tel. 580/338–6515 **A**9 10 20 **F**3 11 13 15 29 34 40 43 45 57 59 64 65 68 70 75 76 79 81 85 89 107 108 110 111 114 119 133 135 146 147 **P**6
Primary Contact: David Rasmussen, Chief Executive Officer
CFO: Michele Reust, Controller
CIO: Sheldon Spence, Director of Revenue Cycle, IT
CHR: Sarah Wagner, Human Resources Officer
CNO: Dondie Rodgers, Interim Chief Nursing Officer
Web address: www.mhtcguymon.org
**Control:** County–Government, nonfederal **Service:** General Medical and Surgical

**Staffed Beds:** 14 **Admissions:** 812 **Census:** 6 **Outpatient Visits:** 29962
**Births:** 318 **Total Expense ($000):** 15779 **Payroll Expense ($000):** 6704
**Personnel:** 159

## HEALDTON—Carter County

★ **MERCY HOSPITAL HEALDTON (371310)**, 918 South 8th Street, Zip 73438–0928, Mailing Address: P.O. Box 928, Zip 73438–0928; tel. 580/229–0701 **A**9 10 18 **F**3 28 34 40 43 64 107 114 127 133 **P**6 **S** Mercy Health, Chesterfield, MO
Primary Contact: Jeremy A. Jones, Administrator
CMO: Mark Newey, D.O., Chief of Staff
CHR: Melinda Sharum, Director Human Resources
Web address: www.mercyok.com
**Control:** Church–operated, Nongovernment, not–for profit **Service:** General Medical and Surgical

**Staffed Beds:** 22 **Admissions:** 191 **Census:** 5 **Outpatient Visits:** 8713
**Births:** 0 **Total Expense ($000):** 5094 **Payroll Expense ($000):** 2618
**Personnel:** 45

---

**Hospital, Medicare Provider Number, Address, Telephone, Approval, Facility, and Physician Codes, Health Care System**

★ American Hospital Association (AHA) membership
☐ The Joint Commission accreditation
○ Healthcare Facilities Accreditation Program
◇ DNV Healthcare Inc. accreditation
⇑ Center for Improvement in Healthcare Quality Accreditation
△ Commission on Accreditation of Rehabilitation Facilities (CARF) accreditation

**OK**

### HENRYETTA—Okmulgee County

★ **HILLCREST HOSPITAL HENRYETTA (370183)**, 2401 West Main Street, Zip 74437–3893, Mailing Address: P.O. Box 1269, Zip 74437–1269; tel. 918/650–1100 **A**9 10 **F**3 15 29 40 45 54 56 64 65 79 81 85 87 93 98 102 103 107 110 111 114 119 129 130 133 143 148 **P**6 **S** Ardent Health Services, Nashville, TN
Primary Contact: Dee Renshaw, Chief Executive Officer
CFO: Joseph Mendoza, Chief Financial Officer
CNO: April Secor, R.N., Chief Nursing Officer
Web address: www.hillcresthenryetta.com/
**Control:** Corporation, Investor–owned, for–profit **Service:** General Medical and Surgical

> **Staffed Beds:** 41 **Admissions:** 964 **Census:** 18 **Outpatient Visits:** 12727 **Births:** 8 **Total Expense ($000):** 14659 **Payroll Expense ($000):** 5755 **Personnel:** 103

### HOBART—Kiowa County

★ **ELKVIEW GENERAL HOSPITAL (370153)**, 429 West Elm Street, Zip 73651–1615; tel. 580/726–3324 **A**9 10 20 **F**3 15 28 29 31 34 35 40 45 56 59 62 79 81 85 89 93 107 108 110 111 115 118 119 129 133 146 148 **P**6
Primary Contact: Lisa Hart, Chief Executive Officer
COO: Harold Moad, Chief Operating Officer
CFO: Lisa Hart, Chief Financial Officer
CMO: Samatha Jackson, M.D., Chief of Staff
CIO: Chris Clark, Chief Technology Officer
CHR: Sharon Moad, Director Personnel
Web address: www.elkviewhospital.com
**Control:** Hospital district or authority, Government, nonfederal **Service:** General Medical and Surgical

> **Staffed Beds:** 38 **Admissions:** 1039 **Census:** 9 **Outpatient Visits:** 11084 **Births:** 1 **Total Expense ($000):** 13059 **Payroll Expense ($000):** 6798 **Personnel:** 160

### HOLDENVILLE—Hughes County

★ **HOLDENVILLE GENERAL HOSPITAL (371321)**, 100 McDougal Drive, Zip 74848–2822; tel. 405/379–4200 **A**9 10 18 **F**3 11 29 30 40 45 57 59 64 65 79 81 82 89 93 97 107 111 119 127 128 133 135 146 148
Primary Contact: Roberta Jeffrey, Chief Executive Officer
CFO: Drew Johnson, Chief Financial Officer
CMO: Tom Osborn, D.O., Chief Medical Staff
CIO: Mike Combs, Manager Information Technology
CHR: Heather Heard, Director Human Resources
CNO: Jackie Smith, R.N., Chief Nursing Officer
Web address: www.holdenvillegeneral.org
**Control:** City–Government, nonfederal **Service:** General Medical and Surgical

> **Staffed Beds:** 25 **Admissions:** 410 **Census:** 4 **Outpatient Visits:** 33754 **Births:** 0 **Total Expense ($000):** 11029 **Payroll Expense ($000):** 4919 **Personnel:** 120

### HOLLIS—Harmon County

★ **HARMON MEMORIAL HOSPITAL (370036)**, 400 East Chestnut Street, Zip 73550–2030, Mailing Address: P.O. Box 791, Zip 73550–0791; tel. 580/688–3363, (Nonreporting) **A**9 10 20
Primary Contact: Sheila Lewis, Administrator
CFO: Willie Mae Copeland, Chief Financial Officer
CMO: Akram Abraham, M.D., Chief of Staff
CHR: Abbey Welch, Director Human Resources
**Control:** Hospital district or authority, Government, nonfederal **Service:** General Medical and Surgical

> **Staffed Beds:** 31

### HUGO—Choctaw County

**CHOCTAW MEMORIAL HOSPITAL (370100)**, 1405 East Kirk Street, Zip 74743–3603; tel. 580/317–9500 **A**9 10 **F**3 15 29 34 35 40 45 49 75 81 87 93 107 110 111 114 119 130 146
Primary Contact: Marcia O'Connor, Chief Executive Officer
CIO: Andy Richmond, Director Information Technology
CHR: Darlene Galyon, Director Human Resources
Web address: www.choctawmemorial.com
**Control:** Hospital district or authority, Government, nonfederal **Service:** General Medical and Surgical

> **Staffed Beds:** 32 **Admissions:** 1298 **Census:** 15

**LANE FROST HEALTH AND REHABILITATION CENTER (372017)**, 2815 East Jackson Street, Zip 74743–4250; tel. 580/326–9200, (Nonreporting) **A**10
Primary Contact: Robert F. Berry, Chief Executive Officer
Web address: www.lanefrosthealth.com/
**Control:** Other not–for–profit (including NFP Corporation) **Service:** Long–Term Acute Care hospital

> **Staffed Beds:** 30

### IDABEL—Mccurtain County

★ **MCCURTAIN MEMORIAL HOSPITAL (370048)**, 1301 Lincoln Road, Zip 74745–7341; tel. 580/286–7623 **A**9 10 20 **F**3 11 13 15 28 29 34 40 45 49 53 57 59 62 64 70 75 76 81 87 93 98 103 107 110 111 114 119 128 130 132 133 148 **P**6 8
Primary Contact: Jahni Tapley, JD, Interim Chief Executive Officer
CFO: Ray B. Whitmore, Chief Financial Officer
CMO: Michael C. West, M.D., Chief of Staff
CIO: Dana A. Stowell, Chief Information Officer
CNO: Pam Johnson, R.N., Chief Nursing Officer
Web address: www.mmhok.com
**Control:** Other not–for–profit (including NFP Corporation) **Service:** General Medical and Surgical

> **Staffed Beds:** 77 **Admissions:** 1600 **Census:** 16

### KINGFISHER—Kingfisher County

★ **MERCY HOSPITAL KINGFISHER (371313)**, 1000 Kingfisher Regional Hospital Drive, Zip 73750–3528, Mailing Address: P.O. Box 59, Zip 73750–0059; tel. 405/375–3141, (Data for 242 days) **A**9 10 18 **F**3 15 29 30 34 35 40 41 43 45 46 50 59 63 64 65 68 75 77 79 81 85 91 93 107 110 111 114 119 129 132 133 146 **S** Mercy Health, Chesterfield, MO
Primary Contact: Brian Denton, Administrator
CMO: Brett Krablin, M.D., Chief of Staff
CIO: Chad Kliewer, Information Technology Specialist
CHR: Carolyn Bjerke, Director Human Resources
CNO: Hannah Powell, Chief Nursing Officer
Web address: www.kingfisherhospital.com
**Control:** Church–operated, Nongovernment, not–for profit **Service:** General Medical and Surgical

> **Staffed Beds:** 25 **Admissions:** 299 **Census:** 6 **Outpatient Visits:** 8260 **Births:** 0 **Total Expense ($000):** 7078 **Payroll Expense ($000):** 3804 **Personnel:** 90

### LAWTON—Comanche County

⊠ △ **COMANCHE COUNTY MEMORIAL HOSPITAL (370056)**, 3401 West Gore Boulevard, Zip 73505–6332, Mailing Address: P.O. Box 129, Zip 73502–0129; tel. 580/355–8620, (Total facility includes 132 beds in nursing home–type unit) **A**1 2 3 5 7 9 10 13 **F**3 7 8 11 12 13 15 17 18 20 22 24 26 28 29 30 31 32 34 35 40 43 45 47 48 49 50 51 54 56 57 58 59 62 63 64 65 66 68 70 72 74 75 76 77 78 79 80 81 82 84 85 86 89 90 91 92 93 96 97 98 103 104 107 108 110 111 114 115 117 118 119 120 121 123 124 127 128 129 130 131 132 134 135 143 144 146 147 148 **P**6
Primary Contact: Randall K. Segler, FACHE, Chief Executive Officer
COO: Sharon Dudley, Chief Operating Officer
CFO: Brent Smith, Chief Financial Officer
CMO: John A. Cox, Jr., M.D., President Medical Staff
CIO: James Wellman, Senior Director Information Services
CHR: Donna Wade, Senior Director Human Resources
CNO: Kim Holland, Senior Director Nursing Services
Web address: www.ccmhonline.com
**Control:** Hospital district or authority, Government, nonfederal **Service:** General Medical and Surgical

> **Staffed Beds:** 378 **Admissions:** 9443 **Census:** 242 **Outpatient Visits:** 163722 **Births:** 1244 **Total Expense ($000):** 227012 **Payroll Expense ($000):** 92687 **Personnel:** 1476

**JIM TALIAFERRO COMMUNITY MENTAL HEALTH (374008)**, 602 S.W. 38th Street, Zip 73505; tel. 580/248–5780 **A**9 10 **F**4 5 29 35 38 98 99 100 101 102 103 104 106
Primary Contact: Brenda Ototibo, Executive Director
Web address: www.odmhsas.org
**Control:** State–Government, nonfederal **Service:** Psychiatric

> **Staffed Beds:** 18 **Admissions:** 518 **Census:** 7 **Outpatient Visits:** 10500 **Births:** 0

☐ **LAWTON INDIAN HOSPITAL (370170)**, 1515 Lawrie Tatum Road, Zip 73507–3099; tel. 580/353–0350, (Nonreporting) **A**1 10 **S** U. S. Indian Health Service, Rockville, MD
Primary Contact: Greg Ketcher, Administrator
COO: John Bear, Hospital Administrator Officer and Supervisor Human Resources
CFO: Sarabeth Sahmaunt, Supervisory Accountant
CMO: Richard Chadek, M.D., Clinical Director
CIO: William R. Harris, Chief Information Officer
CHR: John Bear, Hospital Administrator Officer and Supervisor Human Resources
CNO: Lenora Littledeer, R.N., Director of Nursing
Web address: www.ihs.gov
**Control:** PHS, Indian Service, Government, federal **Service:** General Medical and Surgical

> **Staffed Beds:** 26

**OK**

□ △ **SOUTHWESTERN MEDICAL CENTER (370097)**, 5602 S.W. Lee Boulevard, Zip 73505–9635; tel. 580/531–4700 **A**1 3 5 7 9 10 **F**3 8 13 29 30 34 38 40 41 43 45 47 49 50 51 57 59 60 64 65 67 68 70 74 76 77 78 79 81 85 87 89 90 91 92 93 98 99 100 101 102 104 106 107 108 111 114 118 119 120 121 122 123 124 127 129 130 131 133 135 146 147 148 **P**6 **S** Capella Healthcare, Franklin, TN
Primary Contact: Stephen O. Hyde, FACHE, Chief Executive Officer
CFO: Wayne Colson, Chief Financial Officer
CMO: David Pagnanelli, M.D., Chief of Staff
CIO: Kent Lewis, Director Information Services
CHR: Danny Hale, Director Human Resources
CNO: Steven Vance Owens, RN, Chief Nursing Officer
Web address: www.swmconline.com
**Control:** Corporation, Investor–owned, for–profit **Service:** General Medical and Surgical

**Staffed Beds: 178 Admissions: 4388 Census: 87 Outpatient Visits: 57059 Births: 554 Total Expense ($000): 64347 Payroll Expense ($000): 21721 Personnel: 453**

**LINDSAY—Garvin County**

**LINDSAY MUNICIPAL HOSPITAL (370214)**, Highway 19 West, Zip 73052, Mailing Address: P.O. Box 888, Zip 73052–0888; tel. 405/756–1404, (Nonreporting) **A**9 10
Primary Contact: Jeff Walraven, Chief Executive Officer
**Control:** City–Government, nonfederal **Service:** General Medical and Surgical

**Staffed Beds: 26**

**MADILL—Marshall County**

✠ **ALLIANCEHEALTH MADILL (371326)**, 1 Hospital Drive, Zip 73446, Mailing Address: P.O. Box 827, Zip 73446–0827; tel. 580/795–3384 **A**1 9 10 18 **F**3 11 29 30 34 35 40 43 45 49 59 64 81 87 93 107 114 119 127 130 133 135 146 **P**5 **S** Community Health Systems, Inc., Franklin, TN
Primary Contact: Minnie Burkhardt, Administrator
CFO: Thomas Briggs, Chief Financial Officer
CMO: Joe Potter, M.D., Chief of Staff
CHR: Lori Friend, Director Human Resources
CNO: Holly Bain, Chief Nursing Officer
Web address: www.integrismarshallcounty.com
**Control:** Corporation, Investor–owned, for–profit **Service:** General Medical and Surgical

**Staffed Beds: 21 Admissions: 546 Census: 6**

**MANGUM—Greer County**

**QUARTZ MOUNTAIN MEDICAL CENTER (371330)**, One Wickersham Drive, Zip 73554–9116, Mailing Address: P.O. Box 280, Zip 73554–0280; tel. 580/782–3353 **A**9 10 18 **F**29 40 41 45 57 68 81 82 93 107 111 119 127 128 129 133 148 **P**6
Primary Contact: Kevin Owens, Chief Executive Officer
COO: Danny Avery, Chief Financial Officer and Chief Operating Officer
CIO: Gregg Burnam, Chief Information Officer and Manager Business Office
Web address: www.mangumhealth.com
**Control:** Individual, Investor–owned, for–profit **Service:** General Medical and Surgical

**Staffed Beds: 25 Admissions: 356 Census: 3 Outpatient Visits: 8865 Births: 0 Total Expense ($000): 10380 Payroll Expense ($000): 3667 Personnel: 95**

**MARIETTA—Love County**

★ **MERCY HEALTH LOVE COUNTY (371306)**, 300 Wanda Street, Zip 73448–1200; tel. 580/276–3347 **A**9 10 18 **F**3 29 34 40 43 50 57 59 84 107 114 119 127 128 133 135 143 146 148 **S** Mercy Health, Chesterfield, MO
Primary Contact: Richard Barker, Administrator
CMO: J. T. O'Connor, M.D., Medical Director
CIO: Connie Graham, Public Information Officer
Web address: www.mercyhealthlovecounty.com
**Control:** Church–operated, Nongovernment, not–for profit **Service:** General Medical and Surgical

**Staffed Beds: 35 Admissions: 264 Census: 7 Outpatient Visits: 35226 Births: 0 Total Expense ($000): 13344 Payroll Expense ($000): 7501 Personnel: 136**

**MCALESTER—Pittsburg County**

**CARL ALBERT COMMUNITY MENTAL HEALTH CENTER (374006)**, 1101 East Monroe Avenue, Zip 74501–4826; tel. 918/426–7800 **A**10 **F**5 29 35 38 98 99 100 101 102 103 104 130 132 135 146
Primary Contact: Debbie Moran, Executive Director
CFO: Konnie Taylor, Chief Financial Officer
CMO: William Mings, M.D., Medical Director
CHR: Judy Allen, Human Resource Specialist
Web address: www.odmhsas.org
**Control:** State–Government, nonfederal **Service:** Psychiatric

**Staffed Beds: 15 Admissions: 369 Census: 9 Outpatient Visits: 40610 Births: 0 Personnel: 140**

★ △ ◇ **MCALESTER REGIONAL HEALTH CENTER (370034)**, One Clark Bass Boulevard, Zip 74501–4267, Mailing Address: P.O. Box 1228, Zip 74502–1228; tel. 918/426–1800 **A**7 9 10 13 21 **F**3 10 11 13 15 18 20 22 26 29 30 34 35 40 43 45 49 50 51 53 54 56 57 59 61 62 64 68 69 70 75 76 77 79 81 82 85 86 87 90 91 92 93 107 108 109 110 111 114 115 116 117 118 119 125 127 128 129 130 131 132 135 144 146 147 148 **P**6
Primary Contact: David N. Keith, FACHE, President and Chief Executive Officer
COO: Chris Whybrew, Chief Operating Officer
CFO: Darryl Linnington, Chief Financial Officer
CIO: Frank Hilbert, Senior Vice President and Chief Information Officer
CHR: Scott Lowe, Director Human Resource
CNO: Kimberly Dawn Stout, Chief Nursing Officer
Web address: www.mrhcok.com
**Control:** City–Government, nonfederal **Service:** General Medical and Surgical

**Staffed Beds: 216 Admissions: 5179 Census: 55 Outpatient Visits: 91332 Births: 482 Total Expense ($000): 78547 Payroll Expense ($000): 35244 Personnel: 633**

**MIAMI—Ottawa County**

✠ **INTEGRIS BAPTIST REGIONAL HEALTH CENTER (370004)**, 200 Second Street S.W., Zip 74354–6830; tel. 918/542–6611 **A**1 9 10 20 **F**7 8 11 13 15 18 20 22 26 28 29 30 34 35 40 45 51 57 59 62 63 70 75 76 77 79 81 85 88 89 93 98 100 103 107 108 110 111 114 115 119 125 129 130 131 132 135 144 146 147 148 **S** INTEGRIS Health, Oklahoma City, OK
Primary Contact: Jordan Cash, President
CFO: Valerie Reeves, Chief Financial Officer
CMO: Elaine Mader, M.D., Chief of Staff
CHR: Jamil Haynes, Regional Director Human Resources
CNO: Lisa Halstead, Chief Nursing Officer
Web address: www.integris–health.com
**Control:** Other not–for–profit (including NFP Corporation) **Service:** General Medical and Surgical

**Staffed Beds: 84 Admissions: 2295 Census: 26 Outpatient Visits: 53894 Births: 361 Total Expense ($000): 53942 Payroll Expense ($000): 24815 Personnel: 346**

★ **WILLOW CREST HOSPITAL (374017)**, 130 A Street S.W., Zip 74354–6800; tel. 918/542–1836 **A**9 10 **F**29 75 98 99 101 102 106 130 **P**6
Primary Contact: Anne Anthony, FACHE, President and Chief Executive Officer
COO: Steven Goodman, Chief Operating Officer
CFO: Cindy Bell, Director Finance
CMO: Mark Elkington, M.D., Chief Medical Officer
CIO: Steven Goodman, Chief Operating Officer
CHR: Kathy Henderson, Director Human Resources
CNO: Kassi Davis, Director Patient Care Services
Web address: www.willowcresthospital.com
**Control:** Corporation, Investor–owned, for–profit **Service:** Children's hospital psychiatric

**Staffed Beds: 75 Admissions: 556 Census: 47 Outpatient Visits: 0 Births: 0 Total Expense ($000): 8371 Payroll Expense ($000): 5069 Personnel: 125**

**Hospital, Medicare Provider Number, Address, Telephone, Approval, Facility, and Physician Codes, Health Care System**

★ American Hospital Association (AHA) membership
□ The Joint Commission accreditation
○ Healthcare Facilities Accreditation Program
◇ DNV Healthcare Inc. accreditation
⇑ Center for Improvement in Healthcare Quality Accreditation
△ Commission on Accreditation of Rehabilitation Facilities (CARF) accreditation

**OK**

## MIDWEST CITY—Oklahoma County

☒ **ALLIANCEHEALTH MIDWEST (370094)**, 2825 Parklawn Drive,
Zip 73110–4258; tel. 405/610–4411 **A**1 3 5 9 10 **F**3 7 8 11 13 14 15 17 18
20 22 26 29 30 31 34 40 43 45 46 49 50 57 59 64 70 74 76 77 78 79 80
81 85 86 87 89 91 93 98 100 101 102 103 107 108 110 111 114 115 119
126 130 132 135 143 146 147 **S** Community Health Systems, Inc., Franklin, TN
Primary Contact: Damon Brown, Chief Executive Officer
CFO: Brandon Bullard, Chief Financial Officer
CMO: Rockey Talley, M.D., Chief Medical Officer
CHR: Michael Ward Hartley, Director Human Resources
CNO: Gloria Alicia Ceballos, MSN, Chief Nursing Officer
Web address: www.midwestregional.com
**Control:** Corporation, Investor–owned, for–profit **Service:** General Medical and
Surgical

**Staffed Beds: 255 Admissions: 9859 Census: 126 Outpatient Visits:**
103047 **Births: 732 Total Expense ($000): 133905 Payroll Expense
($000): 46637 Personnel: 735**

☐ **SPECIALTY HOSPITAL OF MIDWEST CITY (372012)**, 8210 National Avenue,
Zip 73110–8518; tel. 405/739–0800 **A**1 9 10 **F**1 3 4 17 18 29 34 40 65 67
70 72 73 75 76 77 79 85 86 87 88 89 90 128 130 135 143 148 **P**5
**S** Encore Healthcare, Columbia, MD
Primary Contact: Bobby Snyder, Chief Executive Officer
CFO: Veronica Scott, Business Office Manager
CHR: Anna Emamghoraishi, Human Resources
CNO: Jason Farris, Chief Nursing Officer
**Control:** Partnership, Investor–owned, for–profit **Service:** Long–Term Acute Care
hospital

**Staffed Beds: 31 Admissions: 312 Census: 21 Outpatient Visits: 0 Births:**
0 **Personnel: 77**

## MOORE—Cleveland County

**MOORE MEDICAL CENTER** See Norman Regional Health System, Norman

## MUSKOGEE—Muskogee County

⇑ **CORNERSTONE HOSPITAL OF OKLAHOMA–MUSKOGEE (372022)**, 351
South 40th Street, Zip 74401–4916; tel. 918/682–6161, (Includes
CORNERSTONE HOSPITAL OF OKLAHOMA–BROKEN ARROW, 1000 West Boise
Circle, Third Floor, Broken Arrow, Zip 74012–4900, Mailing Address: 1000 West
Boise Circle, Zip 74012–4900; tel. 918/994–8300; Craig Koele, Chief Executive
Officer), (Nonreporting) **A**9 10 22 **S** Cornerstone Healthcare Group, Dallas, TX
Primary Contact: Craig Koele, Chief Executive Officer
CMO: Jeremiah Rutherford, Chief Medical Officer
Web address: www.chghospitals.com/muskogee/
**Control:** Corporation, Investor–owned, for–profit **Service:** Long–Term Acute Care
hospital

**Staffed Beds: 64**

☒ **EASTAR HEALTH SYSTEM (370025)**, 300 Rockefeller Drive, Zip 74401–5081;
tel. 918/682–5501, (Includes EASTAR HEALTH SYSTEM, EAST CAMPUS, 2900
North Main Street, Zip 74401–4078; tel. 918/687–7777) **A**1 2 9 10 19 **F**3 8 11
12 13 15 18 20 22 29 30 31 34 35 40 43 45 46 47 48 49 50 51 53 56 57
59 60 62 64 65 68 70 73 74 75 76 77 78 79 81 85 86 87 89 90 93 96 98
100 101 102 103 107 108 110 111 114 115 119 120 121 123 129 130 146
147 148 **S** Capella Healthcare, Franklin, TN
Primary Contact: Anthony R. Young, Chief Executive Officer
COO: James F. Davidson, Chief Operating Officer
CFO: Scott Bailey, Chief Financial Officer
CMO: Jay Gregory, M.D., Chief Medical Officer
CIO: James Tolbert, Director Information Systems
CHR: Bill Peterson, Director Human Resources
CNO: Debbie Kifer, Chief Nursing Officer
Web address: www.eastarhealth.com
**Control:** Corporation, Investor–owned, for–profit **Service:** General Medical and
Surgical

**Staffed Beds: 222 Admissions: 8675 Census: 121 Outpatient Visits: 81022
Births: 732 Total Expense ($000): 121819 Payroll Expense ($000): 41990
Personnel: 844**

**EASTAR HEALTH SYSTEM, EAST CAMPUS** See EASTAR Health System

☒ △ **JACK C. MONTGOMERY VETERANS AFFAIRS MEDICAL CENTER**, 1011
Honor Heights Drive, Zip 74401–1318; tel. 918/577–3000 **A**1 2 3 7 9 **F**5 18 29
30 31 33 34 35 36 38 39 40 44 45 50 53 54 55 56 57 58 59 60 61 63 64
65 67 70 74 75 77 78 79 81 83 84 85 86 87 90 92 93 94 96 97 98 100
101 102 103 104 105 107 108 111 114 119 127 130 132 133 135 143 146
147 148 **S** Department of Veterans Affairs, Washington, DC
Primary Contact: Richard Crockett, Acting Medical Center Director
CFO: Dwight Beal, Chief Fiscal Services
CMO: Thomas D. Schneider, D.O., Chief of Staff
CIO: Mark Carr, Chief Information Resource Management
CNO: Bonnie Pierce, MSN, Associate Director for Patient Care Services
Web address: www.muskogee.va.gov
**Control:** Veterans Affairs, Government, federal **Service:** General Medical and
Surgical

**Staffed Beds: 99 Admissions: 3855 Census: 58 Outpatient Visits: 470942
Births: 0 Personnel: 1219**

**MUSKOGEE REGIONAL MEDICAL CENTER** See EASTAR Health System

## NORMAN—Cleveland County

☐ **GRIFFIN MEMORIAL HOSPITAL (374000)**, 900 East Main Street,
Zip 73071–5305, Mailing Address: P.O. Box 151, Zip 73070–0151;
tel. 405/321–4880 **A**1 3 5 9 10 **F**40 98 102 103 130 135 **P**6 **S** Oklahoma
Department of Mental Health and Substance Abuse Services, Oklahoma City, OK
Primary Contact: Lori Jordan, Executive Director
CFO: Bob Mathew, Director Finance
CMO: Stan Ardoin, M.D., Medical Director
Web address: www.odmhsas.org
**Control:** State–Government, nonfederal **Service:** Psychiatric

**Staffed Beds: 120 Admissions: 1553 Census: 114 Outpatient Visits: 344
Births: 0 Total Expense ($000): 26308 Payroll Expense ($000): 13526
Personnel: 324**

**J. D. MCCARTY CENTER FOR CHILDREN WITH DEVELOPMENTAL
DISABILITIES (373300)**, 2002 East Robinson, Zip 73071–7420;
tel. 405/307–2800 **A**10 **F**3 29 35 64 65 75 77 87 90 91 93 130 135 146
Primary Contact: Vicki Kuestersteffen, Chief Executive Officer
CFO: Erik Paulson, Director of Finance
CMO: Thomas Thurston, M.D., Medical Director
CIO: Jeffery Setzer, Administrator Information Systems
CHR: Tina Martinez, Director Human Resources
Web address: www.jdmc.org
**Control:** State–Government, nonfederal **Service:** Children's rehabilitation

**Staffed Beds: 36 Admissions: 190 Census: 33 Outpatient Visits: 8480
Births: 0 Total Expense ($000): 20311 Payroll Expense ($000): 10783
Personnel: 229**

☒ △ **NORMAN REGIONAL HEALTH SYSTEM (370008)**, 901 North Porter
Street, Zip 73071–6482, Mailing Address: P.O. Box 1308, Zip 73070–1308;
tel. 405/307–1000, (Includes MOORE MEDICAL CENTER, 700 South Telephone
Road, Moore, Zip 73160; tel. 405/793–9355; R. Gehris, Chief Administrative
Officer; NORMAN REGIONAL HOSPITAL, 901 North Porter Street, Mailing Address:
P.O. Box 1308, Zip 73070–1308; tel. 405/307–1000) **A**1 2 7 9 10 13 **F**3 7 11
12 13 15 17 18 20 22 24 28 29 30 31 32 34 35 36 37 39 40 42 43 44 45
47 48 49 50 53 54 55 56 57 58 59 63 64 65 69 70 72 74 75 76 77 78 79
80 81 82 83 84 85 86 87 89 90 93 94 96 97 98 100 101 102 103 104 107
110 111 114 115 117 118 119 120 123 126 127 129 130 131 132 135 143
145 146 147 148 **P**5 6 8
Primary Contact: David D. Whitaker, FACHE, President and Chief Executive Officer
COO: Greg Terrell, Senior Vice President and Chief Operating Officer
CFO: Ken Hopkins, Vice President Finance and Chief Financial Officer
CIO: John Meharg, Director Health Information Technology
CHR: Jim Beyer, Director Human Resources
CNO: Nancy Brown, R.N., Vice President Patient Care Services and Chief Nursing
Officer
Web address: www.normanregional.com
**Control:** Hospital district or authority, Government, nonfederal **Service:** General
Medical and Surgical

**Staffed Beds: 355 Admissions: 16671 Census: 207 Outpatient Visits:**
338019 **Births: 2910 Total Expense ($000): 342371 Payroll Expense
($000): 151402 Personnel: 2555**

☒ **NORMAN SPECIALTY HOSPITAL (372021)**, 1210 West Robinson Street,
Zip 73069–7401; tel. 405/321–8824 **A**1 9 10 **F**1 3 29 30 35 40 60 68 74 75
77 87 91 100 119 130 146 148 **P**8
Primary Contact: Billy Blasingame, Administrator and Chief Executive Officer
CFO: Debra Anderson, Manager Patient Financial Services
CMO: Mehan Shahsavari, M.D., Chief of Staff
CHR: Beth Blankenship, Coordinator Human Resources
CNO: Linda Massey, R.N., Nurse Manager
Web address: www.normanspecialtyhospital.com
**Control:** Individual, Investor–owned, for–profit **Service:** Long–Term Acute Care
hospital

**Staffed Beds: 50 Admissions: 467 Census: 34 Outpatient Visits: 4 Births:**
0 **Personnel: 116**

## NOWATA—Nowata County

★ **JANE PHILLIPS NOWATA HEALTH CENTER (371305)**, 237 South Locust
Street, Zip 74048–3660; tel. 918/273–3102 **A**9 10 18 **F**3 29 30 34 35 40 50
57 64 68 107 114 119 128 133 146 **P**5 **S** Ascension Health, Saint Louis, MO
Primary Contact: Scott Upton, Administrator
CMO: David Caughell, M.D., Chief of Staff
Web address: www.jpmc.org
**Control:** Church–operated, Nongovernment, not–for profit **Service:** General
Medical and Surgical

**Staffed Beds: 13 Admissions: 190 Census: 4 Outpatient Visits: 2534
Births: 0 Total Expense ($000): 4506 Payroll Expense ($000): 2096**

### OKEENE—Blaine County

★ **OKEENE MUNICIPAL HOSPITAL (371327)**, 207 East F Street, Zip 73763–9441, Mailing Address: P.O. Box 489, Zip 73763–0489; tel. 580/822–4417 **A**9 10 18 **F**3 29 34 40 45 50 59 64 68 81 85 93 97 107 111 119 129 130 132 133 135 **P**6
Primary Contact: Shelly Dunham, Chief Executive Officer
COO: Pat Lorenz, Chief Operating Officer
CFO: Sandra Lamle, Chief Financial Officer
CHR: Barbara Creps, Director Human Resources and Accounting
CNO: Tamara Fischer, Chief Nursing Officer
Web address: www.okeenehospital.com
**Control:** Hospital district or authority, Government, nonfederal **Service:** General Medical and Surgical

**Staffed Beds:** 17 **Admissions:** 155 **Census:** 6 **Outpatient Visits:** 19384 **Births:** 0 **Total Expense ($000):** 6115 **Payroll Expense ($000):** 2399 **Personnel:** 55

### OKEMAH—Okfuskee County

★ ◇ **CREEK NATION COMMUNITY HOSPITAL (371333)**, 309 North 14th Street, Zip 74859–2028; tel. 918/623–1424, (Nonreporting) **A**9 10 18 21
Primary Contact: Sheryl Sharber–Howell, Administrator
COO: Rhonda Beaver, Chief Operating Officer
CFO: Tyler McIntosh, Chief Financial Officer
CMO: Lawrence Vark, M.D., Chief Medical Officer
CIO: Robert Coffee, Chief Information Officer
CHR: Russell B. Torbett, Director Human Resources
CNO: Annette James, R.N., Chief Nursing Officer
Web address: www.creekhealth.org
**Control:** Other not–for–profit (including NFP Corporation) **Service:** General Medical and Surgical

**Staffed Beds:** 18

### OKLAHOMA CITY—Oklahoma County

▣ △ **ALLIANCEHEALTH DEACONESS (370032)**, 5501 North Portland Avenue, Zip 73112–2099; tel. 405/604–6000 **A**1 2 5 9 10 **F**3 8 11 13 15 17 18 20 22 24 28 29 30 31 34 35 40 41 43 45 46 47 49 50 56 57 59 60 70 72 73 74 75 76 78 79 80 81 83 84 85 86 87 90 93 97 102 107 108 109 110 111 114 119 120 126 129 130 132 135 146 147 148 **P**8 **S** Community Health Systems, Inc., Franklin, TN
Primary Contact: Devon Hyde, Chief Executive Officer
COO: Brett Kirkham, Chief Operating Officer
CIO: Don Bandy, Director Information Technology
CHR: Ellen Gifford, Director Human Resources
CNO: Jayne Thomas, Chief Nursing Officer
Web address: www.deaconessokc.com
**Control:** Partnership, Investor–owned, for–profit **Service:** General Medical and Surgical

**Staffed Beds:** 238 **Admissions:** 5396 **Census:** 73 **Outpatient Visits:** 67897 **Births:** 792 **Total Expense ($000):** 102229 **Payroll Expense ($000):** 38288 **Personnel:** 696

☐ **CEDAR RIDGE HOSPITAL (374023)**, 6501 N.E. 50th Street, Zip 73141–9118; tel. 405/605–6111, (Nonreporting) **A**1 9 10 **S** Universal Health Services, Inc., King of Prussia, PA
Primary Contact: Diane Bedell, R.N., Chief Executive Officer
Web address: www.cedarridgebhs.com
**Control:** Corporation, Investor–owned, for–profit **Service:** Psychiatric

**Staffed Beds:** 116

**CHILDREN'S HOSPITAL OF OKLAHOMA** See OU Medical Center

◇ **COMMUNITY HOSPITAL (370203)**, 3100 S.W. 89th Street, Zip 73159–7900; tel. 405/378–3755, (Nonreporting) **A**9 10 21
Primary Contact: Brian L. Clemens, President and Chief Executive Officer
Web address: www.communityhospitalokc.com
**Control:** Corporation, Investor–owned, for–profit **Service:** General Medical and Surgical

**Staffed Beds:** 40

**EVERETT TOWER** See OU Medical Center

▣ △ **INTEGRIS BAPTIST MEDICAL CENTER (370028)**, 3300 N.W. Expressway, Zip 73112–4418; tel. 405/949–3011, (Includes INTEGRIS MENTAL HEALTH SYSTEM–SPENCER, 2601 North Spencer Road, Spencer, Zip 73084–3699, Mailing Address: P.O. Box 11137, Oklahoma City, Zip 73136–0137; tel. 405/717–9800) **A**1 2 3 5 7 9 10 13 **F**3 8 11 12 13 15 16 17 18 20 22 24 26 28 29 30 31 32 34 35 36 38 39 40 43 44 45 46 49 50 52 53 54 55 57 58 59 60 62 63 64 68 70 71 72 74 75 76 77 78 79 80 81 82 83 84 85 86 87 88 89 90 92 93 96 97 98 99 100 101 102 104 106 107 108 109 110 111 114 115 116 118 119 120 121 123 124 126 129 130 131 132 133 134 135 137 138 139 140 141 142 143 146 147 148 **P**6 7 **S** INTEGRIS Health, Oklahoma City, OK
Primary Contact: Timothy J. Johnsen, MS, President
CFO: David R. Hadley, Managing Director and Chief Financial Officer
CMO: James P. White, M.D., Chief Medical Officer
CIO: John Delano, Vice President Chief Information Officer
CHR: Jason L. Eliot, Vice President Human Resources
CNO: Joni R. Tiller, R.N., Chief Nursing Officer
Web address: www.integrisok.com
**Control:** Other not–for–profit (including NFP Corporation) **Service:** General Medical and Surgical

**Staffed Beds:** 528 **Admissions:** 20976 **Census:** 405 **Outpatient Visits:** 188198 **Births:** 2834 **Total Expense ($000):** 621838 **Payroll Expense ($000):** 216268 **Personnel:** 2953

▣ △ **INTEGRIS SOUTHWEST MEDICAL CENTER (370106)**, 4401 South Western, Zip 73109–3413; tel. 405/636–7000 **A**1 2 3 5 7 9 10 13 **F**3 11 13 15 18 20 22 24 28 29 30 31 32 34 35 38 40 43 45 47 49 50 53 57 58 59 60 64 68 70 74 75 76 77 78 79 80 81 82 85 86 87 90 91 92 93 95 96 97 98 107 108 110 111 114 118 119 120 121 123 124 129 130 131 132 133 135 143 146 147 148 **S** INTEGRIS Health, Oklahoma City, OK
Primary Contact: James D. Moore, FACHE, President
CFO: Errol Mitchell, Vice President
CMO: Son Nguyen, M.D., President of Medical Staff
CIO: John Delano, Vice President and Chief Information Officer
CHR: Lynn Ketch, Director
CNO: Marva Harrison, R.N., Vice President and Chief Nursing Officer
Web address: www.integris–health.com
**Control:** Other not–for–profit (including NFP Corporation) **Service:** General Medical and Surgical

**Staffed Beds:** 335 **Admissions:** 11657 **Census:** 190 **Outpatient Visits:** 155746 **Births:** 1247 **Total Expense ($000):** 233336 **Payroll Expense ($000):** 89081 **Personnel:** 1668

▣ **KINDRED HOSPITAL– OKLAHOMA CITY (372004)**, 1407 North Robinson Avenue, Zip 73103–4823; tel. 405/232–8000, (Includes KINDRED HOSPITAL–OKLAHOMA CITY SOUTH, 2129 S.W. 59th Street, Zip 73119; tel. 405/713–5955) **A**1 3 5 9 10 **F**29 40 46 60 68 70 85 87 119 130 145 148 **S** Kindred Healthcare, Louisville, KY
Primary Contact: William Patton, Chief Executive Officer
Web address: www.kindredoklahoma.com
**Control:** Corporation, Investor–owned, for–profit **Service:** General Medical and Surgical

**Staffed Beds:** 93 **Admissions:** 714 **Census:** 48 **Outpatient Visits:** 0 **Births:** 0 **Total Expense ($000):** 27056 **Payroll Expense ($000):** 8597 **Personnel:** 239

▣ **LAKESIDE WOMEN'S HOSPITAL (370199)**, 11200 North Portland Avenue, Zip 73120–5045; tel. 405/936–1500 **A**1 9 10 **F**3 12 13 15 30 35 40 45 59 64 73 76 81 85 87 110 119 126 132 147 **P**6 **S** INTEGRIS Health, Oklahoma City, OK
Primary Contact: Kelley Brewer, R.N., MSN, President
CFO: Darla McCallister, Chief Financial Officer
CMO: Margaret Hall, M.D., Chief Medical Officer
Web address: www.lakeside–wh.net
**Control:** Corporation, Investor–owned, for–profit **Service:** Obstetrics and gynecology

**Staffed Beds:** 23 **Admissions:** 1401 **Census:** 9 **Outpatient Visits:** 2498 **Births:** 1295 **Total Expense ($000):** 21733 **Payroll Expense ($000):** 6446 **Personnel:** 144

---

**Hospital, Medicare Provider Number, Address, Telephone, Approval, Facility, and Physician Codes, Health Care System**

★ American Hospital Association (AHA) membership
☐ The Joint Commission accreditation
◯ Healthcare Facilities Accreditation Program
◇ DNV Healthcare Inc. accreditation
⇑ Center for Improvement in Healthcare Quality Accreditation
△ Commission on Accreditation of Rehabilitation Facilities (CARF) accreditation

**OK**

**MCBRIDE CLINIC ORTHOPEDIC HOSPITAL (370222)**, 9600 Broadway Extension, Zip 73114–7408; tel. 405/486–2100 **A**3 5 9 10 **F**3 29 34 40 64 68 77 79 81 82 85 86 87 107 111 114 119 130 131 146 **P**2 6
Primary Contact: Mark Galliart, Chief Executive Officer
COO: Christine H. Weigel, R.N., Clinical Operating Officer
CFO: Annie Bassett, Director Finance
CMO: Thomas Janssen, M.D., Chief of Staff
CIO: Ronnie Green, Director Information Systems
CHR: Cathy Withiam, Director Human Resources
Web address: www.mcbrideclinicorthopedichospital.com
**Control:** Corporation, Investor–owned, for–profit **Service:** Orthopedic

**Staffed Beds:** 60 **Admissions:** 3195 **Census:** 26 **Outpatient Visits:** 161449 **Births:** 0 **Total Expense ($000):** 121254 **Payroll Expense ($000):** 50036 **Personnel:** 623

☒ **MERCY HOSPITAL OKLAHOMA CITY (370013)**, 4300 West Memorial Road, Zip 73120–8362; tel. 405/755–1515 **A**1 2 5 9 10 **F**3 11 13 15 28 29 30 31 32 34 35 39 40 41 43 45 46 47 48 49 50 53 55 57 58 59 60 61 62 63 64 65 68 69 70 72 74 75 76 77 78 79 81 82 83 84 85 86 87 89 90 91 92 93 94 96 100 101 107 108 110 111 114 115 117 118 119 120 121 124 126 129 130 131 132 134 135 143 146 147 148 **P**6 **S** Mercy Health, Chesterfield, MO
Primary Contact: Jim Gebhart, Jr., FACHE, President
COO: Aaron Steffens, Chief Operating Officer
CFO: Jon Vitiello, Chief Financial Officer
CMO: Mark Johnson, M.D., Chief Medical Officer
CIO: Ellen Stephens, Vice President Information Services
CHR: Becky J. Payton, Vice President Human Resources
Web address: www.mercyok.net
**Control:** Church–operated, Nongovernment, not–for profit **Service:** General Medical and Surgical

**Staffed Beds:** 369 **Admissions:** 16006 **Census:** 224 **Outpatient Visits:** 444301 **Births:** 3183 **Total Expense ($000):** 341611 **Payroll Expense ($000):** 107675 **Personnel:** 2163

☐ **MERCY REHABILITATION HOSPITAL OKLAHOMA CITY (373033)**, 5401 West Memorial Road, Zip 73142–2026; tel. 405/752–3935 **A**1 10 **F**3 29 30 87 90 91 96 130 148 **S** Kindred Healthcare, Louisville, KY
Primary Contact: Sharon Smeltzer, Chief Executive Officer
**Control:** Partnership, Investor–owned, for–profit **Service:** Rehabilitation

**Staffed Beds:** 50 **Admissions:** 1044 **Census:** 36 **Outpatient Visits:** 0 **Births:** 0 **Total Expense ($000):** 13968 **Payroll Expense ($000):** 6797 **Personnel:** 122

◇ **NORTHWEST SURGICAL HOSPITAL (370192)**, 9204 North May Avenue, Zip 73120–4419; tel. 405/848–1918, (Nonreporting) **A**9 10 21
Primary Contact: Brian L. Clemens, Chief Executive Officer
CFO: Cindy Thompson, Chief Financial Officer
CMO: Jimmy Conway, M.D., President Medical Staff
Web address: www.nwsurgicalokc.com/
**Control:** Corporation, Investor–owned, for–profit **Service:** Orthopedic

**Staffed Beds:** 9

☒ **OKLAHOMA CENTER FOR ORTHOPEDIC AND MULTI–SPECIALTY SURGERY (370212)**, 8100 South Walker, Suite C., Zip 73139–9402, Mailing Address: P.O. Box 890609, Zip 73189–0609; tel. 405/602–6500 **A**1 9 10 **F**3 8 29 34 35 39 40 45 47 48 54 57 59 64 74 79 81 82 85 86 93 94 97 107 111 129 131 148 **P**6 **S** United Surgical Partners International, Addison, TX
Primary Contact: Mike Kimzey, Chief Executive Officer and Administrator
COO: Jeff Bibb, Chief Operating Officer
CFO: Amy Taylor, Chief Financial Officer
CHR: Sherry Wagner, Director Human Resources
CNO: Jolena Wyer, R.N., Chief Nursing Officer
Web address: www.ocomhospital.com
**Control:** Partnership, Investor–owned, for–profit **Service:** General Medical and Surgical

**Staffed Beds:** 10 **Admissions:** 697 **Census:** 5 **Outpatient Visits:** 39895 **Births:** 0 **Total Expense ($000):** 46205 **Payroll Expense ($000):** 12657 **Personnel:** 320

☒ △ **OKLAHOMA CITY VETERANS AFFAIRS MEDICAL CENTER**, 921 N.E. 13th Street, Zip 73104–5028; tel. 405/456–1000, (Nonreporting) **A**1 2 3 5 7 8 9 **S** Department of Veterans Affairs, Washington, DC
Primary Contact: Gerald K. Darnell, PsyD, Acting Medical Center Director
CFO: Michele Pipgrass, Chief Fiscal Service
CMO: Mark Huycke, M.D., Chief of Staff
CIO: David Buckley, Acting Chief Information Management Services
CHR: Kyle Inhofe, Chief Human Resources Officer
CNO: Donna Delise, Associate Director Patient Care Services
Web address: www.oklahoma.va.gov
**Control:** Veterans Affairs, Government, federal **Service:** General Medical and Surgical

**Staffed Beds:** 192

◇ **OKLAHOMA HEART HOSPITAL (370215)**, 4050 West Memorial Road, Zip 73120–8382; tel. 405/608–3200 **A**9 10 21 **F**17 18 20 22 24 26 28 29 30 34 35 40 64 68 74 75 81 86 87 100 102 107 108 116 117 126 146 **P**2
Primary Contact: John Harvey, M.D., President and Chief Executive Officer
COO: Peggy Tipton, Chief Operating Officer and Chief Nursing Officer
CFO: Carol Walker, Chief Financial Officer
CMO: John Harvey, M.D., President and Chief Executive Officer
CIO: Steve Miller, Chief Information Officer
CHR: Katherine Wynn, Chief Human Resource
Web address: www.okheart.com
**Control:** Corporation, Investor–owned, for–profit **Service:** Heart

**Staffed Beds:** 99 **Admissions:** 7283 **Census:** 78 **Outpatient Visits:** 296298 **Births:** 0 **Total Expense ($000):** 187180 **Payroll Expense ($000):** 74969 **Personnel:** 1362

◇ **OKLAHOMA HEART HOSPITAL SOUTH CAMPUS (370234)**, 5200 East I–240 Service Road, Zip 73135; tel. 405/628–6000 **A**9 10 21 **F**17 18 20 22 24 26 28 29 30 34 35 40 53 64 68 74 75 81 82 100 107 116 117 146 **P**6
Primary Contact: John Harvey, M.D., President and Chief Executive Officer
Web address: www.okheart.com
**Control:** Corporation, Investor–owned, for–profit **Service:** Heart

**Staffed Beds:** 46 **Admissions:** 4498 **Census:** 41 **Outpatient Visits:** 48703 **Births:** 0 **Total Expense ($000):** 97437 **Payroll Expense ($000):** 34825 **Personnel:** 469

◇ **OKLAHOMA SPINE HOSPITAL (370206)**, 14101 Parkway Commons Drive, Zip 73134–6012; tel. 405/749–2700, (Nonreporting) **A**9 10 21
Primary Contact: Kevin Blaylock, Chief Executive Officer
Web address: www.oklahomaspine.com
**Control:** Corporation, Investor–owned, for–profit **Service:** Other specialty

**Staffed Beds:** 12

**ONECORE HEALTH (370220)**, 1044 S.W. 44th Street, Suite 516, Zip 73109–3609; tel. 405/631–3085 **A**10 **F**40 79 81 82 87 111 **P**8
Primary Contact: Steve Hockert, Chief Executive Officer
CMO: Joel L. Frazier, M.D., Medical Director
CNO: Teresa Carter, Vice President Patient Care Services
Web address: www.onecorehealth.com
**Control:** Corporation, Investor–owned, for–profit **Service:** Orthopedic

**Staffed Beds:** 8 **Admissions:** 168 **Census:** 1 **Outpatient Visits:** 1333 **Births:** 0 **Total Expense ($000):** 7872 **Payroll Expense ($000):** 2189

☒ **OU MEDICAL CENTER (370093)**, 1200 Everett Drive, Zip 73104–5047, Mailing Address: P.O. Box 26307, Zip 73126–0307; tel. 405/271–3636, (Includes CHILDREN'S HOSPITAL OF OKLAHOMA, 940 N.E. 13th Street, Zip 73104, Mailing Address: P.O. Box 26307, Zip 73126; tel. 405/271–6165; EVERETT TOWER, 1200 Everett Drive, Zip 73104; tel. 405/271–4700; OU MEDICAL CENTER EDMOND, 1 South Bryant Avenue, Edmond, Zip 73034–6309; tel. 405/341–6100; PRESBYTERIAN TOWER, 700 N.E. 13th Street, Zip 73104–5070; tel. 405/271–5100) **A**1 2 3 5 8 9 10 **F**3 8 11 12 13 15 17 18 19 20 21 22 23 24 25 26 27 28 29 30 31 32 34 35 37 38 39 40 41 43 45 46 47 48 49 50 51 52 55 56 57 58 59 60 61 63 64 65 66 68 70 72 74 75 76 77 78 79 81 82 84 85 86 87 88 89 91 92 93 94 96 97 98 100 102 103 105 107 108 110 111 114 115 116 117 118 119 120 121 123 124 126 129 130 131 132 135 136 138 139 142 145 146 147 148 **S** HCA, Nashville, TN
Primary Contact: Charles Spicer, President and Chief Executive Officer
COO: Kristina Wallace, R.N., Chief Operating Officer
CFO: Mike Reese, Chief Financial Officer
CMO: Curt Steinhart, M.D., Chief Medical Officer
CIO: Larry Forsyth, Director Information Services
CHR: Jed M. Liuzza, Chief Human Resources Officer
CNO: Debra L. Pasley, Chief Nursing Officer
Web address: www.oumedicine.com/oumedicalcenter
**Control:** Corporation, Investor–owned, for–profit **Service:** General Medical and Surgical

**Staffed Beds:** 724 **Admissions:** 33871 **Census:** 542 **Outpatient Visits:** 333898 **Births:** 4540 **Total Expense ($000):** 782911 **Payroll Expense ($000):** 221426 **Personnel:** 3330

**PRESBYTERIAN TOWER** See OU Medical Center

☒ **SELECT SPECIALTY HOSPITAL–OKLAHOMA CITY (372009)**, 3524 N.W. 56th Street, Zip 73112–4518; tel. 405/606–6700 **A**1 9 10 **F**1 3 12 29 40 74 75 79 87 107 119 130 148 **S** Select Medical Corporation, Mechanicsburg, PA
Primary Contact: Connie Strickland, Chief Executive Officer
Web address: www.selectspecialtyhospitals.com/company/locations/oklahomacity.aspx
**Control:** Corporation, Investor–owned, for–profit **Service:** Long–Term Acute Care hospital

**Staffed Beds:** 72 **Admissions:** 876 **Census:** 61 **Outpatient Visits:** 0 **Births:** 0 **Total Expense ($000):** 28099 **Payroll Expense ($000):** 12414 **Personnel:** 229

*Many Facility Codes have changed. Please refer to the AHA Guide Code Chart.* © 2015 AHA Guide

✠ △ **ST. ANTHONY HOSPITAL (370037)**, 1000 North Lee Street, Zip 73102–1080, Mailing Address: P.O. Box 205, Zip 73101–0205; tel. 405/272–7000, (Includes BONE AND JOINT HOSPITAL, 1111 North Dewey Avenue, Zip 73103–2609; tel. 405/272–9671; Tammy Powell, FACHE, M.P.H., President) **A**1 2 3 5 7 9 10 12 13 **F**3 4 5 7 8 11 12 13 15 17 18 20 22 24 26 28 29 30 31 34 35 36 37 40 42 43 45 46 47 48 49 50 54 56 57 59 64 67 70 71 74 76 77 78 79 81 82 84 85 86 87 89 90 91 92 93 96 97 98 99 100 101 102 103 104 105 106 107 108 110 111 114 115 117 118 119 120 121 123 124 126 127 129 130 131 132 136 144 146 147 148 **P**7 **S** SSM Health, Saint Louis, MO
Primary Contact: Tammy Powell, FACHE, M.P.H., President
COO: Marti Jourden, FACHE, Chief Quality Officer
CFO: Shasta Manuel, Executive Director Finance
CMO: Kersey Winfree, M.D., Chief Medical Officer
CIO: Kevin Olson, Director Information Systems
CHR: Cynthia Brundise, Vice President Human Resources
Web address: www.saintsok.com
**Control:** Church–operated, Nongovernment, not–for profit **Service:** General Medical and Surgical

**Staffed Beds: 565 Admissions: 21135 Census: 429 Outpatient Visits: 280502 Births: 1258 Total Expense ($000): 461576 Payroll Expense ($000): 151740 Personnel: 2882**

☐ **SURGICAL HOSPITAL OF OKLAHOMA (370201)**, 100 S.E. 59th Street, Zip 73129–3616; tel. 405/634–9300 **A**1 10 **F**3 40 81 129
Primary Contact: Phil Ross, Chief Executive Officer
Web address: www.sh–ok.com/
**Control:** Partnership, Investor–owned, for–profit **Service:** General Medical and Surgical

**Staffed Beds: 12 Admissions: 159 Census: 1 Outpatient Visits: 5492 Births: 0 Total Expense ($000): 11226 Payroll Expense ($000): 4038 Personnel: 71**

✠ **VALIR REHABILITATION HOSPITAL (373025)**, 700 N.W. Seventh Street, Zip 73102–1212; tel. 405/236–3131, (Nonreporting) **A**1 10
Primary Contact: Stacy Smith, R.N., Chief Executive Officer
COO: Ginger Castleberry, Corporate Risk Manager, Quality and Patient Safety
CFO: Scott Brown, Chief Financial Officer
CMO: Tonya Washburn, M.D., Medical Director
CIO: Mark Dickey, Director Business Development
CHR: Bill Turner, Vice President Human Resources
Web address: www.valir.com
**Control:** Corporation, Investor–owned, for–profit **Service:** Rehabilitation

**Staffed Beds: 45**

**VETERANS AFFAIRS MEDICAL CENTER** See Oklahoma City Veterans Affairs Medical Center

### OKMULGEE—Okmulgee County

**GEORGE NIGH REHABILITATION CENTER** See Muscogee Creek Nation Physical Rehabilitation Center

★ **MUSCOGEE CREEK NATION MEDICAL CENTER (370057)**, 1401 Morris Drive, Zip 74447–6429, Mailing Address: P.O. Box 1038, Zip 74447–1038; tel. 918/756–4233 **A**9 10 **F**3 11 16 23 34 40 43 50 56 57 59 62 68 81 83 85 87 89 92 93 98 103 106 107 108 115 119 128 130 133 146 **P**6
Primary Contact: Sheridan Pickering, Chief Executive Officer
CFO: John W. Crawford, Chief Financial Officer
CMO: Michael Sandlin, M.D., Chief of Staff
CHR: Stacey R. Burton, Director Human Resources
Web address: www.okmulgeehospital.com
**Control:** PHS, Indian Service, Government, federal **Service:** General Medical and Surgical

**Staffed Beds: 46 Admissions: 728 Census: 11 Outpatient Visits: 19768 Births: 4 Total Expense ($000): 15857 Payroll Expense ($000): 8007 Personnel: 192**

**MUSCOGEE CREEK NATION PHYSICAL REHABILITATION CENTER (372023)**, 900 East Airport Road, Zip 74447–9082, Mailing Address: P.O. Box 1118, Zip 74447–1118; tel. 918/756–9211, (Total facility includes 8 beds in nursing home–type unit) (Data for 310 days) **A**10 **F**1 28 29 56 82 90 93 94 96 128 130 135 143 146 148 **P**5
Primary Contact: Gala McBee, Administrator
CFO: Djogan Djogan, Chief Financial Officer
CHR: Denaye Atwell, Manager Human Resources
Web address: www.gnrc.ouhsc.edu/
**Control:** PHS, Indian Service, Government, federal **Service:** Rehabilitation

**Staffed Beds: 38 Admissions: 257 Census: 14 Outpatient Visits: 4522 Births: 0 Total Expense ($000): 6111 Payroll Expense ($000): 3001 Personnel: 106**

### OWASSO—Tulsa County

★ **BAILEY MEDICAL CENTER (370228)**, 10502 North 110th East Avenue, Zip 74055–6655; tel. 918/376–8000 **A**9 10 **F**3 12 13 15 18 29 34 40 45 51 57 70 76 79 81 94 107 108 110 111 115 119 129 132 146 147 **S** Ardent Health Services, Nashville, TN
Primary Contact: Keith Mason, Chief Executive Officer
CFO: Brandon Bullard, Chief Financial Officer
CHR: Tandy Groves, Coordinator Human Resources
Web address: www.baileymedicalcenter.com
**Control:** Corporation, Investor–owned, for–profit **Service:** General Medical and Surgical

**Staffed Beds: 37 Admissions: 1351 Census: 8 Outpatient Visits: 30189 Births: 373 Total Expense ($000): 28894 Payroll Expense ($000): 10161 Personnel: 174**

★ **ST. JOHN OWASSO (370227)**, 12451 East 100th Street North, Zip 74055–4600; tel. 918/274–5000 **A**9 10 **F**3 11 13 15 18 29 30 34 35 40 43 45 57 59 64 68 76 79 81 85 87 93 107 108 110 111 114 115 119 130 131 132 146 **P**5 6 **S** Ascension Health, Saint Louis, MO
Primary Contact: David L. Phillips, President and Chief Executive Officer
CFO: Michael R. Nevins, Chief Financial Officer
CMO: Tim Hepner, M.D., Medical Director
CIO: Mike Reeves, Chief Information Officer
CNO: Dan Hall, R.N., Director of Nursing
Web address: www.stjohnowasso.com
**Control:** Church–operated, Nongovernment, not–for profit **Service:** General Medical and Surgical

**Staffed Beds: 45 Admissions: 1697 Census: 11 Outpatient Visits: 55463 Births: 391 Total Expense ($000): 29094 Payroll Expense ($000): 10147 Personnel: 192**

### PAULS VALLEY—Garvin County

★ **PAULS VALLEY GENERAL HOSPITAL (370156)**, 100 Valley Drive, Zip 73075–6613, Mailing Address: P.O. Box 368, Zip 73075–0368; tel. 405/238–5501 **A**9 10 20 **F**3 7 10 11 29 30 40 57 59 62 63 64 65 77 82 84 87 89 93 107 111 119 129 130 132 133 146 147 148 **P**3
Primary Contact: Nathan Staggs, Chief Executive Officer
CFO: Dale Semar, Controller
CIO: Rusty Weaver, Manager Information Technology
CHR: Stephanie Dancer, Manager Human Resources
CNO: Kari Howard, Interim Director of Nursing
Web address: www.pvgh.net
**Control:** City–Government, nonfederal **Service:** General Medical and Surgical

**Staffed Beds: 53 Admissions: 635 Census: 9 Outpatient Visits: 15299 Births: 0 Total Expense ($000): 13679 Payroll Expense ($000): 6174 Personnel: 152**

### PAWHUSKA—Osage County

★ **PAWHUSKA HOSPITAL (371309)**, 1101 East 15th Street, Zip 74056–1920; tel. 918/287–3232 **A**9 10 18 **F**3 11 29 34 35 40 50 57 64 68 75 77 90 93 107 128 133 135
Primary Contact: Shaun Beggs, Interim Administrator
CMO: Mike Priest, M.D., Chief of Staff
Web address: www.pawhuskahospital.org
**Control:** Church–operated, Nongovernment, not–for profit **Service:** General Medical and Surgical

**Staffed Beds: 15 Admissions: 81 Census: 2 Outpatient Visits: 15537 Births: 0 Total Expense ($000): 5225 Payroll Expense ($000): 2299 Personnel: 53**

### PERRY—Noble County

★ ◇ **PERRY MEMORIAL HOSPITAL (370139)**, 501 North 14th Street, Zip 73077–5099; tel. 580/336–3541 **A**9 10 20 21 **F**3 15 29 34 40 45 57 59 62 64 65 79 81 85 93 97 107 111 114 119 133 146 148 **P**6 **S** QHR, Brentwood, TN
Primary Contact: Howard D. Turner, Chief Executive Officer
CFO: Courtney Kozikuski, Chief Financial Officer
CMO: Michael Hartwig, M.D., Chief of Staff
CIO: Randy Taylor, Chief Information Technology Officer
CHR: Deb Ellis, Director Human Resources
CNO: Jeannie Carey, R.N., Director Patient Care
Web address: www.pmh–ok.org
**Control:** Hospital district or authority, Government, nonfederal **Service:** General Medical and Surgical

**Staffed Beds: 26 Admissions: 314 Census: 6 Outpatient Visits: 19074 Births: 0 Total Expense ($000): 8073 Payroll Expense ($000): 3655 Personnel: 109**

---

**Hospital, Medicare Provider Number, Address, Telephone, Approval, Facility, and Physician Codes, Health Care System**

★ American Hospital Association (AHA) membership ☐ The Joint Commission accreditation ○ Healthcare Facilities Accreditation Program ◇ DNV Healthcare Inc. accreditation ⇑ Center for Improvement in Healthcare Quality Accreditation △ Commission on Accreditation of Rehabilitation Facilities (CARF) accreditation

**OK**

### PONCA CITY—Kay County

✠ **ALLIANCEHEALTH PONCA CITY (370006)**, 1900 North 14th Street, Zip 74601–2099; tel. 580/765–3321 **A**1 9 10 19 **F**3 13 15 20 28 29 30 31 34 35 40 43 46 49 51 53 56 57 59 64 65 66 68 69 70 74 75 76 77 78 79 81 82 85 89 90 93 97 107 108 110 111 114 115 117 118 119 129 130 131 132 133 135 145 146 147 148 **P**6 **S** Community Health Systems, Inc., Franklin, TN
Primary Contact: R. Andrew Wachtel, FACHE, Chief Executive Officer
COO: Nikia Beene, Assistant Chief Executive Officer
CFO: Geoff Blomeley, Interim Chief Financial Officer
CIO: Rob Dreussi, Interim Director Information Systems
CHR: Lisa Zaloudek, Chief Human Resources Officer
CNO: Jeanne Stara, R.N., Chief Nursing Officer
Web address: www.poncamedcenter.com
**Control:** Corporation, Investor–owned, for–profit **Service:** General Medical and Surgical

**Staffed Beds:** 72 **Admissions:** 2801 **Census:** 25 **Outpatient Visits:** 65175 **Births:** 583 **Total Expense ($000):** 51170 **Payroll Expense ($000):** 20661 **Personnel:** 362

### POTEAU—Le Flore County

★ **EASTERN OKLAHOMA MEDICAL CENTER (370040)**, 105 Wall Street, Zip 74953–4433, Mailing Address: P.O. Box 1148, Zip 74953–1148; tel. 918/647–8161 **A**9 10 **F**3 11 13 15 29 40 43 45 50 57 62 68 70 81 85 86 98 107 110 111 114 115 116 119 146 **P**4
Primary Contact: Michael J. Carter, Chief Executive Officer
CFO: Nancy Frier, Chief Financial Officer
CMO: Dennis Carter, M.D., Chief of Staff
CIO: Michael C. Huggins, Administrator Network System
Web address: www.eomchospital.com
**Control:** County–Government, nonfederal **Service:** General Medical and Surgical

**Staffed Beds:** 59 **Admissions:** 1557 **Census:** 19 **Outpatient Visits:** 26980 **Births:** 218 **Total Expense ($000):** 18602 **Payroll Expense ($000):** 8852 **Personnel:** 211

### PRAGUE—Lincoln County

**PRAGUE COMMUNITY HOSPITAL (371301)**, 1322 Klabzuba Avenue, Zip 74864–9005, Mailing Address: P.O. Box S., Zip 74864–1090; tel. 405/567–4922, (Nonreporting) **A**9 10 18 **S** Rural Community Hospitals of America, Kansas City, MO
Primary Contact: William Holland, Chief Executive Officer
CFO: Doug Erickson, Chief Financial Officer
CMO: Darryl Jackson, D.O., Chief of Staff
CIO: Rhonda Whitnum, Director Health Improvement Management
CHR: Angie Brezny, Director Human Resources
Web address: www.praguehospital.com
**Control:** Corporation, Investor–owned, for–profit **Service:** General Medical and Surgical

**Staffed Beds:** 19

### PRYOR—Mayes County

✠ **ALLIANCEHEALTH PRYOR (370015)**, 111 North Bailey Street, Zip 74361–4201, Mailing Address: P.O. Box 278, Zip 74362–0278; tel. 918/825–1600 **A**1 9 10 **F**3 11 15 18 29 30 34 35 40 46 47 48 49 59 62 64 65 68 75 77 79 81 87 92 93 94 97 107 108 111 114 119 130 135 146 147 148 **S** Community Health Systems, Inc., Franklin, TN
Primary Contact: Douglas K. Weaver, FACHE, President
CMO: Jason Joice, M.D., Chief Medical Staff
CHR: Pamela A. Guthrie, Chief Human Resources Officer
CNO: Mary Ozment, Chief Nursing Officer
Web address: www.integrismayescounty.com
**Control:** Corporation, Investor–owned, for–profit **Service:** General Medical and Surgical

**Staffed Beds:** 24 **Admissions:** 584 **Census:** 5 **Outpatient Visits:** 28866 **Births:** 0 **Total Expense ($000):** 15506 **Payroll Expense ($000):** 5601 **Personnel:** 194

### PURCELL—Mcclain County

**PURCELL MUNICIPAL HOSPITAL (370158)**, 1500 North Green Avenue, Zip 73080–1699, Mailing Address: P.O. Box 511, Zip 73080–0511; tel. 405/527–6524 **A**9 10 **F**3 11 13 15 18 29 30 34 35 40 45 48 57 59 64 65 68 75 76 79 81 82 86 87 89 110 114 119 127 130 132 133 **P**4 6
Primary Contact: Kem Scully, Chief Executive Officer
COO: Lisa Roberts, Chief Operating Officer
CFO: Jennifer Warren, Chief Financial Officer
CMO: Heather Lynch, M.D., Chief of Staff
CIO: Jennifer Coates, Coordinator Information Technology
CHR: Tara Selfridge, Manager Human Resources
Web address: www.purcellhospital.com
**Control:** City–Government, nonfederal **Service:** General Medical and Surgical

**Staffed Beds:** 30 **Admissions:** 701 **Census:** 7 **Outpatient Visits:** 51556 **Births:** 10 **Total Expense ($000):** 13755 **Payroll Expense ($000):** 6173 **Personnel:** 133

### SALLISAW—Sequoyah County

**SEQUOYAH MEMORIAL HOSPITAL (370112)**, 213 East Redwood Street, Zip 74955–2811, Mailing Address: P.O. Box 505, Zip 74955–0505; tel. 918/774–1100 **A**9 10 **F**3 8 11 14 15 28 29 30 32 34 35 40 43 45 46 50 57 59 60 62 63 64 65 77 81 84 86 87 91 93 107 109 110 111 114 115 119 128 129 130 132 133 146 **P**4 5
Primary Contact: Debra R. Knoke, Chief Executive Officer
COO: Debra R. Knoke, Chief Executive Officer
CFO: Glenn Click, Chief Financial Officer
CMO: William E. Wood, M.D., Chief of Staff
CIO: Gary McClanahan, Chief Information Officer
Web address: www.sequoyahmemorial.com/home.php
**Control:** Hospital district or authority, Government, nonfederal **Service:** General Medical and Surgical

**Staffed Beds:** 26 **Admissions:** 538 **Census:** 5 **Outpatient Visits:** 16238 **Births:** 1 **Personnel:** 266

### SAPULPA—Creek County

★ **ST. JOHN SAPULPA (371312)**, 519 South Division Street, Zip 74066–4501, Mailing Address: P.O. Box 1368, Zip 74067–1368; tel. 918/224–4280 **A**9 10 18 **F**3 8 11 14 29 30 34 35 40 45 57 59 64 68 79 81 85 86 87 107 111 119 130 132 133 135 143 146 147 **P**5 6 **S** Ascension Health, Saint Louis, MO
Primary Contact: David L. Phillips, Chief Executive Officer
CFO: John W. Crawford, Chief Financial Officer
CMO: Jason Lepak, M.D., Medical Director
CNO: Kelly Johnson, R.N., Chief Nursing Officer
Web address: www.sjmc.org
**Control:** Church–operated, Nongovernment, not–for profit **Service:** General Medical and Surgical

**Staffed Beds:** 25 **Admissions:** 784 **Census:** 10 **Outpatient Visits:** 38652 **Births:** 0 **Total Expense ($000):** 22500 **Payroll Expense ($000):** 7581 **Personnel:** 154

### SAYRE—Beckham County

★ **SAYRE MEMORIAL HOSPITAL (370103)**, 911 Hospital Drive, Zip 73662–1206; tel. 580/928–5541, (Nonreporting) **A**9 10
Primary Contact: Donald Bates, Chief Executive Officer
CFO: Brenda K. Doyel, Chief Financial Officer
Web address: www.sayrehospital.org
**Control:** Other not–for–profit (including NFP Corporation) **Service:** General Medical and Surgical

**Staffed Beds:** 25

### SEILING—Dewey County

★ **SEILING MUNICIPAL HOSPITAL (371332)**, Highway 60 N.E., Zip 73663, Mailing Address: P.O. Box 720, Zip 73663–0720; tel. 580/922–7361, (Nonreporting) **A**9 10 18 **S** Mercy Health, Chesterfield, MO
Primary Contact: Bobby Stitt, R.N., Chief Executive Officer
CFO: Nancy Freed, Chief Financial Officer
CMO: Kenneth Duffy, M.D., Medical Director
CHR: Sandy Landreth, Director Human Resources
Web address: www.seilinghospital.com
**Control:** City–Government, nonfederal **Service:** General Medical and Surgical

**Staffed Beds:** 18

### SEMINOLE—Seminole County

✠ **ALLIANCEHEALTH SEMINOLE (370229)**, 2401 Wrangler Boulevard, Zip 74868–1917; tel. 405/303–4000 **A**1 9 10 **F**3 11 15 18 29 30 34 35 40 41 50 51 59 65 68 79 81 82 93 102 107 108 110 111 114 119 130 133 135 146 148 **P**6 **S** Community Health Systems, Inc., Franklin, TN
Primary Contact: Benjamin Heath, Interim Chief Executive Officer
CMO: Nikki Chawla, M.D., Medical Director
CHR: Lori Friend, Human Resources Director
CNO: Barbara Lewis, Chief Nursing Officer
Web address: www.hma.com
**Control:** Corporation, Investor–owned, for–profit **Service:** General Medical and Surgical

**Staffed Beds:** 32 **Admissions:** 739 **Census:** 6 **Outpatient Visits:** 22699 **Births:** 0 **Total Expense ($000):** 12588 **Payroll Expense ($000):** 4901 **Personnel:** 86

### SHATTUCK—Ellis County

★ **NEWMAN MEMORIAL HOSPITAL (370007)**, 905 South Main Street, Zip 73858–9205; tel. 580/938–2551 **A**9 10 20 **F**3 11 13 15 29 30 34 35 39 40 53 59 62 64 65 69 76 81 87 93 104 107 111 115 119 130 133 146 **P**6
Primary Contact: Steve Stewart, Interim Chief Executive Officer
CFO: Kellcie Skinner, Controller
CMO: Danna Stuart, M.D., Chief Medical Officer
CIO: Robert Neal, Manager Information Technology Services
CNO: Rylee Casper, R.N., Chief Nursing Officer
Web address: www.newmanmemorialhospital.org
**Control:** Other not–for–profit (including NFP Corporation) **Service:** General Medical and Surgical

**Staffed Beds:** 27 **Admissions:** 379 **Census:** 3

*Many Facility Codes have changed. Please refer to the AHA Guide Code Chart.*

**OK**

## SHAWNEE—Pottawatomie County

**CORNERSTONE HOSPITAL OF OKLAHOMA–SHAWNEE (372019)**, 1900 Gordon Cooper Drive, 2nd Floor, Zip 74801–8603, Mailing Address: PO BOX 1245, Zip 74802–1245; tel. 405/395–5800, (Nonreporting) **A**9 10 **S** Cornerstone Healthcare Group, Dallas, TX
Primary Contact: Elizabeth Waytula, Chief Executive Officer
COO: Elizabeth Waytula, Chief Executive Officer
CMO: Keith Conaway, M.D., Chief Medical Officer
Web address: www.chghospitals.com/shawnee/
**Control:** Corporation, Investor–owned, for–profit **Service:** Long–Term Acute Care hospital

**Staffed Beds:** 34

☒ **ST. ANTHONY SHAWNEE HOSPITAL (370149)**, 1102 West MacArthur Street, Zip 74804–1744; tel. 405/273–2270 **A**1 2 9 10 19 **F**3 11 13 15 18 20 29 30 31 34 35 40 43 45 50 57 59 60 64 65 68 69 70 75 76 77 78 79 81 82 87 94 107 110 111 114 119 121 123 129 130 131 132 135 144 146 147 148 **P**6 **S** SSM Health, Saint Louis, MO
Primary Contact: Charles E. Skillings, President and Chief Executive Officer
COO: Angela Mohr, R.N., Vice President Nursing and Chief Operating Officer
CFO: Jennifer Pierce, Administrative Director of Finance
CMO: Gaynell Anderson, M.D., Medical Director
CHR: Michael Spears, Human Resource Leader
CNO: Angela Mohr, R.N., Vice President Nursing and Chief Operating Officer
Web address: www.stanthonyshawnee.com
**Control:** Other not–for–profit (including NFP Corporation) **Service:** General Medical and Surgical

**Staffed Beds:** 76 **Admissions:** 3828 **Census:** 32 **Outpatient Visits:** 103529 **Births:** 865 **Total Expense ($000):** 65583 **Payroll Expense ($000):** 23036 **Personnel:** 430

**UNITY HEALTH CENTER** See St. Anthony Shawnee Hospital

## SPENCER—Oklahoma County

**INTEGRIS MENTAL HEALTH SYSTEM–SPENCER** See Integris Baptist Medical Center, Oklahoma City

## STIGLER—Haskell County

**HASKELL COUNTY COMMUNITY HOSPITAL (371335)**, 401 Northwest H Street, Zip 74462–1625; tel. 918/967–4682 **A**9 10 18 **F**8 11 15 35 40 45 64 81 87 91 92 93 97 107 110 114 119 128 130 133 146 **S** Rural Community Hospitals of America, Kansas City, MO
Primary Contact: Donald E. Buchanan, Interim Chief Executive Officer
CMO: Stephen Woodson, D.O., Chief of Staff
CIO: Steve Hurst, Information Technology Specialist
Web address: www.haskellhospital.com
**Control:** Corporation, Investor–owned, for–profit **Service:** General Medical and Surgical

**Staffed Beds:** 18 **Admissions:** 370 **Census:** 9 **Outpatient Visits:** 11011 **Births:** 0 **Total Expense ($000):** 7294 **Payroll Expense ($000):** 3444 **Personnel:** 100

**HASKELL COUNTY HEALTHCARE SYSTEM** See Haskell County Community Hospital

## STILLWATER—Payne County

★ ◇ **STILLWATER MEDICAL CENTER (370049)**, 1323 West Sixth Avenue, Zip 74074–4399, Mailing Address: P.O. Box 2408, Zip 74076–2408; tel. 405/372–1480 **A**3 5 9 10 21 **F**3 8 11 13 16 20 22 28 29 31 34 35 40 43 45 46 47 48 49 50 51 53 59 62 64 65 68 69 70 74 75 76 78 79 81 82 85 87 90 91 93 94 97 107 108 110 111 115 117 119 126 129 130 132 146 147 148 **P**5 6
Primary Contact: Jerry G. Moeller, FACHE, President and Chief Executive Officer
CFO: Alan Lovelace, Vice President and Chief Financial Officer
CMO: Steve Cummings, M.D., Chief of Medical Staff
CIO: Chris Roark, Chief Information Officer
CHR: Keith Hufnagel, Director Human Resources
CNO: Elizabeth Michael, R.N., Vice President Patient Care Services and Chief Nursing Officer
Web address: www.stillwater–medical.org
**Control:** Hospital district or authority, Government, nonfederal **Service:** General Medical and Surgical

**Staffed Beds:** 87 **Admissions:** 3463 **Census:** 42 **Outpatient Visits:** 114889 **Births:** 942 **Total Expense ($000):** 135157 **Payroll Expense ($000):** 56548 **Personnel:** 983

## STILWELL—Adair County

**MEMORIAL HOSPITAL (370178)**, 1401 West Locust, Zip 74960–3275, Mailing Address: P.O. Box 272, Zip 74960–0272; tel. 918/696–3101, (Nonreporting) **A**9 10
Primary Contact: Alan L. Adams, President
Web address: www.stilwellmemorialhospital.com
**Control:** Corporation, Investor–owned, for–profit **Service:** General Medical and Surgical

**Staffed Beds:** 30

## STROUD—Lincoln County

**STROUD REGIONAL MEDICAL CENTER (371316)**, Highway 66 West, Zip 74079, Mailing Address: P.O. Box 530, Zip 74079–0530; tel. 918/968–3571 **A**9 10 18 **F**3 8 11 29 30 34 35 40 41 43 45 57 59 64 68 81 89 93 107 114 128 130 133 135 148 **P**5 **S** Southern Plains Medical Group, Oklahoma City, OK
Primary Contact: Tommy Smith, Chief Executive Officer
CFO: Richard E. Rentsch, President
CMO: Ken Darvin, M.D., Chief of Staff
CIO: Donna Buchanan, Director Nursing
CHR: Leannette Raffety, Administrative Generalist
Web address: www.stroudhospital.com/
**Control:** Other not–for–profit (including NFP Corporation) **Service:** General Medical and Surgical

**Staffed Beds:** 25 **Admissions:** 206 **Census:** 2 **Outpatient Visits:** 4405 **Births:** 0 **Total Expense ($000):** 18488 **Personnel:** 56

## SULPHUR—Murray County

★ **ARBUCKLE MEMORIAL HOSPITAL (371328)**, 2011 West Broadway Street, Zip 73086–4221; tel. 580/622–2161 **A**9 10 18 **F**3 11 29 32 40 45 56 57 81 87 93 107 119 133 135 148 **P**6 **S** Mercy Health, Chesterfield, MO
Primary Contact: Darin Farrell, Chief Executive Officer
CFO: Denise Welch, Chief Financial Officer
CMO: Ryan Oden, M.D., Chief of Staff
CIO: Tiffany Sands, Manager Health Information
CHR: Sallie Tomlinson, Manager Human Resources
CNO: Sarah Freehill, Chief Nursing Officer
Web address: www.arbucklehospital.com/
**Control:** County–Government, nonfederal **Service:** General Medical and Surgical

**Staffed Beds:** 13 **Admissions:** 671 **Census:** 15 **Outpatient Visits:** 26699 **Births:** 0 **Total Expense ($000):** 14128 **Payroll Expense ($000):** 7179 **Personnel:** 125

## TAHLEQUAH—Cherokee County

★ ◇ **CHEROKEE NATION W.W. HASTINGS INDIAN HOSPITAL (370171)**, 100 South Bliss Avenue, Zip 74464–2512; tel. 918/458–3100, (Nonreporting) **A**10 21 **S** U. S. Indian Health Service, Rockville, MD
Primary Contact: Brian Hail, Chief Executive Officer
COO: Mitchell Thornbrugh, Administrative Officer
CMO: Douglas Nolan, M.D., Medical Director
CIO: Mitchell Thornbrugh, Acting Chief Information Officer
CNO: Valerie J. Rogers, Director of Nursing
Web address: www.cherokee.org
**Control:** PHS, Indian Service, Government, federal **Service:** General Medical and Surgical

**Staffed Beds:** 58

★ **NORTHEASTERN HEALTH SYSTEM (370089)**, 1400 East Downing Street, Zip 74464–3324, Mailing Address: P.O. Box 1008, Zip 74465–1008; tel. 918/456–0641 **A**9 10 13 20 **F**3 7 11 13 15 17 18 20 22 24 28 29 30 31 34 35 39 40 43 45 46 47 51 57 59 60 64 68 70 74 75 76 77 78 79 80 81 82 85 87 89 90 93 97 98 103 107 108 110 111 114 115 116 117 118 119 120 121 123 129 130 135 146 147 148 **P**6
Primary Contact: Brian K. Woodliff, President and Chief Executive Officer Northeastern Health System
COO: Mark McCroskey, Vice President Operations
CFO: Julie Ward, Vice President Finance
CIO: Julie Ward, Vice President Finance
CHR: Phyllis Smith, Vice President Human Resources
CNO: Donna Dallis, R.N., Vice President Patient Care
Web address: www.tch–ok.org
**Control:** City–Government, nonfederal **Service:** General Medical and Surgical

**Staffed Beds:** 90 **Admissions:** 3314 **Census:** 42 **Outpatient Visits:** 126374 **Births:** 363 **Total Expense ($000):** 85677 **Payroll Expense ($000):** 26104 **Personnel:** 703

---

**Hospital, Medicare Provider Number, Address, Telephone, Approval, Facility, and Physician Codes, Health Care System**

★ American Hospital Association (AHA) membership
☐ The Joint Commission accreditation
○ Healthcare Facilities Accreditation Program
◇ DNV Healthcare Inc. accreditation
⇑ Center for Improvement in Healthcare Quality Accreditation
△ Commission on Accreditation of Rehabilitation Facilities (CARF) accreditation

**OK**

## TALIHINA—Latimer County

✠ **CHOCTAW NATION HEALTH CARE CENTER (370172)**, One Choctaw Way, Zip 74571–2022; tel. 918/567–7000 **A**1 10 13 **F**3 11 13 15 18 30 32 34 35 38 39 40 43 45 50 53 54 56 57 58 59 61 64 65 68 71 74 75 76 79 81 85 86 87 89 91 92 93 94 96 97 99 100 101 103 104 107 111 114 115 119 127 129 130 132 134 135 144 146 147 148 **P**6
Primary Contact: Todd Hallmark, Chief Executive Officer
COO: Todd Hallmark, Chief Operating Officer
CMO: Jason Hill, M.D., Chief Medical Officer
CIO: Skip Leader, Chief Information Officer
CHR: Evelyn Jones, Director Human Resources
Web address: www.cnhsa.com
**Control:** PHS, Indian Service, Government, federal **Service:** General Medical and Surgical

**Staffed Beds:** 44 **Admissions:** 1579 **Census:** 12 **Outpatient Visits:** 206733 **Births:** 753 **Personnel:** 381

## TISHOMINGO—Johnston County

**JOHNSTON MEMORIAL HOSPITAL** See Mercy Hospital Tishomingo

★ **MERCY HOSPITAL TISHOMINGO (371304)**, 1000 South Byrd Street, Zip 73460–3299; tel. 580/371–2327 **A**9 10 18 **F**3 29 40 43 107 108 133 134 **S** Mercy Health, Chesterfield, MO
Primary Contact: Gary Sharum, Administrator
CFO: Lisa Dowling, Manager Finance
CHR: Arlita Hummelke, Manager Human Resources
Web address: www.mercy.net/
**Control:** Church–operated, Nongovernment, not–for profit **Service:** General Medical and Surgical

**Staffed Beds:** 25 **Admissions:** 327 **Census:** 5 **Outpatient Visits:** 4768 **Births:** 0 **Total Expense ($000):** 5211 **Payroll Expense ($000):** 2709 **Personnel:** 47

## TULSA—Tulsa County

**AMG SPECIALTY HOSPITAL–TULSA (372011)**, 2408 East 81st Street, Suite 2800, Zip 74104–6510; tel. 918/710–3620, (Includes CONTINUOUS CARE CENTERS OF OKLAHOMA, 744 West Ninth Street, 9th Floor, Zip 74127; tel. 918/599–4604), (Nonreporting) **A**9 10 **S** AMG Integrated Healthcare Management, Lafayette, LA
Primary Contact: Stacy Wilde, Chief Executive Officer
COO: Mike Harris, Chief Operating Officer
CFO: Basil Wyatt, Chief Financial Officer
CMO: Mark Myers, M.D., Chief Medical Officer
CIO: Dana Jetton, Chief Information Officer
CHR: Donna Nagel, Director Human Resources
Web address: www.amgihm.com
**Control:** Other not–for–profit (including NFP Corporation) **Service:** Long–Term Acute Care hospital

**Staffed Beds:** 46

**BROOKHAVEN HOSPITAL (374012)**, 201 South Garnett Road, Zip 74128–1805; tel. 918/438–4257 **A**9 10 **F**4 5 29 30 38 74 75 77 98 104 106 130 132
Primary Contact: Rolf B. Gainer, M.D., Chief Executive Officer and Administrator
CFO: Kenneth Pierce, Chief Financial Officer
CMO: Mark Gage, D.O., Medical Director
CHR: Heather Dudley, Director Administrative Services
CNO: Matt Maxey, R.N., Director of Nursing
Web address: www.brookhavenhospital.com
**Control:** Corporation, Investor–owned, for–profit **Service:** Psychiatric

**Staffed Beds:** 64 **Admissions:** 1167 **Census:** 51 **Outpatient Visits:** 4279 **Births:** 0 **Total Expense ($000):** 11171 **Payroll Expense ($000):** 6383 **Personnel:** 162

**CONTINUOUS CARE CENTERS OF TULSA** See AMG Specialty Hospital–Tulsa

✠ **HILLCREST HOSPITAL – SOUTH (370202)**, 8801 South 101st East Avenue, Zip 74133–5716; tel. 918/294–4000 **A**1 9 10 **F**3 13 15 18 20 22 24 26 28 29 34 40 43 47 49 51 64 70 76 79 81 85 86 87 91 93 97 107 108 110 111 114 115 119 126 129 130 131 145 146 147 148 **S** Ardent Health Services, Nashville, TN
Primary Contact: Lynn M. Mergen, Chief Executive Officer
COO: Matthew Morgan, Associate Administrator
CFO: James Washecka, Chief Financial Officer
CMO: David L. Pohl, M.D., Chief of Staff
CIO: David Graser, Vice President and Chief Information Officer
CHR: Rachel Steward, Director Human Resources
CNO: Dava Baldridge, R.N., Chief Nursing Officer
Web address: www.southcresthospital.com
**Control:** Corporation, Investor–owned, for–profit **Service:** General Medical and Surgical

**Staffed Beds:** 160 **Admissions:** 7263 **Census:** 81 **Outpatient Visits:** 84109 **Births:** 1668 **Total Expense ($000):** 117310 **Payroll Expense ($000):** 35615 **Personnel:** 584

★ ◇ **HILLCREST MEDICAL CENTER (370001)**, 1120 South Utica, Zip 74104–4090; tel. 918/579–1000 **A**3 5 9 10 21 **F**3 11 13 15 16 17 18 20 22 24 26 28 29 30 31 37 40 43 45 46 47 48 49 50 51 53 55 57 58 59 60 68 70 72 74 76 78 79 80 81 84 86 87 90 93 98 99 100 106 107 108 110 111 114 115 116 117 118 119 120 121 123 124 126 129 130 131 135 145 146 147 148 **P**6 **S** Ardent Health Services, Nashville, TN
Primary Contact: Kevin J. Gross, Interim Chief Executive Officer
CFO: Steve Winegeart, Chief Financial Officer
CMO: Steven Landgarten, M.D., Chief Medical Officer
CHR: Julie Eccleston, Vice President Human Resources
Web address: www.hillcrest.com/home
**Control:** Corporation, Investor–owned, for–profit **Service:** General Medical and Surgical

**Staffed Beds:** 557 **Admissions:** 24085 **Census:** 365 **Outpatient Visits:** 180661 **Births:** 2817 **Total Expense ($000):** 413246 **Payroll Expense ($000):** 114516 **Personnel:** 1766

✠ **LAUREATE PSYCHIATRIC CLINIC AND HOSPITAL (374020)**, 6655 South Yale Avenue, Zip 74136–3329; tel. 918/481–4000 **A**1 3 5 9 10 **F**4 5 40 98 99 100 101 102 103 104 105 106 146 **P**6 **S** Saint Francis Health System, Tulsa, OK
Primary Contact: William Schloss, Senior Vice President and Administrator
COO: William Schloss, Senior Vice President and Administrator
CFO: Barry L. Steichen, Executive Vice President, Chief Administrative Officer and Chief Financial Officer
CMO: Mark I. Frost, M.D., Vice President Medical Staff Affairs
CHR: Amy B. Adams, Executive Director Human Resources
CNO: Lynn A. Sund, R.N., Senior Vice President, Administrator and Chief Nursing Executive
Web address: www.laureate.com
**Control:** Other not–for–profit (including NFP Corporation) **Service:** Psychiatric

**Staffed Beds:** 75 **Admissions:** 3099 **Census:** 67 **Outpatient Visits:** 67906 **Births:** 0 **Total Expense ($000):** 30809 **Payroll Expense ($000):** 18629 **Personnel:** 346

**MEADOWBROOK SPECIALTY HOSPITAL OF TULSA** See Post Acute Medical Specialty Hospital of Tulsa

◇ **OKLAHOMA STATE UNIVERSITY MEDICAL CENTER (370078)**, 744 West Ninth Street, Zip 74127–9020; tel. 918/599–1000 **A**9 10 11 12 13 **F**3 8 13 15 18 20 22 24 26 28 29 30 31 34 35 40 43 45 47 49 50 56 57 59 64 65 70 71 72 74 75 76 77 78 79 81 84 85 87 89 92 93 96 97 107 108 110 111 115 119 130 135 146 148 **P**6
Primary Contact: Rhett Stover, Chief Executive Officer
COO: Jeff Stroup, Chief Operating Officer
CFO: Sara Bradley, Chief Financial Officer
CMO: Damon Baker, D.O., Chief Medical Officer
CIO: Heidi Holmes, Chief Information Officer
CHR: Sunny J. Benjamin, Chief Human Resources Officer
CNO: Joy Upshaw, Chief Nursing Officer
Web address: www.osumc.net
**Control:** City–Government, nonfederal **Service:** General Medical and Surgical

**Staffed Beds:** 191 **Admissions:** 5900 **Census:** 78

**OKLAHOMA SURGICAL HOSPITAL (370210)**, 2408 East 81st Street, Suite 300, Zip 74137–4215; tel. 918/477–5000 **A**3 5 9 10 **F**3 12 29 30 34 35 40 41 44 45 49 50 51 64 65 68 74 75 77 79 81 82 85 86 87 93 94 107 108 111 114 119 126 130 131 **P**2
Primary Contact: Rick Ferguson, Chief Executive Officer
CFO: Dub Cleland, Chief Financial Officer
Web address: www.oklahomasurgicalhospital.com
**Control:** Partnership, Investor–owned, for–profit **Service:** General Medical and Surgical

**Staffed Beds:** 60 **Admissions:** 3606 **Census:** 24 **Outpatient Visits:** 25811 **Births:** 0 **Total Expense ($000):** 80320 **Payroll Expense ($000):** 17639 **Personnel:** 363

**PARKSIDE PSYCHIATRIC HOSPITAL AND CLINIC (374021)**, 1620 East 12th Street, Zip 74120–5407; tel. 918/582–2131 **A**3 5 9 10 **F**3 5 35 38 59 98 99 102 103 104 105 106 146
Primary Contact: Debra Moore, Chief Executive Officer
CFO: Saunya Moore, Chief Financial Officer
CMO: Marvin Jin, M.D., Medical Director
CIO: Joe Vitali, Director Information Technology
CHR: David Patterson, Director Human Resources
Web address: www.parksideinc.org
**Control:** Other not–for–profit (including NFP Corporation) **Service:** Psychiatric

**Staffed Beds:** 60 **Admissions:** 1850 **Census:** 60

◇ **PINNACLE SPECIALTY HOSPITAL (370233)**, 2408 East 81st Street, Suite 600, Zip 74137–4200; tel. 918/392–2780 **A**10 11 **F**12 29 33 75 84 129 148
Primary Contact: Mark Stearns, Administrator
Web address: www.pinnaclespecialtyhospital.com/
**Control:** State–Government, nonfederal **Service:** General Medical and Surgical

**Staffed Beds:** 4 **Admissions:** 54 **Census:** 1 **Births:** 0

✠ **POST ACUTE MEDICAL SPECIALTY HOSPITAL OF TULSA (372018)**, 3219 South 79th East Avenue, Zip 74145–1343; tel. 918/663–8183 **A**1 9 10 **F**1 3 29 40 60 68 70 75 87 94 100 107 108 114 130 143 148 **S** Post Acute Medical, LLC, Enola, PA
Primary Contact: Lee A. Simpson, Jr., Chief Executive Officer
CFO: Lee A. Simpson, Jr., Chief Executive Officer
Web address: www.postacutetulsa.com
**Control:** Corporation, Investor–owned, for–profit **Service:** Long–Term Acute Care hospital

**Staffed Beds:** 60 **Admissions:** 478 **Census:** 35 **Outpatient Visits:** 14 **Births:** 0 **Total Expense ($000):** 18476 **Payroll Expense ($000):** 7108 **Personnel:** 106

**SAINT FRANCIS HEART HOSPITAL** See Saint Francis Hospital

✠ **SAINT FRANCIS HOSPITAL (370091)**, 6161 South Yale Avenue, Zip 74136–1902; tel. 918/494–2200, (Includes CHILDREN'S HOSPITAL AT SAINT FRANCIS, 6161 South Yale Avenue, tel. 918/502–6714; SAINT FRANCIS HEART HOSPITAL, 6161 South Yale Avenue, tel. 918/502–2022) **A**1 2 3 5 9 10 **F**3 7 8 11 12 13 15 17 18 19 20 21 22 23 24 25 26 27 28 29 30 31 32 35 37 39 40 41 43 44 45 46 47 48 49 50 51 54 55 56 57 58 59 60 61 64 66 68 70 72 73 74 75 76 77 78 79 80 81 82 83 84 85 86 87 88 89 90 92 93 107 108 110 111 114 115 116 117 118 119 120 121 123 124 126 129 130 131 132 135 136 138 141 146 148 **P**6 **S** Saint Francis Health System, Tulsa, OK
Primary Contact: Lynn A. Sund, R.N., MS, Senior Vice President, Administrator and Chief Nurse Executive
COO: Lynn A. Sund, R.N., Senior Vice President, Administrator and Chief Nurse Executive
CFO: Barry L. Steichen, Executive Vice President and Chief Operating Officer
CMO: Peter P. Aran, M.D., Senior Vice President and Chief Medical Officer
CHR: Amy B. Adams, Executive Director Human Resources
Web address: www.saintfrancis.com
**Control:** Other not–for–profit (including NFP Corporation) **Service:** General Medical and Surgical

**Staffed Beds:** 833 **Admissions:** 41898 **Census:** 599 **Outpatient Visits:** 372488 **Births:** 3977 **Total Expense ($000):** 693544 **Payroll Expense ($000):** 266652 **Personnel:** 5109

✠ **SAINT FRANCIS HOSPITAL SOUTH (370218)**, 10501 East 91St. Streeet, Zip 74133–5790; tel. 918/455–3535 **A**1 9 10 **F**11 13 15 18 20 22 26 29 30 34 35 37 39 40 44 48 49 50 51 57 58 60 61 64 68 70 72 75 76 79 81 82 85 87 107 108 110 111 114 115 118 119 130 146 148 **P**6 **S** Saint Francis Health System, Tulsa, OK
Primary Contact: David S. Weil, Senior Vice President and Administrator
COO: Barry L. Steichen, Executive Vice President
CFO: Barry L. Steichen, Executive Vice President
CMO: Peter P. Aran, M.D., Senior Vice President and Chief Medical Officer
CHR: Amy B. Adams, Executive Director Human Resources
CNO: Jimmie Cash, R.N., Executive Director and Patient Care
Web address: www.saintfrancis.com/south/
**Control:** Other not–for–profit (including NFP Corporation) **Service:** General Medical and Surgical

**Staffed Beds:** 81 **Admissions:** 4355 **Census:** 44 **Outpatient Visits:** 78390 **Births:** 1397 **Total Expense ($000):** 63721 **Payroll Expense ($000):** 24959 **Personnel:** 420

✠ **SELECT SPECIALTY HOSPITAL–TULSA MIDTOWN (372007)**, 1125 South Trenton Avenue, 3rd Floor, Zip 74120–5418; tel. 918/579–7300 **A**1 9 10 **F**1 3 29 75 85 87 130 148 **S** Select Medical Corporation, Mechanicsburg, PA
Primary Contact: Linda Tiemens, Chief Executive Officer
CMO: E. Joe Schelbar, M.D., Medical Director
CNO: Connie Ryan, Chief Nursing Officer
Web address: www.selectmedical.com
**Control:** Corporation, Investor–owned, for–profit **Service:** Long–Term Acute Care hospital

**Staffed Beds:** 56 **Admissions:** 369 **Census:** 26 **Outpatient Visits:** 0 **Births:** 0 **Total Expense ($000):** 13823 **Payroll Expense ($000):** 6011 **Personnel:** 105

☐ **SHADOW MOUNTAIN BEHAVIORAL HEALTH SYSTEM**, 6262 South Sheridan Road, Zip 74133–4055; tel. 918/492–8200 **A**1 3 5 9 **F**40 41 54 59 98 99 101 102 104 106 **P**6 **S** Universal Health Services, Inc., King of Prussia, PA
Primary Contact: Mike Kistler, Chief Executive Officer
CFO: Kirt Penrod, Chief Financial Officer
CMO: K. Michael Saliba, M.D., Medical Director
CHR: Jordan Cooke, Director Human Resources
Web address: www.shadowmountainbhs.com
**Control:** Corporation, Investor–owned, for–profit **Service:** Children's hospital psychiatric

**Staffed Beds:** 226 **Admissions:** 2298 **Census:** 189 **Outpatient Visits:** 26374 **Births:** 0 **Total Expense ($000):** 32045 **Payroll Expense ($000):** 12554 **Personnel:** 347

☐ **SOUTHWESTERN REGIONAL MEDICAL CENTER (370190)**, 10109 East 79th Street, Zip 74133–4564; tel. 918/286–5000 **A**1 2 3 5 10 13 **F**3 15 29 30 31 34 35 36 40 44 45 46 47 49 53 55 57 58 59 64 67 70 75 77 78 80 81 82 85 86 87 93 100 107 108 110 111 114 116 117 118 119 120 121 123 124 130 132 135 136 143 145 146 148 **P**6 **S** Cancer Treatment Centers of America, Schaumburg, IL
Primary Contact: Richard Haldeman, President and Chief Executive Officer
COO: Jay Foley, Chief Operating Officer
CFO: David Hedges, Chief Financial Officer
CMO: Daniel Nader, D.O., Chief of Staff
CIO: Craig Olson, Director Information Technology
CHR: Ryan Crawford, Director Talent
CNO: Denise Geuder, Vice President Patient Care Service and Chief Nursing Officer
Web address: www.cancercenter.com
**Control:** Corporation, Investor–owned, for–profit **Service:** Cancer

**Staffed Beds:** 40 **Admissions:** 929 **Census:** 19 **Outpatient Visits:** 68640 **Births:** 0 **Personnel:** 767

✠ **ST. JOHN MEDICAL CENTER (370114)**, 1923 South Utica Avenue, Zip 74104–6502; tel. 918/744–2345 **A**1 2 3 5 9 10 **F**3 8 9 11 12 13 14 15 17 18 19 20 22 24 26 28 29 30 31 34 39 40 43 45 46 47 48 49 50 51 53 54 56 57 58 59 60 61 62 63 64 65 66 68 70 72 73 74 75 76 77 78 79 80 81 82 83 84 85 86 87 88 89 90 92 93 94 96 97 100 104 107 108 110 111 114 115 116 117 118 119 120 121 123 124 126 129 130 131 132 135 138 141 143 145 146 147 148 **P**1 5 **S** Ascension Health, Saint Louis, MO
Primary Contact: Jeffrey D. Nowlin, President and Chief Operating Officer
COO: Jeffrey D. Nowlin, President and Chief Operating Officer
CFO: Wayne Walthall, Vice President and Chief Financial Officer
CMO: William Allred, M.D., Vice President Medical Affairs
CIO: Mike Reeves, Vice President
CHR: John Page Bachman, Corporate Vice President
CNO: Pamela Kiser, R.N., Chief Nursing Executive and Vice President of Nursing
Web address: www.sjmc.org
**Control:** Church–operated, Nongovernment, not–for profit **Service:** General Medical and Surgical

**Staffed Beds:** 547 **Admissions:** 28728 **Census:** 403 **Outpatient Visits:** 274307 **Births:** 2205 **Total Expense ($000):** 477102 **Payroll Expense ($000):** 152933 **Personnel:** 2753

✠ **TULSA SPINE AND SPECIALTY HOSPITAL (370216)**, 6901 South Olympia Avenue, Zip 74132–1843; tel. 918/388–5701, (Nonreporting) **A**1 9 10
Primary Contact: Terry L. Woodbeck, Administrator
CFO: Thom Biby, Chief Financial Officer
CMO: David Fell, M.D., Chief Medical Officer
Web address: www.tulsaspinehospital.com
**Control:** Corporation, Investor–owned, for–profit **Service:** General Medical and Surgical

**Staffed Beds:** 21

**VINITA—Craig County**

★ **CRAIG GENERAL HOSPITAL (370065)**, 735 North Foreman Street, Zip 74301–1418, Mailing Address: P.O. Box 326, Zip 74301–0326; tel. 918/256–7551 **A**9 10 20 **F**3 11 13 15 29 30 34 35 40 53 57 59 64 65 75 76 81 85 89 93 97 98 103 104 105 106 107 110 111 115 119 127 128 130 132 133 135 146 147 148
Primary Contact: Herbert Crum, Jr., Chief Executive Officer
CMO: Ed Allensworth, M.D., Medical Director
CHR: Darlene R. Nolte, Chief Human Resource Officer
CNO: Ann Carr, R.N., Chief Nursing Officer
Web address: www.craiggeneralhospital.com
**Control:** Hospital district or authority, Government, nonfederal **Service:** General Medical and Surgical

**Staffed Beds:** 55 **Admissions:** 1483 **Census:** 23 **Outpatient Visits:** 36283 **Births:** 85 **Total Expense ($000):** 26440 **Payroll Expense ($000):** 11113 **Personnel:** 231

**OKLAHOMA FORENSIC CENTER**, 24800 South 4420 Road, Zip 74301–5544, Mailing Address: P.O. Box 69, Zip 74301–0069; tel. 918/256–7841, (Nonreporting) **S** Oklahoma Department of Mental Health and Substance Abuse Services, Oklahoma City, OK
Primary Contact: Kevan Finley, Chief Executive Officer
CFO: Miriam Harris, Director Finance
CMO: Satwant Tandon, M.D., Director of Clinical Services
CIO: Kevin Marble, Director Information Technology
CHR: Julie Jacobs, Director Human Resources
CNO: Glenda Satterwhite, Director of Nursing
Web address: www.odmhsas.org
**Control:** State–Government, nonfederal **Service:** Psychiatric

**Staffed Beds:** 200

---

**Hospital, Medicare Provider Number, Address, Telephone, Approval, Facility, and Physician Codes, Health Care System**

★ American Hospital Association (AHA) membership
☐ The Joint Commission accreditation
○ Healthcare Facilities Accreditation Program
◇ DNV Healthcare Inc. accreditation
⇑ Center for Improvement in Healthcare Quality Accreditation
△ Commission on Accreditation of Rehabilitation Facilities (CARF) accreditation

OK

### WAGONER—Wagoner County

**WAGONER COMMUNITY HOSPITAL (370166)**, 1200 West Cherokee Street, Zip 74467–4624, Mailing Address: P.O. Box 407, Zip 74477–0407; tel. 918/485–5514 **A**9 10 **F**3 11 12 15 28 29 30 34 39 40 41 45 50 51 57 59 64 65 68 70 74 75 79 81 82 85 87 89 98 102 107 108 110 111 114 116 119 130 131 135 146 148
Primary Contact: Jimmy Leopard, FACHE, Chief Executive Officer
COO: Louise Easter, R.N., Chief Operating Officer and Chief Nursing Officer
CFO: Rebecca Sharp, Chief Financial Officer
CMO: John Perry, M.D., Chief of Staff
CIO: Jim Riley, Director Information Technology
CHR: Barnetta Pofahl, Director Human Resources
CNO: Louise Easter, R.N., Chief Nursing Officer
Web address: www.wagonerhospital.com
**Control:** Hospital district or authority, Government, nonfederal **Service:** General Medical and Surgical

**Staffed Beds:** 100 **Admissions:** 2956 **Census:** 36 **Outpatient Visits:** 28054 **Births:** 0 **Total Expense ($000):** 22264 **Payroll Expense ($000):** 8999 **Personnel:** 181

### WATONGA—Blaine County

★ **MERCY HOSPITAL WATONGA (371302)**, 500 North Clarence Nash Boulevard, Zip 73772–2845, Mailing Address: P.O. Box 370, Zip 73772–0370; tel. 580/623–7211 **A**9 10 18 **F**11 29 30 34 40 41 43 57 62 63 64 77 85 91 93 107 111 119 130 133 135 **P**6 **S** Mercy Health, Chesterfield, MO
Primary Contact: Bobby Stitt, R.N., Administrator
CFO: Patricia Dianne Robertson, Chief Financial Officer
CHR: Mary Jo Messelt, Manager Human Resources
Web address: www.mercy.net/watongaok/practice/mercy–hospital–watonga
**Control:** Church–operated, Nongovernment, not–for profit **Service:** General Medical and Surgical

**Staffed Beds:** 17 **Admissions:** 261 **Census:** 2 **Outpatient Visits:** 9479 **Births:** 0 **Total Expense ($000):** 5794 **Payroll Expense ($000):** 3134 **Personnel:** 47

### WAURIKA—Jefferson County

★ **JEFFERSON COUNTY HOSPITAL (371311)**, Highway 70 and 81, Zip 73573–3075, Mailing Address: P.O. Box 90, Zip 73573–0090; tel. 580/228–2344 **A**9 10 18 **F**40 41 42 43 64 93 97 100 107 114 119 127 129 133 146 **P**6
Primary Contact: Richard Gillespie, Chief Executive Officer
CFO: Richard Tallon, Chief Financial Officer
CMO: Rob Linzman, D.O., Chief of Staff
CIO: Nikki McGahey, Information Officer
Web address: www.jeffersoncountyhospital.net
**Control:** Hospital district or authority, Government, nonfederal **Service:** General Medical and Surgical

**Staffed Beds:** 25 **Admissions:** 155 **Census:** 2 **Outpatient Visits:** 9999 **Births:** 0 **Total Expense ($000):** 3189 **Payroll Expense ($000):** 1668 **Personnel:** 40

### WEATHERFORD—Custer County

★ **WEATHERFORD REGIONAL HOSPITAL (371323)**, 3701 East Main Street, Zip 73096–3309; tel. 580/772–5551 **A**9 10 18 **F**3 11 13 15 29 34 40 43 45 64 68 75 76 77 81 86 87 93 107 110 111 115 119 130 133 135 144 146 147 148 **P**6
Primary Contact: Debbie Howe, Chief Executive Officer
CFO: Stephanie Helton, Chief Financial Officer
CMO: Jonathan Ray Long, M.D., Chief of Staff
CIO: Amy Outhier, Director Health Information Management
CHR: Tawnya Paden, Director Human Resources
CNO: Delvin Mast, R.N., Director of Nursing
Web address: www.weatherfordhospital.com
**Control:** Hospital district or authority, Government, nonfederal **Service:** General Medical and Surgical

**Staffed Beds:** 25 **Admissions:** 641 **Census:** 6 **Outpatient Visits:** 42584 **Births:** 176 **Total Expense ($000):** 18124 **Payroll Expense ($000):** 6783 **Personnel:** 163

### WILBURTON—Latimer County

**LATIMER COUNTY GENERAL HOSPITAL (370072)**, 806 Highway 2 North, Zip 74578–3698; tel. 918/465–2391, (Nonreporting) **A**9 10
Primary Contact: Dana Hugle, Administrator
CMO: Richard Valbuena, M.D., Medical Director
CHR: Rachel Chinnock, Chief Human Resources Officer
**Control:** County–Government, nonfederal **Service:** General Medical and Surgical

**Staffed Beds:** 33

### WOODWARD—Woodward County

✠ **ALLIANCEHEALTH WOODWARD (370002)**, 900 17th Street, Zip 73801–2448; tel. 580/256–5511 **A**1 9 10 20 **F**13 15 29 30 31 32 34 35 40 43 45 50 57 59 64 68 69 70 75 76 77 79 81 85 93 107 108 110 111 115 119 124 127 129 130 131 133 135 146 **P**6 **S** Community Health Systems, Inc., Franklin, TN
Primary Contact: David Wallace, Chief Executive Officer
CFO: Tom Earley, Chief Financial Officer
CIO: Larry Churchill, Director Information Services
CHR: Melinda Brock, Director Human Resources
CNO: Kimberly N. Arnold, R.N., Chief Nursing Officer and Interim Chief Quality Officer
Web address: www.woodwardhospital.com
**Control:** Corporation, Investor–owned, for–profit **Service:** General Medical and Surgical

**Staffed Beds:** 40 **Admissions:** 1554 **Census:** 14 **Outpatient Visits:** 63478 **Births:** 276 **Total Expense ($000):** 33441 **Payroll Expense ($000):** 13674 **Personnel:** 261

### YUKON—Canadian County

✠ **INTEGRIS CANADIAN VALLEY HOSPITAL (370211)**, 1201 Health Center Parkway, Zip 73099–6381; tel. 405/717–6800 **A**1 9 10 **F**3 11 13 15 29 30 34 40 45 46 49 57 59 60 64 68 70 76 79 81 87 93 97 107 108 110 111 115 118 119 130 135 144 145 146 148 **S** INTEGRIS Health, Oklahoma City, OK
Primary Contact: Rex Van Meter, President
COO: Cindy White, CPA, Vice President of Operations
CFO: Errol Mitchell, Chief Financial Officer
CHR: Lynn Ketch, Human Resources Recruiter Generalist
CNO: Teresa Gray, Chief Nursing Officer and Assistant Vice President
Web address: www.integris–health.com
**Control:** Other not–for–profit (including NFP Corporation) **Service:** General Medical and Surgical

**Staffed Beds:** 75 **Admissions:** 2380 **Census:** 21 **Outpatient Visits:** 50467 **Births:** 743 **Total Expense ($000):** 50965 **Payroll Expense ($000):** 19647 **Personnel:** 283

*Many Facility Codes have changed. Please refer to the AHA Guide Code Chart.* © 2015 AHA Guide

# OREGON

**OR**

## ALBANY—Linn County

★ ◇ **SAMARITAN ALBANY GENERAL HOSPITAL (380022)**, 1046 Sixth Avenue, S.W., Zip 97321–1999; tel. 541/812–4000 **A**9 10 21 **F**3 5 11 13 15 18 28 29 30 31 34 35 36 37 40 43 45 47 49 53 54 57 59 61 63 64 67 68 70 73 74 76 77 78 79 81 83 84 85 86 87 89 92 93 97 104 107 108 110 111 114 116 117 119 129 130 131 132 135 144 145 146 147 148 **P**6 **S** Samaritan Health Services, Corvallis, OR
Primary Contact: David G. Triebes, Chief Executive Officer
CFO: Daniel B. Smith, Vice President Finance
Web address: www.samhealth.org
**Control:** Other not–for–profit (including NFP Corporation) **Service:** General Medical and Surgical

**Staffed Beds:** 70 **Admissions:** 2507 **Census:** 26 **Outpatient Visits:** 285145 **Births:** 558 **Total Expense ($000):** 161656 **Payroll Expense ($000):** 66272 **Personnel:** 757

## ASHLAND—Jackson County

★ ◇ **ASANTE ASHLAND COMMUNITY HOSPITAL (380005)**, 280 Maple Street, Zip 97520–1593; tel. 541/201–4000 **A**9 10 21 **F**3 11 13 15 29 30 34 35 36 40 43 48 49 50 54 62 63 64 65 68 70 75 76 79 81 82 84 85 86 87 93 97 107 110 114 119 130 132 145 146 147 148 **P**6 **S** Asante Health System, Medford, OR
Primary Contact: Sheila Clough, Chief Executive Officer
CFO: Patrick Hocking, Chief Financial Officer
CMO: Bill Steinsick, M.D., Chief Medical Staff
CIO: Mark Hetz, Chief Information Officer
CHR: Gregg Edwards, Vice President Human Resources
CNO: Susan Montgomery, Chief Nursing Officer
Web address: www.ashlandhospital.org
**Control:** Other not–for–profit (including NFP Corporation) **Service:** General Medical and Surgical

**Staffed Beds:** 36 **Admissions:** 1403 **Census:** 12 **Outpatient Visits:** 58473 **Births:** 304 **Total Expense ($000):** 50278 **Payroll Expense ($000):** 16752 **Personnel:** 282

## ASTORIA—Clatsop County

★ **COLUMBIA MEMORIAL HOSPITAL (381320)**, 2111 Exchange Street, Zip 97103–3329; tel. 503/325–4321 **A**9 10 18 **F**3 8 11 13 15 18 19 28 29 30 31 34 35 36 40 41 42 43 44 46 50 51 53 57 58 59 62 63 64 68 70 75 76 77 78 79 81 85 86 87 89 93 97 107 108 110 111 114 115 119 130 131 132 134 135 143 144 146 147 148 **P**6
Primary Contact: Erik Thorsen, Chief Executive Officer
CFO: Guy Rivers, Chief Financial Officer
CMO: Hugh Sabahi, M.D., President Professional Staff
CIO: Guy Rivers, Chief Financial Officer
CHR: Cheryl Martin, Manager Human Resources
CNO: Joe DaFoe, R.N., Chief Clinical Officer
Web address: www.columbiamemorial.org
**Control:** Other not–for–profit (including NFP Corporation) **Service:** General Medical and Surgical

**Staffed Beds:** 25 **Admissions:** 1589 **Census:** 12 **Outpatient Visits:** 167548 **Births:** 312 **Total Expense ($000):** 75241 **Payroll Expense ($000):** 33268 **Personnel:** 510

## BAKER CITY—Baker County

⊞ **SAINT ALPHONSUS MEDICAL CENTER – BAKER CITY (381315)**, 3325 Pocahontas Road, Zip 97814–1464; tel. 541/523–6461, (Total facility includes 30 beds in nursing home–type unit) **A**1 9 10 18 **F**3 11 13 15 29 31 34 35 36 37 40 43 44 45 50 59 64 67 70 75 76 77 79 81 82 83 85 91 93 97 107 110 115 119 127 128 129 131 133 143 144 146 147 148 **P**6 **S** Trinity Health, Livonia, MI
Primary Contact: H. Ray Gibbons, FACHE, Chief Executive Officer
CFO: Robert D. Wehling, Interim Chief Financial Officer
CHR: Jerry Nickell, Vice President Human Resource and Mission
Web address: www.saintalphonsus.org/bakercity
**Control:** Other not–for–profit (including NFP Corporation) **Service:** General Medical and Surgical

**Staffed Beds:** 55 **Admissions:** 823 **Census:** 30 **Outpatient Visits:** 47778 **Births:** 131 **Total Expense ($000):** 33087 **Payroll Expense ($000):** 15535 **Personnel:** 203

**ST. ELIZABETH HEALTH SERVICES** See Saint Alphonsus Medical Center – Baker City

## BANDON—Coos County

★ **SOUTHERN COOS HOSPITAL AND HEALTH CENTER (381304)**, 900 11th Street S.E., Zip 97411–9114; tel. 541/347–2426 **A**9 10 18 **F**3 15 34 35 40 45 50 57 59 65 68 75 81 82 85 87 97 107 110 114 119 130 132 133 135 148 **P**6
Primary Contact: Charles W. Johnston, Chief Executive Officer
CFO: Robin Triplett, Chief Financial Officer
CIO: Mandy Calvert, Director Information Systems
CHR: Cyndy Vollmer, Director Human Resources
Web address: www.southerncoos.org
**Control:** Hospital district or authority, Government, nonfederal **Service:** General Medical and Surgical

**Staffed Beds:** 19 **Admissions:** 362 **Census:** 3 **Outpatient Visits:** 13934 **Births:** 0 **Total Expense ($000):** 14563 **Payroll Expense ($000):** 5304 **Personnel:** 123

## BEND—Deschutes County

⊞ **ST. CHARLES BEND (380047)**, 2500 N.E. Neff Road, Zip 97701–6015; tel. 541/382–4321 **A**1 2 3 5 9 10 19 **F**3 8 11 12 13 14 15 18 19 20 21 22 24 26 28 29 30 31 34 35 36 37 38 40 42 43 44 45 46 47 49 50 51 54 57 58 59 60 62 63 64 65 67 70 72 74 75 76 77 78 79 81 82 84 85 86 87 89 90 91 92 93 97 98 99 100 101 102 104 107 108 111 112 114 115 119 120 121 122 124 126 129 130 132 135 142 144 146 147 148 **P**6 **S** St. Charles Health System, Inc., Bend, OR
Primary Contact: Robert Gomes, FACHE, Chief Executive Officer
CFO: Karen Shepard, Executive Vice President Finance and Chief Financial Officer
CMO: Michel Boileau, M.D., Chief Clinical Officer
CIO: William Winnenberg, Chief Information Officer
CHR: Rebecca Berry, Senior Director Human Resources
CNO: Karen Reed, R.N., Chief Nursing Officer
Web address: www.scmc.org
**Control:** Other not–for–profit (including NFP Corporation) **Service:** General Medical and Surgical

**Staffed Beds:** 250 **Admissions:** 15255 **Census:** 166 **Outpatient Visits:** 114171 **Births:** 1718 **Total Expense ($000):** 417999 **Payroll Expense ($000):** 155446 **Personnel:** 2369

## BURNS—Harney County

★ **HARNEY DISTRICT HOSPITAL (381307)**, 557 West Washington Street, Zip 97720–1497; tel. 541/573–7281 **A**3 9 10 18 **F**1 3 4 7 13 15 16 17 29 31 34 35 40 43 45 47 53 57 59 64 65 67 70 72 73 75 76 78 80 81 82 85 86 88 89 90 93 98 102 107 111 114 119 128 129 131 132 133 135 146 **P**6
Primary Contact: Dan Grigg, Chief Executive Officer
CFO: Catherine White, Chief Financial Officer
CMO: Sarah Laiosa, M.D., Chief Medical Staff
CIO: Tanya Strong, Manager Information Technology
CHR: Sammie Masterson, Chief Human Resources Officer
CNO: Deana Altman, Chief Nursing Officer
Web address: www.harneydh.com
**Control:** Hospital district or authority, Government, nonfederal **Service:** General Medical and Surgical

**Staffed Beds:** 20 **Admissions:** 327 **Census:** 2 **Outpatient Visits:** 32008 **Births:** 53 **Total Expense ($000):** 20285 **Payroll Expense ($000):** 8918 **Personnel:** 157

---

**Hospital, Medicare Provider Number, Address, Telephone, Approval, Facility, and Physician Codes, Health Care System**

★ American Hospital Association (AHA) membership    ◇ Healthcare Facilities Accreditation Program    ⇑ Center for Improvement in Healthcare Quality Accreditation
□ The Joint Commission accreditation    ◇ DNV Healthcare Inc. accreditation    △ Commission on Accreditation of Rehabilitation Facilities (CARF) accreditation

OR

## CLACKAMAS—Clackamas County

☒ **KAISER PERMANENTE SUNNYSIDE MEDICAL CENTER (380091)**, 10180 S.E. Sunnyside Road, Zip 97015–8970; tel. 503/652–2880 **A**1 2 3 5 10 **F**3 11 12 13 15 17 18 20 22 24 26 29 30 31 34 37 40 45 46 47 49 60 61 64 68 70 72 74 75 76 77 78 79 81 84 85 86 87 93 94 97 102 107 108 110 111 114 115 119 130 135 141 146 147 148 **P**6 **S** Kaiser Foundation Hospitals, Oakland, CA
Primary Contact: Gary Petersen, Administrator and Chief Executive Officer
CFO: Justin Evander, Chief Financial Officer
CMO: Richard Hunt, M.D., Chief Operating Officer
CIO: Mark A. Burmester, Vice President Strategy and Communications
CHR: Rich Smith, Vice President Human Resources
CNO: Lauren M. Bridge, R.N., Chief Nursing Officer
Web address: www.kaiserpermanente.org
**Control:** Other not–for–profit (including NFP Corporation) **Service:** General Medical and Surgical

**Staffed Beds: 299 Admissions: 19229 Census: 167 Outpatient Visits: 69779 Births: 2099 Total Expense ($000): 330585 Payroll Expense ($000): 136677 Personnel: 1903**

## COOS BAY—Coos County

☒ **BAY AREA HOSPITAL (380090)**, 1775 Thompson Road, Zip 97420–2198; tel. 541/269–8111 **A**1 2 3 5 9 10 **F**3 11 12 13 15 18 28 29 31 34 35 37 40 43 45 46 48 50 51 57 59 62 68 70 73 74 75 76 77 78 79 81 82 83 84 85 89 91 92 93 98 99 100 101 102 104 107 108 110 111 114 118 119 120 121 123 126 129 130 132 135 142 146 148
Primary Contact: Paul Janke, FACHE, President and Chief Executive Officer
COO: Ben Pfau, Chief Facility and Information Officer
CFO: Sam Patterson, Chief Financial Officer
CIO: Bob Adams, Director Information Services
CHR: Suzie Q. McDaniel, Chief Human Resource Officer
CNO: Lori L. Krenos, R.N., Chief Nursing Officer
Web address: www.bayareahospital.org
**Control:** Hospital district or authority, Government, nonfederal **Service:** General Medical and Surgical

**Staffed Beds: 144 Admissions: 5770 Census: 60 Outpatient Visits: 72156 Births: 713 Total Expense ($000): 137861 Payroll Expense ($000): 62004 Personnel: 816**

## COQUILLE—Coos County

★ **COQUILLE VALLEY HOSPITAL (381312)**, 940 East Fifth Street, Zip 97423–1699; tel. 541/396–3101 **A**9 10 18 **F**3 11 13 15 29 34 35 40 43 45 50 57 59 62 64 70 75 79 81 82 85 86 87 107 110 111 114 118 119 132 133 135 148 **P**6
Primary Contact: Karen Lautermilch, Chief Executive Officer
CFO: Gail Ludington, Chief Financial Officer
CMO: James Sinnott, M.D., Chief Medical Staff
CIO: Curt Carpenter, Manager Information Technology
CHR: Monte Johnston, Manager Human Resources
Web address: www.cvhospital.org
**Control:** Hospital district or authority, Government, nonfederal **Service:** General Medical and Surgical

**Staffed Beds: 25 Admissions: 614 Census: 6 Outpatient Visits: 24331 Births: 0 Total Expense ($000): 23792 Payroll Expense ($000): 9258 Personnel: 192**

## CORVALLIS—Benton County

★ ◇ **GOOD SAMARITAN REGIONAL MEDICAL CENTER (380014)**, 3600 N.W. Samaritan Drive, Zip 97330–3737, Mailing Address: P.O. Box 1068, Zip 97339–1068; tel. 541/768–5111 **A**2 9 10 12 13 19 21 **F**3 11 12 13 15 17 18 20 22 24 26 28 29 30 31 34 35 36 37 40 43 46 47 49 53 54 56 57 58 59 61 62 64 68 70 73 74 76 77 78 79 81 82 84 85 86 87 89 92 93 97 98 99 100 101 102 103 104 107 108 110 111 114 115 116 117 118 119 120 121 123 124 126 129 130 131 132 135 144 146 147 148 **P**6 **S** Samaritan Health Services, Corvallis, OR
Primary Contact: Larry A. Mullins, FACHE, Chief Executive Officer
COO: Becky A. Pape, R.N., Chief Operating Officer
CFO: Daniel B. Smith, Vice President Finance
CIO: Bob Power, Vice President Information Services
CHR: Doug Boysen, Chief Legal Counsel and Vice President Human Resources
CNO: William Howden, Vice President Nursing
Web address: www.samhealth.org
**Control:** Other not–for–profit (including NFP Corporation) **Service:** General Medical and Surgical

**Staffed Beds: 165 Admissions: 8743 Census: 115 Outpatient Visits: 367597 Births: 1021 Total Expense ($000): 330159 Payroll Expense ($000): 134646 Personnel: 1579**

## COTTAGE GROVE—Lane County

★ **PEACEHEALTH COTTAGE GROVE COMMUNITY MEDICAL CENTER (381301)**, 1515 Village Drive, Zip 97424–9700; tel. 541/942–0511 **A**9 10 18 **F**3 11 15 29 30 32 34 35 40 44 50 56 57 58 59 64 65 66 68 75 85 86 87 93 97 107 110 115 119 127 130 132 133 146 147 148 **P**6 **S** PeaceHealth, Vancouver, WA
Primary Contact: Tim Herrmann, R.N., Administrator
Web address: www.peacehealth.org
**Control:** Church–operated, Nongovernment, not–for profit **Service:** General Medical and Surgical

**Staffed Beds: 14 Admissions: 403 Census: 3 Outpatient Visits: 35848 Births: 0 Total Expense ($000): 26633 Payroll Expense ($000): 10206 Personnel: 114**

## DALLAS—Polk County

**WEST VALLEY HOSPITAL (381308)**, 525 S.E. Washington Street, Zip 97338–2834, Mailing Address: P.O. Box 378, Zip 97338–0378; tel. 503/623–8301 **A**9 10 18 **F**3 15 35 40 43 50 59 64 75 79 81 85 93 97 107 108 110 111 114 119 131 132 133 143 146 148 **P**6 **S** Salem Health, Salem, OR
Primary Contact: James J. Sapienza, Chief Administrative Officer
COO: Cheryl R. Nester Wolfe, R.N., Chief Operating Officer
CFO: James Parr, Chief Financial Officer
CMO: Steve Gordon, M.D., Chief Medical Officer
CIO: Cort Garrison, M.D., Chief Information Officer
CHR: Laurie C. Barr, Vice President Human Resources
CNO: Sarah Horn, Chief Nursing Officer
Web address: www.salemhealth.org/wvh/
**Control:** Other not–for–profit (including NFP Corporation) **Service:** General Medical and Surgical

**Staffed Beds: 6 Admissions: 164 Census: 2 Outpatient Visits: 74815 Births: 0 Total Expense ($000): 20839 Payroll Expense ($000): 10401 Personnel: 118**

## ENTERPRISE—Wallowa County

★ **WALLOWA MEMORIAL HOSPITAL (381306)**, 601 Medical Parkway, Zip 97828–5124; tel. 541/426–3111 **A**3 5 9 10 18 **F**3 7 11 13 15 29 30 31 34 35 40 43 45 46 56 57 59 62 64 68 75 76 78 79 81 82 85 93 102 107 110 114 119 128 129 131 132 133 135 143 148 **P**6
Primary Contact: Larry Davy, Chief Executive Officer
CFO: Joe Wanner, Chief Financial Officer
CMO: Kenneth Rose, M.D., Chief Medical Staff
CIO: John Straughan, Director Information Technology
CHR: Linda Childers, Director Human Resources
CNO: Jenni Word, R.N., Chief Nursing Officer
Web address: www.wchcd.org
**Control:** Hospital district or authority, Government, nonfederal **Service:** General Medical and Surgical

**Staffed Beds: 25 Admissions: 619 Census: 7 Outpatient Visits: 19271 Births: 61 Total Expense ($000): 16917 Payroll Expense ($000): 6760 Personnel: 120**

## EUGENE—Lane County

★ △ ◇ **PEACEHEALTH SACRED HEART MEDICAL CENTER UNIVERSITY DISTRICT (380033)**, 1255 Hilyard Street, Zip 97401–3700, Mailing Address: P.O. Box 10905, Zip 97440–2905; tel. 541/686–7300 **A**7 9 10 21 **F**29 30 40 43 56 68 90 98 102 146 148 **P**6 **S** PeaceHealth, Vancouver, WA
Primary Contact: Rand O'Leary, Chief Executive Officer
CFO: Wendy Apland, Interim Chief Financial Officer
CMO: Bill Moshofsky, M.D., Chief of Staff
CIO: Don McMillan, Chief Information Officer
CHR: Craig Mills, Vice President Human Resources
Web address: www.peacehealth.org
**Control:** Church–operated, Nongovernment, not–for profit **Service:** General Medical and Surgical

**Staffed Beds: 104 Admissions: 2532 Census: 56 Outpatient Visits: 108505 Births: 0 Total Expense ($000): 96229 Payroll Expense ($000): 40089 Personnel: 370**

## FLORENCE—Lane County

★ ◇ **PEACEHEALTH PEACE HARBOR MEDICAL CENTER (381316)**, 400 Ninth Street, Zip 97439–7398; tel. 541/997–8412 **A**9 10 18 21 **F**11 13 15 28 29 30 34 35 40 43 45 50 57 59 62 63 64 68 70 76 77 79 81 85 93 97 107 108 110 111 114 118 119 132 133 135 146 147 148 **P**6 **S** PeaceHealth, Vancouver, WA
Primary Contact: Rick Yecny, Chief Executive Officer and Chief Mission Officer
CMO: Ron Shearer, M.D., Regional Medical Director
CIO: Ginni Boughal, Director Health Information and Information Technology
CHR: Don Bourland, Vice President Human Resources
Web address: www.peacehealth.org
**Control:** Church–operated, Nongovernment, not–for profit **Service:** General Medical and Surgical

**Staffed Beds: 21 Admissions: 1018 Census: 9 Outpatient Visits: 95827 Births: 68 Total Expense ($000): 65923 Payroll Expense ($000): 30185 Personnel: 372**

**FOREST GROVE—Washington County**

**TUALITY FOREST GROVE HOSPITAL** See Tuality Healthcare, Hillsboro

**GOLD BEACH—Curry County**

★ ◇ **CURRY GENERAL HOSPITAL (381322)**, 94220 Fourth Street,
Zip 97444–7756; tel. 541/247–3000 **A**9 10 18 21 **F**3 8 10 11 13 15 28 29
34 35 40 43 56 57 59 64 67 70 75 76 79 81 82 98 105 107 114 119 127
133 135 144 146 147 148
Primary Contact: Virginia Razo, Chief Executive Officer
COO: Kenneth G. Landau, Chief Operating Officer
CFO: Kenneth G. Landau, Chief Financial Officer
CIO: Chris Creighton, Manager Information Technology
CHR: Terri Tomberlin, Director Human Resources
CNO: Lora Maxwell, Chief Nursing Officer
Web address: www.curryhealthnetwork.com
**Control:** Hospital district or authority, Government, nonfederal **Service:** General
Medical and Surgical

**Staffed Beds:** 17 **Admissions:** 334 **Census:** 4 **Outpatient Visits:** 59410
**Births:** 14 **Total Expense ($000):** 27547 **Payroll Expense ($000):** 13955
**Personnel:** 227

**GRANTS PASS—Josephine County**

★ ◇ **ASANTE THREE RIVERS MEDICAL CENTER (380002)**, 500 S.W. Ramsey
Avenue, Zip 97527–5554; tel. 541/472–7000 **A**3 9 10 21 **F**11 13 15 29 30 31
34 35 40 43 45 46 50 57 59 64 65 70 75 76 78 81 87 93 102 107 108 110
111 118 119 122 130 132 143 146 147 148 **P**6 **S** Asante Health System,
Medford, OR
Primary Contact: Win Howard, Chief Executive Officer
COO: David Kinyon, Vice President of Operations and Outpatient Services
CFO: Patrick Hocking, Chief Financial Officer
CMO: Eric Loeliger, Vice President of Medical Affairs
CIO: Mark Hetz, Chief Information Officer
CHR: Gregg Edwards, Chief People Officer
CNO: Nancy Greer, R.N., Vice President Nursing
Web address: www.asante.org/trmc/
**Control:** Other not–for–profit (including NFP Corporation) **Service:** General
Medical and Surgical

**Staffed Beds:** 111 **Admissions:** 7000 **Census:** 61 **Outpatient Visits:** 227634
**Births:** 753 **Total Expense ($000):** 124381 **Payroll Expense ($000):** 43383
**Personnel:** 828

**GRESHAM—Multnomah County**

✠ **LEGACY MOUNT HOOD MEDICAL CENTER (380025)**, 24800 S.E. Stark,
Zip 97030–3378; tel. 503/667–1122 **A**1 2 9 10 **F**3 11 13 15 18 20 26 28 29
30 31 32 34 35 38 40 44 45 46 48 49 50 51 57 59 60 64 68 70 74 75 76
77 78 79 81 85 86 87 93 100 101 102 107 108 110 111 114 115 118 119
120 121 123 126 129 130 132 146 147 148 **P**6 **S** Legacy Health,
Portland, OR
Primary Contact: Gretchen Nichols, R.N., Chief Administrative Officer
COO: Michael Newcomb, D.O., Senior Vice President and Chief Operating Officer
CFO: Linda Hoff, Senior Vice President and Chief Financial Officer
CMO: Lewis Low, M.D., Chief Medical Officer
CIO: John Jay Kenagy, Ph.D., Senior Vice President and Chief Information Officer
CHR: Sonja Steves, Senior Vice President Human Resources
CNO: Marcia Soderling, R.N., Hospital Nurse Executive
Web address: www.legacyhealth.org
**Control:** Other not–for–profit (including NFP Corporation) **Service:** General
Medical and Surgical

**Staffed Beds:** 91 **Admissions:** 5785 **Census:** 55 **Outpatient Visits:** 96409
**Births:** 996 **Total Expense ($000):** 113507 **Payroll Expense ($000):** 43223
**Personnel:** 561

**HEPPNER—Morrow County**

**PIONEER MEMORIAL HOSPITAL (381310)**, 564 East Pioneer Drive,
Zip 97836–7318, Mailing Address: P.O. Box 9, Zip 97836–0009;
tel. 541/676–9133 **A**9 10 18 **F**3 7 17 34 35 40 45 50 57 59 62 63 64 66 68
69 75 97 107 119 127 133 143 148 **P**6
Primary Contact: Nicole Mahoney, Interim Chief Executive Officer
CFO: Nicole Mahoney, Chief Financial Officer
CIO: Shawn Cutsforth, Information Systems Officer
CHR: Patti Allstott, Administrative Coordinator Human Resources and Grant Writer
Web address: www.morrowcountyhealthdistrict.org
**Control:** Hospital district or authority, Government, nonfederal **Service:** General
Medical and Surgical

**Staffed Beds:** 21 **Admissions:** 89 **Census:** 6 **Outpatient Visits:** 5318 **Births:**
0 **Total Expense ($000):** 8882 **Payroll Expense ($000):** 4648 **Personnel:**
60

**HERMISTON—Umatilla County**

★ ◇ **GOOD SHEPHERD HEALTH CARE SYSTEM (381325)**, 610 N.W. 11th
Street, Zip 97838–6601; tel. 541/667–3400 **A**9 10 18 21 **F**3 8 11 13 15 28
29 30 34 35 37 40 43 45 46 50 53 57 59 62 63 64 65 68 70 75 76 77 78
79 81 82 84 85 86 89 93 97 107 108 110 111 114 115 119 126 127 130
131 132 133 135 141 143 146 147 148 **P**3 4 7
Primary Contact: Dennis E. Burke, President and Chief Executive Officer
COO: Jim Schlenker, Chief Operating Officer
CFO: Jan D. Peter, Vice President Fiscal Services and Chief Financial Officer
CMO: Gary Trupp, President Medical Staff
CIO: Rob Rizk, Director Information Technology
CHR: Kelly B. Sanders, Vice President Human Resources
CNO: Theresa Brock, Vice President Nursing
Web address: www.gshealth.org
**Control:** Other not–for–profit (including NFP Corporation) **Service:** General
Medical and Surgical

**Staffed Beds:** 25 **Admissions:** 1791 **Census:** 13 **Outpatient Visits:** 65509
**Births:** 436 **Total Expense ($000):** 63434 **Payroll Expense ($000):** 28417
**Personnel:** 516

**HILLSBORO—Washington County**

✠ **KAISER FOUNDATION HOSPITAL WESTSIDE MEDICAL CENTER (380103)**,
2875 N.W. Stucki Avenue, Zip 97124–5806; tel. 971/310–1000 **A**1 10 **F**3 11
12 13 15 20 22 29 30 31 34 37 40 45 46 47 51 60 61 64 68 70 74 75 76
77 79 81 84 85 86 87 93 94 97 102 107 108 110 111 114 115 119 126
130 135 141 146 147 148 **P**6 **S** Kaiser Foundation Hospitals, Oakland, CA
Primary Contact: Cindy Davis, R.N., Chief Operating Officer
COO: Cindy Davis, R.N., Chief Operating Officer
CFO: Brantley Dettmer, Finance Director
CMO: Carol Unitan, M.D., Chief Medical Officer
CIO: Charles Stearns, Area Information Officer
CHR: Rich Smith, Vice President Human Resources
CNO: Cindy Davis, R.N., Chief Nursing Officer
Web address: www.kp.org
**Control:** Other not–for–profit (including NFP Corporation) **Service:** General
Medical and Surgical

**Staffed Beds:** 122 **Admissions:** 8856 **Census:** 59 **Outpatient Visits:** 35139
**Births:** 1367 **Total Expense ($000):** 141458 **Payroll Expense ($000):**
57866 **Personnel:** 838

✠ **TUALITY HEALTHCARE (380021)**, 335 S.E. Eighth Avenue, Zip 97123–4246;
tel. 503/681–1111, (Includes TUALITY COMMUNITY HOSPITAL, 335 S.E. Eighth
Avenue, Zip 97123, Mailing Address: P.O. Box 309, Zip 97123;
tel. 503/681–1111; Manuel Berman, President and Chief Executive Officer;
TUALITY FOREST GROVE HOSPITAL, 1809 Maple Street, Forest Grove,
Zip 97116–1995; tel. 503/357–2173; Manuel Berman, President and Chief
Executive Officer) **A**1 5 9 10 **F**3 11 13 15 17 18 20 22 24 26 28 29 30 31 32
34 35 36 37 40 44 45 47 49 50 53 54 56 57 59 62 64 68 70 74 75 76
77 78 79 80 81 82 85 86 87 92 93 97 98 100 103 104 107 108 110 111
114 115 118 119 129 130 131 132 135 143 144 145 146 147 148 **P**1 6
Primary Contact: Manuel S. Berman, President and Chief Executive Officer
COO: Steven P. Krautscheid, Ancillary Services Administrator
CFO: Tim Fleischmann, Chief Financial Officer
CMO: Stuart Currie, Chief Medical Officer
CIO: Sonney Sapra, Director Information Systems and Chief Information Officer
CHR: Cheryl Gebhart, Chief Human Resources Officer
CNO: Eunice A. Rech, MSN, Chief Clinical Officer and Administrator of Quality
Services
Web address: www.tuality.org
**Control:** Other not–for–profit (including NFP Corporation) **Service:** General
Medical and Surgical

**Staffed Beds:** 148 **Admissions:** 4617 **Census:** 55 **Outpatient Visits:** 243848
**Births:** 775 **Total Expense ($000):** 173847 **Payroll Expense ($000):** 82031
**Personnel:** 1108

**HOOD RIVER—Hood River County**

✠ **PROVIDENCE HOOD RIVER MEMORIAL HOSPITAL (381318)**, 810 12th
Street, Zip 97031–1587, Mailing Address: P.O. Box 149, Zip 97031–0055;
tel. 541/386–3911 **A**1 3 10 18 **F**2 3 5 8 9 10 11 12 13 15 28 29 30 31 34
35 36 40 43 45 47 48 53 54 56 57 59 60 64 65 68 70 71 75 76 77 79 81
85 86 89 92 97 99 100 101 102 104 107 108 110 111 114 118 119 125
129 132 133 134 135 143 146 147 148 **P**6 **S** Providence Health & Services,
Renton, WA
Primary Contact: Edward E. Freysinger, Chief Executive Officer
CFO: Rochelle Layton, Finance Manager
CHR: Jami McCaslin, Director Human Resources
Web address: www.providence.org/hoodriver
**Control:** Church–operated, Nongovernment, not–for profit **Service:** General
Medical and Surgical

**Staffed Beds:** 25 **Admissions:** 1544 **Census:** 11 **Outpatient Visits:** 160261
**Births:** 463 **Total Expense ($000):** 80009 **Payroll Expense ($000):** 25132
**Personnel:** 364

OR

---

**Hospital, Medicare Provider Number, Address, Telephone, Approval, Facility, and Physician Codes, Health Care System**

★ American Hospital Association (AHA) membership    ◯ Healthcare Facilities Accreditation Program    ⇑ Center for Improvement in Healthcare Quality Accreditation
☐ The Joint Commission accreditation    ◇ DNV Healthcare Inc. accreditation    △ Commission on Accreditation of Rehabilitation Facilities (CARF) accreditation

OR

### JOHN DAY—Grant County

★ **BLUE MOUNTAIN HOSPITAL (381305)**, 170 Ford Road, Zip 97845–2009; tel. 541/575–1311, (Total facility includes 29 beds in nursing home–type unit) **A**3 5 9 10 18 **F**2 3 7 8 11 13 15 17 29 30 31 34 35 36 40 41 43 45 56 57 59 62 63 64 67 68 70 75 76 81 82 86 87 89 93 97 107 110 111 114 119 127 128 130 131 132 133 135 143 144 145 148 **P**6 **S** HealthTech Management Services, Brentwood, TN
Primary Contact: Randall L. Mee, FACHE, Chief Executive Officer
CFO: Carl J. Flanagan, CPA, Chief Financial Officer
CMO: Keith Thomas, M.D., Chief of Staff
CIO: Sean Tsao, Director Information Technology
CHR: Verlene Davis, Director Human Resources
CNO: Les McLeod, Director of Nursing Services
Web address: www.bluemountainhospital.org
**Control:** Hospital district or authority, Government, nonfederal **Service:** General Medical and Surgical

**Staffed Beds:** 45 **Admissions:** 331 **Census:** 25 **Outpatient Visits:** 23968 **Births:** 41 **Total Expense ($000):** 18002 **Payroll Expense ($000):** 9912 **Personnel:** 128

### KLAMATH FALLS—Klamath County

★ ◇ **SKY LAKES MEDICAL CENTER (380050)**, 2865 Daggett Avenue, Zip 97601–1106; tel. 541/882–6311 **A**2 3 5 9 10 21 **F**3 8 11 13 15 18 20 22 29 30 31 34 35 37 40 43 44 45 46 47 48 50 51 53 54 56 57 59 61 62 64 68 70 71 75 76 77 78 79 81 84 85 86 87 89 92 93 94 96 97 100 102 107 108 110 111 114 115 116 117 118 119 120 121 123 130 131 132 134 135 141 142 143 144 145 146 148 **P**6
Primary Contact: Paul R. Stewart, President and Chief Executive Officer
CFO: Richard Rico, Vice President and Chief Financial Officer
CMO: Grant Niskanen, M.D., Vice President Medical Affairs
CHR: Don York, Vice President Human Resources
CNO: Annette E. Cole, R.N., Vice President and Chief Nursing Officer
Web address: www.skylakes.org
**Control:** Other not–for–profit (including NFP Corporation) **Service:** General Medical and Surgical

**Staffed Beds:** 100 **Admissions:** 5270 **Census:** 55 **Outpatient Visits:** 364212 **Births:** 794 **Total Expense ($000):** 183205 **Payroll Expense ($000):** 71082 **Personnel:** 1065

### LA GRANDE—Union County

✉ **GRANDE RONDE HOSPITAL (381321)**, 900 Sunset Drive, Zip 97850–1387, Mailing Address: P.O. Box 3290, Zip 97850–7290; tel. 541/963–8421 **A**1 9 10 18 **F**3 8 11 13 15 17 29 30 31 34 35 37 39 40 41 43 44 45 50 53 54 57 59 62 63 64 66 70 74 75 76 77 78 81 82 84 85 86 87 89 92 93 96 97 107 108 110 111 114 119 128 129 130 131 132 133 135 144 146 147 148 **P**6
Primary Contact: James A. Mattes, President and Chief Executive Officer
CFO: Wade Weis, Senior Director Finance
CIO: Parhez Sattar, Senior Director Information Technology
CHR: Kristi Puckett, Director Human Resources
Web address: www.grh.org
**Control:** Other not–for–profit (including NFP Corporation) **Service:** General Medical and Surgical

**Staffed Beds:** 25 **Admissions:** 1385 **Census:** 11 **Outpatient Visits:** 92736 **Births:** 250 **Total Expense ($000):** 66001 **Payroll Expense ($000):** 36250 **Personnel:** 464

### LAKEVIEW—Lake County

★ **LAKE DISTRICT HOSPITAL (381309)**, 700 South J Street, Zip 97630–1679; tel. 541/947–2114, (Total facility includes 22 beds in nursing home–type unit) **A**5 9 10 18 **F**13 15 18 29 30 31 34 40 45 46 57 59 62 63 64 67 68 76 78 81 82 84 85 87 93 107 111 114 119 128 129 130 132 133 135 146 148 **P**6
Primary Contact: Charles B. Tveit, Chief Executive Officer
CFO: Cheryl J. Cornwell, Chief Financial Officer
CMO: C. Scott Graham, D.O., Chief of Staff
CHR: Linda Michaelson, Director Human Resources
CNO: Teresa Squires, R.N., Chief Nursing Officer
Web address: www.lakehealthdistrict.org
**Control:** Hospital district or authority, Government, nonfederal **Service:** General Medical and Surgical

**Staffed Beds:** 46 **Admissions:** 556 **Census:** 28 **Outpatient Visits:** 25378 **Births:** 64 **Total Expense ($000):** 20691 **Payroll Expense ($000):** 8843 **Personnel:** 176

### LEBANON—Linn County

★ ◇ **SAMARITAN LEBANON COMMUNITY HOSPITAL (381323)**, 525 North Santiam Highway, Zip 97355–4363, Mailing Address: P.O. Box 739, Zip 97355–0739; tel. 541/258–2101 **A**9 10 18 21 **F**3 10 11 13 15 28 29 30 31 34 35 40 43 44 45 46 47 53 59 64 68 70 75 76 78 79 81 85 86 87 89 92 93 97 107 108 110 111 114 116 117 118 119 125 130 131 132 135 144 146 147 148 **P**6 **S** Samaritan Health Services, Corvallis, OR
Primary Contact: Becky A. Pape, R.N., Chief Executive Officer
CFO: Daniel B. Smith, Vice President Finance
CMO: Alan Blake, M.D., President Medical Staff
CIO: Robert Power, Vice President Information Services
CHR: Connie Erwin, Manager
CNO: Wendie Wunderwald, R.N., Vice President Patient Care Services
Web address: www.samhealth.org
**Control:** Other not–for–profit (including NFP Corporation) **Service:** General Medical and Surgical

**Staffed Beds:** 25 **Admissions:** 1605 **Census:** 14 **Outpatient Visits:** 209314 **Births:** 300 **Total Expense ($000):** 92696 **Payroll Expense ($000):** 41289 **Personnel:** 509

### LINCOLN CITY—Lincoln County

★ ◇ **SAMARITAN NORTH LINCOLN HOSPITAL (381302)**, 3043 N.E. 28th Street, Zip 97367–4518, Mailing Address: P.O. Box 767, Zip 97367–0767; tel. 541/994–3661 **A**9 10 18 21 **F**3 8 11 13 15 18 29 30 31 34 35 40 44 45 50 51 57 58 59 62 63 64 68 70 71 75 76 77 78 79 81 85 86 87 93 97 107 108 110 111 114 116 117 118 119 127 130 132 133 135 144 146 147 148 **P**6 **S** Samaritan Health Services, Corvallis, OR
Primary Contact: Marty Cahill, Chief Executive Officer
COO: Lesley Ogden, M.D., Chief Operating Officer
CFO: Kathryn Doksum, Director Finance
CMO: Raj Baman, D.O., President Medical Staff
CHR: Gina Tapp, Director Human Resources
CNO: Virginia Riffle, Vice President Patient Care Services
Web address: www.samhealth.org
**Control:** Other not–for–profit (including NFP Corporation) **Service:** General Medical and Surgical

**Staffed Beds:** 25 **Admissions:** 1052 **Census:** 9 **Outpatient Visits:** 82184 **Births:** 150 **Total Expense ($000):** 48136 **Payroll Expense ($000):** 24105 **Personnel:** 276

### MADRAS—Jefferson County

★ **ST. CHARLES MADRAS (381324)**, 470 N.E. A Street, Zip 97741–1844; tel. 541/475–3882 **A**9 10 18 **F**3 13 15 29 30 34 35 40 43 45 50 57 59 62 63 64 67 68 70 75 76 77 79 80 81 85 87 89 90 98 107 110 115 119 128 132 133 135 146 **P**6 **S** St. Charles Health System, Inc., Bend, OR
Primary Contact: Jeanine Gentry, Chief Executive Officer
CHR: JoDee Tittle, Director Community and Human Resources
Web address: www.mvhd.org
**Control:** Hospital district or authority, Government, nonfederal **Service:** General Medical and Surgical

**Staffed Beds:** 25 **Admissions:** 720 **Census:** 7 **Outpatient Visits:** 22068 **Births:** 175 **Total Expense ($000):** 28514 **Payroll Expense ($000):** 13564 **Personnel:** 184

### MCMINNVILLE—Yamhill County

☐ **WILLAMETTE VALLEY MEDICAL CENTER (380071)**, 2700 S.E. Stratus Avenue, Zip 97128–6255; tel. 503/472–6131 **A**1 2 9 10 **F**3 11 12 13 15 18 20 24 26 27 28 29 30 31 34 35 40 41 45 46 48 50 51 56 57 58 59 60 64 65 70 74 75 76 77 78 79 81 82 84 85 86 87 91 92 93 98 103 107 108 110 111 114 115 118 119 120 123 124 130 131 132 135 146 147 148 **P**6 **S** Capella Healthcare, Franklin, TN
Primary Contact: Peter A. Hofstetter, Chief Executive Officer
CFO: Meredith Nelson, Chief Financial Officer
CIO: Diane Farrow, Manager Information Technology and Systems
CHR: Lisa Clark, Director Human Resources
CNO: Connie Pullen, R.N., Chief Nursing Officer
Web address: www.wvmcweb.com
**Control:** Corporation, Investor–owned, for–profit **Service:** General Medical and Surgical

**Staffed Beds:** 88 **Admissions:** 3411 **Census:** 37 **Outpatient Visits:** 116766 **Births:** 518 **Total Expense ($000):** 75965 **Payroll Expense ($000):** 27900 **Personnel:** 479

*Many Facility Codes have changed. Please refer to the AHA Guide Code Chart.*

## MEDFORD—Jackson County

★ ◇ **ASANTE ROGUE REGIONAL MEDICAL CENTER (380018)**, 2825 East Barnett Road, Zip 97504–8332; tel. 541/789–7000 **A**2 3 9 10 21 **F**11 12 13 15 17 18 19 20 21 22 23 24 25 26 27 28 29 30 31 32 34 35 37 40 43 45 46 50 51 57 58 59 60 63 64 65 70 72 74 75 76 78 79 81 82 85 86 87 89 90 93 94 98 100 102 107 108 110 111 112 115 119 120 121 122 126 130 132 143 146 147 148 **P**6 **S** Asante Health System, Medford, OR
Primary Contact: Scott A. Kelly, Chief Executive Officer
COO: Kristi Blackhurst, Interim Vice President Operations
CFO: Patrick Hocking, Chief Financial Officer
CMO: Jamie Grebosky, M.D., Vice President of Medical Affairs
CIO: Mark Hetz, Chief Information Officer
CHR: Gregg Edwards, Chief People Officer
CNO: Tiffany Oliver, Chief Nursing Officer and Vice President
Web address: www.asante.org
**Control:** Other not–for–profit (including NFP Corporation) **Service:** General Medical and Surgical

**Staffed Beds:** 320 **Admissions:** 15473 **Census:** 202 **Outpatient Visits:** 368685 **Births:** 1536 **Total Expense ($000):** 373218 **Payroll Expense ($000):** 115384 **Personnel:** 1938

⊠ **PROVIDENCE MEDFORD MEDICAL CENTER (380075)**, 1111 Crater Lake Avenue, Zip 97504–6241; tel. 541/732–5000 **A**1 2 9 10 **F**3 11 12 17 18 20 22 28 29 30 31 32 34 35 40 43 45 49 50 51 55 56 57 59 61 62 63 64 68 70 74 75 77 78 79 81 82 84 85 86 87 90 91 92 93 96 97 102 107 110 114 115 118 119 120 121 123 124 126 129 130 132 143 146 147 148 **P**6 **S** Providence Health & Services, Renton, WA
Primary Contact: Cindy Mayo, R.N., FACHE, Chief Executive Officer
COO: Chris Pizzi, Chief Operating Officer and Chief Financial Officer
CFO: Chris Pizzi, Chief Operating Officer and Chief Financial Officer
CHR: Julie Levison, Director Human Resources
CNO: Sherri Steele, Chief Nursing Officer
Web address: www.providence.org
**Control:** Church–operated, Nongovernment, not–for profit **Service:** General Medical and Surgical

**Staffed Beds:** 142 **Admissions:** 6276 **Census:** 72 **Outpatient Visits:** 354139 **Births:** 519 **Total Expense ($000):** 182235 **Payroll Expense ($000):** 60585 **Personnel:** 841

## MILWAUKIE—Clackamas County

⊠ **PROVIDENCE MILWAUKIE HOSPITAL (380082)**, 10150 S.E. 32nd Avenue, Zip 97222–6516; tel. 503/513–8300 **A**1 3 5 9 10 **F**3 15 18 29 30 34 35 36 39 40 44 45 46 50 53 54 57 59 63 64 68 70 71 74 75 77 79 81 82 84 85 87 89 91 92 93 97 100 102 105 107 108 110 111 114 115 119 129 130 131 132 133 135 146 147 148 **P**6 **S** Providence Health & Services, Renton, WA
Primary Contact: Keith Hyde, Chief Executive Officer
COO: Sherri Paris, Chief Operating Officer
CFO: Sheila Waldron, Finance Manager
CHR: Jeannie Mikulic, Director Human Resources
CNO: Lisa Halvorsen, Chief Nurse Executive
Web address: www.providence.org
**Control:** Church–operated, Nongovernment, not–for profit **Service:** General Medical and Surgical

**Staffed Beds:** 51 **Admissions:** 2599 **Census:** 22 **Outpatient Visits:** 243042 **Births:** 0 **Total Expense ($000):** 94804 **Payroll Expense ($000):** 27942 **Personnel:** 364

## NEWBERG—Yamhill County

⊠ **PROVIDENCE NEWBERG MEDICAL CENTER (380037)**, 1001 Providence Drive, Zip 97132–7485; tel. 503/537–1555 **A**1 9 10 **F**3 11 13 15 18 20 29 30 34 35 40 45 49 50 57 59 60 64 68 70 75 76 77 79 81 85 87 93 100 107 108 110 111 114 118 119 129 130 132 135 146 147 148 **P**6 **S** Providence Health & Services, Renton, WA
Primary Contact: Lorinda Van Zanten, MSN, Chief Executive Officer
CFO: Jack R. Sumner, Assistant Administrator Finance
CMO: George Weghorst, M.D., Chief Medical Officer
CIO: Laureen O'Brien, Chief Information Officer
CHR: Cheryl Gebhart, Director Human Resources Providence Health Plan and Providence Medical Group
Web address: www.phsor.org
**Control:** Church–operated, Nongovernment, not–for profit **Service:** General Medical and Surgical

**Staffed Beds:** 40 **Admissions:** 2638 **Census:** 23 **Outpatient Visits:** 218225 **Births:** 580 **Total Expense ($000):** 90603 **Payroll Expense ($000):** 26933 **Personnel:** 391

## NEWPORT—Lincoln County

★ ◇ **SAMARITAN PACIFIC COMMUNITIES HOSPITAL (381314)**, 930 S.W. Abbey Street, Zip 97365–4820, Mailing Address: P.O. Box 945, Zip 97365–0072; tel. 541/265–2244 **A**9 10 18 21 **F**3 8 11 13 15 28 29 30 31 34 35 40 44 45 47 50 54 62 63 64 68 70 75 76 77 78 79 81 85 87 89 92 93 97 107 110 111 114 119 129 130 132 133 135 144 146 147 148 **P**6 **S** Samaritan Health Services, Corvallis, OR
Primary Contact: David C. Bigelow, PharmD, Chief Executive Officer
CFO: Daniel B. Smith, Chief Financial Officer
CIO: Robert Power, Chief Information Officer
CHR: Gina Tapp, Director Human Resources
CNO: Lorie Williams, R.N., Vice President Nursing
Web address: www.samhealth.org
**Control:** Other not–for–profit (including NFP Corporation) **Service:** General Medical and Surgical

**Staffed Beds:** 25 **Admissions:** 1233 **Census:** 11 **Outpatient Visits:** 128306 **Births:** 181 **Total Expense ($000):** 73035 **Payroll Expense ($000):** 33534 **Personnel:** 361

## ONTARIO—Malheur County

**HOLY ROSARY MEDICAL CENTER** See Saint Alphonsus Medical Center – Ontario

⊠ **SAINT ALPHONSUS MEDICAL CENTER – ONTARIO (380052)**, 351 S.W. Ninth Street, Zip 97914–2693; tel. 541/881–7000 **A**1 3 5 9 10 20 **F**3 11 13 15 29 30 31 32 34 35 40 43 44 45 46 50 51 54 55 56 57 59 62 64 65 66 68 70 75 76 77 78 79 81 82 85 87 93 97 107 108 110 114 118 119 129 130 131 132 135 144 146 147 148 **P**6 **S** Trinity Health, Livonia, MI
Primary Contact: Karl Keeler, Chief Executive Officer
COO: Ken Hart, Vice President Operations
CFO: Lannie Checketts, Vice President Finance and Operations
CMO: Paul Gering, M.D., Vice President Medical Affairs
CHR: Stefanie Thiel, Senior Human Resources Business Partner
CNO: Dina Ellwanger, R.N., Chief Nursing Officer
Web address: www.saintalphonsus.org/ontario
**Control:** Church–operated, Nongovernment, not–for profit **Service:** General Medical and Surgical

**Staffed Beds:** 49 **Admissions:** 2552 **Census:** 20 **Outpatient Visits:** 66411 **Births:** 548 **Total Expense ($000):** 61819 **Payroll Expense ($000):** 25521 **Personnel:** 401

## OREGON CITY—Clackamas County

⊠ **PROVIDENCE WILLAMETTE FALLS MEDICAL CENTER (380038)**, 1500 Division Street, Zip 97045–1597; tel. 503/656–1631 **A**1 9 10 **F**13 15 29 30 34 35 36 40 44 45 46 50 53 54 57 59 63 64 68 70 74 75 76 77 78 79 81 82 84 85 87 89 91 92 93 97 98 100 107 108 111 114 119 130 131 132 133 135 146 147 **P**6 **S** Providence Health & Services, Renton, WA
Primary Contact: Russ Reinhard, Chief Executive
COO: Patricia A. Markesino, FACHE, Chief Nurse Executive and Chief Operating Officer
CFO: Elizabeth Sublette, Director Finance
CMO: James Watkins, M.D., President Medical Staff
CHR: Joann M. Pfister, Director Human Resources
CNO: Jessica Bailey-Oetker, Director Quality and Medical Staff
Web address: www.providence.org/pwfmc
**Control:** Church–operated, Nongovernment, not–for profit **Service:** General Medical and Surgical

**Staffed Beds:** 111 **Admissions:** 5063 **Census:** 47 **Outpatient Visits:** 150690 **Births:** 1174 **Total Expense ($000):** 114943 **Payroll Expense ($000):** 35881 **Personnel:** 464

## PENDLETON—Umatilla County

⊠ **CHI ST. ANTHONY HOSPITAL (381319)**, 2801 St. Anthony Way, Zip 97801–3800; tel. 541/276–5121 **A**1 9 10 18 **F**3 11 13 15 17 18 29 30 31 35 40 43 45 50 51 53 54 57 59 62 63 64 65 68 70 75 77 78 79 80 81 85 86 87 89 90 91 93 97 107 108 110 111 114 118 119 127 129 130 131 132 133 134 135 146 147 **P**6 **S** Catholic Health Initiatives, Englewood, CO
Primary Contact: Harold S. Geller, Chief Executive Officer
CMO: Malcolm Townsley, M.D., Chief of Staff
CHR: Janeen K. Reding, Director Human Resources
Web address: www.sahpendleton.org
**Control:** Church–operated, Nongovernment, not–for profit **Service:** General Medical and Surgical

**Staffed Beds:** 25 **Admissions:** 1405 **Census:** 12 **Outpatient Visits:** 69657 **Births:** 331 **Total Expense ($000):** 55142 **Payroll Expense ($000):** 21875 **Personnel:** 300

---

**Hospital, Medicare Provider Number, Address, Telephone, Approval, Facility, and Physician Codes, Health Care System**

★ American Hospital Association (AHA) membership
□ The Joint Commission accreditation
○ Healthcare Facilities Accreditation Program
◇ DNV Healthcare Inc. accreditation
⇑ Center for Improvement in Healthcare Quality Accreditation
△ Commission on Accreditation of Rehabilitation Facilities (CARF) accreditation

**PORTLAND—Multnomah County**

✠ **ADVENTIST MEDICAL CENTER–PORTLAND (380060)**, 10123 S.E. Market Street, Zip 97216–2599; tel. 503/257–2500 **A**1 2 9 10 **F**3 9 11 13 15 18 20 22 24 26 28 29 30 31 34 35 36 37 40 44 45 46 49 54 57 58 59 62 63 64 70 71 74 75 76 77 78 79 81 82 83 84 85 86 93 97 98 100 102 107 108 110 111 114 115 118 119 120 121 123 126 129 130 131 132 135 144 146 147 148 **P**6 7 **S** Adventist Health, Roseville, CA
Primary Contact: Joyce Newmyer, President and Chief Executive Officer
COO: Ronald K. Benfield, Chief Operating Officer
CFO: V. Mark Perry, Chief Financial Officer
CMO: Wesley E. Rippey, M.D., Chief Medical Officer
CHR: Shane Voshell, Director Human Resources
CNO: Ellen Tryon, R.N., Chief Nursing Officer
Web address: www.adventisthealthnw.com
**Control:** Church–operated, Nongovernment, not–for profit **Service:** General Medical and Surgical

**Staffed Beds:** 242 **Admissions:** 11473 **Census:** 123 **Outpatient Visits:** 584450 **Births:** 1179 **Total Expense ($000):** 344763 **Payroll Expense ($000):** 134038 **Personnel:** 1583

☐ **CEDAR HILLS HOSPITAL (384012)**, 10300 S.W. Eastridge Street, Zip 97225–5004; tel. 503/944–5000, (Nonreporting) **A**1 9 10 **S** Universal Health Services, Inc., King of Prussia, PA
Primary Contact: Elizabeth Hutter, Chief Executive Officer
Web address: www.cedarhillshospital.com
**Control:** Corporation, Investor–owned, for–profit **Service:** Psychiatric

**Staffed Beds:** 78

**DOERNBECHER CHILDREN'S HOSPITAL** See OHSU Hospital

**GOOD SAMARITAN HOSPITAL AND MEDICAL CENTER** See Legacy Good Samaritan Hospital and Medical Center

✠ △ ◇ **LEGACY EMANUEL HOSPITAL AND HEALTH CENTER (380007)**, 2801 North Gantenbein Avenue, Zip 97227–1674; tel. 503/413–2200, (Includes RANDALL CHILDREN'S HOSPITAL, 2801 North Gantenbein Avenue, Zip 97227–1623; tel. 503/413–2200) **A**1 2 3 5 7 9 10 21 **F**3 7 11 13 15 16 17 18 19 20 21 22 23 24 25 26 27 29 30 31 32 34 35 38 39 40 41 43 44 45 46 47 49 50 51 54 55 56 57 59 60 61 64 65 66 68 70 72 74 75 76 77 78 79 80 81 83 84 85 86 87 88 89 93 97 98 99 100 101 102 107 108 110 111 112 114 115 118 119 126 127 129 130 131 132 135 144 146 147 148 **P**6 **S** Legacy Health, Portland, OR
Primary Contact: Lori Morgan, M.D., Chief Administrative Officer
CHR: Sonja Steves, Senior Vice President Human Resources and Marketing
Web address: www.legacyhealth.org
**Control:** Other not–for–profit (including NFP Corporation) **Service:** General Medical and Surgical

**Staffed Beds:** 427 **Admissions:** 17852 **Census:** 273 **Outpatient Visits:** 508053 **Births:** 2059 **Total Expense ($000):** 657348 **Payroll Expense ($000):** 288122 **Personnel:** 3455

✠ **LEGACY GOOD SAMARITAN HOSPITAL AND MEDICAL CENTER (380017)**, 1015 N.W. 22nd Avenue, Zip 97210–3099; tel. 503/413–7711, (Includes GOOD SAMARITAN HOSPITAL AND MEDICAL CENTER, 1015 N.W. 22nd Avenue, Zip 97210; tel. 503/229–7711; REHABILITATION INSTITUTE OF OREGON, 2010 N.W. Kearney Street, Zip 97209; tel. 503/226–3774) **A**1 2 3 5 9 10 **F**3 8 11 12 15 18 20 22 24 26 28 29 30 31 34 35 38 40 44 45 46 47 48 49 50 51 55 56 57 58 59 60 61 64 65 68 70 74 75 76 77 78 79 80 81 82 83 84 85 86 87 90 91 93 94 96 97 98 100 101 102 103 107 108 110 111 114 115 116 117 118 119 120 121 123 124 126 129 130 132 135 138 142 143 145 146 147 148 **P**6 **S** Legacy Health, Portland, OR
Primary Contact: Jonathan Avery, Chief Administrative Officer
CIO: C. Matthew Calais, Senior Vice President and Chief Information Officer
CHR: Sonja Steves, Vice President Marketing
CNO: Cindy Evans, R.N., Chief Nursing Officer
Web address: www.legacyhealth.org
**Control:** Other not–for–profit (including NFP Corporation) **Service:** General Medical and Surgical

**Staffed Beds:** 247 **Admissions:** 10087 **Census:** 137 **Outpatient Visits:** 154651 **Births:** 997 **Total Expense ($000):** 274400 **Payroll Expense ($000):** 103979 **Personnel:** 1342

✠ **OHSU HOSPITAL (380009)**, 3181 S.W. Sam Jackson Park Road, Zip 97239–3098; tel. 503/494–8311, (Includes DOERNBECHER CHILDREN'S HOSPITAL, 3181 S.W. Sam Jackson Park Road, Zip 97201; tel. 503/494–8811; Peter F. Rapp, Executive Vice President and Executive Director) **A**1 2 3 5 8 9 10 **F**3 5 6 8 9 12 13 15 17 18 19 20 21 22 23 24 25 26 27 28 29 30 31 32 34 35 36 37 38 39 40 41 43 44 45 46 47 48 49 50 51 52 53 54 55 56 57 58 59 60 61 64 66 68 70 71 72 74 75 76 77 78 79 81 82 84 85 86 87 88 89 92 93 95 96 97 98 100 103 104 107 108 110 111 114 115 117 118 119 120 121 123 124 126 127 129 130 131 132 134 135 136 137 138 139 141 145 146 147 148 **P**1
Primary Contact: Peter F. Rapp, Executive Vice President and Executive Director
COO: Cynthia M. Grueber, Senior Vice President and Chief Operating Officer
CFO: Diana Gernhart, Senior Vice President and Hospital Chief Financial Officer
CMO: Charles M. Kilo, M.D., Chief Medical Officer
CIO: Bridget Haggerty, Chief Information Officer
CHR: Derek Carissimi, Vice President Human Resources
CNO: Dana Bjarnason, R.N., Vice President and Chief Nursing Officer
Web address: www.ohsu.edu
**Control:** Hospital district or authority, Government, nonfederal **Service:** General Medical and Surgical

**Staffed Beds:** 528 **Admissions:** 28535 **Census:** 451 **Outpatient Visits:** 776918 **Births:** 2517 **Total Expense ($000):** 1249384 **Payroll Expense ($000):** 451421 **Personnel:** 6768

✠ **PORTLAND VETERANS AFFAIRS MEDICAL CENTER**, 3710 S.W. U.S. Veterans Hospital Road, Zip 97239–2964, Mailing Address: P.O. Box 1034, Zip 97207–1034; tel. 503/220–8262, (Nonreporting) **A**1 2 3 5 8 **S** Department of Veterans Affairs, Washington, DC
Primary Contact: Joanne Krumberger, R.N., FACHE, Director
CFO: Annette Barkema, Chief Financial Officer
CMO: Thomas Anderson, M.D., Chief of Staff
CIO: James Horner, Chief Information Officer
CHR: Melody Mikutowski, Chief Human Resources Management
Web address: www.portland.va.gov/
**Control:** Veterans Affairs, Government, federal **Service:** General Medical and Surgical

**Staffed Beds:** 303

✠ **PROVIDENCE PORTLAND MEDICAL CENTER (380061)**, 4805 N.E. Glisan Street, Zip 97213–2933; tel. 503/215–5526 **A**1 2 3 5 9 10 **F**3 4 5 9 13 15 17 18 20 22 24 26 27 29 30 31 34 35 36 37 38 40 44 45 46 49 50 51 53 54 56 57 58 59 60 61 62 63 64 65 66 68 70 72 73 74 75 76 77 78 79 81 82 84 85 86 87 89 90 92 93 97 98 99 100 102 103 104 105 107 108 109 110 111 114 116 117 118 119 121 123 124 126 129 130 131 132 133 135 136 137 145 146 147 148 **P**6 **S** Providence Health & Services, Renton, WA
Primary Contact: Paul Gaden, Chief Executive Officer
COO: Krista Farnham, Chief Operating Officer
CFO: Eric Olson, Chief Financial Officer
CMO: Robert Wells, M.D., Chief Medical Officer
CIO: Mark Premo, Senior Director HC Intelligence
CHR: Jeannie Mikulic, Director Human Resources
CNO: Mary T. McFadden, MSN, Chief Nurse Executive
Web address: www.providence.org
**Control:** Church–operated, Nongovernment, not–for profit **Service:** General Medical and Surgical

**Staffed Beds:** 417 **Admissions:** 21796 **Census:** 282 **Outpatient Visits:** 1259244 **Births:** 2594 **Total Expense ($000):** 676770 **Payroll Expense ($000):** 198601 **Personnel:** 2575

✠ **PROVIDENCE ST. VINCENT MEDICAL CENTER (380004)**, 9205 S.W. Barnes Road, Zip 97225–6661; tel. 503/216–1234, (Includes CHILDREN AT PROVIDENCE ST. VINCENT, 9205 S.W. Barnes Road, Zip 97225–6603; tel. 503/216–4400) **A**1 2 3 5 9 10 **F**3 5 13 15 17 18 20 22 24 26 28 29 30 31 34 35 36 37 38 40 41 44 45 46 47 48 49 50 51 53 54 56 57 58 59 60 61 64 65 70 72 74 75 76 77 78 79 81 82 83 84 85 86 87 88 89 91 92 93 97 98 100 102 103 104 105 107 108 109 110 111 112 114 115 116 117 118 119 120 121 123 126 129 130 131 132 133 135 146 147 148 **P**6 **S** Providence Health & Services, Renton, WA
Primary Contact: Janice Burger, Chief Executive
COO: Nancy Roberts, Chief Operating Officer
CFO: Scott Pfister, Director Finance
Web address: www.providence.org/portland/hospitals
**Control:** Church–operated, Nongovernment, not–for profit **Service:** General Medical and Surgical

**Staffed Beds:** 552 **Admissions:** 26181 **Census:** 324 **Outpatient Visits:** 808654 **Births:** 4298 **Total Expense ($000):** 739174 **Payroll Expense ($000):** 205800 **Personnel:** 2626

**REHABILITATION INSTITUTE OF OREGON** See Legacy Good Samaritan Hospital and Medical Center

☐ **SHRINERS HOSPITALS FOR CHILDREN–PORTLAND (383300)**, 3101 S.W. Sam Jackson Park Road, Zip 97239–3009; tel. 503/241–5090 **A**1 3 5 10 **F**3 29 34 35 37 50 53 58 64 68 75 77 79 81 85 86 87 89 91 93 94 130 131 132 134 146 148 **P**6 **S** Shriners Hospitals for Children, Tampa, FL
Primary Contact: J. Craig Patchin, Administrator
CFO: Mark Knudsen, Director Fiscal Services
CMO: Michael Aiona, M.D., Chief of Staff
CIO: Carl Montante, Director Information Systems and Information Technology
CHR: Rhonda Smith, Director Human Resources
CNO: Suzanne Diers, R.N., Director Patient Care Services
Web address: www.shrinershospitalsforchildren.org/Hospitals/Locations/Portland.aspx
**Control:** Other not–for–profit (including NFP Corporation) **Service:** Children's general

**Staffed Beds:** 8 **Admissions:** 419 **Census:** 7 **Outpatient Visits:** 10508
**Births:** 0 **Total Expense ($000):** 37949 **Payroll Expense ($000):** 18684
**Personnel:** 260

**VETERANS AFFAIRS MEDICAL CENTER** See Portland Veterans Affairs Medical Center

⊞ **VIBRA SPECIALTY HOSPITAL OF PORTLAND (382004)**, 10300 N.E. Hancock Street, Zip 97220–3831; tel. 503/257–5500, (Nonreporting) **A**1 9 10 **S** Vibra Healthcare, Mechanicsburg, PA
Primary Contact: David Tupper, Chief Executive Officer
CFO: Stephanie Lawrence, Chief Financial Officer
CMO: Cynthia Wallace, M.D., Medical Director
CIO: Marie Roof, Executive Vice President Information Systems
CHR: Kellie Bernert–Yap, Director Human Resources
CNO: Susan E. Brooker, R.N., Chief Clinical Officer
Web address: www.vshportland.com
**Control:** Corporation, Investor–owned, for–profit **Service:** Long–Term Acute Care hospital

**Staffed Beds:** 73

**PRINEVILLE—Crook County**

★ **PIONEER MEMORIAL HOSPITAL (381313)**, 1201 N.E. Elm Street, Zip 97754–1206; tel. 541/447–6254 **A**9 10 18 **F**3 11 15 29 30 34 35 40 43 45 50 59 64 65 68 70 75 77 79 81 82 84 85 86 87 93 97 100 107 110 115 119 127 128 130 132 133 135 146 **P**6 **S** St. Charles Health System, Inc., Bend, OR
Primary Contact: Jeanine Gentry, Chief Executive Officer
CFO: Karen Shepard, Senior Vice President and Chief Financial Officer
CMO: Michel Boileau, M.D., Chief Clinical Officer
CHR: Rebecca Berry, Senior Director Human Resources
Web address: www.stcharleshealthcare.org
**Control:** Other not–for–profit (including NFP Corporation) **Service:** General Medical and Surgical

**Staffed Beds:** 25 **Admissions:** 658 **Census:** 6 **Outpatient Visits:** 30410
**Births:** 0 **Total Expense ($000):** 33960 **Payroll Expense ($000):** 15000
**Personnel:** 178

**REDMOND—Deschutes County**

⊞ **ST. CHARLES REDMOND (380040)**, 1253 N.W. Canal Boulevard, Zip 97756–1395; tel. 541/548–8131 **A**1 9 10 20 **F**3 11 13 28 29 30 34 40 43 45 47 51 54 57 59 62 63 64 68 70 75 76 79 81 82 84 85 93 97 107 108 114 119 130 132 135 146 148 **P**6 **S** St. Charles Health System, Inc., Bend, OR
Primary Contact: Robert Gomes, FACHE, Chief Executive Officer
CFO: Karen Shepard, Senior Vice President Finance and Chief Financial Officer
CMO: Michel Boileau, M.D., Chief Clinical Officer
CIO: William Winnenberg, Chief Information Officer
CHR: Rebecca Berry, Senior Director Human Resources
CNO: Karen Reed, R.N., Chief Nursing Officer
Web address: www.stcharleshealthcare.org
**Control:** Other not–for–profit (including NFP Corporation) **Service:** General Medical and Surgical

**Staffed Beds:** 48 **Admissions:** 2330 **Census:** 18 **Outpatient Visits:** 52027
**Births:** 413 **Total Expense ($000):** 71929 **Payroll Expense ($000):** 31828
**Personnel:** 400

**REEDSPORT—Douglas County**

**LOWER UMPQUA HOSPITAL DISTRICT (381311)**, 600 Ranch Road, Zip 97467–1795; tel. 541/271–2171 **A**9 10 18 **F**3 7 11 15 29 34 35 40 43 45 46 50 57 64 70 75 77 79 81 82 85 87 93 97 107 108 115 119 127 130 132 133 144 148 **P**6
Primary Contact: Sandra Reese, Administrator
CMO: Ronald Vail, M.D., Chief of Staff
CIO: Timothy Picou, Manager Information Technology
Web address: www.lowerumpquahospital.com
**Control:** Hospital district or authority, Government, nonfederal **Service:** General Medical and Surgical

**Staffed Beds:** 16 **Admissions:** 336 **Census:** 5 **Outpatient Visits:** 15533
**Births:** 0 **Total Expense ($000):** 21553 **Payroll Expense ($000):** 8868
**Personnel:** 131

**ROSEBURG—Douglas County**

⊞ **MERCY MEDICAL CENTER (380027)**, 2700 Stewart Parkway, Zip 97471–1281; tel. 541/673–0611 **A**1 9 10 **F**3 8 11 13 15 17 18 19 20 21 22 23 24 25 26 27 28 29 30 31 32 34 35 37 38 40 43 44 45 46 47 48 49 50 51 54 56 57 59 60 61 62 63 64 65 68 70 74 75 76 77 78 79 81 82 84 85 86 87 89 93 96 102 107 108 110 111 114 115 118 119 129 130 132 135 143 146 147 148 **S** Catholic Health Initiatives, Englewood, CO
Primary Contact: Kelly C. Morgan, President and Chief Executive Officer
COO: Debbie Boswell, Chief Operating Officer and Chief Nursing Officer
CFO: John Kasberger, Vice President and Chief Financial Officer
CMO: Jason Gray, M.D., Chief Medical Officer
CIO: Kathleen Nickel, Director Communications
CHR: Deb Lightcap, Director Human Resources
CNO: Debbie Boswell, Chief Operating Officer and Chief Nursing Officer
Web address: www.mercyrose.org
**Control:** Church–operated, Nongovernment, not–for profit **Service:** General Medical and Surgical

**Staffed Beds:** 141 **Admissions:** 7016 **Census:** 71 **Outpatient Visits:** 350799
**Births:** 916 **Total Expense ($000):** 149881 **Payroll Expense ($000):** 51749
**Personnel:** 738

⊞ **VETERANS AFFAIRS ROSEBURG HEALTHCARE SYSTEM**, 913 N.W. Garden Valley Boulevard, Zip 97471–6513; tel. 541/440–1000, (Nonreporting) **A**1 **S** Department of Veterans Affairs, Washington, DC
Primary Contact: Carol Bogedain, FACHE, Director
COO: Steven Broskey, Associate Director
CHR: Larry Mentzer, Chief Human Resources Officer
CNO: Tracy Weistreich, Ph.D., Associate Director Patient Care Services/Nurse Executive
Web address: www.roseburg.va.gov/
**Control:** Veterans Affairs, Government, federal **Service:** General Medical and Surgical

**Staffed Beds:** 88

**SALEM—Marion County**

☐ **OREGON STATE HOSPITAL (384008)**, 2600 Center Street N.E., Zip 97301–2682; tel. 503/945–2870 **A**1 3 5 10 **F**5 29 30 35 38 39 40 44 53 56 58 59 65 66 74 75 77 82 86 87 91 96 98 101 102 103 106 130 132 135 146
Primary Contact: Greg Roberts, Superintendent
Web address: www.oregon.gov/dhs/mentalhealth/osh/main.shtml
**Control:** State–Government, nonfederal **Service:** Psychiatric

**Staffed Beds:** 659 **Admissions:** 833 **Census:** 247 **Outpatient Visits:** 0
**Births:** 0 **Total Expense ($000):** 209455 **Payroll Expense ($000):** 111678

**OR**

---

**Hospital, Medicare Provider Number, Address, Telephone, Approval, Facility, and Physician Codes, Health Care System**

★ American Hospital Association (AHA) membership   ○ Healthcare Facilities Accreditation Program   ⇑ Center for Improvement in Healthcare Quality Accreditation
☐ The Joint Commission accreditation   ◇ DNV Healthcare Inc. accreditation   △ Commission on Accreditation of Rehabilitation Facilities (CARF) accreditation

**SALEM HOSPITAL (380051)**, 890 Oak Street S.E., Zip 97301–3959, Mailing Address: P.O. Box 14001, Zip 97309–5014; tel. 503/561–5200, (Includes PSYCHIATRIC MEDICINE CENTER, 1127 Oak Street S.E., Zip 97301, Mailing Address: P.O. Box 14001, Zip 97309–5014; REGIONAL REHABILITATION CENTER, 2561 Center Street N.E., Zip 97301, Mailing Address: P.O. Box 14001, Zip 97309–5014; tel. 503/370–5986) **A**1 2 5 9 10 **F**3 11 12 13 15 17 18 19 20 22 24 26 28 29 30 31 34 35 36 37 38 40 43 45 46 47 48 49 50 53 54 55 56 57 58 59 64 67 68 70 72 74 75 76 77 78 79 81 84 85 86 87 89 90 91 92 93 94 95 96 97 98 99 100 102 103 104 105 106 107 108 109 110 111 112 113 114 115 116 117 118 119 120 121 122 123 124 126 129 130 131 132 135 145 146 147 148 **P**6 **S** Salem Health, Salem, OR
Primary Contact: Norman F. Gruber, President and Chief Executive Officer
COO: Cheryl R. Nester Wolfe, R.N., Senior Vice President Operations
CFO: James Parr, Chief Financial Officer
CMO: Steve Gordon, M.D., Chief Medical Officer
CIO: Cort Garrison, M.D., Chief Information Officer
CHR: Laurie C. Barr, Vice President Human Resources
CNO: Sarah Horn, Chief Nursing Officer
Web address: www.salemhealth.org
**Control:** Other not–for–profit (including NFP Corporation) **Service:** General Medical and Surgical

**Staffed Beds:** 428 **Admissions:** 23039 **Census:** 284 **Outpatient Visits:** 336540 **Births:** 3165 **Total Expense ($000):** 579741 **Payroll Expense ($000):** 252180 **Personnel:** 3320

### SEASIDE—Clatsop County

**PROVIDENCE SEASIDE HOSPITAL (381303)**, 725 South Wahanna Road, Zip 97138–7735; tel. 503/717–7000 **A**1 9 10 18 **F**3 12 13 15 18 29 30 31 32 34 35 40 45 46 56 57 59 61 64 65 66 70 75 76 77 78 79 81 82 83 84 85 86 87 91 92 93 97 107 108 110 111 114 119 127 130 132 133 135 143 146 147 148 **P**6 **S** Providence Health & Services, Renton, WA
Primary Contact: Debbie Glass, Interim Chief Executive Officer
COO: Debbie Glass, Interim Chief Operating Officer
CFO: Pamela Cooper, Director Finance
CMO: Susan Heineck, M.D., President Professional Staff
CHR: Theresa Osburne, Human Resources Strategic Partners
CNO: Janiece Zauner, Chief Nursing Officer
Web address: www.providence.org
**Control:** Church–operated, Nongovernment, not–for profit **Service:** General Medical and Surgical

**Staffed Beds:** 25 **Admissions:** 920 **Census:** 15 **Outpatient Visits:** 129931 **Births:** 108 **Total Expense ($000):** 49664 **Payroll Expense ($000):** 22727 **Personnel:** 318

### SILVERTON—Marion County

**SILVERTON HOSPITAL (380029)**, 342 Fairview Street, Zip 97381–1993; tel. 503/873–1500 **A**1 9 10 **F**3 11 13 15 20 26 28 29 30 34 35 40 43 47 50 54 57 59 64 65 66 70 75 76 77 79 81 85 86 87 89 107 108 110 111 114 115 119 124 127 130 131 132 133 135 143 144 146 147 148 **P**4 8
Primary Contact: Sarah Fronza, Interim President and Chief Executive Officer
COO: Karen Brady, Chief Operating Officer and Chief Nursing Officer
CFO: Daniel Jessup, Chief Financial Officer
CMO: Joseph Huang, M.D., Chief Medical and Quality Officer
CIO: Karen Brady, Chief Information Officer
CHR: Natalie Britton, Director Human Resources
CNO: Karen Brady, Chief Operating Officer and Chief Nursing Officer
Web address: www.silvertonhealth.org
**Control:** Other not–for–profit (including NFP Corporation) **Service:** General Medical and Surgical

**Staffed Beds:** 48 **Admissions:** 3157 **Census:** 23 **Outpatient Visits:** 181531 **Births:** 1606 **Total Expense ($000):** 117023 **Payroll Expense ($000):** 51258 **Personnel:** 662

### SPRINGFIELD—Lane County

**MCKENZIE–WILLAMETTE MEDICAL CENTER (380020)**, 1460 G Street, Zip 97477–4197; tel. 541/726–4400 **A**1 9 10 **F**3 11 13 17 18 20 22 24 28 29 30 31 34 35 39 40 41 43 45 46 47 49 50 57 59 70 73 76 78 79 81 82 85 87 89 93 107 108 111 115 118 119 126 129 130 132 146 147 148 **P**6 **S** Community Health Systems, Inc., Franklin, TN
Primary Contact: Chad Campbell, Chief Executive Officer
CFO: Rosanne Devault, Chief Financial Officer
CIO: David Blomquist, Director Information Technology
CHR: Megan A. O'Leary, Vice President Human Resources and Rehabilitation Services
Web address: www.mckweb.com
**Control:** Corporation, Investor–owned, for–profit **Service:** General Medical and Surgical

**Staffed Beds:** 113 **Admissions:** 6476 **Census:** 57 **Outpatient Visits:** 76631 **Births:** 681 **Total Expense ($000):** 126382 **Payroll Expense ($000):** 46392 **Personnel:** 562

★ ◇ **PEACEHEALTH SACRED HEART MEDICAL CENTER AT RIVERBEND (380102)**, 3333 Riverbend Drive, Zip 97477–8800; tel. 541/222–7300 **A**9 10 21 **F**3 11 12 13 19 20 21 22 24 26 28 29 30 31 37 38 40 43 45 46 47 48 49 51 57 60 64 68 70 72 74 75 76 78 79 81 84 85 89 93 102 107 108 111 115 118 119 124 126 129 130 135 146 148 **P**6 **S** PeaceHealth, Vancouver, WA
Primary Contact: Rand O'Leary, Chief Administrative Officer
CFO: Wendy Apland, Regional Vice President of Finance/Chief Financial Officer
CIO: Tom Fricks, Interim Senior Vice President of Information Technology
CHR: Craig Mills, Regional Vice President Culture and People
Web address: www.peacehealth.org
**Control:** Church–operated, Nongovernment, not–for profit **Service:** General Medical and Surgical

**Staffed Beds:** 379 **Admissions:** 23413 **Census:** 288 **Outpatient Visits:** 99420 **Births:** 2943 **Total Expense ($000):** 476531 **Payroll Expense ($000):** 161189 **Personnel:** 2142

### STAYTON—Marion County

**SANTIAM MEMORIAL HOSPITAL (380056)**, 1401 North 10th Avenue, Zip 97383–1399; tel. 503/769–2175 **A**1 9 10 **F**3 7 11 13 15 29 30 40 41 43 50 65 70 76 81 85 87 89 107 111 115 119 128 130 133 135 143 **P**8
Primary Contact: Terry L. Fletchall, Administrator
COO: Maggie Hudson, Chief Financial and Operations Officer
CFO: Rachael Seeder, Controller
CMO: Guesly Dessieux, D.O., Chief Medical Officer
CIO: Trace Jacobs, Director Information Technology
CNO: Genny Baldwin, R.N., Chief Nursing Officer
Web address: www.santiamhospital.org
**Control:** Other not–for–profit (including NFP Corporation) **Service:** General Medical and Surgical

**Staffed Beds:** 40 **Admissions:** 1012 **Census:** 9 **Outpatient Visits:** 38264 **Births:** 100 **Total Expense ($000):** 33205 **Payroll Expense ($000):** 12984 **Personnel:** 245

### THE DALLES—Wasco County

△ **MID–COLUMBIA MEDICAL CENTER (380001)**, 1700 East 19th Street, Zip 97058–3317; tel. 541/296–1111 **A**1 2 7 9 10 **F**3 11 12 13 15 18 28 29 30 31 32 34 35 36 40 41 43 45 46 50 53 57 59 62 65 66 68 70 75 76 77 78 79 81 82 83 84 86 87 89 90 91 92 93 99 100 101 104 107 108 110 111 114 118 119 120 121 123 127 129 130 131 132 133 135 146 147 148 **P**4 6
Primary Contact: Duane Francis, President and Chief Executive Officer
CFO: Don Arbon, Vice President Finance
CMO: Judy Richardson, M.D., President Medical Staff
CIO: Erick Larson, Vice President and Chief Information Officer
CHR: Christine Espy, Division Director
CNO: Regina P. Rose, R.N., Vice President Nursing Services
Web address: www.mcmc.net
**Control:** Other not–for–profit (including NFP Corporation) **Service:** General Medical and Surgical

**Staffed Beds:** 43 **Admissions:** 2109 **Census:** 19 **Outpatient Visits:** 121245 **Births:** 287 **Total Expense ($000):** 87015 **Payroll Expense ($000):** 41171 **Personnel:** 582

### TILLAMOOK—Tillamook County

**TILLAMOOK REGIONAL MEDICAL CENTER (381317)**, 1000 Third Street, Zip 97141–3430; tel. 503/842–4444 **A**1 9 10 18 **F**2 3 7 11 13 18 29 30 31 33 34 35 40 43 45 50 57 59 64 65 68 75 76 77 78 79 81 82 85 87 93 94 97 102 107 108 110 111 115 119 127 129 130 132 133 135 144 146 147 148 **P**6 **S** Adventist Health, Roseville, CA
Primary Contact: David Butler, President and Chief Executive Officer
CFO: Walt Larson, Vice President Finance
CMO: Mark Bowman, M.D., President Medical Staff
CNO: Kathy Saxon, R.N., Vice President Patient Care Services
Web address: www.tillamookregionalmc.com
**Control:** Church–operated, Nongovernment, not–for profit **Service:** General Medical and Surgical

**Staffed Beds:** 25 **Admissions:** 1000 **Census:** 8 **Outpatient Visits:** 128807 **Births:** 193 **Total Expense ($000):** 63746 **Payroll Expense ($000):** 26634 **Personnel:** 360

*Many Facility Codes have changed. Please refer to the AHA Guide Code Chart.*

**TUALATIN—Clackamas County**

✠ **LEGACY MERIDIAN PARK MEDICAL CENTER (380089)**, 19300 S.W. 65th
Avenue, Zip 97062–9741; tel. 503/692–1212 **A**1 2 9 10 **F**3 11 13 15 18 20
22 28 29 30 31 32 34 35 38 40 44 45 46 49 50 51 56 57 59 60 64 68 70
74 75 76 77 78 79 80 81 85 86 87 93 97 107 108 110 111 114 115 116
117 118 119 120 121 126 129 130 132 145 146 147 148 **P**6 **S** Legacy
Health, Portland, OR
Primary Contact: Allyson Anderson, Chief Administrative Officer
COO: Michael Newcomb, D.O., Senior Vice President and Chief Operating Officer
CMO: Lewis Low, M.D., Senior Vice President and Chief Medical Officer
CIO: John Jay Kenagy, Ph.D., Senior Vice President and Chief Information Officer
CHR: Sonja Steves, Vice President Human Resources and Marketing
CNO: Carol Bradley, MSN, Senior Vice President and Chief Nursing Officer
Web address: www.legacyhealth.org
**Control:** Other not–for–profit (including NFP Corporation) **Service:** General
Medical and Surgical

**Staffed Beds:** 130 **Admissions:** 8169 **Census:** 75 **Outpatient Visits:** 160473
**Births:** 1049 **Total Expense ($000):** 173453 **Payroll Expense ($000):**
62055 **Personnel:** 801

---

**Hospital, Medicare Provider Number, Address, Telephone, Approval, Facility, and Physician Codes, Health Care System**

★ American Hospital Association (AHA) membership
☐ The Joint Commission accreditation
○ Healthcare Facilities Accreditation Program
◇ DNV Healthcare Inc. accreditation
⇑ Center for Improvement in Healthcare Quality Accreditation
△ Commission on Accreditation of Rehabilitation Facilities (CARF) accreditation

# PENNSYLVANIA

## ABINGTON—Montgomery County

☒ **ABINGTON MEMORIAL HOSPITAL (390231)**, 1200 Old York Road, Zip 19001–3720; tel. 215/481–2000 **A**1 2 3 5 6 10 13 **F**3 6 8 9 11 12 13 15 17 18 20 22 24 26 28 29 30 31 32 34 35 36 37 38 39 40 43 44 45 46 47 49 50 52 53 54 55 56 57 58 59 60 61 62 63 64 65 66 68 70 72 74 75 76 77 78 79 81 82 83 84 85 86 87 89 90 91 92 93 94 96 97 98 99 100 101 102 103 104 107 108 110 111 114 115 118 119 120 121 124 126 129 130 131 132 135 144 145 146 147 148 **P**6 **S** Jefferson Health, Radnor, PA
Primary Contact: Margaret M. McGoldrick, President
CFO: Michael Walsh, Senior Vice President Finance and Chief Financial Officer
CMO: John J. Kelly, M.D., Chief of Staff
CIO: Alison Ferren, Vice President Information Technology and Chief Information Officer
CHR: Meghan Patton, Vice President Human Resources
CNO: Theresa Reilly, MSN, Senior Vice President Patient Services and Chief Nursing Officer
Web address: www.abingtonhealth.org
**Control:** Other not–for–profit (including NFP Corporation) **Service:** General Medical and Surgical

**Staffed Beds:** 598 **Admissions:** 28575 **Census:** 360 **Outpatient Visits:** 595839 **Births:** 4637 **Total Expense ($000):** 698819 **Payroll Expense ($000):** 328306 **Personnel:** 3910

## ALLENTOWN—Lehigh County

☐ △ **GOOD SHEPHERD REHABILITATION HOSPITAL (393035)**, 850 South 5th Street, Zip 18103–3308; tel. 610/776–3299 **A**1 3 5 7 9 10 **F**28 29 30 32 34 35 36 53 54 56 57 58 59 64 65 66 68 74 75 77 82 86 87 90 91 92 93 94 95 96 107 111 119 130 131 132 143 146 147 148 **P**1 **S** Good Shepherd Rehabilitation Network, Allentown, PA
Primary Contact: John Kristel, President and Chief Executive Officer
CFO: Ron Petula, Chief Financial Officer
Web address: www.goodshepherdrehab.org
**Control:** Other not–for–profit (including NFP Corporation) **Service:** Rehabilitation

**Staffed Beds:** 106 **Admissions:** 1763 **Census:** 79 **Outpatient Visits:** 215164 **Births:** 0 **Total Expense ($000):** 80599 **Payroll Expense ($000):** 32084 **Personnel:** 909

☒ **LEHIGH VALLEY HOSPITAL (390133)**, 1200 South Cedar Crest Boulevard, Zip 18103–6248, Mailing Address: P.O. Box 689, Zip 18105–1556; tel. 610/402–8000, (Includes LEHIGH VALLEY HEALTH NETWORK PEDIATRICS, 17th and Chew Streets, Zip 18102, Mailing Address: PO Box 7017, Zip 18105–7017; tel. 610/402–2273) **A**1 2 3 5 8 9 10 **F**3 6 7 8 12 13 15 16 17 18 19 20 22 24 26 28 29 30 31 32 33 34 35 36 37 38 39 40 41 43 44 45 46 47 48 49 50 51 53 54 55 56 57 58 59 60 61 62 63 64 65 66 68 70 71 72 74 76 77 78 79 80 81 82 84 85 86 87 88 89 90 92 93 96 97 98 99 100 101 102 104 105 106 107 108 110 114 115 118 119 120 121 123 124 126 128 129 130 131 132 134 135 138 141 142 143 144 145 146 147 148 **P**5 6 8 **S** Lehigh Valley Health Network, Allentown, PA
Primary Contact: Brian Nester, D.O., Interim President and Chief Executive Officer
COO: Terry Ann Capuano, R.N., Chief Operating Officer
CFO: Edward O'Dea, Vice President and Chief Financial Officer
CMO: Thomas Whalen, M.D., Chief Medical Officer
CIO: Harry Lukens, Senior Vice President and Chief Information Officer
CHR: Deborah A. Patrick, Senior Vice President Human Resources
CNO: Anne Panik, MS, Senior Vice President Patient Care Services and Chief Nursing Officer
Web address: www.lvhhn.org
**Control:** Other not–for–profit (including NFP Corporation) **Service:** General Medical and Surgical

**Staffed Beds:** 784 **Admissions:** 43363 **Census:** 626 **Outpatient Visits:** 381262 **Births:** 4408 **Total Expense ($000):** 1132229 **Payroll Expense ($000):** 379294 **Personnel:** 6579

☐ △ **SACRED HEART HOSPITAL (390197)**, 421 West Chew Street, Zip 18102–3490; tel. 610/776–4500, (Total facility includes 22 beds in nursing home–type unit) **A**1 3 5 7 9 10 **F**3 11 12 13 15 18 20 22 24 28 29 30 31 32 34 35 38 39 40 43 45 46 47 49 50 56 57 59 61 62 63 64 66 68 74 75 76 77 78 79 80 81 82 84 85 87 91 92 93 97 98 100 101 102 103 107 108 110 111 114 119 121 128 129 130 132 135 143 146 147 148 **P**8
Primary Contact: John L. Nespoli, Chief Executive Officer
CMO: Farrokh Sadr, M.D., Chief Medical Officer
CIO: Tracy Burkhart, Vice President Information Services
CHR: Joseph Mikitka, Vice President Human Resources
Web address: www.shh.org
**Control:** Other not–for–profit (including NFP Corporation) **Service:** General Medical and Surgical

**Staffed Beds:** 143 **Admissions:** 5368 **Census:** 112 **Outpatient Visits:** 173628 **Births:** 366 **Total Expense ($000):** 92377 **Payroll Expense ($000):** 35827 **Personnel:** 830

**ST LUKE'S HOSPITAL – ALLENTOWN CAMPUS** See St. Luke's University Hospital – Bethlehem Campus, Bethlehem

☐ **SURGICAL SPECIALTY CENTER AT COORDINATED HEALTH (390321)**, 1503 North Cedar Crest Boulevard, Zip 18104–2302; tel. 610/861–8080, (Nonreporting) **A**1 9 10
Primary Contact: Emil Dilorio, M.D., Chief Executive Officer
Web address: www.coordinatedhealth.com
**Control:** Other not–for–profit (including NFP Corporation) **Service:** Surgical

**Staffed Beds:** 20

## ALTOONA—Blair County

**ALTOONA REGIONAL HEALTH SYSTEM** See UPMC Altoona

☒ **HEALTHSOUTH REHABILITATION HOSPITAL OF ALTOONA (393040)**, 2005 Valley View Boulevard, Zip 16602–4598; tel. 814/944–3535 **A**1 10 **F**28 29 34 64 74 75 82 90 91 93 94 96 130 131 **P**5 **S** HEALTHSOUTH Corporation, Birmingham, AL
Primary Contact: Scott Filler, Chief Executive Officer
CFO: George Berger, Controller
CMO: Rakesh Patel, D.O., Medical Director
CIO: Kathleen Edwards, Manager Information Systems Operation
CHR: Christine Filer, Director Human Resources
CNO: Mary Gen Boyles, Chief Nursing Officer
Web address: www.healthsouthaltoona.com
**Control:** Corporation, Investor–owned, for–profit **Service:** Rehabilitation

**Staffed Beds:** 80 **Admissions:** 1900 **Census:** 70 **Births:** 0

☒ **JAMES E. VAN ZANDT VETERANS AFFAIRS MEDICAL CENTER**, 2907 Pleasant Valley Boulevard, Zip 16602–4305; tel. 877/626–2500, (Nonreporting) **A**1 **S** Department of Veterans Affairs, Washington, DC
Primary Contact: William H. Mills, Director
CFO: Carl Parrish, Chief Fiscal Service
CMO: Santha Kurian, M.D., Chief of Staff
CIO: Michael Hynoski, Chief Information Resource Management
CHR: Gina Dunio, Chief Human Resources
Web address: www.altoona.va.gov/
**Control:** Veterans Affairs, Government, federal **Service:** General Medical and Surgical

**Staffed Beds:** 68

☒ **UPMC ALTOONA (390073)**, 620 Howard Avenue, Zip 16601–4804; tel. 814/889–2011 **A**1 2 3 5 9 10 12 13 **F**3 5 8 11 12 13 15 18 20 22 24 26 28 29 30 31 34 35 37 38 39 40 43 44 45 47 48 49 50 51 54 56 57 59 60 61 63 64 65 66 68 70 73 74 75 76 77 78 79 81 83 84 85 86 87 89 91 92 93 97 98 100 101 102 103 107 108 110 111 114 115 117 118 119 120 121 123 126 129 130 131 132 135 146 147 148 **S** UPMC, Pittsburgh, PA
Primary Contact: Gerald Murray, President
COO: Ron McConnell, Chief Operating Officer
CFO: Betsy Kreuz, Chief Financial Officer
CMO: Linnane Batzel, M.D., Senior Vice President Quality and Medical Affairs and Chief Medical Officer
CIO: Dale Fuller, Vice President and Chief Information Officer
CHR: Michelle A. Speck, Vice President Human Resources
CNO: Chris Rickens, R.N., Senior Vice President and Chief Nursing Officer
Web address: www.altoonaregional.org
**Control:** Other not–for–profit (including NFP Corporation) **Service:** General Medical and Surgical

**Staffed Beds:** 380 **Admissions:** 17707 **Census:** 228 **Outpatient Visits:** 352620 **Births:** 919 **Total Expense ($000):** 348478 **Payroll Expense ($000):** 134525 **Personnel:** 2015

## AMBLER—Montgomery County

☐ **HORSHAM CLINIC (394034)**, 722 East Butler Pike, Zip 19002–2310; tel. 215/643–7800, (Nonreporting) **A**1 3 5 9 10 **S** Universal Health Services, Inc., King of Prussia, PA
Primary Contact: Phyllis Weisfield, Chief Executive Officer and Managing Director
CFO: Lee Daniels, Chief Financial Officer
CMO: James B. Congdon, M.D., Medical Director
CIO: Suzanne Scholz, Director Medical Records
CHR: Kathleen Nichelson, Director Human Resources
CNO: Calvin Litka, R.N., Director of Nursing
Web address: www.horshamclinic.com
**Control:** Individual, Investor–owned, for–profit **Service:** Psychiatric

**Staffed Beds:** 138

PA

**BEAVER—Beaver County**

☐ **HERITAGE VALLEY HEALTH SYSTEM (390036)**, 1000 Dutch Ridge Road, Zip 15009–9727; tel. 724/728–7000 **A**1 3 9 10 13 **F**3 11 13 14 15 18 20 22 24 26 28 29 30 32 34 35 38 40 46 49 50 53 54 55 57 59 60 64 66 70 73 74 75 76 77 78 79 81 82 84 85 86 89 90 92 93 96 97 98 100 101 102 103 104 107 108 110 111 115 116 118 119 120 121 129 130 131 132 135 145 147 148 **P**6 **S** Heritage Valley Health System, Beaver, PA
Primary Contact: Norman F. Mitry, President and Chief Executive Officer
CFO: Bryan J. Randall, Vice President Finance and Chief Financial Officer
CMO: John Cinicola, M.D., Chief Medical Officer
CIO: David Carleton, Chief Information Officer
CHR: Bruce Edwards, Vice President Human Resources
CNO: Marcia L. Ferrero, MS, Chief Nursing Officer
Web address: www.heritagevalley.org
**Control:** Other not–for–profit (including NFP Corporation) **Service:** General Medical and Surgical

Staffed Beds: 273 Admissions: 14062 Census: 176 Births: 1020

☒ **KINDRED HOSPITAL–HERITAGE VALLEY (392043)**, 1000 Dutch Ridge Road, Zip 15009–9727; tel. 724/773–8480, (Nonreporting) **A**1 9 10 **S** Kindred Healthcare, Louisville, KY
Primary Contact: Dusty Bowers, Chief Executive Officer
CFO: Kevin Varley, Chief Financial Officer
CMO: Jeffrey Erukhimou, M.D., Medical Director
Web address: www.kindredhospitalhv.com/
**Control:** Corporation, Investor–owned, for–profit **Service:** Long–Term Acute Care hospital

Staffed Beds: 35

**BENSALEM—Bucks County**

**LIVENGRIN FOUNDATION**, 4833 Hulmeville Road, Zip 19020–3099; tel. 215/638–5200, (Nonreporting) **A**9
Primary Contact: Richard M. Pine, President and Chief Executive Officer
CFO: James D. Flis, Chief Financial Officer
CMO: William J. Lorman, Ph.D., Clinical Director
CIO: William Miller, Coordinator Management Information Systems
Web address: www.livengrin.org
**Control:** Other not–for–profit (including NFP Corporation) **Service:** Alcoholism and other chemical dependency

Staffed Beds: 76

☐ **ROTHMAN SPECIALTY HOSPITAL (390322)**, 3300 Tillman Drive, Zip 19020–2071; tel. 215/244–7400 **A**1 3 10 **F**29 65 79 81 85 89 107 141 146
Primary Contact: Kelly Doyle, Chief Executive Officer
Web address: www.rothmanspecialtyhospital.com/
**Control:** Partnership, Investor–owned, for–profit **Service:** Surgical

Staffed Beds: 24 Admissions: 1071 Census: 4 Births: 0

**BERWICK—Columbia County**

☒ **BERWICK HOSPITAL CENTER (390072)**, 701 East 16th Street, Zip 18603–2397; tel. 570/759–5000, (Nonreporting) **A**1 9 10 **S** Community Health Systems, Inc., Franklin, TN
Primary Contact: David P. Steitz, Chief Executive Officer
COO: Chad Kramer, Chief Operating Officer
CFO: Whitney Holloway, Chief Financial Officer
CMO: M. Joseph John, M.D., Chief of Staff
CIO: Jeff Leslie, Director Information Technology
CHR: Jackie Ridall, Director Human Resources
CNO: Kathleen Springman, Chief Nursing Officer
Web address: www.berwick–hospital.com
**Control:** Corporation, Investor–owned, for–profit **Service:** General Medical and Surgical

Staffed Beds: 341

**BETHLEHEM—Northampton County**

☐ **COORDINATED HEALTH–BETHLEHEM (390314)**, 2310 Highland Avenue, Zip 18020–8920, Mailing Address: 2300 Highland Avenue, Zip 18020; tel. 610/861–8080 **A**1 10 **F**3 29 34 65 68 79 81 82 85 119 130 131 141 147 148
Primary Contact: Mark Holtz, Chief Operating Officer
Web address: www.coordinatedhealth.com
**Control:** Corporation, Investor–owned, for–profit **Service:** Orthopedic

Staffed Beds: 20 Admissions: 1028 Census: 7 Births: 0

☒ △ **GOOD SHEPHERD SPECIALTY HOSPITAL (392033)**, 2545 Schoenersville Road, 3rd Floor, Zip 18017–7300; tel. 484/884–5051 **A**1 7 9 10 **F**1 3 29 30 36 77 85 87 91 95 130 148 **P**5 **S** Good Shepherd Rehabilitation Network, Allentown, PA
Primary Contact: John Kristel, President and Chief Executive Officer
Web address: www.goodshepherdrehab.org
**Control:** Other not–for–profit (including NFP Corporation) **Service:** Long–Term Acute Care hospital

Staffed Beds: 32 Admissions: 419 Census: 28 Outpatient Visits: 0 Births: 0 Total Expense ($000): 14810 Payroll Expense ($000): 5239 Personnel: 86

☒ **LEHIGH VALLEY HOSPITAL–MUHLENBERG (390263)**, 2545 Schoenersville Road, Zip 18017–7300; tel. 484/884–2201 **A**1 2 3 9 10 12 13 **F**3 7 11 12 15 17 18 20 22 24 26 28 29 30 31 34 35 36 37 38 39 40 44 45 49 50 51 53 54 57 58 59 60 62 63 64 65 68 70 74 77 78 79 80 81 82 84 85 86 87 90 92 93 97 100 102 105 107 108 110 111 115 118 119 120 121 123 124 126 129 130 131 132 134 135 141 143 146 148 **P**5 6 8 **S** Lehigh Valley Health Network, Allentown, PA
Primary Contact: Brian Nester, D.O., Interim President and Chief Executive Officer
COO: Terry Ann Capuano, R.N., Chief Operating Officer
CFO: Edward O'Dea, Chief Financial Officer
CMO: Thomas Whalen, M.D., Chief Medical Officer
CIO: Harry Lukens, Senior Vice President and Chief Information Officer
CHR: Deborah A. Patrick, Vice President Human Resources
CNO: Anne Panik, MS, Senior Vice President Patient Care Services and Chief Nursing Officer
Web address: www.lvhhn.org
**Control:** Other not–for–profit (including NFP Corporation) **Service:** General Medical and Surgical

Staffed Beds: 162 Admissions: 10112 Census: 133 Outpatient Visits: 173751 Births: 0 Total Expense ($000): 205481 Payroll Expense ($000): 73373 Personnel: 1195

☐ △ **ST. LUKE'S UNIVERSITY HOSPITAL – BETHLEHEM CAMPUS (390049)**, 801 Ostrum Street, Zip 18015–1065; tel. 484/526–4000, (Includes ST LUKE'S HOSPITAL – ALLENTOWN CAMPUS, 1736 Hamilton Street, Allentown, Zip 18104–5656; tel. 610/628–8300) **A**1 2 3 6 7 8 9 10 12 13 **F**3 9 11 12 13 15 17 18 19 20 22 24 26 27 28 29 30 31 32 34 35 36 37 38 39 40 42 43 44 45 46 47 48 49 50 51 52 53 54 55 56 57 58 59 60 61 63 64 65 66 68 70 71 72 73 74 75 76 77 78 79 81 82 84 85 86 87 89 90 92 93 96 97 98 99 100 101 102 103 104 105 107 108 109 110 111 115 117 118 119 120 121 123 124 126 129 130 131 132 134 135 144 145 146 147 148 **P**6 8 **S** St. Luke's University Health Network, Bethlehem, PA
Primary Contact: Carol R. Kupler, President and Chief Executive Officer
COO: Carol Kuplen, R.N., Chief Operating Officer and Chief Nursing Officer
CFO: Tom Lichtenwalner, Vice President Finance
CMO: Jeffrey Jahre, M.D., Vice President Medical and Academic Affairs
CIO: Chad Brisendine, Chief Information Officer
CHR: Robert Zimmel, Senior Vice President Human Resources
Web address: www.slhn–lehighvalley.org
**Control:** Other not–for–profit (including NFP Corporation) **Service:** General Medical and Surgical

Staffed Beds: 550 Admissions: 26152 Census: 337 Outpatient Visits: 607668 Births: 3597 Total Expense ($000): 530853 Payroll Expense ($000): 225724 Personnel: 4199

**BLOOMSBURG—Columbia County**

★ **GEISINGER–BLOOMSBURG HOSPITAL (390003)**, 549 Fair Street, Zip 17815–1419; tel. 570/387–2100, (Nonreporting) **A**3 9 10 **S** Geisinger Health System, Danville, PA
Primary Contact: Lissa Bryan–Smith, Chief Administrative Officer
COO: Joseph M. DeVito, Vice President Finance and Chief Operating Officer
CFO: Joseph M. DeVito, Vice President Finance and Chief Operating Officer
CMO: James Joseph, M.D., President Medical Staff
CIO: Thomas Wray, Director Information
CHR: Mary Lenzini Howe, Vice President Human Resources
Web address: www.bloomhealth.net
**Control:** Other not–for–profit (including NFP Corporation) **Service:** General Medical and Surgical

Staffed Beds: 72

**PA**

---

**Hospital, Medicare Provider Number, Address, Telephone, Approval, Facility, and Physician Codes, Health Care System**

★ American Hospital Association (AHA) membership
☐ The Joint Commission accreditation
○ Healthcare Facilities Accreditation Program
◇ DNV Healthcare Inc. accreditation
⇑ Center for Improvement in Healthcare Quality Accreditation
△ Commission on Accreditation of Rehabilitation Facilities (CARF) accreditation

**PA**

## BRADFORD—Mckean County

☐ **BRADFORD REGIONAL MEDICAL CENTER (390118)**, 116 Interstate Parkway, Zip 16701–1036; tel. 814/368–4143, (Total facility includes 95 beds in nursing home–type unit) **A**1 9 10 **F**3 5 11 13 15 18 20 28 29 30 31 34 35 38 39 40 45 47 49 50 53 54 56 57 59 62 63 64 65 70 75 76 77 78 79 81 82 83 84 85 86 87 93 94 96 97 98 100 101 102 103 104 105 107 108 110 111 114 117 118 119 127 128 129 130 131 132 135 146 147 148 **P**6 8 **S** Upper Allegheny Health System, Olean, NY
Primary Contact: Timothy J. Finan, FACHE, President and Chief Executive Officer
CFO: Richard G. Braun, Jr., CPA, Senior Vice President and Chief Financial Officer
CMO: William Mills, M.D., Senior Vice President Quality and Professional Affairs
CIO: Jason Yaworsky, Chief Information Officer
CHR: Timothy M. McNamara, Senior Vice President Human Resources
CNO: Jeff S. Zewe, R.N., Senior Vice President Patient Care and Chief Nursing Officer
Web address: www.brmc.com
**Control:** Other not–for–profit (including NFP Corporation) **Service:** General Medical and Surgical

**Staffed Beds:** 182 **Admissions:** 2869 **Census:** 121 **Outpatient Visits:** 133023 **Births:** 250 **Total Expense ($000):** 68748 **Payroll Expense ($000):** 28997 **Personnel:** 510

## BRISTOL—Bucks County

☐ **LOWER BUCKS HOSPITAL (390070)**, 501 Bath Road, Zip 19007–3190; tel. 215/785–9200, (Nonreporting) **A**1 9 10 13 **S** Prime Healthcare Services, Ontario, CA
Primary Contact: Peter J. Adamo, Chief Executive Officer
COO: Matt Shelak, Chief Operating Officer
CFO: Courtney Coffman, Chief Financial Officer
CMO: Sanjay Bhatia, Chief Medical Officer
CIO: Steve Kane, Director Information Technology
CHR: Kellie T. Pearson, Director Human Resources
CNO: Pat Bain, Chief Nursing Officer
Web address: www.lowerbuckshosp.com
**Control:** Other not–for–profit (including NFP Corporation) **Service:** General Medical and Surgical

**Staffed Beds:** 150

## BROOKVILLE—Jefferson County

**PENN HIGHLANDS BROOKVILLE (391312)**, 100 Hospital Road, Zip 15825–1367; tel. 814/849–2312 **A**9 10 18 **F**3 11 15 18 28 29 30 34 35 39 40 45 46 57 59 62 64 65 75 77 81 82 85 86 93 98 102 103 104 107 108 110 114 118 119 127 129 130 131 132 133 145 146
Primary Contact: Julie Peer, President
CFO: Jessica Park, Director Accounting
CMO: Timothy Pendleton, M.D., President Medical Staff
CIO: Thomas Johnson, Director Information Systems
CHR: Rebecca Edwards, Chief Human Resources Officer
CNO: Debra A. Thomas, Vice President of Patient Care Services and Chief Nursing Officer
Web address: www.phhealthcare.org/
**Control:** Other not–for–profit (including NFP Corporation) **Service:** General Medical and Surgical

**Staffed Beds:** 35 **Admissions:** 792 **Census:** 13 **Outpatient Visits:** 84111 **Births:** 0 **Total Expense ($000):** 26548 **Payroll Expense ($000):** 10409 **Personnel:** 247

## BRYN MAWR—Montgomery County

✠ **BRYN MAWR HOSPITAL (390139)**, 130 South Bryn Mawr Avenue, Zip 19010–3160; tel. 484/337–3000 **A**1 2 3 5 9 10 13 **F**3 5 11 12 13 15 16 17 18 20 22 24 26 28 29 30 31 34 35 36 37 38 39 40 41 44 45 46 48 49 50 54 55 56 57 58 59 64 65 70 72 74 75 76 78 79 80 81 82 84 85 86 87 89 92 97 98 99 100 101 102 103 104 105 107 108 110 111 114 115 118 119 120 121 123 124 126 129 130 131 132 134 135 141 146 147 148 **S** Main Line Health
Primary Contact: Andrea F. Gilbert, FACHE, President
COO: Andrea F. Gilbert, FACHE, President
CFO: Michael J. Buongiorno, Executive Vice President Finance and Chief Financial Officer
CMO: Andrew J. Norton, M.D., Chief Medical Officer
CIO: Karen A. Thomas, Vice President and Chief Information Officer
CHR: Terry Dougherty, Director Human Resources
CNO: Barbara A. Wadsworth, MSN, Chief Nursing Officer
Web address: www.brynmawrhospital.org
**Control:** Other not–for–profit (including NFP Corporation) **Service:** General Medical and Surgical

**Staffed Beds:** 319 **Admissions:** 15090 **Census:** 172 **Outpatient Visits:** 247214 **Births:** 1671 **Total Expense ($000):** 284956 **Payroll Expense ($000):** 101417 **Personnel:** 1494

## BUTLER—Butler County

★ **BUTLER HEALTH SYSTEM (390168)**, 1 Hospital Way, Zip 16001–4697; tel. 724/283–6666, (Total facility includes 25 beds in nursing home–type unit) **A**2 9 10 **F**3 4 5 12 13 15 18 20 22 24 26 28 29 31 32 35 40 45 57 59 70 74 76 79 81 82 85 87 93 98 100 103 107 108 111 114 118 119 128 129 130 132 135 146 147 148 **P**6
Primary Contact: Ken DeFurio, President and Chief Executive Officer
COO: Stephanie Roskovski, Chief Operating Officer
CFO: Anne Krebs, Chief Financial Officer
CMO: John C. Reefer, M.D., Director
CIO: Chuck Oleson, Chief Information Officer
CHR: Thomas A. Genevro, Vice President Human Resources
CNO: Karen A. Allen, R.N., Chief Nursing Officer
Web address: www.butlerhealthsystem.org
**Control:** Other not–for–profit (including NFP Corporation) **Service:** General Medical and Surgical

**Staffed Beds:** 288 **Admissions:** 11950 **Census:** 163 **Outpatient Visits:** 483564 **Births:** 725 **Total Expense ($000):** 205506 **Payroll Expense ($000):** 78849 **Personnel:** 1421

**VETERANS AFFAIRS MEDICAL CENTER** See Veterans Affairs Butler Healthcare

## CAMP HILL—Cumberland County

✠ **HOLY SPIRIT – A GEISINGER AFFILIATE (390004)**, 503 North 21st Street, Zip 17011–2204; tel. 717/763–2100 **A**1 5 9 10 **F**3 8 11 12 13 14 15 17 18 20 22 24 26 28 29 30 31 34 35 37 38 40 44 46 49 50 54 57 58 59 61 62 63 64 65 70 72 73 74 75 76 77 78 79 80 81 82 84 85 86 87 98 99 100 101 102 103 104 105 107 108 110 111 114 115 118 119 124 126 129 130 132 134 135 145 146 147 148
Primary Contact: Sister Romaine Niemeyer, President and Chief Executive Officer
COO: Richard Schaffner, Senior Vice President and Chief Operating Officer
CFO: Manuel J. Evans, Senior Vice President Finance and Chief Financial Officer
CMO: Joseph Torchia, M.D., Senior Vice President Medical Affairs and Chief Medical Officer
CIO: Edith Dees, Vice President Information Services and Chief Information Officer
CHR: William Shartle, Senior Vice President Human Resources
CNO: Lisa F. Lewis, MSN, Vice President and Chief Nursing Officer
Web address: www.hsh.org
**Control:** Other not–for–profit (including NFP Corporation) **Service:** General Medical and Surgical

**Staffed Beds:** 294 **Admissions:** 13136 **Census:** 185 **Births:** 1219

✠ **SELECT SPECIALTY HOSPITAL–CENTRAL PENNSYLVANIA (392039)**, 503 North 21st Street, 5th Floor, Zip 17011–2204; tel. 717/972–4575, (Includes SELECT SPECIALTY HOSPITAL–HARRISBURG, 2501 NorthThird Street, Landis Building, Harrisburg, Zip 17110–1904, Mailing Address: 2501 North Third Street, Landis Building, Zip 17110–1904; tel. 717/724–6605; SELECT SPECIALTY HOSPITAL–YORK, 1001 South George Street, York, Zip 17403–3676; tel. 717/851–2661; Marcia Medlin, Chief Executive Officer) **A**1 9 10 **F**1 3 5 12 28 29 30 31 34 38 39 45 46 47 48 49 50 57 63 74 75 78 79 82 84 87 100 107 108 109 110 111 112 113 114 115 116 117 118 119 130 133 **S** Select Medical Corporation, Mechanicsburg, PA
Primary Contact: Tom Mullin, Chief Executive Officer
Web address: www.selectspecialtyhospitals.com/company/locations/camphill.aspx
**Control:** Corporation, Investor–owned, for–profit **Service:** Long–Term Acute Care hospital

**Staffed Beds:** 61 **Admissions:** 614 **Census:** 46 **Births:** 0

**STATE CORRECTIONAL INSTITUTION AT CAMP HILL**, 2500 Lisburn Road, Zip 17011–8005, Mailing Address: P.O. Box 200, Zip 17001–0200; tel. 717/737–4531, (Nonreporting)
Primary Contact: Kathy Montag, Administrator Health Care
Web address: www.cor.state.pa.us/
**Control:** State–Government, nonfederal **Service:** Hospital unit of an institution (prison hospital, college infirmary, etc.)

**Staffed Beds:** 34

## CANONSBURG—Washington County

✠ **CANONSBURG GENERAL HOSPITAL (390160)**, 100 Medical Boulevard, Zip 15317–9762; tel. 724/745–6100 **A**1 9 10 **F**3 7 11 15 29 30 34 35 40 44 45 46 47 48 49 50 51 55 57 59 64 65 67 68 70 74 75 78 79 81 85 86 90 92 93 107 108 110 111 114 118 119 129 130 131 132 135 146 **S** Allegheny Health Network, Pittsburgh, PA
Primary Contact: Jane B. Sarra, President and Chief Executive Officer
CMO: Thomas B. Corkery, D.O., Chief Medical Officer
CIO: David Vincent, Director Information Systems
CHR: Martha L. Clister, Director Human Resources
Web address: www.wpahs.org
**Control:** Other not–for–profit (including NFP Corporation) **Service:** General Medical and Surgical

**Staffed Beds:** 104 **Admissions:** 2656 **Census:** 33 **Outpatient Visits:** 65700 **Births:** 0 **Total Expense ($000):** 48359 **Payroll Expense ($000):** 15206 **Personnel:** 322

**PA**

## CARLISLE—Cumberland County

☒ **CARLISLE REGIONAL MEDICAL CENTER (390058)**, 361 Alexander Spring Road, Zip 17015–6940; tel. 717/249–1212, (Nonreporting) **A**1 9 10 **S** Community Health Systems, Inc., Franklin, TN
Primary Contact: Ann M. Spade, Interim Chief Executive Officer
COO: P. Mark Harmon, Chief Operating Officer
CFO: Joanna Zimmerman, Chief Financial Officer
CMO: Michael Hilden, M.D., President Medical Staff
CIO: Sherry Aby, Director Information Management
CHR: Leslie Shatto, Director Human Resources
CNO: Ann M. Spade, Chief Nursing Executive
Web address: www.carlislermc.com/default.aspx
**Control:** Corporation, Investor–owned, for–profit **Service:** General Medical and Surgical

**Staffed Beds:** 165

## CENTRE HALL—Centre County

☒ **MEADOWS PSYCHIATRIC CENTER (394040)**, 132 The Meadows Drive, Zip 16828–9231; tel. 814/364–2161 **A**1 9 10 **F**29 38 98 99 103 **S** Universal Health Services, Inc., King of Prussia, PA
Primary Contact: Ann Wayne, Interim Chief Executive Officer
CFO: Rich Armentrout, Chief Financial Officer
CMO: Craig Richman, M.D., Medical Director
CHR: Mary Jane Schreffler, Director Human Resources
CNO: Ann Wayne, Director of Nursing
Web address: www.themeadows.net
**Control:** Corporation, Investor–owned, for–profit **Service:** Psychiatric

**Staffed Beds:** 107 **Admissions:** 2549 **Census:** 95 **Outpatient Visits:** 2822 **Births:** 0 **Personnel:** 209

## CHAMBERSBURG—Franklin County

☒ **CHAMBERSBURG HOSPITAL (390151)**, 112 North Seventh Street, Zip 17201–1720; tel. 717/267–3000 **A**1 2 3 5 9 10 **F**3 11 12 13 15 17 18 20 22 28 29 30 31 32 34 35 36 38 39 40 44 45 49 50 56 57 59 61 64 65 68 70 74 75 76 78 79 81 83 84 85 86 87 89 90 91 93 94 95 98 99 100 101 102 103 104 107 108 110 111 114 115 116 117 118 119 120 126 129 130 131 132 135 146 147 148 **P**8 **S** Summit Health, Chambersburg, PA
Primary Contact: Patrick W. O'Donnell, CPA, President and Chief Executive Officer
COO: John P. Massimilla, FACHE, Vice President Administration and Chief Operating Officer
CFO: Kimberly Rzomp, Vice President and Chief Financial Officer
CMO: Thomas Anderson, M.D., Vice President Medical Affairs
CIO: Michele Zeigler, Vice President and Chief Information Officer
CHR: Cathy A. Puhl, Vice President Human Resources
CNO: Sherri Stahl, R.N., Senior Vice President for Hospital Services
Web address: www.summithealth.org
**Control:** Other not–for–profit (including NFP Corporation) **Service:** General Medical and Surgical

**Staffed Beds:** 248 **Admissions:** 11876 **Census:** 140 **Outpatient Visits:** 330574 **Births:** 1305 **Total Expense ($000):** 242362 **Payroll Expense ($000):** 100431 **Personnel:** 1516

## CLARION—Clarion County

★ ○ **CLARION HOSPITAL (390093)**, One Hospital Drive, Zip 16214–8501; tel. 814/226–9500 **A**9 10 11 12 13 19 20 **F**3 7 11 13 15 29 30 31 35 40 48 49 51 57 59 64 70 76 77 78 79 81 82 84 85 90 107 108 111 115 119 129 130 132 133 135 145 146 148 **S** QHR, Brentwood, TN
Primary Contact: Byron Quinton, Chief Executive Officer
CFO: Vincent M. Lamorella, Chief Financial Officer
CIO: James Confer, Manager Information Systems
CHR: Brooke Divins, Manager Human Resources
CNO: Leslie Walters, R.N., Chief Nursing Officer
Web address: www.clarionhospital.org
**Control:** Other not–for–profit (including NFP Corporation) **Service:** General Medical and Surgical

**Staffed Beds:** 77 **Admissions:** 1882 **Census:** 20 **Outpatient Visits:** 161009 **Births:** 143 **Total Expense ($000):** 50006 **Payroll Expense ($000):** 18019 **Personnel:** 464

## CLARION PSYCHIATRIC CENTER (394043), 2 Hospital Drive,

☒ **CLARION PSYCHIATRIC CENTER (394043)**, 2 Hospital Drive, Zip 16214–8502; tel. 814/226–9545 **A**1 9 10 **F**98 99 101 102 105 **P**6 **S** Universal Health Services, Inc., King of Prussia, PA
Primary Contact: Robert Scheffler, Chief Executive Officer
CFO: Shelly Rhoades, Chief Financial Officer
CMO: Jeffrey Moll, M.D., Medical Director
CHR: Dianne C. Bilunka, Director Human Resources
CNO: Rhonda Massa, Director of Nursing
Web address: www.clarioncenter.com
**Control:** Individual, Investor–owned, for–profit **Service:** Psychiatric

**Staffed Beds:** 74 **Admissions:** 1873 **Census:** 61 **Outpatient Visits:** 0 **Births:** 0

## CLARKS SUMMIT—Lackawanna County

**CLARKS SUMMIT STATE HOSPITAL (394012)**, 1451 Hillside Drive, Zip 18411–9504; tel. 570/586–2011 **A**10 **F**29 30 34 35 38 39 50 53 56 57 59 65 68 75 77 86 87 91 97 98 100 101 103 106 130 132 135 143 146 **P**6
Primary Contact: Monica Bradbury, Chief Executive Officer
COO: Gordon Weber, Chief Operating Officer
CMO: David Waibel, M.D., Medical Director
CHR: William Abda, Chief Human Resources Officer
Web address: www.dpw.state.pa.us/
**Control:** State–Government, nonfederal **Service:** Psychiatric

**Staffed Beds:** 222 **Admissions:** 63 **Census:** 217 **Outpatient Visits:** 0 **Births:** 0

## CLEARFIELD—Clearfield County

**PENN HIGHLANDS CLEARFIELD (390052)**, 809 Turnpike Avenue, Zip 16830–1232, Mailing Address: P.O. Box 992, Zip 16830–0992; tel. 814/765–5341 **A**9 10 **F**3 8 11 13 14 15 17 18 28 29 30 32 34 40 44 45 46 50 57 59 62 63 68 72 75 76 77 79 81 84 85 86 87 93 97 98 103 104 107 108 110 111 115 118 119 129 130 132 133 135 146 148 **P**6
Primary Contact: Gary Macioce, President
CFO: William Cain, Controller
CMO: Kevin L. Tyler, M.D., President Medical Staff
CHR: James G. Glade, Director Human Resources
CNO: Kathy Bedger, Chief Nursing Officer
Web address: www.phhealthcare.org
**Control:** Other not–for–profit (including NFP Corporation) **Service:** General Medical and Surgical

**Staffed Beds:** 96 **Admissions:** 2278 **Census:** 27 **Outpatient Visits:** 122654 **Births:** 113 **Total Expense ($000):** 58474 **Payroll Expense ($000):** 22865

## COALDALE—Schuylkill County

☐ **ST. LUKE'S HOSPITAL – MINERS CAMPUS (390183)**, 360 West Ruddle Street, Zip 18218–1027; tel. 570/645–2131, (Total facility includes 48 beds in nursing home–type unit) **A**1 9 10 **F**3 15 18 28 29 31 34 35 40 43 45 46 49 50 51 54 56 57 59 60 62 64 65 68 70 75 77 78 79 81 85 86 93 107 108 110 111 115 118 119 127 128 129 130 131 132 145 146 148 **P**6 8 **S** St. Luke's University Health Network, Bethlehem, PA
Primary Contact: William E. Moyer, President
COO: Joel Fagerstrom, Executive Vice President and Chief Operating Officer
CFO: Michele Levitz, Director Finance
CMO: Glenn Freed, D.O., Medical Director
CIO: Chad Brisendine, Vice President and Chief Information Officer
CHR: Susan Van Why, Director Human Resources
CNO: Kimberly Sargent, Vice President Patient Services
Web address: www.slhn.org
**Control:** Other not–for–profit (including NFP Corporation) **Service:** General Medical and Surgical

**Staffed Beds:** 92 **Admissions:** 1926 **Census:** 63 **Outpatient Visits:** 78407 **Births:** 0 **Total Expense ($000):** 43355 **Payroll Expense ($000):** 19981 **Personnel:** 268

## COATESVILLE—Chester County

☒ **BRANDYWINE HOSPITAL (390076)**, 201 Reeceville Road, Zip 19320–1536; tel. 610/383–8000 **A**1 2 6 9 10 **F**3 12 15 17 18 20 22 24 26 28 29 31 34 35 40 45 46 50 51 54 56 59 60 62 64 65 66 70 74 75 77 78 79 81 82 92 93 98 103 104 106 107 108 110 111 114 115 116 117 119 126 129 132 146 147 148 **S** Community Health Systems, Inc., Franklin, TN
Primary Contact: W. Jeffrey Hunt, Chief Executive Officer
COO: Jill Tillman, Assistant Chief Executive Officer
CFO: Jay Graham, Interim Chief Financial Officer
Web address: www.brandywinehospital.com
**Control:** Corporation, Investor–owned, for–profit **Service:** General Medical and Surgical

**Staffed Beds:** 169 **Admissions:** 6489 **Census:** 94 **Outpatient Visits:** 68360 **Births:** 0 **Total Expense ($000):** 101601 **Payroll Expense ($000):** 38127 **Personnel:** 634

---

**Hospital, Medicare Provider Number, Address, Telephone, Approval, Facility, and Physician Codes, Health Care System**

★ American Hospital Association (AHA) membership    ○ Healthcare Facilities Accreditation Program    ⇑ Center for Improvement in Healthcare Quality Accreditation
☐ The Joint Commission accreditation    ◇ DNV Healthcare Inc. accreditation    △ Commission on Accreditation of Rehabilitation Facilities (CARF) accreditation

✠ **COATESVILLE VETERANS AFFAIRS MEDICAL CENTER**, 1400 Black Horse Hill Road, Zip 19320–2040; tel. 610/384–7711, (Nonreporting) **A**1 3 5
**S** Department of Veterans Affairs, Washington, DC
Primary Contact: Gary W. Devansky, Director
CFO: Tony Wolfgang, Chief Financial Officer
CMO: Sheila Chellappa, M.D., Chief of Staff
CIO: Ryan McGettigan, Chief Information Officer
CHR: Andrew Sutton, Chief Human Resources Officer
CNO: Nancy A. Schmid, R.N., Associate Director Patient Care Services
Web address: www.coatesville.va.gov/
**Control:** Veterans Affairs, Government, federal **Service:** Alcoholism and other chemical dependency

| Staffed Beds: 145 |
|---|

**VETERANS AFFAIRS MEDICAL CENTER** See Coatesville Veterans Affairs Medical Center

### CONNELLSVILLE—Fayette County

**HIGHLANDS HOSPITAL (390184)**, 401 East Murphy Avenue, Zip 15425–2700; tel. 724/628–1500 **A**9 10 **F**3 11 15 26 27 29 30 34 35 36 39 40 44 45 46 49 50 51 53 54 56 57 59 61 64 65 70 75 77 79 81 82 85 86 87 89 98 99 100 102 103 107 108 111 114 119 129 130 132 133 143 146
Primary Contact: Michelle P. Cunningham, Chief Executive Officer
CFO: John Andursky, Chief Financial Officer
CMO: Richard Grimaldi, President Medical Staff
CIO: John Andursky, Chief Financial Officer
CHR: Mary June Krosoff, Chief Human Resources Officer
CNO: Tammy Donaldson, Director of Nursing
Web address: www.highlandshospital.org
**Control:** Other not–for–profit (including NFP Corporation) **Service:** General Medical and Surgical

| Staffed Beds: 64 Admissions: 2415 Census: 28 Outpatient Visits: 61520 Births: 0 Total Expense ($000): 24186 Payroll Expense ($000): 10538 Personnel: 270 |
|---|

### CORRY—Erie County

**CORRY MEMORIAL HOSPITAL (391308)**, 965 Shamrock Lane, Zip 16407; tel. 814/664–4641, (Nonreporting) **A**9 10 18
Primary Contact: Barbara Nichols, R.N., President and Chief Executive Officer
CFO: Michael Heller, Chief Financial Officer
CMO: Paul McGeehan, M.D., Chief Medical Staff
CIO: Andrew Jackman, Director Information Technology
CHR: Sharon Kimmy, Coordinator Human Resources
CNO: Terry Delellis, R.N., Director of Nursing
Web address: www.corryhospital.com
**Control:** Other not–for–profit (including NFP Corporation) **Service:** General Medical and Surgical

| Staffed Beds: 25 |
|---|

### COUDERSPORT—Potter County

✠ **COLE MEMORIAL (391313)**, 1001 East Second Street, Zip 16915–8161; tel. 814/274–9300, (Total facility includes 49 beds in nursing home–type unit) **A**1 9 10 18 **F**3 10 13 15 28 29 30 31 35 39 40 45 49 53 57 59 62 63 64 68 70 76 77 78 79 81 82 85 87 92 93 98 103 107 108 110 111 115 119 121 127 128 129 130 131 132 133 146 147 148 **P**6
Primary Contact: Edward C. Pitchford, President and Chief Executive Officer
CFO: Ron Rapp, Controller
CMO: Brenda Wahlers, M.D., Chief of Staff
CIO: Janice Walters, Executive Director, Revenue Systems and Information Technology
CHR: James Evans, Executive Director Human Resources
Web address: www.colememorial.org/
**Control:** Other not–for–profit (including NFP Corporation) **Service:** General Medical and Surgical

| Staffed Beds: 84 Admissions: 1952 Census: 70 Outpatient Visits: 221393 Births: 194 Total Expense ($000): 77322 Payroll Expense ($000): 27528 Personnel: 521 |
|---|

### CRANBERRY—Butler County

**UPMC PASSAVANT CRANBERRY** See UPMC Passavant, Pittsburgh

### DANVILLE—Montour County

**DANVILLE STATE HOSPITAL (394004)**, 200 State Hospital Drive, Zip 17821–9198; tel. 570/271–4500 **A**3 10 **F**30 39 65 75 77 98 106 130 135 146 **P**6
Primary Contact: Theresa Long, Chief Executive Officer
COO: Thomas J. Burk, Chief Operating Officer
CFO: Patricia Riegert, Director Fiscal Services
CMO: Vikrant Mittal, M.D., Chief Medical Officer
CHR: Thomas J. Burk, Chief Operating Officer
CNO: Brenda Lahout, Chief Nurse Executive
Web address: www.dpw.state.pa.us/foradults/statehospitals/danvillestatehospital/index.htm
**Control:** State–Government, nonfederal **Service:** Psychiatric

| Staffed Beds: 168 Admissions: 71 Census: 170 Outpatient Visits: 0 Births: 0 Total Expense ($000): 39009 Payroll Expense ($000): 19035 Personnel: 371 |
|---|

✠ **GEISINGER HEALTHSOUTH REHABILITATION HOSPITAL (393047)**, 2 Rehab Lane, Zip 17821–8498; tel. 570/271–6733, (Nonreporting) **A**1 9 10
**S** HEALTHSOUTH Corporation, Birmingham, AL
Primary Contact: Lorie Dillon, Chief Executive Officer
CFO: Sally Shipierski, Controller
CMO: Greg Burke, M.D., Medical Director
CHR: Christian Shirley, Director Human Resources
CNO: Kim Rankin, Chief Nursing Officer
Web address: www.geisingerhealthsouth.com
**Control:** Corporation, Investor–owned, for–profit **Service:** Rehabilitation

| Staffed Beds: 42 |
|---|

✠ **GEISINGER MEDICAL CENTER (390006)**, 100 North Academy Avenue, Zip 17822–2201; tel. 570/271–6211, (Includes GEISINGER–SHAMOKIN AREA COMMUNITY HOSPITAL, 4200 Hospital Road, Coal Township, Zip 17866–9697; tel. 570/644–4200; Thomas R. Harlow, FACHE, Chief Administrative Officer), (Nonreporting) **A**1 2 3 5 8 9 10 13 19 **S** Geisinger Health System, Danville, PA
Primary Contact: Thomas P. Sokola, Chief Administrative Officer
COO: Frank J. Trembulak, Executive Vice President and Chief Operating Officer
CFO: Kevin F. Brennan, CPA, Executive Vice President and Chief Financial Officer
CMO: Albert Bothe, Jr., M.D., Chief Medical Officer
CIO: Frank Richards, Chief Information Officer
CHR: Amy Brayford, Chief Human Resources Officer
CNO: Susan M. Hallick, R.N., Executive Vice President and Chief Nursing Officer
Web address: www.geisinger.org
**Control:** Other not–for–profit (including NFP Corporation) **Service:** General Medical and Surgical

| Staffed Beds: 545 |
|---|

✠ **SELECT SPECIALTY HOSPITAL–DANVILLE (392047)**, 100 North Academy Avenue, 3rd Floor, Zip 17822–3050; tel. 570/214–9653, (Nonreporting) **A**1 9 10
**S** Select Medical Corporation, Mechanicsburg, PA
Primary Contact: Brian Mann, Chief Executive Officer
Web address: www.selectspecialtyhospitals.com/company/locations/danville.aspx
**Control:** Corporation, Investor–owned, for–profit **Service:** Long–Term Acute Care hospital

| Staffed Beds: 30 |
|---|

### DARBY—Delaware County

✠ △ **MERCY FITZGERALD HOSPITAL (390156)**, 1500 Lansdowe Avenue, Zip 19023–1200; tel. 610/237–4000, (Includes MERCY FITZGERALD HOSPITAL, 1500 South Lansdowne Avenue, Zip 19023; tel. 610/237–4000; MERCY PHILADELPHIA HOSPITAL, 501 South 54th Street, Philadelphia, Zip 19143; tel. 215/748–9000) **A**1 2 3 5 7 9 10 12 13 **F**3 4 11 12 15 18 20 22 24 26 28 29 30 31 34 35 38 40 45 46 49 50 51 53 54 55 57 58 59 61 64 65 66 69 70 75 77 78 79 81 82 85 86 87 90 91 92 93 96 97 98 100 101 102 103 104 107 108 110 111 114 115 118 119 120 121 123 124 130 132 135 145 146 147 148 **S** Trinity Health, Livonia, MI
Primary Contact: Kathryn Conallen, Chief Executive Officer
COO: Ruth Thomas, Chief Operating Officer
CFO: Don Snenk, Chief Financial Officer
CMO: Jeff Komins, M.D., Chief Medical Officer
CIO: Jeff Byda, Vice President Information Technology
Web address: www.mercyhealth.org
**Control:** Church–operated, Nongovernment, not–for profit **Service:** General Medical and Surgical

| Staffed Beds: 382 Admissions: 17569 Census: 224 Outpatient Visits: 227651 Births: 0 Total Expense ($000): 308750 Payroll Expense ($000): 116173 Personnel: 1890 |
|---|

### DOWNINGTOWN—Chester County

**ST. JOHN VIANNEY HOSPITAL**, 151 Woodbine Road, Zip 19335–3057; tel. 610/269–2600, (Nonreporting)
Primary Contact: David Shellenberger, Chief Operating Officer
CMO: James MacFadyen, M.D., Medical Director
Web address: www.sjvcenter.org
**Control:** Church–operated, Nongovernment, not–for profit **Service:** Psychiatric

| Staffed Beds: 42 |
|---|

**PA**

*Many Facility Codes have changed. Please refer to the AHA Guide Code Chart.* © 2015 AHA Guide

## DOYLESTOWN—Bucks County

☒ △ **DOYLESTOWN HOSPITAL (390203)**, 595 West State Street, Zip 18901–2597; tel. 215/345–2200, (Total facility includes 107 beds in nursing home–type unit) **A**1 2 3 5 7 9 10 **F**3 8 10 13 15 17 18 20 22 24 26 28 29 30 31 34 35 40 45 46 49 50 51 54 56 57 58 59 62 63 64 70 73 74 75 76 77 78 79 81 82 84 85 86 89 92 93 94 96 107 108 110 111 114 115 118 119 124 125 126 128 130 131 132 141 146 147 **P**2 5 8
Primary Contact: James L. Brexler, President and Chief Executive Officer
COO: Eleanor Wilson, R.N., Vice President and Chief Operating Officer
CFO: Daniel Upton, Vice President and Chief Financial Officer
CMO: Scott S. Levy, M.D., Vice President and Chief Medical Officer
CIO: Richard Lang, Ed.D., Vice President and Chief Information Officer
CHR: Barbara Hebel, Vice President Human Resources
CNO: Patricia A. Stover, Administrator Nursing
Web address: www.dh.org
**Control:** Other not–for–profit (including NFP Corporation) **Service:** General Medical and Surgical

**Staffed Beds:** 339 **Admissions:** 12306 **Census:** 199 **Outpatient Visits:** 298622 **Births:** 1228 **Total Expense ($000):** 256906 **Payroll Expense ($000):** 104014 **Personnel:** 1883

☐ **FOUNDATIONS BEHAVIORAL HEALTH (394038)**, 833 East Butler Avenue, Zip 18901–2280; tel. 215/345–0444 **A**1 9 10 **F**98 99 100 101 102 105 106 **S** Universal Health Services, Inc., King of Prussia, PA
Primary Contact: Robert Weinhold, Chief Executive Officer
Web address: www.fbh.com
**Control:** Corporation, Investor–owned, for–profit **Service:** Children's hospital psychiatric

**Staffed Beds:** 58 **Admissions:** 965 **Census:** 47 **Outpatient Visits:** 0 **Births:** 0

## DREXEL HILL—Delaware County

☒ **DELAWARE COUNTY MEMORIAL HOSPITAL (390081)**, 501 North Lansdowne Avenue, Zip 19026–1114; tel. 610/284–8100, (Nonreporting) **A**1 2 3 5 9 10 **S** Crozer–Keystone Health System, Springfield, PA
Primary Contact: Robert Haffey, R.N., President
CFO: Richard I. Bennett, Senior Vice President and Chief Financial Officer
CMO: Seth Malin, M.D., President Medical and Dental Staff
CIO: Robert E. Wilson, Vice President and Chief Information Officer
Web address: www.crozer.org
**Control:** Other not–for–profit (including NFP Corporation) **Service:** General Medical and Surgical

**Staffed Beds:** 209

## DUBOIS—Clearfield County

☐ **PENN HIGHLANDS DUBOIS (390086)**, 100 Hospital Avenue, Zip 15801–1440, Mailing Address: P.O. Box 447, Zip 15801–0447; tel. 814/371–2200 **A**1 2 9 10 19 **F**5 11 13 15 17 18 19 20 22 24 26 27 28 29 30 31 34 35 40 49 51 54 55 57 58 59 62 63 64 70 72 74 76 77 78 79 81 82 85 89 90 93 97 98 99 104 107 108 111 115 116 117 119 120 121 122 129 130 131 132 133 135 146 147 148
Primary Contact: John Sutika, President
CFO: Brian S. Kline, Vice President and Chief Financial Officer
CMO: Gary Dugan, M.D., Vice President Medical Affairs
CHR: Robert J. McKee, Vice President Human Resources
Web address: www.drmc.org
**Control:** Other not–for–profit (including NFP Corporation) **Service:** General Medical and Surgical

**Staffed Beds:** 219 **Admissions:** 8335 **Census:** 106 **Births:** 1027

## EAGLEVILLE—Montgomery County

★ **EAGLEVILLE HOSPITAL (390278)**, 100 Eagleville Road, Zip 19403–1829, Mailing Address: P.O. Box 45, Zip 19408–0045; tel. 610/539–6000 **A**5 9 10 **F**4 29 34 35 50 61 68 75 86 98 100 101 103 130 132 134 143 146 147 **P**6
Primary Contact: Maureen King Pollock, Chief Executive Officer
COO: Lois Chepak, R.N., Chief Clinical Officer
CFO: Alfred P. Salvitti, Chief Financial Officer
CMO: Robert Wilson, D.O., Director Medical Services
CIO: Richard R. Mitchell, Director Information Technology
CHR: Zoe Yousaitis, Director Human Resources
Web address: www.eaglevillehospital.org
**Control:** Other not–for–profit (including NFP Corporation) **Service:** Alcoholism and other chemical dependency

**Staffed Beds:** 83 **Admissions:** 2378 **Census:** 52 **Outpatient Visits:** 0 **Births:** 0 **Total Expense ($000):** 34403 **Payroll Expense ($000):** 19625 **Personnel:** 370

## EAST NORRITON—Montgomery County

☐ **EINSTEIN MEDICAL CENTER MONTGOMERY (390329)**, 559 West Germantown Pike, Zip 19403–4250; tel. 484/622–1000 **A**1 2 3 9 10 **F**3 11 12 13 15 18 20 22 24 26 29 30 31 34 35 40 46 49 55 57 59 62 63 64 68 70 72 74 75 76 78 79 80 81 82 84 85 87 92 100 107 108 110 111 115 117 119 120 121 123 126 129 130 131 132 135 146 147 148 **S** Einstein Healthcare Network, Philadelphia, PA
Primary Contact: Beth Duffy, Chief Operating Officer
COO: Beth Duffy, Chief Operating Officer
CFO: David Ertel, Chief Financial Officer
CMO: Robert Czincila, D.O., Medical Staff President
CIO: Kenneth Levitan, Vice President and Chief Information Officer
CHR: Lynne R. Kornblatt, Chief Human Resources Officer
CNO: AnnMarie Papa, R.N., Vice President and Chief Nursing Officer
**Control:** Other not–for–profit (including NFP Corporation) **Service:** General Medical and Surgical

**Staffed Beds:** 170 **Admissions:** 9138 **Census:** 103 **Births:** 1940

## EAST STROUDSBURG—Monroe County

☐ △ **POCONO MEDICAL CENTER (390201)**, 206 East Brown Street, Zip 18301–3006; tel. 570/421–4000 **A**1 2 7 9 10 **F**3 11 12 13 14 15 17 18 20 22 24 26 28 29 30 31 32 34 35 36 38 39 40 43 45 47 48 49 50 54 55 56 57 59 61 64 65 66 70 72 74 75 76 77 78 79 81 82 84 85 86 87 89 92 97 98 100 101 102 103 107 108 110 111 114 115 116 117 118 119 120 121 123 124 126 130 132 134 135 144 146 147 148 **P**6 7
Primary Contact: Jeffrey Snyder, Chief Executive Officer
CFO: Michael Wilk, Senior President Financial Services and Chief Financial Officer
CMO: William K. Cors, M.D., Vice President and Chief Medical Quality Officer
CIO: Ferd Feola, Chief Information Officer
CHR: Lynn M. Lansdowne, Vice President Human Resources
Web address: www.pmchealthsystem.org
**Control:** Other not–for–profit (including NFP Corporation) **Service:** General Medical and Surgical

**Staffed Beds:** 235 **Admissions:** 11175 **Census:** 135 **Births:** 1045

## EASTON—Northampton County

☒ **EASTON HOSPITAL (390162)**, 250 South 21st Street, Zip 18042–3892; tel. 610/250–4000 **A**1 2 3 5 9 10 **F**3 34 40 44 45 46 47 48 49 51 54 56 57 58 59 60 61 64 65 66 70 72 74 75 78 79 80 81 82 85 86 87 90 92 97 100 107 108 109 110 111 114 115 116 117 119 120 121 123 124 126 129 130 132 135 144 146 147 148 **S** Community Health Systems, Inc., Franklin, TN
Primary Contact: John A. Zidansek, President and Chief Executive Officer
CMO: David Lyon, M.D., Chief Medical Officer
CIO: Kenneth Castle, Chief Information Officer
CHR: Lori Ofner, Vice President Human Resources
Web address: www.easton–hospital.com
**Control:** Corporation, Investor–owned, for–profit **Service:** General Medical and Surgical

**Staffed Beds:** 224 **Admissions:** 7331 **Census:** 91 **Outpatient Visits:** 165650 **Births:** 458 **Total Expense ($000):** 157226 **Payroll Expense ($000):** 49642 **Personnel:** 1097

☐ **ST. LUKE'S HOSPITAL – ANDERSON CAMPUS (390326)**, 1872 Riverside Circle, Zip 18045–5669; tel. 484/503–3000 **A**1 2 3 9 10 **F**3 11 15 18 20 22 24 26 29 30 31 34 35 38 40 44 45 46 49 50 51 53 54 55 57 59 60 63 64 68 70 74 75 77 78 79 81 82 84 85 87 93 96 102 107 108 110 111 115 118 119 120 121 123 124 130 132 144 145 146 **P**6 8 **S** St. Luke's University Health Network, Bethlehem, PA
Primary Contact: Edward Nawrocki, President
CMO: Justin P. Psaila, M.D., Vice President Medical Affairs
CNO: Darla Frack, RN, R.N., Vice President, Patient Services
Web address: www.mystlukesonline.org
**Control:** Other not–for–profit (including NFP Corporation) **Service:** General Medical and Surgical

**Staffed Beds:** 78 **Admissions:** 5438 **Census:** 55 **Outpatient Visits:** 143053 **Births:** 0 **Total Expense ($000):** 111555 **Payroll Expense ($000):** 36592 **Personnel:** 557

## ELLWOOD CITY—Lawrence County

**ELLWOOD CITY HOSPITAL (390008)**, 724 Pershing Street, Zip 16117–1474; tel. 724/752–0081, (Nonreporting) **A**9 10
Primary Contact: Carolyn Izzo, President and Chief Executive Officer
CFO: Christopher M. Little, Vice President and Chief Financial Officer
CIO: Dennis Crumb, Chief Information Officer
CHR: Paul Landman, Director Human Resources
CNO: Della Stabryla, Director of Nursing
Web address: www.TheEllwoodCityHospital.org
**Control:** Other not–for–profit (including NFP Corporation) **Service:** General Medical and Surgical

**Staffed Beds:** 95

---

**Hospital, Medicare Provider Number, Address, Telephone, Approval, Facility, and Physician Codes, Health Care System**

★ American Hospital Association (AHA) membership
☐ The Joint Commission accreditation
○ Healthcare Facilities Accreditation Program
◇ DNV Healthcare Inc. accreditation
⇑ Center for Improvement in Healthcare Quality Accreditation
△ Commission on Accreditation of Rehabilitation Facilities (CARF) accreditation

**PA**

## EPHRATA—Lancaster County

☐ **EPHRATA COMMUNITY HOSPITAL (390225)**, 169 Martin Avenue, Zip 17522–1724, Mailing Address: P.O. Box 1002, Zip 17522–1002; tel. 717/733–0311 **A**1 2 9 10 **F**3 12 13 15 18 20 28 29 30 31 34 35 36 40 45 49 50 51 54 57 59 60 61 62 64 69 70 72 74 75 76 77 78 79 80 81 82 85 87 89 90 91 97 98 99 100 101 102 107 108 110 111 114 115 116 117 118 119 120 121 129 130 131 132 135 144 146 147 148 **P**6 8 **S** WellSpan Health, York, PA
Primary Contact: John M. Porter, Jr., President and Chief Executive Officer
CFO: David Kreider, Controller
CMO: Mark Jacobson, D.O., Vice President Medical Affairs
CIO: Leon John Jabour, Regional Chief Information Officer
CHR: Jana Salaki, Regional Director Human Resources
CNO: Marcia A. Hansen, R.N., Vice President Operations and Chief Nursing Officer
Web address: www.wellspan.org
**Control:** Other not–for–profit (including NFP Corporation) **Service:** General Medical and Surgical

**Staffed Beds: 130 Admissions: 5586 Census: 64 Outpatient Visits: 355695 Births: 820 Total Expense ($000): 213315 Payroll Expense ($000): 99191 Personnel: 1682**

## ERIE—Erie County

⊠ **ERIE VETERANS AFFAIRS MEDICAL CENTER**, 135 East 38th Street, Zip 16504–1559; tel. 814/860–2576, (Nonreporting) **A**1 **S** Department of Veterans Affairs, Washington, DC
Primary Contact: David Cord, Director
CFO: Joann Pritchard, Chief Financial Officer
CMO: Anthony Behm, D.O., Chief of Staff
CIO: Jonathan Seale, Chief Information Officer
CHR: Lynn Nies, Human Resources Officer
CNO: Dorene M. Sommers, Associate Director Patient Care Services
Web address: www.erie.va.gov/
**Control:** Veterans Affairs, Government, federal **Service:** General Medical and Surgical

**Staffed Beds: 78**

**HAMOT MEDICAL CENTER** See UPMC Hamot

⊠ **HEALTHSOUTH REHABILITATION HOSPITAL OF ERIE (393046)**, 143 East Second Street, Zip 16507–1501; tel. 814/878–1200 **A**1 9 10 **F**29 34 90 91 95 96 132 **S** HEALTHSOUTH Corporation, Birmingham, AL
Primary Contact: John Papalia, Chief Executive Officer
CFO: Lori Gibbens, Controller
CMO: Douglas Grisier, D.O., Medical Director
CIO: Sharon Zielinski, Manager Health Information
CHR: William Robinson, Director Human Resources
CNO: Evelyn Armstrong, Chief Nursing Officer
Web address: www.healthsoutherie.com
**Control:** Corporation, Investor–owned, for–profit **Service:** Rehabilitation

**Staffed Beds: 100 Admissions: 1622 Census: 53 Outpatient Visits: 0 Births: 0**

◯ **MILLCREEK COMMUNITY HOSPITAL (390198)**, 5515 Peach Street, Zip 16509–2695; tel. 814/864–4031, (Nonreporting) **A**9 10 11 12 13
Primary Contact: Mary L. Eckert, President and Chief Executive Officer
CFO: Richard P. Olinger, Chief Financial Officer
CMO: James Y. Lin, D.O., Chief of Staff
CIO: Cheryl Girardier, Director Information Technology
CHR: Polly Momeyer, Manager Human Resources
CNO: Katie Agresti, R.N., Director Patient Care Services
Web address: www.millcreekcommunityhospital.com
**Control:** Other not–for–profit (including NFP Corporation) **Service:** General Medical and Surgical

**Staffed Beds: 168**

⊠ **SAINT VINCENT HEALTH CENTER (390009)**, 232 West 25th Street, Zip 16544–0002; tel. 814/452–5000 **A**1 2 3 5 9 10 12 13 **F**3 8 9 11 12 13 15 17 18 20 22 24 26 28 29 31 32 33 34 35 36 38 39 40 42 44 45 50 51 53 54 56 57 58 59 60 61 62 63 64 65 66 68 70 71 72 74 75 76 77 78 79 80 81 82 84 85 86 87 89 90 92 93 97 98 100 101 102 103 104 107 108 110 111 114 115 117 119 129 132 133 135 144 146 147 148 **P**6 8 **S** Allegheny Health Network, Pittsburgh, PA
Primary Contact: Scott Whalen, Ph.D., FACHE, President and Chief Executive Officer
COO: Thomas Fucci, Chief Operating Officer
CFO: Al Mansfield, Chief Financial Officer
CMO: Chris Clark, M.D., Senior Vice President Medical Affairs and Chief Medical Officer
CIO: Richard B. Ong, Chief Information Officer
CHR: Johnie M. Atkinson, Chief Human Resources Officer
CNO: Maureen C. Chadwick, R.N., Chief Nursing Officer
Web address: www.svhs.org
**Control:** Other not–for–profit (including NFP Corporation) **Service:** General Medical and Surgical

**Staffed Beds: 413 Admissions: 14572 Census: 187 Outpatient Visits: 192540 Births: 1212 Total Expense ($000): 250674 Payroll Expense ($000): 78437 Personnel: 1726**

⊠ **SELECT SPECIALTY HOSPITAL–ERIE (392037)**, 252 West 11th Street, Zip 16501–1702; tel. 814/874–5300, (Nonreporting) **A**1 9 10 **S** Select Medical Corporation, Mechanicsburg, PA
Primary Contact: Randy Neiswonger, Chief Executive Officer
CNO: Keith Christiansen, Chief Nursing Officer
Web address: www.erie.selectspecialtyhospitals.com/
**Control:** Corporation, Investor–owned, for–profit **Service:** Long–Term Acute Care hospital

**Staffed Beds: 50**

☐ **UPMC HAMOT (390063)**, 201 State Street, Zip 16550–0002; tel. 814/877–6000 **A**1 2 3 5 9 10 12 13 **F**3 9 11 12 13 15 17 18 20 22 24 26 28 29 30 31 34 35 36 37 38 39 40 43 44 45 46 47 48 49 50 51 56 57 58 59 60 61 62 63 64 65 66 68 70 72 74 75 76 77 78 79 80 81 82 84 85 86 87 89 92 93 96 97 100 107 108 110 111 114 115 118 119 124 126 129 130 131 132 135 141 146 147 148 **P**6 **S** UPMC, Pittsburgh, PA
Primary Contact: V. James Fiorenzo, President
COO: David Gibbons, Executive Vice President and Chief Operating Officer
CFO: Stephen M. Danch, Chief Financial Officer
CMO: Richard Long, M.D., Chief Medical Officer
CIO: Lisa D. McChesney, R.N., Senior Director Information Systems
CHR: Brian Durniok, Vice President Human Resources
CNO: James E. Donnelly, Chief Nursing Officer and Vice President Patient Care Services
Web address: www.hamot.org
**Control:** Other not–for–profit (including NFP Corporation) **Service:** General Medical and Surgical

**Staffed Beds: 311 Admissions: 18911 Census: 235 Outpatient Visits: 203254 Births: 2064 Total Expense ($000): 333934 Payroll Expense ($000): 100594 Personnel: 1936**

**VETERANS AFFAIRS MEDICAL CENTER** See Erie Veterans Affairs Medical Center

## EVERETT—Bedford County

☐ **UPMC BEDFORD MEMORIAL (390117)**, 10455 Lincoln Highway, Zip 15537–7046; tel. 814/623–6161 **A**1 9 10 20 **F**3 8 11 13 15 18 28 29 30 31 34 35 36 39 40 41 45 50 51 56 57 59 61 64 65 68 70 74 75 76 77 78 79 81 85 86 87 89 93 97 102 104 107 108 110 111 114 119 129 130 131 132 133 135 146 147 **P**6 **S** UPMC, Pittsburgh, PA
Primary Contact: Gerald Murray, President
CFO: Mario Wilfong, Vice President Finance and Administration
CIO: Mark Wiley, Manager Information Systems Development
CHR: Michelle A. Speck, Vice President Human Resources
CNO: Paula Thomas, R.N., Vice President Patient Services
Web address: www.upmcbedfordmemorial.com
**Control:** Other not–for–profit (including NFP Corporation) **Service:** General Medical and Surgical

**Staffed Beds: 27 Admissions: 1670 Census: 13 Outpatient Visits: 110236 Births: 303 Total Expense ($000): 51424 Payroll Expense ($000): 15520 Personnel: 281**

## FARRELL—Mercer County

**SHENANGO VALLEY CAMPUS** See UPMC Horizon, Greenville

## FORT WASHINGTON—Montgomery County

☐ **BROOKE GLEN BEHAVIORAL HOSPITAL (394049)**, 7170 Lafayette Avenue, Zip 19034–2301; tel. 215/641–5300, (Nonreporting) **A**1 3 5 9 10 **S** Universal Health Services, Inc., King of Prussia, PA
Primary Contact: Neil Callahan, Chief Executive Officer
COO: William R. Mason, Chief Operating Officer
CFO: Robert Zagerman, Chief Financial Officer
CMO: Chand Nair, M.D., Medical Director
CHR: Dawn Kownacki, Director Human Resources
Web address: www.brookeglenhospital.com
**Control:** Corporation, Investor–owned, for–profit **Service:** Psychiatric

**Staffed Beds: 146**

## GETTYSBURG—Adams County

⊠ **GETTYSBURG HOSPITAL (390065)**, 147 Gettys Street, Zip 17325–2534; tel. 717/334–2121 **A**1 3 9 10 **F**3 8 11 13 15 18 20 28 29 30 31 35 40 45 46 50 54 55 59 60 64 65 68 70 74 75 76 79 81 82 84 85 87 89 93 102 107 108 110 111 112 114 115 118 119 120 121 129 130 131 132 134 135 146 147 148 **S** WellSpan Health, York, PA
Primary Contact: Jane E. Hyde, President
COO: Joseph H. Edgar, Senior Vice President Operations
CMO: Charles Marley, D.O., Vice President Medical Affairs
CIO: Robin Kimple, Director Information Services
CHR: Kim Brister, Director Human Resources
CNO: Kristen O'Shea, R.N., Vice President Patient Care Services
Web address: www.wellspan.org
**Control:** Other not–for–profit (including NFP Corporation) **Service:** General Medical and Surgical

**Staffed Beds: 76 Admissions: 4091 Census: 46 Outpatient Visits: 184661 Births: 531 Total Expense ($000): 126131 Payroll Expense ($000): 41689 Personnel: 798**

*Many Facility Codes have changed. Please refer to the AHA Guide Code Chart.* © 2015 AHA Guide

## GREENSBURG—Westmoreland County

☐ **EXCELA HEALTH WESTMORELAND HOSPITAL (390145)**, 532 West Pittsburgh Street, Zip 15601–2282; tel. 724/832–4000 **A**1 3 9 10 **F**3 5 8 9 11 12 13 15 17 18 20 22 24 26 28 29 30 32 34 35 36 38 40 44 45 46 48 49 50 51 56 57 59 61 64 65 68 70 73 74 75 76 77 78 79 81 82 84 85 86 87 89 90 91 92 93 96 97 98 100 101 102 103 104 105 107 108 110 111 114 115 118 119 129 130 131 132 134 135 143 146 147 148 **S** Excela Health, Greensburg, PA
Primary Contact: Ronald H. Ott, President
COO: Michael D. Busch, Executive Vice President and Chief Operating Officer
CFO: Jeffrey T. Curry, Executive Vice President and Chief Financial Officer
CMO: Jerome Granato, M.D., Senior Vice President and Chief Medical Officer
CIO: David Gawaluck, Vice President and Chief Information Officer
CHR: John Caverno, Chief Human Resources Officer
CNO: Helen K. Burns, Ph.D., Senior Vice President and Chief Nursing Officer
Web address: www.excelahealth.org
**Control:** Other not–for–profit (including NFP Corporation) **Service:** General Medical and Surgical

**Staffed Beds:** 284 **Admissions:** 15816 **Census:** 203 **Outpatient Visits:** 329718 **Births:** 1601 **Total Expense ($000):** 215740 **Payroll Expense ($000):** 90732 **Personnel:** 1814

## GREENVILLE—Mercer County

☐ ○ **UPMC HORIZON (390178)**, 110 North Main Street, Zip 16125–1726; tel. 724/588–2100, (Includes GREENVILLE CAMPUS, 110 North Main Street, Zip 16125–1795; tel. 724/588–2100; SHENANGO VALLEY CAMPUS, 2200 Memorial Drive, Farrell, Zip 16121–1398; tel. 724/981–3500), (Total facility includes 25 beds in nursing home–type unit) **A**1 2 9 10 11 13 **F**3 11 12 13 15 18 20 26 28 29 30 31 32 34 35 39 40 43 44 45 47 49 50 53 54 56 57 59 61 64 65 68 70 74 75 76 77 78 79 81 82 85 86 87 90 92 97 107 108 110 111 114 115 116 117 118 119 121 123 128 129 130 131 132 133 135 146 147 148 **S** UPMC, Pittsburgh, PA
Primary Contact: Donald R. Owrey, President
CFO: David Shulik, Vice President and Chief Financial Officer
CMO: Samuel Daisley, D.O., Vice President Medical Affairs
CHR: Connie Mayle, Vice President Administrative Services
Web address: www.horizon.upmc.com
**Control:** Other not–for–profit (including NFP Corporation) **Service:** General Medical and Surgical

**Staffed Beds:** 184 **Admissions:** 6719 **Census:** 86 **Outpatient Visits:** 215221 **Births:** 819 **Total Expense ($000):** 147608 **Payroll Expense ($000):** 40203 **Personnel:** 742

## GROVE CITY—Mercer County

**GROVE CITY MEDICAL CENTER (390266)**, 631 North Broad Street Extension, Zip 16127–4603; tel. 724/450–7000, (Total facility includes 20 beds in nursing home–type unit) **A**9 10 **F**3 13 15 18 20 28 29 31 34 35 40 45 46 49 50 51 54 57 59 60 64 70 75 76 78 79 81 82 87 93 107 108 110 111 115 117 118 119 124 127 128 129 130 132 135 146 147 148 **P**6
Primary Contact: Robert Jackson, Jr., Chief Executive Officer
CFO: David Poland, Vice President Finance
CMO: Armando Sciullo, D.O., Chief of Staff
CIO: Philip Swartwood, Director Information Systems
CHR: Donald Henley, Vice President Human Resources and Social Services
Web address: www.gcmcpa.org
**Control:** Other not–for–profit (including NFP Corporation) **Service:** General Medical and Surgical

**Staffed Beds:** 65 **Admissions:** 2047 **Census:** 31 **Outpatient Visits:** 98328 **Births:** 168 **Total Expense ($000):** 44247 **Payroll Expense ($000):** 16870 **Personnel:** 379

## HANOVER—York County

☒ **HANOVER HOSPITAL (390233)**, 300 Highland Avenue, Zip 17331–2297; tel. 717/316–3711 **A**1 9 10 **F**3 11 13 15 18 20 22 28 29 30 31 34 35 36 40 44 45 49 50 53 54 57 59 61 64 65 75 76 77 78 81 84 85 86 87 89 93 94 96 107 108 110 111 115 118 119 129 130 131 132 134 135 143 144 146 147 148
Primary Contact: Michael W. Gaskins, Interim President and Chief Executive Officer
COO: Michael A. Hockenberry, Vice President Operations
CFO: Michael W. Gaskins, Executive Vice President and Chief Financial Officer
CMO: Michael H. Ader, M.D., Vice President Medical Affairs
CIO: Pamela Owens, Director Health Information Management
CHR: Christine Miller, General Counsel and Vice President Human Resources
CNO: M. Patricia Saunders, R.N., Vice President Nursing
Web address: www.hanoverhospital.org
**Control:** Other not–for–profit (including NFP Corporation) **Service:** General Medical and Surgical

**Staffed Beds:** 93 **Admissions:** 5242 **Census:** 63 **Outpatient Visits:** 215386 **Births:** 577 **Total Expense ($000):** 131615 **Payroll Expense ($000):** 53116 **Personnel:** 957

## HARRISBURG—Dauphin County

**COMMUNITY HOSPITAL** See Pinnacle Health System

☒ **HELEN M. SIMPSON REHABILITATION HOSPITAL**, 4300 Londonderry Road, Zip 17109–5317; tel. 717/920–4300, (Nonreporting) **A**1 **S** Select Medical Corporation, Mechanicsburg, PA
Primary Contact: Melissa Gillis, Chief Executive Officer
**Control:** Corporation, Investor–owned, for–profit **Service:** Rehabilitation

**Staffed Beds:** 55

☒ **PENNSYLVANIA PSYCHIATRIC INSTITUTE (394051)**, 2501 North Third Street, Zip 17110–1904; tel. 717/782–6420, (Nonreporting) **A**1 3 5 10
Primary Contact: William Daly, Chief Executive Officer
CFO: Michael Felice, Chief Financial Officer
Web address: www.ppimhs.org/
**Control:** Other not–for–profit (including NFP Corporation) **Service:** Psychiatric

**Staffed Beds:** 80

☐ **PINNACLE HEALTH SYSTEM (390067)**, 111 South Front Street, Zip 17101–2010, Mailing Address: P.O. Box 8700, Zip 17105–8700; tel. 717/782–3131, (Includes COMMUNITY HOSPITAL, 4300 Londonderry Road, Zip 17109–5397, Mailing Address: P.O. Box 3000, Zip 17105–3000; tel. 717/652–3000; HARRISBURG HOSPITAL, 111 South Front Street, Zip 17101–2099; tel. 717/782–3131; POLYCLINIC HOSPITAL, 2501 North Third Street, Zip 17110–1904; tel. 717/782–4141; Roger Longenderfer, M.D., President and Chief Executive Officer) **A**1 2 3 5 9 10 12 13 **F**3 7 8 11 12 13 14 15 17 18 19 20 22 24 26 27 28 29 30 31 32 34 35 36 37 38 40 44 45 46 47 48 49 50 52 53 54 55 56 57 58 59 60 61 64 65 66 68 70 72 74 75 76 77 78 79 81 82 84 85 86 87 89 91 93 97 100 101 102 103 104 107 108 109 110 111 114 115 116 117 118 119 120 121 123 124 126 130 131 132 134 138 142 143 146 147 148 **P**6
Primary Contact: Michael A. Young, FACHE, President and Chief Executive Officer
COO: Philip Guarneschelli, Senior Vice President and Chief Operating Officer
CFO: William H. Pugh, Senior Vice President Corporate Finance and Chief Financial Officer
CMO: Nirmal Joshi, M.D., Senior Vice President Medical Affairs and Chief Medical Officer
CIO: Steven Roth, Vice President Informatics and Chief Information Officer
CHR: Ann H. Gormley, Vice President Human Resources
Web address: www.pinnaclehealth.org
**Control:** Other not–for–profit (including NFP Corporation) **Service:** General Medical and Surgical

**Staffed Beds:** 662 **Admissions:** 31770 **Census:** 417 **Outpatient Visits:** 769600 **Births:** 4025 **Total Expense ($000):** 675153 **Payroll Expense ($000):** 237776 **Personnel:** 5196

**POLYCLINIC HOSPITAL** See Pinnacle Health System

**SELECT SPECIALTY HOSPITAL–HARRISBURG** See Select Specialty Hospital–Central Pennsylvania, Camp Hill

## HASTINGS—Cambria County

★ **CONEMAUGH MINERS MEDICAL CENTER (390130)**, 290 Haida Avenue, Zip 16646–5610, Mailing Address: P.O. Box 689, Zip 16646–0689; tel. 814/247–3100 **A**9 10 20 **F**3 15 18 29 30 31 35 36 40 45 48 56 57 59 64 70 75 78 79 81 86 92 93 96 97 102 107 108 110 119 129 130 131 133 144 146 148 **P**8 **S** Duke LifePoint Healthcare, Brentwood, TN
Primary Contact: William R. Crowe, President
CFO: Kimberly Semelsberger, Vice President Financial Operations
CHR: John Fresh, Vice President Human Resources
Web address: www.minersmedicalcenter.org
**Control:** Other not–for–profit (including NFP Corporation) **Service:** General Medical and Surgical

**Staffed Beds:** 30 **Admissions:** 426 **Census:** 5 **Outpatient Visits:** 51111 **Births:** 1 **Total Expense ($000):** 16478 **Payroll Expense ($000):** 5180 **Personnel:** 121

**PA**

---

**Hospital, Medicare Provider Number, Address, Telephone, Approval, Facility, and Physician Codes, Health Care System**

★ American Hospital Association (AHA) membership  ○ Healthcare Facilities Accreditation Program  ⇑ Center for Improvement in Healthcare Quality Accreditation
☐ The Joint Commission accreditation  ◇ DNV Healthcare Inc. accreditation  △ Commission on Accreditation of Rehabilitation Facilities (CARF) accreditation

**PA**

### HAZLETON—Luzerne County

★ ○ **LEHIGH VALLEY HOSPITAL – HAZLETON (390185)**, 700 East Broad Street, Zip 18201–6897; tel. 570/501–4000 **A**9 10 11 **F**3 8 11 12 13 15 18 28 29 30 31 33 34 35 40 50 53 54 57 59 60 62 64 68 69 70 75 76 77 78 79 81 82 85 86 87 89 90 93 107 108 110 111 114 118 119 124 129 130 131 132 135 143 144 146 147 148 **P**6 **S** Lehigh Valley Health Network, Allentown, PA
Primary Contact: John R. Fletcher, President
CFO: William Bauer, Vice President Finance and Chief Financial Officer
CMO: Anthony Valente, M.D., Vice President Medical Affairs
CIO: Carl Shoener, Chief Information Officer
Web address: www.lvhn.org/hazleton/
**Control:** Other not–for–profit (including NFP Corporation) **Service:** General Medical and Surgical

**Staffed Beds:** 116 **Admissions:** 6719 **Census:** 84 **Outpatient Visits:** 158845 **Births:** 637 **Total Expense ($000):** 98257 **Payroll Expense ($000):** 41144 **Personnel:** 725

### HERSHEY—Dauphin County

⊞ **PENN STATE MILTON S. HERSHEY MEDICAL CENTER (390256)**, 500 University Drive, Zip 17033–2360, Mailing Address: P.O. Box 850, Zip 17033–0850; tel. 717/531–8521, (Includes PENN STATE CHILDREN'S HOSPITAL, 500 University Drive, tel. 717/531–8521) **A**1 2 3 5 8 9 10 **F**3 5 6 7 8 9 11 12 13 14 15 17 18 19 20 21 22 23 24 25 26 27 28 29 30 31 32 34 35 36 37 38 40 41 43 44 45 46 47 48 49 50 51 52 53 54 55 56 57 58 59 60 61 64 65 66 68 70 71 72 73 74 75 76 77 78 79 80 81 82 84 85 86 87 88 89 91 92 93 96 97 99 100 101 102 103 104 105 106 107 108 109 110 111 114 115 116 117 118 119 120 121 123 124 126 129 130 131 132 134 135 136 137 138 139 141 142 143 144 145 146 147 148 **P**6
Primary Contact: A. Craig Hillemeier, M.D., Chief Executive Officer
COO: Robin D. Wittenstein, Ed.D., Director and Chief Operating Officer
CFO: Paul Swinko, Interim Chief Financial Officer
CMO: Carol V. Freer, M.D., Chief Medical Officer
CIO: Rod Dykehouse, Chief Information Officer
CHR: Lisa Abbott, Chief Human Resources Officer
CNO: Sherry M. Kwater, R.N., Chief Nursing Officer
Web address: www.pennstatehershey.org/web/guest/home
**Control:** Other not–for–profit (including NFP Corporation) **Service:** General Medical and Surgical

**Staffed Beds:** 493 **Admissions:** 27396 **Census:** 422 **Outpatient Visits:** 923905 **Births:** 1902 **Total Expense ($000):** 1098461 **Payroll Expense ($000):** 393556 **Personnel:** 8228

### HONESDALE—Wayne County

★ ◇ **WAYNE MEMORIAL HOSPITAL (390125)**, 601 Park Street, Zip 18431–1498; tel. 570/253–8100 **A**9 10 21 **F**3 11 13 15 18 28 30 31 34 35 36 37 39 40 45 46 48 49 50 51 53 54 56 57 59 61 62 63 64 65 75 76 77 78 79 81 86 90 92 93 99 100 101 102 103 104 107 108 110 111 115 116 117 119 124 129 130 131 132 133 134 135 146 147 148
Primary Contact: David L. Hoff, Chief Executive Officer
COO: John D. Conte, Director Facility Services
CFO: Michael J. Clifford, Director Finance
CMO: William Dewar, M.D., Chief of Staff
CIO: Tom Hoffman, Manager Information Systems
CHR: Elizabeth McDonald, Director Human Resources
CNO: Major Jim Pettinato, Director Patient Care Services
Web address: www.wmh.org
**Control:** Other not–for–profit (including NFP Corporation) **Service:** General Medical and Surgical

**Staffed Beds:** 104 **Admissions:** 3609 **Census:** 42 **Outpatient Visits:** 138709 **Births:** 436 **Total Expense ($000):** 71889 **Payroll Expense ($000):** 29970 **Personnel:** 570

### HUMMELSTOWN—Dauphin County

⊞ △ **PENN STATE HERSHEY REHABILITATION HOSPITAL (393053)**, 1135 Old West Chocolate Avenue, Zip 17036; tel. 717/832–2600, (Nonreporting) **A**1 3 7 9 10 **S** Select Medical Corporation, Mechanicsburg, PA
Primary Contact: Scott Guevin, Chief Executive Officer
CMO: Brenda Mallory, M.D., Medical Director
Web address: www.psh-rehab.com
**Control:** Corporation, Investor–owned, for–profit **Service:** Rehabilitation

**Staffed Beds:** 32

### HUNTINGDON—Huntingdon County

⊞ **J. C. BLAIR MEMORIAL HOSPITAL (390056)**, 1225 Warm Springs Avenue, Zip 16652–2398; tel. 814/643–2290 **A**1 9 10 20 **F**3 11 13 15 18 28 29 34 35 40 45 50 53 55 57 59 64 68 70 75 76 77 79 81 85 86 87 89 96 98 99 100 102 103 105 107 108 110 111 114 116 117 118 119 129 130 132 133 135 146 147 148
Primary Contact: Jason F. Hawkins, President and Chief Executive Officer
CFO: Deborah A. Shughart, Vice President and Chief Financial Officer
CMO: James Hayden, M.D., Chief Medical Officer
CIO: Rusty Davis, Director Information Technology
CHR: Michael F. Hubert, Vice President Human Resources
CNO: Pam Matthias, Vice President of Patient Care Services
Web address: www.jcblair.org
**Control:** Other not–for–profit (including NFP Corporation) **Service:** General Medical and Surgical

**Staffed Beds:** 70 **Admissions:** 1819 **Census:** 18 **Outpatient Visits:** 111435 **Births:** 235 **Total Expense ($000):** 40153 **Payroll Expense ($000):** 19035 **Personnel:** 348

### INDIANA—Indiana County

★ ⇑ **INDIANA REGIONAL MEDICAL CENTER (390173)**, 835 Hospital Road, Zip 15701–3629, Mailing Address: P.O. Box 788, Zip 15701–0788; tel. 724/357–7000 **A**2 9 10 20 22 **F**3 11 15 18 20 28 29 31 32 34 35 40 44 45 46 47 49 53 56 57 59 64 65 70 71 74 75 76 77 78 79 81 82 83 84 85 87 89 90 98 102 103 107 108 111 114 115 118 119 120 121 123 124 129 130 132 144 146 147 148 **P**4 6
Primary Contact: Stephen A. Wolfe, President and Chief Executive Officer
COO: Dominic Paccapaniccia, Chief Operating Officer
CFO: Robert Gongaware, Senior Vice President Finance
CMO: Bruce A. Bush, M.D., Senior Vice President Medical Affairs
CIO: Wade Patrick, Senior Vice President Information Services
CHR: James W. Kinneer, Vice President Organizational Development
CNO: Cindy L. Virgil, MSN, Senior Vice President Patient Care Services
Web address: www.indianarmc.org
**Control:** Other not–for–profit (including NFP Corporation) **Service:** General Medical and Surgical

**Staffed Beds:** 164 **Admissions:** 7166 **Census:** 87 **Outpatient Visits:** 279039 **Births:** 588 **Total Expense ($000):** 137171 **Payroll Expense ($000):** 61850 **Personnel:** 866

### JEFFERSON HILLS—Allegheny County

⊞ **JEFFERSON HOSPITAL (390265)**, 565 Coal Valley Road, Zip 15025–3703, Mailing Address: Box 18119, Pittsburgh, Zip 15236–0119; tel. 412/469–5000 **A**1 2 3 9 10 **F**3 8 11 12 13 15 18 20 22 24 26 28 29 30 31 34 35 40 44 45 46 47 48 49 51 54 57 59 60 64 70 73 74 75 76 78 79 81 84 85 86 87 89 90 93 98 100 104 107 110 111 114 115 116 117 118 119 126 129 130 132 146 147 148 **P**6 **S** Allegheny Health Network, Pittsburgh, PA
Primary Contact: Louise Urban, R.N., President and Chief Executive Officer
CMO: Richard F. Collins, M.D., Executive Vice President and Chief Medical Officer
CIO: James Witenske, Chief Information Officer
Web address: www.jeffersonregional.com
**Control:** Other not–for–profit (including NFP Corporation) **Service:** General Medical and Surgical

**Staffed Beds:** 349 **Admissions:** 14055 **Census:** 189 **Outpatient Visits:** 471941 **Births:** 34 **Total Expense ($000):** 305826 **Payroll Expense ($000):** 116725 **Personnel:** 1618

### JERSEY SHORE—Lycoming County

⊞ **JERSEY SHORE HOSPITAL (391300)**, 1020 Thompson Street, Zip 17740–1794; tel. 570/398–0100 **A**1 9 10 18 **F**3 15 18 28 29 30 34 35 40 45 46 47 48 50 57 59 75 77 79 81 82 85 93 107 108 109 110 111 115 119 129 130 131 133 135 144 145 147 148 **S** QHR, Brentwood, TN
Primary Contact: David A. Shannon, President and Chief Executive Officer
CFO: Mark Rice, CPA, Controller
CMO: Thomas Connolly, M.D., Chief Medical Officer
CIO: Christine Haas, Chief Information Officer
CHR: Megan Switzer, Director Human Resources
Web address: www.jsh.org
**Control:** Other not–for–profit (including NFP Corporation) **Service:** General Medical and Surgical

**Staffed Beds:** 25 **Admissions:** 804 **Census:** 9 **Outpatient Visits:** 87089 **Births:** 0 **Total Expense ($000):** 27562 **Payroll Expense ($000):** 11658 **Personnel:** 309

*Many Facility Codes have changed. Please refer to the AHA Guide Code Chart.* © 2015 AHA Guide

**PA**

## JOHNSTOWN—Cambria County

✠ △ **CONEMAUGH MEMORIAL MEDICAL CENTER (390110)**, 1086 Franklin Street, Zip 15905–4398; tel. 814/534–9000, (Includes GOOD SAMARITAN MEDICAL CENTER, 1020 Franklin Street, Zip 15905–4186; tel. 814/533–1000; MEMORIAL MEDICAL CENTER – LEE CAMPUS, 320 Main Street, Zip 15901–1601; tel. 814/533–0123) **A**1 3 5 6 7 9 10 12 13 **F**3 5 8 12 13 14 15 17 18 20 22 24 26 28 29 30 31 32 34 35 40 42 43 44 45 46 49 50 51 53 54 55 56 57 59 61 62 63 64 68 70 72 74 75 76 77 78 79 81 82 83 84 85 86 87 89 90 92 93 97 98 99 100 101 103 104 107 108 110 111 114 115 118 119 126 129 130 131 132 134 135 144 145 146 147 148 **S** Duke LifePoint Healthcare, Brentwood, TN
Primary Contact: Steven E. Tucker, President
COO: Steven E. Tucker, President
CFO: Edward De Pasquale, Chief Financial Officer
CMO: William Carney, M.D., Interim Chief Medical Officer
CIO: Joseph Dado, Chief Information Officer
CHR: Brent J. Mallek, Chief Human Resources Officer
CNO: Claudia Rager, R.N., Vice President Patient Care Services
Web address: www.conemaugh.org
**Control:** Corporation, Investor–owned, for–profit **Service:** General Medical and Surgical

**Staffed Beds: 539 Admissions: 21707 Census: 330 Outpatient Visits: 488083 Births: 1563 Total Expense ($000): 392580 Payroll Expense ($000): 154301 Personnel: 3131**

**MEMORIAL MEDICAL CENTER – LEE CAMPUS** See Conemaugh Memorial Medical Center

✠ **SELECT SPECIALTY HOSPITAL–JOHNSTOWN (392031)**, 320 Main Street, 3rd Floor, Zip 15901–1601; tel. 814/534–7300, (Nonreporting) **A**1 9 10 **S** Select Medical Corporation, Mechanicsburg, PA
Primary Contact: Kelly Blake, Chief Executive Officer
CMO: Gary Davidson, M.D., Medical Director
Web address: www.selectspecialtyhospitals.com/company/locations/johnstown. aspx
**Control:** Corporation, Investor–owned, for–profit **Service:** Long–Term Acute Care hospital

**Staffed Beds: 39**

## KANE—McKean County

**KANE COMMUNITY HOSPITAL (390104)**, 4372 Route 6, Zip 16735–3060; tel. 814/837–8585 **A**9 10 20 **F**3 11 12 15 17 18 28 29 30 31 34 35 40 41 45 46 50 53 57 59 62 64 65 70 75 77 79 81 82 85 89 91 93 107 108 110 111 114 118 119 128 129 130 132 133 135 145 146 147 **P**4
Primary Contact: J. Gary Rhodes, FACHE, Chief Executive Officer
CFO: Angela Hadzega, Chief Financial Officer
CMO: Linda Rettger, M.D., President Medical Staff
CIO: Margaret Twidale, Manager Information Systems
CHR: Marsha Keller, Director Human Resources
CNO: Pam Bray, Director of Nursing and Director Inpatient Services
Web address: www.kanehosp.com
**Control:** Other not–for–profit (including NFP Corporation) **Service:** General Medical and Surgical

**Staffed Beds: 31 Admissions: 741 Census: 9 Outpatient Visits: 72514 Births: 0 Total Expense ($000): 19979 Payroll Expense ($000): 9930 Personnel: 181**

## KINGSTON—Luzerne County

✠ **FIRST HOSPITAL WYOMING VALLEY (394039)**, 562 Wyoming Avenue, Zip 18704–3721; tel. 570/552–3900 **A**1 9 10 **F**42 98 99 103 105 130 **P**6 **S** Community Health Systems, Inc., Franklin, TN
Primary Contact: Rhonda Moffitt Sod, Interim Chief Executive Officer
CFO: Kelly Knorr, Chief Financial Officer
CMO: David Liskov, M.D., Medical Director
CNO: Rhonda Moffitt Sod, Chief Nursing Officer
Web address: www.commonwealthhealth.net/locations/first–hospital
**Control:** Corporation, Investor–owned, for–profit **Service:** Psychiatric

**Staffed Beds: 127 Admissions: 4247 Census: 96 Outpatient Visits: 0 Births: 0 Personnel: 112**

## KITTANNING—Armstrong County

◇ **ACMH HOSPITAL (390163)**, One Nolte Drive, Zip 16201–7111; tel. 724/543–8500 **A**2 9 10 19 21 **F**3 11 13 15 17 18 20 22 26 28 29 30 34 35 40 45 49 59 70 74 75 76 77 78 79 81 82 85 90 93 98 102 103 107 108 110 111 112 114 119 120 127 128 129 130 131 132 135 136 141 142 146 148
Primary Contact: John I. Lewis, President and Chief Executive Officer
CFO: Patrick Burns, Vice President Finance
CMO: Harold Altman, M.D., Chief Medical Officer
CIO: Dianne Emminger, Vice President Information Services
CHR: Anne Remaley, Vice President Human Resources
Web address: www.acmh.org
**Control:** Other not–for–profit (including NFP Corporation) **Service:** General Medical and Surgical

**Staffed Beds: 165 Admissions: 5319 Census: 72 Outpatient Visits: 256421 Births: 580 Total Expense ($000): 94482 Payroll Expense ($000): 43777 Personnel: 634**

## LANCASTER—Lancaster County

✠ **LANCASTER GENERAL HEALTH (390100)**, 555 North Duke Street, Zip 17602–2250, Mailing Address: P.O. Box 3555, Zip 17604–3555; tel. 717/544–5511 **A**1 2 3 5 9 10 **F**3 11 12 13 14 15 17 18 19 20 22 24 26 28 29 30 31 32 34 35 36 37 39 40 43 44 45 46 47 49 50 54 55 56 57 58 59 60 61 64 65 66 68 70 72 73 74 75 76 77 78 79 80 81 82 83 86 87 89 91 92 93 96 97 98 100 102 107 108 110 112 114 115 117 118 119 120 121 123 124 126 129 130 132 135 141 142 145 146 147 148 **P**6 **S** University of Pennsylvania Health System, Philadelphia, PA
Primary Contact: Jan L. Bergen, President and Chief Executive Officer
CFO: Dennis Roemer, Executive Vice President and Chief Financial Officer
CMO: Lee M. Duke, II, M.D., Senior Vice President and Chief Physician Executive
CIO: Gary Davidson, Senior Vice President and Chief Information Officer
CHR: Regina Mingle, Senior Vice President and Chief Leadership Officer
CNO: Admiral Karen Flaherty Oxler, R.N., President, Lancaster General Hospital and Chief Nursing Officer
Web address: www.lghealth.org
**Control:** Other not–for–profit (including NFP Corporation) **Service:** General Medical and Surgical

**Staffed Beds: 630 Admissions: 31642 Census: 394 Outpatient Visits: 1449519 Births: 4348 Total Expense ($000): 793934 Payroll Expense ($000): 321649 Personnel: 4786**

✠ **LANCASTER REGIONAL MEDICAL CENTER (390061)**, 250 College Avenue, Zip 17603–3363, Mailing Address: P.O. Box 3434, Zip 17604–3434; tel. 717/291–8211 **A**1 9 10 **F**3 15 18 20 22 24 26 28 29 30 31 34 35 37 40 45 46 47 48 49 50 51 56 57 59 64 68 70 74 75 77 78 79 81 82 84 85 87 90 91 92 93 96 98 100 101 102 103 107 108 110 111 114 119 121 126 129 130 131 135 146 **S** Community Health Systems, Inc., Franklin, TN
Primary Contact: Russell Baxley, Chief Executive Officer
CFO: Mike Johnson, Chief Financial Officer
CMO: N. A. Mastropietro, M.D., Medical Director
CHR: Brian Hoffman, Director Human Resources
CNO: Michelle Reaser, R.N., Chief Nursing Executive
Web address: www.lancasterregional.com
**Control:** Corporation, Investor–owned, for–profit **Service:** General Medical and Surgical

**Staffed Beds: 150 Admissions: 4534 Census: 69 Outpatient Visits: 91451 Births: 0 Total Expense ($000): 99173 Payroll Expense ($000): 30329 Personnel: 546**

☐ **LANCASTER REHABILITATION HOSPITAL (393054)**, 675 Good Drive, Zip 17601–2426; tel. 717/406–3000, (Nonreporting) **A**1 10 **S** Kindred Healthcare, Louisville, KY
Primary Contact: Tammy L. Ober, Chief Executive Officer
CFO: David Stark, Chief Financial Officer
CHR: Lisa Andrews, Director Human Resources
Web address: www.lancastergeneral.org
**Control:** Corporation, Investor–owned, for–profit **Service:** Rehabilitation

**Staffed Beds: 10**

## LANGHORNE—Bucks County

☐ **BARIX CLINICS OF PENNSYLVANIA (390302)**, 280 Middletown Boulevard, Zip 19047–1816; tel. 267/572–3100, (Nonreporting) **A**1 10
Primary Contact: Vivian Costa, Director
Web address: www.barixclinics.com
**Control:** Partnership, Investor–owned, for–profit **Service:** Surgical

**Staffed Beds: 40**

**BUCKS COUNTY CAMPUS** See Aria Health, Philadelphia

---

**Hospital, Medicare Provider Number, Address, Telephone, Approval, Facility, and Physician Codes, Health Care System**

★ American Hospital Association (AHA) membership
☐ The Joint Commission accreditation
◯ Healthcare Facilities Accreditation Program
◇ DNV Healthcare Inc. accreditation
⇑ Center for Improvement in Healthcare Quality Accreditation
△ Commission on Accreditation of Rehabilitation Facilities (CARF) accreditation

**PA**

✠ **ST. MARY MEDICAL CENTER (390258)**, 1201 Langhorne–Newtown Road, Zip 19047–1201; tel. 215/710–2000 **A**1 2 9 10 **F**2 7 12 15 17 18 20 22 24 26 28 29 30 31 32 34 35 40 41 43 53 55 56 57 58 59 64 66 70 72 74 75 76 77 78 79 81 82 84 86 87 89 90 91 92 93 94 107 108 110 111 114 115 116 117 118 119 120 121 123 124 129 130 132 135 146 147 148 **S** Trinity Health, Livonia, MI
Primary Contact: Gregory T. Wozniak, President and Chief Executive Officer
COO: Jeffrey N. Yarmel, Chief Operating Officer
CFO: Daniel Confalone, Chief Financial Officer and Vice President Finance
CMO: Deirdre Donaghy, M.D., Vice President Medical Affairs
CIO: Bonnie Buehler, Chief Information Officer
CHR: Mary Sweeney, Vice President Colleague Services and Development
CNO: Sharon Brown, R.N., Vice President Patient Care and Chief Nursing Officer
Web address: www.stmaryhealthcare.org
**Control:** Church–operated, Nongovernment, not–for profit **Service:** General Medical and Surgical

**Staffed Beds:** 323 **Admissions:** 23828 **Census:** 283 **Outpatient Visits:** 308559 **Births:** 2495 **Total Expense ($000):** 384027 **Payroll Expense ($000):** 155761 **Personnel:** 2302

### LANSDALE—Montgomery County

✠ **ABINGTON HEALTH LANSDALE HOSPITAL (390012)**, 100 Medical Campus Drive, Zip 19446–1200; tel. 215/368–2100 **A**1 9 10 **F**2 3 11 15 18 28 29 30 31 34 35 40 45 49 57 59 64 65 70 74 77 78 79 81 82 85 86 90 93 107 111 114 115 119 129 130 132 146 147 148 **P**6 **S** Jefferson Health, Radnor, PA
Primary Contact: Gary R. Candia, Ph.D., FACHE, Chief Administrative Officer
COO: Katie Farrell, Chief Operating Officer
CFO: Michael Walsh, Senior Vice President Finance and Chief Financial Officer
CMO: Michel Taupin, M.D., Chief Medical Officer
CIO: Alison Ferren, Vice President Information Technology and Chief Information Officer
CHR: Meghan Patton, Vice President Human Resources
CNO: Kelly Cummings, Chief Nursing Officer
Web address: www.amh.org/lansdale/index.aspx
**Control:** Other not–for–profit (including NFP Corporation) **Service:** General Medical and Surgical

**Staffed Beds:** 139 **Admissions:** 5154 **Census:** 55 **Outpatient Visits:** 77516 **Births:** 0 **Total Expense ($000):** 77028 **Payroll Expense ($000):** 30674 **Personnel:** 328

### LATROBE—Westmoreland County

☐ **EXCELA LATROBE AREA HOSPITAL (390219)**, One Mellon Way, Zip 15650–1096; tel. 724/537–1000 **A**1 2 3 5 9 10 13 **F**3 7 8 11 12 15 28 29 30 34 35 38 40 44 45 46 48 49 50 51 53 56 57 59 60 64 65 68 70 74 75 77 78 79 81 82 85 86 87 92 93 97 98 99 100 101 104 107 108 110 111 114 115 118 119 126 129 130 132 134 135 143 146 147 148 **P**6 **S** Excela Health, Greensburg, PA
Primary Contact: Michael D. Busch, Executive Vice President and Chief Operating Officer
COO: Michael D. Busch, Executive Vice President and Chief Operating Officer
CMO: Carol J. Fox, M.D., Senior Vice President and Chief Medical Officer
CIO: David Gawaluck, Vice President and Chief Information Officer
CHR: Laurie English, Senior Vice President and Chief Human Resource Officer
CNO: Helen K. Burns, Ph.D., Senior Vice President and Chief Nursing Officer
Web address: www.excelahealth.org
**Control:** Other not–for–profit (including NFP Corporation) **Service:** General Medical and Surgical

**Staffed Beds:** 114 **Admissions:** 6380 **Census:** 66 **Outpatient Visits:** 256603 **Births:** 0 **Total Expense ($000):** 114779 **Payroll Expense ($000):** 37357 **Personnel:** 800

✠ **SELECT SPECIALTY HOSPITAL–LAUREL HIGHLANDS (392036)**, One Mellon Way, 3rd Floor, Zip 15650–1197; tel. 724/539–3230, (Nonreporting) **A**1 9 10 **S** Select Medical Corporation, Mechanicsburg, PA
Primary Contact: Laurie Kozorosky, Chief Executive Officer
Web address: www.selectspecialtyhospitals.com/company/locations/laurelhighlands.aspx
**Control:** Corporation, Investor–owned, for–profit **Service:** Long–Term Acute Care hospital

**Staffed Beds:** 40

### LEBANON—Lebanon County

✠ **LEBANON VETERANS AFFAIRS MEDICAL CENTER**, 1700 South Lincoln Avenue, Zip 17042–7529; tel. 717/272–6621, (Nonreporting) **A**1 2 3 5 **S** Department of Veterans Affairs, Washington, DC
Primary Contact: Robert W. Callahan, Jr., Director
CFO: Geoffrey Smith, Chief Financial Officer
CMO: Kanan Chatterjee, M.D., Chief of Staff
CIO: Andru Ditzler, Chief Information Officer
CHR: Cindy Shiner, Manager Human Resources
Web address: www.lebanon.va.gov
**Control:** Veterans Affairs, Government, federal **Service:** General Medical and Surgical

**Staffed Beds:** 213

✠ **THE GOOD SAMARITAN HOSPITAL (390066)**, Fourth and Walnut Streets, Zip 17042–1281, Mailing Address: P.O. Box 1281, Zip 17042–1281; tel. 717/270–7500, (Total facility includes 19 beds in nursing home–type unit) **A**1 3 5 9 10 13 **F**3 8 11 13 14 15 17 18 20 22 24 26 28 29 30 31 34 35 40 45 49 50 51 53 57 59 62 63 64 68 70 75 76 77 78 79 80 81 82 84 85 87 89 90 92 93 94 96 97 107 108 110 111 114 118 119 128 129 130 132 135 145 146 148 **P**8 **S** WellSpan Health, York, PA
Primary Contact: Robert J. Longo, FACHE, President and Chief Executive Officer
COO: Kimberly Feeman, Senior Vice President and Chief Operating Officer
CFO: Robert J. Richards, Vice President Finance and Chief Financial Officer
CMO: Robert D. Shaver, M.D., Vice President Medical Affairs
CIO: Richard Follett, Chief Information Officer
CHR: Denise M. Garman, Director Human Resources
CNO: Jacquelyn M. Gould, MS, Vice President Patient Care Services and Chief Nursing Officer
Web address: www.gshleb.org
**Control:** Other not–for–profit (including NFP Corporation) **Service:** General Medical and Surgical

**Staffed Beds:** 151 **Admissions:** 7582 **Census:** 103 **Outpatient Visits:** 267171 **Births:** 773 **Total Expense ($000):** 169743 **Payroll Expense ($000):** 57528 **Personnel:** 1192

**VETERANS AFFAIRS MEDICAL CENTER** See Lebanon Veterans Affairs Medical Center

### LEHIGHTON—Carbon County

✠ △ **GNADEN HUETTEN MEMORIAL HOSPITAL (390194)**, 211 North 12th Street, Zip 18235–1138; tel. 610/377–1300, (Total facility includes 91 beds in nursing home–type unit) **A**1 7 9 10 **F**3 11 15 28 29 30 34 35 40 50 57 59 62 64 65 68 70 74 75 77 79 81 82 85 87 90 93 94 97 98 102 107 111 114 116 117 119 124 128 130 132 133 135 146 147 148 **S** Blue Mountain Health System, Lehighton, PA
Primary Contact: Andrew E. Harris, Chief Executive Officer
CFO: Andrea Andrae, Chief Financial Officer
CMO: Dennis Kondash, D.O., Vice President Medical Affairs
CIO: Steve Kinkaid, Director Information Systems
CHR: Terrance J. Purcell, Vice President Support Services and Ambulatory Care
CNO: Dorothy Patzek, Vice President Nursing
Web address: www.blmtn.org
**Control:** Other not–for–profit (including NFP Corporation) **Service:** General Medical and Surgical

**Staffed Beds:** 183 **Admissions:** 3271 **Census:** 136 **Outpatient Visits:** 65649 **Births:** 0 **Total Expense ($000):** 60083 **Payroll Expense ($000):** 26445 **Personnel:** 516

### LEWISBURG—Union County

◇ **EVANGELICAL COMMUNITY HOSPITAL (390013)**, One Hospital Drive, Zip 17837–9350; tel. 570/522–2000 **A**9 10 19 21 **F**3 8 11 12 13 15 18 20 22 28 29 30 31 34 35 40 45 49 50 51 53 54 57 59 63 64 65 68 74 75 76 77 78 79 81 82 85 86 87 89 90 93 94 96 107 110 111 114 115 118 119 129 130 131 132 135 144 146 148 **P**7
Primary Contact: Kendra A. Aucker, President and Chief Executive Officer
COO: Kendra A. Aucker, Vice President Operations
CFO: Jim Stopper, CPA, Chief Financial Officer
CMO: J. Lawrence Ginsburg, M.D., Vice President Medical Affairs
CIO: Dale Moyer, Vice President Information Systems
CHR: Angela Hummel, Vice President Human Resources
CNO: Paul E. Tarves, R.N., Vice President Nursing Services
Web address: www.evanhospital.com
**Control:** Other not–for–profit (including NFP Corporation) **Service:** General Medical and Surgical

**Staffed Beds:** 132 **Admissions:** 5508 **Census:** 49 **Outpatient Visits:** 256564 **Births:** 884 **Total Expense ($000):** 140995 **Payroll Expense ($000):** 57267 **Personnel:** 1353

**U. S. PENITENTIARY INFIRMARY**, Route 7, Zip 17837–9303; tel. 570/523–1251, (Nonreporting)
Primary Contact: Arnold Reyes, Administrator
**Control:** Department of Justice, Government, federal **Service:** Hospital unit of an institution (prison hospital, college infirmary, etc.)

**Staffed Beds:** 17

*Many Facility Codes have changed. Please refer to the AHA Guide Code Chart.* © 2015 AHA Guide

## LEWISTOWN—Mifflin County

☒ **GEISINGER–LEWISTOWN HOSPITAL (390048)**, 400 Highland Avenue, Zip 17044–1198; tel. 717/248–5411 **A1** 2 6 9 10 **F3** 11 12 13 15 17 18 19 28 29 30 31 34 35 40 50 51 57 59 64 68 70 71 74 75 76 78 79 81 82 85 86 89 97 98 100 101 102 103 107 108 110 111 114 116 117 118 119 121 124 129 130 132 135 146 147 148 **P6 S** Geisinger Health System, Danville, PA
Primary Contact: Kay A. Hamilton, R.N., MS, Chief Administrative Officer
COO: Kirk E. Thomas, Vice President Operations
CFO: Randy E. Tewksbury, Vice President Finance
CMO: Daniel Reifsnyder, M.D., Chief Medical Officer
CIO: Ronald M. Cowan, Vice President Information Systems
CHR: N. Sue Reinke, Vice President Human Resources
CNO: Christine W. Mathews, R.N., Vice President Nursing Services
Web address: www.geisinger.org
**Control:** Other not–for–profit (including NFP Corporation) **Service:** General Medical and Surgical

**Staffed Beds:** 123 **Admissions:** 4943 **Census:** 52 **Births:** 530

## LITITZ—Lancaster County

☒ **HEART OF LANCASTER REGIONAL MEDICAL CENTER (390068)**, 1500 Highlands Drive, Zip 17543–7694; tel. 717/625–5000 **A1** 9 10 13 **F3** 12 13 15 18 29 30 31 34 35 44 45 47 49 50 57 59 60 64 68 70 72 74 75 76 77 79 81 82 85 87 89 107 108 110 111 115 119 126 130 146 147 148 **S** Community Health Systems, Inc., Franklin, TN
Primary Contact: Deborah J. Willwerth, R.N., MSN, Chief Executive Officer
CIO: David Fisher, Director Information Systems
Web address: www.heartoflancaster.com
**Control:** Corporation, Investor–owned, for–profit **Service:** General Medical and Surgical

**Staffed Beds:** 148 **Admissions:** 2853 **Census:** 32 **Outpatient Visits:** 63041 **Births:** 988 **Total Expense ($000):** 56250 **Payroll Expense ($000):** 18367 **Personnel:** 443

## LOCK HAVEN—Clinton County

☒ **LOCK HAVEN HOSPITAL (390071)**, 24 Cree Drive, Zip 17745–2699; tel. 570/893–5000, (Nonreporting) **A1** 9 10 **S** Community Health Systems, Inc., Franklin, TN
Primary Contact: Steven T. Davis, Chief Executive Officer
CFO: Jennifer Lesher, Chief Financial Officer
CMO: Rajesh Patel, M.D., Chief of Staff
CIO: Judy Chapman, Interim Director Information Systems
CHR: Courtney Kunes, Director Human Resources
Web address: www.lockhavenhospital.com
**Control:** Corporation, Investor–owned, for–profit **Service:** General Medical and Surgical

**Staffed Beds:** 137

## MALVERN—Chester County

☒ △ **BRYN MAWR REHABILITATION HOSPITAL (393025)**, 414 Paoli Pike, Zip 19355–3300, Mailing Address: P.O. Box 3007, Zip 19355–0707; tel. 484/596–5400 **A1** 3 7 9 10 **F3** 11 28 29 30 34 35 36 44 50 65 71 75 82 86 87 90 91 92 93 95 96 119 130 131 132 143 146 **P5 S** Main Line Health
Primary Contact: Donna Phillips, President
CFO: Dave Schmotzer, Chief Financial Officer
CMO: John Kraus, M.D., Chief Medical Officer
CIO: Karen A. Thomas, Chief Information Officer
Web address: www.brynmawrrehab.org
**Control:** Other not–for–profit (including NFP Corporation) **Service:** Rehabilitation

**Staffed Beds:** 148 **Admissions:** 2342 **Census:** 98 **Outpatient Visits:** 62992 **Births:** 0 **Total Expense ($000):** 62635 **Payroll Expense ($000):** 33083 **Personnel:** 517

**DEVEREUX CHILDREN'S BEHAVIORAL HEALTH CENTER**, 655 Sugartown Road, Zip 19355–3303, Mailing Address: 655 Sugartown Road, Zip 19355–3303; tel. 800/345–1292 **F29** 98 99 106 **P6 S** Devereux, Villanova, PA
Primary Contact: David E. Woodward, Executive Director
CFO: Tim Evans, Assistant Financial Director
CMO: Jacquelyn Zavodnick, M.D., Medical Director
CIO: MaryLou Hettinger, Director Quality Management
CHR: Sean Maher, Director Human Resources
CNO: Deanna Reiss, Hospital Director of Nursing
Web address: www.devereux.org
**Control:** Other not–for–profit (including NFP Corporation) **Service:** Children's hospital psychiatric

**Staffed Beds:** 49 **Admissions:** 551 **Census:** 30 **Outpatient Visits:** 0 **Births:** 0

**MALVERN INSTITUTE**, 940 King Road, Zip 19355–3166; tel. 610/647–0330, (Nonreporting) **A9**
Primary Contact: Richard Mangano, Administrator and Chief Executive Officer
CFO: Janet Corley, Accountant
Web address: www.malverninstitute.com
**Control:** Corporation, Investor–owned, for–profit **Service:** Alcoholism and other chemical dependency

**Staffed Beds:** 40

## MC CONNELLSBURG—Fulton County

★ **FULTON COUNTY MEDICAL CENTER (391303)**, 214 Peach Orchard Road, Zip 17233–8559; tel. 717/485–3155, (Total facility includes 67 beds in nursing home–type unit) **A9** 10 18 **F3** 11 12 15 18 28 29 30 34 35 40 50 57 59 62 64 70 75 77 81 87 91 93 97 107 108 111 115 118 119 128 129 130 132 133 135 146 147 148
Primary Contact: Jason F. Hawkins, President and Chief Executive Officer
COO: William Buterbaugh, Director Support Services
CFO: Deborah A. Shughart, Vice President and Chief Financial Officer
CMO: Sharon E. Martin, M.D., President Medical Staff
CIO: Armen Arakelian, Chief Information Officer
CHR: Cheryl Rose, Human Resources Director
Web address: www.fcmcpa.org
**Control:** Other not–for–profit (including NFP Corporation) **Service:** General Medical and Surgical

**Staffed Beds:** 88 **Admissions:** 829 **Census:** 76 **Outpatient Visits:** 58706 **Births:** 0 **Total Expense ($000):** 38127 **Payroll Expense ($000):** 17909 **Personnel:** 341

## MCKEES ROCKS—Allegheny County

☒ **OHIO VALLEY HOSPITAL (390157)**, 25 Heckel Road, Zip 15136–1694; tel. 412/777–6161 **A1** 6 9 10 **F3** 10 15 18 20 29 30 40 45 46 49 51 59 65 70 74 75 77 79 81 82 85 87 90 92 93 98 103 107 108 111 118 119 126 129 130 143 146 148 **P6**
Primary Contact: David W. Scott, President and Chief Executive Officer
CFO: Tad Tefera, Vice President Finance and Chief Financial Officer
CHR: Erin J. Frohnhofer, Vice President Human Resources
CNO: Roni Sue Bell, Director Nursing Services
Web address: www.ohiovalleyhospital.org
**Control:** Other not–for–profit (including NFP Corporation) **Service:** General Medical and Surgical

**Staffed Beds:** 138 **Admissions:** 3426 **Census:** 58 **Outpatient Visits:** 109885 **Births:** 0 **Total Expense ($000):** 67609 **Payroll Expense ($000):** 24965 **Personnel:** 433

## MCKEESPORT—Allegheny County

☒ **SELECT SPECIALTY HOSPITAL–MCKEESPORT (392045)**, 1500 Fifth Avenue, 6th Floor, Zip 15132–2422; tel. 412/664–2900 **A1** 9 10 **F1** 3 91 92 97 130 148 **S** Select Medical Corporation, Mechanicsburg, PA
Primary Contact: Angela Merryman, Chief Executive Officer
Web address: www.mckeesport.selectspecialtyhospitals.com/
**Control:** Corporation, Investor–owned, for–profit **Service:** Long–Term Acute Care hospital

**Staffed Beds:** 30 **Admissions:** 292 **Census:** 21 **Outpatient Visits:** 0 **Births:** 0

☐ **UPMC MCKEESPORT (390002)**, 1500 Fifth Avenue, Zip 15132–2422; tel. 412/664–2000, (Total facility includes 24 beds in nursing home–type unit) **A1** 3 5 9 13 **F3** 8 11 15 17 18 20 22 28 29 30 31 32 34 35 37 40 46 49 50 54 56 57 59 60 61 62 64 65 66 68 70 74 75 77 78 79 81 84 85 86 87 90 93 96 97 98 100 101 102 103 107 111 114 115 118 119 121 128 129 130 131 132 135 143 146 147 148 **S** UPMC, Pittsburgh, PA
Primary Contact: Mark Sevco, President
COO: Amy Bush, Vice President Operations
CFO: Christopher Stockhausen, Chief Financial Officer
CMO: R. Curtis Waligura, D.O., Vice President Medical Affairs, Chief Medical Officer
CIO: Terri Keeling, Vice President Information Systems
CHR: Kelli Reale, Vice President Human Resources
CNO: Leeanna McKibben, R.N., Vice President Patient Services and Chief Nursing Officer
Web address: www.mckeesport.upmc.com
**Control:** Other not–for–profit (including NFP Corporation) **Service:** General Medical and Surgical

**Staffed Beds:** 208 **Admissions:** 8348 **Census:** 140 **Outpatient Visits:** 143219 **Births:** 0 **Total Expense ($000):** 145370 **Payroll Expense ($000):** 46922 **Personnel:** 754

---

**Hospital, Medicare Provider Number, Address, Telephone, Approval, Facility, and Physician Codes, Health Care System**

★ American Hospital Association (AHA) membership
☐ The Joint Commission accreditation
○ Healthcare Facilities Accreditation Program
◇ DNV Healthcare Inc. accreditation
⇑ Center for Improvement in Healthcare Quality Accreditation
△ Commission on Accreditation of Rehabilitation Facilities (CARF) accreditation

**PA**

### MEADOWBROOK—Montgomery County

◇ **HOLY REDEEMER HOSPITAL (390097)**, 1648 Huntingdon Pike, Zip 19046–8001; tel. 215/947–3000, (Total facility includes 21 beds in nursing home–type unit) **A**2 3 5 9 10 21 **F**3 10 13 15 17 18 20 22 29 30 31 34 35 36 39 40 41 44 45 46 49 50 53 54 55 56 57 58 59 61 62 63 64 69 70 72 74 75 76 77 78 79 81 82 84 85 86 87 92 93 97 98 100 103 104 107 108 109 110 114 115 116 117 118 119 120 121 123 128 129 130 131 132 134 135 141 143 146 147 148
Primary Contact: Michael B. Laign, President and Chief Executive Officer
CFO: Russell R. Wagner, Executive Vice President and Chief Financial Officer
CMO: Henry D. Unger, M.D., Senior Vice President and Chief Medical Officer
CIO: Donald F. Friel, Executive Vice President
CHR: Joseph J. Cassidy, Vice President and Chief Human Resources Officer
CNO: Anne Catino, R.N., Vice President and Chief Nursing Officer
Web address: www.holyredeemer.com
**Control:** Other not–for–profit (including NFP Corporation) **Service:** General Medical and Surgical

**Staffed Beds:** 230 **Admissions:** 11159 **Census:** 152 **Outpatient Visits:** 299650 **Births:** 2745 **Total Expense ($000):** 177349 **Payroll Expense ($000):** 71825 **Personnel:** 1326

### MEADVILLE—Crawford County

★ ◇ **MEADVILLE MEDICAL CENTER (390113)**, 751 Liberty Street, Zip 16335–2559; tel. 814/333–5000, (Total facility includes 32 beds in nursing home–type unit) **A**2 9 10 12 13 21 **F**3 4 5 11 13 15 18 20 22 28 29 30 31 35 36 38 43 44 45 46 49 53 57 59 63 64 70 75 76 77 78 79 81 82 85 86 87 89 90 91 93 98 99 103 107 110 111 114 115 118 119 120 128 129 130 131 132 146 147 148 **P**6 7
Primary Contact: Philip Pandolph, Chief Executive Officer
CMO: Denise Johnson, M.D., Medical Director
CIO: Mark Mahoney, Manager Information Systems
CHR: Greg Maras, Vice President Human Resources
Web address: www.mmchs.org
**Control:** Other not–for–profit (including NFP Corporation) **Service:** General Medical and Surgical

**Staffed Beds:** 210 **Admissions:** 6817 **Census:** 104 **Outpatient Visits:** 220244 **Births:** 515 **Total Expense ($000):** 151014 **Payroll Expense ($000):** 59410 **Personnel:** 1096

### MECHANICSBURG—Cumberland County

**HEALTHSOUTH REGIONAL SPECIALTY HOSPITAL** See LifeCare Hospitals of Mechanicsburg

⊞ **HEALTHSOUTH REHABILITATION HOSPITAL OF MECHANICSBURG (393031)**, 175 Lancaster Boulevard, Zip 17055–3562; tel. 717/691–3700 **A**1 9 10 **F**28 29 34 54 57 59 64 68 75 77 79 82 90 91 92 93 94 95 96 130 132 146 148 **S** HEALTHSOUTH Corporation, Birmingham, AL
Primary Contact: Mark Freeburn, Chief Executive Officer
CMO: Michael Lupinacci, M.D., Medical Director
CHR: David Staskin, Director Human Resources
Web address: www.healthsouthpa.com
**Control:** Corporation, Investor–owned, for–profit **Service:** Rehabilitation

**Staffed Beds:** 75 **Admissions:** 1570 **Census:** 51 **Births:** 0

⊞ **LIFECARE HOSPITALS OF MECHANICSBURG (392038)**, 4950 Wilson Lane, Zip 17055–4442; tel. 717/697–7706, (Nonreporting) **A**1 9 10 **S** LifeCare Management Services, Plano, TX
Primary Contact: Mary Ellen Kable, Chief Executive Officer
CFO: Trisha Niemuth, Director of Finance
CMO: Michael Gluck, M.D., Medical Director
CHR: Jennifer Rashford, Manager Human Resources
CNO: Alicia Kuntz, Nurse Manager
Web address: www.lifecare–hospitals.com/hospital.php?id=20
**Control:** Corporation, Investor–owned, for–profit **Service:** Long–Term Acute Care hospital

**Staffed Beds:** 68

### MEDIA—Delaware County

⊞ **RIDDLE HOSPITAL (390222)**, 1068 West Baltimore Pike, Zip 19063–5177; tel. 484/227–9400, (Total facility includes 23 beds in nursing home–type unit) **A**1 2 3 9 10 **F**3 7 11 13 15 18 20 22 28 29 31 34 35 36 38 40 41 44 45 49 50 53 54 55 56 57 59 64 65 70 72 74 75 76 78 79 80 81 82 84 85 86 87 92 100 102 103 107 108 110 111 114 115 118 119 120 124 128 129 130 131 132 135 141 146 148 **S** Main Line Health
Primary Contact: Gary L. Perecko, President
COO: Jeshahnton Essex, Vice President of Administration
CFO: Ed McKillip, Director of Finance
CMO: Joseph D. Hope, D.O., President Medical Staff
CHR: Mary Louise Ciciretti, Director Human Resources
CNO: Ann Marie T. Brooks, R.N., Vice President, Nursing
Web address: www.riddlehospital.org
**Control:** Other not–for–profit (including NFP Corporation) **Service:** General Medical and Surgical

**Staffed Beds:** 204 **Admissions:** 10600 **Census:** 125 **Outpatient Visits:** 139233 **Births:** 965 **Total Expense ($000):** 165847 **Payroll Expense ($000):** 63428 **Personnel:** 837

**RIDDLE MEMORIAL HOSPITAL** See Riddle Hospital

### MEYERSDALE—Somerset County

★ **CONEMAUGH MEYERSDALE MEDICAL CENTER (391302)**, 200 Hospital Drive, Zip 15552–1249; tel. 814/634–5911 **A**9 10 18 **F**15 29 34 40 57 81 85 93 107 110 119 126 129 133 146 148 **S** Duke LifePoint Healthcare, Brentwood, TN
Primary Contact: Heather Smith, President
CMO: Dwayne Platt, M.D., Chief Medical Officer
Web address: www.conemaugh.org
**Control:** Other not–for–profit (including NFP Corporation) **Service:** General Medical and Surgical

**Staffed Beds:** 20 **Admissions:** 325 **Census:** 5 **Births:** 0

### MONONGAHELA—Washington County

⊞ **MONONGAHELA VALLEY HOSPITAL (390147)**, 1163 Country Club Road, Route 88, Zip 15063–1095; tel. 724/258–1000 **A**1 2 9 10 **F**3 8 9 11 12 15 17 18 20 22 28 29 30 31 32 34 35 40 45 48 49 50 51 54 56 57 59 61 64 68 70 74 75 77 78 79 80 81 82 85 86 87 89 90 92 93 96 100 101 102 103 107 108 110 115 118 119 120 121 123 124 129 130 131 132 134 135 144 146 147 148 **P**8
Primary Contact: Louis J. Panza, Jr., President and Chief Executive Officer
COO: Patrick J. Alberts, Senior Vice President and Chief Operating Officer
CFO: Daniel F. Simmons, Senior Vice President and Treasurer
CMO: Walter R. Cox, M.D., President Medical Staff
CIO: Thomas Lamb, Director Information Systems
CHR: Louis Goodman, Senior Vice President Human Resources
CNO: Mary Lou Murt, R.N., Senior Vice President Nursing
Web address: www.monvalleyhospital.com
**Control:** Other not–for–profit (including NFP Corporation) **Service:** General Medical and Surgical

**Staffed Beds:** 210 **Admissions:** 7762 **Census:** 112 **Outpatient Visits:** 283886 **Births:** 0 **Total Expense ($000):** 126837 **Payroll Expense ($000):** 53187 **Personnel:** 1053

### MONROEVILLE—Allegheny County

⊞ **FORBES REGIONAL HOSPITAL (390267)**, 2570 Haymaker Road, Zip 15146–3513; tel. 412/858–2000 **A**1 2 3 5 9 10 **F**3 7 8 11 13 15 17 18 19 20 22 24 26 29 30 31 34 35 36 37 40 43 44 46 49 50 54 55 57 59 60 63 64 65 68 69 70 73 74 75 76 77 78 79 80 81 82 84 85 86 87 89 90 91 96 98 100 101 102 103 107 108 110 111 114 115 119 120 121 123 126 130 132 146 147 148 **P**6 **S** Allegheny Health Network, Pittsburgh, PA
Primary Contact: Duke Rupert, President and Chief Executive Officer
CFO: Tom Hipkiss, Vice President Finance
CMO: Mark Rubino, M.D., Chief Medical Officer
CIO: Sharon Lewis, Director Information Systems
CHR: Georgia Redding, Director Human Resources
CNO: Amber Egyud, Vice President Chief Nursing Officer
Web address: www.ahn.org
**Control:** Other not–for–profit (including NFP Corporation) **Service:** General Medical and Surgical

**Staffed Beds:** 349 **Admissions:** 12755 **Census:** 193 **Outpatient Visits:** 123734 **Births:** 823 **Total Expense ($000):** 193020 **Payroll Expense ($000):** 64841 **Personnel:** 1164

**HEALTHSOUTH HOSPITAL OF PITTSBURGH** See LifeCare Hospitals of Pittsburgh – Monroeville

⊞ **LIFECARE HOSPITALS OF PITTSBURGH – MONROEVILLE (392041)**, 2380 McGinley Road, Zip 15146–4400; tel. 412/856–2400 **A**1 9 10 **F**1 29 93 **P**5 **S** LifeCare Management Services, Plano, TX
Primary Contact: Kim Sperring, Administrator
CMO: Robert Crossey, D.O., Chief Medical Officer
CHR: Chelsea Webber, Director Human Resources
Web address: www.lifecare–hospitals.com/hospital.php?id=8
**Control:** Corporation, Investor–owned, for–profit **Service:** Long–Term Acute Care hospital

**Staffed Beds:** 87 **Admissions:** 509 **Census:** 37 **Births:** 0

**UPMC EAST (390328)**, 2775 Mosside Boulevard, Zip 15146–2760; tel. 412/357–3000 **A**10 **F**3 18 20 22 26 28 29 30 31 34 35 40 45 46 49 50 57 59 60 62 63 64 68 70 74 77 78 79 81 84 85 87 90 92 100 107 108 111 115 119 120 121 122 123 130 132 135 146 148 **S** UPMC, Pittsburgh, PA
Primary Contact: Mark Sevco, President
CNO: Tamra Minton, R.N., Vice President Patient Care Services and Chief Nursing Officer
Web address: www.upmc.com/locations/hospitals/east/Pages/default.aspx
**Control:** Other not–for–profit (including NFP Corporation) **Service:** General Medical and Surgical

**Staffed Beds:** 155 **Admissions:** 6745 **Census:** 84 **Outpatient Visits:** 73740 **Births:** 0 **Total Expense ($000):** 114189 **Payroll Expense ($000):** 35268 **Personnel:** 651

**WESTERN PENNSYLVANIA HOSPITAL – FORBES REGIONAL CAMPUS** See Forbes Regional Hospital

## MONTROSE—Susquehanna County

**ENDLESS MOUNTAIN HEALTH SYSTEMS (391306)**, 25 Grow Avenue,
Zip 18801–1106; tel. 570/278–3801 **A**9 10 18 **F**3 15 34 40 44 45 50 53 57
59 64 65 77 79 81 85 93 107 110 111 114 119 130 132 133 135 146 **P**4
Primary Contact: Rexford Catlin, Chief Executive Officer
CIO: Gary Passmore, Chief Information Officer
CHR: Paula Anderson, Administrative Director Human Resources
Web address: www.endlesscare.org
**Control:** Other not–for–profit (including NFP Corporation) **Service:** General
Medical and Surgical

**Staffed Beds:** 21 **Admissions:** 916 **Census:** 8 **Births:** 0

## MOUNT GRETNA—Lebanon County

✠ **PHILHAVEN (394020)**, 283 South Butler Road, Zip 17064–6085, Mailing
Address: P.O. Box 550, Zip 17064–0550; tel. 717/273–8871 **A**1 9 10 **F**30 98
99 100 101 102 103 104 105 106 130 146 **P**6
Primary Contact: Phil Hess, Chief Executive Officer
COO: Phil Hess, Chief Executive Officer
CFO: Matt Rogers, Chief Financial Officer
CMO: Francis D. Sparrow, M.D., Medical Director
CIO: Lori Nolt, Director Information Technology
CHR: Denis Orthaus, Director Human Resources
CNO: Heidi McMullan, R.N., Chief Nursing Officer
Web address: www.philhaven.org
**Control:** Church–operated, Nongovernment, not–for profit **Service:** Psychiatric

**Staffed Beds:** 103 **Admissions:** 2637 **Census:** 91 **Outpatient Visits:** 130908
**Births:** 0 **Total Expense ($000):** 58847 **Payroll Expense ($000):** 38694
**Personnel:** 902

## MOUNT PLEASANT—Westmoreland County

☐ **EXCELA FRICK HOSPITAL (390217)**, 508 South Church Street,
Zip 15666–1790; tel. 724/547–1500 **A**1 3 9 10 **F**3 8 12 15 29 30 32 34 35
40 45 49 57 59 64 65 68 70 74 75 77 78 79 81 85 86 87 92 93 96 102
107 108 110 111 114 118 119 129 130 132 135 143 146 148 **S** Excela
Health, Greensburg, PA
Primary Contact: Ronald H. Ott, President
COO: Michael D. Busch, Executive Vice President and Chief Operating Officer
CFO: Jeffrey T. Curry, Executive Vice President and Chief Financial Officer
CMO: Jerome Granato, M.D., Senior Vice President and Chief Medical Officer
CIO: David Gawaluck, Vice President and Chief Information Officer
CHR: John Caverno, Chief Human Resources Officer
CNO: Helen K. Burns, Ph.D., Senior Vice President and Chief Nursing Officer
Web address: www.excelahealth.org/PatientsandVisitors/HospitalsFacilities/
Hospitals/Frick.aspx
**Control:** Other not–for–profit (including NFP Corporation) **Service:** General
Medical and Surgical

**Staffed Beds:** 33 **Admissions:** 2964 **Census:** 33 **Outpatient Visits:** 104055
**Births:** 0 **Total Expense ($000):** 41013 **Payroll Expense ($000):** 16076
**Personnel:** 280

## MUNCY—Lycoming County

★ **MUNCY VALLEY HOSPITAL (391301)**, 215 East Water Street,
Zip 17756–8700; tel. 570/546–8282, (Total facility includes 136 beds in nursing
home–type unit) **A**3 9 10 18 **F**6 11 34 40 44 50 56 57 59 64 68 81 86 87 93
107 108 119 128 130 133 144 146 **P**7 **S** Susquehanna Health System,
Williamsport, PA
Primary Contact: Ronald J. Reynolds, President
CFO: Eric D. Pohjala, Executive Vice President and Chief Financial Officer
CIO: Timothy E. Schoener, Chief Information Officer
CHR: Christine A. Ballard, Vice President Human Resources
CNO: C. Cynthia Whipple, Administrative Director and Director of Nursing
Web address: www.susquehannahealth.org
**Control:** Other not–for–profit (including NFP Corporation) **Service:** General
Medical and Surgical

**Staffed Beds:** 156 **Admissions:** 809 **Census:** 139 **Outpatient Visits:** 28113
**Births:** 0 **Total Expense ($000):** 42581 **Payroll Expense ($000):** 13044
**Personnel:** 261

## NATRONA HEIGHTS—Allegheny County

✠ **ALLEGHENY VALLEY HOSPITAL (390032)**, 1301 Carlisle Street,
Zip 15065–1152; tel. 724/224–5100 **A**1 2 3 6 9 10 **F**3 11 15 17 18 24 29 30
31 34 35 38 39 40 44 45 47 49 50 51 54 56 57 58 59 64 65 68 70 74 75
77 78 79 80 81 84 85 86 87 92 93 96 98 100 101 102 103 107 108 111
114 117 118 119 120 121 123 129 130 132 133 135 143 144 146 147 148
**S** Allegheny Health Network, Pittsburgh, PA
Primary Contact: William Englert, Chief Executive Officer
CFO: James A. Kanuch, Vice President Finance
CMO: Thomas McClure, M.D., Vice President Medical Affairs and Chief Medical
Officer
CIO: Linda Fergus, Manager Information Technology
CHR: Cindy Moser, Director Human Resources
Web address: www.wpahs.org
**Control:** Other not–for–profit (including NFP Corporation) **Service:** General
Medical and Surgical

**Staffed Beds:** 228 **Admissions:** 5818 **Census:** 85 **Outpatient Visits:** 201355
**Births:** 0 **Total Expense ($000):** 108016 **Payroll Expense ($000):** 37458

## NEW CASTLE—Lawrence County

☐ **JAMESON HOSPITAL (390016)**, 1211 Wilmington Avenue, Zip 16105–2516;
tel. 724/658–9001, (Total facility includes 20 beds in nursing home–type unit) **A**1
6 9 10 19 **F**3 8 13 15 18 20 22 28 29 30 32 34 35 40 41 45 46 49 57 59
63 64 65 70 74 75 76 77 79 81 82 85 86 90 92 93 96 98 100 101 102 103
105 107 108 110 111 114 115 119 128 129 130 146 147
Primary Contact: Douglas Danko, President and Chief Executive Officer
CFO: James Aubel, Chief Financial Officer
CMO: Robert McGann, M.D., President Medical Staff
CIO: Frank Divito, Manager Information Systems
CHR: Neil A. Chessin, Vice President
CNO: Barbara Bernardi, R.N., Nurse Executive
Web address: www.jamesonhealth.org
**Control:** Other not–for–profit (including NFP Corporation) **Service:** General
Medical and Surgical

**Staffed Beds:** 238 **Admissions:** 8209 **Census:** 113 **Outpatient Visits:**
311914 **Births:** 421 **Total Expense ($000):** 110149 **Payroll Expense
($000):** 46431 **Personnel:** 1001

## NORRISTOWN—Montgomery County

✠ **MERCY SUBURBAN HOSPITAL (390116)**, 2701 DeKalb Pike,
Zip 19401–1820; tel. 610/278–2000 **A**1 2 9 10 12 13 **F**3 12 15 18 28 29 30
31 34 40 45 46 50 54 56 57 59 64 70 74 75 77 78 79 81 82 85 87 93 96
98 103 107 108 110 111 114 115 118 119 120 121 126 129 130 132 135
146 147 **S** Trinity Health, Livonia, MI
Primary Contact: Kathryn Conallen, Interim Chief Executive Officer
COO: Christina Fitz–Patrick, R.N., Executive Director
CFO: David Wajda, Chief Financial Officer
CMO: Michael Magro, M.D., Chief Medical Officer
CIO: Michael Yulich, Director Information Services
CHR: Gretchen Pendleton, Chief Human Resources Officer
CNO: Mary Ellen Rauner, R.N., Chief Nursing Officer
Web address: www.mercyhealth.org
**Control:** Church–operated, Nongovernment, not–for profit **Service:** General
Medical and Surgical

**Staffed Beds:** 126 **Admissions:** 4671 **Census:** 60 **Outpatient Visits:** 66576
**Births:** 0 **Total Expense ($000):** 103682 **Payroll Expense ($000):** 37786
**Personnel:** 643

☐ **MONTGOMERY COUNTY EMERGENCY SERVICE (394033)**, 50 Beech Drive,
Zip 19403–5421; tel. 610/279–6100 **A**1 9 10 **F**4 5 7 29 35 38 50 64 98 99
100 101 102 103 104 130 **P**6
Primary Contact: Rocio Nell, M.D., Chief Executive Officer
COO: William Myers, Chief Operating Officer
CFO: William Myers, Chief Operating Officer
CHR: Byanka Meacham, Director Human Resources
CNO: Naomi Finkel, Nurse Executive
Web address: www.mces.org
**Control:** Other not–for–profit (including NFP Corporation) **Service:** Psychiatric

**Staffed Beds:** 81 **Admissions:** 2131 **Census:** 63 **Outpatient Visits:** 2694
**Births:** 0 **Total Expense ($000):** 18264 **Payroll Expense ($000):** 11069
**Personnel:** 223

**Hospital, Medicare Provider Number, Address, Telephone, Approval, Facility, and Physician Codes, Health Care System**

★ American Hospital Association (AHA) membership ○ Healthcare Facilities Accreditation Program ⇧ Center for Improvement in Healthcare Quality Accreditation
☐ The Joint Commission accreditation ◇ DNV Healthcare Inc. accreditation △ Commission on Accreditation of Rehabilitation Facilities (CARF) accreditation

PA

**PA**

**NORRISTOWN STATE HOSPITAL (394001)**, 1001 Sterigere Street,
Zip 19401–5300; tel. 610/270–1000 **A**3 10 **F**30 35 38 39 53 59 65 98 101
103 146 **P**6
Primary Contact: Edna I. McCutcheon, Chief Executive Officer
COO: Gary Raisner, Chief Operating Officer
CMO: Mia Marcovici, M.D., Chief Medical Officer
CHR: Richard Szczurowski, Director Human Resources
CNO: Taryn Mason–Jones, Chief Nurse Executive
**Control:** State–Government, nonfederal **Service:** Psychiatric

**Staffed Beds: 266 Admissions: 96 Census: 281 Outpatient Visits: 103
Births: 0 Total Expense ($000): 68473 Payroll Expense ($000): 36730
Personnel: 563**

☐ **VALLEY FORGE MEDICAL CENTER AND HOSPITAL (390272)**, 1033 West
Germantown Pike, Zip 19403–3905; tel. 610/539–8500 **A**1 10 **F**3 4 29 61 68
75 82 100 130 132 148 **P**6
Primary Contact: Marian W. Colcher, President and Chief Executive Officer
CFO: Gregg Y. Slocum, Chief Financial Officer
CMO: Robert E. Colcher, M.D., Medical Director
CHR: Frederick D. Jackes, Assistant Administrator and Director Human Resources
Web address: www.vfmc.net
**Control:** Corporation, Investor–owned, for–profit **Service:** Alcoholism and other
chemical dependency

**Staffed Beds: 50 Admissions: 1324 Census: 28 Outpatient Visits: 0 Births:
0**

### OAKDALE—Allegheny County

✠ **KINDRED HOSPITAL–PITTSBURGH (392028)**, 7777 Steubenville Pike,
Zip 15071–3409; tel. 412/494–5500, (Nonreporting) **A**1 9 10 **S** Kindred
Healthcare, Louisville, KY
Primary Contact: Janie Rosenberger–Slampack, Market Chief Executive Officer
CFO: Kevin Varley, Chief Financial Officer
CMO: Ravi Alagar, M.D., Medical Director
CIO: Kurt Segeleon, Director Health Information Management
CHR: Nancy Smocynski, Director Payroll, Personnel and Human Resources
Web address: www.kindredhospitalpittsburgh.com/
**Control:** Corporation, Investor–owned, for–profit **Service:** Long–Term Acute Care
hospital

**Staffed Beds: 63**

### OREFIELD—Lehigh County

**KIDSPEACE CHILDREN'S HOSPITAL**, 5300 Kids Peace Drive,
Zip 18069–2044; tel. 610/799–8800 **A**9 **F**29 39 57 59 98 99 100 101 105
106 **P**7
Primary Contact: William R. Isemann, President and Chief Executive Officer
CMO: Andrew Clark, M.D., Medical Director
CIO: Eileen Tkacik, Vice President Information Technology and Patient Accounts
CHR: Elizabeth Perrong, Vice President Human Resources
CNO: Mary Ann Moore, Director of Nursing
Web address: www.kidspeace.org
**Control:** Other not–for–profit (including NFP Corporation) **Service:** Children's
hospital psychiatric

**Staffed Beds: 96 Admissions: 2071 Census: 68 Outpatient Visits: 0 Births:
0**

### PALMERTON—Carbon County

✠ **PALMERTON HOSPITAL (390019)**, 135 Lafayette Avenue, Zip 18071–1596;
tel. 610/826–3141 **A**1 9 10 **F**2 3 11 12 15 28 29 34 35 40 44 46 47 49 50
56 57 59 64 65 68 70 74 75 77 79 81 85 86 87 92 93 97 98 102 103 107
108 110 119 129 130 132 135 146 **S** Blue Mountain Health System,
Lehighton, PA
Primary Contact: Andrew E. Harris, Chief Executive Officer
CFO: Andrea Andrae, Chief Financial Officer
CMO: Dennis Kondash, D.O., Vice President Medical Affairs
CIO: Steve Kinkaid, Director Information Systems
CHR: Terrance J. Purcell, Vice President Ambulatory Care and Support Services
Web address: www.ghmh.org/content/palmertoncampus.htm
**Control:** Other not–for–profit (including NFP Corporation) **Service:** General
Medical and Surgical

**Staffed Beds: 60 Admissions: 1805 Census: 30 Outpatient Visits: 42555
Births: 0 Total Expense ($000): 29037 Payroll Expense ($000): 12192
Personnel: 286**

### PAOLI—Chester County

✠ **PAOLI HOSPITAL (390153)**, 255 West Lancaster Avenue, Zip 19301–1763;
tel. 484/565–1000 **A**1 2 3 9 10 **F**3 5 11 13 15 18 20 22 24 26 28 29 30 31
32 34 35 36 38 39 40 41 43 44 45 46 47 48 49 50 54 55 56 57 59 64 65
70 72 74 75 76 78 79 80 81 82 84 85 86 87 99 100 101 102 103 104 105
107 108 110 111 114 115 118 119 120 121 123 126 129 130 131 132 134
135 141 144 146 147 148 **P**5 **S** Main Line Health
Primary Contact: James Paradis, President
CFO: John Doyle, Vice President Finance
CMO: Andrew J. Norton, M.D., Chief Medical Officer
CIO: Karen A. Thomas, Vice President and Chief Information Officer
CHR: Deborah Fedora, Director Human Resources
CNO: Jan Nash, Ph.D., Vice President Patient Services and Chief Nursing Officer
Web address: www.mainlinehealth.org
**Control:** Other not–for–profit (including NFP Corporation) **Service:** General
Medical and Surgical

**Staffed Beds: 231 Admissions: 13690 Census: 140 Outpatient Visits:
286339 Births: 2460 Total Expense ($000): 239260 Payroll Expense
($000): 78849 Personnel: 1109**

### PHILADELPHIA—Philadelphia County

**ALBERT EINSTEIN MEDICAL CENTER** See Einstein Medical Center Philadelphia

✠ △ **ARIA HEALTH (390115)**, 10800 Knights Road, Zip 19114–4200;
tel. 215/612–4101, (Includes BUCKS COUNTY CAMPUS, 380 North Oxford Valley
Road, Langhorne, Zip 19047–8399; tel. 215/949–5000; FRANKFORD CAMPUS,
Frankford Avenue and Wakeling Street, Zip 19124; tel. 215/831–2000) **A**1 3 5 6
7 9 10 12 13 **F**3 5 11 12 14 15 17 18 20 22 24 26 28 29 30 31 32 34 35
36 39 40 43 44 45 46 48 49 53 54 57 59 61 62 64 65 66 68 69 70 74 75
77 78 79 80 81 82 85 86 87 100 101 102 103 104 107 108 110 114 115
116 117 118 119 120 121 123 124 126 127 129 130 131 132 135 143 144
145 146 147 148 **P**6
Primary Contact: Kathleen Kinslow, Ed.D., President and Chief Executive Officer
COO: Sandra Gomberg, Chief Operating Officer
CFO: Andrew DeVoe, Chief Financial Officer
CMO: Stanton Segal, M.D., Chief Medical Officer
CIO: Dan Walsh, Chief Information Officer
CHR: Dorinda Carolina, Chief Human Resources Officer
CNO: Michelle E. Conley, R.N., Chief Nursing Officer
Web address: www.ariahealth.org
**Control:** Other not–for–profit (including NFP Corporation) **Service:** General
Medical and Surgical

**Staffed Beds: 460 Admissions: 22494 Census: 285 Outpatient Visits:
298167 Births: 0 Total Expense ($000): 428924 Payroll Expense ($000):
173405 Personnel: 2648**

☐ **BELMONT CENTER FOR COMPREHENSIVE TREATMENT (394023)**, 4200
Monument Road, Zip 19131–1625; tel. 215/877–2000 **A**1 3 5 9 10 **F**5 29 34
35 58 86 87 98 99 103 104 105 130 146 **P**6 **S** Einstein Healthcare Network,
Philadelphia, PA
Primary Contact: Mark Schor, Chief Executive Officer
CFO: Guy Romaniello, Director Fiscal Services
CMO: Richard Jaffe, M.D., Medical Director
CHR: Jenna Pacini, Human Resources Specialist
CNO: Nona Fain, Ph.D., Director of Nursing
Web address: www.einstein.edu/locations/belmont–behavioral–health/
**Control:** Other not–for–profit (including NFP Corporation) **Service:** Psychiatric

**Staffed Beds: 147 Admissions: 3426 Census: 130 Outpatient Visits: 66010
Births: 0 Total Expense ($000): 39863 Payroll Expense ($000): 24893
Personnel: 403**

✠ **CHESTNUT HILL HOSPITAL (390026)**, 8835 Germantown Avenue,
Zip 19118–2718; tel. 215/248–8200, (Nonreporting) **A**1 2 3 5 9 10
**S** Community Health Systems, Inc., Franklin, TN
Primary Contact: John D. Cacciamani, M.D., Chief Executive Officer
CFO: Brian Balutanski, CPA, Chief Financial Officer
CMO: John Scanlon, DPM, Chief Medical Officer
CHR: Marilyn DiCicco, Director Human Resources
CNO: Teresa M. Kelly, MSN, Chief Nursing Officer
Web address: www.chhealthsystem.com
**Control:** Corporation, Investor–owned, for–profit **Service:** General Medical and
Surgical

**Staffed Beds: 212**

*Many Facility Codes have changed. Please refer to the AHA Guide Code Chart.* © 2015 AHA Guide

☐ **CHILDREN'S HOSPITAL OF PHILADELPHIA (393303)**, 3401 Civic Center Boulevard, Zip 19104–4319; tel. 215/590–1000 **A**1 3 5 8 9 10 **F**3 7 8 11 12 13 17 18 19 20 21 22 23 24 25 26 27 28 29 30 31 32 34 35 37 38 39 40 41 43 44 45 46 48 50 53 54 55 57 58 59 60 61 62 64 65 66 68 71 72 74 75 76 77 78 79 81 82 83 84 85 86 87 88 89 90 91 92 93 95 96 97 99 100 101 102 104 107 108 111 112 113 114 115 116 117 118 119 126 129 130 131 132 134 136 137 138 139 140 141 142 143 144 146 148 **P**6
Primary Contact: Madeline Bell, Chief Executive Officer
CFO: Thomas Todorow, Chief Financial Officer and Executive Vice President
CMO: Jan Boswinkel, M.D., Vice President Medical Operations and Chief Safety Officer
CHR: Robert Croner, Senior Vice President and Chief Human Resources Officer
CNO: Paula M. Agosto, R.N., Senior Vice President and Chief Nursing Officer
Web address: www.chop.edu
**Control:** Other not–for–profit (including NFP Corporation) **Service:** Children's general

**Staffed Beds:** 534 **Admissions:** 28156 **Census:** 436 **Outpatient Visits:** 1191174 **Births:** 407 **Total Expense ($000):** 1655506 **Payroll Expense ($000):** 755188 **Personnel:** 9995

☐ **EASTERN REGIONAL MEDICAL CENTER (390312)**, 1331 East Wyoming Avenue, Zip 19124–3808; tel. 800/615–3055 **A**1 2 10 **F**3 15 29 30 31 33 34 35 36 45 46 47 48 49 50 55 56 57 58 59 64 65 68 70 75 78 79 80 81 82 84 85 86 87 91 93 96 97 100 101 104 107 108 110 111 116 117 118 119 120 121 123 124 126 129 130 132 135 136 143 146 148 **P**6 **S** Cancer Treatment Centers of America, Schaumburg, IL
Primary Contact: John McNeil, President and Chief Executive Officer
CFO: Steve Rusinko, Chief Financial Officer
CMO: Steven B. Standiford, M.D., Chief of Staff
CIO: Kristin Darby, Chief Information Officer
CHR: Ronald Gilg, Assistant Vice President Talent
CNO: Nancy Hesse, R.N., Senior Vice President Patient Care Services
Web address: www.cancercenter.com
**Control:** Corporation, Investor–owned, for–profit **Service:** Cancer

**Staffed Beds:** 74 **Admissions:** 1473 **Census:** 33 **Outpatient Visits:** 56576 **Births:** 0

☐ **EINSTEIN MEDICAL CENTER PHILADELPHIA (390142)**, 5501 Old York Road, Zip 19141–3098; tel. 215/456–7890, (Includes EINSTEIN MEDICAL CENTER ELKINS PARK, 60 Township Line Road, Elkins Park, Zip 19027–2220; tel. 215/663–6000; Ruth Lefton, Chief Operating Officer), (Total facility includes 63 beds in nursing home–type unit) **A**1 2 3 5 8 9 10 13 **F**3 5 8 11 12 13 15 17 18 20 22 24 26 29 30 31 32 34 35 37 39 40 41 43 45 46 47 48 49 50 55 56 57 59 60 61 64 65 66 68 70 72 73 74 75 76 78 79 81 82 84 85 86 87 90 92 93 97 98 100 103 107 108 110 111 114 115 119 120 121 123 124 126 128 129 130 131 132 135 138 139 142 145 146 147 148 **P**6 **S** Einstein Healthcare Network, Philadelphia, PA
Primary Contact: Barry R. Freedman, President and Chief Executive Officer
COO: A. Susan Bernini, Chief Operating Officer
CFO: David Ertel, Chief Financial Officer
CMO: Steven Sivak, M.D., Chair, Department of Medicine
CIO: Kenneth Levitan, Vice President and Chief Information Officer
CHR: Lynne R. Kornblatt, Chief Human Resources Officer
CNO: Richard Cuming, R.N., Vice President and Chief Nurse Executive
Web address: www.einstein.edu
**Control:** Other not–for–profit (including NFP Corporation) **Service:** General Medical and Surgical

**Staffed Beds:** 489 **Admissions:** 26732 **Census:** 497 **Outpatient Visits:** 514956 **Births:** 2921 **Total Expense ($000):** 674761 **Payroll Expense ($000):** 307817 **Personnel:** 5242

☐ **FAIRMOUNT BEHAVIORAL HEALTH SYSTEM (394027)**, 561 Fairthorne Avenue, Zip 19128–2499; tel. 215/487–4000 **A**1 9 10 **F**4 98 99 102 105 130 **P**6 **S** Universal Health Services, Inc., King of Prussia, PA
Primary Contact: Lisa McConlogue, PhD, Managing Director
CFO: Anthony Tortella, Chief Financial Officer
CMO: Silvia Gratz, D.O., Chief Medical Officer
CIO: Anthony Tortella, Chief Financial Officer
CHR: Theresa Mahoney, Director Human Resources
Web address: www.fairmountbhs.com
**Control:** Corporation, Investor–owned, for–profit **Service:** Psychiatric

**Staffed Beds:** 235 **Admissions:** 6256 **Census:** 223 **Outpatient Visits:** 8792 **Births:** 0 **Total Expense ($000):** 41730 **Payroll Expense ($000):** 25605

☒ **FOX CHASE CANCER CENTER–AMERICAN ONCOLOGIC HOSPITAL (390196)**, 333 Cottman Avenue, Zip 19111–2434; tel. 215/728–6900 **A**1 2 3 5 9 10 **F**3 8 11 15 29 30 31 34 35 36 45 46 47 49 50 55 57 58 59 60 64 68 70 71 75 77 78 79 81 82 84 85 86 87 93 100 104 107 108 109 110 111 114 115 116 117 118 119 120 121 122 123 124 126 130 132 135 136 144 145 146 147 148 **P**6 **S** Temple University Health System, Philadelphia, PA
Primary Contact: Richard Fisher, President and Chief Executive Officer
COO: Judith Lynn Bachman, Chief Operating Officer
CFO: Joseph Hediger, Chief Financial Officer
CMO: J. Robert Beck, M.D., Chief Medical Officer
CIO: Michael Sweeney, Chief Information Officer
Web address: www.fccc.edu
**Control:** Other not–for–profit (including NFP Corporation) **Service:** General Medical and Surgical

**Staffed Beds:** 100 **Admissions:** 4756 **Census:** 58 **Outpatient Visits:** 89240 **Births:** 0 **Total Expense ($000):** 223375 **Payroll Expense ($000):** 73885 **Personnel:** 1326

☐ **FRIENDS HOSPITAL (394008)**, 4641 Roosevelt Boulevard, Zip 19124–2343; tel. 215/831–4600, (Nonreporting) **A**1 3 5 9 10 **S** Universal Health Services, Inc., King of Prussia, PA
Primary Contact: R. John Repique, MS, R.N., Chief Executive Officer
COO: Diane Carugati, Chief Operating Officer
CFO: Michael Terwilliger, Chief Financial Officer
CMO: Marc Rothman, M.D., Medical Director
CIO: John Healy, Manager Information Technology
CHR: Paul Cavanaugh, Director Human Resources
Web address: www.friendshospital.com
**Control:** Corporation, Investor–owned, for–profit **Service:** Psychiatric

**Staffed Beds:** 192

☒ **GOOD SHEPHERD PENN PARTNERS SPECIALTY HOSPITAL AT RITTENHOUSE (392050)**, 1800 Lombard Street, Zip 19146–1414; tel. 877/969–7342 **A**1 9 10 **F**1 3 28 29 30 34 35 44 50 57 58 60 64 68 75 77 84 85 86 87 90 91 93 94 95 96 100 130 131 132 148 **P**6
Primary Contact: Laura Porter, Interim Executive Director
CFO: Ron Petula, Vice President Finance
CMO: Michael Grippi, M.D., Chief Medical Officer
CHR: Jana Romano, Manager Human Resources
CNO: Lawanda Goehring, MSN, Chief Nursing Officer
Web address: www.phillyrehab.com
**Control:** Other not–for–profit (including NFP Corporation) **Service:** Long–Term Acute Care hospital

**Staffed Beds:** 38 **Admissions:** 334 **Census:** 27 **Outpatient Visits:** 121673 **Births:** 0 **Total Expense ($000):** 40056 **Payroll Expense ($000):** 18068

☒ **HAHNEMANN UNIVERSITY HOSPITAL (390290)**, Broad and Vine Streets, Zip 19102–1192; tel. 215/762–7000 **A**1 2 3 5 8 9 10 13 **F**3 8 12 13 14 15 17 18 20 22 24 26 28 29 31 34 35 40 43 45 46 48 49 50 51 56 57 58 59 64 65 70 72 74 75 76 78 79 80 81 82 85 87 91 92 97 98 100 102 103 105 107 108 110 111 114 115 118 119 120 121 123 124 126 129 130 131 132 136 138 139 142 147 148 **P**6 **S** TENET Healthcare Corporation, Dallas, TX
Primary Contact: Michael P. Halter, Chief Executive Officer
COO: James B. Burke, Chief Operating Officer
CFO: Richard Imbimbo, Chief Financial Officer
CMO: George Amrom, M.D., Vice President Medical Affairs
CIO: Tom Nataloni, Senior Director Information Technology
CHR: Steven Simmons, Chief Human Resources Officer
CNO: Rosemary Dunn, R.N., Chief Nursing Officer
Web address: www.hahnemannhospital.com
**Control:** Corporation, Investor–owned, for–profit **Service:** General Medical and Surgical

**Staffed Beds:** 496 **Admissions:** 18928 **Census:** 268 **Outpatient Visits:** 110576 **Births:** 2046 **Personnel:** 2540

---

**Hospital, Medicare Provider Number, Address, Telephone, Approval, Facility, and Physician Codes, Health Care System**

★ American Hospital Association (AHA) membership   ◯ Healthcare Facilities Accreditation Program   ⇑ Center for Improvement in Healthcare Quality Accreditation
☐ The Joint Commission accreditation   ◇ DNV Healthcare Inc. accreditation   △ Commission on Accreditation of Rehabilitation Facilities (CARF) accreditation

**PA**

✠ △ **HOSPITAL OF THE UNIVERSITY OF PENNSYLVANIA (390111)**, 3400 Spruce Street, Zip 19104–4206; tel. 215/662–4000 **A**1 2 3 5 7 8 9 10 **F**3 6 7 9 11 12 13 14 15 17 18 19 20 21 22 23 24 25 26 27 29 30 31 34 35 37 38 39 40 43 44 45 46 47 48 49 50 51 52 54 55 56 57 58 59 60 61 62 63 64 65 66 68 70 71 72 73 74 75 76 77 78 79 80 81 82 84 85 86 87 90 91 92 93 94 95 96 97 99 100 101 102 104 107 108 110 111 115 117 118 119 121 122 123 126 129 130 131 132 134 135 136 137 138 139 140 141 142 145 146 147 148 **P**6 **S** University of Pennsylvania Health System, Philadelphia, PA
Primary Contact: Garry L. Scheib, Executive Director
COO: Carolyn Jackson, Chief Operating Officer
CFO: Keith Kasper, Chief Financial Officer
CMO: Patrick J. Brennan, M.D., Senior Vice President and Chief Medical Officer
CIO: Michael Restuccia, Chief Information Officer
CHR: Denise Mariotti, Chief Human Resource Officer
CNO: Regina Cunningham, Ph.D., Chief Nurse Executive
Web address: www.pennhealth.com
**Control:** Other not–for–profit (including NFP Corporation) **Service:** General Medical and Surgical

**Staffed Beds:** 789 **Admissions:** 36737 **Census:** 695 **Outpatient Visits:** 1404608 **Births:** 4219 **Total Expense ($000):** 2088467 **Payroll Expense ($000):** 833959 **Personnel:** 12893

✠ **JEANES HOSPITAL (390080)**, 7600 Central Avenue, Zip 19111–2499; tel. 215/728–2000 **A**1 3 5 9 10 **F**3 11 12 15 18 20 22 24 26 28 29 30 31 34 35 40 44 45 56 57 59 60 62 65 68 70 74 75 77 78 79 81 82 85 90 91 92 93 107 108 110 111 114 115 116 117 119 120 124 129 130 132 145 146 147 148 **P**6 **S** Temple University Health System, Philadelphia, PA
Primary Contact: Marc P. Hurowitz, D.O., President and Chief Executive Officer
COO: Judith Lynn Bachman, Chief Operating Officer
CIO: Arthur C. Papacostas, M.D., Vice President and Chief Information Officer
CHR: Elisabeth Donahue, Associate Director Human Resources
CNO: Denise Anne Lavery Frasca, MSN, Vice President Patient Care Services and Chief Nursing Officer
Web address: www.jeanes.com
**Control:** Other not–for–profit (including NFP Corporation) **Service:** General Medical and Surgical

**Staffed Beds:** 146 **Admissions:** 8766 **Census:** 92 **Births:** 0

☐ **KENSINGTON HOSPITAL (390025)**, 136 West Diamond Street, Zip 19122–1721; tel. 215/426–8100, (Nonreporting) **A**1 9 10
Primary Contact: Eileen Hause, Chief Executive Officer
CFO: Kenneth Biddle, Controller
CMO: Luis F. Vera, M.D., Medical Director
CHR: Maria Dimichele, Administrative Assistant
CNO: Aleyamma John, R.N., Director of Nursing
**Control:** State–Government, nonfederal **Service:** General Medical and Surgical

**Staffed Beds:** 33

✠ **KINDRED HOSPITAL SOUTH PHILADELPHIA (392046)**, 1930 South Broad Street, Zip 19145–2328; tel. 267/570–5200, (Nonreporting) **A**1 9 10 **S** Kindred Healthcare, Louisville, KY
Primary Contact: Deborah Karn, Chief Executive Officer
COO: Diane K. White, MSN, Chief Clinical Officer
CFO: Kevin Varley, Chief Financial Officer
CMO: James Dovnarsky, M.D., Director Pulmonary Medical
CHR: Amy Cain, District Director Human Resources
CNO: Diane K. White, MSN, Chief Clinical Officer
Web address: www.khsouthphilly.com
**Control:** Corporation, Investor–owned, for–profit **Service:** Long–Term Acute Care hospital

**Staffed Beds:** 58

✠ **KINDRED HOSPITAL–PHILADELPHIA (392027)**, 6129 Palmetto Street, Zip 19111–5729; tel. 215/722–8555, (Includes KINDRED HOSPITAL PHILADELPHIA – HAVERTOWN, 2000 Old West Chester Pike, Havertown, Zip 19083–2712; tel. 610/536–2100; James Haulihan, Chief Executive Officer) **A**1 9 10 **F**1 3 29 70 75 77 84 87 130 148 **S** Kindred Healthcare, Louisville, KY
Primary Contact: Sandra Larson, Interim Chief Executive Officer
COO: Sandra Collins, Chief Clinical Officer
CFO: Thomas A. McMullen, Chief Financial Officer
Web address: www.kindredphila.com/
**Control:** Corporation, Investor–owned, for–profit **Service:** Long–Term Acute Care hospital

**Staffed Beds:** 52 **Admissions:** 385 **Census:** 33 **Outpatient Visits:** 0 **Births:** 0 **Personnel:** 134

☐ **KIRKBRIDE CENTER (394007)**, 111 North 49th Street, Zip 19139–2718; tel. 215/471–2600, (Nonreporting) **A**1 10
Primary Contact: Scott Weisenberger, Administrator
Web address: www.kirkbridecenter.com
**Control:** Partnership, Investor–owned, for–profit **Service:** Psychiatric

**Staffed Beds:** 205

✠ △ **MAGEE REHABILITATION HOSPITAL (393038)**, 1513 Race Street, Zip 19102–1177; tel. 215/587–3000 **A**1 3 5 7 9 10 **F**2 29 30 34 35 50 60 64 68 74 75 77 79 82 86 90 91 92 93 94 95 96 130 132 146 148 **P**6
Primary Contact: Jack A. Carroll, Ph.D., President and Chief Executive Officer
CFO: Patricia A. Underwood, Chief Financial Officer
CMO: Guy Fried, M.D., Chief Medical Officer
CIO: Travis Gathright, Chief Information and Corporate Compliance Officer
CHR: Scott Agostini, Director
Web address: www.mageerehab.org
**Control:** Other not–for–profit (including NFP Corporation) **Service:** Rehabilitation

**Staffed Beds:** 96 **Admissions:** 1014 **Census:** 74 **Outpatient Visits:** 58095 **Births:** 0 **Total Expense ($000):** 59457 **Payroll Expense ($000):** 33010 **Personnel:** 513

**MERCY PHILADELPHIA HOSPITAL** See Mercy Fitzgerald Hospital, Darby

**METHODIST HOSPITAL** See Thomas Jefferson University Hospitals

✠ △ **NAZARETH HOSPITAL (390204)**, 2601 Holme Avenue, Zip 19152–2096; tel. 215/335–6000, (Total facility includes 28 beds in nursing home–type unit) **A**1 3 7 9 10 **F**3 12 15 18 20 22 29 30 31 34 35 39 40 45 46 49 50 53 56 57 58 59 64 65 70 74 75 77 78 79 80 81 82 84 85 87 90 93 97 100 107 108 110 111 114 115 117 118 119 120 121 128 130 131 132 135 146 147 148 **P**7 **S** Trinity Health, Livonia, MI
Primary Contact: Nancy Cherone, Executive Director and Administrator
CFO: David Wajda, Chief Financial Officer
CMO: Mathew Matthew, M.D., Chief Medical Officer
CIO: Terry O'Neil, Chief Information Technology
CHR: Kathleen M. Pries, Director Human Resources
CNO: Michael Beshel, R.N., Vice President Patient Care and Chief Nursing Officer
Web address: www.nazarethhospital.org
**Control:** Other not–for–profit (including NFP Corporation) **Service:** General Medical and Surgical

**Staffed Beds:** 231 **Admissions:** 9010 **Census:** 131 **Outpatient Visits:** 145727 **Births:** 0 **Total Expense ($000):** 146952 **Payroll Expense ($000):** 57812 **Personnel:** 988

○ **NORTH PHILADELPHIA HEALTH SYSTEM (390132)**, 1524 West Girard Avenue, Zip 19130–1613; tel. 215/787–9000, (Includes GIRARD MEDICAL CENTER, Girard Avenue at Eighth Street, Zip 19122; tel. 215/787–2000; George J. Walmsley, III, CPA, President and Chief Executive Officer; ST. JOSEPH'S HOSPITAL, Girard Avenue at Sixteenth Street, Zip 19130; tel. 215/787–9000; Catherine Kutzler, R.N., Vice President and Administrator), (Nonreporting) **A**3 9 10 11
Primary Contact: George J. Walmsley, III, CPA, President and Chief Executive Officer
CFO: Ronald Kaplan, Chief Financial Officer
CIO: Tony Iero, Director Management Information Systems
CHR: James Gloner, Senior Vice President
Web address: www.nphs.com
**Control:** Other not–for–profit (including NFP Corporation) **Service:** General Medical and Surgical

**Staffed Beds:** 315

✠ **PENN PRESBYTERIAN MEDICAL CENTER (390223)**, 51 North 39th Street, Zip 19104–2699; tel. 215/662–8000, (Total facility includes 26 beds in nursing home–type unit) **A**1 2 3 5 9 10 **F**3 4 5 7 11 12 15 17 18 20 22 24 26 29 30 31 32 34 35 36 37 39 40 44 45 46 49 50 51 52 54 56 57 58 59 60 61 62 63 64 65 66 68 70 74 75 77 78 79 81 82 84 85 86 87 92 94 96 97 98 100 101 104 107 108 110 111 114 115 118 119 126 128 130 131 132 134 135 141 142 143 146 147 148 **P**6 **S** University of Pennsylvania Health System, Philadelphia, PA
Primary Contact: Michele M. Volpe, Executive Director and Chief Executive Officer
COO: Robert J. Russell, Associate Executive Director Operations
CFO: Anthony Zumpano, Chief Financial Officer
CMO: Kevin Fosnocht, M.D., Chief Medical Officer and Associate Executive Director
CIO: Theresa Hiltunen, Entity Information Officer
CHR: Margorie Michele, Chief Human Resources Officer
CNO: James R. Ballinghoff, MSN, Chief Nursing Officer and Associate Executive Director
Web address: www.pennmedicine.org/pmc/
**Control:** Other not–for–profit (including NFP Corporation) **Service:** General Medical and Surgical

**Staffed Beds:** 331 **Admissions:** 14634 **Census:** 207 **Outpatient Visits:** 191582 **Births:** 0 **Total Expense ($000):** 381375 **Payroll Expense ($000):** 162713 **Personnel:** 1775

⊞ **PENNSYLVANIA HOSPITAL (390226)**, 800 Spruce Street, Zip 19107–6192; tel. 215/829–3000 **A**1 2 3 5 9 10 13 **F**3 7 8 11 12 15 17 18 20 22 24 26 29 30 31 34 35 36 37 38 39 40 44 45 46 49 50 54 55 56 57 58 59 60 61 63 64 65 68 70 72 74 75 76 77 78 79 80 81 82 84 85 86 87 92 97 98 99 100 101 102 103 104 107 108 110 111 114 115 116 117 118 119 120 121 123 124 126 129 130 131 132 134 135 141 142 145 146 147 148 **P**6 **S** University of Pennsylvania Health System, Philadelphia, PA
Primary Contact: Theresa M. Larivee, Executive Director
COO: Deborah L. Staples, Chief Operating Officer
CFO: Frank Anastasi, Chief Financial Officer
CMO: Daniel Feinberg, M.D., Chief Medical Officer
CIO: Linda Sinisi, Entity Information Officer
CHR: Sarah Johnson, Chief Human Resources Officer
CNO: Mary Margaret Del Guidice, R.N., Chief Nursing Officer
Web address: www.pahosp.com
**Control:** Other not–for–profit (including NFP Corporation) **Service:** General Medical and Surgical

**Staffed Beds:** 415 **Admissions:** 19852 **Census:** 289 **Outpatient Visits:** 258422 **Births:** 4708 **Total Expense ($000):** 536670 **Payroll Expense ($000):** 172217 **Personnel:** 2307

⊞ △ **PHILADELPHIA VETERANS AFFAIRS MEDICAL CENTER**, 3900 Woodland Avenue, Zip 19104–4594; tel. 215/823–5800, (Nonreporting) **A**1 2 3 5 7 8 **S** Department of Veterans Affairs, Washington, DC
Primary Contact: Daniel Hendee, Director
COO: Jeffrey Beiler, Associate Director
CFO: Graciela McDaniel, Chief Financial Officer
CMO: Dave Oslin, M.D., Chief of Staff
CIO: Adrienne Ficchi, Vice President Information Management
CHR: Gerald Morelli, Director Human Resources
Web address: www.philadelphia.va.gov/
**Control:** Veterans Affairs, Government, federal **Service:** General Medical and Surgical

**Staffed Beds:** 280

☐ **ROXBOROUGH MEMORIAL HOSPITAL (390304)**, 5800 Ridge Avenue, Zip 19128–1737; tel. 215/483–9900 **A**1 6 9 10 **F**3 15 18 24 29 31 34 40 44 49 50 56 57 59 65 68 70 74 77 78 79 81 82 84 85 90 93 96 98 103 104 107 108 110 111 116 119 129 130 143 146 148 **S** Prime Healthcare Services, Ontario, CA
Primary Contact: Peter J. Adamo, Chief Executive Officer
CFO: Thomas Reinboth, Chief Financial Officer
CHR: Michael Henrici, Associate Administrator
Web address: www.roxboroughmemorial.com
**Control:** Corporation, Investor–owned, for–profit **Service:** General Medical and Surgical

**Staffed Beds:** 140 **Admissions:** 4845 **Census:** 64 **Births:** 0

⊞ **SHRINERS HOSPITALS FOR CHILDREN–PHILADELPHIA (393309)**, 3551 North Broad Street, Zip 19140–4160; tel. 215/430–4000 **A**1 3 5 10 **F**29 35 57 58 64 65 68 74 75 77 79 81 82 85 88 89 91 92 93 94 95 96 119 130 132 133 143 146 **S** Shriners Hospitals for Children, Tampa, FL
Primary Contact: Ed Myers, Administrator
CFO: Mario Salvati, Director Fiscal Services
CMO: Scott Kozin, M.D., Chief of Staff
CHR: Megan Hauser, Director Human Resources
Web address: www.shrinershospitalsforchildren.org/Hospitals/Locations/Philadelphia.aspx
**Control:** Other not–for–profit (including NFP Corporation) **Service:** Children's orthopedic

**Staffed Beds:** 39 **Admissions:** 821 **Census:** 13 **Births:** 0

⊞ **ST. CHRISTOPHER'S HOSPITAL FOR CHILDREN (393307)**, 3601 A. Street, Zip 19134–1043; tel. 215/427–5000 **A**1 3 5 8 9 10 **F**3 7 16 17 19 21 23 25 27 29 30 31 32 34 35 39 40 41 42 43 44 48 49 50 54 55 58 64 61 64 68 71 72 73 74 75 77 78 79 80 81 82 83 84 87 88 89 93 97 99 100 101 102 107 111 119 129 130 131 132 134 136 138 143 144 146 **P**6 **S** TENET Healthcare Corporation, Dallas, TX
Primary Contact: J. Mark McLoone, FACHE, Chief Executive Officer
COO: Maria Scenna, Chief Operating Officer
CFO: George Rizzuto, CPA, Chief Financial Officer
CMO: Barbara Hoffman, M.D., Chief Medical Officer
CIO: Robert Taylor, Director Information Services
CHR: Stephen W. Krouse, Chief Human Resource Officer
CNO: Heidi Baur, R.N., Chief Nursing Officer
Web address: www.stchristophershospital.com
**Control:** Corporation, Investor–owned, for–profit **Service:** Children's general

**Staffed Beds:** 189 **Admissions:** 9131 **Census:** 112 **Outpatient Visits:** 148087 **Births:** 0 **Personnel:** 1990

⊞ **TEMPLE UNIVERSITY HOSPITAL (390027)**, 3401 North Broad Street, Zip 19140–5103; tel. 215/707–2000, (Includes TEMPLE UNIVERSITY HOSPITAL – EPISCOPAL DIVISION, 100 East Lehigh Avenue, Zip 19125–1098; tel. 215/427–7000; Kathleen Barron, Executive Director) **A**1 2 3 5 6 8 9 10 **F**3 8 11 12 13 14 15 16 17 18 20 22 24 26 28 29 30 31 34 35 37 38 40 41 43 44 45 46 47 48 49 50 53 54 55 56 57 58 59 60 61 64 68 70 72 73 74 75 77 78 79 80 81 82 83 84 85 86 87 90 92 93 94 96 97 98 99 100 101 102 103 104 107 108 109 110 111 112 114 115 118 119 120 121 123 124 126 129 130 131 132 135 136 137 138 139 140 141 142 146 147 148 **S** Temple University Health System, Philadelphia, PA
Primary Contact: John N. Kastanis, Chief Executive Officer
COO: Rosemary Nolan, R.N., Chief Operating Officer
CFO: Gerald P. Oetzel, Chief Financial Officer
CMO: Herbert Cushing, M.D., Chief Medical Officer
CIO: David Kamowski, Vice President and Chief Information Officer
CHR: John Lasky, Vice President and Chief Human Resources Officer
CNO: Elizabeth J. Craig, MSN, Chief Nursing Officer and Vice President Patient Services
Web address: www.tuh.templehealth.org/content/default.htm
**Control:** Other not–for–profit (including NFP Corporation) **Service:** General Medical and Surgical

**Staffed Beds:** 665 **Admissions:** 36576 **Census:** 517 **Outpatient Visits:** 333436 **Births:** 2981 **Total Expense ($000):** 837276 **Payroll Expense ($000):** 305459 **Personnel:** 4327

⊞ △ **THOMAS JEFFERSON UNIVERSITY HOSPITALS (390174)**, 111 South 11th Street, Zip 19107–5084; tel. 215/955–6000, (Includes METHODIST HOSPITAL, 2301 South Broad Street, Zip 19148; tel. 215/952–9000; Richard Webster, President) **A**1 2 3 5 7 8 9 10 **F**3 5 6 7 8 9 11 12 13 14 15 17 18 20 22 24 26 28 29 30 31 34 35 36 37 38 39 40 43 44 45 46 47 48 49 50 51 52 53 54 55 56 57 58 59 61 64 65 66 68 70 72 73 74 75 76 77 78 79 80 81 82 84 85 86 87 89 90 92 93 94 96 97 98 100 101 102 103 104 107 108 109 110 111 114 115 118 119 120 121 123 124 126 129 130 131 132 134 135 136 137 138 139 141 142 143 145 146 147 148 **P**2 6 8 **S** Jefferson Health, Radnor, PA
Primary Contact: Richard Webster, President
CFO: Neil Lubarsky, Senior Vice President, Finance and Chief Financial Officer
CMO: Anne Docimo, M.D., Executive Vice President and Chief Medical Officer
CIO: Praveen Chopra, Executive Vice President and Chief Information and Transformation Innovative Environment Officer
CHR: Stacy Ann Vahey, Vice President, Human Resources
CNO: Mary Ann McGinley, Senior Vice President, Patient Services and Chief Nursing Officer
Web address: www.jefferson.edu
**Control:** Other not–for–profit (including NFP Corporation) **Service:** General Medical and Surgical

**Staffed Beds:** 937 **Admissions:** 45131 **Census:** 664 **Outpatient Visits:** 471286 **Births:** 1907 **Total Expense ($000):** 1502006 **Payroll Expense ($000):** 481452 **Personnel:** 8076

**TRIUMPH HOSPITAL PHILADELPHIA** See Kindred Hospital South Philadelphia

**VETERANS AFFAIRS MEDICAL CENTER** See Philadelphia Veterans Affairs Medical Center

**PHOENIXVILLE—Chester County**

⊞ **PHOENIXVILLE HOSPITAL (390127)**, 140 Nutt Road, Zip 19460–3900, Mailing Address: P.O. Box 3001, Zip 19460–0916; tel. 610/983–1000 **A**1 2 9 10 **F**1 3 4 8 11 12 13 15 16 17 18 20 22 24 26 28 29 31 32 35 36 38 39 40 45 49 50 51 56 57 59 61 64 67 69 70 72 73 74 75 76 77 78 79 80 81 82 85 86 87 88 90 93 98 100 102 107 108 111 118 119 126 128 130 132 134 135 146 147 **S** Community Health Systems, Inc., Franklin, TN
Primary Contact: Stephen M. Tullman, Chief Executive Officer
CFO: David Paulosky, Chief Financial Officer
CMO: David Stepansky, M.D., Chief Medical Officer
CIO: Terry Murphy, Director Information Services
CHR: Denise Chiolo, Chief Human Resources Officer
CNO: Sarah Strzelecki, Ed.D., Chief Nursing Officer
Web address: www.phoenixvillehospital.com
**Control:** Corporation, Investor–owned, for–profit **Service:** General Medical and Surgical

**Staffed Beds:** 113 **Admissions:** 6741 **Census:** 83 **Outpatient Visits:** 105160 **Births:** 738 **Total Expense ($000):** 158864 **Payroll Expense ($000):** 48570 **Personnel:** 741

PA

---

**Hospital, Medicare Provider Number, Address, Telephone, Approval, Facility, and Physician Codes, Health Care System**

★ American Hospital Association (AHA) membership
☐ The Joint Commission accreditation
◯ Healthcare Facilities Accreditation Program
◇ DNV Healthcare Inc. accreditation
⇑ Center for Improvement in Healthcare Quality Accreditation
△ Commission on Accreditation of Rehabilitation Facilities (CARF) accreditation

**PITTSBURGH—Allegheny County**

⊞ **ALLEGHENY GENERAL HOSPITAL (390050)**, 320 East North Avenue, Zip 15212–4756; tel. 412/359–3131 **A**1 2 3 5 8 9 10 12 13 **F**3 7 8 9 11 12 15 17 18 19 20 22 24 26 28 29 30 31 32 34 35 36 38 39 40 41 43 44 45 46 47 48 49 50 51 53 54 55 57 58 59 61 62 63 64 65 66 68 70 74 75 77 78 79 80 81 82 84 85 86 87 89 92 93 94 95 96 97 99 100 101 102 103 104 105 107 108 110 111 114 115 116 117 118 119 120 121 123 124 126 129 130 131 132 134 135 137 138 139 142 143 145 146 147 148 **P**6 **S** Allegheny Health Network, Pittsburgh, PA
Primary Contact: Michael Harlovic, R.N., President and Chief Executive Officer
CMO: Tony Farah, M.D., President Medical Staff
CIO: John Foley, Chief Information Officer
Web address: www.wpahs.org/locations/allegheny–general–hospital
**Control:** Other not–for–profit (including NFP Corporation) **Service:** General Medical and Surgical

**Staffed Beds: 383 Admissions: 22678 Census: 348 Outpatient Visits: 318992 Births: 0 Total Expense ($000): 638175 Payroll Expense ($000): 188518 Personnel: 3523**

□ **CHILDREN'S HOSPITAL OF PITTSBURGH OF UPMC (393302)**, 4401 Penn Avenue, Zip 15224–1334; tel. 412/692–5325 **A**1 3 5 9 10 **F**3 8 12 17 19 21 22 23 24 25 27 28 29 30 31 32 34 35 39 40 41 43 45 46 48 49 50 53 54 55 57 59 60 64 66 68 71 72 74 75 77 78 79 81 82 84 86 87 88 89 90 91 93 97 100 107 108 109 111 115 116 117 118 119 120 121 123 124 126 129 130 131 132 134 135 136 137 138 139 140 141 142 143 144 146 **S** UPMC, Pittsburgh, PA
Primary Contact: Christopher Gessner, President
COO: Christopher Gessner, President
CNO: Diane Hupp, R.N., Vice President Patient Care Services and Chief Nursing Officer
Web address: www.chp.edu
**Control:** Other not–for–profit (including NFP Corporation) **Service:** Children's general

**Staffed Beds: 304 Admissions: 12796 Census: 211 Outpatient Visits: 308093 Births: 0 Total Expense ($000): 536376 Payroll Expense ($000): 145777 Personnel: 2634**

**EYE AND EAR HOSPITAL OF PITTSBURGH** See UPMC Presbyterian Shadyside

⊞ **HEALTHSOUTH HARMARVILLE REHABILITATION HOSPITAL (393027)**, Guys Run Road, Zip 15238–0460, Mailing Address: P.O. Box 11460, Zip 15238–0460; tel. 412/828–1300 **A**1 10 **F**29 62 64 75 77 79 86 90 93 95 96 132 148 **S** HEALTHSOUTH Corporation, Birmingham, AL
Primary Contact: Mark Van Volkenburg, Chief Executive Officer
CFO: Daniel A. Vrana, Controller
CMO: Thomas Franz, M.D., Medical Director
CHR: Eric Larson, Director Human Resources
Web address: www.healthsouthharmarville.com
**Control:** Corporation, Investor–owned, for–profit **Service:** Rehabilitation

**Staffed Beds: 162 Admissions: 2257 Census: 87 Outpatient Visits: 19314 Births: 0 Total Expense ($000): 28660 Payroll Expense ($000): 15649 Personnel: 271**

⊞ **LIFECARE HOSPITALS OF PITTSBURGH (392024)**, 225 Penn Avenue, Zip 15221–2148; tel. 412/247–2424, (Includes LIFECARE HOSPITALS OF PITTSBURGH – SUBURBAN CAMPUS, 100 South Jackson Avenue, 4th Floor, Zip 15202–3428), (Nonreporting) **A**1 9 10 **S** LifeCare Management Services, Plano, TX
Primary Contact: Kim Sperring, Administrator
CFO: Nikki Aykul, Manager Business Office
CMO: Steven Sotos, M.D., President Medical Staff
CIO: George Fitzgerald, Regional Director Information Systems
CHR: Robin Arslanpay, Director Human Resources
Web address: www.lifecare–hospitals.com
**Control:** Corporation, Investor–owned, for–profit **Service:** Long–Term Acute Care hospital

**Staffed Beds: 236**

⊞ **MAGEE–WOMENS HOSPITAL OF UPMC (390114)**, 300 Halket Street, Zip 15213–3108; tel. 412/641–1000, (Total facility includes 20 beds in nursing home–type unit) **A**1 2 3 5 9 10 **F**3 11 12 13 15 29 30 31 34 35 40 43 44 45 46 49 52 54 55 56 57 58 59 64 65 66 68 70 72 74 75 76 78 79 80 81 82 84 85 86 87 97 107 108 110 111 115 119 120 121 123 126 130 131 132 134 135 146 147 148 **S** UPMC, Pittsburgh, PA
Primary Contact: Leslie C. Davis, President
COO: Lou Baverso, Vice President Operations
CFO: Eileen Simmons, Chief Financial Officer
CMO: Dennis English, M.D., Vice President Medical Affairs
CIO: Harun Rashid, Chief Information Officer
CHR: Rhonda Larimore, Vice President Human Resources
CNO: Maribeth McLaughlin, R.N., Vice President Patient Care Services
Web address: www.magee.edu
**Control:** Other not–for–profit (including NFP Corporation) **Service:** Obstetrics and gynecology

**Staffed Beds: 327 Admissions: 20603 Census: 234 Outpatient Visits: 389987 Births: 9036 Total Expense ($000): 483499 Payroll Expense ($000): 115084 Personnel: 2083**

⊞ **SELECT SPECIALTY HOSPITAL–PITTSBURGH/UPMC (392044)**, 200 Lothrop Street, E824, Zip 15213–2536; tel. 412/586–9800 **A**1 9 10 **F**1 3 29 36 65 85 86 87 91 148 **S** Select Medical Corporation, Mechanicsburg, PA
Primary Contact: John St. Leger, Chief Executive Officer
CMO: Michael Donahue, M.D., Medical Director
CHR: Prudence Sloan, Coordinator Human Resources
CNO: Eli Babich, Chief Nursing Officer
Web address: www.selectspecialtyhospitals.com/company/locations/pittsburghupmc.aspx
**Control:** Corporation, Investor–owned, for–profit **Service:** Long–Term Acute Care hospital

**Staffed Beds: 32 Admissions: 318 Census: 26 Outpatient Visits: 0 Births: 0**

□ **SOUTHWOOD PSYCHIATRIC HOSPITAL**, 2575 Boyce Plaza Road, Zip 15241–3925; tel. 412/257–2290, (Nonreporting) **A**1 9 **S** Acadia Healthcare Company, Inc., Franklin, TN
Primary Contact: Stephen J. Quigley, Chief Executive Officer
CFO: Frank Urban, Chief Financial Officer
CMO: Allan W. Clark, M.D., Medical Director
CHR: Erin J. Frohnhofer, Director Human Resources
Web address: www.southwoodhospital.com
**Control:** Corporation, Investor–owned, for–profit **Service:** Children's hospital psychiatric

**Staffed Beds: 156**

⊞ **ST. CLAIR HOSPITAL (390228)**, 1000 Bower Hill Road, Zip 15243–1873; tel. 412/942–4000 **A**1 2 3 9 10 **F**3 8 13 15 17 18 20 22 24 26 28 29 30 31 34 35 37 40 45 49 51 53 54 56 57 59 60 64 67 70 73 74 75 76 77 78 79 81 82 84 85 86 87 89 90 91 92 93 96 98 100 102 103 104 105 107 108 110 111 114 115 118 119 126 129 130 131 132 134 135 143 144 146 147 148
Primary Contact: James M. Collins, President and Chief Executive Officer
COO: Michael J. Flanagan, Senior Vice President and Chief Operating Officer
CFO: Richard C. Chesnos, Senior Vice President Finance and Chief Financial Officer
CMO: G. Alan Yeasted, M.D., Senior Vice President and Chief Medical Officer
CIO: Richard Schaeffer, Vice President Information Systems and Chief Information Officer
CHR: Andrea Kalina, Vice President External Affairs and Chief Human Resources Officer
CNO: Joan Massella, Administrative Vice President and Chief Nursing Officer
Web address: www.stclair.org
**Control:** Other not–for–profit (including NFP Corporation) **Service:** General Medical and Surgical

**Staffed Beds: 303 Admissions: 15907 Census: 195 Outpatient Visits: 299734 Births: 1321 Total Expense ($000): 234759 Payroll Expense ($000): 91528 Personnel: 1946**

★ **THE CHILDREN'S HOME OF PITTSBURGH (393304)**, 5324 Penn Avenue, Zip 15224–1733; tel. 412/441–4884, (Nonreporting) **A**9 10
Primary Contact: Pamela R. Schanwald, Chief Executive Officer
COO: Kimberly Reblock, M.D., Chief Operating Officer
CFO: Kimberly A. Phillips, Chief Financial Officer
CMO: Frederick C. Sherman, M.D., Chief Medical Officer
Web address: www.childrenshomepgh.org
**Control:** Other not–for–profit (including NFP Corporation) **Service:** Children's general

**Staffed Beds: 15**

★ △ **THE CHILDREN'S INSTITUTE OF PITTSBURGH (393308)**, 1405 Shady Avenue, Zip 15217–1350; tel. 412/420–2400 **A**7 10 **F**3 29 30 34 54 58 59 64 74 75 79 82 85 86 87 90 91 93 96 97 98 99 100 104 107 130 131 132 146 148 **P**6
Primary Contact: David K. Miles, President and Chief Executive Officer
COO: Stacey Vaccaro, Chief Operating Officer
CFO: Jody Mulvihill, Vice President Finance
CMO: Maryanne Henderson, D.O., Chief Medical Officer
CIO: Sharon Dorogy, Director Health Information Management
CHR: Linda M. Allen, Vice President Human Resources
Web address: www.amazingkids.org
**Control:** Other not–for–profit (including NFP Corporation) **Service:** Children's rehabilitation

**Staffed Beds: 62 Admissions: 304 Census: 24 Outpatient Visits: 56352 Births: 0 Total Expense ($000): 27511 Payroll Expense ($000): 15778 Personnel: 285**

PA

**PA**

☐ △ **UPMC MERCY (390028)**, 1400 Locust Street, Zip 15219–5166;
tel. 412/232–8111 **A**1 3 5 6 7 9 10 12 13 **F**3 4 8 13 15 16 17 18 19 20 22
24 26 28 29 30 31 32 34 35 36 39 40 43 44 45 49 50 51 54 57 58 59 60
61 62 64 65 66 68 70 72 74 75 76 77 78 79 81 82 84 85 86 87 90 91 92
93 94 95 96 97 98 101 102 107 108 111 114 115 116 118 119 126 129
130 141 142 146 147 148 **P**6 **S** UPMC, Pittsburgh, PA
Primary Contact: Michael Grace, President
CFO: Jack Gaenzle, Senior Vice President Finance and Administration
CIO: Stephen D. Adams, Executive Vice President and Chief Information Officer
CHR: Kristen Bell, Director Human Resources
CNO: Leeanna McKibben, R.N., Vice President Patient Services and Chief Nursing Officer
Web address: www.upmc.com/HospitalsFacilities/HFHome/Hospitals/Mercy/
**Control:** Other not–for–profit (including NFP Corporation) **Service:** General Medical and Surgical

**Staffed Beds:** 482 **Admissions:** 20571 **Census:** 342 **Outpatient Visits:**
188832 **Births:** 1307 **Total Expense ($000):** 394561 **Payroll Expense**
**($000):** 127561 **Personnel:** 2272

**UPMC MONTEFIORE** See UPMC Presbyterian Shadyside

☐ **UPMC PASSAVANT (390107)**, 9100 Babcock Boulevard, Zip 15237–5815;
tel. 412/748–6700, (Includes UPMC PASSAVANT CRANBERRY, One St. Francis
Way, Cranberry, Zip 16066; tel. 724/772–5300; Teresa G. Petrick, President),
(Total facility includes 12 beds in nursing home–type unit) **A**1 2 5 9 10 **F**3 8 11
15 17 18 20 22 24 26 28 29 30 31 34 35 40 42 43 46 47 48 49 51 56 57
59 64 65 68 70 74 75 77 78 79 81 82 84 85 86 87 90 92 107 108 110 111
114 115 116 117 118 119 120 121 126 128 129 130 132 135 143 145 146
147 148 **S** UPMC, Pittsburgh, PA
Primary Contact: David T. Martin, President
CFO: Thomas M. Newman, Chief Financial Officer
CMO: James W. Boyle, M.D., Chief Medical Officer
CHR: Leeann Cerimele, Vice President Human Resources
CNO: Susan E. Hoolahan, R.N., Vice President Patient Care Services and Chief Nursing Officer
Web address: www.upmc.edu/passavant
**Control:** Other not–for–profit (including NFP Corporation) **Service:** General Medical and Surgical

**Staffed Beds:** 425 **Admissions:** 16328 **Census:** 233 **Outpatient Visits:**
322818 **Births:** 0 **Total Expense ($000):** 371654 **Payroll Expense ($000):**
96682 **Personnel:** 1634

☐ **UPMC PRESBYTERIAN SHADYSIDE (390164)**, 200 Lothrop Street,
Zip 15213–2536; tel. 412/647–2345, (Includes EYE AND EAR HOSPITAL OF
PITTSBURGH, 200 Lothrop Street, Zip 15213–2592; tel. 412/647–2345; UPMC
MONTEFIORE, 3459 Fifth Avenue, Zip 15213; tel. 412/647–2345; John Innocenti,
Sr., President and Chief Executive Officer; UPMC PRESBYTERIAN HOSPITAL, 200
Lothrop Street, Zip 15213; tel. 412/647–2345; UPMC SHADYSIDE, 5230 Centre
Avenue, Zip 15232–1381; tel. 412/623–2121; WESTERN PSYCHIATRIC
INSTITUTE AND CLINIC, 3811 O'Hara Street, Zip 15213–2593;
tel. 412/624–2100), (Total facility includes 30 beds in nursing home–type unit)
**A**1 2 5 6 8 9 10 12 13 **F**2 3 5 6 7 8 9 10 11 12 14 15 17 18 19 20 22 24
25 26 28 29 30 31 32 33 34 35 36 37 38 39 40 43 44 45 46 47 48 49 50
51 52 53 54 55 56 57 58 59 60 61 62 63 64 65 66 68 69 70 71 74 75 77
78 79 81 82 83 84 85 86 87 90 91 92 93 94 97 98 99 100 101 102 103
104 105 106 107 108 109 110 111 112 113 114 115 116 117 118 119 120
121 123 126 128 129 130 131 132 134 135 136 137 138 139 140 141 142
143 144 145 146 147 148 **P**6 **S** UPMC, Pittsburgh, PA
Primary Contact: John Innocenti, Sr., President and Chief Executive Officer
CFO: Eileen Simmons, Chief Financial Officer
CMO: Margaret Reidy, M.D., Vice President Medical Affairs
CIO: James Venturella, Chief Information Officer
CHR: Kathryn Devine, Vice President Human Resources
CNO: Holly Lorenz, R.N., Chief Nurse Executive
Web address: www.upmc.edu
**Control:** Other not–for–profit (including NFP Corporation) **Service:** General Medical and Surgical

**Staffed Beds:** 1517 **Admissions:** 62797 **Census:** 1258 **Outpatient Visits:**
1227180 **Births:** 0 **Total Expense ($000):** 2208327 **Payroll Expense**
**($000):** 531092 **Personnel:** 11899

☐ **UPMC ST. MARGARET (390102)**, 815 Freeport Road, Zip 15215–3301;
tel. 412/784–4000 **A**1 2 3 5 6 9 10 13 **F**3 6 8 9 11 12 15 18 20 29 30 31 34
35 40 44 46 49 50 51 54 56 57 58 59 60 61 63 64 65 68 70 74 75 77 78
79 81 82 84 85 86 87 90 94 97 102 103 104 107 108 111 114 115 118
119 121 129 130 131 132 134 135 146 **S** UPMC, Pittsburgh, PA
Primary Contact: David J. Patton, President
COO: Merle Taylor, Vice President Operations
CFO: Thomas M. Newman, Vice President Finance
CMO: John Lagnese, M.D., Vice President Medical Affairs
CIO: Charles M. Rudek, Chief Information Officer
CHR: Tracey Stange Kolo, Vice President Human Resources
CNO: Mary C. Barkhymer, R.N., Vice President Patient Care Services and Chief
Nursing Officer
Web address: www.upmc.com/locations/hospitals/st–margaret/Pages/default.
aspx
**Control:** Other not–for–profit (including NFP Corporation) **Service:** General
Medical and Surgical

**Staffed Beds:** 249 **Admissions:** 13337 **Census:** 181 **Outpatient Visits:**
175227 **Births:** 0 **Total Expense ($000):** 244305 **Payroll Expense ($000):**
66807 **Personnel:** 1250

⊞ △ **VETERANS AFFAIRS PITTSBURGH HEALTHCARE SYSTEM**, University
Drive, Zip 15240–1001; tel. 866/482–7488, (Includes VETERANS AFFAIRS
MEDICAL CENTER, 7180 Highland Drive, Zip 15206–1297; tel. 412/365–4900;
VETERANS AFFAIRS MEDICAL CENTER, University Drive C, tel. 412/688–6000),
(Total facility includes 285 beds in nursing home–type unit) **A**1 2 3 4 **F**1 2
3 4 5 6 8 9 12 15 17 18 20 22 24 26 28 29 30 31 33 34 35 36 38 39 40 44
45 46 47 48 49 50 51 53 54 55 56 57 58 59 60 61 62 63 64 65 66 67 68
70 74 75 77 78 79 81 82 83 84 85 86 87 90 91 92 93 94 96 97 98 100
101 102 103 104 105 106 107 108 109 110 111 112 113 114 115 116 119
120 121 123 124 128 129 130 132 135 136 137 138 139 140 141 142 143
146 147 148 **P**6 **S** Department of Veterans Affairs, Washington, DC
Primary Contact: David S. Macpherson, M.D., M.P.H., Acting Director
CFO: Charles Thilges, Chief Financial Officer
CMO: Ali Sonel, M.D., Chief of Staff
CIO: John Kovac, Facility Chief Information Officer
CHR: Amber Mesoras, Chief Human Resources Officer
CNO: Ira Richmond, Associate Director Patient Care Services
Web address: www.pittsburgh.va.gov/
**Control:** Veterans Affairs, Government, federal **Service:** General Medical and
Surgical

**Staffed Beds:** 582 **Admissions:** 9842 **Census:** 404 **Outpatient Visits:**
683634 **Births:** 0 **Total Expense ($000):** 583275 **Payroll Expense ($000):**
317413 **Personnel:** 3417

⊞ **WEST PENN HOSPITAL (390090)**, 4800 Friendship Avenue, Zip 15224–1722;
tel. 412/578–5000 **A**1 2 3 5 6 8 9 10 12 13 **F**3 8 11 12 13 15 16 17 18 20
22 24 26 29 30 31 34 35 37 39 40 45 46 47 48 49 50 51 52 54 55 56 57
58 59 63 64 65 68 70 72 74 75 76 77 78 79 80 81 82 84 85 86 87 89 90
91 92 93 96 97 100 102 107 108 109 110 111 114 115 116 117 118 119
120 121 123 124 126 129 130 131 132 135 136 141 145 146 147 148 **P**6
**S** Allegheny Health Network, Pittsburgh, PA
Primary Contact: Ronald J. Andro, President and Chief Executive Officer
CFO: James A. Kanuch, Vice President Finance
CMO: I. William Goldfarb, Chief Medical Officer
CIO: Jacqueline Dailey, Chief Information Officer
CHR: Sally Carozza, Director Human Resources
CNO: Paula A. Lacher, MSN, Chief Nursing Officer
Web address: www.wpahs.org
**Control:** Other not–for–profit (including NFP Corporation) **Service:** General
Medical and Surgical

**Staffed Beds:** 308 **Admissions:** 10202 **Census:** 159 **Outpatient Visits:**
97952 **Births:** 3467 **Total Expense ($000):** 301039 **Payroll Expense**
**($000):** 77974 **Personnel:** 1342

**WESTERN PSYCHIATRIC INSTITUTE AND CLINIC** See UPMC Presbyterian
Shadyside

**PLEASANT GAP—Centre County**

⊞ **HEALTHSOUTH NITTANY VALLEY REHABILITATION HOSPITAL (393039)**,
550 West College Avenue, Zip 16823–7401; tel. 814/359–3421 **A**1 9 10 **F**29
34 44 59 60 64 90 93 148 **S** HEALTHSOUTH Corporation, Birmingham, AL
Primary Contact: Susan Hartman, Chief Executive Officer
CFO: Alan M. Phillips, Controller
CMO: Richard Allatt, M.D., Medical Director
CHR: Michelle Katz, Director Human Resources
CNO: Susan Evans, Chief Nursing Officer
Web address: www.nittanyvalleyrehab.com
**Control:** Corporation, Investor–owned, for–profit **Service:** Rehabilitation

**Staffed Beds:** 73 **Admissions:** 1308 **Census:** 44 **Outpatient Visits:** 18602
**Births:** 0 **Total Expense ($000):** 17561 **Payroll Expense ($000):** 9375
**Personnel:** 174

---

**Hospital, Medicare Provider Number, Address, Telephone, Approval, Facility, and Physician Codes, Health Care System**

★ American Hospital Association (AHA) membership ○ Healthcare Facilities Accreditation Program ⇑ Center for Improvement in Healthcare Quality Accreditation
☐ The Joint Commission accreditation ◇ DNV Healthcare Inc. accreditation △ Commission on Accreditation of Rehabilitation Facilities (CARF) accreditation

**PA**

### POTTSTOWN—Montgomery County

✠ **POTTSTOWN MEMORIAL MEDICAL CENTER (390123)**, 1600 East High Street, Zip 19464–5093; tel. 610/327–7000 **A**1 2 9 10 **F**3 7 8 12 13 15 18 29 30 31 34 35 38 40 44 45 48 49 50 51 54 55 57 59 60 64 68 70 74 75 76 77 78 79 80 81 82 85 89 92 93 96 97 98 100 103 107 108 110 111 117 119 120 121 123 131 132 135 146 147 148 **P**6 **S** Community Health Systems, Inc., Franklin, TN
Primary Contact: Rich Newell, Chief Executive Officer
CFO: Debbie Konarski, Interim Chief Financial Officer
CMO: Richard F. Saylor, M.D., Chief Medical Officer
CIO: Ron Peterson, Chief Information Officer
CHR: Ruta Ore, Director Human Resources
Web address: www.pottstownmemorial.com
**Control:** Corporation, Investor–owned, for–profit **Service:** General Medical and Surgical

> **Staffed Beds:** 232 **Admissions:** 9003 **Census:** 107 **Outpatient Visits:** 101212 **Births:** 519 **Total Expense ($000):** 136771 **Payroll Expense ($000):** 50406 **Personnel:** 912

### POTTSVILLE—Schuylkill County

✠ △ **SCHUYLKILL MEDICAL CENTER – EAST NORWEGIAN STREET (390031)**, 700 East Norwegian Street, Zip 17901–2710; tel. 570/621–4000 **A**1 7 9 10 **F**3 5 11 15 18 29 30 31 34 39 40 45 49 56 57 69 74 75 77 78 79 81 85 86 90 93 98 100 103 107 108 109 110 115 117 118 119 130 132 135 146 147 148 **P**6 **S** Schuylkill Health System, Pottsville, PA
Primary Contact: Mark H. Lory, Chief Executive Officer
CFO: Diane Boris, Vice President and Chief Financial Officer
CMO: Thomas A. Curry, M.D., Vice President Medical Affairs for Clinical Effectiveness and Documentation
CIO: Tina Zanis, Director Information Technology
CHR: Martin Treasure, Director Human Resources
CNO: Susan Curry, Interim Chief Nursing Officer
Web address: www.schuylkillhealth.com
**Control:** Other not–for–profit (including NFP Corporation) **Service:** General Medical and Surgical

> **Staffed Beds:** 109 **Admissions:** 3911 **Census:** 64 **Outpatient Visits:** 101014 **Births:** 0 **Total Expense ($000):** 56682 **Payroll Expense ($000):** 26462 **Personnel:** 513

✠ **SCHUYLKILL MEDICAL CENTER – SOUTH JACKSON STREET (390030)**, 420 South Jackson Street, Zip 17901–3625; tel. 570/621–5000, (Total facility includes 11 beds in nursing home–type unit) **A**1 6 9 10 19 **F**3 11 13 15 18 19 28 29 30 32 34 35 38 40 45 49 51 54 56 57 59 62 64 70 74 75 76 77 78 79 81 82 85 86 89 92 93 96 98 99 100 101 102 104 105 107 108 110 111 115 118 119 124 126 128 129 130 131 132 146 147 **P**6 **S** Schuylkill Health System, Pottsville, PA
Primary Contact: Mark H. Lory, Chief Executive Officer
CFO: Diane Boris, Chief Financial Officer
CMO: Thomas A. Curry, M.D., Vice President Medical Affairs for Clinical Effectiveness and Documentation
CIO: Tina Zanis, Director Information Systems
CHR: Martin Treasure, Director Human Resources
CNO: Susan Curry, Interim Chief Nursing Officer
Web address: www.schuylkillhealth.com
**Control:** Other not–for–profit (including NFP Corporation) **Service:** General Medical and Surgical

> **Staffed Beds:** 190 **Admissions:** 6070 **Census:** 86 **Outpatient Visits:** 113628 **Births:** 842 **Total Expense ($000):** 87874 **Payroll Expense ($000):** 41083 **Personnel:** 747

### PUNXSUTAWNEY—Jefferson County

**PUNXSUTAWNEY AREA HOSPITAL (390199)**, 81 Hillcrest Drive, Zip 15767–2616; tel. 814/938–1800 **A**9 10 20 **F**3 13 15 26 29 30 34 35 40 44 45 46 48 50 51 57 59 62 64 70 74 75 76 77 78 79 81 82 85 86 87 92 93 96 100 104 107 108 110 111 115 118 119 127 130 132 133 146 147 148 **P**6
Primary Contact: Daniel D. Blough, Jr., Chief Executive Officer
CFO: Jack Sisk, Chief Financial Officer
CMO: Dajani Zuhd, M.D., President Medical Staff
CIO: Chuck States, Director Information Systems
CHR: Barbara Kostok, Manager Human Resources
CNO: Paula Spack, R.N., Vice President Nursing
Web address: www.pah.org
**Control:** Other not–for–profit (including NFP Corporation) **Service:** General Medical and Surgical

> **Staffed Beds:** 45 **Admissions:** 1556 **Census:** 16 **Outpatient Visits:** 71750 **Total Expense ($000):** 32195 **Payroll Expense ($000):** 16592 **Personnel:** 330

### QUAKERTOWN—Bucks County

☐ **ST. LUKE'S HOSPITAL – QUAKERTOWN CAMPUS (390035)**, 1021 Park Avenue, Zip 18951–1573; tel. 215/538–4500 **A**1 2 9 10 **F**3 15 18 28 29 30 31 34 35 38 40 44 45 49 50 51 54 56 57 59 64 65 68 69 70 74 75 77 78 79 81 82 85 86 87 92 93 98 100 102 103 107 108 109 110 111 115 118 119 129 130 131 132 135 146 147 148 **P**6 8 **S** St. Luke's University Health Network, Bethlehem, PA
Primary Contact: John B. Sylvia, President
CFO: Theresa Corrado, Director Finance
CMO: Thomas Filipowicz, M.D., Medical Director
CIO: Chad Brisendine, Chief Information Officer
CHR: Shelley Maley, Director Human Resources
Web address: www.slhhn.org
**Control:** Other not–for–profit (including NFP Corporation) **Service:** General Medical and Surgical

> **Staffed Beds:** 57 **Admissions:** 2877 **Census:** 38 **Outpatient Visits:** 74530 **Births:** 0 **Total Expense ($000):** 54799 **Payroll Expense ($000):** 23143 **Personnel:** 304

### READING—Berks County

☐ **HAVEN BEHAVIORAL HEALTH OF EASTERN PENNSYLVANIA (394052)**, 145 North 6th Street, 3rd Floor, Zip 19601–3096; tel. 610/406–4340, (Nonreporting) **A**1 9 10 **S** Haven Behavioral Healthcare, Nashville, TN
Primary Contact: John Baker, Interim Chief Executive Officer
CMO: Mark Putnam, M.D., Medical Director
CHR: Kathy Copenhaver, Director Human Resources
Web address: www.havenbehavioralhospital.com
**Control:** Corporation, Investor–owned, for–profit **Service:** Psychiatric

> **Staffed Beds:** 48

✠ **HEALTHSOUTH READING REHABILITATION HOSPITAL (393026)**, 1623 Morgantown Road, Zip 19607–9455; tel. 610/796–6000, (Nonreporting) **A**1 9 10 **S** HEALTHSOUTH Corporation, Birmingham, AL
Primary Contact: Richard Kruczek, Chief Executive Officer
CFO: Jason Pulaski, Controller
CMO: Patti Brown, M.D., Medical Director
CHR: Edward Werner, Director Human Resources
CNO: Margaret Montgomery, Chief Nursing Officer
Web address: www.healthsouthreading.com
**Control:** Corporation, Investor–owned, for–profit **Service:** Rehabilitation

> **Staffed Beds:** 60

✠ **ST. JOSEPH REGIONAL HEALTH NETWORK (390096)**, 2500 Bernville Road, Zip 19605–9453, Mailing Address: P.O. Box 316, Zip 19603–0316; tel. 610/378–2000, (Includes ST. JOSEPH MEDICAL CENTER–DOWNTOWN READING, 145 North Sixth Street, Zip 19601, Mailing Address: P.O. Box 316, Zip 19603–0316; tel. 610/378–2000; John R. Morahan, FACHE, President and Chief Executive Officer) **A**1 2 9 10 12 13 **F**1 3 4 13 15 16 17 18 20 22 24 26 28 29 30 31 32 34 35 39 40 44 45 46 49 50 51 53 54 57 58 59 64 66 67 68 70 72 73 74 75 76 77 78 79 80 81 82 84 85 87 88 89 90 93 97 98 107 108 111 113 114 115 116 117 118 119 120 121 128 130 131 132 135 144 146 147 148 **P**1 6
Primary Contact: John R. Morahan, FACHE, President and Chief Executive Officer
CFO: Lim David, Vice President Finance and Chief Financial Officer
CMO: Gary Lattin, M.D., Vice President, Medical Affairs
CIO: Amanda Klopp, Director, Innovation and Clinical Integration
CHR: Scott Mengle, Vice President Human Resources
CNO: Sharon Strohecker, R.N., Vice President Clinical Operations and Chief Nursing Officer
Web address: www.thefutureofhealthcare.org
**Control:** Church–operated, Nongovernment, not–for profit **Service:** General Medical and Surgical

> **Staffed Beds:** 180 **Admissions:** 7677 **Census:** 92 **Outpatient Visits:** 251671 **Births:** 682 **Total Expense ($000):** 188879 **Payroll Expense ($000):** 60085 **Personnel:** 1256

### RENOVO—Clinton County

★ **BUCKTAIL MEDICAL CENTER (391304)**, 1001 Pine Street, Zip 17764–1620; tel. 570/923–1000, (Total facility includes 43 beds in nursing home–type unit) **A**9 10 18 **F**3 7 11 34 40 54 56 57 59 65 66 97 127 128 130 133 143 146 **P**6
Primary Contact: Timothy Reeves, Administrator
CFO: Wendy Janerella, Controller
CMO: Alvin Berlot, M.D., Medical Director
Web address: www.bucktailmed.org
**Control:** Other not–for–profit (including NFP Corporation) **Service:** General Medical and Surgical

> **Staffed Beds:** 64 **Admissions:** 147 **Census:** 38 **Outpatient Visits:** 10739 **Births:** 0 **Total Expense ($000):** 5901 **Payroll Expense ($000):** 1556 **Personnel:** 65

### RIDLEY PARK—Delaware County

**TAYLOR HOSPITAL** See Crozer–Chester Medical Center, Upland

*Many Facility Codes have changed. Please refer to the AHA Guide Code Chart.* © 2015 AHA Guide

## ROARING SPRING—Blair County

✠ **NASON HOSPITAL (390062)**, 105 Nason Drive, Zip 16673–1202;
tel. 814/224–2141 **A**1 9 10 **F**3 11 13 15 29 30 34 35 40 45 57 59 62 63 64
68 70 74 75 76 77 79 81 82 85 92 107 108 110 111 114 119 130 132 146
147 148 **P**3 **S** LifePoint Health, Brentwood, TN
Primary Contact: Richard Grogan, Interim Chief Executive Officer
CFO: Raymond C. Askey, CPA, Vice President Fiscal Services
CIO: Brian Lilly, Director Information Systems
CHR: Lorie Smith, Director Human Resources
Web address: www.nasonhospital.org
**Control:** Other not–for–profit (including NFP Corporation) **Service:** General
Medical and Surgical

**Staffed Beds:** 45 **Admissions:** 1837 **Census:** 16 **Outpatient Visits:** 100501
**Births:** 510 **Total Expense ($000):** 32141 **Payroll Expense ($000):** 13594
**Personnel:** 260

## ROYERSFORD—Montgomery County

◇ **PHYSICIANS CARE SURGICAL HOSPITAL (390324)**, 454 Enterprise Drive,
Zip 19468–1200; tel. 610/495–3330 **A**9 10 21 **F**3 8 29 65 81
Primary Contact: Christopher Doyle, Chief Executive Officer
Web address: www.phycarehospital.com
**Control:** Corporation, Investor–owned, for–profit **Service:** Surgical

**Staffed Beds:** 12 **Admissions:** 769 **Census:** 4 **Outpatient Visits:** 4509
**Births:** 0 **Personnel:** 78

## SAINT MARYS—Elk County

**PENN HIGHLANDS ELK (390154)**, 763 Johnsonburg Road, Zip 15857–3498;
tel. 814/788–8000, (Total facility includes 138 beds in nursing home–type unit)
**A**9 10 20 **F**3 6 11 13 15 28 29 30 34 35 40 44 45 56 57 59 70 75 76 77 79
81 82 85 86 87 89 93 98 100 103 107 110 111 114 118 119 128 129 130
131 133 135 144 146 147 148
Primary Contact: Rose Campbell, R.N., President
CFO: Laurie MacDonald, Vice President Finance
CMO: David Johe, M.D., President Medical Staff
CIO: Mary Ann Schwabenbauer, Director Information Technology
CHR: Seanna D'Amore, Director Human Resources
Web address: www.phhealthcare.org
**Control:** Other not–for–profit (including NFP Corporation) **Service:** General
Medical and Surgical

**Staffed Beds:** 218 **Admissions:** 2888 **Census:** 161 **Outpatient Visits:**
159270 **Births:** 210 **Total Expense ($000):** 70148 **Payroll Expense ($000):**
33761 **Personnel:** 634

## SAYRE—Bradford County

✠ **ROBERT PACKER HOSPITAL (390079)**, 1 Guthrie Square, Zip 18840–1698;
tel. 570/888–6666 **A**1 2 3 5 9 10 12 13 19 **F**3 11 12 13 15 17 18 20 22 24
26 28 29 30 31 34 37 38 40 43 45 46 47 48 49 50 51 53 54 58 59 60 61 64
70 73 74 75 76 78 79 81 82 84 85 86 87 89 92 93 98 99 100 101 102 103
105 107 108 110 111 114 115 116 117 118 119 120 121 123 126 129 130
132 141 142 145 146 148 **S** Guthrie Clinic, Sayre, PA
Primary Contact: Marie T. Droege, President
CFO: Minh Dang, Vice President Finance
CMO: Brian Fillipo, M.D., Chief Medical Officer
CIO: Dale Swingle, Vice President Information Services
CHR: Frank Pinkosky, Senior Vice President
CNO: Bonnie J. Onofre, MS, Vice President and Chief Nursing Officer
Web address: www.guthrie.org
**Control:** Other not–for–profit (including NFP Corporation) **Service:** General
Medical and Surgical

**Staffed Beds:** 251 **Admissions:** 14007 **Census:** 178 **Outpatient Visits:**
160930 **Births:** 900 **Total Expense ($000):** 244404 **Payroll Expense
($000):** 75953 **Personnel:** 1316

## SCRANTON—Lackawanna County

✠ △ **ALLIED SERVICES REHABILITATION HOSPITAL (393030)**, 475 Morgan
Highway, Zip 18508–2605, Mailing Address: P.O. Box 1103, Zip 18501–1103;
tel. 570/348–1300 **A**1 7 10 **F**11 29 34 53 56 59 64 74 75 77 78 79 86 87
90 91 93 94 96 130 143 146
Primary Contact: Karen Kearney, Vice President Inpatient Rehabilitation Services
CFO: Michael Avvisato, Senior Vice President and Chief Financial Officer
CMO: Gregory Basting, M.D., Vice President Medical Affairs
CIO: John Regula, Chief Information Officer
CHR: Judy P. Oprisko, Vice President
CNO: Jeana Sluck, R.N., Executive Director Nursing Clinical Inpatient Departments
Web address: www.allied–services.org
**Control:** Other not–for–profit (including NFP Corporation) **Service:** Rehabilitation

**Staffed Beds:** 117 **Admissions:** 2005 **Census:** 57 **Births:** 0

**COMMUNITY MEDICAL CENTER HEALTHCARE SYSTEM** See
Geisinger–Community Medical Center

✠ **GEISINGER–COMMUNITY MEDICAL CENTER (390001)**, 1800 Mulberry
Street, Zip 18510–2369; tel. 570/703–8000, (Nonreporting) **A**1 3 5 9 10
**S** Geisinger Health System, Danville, PA
Primary Contact: David T. Feinberg, M.D., Chief Executive Officer
CFO: Edward Chabalowski, Chief Financial Officer
CMO: Anthony Aquilina, D.O., Chief Medical Officer
CHR: Lois Wolfe, Director Human Resources
Web address: www.cmccare.org/
**Control:** Other not–for–profit (including NFP Corporation) **Service:** General
Medical and Surgical

**Staffed Beds:** 248

**MERCY HOSPITAL OF SCRANTON** See Regional Hospital of Scranton

✠ △ **MOSES TAYLOR HOSPITAL (390119)**, 700 Quincy Avenue,
Zip 18510–1724; tel. 570/770–5000 **A**1 3 5 7 9 10 19 **F**3 7 13 15 18 29 30
31 34 40 49 51 56 57 59 60 61 62 64 65 66 68 70 72 74 75 76 77 78 79
81 85 86 87 89 93 98 103 107 108 110 111 119 124 129 130 132 135
146 147 **P**6 **S** Community Health Systems, Inc., Franklin, TN
Primary Contact: Justin Davis, Chief Executive Officer
CFO: Thomas Bisignani, Chief Financial Officer
CMO: Mary Sewatsky, M.D., Chief Medical Officer
CHR: Elizabeth Leo, Chief Human Resources Officer
CNO: Patricia Seliga, R.N., Chief Nursing Officer
Web address: www.mth.org
**Control:** Corporation, Investor–owned, for–profit **Service:** General Medical and
Surgical

**Staffed Beds:** 217 **Admissions:** 9061 **Census:** 117 **Outpatient Visits:**
165253 **Births:** 2519 **Total Expense ($000):** 130380 **Payroll Expense
($000):** 41262 **Personnel:** 820

✠ △ **REGIONAL HOSPITAL OF SCRANTON (390237)**, 746 Jefferson Avenue,
Zip 18510–1624; tel. 570/348–7100 **A**1 2 3 5 7 9 10 12 **F**7 8 11 12 15 17
18 20 22 24 26 28 29 30 31 34 35 39 40 44 45 46 47 48 49 50 51 53 54
57 58 59 60 61 63 64 65 66 68 70 74 75 77 78 79 81 85 86 87 91 92 93
97 107 108 109 110 111 112 113 114 115 116 117 118 119 120 121 122
123 124 126 130 132 143 144 145 146 147 148 **P**6 **S** Community Health
Systems, Inc., Franklin, TN
Primary Contact: Brooks Turkel, Chief Executive Officer
CFO: Stephen Franko, Vice President Finance and Chief Financial Officer
CMO: Anthony Yanni, M.D., Vice President Medical Affairs
CIO: Jorge Coronel, Chief Information Officer
Web address: www.regionalhospitalofscranton.net
**Control:** Corporation, Investor–owned, for–profit **Service:** General Medical and
Surgical

**Staffed Beds:** 192 **Admissions:** 8689 **Census:** 121 **Outpatient Visits:**
102745 **Births:** 0 **Total Expense ($000):** 153737 **Payroll Expense ($000):**
47772 **Personnel:** 818

## SELLERSVILLE—Bucks County

✠ **GRAND VIEW HEALTH (390057)**, 700 Lawn Avenue, Zip 18960–1548, Mailing
Address: P.O. Box 902, Zip 18960–0902; tel. 215/453–4000 **A**1 2 9 10 **F**3 7
11 13 15 18 19 28 29 32 34 35 37 40 44 45 46 47 48 49 50 51 54 56 57
59 61 62 63 64 65 68 70 71 72 74 75 76 77 78 79 81 84 85 86 87 89 90
93 96 97 107 108 110 111 114 115 117 118 119 120 121 123 130 131
132 134 143 146 147 **P**6
Primary Contact: Jean M. Keeler, President and Chief Executive Officer
COO: J. Mark Horne, Senior Vice President and Chief Operating Officer
CFO: Michael Keen, Senior Vice President and Chief Financial Officer
CMO: Jane Ferry, M.D., Vice President Medical Affairs
CIO: Jane Doll Loveless, Vice President Information Services
CNO: Kathleen Burkey, R.N., Vice President of Nursing
Web address: www.gvh.org
**Control:** Other not–for–profit (including NFP Corporation) **Service:** General
Medical and Surgical

**Staffed Beds:** 202 **Admissions:** 8763 **Census:** 104 **Outpatient Visits:**
319969 **Births:** 1270 **Total Expense ($000):** 173238 **Payroll Expense
($000):** 90462 **Personnel:** 1485

**PA**

---

**Hospital, Medicare Provider Number, Address, Telephone, Approval, Facility, and Physician Codes, Health Care System**

★ American Hospital Association (AHA) membership
□ The Joint Commission accreditation
○ Healthcare Facilities Accreditation Program
◇ DNV Healthcare Inc. accreditation
⇑ Center for Improvement in Healthcare Quality Accreditation
△ Commission on Accreditation of Rehabilitation Facilities (CARF) accreditation

**PA**

### SENECA—Venango County

☐ **UPMC NORTHWEST (390091)**, 100 Fairfield Drive, Zip 16346–2130;
tel. 814/676–7600, (Total facility includes 16 beds in nursing home–type unit) **A**1
2 9 10 19 **F**3 11 13 15 18 28 29 31 34 35 40 44 45 47 50 56 57 59 62 63
64 68 70 74 75 76 78 79 81 83 84 85 86 87 89 90 93 96 97 98 100 101
102 103 107 108 110 111 114 115 118 119 121 128 130 131 132 135 141
142 146 147 148 **S** UPMC, Pittsburgh, PA
Primary Contact: David Gibbons, President
COO: Brian Durniok, Vice President Operations
CFO: Bradley Dinger, Chief Financial Officer
CMO: David McCandless, Vice President Medical Affairs
CHR: Brian Durniok, Vice President Human Resources
CNO: Daniel Shearn, R.N., Vice President Patient Services and Chief Nursing
Officer
Web address: www.upmc.com/locations/hospitals/northwest/Pages/default.aspx
**Control:** Other not–for–profit (including NFP Corporation) **Service:** General
Medical and Surgical

> **Staffed Beds:** 180 **Admissions:** 6800 **Census:** 92 **Outpatient Visits:** 135999
> **Births:** 523 **Total Expense ($000):** 98155 **Payroll Expense ($000):** 28552
> **Personnel:** 585

### SEWICKLEY—Allegheny County

⊞ **HEALTHSOUTH REHABILITATION HOSPITAL OF SEWICKLEY (393045)**, 303
Camp Meeting Road, Zip 15143–8322; tel. 412/741–9500 **A**1 10 **F**29 34 56 57
59 60 64 65 74 75 87 90 91 92 93 95 96 100 132 146 148 **S** HEALTHSOUTH
Corporation, Birmingham, AL
Primary Contact: Leah Laffey, R.N., Chief Executive Officer
CFO: Daniel A. Vrana, Area Controller
CMO: Shelana Gibbs–McElvy, M.D., Medical Director
CIO: Jamie Smith, Supervisor Health Information Management Systems
CHR: Melissa Coleman, Director Human Resources
CNO: Christie Ryan, Chief Nursing Officer
Web address: www.healthsouthsewickley.com
**Control:** Corporation, Investor–owned, for–profit **Service:** Rehabilitation

> **Staffed Beds:** 44 **Admissions:** 877 **Census:** 36 **Outpatient Visits:** 4012
> **Births:** 0 **Total Expense ($000):** 11798 **Payroll Expense ($000):** 6122
> **Personnel:** 96

☐ **SEWICKLEY VALLEY HOSPITAL, (A DIVISION OF VALLEY MEDICAL
FACILITIES) (390037)**, 720 Blackburn Road, Zip 15143–1459;
tel. 412/741–6600 **A**1 9 10 **F**3 8 11 12 13 14 15 18 20 28 29 30 32 34 35
38 40 46 49 50 53 54 55 57 59 60 64 70 74 75 76 77 78 79 81 82 84 85
86 90 92 93 96 97 98 100 101 102 103 104 107 108 109 110 111 115 118
119 120 121 126 129 130 132 135 145 **P**6 **S** Heritage Valley Health System,
Beaver, PA
Primary Contact: Norman F. Mitry, President and Chief Executive Officer
CFO: Bryan J. Randall, Vice President Finance and Chief Financial Officer
CMO: John Cinicola, M.D., Chief Medical Officer
CIO: David Carleton, Chief Information Officer
CHR: Bruce Edwards, Vice President Human Resources
CNO: Linda Homyk, Chief Nursing Officer
Web address: www.heritagevalley.org
**Control:** Other not–for–profit (including NFP Corporation) **Service:** General
Medical and Surgical

> **Staffed Beds:** 179 **Admissions:** 8833 **Census:** 100 **Births:** 844

### SHARON—Mercer County

⊞ **SHARON REGIONAL HEALTH SYSTEM (390211)**, 740 East State Street,
Zip 16146–3395; tel. 724/983–3911, (Nonreporting) **A**1 6 9 10 19
**S** Community Health Systems, Inc., Franklin, TN
Primary Contact: Jason Roebeck, Chief Executive Officer
CFO: Jeffrey Chrobak, Vice President Finance and Chief Financial Officer
CHR: John Davidson, Vice President Human Resources
Web address: www.sharonregional.com
**Control:** Corporation, Investor–owned, for–profit **Service:** General Medical and
Surgical

> **Staffed Beds:** 256

### SHICKSHINNY—Luzerne County

**CLEAR BROOK LODGE**, 890 Bethel Road, Zip 18655;
tel. 570/864–3116, (Nonreporting)
Primary Contact: Nicholas Colangelo, Ph.D., Chief Executive Officer
Web address: www.clearbrookinc.com
**Control:** Other not–for–profit (including NFP Corporation) **Service:** Alcoholism and
other chemical dependency

> **Staffed Beds:** 65

### SHIPPENSBURG—Franklin County

☐ **ROXBURY TREATMENT CENTER (394050)**, 601 Roxbury Road,
Zip 17257–9302; tel. 800/648–4673, (Nonreporting) **A**1 9 10 **S** Universal Health
Services, Inc., King of Prussia, PA
Primary Contact: Shauna Radzieski, Chief Executive Officer
Web address: www.roxburyhospital.com
**Control:** Corporation, Investor–owned, for–profit **Service:** Psychiatric

> **Staffed Beds:** 94

### SOMERSET—Somerset County

★ **SOMERSET HOSPITAL (390039)**, 225 South Center Avenue, Zip 15501–2088;
tel. 814/443–5000 **A**9 10 20 **F**3 8 11 13 15 17 18 20 22 26 28 29 30 32 34
35 40 45 49 50 53 57 59 62 63 64 68 74 76 77 79 80 81 82 85 86 87 89
93 97 98 99 100 103 104 107 108 111 115 119 129 130 131 132 133 135
141 146 147 148
Primary Contact: Craig M. Saylor, Interim CEO
COO: Andy Rush, Senior Vice President and Chief Operating Officer
CFO: Matthew Kociola, Senior Vice President and Chief Financial Officer
CIO: Jonathan Bauer, Director Information Systems
CHR: Mark P. Frick, Senior Vice President Human Resources
CNO: Suellen Lichtenfels, Vice President and Chief Nursing Officer
Web address: www.somersethospital.com
**Control:** Other not–for–profit (including NFP Corporation) **Service:** General
Medical and Surgical

> **Staffed Beds:** 111 **Admissions:** 3382 **Census:** 42 **Outpatient Visits:** 141622
> **Births:** 403 **Total Expense ($000):** 64019 **Payroll Expense ($000):** 26110
> **Personnel:** 597

### SPRINGFIELD—Delaware County

**SPRINGFIELD HOSPITAL** See Crozer–Chester Medical Center, Upland

### STATE COLLEGE—Centre County

⊞ **MOUNT NITTANY MEDICAL CENTER (390268)**, 1800 East Park Avenue,
Zip 16803–6797; tel. 814/231–7000 **A**1 2 3 5 9 10 **F**3 7 13 15 17 20 22 28
29 30 31 35 40 51 57 59 64 68 70 73 74 75 76 77 78 79 80 81 82 85 87
89 93 98 100 101 102 107 108 111 114 115 118 119 121 126 129 130
132 135 143 144 146 148
Primary Contact: Steven E. Brown, FACHE, President and Chief Executive Officer
CFO: Richard Wisniewski, Senior Vice President Finance and Chief Financial Officer
CMO: Jeffrey Ratner, M.D., Senior Vice President Medical Affairs
CIO: Wayne Thompson, Executive Vice President and Chief Information Officer
CHR: Jerry Dittmann, Vice President Human Resources
CNO: Janet Schachtner, R.N., Senior Vice President, Patient Care Services
Web address: www.mountnittany.org
**Control:** Other not–for–profit (including NFP Corporation) **Service:** General
Medical and Surgical

> **Staffed Beds:** 207 **Admissions:** 11874 **Census:** 130 **Outpatient Visits:**
> 289876 **Births:** 1277 **Total Expense ($000):** 335417 **Payroll Expense**
> **($000):** 140403 **Personnel:** 1367

### SUNBURY—Northumberland County

⊞ **SUNBURY COMMUNITY HOSPITAL AND OUTPATIENT CENTER (390084)**,
350 North Eleventh Street, Zip 17801–1611; tel. 570/286–3333, (Nonreporting)
**A**1 9 10 **S** Community Health Systems, Inc., Franklin, TN
Primary Contact: Robert D. Williams, Interim Chief Executive Officer
CFO: James J. Pachucki, Jr., Chief Financial Officer
CMO: Hasan Askari, M.D., Chief of Staff
CIO: Fax Rector, III, Director Information Technology
CHR: Talia Beatty, Director Human Resources
CNO: Catharine L. Keister, Chief Nursing Officer
Web address: www.sunburyhospital.com
**Control:** Other not–for–profit (including NFP Corporation) **Service:** General
Medical and Surgical

> **Staffed Beds:** 76

### SUSQUEHANNA—Susquehanna County

**BARNES–KASSON COUNTY HOSPITAL (391309)**, 2872 Turnpike Street,
Zip 18847–2771; tel. 570/853–3135, (Nonreporting) **A**9 10 18
Primary Contact: Sara F. Adornato, Executive Director
CFO: Kelli R. Kane, Director of Finance
CMO: Pravinchandra Patel, M.D., Chief Medical Officer
CIO: Eric Detwiler, Director Information Technology
Web address: www.barnes–kasson.org
**Control:** Other not–for–profit (including NFP Corporation) **Service:** General
Medical and Surgical

> **Staffed Beds:** 83

### TITUSVILLE—Crawford County

**TITUSVILLE AREA HOSPITAL (391314)**, 406 West Oak Street,
Zip 16354–1404; tel. 814/827–1851, (Nonreporting) **A**9 10 20
Primary Contact: Anthony J. Nasralla, FACHE, President and Chief Executive
Officer
CFO: Paul Mattis, Vice President Finance
CMO: William Sonnenberg, M.D., President Medical Staff
CIO: Deanna Callahan, Director Information Systems
CHR: Jeffrey Saintz, Vice President Human Resources
Web address: www.titusvillehospital.org
**Control:** Other not–for–profit (including NFP Corporation) **Service:** General
Medical and Surgical

> **Staffed Beds:** 50

*Many Facility Codes have changed. Please refer to the AHA Guide Code Chart.*     © 2015 AHA Guide

## TORRANCE—Westmoreland County

**TORRANCE STATE HOSPITAL (394026)**, Torrance Road, Zip 15779–0111, Mailing Address: P.O. Box 111, Zip 15779–0111; tel. 724/459–8000 **A**10 **F**39 75 98 130 135 143 146 147 148
Primary Contact: Edna I. McCutcheon, Chief Executive Officer
COO: R. Brad Snyder, Chief Operating Officer
CFO: Michael Yahner, Chief Financial Officer
CMO: Herbert G. Chissell, M.D., Chief Medical Officer
Web address: www.dpw.state.pa.us
**Control:** State–Government, nonfederal **Service:** Psychiatric

**Staffed Beds:** 328 **Admissions:** 304 **Census:** 313 **Outpatient Visits:** 0 **Births:** 0

## TOWANDA—Bradford County

★ **GUTHRIE TOWANDA MEMORIAL HOSPITAL (390236)**, 91 Hospital Drive, Zip 18848–9702; tel. 570/265–2191, (Nonreporting) **A**9 10 **S** Guthrie Clinic, Sayre, PA
Primary Contact: William K. Rohrbach, Chief Executive Officer
CMO: Joseph Cama, M.D., President Medical Staff
CIO: Karen Brown, Manager Information Technology
CHR: Linda Berry, Vice President Human Resources
CNO: Lynn Dibble, Vice President Patient Care Services
Web address: www.memorialhospital.org
**Control:** Other not–for–profit (including NFP Corporation) **Service:** General Medical and Surgical

**Staffed Beds:** 103

## TRANSFER—Mercer County

**EDGEWOOD SURGICAL HOSPITAL (390307)**, 239 Edgewood Drive Extension, Zip 16154–1817; tel. 724/646–0400, (Nonreporting) **A**9 10
Primary Contact: Michael Torn, Chief Executive Officer
Web address: www.edgewoodsurgical.com
**Control:** Corporation, Investor–owned, for–profit **Service:** Surgical

**Staffed Beds:** 10

## TROY—Bradford County

★ **TROY COMMUNITY HOSPITAL (391305)**, 275 Guthrie Drive, Zip 16947; tel. 570/297–2121 **A**9 10 18 **F**3 11 15 28 30 34 40 45 50 57 64 75 81 82 85 87 93 96 107 110 111 119 129 130 133 135 146 148 **S** Guthrie Clinic, Sayre, PA
Primary Contact: Staci Covey, R.N., MS, President
CFO: Bernie Smith, Chief Financial Officer
CMO: Vance A. Good, M.D., Chief Medical Staff
CIO: Dale Swingle, Vice President Information Services
CHR: Frank Pinkosky, Executive Vice President
CNO: Lori Barnett, R.N., Chief Nursing Officer
Web address: www.guthrie.org
**Control:** Other not–for–profit (including NFP Corporation) **Service:** General Medical and Surgical

**Staffed Beds:** 25 **Admissions:** 790 **Census:** 20 **Outpatient Visits:** 28516 **Births:** 0 **Total Expense ($000):** 18815 **Payroll Expense ($000):** 5047 **Personnel:** 108

## TUNKHANNOCK— County

✠ **TYLER MEMORIAL HOSPITAL (390192)**, 5950 State Route 6, Zip 18657–7905; tel. 570/836–2161, (Nonreporting) **A**1 9 10 **S** Community Health Systems, Inc., Franklin, TN
Primary Contact: Diane Ljungquist, R.N., MS, Chief Executive Officer
CFO: Robert Stiekes, Chief Financial Officer
CMO: Terrance Chilson, Chief of Staff
CNO: Patricia Casals, MSN, Chief Nursing Officer
Web address: www.tylermemorialhospital.net
**Control:** Corporation, Investor–owned, for–profit **Service:** General Medical and Surgical

**Staffed Beds:** 48

## TYRONE—Blair County

**TYRONE HOSPITAL (391307)**, 187 Hospital Drive, Zip 16686–1808; tel. 814/684–1255 **A**9 10 18 **F**3 15 40 75 77 79 81 82 93 107 119 130 133 146
Primary Contact: Stephen Gildea, Chief Executive Officer
CFO: Todd Dieffenbach, Chief Financial Officer
CMO: Kelly Biggs, M.D., Chief Medical Officer
CHR: Rosemary Jorden Best, Director Human Resources
CNO: Sharon Fisher, R.N., Chief Nursing Officer
Web address: www.tyronehospital.org
**Control:** Other not–for–profit (including NFP Corporation) **Service:** General Medical and Surgical

**Staffed Beds:** 25 **Admissions:** 652 **Census:** 5 **Births:** 0

## UNIONTOWN—Fayette County

✠ **UNIONTOWN HOSPITAL (390041)**, 500 West Berkeley Street, Zip 15401–5596; tel. 724/430–5000 **A**1 9 10 **F**11 12 13 15 18 20 22 26 28 29 34 35 40 45 49 51 54 57 59 64 70 73 74 75 77 78 79 81 84 90 92 93 95 96 102 107 108 110 111 114 115 118 119 130 132 135 146 148
Primary Contact: Steven P. Handy, CPA, Chief Executive Officer
CHR: James Proud, Vice President Human Resources and Marketing
CNO: Betty Ann Rock, Vice President Nursing and Chief Nursing Officer
Web address: www.uniontownhospital.com
**Control:** Other not–for–profit (including NFP Corporation) **Service:** General Medical and Surgical

**Staffed Beds:** 143 **Admissions:** 9330 **Census:** 111 **Outpatient Visits:** 220193 **Births:** 1027 **Total Expense ($000):** 119692 **Payroll Expense ($000):** 44235 **Personnel:** 949

## UPLAND—Delaware County

✠ **CROZER–CHESTER MEDICAL CENTER (390180)**, One Medical Center Boulevard, Zip 19013–3995; tel. 610/447–2000, (Includes SPRINGFIELD HOSPITAL, 190 West Sproul Road, Springfield, Zip 19064–2097; tel. 610/328–8700; TAYLOR HOSPITAL, 175 East Chester Pike, Ridley Park, Zip 19078–2212; tel. 610/595–6000) **A**1 2 3 5 10 12 13 **F**2 3 5 6 7 8 11 12 13 14 15 16 17 18 20 22 24 26 28 29 30 31 32 34 35 37 38 40 41 43 44 45 46 49 50 51 52 54 55 56 57 58 59 61 62 63 64 65 66 68 70 72 74 75 76 77 78 79 81 82 83 84 85 86 87 89 90 92 93 94 96 97 98 99 100 101 102 103 104 105 107 108 109 110 111 114 115 116 117 118 119 120 121 123 124 126 129 130 131 132 134 135 138 143 146 147 148 **P**6
**S** Crozer–Keystone Health System, Springfield, PA
Primary Contact: Patrick J. Gavin, President
CMO: Sat Arora, M.D., President Medical and Dental Staff
CIO: Robert E. Wilson, Vice President and Chief Information Officer
Web address: www.crozer.org
**Control:** Other not–for–profit (including NFP Corporation) **Service:** General Medical and Surgical

**Staffed Beds:** 400 **Admissions:** 21237 **Census:** 277 **Births:** 1420

## WARREN—Warren County

**WARREN GENERAL HOSPITAL (390146)**, Two Crescent Park West, Zip 16365–0068, Mailing Address: P.O. Box 68, Zip 16365–0068; tel. 814/723–4973 **A**9 10 **F**4 11 13 15 28 29 30 31 34 35 39 40 44 45 50 51 57 59 62 63 64 70 76 77 78 79 81 84 85 86 87 89 92 93 97 98 103 107 108 110 111 113 114 117 119 120 121 130 131 133 146 **P**6
Primary Contact: Richard Allen, Chief Executive Officer
COO: Randy California, Chief Operating Officer
CFO: Julie Jacobs, Chief Financial Officer
CMO: John Maljovec, M.D., Medical Director
CIO: Helen Rosequist, Manager Information Systems
CHR: Stacy Ryan, Corporate Director Human Resources
CNO: Jolene M. Johnson, R.N., Acting Chief Nursing Officer
Web address: www.wgh.org
**Control:** Other not–for–profit (including NFP Corporation) **Service:** General Medical and Surgical

**Staffed Beds:** 87 **Admissions:** 2950 **Census:** 40 **Outpatient Visits:** 219536 **Births:** 335 **Total Expense ($000):** 75447 **Payroll Expense ($000):** 33208 **Personnel:** 555

**PA**

---

**Hospital, Medicare Provider Number, Address, Telephone, Approval, Facility, and Physician Codes, Health Care System**

★ American Hospital Association (AHA) membership   ○ Healthcare Facilities Accreditation Program   ⇑ Center for Improvement in Healthcare Quality Accreditation
□ The Joint Commission accreditation   ◇ DNV Healthcare Inc. accreditation   △ Commission on Accreditation of Rehabilitation Facilities (CARF) accreditation

---

**WARREN STATE HOSPITAL (394016)**, 33 Main Drive, Zip 16365–5001; tel. 814/723–5500 **A**10 **F**4 39 50 56 75 77 82 98 100 101 103 128 130 132 135 143 146 **P**6
Primary Contact: Charlotte M. Uber, Chief Executive Officer
COO: Ronnie Cropper, Chief Operating Officer
CFO: Terry Crambes, Manager Finance
CMO: Asha Prabhu, M.D., Chief Medical Officer
CIO: Karen Byler, Information Technology Generalist
CHR: Nancy Saullo, Director Human Resources
CNO: Sara Flasher, Chief Nurse Executive
Web address: www.dpw.pa.gov
**Control:** State–Government, nonfederal **Service:** Psychiatric

Staffed Beds: 180 Admissions: 86 Census: 182 Outpatient Visits: 0 Births: 0 Total Expense ($000): 42363 Payroll Expense ($000): 20017 Personnel: 386

### WASHINGTON—Washington County

☐ **ADVANCED SURGICAL HOSPITAL (390323)**, 100 Trich Drive Suite 1, Zip 15301–5990; tel. 724/884–0710, (Nonreporting) **A**1 10
Primary Contact: Anne S. Hast, R.N., Chief Executive Officer
CFO: Diane Hritz, Chief Financial Officer
CNO: Anne S. Hast, R.N., Director of Nursing
Web address: www.ashospital.net
**Control:** Partnership, Investor–owned, for–profit **Service:** Orthopedic

Staffed Beds: 14

✠ **WASHINGTON HOSPITAL (390042)**, 155 Wilson Avenue, Zip 15301–3398; tel. 724/225–7000 **A**1 3 5 6 9 10 13 **F**3 5 11 12 13 15 18 20 22 24 26 28 29 30 31 32 34 35 36 38 39 40 45 46 49 50 53 54 56 57 59 60 61 63 64 65 70 74 75 76 77 78 79 81 82 83 84 85 86 89 90 91 92 93 94 96 97 98 99 100 101 102 103 107 108 110 111 114 115 118 119 126 127 130 131 132 134 135 146 147 148 **P**1 7
Primary Contact: Gary B. Weinstein, President and Chief Executive Officer
COO: Brook Ward, Executive Vice President
CFO: Alisa Rucker, Vice President Finance and Chief Financial Officer
CMO: Paul T. Cullen, M.D., Vice President Medical Affairs
CIO: Rodney Louk, Vice President Information Systems
CHR: Barbara A. McCullough, Vice President Human Resources
CNO: Karen A. Bray, R.N., Vice President Patient Care Services
Web address: www.washingtonhospital.org
**Control:** Other not–for–profit (including NFP Corporation) **Service:** General Medical and Surgical

Staffed Beds: 260 Admissions: 12470 Census: 152 Outpatient Visits: 674028 Births: 1055 Total Expense ($000): 220427 Payroll Expense ($000): 98580 Personnel: 1469

### WAYNESBORO—Franklin County

✠ **WAYNESBORO HOSPITAL (390138)**, 501 East Main Street, Zip 17268–2394; tel. 717/765–4000 **A**1 9 10 **F**3 11 13 15 29 30 34 40 45 49 50 57 59 64 65 68 74 75 76 77 79 81 85 86 87 91 92 93 94 107 108 110 111 115 118 119 129 130 131 132 133 135 146 147 148 **P**8 **S** Summit Health, Chambersburg, PA
Primary Contact: Melissa Dubrow, Chief Operating Officer
COO: Melissa Dubrow, Vice President and Chief Operating Officer
CFO: Kimberly Rzomp, Vice President Finance
CMO: Thomas Anderson, M.D., Vice President Medical Affairs
CIO: Michele Zeigler, Vice President Information Services
CHR: Jennifer Knight, Manager Human Resources
CNO: Jill Keller, R.N., Vice President for Nursing Services, Quality and Risk Management
Web address: www.summithealth.org
**Control:** Other not–for–profit (including NFP Corporation) **Service:** General Medical and Surgical

Staffed Beds: 56 Admissions: 2483 Census: 22 Outpatient Visits: 91559 Births: 448 Total Expense ($000): 51470 Payroll Expense ($000): 25414 Personnel: 402

### WAYNESBURG—Greene County

☐ **WASHINGTON HEALTH SYSTEM GREENE (390150)**, 350 Bonar Avenue, Zip 15370–1608; tel. 724/627–3101, (Nonreporting) **A**1 9 10
Primary Contact: Terry Wiltrout, President
COO: Janel Mudry, Chief Operating Officer
CFO: James C. Rutkowski, Chief Financial Officer
CMO: Jamie Boris, M.D., President Medical Staff
CIO: Leslie Hayhurst, Director Information Systems
CHR: Patricia Marshall, Assistant Administrator Human Resources
Web address: www.sw–rmc.com
**Control:** Corporation, Investor–owned, for–profit **Service:** General Medical and Surgical

Staffed Beds: 77

### WELLSBORO—Tioga County

✠ **SOLDIERS AND SAILORS MEMORIAL HOSPITAL (390043)**, 32–36 Central Avenue, Zip 16901–1899; tel. 570/724–1631 **A**1 9 10 20 **F**3 11 13 15 17 28 31 34 40 48 49 64 65 70 75 76 78 79 81 85 93 98 102 103 104 107 108 110 111 115 118 119 129 130 146 **P**7 **S** Susquehanna Health System, Williamsport, PA
Primary Contact: Janie Hilfiger, President
CFO: Ronald Gilbert, Jr., Chief Financial Officer
CMO: Walter Laibinis, M.D., Chief Medical Officer
CIO: Timothy E. Schoener, Senior Vice President and Chief Information Officer
CHR: Christine A. Ballard, Vice President Human Resources
CNO: Matt Romania, Director of Nursing
Web address: www.susquehannahealth.org
**Control:** Other not–for–profit (including NFP Corporation) **Service:** General Medical and Surgical

Staffed Beds: 83 Admissions: 2328 Census: 27 Outpatient Visits: 104103 Births: 285 Total Expense ($000): 53472 Payroll Expense ($000): 21984 Personnel: 444

### WERNERSVILLE—Berks County

**WERNERSVILLE STATE HOSPITAL (394014)**, Route 422, Zip 19565–0300, Mailing Address: P.O. Box 300, Zip 19565–0300; tel. 610/678–3411 **A**10 **F**30 39 75 77 98 103 130 135 146
Primary Contact: Andrea Kepler, Chief Executive Officer
COO: Cheryl Benson, Chief Operating Officer
CMO: Dale K. Adair, M.D., Chief Medical Officer
CIO: William Edwards, Information Technology Generalist
CHR: Melvin McMinn, Director Human Resources
Web address: www.dpw.state.pa.us/
**Control:** State–Government, nonfederal **Service:** Psychiatric

Staffed Beds: 266 Admissions: 46 Census: 254 Outpatient Visits: 0 Births: 0 Total Expense ($000): 59581 Payroll Expense ($000): 30269 Personnel: 573

### WEST CHESTER—Chester County

✠ **LIFECARE HOSPITALS OF CHESTER COUNTY (392048)**, 400 East Marshall Street, Zip 19380–5412; tel. 484/826–0400 **A**1 9 10 **F**1 77 79 130 148 **P**5 **S** LifeCare Management Services, Plano, TX
Primary Contact: Garrett Arneson, Chief Executive Officer
CMO: Robert Satriale, M.D., Medical Director
CHR: Evan Ganley, Manager Human Resources
CNO: Susan Ferguson, Chief Nursing Officer
Web address: www.lifecare–hospitals.com
**Control:** Corporation, Investor–owned, for–profit **Service:** Long–Term Acute Care hospital

Staffed Beds: 39 Admissions: 314 Census: 23 Outpatient Visits: 0 Births: 0 Total Expense ($000): 14996 Payroll Expense ($000): 6529 Personnel: 100

✠ **PENN MEDICINE CHESTER COUNTY HOSPITAL (390179)**, 701 East Marshall Street, Zip 19380–4412; tel. 610/431–5000 **A**1 2 3 5 9 10 **F**3 11 13 15 17 18 20 22 24 26 28 29 30 31 34 35 36 39 40 44 45 46 49 50 51 54 55 57 58 59 60 63 64 68 70 72 74 75 76 77 78 79 81 82 84 85 86 87 89 93 107 108 110 111 114 115 116 117 119 120 121 126 130 131 132 135 146 147 148 **S** University of Pennsylvania Health System, Philadelphia, PA
Primary Contact: Michael J. Duncan, President and Chief Executive Officer
COO: Michael Barber, Chief Operating Officer
CFO: Kenneth E. Flickinger, Chief Financial Officer
CMO: Richard D. Donze, D.O., Senior Vice President Medical Affairs
CIO: Karen Pinsky, M.D., Chief Medical Information Officer
CHR: Jacqueline Felicetti, Chief Human Resource Officer
CNO: Angela Coladonato, MSN, Chief Nursing Officer
Web address: www.chestercountyhospital.org
**Control:** Other not–for–profit (including NFP Corporation) **Service:** General Medical and Surgical

Staffed Beds: 211 Admissions: 12519 Census: 154 Outpatient Visits: 243091 Births: 2371 Total Expense ($000): 251377 Payroll Expense ($000): 110188 Personnel: 1668

### WEST GROVE—Chester County

✠ **JENNERSVILLE REGIONAL HOSPITAL (390220)**, 1015 West Baltimore Pike, Zip 19390–9459; tel. 610/869–1000 **A**1 2 9 10 **F**3 13 15 18 29 35 40 45 49 50 51 57 59 70 74 75 76 79 81 82 85 87 92 93 107 108 110 111 115 119 129 130 131 132 133 146 147 **P**6 **S** Community Health Systems, Inc., Franklin, TN
Primary Contact: Andrew Guz, Chief Executive Officer
CFO: Tracey Claxton, Chief Financial Officer
CMO: Tracy Carmellini, M.D., Chief of Staff
CHR: Debra Basquill, Director Human Resources
CNO: David Schmidt, R.N., Chief Nursing Officer
Web address: www.jennersville.com
**Control:** Corporation, Investor–owned, for–profit **Service:** General Medical and Surgical

Staffed Beds: 63 Admissions: 3145 Census: 32 Births: 346

## WEST READING—Berks County

☒ △ **READING HOSPITAL (390044)**, Sixth Avenue and Spruce Street, Zip 19611–1428, Mailing Address: P.O. Box 16052, Zip 19612–6052; tel. 610/988–8000 **A**1 2 3 5 6 7 9 10 12 13 **F**3 5 8 11 12 13 15 18 20 22 24 26 28 29 30 31 32 34 35 37 40 41 42 43 44 45 46 48 49 50 54 56 57 58 59 60 61 62 64 65 66 68 70 72 73 74 75 76 77 78 79 81 82 84 85 86 87 89 90 92 93 94 96 97 98 99 100 101 102 103 104 105 106 107 108 110 111 114 115 116 117 118 119 120 121 123 124 125 126 128 129 130 131 132 135 144 146 147 148 **P**6 8
Primary Contact: Clinton Matthews, President and Chief Executive Officer
CFO: Richard W. Jones, Chief Financial Officer
CMO: M. Joseph Grennan, Jr., M.D., Senior Vice President and Chief Medical Officer
CIO: Jayashree Raman, Vice President and Chief Information Officer
CNO: Mary Christine Agnew, R.N., Vice President and Chief Nursing Officer
Web address: www.readinghospital.org
**Control:** Other not–for–profit (including NFP Corporation) **Service:** General Medical and Surgical

**Staffed Beds:** 679 **Admissions:** 27230 **Census:** 344 **Outpatient Visits:** 1093517 **Births:** 3740 **Total Expense ($000):** 754217 **Payroll Expense ($000):** 307909 **Personnel:** 4693

## WILKES BARRE—Luzerne County

☒ **GEISINGER WYOMING VALLEY MEDICAL CENTER (390270)**, 1000 East Mountain Boulevard, Zip 18711–0027; tel. 570/808–7300, (Nonreporting) **A**1 2 3 5 9 10 13 **S** Geisinger Health System, Danville, PA
Primary Contact: Ronald R. Beer, FACHE, Vice President, Clinical Operations
CFO: Thomas A. Bielecki, Chief Financial Officer
CMO: Steven Pierdon, M.D., Executive Vice President and Chief Medical Officer
CIO: Frank Richards, Chief Information Officer
CHR: Margaret Heffers, Assistant Vice President Human Resources
Web address: www.geisinger.org
**Control:** Other not–for–profit (including NFP Corporation) **Service:** General Medical and Surgical

**Staffed Beds:** 238

## WILKES–BARRE—Luzerne County

**CLEAR BROOK MANOR**, 1100 East Northampton Street, Zip 18702–9803; tel. 570/823–1171, (Nonreporting)
Primary Contact: Robert Piccone, President
Web address: www.clearbrookinc.com
**Control:** Other not–for–profit (including NFP Corporation) **Service:** Alcoholism and other chemical dependency

**Staffed Beds:** 50

☒ △ **JOHN HEINZ INSTITUTE OF REHABILITATION MEDICINE (393036)**, 150 Mundy Street, Zip 18702–6830; tel. 570/826–3800, (Nonreporting) **A**1 7 10
Primary Contact: Karen Kearney, Vice President Inpatient Rehabilitation Services
CFO: Mike Avvisato, Vice President and Chief Financial Officer
CMO: Gregory Basting, M.D., Vice President Medical Affairs
CIO: John Regula, Chief Information Officer
CHR: Judy P. Oprisko, Vice President Human Resources
CNO: Maria Berlyn, Assistant Vice President Nursing Services
Web address: www.allied–services.org
**Control:** Other not–for–profit (including NFP Corporation) **Service:** Rehabilitation

**Staffed Beds:** 71

**VETERANS AFFAIRS MEDICAL CENTER** See Wilkes–Barre Veterans Affairs Medical Center

★ △ **WILKES–BARRE GENERAL HOSPITAL (390137)**, 575 North River Street, Zip 18764–0001; tel. 570/829–8111, (Includes WILKES–BARRE GENERAL HOSPITAL, 575 North River Street, Zip 18764; tel. 570/829–8111) **A**2 3 5 7 9 10 **F**3 8 12 13 15 17 18 20 22 24 28 29 30 31 34 37 40 44 45 48 49 50 51 53 54 56 57 59 61 64 66 70 73 74 75 76 78 79 81 85 86 87 89 90 93 96 107 108 111 112 114 115 116 117 118 119 126 129 130 132 145 146 147 148 **S** Community Health Systems, Inc., Franklin, TN
Primary Contact: Cornelio R. Catena, President and Chief Executive Officer
COO: Robert P. Hoffman, Vice President and Director Patient Care Services
CFO: Maggie Koehler, Senior Vice President and Chief Financial Officer
CMO: Ragupathy Veluswamy, M.D., Vice President Medical Affairs
CIO: Chris Galanda, Chief Information Officer
CHR: James Carmody, Vice President Human Resources
Web address: www.wvhc.org
**Control:** Corporation, Investor–owned, for–profit **Service:** General Medical and Surgical

**Staffed Beds:** 374 **Admissions:** 14385 **Census:** 211 **Outpatient Visits:** 506582 **Births:** 1118 **Total Expense ($000):** 262240 **Payroll Expense ($000):** 82614 **Personnel:** 1553

☒ △ **WILKES–BARRE VETERANS AFFAIRS MEDICAL CENTER**, 1111 East End Boulevard, Zip 18711–0030; tel. 570/824–3521, (Nonreporting) **A**1 2 3 5 7 9 **S** Department of Veterans Affairs, Washington, DC
Primary Contact: Michael Adelman, M.D., Medical Center Director
COO: Joesph P. Sharon, Associate Director
CFO: Donald E. Foote, Fiscal Officer
CMO: Mirza Z. Ali, M.D., Chief of Staff
CIO: David Longmore, Chief Information Officer
CHR: Dawn P. DeMorrow, Chief Human Resources Service
Web address: www.va.gov/vamcwb
**Control:** Veterans Affairs, Government, federal **Service:** General Medical and Surgical

**Staffed Beds:** 161

**WYOMING VALLEY HEALTH CARE SYSTEM** See Wilkes–Barre General Hospital

## WILLIAMSPORT—Lycoming County

★ **DIVINE PROVIDENCE HOSPITAL (394048)**, 1100 Grampian Boulevard, Zip 17701–1995; tel. 570/326–8000 **A**3 9 10 **F**10 11 15 31 35 38 44 50 51 53 54 55 56 59 62 63 64 68 75 77 78 79 81 82 83 84 86 87 93 98 99 100 103 108 110 111 115 120 121 129 130 131 132 134 146 147 148 **P**7
**S** Susquehanna Health System, Williamsport, PA
Primary Contact: Robert E. Kane, President
COO: Neil G. Armstrong, FACHE, Vice President and Chief Operating Officer
Web address: www.susquehannahealth.org
**Control:** Other not–for–profit (including NFP Corporation) **Service:** Psychiatric

**Staffed Beds:** 31 **Admissions:** 609 **Census:** 15 **Outpatient Visits:** 296044 **Births:** 0 **Total Expense ($000):** 79693 **Payroll Expense ($000):** 21360 **Personnel:** 228

**WILLIAMSPORT HOSPITAL AND MEDICAL CENTER** See Williamsport Regional Medical Center

☒ **WILLIAMSPORT REGIONAL MEDICAL CENTER (390045)**, 700 High Street, Zip 17701–3100; tel. 570/321–1000 **A**1 2 5 9 10 13 **F**3 7 9 11 12 13 15 17 18 20 22 24 26 28 29 30 32 34 40 44 45 46 47 48 49 50 52 53 54 56 57 58 59 60 61 65 68 70 73 74 75 76 77 79 81 85 86 87 89 90 91 92 93 94 96 97 107 108 110 114 115 116 117 118 119 120 121 123 124 126 130 132 134 135 143 144 146 147 **P**7 **S** Susquehanna Health System, Williamsport, PA
Primary Contact: Jan E. Fisher, President
COO: Jan E. Fisher, Executive Vice President and Chief Operating Officer and Williamsport Regional Medical Center President
CFO: Charles J. Santangelo, CPA, Executive Vice President and Chief Financial Officer
CIO: Timothy E. Schoener, Senior Vice President and Chief Information Officer
CHR: Christine A. Ballard, Senior Vice President Human Resources
CNO: Susan Duchman, R.N., Vice President and Chief Nursing Officer
Web address: www.susquehannahealth.org
**Control:** Other not–for–profit (including NFP Corporation) **Service:** General Medical and Surgical

**Staffed Beds:** 203 **Admissions:** 11872 **Census:** 147 **Outpatient Visits:** 147045 **Births:** 1206 **Total Expense ($000):** 280202 **Payroll Expense ($000):** 93172 **Personnel:** 1316

## WINDBER—Somerset County

★ **WINDBER MEDICAL CENTER (390112)**, 600 Somerset Avenue, Zip 15963–1331; tel. 814/467–3000 **A**9 10 **F**3 11 12 15 18 28 29 30 34 35 36 40 45 53 55 56 57 58 59 62 63 70 75 79 81 83 84 85 93 107 110 111 114 117 118 119 127 129 130 131 132 135 146 147
Primary Contact: Thomas M. Kurtz, President and Chief Executive Officer
CFO: Richard Sukenik, CPA, Vice President Finance and Chief Financial Officer
CIO: Renee Adams, Director Information Technology
CHR: Jamie Brock, Director Human Resources
CNO: Mary Lee Dadey, R.N., Vice President of Nursing
Web address: www.windbercare.org
**Control:** Other not–for–profit (including NFP Corporation) **Service:** General Medical and Surgical

**Staffed Beds:** 45 **Admissions:** 1293 **Census:** 12 **Outpatient Visits:** 101681 **Births:** 0 **Total Expense ($000):** 44534 **Payroll Expense ($000):** 18863 **Personnel:** 393

## WYNNEWOOD—Montgomery County

**LANKENAU HOSPITAL** See Lankenau Medical Center

**PA**

---

**Hospital, Medicare Provider Number, Address, Telephone, Approval, Facility, and Physician Codes, Health Care System**

★ American Hospital Association (AHA) membership ◯ Healthcare Facilities Accreditation Program ⇑ Center for Improvement in Healthcare Quality Accreditation
☐ The Joint Commission accreditation ◇ DNV Healthcare Inc. accreditation △ Commission on Accreditation of Rehabilitation Facilities (CARF) accreditation

---

⊠ **LANKENAU MEDICAL CENTER (390195)**, 100 Lancaster Avenue West, Zip 19096–3411; tel. 484/476–2000, (Total facility includes 22 beds in nursing home–type unit) **A**1 2 3 5 8 10 12 13 **F**3 11 13 15 17 18 20 22 24 26 28 29 30 31 32 34 35 38 39 40 41 43 44 45 46 47 48 49 50 54 55 56 57 58 59 64 65 66 70 71 72 73 74 75 76 77 78 79 81 82 84 85 86 87 92 97 100 102 103 107 108 110 111 114 115 119 120 121 123 124 126 128 129 130 131 132 135 138 141 143 146 148 **S** Main Line Health
Primary Contact: Phillip D. Robinson, President
CFO: Michael J. Buongiorno, Vice President Finance
CMO: Thomas G. McCarter, Jr., M.D., Chief Medical Officer
CIO: Karen A. Thomas, Acting Vice President and Chief Information Officer
CHR: Eileen McAnally, Senior Vice President Human Resources
Web address: www.mainlinehealth.org
**Control:** Other not–for–profit (including NFP Corporation) **Service:** General Medical and Surgical

> **Staffed Beds:** 345 **Admissions:** 17096 **Census:** 227 **Outpatient Visits:** 313984 **Births:** 2936 **Total Expense ($000):** 391057 **Payroll Expense ($000):** 122294 **Personnel:** 2175

## WYOMISSING—Berks County

⊠ **SURGICAL INSTITUTE OF READING (390316)**, 2752 Century Boulevard, Zip 19610–3345; tel. 610/378–8800 **A**1 9 10 **F**8 29 45 79 81 82 85 86 107 114
Primary Contact: Debbie Beissel, Chief Executive Officer
CFO: Cheryl Peterson, Business Office Manager
CHR: Megan Schaffer, Administrative Assistant
Web address: www.sireading.com
**Control:** Partnership, Investor–owned, for–profit **Service:** Surgical

> **Staffed Beds:** 15 **Admissions:** 620 **Census:** 4 **Outpatient Visits:** 8663 **Births:** 0 **Personnel:** 84

## YORK—York County

⊠ **HEALTHSOUTH REHABILITATION HOSPITAL OF YORK (393037)**, 1850 Normandie Drive, Zip 17408–1534; tel. 717/767–6941, (Nonreporting) **A**1 9 10 **S** HEALTHSOUTH Corporation, Birmingham, AL
Primary Contact: Steven Alwine, Chief Executive Officer
CFO: Joyce Henry, Controller
CMO: Bruce Sicilia, M.D., Medical Director
CIO: Laura Emig, Director Marketing Operations
CHR: Bradley Teahl, Director Human Resources
CNO: Julie Scott, Chief Nursing Officer
Web address: www.healthsouthyork.com
**Control:** Corporation, Investor–owned, for–profit **Service:** Rehabilitation

> **Staffed Beds:** 90

★ ○ **MEMORIAL HOSPITAL (390101)**, 325 South Belmont Street, Zip 17403–2609, Mailing Address: P.O. Box 15118, Zip 17405–7118; tel. 717/843–8623 **A**9 10 11 12 13 **F**3 7 8 13 15 18 20 22 26 29 30 31 34 35 40 45 47 48 49 50 51 54 56 57 58 59 60 64 65 66 68 70 75 76 77 78 79 81 84 85 93 97 107 108 111 116 117 118 119 126 129 130 132 135 146 147 **P**6 **S** Community Health Systems, Inc., Franklin, TN
Primary Contact: Sally J. Dixon, Chief Executive Officer
CIO: James Mahoney, Chief Information Officer
CHR: Corey Hudak, Director Human Resources
CNO: Susan Gordon, R.N., Chief Nursing Officer
Web address: www.mhyork.org
**Control:** Other not–for–profit (including NFP Corporation) **Service:** General Medical and Surgical

> **Staffed Beds:** 100 **Admissions:** 4559 **Census:** 46 **Births:** 525

⊠ **OSS ORTHOPAEDIC HOSPITAL (390325)**, 1861 Powder Mill Road, Zip 17402–4723; tel. 717/718–2000 **A**1 3 9 10 **F**3 29 34 62 64 79 81 82 85 86 87 92 94 107 111 114 119 130 131 135 144 148 **P**1 2 6
Primary Contact: Joseph Alhadeff, M.D., President and Chief Executive Officer
COO: Margaret Mooers, R.N., Chief Operating Officer and Chief Nursing Officer
CFO: Dale Bushey, Chief Financial Officer
CMO: Gracia Etienne, M.D., President Medical Staff
CIO: Tricia Wolf, Director Information Technology
CHR: Maureen M. Putnam, Director Human Resources
CNO: Margaret Mooers, R.N., Chief Operating Officer and Chief Nursing Officer
Web address: www.osshealth.com
**Control:** Partnership, Investor–owned, for–profit **Service:** Orthopedic

> **Staffed Beds:** 30 **Admissions:** 1471 **Census:** 9 **Outpatient Visits:** 281879 **Births:** 0 **Total Expense ($000):** 79022 **Payroll Expense ($000):** 31293

**SELECT SPECIALTY HOSPITAL–YORK** See Select Specialty Hospital–Central Pennsylvania, Camp Hill

△ **YORK HOSPITAL (390046)**, 1001 South George Street, Zip 17403–3645; tel. 717/851–2345, (Includes WELLSPAN SURGERY AND REHABILLITATION HOSPITAL, 55 Monument Road, Zip 17403–5023; tel. 717/812–6100; Richard L. Seim, President) **A**1 2 3 5 7 8 9 10 12 13 **F**3 7 11 12 13 14 15 17 18 20 22 24 26 28 29 30 31 34 35 39 40 43 44 45 46 48 49 50 54 55 56 57 58 59 60 61 64 65 66 68 70 72 74 75 76 77 78 79 81 82 84 85 86 87 89 92 93 96 97 98 100 101 102 103 104 107 108 110 111 114 115 117 118 119 120 121 123 124 126 129 130 131 132 135 146 147 148 **S** WellSpan Health, York, PA
Primary Contact: Keith D. Noll, President
COO: Raymond Rosen, FACHE, Vice President Operations
CFO: Michael F. O'Connor, Senior Vice President Finance
CMO: Peter M. Hartmann, M.D., Vice President Medical Affairs
CIO: R. Hal Baker, M.D., Vice President and Chief Information Officer
CHR: Robert J. Batory, Vice President Human Resources
CNO: Astrid Davis, R.N., Chief Nursing Officer
Web address: www.wellspan.org
**Control:** Other not–for–profit (including NFP Corporation) **Service:** General Medical and Surgical

> **Staffed Beds:** 556 **Admissions:** 29129 **Census:** 412 **Outpatient Visits:** 900000 **Births:** 3221 **Total Expense ($000):** 779447 **Payroll Expense ($000):** 243777 **Personnel:** 3915

*Many Facility Codes have changed. Please refer to the AHA Guide Code Chart.*       © 2015 AHA Guide

# RHODE ISLAND

## CRANSTON—Providence County

☐ **ELEANOR SLATER HOSPITAL (412001)**, 111 Howard Avenue, Zip 02920–0269, Mailing Address: P.O. Box 8269, Zip 02920–0269; tel. 401/462–3085, (Nonreporting) **A**1 3 10
Primary Contact: Paul J. Despres, Chief Executive Officer
CMO: Charlene Tate, M.D., Chief Medical Staff and Clinical Services
Web address: www.bhddh.ri.gov/esh/
**Control:** State–Government, nonfederal **Service:** Long–Term Acute Care hospital

**Staffed Beds:** 495

## EAST PROVIDENCE—Providence County

☐ **EMMA PENDLETON BRADLEY HOSPITAL (414003)**, 1011 Veterans Memorial Parkway, Zip 02915–5099; tel. 401/432–1000 **A**1 3 5 9 10 **F**3 29 34 35 38 44 57 58 62 64 68 77 86 87 98 99 100 101 104 105 106 130 132 134 135 **S** Lifespan Corporation, Providence, RI
Primary Contact: Daniel J. Wall, President and Chief Executive Officer
CFO: Mamie Wakefield, Vice President Finance and Chief Financial Officer
CMO: Henry T. Sachs, III, M.D., Medical Director
CIO: Carole Cotter, Senior Vice President and Chief Information Officer
CHR: Rob Duval, Chief Human Resources Officer
CNO: Vareen O'Keefe Domaleski, MS, Vice Patient Care Services and Chief Nursing Officer
Web address: www.lifespan.org
**Control:** Other not–for–profit (including NFP Corporation) **Service:** Children's hospital psychiatric

**Staffed Beds:** 60 **Admissions:** 1613 **Census:** 58 **Outpatient Visits:** 19420 **Births:** 0 **Total Expense ($000):** 75594 **Payroll Expense ($000):** 43530 **Personnel:** 570

## NEWPORT—Newport County

☐ △ **NEWPORT HOSPITAL (410006)**, 11 Friendship Street, Zip 02840–2299; tel. 401/846–6400 **A**1 2 3 7 9 10 **F**3 8 11 13 15 18 28 29 30 31 34 35 40 45 49 50 51 53 54 56 57 59 60 64 68 70 74 75 76 77 78 79 81 82 85 86 87 89 90 91 92 93 96 97 98 99 100 102 103 104 105 107 108 110 111 114 118 119 129 130 132 135 141 143 146 147 148 **S** Lifespan Corporation, Providence, RI
Primary Contact: Crista F. Durand, President
CFO: Frank J. Byrne, Vice President Finance
CMO: Thomas E. McGue, M.D., Vice President Medical Affairs and Chief Medical Officer
CHR: Barbara J. Arcangeli, Vice President Human Resources
CNO: Cathy E. Duquette, Ph.D., Vice President Nursing and Chief Nursing Officer
Web address: www.newporthospital.org
**Control:** Other not–for–profit (including NFP Corporation) **Service:** General Medical and Surgical

**Staffed Beds:** 119 **Admissions:** 4486 **Census:** 65 **Outpatient Visits:** 89985 **Births:** 444 **Total Expense ($000):** 103337 **Payroll Expense ($000):** 46637 **Personnel:** 626

## NORTH PROVIDENCE—Providence County

☐ △ **ST. JOSEPH HEALTH SERVICES OF RHODE ISLAND (410005)**, 200 High Service Avenue, Zip 02904–5199; tel. 401/456–3000, (Includes OUR LADY OF FATIMA HOSPITAL, 200 High Service Avenue, Zip 02904; tel. 401/456–3000; Thomas Hughes, President; ST. JOSEPH HOSPITAL FOR SPECIALTY CARE, 21 Peace Street, Providence, Zip 02907; tel. 401/456–3000), (Nonreporting) **A**1 2 6 7 9 10 **S** CharterCare Health Partners, Providence, RI
Primary Contact: Thomas Hughes, President
CFO: Michael E. Conklin, Jr., Chief Financial Officer
CIO: Susan Cerrone Abely, Chief Information Officer
CHR: Darlene Souza, Vice President
CNO: Patricia A. Nadle, R.N., Chief Nursing Officer
Web address: www.saintjosephri.com
**Control:** Other not–for–profit (including NFP Corporation) **Service:** General Medical and Surgical

**Staffed Beds:** 126

## NORTH SMITHFIELD—Providence County

**LANDMARK MEDICAL CENTER–FOGARTY UNIT** See Landmark Medical Center, Woonsocket

☐ **REHABILITATION HOSPITAL OF RHODE ISLAND (413025)**, 116 Eddie Dowling Highway, Zip 02896–7327; tel. 401/766–0800, (Nonreporting) **A**1 9 10 **S** Prime Healthcare Services, Ontario, CA
Primary Contact: Richard Charest, Chief Executive Officer
COO: Demetra Ouellette, Chief Operating Officer
CFO: Matthew Cotti, Chief Financial Officer
CMO: Jorge Mayoral, M.D., Medical Director
CIO: Colleen Ryan, Chief Information Officer and Vice President Professional Services
CHR: Mona M. Willis, Director Human Resources
Web address: www.rhri.net
**Control:** Corporation, Investor–owned, for–profit **Service:** Rehabilitation

**Staffed Beds:** 40

## PAWTUCKET—Providence County

⊠ △ **MEMORIAL HOSPITAL OF RHODE ISLAND (410001)**, 111 Brewster Street, Zip 02860–4499; tel. 401/729–2000 **A**1 2 3 5 7 8 9 10 **F**3 8 11 13 15 17 18 20 28 29 31 32 34 35 40 45 46 48 49 50 51 54 56 57 58 59 61 64 65 66 68 70 74 75 76 77 78 79 81 82 84 85 86 89 90 93 97 102 107 108 109 110 111 114 115 116 117 118 119 126 129 130 131 132 135 144 146 147 148 **P**6 8 **S** Care New England Health System, Providence, RI
Primary Contact: James E. Fanale, M.D., Interim Chief Operating Officer and Chief Medical Officer
CFO: Paul Beaudoin, Senior Vice President Finance
CMO: Joseph Diaz, M.D., Chief Medical Officer
CHR: Lisa Pratt, Vice President Human Resources
CNO: Eileen Dobbing, R.N., Senior Vice President for Patient Care Services
Web address: www.mhri.org
**Control:** Other not–for–profit (including NFP Corporation) **Service:** General Medical and Surgical

**Staffed Beds:** 152 **Admissions:** 4537 **Census:** 58 **Outpatient Visits:** 227455 **Births:** 488 **Total Expense ($000):** 156594 **Payroll Expense ($000):** 71316 **Personnel:** 939

## PROVIDENCE—Providence County

⊠ **BUTLER HOSPITAL (414000)**, 345 Blackstone Boulevard, Zip 02906–4829; tel. 401/455–6200, (Nonreporting) **A**1 3 5 9 10 **S** Care New England Health System, Providence, RI
Primary Contact: Lawrence Price, M.D., President and Chief Operating Officer
COO: Lawrence Price, M.D., President and Chief Operating Officer
CFO: Bonnie Baker, Vice President Finance and Chief Financial Officer
CMO: James Sullivan, M.D., Chief Medical Officer
CIO: Summa Gaddam, Chief Information Officer
CHR: Timothy Bigelow, Director Human Resources
CNO: Mary Leveillee, Senior Vice President Patient Care Services and Chief Nursing Officer
Web address: www.butler.org
**Control:** Other not–for–profit (including NFP Corporation) **Service:** Psychiatric

**Staffed Beds:** 117

☐ **MIRIAM HOSPITAL (410012)**, 164 Summit Avenue, Zip 02906–2853; tel. 401/793–2500 **A**1 2 3 5 8 9 10 **F**3 8 11 12 15 18 20 22 26 28 29 30 31 34 35 40 44 45 46 49 50 53 54 56 57 58 59 60 61 64 65 66 67 68 70 74 75 77 78 79 81 82 84 85 87 92 93 97 100 103 107 108 110 111 114 115 118 119 126 130 132 135 143 146 147 148 **P**3 5 6 **S** Lifespan Corporation, Providence, RI
Primary Contact: Arthur J. Sampson, FACHE, President
COO: Maria Ducharme, R.N., Interim Chief Nursing Officer
CFO: Mamie Wakefield, Chief Financial Officer
CMO: R. William Corwin, M.D., Vice President and Chief Medical Officer
CIO: Carole Cotter, Vice President and Chief Information Officer
CHR: Nancy McMahon, Vice President Human Resources
Web address: www.lifespan.org
**Control:** Other not–for–profit (including NFP Corporation) **Service:** General Medical and Surgical

**Staffed Beds:** 247 **Admissions:** 16033 **Census:** 174 **Outpatient Visits:** 203761 **Births:** 0 **Total Expense ($000):** 402441 **Payroll Expense ($000):** 176969 **Personnel:** 2221

RI

**RI**

⊞ **PROVIDENCE VETERANS AFFAIRS MEDICAL CENTER**, 830 Chalkstone Avenue, Zip 02908–4799; tel. 401/273–7100 **A**1 2 3 5 **F**3 5 8 12 18 29 30 31 35 37 38 39 40 44 45 46 47 48 49 50 51 53 54 55 56 57 58 59 60 61 62 63 64 65 68 70 74 75 77 78 79 81 82 84 85 86 87 91 92 93 94 97 98 100 101 102 103 104 107 108 111 114 115 118 119 126 130 132 135 143 144 145 146 147 148 **S** Department of Veterans Affairs, Washington, DC
Primary Contact: Susan MacKenzie, Director
COO: Erin Clare Sears, Associate Director of Operations
CMO: Satish C. Sharma, M.D., Chief of Staff
Web address: www.providence.va.gov/
**Control:** Veterans Affairs, Government, federal **Service:** General Medical and Surgical

**Staffed Beds:** 73 **Admissions:** 3078 **Census:** 49 **Outpatient Visits:** 420470 **Births:** 0 **Total Expense ($000):** 245995 **Personnel:** 1346

☐ **RHODE ISLAND HOSPITAL (410007)**, 593 Eddy Street, Zip 02903–4900; tel. 401/444–4000, (Includes HASBRO CHILDREN'S HOSPITAL, 593 Eddy Street, Zip 02903–4923; tel. 401/444–4000) **A**1 2 3 5 8 9 10 **F**3 6 7 8 11 15 16 17 18 19 20 21 22 23 24 26 29 30 31 32 34 35 38 39 40 41 43 44 45 46 47 48 49 50 51 53 54 55 56 57 58 59 60 61 64 65 66 67 68 70 74 75 77 78 79 81 82 84 85 86 87 88 89 90 92 93 94 97 98 99 100 101 102 103 104 105 107 108 110 111 114 115 116 117 118 119 120 121 123 124 129 130 131 132 133 134 135 138 142 143 145 146 147 148 **P**3 5 6 **S** Lifespan Corporation, Providence, RI
Primary Contact: Timothy J. Babineau, M.D., President and Chief Executive Officer
COO: Fredrick Macri, Executive Vice President
CFO: Mamie Wakefield, Senior Vice President and Chief Financial Officer
CMO: John B. Murphy, M.D., Vice President Medical Affairs and Chief Medical Officer
CIO: Carole Cotter, Senior Vice President and Chief Information Officer
CHR: Louis J. Sperling, Vice President Human Resources
Web address: www.rhodeislandhospital.org/
**Control:** Other not–for–profit (including NFP Corporation) **Service:** General Medical and Surgical

**Staffed Beds:** 640 **Admissions:** 33987 **Census:** 490 **Outpatient Visits:** 381006 **Births:** 0 **Total Expense ($000):** 1117113 **Payroll Expense ($000):** 495417 **Personnel:** 5754

⊞ **ROGER WILLIAMS MEDICAL CENTER (410004)**, 825 Chalkstone Avenue, Zip 02908–4735; tel. 401/456–2000, (Nonreporting) **A**1 2 3 5 8 9 10 **S** CharterCare Health Partners, Providence, RI
Primary Contact: Kimberly O'Connell, President
CFO: Addy Kane, Chief Financial Officer
CMO: Elaine Jones, M.D., President Medical Staff
CIO: Susan Cerrone Abely, Vice President and Chief Information Officer
Web address: www.rwmc.com
**Control:** Other not–for–profit (including NFP Corporation) **Service:** General Medical and Surgical

**Staffed Beds:** 95

**ST. JOSEPH HOSPITAL FOR SPECIALTY CARE** See St. Joseph Health Services of Rhode Island, North Providence

**VETERANS AFFAIRS MEDICAL CENTER** See Providence Veterans Affairs Medical Center

⊞ **WOMEN & INFANTS HOSPITAL OF RHODE ISLAND (410010)**, 101 Dudley Street, Zip 02905–2499; tel. 401/274–1100 **A**1 2 3 5 8 9 10 **F**3 5 11 13 15 29 30 31 33 34 35 36 38 40 44 45 46 50 52 54 55 57 58 59 63 64 65 66 68 71 72 74 75 76 77 78 81 82 84 85 86 87 93 97 100 101 102 104 105 107 110 111 114 119 126 130 132 134 135 143 146 147 **P**5 6 8 **S** Care New England Health System, Providence, RI
Primary Contact: Mark R. Marcantano, President and Chief Operating Officer
COO: Mark R. Marcantano, President and Chief Operating Officer
CFO: Robert W. Pacheco, Vice President Finance
CMO: Raymond Powrie, M.D., Senior Vice President Quality and Clinical Effectiveness
CHR: Paul F. Heffernan, Vice President Human Resources
CNO: Angelleen Peters–Lewis, R.N., Chief Nurse and Senior Vice President Patient Care
Web address: www.womenandinfants.org
**Control:** Other not–for–profit (including NFP Corporation) **Service:** Obstetrics and gynecology

**Staffed Beds:** 247 **Admissions:** 11332 **Census:** 153 **Outpatient Visits:** 231666 **Births:** 8587 **Total Expense ($000):** 468889 **Payroll Expense ($000):** 189549 **Personnel:** 2038

**WAKEFIELD—Washington County**

☐ **SOUTH COUNTY HOSPITAL (410008)**, 100 Kenyon Avenue, Zip 02879–4299; tel. 401/782–8000 **A**1 2 9 10 **F**3 11 13 15 18 20 26 28 29 30 31 34 35 36 37 38 40 42 44 45 46 47 48 49 50 51 53 54 57 59 60 64 65 70 71 74 75 76 77 78 79 81 82 85 86 87 89 93 97 99 102 103 104 107 108 110 111 114 119 126 129 130 131 132 135 143 144 146 147 148 **P**4 6
Primary Contact: Louis R. Giancola, President and Chief Executive Officer
CFO: Thomas Breen, Vice President and Chief Financial Officer
CMO: Joseph J. O'Neill, M.D., Vice President Medical Affairs
CIO: Gary Croteau, Assistant Vice President and Chief Information Officer
CHR: Maggie Thomas, Vice President Human Resources and Practice Management
Web address: www.schospital.com
**Control:** Other not–for–profit (including NFP Corporation) **Service:** General Medical and Surgical

**Staffed Beds:** 85 **Admissions:** 4462 **Census:** 47 **Outpatient Visits:** 191699 **Births:** 695 **Total Expense ($000):** 135327 **Payroll Expense ($000):** 58918 **Personnel:** 687

**WARWICK—Kent County**

⊞ △ **KENT COUNTY MEMORIAL HOSPITAL (410009)**, 455 Tollgate Road, Zip 02886–2770; tel. 401/737–7000 **A**1 2 3 5 7 9 10 13 **F**3 8 11 12 13 15 17 18 20 22 26 29 30 31 34 35 36 40 43 44 45 46 47 48 49 50 51 56 57 58 59 60 61 63 64 65 68 70 73 74 75 77 78 79 81 82 84 85 86 87 90 93 94 96 98 100 102 103 105 107 108 110 111 115 119 126 129 130 131 132 143 146 147 148 **P**8 **S** Care New England Health System, Providence, RI
Primary Contact: Michael J. Dacey, M.D., MS, President and Chief Operating Officer
COO: Fran Falsey, Senior Vice President Site Operations
CFO: Paul Beaudoin, Senior Vice President Finance and Chief Financial Officer
CMO: Joseph W. Spinale, D.O., Senior Vice President and Chief Medical Officer
CHR: Marilyn J. Walsh, Vice President Human Resources
CNO: Rebecca Burke, R.N., Senior Vice President and Chief Nursing Officer
Web address: www.kentri.org
**Control:** Other not–for–profit (including NFP Corporation) **Service:** General Medical and Surgical

**Staffed Beds:** 306 **Admissions:** 14087 **Census:** 208 **Outpatient Visits:** 206799 **Births:** 892 **Total Expense ($000):** 285926 **Payroll Expense ($000):** 137821 **Personnel:** 1433

**WESTERLY—Washington County**

★ ◇ **WESTERLY HOSPITAL (410013)**, 25 Wells Street, Zip 02891–2934; tel. 401/596–6000, (Nonreporting) **A**2 9 10 21 **S** L+M Healthcare, New London, CT
Primary Contact: Bruce D. Cummings, President and Chief Executive Officer
CFO: James O'Keefe, Chief Financial Officer
CIO: Christopher Lehrach, M.D., Chief Transformation Officer for Interim Operations
CHR: Jodie Tate, Director Human Resources
Web address: www.westerlyhospital.org
**Control:** Other not–for–profit (including NFP Corporation) **Service:** General Medical and Surgical

**Staffed Beds:** 100

**WOONSOCKET—Providence County**

☐ **LANDMARK MEDICAL CENTER (410011)**, 115 Cass Avenue, Zip 02895–4731; tel. 401/769–4100, (Includes LANDMARK MEDICAL CENTER–FOGARTY UNIT, Eddie Dowling Highway, North Smithfield, Zip 02896; Mailing Address: Woonsocket, tel. 401/766–0800; LANDMARK MEDICAL CENTER–WOONSOCKET UNIT, 115 Cass Avenue, Zip 02895; tel. 401/769–4100) **A**1 2 9 10 **F**3 8 13 15 17 18 20 22 26 28 29 30 31 34 35 38 40 44 45 46 47 48 49 50 51 54 56 57 59 60 61 64 65 68 70 74 75 76 77 78 79 81 82 83 84 85 86 87 97 98 100 102 103 107 108 109 110 111 114 118 119 126 129 130 131 132 133 135 143 144 146 147 148 **P**5 6 **S** Prime Healthcare Services, Ontario, CA
Primary Contact: Richard Charest, President
CFO: Dana Diggins, Chief Financial Officer
CMO: Stanley Balon, M.D., President Medical Staff
CIO: Colleen Ryan, Director Management Information Systems
CHR: Mona M. Willis, Director Human Resources
Web address: www.landmarkmedical.org
**Control:** Individual, Investor–owned, for–profit **Service:** General Medical and Surgical

**Staffed Beds:** 140 **Admissions:** 6279 **Census:** 85 **Outpatient Visits:** 96844 **Births:** 200 **Total Expense ($000):** 112293 **Payroll Expense ($000):** 47949 **Personnel:** 745

# SOUTH CAROLINA

## ABBEVILLE—Abbeville County

★ ◇ **ABBEVILLE AREA MEDICAL CENTER (421301)**, 420 Thomson Circle, Zip 29620–5656, Mailing Address: P.O. Box 887, Zip 29620–0887; tel. 864/366–5011 **A**9 10 18 21 **F**1 3 15 17 29 30 35 40 51 53 54 56 57 59 62 64 67 70 74 75 77 79 81 85 87 89 90 93 103 107 108 110 114 119 127 128 129 130 132 133 135 146 147 148 **P**5 **S** QHR, Brentwood, TN
Primary Contact: Richard D. Osmus, Chief Executive Officer
CFO: Timothy Wren, Chief Financial Officer
CMO: Michael Turner, M.D., Chief of Staff
CIO: Tim Stewart, Chief Information Officer
CHR: Alice Rigney, Chief Human Resources Officer
CNO: Lucile Culbreth, Chief Nursing Officer
Web address: www.abbevilleareamc.com
**Control:** County–Government, nonfederal **Service:** General Medical and Surgical

**Staffed Beds:** 25 **Admissions:** 602 **Census:** 7 **Outpatient Visits:** 14947 **Births:** 0 **Total Expense ($000):** 35914 **Payroll Expense ($000):** 15718 **Personnel:** 359

## AIKEN—Aiken County

☐ **AIKEN REGIONAL MEDICAL CENTERS (420082)**, 302 University Parkway, Zip 29801–6302; tel. 803/641–5000, (Includes AURORA PAVILION, 655 Medical Park Drive, Zip 29801; tel. 803/641–5900) **A**1 3 5 9 10 **F**1 3 4 5 11 12 15 18 20 22 24 29 30 31 34 35 40 46 49 56 57 58 59 64 70 73 74 76 77 78 79 80 81 85 86 87 89 98 99 100 101 102 103 104 105 107 108 110 111 114 115 119 121 123 128 129 130 131 132 135 146 147 148 **S** Universal Health Services, Inc., King of Prussia, PA
Primary Contact: Vance V. Reynolds, FACHE, CPA, Chief Executive Officer
COO: Justin Krueger, Chief Operating Officer
Web address: www.aikenregional.com
**Control:** Corporation, Investor–owned, for–profit **Service:** General Medical and Surgical

**Staffed Beds:** 271 **Admissions:** 11650 **Census:** 168 **Outpatient Visits:** 130762 **Births:** 1094 **Total Expense ($000):** 148282 **Payroll Expense ($000):** 51678 **Personnel:** 828

## ANDERSON—Anderson County

⊠ **ANMED HEALTH MEDICAL CENTER (420027)**, 800 North Fant Street, Zip 29621–5793; tel. 864/512–1000, (Includes ANMED HEALTH WOMEN'S AND CHILDREN'S HOSPITAL, 2000 East Greenville Street, Zip 29621; tel. 864/512–1000; William T. Manson, III, Chief Executive Officer) **A**1 2 3 5 9 10 **F**1 3 4 5 8 11 12 13 14 15 17 18 20 22 24 26 28 29 30 31 34 35 37 39 40 43 45 46 48 49 50 51 53 54 56 57 58 59 60 61 62 64 65 68 70 71 73 74 75 76 77 78 79 81 84 85 86 87 89 90 91 97 98 100 101 102 103 104 105 107 108 110 111 114 115 117 118 119 121 123 126 127 128 129 130 131 132 135 144 146 147 148 **S** AnMed Health, Anderson, SC
Primary Contact: William T. Manson, III, FACHE, Chief Executive Officer
CFO: Christine Pearson, Vice President Finance and Chief Financial Officer
CMO: Mike Tillirson, D.O., Executive Vice President and Chief Medical Officer
CIO: Marty Stewart, Director Information Services
CHR: Rick W. Grooms, Jr., Vice President Human Resources
CNO: Tina M. Jury, MSN, Executive Vice President Hospital Operations and Chief Nursing Officer
Web address: www.anmedhealth.org
**Control:** Other not–for–profit (including NFP Corporation) **Service:** General Medical and Surgical

**Staffed Beds:** 401 **Admissions:** 19504 **Census:** 257 **Outpatient Visits:** 796499 **Births:** 1850 **Personnel:** 3757

⊠ **ANMED HEALTH REHABILITATION HOSPITAL (423029)**, 1 Spring Back Way, Zip 29621–2676; tel. 864/716–2600 **A**1 10 **F**1 3 29 30 56 74 75 79 90 91 93 94 95 96 128 **S** HEALTHSOUTH Corporation, Birmingham, AL
Primary Contact: Michele M. Skripps, R.N., Chief Executive Officer
CFO: Julie Saylors, Controller
CMO: William Vogentiz, M.D., Medical Director
CHR: Tara Myers, Director Human Resources
CNO: Carmella Burton, Chief Nursing Officer
Web address: www.anmedrehab.com
**Control:** Corporation, Investor–owned, for–profit **Service:** Rehabilitation

**Staffed Beds:** 55 **Admissions:** 1439 **Census:** 49 **Births:** 0 **Total Expense ($000):** 13028 **Payroll Expense ($000):** 7977 **Personnel:** 191

☐ **PATRICK B. HARRIS PSYCHIATRIC HOSPITAL (424011)**, 130 Highway 252, Zip 29621–5054; tel. 864/231–2600, (Nonreporting) **A**1 3 5 9 10
Primary Contact: John Fletcher, Chief Executive Officer
Web address: www.patrickbharrispsychiatrichospital.com/index.htm
**Control:** State–Government, nonfederal **Service:** Psychiatric

**Staffed Beds:** 84

## BARNWELL—Barnwell County

☐ **SOUTHERN PALMETTO HOSPITAL (420016)**, 811 Reynolds Road, Zip 29812–1555; tel. 803/259–1000 **A**1 9 10 20 **F**3 34 40 59 63 90 93 107 119 128
Primary Contact: Mary T. Valliant, R.N., MS, Chief Executive Officer
CFO: Troy Pickens, Chief Financial Officer
CMO: Dean Koukos, M.D., Chief Medical Staff
CIO: Randal Padgett, Manager Information Systems
CHR: Sherry Donaldson, Director Human Resources
CNO: Marsha Gantt, Interim Chief Nursing Officer
Web address: www.bchospital.org
**Control:** Corporation, Investor–owned, for–profit **Service:** General Medical and Surgical

**Staffed Beds:** 10 **Admissions:** 456 **Census:** 3 **Births:** 0 **Total Expense ($000):** 11243 **Payroll Expense ($000):** 5273

## BEAUFORT—Beaufort County

⊠ **BEAUFORT MEMORIAL HOSPITAL (420067)**, 955 Ribaut Road, Zip 29902–5441; tel. 843/522–5200, (Nonreporting) **A**1 2 9 10
Primary Contact: Richard Kirk Toomey, FACHE, President and Chief Executive Officer
CFO: Jeffrey L. White, Senior Vice President and Chief Financial Officer
CMO: Kurt Gambla, D.O., Chief Medical Officer
CIO: Edward Ricks, Vice President and Chief Information Officer
CHR: David Homyk, Vice President Human Resources
CNO: Karen Carroll, MSN, Vice President and Chief Nursing Officer
Web address: www.bmhsc.org
**Control:** County–Government, nonfederal **Service:** General Medical and Surgical

**Staffed Beds:** 181

⊠ **NAVAL HOSPITAL BEAUFORT**, 1 Pinckney Boulevard, Zip 29902–6122; tel. 843/228–5301, (Nonreporting) **A**1 5 **S** Bureau of Medicine and Surgery, Department of the Navy, Washington, DC
Primary Contact: Lieutenant Commander Willie Brown, Director Administration
Web address: www.med.navy.mil/sites/nhbeaufort/Pages/Welcome_Page.aspx
**Control:** Navy, Government, federal **Service:** General Medical and Surgical

**Staffed Beds:** 20

## CAMDEN—Kershaw County

⊠ **KERSHAWHEALTH (420048)**, 1315 Roberts Street, Zip 29020–3737, Mailing Address: P.O. Box 7003, Zip 29021–7003; tel. 803/432–4311 **A**1 9 10 **F**1 3 7 11 13 15 18 20 24 28 29 30 31 32 34 35 40 44 45 49 50 51 54 57 59 61 62 63 64 66 67 68 70 75 76 77 78 79 81 85 86 87 89 90 94 97 107 108 110 111 114 115 118 119 127 128 129 130 132 143 144 146 147 148
Primary Contact: Terry Gunn, FACHE, Chief Executive Officer
COO: Mike Bunch, Executive Vice President, Chief Operating Officer and Chief Financial Officer
CHR: Angela F. Nettles, Director Human Resources
Web address: www.kershawhealth.com
**Control:** County–Government, nonfederal **Service:** General Medical and Surgical

**Staffed Beds:** 119 **Admissions:** 4409 **Census:** 52 **Births:** 276 **Total Expense ($000):** 99256 **Payroll Expense ($000):** 43500 **Personnel:** 746

**SC**

---

| Hospital, Medicare Provider Number, Address, Telephone, Approval, Facility, and Physician Codes, Health Care System |
|---|
| ★ American Hospital Association (AHA) membership    ○ Healthcare Facilities Accreditation Program    ⇑ Center for Improvement in Healthcare Quality Accreditation |
| ☐ The Joint Commission accreditation    ◇ DNV Healthcare Inc. accreditation    △ Commission on Accreditation of Rehabilitation Facilities (CARF) accreditation |

**CHARLESTON—Charleston County**

☒ **BON SECOURS ST. FRANCIS XAVIER HOSPITAL (420065)**, 2095 Henry Tecklenburg Drive, Zip 29414–5733; tel. 843/402–1000 **A**1 9 10 **F**1 3 7 12 13 14 15 20 28 29 30 31 34 35 40 45 46 47 48 49 50 51 56 57 59 60 64 68 70 73 74 75 76 77 78 79 80 81 82 84 85 86 87 89 93 94 100 107 108 110 111 114 117 118 119 120 121 123 128 130 131 132 145 146 147 148 **S** Carolinas Healthcare System, Charlotte, NC
Primary Contact: Allen P. Carroll, Senior Vice President and Chief Executive Officer
CFO: Bret Johnson, Chief Financial Officer
CMO: Steven D. Shapiro, M.D., Chief Medical Officer
CIO: Michael Taylor, Chief Information Officer
CNO: Pennie Peralta, R.N., VP, Nursing & Chief Nursing Officer
Web address: www.rsfh.com/
**Control:** Other not–for–profit (including NFP Corporation) **Service:** General Medical and Surgical

**Staffed Beds:** 172 **Admissions:** 9035 **Census:** 92 **Outpatient Visits:** 156246 **Births:** 2598 **Total Expense ($000):** 163188 **Payroll Expense ($000):** 52624 **Personnel:** 1050

☒ **HEALTHSOUTH REHABILITATION HOSPITAL OF CHARLESTON (423027)**, 9181 Medcom Street, Zip 29406–9168; tel. 843/820–7777 **A**1 10 **F**1 90 94 128 **S** HEALTHSOUTH Corporation, Birmingham, AL
Primary Contact: Troy Powell, Chief Executive Officer
CFO: Beckye Lariviere, Controller
CMO: William Livesay, Jr., D.O., Medical Director
CHR: Donna White, Director Human Resources
Web address: www.healthsouthcharleston.com
**Control:** Corporation, Investor–owned, for–profit **Service:** Rehabilitation

**Staffed Beds:** 49 **Admissions:** 1008 **Census:** 39 **Total Expense ($000):** 15275 **Payroll Expense ($000):** 6733 **Personnel:** 172

☒ **MUSC MEDICAL CENTER OF MEDICAL UNIVERSITY OF SOUTH CAROLINA (420004)**, 169 Ashley Avenue, Zip 29425–8905; tel. 843/792–2300, (Includes CHILDREN'S HOSPITAL OF SOUTH CAROLINA AT MUSC, 171 Ashley Avenue, Zip 29425–8908; tel. 843/792–1414; Patrick J. Cawley, M.D., Vice President of Clinical Operations and Chief Executive Officer) **A**1 2 3 5 8 9 10 **F**1 3 4 5 6 7 8 9 11 12 13 14 15 16 17 18 19 20 21 22 23 24 25 26 27 28 29 30 31 32 34 35 37 38 39 40 41 43 44 45 46 47 48 49 50 51 52 53 54 55 56 57 58 59 60 61 64 65 66 67 68 70 71 72 73 74 75 76 77 78 79 80 81 82 84 85 86 87 88 89 92 93 94 97 98 99 100 101 102 103 104 105 107 108 109 110 111 114 115 116 117 118 119 120 121 123 124 126 128 129 130 131 132 134 135 136 137 138 139 140 141 142 144 145 146 147 148
Primary Contact: Patrick J. Cawley, M.D., FACHE, Chief Executive Officer and Vice President for Clinical Operations
COO: Matthew Wain, Chief Operating Officer
CFO: Stephen Hargett, Administrator Finance and Support Services
CMO: Daniel Handel, M.D., Chief Medical Officer
CIO: John Long, Chief Information Officer & Chief Analytics Officer
CHR: Betts Ellis, Administrator Institutional Relations
CNO: Marilyn J. Schaffner, Ph.D., Administrator Clinical Services and Chief Nursing Officer
Web address: www.muschealth.com
**Control:** State–Government, nonfederal **Service:** General Medical and Surgical

**Staffed Beds:** 732 **Admissions:** 34701 **Census:** 619 **Outpatient Visits:** 994531 **Births:** 2362 **Total Expense ($000):** 1160768 **Payroll Expense ($000):** 391699 **Personnel:** 6481

☐ **PALMETTO LOWCOUNTRY BEHAVIORAL HEALTH (424006)**, 2777 Speissegger Drive, Zip 29405–8229; tel. 843/747–5830 **A**1 10 **F**1 4 5 64 98 99 102 103 104 105 128 **P**5 **S** Universal Health Services, Inc., King of Prussia, PA
Primary Contact: Shari Baker, Chief Executive Officer
CFO: Stan Markowski, Chief Financial Officer
CMO: Steven Lopez, M.D., Chief Medical Officer
CHR: Sheila Simpson, Vice President Human Resources
CNO: Jo Good, Director of Nursing
Web address: www.palmettobehavioralhealth.com
**Control:** Corporation, Investor–owned, for–profit **Service:** Psychiatric

**Staffed Beds:** 84 **Admissions:** 2607 **Census:** 65 **Outpatient Visits:** 5403 **Births:** 0 **Total Expense ($000):** 15336 **Payroll Expense ($000):** 7352 **Personnel:** 153

☒ **RALPH H. JOHNSON VETERANS AFFAIRS MEDICAL CENTER**, 109 Bee Street, Zip 29401–5799; tel. 843/577–5011, (Nonreporting) **A**1 2 3 5 8 **S** Department of Veterans Affairs, Washington, DC
Primary Contact: Scott R. Isaacks, FACHE, Interim Director
COO: Scott R. Isaacks, FACHE, Associate Director
CFO: Cassandra Helfer, Chief Financial Officer
CMO: Florence N. Hutchison, M.D., Chief of Staff
CIO: Marlon Ball, Chief Information Officer
CHR: Amanda Dean, Human Resources Officer
CNO: Mary C. Fraggos, R.N., Associate Director of Nursing and Patient Care Services
Web address: www.charleston.va.gov/
**Control:** Veterans Affairs, Government, federal **Service:** General Medical and Surgical

**Staffed Beds:** 98

☒ △ **ROPER HOSPITAL (420087)**, 316 Calhoun Street, Zip 29401–1125; tel. 843/724–2000 **A**1 2 3 5 7 9 10 **F**1 3 7 8 9 14 15 17 18 20 22 24 26 28 29 30 31 34 35 37 40 42 43 45 49 50 51 53 54 55 56 57 58 59 60 61 62 63 64 65 67 68 69 70 74 75 77 78 79 80 81 82 84 85 86 87 90 92 93 94 95 96 100 107 108 110 111 114 115 118 119 120 121 123 124 126 128 129 130 131 132 135 136 143 144 146 147 148 **S** Carolinas Healthcare System, Charlotte, NC
Primary Contact: Matthew J. Severance, FACHE, Chief Executive Officer
CFO: Bret Johnson, Chief Financial Officer
CMO: Steven D. Shapiro, M.D., Vice President Medical Affairs
CIO: Melinda H. Cardell, Interim Vice President and Chief Information Officer
CHR: Melanie Stith, Vice President Human Resources
CNO: Carolyn Viall Donohue, MSN, Vice President Nursing
Web address: www.rsfh.com/
**Control:** Other not–for–profit (including NFP Corporation) **Service:** General Medical and Surgical

**Staffed Beds:** 308 **Admissions:** 12528 **Census:** 190 **Outpatient Visits:** 213155 **Births:** 0 **Total Expense ($000):** 323039 **Payroll Expense ($000):** 100307 **Personnel:** 2007

☒ **TRIDENT MEDICAL CENTER (420079)**, 9330 Medical Plaza Drive, Zip 29406–9195; tel. 843/797–7000, (Includes MONCKS CORNER MEDICAL CENTER, 401 North Live Oak Drive, Highway 17A, Moncks Corner, Zip 29461–5603; tel. 843/761–8721; SUMMERVILLE MEDICAL CENTER, 295 Midland Parkway, Summerville, Zip 29485–8104; tel. 843/832–5000) **A**1 2 3 5 9 10 **F**1 3 8 12 13 15 16 18 20 22 24 26 28 29 30 31 34 35 40 42 43 45 46 48 49 50 54 55 56 57 59 60 61 64 70 72 73 74 75 76 77 78 79 81 84 85 86 87 89 90 93 94 98 102 107 108 110 111 114 115 116 117 118 119 120 121 123 124 126 128 129 130 131 132 135 145 146 147 148 **S** HCA, Nashville, TN
Primary Contact: Todd Gallati, FACHE, President and Chief Executive Officer
CFO: Teresa Finch, Chief Financial Officer
CIO: Susan Murray, Director Information Services
CHR: Joe B. Hill, Jr., Vice President Human Resources
Web address: www.tridenthealthsystem.com
**Control:** Corporation, Investor–owned, for–profit **Service:** General Medical and Surgical

**Staffed Beds:** 421 **Admissions:** 21565 **Census:** 253 **Births:** 2798 **Personnel:** 1760

**CHERAW—Chesterfield County**

☒ **MCLEOD HEALTH CHERAW (420062)**, 711 Chesterfield Highway, Zip 29520–7002; tel. 843/537–7881 **A**1 9 10 **F**1 3 8 13 15 18 28 29 30 34 35 40 45 56 57 59 68 70 76 77 79 81 85 86 87 89 90 102 107 108 114 118 119 128 130 132 133 135 **S** McLeod Health, Florence, SC
Primary Contact: Mib Scoggins, Chief Executive Officer
CFO: Louis Anderson, Chief Financial Officer
CMO: David Bersinger, M.D., Chief of Staff
CIO: Jim Spencer, Director Information System
Web address: www.chesterfieldgeneral.com
**Control:** Other not–for–profit (including NFP corporation) **Service:** General Medical and Surgical

**Staffed Beds:** 59 **Admissions:** 1742 **Census:** 16 **Outpatient Visits:** 25661 **Births:** 215 **Total Expense ($000):** 30361 **Payroll Expense ($000):** 10448 **Personnel:** 201

**CHESTER—Chester County**

☒ **CHESTER REGIONAL MEDICAL CENTER (420019)**, 1 Medical Park Drive, Zip 29706–9769; tel. 803/581–3151 **A**1 9 10 **F**1 15 28 29 34 35 40 50 56 57 59 70 75 77 79 81 85 86 87 89 90 94 107 108 110 111 119 128 129 130 131 132 135 **S** Community Health Systems, Inc., Franklin, TN
Primary Contact: Page H. Vaughan, Chief Executive Officer
CFO: Tracey Claxton, Chief Financial Officer
CMO: Terry Dodge, M.D., Chief of Staff
CIO: Shaw Laird, Chief Information Officer
CHR: Karen Chapman, Director Human Resources
CNO: Betty Griffin, Interim Chief Nursing Officer
Web address: www.chesterregional.com
**Control:** Corporation, Investor–owned, for–profit **Service:** General Medical and Surgical

**Staffed Beds:** 36 **Admissions:** 1017 **Census:** 8

**SC**

## CLINTON—Laurens County

✠ **GREENVILLE HEALTH SYSTEM – LAURENS COUNTY MEMORIAL HOSPITAL (420038)**, 22725 Highway 76 East, Zip 29325–7527, Mailing Address: P.O. Drawer 976, Zip 29325–0976; tel. 864/833–9100, (Includes GHS – LAURENS COUNTY MEMORIAL HOSPITAL, 22725 Highway 76 E., Mailing Address: P.O. Box 976, Zip 29325; tel. 803/833–9100), (Total facility includes 10 beds in nursing home–type unit) **A**1 5 9 10 20 **F**1 3 11 13 15 18 28 29 30 34 35 40 45 46 59 70 76 79 80 81 87 89 90 107 108 110 119 128 129 130 132 146 147 **S** Greenville Health System, Greenville, SC
Primary Contact: Richard E. D'Alberto, FACHE, Campus President
CFO: Todd Walker, Director Operations
CMO: Randy Reinhardt, Chief of Staff
CIO: Gina Driggers, Manager Information Technology
CHR: Cathy M. Rogers, Manager Human Resources
CNO: Kay Swisher, Chief Nursing Officer
Web address: www.ghs.org/laurens
**Control:** Hospital district or authority, Government, nonfederal **Service:** General Medical and Surgical

**Staffed Beds: 50 Admissions: 145 Census: 35 Outpatient Visits: 69129 Births: 315 Total Expense ($000): 59515 Payroll Expense ($000): 20238 Personnel: 373**

**WHITTEN CENTER**, Highway 76 East, Zip 29325, Mailing Address: P.O. Box 239, Zip 29325–0239; tel. 864/833–2733, (Nonreporting)
Primary Contact: Wes Leonard, Chief Executive Officer
**Control:** State–Government, nonfederal **Service:** Intellectual disabilites

**Staffed Beds: 22**

## COLUMBIA—Richland County

**EARLE E. MORRIS ALCOHOL AND DRUG TREATMENT CENTER**, 610 Faison Drive, Zip 29203–3218; tel. 803/935–7100, (Nonreporting)
Primary Contact: George McConnell, Director
Web address: www.state.sc.us/dmh/morris_village/
**Control:** State–Government, nonfederal **Service:** Alcoholism and other chemical dependency

**Staffed Beds: 107**

☐ **G. WERBER BRYAN PSYCHIATRIC HOSPITAL (424005)**, 220 Faison Drive, Zip 29203–3210; tel. 803/935–7146, (Nonreporting) **A**1 3 10
Primary Contact: Harvey Miller, Director
COO: Jaclyn Upfield, Chief Operating Officer
CIO: Sam Livingston, Information Resource Consultant
CHR: Kim Church, Manager Human Resources
Web address: www.scdmh.org
**Control:** State–Government, nonfederal **Service:** Psychiatric

**Staffed Beds: 166**

✠ **HEALTHSOUTH REHABILITATION HOSPITAL OF COLUMBIA (423025)**, 2935 Colonial Drive, Zip 29203–6811; tel. 803/254–7777 **A**1 10 **F**29 50 53 60 64 77 90 91 92 93 94 95 96 97 119 **S** HEALTHSOUTH Corporation, Birmingham, AL
Primary Contact: W. Anthony Jackson, Chief Executive Officer
CFO: Jessica Burriss, Chief Financial Officer
CMO: Devin Troyer, M.D., Medical Director
CHR: Luanne Burton, Director Human Resources
CNO: April Brooks, Chief Nursing Officer
Web address: www.healthsouthcolumbia.com
**Control:** Corporation, Investor–owned, for–profit **Service:** Rehabilitation

**Staffed Beds: 96 Admissions: 1690 Census: 65 Births: 0 Total Expense ($000): 18246 Payroll Expense ($000): 10298 Personnel: 184**

**INTERMEDICAL HOSPITAL OF SOUTH CAROLINA (422006)**, Taylor at Marion Street, Zip 29220, Mailing Address: PO BOX 11069, Zip 29211–1069; tel. 803/296–3757, (Nonreporting) **A**9 10
Primary Contact: Armando Colombo, Chief Executive Officer
Web address: www.intermedicalhospital.com
**Control:** Other not–for–profit (including NFP Corporation) **Service:** Long–Term Acute Care hospital

**Staffed Beds: 35**

✠ **PALMETTO HEALTH BAPTIST (420086)**, Taylor at Marion Street, Zip 29220–0001; tel. 803/296–5010, (Total facility includes 22 beds in nursing home–type unit) **A**1 2 3 5 9 10 **F**1 3 5 11 12 13 15 18 20 29 30 31 34 35 40 45 47 48 49 51 54 57 59 61 62 63 64 69 70 71 72 73 74 75 76 77 78 79 80 81 82 84 85 86 87 89 90 93 94 98 99 100 101 102 103 104 105 107 108 110 111 112 114 115 116 117 118 119 124 128 130 132 145 146 147 148 **S** Palmetto Health, Columbia, SC
Primary Contact: Gregory B. Gattman, Acute Care Executive
COO: James M. Bridges, Executive Vice President and Chief Operating Officer
CFO: Paul K. Duane, Chief Financial Officer and Office of Health Reform
CMO: Mark J. Mayson, M.D., Medical Director
CIO: Michelle Edwards, Executive Vice President Information Technology
CHR: Trip Gregory, Senior Vice President Human Resources
Web address: www.palmettohealth.org
**Control:** Other not–for–profit (including NFP Corporation) **Service:** General Medical and Surgical

**Staffed Beds: 404 Admissions: 18850 Census: 250 Outpatient Visits: 217333 Births: 2974 Total Expense ($000): 303794 Payroll Expense ($000): 120588 Personnel: 1900**

✠ **PALMETTO HEALTH BAPTIST PARKRIDGE (420106)**, 400 Palmetto Health Parkway, Zip 29212–1760, Mailing Address: P.O. BOX 2266, Zip 29202–2266; tel. 803/907–7000, (Data for 196 days) **A**1 10 **F**1 3 8 13 15 29 30 31 34 35 40 45 46 50 55 57 59 64 68 70 75 76 77 78 79 81 86 87 89 90 93 94 107 110 111 119 128 130 132 143 144 146 147 **S** Palmetto Health, Columbia, SC
Primary Contact: Sarah Kirby, R.N., MSN, FACHE, Acute Care Executive
Web address: www.palmettohealth.org
**Control:** Other not–for–profit (including NFP Corporation) **Service:** General Medical and Surgical

**Staffed Beds: 75 Admissions: 1604 Census: 29 Outpatient Visits: 25625 Births: 224 Personnel: 494**

✠ **PALMETTO HEALTH RICHLAND (420018)**, Five Richland Medical Park Drive, Zip 29203–6897; tel. 803/434–7000, (Includes PALMETTO HEALTH CHILDREN'S HOSPITAL, Five Richland Medical Park Drive, Zip 29203–6863; tel. 803/434–6882) **A**1 2 3 5 8 9 10 **F**1 2 3 4 5 6 11 13 15 17 18 20 22 24 28 29 30 31 32 34 35 39 40 41 43 45 46 50 54 55 56 57 58 59 60 61 64 68 70 72 73 74 75 76 77 78 79 81 86 87 88 89 90 93 94 98 99 100 101 102 103 104 105 107 108 110 111 114 118 119 121 126 128 129 130 131 132 134 135 143 146 147 148 **S** Palmetto Health, Columbia, SC
Primary Contact: Jay Hamm, R.N., FACHE, Chief Acute Care Executive
CFO: Paul K. Duane, Chief Financial Officer and Office of Health Reform
CMO: Eric Brown, M.D., Physician Executive
CNO: Carole A. Siegfried, MSN, Campus Nurse Executive
Web address: www.palmettohealth.org
**Control:** Other not–for–profit (including NFP Corporation) **Service:** General Medical and Surgical

**Staffed Beds: 694 Admissions: 30701 Census: 550 Outpatient Visits: 476129 Births: 2319 Total Expense ($000): 690119 Payroll Expense ($000): 265835 Personnel: 4466**

★ ◇ **PROVIDENCE HOSPITAL (420026)**, 2435 Forest Drive, Zip 29204–2098; tel. 803/865–4500, (Includes PROVIDENCE HOSPITAL NORTHEAST, 120 Gateway Corporate Boulevard, Zip 29203–9611; tel. 803/865–4500; Ryan Hall, Vice President) **A**9 10 21 **F**1 3 8 11 15 17 18 20 22 24 26 28 29 30 34 35 38 40 44 45 49 50 53 54 56 57 58 59 61 63 64 68 70 74 75 77 79 80 81 83 84 85 86 87 89 90 92 93 94 100 107 108 111 114 118 119 128 129 130 131 132 141 146 147 148 **P**5 **S** Sisters of Charity Health System, Cleveland, OH
Primary Contact: Terrence Kessler, Interim Chief Executive Officer
COO: W. Carl Martin, Chief Operating Officer
CFO: Pamela Gallagher, Chief Financial Officer
CMO: Wayne Sribnick, M.D., Senior Vice President and Chief Medical Officer
CIO: Lib Cumbee, Director Information Systems
CHR: Justin A. Lofurno, Director Human Resources
Web address: www.sistersofcharityhealth.org/health–care/providence–hospitals/
**Control:** Church–operated, Nongovernment, not–for profit **Service:** General Medical and Surgical

**Staffed Beds: 314 Admissions: 10630 Census: 132 Births: 0 Total Expense ($000): 228922 Payroll Expense ($000): 72832 Personnel: 1177**

**PROVIDENCE HOSPITAL NORTHEAST** See Providence Hospital

**SOUTH CAROLINA DEPARTMENT OF CORRECTIONS HOSPITAL**, 4344 Broad River Road, Zip 29210–4098; tel. 803/896–8567, (Nonreporting)
Primary Contact: John Solomon, M.D., Director
Web address: www.doc.sc.gov/
**Control:** State–Government, nonfederal **Service:** Hospital unit of an institution (prison hospital, college infirmary, etc.)

**Staffed Beds: 70**

---

**Hospital, Medicare Provider Number, Address, Telephone, Approval, Facility, and Physician Codes, Health Care System**

★ American Hospital Association (AHA) membership   ◯ Healthcare Facilities Accreditation Program   ⇑ Center for Improvement in Healthcare Quality Accreditation
☐ The Joint Commission accreditation   ◇ DNV Healthcare Inc. accreditation   △ Commission on Accreditation of Rehabilitation Facilities (CARF) accreditation

SC

☐ **WILLIAM S. HALL PSYCHIATRIC INSTITUTE (424003)**, 1800 Colonial Drive, Zip 29203–6827; tel. 803/898–1693, (Nonreporting) **A**1 3 5 10
Primary Contact: Angela Forand, Director
COO: Doug Glover, Controller
CFO: Doug Glover, Controller
CMO: Phyllis Bryant–Mobley, M.D., Director Medical Services
CIO: Mesa Foard, Director Information technology
CHR: Kim Church, Manager Human Resources
Web address: www.scdmh.org
**Control:** State–Government, nonfederal **Service:** Psychiatric

**Staffed Beds:** 38

☒ △ **WM. JENNINGS BRYAN DORN VETERANS AFFAIRS MEDICAL CENTER**, 6439 Garners Ferry Road, Zip 29209–1639; tel. 803/776–4000, (Nonreporting) **A**1 2 3 5 7 **S** Department of Veterans Affairs, Washington, DC
Primary Contact: Timothy McMurry, Director
COO: David Omura, Associate Director
CMO: Bernard L. DeKoning, M.D., Chief of Staff
CIO: Steve Chalphant, Director Information Management Service Line
CHR: Phyllis Jones, Chief Human Resources
CNO: Ruth W. Mustard, R.N., Associate Director Nursing and Patient Services
Web address: www.columbiasc.va.gov/
**Control:** Veterans Affairs, Government, federal **Service:** General Medical and Surgical

**Staffed Beds:** 216

### CONWAY—Horry County

★ ◇ **CONWAY MEDICAL CENTER (420049)**, 300 Singleton Ridge Road, Zip 29526–9142, Mailing Address: P.O. Box 829, Zip 29528–0829; tel. 843/347–7111, (Total facility includes 88 beds in nursing home–type unit) **A**9 10 21 **F**1 3 8 11 12 13 15 18 20 26 28 29 30 34 35 40 45 46 49 50 51 53 57 59 60 61 68 70 71 73 75 76 77 79 81 83 84 85 86 87 89 90 93 94 100 102 107 108 110 111 114 115 118 119 128 129 130 132 135 145 146 147 148
Primary Contact: Philip A. Clayton, President and Chief Executive Officer
CFO: Bret Barr, Vice President Fiscal Services
CMO: Preston Strosnider, M.D., Vice President Medical Affairs
CIO: Mickey Waters, Director Information Technology
CHR: Matthew J. Securro, Vice President Human Resources
Web address: www.conwaymedicalcenter.com
**Control:** Other not–for–profit (including NFP Corporation) **Service:** General Medical and Surgical

**Staffed Beds:** 262 **Admissions:** 8812 **Census:** 164 **Outpatient Visits:** 114583 **Births:** 1348 **Total Expense ($000):** 133125 **Payroll Expense ($000):** 50302

☐ **LIGHTHOUSE CARE CENTER OF CONWAY (424002)**, 152 Waccamaw Medical Park Drive, Zip 29526–8901; tel. 843/347–8871 **A**1 9 10 **F**1 4 98 101 102 103 106 128 130 **S** Universal Health Services, Inc., King of Prussia, PA
Primary Contact: Thomas L. Ryba, Chief Executive Officer
CFO: Gabrielle Gale, Chief Financial Officer
CMO: Adedapo Oduwole, M.D., Medical Director
CIO: Gabrielle Gale, Chief Financial Officer
CHR: Lois Woodall, Director Human Resources
Web address: www.lighthousecarecenterofconway.com/
**Control:** Corporation, Investor–owned, for–profit **Service:** Psychiatric

**Staffed Beds:** 72 **Admissions:** 2255 **Census:** 62 **Personnel:** 183

### DARLINGTON—Darlington County

☐ **MCLEOD MEDICAL CENTER–DARLINGTON (420057)**, 701 Cashua Ferry Road, Zip 29532–8488, Mailing Address: P.O. Box 1859, Zip 29540; tel. 843/395–1100 **A**1 10 **F**1 3 4 15 34 35 38 56 57 59 61 64 67 68 77 81 85 90 93 94 97 98 100 101 103 104 107 110 114 119 127 128 130 132 133 135 147 148 **P**6 **S** McLeod Health, Florence, SC
Primary Contact: Tim Smoak, Administrator
Web address: www.mcleodhealth.org
**Control:** Other not–for–profit (including NFP Corporation) **Service:** General Medical and Surgical

**Staffed Beds:** 72 **Admissions:** 1283 **Census:** 55 **Births:** 0 **Total Expense ($000):** 14435 **Payroll Expense ($000):** 6380 **Personnel:** 98

### DILLON—Dillon County

☐ **MCLEOD MEDICAL CENTER DILLON (420005)**, 301 East Jackson Street, Zip 29536–2509, Mailing Address: P.O. Box 1327, Zip 29536–1327; tel. 843/774–4111 **A**1 9 10 **F**1 3 11 13 15 28 29 30 32 34 35 40 50 57 59 64 68 70 75 76 79 80 81 82 85 87 89 90 94 107 111 114 119 128 130 132 134 135 146 147 148 **P**6 **S** McLeod Health, Florence, SC
Primary Contact: Joan Gruin, RN, MN, Administrator
CFO: Fulton Ervin, Senior Vice President and Chief Financial Officer
CMO: Walter B. Blum, M.D., Chief of Staff
CIO: Jenean Blackmon, Assistant Vice President and Chief Information Officer
CHR: Cynthia Causey, Associate Administrator Human and Mission Services
Web address: www.mcleodhealth.org
**Control:** Other not–for–profit (including NFP Corporation) **Service:** General Medical and Surgical

**Staffed Beds:** 58 **Admissions:** 2507 **Census:** 22 **Outpatient Visits:** 14434 **Births:** 268 **Total Expense ($000):** 38341 **Payroll Expense ($000):** 15588 **Personnel:** 298

### EASLEY—Pickens County

☒ **BAPTIST EASLEY HOSPITAL (420015)**, 200 Fleetwood Drive, Zip 29640–2022, Mailing Address: P.O. Box 2129, Zip 29641–2129; tel. 864/442–7200 **A**1 5 9 10 **F**1 3 11 13 15 20 28 29 30 34 35 39 40 56 57 59 64 70 76 79 81 85 86 87 89 107 108 111 114 115 119 124 128 130 132 146 147 **S** Palmetto Health, Columbia, SC
Primary Contact: Michael Batchelor, Chief Executive Officer
CFO: J. Larry Pope, Vice President Finance
CIO: Cynthia Ellenburg, Director Health Information Services
CHR: Richard B. Posey, Director Human Resources
CNO: Mary Ann Hunter, Director Nursing Services
Web address: www.baptisteasley.org
**Control:** Other not–for–profit (including NFP Corporation) **Service:** General Medical and Surgical

**Staffed Beds:** 89 **Admissions:** 3995 **Census:** 52 **Outpatient Visits:** 105855 **Births:** 499 **Total Expense ($000):** 73301 **Payroll Expense ($000):** 27499 **Personnel:** 715

### EDGEFIELD—Edgefield County

★ **EDGEFIELD COUNTY HOSPITAL (421304)**, 300 Ridge Medical Plaza, Zip 29824–4525; tel. 803/637–3174 **A**9 10 18 **F**1 3 28 29 34 40 45 59 65 68 77 79 81 84 90 93 94 107 115 119 127 128 130 133 146 **P**1
Primary Contact: Carlos R. Milanes, Interim Chief Executive Officer
CFO: William Garry, Chief Financial Officer
CMO: W. Hugh Morgan, M.D., Chief Medical Staff
CIO: Faye Burton, Director Health Information Management
CHR: Leslie G. Seigler, Executive Assistant and Coordinator Human Resources
Web address: www.myech.org
**Control:** County–Government, nonfederal **Service:** General Medical and Surgical

**Staffed Beds:** 25 **Admissions:** 378 **Census:** 3 **Outpatient Visits:** 6994 **Births:** 0 **Total Expense ($000):** 12707 **Payroll Expense ($000):** 6523 **Personnel:** 180

### FAIRFAX—Allendale County

★ **ALLENDALE COUNTY HOSPITAL (421300)**, 1787 Allendale Fairfax Highway, Zip 29827–9133, Mailing Address: P.O. Box 218, Zip 29827–0218; tel. 803/632–3311, (Nonreporting) **A**9 10 18
Primary Contact: Lari Gooding, MBA, Chief Executive Officer
Web address: www.achospital.org
**Control:** County–Government, nonfederal **Service:** General Medical and Surgical

**Staffed Beds:** 69

### FLORENCE—Florence County

☒ △ **CAROLINAS HOSPITAL SYSTEM (420091)**, 805 Pamplico Highway, Zip 29505–6050, Mailing Address: P.O. Box 100550, Zip 29502–0550; tel. 843/674–5000, (Nonreporting) **A**1 7 9 10 **S** Community Health Systems, Inc., Franklin, TN
Primary Contact: Darcy Craven, Chief Executive Officer
CFO: Loren Rials, Chief Financial Officer
CMO: Kevin Shea, M.D., Chief of Staff
CIO: Lynn Northcutt, Chief Information Officer
CHR: Donna Damico, Director Human Resources
Web address: www.carolinashospital.com
**Control:** Corporation, Investor–owned, for–profit **Service:** General Medical and Surgical

**Staffed Beds:** 429

☒ **HEALTHSOUTH REHABILITATION HOSPITAL OF FLORENCE (423026)**, 900 East Cheves Street, Zip 29506–2704; tel. 843/679–9000, (Nonreporting) **A**1 10 **S** HEALTHSOUTH Corporation, Birmingham, AL
Primary Contact: Jill Strawn, Chief Executive Officer
CFO: Robert Wheeler, Controller
CMO: Adora Matthews, M.D., Medical Director
CHR: Susan Trantham, Director Human Resources
Web address: www.healthsouthflorence.com
**Control:** Corporation, Investor–owned, for–profit **Service:** Rehabilitation

**Staffed Beds:** 88

SC

☒ **MCLEOD REGIONAL MEDICAL CENTER (420051)**, 555 East Cheves Street, Zip 29506–2617, Mailing Address: P.O. Box 100551, Zip 29502–0551; tel. 843/777–2000 **A**1 2 3 5 9 10 **F**1 3 7 8 11 13 15 17 18 20 22 24 26 28 29 30 31 32 34 35 39 40 43 45 46 47 48 49 50 51 53 54 56 57 58 59 60 61 62 63 64 68 70 71 72 73 74 75 76 77 78 79 80 81 82 84 85 86 87 88 89 90 92 94 96 97 100 102 107 108 110 111 114 115 116 119 121 128 129 130 131 132 135 143 145 146 147 148 **P**6 **S** McLeod Health, Florence, SC
Primary Contact: Robert L. Colones, President and Chief Executive Officer
COO: Ronald L. Boring, Senior Vice President and Chief Operating Officer
CFO: Fulton Ervin, Chief Financial Officer
CMO: Alva W. Whitehead, M.D., Vice President Medical Services
CIO: Jenean Blackmon, Associate Vice President and Chief Information Officer
CHR: Jeannette Glenn, Vice President Human Resources, Education and Training
Web address: www.mcleodhealth.org
**Control:** Other not–for–profit (including NFP Corporation) **Service:** General Medical and Surgical

| | |
|---|---|
| **Staffed Beds:** 493 **Admissions:** 24080 **Census:** 368 **Outpatient Visits:** 137921 **Births:** 1971 **Total Expense ($000):** 502010 **Payroll Expense ($000):** 173450 **Personnel:** 3107 | |

☒ **REGENCY HOSPITAL OF FLORENCE (422007)**, 121 East Cedar Street, 4th Floor, Zip 29506–2576; tel. 843/661–3471 **A**1 10 **F**1 3 29 34 35 57 58 70 77 80 85 90 100 128 130 148 **S** Select Medical Corporation, Mechanicsburg, PA
Primary Contact: Amy Metz, Chief Executive Officer
CMO: Stephen Dersch, M.D., President Medical Staff
CHR: Tina Stokes, Manager Human Resources
Web address: www.regencyhospital.com
**Control:** Corporation, Investor–owned, for–profit **Service:** Long–Term Acute Care hospital

| | |
|---|---|
| **Staffed Beds:** 40 **Admissions:** 435 **Census:** 34 **Outpatient Visits:** 0 **Births:** 0 **Total Expense ($000):** 16668 **Payroll Expense ($000):** 6978 **Personnel:** 92 | |

### FORT JACKSON—Richland County

☒ **MONCRIEF ARMY COMMUNITY HOSPITAL**, 4500 Stuart Street, Zip 29207–5700; tel. 803/751–2160, (Nonreporting) **A**1 3 5 **S** Department of the Army, Office of the Surgeon General, Falls Church, VA
Primary Contact: Colonel Traci Crawford, R.N., Commander
Web address: www.moncrief.amedd.army.mil
**Control:** Army, Government, federal **Service:** General Medical and Surgical

| | |
|---|---|
| **Staffed Beds:** 60 | |

### GAFFNEY—Cherokee County

☒ **MARY BLACK HEALTH SYSTEM – GAFFNEY (420043)**, 1530 North Limestone Street, Zip 29340–4738; tel. 864/487–4271 **A**1 9 10 **F**1 3 11 13 15 18 19 29 34 35 40 45 46 51 57 59 64 65 67 70 75 76 79 81 82 85 86 87 89 107 108 110 111 113 119 128 129 130 131 132 135 145 146 147 148 **S** Community Health Systems, Inc., Franklin, TN
Primary Contact: Joshua Self, Chief Executive Officer
COO: Leslie Glover, Director Operations
CMO: Frank Phillips, M.D., Chief of Staff
CIO: Richard Bledsoe, Director Information Systems
CHR: Connie Gibson, R.N., Director Human Resources
CNO: Brian Nunn, R.N., Chief Nursing Officer
Web address: www.upstatecarolina.org
**Control:** Corporation, Investor–owned, for–profit **Service:** General Medical and Surgical

| | |
|---|---|
| **Staffed Beds:** 125 **Admissions:** 2270 **Census:** 27 **Outpatient Visits:** 7762 **Births:** 281 **Total Expense ($000):** 41695 **Payroll Expense ($000):** 15324 **Personnel:** 362 | |

### GEORGETOWN—Georgetown County

☒ **TIDELANDS GEORGETOWN MEMORIAL HOSPITAL (420020)**, 606 Black River Road, Zip 29440–3368, Mailing Address: Drawer 421718, Zip 29442–4203; tel. 843/527–7000 **A**1 3 5 9 10 19 **F**1 3 8 11 12 13 15 17 18 20 22 24 29 30 31 32 34 35 39 40 45 50 51 53 54 56 57 59 60 61 64 65 68 70 73 74 75 76 77 78 79 81 82 84 85 86 87 89 90 93 94 97 100 102 107 108 110 111 115 118 119 128 130 131 132 135 146 147 148 **S** QHR, Brentwood, TN
Primary Contact: Gayle L. Resetar, Chief Operating Officer
COO: Gayle L. Resetar, Vice President and Chief Operating Officer
CFO: Terry L. Kiser, Vice President and Chief Financial Officer
CIO: Frank Scafidi, Vice President and Chief Information Officer
CHR: James F. Harper, Senior Vice President and Chief Human Resources Officer
Web address: www.georgetownhospitalsystem.org
**Control:** Other not–for–profit (including NFP Corporation) **Service:** General Medical and Surgical

| | |
|---|---|
| **Staffed Beds:** 136 **Admissions:** 4021 **Census:** 47 **Outpatient Visits:** 172077 **Births:** 267 **Total Expense ($000):** 117357 **Payroll Expense ($000):** 46193 **Personnel:** 743 | |

### GREENVILLE—Greenville County

☒ △ **BON SECOURS ST. FRANCIS HEALTH SYSTEM (420023)**, One St. Francis Drive, Zip 29601–3207; tel. 864/255–1000, (Includes ST. FRANCIS EASTSIDE, 125 Commonwealth Drive, Zip 29615–4812; tel. 864/675–4000), (Nonreporting) **A**1 2 7 9 10 **S** Bon Secours Health System, Inc., Marriottsville, MD
Primary Contact: Craig McCoy, Chief Executive Officer
COO: Daniel Duggan, Chief Operating Officer
CFO: Ronnie Hyatt, Senior Vice President Finance and Chief Financial Officer
CMO: Saria Saccoio, M.D., Chief Medical Officer
CIO: Rita Hooker, Administrative Director Information Services
CHR: Fernando Fleites, Senior Vice President Human Resources
CNO: Teri Ficicchy, R.N., Chief Nursing Officer
Web address: www.stfrancishealth.org
**Control:** Other not–for–profit (including NFP Corporation) **Service:** General Medical and Surgical

| | |
|---|---|
| **Staffed Beds:** 331 | |

☒ △ **GREENVILLE MEMORIAL HOSPITAL (420078)**, 701 Grove Road, Zip 29605–4295; tel. 864/455–7000, (Includes CHILDREN'S HOSPITAL, 701 Grove Road, Zip 29605–5611; tel. 864/455–7000; MARSHALL I. PICKENS HOSPITAL, 701 Grove Road, Zip 29605–5601; tel. 864/455–8988; ROGER C. PEACE REHABILITATION HOSPITAL, 701 Grove Road, tel. 864/455–7000), (Total facility includes 15 beds in nursing home–type unit) **A**1 2 3 5 7 8 9 10 **F**3 4 5 11 13 15 17 18 19 20 22 24 26 27 28 29 30 31 34 35 36 38 39 40 41 43 44 45 46 47 48 49 50 52 53 54 56 57 59 60 64 65 66 70 72 73 74 75 76 77 78 79 81 82 84 85 86 87 88 89 90 92 93 94 96 97 98 99 100 101 102 103 104 105 106 107 110 111 114 115 116 117 118 119 120 121 124 126 128 129 130 132 134 135 136 141 142 145 146 147 148 **S** Greenville Health System, Greenville, SC
Primary Contact: Paul F. Johnson, President
CNO: Michelle T. Smith, R.N., Chief Nursing Officer
Web address: www.ghs.org
**Control:** Other not–for–profit (including NFP Corporation) **Service:** General Medical and Surgical

| | |
|---|---|
| **Staffed Beds:** 759 **Admissions:** 35889 **Census:** 613 **Outpatient Visits:** 252212 **Births:** 5587 **Total Expense ($000):** 747579 **Payroll Expense ($000):** 221289 **Personnel:** 5463 | |

☒ **PATEWOOD MEMORIAL HOSPITAL (420102)**, 175 Patewood Drive, Zip 29615–3570; tel. 864/797–1000 **A**1 5 9 10 **F**1 3 11 29 30 37 45 50 64 74 77 79 81 85 128 130 135 146 **S** Greenville Health System, Greenville, SC
Primary Contact: Beverly J. Haines, R.N., President
Web address: www.ghs.org/patewood
**Control:** Other not–for–profit (including NFP Corporation) **Service:** Surgical

| | |
|---|---|
| **Staffed Beds:** 16 **Admissions:** 1065 **Census:** 6 **Outpatient Visits:** 5701 **Births:** 0 **Total Expense ($000):** 37471 **Payroll Expense ($000):** 9796 **Personnel:** 172 | |

☒ **REGENCY HOSPITAL OF GREENVILLE (422009)**, One St. Francis Drive, 4th Floor, Zip 29601–3955; tel. 864/255–1438 **A**1 10 **F**1 3 29 60 75 77 85 97 128 **S** Select Medical Corporation, Mechanicsburg, PA
Primary Contact: Stephanie James, Chief Executive Officer
Web address: www.regencyhospital.com
**Control:** Corporation, Investor–owned, for–profit **Service:** Long–Term Acute Care hospital

| | |
|---|---|
| **Staffed Beds:** 32 **Admissions:** 379 **Census:** 27 **Outpatient Visits:** 0 **Births:** 0 **Total Expense ($000):** 14140 **Payroll Expense ($000):** 6169 **Personnel:** 96 | |

☐ **SHRINERS HOSPITALS FOR CHILDREN–GREENVILLE (423300)**, 950 West Faris Road, Zip 29605–4277; tel. 864/271–3444 **A**1 3 5 9 10 **F**1 59 64 68 75 77 79 81 85 87 89 90 93 94 128 130 131 146 148 **P**6 **S** Shriners Hospitals for Children, Tampa, FL
Primary Contact: Randall R. Romberger, Administrator
CFO: John Conti, Director Finance
CMO: J. Michael Wattenbarger, M.D., Chief of Staff
CHR: Willis E. Tisdale, Director Human Resources
CNO: Allison Leigh Windas, Director of Patient Care Services
Web address: www.greenvilleshrinershospital.org
**Control:** Other not–for–profit (including NFP Corporation) **Service:** Children's orthopedic

| | |
|---|---|
| **Staffed Beds:** 15 **Admissions:** 261 **Census:** 2 **Outpatient Visits:** 15440 **Births:** 0 **Total Expense ($000):** 21878 **Payroll Expense ($000):** 9743 **Personnel:** 182 | |

**SC**

| Hospital, Medicare Provider Number, Address, Telephone, Approval, Facility, and Physician Codes, Health Care System | | |
|---|---|---|
| ★ American Hospital Association (AHA) membership | ○ Healthcare Facilities Accreditation Program | ⇑ Center for Improvement in Healthcare Quality Accreditation |
| ☐ The Joint Commission accreditation | ◇ DNV Healthcare Inc. accreditation | △ Commission on Accreditation of Rehabilitation Facilities (CARF) accreditation |

**SC**

## GREENWOOD—Greenwood County

☐ **GREENWOOD REGIONAL REHABILITATION HOSPITAL (423030)**, 1530 Parkway, Zip 29646–4027; tel. 864/330–9070, (Total facility includes 7 beds in nursing home–type unit) **A**1 10 **F**1 3 29 75 90 128 130 132 143 148 **S** Ernest Health, Inc., Albuquerque, NM
Primary Contact: Kristin Manske, Chief Executive Officer
CFO: Charity Walker, Controller and Regional Business Officer Manager
CMO: Cam Monda, D.O., Medical Director
CNO: Teresa Nabors, Director of Nursing
Web address: www.grrh.ernesthealth.com
**Control:** Corporation, Investor–owned, for–profit **Service:** Rehabilitation

**Staffed Beds:** 49 **Admissions:** 998 **Census:** 39 **Outpatient Visits:** 0 **Births:** 0 **Total Expense ($000):** 16529 **Payroll Expense ($000):** 6617 **Personnel:** 119

★ ◇ **SELF REGIONAL HEALTHCARE (420071)**, 1325 Spring Street, Zip 29646–3860; tel. 864/725–4111 **A**2 3 5 9 10 21 **F**1 3 8 11 13 15 17 18 20 22 24 26 28 29 30 31 32 34 35 39 40 43 49 50 51 53 57 59 60 62 64 68 70 72 73 74 75 76 77 78 79 80 81 82 86 87 89 90 93 94 97 98 102 103 104 107 108 110 111 114 115 117 119 120 121 123 124 128 129 130 131 132 134 135 144 146 147 148 **P**5 8
Primary Contact: James A. Pfeiffer, FACHE, President and Chief Executive Officer
CFO: Timothy Evans, Vice President and Chief Financial Officer
CMO: F Gregory Mappin, M.D., Vice President Medical Affairs and Chief Medical Officer
CIO: Andy Hartung, Director Information Systems
CHR: Michael Dixon, Director Human Resources
CNO: Linda Russell, Vice President and Chief Nursing Officer
Web address: www.selfregional.org
**Control:** County–Government, nonfederal **Service:** General Medical and Surgical

**Staffed Beds:** 326 **Admissions:** 11865 **Census:** 155 **Outpatient Visits:** 234146 **Births:** 1450 **Total Expense ($000):** 300673 **Payroll Expense ($000):** 100689 **Personnel:** 1800

## GREER—Greenville County

☐ **CAROLINA CENTER FOR BEHAVIORAL HEALTH (424010)**, 2700 East Phillips Road, Zip 29650–4816; tel. 864/235–2335, (Nonreporting) **A**1 9 10 **S** Universal Health Services, Inc., King of Prussia, PA
Primary Contact: John Willingham, Chief Executive Officer and Managing Director
CFO: James P. Boynton, Jr., Chief Financial Officer
CMO: Gergana Dimitrova, M.D., Medical Director
CHR: George Hammett, Director Human Resources
Web address: www.thecarolinacenter.com
**Control:** Corporation, Investor–owned, for–profit **Service:** Psychiatric

**Staffed Beds:** 112

✖ **GREER MEMORIAL HOSPITAL (420033)**, 830 South Bumcombe Road, Zip 29650–2400; tel. 864/797–8000, (Includes ROGER HUNTINGTON NURSING CENTER ) **A**1 5 9 10 **F**1 3 11 13 15 18 28 29 30 34 35 40 44 47 49 50 57 59 61 64 65 68 70 76 77 79 81 82 85 86 87 89 94 107 110 111 114 119 128 129 130 146 147 **S** Greenville Health System, Greenville, SC
Primary Contact: John F. Mansure, FACHE, President
Web address: www.ghs.org
**Control:** Other not–for–profit (including NFP Corporation) **Service:** General Medical and Surgical

**Staffed Beds:** 35 **Admissions:** 3499 **Census:** 29 **Outpatient Visits:** 104822 **Births:** 694 **Total Expense ($000):** 74217 **Payroll Expense ($000):** 24357 **Personnel:** 393

★ **PELHAM MEDICAL CENTER (420103)**, 250 Westmoreland Road, Zip 29651–9013; tel. 864/530–6000 **A**9 10 **F**1 3 11 15 18 20 26 29 30 34 35 37 40 45 49 50 54 57 59 64 68 70 74 75 77 79 81 82 84 85 86 87 90 94 107 108 110 111 114 115 118 119 128 130 146 **S** Spartanburg Regional Healthcare System, Spartanburg, SC
Primary Contact: Anthony Kouskolekas, FACHE, President
CNO: Connie Spykerman, Chief Nursing Officer
Web address: www.villageatpelham.com
**Control:** Hospital district or authority, Government, nonfederal **Service:** General Medical and Surgical

**Staffed Beds:** 39 **Admissions:** 1956 **Census:** 19 **Outpatient Visits:** 43033 **Births:** 0 **Total Expense ($000):** 48025 **Payroll Expense ($000):** 16408 **Personnel:** 645

## HARDEEVILLE—Jasper County

✖ **COASTAL CAROLINA HOSPITAL (420101)**, 1000 Medical Center Drive, Zip 29927–3446; tel. 843/784–8000 **A**1 9 10 **F**1 3 11 13 15 28 29 30 34 35 40 45 46 47 48 49 51 57 59 60 64 70 74 75 76 77 79 81 85 89 90 93 94 107 108 110 111 115 119 127 128 130 132 135 146 147 148 **S** TENET Healthcare Corporation, Dallas, TX
Primary Contact: Bradley S. Talbert, FACHE, Chief Executive Officer
CFO: Amanda Dyle, Chief Financial Officer
CMO: Robert Bernasek, M.D., Chief Medical Officer
CIO: Cheryl Grant, Director Information Systems
CHR: Darlene Nester, Market Chief Human Resources Officer
CNO: Ashley Marie VonNida, Chief Nursing Officer
Web address: www.coastalhospital.com
**Control:** Corporation, Investor–owned, for–profit **Service:** General Medical and Surgical

**Staffed Beds:** 35 **Admissions:** 2489 **Census:** 22 **Outpatient Visits:** 42529 **Births:** 453 **Total Expense ($000):** 38651 **Payroll Expense ($000):** 13255 **Personnel:** 263

## HARTSVILLE—Darlington County

✖ **CAROLINA PINES REGIONAL MEDICAL CENTER (420010)**, 1304 West Bobo Newsom Highway, Zip 29550–4710; tel. 843/339–2100 **A**1 9 10 **F**1 3 11 13 15 20 28 29 30 34 35 40 43 46 49 57 64 70 73 75 76 79 81 82 85 86 87 89 90 93 107 108 110 111 115 118 119 128 129 130 131 132 135 146 147 148 **S** Capella Healthcare, Franklin, TN
Primary Contact: J. Timothy Browne, FACHE, Chief Executive Officer
COO: Susan C. Shugart, Chief Operating Officer
CFO: Rodney VanDonkelaar, Chief Financial Officer
CIO: Denise Barefoot, Director Health Information Systems
CHR: Charlotte Adams, Director Associate Resources
CNO: Debbie Brand, Chief Nursing Officer
Web address: www.cprmc.com
**Control:** Corporation, Investor–owned, for–profit **Service:** General Medical and Surgical

**Staffed Beds:** 120 **Admissions:** 5256 **Census:** 50 **Outpatient Visits:** 39251 **Births:** 601 **Personnel:** 440

## HILTON HEAD ISLAND—Beaufort County

✖ **HILTON HEAD HOSPITAL (420080)**, 25 Hospital Center Boulevard, Zip 29926–2738; tel. 843/681–6122 **A**1 9 10 20 **F**1 3 11 13 15 17 18 20 22 24 26 28 29 30 34 35 37 40 45 46 47 48 49 50 51 53 54 57 59 60 61 64 65 68 70 74 76 77 78 79 81 85 86 89 94 96 107 110 111 114 115 118 119 128 130 131 132 135 146 147 148 **S** TENET Healthcare Corporation, Dallas, TX
Primary Contact: Jeremy Clark, President and Chief Executive Officer
CFO: Cassie Ball, Chief Financial Officer
CMO: Glenn Neil Love, M.D., Medical Director
CIO: Stephen Brendler, Director Information Systems
CHR: Darlene Nester, Chief Human Resources Officer
Web address: www.hiltonheadregional.com
**Control:** Partnership, Investor–owned, for–profit **Service:** General Medical and Surgical

**Staffed Beds:** 93 **Admissions:** 5418 **Census:** 57 **Outpatient Visits:** 60017 **Births:** 593 **Total Expense ($000):** 91371 **Payroll Expense ($000):** 25230 **Personnel:** 525

## KINGSTREE—Williamsburg County

✖ **WILLIAMSBURG REGIONAL HOSPITAL (421303)**, 500 Nelson Boulevard, Zip 29556–4027; tel. 843/355–8888 **A**1 9 10 18 **F**1 3 11 15 18 24 29 30 34 35 40 50 57 59 64 70 77 81 85 86 87 89 90 94 97 107 108 114 119 127 128 130 133 135 146 148
Primary Contact: Sharon Poston, President and Chief Executive Officer
COO: Dan Harrington, Chief Operating Officer and Director Human Resources
CMO: Troy B. Gamble, Jr., M.D., Chief Medical Staff
CIO: David Slenszak, Director, Information Services
CHR: Dan Harrington, Chief Operating Officer and Director Human Resources
CNO: Kelly Lawson, Chief Nursing Officer
Web address: www.wmbgrh.com/
**Control:** Other not–for–profit (including NFP Corporation) **Service:** General Medical and Surgical

**Staffed Beds:** 25 **Admissions:** 1079 **Census:** 17 **Outpatient Visits:** 34099 **Births:** 0 **Personnel:** 218

*Many Facility Codes have changed. Please refer to the AHA Guide Code Chart.* © 2015 AHA Guide

## LAKE CITY—Florence County

★ **LAKE CITY COMMUNITY HOSPITAL (420066)**, 258 North Ron McNair Boulevard, Zip 29560–2462, Mailing Address: P.O. Box 1479, Zip 29560–1479; tel. 843/374–2036 **A**9 10 **F**1 3 11 15 28 29 34 35 40 50 56 57 59 61 64 65 69 75 77 79 81 85 86 87 93 94 107 108 111 113 114 119 127 128 130 132 144 146
Primary Contact: Henry McCutcheon, Jr., Chief Executive Officer
CFO: Henry McCutcheon, Jr., Chief Financial Officer
CMO: Stephen Askins, M.D., Chief of Staff
CIO: David Moon, Jr., Director Information Systems
CHR: Anne Poston, Director of Human Resources/Compliance
CNO: Renate Browder, R.N., Director of Nursing
Web address: www.lcchospital.org
**Control:** Hospital district or authority, Government, nonfederal **Service:** General Medical and Surgical

**Staffed Beds:** 30 **Admissions:** 790 **Census:** 11 **Outpatient Visits:** 18862 **Births:** 0 **Total Expense ($000):** 16033 **Payroll Expense ($000):** 7006 **Personnel:** 181

## LANCASTER—Lancaster County

⊞ **SPRINGS MEMORIAL HOSPITAL (420036)**, 800 West Meeting Street, Zip 29720–2298; tel. 803/286–1214, (Total facility includes 14 beds in nursing home–type unit) **A**1 5 9 10 **F**1 3 8 11 13 15 17 18 20 29 30 31 34 35 40 47 48 49 51 57 59 62 63 64 68 70 72 73 74 75 76 78 79 80 81 85 89 90 93 94 102 107 108 110 111 114 115 118 119 128 129 130 132 135 146 147 148 **S** Community Health Systems, Inc., Franklin, TN
Primary Contact: Janice Dabney, Chief Executive Officer
CFO: Holt Smith, Chief Financial Officer
CMO: Douglas Tiedt, M.D., Chief of Staff
CIO: Chrys Steele, Director Information Systems
CHR: Trent Elmore, Director Human Resources
CNO: Karen Martin, Chief Nursing Officer
Web address: www.springsmemorial.com
**Control:** Corporation, Investor–owned, for–profit **Service:** General Medical and Surgical

**Staffed Beds:** 168 **Admissions:** 6798 **Census:** 87 **Outpatient Visits:** 32539 **Births:** 726 **Total Expense ($000):** 91717 **Payroll Expense ($000):** 29620 **Personnel:** 608

## LORIS—Horry County

⊞ **MCLEOD LORIS SEACOAST HOSPITAL (420105)**, 3655 Mitchell Street, Zip 29569–2827; tel. 843/716–7000, (Includes MCLEOD SEACOAST, 4000 Highway 9 East, Little River, Zip 29566–7833; tel. 843/390–8100), (Total facility includes 88 beds in nursing home–type unit) **A**1 9 10 **F**1 3 11 13 15 17 18 20 28 29 30 32 34 35 40 50 53 57 59 60 64 68 70 74 75 76 77 79 81 82 85 86 87 89 90 94 96 107 108 110 111 114 115 118 119 128 130 131 132 134 135 146 148 **S** McLeod Health, Florence, SC
Primary Contact: Edward D. Tinsley, III, Chief Executive Officer
COO: Arnold Green, Senior Vice President and Chief Operating Officer
CFO: Fred O. Todd, Senior Vice President Finance
CMO: James N. Craigie, M.D., Vice President Medical Affairs
CHR: Teresa Pougnaud, Vice President Human Resources
Web address: www.mcleodhealth.org
**Control:** Other not–for–profit (including NFP Corporation) **Service:** General Medical and Surgical

**Staffed Beds:** 193 **Admissions:** 4563 **Census:** 115 **Outpatient Visits:** 93939 **Births:** 450 **Total Expense ($000):** 95077 **Payroll Expense ($000):** 36753 **Personnel:** 353

## MANNING—Clarendon County

★ ◇ **CLARENDON MEMORIAL HOSPITAL (420069)**, 10 Hospital Street, Zip 29102–3153, Mailing Address: P.O. Box 550, Zip 29102–0550; tel. 803/433–3000 **A**9 10 21 **F**1 3 7 11 13 15 18 26 28 29 34 35 39 40 45 50 51 53 54 56 57 59 62 64 65 67 70 75 76 77 79 81 85 89 90 91 93 94 96 97 107 108 110 111 114 118 119 127 128 129 130 132 135 143 146 147 148
Primary Contact: Richard W. Stokes, Jr., CPA, Chief Executive Officer
COO: Paul Schumacher, Chief Operating Officer
CFO: John Shaughnessy, Chief Financial Officer
CMO: Catherine Rabon, M.D., Chief Medical Officer
CIO: Pat Kolb, Manager Information Technology
CHR: Gail A. Richbourg, Director Human Resources
CNO: Natalie Davis, R.N., Interim Chief Nursing Officer
Web address: www.clarendonhealth.com
**Control:** Hospital district or authority, Government, nonfederal **Service:** General Medical and Surgical

**Staffed Beds:** 48 **Admissions:** 2375 **Census:** 30 **Outpatient Visits:** 20699 **Births:** 448 **Total Expense ($000):** 45087 **Payroll Expense ($000):** 18460 **Personnel:** 471

## MOUNT PLEASANT—Charleston County

⊞ **EAST COOPER MEDICAL CENTER (420089)**, 2000 Hospital Drive, Zip 29464–3764; tel. 843/881–0100 **A**1 3 5 9 10 **F**1 3 13 15 18 29 31 34 35 40 43 46 51 57 59 60 64 68 70 73 74 75 76 77 78 79 80 81 82 84 85 86 90 92 93 94 100 102 107 108 110 111 114 115 119 126 128 129 130 131 132 135 146 147 148 **S** TENET Healthcare Corporation, Dallas, TX
Primary Contact: Jason P. Alexander, FACHE, Chief Executive Officer
COO: Ramona Pickens, Chief Operating Officer
CFO: Brandon Willams, Chief Financial Officer
CMO: William Stroud, M.D., Chief Medical Officer
CIO: Michael Foster, Director Information Systems
CHR: Tracy Hunter, Chief Human Resources Officer
CNO: Terri Harris, R.N., Chief Nursing Officer
Web address: www.eastcoopermedctr.com
**Control:** Corporation, Investor–owned, for–profit **Service:** General Medical and Surgical

**Staffed Beds:** 140 **Admissions:** 5076 **Census:** 42 **Outpatient Visits:** 51924 **Births:** 1473 **Total Expense ($000):** 108830 **Payroll Expense ($000):** 27611 **Personnel:** 425

**EAST COOPER REGIONAL MEDICAL CENTER** See East Cooper Medical Center

⊞ **ROPER ST. FRANCIS MOUNT PLEASANT HOSPITAL (420104)**, 3500 Highway 17 North, Zip 29466–9123, Mailing Address: 3500 North Highway 17, Zip 29466–9123; tel. 843/606–7000 **A**1 9 10 **F**1 3 7 13 15 29 30 34 40 45 54 57 59 68 70 75 76 79 81 84 85 87 89 94 107 108 110 111 115 118 119 128 129 143 146 147 148 **S** Carolinas Healthcare System, Charlotte, NC
Primary Contact: Tavia Buck, Interim Chief Executive Officer
CFO: Bret Johnson, Chief Financial Officer
CMO: Steven D. Shapiro, M.D., Chief Medical Officer
CIO: Melinda H. Cardell, Interim Chief Information Officer
CHR: Melanie Stith, Vice President Human Resources
CNO: Tavia Buck, Chief Nursing Officer
Web address: www.mymountpleasanthospital.com
**Control:** Other not–for–profit (including NFP Corporation) **Service:** General Medical and Surgical

**Staffed Beds:** 50 **Admissions:** 1650 **Census:** 13 **Outpatient Visits:** 38702 **Births:** 518 **Total Expense ($000):** 52148 **Payroll Expense ($000):** 13044 **Personnel:** 291

## MT. PLEASANT—Mt. Pleasant County

**KINDRED HOSPITAL–CHARLESTON** See Vibra Hospital of Charleston

⊞ **VIBRA HOSPITAL OF CHARLESTON (422005)**, 1200 Hospital Drive, Zip 29464; tel. 843/375–4000, (Total facility includes 35 beds in nursing home–type unit) **A**1 10 **F**1 3 29 35 85 90 107 114 119 128 148 **S** Vibra Healthcare, Mechanicsburg, PA
Primary Contact: Joseph E. Roche, Chief Executive Officer
CFO: Julia Smith, Chief Financial Officer
CMO: Athena Beldecos, M.D., Medical Director
CHR: Julia Taylor, Area Director Human Resources
Web address: www.vhcharleston.com
**Control:** Corporation, Investor–owned, for–profit **Service:** Long–Term Acute Care hospital

**Staffed Beds:** 94 **Admissions:** 731 **Census:** 63 **Outpatient Visits:** 0 **Births:** 0 **Total Expense ($000):** 25774 **Payroll Expense ($000):** 11567

## MULLINS—Marion County

⊞ **CAROLINAS HOSPITAL SYSTEM MARION (420055)**, 2829 East Highway 76, Zip 29574–6035, Mailing Address: P.O. Drawer 1150, Marion, Zip 29571–1150; tel. 843/431–2000, (Total facility includes 92 beds in nursing home–type unit) **A**1 9 10 **F**1 3 13 15 28 29 34 40 45 46 53 57 59 67 70 75 76 77 79 81 82 85 86 89 90 94 107 111 119 128 129 130 131 133 146 148 **S** Community Health Systems, Inc., Franklin, TN
Primary Contact: Parkes Coggins, Interim Chief Executive Officer
CFO: Christopher Green, Chief Financial Officer
CMO: Alvin Abinsay, M.D., Chief Medical Staff
CIO: Charlie Grantham, Manager Information Systems
CHR: Kay White, Director Human Resources and Diversity
Web address: www.carolinashospitalmarion.com/Pages/Home.aspx
**Control:** Corporation, Investor–owned, for–profit **Service:** General Medical and Surgical

**Staffed Beds:** 216 **Admissions:** 2640 **Census:** 103 **Outpatient Visits:** 46806 **Births:** 284 **Total Expense ($000):** 55980 **Payroll Expense ($000):** 16515

**MARION COUNTY MEDICAL CENTER** See Carolinas Hospital System Marion

SC

---

**Hospital, Medicare Provider Number, Address, Telephone, Approval, Facility, and Physician Codes, Health Care System**

★ American Hospital Association (AHA) membership  ◯ Healthcare Facilities Accreditation Program  ⇑ Center for Improvement in Healthcare Quality Accreditation
☐ The Joint Commission accreditation  ◇ DNV Healthcare Inc. accreditation  △ Commission on Accreditation of Rehabilitation Facilities (CARF) accreditation

## MURRELLS INLET—Georgetown County

✠ △ **TIDELANDS WACCAMAW COMMUNITY HOSPITAL (420098)**, 4070 Highway 17 Bypass, Zip 29576–5033, Mailing Address: P.O. Drawer 3350, Zip 29576–2673; tel. 843/652–1000 **A**1 2 7 9 10 **F**1 3 8 11 13 15 17 18 28 29 30 31 32 35 37 39 40 45 50 51 56 60 61 64 65 68 70 73 74 75 76 77 78 79 81 82 84 85 86 87 89 90 93 94 96 97 100 102 107 108 110 111 114 115 118 119 128 130 146 147 148 **S** QHR, Brentwood, TN
Primary Contact: Gayle L. Resetar, Chief Operating Officer
CFO: Terry L. Kiser, Chief Financial Officer
CIO: Frank Scafidi, Chief Information Officer
Web address: www.tidelandshealth.org
**Control:** Other not–for–profit (including NFP Corporation) **Service:** General Medical and Surgical

**Staffed Beds:** 169 **Admissions:** 7493 **Census:** 106 **Outpatient Visits:** 108844 **Births:** 624 **Total Expense ($000):** 134670 **Payroll Expense ($000):** 35359 **Personnel:** 605

## MYRTLE BEACH—Horry County

✠ **GRAND STRAND REGIONAL MEDICAL CENTER (420085)**, 809 82nd Parkway, Zip 29572–4607; tel. 843/692–1000 **A**1 2 3 9 10 19 **F**1 3 11 13 15 17 18 20 22 24 26 28 29 30 31 34 35 37 39 40 42 43 46 47 49 50 54 56 57 59 60 64 70 73 74 75 76 77 78 79 81 82 85 86 87 88 89 90 107 108 110 111 114 115 118 119 126 128 130 132 135 146 147 **S** HCA, Nashville, TN
Primary Contact: Mark E. Sims, Chief Executive Officer
CFO: Turner Wortham, Chief Financial Officer
Web address: www.grandstrandmed.com
**Control:** Corporation, Investor–owned, for–profit **Service:** General Medical and Surgical

**Staffed Beds:** 271 **Admissions:** 17221 **Census:** 215 **Births:** 865 **Personnel:** 1011

## NEWBERRY—Newberry County

✠ **NEWBERRY COUNTY MEMORIAL HOSPITAL (420053)**, 2669 Kinard Street, Zip 29108–2911, Mailing Address: P.O. Box 497, Zip 29108–0497; tel. 803/276–7570 **A**1 9 10 20 **F**1 3 7 11 13 15 17 28 29 30 31 32 34 35 40 45 47 49 53 56 57 59 64 68 70 75 76 77 78 79 81 82 85 86 87 89 90 93 94 103 104 107 108 109 110 111 114 119 128 129 130 133 135 143 146 147 148 **P**6 **S** QHR, Brentwood, TN
Primary Contact: Bruce A. Baldwin, Chief Executive Officer
CFO: Mike Reynolds, Chief Financial Officer
CMO: Mark Davis, M.D., Chief of Staff
CIO: David Wolff, Director Information Technology
CHR: Dyan Bowman, Director Human Resources
Web address: www.newberryhospital.org
**Control:** County–Government, nonfederal **Service:** General Medical and Surgical

**Staffed Beds:** 52 **Admissions:** 1980 **Census:** 23 **Outpatient Visits:** 40171 **Births:** 322 **Total Expense ($000):** 47907 **Payroll Expense ($000):** 18074 **Personnel:** 394

## ORANGEBURG—Orangeburg County

✠ **REGIONAL MEDICAL CENTER (420068)**, 3000 St. Matthews Road, Zip 29118–1442; tel. 803/395–2200 **A**1 2 9 10 13 **F**1 3 11 13 14 15 17 18 20 28 29 30 31 32 35 39 40 44 45 46 47 48 50 53 57 58 59 60 61 62 65 68 70 71 73 74 75 76 77 78 79 81 82 84 85 86 87 89 90 93 94 97 98 100 101 102 103 107 108 110 111 114 115 119 121 127 128 129 130 131 132 134 135 144 146 147 148 **S** QHR, Brentwood, TN
Primary Contact: Thomas C. Dandridge, FACHE, President and Chief Executive Officer
CFO: Cheryl S. Mason, Chief Financial Officer
CIO: Diana Sharkey, Interim Chief Information Officer
CHR: Howard Harris, Vice President Human Resources
CNO: Julia K. Yawn, MSN, Chief Nursing Officer and Vice President for Patient Care Services
Web address: www.trmchealth.org
**Control:** County–Government, nonfederal **Service:** General Medical and Surgical

**Staffed Beds:** 283 **Admissions:** 9653 **Census:** 146 **Outpatient Visits:** 209891 **Births:** 1021

☐ **WILLIAM J. MCCORD ADOLESCENT AND TREATMENT CENTER (424013)**, 910 Cook Road, Zip 29118–2124, Mailing Address: P.O. Box 1166, Zip 29116–1166; tel. 803/534–2328 **A**1 10 **F**1 4 5 29 34 38 57 61 98 99 128 130 132 134 135
Primary Contact: Michael Dennis, Director
Web address: www.mccordcenter.com
**Control:** Other not–for–profit (including NFP Corporation) **Service:** Alcoholism and other chemical dependency

**Staffed Beds:** 15 **Admissions:** 107 **Census:** 13 **Outpatient Visits:** 0 **Births:** 0 **Total Expense ($000):** 4225 **Payroll Expense ($000):** 2375 **Personnel:** 35

## PICKENS—Pickens County

★ ◇ **CANNON MEMORIAL HOSPITAL (420011)**, 123 West G. Acker Drive, Zip 29671–2739, Mailing Address: P.O. Box 188, Zip 29671–0188; tel. 864/878–4791 **A**9 10 21 **F**1 3 11 15 29 34 40 50 51 53 56 57 59 61 64 65 70 75 79 81 85 94 97 107 108 110 111 114 119 127 128 130 146 **P**8 **S** Carolinas Healthcare System, Charlotte, NC
Primary Contact: Norman G. Rentz, President and Chief Executive Officer
CFO: Will Grant, Chief Financial Officer
CMO: Daniel J. Dahlhausen, M.D., President of Medical Staff/Chief Medical Officer
CIO: Robert Furr, Director Information Services
CHR: Lisa G. Bryant, Director Human Resources
CNO: Donna K. Anderson, R.N., Chief Nursing Officer
Web address: www.cannonhospital.org
**Control:** Other not–for–profit (including NFP Corporation) **Service:** General Medical and Surgical

**Staffed Beds:** 35 **Admissions:** 1015 **Census:** 10 **Outpatient Visits:** 40341 **Births:** 0 **Total Expense ($000):** 23176 **Payroll Expense ($000):** 10092 **Personnel:** 246

## ROCK HILL—York County

✠ **HEALTHSOUTH REHABILITATION HOSPITAL OF ROCK HILL (423028)**, 1795 Dr. Frank Gaston Boulevard, Zip 29732–1190; tel. 803/326–3500 **A**1 10 **F**1 29 56 64 75 90 94 95 128 **S** HEALTHSOUTH Corporation, Birmingham, AL
Primary Contact: Deanna Martin, Chief Executive Officer
Web address: www.healthsouthrockhill.com
**Control:** Corporation, Investor–owned, for–profit **Service:** General Medical and Surgical

**Staffed Beds:** 50 **Admissions:** 1182 **Census:** 40 **Outpatient Visits:** 0 **Births:** 0 **Total Expense ($000):** 13023 **Payroll Expense ($000):** 6674 **Personnel:** 85

✠ **PIEDMONT MEDICAL CENTER (420002)**, 222 Herlong Avenue, Zip 29732; tel. 803/329–1234 **A**1 2 9 10 **F**1 3 7 11 12 13 15 17 18 20 22 24 26 28 29 30 31 34 35 40 43 45 49 50 57 59 60 64 70 73 74 75 76 77 78 79 81 82 85 86 89 90 91 93 98 100 102 107 108 110 111 114 115 118 119 126 128 130 132 135 146 147 148 **S** TENET Healthcare Corporation, Dallas, TX
Primary Contact: William Masterton, Chief Executive Officer
CFO: Alice W. Rigdon, Chief Financial Officer
CIO: Joel Dean, Director Information Services
CHR: Donald L. Currier, Vice President Human Resources
CNO: Ursula Lawrence, MSN, Chief Nursing Officer
Web address: www.piedmontmedicalcenter.com
**Control:** Corporation, Investor–owned, for–profit **Service:** General Medical and Surgical

**Staffed Beds:** 280 **Admissions:** 13931 **Census:** 173 **Outpatient Visits:** 133207 **Births:** 1718 **Total Expense ($000):** 206955 **Payroll Expense ($000):** 67609 **Personnel:** 1497

## SENECA—Oconee County

✠ **OCONEE MEMORIAL HOSPITAL (420009)**, 298 Memorial Drive, Zip 29672–9499; tel. 864/882–3351, (Includes LILA DOYLE NURSING CARE FACILITY ), (Total facility includes 120 beds in nursing home–type unit) **A**1 3 5 9 10 20 **F**1 3 11 15 18 20 28 29 30 31 34 35 39 40 44 50 54 56 57 59 61 62 63 64 67 70 71 74 75 76 77 78 79 81 82 84 85 86 87 89 90 93 94 97 100 107 108 114 119 128 130 132 135 143 146 148 **S** Greenville Health System, Greenville, SC
Primary Contact: Hunter Kome, Campus President
CMO: Conrad K. Shuler, M.D., Chief Medical Officer
CIO: Jay Hansen, Director Information Services
CNO: Patricia Smith, Chief Nursing Officer
Web address: www.oconeemed.org
**Control:** Hospital district or authority, Government, nonfederal **Service:** General Medical and Surgical

**Staffed Beds:** 248 **Admissions:** 5721 **Census:** 160 **Outpatient Visits:** 102117 **Births:** 537 **Total Expense ($000):** 116216 **Payroll Expense ($000):** 43562 **Personnel:** 938

## SIMPSONVILLE—Greenville County

✠ **HILLCREST MEMORIAL HOSPITAL (420037)**, 729 S.E. Main Street, Zip 29681–3280; tel. 864/454–6100 **A**1 5 9 10 **F**1 3 11 12 15 18 29 30 34 35 40 44 45 50 57 58 59 61 64 68 70 79 81 85 86 90 107 110 111 114 119 128 129 130 132 135 146 **S** Greenville Health System, Greenville, SC
Primary Contact: Eric Bour, M.D., FACS, President
CFO: Pam DeVore, Financial Manager
Web address: www.ghs.org
**Control:** Other not–for–profit (including NFP Corporation) **Service:** General Medical and Surgical

**Staffed Beds:** 19 **Admissions:** 1898 **Census:** 16 **Outpatient Visits:** 65305 **Births:** 0 **Total Expense ($000):** 52451 **Payroll Expense ($000):** 15541 **Personnel:** 245

*Many Facility Codes have changed. Please refer to the AHA Guide Code Chart.*      © 2015 AHA Guide

## SPARTANBURG—Spartanburg County

☒ △ **MARY BLACK HEALTH SYSTEM - SPARTANBURG (420083)**, 1700 Skylyn Drive, Zip 29307–1061, Mailing Address: P.O. Box 3217, Zip 29304–3217; tel. 864/573–3000 **A**1 3 5 7 9 10 **F**1 3 11 13 15 18 20 29 30 31 34 35 40 45 47 49 50 51 56 57 59 60 64 68 70 73 74 76 77 78 79 81 85 89 90 93 94 96 98 102 103 107 108 110 111 114 115 119 126 128 129 130 135 146 147 148 **S** Community Health Systems, Inc., Franklin, TN
Primary Contact: Sean T. Dardeau, FACHE, Chief Executive Officer
CFO: Richard A. Meyer, Chief Financial Officer
CMO: Howard Bean, M.D., Chief Medical Officer
CIO: Jeff Nash, Director Information Technology and Services
CHR: Mark E. Garber, Director Human Resources
CNO: Chanda Flynn, R.N., Chief Nursing Officer
Web address: www.maryblackhealthsystem.com
**Control:** Corporation, Investor–owned, for–profit **Service:** General Medical and Surgical

**Staffed Beds:** 181 **Admissions:** 6136 **Census:** 74 **Outpatient Visits:** 56790 **Births:** 925 **Personnel:** 907

☒ **SPARTANBURG HOSPITAL FOR RESTORATIVE CARE (422004)**, 389 Serpentine Drive, Zip 29303–3026; tel. 864/560–3280, (Total facility includes 25 beds in nursing home–type unit) **A**1 10 **F**1 29 30 31 35 57 59 60 68 70 75 77 79 82 84 85 87 90 119 128 130 148 **S** Spartanburg Regional Healthcare System, Spartanburg, SC
Primary Contact: Anita M. Butler, Chief Executive Officer
Web address: www.srhs.com
**Control:** Hospital district or authority, Government, nonfederal **Service:** Long–Term Acute Care hospital

**Staffed Beds:** 116 **Admissions:** 847 **Census:** 45 **Outpatient Visits:** 0 **Births:** 0 **Total Expense ($000):** 20981 **Payroll Expense ($000):** 11074 **Personnel:** 224

★ **SPARTANBURG REGIONAL MEDICAL CENTER (420007)**, 101 East Wood Street, Zip 29303–3040; tel. 864/560–6000, (Total facility includes 25 beds in nursing home–type unit) **A**2 3 5 9 10 13 **F**1 3 7 11 12 13 15 17 18 20 22 24 26 28 29 30 31 34 35 36 37 38 39 40 43 45 46 47 48 49 50 53 54 56 57 58 59 60 61 62 63 64 65 66 68 70 71 72 73 74 75 76 77 78 79 81 82 83 84 85 86 87 88 89 90 94 97 98 99 100 101 102 103 104 105 107 108 110 111 114 115 117 118 119 120 123 124 126 128 129 130 131 132 135 143 144 145 146 147 148 **S** Spartanburg Regional Healthcare System, Spartanburg, SC
Primary Contact: Bruce Holstien, President and Chief Executive Officer
COO: Mark Aycock, Chief Operating Officer
CFO: Kenneth Meinke, Senior Vice President Administrative Services, Finance and Chief Financial Officer
CMO: Charles Morrow, M.D., Chief Medical Officer
CIO: Harold Moore, Chief Information Technology Officer
CHR: Kathy Sinclair, Vice President Human Resources
CNO: Susan Duggar, R.N., Vice President Nursing
Web address: www.spartanburgregional.com
**Control:** Hospital district or authority, Government, nonfederal **Service:** General Medical and Surgical

**Staffed Beds:** 539 **Admissions:** 26121 **Census:** 417 **Outpatient Visits:** 353423 **Births:** 2688 **Total Expense ($000):** 532070 **Payroll Expense ($000):** 187300 **Personnel:** 3736

## SUMTER—Sumter County

☒ **TUOMEY HEALTHCARE SYSTEM (420070)**, 129 North Washington Street, Zip 29150–4983; tel. 803/774–9000, (Total facility includes 18 beds in nursing home–type unit) **A**1 9 10 19 **F**1 3 13 15 20 28 29 30 31 32 34 35 40 48 49 50 51 54 56 59 60 62 63 64 68 70 71 73 75 76 77 78 79 81 84 85 86 87 89 90 94 102 107 108 110 111 114 117 119 121 128 129 130 131 132 135 146 147 148 **P**6
Primary Contact: Michelle Logan-Owens, M.D., Interim Chief Executive Officer and President
CFO: Mark Lovell, Vice President and Chief Financial Officer
CMO: Gene Dickerson, M.D., Vice President Medical Affairs
CIO: Cheryl Martin, Chief Information Officer
CHR: Letitia Pringle–Miller, Administrative Director
CNO: Terrie Carlton, R.N., Vice President & Chief Nursing Officer
Web address: www.tuomey.com
**Control:** Other not–for–profit (including NFP Corporation) **Service:** General Medical and Surgical

**Staffed Beds:** 238 **Admissions:** 4569 **Census:** 165 **Outpatient Visits:** 130571 **Births:** 1275 **Personnel:** 1429

## TRAVELERS REST—Greenville County

☒ △ **NORTH GREENVILLE HOSPITAL (422008)**, 807 North Main Street, Zip 29690–1551; tel. 864/455–9206 **A**1 5 7 10 **F**1 3 15 29 30 34 35 40 44 50 64 68 75 79 85 86 87 107 110 111 114 119 128 130 146 148
Primary Contact: Stan Healy, Administrator
CMO: Amy Treece, M.D., Medical Director
CHR: Carol Bish, Human Resources Coordinator
CNO: Marian McVey, Chief Nursing Officer
Web address: www.ghs.org
**Control:** Other not–for–profit (including NFP Corporation) **Service:** Long–Term Acute Care hospital

**Staffed Beds:** 22 **Admissions:** 255 **Census:** 21 **Outpatient Visits:** 25238 **Births:** 0 **Total Expense ($000):** 26790 **Payroll Expense ($000):** 8150 **Personnel:** 150

☐ **SPRINGBROOK BEHAVIORAL HEALTH SYSTEM (424007)**, One Havenwood Lane, Zip 29690–9447, Mailing Address: P.O. Box 1005, Zip 29690–1005; tel. 864/834–8013, (Total facility includes 68 beds in nursing home–type unit) **A**1 9 10 **F**1 98 99 104 106 128
Primary Contact: Mike Rowley, Chief Executive Officer
COO: Mary Ann Bennett, R.N., Chief Operating Officer and Chief Nursing Officer
CFO: Bart Bennett, Chief Financial Officer
CMO: Mathew Fisher, M.D., Medical Director
CIO: Bart Bennett, Chief Information Technology Officer
CHR: Teresa Lipscomb, Director Human Resources
CNO: Mary Ann Bennett, R.N., Chief Operating Officer and Chief Nursing Officer
Web address: www.springbrookbehavioral.com
**Control:** Corporation, Investor–owned, for–profit **Service:** Psychiatric

**Staffed Beds:** 112 **Admissions:** 1126 **Census:** 97 **Births:** 0 **Total Expense ($000):** 14035 **Payroll Expense ($000):** 8863 **Personnel:** 253

## UNION—Union County

☐ **UNION MEDICAL CENTER (420039)**, 322 West South Street, Zip 29379–2857, Mailing Address: P.O. Box 789, Zip 29379–0789; tel. 864/427–0351 **A**1 9 10 **F**1 3 7 13 15 29 34 35 40 57 59 64 69 70 75 76 79 81 89 107 111 119 128 129 130 135 146 147 **S** Spartanburg Regional Healthcare System, Spartanburg, SC
Primary Contact: Paul R. Newhouse, Chief Executive Officer
CFO: Jeff W. Rush, Chief Financial Officer
CIO: Billy Helmandollar, Director Information Services
CHR: Michelle Helton, Director Human Resources
Web address: www.wallacethomson.com
**Control:** Hospital district or authority, Government, nonfederal **Service:** General Medical and Surgical

**Staffed Beds:** 59 **Admissions:** 1792 **Census:** 19 **Outpatient Visits:** 19233 **Births:** 123

## VARNVILLE—Hampton County

★ **HAMPTON REGIONAL MEDICAL CENTER (420072)**, 503 Carolina Avenue West, Zip 29944–4735, Mailing Address: P.O. Box 338, Zip 29944–0338; tel. 803/943–2771, (Nonreporting) **A**9 10 20
Primary Contact: Dave H. Hamill, President and Chief Executive Officer
Web address: www.hamptonregional.com
**Control:** Other not–for–profit (including NFP Corporation) **Service:** General Medical and Surgical

**Staffed Beds:** 32

## WALTERBORO—Colleton County

☒ **COLLETON MEDICAL CENTER (420030)**, 501 Robertson Boulevard, Zip 29488–5714; tel. 843/782–2000 **A**1 9 10 20 **F**1 3 11 13 15 18 26 29 30 32 34 35 36 40 41 45 47 49 56 57 59 60 64 68 70 75 76 77 79 81 82 85 86 87 89 90 93 94 96 98 102 107 108 110 111 114 115 119 128 129 130 131 132 146 147 148 **P**5 **S** HCA, Nashville, TN
Primary Contact: Brad Griffin, Chief Executive Officer
CFO: Jimmy O. Hiott, III, Chief Financial Officer
CMO: Kim Rakes–Stephens, M.D., Chief Medical Staff
CIO: Damien Noble, Director Information Technology and System
CHR: Wendy Glass, Director Human Resources
CNO: Anna Jonason, Ph.D., Chief Nursing Officer
Web address: www.colletonmedical.com
**Control:** Public Health Service, Government, federal **Service:** General Medical and Surgical

**Staffed Beds:** 131 **Admissions:** 4633 **Census:** 65 **Outpatient Visits:** 33134 **Births:** 302 **Total Expense ($000):** 59452 **Payroll Expense ($000):** 21538 **Personnel:** 396

**SC**

---

**Hospital, Medicare Provider Number, Address, Telephone, Approval, Facility, and Physician Codes, Health Care System**

★ American Hospital Association (AHA) membership
☐ The Joint Commission accreditation
○ Healthcare Facilities Accreditation Program
◇ DNV Healthcare Inc. accreditation
⇑ Center for Improvement in Healthcare Quality Accreditation
△ Commission on Accreditation of Rehabilitation Facilities (CARF) accreditation

**WEST COLUMBIA—Lexington County**

★ ◇ **LEXINGTON MEDICAL CENTER (420073)**, 2720 Sunset Boulevard,
Zip 29169–4810; tel. 803/791–2000 **A**2 3 9 10 21 **F**1 3 8 11 12 13 15 18 20
22 24 26 28 29 30 31 32 34 35 38 39 40 43 44 45 48 49 50 53 54 57 58
59 60 61 64 68 70 72 73 74 75 76 77 78 79 80 81 82 85 86 87 89 90 92
93 94 107 108 110 111 114 115 118 119 120 121 123 127 128 129 130
131 132 135 141 142 144 145 146 147 148 **P**6
Primary Contact: Tod Augsburger, President
CFO: Melinda Kruzner, Chief Financial Officer
CMO: Brent Powers, M.D., Vice President/Chief Medical Officer
CIO: Kathleen R. Herald, Vice President and Chief Information Officer
CHR: Kathy A. Howell, Vice President Human Resources
CNO: Cindy Rohman, R.N., Vice President/Chief Nursing Officer
Web address: www.lexmed.com
**Control:** Hospital district or authority, Government, nonfederal **Service:** General
Medical and Surgical

**Staffed Beds:** 434 **Admissions:** 25958 **Census:** 348 **Outpatient Visits:**
305007 **Births:** 3692 **Total Expense ($000):** 465434 **Payroll Expense**
**($000):** 181786 **Personnel:** 3281

☐ **THREE RIVERS BEHAVIORAL HEALTH (424008)**, 2900 Sunset Boulevard,
Zip 29169–3422; tel. 803/796–9911, (Total facility includes 20 beds in nursing
home–type unit) **A**1 9 10 **F**1 4 5 35 98 99 100 101 103 104 105 106 128
**S** Universal Health Services, Inc., King of Prussia, PA
Primary Contact: Nannette M. Lewis, Chief Executive Officer
CFO: Christopher Jensen, Chief Financial Officer
CMO: Cheryl Dodds, M.D., Medical Director
CHR: Nita Sundberg, Director Human Resources
CNO: Regena Sellers, Chief Nursing Officer
Web address: www.threeriversbehavioral.org
**Control:** Corporation, Investor–owned, for–profit **Service:** Psychiatric

**Staffed Beds:** 118 **Admissions:** 3155 **Census:** 98 **Outpatient Visits:** 0
**Births:** 0 **Total Expense ($000):** 19229 **Payroll Expense ($000):** 9184
**Personnel:** 182

**WINNSBORO—Fairfield County**

☐ **FAIRFIELD MEMORIAL HOSPITAL (421302)**, 102 U.S. Highway 321 By–Pass
N., Zip 29180–9251, Mailing Address: P.O. Box 620, Zip 29180–0620;
tel. 803/635–5548, (Total facility includes 15 beds in nursing home–type unit) **A**1
5 9 10 18 **F**1 3 11 15 18 28 29 30 34 35 40 50 56 57 59 62 63 64 65 68
75 77 79 86 87 90 94 102 107 110 111 114 119 121 127 128 129 130 132
133 135 146 148
Primary Contact: Suzanne C. Doscher, Chief Executive Officer
CFO: Timothy Mitchell, Chief Financial Officer
CMO: Charles D. McElmurray, M.D., Chief Medical Officer
CIO: Donnie Doherty, Director Information Systems
CHR: Shawna Martin Lyde, Director Human Resources
CNO: Starr Connor, Chief Nursing Officer
Web address: www.fairfieldmemorial.com
**Control:** County–Government, nonfederal **Service:** General Medical and Surgical

**Staffed Beds:** 40 **Admissions:** 460 **Census:** 18 **Births:** 1 **Personnel:** 164

**SC**

*Many Facility Codes have changed. Please refer to the AHA Guide Code Chart.*

# SOUTH DAKOTA

## ABERDEEN—Brown County

★ △ **AVERA ST. LUKE'S HOSPITAL (430014)**, 305 South State Street, Zip 57401–4527; tel. 605/622–5000, (Total facility includes 137 beds in nursing home–type unit) **A**2 7 9 10 19 **F**2 3 5 7 10 11 13 15 17 18 20 22 28 29 30 31 32 34 35 36 39 40 43 45 46 48 56 57 59 60 61 64 70 71 74 75 76 77 78 79 81 82 84 85 86 87 89 90 92 93 96 97 98 99 100 101 102 103 104 107 108 110 111 114 115 118 119 120 121 123 125 127 128 129 130 131 132 133 135 146 147 148 **P**6 **S** Avera Health, Sioux Falls, SD
Primary Contact: Todd Forkel, President and Chief Executive Officer
CFO: Geoff Durst, Vice President Finance
CMO: Shahid Chaudhary, M.D., Chief Medical Officer
CIO: Julie Kusler, Manager Information Services
CHR: Tracy Olson, Human Resource Officer
CNO: Jan Patterson, Chief Nursing Officer
Web address: www.avera.org/st–lukes–hospital/
**Control:** Church–operated, Nongovernment, not–for profit **Service:** General Medical and Surgical

**Staffed Beds:** 236 **Admissions:** 4416 **Census:** 182 **Outpatient Visits:** 281031 **Births:** 564 **Total Expense ($000):** 168041 **Payroll Expense ($000):** 76453 **Personnel:** 1125

**DAKOTA PLAINS SURGICAL CENTER (430092)**, 701 8th Avenue N.W., Suite C., Zip 57401–1865; tel. 605/225–3300, (Nonreporting) **A**9 10
Primary Contact: Charles Livingston, Administrator
**Control:** Corporation, Investor–owned, for–profit **Service:** Surgical

**Staffed Beds:** 15

★ **SANFORD ABERDEEN MEDICAL CENTER (430097)**, 2905 3rd Avenue S.E., Zip 57401–5420; tel. 605/626–4200, (Nonreporting) **A**9 10 **S** Sanford Health, Sioux Falls, SD
Primary Contact: Ashley M. Erickson, Chief Executive Officer
CFO: Jeffrey Poppen, Chief Financial Officer
CMO: Samuel Nyamu, M.D., Chief Medical Officer
CHR: Katie Palmer, Manager Human Resources
CNO: Kila Legrand, Chief Nursing Officer
Web address: www.sanfordaberdeen.org/
**Control:** Other not–for–profit (including NFP Corporation) **Service:** General Medical and Surgical

**Staffed Beds:** 48

## ARMOUR—Douglas County

**DOUGLAS COUNTY MEMORIAL HOSPITAL (431305)**, 708 Eighth Street, Zip 57313–2102; tel. 605/724–2159, (Nonreporting) **A**9 10 18
Primary Contact: Heath Brouwer, Administrator
CFO: Dorothy Spease, Manager Business Office
Web address: www.dcmhsd.org
**Control:** Other not–for–profit (including NFP Corporation) **Service:** General Medical and Surgical

**Staffed Beds:** 11

## BOWDLE— County

★ **BOWDLE HOSPITAL (431318)**, 8001 West Fifth Street, Zip 57428, Mailing Address: P.O. Box 556, Zip 57428–0556; tel. 605/285–6146, (Nonreporting) **A**9 10 18
Primary Contact: Sandy Schlechter, Chief Executive Officer
CFO: Lucas Turner, Chief Financial Officer
CMO: John Ottenbacher, Chief of Staff
Web address: www.bowdlehc.com
**Control:** City–Government, nonfederal **Service:** General Medical and Surgical

**Staffed Beds:** 48

## BRITTON—Marshall County

★ **MARSHALL COUNTY HEALTHCARE CENTER AVERA (431312)**, 413 Ninth Street, Zip 57430–2274; tel. 605/448–2253, (Nonreporting) **A**9 10 18 **S** Avera Health, Sioux Falls, SD
Primary Contact: Nick Fosness, Chief Executive Officer
Web address: www.avera.org
**Control:** Other not–for–profit (including NFP Corporation) **Service:** General Medical and Surgical

**Staffed Beds:** 18

## BROOKINGS—Brookings County

★ **BROOKINGS HEALTH SYSTEM (430008)**, 300 22nd Avenue, Zip 57006–2496; tel. 605/696–9000, (Total facility includes 79 beds in nursing home–type unit) **A**9 10 20 **F**3 7 8 11 13 28 29 30 31 32 34 35 40 41 43 45 57 59 62 63 64 65 69 70 75 76 77 79 81 82 85 87 89 93 102 107 111 114 118 119 125 126 127 128 129 130 133 146 147 148
Primary Contact: Jason R. Merkley, Chief Executive Officer
CFO: Steve Lindemann, Chief Financial Officer
CMO: Richard Gudvangen, M.D., Medical Director and Chief of Staff
CHR: September Bessler, Manager Human Resources
CNO: Tammy Hillestad, Chief Nursing Officer
Web address: www.brookingshealth.org
**Control:** City–Government, nonfederal **Service:** General Medical and Surgical

**Staffed Beds:** 128 **Admissions:** 1384 **Census:** 88 **Outpatient Visits:** 61632 **Births:** 291 **Total Expense ($000):** 52214 **Payroll Expense ($000):** 25734 **Personnel:** 256

## BURKE—Gregory County

★ **COMMUNITY MEMORIAL HOSPITAL (431309)**, 809 Jackson Street, Zip 57523–2065, Mailing Address: P.O. Box 319, Zip 57523–0319; tel. 605/775–2621 **A**9 10 18 **F**1 3 11 28 31 34 40 57 59 64 65 67 87 97 107 114 127 128 133 **S** Sanford Health, Sioux Falls, SD
Primary Contact: Mistie Sachtjen, Chief Executive Officer
CMO: Megan Smith, M.D., Chief Medical Staff
CHR: Tami Lyon, Director Human Resources
Web address: www.sanfordhealth.org
**Control:** Other not–for–profit (including NFP Corporation) **Service:** General Medical and Surgical

**Staffed Beds:** 16 **Admissions:** 199 **Census:** 4 **Outpatient Visits:** 3042 **Births:** 0 **Total Expense ($000):** 4175 **Payroll Expense ($000):** 1990 **Personnel:** 57

## CANTON—Lincoln County

★ **SANFORD CANTON–INWOOD MEDICAL CENTER (431333)**, 440 North Hiawatha Drive, Zip 57013–5800; tel. 605/764–1400 **A**9 10 18 **F**7 10 15 28 40 45 59 71 77 81 93 107 130 133 **S** Sanford Health, Sioux Falls, SD
Primary Contact: Scott C. Larson, Chief Executive Officer
CFO: Paul Gerhart, Chief Financial Officer
Web address: www.sanfordcantoninwood.org
**Control:** Other not–for–profit (including NFP Corporation) **Service:** General Medical and Surgical

**Staffed Beds:** 16 **Admissions:** 146 **Census:** 2 **Outpatient Visits:** 19058 **Births:** 0 **Total Expense ($000):** 6183 **Payroll Expense ($000):** 2652 **Personnel:** 75

## CHAMBERLAIN—Brule County

★ **SANFORD CHAMBERLAIN MEDICAL CENTER (431329)**, 300 South Byron Boulevard, Zip 57325–9741; tel. 605/234–5511, (Total facility includes 44 beds in nursing home–type unit) **A**9 10 18 **F**3 8 13 15 18 19 28 29 31 34 35 40 43 50 57 59 68 70 75 76 77 78 81 85 86 87 89 93 100 101 102 103 107 110 114 119 130 131 132 133 146 148 **P**6 **S** Sanford Health, Sioux Falls, SD
Primary Contact: Erica Peterson, Chief Executive Officer
COO: Paul Miller, Director of Operations
CFO: Erica Peterson, Chief Executive Officer and Chief Financial Officer
CMO: John Jones, M.D., Chief Medical Staff
CHR: Dorothy Hieb, Director Human Resources
CNO: Sarah Talbott, Chief Nursing Officer
Web address: www.sanfordmiddakota.org
**Control:** Other not–for–profit (including NFP Corporation) **Service:** General Medical and Surgical

**Staffed Beds:** 69 **Admissions:** 445 **Census:** 46 **Outpatient Visits:** 25643 **Births:** 92 **Total Expense ($000):** 18560 **Payroll Expense ($000):** 8695 **Personnel:** 163

**SANFORD MID DAKOTA MEDICAL CENTER** See Sanford Chamberlain Medical Center

---

**Hospital, Medicare Provider Number, Address, Telephone, Approval, Facility, and Physician Codes, Health Care System**

★ American Hospital Association (AHA) membership    ○ Healthcare Facilities Accreditation Program    ⇑ Center for Improvement in Healthcare Quality Accreditation
□ The Joint Commission accreditation    ◇ DNV Healthcare Inc. accreditation    △ Commission on Accreditation of Rehabilitation Facilities (CARF) accreditation

**SD**

**CLEAR LAKE—Deuel County**

★ **SANFORD CLEAR LAKE MEDICAL CENTER (431307)**, 701 Third Avenue South, Zip 57226–2016; tel. 605/874–2141 **A**9 10 18 **F**3 28 29 34 35 40 43 45 50 53 57 59 62 64 65 68 81 86 87 92 97 107 119 127 128 133 135 144 147 148 **P**6 **S** Sanford Health, Sioux Falls, SD
Primary Contact: Lori Sisk, R.N., Chief Executive Officer
CFO: Allison Nelson, Chief Financial Officer
CMO: Terrance Smith, M.D., Chairman Medical Staff
CNO: Stephanie Dobbs, Chief Nursing Officer
Web address: www.sanforddeuelcounty.org
**Control:** Other not–for–profit (including NFP Corporation) **Service:** General Medical and Surgical

**Staffed Beds: 10 Admissions: 175 Census: 2 Outpatient Visits: 15796 Births: 0 Total Expense ($000): 5561 Payroll Expense ($000): 2698 Personnel: 50**

**CUSTER—Custer County**

★ **CUSTER REGIONAL HOSPITAL (431323)**, 1039 Montgomery Street, Zip 57730–1397; tel. 605/673–2229, (Nonreporting) **A**9 10 18 **S** Regional Health, Rapid City, SD
Primary Contact: Veronica Schmidt, President
Web address: www.regionalhealth.com
**Control:** Other not–for–profit (including NFP Corporation) **Service:** General Medical and Surgical

**Staffed Beds: 87**

**DAKOTA DUNES—Union County**

**SIOUXLAND SURGERY CENTER (430089)**, 600 North Sioux Point Road, Zip 57049–5000; tel. 605/232–3332, (Nonreporting) **A**9 10
Primary Contact: Greg Miner, Administrator
Web address: www.siouxlandsurg.com/
**Control:** Corporation, Investor–owned, for–profit **Service:** Other specialty

**Staffed Beds: 40**

**DE SMET—Kingsbury County**

★ **AVERA DE SMET MEMORIAL HOSPITAL (431332)**, 306 Prairie Avenue S.W., Zip 57231–2285, Mailing Address: P.O. Box 160, Zip 57231–0160; tel. 605/854–3329 **A**9 10 18 **F**3 15 28 34 35 40 59 68 93 133 **P**6 **S** Avera Health, Sioux Falls, SD
Primary Contact: Janice Schardin, R.N., MS, Administrator and Chief Executive Officer
Web address: www.desmetmemorial.org
**Control:** Other not–for–profit (including NFP Corporation) **Service:** General Medical and Surgical

**Staffed Beds: 6 Admissions: 75 Census: 1 Outpatient Visits: 11182 Births: 0 Total Expense ($000): 3910 Payroll Expense ($000): 1639 Personnel: 24**

**DEADWOOD—Lawrence County**

★ **LEAD–DEADWOOD REGIONAL HOSPITAL (431320)**, 61 Charles Street, Zip 57732–1303; tel. 605/717–6000 **A**9 10 18 **F**3 7 15 28 29 30 31 34 40 42 43 59 64 65 68 69 70 77 78 81 85 87 93 107 114 115 117 119 132 133 148 **S** Regional Health, Rapid City, SD
Primary Contact: Mark C. Schmidt, President
CMO: Elizabeth Sayler, M.D., Chief of Staff
CHR: Kathryn L. Shockey, Director Human Resources
Web address: www.regionalhealth.com
**Control:** State–Government, nonfederal **Service:** General Medical and Surgical

**Staffed Beds: 8 Admissions: 292 Census: 7 Outpatient Visits: 11025 Births: 0 Total Expense ($000): 8649 Payroll Expense ($000): 4418 Personnel: 69**

**DELL RAPIDS—Minnehaha County**

**AVERA DELLS AREA HEALTH CENTER** See Avera Dells Area Hospital

★ **AVERA DELLS AREA HOSPITAL (431331)**, 909 North Iowa Avenue, Zip 57022–1231; tel. 605/428–5431 **A**9 10 18 **F**3 11 15 18 28 34 35 40 45 53 57 59 64 65 75 81 86 92 93 94 97 107 110 128 132 133 146 148 **P**6 **S** Avera Health, Sioux Falls, SD
Primary Contact: Lindsay Flannery, R.N., Administrator and Chief Executive Officer
CFO: Kory Holt, Division Controller Network Operations
CMO: Matt Herber, M.D., Chief of Staff
CIO: Thelma Haak, Manager Health Information
CHR: Dawn Ingalls, Regional Manager Human Resources
CNO: Karla Carstensen, Director Patient Care
Web address: www.www1.avera.org/amck/regionalfacilities/dellsareahealth/index.aspx
**Control:** Other not–for–profit (including NFP Corporation) **Service:** General Medical and Surgical

**Staffed Beds: 23 Admissions: 216 Census: 3 Outpatient Visits: 17875 Births: 0 Total Expense ($000): 5243 Payroll Expense ($000): 2157 Personnel: 51**

**EAGLE BUTTE—Dewey County**

◇ **U. S. PUBLIC HEALTH SERVICE INDIAN HOSPITAL (430083)**, 317 Main Street, Zip 57625–1012, Mailing Address: P.O. Box 1012, Zip 57625–1012; tel. 605/964–7724, (Nonreporting) **A**10 21 **S** U. S. Indian Health Service, Rockville, MD
Primary Contact: Charles Fisher, Chief Executive Officer
CFO: Lisa Deal, Budget Analyst
Web address: www.ihs.gov
**Control:** Public Health Service, Government, federal **Service:** General Medical and Surgical

**Staffed Beds: 11**

**EUREKA—Mcpherson County**

★ **EUREKA COMMUNITY HEALTH SERVICES AVERA (431308)**, 410 Ninth Street, Zip 57437–2182, Mailing Address: P.O. Box 517, Zip 57437–0517; tel. 605/284–2661 **A**9 10 18 **F**10 28 34 35 40 41 45 59 62 65 93 133 **S** Avera Health, Sioux Falls, SD
Primary Contact: Carmen Weber, Administrator
CFO: Joyce Schwingler, Chief Financial Officer
Web address: www.avera.org
**Control:** Other not–for–profit (including NFP Corporation) **Service:** General Medical and Surgical

**Staffed Beds: 6 Admissions: 79 Census: 1 Outpatient Visits: 5692 Births: 0 Total Expense ($000): 2199 Payroll Expense ($000): 897 Personnel: 35**

**FAULKTON—Faulk County**

**FAULKTON AREA MEDICAL CENTER (431301)**, 1300 Oak Street, Zip 57438–2149, Mailing Address: P.O. Box 100, Zip 57438–0100; tel. 605/598–6263 **A**9 10 18 **F**3 17 28 29 40 45 57 59 77 93 97 107 127 133 **P**5
Primary Contact: Jay A. Jahnig, Chief Executive Officer
COO: Jay A. Jahnig, Chief Executive Officer
CFO: Susan Miller, Financial Administrator
CMO: K. A. Bartholomew, M.D., Medical Director
CIO: Cheryl Bue, Health Information Transcriptionist
CHR: Blythe Smith, Administrative Assistant
CNO: Shannon Stuwe, Director of Nursing
Web address: www.faulktonmedical.org
**Control:** Other not–for–profit (including NFP Corporation) **Service:** General Medical and Surgical

**Staffed Beds: 12 Admissions: 273 Census: 4 Outpatient Visits: 13557 Births: 0 Total Expense ($000): 8476 Payroll Expense ($000): 3697 Personnel: 71**

**FLANDREAU—Moody County**

★ **AVERA FLANDREAU HOSPITAL (431310)**, 214 North Prairie Street, Zip 57028–1243; tel. 605/997–2433 **A**9 10 18 **F**3 28 34 35 40 45 57 59 64 65 75 81 86 92 93 97 107 127 128 132 133 146 148 **P**6 **S** Avera Health, Sioux Falls, SD
Primary Contact: Lindsay Flannery, R.N., Administrator and Chief Executive Officer
CFO: Kory Holt, Assistant Vice President for Financial Integration
CMO: Scott Peterson, M.D., President Medical Staff
CIO: Rose Reynolds, Director Health Information
CHR: Amy Aukes, Human Resources Analyst
Web address: www.avera.org/flandreau–medical/
**Control:** Other not–for–profit (including NFP Corporation) **Service:** General Medical and Surgical

**Staffed Beds: 18 Admissions: 127 Census: 1 Outpatient Visits: 12784 Births: 0 Total Expense ($000): 4870 Payroll Expense ($000): 2064 Personnel: 49**

**AVERA FLANDREAU MEDICAL CENTER** See Avera Flandreau Hospital

**FORT MEADE—Meade County**

⌧ **VETERANS AFFAIRS BLACK HILLS HEALTH CARE SYSTEM**, 113 Comanche Road, Zip 57741–1099; tel. 605/347–2511, (Includes VETERANS AFFAIRS MEDICAL CENTER HOT SPRINGS CAMPUS, 500 North Fifth Street, Hot Springs, Zip 57747; tel. 605/745–2052), (Total facility includes 53 beds in nursing home–type unit) **A**1 5 9 **F**3 4 5 8 12 15 29 30 31 34 35 36 37 38 39 40 44 45 46 47 48 49 53 54 56 57 59 60 61 62 63 64 65 66 68 70 74 75 77 78 79 81 82 83 84 85 86 87 91 92 93 94 96 97 98 100 101 102 104 106 107 108 111 112 115 119 127 129 130 132 135 143 144 146 147 148 **S** Department of Veterans Affairs, Washington, DC
Primary Contact: Stephen R. DiStasio, Director
CFO: Joseph Ferris, Chief Financial Officer
CHR: Denis Sullivan, Chief Human Resources Management
Web address: www.blackhills.va.gov/
**Control:** Veterans Affairs, Government, federal **Service:** General Medical and Surgical

**Staffed Beds: 243 Admissions: 2454 Census: 185 Outpatient Visits: 250530 Births: 0 Total Expense ($000): 189555 Payroll Expense ($000): 74619 Personnel: 1135**

*Many Facility Codes have changed. Please refer to the AHA Guide Code Chart.*

© 2015 AHA Guide

**SD**

### FREEMAN—Hutchinson County

★ **FREEMAN REGIONAL HEALTH SERVICES (431313)**, 510 East Eighth Street, Zip 57029–2086, Mailing Address: P.O. Box 370, Zip 57029–0370; tel. 605/925–4000, (Total facility includes 56 beds in nursing home–type unit) **A**9 10 18 **F**2 3 6 11 15 28 30 31 34 35 40 43 45 49 54 56 57 59 64 65 68 69 70 75 77 79 81 82 86 90 93 97 107 114 119 125 127 128 130 132 133 146 **P**6
Primary Contact: Nicholas R. Brandner, Chief Executive Officer
CFO: Mark Miller, Chief Financial Officer
Web address: www.freemanregional.com
**Control:** Other not–for–profit (including NFP Corporation) **Service:** General Medical and Surgical

| | |
|---|---|
| **Staffed Beds:** 81 **Admissions:** 286 **Census:** 56 **Outpatient Visits:** 10957 **Total Expense ($000):** 9712 **Payroll Expense ($000):** 4157 **Personnel:** 119 | |

### GETTYSBURG—Potter County

★ **AVERA GETTYSBURG HOSPITAL (431302)**, 606 East Garfield Avenue, Zip 57442–1398; tel. 605/765–2480, (Total facility includes 45 beds in nursing home–type unit) **A**9 10 18 **F**3 6 11 28 29 30 34 35 36 40 50 59 64 67 75 77 79 81 82 86 87 93 107 125 128 130 132 133 146 **S** Avera Health, Sioux Falls, SD
Primary Contact: Bob Sutton, Interim Chief Executive Officer
Web address: www.avera.org/st–marys–pierre/gettysburg–hospital/
**Control:** Church–operated, Nongovernment, not–for profit **Service:** General Medical and Surgical

| | |
|---|---|
| **Staffed Beds:** 55 **Admissions:** 72 **Census:** 43 **Outpatient Visits:** 4534 **Births:** 0 **Total Expense ($000):** 5693 **Payroll Expense ($000):** 2593 **Personnel:** 60 | |

### GREGORY—Gregory County

★ **AVERA GREGORY HOSPITAL (431338)**, 400 Park Avenue, Zip 57533–1302, Mailing Address: P.O. Box 408, Zip 57533–0408; tel. 605/835–8394, (Nonreporting) **A**9 10 18 **S** Avera Health, Sioux Falls, SD
Primary Contact: Anthony Timanus, Chief Executive Officer
CFO: Trish Keiser, Comptroller
CMO: Rich Kafka, M.D., Chief Medical Officer
CIO: Justin Keegan, Director Support Services
CHR: Carol Postulka, Administrative Coordinator
Web address: www.gregoryhealthcare.org
**Control:** Church–operated, Nongovernment, not–for profit **Service:** General Medical and Surgical

| | |
|---|---|
| **Staffed Beds:** 67 | |

### HOT SPRINGS—Fall River County

★ **FALL RIVER HOSPITAL (431322)**, 1201 Highway 71 South, Zip 57747–8800; tel. 605/745–3159, (Includes CASTLE MANOR ), (Total facility includes 48 beds in nursing home–type unit) **A**9 10 18 **F**3 28 34 40 43 45 56 57 59 64 65 74 77 79 81 93 102 107 111 114 119 127 128 129 130 131 133 146 148 **P**6
Primary Contact: Tricia Uhlir, Chief Executive Officer
CFO: Jesse Naze, Chief Financial Officer
CMO: Rodney Larson, M.D., Medical Director
CIO: Dustin Kleinsasser, Information Technology and BioMed
CHR: Cindy Trent, Manager Personnel
Web address: www.frhssd.org
**Control:** Other not–for–profit (including NFP Corporation) **Service:** General Medical and Surgical

| | |
|---|---|
| **Staffed Beds:** 73 **Admissions:** 414 **Census:** 13 **Outpatient Visits:** 15805 **Births:** 0 **Total Expense ($000):** 13448 **Payroll Expense ($000):** 5440 **Personnel:** 134 | |

**VETERANS AFFAIRS MEDICAL CENTER HOT SPRINGS CAMPUS** See Veterans Affairs Black Hills Health Care System, Fort Meade

### HURON—Beadle County

★ **HURON REGIONAL MEDICAL CENTER (431335)**, 172 Fourth Street S.E., Zip 57350–2590; tel. 605/353–6200 **A**9 10 18 **F**3 11 13 14 15 28 29 31 34 35 40 41 43 45 57 59 60 62 63 64 68 70 75 77 78 79 81 85 86 93 102 107 108 110 111 115 118 119 130 132 133 146 148 **P**6 **S** QHR, Brentwood, TN
Primary Contact: David Dick, Chief Executive Officer
CFO: Marcia Zwanziger, Vice President Finance
CMO: Jim Schwaiger, M.D., Chief of Staff
CHR: Rhonda Hanson, Director Human Resources
CNO: Gail Robeson, Vice President Patient Services
Web address: www.huronregional.org
**Control:** Other not–for–profit (including NFP Corporation) **Service:** General Medical and Surgical

| | |
|---|---|
| **Staffed Beds:** 25 **Admissions:** 1278 **Census:** 12 **Outpatient Visits:** 58568 **Births:** 320 **Total Expense ($000):** 29434 **Payroll Expense ($000):** 13994 **Personnel:** 238 | |

### MADISON—Lake County

★ **MADISON COMMUNITY HOSPITAL (431300)**, 917 North Washington Avenue, Zip 57042–1696; tel. 605/256–6551 **A**9 10 18 **F**7 11 13 15 28 31 34 35 40 41 43 57 59 62 64 70 75 76 77 81 82 85 87 89 93 97 107 110 114 119 129 132 133 135 143 144 145 146 148 **P**6
Primary Contact: Tamara Miller, R.N., Administrator
CFO: Teresa Mallett, Chief Financial Officer
CNO: Charlotte Charles, Director Acute Patient Services
Web address: www.madisonhospital.com
**Control:** Other not–for–profit (including NFP Corporation) **Service:** General Medical and Surgical

| | |
|---|---|
| **Staffed Beds:** 25 **Admissions:** 442 **Census:** 7 **Outpatient Visits:** 28946 **Births:** 10 **Total Expense ($000):** 14019 **Payroll Expense ($000):** 6986 **Personnel:** 199 | |

### MARTIN—Bennett County

**BENNETT COUNTY HOSPITAL AND NURSING HOME (431314)**, 102 Major Allen Street, Zip 57551–6005, Mailing Address: P.O. Box 70, Zip 57551–0070; tel. 605/685–6622, (Total facility includes 42 beds in nursing home–type unit) **A**9 10 18 **F**7 10 28 34 40 50 53 57 59 62 65 66 67 68 77 84 93 107 130 133 143
Primary Contact: Ethel Frein, Chief Executive Officer
CFO: Jean Kirk, Chief Financial Officer
CMO: Peter Knowles–Smith, M.D., Medical Director
CIO: Jean Kirk, Chief Financial Officer
CHR: T. J. Porter, Director Human Resources
Web address: www.bennettcountyhospital.com/
**Control:** Other not–for–profit (including NFP Corporation) **Service:** General Medical and Surgical

| | |
|---|---|
| **Staffed Beds:** 53 **Admissions:** 140 **Census:** 40 **Outpatient Visits:** 45116 **Births:** 5 **Total Expense ($000):** 6529 **Payroll Expense ($000):** 3267 **Personnel:** 99 | |

### MILBANK—Grant County

★ **MILBANK AREA HOSPITAL AVERA (431326)**, 901 East Virgil Avenue, Zip 57252–2124; tel. 605/432–4538, (Includes ST. WILLIAM HOME FOR THE AGED ), (Nonreporting) **A**9 10 18 **S** Avera Health, Sioux Falls, SD
Primary Contact: Natalie Gauer, Administrator
CMO: Kevin Bjordahl, M.D., Chief Medical Officer
CHR: Mona Schafer, Regional Manager Human Resources
Web address: www.averamilbank.org
**Control:** Other not–for–profit (including NFP Corporation) **Service:** General Medical and Surgical

| | |
|---|---|
| **Staffed Beds:** 25 | |

### MILLER—Hand County

★ **AVERA HAND COUNTY MEMORIAL HOSPITAL (431337)**, 300 West Fifth Street, Zip 57362–1238; tel. 605/853–2421 **A**9 10 18 **F**3 8 11 15 17 28 29 34 35 40 43 45 46 50 53 57 59 76 79 81 86 87 93 107 114 119 128 129 132 133 146 148 **S** Avera Health, Sioux Falls, SD
Primary Contact: Bryan Breitling, Administrator
CFO: Debbie Pullman, Director Finance
CMO: Steve Schroeder, M.D., Chief of Staff
CIO: Janice Purrington, Coordinator Medical Records
CNO: Teresa E. Fanning, Director of Patient Care
Web address: www.avera.org
**Control:** Other not–for–profit (including NFP Corporation) **Service:** General Medical and Surgical

| | |
|---|---|
| **Staffed Beds:** 9 **Admissions:** 292 **Census:** 4 **Outpatient Visits:** 12171 **Births:** 0 **Total Expense ($000):** 6792 **Payroll Expense ($000):** 3098 **Personnel:** 47 | |

## MITCHELL—Davison County

✠ **AVERA QUEEN OF PEACE HOSPITAL (430013)**, 525 North Foster, Zip 57301–2999; tel. 605/995–2000, (Total facility includes 109 beds in nursing home–type unit) **A**1 2 9 10 **F**3 10 12 13 15 28 29 30 31 34 39 40 43 45 48 50 51 53 54 57 59 64 69 70 71 75 76 77 78 79 81 82 84 85 86 89 93 94 96 104 107 108 110 111 114 117 118 119 121 123 127 128 129 130 131 132 133 135 144 146 147 148 **P**6 **S** Avera Health, Sioux Falls, SD
Primary Contact: Thomas A. Clark, Regional President and Chief Executive Officer
CFO: Will Flett, Vice President Finance and Chief Financial Officer
CMO: David Balt, D.O., Chief Medical Officer
CIO: Patti Brooks, Director Information Systems
CHR: Rita Lemon, Director Human Resources
CNO: Rochelle Reider, Vice President Patient Care
Web address: www.averaqueenofpeace.org
**Control:** Church–operated, Nongovernment, not–for profit **Service:** General Medical and Surgical

**Staffed Beds:** 176 **Admissions:** 2497 **Census:** 106 **Outpatient Visits:** 129778 **Births:** 498 **Total Expense ($000):** 85051 **Payroll Expense ($000):** 39412 **Personnel:** 378

## MOBRIDGE—Walworth County

★ **MOBRIDGE REGIONAL HOSPITAL (431325)**, 1401 Tenth Avenue West, Zip 57601–1106, Mailing Address: P.O. Box 580, Zip 57601–0580; tel. 605/845–3692 **A**9 10 18 **F**3 7 10 11 13 15 17 28 32 34 35 40 43 45 50 56 57 59 62 64 65 70 76 81 89 93 94 97 107 108 110 114 119 125 127 128 129 130 131 132 133 147 148 **P**6
Primary Contact: Angelia K. Svihovec, Chief Executive Officer
COO: Beth Jensen, Director Clinic Operations
CFO: Renae Tisdall, Chief Financial Officer
CMO: Travis Henderson, M.D., Chief of Staff
CIO: Lynn Schott, Director Information Technology
CHR: Keri Wientjes, Director Human Resources
CNO: Kristi Voller, Director of Nursing
Web address: www.mobridgehospital.org
**Control:** Other not–for–profit (including NFP Corporation) **Service:** General Medical and Surgical

**Staffed Beds:** 25 **Admissions:** 662 **Census:** 6 **Outpatient Visits:** 52908 **Births:** 79 **Total Expense ($000):** 16717 **Payroll Expense ($000):** 7807 **Personnel:** 154

## PARKSTON—Hutchinson County

★ **AVERA ST. BENEDICT HEALTH CENTER (431330)**, 401 West Glynn Drive, Zip 57366–9605; tel. 605/928–3311, (Total facility includes 74 beds in nursing home–type unit) **A**9 10 18 **F**2 3 8 10 13 15 28 29 30 31 32 34 35 38 40 45 53 56 57 59 64 65 69 75 76 81 82 83 85 86 87 89 107 110 111 114 116 119 128 129 130 131 132 133 135 146 148 **P**6 **S** Avera Health, Sioux Falls, SD
Primary Contact: Gale N. Walker, President and Chief Executive Officer
CFO: Rita Blasius, Assistant Administrator and Chief Financial Officer
CMO: Jason Wickersham, M.D., Chief of Staff
CIO: Adam Popp, Director Information Systems
CHR: Phyllis Ehler, Director Human Resources
CNO: Denise Muntefering, Vice President Patient Care Services
Web address: www.averastbenedict.org
**Control:** Church–operated, Nongovernment, not–for profit **Service:** General Medical and Surgical

**Staffed Beds:** 99 **Admissions:** 568 **Census:** 79 **Outpatient Visits:** 21979 **Births:** 50 **Total Expense ($000):** 17971 **Payroll Expense ($000):** 9374 **Personnel:** 177

## PHILIP—Haakon County

**HANS P. PETERSON MEMORIAL HOSPITAL** See Philip Health Services

★ **PHILIP HEALTH SERVICES (431319)**, 503 West Pine Street, Zip 57567–3300, Mailing Address: P.O. Box 790, Zip 57567–0790; tel. 605/859–2511, (Total facility includes 30 beds in nursing home–type unit) **A**9 10 18 **F**10 11 40 43 57 59 62 85 93 107 114 119 125 127 128 130 131 133 148 **P**6
Primary Contact: Kent Olson, Administrator and Chief Executive Officer
**Control:** Other not–for–profit (including NFP Corporation) **Service:** General Medical and Surgical

**Staffed Beds:** 48 **Admissions:** 136 **Census:** 31 **Outpatient Visits:** 9147 **Births:** 0 **Total Expense ($000):** 8525 **Payroll Expense ($000):** 4952 **Personnel:** 140

## PIERRE—Hughes County

✠ **AVERA ST. MARY'S HOSPITAL (430015)**, 801 East Sioux Avenue, Zip 57501–3323; tel. 605/224–3100, (Total facility includes 90 beds in nursing home–type unit) **A**1 9 10 20 **F**2 8 11 13 15 28 29 30 31 34 38 40 41 45 48 49 50 51 59 60 64 68 77 78 79 82 83 84 85 87 93 107 110 111 114 119 125 129 130 133 **P**5 **S** Avera Health, Sioux Falls, SD
Primary Contact: Bob Sutton, President and Chief Executive Officer
CFO: Tom Wagner, Interim Vice President Finance
CMO: Denise Hanisch, M.D., Chief of Staff
CIO: Jamie Raske, Information Technology Lead
CHR: Paul Marso, Vice President Human Resources
Web address: www.avera.org/st–marys–pierre/
**Control:** Other not–for–profit (including NFP Corporation) **Service:** General Medical and Surgical

**Staffed Beds:** 164 **Admissions:** 1442 **Census:** 76 **Outpatient Visits:** 48229 **Births:** 498 **Total Expense ($000):** 43732 **Payroll Expense ($000):** 17460 **Personnel:** 268

## PINE RIDGE—Shannon County

◇ **U. S. PUBLIC HEALTH SERVICE INDIAN HOSPITAL (430081)**, East Highway 18, Zip 57770, Mailing Address: P.O. Box 1201, Zip 57770–1201; tel. 605/867–5131, (Nonreporting) **A**10 21 **S** U. S. Indian Service, Rockville, MD
Primary Contact: Ellen Davis, Service Unit Director
CFO: Sophia Conny, Deputy Administrative Officer
CMO: Jan Colton, M.D., Acting Clinical Director
CHR: Annabelle Blackbear, Human Resources Specialist
Web address: www.ihs.gov
**Control:** Public Health Service, Government, federal **Service:** General Medical and Surgical

**Staffed Beds:** 45

## PLATTE—Charles Mix County

★ **PLATTE HEALTH CENTER AVERA (431306)**, 601 East Seventh, Zip 57369–2123, Mailing Address: P.O. Box 200, Zip 57369–0200; tel. 605/337–3364, (Nonreporting) **A**9 10 18 **S** Avera Health, Sioux Falls, SD
Primary Contact: Mark Burket, Chief Executive Officer
CFO: Jerry Hoffman, Chief Financial Officer
Web address: www.phcavera.org
**Control:** Other not–for–profit (including NFP Corporation) **Service:** General Medical and Surgical

**Staffed Beds:** 65

## RAPID CITY—Pennington County

**BLACK HILLS SURGERY CENTER (430091)**, 216 Anamaria Drive, Zip 57701–7366, Mailing Address: 1868 Lombardy Drive, Zip 57703–4130; tel. 605/721–4900, (Nonreporting) **A**9 10
Primary Contact: Franklin Shobe, Administrator and Chief Executive Officer
Web address: www.bhsc.com
**Control:** Partnership, Investor–owned, for–profit **Service:** General Medical and Surgical

**Staffed Beds:** 26

◇ **INDIAN HEALTH SERVICE HOSPITAL (430082)**, 3200 Canyon Lake Drive, Zip 57702–8197; tel. 605/355–2280 **A**10 21 **F**3 5 15 29 34 39 40 44 50 53 59 64 65 87 89 93 97 104 110 130 134 135 **P**6 **S** U. S. Indian Service, Rockville, MD
Primary Contact: Kevin J. Stiffarm, Chief Executive Officer
Web address: www.ihs.gov
**Control:** PHS, Indian Service, Government, federal **Service:** General Medical and Surgical

**Staffed Beds:** 9 **Admissions:** 54 **Census:** 1 **Outpatient Visits:** 174634 **Births:** 0 **Personnel:** 214

✠ **RAPID CITY REGIONAL HOSPITAL (430077)**, 353 Fairmont Boulevard, Zip 57701–7393, Mailing Address: P.O. Box 6000, Zip 57709–6000; tel. 605/755–1000 **A**1 3 5 9 10 **F**3 5 11 12 13 15 17 18 20 22 24 26 28 29 30 31 34 35 36 38 40 43 44 45 46 47 48 49 51 56 57 58 59 60 62 63 64 65 66 68 70 72 73 74 75 76 77 78 79 80 81 82 84 85 86 87 88 89 90 91 92 93 98 99 100 101 102 104 107 108 110 111 115 119 120 121 122 123 124 126 129 130 131 132 135 141 143 144 146 148 **P**5 6 **S** Regional Health, Rapid City, SD
Primary Contact: Mick Gibbs, President
CFO: Mark Thompson, Vice President Financial Services
CMO: David Houser, M.D., Vice President Medical Affairs
CIO: Richard Latuchie, Vice President Business Development
CHR: Maureen Henson, Vice President Human Resources
CNO: Rita K. Haxton, R.N., Vice President Patient Care Nursing
Web address: www.regionalhealth.com
**Control:** Other not–for–profit (including NFP Corporation) **Service:** General Medical and Surgical

**Staffed Beds:** 369 **Admissions:** 18256 **Census:** 261 **Outpatient Visits:** 187379 **Births:** 2295 **Total Expense ($000):** 388576 **Payroll Expense ($000):** 169606 **Personnel:** 2559

SD

*Many Facility Codes have changed. Please refer to the AHA Guide Code Chart.* © 2015 AHA Guide

**SAME DAY SURGERY CENTER (430093)**, 651 Cathedral Drive, Zip 57701–7368; tel. 605/755–9000, (Nonreporting) **A**9 10
Primary Contact: Doris Fritts, R.N., Executive Director
Web address: www.regionalhealth.com
**Control:** Corporation, Investor–owned, for–profit **Service:** Surgical

Staffed Beds: 8

### REDFIELD—Spink County

**COMMUNITY MEMORIAL HOSPITAL (431316)**, 110 West Tenth Avenue, Zip 57469–1520, Mailing Address: P.O. Box 420, Zip 57469–0420; tel. 605/472–1110 **A**9 10 18 **F**7 11 34 35 40 45 53 57 59 62 63 64 65 77 107 117 119 127 130 132 133 145 146 **P**6
Primary Contact: Michael O'Keefe, Interim Chief Executive Officer
CFO: William Boyer, Chief Financial Officer
CHR: Rhonda Stroh, Chief Human Resources Officer
CNO: Julene J. Cass, R.N., Director of Nursing
Web address: www.redfield–sd.com/hospital.html
**Control:** City–Government, nonfederal **Service:** General Medical and Surgical

Staffed Beds: 18 Admissions: 506 Census: 2 Outpatient Visits: 18544 Births: 0 Total Expense ($000): 10888 Payroll Expense ($000): 5011 Personnel: 112

### ROSEBUD—Todd County

**U. S. PUBLIC HEALTH SERVICE INDIAN HOSPITAL (430084)**, Highway 18, Soldier Creek Road, Zip 57570; tel. 605/747–2231, (Nonreporting) **A**10 **S** U. S. Indian Health Service, Rockville, MD
Primary Contact: Kathey Wilson, Acting Chief Executive Officer
COO: Romeo Vivit, Chief Surgeon
CMO: Valerie Parker, M.D., Clinical Director
CHR: Michelle Zephier, Human Resource Specialist
Web address: www.ihs.gov
**Control:** PHS, Indian Service, Government, federal **Service:** General Medical and Surgical

Staffed Beds: 35

### SCOTLAND—Bon Homme County

★ **LANDMANN–JUNGMAN MEMORIAL HOSPITAL AVERA (431317)**, 600 Billars Street, Zip 57059–2026; tel. 605/583–2226 **A**9 11 30 40 41 45 59 64 65 77 89 93 97 107 119 125 128 133 148 **P**6 **S** Avera Health, Sioux Falls, SD
Primary Contact: Jonathan Moe, Chief Executive Officer
CFO: Darcy Permann, Manager Business Office
Web address: www.ljmh.org
**Control:** Other not–for–profit (including NFP Corporation) **Service:** General Medical and Surgical

Staffed Beds: 17 Admissions: 48 Census: 1 Outpatient Visits: 2323 Births: 0

### SIOUX FALLS—Lincoln County

☐ **AVERA HEART HOSPITAL OF SOUTH DAKOTA (430095)**, 4500 West 69th Street, Zip 57108–8148; tel. 605/977–7000 **A**1 5 9 10 **F**3 11 17 18 20 22 24 26 28 29 30 34 35 40 43 45 57 59 61 74 75 79 81 84 85 87 108 111 115 118 119 121 124 130 132 135 **S** Avera Health, Sioux Falls, SD
Primary Contact: Jon Soderholm, President
CFO: Jean White, Vice President Finance
Web address: www.avera.org/heart–hospital
**Control:** Corporation, Investor–owned, for–profit **Service:** Heart

Staffed Beds: 53 Admissions: 2439 Census: 27 Outpatient Visits: 5446 Births: 0 Personnel: 370

✠ △ **AVERA McKENNAN HOSPITAL AND UNIVERSITY HEALTH CENTER (430016)**, 1325 South Cliff Avenue, Zip 57105–1007, Mailing Address: P.O. Box 5045, Zip 57117–5045; tel. 605/322–8000, (Includes AVERA BEHAVIORAL HEALTH CENTER, 440 West 69th Street, Zip 57108; tel. 605/322–4065; Steve Lindquist, Assistant Vice President, Behavioral Health; AVERA CHILDREN'S HOSPITAL, 1325 South Cliff Avenue, Zip 57105–1016, Mailing Address: PO Box 5045, Zip 57117–5045; tel. 605/322–5437), (Total facility includes 90 beds in nursing home–type unit) **A**1 2 3 5 7 9 10 **F**3 5 7 10 11 12 13 15 18 19 20 21 22 23 24 29 30 31 32 34 35 36 38 39 40 41 43 44 46 49 50 53 54 55 56 57 58 59 60 61 63 64 65 66 67 68 70 71 72 74 75 76 77 78 79 81 82 84 85 86 87 88 89 90 92 93 94 96 97 98 99 100 101 102 103 104 105 107 108 110 111 114 115 116 117 118 119 120 121 123 124 125 126 128 129 130 131 132 134 135 136 138 141 142 143 144 145 146 147 148 **P**6
**S** Avera Health, Sioux Falls, SD
Primary Contact: David Kapaska, D.O., Regional President and Chief Executive Officer
COO: Judy Blauwet, M.P.H., Senior Vice President Operations and Chief Nursing Officer
CFO: Julie Norton, Chief Financial Officer
CMO: Michael Elliott, M.D., Chief Medical Officer and Senior Vice President of Medical Affairs
CIO: Kristin Gross, Director Information Technology Center
CHR: Lynne D. Hagen, Human Resources Officer
CNO: Judy Blauwet, M.P.H., Senior Vice President of Hospital Operations and Chief Nursing Officer
Web address: www.averamckennan.org
**Control:** Church–operated, Nongovernment, not–for profit **Service:** General Medical and Surgical

Staffed Beds: 400 Admissions: 20823 Census: 299 Outpatient Visits: 212422 Births: 2139 Total Expense ($000): 685967 Payroll Expense ($000): 312784 Personnel: 3574

**CHILDRENS CARE HOSPITAL AND SCHOOL (433300)**, 2501 West 26th Street, Zip 57105–2498; tel. 605/782–2300, (Nonreporting) **A**9 10
Primary Contact: David A. Timpe, Interim President and Chief Executive Officer
CFO: John Clark, Chief Financial Officer
CMO: Christiane Maroun, M.D., Chief of Staff
CHR: Tiffany Reilly, Director Human Resources
Web address: www.cchs.org
**Control:** Other not–for–profit (including NFP Corporation) **Service:** Children's rehabilitation

Staffed Beds: 114

✠ △ **SANFORD USD MEDICAL CENTER (430027)**, 1305 West 18th Street, Zip 57105–0496, Mailing Address: P.O. Box 5039, Zip 57117–5039; tel. 605/333–1000, (Includes SANFORD CHILDREN'S HOSPITAL, 1600 West 22nd Street, Zip 57105, Mailing Address: PO Box 5039, Zip 57117–5039; tel. 605/333–1000) **A**1 2 3 5 7 8 9 10 **F**3 7 8 9 11 12 13 14 15 17 18 19 20 21 22 23 24 25 26 27 28 29 30 31 32 34 35 36 37 38 40 43 44 45 46 48 49 50 51 52 53 54 55 56 57 58 59 60 61 63 64 65 68 70 71 72 73 74 75 76 77 78 79 80 81 82 83 84 85 86 87 88 89 90 91 92 93 94 96 97 99 100 101 103 104 105 107 108 110 111 114 115 116 117 118 119 120 121 123 124 126 129 130 131 132 134 135 138 141 142 143 146 147 148 **P**6
**S** Sanford Health, Sioux Falls, SD
Primary Contact: Paul A. Hanson, FACHE, President
COO: Brad J. Schipper, Chief Operating Officer
CFO: Merrilee Schultz, Chief Finance
CIO: Arlyn Broekhuis, Vice President and Chief Information Officer
CHR: Evan Burkett, Chief Human Resource Officer
Web address: www.sanfordhealth.org
**Control:** Other not–for–profit (including NFP Corporation) **Service:** General Medical and Surgical

Staffed Beds: 511 Admissions: 23241 Census: 289 Outpatient Visits: 1294055 Births: 3296 Total Expense ($000): 742682 Payroll Expense ($000): 244482 Personnel: 4958

✠ **SELECT SPECIALTY HOSPITAL–SIOUX FALLS (432002)**, 1305 West 18th Street, Zip 57105–0401; tel. 605/312–9500, (Nonreporting) **A**1 9 10 **S** Select Medical Corporation, Mechanicsburg, PA
Primary Contact: Carol Ulmer, Chief Executive Officer
CNO: Dawn Anderson, Chief Nursing Officer
Web address: www.selectspecialtyhospitals.com/company/locations/siouxfalls.aspx
**Control:** Corporation, Investor–owned, for–profit **Service:** Long–Term Acute Care hospital

Staffed Beds: 24

| Hospital, Medicare Provider Number, Address, Telephone, Approval, Facility, and Physician Codes, Health Care System | | |
|---|---|---|
| ★ American Hospital Association (AHA) membership | ○ Healthcare Facilities Accreditation Program | ⇧ Center for Improvement in Healthcare Quality Accreditation |
| ☐ The Joint Commission accreditation | ◇ DNV Healthcare Inc. accreditation | △ Commission on Accreditation of Rehabilitation Facilities (CARF) accreditation |

**SIOUX FALLS SPECIALTY HOSPITAL (430090)**, 910 East 20th Street, Zip 57105–1012; tel. 605/334–6730, (Nonreporting) **A**9 10
Primary Contact: R. Blake Curd, M.D., Chief Executive Officer
CFO: Kyle Goldammer, Chief Financial Officer
Web address: www.sfsurgical.com
**Control:** Partnership, Investor–owned, for–profit **Service:** General Medical and Surgical

**Staffed Beds:** 35

☒ **SIOUX FALLS VETERANS AFFAIRS HEALTH CARE SYSTEM**, 2501 West 22nd Street, Zip 57105–1305, Mailing Address: P.O. Box 5046, Zip 57117–5046; tel. 605/336–3230, (Total facility includes 58 beds in nursing home–type unit) **A**1 3 5 8 9 **F**5 8 18 29 30 31 33 34 35 36 38 39 40 45 46 50 53 54 56 57 58 59 60 62 63 64 65 68 70 71 74 75 77 78 79 81 82 84 85 86 87 91 92 93 94 97 98 100 101 102 103 104 107 111 118 119 127 130 131 132 134 143 146 147 148 **S** Department of Veterans Affairs, Washington, DC
Primary Contact: Darwin Goodspeed, Director
COO: Sara Ackert, Associate Director
CFO: Daniel Hubbard, Chief Financial Officer
CIO: Eric Heiser, Chief Information Resource Management
CHR: Betsy Geiver, Chief Human Resources Officer
CNO: Barbara Teal, R.N., Associate Director Patient Care Services and Nurse Executive
Web address: www.siouxfalls.va.gov
**Control:** Veterans Affairs, Government, federal **Service:** General Medical and Surgical

**Staffed Beds:** 98 **Admissions:** 2722 **Census:** 80 **Outpatient Visits:** 280881 **Births:** 0 **Personnel:** 999

SISSETON—Roberts County

★ **COTEAU DES PRAIRIES HOSPITAL (431339)**, 205 Orchard Drive, Zip 57262–2398; tel. 605/698–7647 **A**9 10 18 **F**13 15 28 31 34 35 40 43 45 53 57 59 62 64 75 77 81 86 93 107 110 119 127 130 133 135 146 147 **P**6
Primary Contact: Michael F. Coyle, Chief Executive Officer
CFO: Larry Moen, Chief Financial Officer
CMO: David Staub, M.D., Chief of Staff
CIO: Cheryl Kaufman, Information Technology Technician
CHR: Leslie Hendrickson, Director Human Resources
CNO: Brenda Bostrom, Director of Nursing
Web address: www.cdphospital.com
**Control:** Other not–for–profit (including NFP Corporation) **Service:** General Medical and Surgical

**Staffed Beds:** 25 **Admissions:** 497 **Census:** 4 **Outpatient Visits:** 43159 **Births:** 142

SPEARFISH—Lawrence County

★ **SPEARFISH REGIONAL HOSPITAL (430048)**, 1440 North Main Street, Zip 57783–1504; tel. 605/644–4000, (Includes SPEARFISH REGIONAL SURGERY CENTER, 1316 North 10th Street, Zip 57783–1530; tel. 605/642–3113; Michael DeLano, Administrator) **A**9 10 20 **F**3 11 13 15 28 29 31 34 40 43 45 57 59 62 63 70 75 76 79 81 82 84 85 89 93 97 107 108 110 111 114 119 128 129 130 132 135 146 147 148 **P**6 **S** Regional Health, Rapid City, SD
Primary Contact: Larry W. Veitz, President
CFO: Marcia Olson, Director Finance
CHR: Colleen De Rosier, Coordinator Human Resource
CNO: Cathy Dill, R.N., Director Patient Services
Web address: www.regionalhealth.com/Our–Locations/Regional–Hospitals/ Spearfish–Regional–Hospital.aspx
**Control:** Other not–for–profit (including NFP Corporation) **Service:** General Medical and Surgical

**Staffed Beds:** 35 **Admissions:** 1421 **Census:** 9 **Outpatient Visits:** 42948 **Births:** 486 **Total Expense ($000):** 33225 **Payroll Expense ($000):** 13364 **Personnel:** 268

STURGIS—Meade County

★ **STURGIS REGIONAL HOSPITAL (431321)**, 949 Harmon Street, Zip 57785–2452; tel. 605/720–2400, (Nonreporting) **A**9 10 18 **S** Regional Health, Rapid City, SD
Primary Contact: Mark Schulte, FACHE, Chief Executive Officer
CFO: Jodie Mitchell, Facility Financial Director
CMO: Tom Hermann, Chief of Staff
CHR: Ginger Chord, Coordinator Human Resources
CNO: Rikki Plaggemeyer, Director Acute Care Nursing
Web address: www.regionalhealth.com/Our–Locations/Regional–Hospitals/ Sturgis–Regional–Hospital.aspx
**Control:** Other not–for–profit (including NFP Corporation) **Service:** General Medical and Surgical

**Staffed Beds:** 109

TYNDALL—Bon Homme County

★ **ST. MICHAEL'S HOSPITAL AVERA (431327)**, 410 West 16th Avenue, Zip 57066–2318; tel. 605/589–2152 **A**9 10 18 **F**3 15 28 31 34 40 43 45 53 57 59 64 65 67 70 75 77 81 86 89 92 93 94 107 110 114 119 127 128 129 131 133 148 **P**6 **S** Avera Health, Sioux Falls, SD
Primary Contact: Carol Deurmier, Chief Executive Officer
CFO: Lisa Ronke, Director Finance
CMO: Melvin Wallinga, M.D., Medical Director
Web address: www.stmichaels–bhfp.org
**Control:** Church–operated, Nongovernment, not–for profit **Service:** General Medical and Surgical

**Staffed Beds:** 25 **Admissions:** 223 **Census:** 6 **Outpatient Visits:** 10159 **Births:** 0 **Total Expense ($000):** 8142 **Payroll Expense ($000):** 3186 **Personnel:** 60

VERMILLION—Clay County

★ **SANFORD VERMILLION MEDICAL CENTER (431336)**, 20 South Plum Street, Zip 57069–3346; tel. 605/624–2611, (Total facility includes 66 beds in nursing home–type unit) **A**9 10 18 **F**15 28 29 31 34 35 40 43 45 57 59 67 76 81 91 92 93 97 107 110 114 116 119 125 129 130 131 132 133 135 **P**8 **S** Sanford Health, Sioux Falls, SD
Primary Contact: Timothy J. Tracy, Chief Executive Officer
CFO: Valerie Osterberg, Chief Financial Officer
CMO: Roy Mortinsen, M.D., Chief of Staff
CIO: Mary C. Merrigan, Manager Public Relations
CHR: Cindy Benzel, Manager Human Resources
CNO: Jeff Berens, MS, Chief Nursing Officer
Web address: www.sanfordvermillion.org
**Control:** Other not–for–profit (including NFP Corporation) **Service:** General Medical and Surgical

**Staffed Beds:** 114 **Admissions:** 493 **Census:** 71 **Outpatient Visits:** 36989 **Births:** 94 **Total Expense ($000):** 19005 **Payroll Expense ($000):** 9239 **Personnel:** 135

VIBORG—Turner County

★ **PIONEER MEMORIAL HOSPITAL AND HEALTH SERVICES (431328)**, 315 North Washington Street, Zip 57070–2002, Mailing Address: P.O. Box 368, Zip 57070–0368; tel. 605/326–5161, (Total facility includes 52 beds in nursing home–type unit) **A**9 10 18 **F**6 10 15 28 30 34 40 43 45 53 56 57 59 63 65 69 75 79 81 87 97 107 111 119 125 127 128 130 132 133 **P**6 **S** Sanford Health, Sioux Falls, SD
Primary Contact: Thomas V. Richter, Chief Executive Officer
CFO: Anne Christiansen, Chief Financial Officer
CMO: Syed Shah, M.D., Chief of Staff
Web address: www.pioneermemorial.org
**Control:** Other not–for–profit (including NFP Corporation) **Service:** General Medical and Surgical

**Staffed Beds:** 64 **Admissions:** 159 **Census:** 53 **Outpatient Visits:** 30480 **Births:** 0 **Total Expense ($000):** 11752 **Payroll Expense ($000):** 6585 **Personnel:** 149

WAGNER—Charles Mix County

★ **WAGNER COMMUNITY MEMORIAL HOSPITAL AVERA (431315)**, 513 Third Street S.W., Zip 57380–9675, Mailing Address: P.O. Box 280, Zip 57380–0280; tel. 605/384–3611 **A**9 10 18 **F**3 11 15 17 18 28 31 34 40 43 45 57 59 64 67 70 75 77 81 93 97 107 110 114 119 125 128 130 133 148 **P**6 **S** Avera Health, Sioux Falls, SD
Primary Contact: Bryan Slaba, Chief Executive Officer
CFO: Lisa Weisser, Supervisor Finance
CIO: Cindy Minder, Coordinator Information Systems
CHR: Marcia Podzimek, Chief Human Resources Officer
Web address: www.avera.org/wagnerhospital
**Control:** Other not–for–profit (including NFP Corporation) **Service:** General Medical and Surgical

**Staffed Beds:** 20 **Admissions:** 205 **Census:** 2 **Outpatient Visits:** 8699 **Births:** 0 **Total Expense ($000):** 8188 **Payroll Expense ($000):** 2873 **Personnel:** 57

WATERTOWN—Codington County

★ **PRAIRIE LAKES HEALTHCARE SYSTEM (430005)**, 401 9th Avenue N.W., Zip 57201–1548, Mailing Address: P.O. Box 1210, Zip 57201–6210; tel. 605/882–7000, (Nonreporting) **A**9 10 20
Primary Contact: Jill Fuller, R.N., Ph.D., President and Chief Executive Officer
COO: Traci Rabine, Vice President Clinic Operations
CFO: Adam Paul, Chief Financial Officer
CMO: Daniel Flaherty, M.D., Chief Medical Staff
CHR: Nathan Lake, Vice President Human Resources
CNO: Shelly Turbak, R.N., Chief Nursing Officer
Web address: www.prairielakes.com
**Control:** Other not–for–profit (including NFP Corporation) **Service:** General Medical and Surgical

**Staffed Beds:** 81

**SD**

*Many Facility Codes have changed. Please refer to the AHA Guide Code Chart.* © 2015 AHA Guide

## WEBSTER—Day County

★ **SANFORD WEBSTER MEDICAL CENTER (431311)**, 1401 West 1st Street,
Zip 57274–1054, Mailing Address: P.O. Box 489, Zip 57274–0489;
tel. 605/345–3336, (Nonreporting) **A**9 10 18 **S** Sanford Health, Sioux Falls, SD
Primary Contact: David Rogers, Chief Executive Officer
CFO: Sheryl L. Pappas, Chief Financial Officer
Web address: www.sanfordhealth.org
**Control:** Other not–for–profit (including NFP Corporation) **Service:** General
Medical and Surgical

**Staffed Beds:** 25

## WESSINGTON SPRINGS—Jerauld County

★ **AVERA WESKOTA MEMORIAL HOSPITAL (431324)**, 604 First Street N.E.,
Zip 57382–2166; tel. 605/539–1201 **A**9 10 18 **F**3 15 28 31 35 40 53 57 59
64 75 77 81 85 93 107 114 119 128 130 131 132 133 **P**5 **S** Avera Health,
Sioux Falls, SD
Primary Contact: Gaea Blue, R.N., Administrator and Chief Executive Officer
CFO: Linda Jager, Director Finance
CMO: Thomas Dean, M.D., Chief of Staff
CNO: JoAnn Hettinger, R.N., Director of Patient Care Services
Web address: www.averaweskota.org
**Control:** Other not–for–profit (including NFP Corporation) **Service:** General
Medical and Surgical

**Staffed Beds:** 23 **Admissions:** 109 **Census:** 2 **Outpatient Visits:** 5129
**Births:** 0 **Total Expense ($000):** 4018 **Payroll Expense ($000):** 1655
**Personnel:** 26

## WINNER—Tripp County

★ **WINNER REGIONAL HEALTHCARE CENTER (431334)**, 745 East Eighth
Street, Zip 57580–2631; tel. 605/842–7100, (Total facility includes 79 beds in
nursing home–type unit) **A**9 10 18 **F**11 13 15 17 28 29 31 34 35 40 43 47 56
57 59 62 64 65 68 81 85 97 107 108 119 127 128 129 131 132 133 148
**P**3 **S** Sanford Health, Sioux Falls, SD
Primary Contact: Kevin Coffey, Chief Executive Officer
COO: Debra K. Davis, Director of Operations
CFO: Phil Husher, Chief Financial Officer
CMO: Tony L. Berg, M.D., Chief of Staff
CIO: Gary Burrus, Director Information Technology
CHR: Susan Hughes, Interim Director Human Resources
CNO: Julie Hennebold, R.N., Interim Chief Nursing Officer
Web address: www.winnerregional.org
**Control:** Other not–for–profit (including NFP Corporation) **Service:** General
Medical and Surgical

**Staffed Beds:** 104 **Admissions:** 667 **Census:** 73 **Outpatient Visits:** 9863
**Births:** 180 **Total Expense ($000):** 19746 **Payroll Expense ($000):** 7318
**Personnel:** 259

## YANKTON—Yankton County

⊠ **AVERA SACRED HEART HOSPITAL (430012)**, 501 Summit Avenue,
Zip 57078–3855; tel. 605/668–8000, (Total facility includes 187 beds in nursing
home–type unit) **A**1 2 5 9 10 **F**2 3 6 8 10 13 15 18 20 28 29 30 31 34 35 39
40 43 45 46 47 48 53 57 59 60 62 63 64 70 71 73 76 77 78 79 81 82 84
85 86 87 89 91 93 96 100 103 104 107 108 110 111 114 115 118 119 120
121 127 128 129 130 132 133 146 147 148 **S** Avera Health, Sioux Falls, SD
Primary Contact: Douglas R. Ekeren, Regional President and Chief Executive
Officer
CFO: Jamie Schaefer, Vice President Finance
CIO: Kathy Quinlivan, Director Management Information Systems
CHR: Jane E. Miller, Human Resources Officer
CNO: Laurie McKee, Vice President Patient Care Services
Web address: www.averasacredheart.com
**Control:** Church–operated, Nongovernment, not–for profit **Service:** General
Medical and Surgical

**Staffed Beds:** 293 **Admissions:** 3598 **Census:** 218 **Outpatient Visits:** 90501
**Births:** 582 **Total Expense ($000):** 92375 **Payroll Expense ($000):** 37996
**Personnel:** 627

**LEWIS AND CLARK SPECIALTY HOSPITAL (430096)**, 2601 Fox Run Parkway,
Zip 57078–5341; tel. 605/665–5100, (Nonreporting) **A**9 10
Primary Contact: Michelle J. Jordan, Administrator
CFO: Terry Steichen, Business Officer
CHR: Elizabeth Steichen, Human Resources
Web address: www.lewisandclarkspecialty.com
**Control:** Corporation, Investor–owned, for–profit **Service:** Other specialty

**Staffed Beds:** 6

---

**Hospital, Medicare Provider Number, Address, Telephone, Approval, Facility, and Physician Codes, Health Care System**

★ American Hospital Association (AHA) membership
☐ The Joint Commission accreditation
◯ Healthcare Facilities Accreditation Program
◇ DNV Healthcare Inc. accreditation
⇑ Center for Improvement in Healthcare Quality Accreditation
△ Commission on Accreditation of Rehabilitation Facilities (CARF) accreditation

# TENNESSEE

**TN**

## ASHLAND CITY—Cheatham County

★ **TRISTAR ASHLAND CITY MEDICAL CENTER (441311)**, 313 North Main Street, Zip 37015–1347; tel. 615/792–3030, (Nonreporting) **A**9 10 18 **S** HCA, Nashville, TN
Primary Contact: Heather J. Rohan, Chief Executive Officer
COO: Brian Marger, Chief Operating Officer
CFO: David A. Summers, Chief Financial Officer
CMO: Divya Shroff, Chief Medical Officer
CIO: David Archer, Director Information Systems
CNO: Darrell White, R.N., Administrator and Chief Nursing Officer
Web address: www.tristarashlandcity.com/
**Control:** Corporation, Investor–owned, for–profit **Service:** General Medical and Surgical

**Staffed Beds:** 12

## ATHENS—Mcminn County

⊞ **STARR REGIONAL MEDICAL CENTER (440068)**, 1114 West Madison Avenue, Zip 37303–4150, Mailing Address: P.O. Box 250, Zip 37371–0250; tel. 423/745–1411, (Nonreporting) **A**1 3 5 9 10 **S** LifePoint Health, Brentwood, TN
Primary Contact: Mark Nichols, FACHE, Chief Executive Officer
CFO: David Alley, Chief Financial Officer
CNO: Margie Brusseau, R.N., Chief Nursing Officer
Web address: www.starrregional.com
**Control:** Corporation, Investor–owned, for–profit **Service:** General Medical and Surgical

**Staffed Beds:** 190

## BARTLETT—Shelby County

⊞ **SAINT FRANCIS HOSPITAL–BARTLETT (440228)**, 2986 Kate Bond Road, Zip 38133–4003; tel. 901/820–7000 **A**1 9 10 **F**3 11 13 15 18 20 22 29 30 31 34 35 38 39 40 44 45 47 48 49 50 54 57 59 60 61 64 68 70 72 74 75 76 77 78 79 81 82 84 85 86 87 93 107 108 110 111 114 115 119 126 130 131 141 142 144 146 147 148 **P**5 **S** TENET Healthcare Corporation, Dallas, TX
Primary Contact: Christopher Locke, Chief Executive Officer
COO: Gwen Bonner, Chief Operating Officer
CFO: Tina Kovacs, Chief Financial Officer
CMO: David Schwartz, Chief Medical Officer
CIO: Mark Lawrence, Director Information Systems
CHR: Bill Stone, Chief Human Resources Officer
CNO: Kris Cherry, Chief Nursing Officer
Web address: www.saintfrancisbartlett.com
**Control:** Corporation, Investor–owned, for–profit **Service:** General Medical and Surgical

**Staffed Beds:** 156 **Admissions:** 6571 **Census:** 89 **Outpatient Visits:** 66789 **Births:** 611 **Total Expense ($000):** 98498 **Payroll Expense ($000):** 30820 **Personnel:** 478

## BOLIVAR—Hardeman County

⊞ **BOLIVAR GENERAL HOSPITAL (440181)**, 650 Nuckolls Road, Zip 38008–1532, Mailing Address: PO Box 509, Zip 38008–0509; tel. 731/658–3100 **A**1 9 10 **F**3 15 29 30 35 40 44 45 57 59 64 75 81 87 93 107 119 130 132 133 146 **S** West Tennessee Healthcare, Jackson, TN
Primary Contact: Ruby Kirby, Administrator
CFO: Terry Swindell, Controller
CMO: Felix Nnaji, Chief Medical Staff
CNO: Angela Lacy, Director of Nursing
Web address: www.wth.net
**Control:** Hospital district or authority, Government, nonfederal **Service:** General Medical and Surgical

**Staffed Beds:** 15 **Admissions:** 171 **Census:** 2 **Outpatient Visits:** 14148 **Births:** 1 **Total Expense ($000):** 6464 **Payroll Expense ($000):** 2605 **Personnel:** 59

☐ **WESTERN MENTAL HEALTH INSTITUTE (444008)**, 11100 Old Highway 64, West, Zip 38008–1554; tel. 731/228–2000, (Nonreporting) **A**1 10
Primary Contact: Roger Pursley, Chief Executive Officer
CFO: Richard Taylor, Chief Financial Officer
CMO: Doug King, M.D., Director Clinical Services
CIO: Earl Bates, Director Information Technology
CHR: Barry Young, Director Human Resources
**Control:** State–Government, nonfederal **Service:** Psychiatric

**Staffed Beds:** 247

## BRISTOL—Sullivan County

⊞ **SELECT SPECIALTY HOSPITAL–TRI CITIES (442016)**, One Medical Park Boulevard, 5th Floor, Zip 37620–8964; tel. 423/844–5900, (Nonreporting) **A**1 9 10 **S** Select Medical Corporation, Mechanicsburg, PA
CMO: John Byers, M.D., Medical Director
CHR: William G. Ison, Human Resources Manager
CNO: Jeffrey Radford, Chief Nursing Officer
Web address: www.selectspecialtyhospitals.com/company/locations/tricities.aspx
**Control:** Corporation, Investor–owned, for–profit **Service:** Long–Term Acute Care hospital

**Staffed Beds:** 33

⊞ **WELLMONT BRISTOL REGIONAL MEDICAL CENTER (440012)**, 1 Medical Park Boulevard, Zip 37620–7430; tel. 423/844–1121 **A**1 2 3 5 9 10 **F**3 8 11 13 15 17 18 20 22 24 28 29 30 31 34 35 37 38 39 40 43 44 45 46 47 49 51 54 56 57 58 59 60 61 63 64 67 70 73 74 75 76 77 78 79 81 82 83 84 85 86 87 89 91 92 93 94 96 97 98 100 101 102 103 104 106 107 108 110 111 114 115 118 119 120 121 123 124 126 129 130 131 132 135 144 145 146 147 148 **P**1 6 **S** Wellmont Health System, Kingsport, TN
Primary Contact: Greg Neal, President
COO: Christopher Hobson, Chief Operating Officer
CFO: Dale Poe, Vice President and Chief Financial Officer
CIO: Will Showalter, Senior Vice President Information Technology
CHR: Hamlin J. Wilson, Senior Vice President Human Resources
CNO: Timothy Craig Anderson, Jr., Chief Nursing Officer
Web address: www.wellmont.org
**Control:** Other not–for–profit (including NFP Corporation) **Service:** General Medical and Surgical

**Staffed Beds:** 312 **Admissions:** 14844 **Census:** 187 **Outpatient Visits:** 100911 **Births:** 854 **Total Expense ($000):** 219441 **Payroll Expense ($000):** 56539 **Personnel:** 1599

## CAMDEN—Benton County

⊞ **CAMDEN GENERAL HOSPITAL (441316)**, 175 Hospital Drive, Zip 38320–1617; tel. 731/584–6135 **A**1 9 10 18 **F**3 15 29 30 35 40 44 57 59 64 75 79 81 85 87 93 107 111 119 130 132 133 146 **S** West Tennessee Healthcare, Jackson, TN
Primary Contact: Denny R. Smith, Administrator
COO: James E. Ross, Chief Operating Officer
CFO: Terry Swindell, Chief Financial Officer
CMO: Jon R. Winter, D.O., Chief of Staff
CIO: Jeff Frieling, Vice President Information Systems
CHR: Barry Phillips, Executive Director Human Resources
Web address: www.wth.net
**Control:** Hospital district or authority, Government, nonfederal **Service:** General Medical and Surgical

**Staffed Beds:** 25 **Admissions:** 298 **Census:** 5 **Outpatient Visits:** 13012 **Births:** 0 **Total Expense ($000):** 6711 **Payroll Expense ($000):** 2753 **Personnel:** 70

## CARTHAGE—Smith County

⊞ **RIVERVIEW REGIONAL MEDICAL CENTER (441307)**, 158 Hospital Drive, Zip 37030–1096; tel. 615/735–1560, (Nonreporting) **A**1 9 10 18 **S** LifePoint Health, Brentwood, TN
Primary Contact: Rod Harkleroad, R.N., Administrator
CHR: Gina Anderson, Human Resources Officer
CNO: Kathy Lewis, Chief Nursing Officer and Vice President Clinical Services
Web address: www.myriverviewmedical.com/
**Control:** Corporation, Investor–owned, for–profit **Service:** General Medical and Surgical

**Staffed Beds:** 35

## CELINA—Clay County

☐ **CUMBERLAND RIVER HOSPITAL (440141)**, 100 Old Jefferson Street, Zip 38551–4040, Mailing Address: P. O. Box 427, Zip 38551–0427; tel. 931/243–3581, (Nonreporting) **A**1 9 10
Primary Contact: Patricia Strong, Interim Chief Executive Officer
CFO: Patricia Strong, Chief Financial Officer
CMO: Harry Horne, D.O., Chief of Staff
CIO: Margie Boone, Registered Health Information Technician
CHR: Angel Lewis, Senior Vice President
CNO: Patsy Marinich, Chief Nursing Officer
Web address: www.cumberlandriverhospital.com
**Control:** Corporation, Investor–owned, for–profit **Service:** General Medical and Surgical

**Staffed Beds:** 34

*Many Facility Codes have changed. Please refer to the AHA Guide Code Chart.*   © 2015 AHA Guide

## CENTERVILLE—Hickman County

☒ **SAINT THOMAS HICKMAN HOSPITAL (441300)**, 135 East Swan Street, Zip 37033–1417; tel. 931/729–4271, (Total facility includes 40 beds in nursing home–type unit) **A**1 9 10 18 **F**3 29 30 34 35 40 41 45 56 57 59 62 64 65 67 77 81 86 87 89 90 91 93 104 107 119 127 128 130 133 135 148 **P**6 **S** Ascension Health, Saint Louis, MO
Primary Contact: Jack M. Keller, Chief Executive Officer
COO: Robin Crowell, Chief Nursing Officer and Chief Operating Officer
CFO: Bailey Pratt, Chief Financial Officer
CMO: Zachary Hutchens, M.D., Chief Medical Officer
CHR: Patty Matney, Human Resources Consultant
CNO: Robin Crowell, Chief Nursing Officer and Chief Operating Officer
Web address: www.hickmanhospital.com
**Control:** Other not–for–profit (including NFP Corporation) **Service:** General Medical and Surgical

**Staffed Beds:** 65 **Admissions:** 178 **Census:** 40 **Outpatient Visits:** 12829 **Births:** 0 **Total Expense ($000):** 13678 **Payroll Expense ($000):** 6255 **Personnel:** 121

## CHATTANOOGA—Hamilton County

☒ **CHI MEMORIAL (440091)**, 2525 De Sales Avenue, Zip 37404–1161; tel. 423/495–2525, (Includes MEMORIAL HOSPITAL HIXSON, 2051 Hamill Road, Hixson, Zip 37343–4026; tel. 423/495–7100), (Nonreporting) **A**1 2 3 9 10 **S** Catholic Health Initiatives, Englewood, CO
Primary Contact: James M. Hobson, Chief Executive Officer
CMO: Kevin Lewis, M.D., Chief Medical Officer
CHR: Brad W. Pope, Vice President Human Resources
CNO: Rhonda Poulson, Chief Nursing Officer and Vice President of Clinical Operations
Web address: www.memorial.org
**Control:** Church–operated, Nongovernment, not–for profit **Service:** General Medical and Surgical

**Staffed Beds:** 336

☒ **ERLANGER MEDICAL CENTER (440104)**, 975 East Third Street, Zip 37403–2147; tel. 423/778–7000, (Includes ERLANGER EAST HOSPITAL, 1755 Gunbarrel Road, Zip 37421; tel. 423/778–8700; Teresa Radeker, Administrator; ERLANGER NORTH HOSPITAL, 632 Morrison Springs Road, Zip 37415; tel. 615/778–3300; T. C. THOMPSON CHILDREN'S HOSPITAL, 910 Blackford Street, Zip 37403; tel. 615/778–6011; Cynthia Rhodes, Administrator; WILLIE D. MILLER EYE CENTER, 975 East Third Street, Zip 37403; tel. 615/778–6011) **A**1 2 3 5 8 9 10 **F**3 5 6 7 8 9 11 12 13 14 15 16 17 18 19 20 21 22 23 24 25 26 27 28 29 30 31 32 34 35 36 37 38 40 42 43 44 45 46 47 48 49 50 51 52 53 54 55 56 57 58 59 60 61 62 63 64 65 66 68 70 71 72 73 74 75 76 77 78 79 80 81 82 83 84 85 86 87 88 89 91 92 93 94 97 98 99 100 101 102 103 104 105 107 108 109 110 111 112 114 115 116 117 118 119 120 121 123 124 126 127 129 130 131 132 133 134 135 138 141 142 143 144 145 146 147 148 **P**2 4 6 7 **S** Erlanger Health System, Chattanooga, TN
Primary Contact: Kevin M. Spiegel, FACHE, Chief Executive Officer
COO: Robert E. Brooks, FACHE, Executive Vice President and Chief Operating Officer
CFO: J. Britton Tabor, Senior VP and Chief Financial Officer
CMO: James Creel, M.D., Chief Medical Officer
CIO: Laurene Vamprine, Senior Vice President Information Systems
CHR: Gregg Gentry, Senior Vice President Human Resources
CNO: Janice Colleen Keys, MSN, Chief Nurse Executive
Web address: www.erlanger.org
**Control:** Hospital district or authority, Government, nonfederal **Service:** General Medical and Surgical

**Staffed Beds:** 540 **Admissions:** 30098 **Census:** 386 **Outpatient Visits:** 422841 **Births:** 5396 **Total Expense ($000):** 565651 **Payroll Expense ($000):** 240761 **Personnel:** 3765

**ERLANGER WOMEN'S EAST HOSPITAL** See Erlanger East Hospital

☒ **HEALTHSOUTH CHATTANOOGA REHABILITATION HOSPITAL (443032)**, 2412 McCallie Avenue, Zip 37404–3398; tel. 423/698–0221 **A**1 10 **F**29 34 90 92 95 96 130 132 148 **S** HEALTHSOUTH Corporation, Birmingham, AL
Primary Contact: Scott Rowe, Chief Executive Officer
COO: Scott Rowe, Chief Executive Officer
CFO: Karen Klassen, Controller
CMO: Amjad Munir, M.D., Medical Director
CIO: Denise Smith, Director Health Information
CHR: Deborah Hersom, Director Human Resources
CNO: Michelle Cowart, Chief Nursing Officer
Web address: www.healthsouthchattanooga.com
**Control:** Corporation, Investor–owned, for–profit **Service:** Rehabilitation

**Staffed Beds:** 69 **Admissions:** 1083 **Census:** 38 **Outpatient Visits:** 0 **Births:** 0 **Total Expense ($000):** 14764 **Payroll Expense ($000):** 6838 **Personnel:** 58

☒ **KINDRED HOSPITAL–CHATTANOOGA (442007)**, 709 Walnut Street, Zip 37402–1916; tel. 423/266–7721, (Nonreporting) **A**1 9 10 **S** Kindred Healthcare, Louisville, KY
Primary Contact: Gigi Johnson, Interim Chief Executive Officer
COO: Rick Rheinheimer, Chief Clinical Officer
CFO: Julia Smith, Chief Financial Officer
CMO: Randy Heisser, M.D., Medical Director
CHR: Kellie McCampbell, Coordinator Human Resources
CNO: Gigi Johnson, Chief Nursing Officer
Web address: www.kindredchattanooga.com/
**Control:** Corporation, Investor–owned, for–profit **Service:** Long–Term Acute Care hospital

**Staffed Beds:** 44

☐ **MOCCASIN BEND MENTAL HEALTH INSTITUTE (444002)**, 100 Moccasin Bend Road, Zip 37405–4415; tel. 423/265–2271, (Nonreporting) **A**1 10 Primary Contact: Mary C. Young, Chief Executive Officer
COO: Rob Cotterman, Assistant Superintendent Program Services
CFO: Sylvia Harris, Fiscal Director
CMO: Terry R. Holmes, M.D., Clinical Director
CIO: Mickey Williams, Manager Information Technology
CHR: Cynthia Honeycutt, Director Human Resources
CNO: Charlynne Parson, Nurse Executive
Web address: www.state.tn.us/mental/mhs/mbhmhi/moc.htm
**Control:** State–Government, nonfederal **Service:** Psychiatric

**Staffed Beds:** 150

☒ **PARKRIDGE MEDICAL CENTER (440156)**, 2333 McCallie Avenue, Zip 37404–3258; tel. 423/698–6061, (Includes EAST RIDGE HOSPITAL, 941 Spring Creek Road, East Ridge, Zip 37412, Mailing Address: P.O. Box 91229, Zip 37412–6229; tel. 423/855–3500; Jarrett B. Millsaps, Jr., FACHE, Chief Executive Officer; PARKRIDGE EAST HOSPITAL, 941 Spring Creek Road, Zip 37412–3909; tel. 423/894–7870; Jarrett B. Millsaps, Jr., FACHE, Chief Executive Officer; PARKRIDGE VALLEY CHILD AND ADOLESCENT CAMPUS, 2200 Morris Hill Road, Zip 37421; tel. 423/894–4220; Brennan Francois, Chief Executive Officer; PARKRIDGE WEST HOSPITAL, 1000 Highway 28, Jasper, Zip 37347–3638; tel. 423/837–9500; Shirley K. Scarlatti, Associate Chief Nursing Officer) **A**1 2 3 5 9 10 **F**3 5 13 15 18 20 22 24 26 28 29 30 31 39 40 45 46 49 50 51 55 56 57 58 59 60 70 72 75 76 77 78 79 81 85 90 93 98 99 103 104 105 106 107 108 110 111 114 115 119 120 121 124 126 129 130 131 132 146 148 **S** HCA, Nashville, TN
Primary Contact: Darrell W. Moore, Chief Executive Officer
COO: Jim L. Coleman, Jr., Chief Operating Officer
CFO: Tom Jackson, Chief Financial Officer
CMO: Gary Lanham, Chief Medical Officer
CIO: David Cornelius, Director Information Systems
CHR: Carole Hoffman, Vice President
CNO: Jerri C. Underwood, R.N., Chief Nursing Officer
Web address: www.parkridgemedicalcenter.com
**Control:** Corporation, Investor–owned, for–profit **Service:** General Medical and Surgical

**Staffed Beds:** 513 **Admissions:** 17171 **Census:** 294 **Outpatient Visits:** 155498 **Births:** 2082 **Total Expense ($000):** 241833 **Payroll Expense ($000):** 88171 **Personnel:** 1312

☒ △ **SISKIN HOSPITAL FOR PHYSICAL REHABILITATION (443025)**, One Siskin Plaza, Zip 37403–1306; tel. 423/634–1200, (Nonreporting) **A**1 7 10 Primary Contact: Carol Sim, President and Chief Executive Officer
CFO: Carol Arnhart, Vice President and Chief Financial Officer
CMO: David N. Bowers, M.D., Medical Director
CIO: Baret H. Avery, Chief Information Officer
CHR: Angela Chaffin, Administrative Director Human Resources
CNO: Kathy Campbell, R.N., Interim Director of Nursing
Web address: www.siskinrehab.org
**Control:** Other not–for–profit (including NFP Corporation) **Service:** Rehabilitation

**Staffed Beds:** 109

**T. C. THOMPSON CHILDREN'S HOSPITAL** See Erlanger Medical Center

**WILLIE D. MILLER EYE CENTER** See Erlanger Medical Center

## CLARKSVILLE—Montgomery County

★ **BEHAVIORAL HEALTHCARE CENTER AT CLARKSVILLE (444019)**, 930 Professional Park Drive, Zip 37040–5136; tel. 931/538–6420, (Nonreporting) **A**10 **S** Tennessee Health Management, Parsons, TN
Primary Contact: Jennifer Robinson, Administrator
CMO: Michael McGhee, M.D., Medical Director
CNO: Chrissy Myers, R.N., Director of Nursing
Web address: www.bhcclarksville.com
**Control:** Partnership, Investor–owned, for–profit **Service:** Psychiatric

**Staffed Beds:** 26

**TN**

---

**Hospital, Medicare Provider Number, Address, Telephone, Approval, Facility, and Physician Codes, Health Care System**

★ American Hospital Association (AHA) membership
☐ The Joint Commission accreditation
◯ Healthcare Facilities Accreditation Program
◇ DNV Healthcare Inc. accreditation
⇑ Center for Improvement in Healthcare Quality Accreditation
△ Commission on Accreditation of Rehabilitation Facilities (CARF) accreditation

✠ **GATEWAY MEDICAL CENTER (440035)**, 651 Dunlop Lane, Zip 37040–5015, Mailing Address: P.O. Box 31629, Zip 37040–0028; tel. 931/502–1000, (Nonreporting) **A**1 9 10 **S** Community Health Systems, Inc., Franklin, TN
Primary Contact: Mark A. Marsh, Chief Executive Officer
COO: Shawn Molsberger, Chief Operating Officer
CFO: George Sprinkel, Chief Financial Officer
CMO: Thomas L. Ely, D.O., Chief Medical Officer
CIO: Scott Greene, Chief Information Officer
CHR: Liza Edmunds, Director Human Resources
CNO: Faye Perry, Chief Nursing Officer
Web address: www.ghsystem.com
**Control:** Partnership, Investor–owned, for–profit **Service:** General Medical and Surgical

| |
|---|
| **Staffed Beds:** 247 |

### CLEVELAND—Bradley County

✠ **SKYRIDGE MEDICAL CENTER (440185)**, 2305 Chambliss Avenue N.W., Zip 37311–3847, Mailing Address: P.O. Box 3060, Zip 37320–3060; tel. 423/559–6000, (Includes SKYRIDGE MEDICAL CENTER – WESTSIDE CAMPUS, 2800 Westside Drive N.W., Zip 37312–3599; tel. 423/339–4100; R. Coleman Foss, Chief Executive Officer) **A**1 3 5 9 10 **F**3 5 13 15 18 20 22 28 29 30 31 34 35 39 40 45 49 51 57 59 60 68 70 73 76 77 78 79 81 82 85 87 89 93 98 104 105 107 108 110 111 114 115 118 119 124 129 135 146 148 **S** Community Health Systems, Inc., Franklin, TN
Primary Contact: R. Coleman Foss, Chief Executive Officer
COO: Bernadette De Prez, Chief Operating Officer
CFO: Bill Ziesmer, Chief Financial Officer
CMO: Stephen Jackson, M.D., Chief of Staff
CHR: Kristine Godfrey, Director Human Resources
Web address: www.skyridgemedicalcenter.net
**Control:** Corporation, Investor–owned, for–profit **Service:** General Medical and Surgical

| |
|---|
| **Staffed Beds:** 186 **Admissions:** 7957 **Census:** 98 **Outpatient Visits:** 97490 **Births:** 1072 **Total Expense ($000):** 129857 **Payroll Expense ($000):** 43492 **Personnel:** 906 |

### COLLIERVILLE—Shelby County

★ **BAPTIST MEMORIAL HOSPITAL–COLLIERVILLE (440217)**, 1500 West Poplar Avenue, Zip 38017–0601; tel. 901/861–9400 **A**5 9 **F**3 7 8 12 15 18 19 20 21 22 23 24 25 26 27 28 29 30 31 32 34 35 36 37 38 40 41 45 46 47 48 49 52 53 54 55 56 57 58 59 60 61 62 63 64 65 66 68 70 71 74 75 77 78 79 81 82 83 84 85 86 87 92 93 96 107 108 109 110 111 112 113 114 115 116 117 118 119 120 121 123 124 126 129 130 132 135 136 137 143 144 145 146 147 148 **S** Baptist Memorial Health Care Corporation, Memphis, TN
Primary Contact: Kyle E. Armstrong, Administrator and Chief Executive Officer
CFO: Terri Seago, Chief Financial Officer
CIO: Doug Reiselt, Vice President and Chief Information Officer
CHR: Brenda Johnson, Director Human Resources
CNO: Denise Ferguson, Chief Nursing Officer
Web address: www.baptistonline.org/collierville/
**Control:** Other not–for–profit (including NFP Corporation) **Service:** General Medical and Surgical

| |
|---|
| **Staffed Beds:** 61 **Admissions:** 2379 **Census:** 22 **Outpatient Visits:** 26763 **Births:** 0 **Total Expense ($000):** 51851 **Payroll Expense ($000):** 17074 **Personnel:** 284 |

### COLUMBIA—Maury County

**BEHAVIORAL HEALTHCARE CENTER AT COLUMBIA (440230)**, 1400 Rosewood Drive, Zip 38401–4878; tel. 931/388–6573 **A**10 **F**29 34 38 56 98 103 130 **S** Tennessee Health Management, Parsons, TN
Primary Contact: Paula Chennault, Administrator
CMO: Rodney Poling, M.D., Medical Director
CHR: Pam Brown, Human Resources Manager
CNO: Sheila Ridner, R.N., Director of Nursing
Web address: www.bhccolumbia.com
**Control:** Corporation, Investor–owned, for–profit **Service:** Psychiatric

| |
|---|
| **Staffed Beds:** 16 **Admissions:** 307 **Census:** 11 **Outpatient Visits:** 0 **Births:** 0 |

✠ **MAURY REGIONAL HOSPITAL (440073)**, 1224 Trotwood Avenue, Zip 38401–4802; tel. 931/381–1111, (Total facility includes 17 beds in nursing home–type unit) **A**1 2 9 10 19 **F**7 8 11 13 15 17 18 20 22 24 28 29 30 31 34 35 40 44 45 46 48 50 51 54 57 59 60 62 64 68 70 73 74 75 76 77 78 79 80 81 85 86 87 93 97 107 108 111 114 116 117 118 119 121 123 128 129 130 131 132 135 144 146 147 148 **S** Maury Regional Health System, Columbia, TN
Primary Contact: H. Alan Watson, FACHE, Chief Executive Officer
COO: Paul Betz, FACHE, Chief Operating Officer and Senior Vice President
CFO: Nick Swift, Chief Financial Officer
CMO: Chris Edwards, M.D., Chief Medical Officer
CIO: Jim Parcel, Director Information Technology
CHR: Kaye Brewer, Vice President Human Resources
CNO: Deborah Lumpkins, MSN, Chief Nursing Officer
Web address: www.mauryregional.com
**Control:** County–Government, nonfederal **Service:** General Medical and Surgical

| |
|---|
| **Staffed Beds:** 211 **Admissions:** 12664 **Census:** 133 **Outpatient Visits:** 225278 **Births:** 1528 **Total Expense ($000):** 236489 **Payroll Expense ($000):** 94176 **Personnel:** 1603 |

### COOKEVILLE—Putnam County

✠ **COOKEVILLE REGIONAL MEDICAL CENTER (440059)**, 1 Medical Center Boulevard, Zip 38501–4294; tel. 931/783–2000 **A**1 2 9 10 19 **F**3 8 11 12 13 15 17 18 20 22 24 26 28 29 30 31 34 35 40 44 45 49 50 51 54 57 59 62 64 65 68 70 73 74 75 76 77 78 79 81 85 86 87 89 90 93 96 107 108 110 111 114 115 117 118 119 120 121 123 126 129 130 132 135 146 147 148 **P**7
Primary Contact: Paul Korth, Chief Executive Officer
COO: Scott Williams, Chief Operating Officer
CFO: Paul Korth, Chief Financial Officer
CMO: Jeffrey J. Gleason, M.D., Chief Medical Officer
CIO: Les Bernstein, Chief Information Officer
CHR: Angel Lewis, Senior Vice President Administration
CNO: Linda Crawford, R.N., Chief Nursing Officer
Web address: www.crmchealth.org
**Control:** Hospital district or authority, Government, nonfederal **Service:** General Medical and Surgical

| |
|---|
| **Staffed Beds:** 243 **Admissions:** 13145 **Census:** 154 **Outpatient Visits:** 192884 **Births:** 1603 **Total Expense ($000):** 219488 **Payroll Expense ($000):** 93198 **Personnel:** 1798 |

◇ **TEN BROECK TENNESSEE TREATMENT FACILITY (444022)**, 1 Medical Center Boulevard, 5 West, Zip 38501; tel. 931/783–2570, (Nonreporting) **A**10 21 **S** United Medical Corporation, Windermere, FL
Primary Contact: Jane Wilson–Mitchell, Interim Chief Executive Officer
CFO: David Corddry, Chief Financial Officer
CMO: Glenn T. Webb, M.D., Medical Director
CNO: Shannon Beaty, Nursing Director
Web address: www.tenbroeck.com
**Control:** Corporation, Investor–owned, for–profit **Service:** General Medical and Surgical

| |
|---|
| **Staffed Beds:** 32 |

### COPPERHILL—Polk County

□ **COPPER BASIN MEDICAL CENTER (441315)**, 144 Medical Center Drive, Zip 37317–5005, Mailing Address: P.O. Box 990, Zip 37317–0990; tel. 423/496–5511, (Nonreporting) **A**1 9 10 18
Primary Contact: Anna Clark, Interim Chief Executive Officer
COO: Anna Clark, Chief Operating Officer
CMO: Allen Uhlik, M.D., Chief of Staff
CIO: Florence Tichenor, Director Information Technology
CHR: Kathy Pack, Manager Human Resources
CNO: Sonya Standridge, Chief Nursing Officer
Web address: www.copperbasin.org
**Control:** Other not–for–profit (including NFP Corporation) **Service:** General Medical and Surgical

| |
|---|
| **Staffed Beds:** 25 |

### COVINGTON—Tipton County

✠ **BAPTIST MEMORIAL HOSPITAL–TIPTON (440131)**, 1995 Highway 51 South, Zip 38019–3635; tel. 901/476–2621 **A**1 9 10 **F**3 11 15 29 30 31 34 35 40 45 55 57 58 59 65 70 74 75 76 78 79 81 85 87 89 93 100 107 108 110 111 114 115 119 120 121 129 130 135 146 148 **P**6 **S** Baptist Memorial Health Care Corporation, Memphis, TN
Primary Contact: Samuel Lynd, Administrator and Chief Executive Officer
CFO: Monique Hart, Chief Financial Officer
CMO: Kenneth Afenya, M.D., Chief of Staff
CHR: Myra Cousar, Director Human Resources
CNO: Cheryl Furdge Berry, Chief Nursing Officer
Web address: www.baptistonline.org/tipton/
**Control:** Other not–for–profit (including NFP Corporation) **Service:** General Medical and Surgical

| |
|---|
| **Staffed Beds:** 44 **Admissions:** 1221 **Census:** 9 **Outpatient Visits:** 43920 **Births:** 415 **Total Expense ($000):** 72048 **Payroll Expense ($000):** 15427 **Personnel:** 263 |

**TN**

*Many Facility Codes have changed. Please refer to the AHA Guide Code Chart.* © 2015 AHA Guide

## CROSSVILLE—Cumberland County

✠ **CUMBERLAND MEDICAL CENTER (440009)**, 421 South Main Street, Zip 38555–5031; tel. 931/484–9511 **A**1 2 9 10 20 **F**3 11 13 15 18 20 22 28 29 30 31 34 35 40 45 47 48 49 51 53 57 58 59 62 68 70 74 75 76 77 78 79 81 85 86 87 93 107 108 110 111 114 119 120 121 129 130 132 135 146 147 148 **S** Covenant Health, Knoxville, TN
Primary Contact: Jeremy Biggs, President and Chief Administrative Officer
COO: Larry E. Moore, Executive Vice President and Chief Operating Officer and Chief Financial Officer
CFO: Larry E. Moore, Executive Vice President and Chief Operating Officer and Chief Financial Officer
CIO: Joe Lowe, Director Management Information Systems
CHR: Charles Sexton, Manager Human Resources
CNO: Rebecca Foster, Chief Nursing Officer
Web address: www.cmchealthcare.org
**Control:** Other not–for–profit (including NFP Corporation) **Service:** General Medical and Surgical

**Staffed Beds:** 110 **Admissions:** 5721 **Census:** 69 **Outpatient Visits:** 88007 **Births:** 624 **Total Expense ($000):** 87062 **Payroll Expense ($000):** 39063 **Personnel:** 686

## DAYTON—Rhea County

✠ **RHEA MEDICAL CENTER (441310)**, 9400 Rhea County Highway, Zip 37321–7922; tel. 423/775–1121, (Nonreporting) **A**1 9 10 18 **S** QHR, Brentwood, TN
Primary Contact: Kennedy L. Croom, Jr., Administrator and Chief Executive Officer
CFO: Harv Sanders, Chief Financial Officer
CMO: Michael Prostko, M.D., Chief of Staff
CHR: Peri Meadows, Director Human Resources
Web address: www.rheamedical.org
**Control:** County–Government, nonfederal **Service:** General Medical and Surgical

**Staffed Beds:** 25

## DICKSON—Dickson County

✠ **TENNOVA HEALTHCARE – DYERSBURG REGIONAL HOSPITAL (440046)**, 111 Highway 70 East, Zip 37055–2080; tel. 615/446–0446, (Nonreporting) **A**1 2 9 10 **S** HCA, Nashville, TN
Primary Contact: Dustin Greene, Chief Executive Officer
CFO: Clarence Gray, Chief Financial Officer
CIO: Rick Stoker, Director Management Information Systems
CHR: Sheila Kight, Director Human Resources
CNO: Gina Bullington, Chief Nursing Officer
Web address: www.horizonmedicalcenter.com
**Control:** Corporation, Investor–owned, for–profit **Service:** General Medical and Surgical

**Staffed Beds:** 130

## DYERSBURG—Dyer County

✠ **DYERSBURG REGIONAL MEDICAL CENTER (440072)**, 400 East Tickle Street, Zip 38024–3120; tel. 731/285–2410, (Nonreporting) **A**1 9 10 20 **S** Community Health Systems, Inc., Franklin, TN
Primary Contact: Reba Celsor, Chief Executive Officer
CFO: Meredith Malone, Chief Financial Officer
CMO: Darren Johnson, M.D., Chief of Staff
CIO: Russ Shephard, Senior Systems Analyst
CHR: Beverly Ray, Director Human Resources
Web address: www.dyersburgregionalmc.com
**Control:** Corporation, Investor–owned, for–profit **Service:** General Medical and Surgical

**Staffed Beds:** 120

## EAST RIDGE—Hamilton County

**EAST RIDGE HOSPITAL** See Parkridge Medical Center, Chattanooga

## ELIZABETHTON—Carter County

☐ **SYCAMORE SHOALS HOSPITAL (440018)**, 1501 West Elk Avenue, Zip 37643–2874; tel. 423/542–1300 **A**1 9 10 **F**3 11 15 18 29 30 34 35 40 44 45 48 49 50 53 54 56 57 62 63 64 68 70 75 77 78 79 81 85 87 93 98 103 107 110 111 115 118 119 130 132 135 146 147 148 **P**6 8 **S** Mountain States Health Alliance, Johnson City, TN
Primary Contact: Dwayne Taylor, Chief Executive Officer
COO: Melanie Stanton, R.N., Chief Nursing Officer
CFO: Bradley Logan, Chief Financial Officer
CMO: Morris H. Seligman, M.D., Chief Medical Officer and Chief Medical Information Officer
CIO: Paul Merrywell, Chief Information Officer
CHR: Sharon Sheppard, Manager Human Resources
Web address: www.msha.com
**Control:** Other not–for–profit (including NFP Corporation) **Service:** General Medical and Surgical

**Staffed Beds:** 121 **Admissions:** 3201 **Census:** 41 **Outpatient Visits:** 62812 **Births:** 0 **Total Expense ($000):** 38794 **Payroll Expense ($000):** 15945 **Personnel:** 326

## ERIN—Houston County

✠ **HOUSTON COUNTY COMMUNITY HOSPITAL (440232)**, 5001 East Main Street, Zip 37061–4115, Mailing Address: P.O. Box 489, Zip 37061–0489; tel. 931/289–4211 **A**1 9 10 **F**15 29 40 41 81 93 107 115 119 133
Primary Contact: Scott Bradley, Interim Chief Executive Officer
CFO: Shannon Allison, Chief Financial Officer
CMO: Erin Chambers, M.D., Chief Medical Officer
Web address: www.pcmc–erintn.com/
**Control:** County–Government, nonfederal **Service:** General Medical and Surgical

**Staffed Beds:** 25 **Admissions:** 465 **Census:** 6 **Outpatient Visits:** 11855 **Births:** 0 **Total Expense ($000):** 5946 **Payroll Expense ($000):** 2746 **Personnel:** 71

## ERWIN—Unicoi County

✠ **UNICOI COUNTY MEMORIAL HOSPITAL (440001)**, 100 Greenway Circle, Zip 37650–2196, Mailing Address: P.O. Box 802, Zip 37650–0802; tel. 423/743–3141, (Total facility includes 46 beds in nursing home–type unit) **A**1 9 10 **F**11 15 29 30 34 35 40 45 62 64 67 70 75 77 79 81 85 87 107 110 111 115 130 131 146 **P**6 8
Primary Contact: Eric Carroll, Chief Executive Officer
CFO: Toni Buchanan, Chief Financial Officer
CMO: Jose Picaza, M.D., Chief of Staff
CIO: Maggie Tipton, Chief Information Officer
CHR: Susan Broyles, Director Human Resources and Safety
CNO: Melanie Stanton, R.N., Chief Nursing Officer
Web address: www.msha.com
**Control:** Other not–for–profit (including NFP Corporation) **Service:** General Medical and Surgical

**Staffed Beds:** 94 **Admissions:** 749 **Census:** 37 **Outpatient Visits:** 18264 **Births:** 0 **Total Expense ($000):** 20835 **Payroll Expense ($000):** 5548 **Personnel:** 135

## FAYETTEVILLE—Lincoln County

✠ **LINCOLN COUNTY HEALTH SYSTEM (440102)**, 106 Medical Center Boulevard, Zip 37334–2684; tel. 931/438–1100, (Total facility includes 264 beds in nursing home–type unit) **A**1 9 10 **F**3 7 10 11 13 15 18 29 30 34 35 40 45 50 53 56 57 59 62 63 64 67 68 70 74 75 76 77 79 81 85 93 98 103 104 107 108 110 111 114 118 119 128 129 132 135 143 146 148 **P**6 **S** QHR, Brentwood, TN
Primary Contact: John Harding, Interim Chief Executive Officer
CFO: Bailey Pratt, Interim Chief Financial Officer
CMO: Richard Cline, D.O., Chief of Staff
CHR: Wendy Nogler, Director Human Resources
CNO: Vicky Groce, Chief Nursing Officer
Web address: www.lchealthsystem.com
**Control:** County–Government, nonfederal **Service:** General Medical and Surgical

**Staffed Beds:** 323 **Admissions:** 1919 **Census:** 214 **Outpatient Visits:** 44354 **Births:** 227 **Total Expense ($000):** 40606 **Payroll Expense ($000):** 18133 **Personnel:** 507

## FRANKLIN—Williamson County

☐ **ROLLING HILLS HOSPITAL (444007)**, 2014 Quail Hollow Circle, Zip 37067–5967; tel. 615/628–5700, (Nonreporting) **A**1 10 **S** Universal Health Services, Inc., King of Prussia, PA
Primary Contact: Laurel Roberts, R.N., Interim Chief Executive Officer
Web address: www.rollinghillshospital.org/
**Control:** Corporation, Investor–owned, for–profit **Service:** Psychiatric

**Staffed Beds:** 80

**TN**

---

**Hospital, Medicare Provider Number, Address, Telephone, Approval, Facility, and Physician Codes, Health Care System**

★ American Hospital Association (AHA) membership
☐ The Joint Commission accreditation
○ Healthcare Facilities Accreditation Program
◇ DNV Healthcare Inc. accreditation
⇑ Center for Improvement in Healthcare Quality Accreditation
△ Commission on Accreditation of Rehabilitation Facilities (CARF) accreditation

☐ **WILLIAMSON MEDICAL CENTER (440029)**, 4321 Carothers Parkway,
Zip 37067–8542; tel. 615/435–5000 **A**1 2 9 10 **F**3 7 11 13 15 17 18 20 22
28 29 30 31 34 35 40 43 45 49 50 54 57 59 64 67 68 70 72 74 75 76 78
79 80 81 85 86 87 93 97 102 107 108 110 111 114 115 118 119 124 126
129 130 132 135 146 148 **P**6 8
Primary Contact: Donald Webb, Chief Executive Officer
COO: Julie Miller, Chief Operating Officer
CMO: Starling C. Evins, M.D., Chief of Staff
CIO: Steve Dycus, Director Marketing and Public Relations
CHR: Phyllis Molyneux, Associate Administrator Human Resources and Education
Web address: www.williamsonmedicalcenter.org
**Control:** County–Government, nonfederal **Service:** General Medical and Surgical

**Staffed Beds:** 185 **Admissions:** 9732 **Census:** 80 **Outpatient Visits:** 106357
**Births:** 1641 **Total Expense ($000):** 159935 **Payroll Expense ($000):**
66636 **Personnel:** 1130

### GALLATIN—Sumner County

☒ **SUMNER REGIONAL MEDICAL CENTER (440003)**, 555 Hartsville Pike,
Zip 37066–2400, Mailing Address: P.O. Box 1558, Zip 37066–1558;
tel. 615/452–4210, (Nonreporting) **A**1 2 3 9 10 **S** LifePoint Health,
Brentwood, TN
Primary Contact: Susan M. Peach, R.N., Chief Executive Officer
COO: Michael Herman, Chief Operating Officer
CIO: Vickie Carter, Information Systems Director
CNO: Anne Melton, Chief Nursing Officer
Web address: www.mysumnermedical.com
**Control:** Corporation, Investor–owned, for–profit **Service:** General Medical and Surgical

**Staffed Beds:** 155

### GERMANTOWN—Shelby County

☐ **BAPTIST MEMORIAL REHABILITATION HOSPITAL (443034)**, 1240 South
Germantown Road, Zip 38138–2226; tel. 901/275–3300, (Nonreporting) **A**1 10
**S** Baptist Memorial Health Care Corporation, Memphis, TN
Primary Contact: Brian Hogan, Chief Executive Officer and Administrator
CFO: Carlos Mendoza, Controller
CHR: Stacie Schroeppel, Director of Human Resources
CNO: Donna Hale, Director of Nursing
Web address: www.baptistrehab.com
**Control:** Partnership, Investor–owned, for–profit **Service:** Rehabilitation

**Staffed Beds:** 49

☒ △ **BAPTIST REHABILITATION–GERMANTOWN (440147)**, 2100 Exeter
Road, Zip 38138–3978; tel. 901/757–1350, (Total facility includes 18 beds in
nursing home–type unit) **A**1 7 9 10 **F**3 29 30 34 35 54 57 59 64 68 75 77 79
86 87 90 91 92 93 96 107 111 114 119 128 130 131 132 135 143 146 148
**S** Baptist Memorial Health Care Corporation, Memphis, TN
Primary Contact: Janice Hill, R.N., President and Chief Executive Officer
CFO: Catherine Saltz, Chief Financial Officer
CMO: Sunita Jain, M.D., Chief Medical Officer
CHR: Pam Hill, Director Human Resources
CNO: Donna Hale, Chief Nursing Officer
Web address: www.baptistonline.org/germantown/
**Control:** Other not–for–profit (including NFP Corporation) **Service:** Rehabilitation

**Staffed Beds:** 68 **Admissions:** 1128 **Census:** 35 **Outpatient Visits:** 10642
**Births:** 0 **Total Expense ($000):** 23256 **Payroll Expense ($000):** 11369
**Personnel:** 176

**METHODIST LE BONHEUR GERMANTOWN HOSPITAL** See Methodist
Healthcare Memphis Hospitals, Memphis

### GREENEVILLE—Greene County

☒ **LAUGHLIN MEMORIAL HOSPITAL (440025)**, 1420 Tusculum Boulevard,
Zip 37745–5825; tel. 423/787–5000, (Total facility includes 81 beds in nursing
home–type unit) **A**1 2 9 10 19 **F**2 12 13 15 18 20 28 29 31 34 35 37 40
45 46 48 49 50 56 57 59 62 64 68 70 73 74 75 76 77 78 79 81 85 86 87
89 93 97 107 108 110 111 114 115 118 119 120 121 123 128 129 130
131 132 134 135 146 147 148 **P**6
Primary Contact: Charles H. Whitfield, Jr., President and Chief Executive Officer
CFO: Mark Compton, Chief Financial Officer
CMO: Mark Patterson, M.D., Chief Medical Officer
CIO: Rex Arrington, Chief Information Officer
CHR: Robert Roark, Director Human Resources
CNO: Brenda Cannon, R.N., Director of Nursing
Web address: www.laughlinmemorial.org
**Control:** Other not–for–profit (including NFP Corporation) **Service:** General
Medical and Surgical

**Staffed Beds:** 143 **Admissions:** 5972 **Census:** 113 **Outpatient Visits:** 95668
**Births:** 233 **Total Expense ($000):** 73326 **Payroll Expense ($000):** 32144
**Personnel:** 727

☒ **TAKOMA REGIONAL HOSPITAL (440050)**, 401 Takoma Avenue,
Zip 37743–4647; tel. 423/639–3151 **A**1 9 **F**3 11 13 15 29 30 34 40 45
50 57 59 70 75 76 77 79 81 87 89 90 93 97 98 101 102 103 104 107 108
110 111 119 129 130 131 144 146 148 **S** Adventist Health System Sunbelt
Health Care Corporation, Altamonte Springs, FL
Primary Contact: Dennis Kiley, Interim Chief Executive Officer
CFO: Steven Miller, Chief Financial Officer
CMO: Daniel Lewis, Chief Medical Officer
CHR: Jack Lister, Director Human Resources
CNO: Tammy Albright, Chief Nursing Officer
Web address: www.takoma.org
**Control:** Church–operated, Nongovernment, not–for profit **Service:** General
Medical and Surgical

**Staffed Beds:** 32 **Admissions:** 2407 **Census:** 31 **Outpatient Visits:** 206308
**Births:** 287 **Total Expense ($000):** 57311 **Payroll Expense ($000):** 26417

### HARRIMAN—Roane County

☒ **ROANE MEDICAL CENTER (440031)**, 8045 Roane Medical Center Drive,
Zip 37748–8333; tel. 865/316–1000 **A**1 9 10 **F**3 11 15 18 20 28 29 30 40
45 57 59 68 70 77 79 81 85 93 107 108 110 111 119 129 130 136 141
142 146 **S** Covenant Health, Knoxville, TN
Primary Contact: Gaye Jolly, FACHE, President/Chief Administrative Officer
COO: Jason B. Pilant, Chief Operating Officer
CFO: Julie Utterback, Chief Financial Officer
CMO: Mark Browne, M.D., Chief Medical Officer
CIO: Mike Ward, Senior Vice President Chief Information Officer
CHR: Randall Carr, Director Human Resources
CNO: Carolyn Shipley, Chief Nursing Officer
Web address: www.roanemedical.com
**Control:** Other not–for–profit (including NFP Corporation) **Service:** General
Medical and Surgical

**Staffed Beds:** 54 **Admissions:** 2219 **Census:** 23 **Outpatient Visits:** 57874
**Total Expense ($000):** 33849 **Payroll Expense ($000):** 11550 **Personnel:**
220

### HARTSVILLE—Trousdale County

☒ **TROUSDALE MEDICAL CENTER (441301)**, 500 Church Street,
Zip 37074–1744; tel. 615/374–2221, (Nonreporting) **A**1 9 10 18 **S** LifePoint
Health, Brentwood, TN
Primary Contact: Rod Harkleroad, R.N., Chief Executive Officer
COO: William D. Mize, Chief Operating Officer
CFO: David Wilhoite, CPA, Senior Vice President Finance and Chief Financial
Officer
CIO: David Young, Senior Vice President Planning and Technology
CHR: Amy Overstreet, Director Human Resources
Web address: www.mytrousdalemedical.com
**Control:** Corporation, Investor–owned, for–profit **Service:** General Medical and Surgical

**Staffed Beds:** 25

### HENDERSONVILLE—Sumner County

☒ **TRISTAR HENDERSONVILLE MEDICAL CENTER (440194)**, 355 New Shackle
Island Road, Zip 37075–2479; tel. 615/338–1000, (Nonreporting) **A**1 9 10
**S** HCA, Nashville, TN
Primary Contact: Regina Bartlett, Chief Executive Officer
COO: Cory Darling, Chief Operating Officer
CFO: Michael Morrison, Chief Financial Officer
CMO: Brett Branson, M.D., Chief of Staff
CIO: Hal Schultheis, Director Information Systems
CNO: Lisa Gann, R.N., Chief Nursing Officer
Web address: www.hendersonvillemedicalcenter.com
**Control:** Corporation, Investor–owned, for–profit **Service:** General Medical and Surgical

**Staffed Beds:** 70

### HERMITAGE—Davidson County

☒ **TRISTAR SUMMIT MEDICAL CENTER (440150)**, 5655 Frist Boulevard,
Zip 37076–2053; tel. 615/316–3000 **A**1 2 9 10 **F**3 11 13 15 18 20 22 26 28
29 30 31 34 35 37 38 39 40 43 45 46 47 48 49 50 53 56 57 59 61 64 70
72 74 75 76 77 78 79 80 81 82 85 87 89 93 96 97 98 100 102 107 108
110 111 114 115 118 119 121 123 124 126 129 130 131 135 145 146 147
148 **S** HCA, Nashville, TN
Primary Contact: Jeffrey T. Whitehorn, Chief Executive Officer
COO: Greg Caples, Chief Operating Officer
CFO: Bryan Shephard, Chief Financial Officer
CIO: Joel Bain, Director Information Services
CHR: Emily Dye, Vice President Human Resources
CNO: Mary Ann Angle, R.N., Chief Nursing Officer
Web address: www.summitmedctr.com
**Control:** Corporation, Investor–owned, for–profit **Service:** General Medical and Surgical

**Staffed Beds:** 196 **Admissions:** 10552 **Census:** 123 **Outpatient Visits:**
123066 **Births:** 1159 **Total Expense ($000):** 130067 **Payroll Expense
($000):** 48094

TN

## HUNTINGDON—Carroll County

✠ **BAPTIST MEMORIAL HOSPITAL–HUNTINGDON (440016)**, 631 R.B. Wilson Drive, Zip 38344–1727; tel. 731/986–4461 **A**1 9 10 **F**3 7 15 18 28 29 30 32 34 35 40 50 56 57 59 61 62 63 64 65 68 70 75 77 79 81 82 85 86 87 93 102 103 107 111 115 118 119 130 131 132 133 135 146 148 **S** Baptist Memorial Health Care Corporation, Memphis, TN
Primary Contact: Susan M. Breeden, Administrator and Chief Executive Officer
CFO: Sharron Holland, Chief Financial Officer
CHR: Kim King, Director Human Resources and Public Relations
CNO: Kimberly Sanders, Chief Nursing Officer
Web address: www.baptistonline.org/huntingdon/
**Control:** Other not–for–profit (including NFP Corporation) **Service:** General Medical and Surgical

**Staffed Beds:** 33 **Admissions:** 588 **Census:** 6 **Outpatient Visits:** 15246 **Births:** 0 **Total Expense ($000):** 16315 **Payroll Expense ($000):** 6417 **Personnel:** 146

## JACKSON—Madison County

✠ △ **JACKSON–MADISON COUNTY GENERAL HOSPITAL (440002)**, 620 Skyline Drive, Zip 38301–3923; tel. 731/541–5000 **A**1 2 3 5 7 9 10 19 **F**3 7 8 11 13 15 17 18 20 22 24 26 28 29 30 31 34 35 40 44 45 46 47 48 49 51 53 56 57 58 59 60 63 64 65 68 70 72 74 75 76 77 78 79 80 81 82 83 84 85 86 87 89 90 92 93 94 96 97 107 108 109 110 111 112 114 115 116 117 118 119 120 121 124 126 129 130 131 132 135 145 146 147 148 **P**5 8 **S** West Tennessee Healthcare, Jackson, TN
Primary Contact: Bobby Arnold, President and Chief Executive Officer
COO: James E. Ross, Vice President and Chief Operating Officer
CFO: Jeff Blankenship, CPA, Vice President and Chief Financial Officer
CMO: Robert Gilroy, M.D., Chief of Staff
CIO: Jeff Frieling, Vice President and Chief Information Officer
CHR: Wendie Carlson, Vice President, Human Resources
CNO: Tina Prescott, Vice President, Hospital Services
Web address: www.wth.org
**Control:** Hospital district or authority, Government, nonfederal **Service:** General Medical and Surgical

**Staffed Beds:** 635 **Admissions:** 26732 **Census:** 422 **Outpatient Visits:** 188420 **Births:** 3145 **Total Expense ($000):** 520297 **Payroll Expense ($000):** 195152 **Personnel:** 3996

★ **PATHWAYS OF TENNESSEE (444010)**, 238 Summar Drive, Zip 38301–3906; tel. 731/541–8200 **A**10 **F**4 5 29 35 38 44 57 59 98 99 100 101 102 103 104 132 134 **S** West Tennessee Healthcare, Jackson, TN
Primary Contact: Pam Henson, Executive Director
CFO: Jeff Blankenship, CPA, Chief Financial Officer
CMO: Vadankumar Patel, M.D., Medical Director
CIO: Jeff Frieling, Chief Information Officer
CHR: Wendy Carlson, Director Human Resources
CNO: Paula Terry, Director of Nursing
Web address: www.wth.net/pathways
**Control:** Hospital district or authority, Government, nonfederal **Service:** Psychiatric

**Staffed Beds:** 25 **Admissions:** 706 **Census:** 10 **Outpatient Visits:** 129230 **Births:** 0 **Total Expense ($000):** 17204 **Payroll Expense ($000):** 9327 **Personnel:** 209

✠ **TENNOVA HEALTHCARE – REGIONAL HOSPITAL OF JACKSON (440189)**, 367 Hospital Boulevard, Zip 38305–2080; tel. 731/661–2000, (Nonreporting) **A**1 3 9 10 **S** Community Health Systems, Inc., Franklin, TN
Primary Contact: Charles F. Miller, Chief Executive Officer
CFO: Richard Read, Chief Financial Officer
CMO: Michael Saridakis, M.D., Physician Adviser
CIO: Jimmy Anderson, Director of Information Systems
CHR: Barbara Euler, Director Human Resources
CNO: Jan Zimmer, R.N., Chief Nursing Officer
Web address: www.regionalhospitaljackson.com/Pages/Home.aspx
**Control:** Corporation, Investor–owned, for–profit **Service:** General Medical and Surgical

**Staffed Beds:** 129

## JAMESTOWN—Fentress County

✠ **JAMESTOWN REGIONAL MEDICAL CENTER (440083)**, 436 Central Avenue W., Zip 38556–3031, Mailing Address: P.O. Box 1500, Zip 38556–1500; tel. 931/879–8171, (Nonreporting) **A**1 9 10 20 **S** Community Health Systems, Inc., Franklin, TN
Primary Contact: Lynette Pritchett, Chief Executive Officer
CMO: Mark Hendrixson, M.D., Chief Medical Officer
CIO: Rick Smith, Director Information Systems
CHR: Shelia Russell, Director Human Resources
Web address: www.jamestownregional.org
**Control:** Corporation, Investor–owned, for–profit **Service:** General Medical and Surgical

**Staffed Beds:** 85

## JEFFERSON CITY—Jefferson County

**ST. MARY'S JEFFERSON MEMORIAL HOSPITAL** See Tennova Healthcare–Jefferson Memorial Hospital

✠ **TENNOVA HEALTHCARE–JEFFERSON MEMORIAL HOSPITAL (440056)**, 110 Hospital Drive, Zip 37760–5281; tel. 865/471–2500, (Nonreporting) **A**1 9 10 **S** Community Health Systems, Inc., Franklin, TN
Primary Contact: Colin McRae, Chief Executive Officer
CFO: Roseann M. Devault, Chief Financial Officer
CMO: Richard Carter, M.D., Chief of Staff
Web address: www.tennova.com/
**Control:** Corporation, Investor–owned, for–profit **Service:** General Medical and Surgical

**Staffed Beds:** 54

## JELLICO—Campbell County

✠ **JELLICO COMMUNITY HOSPITAL (440180)**, 188 Hospital Lane, Zip 37762–4400; tel. 423/784–7252 **A**1 9 10 **F**3 7 11 13 15 29 30 34 35 40 43 44 48 50 53 54 57 59 62 64 65 68 70 75 76 77 81 85 86 87 93 97 107 108 110 111 114 119 130 131 132 133 135 143 146 148 **P**6 **S** Community Hospital Corporation, Plano, TX
Primary Contact: Keith Richardson, Chief Executive Officer
COO: Pamela Hodge, R.N., Chief Nursing Officer and Coordinator Performance Improvement
CFO: Keith Richardson, Chief Financial Officer
CMO: Gregory Wilkens, M.D., Chief of Staff
CIO: Derek Brown, Chief Information Officer
CHR: Vince Vannett, Director Human Resources
CNO: Pamela Hodge, R.N., Registered Nurse and Chief Nursing Officer
Web address: www.jellicohospital.com
**Control:** Other not–for–profit (including NFP Corporation) **Service:** General Medical and Surgical

**Staffed Beds:** 31 **Admissions:** 1390 **Census:** 10 **Outpatient Visits:** 38912 **Births:** 186 **Total Expense ($000):** 24821 **Payroll Expense ($000):** 9476 **Personnel:** 264

## JOHNSON CITY—Washington County

✠ **FRANKLIN WOODS COMMUNITY HOSPITAL (440184)**, 300 MedTech Parkway, Zip 37604–2277; tel. 423/302–1000 **A**1 3 9 10 **F**3 11 13 29 30 34 35 40 44 50 56 59 68 70 74 75 76 77 79 81 86 87 93 97 107 108 111 114 115 118 119 126 130 143 146 147 **P**6 8 **S** Mountain States Health Alliance, Johnson City, TN
Primary Contact: Lindy P. White, Chief Executive Officer
CFO: Bradley Logan, Chief Financial Officer
CHR: Brooke Graham, Human Resources Manager
CNO: Rhonda Mann, Chief Nursing Officer
Web address: www.msha.com
**Control:** Other not–for–profit (including NFP Corporation) **Service:** General Medical and Surgical

**Staffed Beds:** 80 **Admissions:** 4993 **Census:** 55 **Outpatient Visits:** 42046 **Births:** 1156 **Total Expense ($000):** 59730 **Payroll Expense ($000):** 20225 **Personnel:** 404

TN

---

**Hospital, Medicare Provider Number, Address, Telephone, Approval, Facility, and Physician Codes, Health Care System**

★ American Hospital Association (AHA) membership
□ The Joint Commission accreditation
○ Healthcare Facilities Accreditation Program
◇ DNV Healthcare Inc. accreditation
⇑ Center for Improvement in Healthcare Quality Accreditation
△ Commission on Accreditation of Rehabilitation Facilities (CARF) accreditation

⊞ **JOHNSON CITY MEDICAL CENTER (440063)**, 400 North State of Franklin
Road, Zip 37604–6094; tel. 423/431–6111, (Includes NISWONGER CHILDREN'S
HOSPITAL, 400 North State Of Franklin Road, Zip 37604–6035;
tel. 423/431–6111; WOODRIDGE HOSPITAL, 403 State of Franklin Road,
Zip 37604–6034; tel. 423/431–7111; Grace Pereira, Interim Chief Executive
Officer), (Total facility includes 34 beds in nursing home–type unit) **A**1 2 3 5 8 9
10 **F**3 5 7 11 12 13 15 17 18 19 20 21 22 24 26 27 28 29 30 31 32 34 35
38 39 40 41 43 44 45 46 47 48 49 50 51 52 53 54 55 56 57 58 59 60 61
62 63 64 68 70 72 74 75 76 77 78 79 81 82 84 85 86 87 88 89 90 91 93
97 99 100 101 102 103 104 105 107 108 110 111 114 115 117 118 119
120 121 123 124 128 129 130 131 132 134 135 143 146 147 148 **P**6 8
**S** Mountain States Health Alliance, Johnson City, TN
Primary Contact: Melody Trimble, Chief Executive Officer
CFO: Richard Boone, Chief Financial Officer
CMO: Clay Runnels, Vice President Chief Medical Officer Washington County
CHR: Jamie Parsons, Human Resources Director
CNO: Rhonda Mann, Vice President and Chief Nursing Officer
Web address: www.msha.com
**Control:** Other not–for–profit (including NFP Corporation) **Service:** General
Medical and Surgical

**Staffed Beds:** 658 **Admissions:** 27965 **Census:** 421 **Outpatient Visits:**
260021 **Births:** 1347 **Total Expense ($000):** 396444 **Payroll Expense
($000):** 132758 **Personnel:** 2510

**NORTH SIDE HOSPITAL** See Franklin Woods Community Hospital

⊞ △ **QUILLEN REHABILITATION HOSPITAL (443033)**, 2511 Wesley Street,
Zip 37601–1723; tel. 423/283–0700, (Nonreporting) **A**1 7 10 **S** HEALTHSOUTH
Corporation, Birmingham, AL
Primary Contact: Brian Luff, Chief Executive Officer
Web address: www.quillenrehabilitationhospital.com/
**Control:** Other not–for–profit (including NFP Corporation) **Service:** Long–Term
Acute Care hospital

**Staffed Beds:** 60

### KINGSPORT—Sullivan County

⊞ **HEALTHSOUTH REHABILITATION HOSPITAL (443027)**, 113 Cassel Drive,
Zip 37660–3775; tel. 423/246–7240, (Nonreporting) **A**1 10 **S** HEALTHSOUTH
Corporation, Birmingham, AL
Primary Contact: Troy Clark, Chief Executive Officer
CFO: Natalie Tilson, Controller
CMO: James P. Little, M.D., Medical Director
CIO: Natalie Tilson, Controller
CHR: Joyce Jones, Director Human Resources
CNO: Debra Smith, Chief Nursing Officer
Web address: www.healthsouthkingsport.com
**Control:** Corporation, Investor–owned, for–profit **Service:** Rehabilitation

**Staffed Beds:** 50

☐ **INDIAN PATH MEDICAL CENTER (440176)**, 2000 Brookside Drive,
Zip 37660–4627; tel. 423/857–7000 **A**1 3 9 10 **F**3 8 11 13 15 18 20 22 26
28 29 30 31 34 35 36 38 40 44 45 46 47 49 50 51 53 54 56 57 58 59 60
62 63 64 65 68 70 71 73 74 75 76 77 78 79 81 85 86 87 91 97 107 108
110 111 114 115 116 117 118 119 121 123 129 130 132 135 143 144 146
147 148 **P**6 8 **S** Mountain States Health Alliance, Johnson City, TN
Primary Contact: Monty E. McLaurin, President and Chief Executive Officer
CFO: Steven Sawyer, Chief Financial Officer
CMO: Mark Wilkinson, M.D., Chief Medical Officer
CIO: Matthew Grissinger, Site Manager Information Systems
CHR: Kevin M. Smith, Director Human Resources
CNO: Susan Fannon, Chief Nursing Officer
Web address: www.msha.com
**Control:** Other not–for–profit (including NFP Corporation) **Service:** General
Medical and Surgical

**Staffed Beds:** 239 **Admissions:** 6151 **Census:** 83 **Outpatient Visits:** 117137
**Births:** 751 **Total Expense ($000):** 87716 **Payroll Expense ($000):** 32214
**Personnel:** 590

⊞ **WELLMONT HOLSTON VALLEY MEDICAL CENTER (440017)**, 130 West
Ravine Street, Zip 37660–3837, Mailing Address: P.O. Box 238,
Zip 37662–0238; tel. 423/224–4000 **A**1 2 3 5 9 10 13 19 **F**3 11 12 13 15 17
18 19 20 22 24 26 28 29 30 31 32 34 35 40 41 43 45 46 47 48 49 50 51
54 55 57 58 59 60 61 64 65 70 72 74 75 76 77 78 79 81 82 83 84 85 87
88 89 92 93 107 108 110 111 114 115 118 119 120 121 122 123 126 129
130 131 132 135 146 147 148 **S** Wellmont Health System, Kingsport, TN
Primary Contact: Tim Attebery, Chief Executive Officer
COO: Fred L. Pelle, FACHE, Chief Operating Officer
CFO: Dale Poe, Vice President Finance and Operations
CMO: Daniel Carlson, M.D., Chief Medical Officer
CIO: Will Showalter, Senior Vice President Information Technology
CHR: Hamlin J. Wilson, Senior Vice President Human Resources
CNO: Kathy Campbell, Interim Chief Nursing Officer
Web address: www.wellmont.org
**Control:** Other not–for–profit (including NFP Corporation) **Service:** General
Medical and Surgical

**Staffed Beds:** 345 **Admissions:** 17503 **Census:** 216 **Outpatient Visits:**
73483 **Births:** 1133 **Total Expense ($000):** 304570 **Payroll Expense
($000):** 77292 **Personnel:** 1698

### KNOXVILLE—Knox County

☐ **EAST TENNESSEE CHILDREN'S HOSPITAL (443303)**, 2018 Clinch Avenue,
Zip 37916–2393, Mailing Address: P.O. Box 15010, Zip 37901–5010;
tel. 865/541–8000, (Nonreporting) **A**1 3 5 9 10
Primary Contact: Keith D. Goodwin, President and Chief Executive Officer
COO: Rudolph McKinley, Jr., Vice President Operations and Chief Operating Officer
CFO: Zane Goodrich, Vice President Finance
CMO: Joe Childs, M.D., Vice President Medical Services
CIO: John Hanks, Director Information Systems
CHR: Sue Wilburn, Vice President Human Resources and Organizational
Development
CNO: Laura P. Barnes, MSN, Vice President Patient Care Services and Chief
Nursing Officer
Web address: www.etch.com
**Control:** Other not–for–profit (including NFP Corporation) **Service:** Children's
general

**Staffed Beds:** 152

⊞ △ **FORT SANDERS REGIONAL MEDICAL CENTER (440125)**, 1901 West
Clinch Avenue, Zip 37916–2307; tel. 865/541–1111, (Total facility includes 24
beds in nursing home–type unit) **A**1 2 7 9 10 **F**3 11 12 13 15 17 18 20 22 24
26 28 29 30 31 34 35 40 45 46 47 48 49 50 51 54 55 57 58 59 60 61 64
68 74 75 76 77 78 79 80 81 84 85 86 87 90 91 92 93 94 96 100 102 107
108 110 111 114 115 116 117 118 119 120 121 123 124 126 128 129 130
131 132 136 141 142 146 147 148 **S** Covenant Health, Knoxville, TN
Primary Contact: Keith Altshuler, President and Chief Administrative Officer
Web address: www.covenanthealth.com
**Control:** Other not–for–profit (including NFP Corporation) **Service:** General
Medical and Surgical

**Staffed Beds:** 384 **Admissions:** 15958 **Census:** 234 **Outpatient Visits:**
217733 **Births:** 2504 **Total Expense ($000):** 264593 **Payroll Expense
($000):** 85267 **Personnel:** 1532

**MERCY MEDICAL CENTER WEST** See Tennova Turkey Creek Medical Center

⊞ **PARKWEST MEDICAL CENTER (440173)**, 9352 Park West Boulevard,
Zip 37923–4325, Mailing Address: P.O. Box 22993, Zip 37933–0993;
tel. 865/373–1000 **A**1 2 9 10 **F**3 13 15 17 18 20 22 24 26 28 29 30 31 34
35 37 40 45 46 47 48 49 50 51 56 58 60 64 68 70 74 75 76 77 78 79 80
81 84 85 87 92 93 98 103 107 108 110 111 115 116 117 118 119 120 121
123 124 126 129 130 131 132 135 141 142 146 147 148 **S** Covenant Health,
Knoxville, TN
Primary Contact: Rick Lassiter, President and Chief Administrative Officer
COO: Emlyn Cobble, Vice President and Chief Support Officer
CFO: Scott Hamilton, Vice President and Chief Financial Officer
CHR: Randall Carr, Director Human Resources
CNO: Diane Oliver, R.N., Chief Nursing Officer
Web address: www.yesparkwest.com
**Control:** Other not–for–profit (including NFP Corporation) **Service:** General
Medical and Surgical

**Staffed Beds:** 297 **Admissions:** 16054 **Census:** 213 **Outpatient Visits:**
151208 **Births:** 1594 **Total Expense ($000):** 241835 **Payroll Expense
($000):** 76045 **Personnel:** 1389

⊞ **SELECT SPECIALTY HOSPITAL–KNOXVILLE (442012)**, 1901 Clinch Avenue,
4th Floor North, Zip 37916–2307; tel. 865/541–2615, (Nonreporting) **A**1 9 10
**S** Select Medical Corporation, Mechanicsburg, PA
Primary Contact: Steve Plumlee, Interim Chief Executive Officer
CFO: David Elledge, Controller
CMO: Jano Janoyan, M.D., Medical Director
CHR: Christina Blanton, Administrative Assistant and Human Resources
Coordinator
CNO: Danielle Connolly Robbins, Chief Nursing Officer
Web address: www.knoxville.selectspecialtyhospitals.com/
**Control:** Corporation, Investor–owned, for–profit **Service:** Long–Term Acute Care
hospital

**Staffed Beds:** 35

⊞ △ **TENNOVA PHYSICIANS REGIONAL MEDICAL CENTER (440120)**, 900
East Oak Hill Avenue, Zip 37917–4556; tel. 865/545–8000, (Includes TENNOVA
NORTH KNOXVILLE MEDICAL CENTER, 7565 Dannaher Way, Powell,
Zip 37849–4029; tel. 865/859–7000; Rob Followell, Chief Executive Officer;
TENNOVA TURKEY CREEK MEDICAL CENTER, 10820 Parkside Drive,
Zip 37934–1956; tel. 865/218–7092; Ben Youree, Chief Executive Officer;
TENNOVA TURKEY CREEK MEDICAL CENTER, 10820 Parkside Drive,
Zip 37922–1956; tel. 865/218–7090), (Nonreporting) **A**1 2 7 9 10 **S** Community
Health Systems, Inc., Franklin, TN
Primary Contact: Neil Heatherly, Interim Chief Executive Officer
CFO: Rhonda Maynard, Chief Financial Officer
CIO: Tom Lakins, Director Information Systems
CHR: Sarah M. Laboranti, Interim Director Human Resources
Web address: www.hma.com/content/physicians–regional–medical–center
**Control:** Corporation, Investor–owned, for–profit **Service:** General Medical and
Surgical

**Staffed Beds:** 233

**TN**

✠ **UNIVERSITY OF TENNESSEE MEDICAL CENTER (440015)**, 1924 Alcoa Highway, Zip 37920–6900; tel. 865/305–9000 **A**1 2 3 5 8 9 10 **F**3 6 8 9 11 12 13 15 17 18 19 20 21 22 23 24 25 26 27 28 29 30 31 34 35 36 39 40 41 43 44 45 46 47 48 49 50 51 53 54 55 56 57 58 59 60 61 64 65 70 71 72 74 75 76 77 78 79 81 82 84 85 86 87 88 91 92 93 94 96 97 100 102 103 107 108 109 110 111 114 115 116 117 118 119 120 121 123 124 126 129 130 131 132 135 138 141 144 145 146 147 148 **P**5 6
Primary Contact: Joseph Landsman, President and Chief Executive Officer
COO: David Hall, Senior Vice President and Chief Operating Officer
CFO: Thomas Fisher, Senior Vice President and Chief Financial Officer
CMO: John W. Lacey, III, M.D., Senior Vice President and Chief Medical Officer
CIO: Eileen Clark, Director Computer Services
CHR: Betty Gissel, Vice President Human Resources
CNO: Janell Cecil, R.N., Senior Vice President and Chief Nursing Officer
Web address: www.utmedicalcenter.org
**Control:** Other not–for–profit (including NFP Corporation) **Service:** General Medical and Surgical

Staffed Beds: 553 Admissions: 25397 Census: 412 Outpatient Visits: 254396 Births: 3296 Total Expense ($000): 683541 Payroll Expense ($000): 238211 Personnel: 3455

---

### LA FOLLETTE—Campbell County

✠ **TENNOVA HEALTHCARE–LAFOLLETTE MEDICAL CENTER (440033)**, 923 East Central Avenue, Zip 37766–2768, Mailing Address: P.O. Box 1301, Zip 37766–1301; tel. 423/907–1200, (Nonreporting) **A**1 9 10 20 **S** Community Health Systems, Inc., Franklin, TN
Primary Contact: Mark Cain, Chief Executive Officer
COO: Sara Heatherly–Lloyd, Chief Operating Officer
CFO: Wes Griffith, Chief Financial Officer
CMO: Jan Robbins, M.D., Chief of Staff
CIO: Dillon Ward, Management Information Systems Specialist
CHR: Bess Stout, Director Human Resources
CNO: Kathy R. Myers, MS, Chief Nursing Officer
Web address: www.tennova.com
**Control:** Corporation, Investor–owned, for–profit **Service:** General Medical and Surgical

Staffed Beds: 164

---

### LAFAYETTE—Macon County

★ ◇ **MACON COUNTY GENERAL HOSPITAL (441305)**, 204 Medical Drive, Zip 37083–1799, Mailing Address: P.O. Box 378, Zip 37083–0378; tel. 615/666–2147 **A**9 10 18 21 **F**3 15 18 29 30 34 35 40 57 59 65 75 77 81 86 93 107 111 114 119 128 130 132 133 146 **S** QHR, Brentwood, TN
Primary Contact: Dennis A. Wolford, FACHE, Chief Executive Officer
CFO: Thomas J. Kidd, Assistant Administrator and Chief Financial Officer
Web address: www.mcgh.net
**Control:** Other not–for–profit (including NFP Corporation) **Service:** General Medical and Surgical

Staffed Beds: 25 Admissions: 817 Census: 9 Outpatient Visits: 30949 Births: 2 Personnel: 128

---

### LAWRENCEBURG—Lawrence County

✠ **SOUTHERN TENNESSEE REGIONAL HEALTH SYSTEM–LAWRENCEBURG (440175)**, 1607 South Locust Avenue, Zip 38464–4011, Mailing Address: P.O. Box 847, Zip 38464–0847; tel. 931/762–6571, (Nonreporting) **A**1 9 10 **S** LifePoint Health, Brentwood, TN
Primary Contact: Jeff Noblin, FACHE, Chief Executive Officer
CFO: Kristie Taylor, Chief Financial Officer
CIO: Jason Weaver, Director Information Systems
CHR: Robert Augustin, Director Human Resources
CNO: Carol Laird, R.N., Chief Nursing Officer
Web address: www.crocketthospital.com
**Control:** Corporation, Investor–owned, for–profit **Service:** General Medical and Surgical

Staffed Beds: 99

---

### LEBANON—Wilson County

✠ **UNIVERSITY MEDICAL CENTER (440193)**, 1411 Baddour Parkway, Zip 37087–2513; tel. 615/444–8262, (Includes MCFARLAND SPECIALTY HOSPITAL, 500 Park Avenue, Zip 37087–3720; tel. 615/449–0500), (Nonreporting) **A**1 5 9 10 **S** Community Health Systems, Inc., Franklin, TN
Primary Contact: Matthew T. Caldwell, Chief Executive Officer
CMO: Andrew Jordan, M.D., Chief of Staff
CIO: Adrian Fung, Director Information Systems
Web address: www.universitymedicalcenter.com
**Control:** Corporation, Investor–owned, for–profit **Service:** General Medical and Surgical

Staffed Beds: 245

---

### LENOIR CITY—Loudon County

✠ **FORT LOUDOUN MEDICAL CENTER (440110)**, 550 Fort Loudoun Medical Center Drive, Zip 37772–5673; tel. 865/271–6000 **A**1 9 10 **F**3 15 18 28 29 30 34 35 40 50 57 59 68 70 77 79 81 85 93 102 107 108 110 111 114 118 119 130 135 146 148 **S** Covenant Health, Knoxville, TN
Primary Contact: Jeffrey Feike, President and Chief Administrative Officer
CNO: Teresa Fisher, R.N., Chief Nursing Officer
Web address: www.covenanthealth.com
**Control:** Other not–for–profit (including NFP Corporation) **Service:** General Medical and Surgical

Staffed Beds: 30 Admissions: 1814 Census: 20 Outpatient Visits: 60228 Births: 0 Total Expense ($000): 27049 Payroll Expense ($000): 10740 Personnel: 191

---

### LEWISBURG—Marshall County

✠ **MARSHALL MEDICAL CENTER (441309)**, 1080 North Ellington Parkway, Zip 37091–2227, Mailing Address: P.O. Box 1609, Zip 37091–1609; tel. 931/359–6241 **A**1 9 10 18 **F**3 11 15 29 30 34 40 45 50 56 57 59 68 75 77 81 92 93 104 108 110 111 114 119 129 131 132 133 135 146 **S** Maury Regional Health System, Columbia, TN
Primary Contact: Phyllis Brown, Chief Executive Officer
CFO: Kyle Jones, Controller
CMO: Tim Nash, M.D., Chief of Staff
CHR: Jeff M. Pierce, Manager Human Resources
CNO: Karen Martin, R.N., Chief Nursing Officer
Web address: www.mauryregional.com
**Control:** County–Government, nonfederal **Service:** General Medical and Surgical

Staffed Beds: 12 Admissions: 193 Census: 1 Outpatient Visits: 39377 Births: 0 Total Expense ($000): 13802 Payroll Expense ($000): 6186 Personnel: 134

---

### LEXINGTON—Henderson County

✠ **HENDERSON COUNTY COMMUNITY HOSPITAL (440008)**, 200 West Church Street, Zip 38351–2038; tel. 731/968–3646 **A**1 9 10 **F**7 15 18 29 30 34 35 40 50 57 59 68 75 79 81 82 86 87 93 97 107 108 110 111 114 119 120 127 132 145 146 **S** Community Health Systems, Inc., Franklin, TN
Primary Contact: Dale Humphrey, Chief Executive Officer
CFO: John Bostwick, Interim Chief Financial Officer
CHR: Linda Durham, Director Human Resources
CNO: Charlene Morgan, Chief Nursing Officer
Web address: www.hendersoncchospital.com
**Control:** Corporation, Investor–owned, for–profit **Service:** General Medical and Surgical

Staffed Beds: 45 Admissions: 411 Census: 23 Outpatient Visits: 46942 Births: 0

---

### LINDEN—Perry County

**PERRY COMMUNITY HOSPITAL (440040)**, 2718 Squirrel Hollow Drive, Zip 37096–3526; tel. 931/589–2121, (Nonreporting) **A**9 10
Primary Contact: John B. Avery, III, Administrator
**Control:** Other not–for–profit (including NFP Corporation) **Service:** General Medical and Surgical

Staffed Beds: 53

---

### LIVINGSTON—Overton County

✠ **LIVINGSTON REGIONAL HOSPITAL (440187)**, 315 Oak Street, Zip 38570–1728, Mailing Address: P.O. Box 550, Zip 38570–0550; tel. 931/823–5611, (Nonreporting) **A**1 9 10 **S** LifePoint Health, Brentwood, TN
Primary Contact: Ronald Tyrer, Interim Chief Executive Officer
CFO: Joseph Ross, Chief Financial Officer
CMO: Donnie Huff, M.D., Chief Medical Officer
CIO: Joseph Ross, Chief Financial Officer
CNO: Colleen Tuck, Chief Nursing Officer
Web address: www.MyLivingstonHospital.com
**Control:** Corporation, Investor–owned, for–profit **Service:** General Medical and Surgical

Staffed Beds: 114

---

**TN**

---

**Hospital, Medicare Provider Number, Address, Telephone, Approval, Facility, and Physician Codes, Health Care System**

★ American Hospital Association (AHA) membership  ◯ Healthcare Facilities Accreditation Program  ⇧ Center for Improvement in Healthcare Quality Accreditation
☐ The Joint Commission accreditation  ◇ DNV Healthcare Inc. accreditation  △ Commission on Accreditation of Rehabilitation Facilities (CARF) accreditation

---

## LOUISVILLE—Blount County

★ **PENINSULA HOSPITAL**, 2347 Jones Bend Road, Zip 37777–5213, Mailing Address: P.O. Box 2000, Zip 37777–2000; tel. 865/970–9800 **F**4 5 29 30 34 35 38 50 64 68 98 99 101 104 130 **P**6
Primary Contact: Elizabeth P. Clary, R.N., Vice President Behavioral Health
COO: Todd Roberts, Manager Business Operations
CFO: Scott Hamilton, Chief Financial Officer
CMO: Reggie Raman, M.D., Medical Director
CIO: Shelby Bowers, Director Marketing and Public Relations
CHR: Anita Rivera, Director Human Resources
CNO: Heather Jett, Director Patient Care Services
Web address: www.peninsula–hospital.org
**Control:** Other not-for-profit (including NFP Corporation) **Service:** Psychiatric

**Staffed Beds:** 137 **Admissions:** 4948 **Census:** 83 **Outpatient Visits:** 85404 **Births:** 0 **Total Expense ($000):** 30659 **Payroll Expense ($000):** 16013 **Personnel:** 312

## MADISON—Davidson County

★ **TRISTAR SKYLINE MADISON CAMPUS (440135)**, 500 Hospital Drive, Zip 37115–5032; tel. 615/769–5000, (Nonreporting) **A**9 **S** HCA, Nashville, TN
Primary Contact: Steve Otto, Chief Executive Officer
COO: Jill Howard, R.N., Chief Operating Officer
CFO: Bradley Schultz, Chief Financial Officer
CMO: Sunil Kaza, M.D., President Medical Staff
CIO: Troy Sypien, Director Information Technology and Systems
CHR: Robert A. Hooper, Director Human Resources
CNO: Laurie Turner, Chief Nursing Officer
Web address: www.skylinemadison.com
**Control:** Corporation, Investor–owned, for–profit **Service:** General Medical and Surgical

**Staffed Beds:** 284

## MANCHESTER—Coffee County

**MEDICAL CENTER OF MANCHESTER (441308)**, 481 Interstate Drive, Zip 37355–3108, Mailing Address: P.O. Box 1409, Zip 37349–4409; tel. 931/728–6354, (Nonreporting) **A**9 10 18
Primary Contact: Robert J. Couch, Chief Executive Officer
CMO: W. D. Daniel, D.O., Chief of Staff
CHR: Shelly Turner, Chief Clinical Services Officer
**Control:** Corporation, Investor–owned, for–profit **Service:** General Medical and Surgical

**Staffed Beds:** 25

**UNITED REGIONAL MEDICAL CENTER (440007)**, 1001 McArthur Drive, Zip 37355–2455, Mailing Address: P.O. Box 1079, Zip 37349–1079; tel. 931/728–3586, (Nonreporting) **A**9 10
Primary Contact: Martha McCormick, Chief Executive Officer
CFO: Pam Jernigan, Chief Financial Officer
CMO: James Van Winkle, M.D., Chief of Staff
CIO: Matt Burks, Director Information Technology
CHR: Sherry Holt, Director Human Resources
CNO: Stephanie Byars, Chief Nursing Officer
Web address: www.urmchealthcare.com
**Control:** Corporation, Investor–owned, for–profit **Service:** General Medical and Surgical

**Staffed Beds:** 36

## MARTIN—Weakley County

★ **BEHAVIORAL HEALTHCARE CENTER AT MARTIN (444005)**, 458 Hannings Lane, Zip 38237–3308; tel. 731/588–2830, (Nonreporting) **A**10 **S** Tennessee Health Management, Parsons, TN
Primary Contact: Carrie Brawley, Administrator
Web address: www.tnhealthmanagement.com/BHC/martin/
**Control:** Partnership, Investor–owned, for–profit **Service:** Psychiatric

**Staffed Beds:** 16

✠ **HEALTHSOUTH CANE CREEK REHABILITATION HOSPITAL (443030)**, 180 Mount Pelia Road, Zip 38237–3812; tel. 731/587–4231 **A**1 10 **F**30 56 82 90 94 95 96 130 132 143 **S** HEALTHSOUTH Corporation, Birmingham, AL
Primary Contact: Amy Vieth, Chief Executive Officer
CFO: Bethany Smith, Controller
CMO: Belinda Merritt, M.D., Medical Director
CIO: Jan Trowhill, Director Health Information Management Systems
CHR: Sharon Shihady, Director Human Resources
CNO: Lindsey Rotger, Chief Nursing Officer
Web address: www.healthsouthcanecreek.com
**Control:** Corporation, Investor–owned, for–profit **Service:** Rehabilitation

**Staffed Beds:** 40 **Admissions:** 733 **Census:** 26 **Outpatient Visits:** 0 **Births:** 0 **Total Expense ($000):** 8484 **Payroll Expense ($000):** 4633 **Personnel:** 97

✠ **TENNOVA HEALTHCARE – VOLUNTEER COMMUNITY HOSPITAL (440061)**, 161 Mount Pelia Road, Zip 38237–3811; tel. 731/587–4261, (Nonreporting) **A**1 9 10 **S** Community Health Systems, Inc., Franklin, TN
Primary Contact: Darrell Blaylock, Chief Executive Officer
CFO: Jason Draper, Chief Financial Officer
CMO: Elizabeth Lund, M.D., Chief of Staff
CHR: Tammie Bell, Director Human Resources
CNO: Donna Barfield, Chief Nursing Officer
Web address: www.volunteercommunityhospital.com
**Control:** Corporation, Investor–owned, for–profit **Service:** General Medical and Surgical

**Staffed Beds:** 65

## MARYVILLE—Blount County

✠ **BLOUNT MEMORIAL HOSPITAL (440011)**, 907 East Lamar Alexander Parkway, Zip 37804–5016; tel. 865/983–7211, (Total facility includes 76 beds in nursing home–type unit) **A**1 2 9 10 **F**3 4 10 11 12 13 15 17 18 20 22 26 28 29 30 31 32 35 38 40 43 45 46 49 53 54 56 57 59 62 63 64 67 68 70 74 75 76 77 78 79 80 81 84 85 86 87 90 93 96 97 98 99 100 101 102 103 104 105 107 108 110 111 114 115 116 117 118 119 120 121 122 123 125 126 128 129 130 131 132 134 135 144 146 147 148 **P**6
Primary Contact: Don Heinemann, Administrator and Chief Executive Officer
CFO: Jonathan Smith, Assistant Administrator and Chief Financial Officer
CMO: G. Harold Naramore, M.D., Chief Medical Officer and In house Legal Counsel
CIO: Clay Puckett, Assistant Administrator and Chief Information Officer
CHR: Chris Wilkes, MS, Director Human Resources
CNO: Sonya Newman, R.N., Chief Nursing Officer
Web address: www.blountmemorial.org
**Control:** County–Government, nonfederal **Service:** General Medical and Surgical

**Staffed Beds:** 314 **Admissions:** 12159 **Census:** 216 **Outpatient Visits:** 272692 **Births:** 713 **Total Expense ($000):** 225455 **Payroll Expense ($000):** 105021 **Personnel:** 2172

## MC MINNVILLE—Warren County

✠ **SAINT THOMAS RIVER PARK HOSPITAL (440151)**, 1559 Sparta Street, Zip 37110–1316; tel. 931/815–4000 **A**1 9 10 **F**8 11 13 15 28 29 30 34 35 40 50 51 53 57 59 64 70 74 75 76 79 81 89 90 93 107 110 111 114 115 119 128 129 130 133 146 **P**6 **S** Ascension Health, Saint Louis, MO
Primary Contact: Timothy W. McGill, Chief Executive Officer
COO: Joseph Mazzo, Chief Operating Officer
CFO: Christina Patterson, Chief Financial Officer
CMO: Randal D. Rampp, M.D., Chief Medical Officer
CIO: Jeff Johnson, Director Information Systems
CHR: Deeann Johnson, Director Human Resources
Web address: www.riverparkhospital.com
**Control:** Corporation, Investor–owned, for–profit **Service:** General Medical and Surgical

**Staffed Beds:** 85 **Admissions:** 2937 **Census:** 31 **Outpatient Visits:** 45789 **Births:** 395 **Total Expense ($000):** 44566 **Payroll Expense ($000):** 14653 **Personnel:** 345

## MCKENZIE—Carroll County

✠ **MCKENZIE REGIONAL HOSPITAL (440182)**, 161 Hospital Drive, Zip 38201–1636; tel. 731/352–5344 **A**1 9 10 **F**3 13 29 34 40 53 59 76 81 85 89 93 107 115 119 131 133 146 **S** Community Health Systems, Inc., Franklin, TN
Primary Contact: Michael G. Morrical, Chief Executive Officer
CFO: Kevin Harvey, Chief Financial Officer
CHR: Tammie Bell, Director Human Resources
CNO: Penny V. Kirby, MSN, Chief Nursing Officer
Web address: www.mckenzieregionalhospital.com
**Control:** Corporation, Investor–owned, for–profit **Service:** General Medical and Surgical

**Staffed Beds:** 35 **Admissions:** 1112 **Census:** 8 **Outpatient Visits:** 11906 **Births:** 370 **Total Expense ($000):** 14171 **Payroll Expense ($000):** 5179 **Personnel:** 99

*Many Facility Codes have changed. Please refer to the AHA Guide Code Chart.*  © 2015 AHA Guide

**TN**

**MEMPHIS—Shelby County**

✠ **BAPTIST MEMORIAL HOSPITAL – MEMPHIS (440048)**, 6019 Walnut Grove
Road, Zip 38120–2173; tel. 901/226–5000 **A**1 2 3 5 9 10 **F**3 6 8 12 17 18 19
20 21 22 24 26 28 29 30 31 34 35 36 37 40 41 45 46 47 48 49 53 54 56
57 58 59 63 64 65 68 70 74 75 77 78 79 80 81 82 84 85 86 87 91 92 93
107 108 109 111 112 114 115 116 117 118 119 120 121 123 124 126 130
132 135 136 137 143 146 148 **S** Baptist Memorial Health Care Corporation,
Memphis, TN
Primary Contact: Dana Dye, R.N., Vice President, Administrator and Chief
Executive Officer
CFO: Cyndi Pittman, Chief Financial Officer
CMO: Christian C. Patrick, M.D., Chief Medical Officer
CIO: Doug Reiselt, Vice President and Chief Information Officer
CHR: Jerry Barbaree, Director Human Resources
CNO: Becky Hunter, R.N., Chief Nursing Officer
Web address: www.baptistonline.org/memphis/
**Control:** Other not–for–profit (including NFP Corporation) **Service:** General
Medical and Surgical

**Staffed Beds:** 547 **Admissions:** 24737 **Census:** 426 **Outpatient Visits:**
123541 **Births:** 0 **Total Expense ($000):** 515344 **Payroll Expense ($000):**
155147 **Personnel:** 2667

★ **BAPTIST MEMORIAL HOSPITAL FOR WOMEN (440222)**, 6225 Humphreys
Boulevard, Zip 38120–2373; tel. 901/227–9000 **A**3 9 **F**3 7 8 12 13 15 18 19
20 21 22 23 24 25 26 27 28 29 30 31 32 34 35 36 37 38 41 45 46 47 48
49 52 53 54 55 56 57 58 59 60 61 64 65 66 68 70 71 72 73 74 75 76 77
78 79 81 82 83 84 85 86 87 89 92 93 96 107 108 109 110 111 112 113
114 115 116 117 118 119 120 121 123 124 126 129 130 132 135 136 137
143 144 145 146 147 148 **S** Baptist Memorial Health Care Corporation,
Memphis, TN
Primary Contact: Anita Vaughn, Administrator and Chief Executive Officer
CFO: Margaret Williams, Chief Financial Officer
CMO: Judi Carney, M.D., President Medical Staff
CIO: Melissa Nelson, Assistant Administrator
CHR: Karen Ingram, Director Human Resources
CNO: Carol Thetford, Chief Nursing Officer
Web address: www.baptistonline.org/womens/
**Control:** Other not–for–profit (including NFP Corporation) **Service:** Obstetrics and
gynecology

**Staffed Beds:** 140 **Admissions:** 6022 **Census:** 66 **Outpatient Visits:** 36793
**Births:** 4596 **Total Expense ($000):** 90914 **Payroll Expense ($000):** 31887
**Personnel:** 498

✠ **BAPTIST MEMORIAL RESTORATIVE CARE HOSPITAL (442010)**, 6019 Walnut
Grove Road, Zip 38120–2113; tel. 901/226–1400 **A**1 9 10 **F**1 3 29 68 75 130
148 **S** Baptist Memorial Health Care Corporation, Memphis, TN
Primary Contact: Janice Hill, R.N., Administrator
Web address: www.baptistonline.org/restorative–care/
**Control:** Other not–for–profit (including NFP Corporation) **Service:** Long–Term
Acute Care hospital

**Staffed Beds:** 30 **Admissions:** 262 **Census:** 24 **Outpatient Visits:** 0 **Births:**
0 **Total Expense ($000):** 16875 **Payroll Expense ($000):** 5104 **Personnel:**
79

☐ **DELTA MEDICAL CENTER (440159)**, 3000 Getwell Road, Zip 38118–2299;
tel. 901/369–8100 **A**1 9 10 **F**4 5 8 18 29 38 40 42 45 56 60 81 90 98 103
104 105 107 111 114 119 129 130 143 148 **P**5 **S** Acadia Healthcare
Company, Inc., Franklin, TN
Primary Contact: James W. Hahn, Chief Executive Officer
CFO: Mike Reynolds, Chief Financial Officer
CMO: David Richardson, M.D., Chief of Staff
CIO: Patrick Duffee, Director Medical Information Systems
CHR: Karyn Erickson, Director Human Resources
CNO: Donna Lanier, R.N., Chief Nursing Officer
Web address: www.deltamedcenter.com
**Control:** Corporation, Investor–owned, for–profit **Service:** Psychiatric

**Staffed Beds:** 173 **Admissions:** 4641 **Census:** 124 **Outpatient Visits:** 47036
**Births:** 0 **Total Expense ($000):** 47962 **Payroll Expense ($000):** 23354
**Personnel:** 436

✠ **HEALTHSOUTH REHABILITATION HOSPITAL MEMPHIS–NORTH (443031)**,
4100 Austin Peay Highway, Zip 38128–2502; tel. 901/213–5400, (Nonreporting)
**A**1 10 **S** HEALTHSOUTH Corporation, Birmingham, AL
Primary Contact: Marcia Taylor, Chief Executive Officer
CFO: Thaddeus Williams, Controller
CMO: Donald Sullivan, M.D., Medical Director
CHR: Adrienne Huntley, Director Human Resources
CNO: Charlotte Boyce, Chief Nursing Officer
Web address: www.healthsouthnorthmemphis.com
**Control:** Corporation, Investor–owned, for–profit **Service:** Rehabilitation

**Staffed Beds:** 40

✠ **HEALTHSOUTH REHABILITATION HOSPITAL OF MEMPHIS (443029)**, 1282
Union Avenue, Zip 38104–3414; tel. 901/722–2000 **A**1 3 5 10 **F**3 28 29 30 34
60 68 75 87 90 91 93 96 130 148 **S** HEALTHSOUTH Corporation,
Birmingham, AL
Primary Contact: Kevin Spears, Chief Executive Officer
CFO: Eric Gray, Chief Financial Officer
CMO: Jonathan D. Ellen, M.D., Medical Director
CHR: Sandra Milburn, Director Human Resources
CNO: Jennifer Ferrell, Chief Nursing Officer
Web address: www.healthsouthmemphis.com
**Control:** Partnership, Investor–owned, for–profit **Service:** Rehabilitation

**Staffed Beds:** 72 **Admissions:** 1348 **Census:** 48 **Outpatient Visits:** 6425
**Births:** 0 **Total Expense ($000):** 16978 **Payroll Expense ($000):** 8550
**Personnel:** 170

☐ **LAKESIDE BEHAVIORAL HEALTH SYSTEM (444004)**, 2911 Brunswick Road,
Zip 38133–4199; tel. 901/377–4700 **A**1 3 5 10 **F**4 5 34 38 54 56 98 99 100
101 102 103 104 105 106 130 132 **S** Universal Health Services, Inc., King of
Prussia, PA
Primary Contact: Joy Golden, Chief Executive Officer
CFO: Thomas Joyner, Chief Financial Officer
CMO: C. Hal Brunt, M.D., Medical Director
CIO: Jacob Arnett, Chief Information Technology Officer
CHR: Stacie Schroeppel, Director Human Resources
CNO: Lisa Weaver, Nurse Executive
Web address: www.lakesidebhs.com
**Control:** Corporation, Investor–owned, for–profit **Service:** Psychiatric

**Staffed Beds:** 319 **Admissions:** 8456 **Census:** 228 **Outpatient Visits:** 22350
**Births:** 0 **Total Expense ($000):** 38463 **Payroll Expense ($000):** 20117
**Personnel:** 456

**LE BONHEUR CHILDREN'S HOSPITAL** See Methodist Healthcare Memphis
Hospitals

☐ **MEMPHIS MENTAL HEALTH INSTITUTE (444001)**, 951 Court Avenue,
Zip 38103–2813, Mailing Address: P.O. Box 40966, Zip 38174–0966;
tel. 901/577–1800, (Nonreporting) **A**1 3 5 10
Primary Contact: Lisa Daniel, Chief Executive Officer
CFO: Donny Hornsby, Director Fiscal Services
CHR: Claudette Seymour, Director Personnel
Web address: www.tn.gov/mental/mhs/mhs2.html
**Control:** State–Government, nonfederal **Service:** Psychiatric

**Staffed Beds:** 75

✠ △ **MEMPHIS VETERANS AFFAIRS MEDICAL CENTER**, 1030 Jefferson
Avenue, Zip 38104–2193; tel. 901/523–8990 **A**1 3 5 7 8 **F**3 4 8 9 17 18 20
22 24 29 30 31 35 38 39 40 44 45 48 49 51 53 54 56 58 59 60 61 62 63
64 65 70 71 74 75 77 78 79 80 81 82 83 84 85 86 87 91 92 93 94 96 97
98 100 101 102 103 104 105 106 107 108 111 114 115 116 117 118 119
120 121 123 129 130 131 132 135 139 140 141 146 147 148 **S** Department
of Veterans Affairs, Washington, DC
Primary Contact: C. Diane Knight, M.D., Director and Chief Executive Officer
CFO: Kristi Depperman, Chief Financial Officer
CMO: Christopher Marino, M.D., Chief of Staff
CIO: Robert Page, III, Chief Information and Technology Officer
CHR: Natalie Brown, Chief Human Resources Management Services
CNO: Karen Gillette, Associate Director Patient Care Services
Web address: www.memphis.va.gov/
**Control:** Veterans Affairs, Government, federal **Service:** General Medical and
Surgical

**Staffed Beds:** 251 **Admissions:** 3302 **Census:** 79 **Outpatient Visits:** 639872
**Births:** 0 **Total Expense ($000):** 420261 **Payroll Expense ($000):** 176758
**Personnel:** 2299

☐ **METHODIST EXTENDED CARE HOSPITAL (442013)**, 225 South Claybrook
Street, Zip 38104–3537; tel. 901/516–2595 **A**1 10 **F**1 3 18 29 30 35 38 44
56 60 68 74 75 77 82 84 86 87 130 132 148 **S** Methodist Le Bonheur
Healthcare, Memphis, TN
Primary Contact: Sandra Bailey–DeLeeuw, Chief Executive Officer
COO: Sandra Hugueley, Assistant Administrator and Chief Nursing Officer
CFO: Alison Moore, Chief Financial Officer
CMO: Hany Mounir Habashy, M.D., Chief Medical Director
CHR: Mayzelle Moore, Director Human Resources
CNO: Sandra Hugueley, Assistant Administrator and Chief Nursing Officer
Web address: www.methodisthealth.org
**Control:** Other not–for–profit (including NFP Corporation) **Service:** Long–Term
Acute Care hospital

**Staffed Beds:** 36 **Admissions:** 453 **Census:** 31 **Outpatient Visits:** 0 **Births:**
0 **Total Expense ($000):** 15875 **Payroll Expense ($000):** 7244 **Personnel:**
117

---

**Hospital, Medicare Provider Number, Address, Telephone, Approval, Facility, and Physician Codes, Health Care System**

★ American Hospital Association (AHA) membership    ○ Healthcare Facilities Accreditation Program    ⇑ Center for Improvement in Healthcare Quality Accreditation
☐ The Joint Commission accreditation    ◇ DNV Healthcare Inc. accreditation    △ Commission on Accreditation of Rehabilitation Facilities (CARF) accreditation

TN

**TN**

☐ **METHODIST HEALTHCARE MEMPHIS HOSPITALS (440049)**, 1265 Union Avenue, Zip 38104–3415; tel. 901/516–7000, (Includes LE BONHEUR CHILDREN'S HOSPITAL, 50 North Dunlap Street, Zip 38103; tel. 901/287–5437; Meri Armour, Chief Executive Officer; METHODIST HEALTHCARE–NORTH HOSPITAL, 3960 New Covington Pike, Zip 38128; tel. 901/384–5389; Gyasi Chisley, Chief Executive Officer; METHODIST HEALTHCARE–SOUTH HOSPITAL, 1300 Wesley Drive, Zip 38116; tel. 901/516–3081; James L. Robinson, III, PsyD, Chief Executive Officer; METHODIST LE BONHEUR GERMANTOWN HOSPITAL, 7691 Poplar Avenue, Germantown, Zip 38138; tel. 901/516–6000; William A. Kenley, Chief Executive Officer) **A**1 2 3 5 8 9 10 **F**3 7 8 9 11 12 13 15 17 18 19 20 21 22 23 24 25 26 27 28 29 30 31 32 34 35 37 38 39 40 41 43 44 45 46 47 48 49 50 54 55 56 57 58 59 60 61 64 65 68 70 71 72 73 74 75 76 78 79 80 81 82 84 85 86 87 88 89 92 93 94 96 97 98 99 100 101 102 103 104 105 107 108 110 111 112 113 114 115 117 118 119 120 121 123 126 129 130 131 132 134 135 136 138 139 141 142 143 144 146 147 148 **P**5 6 8 **S** Methodist Le Bonheur Healthcare, Memphis, TN
Primary Contact: Michael O. Ugwueke, President and Chief Executive Officer
COO: James R. Carter, Jr., Chief Operating Officer
CFO: Chris J. McLean, Chief Financial Officer
CMO: Robin Womeodu, M.D., Chief Medical Officer
CIO: Andy Fowler, Senior Vice President Information Systems
CHR: Carol Ross–Spang, Senior Vice President
Web address: www.methodisthealth.org
**Control:** Other not–for–profit (including NFP Corporation) **Service:** General Medical and Surgical

**Staffed Beds:** 1446 **Admissions:** 62342 **Census:** 917 **Outpatient Visits:** 599253 **Births:** 5635 **Total Expense ($000):** 1380839 **Payroll Expense ($000):** 438468 **Personnel:** 9602

☒ **REGIONAL ONE HEALTH (440152)**, 877 Jefferson Avenue, Zip 38103–2897; tel. 901/545–7100, (Nonreporting) **A**1 3 5 8 9 10
Primary Contact: Reginald W. Coopwood, M.D., President and Chief Executive Officer
COO: Rob Sumter, Executive Vice President and Chief Operating Officer
CFO: Rick Wagers, Senior Executive Vice President and Chief Financial Officer
CIO: Rob Sumter, Executive Vice President and Chief Operation Officer
CHR: Sarah Colley, Senior Vice President Human Resources
CNO: Pam Castleman, MSN, Chief Nursing Officer
Web address: www.regionalonehealth.org
**Control:** Other not–for–profit (including NFP Corporation) **Service:** General Medical and Surgical

**Staffed Beds:** 348

**REGIONAL ONE HEALTH EXTENDED CARE HOSPITAL**, 890 Madison Avenue, Turner Tower, Zip 38103–3409; tel. 901/515–3000, (Nonreporting)
Primary Contact: Mark Kelly, Administrator
CNO: Paula Harrell, Chief Nursing Officer
Web address: www.regionalonehealth.org/extended–care–hospital/
**Control:** Other not–for–profit (including NFP Corporation) **Service:** Long–Term Acute Care hospital

**Staffed Beds:** 25

☒ **SAINT FRANCIS HOSPITAL (440183)**, 5959 Park Avenue, Zip 38119–5198, Mailing Address: P.O. Box 171808, Zip 38187–1808; tel. 901/765–1000 **A**1 2 3 5 9 10 **F**3 8 11 12 13 15 17 18 20 22 24 26 28 29 30 31 34 35 38 39 40 44 45 46 47 48 49 50 51 54 56 57 58 59 64 68 70 72 74 75 76 77 78 79 81 82 84 85 86 87 90 93 96 97 98 99 100 101 102 103 104 107 108 110 111 114 115 118 119 121 123 124 126 129 130 131 132 143 146 147 148 **S** TENET Healthcare Corporation, Dallas, TX
Primary Contact: David L. Archer, Chief Executive Officer
CFO: Bradley Robertson, Chief Financial Officer
CIO: Keith Scarbrough, Chief Information Officer
CHR: Keith Stanhill, Chief Human Resources Officer
CNO: Terri L. Stewart, R.N., Chief Nursing Officer
Web address: www.saintfrancishosp.com
**Control:** Corporation, Investor–owned, for–profit **Service:** General Medical and Surgical

**Staffed Beds:** 511 **Admissions:** 15982 **Census:** 241 **Outpatient Visits:** 98939 **Births:** 1469 **Total Expense ($000):** 257611 **Payroll Expense ($000):** 74116 **Personnel:** 1383

☒ **SELECT SPECIALTY HOSPITAL–MEMPHIS (442014)**, 5959 Park Avenue, 12th Floor, Zip 38119–5200; tel. 901/765–1245, (Nonreporting) **A**1 9 10 **S** Select Medical Corporation, Mechanicsburg, PA
Primary Contact: Patricia A. Rice, Chief Executive Officer
Web address: www.selectspecialtyhospitals.com/company/locations/memphis.aspx
**Control:** Corporation, Investor–owned, for–profit **Service:** Long–Term Acute Care hospital

**Staffed Beds:** 39

☒ **ST. JUDE CHILDREN'S RESEARCH HOSPITAL (443302)**, 262 Danny Thomas Place, Zip 38105–3678; tel. 901/595–3300, (Nonreporting) **A**1 3 5 9 10
Primary Contact: James Downing, M.D., Chief Executive Officer
CFO: Mike Canarios, Vice President and Chief Financial Officer
CIO: Clayton Naeve, Vice President and Chief Information Officer
CHR: Mary Anna Quinn, Vice President
Web address: www.stjude.org
**Control:** Other not–for–profit (including NFP Corporation) **Service:** Children's other specialty

**Staffed Beds:** 56

**VETERANS AFFAIRS MEDICAL CENTER** See Memphis Veterans Affairs Medical Center

**MILAN—Gibson County**

☒ **MILAN GENERAL HOSPITAL (440060)**, 4039 Highland Street, Zip 38358–3483; tel. 731/686–1591 **A**1 9 10 **F**3 15 29 30 35 40 44 45 57 59 64 68 70 81 85 87 107 110 114 119 130 132 133 146 **S** West Tennessee Healthcare, Jackson, TN
Primary Contact: Sherry Scruggs, Administrator
CMO: Joe Appleton, M.D., Chief of Surgery
CNO: Carolyn Drake, Director of Nursing
Web address: www.wth.org
**Control:** Hospital district or authority, Government, nonfederal **Service:** General Medical and Surgical

**Staffed Beds:** 28 **Admissions:** 411 **Census:** 5 **Outpatient Visits:** 12413 **Births:** 1 **Total Expense ($000):** 8453 **Payroll Expense ($000):** 3439 **Personnel:** 72

**MORRISTOWN—Hamblen County**

☒ **LAKEWAY REGIONAL HOSPITAL (440067)**, 726 McFarland Street, Zip 37814–3990; tel. 423/586–2302, (Nonreporting) **A**1 9 10 19 **S** Community Health Systems, Inc., Franklin, TN
Primary Contact: Clyde Wood, Chief Executive Officer
CMO: Paul Cardali, M.D., Chief of Staff
CHR: Deirdre Helton, Director Human Resources
Web address: www.tennova.com
**Control:** Corporation, Investor–owned, for–profit **Service:** General Medical and Surgical

**Staffed Beds:** 135

☒ **MORRISTOWN–HAMBLEN HEALTHCARE SYSTEM (440030)**, 908 West Fourth North Street, Zip 37814–3894, Mailing Address: P.O. Box 1178, Zip 37816–1178; tel. 423/492–9000 **A**1 5 9 10 **F**3 11 13 15 18 19 20 22 26 28 29 30 31 34 35 40 45 46 47 49 50 56 57 59 60 64 74 76 78 79 80 81 85 93 98 102 103 107 108 110 111 114 115 117 118 119 121 123 129 141 142 146 147 148 **S** Covenant Health, Knoxville, TN
Primary Contact: Gordon Lintz, Chief Administrative Officer
CFO: Amy Herndon, Director Finance
CIO: Mike Ward, Chief Information Officer
CNO: Dedra Whitaker, R.N., Chief Nursing Officer
Web address: www.mhhs1.org
**Control:** Other not–for–profit (including NFP Corporation) **Service:** General Medical and Surgical

**Staffed Beds:** 131 **Admissions:** 6479 **Census:** 71 **Outpatient Visits:** 87350 **Births:** 915 **Total Expense ($000):** 76820 **Payroll Expense ($000):** 28535 **Personnel:** 543

**MOUNTAIN CITY—Johnson County**

★ **JOHNSON COUNTY COMMUNITY HOSPITAL (441304)**, 1901 South Shady Street, Zip 37683–2271; tel. 423/727–1100 **A**5 9 10 18 **F**3 15 18 28 30 34 35 40 44 50 57 62 64 68 87 93 97 104 107 108 110 111 114 119 127 **P**6 8 **S** Mountain States Health Alliance, Johnson City, TN
Primary Contact: Chastity Trivette, Chief Executive Officer
CNO: Helen Pardue, Interim Chief Nursing Officer
Web address: www.msha.com
**Control:** Other not–for–profit (including NFP Corporation) **Service:** General Medical and Surgical

**Staffed Beds:** 2 **Admissions:** 14 **Census:** 1 **Outpatient Visits:** 41361 **Births:** 0 **Total Expense ($000):** 8176 **Payroll Expense ($000):** 4075 **Personnel:** 63

*Many Facility Codes have changed. Please refer to the AHA Guide Code Chart.*

## MOUNTAIN HOME— County

⊞ **JAMES H. QUILLEN VETERANS AFFAIRS MEDICAL CENTER**, Corner of Lamont & Veterans Way, Zip 37684, Mailing Address: P.O. Box 4000, Zip 37684–4000; tel. 423/926–1171, (Nonreporting) **A**1 2 3 5 **S** Department of Veterans Affairs, Washington, DC
Primary Contact: Charlene S. Ehret, FACHE, Director
CFO: Sandra Nash, Chief Fiscal Service
CMO: David Hecht, M.D., Chief of Staff
CIO: Karen Perry, Chief Information Resource Management Services
CHR: John Henderson, Chief Human Resources Management
CNO: Linda M. McConnell, R.N., Associate Medical Center Director Patient Care Services
Web address: www.mountainhome.va.gov/
**Control:** Veterans Affairs, Government, federal **Service:** General Medical and Surgical

**Staffed Beds:** 98

## MURFREESBORO—Rutherford County

**ALVIN C. YORK CAMPUS** See Tennessee Valley Healthcare System, Nashville

⊞ **SAINT THOMAS RUTHERFORD HOSPITAL (440053)**, 1700 Medical Center Parkway, Zip 37129–2245; tel. 615/396–4100, (Nonreporting) **A**1 2 3 5 9 10 **S** Ascension Health, Saint Louis, MO
Primary Contact: Gordon B. Ferguson, President and Chief Executive Officer
COO: Elizabeth Lemons, Chief Operating Officer
CFO: Larry Spratlin, Chief Financial Officer
CMO: Scott Corlew, M.D., Chief Medical Officer
CHR: Carol Bragdon, Director Human Resources
CNO: Stacey Beaven, R.N., Chief Nursing Officer
Web address: www.mtmc.org
**Control:** Church–operated, Nongovernment, not–for profit **Service:** General Medical and Surgical

**Staffed Beds:** 286

☐ **TRUSTPOINT HOSPITAL (440231)**, 1009 North Thompson Lane, Zip 37129–4351; tel. 615/867–1111, (Nonreporting) **A**1 10 **S** Polaris Hospital Company, Brentwood, TN
Primary Contact: Jeffrey Woods, Chief Executive Officer
Web address: www.trustpointhospital.com
**Control:** Partnership, Investor–owned, for–profit **Service:** Rehabilitation

**Staffed Beds:** 60

## NASHVILLE—Davidson County

**CENTENNIAL MEDICAL CENTER** See TriStar Centennial Medical Center

⊞ **KINDRED HOSPITAL–NASHVILLE (442006)**, 1412 County Hospital Road, Zip 37218–3007; tel. 615/687–2600, (Nonreporting) **A**1 10 **S** Kindred Healthcare, Louisville, KY
Primary Contact: William P. Macri, Chief Executive Officer
CFO: Philip L. Jones, Chief Financial Officer
CMO: Clyde Heflin, M.D., Chief Medical Officer
CHR: Robyn Dunman, Coordinator Human Resources
CNO: Tom Rone, Chief Clinical Officer
Web address: www.khnashville.com/
**Control:** Corporation, Investor–owned, for–profit **Service:** Long–Term Acute Care hospital

**Staffed Beds:** 58

☐ **MIDDLE TENNESSEE MENTAL HEALTH INSTITUTE (444014)**, 221 Stewarts Ferry Pike, Zip 37214–3325; tel. 615/902–7535 **A**1 3 5 10 **F**3 29 30 75 98 101 102 103 106 130
Primary Contact: Bob Micinski, Chief Executive Officer
CFO: Mark Stanley, Director Fiscal Services
CMO: Mohammad S. Jahan, M.D., Clinical Director
CHR: Margie Dunn, Director Human Resources
Web address: www.tn.gov/mental/mhs/mhs2.html
**Control:** State–Government, nonfederal **Service:** Psychiatric

**Staffed Beds:** 207 **Admissions:** 3642 **Census:** 177 **Outpatient Visits:** 0 **Births:** 0 **Total Expense ($000):** 45396 **Payroll Expense ($000):** 24032 **Personnel:** 516

**MONROE CARELL JR. CHILDREN'S HOSPITAL AT VANDERBILT** See Vanderbilt Hospital and Clinics

☐ **NASHVILLE GENERAL HOSPITAL (440111)**, 1818 Albion Street, Zip 37208–2918; tel. 615/341–4000, (Nonreporting) **A**1 2 3 5 9 10
Primary Contact: Joseph Webb, Chief Executive Officer
CFO: Robert Lonis, Interim Chief Financial Officer
CMO: Chike Nzerue, M.D., Chief Medical Officer
CIO: Chris Whorley, Chief Information Officer
CHR: Diana Wohlfardt, Director Human Resources
CNO: Leonora Collins, Chief Nursing Officer
Web address: www.nashvilleha.org
**Control:** City–County, Government, nonfederal **Service:** General Medical and Surgical

**Staffed Beds:** 116

⊞ **SAINT THOMAS HOSPITAL FOR SPINAL SURGERY (440218)**, 2011 Murphy Avenue, Suite 400, Zip 37203–2065; tel. 615/341–7500, (Nonreporting) **A**1 9 10 **S** Ascension Health, Saint Louis, MO
Primary Contact: Kathy Watson, R.N., Administrator and Chief Nursing Officer
CFO: Angie Crow, Director Finance
CMO: Carl Hampf, M.D., Chief Medical Officer
Web address: www.hospitalforspinalsurgery.com
**Control:** Partnership, Investor–owned, for–profit **Service:** General Medical and Surgical

**Staffed Beds:** 23

⊞ **SAINT THOMAS MIDTOWN HOSPITAL (440133)**, 2000 Church Street, Zip 37236–0002; tel. 615/284–5555, (Nonreporting) **A**1 2 3 5 9 10 **S** Ascension Health, Saint Louis, MO
Primary Contact: Don King, Chief Executive Officer
COO: Renee A. Kessler, Chief Operating Officer
CFO: Carrie Teaford, Vice President Finance
CMO: William Thompson, M.D., Chief Medical Officer
CIO: Jim Drew, Chief Information Officer
CHR: Martha Underwood, Chief Human Resources Officer
Web address: www.sths.com
**Control:** Other not–for–profit (including NFP Corporation) **Service:** General Medical and Surgical

**Staffed Beds:** 425

⊞ **SAINT THOMAS WEST HOSPITAL (440082)**, 4220 Harding Road, Zip 37205–2095, Mailing Address: P.O. Box 380, Zip 37202–0380; tel. 615/222–2111, (Nonreporting) **A**1 2 3 5 9 10 **S** Ascension Health, Saint Louis, MO
Primary Contact: Don King, Chief Executive Officer
CFO: Lisa Davis, Vice President Finance
CMO: Dale Batchelor, M.D., Chief Medical Officer
CIO: Randy Cox, Vice President and Chief Information Officer
CHR: Bud Wood, Chief Human Resources Officer
CNO: Jennifer Elliott, Chief Nursing Officer
Web address: www.stthomas.org
**Control:** Church–operated, Nongovernment, not–for profit **Service:** General Medical and Surgical

**Staffed Beds:** 395

⊞ **SELECT SPECIALTY HOSPITAL–NASHVILLE (442011)**, 2000 Hayes Street, Zip 37203–2318; tel. 615/284–4599, (Nonreporting) **A**1 9 10 **S** Select Medical Corporation, Mechanicsburg, PA
Primary Contact: Jennifer Causey, Chief Executive Officer
CNO: Karen Cagle, Chief Nursing Officer
Web address: www.selectspecialtyhospitals.com/company/locations/nashville.aspx
**Control:** Corporation, Investor–owned, for–profit **Service:** Long–Term Acute Care hospital

**Staffed Beds:** 47

**TN**

---

**Hospital, Medicare Provider Number, Address, Telephone, Approval, Facility, and Physician Codes, Health Care System**

★ American Hospital Association (AHA) membership ◯ Healthcare Facilities Accreditation Program ⇑ Center for Improvement in Healthcare Quality Accreditation
☐ The Joint Commission accreditation ◇ DNV Healthcare Inc. accreditation △ Commission on Accreditation of Rehabilitation Facilities (CARF) accreditation

---

✠ **TENNESSEE VALLEY HEALTHCARE SYSTEM**, 1310 24th Avenue South, Zip 37212–2637; tel. 615/327–4751, (Includes ALVIN C. YORK CAMPUS, 3400 Lebanon Pike, Murfreesboro, Zip 37129–1236; tel. 615/867–6000; NASHVILLE CAMPUS, 1310 24th Avenue South, tel. 615/327–4751), (Total facility includes 238 beds in nursing home–type unit) **A**1 2 3 5 8 **F**1 3 5 12 15 17 18 20 22 24 26 28 30 31 38 39 40 45 54 56 57 58 60 62 63 64 70 74 75 77 78 79 81 82 83 84 87 90 91 92 93 94 97 98 100 102 103 104 107 108 110 111 114 115 116 117 118 119 129 130 135 136 142 143 146 147 148 **S** Department of Veterans Affairs, Washington, DC
Primary Contact: Juan A. Morales, R.N., MSN, Health System Director
COO: Suzanne Jene, Chief Operating Officer
CFO: Lynn Menthcoast, Chief Fiscal Service
CMO: Roger Jones, M.D., Interim Chief of Staff
CIO: Paul Mardy, Chief Information Technology Officer
CHR: Shirley F. Pettite, Chief Human Resources Officer
CNO: Janice M. Cobb, R.N., Chief Nursing Officer
Web address: www.tennesseevalley.va.gov
**Control:** Veterans Affairs, Government, federal **Service:** General Medical and Surgical

**Staffed Beds:** 546 **Admissions:** 11306 **Census:** 335 **Outpatient Visits:** 1000934 **Births:** 0 **Total Expense ($000):** 677048 **Payroll Expense ($000):** 299128 **Personnel:** 3553

✠ **TRISTAR CENTENNIAL MEDICAL CENTER (440161)**, 2300 Patterson Street, Zip 37203–1528; tel. 615/342–1000, (Includes TRISTAR CENTENNIAL WOMEN'S & CHILDREN'S, 2221 Murphy Avenue, Zip 37203; tel. 615/342–1000), (Nonreporting) **A**1 2 3 5 9 10 **S** HCA, Nashville, TN
Primary Contact: Heather J. Rohan, Chief Executive Officer
COO: Micki J. Slingerland, Chief Operating Officer
CFO: David A. Summers, Chief Financial Officer
CHR: Jennifer Burden, Human Resources Director
Web address: www.tristarcentennial.com
**Control:** Corporation, Investor–owned, for–profit **Service:** General Medical and Surgical

**Staffed Beds:** 641

✠ △ **TRISTAR SKYLINE MEDICAL CENTER (440006)**, 3441 Dickerson Pike, Zip 37207–2539; tel. 615/769–2000, (Nonreporting) **A**1 2 3 5 7 9 10 **S** HCA, Nashville, TN
Primary Contact: Steve Otto, Chief Executive Officer
CFO: Bradley Schultz, Chief Financial Officer
CMO: Sunil Kaza, M.D., President Medical Staff
CIO: Troy Sypien, Director Information Technology and Systems
CHR: Robert A. Hooper, Director Human Resources
CNO: Laurie Turner, Chief Nursing Officer
Web address: www.skylinemedicalcenter.com
**Control:** Corporation, Investor–owned, for–profit **Service:** General Medical and Surgical

**Staffed Beds:** 295

✠ **TRISTAR SOUTHERN HILLS MEDICAL CENTER (440197)**, 391 Wallace Road, Zip 37211–4859; tel. 615/781–4000, (Nonreporting) **A**1 2 9 10 **S** HCA, Nashville, TN
Primary Contact: Thomas H. Ozburn, Chief Executive Officer
COO: Richard Tumlin, Chief Operating Officer
CFO: John Porada, Chief Financial Officer
CIO: Ronnie Gannon, Director Information Services
CHR: Gary Briggs, Vice President Human Resources
CNO: Chris Staigl, Chief Nursing Officer
Web address: www.tristarsouthernhills.com
**Control:** Corporation, Investor–owned, for–profit **Service:** General Medical and Surgical

**Staffed Beds:** 87

✠ **VANDERBILT HOSPITAL AND CLINICS (440039)**, 1211 22nd Avenue North, Zip 37232–2102; tel. 615/322–5000, (Includes MONROE CARELL JR. CHILDREN'S HOSPITAL AT VANDERBILT, 2200 Children's Way, Zip 37232; tel. 615/936–1000; Luke Gregory, Chief Executive Officer; VANDERBILT PSYCHIATRIC HOSPITAL, 1601 23rd Avenue South, Zip 37212–3198; tel. 615/320–7770; William Parsons, D.O., Chief Administrative Officer) **A**1 2 3 5 8 9 10 **F**2 3 4 5 6 7 8 9 11 12 13 15 16 17 18 19 20 21 22 23 24 25 26 27 28 29 30 31 32 34 35 36 37 38 39 40 41 42 43 44 45 46 47 48 49 50 51 52 53 54 55 56 57 58 59 60 61 62 63 64 65 66 68 70 72 74 75 76 77 78 79 80 81 82 83 84 85 86 87 88 89 91 92 93 94 95 96 97 98 99 100 101 102 103 104 105 106 107 108 109 110 111 114 115 116 117 118 119 120 121 123 124 126 129 130 131 132 133 134 135 136 137 138 139 140 141 142 143 144 146 147 148 **P**6 **S** Vanderbilt Health, Nashville, TN
Primary Contact: David R. Posch, Chief Executive Officer
COO: Mitch Edgeworth, Adult Enterprise Chief Operating Officer
CFO: Cecelia B. Moore, CPA, Associate Vice Chancellor Finance
CMO: Paul Sternberg, M.D., Professor and Chairman
CIO: William Stead, Associate Vice Chancellor Health Affairs, Director Informatics Center and Chief Strategy and Information Officer
CHR: Traci Nordberg, Chief Human Resources Officer
CNO: Pam Jones, MSN, Associate Hospital Director and Chief Nursing Officer
Web address: www.mc.vanderbilt.edu
**Control:** Other not–for–profit (including NFP Corporation) **Service:** General Medical and Surgical

**Staffed Beds:** 1004 **Admissions:** 59112 **Census:** 850 **Outpatient Visits:** 1987609 **Births:** 4541 **Total Expense ($000):** 1893402 **Payroll Expense ($000):** 655909 **Personnel:** 13510

**VANDERBILT PSYCHIATRIC HOSPITAL** See Vanderbilt Hospital and Clinics

✠ **VANDERBILT STALLWORTH REHABILITATION HOSPITAL (443028)**, 2201 Childrens Way, Zip 37212–3165; tel. 615/320–7600, (Nonreporting) **A**1 3 5 9 10 **S** HEALTHSOUTH Corporation, Birmingham, AL
Primary Contact: Scott J. Peterson, Acting Chief Executive Officer
CFO: Peggy Belyeu, Controller
CMO: Jeffery Johns, M.D., Medical Director
CHR: Ruth Beasley, Director Human Resources
CNO: Karen Lasher, Chief Nursing Officer
Web address: www.vanderbiltstallworthrehab.com
**Control:** Corporation, Investor–owned, for–profit **Service:** Rehabilitation

**Staffed Beds:** 80

**VETERANS AFFAIRS TENNESSEE VALLEY HEALTHCARE SYSTEM** See Tennessee Valley Healthcare System

**NEWPORT—Cocke County**

**BAPTIST HOSPITAL OF COCKE COUNTY** See Tennova Newport Medical Center

✠ **TENNOVA NEWPORT MEDICAL CENTER (440153)**, 435 Second Street, Zip 37821–3799; tel. 423/625–2200, (Nonreporting) **A**1 9 10 **S** Community Health Systems, Inc., Franklin, TN
Primary Contact: Trevor Castaneda, Chief Executive Officer
CFO: Jon Richards, Chief Financial Officer
CMO: Larry Mathers, M.D., Chief of Staff
CNO: Tonia Hale, Chief Nursing Officer
Web address: www.tennova.com
**Control:** Corporation, Investor–owned, for–profit **Service:** General Medical and Surgical

**Staffed Beds:** 47

**OAK RIDGE—Anderson County**

✠ **METHODIST MEDICAL CENTER OF OAK RIDGE (440034)**, 990 Oak Ridge Turnpike, Zip 37830–6976, Mailing Address: P.O. Box 2529, Zip 37831–2529; tel. 865/835–1000 **A**1 2 3 9 10 **F**3 11 13 15 17 18 20 22 24 26 28 29 30 31 34 35 37 40 45 46 47 48 49 50 51 54 57 58 59 60 64 68 70 74 75 76 77 78 79 80 81 84 85 86 87 92 93 102 107 108 110 111 114 115 118 119 120 121 123 124 126 129 130 132 135 141 142 146 148 **S** Covenant Health, Knoxville, TN
Primary Contact: Michael Belbeck, President and Chief Administrative Officer
COO: Connie Martin, Vice President and Chief Support Officer
CFO: Rick Carringer, Vice President and Chief Financial Officer
CMO: Mark Browne, M.D., Covenant Health, Senior Vice President and Chief Medical Officer
CIO: Mike Ward, Covenant Health, Senior Vice President and Chief Information Officer
CHR: Rick Akens, Director Human Resources and Labor Relations
CNO: Sue Harris, Vice President and Chief Nursing Officer
Web address: www.mmcoakridge.com
**Control:** Other not–for–profit (including NFP Corporation) **Service:** General Medical and Surgical

**Staffed Beds:** 210 **Admissions:** 10703 **Census:** 129 **Outpatient Visits:** 157377 **Births:** 608 **Total Expense ($000):** 156890 **Payroll Expense ($000):** 53343 **Personnel:** 895

**TN**

**RIDGEVIEW PSYCHIATRIC HOSPITAL AND CENTER (444003)**, 240 West Tyrone Road, Zip 37830–6571; tel. 865/482–1076, (Nonreporting) **A**10
Primary Contact: Brian Buuck, Chief Executive Officer
CFO: Mary Claire Duff, CPA, Chief Financial Officer
CMO: Renu Bhateja, M.D., President Medical Staff
CHR: Julie M. Wright, Director Human Resources
Web address: www.ridgeviewresources.com
**Control:** Other not–for–profit (including NFP Corporation) **Service:** Psychiatric

**Staffed Beds:** 20

### PARIS—Henry County

✠ **HENRY COUNTY MEDICAL CENTER (440132)**, 301 Tyson Avenue, Zip 38242–4544, Mailing Address: P.O. Box 1030, Zip 38242–1030; tel. 731/642–1220, (Total facility includes 150 beds in nursing home–type unit) **A**1 9 10 **F**3 7 8 11 13 15 18 20 28 29 30 31 32 34 35 39 40 44 51 53 54 57 59 62 63 64 65 67 68 70 71 76 77 78 79 81 82 85 86 87 89 93 98 102 103 107 108 110 111 114 118 119 121 126 128 129 130 131 132 133 135 146 148 **P**6
Primary Contact: Thomas H. Gee, Administrator
CFO: Lisa Casteel, Assistant Administrator and Chief Financial Officer
CIO: Pam Ridley, Director Information Systems
CHR: Edwin L. Ledden, Assistant Administrator and Director Human Resources
CNO: James Caldwell, R.N., Chief Nursing Officer
Web address: www.hcmc–tn.org
**Control:** Hospital district or authority, Government, nonfederal **Service:** General Medical and Surgical

**Staffed Beds:** 251 **Admissions:** 3722 **Census:** 138 **Outpatient Visits:** 80322 **Births:** 252 **Total Expense ($000):** 72632 **Payroll Expense ($000):** 29480 **Personnel:** 662

### PARSONS—Decatur County

☐ **DECATUR COUNTY GENERAL HOSPITAL (440070)**, 969 Tennessee Avenue South, Zip 38363–3700, Mailing Address: P.O. Box 250, Zip 38363–0250; tel. 731/847–3031, (Nonreporting) **A**1 9 10
Primary Contact: Scott Barber, Chief Executive Officer
CFO: Donna Hayes, Controller
CMO: Tom Hamilton, M.D., Chief of Staff
CHR: Shelley Bartholomew, Director Human Resources
Web address: www.dcgh.org
**Control:** County–Government, nonfederal **Service:** General Medical and Surgical

**Staffed Beds:** 40

### PIKEVILLE—Bledsoe County

**ERLANGER BLEDSOE HOSPITAL (441306)**, 71 Wheeler Avenue, Zip 37367, Mailing Address: P.O. Box 699, Zip 37367–0699; tel. 423/447–2112 **A**9 10 18 **F**3 11 15 18 28 29 30 34 35 38 40 41 42 44 50 54 56 57 59 61 63 64 65 66 67 68 75 82 84 86 87 92 93 97 102 103 107 110 114 119 127 128 130 131 133 135 144 146 147 148 **P**6 **S** Erlanger Health System, Chattanooga, TN
Primary Contact: Stephanie Boynton, Administrator
CMO: Arturo L. Quito, M.D., Chief of Staff
CIO: Debbie Rains, Coordinator Health Information Management
CHR: Patsy Brown, Site Coordinator Human Resources
Web address: www.erlanger.org
**Control:** Hospital district or authority, Government, nonfederal **Service:** General Medical and Surgical

**Staffed Beds:** 25 **Admissions:** 296 **Census:** 4 **Outpatient Visits:** 13896 **Births:** 0 **Total Expense ($000):** 8540 **Payroll Expense ($000):** 3480 **Personnel:** 89

### POWELL—Knox County

**MERCY MEDICAL CENTER NORTH** See Tennova North Knoxville Medical Center

✠ **SELECT SPECIALTY HOSPITAL–NORTH KNOXVILLE (442015)**, 7557B Dannaher Drive, Suite 145, Zip 37849–3568; tel. 865/512–2450, (Nonreporting) **A**1 9 10 **S** Select Medical Corporation, Mechanicsburg, PA
Primary Contact: Steve Plumlee, Chief Executive Officer
CFO: David Elledge, Controller
CMO: Jeff Summers, M.D., Medical Director
CIO: Steve Plumlee, Chief Executive Officer
CHR: Mallory Wilson, Administrative Assistant and Human Resources Coordinator
CNO: Nancy Johnson, Chief Nursing Officer
Web address: www.northknoxville.selectspecialtyhospitals.com/
**Control:** Corporation, Investor–owned, for–profit **Service:** Long–Term Acute Care hospital

**Staffed Beds:** 33

### PULASKI—Giles County

✠ **SOUTHERN TENNESSEE REGIONAL HEALTH SYSTEM–PULASKI (440020)**, 1265 East College Street, Zip 38478–4541; tel. 931/363–7531, (Nonreporting) **A**1 9 10 **S** LifePoint Health, Brentwood, TN
Primary Contact: James H. Edmondson, Chief Executive Officer
CFO: Donald Gavin, Chief Financial Officer
CMO: J. Michael Windland, M.D., Chief of Staff
CIO: Mitzi Foster, Director Information Services
CHR: Jane Petty, Director Human Resources
CNO: Sherry Sands, R.N., Chief Nursing Officer
Web address: www.hillsidehospital.com
**Control:** Corporation, Investor–owned, for–profit **Service:** General Medical and Surgical

**Staffed Beds:** 95

### RIPLEY—Lauderdale County

◇ **LAUDERDALE COMMUNITY HOSPITAL (441314)**, 326 Asbury Avenue, Zip 38063–5577; tel. 731/221–2200 **A**9 10 18 21 **F**3 11 15 28 29 30 34 35 40 45 57 59 64 74 75 77 79 81 85 87 93 107 114 119 130 132 133 134 135 146 148 **S** Rural Community Hospitals of America, Kansas City, MO
Primary Contact: Tammie H. Hardy, Chief Executive Officer
CFO: Scott A. Tongate, Chief Financial Officer
CMO: Syed A. Zaidi, M.D., Chief of Staff
CIO: Jim Vaden, Director Information Systems
CHR: Joan W. Simpson, Manager Human Resources
CNO: Michelle Simpson, Chief Nursing Officer and Quality Leader
Web address: www.lauderdalehospital.com/
**Control:** Corporation, Investor–owned, for–profit **Service:** General Medical and Surgical

**Staffed Beds:** 25 **Admissions:** 263 **Census:** 3 **Outpatient Visits:** 18459 **Births:** 0 **Total Expense ($000):** 14674 **Payroll Expense ($000):** 6292 **Personnel:** 163

### ROGERSVILLE—Hawkins County

✠ **WELLMONT HAWKINS COUNTY MEMORIAL HOSPITAL (440032)**, 851 Locust Street, Zip 37857–2407, Mailing Address: P.O. Box 130, Zip 37857–0130; tel. 423/921–7000 **A**1 5 9 10 **F**3 11 15 29 30 31 34 35 40 45 50 57 59 64 68 75 77 78 81 82 85 87 93 97 107 108 118 119 129 130 133 146 **S** Wellmont Health System, Kingsport, TN
Primary Contact: Rebecca Beck, President
CFO: Dale Poe, Vice President and Chief Financial Officer
CHR: Robin Poteete, Manager Human Resources
Web address: www.wellmont.org
**Control:** Other not–for–profit (including NFP Corporation) **Service:** General Medical and Surgical

**Staffed Beds:** 20 **Admissions:** 1057 **Census:** 8 **Outpatient Visits:** 36999 **Births:** 0 **Total Expense ($000):** 49682 **Payroll Expense ($000):** 6197 **Personnel:** 153

### SAVANNAH—Hardin County

★ ◇ **HARDIN MEDICAL CENTER (440109)**, 935 Wayne Road, Zip 38372–1904; tel. 731/926–8000, (Total facility includes 73 beds in nursing home–type unit) **A**9 10 21 **F**2 3 7 11 13 15 18 19 28 29 31 34 40 45 57 59 65 69 75 76 77 78 79 80 81 89 93 107 110 111 115 119 124 128 129 130 133 144 148 **P**6
Primary Contact: Nicholas P. Lewis, Chief Executive Officer
CFO: Leigh Ann Hughes, Chief Financial Officer
CMO: Gilbert M. Thayer, M.D., Chief Medical Staff
CIO: Jacob Bomar, Director Information Technology
CHR: Jimmy Davis, Director Human Resources
CNO: Jesse Wint, Director of Nursing
Web address: www.hardinmedicalcenter.org
**Control:** County–Government, nonfederal **Service:** General Medical and Surgical

**Staffed Beds:** 122 **Admissions:** 1697 **Census:** 79 **Outpatient Visits:** 54083 **Births:** 306 **Total Expense ($000):** 33984 **Payroll Expense ($000):** 14778 **Personnel:** 381

### SELMER—Mcnairy County

✠ **TENNOVA HEALTHCARE – MCNAIRY REGIONAL HOSPITAL (440051)**, 705 East Poplar Avenue, Zip 38375–1828; tel. 731/645–3221, (Nonreporting) **A**1 9 10 **S** Community Health Systems, Inc., Franklin, TN
Primary Contact: Pamela W. Roberts, Chief Executive Officer
CFO: Meredith Jones, Chief Financial Officer
CMO: Ryan Bartz, D.O., Chief of Staff
CHR: Linda Durham, Director Human Resources
Web address: www.mcnairyregionalhospital.com
**Control:** Other not–for–profit (including NFP Corporation) **Service:** General Medical and Surgical

**Staffed Beds:** 45

**TN**

---

**Hospital, Medicare Provider Number, Address, Telephone, Approval, Facility, and Physician Codes, Health Care System**

★ American Hospital Association (AHA) membership
☐ The Joint Commission accreditation
◯ Healthcare Facilities Accreditation Program
◇ DNV Healthcare Inc. accreditation
⇑ Center for Improvement in Healthcare Quality Accreditation
△ Commission on Accreditation of Rehabilitation Facilities (CARF) accreditation

## SEVIERVILLE—Sevier County

☒ **LECONTE MEDICAL CENTER (440081)**, 742 Middle Creek Road, Zip 37862–5019, Mailing Address: P.O. Box 8005, Zip 37864–8005; tel. 865/446–7000, (Total facility includes 54 beds in nursing home–type unit) **A**1 5 9 10 **F**3 11 13 15 18 20 28 29 30 31 34 35 40 45 50 51 53 57 59 61 64 67 68 70 75 76 77 78 79 81 85 87 93 107 110 111 114 119 120 121 123 124 128 129 130 131 135 146 147 **S** Covenant Health, Knoxville, TN
Primary Contact: Jennifer Hanson, MS, R.N., President and Chief Administrative Officer
COO: Rick Carringer, Vice President Finance and Support Services
CFO: Rick Carringer, Vice President Finance and Support Services
CMO: Stephen Dill, M.D., Chief of Staff
CIO: Amanda Paletz, Director Marketing and Public Relations
CHR: Derek Winkle, Director Human Resources
Web address: www.lecontemedicalcenter.com
**Control:** Other not–for–profit (including NFP Corporation) **Service:** General Medical and Surgical

**Staffed Beds:** 129 **Admissions:** 4773 **Census:** 83 **Outpatient Visits:** 117448 **Births:** 1071 **Total Expense ($000):** 67617 **Payroll Expense ($000):** 24130 **Personnel:** 440

## SEWANEE—Franklin County

**SOUTHERN TENNESSEE REGIONAL HEALTH SYSTEM–SEWANEE** See Southern Tennessee Regional Health System–Winchester, Winchester

## SHELBYVILLE—Bedford County

☒ **HERITAGE MEDICAL CENTER (440137)**, 2835 Highway 231 North, Zip 37160–7327; tel. 931/685–5433, (Nonreporting) **A**1 9 10 **S** Community Health Systems, Inc., Franklin, TN
Primary Contact: David V. Bunch, Chief Executive Officer
CFO: Mitchell Frank, Chief Financial Officer
CIO: Jonathon Willis, Director Information Services
CHR: Brian Woods, Director Human Resources
CNO: Vickie Vaughn, Chief Nursing Officer
Web address: www.heritagemedicalcenter.com
**Control:** County–Government, nonfederal **Service:** General Medical and Surgical

**Staffed Beds:** 70

## SMITHVILLE—Dekalb County

☒ **SAINT THOMAS DEKALB HOSPITAL (440148)**, 520 West Main Street, Zip 37166–1138, Mailing Address: P.O. Box 640, Zip 37166–0640; tel. 615/215–5000 **A**1 9 10 **F**3 15 17 18 26 29 30 31 34 35 40 43 45 47 48 57 59 64 65 70 74 75 77 78 79 81 85 89 90 91 93 107 108 111 114 119 129 133 **S** Ascension Health, Saint Louis, MO
Primary Contact: Susan Conley, Chief Executive Officer
CMO: Hugh Don Cripps, M.D., Chief of Staff
CHR: Gingie Braswell, Director Human Resources
CNO: Kimberly Frazier, Chief Nursing Officer
Web address: www.dekalbcommunityhospital.com
**Control:** Corporation, Investor–owned, for–profit **Service:** General Medical and Surgical

**Staffed Beds:** 56 **Admissions:** 941 **Census:** 9 **Outpatient Visits:** 21091 **Births:** 0 **Total Expense ($000):** 15885 **Payroll Expense ($000):** 6623

## SMYRNA—Rutherford County

☒ **TRISTAR STONECREST MEDICAL CENTER (440227)**, 200 StoneCrest Boulevard, Zip 37167–6810; tel. 615/768–2000, (Nonreporting) **A**1 2 9 10 **S** HCA, Nashville, TN
Primary Contact: Louis Caputo, Chief Executive Officer
COO: Andrew Tyrer, Chief Operating Officer
CFO: Joseph E. Bowman, Chief Financial Officer
CMO: William Mayfield, M.D., Chief of Staff
CHR: Cynthia Adams, Vice President Human Resources
CNO: Ruth Willard, Chief Nursing Officer
Web address: www.stonecrestmedical.com
**Control:** Corporation, Investor–owned, for–profit **Service:** General Medical and Surgical

**Staffed Beds:** 101

## SNEEDVILLE—Hancock County

★ **WELLMONT HANCOCK COUNTY HOSPITAL (441313)**, 1519 Main Street, Zip 37869–3657; tel. 423/733–5000 **A**9 10 18 **F**3 29 30 34 40 50 57 59 68 85 87 107 108 118 119 133 **S** Wellmont Health System, Kingsport, TN
Primary Contact: Rebecca Beck, President
COO: Eric Deaton, Executive Vice President, Chief Operating Officer and Corporate Operating
CFO: Regina Day, Director of Finance
CIO: Martha O'Regan Chill, Interim Chief Information Officer
CHR: Robin Poteete, Manager Human Resources
CNO: Phyllis Dossett, Director of Clinical Services
Web address: www.wellmont.org/Hospitals/Hancock–County–Hospital.aspx
**Control:** Other not–for–profit (including NFP Corporation) **Service:** General Medical and Surgical

**Staffed Beds:** 10 **Admissions:** 252 **Census:** 3 **Outpatient Visits:** 7936 **Births:** 0 **Total Expense ($000):** 5813 **Payroll Expense ($000):** 1776 **Personnel:** 39

## SPARTA—White County

☒ **SAINT THOMAS HIGHLANDS HOSPITAL (440192)**, 401 Sewell Road, Zip 38583–1299; tel. 931/738–9211, (Nonreporting) **A**1 9 10 **S** Ascension Health, Saint Louis, MO
Primary Contact: William Little, Chief Executive Officer
CFO: Rodney VanDonkelaar, Chief Financial Officer
CMO: Robert Knowles, M.D., Chief of Staff
CIO: Glenn Wade, Director Information Systems
CHR: Kent Frisbee, Director Human Resources
CNO: Gearline Copeland, R.N., Chief Nursing Officer
Web address: www.whitecountyhospital.com
**Control: Service:** General Medical and Surgical

**Staffed Beds:** 60

## SPRINGFIELD—Robertson County

☒ **NORTHCREST MEDICAL CENTER (440065)**, 100 North Crest Drive, Zip 37172–3961; tel. 615/384–2411, (Nonreporting) **A**1 9 10
Primary Contact: Randy Davis, Chief Executive Officer
CFO: Kim Pridgen, Chief Financial Officer
CMO: Tommy Crunk, M.D., Chief of Staff
CHR: Amber King, Director Human Resources
CNO: Angie Beard, Chief Nursing Officer
Web address: www.northcrest.com
**Control:** Other not–for–profit (including NFP Corporation) **Service:** General Medical and Surgical

**Staffed Beds:** 81

## SWEETWATER—Monroe County

☒ **SWEETWATER HOSPITAL (440084)**, 304 Wright Street, Zip 37874–2823; tel. 865/213–8200, (Nonreporting) **A**1 9 10
Primary Contact: Scott Bowman, Administrator
CFO: Debbie Thompson, Chief Financial Officer
CMO: Tracey Beverley, M.D., Chief Medical Staff
CIO: Tony Sharp, Supervisor Information System
CHR: Lucretia Santelli, Director Human Resources
CNO: Andrea Henry, Director of Nursing
Web address: www.sweetwaterhospital.org
**Control:** Other not–for–profit (including NFP Corporation) **Service:** General Medical and Surgical

**Staffed Beds:** 59

## TAZEWELL—Claiborne County

☒ **CLAIBORNE MEDICAL CENTER (440057)**, 1850 Old Knoxville Road, Zip 37879–3625; tel. 423/626–4211, (Nonreporting) **A**1 9 10 20 **S** Covenant Health, Knoxville, TN
Primary Contact: Patricia P. Ketterman, R.N., President and Chief Administrative Officer
CFO: Tracee McFarland, Chief Financial Officer
CHR: Susan Stone, Director Human Resources
Web address: www.claibornehospital.org
**Control:** County–Government, nonfederal **Service:** General Medical and Surgical

**Staffed Beds:** 62

## TULLAHOMA—Coffee County

☒ **HARTON REGIONAL MEDICAL CENTER (440144)**, 1801 North Jackson Street, Zip 37388–8259; tel. 931/393–3000, (Nonreporting) **A**1 9 10 19 **S** Community Health Systems, Inc., Franklin, TN
Primary Contact: William R. Spray, Chief Executive Officer
CFO: Shaun Adams, Chief Financial Officer
CMO: John D. Crabtree, M.D., Chief of Staff
CIO: Donald Cooper, Director Information Systems
CHR: Lenore Blackwell, Director Human Resources
Web address: www.hartonmedicalcenter.com
**Control:** Corporation, Investor–owned, for–profit **Service:** General Medical and Surgical

**Staffed Beds:** 104

*Many Facility Codes have changed. Please refer to the AHA Guide Code Chart.* © 2015 AHA Guide

**TN**

## UNION CITY—Obion County

✠ **BAPTIST MEMORIAL HOSPITAL–UNION CITY (440130)**, 1201 Bishop Street,
Zip 38261–5403, Mailing Address: P.O. Box 310, Zip 38281–0310;
tel. 731/885–2410 **A**1 9 10 **F**4 5 7 11 13 15 18 20 26 29 30 34 35 40 45 48
50 51 53 57 58 59 63 64 70 75 76 79 80 81 82 84 85 86 87 89 91 93 98
99 100 101 102 104 105 107 108 109 110 111 115 118 119 124 130 132
135 146 **P**3 **S** Baptist Memorial Health Care Corporation, Memphis, TN
Primary Contact: Barry Bondurant, Administrator and Chief Executive Officer
CFO: Mike Perryman, Chief Financial Officer
CMO: Kofi Nuako, M.D., President Medical Staff
CIO: David Mercer, Coordinator Information Systems
CHR: Nicky Thomas, Director Human Resources
CNO: Lori Brown, Chief Nursing Officer
Web address: www.baptistonline.org/union–city/
**Control:** Other not–for–profit (including NFP Corporation) **Service:** General
Medical and Surgical

**Staffed Beds:** 85 **Admissions:** 2599 **Census:** 27 **Outpatient Visits:** 44607
**Births:** 242 **Total Expense ($000):** 43580 **Payroll Expense ($000):** 16355
**Personnel:** 320

## WAVERLY—Humphreys County

**THREE RIVERS HOSPITAL (441303)**, 451 Highway 13 South,
Zip 37185–2109, Mailing Address: P.O. Box 437, Zip 37185–0437;
tel. 931/296–4203, (Nonreporting) **A**9 10 18
Primary Contact: Freda Russell, R.N., Chief Executive Officer and Chief Nursing
Officer
CFO: Sandra Patrick, Chief Financial Officer
CMO: George Mathai, M.D., Chief of Staff
CIO: Joe Hildreth, Director Information Technology
CHR: Linda Rawlings, Director Human Resources and Personnel
CNO: Freda Russell, R.N., Chief Executive Officer and Chief Nursing Officer
Web address: www.threerivershospital.org
**Control:** Other not–for–profit (including NFP Corporation) **Service:** General
Medical and Surgical

**Staffed Beds:** 25

## WAYNESBORO—Wayne County

✠ **WAYNE MEDICAL CENTER (440010)**, 103 J. V. Mangubat Drive,
Zip 38485–2440, Mailing Address: P.O. Box 580, Zip 38485–0580;
tel. 931/722–5411, (Nonreporting) **A**1 9 10 20 **S** Maury Regional Health System,
Columbia, TN
Primary Contact: Teresa Grimmett, Chief Executive Officer
CMO: Harish Veeramachaneni, M.D., Chief of Staff
CHR: Jeff M. Pierce, Manager Human Resources
Web address: www.mauryregional.com
**Control:** Other not–for–profit (including NFP Corporation) **Service:** General
Medical and Surgical

**Staffed Beds:** 78

## WINCHESTER—Franklin County

✠ **SOUTHERN TENNESSEE REGIONAL HEALTH SYSTEM–WINCHESTER**
**(440058)**, 185 Hospital Road, Zip 37398–2404; tel. 931/967–8200, (Includes
SOUTHERN TENNESSEE REGIONAL HEALTH SYSTEM–SEWANEE, 1260 University
Avenue, Sewanee, Zip 37375–2303; tel. 931/598–5691; Ralph Underwood,
Administrator), (Nonreporting) **A**1 9 10 **S** LifePoint Health, Brentwood, TN
Primary Contact: J. Phillip Young, FACHE, Chief Executive Officer
CFO: Steve Moore, Chief Financial Officer
CIO: James Payne, Director Information Systems
CHR: Linda Tipps, Director Human Resources
Web address: www.southerntennessee.com
**Control:** Corporation, Investor–owned, for–profit **Service:** General Medical and
Surgical

**Staffed Beds:** 198

## WOODBURY—Cannon County

✠ **SAINT THOMAS STONES RIVER HOSPITAL (440200)**, 324 Doolittle Road,
Zip 37190–1139; tel. 615/563–4001, (Nonreporting) **A**1 9 10 **S** Ascension
Health, Saint Louis, MO
Primary Contact: Susan Conley, Chief Executive Officer
CMO: J. C. Wall, M.D., Chief of Staff
CNO: Kimberly Frazier, Chief Nursing Officer
Web address: www.stonesriverhospital.com
**Control:** **Service:** General Medical and Surgical

**Staffed Beds:** 60

**TN**

# TEXAS

## ABILENE—Taylor County

**ABILENE BEHAVIORAL HEALTH (454098)**, 4225 Woods Place,
Zip 79602–7991, Mailing Address: P.O. Box 5559, Zip 79608–5559;
tel. 325/698–6600 **A**1 9 10 **F**4 5 16 29 54 56 64 87 98 99 101 103 104 105
106 130 135 143 **S** Acadia Healthcare Company, Inc., Franklin, TN
Primary Contact: Keith Broach, Chief Executive Officer
Web address: www.abilenebehavioralhealth.com/
**Control:** Corporation, Investor–owned, for–profit **Service:** Psychiatric

**Staffed Beds: 92 Admissions: 1809 Census: 55 Outpatient Visits: 4265
Births: 0 Total Expense ($000): 9428 Payroll Expense ($000): 5298
Personnel: 133**

**ABILENE REGIONAL MEDICAL CENTER (450558)**, 6250 U.S. Highway 83,
Zip 79606–5299; tel. 325/428–1000, (Total facility includes 25 beds in nursing
home–type unit) **A**1 9 10 **F**8 11 13 15 17 18 20 22 24 26 28 29 30 31 34 35
40 41 43 45 46 49 50 53 56 57 59 64 68 70 72 75 76 77 78 79 81 85 86
87 89 91 93 107 108 110 111 114 115 118 119 126 128 130 132 135 146
147 148 **P**3 **S** Community Health Systems, Inc., Franklin, TN
Primary Contact: Michael D. Murphy, Chief Executive Officer
CFO: Ron Bennett, Chief Financial Officer
CMO: Tim Bumann, D.O., Chief of Staff
CIO: Dennis Newquist, Director Information Systems
CHR: John J. Jeziorske, Director Human Resources
CNO: Jessica Kiehle, R.N., Chief Nursing Officer
Web address: www.abileneregional.com
**Control:** Partnership, Investor–owned, for–profit **Service:** General Medical and
Surgical

**Staffed Beds: 205 Admissions: 6001 Census: 75 Outpatient Visits: 73857
Births: 1214 Total Expense ($000): 95980 Payroll Expense ($000): 32995
Personnel: 627**

**ACADIA ABILENE HOSPITAL** See Abilene Behavioral Health

★ **CONTINUECARE HOSPITAL AT HENDRICK MEDICAL CENTER (452029)**,
1900 Pine Street, Zip 79601–2432; tel. 325/670–6251, (Data for 181 days)
**A**10 **F**1 3 29 34 35 68 85 87 **S** Community Hospital Corporation, Plano, TX
Primary Contact: Thomas P. Harlan, Chief Executive Officer
CFO: Kliff Rodgers, Vice President and Chief Financial Officer
CHR: Laurie Fields, Director Human Resources
CNO: Sherry Hendricksen, R.N., Chief Nursing Officer
Web address: www.continuecare.org/hendrick/
**Control:** Other not–for–profit (including NFP Corporation) **Service:** Long–Term
Acute Care hospital

**Staffed Beds: 19 Admissions: 94 Census: 15 Outpatient Visits: 0 Births: 0
Total Expense ($000): 2771 Payroll Expense ($000): 1100 Personnel: 50**

**HENDRICK HEALTH SYSTEM (450229)**, 1900 Pine Street, Zip 79601–2432;
tel. 325/670–2000, (Total facility includes 20 beds in nursing home–type unit) **A**1
9 10 **F**3 11 12 13 14 15 17 18 20 22 24 26 28 29 30 31 32 34 35 36 39 40
43 44 45 48 49 50 51 53 56 57 59 60 61 62 64 68 70 73 74 75 76 77 78
79 80 81 84 85 86 87 88 89 90 92 93 96 97 102 107 108 110 111 114 115
118 119 121 123 128 129 130 131 132 135 143 146 147 148 **P**8
Primary Contact: Tim Lancaster, FACHE, President and Chief Executive Officer
CFO: Jeremy Tyler Walker, Vice President and Chief Financial Officer
CMO: Steve Faehnle, M.D., Vice President Medical Affairs
CIO: Duane Donaway, Director Information Technology
CHR: Susan Wade, Assistant Vice President
CNO: Susie Cassle, R.N., Assistant Vice President Nursing Services
Web address: www.ehendrick.org
**Control:** Church–operated, Nongovernment, not–for profit **Service:** General
Medical and Surgical

**Staffed Beds: 391 Admissions: 16003 Census: 246 Outpatient Visits:
285937 Births: 1601 Total Expense ($000): 299531 Payroll Expense
($000): 103128 Personnel: 1846**

**OCEANS BEHAVIORAL HOSPITAL ABILENE (454122)**, 6401 Directors
Parkway, Suite 200, Zip 79606–5869; tel. 325/691–0030 **A**1 10 **F**29 68 98
100 101 103 **P**6
Primary Contact: Stacy Sanford, Chief Executive Officer
Web address: www.oceansabilene.com
**Control:** Corporation, Investor–owned, for–profit **Service:** Psychiatric

**Staffed Beds: 35 Admissions: 486 Census: 14 Outpatient Visits: 0 Births:
0 Total Expense ($000): 3666 Payroll Expense ($000): 1494 Personnel:
55**

**RELIANT REHABILITATION HOSPITAL ABILENE (673039)**, 6401 Directors
Parkway, Zip 79606–5869; tel. 325/691–1600 **A**1 9 10 **F**3 29 90 96 130 148
**S** Reliant Healthcare Partners, Richardson, TX
Primary Contact: Joe Roberson, Chief Executive Officer
Web address: www.reliantabilene.com
**Control:** Partnership, Investor–owned, for–profit **Service:** Rehabilitation

**Staffed Beds: 30 Admissions: 495 Census: 12 Outpatient Visits: 0 Births:
0 Total Expense ($000): 6544 Payroll Expense ($000): 2542 Personnel:
50**

## ADDISON—Dallas County

◇ **METHODIST HOSPITAL FOR SURGERY (670073)**, 17101 North Dallas
Parkway, Zip 75001–7103; tel. 469/248–3900 **A**9 10 21 **F**3 29 30 35 40 64
70 81 93 107 111 112 119 130 146 **P**2
Primary Contact: Daniel L. Gideon, President
CFO: Kelly Hayes, Chief Financial Officer
CMO: Robert Fischer, M.D., Medical Director
CHR: Erik Leopard, Manager Human Resource
CNO: Patti Griffith, R.N., Chief Nursing Officer
Web address: www.methodisthospitalforsurgery.com/
**Control:** Corporation, Investor–owned, for–profit **Service:** Surgical

**Staffed Beds: 32 Admissions: 2336 Census: 16 Outpatient Visits: 8857
Births: 0 Total Expense ($000): 91715 Payroll Expense ($000): 12939
Personnel: 241**

## ALICE—Jim Wells County

**CHRISTUS SPOHN HOSPITAL ALICE (450828)**, 2500 East Main Street,
Zip 78332–4169; tel. 361/661–8000 **A**1 9 10 20 **F**3 11 13 15 18 20 22 28
29 30 35 39 40 42 43 45 46 49 50 57 59 68 70 75 76 77 79 81 85 86 87
89 93 97 98 100 101 102 103 107 108 111 114 119 127 130 146 148 **P**8
**S** CHRISTUS Health, Irving, TX
Primary Contact: Steven G. Daniel, Senior Vice President and Chief Operating
Officer
COO: Steven G. Daniel, Senior Vice President and Chief Operating Officer
CFO: Michael Guajardo, Director Finance
CMO: Jerry Liles, D.O.
CHR: Mindy Soliz, Director Human Resources
CNO: Margot Rios, R.N., Chief Nursing Officer
Web address: www.christusspohn.org/locations_alice.htm
**Control:** Church–operated, Nongovernment, not–for profit **Service:** General
Medical and Surgical

**Staffed Beds: 73 Admissions: 2732 Census: 34 Outpatient Visits: 51944
Births: 396 Total Expense ($000): 46067 Payroll Expense ($000): 16200
Personnel: 225**

## ALLEN—Collin County

**POST ACUTE/WARM SPRINGS REHABILITATION HOSPITAL OF ALLEN
(673025)**, 1001 Raintree Circle, Zip 75013–4912; tel. 972/908–2015 **A**1 9 10
**F**3 28 29 30 34 40 56 59 60 74 75 79 87 90 91 94 96 100 130 132 146
148 **S** Post Acute Medical, LLC, Enola, PA
Primary Contact: Bill Kaupas, Chief Executive Officer
Web address: www.warmsprings.org
**Control:** Partnership, Investor–owned, for–profit **Service:** Rehabilitation

**Staffed Beds: 39 Admissions: 863 Census: 26 Outpatient Visits: 0 Births:
0 Total Expense ($000): 12018 Payroll Expense ($000): 5451 Personnel:
106**

**TEXAS HEALTH PRESBYTERIAN HOSPITAL ALLEN (450840)**, 1105 Central
Expressway North, Zip 75013–6103; tel. 972/747–1000 **A**1 9 10 **F**3 13 15 18
20 28 29 30 34 35 38 40 45 47 49 51 54 55 57 59 64 65 70 73 74 75 76
78 79 81 89 93 107 110 111 114 115 118 119 126 129 130 132 135 146
147 148 **S** Texas Health Resources, Arlington, TX
Primary Contact: Jeff Reecer, President
COO: Crispin P. Hocate, Professional and Support Services Officer
CFO: Lisa Gildon, Group Financial Officer
CMO: Bob Schwab, M.D., Chief Medical Officer
CHR: Sharon Chisholm, Entity Human Resource Officer
Web address: www.texashealth.org
**Control:** Other not–for–profit (including NFP Corporation) **Service:** General
Medical and Surgical

**Staffed Beds: 73 Admissions: 3126 Census: 28 Outpatient Visits: 43414
Births: 578 Total Expense ($000): 69873 Payroll Expense ($000): 25857
Personnel: 286**

TX

*Many Facility Codes have changed. Please refer to the AHA Guide Code Chart.*

## ALPINE—Brewster County

✠ **BIG BEND REGIONAL MEDICAL CENTER (451378)**, 2600 Highway 118
North, Zip 79830–2002; tel. 432/837–3447 **A**1 3 9 10 18 **F**3 29 30 34 35 40
43 45 49 57 59 64 68 70 75 76 81 85 93 107 119 132 133 146 147 148 **P**6
**S** Community Health Systems, Inc., Franklin, TN
Primary Contact: John Hughson, Chief Executive Officer
CFO: Diane Moore, Chief Financial Officer
CNO: Keith Ellison, Chief Nursing Officer
Web address: www.bigbendhealthcare.com
**Control:** Corporation, Investor–owned, for–profit **Service:** General Medical and
Surgical

**Staffed Beds:** 25 **Admissions:** 776 **Census:** 6 **Outpatient Visits:** 11890
**Births:** 187 **Total Expense ($000):** 19235 **Payroll Expense ($000):** 6630
**Personnel:** 108

## ALVIN—Brazoria County

**ALVIN DIAGNOSTIC AND URGENT CARE CENTER** See Clear Lake Regional
Medical Center, Webster

## AMARILLO—Potter County

✠ **AMARILLO VETERANS AFFAIRS HEALTH CARE SYSTEM**, 6010 West Amarillo
Boulevard, Zip 79106–1992; tel. 806/355–9703, (Nonreporting) **A**1 2 3 5 9
**S** Department of Veterans Affairs, Washington, DC
Primary Contact: Walt Dannenberg, Interim Director
COO: Lance Robinson, Associate Director
CMO: James Gray, M.D., Chief Medical Service
CIO: Modesto Baca, Chief Information Officer
CHR: Ken Creamer, Chief Human Resource
Web address: www.amarillo.va.gov/
**Control:** Veterans Affairs, Government, federal **Service:** General Medical and
Surgical

**Staffed Beds:** 55

★ **BAPTIST ST. ANTHONY HEALTH SYSTEM (450231)**, 1600 Wallace
Boulevard, Zip 79106–1799; tel. 806/212–2000 **A**2 3 5 9 10 **F**3 7 8 11 13 15
17 18 20 22 24 26 28 29 30 31 34 35 40 45 46 48 49 51 53 54 57 58 59
62 70 72 74 75 76 77 78 79 81 82 85 86 87 88 89 90 91 93 96 107 108
110 111 114 115 117 119 120 121 123 124 126 129 130 135 146 147 148
**S** Ardent Health Services, Nashville, TN
Primary Contact: Bob Williams, President and Chief Executive Officer
COO: Michael Cruz, Senior Vice President Operations
CFO: Lorenzo Olivarez, Senior Vice President and Chief Financial Officer
CMO: Mike Lamanteer, M.D., Senior Vice President Medical Affairs
CIO: Lewis Brown, Director Information Technology
CHR: Cheryl L. Jones, Vice President Human Resources and Organizational
Development
CNO: Belinda D. Gibson, R.N., Senior Vice President Patient Services
Web address: www.bsahs.org
**Control:** Corporation, Investor–owned, for–profit **Service:** General Medical and
Surgical

**Staffed Beds:** 312 **Admissions:** 20696 **Census:** 256 **Outpatient Visits:**
167739 **Births:** 2211 **Total Expense ($000):** 310016 **Payroll Expense
($000):** 113594 **Personnel:** 1877

**KINDRED HOSPITAL–AMARILLO** See Vibra Hospital of Amarillo

**KINDRED REHABILITATION HOSPITAL AMARILLO** See Vibra Rehabilitation
Hospital of Amarillo

✠ **NORTHWEST TEXAS HEALTHCARE SYSTEM (450209)**, 1501 South Coulter
Avenue, Zip 79106–1770, Mailing Address: P.O. Box 1110, Zip 79105–1110;
tel. 806/354–1000, (Includes NORTHWEST CHILDREN'S HOSPITAL, 1501 South
Coulter Street, tel. 806/354–1000; NORTHWEST PAVILION, 7201 Evans,
Zip 79106, Mailing Address: P.O. Box 1110, Zip 79105–1110;
tel. 806/354–1000) **A**1 2 3 5 9 10 **F**3 4 5 11 12 13 15 17 18 20 22 24 26 28
29 30 31 32 34 35 37 38 39 40 43 44 45 46 48 49 50 54 56 57 59 60 61
64 66 68 70 72 74 75 76 77 78 79 80 81 84 86 87 88 89 90 92 93 94 96
97 98 99 100 101 102 103 104 105 107 108 110 111 115 118 119 135
130 132 135 144 146 147 148 **P**6 **S** Universal Health Services, Inc., King of
Prussia, PA
Primary Contact: Mark W. Crawford, Chief Executive Officer
COO: John McDonald, Chief Operating Officer
CFO: Gene Winters, Chief Financial Officer
CMO: Brian Weis, M.D., Chief Medical Officer
CIO: Bach Nguyen, Director Information Systems
CHR: Samuel Lynn, Director Human Resources
CNO: Valerie Kiper, MSN, Chief Nursing Officer
Web address: www.nwtexashealthcare.com
**Control:** Corporation, Investor–owned, for–profit **Service:** General Medical and
Surgical

**Staffed Beds:** 417 **Admissions:** 18295 **Census:** 241 **Outpatient Visits:**
217033 **Births:** 2568 **Total Expense ($000):** 260740 **Payroll Expense
($000):** 83266 **Personnel:** 1566

**NORTHWEST TEXAS SURGERY CENTER (450796)**, 3501 South Soncy Road
Suite 118, Zip 79119–6405; tel. 806/359–7999 **A**10 **F**26 39 40 58 68 79 81
82 85 126 131
Primary Contact: Jeff Barnhart, Administrator
**Control:** Corporation, Investor–owned, for–profit **Service:** General Medical and
Surgical

**Staffed Beds:** 4 **Admissions:** 181 **Census:** 1 **Outpatient Visits:** 3768 **Births:**
0 **Total Expense ($000):** 7691 **Payroll Expense ($000):** 2551 **Personnel:**
39

★ **PHYSICIANS SURGICAL HOSPITAL – PANHANDLE CAMPUS**, 7100 West 9th
Avenue, Zip 79106–1704; tel. 806/212–0247, (Nonreporting) **S** Ardent Health
Services, Nashville, TN
Primary Contact: Brad McCall, President and Chief Executive Officer
CFO: Austin Jones, CPA, Chief Financial Officer
CMO: Robert Crabtree, M.D., Chief of Staff and Medical Director
CNO: Debbie Inman, Chief Nursing Officer
Web address: www.physurg.com/
**Control:** Partnership, Investor–owned, for–profit **Service:** General Medical and
Surgical

**Staffed Beds:** 11

★ **PHYSICIANS SURGICAL HOSPITAL – QUAIL CREEK (450875)**, 6819 Plum
Creek, Zip 79124–1602; tel. 806/354–6100 **A**9 10 **F**3 29 30 40 44 68 75 79
81 82 85 89 130 135 **S** Ardent Health Services, Nashville, TN
Primary Contact: Brad McCall, President and Chief Executive Officer
CFO: Austin Jones, CPA, Chief Financial Officer
CMO: Robert Crabtree, M.D., Chief of Staff and Medical Director
CNO: Debbie Inman, Chief Nursing Officer
Web address: www.physurg.com
**Control:** Corporation, Investor–owned, for–profit **Service:** Surgical

**Staffed Beds:** 41 **Admissions:** 1752 **Census:** 10 **Outpatient Visits:** 13817
**Births:** 0 **Total Expense ($000):** 39908 **Payroll Expense ($000):** 10302
**Personnel:** 170

☐ **PLUM CREEK SPECIALTY HOSPITAL (452066)**, 5601 Plum Creek Drive,
Zip 79124–1801; tel. 806/351–1000 **A**1 9 10 **F**1 3 29 75 85 148 **S** Encore
Healthcare, Columbia, MD
Primary Contact: Timothy Deaton, Chief Executive Officer
Web address: www.plumcreekspecialtyhosp.com/
**Control:** Corporation, Investor–owned, for–profit **Service:** Long–Term Acute Care
hospital

**Staffed Beds:** 47 **Admissions:** 259 **Census:** 17 **Outpatient Visits:** 0 **Births:**
0 **Total Expense ($000):** 7594 **Payroll Expense ($000):** 2891 **Personnel:**
65

**SPECIALTY HOSPITAL AT PLUM CREEK** See Plum Creek Specialty Hospital

✠ **VIBRA HOSPITAL OF AMARILLO (452060)**, 7501 Wallace Boulevard,
Zip 79124–2150; tel. 806/467–7000 **A**1 9 10 **F**1 3 29 45 46 50 56 59 60 61
70 74 75 77 79 82 84 85 86 87 91 96 107 114 130 148 **S** Vibra Healthcare,
Mechanicsburg, PA
Primary Contact: Jerry Jasper, Chief Executive Officer
CFO: Carlene Wright, Chief Financial Officer
CMO: Pablo Rodrigues, M.D., Medical Director
CNO: Melany McCarty, R.N., Chief Clinical Officer
Web address: www.vhamarillo.com
**Control:** Corporation, Investor–owned, for–profit **Service:** Long–Term Acute Care
hospital

**Staffed Beds:** 72 **Admissions:** 833 **Census:** 62 **Outpatient Visits:** 0 **Births:**
0 **Total Expense ($000):** 20155 **Payroll Expense ($000):** 11273
**Personnel:** 215

✠ △ **VIBRA REHABILITATION HOSPITAL OF AMARILLO (453096)**, 7200 West
9th Avenue, Zip 79106–1703; tel. 806/468–2900 **A**1 7 10 **F**3 28 29 56 75 77
82 87 90 91 96 130 143 148 **S** Vibra Healthcare, Mechanicsburg, PA
Primary Contact: Jerry Jasper, Chief Executive Officer
Web address: www.vrhamarillo.com
**Control:** Corporation, Investor–owned, for–profit **Service:** Rehabilitation

**Staffed Beds:** 44 **Admissions:** 811 **Census:** 23 **Outpatient Visits:** 0 **Births:**
0 **Total Expense ($000):** 7894 **Payroll Expense ($000):** 5590 **Personnel:**
119

**TX**

## ANAHUAC—Chambers County

★ **CHAMBERS COUNTY PUBLIC HOSPITAL DISTRICT 1 (451320)**, 200 Hospital Drive, Zip 77514, Mailing Address: P.O. Box 398, Zip 77514-0398; tel. 409/267-3143 **A**9 10 18 **F**3 8 11 29 34 35 40 43 45 47 50 53 54 56 57 59 64 70 81 86 88 93 107 111 114 119 128 130 133 **P**3
Primary Contact: Steven Gularte, Chief Executive Officer
CFO: Theresa Cheaney, Controller
CMO: Anthony Capili, M.D., Chief of Staff
CNO: Christi Morris, Director of Nursing
Web address: www.chambershealth.org
**Control:** Hospital district or authority, Government, nonfederal **Service:** General Medical and Surgical

**Staffed Beds:** 14 **Admissions:** 135 **Census:** 1 **Outpatient Visits:** 26514 **Births:** 0 **Total Expense ($000):** 15066 **Payroll Expense ($000):** 5495 **Personnel:** 112

## ANDREWS—Andrews County

★ ◇ **PERMIAN REGIONAL MEDICAL CENTER (450144)**, Northeast By-Pass, Zip 79714, Mailing Address: P.O. Box 2108, Zip 79714-2108; tel. 432/523-2200 **A**9 10 20 21 **F**3 11 13 15 29 34 35 36 38 40 43 44 50 53 56 57 59 62 64 65 68 70 73 75 76 77 81 82 84 85 86 87 89 93 97 107 108 110 111 115 119 127 129 130 131 132 133 135 145 146 148 **P**5 6
Primary Contact: Russell Tippin, Chief Executive Officer and Administrator
CFO: Sandra Cox, Controller
CIO: Dan Smart, Chief Information Management Officer
CHR: Pam McCormick, Director Human Resources
Web address: www.permianregional.com
**Control:** Hospital district or authority, Government, nonfederal **Service:** General Medical and Surgical

**Staffed Beds:** 42 **Admissions:** 710 **Census:** 5 **Outpatient Visits:** 34978 **Births:** 256 **Total Expense ($000):** 37748 **Payroll Expense ($000):** 17929 **Personnel:** 255

## ANSON—Jones County

★ **ANSON GENERAL HOSPITAL (450078)**, 101 Avenue J, Zip 79501-2198; tel. 325/823-3231 **A**9 10 **F**7 11 29 40 45 62 75 77 81 107 127 133 **P**8
Primary Contact: Pamela Gonzales, Administrator
CIO: Lynna B. Cox, Director Health Information Services
**Control:** City-Government, nonfederal **Service:** General Medical and Surgical

**Staffed Beds:** 30 **Admissions:** 229 **Census:** 4 **Outpatient Visits:** 9575 **Births:** 0 **Total Expense ($000):** 7911 **Payroll Expense ($000):** 3952 **Personnel:** 127

## ARANSAS PASS—San Patricio County

**CARE REGIONAL MEDICAL CENTER (450605)**, 1711 West Wheeler Avenue, Zip 78336-4536; tel. 361/758-8585 **A**9 10 **F**3 11 15 18 29 34 35 40 44 45 50 56 57 59 64 65 68 70 75 77 78 79 81 82 85 86 87 93 97 98 101 102 103 107 108 111 114 119 130 132 133 146 148 **P**7
Primary Contact: Sunil Reddy, Chief Executive Officer
CMO: Salim Surani, M.D., Chief of Staff
CIO: Greg Palmer, Administrator Information Technology Network
CHR: Kerry L. Upton, Administrative Director Human Resources
CNO: Christal Burns, R.N., Chief Nursing Officer
Web address: www.crmctx.com
**Control:** Corporation, Investor-owned, for-profit **Service:** General Medical and Surgical

**Staffed Beds:** 54 **Admissions:** 1104 **Census:** 16 **Outpatient Visits:** 25950 **Births:** 0 **Total Expense ($000):** 14635 **Payroll Expense ($000):** 6570 **Personnel:** 154

**NORTH BAY HOSPITAL** See Care Regional Medical Center

## ARLINGTON—Tarrant County

**ARLINGTON REHABILITATION HOSPITAL** See Kindred Rehabilitation Hospital Arlington

☐ **BAYLOR ORTHOPEDIC AND SPINE HOSPITAL AT ARLINGTON (670067)**, 707 Highlander Boulevard, Zip 76015-4319; tel. 817/583-7100 **A**1 9 10 **F**3 29 40 75 79 81 82 85 86 107 111 114
Primary Contact: Allan Beck, Chief Executive Officer
Web address: www.baylorarlington.com/
**Control:** Partnership, Investor-owned, for-profit **Service:** General Medical and Surgical

**Staffed Beds:** 24 **Admissions:** 1212 **Census:** 8 **Outpatient Visits:** 8826 **Births:** 0 **Total Expense ($000):** 41869 **Payroll Expense ($000):** 7572 **Personnel:** 116

☒ **HEALTHSOUTH REHABILITATION HOSPITAL OF ARLINGTON (453040)**, 3200 Matlock Road, Zip 76015-2911; tel. 817/468-4000 **A**1 9 10 **F**3 29 74 75 77 79 90 91 94 95 96 130 148 **S** HEALTHSOUTH Corporation, Birmingham, AL
Primary Contact: Sheryl Appel, Chief Executive Officer
CFO: Kathy Dickerson, Chief Financial Officer
CMO: Todd Daniels, M.D., Medical Director
CHR: Nancy Rosiles, Director Human Resources
CNO: David Jones, Chief Nursing Officer
Web address: www.healthsoutharlington.com
**Control:** Corporation, Investor-owned, for-profit **Service:** Rehabilitation

**Staffed Beds:** 85 **Admissions:** 1723 **Census:** 63 **Outpatient Visits:** 0 **Births:** 0 **Total Expense ($000):** 25690 **Payroll Expense ($000):** 12189 **Personnel:** 225

☒ **KINDRED HOSPITAL TARRANT COUNTY–ARLINGTON (452028)**, 1000 North Cooper Street, Zip 76011-5540; tel. 817/548-3400 **A**1 9 10 **F**1 3 29 30 40 56 57 77 80 82 93 130 148 **S** Kindred Healthcare, Louisville, KY
Primary Contact: Christina Richard, Administrator
CFO: Jennifer Penland, Controller
CMO: Bernard A. McGowen, M.D., Medical Director
Web address: www.kindredhospitalarl.com/
**Control:** Corporation, Investor-owned, for-profit **Service:** Long-Term Acute Care hospital

**Staffed Beds:** 55 **Admissions:** 555 **Census:** 39 **Outpatient Visits:** 623 **Births:** 0 **Total Expense ($000):** 18694 **Payroll Expense ($000):** 8049 **Personnel:** 141

☒ **KINDRED REHABILITATION HOSPITAL ARLINGTON (453094)**, 2601 West Randol Mill Road, Zip 76012-4289; tel. 817/804-4400 **A**1 9 10 **F**3 29 34 57 59 74 75 86 87 90 94 96 130 132 146 148 **S** Kindred Healthcare, Louisville, KY
Primary Contact: Amy Hoffner, Administrator
CFO: Jennifer Penland, Controller
CNO: Katherine Kreis, Chief Clinical Officer
Web address: www.khrehabarlington.com
**Control:** Corporation, Investor-owned, for-profit **Service:** Rehabilitation

**Staffed Beds:** 24 **Admissions:** 606 **Census:** 20 **Outpatient Visits:** 0 **Births:** 0 **Total Expense ($000):** 7628 **Payroll Expense ($000):** 3975 **Personnel:** 68

☒ **MEDICAL CENTER ARLINGTON (450675)**, 3301 Matlock Road, Zip 76015-2908; tel. 817/465-3241 **A**1 2 3 9 10 **F**3 11 12 13 15 17 18 20 22 24 26 28 29 31 34 35 39 40 42 43 45 46 47 48 49 50 56 57 59 64 68 70 72 73 74 75 76 78 79 81 82 85 86 87 92 93 107 108 110 111 114 115 119 126 130 131 132 135 145 146 147 148 **S** HCA, Nashville, TN
Primary Contact: Winston Borland, FACHE, President and Chief Executive Officer
CFO: Jeff Ardemagni, Chief Financial Officer
CMO: Edwin Duppstadt, M.D., Chief Medical Officer
CIO: Basil Holloway, Director Information Services
CHR: Jennifer C. Morris, Vice President Human Resources
CNO: Omar Pineda, R.N., Chief Nursing Officer
Web address: www.medicalcenterarlington.com
**Control:** Partnership, Investor-owned, for-profit **Service:** General Medical and Surgical

**Staffed Beds:** 265 **Admissions:** 15443 **Census:** 212 **Outpatient Visits:** 101508 **Births:** 4266 **Total Expense ($000):** 196491 **Payroll Expense ($000):** 73448 **Personnel:** 1081

☐ **MILLWOOD HOSPITAL (454012)**, 1011 North Cooper Street, Zip 76011-5517; tel. 817/261-3121 **A**1 9 10 **F**4 5 29 30 35 54 56 71 87 98 99 100 101 102 103 104 105 130 132 **S** Universal Health Services, Inc., King of Prussia, PA
Primary Contact: Dwight A. Lacy, Chief Executive Officer
CFO: Jeff Epperson, Chief Financial Officer
CMO: Robert Bennett, M.D., Medical Director
CIO: William Jackson, Director Medical Records
CHR: Betty Nuru, Director Human Resources
CNO: Nancy Stewart, Chief Nursing Officer
Web address: www.millwoodhospital.com
**Control:** Partnership, Investor-owned, for-profit **Service:** Psychiatric

**Staffed Beds:** 122 **Admissions:** 3935 **Census:** 91 **Outpatient Visits:** 27919 **Births:** 0 **Total Expense ($000):** 25150 **Payroll Expense ($000):** 11179 **Personnel:** 205

☐ **SUNDANCE HOSPITAL (454113)**, 7000 U.S. Highway 287 South, Zip 76001; tel. 817/583-8080 **A**1 9 10 **F**4 98 99 101 102 103
Primary Contact: Rick Harding, Chief Executive Officer
Web address: www.sundancehealthcare.com
**Control:** Corporation, Investor-owned, for-profit **Service:** Psychiatric

**Staffed Beds:** 116 **Admissions:** 3825 **Census:** 87 **Outpatient Visits:** 0 **Births:** 0 **Total Expense ($000):** 12674 **Payroll Expense ($000):** 7354 **Personnel:** 201

TX

*Many Facility Codes have changed. Please refer to the AHA Guide Code Chart.*

© 2015 AHA Guide

✠ **TEXAS HEALTH ARLINGTON MEMORIAL HOSPITAL (450064)**, 800 West Randol Mill Road, Zip 76012–2503; tel. 817/548–6100 **A**1 2 9 10 **F**3 11 12 13 15 18 26 28 29 30 31 34 35 37 40 45 46 47 48 49 51 53 54 57 59 60 63 64 65 66 68 70 72 74 75 76 77 78 79 80 81 82 85 86 87 93 98 99 100 101 102 103 104 105 107 108 110 111 114 115 118 119 123 124 126 130 131 132 135 136 141 142 145 146 147 148 **S** Texas Health Resources, Arlington, TX
Primary Contact: Blake Kretz, President
COO: Sandra L. Harris, R.N., Senior Vice President and Chief Operating Officer
CMO: Robert N. Cluck, M.D., Vice President and Medical Director
CHR: Yvonne Kyler, Director Human Resources
Web address: www.arlingtonmemorial.org
**Control:** Other not–for–profit (including NFP Corporation) **Service:** General Medical and Surgical

**Staffed Beds:** 266 **Admissions:** 12579 **Census:** 173 **Outpatient Visits:** 108040 **Births:** 1927 **Total Expense ($000):** 233712 **Payroll Expense ($000):** 98318 **Personnel:** 1545

☐ **TEXAS HEALTH HEART & VASCULAR HOSPITAL ARLINGTON (670071)**, 811 Wright Street, Zip 76012–4708; tel. 817/960–3500 **A**1 9 10 **F**3 17 18 20 22 24 26 29 30 60 64 65 68 81 85
Primary Contact: Shelly Emerson, President
CFO: Kay Mason, Chief Financial Officer
CMO: William Nesbitt, M.D., President Medical Staff
CHR: Yvonne Kyler, Director Human Resources
Web address: www.texashealthheartandvascular.org/
**Control:** Partnership, Investor–owned, for–profit **Service:** Heart

**Staffed Beds:** 48 **Admissions:** 1251 **Census:** 16 **Outpatient Visits:** 2257 **Births:** 0 **Total Expense ($000):** 39326 **Payroll Expense ($000):** 8556 **Personnel:** 109

✠ **USMD HOSPITAL AT ARLINGTON (450872)**, 801 West Interstate 20, Zip 76017–5851; tel. 817/472–3400 **A**1 9 10 **F**3 12 29 34 35 39 40 45 49 50 51 57 58 59 64 70 74 75 78 79 81 82 85 87 92 107 108 111 114 119 124 126 132 **S** USMD Inc., Irving, TX
Primary Contact: Marcia Crim, R.N., MSN, Chief Executive Officer
CFO: Andrew Summers, Chief Financial Officer
CMO: M. Patrick Collini, M.D., President Medical Staff
CIO: Bob Rick, Vice President Information Technology
CHR: Bernardo Valle, Vice President Human Resources
CNO: Marcia Crim, R.N., Chief Nursing Officer and Chief Executive Officer
Web address: www.usmdarlington.com
**Control:** Partnership, Investor–owned, for–profit **Service:** General Medical and Surgical

**Staffed Beds:** 34 **Admissions:** 1714 **Census:** 14 **Outpatient Visits:** 33890 **Births:** 0 **Total Expense ($000):** 74196 **Payroll Expense ($000):** 16188 **Personnel:** 310

### ASPERMONT—Stonewall County

**STONEWALL MEMORIAL HOSPITAL (451318)**, 821 North Broadway, Zip 79502–2029, Mailing Address: P.O. Box C, Zip 79502–0902; tel. 940/989–3551 **A**9 10 18 **F**3 29 34 35 40 41 56 57 59 64 93 97 103 107 114 119 127 128 133 148 **P**5
Primary Contact: Andy Kolb, Chief Executive Officer
COO: Billie Carter, Chief Operating Officer and Assistant Administrator
CFO: Andy Kolb, Chief Executive Officer
CMO: Frederic K. Passmann, M.D., Chief of Staff
CIO: Billie Carter, Chief Operating Officer and Assistant Administrator
CHR: Andy Kolb, Chief Executive Officer
CNO: Jan Harris, R.N., Director of Nursing
Web address: www.smhdhealth.org/
**Control:** Hospital district or authority, Government, nonfederal **Service:** General Medical and Surgical

**Staffed Beds:** 12 **Admissions:** 142 **Census:** 2 **Outpatient Visits:** 3441 **Births:** 0 **Total Expense ($000):** 8567 **Payroll Expense ($000):** 3982 **Personnel:** 48

### ATHENS—Henderson County

✠ **EAST TEXAS MEDICAL CENTER ATHENS (450389)**, 2000 South Palestine Street, Zip 75751–5610; tel. 903/676–1000 **A**1 9 10 **F**3 11 13 15 18 20 29 34 40 42 43 45 49 50 70 74 76 79 81 85 89 107 108 110 111 114 115 118 119 127 130 132 146 **S** East Texas Medical Center Regional Healthcare System, Tyler, TX
Primary Contact: Patrick L. Wallace, Administrator
CFO: David A. Travis, Chief Financial Officer
CMO: Curtis E. Grey, M.D., Chief of Staff
CHR: Jennifer Rummel, Director Human Resources
CNO: Kevin M. Jablonski, Chief Nursing Officer
Web address: www.etmc.org
**Control:** Other not–for–profit (including NFP Corporation) **Service:** General Medical and Surgical

**Staffed Beds:** 127 **Admissions:** 5711 **Census:** 56 **Outpatient Visits:** 76443 **Births:** 924 **Total Expense ($000):** 71495 **Payroll Expense ($000):** 22211 **Personnel:** 407

### AUBREY—Denton County

★ ◇ **BAYLOR EMERGENCY MEDICAL CENTER AT AUBREY (670062)**, 26791 Highway 380, Zip 76227; tel. 972/347–2525 **A**9 10 21 **F**3 29 40 75 87 107 119 **P**5 **S** Emerus, The Woodlands, TX
Primary Contact: John Wood, Chief Executive Officer
CFO: Michael Rzendzian, Chief Financial Officer
CMO: Amynah Kara, M.D., Chief Medical Officer
CIO: Trang Dawson, Chief Information Officer
CHR: Larry Guillory, Chief Human Resources Officer
CNO: Daniel Baas, R.N., Chief Nursing Officer
Web address: www.bemcataubrey.com
**Control:** Partnership, Investor–owned, for–profit **Service:** General Medical and Surgical

**Staffed Beds:** 32 **Admissions:** 178 **Census:** 1 **Outpatient Visits:** 29687 **Births:** 0 **Total Expense ($000):** 22858 **Payroll Expense ($000):** 6572 **Personnel:** 149

### AUSTIN—Travis County

☐ **ARISE AUSTIN MEDICAL CENTER (450871)**, 3003 Bee Caves Road, Zip 78746–5542; tel. 512/314–3800 **A**1 9 10 **F**29 33 37 40 51 54 59 64 65 68 70 79 81 82 85 91 92 93 107 111 114 119 126 131 148
Primary Contact: Diana Zamora Magallanes, Chief Executive Officer
CFO: Lawrence Oldham, Chief Financial Officer
CMO: Robert Wills, M.D., Chief Medical Officer
CHR: Marilyn Jennings, Director Human Resources
Web address: www.austinsurgicalhospital.com
**Control:** Corporation, Investor–owned, for–profit **Service:** General Medical and Surgical

**Staffed Beds:** 23 **Admissions:** 835 **Census:** 5 **Outpatient Visits:** 21490 **Births:** 0 **Total Expense ($000):** 39659 **Payroll Expense ($000):** 7772 **Personnel:** 167

☐ **AUSTIN LAKES HOSPITAL (454069)**, 1025 East 32nd Street, Zip 78705–2714; tel. 512/544–5253 **A**1 5 9 10 **F**98 103 104 105 130 **S** Universal Health Services, Inc., King of Prussia, PA
Primary Contact: Rick Buckelew, Chief Executive Officer
CFO: Greg Wysocki, Chief Financial Officer
CMO: Shiva Lam, M.D., Executive Medical Director
CHR: Dan Smith, Director Human Resources
CNO: Barbara Powers, R.N., Chief Nursing Officer
Web address: www.austinlakeshospital.com
**Control:** Corporation, Investor–owned, for–profit **Service:** Psychiatric

**Staffed Beds:** 58 **Admissions:** 2654 **Census:** 50 **Outpatient Visits:** 6984 **Births:** 0 **Total Expense ($000):** 11458 **Payroll Expense ($000):** 6315 **Personnel:** 122

☐ **AUSTIN OAKS HOSPITAL (454121)**, 1407 West Stassney Lane, Zip 78745–2947; tel. 512/440–4800 **A**1 10 **F**29 38 64 98 99 100 101 103 104 105 130 **S** Universal Health Services, Inc., King of Prussia, PA
Primary Contact: Steve Kelly, Interim Chief Executive Officer
Web address: www.austinoakshospital.com
**Control:** Partnership, Investor–owned, for–profit **Service:** Psychiatric

**Staffed Beds:** 80 **Admissions:** 2005 **Census:** 43 **Outpatient Visits:** 1915 **Births:** 0 **Total Expense ($000):** 11019 **Payroll Expense ($000):** 5817 **Personnel:** 123

**TX**

---

**Hospital, Medicare Provider Number, Address, Telephone, Approval, Facility, and Physician Codes, Health Care System**

★ American Hospital Association (AHA) membership
☐ The Joint Commission accreditation
◯ Healthcare Facilities Accreditation Program
◇ DNV Healthcare Inc. accreditation
⇑ Center for Improvement in Healthcare Quality Accreditation
△ Commission on Accreditation of Rehabilitation Facilities (CARF) accreditation

☐ **AUSTIN STATE HOSPITAL (454084)**, 4110 Guadalupe Street,
Zip 78751–4296; tel. 512/452–0381 **A**1 3 5 10 **F**29 30 39 50 56 59 65 68
75 82 86 98 99 101 103 130 132 143 146 **P**1 **S** Texas Department of State
Health Services, Austin, TX
Primary Contact: Cathy Nottebart, Acting Superintendent
CMO: Ross Taylor, M.D., Clinical Director
CIO: Cindy Reed, Director Community Relations
Web address: www.dshs.state.tx.us/mhhospitals/austinsh/default.shtm
**Control:** State–Government, nonfederal **Service:** Psychiatric

**Staffed Beds:** 314 **Admissions:** 2539 **Census:** 266 **Outpatient Visits:** 0
**Births:** 0 **Total Expense ($000):** 80762 **Payroll Expense ($000):** 36996
**Personnel:** 823

⊞ **CENTRAL TEXAS REHABILITATION HOSPITAL (673027)**, 700 West 45th
Street, Zip 78751–2800; tel. 512/407–2111 **A**1 3 9 10 **F**3 29 59 74 79 82 90
91 96 130 132 148 **S** Kindred Healthcare, Louisville, KY
Primary Contact: Peggy Barrett, R.N., Chief Executive Officer
CFO: Tracey Allen, Controller
CMO: Mary Ann Gonzales, M.D., Medical Director
CIO: Peggy Barrett, R.N., Chief Executive Officer
CHR: Liza Cuero, Coordinator Human Resources
CNO: Kerry Radcliffe, JD, Chief Nursing Officer
Web address: www.khrehabcentraltexas.com/
**Control:** Partnership, Investor–owned, for–profit **Service:** Rehabilitation

**Staffed Beds:** 50 **Admissions:** 1130 **Census:** 42 **Outpatient Visits:** 26
**Births:** 0 **Total Expense ($000):** 18797 **Payroll Expense ($000):** 8541
**Personnel:** 117

☐ **CORNERSTONE HOSPITAL OF AUSTIN (452034)**, 4207 Burnet Road,
Zip 78756–3396; tel. 512/706–1900, (Includes CORNERSTONE HOSPITAL OF
AUSTIN, 1005 East 32nd Street, Zip 78705; tel. 512/867–5822; Edward J.
Sherwood, M.D., Chief Executive Officer; CORNERSTONE HOSPITAL OF ROUND
ROCK, 4681 College Park Drive, Round Rock, Zip 78665; tel. 512/533–2525;
Edward L. Dyer, Chief Executive Officer) **A**1 9 10 **F**1 3 29 30 45 75 77 87 91
148 **S** Cornerstone Healthcare Group, Dallas, TX
Primary Contact: Scott Galliardt, Chief Executive Officer
CMO: David F. Pohl, M.D., Chief of Staff
Web address: www.chghospitals.com/austin/
**Control:** Corporation, Investor–owned, for–profit **Service:** Long–Term Acute Care
hospital

**Staffed Beds:** 118 **Admissions:** 765 **Census:** 55 **Outpatient Visits:** 0 **Births:**
0 **Total Expense ($000):** 23579 **Payroll Expense ($000):** 11945
**Personnel:** 209

⊞ **DELL CHILDREN'S MEDICAL CENTER OF CENTRAL TEXAS (453310)**, 4900
Mueller Boulevard, Zip 78723–3079; tel. 512/324–0000 **A**1 2 3 5 9 10 **F**3 11
19 21 23 25 27 29 30 31 32 34 40 41 43 44 46 49 50 53 54 58 59
61 64 65 68 71 72 74 75 77 78 79 80 81 82 83 84 85 86 87 88 89 93 99
100 101 104 107 108 111 112 114 115 118 119 126 129 130 131 132 135
143 146 148 **P**3 8 **S** Ascension Health, Saint Louis, MO
Primary Contact: Robert I. Bonar, Jr., Chief Executive Officer
Web address: www.dellchildrens.net
**Control:** Church–operated, Nongovernment, not–for profit **Service:** Children's
general

**Staffed Beds:** 248 **Admissions:** 8606 **Census:** 111 **Outpatient Visits:**
309833 **Births:** 0 **Total Expense ($000):** 344951 **Payroll Expense ($000):**
170515 **Personnel:** 2451

⊞ **HEALTHSOUTH REHABILITATION HOSPITAL OF AUSTIN (453044)**, 1215
Red River Street, Zip 78701–1921; tel. 512/474–5700 **A**1 9 10 **F**3 29 56 62
74 75 77 79 86 87 90 91 130 132 143 148 **P**5 **S** HEALTHSOUTH Corporation,
Birmingham, AL
Primary Contact: Sandra Hegland, Chief Executive Officer
CFO: Pamela McLaughlin, Chief Financial Officer
CMO: Johnny Shane Ross, Executive Medical Director
CHR: Debbie Belcher, Director Human Resources
CNO: Paul Bruce, Chief Nursing Officer
Web address: www.healthsouthaustin.com
**Control:** Corporation, Investor–owned, for–profit **Service:** Rehabilitation

**Staffed Beds:** 40 **Admissions:** 802 **Census:** 29 **Outpatient Visits:** 10455
**Births:** 0 **Total Expense ($000):** 15255 **Payroll Expense ($000):** 7393
**Personnel:** 125

☐ **NORTHWEST HILLS SURGICAL HOSPITAL (450808)**, 6818 Austin Center
Boulevard, Suite 100, Zip 78731–3199; tel. 512/346–1994 **A**1 9 10 **F**3 40 45
64 79 81
Primary Contact: Scott Cullen, Chief Executive Officer
CFO: Jenny Salome, Chief Financial Officer and Assistant Administrator
Web address: www.northwesthillssurgical.com
**Control:** Partnership, Investor–owned, for–profit **Service:** General Medical and
Surgical

**Staffed Beds:** 8 **Admissions:** 413 **Census:** 1 **Outpatient Visits:** 6014 **Births:**
0 **Total Expense ($000):** 23709 **Payroll Expense ($000):** 4527 **Personnel:**
93

☐ **RELIANT AUSTIN (673054)**, 330 West Ben White Boulevard, Zip 78704;
tel. 512/730–4800 **A**1 9 10 **F**3 29 90 96 130 148
Primary Contact: Jack Boggess, Chief Executive Officer
CNO: Vidette J. Forbes, R.N., Chief Nursing Officer and Chief Operating Officer
Web address: www.reliantaustin.com
**Control:** Partnership, Investor–owned, for–profit **Service:** Rehabilitation

**Staffed Beds:** 60 **Admissions:** 647 **Census:** 18 **Outpatient Visits:** 0 **Births:**
0 **Total Expense ($000):** 10370 **Payroll Expense ($000):** 3722 **Personnel:**
74

⊞ ◇ **SETON MEDICAL CENTER AUSTIN (450056)**, 1201 West 38th Street,
Zip 78705–1006; tel. 512/324–1000 **A**1 2 3 5 9 10 21 **F**3 11 12 13 15 18 20
22 24 26 28 29 30 31 34 35 40 43 44 45 46 49 50 51 57 58 59 60 61 64
68 70 72 74 75 76 77 78 79 80 81 82 84 85 86 87 93 107 108 111 114
115 119 126 130 131 132 135 137 145 146 147 148 **P**3 8 **S** Ascension
Health, Saint Louis, MO
Primary Contact: Katherine Henderson, Chief Executive Officer
COO: Charlotte Thrasher, Vice President and Chief Operating Officer
CFO: Douglas D. Waite, Chief Financial Officer
CMO: Carol Wratten, M.D., Vice President Medical Affairs
CIO: Gerry Lewis, Chief Information Officer
CHR: Fenorris Pearson, Chief Human Resources Officer
CNO: Angela Stalbaum, R.N., Chief Nursing Officer
Web address: www.seton.net
**Control:** Church–operated, Nongovernment, not–for profit **Service:** General
Medical and Surgical

**Staffed Beds:** 422 **Admissions:** 20487 **Census:** 274 **Outpatient Visits:**
77333 **Births:** 3857 **Total Expense ($000):** 392321 **Payroll Expense
($000):** 148883 **Personnel:** 2344

⊞ **SETON NORTHWEST HOSPITAL (450867)**, 11113 Research Boulevard,
Zip 78759–5236; tel. 512/324–6000 **A**1 2 3 5 9 10 **F**3 11 12 13 15 18 29 30
31 34 35 36 37 40 43 44 45 47 49 50 51 57 59 64 68 70 73 74 75 76 77
78 79 80 81 85 86 87 93 107 111 114 119 130 131 132 135 146 148 **P**3 8
**S** Ascension Health, Saint Louis, MO
Primary Contact: Karen Litterer, R.N., MSN, Administrator and Chief Operating
Officer
COO: Karen Litterer, R.N., Administrator and Chief Operating Officer
CFO: Douglas D. Waite, Chief Financial Officer
CMO: Ed LeBlanc, M.D., Vice President Medical Affairs
CIO: Gerry Lewis, Chief Information Officer
CHR: Trennis Jones, Senior Vice President and Chief Administrative Officer
Web address: www.seton.net
**Control:** Church–operated, Nongovernment, not–for profit **Service:** General
Medical and Surgical

**Staffed Beds:** 74 **Admissions:** 5206 **Census:** 48 **Outpatient Visits:** 51393
**Births:** 1186 **Total Expense ($000):** 76385 **Payroll Expense ($000):** 35024
**Personnel:** 450

⊞ **SETON SHOAL CREEK HOSPITAL (454029)**, 3501 Mills Avenue,
Zip 78731–6391; tel. 512/324–2000 **A**1 3 9 10 **F**4 5 29 30 34 68 86 87 98
99 100 101 103 104 130 132 135 146 **P**3 8 **S** Ascension Health, Saint
Louis, MO
Primary Contact: William Henricks, Vice President and Chief Operating Officer
CFO: Alan Strauss, Senior Vice President and Chief Financial Officer
CMO: Kari Wolf, M.D., Medical Director
CIO: Gerry Lewis, Chief Information Officer
CHR: Joe Canales, Director Human Resources
CNO: Elizabeth Steger, Chief Nursing Officer
Web address: www.seton.net
**Control:** Church–operated, Nongovernment, not–for profit **Service:** Psychiatric

**Staffed Beds:** 92 **Admissions:** 4361 **Census:** 66 **Outpatient Visits:** 37252
**Births:** 0 **Total Expense ($000):** 29127 **Payroll Expense ($000):** 17211
**Personnel:** 302

⊞ **SETON SOUTHWEST HOSPITAL (450865)**, 7900 F. M. 1826,
Zip 78737–1407; tel. 512/324–9000 **A**1 9 10 **F**3 11 13 15 28 29 30 34 35
36 40 43 44 45 57 59 64 68 71 72 75 76 79 81 85 87 93 107 110 111 115
119 130 131 132 135 146 147 **P**3 8 **S** Ascension Health, Saint Louis, MO
Primary Contact: Mary Faria, FACHE, Ph.D., Vice President and Chief Operating
Officer
Web address: www.seton.net
**Control:** Church–operated, Nongovernment, not–for profit **Service:** General
Medical and Surgical

**Staffed Beds:** 33 **Admissions:** 914 **Census:** 7 **Outpatient Visits:** 30932
**Births:** 709 **Total Expense ($000):** 26569 **Payroll Expense ($000):** 11843
**Personnel:** 117

**TX**

☒ ◇ **ST. DAVID'S MEDICAL CENTER (450431)**, 919 East 32nd Street, Zip 78705–2709, Mailing Address: P.O. Box 4039, Zip 78765–4039; tel. 512/476–7111, (Includes HEART HOSPITAL OF AUSTIN, 3801 North Lamar Boulevard, Zip 78756–4080; tel. 512/407–7000; David Laird, Chief Executive Officer; ST. DAVID'S GEORGETOWN HOSPITAL, 2000 Scenic Drive, Georgetown, Zip 78626–7726; tel. 512/943–3000; Hugh Brown, Chief Executive Officer; ST. DAVID'S REHABILITATION CENTER, 1005 East 32nd Street, Zip 78705–2713, Mailing Address: P.O. Box 4270, Zip 78765–4270; tel. 512/544–5100; Diane Owens, Assistant Administrator) **A**1 2 3 5 9 10 21 **F**3 11 12 13 15 17 18 20 22 24 26 28 29 30 31 34 35 36 37 39 40 43 45 46 47 48 49 52 53 56 57 58 59 61 64 68 70 72 73 74 75 76 77 78 79 81 85 86 87 90 93 95 96 107 108 109 110 111 114 115 116 119 126 130 131 132 135 146 147 148 **P**3 6 8 **S** HCA, Nashville, TN
Primary Contact: Donald H. Wilkerson, Chief Executive Officer
COO: David Shimp, Chief Operating Officer
CFO: Julie Perez, Chief Financial Officer
CMO: John Marietta, M.D., Chief Medical Officer
CIO: Richard Lear, Director Information Systems
CHR: Julie Hajek, Director Human Resources
Web address: www.stdavids.com
**Control:** Other not–for–profit (including NFP Corporation) **Service:** General Medical and Surgical

**Staffed Beds:** 553 **Admissions:** 25927 **Census:** 392 **Outpatient Visits:** 207831 **Births:** 5518 **Total Expense ($000):** 467452 **Payroll Expense ($000):** 154097 **Personnel:** 2554

☒ **ST. DAVID'S NORTH AUSTIN MEDICAL CENTER (450809)**, 12221 North MoPac Expressway, Zip 78758–2496; tel. 512/901–1000 **A**1 2 3 10 **F**3 12 13 15 18 20 22 24 26 28 29 30 31 34 35 37 40 41 42 43 45 47 49 53 54 56 57 59 64 68 70 72 73 74 75 76 77 78 79 81 82 85 86 87 88 89 90 93 107 108 111 115 118 119 126 129 130 131 132 138 144 145 146 147 148 **P**3 6 8 **S** HCA, Nashville, TN
Primary Contact: Allen Harrison, Chief Executive Officer
COO: Sheri Dube, Chief Operating Officer
CFO: Natalie Pack, Chief Financial Officer
CMO: Kenneth W. Mitchell, M.D., Medical Director
CIO: Marshall Pearson, Director Management Information Systems
CHR: Laura Light, Director Human Resources
Web address: www.northaustin.com
**Control:** Other not–for–profit (including NFP Corporation) **Service:** General Medical and Surgical

**Staffed Beds:** 363 **Admissions:** 18162 **Census:** 252 **Outpatient Visits:** 139556 **Births:** 6465 **Total Expense ($000):** 239738 **Payroll Expense ($000):** 84466 **Personnel:** 1437

☒ **ST. DAVID'S SOUTH AUSTIN MEDICAL CENTER (450713)**, 901 West Ben White Boulevard, Zip 78704–6903; tel. 512/447–2211 **A**1 2 3 5 9 10 **F**11 12 13 15 17 18 20 22 24 26 28 29 30 31 34 35 37 40 42 43 45 46 49 54 56 59 64 68 70 73 74 75 76 77 78 79 80 81 82 84 85 87 93 107 108 110 111 114 115 119 124 126 129 130 136 144 145 146 147 148 **P**3 6 8 **S** HCA, Nashville, TN
Primary Contact: Todd E. Steward, Chief Executive Officer
COO: Brett Matens, Chief Operating Officer
CFO: Wesley D. Fountain, Chief Financial Officer
CMO: Albert Gros, M.D., Chief Medical Officer
CIO: Richard Lear, Director Information Systems
CHR: Lisa Talbot, Director Human Resources
CNO: Sally A. Gillam, R.N., Chief Nursing Officer
Web address: www.southaustinmc.com
**Control:** Other not–for–profit (including NFP Corporation) **Service:** General Medical and Surgical

**Staffed Beds:** 266 **Admissions:** 15318 **Census:** 194 **Outpatient Visits:** 142423 **Births:** 1621 **Total Expense ($000):** 199799 **Payroll Expense ($000):** 68626 **Personnel:** 1174

☒ **TEXAS NEUROREHAB CENTER (452038)**, 1106 West Dittmar, Zip 78745–6328, Mailing Address: P.O. Box 150459, Zip 78715–0459; tel. 512/444–4835 **A**1 9 10 **F**1 10 29 43 54 74 75 79 93 108 130 148 **P**5 **S** Universal Health Services, Inc., King of Prussia, PA
Primary Contact: Cindy Mostaffa, Chief Executive Officer
COO: Janet Bitner, Chief Operating Officer
CFO: Omar Correa, Chief Financial Officer
CMO: James Boysen, M.D., Executive Medical Director
CHR: Colleen Lewis, Director Human Resources
Web address: www.texasneurorehab.com
**Control:** Partnership, Investor–owned, for–profit **Service:** Long–Term Acute Care hospital

**Staffed Beds:** 47 **Admissions:** 470 **Census:** 41 **Outpatient Visits:** 6212 **Births:** 0 **Total Expense ($000):** 12195 **Payroll Expense ($000):** 7265 **Personnel:** 294

☐ **TEXAS STAR RECOVERY (454111)**, 1106 West Dittmar Road, Zip 78745–6328; tel. 512/462–6729, (Nonreporting) **A**1 10
Primary Contact: Janet Bitner, Chief Operating Officer
Web address: www.texasstarrecovery.com
**Control:** Partnership, Investor–owned, for–profit **Service:** Psychiatric

**Staffed Beds:** 28

**THE HOSPITAL AT WESTLAKE MEDICAL CENTER (670006)**, 5656 Bee Caves Road, Zip 78746–5280; tel. 512/327–0000 **A**9 10 **F**3 18 20 22 24 26 28 29 37 40 45 51 53 58 59 64 68 70 75 77 79 81 82 85 93 96 107 108 111 114 118 119 129 130 131 135 148
Primary Contact: Rip Miller, Chief Executive Officer
CFO: Devon Culbert, Controller
CMO: Tom Burns, M.D., Chief of Staff
CHR: Kellie Bryson, Director Human Resources
Web address: www.westlakemedical.com
**Control:** Partnership, Investor–owned, for–profit **Service:** General Medical and Surgical

**Staffed Beds:** 23 **Admissions:** 1049 **Census:** 7 **Outpatient Visits:** 10066 **Births:** 0 **Total Expense ($000):** 38136 **Payroll Expense ($000):** 11201 **Personnel:** 194

☒ ◇ **UNIVERSITY MEDICAL CENTER AT BRACKENRIDGE (450124)**, 601 East 15th Street, Zip 78701–1996; tel. 512/324–7000 **A**1 2 3 5 9 10 21 **F**3 11 13 15 18 20 22 24 26 29 30 31 34 35 37 39 40 43 44 45 47 49 55 57 58 59 60 64 65 66 68 70 71 72 74 75 76 77 78 79 81 82 84 85 87 93 97 102 104 107 108 110 111 114 115 118 119 124 130 132 135 143 146 148 **P**3 8 **S** Ascension Health, Saint Louis, MO
Primary Contact: Christann Vasquez, President
COO: Debra T. Hernandez, R.N., Vice President Chief Operating Officer
CFO: Alan Strauss, Chief Financial Officer
CMO: Tom Caven, M.D., Vice President Medical Affairs
CIO: Thomas Ellinger, Vice President
CHR: Joe Canales, Vice President Human Resources
CNO: Debra T. Hernandez, R.N., Chief Nursing Officer
Web address: www.seton.net
**Control:** Church–operated, Nongovernment, not–for profit **Service:** General Medical and Surgical

**Staffed Beds:** 188 **Admissions:** 13184 **Census:** 175 **Outpatient Visits:** 608186 **Births:** 1387 **Total Expense ($000):** 608868 **Payroll Expense ($000):** 254167 **Personnel:** 3405

**AZLE—Tarrant County**

☒ **TEXAS HEALTH HARRIS METHODIST HOSPITAL AZLE (450419)**, 108 Denver Trail, Zip 76020–3614; tel. 817/444–8600 **A**1 9 10 **F**3 11 15 18 29 30 34 35 40 43 45 56 57 59 64 70 75 77 79 81 85 93 107 110 114 119 130 135 146 147 148 **S** Texas Health Resources, Arlington, TX
Primary Contact: Bob S. Ellzey, FACHE, President
CFO: Brian Blessing, Chief Financial Officer
CMO: Judy Laviolette, M.D., Chief Medical Officer
CIO: Patricia Johnston, Vice President Information Services
CHR: Lance Waring, Director Human Resources
CNO: Valarie Gilbert, R.N., Chief Nursing Officer
Web address: www.texashealth.org/Azle
**Control:** Other not–for–profit (including NFP Corporation) **Service:** General Medical and Surgical

**Staffed Beds:** 31 **Admissions:** 1370 **Census:** 13 **Outpatient Visits:** 33423 **Births:** 0 **Total Expense ($000):** 30820 **Payroll Expense ($000):** 14079 **Personnel:** 198

**BALLINGER—Runnels County**

**BALLINGER MEMORIAL HOSPITAL (451310)**, 608 Avenue B, Zip 76821–2499, Mailing Address: P.O. Box 617, Zip 76821–0617; tel. 325/365–2531 **A**9 10 18 **F**3 7 11 29 34 40 43 53 57 64 65 68 77 93 107 114 127 128 130 133 **P**5
Primary Contact: Becky Ellis, Interim Chief Executive Officer
CFO: Josilyn Peterson, Chief Financial Officer
CHR: Roselyn Hudgens, Director Human Resources
Web address: www.ballingerhospital.org
**Control:** Hospital district or authority, Government, nonfederal **Service:** General Medical and Surgical

**Staffed Beds:** 16 **Admissions:** 128 **Census:** 2 **Outpatient Visits:** 15372 **Births:** 0 **Total Expense ($000):** 7681 **Payroll Expense ($000):** 3318 **Personnel:** 79

**TX**

---

**Hospital, Medicare Provider Number, Address, Telephone, Approval, Facility, and Physician Codes, Health Care System**

★ American Hospital Association (AHA) membership  ○ Healthcare Facilities Accreditation Program  ⇑ Center for Improvement in Healthcare Quality Accreditation
☐ The Joint Commission accreditation  ◇ DNV Healthcare Inc. accreditation  △ Commission on Accreditation of Rehabilitation Facilities (CARF) accreditation

**BAY CITY—Matagorda County**

✠ **MATAGORDA REGIONAL MEDICAL CENTER (450465)**, 104 7th Street, Zip 77414–4853; tel. 979/245–6383 **A**1 9 10 20 **F**3 11 13 15 18 20 22 28 29 30 32 34 38 39 40 43 46 47 50 51 53 56 57 59 64 65 66 68 70 75 76 77 79 81 82 85 86 89 93 98 103 107 108 110 111 114 119 130 132 135 146 147 148 **S** QHR, Brentwood, TN
Primary Contact: Steven L. Smith, Chief Executive Officer
CFO: Bryan Prochnow, Chief Financial Officer
CIO: Mary Ann Cervantes, District Director Management Information Systems
CHR: Cindy Krebs, District Director Human Resources
CNO: Mike Lee, R.N., Chief Nursing Officer
Web address: www.matagordaregional.org
**Control:** Hospital district or authority, Government, nonfederal **Service:** General Medical and Surgical

**Staffed Beds:** 58 **Admissions:** 2136 **Census:** 25 **Outpatient Visits:** 47166 **Births:** 553 **Total Expense ($000):** 54629 **Payroll Expense ($000):** 18173 **Personnel:** 291

**BAYTOWN—Harris County**

★ ◇ **HOUSTON METHODIST SAN JACINTO HOSPITAL (450424)**, 4401 Garth Road, Zip 77521–2122; tel. 281/420–8600, (Includes HOUSTON METHODIST SAN JACINTO HOSPITAL – ALEXANDER, 1700 James Bowie Drive, Zip 77520–3386; tel. 281/420–6100), (Total facility includes 30 beds in nursing home–type unit) **A**2 3 9 10 13 21 **F**3 4 8 11 12 13 15 18 20 22 24 26 28 29 30 31 34 35 38 40 41 44 48 49 50 51 53 57 59 61 64 65 67 68 70 71 73 74 75 76 77 78 79 81 82 85 86 87 90 91 93 96 97 98 102 103 107 108 110 111 114 115 116 117 118 119 120 121 123 126 128 129 130 132 145 146 147 148 **S** Houston Methodist, Houston, TX
Primary Contact: David P. Bernard, Administrator
CFO: Jonathan Sturgis, Chief Financial Officer
CMO: Bruce Kennedy, M.D., Chief Medical Officer
CHR: Sherri Davis–Sampson, Director Human Resources
CNO: Jane DeStefano, R.N., Chief Nursing Officer
Web address: www.houstonmethodist.org
**Control:** Other not–for–profit (including NFP Corporation) **Service:** General Medical and Surgical

**Staffed Beds:** 275 **Admissions:** 12644 **Census:** 178 **Outpatient Visits:** 117494 **Births:** 1659 **Total Expense ($000):** 220669 **Payroll Expense ($000):** 83869 **Personnel:** 1349

**BEAUMONT—Jefferson County**

★ ◇ **BAPTIST HOSPITALS OF SOUTHEAST TEXAS (450346)**, 3080 College Street, Zip 77701–4689, Mailing Address: P.O. Box 1591, Zip 77704–1591; tel. 409/212–5000, (Includes BAPTIST HOSPITALS OF SOUTHEAST TEXAS FANNIN BEHAVIORAL HEALTH CENTER, 3250 Fannin Street, Zip 77701; tel. 409/212–7000) **A**2 9 10 21 **F**3 5 11 13 15 17 18 20 22 24 26 28 29 30 31 34 35 37 40 41 43 45 49 51 55 57 59 60 64 70 72 73 74 75 76 77 78 79 81 82 84 85 86 87 88 89 90 93 96 98 99 100 101 102 103 104 105 107 108 110 111 114 115 117 118 119 120 121 123 124 130 132 135 144 146 147 **P**6 **S** Community Hospital Corporation, Plano, TX
Primary Contact: David N. Parmer, Chief Executive Officer
CFO: Gary Troutman, CPA, Chief Financial Officer
CIO: William Toon, Chief Information Officer
CHR: Deborah Verret, JD, Chief Human Resources Officer
Web address: www.bhset.net
**Control:** Other not–for–profit (including NFP Corporation) **Service:** General Medical and Surgical

**Staffed Beds:** 349 **Admissions:** 15293 **Census:** 197 **Outpatient Visits:** 137352 **Births:** 1195 **Total Expense ($000):** 212116 **Payroll Expense ($000):** 79401 **Personnel:** 1315

**BEAUMONT BONE AND JOINT INSTITUTE (670007)**, 3650 Laurel Street, Zip 77707–2216; tel. 409/838–0346, (Nonreporting) **A**9 10
Primary Contact: Duane N. Hill, Chief Executive Officer
Web address: www.orthodoc.aaos.org/bbji/
**Control:** Partnership, Investor–owned, for–profit **Service:** General Medical and Surgical

**Staffed Beds:** 6

✠ **CHRISTUS DUBUIS HOSPITAL OF BEAUMONT (452042)**, 2830 Calder Avenue, 4th Floor, Zip 77702–1809; tel. 409/899–8154 **A**1 9 10 **F**1 3 18 29 30 31 35 130 148 **S** CHRISTUS Health, Irving, TX
Primary Contact: Kathie Reese, Interim Administrator
Web address: www.christusdubuis.org/BeaumontandPortArthurSystem–CHRISTUSDubuisHospitalofBeaumont
**Control:** Church–operated, Nongovernment, not–for–profit **Service:** Long–Term Acute Care hospital

**Staffed Beds:** 51 **Admissions:** 498 **Census:** 34 **Outpatient Visits:** 0 **Births:** 0 **Total Expense ($000):** 15465 **Payroll Expense ($000):** 6141 **Personnel:** 106

✠ **CHRISTUS HOSPITAL–ST. ELIZABETH (450034)**, 2830 Calder Avenue, Zip 77702–1809, Mailing Address: P.O. Box 5405, Zip 77726–5405; tel. 409/892–7171, (Includes CHRISTUS HOSPITAL–ST. MARY, 3600 Gates Boulevard, Port Arthur, Zip 77642–3601, Mailing Address: P.O. Box 3696, Zip 77643–3696; tel. 409/985–7431; Wayne Moore, Administrator) **A**1 2 3 9 10 **F**3 11 12 13 15 17 18 20 22 24 26 28 29 30 31 34 35 36 38 40 43 44 45 46 49 50 51 54 57 59 60 63 64 70 72 74 75 76 77 78 79 81 82 85 86 87 88 89 93 94 107 108 111 114 118 119 124 126 130 131 132 144 146 147 148 **P**8 **S** CHRISTUS Health, Irving, TX
Primary Contact: Paul Trevino, Chief Executive Officer
CFO: Shawn Adams, Chief Financial Officer
CMO: Rick Tyler, M.D., Vice President Medical Affairs
CIO: Robert Jacobs, Regional Director Information Management
CHR: Charles Foster, Regional Director Human Resources
Web address: www.christushospital.org
**Control:** Church–operated, Nongovernment, not–for profit **Service:** General Medical and Surgical

**Staffed Beds:** 436 **Admissions:** 17943 **Census:** 215 **Outpatient Visits:** 347374 **Births:** 2579 **Total Expense ($000):** 319247 **Payroll Expense ($000):** 102749 **Personnel:** 1441

**HARBOR HOSPITAL OF SOUTHEAST TEXAS (452093)**, 860 South 8th Street, Zip 77701–4626; tel. 409/840–3200 **A**9 10 **F**1 3 29 30 35 45 85 130 148
Primary Contact: Ronald Hunt, Chief Executive Officer
Web address: www.hhsetx.com
**Control:** Partnership, Investor–owned, for–profit **Service:** Long–Term Acute Care hospital

**Staffed Beds:** 30 **Admissions:** 351 **Census:** 22 **Outpatient Visits:** 0 **Births:** 0 **Total Expense ($000):** 10890 **Payroll Expense ($000):** 3896 **Personnel:** 53

✠ **HEALTHSOUTH REHABILITATION HOSPITAL OF BEAUMONT (453048)**, 3340 Plaza 10 Boulevard, Zip 77707–2551; tel. 409/835–0835 **A**1 9 10 **F**3 28 29 30 62 64 74 75 77 79 87 90 91 93 95 96 131 132 148 **S** HEALTHSOUTH Corporation, Birmingham, AL
Primary Contact: H. J. Gaspard, Chief Executive Officer
CFO: David Pipkins, Controller
CMO: Linda C. Smith, M.D., Medical Director
CHR: Joanna Donica, Director Human Resource
CNO: Barbara Morris, R.N., Chief Nursing Officer
Web address: www.healthsouthbeaumont.com
**Control:** Corporation, Investor–owned, for–profit **Service:** Rehabilitation

**Staffed Beds:** 61 **Admissions:** 691 **Census:** 24 **Outpatient Visits:** 6834 **Births:** 0 **Total Expense ($000):** 11821 **Payroll Expense ($000):** 6069 **Personnel:** 118

**MEMORIAL HERMANN BAPTIST FANNIN BEHAVIORAL HEALTH CENTER**
See Baptist Hospitals of Southeast Texas Fannin Behavioral Health Center

☐ **VICTORY MEDICAL CENTER BEAUMONT**, 6025 Metropolitan Drive, Zip 77706–2407; tel. 409/617–7700 **A**1 **F**3 29 40 45 49 79 81 82 85 86 97 107 111 114 119 143 **P**5 **S** Victory Healthcare, The Woodlands, TX
Primary Contact: Becky Ames, Chief Executive Officer
Web address: www.victory–healthcare.com/beaumont
**Control:** Partnership, Investor–owned, for–profit **Service:** Surgical

**Staffed Beds:** 17 **Admissions:** 166 **Census:** 1 **Outpatient Visits:** 5029 **Births:** 0 **Total Expense ($000):** 28005 **Payroll Expense ($000):** 6493 **Personnel:** 99

**BEDFORD—Tarrant County**

☐ **RELIANT REHABILITATION HOSPITAL MID–CITIES (673044)**, 2304 State Highway 121, Zip 76021–5985; tel. 817/684–2000 **A**1 9 10 **F**3 29 90 96 148
Primary Contact: Robert M. Smart, Chief Executive Officer
CFO: Mary Mwaniki, Chief Financial Officer
CMO: Toni Willis, M.D., Medical Director
CHR: Christie Moore, Director Human Resources
Web address: www.relianthcp.com
**Control:** Partnership, Investor–owned, for–profit **Service:** Rehabilitation

**Staffed Beds:** 60 **Admissions:** 1353 **Census:** 39 **Outpatient Visits:** 0 **Births:** 0 **Total Expense ($000):** 14846 **Payroll Expense ($000):** 6468 **Personnel:** 117

**TX**

✠ **TEXAS HEALTH HARRIS METHODIST HOSPITAL HURST–EULESS–BEDFORD (450639)**, 1600 Hospital Parkway, Zip 76022–6913, Mailing Address: P.O. Box 669, Zip 76095–0669; tel. 817/685–4000, (Includes TEXAS HEALTH SPRINGWOOD, 1608 Hospital Parkway, Zip 76022; tel. 817/355–7700; Ramona Osburn, Senior Vice President, Texas Health Resources Behavioral Health) **A**1 2 9 10 **F**9 11 12 13 15 18 20 22 24 26 28 29 30 31 34 35 40 43 47 49 50 53 60 64 70 72 74 75 76 78 79 80 81 82 86 87 93 107 108 111 114 118 119 126 130 131 132 134 135 146 147 148 **S** Texas Health Resources, Arlington, TX
Primary Contact: Deborah Paganelli, President
COO: Alice Landers, Administrative Director Operations
CFO: Jaime James, Entity Finance Officer
CMO: Susann Land, M.D., Chief Medical Officer
CHR: Lee Mulvey, Human Resource Officer
CNO: Debra Grant, R.N., Chief Nursing Officer
Web address: www.texashealth.org
**Control:** Other not–for–profit (including NFP Corporation) **Service:** General Medical and Surgical

**Staffed Beds:** 210 **Admissions:** 14392 **Census:** 180 **Outpatient Visits:** 83022 **Births:** 2086 **Total Expense ($000):** 231873 **Payroll Expense ($000):** 94222 **Personnel:** 1358

### BEEVILLE—Bee County

✠ **CHRISTUS SPOHN HOSPITAL BEEVILLE (450082)**, 1500 East Houston Street, Zip 78102–5312; tel. 361/354–2000 **A**1 9 10 20 **F**3 11 13 15 29 30 32 34 35 40 43 45 50 57 59 64 70 75 76 77 79 81 85 86 87 93 97 107 108 111 119 130 132 146 147 148 **P**8 **S** CHRISTUS Health, Irving, TX
Primary Contact: Nathan Tudor, Vice President and Chief Executive Officer
Web address: www.christusspohn.org
**Control:** Church–operated, Nongovernment, not–for profit **Service:** General Medical and Surgical

**Staffed Beds:** 49 **Admissions:** 1918 **Census:** 18 **Outpatient Visits:** 39245 **Births:** 401 **Total Expense ($000):** 27958 **Payroll Expense ($000):** 11489 **Personnel:** 149

### BELLAIRE—Harris County

◇ **FIRST SURGICAL HOSPITAL**, 4801 Bissonnet, Zip 77401–4028; tel. 713/275–1111, (Data for 95 days) **A**9 10 21 **F**3 12 29 40 48 49 64 65 79 81 82 85 107 111 119 126 130
Primary Contact: David Kreye, Chief Executive Officer
Web address: www.firststreethospital.com
**Control:** Other not–for–profit (including NFP Corporation) **Service:** General Medical and Surgical

**Staffed Beds:** 19 **Admissions:** 399 **Census:** 5 **Outpatient Visits:** 998 **Births:** 0 **Total Expense ($000):** 28810 **Payroll Expense ($000):** 2775 **Personnel:** 142

☐ **HOUSTON ORTHOPEDIC AND SPINE HOSPITAL (670012)**, 5410 West Loop South, Zip 77401–2103; tel. 713/314–4500 **A**1 3 5 9 10 **F**3 29 37 40 57 64 74 77 79 81 82 85 91 93 107 111 114 119 126 130 131 **S** Foundation Surgical Hospital Affiliates, Oklahoma City, OK
Primary Contact: Andrew Knizley, Chief Executive Officer
CMO: L. V. Ansell, M.D., Medical Director
Web address: www.foundationsurgicalhospital.com
**Control:** Partnership, Investor–owned, for–profit **Service:** Surgical

**Staffed Beds:** 64 **Admissions:** 2081 **Census:** 15 **Outpatient Visits:** 10557 **Births:** 0 **Total Expense ($000):** 66165 **Payroll Expense ($000):** 15393 **Personnel:** 277

### BELLVILLE—Austin County

**BELLVILLE GENERAL HOSPITAL** See Bellville St. Joseph Health Center

✠ **BELLVILLE ST. JOSEPH HEALTH CENTER (450253)**, 44 North Cummings Street, Zip 77418–1347, Mailing Address: P.O. Box 977, Zip 77418–0977; tel. 979/413–7400 **A**1 9 10 **F**3 11 15 29 34 40 43 45 50 53 57 59 64 65 68 75 81 93 107 110 111 114 119 127 130 133 146 **S** Catholic Health Initiatives, Englewood, CO
Primary Contact: Mark Riggins, Administrator
CMO: Christophe Gay, M.D., Chief of Staff
CHR: Jacqueline McEuen, Coordinator Human Resources
Web address: www.st-joseph.org/body.cfm?id=773
**Control:** Other not–for–profit (including NFP Corporation) **Service:** General Medical and Surgical

**Staffed Beds:** 23 **Admissions:** 227 **Census:** 2 **Outpatient Visits:** 19036 **Births:** 0 **Total Expense ($000):** 12106 **Payroll Expense ($000):** 4385 **Personnel:** 87

### BELTON—Bell County

☐ **CEDAR CREST HOSPITAL AND RESIDENTIAL TREATMENT CENTER (454114)**, 3500 I–35 South, Zip 76513; tel. 254/939–2100 **A**1 9 10 **F**4 29 34 35 59 68 86 87 98 99 100 101 102 103 104 105 106 130 143 **P**4 **S** Acadia Healthcare Company, Inc., Franklin, TN
Primary Contact: Rob Marsh, Chief Executive Officer
CFO: Melissa West, Chief Financial Officer
CMO: Sarah Guzman, M.D., Medical Director
CIO: Cesar Osario, Specialist Information Technology
CHR: Tracy McHaney, Director Human Resources
CNO: Donna Chisholm, Interim Director of Nursing Services
Web address: www.cedarcresthospital.com
**Control:** Corporation, Investor–owned, for–profit **Service:** Psychiatric

**Staffed Beds:** 88 **Admissions:** 2103 **Census:** 54 **Outpatient Visits:** 1988 **Births:** 0 **Total Expense ($000):** 9268 **Payroll Expense ($000):** 5132 **Personnel:** 128

### BIG LAKE—Reagan County

★ **REAGAN MEMORIAL HOSPITAL (451301)**, 805 North Main Street, Zip 76932–3999; tel. 325/884–2561 **A**9 10 18 **F**3 40 43 53 57 89 93 107 114 115 128 130 133 143 **P**5
Primary Contact: Keith L. Butler, Administrator
CMO: Joseph Sudolcan, M.D., Medical Director
**Control:** Hospital district or authority, Government, nonfederal **Service:** General Medical and Surgical

**Staffed Beds:** 7 **Admissions:** 23 **Census:** 1 **Outpatient Visits:** 4028 **Births:** 0 **Total Expense ($000):** 9525 **Payroll Expense ($000):** 2174 **Personnel:** 37

### BIG SPRING—Howard County

☐ **BIG SPRING STATE HOSPITAL (454000)**, 1901 North Highway 87, Zip 79720–0283; tel. 432/267–8216 **A**1 3 5 10 **F**3 30 39 50 56 59 61 68 74 75 77 86 87 98 101 103 106 130 132 135 146 **P**6 **S** Texas Department of State Health Services, Austin, TX
Primary Contact: Lorie Dunnam, Superintendent
CFO: Adrienne Bides, Assistant Chief Financial Officer and Budget Analyst
CMO: Ba Han, M.D., Clinical Director
CIO: Elizabeth Correa, Director Information Management
CHR: Lorie Couch, Assistant Superintendent
CNO: Stormy Ward, Chief Nurse Executive
Web address: www.dshs.state.tx.us/mhhospitals/BigSpringSH/default.shtm
**Control:** State–Government, nonfederal **Service:** Psychiatric

**Staffed Beds:** 200 **Admissions:** 547 **Census:** 189 **Outpatient Visits:** 0 **Births:** 0 **Total Expense ($000):** 23181 **Payroll Expense ($000):** 15325 **Personnel:** 551

✠ **SCENIC MOUNTAIN MEDICAL CENTER (450653)**, 1601 West 11th Place, Zip 79720–4198; tel. 432/263–1211 **A**1 9 10 20 **F**3 8 11 13 15 18 20 29 30 34 35 39 40 43 47 50 51 57 59 64 65 68 69 70 75 76 77 79 81 85 87 89 93 107 108 110 111 114 119 129 130 133 146 147 148 **P**6 **S** Community Health Systems, Inc., Franklin, TN
Primary Contact: Emma Krabill, Interim Chief Executive Officer
CFO: Rodger W. Bowen, M.P.H., Chief Financial Officer
CMO: Keith Ledford, M.D., Chief of Staff
CIO: Gene Mills, Director Information Technology
CHR: Dwight Linton, Director Human Resources
CNO: Judy Roever, MSN, Chief Nursing Officer
Web address: www.smmccares.com
**Control:** Corporation, Investor–owned, for–profit **Service:** General Medical and Surgical

**Staffed Beds:** 75 **Admissions:** 2105 **Census:** 19 **Outpatient Visits:** 30373 **Births:** 266 **Total Expense ($000):** 40119 **Payroll Expense ($000):** 13137 **Personnel:** 200

★ **WEST TEXAS VETERANS AFFAIRS HEALTH CARE SYSTEM**, 300 Veterans Boulevard, Zip 79720–5500; Mailing Address: Big Springs, tel. 432/263–7361, (Nonreporting) **A**3 5 9 **S** Department of Veterans Affairs, Washington, DC
Primary Contact: Adam M. Welch, Interim Director
CFO: Ray Olivas, Chief Fiscal Service
CMO: Martin Schnier, D.O., Chief of Staff
CIO: Mike McKinley, Information Security Officer
CHR: Anna Osborne, Chief Human Resources Management Service
Web address: www.bigspring.va.gov/about/
**Control:** Veterans Affairs, Government, federal **Service:** General Medical and Surgical

**Staffed Beds:** 149

**TX**

---

| **Hospital, Medicare Provider Number, Address, Telephone, Approval, Facility, and Physician Codes, Health Care System** | | |
|---|---|---|
| ★ American Hospital Association (AHA) membership | ◯ Healthcare Facilities Accreditation Program | ⇑ Center for Improvement in Healthcare Quality Accreditation |
| ☐ The Joint Commission accreditation | ◇ DNV Healthcare Inc. accreditation | △ Commission on Accreditation of Rehabilitation Facilities (CARF) accreditation |

## BONHAM—Fannin County

**SAM RAYBURN MEMORIAL VETERANS CENTER** See Veterans Affairs North Texas Health Care System, Dallas

★ ◇ **TMC BONHAM HOSPITAL (451370)**, 504 Lipscomb Street, Zip 75418–4028; tel. 903/583–8585 **A**9 10 18 21 **F**3 11 15 28 29 30 34 35 40 46 50 57 59 64 65 70 75 81 87 93 107 108 110 111 118 119 130 133 135 146
Primary Contact: Harley Smith, Chief Executive Officer
CFO: Jay Hodges, Chief Financial Officer
CMO: Michael Brown, D.O., Chief of Staff
CIO: Jack Farguson, Director Information Technology
CHR: Brenda Bagley, Director Human Resources
CNO: William Kiefer, Chief Nursing Officer
Web address: www.redriverregional.com/
**Control:** Hospital district or authority, Government, nonfederal **Service:** General Medical and Surgical

**Staffed Beds:** 25 **Admissions:** 682 **Census:** 8 **Outpatient Visits:** 14378 **Births:** 0 **Total Expense ($000):** 16257 **Payroll Expense ($000):** 6371 **Personnel:** 112

## BORGER—Hutchinson County

**GOLDEN PLAINS COMMUNITY HOSPITAL (451369)**, 100 Medical Drive, Zip 79007–7579; tel. 806/467–5700 **A**9 10 18 **F**11 13 15 29 30 34 35 40 43 45 50 54 57 59 62 64 65 66 68 70 75 76 77 79 81 85 86 87 93 107 108 115 119 127 130 131 132 133 146 147 148 **P**6
Primary Contact: Kevin Storey, Chief Executive Officer
COO: Melody Henderson, R.N., Chief Operating Officer and Chief Nursing Officer
CFO: Dennis P. Kilday, Chief Financial Officer
CMO: Bard Rogers, M.D., Chief of Staff
CHR: Sally Mason, Director Human Resources
Web address: www.goldenplains.org
**Control:** Corporation, Investor–owned, for–profit **Service:** General Medical and Surgical

**Staffed Beds:** 25 **Admissions:** 910 **Census:** 8 **Outpatient Visits:** 53498 **Births:** 340 **Total Expense ($000):** 25616 **Payroll Expense ($000):** 7522 **Personnel:** 194

## BOWIE—Montague County

**BOWIE MEMORIAL HOSPITAL (450497)**, 705 East Greenwood Avenue, Zip 76230–3199; tel. 940/872–1126 **A**9 10 **F**3 28 29 40 43 45 53 57 62 63 64 70 75 77 81 82 84 93 103 107 115 119 129 130 131 132 133 148 **P**4
Primary Contact: Michael L. McEachern, Chief Executive Officer
CFO: Kim Lee, Chief Financial Officer
CMO: Surinder Aujla, M.D., Chief of Staff
CIO: Randell Cox, Director Data Processing
CHR: Mary Bates, Director Human Resources
CNO: Pam Alexander, R.N., Chief Nursing Officer
Web address: www.bowiememorial.com
**Control:** Hospital district or authority, Government, nonfederal **Service:** General Medical and Surgical

**Staffed Beds:** 44 **Admissions:** 593 **Census:** 9 **Outpatient Visits:** 27751 **Births:** 0 **Total Expense ($000):** 13767 **Payroll Expense ($000):** 5484 **Personnel:** 189

## BRADY—Mcculloch County

**HEART OF TEXAS MEMORIAL HOSPITAL (451348)**, 2008 Nine Road, Zip 76825–7210, Mailing Address: P.O. Box 1150, Zip 76825–1150; tel. 325/597–2901 **A**9 10 18 **F**15 28 40 43 45 64 81 93 107 111 114 119 127 133 **P**4
Primary Contact: Tim Jones, Chief Executive Officer
CFO: Brad Burnett, Chief Financial Officer
CMO: Pete Castro, D.O., Chief of Staff
Web address: www.bradyhospital.com/
**Control:** Other not–for–profit (including NFP Corporation) **Service:** General Medical and Surgical

**Staffed Beds:** 25 **Admissions:** 376 **Census:** 3 **Outpatient Visits:** 29403 **Births:** 0 **Total Expense ($000):** 12851 **Payroll Expense ($000):** 3777 **Personnel:** 80

## BRECKENRIDGE—Stephens County

**STEPHENS MEMORIAL HOSPITAL (450498)**, 200 South Geneva Street, Zip 76424–4799; tel. 254/559–2242 **A**9 10 20 **F**3 7 8 11 15 28 30 34 35 40 43 45 50 53 56 57 59 63 64 68 69 81 85 87 89 93 97 103 107 114 130 133 146 **P**6
Primary Contact: Matthew Kempton, Chief Executive Officer and Administrator
CFO: Samuel Grant, Chief Financial Officer
CMO: Cynthia Perry, M.D., Chief of Staff
CIO: Bobby Thompson, Director Information Technology
CHR: Michelle Funderburg, Director Human Resources
CNO: Alicia Whitt, R.N., Chief Nursing Officer
Web address: www.smhtx.com
**Control:** Hospital district or authority, Government, nonfederal **Service:** General Medical and Surgical

**Staffed Beds:** 21 **Admissions:** 398 **Census:** 5 **Outpatient Visits:** 13836 **Births:** 0 **Total Expense ($000):** 10942 **Payroll Expense ($000):** 5590 **Personnel:** 127

## BRENHAM—Washington County

⊠ **SCOTT & WHITE HOSPITAL – BRENHAM (450187)**, 700 Medical Parkway, Zip 77833–5498; tel. 979/337–5000, (Data for 303 days) **A**1 9 10 **F**3 13 29 30 34 35 40 41 50 51 57 59 66 70 76 77 80 81 82 85 87 93 107 111 119 120 121 129 130 132 133 146 **S** Baylor Scott & White Health, Dallas, TX
Primary Contact: Michael Pittman, Chief Operating Officer and Chief Nursing Officer
CFO: Jane Wellmann, Chief Financial Officer
CMO: Michael Schlabach, M.D., Chief Medical Officer
CIO: Sharon Schwartz, Director Medical Records
CHR: Virginia Counts, Manager Human Resources
Web address: www.swbrenham.org
**Control:** Other not–for–profit (including NFP Corporation) **Service:** General Medical and Surgical

**Staffed Beds:** 60 **Admissions:** 1183 **Census:** 14 **Outpatient Visits:** 29406 **Births:** 268 **Total Expense ($000):** 23394 **Payroll Expense ($000):** 11368 **Personnel:** 187

## BROWNFIELD—Terry County

★ **BROWNFIELD REGIONAL MEDICAL CENTER (450399)**, 705 East Felt Street, Zip 79316–3439; tel. 806/637–3551 **A**9 10 20 **F**3 7 13 28 29 30 34 40 43 45 50 53 57 59 62 64 65 68 75 76 80 81 85 86 87 89 90 93 97 102 107 119 127 130 135 148 **P**4
Primary Contact: Mike Click, Administrator
CFO: Grady Paul Gafford, Chief Financial Officer
CIO: Sheryl Holcombe, Administrative Assistant
CHR: Kelly Barnett, Human Resource Officer
CNO: Yvonne Schue, R.N., Chief Nursing Officer
Web address: www.brownfield-rmc.org
**Control:** Hospital district or authority, Government, nonfederal **Service:** General Medical and Surgical

**Staffed Beds:** 26 **Admissions:** 847 **Census:** 8 **Outpatient Visits:** 48453 **Births:** 134 **Total Expense ($000):** 15913 **Payroll Expense ($000):** 7797 **Personnel:** 198

## BROWNSVILLE—Cameron County

☐ **SOUTH TEXAS REHABILITATION HOSPITAL (453092)**, 425 East Alton Gloor Boulevard, Zip 78526–3361; tel. 956/554–6000 **A**1 9 10 **F**3 28 29 34 35 59 64 75 77 86 87 90 93 94 96 130 132 148 **P**6 **S** Ernest Health, Inc., Albuquerque, NM
Primary Contact: Jessie Eason Smedley, Chief Executive Officer
COO: Mary Valdez, Chief Operating Officer
CFO: Sue Thomsen, Chief Financial Officer
CMO: Christopher Wilson, M.D., Inpatient Medical Director
CIO: Deborah Alcocer, Chief Information Officer
CHR: Tony Rodriguez, Director Human Resources
CNO: Cheryl Sexton, Director Nursing Operations
Web address: www.strh.ernesthealth.com
**Control:** Partnership, Investor–owned, for–profit **Service:** Rehabilitation

**Staffed Beds:** 40 **Admissions:** 828 **Census:** 33 **Outpatient Visits:** 3553 **Births:** 0 **Total Expense ($000):** 14693 **Payroll Expense ($000):** 6395 **Personnel:** 118

**TX**

*Many Facility Codes have changed. Please refer to the AHA Guide Code Chart.*   © 2015 AHA Guide

★ **VALLEY BAPTIST MEDICAL CENTER–BROWNSVILLE (450028)**, 1040 West Jefferson Street, Zip 78520–6338, Mailing Address: P.O. Box 3590, Zip 78523–3590; tel. 956/698–5400, (Total facility includes 11 beds in nursing home–type unit) **A**9 10 **F**3 11 12 13 15 18 20 22 24 26 28 29 30 34 35 37 39 40 43 44 45 49 50 54 56 57 59 60 63 64 65 70 72 74 75 76 77 79 81 82 84 85 86 87 89 93 98 100 101 102 103 104 105 106 107 109 110 111 112 114 115 119 126 128 129 130 132 146 147 148 **S** TENET Healthcare Corporation, Dallas, TX
Primary Contact: Leslie Bingham, Senior Vice President and Chief Executive Officer
COO: Marisa Aguilar, Chief Operating Officer
CFO: Harvey Torres, Chief Financial Officer
CMO: Jose L. Ayala, M.D., Chief Medical Officer
CIO: Mary Garrido, Vice President and Regional Chief Information Officer
CHR: Irma L. Pye, Chief Human Resource Officer
CNO: Aniceta Mendoza, R.N., Chief Nursing Officer
Web address: www.valleybaptist.net/brownsville/index.htm
**Control:** Corporation, Investor–owned, for–profit **Service:** General Medical and Surgical

**Staffed Beds:** 262 **Admissions:** 10687 **Census:** 147 **Outpatient Visits:** 69443 **Births:** 2168 **Total Expense ($000):** 121962 **Payroll Expense ($000):** 49483 **Personnel:** 631

⊞ **VALLEY REGIONAL MEDICAL CENTER (450662)**, 100A Alton Gloor Boulevard, Zip 78526–3354, Mailing Address: P.O. Box 3710, Zip 78523–3710; tel. 956/350–7101 **A**1 9 10 **F**3 11 13 15 18 20 22 24 26 29 30 31 32 34 35 40 43 44 45 47 49 50 53 57 59 60 61 64 65 68 70 72 73 74 75 76 77 78 79 81 82 84 85 86 87 89 93 107 108 110 111 115 118 119 124 130 132 135 146 147 148 **P**7 **S** HCA, Nashville, TN
Primary Contact: Art Garza, Interim Chief Executive Officer
COO: Steven C. Hoelscher, Chief Operating Officer
CFO: Marcia Patterson, Chief Financial Officer
CIO: Carlos Leal, Director Information Technology
CHR: Vicky Kahl, Director Human Resources
Web address: www.valleyregionalmedicalcenter.com
**Control:** Partnership, Investor–owned, for–profit **Service:** General Medical and Surgical

**Staffed Beds:** 214 **Admissions:** 9903 **Census:** 147 **Outpatient Visits:** 67564 **Births:** 2602 **Total Expense ($000):** 122022 **Payroll Expense ($000):** 51570 **Personnel:** 764

**BROWNWOOD—Brown County**

⊞ **BROWNWOOD REGIONAL MEDICAL CENTER (450587)**, 1501 Burnet Road, Zip 76801–8520, Mailing Address: P.O. Box 760, Zip 76804–0760; tel. 325/646–8541, (Total facility includes 20 beds in nursing home–type unit) **A**1 9 10 20 **F**11 13 15 18 28 29 30 31 34 35 39 40 45 48 49 50 51 53 54 56 57 59 63 64 68 70 74 75 77 78 79 81 82 85 86 87 93 97 107 108 111 114 119 120 121 123 128 129 130 132 146 147 148 **P**3 8 **S** Community Health Systems, Inc., Franklin, TN
Primary Contact: Claude E. Chip™ Camp, III, FACHE, Chief Executive Officer
COO: Curt M. Junkins, Assistant Chief Executive Officer
CFO: Joseph Wooldridge, Chief Financial Officer
CMO: Eric Wiley, M.D., Chief of Staff
CIO: Jay Smith, Director Information Systems
CHR: Mikeana Bailey, Director Human Resources
CNO: Alicia R. Kayga, R.N., Chief Nursing Officer
Web address: www.brmc–cares.com
**Control:** Partnership, Investor–owned, for–profit **Service:** General Medical and Surgical

**Staffed Beds:** 168 **Admissions:** 3980 **Census:** 47 **Outpatient Visits:** 64576 **Births:** 643 **Total Expense ($000):** 77929 **Payroll Expense ($000):** 22811 **Personnel:** 507

**BRYAN—Brazos County**

⊞ **CHRISTUS DUBUIS HOSPITAL OF BRYAN (452113)**, 1600 Joseph Drive, 2nd Floor, Zip 77802–1502; tel. 979/821–5000 **A**1 9 10 **F**1 3 29 30 34 75 80 82 85 86 87 91 130 148 **P**8 **S** CHRISTUS Health, Irving, TX
Primary Contact: Terry W. Kepler, Chief Executive Officer
Web address: www.dubuis.org/CHRISTUSDubuisHospitalofBryan
**Control:** Church–operated, Nongovernment, not–for profit **Service:** Long–Term Acute Care hospital

**Staffed Beds:** 30 **Admissions:** 189 **Census:** 14 **Outpatient Visits:** 0 **Births:** 0 **Total Expense ($000):** 6711 **Payroll Expense ($000):** 2573 **Personnel:** 49

⊞ **ST. JOSEPH REGIONAL HEALTH CENTER (450011)**, 2801 Franciscan Drive, Zip 77802–2599; tel. 979/776–3777 **A**1 2 3 5 9 10 **F**3 7 11 12 13 15 17 18 20 22 24 28 29 30 31 32 34 35 37 40 42 43 44 45 46 48 49 50 53 54 57 59 64 65 68 70 74 75 76 77 78 79 80 81 84 85 86 87 89 90 93 96 107 110 111 114 118 119 121 123 124 126 127 129 130 131 132 135 143 144 146 148 **S** Catholic Health Initiatives, Englewood, CO
Primary Contact: Kathleen R. Krusie, FACHE, Chief Executive Officer
CFO: Lisa McNair, CPA, Senior Vice President and Chief Financial Officer
CIO: John Phillips, Vice President Information Services
CHR: Michael G. Costa, Vice President Human Resources
Web address: www.st–joseph.org
**Control:** Church–operated, Nongovernment, not–for profit **Service:** General Medical and Surgical

**Staffed Beds:** 229 **Admissions:** 14093 **Census:** 164 **Outpatient Visits:** 255636 **Births:** 1491 **Total Expense ($000):** 255552 **Payroll Expense ($000):** 90140 **Personnel:** 1616

☐ **THE PHYSICIANS CENTRE HOSPITAL (450834)**, 3131 University Drive East, Zip 77802–3473; tel. 979/731–3100 **A**1 9 10 **F**3 12 15 29 34 35 40 44 45 50 51 59 64 68 74 75 77 79 81 82 85 86 87 89 107 111 114 119 130 131 132 135
Primary Contact: Kori Rich, Chief Executive Officer
CFO: Paul Tannos, Chief Financial Officer
CMO: Barry Solcher, M.D., Chief of Staff
CIO: Shawn Clark, Director Information Systems
CHR: LeeAnn Ford, Director Human Resources and Imaging
CNO: Robert Raymond Lemay, R.N., Chief Nursing Officer
Web address: www.thephysicianscentre.com
**Control:** Corporation, Investor–owned, for–profit **Service:** General Medical and Surgical

**Staffed Beds:** 16 **Admissions:** 324 **Census:** 2 **Outpatient Visits:** 7881 **Births:** 0 **Total Expense ($000):** 15807 **Payroll Expense ($000):** 4034 **Personnel:** 83

**BURNET—Burnet County**

⊞ **SETON HIGHLAND LAKES (451365)**, 3201 South Water Street, Zip 78611–4510, Mailing Address: P.O. Box 1219, Zip 78611–7219; tel. 512/715–3000 **A**1 3 9 10 18 **F**3 11 15 18 28 29 30 34 35 40 43 44 50 57 59 62 63 64 65 66 68 70 71 74 75 77 78 79 81 82 84 85 86 87 91 92 93 97 107 110 111 115 119 127 130 132 133 135 146 148 **P**3 8 **S** Ascension Health, Saint Louis, MO
Primary Contact: Karen Litterer, R.N., MSN, Administrator and Chief Operating Officer
COO: Karen Litterer, R.N., Administrator and Chief Operating Officer
CFO: Douglas D. Waite, Senior Vice President and Chief Financial Officer
CIO: Gerry Lewis, Chief Information Officer
Web address: www.seton.net
**Control:** Church–operated, Nongovernment, not–for profit **Service:** General Medical and Surgical

**Staffed Beds:** 23 **Admissions:** 1179 **Census:** 11 **Outpatient Visits:** 104113 **Births:** 0 **Total Expense ($000):** 43040 **Payroll Expense ($000):** 18272 **Personnel:** 260

**CALDWELL—Burleson County**

⊞ **BURLESON ST. JOSEPH HEALTH CENTER (451305)**, 1101 Woodson Drive, Zip 77836–1052, Mailing Address: P.O. Box 360, Zip 77836–0360; tel. 979/567–3245 **A**1 9 10 18 **F**3 7 11 28 29 30 34 35 40 43 57 59 64 93 130 133 135 143 **S** Catholic Health Initiatives, Englewood, CO
Primary Contact: Brian Stanford, Administrator
CFO: Daniel Goggin, Senior Vice President and Chief Financial Officer
CMO: Scott Chennault, M.D., Chief of Staff
CHR: Michael G. Costa, Vice President Human Resources
Web address: www.st–joseph.org/
**Control:** Church–operated, Nongovernment, not–for profit **Service:** General Medical and Surgical

**Staffed Beds:** 25 **Admissions:** 215 **Census:** 5 **Outpatient Visits:** 22713 **Births:** 0 **Total Expense ($000):** 9780 **Payroll Expense ($000):** 4243 **Personnel:** 77

**CAMERON—Milam County**

**LITTLE RIVER CAMERON HOSPITAL (670094)**, 806 North Crockett Avenue, Zip 76520–2553; tel. 254/605–1300, (Nonreporting)
Primary Contact: Troy Zinn, Chief Executive Officer
Web address: www.lrhealthcare.com/cameronhospital
**Control:** Corporation, Investor–owned, for–profit **Service:** General Medical and Surgical

**Staffed Beds:** 25

**TX**

**Hospital, Medicare Provider Number, Address, Telephone, Approval, Facility, and Physician Codes, Health Care System**

★ American Hospital Association (AHA) membership
☐ The Joint Commission accreditation
○ Healthcare Facilities Accreditation Program
◇ DNV Healthcare Inc. accreditation
⇑ Center for Improvement in Healthcare Quality Accreditation
△ Commission on Accreditation of Rehabilitation Facilities (CARF) accreditation

## CANADIAN—Hemphill County

**HEMPHILL COUNTY HOSPITAL (450578)**, 1020 South Fourth Street, Zip 79014–3315; tel. 806/323–6422 **A**9 10 20 **F**2 7 29 35 40 45 56 57 62 63 64 68 69 87 89 93 97 102 107 108 130 133 146 148
Primary Contact: Christy Francis, Chief Executive Officer
COO: Patrick Murfee, Chief Operating Officer
CFO: Bob Ericson, Chief Financial Officer
CMO: G. Anthony Cook, M.D., Medical Director
CIO: Brian Goza, Chief Information Officer
CHR: David Troublefield, Chief Communications Officer
CNO: Debra Sappenfield, R.N., Chief Nursing Officer
Web address: www.hchdst.org
**Control:** Hospital district or authority, Government, nonfederal **Service:** General Medical and Surgical

**Staffed Beds:** 19 **Admissions:** 214 **Census:** 3 **Outpatient Visits:** 13535 **Births:** 0 **Total Expense ($000):** 8445 **Payroll Expense ($000):** 3124 **Personnel:** 92

## CARRIZO SPRINGS—Dimmit County

★ **DIMMIT REGIONAL HOSPITAL (450620)**, 704 Hospital Drive, Zip 78834–3836, Mailing Address: P.O. Box 1016, Zip 78834–7016; tel. 830/876–2424 **A**9 10 20 **F**11 13 40 43 45 57 62 64 70 76 81 89 93 107 115 119
Primary Contact: James E. Buckner, Jr., FACHE, Chief Executive Officer
CFO: Alma Melendez, Controller
Web address: www.dcmhospital.org
**Control:** Other not–for–profit (including NFP Corporation) **Service:** General Medical and Surgical

**Staffed Beds:** 35 **Admissions:** 747 **Census:** 7 **Outpatient Visits:** 20500 **Births:** 242 **Total Expense ($000):** 14006 **Payroll Expense ($000):** 6338 **Personnel:** 160

## CARROLLTON—Denton County

⊞ **BAYLOR MEDICAL CENTER AT CARROLLTON (450730)**, 4343 North Josey Lane, Zip 75010–4691; tel. 972/492–1010 **A**1 2 9 10 **F**3 11 12 13 15 18 20 22 29 30 31 34 35 40 45 48 49 50 51 54 55 56 57 59 64 70 72 73 74 75 76 77 78 79 81 82 84 85 86 87 88 93 107 108 111 114 115 119 129 130 131 132 135 146 147 148 **S** Baylor Scott & White Health, Dallas, TX
Primary Contact: Mike McAllister, Interim Chief Executive Officer
CFO: James McNatt, Chief Financial Officer
CMO: Matthew Smith, M.D., Vice President Medical Affairs and Chief Medical Officer
CIO: Paul Ratcliff, Director Information Services
CHR: Drew Smith, Director Human Resources
CNO: Barbara Vaughn, Chief Nursing Officer
Web address: www.baylorhealth.com
**Control:** Other not–for–profit (including NFP Corporation) **Service:** General Medical and Surgical

**Staffed Beds:** 123 **Admissions:** 5942 **Census:** 68 **Outpatient Visits:** 59199 **Births:** 1399 **Total Expense ($000):** 124183 **Payroll Expense ($000):** 43700 **Personnel:** 417

☐ **CARROLLTON SPRINGS (454119)**, 2225 Parker Road, Zip 75010–4711; tel. 972/242–4114 **A**1 9 10 **F**4 98 102 103 104 105
Primary Contact: Shanti Carter, Chief Executive Officer
Web address: www.carrolltonsprings.com
**Control:** Corporation, Investor–owned, for–profit **Service:** Psychiatric

**Staffed Beds:** 45 **Admissions:** 1663 **Census:** 40 **Outpatient Visits:** 9581 **Births:** 0 **Total Expense ($000):** 9815 **Payroll Expense ($000):** 6142 **Personnel:** 126

⊞ **SELECT SPECIALTY HOSPITAL–DALLAS (452022)**, 2329 West Parker Road, Zip 75010–4713; tel. 469/892–1400 **A**1 9 10 **F**1 3 29 56 74 75 77 85 91 107 114 119 130 135 148 **S** Select Medical Corporation, Mechanicsburg, PA
Primary Contact: John M. Griffes, Chief Executive Officer
Web address: www.selectspecialtyhospitals.com/company/locations/dallas.aspx
**Control:** Corporation, Investor–owned, for–profit **Service:** Long–Term Acute Care hospital

**Staffed Beds:** 60 **Admissions:** 516 **Census:** 40 **Outpatient Visits:** 0 **Births:** 0 **Total Expense ($000):** 23318 **Payroll Expense ($000):** 10389 **Personnel:** 181

## CARTHAGE—Panola County

⊞ **EAST TEXAS MEDICAL CENTER CARTHAGE (450210)**, 409 Cottage Road, Zip 75633–1466; tel. 903/693–3841 **A**1 9 10 20 **F**3 8 11 15 28 29 30 34 35 40 43 45 50 57 59 64 65 75 81 85 107 108 110 111 115 119 127 129 145 146 **S** East Texas Medical Center Regional Healthcare System, Tyler, TX
Primary Contact: Gary Mikeal Hudson, Administrator
COO: Gary Mikeal Hudson, Administrator
CFO: Phillip A. Caron, Chief Financial Officer
CMO: Salah Almohammed, Chief of Staff
CIO: Renee Lawhorn, Director Medical Records
CHR: Amber Cox, Director Human Resources
CNO: Judy Peterson, R.N., Chief Nursing Officer
Web address: www.etmc.org
**Control:** Other not–for–profit (including NFP Corporation) **Service:** General Medical and Surgical

**Staffed Beds:** 25 **Admissions:** 815 **Census:** 6 **Outpatient Visits:** 86578 **Births:** 0 **Total Expense ($000):** 21855 **Payroll Expense ($000):** 7721 **Personnel:** 151

## CEDAR PARK—Williamson County

⊞ **CEDAR PARK REGIONAL MEDICAL CENTER (670043)**, 1401 Medical Parkway, Zip 78613–7763; tel. 512/528–7000 **A**1 9 10 **F**3 12 13 15 18 20 22 29 34 35 40 45 47 49 50 54 57 59 64 70 73 74 75 76 77 78 79 81 82 85 87 89 93 107 108 110 111 114 115 119 126 129 130 132 135 146 147 148 **S** Community Health Systems, Inc., Franklin, TN
Primary Contact: Brad D. Holland, Chief Executive Officer
COO: Megan Drake, Assistant Administrator
CFO: Erich Wallschlaeger, Chief Financial Officer
CIO: Brad Hoar, Director Information and Technology
CNO: Krista Baty, R.N., Chief Nursing Officer
Web address: www.cedarparkregional.com
**Control:** Corporation, Investor–owned, for–profit **Service:** General Medical and Surgical

**Staffed Beds:** 93 **Admissions:** 3773 **Census:** 36 **Outpatient Visits:** 45390 **Births:** 944 **Total Expense ($000):** 75360 **Payroll Expense ($000):** 26006 **Personnel:** 382

★ ◇ **SCOTT & WHITE EMERGENCY HOSPITAL– CEDAR PARK (670087)**, 900 East Whitestone Boulevard, Zip 78613–9093; tel. 512/684–4911 **A**10 21 **F**3 29 40 75 87 107 119 **P**5 **S** Baylor Scott & White Health, Dallas, TX
Primary Contact: John Wood, Administrator
Web address: www.sweh.org
**Control:** Partnership, Investor–owned, for–profit **Service:** General Medical and Surgical

**Staffed Beds:** 8 **Admissions:** 37 **Census:** 1 **Outpatient Visits:** 9435 **Births:** 0 **Total Expense ($000):** 5650 **Payroll Expense ($000):** 1861 **Personnel:** 45

## CHILDRESS—Childress County

★ **CHILDRESS REGIONAL MEDICAL CENTER (450369)**, Highway 83 North, Zip 79201–5800, Mailing Address: P.O. Box 1030, Zip 79201–1030; tel. 940/937–6371 **A**9 10 20 **F**3 7 8 13 15 29 31 32 34 35 40 43 45 50 56 57 59 60 61 62 63 64 65 66 79 81 84 91 92 93 107 111 119 127 129 130 133 **P**6
Primary Contact: John Henderson, Chief Executive Officer
COO: Holly Holcomb, R.N., Chief Operating Officer
CFO: Kathy McLain, Chief Financial Officer
CMO: Dustin Pratt, M.D., Chief of Staff
CIO: Holly Holcomb, R.N., Chie Operating Officer
CHR: Gayle Cannon, Director Human Resources
CNO: Sulynn Mester, R.N., Chief Nursing Officer
Web address: www.childresshospital.com
**Control:** Hospital district or authority, Government, nonfederal **Service:** General Medical and Surgical

**Staffed Beds:** 35 **Admissions:** 932 **Census:** 7 **Outpatient Visits:** 159011 **Births:** 213 **Total Expense ($000):** 24865 **Payroll Expense ($000):** 10499 **Personnel:** 242

## CHILLICOTHE—Hardeman County

★ **CHILLICOTHE HOSPITAL DISTRICT (451326)**, 303 Avenue I, Zip 79225, Mailing Address: P.O. Box 370, Zip 79225–0370; tel. 940/852–5131 **A**9 10 18 **F**29 34 40 43 45 57 59 69 81 89 132 133 **P**5
Primary Contact: Linda Hall, Administrator and Chief Executive Officer
COO: Linda Hall, Administrator and Chief Executive Officer
CFO: Linda Hall, Administrator and Chief Executive Officer
CMO: Weldon Glidden, M.D., Chief of Staff
CIO: Kathy Busby, Medical Record Technician
CHR: Linda Hall, Administrator and Chief Executive Officer
CNO: Sonya Richardson, Chief Nursing Officer
Web address: www.chillhd.org
**Control:** Hospital district or authority, Government, nonfederal **Service:** General Medical and Surgical

**Staffed Beds:** 13 **Admissions:** 39 **Census:** 1 **Outpatient Visits:** 5040 **Births:** 0 **Total Expense ($000):** 2210 **Payroll Expense ($000):** 1097 **Personnel:** 23

## CLEBURNE—Johnson County

✠ **TEXAS HEALTH HARRIS METHODIST HOSPITAL CLEBURNE (450148)**, 201 Walls Drive, Zip 76033–4007; tel. 817/641–2551 **A**1 9 10 **F**3 11 13 15 18 29 30 32 34 35 40 43 44 45 46 49 50 51 56 57 59 64 65 66 68 70 75 76 77 79 81 85 89 93 107 108 110 114 119 124 126 129 130 146 148 **P**6 **S** Texas Health Resources, Arlington, TX
Primary Contact: Lorrie Normand, R.N., Interim Chief Executive Officer
CFO: Shelly Miland, Group Finance Officer
CMO: Judy Laviolette, M.D., Chief Medical Officer
CIO: Brenda Taylor, Director Information Systems
CHR: Marsha Adams, Interim Director Human Resources
CNO: Lorrie Normand, R.N., Chief Nursing Officer
Web address: www.texashealth.org
**Control:** Other not–for–profit (including NFP Corporation) **Service:** General Medical and Surgical

**Staffed Beds:** 85 **Admissions:** 3984 **Census:** 40 **Outpatient Visits:** 45987
**Births:** 683 **Total Expense ($000):** 62166 **Payroll Expense ($000):** 25432
**Personnel:** 270

## CLIFTON—Bosque County

★ **GOODALL–WITCHER HOSPITAL AUTHORITY (450052)**, 101 South Avenue T, Zip 76634–1897, Mailing Address: P.O. Box 549, Zip 76634–0549; tel. 254/675–8322 **A**9 10 20 **F**3 11 13 15 28 29 30 34 35 36 40 43 45 50 53 57 59 62 64 65 68 76 77 81 93 107 108 114 119 127 130 133 146 147 148 **P**3
Primary Contact: Adam Willmann, President and Chief Executive Officer
CFO: Vicki Gloff, Chief Financial Officer
CMO: Kevin Blanton, D.O., Chief of Staff
CHR: Jennie Oldham, Director Human Resources
CNO: Donna Nichols, R.N., Chief Nursing Officer
Web address: www.gwhf.org
**Control:** Hospital district or authority, Government, nonfederal **Service:** General Medical and Surgical

**Staffed Beds:** 33 **Admissions:** 579 **Census:** 9 **Outpatient Visits:** 34713
**Births:** 70 **Total Expense ($000):** 16038 **Payroll Expense ($000):** 6845
**Personnel:** 170

## COLEMAN—Coleman County

**COLEMAN COUNTY MEDICAL CENTER (451347)**, 310 South Pecos Street, Zip 76834–4159; tel. 325/625–2135 **A**9 10 18 **F**3 11 13 28 29 32 34 35 40 43 45 57 59 64 65 66 68 75 77 81 84 93 97 107 114 127 133 134 **S** Preferred Management Corporation, Shawnee, OK
Primary Contact: Michael W. Pruitt, Administrator and Chief Executive Officer
CMO: Paul Reynolds, M.D., Medical Director
CIO: Harvey Ramirez, Chief Information Officer
CHR: Sue Titsworth, Director Human Resources
CNO: Melissa Ereman, R.N., Chief Nursing Officer
Web address: www.colemantexas.org/hospital.html
**Control:** Corporation, Investor–owned, for–profit **Service:** General Medical and Surgical

**Staffed Beds:** 25 **Admissions:** 592 **Census:** 7 **Outpatient Visits:** 26584
**Births:** 24 **Total Expense ($000):** 9800 **Payroll Expense ($000):** 4411
**Personnel:** 105

## COLLEGE STATION—Brazos County

✠ **COLLEGE STATION MEDICAL CENTER (450299)**, 1604 Rock Prairie Road, Zip 77845–8345, Mailing Address: P.O. Box 10000, Zip 77842–3500; tel. 979/764–5100 **A**1 2 3 5 9 10 **F**3 11 13 15 18 20 22 24 26 28 29 30 31 34 40 43 45 46 49 53 57 61 70 72 74 76 77 78 79 81 82 84 85 87 89 90 91 93 107 108 111 113 115 118 119 124 127 129 130 131 132 135 146 147 148 **P**7 **S** Community Health Systems, Inc., Franklin, TN
Primary Contact: Larry Rodgers, Chief Executive Officer
COO: Vicky Cha Bridier, Chief Operating Officer
CFO: Ken Pannell, Chief Financial Officer
CIO: Daphne Hartman, Director Information Systems
CHR: Sharon Bond, Director Human Resources
CNO: Sherri Welch, R.N., Chief Nursing Officer
Web address: www.csmedcenter.com
**Control:** Corporation, Investor–owned, for–profit **Service:** General Medical and Surgical

**Staffed Beds:** 148 **Admissions:** 5094 **Census:** 69 **Outpatient Visits:** 58945
**Births:** 1304 **Total Expense ($000):** 89138 **Payroll Expense ($000):** 29502
**Personnel:** 497

□ **ROCK PRAIRIE BEHAVIORAL HEALTH (454125)**, 3550 Normand Drive, Zip 77845–6399; tel. 979/703–8848, (Nonreporting) **A**1 10 **S** Strategic Behavioral Health, LLC, Memphis, TN
Primary Contact: Jim Serratt, Chief Executive Officer
CFO: Doug Smith, Chief Financial Officer
CMO: Jason Boley, M.D., Medical Director
CHR: MaxAnne Jones, Director Human Resources
**Control:** Investor–owned, for–profit **Service:** Children's hospital psychiatric

**Staffed Beds:** 55 **Admissions:** 772 **Census:** 19 **Outpatient Visits:** 666
**Births:** 0 **Total Expense ($000):** 5879 **Payroll Expense ($000):** 2959
**Personnel:** 88

✠ **SCOTT & WHITE HOSPITAL – COLLEGE STATION (670088)**, 700 Scott & White Drive, Zip 77845; tel. 979/207–0100, (Data for 303 days) **A**1 5 10 **F**3 11 13 18 20 22 24 26 29 30 34 35 38 40 45 46 47 49 50 51 57 59 60 65 68 70 72 74 75 76 77 79 81 82 85 86 87 89 93 96 107 108 111 115 119 130 131 132 135 145 146 148 **S** Baylor Scott & White Health, Dallas, TX
Primary Contact: Jason Jennings, Chief Executive Officer
Web address: www.sw.org/location/college–station–hospital
**Control:** Other not–for–profit (including NFP Corporation) **Service:** General Medical and Surgical

**Staffed Beds:** 95 **Admissions:** 3530 **Census:** 40 **Outpatient Visits:** 188009
**Births:** 806 **Total Expense ($000):** 85698 **Payroll Expense ($000):** 29779
**Personnel:** 838

## COLORADO CITY—Mitchell County

★ **MITCHELL COUNTY HOSPITAL (451342)**, 997 West Interstate 20, Zip 79512–2685; tel. 325/728–3431 **A**9 10 18 **F**3 7 11 28 29 40 43 45 50 57 59 64 68 81 93 107 119 133 146 **P**6
Primary Contact: Robbie Dewberry, Chief Executive Officer
CFO: Joe Wright, Chief Financial Officer
CMO: Dee A. Roach, M.D., Chief of Staff
CIO: Randy Myers, Chief Information Officer, Information Technology
CHR: Deana Overton, Director Human Resources
CNO: Donna Goebel, M.D., Chief Nursing Officer
Web address: www.mitchellcountyhospital.com
**Control:** Hospital district or authority, Government, nonfederal **Service:** General Medical and Surgical

**Staffed Beds:** 25 **Admissions:** 473 **Census:** 5 **Outpatient Visits:** 31784
**Births:** 0 **Total Expense ($000):** 18884 **Payroll Expense ($000):** 8927
**Personnel:** 210

## COLUMBUS—Colorado County

**COLUMBUS COMMUNITY HOSPITAL (450370)**, 110 Shult Drive, Zip 78934–3010; tel. 979/732–2371 **A**3 5 9 10 **F**11 13 15 29 35 40 43 57 68 76 79 81 107 110 111 114 119 127 130 133 135
Primary Contact: James Vanek, Chief Executive Officer
CFO: Regina Wicke, Chief Financial Officer
CMO: Jorge Duchicela, M.D., Chief of Staff
CIO: Ashley Mathis, Privacy Officer
CHR: Janie Hammonds, Human Resources Officer
CNO: Jeno Hargrove, R.N., Director of Nursing
Web address: www.columbusch.com
**Control:** Other not–for–profit (including NFP Corporation) **Service:** General Medical and Surgical

**Staffed Beds:** 40 **Admissions:** 1252 **Census:** 13 **Outpatient Visits:** 81552
**Births:** 225 **Total Expense ($000):** 26496 **Payroll Expense ($000):** 8644
**Personnel:** 153

## COMANCHE—Comanche County

★ **COMANCHE COUNTY MEDICAL CENTER (451382)**, 10201 Highway 16 North, Zip 76442–4462; tel. 254/879–4900 **A**9 10 18 **F**3 11 15 28 29 30 34 35 40 43 45 50 57 59 64 65 68 70 75 77 79 81 85 86 87 93 97 107 108 110 111 115 119 127 129 130 131 133 145 146 148
Primary Contact: Carl (Jim) Christensen, Chief Executive Officer
CFO: David Freshour, Chief Financial Officer
CMO: Guyle Donham, M.D., Chief of Staff
CIO: Ismelda Garza, Director Information Systems
CHR: Karen DeLavan, Interim Director Human Resources
CNO: Colleen Jedlicka, R.N., Chief Nursing Officer
Web address: www.comanchecmc.org
**Control:** Other not–for–profit (including NFP Corporation) **Service:** General Medical and Surgical

**Staffed Beds:** 25 **Admissions:** 711 **Census:** 8 **Outpatient Visits:** 53541
**Births:** 0 **Total Expense ($000):** 19007 **Payroll Expense ($000):** 6280
**Personnel:** 144

**TX**

---

**Hospital, Medicare Provider Number, Address, Telephone, Approval, Facility, and Physician Codes, Health Care System**

★ American Hospital Association (AHA) membership  ○ Healthcare Facilities Accreditation Program  ⇑ Center for Improvement in Healthcare Quality Accreditation
□ The Joint Commission accreditation  ◇ DNV Healthcare Inc. accreditation  △ Commission on Accreditation of Rehabilitation Facilities (CARF) accreditation

## COMMERCE—Hunt County

✠ **HUNT REGIONAL COMMUNITY HOSPITAL (451321)**, 2900 Sterling Hart Drive, Zip 75428–3912; tel. 903/886–3161 **A**1 9 10 18 **F**3 11 29 30 40 41 57 75 85 87 93 105 107 114 119 130 133 135 146 **S** Hunt Regional Healthcare, Greenville, TX
Primary Contact: Michael R. Klepin, Associate Administrator
COO: John Heatherly, Assistant Administrator Support Services
CFO: Jeri Rich, Assistant Administrator and Chief Financial Officer
CMO: Richard Selvaggi, M.D., Chief of Staff
CIO: Jonathan Schafft, Director Information Systems
CHR: Stacey Lane, Director Human Resources
CNO: Deborah Clack, Chief Nursing Officer
Web address: www.huntregional.org
**Control:** Hospital district or authority, Government, nonfederal **Service:** General Medical and Surgical

**Staffed Beds:** 15 **Admissions:** 195 **Census:** 3 **Outpatient Visits:** 8418
**Births:** 0 **Total Expense ($000):** 8025 **Payroll Expense ($000):** 2714
**Personnel:** 41

## CONROE—Montgomery County

✠ **ASPIRE HOSPITAL (454112)**, 2006 South Loop 336 West, Suite 500, Zip 77304–3315; tel. 936/647–3500 **A**1 9 10 **F**3 15 34 54 55 56 57 59 78 79 93 96 98 102 103 104 105 106 107 108 110 111 112 113 114 115 117 118 119 120 121 123 124 129 130 131 147
Primary Contact: Kostas Gotsoulias, Interim Chief Executive Officer
CFO: Bob Gray, Chief Financial Officer
CIO: John Heemann, Chief Information Officer
CHR: Angela Walker, Manager Human Resources
CNO: Troy Ryder, Director of Nursing
Web address: www.aspirehospital.com
**Control:** Partnership, Investor–owned, for–profit **Service:** Psychiatric

**Staffed Beds:** 24 **Admissions:** 698 **Census:** 17 **Outpatient Visits:** 10743
**Births:** 0 **Total Expense ($000):** 8605 **Payroll Expense ($000):** 4128
**Personnel:** 63

✠ **CONROE REGIONAL MEDICAL CENTER (450222)**, 504 Medical Boulevard, Zip 77304, Mailing Address: P.O. Box 1538, Zip 77305–1538; tel. 936/539–1111 **A**1 3 9 10 13 **F**3 11 12 13 15 17 18 20 22 24 26 28 29 31 34 35 40 41 43 45 46 53 54 57 59 64 68 70 72 73 74 75 76 78 79 81 82 85 86 89 90 91 93 107 108 111 114 115 118 119 121 124 129 130 132 135 146 147 148 **S** HCA, Nashville, TN
Primary Contact: Matt Davis, Chief Executive Officer
COO: Tripp Montalbo, Chief Operating Officer
CFO: Thomas A. Holt, Chief Financial Officer
CIO: Jeremy Fuller, Director Information Systems
CHR: Diana Howell, Director Human Resources
Web address: www.conroeregional.com/
**Control:** Partnership, Investor–owned, for–profit **Service:** General Medical and Surgical

**Staffed Beds:** 312 **Admissions:** 15335 **Census:** 213 **Outpatient Visits:** 123310 **Births:** 1236 **Total Expense ($000):** 210775 **Payroll Expense ($000):** 74167 **Personnel:** 1021

✠ **HEALTHSOUTH REHABILITATION HOSPITAL THE WOODLANDS (453059)**, 18550 'IH' 45 South, Zip 77384; tel. 281/364–2000 **A**1 10 **F**3 28 29 34 35 44 57 59 62 65 68 74 75 77 79 82 86 87 90 91 95 96 130 132 148 **S** HEALTHSOUTH Corporation, Birmingham, AL
Primary Contact: Krista Uselman, Chief Executive Officer
CMO: Ben Agana, M.D., Medical Director
CHR: Valerie Wells, Manager Human Resources
Web address: www.healthsouththewoodlands.com
**Control:** Corporation, Investor–owned, for–profit **Service:** Rehabilitation

**Staffed Beds:** 84 **Admissions:** 1127 **Census:** 37 **Outpatient Visits:** 10405
**Births:** 0 **Total Expense ($000):** 17207 **Payroll Expense ($000):** 8769
**Personnel:** 107

☐ **SOLARA HOSPITAL CONROE (452107)**, 1500 Grand Lake Drive, Zip 77304–2891; tel. 936/523–1800 **A**1 9 10 **F**1 3 29 34 40 74 75 77 79 85 86 87 91 148 **S** Cornerstone Healthcare Group, Dallas, TX
Primary Contact: Suzanne Kretschmer, Interim Hospital Administrator
Web address: www.chghospitals.com/conroe/
**Control:** Partnership, Investor–owned, for–profit **Service:** Long–Term Acute Care hospital

**Staffed Beds:** 41 **Admissions:** 507 **Census:** 34 **Outpatient Visits:** 0 **Births:** 0 **Total Expense ($000):** 15796 **Payroll Expense ($000):** 6465 **Personnel:** 137

## CORINTH—Denton County

◇ **ATRIUM MEDICAL CENTER OF CORINTH (452111)**, 3305 Corinth Parkway, Zip 76208–5380; tel. 940/270–4100 **A**9 10 21 **F**1 3 28 29 40 45 47 60 64 68 70 75 77 81 86 87 96 107 111 114 119 148 **P**2
Primary Contact: Barbara Callaghan, Interim Chief Executive Officer
COO: Kathy Mason, Chief Operating Officer
CFO: Anbu Nachimuthu, Chief Financial Officer
CMO: Jalil Kahn, M.D., Chief of Staff
CIO: Wendy Keller, Director Health Information Management
CHR: Melissa Dovel, Manager Human Resources
CNO: Michelle Gray, Nurse Executive
Web address: www.atriumhealthcare.net
**Control:** Corporation, Investor–owned, for–profit **Service:** Long–Term Acute Care hospital

**Staffed Beds:** 60 **Admissions:** 468 **Census:** 34 **Outpatient Visits:** 4293
**Births:** 0 **Total Expense ($000):** 23213 **Payroll Expense ($000):** 9632
**Personnel:** 165

## CORPUS CHRISTI—Nueces County

✠ **CHRISTUS SPOHN HOSPITAL CORPUS CHRISTI MEMORIAL (450046)**, 2606 Hospital Boulevard, Zip 78405–1804, Mailing Address: P.O. Box 5280, Zip 78465–5280; tel. 361/902–4000, (Includes CHRISTUS SPOHN HOSPITAL CORPUS CHRISTI SHORELINE, 600 Elizabeth Street, Zip 78404–2235; tel. 361/881–3000; Xavier Villarreal, Chief Executive Officer; CHRISTUS SPOHN HOSPITAL CORPUS CHRISTUS SOUTH, 5950 Saratoga, Zip 78414–4100; tel. 361/985–5000), (Total facility includes 22 beds in nursing home–type unit) **A**1 2 3 5 9 10 **F**3 8 11 13 15 18 20 22 24 26 28 29 30 34 35 37 38 39 40 43 45 46 47 48 49 50 51 53 54 56 57 58 59 60 64 66 67 68 70 72 74 75 76 77 78 79 81 85 86 87 90 93 96 97 98 99 100 101 102 103 107 108 111 114 115 118 119 120 121 123 126 127 128 130 146 147 148 **P**8 **S** CHRISTUS Health, Irving, TX
Primary Contact: Xavier Villarreal, Chief Executive Officer
COO: Xavier Villareal, Chief Operating Officer
CFO: Brower Pam, Chief Financial Officer
CMO: Charles T. Volk, M.D., Regional Chief Medical Officer
CHR: Mary LaFrancois, Vice President Human Resources
CNO: Jennifer Gentry, R.N., Chief Nursing Officer
Web address: www.christusspohn.org
**Control:** Church–operated, Nongovernment, not–for profit **Service:** General Medical and Surgical

**Staffed Beds:** 710 **Admissions:** 35406 **Census:** 506 **Outpatient Visits:** 279798 **Births:** 3223 **Total Expense ($000):** 522735 **Payroll Expense ($000):** 180286 **Personnel:** 2956

✠ **CORPUS CHRISTI MEDICAL CENTER (450788)**, 3315 South Alameda Street, Zip 78411–1883, Mailing Address: P.O. Box 8991, Zip 78468–8991; tel. 361/761–1400, (Includes BAYVIEW BEHAVIORAL HOSPITAL, 6629 Wooldridge Road, Zip 78414; tel. 361/986–9444; Jamie Molbert, Associate Administrator; CORPUS CHRISTI MEDICAL CENTER BAY AREA, 7101 South Padre Island Drive, Zip 78412–4999; tel. 361/985–1200) **A**1 9 10 13 **F**3 4 5 11 12 13 15 17 18 20 22 24 26 28 29 31 34 35 37 38 40 42 44 47 49 50 53 57 58 59 64 68 70 72 73 74 75 76 77 78 79 81 82 85 86 87 90 93 97 98 99 100 101 102 103 104 105 107 108 110 111 114 115 118 119 120 121 124 126 130 131 132 146 147 148 **P**3 8 **S** HCA, Nashville, TN
Primary Contact: Jay Woodall, Chief Executive Officer
CFO: Chris Nicosia, Chief Financial Officer
CMO: Lawrence Brenner, M.D., Chief of Staff
CIO: Bryan Brown, Director Information Services and Technology
CHR: Michael Conwill, Director Human Resources
CNO: Kathleen A. Rubano, MSN, Chief Nursing Officer
Web address: www.ccmedicalcenter.com
**Control:** Partnership, Investor–owned, for–profit **Service:** General Medical and Surgical

**Staffed Beds:** 436 **Admissions:** 19641 **Census:** 268 **Outpatient Visits:** 121710 **Births:** 4356 **Total Expense ($000):** 263155 **Payroll Expense ($000):** 86516 **Personnel:** 1581

✠ **DRISCOLL CHILDREN'S HOSPITAL (453301)**, 3533 South Alameda Street, Zip 78411–1785, Mailing Address: P.O. Box 6530, Zip 78466–6530; tel. 361/694–5000 **A**1 3 5 9 10 13 **F**3 7 11 12 19 21 23 25 27 29 30 31 32 34 35 38 39 40 41 43 49 50 54 55 57 58 59 60 61 64 65 68 72 74 75 77 78 79 81 82 85 86 87 88 89 92 93 97 99 104 107 108 111 115 118 119 130 132 134 138 143 144 146 148
Primary Contact: Steve Woerner, President and Chief Executive Officer
COO: Donna Quinn, Vice President Operations and Quality
CFO: Eric Hamon, Chief Financial Officer
CIO: Miguel Perez, Director Information Systems
CHR: Bill Larsen, Vice President Human Resources
Web address: www.driscollchildrens.org
**Control:** Other not–for–profit (including NFP Corporation) **Service:** Children's general

**Staffed Beds:** 162 **Admissions:** 4285 **Census:** 73 **Outpatient Visits:** 133758
**Births:** 0 **Total Expense ($000):** 227950 **Payroll Expense ($000):** 85019
**Personnel:** 1849

**KINDRED HOSPITAL–CORPUS CHRISTI** See Post Acute Medical Specialty Hospital of Corpus Christi

**TX**

*Many Facility Codes have changed. Please refer to the AHA Guide Code Chart.* © 2015 AHA Guide

✠ **POST ACUTE MEDICAL SPECIALTY HOSPITAL OF CORPUS CHRISTI (452086)**, 600 Elizabeth Street, 3rd Floor, Zip 78404–2235; tel. 361/881–3223 **A**1 9 10 **F**1 3 29 30 31 75 85 87 148 **P**5 **S** Post Acute Medical, LLC, Enola, PA
Primary Contact: Hector Bernal, Chief Executive Officer
Web address: www.postacutemedical.com/our–facilities/hospitals/post–acute–medical–specialty–hospital–corpus–christi/
**Control:** Church–operated, Nongovernment, not–for profit **Service:** Long–Term Acute Care hospital

**Staffed Beds:** 22 **Admissions:** 215 **Census:** 17 **Outpatient Visits:** 0 **Births:** 0 **Total Expense ($000):** 8892 **Payroll Expense ($000):** 3451 **Personnel:** 55

✠ **POST ACUTE MEDICAL SPECIALTY HOSPITAL OF CORPUS CHRISTI (452092)**, 6226 Saratoga Boulevard, Zip 78414–3421; tel. 361/986–1600 **A**1 9 10 **F**1 3 29 30 34 35 45 57 59 60 70 74 75 77 79 82 85 86 87 90 97 100 107 130 146 148 **S** Post Acute Medical, LLC, Enola, PA
Primary Contact: Michael L. Pierce, Chief Executive Officer
CFO: Eva De La Paz, Chief Financial Officer
CHR: Kasey Parkey, Coordinator Payroll and Benefits
Web address: www.postacutemedical.com
**Control:** Corporation, Investor–owned, for–profit **Service:** Long–Term Acute Care hospital

**Staffed Beds:** 74 **Admissions:** 552 **Census:** 43 **Outpatient Visits:** 0 **Births:** 0 **Total Expense ($000):** 19713 **Payroll Expense ($000):** 7628 **Personnel:** 160

☐ **SOUTH TEXAS SURGICAL HOSPITAL (670061)**, 6130 Parkway Drive, Zip 78414–2455; tel. 361/993–2000 **A**1 9 10 **F**3 29 40 45 54 64 68 75 79 81 82 85 119 130 **S** National Surgical Healthcare, Chicago, IL
Primary Contact: James Murphy, Chief Executive Officer
CFO: Julie Wittwer, Chief Financial Officer
CMO: Michael Mintz, M.D., Chief Medical Officer
CHR: Crystal Matthys, Director Human Resources
CNO: Jan O'Donnell, Chief Nursing Officer
Web address: www.southtexassurgicalhospital.com
**Control:** Partnership, Investor–owned, for–profit **Service:** General Medical and Surgical

**Staffed Beds:** 20 **Admissions:** 1136 **Census:** 10 **Outpatient Visits:** 9234 **Births:** 0 **Total Expense ($000):** 27993 **Payroll Expense ($000):** 6331 **Personnel:** 161

## CORSICANA—Navarro County

✠ **NAVARRO REGIONAL HOSPITAL (450447)**, 3201 West State Highway 22, Zip 75110–2469; tel. 903/654–6800 **A**1 9 10 19 **F**3 11 13 14 15 18 29 30 34 35 39 40 43 45 47 49 50 51 57 59 60 64 68 70 75 79 81 82 85 93 107 108 110 111 114 119 129 132 135 146 148 **P**7 **S** Community Health Systems, Inc., Franklin, TN
Primary Contact: Michael K. Stewart, Chief Executive Officer
CFO: Joseph Woolridge, Chief Financial Officer
CIO: Bryan Chilton, Director Information Systems
CHR: Melodee Pugh, Director Human Resources
CNO: Angie K. Merrell, R.N., Chief Nursing Officer
Web address: www.navarrohospital.com
**Control:** Partnership, Investor–owned, for–profit **Service:** General Medical and Surgical

**Staffed Beds:** 148 **Admissions:** 2732 **Census:** 24 **Outpatient Visits:** 45166 **Births:** 577 **Total Expense ($000):** 40755 **Payroll Expense ($000):** 14416 **Personnel:** 244

## CRANE—Crane County

★ **CRANE MEMORIAL HOSPITAL (451353)**, 1310 South Alford Street, Zip 79731–3899; tel. 432/558–3555 **A**9 10 18 **F**3 29 32 34 40 57 59 64 65 68 75 81 86 97 107 114 119 127 133 145 147 148 **P**2 6
Primary Contact: Dianne Yeager, Chief Executive Officer
CMO: Jay Sigel, M.D., Chief Medical Staff
Web address: www.cranememorial.org
**Control:** Hospital district or authority, Government, nonfederal **Service:** General Medical and Surgical

**Staffed Beds:** 9 **Admissions:** 87 **Census:** 1 **Outpatient Visits:** 11591 **Births:** 0 **Total Expense ($000):** 6222 **Payroll Expense ($000):** 2480 **Personnel:** 47

## CROCKETT—Houston County

★ **HOUSTON COUNTY MEDICAL CENTER (450580)**, 1100 Loop 304 East, Zip 75835–1810; tel. 936/546–3862 **A**3 5 9 10 20 **F**3 11 13 15 28 29 32 35 40 43 46 50 54 57 58 59 61 64 70 75 76 81 87 97 107 108 111 114 118 119 127 129 146 **P**7
Primary Contact: William A. Rohloff, FACHE, Interim Chief Executive Officer
Web address: www.etmc.org
**Control:** Other not–for–profit (including NFP Corporation) **Service:** General Medical and Surgical

**Staffed Beds:** 46 **Admissions:** 946 **Census:** 8 **Outpatient Visits:** 50382 **Births:** 201 **Total Expense ($000):** 21284 **Payroll Expense ($000):** 5603 **Personnel:** 96

## CROSBYTON—Crosby County

**CROSBYTON CLINIC HOSPITAL (451345)**, 710 West Main Street, Zip 79322–2143; tel. 806/675–2382 **A**9 10 18 **F**7 10 29 34 40 50 57 59 63 64 68 87 93 111 119 127 130 133 148 **P**6
Primary Contact: Debra Miller, Administrator
CFO: Cherie Parkhill, Chief Financial Officer
CMO: Steve B. Alley, M.D., Chief of Staff
CHR: Janie Cantu, Director Human Resources
CNO: Anna Bradford, R.N., Chief Nursing Officer
Web address: www.crosbytonclinichospital.com
**Control:** Other not–for–profit (including NFP Corporation) **Service:** General Medical and Surgical

**Staffed Beds:** 25 **Admissions:** 209 **Census:** 3 **Outpatient Visits:** 16925 **Births:** 0 **Total Expense ($000):** 6102 **Payroll Expense ($000):** 2624 **Personnel:** 78

## CUERO—Dewitt County

★ **CUERO COMMUNITY HOSPITAL (450597)**, 2550 North Esplanade Street, Zip 77954–4716; tel. 361/275–6191 **A**9 10 **F**3 7 11 13 15 29 34 40 43 45 57 59 62 64 68 70 75 76 77 79 81 85 86 93 103 107 108 111 115 118 119 129 130 131 **P**6
Primary Contact: Skip Gjolberg, FACHE, Chief Executive Officer
CFO: Greg Pritchett, Chief Financial Officer
CMO: Michael McLeod, M.D., Chief Medical Officer
CIO: Arthur Mueller, Director Management Information Systems
CHR: Wanda S. Kolodziejcyk, Director Human Resources
CNO: Judith Krupala, R.N., Chief Nursing Officer
Web address: www.cuerohospital.org
**Control:** Hospital district or authority, Government, nonfederal **Service:** General Medical and Surgical

**Staffed Beds:** 29 **Admissions:** 944 **Census:** 9 **Outpatient Visits:** 104763 **Births:** 146 **Total Expense ($000):** 29082 **Payroll Expense ($000):** 12138 **Personnel:** 329

## CYPRESS—Harris County

☐ ◇ **LONE STAR BEHAVIORAL HEALTH (454118)**, 16303 Grant Road, Zip 77429–1253; tel. 281/516–6200 **A**1 9 10 21 **F**40 98 104 105 **P**5
Primary Contact: Nathan Daniel Ingram, Chief Executive Officer and Owner
Web address: www.lonestarbehavioralhealth.com
**Control:** Partnership, Investor–owned, for–profit **Service:** Psychiatric

**Staffed Beds:** 24 **Admissions:** 527 **Census:** 15 **Outpatient Visits:** 34545 **Births:** 0 **Total Expense ($000):** 6212 **Payroll Expense ($000):** 4051 **Personnel:** 82

☐ **NORTH CYPRESS MEDICAL CENTER (670024)**, 21214 Northwest Freeway, Zip 77429–3373; tel. 832/912–3500 **A**1 9 10 **F**3 8 12 15 17 18 19 20 22 24 26 28 29 31 34 35 37 39 40 41 42 44 45 46 47 48 49 50 51 55 56 57 58 59 60 61 64 70 74 75 77 78 79 80 81 82 84 85 86 87 89 91 92 93 96 97 107 108 109 110 111 114 115 116 117 118 119 120 121 123 124 126 129 130 131 132 135 141 142 146 148
Primary Contact: Robert Behar, M.D., Chief Executive Officer
Web address: www.ncmc–hospital.com
**Control:** Partnership, Investor–owned, for–profit **Service:** General Medical and Surgical

**Staffed Beds:** 139 **Admissions:** 9543 **Census:** 117 **Outpatient Visits:** 204960 **Births:** 0 **Total Expense ($000):** 208336 **Payroll Expense ($000):** 70740 **Personnel:** 1332

**TX**

---

**Hospital, Medicare Provider Number, Address, Telephone, Approval, Facility, and Physician Codes, Health Care System**

★ American Hospital Association (AHA) membership
☐ The Joint Commission accreditation
◯ Healthcare Facilities Accreditation Program
◇ DNV Healthcare Inc. accreditation
⇑ Center for Improvement in Healthcare Quality Accreditation
△ Commission on Accreditation of Rehabilitation Facilities (CARF) accreditation

**DALHART—Hartley County**

**COON MEMORIAL HOSPITAL (451331)**, 1411 Denver Avenue,
Zip 79022–4809, Mailing Address: P.O. Box 2014, Zip 79022–6014;
tel. 806/244–4571 **A**9 10 18 **F**3 7 10 11 13 30 34 35 40 43 45 50 53 57 59
62 63 64 65 68 69 71 77 79 81 82 83 85 87 93 97 103 107 114 119 125
127 131 133 143 144 146 148 **P**5
Primary Contact: Leroy Schaffner, Chief Executive Officer
CFO: Donny Pettit, Chief Financial Officer
CMO: Randy Herring, M.D., Chief of Staff
CIO: Anthony Lovato, Director Information Technology
CHR: Dee Dawn McCormick, Director Personnel and Human Resources
Web address: www.coonmemorial.org
**Control:** Hospital district or authority, Government, nonfederal **Service:** General
Medical and Surgical

**Staffed Beds:** 21 **Admissions:** 410 **Census:** 4 **Outpatient Visits:** 18315
**Births:** 152 **Total Expense ($000):** 25129 **Payroll Expense ($000):** 8819
**Personnel:** 176

**DALLAS—Dallas County**

**A. WEBB ROBERTS HOSPITAL** See Baylor University Medical Center

⊞ **BAYLOR INSTITUTE FOR REHABILITATION (453036)**, 909 North Washington
Avenue, Zip 75246–1520; tel. 214/820–9300 **A**1 9 10 **F**3 29 30 34 35 44 62
64 65 68 74 75 77 85 86 87 90 92 93 94 96 130 131 132 135 143 148
**S** Baylor Scott & White Health, Dallas, TX
Primary Contact: Fabian Polo, Chief Executive Officer
CMO: Amy Wilson, M.D., Medical Director
CHR: Karen Hill, Director Human Resources
CNO: Beth Hudson, Chief Nursing Officer
Web address: www.baylorhealth.com/PhysiciansLocations/BIR/Pages/Default.aspx
**Control:** Partnership, Investor–owned, for–profit **Service:** Rehabilitation

**Staffed Beds:** 89 **Admissions:** 1531 **Census:** 81 **Outpatient Visits:** 124
**Births:** 0 **Total Expense ($000):** 65802 **Payroll Expense ($000):** 37573
**Personnel:** 269

⊞ **BAYLOR INSTITUTE FOR REHABILITATION AT NORTHWEST DALLAS
(673033)**, 1340 Empire Central Drive, Zip 75247–4022; tel. 214/879–7300 **A**1
10 **F**3 28 29 30 68 75 90 91 96 100 130 148 **S** GLOBALREHAB, Dallas, TX
Primary Contact: David Smith, Chief Executive Officer
CNO: Judy Cash, MSN, Chief Nursing Officer
Web address: www.baylorhealth.com/bir
**Control:** Partnership, Investor–owned, for–profit **Service:** Rehabilitation

**Staffed Beds:** 42 **Admissions:** 696 **Census:** 25 **Outpatient Visits:** 0 **Births:**
0 **Total Expense ($000):** 14857 **Payroll Expense ($000):** 6587 **Personnel:**
109

☐ **BAYLOR JACK AND JANE HAMILTON HEART AND VASCULAR HOSPITAL
(450851)**, 621 North Hall Street, Zip 75226–1339; tel. 214/820–0600 **A**1 5 9
10 **F**3 11 18 20 21 22 26 28 29 30 34 35 57 58 59 64 68 75 81 85 86 87
93 96 100 107 115 119 132 135
Primary Contact: Nancy Vish, Ph.D., President
CFO: Julius Wicke, III, Vice President Finance and Hospital Financial Officer
CMO: Kevin Wheelan, M.D., Medical Director
CHR: Kim Krause, Director Human Resources
Web address: www.baylorhearthospital.com
**Control:** Partnership, Investor–owned, for–profit **Service:** General Medical and
Surgical

**Staffed Beds:** 54 **Admissions:** 2151 **Census:** 21 **Outpatient Visits:** 24443
**Births:** 0 **Total Expense ($000):** 88211 **Payroll Expense ($000):** 25818
**Personnel:** 257

⊞ **BAYLOR MEDICAL CENTER AT UPTOWN (450422)**, 2727 East Lemmon
Avenue, Zip 75204–2895; tel. 214/443–3000 **A**1 3 5 9 10 **F**29 40 68 79 81
82 85 107 111 **P**4 **S** United Surgical Partners International, Addison, TX
Primary Contact: Jon Duckert, Chief Executive Officer
CFO: Colene Fielding, Manager Business Office
CMO: Mark Armstrong, M.D., Medical Director
CIO: Javier Vela, Director Information Technology
CHR: Emalie Sanchez, Director Human Resources
CNO: Verette Neeb, R.N., Chief Nursing Officer
Web address: www.bmcuptown.com
**Control:** Partnership, Investor–owned, for–profit **Service:** General Medical and
Surgical

**Staffed Beds:** 24 **Admissions:** 1140 **Census:** 6 **Outpatient Visits:** 8933
**Births:** 0 **Total Expense ($000):** 46051 **Payroll Expense ($000):** 9524
**Personnel:** 173

⊞ **BAYLOR SPECIALTY HOSPITAL (452017)**, 3504 Swiss Avenue,
Zip 75204–6224; tel. 214/820–9700 **A**1 9 10 **F**1 30 50 75 77 85 130 148
**S** Baylor Scott & White Health, Dallas, TX
Primary Contact: Elizabeth Youngblood, President
CFO: Trey Wicke, Vice President
CHR: Stacie Roberts, Coordinator Human Resources
CNO: Kelli Terpstra, R.N., Chief Nursing Officer
Web address: www.baylorhealth.com/PhysiciansLocations/BSH/Pages/Default.
aspx
**Control:** Other not–for–profit (including NFP Corporation) **Service:** Long–Term
Acute Care hospital

**Staffed Beds:** 57 **Admissions:** 484 **Census:** 39 **Outpatient Visits:** 0 **Births:**
0 **Total Expense ($000):** 24863 **Payroll Expense ($000):** 9923 **Personnel:**
97

⊞ **BAYLOR UNIVERSITY MEDICAL CENTER (450021)**, 3500 Gaston Avenue,
Zip 75246–2088; tel. 214/820–0111, (Includes A. WEBB ROBERTS HOSPITAL,
Zip 75246; ERIK AND MARGARET JONSSON HOSPITAL, Zip 75246; GEORGE W.
TRUETT MEMORIAL HOSPITAL, 3500 Gaston Avenue, Zip 75246; KARL AND
ESTHER HOBLITZELLE MEMORIAL HOSPITAL, 3500 Gaston Avenue, Zip 75246)
**A**1 2 3 5 8 9 10 **F**3 6 11 12 13 14 15 17 18 20 22 24 26 28 29 30 31 34 35
36 37 38 39 40 43 44 45 46 47 48 49 50 51 54 55 56 57 58 59 60 61 63
64 65 66 68 70 71 72 74 75 76 78 79 80 82 84 85 86 87 91 92 94 95
96 97 102 107 108 110 111 112 114 115 116 117 118 119 120 121 123
124 126 129 130 132 135 136 137 138 139 140 141 142 143 144 145 146
147 148 **S** Baylor Scott & White Health, Dallas, TX
Primary Contact: John B. McWhorter, III, President
COO: Doug Lawson, Chief Operating Officer
CFO: Jay Whitfield, Chief Financial Officer
CMO: Brad Lembcke, M.D., Vice President Medical Staff Affairs
CHR: Julie Strittmatter, Director Human Resources
CNO: Claudia Wilder, R.N., Chief Nursing Officer
Web address: www.baylorhealth.com/PhysiciansLocations/Dallas/Pages/Default.
aspx
**Control:** Other not–for–profit (including NFP Corporation) **Service:** General
Medical and Surgical

**Staffed Beds:** 844 **Admissions:** 35366 **Census:** 627 **Outpatient Visits:**
242860 **Births:** 4794 **Total Expense ($000):** 921404 **Payroll Expense
($000):** 307770 **Personnel:** 3058

⊞ **CHILDREN'S HEALTH SYSTEM OF TEXAS (453302)**, 1935 Medical District
Drive, Zip 75235; tel. 214/456–7000 **A**1 3 5 8 9 10 **F**3 7 8 11 12 17 19 21
23 25 27 29 30 31 32 34 35 38 39 41 43 44 45 46 47 48 49 50 51 54
55 57 58 59 60 61 62 64 65 66 68 72 74 75 77 78 79 81 82 84 85 86 87
88 89 91 92 93 94 97 98 99 100 101 102 104 105 106 107 108 111 114
116 117 118 119 126 127 129 130 131 132 134 136 137 138 139 140 141
142 143 144 145 146 148
Primary Contact: Christopher J. Durovich, President and Chief Executive Officer
COO: Douglas G. Hock, President and Chief Operating Officer, Children's Medical
Center
CFO: David Eager, Senior Vice President and Chief Financial Officer
CMO: W. Robert Morrow, M.D., Executive Vice President and Chief Medical Officer
CIO: Pamela Arora, Senior Vice President Information Systems
CHR: Kim Besse, Senior Vice President and Chief Human Resource Officer
CNO: Mary Stowe, R.N., Senior Vice President and Chief Nursing Officer
Web address: www.childrens.com
**Control:** Other not–for–profit (including NFP Corporation) **Service:** Children's
general

**Staffed Beds:** 418 **Admissions:** 29181 **Census:** 264 **Outpatient Visits:**
608571 **Births:** 0 **Total Expense ($000):** 994117 **Payroll Expense ($000):**
396802 **Personnel:** 5851

☐ **DALLAS MEDICAL CENTER (450379)**, Seven Medical Parkway,
Zip 75234–7823, Mailing Address: P.O. Box 819094, Zip 75381–9094;
tel. 972/247–1000 **A**1 10 **F**3 12 13 15 18 20 22 26 29 34 40 44 45 49 56
57 59 68 70 74 75 76 77 78 79 81 82 84 85 86 93 97 107 108 111 114
116 119 130 131 132 141 142 146 147 148 **S** Prime Healthcare Services,
Ontario, CA
Primary Contact: Raji Kumar, Chief Executive Officer
CFO: Karen Bomersbach, Chief Financial Officer
CIO: Mary Jo Tallant–Ball, Director Health Information Systems
CHR: Sheila K. Richards, Human Resources Director
Web address: www.dallasmedcenter.com
**Control:** Corporation, Investor–owned, for–profit **Service:** General Medical and
Surgical

**Staffed Beds:** 83 **Admissions:** 3942 **Census:** 40 **Outpatient Visits:** 38579
**Births:** 592 **Total Expense ($000):** 83603 **Payroll Expense ($000):** 26548

*Many Facility Codes have changed. Please refer to the AHA Guide Code Chart.*

✠ **DOCTORS HOSPITAL AT WHITE ROCK LAKE (450678)**, 9440 Poppy Drive, Zip 75218–3694; tel. 214/324–6100 **A**1 9 10 **F**3 11 12 13 15 17 18 20 22 24 26 28 29 30 31 34 35 37 40 45 47 49 50 51 53 56 57 59 64 70 72 73 74 75 76 77 78 79 81 85 93 107 108 110 111 114 115 119 120 124 126 129 130 132 135 144 146 147 148 **S** TENET Healthcare Corporation, Dallas, TX
Primary Contact: Jaikumar Krishnaswamy, Chief Executive Officer
CFO: Drew Shea, Chief Financial Officer
CMO: Tom Jones, D.O., Chief Medical Officer
CHR: Lorinnsa Bridges-Kee, Chief Human Resources Officer
Web address: www.doctorshospitaldallas.com
**Control:** Partnership, Investor–owned, for–profit **Service:** General Medical and Surgical

**Staffed Beds:** 151 **Admissions:** 6900 **Census:** 77 **Outpatient Visits:** 64649 **Births:** 864 **Total Expense ($000):** 104562 **Payroll Expense ($000):** 37378 **Personnel:** 553

○ **FOREST PARK MEDICAL CENTER (670057)**, 11990 North Central Expressway, Zip 75243–3714; tel. 972/234–1900 **A**9 11 **F**3 8 12 29 34 35 37 40 45 47 48 49 57 70 75 79 81 82 85 107 111 115 126 130 132 **S** Vibrant Healthcare, Dallas, TX
Primary Contact: Cindy Bledsoe, Chief Executive Officer
Web address: www.forestparkmc.com/
**Control:** Partnership, Investor–owned, for–profit **Service:** Surgical

**Staffed Beds:** 84 **Admissions:** 2113 **Census:** 14 **Outpatient Visits:** 8736 **Births:** 0 **Total Expense ($000):** 109507 **Payroll Expense ($000):** 21975 **Personnel:** 295

✠ **GREEN OAKS HOSPITAL (454094)**, 7808 Clodus Fields Drive, Zip 75251–2206; tel. 972/991–9504 **A**1 5 9 10 **F**4 5 29 54 87 98 99 102 103 104 105 130 132 **P**5 **S** HCA, Nashville, TN
Primary Contact: Thomas M. Collins, President, Chairman and Chief Executive Officer
COO: Pam Whitley, R.N., Chief Operating Officer and Chief Nursing Officer
CFO: Aaron Rowe, Chief Financial Officer
CMO: Joel Holiner, M.D., Executive Medical Director
CIO: Richard Fontenault, Director Information Systems
CHR: Kevin Adkins, Director Human Resources
CNO: Pam Whitley, R.N., Chief Nursing Officer and Chief Operating Officer
Web address: www.greenoakspsych.com
**Control:** Corporation, Investor–owned, for–profit **Service:** Psychiatric

**Staffed Beds:** 124 **Admissions:** 4597 **Census:** 124 **Outpatient Visits:** 34899 **Births:** 0 **Total Expense ($000):** 45198 **Payroll Expense ($000):** 20571 **Personnel:** 363

✠ **KINDRED HOSPITAL DALLAS CENTRAL (452108)**, 8050 Meadows Road, Zip 75231–3406; tel. 469/232–6500 **A**1 9 10 **F**1 3 29 75 77 85 87 96 107 114 148 **P**8 **S** Kindred Healthcare, Louisville, KY
Primary Contact: Stephanie Madrid, Chief Executive Officer
CFO: Joni Gonzalez, Controller
CNO: Jackie Gordon, Chief Clinical Officer
Web address: www.khdallascentral.com/
**Control:** Corporation, Investor–owned, for–profit **Service:** Long–Term Acute Care hospital

**Staffed Beds:** 60 **Admissions:** 559 **Census:** 40 **Outpatient Visits:** 300 **Births:** 0 **Total Expense ($000):** 25116 **Payroll Expense ($000):** 8292 **Personnel:** 130

**KINDRED HOSPITAL DALLAS–WALNUT HILL** See Kindred Hospital–Dallas

✠ **KINDRED HOSPITAL–DALLAS (452015)**, 9525 Greenville Avenue, Zip 75243–4116; tel. 214/355–2600, (Includes KINDRED HOSPITAL DALLAS–WALNUT HILL, 8200 Walnut Hill Lane, Zip 75231; tel. 214/345–6500) **A**1 9 10 **F**1 3 29 70 107 114 130 148 **S** Kindred Healthcare, Louisville, KY
Primary Contact: James Mendez, Chief Executive Officer
CFO: Jean McDowell, Chief Financial Officer
Web address: www.khdallas.com
**Control:** Partnership, Investor–owned, for–profit **Service:** Long–Term Acute Care hospital

**Staffed Beds:** 50 **Admissions:** 479 **Census:** 32 **Outpatient Visits:** 0 **Births:** 0 **Total Expense ($000):** 19516 **Payroll Expense ($000):** 6779 **Personnel:** 196

✠ **KINDRED HOSPITAL–WHITE ROCK (452071)**, 9440 Poppy Drive, 5th Floor, Zip 75218–3652; tel. 214/324–6562 **A**1 9 10 **F**1 29 85 86 87 130 148 **P**5 **S** Kindred Healthcare, Louisville, KY
Primary Contact: Kelly Bailey, Administrator
COO: Kim Chipman, Chief Clinical Officer
CFO: Jennifer Penland, Controller
CMO: Mark Ferris, M.D., Medical Director
CNO: Brenda Perez, R.N., Chief Clinical Officer
Web address: www.khwhiterock.com
**Control:** Corporation, Investor–owned, for–profit **Service:** Long–Term Acute Care hospital

**Staffed Beds:** 25 **Admissions:** 218 **Census:** 18 **Outpatient Visits:** 0 **Births:** 0 **Total Expense ($000):** 9279 **Payroll Expense ($000):** 3890 **Personnel:** 60

✠ **LIFECARE HOSPITALS OF DALLAS (452044)**, 1950 Record Crossing Road, Zip 75235–6223; tel. 214/640–9600 **A**1 9 10 **F**1 3 29 40 64 75 91 107 119 130 148 **S** LifeCare Management Services, Plano, TX
Primary Contact: Kevin S. Cooper, R.N., Chief Executive Officer
CFO: Amie Gratch, Director Financial Services
CMO: Jonathan Weissler, M.D., Chief Medical Officer
CHR: Linzie Riley, Interim Human Resource Manager
CNO: Kathy Mason, R.N., Chief Nursing Officer
Web address: www.lifecare–hospitals.com/hospital/dallas
**Control:** Corporation, Investor–owned, for–profit **Service:** Long–Term Acute Care hospital

**Staffed Beds:** 173 **Admissions:** 1661 **Census:** 119 **Outpatient Visits:** 7741 **Births:** 0 **Total Expense ($000):** 67009 **Payroll Expense ($000):** 27713 **Personnel:** 408

**LIFECARE HOSPITALS OF NORTH TEXAS** See LifeCare Hospitals of Dallas

**MARY SHIELS HOSPITAL** See Baylor Medical Center at Uptown

✠ **MEDICAL CITY DALLAS HOSPITAL (450647)**, 7777 Forest Lane, Zip 75230–2598; tel. 972/566–7000, (Includes MEDICAL CITY CHILDREN'S HOSPITAL, 7777 Forest Lane, Zip 75230–2505; tel. 972/566–7000; Keith Zimmerman, Chief Executive Officer) **A**1 2 3 5 9 10 **F**3 8 11 12 13 15 17 18 19 20 21 22 23 24 25 26 27 28 29 30 31 34 35 37 40 41 43 44 45 46 47 49 50 51 55 56 57 58 59 60 63 64 65 68 70 72 73 74 75 76 77 78 79 81 82 84 85 86 87 88 89 93 97 105 107 108 110 111 114 115 116 117 118 119 126 129 130 132 135 136 137 138 141 142 143 144 146 147 148 **P**6 **S** HCA, Nashville, TN
Primary Contact: Troy Villarreal, President and Chief Executive Officer
CFO: Mark Atchley, Vice President and Chief Financial Officer
CMO: Mark Hebert, M.D., President Medical Staff
CIO: Troy Sypien, Director Information Technology and Systems
CHR: Jenifer K. Tertel, Director Human Resources
Web address: www.medicalcityhospital.com
**Control:** Corporation, Investor–owned, for–profit **Service:** General Medical and Surgical

**Staffed Beds:** 534 **Admissions:** 25139 **Census:** 404 **Outpatient Visits:** 162572 **Births:** 3747 **Total Expense ($000):** 482683 **Payroll Expense ($000):** 171826 **Personnel:** 2071

✠ **METHODIST CHARLTON MEDICAL CENTER (450723)**, 3500 West Wheatland Road, Zip 75237–3460, Mailing Address: P.O. Box 225357, Zip 75222–5357; tel. 214/947–7777 **A**1 3 9 10 13 **F**3 11 13 15 18 20 22 24 28 29 30 31 34 35 40 45 46 47 49 50 53 58 59 60 64 66 68 70 74 76 78 79 81 82 84 85 86 87 97 107 108 110 111 114 115 118 119 126 130 131 132 146 148 **P**1 7 **S** Methodist Health System, Dallas, TX
Primary Contact: Fran Laukaitis, R.N., Interim Chief Executive Officer and Chief Nursing Officer
COO: Pamela Stoyanoff, Executive Vice President and Chief Operating Officer
CFO: Michael J. Schaefer, Executive Vice President and Chief Financial Officer
CIO: Pamela McNutt, Vice President Information Systems
CHR: Cheryl Flynn, Senior Vice President Chief Human Resources Officer
CNO: Fran Laukaitis, R.N., Vice President Nursing
Web address: www.methodisthealthsystem.org/charlton
**Control:** Other not–for–profit (including NFP Corporation) **Service:** General Medical and Surgical

**Staffed Beds:** 304 **Admissions:** 13972 **Census:** 181 **Outpatient Visits:** 152411 **Total Expense ($000):** 216053 **Payroll Expense ($000):** 101668 **Personnel:** 1443

---

**Hospital, Medicare Provider Number, Address, Telephone, Approval, Facility, and Physician Codes, Health Care System**

★ American Hospital Association (AHA) membership
□ The Joint Commission accreditation
○ Healthcare Facilities Accreditation Program
◇ DNV Healthcare Inc. accreditation
⇑ Center for Improvement in Healthcare Quality Accreditation
△ Commission on Accreditation of Rehabilitation Facilities (CARF) accreditation

**TX**

✠ **METHODIST DALLAS MEDICAL CENTER (450051)**, 1441 North Beckley Avenue, Zip 75203–1201, Mailing Address: P.O. Box 655999, Zip 75265–5999; tel. 214/947–8181 **A**1 2 3 5 8 9 10 **F**3 11 12 13 15 18 20 22 24 26 28 29 30 31 34 35 37 40 43 45 46 47 48 49 50 53 54 58 59 60 64 66 68 70 72 74 76 78 79 81 82 84 85 87 92 93 97 107 108 110 111 118 119 126 130 132 138 139 142 146 148 **P**1 7 **S** Methodist Health System, Dallas, TX
Primary Contact: David D. Clark, President
COO: Pamela Stoyanoff, Executive Vice President and Chief Operating Officer
CFO: Randy Walker, Vice President
CIO: Pamela McNutt, Senior Vice President and Chief Information Officer
CHR: Jackie Middleton, Vice President Human Resources
Web address: www.methodisthealthsystem.org/Dallas
**Control:** Other not–for–profit (including NFP Corporation) **Service:** General Medical and Surgical

**Staffed Beds:** 408 **Admissions:** 16761 **Census:** 250 **Outpatient Visits:** 156387 **Births:** 3472 **Total Expense ($000):** 373775 **Payroll Expense ($000):** 154580 **Personnel:** 2266

☐ **METHODIST REHABILITATION HOSPITAL (673031)**, 3020 West Wheatland Road, Zip 75237–3537; tel. 972/708–8600 **A**1 9 10 **F**29 30 60 90 91 93 96
Primary Contact: Chris Ensmann, MS, Chief Executive Officer
Web address: www.methodist–rehab.com
**Control:** Partnership, Investor–owned, for–profit **Service:** Rehabilitation

**Staffed Beds:** 40 **Admissions:** 992 **Census:** 34 **Outpatient Visits:** 11173 **Births:** 0 **Total Expense ($000):** 16039 **Payroll Expense ($000):** 8287 **Personnel:** 154

☐ **NORTH CENTRAL SURGICAL CENTER (670049)**, 9301 North Central Expressway, Suite 100, Zip 75231–0802; tel. 214/265–2810 **A**1 9 10 **F**3 40 45 79 81 82 85 107 111 114 115 119
Primary Contact: Suzanne Greever, Chief Executive Officer
COO: Thanh Tran, Chief Operating Officer
CMO: Stuart Simon, M.D., Medical Director
CNO: Katherine Martinez, Chief Nursing Officer
Web address: www.northcentralsurgical.com
**Control:** Partnership, Investor–owned, for–profit **Service:** Surgical

**Staffed Beds:** 23 **Admissions:** 1228 **Census:** 8 **Outpatient Visits:** 19886 **Births:** 0 **Total Expense ($000):** 63927 **Payroll Expense ($000):** 14665 **Personnel:** 297

★ **OUR CHILDREN'S HOUSE AT BAYLOR (453308)**, 1208 North Hall Street, Zip 75204; tel. 214/820–9838 **A**3 5 9 10 **F**3 29 30 32 34 35 39 50 54 58 59 74 75 81 85 86 87 89 90 93 129 130 132 146 148 **S** Baylor Scott & White Health, Dallas, TX
Primary Contact: Elizabeth Youngblood, President
CMO: Andrew Gelfand, M.D., Medical Director
CHR: Stacie Roberts, Coordinator Human Resources
CNO: Kelli Terpstra, R.N., Chief Nursing Officer
Web address: www.baylorhealth.com/PhysiciansLocations/OCH/Pages/Default.aspx
**Control:** Other not–for–profit (including NFP Corporation) **Service:** Children's general

**Staffed Beds:** 54 **Admissions:** 394 **Census:** 22 **Outpatient Visits:** 97678 **Births:** 0 **Total Expense ($000):** 34825 **Payroll Expense ($000):** 18252 **Personnel:** 214

✠ **PARKLAND HEALTH & HOSPITAL SYSTEM (450015)**, 5200 Harry Hines Boulevard, Zip 75235–7708; tel. 214/590–8000 **A**1 2 3 5 8 9 10 **F**3 8 9 11 12 13 15 16 17 18 20 22 26 28 29 30 31 34 35 37 38 39 40 43 46 47 48 49 50 51 54 55 56 57 58 59 60 61 64 65 66 68 70 72 74 75 76 77 78 79 81 82 83 84 85 86 87 90 91 92 93 94 97 98 99 100 101 102 103 104 105 107 108 110 111 114 115 118 119 129 130 131 132 134 135 138 141 144 146 147 148 **P**1
Primary Contact: Fred Cerise, M.D., Chief Executive Officer
CIO: Fernando Martinez, Senior Vice President and Chief Information Officer
CNO: Mary K. Eagen, R.N., Executive Vice President, Chief Nursing Officer
Web address: www.parklandhospital.com
**Control:** Hospital district or authority, Government, nonfederal **Service:** General Medical and Surgical

**Staffed Beds:** 858 **Admissions:** 38905 **Census:** 581 **Outpatient Visits:** 1223266 **Births:** 10222 **Total Expense ($000):** 1314726 **Payroll Expense ($000):** 670006 **Personnel:** 10089

☐ **PINE CREEK MEDICAL CENTER (450894)**, 9032 Harry Hines Boulevard, Zip 75235–1720; tel. 214/231–2273 **A**1 9 10 **F**3 12 18 24 29 30 34 40 42 45 49 51 64 79 81 82 85 93 107 111 114
Primary Contact: Corazon Ramirez, M.D., Chief Executive Officer
CFO: Michael Conroy, Chief Financial Officer
CIO: Kevin Carney, Senior Information Systems Analyst
Web address: www.pinecreekmedicalcenter.com
**Control:** Partnership, Investor–owned, for–profit **Service:** General Medical and Surgical

**Staffed Beds:** 15 **Admissions:** 1226 **Census:** 8 **Outpatient Visits:** 6423 **Births:** 0 **Total Expense ($000):** 54577 **Payroll Expense ($000):** 9398 **Personnel:** 145

☐ **PROMISE HOSPITAL OF DALLAS (452067)**, 7955 Harry Hines Boulevard, Zip 75235–3305; tel. 214/637–0000 **A**1 9 10 **F**1 3 29 30 64 75 148 **S** Promise Healthcare, Boca Raton, FL
Primary Contact: Mary Alexander, Interim Chief Executive Officer
CFO: Diana B. Smith, Chief Financial Officer
CMO: Gary E. Goff, M.D., Medical Director
CHR: Ginger Davenport, Director Human Resources
Web address: www.promise–dallas.com/
**Control:** Corporation, Investor–owned, for–profit **Service:** Long–Term Acute Care hospital

**Staffed Beds:** 62 **Admissions:** 248 **Census:** 17 **Outpatient Visits:** 1481 **Births:** 0 **Total Expense ($000):** 8655 **Payroll Expense ($000):** 3300 **Personnel:** 74

☐ **RELIANT REHABILITATION HOSPITAL DALLAS (673043)**, 7930 Northaven Road, Zip 75230–3331; tel. 214/706–8200 **A**1 9 10 **F**3 29 90 96 130 148
Primary Contact: Kasey Norman, Chief Executive Officer
CFO: Mary Mwaniki, Chief Financial Officer
CMO: Anna Freed–Sigurdsson, M.D., Medical Director
CIO: James E. King, Corporate Director Information Technology
CHR: Ieesha Cannida, Director Human Resources
CNO: Nancy Faas, R.N., Chief Nursing Officer
Web address: www.relianthcp.com
**Control:** Partnership, Investor–owned, for–profit **Service:** Rehabilitation

**Staffed Beds:** 60 **Admissions:** 790 **Census:** 26 **Outpatient Visits:** 0 **Births:** 0 **Total Expense ($000):** 12095 **Payroll Expense ($000):** 4729 **Personnel:** 107

★ **SELECT SPECIALTY HOSPITAL – DALLAS DOWNTOWN**, 3500 Gaston Avenue, Floors 3&4 Jonnson, Zip 75246–2017; tel. 409/801–4500, (Nonreporting) **S** Select Medical Corporation, Mechanicsburg, PA
Primary Contact: Melody Nagel, Chief Executive Officer
Web address: www.dallasdowntown.selectspecialtyhospitals.com/
**Control:** Corporation, Investor–owned, for–profit **Service:** Long–Term Acute Care hospital

**Staffed Beds:** 46

✠ **SELECT SPECIALTY HOSPITAL–SOUTH DALLAS (452078)**, 3500 West Wheatland Road, 4th Floor, Zip 75237–3460; tel. 972/780–6500 **A**1 9 10 **F**1 3 29 85 130 148 **S** Select Medical Corporation, Mechanicsburg, PA
Primary Contact: Richard Knowland, Chief Executive Officer
Web address: www.selectspecialtyhospitals.com/company/locations/southdallas.aspx
**Control:** Corporation, Investor–owned, for–profit **Service:** Long–Term Acute Care hospital

**Staffed Beds:** 69 **Admissions:** 578 **Census:** 41 **Outpatient Visits:** 0 **Births:** 0 **Total Expense ($000):** 22437 **Payroll Expense ($000):** 8832 **Personnel:** 148

✠ △ **TEXAS HEALTH PRESBYTERIAN HOSPITAL DALLAS (450462)**, 8200 Walnut Hill Lane, Zip 75231–4426; tel. 214/345–6789 **A**1 2 3 5 7 9 10 **F**3 5 11 12 13 15 17 18 20 22 24 26 28 29 30 31 32 34 35 36 37 38 40 44 45 46 47 49 50 51 52 53 54 55 56 57 58 59 60 61 63 64 65 66 68 70 72 74 75 76 77 78 79 81 82 85 86 87 90 91 92 93 94 95 96 97 98 100 101 102 103 104 105 107 108 110 111 112 114 115 118 119 124 126 129 130 131 132 135 141 143 144 146 147 148 **P**6 **S** Texas Health Resources, Arlington, TX
Primary Contact: James Berg, FACHE, President
CFO: Brian Craft, Group Finance Officer
CMO: Aurora Estevez, M.D., Chief Medical Officer
CIO: Tammy Phillips, Director, Information Systems
CHR: Stacy Miller, Entity Human Resources Officer
CNO: Cole Edmonson, R.N., Vice President and Chief Nursing Officer
Web address: www.texashealth.org
**Control:** Other not–for–profit (including NFP Corporation) **Service:** General Medical and Surgical

**Staffed Beds:** 644 **Admissions:** 26426 **Census:** 412 **Outpatient Visits:** 350966 **Births:** 5817 **Total Expense ($000):** 592817 **Payroll Expense ($000):** 199052 **Personnel:** 2753

**TEXAS HOSPITAL FOR ADVANCED MEDICINE** See Dallas Medical Center

☐ **TEXAS INSTITUTE FOR SURGERY AT TEXAS HEALTH PRESBYTERIAN DALLAS (450889)**, 7115 Greenville Avenue, Zip 75231–5100; tel. 214/647–5300 **A**1 9 10 **F**40 51 64 79 81 82 107 114 115 119
Primary Contact: David Helfer, President
CFO: John S. Croley, Vice President Business Operations
CMO: Presley Mock, M.D., Chief of Staff
CHR: Jennifer Cherrnay, Director Human Resources
CNO: Joy Dier, R.N., Vice President Clinical Services and Chief Nursing Officer
Web address: www.texasinstituteforsurgery.com
**Control:** Partnership, Investor–owned, for–profit **Service:** General Medical and Surgical

**Staffed Beds:** 9 **Admissions:** 374 **Census:** 2 **Outpatient Visits:** 10808 **Births:** 0 **Total Expense ($000):** 49120 **Payroll Expense ($000):** 11491 **Personnel:** 177

**TX**

✠ **TEXAS SCOTTISH RITE HOSPITAL FOR CHILDREN (453314)**, 2222 Welborn Street, Zip 75219–3924, Mailing Address: P.O. Box 190567, Zip 75219–0567; tel. 214/559–5000 **A**1 3 5 10 **F**3 9 11 29 34 35 50 53 58 64 68 74 75 77 79 81 82 85 86 87 89 92 94 107 111 115 119 130 131 132 143 146 148 **P**6
Primary Contact: Robert L. Walker, President and Chief Executive Officer
CFO: William R. Huston, Senior Vice President and Chief Financial Officer
CMO: Daniel J. Sucato, M.D., Chief of Staff
CIO: Amy Bailey, Director Information Systems
CHR: James D. Sturgis, Associate Administrator
CNO: Debbie A. Sayles, R.N., Vice President and Chief Nursing Officer
Web address: www.tsrhc.org
**Control:** Other not–for–profit (including NFP Corporation) **Service:** Children's orthopedic

**Staffed Beds:** 52 **Admissions:** 923 **Census:** 13 **Outpatient Visits:** 32502 **Births:** 0 **Total Expense ($000):** 153858 **Payroll Expense ($000):** 64699 **Personnel:** 846

☐ **TIMBERLAWN MENTAL HEALTH SYSTEM (454081)**, 4600 Samuell Boulevard, Zip 75228–6800; tel. 214/381–7181 **A**1 5 9 10 **F**4 5 54 56 59 64 87 98 99 100 101 102 103 104 105 130 132 143 **S** Universal Health Services, Inc., King of Prussia, PA
Primary Contact: Shelah Adams, Chief Executive Officer
COO: Rick Paczkowski, Chief Operating Officer
CFO: Lori Verbeke, Chief Financial Officer
CMO: John Pascoe, M.D., Executive Medical Director
CIO: Twila Ragar–Thomas, Director Health Information Management and Quality Improvement
CHR: Winnie Boehnke, Director Human Resources
CNO: Paula Hirschberg, R.N., Director of Nursing
Web address: www.timberlawn.com
**Control:** Corporation, Investor–owned, for–profit **Service:** Psychiatric

**Staffed Beds:** 144 **Admissions:** 6747 **Census:** 126 **Outpatient Visits:** 19229 **Births:** 0 **Total Expense ($000):** 25606 **Payroll Expense ($000):** 12150 **Personnel:** 265

✠ △ **UNIVERSITY OF TEXAS SOUTHWESTERN MEDICAL CENTER (450766)**, 5323 Harry Hines Boulevard, Zip 75390–9265; tel. 214/645–5555, (Includes UNIVERSITY OF TEXAS SOUTHWESTERN MEDICAL CENTER – ST. PAUL, 5909 Harry Hines Boulevard, Zip 75390–9200; tel. 214/645–5555; UNIVERSITY OF TEXAS SOUTHWESTERN MEDICAL CENTER – ZALE LIPSHY, 5151 Harry Hines Boulevard, Zip 75390–9265; tel. 214/645–5555; Daniel Podolsky, M.D., President) **A**1 2 3 5 7 8 9 10 **F**3 6 7 8 9 10 11 12 13 15 17 18 20 22 24 26 28 29 30 31 34 35 36 38 39 40 44 45 46 47 48 49 50 52 53 54 55 56 57 58 59 60 61 62 64 65 68 70 71 72 74 75 76 77 78 79 80 81 82 84 85 86 87 90 91 92 93 94 95 96 97 98 99 100 101 102 103 104 107 108 109 110 111 114 115 116 117 118 119 120 121 123 124 126 129 130 131 132 135 136 137 138 139 140 141 142 143 145 146 147 148 **P**4 6
Primary Contact: John Warner, M.D., Chief Executive Officer
COO: Becky McCulley, Chief Operating Officer
CFO: Elizabeth S. Ward, Chief Financial Officer
CMO: Steven Leach, M.D., Chief Medical Officer
CIO: Suresh Gunasekaran, Assistant Vice President Information Resources
CHR: William Behrendt, Ph.D., Vice President Human Resources
CNO: Susan Hernandez, Chief Nursing Officer
Web address: www.utsouthwestern.edu
**Control:** State–Government, nonfederal **Service:** General Medical and Surgical

**Staffed Beds:** 459 **Admissions:** 21828 **Census:** 357 **Outpatient Visits:** 375457 **Births:** 1750 **Total Expense ($000):** 802955 **Payroll Expense ($000):** 320899 **Personnel:** 4234

✠ △ **VETERANS AFFAIRS NORTH TEXAS HEALTH CARE SYSTEM**, 4500 South Lancaster Road, Zip 75216–7167; tel. 214/742–8387, (Includes SAM RAYBURN MEMORIAL VETERANS CENTER, 1201 East Ninth Street, Bonham, Zip 75418–4091; tel. 903/583–2111; Angela Nix, Administrator), (Nonreporting) **A**1 2 3 5 7 9 **S** Department of Veterans Affairs, Washington, DC
Primary Contact: Jeffrey Milligan, Director
CFO: Garry Martin, Chief Fiscal
CIO: Lucy Rogers, Chief Information Resource Management Systems
Web address: www.northtexas.va.gov/
**Control:** Veterans Affairs, Government, federal **Service:** General Medical and Surgical

**Staffed Beds:** 875

☐ **WALNUT HILL MEDICAL CENTER (670092)**, 7502 Greenville Avenue, Zip 75231–3802; tel. 972/863–6000, (Data for 333 days) **A**1 10 **F**3 15 18 20 22 24 26 29 34 40 47 49 57 58 59 60 70 74 75 77 79 81 84 85 87 97 102 107 108 110 111 114 119 129 130 145 148
Primary Contact: Cory Countryman, Chief Executive Officer
Web address: www.walnuthillmc.com
**Control:** Partnership, Investor–owned, for–profit **Service:** General Medical and Surgical

**Staffed Beds:** 52 **Admissions:** 814 **Census:** 9 **Outpatient Visits:** 4892 **Births:** 0 **Total Expense ($000):** 67093 **Payroll Expense ($000):** 11793 **Personnel:** 289

### DECATUR—Wise County

✠ **WISE REGIONAL HEALTH SYSTEM (450271)**, 609 Medical Center Drive, Zip 76234–3836; tel. 940/627–5921, (Includes PARKWAY SURGICAL & CARDIOVASCULAR HOSPITAL, 3200 North Tarrant Parkway, Fort Worth, Zip 76177–8611; tel. 817/502–7300; WISE REGIONAL HEALTH SYSTEM – BRIDGEPORT CAMPUS, 1905 Doctors Hospital Drive, Bridgeport, Zip 76426–2260; tel. 940/683–0300; WISE REGIONAL HEALTH SYSTEM, EAST CAMPUS DECATUR, 609 Medical Center Drive, tel. 940/627–5921; WISE REGIONAL HEALTH SYSTEM, WEST CAMPUS DECATUR, 2000 South Fm 51, Zip 76234–3702; tel. 940/627–5921) **A**1 2 9 10 **F**3 11 12 13 15 17 18 20 22 24 26 28 29 30 31 32 34 40 43 45 47 49 51 53 54 56 57 59 60 62 70 74 75 76 77 78 79 81 85 87 89 90 93 96 97 98 103 104 107 108 110 111 114 115 116 118 119 129 130 131 132 135 147 148 **P**7
Primary Contact: Stephen M. Summers, CPA, FACHE, Chief Executive Officer
COO: Leon Fuqua, Chief Operating Officer
CFO: Jim Eaton, Chief Financial Officer
CMO: Jason Schuh, M.D., Chief of Staff
CIO: Joe Arispe, Director Information Systems
CHR: Mike McQuiston, Administrative Director Human Resources
CNO: Sue Sewell, Chief Nursing Officer
Web address: www.wiseregional.com
**Control:** Hospital district or authority, Government, nonfederal **Service:** General Medical and Surgical

**Staffed Beds:** 145 **Admissions:** 5128 **Census:** 72 **Outpatient Visits:** 253395 **Births:** 592 **Total Expense ($000):** 196306 **Payroll Expense ($000):** 66546 **Personnel:** 1260

### DEL RIO—Val Verde County

✠ ⇑ **VAL VERDE REGIONAL MEDICAL CENTER (450154)**, 801 Bedell Avenue, Zip 78840–4112, Mailing Address: 801 North Bedell Avenue, Zip 78840–4112; tel. 830/775–8566 **A**1 9 10 20 22 **F**3 7 11 13 15 18 20 29 30 34 35 40 43 46 48 54 57 59 63 73 75 76 77 79 81 82 84 85 87 89 93 96 107 108 110 111 114 119 129 131 132 133 146 147
Primary Contact: Xochy Hurtado, Chief Executive Officer
COO: Steven Hale, Chief Operating Officer
CFO: Eddie Read, Interim Chief Financial Officer
CMO: Mohamed Shafiu, M.D., Chief of Staff
CIO: Val King, Chief Information Officer
CHR: Leigh Ann Qualia, Director Human Resources
CNO: Kathy Fletcher, R.N., Interim Chief Nursing Officer
Web address: www.vvrmc.org
**Control:** Hospital district or authority, Government, nonfederal **Service:** General Medical and Surgical

**Staffed Beds:** 80 **Admissions:** 2904 **Census:** 27 **Outpatient Visits:** 57229 **Births:** 935 **Total Expense ($000):** 49746 **Payroll Expense ($000):** 21506 **Personnel:** 477

### DENISON—Grayson County

☐ **TEXOMA MEDICAL CENTER (450324)**, 5016 South U.S. Highway 75, Zip 75020–4584, Mailing Address: P.O. Box 890, Zip 75021–0890; tel. 903/416–4000 **A**1 9 10 13 **F**3 11 12 13 15 17 18 20 22 24 28 29 30 31 34 40 43 45 46 47 49 50 53 54 57 59 62 64 70 74 75 76 77 78 79 80 81 85 86 89 90 91 93 96 98 100 101 102 103 104 105 107 108 110 111 115 119 126 129 130 132 144 145 146 147 148 **S** Universal Health Services, Inc., King of Prussia, PA
Primary Contact: Ronald T. Seal, Chief Executive Officer
CFO: Gerard Hebert, Chief Financial Officer
CMO: Robert Sanders, M.D., Chief Medical Officer
CIO: Lisa Engle, Director Information Technology
CHR: Bill Heinzmann, Director Human Resources
CNO: Andrea Brenn, R.N., Chief Nursing Officer
Web address: www.texomamedicalcenter.net
**Control:** Corporation, Investor–owned, for–profit **Service:** General Medical and Surgical

**Staffed Beds:** 294 **Admissions:** 13319 **Census:** 188 **Outpatient Visits:** 109778 **Births:** 1107 **Total Expense ($000):** 195181 **Payroll Expense ($000):** 73694 **Personnel:** 1517

**TX**

---

**Hospital, Medicare Provider Number, Address, Telephone, Approval, Facility, and Physician Codes, Health Care System**

★ American Hospital Association (AHA) membership
☐ The Joint Commission accreditation
◯ Healthcare Facilities Accreditation Program
◇ DNV Healthcare Inc. accreditation
⇑ Center for Improvement in Healthcare Quality Accreditation
△ Commission on Accreditation of Rehabilitation Facilities (CARF) accreditation

## DENTON—Denton County

☒ **DENTON REGIONAL MEDICAL CENTER (450634)**, 3535 South I–35 East, Zip 76210; tel. 940/384–3535 **A**1 3 9 10 **F**3 13 15 18 20 22 24 26 28 29 30 34 35 40 43 45 46 47 49 50 57 59 64 69 70 73 74 75 76 77 79 81 82 84 85 86 87 93 107 108 110 111 114 115 118 119 126 130 132 144 146 147 148 **S** HCA, Nashville, TN
Primary Contact: Caleb F. O'Rear, Chief Executive Officer
COO: Jeffrey T. Lawrence, Chief Operating Officer
CFO: Todd Gibson, Chief Financial Officer
CMO: Stanley Evans, M.D., Chief of Staff
CHR: Stacey Bravo, Vice President Human Resources
CNO: Nicki Roderman, Chief Nursing Officer
Web address: www.dentonregional.com
**Control:** Partnership, Investor–owned, for–profit **Service:** General Medical and Surgical

> **Staffed Beds:** 185 **Admissions:** 9336 **Census:** 123 **Outpatient Visits:** 96026 **Births:** 1067 **Total Expense ($000):** 137549 **Payroll Expense ($000):** 51973 **Personnel:** 686

☐ **INTEGRITY TRANSITIONAL HOSPITAL (452109)**, 2813 South Mayhill Road, Zip 76208–5910; tel. 940/320–2300 **A**1 9 10 **F**1 3 29 40 42 77 80 82 84 86 87 91 130 148
Primary Contact: Israel Navarro, Chief Executive Officer
CNO: Michele Andrews, Chief Clinical Officer
Web address: www.ithcare.com
**Control:** Partnership, Investor–owned, for–profit **Service:** Long–Term Acute Care hospital

> **Staffed Beds:** 44 **Admissions:** 353 **Census:** 21 **Outpatient Visits:** 408 **Births:** 0 **Personnel:** 85

☒ **MAYHILL HOSPITAL (670010)**, 2809 South Mayhill Road, Zip 76208–5910; tel. 940/239–3000 **A**1 9 10 **F**4 5 29 40 56 82 98 101 102 103 104 130 **S** Universal Health Services, Inc., King of Prussia, PA
Primary Contact: Adam Vincent, Chief Executive Officer
CFO: Emmy Adams, Chief Financial Officer
CMO: Asad Islam, M.D., Chief Medical Officer
CIO: Kyle Murphy, Director Information Technology
CHR: Patricia Gloria–Barraza, Coordinator Human Resources
Web address: www.mayhillhospital.com
**Control:** Partnership, Investor–owned, for–profit **Service:** Psychiatric

> **Staffed Beds:** 59 **Admissions:** 1456 **Census:** 44 **Outpatient Visits:** 1387 **Births:** 0 **Total Expense ($000):** 8896 **Payroll Expense ($000):** 4516 **Personnel:** 94

☒ **SELECT REHABILITATION HOSPITAL OF DENTON (673036)**, 2620 Scripture Street, Zip 76201–4315; tel. 940/297–6500 **A**1 9 10 **F**3 29 40 60 64 68 74 75 77 79 86 87 90 93 96 132 135 148 **P**6 **S** Select Medical Corporation, Mechanicsburg, PA
Primary Contact: Michelle Powell, Chief Executive Officer
CFO: Doug Selsor, Director Finance
CHR: Patsy Martin, Manager Human Resources
CNO: Lee Ann Elliott, R.N., Director of Nursing
Web address: www.selectrehab–denton.com/
**Control:** Partnership, Investor–owned, for–profit **Service:** Rehabilitation

> **Staffed Beds:** 44 **Admissions:** 744 **Census:** 26 **Outpatient Visits:** 8755 **Births:** 0 **Total Expense ($000):** 13296 **Payroll Expense ($000):** 7009 **Personnel:** 95

☒ **TEXAS HEALTH PRESBYTERIAN HOSPITAL DENTON (450743)**, 3000 North I–35, Zip 76201–5119; tel. 940/898–7000 **A**1 9 10 **F**3 11 12 13 15 17 18 20 22 24 26 28 29 30 31 34 35 40 45 46 48 49 57 59 66 70 72 74 75 76 78 79 81 82 84 85 86 89 93 107 108 110 111 114 115 118 119 126 129 130 131 132 135 145 146 147 148 **S** Texas Health Resources, Arlington, TX
Primary Contact: Stan C. Morton, FACHE, President
CFO: David B. Meltzer, Chief Financial Officer
CMO: Timothy Harris, M.D., Chief Quality Officer
CIO: Melissa Smart, Communication ad Public Relations Specialist
CHR: Kathy Hardcastle, Director Human Resources
CNO: Deborah Bostic, R.N., Chief Nursing Officer
Web address: www.dentonhospital.com
**Control:** Other not–for–profit (including NFP Corporation) **Service:** General Medical and Surgical

> **Staffed Beds:** 208 **Admissions:** 9339 **Census:** 112 **Outpatient Visits:** 66602 **Births:** 1912 **Total Expense ($000):** 165290 **Payroll Expense ($000):** 61219 **Personnel:** 904

★ ◇ **THE HEART HOSPITAL BAYLOR DENTON (450893)**, 2801 South Mayhill Road, Zip 76208–5910; tel. 940/220–0600 **A**9 10 21 **F**3 17 18 20 22 24 26 28 29 30 34 40 54 57 59 64 75 81 84 85 86 87 91 92 93 97 107 108 111 112 114 115 116 117 118 119 120 121 123 124 126 130 137 146 147
Primary Contact: Mark Valentine, President
COO: Bradley Morgan, Vice President of Operations
Web address: www.https://denton.thehearthospitalbaylor.com
**Control:** Partnership, Investor–owned, for–profit **Service:** Heart

> **Staffed Beds:** 22 **Admissions:** 156 **Census:** 1 **Outpatient Visits:** 1825 **Births:** 0 **Total Expense ($000):** 25180 **Payroll Expense ($000):** 8001 **Personnel:** 85

☒ **UNIVERSITY BEHAVIORAL HEALTH OF DENTON (454104)**, 2026 West University Drive, Zip 76201–0644; tel. 940/320–8100 **A**1 9 10 **F**4 5 34 54 98 99 100 101 104 105 **S** Universal Health Services, Inc., King of Prussia, PA
Primary Contact: Chris Rupert, Chief Executive Officer
CFO: Ed Sopiarz, Chief Financial Officer
CMO: Atique Khan, M.D., Medical Director
CIO: Marsh Smith, Manager Health Information
CHR: Dorie Atherton, Manager Human Resources
CNO: Vicki Stoker, Chief Nursing Officer
Web address: www.ubhdenton.com
**Control:** Partnership, Investor–owned, for–profit **Service:** Psychiatric

> **Staffed Beds:** 104 **Admissions:** 2888 **Census:** 72 **Outpatient Visits:** 10416 **Births:** 0 **Total Expense ($000):** 20845 **Payroll Expense ($000):** 8818 **Personnel:** 171

## DENVER CITY—Yoakum County

★ **YOAKUM COUNTY HOSPITAL (451308)**, 412 Mustang Avenue, Zip 79323–2762, Mailing Address: P.O. Box 1130, Zip 79323–1130; tel. 806/592–2121 **A**9 10 18 **F**3 11 13 28 34 35 40 43 50 53 57 59 60 62 64 76 81 87 89 93 107 114 119 127 129 133 **P**6
Primary Contact: Jerry Osburn, Chief Executive Officer
CFO: Suann Parrish, Chief Financial Officer
CMO: Dan Khan, M.D., Chief Medical Officer
CIO: Todd Carrillo, Chief Information Officer
CHR: Teresa Howard, Manager Human Resources
Web address: www.ych.us
**Control:** County–Government, nonfederal **Service:** General Medical and Surgical

> **Staffed Beds:** 22 **Admissions:** 580 **Census:** 6 **Outpatient Visits:** 47925 **Births:** 165 **Total Expense ($000):** 23023 **Payroll Expense ($000):** 7723 **Personnel:** 180

## DESOTO—Dallas County

☐ **DALLAS BEHAVIORAL HEALTHCARE HOSPITAL**, 800 Kirnwood Drive, Zip 75115–2000; tel. 855/982–0897, (Data for 350 days) **A**1 **F**4 5 56 87 98 99 100 101 103 104 105 130 **S** Signature Healthcare Services, Corona, CA
Primary Contact: Selene Q. Hammon, Chief Executive Officer
CMO: Rahim Haqqani, M.D., Medical Director
CIO: Rhonda Nash, Director Health Information Management
CHR: Henry In, Director Human Resources
CNO: Susie Edler, R.N., Chief Nursing Officer
Web address: www.dallasbehavioral.com
**Control:** Individual, Investor–owned, for–profit **Service:** Psychiatric

> **Staffed Beds:** 44 **Admissions:** 595 **Census:** 14 **Outpatient Visits:** 361 **Births:** 0 **Total Expense ($000):** 10279 **Payroll Expense ($000):** 4091 **Personnel:** 83

☐ **HICKORY TRAIL HOSPITAL (454065)**, 2000 Old Hickory Trail, Zip 75115–2242; tel. 972/298–7323 **A**1 9 10 **F**4 5 29 38 98 99 103 104 105 130 **S** Universal Health Services, Inc., King of Prussia, PA
Primary Contact: Lance Folske, Chief Executive Officer
CFO: Terri Logsdon, Chief Financial Officer
CMO: Manoochehr Khatami, M.D., Medical Director
CHR: Sarah Warren, Coordinator Human Resources
Web address: www.hickorytrail.com
**Control:** Corporation, Investor–owned, for–profit **Service:** Psychiatric

> **Staffed Beds:** 86 **Admissions:** 2844 **Census:** 67 **Outpatient Visits:** 8780 **Births:** 0 **Total Expense ($000):** 16325 **Payroll Expense ($000):** 7908 **Personnel:** 184

☒ **VIBRA SPECIALTY HOSPITAL AT DESOTO (452097)**, 2700 Walker Way, Zip 75115–2088; tel. 972/298–1100 **A**1 10 **F**1 3 29 70 75 77 87 91 107 130 148 **S** Vibra Healthcare, Mechanicsburg, PA
Primary Contact: Thomas Alexander, Chief Executive Officer
CFO: Donald Trimble, CPA, Chief Financial Officer
CMO: Ed Dominguez, President Medical Staff
CHR: Tim Lozier, Director Human Resources
CNO: Mae C. Weathersby, R.N., Chief Clinical Officer
Web address: www.vshdesoto.com
**Control:** Corporation, Investor–owned, for–profit **Service:** Long–Term Acute Care hospital

> **Staffed Beds:** 40 **Admissions:** 463 **Census:** 34 **Outpatient Visits:** 0 **Births:** 0 **Total Expense ($000):** 18758 **Payroll Expense ($000):** 8539 **Personnel:** 110

**TX**

*Many Facility Codes have changed. Please refer to the AHA Guide Code Chart.*
© 2015 AHA Guide

## DILLEY—Frio County

☐ **NIX COMMUNITY GENERAL HOSPITAL (670089)**, 230 West Miller,
Zip 78017–3818; tel. 830/965–2003 **A**1 9 10 **F**34 35 40 57 97 107 127
Primary Contact: Allen Tinker, Administrator
CFO: Lester Surrock, Chief Financial Officer
CHR: Blake W. Hubbard, FACHE, Senior Vice President and Chief Operating Officer
Medical Surgical Operations and Human Resources
CNO: Amy Lieck, Chief Nursing Officer
Web address: www.nixhealth.com/home/facilities/nix–community–general–
hospital?headerbar=2
**Control:** Corporation, Investor–owned, for–profit **Service:** General Medical and
Surgical

**Staffed Beds:** 10 **Admissions:** 123 **Census:** 1 **Outpatient Visits:** 10800
**Births:** 0 **Total Expense ($000):** 6000 **Payroll Expense ($000):** 1814
**Personnel:** 65

## DIMMITT—Castro County

★ **PLAINS MEMORIAL HOSPITAL (451350)**, 310 West Halsell Street,
Zip 79027–1846, Mailing Address: P.O. Box 278, Zip 79027–0278;
tel. 806/647–2191 **A**9 10 18 **F**3 7 32 34 35 40 43 53 57 59 64 65 69 75 77
85 86 87 93 97 107 114 115 119 127 130 133 135 **P**6
Primary Contact: Linda Rasor, R.N., Chief Executive Officer
CFO: Terri Martinez, Chief Financial Officer
CMO: Gary R. Hardee, M.D., Medical Director
CIO: Terry Young, Chief Information Officer
CHR: Debbie Underwood, Manager Human Resources
CNO: Renee Castillo, Chief Nursing Officer
Web address: www.plainsmemorial.com
**Control:** Hospital district or authority, Government, nonfederal **Service:** General
Medical and Surgical

**Staffed Beds:** 25 **Admissions:** 167 **Census:** 3 **Outpatient Visits:** 22222
**Births:** 0 **Total Expense ($000):** 10561 **Payroll Expense ($000):** 4200
**Personnel:** 94

## DUMAS—Moore County

☐ **MOORE COUNTY HOSPITAL DISTRICT (450221)**, 224 East Second Street,
Zip 79029–3808; tel. 806/935–7171 **A**1 9 10 20 **F**3 7 11 13 15 28 34 35 39
40 43 46 50 51 57 59 62 63 70 75 76 77 79 81 85 86 89 91 93 107 111
115 119 130 131 132 133 146 147 148
Primary Contact: Jeff Turner, FACHE, Chief Executive Officer
COO: Yvonne Blue, Chief Operations Officer
CFO: John E. Bailey, Chief Financial Officer
CHR: Ashleigh Wiswell, Director Human Resources
CNO: Stacey Cropley, M.D., Chief Nursing Officer
Web address: www.mchd.net
**Control:** Hospital district or authority, Government, nonfederal **Service:** General
Medical and Surgical

**Staffed Beds:** 47 **Admissions:** 942 **Census:** 8 **Outpatient Visits:** 38534
**Births:** 315 **Total Expense ($000):** 27433 **Payroll Expense ($000):** 12307
**Personnel:** 261

## EAGLE LAKE—Colorado County

★ **RICE MEDICAL CENTER (451312)**, 600 South Austin Road, Zip 77434–3298,
Mailing Address: P.O. Box 277, Zip 77434–0277; tel. 979/234–5571 **A**9 10 18
**F**3 11 13 15 29 34 40 43 57 59 64 65 70 76 79 81 107 119 127 133 **P**6
Primary Contact: James D. Janek, Chief Executive Officer
CFO: Brian Mc Bride, Chief Financial Officer
CMO: Russell Thomas, M.D., Chief of Staff
CHR: Velma Loya, Administrative Human Resource Coordinator
CNO: Susan Hernandez, R.N., Chief Nursing Officer
Web address: www.ricemedicalcenter.net/
**Control:** Corporation, Investor–owned, for–profit **Service:** General Medical and
Surgical

**Staffed Beds:** 15 **Admissions:** 249 **Census:** 3 **Outpatient Visits:** 26962
**Births:** 37 **Total Expense ($000):** 12120 **Payroll Expense ($000):** 3362
**Personnel:** 148

## EAGLE PASS—Maverick County

☐ **FORT DUNCAN REGIONAL MEDICAL CENTER (450092)**, 3333 North Foster
Maldonado Boulevard, Zip 78852–5893; tel. 830/773–5321 **A**1 9 10 20 **F**3 13
15 18 29 40 43 45 53 57 60 65 68 70 75 76 77 79 81 85 87 89 90 91 93
107 108 110 111 114 118 119 130 146 147 148 **S** Universal Health Services,
Inc., King of Prussia, PA
Primary Contact: Richard Prati, Chief Executive Officer
COO: Richard Prati, Chief Executive Officer
CFO: Joel Morales, Chief Financial Officer
CMO: David Land, D.O., Chief Medical Staff
CIO: Tony Hernandez, Director Information Technology
CHR: Daisy Rodriquez, Director Human Resources
CNO: Wilma Carbonel Mason, Chief Nursing Officer
Web address: www.fortduncanmedicalcenter.com
**Control:** Corporation, Investor–owned, for–profit **Service:** General Medical and
Surgical

**Staffed Beds:** 101 **Admissions:** 4766 **Census:** 60 **Outpatient Visits:** 44047
**Births:** 1242 **Total Expense ($000):** 47796 **Payroll Expense ($000):** 21156
**Personnel:** 371

## EASTLAND—Eastland County

**EASTLAND MEMORIAL HOSPITAL (450411)**, 304 South Daugherty Street,
Zip 76448–2609, Mailing Address: P.O. Box 897, Zip 76448–0897;
tel. 254/629–2601 **A**9 10 20 **F**7 11 15 28 30 34 40 43 45 49 50 53 56 57
59 64 65 68 75 81 85 86 87 93 107 111 114 119 128 129 130 131 133
146 148
Primary Contact: Ted Matthews, Chief Executive Officer
CFO: Jamie Hayden, Chief Financial Officer
CHR: Leisha Hodges, Human Resources Officer
Web address: www.eastlandmemorial.com
**Control:** Hospital district or authority, Government, nonfederal **Service:** General
Medical and Surgical

**Staffed Beds:** 36 **Admissions:** 664 **Census:** 9 **Outpatient Visits:** 22324
**Births:** 2 **Total Expense ($000):** 11665 **Payroll Expense ($000):** 5651
**Personnel:** 137

## EDEN—Concho County

**CONCHO COUNTY HOSPITAL (451325)**, 614 Eaker Street, Zip 76837–0359,
Mailing Address: P.O. Box 987, Zip 76837–0987; tel. 325/869–5911 **A**9 10 18
**F**3 40 43 50 59 77 87 107 133 146
Primary Contact: Dudley R. White, Administrator and Chief Executive Officer
CFO: Melanie Lozano, Chief Financial Officer
CNO: Toby Lehn, Director of Nurses
Web address: www.conchocountyhospital.com
**Control:** Hospital district or authority, Government, nonfederal **Service:** General
Medical and Surgical

**Staffed Beds:** 16 **Admissions:** 147 **Census:** 1 **Outpatient Visits:** 4864
**Births:** 0 **Total Expense ($000):** 6522 **Payroll Expense ($000):** 2334
**Personnel:** 43

## EDINBURG—Hidalgo County

⌧ **CORNERSTONE REGIONAL HOSPITAL (450825)**, 2302 Cornerstone
Boulevard, Zip 78539–8471; tel. 956/618–4444 **A**1 9 10 **F**3 8 29 34 35 37 39
40 45 46 47 51 57 59 74 79 81 82 85 119 126 **S** Universal Health Services,
Inc., King of Prussia, PA
Primary Contact: Roxanna M. Godinez, Chief Executive Officer
CFO: Janie Alvarez, Accounting Director
CMO: Omar Gomez, M.D., Chief of Staff
CHR: Erika Betancourt, Coordinator Human Resources
CNO: Roxanne Reyes, Director of Nursing
Web address: www.cornerstoneregional.com
**Control:** Partnership, Investor–owned, for–profit **Service:** General Medical and
Surgical

**Staffed Beds:** 14 **Admissions:** 631 **Census:** 4 **Outpatient Visits:** 2811
**Births:** 0 **Total Expense ($000):** 12572 **Payroll Expense ($000):** 3307
**Personnel:** 68

**TX**

---

**Hospital, Medicare Provider Number, Address, Telephone, Approval, Facility, and Physician Codes, Health Care System**

★ American Hospital Association (AHA) membership    ○ Healthcare Facilities Accreditation Program    ⇑ Center for Improvement in Healthcare Quality Accreditation
☐ The Joint Commission accreditation    ◇ DNV Healthcare Inc. accreditation    △ Commission on Accreditation of Rehabilitation Facilities (CARF) accreditation

☐ **DOCTOR'S HOSPITAL AT RENAISSANCE (450869)**, 5501 South McColl Road, Zip 78539–9152; tel. 956/362–7360 **A**1 2 3 5 9 10 **F**3 12 13 15 17 18 19 20 22 24 26 28 29 30 31 34 35 38 39 40 43 45 46 47 48 49 50 51 52 53 54 55 56 57 58 59 60 64 65 66 70 71 72 73 74 75 76 77 78 79 80 81 82 84 85 86 87 88 89 90 91 92 93 96 97 98 99 100 101 102 103 104 105 107 108 109 110 111 112 113 114 115 116 117 118 119 120 121 123 124 126 130 132 145 146 147 148 **P**3 8
Primary Contact: Israel Rocha, Chief Executive Officer
COO: Marissa Castaneda, Chief Operating Officer and Director Marketing
CFO: Susan S. Turley, Chief Financial Officer
Web address: www.dhr–rgv.com
**Control:** Partnership, Investor–owned, for–profit **Service:** General Medical and Surgical

**Staffed Beds:** 525 **Admissions:** 31840 **Census:** 392 **Outpatient Visits:** 220396 **Births:** 9490 **Total Expense ($000):** 363818 **Payroll Expense ($000):** 161937 **Personnel:** 3533

☐ **SOUTH TEXAS HEALTH SYSTEM (450119)**, 1102 West Trenton Road, Zip 78539–9105; tel. 956/388–6000, (Includes EDINBURG CHILDREN'S HOSPITAL, 1400 West Trenton Road, Zip 78539; tel. 956/388–8000; EDINBURG REGIONAL MEDICAL CENTER, 1102 West Trenton Road, Zip 78539–6199; tel. 956/388–6000; MCALLEN HEART HOSPITAL, 1900 South D. Street, McAllen, Zip 78503; tel. 956/994–2000; MCALLEN MEDICAL CENTER, 301 West Expressway 83, McAllen, Zip 78503–3045; tel. 956/632–4000; SOUTH TEXAS BEHAVIORAL HEALTH CENTER, 2101 West Trenton Road, Zip 78539; tel. 956/388–1300; Joe Rodriguez, Chief Executive Officer) **A**1 3 9 10 **F**3 4 5 11 12 13 15 17 18 19 20 22 24 26 29 30 31 34 35 37 38 39 40 41 42 43 45 46 47 48 49 50 53 57 59 60 64 68 70 72 74 75 76 77 78 79 81 85 86 87 88 89 90 96 98 99 100 101 102 103 104 107 108 110 111 114 115 119 129 130 135 138 146 148 **P**6 **S** Universal Health Services, Inc., King of Prussia, PA
Primary Contact: Jennifer Garza, Chief Executive Officer
COO: Jerome M. Brooks, Chief Operating Officer
CFO: Carlos Guajardo, Chief Financial Officer
CMO: Yuri Bermudez, M.D., Chief of Staff
CIO: Rosie L. Mendiola–Balderas, Director Information Systems
CHR: Patricia Mcclelland, Director Human Resources
CNO: Catherine Domian, R.N., Chief Nursing Officer
Web address: www.southtexashealthsystem.com
**Control:** Partnership, Investor–owned, for–profit **Service:** General Medical and Surgical

**Staffed Beds:** 788 **Admissions:** 24423 **Census:** 315 **Outpatient Visits:** 129689 **Births:** 1604 **Total Expense ($000):** 271267 **Payroll Expense ($000):** 106480 **Personnel:** 1926

### EDNA—Jackson County

★ **JACKSON COUNTY HOSPITAL DISTRICT (451363)**, 1013 South Wells Street, Zip 77957–4098; tel. 361/782–7800 **A**9 10 18 **F**3 7 15 34 40 43 45 50 56 57 59 62 64 65 68 75 81 87 93 103 104 107 110 111 114 119 127 129 130 131 133 146 148 **P**8
Primary Contact: Bill Jones, Chief Executive Officer
CFO: Lance Smiga, Chief Financial Officer
CMO: Francisco Ortiz, M.D., Chief of Staff
CIO: Jeff Prukop, Director Professional Services
CHR: Donna Coleman, Coordinator Human Resources
CNO: Tammy Zajicek, Director of Nursing
Web address: www.jchd.org
**Control:** Hospital district or authority, Government, nonfederal **Service:** General Medical and Surgical

**Staffed Beds:** 17 **Admissions:** 243 **Census:** 3 **Outpatient Visits:** 18950 **Births:** 0 **Total Expense ($000):** 19764 **Payroll Expense ($000):** 6923 **Personnel:** 161

### EL CAMPO—Wharton County

**EL CAMPO MEMORIAL HOSPITAL (450694)**, 303 Sandy Corner Road, Zip 77437–9535; tel. 979/543–6251 **A**9 10 **F**3 11 15 29 34 35 40 43 45 56 57 59 60 62 64 68 70 77 79 81 85 86 93 97 107 108 110 111 114 119 127 129 130 131 132 148 **P**6
Primary Contact: Tisha Zalman, Chief Executive Officer
CFO: Laurie Harvey, Controller
CMO: Laurie Hulsman, M.D., Chief of Staff
CIO: Bill Eller, Director Information Technology
CHR: Ginger Andreas, Coordinator Personnel and Credentialing
CNO: Desiree Cernoch, Director of Nurses
Web address: www.ecmh.org
**Control:** Other not–for–profit (including NFP Corporation) **Service:** General Medical and Surgical

**Staffed Beds:** 26 **Admissions:** 316 **Census:** 3 **Outpatient Visits:** 51072 **Births:** 0 **Total Expense ($000):** 18547 **Payroll Expense ($000):** 6753 **Personnel:** 139

### EL PASO—El Paso County

**EAST EL PASO PHYSICIANS MEDICAL CENTER** See Foundation Surgical Hospital of El Paso

☐ **EL PASO CHILDREN'S HOSPITAL (453313)**, 4845 Alameda Avenue, Zip 79905–2705; tel. 915/298–5444 **A**1 3 5 9 10 **F**3 11 29 31 40 41 44 45 46 47 48 49 50 58 64 65 72 73 74 75 78 81 85 86 87 88 89 93 96 111 119 130 146 148 **P**6
Primary Contact: Mark C. Herbers, Chief Executive Officer
COO: Elias Armendariz, Chief Operating Officer and Chief Nursing Officer
CFO: David Mier, Chief Financial Officer
CMO: Bradley Fuhrman, M.D., Physician in Chief
CIO: Janina Prada, Director Information Technology
CHR: Natalia Chaparro, Manager Human Resources
CNO: Elias Armendariz, Chief Operating Officer and Chief Nursing Officer
Web address: www.elpasochildrens.org
**Control:** Other not–for–profit (including NFP Corporation) **Service:** Children's general

**Staffed Beds:** 122 **Admissions:** 4131 **Census:** 58 **Outpatient Visits:** 39705 **Births:** 0 **Total Expense ($000):** 103497 **Payroll Expense ($000):** 27936 **Personnel:** 478

**EL PASO LTAC HOSPITAL (452103)**, 1221 North Cotton Street, 3rd Floor, Zip 79902–3015; tel. 915/546–5822 **A**9 10 **F**1 3 7 29 30 34 57 60 75 77 82 84 85 86 87 91 100 103 119 130 148
Primary Contact: Eddie Martinez, Chief Executive Officer
CNO: Skylier Blake, R.N., Director of Nursing
Web address: www.epltachospital.com/
**Control:** Partnership, Investor–owned, for–profit **Service:** Long–Term Acute Care hospital

**Staffed Beds:** 33 **Admissions:** 257 **Census:** 17 **Outpatient Visits:** 0 **Births:** 0 **Total Expense ($000):** 7556 **Payroll Expense ($000):** 2835 **Personnel:** 74

☐ **EL PASO PSYCHIATRIC CENTER (454100)**, 4615 Alameda Avenue, Zip 79905–2702; tel. 915/532–2202 **A**1 3 5 9 10 **F**29 98 99 103 130 135 **P**6 **S** Texas Department of State Health Services, Austin, TX
Primary Contact: Zulema Carrillo, Superintendent
CFO: David Osterhout, Assistant Superintendent and Chief Financial Officer
CMO: Nicolas Baida–Fragoso, M.D., Clinical Director
CNO: Raul D. Luna, Chief Nurse Executive
Web address: www.dshs.state.tx.us/mhhospitals/ElPasoPC/default.shtm
**Control:** State–Government, nonfederal **Service:** Psychiatric

**Staffed Beds:** 74 **Admissions:** 988 **Census:** 66 **Outpatient Visits:** 0 **Births:** 0 **Total Expense ($000):** 18797 **Payroll Expense ($000):** 10406 **Personnel:** 259

☐ **EL PASO SPECIALTY HOSPITAL (450845)**, 1755 Curie Drive, Zip 79902–2919; tel. 915/544–3636 **A**1 3 9 10 **F**3 29 34 35 40 59 64 68 75 79 81 82 85 87 107 130 131 148 **S** National Surgical Healthcare, Chicago, IL
Primary Contact: James Wilcox, Chief Executive Officer
CFO: Greg Watters, Chief Financial Officer
CMO: David Mansfield, M.D., Chief of Staff
CNO: Anne Harvey, MSN, Chief Nursing Officer
Web address: www.elpasospecialtyhospital.com
**Control:** Partnership, Investor–owned, for–profit **Service:** Orthopedic

**Staffed Beds:** 27 **Admissions:** 734 **Census:** 5 **Outpatient Visits:** 21068 **Births:** 0 **Total Expense ($000):** 30634 **Payroll Expense ($000):** 8065 **Personnel:** 134

◇ **FOUNDATION SURGICAL HOSPITAL OF EL PASO (450877)**, 1416 George Dieter Drive, Zip 79936–7601; tel. 915/598–4240 **A**3 9 10 21 **F**3 29 40 45 49 79 81 82 85 86 107 111 114 119 **S** Foundation Surgical Hospital Affiliates, Oklahoma City, OK
Primary Contact: Don Burris, Chief Executive Officer
COO: Marta Contreras, Chief Nursing Officer and Chief Operating Officer
CIO: Louie Aguilera, Director Information Technology
CHR: Grace Beltran, Director Human Resources
CNO: Marta Contreras, Chief Nursing Officer and Chief Operating Officer
Web address: www.physiciansmedcenter.com
**Control:** Corporation, Investor–owned, for–profit **Service:** Surgical

**Staffed Beds:** 20 **Admissions:** 1034 **Census:** 5 **Outpatient Visits:** 44465 **Births:** 0 **Total Expense ($000):** 50984 **Payroll Expense ($000):** 7138 **Personnel:** 126

☐ △ **HIGHLANDS REGIONAL REHABILITATION HOSPITAL (453086)**, 1395 George Dieter Drive, Zip 79936–7410; tel. 915/298–7222 **A**1 7 9 10 **F**3 29 30 34 57 59 64 74 75 79 86 87 90 93 96 100 130 132 143 146 148
Primary Contact: Mariaelena Carmona, Chief Executive Officer
CHR: Janet Straughan, Manager Human Resources
CNO: Oscar Mendizabal, Chief Nursing Officer
Web address: www.highlandsrehab.com
**Control:** Partnership, Investor–owned, for–profit **Service:** Rehabilitation

**Staffed Beds:** 41 **Admissions:** 909 **Census:** 28 **Outpatient Visits:** 4423 **Births:** 0 **Total Expense ($000):** 7884 **Personnel:** 130

*Many Facility Codes have changed. Please refer to the AHA Guide Code Chart.* © 2015 AHA Guide

⊞ **KINDRED HOSPITAL EL PASO (452079)**, 1740 Curie Drive, Zip 79902–2901; tel. 915/351–9044 **A**1 9 10 **F**1 3 29 30 34 75 77 87 130 148 **S** Kindred Healthcare, Louisville, KY
Primary Contact: Diana Schultz, Chief Executive Officer
CFO: Melissa Campa, Controller
CMO: Edward Juarez, M.D., Chief Medical Officer
CHR: Laura Anchondo, Administrator Human Resources
Web address: www.khelpaso.com
**Control:** Corporation, Investor–owned, for–profit **Service:** Long–Term Acute Care hospital

**Staffed Beds:** 72 **Admissions:** 697 **Census:** 47 **Outpatient Visits:** 656 **Births:** 0 **Total Expense ($000):** 21960 **Payroll Expense ($000):** 8725 **Personnel:** 149

⊞ △ **LAS PALMAS MEDICAL CENTER (450107)**, 1801 North Oregon Street, Zip 79902–3591; tel. 915/521–1200, (Includes DEL SOL MEDICAL CENTER, 10301 West Gateway Boulevard, Zip 79925–7798; tel. 915/595–9000; Jacob Cintron, FACHE, Chief Executive Officer; LAS PALMAS REHABILITATION HOSPITAL, 300 Waymore Drive, Zip 79902–1628; tel. 915/577–2600; Don Karl, Interim Chief Executive Officer) **A**1 3 5 7 9 10 **F**3 8 11 12 13 15 17 18 19 20 22 24 26 27 28 29 30 31 34 35 37 38 39 40 41 43 45 46 47 48 49 50 51 53 54 56 57 58 59 60 64 68 70 72 73 74 75 76 77 78 79 81 82 85 86 87 88 89 90 91 92 93 96 103 107 108 110 111 112 114 115 119 120 121 122 124 126 127 129 130 132 134 135 136 138 143 144 145 146 147 148 **S** HCA, Nashville, TN
Primary Contact: Don Karl, Interim Chief Executive Officer
COO: Don Karl, Chief Operating Officer
Web address: www.laspalmashealth.com
**Control:** Partnership, Investor–owned, for–profit **Service:** General Medical and Surgical

**Staffed Beds:** 570 **Admissions:** 26153 **Census:** 348 **Outpatient Visits:** 212320 **Births:** 5092 **Total Expense ($000):** 348186 **Payroll Expense ($000):** 129813 **Personnel:** 2046

☐ **MESA HILLS SPECIALTY HOSPITAL (452035)**, 2311 North Oregon Street, Zip 79902–3216; tel. 915/545–1823 **A**1 9 10 **F**1 3 29 54 59 61 64 65 74 75 77 82 83 84 85 94 130 143 148 **S** Encore Healthcare, Columbia, MD
Primary Contact: Jesus Ruiz, Chief Executive Officer
COO: Elena Pino, Chief Operating Officer and Chief Nursing Officer
CFO: Priscilla Carter, Chief Financial Officer
Web address: www.mesahillsspecialtyhospital.com/mesa_hills/index.aspx
**Control:** Corporation, Investor–owned, for–profit **Service:** Children's Long–Term Acute Care

**Staffed Beds:** 32 **Admissions:** 297 **Census:** 18 **Outpatient Visits:** 0 **Births:** 0 **Total Expense ($000):** 10124 **Payroll Expense ($000):** 2822 **Personnel:** 84

⊞ **THE HOSPITALS OF PROVIDENCE MEMORIAL CAMPUS (450002)**, 2001 North Oregon Street, Zip 79902–3368; tel. 915/577–6625, (Includes PROVIDENCE CHILDREN'S HOSPITAL, 2001 North Oregon Street, Zip 79902–3320; tel. 915/577–7746) **A**1 2 9 10 **F**3 11 12 13 14 15 17 18 19 20 21 22 23 24 25 28 29 31 32 34 35 40 41 42 43 45 46 49 50 51 54 56 57 59 63 64 65 70 72 73 74 75 76 77 78 79 81 84 85 86 87 88 89 91 92 93 98 103 107 108 110 111 114 118 119 126 129 130 132 134 145 146 147 148 **P**1 **S** TENET Healthcare Corporation, Dallas, TX
Primary Contact: Sally A. Hurt–Deitch, FACHE, Chief Executive Officer
COO: Daniel Fink, Chief Operating Officer
CFO: Charles Handley, Chief Financial Officer
CMO: Enrique Martinez, M.D., Chief Medical Officer
CIO: Ray Davis, Administrative Director
CHR: Stephanie S. Talley, Interim Chief Human Resource Officer
CNO: Karen Fowler, R.N., Chief Nursing Officer
Web address: www.sphn.com
**Control:** Partnership, Investor–owned, for–profit **Service:** General Medical and Surgical

**Staffed Beds:** 351 **Admissions:** 16920 **Census:** 209 **Outpatient Visits:** 149367 **Births:** 3159 **Total Expense ($000):** 260384 **Payroll Expense ($000):** 78514 **Personnel:** 1347

⊞ **THE HOSPITALS OF PROVIDENCE SIERRA CAMPUS (450668)**, 1625 Medical Center Drive, Zip 79902–5044; tel. 915/747–4000 **A**1 2 5 9 10 **F**3 11 13 15 17 18 20 22 24 26 29 30 31 34 37 40 42 43 45 47 48 49 50 54 55 57 58 59 60 61 64 68 69 70 72 74 75 76 77 78 79 81 82 85 86 90 96 97 107 108 110 111 114 115 118 119 120 124 126 130 132 134 144 145 146 147 148 **P**1 **S** TENET Healthcare Corporation, Dallas, TX
Primary Contact: Monica Vargas–Mahar, FACHE, Chief Executive Officer
COO: Benson Chacko, Chief Operating Officer
CFO: David Byrd, Chief Financial Officer
CMO: Enrique Martinez, M.D., Chief Medical Officer
CIO: Ray Davis, Administrative Director Information Systems
CHR: Stephanie S. Talley, Interim Chief Human Resource Officer
CNO: Erik Cazares, Interim Chief Nursing Officer
Web address: www.sphn.com
**Control:** Corporation, Investor–owned, for–profit **Service:** General Medical and Surgical

**Staffed Beds:** 349 **Admissions:** 10559 **Census:** 137 **Outpatient Visits:** 101066 **Births:** 1410 **Total Expense ($000):** 160899 **Payroll Expense ($000):** 49497 **Personnel:** 898

⊞ **THE HOSPITALS OF SIERRA PROVIDENCE EAST CAMPUS (670047)**, 3280 Joe Battle Boulevard, Zip 79938–2622; tel. 915/832–2000 **A**1 2 5 9 10 **F**3 13 15 18 20 22 26 29 30 31 34 35 37 40 45 46 47 49 50 57 59 60 63 64 68 70 72 73 74 75 76 77 78 79 81 84 85 86 87 93 107 108 110 111 115 119 126 130 134 146 147 148 **P**4 **S** TENET Healthcare Corporation, Dallas, TX
Primary Contact: Nicholas R. Tejeda, FACHE, Chief Executive Officer
COO: Lauren Morton, Chief Operating Officer
Web address: www.sphn.com
**Control:** Individual, Investor–owned, for–profit **Service:** General Medical and Surgical

**Staffed Beds:** 170 **Admissions:** 9030 **Census:** 98 **Outpatient Visits:** 83572 **Births:** 1983 **Total Expense ($000):** 129017 **Payroll Expense ($000):** 40241 **Personnel:** 765

**TRIUMPH HOSPITAL EL PASO** See Kindred Hospital El Paso

☐ **UNIVERSITY BEHAVIORAL HEALTH OF EL PASO (454109)**, 1900 Denver Avenue, Zip 79902–3008; tel. 915/544–4000 **A**1 3 5 9 10 **F**4 5 56 57 75 86 87 98 99 101 102 103 104 105 130 **S** Universal Health Services, Inc., King of Prussia, PA
Primary Contact: David W. Morris, Chief Executive Officer
CFO: Phillip Sosa, Chief Financial Officer
CMO: Arthur L. Ramirez, M.D., Medical Director
CIO: Victor Torres, Information Technology Specialist Administrator
CHR: Brenda Holguin, Manager Human Resources
CNO: Susan Brown, Chief Nursing Officer
Web address: www.ubhelpaso.com/
**Control:** Corporation, Investor–owned, for–profit **Service:** Psychiatric

**Staffed Beds:** 163 **Admissions:** 5359 **Census:** 137 **Outpatient Visits:** 26608 **Births:** 0 **Total Expense ($000):** 22895 **Payroll Expense ($000):** 13185 **Personnel:** 301

⊞ **UNIVERSITY MEDICAL CENTER OF EL PASO (450024)**, 4815 Alameda Avenue, Zip 79905–2794, Mailing Address: P.O. Box 20009, Zip 79998–0009; tel. 915/544–1200 **A**1 2 3 5 8 9 10 **F**3 8 11 13 15 17 18 20 22 24 26 28 29 30 31 34 35 37 40 43 45 46 47 48 49 50 51 53 54 56 57 59 60 61 64 65 68 70 74 75 76 77 79 81 82 85 86 87 91 92 93 94 96 97 100 102 107 108 110 111 112 113 114 115 118 119 126 127 130 131 134 143 144 145 146 147 148 **P**6
Primary Contact: James N. Valenti, FACHE, President and Chief Executive Officer
COO: Maria Zampini, Chief Operating Officer
CFO: Michael Nunez, Chief Financial Officer
CMO: Carmela Morales, M.D., Chief of Staff
CIO: Janina Prada, Director Information Services
CHR: Janice M. Harris, Director Human Resources
CNO: Diana Fancher, Chief Nursing Officer
Web address: www.thomasoncares.org
**Control:** Hospital district or authority, Government, nonfederal **Service:** General Medical and Surgical

**Staffed Beds:** 261 **Admissions:** 15409 **Census:** 183 **Outpatient Visits:** 760118 **Births:** 3636 **Total Expense ($000):** 514477 **Payroll Expense ($000):** 136204 **Personnel:** 2483

⊞ **WILLIAM BEAUMONT ARMY MEDICAL CENTER**, 5005 North Piedras Street, Zip 79920–5001; tel. 915/742–2121, (Nonreporting) **A**1 2 3 5 9 **S** Department of the Army, Office of the Surgeon General, Falls Church, VA
Primary Contact: Colonel Michael S. Heimall, Commander
CIO: Major Rion Koon, Chief Information Management Division
Web address: www.wbamc.amedd.army.mil
**Control:** Army, Government, federal **Service:** General Medical and Surgical

**Staffed Beds:** 209

### ELDORADO—Schleicher County

★ **SCHLEICHER COUNTY MEDICAL CENTER (451304)**, 400 West Murchison, Zip 76936, Mailing Address: P.O. Box V., Zip 76936–1246; tel. 325/853–2507 **A**9 10 18 **F**34 40 57 59 64 65 66 68 93 107 127 133 **S** Preferred Management Corporation, Shawnee, OK
Primary Contact: Paul Burke, Administrator
CFO: Larry Stephens, Chief Financial Officer
CMO: Gordy Day, M.D., Medical Director
CHR: Beverly Minor, Chief Human Resources
Web address: www.scmc.us
**Control:** Corporation, Investor–owned, for–profit **Service:** General Medical and Surgical

**Staffed Beds:** 14 **Admissions:** 78 **Census:** 1 **Outpatient Visits:** 8327 **Births:** 0 **Total Expense ($000):** 4350 **Payroll Expense ($000):** 1916 **Personnel:** 45

### ELECTRA—Wichita County

★ **ELECTRA MEMORIAL HOSPITAL (451343)**, 1207 South Bailey Street, Zip 76360–3221, Mailing Address: P.O. Box 1112, Zip 76360–1112; tel. 940/495–3981 **A**9 10 18 **F**3 7 11 28 32 34 40 43 45 53 59 62 64 65 66 75 77 82 86 93 97 107 114 119 129 130 131 133 148
Primary Contact: Rebecca McCain, Chief Executive Officer
CIO: Brandon Huffstutler, Chief Information Officer
CNO: Kim Gilbert, R.N., Chief Nursing Officer
Web address: www.electrahospital.com
**Control:** Hospital district or authority, Government, nonfederal **Service:** General Medical and Surgical

**Staffed Beds:** 19 **Admissions:** 513 **Census:** 7 **Outpatient Visits:** 18331 **Births:** 0 **Total Expense ($000):** 13885 **Payroll Expense ($000):** 7009 **Personnel:** 113

### ENNIS—Ellis County

✠ **ENNIS REGIONAL MEDICAL CENTER (450833)**, 2201 West Lampasas Street, Zip 75119–5644; tel. 972/875–0900 **A**1 9 10 **F**3 11 13 15 18 29 30 34 35 40 43 45 50 51 57 59 64 65 70 75 76 77 79 81 82 85 93 107 108 110 111 115 119 146 **S** LifePoint Health, Brentwood, TN
Primary Contact: Alan Daugherty, Interim Chief Executive Officer
CFO: Jack Wilcox, Chief Financial Officer
CMO: Raymond W. Blair, Jr., M.D., Chief of Staff
CHR: Selena Cryer, Director Human Resources
CNO: Edwina A. Miner, R.N., Chief Nursing Officer
Web address: www.ennisregional.com
**Control:** Partnership, Investor–owned, for–profit **Service:** General Medical and Surgical

**Staffed Beds:** 58 **Admissions:** 1735 **Census:** 14 **Outpatient Visits:** 31807 **Births:** 698 **Total Expense ($000):** 23256 **Payroll Expense ($000):** 9864 **Personnel:** 171

### FAIRFIELD—Freestone County

★ **EAST TEXAS MEDICAL CENTER FAIRFIELD (450658)**, 125 Newman Street, Zip 75840–1499; tel. 903/389–2121 **A**9 10 20 **F**15 28 34 40 43 45 50 57 59 68 75 81 82 107 110 115 119 127 130 132 **P**7 **S** East Texas Medical Center Regional Healthcare System, Tyler, TX
Primary Contact: Ruth Cook, Administrator
CFO: David A. Travis, Chief Financial Officer
CMO: Darryl White, M.D., Chief of Staff
CHR: Jennifer Rummel, Director Human Resources
Web address: www.etmc.org
**Control:** Other not–for–profit (including NFP Corporation) **Service:** General Medical and Surgical

**Staffed Beds:** 44 **Admissions:** 405 **Census:** 4 **Outpatient Visits:** 42180 **Births:** 0 **Total Expense ($000):** 28495 **Payroll Expense ($000):** 3784 **Personnel:** 82

### FLORESVILLE—Wilson County

**CONNALLY MEMORIAL MEDICAL CENTER (450108)**, 499 10th Street, Zip 78114–3175; tel. 830/393–1300 **A**9 10 **F**3 15 18 29 34 35 40 43 45 47 54 57 59 62 64 70 75 81 82 85 86 87 107 111 114 119 130 132 133 146 148 **P**4
Primary Contact: Brian D. Burnside, FACHE, Chief Executive Officer
COO: Thomas Repino, Executive Director Ancillary Services
CFO: Jamie R. Jacoby, Chief Financial Officer
CMO: Carl Blond, M.D., Chief of Staff
CIO: Kim Schultz, Senior Application Analyst
CHR: Dane Bonecutter, Director Human Resources
CNO: Sue Tackitt, Chief Nursing Officer
Web address: www.connallymmc.org
**Control:** Hospital district or authority, Government, nonfederal **Service:** General Medical and Surgical

**Staffed Beds:** 30 **Admissions:** 859 **Census:** 9 **Outpatient Visits:** 80717 **Births:** 0 **Total Expense ($000):** 28418 **Payroll Expense ($000):** 10019 **Personnel:** 233

### FLOWER MOUND—Denton County

◇ **CONTINUUM REHABILITATION HOSPITAL OF NORTH TEXAS (673047)**, 3100 Peters Colony Road, Zip 75022–2949; tel. 214/513–0310, (Total facility includes 12 beds in nursing home–type unit) **A**9 10 21 **F**3 34 57 59 60 64 90 93 96 128 130 148
Primary Contact: William Conway, Chief Executive Officer
Web address: www.continuumhs.com
**Control:** Individual, Investor–owned, for–profit **Service:** Rehabilitation

**Staffed Beds:** 41 **Admissions:** 563 **Census:** 19 **Outpatient Visits:** 2577 **Births:** 0 **Total Expense ($000):** 10242 **Payroll Expense ($000):** 4508 **Personnel:** 95

□ ◇ **TEXAS HEALTH PRESBYTERIAN HOSPITAL FLOWER MOUND (670068)**, 4400 Long Prairie Road, Zip 75028–1892; tel. 469/322–7000 **A**1 9 10 21 **F**3 13 15 18 20 29 30 31 34 40 45 49 57 59 70 73 75 76 77 78 79 81 82 85 87 93 107 108 110 111 114 115 119 126 130 146 147
Primary Contact: Spencer Turner, Chief Executive Officer
COO: Shelley R. Tobey, R.N., Chief Operating Officer and Chief Nursing Officer
CFO: Tom Howard, Chief Financial Officer
CHR: Nicole Schweigert, Director Human Resources
CNO: Shelley R. Tobey, R.N., Chief Operating Officer and Chief Nursing Officer
Web address: www.texashealthflowermound.com/
**Control:** Partnership, Investor–owned, for–profit **Service:** General Medical and Surgical

**Staffed Beds:** 92 **Admissions:** 4805 **Census:** 51 **Outpatient Visits:** 33467 **Births:** 1327 **Total Expense ($000):** 97556 **Payroll Expense ($000):** 33102 **Personnel:** 693

### FORT HOOD—Bell County

✠ **CARL R. DARNALL ARMY MEDICAL CENTER**, 36000 Darnall Loop, Zip 76544–5095; tel. 254/288–8000, (Nonreporting) **A**1 3 5 9 **S** Department of the Army, Office of the Surgeon General, Falls Church, VA
Primary Contact: Colonel Patricia Darnauer, Medical Center Commander
CMO: Colonel Carolyn Tiffany, Deputy Commander Clinical Service
CHR: Charles Burton, Chief Human Resources
Web address: www.crdamc.amedd.army.mil
**Control:** Army, Government, federal **Service:** General Medical and Surgical

**Staffed Beds:** 109

### FORT SAM HOUSTON—Bexar County

✠ **BROOKE ARMY MEDICAL CENTER**, 3851 Roger Brookes Drive, Zip 78234–4501; tel. 210/916–4141, (Nonreporting) **A**1 2 3 5 9 **S** Department of the Army, Office of the Surgeon General, Falls Church, VA
Primary Contact: Colonel Kyle D. Campbell, Commander
CMO: Colonel Joseph P. Chozinski, M.D., Deputy Commander Clinical Services
CIO: Lieutenant Colonel David Broyhill, Chief Information Management
CHR: Rose Juarez, Chief Civilian Personnel Branch
CNO: Colonel Sheri Howell, Deputy Commander Nursing
Web address: www.bamc.amedd.army.mil
**Control:** Army, Government, federal **Service:** General Medical and Surgical

**Staffed Beds:** 226

### FORT STOCKTON—Pecos County

★ **PECOS COUNTY MEMORIAL HOSPITAL (450178)**, 387 West I. H–10, Zip 79735–8912, Mailing Address: P.O. Box 1648, Zip 79735–1648; tel. 432/336–2004 **A**9 10 20 **F**3 11 13 28 29 30 32 34 35 40 43 53 57 59 62 63 64 65 75 76 81 93 107 111 119 127 129 130 146 148 **P**5 6
Primary Contact: James E. Koulovatos, Interim Chief Executive Officer
CFO: Leticia Fox, Chief Financial Officer
CMO: Larry Boyd, M.D., Chief of Staff
CHR: Malissa Trevino, Director Human Resources
CNO: Gina Kalka, R.N., Chief Nursing Officer
Web address: www.pcmhfs.com
**Control:** County–Government, nonfederal **Service:** General Medical and Surgical

**Staffed Beds:** 31 **Admissions:** 1343 **Census:** 12 **Outpatient Visits:** 107269 **Births:** 172 **Total Expense ($000):** 30614 **Payroll Expense ($000):** 14865 **Personnel:** 242

**TX**

*Many Facility Codes have changed. Please refer to the AHA Guide Code Chart.* © 2015 AHA Guide

**FORT WORTH—Tarrant County**

✠ **BAYLOR ALL SAINTS MEDICAL CENTER AT FORT WORTH (450137)**, 1400 Eighth Avenue, Zip 76104–4192; tel. 817/926–2544 **A**1 2 3 5 9 10 **F**3 11 12 13 17 18 20 22 24 26 28 29 30 31 34 35 38 40 45 46 47 49 53 55 59 64 70 72 73 74 75 76 77 78 79 80 81 82 84 86 87 90 96 97 100 101 102 103 104 105 107 108 111 114 115 119 124 126 130 131 132 138 139 142 146 147 148 **S** Baylor Scott & White Health, Dallas, TX
Primary Contact: David G. Klein, M.D., President
COO: Janice L. Walker, R.N., Chief Operating Officer
CFO: Lucy Catala, Vice President Finance
CMO: Dahlia Hassani, Vice President of Medical Affairs
CIO: Sandy Vaughn, Director Information Services
CHR: Tracy Stanford, Director Human Resources
CNO: Ellen Pitcher, MSN, Vice President and Chief Nursing Officer
Web address: www.baylorhealth.com/PhysiciansLocations/AllSaints/Pages/Default.aspx
**Control:** Other not–for–profit (including NFP Corporation) **Service:** General Medical and Surgical

**Staffed Beds:** 449 **Admissions:** 18192 **Census:** 237 **Outpatient Visits:** 72984 **Births:** 5659 **Total Expense ($000):** 320716 **Payroll Expense ($000):** 117759 **Personnel:** 1134

✠ **BAYLOR INSTITUTE FOR REHABILITATION AT FORT WORTH (673035)**, 6601 Harris Parkway, Zip 76132–6108; tel. 817/433–9600 **A**1 10 **F**3 28 29 30 64 75 90 93 130 **S** GLOBALREHAB, Dallas, TX
Primary Contact: Jeffrey D. Thompson, Chief Executive Officer
CMO: Ade Adedokun, M.D., Medical Director
CHR: Lenae Romack, Manager Human Resources
CNO: Fred J. Andrews, Director of Nursing and Ancillary Services
Web address: www.globalrehabhospitals.com
**Control:** Partnership, Investor–owned, for–profit **Service:** Rehabilitation

**Staffed Beds:** 42 **Admissions:** 983 **Census:** 32 **Outpatient Visits:** 3579 **Births:** 0 **Total Expense ($000):** 15745 **Payroll Expense ($000):** 7243 **Personnel:** 122

☐ **BAYLOR SURGICAL HOSPITAL AT FORT WORTH (450880)**, 1800 Park Place Avenue, Zip 76110–1302; tel. 682/703–5600 **A**1 9 10 **F**3 29 40 54 70 79 81 107 119 120
Primary Contact: Chris Fromme, Acting Chief Executive Officer
CFO: Jane Mathis, Chief Financial Officer
CMO: Bruce Bollinger, M.D., Medical Director
CNO: Stacie Merrill, Chief Nursing Officer
Web address: www.mcsh–hospital.com
**Control:** Partnership, Investor–owned, for–profit **Service:** General Medical and Surgical

**Staffed Beds:** 30 **Admissions:** 958 **Census:** 8 **Outpatient Visits:** 10999 **Births:** 0 **Total Expense ($000):** 61966 **Payroll Expense ($000):** 11596 **Personnel:** 180

✠ **COOK CHILDREN'S MEDICAL CENTER (453300)**, 801 Seventh Avenue, Zip 76104–2796; tel. 682/885–4000 **A**1 3 5 9 10 **F**3 7 8 17 19 21 23 25 27 29 30 31 32 34 35 38 39 40 41 43 44 45 48 50 54 55 57 58 59 60 61 64 68 72 74 75 77 78 79 80 81 82 84 85 86 87 88 89 90 93 97 98 99 100 101 102 104 105 106 107 108 111 112 113 114 118 119 129 130 131 132 134 136 138 143 144 146 148 **P**6
Primary Contact: Rick W. Merrill, President and Chief Executive Officer
CFO: Stephen Kimmel, Chief Financial Officer
CMO: James C. Cunningham, M.D., Chief Medical Officer
CIO: Theresa Meadows, Chief Information Officer
CHR: Keith Holtz, Chief Human Resources Officer
CNO: Teresa J. Clark, R.N., Chief Nursing Officer
Web address: www.cookchildrens.org
**Control:** Other not–for–profit (including NFP Corporation) **Service:** Children's general

**Staffed Beds:** 363 **Admissions:** 11615 **Census:** 213 **Outpatient Visits:** 264343 **Births:** 0 **Total Expense ($000):** 654743 **Payroll Expense ($000):** 222758 **Personnel:** 3440

✠ **HEALTHSOUTH CITY VIEW REHABILITATION HOSPITAL (453042)**, 6701 Oakmont Boulevard, Zip 76132–2957; tel. 817/370–4700 **A**1 9 10 **F**3 29 62 77 90 91 94 95 96 118 130 148 **S** HEALTHSOUTH Corporation, Birmingham, AL
Primary Contact: Trent Pierce, R.N., Chief Executive Officer
Web address: www.healthsouthcityview.com
**Control:** Corporation, Investor–owned, for–profit **Service:** Rehabilitation

**Staffed Beds:** 62 **Admissions:** 1099 **Census:** 40 **Outpatient Visits:** 8947 **Births:** 0 **Total Expense ($000):** 14359 **Payroll Expense ($000):** 8485 **Personnel:** 158

✠ **HEALTHSOUTH REHABILITATION HOSPITAL OF FORT WORTH (453041)**, 1212 West Lancaster Avenue, Zip 76102–4510; tel. 817/870–2336 **A**1 9 10 **F**3 29 30 60 68 74 75 77 79 86 90 91 95 96 130 131 148 **S** HEALTHSOUTH Corporation, Birmingham, AL
Primary Contact: Trent Pierce, R.N., Chief Executive Officer
CFO: Sherry Hapney, Chief Financial Officer
CMO: Patrick Donovan, M.D., Director Medical Staff
CHR: Tara Kleas, Director Human Resources
Web address: www.healthsouthfortworth.com
**Control:** Corporation, Investor–owned, for–profit **Service:** Rehabilitation

**Staffed Beds:** 60 **Admissions:** 1125 **Census:** 40 **Outpatient Visits:** 0 **Births:** 0 **Total Expense ($000):** 14932 **Payroll Expense ($000):** 7796 **Personnel:** 149

**JOHN PETER SMITH HOSPITAL** See JPS Health Network

✠ **JPS HEALTH NETWORK (450039)**, 1500 South Main Street, Zip 76104–4917; tel. 817/921–3431, (Includes JOHN PETER SMITH HOSPITAL, 1500 South Main Street, Zip 76104; tel. 817/921–3431; TRINITY SPRINGS PAVILION, 1500 South Main Street, tel. 817/927–3636; Lily Wong, Director Psychiatry), (Total facility includes 15 beds in nursing home–type unit) **A**1 2 3 5 8 9 10 12 13 **F**3 8 11 13 15 17 18 20 22 24 26 28 29 30 31 32 34 35 36 37 38 39 40 43 45 47 49 50 54 55 56 57 58 59 60 61 64 65 66 68 70 72 74 75 76 77 78 79 80 81 82 84 85 86 87 89 91 92 93 97 98 99 100 101 102 103 104 105 107 108 110 111 114 115 118 119 120 121 123 124 126 128 130 131 132 134 135 142 143 144 146 147 148
Primary Contact: Robert Earley, President and Chief Executive Officer
CFO: Alan Townsend, Interim Chief Financial Officer
CIO: Melinda Custin, Chief Information Officer
CHR: Nikki Sumpter, Senior Vice President Human Resources
CNO: Wanda V. Peebles, Chief Nursing Officer
Web address: www.jpshealthnet.org
**Control:** Hospital district or authority, Government, nonfederal **Service:** General Medical and Surgical

**Staffed Beds:** 510 **Admissions:** 24907 **Census:** 386 **Outpatient Visits:** 1043294 **Births:** 4833 **Total Expense ($000):** 770841 **Payroll Expense ($000):** 299658 **Personnel:** 5236

✠ **KINDRED HOSPITAL–FORT WORTH (452088)**, 815 Eighth Avenue, Zip 76104–2609; tel. 817/332–4812, (Includes KINDRED HOSPITAL TARRANT COUNTY–FORT WORTH SOUTHWEST, 7800 Oakmont Boulevard, Zip 76132–4299; tel. 817/346–0094; Anna Rojas, Chief Executive Officer) **A**1 9 10 **F**3 29 46 48 60 70 77 79 82 85 107 114 130 148 **S** Kindred Healthcare, Louisville, KY
Primary Contact: Angela Harris, Chief Executive Officer
CFO: Susan Popp, Controller
CMO: Stuart McDonald, M.D., President Medical Staff
CIO: Norma Warner, Area Director Health Information Management
CHR: Nicole Newpower, Coordinator Human Resources
Web address: www.kindredfortworth.com/
**Control:** Corporation, Investor–owned, for–profit **Service:** Long–Term Acute Care hospital

**Staffed Beds:** 54 **Admissions:** 636 **Census:** 45 **Outpatient Visits:** 0 **Births:** 0 **Total Expense ($000):** 24345 **Payroll Expense ($000):** 9216 **Personnel:** 165

**MEDICAL CENTER ALLIANCE**, 3101 North Tarrant Parkway, Zip 76177; tel. 817/639–1000
Primary Contact: Glenn Wallace, Chief Executive Officer

**Control:** Corporation, Investor–owned, for–profit **Service:** General

☐ **MESA SPRINGS (454124)**, 5560 Mesa Springs Drive, Zip 76123; tel. 817/292–4600 **A**1 10 **F**5 29 54 98 99 101 103 104 105
Primary Contact: Barbara Schmidt, Chief Executive Officer
CFO: Jessica Knox, Chief Financial Officer
CMO: Stewart Keller, M.D., Medical Director
CHR: Jill Housand, Director Human Resources
CNO: Lisa Thames, Director of Nursing
Web address: www.springstone.com/hospitals.stmhl
**Control:** Corporation, Investor–owned, for–profit **Service:** Psychiatric

**Staffed Beds:** 72 **Admissions:** 1116 **Census:** 23 **Outpatient Visits:** 4998 **Births:** 0 **Total Expense ($000):** 8991 **Payroll Expense ($000):** 4465 **Personnel:** 90

TX

---

**Hospital, Medicare Provider Number, Address, Telephone, Approval, Facility, and Physician Codes, Health Care System**

★ American Hospital Association (AHA) membership    ○ Healthcare Facilities Accreditation Program    ⇑ Center for Improvement in Healthcare Quality Accreditation
☐ The Joint Commission accreditation    ◇ DNV Healthcare Inc. accreditation    △ Commission on Accreditation of Rehabilitation Facilities (CARF) accreditation

✠ **PLAZA MEDICAL CENTER OF FORT WORTH (450672)**, 900 Eighth Avenue, Zip 76104–3902; tel. 817/336–2100 **A**1 2 3 9 10 13 **F**3 11 12 17 18 20 22 24 26 28 29 30 31 34 35 40 42 45 46 48 49 53 56 58 64 67 70 74 77 78 79 81 85 87 91 93 107 108 111 114 115 119 130 138 145 146 148 **P**8 **S** HCA, Nashville, TN
Primary Contact: Clay Franklin, Chief Executive Officer
COO: Gregory Haralson, Chief Operating Officer
CFO: Elia Stokes, Chief Financial Officer
CMO: Amir Malik, M.D., Cardiologist
CIO: Kelley Fredrickson, Director Information Services
CHR: Cyndi Roberts, Director Human Resources
Web address: www.plazamedicalcenter.com
**Control:** Partnership, Investor–owned, for–profit **Service:** General Medical and Surgical

**Staffed Beds:** 212 **Admissions:** 9177 **Census:** 136 **Outpatient Visits:** 42824 **Births:** 1 **Total Expense ($000):** 164813 **Payroll Expense ($000):** 53641 **Personnel:** 743

✠ **REGENCY HOSPITAL OF FORT WORTH (452099)**, 6801 Oakmont Boulevard, Zip 76132–3918; tel. 817/840–2500 **A**1 9 10 **F**1 3 29 45 75 77 85 86 87 107 130 148 **P**5 **S** Select Medical Corporation, Mechanicsburg, PA
Primary Contact: Natalie D. Lamberton, Chief Executive Officer
Web address: www.regencyhospital.com
**Control:** Corporation, Investor–owned, for–profit **Service:** Long–Term Acute Care hospital

**Staffed Beds:** 44 **Admissions:** 280 **Census:** 19 **Outpatient Visits:** 0 **Births:** 0 **Total Expense ($000):** 13213 **Payroll Expense ($000):** 6399 **Personnel:** 106

✠ **TEXAS HEALTH HARRIS METHODIST HOSPITAL ALLIANCE (670085)**, 10864 Texas Health Trail, Zip 76244–4897; tel. 682/212–2000 **A**1 9 10 **F**3 11 12 13 15 18 20 29 30 34 35 40 45 46 48 49 57 59 64 70 72 74 75 76 77 79 81 82 85 86 91 93 107 108 110 111 113 114 115 118 119 130 131 132 135 145 146 147 148 **S** Texas Health Resources, Arlington, TX
Primary Contact: Clint Abernathy, Interim Chief Executive Officer
**Control:** Other not–for–profit (including NFP Corporation) **Service:** General Medical and Surgical

**Staffed Beds:** 58 **Admissions:** 4024 **Census:** 37 **Outpatient Visits:** 36705 **Births:** 1146 **Total Expense ($000):** 71617 **Payroll Expense ($000):** 26656 **Personnel:** 361

✠ △ **TEXAS HEALTH HARRIS METHODIST HOSPITAL FORT WORTH (450135)**, 1301 Pennsylvania Avenue, Zip 76104–2122; tel. 817/250–2000 **A**1 2 7 9 10 **F**3 8 11 12 13 15 17 18 20 22 24 26 28 29 30 31 34 35 36 40 42 43 45 46 47 48 49 53 54 56 57 58 59 60 61 64 65 68 70 71 72 74 75 76 77 78 79 81 82 83 84 85 86 87 91 92 93 94 95 96 107 108 110 111 112 114 115 116 117 118 119 120 126 130 131 132 135 138 146 147 148 **S** Texas Health Resources, Arlington, TX
Primary Contact: Lillie Biggins, RN, R.N., President
CFO: Shelly Miland, Group Financial Officer
CMO: Joseph Prosser, M.D., Chief Medical Officer
CHR: Joseph Condon, Entity Human Resources Officer
CNO: Elaine Nelson, R.N., Chief Nursing Officer
Web address: www.texashealth.org
**Control:** Other not–for–profit (including NFP Corporation) **Service:** General Medical and Surgical

**Staffed Beds:** 641 **Admissions:** 33377 **Census:** 486 **Outpatient Visits:** 184426 **Births:** 2885 **Total Expense ($000):** 633752 **Payroll Expense ($000):** 249751 **Personnel:** 3890

✠ **TEXAS HEALTH HARRIS METHODIST HOSPITAL SOUTHWEST FORT WORTH (450779)**, 6100 Harris Parkway, Zip 76132–4199; tel. 817/433–5000 **A**1 2 9 10 **F**3 11 13 15 18 20 29 30 31 34 35 36 37 40 45 46 47 48 49 50 57 59 64 67 68 70 72 75 76 77 78 79 81 84 85 86 87 93 102 107 110 111 114 115 119 126 130 131 146 147 **S** Texas Health Resources, Arlington, TX
Primary Contact: Joseph DeLeon, President
CFO: Charlotte Ward, Entity Financial Officer
CMO: Mark Montgomery, M.D., Chief Medical Officer
CHR: Leanna W. Nalley, Director Human Resources
CNO: Mary Robinson, Chief Nursing Officer and Vice President Patient Care Services
Web address: www.texashealth.org
**Control:** Other not–for–profit (including NFP Corporation) **Service:** General Medical and Surgical

**Staffed Beds:** 199 **Admissions:** 13051 **Census:** 123 **Outpatient Visits:** 97688 **Births:** 3197 **Total Expense ($000):** 197461 **Payroll Expense ($000):** 65089 **Personnel:** 826

✠ **TEXAS HEALTH HUGULEY HOSPITAL FORT WORTH SOUTH (450677)**, 11801 South Freeway, Zip 76028–7021, Mailing Address: P.O. Box 6337, Zip 76115–0337; tel. 817/293–9110 **A**1 10 **F**3 5 8 11 13 15 17 18 20 22 24 28 29 30 31 32 34 35 38 40 44 45 49 51 53 54 56 57 59 60 64 65 68 70 71 74 75 76 77 78 79 80 81 82 85 86 87 89 93 98 100 101 102 103 104 105 107 108 110 111 114 118 119 120 121 126 130 132 135 146 147 148 **S** Adventist Health System Sunbelt Health Care Corporation, Altamonte Springs, FL
Primary Contact: Kenneth A. Finch, President and Chief Executive Officer
CFO: Penny Johnson, Chief Financial Officer
CMO: Edward Laue, M.D., Chief Medical Officer
CIO: David Smith, Manager Data Center
CHR: Laura Fisher, Director Human Resources
CNO: Tammy Collier, R.N., Vice President Patient Services
Web address: www.TexasHealthHuguley.org
**Control:** Church–operated, Nongovernment, not–for profit **Service:** General Medical and Surgical

**Staffed Beds:** 197 **Admissions:** 9457 **Census:** 108 **Outpatient Visits:** 130720 **Births:** 1166 **Total Expense ($000):** 155646 **Payroll Expense ($000):** 62556 **Personnel:** 1035

✠ **TEXAS HEALTH SPECIALTY HOSPITAL (452018)**, 1301 Pennsylvania Avenue, 4th Floor, Zip 76104–2190; tel. 817/250–5500 **A**1 9 10 **F**1 3 42 44 87 130 148 **S** Texas Health Resources, Arlington, TX
Primary Contact: Cheryl Mobley, FACHE, President
CFO: Vicki L. Galati, Chief Financial Officer
CMO: Joseph Prosser, M.D., Chief Medical Officer
CHR: Joseph Condon, Director Human Resources
CNO: Pam Duffey, MSN, Chief Nursing Officer
Web address: www.texashealth.org
**Control:** Church–operated, Nongovernment, not–for profit **Service:** Long–Term Acute Care hospital

**Staffed Beds:** 10 **Admissions:** 96 **Census:** 9 **Outpatient Visits:** 0 **Births:** 0 **Total Expense ($000):** 7280 **Payroll Expense ($000):** 3039 **Personnel:** 39

☐ △ **TEXAS REHABILITATION HOSPITAL OF FORT WORTH (673048)**, 425 Alabama Avenue, Zip 76104–1022; tel. 817/820–3400 **A**1 7 9 10 **F**3 29 74 79 90 91 96 130 132 148 **S** Kindred Healthcare, Louisville, KY
Primary Contact: Russell Bailey, Chief Executive Officer
Web address: www.texasrehabhospital.com/
**Control:** Corporation, Investor–owned, for–profit **Service:** Rehabilitation

**Staffed Beds:** 66 **Admissions:** 1262 **Census:** 48 **Outpatient Visits:** 0 **Births:** 0 **Total Expense ($000):** 18578 **Payroll Expense ($000):** 8872 **Personnel:** 148

☐ **USMD HOSPITAL AT FORT WORTH (670046)**, 5900 Altamesa Boulevard, Zip 76132–5473; tel. 817/433–9100 **A**1 9 10 **F**3 29 39 40 51 64 68 81 85 89 107 114 119 130 **S** USMD Inc., Irving, TX
Primary Contact: Stephanie Atkins–Guidry, Administrator and Chief Nursing Officer
CHR: Michelle Speck, Senior Vice President Human Resources
CNO: Stephanie Atkins–Guidry, Administrator and Chief Nursing Officer
Web address: www.usmdfortworth.com/
**Control:** Partnership, Investor–owned, for–profit **Service:** Surgical

**Staffed Beds:** 8 **Admissions:** 391 **Census:** 3 **Outpatient Visits:** 5021 **Births:** 0 **Total Expense ($000):** 28680 **Payroll Expense ($000):** 4919 **Personnel:** 109

**FREDERICKSBURG—Gillespie County**

✠ **HILL COUNTRY MEMORIAL HOSPITAL (450604)**, 1020 South State Highway 16, Zip 78624–4471, Mailing Address: P.O. Box 835, Zip 78624–0835; tel. 830/997–4353 **A**1 9 10 **F**3 11 13 15 18 20 28 29 30 31 32 34 35 37 40 43 46 49 50 51 53 57 59 62 63 64 68 70 74 75 76 77 78 79 81 82 84 85 86 87 90 93 96 107 108 110 111 114 115 119 124 129 130 131 132 135 145 146 148 **P**8
Primary Contact: Jayne E. Pope, Chief Executive Officer
COO: Mike Reno, Chief Operating Officer
CFO: Mark Jones, Chief Financial Officer
CMO: James R. Partin, M.D., Chief Medical Director
CIO: Holly Schmidt, Chief Information Officer
CHR: Alysha Metzger, Director Human Resources
CNO: Maureen Polivka, Chief Nursing Officer
Web address: www.hcmhs.org
**Control:** Other not–for–profit (including NFP Corporation) **Service:** General Medical and Surgical

**Staffed Beds:** 57 **Admissions:** 2809 **Census:** 24 **Outpatient Visits:** 79414 **Births:** 472 **Total Expense ($000):** 68428 **Payroll Expense ($000):** 26998 **Personnel:** 486

**FRIONA—Parmer County**

**PARMER COUNTY COMMUNITY HOSPITAL** See Parmer Medical Center

**TX**

*Many Facility Codes have changed. Please refer to the AHA Guide Code Chart.* © 2015 AHA Guide

**PARMER MEDICAL CENTER (451300)**, 1307 Cleveland Avenue, Zip 79035–1121; tel. 806/250–2754 **A**9 10 18 **F**11 30 34 35 40 43 57 64 75 77 89 93 107 119 127 130 133 148 **S** Preferred Management Corporation, Shawnee, OK
Primary Contact: Gayla Quillin, Administrator
Web address: www.parmermedicalcenter.com
**Control:** Other not–for–profit (including NFP Corporation) **Service:** General Medical and Surgical

**Staffed Beds:** 15 **Admissions:** 240 **Census:** 4 **Outpatient Visits:** 9854 **Births:** 0 **Total Expense ($000):** 10481 **Payroll Expense ($000):** 3982 **Personnel:** 91

---

**FRISCO—Collin County**

✠ **BAYLOR INSTITUTE FOR REHABILITATION AT FRISCO (673046)**, 2990 Legacy Drive, Zip 75034–6066; tel. 469/888–5100 **A**1 9 10 **F**3 29 30 34 64 75 90 91 92 93 96 130 132 148 **S** Select Medical Corporation, Mechanicsburg, PA
Primary Contact: Mark D. Boles, Chief Executive Officer
Web address: www.baylorhealth.com/bir
**Control:** Partnership, Investor–owned, for–profit **Service:** Rehabilitation

**Staffed Beds:** 44 **Admissions:** 827 **Census:** 26 **Outpatient Visits:** 7209 **Births:** 0 **Total Expense ($000):** 15299 **Payroll Expense ($000):** 6793 **Personnel:** 97

☐ **BAYLOR MEDICAL CENTER AT FRISCO (450853)**, 5601 Warren Parkway, Zip 75034–4069; tel. 214/407–5000 **A**1 3 5 9 10 **F**3 13 29 34 40 51 54 57 64 68 72 74 75 76 79 81 85 87 107 111 114 119 126 129 144 **S** United Surgical Partners International, Addison, TX
Primary Contact: William A. Keaton, Chief Executive Officer
COO: Kevin Coats, Chief Operating Officer and Chief Financial Officer
CFO: Kevin Coats, Chief Financial Officer
CMO: Jimmy Laferney, M.D., Vice President Medical Staff Affairs
CIO: Rick Barry, Director Information Systems
CHR: Margaret Garcia, Manager Human Resources
CNO: Randi Elliott MSN, Chief Nursing Officer
Web address: www.bmcf.com
**Control:** Partnership, Investor–owned, for–profit **Service:** General Medical and Surgical

**Staffed Beds:** 68 **Admissions:** 4487 **Census:** 39 **Outpatient Visits:** 24732 **Births:** 2613 **Total Expense ($000):** 118767 **Payroll Expense ($000):** 39192 **Personnel:** 567

✠ **CENTENNIAL MEDICAL CENTER (450885)**, 12505 Lebanon Road, Zip 75035–8298; tel. 972/963–3333 **A**1 9 10 **F**3 8 13 15 18 20 22 24 29 30 34 35 40 45 46 47 48 49 50 51 57 59 64 65 70 72 74 75 76 78 79 81 82 85 86 89 92 93 107 108 110 111 114 115 119 124 126 130 131 144 146 147 148 **S** TENET Healthcare Corporation, Dallas, TX
Primary Contact: Joe D. Thomason, Chief Executive Officer
COO: Reed Hammond, Chief Operating Officer
CFO: Blaise Bondi, Chief Financial Officer
CMO: Robert S. Hendler, M.D., Regional Chief Medical Officer
CIO: Dianne Yarborough, Director of Information Technology
CHR: Stephanie S. Talley, Director Human Resources
CNO: Calee Travis, R.N., Chief Nursing Officer
Web address: www.centennialmedcenter.com
**Control:** Corporation, Investor–owned, for–profit **Service:** General Medical and Surgical

**Staffed Beds:** 118 **Admissions:** 3918 **Census:** 43 **Outpatient Visits:** 33528 **Births:** 735 **Total Expense ($000):** 77420 **Payroll Expense ($000):** 26848 **Personnel:** 335

○ **FOREST PARK MEDICAL CENTER FRISCO**, 5500 Frisco Square Boulevard, Zip 75034–3305; tel. 214/618–0500 **A**11 **F**29 34 40 45 49 57 59 64 70 74 75 77 79 81 85 86 87 107 108 111 112 114 115 119 126 130 **P**5 **S** Vibrant Healthcare, Dallas, TX
Primary Contact: Julie A. Camp, R.N., Chief Executive Officer
COO: Kathryn Murphy, Chief Operating Officer and Chief Nursing Officer
CFO: Elisa Banigan, Chief Financial Officer
CMO: Robert Wyatt, M.D., Chief Medical Officer
CHR: Bryan Jewell, Director Human Resources
CNO: Kathryn Murphy, Chief Operating Officer and Chief Nursing Officer
Web address: www.forestparkfrisco.com/default.aspx
**Control:** Corporation, Investor–owned, for–profit **Service:** Surgical

**Staffed Beds:** 54 **Admissions:** 656 **Census:** 4 **Outpatient Visits:** 5171 **Births:** 0 **Total Expense ($000):** 59981 **Payroll Expense ($000):** 12481 **Personnel:** 170

☐ **HAVEN BEHAVIORAL HOSPITAL OF FRISCO**, 5680 Frisco Square Boulevard, Zip 75034–3300; tel. 469/353–2219, (Nonreporting) **A**1
Primary Contact: William W. Brattvet, Chief Executive Officer
Web address: www.frisco.havenbehavioral.com/
**Control:** Corporation, Investor–owned, for–profit **Service:** Psychiatric

**Staffed Beds:** 36

---

**GAINESVILLE—Cooke County**

**NORTH TEXAS MEDICAL CENTER (450090)**, 1900 Hospital Boulevard, Zip 76240–2002; tel. 940/665–1751 **A**9 10 20 **F**3 11 13 15 28 29 30 34 35 40 43 45 50 59 60 62 64 68 70 75 76 77 79 81 82 85 87 93 104 107 108 110 111 115 118 119 127 130 132 133 146 147
Primary Contact: Randy A. Bacus, FACHE, Chief Executive Officer
CFO: Kelly Hayes, Chief Financial Officer
CHR: Teresa Krebs, Director Human Resources
Web address: www.ntmconline.net
**Control:** Hospital district or authority, Government, nonfederal **Service:** General Medical and Surgical

**Staffed Beds:** 48 **Admissions:** 1365 **Census:** 12 **Outpatient Visits:** 63976 **Births:** 333 **Total Expense ($000):** 36446 **Payroll Expense ($000):** 16904 **Personnel:** 268

---

**GALVESTON—Galveston County**

☐ **SHRINERS HOSPITALS FOR CHILDREN–GALVESTON (453311)**, (Burn Care), 815 Market Street, Zip 77550–2725; tel. 409/770–6600 **A**1 3 5 10 **F**3 11 16 29 30 32 34 35 38 64 68 75 77 81 82 85 86 93 99 100 101 104 119 130 132 146 148 **S** Shriners Hospitals for Children, Tampa, FL
Primary Contact: Mary Jaco, R.N., MSN, Administrator
CFO: Michael B. Schimming, Director Financial Services
CMO: David N. Herndon, M.D., Chief of Staff
CHR: Ushma Lakhani, Interim Director Human Resources
CNO: Angel Martinez, RN, BSN, Director Patient Care Services
Web address: www.shrinershospitalsforchildren.org/Hospitals/Locations/Galveston.aspx
**Control:** Other not–for–profit (including NFP Corporation) **Service:** Children's other specialty

**Staffed Beds:** 15 **Admissions:** 216 **Census:** 7 **Outpatient Visits:** 8732 **Births:** 0 **Total Expense ($000):** 30669 **Payroll Expense ($000):** 12282 **Personnel:** 209

✠ **UNIVERSITY OF TEXAS MEDICAL BRANCH (450018)**, 301 University Boulevard, Zip 77555–0128; tel. 409/772–1011, (Includes ANGLETON DANBURY CAMPUS, 132 East Hospital Drive, Angleton, Zip 77515–4112; tel. 979/849–7721; Donna K. Sollenberger, Executive Vice President and Chief Executive Officer) **A**1 2 3 5 9 10 **F**3 8 11 12 13 14 15 16 17 18 19 20 22 24 26 28 29 30 31 34 35 36 38 39 40 41 43 44 45 46 49 50 51 52 53 54 55 56 57 58 59 60 61 64 65 66 68 70 71 72 73 74 75 76 77 78 79 81 82 84 85 86 87 88 89 90 92 93 94 96 97 99 100 101 102 103 104 107 108 110 111 114 115 117 118 119 120 121 123 124 126 129 130 131 132 134 135 137 138 141 142 144 145 146 147 148 **P**6 **S** University of Texas System, Austin, TX
Primary Contact: Donna K. Sollenberger, Executive Vice President and Chief Executive Officer
COO: Deborah A. McGrew, Vice President and Chief Operating Officer
CFO: Cheryl A. Sadro, Executive Vice President Chief Business and Finance Officer
CMO: Selwyn O. Rogers, M.D., Vice President and Chief Medical Officer
CIO: Todd Leach, Vice President and Chief Information Officer
CHR: Ronald McKinley, Ph.D., Vice President Human Resources and Employee Services
CNO: David R. Marshall, JD, Chief Nursing and Patient Care Services Officer
Web address: www.utmb.edu
**Control:** State–Government, nonfederal **Service:** General Medical and Surgical

**Staffed Beds:** 437 **Admissions:** 23678 **Census:** 332 **Outpatient Visits:** 791180 **Births:** 5412 **Total Expense ($000):** 715921 **Payroll Expense ($000):** 244752 **Personnel:** 3689

**TX**

---

### GARLAND—Dallas County

✠ **BAYLOR MEDICAL CENTER AT GARLAND (450280)**, 2300 Marie Curie Drive, Zip 75042–5706; tel. 972/487–5000 **A**1 2 3 5 9 10 **F**3 11 13 15 18 20 22 24 26 28 29 30 31 34 35 40 45 47 50 54 56 57 59 60 64 65 66 70 74 75 76 78 79 81 82 84 86 87 98 102 103 107 108 110 111 114 118 119 124 126 129 130 132 135 145 146 147 148 **S** Baylor Scott & White Health, Dallas, TX
Primary Contact: Thomas J. Trenary, President
COO: Janice L. Walker, R.N., Chief Nursing Officer and Chief Operating Officer
CFO: Robert Knowlton, Vice President and Chief Financial Officer
CMO: Steven Arze, M.D., Chief Medical Officer and Vice President Medical Affairs
CIO: Michael Larsen, Director Information Systems
CHR: Laura Settles, Director Human Resources
CNO: Janice L. Walker, R.N., Chief Nursing Officer and Chief Operating Officer
Web address: www.baylorhealth.com/PhysiciansLocations/Garland/Pages/Default. aspx
**Control:** Other not–for–profit (including NFP Corporation) **Service:** General Medical and Surgical

**Staffed Beds:** 185 **Admissions:** 9599 **Census:** 116 **Outpatient Visits:** 104634 **Births:** 802 **Total Expense ($000):** 173954 **Payroll Expense ($000):** 64955 **Personnel:** 592

✠ **SELECT SPECIALTY HOSPITAL – DALLAS GARLAND (450280)**, 2300 Marie Curie Drive, Floors 3E and 3W, Zip 75042–5706; tel. 469/440–5800, (Nonreporting) **A**1 **S** Select Medical Corporation, Mechanicsburg, PA
Primary Contact: Ron Norris, Chief Executive Officer
Web address: www.dallasgarland.selectspecialtyhospitals.com/
**Control:** Corporation, Investor–owned, for–profit **Service:** Long–Term Acute Care hospital

**Staffed Beds:** 40

### GATESVILLE—Coryell County

☐ **CORYELL MEMORIAL HOSPITAL (451379)**, 1507 West Main Street, Zip 76528–1098; tel. 254/865–8251 **A**1 9 10 18 **F**3 7 10 11 15 18 20 28 40 43 50 57 58 59 61 62 65 70 74 81 82 84 87 93 97 107 111 115 119 125 127 129 130 133 **P**6
Primary Contact: David Byrom, Chief Executive Officer
COO: David Byrom, Chief Executive Officer
CFO: Carol Jones, Controller and Manager Business Office
CMO: Diedra Wuenschel, D.O., President Medical Staff
CIO: Mike Huckabee, Network Administrator
CHR: Paula Smithhart, Director Human Resources
CNO: Jeanne Griffith, Chief Nursing Officer
Web address: www.cmhos.org
**Control:** Hospital district or authority, Government, nonfederal **Service:** General Medical and Surgical

**Staffed Beds:** 25 **Admissions:** 811 **Census:** 11 **Outpatient Visits:** 56130 **Births:** 0 **Total Expense ($000):** 31438 **Payroll Expense ($000):** 12343 **Personnel:** 349

### GEORGETOWN—Williamson County

☐ **GEORGETOWN BEHAVIORAL HEALTH INSTITUTE**, 3101 South Austin Avenue, Zip 78626–7541; tel. 512/819–1100, (Nonreporting) **A**1 **S** Signature Healthcare Services, Corona, CA
Primary Contact: Sheila McDermott–Lord, Chief Executive Officer
CFO: Shelli Surcouf, Chief Financial Officer
CHR: Kristi Hynes, Director Human Resources
CNO: Nini Perry, Chief Nursing Officer
Web address: www.georgetownbehavioral.co
**Control:** Investor–owned, for–profit **Service:** Psychiatric

**Staffed Beds:** 118

★ **ROCK SPRINGS**, 700 Southeast Inner Loop, Zip 78626; tel. 512/819–9400, (Data for 309 days) **F**98 99 100 102 104 105
Primary Contact: Edgar E. Prettyman, PsyD, Chief Executive Officer
Web address: www.rockspringshealth.com/
**Control:** Corporation, Investor–owned, for–profit **Service:** Psychiatric

**Staffed Beds:** 72 **Admissions:** 1088 **Census:** 25 **Outpatient Visits:** 2923 **Births:** 0 **Total Expense ($000):** 8767 **Payroll Expense ($000):** 4302 **Personnel:** 171

### GLEN ROSE—Somervell County

✠ **GLEN ROSE MEDICAL CENTER (450451)**, 1021 Holden Street, Zip 76043–4937, Mailing Address: P.O. Box 2099, Zip 76043–2099; tel. 254/897–2215 **A**1 9 10 **F**2 15 29 34 40 43 45 48 51 56 57 59 65 81 93 103 104 107 108 110 111 119 129 130 132 133 143 146 **P**7
Primary Contact: Ray Reynolds, Chief Executive Officer
CFO: Michael Honea, Chief Financial Officer
CHR: Ladonna Green, Director Human Resources
CNO: Laura Hodnett, Interim Chief Nursing Officer
Web address: www.glenrosemedicalcenter.com
**Control:** Hospital district or authority, Government, nonfederal **Service:** General Medical and Surgical

**Staffed Beds:** 16 **Admissions:** 684 **Census:** 6 **Outpatient Visits:** 19740 **Births:** 0 **Total Expense ($000):** 16383 **Payroll Expense ($000):** 5973 **Personnel:** 157

### GONZALES—Gonzales County

★ **MEMORIAL HOSPITAL (450235)**, 1110 Sarah Dewitt Drive, Zip 78629–3311, Mailing Address: P.O. Box 587, Zip 78629–0587; tel. 830/672–7581 **A**9 10 **F**3 11 13 15 29 34 35 38 40 43 53 57 59 62 64 65 68 70 75 76 77 81 85 87 93 97 107 110 111 115 119 127 129 130 132 148 **S** QHR, Brentwood, TN
Primary Contact: Charles Norris, Chief Executive Officer
CFO: Patty Stewart, Chief Financial Officer
CMO: Commie Hisey, D.O., Chief of Staff
CHR: Joni Leland, Director Human Resources
CNO: Valerie Hohenshell, Director of Clinical Services
Web address: www.gonzaleshealthcare.com
**Control:** Hospital district or authority, Government, nonfederal **Service:** General Medical and Surgical

**Staffed Beds:** 33 **Admissions:** 788 **Census:** 6 **Outpatient Visits:** 73436 **Births:** 184 **Total Expense ($000):** 30223 **Payroll Expense ($000):** 10226 **Personnel:** 287

### GRAHAM—Young County

★ **GRAHAM REGIONAL MEDICAL CENTER (450085)**, 1301 Montgomery Road, Zip 76450–4240, Mailing Address: P.O. Box 1390, Zip 76450–1390; tel. 940/549–3400 **A**9 10 20 **F**7 11 13 15 28 29 40 43 53 57 59 62 63 70 75 76 79 81 85 89 93 104 107 111 115 119 127 130 133 135 **P**5 **S** QHR, Brentwood, TN
Primary Contact: Scott M. Landrum, Interim Administrator
CIO: Jeff Clark, Director Information Systems
CHR: Judy Guinn, Chief Human Resources Officer
Web address: www.grahamrmc.com
**Control:** Hospital district or authority, Government, nonfederal **Service:** General Medical and Surgical

**Staffed Beds:** 25 **Admissions:** 916 **Census:** 8 **Outpatient Visits:** 62147 **Births:** 220 **Total Expense ($000):** 26013 **Payroll Expense ($000):** 9724 **Personnel:** 200

### GRANBURY—Hood County

✠ **LAKE GRANBURY MEDICAL CENTER (450596)**, 1310 Paluxy Road, Zip 76048–5655; tel. 817/573–2273 **A**1 9 10 **F**3 8 11 12 13 15 18 20 22 26 28 29 30 34 37 40 43 45 49 53 57 59 64 68 70 74 75 76 77 79 81 82 85 86 93 107 108 110 111 114 118 119 126 129 133 135 146 147 **S** Community Health Systems, Inc., Franklin, TN
Primary Contact: Derrick Cuenca, Chief Executive Officer
CFO: Noe Gutierrez, Chief Financial Officer
CIO: Kevin Myers, Director Information Systems
CHR: Brooke Montoya, Director Human Resources
CNO: Abigail Kendall, Chief Nursing Officer
Web address: www.lakegranburymedicalcenter.com
**Control:** Corporation, Investor–owned, for–profit **Service:** General Medical and Surgical

**Staffed Beds:** 83 **Admissions:** 2640 **Census:** 22 **Outpatient Visits:** 60561 **Births:** 487 **Total Expense ($000):** 57997 **Payroll Expense ($000):** 18962 **Personnel:** 323

### GRAND PRAIRIE—Dallas County

◇ **TEXAS GENERAL HOSPITAL (670083)**, 2709 Hospital Boulevard, Zip 75051–1017; tel. 469/999–0000 **A**10 21 **F**3 18 20 22 29 34 40 45 46 48 50 57 59 64 70 74 75 79 81 82 85 87 107 108 111 115 119 148
Primary Contact: Suleman Hashmi, President and Chief Executive Officer
Web address: www.texasgeneralhospital.com
**Control:** Partnership, Investor–owned, for–profit **Service:** General Medical and Surgical

**Staffed Beds:** 41 **Admissions:** 497 **Census:** 4 **Outpatient Visits:** 12543 **Births:** 0 **Total Expense ($000):** 30746 **Payroll Expense ($000):** 10805 **Personnel:** 202

### GRAPEVINE—Tarrant County

✠ **BAYLOR REGIONAL MEDICAL CENTER AT GRAPEVINE (450563)**, 1650 West College Street, Zip 76051–3565; tel. 817/481–1588 **A**1 2 3 9 10 **F**3 11 12 13 15 18 20 22 24 26 28 29 30 31 34 35 40 45 46 47 48 49 56 57 59 61 64 65 70 72 74 75 76 77 78 79 80 81 82 84 86 87 107 108 110 111 114 115 119 126 129 130 131 132 135 145 146 147 **S** Baylor Scott & White Health, Dallas, TX
Primary Contact: Steven R. Newton, President
CFO: Terri Foster, Hospital Finance Officer
CMO: Ron Jensen, D.O., Chief Medical Officer and Vice President
CIO: Sandy Vaughn, Director Information Systems
CHR: Donna Stark, Director Human Resources
CNO: Beth P. Beckman, R.N., Chief Nursing Officer
Web address: www.https://www.baylorhealth.com/PhysiciansLocations/Grapevine/Pages/Default.aspx
**Control:** Other not–for–profit (including NFP Corporation) **Service:** General Medical and Surgical

**Staffed Beds:** 233 **Admissions:** 11501 **Census:** 140 **Outpatient Visits:** 62614 **Births:** 2637 **Total Expense ($000):** 185045 **Payroll Expense ($000):** 67442 **Personnel:** 661

*Many Facility Codes have changed. Please refer to the AHA Guide Code Chart.* © 2015 AHA Guide

☐ **ETHICUS HOSPITAL – GRAPEVINE (452110)**, 4201 William D. Tate Avenue, Zip 76051–5736; tel. 817/288–1300 **A**1 9 10 **F**1 3 29 40 64 74 75 77 87 93 96 107 119 130 148
Primary Contact: Roger T. Jenkins, Chief Executive Officer
Web address: www.ethicusgrapevine.com
**Control:** Partnership, Investor–owned, for–profit **Service:** Long–Term Acute Care hospital

**Staffed Beds:** 22 **Admissions:** 404 **Census:** 29 **Outpatient Visits:** 11 **Births:** 0 **Total Expense ($000):** 19681 **Payroll Expense ($000):** 8014 **Personnel:** 105

### GREENVILLE—Hunt County

☐ **GLEN OAKS HOSPITAL (454050)**, 301 Division Street, Zip 75401–4101; tel. 903/454–6000 **A**1 9 10 **F**4 5 29 34 40 98 99 100 101 102 103 104 105 **S** Universal Health Services, Inc., King of Prussia, PA
Primary Contact: Greg Garland, Interim Chief Executive Officer
CFO: Lowell K. Hudson, Chief Financial Officer
CHR: Joe Carson, Director Human Resources
Web address: www.glenoakshospital.com
**Control:** Corporation, Investor–owned, for–profit **Service:** Psychiatric

**Staffed Beds:** 54 **Admissions:** 1640 **Census:** 34 **Outpatient Visits:** 4616 **Births:** 0 **Total Expense ($000):** 8172 **Payroll Expense ($000):** 3910 **Personnel:** 77

⊠ **HUNT REGIONAL MEDICAL CENTER (450352)**, 4215 Joe Ramsey Boulevard, Zip 75401–7899, Mailing Address: P.O. Box 1059, Zip 75403–1059; tel. 903/408–5000, (Includes HUNT REGIONAL MEDICAL CENTER, 4215 Joe Ramsey Boulevard, Zip 75403–1059, Mailing Address: Drawer 1059, Zip 75403–1059; tel. 903/408–5000), (Nonreporting) **A**1 9 10 **S** Hunt Regional Healthcare, Greenville, TX
Primary Contact: Richard Carter, District Chief Executive Officer
COO: Michael R. Klepin, Administrator
CFO: Lee Boles, Assistant Administrator and Chief Financial Officer
CMO: James H. Sandin, M.D., Assistant Administrator Medical Affairs
CIO: Richard Montanye, Director Information Systems
CHR: John Heatherly, Assistant Administrator Support Services
CNO: Deborah Clack, Chief Nursing Officer
Web address: www.huntregional.org
**Control:** Hospital district or authority, Government, nonfederal **Service:** General Medical and Surgical

**Staffed Beds:** 225

### GROESBECK—Limestone County

**LIMESTONE MEDICAL CENTER (451303)**, 701 Mcclintic Drive, Zip 76642–2128; tel. 254/729–3281 **A**9 10 18 **F**3 7 11 28 32 34 35 40 41 43 45 57 64 65 75 77 84 85 90 93 96 97 104 107 114 127 129 130 133 135 146 148
Primary Contact: Larry Price, Chief Executive Officer
CFO: Mike Williams, Accountant
CMO: Sheer Rahaman, M.D., Chief of Medical Staff
CIO: Byong Lee, Manager Information Technology and PACS Administrator
CHR: Jean Koester, Manager Human Resources
CNO: Jean Wragge, Director of Nurses
Web address: www.lmchospital.com
**Control:** Hospital district or authority, Government, nonfederal **Service:** General Medical and Surgical

**Staffed Beds:** 20 **Admissions:** 383 **Census:** 8 **Outpatient Visits:** 17935 **Births:** 0 **Total Expense ($000):** 17978 **Payroll Expense ($000):** 7232 **Personnel:** 168

### HALLETTSVILLE—Lavaca County

**LAVACA MEDICAL CENTER (451376)**, 1400 North Texana Street, Zip 77964–2099; tel. 361/798–3671 **A**9 10 18 **F**3 11 15 18 29 34 40 41 43 45 47 53 56 57 59 64 65 68 75 77 81 85 86 87 93 107 108 110 111 114 118 119 127 133 135 146 148
Primary Contact: Michael Morris, Interim Chief Executive Officer
**Control:** Hospital district or authority, Government, nonfederal **Service:** General Medical and Surgical

**Staffed Beds:** 25 **Admissions:** 535 **Census:** 7 **Outpatient Visits:** 38701 **Births:** 0 **Total Expense ($000):** 16297 **Payroll Expense ($000):** 5560 **Personnel:** 139

### HAMILTON—Hamilton County

★ **HAMILTON GENERAL HOSPITAL (450754)**, 400 North Brown Street, Zip 76531–1518; tel. 254/386–1600 **A**9 10 20 **F**3 7 11 15 28 29 34 40 43 44 45 50 53 56 57 59 64 68 79 80 81 82 85 86 93 97 103 104 107 110 114 127 130 132
Primary Contact: James R. Shafer, Interim Chief Executive Officer
CIO: Chad Reinert, Director Information Technology
CHR: Emily Dossey, Director Human Resources
CNO: Debra Martin, Director of Nursing
Web address: www.hamiltonhospital.org
**Control:** Hospital district or authority, Government, nonfederal **Service:** General Medical and Surgical

**Staffed Beds:** 42 **Admissions:** 1173 **Census:** 12 **Outpatient Visits:** 80484 **Births:** 0 **Total Expense ($000):** 20438 **Payroll Expense ($000):** 7821 **Personnel:** 211

### HAMLIN—Jones County

**HAMLIN MEMORIAL HOSPITAL (450243)**, 632 Northwest Second Street, Zip 79520–3831, Mailing Address: P.O. Box 400, Zip 79520–0400; tel. 325/576–3646 **A**9 10 **F**3 7 11 28 29 40 43 64 68 69 107 133 135 146 148 **P**5
Primary Contact: Clay Vogel, Chief Executive Officer
CMO: Krishna Sunkavalle, M.D., Chief Medical Officer
**Control:** Hospital district or authority, Government, nonfederal **Service:** General Medical and Surgical

**Staffed Beds:** 23 **Admissions:** 134 **Census:** 2 **Outpatient Visits:** 3475 **Births:** 0 **Total Expense ($000):** 3460 **Payroll Expense ($000):** 1739 **Personnel:** 44

### HARKER HEIGHTS—Bell County

⊠ **SETON MEDICAL CENTER HARKER HEIGHTS (670080)**, 850 West Central Texas Expressway, Zip 76548–1890; tel. 254/690–0900 **A**1 9 10 **F**3 13 15 18 20 22 26 28 29 30 34 35 40 43 45 50 51 57 59 60 66 70 74 75 76 79 81 91 107 108 110 111 115 119 129 130 146 147 148 **P**3 **S** LHP Hospital Group, Plano, TX
Primary Contact: Matt T. Maxfield, FACHE, Chief Executive Officer
CFO: John K. Sharp, Chief Financial Officer
CHR: Mona Tucker, Director Human Resources
CNO: Pamela Craig, R.N., Chief Nursing Officer
Web address: www.setonharkerheights.net
**Control:** Partnership, Investor–owned, for–profit **Service:** General Medical and Surgical

**Staffed Beds:** 60 **Admissions:** 3566 **Census:** 30 **Outpatient Visits:** 71177 **Births:** 930 **Total Expense ($000):** 119050 **Payroll Expense ($000):** 21648 **Personnel:** 340

### HARLINGEN—Cameron County

⊠ **HARLINGEN MEDICAL CENTER (450855)**, 5501 South Expressway 77, Zip 78550–3213; tel. 956/365–1000 **A**1 3 5 9 10 **F**3 12 13 15 17 18 20 22 24 29 30 40 43 49 50 51 57 59 64 68 70 74 75 76 79 81 85 86 107 108 110 111 114 115 118 119 129 130 146 147 148 **S** Prime Healthcare Services, Ontario, CA
Primary Contact: Brenda Ivory, Chief Executive Officer
CFO: David Glassburn, Vice President Finance and Chief Financial Officer
CMO: Elizabeth Juarez, M.D., Chief Medical Officer
CHR: Emmett Craig, Director Human Resources
CNO: Deborah Meeks, Chief Nursing Officer
Web address: www.harlingenmedicalcenter.com
**Control:** Partnership, Investor–owned, for–profit **Service:** General Medical and Surgical

**Staffed Beds:** 88 **Admissions:** 4868 **Census:** 52 **Outpatient Visits:** 62806 **Births:** 671 **Total Expense ($000):** 92819 **Payroll Expense ($000):** 29408 **Personnel:** 478

**TX**

---

**Hospital, Medicare Provider Number, Address, Telephone, Approval, Facility, and Physician Codes, Health Care System**

★ American Hospital Association (AHA) membership
☐ The Joint Commission accreditation
○ Healthcare Facilities Accreditation Program
◇ DNV Healthcare Inc. accreditation
⇑ Center for Improvement in Healthcare Quality Accreditation
△ Commission on Accreditation of Rehabilitation Facilities (CARF) accreditation

☐ **RIO GRANDE STATE CENTER/SOUTH TEXAS HEALTH CARE SYSTEM (454088)**, 1401 South Rangerville Road, Zip 78552–7638; tel. 956/364–8000, (Includes RIO GRANDE STATE CENTER, 1401 South Rangerville Road, tel. 956/364–8000; SOUTH TEXAS HEALTH CARE SYSTEM, 1401 Rangerville Road, Zip 78552–7609; tel. 956/364–8000) **A**1 3 5 10 **F**30 53 54 57 65 66 68 75 87 97 98 101 107 119 130 132 135 143 146 147 **P**6 **S** Texas Department of State Health Services, Austin, TX
Primary Contact: Sonia Hernandez–Keeble, Superintendent
CFO: Tom Garza, Director Fiscal and Support
CMO: David Moron, M.D., Clinical Director
CIO: Blas Ortiz, Jr., Assistant Superintendent and Public Information Officer
CHR: Irma Garcia, Job Coordinator
CNO: Maia Baker, MSN, Chief Nurse Executive
Web address: www.dshs.state.tx.us/mhhospitals/RioGrandeSC/default.shtm
**Control:** State–Government, nonfederal **Service:** Psychiatric

**Staffed Beds:** 128 **Admissions:** 663 **Census:** 51 **Outpatient Visits:** 35190 **Births:** 0 **Total Expense ($000):** 22419 **Payroll Expense ($000):** 8895 **Personnel:** 522

⇑ **SOLARA HOSPITAL HARLINGEN (452101)**, 508 Victoria Lane, Zip 78550–3225; tel. 956/425–9600, (Includes SOLARA HOSPITAL – BROWNSVILLE CAMPUS, 333 Lorenaly Drive, Brownsville, Zip 78526–4333; tel. 956/546–0808) **A**9 10 22 **F**1 3 29 30 35 40 57 75 85 86 130 148 **S** Cornerstone Healthcare Group, Dallas, TX
Primary Contact: Cary L. Montalvo, Chief Executive Officer
CFO: Kurt Schultz, Chief Financial Officer
CIO: Adam Davis, Chief Information Officer
CHR: Dan Perkins, Vice President of Human Resources
Web address: www.chghospitals.com/harlingen/
**Control:** Partnership, Investor–owned, for–profit **Service:** Long–Term Acute Care hospital

**Staffed Beds:** 82 **Admissions:** 814 **Census:** 59 **Outpatient Visits:** 0 **Births:** 0 **Total Expense ($000):** 26952 **Payroll Expense ($000):** 10449 **Personnel:** 196

⊠ **VALLEY BAPTIST MEDICAL CENTER–HARLINGEN (450033)**, 2101 Pease Street, Zip 78550–8307, Mailing Address: P.O. Drawer 2588, Zip 78551–2588; tel. 956/389–1100 **A**1 3 5 9 10 **F**3 11 12 13 14 15 17 18 20 22 24 26 28 29 30 31 34 35 39 40 43 44 45 46 47 48 49 50 54 56 57 59 60 63 64 65 68 70 71 72 73 74 75 76 77 78 79 80 81 82 84 85 86 87 88 89 90 91 92 93 94 100 103 104 107 108 110 111 112 114 115 119 126 129 130 132 144 146 147 148 **S** TENET Healthcare Corporation, Dallas, TX
Primary Contact: Todd Mann, Senior Vice President and Chief Executive Officer
COO: Daniel Listi, Chief Operating Officer
CFO: Marco Rodriguez, Chief Financial Officer
CHR: Irma L. Pye, Senior Vice President and Chief Human Resource Officer
CNO: Stephen Hill, Vice President and Chief Nursing Officer
Web address: www.valleybaptist.net/harlingen/index.htm
**Control:** Corporation, Investor–owned, for–profit **Service:** General Medical and Surgical

**Staffed Beds:** 416 **Admissions:** 17690 **Census:** 232 **Outpatient Visits:** 117318 **Births:** 2573 **Total Expense ($000):** 261669 **Payroll Expense ($000):** 85704 **Personnel:** 1153

### HASKELL—Haskell County

**HASKELL MEMORIAL HOSPITAL (451341)**, 1 North Avenue N, Zip 79521–5499, Mailing Address: P.O. Box 1117, Zip 79521–1117; tel. 940/864–2621 **A**9 10 18 **F**11 28 29 34 35 40 53 54 57 59 64 68 75 77 86 87 93 97 119 130 131 133 146 **P**1
Primary Contact: Fran McCown, Administrator
CHR: Emily Moore, Director Human Resources and Information Technology
CNO: Teri Turner, Chief Nursing Officer
**Control:** Hospital district or authority, Government, nonfederal **Service:** General Medical and Surgical

**Staffed Beds:** 15 **Admissions:** 243 **Census:** 3 **Outpatient Visits:** 16711 **Births:** 0 **Total Expense ($000):** 5489 **Payroll Expense ($000):** 2307 **Personnel:** 80

### HEMPHILL—Sabine County

☐ **SABINE COUNTY HOSPITAL (451361)**, 2301 Worth Street, Zip 75948–7216, Mailing Address: P.O. Box 750, Zip 75948–0750; tel. 409/787–3300 **A**1 9 10 18 **F**3 29 34 35 40 43 50 57 59 64 65 68 75 83 84 87 91 93 94 107 114 119 127 132 133 **S** Preferred Management Corporation, Shawnee, OK
Primary Contact: Diana Taylor, Administrator
COO: Mike Easley, Vice President and Chief Operating Officer
CFO: Larry Stephens, Chief Financial Officer
CMO: Vera Luther, M.D., Chief of Staff
CIO: Margaret Moore, Director Business Office
CHR: Laura Simpson, Director Human Resources
CNO: Margie Watson, MSN, RN–B, Chief Nursing Officer
Web address: www.sabinecountyhospital.com/
**Control:** Corporation, Investor–owned, for–profit **Service:** General Medical and Surgical

**Staffed Beds:** 25 **Admissions:** 275 **Census:** 3 **Outpatient Visits:** 22810 **Births:** 0 **Total Expense ($000):** 9382 **Payroll Expense ($000):** 3209 **Personnel:** 80

### HENDERSON—Rusk County

⊠ **EAST TEXAS MEDICAL CENTER HENDERSON (450475)**, 300 Wilson Street, Zip 75652–5956; tel. 903/657–7541 **A**1 9 10 **F**3 8 11 13 15 18 28 29 30 34 35 37 40 43 45 50 57 59 64 65 75 76 79 81 85 107 108 110 111 115 119 127 129 133 135 145 146 147 148 **S** East Texas Medical Center Regional Healthcare System, Tyler, TX
Primary Contact: Mark Leitner, Administrator
CFO: Phillip A. Caron, Chief Financial Officer
CHR: William Henry, Director Human Resources
CNO: Miguel Casas, R.N., Chief Clinical Officer
Web address: www.etmc.org/etmchenderson/
**Control:** Other not–for–profit (including NFP Corporation) **Service:** General Medical and Surgical

**Staffed Beds:** 41 **Admissions:** 1498 **Census:** 12 **Outpatient Visits:** 47040 **Births:** 240 **Total Expense ($000):** 27990 **Payroll Expense ($000):** 8038 **Personnel:** 148

### HENRIETTA—Clay County

**CLAY COUNTY MEMORIAL HOSPITAL (451362)**, 310 West South Street, Zip 76365–3346; tel. 940/538–5621 **A**9 10 18 **F**7 8 11 28 34 35 40 50 53 57 62 68 80 81 90 93 107 111 119 130 132 133 148 **P**5
Primary Contact: Jeff Huskey, Chief Executive Officer and Administrator
COO: Michael Clark, Director Operations
CFO: Debra Haehn, Chief Financial Officer
CMO: Mitchell Wolfe, M.D., Chief of Staff
CIO: Larry Evangelista, Supervisor Information Technology
CHR: Linda Burleson, Administrative Secretary
Web address: www.ccmhospital.com
**Control:** County–Government, nonfederal **Service:** General Medical and Surgical

**Staffed Beds:** 25 **Admissions:** 197 **Census:** 3 **Outpatient Visits:** 8296 **Births:** 0 **Total Expense ($000):** 5101 **Payroll Expense ($000):** 2602 **Personnel:** 75

### HEREFORD—Deaf Smith County

**HEREFORD REGIONAL MEDICAL CENTER (450155)**, 540 West 15th Street, Zip 79045–2820; tel. 806/364–2141 **A**9 10 **F**3 7 11 13 15 29 35 40 43 50 57 59 62 65 70 76 77 81 85 93 107 111 114 119 127 130 133 147 **P**5
Primary Contact: Nathan A. Flood, Chief Executive Officer
COO: Meri Killingsworth, Chief Operating Officer
CFO: Greg Reinart, Chief Financial Officer
CNO: Anthony T. Jerina, Chief Nursing Officer
Web address: www.herefordregional.com
**Control:** Hospital district or authority, Government, nonfederal **Service:** General Medical and Surgical

**Staffed Beds:** 39 **Admissions:** 723 **Census:** 8 **Outpatient Visits:** 64857 **Births:** 295 **Total Expense ($000):** 23796 **Payroll Expense ($000):** 7408 **Personnel:** 192

### HILLSBORO—Hill County

⊠ **HILL REGIONAL HOSPITAL (450192)**, 101 Circle Drive, Zip 76645–2670; tel. 254/580–8500 **A**1 9 10 **F**3 13 15 17 18 19 29 34 35 40 43 45 50 57 59 64 65 68 70 75 76 77 78 79 81 82 86 87 88 89 93 107 114 118 119 133 146 147 **S** Community Health Systems, Inc., Franklin, TN
Primary Contact: Michael J. Ellis, Chief Executive Officer
CFO: Judy Culp, Chief Financial Officer
CHR: Becky Hale, Director Human Resources
Web address: www.chs.net
**Control:** Corporation, Investor–owned, for–profit **Service:** General Medical and Surgical

**Staffed Beds:** 66 **Admissions:** 1280 **Census:** 11 **Outpatient Visits:** 22241 **Births:** 239 **Total Expense ($000):** 28510 **Payroll Expense ($000):** 8012 **Personnel:** 157

### HONDO—Medina County

**MEDINA COMMUNITY HOSPITAL** See Medina Regional Hospital

**MEDINA REGIONAL HOSPITAL (451330)**, 3100 Avenue E., Zip 78861–3599; tel. 830/426–7700 **A**9 10 18 **F**3 11 13 15 29 34 35 40 43 45 50 57 59 64 76 81 87 93 97 107 111 114 119 127 133 146 **P**4
Primary Contact: Janice Simons, FACHE, Chief Executive Officer
CFO: Kevin Frosch, Chief Financial Officer
CMO: Matthew Windrow, M.D., Chief of Staff
CIO: Ken Gallegos, Director Support Services and Information Technology
CHR: Sharon Garcia, Human Resources Representative
CNO: Rebecca Hinojoza, Chief Nursing Officer
Web address: www.medinahospital.net
**Control:** Hospital district or authority, Government, nonfederal **Service:** General Medical and Surgical

**Staffed Beds:** 25 **Admissions:** 939 **Census:** 11 **Outpatient Visits:** 99659 **Births:** 166 **Total Expense ($000):** 22967 **Payroll Expense ($000):** 9093 **Personnel:** 222

**TX**

*Many Facility Codes have changed. Please refer to the AHA Guide Code Chart.* © 2015 AHA Guide

**HOUSTON—Harris County**

★ ◇ **BAYLOR ST. LUKE'S MEDICAL CENTER (450193)**, 6720 Bertner Avenue, Zip 77030–2697, Mailing Address: P.O. Box 20269, Zip 77225–0269; tel. 832/355–1000, (Data for 181 days) **A**2 3 5 8 9 10 21 **F**3 11 14 15 17 18 20 22 24 26 28 29 30 31 34 35 36 44 45 46 47 48 49 50 51 54 56 57 58 59 60 61 64 65 66 68 70 71 74 75 76 77 78 79 81 82 84 85 86 87 90 91 92 96 97 100 107 108 110 111 114 115 116 117 118 119 120 121 123 124 126 129 130 132 135 137 138 139 140 145 146 147 148 **P**5 6 **S** Catholic Health Initiatives, Englewood, CO
Primary Contact: Michael H. Covert, FACHE, President and Chief Executive Officer
CFO: William Brosius, Vice President and Chief Financial Officer
CIO: James Albin, Chief Information Officer
CHR: Susan Bailey–Newell, Vice President Human Resources
CNO: Karen K. Myers, MSN, Vice President and Chief Nursing Officer
Web address: www.stlukestexas.com
**Control:** Church–operated, Nongovernment, not–for profit **Service:** General Medical and Surgical

Staffed Beds: 690 Admissions: 12381 **Census:** 482 **Outpatient Visits:** 127213 Births: 0 Total Expense ($000): 395466 Payroll Expense ($000): 147039 Personnel: 3528

☐ **BEHAVIORAL HOSPITAL OF BELLAIRE (454107)**, 5314 Dashwood Drive, Zip 77081–4603; tel. 713/600–9500 **A**1 9 10 **F**4 5 29 98 99 100 101 104 105 130 **S** Universal Health Services, Inc., King of Prussia, PA
Primary Contact: Ethan Permenter, Chief Executive Officer
Web address: www.bhbhospital.com
**Control:** Corporation, Investor–owned, for–profit **Service:** Psychiatric

Staffed Beds: 84 Admissions: 2649 **Census:** 63 **Outpatient Visits:** 1673 Births: 0 Total Expense ($000): 13925 Payroll Expense ($000): 7956 Personnel: 158

**BEN TAUB GENERAL HOSPITAL** See Harris Health System

**CAMBRIDGE HOSPITAL IN HOUSTON (454120)**, 7601 Fannin Street, Zip 77054–1905; tel. 713/795–5025 **A**9 10 **F**4 29 44 86 87 98 99 100 101 103 105 130 132 135
Primary Contact: Trey Miller, Chief Executive Officer
COO: Nona Fain, M.D., Chief Operations Officer
CHR: Missy Wagenhauser, Director Human Resources
CNO: Nona Fain, M.D., Chief Nursing Officer
Web address: www.cambridgehospitalhouston.com
**Control:** Corporation, Investor–owned, for–profit **Service:** Psychiatric

Staffed Beds: 100 Admissions: 2800 **Census:** 41 **Outpatient Visits:** 0 Births: 0 Total Expense ($000): 7692 Payroll Expense ($000): 4325 Personnel: 119

**CHILDREN'S MEMORIAL HERMANN HOSPITAL** See Memorial Hermann – Texas Medical Center

⇑ **CORNERSTONE HOSPITAL–MEDICAL CENTER OF HOUSTON (452055)**, 2001 Hermann Drive, Zip 77004; tel. 832/649–6200 **A**10 22 **F**1 3 29 31 77 85 86 87 119 130 148 **S** Cornerstone Healthcare Group, Dallas, TX
Primary Contact: Michael Higginbotham, Chief Executive Officer
Web address: www.chghospitals.com
**Control:** Partnership, Investor–owned, for–profit **Service:** Long–Term Acute Care hospital

Staffed Beds: 35 Admissions: 385 **Census:** 25 **Outpatient Visits:** 0 **Births:** 0 **Total Expense ($000):** 13920 **Payroll Expense ($000):** 5720 **Personnel:** 95

☐ **CYPRESS CREEK HOSPITAL (454108)**, 17750 Cali Drive, Zip 77090–2700; tel. 281/586–7600 **A**1 9 10 **F**4 5 29 30 64 87 98 99 100 102 104 105 130 132 **S** Universal Health Services, Inc., King of Prussia, PA
Primary Contact: Brian Brooker, Chief Executive Officer
CFO: Leslie Stuart, Chief Financial Officer
CMO: Marshall Lucas, M.D., Medical Director
CIO: James Harmon, Information Technology
CHR: Brenda Dominguez, Director Human Resources
CNO: Shazetta Richardson, Director of Nursing
Web address: www.cypresscreekhospital.com
**Control:** Corporation, Investor–owned, for–profit **Service:** Psychiatric

Staffed Beds: 96 Admissions: 3932 **Census:** 86 **Outpatient Visits:** 8428 Births: 0 Total Expense ($000): 20870 Payroll Expense ($000): 9970 Personnel: 184

⊠ **CYPRESS FAIRBANKS MEDICAL CENTER (450716)**, 10655 Steepletop Drive, Zip 77065–4297; tel. 281/890–4285 **A**1 9 10 **F**3 11 12 13 15 18 20 22 24 29 30 31 34 35 40 42 43 45 46 47 49 50 53 55 57 59 64 65 70 72 74 75 76 77 78 79 81 82 85 87 89 93 107 108 110 111 114 115 119 120 121 124 129 130 132 144 146 147 148 **P**1 8 **S** TENET Healthcare Corporation, Dallas, TX
Primary Contact: Terry J. Wheeler, Chief Executive Officer
CFO: James Wright, M.D., Chief Financial Officer
CMO: Arturo Bravo, M.D., Chief of Staff
CIO: Donna Cain, Director Information Systems Department
CHR: Linda Creswell, Director Human Resource
CNO: Lisa D. Cox, R.N., Chief Nursing Officer
Web address: www.cyfairhospital.com
**Control:** Corporation, Investor–owned, for–profit **Service:** General Medical and Surgical

Staffed Beds: 181 Admissions: 8521 **Census:** 86 **Outpatient Visits:** 121122 **Births:** 3104 **Total Expense ($000):** 131913 **Payroll Expense ($000):** 51512 **Personnel:** 755

⇑ **DOCTOR'S HOSPITAL – TIDWELL (450803)**, 510 West Tidwell Road, Zip 77091–4399; tel. 713/691–1111, (Includes DOCTORS HOSPITAL PARKWAY, 233 West Parker Road, Zip 77076–2999; tel. 281/765–2600) **A**9 10 22 **F**22 29 40 43 50 64 68 70 75 79 81 92 107 114 119 130 148
Primary Contact: Farida Moeen, M.D., Interim Administrator
COO: Farida Moeen, M.D., Chief Operating Officer
CFO: Theresa Eatherly, Chief Financial Officer
CMO: Cesar Ortega, M.D., Chief of Staff
CIO: Dell Davis, Director Information Systems
CHR: Carolyn Washington, Director of Human Resources
Web address: www.dhthou.com/
**Control:** Partnership, Investor–owned, for–profit **Service:** General Medical and Surgical

Staffed Beds: 42 Admissions: 934 **Census:** 10 **Outpatient Visits:** 13592 **Births:** 0 **Total Expense ($000):** 23334 **Payroll Expense ($000):** 9482 **Personnel:** 215

**DUBUIS HOSPITAL OF HOUSTON** See Cornerstone Hospital–Medical Center of Houston

★ △ ◇ **HARRIS HEALTH SYSTEM (450289)**, 2525 Holly Hall Street, Zip 77054–4108, Mailing Address: P.O. Box 66769, Zip 77266–6769; tel. 713/566–6403, (Includes BEN TAUB GENERAL HOSPITAL, 1504 Taub Loop, Zip 77030; tel. 713/873–2300; LYNDON B JOHNSON GENERAL HOSPITAL, 5656 Kelley, Zip 77026; tel. 713/566–5000; Jesse Lee Tucker, Administrator; QUENTIN MEASE HOSPITAL, 3601 North MacGregor, Zip 77004; tel. 713/873–3700; Jeffrey Webster, Administrator), (Total facility includes 24 beds in nursing home–type unit) **A**2 3 5 7 8 9 10 21 **F**3 5 7 13 15 17 18 20 22 24 26 29 30 31 32 34 35 39 40 41 43 45 46 49 50 51 54 55 56 57 58 59 60 61 64 65 68 70 71 72 73 74 75 76 77 78 79 81 82 84 87 89 90 91 92 93 94 97 98 99 100 101 102 103 104 107 110 111 112 114 115 118 119 120 121 124 128 129 130 132 134 135 143 144 145 146 147 148 **P**6
Primary Contact: George V. Masi, Chief Executive Officer
CFO: Michael Norby, Chief Financial Officer
CMO: Fred Sutton, M.D., Chief Medical Officer
CIO: Tim Tindle, Chief Information Officer
CHR: Diane Poirot, Vice President Human Resources
CNO: Elizabeth Cloyd, R.N., Chief Nurse Executive and Executive Vice President
Web address: www.hchdonline.com
**Control:** Hospital district or authority, Government, nonfederal **Service:** General Medical and Surgical

Staffed Beds: 789 Admissions: 35934 **Census:** 561 **Outpatient Visits:** 1828412 **Births:** 6288 **Total Expense ($000):** 1267411 **Payroll Expense ($000):** 522942 **Personnel:** 7297

◇ **HEALTHBRIDGE CHILDREN'S HOSPITAL OF HOUSTON (453309)**, 2929 Woodland Park Drive, Zip 77082–2687; tel. 281/293–7774 **A**9 10 21 **F**3 29 74 75 79 85 87 89 93 100 130 146 148 **S** Nexus Health Systems, Houston, TX
Primary Contact: Tony Bonilla, Chief Executive Officer
CMO: Robert Yetman, M.D., Medical Director
CHR: Guy Murdock, Vice President Human Resources
Web address: www.healthbridgehouston.com/
**Control:** Partnership, Investor–owned, for–profit **Service:** Children's general

Staffed Beds: 37 Admissions: 210 **Census:** 20 **Outpatient Visits:** 167 **Births:** 0 **Total Expense ($000):** 12158 **Payroll Expense ($000):** 5458 **Personnel:** 102

**TX**

✠ **HEALTHSOUTH REHABILITATION HOSPITAL OF CYPRESS (673050)**, 13031 Wortham Center Drive, Zip 77065–5662; tel. 832/280–2500 **A**1 10 **F**3 29 34 57 60 62 64 68 75 77 87 90 91 93 94 95 96 100 130 132 146 148 **S** HEALTHSOUTH Corporation, Birmingham, AL
Primary Contact: Sheila A. Bollier, Chief Executive Officer
CFO: Melissa Haddox, Controller
CMO: Ignazio LaChina, M.D., Medical Director
CHR: Keisha Pittman, Director Human Resources
CNO: Roshonda Henry, Chief Nursing Officer
Web address: www.healthsouthcypress.com
**Control:** Corporation, Investor–owned, for–profit **Service:** Rehabilitation

**Staffed Beds:** 60 **Admissions:** 1153 **Census:** 39 **Outpatient Visits:** 3654 **Births:** 0 **Total Expense ($000):** 15781 **Payroll Expense ($000):** 8186 **Personnel:** 162

◇ **HOPEBRIDGE HOSPITAL (670072)**, 5556 Gasmer Drive, Zip 77035–4502; tel. 713/422–2625 **A**9 10 21 **F**3 29 35 38 64 68 98 99 100 101 103 104 105 130
Primary Contact: Tim C. Simmons, Chief Executive Officer
**Control:** Corporation, Investor–owned, for–profit **Service:** Psychiatric

**Staffed Beds:** 85 **Admissions:** 2736 **Census:** 53 **Outpatient Visits:** 43596 **Births:** 0 **Total Expense ($000):** 19022 **Payroll Expense ($000):** 9764 **Personnel:** 167

☐ **HOUSTON HOSPITAL FOR SPECIALIZED SURGERY (450797)**, 5445 La Branch Street, Zip 77004–6835; tel. 713/528–6800 **A**1 3 9 10 **F**3 8 40 45 46 47 48 49 79 81 82
Primary Contact: Gary Williams, Administrator
CFO: Deborah Jones, Controller
Web address: www.scasurgery.com
**Control:** Partnership, Investor–owned, for–profit **Service:** General Medical and Surgical

**Staffed Beds:** 7 **Admissions:** 131 **Census:** 1 **Outpatient Visits:** 4294 **Births:** 0 **Total Expense ($000):** 10514 **Payroll Expense ($000):** 3856 **Personnel:** 55

★ △ ◇ **HOUSTON METHODIST HOSPITAL (450358)**, 6565 Fannin Street, Zip 77030–2707; tel. 713/790–3311, (Total facility includes 25 beds in nursing home–type unit) **A**2 3 5 7 8 9 10 21 **F**3 6 8 9 11 12 13 14 15 16 20 22 24 26 28 29 30 31 34 35 36 37 38 39 40 41 42 44 45 46 47 48 49 50 51 53 54 55 56 57 58 59 60 61 64 65 66 68 70 72 73 74 75 76 77 78 79 81 82 84 85 86 87 90 91 92 93 96 97 98 100 101 103 107 108 110 111 114 115 116 117 118 119 120 121 123 124 126 128 129 130 131 132 135 136 137 138 139 140 141 142 145 146 147 148 **P**6 **S** Houston Methodist, Houston, TX
Primary Contact: Roberta Schwartz, Executive Vice President
CMO: Dirk Sostman, M.D., Executive Vice President, Chief Medical Officer and Chief Academic Officer
CIO: Timothy L. Thompson, Sr., Senior Vice President and Chief Information Officer
CHR: Lauren P. Rykert, Senior Vice President
Web address: www.methodisthealth.com
**Control:** Other not–for–profit (including NFP Corporation) **Service:** General Medical and Surgical

**Staffed Beds:** 856 **Admissions:** 36680 **Census:** 662 **Outpatient Visits:** 377765 **Births:** 1102 **Total Expense ($000):** 1385119 **Payroll Expense ($000):** 376675 **Personnel:** 7472

★ ◇ **HOUSTON METHODIST WEST HOSPITAL (670077)**, 18500 Katy Freeway, Zip 77094–1110; tel. 832/522–1000 **A**3 9 10 21 **F**3 12 13 15 18 20 22 24 26 28 29 30 31 34 35 36 40 45 49 50 51 53 57 59 61 64 70 73 74 75 76 77 78 79 81 82 85 87 93 107 108 109 110 111 114 115 119 120 121 123 124 126 130 131 132 135 146 147 **P**1 **S** Houston Methodist, Houston, TX
Primary Contact: Wayne M. Voss, Chief Executive Officer
COO: Peyton Elliott, Vice President Operations
CNO: Victoria Brownewell, Chief Nursing Officer
Web address: www.methodisthealth.com
**Control:** Other not–for–profit (including NFP Corporation) **Service:** General Medical and Surgical

**Staffed Beds:** 176 **Admissions:** 10315 **Census:** 105 **Outpatient Visits:** 106280 **Births:** 2692 **Total Expense ($000):** 184375 **Payroll Expense ($000):** 66253 **Personnel:** 1142

★ ◇ **HOUSTON METHODIST WILLOWBROOK HOSPITAL (450844)**, 18220 Tomball Parkway, Zip 77070–4347; tel. 281/477–1000 **A**3 9 10 21 **F**3 8 12 13 15 17 18 20 22 24 26 28 29 30 31 34 35 36 37 40 44 45 49 53 57 59 64 65 67 70 72 73 74 75 76 77 78 79 81 85 86 87 93 97 102 107 108 110 111 112 115 119 120 121 123 126 130 131 132 135 146 147 **S** Houston Methodist, Houston, TX
Primary Contact: Debbie Sakin, PhD, Interim Chief Executive Officer
CHR: Sherene Thompson, Director Human Resources
Web address: www.methodisthealth.com
**Control:** Other not–for–profit (including NFP Corporation) **Service:** General Medical and Surgical

**Staffed Beds:** 261 **Admissions:** 15274 **Census:** 172 **Outpatient Visits:** 146626 **Births:** 3349 **Total Expense ($000):** 254529 **Payroll Expense ($000):** 90454 **Personnel:** 1471

✠ **HOUSTON NORTHWEST MEDICAL CENTER (450638)**, 710 FM 1960 Road West, Zip 77090–3402; tel. 281/440–1000 **A**1 2 3 5 9 10 **F**3 11 12 13 15 18 20 22 24 26 28 29 30 31 34 35 40 43 45 46 49 50 57 59 64 65 70 72 74 75 76 77 78 79 81 82 84 85 86 87 89 91 92 93 96 102 107 108 109 110 111 114 115 117 118 119 126 129 130 132 135 144 145 146 147 148 **S** TENET Healthcare Corporation, Dallas, TX
Primary Contact: Timothy Puthoff, Chief Executive Officer
COO: Juan Fresquez, Chief Operating Officer
CFO: Bryan Forry, Chief Financial Officer
CIO: Ed Roberson, Director Information Systems
CHR: Melanie R. Webb, Director Human Resources
CNO: Cindy Henning, R.N., Chief Nursing Officer
Web address: www.hnmc.com
**Control:** Partnership, Investor–owned, for–profit **Service:** General Medical and Surgical

**Staffed Beds:** 339 **Admissions:** 16108 **Census:** 185 **Outpatient Visits:** 145930 **Births:** 4408 **Total Expense ($000):** 298354 **Payroll Expense ($000):** 85230 **Personnel:** 1226

☐ **INTRACARE NORTH HOSPITAL (454083)**, 1120 Cypress Station Drive, Zip 77090–3031; tel. 281/893–7200 **A**1 9 10 **F**5 98 99 100 101 103 104 105
Primary Contact: Terry Scovill, Chief Executive Officer
CFO: Fred Chan, Chief Financial Officer
CMO: Javier Ruiz, M.D., Medical Director
Web address: www.intracare.org
**Control:** Other not–for–profit (including NFP Corporation) **Service:** Psychiatric

**Staffed Beds:** 86 **Admissions:** 2873 **Census:** 60 **Outpatient Visits:** 61350 **Births:** 0 **Total Expense ($000):** 19546 **Payroll Expense ($000):** 8644 **Personnel:** 259

✠ **KINDRED HOSPITAL–HOUSTON (452023)**, 6441 Main Street, Zip 77030–1596; tel. 713/790–0500 **A**1 3 5 9 10 **F**1 3 29 30 70 75 77 85 107 130 148 **S** Kindred Healthcare, Louisville, KY
Primary Contact: Robert Stein, Chief Executive Officer
CFO: Sara Langlitz, Controller
Web address: www.khhouston.com/
**Control:** Corporation, Investor–owned, for–profit **Service:** Long–Term Acute Care hospital

**Staffed Beds:** 105 **Admissions:** 1030 **Census:** 86 **Outpatient Visits:** 0 **Births:** 0 **Total Expense ($000):** 42536 **Payroll Expense ($000):** 19465 **Personnel:** 250

✠ **KINDRED HOSPITAL–HOUSTON NORTHWEST (452039)**, 11297 Fallbrook Drive, Zip 77065–4292; tel. 281/897–8114 **A**1 9 10 **F**1 3 29 49 57 64 70 77 85 87 107 114 130 148 **P**5 **S** Kindred Healthcare, Louisville, KY
Primary Contact: Larkin Virden, Chief Executive Officer
Web address: www.khhoustonnw.com/
**Control:** Corporation, Investor–owned, for–profit **Service:** Long–Term Acute Care hospital

**Staffed Beds:** 84 **Admissions:** 660 **Census:** 46 **Outpatient Visits:** 326 **Births:** 0 **Total Expense ($000):** 29270 **Payroll Expense ($000):** 10440 **Personnel:** 148

**LYNDON B JOHNSON GENERAL HOSPITAL** See Harris Health System

✠ **MEMORIAL HERMANN – TEXAS MEDICAL CENTER (450068)**, 6411 Fannin Street, Zip 77030–1501; tel. 713/704–4000, (Includes CHILDREN'S MEMORIAL HERMANN HOSPITAL, 6411 Fannin, Zip 77030; tel. 713/704–5437), (Total facility includes 8 beds in nursing home–type unit) **A**1 2 3 5 8 9 10 **F**3 7 12 13 15 16 17 18 19 20 21 22 23 24 25 26 27 28 29 30 31 32 34 35 36 37 40 41 43 44 45 46 47 48 49 50 51 55 56 57 58 59 60 61 64 68 70 72 73 74 75 76 77 78 79 81 82 84 85 86 87 88 89 90 91 92 93 96 97 100 102 107 108 109 110 111 113 114 115 116 118 119 120 121 123 124 126 128 129 130 131 132 135 137 138 139 141 142 144 146 147 148 **P**1 5 6 **S** Memorial Hermann Healthcare System, Houston, TX
Primary Contact: Craig Cordola, Chief Executive Officer
COO: Tom Flanagan, Chief Operating Officer
CFO: William Pack, Chief Financial Officer
CMO: Jeffrey Katz, M.D., Chief Medical Officer
CIO: David Bradshaw, Chief Information Officer
CHR: Vivian Kardow, Chief Human Resources Officer
Web address: www.mhhs.org
**Control:** Other not–for–profit (including NFP Corporation) **Service:** General Medical and Surgical

**Staffed Beds:** 877 **Admissions:** 35888 **Census:** 660 **Outpatient Visits:** 202781 **Births:** 4742 **Total Expense ($000):** 1143366 **Payroll Expense ($000):** 345586 **Personnel:** 4559

*Many Facility Codes have changed. Please refer to the AHA Guide Code Chart.* © 2015 AHA Guide

✠ **MEMORIAL HERMANN MEMORIAL CITY MEDICAL CENTER (450610)**, 921 Gessner Road, Zip 77024–2501; tel. 713/242–3000 **A**1 2 3 5 9 10 **F**3 12 13 15 18 20 22 24 26 28 29 30 31 34 35 37 40 41 43 45 46 49 51 56 57 59 60 65 70 72 74 75 76 77 78 79 80 81 82 84 85 87 89 107 108 110 111 114 115 117 118 119 120 121 123 124 126 129 130 131 132 135 146 147 148 **P**1 5 6 **S** Memorial Hermann Healthcare System, Houston, TX
Primary Contact: Paul O'Sullivan, Chief Executive Officer
COO: Allen Tseng, Chief Operations Officer
CFO: Lisa Kendler, Chief Financial Officer
CMO: Harold Gottlieb, M.D., Chief Medical Officer
CIO: David Bradshaw, Chief Information, Planning and Marketing Officer
CHR: Suzanne S. Meier, System Director, Compensation and Human Resources Technology
CNO: Dan Kelly, R.N., Chief Nursing Officer
Web address: www.memorialhermann.org
**Control:** Other not–for–profit (including NFP Corporation) **Service:** General Medical and Surgical

**Staffed Beds:** 383 **Admissions:** 20360 **Census:** 238 **Outpatient Visits:** 200051 **Births:** 3337 **Total Expense ($000):** 398704 **Payroll Expense ($000):** 108597 **Personnel:** 1494

✠ **MEMORIAL HERMANN NORTHWEST HOSPITAL (450184)**, 1635 North Loop West, Zip 77008–1532; tel. 713/867–3380, (Includes MEMORIAL HERMANN SOUTHEAST HOSPITAL, 11800 Astoria Boulevard, Zip 77089–6041; tel. 281/929–6100; Kyle Price, Interim Chief Executive Officer; MEMORIAL HERMANN SOUTHWEST HOSPITAL, 7600 Beechnut, Zip 77074–1850; tel. 713/456–5000; Gary Kerr, Chief Executive Officer; MEMORIAL HERMANN THE WOODLANDS HOSPITAL, 9250 Pinecroft Drive, The Woodlands, Zip 77380–3225; tel. 281/364–2300) **A**1 2 3 5 9 10 **F**3 8 9 11 12 13 15 17 18 20 22 24 26 28 29 30 31 34 35 37 40 41 42 43 44 45 46 47 48 49 50 51 53 54 55 56 57 58 59 60 61 62 63 64 65 68 69 70 72 73 74 75 76 77 78 79 80 81 82 83 84 85 86 87 89 90 91 92 93 94 96 97 98 100 101 102 103 107 108 109 110 111 114 115 116 117 118 119 120 121 123 126 129 130 131 132 135 143 146 147 148 **P**1 5 6 **S** Memorial Hermann Healthcare System, Houston, TX
Primary Contact: Susan Jadlowski, MSN, R.N., Chief Executive Officer
COO: Wesley Tidwell, Chief Operating Officer
CFO: James R. Shallock, Chief Financial Officer
CMO: Maurice Leibman, M.D., Chief Medical Officer
CIO: David Bradshaw, Chief Information Officer
CNO: Melody Ford Dickerson, Chief Nursing Officer
Web address: www.mhbh.org
**Control:** Other not–for–profit (including NFP Corporation) **Service:** General Medical and Surgical

**Staffed Beds:** 1217 **Admissions:** 59340 **Census:** 745 **Outpatient Visits:** 537347 **Births:** 12096 **Total Expense ($000):** 1033553 **Payroll Expense ($000):** 355573 **Personnel:** 4765

**MEMORIAL HERMANN SOUTHEAST HOSPITAL** See Memorial Hermann Northwest Hospital

**MEMORIAL HERMANN SOUTHWEST HOSPITAL** See Memorial Hermann Northwest Hospital

☐ **MENNINGER CLINIC**, 12301 Main Street, Zip 77035–6207; tel. 713/275–5000 **A**1 3 5 **F**30 35 98 99 101 104 106 130 132
Primary Contact: C. Edward Coffey, M.D., President
COO: Shawna Morris, Senior Vice President Operations and Chief Operating Officer
CMO: John M. Oldham, M.D., Senior Vice President and Chief of Staff
CHR: Shawna Morris, Senior Vice President Operations and Chief Operating Officer
Web address: www.menningerclinic.com
**Control:** Other not–for–profit (including NFP Corporation) **Service:** Psychiatric

**Staffed Beds:** 102 **Admissions:** 813 **Census:** 88 **Outpatient Visits:** 1967 **Births:** 0 **Total Expense ($000):** 57227 **Payroll Expense ($000):** 24250 **Personnel:** 398

**METHODIST WEST HOUSTON HOSPITAL** See Houston Methodist West Hospital
**METHODIST WILLOWBROOK HOSPITAL** See Houston Methodist Willowbrook Hospital

✠ △ **MICHAEL E. DEBAKEY VETERANS AFFAIRS MEDICAL CENTER**, 2002 Holcombe Boulevard, Zip 77030–4298; tel. 713/791–1414, (Nonreporting) **A**1 2 3 5 7 9 **S** Department of Veterans Affairs, Washington, DC
Primary Contact: Adam C. Walmus, Director
COO: Christopher Sandles, Associate Director
CFO: Alisa Cooper, Manager Financial Resources
CMO: Jagadeesh S. Kalavar, M.D., Chief of Staff
CIO: Kevin Lenamond, Information Management Service Line Executive
CHR: Mark Muhammad, Manager Human Resources
CNO: Kelly Ann Irving, MSN, RN–B, Associate Director for Patient Care Services
Web address: www.houston.va.gov
**Control:** Veterans Affairs, Government, federal **Service:** General Medical and Surgical

**Staffed Beds:** 479

✠ **PARK PLAZA HOSPITAL (450659)**, 1313 Hermann Drive, Zip 77004–7092; tel. 713/527–5000 **A**1 2 3 9 10 **F**3 12 15 18 20 22 29 31 34 35 40 45 49 50 56 57 59 70 74 78 79 81 85 92 107 108 110 111 114 115 118 119 120 121 123 129 130 132 146 147 148 **S** TENET Healthcare Corporation, Dallas, TX
Primary Contact: Steven D. Patonai, Interim Chief Executive Officer
COO: Mary Jo Goodman, Chief Operating Officer
CMO: Robert Brown, M.D., Chief Medical Officer
CIO: Terry Janis, Assistant Vice President
CHR: Melanie R. Webb, Chief Human Resources Officer
CNO: Martha M. Smith, R.N., Chief Nursing Officer
Web address: www.parkplazahospital.com
**Control:** Partnership, Investor–owned, for–profit **Service:** General Medical and Surgical

**Staffed Beds:** 157 **Admissions:** 3669 **Census:** 53 **Outpatient Visits:** 33198 **Births:** 0 **Total Expense ($000):** 81099 **Payroll Expense ($000):** 27861 **Personnel:** 470

✠ **PLAZA SPECIALTY HOSPITAL (452046)**, 1300 Binz, Zip 77004–7016; tel. 713/285–1000 **A**1 9 10 **F**1 3 70 85 87 **P**8 **S** TENET Healthcare Corporation, Dallas, TX
Primary Contact: Richard Pletz, Chief Executive Officer
CFO: Charles R. Handley, Chief Financial Officer
CMO: Wasae S. Tabibi, M.D., President Medical Staff
CIO: Steve Peacock, Assistant Vice President
Web address: www.plazaspecialtyhospital.com
**Control:** Corporation, Investor–owned, for–profit **Service:** Long–Term Acute Care hospital

**Staffed Beds:** 39 **Admissions:** 340 **Census:** 29 **Outpatient Visits:** 0 **Births:** 0 **Total Expense ($000):** 22151 **Payroll Expense ($000):** 6087 **Personnel:** 77

☐ **PROMISE HOSPITAL OF HOUSTON (452043)**, 6160 South Loop East, Zip 77087–1010; tel. 713/640–2400, (Data for 289 days) **A**1 9 10 **F**1 3 29 75 77 85 87 130 148 **S** Promise Healthcare, Boca Raton, FL
Primary Contact: Tom Omondi, Interim Chief Executive Officer
CFO: Betty Priestley, Manager Business Office
CMO: Alfred Louis, M.D., Chief Medical Staff
CHR: Laura Garza, Director Human Resources
Web address: www.promise–houston.com
**Control:** Corporation, Investor–owned, for–profit **Service:** Long–Term Acute Care hospital

**Staffed Beds:** 35 **Admissions:** 165 **Census:** 14 **Outpatient Visits:** 0 **Births:** 0 **Total Expense ($000):** 7563 **Payroll Expense ($000):** 3027 **Personnel:** 57

**QUENTIN MEASE HOSPITAL** See Harris Health System

☐ **RELIANT NORTHWEST HOUSTON (673052)**, 20180 Chasewood Park Drive, Zip 77070–1436; tel. 281/205–5100 **A**1 9 10 **F**3 29 65 90 96 130 148
Primary Contact: Jeff Crawford, Chief Executive Officer
CNO: Stanley F. Kiebzak, R.N., Chief Nursing Officer
Web address: www.reliantnwhouston.com
**Control:** Partnership, Investor–owned, for–profit **Service:** Rehabilitation

**Staffed Beds:** 60 **Admissions:** 1002 **Census:** 30 **Outpatient Visits:** 5889 **Births:** 0 **Total Expense ($000):** 13466 **Payroll Expense ($000):** 5806 **Personnel:** 103

★ **SELECT SPECIALTY HOSPITAL–HOUSTON WEST (452049)**, 9430 Old Katy Road, Zip 77055; tel. 713/984–2273, (Includes SELECT SPECIALTY HOSPITAL–HOUSTON MEDICAL CENTER, 2130 West Holcombe, Zip 77030–1502; tel. 713/218–2300; Michael A. Anaya, FACHE, Chief Executive Officer), (Nonreporting) **S** Select Medical Corporation, Mechanicsburg, PA
Primary Contact: Mitali Paul, Chief Executive Officer
Web address: www.selectmedicalcorp.com
**Control:** Corporation, Investor–owned, for–profit **Service:** Long–Term Acute Care hospital

**Staffed Beds:** 72

**TX**

□ **SHRINERS HOSPITALS FOR CHILDREN–HOUSTON (453312)**, 6977 Main Street, Zip 77030–3701; tel. 713/797–1616 **A**1 3 5 10 **F**3 4 29 30 35 50 59 64 68 74 75 77 79 81 86 87 89 93 94 96 130 131 132 134 143 146 148 **P**6 **S** Shriners Hospitals for Children, Tampa, FL
Primary Contact: David A. Ferrell, Regional Administrator
COO: Cathy Moniaci, Chief Operating Officer
CFO: Lona Pope, Director Fiscal Services
CMO: Douglas A. Barnes, M.D., Chief of Staff
CHR: Lynn Clements, Director Human Resources
Web address: www.shrinershospitalsforchildren.org/Hospitals/Locations/Houston.aspx
**Control:** Other not–for–profit (including NFP Corporation) **Service:** Children's orthopedic

**Staffed Beds:** 40 **Admissions:** 535 **Census:** 11 **Outpatient Visits:** 10633 **Births:** 0 **Total Expense ($000):** 24973 **Payroll Expense ($000):** 13286 **Personnel:** 163

◇ **ST. JOSEPH MEDICAL CENTER (450035)**, 1401 St. Joseph Parkway, Zip 77002–8301; tel. 713/757–1000, (Total facility includes 18 beds in nursing home–type unit) **A**3 5 9 10 21 **F**3 11 12 13 15 18 20 22 24 26 29 30 31 34 35 40 42 43 47 49 50 51 53 55 57 58 59 60 64 68 70 72 74 75 76 77 78 79 81 82 84 85 86 87 90 93 94 97 98 101 102 103 104 105 107 108 110 111 114 115 116 117 118 119 121 123 124 126 128 129 130 131 132 135 143 144 146 147 148 **P**8 **S** IASIS Healthcare, Franklin, TN
Primary Contact: Mark L. Bernard, Chief Executive Officer
COO: Laura Fortin, R.N., Chief Operating Officer
CIO: Robin Brown, Chief Information Officer and Compliance Officer
CHR: Kris Clatanoff, Director Human Resources
Web address: www.sjmctx.com
**Control:** Partnership, Investor–owned, for–profit **Service:** General Medical and Surgical

**Staffed Beds:** 374 **Admissions:** 15786 **Census:** 212 **Outpatient Visits:** 113061 **Births:** 5078 **Total Expense ($000):** 194066 **Payroll Expense ($000):** 88754 **Personnel:** 1451

★ ◇ **ST. LUKE'S HOSPITAL – THE VINTAGE HOSPITAL (670075)**, 20171 Chasewood Park Drive, Zip 77070–1437; tel. 832/534–5000, (Data for 181 days) **A**9 10 21 **F**3 11 12 13 15 18 20 22 24 26 29 30 34 35 40 45 49 50 57 59 60 64 68 70 72 75 76 77 79 81 82 85 87 107 108 110 111 114 115 118 119 130 146 147 **P**5 **S** Catholic Health Initiatives, Englewood, CO
Primary Contact: Norman F. Stephens, President
Web address: www.stlukesvintage.com/
**Control:** Church–operated, Nongovernment, not–for profit **Service:** General Medical and Surgical

**Staffed Beds:** 78 **Admissions:** 1559 **Census:** 41 **Outpatient Visits:** 12522 **Births:** 207 **Total Expense ($000):** 37635 **Payroll Expense ($000):** 11153 **Personnel:** 430

□ **TEXAS CHILDREN'S HOSPITAL (453304)**, 6621 Fannin Street, Zip 77030–2399, Mailing Address: Box 300630, Zip 77230–0630; tel. 832/824–1000, (Includes TEXAS CHILDREN'S HOSPITAL WEST CAMPUS, 18200 Katy Freeway, Zip 77094–1285; tel. 832/227–1000) **A**1 3 5 8 9 10 **F**3 7 11 12 13 17 19 21 23 25 29 30 31 32 34 35 38 39 40 41 43 48 49 50 52 55 57 58 59 60 61 64 65 68 71 72 73 74 75 76 77 78 79 80 81 84 85 86 87 88 89 90 92 93 94 95 96 97 99 100 101 104 107 108 111 114 115 116 117 118 119 129 130 131 132 134 136 137 138 139 140 143 144 146 147 148
Primary Contact: Mark A. Wallace, President and Chief Executive Officer
CFO: Benjamin B. Melson, CPA, Executive Vice President and Chief Financial Officer
CMO: Mark W. Kline, M.D., Physician in Chief
CHR: Linda W. Aldred, Senior Vice President
Web address: www.texaschildrenshospital.org
**Control:** Other not–for–profit (including NFP Corporation) **Service:** Children's general

**Staffed Beds:** 629 **Admissions:** 32446 **Census:** 518 **Outpatient Visits:** 1043779 **Births:** 5588 **Total Expense ($000):** 1442946 **Payroll Expense ($000):** 551176 **Personnel:** 7085

⊠ **TEXAS ORTHOPEDIC HOSPITAL (450804)**, 7401 South Main Street, Zip 77030–4509; tel. 713/799–8600 **A**1 3 5 9 10 **F**3 29 30 40 59 64 68 70 79 81 82 85 86 87 93 94 97 107 111 115 119 146 **S** HCA, Nashville, TN
Primary Contact: Trent Lind, Chief Executive Officer
CFO: Virgil Winslow, Chief Financial Officer
CMO: Gregory Stocks, M.D., Chief of Staff
CNO: Troy Sarver, R.N., Chief Nursing Officer
Web address: www.texasorthopedic.com
**Control:** Partnership, Investor–owned, for–profit **Service:** Orthopedic

**Staffed Beds:** 49 **Admissions:** 3523 **Census:** 24 **Outpatient Visits:** 34556 **Births:** 0 **Total Expense ($000):** 77126 **Payroll Expense ($000):** 23722 **Personnel:** 371

**THE METHODIST HOSPITAL** See Houston Methodist Hospital

⊠ △ **TIRR MEMORIAL HERMANN (453025)**, 1333 Moursund Street, Zip 77030–3405; tel. 713/799–5000 **A**1 3 5 7 9 10 **F**11 29 30 34 35 44 50 52 54 58 59 60 64 68 74 75 77 79 82 86 87 90 91 93 95 96 97 100 104 107 114 119 129 130 131 132 146 148 **P**1 5 6 **S** Memorial Hermann Healthcare System, Houston, TX
Primary Contact: Carl E. Josehart, Chief Executive Officer
COO: Mary Ann Euliarte, R.N., Chief Operating Officer and Chief Nursing Officer
CFO: Wayne Gordon, Chief Financial Officer
CMO: Gerard E. Francisco, M.D., Chief Medical Officer
CIO: Gina Tripp, Director Information Systems
CHR: Vivian Kardow, Chief Human Resources Officer
CNO: Mary Ann Euliarte, R.N., Chief Operating Officer and Chief Nursing Officer
Web address: www.memorialhermann.org/locations/tirr.html
**Control:** Other not–for–profit (including NFP Corporation) **Service:** Rehabilitation

**Staffed Beds:** 134 **Admissions:** 1184 **Census:** 83 **Outpatient Visits:** 20767 **Births:** 0 **Total Expense ($000):** 88239 **Payroll Expense ($000):** 42372 **Personnel:** 611

□ **TOPS SURGICAL SPECIALTY HOSPITAL (450774)**, 17080 Red Oak Drive, Zip 77090–2602; tel. 281/539–2900 **A**1 9 10 **F**3 15 29 40 45 51 79 81 82 107 119 **S** United Surgical Partners International, Addison, TX
Primary Contact: Daniel Smith, Interim Chief Executive Officer
CFO: Daniel Smith, Chief Financial Officer
CMO: Thomas Barton, M.D., Medical Director
CIO: Maud Jones, Manager Medical Records
CHR: Ashley Monzingo, Human Resources, Accounts Payable and Payroll
CNO: Andrea Wappelhorst, Chief Nursing Officer
Web address: www.tops–hospital.com
**Control:** Partnership, Investor–owned, for–profit **Service:** General Medical and Surgical

**Staffed Beds:** 15 **Admissions:** 784 **Census:** 5 **Outpatient Visits:** 43805 **Births:** 0 **Total Expense ($000):** 32968 **Payroll Expense ($000):** 8620 **Personnel:** 169

**TRIUMPH HOSPITAL NORTHWEST** See Kindred Hospital Spring

□ ⇑ **UNIVERSITY GENERAL HOSPITAL (670019)**, 7501 Fannin Street, Zip 77054–1938; tel. 713/375–7000 **A**1 9 10 **F**3 8 12 18 20 22 29 31 40 45 47 49 54 57 59 67 70 75 79 81 82 85 86 107 108 111 114 119 130 132 148
Primary Contact: Harmony Vice, Chief Executive Officer
Web address: www.ughospital.com
**Control:** Partnership, Investor–owned, for–profit **Service:** General Medical and Surgical

**Staffed Beds:** 69 **Admissions:** 2884 **Census:** 34 **Outpatient Visits:** 11488 **Births:** 0 **Total Expense ($000):** 82109 **Payroll Expense ($000):** 24717 **Personnel:** 510

★ **UNIVERSITY OF TEXAS HARRIS COUNTY PSYCHIATRIC CENTER (454076)**, 2800 South MacGregor Way, Zip 77021–1000, Mailing Address: P.O. Box 20249, Zip 77225–0249; tel. 713/741–7870 **A**5 9 10 **F**29 30 34 35 57 58 68 75 86 87 98 99 100 101 103 106 130 146 **P**6 **S** University of Texas System, Austin, TX
Primary Contact: Jair C. Soares, M.D., Executive Director
COO: Stephen Glazier, Chief Operating Officer
CFO: Lois K. Pierson, Chief Financial Officer
CMO: R. Andrew Harper, M.D., Medical Director
CHR: Jill Strutton, Director Personnel Systems
CNO: Margaret Pung, R.N., Chief Nursing Officer
Web address: www.hcpc.uth.tmc.edu
**Control:** State–Government, nonfederal **Service:** Psychiatric

**Staffed Beds:** 204 **Admissions:** 8431 **Census:** 184 **Outpatient Visits:** 0 **Births:** 0 **Total Expense ($000):** 47552 **Payroll Expense ($000):** 30278 **Personnel:** 495

⊠ **UNIVERSITY OF TEXAS M.D. ANDERSON CANCER CENTER (450076)**, 1515 Holcombe Boulevard, Box 91, Zip 77030–4000; tel. 713/792–2121 **A**1 2 3 5 8 9 10 **F**3 8 11 14 15 18 20 22 26 29 30 31 32 34 35 36 37 38 39 40 41 44 45 46 47 49 50 54 55 57 58 59 63 64 66 68 70 71 74 75 77 78 79 80 81 82 83 84 85 86 87 88 89 92 93 94 96 97 99 100 101 102 104 107 108 110 111 112 114 115 117 118 119 120 121 122 123 124 126 129 130 132 134 135 136 141 145 146 147 148 **P**6 **S** University of Texas System, Austin, TX
Primary Contact: Ronald A. DePinho, M.D., President
CMO: Thomas Buchholz, M.D., Physician–in–Chief and Executive Vice President
CIO: Chris Belmont, Chief Information Officer and Vice President
CHR: Shibu Varghese, Vice President Human Resources
CNO: Barbara L. Summers, Ph.D., Vice President Nursing Practice and Chief Nursing Officer
Web address: www.mdanderson.org
**Control:** State–Government, nonfederal **Service:** Cancer

**Staffed Beds:** 654 **Admissions:** 27761 **Census:** 555 **Outpatient Visits:** 1374160 **Births:** 0 **Total Expense ($000):** 3813352 **Payroll Expense ($000):** 1670023 **Personnel:** 19498

**TX**

☐ **VICTORY MEDICAL CENTER HOUSTON**, 2001 Hermann Drive,
Zip 77004–7643; tel. 713/285–5500 **A**1 **F**3 12 29 40 45 68 81 85 86 107
114 **S** Victory Healthcare, The Woodlands, TX
Primary Contact: Nicholas Crafts, Chief Executive Officer
Web address: www.victory–healthcare.com
**Control:** Corporation, Investor–owned, for–profit **Service:** Surgical

> **Staffed Beds: 25 Admissions: 458 Census: 3 Outpatient Visits: 1586
> Births: 0 Total Expense ($000): 27419 Payroll Expense ($000): 5164
> Personnel: 60**

☐ **VICTORY SURGICAL HOSPITAL EAST HOUSTON**, 12950 East Freeway,
Zip 77015–5710; tel. 713/330–3887 **A**1 **F**3 12 15 29 40 68 81 85 107 114
119 **S** Victory Healthcare, The Woodlands, TX
Primary Contact: Steve Winnett, Chief Executive Officer
CFO: Carol Files, Chief Financial Officer
CMO: Ian Reynolds, Chief Medical Officer
CIO: Yobi Kasper, Chief Information Officer
CHR: Gabby Myers, Human Resources Director
CNO: David Gonzalez, Chief Clinical Officer
Web address: www.victory–healthcare.com/easthouston
**Control:** Corporation, Investor–owned, for–profit **Service:** Surgical

> **Staffed Beds: 4 Admissions: 58 Census: 1 Outpatient Visits: 645 Births: 0
> Total Expense ($000): 10398 Payroll Expense ($000): 2660 Personnel: 34**

⊠ **WEST HOUSTON MEDICAL CENTER (450644)**, 12141 Richmond Avenue,
Zip 77082–2499; tel. 281/558–3444 **A**1 9 10 **F**3 11 12 13 15 18 20 22 24
26 28 29 30 31 39 40 42 45 46 47 48 49 50 51 56 57 59 60 64 70 73 74
75 76 77 78 79 80 81 82 85 90 93 96 98 102 103 107 110 111 115 116
117 118 119 121 124 129 130 132 143 145 146 147 148 **S** HCA, Nashville, TN
Primary Contact: Todd Caliva, Chief Executive Officer
CFO: Stanley K. Nord, Chief Financial Officer
CMO: Magdy Rizk, M.D., Chief of Staff
CIO: Sergio Almeida, Director Information Systems
CHR: Carol Melville, Director Human Resources
Web address: www.westhoustonmedical.com
**Control:** Partnership, Investor–owned, for–profit **Service:** General Medical and
Surgical

> **Staffed Beds: 238 Admissions: 12866 Census: 191 Outpatient Visits:
> 104518 Births: 2911 Total Expense ($000): 180708 Payroll Expense
> ($000): 73224 Personnel: 1035**

☐ **WEST OAKS HOSPITAL (454026)**, 6500 Hornwood Drive, Zip 77074–5095;
tel. 713/995–0909 **A**1 3 5 9 10 **F**5 29 54 56 64 68 98 99 100 101 103 104
105 132 **S** Universal Health Services, Inc., King of Prussia, PA
Primary Contact: Gregory Drummond, Chief Executive Officer
CFO: Rob Tyler, Chief Financial Officer
CMO: Vernon Walling, M.D., Executive Medical Director
CIO: James Harmon, Network Administrator
CHR: Janice Webster, Director Human Resources
CNO: Israel Ahaine, Chief Nursing Officer
Web address: www.westoakshospital.com
**Control:** Corporation, Investor–owned, for–profit **Service:** Psychiatric

> **Staffed Beds: 144 Admissions: 5951 Census: 110 Outpatient Visits: 23060
> Births: 0 Total Expense ($000): 22355 Payroll Expense ($000): 13800
> Personnel: 306**

★ **WESTSIDE SURGICAL HOSPITAL**, 4200 Twelve Oaks Drive, Zip 77027;
tel. 713/621–5010 **F**3 15 20 29 35 40 45 64 75 79 81 82 85 86 107 119
126 132 147
Primary Contact: Angie Kauffman, R.N., MSN, Chief Executive Officer
**Control:** Partnership, Investor–owned, for–profit **Service:** Surgical

> **Staffed Beds: 12 Admissions: 301 Census: 2 Outpatient Visits: 2959
> Births: 0 Total Expense ($000): 31829 Payroll Expense ($000): 6725
> Personnel: 106**

⊠ **WOMAN'S HOSPITAL OF TEXAS (450674)**, 7600 Fannin Street,
Zip 77054–1906; tel. 713/790–1234 **A**1 3 5 9 10 **F**3 15 29 30 34 40 41
45 46 58 68 70 72 73 75 76 77 81 85 86 87 88 89 93 107 108 110 111
118 119 126 130 132 146 **S** HCA, Nashville, TN
Primary Contact: Ashley McClellan, Chief Executive Officer
COO: Eric Evans, Chief Operating Officer
CFO: Scott Bentley, Chief Financial Officer
CMO: Eberhard Lotze, M.D., Chief Medical Officer
CIO: Emily Le, Director Information Technology and Services
CHR: Arnita Crawford, Director Human Resources
CNO: Holley Tyler, R.N., Chief Nursing Officer
Web address: www.womanshospital.com
**Control:** Partnership, Investor–owned, for–profit **Service:** Obstetrics and
gynecology

> **Staffed Beds: 345 Admissions: 14884 Census: 223 Outpatient Visits:
> 47263 Births: 10678 Total Expense ($000): 180611 Payroll Expense
> ($000): 90671 Personnel: 1293**

**HUMBLE—Harris County**

⊠ **HEALTHSOUTH REHABILITATION HOSPITAL OF HUMBLE, LLC (453029)**,
19002 McKay Drive, Zip 77338–5701; tel. 281/446–6148 **A**1 9 10 **F**29 56 64
75 77 82 86 87 90 91 92 93 95 96 130 132 143 148 **P**5 **S** HEALTHSOUTH
Corporation, Birmingham, AL
Primary Contact: Angela L. Simmons, Chief Executive Officer
CFO: Sheila Shepard, Controller
CMO: Emile Mathurin, Jr., M.D., Medical Director
CHR: Christy Dixon, Chief Human Resources Officer
CNO: Christie Griffin–Jones, R.N., Chief Nursing Officer
Web address: www.healthsouthhumble.com
**Control:** Corporation, Investor–owned, for–profit **Service:** Rehabilitation

> **Staffed Beds: 60 Admissions: 1060 Census: 38 Outpatient Visits: 4084
> Births: 0 Total Expense ($000): 11659 Payroll Expense ($000): 8525
> Personnel: 143**

⊠ **ICON HOSPITAL (452112)**, 19211 McKay Boulevard, Zip 77338–5502;
tel. 281/883–5500 **A**1 9 10 **F**1 3 29 40 45 64 77 82 85 107 114 119 130
146 148 **S** AcuityHealthcare, LP, Charlotte, NC
Primary Contact: Hilda Long, Chief Executive Officer
Web address: www.acuityhealthcare.net
**Control:** Partnership, Investor–owned, for–profit **Service:** Long–Term Acute Care
hospital

> **Staffed Beds: 32 Admissions: 507 Census: 36 Outpatient Visits: 526
> Births: 0 Total Expense ($000): 20296 Payroll Expense ($000): 9519
> Personnel: 149**

⊠ **KINDRED REHABILITATION HOSPITAL NORTHEAST HOUSTON (673051)**,
18839 McKay Road, Zip 77338–5721; tel. 281/964–6600 **A**1 9 10 **F**3 29 64
77 90 91 93 130 148 **S** Kindred Healthcare, Louisville, KY
Primary Contact: Reagan Simpson, Chief Executive Officer
CFO: Cheryl Csepke, Controller
CMO: Helen Schilling, M.D., Medical Director
CHR: Stephanie Williams, Coordinator Human Resources
CNO: Albert J. Chapple, R.N., Chief Clinical Officer
Web address: www.khrehabnortheasthouston.com
**Control:** Corporation, Investor–owned, for–profit **Service:** Rehabilitation

> **Staffed Beds: 46 Admissions: 715 Census: 27 Outpatient Visits: 2846
> Births: 0 Total Expense ($000): 15064 Payroll Expense ($000): 6300
> Personnel: 162**

⊠ **MEMORIAL HERMANN NORTHEAST (450684)**, 18951 North Memorial Drive,
Zip 77338–4297; tel. 281/540–7700 **A**1 2 3 9 10 **F**3 11 13 15 18 20 22 24
26 29 30 31 34 35 40 42 45 46 49 53 54 57 59 64 65 68 70 72 73 74 75
76 77 78 79 80 81 85 86 87 93 100 107 108 109 110 111 114 115 119
120 121 123 126 129 130 131 132 135 146 147 148 **P**1 5 6 **S** Memorial
Hermann Healthcare System, Houston, TX
Primary Contact: Heath Rushing, Interim Chief Executive Officer
COO: Heath Rushing, Chief Operating Officer
CFO: Rebecca Tucker, Chief Financial Officer
CMO: Susan Curling, M.D., Chief Medical Officer
CHR: Monica Baisden, Director Human Resources
CNO: Linda Stephens, R.N., Chief Nursing Officer
Web address: www.memorialhermann.org
**Control:** Other not–for–profit (including NFP Corporation) **Service:** General
Medical and Surgical

> **Staffed Beds: 216 Admissions: 11536 Census: 149 Outpatient Visits:
> 108284 Births: 1423 Total Expense ($000): 193754 Payroll Expense
> ($000): 68150 Personnel: 840**

**HUNTSVILLE—Walker County**

⊠ **HUNTSVILLE MEMORIAL HOSPITAL (450347)**, 110 Memorial Hospital Drive,
Zip 77340–4940, Mailing Address: P.O. Box 4001, Zip 77342–4001;
tel. 936/291–3411 **A**1 9 10 **F**3 8 11 12 13 15 18 20 22 26 28 29 32 34 35
39 40 42 43 45 46 47 49 50 53 54 57 59 63 64 65 66 67 68 70 71 74 75
76 77 79 81 82 85 86 87 89 90 91 92 93 96 97 102 107 108 110 111 114
115 118 119 127 130 131 132 135 146 147 148
Primary Contact: Shannon Brown, Chief Executive Officer
CFO: Guy Gyros, Chief Financial Officer
CIO: Raul Velez, Director Information Systems
CHR: Brenda Ray, Director Human Resources
CNO: Sheila Ard, Chief Nursing Officer
Web address: www.huntsvillememorial.com
**Control:** Other not–for–profit (including NFP Corporation) **Service:** General
Medical and Surgical

> **Staffed Beds: 98 Admissions: 4606 Census: 52 Outpatient Visits: 86781
> Births: 502 Total Expense ($000): 77231 Payroll Expense ($000): 29926
> Personnel: 473**

**TX**

---

**Hospital, Medicare Provider Number, Address, Telephone, Approval, Facility, and Physician Codes, Health Care System**

★ American Hospital Association (AHA) membership ◯ Healthcare Facilities Accreditation Program ⇧ Center for Improvement in Healthcare Quality Accreditation
☐ The Joint Commission accreditation ◇ DNV Healthcare Inc. accreditation △ Commission on Accreditation of Rehabilitation Facilities (CARF) accreditation

---

## HURST—Tarrant County

**⊠ COOK CHILDREN'S NORTHEAST HOSPITAL (670045)**, 6316 Precinct Line Road, Zip 76054–2766; tel. 817/605–2500 **A**1 9 10 **F**3 40 41 45 48 64 68 79 81 85 89 107 111 114 119 144
Primary Contact: Kyllan Cody, Chief Executive Officer
CMO: Christopher Mann, M.D., Medical Director
CHR: Laurie Stanley, Manager Human Resources
CNO: Jan Milligan, Chief Nursing Officer
Web address: www.cookchildrensneh.org
**Control:** Corporation, Investor–owned, for–profit **Service:** Children's general

**Staffed Beds: 3 Admissions: 4 Census: 1 Outpatient Visits: 53727 Births:** 0 **Total Expense ($000):** 26021 **Payroll Expense ($000):** 9248 **Personnel:** 170

**☐ VICTORY MEDICAL CENTER MID–CITIES (450886)**, 1612 Hurst Town Center Drive, Zip 76054–6236; tel. 817/345–4100 **A**1 9 10 **F**3 12 29 40 45 46 48 49 77 79 81 82 85 86 87 107 108 114 **S** Victory Healthcare, The Woodlands, TX
Primary Contact: Barbara Millwood, Chief Executive Officer
CFO: Michelle Brost, Financial Officer
CMO: Dale Brancel, D.O., Chief of Staff
CHR: Donna Irvin, Director Human Resources
Web address: www.victory–healthcare.com
**Control:** Partnership, Investor–owned, for–profit **Service:** Surgical

**Staffed Beds: 16 Admissions: 240 Census: 2 Outpatient Visits: 1670 Births:** 0 **Total Expense ($000):** 33915 **Payroll Expense ($000):** 6203 **Personnel:** 80

## IRAAN—Pecos County

**IRAAN GENERAL HOSPITAL (451307)**, 600 349 North, Zip 79744, Mailing Address: P.O. Box 665, Zip 79744–0665; tel. 432/639–2871 **A**9 10 18 **F**28 40 43 56 57 59 64 65 75 86 93 104 107 119 127 130 133
Primary Contact: Teresa Callahan, R.N., MSN, Chief Executive Officer
CFO: Tami Burks, Chief Fiscal Services
CMO: Robert W. Garcia, M.D., Chief Medical Officer
CHR: Cathy Tucker, Director Human Resources
Web address: www.igh–hospital.com
**Control:** Hospital district or authority, Government, nonfederal **Service:** General Medical and Surgical

**Staffed Beds: 13 Admissions: 98 Census: 2 Outpatient Visits: 8341 Births:** 0 **Total Expense ($000):** 8386 **Payroll Expense ($000):** 3105 **Personnel:** 51

## IRVING—Dallas County

**⊠ BAYLOR MEDICAL CENTER AT IRVING (450079)**, 1901 North MacArthur Boulevard, Zip 75061–2220; tel. 972/579–8100 **A**1 2 3 5 9 10 **F**3 6 11 12 13 15 17 18 20 22 24 26 28 29 30 31 34 35 40 45 46 47 49 54 55 57 58 59 64 65 70 73 74 75 76 77 78 79 80 81 82 84 85 86 87 90 93 94 98 100 107 108 110 111 114 115 116 117 118 119 120 121 122 126 129 130 141 143 146 147 148 **S** Baylor Scott & White Health, Dallas, TX
Primary Contact: Cindy K. Schamp, President
COO: Brenda K. Blain, FACHE, Chief Nursing Officer and Chief Operating Officer
CMO: Jeffrey Embrey, M.D., Vice President Medical Affairs
CIO: Catherine Shisler, Director Information Services
CHR: Donna Stark, Director Human Resources
CNO: Brenda K. Blain, FACHE, Chief Nursing Officer and Chief Operating Officer
Web address: www.baylorhealth.com/PhysiciansLocations/Irving/Pages/Default.aspx
**Control:** Other not–for–profit (including NFP Corporation) **Service:** General Medical and Surgical

**Staffed Beds: 220 Admissions: 10268 Census: 133 Outpatient Visits:** 98325 **Births:** 2151 **Total Expense ($000):** 194834 **Payroll Expense ($000):** 73952 **Personnel:** 707

**☐ IRVING COPPELL SURGICAL HOSPITAL (450874)**, 400 West Interstate 635, Zip 75063; tel. 972/868–4000 **A**1 9 10 **F**3 29 40 51 81 85 99 100 101 102 103 **S** United Surgical Partners International, Addison, TX
Primary Contact: Deonna Unell, Chief Executive Officer
CFO: Gabrielle Holland, Chief Financial Officer
CMO: Scott McGraw, M.D., Medical Director
Web address: www.ic–sh.com
**Control:** Partnership, Investor–owned, for–profit **Service:** General Medical and Surgical

**Staffed Beds: 12 Admissions: 664 Census: 4 Outpatient Visits: 18480 Births:** 0 **Total Expense ($000):** 37461 **Payroll Expense ($000):** 7111 **Personnel:** 133

**⊠ LAS COLINAS MEDICAL CENTER (450822)**, 6800 North MacArthur Boulevard, Zip 75039–2422; tel. 972/969–2000 **A**1 9 10 **F**3 8 13 15 18 20 22 24 29 30 31 34 35 37 40 45 46 47 48 49 50 57 59 60 64 68 70 72 73 74 75 76 77 78 79 81 87 93 100 102 107 108 110 111 114 118 119 126 129 130 147 148 **S** HCA, Nashville, TN
Primary Contact: Daniela Decell, Chief Executive Officer
COO: Chip Zahn, Chief Operating Officer
CFO: Nick Galt, Chief Financial Officer
Web address: www.lascolinasmedical.com
**Control:** Corporation, Investor–owned, for–profit **Service:** General Medical and Surgical

**Staffed Beds: 90 Admissions: 4783 Census: 47 Outpatient Visits: 54259 Births:** 1604 **Total Expense ($000):** 74946 **Payroll Expense ($000):** 25833 **Personnel:** 377

## JACKSBORO—Jack County

**FAITH COMMUNITY HOSPITAL (450241)**, 717 Magnolia Street, Zip 76458–1111; tel. 940/567–6633 **A**9 10 20 **F**7 11 28 34 35 40 43 57 59 76 77 81 93 107 114 119 127 130 133 **P**6
Primary Contact: Frank Beaman, Administrator
CFO: James Bartlett, Chief Financial Officer
CMO: Sushil Chokshi, M.D., Chief Medical Officer
CIO: Bradlee Landis, Chief Information Officer
CHR: James Bartlett, Human Resources
CNO: Joy Henry, R.N., Director Nurses
Web address: www.faithcommunityhospital.com
**Control:** Hospital district or authority, Government, nonfederal **Service:** General Medical and Surgical

**Staffed Beds: 17 Admissions: 204 Census: 2 Outpatient Visits: 21299 Births:** 33 **Total Expense ($000):** 15069 **Payroll Expense ($000):** 4144 **Personnel:** 104

## JACKSONVILLE—Cherokee County

**⊠ EAST TEXAS MEDICAL CENTER JACKSONVILLE (450194)**, 501 South Ragsdale Street, Zip 75766–2413; tel. 903/541–5000 **A**1 9 10 20 **F**3 8 11 13 15 18 26 29 34 35 37 39 40 43 45 50 57 59 64 65 70 75 76 79 81 82 85 97 107 108 110 111 115 119 127 129 145 146 147 148 **S** East Texas Medical Center Regional Healthcare System, Tyler, TX
Primary Contact: Jack R. Endres, JD, FACHE, Administrator
CFO: Phillip A. Caron, Chief Financial Officer
CMO: Sharlet Slough, D.O., Chief of Staff
CHR: Elysia Epperson, Director Human Resources
CNO: Jana Bateman, R.N., Chief Nursing Officer
Web address: www.etmc.org
**Control:** Other not–for–profit (including NFP Corporation) **Service:** General Medical and Surgical

**Staffed Beds: 38 Admissions: 1821 Census: 15 Outpatient Visits: 79990 Births:** 446 **Total Expense ($000):** 34129 **Payroll Expense ($000):** 9971 **Personnel:** 176

**⊠ MOTHER FRANCES HOSPITAL – JACKSONVILLE (451319)**, 2026 South Jackson, Zip 75766–5822; tel. 903/541–4500 **A**1 9 10 18 **F**3 15 18 29 30 32 34 35 40 43 45 50 53 56 57 59 64 65 68 77 79 81 82 85 93 97 107 108 110 111 114 119 129 130 133 145 147 **P**5 6 7 8 **S** Trinity Mother Frances Hospitals and Clinics, Tyler, TX
Primary Contact: Anne Pileggi, Chief Executive Officer
COO: Michael Lewis, Chief Operating Officer
CFO: Elizabeth Pulliam, Chief Financial Officer
CMO: Matthew Vierkant, M.D., President Medical Staff
CIO: Jeff Pearson, Chief Information Officer
CHR: Denise Abrams, Human Resources
CNO: Kerry F. Bolin, Chief Nursing Officer
Web address: www.tmfhs.org/jacksonville
**Control:** Other not–for–profit (including NFP Corporation) **Service:** General Medical and Surgical

**Staffed Beds: 21 Admissions: 1058 Census: 8 Outpatient Visits: 71774 Births:** 0 **Total Expense ($000):** 33864 **Payroll Expense ($000):** 7978 **Personnel:** 159

## JASPER—Jasper County

**⊠ CHRISTUS JASPER MEMORIAL HOSPITAL (450573)**, 1275 Marvin Hancock Drive, Zip 75951–4995; tel. 409/384–5461 **A**1 9 10 **F**3 11 13 15 29 30 34 40 43 50 51 57 59 64 70 76 77 79 81 82 89 107 111 119 127 130 135 146 **P**8 **S** CHRISTUS Health, Irving, TX
Primary Contact: Lance Beus, Chief Executive Officer
COO: Mark Durand, Assistant Administrator Operations
CFO: Nikki Martin, Chief Financial Officer
CIO: Robert Jacobs, Regional Information Management Executive
CHR: Kay Powell, Director Human Resources
Web address: www.christusjasper.org
**Control:** Church–operated, Nongovernment, not–for profit **Service:** General Medical and Surgical

**Staffed Beds: 40 Admissions: 1359 Census: 11 Outpatient Visits: 65458 Births:** 310 **Total Expense ($000):** 25048 **Payroll Expense ($000):** 9769 **Personnel:** 171

*Many Facility Codes have changed. Please refer to the AHA Guide Code Chart.* © 2015 AHA Guide

**JOURDANTON—Atascosa County**

✠ **SOUTH TEXAS REGIONAL MEDICAL CENTER (450165)**, 1905 Highway 97 East, Zip 78026–1504; tel. 830/769–3515 **A**1 9 10 20 **F**3 11 13 15 18 20 29 30 34 35 39 40 43 45 57 59 63 64 68 70 75 76 77 79 81 85 93 107 108 110 111 114 119 129 130 132 133 144 146 147 148 **P**6 **S** Community Health Systems, Inc., Franklin, TN
Primary Contact: James R. Resendez, Chief Executive Officer
CFO: Gary Redmon, Chief Financial Officer
CIO: Rita S. Castillo, R.N., Chief Quality Officer and Risk Management
Web address: www.strmc.com
**Control:** Corporation, Investor–owned, for–profit **Service:** General Medical and Surgical

> **Staffed Beds:** 67 **Admissions:** 1562 **Census:** 15 **Outpatient Visits:** 31898 **Births:** 265 **Total Expense ($000):** 31721 **Payroll Expense ($000):** 11808 **Personnel:** 231

**JUNCTION—Kimble County**

**KIMBLE HOSPITAL (451306)**, 349 Reid Road, Zip 76849–3049; tel. 325/446–3321 **A**9 10 18 **F**3 34 35 40 43 45 56 57 59 65 66 75 93 97 107 114 127 133 146 **S** Preferred Management Corporation, Shawnee, OK
Primary Contact: Steve Bowen, Administrator
COO: Teena Hagood, Chief Nursing Officer
CFO: Larry Stephens, Chief Financial Officer
CMO: Ben Udall, M.D., Chief of Staff
CIO: Anna Henry, Chief Information Officer
CHR: Hope Lamb, Manager Human Resources
Web address: www.kimblehospital.org/
**Control:** Corporation, Investor–owned, for–profit **Service:** General Medical and Surgical

> **Staffed Beds:** 15 **Admissions:** 153 **Census:** 2 **Outpatient Visits:** 13966 **Births:** 0 **Total Expense ($000):** 6934 **Payroll Expense ($000):** 2901 **Personnel:** 67

**KATY—Harris County**

**CHRISTUS ST. CATHERINE HOSPITAL** See Houston Methodist St. Catherine Hospital

★ ◇ **HOUSTON METHODIST ST. CATHERINE HOSPITAL (450832)**, 701 Fry Road, Zip 77450–2255; tel. 281/599–5700, (Data for 334 days) **A**2 9 10 21 **F**1 29 30 34 35 50 53 57 59 75 82 84 85 87 130 132 135 146 148 **S** Houston Methodist, Houston, TX
Primary Contact: Gary L. Kempf, R.N., Administrator
CFO: Nancy Brock, Chief Financial Officer
CHR: James A. Fitch, Director Human Resources
Web address: www.houstonmethodist.org/katy–st–catherine–hospital
**Control:** Other not–for–profit (including NFP Corporation) **Service:** Long–Term Acute Care hospital

> **Staffed Beds:** 30 **Admissions:** 152 **Census:** 10 **Outpatient Visits:** 0 **Births:** 0 **Total Expense ($000):** 21692 **Payroll Expense ($000):** 5674 **Personnel:** 107

✠ **MEMORIAL HERMANN KATY HOSPITAL (450847)**, 23900 Katy Freeway, Zip 77494–1323; tel. 281/644–7000 **A**1 3 5 9 10 **F**3 8 11 13 15 18 20 22 29 30 34 35 39 40 43 45 46 49 50 51 57 59 61 64 65 68 69 70 73 74 75 77 78 79 81 85 87 89 93 102 107 108 110 111 114 119 126 130 131 132 145 146 147 **P**1 5 6 **S** Memorial Hermann Healthcare System, Houston, TX
Primary Contact: James Parisi, Chief Executive Officer
CFO: Linda Kulhanek, Chief Financial Officer
Web address: www.memorialhermann.org/locations/katy/
**Control:** Other not–for–profit (including NFP Corporation) **Service:** General Medical and Surgical

> **Staffed Beds:** 142 **Admissions:** 9323 **Census:** 90 **Outpatient Visits:** 86154 **Births:** 2202 **Total Expense ($000):** 146180 **Payroll Expense ($000):** 51585 **Personnel:** 670

✠ **MEMORIAL HERMANN REHABILITATION HOSPITAL – KATY (673038)**, 21720 Kingsland Boulevard, Zip 77450–2550; tel. 281/579–5555 **A**1 9 10 **F**3 29 30 64 79 90 92 93 107 111 114 119 129 130 131 148 **P**1 5 6 **S** Memorial Hermann Healthcare System, Houston, TX
Primary Contact: Carl E. Josehart, Chief Executive Officer
COO: Mary Ann Euliarte, R.N., Chief Operating Officer
CFO: Wayne Gordon, Chief Financial Officer
CMO: Shalin Patel, M.D., Chief Medical Officer
CIO: David Bradshaw, Chief Information Officer
CHR: Joyce Williams, Consultant Human Resources and Organizational Development
CNO: Mary Ann Euliarte, R.N., Chief Nursing Officer
Web address: www.memorialhermann.com
**Control:** Partnership, Investor–owned, for–profit **Service:** Rehabilitation

> **Staffed Beds:** 35 **Admissions:** 483 **Census:** 20 **Outpatient Visits:** 11129 **Births:** 0 **Total Expense ($000):** 17190 **Payroll Expense ($000):** 6985 **Personnel:** 95

**KAUFMAN—Kaufman County**

✠ **TEXAS HEALTH PRESBYTERIAN HOSPITAL KAUFMAN (450292)**, 850 Ed Hall Drive, Zip 75142–1861, Mailing Address: P.O. Box 1108, Zip 75142–5401; tel. 972/932–7200 **A**1 9 10 **F**3 11 13 15 18 29 30 34 35 40 43 45 53 57 59 64 65 68 70 75 76 79 81 85 86 87 93 100 102 107 108 111 114 118 119 130 132 135 146 147 148 **P**5 **S** Texas Health Resources, Arlington, TX
Primary Contact: Patsy Youngs, President
CMO: Benjamin Bradshaw, M.D., President Medical Staff
CHR: Mark J. Rainey, Director Human Resources
CNO: Denise Claussen, R.N., Chief Nursing Officer
Web address: www.texashealth.org/Kaufman
**Control:** Other not–for–profit (including NFP Corporation) **Service:** General Medical and Surgical

> **Staffed Beds:** 68 **Admissions:** 2019 **Census:** 18 **Outpatient Visits:** 67662 **Births:** 239 **Total Expense ($000):** 34896 **Payroll Expense ($000):** 14049 **Personnel:** 198

**KENEDY—Karnes County**

★ **OTTO KAISER MEMORIAL HOSPITAL (451364)**, 3349 South Highway 181, Zip 78119–5247; tel. 830/583–3401 **A**9 10 18 **F**3 11 15 29 30 34 40 45 46 57 62 64 68 77 81 93 107 111 114 119 133 135 148 **P**8
Primary Contact: David Lee, Chief Executive Officer
CIO: Joseph Wiatrek, Director Information Technology
CHR: Christina Benavides, Director Employee Services
CNO: Vincent Sowell, Chief Nursing Officer
Web address: www.okmh.org/
**Control:** Hospital district or authority, Government, nonfederal **Service:** General Medical and Surgical

> **Staffed Beds:** 25 **Admissions:** 317 **Census:** 5 **Outpatient Visits:** 25627 **Births:** 0 **Total Expense ($000):** 15827 **Payroll Expense ($000):** 7131 **Personnel:** 132

**KERMIT—Winkler County**

**WINKLER COUNTY MEMORIAL HOSPITAL (451314)**, 821 Jeffee Drive, Zip 79745–4696, Mailing Address: P.O. Box H., Zip 79745–6008; tel. 432/586–5864 **A**9 10 18 **F**3 32 34 36 40 57 59 64 65 69 93 97 107 114 119 127 133
Primary Contact: John Clark, Interim Administrator
CFO: Wannah Hartley, Controller
CMO: K. Pham, M.D., Chief of Staff
CIO: Keith Palmer, Assistant Administrator
**Control:** County–Government, nonfederal **Service:** General Medical and Surgical

> **Staffed Beds:** 19 **Admissions:** 157 **Census:** 1 **Outpatient Visits:** 7867 **Births:** 0 **Total Expense ($000):** 8789 **Payroll Expense ($000):** 2990 **Personnel:** 73

**KERRVILLE—Kerr County**

**KERRVILLE DIVISION** See South Texas Veterans Health Care System, San Antonio

**TX**

---

| Hospital, Medicare Provider Number, Address, Telephone, Approval, Facility, and Physician Codes, Health Care System |
|---|

★ American Hospital Association (AHA) membership  ○ Healthcare Facilities Accreditation Program  ⇑ Center for Improvement in Healthcare Quality Accreditation
☐ The Joint Commission accreditation  ◇ DNV Healthcare Inc. accreditation  △ Commission on Accreditation of Rehabilitation Facilities (CARF) accreditation

☐ **KERRVILLE STATE HOSPITAL (454014)**, 721 Thompson Drive, Zip 78028–5154; tel. 830/896–2211 **A**1 3 5 10 **F**11 30 34 39 44 50 56 65 68 75 86 87 97 98 101 103 130 132 135 146 **S** Texas Department of State Health Services, Austin, TX
Primary Contact: Leigh Ann Fitzpatrick, Superintendent
CFO: Laurie Harris, Chief Accountant
CMO: Matthew Faubion, M.D., Clinical Director
CNO: Lee McGuire, Chief Nurse Executive
Web address: www.dshs.state.tx.us/mhhospitals/KerrvilleSH/default.shtm
**Control:** State–Government, nonfederal **Service:** Psychiatric

**Staffed Beds:** 202 **Admissions:** 77 **Census:** 194 **Outpatient Visits:** 0 **Births:** 0 **Total Expense ($000):** 35421 **Payroll Expense ($000):** 21642 **Personnel:** 549

✠ **PETERSON REGIONAL MEDICAL CENTER (450007)**, 551 Hill Country Drive, Zip 78028–6085; tel. 830/896–4200 **A**1 9 10 19 **F**3 8 11 13 15 18 20 26 29 30 31 34 35 39 40 44 45 49 54 57 59 62 63 64 65 68 70 74 75 76 77 78 79 80 81 82 84 85 86 87 90 93 96 97 100 107 110 111 114 115 118 119 126 130 131 132 135 145 146 147 148 **P**1 6
Primary Contact: James Patrick Murray, FACHE, President and Chief Executive Officer
COO: Stephen Pautler, FACHE, Chief Operating Officer
CFO: Lisa Medovich, Chief Financial Officer
CMO: Kerri Truelock, M.D., Chief of Staff
CIO: Richard Cruthirds, Director Information Systems
CHR: Buddy Volpe, Director Human Resources
CNO: Kaeli Dressler, R.N., Chief Nursing Officer
Web address: www.petersonrmc.com
**Control:** Other not–for–profit (including NFP Corporation) **Service:** General Medical and Surgical

**Staffed Beds:** 124 **Admissions:** 4526 **Census:** 57 **Outpatient Visits:** 138903 **Births:** 430 **Total Expense ($000):** 98061 **Payroll Expense ($000):** 39613 **Personnel:** 803

### KILGORE—Gregg County

◇ **ALLEGIANCE SPECIALTY HOSPITAL OF KILGORE (450488)**, 1612 South Henderson Boulevard, Zip 75662–3594; tel. 903/984–3505 **A**9 10 21 **F**3 29 34 35 56 59 98 101 103 104 130 **S** Allegiance Health Management, Shreveport, LA
Primary Contact: Karen Ross, Chief Executive Officer
CHR: Stephenie Edmons, Human Resources Clerk
CNO: Shelley Pierce, Chief Nursing Officer
Web address: www.ahmgt.com
**Control:** Corporation, Investor–owned, for–profit **Service:** Psychiatric

**Staffed Beds:** 60 **Admissions:** 470 **Census:** 14 **Outpatient Visits:** 16989 **Births:** 0 **Total Expense ($000):** 7867 **Payroll Expense ($000):** 4069 **Personnel:** 124

### KILLEEN—Bell County

✠ **METROPLEX ADVENTIST HOSPITAL (450152)**, 2201 South Clear Creek Road, Zip 76549–4110; tel. 254/526–7523 **A**1 3 9 10 **F**3 8 11 12 13 15 18 20 22 26 28 29 30 34 35 39 40 43 45 46 48 49 54 57 59 62 65 68 70 71 74 75 76 77 78 79 81 82 83 85 86 87 89 91 93 98 99 100 101 102 103 104 105 107 108 110 111 114 115 118 119 129 130 131 132 135 146 147 148 **P**8 **S** Adventist Health System Sunbelt Health Care Corporation, Altamonte Springs, FL
Primary Contact: Carlyle L. E. Walton, FACHE, Chief Executive Officer
CFO: Penny Johnson, Chief Financial Officer
CMO: Frederick Barnett, M.D., Chief of Staff
CIO: Dale Koebnick, Director Management Information Systems and Patient Access
CHR: Brenda Coley, Executive Director
Web address: www.mplex.org
**Control:** Church–operated, Nongovernment, not–for profit **Service:** General Medical and Surgical

**Staffed Beds:** 177 **Admissions:** 6105 **Census:** 61 **Outpatient Visits:** 97402 **Births:** 1335 **Total Expense ($000):** 95633 **Payroll Expense ($000):** 38782 **Personnel:** 905

### KINGSVILLE—Kleberg County

✠ **CHRISTUS SPOHN HOSPITAL KLEBERG (450163)**, 1311 General Cavazos Boulevard, Zip 78363–7130; tel. 361/595–1661 **A**1 9 10 20 **F**3 11 13 15 29 30 34 35 40 43 53 54 57 59 62 63 64 65 68 86 87 89 93 102 108 110 111 119 130 146 **P**8 **S** CHRISTUS Health, Irving, TX
Primary Contact: David LeMonte, Vice President and Chief Operating Officer
CFO: Lauralinda Moore, Manager Finance
CHR: Candace Jefferson, Manager Human Resources
Web address: www.christusspohn.org
**Control:** Church–operated, Nongovernment, not–for profit **Service:** General Medical and Surgical

**Staffed Beds:** 50 **Admissions:** 3211 **Census:** 37 **Outpatient Visits:** 37705 **Births:** 338 **Total Expense ($000):** 37611 **Payroll Expense ($000):** 15122 **Personnel:** 199

✠ **KINGWOOD MEDICAL CENTER (450775)**, 22999 U.S. Highway 59 North, Zip 77339; tel. 281/348–8000 **A**1 9 10 **F**3 13 15 18 20 22 24 26 28 29 31 34 35 40 42 45 49 57 58 59 61 64 70 72 74 76 78 79 81 85 86 87 89 90 96 107 108 110 111 115 119 126 129 130 132 146 147 **S** HCA, Nashville, TN
Primary Contact: Melinda Stephenson, Chief Executive Officer
COO: Megan Marietta, Chief Operating Officer
CFO: Daniel E. Davis, Chief Financial Officer
CMO: Eugene Ogrod, M.D., Chief Medical Officer
CNO: Lisa Hoyle, R.N., Chief Nursing Officer
Web address: www.kingwoodmedical.com
**Control:** Corporation, Investor–owned, for–profit **Service:** General Medical and Surgical

**Staffed Beds:** 345 **Admissions:** 16549 **Census:** 229 **Outpatient Visits:** 104518 **Births:** 2807 **Total Expense ($000):** 187135 **Payroll Expense ($000):** 75170 **Personnel:** 884

☐ **KINGWOOD PINES HOSPITAL (454103)**, 2001 Ladbrook Drive, Zip 77339–3004; tel. 281/404–1001 **A**1 9 10 **F**4 5 29 75 86 87 98 99 101 102 103 104 105 130 132 **S** Universal Health Services, Inc., King of Prussia, PA
Primary Contact: James Burroughs, Chief Executive Officer
COO: Grey Mc Kellar, Chief Operating Officer and Director of Performance Improvement and Risk
CFO: Sharon Corum, Chief Financial Officer
CMO: Javier Ruiz, M.D., Medical Director
CNO: Kim Wheeler, R.N., Director of Nursing
Web address: www.kingwoodpines.com
**Control:** Corporation, Investor–owned, for–profit **Service:** Psychiatric

**Staffed Beds:** 116 **Admissions:** 4012 **Census:** 91 **Outpatient Visits:** 3340 **Births:** 0 **Total Expense ($000):** 20976 **Payroll Expense ($000):** 10479 **Personnel:** 211

**KINGWOOD SPECIALTY HOSPITAL** See Memorial Hermann Surgical Hospital Kingwood

☐ **MEMORIAL HERMANN SURGICAL HOSPITAL KINGWOOD (670005)**, 300 Kingwood Medical Drive, Zip 77339–6400; tel. 281/312–4000 **A**1 9 10 **F**3 29 40 45 51 64 68 79 81 82 85 86 87
Primary Contact: Teal A. Holden, Chief Executive Officer
CFO: Jay Michael Gomez, Chief Financial Officer
CNO: Shawna Fugler, R.N., Chief Nursing Officer
Web address: www.memorialhermannkingwood.com
**Control:** Corporation, Investor–owned, for–profit **Service:** General Medical and Surgical

**Staffed Beds:** 10 **Admissions:** 227 **Census:** 2 **Outpatient Visits:** 6009 **Births:** 0 **Total Expense ($000):** 20495 **Payroll Expense ($000):** 4370 **Personnel:** 78

**KNOX COUNTY HOSPITAL (450746)**, 701 South Fifth Street, Zip 79529–2107, Mailing Address: P.O. Box 608, Zip 79529–0608; tel. 940/657–3535 **A**9 10 20 **F**7 11 28 33 34 35 40 43 57 59 62 127 133 **P**6
Primary Contact: Stephan A. Kuehler, Administrator
CFO: Dan Offutt, Manager Finance
CMO: Kevin Finley, D.O., Chief of Staff
CIO: Sue Marion, Manager Business Office
CNO: Sheila Kuehler, R.N., Director of Nursing
Web address: www.knoxcountyhospital–texas.com
**Control:** Hospital district or authority, Government, nonfederal **Service:** General Medical and Surgical

**Staffed Beds:** 14 **Admissions:** 115 **Census:** 1 **Outpatient Visits:** 29585 **Births:** 0 **Total Expense ($000):** 6018 **Payroll Expense ($000):** 2603 **Personnel:** 53

✠ **SETON MEDICAL CENTER HAYS (670056)**, 6001 Kyle Parkway, Zip 78640–6112, Mailing Address: 6001 Kyle Prkway, Zip 78640–6112; tel. 512/504–5000 **A**1 3 9 10 **F**3 11 13 15 18 20 22 24 28 29 30 31 34 35 40 43 44 45 46 49 50 57 60 64 65 68 70 72 74 75 76 77 78 79 81 82 85 87 107 108 110 111 114 115 118 119 129 130 131 135 146 148 **P**3 8 **S** Ascension Health, Saint Louis, MO
Primary Contact: Christopher L. Hartle, President
COO: Neal Kelley, Vice President and Chief Operating Officer
Web address: www.seton.net/locations/seton_medical_center_hays/
**Control:** Church–operated, Nongovernment, not–for profit **Service:** General Medical and Surgical

**Staffed Beds:** 96 **Admissions:** 6115 **Census:** 75 **Outpatient Visits:** 49769 **Births:** 869 **Total Expense ($000):** 106444 **Payroll Expense ($000):** 42840 **Personnel:** 617

**TX**

## LA GRANGE—Fayette County

★ **ST. MARK'S MEDICAL CENTER (670004)**, One St. Mark's Place, Zip 78945; tel. 979/242–2200 **A**3 5 9 10 **F**3 8 11 12 13 15 17 29 30 34 40 43 45 50 56 57 59 68 70 74 75 76 79 81 82 84 85 87 89 93 107 110 111 114 119 128 129 130 133 145 146 147 **P**6 **S** Community Hospital Corporation, Plano, TX
Primary Contact: Shane Kernell, Chief Executive Officer
COO: Carol Drozd, Chief Operating Officer
CFO: Dennis Boyd, Chief Financial Officer
CMO: Russell Juno, M.D., Chief of Staff
CHR: Tammy Oehlke, Director Human Resources
Web address: www.smmctx.org
**Control:** Other not–for–profit (including NFP Corporation) **Service:** General Medical and Surgical

**Staffed Beds:** 44 **Admissions:** 1668 **Census:** 17 **Outpatient Visits:** 49799 **Births:** 295 **Total Expense ($000):** 25949 **Payroll Expense ($000):** 10065 **Personnel:** 188

## LAKE JACKSON—Brazoria County

⊞ **BRAZOSPORT REGIONAL HEALTH SYSTEM (450072)**, 100 Medical Drive, Zip 77566–5674; tel. 979/297–4411 **A**1 2 9 10 **F**3 11 13 15 18 20 22 28 29 30 31 34 37 40 41 43 45 47 48 49 50 51 54 57 59 60 62 64 65 68 70 74 75 76 78 79 81 82 85 86 87 89 90 91 93 94 107 108 110 111 114 117 118 119 120 121 123 129 130 131 132 146 147 148 **P**8 **S** QHR, Brentwood, TN
Primary Contact: Al Guevara, FACHE, President and Chief Executive Officer
CFO: Chuck Jeffress, Vice President Fiscal Services
CMO: Michael Gilliand, M.D., Chief of Staff
CIO: Todd Edwards, Director Information Management Systems
CHR: Christopher Calia, Director Human Resources
CNO: Jerrie Patterson, Chief Nursing Officer
Web address: www.brhstx.org
**Control:** Other not–for–profit (including NFP Corporation) **Service:** General Medical and Surgical

**Staffed Beds:** 103 **Admissions:** 4570 **Census:** 47 **Outpatient Visits:** 132339 **Births:** 558 **Total Expense ($000):** 76296 **Payroll Expense ($000):** 30515 **Personnel:** 565

## LAKEWAY—Travis County

⊞ **LAKEWAY REGIONAL MEDICAL CENTER (670079)**, 100 Medical Parkway, Zip 78738–5621; tel. 512/571–5000 **A**1 9 10 **F**3 13 15 17 18 20 22 24 29 30 34 38 40 45 46 49 50 51 54 57 59 60 64 69 70 72 74 75 76 78 79 81 82 85 86 87 91 92 93 107 108 110 111 115 116 117 118 119 129 130 135 146 147 148 **P**6
Primary Contact: Philippe Bochaton, Chief Executive Officer
CFO: Thomas Marshall, Chief Financial Officer
CIO: Matt Pace, Information Technology Director
CHR: Ron Morrison, Chief Human Resources Officer
CNO: Laura L. Miller, MSN, Chief Nursing Officer
Web address: www.lakewayregional.com
**Control:** Corporation, Investor–owned, for–profit **Service:** General Medical and Surgical

**Staffed Beds:** 48 **Admissions:** 2030 **Census:** 22 **Outpatient Visits:** 23911 **Births:** 315 **Total Expense ($000):** 93427 **Payroll Expense ($000):** 16485 **Personnel:** 334

⊞ **VIBRA REHABILITATION HOSPITAL LAKE TRAVIS (673058)**, 2000 Medical Drive, Zip 78734–4200; tel. 512/263–4500, (Nonreporting) **A**1 **S** Vibra Healthcare, Mechanicsburg, PA
Primary Contact: Deborah Hopps, Chief Executive Officer
Web address: www.vrhlaketravis.com
**Control:** Corporation, Investor–owned, for–profit **Service:** Rehabilitation

**Staffed Beds:** 36

## LAMESA—Dawson County

**MEDICAL ARTS HOSPITAL (450489)**, 2200 North Bryan Avenue, Zip 79331–2451; tel. 806/872–2183 **A**9 10 20 **F**3 7 11 13 28 29 30 35 40 43 45 50 57 59 62 64 75 76 81 87 97 107 111 115 119 127 128 130 133 146 148 **P**6
Primary Contact: Letha Stokes, Chief Executive Officer
COO: JoBeth Smith, Chief Operating Officer and Director of Human Resources
CFO: Jeff Weaver, Chief Financial Officer
CMO: Mark Key, M.D., Chief of Staff
CHR: Traci Brown, Human Resources Generalist
CNO: Heidi Cobb, R.N., Chief Nursing Officer
Web address: www.medicalartshospital.org
**Control:** Hospital district or authority, Government, nonfederal **Service:** General Medical and Surgical

**Staffed Beds:** 22 **Admissions:** 333 **Census:** 3 **Outpatient Visits:** 75543 **Births:** 100 **Total Expense ($000):** 21939 **Payroll Expense ($000):** 7600 **Personnel:** 211

## LAMPASAS—Lampasas County

⊞ **ROLLINS–BROOK COMMUNITY HOSPITAL (451323)**, 608 North Key Avenue, Zip 76550–1106, Mailing Address: P.O. Box 589, Zip 76550–0032; tel. 512/556–3682 **A**1 9 10 18 **F**3 8 15 29 35 40 43 45 46 61 81 85 87 93 97 107 110 111 114 119 130 131 133 146 **P**4 8 **S** Adventist Health System Sunbelt Health Care Corporation, Altamonte Springs, FL
Primary Contact: Carlyle L. E. Walton, FACHE, Chief Executive Officer
CFO: Robert Brock, Chief Financial Officer and Vice President
CMO: Don Daniels, M.D., Chief Medical Officer
CIO: Carl Elkins, Director Information Technology
CHR: Brenda Coley, Executive Director
CNO: Tammy Rodriguez, Vice President of Patient Care Services
Web address: www.mplex.org
**Control:** Church–operated, Nongovernment, not–for profit **Service:** General Medical and Surgical

**Staffed Beds:** 35 **Admissions:** 732 **Census:** 9 **Outpatient Visits:** 16457 **Births:** 0 **Total Expense ($000):** 13806 **Payroll Expense ($000):** 4349 **Personnel:** 101

## LANCASTER—Dallas County

◇ **CRESCENT MEDICAL CENTER LANCASTER (670090)**, 2600 West Pleasant Run Road, Zip 75146–1114; tel. 972/230–8888 **A**10 21 **F**3 18 40 41 46 51 59 70 79 81 85 87 107 114 119 124 130 135 143 148
Primary Contact: Susie Elder, Interim Chief Executive Officer
**Control:** Individual, Investor–owned, for–profit **Service:** General Medical and Surgical

**Staffed Beds:** 84 **Admissions:** 274 **Census:** 2 **Outpatient Visits:** 8129 **Births:** 0 **Total Expense ($000):** 10824 **Payroll Expense ($000):** 4570 **Personnel:** 93

## LAREDO—Webb County

☐ **DOCTORS HOSPITAL OF LAREDO (450643)**, 10700 McPherson Road, Zip 78045–6268; tel. 956/523–2000 **A**1 2 9 10 **F**3 11 12 13 15 18 20 22 26 29 30 31 32 34 37 39 40 43 45 48 49 50 51 54 59 60 63 64 70 71 72 74 75 76 77 78 79 81 85 87 89 90 91 93 107 108 111 114 119 121 129 130 132 146 147 148 **P**5 **S** Universal Health Services, Inc., King of Prussia, PA
Primary Contact: Rene Lopez, Chief Executive Officer
CMO: Ralph Nimchan, M.D., Chief of Staff
CIO: Maribel Mata, Director Information Services
CHR: Roseann Figueroa, Director Human Resources
CNO: Daniel Cabrera, Chief Nursing Officer
Web address: www.doctorshosplaredo.com
**Control:** Partnership, Investor–owned, for–profit **Service:** General Medical and Surgical

**Staffed Beds:** 183 **Admissions:** 8170 **Census:** 108 **Outpatient Visits:** 109474 **Births:** 2538 **Total Expense ($000):** 93495 **Payroll Expense ($000):** 37440 **Personnel:** 659

⊞ **LAREDO MEDICAL CENTER (450029)**, 1700 East Saunders Avenue, Zip 78041–5474, Mailing Address: P.O. Box 2068, Zip 78044–2068; tel. 956/796–5000, (Total facility includes 18 beds in nursing home–type unit) **A**1 9 10 **F**3 8 11 12 13 15 18 20 22 24 26 28 29 30 31 32 34 35 36 37 40 43 45 46 49 50 51 53 54 56 57 59 60 64 68 72 74 75 76 77 78 79 81 85 86 87 89 92 107 108 110 111 114 119 120 121 123 128 132 135 146 147 148 **S** Community Health Systems, Inc., Franklin, TN
Primary Contact: Enrique Gallegos, Chief Executive Officer
COO: John E. Ulbricht, Chief Operating Officer
CIO: Joe Rivera, Chief Information Technology Officer
Web address: www.laredomedical.com
**Control:** Corporation, Investor–owned, for–profit **Service:** General Medical and Surgical

**Staffed Beds:** 326 **Admissions:** 14508 **Census:** 209 **Outpatient Visits:** 148444 **Births:** 3436 **Total Expense ($000):** 276701 **Payroll Expense ($000):** 54657 **Personnel:** 1110

☐ **LAREDO SPECIALTY HOSPITAL (452096)**, 2005 Bustamante Street, Zip 78041–5470; tel. 956/753–5353 **A**1 10 **F**1 3 29 30 75 85 91 96 130 148 **S** Ernest Health, Inc., Albuquerque, NM
Primary Contact: Mario Rodriguez, Chief Executive Officer
CFO: Robert Voss, Chief Financial Officer
CMO: Marisa Guerrero, Director Human Resources
Web address: www.lsh.ernesthealth.com
**Control:** Partnership, Investor–owned, for–profit **Service:** Long–Term Acute Care hospital

**Staffed Beds:** 40 **Admissions:** 503 **Census:** 34 **Outpatient Visits:** 0 **Births:** 0 **Total Expense ($000):** 20170 **Payroll Expense ($000):** 7444 **Personnel:** 152

**TX**

---

## LEAGUE CITY—Galveston County

☐ **DEVEREUX TEXAS TREATMENT NETWORK (454085)**, 1150 Devereux Drive, Zip 77573–2043; tel. 281/335–1000 **A**1 9 10 **F**4 5 29 32 35 38 53 54 59 64 75 86 87 98 99 100 101 103 104 106 130 132 134 **S** Devereux, Villanova, PA
Primary Contact: Pamela E. Helm, Executive Director
Web address: www.devereux.org
**Control:** Other not–for–profit (including NFP Corporation) **Service:** Children's hospital psychiatric

**Staffed Beds:** 39 **Admissions:** 55 **Census:** 39 **Outpatient Visits:** 1808 **Births:** 0 **Total Expense ($000):** 7639 **Payroll Expense ($000):** 2590 **Personnel:** 61

## LEVELLAND—Hockley County

★ **COVENANT HOSPITAL–LEVELLAND (450755)**, 1900 South College Avenue, Zip 79336–6508; tel. 806/894–4963 **A**9 10 **F**11 13 15 29 30 34 40 43 45 50 54 57 59 64 65 68 75 76 77 81 82 85 86 87 89 90 91 93 97 107 110 111 114 115 119 127 130 133 146 **P**4 **S** Covenant Health System, Lubbock, TX
Primary Contact: Bruce White, Administrator
CFO: Newman Wheeler, Chief Financial Officer and Chief Operating Officer
CMO: Harry Weaver, M.D., Chief of Staff
CIO: Kevin Elmore, Chief Information Officer
CHR: Tammy Franklin, Manager Personnel and Marketing
CNO: Connie Thomman, Director of Nursing
Web address: www.covenanthospitallevelland.com/
**Control:** Church–operated, Nongovernment, not–for profit **Service:** General Medical and Surgical

**Staffed Beds:** 26 **Admissions:** 886 **Census:** 9 **Outpatient Visits:** 40051 **Births:** 250 **Total Expense ($000):** 20207 **Payroll Expense ($000):** 7761 **Personnel:** 185

## LEWISVILLE—Denton County

☒ **MEDICAL CENTER OF LEWISVILLE (450669)**, 500 West Main, Zip 75057–3699; tel. 972/420–1000 **A**1 9 10 **F**3 13 15 18 20 22 24 26 28 29 30 31 34 35 40 42 43 46 49 50 56 57 59 68 70 72 74 75 76 78 79 81 85 87 89 90 93 96 107 108 110 111 114 118 119 129 130 131 132 135 146 147 148 **S** HCA, Nashville, TN
Primary Contact: LaSharndra Barbarin, Chief Executive Officer and Chief Operating Officer
CFO: Lisa Brodbeck, Chief Financial Officer
CIO: Shirley Archambeault, Chief Information Officer
CHR: Dara Biegert, Vice President Human Resources
CNO: Lynn O'Neill, R.N., Chief Nursing Officer
Web address: www.lewisvillemedical.com
**Control:** Corporation, Investor–owned, for–profit **Service:** General Medical and Surgical

**Staffed Beds:** 166 **Admissions:** 7092 **Census:** 97 **Outpatient Visits:** 70586 **Births:** 1368 **Total Expense ($000):** 131852 **Payroll Expense ($000):** 51115 **Personnel:** 670

## LIBERTY—Liberty County

☐ **LIBERTY DAYTON REGIONAL MEDICAL CENTER (451375)**, 1353 North Travis, Zip 77575–3549; tel. 936/336–7316 **A**1 9 10 18 **F**3 29 40 45 64 81 85 107 114 115 119 130 133
Primary Contact: James E. Koulovatos, Chief Executive Officer
CFO: Hal Mayo, Chief Financial Officer
CMO: Don Callens, M.D., Chief Medical Officer
CIO: Matt Thornton, Chief Information Officer
CNO: Cindy Griffin, Chief Nursing Officer
Web address: www.libertydaytonrmc.com
**Control:** Other not–for–profit (including NFP Corporation) **Service:** General Medical and Surgical

**Staffed Beds:** 14 **Admissions:** 175 **Census:** 1 **Outpatient Visits:** 19959 **Births:** 0 **Total Expense ($000):** 8320 **Payroll Expense ($000):** 3282 **Personnel:** 84

## LITTLEFIELD—Lamb County

★ **LAMB HEALTHCARE CENTER (450698)**, 1500 South Sunset, Zip 79339–4899; tel. 806/385–6411 **A**9 10 20 **F**13 35 40 43 45 57 59 64 66 75 76 81 86 87 89 107 114 119 127 132 133 134 147 **P**6
Primary Contact: Dennis Fleenor, R.N., Administrator and Chief Executive Officer
CFO: Cindy Klein, Chief Financial Officer
CMO: Isabel Molina, M.D., Chief Medical Officer
CHR: Joan Williams, Administrative Assistant/Human Resources
CNO: Stacie Styron, Chief Nursing Officer
**Control:** County–Government, nonfederal **Service:** General Medical and Surgical

**Staffed Beds:** 41 **Admissions:** 438 **Census:** 6 **Outpatient Visits:** 21526 **Births:** 110 **Total Expense ($000):** 10968 **Payroll Expense ($000):** 4262 **Personnel:** 127

## LIVINGSTON—Polk County

☒ **CHI ST. LUKE'S HEALTH MEMORIAL LIVINGSTON (450395)**, 1717 Highway 59 Bypass, Zip 77351–1257, Mailing Address: P.O. Box 1257, Zip 77351–0022; tel. 936/329–8700, (Data for 181 days) **A**1 9 10 **F**3 11 13 15 29 34 35 40 43 45 46 50 57 59 62 64 68 70 74 75 76 79 81 85 87 89 107 108 110 111 114 119 129 130 132 146 **S** Catholic Health Initiatives, Englewood, CO
Primary Contact: Randy Slack, Chief Executive Officer
CFO: Ken Miller, Chief Financial Officer
CMO: Shane Shaw, M.D., Chief of Staff
CIO: Mark Clifton, Interim Chief Financial Officer
CHR: Donald Morris, System Vice President Human Resources
CNO: Jacqueline Gordon, R.N., Chief Nursing Officer
Web address: www.memorialhealth.org
**Control:** Other not–for–profit (including NFP Corporation) **Service:** General Medical and Surgical

**Staffed Beds:** 66 **Admissions:** 1188 **Census:** 23 **Outpatient Visits:** 25751 **Births:** 196 **Total Expense ($000):** 21776 **Payroll Expense ($000):** 8727 **Personnel:** 261

## LLANO—Llano County

★ **SCOTT & WHITE HOSPITAL – LLANO (450219)**, 200 West Ollie Street, Zip 78643–2628; tel. 325/247–5040, (Data for 303 days) **A**9 10 20 **F**3 7 13 15 18 29 40 43 45 50 57 59 64 68 76 79 81 85 87 107 108 111 114 119 127 146 147 **S** Baylor Scott & White Health, Dallas, TX
Primary Contact: Eric N. Looper, Chief Executive Officer
COO: Linda Meredith, MSN, Chief Operating Officer
CFO: Jason Cole, Director Finance
CMO: Kim Russell, M.D., Chief of Staff
CIO: Rodney Lott, Director Management Information Systems and Facility Operations
CHR: Pearl Oestreich, Director Human Resources
CNO: Reta Hunt, Director of Nursing
Web address: www.llanomemorial.org
**Control:** Other not–for–profit (including NFP Corporation) **Service:** General Medical and Surgical

**Staffed Beds:** 20 **Admissions:** 721 **Census:** 6 **Outpatient Visits:** 7566 **Births:** 205 **Total Expense ($000):** 36171 **Payroll Expense ($000):** 13918 **Personnel:** 313

## LOCKNEY—Floyd County

★ **W. J. MANGOLD MEMORIAL HOSPITAL (451337)**, 320 North Main Street, Zip 79241–0037, Mailing Address: Box 37, Zip 79241–0037; tel. 806/652–3373 **A**9 10 18 **F**1 3 4 13 16 17 35 40 43 45 53 57 59 62 64 65 67 70 72 73 76 80 81 85 88 90 93 97 98 107 111 119 127 128 130 133 148 **P**4
Primary Contact: Larry Mullins, Chief Executive Officer and Administrator
CFO: Alyssa McCarter, Chief Financial Officer
CMO: Kevin T. Stennett, M.D., Chief of Staff
CIO: Sam Vanderbeek, Chief Information Officer
CHR: Janice Yearwood, Director Human Resources
CNO: Billie Hendrix, R.N., Director of Nursing
Web address: www.mangoldmemorial.org
**Control:** Hospital district or authority, Government, nonfederal **Service:** General Medical and Surgical

**Staffed Beds:** 25 **Admissions:** 496 **Census:** 6 **Outpatient Visits:** 25782 **Births:** 35 **Total Expense ($000):** 10537 **Payroll Expense ($000):** 4538 **Personnel:** 121

## LONGVIEW—Gregg County

☐ **BEHAVIORAL HOSPITAL OF LONGVIEW (454105)**, 22 Bermuda Lane, Zip 75605–2902; tel. 903/291–3456 **A**1 9 10 **F**98 100 130 **P**6
Primary Contact: Andre Deshong, Administrator
Web address: www.longviewhospital.com
**Control:** Corporation, Investor–owned, for–profit **Service:** Psychiatric

**Staffed Beds:** 76 **Admissions:** 1073 **Census:** 43 **Outpatient Visits:** 0 **Births:** 0 **Total Expense ($000):** 9611 **Payroll Expense ($000):** 4997 **Personnel:** 112

*Many Facility Codes have changed. Please refer to the AHA Guide Code Chart.*

✠ △ **GOOD SHEPHERD MEDICAL CENTER (450037)**, 700 East Marshall Avenue, Zip 75601–5580; tel. 903/315–2000 **A**1 3 7 9 10 **F**3 11 12 13 15 18 20 22 24 26 28 29 30 31 32 34 35 37 40 42 43 45 46 49 50 51 53 54 56 57 59 60 61 63 64 68 70 71 72 73 74 75 76 77 78 79 80 81 82 84 85 86 87 89 90 92 93 97 102 107 108 111 114 115 118 119 126 129 130 131 132 135 143 144 146 147 148 **P**8 **S** Good Shepherd Health System, Longview, TX
Primary Contact: Steve Altmiller, President and Chief Executive Officer
CFO: Tim Pileggi, Interim Chief Financial Officer
CMO: Larry Verfurth, D.O., Chief Medical Officer and Senior Vice President
CIO: Chris Blakemore, Interim Chief Information Officer
CHR: Ginger Morrow, Executive Vice President Human Resources
CNO: Patti Bennett, Chief Nursing Officer and Senior Vice President
Web address: www.gsmc.org
**Control:** Other not–for–profit (including NFP Corporation) **Service:** General Medical and Surgical

**Staffed Beds: 393 Admissions: 15781 Census: 210 Outpatient Visits: 204945 Births: 2170 Total Expense ($000): 267272 Payroll Expense ($000): 89162 Personnel: 1321**

✠ **LONGVIEW REGIONAL MEDICAL CENTER (450702)**, 2901 North Fourth Street, Zip 75605–5191, Mailing Address: P.O. Box 14000, Zip 75607–4000; tel. 903/758–1818, (Total facility includes 15 beds in nursing home–type unit) **A**1 9 10 **F**3 8 11 12 13 15 18 20 22 24 26 28 29 30 31 34 35 37 39 40 43 45 46 47 49 50 57 59 61 64 65 67 70 72 74 75 76 77 78 79 81 85 86 87 89 91 93 107 108 110 111 114 115 118 119 120 126 128 130 146 148 **P**8 **S** Community Health Systems, Inc., Franklin, TN
Primary Contact: Jim R. Kendrick, Chief Executive Officer
COO: Roy Finch, Chief Operating Officer
CFO: Todd Johnson, Chief Financial Officer
CMO: Kenneth McClure, M.D., Chief of Staff
CIO: Keith Jarvis, Director Information Systems
CHR: Terry Hardan, Director Human Resources
CNO: Stephanie Foster, MSN, Chief Nursing Officer
Web address: www.longviewregional.com
**Control:** Partnership, Investor–owned, for–profit **Service:** General Medical and Surgical

**Staffed Beds: 198 Admissions: 8283 Census: 94 Outpatient Visits: 83974 Births: 1717 Total Expense ($000): 132785 Payroll Expense ($000): 48109 Personnel: 917**

☐ **OCEANS BEHAVIORAL HOSPITAL LONGVIEW (454117)**, 615 Clinic Drive, Zip 75605–5172; tel. 903/212–3105 **A**1 10 **F**64 68 98 100 101 103 104 **S** Audubon Behavioral Healthcare, Longview, TX
Primary Contact: Lauren Weber, Administrator
Web address: www.oceanslongview.com/
**Control:** Corporation, Investor–owned, for–profit **Service:** Psychiatric

**Staffed Beds: 24 Admissions: 390 Census: 16 Outpatient Visits: 7383 Births: 0 Total Expense ($000): 4930 Payroll Expense ($000): 2049 Personnel: 59**

✠ **SELECT SPECIALTY HOSPITAL–LONGVIEW (452087)**, 700 East Marshall Avenue, 1st Floor, Zip 75601–5580; tel. 903/315–1100 **A**1 9 10 **F**1 3 28 29 40 75 77 85 91 92 130 148 **S** Select Medical Corporation, Mechanicsburg, PA
Primary Contact: Dennis Baker, Chief Executive Officer
Web address: www.selectspecialtyhospitals.com/company/locations/longview.aspx
**Control:** Corporation, Investor–owned, for–profit **Service:** Long–Term Acute Care hospital

**Staffed Beds: 32 Admissions: 415 Census: 31 Outpatient Visits: 0 Births: 0 Total Expense ($000): 14404 Payroll Expense ($000): 6726 Personnel: 121**

**LUBBOCK—Lubbock County**

✠ **COVENANT CHILDREN'S HOSPITAL (453306)**, 4015 22nd Place, Zip 79410; tel. 806/725–1011 **A**1 3 5 9 10 **F**3 19 21 23 25 27 30 31 32 40 41 43 50 59 72 73 81 89 **P**8 **S** Covenant Health System, Lubbock, TX
Primary Contact: Christopher J. Dougherty, Chief Executive Officer
CMO: Scott Robins, M.D., Chief Medical Officer
CIO: Jim Reid, Vice President and Chief Information Officer
CHR: Rodney Cates, Senior Vice President Human Resources
Web address: www.covenanthealth.org/About–Us/Facilities/Childrens–Hospital.aspx
**Control:** Other not–for–profit (including NFP Corporation) **Service:** Children's general

**Staffed Beds: 73 Admissions: 2377 Census: 52 Outpatient Visits: 30117 Births: 0 Total Expense ($000): 62543 Payroll Expense ($000): 21051 Personnel: 201**

✠ **COVENANT MEDICAL CENTER (450040)**, 3615 19th Street, Zip 79410–1203, Mailing Address: P.O. Box 1201, Zip 79408–1201; tel. 806/725–0000, (Includes COVENANT MEDICAL CENTER–LAKESIDE, 4000 24th Street, Zip 79410–1894; tel. 806/725–0000) **A**1 3 6 9 10 **F**7 8 15 17 18 19 20 22 23 26 27 28 30 34 35 37 39 40 43 46 47 48 49 50 51 53 54 55 57 58 59 60 61 63 64 65 68 70 71 74 75 77 78 79 81 82 83 84 85 86 87 90 91 92 93 94 96 98 102 105 107 108 109 111 114 115 116 117 119 120 121 123 129 130 131 132 135 143 144 146 147 148 **P**6 8 **S** Covenant Health System, Lubbock, TX
Primary Contact: Walt Cathey, Chief Executive Officer
CFO: John A. Grigson, Vice President and Chief Financial Officer
CMO: Craig Rhyne, M.D., Chief Medical Officer
CIO: Troy Pratt, Information Technology Site Director
CHR: Chris Shaver, Vice President Human Resources
CNO: Karen Baggerly, Chief Nursing Officer and Vice President
Web address: www.covenanthealth.org
**Control:** Other not–for–profit (including NFP Corporation) **Service:** General Medical and Surgical

**Staffed Beds: 551 Admissions: 22407 Census: 329 Outpatient Visits: 65137 Births: 2495 Total Expense ($000): 498952 Payroll Expense ($000): 148858 Personnel: 3049**

**COVENANT SPECIALTY HOSPITAL (452102)**, 3815 20th Street, Zip 79410–1235; tel. 806/725–9200 **A**10 **F**1 3 29 30 31 60 63 68 75 77 78 79 87 119 130 143 148 **S** Covenant Health System, Lubbock, TX
Primary Contact: Stuart Oertli, Executive Director
CFO: John Carigson, Chief Financial Officer
CMO: Naidu Chekuru, M.D., Chief Medical Officer
CHR: Chris Shaver, Vice President Human Resources
CNO: Julie Bell, Director of Nursing
Web address: www.covenanthealth.org/view/Facilities/Specialty_Hospital
**Control:** Partnership, Investor–owned, for–profit **Service:** Long–Term Acute Care hospital

**Staffed Beds: 56 Admissions: 486 Census: 33 Outpatient Visits: 0 Births: 0 Total Expense ($000): 17761 Payroll Expense ($000): 6306 Personnel: 124**

✠ **GRACE MEDICAL CENTER (450162)**, 2412 50th Street, Zip 79412–2494; tel. 806/788–4100 **A**1 3 9 10 **F**3 8 11 12 15 29 34 35 40 44 45 47 49 50 51 59 64 70 75 78 79 81 82 85 87 107 108 110 111 114 115 118 119 135 146
Primary Contact: Vanessa Reasoner, Chief Executive Officer
CMO: Howard Beck, M.D., Chief of Staff
CIO: Jason Derouen, Director Management Information Systems
CHR: Sally Charles, Coordinator Human Resources
Web address: www.gracehealthsystem.com
**Control:** Partnership, Investor–owned, for–profit **Service:** General Medical and Surgical

**Staffed Beds: 43 Admissions: 925 Census: 7 Outpatient Visits: 77833 Births: 0 Total Expense ($000): 43706 Payroll Expense ($000): 8676 Personnel: 194**

**LUBBOCK HEART HOSPITAL (450876)**, 4810 North Loop 289, Zip 79416–3025; tel. 806/687–7777 **A**3 5 9 10 **F**3 17 18 20 22 24 26 29 34 40 45 57 59 79 81 82 85 107 108 115 119 130 131 148
Primary Contact: Charley O. Trimble, Chief Executive Officer
Web address: www.lubbockhearthospital.com
**Control:** Partnership, Investor–owned, for–profit **Service:** General Medical and Surgical

**Staffed Beds: 73 Admissions: 3251 Census: 32 Outpatient Visits: 94498 Births: 0 Total Expense ($000): 61963 Payroll Expense ($000): 18342 Personnel: 421**

☐ **SUNRISE CANYON HOSPITAL (454093)**, 1950 Aspen Avenue, Zip 79404–1211, Mailing Address: P.O. Box 2828, Zip 79408–2828; tel. 806/740–1420 **A**1 10 **F**29 35 38 42 53 56 61 86 98 99 101 103 130 132 143 146 **P**5
Primary Contact: Leonard Valderaz, Administrator
CFO: Jerome Flores, Chief Financial Officer
CMO: Dana Butler, M.D., Medical Director
CIO: Wendy Potitadkul, Chief Information Officer
CHR: Barbara McCann, Director Human Resources
Web address: www.starcarelubbock.org
**Control:** Other not–for–profit (including NFP Corporation) **Service:** Psychiatric

**Staffed Beds: 30 Admissions: 470 Census: 24 Outpatient Visits: 0 Births: 0 Total Expense ($000): 4617 Payroll Expense ($000): 1696 Personnel: 39**

TX

□ **TEXAS SPECIALTY HOSPITAL AT LUBBOCK (452116)**, 4302 Princeton Street, Zip 79415–1304; tel. 806/723–8700 **A**1 9 10 **F**1 12 29 60 92 107 111 119 148 **S** Fundamental Long Term Care Holdings, LLC, Sparks Glencoe, MD
Primary Contact: Deanna Graves, Chief Executive Officer
CFO: Robert Stanley, Chief Financial Officer
CMO: Michael Ragain, M.D., Chief Medical Officer
CNO: Bernadette Hernandez, R.N., Chief Nursing Officer
**Control:** Corporation, Investor–owned, for–profit **Service:** Long–Term Acute Care hospital

**Staffed Beds: 25 Admissions: 322 Census: 25 Outpatient Visits: 0 Births: 0 Total Expense ($000): 10036 Payroll Expense ($000): 3910 Personnel: 58**

□ **TRUSTPOINT HOSPITAL (670050)**, 4302 Princeton Street, Zip 79415–1304; tel. 806/749–2222 **A**1 3 5 9 10 **F**3 29 34 35 40 56 64 68 74 75 77 79 85 86 87 90 91 94 96 98 101 103 130 148 **S** Polaris Hospital Company, Brentwood, TN
Primary Contact: Craig Bragg, Chief Executive Officer
CFO: Crystal Roach, Chief Financial Officer
CNO: John Parsons, R.N., Chief Nursing Officer
Web address: www.trustpointhospital.com/
**Control:** Partnership, Investor–owned, for–profit **Service:** Rehabilitation

**Staffed Beds: 67 Admissions: 1392 Census: 49 Outpatient Visits: 7 Births: 0 Total Expense ($000): 19346 Payroll Expense ($000): 7631 Personnel: 190**

◇ **UNIVERSITY MEDICAL CENTER (450686)**, 602 Indiana Avenue, Zip 79415–3364, Mailing Address: P.O. Box 5980, Zip 79408–5980; tel. 806/775–8200 **A**2 3 5 8 9 10 21 **F**3 7 8 11 12 13 15 16 17 18 19 20 22 24 26 27 28 29 30 31 34 35 38 40 41 43 45 46 47 48 49 50 54 55 58 59 60 62 64 65 66 68 70 72 74 75 76 77 78 79 80 81 82 83 84 85 86 87 88 89 93 94 96 97 102 107 108 109 110 111 112 114 115 116 117 118 119 120 121 123 124 126 127 130 131 132 135 136 143 144 146 147 148
Primary Contact: David G. Allison, President and Chief Executive Officer
COO: Mark Funderburk, Executive Vice President and Administrator
CFO: Jeff Dane, Executive Vice President and Chief Financial Officer
CMO: Michael Ragain, M.D., Chief Medical Officer and Senior Vice President
CIO: Bill Eubanks, Senior Vice President and Chief Information Officer
CHR: Adrienne Cozart, Vice President Human Resources
CNO: Tammy J. Williams, R.N., Chief Nursing Officer and Senior Vice President
Web address: www.umchealthsystem.com
**Control:** Hospital district or authority, Government, nonfederal **Service:** General Medical and Surgical

**Staffed Beds: 446 Admissions: 27110 Census: 335 Outpatient Visits: 292301 Births: 2974 Total Expense ($000): 456455 Payroll Expense ($000): 171698 Personnel: 2964**

### LUFKIN—Angelina County

★ **CHI ST. LUKE'S HEALTH MEMORIAL LUFKIN (450211)**, 1201 West Frank Avenue, Zip 75904–3357, Mailing Address: P.O. Box 1447, Zip 75902–1447; tel. 936/634–8111, (Data for 181 days) **A**2 9 10 19 **F**3 11 12 13 14 15 17 18 20 21 22 23 24 26 28 29 30 31 34 35 37 38 40 44 45 46 47 48 49 50 51 56 57 59 60 61 62 63 64 68 70 71 74 75 76 77 78 79 81 82 83 84 85 86 87 90 91 92 93 97 100 101 102 107 108 110 111 112 114 115 116 117 119 121 126 129 130 132 135 143 144 146 147 148 **S** Catholic Health Initiatives, Englewood, CO
Primary Contact: Gary N. Looper, Chief Executive Officer
CFO: Kristi Gay, Chief Financial Officer
CHR: Tanya Tyler, Vice President Human Resources
Web address: www.memorialhealth.us/centers/lufkin
**Control:** Other not–for–profit (including NFP Corporation) **Service:** General Medical and Surgical

**Staffed Beds: 217 Admissions: 3359 Census: 96 Outpatient Visits: 40913 Births: 173 Total Expense ($000): 66196 Payroll Expense ($000): 18525 Personnel: 934**

★ **CHI ST. LUKE'S HEALTH MEMORIAL SPECIALTY HOSPITAL (452031)**, 1201 West Frank Avenue, Zip 75904–3357, Mailing Address: P.O. Box 1447, Zip 75902–1447; tel. 936/639–7530, (Data for 181 days) **A**9 10 **F**1 3 29 31 50 61 68 74 75 85 86 130 145 **S** Catholic Health Initiatives, Englewood, CO
Primary Contact: Leslie Leach, Administrator
CFO: Ken Miller, Chief Financial Officer
CMO: Karl Krohn, M.D., President Medical Staff
CHR: Donald Morris, Vice President Human Resources
CNO: Brenda Broadway, Chief Nursing Officer
Web address: www.memorialhealth.org
**Control:** Other not–for–profit (including NFP Corporation) **Service:** Long–Term Acute Care hospital

**Staffed Beds: 20 Admissions: 124 Census: 19 Outpatient Visits: 0 Births: 0 Total Expense ($000): 4936 Payroll Expense ($000): 3024 Personnel: 71**

□ **OCEANS BEHAVIORAL HOSPITAL LUFKIN (454123)**, 302 Gobblers Knob, Zip 75904–5419; tel. 936/632–2276 **A**1 10 **F**64 98 100 101 103 104 130 **P**6 **S** Audubon Behavioral Healthcare, Longview, TX
Primary Contact: Frances Dick, Chief Executive Officer
Web address: www.oceanslufkin.com/
**Control:** Corporation, Investor–owned, for–profit **Service:** Psychiatric

**Staffed Beds: 24 Admissions: 305 Census: 14 Outpatient Visits: 3207 Births: 0 Total Expense ($000): 4295 Payroll Expense ($000): 1740 Personnel: 58**

✦ **WOODLAND HEIGHTS MEDICAL CENTER (450484)**, 505 South John Reddit Drive, Zip 75904–3157, Mailing Address: P.O. Box 150610, Zip 75904; tel. 936/634–8311, (Total facility includes 15 beds in nursing home–type unit) **A**1 9 10 19 **F**8 11 12 13 15 18 20 22 24 26 28 29 30 34 35 40 41 46 49 50 51 53 57 59 64 68 70 72 74 75 76 77 78 79 81 82 85 86 87 93 102 107 108 111 114 115 118 119 126 128 129 130 131 146 147 148 **S** Community Health Systems, Inc., Franklin, TN
Primary Contact: Kyle Swift, Chief Executive Officer
COO: Conner Hickey, Chief Operating Officer
CFO: William Whiddon, Chief Financial Officer
CMO: William Strinden, M.D., Chief of Staff
CIO: Kalvin Buckley, Director Information Systems
CHR: Emilie Hobbs, Director Human Resources
CNO: Cathy L. Busbee, Chief Nursing Officer
Web address: www.woodlandheights.net
**Control:** Partnership, Investor–owned, for–profit **Service:** General Medical and Surgical

**Staffed Beds: 115 Admissions: 5184 Census: 66 Outpatient Visits: 49059 Births: 1042 Total Expense ($000): 79358 Payroll Expense ($000): 30630 Personnel: 539**

### LULING—Caldwell County

✦ **POST ACUTE/WARM SPRINGS SPECIALTY HOSPITAL OF LULING (452062)**, 200 Memorial Drive, Zip 78648–3213; tel. 830/875–8400 **A**1 9 10 **F**1 3 29 53 64 93 96 130 133 148 **S** Post Acute Medical, LLC, Enola, PA
Primary Contact: Jana Kuykendall, Chief Executive Officer
CFO: James Asberry, Chief Financial Officer
Web address: www.warmsprings.org
**Control:** Partnership, Investor–owned, for–profit **Service:** Long–Term Acute Care hospital

**Staffed Beds: 34 Admissions: 399 Census: 33 Outpatient Visits: 11303 Births: 0 Total Expense ($000): 13840 Payroll Expense ($000): 6059 Personnel: 152**

✦ **SETON EDGAR B. DAVIS HOSPITAL (451371)**, 130 Hays Street, Zip 78648–3207; tel. 830/875–7000 **A**1 9 10 18 **F**3 11 15 18 29 30 35 40 43 44 45 50 56 68 71 75 77 78 79 81 83 97 103 107 110 111 114 119 127 130 133 135 143 146 **P**3 8 **S** Ascension Health, Saint Louis, MO
Primary Contact: Apryl Haynes, R.N., Vice President, Chief Operating Officer, Chief Nursing Officer and Administrator
CFO: Thomas E. Gallagher, Chief Financial Officer
CMO: Martin E. Weiner, M.D., Chief of Staff
CIO: Mike Minks, Chief Information Officer
CHR: Joe Canales, Director Human Resources
CNO: Apryl Haynes, R.N., Vice President, Chief Operating Officer, Chief Nursing Officer and Administrator
Web address: www.seton.net/locations/edgar_davis/
**Control:** Church–operated, Nongovernment, not–for profit **Service:** General Medical and Surgical

**Staffed Beds: 25 Admissions: 804 Census: 9 Outpatient Visits: 64729 Births: 0 Total Expense ($000): 22888 Payroll Expense ($000): 10967 Personnel: 146**

**WARM SPRINGS SPECIALTY HOSPITAL OF LULING** See Post Acute/Warm Springs Specialty Hospital of Luling

### MADISONVILLE—Madison County

✦ **MADISON ST. JOSEPH HEALTH CENTER (451316)**, 100 West Cross Street, Zip 77864–2432, Mailing Address: Box 698, Zip 77864–0698; tel. 936/348–2631 **A**1 9 10 18 **F**3 7 11 15 30 40 43 50 57 59 64 68 75 77 93 103 107 108 110 119 130 133 135 146 148 **S** Catholic Health Initiatives, Englewood, CO
Primary Contact: Reed Edmundson, Administrator
COO: Reed Edmundson, Administrator
CFO: Kris Smith, Controller
CMO: Grover Hubley, M.D., President Medical Staff
CIO: Maurita Turner, Team Leader Health Information Systems Services
CHR: Marybeth Murphy, Director Human Resources
CNO: Roxanne Hass, Director of Nursing
Web address: www.st-joseph.org
**Control:** Church–operated, Nongovernment, not–for profit **Service:** General Medical and Surgical

**Staffed Beds: 25 Admissions: 230 Census: 7 Outpatient Visits: 18185 Births: 0 Total Expense ($000): 10568 Payroll Expense ($000): 4832 Personnel: 88**

**TX**

*Many Facility Codes have changed. Please refer to the AHA Guide Code Chart.*   © 2015 AHA Guide

## MANSFIELD—Tarrant County

⊠ **KINDRED HOSPITAL–MANSFIELD (452019)**, 1802 Highway 157 North, Zip 76063–3923; tel. 817/473–6101 **A**1 9 10 **F**1 3 29 30 45 46 60 70 75 82 85 107 130 132 148 **S** Kindred Healthcare, Louisville, KY
Primary Contact: Susan Schaetti, Chief Executive Officer
CFO: Judy Baker, Chief Financial Officer
Web address: www.kindredmansfield.com
**Control:** Corporation, Investor–owned, for–profit **Service:** Long–Term Acute Care hospital

**Staffed Beds:** 55 **Admissions:** 439 **Census:** 31 **Outpatient Visits:** 90 **Births:** 0 **Total Expense ($000):** 16020 **Payroll Expense ($000):** 6514 **Personnel:** 111

⊠ **METHODIST MANSFIELD MEDICAL CENTER (670023)**, 2700 East Broad Street, Zip 76063–5899; tel. 682/622–2000 **A**1 9 10 **F**3 11 13 15 18 20 22 24 29 30 31 34 35 37 40 45 46 48 49 50 58 59 60 64 68 70 72 74 76 78 79 81 82 85 87 93 97 107 108 110 111 115 118 119 126 130 132 146 148 **P**1 7 **S** Methodist Health System, Dallas, TX
Primary Contact: John E. Phillips, FACHE, President
CFO: Jary Ganske, Chief Financial Officer
CMO: Sam Bagchi, Chief Medical Officer
CIO: Pamela McNutt, Senior Vice President and Chief Information Officer
CHR: Judy K. Laister, Director, Human Resources
CNO: Nora Frasier, R.N., Chief Nursing Officer
Web address: www.methodisthealthsystem.org/mansfield
**Control:** Other not–for–profit (including NFP Corporation) **Service:** General Medical and Surgical

**Staffed Beds:** 175 **Admissions:** 10269 **Census:** 117 **Outpatient Visits:** 78391 **Births:** 2148 **Total Expense ($000):** 134949 **Payroll Expense ($000):** 62146 **Personnel:** 823

## MARLIN—Falls County

★ **FALLS COMMUNITY HOSPITAL AND CLINIC (450348)**, 322 Coleman Street, Zip 76661–2358, Mailing Address: P.O. Box 60, Zip 76661–0060; tel. 254/803–3561 **A**9 10 20 **F**3 11 32 33 34 35 36 40 43 45 53 56 57 59 64 65 66 68 75 82 87 91 93 97 99 103 104 107 114 127 129 131 133 135 146 148
Primary Contact: Willis L. Reese, Administrator
COO: Becca Brewer, Chief Operations Officer
CFO: Willis L. Reese, Administrator
CMO: James Scott Crockett, M.D., Chief of Staff
CIO: Chris Smith, Chief Information Officer
CHR: Peggy Polster, Manager Personnel and Administrative Assistant
CNO: Tasha Burnett, Director of Nursing
Web address: www.fallshospital.com
**Control:** Other not–for–profit (including NFP Corporation) **Service:** General Medical and Surgical

**Staffed Beds:** 32 **Admissions:** 447 **Census:** 5 **Outpatient Visits:** 73598 **Births:** 0 **Total Expense ($000):** 18947 **Payroll Expense ($000):** 6109 **Personnel:** 165

## MARSHALL—Harrison County

☐ **GOOD SHEPHERD MEDICAL CENTER–MARSHALL (450032)**, 811 South Washington Avenue, Zip 75670–5336, Mailing Address: P.O. Box 1599, Zip 75671–1599; tel. 903/927–6000 **A**1 3 9 10 **F**3 11 13 15 18 28 29 30 34 35 40 43 49 50 53 54 57 59 60 64 65 68 70 75 77 79 80 81 86 87 90 93 97 102 103 107 110 115 119 127 129 130 131 132 145 146 147 148 **P**7 8 **S** Good Shepherd Health System, Longview, TX
Primary Contact: Russell J. Collier, FACHE, President and Chief Executive Officer
COO: Keith Creel, Vice President Operations
CFO: Tim Pileggi, Interim Chief Financial Officer
CMO: Larry Verfurth, D.O., Executive Vice President and Chief Medical Officer
CIO: Walter Grimes, Director Information Technology
CHR: Ginger Morrow, Executive Vice President Human Resources
CNO: Keith Kirbow, R.N., Vice President and Chief Nursing Officer
Web address: www.gsmcmarshall.org
**Control:** Other not–for–profit (including NFP Corporation) **Service:** General Medical and Surgical

**Staffed Beds:** 140 **Admissions:** 4156 **Census:** 41 **Outpatient Visits:** 97811 **Births:** 531 **Total Expense ($000):** 61386 **Payroll Expense ($000):** 21373 **Personnel:** 485

## MCALLEN—Hidalgo County

**LIFECARE HOSPITALS OF SOUTH TEXAS–MCALLEN** See Lifecare Hospitals of South Texas–North McAllen

⊠ **LIFECARE HOSPITALS OF SOUTH TEXAS–NORTH MCALLEN (452063)**, 5101 North Jackson, Zip 78504–6343; tel. 956/926–7000, (Includes LIFECARE HOSPITALS OF SOUTH TEXAS–MCALLEN, 2001 South M Street, Zip 78503; tel. 956/688–4300) **A**1 9 10 **F**1 3 29 57 75 77 85 87 148 **S** LifeCare Management Services, Plano, TX
Primary Contact: Angel Lozano, Chief Executive Officer
Web address: www.lifecare–hospitals.com/hospital/southtexas
**Control:** Corporation, Investor–owned, for–profit **Service:** Long–Term Acute Care hospital

**Staffed Beds:** 84 **Admissions:** 836 **Census:** 58 **Outpatient Visits:** 0 **Births:** 0 **Total Expense ($000):** 24923 **Payroll Expense ($000):** 10588 **Personnel:** 206

⊠ **RIO GRANDE REGIONAL HOSPITAL (450711)**, 101 East Ridge Road, Zip 78503–1299; tel. 956/632–6000 **A**1 3 9 10 **F**3 8 11 12 13 15 18 19 20 21 22 23 24 25 26 27 29 30 31 34 35 39 40 42 43 45 46 49 50 54 56 57 59 60 64 68 70 71 72 73 74 75 76 78 79 81 85 87 88 89 93 107 108 110 111 114 118 119 126 130 132 146 147 148 **P**7 **S** HCA, Nashville, TN
Primary Contact: Cristina Rivera, Chief Executive Officer
COO: David Elgarico, Chief Operating Officer
CFO: William Saller, Chief Financial Officer
CHR: Marjorie Whittemore, Director Human Resources
Web address: www.riohealth.com
**Control:** Partnership, Investor–owned, for–profit **Service:** General Medical and Surgical

**Staffed Beds:** 320 **Admissions:** 14323 **Census:** 168 **Outpatient Visits:** 103122 **Births:** 2474 **Total Expense ($000):** 134486 **Payroll Expense ($000):** 60718 **Personnel:** 806

**SOLARA HOSPITAL MCALLEN (452095)**, 301 West Expressway 83, Zip 78503–3045; tel. 956/632–4880 **A**9 10 22 **F**1 3 29 30 56 57 68 70 75 77 85 86 87 91 130 148 **S** Cornerstone Healthcare Group, Dallas, TX
Primary Contact: Chris Chizek, Chief Executive Officer
Web address: www.chghospitals.com/mcallen/
**Control:** Partnership, Investor–owned, for–profit **Service:** Long–Term Acute Care hospital

**Staffed Beds:** 71 **Admissions:** 630 **Census:** 45 **Outpatient Visits:** 0 **Births:** 0 **Total Expense ($000):** 20025 **Payroll Expense ($000):** 8967 **Personnel:** 156

## MCCAMEY—Upton County

★ **MCCAMEY COUNTY HOSPITAL DISTRICT (451309)**, 2500 Highway 305 South, Zip 79752, Mailing Address: P.O. Box 1200, Zip 79752–1200; tel. 432/652–8626, (Total facility includes 30 beds in nursing home–type unit) **A**9 10 18 **F**3 40 53 59 64 65 66 93 127 128 133
Primary Contact: Jaime Ramirez, Chief Executive Officer
COO: Tana Robertson, Chief Operating Officer
CFO: Jason J. Menefee, Chief Financial Officer
CMO: Ramon Domingo, M.D., Chief of Staff
CIO: Larry Rollins, Supervisor Information Technology
CHR: Judith Gulihur, Director Human Resources
CNO: Cheryl Roberts, Chief Nursing Officer
Web address: www.mccameyhospital.org
**Control:** Hospital district or authority, Government, nonfederal **Service:** General Medical and Surgical

**Staffed Beds:** 44 **Admissions:** 53 **Census:** 23 **Outpatient Visits:** 5686 **Births:** 0 **Total Expense ($000):** 9072 **Payroll Expense ($000):** 3696 **Personnel:** 96

## MCKINNEY—Collin County

⊠ **BAYLOR MEDICAL CENTER AT MCKINNEY (670082)**, 5252 West University Drive, Zip 75071–7822; tel. 469/764–1000 **A**1 5 9 10 **F**3 13 15 18 20 22 26 29 30 34 35 40 45 46 47 49 50 51 57 67 70 72 73 74 75 76 77 78 79 81 85 87 107 110 111 114 115 119 126 130 131 132 146 147 148 **S** Baylor Scott & White Health, Dallas, TX
Primary Contact: Scott Peek, FACHE, President
COO: Melissa Winter, R.N., Chief Operating Officer and Chief Nursing Officer
CFO: Steve Roussel, Chief Financial Officer
CMO: Jeff Kerr, M.D., Chief Medical Officer
CNO: Melissa Winter, R.N., Chief Operating Officer and Chief Nursing Officer
Web address: www.baylorhealth.com/PhysiciansLocations/McKinney/Pages/Default.aspx
**Control:** Other not–for–profit (including NFP Corporation) **Service:** General Medical and Surgical

**Staffed Beds:** 78 **Admissions:** 5973 **Census:** 62 **Outpatient Visits:** 41025 **Births:** 1774 **Total Expense ($000):** 113721 **Payroll Expense ($000):** 37620 **Personnel:** 382

**TX**

| **Hospital, Medicare Provider Number, Address, Telephone, Approval, Facility, and Physician Codes, Health Care System** | | |
|---|---|---|
| ★ American Hospital Association (AHA) membership | ○ Healthcare Facilities Accreditation Program | ⇑ Center for Improvement in Healthcare Quality Accreditation |
| ☐ The Joint Commission accreditation | ◇ DNV Healthcare Inc. accreditation | △ Commission on Accreditation of Rehabilitation Facilities (CARF) accreditation |

⊞ **MEDICAL CENTER OF MCKINNEY (450403)**, 4500 Medical Center Drive, Zip 75069–1650; tel. 972/547–8000, (Includes WYSONG CAMPUS, 130 South Central Expressway, Zip 75070; tel. 972/548–5300) **A**1 9 10 **F**3 4 11 13 18 20 22 24 26 28 29 30 34 37 40 45 49 50 56 57 59 60 64 68 70 72 74 75 76 77 78 79 81 82 85 87 90 91 92 93 94 96 97 98 102 103 107 108 109 111 114 115 119 126 130 131 132 146 147 148 **S** HCA, Nashville, TN
Primary Contact: Ernest C. Lynch, III, President and Chief Executive Officer
COO: LaSharndra Barbarin, Chief Operating Officer
CFO: Dwayne Ray, Chief Financial Officer
CIO: Kevin Fletcher, Director Information Systems
CHR: Senta Miles, Director Human Resources
CNO: Kimberly Kay Hatchel, Chief Nursing Officer
Web address: www.medicalcenterofmckinney.com
**Control:** Partnership, Investor–owned, for–profit **Service:** General Medical and Surgical

**Staffed Beds:** 219 **Admissions:** 10794 **Census:** 162 **Outpatient Visits:** 61568 **Births:** 1001 **Total Expense ($000):** 120348 **Payroll Expense ($000):** 52817 **Personnel:** 793

☐ **METHODIST MCKINNEY HOSPITAL (670069)**, 8000 West Eldorado Parkway, Zip 75070–5940; tel. 972/569–2700 **A**1 9 10 **F**3 15 29 34 40 45 51 70 75 79 81 82 85 93 107 110 111 119 126 129 130 131
Primary Contact: Joseph Minissale, President
CFO: Mike Conroy, Chief Financial Officer
CIO: Sharon Stark, R.N., Manager Clinical Information Systems
CHR: Diana Hume, Manager Human Resources
CNO: Staci Jones, R.N., Chief Nursing Officer
Web address: www.methodistmckinneyhospital.com
**Control:** Partnership, Investor–owned, for–profit **Service:** General Medical and Surgical

**Staffed Beds:** 21 **Admissions:** 730 **Census:** 6 **Outpatient Visits:** 26724 **Births:** 0 **Total Expense ($000):** 44690 **Payroll Expense ($000):** 8122 **Personnel:** 137

☐ **VICTORY MEDICAL CENTER CRAIG RANCH**, 6045 Alma Road, Zip 75070–2188; tel. 972/908–1215 **A**1 **F**3 12 29 40 45 46 47 48 49 70 79 81 82 85 86 87 130 141 **S** Victory Healthcare, The Woodlands, TX
Primary Contact: Ashley Anson, Chief Executive Officer
CFO: Ron Collins, Chief Financial Officer
CHR: Dorie Alston, Manager Human Resources
CNO: Cathy Woodard, R.N., Chief Clinical Officer
Web address: www.victory–healthcare.com/craig–ranch/
**Control:** Partnership, Investor–owned, for–profit **Service:** Surgical

**Staffed Beds:** 24 **Admissions:** 156 **Census:** 1 **Outpatient Visits:** 2361 **Births:** 0 **Total Expense ($000):** 32270 **Payroll Expense ($000):** 5521 **Personnel:** 83

**MESQUITE—Dallas County**

⊞ **DALLAS REGIONAL MEDICAL CENTER (450688)**, 1011 North Galloway Avenue, Zip 75149–2433; tel. 214/320–7000 **A**1 9 10 **F**3 12 15 18 20 22 24 26 29 30 34 35 40 41 43 45 46 49 50 54 56 57 59 64 65 67 68 70 74 75 79 80 81 85 87 107 108 110 111 114 119 126 130 134 135 146 148 **S** Prime Healthcare Services, Ontario, CA
Primary Contact: Raji Kumar, Regional Chief Executive Officer
CMO: Srinivas Gunukula, M.D., Chief of Staff
Web address: www.dallasregionalmedicalcenter.com
**Control:** Corporation, Investor–owned, for–profit **Service:** General Medical and Surgical

**Staffed Beds:** 100 **Admissions:** 3441 **Census:** 42 **Outpatient Visits:** 59745 **Births:** 0 **Total Expense ($000):** 60691 **Payroll Expense ($000):** 22165 **Personnel:** 397

☐ **MESQUITE REHABILITATION INSTITUTE (673045)**, 1023 North Belt Line Road, Zip 75149–1788; tel. 972/216–2400 **A**1 9 10 **F**3 28 29 30 34 35 57 59 64 82 90 91 93 96 148 **S** Ernest Health, Inc., Albuquerque, NM
Primary Contact: Brian Abraham, Chief Operating Officer
Web address: www.mesquiterehab.ernesthealth.com/
**Control:** Corporation, Investor–owned, for–profit **Service:** Rehabilitation

**Staffed Beds:** 20 **Admissions:** 496 **Census:** 18 **Outpatient Visits:** 2204 **Births:** 0 **Total Expense ($000):** 6133 **Payroll Expense ($000):** 3784 **Personnel:** 48

☐ **MESQUITE SPECIALTY HOSPITAL (452100)**, 1024 North Galloway Avenue, Zip 75149–2434; tel. 972/216–2300 **A**1 9 10 **F**1 3 29 74 75 77 79 85 87 130 135 148 **S** Ernest Health, Inc., Albuquerque, NM
Primary Contact: Louis Bradley, Chief Executive Officer
Web address: www.msh.ernesthealth.com
**Control:** Partnership, Investor–owned, for–profit **Service:** Long–Term Acute Care hospital

**Staffed Beds:** 40 **Admissions:** 492 **Census:** 35 **Outpatient Visits:** 0 **Births:** 0 **Total Expense ($000):** 18896 **Payroll Expense ($000):** 7269 **Personnel:** 135

**MEXIA—Limestone County**

⊞ **PARKVIEW REGIONAL HOSPITAL (450400)**, 600 South Bonham, Zip 76667–3603; tel. 254/562–5332 **A**1 9 10 20 **F**3 11 15 29 30 34 35 40 43 45 51 53 56 57 59 64 65 70 75 77 78 79 81 85 86 87 97 98 103 107 108 110 111 114 119 127 130 132 133 146 **P**5 6 **S** LifePoint Health, Brentwood, TN
Primary Contact: Alan Daugherty, Interim Chief Executive Officer
Web address: www.parkviewregional.com
**Control:** Partnership, Investor–owned, for–profit **Service:** General Medical and Surgical

**Staffed Beds:** 58 **Admissions:** 734 **Census:** 8 **Outpatient Visits:** 22347 **Births:** 0 **Total Expense ($000):** 16221 **Payroll Expense ($000):** 7592 **Personnel:** 149

**MIDLAND—Midland County**

⇑ **CONTINUECARE HOSPITAL AT MIDLAND MEMORIAL (670091)**, 4214 Andrews Highway, 3rd Floor, Zip 79703–4822; tel. 432/221–3563, (Nonreporting) **A**10 22 **S** Community Hospital Corporation, Plano, TX
Web address: www.continuecare.org/midland/
**Control:** Hospital district or authority, Government, nonfederal **Service:** Long–Term Acute Care hospital

**Staffed Beds:** 29

⊞ **HEALTHSOUTH REHABILITATION HOSPITAL MIDLAND–ODESSA (453057)**, 1800 Heritage Boulevard, Zip 79707–9750; tel. 432/520–1600 **A**1 5 9 10 **F**3 29 57 59 62 74 75 77 90 91 96 130 143 148 **S** HEALTHSOUTH Corporation, Birmingham, AL
Primary Contact: Christopher Wortham, Chief Executive Officer
CFO: Vivian Irwin, Chief Financial Officer and Controller
CMO: Mark A. Fredrickson, M.D., Medical Director
CHR: Tina Parker, Director Human Resources
Web address: www.healthsouthmidland.com
**Control:** Corporation, Investor–owned, for–profit **Service:** Rehabilitation

**Staffed Beds:** 60 **Admissions:** 1270 **Census:** 46 **Outpatient Visits:** 4971 **Births:** 0 **Total Expense ($000):** 16937 **Payroll Expense ($000):** 10756 **Personnel:** 179

★ ◇ **MIDLAND MEMORIAL HOSPITAL (450133)**, 400 Rosalind Redfern Grover Parkway, Zip 79701–6499; tel. 432/221–1111, (Includes MIDLAND MEMORIAL HOSPITAL, 400 Rosalind Redfern Grover Parkway, Zip 79701–5846; tel. 432/221–1111) **A**2 3 5 9 10 21 **F**3 8 11 12 13 15 17 18 20 22 24 26 28 29 30 31 32 34 35 37 40 43 45 49 50 56 57 59 61 64 68 70 73 74 75 76 77 78 79 81 82 83 84 85 86 87 88 89 93 97 107 108 111 114 115 116 117 118 119 124 126 129 130 131 132 135 145 146 147 148 **P**8
Primary Contact: Russell Meyers, President and Chief Executive Officer
COO: Robert L. Dent, R.N., Senior Vice President and Chief Operating Officer
CFO: Stephen Bowerman, Senior Vice President, Chief Financial Officer
CMO: Lawrence Wilson, M.D., Vice President, Chief Medical Officer
CIO: Taylor Weems, Vice President, Chief Information Officer
CHR: Roberta SoloRio, Vice President, Chief Human Resource Officer
CNO: Cori Armstead, MSN, Vice President, Chief Nursing Officer
Web address: www.midland–memorial.com
**Control:** Hospital district or authority, Government, nonfederal **Service:** General Medical and Surgical

**Staffed Beds:** 244 **Admissions:** 11690 **Census:** 147 **Outpatient Visits:** 148426 **Births:** 2548 **Total Expense ($000):** 242061 **Payroll Expense ($000):** 97316 **Personnel:** 1645

☐ **OCEANS BEHAVIORAL HEALTH CENTER PERMIAN BASIN (454110)**, 3300 South FM 1788, Zip 79706–2601; tel. 432/561–5915, (Nonreporting) **A**1 3 10 **S** Oceans Healthcare, Lake Charles, LA
Primary Contact: Kristin Harris, Interim Chief Executive Officer
Web address: www.oceanspermianbasin.com/
**Control:** Corporation, Investor–owned, for–profit **Service:** Psychiatric

**Staffed Beds:** 48

**MINERAL WELLS—Palo Pinto County**

⊞ **PALO PINTO GENERAL HOSPITAL (450565)**, 400 S.W. 25th Avenue, Zip 76067–8246; tel. 940/328–6403 **A**1 9 10 **F**11 13 15 17 18 28 29 32 34 40 43 45 46 51 53 54 57 59 62 63 64 65 66 68 69 71 74 75 76 77 79 81 84 86 87 91 93 107 108 110 111 114 119 127 129 130 131 133 135 146 147 **P**1
Primary Contact: Harris W. Brooks, Administrator and Chief Executive Officer
CFO: Dee Waldow, Chief Financial Officer
CMO: Alice Ramsey, M.D., Chief of Staff
CHR: Mary B. Braddock, Director Human Resources
CNO: Cheryl Kirby, Chief Nursing Officer
Web address: www.ppgh.com
**Control:** Hospital district or authority, Government, nonfederal **Service:** General Medical and Surgical

**Staffed Beds:** 42 **Admissions:** 1877 **Census:** 18 **Outpatient Visits:** 85090 **Births:** 344 **Total Expense ($000):** 36765 **Payroll Expense ($000):** 15734 **Personnel:** 298

*Many Facility Codes have changed. Please refer to the AHA Guide Code Chart.*   © 2015 AHA Guide

TX

## MISSION—Hidalgo County

✠ △ **MISSION REGIONAL MEDICAL CENTER (450176)**, 900 South Bryan Road, Zip 78572–6613; tel. 956/323–9103 **A**1 7 9 10 **F**3 11 12 13 15 18 20 22 29 30 31 34 35 40 43 45 46 49 50 51 57 59 60 64 65 66 68 70 72 74 75 76 77 79 81 85 87 89 90 93 96 107 108 110 111 115 119 130 132 146 147 148 **P**8
Primary Contact: Javier Iruegas, FACHE, Chief Executive Officer
COO: Carlos Trevino, Chief Operating Officer
CFO: Timothy J. McVey, Chief Financial Officer
CNO: Kennetha Foster, Chief Nursing Officer
Web address: www.missionrmc.org
**Control:** Other not–for–profit (including NFP Corporation) **Service:** General Medical and Surgical

**Staffed Beds:** 249 **Admissions:** 9097 **Census:** 131 **Outpatient Visits:** 76927 **Births:** 2358 **Total Expense ($000):** 116921 **Payroll Expense ($000):** 53215 **Personnel:** 973

## MONAHANS—Ward County

★ **WARD MEMORIAL HOSPITAL (451373)**, 406 South Gary Street, Zip 79756–4798, Mailing Address: P.O. Box 40, Zip 79756–0040; tel. 432/943–2511 **A**9 10 18 **F**3 40 43 45 64 65 66 81 82 89 93 107 114 119 127 131 133 148 **P**6
Primary Contact: Leticia Rodriguez, Chief Executive Officer
CFO: Leticia Rodriguez, Controller
CHR: Donna Lemon, Director Human Resources
Web address: www.wardmemorial.com
**Control:** County–Government, nonfederal **Service:** General Medical and Surgical

**Staffed Beds:** 25 **Admissions:** 360 **Census:** 3 **Outpatient Visits:** 23418 **Births:** 0 **Total Expense ($000):** 10143 **Payroll Expense ($000):** 4845 **Personnel:** 91

## MORTON—Cochran County

**COCHRAN MEMORIAL HOSPITAL (451366)**, 201 East Grant Street, Zip 79346–3444; tel. 806/266–5565 **A**9 10 18 **F**34 40 57 59 65 127 **P**6
Primary Contact: Larry Turney, Administrator
CHR: Niona Tunney, Director Human Resources
**Control:** Hospital district or authority, Government, nonfederal **Service:** General Medical and Surgical

**Staffed Beds:** 13 **Admissions:** 20 **Census:** 1 **Outpatient Visits:** 5227 **Births:** 0 **Total Expense ($000):** 3656 **Payroll Expense ($000):** 1769 **Personnel:** 45

## MOUNT PLEASANT—Titus County

✠ **TITUS REGIONAL MEDICAL CENTER (450080)**, 2001 North Jefferson Avenue, Zip 75455–2398; tel. 903/577–6000, (Total facility includes 7 beds in nursing home–type unit) **A**1 9 10 19 **F**3 7 11 12 13 15 18 19 20 24 26 28 29 30 34 35 39 40 43 45 47 50 51 53 54 56 57 58 59 64 68 70 73 74 75 76 78 79 81 82 85 89 90 93 97 98 103 108 110 111 114 115 117 118 119 121 123 127 128 129 130 132 135 147 148
Primary Contact: John P. Allen, Chief Executive Officer
CFO: Terry Scoggin, Chief Financial Officer
CMO: Chris Burling, M.D., Chief of Staff
CIO: Kevin Harris, Director Information Systems
CHR: Tony Piazza, Director Human Resources
CNO: Carol Slider, Chief Nursing Officer
Web address: www.titusregional.com
**Control:** Hospital district or authority, Government, nonfederal **Service:** General Medical and Surgical

**Staffed Beds:** 73 **Admissions:** 4504 **Census:** 48 **Outpatient Visits:** 194812 **Births:** 1092 **Total Expense ($000):** 67809 **Payroll Expense ($000):** 24715 **Personnel:** 504

## MUENSTER—Cooke County

**MUENSTER MEMORIAL HOSPITAL (451335)**, 605 North Maple Street, Zip 76252–2424, Mailing Address: P.O. Box 370, Zip 76252–0370; tel. 940/759–2271 **A**9 10 18 **F**11 35 40 43 45 53 57 59 62 64 65 75 77 81 93 107 114 119 127 130 133 146 **P**8
Primary Contact: Brian Roland, Chief Executive Officer
CFO: Richard Teeter, Chief Financial Officer
CMO: J. Stephen Jones, M.D., Chief of Staff
CIO: Sheri Hutchins, Director Health Information Management
**Control:** Hospital district or authority, Government, nonfederal **Service:** General Medical and Surgical

**Staffed Beds:** 18 **Admissions:** 257 **Census:** 9 **Outpatient Visits:** 4212 **Births:** 0 **Total Expense ($000):** 10408 **Payroll Expense ($000):** 4507 **Personnel:** 110

## MULESHOE—Bailey County

★ **MULESHOE AREA MEDICAL CENTER (451372)**, 708 South First Street, Zip 79347–3627; tel. 806/272–4524 **A**9 10 18 **F**3 11 29 34 35 40 43 50 59 64 65 68 69 75 77 93 107 114 119 127 130 133
Primary Contact: Tommy Johnson, Chief Executive Officer
CMO: Bruce Purdy, M.D., Chief of Staff
CHR: Suzanne Nichols, Director Human Resources
Web address: www.mahdtx.org
**Control:** Hospital district or authority, Government, nonfederal **Service:** General Medical and Surgical

**Staffed Beds:** 25 **Admissions:** 403 **Census:** 5 **Outpatient Visits:** 29648 **Births:** 0 **Total Expense ($000):** 8282 **Payroll Expense ($000):** 3127 **Personnel:** 103

## NACOGDOCHES—Nacogdoches County

✠ **NACOGDOCHES MEDICAL CENTER (450656)**, 4920 N.E. Stallings Drive, Zip 75965–1200; tel. 936/569–9481 **A**1 2 9 10 19 **F**13 15 18 20 22 23 24 26 29 31 34 35 39 40 42 45 46 47 48 49 50 51 56 57 59 60 64 68 70 74 75 76 77 78 79 81 82 85 86 87 93 107 108 110 111 114 115 116 117 118 119 120 121 123 129 130 131 132 135 146 147 148 **S** TENET Healthcare Corporation, Dallas, TX
Primary Contact: Gary L. Stokes, Chief Executive Officer
COO: Clay Farell, Chief Operating Officer
CFO: Frank Malek, Chief Financial Officer
CMO: Charles Thompson, M.D., Chief Medical Officer
CIO: Teresa Simon, Director Information Systems
CHR: Teresa Farrell, Chief Human Resources Officer
CNO: Mario B. Estrella, R.N., Chief Nursing Officer
Web address: www.nacmedicalcenter.com
**Control:** Partnership, Investor–owned, for–profit **Service:** General Medical and Surgical

**Staffed Beds:** 109 **Admissions:** 3861 **Census:** 40 **Outpatient Visits:** 52418 **Births:** 556 **Total Expense ($000):** 56535 **Payroll Expense ($000):** 19491 **Personnel:** 344

☐ **NACOGDOCHES MEMORIAL HOSPITAL (450508)**, 1204 North Mound Street, Zip 75961–4061; tel. 936/564–4611 **A**1 9 10 19 **F**3 7 11 13 15 18 20 22 24 28 29 30 31 34 35 38 40 43 49 50 57 59 61 64 68 70 74 76 77 78 79 80 81 85 86 89 90 93 96 107 108 110 111 114 118 119 126 130 132 146 147 148 **P**8
Primary Contact: Scott Street, Chief Executive Officer
CFO: Jane Ann Bridges, Chief Financial Officer
CNO: Beth Knight, Chief Nursing Officer
Web address: www.nacmem.org
**Control:** Hospital district or authority, Government, nonfederal **Service:** General Medical and Surgical

**Staffed Beds:** 116 **Admissions:** 4405 **Census:** 65 **Outpatient Visits:** 60452 **Births:** 750 **Total Expense ($000):** 83551 **Payroll Expense ($000):** 30099 **Personnel:** 748

## NASSAU BAY—Harris County

★ ◇ **HOUSTON METHODIST ST. JOHN HOSPITAL (450709)**, 18300 St. John Drive, Zip 77058–6302; tel. 281/333–5503, (Data for 334 days) **A**2 3 5 10 21 **F**3 8 11 13 15 18 20 22 26 28 29 30 34 35 39 40 41 44 45 47 49 50 51 53 54 57 59 63 64 65 68 69 70 73 74 75 76 77 78 79 81 82 84 85 86 87 93 94 102 107 108 110 111 115 118 119 130 131 132 135 146 147 **S** Houston Methodist, Houston, TX
Primary Contact: Dan Newman, Chief Executive Officer
CFO: David A. Witt, Vice President Finances
CHR: Becky A. Merritt, Director Human Resources
Web address: www.houstonmethodist.org/st-john-clear-lake
**Control:** Other not–for–profit (including NFP Corporation) **Service:** General Medical and Surgical

**Staffed Beds:** 137 **Admissions:** 6049 **Census:** 72 **Outpatient Visits:** 152282 **Births:** 501 **Total Expense ($000):** 106441 **Payroll Expense ($000):** 40569 **Personnel:** 668

TX

---

**Hospital, Medicare Provider Number, Address, Telephone, Approval, Facility, and Physician Codes, Health Care System**

★ American Hospital Association (AHA) membership    ◯ Healthcare Facilities Accreditation Program    ⇑ Center for Improvement in Healthcare Quality Accreditation
☐ The Joint Commission accreditation    ◇ DNV Healthcare Inc. accreditation    △ Commission on Accreditation of Rehabilitation Facilities (CARF) accreditation

## NAVASOTA—Grimes County

☒ **GRIMES ST. JOSEPH HEALTH CENTER (451322)**, 210 South Judson Street, Zip 77868–3704; tel. 936/825–6585 **A**1 9 10 18 **F**3 29 34 40 43 56 57 59 75 77 81 93 103 107 111 119 130 132 133 135 146 **S** Catholic Health Initiatives, Englewood, CO
Primary Contact: Reed Edmundson, Regional Administrator
CFO: Daniel Goggin, Senior Vice President and Chief Financial Officer
CMO: Luke P. Scamardo, II, M.D., Chief of Staff
CIO: Mike Russo, Vice President Information Systems
CHR: Michael G. Costa, Director Human Resources
CNO: Cesar Lopez, R.N., Director of Nurses
Web address: www.st–joseph.org
**Control:** Church–operated, Nongovernment, not–for profit **Service:** General Medical and Surgical

**Staffed Beds: 18 Admissions: 305 Census: 6 Outpatient Visits:** 18105
**Births:** 0 **Total Expense ($000):** 10515 **Payroll Expense ($000):** 4695
**Personnel:** 102

## NEDERLAND—Jefferson County

**MID–JEFFERSON EXTENDED CARE HOSPITAL (452083)**, 2600 Highway 365, Zip 77627–6237; tel. 409/726–8700 **A**9 10 **F**1 3 29 30 34 35 40 70 74 75 77 79 85 130 148
Primary Contact: Mark Rice, Administrator
COO: Wade K. Lester, Chief Nursing and Operations Officer
Web address: www.midjeffextendedcare.com/index.php
**Control:** Corporation, Investor–owned, for–profit **Service:** Long–Term Acute Care hospital

**Staffed Beds: 48 Admissions: 605 Census: 42 Outpatient Visits:** 0 **Births:** 0 **Total Expense ($000):** 18430 **Payroll Expense ($000):** 8207 **Personnel:** 166

## NEW BRAUNFELS—Comal County

**GULF STATES LONG TERM ACUTE CARE OF NEW BRAUNFELS** See Post Acute/Warm Springs Specialty Hospital of New Braunfels

☐ **NEW BRAUNFELS REGIONAL REHABILITATION HOSPITAL (673049)**, 2041 Sundance Parkway, Zip 78130–2779; tel. 830/625–6700 **A**1 9 10 **F**29 34 57 64 90 91 93 130 132 148 **S** Ernest Health, Inc., Albuquerque, NM
Primary Contact: Jennifer Malatek, Chief Executive Officer
CFO: Sue Thomsen, Chief Financial Officer
CMO: Maria R. Lomba, Medical Director
CHR: Cheryl Smith, Manager Human Resources
CNO: Peggy Schmits, Director, Nursing Operations
Web address: www.nbrrh.ernesthealth.com
**Control:** Corporation, Investor–owned, for–profit **Service:** Rehabilitation

**Staffed Beds: 40 Admissions: 786 Census: 30 Outpatient Visits:** 3724
**Births:** 0 **Total Expense ($000):** 12611 **Payroll Expense ($000):** 5891
**Personnel:** 135

☒ **POST ACUTE/WARM SPRINGS SPECIALTY HOSPITAL OF NEW BRAUNFELS (452106)**, 1445 Hanz Drive, Zip 78130–2567; tel. 830/627–7600 **A**1 9 10 **F**1 3 29 30 34 85 130 148 **S** Post Acute Medical, LLC, Enola, PA
Primary Contact: Shayne Goode, Administrator
Web address: www.warmsprings.org/locations/hos/h1/
**Control:** Partnership, Investor–owned, for–profit **Service:** Long–Term Acute Care hospital

**Staffed Beds: 40 Admissions: 395 Census: 27 Outpatient Visits:** 0 **Births:** 0 **Total Expense ($000):** 12900 **Payroll Expense ($000):** 5783 **Personnel:** 99

☒ **RESOLUTE HEALTH (670098)**, 555 Creekside Crossing, Zip 78130–2594; tel. 830/500–6000, (Data for 190 days) **A**1 10 **F**3 13 18 20 29 30 34 35 40 45 48 49 50 53 64 65 70 72 74 75 76 77 79 81 85 87 107 108 111 114 115 119 130 146 **P**8 **S** TENET Healthcare Corporation, Dallas, TX
Primary Contact: Matt Stone, Chief Executive Officer
Web address: www.resolutehealth.com
**Control:** Corporation, Investor–owned, for–profit **Service:** General Medical and Surgical

**Staffed Beds: 54 Admissions: 1112 Census: 18 Outpatient Visits:** 8388
**Births:** 253 **Total Expense ($000):** 53557 **Payroll Expense ($000):** 16375
**Personnel:** 379

## NOCONA—Montague County

**NOCONA GENERAL HOSPITAL (450641)**, 100 Park Road, Zip 76255–3616; tel. 940/825–3235 **A**9 10 **F**7 11 28 29 30 34 35 40 43 45 50 53 57 59 62 64 65 66 68 75 81 82 83 84 86 87 91 93 107 108 114 119 130 131 133 143 146 148 **P**5
Primary Contact: Lance Meekins, Administrator
CFO: Lance Meekins, Administrator
CMO: Chance Dingler, M.D., Chief Medical Officer
CHR: Paula Monkres, Administrative Assistant and Director Human Resources
Web address: www.noconageneral.com/
**Control:** Hospital district or authority, Government, nonfederal **Service:** General Medical and Surgical

**Staffed Beds: 25 Admissions: 432 Census: 7 Outpatient Visits:** 5310
**Births:** 0 **Total Expense ($000):** 7484 **Payroll Expense ($000):** 3772
**Personnel:** 97

## NORTH RICHLAND HILLS—Tarrant County

☒ **NORTH HILLS HOSPITAL (450087)**, 4401 Booth Calloway Road, Zip 76180–7399; tel. 817/255–1000 **A**1 9 10 **F**3 8 12 13 15 17 18 20 22 24 28 29 30 31 34 37 40 42 43 45 49 53 56 57 59 64 70 74 75 76 77 78 79 81 84 85 86 87 93 107 108 110 111 115 118 119 126 130 132 135 146 147 148 **P**3 **S** HCA, Nashville, TN
Primary Contact: Randy Moresi, Chief Executive Officer
COO: Nancy L. Hill, R.N., Chief Operating Officer
CFO: Nick Galt, Chief Financial Officer
CMO: John McDonald, M.D., Chief Medical Officer
CIO: Jason Sims, Facility Information Security Officer
CHR: Cynthia Dang, Vice President Human Resources
CNO: Tracey Smithson, Chief Nursing Officer
Web address: www.northhillshospital.com
**Control:** Partnership, Investor–owned, for–profit **Service:** General Medical and Surgical

**Staffed Beds: 176 Admissions: 6717 Census: 76 Outpatient Visits:** 79504
**Births:** 556 **Total Expense ($000):** 104457 **Payroll Expense ($000):** 39334
**Personnel:** 470

## ODESSA—Ector County

☐ **BASIN HEALTHCARE CENTER (670066)**, 900 East 4th Street, Zip 79761–5255; tel. 432/362–9900 **A**1 9 10 **F**3 29 40 45 64 68 81 82 85 98 107 111 114 119
Primary Contact: Gail Knous, Interim Administrator
CFO: Carl J. Flanagan, CPA, Chief Financial Officer
CMO: Richard Bartlett, M.D., Chief Medical Officer
CIO: Carl J. Flanagan, CPA, Chief Financial Officer
CHR: Gail Knous, Chief Executive Officer and Chief Compliance Officer
Web address: www.bhcodessa.com
**Control:** Partnership, Investor–owned, for–profit **Service:** Surgical

**Staffed Beds: 14 Admissions: 106 Census: 1 Outpatient Visits:** 9595
**Births:** 0 **Total Expense ($000):** 12233 **Payroll Expense ($000):** 3699
**Personnel:** 67

☒ **MEDICAL CENTER HEALTH SYSTEM (450132)**, 500 West Fourth Street, Zip 79761–5059, Mailing Address: P.O. Drawer 7239, Zip 79760–7239; tel. 432/640–4000 **A**1 2 3 5 8 9 10 **F**3 8 11 12 13 15 17 18 20 22 24 26 28 29 30 31 34 35 39 40 43 46 47 48 49 50 53 54 57 59 64 65 66 68 70 71 72 74 75 76 77 78 79 81 85 87 89 90 93 107 111 114 115 116 117 118 119 126 129 130 131 132 135 144 146 147 148 **P**6 8
Primary Contact: William W. Webster, FACHE, Chief Executive Officer
COO: Tony Ruiz, Chief Operating Officer
CFO: Jon Riggs, Chief Financial Officer
CMO: Bruce Becker, M.D., Chief Medical Officer
CIO: Gary Barnes, Chief Information Officer
CHR: Robbi Banks, Executive Director Human Resources
CNO: Chad Dunavan, R.N., Chief Nursing Officer
Web address: www.mchodessa.com
**Control:** Hospital district or authority, Government, nonfederal **Service:** General Medical and Surgical

**Staffed Beds: 368 Admissions: 13737 Census: 197 Outpatient Visits:** 323938 **Births:** 1805 **Total Expense ($000):** 249352 **Payroll Expense ($000):** 103751 **Personnel:** 1625

**MEDICAL CENTER HOSPITAL** See Medical Center Health System

*Many Facility Codes have changed. Please refer to the AHA Guide Code Chart.* © 2015 AHA Guide

TX

◇ **ODESSA REGIONAL MEDICAL CENTER (450661)**, 520 East Sixth Street, Zip 79761–4565, Mailing Address: P.O. Box 4859, Zip 79760–4859; tel. 432/582–8000 **A**3 5 9 10 21 **F**3 12 13 15 17 18 20 22 23 24 25 29 34 35 40 43 46 49 50 51 52 55 57 59 60 64 72 74 75 76 79 80 81 82 85 86 87 89 90 91 107 108 111 115 119 124 130 132 146 147 148 **P**8 **S** IASIS Healthcare, Franklin, TN
Primary Contact: Stacey L. Gerig, Chief Executive Officer
CIO: Jimmy Diaz, Director Information Technology
CHR: Jill Sparkman, Director Human Resources
CNO: Levi Stone, R.N., Chief Nursing Officer
Web address: www.odessaregionalmedicalcenter.com
**Control:** Partnership, Investor–owned, for–profit **Service:** General Medical and Surgical

**Staffed Beds:** 213 **Admissions:** 5850 **Census:** 83 **Outpatient Visits:** 43331 **Births:** 2584 **Total Expense ($000):** 97786 **Payroll Expense ($000):** 36706 **Personnel:** 566

### OLNEY—Young County

★ **HAMILTON HOSPITAL (451354)**, 901 West Hamilton Street, Zip 76374–1725, Mailing Address: P.O. Box 158, Zip 76374–0158; tel. 940/564–5521 **A**9 10 18 **F**7 11 13 28 29 30 34 40 43 53 57 76 77 81 86 89 93 107 114 119 127 129 133 146 148
Primary Contact: Michael H. Huff, Chief Executive Officer
CFO: Coy Noles, Chief Financial Officer Consultant
CMO: Mark L. Mankins, M.D., Chief of Staff
CIO: Rick Oliver, Information Technology
CHR: Amy Moore, Human Resources
CNO: Samantha Isbell, R.N., Chief Nursing Officer
Web address: www.olneyhamiltonhospital.com
**Control:** Hospital district or authority, Government, nonfederal **Service:** General Medical and Surgical

**Staffed Beds:** 25 **Admissions:** 672 **Census:** 10 **Outpatient Visits:** 13517 **Births:** 39 **Total Expense ($000):** 12254 **Payroll Expense ($000):** 5248 **Personnel:** 119

### PALACIOS—Matagorda County

**PALACIOS COMMUNITY MEDICAL CENTER (451332)**, 311 Green Street, Zip 77465–3213; tel. 361/972–2511 **A**9 10 18 **F**29 34 40 41 50 54 57 59 64 65 87 91 93 97 107 127 133 146 148
Primary Contact: Alden M. Vandeveer, Jr., FACHE, Chief Executive Officer
COO: Lisa Henderson, Chief Operating Officer
CFO: Claude Manning, Chief Financial Officer
CIO: Angela Yeager, Director Information Technology
CHR: Lisa Henderson, Chief Operations Officer
CNO: Susan Easter, Chief Nursing Officer
Web address: www.palacioshospital.net/
**Control:** Other not–for–profit (including NFP Corporation) **Service:** General Medical and Surgical

**Staffed Beds:** 17 **Admissions:** 125 **Census:** 2 **Outpatient Visits:** 12772 **Births:** 0 **Total Expense ($000):** 5771 **Payroll Expense ($000):** 3119 **Personnel:** 50

### PALESTINE—Anderson County

⊞ **PALESTINE REGIONAL MEDICAL CENTER (453089)**, 2900 South Loop 256, Zip 75801–6958; tel. 903/731–1000, (Nonreporting) **A**1 **S** LifePoint Health, Brentwood, TN
Primary Contact: Alan E. George, Chief Executive Officer
CFO: Louis D. Ferguson, Chief Financial Officer
CIO: Rebecca Chou, Directory Information Systems
CHR: Rhonda Beard, Director Human Resources
CNO: Christi Watkins, R.N., Chief Operating Officer
Web address: www.palestineregional.com
**Control:** Corporation, Investor–owned, for–profit **Service:** Rehabilitation

**Staffed Beds:** 12

⊞ **PALESTINE REGIONAL MEDICAL CENTER–EAST (450747)**, 2900 South Loop 256, Zip 75801–6958; tel. 903/731–1000 **A**1 9 10 **F**3 7 11 13 15 18 20 22 26 28 29 30 34 40 43 44 47 48 49 50 51 56 57 59 63 70 76 79 81 82 85 86 87 89 90 93 96 97 98 100 101 102 103 104 107 108 110 111 114 118 119 129 130 131 143 146 147 148 **S** LifePoint Health, Brentwood, TN
Primary Contact: Alan E. George, Chief Executive Officer
CFO: Louis D. Ferguson, Chief Financial Officer
CIO: Rebecca Chou, Director Information Systems
CHR: Rhonda Beard, Director Human Resources
Web address: www.palestineregional.com
**Control:** Partnership, Investor–owned, for–profit **Service:** General Medical and Surgical

**Staffed Beds:** 139 **Admissions:** 5018 **Census:** 57 **Outpatient Visits:** 84176 **Births:** 617 **Total Expense ($000):** 59283 **Payroll Expense ($000):** 27669 **Personnel:** 489

### PAMPA—Gray County

⊞ **PAMPA REGIONAL MEDICAL CENTER (450099)**, One Medical Plaza, Zip 79065; tel. 806/665–3721 **A**1 9 10 20 **F**3 11 12 13 15 18 20 22 29 30 34 40 43 45 46 47 48 49 50 51 52 54 56 57 58 59 60 61 63 64 65 66 68 70 75 76 77 79 81 83 84 85 86 87 91 92 93 96 97 98 100 101 103 104 105 107 108 110 111 114 115 119 130 132 134 135 146 147 148 **P**7 **S** Prime Healthcare Services, Ontario, CA
Primary Contact: Brad S. Morse, Chief Executive Officer
CFO: Paul Christenson, Chief Financial Officer
CMO: David Hampton, M.D., Chief Medical Staff
CIO: Joy Patton, Chief Information Services
CHR: Debbie Dixon, Director Human Resources
CNO: Catherine Kenney, Chief Nursing Officer
Web address: www.prmctx.com
**Control:** Other not–for–profit (including NFP Corporation) **Service:** General Medical and Surgical

**Staffed Beds:** 72 **Admissions:** 1660 **Census:** 18 **Outpatient Visits:** 37858 **Births:** 190 **Total Expense ($000):** 35689 **Payroll Expense ($000):** 11566 **Personnel:** 205

### PARIS—Lamar County

★ **CHRISTUS DUBUIS HOSPITAL OF PARIS (452082)**, 865 Deshong Drive, 5th Floor, Zip 75460–9313; tel. 903/782–2961 **A**9 10 **F**1 3 29 30 85 148 **S** CHRISTUS Health, Irving, TX
Primary Contact: Kathie Reese, Administrator
CMO: James E. Gulde, M.D., Medical Director
CNO: Janice Cochran, R.N., Director of Patient Care
Web address: www.dubuis.org/CHRISTUSDubuisHospitalofParis
**Control:** Church–operated, Nongovernment, not–for profit **Service:** Long–Term Acute Care hospital

**Staffed Beds:** 25 **Admissions:** 222 **Census:** 16 **Outpatient Visits:** 0 **Births:** 0 **Total Expense ($000):** 6264 **Payroll Expense ($000):** 1977 **Personnel:** 41

☐ **PARIS REGIONAL MEDICAL CENTER (450196)**, 865 Deshong Drive, Zip 75460–9313, Mailing Address: P.O. Box 9070, Zip 75461–9070; tel. 903/785–4521, (Includes PARIS REGIONAL MEDICAL CENTER, 865 Deshong Drive, Zip 75462–2097; tel. 903/785–4521; PARIS REGIONAL MEDICAL CENTER–SOUTH CAMPUS, 820 Clarksville Street, Zip 75460–9070, Mailing Address: P.O. Box 9070, Zip 75461–9070; tel. 903/785–4521) **A**1 9 10 19 **F**3 8 11 13 15 17 18 20 22 24 26 28 29 30 31 34 35 36 39 40 45 49 50 51 55 57 59 60 64 65 66 68 70 72 74 75 76 77 78 79 81 82 85 86 87 89 90 91 93 97 98 102 103 107 108 111 115 119 126 127 130 132 135 144 145 146 147 148 **P**5 **S** RegionalCare Hospital Partners, Brentwood, TN
Primary Contact: Patti Monczewski, Interim Chief Executive Officer
COO: Patti Monczewski, Chief Operating Officer
CFO: Janet Montel, Chief Financial Officer
CMO: Richard Bercher, M.D., Chief Medical Officer
CHR: Cheryl Perry, Director Human Resources
CNO: Debra Taylor, Chief Nursing Officer
Web address: www.parisrmc.com
**Control:** Partnership, Investor–owned, for–profit **Service:** General Medical and Surgical

**Staffed Beds:** 192 **Admissions:** 7200 **Census:** 97 **Outpatient Visits:** 76859 **Births:** 808 **Total Expense ($000):** 103278 **Payroll Expense ($000):** 34402 **Personnel:** 772

### PASADENA—Harris County

⊞ **BAYSHORE MEDICAL CENTER (450097)**, 4000 Spencer Highway, Zip 77504–1202; tel. 713/359–2000, (Includes EAST HOUSTON REGIONAL MEDICAL CENTER, 13111 East Freeway, Houston, Zip 77015–5820; tel. 713/393–2000; Alice G. Adams, R.N., Chief Executive Officer) **A**1 2 3 9 10 **F**3 8 12 13 15 17 18 20 22 24 26 28 29 31 34 35 40 41 42 43 47 49 51 55 56 57 59 60 64 70 72 74 75 76 77 78 79 81 82 84 86 89 90 91 93 98 100 102 103 107 108 111 114 115 116 117 118 119 120 121 123 129 130 131 144 146 147 148 **S** HCA, Nashville, TN
Primary Contact: Jeanna Barnard, Chief Executive Officer
CFO: John Armour, Chief Financial Officer
CIO: Clifford Ferguson, Director Information Technology and Systems
Web address: www.bayshoremedical.com
**Control:** Partnership, Investor–owned, for–profit **Service:** General Medical and Surgical

**Staffed Beds:** 451 **Admissions:** 22042 **Census:** 308 **Outpatient Visits:** 190556 **Births:** 4424 **Total Expense ($000):** 268369 **Payroll Expense ($000):** 113362 **Personnel:** 1617

**TX**

---

**Hospital, Medicare Provider Number, Address, Telephone, Approval, Facility, and Physician Codes, Health Care System**

★ American Hospital Association (AHA) membership
☐ The Joint Commission accreditation
○ Healthcare Facilities Accreditation Program
◇ DNV Healthcare Inc. accreditation
⇑ Center for Improvement in Healthcare Quality Accreditation
△ Commission on Accreditation of Rehabilitation Facilities (CARF) accreditation

★ **KINDRED HOSPITAL–BAY AREA (452039)**, 4801 East Sam Houston Parkway South, Zip 77505–3955; tel. 281/991–5463 **A**9 **F**1 3 29 30 34 45 46 47 60 64 70 77 93 107 114 130 132 146 148 **S** Kindred Healthcare, Louisville, KY
Primary Contact: Jeffrey Smith, Chief Executive Officer
CHR: Nellie Moen, Coordinator Human Resources
Web address: www.khbayareahouston.com/
**Control:** Corporation, Investor–owned, for–profit **Service:** Long–Term Acute Care hospital

> **Staffed Beds:** 74 **Admissions:** 915 **Census:** 64 **Outpatient Visits:** 44 **Births:** 0 **Total Expense ($000):** 32742 **Payroll Expense ($000):** 11891
> **Personnel:** 172

**PATIENTS MEDICAL CENTER** See St. Luke's Patients Medical Center

★ ◇ **ST. LUKE'S PATIENTS MEDICAL CENTER (670031)**, 4600 East Sam Houston Parkway South, Zip 77505–3948; tel. 713/948–7000, (Data for 181 days) **A**9 10 21 **F**15 18 20 22 24 29 30 31 35 40 45 46 54 64 70 74 77 81 82 86 87 91 93 94 107 111 114 115 116 117 119 129 130 135 146 147 148 **S** Catholic Health Initiatives, Englewood, CO
Primary Contact: William Simmons, Chief Executive Officer
Web address: www.stlukestexas.com
**Control:** Corporation, Investor–owned, for–profit **Service:** General Medical and Surgical

> **Staffed Beds:** 61 **Admissions:** 1945 **Census:** 53 **Outpatient Visits:** 22782
> **Births:** 0 **Total Expense ($000):** 32017 **Payroll Expense ($000):** 11840
> **Personnel:** 408

○ **SURGERY SPECIALTY HOSPITALS OF AMERICA (450831)**, 4301B Vista Road, Zip 77504; tel. 713/378–3000 **A**10 11 **F**3 12 29 34 40 45 56 57 59 65 70 75 79 81 82 85 86 97 107 109 111 112 114 119 129 130 131 132 145 148
Primary Contact: Eric Chan, Chief Executive Officer
COO: Hemant Khemka, Chief Operating Officer
CFO: Hemant Khemka, Chief Financial Officer
CMO: Xiao H. Li, M.D., Chief of Staff
CIO: Ringo Cheng, Director Information Technology
Web address: www.surgeryspecialty.com/
**Control:** Partnership, Investor–owned, for–profit **Service:** General Medical and Surgical

> **Staffed Beds:** 37 **Admissions:** 155 **Census:** 1 **Outpatient Visits:** 1562
> **Births:** 0 **Total Expense ($000):** 14400 **Payroll Expense ($000):** 3448
> **Personnel:** 81

□ **PEARLAND MEDICAL CENTER**, 11100 Shadow Creek Parkway, Zip 77584–7285; tel. 713/770–7000, (Nonreporting) **A**1 **S** HCA, Nashville, TN
Primary Contact: Matt Dixon, Chief Executive Officer
Web address: www.pearlandmc.com
**Control:** Investor–owned, for–profit **Service:** General Medical and Surgical

> **Staffed Beds:** 33

★ **FRIO REGIONAL HOSPITAL (450293)**, 200 South I. H. 35, Zip 78061–3998; tel. 830/334–3617 **A**9 10 **F**3 8 15 29 34 35 40 43 45 53 57 59 62 64 68 76 77 81 87 107 114 119 130 133 148 **P**6
Primary Contact: Michael S. Thompson, Chief Executive Officer
CFO: Rhett D. Fricke, Chief Financial Officer
CMO: Oscar Garza, M.D., Chief Medical Staff
CIO: Jacob Flores, Chief Information Officer
CHR: Nancy Ortiz, Director Human Resource and Marketing
CNO: Louisa Martinez, Director of Nursing
Web address: www.frioregionalhospital.com
**Control:** Other not–for–profit (including NFP Corporation) **Service:** General Medical and Surgical

> **Staffed Beds:** 22 **Admissions:** 295 **Census:** 3 **Outpatient Visits:** 15618
> **Births:** 125 **Total Expense ($000):** 11962 **Payroll Expense ($000):** 4768
> **Personnel:** 126

**REEVES COUNTY HOSPITAL (451377)**, 2323 Texas Street, Zip 79772–7338; tel. 432/447–3551 **A**9 10 18 **F**3 11 13 35 40 43 57 60 64 68 70 81 87 93 107 110 114 119 127 130 131 133 146 147 148
Primary Contact: Albert LaRochelle, Chief Executive Officer
CFO: Brenda Mckinney, Chief Financial Officer
CMO: W. J. Bang, M.D., Chief of Staff
CHR: Nadine Smith, Director Human Resources
CNO: Faye Lease, Director of Nursing
Web address: www.reevescountyhospital.com
**Control:** Hospital district or authority, Government, nonfederal **Service:** General Medical and Surgical

> **Staffed Beds:** 25 **Admissions:** 939 **Census:** 11 **Outpatient Visits:** 59964
> **Births:** 126 **Total Expense ($000):** 22256 **Payroll Expense ($000):** 9431
> **Personnel:** 207

★ **OCHILTREE GENERAL HOSPITAL (451359)**, 3101 Garrett Drive, Zip 79070–5323; tel. 806/435–3606 **A**9 10 18 **F**10 11 13 15 30 35 40 43 57 59 62 63 64 69 76 81 85 89 93 107 108 114 119 127 130 133 143 146 147 **P**1
Primary Contact: Richard Hoeth, Interim Chief Executive Officer and Administrator
CFO: Debbie Blodgett, Director of Fiscal Services
CIO: Dyan Harrison, Manager Health Information
CNO: Judy Russell, Director of Nurses
Web address: www.ochiltreehospital.com
**Control:** Hospital district or authority, Government, nonfederal **Service:** General Medical and Surgical

> **Staffed Beds:** 25 **Admissions:** 594 **Census:** 5 **Outpatient Visits:** 36415
> **Births:** 193 **Total Expense ($000):** 15109 **Payroll Expense ($000):** 6203
> **Personnel:** 142

★ **EAST TEXAS MEDICAL CENTER PITTSBURG (451367)**, 2701 Highway 271 North, Zip 75686–1032; tel. 903/946–5000 **A**9 10 18 **F**3 11 12 28 29 35 40 43 45 50 53 57 59 64 68 70 75 77 81 85 87 89 92 93 97 107 108 111 115 119 127 129 130 133 **P**6 **S** East Texas Medical Center Regional Healthcare System, Tyler, TX
Primary Contact: James Warren Robicheaux, Senior Administrator
CMO: W. R. Christensen, M.D., Chief of Staff
CIO: Paula Anthony, Vice President Information Services
CHR: Kathy Shelton, Director Human Resources
CNO: Casey Mayben, Chief Nursing Officer
Web address: www.etmc.org/newpittsburg.htm
**Control:** Other not–for–profit (including NFP Corporation) **Service:** General Medical and Surgical

> **Staffed Beds:** 25 **Admissions:** 963 **Census:** 11 **Outpatient Visits:** 84098
> **Births:** 0 **Total Expense ($000):** 31834 **Payroll Expense ($000):** 8863
> **Personnel:** 185

**ALLEGIANCE BEHAVIORAL HEALTH CENTER OF PLAINVIEW (454101)**, 2601 Dimmit Road, 4th Floor, Zip 79072–1833; tel. 806/296–9191 **A**10 **F**29 35 56 64 98 101 103 104 **S** Allegiance Health Management, Shreveport, LA
Primary Contact: Angie Alexander, Chief Executive Officer
COO: Don Cameron, Chief Operating Officer
CFO: Jim Turgeon, Vice President Finance
CMO: Victor A. Gutierrez, M.D., Medical Director
CIO: Richard Merk, Executive Vice President
CHR: Rob Lindsey, Jr., Vice President Human Resources
Web address: www.ahmgt.com
**Control:** Corporation, Investor–owned, for–profit **Service:** Psychiatric

> **Staffed Beds:** 20 **Admissions:** 303 **Census:** 11 **Outpatient Visits:** 27495
> **Births:** 0 **Total Expense ($000):** 5068 **Payroll Expense ($000):** 2013
> **Personnel:** 37

⊠ **COVENANT HOSPITAL PLAINVIEW (450539)**, 2601 Dimmitt Road, Zip 79072–1833; tel. 806/296–5531 **A**1 3 9 10 20 **F**3 11 12 13 15 18 29 30 32 34 35 38 40 41 43 44 45 46 48 50 51 54 56 57 59 61 64 65 68 70 75 76 77 79 80 81 85 86 87 97 107 108 110 114 119 127 129 130 131 132 135 146 147 148 **S** Covenant Health System, Lubbock, TX
Primary Contact: Clay Taylor, Chief Executive Officer
COO: Mike McNutt, Assistant Administrator
CFO: Cassie Mogg, Chief Financial Officer
CMO: Sergio Lara, M.D., Chief Medical Officer
CNO: Leslie Hackett, Chief Nursing Officer
Web address: www.covenantplainview.org
**Control:** Church–operated, Nongovernment, not–for profit **Service:** General Medical and Surgical

> **Staffed Beds:** 68 **Admissions:** 2235 **Census:** 19 **Births:** 498 **Total Expense ($000):** 36808 **Payroll Expense ($000):** 12259 **Personnel:** 295

⊠ **BAYLOR REGIONAL MEDICAL CENTER AT PLANO (450890)**, 4700 Alliance Boulevard, Zip 75093–5323; tel. 469/814–2000 **A**1 2 3 5 9 10 **F**3 12 15 29 30 31 34 35 40 45 46 47 49 54 57 59 64 70 74 75 77 78 79 80 81 82 84 85 86 87 107 108 110 111 114 118 119 126 130 131 132 135 145 146 147 148 **S** Baylor Scott & White Health, Dallas, TX
Primary Contact: Jerri Garison, R.N., President
COO: Joseph Brown, Vice President Operations
CFO: Deanne Kindered, Vice President Finance
CMO: John Marcucci, M.D., Vice President Medical Affairs
CHR: Kriss Gamez, Director Human Resources
Web address: www.baylorhealth.com/PhysiciansLocations/Plano/Pages/Default.aspx
**Control:** Other not–for–profit (including NFP Corporation) **Service:** General Medical and Surgical

> **Staffed Beds:** 110 **Admissions:** 5962 **Census:** 85 **Outpatient Visits:** 52114
> **Births:** 0 **Total Expense ($000):** 159538 **Payroll Expense ($000):** 52121
> **Personnel:** 525

**TX**

**CHILDREN'S MEDICAL CENTER PLANO**, 7601 Preston Road, Zip 75024–3214; tel. 469/303–7000, (Nonreporting) **A**3 5
Primary Contact: Christopher J. Durovich, President and Chief Executive
Web address: www.https://www.childrens.com/location–landing/locations–and–directions/childrens–health–plano
**Control:** Other not–for–profit (including NFP Corporation) **Service:** Children's general

Staffed Beds: 72

✠ **HEALTHSOUTH PLANO REHABILITATION HOSPITAL (453047)**, 2800 West 15th Street, Zip 75075–7526; tel. 972/612–9000 **A**1 9 10 **F**34 57 59 62 90 93 95 96 130 132 148 **S** HEALTHSOUTH Corporation, Birmingham, AL
Primary Contact: Jennifer Lynn Brewer, Chief Executive Officer
CFO: Catrina Madkins, Controller and Chief Financial Officer
CMO: Omar Colon, M.D., Medical Director
Web address: www.healthsouthplano.com
**Control:** Corporation, Investor–owned, for–profit **Service:** Rehabilitation

Staffed Beds: 83 Admissions: 1564 Census: 52 Outpatient Visits: 11615 Births: 0 Total Expense ($000): 19827 Payroll Expense ($000): 11364 Personnel: 216

✠ ◇ **MEDICAL CENTER OF PLANO (450651)**, 3901 West 15th Street, Zip 75075–7738; tel. 972/596–6800 **A**1 2 3 9 10 13 21 **F**3 12 13 15 18 19 20 22 24 26 28 29 30 31 34 35 40 42 43 45 46 47 48 49 51 54 55 57 58 59 60 64 70 72 74 75 76 78 79 81 82 84 85 86 87 91 93 107 108 110 111 112 114 115 117 118 119 124 126 130 132 135 145 146 147 148 **P**5 **S** HCA, Nashville, TN
Primary Contact: Charles Gressle, Chief Executive Officer
COO: Glenn Wallace, Chief Operating Officer
CFO: W. Patrick Whitmore, Chief Financial Officer
CMO: Ann Arnold, M.D., Medical Director
CIO: Michael Gfeller, Director Information Systems
CHR: Shanna Warren, Director Human Resources
Web address: www.medicalcenterplano.com
**Control:** Partnership, Investor–owned, for–profit **Service:** General Medical and Surgical

Staffed Beds: 362 Admissions: 16782 Census: 248 Outpatient Visits: 131258 Births: 2405 Total Expense ($000): 290288 Payroll Expense ($000): 94010 Personnel: 1320

☐ **PLANO SPECIALTY HOSPITAL (452054)**, 1621 Coit Road, Zip 75075–6141; tel. 972/758–5200 **A**1 9 10 **F**1 3 29 75 82 84 85 86 87 96 130 135 148 **S** Encore Healthcare, Columbia, MD
Primary Contact: Jay Lindsey, Chief Executive Officer
CFO: Deanna Lankford, Business Office Manager
CHR: Robbie McCranie, Director Human Resources
Web address: www.specialtyhospital–plano.com
**Control:** Corporation, Investor–owned, for–profit **Service:** Long–Term Acute Care hospital

Staffed Beds: 43 Admissions: 285 Census: 22 Outpatient Visits: 0 Births: 0 Total Expense ($000): 10206 Payroll Expense ($000): 3338 Personnel: 89

☐ **TEXAS HEALTH CENTER FOR DIAGNOSTIC & SURGERY (450891)**, 6020 West Parker Road, Zip 75093–8171; tel. 972/403–2700 **A**1 2 9 10 **F**3 29 40 45 54 64 79 81 82 85 87 107 111 114 119 126 129
Primary Contact: Larry Robertson, President
CFO: Douglas Browning, Chief Financial Officer
CHR: Cookie Tedder, Human Resources Manager
CNO: Ellen Baldwin, R.N., Chief Nursing Officer
Web address: www.thcds.com
**Control:** Partnership, Investor–owned, for–profit **Service:** General Medical and Surgical

Staffed Beds: 18 Admissions: 675 Census: 4 Outpatient Visits: 17456 Births: 0 Total Expense ($000): 51974 Payroll Expense ($000): 11003 Personnel: 153

✠ **TEXAS HEALTH PRESBYTERIAN HOSPITAL PLANO (450771)**, 6200 West Parker Road, Zip 75093–8185; tel. 972/981–8000 **A**1 3 9 10 **F**3 12 13 15 18 20 22 24 26 28 29 30 31 32 34 35 37 38 40 43 44 45 46 48 49 50 52 54 55 57 58 59 60 64 65 68 70 72 74 75 76 77 78 79 81 84 85 86 87 89 93 107 108 110 111 114 115 118 119 126 130 131 132 134 135 141 145 146 147 148 **P**6 **S** Texas Health Resources, Arlington, TX
Primary Contact: Joshua Floren, Interim President
CFO: Lisa Gildon, Vice President and Chief Financial Officer
CMO: Gwen Webster, M.D., President Medical Staff
CIO: Susan Anderson, Director Information Systems
CHR: Kelly K. Martin, Human Resource Officer
CNO: Raymond Kelly, R.N., Chief Nursing Officer
Web address: www.texashealth.org
**Control:** Other not–for–profit (including NFP Corporation) **Service:** General Medical and Surgical

Staffed Beds: 307 Admissions: 16187 Census: 212 Outpatient Visits: 92384 Births: 3828 Total Expense ($000): 224083 Payroll Expense ($000): 101242 Personnel: 1360

✠ **THE HEART HOSPITAL BAYLOR PLANO (670025)**, 1100 Allied Drive, Zip 75093–5348; tel. 469/814–3278 **A**1 5 9 10 **F**3 17 18 20 22 24 26 28 29 30 34 40 54 57 59 64 75 81 84 85 86 87 91 92 93 96 97 107 108 111 112 114 115 116 117 118 119 120 121 123 124 126 130 146 147
Primary Contact: Mark Valentine, President
CFO: Bryan Nichols, Chief Financial Officer
CMO: Trent Pettijohn, M.D., Chief Medical Officer
CIO: Nayan Patel, Director Information Systems
CHR: Kriss Gamez, Director Human Resources
CNO: Susan Moats, R.N., Vice President of Patient Care Services and Chief Nursing Officer
Web address: www.https://www.thehearthospitalbaylor.com
**Control:** Partnership, Investor–owned, for–profit **Service:** Heart

Staffed Beds: 116 Admissions: 4253 Census: 65 Outpatient Visits: 23908 Births: 0 Total Expense ($000): 182937 Payroll Expense ($000): 56541 Personnel: 551

☐ **VICTORY MEDICAL CENTER PLANO (673055)**, 2301 Marsh Lane, Zip 75093–8497; tel. 972/820–2600 **A**1 10 **F**3 8 29 40 45 46 49 68 81 82 85 86 87 **S** Victory Healthcare, The Woodlands, TX
Primary Contact: Steve Williams, Chief Executive Officer
Web address: www.victory–healthcare.com/plano
**Control:** Partnership, Investor–owned, for–profit **Service:** Surgical

Staffed Beds: 26 Admissions: 473 Census: 2 Outpatient Visits: 1820 Births: 0 Total Expense ($000): 39842 Payroll Expense ($000): 7023 Personnel: 85

**PORT ARTHUR—Jefferson County**

★ **CHRISTUS DUBUIS HOSPITAL OF PORT ARTHUR**, 3600 Gates Boulevard, Zip 77642–3858; tel. 409/989–5300, (Nonreporting) **A**9 **S** CHRISTUS Health, Irving, TX
Primary Contact: Kathie Reese, Interim Administrator
Web address: www.christusdubuis.org/CHRISTUSDubuisHospitalofPortArthur
**Control:** Church–operated, Nongovernment, not–for profit **Service:** Other specialty

Staffed Beds: 15

**DUBUIS HOSPITAL OF PORT ARTHUR** See CHRISTUS Dubuis Hospital of Port Arthur

◇ **THE MEDICAL CENTER OF SOUTHEAST TEXAS (450518)**, 2555 Jimmy Johnson Boulevard, Zip 77640–2007; tel. 409/724–7389 **A**9 10 21 **F**3 8 11 12 13 15 18 20 22 24 28 29 30 34 35 40 44 45 47 49 50 56 57 59 64 72 74 76 77 78 79 81 82 85 86 87 89 90 91 92 93 94 98 101 102 103 104 105 107 108 110 111 114 115 119 121 129 130 132 135 146 147 148 **P**2 **S** IASIS Healthcare, Franklin, TN
Primary Contact: Richard Gonzalez, Chief Executive Officer
COO: Chris McMahon, Chief Operating Officer
CFO: Jason R. Miller, Chief Financial Officer
CMO: Don Duplan, M.D., Chief of Staff
CIO: Bryan Hebert, Director Information Systems
CHR: Carol Hebert, Director Human Resources
CNO: Heidi Wolf, R.N., Chief Nursing Officer
Web address: www.medicalcentersetexas.com
**Control:** Partnership, Investor–owned, for–profit **Service:** General Medical and Surgical

Staffed Beds: 185 Admissions: 8222 Census: 99 Outpatient Visits: 68646 Births: 1305 Total Expense ($000): 109536 Payroll Expense ($000): 39192 Personnel: 685

TX

**PORT LAVACA—Calhoun County**

★ **MEMORIAL MEDICAL CENTER (451356)**, 815 North Virginia Street,
Zip 77979–3025, Mailing Address: P.O. Box 25, Zip 77979–0025;
tel. 361/552–6713 **A**9 10 18 **F**3 11 13 15 18 29 30 32 34 35 40 43 44 45
46 49 50 57 59 64 65 68 70 75 76 77 78 79 81 84 85 86 87 93 107 108
111 115 118 119 129 130 132 133 134 135 146 147 148
Primary Contact: Jason Anglin, Chief Executive Officer
COO: Roshanda Gray, Assistant Administrator
CMO: Jeannine Griffin, M.D., Chief of Staff
CIO: Adam Besio, Chief Information Officer
CNO: Erin R. Clevenger, Chief Nursing Officer and Director of Quality
Web address: www.mmcportlavaca.com
**Control:** County–Government, nonfederal **Service:** General Medical and Surgical

**Staffed Beds:** 25 **Admissions:** 1324 **Census:** 14 **Outpatient Visits:** 51094
**Births:** 113 **Total Expense ($000):** 22250 **Payroll Expense ($000):** 8733
**Personnel:** 182

**QUANAH—Hardeman County**

**HARDEMAN COUNTY MEMORIAL HOSPITAL (451352)**, 402 Mercer Street,
Zip 79252–4026, Mailing Address: P.O. Box 90, Zip 79252–0090;
tel. 940/663–2795 **A**9 10 18 **F**28 29 30 34 40 43 50 56 59 62 63 64 75 77
87 93 100 101 103 104 107 127 130 133 147 **P**5
Primary Contact: Dave Clark, Interim Chief Executive Officer
CFO: Tracy Betts, Chief Financial Officer
CMO: Kevin Lane, D.O., Chief of Staff
CNO: Dennis Thomas, Chief Nursing Officer
Web address: www.hcmhosp.com/
**Control:** Hospital district or authority, Government, nonfederal **Service:** General Medical and Surgical

**Staffed Beds:** 18 **Admissions:** 284 **Census:** 5 **Outpatient Visits:** 15825
**Births:** 0 **Total Expense ($000):** 6999 **Payroll Expense ($000):** 3328
**Personnel:** 77

**QUITMAN—Wood County**

★ **EAST TEXAS MEDICAL CENTER–QUITMAN (451380)**, 117 Winnsboro Street,
Zip 75783–2144, Mailing Address: P.O. Box 1000, Zip 75783–1000;
tel. 903/763–6300 **A**9 10 18 **F**3 11 15 29 30 35 40 43 45 50 57 59 64 65
68 79 81 85 87 107 108 110 111 115 119 127 129 130 133 **P**7 **S** East
Texas Medical Center Regional Healthcare System, Tyler, TX
Primary Contact: Patrick Swindle, Administrator
CHR: William Henry, Director Human Resources
CNO: Teresa Meeks, Chief Nursing Officer
Web address: www.etmc.org/etmcquitman/
**Control:** Other not–for–profit (including NFP Corporation) **Service:** General Medical and Surgical

**Staffed Beds:** 25 **Admissions:** 1019 **Census:** 12 **Outpatient Visits:** 39793
**Births:** 0 **Total Expense ($000):** 19318 **Payroll Expense ($000):** 5906
**Personnel:** 109

**RANKIN—Upton County**

★ **RANKIN HOSPITAL DISTRICT (451329)**, 1105 Elizabeth Street, Zip 79778,
Mailing Address: P.O. Box 327, Zip 79778–0327; tel. 432/693–2443 **A**9 10 18
**F**8 29 35 40 59 64 65 68 93 97 119 133
Primary Contact: Jim Horton, Chief Executive Officer
CFO: Tami Burks, Comptroller
CMO: Thomas J. Curvin, M.D., Chief of Staff
**Control:** Hospital district or authority, Government, nonfederal **Service:** General Medical and Surgical

**Staffed Beds:** 10 **Admissions:** 95 **Census:** 1 **Outpatient Visits:** 4200 **Births:**
0 **Total Expense ($000):** 7262 **Payroll Expense ($000):** 3521 **Personnel:**
53

**REFUGIO—Refugio County**

**REFUGIO COUNTY MEMORIAL HOSPITAL (451317)**, 107 Swift Street,
Zip 78377–2425; tel. 361/526–2321 **A**9 10 18 **F**3 7 29 40 43 57 61 64 75
81 86 87 93 97 107 119 127 133 **P**6
Primary Contact: Louis R. Willeke, Administrator
Web address: www.refugiohospital.com/
**Control:** Hospital district or authority, Government, nonfederal **Service:** General Medical and Surgical

**Staffed Beds:** 20 **Admissions:** 167 **Census:** 3 **Outpatient Visits:** 24130
**Births:** 0 **Total Expense ($000):** 13110 **Payroll Expense ($000):** 5223
**Personnel:** 132

**RICHARDSON—Collin County**

✖ **METHODIST RICHARDSON MEDICAL CENTER (450537)**, 2831 East
President George Bush Highway, Zip 75082–3561; tel. 469/204–1000 **A**1 2 9
10 **F**3 5 11 13 15 18 20 22 24 29 30 31 34 35 38 40 45 46 49 54 55 56 57
59 64 65 68 70 72 74 75 76 77 78 79 81 82 85 86 87 93 97 98 100 101
102 103 104 105 107 108 109 110 111 112 115 116 117 119 120 121 123
124 126 129 130 131 132 135 146 147 148 **P**1 7 **S** Methodist Health System,
Dallas, TX
Primary Contact: E. Kenneth Hutchenrider, President and Chief Executive Officer
COO: Robert Simpson, Vice President Operations
CFO: Amy Bodwell, Vice President Finance
CMO: Mark Smith, M.D., Chief Medical Officer
CIO: Terri Morris, Director Information Systems
CHR: Chris Loyd, Director Human Resources
CNO: Irene T. Strejc, R.N., Vice President, Nursing
Web address: www.methodisthealthsystem.org/richardson
**Control:** Other not–for–profit (including NFP Corporation) **Service:** General Medical and Surgical

**Staffed Beds:** 164 **Admissions:** 7309 **Census:** 94 **Outpatient Visits:** 75876
**Births:** 1262 **Total Expense ($000):** 140812 **Payroll Expense ($000):**
58487 **Personnel:** 755

✖ **RELIANT REHABILITATION HOSPITAL NORTH TEXAS (673029)**, 3351
Waterview Parkway, Zip 75080–1449; tel. 972/398–5700 **A**1 9 10 **F**3 29 90 93
96 148 **S** Reliant Healthcare Partners, Richardson, TX
Primary Contact: Jim Ransom, Chief Executive Officer
CFO: Nichole Dykes, Chief Financial Officer
CMO: Richard Jones, M.D., Medical Director
CNO: Pam Smith, Chief Nursing Officer
Web address: www.relianthcp.com
**Control:** Partnership, Investor–owned, for–profit **Service:** Rehabilitation

**Staffed Beds:** 50 **Admissions:** 1206 **Census:** 38 **Outpatient Visits:** 6656
**Births:** 0 **Total Expense ($000):** 14437 **Payroll Expense ($000):** 6949
**Personnel:** 132

**RICHMOND—Fort Bend County**

☐ △ **OAKBEND MEDICAL CENTER (450330)**, 1705 Jackson Street,
Zip 77469–3289; tel. 281/341–3000, (Total facility includes 21 beds in nursing
home–type unit) **A**1 3 7 9 10 **F**3 11 13 15 18 20 22 24 26 28 29 30 31 34 35
40 41 42 43 45 46 48 49 50 56 57 59 64 68 70 72 74 75 76 77 78 79 81
82 85 86 87 89 97 98 102 107 108 111 114 119 120 124 128 129 130 131
146 147 148 **P**6
Primary Contact: Joe Freudenberger, Chief Executive Officer
CFO: Rodney Lenfant, Chief Financial Officer
CMO: Douglas Thibodeaux, M.D., Chief Medical Officer
CIO: Tim McCarty, Chief Information Officer
CHR: Eileen Gamboa, Director Human Resources
Web address: www.oakbendmedcenter.org
**Control:** Hospital district or authority, Government, nonfederal **Service:** General Medical and Surgical

**Staffed Beds:** 160 **Admissions:** 5656 **Census:** 81 **Outpatient Visits:** 181408
**Births:** 1607 **Total Expense ($000):** 117652 **Payroll Expense ($000):**
34494 **Personnel:** 510

**RIO GRANDE CITY—Starr County**

★ **STARR COUNTY MEMORIAL HOSPITAL (450654)**, 2753 Hospital Court,
Zip 78582–6859, Mailing Address: P.O. Box 78, Zip 78582–0078;
tel. 956/487–5561 **A**9 10 20 **F**7 11 13 15 29 34 40 43 45 46 50 57 59 64
65 66 68 75 76 81 89 107 110 111 114 119 127 130 135 145 148 **P**5
Primary Contact: Thalia H. Munoz, R.N., MS, Chief Executive Officer
CFO: Rafael Olivares, Controller
CHR: Amaro Salinas, Assistant Administrator and Human Resource Officer
CNO: Mario Segura, Director of Nursing
Web address: www.starrcountyhospital.com
**Control:** Hospital district or authority, Government, nonfederal **Service:** General Medical and Surgical

**Staffed Beds:** 47 **Admissions:** 1317 **Census:** 13 **Outpatient Visits:** 41748
**Births:** 263 **Total Expense ($000):** 25990 **Payroll Expense ($000):** 12229
**Personnel:** 276

**ROCKDALE—Milam County**

◇ **LITTLE RIVER ROCKDALE HOSPITAL (451357)**, 1700 Brazos Street,
Zip 76567–2517, Mailing Address: Drawer 1010, Zip 76567–1010;
tel. 512/446–4500 **A**9 10 18 21 **F**3 7 15 18 20 22 29 34 40 43 45 46 47 54
56 57 59 64 65 68 74 75 77 79 81 82 84 85 87 91 93 107 108 110 111
114 116 117 127 129 131 133 135 146 147 148
Primary Contact: Jeffrey Madison, Chief Executive Officer
CMO: John Weed, III, M.D., Medical Director
CHR: Crystal Foley, Director Human Resources
Web address: www.lrhealthcare.com
**Control:** Corporation, Investor–owned, for–profit **Service:** General Medical and Surgical

**Staffed Beds:** 21 **Admissions:** 335 **Census:** 3 **Outpatient Visits:** 143170
**Births:** 1 **Total Expense ($000):** 68773 **Payroll Expense ($000):** 25301
**Personnel:** 393

TX

*Many Facility Codes have changed. Please refer to the AHA Guide Code Chart.*   © 2015 AHA Guide

## ROCKWALL—Rockwall County

✦ **TEXAS HEALTH PRESBYTERIAN HOSPITAL OF ROCKWALL (670044)**, 3150 Horizon Road, Zip 75032–7805; tel. 469/698–1000 **A**1 3 9 10 **F**3 12 13 15 29 30 34 35 40 42 45 46 47 49 50 54 68 70 75 76 77 79 81 82 84 85 87 107 108 110 111 115 119 130 146 147 148
Primary Contact: Cynthia K. Paris, R.N., President and Chief Executive Officer
CFO: Gorman Warren, Chief Financial Officer
CMO: Gary Bonacquisti, M.D., Chief Medical Officer
CIO: Kenneth Huckaby, Senior Director Information Technology Systems Operations
CNO: Tami Hawkins, R.N., Vice President Patient Care and Chief Nursing Officer
Web address: www.phrtexas.com
**Control:** Corporation, Investor–owned, for–profit **Service:** General Medical and Surgical

**Staffed Beds:** 50 **Admissions:** 4324 **Census:** 41 **Outpatient Visits:** 53077 **Births:** 893 **Total Expense ($000):** 96500 **Payroll Expense ($000):** 33548 **Personnel:** 504

## ROTAN—Fisher County

**FISHER COUNTY HOSPITAL DISTRICT (451313)**, 774 State Highway 70 North, Zip 79546–6918, Mailing Address: P.O. Drawer F, Zip 79546–4019; tel. 325/735–2256 **A**9 10 18 **F**7 28 32 34 35 40 43 50 53 56 57 59 64 66 75 93 97 107 119 127 133 **P**6
Primary Contact: Steve Lefevre, Chief Executive Officer and Administrator
CFO: Debbie Hull, Chief Financial Officer
CMO: C. M. Callan, M.D., Chief of Staff
Web address: www.fishercountyhospital.com
**Control:** Hospital district or authority, Government, nonfederal **Service:** General Medical and Surgical

**Staffed Beds:** 10 **Admissions:** 126 **Census:** 2 **Outpatient Visits:** 18438 **Births:** 0 **Total Expense ($000):** 7893 **Payroll Expense ($000):** 3474 **Personnel:** 70

## ROUND ROCK—Williamson County

☐ **RELIANT REHABILITATION HOSPITAL CENTRAL TEXAS (673032)**, 1400 Hester's Crossing, Zip 78681–8025; tel. 512/244–4400, (Total facility includes 25 beds in nursing home–type unit) **A**1 9 10 **F**3 29 90 93 96 128 130 148 **S** Reliant Healthcare Partners, Richardson, TX
Primary Contact: Eric Mueller, Chief Executive Officer
CNO: Vidette J. Forbes, R.N., Chief Nursing Officer and Chief Operating officer
Web address: www.reliantcentraltx.com/
**Control:** Partnership, Investor–owned, for–profit **Service:** Rehabilitation

**Staffed Beds:** 75 **Admissions:** 1391 **Census:** 48 **Outpatient Visits:** 4768 **Births:** 0 **Total Expense ($000):** 15709 **Payroll Expense ($000):** 7369 **Personnel:** 143

✦ **SCOTT & WHITE HOSPITAL AT ROUND ROCK (670034)**, 300 University Boulevard, Zip 78665–1032; tel. 512/509–0100, (Data for 303 days) **A**1 9 10 **F**3 7 11 13 15 18 20 22 24 28 29 30 34 35 36 40 43 44 46 49 52 54 57 59 60 64 65 66 70 74 75 76 77 78 79 81 82 85 87 93 97 99 104 107 108 110 111 115 118 119 129 130 131 132 135 144 145 146 147 148 **S** Baylor Scott & White Health, Dallas, TX
Primary Contact: Jay Fox, Chief Executive Officer
COO: Kevin E. Smith, Chief Operating Officer
CFO: Jason Cole, Senior Director Finance
CMO: Rob Watson, M.D., Chief Medical Officer
CIO: Matthew Chambers, Chief Information Officer
CHR: Mark A. Sherry, Director Human Resources
CNO: Leslie Gembol, MSN, Chief Nursing Officer
Web address: www.sw.org
**Control:** Other not–for–profit (including NFP Corporation) **Service:** General Medical and Surgical

**Staffed Beds:** 101 **Admissions:** 4643 **Census:** 54 **Outpatient Visits:** 392965 **Births:** 484 **Total Expense ($000):** 118195 **Payroll Expense ($000):** 33456 **Personnel:** 885

✦ **SETON MEDICAL CENTER WILLIAMSON (670041)**, 201 Seton Parkway, Zip 78665–8000; tel. 512/324–4000 **A**1 3 5 9 10 **F**3 11 12 13 15 18 20 22 24 26 28 29 30 31 34 35 37 40 43 44 45 46 49 50 51 53 54 57 58 59 60 64 68 70 72 74 75 76 77 78 79 81 82 83 84 86 87 93 96 107 108 110 111 114 115 119 124 126 130 131 132 135 146 147 148 **P**3 8 **S** Ascension Health, Saint Louis, MO
Primary Contact: Michelle Robertson, R.N., President
CFO: Douglas D. Waite, Senior Vice President and Chief Financial Officer
CMO: Hugh V. Gilmore, M.D., Vice President Medical Affairs
CIO: Gerry Lewis, Chief Information Officer
CHR: Thomas Wilken, Vice President Human Resources
Web address: www.seton.net/williamson
**Control:** Church–operated, Nongovernment, not–for profit **Service:** General Medical and Surgical

**Staffed Beds:** 143 **Admissions:** 7155 **Census:** 92 **Outpatient Visits:** 63088 **Births:** 708 **Total Expense ($000):** 144429 **Payroll Expense ($000):** 54678 **Personnel:** 715

✦ **ST. DAVID'S ROUND ROCK MEDICAL CENTER (450718)**, 2400 Round Rock Avenue, Zip 78681–4097; tel. 512/341–1000 **A**1 2 5 9 10 **F**3 11 12 13 15 18 20 22 24 26 28 29 30 31 34 35 40 42 43 57 60 64 66 70 72 74 75 76 77 78 79 81 85 87 90 92 93 96 107 108 110 111 114 115 116 118 119 124 126 129 130 132 135 144 146 147 148 **P**3 6 8 **S** HCA, Nashville, TN
Primary Contact: Deborah L. Ryle, Administrator and Chief Executive Officer
COO: Tad Hatton, Chief Operating Officer
CFO: Cindy Sexton, Chief Financial Officer
CHR: Amy Noak, Director Human Resources
Web address: www.stdavids.com
**Control:** Other not–for–profit (including NFP Corporation) **Service:** General Medical and Surgical

**Staffed Beds:** 148 **Admissions:** 9433 **Census:** 100 **Outpatient Visits:** 64008 **Births:** 1940 **Total Expense ($000):** 127405 **Payroll Expense ($000):** 42329 **Personnel:** 712

## ROWLETT—Rockwall County

✦ **LAKE POINTE MEDICAL CENTER (450742)**, 6800 Scenic Drive, Zip 75088–4552, Mailing Address: P.O. Box 1550, Zip 75030–1550; tel. 972/412–2273 **A**1 9 10 **F**3 12 13 15 18 20 22 24 28 29 30 34 35 40 42 45 46 49 50 53 54 57 59 60 64 65 70 72 73 74 75 77 78 79 81 82 85 86 87 93 107 108 110 111 114 115 118 119 120 121 126 129 130 131 132 144 146 147 148 **S** TENET Healthcare Corporation, Dallas, TX
Primary Contact: Brett D. Lee, Chief Executive Officer
COO: Deborah A. Moeller, R.N., Chief Operating Officer
CFO: Becky Speight, Chief Financial Officer
CMO: Larry Dencklau, D.O., Chief of Staff
CIO: Mark Slater, Director Information Systems
CHR: David Olmstead, Associate Administrator and Director Human Resources
CNO: Patti Gilliano, Chief Nursing Officer
Web address: www.lakepointemedical.com
**Control:** Corporation, Investor–owned, for–profit **Service:** General Medical and Surgical

**Staffed Beds:** 112 **Admissions:** 6838 **Census:** 65 **Outpatient Visits:** 102767 **Births:** 1399 **Total Expense ($000):** 107121 **Payroll Expense ($000):** 38263 **Personnel:** 595

## RUSK—Cherokee County

☐ **RUSK STATE HOSPITAL (454009)**, 805 North Dickinson, Zip 75785–2333, Mailing Address: P.O. Box 318, Zip 75785–0318; tel. 903/683–3421 **A**1 10 **F**3 30 39 44 50 68 75 86 87 98 103 106 130 135 146 148 **P**6 **S** Texas Department of State Health Services, Austin, TX
Primary Contact: Brenda Slaton, Superintendent
COO: Lynda Roberson, Senior Program Director
CFO: Rhonda Transier, Financial Officer
CMO: Joe Bates, M.D., Clinical Director
CHR: Kendra Brown, Job Requisition Coordinator
Web address: www.dshs.state.tx.us/mhhospitals/RuskSH/default.shtm
**Control:** State–Government, nonfederal **Service:** Psychiatric

**Staffed Beds:** 325 **Admissions:** 606 **Census:** 339 **Outpatient Visits:** 0 **Births:** 0 **Total Expense ($000):** 57583 **Payroll Expense ($000):** 33945 **Personnel:** 1026

**TX**

## SAN ANGELO—Tom Green County

☐ **RIVER CREST HOSPITAL (454064)**, 1636 Hunters Glen Road, Zip 76901–5016; tel. 325/949–5722 **A**1 9 10 **F**4 5 29 64 87 98 99 100 101 102 103 104 105 130 132 **S** Universal Health Services, Inc., King of Prussia, PA
Primary Contact: Mandy Westerman, Chief Executive Officer
CFO: Juana Giralt, Chief Financial Officer
CMO: Raymond Mays, M.D., Medical Director
CHR: Lydia Cardenas, Director Human Resources
CNO: Melissa Gabrielli, MSN, RN–B, Director of Nursing
Web address: www.rivercresthospital.com
**Control:** Corporation, Investor–owned, for–profit **Service:** Psychiatric

| | |
|---|---|
| **Staffed Beds:** 80 **Admissions:** 2755 **Census:** 54 **Outpatient Visits:** 1366 **Births:** 0 **Total Expense ($000):** 11770 **Payroll Expense ($000):** 5702 **Personnel:** 143 | |

✠ **SAN ANGELO COMMUNITY MEDICAL CENTER (450340)**, 3501 Knickerbocker Road, Zip 76904–7698; tel. 325/949–9511 **A**1 9 10 **F**3 8 11 13 15 18 20 22 24 28 29 30 31 34 35 37 40 43 45 49 51 53 54 57 59 60 63 64 68 70 72 74 75 76 77 78 79 81 82 85 89 93 107 108 110 111 115 118 119 126 129 130 131 135 144 145 146 147 148 **P**8 **S** Community Health Systems, Inc., Franklin, TN
Primary Contact: Jeremy Riney, Chief Executive Officer
CHR: Lisa Bibb, Director Human Resources
Web address: www.sacmc.com
**Control:** Partnership, Investor–owned, for–profit **Service:** General Medical and Surgical

| | |
|---|---|
| **Staffed Beds:** 131 **Admissions:** 4634 **Census:** 50 **Outpatient Visits:** 76452 **Births:** 852 **Total Expense ($000):** 95524 **Payroll Expense ($000):** 29291 **Personnel:** 519 | |

★ ⇑ **SHANNON MEDICAL CENTER (450571)**, 120 East Harris Street, Zip 76903–5976, Mailing Address: P.O. Box 1879, Zip 76902–1879; tel. 325/653–6741, (Includes SHANNON MEDICAL CENTER– ST. JOHN'S CAMPUS, 2018 Pulliam Street, Zip 76905–5197; tel. 915/659–7100), (Total facility includes 24 beds in nursing home–type unit) **A**2 3 5 9 10 22 **F**3 7 8 11 13 15 18 20 22 24 26 28 29 30 31 32 34 35 37 38 40 43 45 47 48 49 50 51 53 54 56 57 58 59 60 61 62 64 68 70 72 73 74 75 76 77 78 79 80 81 82 84 85 86 87 89 90 92 93 94 96 98 100 101 102 103 107 108 110 111 114 115 117 119 128 130 132 145 146 147 148
Primary Contact: Bryan Horner, President and Chief Executive Officer
CFO: Shane Plymell, Chief Financial Officer
CMO: Irvin Zeitler, D.O., Vice President Medical Affairs
CIO: Tom Perkins, Chief Information Officer
CHR: Teresa Morgan, Assistant Vice President Human Resources
Web address: www.shannonhealth.com
**Control:** Other not–for–profit (including NFP Corporation) **Service:** General Medical and Surgical

| | |
|---|---|
| **Staffed Beds:** 298 **Admissions:** 11749 **Census:** 161 **Outpatient Visits:** 110531 **Births:** 1209 **Total Expense ($000):** 213624 **Payroll Expense ($000):** 79915 **Personnel:** 1557 | |

## SAN ANTONIO—Bexar County

✠ **ACUITY HOSPITAL OF SOUTH TEXAS (452040)**, 718 Lexington Avenue, Zip 78212–4768; tel. 210/572–4600 **A**1 9 10 **F**1 3 29 45 75 85 87 91 107 119 148 **S** AcuityHealthcare, LP, Charlotte, NC
Primary Contact: Kris Karns, Ph.D., FACHE, Chief Executive Officer
CFO: Wayne Hegwood, Chief Financial Officer
CMO: Qasim Butt, M.D., Chief Medical Officer
CHR: Sheree Allstrom, Director Human Resources
CNO: Danny Fraley, Chief Clinical Officer
Web address: www.acuitysouthtexas.com
**Control:** Corporation, Investor–owned, for–profit **Service:** Long–Term Acute Care hospital

| | |
|---|---|
| **Staffed Beds:** 30 **Admissions:** 345 **Census:** 28 **Outpatient Visits:** 0 **Births:** 0 **Total Expense ($000):** 18251 **Payroll Expense ($000):** 7836 **Personnel:** 118 | |

◇ **BAPTIST EMERGENCY HOSPITAL (670078)**, 16088 San Pedro, Zip 78232–2249; tel. 210/402–4092 **A**10 21 **F**3 40 41 75 107 108 **P**5
Primary Contact: Laura Salgado, Administrator
Web address: www.baptistemergencyhospital.com
**Control:** Corporation, Investor–owned, for–profit **Service:** General Medical and Surgical

| | |
|---|---|
| **Staffed Beds:** 42 **Admissions:** 602 **Census:** 3 **Outpatient Visits:** 70760 **Births:** 0 **Total Expense ($000):** 31116 **Payroll Expense ($000):** 11164 **Personnel:** 206 | |

✠ △ **BAPTIST MEDICAL CENTER (450058)**, 111 Dallas Street, Zip 78205–1230; tel. 210/297–7000, (Includes MISSION TRAIL BAPTIST HOSPITAL, 3333 Research Plaza, Zip 78235–5154; tel. 210/297–3000; Andrew M. Harris, Chief Executive Officer; NORTH CENTRAL BAPTIST HOSPITAL, 520 Madison Oak Drive, Zip 78258–3912; tel. 210/297–4000; NORTHEAST BAPTIST HOSPITAL, 8811 Village Drive, Zip 78217–5440; tel. 210/297–2000; ST. LUKE'S BAPTIST HOSPITAL, 7930 Floyd Curl Drive, Zip 78229–0100; tel. 210/297–5000; John E. Knox, FACHE, Chief Executive Officer) **A**1 2 3 5 6 7 9 10 **F**1 3 11 12 13 14 15 17 18 19 20 22 24 26 28 29 30 31 35 37 38 40 41 42 43 44 45 46 47 50 54 55 56 57 59 60 64 65 68 70 72 73 74 75 77 78 79 80 81 82 85 86 87 88 90 91 92 93 95 96 98 101 102 103 107 108 111 114 115 116 117 119 124 126 129 130 132 135 145 146 147 148 **P**8 **S** TENET Healthcare Corporation, Dallas, TX
Primary Contact: Jonathan Turton, FACHE, Interim President
COO: Sandy Ethridge, Interim Chief Operating Officer
CFO: Linda Kirks, Chief Financial Officer
CMO: Richard Marple, M.D., Chief Medical Officer
CIO: Gary Davis, Vice President Information Systems
CHR: Sarah Spinharney, Senior Vice President
CNO: Nelson Tuazon, Chief Nursing Officer
Web address: www.baptisthealthsystem.com
**Control:** Partnership, Investor–owned, for–profit **Service:** General Medical and Surgical

| | |
|---|---|
| **Staffed Beds:** 1672 **Admissions:** 66413 **Census:** 796 **Outpatient Visits:** 286096 **Births:** 10756 **Total Expense ($000):** 785574 **Payroll Expense ($000):** 319934 **Personnel:** 4467 | |

✠ **CHRISTUS SANTA ROSA HEALTH SYSTEM (450237)**, 333 North Santa Rosa Street, Zip 78207–3108; tel. 210/704–4184, (Includes CHILDREN'S HOSPITAL OF SAN ANTONIO, 333 North Santa Rosa Street, Zip 78207; tel. 210/704–2011; Elias Neujahr, Administrator; CHRISTUS SANTA ROSA HOSPITAL – NEW BRAUNFELS, 600 North Union Avenue, New Braunfels, Zip 78130–4191; tel. 830/606–9111; Jim D. Wesson, Vice President and Administrator; CHRISTUS SANTA ROSA–MEDICAL CENTER, 2827 Babcock Road, Zip 78229–4813; tel. 210/705–6300; Christopher Bowe, Vice President and Administrator), (Nonreporting) **A**1 3 5 9 10 **S** CHRISTUS Health, Irving, TX
Primary Contact: Ken Haynes, President and Chief Executive Officer
CFO: Shawn Barnett, Vice President and Chief Financial Officer
CMO: James C. Martin, M.D., Vice President and Chief Medical Officer
CHR: Crystal H. Kohanke, Vice President Human Resources
CNO: Patty Toney, R.N., Chief Nurse Executive
Web address: www.christussantarosa.org
**Control:** Church–operated, Nongovernment, not–for profit **Service:** General Medical and Surgical

| | |
|---|---|
| **Staffed Beds:** 766 | |

☐ **CLARITY CHILD GUIDANCE CENTER**, 8535 Tom Slick, Zip 78229–3363; tel. 210/616–0300 **A**1 3 5 9 **F**29 41 98 99 101 102 104 105 106 130
Primary Contact: Frederick W. Hines, President and Chief Executive Officer
CFO: Michael Bernick, Executive Vice President and Chief Financial Officer
CMO: Soad Michelson, M.D., Senior Medical Director
CHR: Gina Massey, Vice President Human Resources
CNO: Carol Carver, MSN, Vice President Patient Services
Web address: www.claritycgc.org
**Control:** Other not–for–profit (including NFP Corporation) **Service:** Children's hospital psychiatric

| | |
|---|---|
| **Staffed Beds:** 52 **Admissions:** 1682 **Census:** 46 **Outpatient Visits:** 16474 **Births:** 0 **Total Expense ($000):** 18981 **Payroll Expense ($000):** 11421 **Personnel:** 235 | |

◇ **FOUNDATION SURGICAL HOSPITAL OF SAN ANTONIO (670054)**, 9522 Huebner Road, Zip 78240–1548; tel. 210/478–5400 **A**3 5 9 10 21 **F**3 12 29 30 35 37 40 44 45 51 53 68 74 75 77 79 81 85 86 87 107 114 119 129 130 132 135 148 **S** Foundation Surgical Hospital Affiliates, Oklahoma City, OK
Primary Contact: Kenneth Crouch, Chief Executive Officer
Web address: www.fshsanantonio.com/bariatric–foundation–surgical.html
**Control:** Corporation, Investor–owned, for–profit **Service:** Surgical

| | |
|---|---|
| **Staffed Beds:** 20 **Admissions:** 1041 **Census:** 6 **Outpatient Visits:** 2361 **Births:** 0 **Total Expense ($000):** 30723 **Payroll Expense ($000):** 5951 **Personnel:** 94 | |

✠ **HEALTHSOUTH REHABILITATION INSTITUTE OF SAN ANTONIO (453031)**, 9119 Cinnamon Hill, Zip 78240–5401; tel. 210/691–0737 **A**1 9 10 **F**29 62 90 91 96 130 132 148 **P**5 **S** HEALTHSOUTH Corporation, Birmingham, AL
Primary Contact: Scott Butcher, Chief Executive Officer
CFO: Larry Spriggs, Controller
CMO: Richard Senelick, M.D., Medical Director
CHR: Vanessa Tejada, Director Human Resources
CNO: Felipe Gregorio, Chief Nursing Officer
Web address: www.hsriosa.com
**Control:** Corporation, Investor–owned, for–profit **Service:** Rehabilitation

| | |
|---|---|
| **Staffed Beds:** 96 **Admissions:** 1164 **Census:** 56 **Outpatient Visits:** 3155 **Births:** 0 **Total Expense ($000):** 18861 **Payroll Expense ($000):** 10404 **Personnel:** 198 | |

*Many Facility Codes have changed. Please refer to the AHA Guide Code Chart.*

**TX**

✠ **KINDRED HOSPITAL–SAN ANTONIO (452016)**, 3636 Medical Drive,
Zip 78229–2183; tel. 210/616–0616 **A**1 9 10 **F**1 3 29 70 75 77 85 87 91
107 130 148 **S** Kindred Healthcare, Louisville, KY
Primary Contact: Kay E. Peck, Ph.D., Chief Executive Officer
CFO: Erin Russell, Controller
CMO: Charles Duncan, M.D., Medical Director
CHR: Stanley Richardson, Coordinator Human Resources and Payroll Benefits
Web address: www.khsanantonio.com/
**Control:** Corporation, Investor–owned, for–profit **Service:** Long–Term Acute Care hospital

**Staffed Beds:** 59 **Admissions:** 481 **Census:** 33 **Outpatient Visits:** 0 **Births:** 0 **Total Expense ($000):** 21010 **Payroll Expense ($000):** 7800 **Personnel:** 94

✠ **LAUREL RIDGE TREATMENT CENTER (454060)**, 17720 Corporate Woods
Drive, Zip 78259–3500; tel. 210/491–9400 **A**1 3 5 9 10 **F**5 29 35 38 75 77
98 99 100 101 103 105 106 130 132 **S** Universal Health Services, Inc., King of Prussia, PA
Primary Contact: Jacob Cuellar, M.D., Chief Executive Officer
COO: Debra Ward, Chief Operating Officer
CFO: Linda Maenius, Chief Financial Officer
CMO: Benigno J. Fernandez, M.D., Executive Medical Director
CHR: Brenda Frederick, Director Human Resources
CNO: Kathy Rosetta, Chief Nursing Officer
Web address: www.laurelridgetc.com
**Control:** Partnership, Investor–owned, for–profit **Service:** Psychiatric

**Staffed Beds:** 208 **Admissions:** 7024 **Census:** 167 **Outpatient Visits:** 19490 **Births:** 0 **Total Expense ($000):** 46684 **Payroll Expense ($000):** 19295 **Personnel:** 352

✠ **LIFECARE HOSPITALS OF SAN ANTONIO (452059)**, 8902 Floyd Curl Drive,
Zip 78240–1681; tel. 210/690–7000 **A**1 9 10 **F**1 3 29 45 75 77 85 86 87 96
97 107 114 130 148 **S** LifeCare Management Services, Plano, TX
Primary Contact: Randell G. Stokes, Chief Executive Officer
CMO: Randall C. Bell, M.D., Medical Director
CIO: Mike Wattenbarger, Chief Information Officer
Web address: www.lifecare–hospitals.com
**Control:** Corporation, Investor–owned, for–profit **Service:** Long–Term Acute Care hospital

**Staffed Beds:** 62 **Admissions:** 731 **Census:** 53 **Outpatient Visits:** 0 **Births:** 0 **Total Expense ($000):** 27395 **Payroll Expense ($000):** 12278 **Personnel:** 196

✠ **METHODIST AMBULATORY SURGERY HOSPITAL – NORTHWEST (450780)**,
9150 Huebner Road, Suite 100, Zip 78240–1545; tel. 210/575–5000 **A**1 9 10
**F**3 29 40 65 68 79 81 85 87 **P**8 **S** HCA, Nashville, TN
Primary Contact: Andrew G. Williams, Chief Executive Officer and Administrator
CFO: Tim Carr, Chief Financial Officer
CHR: Barry Burns, Vice President
CNO: Cathy Bump, R.N., Chief Nursing Officer
Web address: www.sahealth.com
**Control:** Partnership, Investor–owned, for–profit **Service:** General Medical and Surgical

**Staffed Beds:** 23 **Admissions:** 469 **Census:** 3 **Outpatient Visits:** 6989 **Births:** 0 **Total Expense ($000):** 20316 **Payroll Expense ($000):** 6448 **Personnel:** 107

✠ **METHODIST HOSPITAL (450388)**, 7700 Floyd Curl Drive, Zip 78229–3993;
tel. 210/575–4000, (Includes METHODIST CHILDREN'S HOSPITAL, 7700 Floyd
Curl Drive, Zip 78229–3383; tel. 210/575–7000; METHODIST SPECIALTY AND
TRANSPLANT HOSPITAL, 8026 Floyd Curl Drive, Zip 78229–3915;
tel. 210/575–8090; David Handley, Chief Executive Officer; METHODIST TEXSAN
HOSPITAL, 6700 IH–10 West, Zip 78201; tel. 210/736–6700; Scott Davis, Chief
Executive Officer; METROPOLITAN METHODIST HOSPITAL, 1310 McCullough
Avenue, Zip 78212–2617; tel. 210/757–2909; Gregory A. Seiler, Chief Executive
Officer; NORTHEAST METHODIST HOSPITAL, 12412 Judson Road, Live Oak,
Zip 78233–3255; tel. 210/757–5000; Michael D. Beaver, Chief Executive Officer)
**A**1 2 3 5 9 10 **F**3 4 5 8 11 12 13 15 17 18 19 20 21 22 23 24 25 26 27 28
29 30 31 34 35 38 40 41 42 43 44 45 46 47 48 49 51 53 54 56 57 58 59
60 64 65 68 70 72 74 75 76 77 78 79 80 81 82 84 85 86 87 88 89 90 93
95 96 98 100 101 102 103 104 105 107 108 111 114 115 119 121 124
126 127 129 130 132 135 136 137 138 139 142 143 145 146 147 148 **P**7
**S** HCA, Nashville, TN
Primary Contact: Gay Nord, Chief Executive Officer
CFO: Nancy Meadows, Chief Financial Officer
CMO: Russell Woodward, M.D., Chief Medical Officer
CIO: Eddie Cuellar, Vice President Information Systems
CHR: Nancy Edgar, Vice President Human Resources
Web address: www.sahealth.com
**Control:** Partnership, Investor–owned, for–profit **Service:** General Medical and Surgical

**Staffed Beds:** 1585 **Admissions:** 76310 **Census:** 1098 **Outpatient Visits:** 448301 **Births:** 9749 **Total Expense ($000):** 1110529 **Payroll Expense ($000):** 407873 **Personnel:** 5721

✠ **METHODIST STONE OAK HOSPITAL (670055)**, 1139 East Sonterra
Boulevard, Zip 78258–4347; tel. 210/638–2100 **A**1 3 5 9 10 **F**3 13 15 18 20
22 24 29 30 31 34 38 40 44 45 46 47 49 52 57 59 60 64 65 68 70 72 74
75 76 77 78 79 80 81 82 85 86 87 107 108 111 114 119 126 130 145 146
147 148 **S** HCA, Nashville, TN
Primary Contact: Marc Strode, Chief Executive Officer
COO: Candie Starr, Chief Operating Officer and Ethics and Compliance Officer
CFO: Gabriel Marrufo, Chief Financial Officer
CNO: Ann M. Winn, M.D., Chief Nursing Officer
Web address: www.sahealth.com/locations/methodist–stone–oak–hospital/
**Control:** Partnership, Investor–owned, for–profit **Service:** General Medical and Surgical

**Staffed Beds:** 140 **Admissions:** 10016 **Census:** 108 **Outpatient Visits:** 41898 **Births:** 2013 **Total Expense ($000):** 139162 **Payroll Expense ($000):** 39075 **Personnel:** 516

◇ **NIX HEALTH CARE SYSTEM (450130)**, 414 Navarro Street, Zip 78205–2516;
tel. 210/271–1800 **A**3 5 9 10 21 **F**3 5 12 15 18 20 22 24 26 29 30 31 34 35
40 44 45 49 50 54 56 57 59 60 62 64 68 70 74 75 78 79 81 82 85 87 90
93 97 98 99 103 107 108 110 111 114 118 119 129 130 132 142 143 146
147 148
Primary Contact: John F. Strieby, Chief Executive Officer
COO: Blake W. Hubbard, FACHE, Senior Vice President and Chief Operating Officer
CFO: Lester Surrock, Chief Financial Officer
CMO: Dina Goytia–Leos, M.D., Chief of Staff
CIO: Adrian Dickreiter, Vice President Technology
CHR: Blake W. Hubbard, FACHE, Senior Vice President and Chief Operating Officer
CNO: Maria Rose Lopez, R.N., Chief of Nursing
Web address: www.nixhealth.com
**Control:** Corporation, Investor–owned, for–profit **Service:** General Medical and Surgical

**Staffed Beds:** 246 **Admissions:** 9494 **Census:** 150 **Outpatient Visits:** 89088 **Births:** 0 **Total Expense ($000):** 113591 **Payroll Expense ($000):** 42605 **Personnel:** 1286

**TX**

**TX**

⊠ **POST ACUTE/WARM SPRINGS REHABILITATION HOSPITAL OF SAN ANTONIO (453035)**, 5101 Medical Drive, Zip 78229–4801; tel. 210/616–0100, (Includes WARM SPRINGS REHABILITATION HOSPITAL OF THOUSAND OAKS, 14747 Jones Maltsberger Road, Zip 78247–3713; tel. 210/581–5300; Kasondra Kistner, Chief Executive Officer; WARM SPRINGS REHABILITATION HOSPITAL OF WESTOVER HILLS, 10323 State Highway 151, Zip 78251–4557; tel. 210/581–5306; Steve Flaherty, Chief Executive Officer), (Total facility includes 4 beds in nursing home–type unit) **A**1 3 5 9 10 **F**3 11 29 30 57 64 68 74 75 79 82 90 91 93 94 96 128 130 132 146 148 **S** Post Acute Medical, LLC, Enola, PA
Primary Contact: Kasondra Kistner, Chief Executive Officer
CFO: James Asberry, Chief Financial Officer
CMO: Alex Willingham, M.D., Medical Director
CIO: Rick Marek, Vice President Medical Information Systems
CHR: Waynea Finley, System Director Human Resources
Web address: www.postacutemedical.com/our–facilities/hospitals/warm–springs–rehabilitation–hospital–san–antonio/
**Control:** Partnership, Investor–owned, for–profit **Service:** Rehabilitation

**Staffed Beds:** 138 **Admissions:** 2655 **Census:** 99 **Outpatient Visits:** 27479 **Births:** 0 **Total Expense ($000):** 45670 **Payroll Expense ($000):** 22805 **Personnel:** 466

⊠ **POST ACUTE/WARM SPRINGS SPECIALTY HOSPITAL OF SAN ANTONIO (452090)**, 7400 Barlite Boulevard, 2nd Floor, Zip 78224–1308; tel. 210/921–3550 **A**1 9 10 **F**1 3 29 30 148 **S** Post Acute Medical, LLC, Enola, PA
Primary Contact: Karen Pitcher, Chief Executive Officer and Vice President
CNO: Carrie Nims, Director of Nursing
Web address: www.postacutemedical.com
**Control:** Partnership, Investor–owned, for–profit **Service:** Long–Term Acute Care hospital

**Staffed Beds:** 26 **Admissions:** 195 **Census:** 13 **Outpatient Visits:** 0 **Births:** 0 **Total Expense ($000):** 8758 **Payroll Expense ($000):** 3688 **Personnel:** 75

☐ **SAN ANTONIO STATE HOSPITAL (454011)**, 6711 South New Braunfels, Suite 100, Zip 78223–3006; tel. 210/531–7711 **A**1 3 5 10 **F**30 39 53 56 57 59 68 75 77 86 87 91 98 99 100 101 103 106 130 132 135 146 **P**1 **S** Texas Department of State Health Services, Austin, TX
Primary Contact: Robert C. Arizpe, Superintendent
CFO: Janie Rabago, Chief Accountant
CMO: Terresa Stallworth, M.D., Clinical Director
CIO: Chris Stanush, Director Information Management
CHR: Renee Bourland, Human Resources Specialist
CNO: Maria DC Ostrander, R.N., Chief Nurse Executive
Web address: www.dshs.state.tx.us/mhhospitals/SanAntonioSH/default.shtm
**Control:** State–Government, nonfederal **Service:** Psychiatric

**Staffed Beds:** 302 **Admissions:** 1794 **Census:** 271 **Outpatient Visits:** 0 **Births:** 0 **Total Expense ($000):** 73134 **Payroll Expense ($000):** 34960 **Personnel:** 783

★ ○ **SELECT REHABILITATION HOSPITAL OF SAN ANTONIO (673040)**, 19126 Stonehue Road, Zip 78258–3490; tel. 210/482–3400 **A**9 10 11 **F**3 29 30 75 90 91 96 130 148 **S** GLOBALREHAB, Dallas, TX
Primary Contact: Robert Ward, Chief Executive Officer
Web address: www.globalrehabhospitals.com
**Control:** Partnership, Investor–owned, for–profit **Service:** Rehabilitation

**Staffed Beds:** 42 **Admissions:** 866 **Census:** 33 **Outpatient Visits:** 0 **Births:** 0 **Total Expense ($000):** 14775 **Payroll Expense ($000):** 6932 **Personnel:** 145

⊠ **SELECT SPECIALTY HOSPITAL–SAN ANTONIO (452073)**, 111 Dallas Street, 4th Floor, Zip 78205–1201; tel. 210/297–7185 **A**1 9 10 **F**1 29 148 **P**8 **S** Select Medical Corporation, Mechanicsburg, PA
Primary Contact: Sean Stricker, Chief Executive Officer
Web address: www.selectspecialtyhospitals.com/company/locations/sanantonio.aspx
**Control:** Corporation, Investor–owned, for–profit **Service:** Long–Term Acute Care hospital

**Staffed Beds:** 44 **Admissions:** 455 **Census:** 36 **Outpatient Visits:** 0 **Births:** 0 **Total Expense ($000):** 19862 **Payroll Expense ($000):** 7669 **Personnel:** 108

☐ **SOUTH TEXAS SPINE AND SURGICAL HOSPITAL (450856)**, 18600 Hardy Oak Boulevard, Zip 78258–4206; tel. 210/507–4090 **A**1 3 5 9 10 **F**3 29 40 41 70 75 77 79 81 85 86 87 89 **S** National Surgical Healthcare, Chicago, IL
Primary Contact: Debbie Kelly, Chief Executive Officer
CFO: Sylvia Garcia, Chief Accounting Officer
CHR: Sally Hall, Manager Human Resources
CNO: Jennifer West, Chief Nursing Officer
Web address: www.southtexassurgical.com
**Control:** Partnership, Investor–owned, for–profit **Service:** General Medical and Surgical

**Staffed Beds:** 30 **Admissions:** 1010 **Census:** 7 **Outpatient Visits:** 2230 **Births:** 0 **Total Expense ($000):** 25913 **Payroll Expense ($000):** 5755 **Personnel:** 106

⊠ △ **SOUTH TEXAS VETERANS HEALTH CARE SYSTEM**, 7400 Merton Minter Boulevard, Zip 78229–4404; tel. 210/617–5300, (Includes KERRVILLE DIVISION, 3600 Memorial Boulevard, Kerrville, Zip 78028; tel. 210/896–2020; SAN ANTONIO DIVISION, 7400 Merton Minter Boulevard, Zip 78284–5799; tel. 210/617–5300), (Nonreporting) **A**1 3 5 7 8 **S** Department of Veterans Affairs, Washington, DC
Primary Contact: Julianne Flynn, M.D., Acting Director
CFO: I. M. Rachal, Chief Fiscal Service
CMO: Richard Bauer, M.D., Chief of Staff
CIO: Simon Willett, Director Administrative Operations
CHR: Leslie Cruthirds, Chief Human Resource Management Service
Web address: www.southtexas.va.gov/
**Control:** Veterans Affairs, Government, federal **Service:** General Medical and Surgical

**Staffed Beds:** 838

⊠ **SOUTHWEST GENERAL HOSPITAL (450697)**, 7400 Barlite Boulevard, Zip 78224–1399; tel. 210/921–2000 **A**9 10 **F**3 12 13 15 18 20 22 24 29 30 35 37 40 43 44 45 46 49 50 51 56 57 59 60 64 65 70 72 73 74 75 76 77 78 79 80 81 85 87 90 93 98 100 102 103 105 107 108 110 111 114 115 119 126 129 130 132 135 146 147 148 **S** IASIS Healthcare, Franklin, TN
Primary Contact: P. Craig Desmond, Chief Executive Officer
COO: Sarah Humme, MSN, Chief Operating Officer
CFO: Joe Sereno, Chief Financial Officer
CIO: Matthew D'Ambrosio, Director Information Systems
CHR: Christina Rivera, Director Human Resources
CNO: Sarah Humme, MSN, Chief Nursing Officer
Web address: www.swgeneralhospital.com
**Control:** Corporation, Investor–owned, for–profit **Service:** General Medical and Surgical

**Staffed Beds:** 253 **Admissions:** 9092 **Census:** 132 **Outpatient Visits:** 61961 **Births:** 1887 **Total Expense ($000):** 98093 **Payroll Expense ($000):** 44487 **Personnel:** 637

**ST. LUKE'S BAPTIST HOSPITAL** See Baptist Medical Center

☐ **TEXAS CENTER FOR INFECTIOUS DISEASE (452033)**, 2303 S.E. Military Drive, Zip 78223–3597; tel. 210/534–8857 **A**1 10 **F**1 3 29 30 50 53 54 61 64 68 75 87 130 132 135 143 146 **P**6 **S** Texas Department of State Health Services, Austin, TX
Primary Contact: James N. Elkins, FACHE, Superintendent
CFO: Glenda Armstrong–Huff, Assistant Superintendent
CMO: David Griffith, M.D., Medical Director
CIO: Andre Avant, Facility Automation Manager
CHR: Gerald Shackelford, Staff Support Specialist
CNO: Rebecca Sanchez, R.N., Director of Nursing
Web address: www.dshs.state.tx.us/tcid/default.shtm
**Control:** State–Government, nonfederal **Service:** Tuberculosis and other respiratory diseases

**Staffed Beds:** 40 **Admissions:** 67 **Census:** 35 **Outpatient Visits:** 882 **Births:** 0 **Total Expense ($000):** 11429 **Payroll Expense ($000):** 6595 **Personnel:** 149

⊠ **UNIVERSITY HEALTH SYSTEM (450213)**, 4502 Medical Drive, Zip 78229–4493; tel. 210/358–2000, (Includes UNIVERSITY HEALTH CENTER – DOWNTOWN, 4502 Medical Drive, tel. 210/358–3400; UNIVERSITY HOSPITAL, 4502 Medical Drive, tel. 210/358–4000) **A**1 2 3 5 8 9 10 **F**3 4 7 11 13 14 15 16 17 18 19 20 21 22 23 24 25 26 27 29 30 31 32 34 35 38 40 41 43 44 45 46 47 48 49 50 51 52 54 55 56 57 58 59 60 61 64 65 66 68 72 73 74 75 76 77 78 79 80 81 82 84 85 86 87 88 89 90 92 93 95 96 98 100 101 107 108 110 111 115 118 119 124 126 129 130 132 135 138 139 140 141 142 143 144 145 146 147 148
Primary Contact: George B. Hernandez, Jr., President and Chief Executive Officer
COO: Christann Vasquez, Executive Vice President and Chief Operating Officer
CFO: Peggy Deming, Executive Vice President and Chief Financial Officer
CMO: Bryan Alsip, M.D., Executive Vice President, Chief Medical Officer
CIO: Bill Phillips, Vice President Information Services
CHR: Theresa Scepanski, Vice President People and Organizational Development
CNO: Nancy L. Ray, R.N., Executive Vice President, Chief Nursing Executive
Web address: www.universityhealthsystem.com
**Control:** Hospital district or authority, Government, nonfederal **Service:** General Medical and Surgical

**Staffed Beds:** 426 **Admissions:** 22810 **Census:** 398 **Outpatient Visits:** 2230674 **Births:** 2836 **Total Expense ($000):** 918060 **Payroll Expense ($000):** 313483 **Personnel:** 6212

☐ **VICTORY MEDICAL CENTER – SOUTHCROSS (670021)**, 5330 N. Loop 1604 W., Zip 78249; tel. 210/877–8000 **A**1 10 **F**3 12 29 40 45 75 79 81 82 86 132 **S** Victory Healthcare, The Woodlands, TX
Primary Contact: Louis O. Garcia, Chief Executive Officer
COO: Leroy Bernal, Chief Operating Officer
CFO: Julie Churchill, Chief Financial Officer
CHR: Regina Woolridge, Director Human Resources
CNO: Adam Apolinar, Chief Clinical Officer
Web address: www.victory–healthcare.com/san–antonio–location/
**Control:** Corporation, Investor–owned, for–profit **Service:** Surgical

**Staffed Beds:** 9 **Admissions:** 33 **Census:** 1 **Outpatient Visits:** 284 **Births:** 0

☐ **VICTORY MEDICAL CENTER LANDMARK**, 5330 North Loop 1604 West,
Zip 78249–1371; tel. 210/877–8000 **A**1 **F**3 12 29 40 45 51 75 79 81 82 107
**S** Victory Healthcare, The Woodlands, TX
Primary Contact: Alex Garcia, Chief Executive Officer
Web address: www.victory–healthcare.com/sanantoniolandmark
**Control:** Corporation, Investor–owned, for–profit **Service:** Surgical

**Staffed Beds:** 25 **Admissions:** 476 **Census:** 4 **Outpatient Visits:** 1060
**Births:** 0 **Total Expense ($000):** 51009 **Payroll Expense ($000):** 6149
**Personnel:** 103

### SAN AUGUSTINE—San Augustine County

★ **CHI ST. LUKE'S HEALTH MEMORIAL SAN AUGUSTINE (451360)**, 511 East
Hospital Street, Zip 75972–2121, Mailing Address: P.O. Box 658,
Zip 75972–0658; tel. 936/275–3446, (Data for 181 days) **A**9 10 18 **F**29 35 40
57 59 64 102 107 119 132 133 **S** Catholic Health Initiatives, Englewood, CO
Primary Contact: Darlene Williams, R.N., Administrator
CFO: Kristi Gay, Chief Financial Officer
Web address: www.memorialhealth.org
**Control:** Other not–for–profit (including NFP Corporation) **Service:** General
Medical and Surgical

**Staffed Beds:** 8 **Admissions:** 180 **Census:** 3 **Outpatient Visits:** 6451 **Births:**
0 **Total Expense ($000):** 2997 **Payroll Expense ($000):** 1452 **Personnel:**
55

### SAN MARCOS—Hays County

⊞ **CENTRAL TEXAS MEDICAL CENTER (450272)**, 1301 Wonder World Drive,
Zip 78666–7544; tel. 512/353–8979 **A**1 9 10 **F**3 11 13 15 18 20 29 30 32
34 35 39 40 43 44 45 49 50 51 54 57 59 60 62 63 64 65 66 68 70 72 75
76 77 79 80 81 82 85 86 87 92 93 94 98 107 108 109 110 111 114 116
117 118 119 126 129 130 131 132 146 147 148 **P**6 8 **S** Adventist Health
System Sunbelt Health Care Corporation, Altamonte Springs, FL
Primary Contact: Sam Huenergardt, President and Chief Executive Officer
CFO: Jesse Sutton, Chief Financial Officer
CHR: Debbie D. Cox, Administrative Director Human Resources
CNO: Lana Cameron, Chief Nursing Officer
Web address: www.ctmc.org
**Control:** Church–operated, Nongovernment, not–for profit **Service:** General
Medical and Surgical

**Staffed Beds:** 111 **Admissions:** 4200 **Census:** 40 **Outpatient Visits:** 78029
**Births:** 1021 **Total Expense ($000):** 89261 **Payroll Expense ($000):** 31437
**Personnel:** 567

### SEGUIN—Guadalupe County

⊞ **GUADALUPE REGIONAL MEDICAL CENTER (450104)**, 1215 East Court
Street, Zip 78155–5189; tel. 830/379–2411 **A**1 9 10 **F**3 5 8 11 13 15 18 20
22 28 29 30 31 34 35 39 40 43 45 46 49 50 51 53 56 57 59 60 62 63 64
66 68 70 74 75 76 77 78 79 81 82 84 85 86 90 93 96 103 104 107 108
110 111 112 114 118 119 126 129 130 132 143 145 146 148 **P**1
Primary Contact: Robert Haynes, FACHE, Chief Executive Officer
COO: Michelle Rumbaut, Chief Strategy Officer
CFO: Penny Wallace, Chief Financial Officer
CMO: Robert Ryan, M.D., Chief Medical Officer
CIO: Steve Ratliff, Director Information Technology
CHR: Fay Bennett, Vice President Employee Services
CNO: Daphne Blake, R.N., Chief Nursing Officer
Web address: www.grmedcenter.com
**Control:** City–County, Government, nonfederal **Service:** General Medical and
Surgical

**Staffed Beds:** 95 **Admissions:** 3936 **Census:** 39 **Outpatient Visits:** 133682
**Births:** 852 **Total Expense ($000):** 86503 **Payroll Expense ($000):** 31253
**Personnel:** 628

### SEMINOLE—Gaines County

★ **MEMORIAL HOSPITAL (451358)**, 209 N.W. Eighth Street, Zip 79360–3447;
tel. 432/758–5811 **A**9 10 18 **F**3 10 11 13 28 29 30 32 34 35 40 43 45 53
56 57 59 62 63 64 65 75 76 81 87 93 97 102 107 114 119 129 130 131
132 133 143 146 147 148
Primary Contact: Betsy Briscoe, Chief Executive Officer
COO: Heath Mitchell, Chief Operating Officer
CFO: Traci Anderson, Chief Financial Officer
CMO: Michael Watson, M.D., Chief of Staff
Web address: www.seminolehospitaldistrict.com
**Control:** Hospital district or authority, Government, nonfederal **Service:** General
Medical and Surgical

**Staffed Beds:** 25 **Admissions:** 924 **Census:** 10 **Outpatient Visits:** 76584
**Births:** 271 **Total Expense ($000):** 36119 **Payroll Expense ($000):** 8136
**Personnel:** 183

### SEYMOUR—Baylor County

**SEYMOUR HOSPITAL (450586)**, 200 Stadium Drive, Zip 76380–2344;
tel. 940/889–5572 **A**9 10 20 **F**3 7 8 11 13 14 28 29 34 36 40 43 45 50 53
56 57 59 62 64 65 66 68 70 75 81 85 86 87 93 94 100 102 103 104 107
119 127 130 133 135 146 147 148 **P**1
Primary Contact: Leslie Hardin, Chief Executive Officer and Chief Financial Officer
CFO: Leslie Hardin, Chief Executive Officer and Chief Financial Officer
CMO: Kory Lann Martin, M.D., Chief of Staff
CHR: Linda Moore, Manager Human Resources
CNO: Julie Smajstrla, Director Nursing
Web address: www.seymourhospital.com/
**Control:** Hospital district or authority, Government, nonfederal **Service:** General
Medical and Surgical

**Staffed Beds:** 38 **Admissions:** 487 **Census:** 7 **Outpatient Visits:** 37986
**Total Expense ($000):** 10837 **Payroll Expense ($000):** 5266 **Personnel:**
118

### SHAMROCK—Wheeler County

**SHAMROCK GENERAL HOSPITAL (451340)**, 1000 South Main Street,
Zip 79079–2896, Mailing Address: P. O. Box 511, Zip 79079–0511;
tel. 806/256–2114 **A**9 10 18 **F**7 11 29 32 34 40 43 63 65 68 93 107 119
127 130 133 **P**4
Primary Contact: Wiley M. Fires, Administrator
CFO: Wiley M. Fires, Administrator
CHR: Cecille Williams, Assistant Administrator
CNO: Jeanne Crossland, Director of Nursing
**Control:** Hospital district or authority, Government, nonfederal **Service:** General
Medical and Surgical

**Staffed Beds:** 13 **Admissions:** 132 **Census:** 2 **Outpatient Visits:** 11481
**Births:** 0 **Total Expense ($000):** 6101 **Payroll Expense ($000):** 3044
**Personnel:** 74

### SHENANDOAH—Montgomery County

◇ **NEXUS SPECIALTY HOSPITAL**, 123 Vision Park Boulevard, Zip 77384–3001;
tel. 281/364–0317 **A**9 21 **F**1 3 70 74 75 77 82 84 85 91 92 93 100 101 107
119 130 132 135 148 **S** Nexus Health Systems, Houston, TX
Primary Contact: Judith Butryn, Chief Executive Officer
COO: Guido J. Cubellis, Chief Operating Officer
CFO: Julia Hatton, Chief Financial Officer
CMO: Ather Siddiqi, M.D., Medical Director
CIO: Deepak Chaudhry, Vice President Information Technology
CHR: Marc Leighton, Vice President Human Resources
CNO: Patrick Laird, Chief Clinical Officer
Web address: www.nexusspecialty.com
**Control:** Partnership, Investor–owned, for–profit **Service:** Long–Term Acute Care
hospital

**Staffed Beds:** 75 **Admissions:** 635 **Census:** 46 **Outpatient Visits:** 527
**Births:** 0 **Total Expense ($000):** 27015 **Payroll Expense ($000):** 10987
**Personnel:** 204

☐ **RELIANT REHABILITATION HOSPITAL NORTH HOUSTON (673034)**, 117
Vision Park Boulevard, Zip 77384–3001; tel. 936/444–1700 **A**1 9 10 **F**3 29 65
90 93 96 130 148 **S** Reliant Healthcare Partners, Richardson, TX
Primary Contact: Jeff Crawford, Chief Executive Officer
CFO: Terri Weiss, Chief Financial Officer
Web address: www.reliantnorthhouston.com/
**Control:** Partnership, Investor–owned, for–profit **Service:** Rehabilitation

**Staffed Beds:** 60 **Admissions:** 1350 **Census:** 39 **Outpatient Visits:** 12239
**Births:** 0 **Total Expense ($000):** 16243 **Payroll Expense ($000):** 7600
**Personnel:** 140

### SHERMAN—Grayson County

◇ **CARRUS REHABILITATION HOSPITAL (673041)**, 1810 West U.S. Highway 82,
Suite 100, Zip 75092–7069; tel. 903/870–2600 **A**9 10 21 **F**3 29 40 41 44 65
74 75 77 79 85 86 87 90 91 96 130 **S** Carrus Hospitals, Sherman, TX
Primary Contact: Dorothy J. Elford, Chief Executive Officer
CFO: Michael Exline, Chief Financial Officer
CMO: Jose Matus, M.D., Director Medical
CIO: Gary Glenn, Director Information Technology
CHR: Charlene Shupert, Director Staff Services
CNO: Marie Johnson, Chief Nursing Officer
Web address: www.carrushospital.com
**Control:** Corporation, Investor–owned, for–profit **Service:** Rehabilitation

**Staffed Beds:** 24 **Admissions:** 605 **Census:** 23 **Outpatient Visits:** 0 **Births:**
0 **Total Expense ($000):** 7204 **Payroll Expense ($000):** 3265 **Personnel:**
58

**TX**

---

**Hospital, Medicare Provider Number, Address, Telephone, Approval, Facility, and Physician Codes, Health Care System**

★ American Hospital Association (AHA) membership    ○ Healthcare Facilities Accreditation Program    ⇑ Center for Improvement in Healthcare Quality Accreditation
☐ The Joint Commission accreditation    ◇ DNV Healthcare Inc. accreditation    △ Commission on Accreditation of Rehabilitation Facilities (CARF) accreditation

◇ **CARRUS SPECIALTY HOSPITAL (452041)**, 1810 West U.S. Highway 82, Zip 75092–7069; tel. 903/870–2600 **A**9 10 21 **F**1 3 29 40 41 44 56 65 74 75 77 78 79 83 85 86 87 91 107 114 129 130 148 **S** Carrus Hospitals, Sherman, TX
Primary Contact: Jon Michael Rains, Chief Executive Officer
CFO: Michael Exline, Chief Financial Officer
CMO: Nathan Watson, Jr., M.D., Chief of Staff
CIO: Gary Glenn, Director Information Technology
CHR: Charlene Shupert, Director Staff Services
CNO: Marie Johnson, Chief Nursing Officer
Web address: www.carrushospital.com
**Control:** Corporation, Investor–owned, for–profit **Service:** Long–Term Acute Care hospital

> **Staffed Beds:** 16 **Admissions:** 218 **Census:** 15 **Outpatient Visits:** 2891 **Births:** 0 **Total Expense ($000):** 10268 **Payroll Expense ($000):** 3056 **Personnel:** 80

◇ **HERITAGE PARK SURGICAL HOSPITAL (670076)**, 3601 North Calais Street, Zip 75090–1785; tel. 903/870–0999 **A**9 10 21 **F**3 8 29 34 39 40 45 47 54 57 64 75 77 79 81 82 85 86 87 107 111 114 119 131 135 **S** Foundation Surgical Hospital Affiliates, Oklahoma City, OK
Primary Contact: Marc Devorsetz, Chief Executive Officer
CMO: Curtis Holbrook, M.D., Chief Medical Officer
CIO: Grant Hulsey, Director Information Technology
CHR: Terrie Langford, Director Human Resources
CNO: Teresa Dutton, R.N., Chief Nursing Officer
Web address: www.heritageparksurgicalhospital.com
**Control:** Corporation, Investor–owned, for–profit **Service:** General Medical and Surgical

> **Staffed Beds:** 10 **Admissions:** 295 **Census:** 2 **Outpatient Visits:** 30919 **Births:** 0 **Total Expense ($000):** 28231 **Payroll Expense ($000):** 8243 **Personnel:** 164

**WILSON N. JONES MEDICAL CENTER** See Wilson N. Jones Regional Medical Center

✠ **WILSON N. JONES REGIONAL MEDICAL CENTER (450469)**, 500 North Highland Avenue, Zip 75092–7354; tel. 903/870–4611 **A**1 9 10 **F**3 11 13 15 17 18 20 22 24 26 28 29 30 31 35 40 41 43 45 53 54 56 57 58 59 61 64 70 74 76 77 78 79 81 84 86 87 93 96 98 100 103 106 107 108 111 118 119 129 130 132 146 147 148
Primary Contact: Kitty J. Richardson, Administrator
CMO: Al Cardenas, M.D., President Medical Staff
CIO: Michael Wooton, Manager Information Technology Service Delivery
CHR: Tammy Dawn Johnson, Vice President Human Resources
CNO: Tonya Price, Chief Nursing Officer
Web address: www.wnj.org
**Control:** Corporation, Investor–owned, for–profit **Service:** General Medical and Surgical

> **Staffed Beds:** 235 **Admissions:** 5764 **Census:** 79 **Outpatient Visits:** 46542 **Births:** 428 **Total Expense ($000):** 102017 **Payroll Expense ($000):** 27449 **Personnel:** 496

### SMITHVILLE—Bastrop County

✠ **SETON SMITHVILLE REGIONAL HOSPITAL (450143)**, 800 East Highway 71, Zip 78957–1730; tel. 512/237–3214 **A**1 9 10 **F**3 11 15 29 30 34 40 43 53 57 62 64 68 77 79 81 85 87 93 107 110 111 114 119 146 148 **P**3 8 **S** Ascension Health, Saint Louis, MO
Primary Contact: Robbie G. Rabe, Interim Chief Executive Officer
CFO: Melissa Nordyke, Chief Financial Officer
CHR: Sara Rodriguez, Human Resources
CNO: Christine Laflamme, R.N., Chief Nursing Officer
Web address: www.seton.org
**Control:** Church–operated, Nongovernment, not–for profit **Service:** General Medical and Surgical

> **Staffed Beds:** 10 **Admissions:** 301 **Census:** 3 **Outpatient Visits:** 29177 **Births:** 0 **Total Expense ($000):** 18524 **Payroll Expense ($000):** 8645 **Personnel:** 126

### SNYDER—Scurry County

**COGDELL MEMORIAL HOSPITAL (450073)**, 1700 Cogdell Boulevard, Zip 79549–6198; tel. 325/573–6374 **A**9 10 20 **F**8 11 13 15 18 19 29 30 34 40 43 45 46 47 48 49 50 53 56 57 59 62 64 65 68 75 76 77 79 81 85 86 87 91 92 93 97 107 108 111 115 119 127 130 131 132 133 145 146 147 148 **P**6
Primary Contact: William W. Weldon, Ph.D., Interim Chief Executive Officer
CFO: John Everett, Chief Financial Officer
CMO: Robert Rakov, M.D., Chief Medical Officer
CHR: Linda Warren, Director Human Resources
Web address: www.cogdellhospital.com
**Control:** Hospital district or authority, Government, nonfederal **Service:** General Medical and Surgical

> **Staffed Beds:** 49 **Admissions:** 656 **Census:** 6 **Outpatient Visits:** 60571 **Births:** 159 **Total Expense ($000):** 36945 **Payroll Expense ($000):** 13068 **Personnel:** 217

### SONORA—Sutton County

★ **LILLIAN M. HUDSPETH MEMORIAL HOSPITAL (451324)**, 308 Hudspeth Avenue, Zip 76950–8003, Mailing Address: P.O. Box 455, Zip 76950–0455; tel. 325/387–2521 **A**9 10 18 **F**3 7 11 12 15 18 28 29 30 32 34 35 40 43 44 45 50 53 57 59 64 65 66 68 74 75 79 86 87 90 93 96 97 107 110 111 115 119 127 128 131 132 133 134 135 147 148
Primary Contact: John A. Graves, Chief Executive Officer
CFO: Michelle Schaefer, Chief Financial Officer
CMO: Kristy Edwards, M.D., Chief Medical Officer
CNO: Jon–Michael Parker, R.N., Chief Nursing Officer
Web address: www.sonora–hospital.org
**Control:** Hospital district or authority, Government, nonfederal **Service:** General Medical and Surgical

> **Staffed Beds:** 12 **Admissions:** 137 **Census:** 1 **Outpatient Visits:** 8619 **Births:** 0 **Total Expense ($000):** 9694 **Payroll Expense ($000):** 4476 **Personnel:** 74

### SOUTHLAKE—Tarrant County

○ **FOREST PARK MEDICAL CENTER–SOUTHLAKE**, 421 East State Highway 114, Zip 76092–4400 **A**11 **F**3 12 29 40 45 47 49 70 74 79 81 82 85 87 89 107 111 115 119 126 130 132 **P**2 **S** Vibrant Healthcare, Dallas, TX
Primary Contact: Dawn Beljin, R.N., Chief Operating Officer
COO: Dawn Beljin, R.N., Chief Operating Officer
Web address: www.forestparksouthlake.com
**Control:** Corporation, Investor–owned, for–profit **Service:** General Medical and Surgical

> **Staffed Beds:** 18 **Admissions:** 603 **Census:** 4 **Outpatient Visits:** 8865 **Births:** 0 **Personnel:** 193

□ **TEXAS HEALTH HARRIS METHODIST HOSPITAL SOUTHLAKE (450888)**, 1545 East Southlake Boulevard, Zip 76092–6422; tel. 817/748–8700 **A**1 9 10 **F**3 29 30 40 64 74 79 81 85 107 111 113 114 119 130 146 **P**2
Primary Contact: Traci Bernard, President
CFO: Douglas Browning, Group Financial Officer
CMO: David Taunton, M.D., Chief of Staff
CHR: Tasha Sledge, Director Human Resources
CNO: Jessica Hill, Vice President, Chief Nursing Officer
Web address: www.texashealthsouthlake.com
**Control:** Corporation, Investor–owned, for–profit **Service:** General Medical and Surgical

> **Staffed Beds:** 18 **Admissions:** 1006 **Census:** 8 **Outpatient Visits:** 10601 **Births:** 0 **Total Expense ($000):** 50865 **Payroll Expense ($000):** 11970 **Personnel:** 150

### SPEARMAN—Hansford County

★ **HANSFORD HOSPITAL (451344)**, 707 South Roland Street, Zip 79081–3441; tel. 806/659–2535 **A**9 10 18 **F**3 11 31 32 34 35 40 43 56 57 59 62 63 64 65 68 69 78 93 107 114 127 130 133 **P**6
Primary Contact: Jonathan D. Bailey, Chief Executive Officer and Administrator
CFO: Scott Beedy, Chief Financial Officer
CMO: Mark Garnett, M.D., Chief of Staff
CHR: Jackie Nelson, Director Human Resources
Web address: www.hchd.net
**Control:** Hospital district or authority, Government, nonfederal **Service:** General Medical and Surgical

> **Staffed Beds:** 14 **Admissions:** 186 **Census:** 3 **Outpatient Visits:** 26084 **Births:** 0 **Total Expense ($000):** 10115 **Payroll Expense ($000):** 4057 **Personnel:** 92

### SPRING—Montgomery County

**NEXUS SPECIALTY HOSPITAL THE WOODLANDS (452057)**, 25440 I–45 North, Zip 77386–3670, Mailing Address: 9182 Six Pines Drive, Zip 77380–3670; tel. 281/364–0317, (Nonreporting) **A**10
Primary Contact: Judith Butryn, Chief Executive Officer
COO: Guido J. Cubellis, Chief Operating Officer
CFO: Julia Hatton, Chief Financial Officer
CMO: Ather Siddiqi, M.D., Medical Director
CIO: Deepak Chaudhry, Vice President Information Technology
CHR: Marc Leighton, Vice President Human Resources
CNO: Patrick Laird, Chief Clinical Officer
Web address: www.nexusspecialty.com
**Control:** Partnership, Investor–owned, for–profit **Service:** Long–Term Acute Care hospital

> **Staffed Beds:** 21

★ **WOODLANDS SPECIALTY HOSPITAL**, 25440 I–45 North, Zip 77386–3670, Mailing Address: 25540 I–45 North, Suite 100, Zip 77380–3670; tel. 281/602–8160, (Nonreporting)
Primary Contact: Timothy J. Bevelacqua, R.N., Chief Executive Officer
CFO: Virginia de Bond, Chief Financial Officer
**Control:** Partnership, Investor–owned, for–profit **Service:** General Medical and Surgical

> **Staffed Beds:** 6

**TX**

*Many Facility Codes have changed. Please refer to the AHA Guide Code Chart.* © 2015 AHA Guide

**STAFFORD—Fort Bend County**

◇ **ATRIUM MEDICAL CENTER (452114)**, 11929 West Airport Boulevard,
Zip 77477–2451; tel. 281/207–8200 **A**9 10 21 **F**1 3 18 26 28 29 45 46 56
59 60 65 70 74 77 82 83 85 90 107 114 119 130 146 148
Primary Contact: Ahmad Zaid, Chief Executive Officer
Web address: www.atriummedicalcenter.com
**Control:** Partnership, Investor–owned, for–profit **Service:** Long–Term Acute Care
hospital

> **Staffed Beds:** 68 **Admissions:** 555 **Census:** 37 **Outpatient Visits:** 150
> **Births:** 0 **Total Expense ($000):** 20331 **Payroll Expense ($000):** 7355
> **Personnel:** 169

**STAMFORD—Jones County**

**STAMFORD MEMORIAL HOSPITAL (450306)**, 1601 Columbia Street,
Zip 79553–6863, Mailing Address: P.O. Box 911, Zip 79553–0911;
tel. 325/773–2725 **A**9 10 **F**1 10 11 28 30 34 35 36 40 41 43 50 53 57 59
62 64 65 67 81 89 93 107 114 119 127 128 133 144 146 148 **P**4
Primary Contact: Richard G. DeFoore, FACHE, Chief Executive Officer
CFO: Elizabeth Miller, CPA, Chief Financial Officer
CMO: Michael Hart, M.D., Medical Director
CHR: Cheryl Hertel, Coordinator Human Resources
CNO: Angela Gass, Chief Nursing Officer
Web address: www.stamfordhosp.com/
**Control:** Other not–for–profit (including NFP Corporation) **Service:** General
Medical and Surgical

> **Staffed Beds:** 12 **Admissions:** 246 **Census:** 4 **Outpatient Visits:** 18962
> **Births:** 0 **Total Expense ($000):** 9501 **Payroll Expense ($000):** 3941
> **Personnel:** 87

**STANTON—Martin County**

**MARTIN COUNTY HOSPITAL DISTRICT (451333)**, 600 Interstate 20E,
Zip 79782, Mailing Address: P.O. Box 640, Zip 79782–0640; tel. 432/607–3200
**A**9 10 18 **F**3 7 29 34 35 39 40 45 50 57 59 62 64 65 75 81 87 93 107 114
119 127 130 133 **P**6
Primary Contact: Paul McKinney, Chief Executive Officer
COO: Rance Ramsey, Chief Operating Officer
CFO: Michele Cathey, Interim Chief Financial officer
CIO: Freddy Oliveras, Chief Information Officer
CHR: Paula Dority, Director Human Resources
CNO: Brandi Avila, Chief Nursing Officer
**Control:** Hospital district or authority, Government, nonfederal **Service:** General
Medical and Surgical

> **Staffed Beds:** 18 **Admissions:** 123 **Census:** 3 **Outpatient Visits:** 10059
> **Births:** 2 **Total Expense ($000):** 14849 **Payroll Expense ($000):** 5033
> **Personnel:** 138

**STEPHENVILLE—Erath County**

✠ **TEXAS HEALTH HARRIS METHODIST HOSPITAL STEPHENVILLE (450351)**,
411 North Belknap Street, Zip 76401–3415; tel. 254/965–1500 **A**1 9 10 20 **F**3
13 15 29 30 34 35 39 40 41 43 45 50 57 59 65 68 70 75 76 77 79 81 85
86 89 107 108 111 114 118 119 129 130 146 147 148 **P**6 **S** Texas Health
Resources, Arlington, TX
Primary Contact: Christopher Leu, President
CFO: Carol Cross, Director Finance
CMO: Marilyn Brister, M.D., Chief of Staff
CHR: Kimberly Leondar, Director Human Resources
CNO: Cynthia L. McCarthy, R.N., Chief Nursing Officer
Web address: www.texashealth.org/landing.cfm?id=108
**Control:** Other not–for–profit (including NFP Corporation) **Service:** General
Medical and Surgical

> **Staffed Beds:** 54 **Admissions:** 1914 **Census:** 17 **Outpatient Visits:** 30765
> **Births:** 470 **Total Expense ($000):** 37718 **Payroll Expense ($000):** 14923
> **Personnel:** 184

**SUGAR LAND—Fort Bend County**

◇ **EMERUS (670058)**, 16000 Southwest Freeway, Suite 100, Zip 77479–2674;
tel. 281/277–0911 **A**10 21 **F**3 40 75 107 114 119 **P**5 **S** Emerus, The
Woodlands, TX
Primary Contact: Mike Kohler, Chief Executive Officer
Web address: www.emerus.com
**Control:** Corporation, Investor–owned, for–profit **Service:** General Medical and
Surgical

> **Staffed Beds:** 7 **Admissions:** 86 **Census:** 1 **Outpatient Visits:** 7089 **Births:**
> 0 **Total Expense ($000):** 5037 **Payroll Expense ($000):** 1762 **Personnel:**
> 33

✠ **HEALTHSOUTH SUGAR LAND REHABILITATION HOSPITAL (673042)**, 1325
Highway 6, Zip 77478–4906; tel. 281/276–7574 **A**1 9 10 **F**3 29 34 75 87 90
95 96 130 132 146 148 **S** HEALTHSOUTH Corporation, Birmingham, AL
Primary Contact: Nicholas Hardin, Chief Executive Officer
CFO: Carol Neilson, CPA, Controller
CNO: Steve Midgett, R.N., Chief Nursing Officer
Web address: www.healthsouthsugarland.com
**Control:** Corporation, Investor–owned, for–profit **Service:** Rehabilitation

> **Staffed Beds:** 50 **Admissions:** 1191 **Census:** 44 **Outpatient Visits:** 0 **Births:**
> 0 **Total Expense ($000):** 17433 **Payroll Expense ($000):** 8650 **Personnel:**
> 180

★ ◇ **HOUSTON METHODIST SUGAR LAND HOSPITAL (450820)**, 16655 S.W.
Freeway, Zip 77479–2329; tel. 281/274–7000 **A**2 3 9 10 21 **F**3 12 13 15 18
20 22 24 26 29 30 31 33 34 35 36 37 38 39 40 41 42 44 45 46 47 49 50
51 53 54 57 58 59 60 61 64 65 68 70 73 74 75 76 77 78 79 81 82 84 85
86 87 92 93 94 96 100 102 107 108 110 111 114 115 119 120 121 123
124 126 130 131 132 135 145 146 147 148 **S** Houston Methodist,
Houston, TX
Primary Contact: Christopher Siebenaler, Chief Executive Officer
CFO: Lowell Stanton, Chief Financial Officer
CMO: Jeffrey Jackson, M.D., Medical Director
CHR: Luis Mario Garcia, Jr., Director Human Resources
Web address: www.methodisthealth.com
**Control:** Other not–for–profit (including NFP Corporation) **Service:** General
Medical and Surgical

> **Staffed Beds:** 243 **Admissions:** 14689 **Census:** 166 **Outpatient Visits:**
> 176436 **Births:** 3043 **Total Expense ($000):** 279411 **Payroll Expense**
> **($000):** 97213 **Personnel:** 1831

✠ **KINDRED HOSPITAL SUGAR LAND (452080)**, 1550 First Colony Boulevard,
Zip 77479–4000; tel. 281/275–6000 **A**1 9 10 **F**1 3 29 31 35 45 57 65 75 77
85 87 91 107 130 148 **S** Kindred Healthcare, Louisville, KY
Primary Contact: Lorene Perona, Market Chief Executive Officer
CFO: Sara Rodriguez, Chief Financial Officer
CMO: Subodh Bhuchar, M.D., Chief of Staff
CIO: Artie Dmello, Director Case Management
CHR: Craig King, Coordinator Human Resources
CNO: Laura Jane Griffin, M.D., Chief Nursing Executive
Web address: www.khsugarland.com
**Control:** Corporation, Investor–owned, for–profit **Service:** Long–Term Acute Care
hospital

> **Staffed Beds:** 171 **Admissions:** 1715 **Census:** 126 **Outpatient Visits:** 264
> **Births:** 0 **Total Expense ($000):** 67518 **Payroll Expense ($000):** 22730
> **Personnel:** 335

✠ **MEMORIAL HERMANN SUGAR LAND HOSPITAL (450848)**, 17500 West
Grand Parkway South, Zip 77479–2562; tel. 281/725–5000 **A**1 3 5 9 10 **F**3 8
11 13 15 18 20 22 29 30 34 35 36 37 40 41 43 44 45 46 47 48 49 50 51
55 56 57 59 60 64 68 70 72 74 75 76 77 78 79 81 82 85 86 87 89 91 92
93 97 107 108 109 110 111 112 114 117 119 126 129 130 135 146 147
148 **P**1 5 6 **S** Memorial Hermann Healthcare System, Houston, TX
Primary Contact: Gregory Haralson, Chief Executive Officer
CFO: Lisa Kendler, Chief Financial Officer
CMO: William Riley, Jr., M.D., Chief of Staff
CHR: Robert Blake, Chief Human Resources Officer Southwest Market
Web address: www.memorialhermann.org
**Control:** Other not–for–profit (including NFP Corporation) **Service:** General
Medical and Surgical

> **Staffed Beds:** 81 **Admissions:** 5263 **Census:** 51 **Outpatient Visits:** 79076
> **Births:** 1391 **Total Expense ($000):** 105133 **Payroll Expense ($000):**
> 33919 **Personnel:** 441

☐ **MEMORIAL HERMANN SURGICAL HOSPITAL‰(FIRST COLONY (450860)**,
16906 Southwest Freeway, Zip 77479–2350; tel. 281/243–1000 **A**1 9 10 **F**3
29 40 48 50 79 81 85 87 107 111 114 119 **P**2 **S** Memorial Hermann
Healthcare System, Houston, TX
Primary Contact: Daniel Smith, Interim Chief Executive Officer
CFO: Raquel Hebert, Business Manager
CMO: Ken Thomson, M.D., Medical Director
Web address: www.memorialhermannfirstcolony.com
**Control:** Partnership, Investor–owned, for–profit **Service:** General Medical and
Surgical

> **Staffed Beds:** 6 **Admissions:** 342 **Census:** 2 **Outpatient Visits:** 9876 **Births:**
> 0 **Total Expense ($000):** 27224 **Payroll Expense ($000):** 5887 **Personnel:**
> 120

**METHODIST SUGAR LAND HOSPITAL** See Houston Methodist Sugar Land
Hospital

**TX**

---

**Hospital, Medicare Provider Number, Address, Telephone, Approval, Facility, and Physician Codes, Health Care System**

★ American Hospital Association (AHA) membership    ○ Healthcare Facilities Accreditation Program    ⇑ Center for Improvement in Healthcare Quality Accreditation
☐ The Joint Commission accreditation    ◇ DNV Healthcare Inc. accreditation    △ Commission on Accreditation of Rehabilitation Facilities (CARF) accreditation

★ ◇ **ST. LUKE'S SUGAR LAND HOSPITAL (670053)**, 1317 Lake Pointe Parkway, Zip 77478–3997; tel. 281/637–7000, (Data for 181 days) **A**9 10 21 **F**3 15 18 20 22 26 29 30 34 35 37 39 40 41 44 45 46 49 50 57 60 64 68 70 74 75 79 81 82 85 107 108 110 111 115 119 129 130 146 147 148 **P**5 **S** Catholic Health Initiatives, Englewood, CO
Primary Contact: Robert A. Heifner, Chief Executive Officer
CFO: Bill Beauchamp, Chief Financial Officer
CNO: Wes Garrison
Web address: www.stlukessugarland.com
**Control:** Church–operated, Nongovernment, not–for profit **Service:** General Medical and Surgical

**Staffed Beds:** 58 **Admissions:** 1526 **Census:** 40 **Outpatient Visits:** 11459 **Births:** 0 **Total Expense ($000):** 35894 **Payroll Expense ($000):** 10595 **Personnel:** 297

**SUGAR LAND REHABILITATION HOSPITAL** See HEALTHSOUTH Sugar Land Rehabilitation Hospital

**TRIUMPH HOSPITAL SOUTHWEST** See Kindred Hospital Sugar Land

### SULPHUR SPRINGS—Hopkins County

★ **HOPKINS COUNTY MEMORIAL HOSPITAL (450236)**, 115 Airport Road, Zip 75482–2105; tel. 903/885–7671 **A**9 10 **F**1 7 11 13 15 26 28 29 34 35 40 43 56 59 70 73 76 79 80 81 93 96 107 110 111 114 119 127 130 146 **P**6
Primary Contact: Michael McAndrew, Chief Executive Officer
COO: Donna Geiken Wallace, Chief Operating Officer and Chief Financial Officer
CFO: Donna Geiken Wallace, Chief Operating Officer and Chief Financial Officer
CMO: Chris Gallagher, M.D., Chief Medical Officer
CIO: Steve B. Longino, III, Director Information Systems
CHR: Donna Rudzik, Director Human Resources
CNO: Terri Bunch, R.N., Chief Nursing Officer
Web address: www.hcmh.com
**Control:** Hospital district or authority, Government, nonfederal **Service:** General Medical and Surgical

**Staffed Beds:** 50 **Admissions:** 3286 **Census:** 29 **Outpatient Visits:** 65022 **Births:** 779 **Total Expense ($000):** 51643 **Payroll Expense ($000):** 19173 **Personnel:** 449

### SUNNYVALE—Dallas County

☐ **TEXAS REGIONAL MEDICAL CENTER AT SUNNYVALE (670060)**, 231 South Collins Road, Zip 75182–4624; tel. 972/892–3000 **A**1 9 10 **F**3 13 15 18 20 22 24 29 34 35 40 45 49 57 59 64 70 74 75 76 79 80 81 82 85 87 107 108 110 111 114 115 119 130 135 146 147 148 **P**2
Primary Contact: Collin LeMaistre, Chief Executive Officer
CFO: Ben Dunford, Chief Financial Officer
Web address: www.texasregionalmedicalcenter.com
**Control:** Partnership, Investor–owned, for–profit **Service:** General Medical and Surgical

**Staffed Beds:** 70 **Admissions:** 4889 **Census:** 51 **Outpatient Visits:** 46086 **Births:** 1360 **Total Expense ($000):** 74175 **Payroll Expense ($000):** 26620 **Personnel:** 383

### SWEENY—Brazoria County

**SWEENY COMMUNITY HOSPITAL (451311)**, 305 North McKinney Street, Zip 77480–2895; tel. 979/548–1500 **A**9 10 **F**3 7 10 11 15 29 34 35 40 43 45 53 56 57 59 65 69 70 75 81 85 93 103 104 107 110 114 119 130 132 133 143 145 148 **P**6
Primary Contact: William H. Barnes, Administrator
CFO: Hong Wade, Chief Financial Officer
CMO: Fabio Aglieco, D.O., Chief of Staff
CIO: Stuart Butler, Director Information Technology
CHR: Grace Baty, Director Human Resources
Web address: www.sweenyhospital.org
**Control:** Hospital district or authority, Government, nonfederal **Service:** General Medical and Surgical

**Staffed Beds:** 14 **Admissions:** 245 **Census:** 2 **Outpatient Visits:** 16472 **Births:** 0 **Total Expense ($000):** 15623 **Payroll Expense ($000):** 7053 **Personnel:** 175

### SWEETWATER—Nolan County

★ ◇ **ROLLING PLAINS MEMORIAL HOSPITAL (450055)**, 200 East Arizona Street, Zip 79556–7199, Mailing Address: P.O. Box 690, Zip 79556–0690; tel. 325/235–1701 **A**9 10 20 21 **F**3 11 13 15 28 29 34 40 43 45 53 57 59 62 70 76 77 79 81 85 89 91 93 107 108 114 119 130 133 135 146 148
Primary Contact: Donna Boatright, MSN, Administrator
COO: Rhonda Guelker, Senior Director Finance
CFO: Rhonda Guelker, Senior Director Finance
CMO: Ronnie Dennis, Chief of Staff
CIO: Rhonda Guelker, Senior Director Finance
CHR: Ame Monroe, Director Human Resources
CNO: Rosa Best, Chief Nursing Officer
Web address: www.rpmh.net
**Control:** Hospital district or authority, Government, nonfederal **Service:** General Medical and Surgical

**Staffed Beds:** 52 **Admissions:** 1275 **Census:** 15 **Outpatient Visits:** 69565 **Births:** 227 **Total Expense ($000):** 24852 **Payroll Expense ($000):** 12636 **Personnel:** 259

### TAHOKA—Lynn County

★ **LYNN COUNTY HOSPITAL DISTRICT (451351)**, 2600 Lockwood, Zip 79373–4118, Mailing Address: Box 1310, Zip 79373–1310; tel. 806/998–4533 **A**9 10 18 **F**3 7 10 13 29 32 34 35 40 43 44 53 54 56 57 59 65 66 75 86 93 97 107 133 147 148 **P**5
Primary Contact: Jeff Barnhart, Chief Executive Officer
CFO: Steve Brock, Chief Financial Officer
CMO: Donald Freitag, M.D., Chief Medical Officer
CIO: Jim Brown, Director Information Technology
CHR: Jill Stone, Manager Human Resources
CNO: Angie Jalomo, Chief Nursing Officer
Web address: www.lchdhealthcare.org
**Control:** Hospital district or authority, Government, nonfederal **Service:** General Medical and Surgical

**Staffed Beds:** 24 **Admissions:** 193 **Census:** 2 **Outpatient Visits:** 13036 **Births:** 0 **Total Expense ($000):** 8390 **Payroll Expense ($000):** 2654 **Personnel:** 96

### TAYLOR—Williamson County

**JOHNS COMMUNITY HOSPITAL** See Scott & White Hospital – Taylor

⊞ **SCOTT & WHITE HOSPITAL – TAYLOR (451374)**, 305 Mallard Lane, Zip 76574–1208; tel. 512/352–7611, (Data for 303 days) **A**1 9 10 18 **F**14 15 29 34 40 43 45 54 64 75 77 81 85 93 107 119 129 130 146 147 **S** Baylor Scott & White Health, Dallas, TX
Primary Contact: Jay Fox, Chief Executive Officer, Round Rock Region
CIO: Tim Tarbell, Assistant Administrator Support Services
Web address: www.swtaylor.org
**Control:** Other not–for–profit (including NFP Corporation) **Service:** General Medical and Surgical

**Staffed Beds:** 25 **Admissions:** 458 **Census:** 10 **Outpatient Visits:** 10674 **Births:** 0 **Total Expense ($000):** 11805 **Payroll Expense ($000):** 6288 **Personnel:** 120

### TEMPLE—Bell County

**CENTRAL TEXAS VETERANS AFFAIRS HEALTH CARE SYSTEM, OLIN E. TEAGUE VETERANS CENTER** See Central Texas Veterans Health Care System

⊞ △ **CENTRAL TEXAS VETERANS HEALTH CARE SYSTEM**, 1901 Veterans Memorial Drive, Zip 76504–7493; tel. 254/778–4811, (Includes CENTRAL TEXAS VETERANS AFFAIRS HEALTH CARE SYSTEM, OLIN E. TEAGUE VETERANS CENTER, 1901 Veterans Memorial Drive, Zip 76504; tel. 817/778–4811; WACO VETERANS AFFAIRS HOSPITAL, 4800 Memorial Drive, Waco, Zip 76711–1397; tel. 254/752–6581), (Nonreporting) **A**1 2 3 5 7 8 9 **S** Department of Veterans Affairs, Washington, DC
Primary Contact: Sallie Houser–Hanfelder, FACHE, Director
CFO: Amy Maynard, Acting Chief Finance Service
CIO: Victor Vitolas, Acting Chief Information Technology Services
CHR: Mary P. Doerfler, Chief Human Resources Officer
CNO: Bryan W. Sisk, Associate Director Patient and Nursing Services
Web address: www.centraltexas.va.gov/
**Control:** Veterans Affairs, Government, federal **Service:** General Medical and Surgical

**Staffed Beds:** 1532

**MCLANE CHILDREN'S HOSPITAL SCOTT & WHITE** See Scott & White Memorial Hospital

**TX**

✠ **SCOTT & WHITE MEMORIAL HOSPITAL (450054)**, 2401 South 31st Street, Zip 76508–0002; tel. 254/724–2111, (Includes MCLANE CHILDREN'S HOSPITAL SCOTT & WHITE, 2401 South 31st Street, Zip 76508–0001; tel. 877/724–5437; John Boyd, III, M.D., Chief Executive Officer and Chief Medical Officer; MCLANE CHILDREN'S HOSPITAL SCOTT & WHITE, 1901 S.W. H. K. Dodgen Loop, Zip 76502–1896; tel. 254/771–8600; John Boyd, III, M.D., Chief Executive Officer), (Total facility includes 29 beds in nursing home–type unit) (Data for 303 days) **A**1 2 3 5 8 9 10 **F**3 4 5 7 8 11 12 13 14 15 17 18 19 20 22 24 26 27 28 29 30 31 32 34 35 38 39 40 41 43 45 46 47 48 49 50 51 52 54 55 56 57 58 59 60 61 62 63 64 65 68 70 72 74 75 76 77 78 79 81 82 84 85 86 87 88 89 91 92 93 94 96 97 98 99 100 102 103 104 107 108 111 113 114 115 116 117 119 120 121 123 124 126 127 128 129 130 131 132 134 135 136 137 138 140 141 143 144 145 146 148 **S** Baylor Scott & White Health, Dallas, TX
Primary Contact: Shahin Motakef, Chief Executive Officer
CFO: Alita Prosser, Chief Financial Officer
CMO: Stephen Sibbitt, M.D., Chief Medical Officer
CIO: Matthew Chambers, Chief Information Officer
CHR: Lorraine Bell, Vice President Operations Human Resources
CNO: Gerald W. Bryant, R.N., Chief Nursing Officer
Web address: www.sw.org/location/temple–hospital
**Control:** Other not–for–profit (including NFP Corporation) **Service:** General Medical and Surgical

**Staffed Beds:** 614 **Admissions:** 26230 **Census:** 428 **Outpatient Visits:** 1396815 **Births:** 2154 **Total Expense ($000):** 680730 **Payroll Expense ($000):** 217158 **Personnel:** 6263

★ **SCOTT AND WHITE CONTINUING CARE HOSPITAL (452105)**, 546 North Kegley Road, Zip 76502–4069; tel. 254/215–0900, (Data for 303 days) **A**9 10 **F**1 3 29 30 43 60 85 107 119 130 **S** Baylor Scott & White Health, Dallas, TX
Primary Contact: Kimberly K. Langston, R.N., Chief Executive Officer
CMO: David P. Ciceri, M.D., Chief Medical Officer
Web address: www.sw.org/location/temple–cch
**Control:** Other not–for–profit (including NFP Corporation) **Service:** Long–Term Acute Care hospital

**Staffed Beds:** 50 **Admissions:** 274 **Census:** 28 **Outpatient Visits:** 0 **Births:** 0 **Total Expense ($000):** 15142 **Payroll Expense ($000):** 6064 **Personnel:** 104

### TERRELL—Kaufman County

☐ **TERRELL STATE HOSPITAL (454006)**, 1200 East Brin Street, Zip 75160–2938, Mailing Address: P.O. Box 70, Zip 75160–9000; tel. 972/524–6452 **A**1 9 10 **F**30 34 39 57 68 75 86 87 98 99 100 101 103 130 132 135 146 **P**6 **S** Texas Department of State Health Services, Austin, TX
Primary Contact: Dorothy Floyd, Ph.D., Superintendent
CFO: Mike Verseckes, Financial Officer
CMO: Anthony Claxton, M.D., Clinical Director
CIO: Sims Anderson, Manager Facility Automation
Web address: www.dshs.state.tx.us/mhhospitals/terrellsh
**Control:** State–Government, nonfederal **Service:** Psychiatric

**Staffed Beds:** 288 **Admissions:** 2144 **Census:** 243 **Outpatient Visits:** 0 **Births:** 0 **Total Expense ($000):** 65237 **Payroll Expense ($000):** 36737 **Personnel:** 909

### TEXARKANA—Bowie County

✠ **CHRISTUS ST. MICHAEL HEALTH SYSTEM (450801)**, 2600 St. Michael Drive, Zip 75503–5220; tel. 903/614–1000, (Includes CHRISTUS ST. MICHAEL HOSPITAL–ATLANTA, 1007 South William Street, Atlanta, Zip 75551–3245; tel. 903/799–3000; Thomas McKinney, Administrator) **A**1 2 9 10 **F**3 11 13 15 17 18 20 22 24 28 29 30 31 34 35 40 41 43 45 48 49 51 53 55 56 57 59 60 64 65 68 70 71 72 74 75 76 77 78 79 80 81 82 84 85 86 87 89 92 97 98 107 108 109 110 111 114 115 118 119 120 121 122 123 124 126 129 130 131 132 135 143 144 146 147 148 **P**8 **S** CHRISTUS Health, Irving, TX
Primary Contact: Chris Karam, President and Chief Executive Officer
COO: Jason Rounds, Chief Operating Officer and Administrator
CFO: Glen Boles, Vice President and Chief Financial Officer
CMO: Mike Finley, M.D., Chief Medical Officer
CIO: Alana Higgins, Regional Information Management Executive
CHR: Pam Kennedy, Vice President Regional Human Resources and Organizational Department
CNO: Nancy C. Keenan, R.N., Chief Nursing Officer
Web address: www.christusstmichael.org
**Control:** Church–operated, Nongovernment, not–for profit **Service:** General Medical and Surgical

**Staffed Beds:** 376 **Admissions:** 13506 **Census:** 167 **Outpatient Visits:** 155963 **Births:** 1457 **Total Expense ($000):** 222726 **Payroll Expense ($000):** 71366 **Personnel:** 1492

✠ △ **CHRISTUS ST. MICHAEL REHABILITATION HOSPITAL (453065)**, 2400 St. Michael Drive, Zip 75503–2374; tel. 903/614–4000 **A**1 7 9 10 **F**3 11 18 28 29 30 34 35 57 59 65 68 75 77 79 82 87 90 93 96 132 135 143 148 **S** CHRISTUS Health, Irving, TX
Primary Contact: Aloma Gender, R.N., MSN, Administrator and Chief Nursing Officer
CFO: Glen Boles, Vice President and Chief Financial Officer
CMO: Richard Sharp, M.D., Medical Director
CIO: Alana Higgins, Regional Information Management Executive
CHR: Pam Kennedy, Director Human Resources
CNO: Aloma Gender, R.N., Administrator and Chief Nursing Officer
Web address: www.christusstmichael.org/rehab
**Control:** Church–operated, Nongovernment, not–for profit **Service:** Rehabilitation

**Staffed Beds:** 50 **Admissions:** 1090 **Census:** 32 **Outpatient Visits:** 12241 **Births:** 0 **Total Expense ($000):** 19056 **Payroll Expense ($000):** 9123 **Personnel:** 172

✠ **HEALTHSOUTH REHABILITATION HOSPITAL OF TEXARKANA (453053)**, 515 West 12th Street, Zip 75501–4416; tel. 903/735–5000 **A**1 9 10 **F**3 28 29 42 62 64 74 77 79 90 91 93 95 96 130 131 132 143 148 **P**5 **S** HEALTHSOUTH Corporation, Birmingham, AL
Primary Contact: Harlo McCall, Chief Executive Officer
CFO: Phylis Buck, Controller
CMO: Mark A. Wren, M.D., Medical Director
CHR: Ann R. Clapp, Director Human Resources
CNO: Lametria Griffie, Interim Chief Nursing Officer
Web address: www.healthsouthtexarkana.com
**Control:** Corporation, Investor–owned, for–profit **Service:** Rehabilitation

**Staffed Beds:** 60 **Admissions:** 1155 **Census:** 44 **Outpatient Visits:** 10498 **Births:** 0 **Total Expense ($000):** 14096 **Payroll Expense ($000):** 8243 **Personnel:** 169

✠ **POST ACUTE MEDICAL SPECIALTY HOSPITAL OF TEXARKANA (452061)**, 2400 St. Michael Drive, 2nd Floor, Zip 75503–2372; tel. 903/614–7600 **A**1 9 10 **F**1 3 29 77 82 84 86 87 130 148 **S** Post Acute Medical, LLC, Enola, PA
Primary Contact: Holly Powell, Administrator
Web address: www.postacutemedical.com
**Control:** Church–operated, Nongovernment, not–for profit **Service:** Long–Term Acute Care hospital

**Staffed Beds:** 49 **Admissions:** 466 **Census:** 32 **Outpatient Visits:** 0 **Births:** 0 **Total Expense ($000):** 13705 **Payroll Expense ($000):** 5013 **Personnel:** 93

☐ **WADLEY REGIONAL MEDICAL CENTER (450200)**, 1000 Pine Street, Zip 75501–5170; tel. 903/798–8000 **A**1 3 9 10 **F**3 11 13 15 18 20 22 24 28 29 30 31 34 35 40 43 45 49 50 56 57 59 60 64 65 70 71 73 74 75 76 77 78 79 81 85 86 87 89 98 103 107 108 110 111 114 115 119 126 130 146 147 **S** IASIS Healthcare, Franklin, TN
Primary Contact: Thomas D. Gilbert, FACHE, Chief Executive Officer
CFO: Bonny Sorensen, Chief Financial Officer
CIO: Matt Kesterson, Director Information Services
CHR: Debby Butler, Director Human Resources
CNO: Shelly Strayhorn, R.N., Chief Nursing Officer
Web address: www.wadleyhealth.com
**Control:** Corporation, Investor–owned, for–profit **Service:** General Medical and Surgical

**Staffed Beds:** 179 **Admissions:** 6844 **Census:** 85 **Outpatient Visits:** 74883 **Births:** 1332 **Total Expense ($000):** 98154 **Payroll Expense ($000):** 35364 **Personnel:** 684

### THE WOODLANDS—Montgomery County

**MEMORIAL HERMANN THE WOODLANDS HOSPITAL** See Memorial Hermann Northwest Hospital, Houston

★ ◇ **ST. LUKE'S LAKESIDE HOSPITAL (670059)**, 17400 St. Luke's Way, Zip 77384–8036; tel. 936/266–9000, (Data for 180 days) **A**9 10 21 **F**3 18 20 22 26 29 30 34 35 40 50 57 59 64 68 75 79 81 87 94 107 111 115 119 130 131 135 **P**5 **S** Catholic Health Initiatives, Englewood, CO
Primary Contact: David Argueta, Chief Executive Officer
CFO: Mary Sue Lipham, Chief Financial Officer
CMO: Bruce Lachterman, M.D., Chief of Medical Staff
CIO: Paul Solverson, Chief Information Officer
CHR: Debra Roberts, Director of Human Resources
CNO: Diane Freeman, R.N., Assistant Vice President and Chief Nursing Officer
Web address: www.stlukeslakeside.com/
**Control:** Corporation, Investor–owned, for–profit **Service:** General Medical and Surgical

**Staffed Beds:** 30 **Admissions:** 398 **Census:** 6 **Outpatient Visits:** 6485 **Births:** 0 **Total Expense ($000):** 19110 **Payroll Expense ($000):** 3511 **Personnel:** 123

**TX**

---

**Hospital, Medicare Provider Number, Address, Telephone, Approval, Facility, and Physician Codes, Health Care System**

★ American Hospital Association (AHA) membership
☐ The Joint Commission accreditation
○ Healthcare Facilities Accreditation Program
◇ DNV Healthcare Inc. accreditation
⇑ Center for Improvement in Healthcare Quality Accreditation
△ Commission on Accreditation of Rehabilitation Facilities (CARF) accreditation

★ ◇ **ST. LUKE'S THE WOODLANDS HOSPITAL (450862)**, 17200 St. Luke's Way, Zip 77384–8007; tel. 936/266–2000, (Data for 180 days) **A**9 10 21 **F**3 11 12 13 15 18 20 22 24 26 28 29 30 34 35 38 40 41 45 49 50 57 58 59 64 68 70 72 74 75 76 78 79 81 82 85 86 87 89 93 107 108 109 110 111 114 118 119 124 126 129 130 131 135 145 146 147 148 **P**5 **S** Catholic Health Initiatives, Englewood, CO
Primary Contact: David Argueta, President
CFO: Mary Sue Lipham, Controller
CMO: Charles Sims, M.D., Chief of Staff
Web address: www.stlukeswoodlands.com
**Control:** Church–operated, Nongovernment, not–for profit **Service:** General Medical and Surgical

**Staffed Beds: 192 Admissions: 5607 Census: 125 Outpatient Visits: 33018 Births: 993 Total Expense ($000): 79623 Payroll Expense ($000): 26550 Personnel: 880**

**THROCKMORTON—Throckmorton County**

★ **THROCKMORTON COUNTY MEMORIAL HOSPITAL (451339)**, 802 North Minter Street, Zip 76483–5357, Mailing Address: P.O. Box 729, Zip 76483–0729; tel. 940/849–2151 **A**9 10 18 **F**7 40 41 43 50 64 65 68 75 87 127 128 133 148 **P**5 6
Primary Contact: Kirby Gober, Chief Executive Officer
CFO: Cindy Parker, Chief Financial Officer and Director Human Resources
CMO: Ruth Ebangit, M.D., Chief of Staff and Medical Officer
CIO: Amber Myer, Director Medical Technology
CHR: Cindy Parker, Chief Financial Officer and Director Human Resources
CNO: Pam Stamm, Chief Nursing Officer
Web address: www.throckmortonhospital.com/index.html
**Control:** County–Government, nonfederal **Service:** General Medical and Surgical

**Staffed Beds: 14 Admissions: 226 Census: 2 Outpatient Visits: 7998 Births: 0 Total Expense ($000): 3627 Payroll Expense ($000): 1067 Personnel: 38**

**TOMBALL—Harris County**

⊞ **KINDRED HOSPITAL TOMBALL (452074)**, 505 Graham Drive, Zip 77375–3368; tel. 281/255–5600, (Includes KINDRED HOSPITAL SPRING, 205 Hollow Tree Lane, Houston, Zip 77090; tel. 832/249–2700; Tracy Kohler, Chief Executive Officer), (Nonreporting) **A**1 9 10 **S** Kindred Healthcare, Louisville, KY
Primary Contact: Eric Cantrell, Chief Executive Officer
Web address: www.khtomball.com/
**Control:** Corporation, Investor–owned, for–profit **Service:** Long–Term Acute Care hospital

**Staffed Beds: 74**

⊞ **TOMBALL REGIONAL MEDICAL CENTER (450670)**, 605 Holderrieth Street, Zip 77375–6445; tel. 281/401–7500 **A**1 9 10 **F**3 8 13 15 18 20 22 24 26 28 29 30 34 40 44 45 46 47 48 49 50 51 53 54 57 59 60 64 70 72 74 75 76 78 79 80 81 82 85 86 87 90 91 94 96 98 102 103 107 108 110 111 114 115 119 120 121 123 124 126 129 130 131 132 146 148 **P**6 **S** Community Health Systems, Inc., Franklin, TN
Primary Contact: Thomas W. Jackson, Chief Executive Officer
COO: Brett Kinman, Chief Operating Officer
CFO: Richard Ervin, Chief Financial Officer
CMO: Ian Glass, M.D., Chief Medical Officer
CIO: Marisa Smith, Director
CHR: Vanessa Anyaso, Chief Human Resources
Web address: www.tomballregionalmedicalcenter.com
**Control:** Corporation, Investor–owned, for–profit **Service:** General Medical and Surgical

**Staffed Beds: 160 Admissions: 9609 Census: 136 Outpatient Visits: 69399 Births: 915 Total Expense ($000): 161592 Payroll Expense ($000): 58631 Personnel: 878**

**TRINITY—Trinity County**

★ **EAST TEXAS MEDICAL CENTER TRINITY (450749)**, 317 Prospect Drive, Zip 75862–6202, Mailing Address: P.O. Box 3169, Zip 75862–3169; tel. 936/744–1100 **A**9 10 **F**11 29 40 43 45 64 81 97 107 114 115 119 127 146 **P**7 **S** East Texas Medical Center Regional Healthcare System, Tyler, TX
Primary Contact: Ruth Cook, Chief Executive Officer and Administrator
CFO: Jerry A. Dominguez, CPA, Chief Financial Officer
CMO: David Mandel, M.D., Chief of Staff
CHR: Kathy Turner, Director Human Resources
CNO: Roxann Langston, Chief Nursing Officer
Web address: www.etmc.org
**Control:** Other not–for–profit (including NFP Corporation) **Service:** General Medical and Surgical

**Staffed Beds: 22 Admissions: 435 Census: 4 Outpatient Visits: 26589 Births: 0 Total Expense ($000): 21377 Payroll Expense ($000): 3049 Personnel: 49**

**TROPHY CLUB—Denton County**

☐ **BAYLOR MEDICAL CENTER AT TROPHY CLUB (450883)**, 2850 East State Highway 114, Zip 76262–5302; tel. 817/837–4600 **A**1 9 10 **F**3 12 29 40 64 70 75 79 81 85 87 107 108 111 114 118 121 123 141
Primary Contact: Melanie Chick, Chief Executive Officer
CFO: Jonathan Saunders, Chief Financial Officer
CMO: Mike Stanton, D.O., Medical Director
CIO: Scot Bradford, Chief Information Officer
CHR: Donna Irvin, Director Human Resources
CNO: Tina Huddleston, Chief Nursing Officer
Web address: www.baylortrophyclub.com
**Control:** Partnership, Investor–owned, for–profit **Service:** General Medical and Surgical

**Staffed Beds: 20 Admissions: 539 Census: 3 Outpatient Visits: 6832 Births: 0 Total Expense ($000): 39175 Payroll Expense ($000): 7973 Personnel: 140**

**TULIA—Swisher County**

**SWISHER MEMORIAL HOSPITAL DISTRICT (451349)**, 539 Southeast Second, Zip 79088–2400, Mailing Address: P.O. Box 808, Zip 79088–0808; tel. 806/995–3581 **A**9 10 18 **F**3 7 10 11 29 34 35 40 43 50 53 59 62 64 65 68 77 93 107 114 127 129 130 133 **P**4
Primary Contact: Ryan Barnard, Chief Executive Officer
CFO: Connie Wilhelm, Chief Financial Officer
CIO: Brad Roberts, Network Administrator
Web address: www.swisherhospital.com
**Control:** Other not–for–profit (including NFP Corporation) **Service:** General Medical and Surgical

**Staffed Beds: 20 Admissions: 259 Census: 2 Outpatient Visits: 22769 Births: 0 Total Expense ($000): 10221 Payroll Expense ($000): 4429 Personnel: 100**

**TYLER—Smith County**

⊞ △ **EAST TEXAS MEDICAL CENTER REHABILITATION HOSPITAL (453072)**, 701 Olympic Plaza Circle, Zip 75701–1950, Mailing Address: P.O. Box 7530, Zip 75711–7530; tel. 903/596–3000 **A**1 7 9 10 **F**3 28 29 30 34 53 57 75 86 90 91 93 96 130 131 132 148 **S** East Texas Medical Center Regional Healthcare System, Tyler, TX
Primary Contact: Eddie L. Howard, Vice President and Chief Operating Officer
COO: Eddie L. Howard, Chief Operating Officer
CFO: James Blanton, Chief Financial Officer
CMO: Jerry Schwarzbach, M.D., Medical Director
CIO: Paula Anthony, Vice President Information Services
CHR: David L. Langston, Corporate Vice President Human Resources
CNO: Laurie Lehnhof–Watts, Assistant Administrator Patient Services
Web address: www.etmc.org
**Control:** Other not–for–profit (including NFP Corporation) **Service:** Rehabilitation

**Staffed Beds: 49 Admissions: 916 Census: 32 Outpatient Visits: 79387 Births: 0 Total Expense ($000): 25162 Payroll Expense ($000): 11547 Personnel: 186**

⊞ **EAST TEXAS MEDICAL CENTER SPECIALTY HOSPITAL (452051)**, 1000 South Beckham, 5th Floor, Zip 75701–1908, Mailing Address: P.O. Box 7018, Zip 75711–7018; tel. 903/596–3600 **A**1 9 10 **F**1 3 29 30 75 84 130 148 **S** East Texas Medical Center Regional Healthcare System, Tyler, TX
Primary Contact: Eddie L. Howard, Vice President and Chief Operating Officer
CFO: James Blanton, Chief Financial Officer
CMO: J. David Johnson, M.D., Chief of Staff
CIO: Paula Anthony, Vice President Information Services
CHR: David L. Langston, Corporate Vice President Human Resources
CNO: Laurie Lehnhof–Watts, Assistant Administrator Risk Management Performance Improvement and Education
Web address: www.etmc.org
**Control:** Other not–for–profit (including NFP Corporation) **Service:** Long–Term Acute Care hospital

**Staffed Beds: 36 Admissions: 387 Census: 29 Outpatient Visits: 0 Births: 0 Total Expense ($000): 15458 Payroll Expense ($000): 4997 Personnel: 73**

**TX**

*Many Facility Codes have changed. Please refer to the AHA Guide Code Chart.* © 2015 AHA Guide

✠ **EAST TEXAS MEDICAL CENTER TYLER (450083)**, 1000 South Beckham Street, Zip 75701–1908, Mailing Address: Box 6400, Zip 75711–6400; tel. 903/597–0351, (Includes EAST TEXAS MEDICAL CENTER BEHAVIORAL HEALTH CENTER, 4101 University Boulevard, Zip 75701–6600; tel. 903/566–8668; Jerry W. Echols, Administrator and Chief Executive Officer) **A**1 2 3 5 9 10 **F**3 5 8 11 12 13 15 17 18 20 22 24 25 26 28 29 30 31 34 35 37 38 40 42 43 44 45 46 47 48 49 51 56 58 59 60 61 64 65 68 70 71 73 74 75 76 78 79 80 81 82 84 85 86 87 89 93 98 99 100 101 102 103 104 105 107 110 111 114 115 117 118 119 120 121 123 124 126 129 130 132 138 141 145 146 147 148 **S** East Texas Medical Center Regional Healthcare System, Tyler, TX
Primary Contact: Robert B. Evans, Administrator and Chief Executive Officer
CFO: Byron Hale, Chief Financial Officer
CMO: John Andrews, M.D., Chief of Staff
CIO: Paula Anthony, Vice President Information Services
CHR: Mike Gray, Corporate Vice President Human Resources
CNO: Mariarose Kulma, R.N., Vice President Patient Services
Web address: www.etmc.org
**Control:** Other not–for–profit (including NFP Corporation) **Service:** General Medical and Surgical

**Staffed Beds: 437 Admissions: 20120 Census: 293 Outpatient Visits: 131819 Births: 768 Total Expense ($000): 385636 Payroll Expense ($000): 131048 Personnel: 1765**

✠ **MOTHER FRANCES HOSPITAL – TYLER (450102)**, 800 East Dawson Street, Zip 75701–2036; tel. 903/593–8441, (Includes LOUIS & PEACHES OWEN HEART HOSPITAL, 703 South Fleishel Avenue, Zip 75701–2015; tel. 903/606–3000; John McGreevy, Chief Executive Officer) **A**1 2 3 9 10 **F**3 7 8 11 12 13 15 17 18 19 20 22 24 26 28 29 30 31 32 34 37 40 43 45 46 47 48 49 50 51 53 54 55 59 60 64 66 68 70 72 73 74 75 76 77 78 79 80 81 82 83 84 85 86 87 89 93 107 108 110 111 114 115 118 119 124 126 127 129 130 131 132 134 144 146 147 148 **P**5 6 7 8 **S** Trinity Mother Frances Hospitals and Clinics, Tyler, TX
Primary Contact: John McGreevy, Chief Executive Officer
COO: Todd Hancock, Senior Vice President and Chief Operating Officer
CFO: Joyce Hester, CPA, Senior Vice President and Chief Financial Officer
CMO: Fadi Nasrallah, M.D., Vice President Medical Affairs
CIO: Jeff Pearson, Vice President and Chief Information Officer
CHR: Thomas Wilken, Senior Vice President and Chief Human Resources Officer
CNO: Robert Rose, R.N., Senior Vice President and System Chief Nursing Officer
Web address: www.tmfhc.org
**Control:** Other not–for–profit (including NFP Corporation) **Service:** General Medical and Surgical

**Staffed Beds: 458 Admissions: 23231 Census: 302 Outpatient Visits: 540609 Births: 2518 Total Expense ($000): 479627 Payroll Expense ($000): 151354 Personnel: 3066**

✠ **TEXAS SPINE & JOINT HOSPITAL (450864)**, 1814 Roseland Boulevard, Suite 100, Zip 75701–4262; tel. 903/525–3300 **A**1 10 **F**8 29 39 40 77 79 81 82 85 107 111 114 119 144
Primary Contact: Tony Wahl, Chief Executive Officer
CFO: Greg Cummings, Chief Financial Officer
CMO: Kim Foreman, M.D., Chief of Staff
CNO: Deborah Pelton, R.N., Chief Nursing Officer
Web address: www.tsjh.org
**Control:** Partnership, Investor–owned, for–profit **Service:** Orthopedic

**Staffed Beds: 18 Admissions: 1985 Census: 13 Outpatient Visits: 37219 Births: 0 Total Expense ($000): 68080 Payroll Expense ($000): 16256 Personnel: 298**

✠ **TRINITY MOTHER FRANCES REHABILITATION HOSPITAL (453056)**, 3131 Troup Highway, Zip 75701–8352; tel. 903/510–7000 **A**1 9 10 **F**3 9 28 29 56 62 64 74 75 77 79 82 87 90 91 93 95 96 130 131 132 143 147 148 **S** HEALTHSOUTH Corporation, Birmingham, AL
Primary Contact: Sharla Anderson, Chief Executive Officer
CFO: Michael G. Treadway, Controller
CMO: Bradley Merritt, M.D., Medical Director
Web address: www.tmfrehabhospital.com
**Control:** Partnership, Investor–owned, for–profit **Service:** Rehabilitation

**Staffed Beds: 74 Admissions: 1906 Census: 66 Outpatient Visits: 13736 Births: 0 Total Expense ($000): 19455 Payroll Expense ($000): 11136 Personnel: 183**

**TYLER CONTINUECARE HOSPITAL AT MOTHER FRANCES (452091)**, 800 East Dawson, 4th Floor, Zip 75701–2036; tel. 903/531–4080 **A**9 10 **F**1 3 29 34 59 74 75 77 85 86 87 130 135 148 **P**4 **S** Community Hospital Corporation, Plano, TX
Primary Contact: Stephanie Hyde, Chief Executive Officer
Web address: www.continuecare.org
**Control:** Other not–for–profit (including NFP Corporation) **Service:** Long–Term Acute Care hospital

**Staffed Beds: 51 Admissions: 610 Census: 46 Outpatient Visits: 0 Births: 0 Total Expense ($000): 23549 Payroll Expense ($000): 9336 Personnel: 124**

✠ **UNIVERSITY OF TEXAS HEALTH NORTHEAST (450690)**, 11937 Highway 271, Zip 75708–3154; tel. 903/877–7777 **A**1 9 10 **F**3 8 11 15 18 20 22 24 26 28 29 30 31 32 34 35 40 43 45 46 47 49 50 53 55 56 57 58 59 64 65 68 70 71 75 77 78 79 81 84 85 86 87 93 97 107 108 110 111 114 115 116 117 118 119 120 121 123 124 129 130 132 135 146 147 148 **P**6 **S** University of Texas System, Austin, TX
Primary Contact: Kirk A. Calhoun, M.D., President
COO: Joe Woelkers, Executive Vice President and Chief Staff
CFO: Vernon Moore, Senior Vice President Chief Business and Finance
CMO: Steven Cox, M.D., Chief Medical Officer
CIO: Vernon Moore, Senior Vice President Chief Business and Finance
CHR: Jesse Gomez, Vice President Human Resources
CNO: Don Hunt, M.D., Vice President Patient Centered Care and Chief Nursing Officer
Web address: www.uthct.edu
**Control:** State–Government, nonfederal **Service:** General Medical and Surgical

**Staffed Beds: 111 Admissions: 1731 Census: 22 Outpatient Visits: 236558 Births: 0 Total Expense ($000): 106277 Payroll Expense ($000): 50415 Personnel: 1046**

**UVALDE—Uvalde County**

✠ **UVALDE COUNTY HOSPITAL AUTHORITY (450177)**, 1025 Garner Field Road, Zip 78801–4809; tel. 830/278–6251 **A**1 9 10 20 **F**3 11 13 15 18 29 30 39 40 43 45 50 56 57 59 63 64 68 70 79 81 84 85 86 87 93 104 107 108 111 115 119 130 132 133 146 147 148 **P**3
Primary Contact: Thomas Nordwick, Chief Executive Officer
CFO: Valerie Lopez, CPA, Chief Financial Officer
CMO: Clifford White, M.D., Chief of Staff
CIO: Carolina Velasquez, Director Information Services
CHR: Charla Carter, Human Resource Officer
CNO: Jeanne E. Leake, R.N., Chief Nursing Officer
Web address: www.umhtx.org
**Control:** Hospital district or authority, Government, nonfederal **Service:** General Medical and Surgical

**Staffed Beds: 48 Admissions: 1825 Census: 19 Outpatient Visits: 67538 Births: 371 Total Expense ($000): 50125 Payroll Expense ($000): 21469 Personnel: 422**

**VAN HORN—Culberson County**

**CULBERSON HOSPITAL (451338)**, Eisenhower–Farm Market Road 2185, Zip 79855, Mailing Address: P.O. Box 609, Zip 79855–0609; tel. 432/283–2760 **A**9 10 18 **F**3 7 34 40 43 57 59 65 66 68 93 107 114 119 127 133 148 **P**6 **S** Preferred Management Corporation, Shawnee, OK
Primary Contact: Jared Chanski, Administrator
CMO: John A. Thomas, M.D., Chief Medical Staff
Web address: www.culbersonhospital.org
**Control:** Corporation, Investor–owned, for–profit **Service:** General Medical and Surgical

**Staffed Beds: 14 Admissions: 102 Census: 2 Outpatient Visits: 10849 Births: 0 Total Expense ($000): 5787 Payroll Expense ($000): 2481 Personnel: 59**

**VERNON—Wilbarger County**

**NORTH TEXAS STATE HOSPITAL**, Highway 70 Northwest, Zip 76384, Mailing Address: P.O. Box 2231, Zip 76385–2231; tel. 940/552–9901 **F**11 30 34 39 44 50 56 57 68 75 86 87 96 97 98 99 103 130 132 135 146 **P**6 **S** Texas Department of State Health Services, Austin, TX
Primary Contact: James E. Smith, Superintendent
CFO: William Lowery, Financial Officer
CIO: Chad Hughes, Information Officer
Web address: www.dshs.state.tx.us/mhhospitals/NorthTexasSH/default.shtm
**Control:** State–Government, nonfederal **Service:** Psychiatric

**Staffed Beds: 640 Admissions: 1865 Census: 553 Outpatient Visits: 0 Births: 0 Total Expense ($000): 169884 Payroll Expense ($000): 72733 Personnel: 2059**

TX

---

**Hospital, Medicare Provider Number, Address, Telephone, Approval, Facility, and Physician Codes, Health Care System**

★ American Hospital Association (AHA) membership
□ The Joint Commission accreditation
○ Healthcare Facilities Accreditation Program
◇ DNV Healthcare Inc. accreditation
⇑ Center for Improvement in Healthcare Quality Accreditation
△ Commission on Accreditation of Rehabilitation Facilities (CARF) accreditation

**WILBARGER GENERAL HOSPITAL (450584)**, 920 Hillcrest Drive, Zip 76384–3196; tel. 940/552–9351 **A**9 10 20 **F**3 11 15 29 34 35 40 43 45 54 56 57 60 62 75 81 85 86 87 93 98 101 103 104 107 111 115 119 124 127 130 132 133 143 146 148
Primary Contact: Claudia Eisenmann, Chief Executive Officer
CFO: Kim Fenter, Chief Financial Officer
CMO: Randall Schaffner, M.D., Chief of Staff and Medical Director
CIO: Ed Nary, Director Information Technology and Chief Compliance Officer
CHR: Cathie Bristo, Director Human Resources
CNO: Pam Akin, Interim Chief Nursing Officer
Web address: www.wghospital.com
**Control:** Hospital district or authority, Government, nonfederal **Service:** General Medical and Surgical

**Staffed Beds:** 27 **Admissions:** 432 **Census:** 5 **Outpatient Visits:** 12895 **Births:** 0 **Total Expense ($000):** 18772 **Payroll Expense ($000):** 7995 **Personnel:** 177

### VICTORIA—Victoria County

★ ◇ **CITIZENS MEDICAL CENTER (450023)**, 2701 Hospital Drive, Zip 77901–5749; tel. 361/573–9181, (Total facility includes 20 beds in nursing home–type unit) **A**2 9 10 21 **F**1 3 4 11 12 13 15 16 17 18 20 22 24 28 29 30 31 34 35 38 40 41 42 43 45 49 50 51 53 54 56 57 59 62 64 65 67 70 72 73 74 75 76 77 78 79 80 81 82 85 86 87 88 89 90 93 94 97 98 102 107 108 109 110 111 113 114 115 116 117 118 119 120 121 124 126 128 129 130 131 132 135 144 146 147 148 **P**6
Primary Contact: S. Jeffrey Ackerman, M.D., Chief Executive Officer
CFO: Carolyn Zafereo, Chief Accounting Officer
CMO: Daniel Cano, M.D., Chief Medical Officer
CIO: Russell Witte, Director Information Technology
CHR: Kathleen C. Mosmeyer, Director Human Resources
Web address: www.citizensmedicalcenter.org
**Control:** County–Government, nonfederal **Service:** General Medical and Surgical

**Staffed Beds:** 296 **Admissions:** 8068 **Census:** 109 **Outpatient Visits:** 116246 **Births:** 802 **Total Expense ($000):** 135066 **Payroll Expense ($000):** 57674 **Personnel:** 949

☒ **DETAR HEALTHCARE SYSTEM (450147)**, 506 East San Antonio Street, Zip 77901–6060, Mailing Address: P.O. Box 2089, Zip 77902–2089; tel. 361/575–7441, (Includes DETAR HOSPITAL NORTH, 101 Medical Drive, Zip 77904–3198; tel. 361/573–6100; William R. Blanchard, Chief Executive Officer) **A**1 3 9 10 **F**3 12 13 15 18 20 22 24 26 28 29 30 31 39 40 41 43 47 49 50 51 53 56 64 70 72 74 75 76 77 78 79 81 82 85 86 87 89 90 91 93 98 103 104 105 107 108 110 111 114 118 119 126 130 132 146 147 148 **P**3 5 **S** Community Health Systems, Inc., Franklin, TN
Primary Contact: William R. Blanchard, Chief Executive Officer
COO: George N. Parsley, Chief Operating Officer
CFO: Donald E. Hagan, Chief Financial Officer
CMO: Conde Nevin Anderson, M.D., Chief of Staff
CIO: Kim Tompkins, Director Information Services
CHR: John Furman, Interim Director Human Resources
CNO: Sammie Drehr, Chief Nursing Officer
Web address: www.detar.com
**Control:** Corporation, Investor–owned, for–profit **Service:** General Medical and Surgical

**Staffed Beds:** 245 **Admissions:** 8053 **Census:** 97 **Outpatient Visits:** 88900 **Births:** 1354 **Total Expense ($000):** 125143 **Payroll Expense ($000):** 46889 **Personnel:** 878

☒ **POST ACUTE MEDICAL SPECIALTY HOSPITAL OF VICTORIA (452056)**, 506 East San Antonio Street, 3rd Floor, Zip 77901–6060; tel. 361/575–1445 **A**1 9 10 **F**1 3 29 30 31 82 85 86 87 97 130 148 **S** Post Acute Medical, LLC, Enola, PA
Primary Contact: Portlyn Brogger, Chief Executive Officer
CHR: Rachel Reeves, Manager Human Resources
Web address: www.khvictoria.com
**Control:** Partnership, Investor–owned, for–profit **Service:** Long–Term Acute Care hospital

**Staffed Beds:** 23 **Admissions:** 301 **Census:** 22 **Outpatient Visits:** 0 **Births:** 0 **Total Expense ($000):** 10438 **Payroll Expense ($000):** 3794 **Personnel:** 78

☒ **POST ACUTE/WARM SPRINGS SPECIALTY HOSPITAL OF VICTORIA (452094)**, 102 Medical Drive, Zip 77904–3101; tel. 361/576–6200 **A**1 9 10 **F**1 3 29 75 77 85 93 94 96 148 **S** Post Acute Medical, LLC, Enola, PA
Primary Contact: Portlyn Brogger, Chief Executive Officer
CFO: James Asberry, Chief Financial Officer
CMO: Behram Khan, M.D., Medical Director
CHR: Waynea Finley, Corporate Director Human Resources
Web address: www.warmsprings.org
**Control:** Partnership, Investor–owned, for–profit **Service:** Long–Term Acute Care hospital

**Staffed Beds:** 26 **Admissions:** 318 **Census:** 24 **Outpatient Visits:** 7219 **Births:** 0 **Total Expense ($000):** 12965 **Payroll Expense ($000):** 4776 **Personnel:** 111

### WACO—Mclennan County

☒ **BAYLOR SCOTT & WHITE HILLCREST MEDICAL CENTER (450101)**, 100 Hillcrest Medical Boulevard, Zip 76712–8897, Mailing Address: P.O. Box 21146, Zip 76702–1146; tel. 254/202–2000, (Includes HILLCREST BAPTIST MEDICAL CENTER – HERRING AVENUE CAMPUS, 3000 HERRING AVENUE, ZIP 76708 ), (Total facility includes 20 beds in nursing home–type unit) (Data for 303 days) **A**1 2 3 9 10 **F**3 11 13 15 18 20 22 24 26 28 29 30 31 34 40 43 44 45 46 47 48 49 50 51 53 54 56 57 59 60 61 63 64 68 70 72 74 75 76 78 79 81 82 84 85 86 87 89 90 93 96 97 107 108 110 111 113 114 115 116 117 118 119 120 121 123 128 129 130 131 132 134 135 145 146 147 148 **P**6 **S** Baylor Scott & White Health, Dallas, TX
Primary Contact: Glenn A. Robinson, Chief Executive Officer
CFO: Richard Perkins, Chief Financial Officer
CMO: J. E. Morrison, M.D., Chief Medical Officer
CIO: Richard Warren, Chief Information Officer
Web address: www.hillcrest.net
**Control:** Other not–for–profit (including NFP Corporation) **Service:** General Medical and Surgical

**Staffed Beds:** 277 **Admissions:** 11023 **Census:** 172 **Outpatient Visits:** 163945 **Births:** 2868 **Total Expense ($000):** 162819 **Payroll Expense ($000):** 59069 **Personnel:** 1222

☒ **PROVIDENCE HEALTHCARE NETWORK (450042)**, 6901 Medical Parkway, Zip 76712–7998, Mailing Address: P.O. Box 2589, Zip 76702–2589; tel. 254/751–4000, (Includes DEPAUL CENTER, 301 Londonderry Drive, Zip 76712; tel. 254/776–5970; Vicky Campbell, Vice President Mental Health and Support Services), (Nonreporting) **A**1 2 3 9 10 **S** Ascension Health, Saint Louis, MO
Primary Contact: Brett A. Esrock, President and Chief Executive Officer
COO: Steven Province, Senior Vice President and Chief Operating Officer
CFO: Karen K. Richardson, Senior Vice President and Chief Financial Officer
CMO: T. Marc Barrett, M.D., Senior Vice President and Chief Medical Officer
CIO: Jay Scherler, Vice President Finance and Chief Information Officer
CHR: Chuck Sivess, Vice President Human Resources
CNO: Christine Courtney, R.N., Vice President and Chief Nursing Officer
Web address: www.providence.net
**Control:** Church–operated, Nongovernment, not–for profit **Service:** General Medical and Surgical

**Staffed Beds:** 647

**WACO VETERANS AFFAIRS HOSPITAL** See Central Texas Veterans Health Care System, Temple

### WAXAHACHIE—Ellis County

☒ **BAYLOR MEDICAL CENTER AT WAXAHACHIE (450372)**, 2400 North I–35E, Zip 75165; tel. 469/843–4000 **A**1 2 3 9 10 **F**3 11 12 15 28 29 30 34 35 40 41 53 57 59 64 65 68 70 71 74 75 77 78 79 81 82 84 85 93 107 108 110 111 114 119 124 129 130 135 147 148 **S** Baylor Scott & White Health, Dallas, TX
Primary Contact: Christopher York, FACHE, Chief Executive Officer
COO: Cindy Murray, R.N., Chief Nursing Officer and Chief Operating Officer
CFO: Steve Roussel, Vice President Finance
CMO: Valerie Goman, M.D., President Medical Staff
CIO: Gary Beazley, Coordinator Information Systems
CHR: Marcos A. Ramirez, Human Resources Business Partner
Web address: www.baylorhealth.com/PhysiciansLocations/Waxahachie/Pages/Default.aspx
**Control:** Other not–for–profit (including NFP Corporation) **Service:** General Medical and Surgical

**Staffed Beds:** 41 **Admissions:** 3014 **Census:** 29 **Outpatient Visits:** 63640 **Births:** 0 **Total Expense ($000):** 60850 **Payroll Expense ($000):** 24538 **Personnel:** 252

### WEATHERFORD—Parker County

☒ **WEATHERFORD REGIONAL MEDICAL CENTER (450203)**, 713 East Anderson Street, Zip 76086–5705; tel. 817/596–8751 **A**1 9 10 12 13 **F**3 8 13 15 17 18 20 22 28 29 34 35 40 43 49 51 57 59 60 68 70 74 75 76 77 79 81 82 85 93 107 110 111 114 115 119 131 132 133 135 146 148 **P**8 **S** Community Health Systems, Inc., Franklin, TN
Primary Contact: David Orcutt, Chief Executive Officer
CFO: Nancy Cooke, Chief Financial Officer
CMO: Scott Walker, M.D., Chief Medical Staff
CIO: Merri Roy, Director Information Services
CNO: Donna Boone, R.N., Chief Nursing Officer
Web address: www.weatherfordregional.com
**Control:** Corporation, Investor–owned, for–profit **Service:** General Medical and Surgical

**Staffed Beds:** 86 **Admissions:** 4550 **Census:** 43 **Outpatient Visits:** 69053 **Births:** 629 **Total Expense ($000):** 80610 **Payroll Expense ($000):** 24679 **Personnel:** 503

**TX**

*Many Facility Codes have changed. Please refer to the AHA Guide Code Chart.* © 2015 AHA Guide

## WEBSTER—Harris County

☐ **BAY AREA REGIONAL MEDICAL CENTER (670096)**, 200 Blossom Street,
Zip 77598–4204; tel. 281/525–7000, (Data for 164 days) **A**1 **F**3 15 17 18 20
22 26 29 34 40 45 49 50 59 64 70 74 75 77 78 79 80 81 82 84 85 87 107
108 110 111 115 119 130 135 148
Primary Contact: Tim Schmidt, Chief Executive Officer
Web address: www.barmc.us/
**Control:** Corporation, Investor–owned, for–profit **Service:** General Medical and
Surgical

**Staffed Beds:** 79 **Admissions:** 940 **Census:** 19 **Outpatient Visits:** 7042
**Births:** 0 **Total Expense ($000):** 55685 **Payroll Expense ($000):** 13709
**Personnel:** 420

✠ **CLEAR LAKE REGIONAL MEDICAL CENTER (450617)**, 500 Medical Center
Boulevard, Zip 77598–4220; tel. 281/332–2511, (Includes ALVIN DIAGNOSTIC
AND URGENT CARE CENTER, 301 Medic Lane, Alvin, Zip 77511–5597;
tel. 281/331–6141; MAINLAND MEDICAL CENTER, 6801 E F Lowry Expressway,
Texas City, Zip 77591; tel. 409/938–5000; Michael Roussos, Chief Executive
Officer) **A**1 3 5 9 10 **F**3 11 13 15 17 18 20 22 24 26 28 29 30 31 34 35 40
41 42 43 44 45 46 47 49 50 51 54 56 57 59 60 64 70 72 73 74 75 76 77
78 79 81 85 86 87 88 89 90 93 94 96 98 100 101 103 104 105 107 108
110 111 114 115 119 124 126 129 130 132 135 146 147 148 **S** HCA,
Nashville, TN
Primary Contact: Stephen K. Jones, Jr., FACHE, Chief Executive Officer
CFO: Jeff Sliwinski, Chief Financial Officer
CMO: Richard Marietta, M.D., Medical Director
CIO: Ley Samson, Director Management Information Systems
CHR: Brad Horst, Director Human Resources
Web address: www.clearlakermc.com
**Control:** Partnership, Investor–owned, for–profit **Service:** General Medical and
Surgical

**Staffed Beds:** 680 **Admissions:** 30260 **Census:** 413 **Outpatient Visits:**
224033 **Births:** 4212 **Total Expense ($000):** 402133 **Payroll Expense**
**($000):** 166025 **Personnel:** 2422

**CLEAR LAKE REHABILITATION HOSPITAL** See Kindred Rehabilitation Hospital
Clear Lake

☐ **CORNERSTONE HOSPITAL OF HOUSTON AT CLEARLAKE (452032)**, 709
Medical Center Boulevard, Zip 77598; tel. 281/332–3322, (Includes
CORNERSTONE HOSPITAL OF HOUSTON – BELLAIRE, 5314 Dashwood, Houston,
Zip 77081–4603; tel. 713/295–5300; Colin O'Sullivan, Interim Chief Executive
Officer), (Nonreporting) **A**1 9 10 **S** Cornerstone Healthcare Group, Dallas, TX
Primary Contact: Amy Stasney, Chief Executive Officer
COO: Brenda Lucero, Chief Clinical Officer
CFO: A. Shane Wells, Chief Financial Officer
CMO: Mark Barlow, M.D., Chief Medical Officer and President Medical Staff
CIO: Jerald Harris, Chief Information Officer
CHR: Yolanda Jacobs, Coordinator Human Resources
Web address: www.cornerstonehealthcaregroup.com
**Control:** Partnership, Investor–owned, for–profit **Service:** Long–Term Acute Care
hospital

**Staffed Beds:** 130

◇ **HOUSTON PHYSICIANS HOSPITAL (670008)**, 333 North Texas Avenue,
Zip 77598–4966; tel. 281/557–5620 **A**9 10 21 **F**3 29 40 51 64 74 79 81 82
85 86 89 91 93 107 111 114 141
Primary Contact: Susan Barragy, Chief Executive Officer
Web address: www.houstonphysicianshospital.com
**Control:** Corporation, Investor–owned, for–profit **Service:** Surgical

**Staffed Beds:** 21 **Admissions:** 550 **Census:** 3 **Outpatient Visits:** 13836
**Births:** 0 **Total Expense ($000):** 38527 **Payroll Expense ($000):** 9554
**Personnel:** 161

☐ **KINDRED HOSPITAL CLEAR LAKE (452075)**, 350 Blossom Street, Zip 77598;
tel. 281/316–7800, (Includes KINDRED HOSPITAL BAYTOWN, 1700 James Bowie
Drive, 3rd Floor, Baytown, Zip 77520; tel. 281/420–7800; Angel Gradney, Chief
Executive Officer), (Nonreporting) **A**1 9 **S** Kindred Healthcare, Louisville, KY
Primary Contact: Meridell Sloterbeek, Chief Executive Officer
Web address: www.khclearlake.com
**Control:** Corporation, Investor–owned, for–profit **Service:** Long–Term Acute Care
hospital

**Staffed Beds:** 110

✠ **KINDRED REHABILITATION HOSPITAL CLEAR LAKE (453052)**, 655 East
Medical Center Boulevard, Zip 77598–4328; tel. 281/286–1500 **A**1 9 10 **F**3 29
64 74 75 79 90 93 95 130 131 132 143 146 148 **S** Kindred Healthcare,
Louisville, KY
Primary Contact: Dale R. Mulder, Chief Executive Officer
CFO: Michael McFall, Chief Financial Officer
CMO: Michael Rosenblatt, M.D., Medical Director
CHR: Monica Little, Coordinator Human Resources
CNO: Kathy Hutchins–Otero, Chief Clinical Officer
Web address: www.khrehabclearlake.com/
**Control:** Corporation, Investor–owned, for–profit **Service:** Rehabilitation

**Staffed Beds:** 60 **Admissions:** 1096 **Census:** 40 **Outpatient Visits:** 6956
**Births:** 0 **Total Expense ($000):** 16090 **Payroll Expense ($000):** 8035
**Personnel:** 120

## WELLINGTON—Collingsworth County

**COLLINGSWORTH GENERAL HOSPITAL (451355)**, 1013 15th Street,
Zip 79095–3703, Mailing Address: P.O. Box 1112, Zip 79095–1112;
tel. 806/447–2521 **A**9 10 18 **F**3 16 40 43 57 59 68 93 97 107 114 127 133
**S** Preferred Management Corporation, Shawnee, OK
Primary Contact: Candy Powell, Administrator
CFO: Larry Stephens, Chief Financial Officer
CMO: Wesley Nickens, M.D., Chief of Staff
CIO: Thomas T. Ng, Chief Information Officer
CHR: April Wright, Human Resources Officer
CNO: Vikki Barton, R.N., Chief Nursing Officer
Web address: www.collingsworthgeneral.net
**Control:** Corporation, Investor–owned, for–profit **Service:** General Medical and
Surgical

**Staffed Beds:** 13 **Admissions:** 155 **Census:** 3 **Outpatient Visits:** 10956
**Births:** 0 **Total Expense ($000):** 5917 **Payroll Expense ($000):** 2375
**Personnel:** 59

## WESLACO—Hidalgo County

✠ **KNAPP MEDICAL CENTER (450128)**, 1401 East Eighth Street,
Zip 78596–6640, Mailing Address: P.O. Box 1110, Zip 78599–1110;
tel. 956/968–8567 **A**1 3 5 9 10 **F**3 8 11 12 13 15 20 22 29 30 31 34 35 39
40 43 44 46 49 50 51 56 57 59 60 63 64 70 73 74 75 76 77 78 79 81 82
84 85 86 87 89 93 107 108 110 111 114 115 119 130 131 132 134 135
143 146 147 148 **P**8 **S** Prime Healthcare Services, Ontario, CA
Primary Contact: William D. Adams, Chief Executive Officer
CFO: Dinah L. Gonzalez, Chief Financial Officer
CIO: Teri Garza, Director Health Information Services
CHR: Emmett Craig, Chief Human Resources Officer
CNO: Anna Hinojosa, MSN, Interim Chief Nursing Officer
Web address: www.knappmed.org
**Control:** Other not–for–profit (including NFP Corporation) **Service:** General
Medical and Surgical

**Staffed Beds:** 192 **Admissions:** 9398 **Census:** 98 **Outpatient Visits:** 76021
**Births:** 1870 **Total Expense ($000):** 101310 **Payroll Expense ($000):**
43547 **Personnel:** 764

△ **WESLACO REHABILITATION HOSPITAL (453091)**, 906 South James Street,
Zip 78596–9840; tel. 956/969–2222 **A**9 10 **F**3 29 30 90 130 **P**5
Primary Contact: Maggie E. Barreiro, Administrator
CFO: Annette Garza, Controller
CMO: Daisy Arce, Chief of Medical Staff
CHR: Debbie Pendleton, Human Resources Specialist
CNO: Rita Mata–Guerrero, Nurse Director
Web address: www.weslacorehabhospital.com
**Control:** Partnership, Investor–owned, for–profit **Service:** Rehabilitation

**Staffed Beds:** 32 **Admissions:** 577 **Census:** 19 **Outpatient Visits:** 0 **Births:**
0 **Total Expense ($000):** 7557 **Payroll Expense ($000):** 4675 **Personnel:**
70

## WHARTON—Wharton County

☐ **GULF COAST MEDICAL CENTER (450214)**, 10141 Highway 59,
Zip 77488–3004; tel. 979/282–6100 **A**1 9 10 **F**11 29 40 43 49 64 70 77 81
82 93 98 101 102 103 107 108 114 118 119 121 130 146 148 **S** Southwest
Healthcare System, Scottsdale, AZ
Primary Contact: Loretta Flynn, Chief Executive Officer
CFO: Barbara Starling, Chief Financial Officer
CHR: Loretta Flynn, Director Human Resources
Web address: www.gulfcoastmedical.com
**Control:** Partnership, Investor–owned, for–profit **Service:** General Medical and
Surgical

**Staffed Beds:** 159 **Admissions:** 1079 **Census:** 16 **Outpatient Visits:** 14745
**Births:** 0 **Total Expense ($000):** 19502 **Payroll Expense ($000):** 7117
**Personnel:** 140

**TX**

**TX**

### WHEELER—Wheeler County

**PARKVIEW HOSPITAL (451334)**, 901 Sweetwater Street, Zip 79096–2421,
Mailing Address: P.O. Box 1030, Zip 79096–1030; tel. 806/826–5581 **A**9 10 18
**F**3 7 10 40 43 59 62 65 68 90 91 93 107 114 128 130 133 148
Primary Contact: Monica Kidd, R.N., MSN, Administrator
CFO: Jace Henderson, Chief Financial Officer
CMO: John P. Lavelle, M.D., Chief Medical Officer
CNO: Melisa Scales, Director of Nursing
Web address: www.parkviewhosp.org
**Control:** Hospital district or authority, Government, nonfederal **Service:** General
Medical and Surgical

**Staffed Beds:** 16 **Admissions:** 109 **Census:** 2 **Outpatient Visits:** 2407
**Births:** 0 **Total Expense ($000):** 6233 **Payroll Expense ($000):** 2761
**Personnel:** 103

### WHITNEY—Hill County

**LAKE WHITNEY MEDICAL CENTER (450270)**, 200 North San Jacinto Street,
Zip 76692–2388, Mailing Address: P.O. Box 458, Zip 76692–0458;
tel. 254/694–3165, (Nonreporting) **A**9 10
Primary Contact: Ruth Ann Crow, Administrator
COO: Tariq Mahmood, Chief Executive Officer
CFO: Joe White, Chief Financial Officer
CMO: Aman Ali Shah, M.D., Chief Medical Staff
CIO: Patricia Daniel, Chief Information Officer
CHR: Darleen Towers, Director Human Resources
Web address: www.lakewhitneychamber.com/lake–whitney–medical–center.html
**Control:** Corporation, Investor–owned, for–profit **Service:** General Medical and
Surgical

**Staffed Beds:** 25

### WICHITA FALLS—Wichita County

⊞ **HEALTHSOUTH REHABILITATION HOSPITAL–WICHITA FALLS (453054)**,
3901 Armory Road, Zip 76302–2204; tel. 940/720–5700 **A**1 9 10 **F**3 28 29 44
50 53 62 64 68 74 75 77 79 82 86 87 90 91 92 93 95 96 132 143 146 148
**S** HEALTHSOUTH Corporation, Birmingham, AL
Primary Contact: Michael L. Bullitt, Chief Executive Officer
CFO: Tom Box, CPA, Chief Financial Officer
CMO: Virgil Frardo, M.D., Medical Director
CIO: Mary Walker, Manager Information Technology
CHR: Kathleen Pirtle, Director Human Resources
CNO: Karla Dwyer, R.N., Chief Nursing Officer
Web address: www.healthsouthwichitafalls.com
**Control:** Partnership, Investor–owned, for–profit **Service:** Rehabilitation

**Staffed Beds:** 63 **Admissions:** 1219 **Census:** 43 **Outpatient Visits:** 9930
**Births:** 0 **Total Expense ($000):** 14772 **Payroll Expense ($000):** 8032
**Personnel:** 162

☐ **KELL WEST REGIONAL HOSPITAL (450827)**, 5420 Kell West Boulevard,
Zip 76310–1610; tel. 940/692–5888 **A**1 9 10 **F**3 31 39 40 49 50 51 74 75
78 79 81 82 85 87 91 93 107 108 111 114 119 129 130
Primary Contact: Jerry Myers, M.D., Chief Executive Officer
CFO: Fran Lindemann, Director Finance
Web address: www.kellwest.com
**Control:** Partnership, Investor–owned, for–profit **Service:** General Medical and
Surgical

**Staffed Beds:** 41 **Admissions:** 1097 **Census:** 9 **Outpatient Visits:** 25913
**Births:** 0 **Total Expense ($000):** 27568 **Payroll Expense ($000):** 8776
**Personnel:** 233

☐ **NORTH TEXAS STATE HOSPITAL, WICHITA FALLS CAMPUS (454008)**,
6515 Lake Road, Zip 76308–5419, Mailing Address: Box 300, Zip 76307–0300;
tel. 940/692–1220, (Nonreporting) **A**1 10
Primary Contact: James E. Smith, Superintendent
CFO: Bill Lowery, Chief Financial Officer
CMO: Lauren Parsons, M.D., Clinical Director
CIO: Crystal Dennstedt, Chief Information Officer
Web address: www.mhmr.state.tx.us
**Control:** State–Government, nonfederal **Service:** Psychiatric

**Staffed Beds:** 381

☐ **PROMISE HOSPITAL OF WICHITA FALLS (452068)**, 1103 Grace Street,
Zip 76301–4414; tel. 940/720–6633 **A**1 9 10 **F**1 3 29 30 31 56 75 77 82 85
86 87 91 100 130 143 148 **S** Promise Healthcare, Boca Raton, FL
Primary Contact: Delnita Bray, Administrator
CFO: Debbie Herder, Controller
CMO: Robert McBroom, M.D., Medical Director
CIO: Gail McIlroy, Director Medical Records
CNO: Deanna Dowling, R.N., Chief Nursing Officer
Web address: www.promise–wichitafalls.com
**Control:** Corporation, Investor–owned, for–profit **Service:** Long–Term Acute Care
hospital

**Staffed Beds:** 31 **Admissions:** 237 **Census:** 16 **Outpatient Visits:** 0 **Births:**
0 **Total Expense ($000):** 7047 **Payroll Expense ($000):** 3270 **Personnel:**
72

☐ **RED RIVER HOSPITAL, LLC (454018)**, 1505 Eighth Street, Zip 76301–3106;
tel. 940/322–3171 **A**1 9 10 **F**4 5 29 86 87 98 99 101 102 103 104 105 130
132 135 143 **S** Acadia Healthcare Company, Inc., Franklin, TN
Primary Contact: John B. Warburton, Chief Executive Officer
CFO: Bruce Porter, Chief Financial Officer
CMO: Harvey C. Martin, M.D., Medical Director
CIO: Fay Helton, Director Medical Records
CHR: Degie White, Director Human Resources
CNO: Peggy Huey, Chief Nursing Officer
Web address: www.redriverhospital.com
**Control:** Corporation, Investor–owned, for–profit **Service:** Psychiatric

**Staffed Beds:** 74 **Admissions:** 2051 **Census:** 59 **Outpatient Visits:** 5446
**Births:** 0 **Total Expense ($000):** 10279 **Payroll Expense ($000):** 5701
**Personnel:** 147

⊞ **UNITED REGIONAL HEALTH CARE SYSTEM (450010)**, 1600 11th Street,
Zip 76301–4300; tel. 940/764–7000, (Includes UNITED REGIONAL HEALTH
CARE SYSTEM–EIGHTH STREET CAMPUS, 1600 Eighth Street, Zip 76301–3164;
UNITED REGIONAL HEALTH CARE SYSTEM–ELEVENTH STREET CAMPUS, 1600
11th Street, Zip 76301–9988; tel. 940/764–0055) **A**1 2 3 9 10 20 **F**3 11 12
13 15 17 18 20 21 22 24 26 28 29 30 31 32 34 35 37 39 40 43 44 45 46
47 48 49 50 51 53 57 59 60 61 64 65 68 70 73 74 75 76 77 78 79 80 81
82 84 85 86 87 89 92 93 102 107 110 111 114 115 116 117 118 119 126
130 131 132 134 146 147 148 **P**3
Primary Contact: Phyllis A. Cowling, CPA, President and Chief Executive Officer
COO: Nancy Townley, R.N., Senior Vice President Operations
CFO: Robert M. Pert, Vice President Finance and Chief Financial Officer
CMO: Scott Hoyer, M.D., Vice President Quality and Chief Medical Officer
CIO: Jerry Marshall, Director Information Services, Information Technology
Security Officer
CHR: Kristi Faulkner, Director Human Resources
Web address: www.urhcs.org
**Control:** Other not–for–profit (including NFP Corporation) **Service:** General
Medical and Surgical

**Staffed Beds:** 304 **Admissions:** 14546 **Census:** 175 **Outpatient Visits:**
134911 **Births:** 2236 **Total Expense ($000):** 279735 **Payroll Expense**
**($000):** 119816 **Personnel:** 1780

### WINNIE—Chambers County

**WINNIE COMMUNITY HOSPITAL (451328)**, 538 Broadway, Zip 77665–7600,
Mailing Address: P.O. Box 1249, Zip 77665–1249; tel. 409/296–6000 **A**9 10 18
**F**3 29 34 40 59 65 105 107 119 127 133 146 **P**6
Primary Contact: Daniel Yancy, Administrator and Chief Executive Officer
CFO: Julie Harris, Chief Financial Officer
CMO: Leonidas Andres, M.D., Chief of Staff
CHR: Anha Simon, Director Human Resources
Web address: www.winniehospital.com
**Control:** Partnership, Investor–owned, for–profit **Service:** General Medical and
Surgical

**Staffed Beds:** 25 **Admissions:** 364 **Census:** 3 **Outpatient Visits:** 31501
**Births:** 0 **Total Expense ($000):** 12312 **Payroll Expense ($000):** 3941
**Personnel:** 91

### WINNSBORO—Wood County

⊞ **MOTHER FRANCES HOSPITAL – WINNSBORO (451381)**, 719 West Coke
Road, Zip 75494–3011, Mailing Address: P.O. Box 628, Zip 75494–0628;
tel. 903/342–5227 **A**1 9 10 18 **F**3 18 29 30 34 40 43 45 57 59 64 68 70 75
79 81 82 85 87 91 93 102 107 108 111 114 118 119 127 129 130 131 132
133 146 148 **P**5 6 7 8 **S** Trinity Mother Frances Hospitals and Clinics, Tyler, TX
Primary Contact: Janet E. Coates, R.N., President and Chief Executive Officer
CFO: Glenn Peltier, Chief Financial Officer
CNO: Kevin Jablonski, Chief Nursing Officer
Web address: www.tmfhs.org
**Control:** Other not–for–profit (including NFP Corporation) **Service:** General
Medical and Surgical

**Staffed Beds:** 23 **Admissions:** 664 **Census:** 6 **Outpatient Visits:** 20821
**Births:** 0 **Total Expense ($000):** 17554 **Payroll Expense ($000):** 4989
**Personnel:** 102

**TEXAS HEALTH PRESBYTERIAN HOSPITAL WINNSBORO** See Mother Frances
Hospital – Winnsboro

### WINTERS—Runnels County

★ **NORTH RUNNELS HOSPITAL (451315)**, 7821 State Highway 153,
Zip 79567–7345, Mailing Address: P.O. Box 185, Zip 79567–0185;
tel. 325/754–1317 **A**9 10 18 **F**7 11 40 57 59 62 65 66 68 97 119 127
133 **P**5
Primary Contact: Judy Espitia, Chief Executive Officer
CFO: Judy Espitia, Chief Financial Officer
CMO: Mark McKinnon, M.D., Chief of Staff
CHR: Judy Espitia, Chief Financial Officer
CNO: Bobbie Collom, Nursing Director
**Control:** Hospital district or authority, Government, nonfederal **Service:** General
Medical and Surgical

**Staffed Beds:** 21 **Admissions:** 146 **Census:** 2 **Outpatient Visits:** 7085
**Births:** 0 **Total Expense ($000):** 4390 **Payroll Expense ($000):** 2442
**Personnel:** 52

*Many Facility Codes have changed. Please refer to the AHA Guide Code Chart.*
© 2015 AHA Guide

**WOODVILLE—Tyler County**

★ **TYLER COUNTY HOSPITAL (450460)**, 1100 West Bluff Street,
Zip 75979–4799, Mailing Address: P.O. Box 549, Zip 75979–0549;
tel. 409/283–8141 **A**9 10 20 **F**3 11 30 35 40 43 46 57 59 64 81 107 114
119 127 146 **P**5
Primary Contact: Sandra Gayle Wright, R.N., Ed.D., Chief Executive Officer
CFO: Christopher John Torres, Assistant Administrator Chief Financial Officer and
Controller
CMO: Paula Lajean Denson, M.D., President
CIO: Rachel Joy Haygood, Director Information Technology
CHR: Kenneth Lynn Jobe, Director Human Resources
CNO: Sondra Dianne Wilson RN, MSN,CEN, R.N., Assistant Administrator and
Chief Nursing Officer
Web address: www.tchospital.us
**Control:** Hospital district or authority, Government, nonfederal **Service:** General
Medical and Surgical

> **Staffed Beds:** 25 **Admissions:** 537 **Census:** 5 **Outpatient Visits:** 24564
> **Births:** 0 **Total Expense ($000):** 10850 **Payroll Expense ($000):** 4207
> **Personnel:** 120

**YOAKUM—Lavaca County**

★ **YOAKUM COMMUNITY HOSPITAL (451346)**, 1200 Carl Ramert Drive,
Zip 77995–4868; tel. 361/293–2321 **A**9 10 18 **F**3 11 13 15 29 34 35 40 43
56 57 59 64 70 76 79 81 85 86 93 107 108 111 114 119 129 132 133 134
146 148 **S** Community Hospital Corporation, Plano, TX
Primary Contact: Karen Barber, R.N., Chief Executive Officer
CFO: Robert Foret, Chief Financial Officer
CMO: Timothy Wagner, M.D., Chief Medical Staff
CIO: Barbara Vasek, Director Information Technology
CHR: Karen Roznovsky, Director Human Resources
CNO: Jennifer Franklin, R.N., Chief Clinical Officer
Web address: www.yoakumhospital.org
**Control:** Other not–for–profit (including NFP Corporation) **Service:** General
Medical and Surgical

> **Staffed Beds:** 25 **Admissions:** 905 **Census:** 12 **Outpatient Visits:** 19590
> **Births:** 68 **Total Expense ($000):** 16691 **Payroll Expense ($000):** 7160
> **Personnel:** 122

TX

---

**Hospital, Medicare Provider Number, Address, Telephone, Approval, Facility, and Physician Codes, Health Care System**

★ American Hospital Association (AHA) membership  ◯ Healthcare Facilities Accreditation Program  ⇑ Center for Improvement in Healthcare Quality Accreditation
◻ The Joint Commission accreditation  ◇ DNV Healthcare Inc. accreditation  △ Commission on Accreditation of Rehabilitation Facilities (CARF) accreditation

# UTAH

### AMERICAN FORK—Utah County

✠ **AMERICAN FORK HOSPITAL (460023)**, 170 North 1100 East,
Zip 84003–2096; tel. 801/855–3300 **A**1 10 **F**3 13 15 29 31 32 34 38 39 40
43 44 45 48 54 57 59 62 64 70 72 75 76 77 78 81 82 85 86 87 89 107
110 111 114 116 117 119 123 128 130 131 132 134 144 146 147 148
**S** Intermountain Healthcare, Inc., Salt Lake City, UT
Primary Contact: Michael R. Olson, Administrator
CMO: Paul H. Robinson, M.D., Medical Director
CIO: Mary Gathers, Manager Information Systems
CHR: Luke P. Morris, Regional Director Human Resources
CNO: Maria Black, MSN, Nurse Administrator
Web address: www.intermountainhealthcare.org
**Control:** Other not–for–profit (including NFP Corporation) **Service:** General
Medical and Surgical

**Staffed Beds: 90 Admissions:** 5920 **Census:** 43 **Outpatient Visits:** 309050
**Births:** 3032 **Total Expense ($000):** 101487 **Payroll Expense ($000):**
31727 **Personnel:** 633

### BEAVER—Beaver County

**BEAVER VALLEY HOSPITAL (460035)**, 1109 North 100 West, Zip 84713,
Mailing Address: P.O. Box 1670, Zip 84713–1670; tel. 435/438–7100,
(Nonreporting) **A**9 10 20
Primary Contact: Craig Val Davidson, Chief Executive Officer and Administrator
Web address: www.bvhospital.com/
**Control:** City–Government, nonfederal **Service:** General Medical and Surgical

**Staffed Beds:** 49

### BLANDING—San Juan County

✠ **BLUE MOUNTAIN HOSPITAL (461310)**, 802 South 200 West,
Zip 84511–3910, Mailing Address: 802 South 200 West, Suite A.,
Zip 84511–3910; tel. 435/678–3993 **A**1 9 10 18 **F**3 8 13 15 40 45 50 60 65
68 75 76 81 107 110 111 119 133 146
Primary Contact: Jeremy Lyman, Chief Executive Officer
CFO: Jimmy Johnson, Chief Financial Officer
CMO: Mahana Fisher, M.D., Medical Director
CIO: Anthony Torres, Manager Information Technology
CHR: Gail M. Northern, Director Human Resources
CNO: Derrill Kent Turek, R.N., Chief Nursing Officer
Web address: www.bmhutah.org/
**Control:** Other not–for–profit (including NFP Corporation) **Service:** General
Medical and Surgical

**Staffed Beds: 11 Admissions:** 375 **Census:** 3 **Outpatient Visits:** 7907
**Births:** 133 **Total Expense ($000):** 12041 **Payroll Expense ($000):** 3325
**Personnel:** 77

### BOUNTIFUL—Davis County

✠ **LAKEVIEW HOSPITAL (460042)**, 630 East Medical Drive, Zip 84010–4908;
tel. 801/299–2200 **A**1 9 10 13 **F**3 8 11 13 15 18 20 22 26 28 29 30 34 37
38 40 43 44 45 49 50 51 53 56 57 59 60 64 65 67 68 70 72 74 75 76 77
79 81 82 85 86 87 89 91 93 96 97 98 100 101 102 103 107 108 110 111
114 115 118 119 129 130 132 135 146 147 148 **P**6 **S** HCA, Nashville, TN
Primary Contact: Rand Kerr, Chief Executive Officer
COO: Joe Mazzo, Chief Operating Officer
CFO: Wayne Dalton, Chief Financial Officer
CMO: Michael Hess, M.D., Chief Medical Officer
CIO: Mark Ellis, Director Information Technology
CHR: Julie Isom, Director Human Resources
CNO: Marilyn Mariani, R.N., Chief Nursing Officer
Web address: www.lakeviewhospital.com
**Control:** Corporation, Investor–owned, for–profit **Service:** General Medical and
Surgical

**Staffed Beds: 119 Admissions:** 3999 **Census:** 42 **Outpatient Visits:** 43713
**Births:** 519 **Personnel:** 435

**SOUTH DAVIS COMMUNITY HOSPITAL (462003)**, 401 South 400 East,
Zip 84010–4933; tel. 801/295–2361, (Nonreporting) **A**9 10
Primary Contact: David Bland, Chief Executive Officer
CFO: Daniel J. Foster, Chief Financial Officer
CMO: Scott Southworth, M.D., Medical Director
CHR: Jamey Sulser, Director Human Resources
Web address: www.sdch.com
**Control:** Other not–for–profit (including NFP Corporation) **Service:** Long–Term
Acute Care hospital

**Staffed Beds:** 176

### BRIGHAM CITY—Box Elder County

✠ **BRIGHAM CITY COMMUNITY HOSPITAL (460017)**, 950 South Medical Drive,
Zip 84302–4724; tel. 435/734–9471, (Nonreporting) **A**1 9 10 **S** HCA,
Nashville, TN
Primary Contact: Richard Spuhler, Chief Executive Officer
CMO: Lance Bryce, M.D., Chief Medical Officer
CIO: Steve Reichard, Manager Information Systems
CHR: Jordan Lang, Director Human Resources
CNO: Jerry Bushman, Chief Nursing Officer
Web address: www.brighamcityhospital.com
**Control:** Corporation, Investor–owned, for–profit **Service:** General Medical and
Surgical

**Staffed Beds:** 39

### CEDAR CITY—Iron County

✠ **VALLEY VIEW MEDICAL CENTER (460007)**, 1303 North Main Street,
Zip 84721–9746; tel. 435/868–5000 **A**1 9 10 20 **F**8 11 13 15 18 28 29 31
35 70 76 89 **S** Intermountain Healthcare, Inc., Salt Lake City, UT
Primary Contact: Jason Wilson, Administrator
CFO: Reed Sargent, Assistant Administrator Finance
Web address: www.ihc.com
**Control:** Other not–for–profit (including NFP Corporation) **Service:** General
Medical and Surgical

**Staffed Beds: 48 Admissions:** 3460 **Census:** 20

### DELTA—Millard County

★ **DELTA COMMUNITY MEDICAL CENTER (461300)**, 126 South White Sage
Avenue, Zip 84624–8937; tel. 435/864–5591 **A**9 10 18 **F**3 8 11 13 15 29 31
34 38 40 41 42 43 45 54 57 59 64 68 71 75 76 81 82 86 87 89 102 107
111 119 128 133 144 145 146 **P**5 8 **S** Intermountain Healthcare, Inc., Salt Lake
City, UT
Primary Contact: Lenny Lyons, Administrator
CFO: Chris Thompson, Chief Financial Officer
Web address: www.ihc.com
**Control:** Other not–for–profit (including NFP Corporation) **Service:** General
Medical and Surgical

**Staffed Beds: 18 Admissions:** 287 **Census:** 3 **Outpatient Visits:** 18829
**Births:** 93 **Total Expense ($000):** 8083 **Payroll Expense ($000):** 2847
**Personnel:** 52

### DRAPER—Salt Lake County

✠ **LONE PEAK HOSPITAL (460060)**, 1925 South State Street, Zip 84020;
tel. 801/545–8000 **A**1 10 **F**3 8 13 15 29 34 40 45 48 49 50 51 64 73 75 76
79 81 85 87 107 108 110 111 115 119 129 131 147 **S** HCA, Nashville, TN
Primary Contact: Mark Meadows, Chief Executive Officer
Web address: www.lonepeakhospital.com
**Control:** Corporation, Investor–owned, for–profit **Service:** General Medical and
Surgical

**Staffed Beds: 32 Admissions:** 1268 **Census:** 8 **Outpatient Visits:** 24179
**Births:** 585 **Total Expense ($000):** 36389 **Payroll Expense ($000):** 9362
**Personnel:** 153

### FILLMORE—Millard County

★ **FILLMORE COMMUNITY MEDICAL CENTER (461301)**, 674 South Highway
99, Zip 84631–5013; tel. 435/743–5591 **A**9 10 18 **F**3 8 11 13 15 29 31 34
38 40 41 50 56 57 59 62 63 64 67 68 75 76 81 82 86 87 89 93 107 110
119 128 133 145 146 147 148 **S** Intermountain Healthcare, Inc., Salt Lake
City, UT
Primary Contact: Lenny Lyons, Administrator
CFO: Chris Thompson, Chief Financial Officer
Web address: www.ihc.com
**Control:** Other not–for–profit (including NFP Corporation) **Service:** General
Medical and Surgical

**Staffed Beds: 19 Admissions:** 192 **Census:** 11 **Outpatient Visits:** 10830
**Births:** 38 **Total Expense ($000):** 7543 **Payroll Expense ($000):** 2733
**Personnel:** 52

*Many Facility Codes have changed. Please refer to the AHA Guide Code Chart.* © 2015 AHA Guide

## GUNNISON—Sanpete County

★ **GUNNISON VALLEY HOSPITAL (461306)**, 64 East 100 North, Zip 84634,
Mailing Address: P.O. Box 759, Zip 84634–0759; tel. 435/528–7246 **A**9 10 18
**F**7 11 13 15 18 34 35 39 40 56 57 59 62 63 64 65 76 79 81 82 85 97 100
102 107 115 119 129 130 133 135 146 147 148
Primary Contact: Mark F. Dalley, Administrator
CFO: Brian Murray, Chief Financial Officer
CIO: Mike Ryan, Director of Information Services
CHR: Liz Brown, Manager Human Resources
CNO: Brenda Bartholomew, Chief Nursing Officer
Web address: www.gvhospital.org
**Control:** County–Government, nonfederal **Service:** General Medical and Surgical

**Staffed Beds: 25 Admissions: 859 Census: 10 Outpatient Visits: 29287
Births: 168 Total Expense ($000): 15373 Payroll Expense ($000): 5509
Personnel: 139**

## HEBER CITY—Wasatch County

★ **HEBER VALLEY MEDICAL CENTER (461307)**, 1485 South Highway 40,
Zip 84032–3522; tel. 435/654–2500 **A**9 10 18 **F**13 15 29 32 34 35 38 40 41
43 45 46 50 57 59 60 63 75 76 77 79 81 82 91 93 107 108 119 129 130
131 133 144 147 **S** Intermountain Healthcare, Inc., Salt Lake City, UT
Primary Contact: Shawn Morrow, Administrator
CFO: Craig Mills, Chief Financial Officer
CMO: Stanton B. McDonald, M.D., Medical Director
CHR: Bruce Dent, Human Resources Director
CNO: Gayle Sturgis, R.N., Nurse Administrator
Web address: www.intermountainhealthcare.org
**Control:** Other not–for–profit (including NFP Corporation) **Service:** General
Medical and Surgical

**Staffed Beds: 19 Admissions: 690 Census: 6**

## KANAB—Kane County

**KANE COUNTY HOSPITAL (461309)**, 355 North Main Street,
Zip 84741–3260; tel. 435/644–5811, (Nonreporting) **A**9 10 18
Primary Contact: Sherrie Pandya, Administrator
CFO: Stephen Howells, Chief Financial Officer
CMO: Darin Ott, D.O., Chief of Staff
CHR: Laurali Noteman, Director Human Resources
CNO: Charlene Kelly, Chief Nursing Officer
Web address: www.kanecountyhospital.net
**Control:** Hospital district or authority, Government, nonfederal **Service:** General
Medical and Surgical

**Staffed Beds: 25**

## LAYTON—Davis County

★ ◇ **DAVIS HOSPITAL AND MEDICAL CENTER (460041)**, 1600 West
Antelope Drive, Zip 84041–1142; tel. 801/807–1000 **A**3 9 10 21 **F**3 11 12 13
15 17 18 20 22 26 28 29 31 34 35 40 42 45 46 47 48 49 55 57 59 64 65
68 70 72 73 74 75 76 77 78 79 81 82 85 86 87 89 90 93 94 98 102 105
107 108 109 110 111 114 115 116 117 119 120 126 129 130 146 147 148
**S** IASIS Healthcare, Franklin, TN
Primary Contact: Michael E. Jensen, Chief Executive Officer
CFO: Jared Spackman, Chief Financial Officer
CMO: Jason Hoagland, M.D., President, Medical Staff
CIO: Shane Williams, Director Information Systems
CHR: Tara Cantrell, Director Human Resources
CNO: Chris Johnson, R.N., Chief Nursing Officer
Web address: www.davishospital.com
**Control:** Corporation, Investor–owned, for–profit **Service:** General Medical and
Surgical

**Staffed Beds: 200 Admissions: 6125 Census: 58 Outpatient Visits: 162145
Births: 1716 Personnel: 670**

## LOGAN—Cache County

☒ **LOGAN REGIONAL HOSPITAL (460015)**, 1400 North 500 East,
Zip 84341–2455; tel. 435/716–1000, (Total facility includes 11 beds in nursing
home–type unit) **A**1 9 10 **F**3 8 11 13 14 15 18 20 22 28 29 31 32 34 35 36
37 40 43 45 46 49 50 51 57 59 60 64 66 68 70 73 74 75 76 77 78 79 81
82 85 86 87 89 91 93 97 98 99 100 101 102 103 104 105 107 108 109
110 111 114 115 119 120 121 123 128 129 130 131 132 135 146 147 148
**P**6 **S** Intermountain Healthcare, Inc., Salt Lake City, UT
Primary Contact: Kyle A. Hansen, Chief Executive Officer
COO: Brandon McBride, Operations Officer
CFO: Alan Robinson, Chief Financial Officer
CMO: Todd A. Brown, M.D., Medical Director
CIO: Dave Felts, Chief Information Systems
CHR: Jolene Clonts, Director Human Resources
CNO: Neil C. Perkes, Operations Officer
Web address: www.loganregionalhospital.org
**Control:** Other not–for–profit (including NFP Corporation) **Service:** General
Medical and Surgical

**Staffed Beds: 139 Admissions: 6728 Census: 54 Outpatient Visits: 307175
Births: 2565 Total Expense ($000): 132427 Payroll Expense ($000):
43163 Personnel: 982**

## MILFORD—Beaver County

★ **MILFORD VALLEY MEMORIAL HOSPITAL (461305)**, 850 North Main Street,
Zip 84751–0640, Mailing Address: P.O. Box 640, Zip 84751–0640;
tel. 435/387–2411, (Nonreporting) **A**9 10 18
Primary Contact: Craig Val Davidson, Chief Executive Officer
Web address: www.bvhospital.com/directions–2.htm
**Control:** Hospital district or authority, Government, nonfederal **Service:** General
Medical and Surgical

**Staffed Beds: 25**

## MOAB—Grand County

★ **MOAB REGIONAL HOSPITAL (461302)**, 450 West Williams Way,
Zip 84532–2065, Mailing Address: P.O. Box 998, Zip 84532–0998;
tel. 435/719–3500 **A**9 10 18 **F**3 13 15 29 30 31 34 35 40 43 45 57 59 63
64 65 66 68 75 76 79 81 82 85 86 89 90 97 107 110 111 115 119 130 131
132 133 144 148 **P**6
Primary Contact: Jennifer Sadoff, Chief Executive Officer
COO: Vicki Gigliotti, Chief Clinical Officer
CFO: Craig M. Daniels, Chief Financial Officer
CMO: J.C. Vasquez, M.D., Chief Medical Staff
CIO: Mike Foster, Manager Information Systems
CHR: Katherine Sullivan, Director, Human Resources
Web address: www.amhmoab.com
**Control:** Other not–for–profit (including NFP Corporation) **Service:** General
Medical and Surgical

**Staffed Beds: 17 Admissions: 602 Census: 6 Outpatient Visits: 19812
Births: 86 Total Expense ($000): 23528 Payroll Expense ($000): 8690
Personnel: 160**

## MONTICELLO—San Juan County

**SAN JUAN HOSPITAL (461308)**, 380 West 100 North, Zip 84535, Mailing
Address: P.O. Box 308, Zip 84535–0308; tel. 435/587–2116 **A**9 10 18 **F**3 13
15 29 31 32 34 35 40 41 45 56 59 64 65 66 68 76 79 81 82 89 107 110
119 127 128 133 **P**6
Primary Contact: Clayton Holt, Chief Executive Officer
CFO: Lyman Duncan, Chief Financial Officer
CMO: Kelly Jeppesen, Chief Medical Officer
CIO: Julie Bingham, IT Supervisor
CHR: Deana Dalton, Human Resources
CNO: Laurie Schafer, Chief Nursing Officer
Web address: www.sanjuanhealthservices.org/
**Control:** Hospital district or authority, Government, nonfederal **Service:** General
Medical and Surgical

**Staffed Beds: 25 Admissions: 348 Census: 3 Outpatient Visits: 7635
Births: 34 Total Expense ($000): 12457 Payroll Expense ($000): 4797
Personnel: 90**

**UT**

---

**Hospital, Medicare Provider Number, Address, Telephone, Approval, Facility, and Physician Codes, Health Care System**

★ American Hospital Association (AHA) membership    ○ Healthcare Facilities Accreditation Program    ⇑ Center for Improvement in Healthcare Quality Accreditation
☐ The Joint Commission accreditation    ◇ DNV Healthcare Inc. accreditation    △ Commission on Accreditation of Rehabilitation Facilities (CARF) accreditation

## MOUNT PLEASANT—Sanpete County

★ **SANPETE VALLEY HOSPITAL (461303)**, 1100 South Medical Drive,
Zip 84647–2222; tel. 435/462–2441, (Nonreporting) **A**9 10 18 **S** Intermountain
Healthcare, Inc., Salt Lake City, UT
Primary Contact: Aaron Wood, Administrator
COO: Jody Green, Chief Quality Manager
CFO: Chris Thompson, Chief Financial Officer
CMO: Eileen Jackson, M.D., President Medical Staff
CIO: Michael Ence, Computer Specialist
CNO: Ryan Robison, Chief Nursing Officer
Web address: www.intermountainhealthcare.com
**Control:** Other not–for–profit (including NFP Corporation) **Service:** General
Medical and Surgical

**Staffed Beds:** 18

## MURRAY—Salt Lake County

□ △ **INTERMOUNTAIN MEDICAL CENTER (460010)**, 5121 South Cottonwood
Street, Zip 84107–5701; tel. 801/507–7000 **A**1 2 3 5 7 10 **F**3 7 8 12 13 15
17 18 20 22 24 26 28 29 30 31 34 35 37 38 39 40 43 44 45 46 47 48 49
50 51 52 53 54 55 56 57 58 59 60 61 64 68 70 72 74 75 76 77 78 79
81 82 84 85 86 87 90 91 92 93 94 95 96 97 100 102 107 108 109 110 111
112 114 115 116 117 118 119 120 121 122 123 124 126 129 130 131 132
137 138 139 141 142 146 147 148 **S** Intermountain Healthcare, Inc., Salt Lake
City, UT
Primary Contact: David Grauer, Chief Executive Officer and Administrator
COO: Kelly L. Duffin, Operations Officer
CFO: Jeff Jensen, Finance Director
CMO: William L. Hamilton, M.D., Urban Central Region Medical Director
CIO: David Baird, Director of Information Systems
CHR: Cari Vande Veegaete, Human Resources Manager
CNO: Suzanne P. Anderson, Nurse Administrator
Web address: www.intermountainhealthcare.org
**Control:** Other not–for–profit (including NFP Corporation) **Service:** General
Medical and Surgical

**Staffed Beds:** 464 **Admissions:** 25054 **Census:** 317 **Births:** 4821 **Total
Expense ($000):** 704139 **Payroll Expense ($000):** 215873 **Personnel:**
3667

◇ **LANDMARK HOSPITAL OF SALT LAKE CITY (462006)**, 4252 South Birkhill
Boulevard, Zip 84107–5715; tel. 801/268–5400, (Nonreporting) **A**10 21
**S** Landmark Hospitals, Cape Girardeau, MO
Primary Contact: Ken D'Amico, Chief Executive Officer
Web address: www.landmarkhospitals.com/utah.aspx
**Control:** Partnership, Investor–owned, for–profit **Service:** Long–Term Acute Care
hospital

**Staffed Beds:** 38

⊠ **THE ORTHOPEDIC SPECIALTY HOSPITAL (460049)**, 5848 South 300 East,
Zip 84107–6121; tel. 801/314–4100 **A**1 10 **F**3 9 29 32 34 35 37 53 57 58
59 64 68 74 75 77 79 81 85 86 87 91 93 94 100 107 111 114 115 119 130
131 132 134 135 146 **S** Intermountain Healthcare, Inc., Salt Lake City, UT
Primary Contact: Barbara Ohm, Administrator
CFO: Sherlyn Lewis, Manager Finance
CMO: Jon Sundin, M.D., Medical Director
CIO: David Baird, Chief Information Officer
CHR: Tina Tasso, Manager Human Resources
CNO: Terri Lynn Hunter, Nurse Administrator
Web address: www.intermountainhealthcare.org
**Control:** Other not–for–profit (including NFP Corporation) **Service:** Orthopedic

**Staffed Beds:** 40 **Admissions:** 1870 **Census:** 12 **Births:** 0 **Total Expense
($000):** 65142 **Payroll Expense ($000):** 17432 **Personnel:** 345

## NEPHI—Juab County

★ **CENTRAL VALLEY MEDICAL CENTER (461304)**, 48 West 1500 North,
Zip 84648–8900; tel. 435/623–3000 **A**9 10 18 **F**3 13 15 29 34 35 40 41 43
45 50 57 62 63 64 65 75 77 79 81 82 85 86 93 94 97 100 101 103 104
107 110 111 114 119 128 129 130 131 133 147 148 **P**6 **S** Rural Health
Group, Nephi, UT
Primary Contact: Mark R. Stoddard, President
CFO: Brent Davis, Chief Financial Officer
CMO: Joel Holman, Chief of Staff
CIO: Ken Richens, Chief Information Officer
CHR: Brian Allsop, Director Human Resources
CNO: Randy Allinson, R.N., Patient Care Services Director
Web address: www.cvmed.net
**Control:** Other not–for–profit (including NFP Corporation) **Service:** General
Medical and Surgical

**Staffed Beds:** 27 **Admissions:** 1083 **Census:** 11 **Outpatient Visits:** 30973
**Births:** 149 **Total Expense ($000):** 28791 **Payroll Expense ($000):** 8849
**Personnel:** 163

## NORTH LOGAN—Cache County

⊠ **CACHE VALLEY HOSPITAL (460054)**, 2380 North 400 East,
Zip 84341–6000; tel. 435/713–9700 **A**1 10 **F**3 8 15 29 34 35 39 40 41 43
51 57 59 68 70 77 79 81 82 83 84 85 87 91 92 93 96 97 107 110 111 114
119 130 131 143 148 **P**6 **S** HCA, Nashville, TN
Primary Contact: John C. Worley, III, Chief Executive Officer
CFO: David S. Geary, Chief Financial Officer
CMO: Matt Welter, Chief Medical Officer
Web address: www.cachevalleyhospital.com/
**Control:** Corporation, Investor–owned, for–profit **Service:** General Medical and
Surgical

**Staffed Beds:** 22 **Admissions:** 638 **Census:** 4 **Outpatient Visits:** 65835
**Births:** 0 **Total Expense ($000):** 35749 **Payroll Expense ($000):** 11207
**Personnel:** 240

## OGDEN—Weber County

⊠ **MCKAY–DEE HOSPITAL CENTER (460004)**, 4401 Harrison Boulevard,
Zip 84403–3195; tel. 801/387–2800 **A**1 2 3 10 **F**3 8 11 12 13 15 17 18 20
22 24 26 28 29 30 31 34 35 38 39 40 43 44 45 46 49 50 51 53 54 55 57
58 59 60 61 64 65 66 67 68 70 72 74 75 76 77 78 79 81 82 84 85 86 87
89 90 91 93 97 98 99 100 101 102 104 105 107 108 110 111 114 115 116
117 118 119 120 121 123 126 129 130 131 132 134 135 146 147 148 **P**6
**S** Intermountain Healthcare, Inc., Salt Lake City, UT
Primary Contact: Michael A. Clark, Administrator
COO: Michael A. Clark, Chief Operating Officer
CFO: Doug Smith, Chief Financial Officer
CMO: Christine Nefcy, M.D., Chief Medical Officer
CIO: Mary Gathers, Director Information Systems
CHR: Lee Lorimer, IV, Regional Director Human Resources
CNO: Bonnie Jacklin, R.N., Chief Nursing Officer
Web address: www.mckay–dee.org
**Control:** Other not–for–profit (including NFP Corporation) **Service:** General
Medical and Surgical

**Staffed Beds:** 312 **Admissions:** 17511 **Census:** 178 **Outpatient Visits:**
256166 **Births:** 3836 **Total Expense ($000):** 355439 **Payroll Expense
($000):** 113605 **Personnel:** 2413

⊠ **OGDEN REGIONAL MEDICAL CENTER (460005)**, 5475 South 500 East,
Zip 84405–6905; tel. 801/479–2111, (Nonreporting) **A**1 9 10 13 **S** HCA,
Nashville, TN
Primary Contact: Mark B. Adams, Chief Executive Officer
COO: Brian Lines, Chief Operating Officer
CFO: Judd Taylor, Chief Financial Officer
CMO: Jeffrey Abel, M.D., Chief Medical Officer
CIO: Eric Peterson, Director
CHR: Chris Bissenden, Director Human Resources
CNO: Elizabeth B. Later, R.N., Chief Nursing Officer
Web address: www.ogdenregional.com
**Control:** Corporation, Investor–owned, for–profit **Service:** General Medical and
Surgical

**Staffed Beds:** 167

## OREM—Utah County

⊠ **OREM COMMUNITY HOSPITAL (460043)**, 331 North 400 West,
Zip 84057–1999; tel. 801/224–4080 **A**1 10 **F**3 11 13 15 29 32 35 38 40 43
44 54 59 64 75 76 81 82 86 87 93 97 107 111 119 132 135 146
**S** Intermountain Healthcare, Inc., Salt Lake City, UT
Primary Contact: Scott Mortensen, Administrator
CMO: Neil Whitaker, M.D., Chief Medical Director
CIO: Diane Rindlisbacher, Manager Information Systems
CHR: Pamela S. Niece, Director Human Resources
Web address: www.intermountainhealthcare.org
**Control:** Other not–for–profit (including NFP Corporation) **Service:** General
Medical and Surgical

**Staffed Beds:** 18 **Admissions:** 1215 **Census:** 7 **Outpatient Visits:** 96178
**Births:** 1183 **Total Expense ($000):** 40397 **Payroll Expense ($000):** 8916
**Personnel:** 185

□ **PROVO CANYON BEHAVIORAL HOSPITAL (464014)**, 1350 East 750 North,
Zip 84097–4345; tel. 801/852–2273, (Nonreporting) **A**1 10 **S** Universal Health
Services, Inc., King of Prussia, PA
Primary Contact: Jeremy Cottle, Ph.D., Chief Executive Officer
Web address: www.pcbh.com
**Control:** Corporation, Investor–owned, for–profit **Service:** Psychiatric

**Staffed Beds:** 80

UT

*Many Facility Codes have changed. Please refer to the AHA Guide Code Chart.*  © 2015 AHA Guide

✠ **TIMPANOGOS REGIONAL HOSPITAL (460052)**, 750 West 800 North, Zip 84057–3660; tel. 801/714–6000, (Nonreporting) **A**1 9 10 **S** HCA, Nashville, TN
Primary Contact: Kimball Anderson, FACHE, Chief Executive Officer
COO: Austin Lane Manning, Chief Operating Officer
CFO: Jody S. Dial, Chief Financial Officer
CMO: Steven B. Cherrington, M.D., Chief of Staff
CIO: Richard Neilson, Director of Information Services
CHR: Tim Black, Director Human Resources
CNO: Sandy Ewell, Chief Nursing Officer
Web address: www.timpanogosregionalhospital.com
**Control:** Corporation, Investor–owned, for–profit **Service:** General Medical and Surgical

**Staffed Beds:** 105

### PANGUITCH—Garfield County

★ **GARFIELD MEMORIAL HOSPITAL AND CLINICS (460033)**, 200 North 400 East, Zip 84759, Mailing Address: P.O. Box 389, Zip 84759–0389; tel. 435/676–8811, (Total facility includes 27 beds in nursing home–type unit) **A**9 10 20 **F**2 13 15 28 29 32 34 35 40 45 56 57 59 64 65 67 75 76 81 82 87 97 107 110 119 127 128 129 130 132 133 148 **P**6 **S** Intermountain Healthcare, Inc., Salt Lake City, UT
Primary Contact: Alberto Vasquez, Administrator
CFO: Reed Sargent, Assistant Administrator Finance
Web address: www.ihc.com/hospitals/garfield
**Control:** Other not–for–profit (including NFP Corporation) **Service:** General Medical and Surgical

**Staffed Beds:** 41 **Admissions:** 549 **Census:** 22 **Outpatient Visits:** 30044
**Births:** 30 **Total Expense ($000):** 11369 **Payroll Expense ($000):** 5504

### PARK CITY—Summit County

✠ **PARK CITY MEDICAL CENTER (460057)**, 900 Round Valley Drive, Zip 84060–7552; tel. 435/658–7000 **A**1 9 10 **F**3 13 15 18 29 34 35 36 38 40 43 45 48 50 51 53 57 59 65 68 74 75 76 79 81 82 85 87 89 93 96 102 107 108 110 111 115 119 129 130 131 135 146 147 **P**6 **S** Intermountain Healthcare, Inc., Salt Lake City, UT
Primary Contact: Si Hutt, Administrator
CFO: Craig Mills, Senior Financial Advisor
CMO: Wain Allen, M.D., Medical Director
CHR: Bruce Dent, Director Human Resources
CNO: Dan Davis, R.N., Nurse Administrator
Web address: www.intermountainhealthcare.org
**Control:** Other not–for–profit (including NFP Corporation) **Service:** General Medical and Surgical

**Staffed Beds:** 26 **Admissions:** 1877 **Census:** 12

### PAYSON—Utah County

✠ **MOUNTAIN VIEW HOSPITAL (460013)**, 1000 East 100 North, Zip 84651–1600; tel. 801/465–7000, (Nonreporting) **A**1 9 10 **S** HCA, Nashville, TN
Primary Contact: Kevin Johnson, Chief Executive Officer
COO: Ric Johnson, Associate Administrator
CFO: Steven R. Schramm, Chief Financial Officer
CMO: Max Crouch, M.D., Chief Medical Staff
CIO: Cindy Mecham, Health Information Director
CHR: Wally Trotter, Director Human Resources
CNO: Lisa Taylor, Director of Nursing
Web address: www.mvhpayson.com
**Control:** Corporation, Investor–owned, for–profit **Service:** General Medical and Surgical

**Staffed Beds:** 114

### PRICE—Carbon County

✠ **CASTLEVIEW HOSPITAL (460011)**, 300 North Hospital Drive, Zip 84501–4200; tel. 435/637–4800 **A**1 9 10 20 **F**3 8 11 12 13 15 29 31 34 39 40 41 45 47 48 50 51 57 59 68 70 75 76 77 78 79 81 82 85 86 87 89 93 107 108 110 115 119 127 130 131 133 146 147 148 **S** LifePoint Health, Brentwood, TN
Primary Contact: Mark Holyoak, Chief Executive Officer
CFO: Greg Cook, Chief Financial Officer
CMO: Scott Justesen, M.D., Chief of Staff
CIO: Keenan Johnson, Director Information Systems
CHR: Misty Birch, Director Human Resources
CNO: Terri Watkins, R.N., Chief Nursing Officer
Web address: www.castleviewhospital.net
**Control:** Corporation, Investor–owned, for–profit **Service:** General Medical and Surgical

**Staffed Beds:** 49 **Admissions:** 1621 **Census:** 13 **Outpatient Visits:** 44520
**Births:** 275 **Total Expense ($000):** 32637 **Payroll Expense ($000):** 13093
**Personnel:** 307

### PROVO—Utah County

☐ **UTAH STATE HOSPITAL (464001)**, 1300 East Center Street, Zip 84606–3554, Mailing Address: P.O. Box 270, Zip 84603–0270; tel. 801/344–4400 **A**1 3 10 **F**30 34 56 75 77 86 87 91 98 99 100 101 103 130 135 143 146 **P**6
Primary Contact: Dallas Earnshaw, Superintendent
COO: Dallas Earnshaw, Superintendent
CFO: Robert Burton, Manager Finance
CMO: Madhu Gundlapalli, M.D., Clinical Director
CIO: Jill Hill, Director Information Technology
CHR: Devin Patrick, Manager Human Resources
CNO: Chris Metcalf, Director of Nursing
Web address: www.ush.utah.gov
**Control:** State–Government, nonfederal **Service:** Psychiatric

**Staffed Beds:** 329 **Admissions:** 391 **Census:** 297 **Outpatient Visits:** 0
**Births:** 0 **Total Expense ($000):** 55203 **Payroll Expense ($000):** 28035
**Personnel:** 745

✠ △ **UTAH VALLEY REGIONAL MEDICAL CENTER (460001)**, 1034 North 500 West, Zip 84604–3337; tel. 801/357–7850 **A**1 2 3 7 10 **F**3 11 13 15 17 18 20 21 22 23 24 25 28 29 30 31 32 34 35 38 39 40 43 44 45 48 49 50 51 53 54 56 57 58 59 60 61 62 63 64 68 69 70 72 74 75 76 77 78 81 82 84 85 86 87 88 89 90 91 92 93 94 97 98 99 100 101 102 103 104 105 107 108 110 111 114 115 116 117 118 119 121 123 128 129 130 131 132 133 144 146 147 148 **P**6 **S** Intermountain Healthcare, Inc., Salt Lake City, UT
Primary Contact: Steve Smoot, Administrator
CFO: Rod Lisonbee, Chief Financial Officer
CIO: Mary Gathers, Director Information Systems
CHR: Luke P. Morris, Regional Director Human Resources
CNO: Lisa A. Paletta, R.N., Chief Nursing Officer
Web address: www.utahvalleyregional.org
**Control:** Other not–for–profit (including NFP Corporation) **Service:** General Medical and Surgical

**Staffed Beds:** 375 **Admissions:** 18899 **Census:** 225 **Outpatient Visits:** 627385 **Births:** 4193 **Total Expense ($000):** 395706 **Payroll Expense ($000):** 133748 **Personnel:** 2816

☐ **UTAH VALLEY SPECIALTY HOSPITAL (462005)**, 306 River Bend Lane, Zip 84604–5625; tel. 801/226–8880, (Nonreporting) **A**1 9 10 **S** Ernest Health, Inc., Albuquerque, NM
Primary Contact: Ezra Segura, Chief Executive Officer
Web address: www.uvsh.ernesthealth.com
**Control:** Corporation, Investor–owned, for–profit **Service:** Long–Term Acute Care hospital

**Staffed Beds:** 40

### RICHFIELD—Sevier County

✠ **SEVIER VALLEY MEDICAL CENTER (460026)**, 1000 North Main Street, Zip 84701–1857; tel. 435/893–4100, (Nonreporting) **A**1 9 10 20 **S** Intermountain Healthcare, Inc., Salt Lake City, UT
Primary Contact: Gary E. Beck, Administrator
CFO: Chris Thompson, Chief Financial Officer
CMO: Justin Abbott, M.D., Medical Director
CHR: Katey Nelson, Director Human Resources
CNO: Cami Blackham, R.N., Nurse Administrator
Web address: www.sevierhospital.org
**Control:** Other not–for–profit (including NFP Corporation) **Service:** General Medical and Surgical

**Staffed Beds:** 27

### RIVERTON—Salt Lake County

✠ **RIVERTON HOSPITAL (460058)**, 3741 West 12600 South, Zip 84065–7215; tel. 801/285–4000 **A**1 3 9 10 **F**3 13 15 29 30 31 34 35 39 40 41 44 45 46 47 48 49 50 51 57 59 64 68 70 73 75 76 77 78 79 81 85 86 87 89 91 93 94 97 107 108 110 111 114 115 118 119 129 130 131 146 147 148 **S** Intermountain Healthcare, Inc., Salt Lake City, UT
Primary Contact: Blair Kent, Administrator
CFO: Royce Stephens, Chief Financial Officer
CMO: David Haselton, Chief Medical Officer
CNO: Judy Williamson, R.N., Chief Nursing Officer
Web address: www.intermountainhealthcare.org/
**Control:** Other not–for–profit (including NFP Corporation) **Service:** General Medical and Surgical

**Staffed Beds:** 88 **Admissions:** 4970 **Census:** 31 **Outpatient Visits:** 130544
**Births:** 2450 **Total Expense ($000):** 87192 **Payroll Expense ($000):** 24769
**Personnel:** 436

UT

---

**Hospital, Medicare Provider Number, Address, Telephone, Approval, Facility, and Physician Codes, Health Care System**

★ American Hospital Association (AHA) membership   ◯ Healthcare Facilities Accreditation Program   ⇑ Center for Improvement in Healthcare Quality Accreditation
☐ The Joint Commission accreditation   ◇ DNV Healthcare Inc. accreditation   △ Commission on Accreditation of Rehabilitation Facilities (CARF) accreditation

## ROOSEVELT—Duchesne County

★ **UINTAH BASIN MEDICAL CENTER (460019)**, 250 West 300 North, 75–2, Zip 84066–2336; tel. 435/722–6163, (Total facility includes 90 beds in nursing home–type unit) **A**9 10 20 **F**6 7 11 13 15 17 35 40 43 45 50 52 53 54 57 59 60 62 63 70 73 76 77 79 81 82 84 85 87 89 93 107 110 111 114 118 119 128 129 130 131 132 135 144 146 147 148 **P**7
Primary Contact: James I. Marshall, President and Chief Executive Officer
CFO: Brent Hales, Chief Financial Officer
CMO: Gary B. White, M.D., Chief Medical Staff
CHR: Randall Bennett, Assistant Administrator
Web address: www.ubmc.org
**Control:** Other not–for–profit (including NFP Corporation) **Service:** General Medical and Surgical

**Staffed Beds:** 124 **Admissions:** 1740 **Census:** 79

## SAINT GEORGE—Washington County

✠ △ **DIXIE REGIONAL MEDICAL CENTER (460021)**, 1380 East Medical Center Drive, Zip 84790–2123; tel. 435/251–1000, (Includes DIXIE REGIONAL MEDICAL CENTER, 544 South 400 East, St. George, Zip 84770) **A**1 2 7 9 10 **F**3 7 11 12 13 15 18 19 20 21 22 23 24 25 28 29 31 34 35 38 40 43 45 46 50 53 54 57 59 64 67 68 70 72 74 75 76 77 78 79 80 81 82 83 84 85 89 90 93 98 102 107 108 110 111 114 115 117 119 120 121 127 129 130 131 132 135 146 147 148 **P**5 **S** Intermountain Healthcare, Inc., Salt Lake City, UT
Primary Contact: Terri Kane, Chief Executive Officer
CFO: Steven Vance, Chief Financial Officer
CMO: Steven Van Norman, M.D., Medical Director
CIO: Lance Bedingfield, Director Information Services
CHR: Vicki Wilson, Human Resources Director
CNO: Gary Cunningham, Chief Nursing Officer
Web address: www.intermountainhealthcare.org
**Control:** Other not–for–profit (including NFP Corporation) **Service:** General Medical and Surgical

**Staffed Beds:** 261 **Admissions:** 15326 **Census:** 154 **Outpatient Visits:** 501320 **Births:** 2378 **Total Expense ($000):** 361375 **Payroll Expense ($000):** 100427 **Personnel:** 1615

## SALT LAKE CITY—Salt Lake County

✠ **LDS HOSPITAL (460006)**, Eighth Avenue and C Street, Zip 84143–0001; tel. 801/408–1100 **A**1 2 3 5 10 **F**3 4 5 7 8 12 13 15 18 28 29 30 31 34 35 36 37 38 39 40 43 44 45 46 48 49 50 51 52 53 54 55 56 57 58 59 60 61 63 64 65 66 68 70 73 74 75 76 77 78 79 81 82 84 85 86 87 91 92 93 94 96 98 100 101 102 103 104 105 107 108 109 110 111 114 115 119 121 123 124 126 129 130 131 132 135 136 146 147 148 **S** Intermountain Healthcare, Inc., Salt Lake City, UT
Primary Contact: Jim Sheets, Chief Executive Officer and Administrator
COO: David Gardiner, Operations Officer
CFO: Dave M. Larsen, Chief Financial Officer
CMO: William L. Hamilton, M.D., Chief Medical Officer
CIO: David Baird, Chief Information Officer
CHR: Pamela S. Niece, Chief Human Resources Officer
CNO: Todd Neubert, Nurse Administrator
Web address: www.intermountainhealthcare.org
**Control:** Other not–for–profit (including NFP Corporation) **Service:** General Medical and Surgical

**Staffed Beds:** 262 **Admissions:** 9975 **Census:** 113 **Outpatient Visits:** 229701 **Births:** 2369 **Total Expense ($000):** 224420 **Payroll Expense ($000):** 62592 **Personnel:** 1147

✠ **MARIAN CENTER (464012)**, 451 East Bishop Federal Lane, Zip 84115–2357; tel. 801/487–7557 **A**1 10 **F**29 55 98 100 101 102 103 104 130 **P**8
Primary Contact: Bradley C. Albrechtsen, Chief Executive Officer and Administrator
Web address: www.stjosephvilla.com
**Control:** Corporation, Investor–owned, for–profit **Service:** Psychiatric

**Staffed Beds:** 14 **Admissions:** 216 **Census:** 9 **Outpatient Visits:** 1344 **Births:** 0 **Total Expense ($000):** 2344 **Payroll Expense ($000):** 1226 **Personnel:** 29

☐ **PRIMARY CHILDREN'S HOSPITAL (463301)**, 100 North Mario Capecchi Drive, Zip 84113–1100; tel. 801/662–1000, (Nonreporting) **A**1 3 5 9 10 **S** Intermountain Healthcare, Inc., Salt Lake City, UT
Primary Contact: Katy Welkie, R.N., Chief Executive Officer
CFO: Jeremiah Radandt, Chief Financial Officer
CMO: Ed Clark, M.D., Chief Medical Officer
CIO: Joe Hales, Director Information Systems
CHR: Albert Bennett Buckworth, Director Human Resources
CNO: Judy Geiger, R.N., Chief Nursing Officer
Web address: www.intermountainhealthcare.org
**Control:** Other not–for–profit (including NFP Corporation) **Service:** Children's general

**Staffed Beds:** 289

☐ **PROMISE HOSPITAL OF SALT LAKE (462004)**, 8 Avenue, C. Street, Zip 84143; tel. 801/408–7110, (Nonreporting) **A**9 10 **S** Promise Healthcare, Boca Raton, FL
Primary Contact: Wayne Kinsey, Chief Executive Officer
CMO: Geoff Harding, Chief Clinical Officer
Web address: www.promise–saltlake.com
**Control:** Corporation, Investor–owned, for–profit **Service:** Long–Term Acute Care hospital

**Staffed Beds:** 32

☐ **SALT LAKE BEHAVIORAL HEALTH (464013)**, 3802 South 700 East, Zip 84106–1182; tel. 801/264–6000, (Nonreporting) **A**1 9 10 **S** Universal Health Services, Inc., King of Prussia, PA
Primary Contact: Kreg Gillman, Chief Executive Officer
COO: Jim Hess, Chief Operations Officer
CFO: Nancy MacGregor, Chief Financial Officer
CMO: Sajid Faizi, M.D., Medical Director
CHR: Robyn Holsten, Human Resources Director
CNO: Suzanne Nelson, RN, Director of Nursing
Web address: www.saltlakebehavioralhealth.com
**Control:** Corporation, Investor–owned, for–profit **Service:** Psychiatric

**Staffed Beds:** 118

★ ◇ **SALT LAKE REGIONAL MEDICAL CENTER (460003)**, 1050 East South Temple, Zip 84102–1507; tel. 801/350–4111, (Nonreporting) **A**3 5 9 10 21 **S** IASIS Healthcare, Franklin, TN
Primary Contact: Dale Johns, Chief Executive Officer
CFO: Scott Banks, Chief Financial Officer
CMO: Ben Howard, D.O., Chief of Staff
CIO: Mark Runyan, Director Information Services
CHR: Carolyn Livingston, Director Human Resources
CNO: Terron Arbon, R.N., Chief Nursing Officer
Web address: www.saltlakeregional.com
**Control:** Corporation, Investor–owned, for–profit **Service:** General Medical and Surgical

**Staffed Beds:** 132

☐ **SHRINERS HOSPITALS FOR CHILDREN–SALT LAKE CITY (463302)**, Fairfax Road & Virginia Street, Zip 84103–4399; tel. 801/536–3500, (Nonreporting) **A**1 3 5 10 **S** Shriners Hospitals for Children, Tampa, FL
Primary Contact: Kevin Martin, M.P.H., R.N., Administrator
CFO: Randy Lindberg, Director Fiscal Services
CMO: Suzanne Yandow, M.D., Chief of Staff
CIO: Mike Allen, Director Information Technology
CHR: Russ Crockett, Director Human Resources
CNO: Gail McGuill, R.N., Chief Nursing Officer and Administrative Director of Patient Care Services
Web address: www.shrinershospitalsforchildren.org/Hospitals/Locations/SaltLakeCity.aspx
**Control:** Other not–for–profit (including NFP Corporation) **Service:** Children's orthopedic

**Staffed Beds:** 40

✠ **ST. MARK'S HOSPITAL (460047)**, 1200 East 3900 South, Zip 84124–1390; tel. 801/268–7111 **A**1 2 3 9 10 **F**3 8 11 12 13 15 17 18 20 22 24 26 28 29 30 31 34 35 36 38 40 43 46 49 50 53 55 56 57 58 59 60 64 65 67 70 72 73 74 75 76 77 78 79 81 82 84 85 86 87 90 91 92 98 102 107 108 110 111 115 118 119 124 126 128 129 130 132 135 145 146 147 148 **S** HCA, Nashville, TN
Primary Contact: Steven B. Bateman, Chief Executive Officer
CFO: Bryan McKinley, Chief Financial Officer
CMO: J. Eric Vanderhooft, M.D., President Medical Staff
CIO: Jesse Trujillo, Chief Information Officer
CHR: Robyn Opheikens, Assistant Administrator Human Resources
Web address: www.stmarkshospital.com
**Control:** Corporation, Investor–owned, for–profit **Service:** General Medical and Surgical

**Staffed Beds:** 277 **Admissions:** 14490 **Census:** 178 **Outpatient Visits:** 95692 **Births:** 2681

**UT**

*Many Facility Codes have changed. Please refer to the AHA Guide Code Chart.*
© 2015 AHA Guide

★ △ ◇ **UNIVERSITY OF UTAH HEALTH CARE – HOSPITAL AND CLINICS (460009)**, 50 North Medical Drive, Zip 84132–0002; tel. 801/587–3572 **A**3 5 7 8 9 10 21 **F**3 5 6 7 8 9 11 12 13 15 16 17 18 20 22 24 26 28 29 30 31 33 34 35 36 37 38 39 40 42 43 44 45 46 47 48 49 50 51 52 53 54 55 56 57 58 59 60 61 64 65 68 70 71 72 73 74 75 76 77 78 79 80 81 82 83 84 85 86 87 90 91 92 93 94 95 96 97 98 99 100 101 102 103 104 105 106 107 108 109 110 111 112 113 114 115 116 117 118 119 120 121 123 124 126 129 130 131 132 134 135 136 137 138 139 140 141 142 143 144 145 146 147 148 **P**1
Primary Contact: David Entwistle, Chief Executive Officer
COO: Quinn McKenna, Chief Operating Officer
CFO: Gordon Crabtree, Chief Financial Officer
CMO: Thomas Miller, M.D., Medical Director
CIO: James Turnbull, Chief Information Officer
CHR: Dale A. Spartz, Chief Human Resources Officer
CNO: Margaret Pearce, R.N., Chief Nursing Officer
Web address: www.uuhsc.utah.edu
**Control:** State–Government, nonfederal **Service:** General Medical and Surgical

**Staffed Beds: 528 Admissions: 23390 Census: 390 Outpatient Visits:** 1591326 **Births: 2722 Total Expense ($000): 1083205 Payroll Expense ($000): 373528 Personnel: 7866**

◇ **UNIVERSITY OF UTAH NEUROPSYCHIATRIC INSTITUTE (464009)**, 501 South Chipeta Way, Zip 84108–1222; tel. 801/583–2500 **A**3 5 9 10 21 **F**4 5 30 34 35 38 54 57 64 68 75 87 98 99 100 101 103 104 105 106 130 132 **P**1
Primary Contact: Ross Van Vranken, Executive Director
CFO: Becky Schaefer, Chief Financial Officer
CMO: Michael Lowry, M.D., Medical Director
Web address: www.med.utah.edu/uni
**Control:** State–Government, nonfederal **Service:** Psychiatric

**Staffed Beds: 94 Admissions: 4514 Census: 109 Births: 0**

⊠ △ **VETERANS AFFAIRS SALT LAKE CITY HEALTH CARE SYSTEM**, 500 Foothill Drive, Zip 84148–0002; tel. 801/582–1565 **A**1 3 5 7 **F**3 4 5 8 12 18 20 22 24 28 29 30 34 35 36 38 39 40 44 45 46 47 48 49 50 53 54 55 56 57 58 59 60 61 62 63 64 65 70 71 74 75 77 78 79 81 82 83 84 85 86 87 90 92 93 94 96 97 98 100 101 102 103 104 105 106 107 108 109 111 114 115 116 117 118 119 126 127 129 130 132 133 137 143 144 146 147 148 **P**6 **S** Department of Veterans Affairs, Washington, DC
Primary Contact: Steven W. Young, Director
CFO: Val Martin, Director Financial Management Services Center
CMO: Ronald J. Gebhart, M.D., Chief of Staff
CIO: Lisa Leonelis, Chief Information Officer
CHR: Lisa Porter, Director Human Resources, Leadership and Education
Web address: www.saltlakecity.va.gov/
**Control:** Veterans Affairs, Government, federal **Service:** General Medical and Surgical

**Staffed Beds: 121 Admissions: 4983 Census: 89 Outpatient Visits: 636573 Births: 0 Personnel: 2153**

### SANDY—Salt Lake County

⊠ **ALTA VIEW HOSPITAL (460044)**, 9660 South 1300 East, Zip 84094–3793; tel. 801/501–2600 **A**1 2 10 **F**3 8 12 13 15 29 30 31 34 35 38 39 40 44 45 46 47 48 49 50 51 53 54 56 57 59 64 68 70 75 76 77 78 79 81 85 86 87 92 93 102 107 108 110 111 115 119 129 130 131 132 135 146 147 **S** Intermountain Healthcare, Inc., Salt Lake City, UT
Primary Contact: Bryan L. Johnson, Administrator
CFO: Chris Hargis, Manager Finance
CHR: Leslie Bates, Manager Human Resources
Web address: www.intermountainhealthcare.org
**Control:** Other not–for–profit (including NFP Corporation) **Service:** General Medical and Surgical

**Staffed Beds: 69 Admissions: 3332 Census: 22 Births: 1240 Total Expense ($000): 85599 Payroll Expense ($000): 24116 Personnel: 413**

⊠ **HEALTHSOUTH REHABILITATION HOSPITAL OF UTAH (463025)**, 8074 South 1300 East, Zip 84094–0743; tel. 801/561–3400, (Nonreporting) **A**1 10 **S** HEALTHSOUTH Corporation, Birmingham, AL
Primary Contact: Jeff Frandsen, Chief Executive Officer
CFO: Daren Woolstenhulme, Chief Financial Officer
CMO: Joseph VickRoy, M.D., Medical Director
CHR: Troy Jensen, Director Human Resources
Web address: www.healthsouthutah.com
**Control:** Corporation, Investor–owned, for–profit **Service:** Rehabilitation

**Staffed Beds: 105**

### TOOELE—Tooele County

⊠ **MOUNTAIN WEST MEDICAL CENTER (460014)**, 2055 North Main Street, Zip 84074–9819; tel. 435/843–3600, (Nonreporting) **A**1 9 10 **S** Community Health Systems, Inc., Franklin, TN
Primary Contact: Philip Eaton, Interim Chief Executive Officer
CMO: James Antinori, M.D., Chief of Staff
CIO: Marc Taylor, IS Director
CHR: Matthew Flygare, Director Human Resources
CNO: Yvonne Nielson, Chief Nursing Officer, Director Quality Management and Regulatory Compliance
Web address: www.mountainwestmc.com
**Control:** Corporation, Investor–owned, for–profit **Service:** General Medical and Surgical

**Staffed Beds: 31**

### TREMONTON—Box Elder County

★ **BEAR RIVER VALLEY HOSPITAL (460039)**, 905 North 1000 West, Zip 84337–2497; tel. 435/207–4500, (Nonreporting) **A**9 10 **S** Intermountain Healthcare, Inc., Salt Lake City, UT
Primary Contact: Eric Packer, Administrator
CHR: Joy Sadler, Director Human Resources
CNO: Penny Marshall, Chief Nursing Officer
Web address: www.intermountainhealthcare.org/hospitals/bearriver
**Control:** Other not–for–profit (including NFP Corporation) **Service:** General Medical and Surgical

**Staffed Beds: 14**

### VERNAL—Uintah County

⊠ **ASHLEY REGIONAL MEDICAL CENTER (460030)**, 150 West 100 North, Zip 84078–2036; tel. 435/789–3342, (Nonreporting) **A**1 9 10 20 **S** LifePoint Health, Brentwood, TN
Primary Contact: Ben Cluff, Chief Executive Officer
CFO: Chad Labrum, Chief Financial Officer
CMO: Karl L. Breitenbach, M.D., Chief of Staff
CIO: Mark Rich, Chief Information Officer
CHR: Deena Mansfield, Director Human Resources
CNO: Greg Gardiner, Chief Clinical Officer
Web address: www.ashleyregional.com
**Control:** Corporation, Investor–owned, for–profit **Service:** General Medical and Surgical

**Staffed Beds: 39**

### WEST JORDAN—Salt Lake County

★ ◇ **JORDAN VALLEY MEDICAL CENTER (460051)**, 3580 West 9000 South, Zip 84088–8812; tel. 801/561–8888, (Includes MOUNTAIN POINT MEDICAL CENTER, 3000 North Triumph Boulevard, Lehii, Zip 84043; Mailing Address: Lehi, tel. 385/345–3000), (Nonreporting) **A**9 10 21 **S** IASIS Healthcare, Franklin, TN
Primary Contact: Steven Anderson, Chief Executive Officer
COO: Jon Butterfield, Chief Operating Officer
CFO: Kurt Shipley, Chief Financial Officer
CMO: B. Dee Allred, M.D., President Medical Staff
Web address: www.jordanvalleymc.com
**Control:** Partnership, Investor–owned, for–profit **Service:** General Medical and Surgical

**Staffed Beds: 183**

### WEST VALLEY CITY—Salt Lake County

★ **JORDAN VALLEY MEDICAL CENTER–WVC CAMPUS**, 3460 South Pioneer Parkway, Zip 84120–2049; tel. 801/561–8888, (Nonreporting) **S** IASIS Healthcare, Franklin, TN
Primary Contact: Steven Anderson, Chief Executive Officer
COO: Jon Butterfield, Administrator and Chief Operating Officer
CFO: Steven Payne, Chief Financial Officer
CMO: Justin Parkinson, M.D., President Medical Staff
CIO: Mark Runyan, Director Information Systems
CHR: Rob Burnett, Director Human Resources
Web address: www.pioneervalleyhospital.com
**Control:** Corporation, Investor–owned, for–profit **Service:** General Medical and Surgical

**Staffed Beds: 101**

UT

---

**Hospital, Medicare Provider Number, Address, Telephone, Approval, Facility, and Physician Codes, Health Care System**

★ American Hospital Association (AHA) membership ◯ Healthcare Facilities Accreditation Program ⇑ Center for Improvement in Healthcare Quality Accreditation
☐ The Joint Commission accreditation ◇ DNV Healthcare Inc. accreditation △ Commission on Accreditation of Rehabilitation Facilities (CARF) accreditation

# VERMONT

## BENNINGTON—Bennington County

☒ **SOUTHWESTERN VERMONT MEDICAL CENTER (470012)**, 100 Hospital Drive, Zip 05201–5004; tel. 802/442–6361, (Nonreporting) **A**1 2 9 10
Primary Contact: Thomas A. Dee, Chief Executive Officer
CFO: Stephen D. Majetich, CPA, Chief Financial Officer
CMO: Trey Dobson, M.D., Chief Medical Officer
CIO: Richard Ogilvie, Chief Information Officer
CHR: Rudolph D. Weaver, Vice President Human Resources
CNO: Carol Conroy, R.N., Chief Nursing Officer
Web address: www.svhealthcare.org
**Control:** Other not–for–profit (including NFP Corporation) **Service:** General Medical and Surgical

**Staffed Beds:** 77

## BERLIN—Washington County

☒ **THE UNIVERSITY OF VERMONT HEALTH NETWORK CENTRAL VERMONT MEDICAL CENTER (470001)**, 130 Fisher Road, Zip 05602–9516, Mailing Address: P.O. Box 547, Barre, Zip 05641–0547; tel. 802/371–4100, (Total facility includes 153 beds in nursing home–type unit) **A**1 2 3 9 10 **F**3 8 11 13 15 28 29 30 31 34 35 36 40 43 44 45 46 49 50 51 52 53 54 57 58 59 64 65 70 74 75 76 77 78 79 81 82 83 84 85 87 93 94 96 97 98 99 100 102 103 104 107 108 110 111 114 115 116 117 118 119 128 130 131 132 135 143 144 146 147 148
Primary Contact: Judith C. Tartaglia, President and Chief Executive Officer
COO: Nancy Lothian, Chief Operating Officer and Chief Information Officer
CFO: Cheyenne Follard, Chief Financial Officer
CMO: Philip Brown, D.O., Vice President Medical Affairs
CIO: Nancy Lothian, Chief Operating Officer and Chief Information Officer
CHR: Robert Patterson, Vice President Human Resources and Rehabilitation Services
Web address: www.cvmc.org/
**Control:** Other not–for–profit (including NFP Corporation) **Service:** General Medical and Surgical

**Staffed Beds:** 233 **Admissions:** 3875 **Census:** 176 **Outpatient Visits:** 313556 **Births:** 368 **Total Expense ($000):** 121009 **Payroll Expense ($000):** 57649

## BRATTLEBORO—Windham County

★ **BRATTLEBORO MEMORIAL HOSPITAL (470011)**, 17 Belmont Avenue, Zip 05301–3498; tel. 802/257–0341 **A**9 10 **F**3 11 13 15 18 28 29 30 31 34 35 39 40 45 49 51 53 55 57 59 64 68 70 74 75 76 77 78 79 81 85 87 93 107 108 110 111 115 118 119 130 131 132 135 146 147 148
Primary Contact: Steven R. Gordon, President and Chief Executive Officer
CFO: Michael Rogers, Vice President Fiscal Services
CMO: Kathleen McGraw, M.D., Chief Medical Officer
CIO: Jonathan Farina, Chief Information Officer
CHR: Robin R. Heald, Vice President Human Resources
CNO: Mary Urquhart, R.N., Vice President Patient Care
Web address: www.bmhvt.org
**Control:** Other not–for–profit (including NFP Corporation) **Service:** General Medical and Surgical

**Staffed Beds:** 42 **Admissions:** 1555 **Census:** 15 **Outpatient Visits:** 80237 **Births:** 320 **Total Expense ($000):** 72612 **Payroll Expense ($000):** 30703 **Personnel:** 391

☒ **BRATTLEBORO RETREAT (474001)**, Anna Marsh Lane, Zip 05301, Mailing Address: P.O. Box 803, Zip 05302–0803; tel. 802/257–7785 **A**1 5 9 10 **F**29 34 35 50 68 98 99 100 101 102 103 104 105 106 **P**6
Primary Contact: Robert E. Simpson, Jr., M.P.H., President and Chief Executive Officer
COO: Gerri Cote, Vice President Operations
CFO: John E. Blaha, Vice President Finance and Chief Financial Officer
CMO: Frederick Engstrom, M.D., Chief Medical Officer
CHR: Jeffrey T. Corrigan, Vice President Human Resources
CNO: Linda J. Nagy, MSN, Chief Nursing Officer
Web address: www.brattlebororetreat.org
**Control:** Other not–for–profit (including NFP Corporation) **Service:** Psychiatric

**Staffed Beds:** 122 **Admissions:** 3541 **Census:** 104 **Outpatient Visits:** 34543 **Births:** 0 **Total Expense ($000):** 65114 **Payroll Expense ($000):** 38601 **Personnel:** 478

## BURLINGTON—Chittenden County

☒ **THE UNIVERSITY OF VERMONT HEALTH NETWORK UNIVERSITY OF VERMONT MEDICAL CENTER (470003)**, 111 Colchester Avenue, Zip 05401–1473; tel. 802/847–0000, (Includes FANNY ALLEN CAMPUS, 101 College Parkway, Colchester, Zip 05446–3035; tel. 802/655–1234; MEDICAL CENTER HOSPITAL CAMPUS, Colchester Avenue, Zip 05401; tel. 802/847–2345; VERMONT CHILDREN'S HOSPITAL, 111 Colchester Avenue, tel. 802/847–0000) **A**1 2 3 5 8 9 10 **F**3 4 5 6 7 9 11 12 13 15 17 18 19 20 21 22 23 24 25 26 28 29 30 31 32 34 35 36 37 39 40 43 44 45 46 47 48 49 50 51 52 54 55 56 57 58 59 60 61 63 64 65 66 68 70 72 73 74 75 77 78 79 81 82 84 85 86 87 88 90 91 92 93 94 96 97 98 99 100 101 102 103 104 105 107 108 110 111 114 115 116 117 118 119 120 121 123 124 126 128 129 130 131 132 135 136 138 141 142 143 144 145 146 147 148 **P**6
Primary Contact: John R. Brumsted, M.D., President and Chief Executive Officer
CFO: Todd Keating, Chief Financial Officer
CMO: Stephen Leffler, Chief Medical Officer
CIO: Charles H. Podesta, Vice President Information Services
CHR: Paul Macuga, Chief Human Resources Officer
Web address: www.fletcherallen.org
**Control:** Other not–for–profit (including NFP Corporation) **Service:** General Medical and Surgical

**Staffed Beds:** 426 **Admissions:** 18240 **Census:** 305 **Outpatient Visits:** 1450345 **Births:** 2245 **Total Expense ($000):** 1013883 **Payroll Expense ($000):** 491522 **Personnel:** 6405

## MIDDLEBURY—Addison County

★ **PORTER MEDICAL CENTER (471307)**, 115 Porter Drive, Zip 05753–8423; tel. 802/388–4701 **A**9 10 18 **F**1 3 4 8 11 13 15 16 17 18 26 29 30 40 43 45 50 59 64 67 68 70 72 73 75 76 79 80 81 83 85 86 88 89 90 93 97 98 107 108 110 111 114 115 119 128 130 133 146 **P**6
Primary Contact: Lynn Ingram Boggs, Chief Executive Officer
CFO: Steve Ciampa, Vice President Finance
CMO: Fred Kniffin, M.D., Chief Medical Officer
CIO: Rebecca Woods, Chief Information Officer
CHR: David Fuller, Director Human Resources
CNO: Lorraina Smith–Zuba, R.N., Chief Nursing Officer
Web address: www.portermedical.org
**Control:** Other not–for–profit (including NFP Corporation) **Service:** General Medical and Surgical

**Staffed Beds:** 25 **Admissions:** 1580 **Census:** 14 **Outpatient Visits:** 67784 **Births:** 387 **Total Expense ($000):** 71704 **Payroll Expense ($000):** 32200 **Personnel:** 483

## MORRISVILLE—Lamoille County

★ **COPLEY HOSPITAL (471305)**, 528 Washington Highway, Zip 05661–8973; tel. 802/888–8888 **A**9 10 18 **F**3 11 13 15 18 28 29 30 31 34 35 39 40 44 45 58 59 64 65 70 74 75 76 77 78 79 81 85 86 93 107 110 111 119 129 130 131 133 135 146 147
Primary Contact: Melvyn Patashnick, President and Chief Executive Officer
COO: Greg Ward, Vice President Operations
CFO: Rassoul Rangaviz, Chief Financial Officer
CMO: Joel Silverstein, M.D., Chief Medical Officer
CIO: Greg Ward, Vice President Operations
CHR: Jennifer Archambault, Vice President Human Resources and Compliance
CNO: Carolyn J. Roe, R.N., Chief Nursing Officer
Web address: www.copleyvt.org
**Control:** Other not–for–profit (including NFP Corporation) **Service:** General Medical and Surgical

**Staffed Beds:** 25 **Admissions:** 1566 **Census:** 12 **Outpatient Visits:** 79640 **Births:** 229 **Total Expense ($000):** 57515 **Payroll Expense ($000):** 27690 **Personnel:** 341

## NEWPORT—Orleans County

★ **NORTH COUNTRY HOSPITAL AND HEALTH CENTER (471304)**, 189 Prouty Drive, Zip 05855–9326; tel. 802/334–7331 **A**9 10 18 **F**11 13 15 28 29 30 31 34 40 45 51 53 70 74 75 76 77 78 79 81 82 84 89 93 107 108 110 111 114 119 127 129 130 131 133 135 146 148
Primary Contact: Claudio D. Fort, President and Chief Executive Officer
COO: Thomas Frank, Chief Operating Officer
CFO: Andre Bissonnette, Chief Financial Officer
CHR: William Perket, Vice President Human Resources
CNO: Brenda Neff, MSN, Vice President Patient Care Services and Chief Nursing Officer
Web address: www.nchsi.org
**Control:** Other not–for–profit (including NFP Corporation) **Service:** General Medical and Surgical

**Staffed Beds:** 25 **Admissions:** 1371 **Census:** 15 **Outpatient Visits:** 69862 **Births:** 210 **Total Expense ($000):** 76155 **Payroll Expense ($000):** 33844 **Personnel:** 415

**VT**

*Many Facility Codes have changed. Please refer to the AHA Guide Code Chart.* © 2015 AHA Guide

## RANDOLPH—Orange County

★ **GIFFORD MEDICAL CENTER (471301)**, 44 South Main Street,
Zip 05060–1381, Mailing Address: P.O. Box 2000, Zip 05060–2000;
tel. 802/728–7000, (Nonreporting) **A**2 9 10 18
Primary Contact: Joseph L. Woodin, President and Chief Executive Officer
CFO: Jeff Hebert, Interim Vice President Finance
CMO: Joshua Plavin, M.D., Medical Director Medicine Division
CIO: Sean Patrick, Director Information Systems
CHR: Janice Davis, Interim Director Human Resources
CNO: Linda Minsinger, Vice President Hospital Division
Web address: www.giffordmed.org
**Control:** Other not–for–profit (including NFP Corporation) **Service:** General
Medical and Surgical

**Staffed Beds:** 52

## RUTLAND—Rutland County

⊞ **RUTLAND REGIONAL MEDICAL CENTER (470005)**, 160 Allen Street,
Zip 05701–4595; tel. 802/775–7111 **A**1 2 9 10 **F**13 15 18 20 22 23 24 28
29 31 34 36 38 40 45 47 48 49 50 51 55 57 59 61 64 65 70 76 77 78 79
81 82 83 84 85 87 92 93 94 98 100 101 102 103 104 107 108 111 115
116 117 118 119 128 129 130 133 135 146 147 148
Primary Contact: Thomas W. Huebner, President
CFO: Ed Ogorzalek, Chief Financial Officer
CMO: Baxter C. Holland, M.D., Chief Medical Officer
CHR: Allison Wollen, Vice President Human Resources
CNO: Carol Egen, R.N., Chief Nursing Officer
Web address: www.rrmc.org
**Control:** Other not–for–profit (including NFP Corporation) **Service:** General
Medical and Surgical

**Staffed Beds:** 126 **Admissions:** 5694 **Census:** 80 **Outpatient Visits:** 225383
**Births:** 412 **Total Expense ($000):** 220537 **Payroll Expense ($000):**
101668 **Personnel:** 1212

## SAINT ALBANS—Franklin County

⊞ **NORTHWESTERN MEDICAL CENTER (470024)**, 133 Fairfield Street,
Zip 05478–1726; tel. 802/524–5911 **A**1 2 9 10 20 **F**3 11 13 15 28 29 30 32
34 35 36 37 38 40 43 44 45 50 51 57 58 59 63 69 70 75 76 77 78 79 81
82 84 85 86 87 89 93 96 107 108 111 114 119 130 131 132 133 134 135
143 144 146 147 148 **P**6 8 **S** QHR, Brentwood, TN
Primary Contact: Jill Berry Bowen, President and Chief Executive Officer
COO: Jane Catton, R.N., Chief Operating Officer and Chief Nursing Officer
CFO: Ted D. Sirotta, Chief Financial Officer
CMO: Lowery Sullivan, M.D., Chief Medical Officer
CIO: Joel Benware, Vice President Information Technology and Compliance
CHR: Thomas C. Conley, Vice President, Human Resources and Organizational
Development
CNO: Jane Catton, R.N., Chief Operating Officer and Chief Nursing Officer
Web address: www.northwesternmedicalcenter.org
**Control:** Other not–for–profit (including NFP Corporation) **Service:** General
Medical and Surgical

**Staffed Beds:** 55 **Admissions:** 2405 **Census:** 22 **Outpatient Visits:** 76342
**Births:** 469 **Total Expense ($000):** 86318 **Payroll Expense ($000):** 39318
**Personnel:** 590

## SAINT JOHNSBURY—Caledonia County

★ **NORTHEASTERN VERMONT REGIONAL HOSPITAL (471303)**, 1315 Hospital
Drive, Zip 05819–9210, Mailing Address: PO Box 905, Zip 05819–0905;
tel. 802/748–8141 **A**9 10 18 **F**3 11 13 15 18 26 28 29 30 34 35 40 44 45
50 51 59 64 68 70 74 75 76 77 78 79 81 82 84 85 86 87 89 93 97 107
108 110 111 115 118 119 127 130 131 132 133 135 146 147 **P**6
Primary Contact: Paul R. Bengtson, Chief Executive Officer
CFO: Robert Hersey, Chief Financial Officer
CIO: Andrea Lott, Vice President Information Services
CHR: Betty Ann Gwatkin, Vice President Human Resources
CNO: Seleem Choudhury, R.N., Chief Nursing Officer
Web address: www.nvrh.org
**Control:** Other not–for–profit (including NFP Corporation) **Service:** General
Medical and Surgical

**Staffed Beds:** 25 **Admissions:** 1317 **Census:** 13 **Outpatient Visits:** 153390
**Births:** 194 **Total Expense ($000):** 67007 **Payroll Expense ($000):** 29988
**Personnel:** 395

## SPRINGFIELD—Windsor County

**SPRINGFIELD HOSPITAL (471306)**, 25 Ridgewood Road, Zip 05156–3050,
Mailing Address: 25 Ridgewood Road, Zip 05156–3050; tel. 802/885–2151,
(Nonreporting) **A**9 10 18
Primary Contact: Timothy R. Ford, President and Chief Executive Officer
CFO: Andrew Majka, Chief Financial Officer
CMO: Richard Marasa, M.D., President Medical Staff
CIO: Kyle Peoples, Director Technology Management Services
CHR: Janet Lyle, Chief Human Resources and Allied Health Services
CNO: Janet Sherer, Chief of Patient Care Services
Web address: www.springfieldmed.org
**Control:** Other not–for–profit (including NFP Corporation) **Service:** General
Medical and Surgical

**Staffed Beds:** 35

## TOWNSHEND—Windham County

★ **GRACE COTTAGE HOSPITAL (471300)**, 185 Grafton Road, Zip 05353–0216,
Mailing Address: P.O. Box 216, Zip 05353–0216; tel. 802/365–7357,
(Nonreporting) **A**9 10 18
Primary Contact: Roger Allbee, Chief Executive Officer and Administrator
COO: Jeanne M. Fortier, R.N., Chief Nursing Officer and Interim Chief Operating
Officer
CFO: Stephen A. Brown, Chief Financial Officer
CMO: Timothy Shafer, M.D., Medical Director
CIO: Tony Marques, Director Information Systems
CHR: Christopher J. Lackney, Director Human Resources
CNO: Jeanne M. Fortier, R.N., Chief Nursing Officer and Interim Chief Operating
Officer
Web address: www.gracecottage.org
**Control:** Other not–for–profit (including NFP Corporation) **Service:** General
Medical and Surgical

**Staffed Beds:** 19

## WHITE RIVER JUNCTION—Windsor County

⊞ **WHITE RIVER JUNCTION VETERANS AFFAIRS MEDICAL CENTER**, 215 North
Main Street, Zip 05009–0001; tel. 802/295–9363 **A**1 3 5 8 **F**3 4 5 8 9 12 18
26 28 29 30 31 33 34 35 36 38 39 40 44 45 46 47 48 49 50 53 54 55 56
57 58 59 60 61 63 64 65 70 74 75 77 78 79 81 82 83 84 85 86 87 91 93
94 97 98 100 101 102 103 104 105 106 107 108 111 115 116 117 118
119 127 130 131 132 135 141 143 144 146 147 148 **P**6 **S** Department of
Veterans Affairs, Washington, DC
Primary Contact: Deborah Amdur, Director
CFO: Joan Wilmot, Chief Finance Officer
CMO: M. Ganga Hematillake, M.D., Chief of Staff
CIO: Matthew Rafus, Chief Information Officer
CHR: Barbara Nadeau, Chief Human Resources Management Service
Web address: www.whiteriver.va.gov/
**Control:** Veterans Affairs, Government, federal **Service:** General Medical and
Surgical

**Staffed Beds:** 60 **Admissions:** 2680 **Census:** 40 **Outpatient Visits:** 263369
**Births:** 0 **Total Expense ($000):** 187253 **Payroll Expense ($000):** 74869
**Personnel:** 870

## WINDSOR—Windsor County

★ △ **MT. ASCUTNEY HOSPITAL AND HEALTH CENTER (471302)**, 289
County Road, Zip 05089–9000; tel. 802/674–6711 **A**7 9 10 18 **F**3 8 10 11 15
28 29 30 31 32 34 35 36 40 41 44 45 49 50 54 56 57 59 63 64 65 66 68
69 70 71 75 77 78 79 81 82 84 85 86 87 90 91 92 93 94 96 97 100 104
107 110 111 114 119 125 130 131 132 133 134 135 143 146 148 **P**6
Primary Contact: Kevin Donovan, Chief Executive Officer
COO: Paul Calandrella, Chief Operating Officer
CFO: David Sanville, Chief Financial Officer
CMO: Joseph Perras, Chief Medical Officer
CIO: Brenna Heighes, Manager Information Technology
CHR: Jean Martaniuk, Director Human Resources
CNO: Jill Lord, MS, Director Patient Care Services
Web address: www.mtascutneyhospital.org
**Control:** Other not–for–profit (including NFP Corporation) **Service:** General
Medical and Surgical

**Staffed Beds:** 35 **Admissions:** 943 **Census:** 24 **Outpatient Visits:** 80503
**Births:** 0 **Total Expense ($000):** 49189 **Payroll Expense ($000):** 22638
**Personnel:** 368

**VT**

---

**Hospital, Medicare Provider Number, Address, Telephone, Approval, Facility, and Physician Codes, Health Care System**

★ American Hospital Association (AHA) membership    ○ Healthcare Facilities Accreditation Program    ⇧ Center for Improvement in Healthcare Quality Accreditation
□ The Joint Commission accreditation    ◇ DNV Healthcare Inc. accreditation    △ Commission on Accreditation of Rehabilitation Facilities (CARF) accreditation

# VIRGINIA

### ABINGDON—Washington County

✠ **JOHNSTON MEMORIAL HOSPITAL (490053)**, 16000 Johnston Memorial Drive, Zip 24211–7659; tel. 276/676–7000 **A**1 2 9 10 13 **F**3 7 8 11 13 15 18 20 22 26 28 29 30 31 34 35 39 44 45 46 48 49 50 51 54 57 59 60 62 63 64 68 70 74 75 76 77 78 79 81 82 84 85 87 93 97 100 107 108 110 111 115 116 118 119 120 121 123 129 130 132 133 135 143 144 146 147 148 **P**6 8 **S** Mountain States Health Alliance, Johnson City, TN
Primary Contact: Sean S. McMurray, FACHE, Vice President and Chief Executive Officer
CFO: John Jeter, Assistant Administrator and Chief Financial Officer
CIO: Jackson Dale, Director Management Information Services
CHR: Jackie G. Phipps, Director Human Resources
Web address: www.jmh.org
**Control:** Other not–for–profit (including NFP Corporation) **Service:** General Medical and Surgical

**Staffed Beds:** 116 **Admissions:** 7109 **Census:** 64 **Outpatient Visits:** 145692 **Births:** 763 **Total Expense ($000):** 113243 **Payroll Expense ($000):** 33059 **Personnel:** 687

### ALDIE—Loudoun County

✠ **HEALTHSOUTH REHABILITATION HOSPITAL OF NORTHERN VIRGINIA (493033)**, 24430 Millstream Drive, Zip 20105–3098; tel. 703/957–2000, (Nonreporting) **A**1 10 **S** HEALTHSOUTH Corporation, Birmingham, AL
Primary Contact: Jason Waibel, Interim Chief Executive Officer
Web address: www.healthsouthnorthernvirginia.com
**Control:** Corporation, Investor–owned, for–profit **Service:** Rehabilitation

**Staffed Beds:** 40

### ALEXANDRIA—Alexandria City County

✠ **INOVA ALEXANDRIA HOSPITAL (490040)**, 4320 Seminary Road, Zip 22304–1535; tel. 703/504–3167 **A**1 2 5 9 10 **F**3 11 13 14 15 17 18 20 22 24 26 28 29 30 31 34 35 40 42 44 45 48 49 50 51 54 55 57 59 60 61 63 64 65 66 68 70 72 74 75 77 78 79 80 81 82 84 85 86 87 91 92 93 100 102 107 108 110 111 114 115 117 118 119 120 121 123 124 129 130 131 132 135 145 146 147 148 **S** Inova Health System, Falls Church, VA
Primary Contact: Susan Carroll, Chief Executive Officer
CFO: Todd Lockcuff, Chief Financial Officer
CMO: William L. Jackson, Chief Medical Officer
CHR: Hugo Aguas, Vice President Human Resources
Web address: www.inova.org
**Control:** Other not–for–profit (including NFP Corporation) **Service:** General Medical and Surgical

**Staffed Beds:** 334 **Admissions:** 16732 **Census:** 209 **Outpatient Visits:** 174866 **Births:** 3550 **Total Expense ($000):** 280277 **Payroll Expense ($000):** 101681 **Personnel:** 1362

✠ △ **INOVA MOUNT VERNON HOSPITAL (490122)**, 2501 Parker's Lane, Zip 22306–3209; tel. 703/664–7000 **A**1 2 3 5 7 9 10 **F**3 5 11 14 15 18 26 28 29 30 31 34 35 37 38 39 40 42 44 45 48 49 50 51 54 55 57 58 59 60 61 63 64 65 66 68 69 70 74 75 77 78 79 80 81 82 84 85 86 87 90 91 92 93 94 98 100 101 102 103 104 105 107 108 110 111 114 115 118 119 130 131 132 135 145 146 147 148 **P**6 **S** Inova Health System, Falls Church, VA
Primary Contact: Deborah Addo–Samuels, Chief Executive Officer
CFO: Tammy Razmic, Associate Administrator Finance and Chief Financial Officer
CMO: Donald Brideau, M.D., Chief Medical Officer
CHR: Bev Sugar, Associate Administrator and Director Human Resources
Web address: www.inova.org
**Control:** Other not–for–profit (including NFP Corporation) **Service:** General Medical and Surgical

**Staffed Beds:** 237 **Admissions:** 8680 **Census:** 135 **Outpatient Visits:** 84940 **Births:** 0 **Total Expense ($000):** 165166 **Payroll Expense ($000):** 58326 **Personnel:** 785

### ARLINGTON—Arlington County

**CAPITAL HOSPICE (490129)**, 4715 15th Street North, Zip 22205–2640; tel. 703/538–2065, (Nonreporting) **A**3 10
Primary Contact: Malene S. Davis, R.N., President and Chief Executive Officer
CFO: David Schwind, Chief Financial Officer
CIO: Diane Rigsby, Chief Information Officer
Web address: www.capitalhospice.org
**Control:** Other not–for–profit (including NFP Corporation) **Service:** Other specialty

**Staffed Beds:** 15

✠ △ **VIRGINIA HOSPITAL CENTER – ARLINGTON (490050)**, 1701 North George Mason Drive, Zip 22205–3698; tel. 703/558–5000 **A**1 2 3 5 7 9 10 **F**3 4 5 8 11 12 13 15 17 18 20 22 24 26 28 29 30 31 34 35 37 38 40 45 46 47 48 49 50 51 54 57 59 60 61 64 65 66 68 70 72 73 74 75 76 78 79 81 84 85 86 87 89 90 91 92 93 94 95 96 97 98 100 102 103 104 105 107 110 111 114 115 116 117 118 119 120 121 123 124 126 129 130 132 135 144 145 146 147 148
Primary Contact: James B. Cole, Chief Executive Officer
COO: Carl Bahnlein, Executive Vice President and Chief Operating Officer
CFO: Robin Norman, Senior Vice President and Chief Financial Officer
CMO: Jeffrey P. DiLisi, Vice President and Chief Medical Officer
CIO: Russ McWey, M.D., Vice President and Chief Information Officer
CHR: Michael Malone, Vice President and Chief Human Resources Officer
CNO: Darlene Vrotsos, R.N., Senior Vice President and Chief Nursing Officer
Web address: www.virginiahospitalcenter.com
**Control:** Other not–for–profit (including NFP Corporation) **Service:** General Medical and Surgical

**Staffed Beds:** 357 **Admissions:** 22434 **Census:** 273 **Outpatient Visits:** 340802 **Births:** 5825 **Total Expense ($000):** 366424 **Payroll Expense ($000):** 147313 **Personnel:** 2441

### BEDFORD—Bedford City County

✠ **BEDFORD MEMORIAL HOSPITAL (490088)**, 1613 Oakwood Street, Zip 24523–1213, Mailing Address: P.O. Box 688, Zip 24523–0688; tel. 540/586–2441, (Nonreporting) **A**1 9 10 **S** Centra Health, Inc., Lynchburg, VA
Primary Contact: Patti Jurkus, Chief Executive Officer
CFO: Donald E. Lorton, Executive Vice President
CMO: E. Allen Joslyn, M.D., Chief Medical Officer
Web address: www.bmhva.com
**Control:** Other not–for–profit (including NFP Corporation) **Service:** General Medical and Surgical

**Staffed Beds:** 124

### BIG STONE GAP—Wise County

✠ **WELLMONT LONESOME PINE HOSPITAL (490114)**, 1990 Holton Avenue East, Zip 24219–3350; tel. 276/523–3111 **A**1 9 10 13 **F**3 11 13 15 18 29 30 31 34 35 40 45 49 50 57 59 68 76 77 78 79 81 82 85 87 89 93 107 108 110 111 118 119 120 121 129 130 146 148 **S** Wellmont Health System, Kingsport, TN
Primary Contact: Dale Clark, President
CFO: Regina Day, Executive Vice President of Finance
CMO: James Raj, M.D., Chief Medical Officer
CHR: Bobby Collins, Director Human Resources
CNO: Cindy Stidham, R.N., Director of Patient Care Services
Web address: www.wellmont.org
**Control:** Other not–for–profit (including NFP Corporation) **Service:** General Medical and Surgical

**Staffed Beds:** 30 **Admissions:** 1317 **Census:** 10 **Outpatient Visits:** 36813 **Births:** 288 **Total Expense ($000):** 34489 **Payroll Expense ($000):** 8127 **Personnel:** 203

### BLACKSBURG—Montgomery County

✠ **LEWISGALE HOSPITAL MONTGOMERY (490110)**, 3700 South Main Street, Zip 24060–7081, Mailing Address: P.O. Box 90004, Zip 24062–9004; tel. 540/951–1111, (Nonreporting) **A**1 9 10 12 13 **S** HCA, Nashville, TN
Primary Contact: Alan J. Fabian, Chief Executive Officer
COO: Matt Mathias, Chief Operating Officer
CFO: Timothy W. Haasken, Chief Financial Officer
CIO: Diron Lane, Director Information Systems
CNO: Ellen Linkenhoker, Chief Nursing Officer
Web address: www.lewisgale.com
**Control:** Corporation, Investor–owned, for–profit **Service:** General Medical and Surgical

**Staffed Beds:** 89

### BRISTOL—Bristol City County

✠ **REHABILITATION HOSPITAL OF SOUTHWEST VIRGINIA (493034)**, 103 North Street, Zip 24201–3201; tel. 276/642–7900, (Nonreporting) **A**1 10 **S** HEALTHSOUTH Corporation, Birmingham, AL
Primary Contact: Georgeanne Cole, Chief Executive Officer
Web address: www.rehabilitationhospitalswvirginia.com
**Control:** Corporation, Investor–owned, for–profit **Service:** Rehabilitation

**Staffed Beds:** 25

*Many Facility Codes have changed. Please refer to the AHA Guide Code Chart.*

## BURKEVILLE—Nottoway County

**PIEDMONT GERIATRIC HOSPITAL (490134)**, 5001 East Patrick Henry Highway, Zip 23922–3460, Mailing Address: P.O. Box 427, Zip 23922–0427; tel. 434/767–4401, (Nonreporting) **A9 S** Virginia Department of Mental Health, Richmond, VA
Primary Contact: Stephen M. Herrick, Ph.D., Director
CFO: James G. Ayers, Chief Financial Officer
CMO: Hugo Falcon, M.D., Director Medical Services
CHR: Michael Wimsatt, Director Human Resources
Web address: www.pgh.dmhmrsas.virginia.gov
**Control:** State–Government, nonfederal **Service:** Other specialty

**Staffed Beds:** 150

## CATAWBA—Roanoke County

☐ **CATAWBA HOSPITAL (490135)**, 5525 Catawba Hospital Drive, Zip 24070–2115, Mailing Address: P.O. Box 200, Zip 24070–0200; tel. 540/375–4200 **A**1 3 9 10 **F**29 30 35 38 39 44 50 68 75 77 98 103 130 146 **P**6 **S** Virginia Department of Mental Health, Richmond, VA
Primary Contact: Walton F. Mitchell, III, Director
COO: Charles Law, Ph.D., Chief Operating Officer
CFO: Cecil Hardin, CPA, Chief Financial Officer
CMO: Yad Jabbarpour, M.D., Chief of Staff
CIO: Charles Law, Ph.D., Chief Operating Officer
CHR: Patricia Ebbett, Chief Human Resources Officer
CNO: Vicky Fisher, Ph.D., Chief Nurse Executive
Web address: www.catawba.dbhds.virginia.gov
**Control:** State–Government, nonfederal **Service:** Psychiatric

**Staffed Beds:** 110 **Admissions:** 240 **Census:** 101 **Outpatient Visits:** 0
**Births:** 0 **Total Expense ($000):** 21591 **Payroll Expense ($000):** 11796
**Personnel:** 263

## CHARLOTTESVILLE—Charlottesville City County

★ ◇ **MARTHA JEFFERSON HOSPITAL (490077)**, 500 Martha Jefferson Drive, Zip 22911–4668; tel. 434/654–7000 **A**2 3 5 9 10 21 **F**3 8 12 13 15 18 20 22 26 28 29 30 31 34 35 36 40 42 44 45 46 47 48 49 50 54 55 57 58 59 64 66 68 70 74 75 76 77 78 79 81 82 84 85 86 87 89 92 93 94 97 107 108 110 111 114 115 116 117 118 119 120 121 123 124 129 130 131 132 135 145 146 147 148 **P**1 **S** Sentara Healthcare, Norfolk, VA
Primary Contact: Jonathan S. Davis, FACHE, President
COO: Amy Black, R.N., Chief Operating Officer
CFO: J. Michael Burris, Vice President Corporate Services and Chief Financial Officer
CMO: F. Michael Ashby, M.D., Vice President and Medical Director
CIO: Marijo Lecker, Vice President
CHR: Debbie Desmond, Director Human Resources
Web address: www.marthajefferson.org
**Control:** Other not-for-profit (including NFP Corporation) **Service:** General Medical and Surgical

**Staffed Beds:** 139 **Admissions:** 9397 **Census:** 88 **Outpatient Visits:** 457547
**Births:** 1741 **Total Expense ($000):** 237201 **Payroll Expense ($000):** 105380 **Personnel:** 1433

⊠ △ **UNIVERSITY OF VIRGINIA MEDICAL CENTER (490009)**, 1215 Lee Street, Zip 22908–0001, Mailing Address: P.O. Box 800809, Zip 22908–0809; tel. 434/924–0211, (Includes UNIVERSITY OF VIRGINIA CHILDREN'S HOSPITAL, 1215 Lee Street, Zip 22908, Mailing Address: PO Box 800566, Zip 22908; tel. 434/243–5500) **A**1 2 3 5 7 8 9 10 **F**3 4 5 6 7 8 9 11 12 13 15 16 17 18 19 20 21 22 23 24 25 26 27 28 29 30 31 32 34 35 36 37 38 39 40 41 43 44 45 46 47 48 49 50 51 52 54 55 56 57 58 59 60 61 62 64 65 66 68 69 70 71 72 73 74 75 76 77 78 79 80 81 82 83 84 85 86 87 88 89 90 91 92 93 94 97 98 99 100 101 102 103 104 107 108 110 111 112 114 115 116 117 118 119 120 121 123 124 126 129 130 131 132 134 135 136 137 138 139 140 141 142 143 145 146 147 148 **P**3 4 **S** UVA Health System, Charlottesville, VA
Primary Contact: Pamela Sutton–Wallace, Chief Executive Officer
COO: James Amato, Interim Chief Operating Officer
CFO: Nick Mendyka, Chief Financial Officer
CMO: Chris A. Ghaemmaghami, M.D., Chief Medical Officer
CIO: Richard Skinner, Chief Information Technology Officer
CHR: John Boswell, Chief Human Resources Officer
CNO: Lorna M. Facteau, Ph.D., Chief Nursing Officer
Web address: www.healthsystem.virginia.edu
**Control:** State–Government, nonfederal **Service:** General Medical and Surgical

**Staffed Beds:** 584 **Admissions:** 28274 **Census:** 446 **Outpatient Visits:** 1832429 **Births:** 1717 **Total Expense ($000):** 1203070 **Payroll Expense ($000):** 417656 **Personnel:** 5961

⊠ **UVA TRANSITIONAL CARE HOSPITAL (492011)**, 2965 Ivy Road (250 West), Zip 22903–9330; tel. 434/924–7897 **A**1 10 **F**1 3 29 30 60 77 85 94 114 130 146 148 **P**3 4 **S** UVA Health System, Charlottesville, VA
Primary Contact: Michelle Hereford, Chief
Web address: www.uvahealth.com/services/transitional–care–hospital
**Control:** State–Government, nonfederal **Service:** Long–Term Acute Care hospital

**Staffed Beds:** 40 **Admissions:** 316 **Census:** 26 **Outpatient Visits:** 0 **Births:** 0 **Total Expense ($000):** 17400 **Payroll Expense ($000):** 7037 **Personnel:** 125

⊠ **UVA–HEALTHSOUTH REHABILITATION HOSPITAL (493029)**, 515 Ray C. Hunt Drive, Zip 22903–2981; tel. 434/244–2000 **A**1 3 5 10 **F**28 29 30 34 54 57 59 64 74 75 77 90 91 93 94 96 131 148 **P**5 **S** HEALTHSOUTH Corporation, Birmingham, AL
Primary Contact: Thomas J. Cook, Chief Executive Officer
Web address: www.uvahealthsouth.com
**Control:** Corporation, Investor–owned, for–profit **Service:** Rehabilitation

**Staffed Beds:** 50 **Admissions:** 1255 **Census:** 41 **Outpatient Visits:** 27366 **Births:** 0 **Total Expense ($000):** 20282 **Payroll Expense ($000):** 12461 **Personnel:** 218

## CHESAPEAKE—Chesapeake City County

★ ○ **CHESAPEAKE REGIONAL MEDICAL CENTER (490120)**, 736 Battlefield Boulevard North, Zip 23320–4941, Mailing Address: P.O. Box 2028, Zip 23327–2028; tel. 757/312–8121 **A**2 3 9 10 11 **F**3 6 10 11 12 13 15 18 20 22 24 26 28 29 30 31 34 35 37 40 44 45 46 49 50 53 54 57 58 59 61 62 63 64 65 66 68 69 70 71 73 74 75 76 77 78 79 81 83 84 85 86 87 89 91 93 100 101 102 103 107 108 110 111 114 115 118 119 120 121 123 126 129 130 132 135 141 142 143 146 147 148 **P**6 8
Primary Contact: Peter F. Bastone, Chief Executive Officer
CMO: Paul Brainstein, M.D., Interim Chief Medical Officer
CIO: Ken Deans, Chief Information Officer
CHR: Deborah L. Rosenburg, Vice President Human Resources
CNO: Elaine Griffiths, R.N., Chief Nursing Officer
Web address: www.chesapeakeregional.com
**Control:** Hospital district or authority, Government, nonfederal **Service:** General Medical and Surgical

**Staffed Beds:** 309 **Admissions:** 15069 **Census:** 190 **Outpatient Visits:** 187197 **Births:** 2412 **Total Expense ($000):** 263923 **Payroll Expense ($000):** 102874 **Personnel:** 1695

## CHRISTIANSBURG—Montgomery County

⊠ **CARILION NEW RIVER VALLEY MEDICAL CENTER (490042)**, 2900 Lamb Circle, Zip 24073–6344, Mailing Address: P.O. Box 5, Radford, Zip 24143–0005; tel. 540/731–2000, (Includes CARILION CLINIC SAINT ALBANS HOSPITAL, 2900 Lamb Circle, tel. 540/731–2000) **A**1 3 9 10 13 19 **F**3 5 12 13 15 18 20 22 26 28 29 30 31 34 35 36 40 43 45 47 48 49 50 51 57 59 60 62 63 64 68 70 74 75 76 77 79 81 82 84 85 86 87 89 91 92 93 96 98 99 102 103 104 105 107 108 110 111 114 115 118 119 126 129 130 131 135 146 147 148 **S** Carilion Clinic, Roanoke, VA
Primary Contact: William Flattery, Vice President and Administrator Western Division
CFO: Rob Vaughan, Chief Financial Officer
CMO: Dennis Means, M.D., Vice President Medical Affairs
CIO: Daniel Borchi, Chief Information Officer
CHR: Patti Jurkus, Director Human Resources
Web address: www.carilionclinic.org/Carilion/cnrv
**Control:** Other not-for-profit (including NFP Corporation) **Service:** General Medical and Surgical

**Staffed Beds:** 94 **Admissions:** 8079 **Census:** 87 **Outpatient Visits:** 91630 **Births:** 1258 **Total Expense ($000):** 141722 **Payroll Expense ($000):** 53276 **Personnel:** 850

## CLINTWOOD—Dickenson County

**DICKENSON COMMUNITY HOSPITAL (491303)**, 312 Hospital Drive, Zip 24228, Mailing Address: P.O. Box 1440, Zip 24228–1440; tel. 276/926–0300 **A**9 10 18 **F**3 29 40 44 64 87 97 104 107 111 119 130 148 **P**6 8 **S** Mountain States Health Alliance, Johnson City, TN
Primary Contact: Mark T. Leonard, Chief Executive Officer
CFO: Kevin Morrison, Chief Financial Officer
CMO: Erin Mullins, D.O., Chief Medical Staff
CHR: Valeri J. Colyer, Director Human Resources
CNO: Terri Roop, Director Patient Care Services
Web address: www.msha.com/dch
**Control:** Other not-for-profit (including NFP Corporation) **Service:** General Medical and Surgical

**Staffed Beds:** 25 **Admissions:** 8 **Census:** 1 **Outpatient Visits:** 21348 **Births:** 0 **Total Expense ($000):** 6301 **Payroll Expense ($000):** 2462 **Personnel:** 45

**VA**

---

## CULPEPER—Culpeper County

✠ **UVA CULPEPER HOSPITAL (490019)**, 501 Sunset Lane, Zip 22701–3917,
Mailing Address: P.O. Box 592, Zip 22701–0500; tel. 540/829–4100 **A**1 3 5 9
10 **F**3 7 8 11 13 15 18 28 29 30 34 35 36 37 38 40 45 50 54 57 59 64 68
70 74 75 76 77 78 79 81 82 85 87 89 93 97 102 107 108 110 111 114 115
119 120 121 123 130 132 133 135 143 146 148 **P**8 **S** UVA Health System,
Charlottesville, VA
Primary Contact: Greg Napps, Chief Executive Officer
COO: Greg Napps, Chief Executive Officer
CFO: David J. Plaviak, Interim Chief Financial Officer
CMO: Morton Chiles, M.D., Chief Medical Officer
CIO: Steven Speelman, Director Information Systems
CHR: Susan Edwards, Vice President Human Resources
Web address: www.culpeperhealth.org
**Control:** Other not–for–profit (including NFP Corporation) **Service:** General
Medical and Surgical

**Staffed Beds:** 68 **Admissions:** 3038 **Census:** 31 **Outpatient Visits:** 71704
**Births:** 352 **Total Expense ($000):** 72472 **Payroll Expense ($000):** 29365
**Personnel:** 446

## DANVILLE—Danville City County

✠ **DANVILLE REGIONAL MEDICAL CENTER (490075)**, 142 South Main Street,
Zip 24541–2922; tel. 434/799–2100, (Nonreporting) **A**1 2 9 10 12 13
**S** LifePoint Health, Brentwood, TN
Primary Contact: Alan Larson, Chief Executive Officer
CFO: Mark T. Anderson, Chief Financial Officer
CMO: James F. Starling, M.D., Chief Medical Officer
CIO: David Cartwright, Director Management Information Systems
Web address: www.danvilleregional.org
**Control:** Other not–for–profit (including NFP Corporation) **Service:** General
Medical and Surgical

**Staffed Beds:** 250

☐ **SOUTHERN VIRGINIA MENTAL HEALTH INSTITUTE (494017)**, 382 Taylor
Drive, Zip 24541–4023; tel. 434/799–6220 **A**1 9 10 **F**34 50 57 68 75 77 86
87 98 100 101 102 106 130 132 146 **P**6 **S** Virginia Department of Mental
Health, Richmond, VA
Primary Contact: William Cook, Director
CFO: Wayne Peters, Administrator
CMO: Pravin Patel, M.D., Acting President and Chief Executive Officer
CIO: Larry Hays, Director Information Technology
CHR: Stephanie Haywood, Director Human Resources
CNO: Kathy M. Dodd, Director of Nursing
Web address: www.svmhi.dbhds.virginia.gov
**Control:** State–Government, nonfederal **Service:** Psychiatric

**Staffed Beds:** 72 **Admissions:** 310 **Census:** 67 **Outpatient Visits:** 0 **Births:**
0

## EMPORIA—Emporia City County

✠ **SOUTHERN VIRGINIA REGIONAL MEDICAL CENTER (490097)**, 727 North
Main Street, Zip 23847–1274; tel. 434/348–4400 **A**1 9 10 **F**3 11 15 26 28 29
30 31 39 40 45 49 57 59 62 64 70 77 78 79 81 82 85 89 93 98 103 107
115 119 124 129 130 133 146 148 **S** Community Health Systems, Inc.,
Franklin, TN
Primary Contact: Matt Tavenner, Chief Executive Officer
CMO: Fitzgerald Marcelin, M.D., Chief of Staff
CIO: Willie Gaines, Director Management Information Systems
CHR: Becky Parrish, Director Human Resources
CNO: Linda Burnette, R.N., Chief Nursing Officer
Web address: www.svrmc.com
**Control:** Corporation, Investor–owned, for–profit **Service:** General Medical and
Surgical

**Staffed Beds:** 80 **Admissions:** 1833 **Census:** 24 **Outpatient Visits:** 23605
**Births:** 0 **Total Expense ($000):** 32456 **Payroll Expense ($000):** 11578
**Personnel:** 245

## FAIRFAX—Fairfax County

✠ **INOVA FAIR OAKS HOSPITAL (490101)**, 3600 Joseph Siewick Drive,
Zip 22033–1798; tel. 703/391–3600 **A**1 2 3 5 9 10 **F**3 11 12 13 14 15 18 29
30 31 32 34 35 37 38 39 40 44 45 46 47 48 50 51 54 55 57 59 60 61 63
64 65 66 68 69 70 72 74 75 76 77 78 79 80 81 82 84 85 86 87 89 91 92
93 100 101 102 107 108 110 111 114 115 118 119 120 121 123 126 129
130 131 132 135 145 146 147 148 **S** Inova Health System, Falls Church, VA
Primary Contact: John L. Fitzgerald, Chief Executive Officer
CFO: Jerry Seager, Assistant Vice President and Chief Financial Officer
CMO: G. Michael Lynch, M.D., Chief Medical Officer
CIO: Geoffrey Brown, Chief Information Officer
CHR: Jeanne Robinson, Director Human Resources
CNO: Cheri Goll, MSN, Chief Nursing Officer
Web address: www.inova.org
**Control:** Other not–for–profit (including NFP Corporation) **Service:** General
Medical and Surgical

**Staffed Beds:** 196 **Admissions:** 13748 **Census:** 127 **Outpatient Visits:**
107077 **Births:** 3829 **Total Expense ($000):** 223508 **Payroll Expense
($000):** 69144 **Personnel:** 945

## FALLS CHURCH—Fairfax County

✠ **DOMINION HOSPITAL (494023)**, 2960 Sleepy Hollow Road, Zip 22044–2030;
tel. 703/536–2000 **A**1 9 10 **F**99 100 101 102 104 105 130 **S** HCA,
Nashville, TN
Primary Contact: C. Alan Eaks, Chief Executive Officer
CFO: Edward R. Stojakovich, Chief Financial Officer
CMO: Gary Litovitz, M.D., Medical Director
CIO: Leslie Gilliam, Director Health Information Management
CHR: Lesley Channell, Vice President Human Resources
CNO: Teresa Brooke, Chief Nursing Officer
Web address: www.dominionhospital.com
**Control:** Corporation, Investor–owned, for–profit **Service:** Psychiatric

**Staffed Beds:** 100 **Admissions:** 3201 **Census:** 78 **Outpatient Visits:** 575
**Births:** 0

✠ **INOVA FAIRFAX HOSPITAL (490063)**, 3300 Gallows Road, Zip 22042–3300;
tel. 703/776–4001, (Includes INOVA FAIRFAX HOSPITAL FOR CHILDREN, 3300
Gallows Road, Zip 22042–3307; tel. 703/776–4002) **A**1 2 3 5 8 9 10 **F**3 4 5 6
8 9 11 12 13 14 15 17 18 19 20 21 22 23 24 25 26 27 28 34 36 39 40 41
42 43 44 45 46 47 48 49 50 51 54 55 56 57 58 59 60 61 63 64 65 66 68
69 70 71 72 74 75 76 77 78 79 80 81 82 83 84 85 86 87 88 89 91 92 93
94 96 97 98 99 100 101 102 103 104 105 107 108 109 110 111 114 115
118 119 120 121 123 124 126 129 130 131 132 134 135 136 137 138 140
141 142 145 146 147 148 **P**6 **S** Inova Health System, Falls Church, VA
Primary Contact: Patrick Christiansen, Ph.D., Chief Executive Officer
COO: Maureen Swick, R.N., Senior Vice President, Chief Operating Officer
CFO: Ronald Ewald, Chief Financial Officer
CMO: Joseph Hallal, M.D., Chief Medical Officer
CIO: Geoffrey Brown, Vice President Information Systems
CHR: Ken Hull, Director Human Resources
Web address: www.inova.org
**Control:** Other not–for–profit (including NFP Corporation) **Service:** General
Medical and Surgical

**Staffed Beds:** 926 **Admissions:** 45197 **Census:** 649 **Outpatient Visits:**
284606 **Births:** 8543 **Total Expense ($000):** 1182421 **Payroll Expense
($000):** 417692 **Personnel:** 5127

☐ **NORTHERN VIRGINIA MENTAL HEALTH INSTITUTE (494010)**, 3302 Gallows
Road, Zip 22042–3398; tel. 703/207–7110 **A**1 3 5 9 10 **F**29 30 98 101 130
132 **S** Virginia Department of Mental Health, Richmond, VA
Primary Contact: James R. Newton, Facility Director
CFO: John Poffenbarger, Director Fiscal Services
CMO: R. Maximilien del Rio, M.D., Medical Director
CHR: Cynthia Lott, Director Human Resources
Web address: www.nvmhi.dmhmrsas.virginia.gov
**Control:** State–Government, nonfederal **Service:** Psychiatric

**Staffed Beds:** 134 **Admissions:** 822 **Census:** 128 **Outpatient Visits:** 0
**Births:** 0 **Total Expense ($000):** 29979 **Payroll Expense ($000):** 16304
**Personnel:** 310

## FARMVILLE—Prince Edward County

✠ **CENTRA SOUTHSIDE COMMUNITY HOSPITAL (490090)**, 800 Oak Street,
Zip 23901–1199; tel. 434/392–8811 **A**1 5 9 10 20 **F**3 11 13 15 28 29 30 34
35 40 44 45 49 50 57 59 62 64 70 74 75 76 77 79 81 85 86 87 89 93 107
108 110 111 115 118 119 129 130 132 133 146 147 148 **P**6 **S** Centra
Health, Inc., Lynchburg, VA
Primary Contact: Thomas Angelo, Chief Executive Officer
Web address: www.sch.centrahealth.com/
**Control:** Other not–for–profit (including NFP Corporation) **Service:** General
Medical and Surgical

**Staffed Beds:** 86 **Admissions:** 3841 **Census:** 32 **Outpatient Visits:** 119839
**Births:** 443 **Total Expense ($000):** 69091 **Payroll Expense ($000):** 32524
**Personnel:** 438

**SOUTHSIDE COMMUNITY HOSPITAL** See Centra Southside Community Hospital

## FISHERSVILLE—Augusta County

✠ **AUGUSTA HEALTH (490018)**, 78 Medical Center Drive, Zip 22939–2332,
Mailing Address: P.O. Box 1000, Zip 22939–1000; tel. 540/932–4000 **A**1 2 3 9
10 **F**3 5 7 11 13 15 18 20 22 26 28 29 30 31 34 35 36 39 40 45 46 48 49
50 51 53 54 56 57 58 59 61 62 63 64 65 66 68 70 74 75 76 77 78 79 81
82 84 85 86 87 89 90 91 92 93 96 97 98 100 101 102 103 104 107 108
110 111 114 115 118 119 120 121 123 128 129 130 131 132 135 144 145
146 147 148 **P**6
Primary Contact: Mary N. Mannix, FACHE, President and Chief Executive Officer
CFO: John R. Heider, Vice President Finance
CMO: Fred Castello, M.D., Chief Medical Officer
CIO: Velma Carroll, Chief Information Officer
CHR: Sue Krzastek, Vice President Human Resources
Web address: www.augustahealth.com
**Control:** Other not–for–profit (including NFP Corporation) **Service:** General
Medical and Surgical

**Staffed Beds:** 224 **Admissions:** 10999 **Census:** 120 **Outpatient Visits:**
650875 **Births:** 1145 **Total Expense ($000):** 270132 **Payroll Expense
($000):** 116634 **Personnel:** 1887

**VA**

**WOODROW WILSON REHABILITATION CENTER**, 243 Woodrow Wilson Avenue, Zip 22939, Mailing Address: P.O. Box 1500, Zip 22939–1500; tel. 540/332–7000, (Nonreporting)
Primary Contact: Richard Luck, Ed.D., Facility Director
COO: Richard Luck, Ed.D., Facility Director
CFO: Ernie Steidle, Chief Operating Officer
CMO: Mammen Mathew, M.D., Chief Rehabilitation Medicine
CIO: Keith Burt, Director Marketing
CHR: Debbie Mitchell, Director Human Resources
Web address: www.wwrc.net
**Control:** State–Government, nonfederal **Service:** Rehabilitation

| Staffed Beds: 30 |
|---|

### FORT BELVOIR—Fairfax County

⊞ **FORT BELVOIR COMMUNITY HOSPITAL**, 9300 Dewitt Loop, Zip 22060–5285; tel. 571/231–3224, (Nonreporting) **A**1 3 5 9 **S** Department of the Army, Office of the Surgeon General, Falls Church, VA
Primary Contact: Captain Jennifer Vedral–Baron, Commander
CMO: Lieutenant Colonel Mark D. Harris, Deputy Commander Clinical Services
CIO: Terrance Branch, Chief Information Management
Web address: www.fbch.capmed.mil/SitePages/Home.aspx
**Control:** Army, Government, federal **Service:** General Medical and Surgical

| Staffed Beds: 46 |
|---|

### FRANKLIN—Franklin City County

⊞ **SOUTHAMPTON MEMORIAL HOSPITAL (490092)**, 100 Fairview Drive, Zip 23851–1238, Mailing Address: P.O. Box 817, Zip 23851–0817; tel. 757/569–6100, (Nonreporting) **A**1 9 10 20 **S** Community Health Systems, Inc., Franklin, TN
Primary Contact: Kimberly W. Marks, Interim Chief Executive Officer
CFO: Steve Ramey, Chief Financial Officer
CMO: Donald Bowling, M.D., Chief Medical Staff
CIO: Kristie Howell, System Information Technology Director
CHR: Kimberly W. Marks, Director Human Resources
CNO: Laurie Ross, Chief Nursing Officer
Web address: www.smhfranklin.com
**Control:** Corporation, Investor–owned, for–profit **Service:** General Medical and Surgical

| Staffed Beds: 72 |
|---|

### FREDERICKSBURG—Fredericksburg City County

⊞ **HEALTHSOUTH REHABILITATION HOSPITAL OF FREDERICKSBURG (493032)**, 300 Park Hill Drive, Zip 22401–3387; tel. 540/368–7300, (Nonreporting) **A**1 10 **S** HEALTHSOUTH Corporation, Birmingham, AL
Primary Contact: Gary J. Herbek, Chief Executive Officer
Web address: www.fredericksburgrehabhospital.com
**Control:** Corporation, Investor–owned, for–profit **Service:** Rehabilitation

| Staffed Beds: 40 |
|---|

⊞ **MARY WASHINGTON HOSPITAL (490022)**, 1001 Sam Perry Boulevard, Zip 22401–3354; tel. 540/741–1100 **A**1 2 3 9 10 **F**3 5 13 15 18 20 22 24 26 28 29 30 31 34 35 40 42 43 44 45 46 47 48 49 50 54 55 57 58 59 62 64 70 72 74 75 76 77 78 79 81 83 84 85 86 87 89 92 93 96 98 99 100 101 102 104 105 107 108 111 114 115 118 119 120 121 122 124 126 129 130 132 146 147 148 **P**8 **S** Mary Washington Healthcare, Fredericksburg, VA
Primary Contact: Michael McDermott, M.D., President and Chief Executive Officer
CFO: Sean Barden, Executive Vice President and Chief Financial Officer
CMO: Rebecca Bigoney, M.D., Executive Vice President and Chief Medical Officer
CIO: Joyce Hanscome, Senior Vice President and Chief Information Officer
CHR: Kathryn S. Wall, Executive Vice President Human Resources and Organizational Development
CNO: Eileen L. Dohmann, R.N., Senior Vice President and Chief Nursing Officer
Web address: www.marywashingtonhealthcare.com
**Control:** Other not–for–profit (including NFP Corporation) **Service:** General Medical and Surgical

| Staffed Beds: 437 Admissions: 22564 Census: 288 Outpatient Visits: 323897 Births: 2942 Total Expense ($000): 390905 Payroll Expense ($000): 134580 Personnel: 1746 |
|---|

**SNOWDEN AT FREDERICKSBURG**, 1200 Sam Perry Boulevard, Zip 22401–4456; tel. 540/741–3900, (Nonreporting) **A**9
Primary Contact: Charles Scercy, Corporate Director
Web address: www.marywashingtonhealthcare.com/locations/snowden–at–fredericksburg
**Control:** Other not–for–profit (including NFP Corporation) **Service:** Psychiatric

| Staffed Beds: 30 |
|---|

⊞ **SPOTSYLVANIA REGIONAL MEDICAL CENTER (490141)**, 4600 Spotsylvania Parkway, Zip 22408–7762; tel. 540/498–4000, (Nonreporting) **A**1 9 10 **S** HCA, Nashville, TN
Primary Contact: Greg T. Madsen, Chief Executive Officer
COO: Roberta Barton–Joe, Chief Operations Officer
CFO: Michael Sean Thomson, CPA, Chief Financial Officer
CNO: Teresa L. Collins, Chief Nursing Officer
Web address: www.spotsrmc.com
**Control:** Corporation, Investor–owned, for–profit **Service:** General Medical and Surgical

| Staffed Beds: 100 |
|---|

### FRONT ROYAL—Warren County

⊞ **WARREN MEMORIAL HOSPITAL (490033)**, 1000 North Shenandoah Avenue, Zip 22630–3598; tel. 540/636–0300, (Total facility includes 120 beds in nursing home–type unit) **A**1 3 9 10 13 **F**3 11 13 15 28 29 30 34 35 36 40 50 53 54 56 57 59 64 65 67 70 75 76 77 79 81 82 85 86 87 93 96 107 108 111 114 118 119 128 130 132 135 144 146 147 148 **P**6 **S** Valley Health System, Winchester, VA
Primary Contact: Floyd Heater, Interim President and Chief Executive Officer
CFO: Phillip Graybeal, Chief Financial Officer
CMO: Robert Meltvedt, Jr., M.D., Vice President Medical Affairs
Web address: www.valleyhealthlink.com/WMH
**Control:** Other not–for–profit (including NFP Corporation) **Service:** General Medical and Surgical

| Staffed Beds: 166 Admissions: 2578 Census: 136 Outpatient Visits: 56041 Births: 275 Total Expense ($000): 53999 Payroll Expense ($000): 24788 Personnel: 461 |
|---|

### GALAX—Galax City County

⊞ **TWIN COUNTY REGIONAL HEALTHCARE (490115)**, 200 Hospital Drive, Zip 24333–2227; tel. 276/236–8181, (Nonreporting) **A**1 9 10 20 **S** Duke LifePoint Healthcare, Brentwood, TN
Primary Contact: Jon D. Applebaum, Chief Executive Officer
CFO: Michael Widener, Chief Financial Officer
CIO: Jack Roberts, Director Information Systems
CHR: Kristal Harrington, Director Human Resources
CNO: Agnes A. Smith, R.N., Chief Nursing Officer
Web address: www.tcrh.org
**Control:** Other not–for–profit (including NFP Corporation) **Service:** General Medical and Surgical

| Staffed Beds: 141 |
|---|

### GLOUCESTER—Gloucester County

⊞ **RIVERSIDE WALTER REED HOSPITAL (490130)**, 7519 Hospital Drive, Zip 23061–4178, Mailing Address: P.O. Box 1130, Zip 23061–1130; tel. 804/693–8800, (Nonreporting) **A**1 2 3 9 10 **S** Riverside Health System, Newport News, VA
Primary Contact: Megan Kleckner, Vice President and Administrator
CHR: Kent Taylor, Director Human Resources
Web address: www.riversideonline.com
**Control:** Other not–for–profit (including NFP Corporation) **Service:** General Medical and Surgical

| Staffed Beds: 32 |
|---|

### GRUNDY—Buchanan County

⊞ **BUCHANAN GENERAL HOSPITAL (490127)**, 1535 Slate Creek Road, Zip 24614–6974; tel. 276/935–1000 **A**1 9 10 20 **F**3 15 18 28 29 30 34 35 40 41 45 57 59 62 64 70 81 82 85 87 89 93 107 108 110 115 119 130 132 135 146
Primary Contact: Robert D. Ruchti, Chief Executive Officer
COO: Scott M. Pittman, Chief Operating Officer
CFO: Kim Boyd, Chief Financial Officer
CIO: Rita Ramey, Director Information Systems
CHR: Wanda Stiltner, Director Human Resources
CNO: Patty Dorton, Director of Nursing
Web address: www.bgh.org
**Control:** Other not–for–profit (including NFP Corporation) **Service:** General Medical and Surgical

| Staffed Beds: 49 Admissions: 1260 Census: 14 Outpatient Visits: 42703 Births: 0 Total Expense ($000): 22358 Payroll Expense ($000): 8867 Personnel: 216 |
|---|

**VA**

---

**Hospital, Medicare Provider Number, Address, Telephone, Approval, Facility, and Physician Codes, Health Care System**

★ American Hospital Association (AHA) membership    ○ Healthcare Facilities Accreditation Program    ⇑ Center for Improvement in Healthcare Quality Accreditation
☐ The Joint Commission accreditation    ◇ DNV Healthcare Inc. accreditation    △ Commission on Accreditation of Rehabilitation Facilities (CARF) accreditation

## HAMPTON—Hampton City County

☒ **HAMPTON VETERANS AFFAIRS MEDICAL CENTER**, 100 Emancipation Drive, Zip 23667–0001; tel. 757/722–9961, (Nonreporting) **A**1 3 5 **S** Department of Veterans Affairs, Washington, DC
Primary Contact: Michael H. Dunfee, Director
COO: Lorraine B. Price, Associate Director
CFO: Terry Grew, Chief Business Office
CMO: Val Gibberman, M.D., Acting Chief of Staff
CIO: Cary Parks, Chief Information Resource Management
Web address: www.hampton.va.gov/
**Control:** Veterans Affairs, Government, federal **Service:** General Medical and Surgical

**Staffed Beds:** 468

☐ **RIVERSIDE BEHAVIORAL HEALTH CENTER (494001)**, 2244 Executive Drive, Zip 23666–2430; tel. 757/827–1001, (Nonreporting) **A**1 5 9 10 **S** Riverside Health System, Newport News, VA
Primary Contact: Debra Campbell, R.N., Administrator
COO: Wade Broughman, Chief Operating Officer
CFO: W. William Austin, Jr., Senior Vice President Finance
CMO: Gary Starkey, M.D., Medical Director
CHR: Ashleigh Andrews, Director Human Resources
CNO: Terris Kennedy, Ph.D., Chief Nursing Officer
Web address: www.riversideonline.com
**Control:** Other not–for–profit (including NFP Corporation) **Service:** Psychiatric

**Staffed Beds:** 79

★ ◇ **SENTARA CAREPLEX HOSPITAL (490093)**, 3000 Coliseum Drive, Zip 23666–5963; tel. 757/736–1000 **A**2 3 5 9 10 21 **F**3 8 11 12 15 18 20 22 26 28 29 30 31 34 35 36 37 39 40 41 42 44 45 47 49 50 54 57 58 59 60 61 64 65 68 70 74 75 77 78 79 80 81 82 83 84 85 86 87 91 92 93 94 96 97 100 107 108 110 111 114 118 119 120 121 123 126 129 130 131 132 144 146 147 148 **P**6 **S** Sentara Healthcare, Norfolk, VA
Primary Contact: Debra A. Flores, R.N., MS, President and Administrator
COO: Chet Hart, Vice President Operations
CFO: Cheryl Larner, Chief Financial Officer
CMO: Arthur Greene, M.D., Vice President Medical Affairs
CIO: Thomas Ewing, Director Information Technology
CHR: David Kidd, Manager Human Resources
Web address: www.sentara.com
**Control:** Other not–for–profit (including NFP Corporation) **Service:** General Medical and Surgical

**Staffed Beds:** 136 **Admissions:** 8624 **Census:** 117 **Outpatient Visits:** 441741 **Births:** 0 **Total Expense ($000):** 203268 **Payroll Expense ($000):** 80320 **Personnel:** 1136

☒ **U. S. AIR FORCE HOSPITAL**, 77 Nealy Avenue, Zip 23665–2040; tel. 757/764–6969, (Nonreporting) **A**1 **S** Department of the Air Force, Washington, DC
Primary Contact: Colonel Wayne M. Pritt, Commander
COO: Colonel Michael Dietz, Administrator
CFO: Major Steven Dadd, Flight Commander Resource Management
CMO: Colonel Paul Gourley, M.D., Chief Hospital Services
CIO: Major Merlinda Vergonio, Chief Information Management and Technology
CHR: Major Steven Dadd, Flight Commander Resource Management
CNO: Colonel Marlene Kerchenski, Chief Nurse
Web address: www.jble.af.mil
**Control:** Air Force, Government, federal **Service:** General Medical and Surgical

**Staffed Beds:** 65

## HARRISONBURG—Harrisonburg City County

★ ◇ **SENTARA RMH MEDICAL CENTER (490004)**, 2010 Health Campus Drive, Zip 22801–3293; tel. 540/689–1000 **A**2 5 9 10 21 **F**3 5 8 11 12 13 15 17 18 20 22 24 26 28 29 30 31 32 34 35 36 40 44 45 49 50 53 54 55 56 57 59 62 63 64 68 70 71 73 74 77 78 79 81 82 84 85 86 87 93 97 98 99 102 104 105 107 108 110 111 114 115 118 119 120 121 129 130 131 132 135 145 146 147 148 **P**6 8 **S** Sentara Healthcare, Norfolk, VA
Primary Contact: James D. Krauss, President
COO: Richard L. Haushalter, Senior Vice President Operations and Chief Operating Officer
CFO: J. Michael Burris, Chief Financial Officer
CMO: Dale Carroll, M.D., Senior Vice President Medical Affairs and Performance Improvement
CIO: Mike Rozmus, Director Information Systems
CNO: Donna S. Hahn, R.N., Vice President Acute Care and Chief Nurse Executive
Web address: www.rmhonline.com
**Control:** Other not–for–profit (including NFP Corporation) **Service:** General Medical and Surgical

**Staffed Beds:** 244 **Admissions:** 12786 **Census:** 131 **Outpatient Visits:** 413745 **Births:** 1748 **Total Expense ($000):** 348186 **Payroll Expense ($000):** 146434 **Personnel:** 2074

## HAYMARKET—Prince William County

☒ **NOVANT HEALTH HAYMARKET MEDICAL CENTER (490144)**, 15225 Heathcote Boulevard, Zip 20155–4023, Mailing Address: 14535 John Marshall Highway, Gainesville, Zip 20155–4023; tel. 571/284–1000, (Data for 281 days) **A**1 10 **F**3 11 13 14 15 18 29 30 34 35 37 40 44 45 47 49 50 56 57 58 59 60 63 64 70 71 74 75 76 78 79 81 84 85 87 89 93 107 110 111 119 130 131 132 135 146 147 148 **P**6 **S** Novant Health, Winston Salem, NC
Primary Contact: Don Sedgley, President
CNO: Jason Jenkins, Senior Director of Nursing
Web address: www.novanthealth.org
**Control:** Other not–for–profit (including NFP Corporation) **Service:** General Medical and Surgical

**Staffed Beds:** 14 **Admissions:** 1380 **Census:** 14 **Outpatient Visits:** 85377 **Births:** 356 **Total Expense ($000):** 39057 **Payroll Expense ($000):** 16492 **Personnel:** 269

## HOPEWELL—Hopewell City County

☒ **JOHN RANDOLPH MEDICAL CENTER (490020)**, 411 West Randolph Road, Zip 23860–2938; tel. 804/541–1600 **A**1 2 9 10 **F**3 5 11 15 17 18 20 28 29 30 31 34 38 40 44 45 49 50 54 57 59 61 63 64 70 74 75 77 78 79 81 85 86 87 92 93 96 98 100 101 102 103 105 107 108 110 111 114 115 118 119 130 131 132 135 144 146 148 **S** HCA, Nashville, TN
Primary Contact: Suzanne B. Jackson, FACHE, Chief Executive Officer
CFO: Chigger Bynum, Chief Financial Officer
CHR: MaDena DuChemin, Assistant Administrator Human Resources
Web address: www.johnrandolphmed.com
**Control:** Corporation, Investor–owned, for–profit **Service:** General Medical and Surgical

**Staffed Beds:** 112 **Admissions:** 4885 **Census:** 69 **Outpatient Visits:** 68956 **Births:** 0 **Personnel:** 457

## HOT SPRINGS—Bath County

☒ **BATH COMMUNITY HOSPITAL (491300)**, 83 Park Drive, Zip 24445–2788, Mailing Address: P.O. Box Z, Zip 24445–0750; tel. 540/839–7000 **A**1 9 10 18 **F**3 7 8 15 34 35 40 49 50 59 64 71 75 77 79 81 85 89 90 93 107 110 111 119 120 127 128 129 130 133
Primary Contact: Kathy Landreth, Interim Chief Executive Officer
COO: Mitzi Grey, Chief Operating Officer
CMO: James Redington, M.D., Chief of Staff
CIO: Tracy Bartley, Manager Information Technology
CHR: Patricia Foutz, Director Human Resources
CNO: Kyna Moore, R.N., Director of Nursing
Web address: www.bcchospital.org
**Control:** Other not–for–profit (including NFP Corporation) **Service:** General Medical and Surgical

**Staffed Beds:** 25 **Admissions:** 378 **Census:** 6 **Outpatient Visits:** 18832 **Births:** 2 **Total Expense ($000):** 19478 **Payroll Expense ($000):** 8462 **Personnel:** 127

## KILMARNOCK—Lancaster County

☒ **RAPPAHANNOCK GENERAL HOSPITAL (490123)**, 101 Harris Drive, Zip 22482–3880, Mailing Address: P.O. Box 1449, Zip 22482–1449; tel. 804/435–8000, (Nonreporting) **A**1 9 10 20 **S** Bon Secours Health System, Inc., Marriottsville, MD
Primary Contact: James M. Holmes, Jr., President and Chief Executive Officer
Web address: www.rgh–hospital.com
**Control:** Other not–for–profit (including NFP Corporation) **Service:** General Medical and Surgical

**Staffed Beds:** 76

## LEBANON—Russell County

☐ **RUSSELL COUNTY MEDICAL CENTER (490002)**, 58 Carroll Street, Zip 24266, Mailing Address: P.O. Box 3600, Zip 24266–0200; tel. 276/883–8000 **A**1 9 10 **F**3 11 15 29 30 34 35 40 44 45 50 56 57 59 62 63 64 68 70 75 81 85 87 93 98 99 100 101 102 103 104 107 108 110 111 114 118 119 127 129 130 133 146 147 148 **P**6 8 **S** Mountain States Health Alliance, Johnson City, TN
Primary Contact: Stephen K. Givens, Assistant Vice President and Administrator
CFO: John Jeter, Chief Financial Officer
CMO: Brian Condit, Vice President Chief Medical Officer, Virginia Operations Medical Staff Services
CHR: Beth Hill, Director Human Resources
CNO: Melanie Paige Horton, Chief Nursing Officer
Web address: www.msha.com/rcmc
**Control:** Other not–for–profit (including NFP Corporation) **Service:** General Medical and Surgical

**Staffed Beds:** 78 **Admissions:** 2122 **Census:** 27 **Outpatient Visits:** 27885 **Births:** 0 **Total Expense ($000):** 15030 **Payroll Expense ($000):** 8684 **Personnel:** 173

**VA**

*Many Facility Codes have changed. Please refer to the AHA Guide Code Chart.* © 2015 AHA Guide

**LEESBURG—Loudoun County**

⊞ **INOVA LOUDOUN HOSPITAL (490043)**, 44045 Riverside Parkway, Zip 20176–5101, Mailing Address: P.O. Box 6000, Zip 20177–0600; tel. 703/858–6000, (Total facility includes 100 beds in nursing home–type unit) **A**1 2 5 9 10 **F**3 5 11 13 14 15 18 20 22 26 28 29 30 31 34 35 37 38 39 40 41 42 44 45 48 49 50 54 55 57 59 60 61 63 64 65 66 67 68 69 70 71 72 74 75 76 77 78 79 80 81 82 84 85 86 87 89 91 92 93 96 98 100 101 102 103 104 105 107 108 110 111 114 115 118 119 120 121 123 126 128 130 131 132 135 145 146 147 148 **P**6 **S** Inova Health System, Falls Church, VA
Primary Contact: Patrick Walters, Chief Executive Officer
CFO: William Bane, Chief Financial Officer
CMO: Christopher Chiantella, M.D., Chief Medical Officer
CHR: Sarah Pavik, Director Human Resources and Guest Services
CNO: Elizabeth Dugan, Ph.D., Chief Nursing Officer
Web address: www.inova.org
**Control:** Other not–for–profit (including NFP Corporation) **Service:** General Medical and Surgical

> **Staffed Beds:** 286 **Admissions:** 12145 **Census:** 216 **Outpatient Visits:** 133177 **Births:** 2560 **Total Expense ($000):** 226604 **Payroll Expense ($000):** 78241 **Personnel:** 1366

**LEXINGTON—Lexington City County**

⊞ **CARILION STONEWALL JACKSON HOSPITAL (491304)**, 1 Health Circle, Zip 24450–2492; tel. 540/458–3300 **A**1 9 10 18 **F**3 8 11 15 18 19 28 29 34 35 40 42 45 50 53 56 57 59 65 70 75 77 79 81 85 87 91 93 97 107 108 110 111 115 119 129 130 131 132 133 135 146 148 **S** Carilion Clinic, Roanoke, VA
Primary Contact: Charles E. Carr, Vice President and Administrator
CMO: Lyle McClung, M.D., Chief of Staff
Web address: www.carilionclinic.org/Carilion/csjh
**Control:** Other not–for–profit (including NFP Corporation) **Service:** General Medical and Surgical

> **Staffed Beds:** 13 **Admissions:** 1200 **Census:** 14 **Outpatient Visits:** 29140 **Births:** 0 **Total Expense ($000):** 25867 **Payroll Expense ($000):** 9084 **Personnel:** 174

**LOW MOOR—Alleghany County**

⊞ **LEWISGALE HOSPITAL ALLEGHANY (490126)**, One ARH Lane, Zip 24457, Mailing Address: P.O. Box 7, Zip 24457–0007; tel. 540/862–6011, (Nonreporting) **A**1 9 10 20 **S** HCA, Nashville, TN
Primary Contact: Charlotte C. Tyson, Chief Executive Officer
CMO: Michele Ballou, M.D., Chief Medical Staff
CIO: Jeffrey Steelman, Director Information Systems
CHR: Bernard M. Campbell, Administrator Human Resources
CNO: Robin Broughman, R.N., Chief Nursing Officer
Web address: www.alleghanyregional.com
**Control:** Corporation, Investor–owned, for–profit **Service:** General Medical and Surgical

> **Staffed Beds:** 146

**LURAY—Page County**

⊞ **PAGE MEMORIAL HOSPITAL (491307)**, 200 Memorial Drive, Zip 22835–1005; tel. 540/743–4561 **A**1 9 10 18 **F**3 7 8 11 15 28 29 30 34 35 40 43 53 56 57 59 60 64 66 68 74 75 77 79 81 85 90 93 107 108 110 111 114 119 127 128 129 130 133 135 143 146 **P**2 **S** Valley Health System, Winchester, VA
Primary Contact: N. Travis Clark, President
CFO: Phillip Graybeal, Chief Financial Officer
Web address: www.valleyhealthlink.com/page
**Control:** Other not–for–profit (including NFP Corporation) **Service:** General Medical and Surgical

> **Staffed Beds:** 25 **Admissions:** 706 **Census:** 13 **Outpatient Visits:** 76841 **Births:** 0 **Total Expense ($000):** 25968 **Payroll Expense ($000):** 11876 **Personnel:** 178

**LYNCHBURG—Lynchburg City County**

**CENTER FOR RESTORATIVE CARE AND REHABILITATION (492010)**, 3300 Rivermont Avenue, Zip 24503–2030; tel. 434/200–1799 **A**10 **F**1 3 29 31 68 75 82 85 100 130 148 **P**6
Primary Contact: Kay Bowling, Chief Executive Officer
**Control:** Other not–for–profit (including NFP Corporation) **Service:** Long–Term Acute Care hospital

> **Staffed Beds:** 36 **Admissions:** 294 **Census:** 22 **Outpatient Visits:** 0 **Births:** 0 **Total Expense ($000):** 9383 **Payroll Expense ($000):** 3988 **Personnel:** 67

**CENTRA HEALTH** See Centra Lynchburg General Hospital

☐ **CENTRA LYNCHBURG GENERAL HOSPITAL (490021)**, 1920 Atherholt Road, Zip 24501–1104; tel. 434/200–4700, (Includes CENTRA VIRGINIA BAPTIST HOSPITAL, 3300 Rivermont Avenue, Zip 24503–2053; tel. 434/200–4000; LYNCHBURG GENERAL HOSPITAL, 1901 Tate Springs Road, Zip 24501–1167; tel. 434/200–3000), (Total facility includes 544 beds in nursing home–type unit) **A**1 2 3 5 6 9 10 20 **F**1 2 3 5 7 10 11 13 15 17 18 19 20 22 24 26 28 29 30 31 32 34 35 37 38 40 42 43 44 45 46 47 48 49 50 53 54 55 56 57 59 60 61 62 63 64 67 68 70 71 72 73 74 75 76 77 78 79 80 81 82 84 85 86 87 89 90 93 94 96 98 99 100 101 102 103 104 105 106 107 108 110 111 115 119 120 125 126 127 128 129 130 131 132 133 135 143 144 146 147 148 **P**7 **S** Centra Health, Inc., Lynchburg, VA
Primary Contact: E. W. Tibbs, President and Chief Executive Officer
CFO: Lewis C. Addison, Senior Vice President and Chief Financial Officer
CMO: Chalmers Nunn, M.D., Chief Medical Officer and Senior Vice President
CIO: Ben Clark, Vice President and Chief Information Officer
CHR: Jan Walker, Director Human Resources
Web address: www.centrahealth.com
**Control:** Other not–for–profit (including NFP Corporation) **Service:** General Medical and Surgical

> **Staffed Beds:** 1206 **Admissions:** 29789 **Census:** 812 **Outpatient Visits:** 547870 **Births:** 2540 **Total Expense ($000):** 654087 **Payroll Expense ($000):** 297509 **Personnel:** 4932

**MADISON HEIGHTS—Amherst County**

**CENTRAL VIRGINIA TRAINING CENTER (490108)**, 210 East Colony Road, Zip 24572–2005, Mailing Address: P.O. Box 1098, Lynchburg, Zip 24505–1098; tel. 434/947–6326, (Nonreporting) **A**10 **S** Virginia Department of Mental Health, Richmond, VA
Primary Contact: Denise D. Micheletti, R.N., Director
COO: Denise D. Micheletti, R.N., Director
CFO: Charles Felmlee, Assistant Director Fiscal Services
CMO: Balraj Bawa, M.D., Assistant Director Medical Services
CHR: Burchkhard Blob, Manager Human Resources
Web address: www.cvtc.dmhmrsas.virginia.gov/
**Control:** State–Government, nonfederal **Service:** Intellectual disabilites

> **Staffed Beds:** 1112

**MANASSAS—Manassas City County**

⊞ **NOVANT HEALTH PRINCE WILLIAM MEDICAL CENTER (490045)**, 8700 Sudley Road, Zip 20110–4418, Mailing Address: P.O. Box 2610, Zip 20108–0867; tel. 703/369–8000 **A**1 2 3 9 10 **F**3 5 8 10 11 13 15 18 19 20 22 26 28 29 30 31 32 34 35 36 37 38 39 40 44 45 46 47 48 49 50 51 53 54 57 59 64 65 68 70 71 72 74 75 76 77 78 79 81 82 84 85 86 87 89 93 97 98 99 100 101 102 103 104 107 108 110 111 114 115 116 117 118 119 120 121 123 126 129 130 131 132 134 135 146 147 148 **P**6 **S** Novant Health, Winston Salem, NC
Primary Contact: Melissa Robson, President
COO: Bebe Holt, Vice President Chief Operating Officer
CMO: Doug Wall, M.D., Vice President Medical Affairs
CHR: Tracy Bowers, Director Human Resources
CNO: Bebe Holt, Vice President and Chief Nursing Officer
Web address: www.pwhs.org
**Control:** Other not–for–profit (including NFP Corporation) **Service:** General Medical and Surgical

> **Staffed Beds:** 93 **Admissions:** 8202 **Census:** 85 **Outpatient Visits:** 272799 **Births:** 1687 **Total Expense ($000):** 158475 **Payroll Expense ($000):** 60465 **Personnel:** 804

**MARION—Smyth County**

☐ **SMYTH COUNTY COMMUNITY HOSPITAL (490038)**, 245 Medical Park Drive, Zip 24354, Mailing Address: P.O. Box 880, Zip 24354–0880; tel. 276/378–1000, (Total facility includes 109 beds in nursing home–type unit) **A**1 9 10 **F**2 3 11 15 18 28 29 30 31 34 35 40 45 50 51 54 57 59 62 64 67 68 70 75 77 78 79 81 85 87 90 93 97 107 110 111 115 118 119 128 129 130 131 132 133 135 146 147 148 **P**6 8 **S** Mountain States Health Alliance, Johnson City, TN
Primary Contact: James E. Tyler, Vice President and Hospital Chief Executive Officer
CFO: John Jeter, Assistant Vice President and Chief Financial Officer
CHR: Sue Henderson, Human Resource Manager
CNO: Cathy L. Maine, MSN, RN–B, Chief Nursing Officer and Assistant Administrator
Web address: www.msha.com/scch
**Control:** Other not–for–profit (including NFP Corporation) **Service:** General Medical and Surgical

> **Staffed Beds:** 153 **Admissions:** 1942 **Census:** 115 **Outpatient Visits:** 62566 **Births:** 0 **Total Expense ($000):** 43876 **Payroll Expense ($000):** 16536 **Personnel:** 216

**VA**

---

**Hospital, Medicare Provider Number, Address, Telephone, Approval, Facility, and Physician Codes, Health Care System**

★ American Hospital Association (AHA) membership
☐ The Joint Commission accreditation
○ Healthcare Facilities Accreditation Program
◇ DNV Healthcare Inc. accreditation
⇑ Center for Improvement in Healthcare Quality Accreditation
△ Commission on Accreditation of Rehabilitation Facilities (CARF) accreditation

☐ **SOUTHWESTERN VIRGINIA MENTAL HEALTH INSTITUTE (490105)**, 340 Bagley Circle, Zip 24354–3390; tel. 276/783–1200 **A**1 9 10 **F**3 87 98 101 103 130 132 135 143 146 **P**6 **S** Virginia Department of Mental Health, Richmond, VA
Primary Contact: Cynthia McClaskey, Ph.D., Director
CIO: Kim Ratliff, Director Health Information Management
Web address: www.swvmhi.dmhmrsas.virginia.gov/
**Control:** State–Government, nonfederal **Service:** Psychiatric

**Staffed Beds:** 166 **Admissions:** 772 **Census:** 169 **Outpatient Visits:** 0 **Births:** 0

### MARTINSVILLE—Martinsville City County

☒ **MEMORIAL HOSPITAL (490079)**, 320 Hospital Drive, Zip 24112–1981, Mailing Address: P.O. Box 4788, Zip 24115–4788; tel. 276/666–7200, (Nonreporting) **A**1 2 9 10 19 **S** LifePoint Health, Brentwood, TN
Primary Contact: Michael Ehrat, Chief Executive Officer
COO: John Maxwell, Chief Operating Officer
CFO: Brandy Hanners, Chief Financial Officer
CIO: Jeff Butker, Chief Information Officer
CHR: Sherry Schofield, Director Human Resources
CNO: Michael Pittman, Chief Nursing Officer
Web address: www.martinsvillehospital.com
**Control:** Corporation, Investor–owned, for–profit **Service:** General Medical and Surgical

**Staffed Beds:** 220

### MECHANICSVILLE—Hanover County

☒ **BON SECOURS MEMORIAL REGIONAL MEDICAL CENTER (490069)**, 8260 Atlee Road, Zip 23116–1844; tel. 804/764–6000 **A**1 2 3 5 9 10 **F**3 7 8 11 13 15 17 18 20 22 24 26 28 29 30 31 33 34 35 38 40 46 48 49 50 54 57 58 59 60 63 64 65 66 68 70 72 74 75 76 77 78 79 81 84 86 87 100 104 107 108 109 110 111 114 115 119 126 129 130 131 132 133 144 146 147 148 **P**6 **S** Bon Secours Health System, Inc., Marriottsville, MD
Primary Contact: Michael Robinson, Chief Executive Officer
COO: Gary A. Welch, Assistant to the Chief Executive Officer and Administrative Director Support Systems
CFO: Stephan F. Quiriconi, Vice President Finance
CMO: Sunil K. Sinha, M.D., Chief Medical Officer
CIO: Gwen Harding, Site Manager Information Systems
CHR: Rebecca Kamguia, Administrative Director Human Resources
CNO: Jill M. Kennedy, R.N., Vice President Patient Care Services and Chief Nursing Officer
Web address: www.bonsecours.com
**Control:** Other not–for–profit (including NFP Corporation) **Service:** General Medical and Surgical

**Staffed Beds:** 225 **Admissions:** 13896 **Census:** 172 **Outpatient Visits:** 85507 **Births:** 1572 **Total Expense ($000):** 329257 **Payroll Expense ($000):** 99382 **Personnel:** 1557

☒ **SHELTERING ARMS REHABILITATION HOSPITAL (493025)**, 8254 Atlee Road, Zip 23116–1844; tel. 804/764–1000 **A**1 3 10 **F**29 30 34 53 54 57 59 64 68 75 77 79 82 86 87 90 91 92 93 95 96 130 131 132 143 146 148 **P**6
Primary Contact: James E. Sok, FACHE, President and Chief Executive Officer
COO: Mary A. Zweifel, Chief Operating Officer
CFO: Michael E. Dacus, Vice President and Chief Financial Officer
CMO: Hillary Hawkins, M.D., Medical Director
CIO: Chris Sorenson, Chief Information Officer
CHR: Ellen B. Vance, Chief Human Resource Officer
CNO: Sandra Eyler, MS, Chief Nursing Officer
Web address: www.shelteringarms.com
**Control:** Other not–for–profit (including NFP Corporation) **Service:** Rehabilitation

**Staffed Beds:** 40 **Admissions:** 894 **Census:** 36 **Outpatient Visits:** 73534 **Births:** 0 **Total Expense ($000):** 42694 **Payroll Expense ($000):** 25899 **Personnel:** 172

### MIDLOTHIAN—Chesterfield County

☒ **BON SECOURS ST. FRANCIS MEDICAL CENTER (490136)**, 13710 St. Francis Boulevard, Zip 23114–3267; tel. 804/594–7300, (Nonreporting) **A**1 2 3 9 10 **S** Bon Secours Health System, Inc., Marriottsville, MD
Primary Contact: Mark M. Gordon, Chief Executive Officer
COO: Peter J. Bernard, Chief Executive Officer
CIO: Mike Lokie, Project Director
CHR: Paul Catucci, Administrative Director Human Resources
Web address: www.bonsecours.com/sfmc/default.asp
**Control:** Other not–for–profit (including NFP Corporation) **Service:** General Medical and Surgical

**Staffed Beds:** 130

☐ **SHELTERING ARMS HOSPITAL SOUTH (493030)**, 13700 St. Francis Boulevard, Suite 400, Zip 23114–3222; tel. 804/764–1000 **A**1 5 10 **F**29 30 34 53 54 57 59 64 75 77 79 82 86 87 90 91 92 93 95 96 130 132 143 146 148 **P**6
Primary Contact: James E. Sok, FACHE, President and Chief Executive Officer
COO: Mary A. Zweifel, Chief Operating Officer
CFO: Michael E. Dacus, Vice President and Chief Financial Officer
CMO: Timothy Silver, M.D., Medical Director
CIO: Chris Sorenson, Chief Information Officer
CHR: Ellen B. Vance, Chief Human Resources Officer
CNO: Sandra Eyler, MS, Chief Nursing Officer
Web address: www.shelteringarms.com
**Control:** Other not–for–profit (including NFP Corporation) **Service:** Rehabilitation

**Staffed Beds:** 28 **Admissions:** 689 **Census:** 22 **Outpatient Visits:** 5727 **Births:** 0 **Total Expense ($000):** 11090 **Payroll Expense ($000):** 5411 **Personnel:** 80

### NASSAWADOX—Northampton County

☐ **RIVERSIDE SHORE MEMORIAL HOSPITAL (490037)**, 9507 Hospital Avenue, Zip 23413–1821, Mailing Address: P.O. Box 17, Zip 23413–0017; tel. 757/414–8000, (Nonreporting) **A**1 2 3 9 10 20 **S** Riverside Health System, Newport News, VA
Primary Contact: John Peterman, Vice President and Administrator
CFO: W. William Austin, Jr., Senior Vice President Finance
CMO: Charles Goldstein, M.D., President Medical Staff
CIO: Andrew Woughter, Information Systems
CHR: Nicole Miller, Director Human Resources
Web address: www.riversideonline.com
**Control:** Other not–for–profit (including NFP Corporation) **Service:** General Medical and Surgical

**Staffed Beds:** 51

**SHORE MEMORIAL HOSPITAL** See Riverside Shore Memorial Hospital

### NEW KENT—New Kent County

☐ **CUMBERLAND HOSPITAL (493300)**, 9407 Cumberland Road, Zip 23124–2029; tel. 804/966–2242, (Nonreporting) **A**1 10 **S** Universal Health Services, Inc., King of Prussia, PA
Primary Contact: Patrice Gay Brooks, Chief Executive Officer
CFO: Joanne Rial, Chief Financial Officer
CMO: Daniel N. Davidow, M.D., Medical Director
CIO: Towanda Brown, Director Standards and Regulatory Compliance
CHR: Lauren Bonner, Director Human Resources
Web address: www.cumberlandhospital.com
**Control:** Corporation, Investor–owned, for–profit **Service:** Children's rehabilitation

**Staffed Beds:** 132

### NEWPORT NEWS—Newport News City County

☐ **HAMPTON ROADS SPECIALTY HOSPITAL (492008)**, 245 Chesapeake Avenue, Zip 23607–6038; tel. 757/534–5000, (Nonreporting) **A**1 10 **S** Riverside Health System, Newport News, VA
Primary Contact: Courtney Detwiler, R.N., Administrator
Web address: www.hamptonroadsspecialtyhospital.com
**Control:** Other not–for–profit (including NFP Corporation) **Service:** Long–Term Acute Care hospital

**Staffed Beds:** 25

**KEYSTONE NEWPORT NEWS**, 17579 Warwick Boulevard, Zip 23603–1343; tel. 757/888–0400 **F**29 30 32 50 75 99 101 106 132 143
Primary Contact: Paul Kirkham, Chief Executive Officer
COO: Paul Kirkham, Chief Executive Officer
CFO: Joe Brooks, Chief Financial Officer
CMO: Avtar Dhillon, M.D., Medical Director
CIO: Gene Yelton, Director Support Services
CHR: Shawn Marston, Director Human Resources
CNO: Karen Bruce, Director of Nursing
Web address: www.newportnewsbhc.com/
**Control:** Corporation, Investor–owned, for–profit **Service:** Psychiatric

**Staffed Beds:** 108 **Admissions:** 171 **Census:** 99 **Outpatient Visits:** 0 **Births:** 0 **Total Expense ($000):** 15893 **Payroll Expense ($000):** 7612 **Personnel:** 181

**VA**

*Many Facility Codes have changed. Please refer to the AHA Guide Code Chart.* © 2015 AHA Guide

✠ **MARY IMMACULATE HOSPITAL (490041)**, 2 Bernardine Drive, Zip 23602–4499; tel. 757/886–6000, (Includes ST. FRANCIS NURSING CENTER ), (Total facility includes 115 beds in nursing home–type unit) **A**1 9 10 **F**3 5 11 12 13 15 18 20 22 24 26 28 29 30 31 32 34 35 36 37 38 40 44 45 46 50 51 57 59 61 63 64 67 68 70 71 73 74 75 76 77 78 79 81 82 84 85 86 87 91 93 102 107 108 111 114 118 119 130 131 132 143 145 146 147 148 **P**6 **S** Bon Secours Health System, Inc., Marriottsville, MD
Primary Contact: Darlene Stephenson, Chief Executive Officer
COO: Darlene Stephenson, Vice President Operations
CIO: Terri Spence, Vice President Information Services
CHR: Vickie Witcher Humphries, Vice President Human Resources
CNO: Jeffrey N. Doucette, R.N., Chief Nursing Officer
Web address: www.bonsecourshamptonroads.com
**Control:** Other not–for–profit (including NFP Corporation) **Service:** General Medical and Surgical

**Staffed Beds:** 238 **Admissions:** 8580 **Census:** 168 **Births:** 1542 **Total Expense ($000):** 166556 **Payroll Expense ($000):** 48067 **Personnel:** 658

☐ **RIVERSIDE REGIONAL MEDICAL CENTER (490052)**, 500 J. Clyde Morris Boulevard, Zip 23601–1929; tel. 757/594–2000, (Includes RIVERSIDE PSYCHIATRIC INSTITUTE ) **A**1 2 3 5 6 9 10 13 **F**3 8 11 12 13 15 18 20 22 24 26 28 30 31 36 38 40 43 44 45 49 50 54 56 58 60 64 70 72 74 75 76 77 78 79 81 82 84 85 86 87 93 94 96 97 102 107 108 110 111 114 115 116 117 118 119 120 121 123 124 126 129 131 132 141 143 146 148 **P**6 **S** Riverside Health System, Newport News, VA
Primary Contact: Michael J. Doucette, Senior Vice President and Administrator
COO: William B. Downey, Chief Operating Officer
CFO: Wade Broughman, Executive Vice President and Chief Financial Officer
CMO: Barry L. Gross, M.D., Executive Vice President and Chief Medical Officer
CIO: Dennis Loftus, Senior Vice President and Chief Information Officer
CHR: Sally Hartman, Senior Vice President
Web address: www.riverside–online.com
**Control:** Other not–for–profit (including NFP Corporation) **Service:** General Medical and Surgical

**Staffed Beds:** 293 **Admissions:** 17492 **Census:** 213 **Outpatient Visits:** 323700 **Births:** 2656 **Total Expense ($000):** 621586 **Payroll Expense ($000):** 162973 **Personnel:** 1245

✠ **RIVERSIDE REHABILITATION INSTITUTE (493027)**, 245 Chesapeake Avenue, Zip 23607–6038; tel. 757/928–8000, (Nonreporting) **A**1 5 10 **S** Riverside Health System, Newport News, VA
Primary Contact: Edward Heckler, Administrator
COO: William B. Downey, President and Chief Executive Officer
CFO: Wade Broughman, Executive Vice President and Chief Financial Officer
CMO: C. Renee Moss, M.D., Chief Medical Officer
CIO: John T. Stanley, Vice President Planning and Information Systems
CHR: Ashleigh Andrews, Manager Human Resources
CNO: Debbie Outlaw, R.N., Director Patient Care Services
Web address: www.riverside–online.com
**Control:** Other not–for–profit (including NFP Corporation) **Service:** Rehabilitation

**Staffed Beds:** 32

### NORFOLK—Norfolk City County

✠ **BON SECOURS–DEPAUL MEDICAL CENTER (490011)**, 150 Kingsley Lane, Zip 23505–4650; tel. 757/889–5000, (Total facility includes 24 beds in nursing home–type unit) **A**1 2 3 5 9 10 **F**3 11 13 15 18 20 22 29 30 31 34 35 40 44 45 46 50 51 56 57 59 61 64 68 70 71 74 75 76 78 79 81 82 84 85 86 87 93 97 102 107 108 110 111 114 115 118 119 120 121 128 129 130 131 132 143 145 146 147 148 **S** Bon Secours Health System, Inc., Marriottsville, MD
Primary Contact: John E. Barrett, III, Chief Executive Officer
CFO: Charmaine Rochester, Vice President Finance
CMO: Raymond McCue, M.D., Chief Medical Officer
CIO: Lynne Zultanky, Director Corporate Communications and Media Relations
CHR: Vickie Witcher Humphries, Vice President Human Resources
CNO: Michael J. Bratton, R.N., Chief Nurse Executive and Vice President Patient Care Services
Web address: www.bonsecourshamptonroads.com
**Control:** Other not–for–profit (including NFP Corporation) **Service:** General Medical and Surgical

**Staffed Beds:** 204 **Admissions:** 6880 **Census:** 87 **Outpatient Visits:** 167371 **Births:** 1329 **Total Expense ($000):** 175550 **Payroll Expense ($000):** 62066

☐ **CHILDREN'S HOSPITAL OF THE KING'S DAUGHTERS (493301)**, 601 Children's Lane, Zip 23507–1910; tel. 757/668–7000 **A**1 3 5 9 10 **F**3 7 8 9 12 16 17 19 21 23 25 27 29 30 31 32 34 35 39 40 41 44 45 48 49 50 54 55 57 58 59 60 61 64 65 66 68 72 73 74 75 77 78 79 80 81 82 84 85 86 87 88 89 90 91 92 93 94 97 99 100 102 107 111 115 118 119 129 130 131 132 134 138 145 146 148 **P**8
Primary Contact: James D. Dahling, President and Chief Executive Officer
COO: John P. Harding, Chief Operating Officer
CFO: Dennis Ryan, Senior Vice President and Chief Financial Officer
CMO: Chris Foley, Chief of Medicine
CIO: Deborah Barnes, Vice President and Chief Information Officer
CHR: Paul J. Morlock, FACHE, Vice President Human Resources
CNO: Karen Mitchell, Vice President Patient Care Services
Web address: www.chkd.org
**Control:** Other not–for–profit (including NFP Corporation) **Service:** Children's general

**Staffed Beds:** 186 **Admissions:** 4602 **Census:** 125 **Outpatient Visits:** 206763 **Births:** 0 **Total Expense ($000):** 290397 **Payroll Expense ($000):** 128586 **Personnel:** 2335

**HOSPITAL FOR EXTENDED RECOVERY (492007)**, 600 Gresham Drive, Suite 700, Zip 23507–1904; tel. 757/388–1700, (Nonreporting) **A**9 10
Primary Contact: Linda B. O'Neil, R.N., Chief Executive Officer
**Control:** Other not–for–profit (including NFP Corporation) **Service:** Long–Term Acute Care hospital

**Staffed Beds:** 35

☐ **KEMPSVILLE CENTER FOR BEHAVIORAL HEALTH**, 860 Kempsville Road, Zip 23502–3980; tel. 757/461–4565, (Nonreporting) **A**1
Primary Contact: Jaime Hernandez, Chief Executive Officer
**Control:** Corporation, Investor–owned, for–profit **Service:** Psychiatric

**Staffed Beds:** 77

**LAKE TAYLOR TRANSITIONAL CARE HOSPITAL (492001)**, 1309 Kempsville Road, Zip 23502–2286; tel. 757/461–5001, (Nonreporting) **A**3 5 10
Primary Contact: Thomas J. Orsini, President and Chief Executive Officer
CFO: Robert W. Fogg, Director Finance
CMO: Kevin Murray, M.D., Director Medical Services
CIO: Mark Davis, Director Information Systems
CHR: LeeAnn Lowman, Director Human Resources
Web address: www.laketaylor.org
**Control:** Hospital district or authority, Government, nonfederal **Service:** Long–Term Acute Care hospital

**Staffed Beds:** 293

★ ◇ **SENTARA LEIGH HOSPITAL (490046)**, 830 Kempsville Road, Zip 23502–3920; tel. 757/261–6000 **A**2 3 5 9 10 21 **F**3 8 9 13 15 18 20 22 26 28 29 30 31 34 35 36 37 38 39 40 44 45 46 47 48 49 50 54 55 57 58 59 60 61 63 64 68 70 71 74 75 76 77 78 79 81 82 84 85 86 87 92 93 94 96 97 100 102 107 108 110 111 114 119 126 130 131 132 141 144 146 147 148 **P**6 **S** Sentara Healthcare, Norfolk, VA
Primary Contact: Teresa L. Edwards, President and Administrator
COO: Howard P. Kern, President and Chief Operating Officer
CFO: Robert Broermann, Senior Vice President and Chief Financial Officer
CMO: Terry Gilliland, M.D., Chief Medical Officer
CIO: Bert Reese, Chief Information Officer
CHR: Michael V. Taylor, Senior Vice President Human Resources
CNO: Genemarie McGee, R.N., Chief Nursing Officer
Web address: www.sentara.com
**Control:** Other not–for–profit (including NFP Corporation) **Service:** General Medical and Surgical

**Staffed Beds:** 238 **Admissions:** 14036 **Census:** 166 **Outpatient Visits:** 503689 **Births:** 1881 **Total Expense ($000):** 235866 **Payroll Expense ($000):** 91659 **Personnel:** 1334

★ ◇ **SENTARA NORFOLK GENERAL HOSPITAL (490007)**, 600 Gresham Drive, Zip 23507–1904; tel. 757/388–3000 **A**2 3 5 8 9 10 21 **F**3 7 12 13 15 16 17 18 20 22 24 26 28 29 30 31 34 35 36 38 39 40 41 43 44 45 46 47 48 49 50 51 54 56 57 58 59 60 61 63 64 65 66 68 70 71 72 74 75 76 77 78 79 81 82 84 85 86 87 90 91 93 94 97 98 100 101 102 103 105 107 108 110 111 114 115 116 117 118 119 120 121 123 124 126 129 130 131 132 135 136 137 138 141 142 144 146 147 148 **P**6 **S** Sentara Healthcare, Norfolk, VA
Primary Contact: Kurt T. Hofelich, President
CFO: Robert Broermann, Senior Vice President and Chief Financial Officer
CIO: Bert Reese, Chief Information Officer
Web address: www.sentara.com
**Control:** Other not–for–profit (including NFP Corporation) **Service:** General Medical and Surgical

**Staffed Beds:** 495 **Admissions:** 24905 **Census:** 413 **Outpatient Visits:** 1185286 **Births:** 2735 **Total Expense ($000):** 672199 **Payroll Expense ($000):** 227672 **Personnel:** 3457

**VA**

---

**Hospital, Medicare Provider Number, Address, Telephone, Approval, Facility, and Physician Codes, Health Care System**

★ American Hospital Association (AHA) membership
☐ The Joint Commission accreditation
○ Healthcare Facilities Accreditation Program
◇ DNV Healthcare Inc. accreditation
⇑ Center for Improvement in Healthcare Quality Accreditation
△ Commission on Accreditation of Rehabilitation Facilities (CARF) accreditation

## NORTON—Norton City County

★ **MOUNTAIN VIEW REGIONAL MEDICAL CENTER (490027)**, 310 Third Street N.E., Zip 24273–1137; tel. 276/679–9100, (Total facility includes 44 beds in nursing home–type unit) **A**9 **F**3 11 15 28 29 30 34 35 40 45 48 49 50 57 59 68 70 77 81 85 87 92 93 97 107 108 111 115 117 118 119 130 146 **S** Wellmont Health System, Kingsport, TN
Primary Contact: Dale Clark, President
CFO: Regina Day, Executive Director Finance
CMO: Souhail Shamiyeh, M.D., Chief of Staff
CHR: Bobby Collins, Director Human Resources
CNO: Sheri Ives, R.N., Vice President Patient Care Services
Web address: www.wellmont.org
**Control:** Other not–for–profit (including NFP Corporation) **Service:** General Medical and Surgical

**Staffed Beds:** 72 **Admissions:** 1782 **Census:** 46 **Outpatient Visits:** 37211 **Births:** 0 **Total Expense ($000):** 26034 **Payroll Expense ($000):** 7009 **Personnel:** 190

○ △ **NORTON COMMUNITY HOSPITAL (490001)**, 100 15th Street N.W., Zip 24273–1616; tel. 276/679–9600 **A**7 9 10 11 13 **F**3 11 13 15 18 28 29 30 34 35 40 44 45 51 53 57 62 63 64 68 70 75 76 77 79 81 82 87 90 91 93 107 108 110 111 115 116 117 118 119 129 130 131 133 135 146 147 148 **P**6 8 **S** Mountain States Health Alliance, Johnson City, TN
Primary Contact: Mark T. Leonard, Chief Executive Officer
CFO: Stephen Sawyer, Chief Financial Officer
CMO: Allen Mullens, M.D., Chief Medical Staff
CIO: Judy Lawson, Director Information Services
CHR: Valeri J. Colyer, Director Human Resources
Web address: www.msha.com/nch
**Control:** Other not–for–profit (including NFP Corporation) **Service:** General Medical and Surgical

**Staffed Beds:** 129 **Admissions:** 3334 **Census:** 33 **Outpatient Visits:** 74888 **Births:** 248 **Total Expense ($000):** 34709 **Payroll Expense ($000):** 19157 **Personnel:** 357

## PEARISBURG—Giles County

☒ **CARILION GILES COMMUNITY HOSPITAL (491302)**, 159 Hartley Way, Zip 24134–2471; tel. 540/921–6000 **A**1 9 10 18 **F**3 11 15 18 28 29 34 35 36 40 45 50 53 57 59 64 65 68 70 75 77 79 81 85 86 87 91 93 96 107 108 110 111 115 119 130 133 135 146 147 148 **S** Carilion Clinic, Roanoke, VA
Primary Contact: William Flattery, Vice President and Administrator Western Division
CMO: John Tamminen, M.D., President Medical Staff
CHR: Carrie Boggess, Human Resource Generalist
CNO: Veronica Stump, Chief Nursing Officer
Web address: www.carilionclinic.org/Carilion/cgch
**Control:** Other not–for–profit (including NFP Corporation) **Service:** General Medical and Surgical

**Staffed Beds:** 16 **Admissions:** 1107 **Census:** 15 **Outpatient Visits:** 25297 **Births:** 0 **Total Expense ($000):** 25939 **Payroll Expense ($000):** 9164 **Personnel:** 162

## PETERSBURG—Petersburg City County

☐ **CENTRAL STATE HOSPITAL**, 26317 West Washington Street, Zip 23803–2727; Mailing Address: P.O. Box 4030, Zip 23803–0030; tel. 804/524–7000, (Nonreporting) **A**1 9 **S** Virginia Department of Mental Health, Richmond, VA
Primary Contact: Vicki Montgomery, Director and Chief Executive Officer
COO: Ann Bailey, Assistant Director Administration
CFO: Robert Kaufman, Director Financial Services
CMO: Ronald O. Forbes, M.D., Medical Director
CIO: Jonathan Baber, Director Information Technology
CHR: Tracy Salisbury, Regional Manager Human Resources
CNO: Eva Parham, R.N., Chief Nurse Executive
Web address: www.csh.dbhds.virginia.gov
**Control:** State–Government, nonfederal **Service:** Psychiatric

**Staffed Beds:** 277

☒ **HEALTHSOUTH REHABILITATION HOSPITAL OF PETERSBURG (493031)**, 95 Medical Park Boulevard, Zip 23805–9233; tel. 804/504–8100, (Nonreporting) **A**1 10 **S** HEALTHSOUTH Corporation, Birmingham, AL
Primary Contact: Tracy Penn Turman, Chief Executive Officer
Web address: www.healthsouthpetersburg.com
**Control:** Corporation, Investor–owned, for–profit **Service:** Rehabilitation

**Staffed Beds:** 53

☐ **HIRAM W. DAVIS MEDICAL CENTER (490104)**, 26317 West Washington Street, Zip 23803–2727, Mailing Address: P.O. Box 4030, Zip 23803–0030; tel. 804/524–7344, (Nonreporting) **A**1 10 **S** Virginia Department of Mental Health, Richmond, VA
Primary Contact: Brenda Buenvenida, Director
CFO: Robert Kaufman, Fiscal Officer
CHR: Tracy Salisbury, Director Human Resources
**Control:** State–Government, nonfederal **Service:** Other specialty

**Staffed Beds:** 10

☒ **POPLAR SPRINGS HOSPITAL (494022)**, 350 Poplar Drive, Zip 23805–9367; tel. 804/733–6874 **A**1 9 10 **F**4 29 64 87 98 99 100 101 102 103 104 105 106 130 143 **P**5 6 **S** Universal Health Services, Inc., King of Prussia, PA
Primary Contact: Joseph Trapani, Chief Executive Officer
COO: Kate McBride, Chief Operating Officer
CFO: Bettie Hill, Chief Financial Officer
CMO: Thresa Simon, M.D., Medical Director
CHR: Morris Mitchell, Director Human Resources
Web address: www.poplarsprings.com
**Control:** Corporation, Investor–owned, for–profit **Service:** Psychiatric

**Staffed Beds:** 180 **Admissions:** 3566 **Census:** 145 **Outpatient Visits:** 2245 **Births:** 0 **Total Expense ($000):** 35520 **Payroll Expense ($000):** 13523 **Personnel:** 295

☒ **SOUTHSIDE REGIONAL MEDICAL CENTER (490067)**, 200 Medical Park Boulevard, Zip 23805–9274; tel. 804/765–5000, (Nonreporting) **A**1 2 3 6 9 10 **S** Community Health Systems, Inc., Franklin, TN
Primary Contact: Douglas J. Moyer, Chief Executive Officer
COO: Jerad Hanlon, Chief Operating Officer
CFO: Charles Coder, Chief Financial Officer
CMO: Boyd Wickizer, Jr., M.D., Chief Medical Officer
CIO: Eric Synnestvedt, Director Information Technology
CHR: Irene Buskey, Director Human Resources
CNO: Beverly Bzdek Smith, Chief Nursing Officer
Web address: www.srmconline.com
**Control:** Corporation, Investor–owned, for–profit **Service:** General Medical and Surgical

**Staffed Beds:** 300

## PORTSMITH—Kings County

★ **NAVAL HOSPITAL LEMOORE**, 620 John Paul Jones Circle, Zip 23708, Mailing Address: 937 Franklin Avenue, Lemoore, CA, Zip 93246–0001; tel. 559/998–4481, (Nonreporting) **S** Bureau of Medicine and Surgery, Department of the Navy, Washington, DC
Primary Contact: Captain Mary A. Mahony, Commanding Officer
CFO: Thomas M. Brui, Director Resource Management
CMO: Scott Cota, M.D., Director Medical Services
CIO: Victor Dela Torre, Command Legal Officer
CHR: Billy Newman, Department Head
Web address: www.med.navy.mil/sites/nhlem/Pages/index.aspx
**Control:** Navy, Government, federal **Service:** General Medical and Surgical

**Staffed Beds:** 16

## PORTSMOUTH—Portsmouth City County

☒ **BON SECOURS MARYVIEW MEDICAL CENTER (490017)**, 3636 High Street, Zip 23707–3270; tel. 757/398–2200, (Total facility includes 120 beds in nursing home–type unit) **A**1 2 3 5 9 10 **F**3 4 5 11 12 13 15 17 18 20 22 24 26 28 29 30 31 34 35 36 37 38 40 42 44 45 46 50 51 54 57 59 61 62 63 64 66 67 68 70 71 73 74 75 76 77 78 79 81 82 84 85 86 87 90 91 93 96 97 98 99 100 101 102 103 104 105 106 107 108 110 111 114 115 118 119 121 126 128 129 130 131 132 134 135 143 145 146 147 **S** Bon Secours Health System, Inc., Marriottsville, MD
Primary Contact: Joseph M. Oddis, Chief Executive Officer
CFO: Ernest C. Padden, Chief Financial Officer
CMO: Warren Austin, M.D., Vice President Medical Affairs
CIO: Terri Spence, Chief Information Officer
CHR: Vickie Witcher Humphries, Director Human Resources
CNO: Leana Fox, MSN, Interim Chief Nurse Executive
Web address: www.bonsecourshamptonroads.com
**Control:** Other not–for–profit (including NFP Corporation) **Service:** General Medical and Surgical

**Staffed Beds:** 466 **Admissions:** 12302 **Census:** 272 **Outpatient Visits:** 402983 **Births:** 1012 **Total Expense ($000):** 324561 **Payroll Expense ($000):** 123851

☒ **NAVAL MEDICAL CENTER**, 620 John Paul Jones Circle, Zip 23708–2197; tel. 757/953–1980, (Nonreporting) **A**1 2 3 5 **S** Bureau of Medicine and Surgery, Department of the Navy, Washington, DC
Primary Contact: Commander Matthew Case, MSC, USN, Director For Administration
CFO: Commander Carlos J. Martinez, Director Resource Management
CIO: Lieutenant Colonel Karen Albany, Chief Information Officer
Web address: www.nmcphc.med.navy.mil/
**Control:** Navy, Government, federal **Service:** General Medical and Surgical

**Staffed Beds:** 274

*Many Facility Codes have changed. Please refer to the AHA Guide Code Chart.*

VA

## PULASKI—Pulaski County

✠ **LEWISGALE HOSPITAL PULASKI (490116)**, 2400 Lee Highway, Zip 24301–2326, Mailing Address: P.O. Box 759, Zip 24301–0759; tel. 540/994–8100, (Nonreporting) **A**1 2 9 10 **S** HCA, Nashville, TN
Primary Contact: Derek Vance, Chief Executive Officer
CFO: Jeff Kurcab, Chief Financial Officer
CMO: Karanita Ojomo, M.D., Chief of Staff
CIO: Diron Lane, Director Information Systems
CHR: Jana Beckner, Director Human Resources
CNO: Linda M. Shepherd, RN, BSN, Chief Nursing Officer
Web address: www.lewisgale.com/
**Control:** Corporation, Investor–owned, for–profit **Service:** General Medical and Surgical

> **Staffed Beds:** 54

## RESTON—Fairfax County

✠ **RESTON HOSPITAL CENTER (490107)**, 1850 Town Center Parkway, Zip 20190–3219; tel. 703/689–9000, (Nonreporting) **A**1 2 3 9 10 **S** HCA, Nashville, TN
Primary Contact: John A. Deardorff, Chief Executive Officer
COO: Jane Raymond, Vice President and Chief Operating Officer
CFO: Edward R. Stojakovich, Chief Financial Officer
CMO: Walter R. Zolkiwsky, M.D., Chief Medical Officer
CIO: Paresh Shah, Director Information Systems
CHR: Lesley Channell, Vice President Human Resources
CNO: Cynthia Glover, R.N., Vice President and Chief Nursing Officer
Web address: www.restonhospital.com
**Control:** Corporation, Investor–owned, for–profit **Service:** General Medical and Surgical

> **Staffed Beds:** 147

## RICHLANDS—Tazewell County

✠ **CLINCH VALLEY MEDICAL CENTER (490060)**, 6801 Governor G. C. Peery Highway, Zip 24641–2194; tel. 276/596–6000, (Total facility includes 14 beds in nursing home–type unit) **A**1 9 10 **F**3 12 13 14 15 17 18 20 22 28 29 30 31 34 35 39 40 41 45 49 50 56 57 59 64 70 74 75 76 77 78 79 81 85 86 87 89 90 93 94 97 107 108 110 111 114 115 118 119 120 121 128 129 130 132 134 135 143 146 147 148 **S** LifePoint Health, Brentwood, TN
Primary Contact: Peter Mulkey, Chief Executive Officer
COO: Jennifer Coello, Chief Operating Officer
CFO: Jason Schmiedt, Chief Financial Officer
CMO: George Farrell, M.D., Chief Medical Officer
CIO: Chris Perkins, Director Information Services
CHR: John Knowles, Director Human Resources
CNO: Clint Kendall, R.N., Chief Nursing Officer
Web address: www.clinchvalleymedicalcenter.com
**Control:** Corporation, Investor–owned, for–profit **Service:** General Medical and Surgical

> **Staffed Beds:** 111 **Admissions:** 4373 **Census:** 48 **Outpatient Visits:** 91019 **Births:** 358 **Personnel:** 455

## RICHMOND—Henrico County

✠ **BON SECOURS ST. MARY'S HOSPITAL (490059)**, 5801 Bremo Road, Zip 23226–1907; tel. 804/285–2011, (Includes BON SECOURS ST. MARY'S CHILDREN'S SERVICES, 5801 Bremo Road, tel. 804/285–2011) **A**1 2 3 5 9 10 **F**3 8 11 12 13 15 17 18 20 22 24 26 28 29 30 31 34 36 37 40 41 44 45 46 47 49 50 51 56 57 59 60 63 64 70 72 73 74 75 76 78 79 80 81 82 84 85 86 87 88 89 98 102 103 107 108 110 111 114 115 116 117 118 119 120 121 123 124 126 131 132 145 146 147 148 **P**2 3 4 5 6 **S** Bon Secours Health System, Inc., Marriottsville, MD
Primary Contact: Toni R. Ardabell, R.N., Chief Executive Officer
COO: Francine Barr, R.N., Vice President and Chief Operating Officer
CFO: Stephan F. Quiriconi, Chief Financial Officer
CMO: Khiet Trinh, M.D., Chief Medical Officer
CIO: Terri Spence, Chief Information Officer
CHR: Kristin Crandall, Director Human Resources
Web address: www.bonsecours.com
**Control:** Church–operated, Nongovernment, not–for profit **Service:** General Medical and Surgical

> **Staffed Beds:** 391 **Admissions:** 21852 **Census:** 280 **Outpatient Visits:** 164592 **Births:** 2197 **Total Expense ($000):** 484505 **Payroll Expense ($000):** 164635 **Personnel:** 2304

✠ **BON SECOURS–RICHMOND COMMUNITY HOSPITAL (490094)**, 1500 North 28th Street, Zip 23223–5396, Mailing Address: P.O. Box 27184, Zip 23261–7184; tel. 804/225–1700 **A**1 3 9 10 **F**3 11 15 18 20 22 24 26 28 29 30 31 34 35 38 40 41 44 45 46 50 57 59 60 64 68 70 74 75 78 81 84 85 86 87 98 100 103 104 105 107 108 111 115 118 119 130 145 146 148 **P**6 8 **S** Bon Secours Health System, Inc., Marriottsville, MD
Primary Contact: Michael Robinson, Executive Vice President and Administrator
CIO: Jeff Burke, Chief Information Officer
CHR: Shelia White, Director Human Resources
Web address: www.bonsecours.com
**Control:** Other not–for–profit (including NFP Corporation) **Service:** General Medical and Surgical

> **Staffed Beds:** 85 **Admissions:** 2788 **Census:** 36 **Outpatient Visits:** 31407 **Births:** 1 **Total Expense ($000):** 67462 **Payroll Expense ($000):** 18634 **Personnel:** 279

★ **CHILDREN'S HOSPITAL OF RICHMOND AT VCU–BROOK ROAD CAMPUS (493302)**, 2924 Brook Road, Zip 23220–1298; tel. 804/321–7474, (Nonreporting) **A**3 5 9 10 **S** VCU Health System, Richmond, VA
Primary Contact: Leslie G. Wyatt, Senior Vice President Children's Services and Executive Director
COO: Leslie G. Wyatt, Senior Vice President Children's Services and Executive Director
CFO: James A. Deyarmin, Controller
CMO: Eugene A. Monasterio, M.D., Medical Director
CIO: Greg Friedman, Director Information Technology
CNO: Sharon Darby, R.N., Vice President, Clinical Operations
Web address: www.chrichmond.org
**Control:** Other not–for–profit (including NFP Corporation) **Service:** Children's rehabilitation

> **Staffed Beds:** 36

✠ **CHIPPENHAM HOSPITAL (490112)**, 7101 Jahnke Road, Zip 23225–4044; tel. 804/320–3911, (Includes CHIPPENHAM MEDICAL CENTER, 7101 Jahnke Road, Zip 23225; tel. 804/320–3911; JOHNSTON–WILLIS HOSPITAL, 1401 Johnston–Willis Drive, Zip 23235; tel. 804/330–2000; Brandon Haushalter, Chief Executive Officer) **A**1 2 3 5 9 10 **F**3 4 8 13 15 17 18 19 20 22 24 26 28 29 30 31 34 35 37 38 40 41 43 45 46 47 49 50 55 57 58 59 60 64 68 70 72 73 74 75 76 77 78 79 80 81 84 85 86 87 88 89 90 96 98 99 100 101 102 103 104 105 107 108 109 110 111 114 115 118 119 120 121 123 124 126 129 130 131 135 146 147 148 **S** HCA, Nashville, TN
Primary Contact: Tim McManus, President and Chief Executive Officer
COO: Betsy Blair, R.N., Chief Operating Officer
CFO: Lynn Strader, Chief Financial Officer
CMO: Georgean DeBlois, M.D., Chairman Medical Staff
CIO: Tracy Hechler, Healthcare Director Information Services
CHR: Kris Lukish, Human Resources Officer
Web address: www.cjwmedical.com
**Control:** Corporation, Investor–owned, for–profit **Service:** General Medical and Surgical

> **Staffed Beds:** 667 **Admissions:** 32865 **Census:** 464 **Outpatient Visits:** 280772 **Births:** 2681

**HALLMARK YOUTHCARE – RICHMOND**, 12800 West Creek Parkway, Zip 23238–1116; tel. 804/784–2200, (Nonreporting)
Primary Contact: Di Hayes, Chief Executive Officer
Web address: www.hallmarkyouthcare.org
**Control:** State–Government, nonfederal **Service:** Children's hospital psychiatric

> **Staffed Beds:** 84

✠ **HEALTHSOUTH REHABILITATION HOSPITAL OF VIRGINIA (493028)**, 5700 Fitzhugh Avenue, Zip 23226–1800; tel. 804/288–5700, (Nonreporting) **A**1 9 10 **S** HEALTHSOUTH Corporation, Birmingham, AL
Primary Contact: David Cashwell, Chief Executive Officer
CMO: Roger Giordano, M.D., Medical Director
CIO: Faye Encke, Director Information Management
CHR: Tonya Ferguson, Director Human Resources
CNO: Michelle Anthony, Chief Nursing Officer
Web address: www.healthsouthrichmond.com
**Control:** Corporation, Investor–owned, for–profit **Service:** Rehabilitation

> **Staffed Beds:** 40

**VA**

---

**Hospital, Medicare Provider Number, Address, Telephone, Approval, Facility, and Physician Codes, Health Care System**

★ American Hospital Association (AHA) membership   ◯ Healthcare Facilities Accreditation Program   ⇧ Center for Improvement in Healthcare Quality Accreditation
☐ The Joint Commission accreditation   ◇ DNV Healthcare Inc. accreditation   △ Commission on Accreditation of Rehabilitation Facilities (CARF) accreditation

✠ **HENRICO DOCTORS' HOSPITAL (490118)**, 1602 Skipwith Road,
Zip 23229–5205; tel. 804/289–4500, (Includes HENRICO DOCTORS' HOSPITAL –
FOREST, 1602 Skipwith Road, Zip 23229–5298; tel. 804/289–4500; HENRICO
DOCTORS' HOSPITAL – PARHAM, 7700 East Parham Road, Zip 23294–4301;
tel. 804/747–5600; William Wagnon, Chief Executive Officer; HENRICO DOCTORS'
HOSPITAL – RETREAT CAMPUS, 2621 Grove Avenue, Zip 23220–4308;
tel. 804/254–5100; William Wagnon, Chief Executive Officer) **A**1 2 9 10 **F**3 8 12
13 15 17 18 20 22 24 26 28 29 30 31 34 35 37 40 42 44 45 46 47 49 50
51 54 55 56 57 59 64 65 68 70 71 72 73 74 75 76 77 78 79 81 85 86 87
88 89 90 93 96 97 98 102 105 107 108 109 110 111 112 114 115 119 120
121 123 126 129 130 131 132 135 138 141 146 147 148 **S** HCA,
Nashville, TN
Primary Contact: William Wagnon, Chief Executive Officer
COO: Lisa R. Valentine, Chief Operating Officer
CFO: Christopher Denton, Chief Financial Officer
CIO: Daniel Patton, Director Information Systems
CHR: Steven Burgess, Administrator Human Resources
Web address: www.henricodoctorshospital.com
**Control:** Corporation, Investor–owned, for–profit **Service:** General Medical and
Surgical

**Staffed Beds:** 559 **Admissions:** 20996 **Census:** 297 **Outpatient Visits:**
130429 **Births:** 3525 **Total Expense ($000):** 380111 **Payroll Expense
($000):** 135803 **Personnel:** 1893

✠ △ **HUNTER HOLMES MCGUIRE VETERANS AFFAIRS MEDICAL
CENTER–RICHMOND**, 1201 Broad Rock Boulevard, Zip 23249–0002;
tel. 804/675–5000, (Total facility includes 98 beds in nursing home–type unit) **A**1
2 3 5 7 8 **F**3 4 5 7 8 12 15 17 18 20 22 24 26 28 29 30 31 34 35 36 38 39
40 41 44 45 46 47 48 49 50 51 53 54 56 57 58 59 60 61 62 63 64 65 68
70 71 74 75 77 78 79 81 82 83 84 85 86 87 90 91 92 93 94 95 96 97 98
100 102 103 104 106 107 108 110 111 115 116 117 118 119 120 121 124
126 127 128 129 130 131 132 135 137 141 143 144 145 146 147 148 **P**6
**S** Department of Veterans Affairs, Washington, DC
Primary Contact: John A. Brandecker, Director
COO: David P. Budinger, Associate Director
CFO: Roger T. Vergne, Chief Fiscal Service
CMO: Judy Brannen, M.D., Interim Chief of Staff
CIO: David Dahlstrand, Associate Chief of Staff Information Technology
CHR: Heather Moody, Chief Human Resource Management
Web address: www.richmond.va.gov/
**Control:** Veterans Affairs, Government, federal **Service:** General Medical and
Surgical

**Staffed Beds:** 389 **Admissions:** 7438 **Census:** 243 **Outpatient Visits:**
595729 **Births:** 0 **Total Expense ($000):** 538281 **Payroll Expense ($000):**
29650 **Personnel:** 3085

**JOHNSTON–WILLIS HOSPITAL** See Chippenham Hospital

**KINDRED HOSPITAL RICHMOND** See Vibra Hospital of Richmond

✠ **VCU MEDICAL CENTER (490032)**, 1250 East Marshall Street,
Zip 23298–5051, Mailing Address: P.O. Box 980510, Zip 23298–0510;
tel. 804/828–9000, (Includes VCU HEALTH SYSTEM CHILDREN'S MEDICAL
CENTER, 1001 East Marshall Street, Zip 23219–1918, Mailing Address: PO Box
980646, Zip 23298–0646; tel. 804/828–9602) **A**1 3 5 8 9 10 **F**2 3 6 8 9 11
12 13 15 16 17 18 19 20 21 23 24 25 26 27 28 29 30 31 32 34 35 36
37 38 39 40 41 43 44 45 46 47 48 49 50 51 52 54 55 56 57 58 59 60 61
62 64 65 66 68 70 72 73 74 75 76 78 79 80 81 82 83 84 85 86 87 88 89
90 92 93 95 96 97 98 99 100 101 102 103 104 107 108 109 110 111 114
115 116 117 118 119 120 121 123 124 126 129 130 131 132 134 135 136
137 138 139 141 142 143 145 146 147 148 **P**6 **S** VCU Health System,
Richmond, VA
Primary Contact: John Duval, Chief Executive Officer
COO: Deborah W. Davis, Chief Operating Officer
CFO: Dominic J. Pulco, Executive Vice President Finance and Chief Financial
Officer
CMO: Ron Clark, M.D., Vice President Clinical Activities and Chief Medical Officer
CIO: Richard Pollack, Vice President Information Services
CHR: Maria Curran, Vice President Human Resources
CNO: Deb T. Zimmermann, R.N., Chief Nursing Officer and Vice President Patient
Care Services
Web address: www.vcuhealth.org
**Control:** Hospital district or authority, Government, nonfederal **Service:** General
Medical and Surgical

**Staffed Beds:** 774 **Admissions:** 33146 **Census:** 585 **Outpatient Visits:**
710409 **Births:** 2367 **Total Expense ($000):** 1133429 **Payroll Expense
($000):** 401345 **Personnel:** 8160

✠ **VIBRA HOSPITAL OF RICHMOND (492009)**, 2220 Edward Holland Drive,
Zip 23230–2519; tel. 804/678–7000 **A**1 10 **F**1 3 29 75 107 148 **P**6 **S** Vibra
Healthcare, Mechanicsburg, PA
Primary Contact: Peter Miller, Interim Chief Executive Officer
Web address: www.vhrichmond.com
**Control:** Corporation, Investor–owned, for–profit **Service:** Long–Term Acute Care
hospital

**Staffed Beds:** 60 **Admissions:** 621 **Census:** 44 **Outpatient Visits:** 0 **Births:**
0 **Total Expense ($000):** 24637 **Payroll Expense ($000):** 8941 **Personnel:**
135

**VA**

✠ **CARILION ROANOKE MEMORIAL HOSPITAL (490024)**, Belleview at Jefferson
Street, Zip 24014, Mailing Address: P.O. Box 13367, Zip 24033–3367;
tel. 540/981–7000, (Includes CARILION CLINIC CHILDREN'S HOSPITAL, 1906
Belleview Avenue, S.E., Zip 24014–1838; tel. 540/981–7000; CARILION
ROANOKE COMMUNITY HOSPITAL, 101 Elm Avenue S.E., Zip 24013–2230,
Mailing Address: P.O. Box 12946, Zip 24029–2946; tel. 540/985–8000;
ROANOKE MEMORIAL REHABILITATION CENTER, South Jefferson and McClanahan
Streets, Mailing Address: P.O. Box 13367, Zip 24033; tel. 703/342–4541) **A**1 2
3 5 8 9 10 12 13 **F**3 5 7 8 9 11 12 13 15 17 18 19 20 22 24 26 28 29 30
31 32 33 34 35 36 37 38 39 40 41 43 44 45 46 47 48 49 50 51 52 53 54
55 56 57 58 59 60 61 62 63 64 65 66 68 70 71 72 73 74 75 76 77 78 79
81 82 83 84 85 86 87 88 89 90 92 93 96 97 98 99 100 101 102 103 104
106 107 108 110 111 113 114 115 117 118 119 120 121 123 124 126 129
130 131 132 134 135 143 144 146 147 148 **P**6 **S** Carilion Clinic, Roanoke, VA
Primary Contact: Steven C. Arner, President
COO: Steven C. Arner, President
CFO: Donald B. Halliwill, Executive Vice President and Chief Financial Officer
CHR: Heather S. Shepardson, Vice President Human Resources
Web address: www.carilionclinic.org
**Control:** Other not–for–profit (including NFP Corporation) **Service:** General
Medical and Surgical

**Staffed Beds:** 646 **Admissions:** 36485 **Census:** 530 **Outpatient Visits:**
243266 **Births:** 3181 **Total Expense ($000):** 966195 **Payroll Expense
($000):** 445288 **Personnel:** 5924

✠ **CARILION FRANKLIN MEMORIAL HOSPITAL (490089)**, 180 Floyd Avenue,
Zip 24151–1389; tel. 540/483–5277 **A**1 3 9 10 **F**3 11 15 18 28 29 30 34 35
40 45 50 53 59 62 63 68 70 75 81 84 85 91 93 96 107 110 115 119 130
132 135 146 **S** Carilion Clinic, Roanoke, VA
Primary Contact: William D. Jacobsen, Vice President and Administrator
COO: Steven C. Arner, Chief Operating Officer
CFO: Donald B. Halliwill, Chief Financial Officer
CMO: Patrice M. Weiss, Chief Medical Officer
CHR: Heather S. Shepardson, Chief Human Resource Officer
Web address: www.carilionclinic.org/Carilion/Franklin+Memorial+Hospital
**Control:** Other not–for–profit (including NFP Corporation) **Service:** General
Medical and Surgical

**Staffed Beds:** 18 **Admissions:** 1482 **Census:** 14 **Outpatient Visits:** 39001
**Births:** 0 **Total Expense ($000):** 33105 **Payroll Expense ($000):** 13414
**Personnel:** 235

✠ **LEWIS–GALE MEDICAL CENTER (490048)**, 1900 Electric Road,
Zip 24153–7494; tel. 540/776–4000, (Includes LEWIS–GALE PAVILION, 1902
Braeburn Drive, Zip 24153–7391; tel. 703/772–2800), (Nonreporting) **A**1 2 9 10
**S** HCA, Nashville, TN
Primary Contact: Jonathan L. Bartlett, Chief Executive Officer
CFO: Angela D. Reynolds, Chief Financial Officer
CMO: Joseph Nelson, M.D., President Medical Staff
CIO: Beth Cole, Director Information Services
CHR: Dale Beaudoin, Vice President Human Resources
Web address: www.lewis–gale.com
**Control:** Corporation, Investor–owned, for–profit **Service:** General Medical and
Surgical

**Staffed Beds:** 521

✠ **SALEM VETERANS AFFAIRS MEDICAL CENTER**, 1970 Roanoke Boulevard,
Zip 24153–6478; tel. 540/982–2463, (Nonreporting) **A**1 2 3 5 8 **S** Department
of Veterans Affairs, Washington, DC
Primary Contact: Miguel H. LaPuz, M.D., Director
CFO: Codie Walker, Chief Financial Officer
CMO: Anne Hutchins, M.D., Chief of Staff
CIO: Sharon Collins, Chief Information Officer
CHR: Brian Zeman, Chief Human Resources
CNO: Teresa England, R.N., Nurse Executive
Web address: www.salem.va.gov
**Control:** Veterans Affairs, Government, federal **Service:** General Medical and
Surgical

**Staffed Beds:** 200

*Many Facility Codes have changed. Please refer to the AHA Guide Code Chart.* © 2015 AHA Guide

## SOUTH BOSTON—Halifax County

⊞ **SENTARA HALIFAX REGIONAL HOSPITAL (490013)**, 2204 Wilborn Avenue, Zip 24592–1638; tel. 434/517–3100, (Total facility includes 348 beds in nursing home–type unit) **A**1 9 10 **F**3 13 14 15 17 18 20 28 29 30 31 35 36 38 40 44 45 46 47 48 51 60 62 63 64 65 67 68 70 74 75 76 77 78 79 81 82 84 85 86 87 89 92 93 94 96 97 100 101 102 103 104 107 108 110 111 114 115 116 117 118 119 127 128 129 130 131 132 135 146 147 148 **P**1 7 **S** Sentara Healthcare, Norfolk, VA
Primary Contact: Chris A. Lumsden, Chief Executive Officer
COO: Thomas S. Kluge, Chief Operating Officer
CFO: Stewart R. Nelson, Chief Financial Officer
CMO: Said Iskandar, M.D., Chief Medical Officer
CIO: William Zirkle, Manager Information Systems
CHR: Catherine Howard, Director Human Resources
CNO: Patricia F. Thomas, Chief Nursing Officer
Web address: www.hrhs.org
**Control:** Other not–for–profit (including NFP Corporation) **Service:** General Medical and Surgical

**Staffed Beds:** 438 **Admissions:** 4238 **Census:** 379 **Outpatient Visits:** 115464 **Births:** 416 **Total Expense ($000):** 123351 **Payroll Expense ($000):** 54574 **Personnel:** 633

## SOUTH HILL—Mecklenburg County

⊞ **VCU COMMUNITY MEMORIAL HOSPITAL (490098)**, 125 Buena Vista Circle, Zip 23970–1431, Mailing Address: P.O. Box 90, Zip 23970–0090; tel. 434/447–3151, (Total facility includes 110 beds in nursing–type unit) **A**1 2 9 10 20 **F**3 11 15 18 28 29 30 31 34 35 39 40 45 46 49 50 53 54 56 59 62 63 64 65 70 74 75 77 78 79 81 82 84 85 86 87 93 96 97 107 108 110 111 115 118 119 127 128 130 131 132 133 135 146 147 148 **P**8 **S** VCU Health System, Richmond, VA
Primary Contact: W. Scott Burnette, Chief Executive Officer
CFO: Kenneth Libby, Vice President Finance
CMO: Manhal Saleeby, M.D., Chief of Staff
CIO: Brian Rock, Director of Information Systems
CHR: Maria Stephens, PHR, Director Human Resources, Education and Occupational Health and Wellness
CNO: Ursula N. Butts, FACHE, Vice President of Patient Care Services
Web address: www.cmh–sh.org
**Control:** Other not–for–profit (including NFP Corporation) **Service:** General Medical and Surgical

**Staffed Beds:** 178 **Admissions:** 3118 **Census:** 143 **Outpatient Visits:** 128185 **Births:** 0 **Total Expense ($000):** 72130 **Payroll Expense ($000):** 30327 **Personnel:** 625

## STAFFORD—Stafford County

⊞ **STAFFORD HOSPITAL (490140)**, 101 Hospital Center Boulevard, Zip 22554–6200; tel. 540/741–9000 **A**1 9 10 **F**3 13 15 18 20 22 26 29 30 31 34 35 40 44 45 46 47 48 49 50 54 57 58 59 60 64 70 73 74 75 76 77 78 79 81 84 85 86 87 92 93 96 107 108 110 111 115 118 119 120 121 122 129 130 132 146 148 **P**8 **S** Mary Washington Healthcare, Fredericksburg, VA
Primary Contact: Michael McDermott, M.D., President and Chief Executive Officer
CFO: Sean Barden, Executive Vice President and Chief Financial Officer
CMO: Rebecca Bigoney, M.D., Executive Vice President and Chief Medical Officer
CIO: Joyce Hanscome, Senior Vice President and Chief Information Officer
CHR: Kathryn S. Wall, Executive Vice President Human Resources and Organizational Development
CNO: Eileen L. Dohmann, R.N., Senior Vice President and Chief Nursing Officer
Web address: www.mwhc.com
**Control:** Other not–for–profit (including NFP Corporation) **Service:** General Medical and Surgical

**Staffed Beds:** 100 **Admissions:** 4420 **Census:** 42 **Outpatient Visits:** 118141 **Births:** 967 **Total Expense ($000):** 78220 **Payroll Expense ($000):** 26432 **Personnel:** 308

## STAUNTON—Staunton City County

**COMMONWEALTH CENTER FOR CHILDREN AND ADOLESCENTS**, 1355 Richmond Road, Zip 24401–9146, Mailing Address: Box 4000, Zip 24402–4000; tel. 540/332–2100, (Nonreporting) **A**3 5 9 **S** Virginia Department of Mental Health, Richmond, VA
Primary Contact: William J. Tuell, MSN, Facility Director
Web address: www.ccca.dbhds.virginia.gov
**Control:** State–Government, nonfederal **Service:** Children's other specialty

**Staffed Beds:** 60

## WESTERN STATE HOSPITAL (490106), 1301 Richmond Avenue

☐ **WESTERN STATE HOSPITAL (490106)**, 1301 Richmond Avenue, Zip 24401–9146, Mailing Address: P.O. Box 2500, Zip 24402–2500; tel. 540/332–8000, (Nonreporting) **A**1 3 5 9 10 **S** Virginia Department of Mental Health, Richmond, VA
Primary Contact: Jack W. Barber, M.D., Director
CFO: David Mawyer, Chief Financial Officer
CMO: Mary Clare Smith, M.D., Medical Director
CIO: Sharon Johnson, Director Health Information Management
CHR: Kimberly Harman, Regional Manager Human Resources
Web address: www.dbhds.virginia.gov
**Control:** State–Government, nonfederal **Service:** Psychiatric

**Staffed Beds:** 260

## STUART—Patrick County

★ ◇ **PIONEER COMMUNITY HOSPITAL OF PATRICK (491306)**, 18688 Jeb Stuart Highway, Zip 24171–1559; tel. 276/694–3151, (Nonreporting) **A**9 10 18 21 **S** Pioneer Health Services, Magee, MS
Primary Contact: Jeanette Filpi, Chief Executive Officer
CFO: Julie Gieger, Chief Financial Officer
CMO: Nicholas Kipreos, M.D., Chief Medical Staff
CIO: Jack York, Chief Information Officer
CHR: Gregory D. Baldwin, Vice President Human Resources
CNO: Leslie Mordue, Chief Nursing Officer
Web address: www.pchpatrick.com
**Control:** Corporation, Investor–owned, for–profit **Service:** General Medical and Surgical

**Staffed Beds:** 25

## SUFFOLK—Suffolk City County

★ ◇ **SENTARA OBICI HOSPITAL (490044)**, 2800 Godwin Boulevard, Zip 23434–8038; tel. 757/934–4000 **A**2 3 5 9 10 21 **F**3 11 13 15 18 20 26 28 29 30 31 34 35 36 37 40 42 45 47 48 49 50 54 56 57 58 59 60 64 68 70 73 74 75 76 77 78 79 81 84 85 86 87 91 92 93 94 96 97 98 107 108 110 111 117 118 119 120 121 123 128 129 130 131 132 144 146 147 148 **P**6 **S** Sentara Healthcare, Norfolk, VA
Primary Contact: Steve Julian, M.D., President
CFO: Mike Mounie, Director Finance
CMO: Steve Julian, M.D., Vice President Medical Affairs
CIO: Alice Oxton, Director Information Technology
CHR: Deborah Ferguson, Human Resources Consultant
Web address: www.sentara.com
**Control:** Other not–for–profit (including NFP Corporation) **Service:** General Medical and Surgical

**Staffed Beds:** 176 **Admissions:** 8923 **Census:** 101 **Outpatient Visits:** 344719 **Births:** 1302 **Total Expense ($000):** 162320 **Payroll Expense ($000):** 64727 **Personnel:** 1006

## TAPPAHANNOCK—Essex County

☐ **RIVERSIDE TAPPAHANNOCK HOSPITAL (490084)**, 618 Hospital Road, Zip 22560–5000; tel. 804/443–3311, (Nonreporting) **A**1 9 10 20 **S** Riverside Health System, Newport News, VA
Primary Contact: John Peterman, Vice President and Administrator
CFO: Jeri Sibley, Director Revenue Cycle
CMO: Randy Ferrance, M.D., President Medical Staff
CHR: Jaime Cook, Director Human Resources
Web address: www.riverside–online.com
**Control:** Other not–for–profit (including NFP Corporation) **Service:** General Medical and Surgical

**Staffed Beds:** 16

## TAZEWELL—Tazewell County

⊞ **CARILION TAZEWELL COMMUNITY HOSPITAL (490117)**, 141 Ben Bolt Avenue, Zip 24651–9700; tel. 276/988–8700 **A**1 9 10 **F**3 11 15 29 30 34 39 40 44 45 50 59 62 64 68 75 77 79 81 85 87 91 107 111 114 119 133 135 146 **S** Carilion Clinic, Roanoke, VA
Primary Contact: Kathren Dowdy, MSN, Regional Hospital Senior Director
CMO: Kerry Moore, M.D., Chief of Staff
CHR: Carrie Boggess, Human Resources Generalist
Web address: www.carilionclinic.org/Carilion/Carilion+Tazewell+Community+Hospital
**Control:** Other not–for–profit (including NFP Corporation) **Service:** General Medical and Surgical

**Staffed Beds:** 7 **Admissions:** 580 **Census:** 6 **Outpatient Visits:** 14380 **Births:** 0 **Total Expense ($000):** 13025 **Payroll Expense ($000):** 4961 **Personnel:** 97

**VA**

## VIRGINIA BEACH—Virginia Beach City County

★ ◇ **SENTARA PRINCESS ANNE HOSPITAL (490119)**, 2025 Glenn Mitchell Drive, Zip 23456-0178; tel. 757/507-1000 **A**2 3 5 9 10 21 **F**3 13 15 18 20 22 26 29 30 31 34 35 36 38 39 40 41 44 45 46 47 49 50 54 55 57 58 59 60 61 63 64 65 68 70 71 72 73 74 75 76 77 78 79 81 82 84 85 86 87 91 92 93 94 96 97 100 102 107 108 110 111 114 115 118 119 129 130 131 132 144 145 146 147 148 **P**6 **S** Sentara Healthcare, Norfolk, VA
Primary Contact: Thomas B. Thames, M.D., President
COO: Howard P. Kern, Chief Operating Officer
CFO: Robert Broermann, Senior Vice President and Chief Financial Officer
CMO: Terry Gilliland, M.D., Senior Vice President and Chief Medical Officer
CIO: Bert Reese, Chief Information Officer
CHR: Michael V. Taylor, Vice President Human Resources
CNO: Grace Myers, MSN, Vice President, Nurse Executive
Web address: www.sentara.com
**Control:** Other not-for-profit (including NFP Corporation) **Service:** General Medical and Surgical

**Staffed Beds: 160 Admissions: 11138 Census: 135 Outpatient Visits:** 352177 **Births: 2697 Total Expense ($000):** 189726 **Payroll Expense ($000): 62180 Personnel: 1132**

★ ◇ **SENTARA VIRGINIA BEACH GENERAL HOSPITAL (490057)**, 1060 First Colonial Road, Zip 23454-3002; tel. 757/395-8000 **A**2 3 5 9 10 21 **F**3 11 15 17 18 20 22 24 26 28 29 30 31 34 36 37 38 39 40 41 43 44 45 46 47 49 50 51 53 54 57 58 59 60 61 63 64 65 68 70 74 75 77 78 79 80 81 82 84 85 86 87 90 92 93 94 96 97 98 100 101 102 103 107 108 109 110 111 114 115 118 119 120 121 123 126 129 130 131 132 141 142 144 145 146 147 148 **P**6 **S** Sentara Healthcare, Norfolk, VA
Primary Contact: Elwood Bernard Boone, III, FACHE, President
COO: Joanne Inman, Vice President Operations
CFO: Marley Nacey, Director Finance
CHR: Michelle Meekins, Manager Human Resources
CNO: Peggy Braun, R.N., Vice President Patient Care Services and Chief Nurse Executive
Web address: www.sentara.com
**Control:** Other not-for-profit (including NFP Corporation) **Service:** General Medical and Surgical

**Staffed Beds: 259 Admissions: 12954 Census: 192 Outpatient Visits:** 434724 **Births: 0 Total Expense ($000):** 240891 **Payroll Expense ($000):** 97334 **Personnel: 1444**

☐ **VIRGINIA BEACH PSYCHIATRIC CENTER (494025)**, 1100 First Colonial Road, Zip 23454-2403; tel. 757/496-6000, (Nonreporting) **A**1 9 10 **S** Universal Health Services, Inc., King of Prussia, PA
Primary Contact: Dustin Davis, Chief Executive Officer
Web address: www.vbpcweb.com
**Control:** Corporation, Investor-owned, for-profit **Service:** Psychiatric

**Staffed Beds: 100**

## WARRENTON—Fauquier County

✠ △ **FAUQUIER HOSPITAL (490023)**, 500 Hospital Drive, Zip 20186-3099; tel. 540/316-5000, (Nonreporting) **A**1 3 7 9 10 **S** LifePoint Health, Brentwood, TN
Primary Contact: Rodger H. Baker, President and Chief Executive Officer
CFO: Lionel J. Phillips, Vice President Financial Services
CMO: Anhtai H. Nguyen, M.D., Vice President Medical Affairs and Chief Medical Officer
CIO: Donna Staton, Chief Information Officer
CHR: Katy Reeves, Vice President Human Resources
CNO: Linda Sharkey, R.N., Vice President Patient Care Services and Chief Nurse Executive
Web address: www.fauquierhospital.org
**Control:** Other not-for-profit (including NFP Corporation) **Service:** General Medical and Surgical

**Staffed Beds: 97**

## WILLIAMSBURG—James City County

☐ **EASTERN STATE HOSPITAL (490109)**, 4601 Ironbound Road, Zip 23188-2652; tel. 757/253-5161, (Nonreporting) **A**1 3 5 9 10 **S** Virginia Department of Mental Health, Richmond, VA
Primary Contact: John M. Favret, Director
CFO: E. Clifford Love, Director Fiscal Services
CMO: Guillermo Schrader, M.D., Acting Medical Director
CIO: Barbara Lambert, Director Healthcare Compliance
CHR: Edie Rogan, Manager Human Resources
Web address: www.esh.dmhmrsas.virginia.gov/
**Control:** State-Government, nonfederal **Service:** Psychiatric

**Staffed Beds: 334**

☐ **RIVERSIDE DOCTORS' HOSPITAL (490143)**, 1500 Commonwealth Avenue, Zip 23185-5229; tel. 757/585-2200, (Nonreporting) **A**1 10 **S** Riverside Health System, Newport News, VA
Primary Contact: Steve C. McCary, Administrator
CNO: Arlene Messina, R.N., Director of Nursing
Web address: www.riversideonline.com
**Control:** Other not-for-profit (including NFP Corporation) **Service:** General Medical and Surgical

**Staffed Beds: 40**

★ ◇ **SENTARA WILLIAMSBURG REGIONAL MEDICAL CENTER (490066)**, 100 Sentara Circle, Zip 23188-5713; tel. 757/984-6000 **A**2 9 10 21 **F**3 8 11 13 15 18 20 22 28 29 30 31 34 35 36 37 39 40 41 44 45 46 47 48 49 50 51 54 56 57 58 59 60 63 64 65 68 70 74 75 76 77 78 79 81 83 84 85 86 87 89 90 91 92 93 94 96 97 100 102 103 107 108 110 111 114 115 116 117 118 119 129 130 131 132 135 144 146 147 148 **P**6 **S** Sentara Healthcare, Norfolk, VA
Primary Contact: David J. Masterson, President
CFO: Andreas Roehrle, Director Finance
CMO: Joe Robbins, M.D., Vice President Medical Affairs
CIO: Mike Freeman, Director Information Technology
CHR: Lois B. Demerich, Director Human Resources
CNO: Donna Wilmoth, Vice President Patient Care Services and Chief Nursing Officer
Web address: www.sentara.com
**Control:** Other not-for-profit (including NFP Corporation) **Service:** General Medical and Surgical

**Staffed Beds: 145 Admissions: 6766 Census: 69 Outpatient Visits:** 298609 **Births: 940 Total Expense ($000):** 138616 **Payroll Expense ($000):** 53513 **Personnel: 701**

☐ **THE PAVILION AT WILLIAMSBURG PLACE (494032)**, 5483 Mooretown Road, Zip 23188-2108; tel. 757/565-0106, (Nonreporting) **A**1 10
Primary Contact: Gary Williams, Executive Director
CNO: Vicki Smith, Director of Nursing
Web address: www.pavilionwp.com
**Control:** Corporation, Investor-owned, for-profit **Service:** Psychiatric

**Staffed Beds: 57**

## WINCHESTER—Winchester City County

✠ **WINCHESTER MEDICAL CENTER (490005)**, 1840 Amherst Street, Zip 22601-2808, Mailing Address: P.O. Box 3340, Zip 22604-2540; tel. 540/536-8000 **A**1 2 3 5 9 10 **F**3 5 11 12 13 15 17 18 20 22 24 26 28 29 30 31 32 34 35 38 39 40 41 43 44 45 47 49 50 51 54 56 57 58 59 60 61 62 64 65 68 70 71 72 74 75 76 77 78 79 80 81 82 84 85 86 87 89 90 91 92 93 97 98 100 101 102 103 107 108 110 111 114 115 116 117 118 119 120 121 123 124 129 130 131 132 135 136 146 147 148 **P**5 **S** Valley Health System, Winchester, VA
Primary Contact: Mark H. Merrill, President
COO: Grady W. Philips, III, Senior Vice President and Chief Operating Officer
CFO: Robert Amos, Vice President and Chief Financial Officer
CMO: Nicolas Restrepo, M.D., Vice President Medical Affairs
CIO: Joan Roscoe, Chief Information Officer
CHR: Elizabeth Savage-Tracy, Vice President and Human Resources Officer
CNO: Anne Whiteside, Vice President Nursing
Web address: www.valleyhealthlink.com/WMC
**Control:** Other not-for-profit (including NFP Corporation) **Service:** General Medical and Surgical

**Staffed Beds: 475 Admissions: 22901 Census: 309 Outpatient Visits:** 309804 **Births: 2233 Total Expense ($000):** 474343 **Payroll Expense ($000):** 154890 **Personnel: 2782**

## WOODBRIDGE—Prince William County

★ ◇ **SENTARA NORTHERN VIRGINIA MEDICAL CENTER (490113)**, 2300 Opitz Boulevard, Zip 22191-3399; tel. 703/523-1000 **A**2 9 10 21 **F**3 7 8 11 12 13 15 18 20 22 28 29 30 31 34 35 36 40 41 42 45 49 50 51 54 57 59 60 63 65 68 70 71 74 75 76 77 78 79 81 82 84 85 87 89 97 102 107 108 110 111 114 115 118 119 121 126 129 130 132 135 146 147 148 **P**6 **S** Sentara Healthcare, Norfolk, VA
Primary Contact: Stephen D. Porter, President
COO: Valerie E. Keane, FACHE, Vice President Operations
CMO: David M. Schwartz, D.O., Vice President, Medical Affairs
CIO: Thomas Ewing, Director Information Technology
CHR: Brett Willsie, Vice President Human Resources
CNO: Patricia Hill, Senior Director Nurse Executive
Web address: www.sentara.com/northernvirginia
**Control:** Other not-for-profit (including NFP Corporation) **Service:** General Medical and Surgical

**Staffed Beds: 181 Admissions: 10032 Census: 109 Outpatient Visits:** 367978 **Births: 1942 Total Expense ($000):** 210081 **Payroll Expense ($000): 89585 Personnel: 1143**

**VA**

**WOODSTOCK—Shenandoah County**

✠ **SHENANDOAH MEMORIAL HOSPITAL (491305)**, 759 South Main Street,
Zip 22664–1127; tel. 540/459–1100 **A**1 9 10 18 **F**3 11 15 28 29 30 35 40
45 50 53 57 59 64 65 68 69 70 75 77 79 81 82 87 92 93 97 107 108 110
114 118 119 130 132 133 135 146 148 **S** Valley Health System,
Winchester, VA
Primary Contact: Floyd Heater, President
CMO: Greg Byrd, Vice President Medical Affairs
CIO: James Burton, Vice President and Chief Information Officer, Valley Health
CNO: April McClain, R.N., Director, Inpatient Nursing
Web address: www.valleyhealthlink.com/shenandoah
**Control:** Other not–for–profit (including NFP Corporation) **Service:** General
Medical and Surgical

| | |
|---|---|
| **Staffed Beds:** 25 **Admissions:** 1614 **Census:** 17 **Outpatient Visits:** 63580 **Births:** 0 **Total Expense ($000):** 46290 **Payroll Expense ($000):** 15992 **Personnel:** 267 | |

**WYTHEVILLE—Wythe County**

✠ **WYTHE COUNTY COMMUNITY HOSPITAL (490111)**, 600 West Ridge Road,
Zip 24382–1099; tel. 276/228–0200 **A**1 2 9 10 20 **F**3 12 15 28 29 34 35 40
45 50 51 55 57 62 63 64 68 70 77 79 81 82 84 85 87 91 92 93 99 107
108 111 119 128 129 132 133 135 146 147 148 **P**6 **S** LifePoint Health,
Brentwood, TN
Primary Contact: Chad Melton, Chief Executive Officer
CFO: John D. White, Chief Financial Officer
CMO: George Farrell, M.D., Chief of Staff
CIO: Andrea Harless, Director Information Services
CHR: Kristie Walker, Director of Human Resources
CNO: Theresa Dix, R.N., Chief Nursing Officer
Web address: www.wcchcares.com
**Control:** Corporation, Investor–owned, for–profit **Service:** General Medical and
Surgical

| | |
|---|---|
| **Staffed Beds:** 70 **Admissions:** 2510 **Census:** 24 **Outpatient Visits:** 36000 **Births:** 327 **Total Expense ($000):** 43600 **Payroll Expense ($000):** 21000 | |

**VA**

---

**Hospital, Medicare Provider Number, Address, Telephone, Approval, Facility, and Physician Codes, Health Care System**

★ American Hospital Association (AHA) membership ○ Healthcare Facilities Accreditation Program ⇑ Center for Improvement in Healthcare Quality Accreditation
☐ The Joint Commission accreditation ◇ DNV Healthcare Inc. accreditation △ Commission on Accreditation of Rehabilitation Facilities (CARF) accreditation

# WASHINGTON

## ABERDEEN—Grays Harbor County

☐ **GRAYS HARBOR COMMUNITY HOSPITAL (500031)**, 915 Anderson Drive, Zip 98520–1097; tel. 360/532–8330 **A**1 9 10 20 **F**1 3 15 32 34 35 40 43 50 54 59 64 65 67 75 82 86 90 97 107 110 119 127 128 130 146
Primary Contact: Tom Jensen, Chief Executive Officer
COO: Thomas Hightower, R.N., Chief Operating Officer
CFO: Joe Vessey, Chief Financial Officer
CMO: Bill Hofmann, M.D., Chief Medical Staff
CIO: Scott Quigley, Director Information Services
CHR: Julie Feller, Director Human Resources
Web address: www.ghchwa.org
**Control:** Other not–for–profit (including NFP Corporation) **Service:** General Medical and Surgical

**Staffed Beds:** 105 **Admissions:** 4322 **Census:** 47 **Births:** 536 **Total Expense ($000):** 101331 **Payroll Expense ($000):** 38428

## ANACORTES—Skagit County

★ ◇ **ISLAND HOSPITAL (500007)**, 1211 24th Street, Zip 98221–2562; tel. 360/299–1300 **A**2 9 10 21 **F**3 8 11 13 15 28 29 30 31 34 35 40 43 45 50 53 57 59 62 64 70 75 76 77 78 79 81 82 85 86 89 93 99 100 102 104 107 108 110 111 114 115 116 119 127 129 130 132 134 135 144 146 147 148 **P**6 8
Primary Contact: Vincent Oliver, Administrator
CFO: Elise Cutter, Chief Financial Officer
CIO: Tom Bluhm, Director Information Systems
CNO: Lois Pate, R.N., Chief Nursing Officer
Web address: www.islandhospital.org
**Control:** Hospital district or authority, Government, nonfederal **Service:** General Medical and Surgical

**Staffed Beds:** 43 **Admissions:** 2993 **Census:** 27 **Outpatient Visits:** 197972 **Births:** 422 **Total Expense ($000):** 86948 **Payroll Expense ($000):** 37319 **Personnel:** 438

## ARLINGTON—Snohomish County

◇ **CASCADE VALLEY HOSPITAL AND CLINICS (500060)**, 330 South Stillaguamish Avenue, Zip 98223–1642; tel. 360/435–2133, (Nonreporting) **A**9 10 21
Primary Contact: W. Clark Jones, Superintendent and Administrator
CFO: Ardis Schmiege, Chief Financial Officer
CMO: Peter Wolff, M.D., President Medical Staff
CIO: Heather Logan, Assistant Administrator Diagnostic and Support Services
CHR: Barbara White, Director Human Resources
CNO: Michelle Sand, R.N., Assistant Administrator Patient Care Serices and Risk Manager
Web address: www.cascadevalley.org
**Control:** Hospital district or authority, Government, nonfederal **Service:** General Medical and Surgical

**Staffed Beds:** 48

## AUBURN—King County

☐ △ **MULTICARE AUBURN MEDICAL CENTER (500015)**, 202 North Division, Plaza One, Zip 98001–4908; tel. 253/833–7711 **A**1 7 9 10 **F**3 13 15 18 20 22 28 29 30 34 35 40 41 43 45 49 51 57 64 65 68 70 73 74 75 76 77 79 81 84 85 87 93 98 102 103 107 108 110 111 114 115 119 124 126 129 130 132 135 146 148 **S** MultiCare Health System, Tacoma, WA
Primary Contact: David Nicewonger, Chief Operating Officer
COO: David Nicewonger, Chief Operating Officer
CMO: Chad Krilich, M.D., Physician Executive
CNO: Roseanna Bell, Nurse Executive
Web address: www.auburnregional.com
**Control:** Other not–for–profit (including NFP Corporation) **Service:** General Medical and Surgical

**Staffed Beds:** 173 **Admissions:** 6828 **Census:** 93 **Outpatient Visits:** 60937 **Births:** 1207 **Total Expense ($000):** 116839 **Payroll Expense ($000):** 59189 **Personnel:** 647

## BELLEVUE—King County

✪ **OVERLAKE MEDICAL CENTER (500051)**, 1035 116th Avenue N.E., Zip 98004–4604; tel. 425/688–5000 **A**1 2 9 10 **F**3 11 12 13 15 17 18 20 22 24 26 29 30 31 34 35 40 43 44 45 46 48 49 56 57 58 59 64 68 70 72 74 75 76 77 78 79 81 84 85 86 87 91 92 93 97 98 100 102 104 105 107 108 110 111 114 115 116 117 118 119 120 121 123 124 126 130 132 134 144 145 146 147 148 **P**6
Primary Contact: J. Michael Marsh, President and Chief Executive Officer
COO: Thomas DeBord, Chief Operating Officer
CFO: Gary McLaughlin, Executive Vice President Finance and Chief Financial Officer
CMO: David Knoepfler, M.D., Chief Medical Officer
CHR: Lisa M. Brock, Chief Human Resource Officer
CNO: Julie Clayton, R.N., Chief Nursing Officer and Vice President Patient Care Services
Web address: www.overlakehospital.org
**Control:** Other not–for–profit (including NFP Corporation) **Service:** General Medical and Surgical

**Staffed Beds:** 281 **Admissions:** 17207 **Census:** 170 **Outpatient Visits:** 231584 **Births:** 3551 **Total Expense ($000):** 418477 **Payroll Expense ($000):** 186937 **Personnel:** 1941

## BELLINGHAM—Whatcom County

★ △ ◇ **PEACEHEALTH ST. JOSEPH MEDICAL CENTER (500030)**, 2901 Squalicum Parkway, Zip 98225–1851; tel. 360/734–5400 **A**2 5 7 9 10 20 21 **F**2 3 13 17 18 20 22 24 26 28 29 30 31 34 35 40 41 43 45 46 47 48 49 50 51 56 57 58 59 63 64 65 70 74 75 76 77 78 79 81 84 85 86 87 89 90 92 93 94 96 97 98 106 107 108 109 114 115 118 119 120 121 123 129 130 131 132 135 141 146 148 **S** PeaceHealth, Vancouver, WA
Primary Contact: Nancy Steiger, R.N., FACHE, Chief Executive Officer and Chief Mission Officer, Northwest Network
COO: Stephen R. Omta, Chief Operating Officer
CFO: Dale Zender, Regional Vice President Finance and Chief Financial Officer
CMO: Chris Sprowl, M.D., Vice President
CIO: Marc Pierson, M.D., Vice President Clinical Information and Quality
CHR: Cindy C. Klein, Vice President Human Resources
Web address: www.peacehealth.org
**Control:** Church–operated, Nongovernment, not–for profit **Service:** General Medical and Surgical

**Staffed Beds:** 253 **Admissions:** 14845 **Census:** 165 **Births:** 1705 **Total Expense ($000):** 418206 **Payroll Expense ($000):** 165541

**ST. JOSEPH HOSPITAL** See PeaceHealth St. Joseph Medical Center

## BREMERTON—Kitsap County

✪ **HARRISON MEDICAL CENTER (500039)**, 2520 Cherry Avenue, Zip 98310–4229; tel. 360/744–3911 **A**1 2 9 10 **F**3 11 12 13 15 18 20 22 24 26 28 29 30 31 34 35 37 38 40 43 44 45 46 49 50 54 57 59 64 65 70 73 74 75 76 77 78 79 80 81 82 84 85 86 87 93 94 96 107 108 110 111 114 115 117 119 120 121 124 126 129 130 132 135 144 146 147 148 **S** Catholic Health Initiatives, Englewood, CO
Primary Contact: David W. Schultz, FACHE, President
COO: Adar Palis, Executive Vice President and Chief Operating Officer
CFO: Mike Fitzgerald, Chief Financial Officer
CMO: Michael Anderson, M.D., Senior Vice President Quality and Chief Medical Officer
CIO: Rand Strobel, Regional Chief Information Officer, Information Technology Services
CHR: Marie LaMarche, Executive Director, Human Resources, Organizational Development, Employee Health
CNO: Jeanell Rasmussen, R.N., Senior Vice President and Chief Nursing Officer
Web address: www.harrisonmedical.org
**Control:** Church–operated, Nongovernment, not–for profit **Service:** General Medical and Surgical

**Staffed Beds:** 260 **Admissions:** 13760 **Census:** 154 **Outpatient Visits:** 194693 **Births:** 1765 **Total Expense ($000):** 384370 **Payroll Expense ($000):** 161799 **Personnel:** 2019

✪ **NAVAL HOSPITAL BREMERTON**, One Boone Road, Zip 98312–1898; tel. 360/475–4000 **A**1 3 5 **F**3 5 8 13 15 18 29 30 32 33 34 35 38 39 40 43 45 46 47 50 53 54 57 58 59 64 65 70 74 75 76 77 79 81 82 85 86 87 92 93 97 99 100 101 104 107 108 110 111 114 115 119 130 131 132 134 135 144 146 147 **S** Bureau of Medicine and Surgery, Department of the Navy, Washington, DC
Primary Contact: Commander Jeffrey Klinger, Director for Administration
CFO: Judith Hogan, Comptroller and Director Resources and Logistics
CIO: Patrick Flaherty, Director Management Information
Web address: www.med.navy.mil/sites/nhbrem/Pages/default.aspx
**Control:** Navy, Government, federal **Service:** General Medical and Surgical

**Staffed Beds:** 30 **Admissions:** 1924 **Census:** 11 **Outpatient Visits:** 304484 **Births:** 710 **Personnel:** 1594

## BREWSTER—Okanogan County

**THREE RIVERS HOSPITAL (501324)**, 507 Hospital Way, Zip 98812–0577, Mailing Address: P.O. Box 577, Zip 98812–0577; tel. 509/689–2517, (Nonreporting) **A**9 10 18
Primary Contact: Scott Graham, Chief Executive Officer
CFO: Jennifer Munson, Chief Financial Officer
CMO: Gordon Tagge, M.D., President Medical Staff
CIO: Edgar Alejandro Arellano, Chief Information Technologist
CHR: Anita Fisk, Director Human Resources
CNO: Gretchen Aguilar, Director Patient Care and Chief Nursing Officer
Web address: www.threerivershospital.net
**Control:** Hospital district or authority, Government, nonfederal **Service:** General Medical and Surgical

**Staffed Beds:** 20

## BURIEN—King County

✠ △ **HIGHLINE MEDICAL CENTER (500011)**, 16251 Sylvester Road S.W., Zip 98166–3052; tel. 206/244–9970, (Includes HIGHLINE SPECIALTY CENTER, 12844 MILITARY ROAD FORK, TUKWILA, ZIP 98168; MARK BENEDUM, ADMINISTRATOR ) **A**1 2 7 9 10 **F**3 8 11 13 15 18 22 29 30 34 35 38 40 43 44 45 49 50 51 57 59 70 72 74 75 76 80 81 85 86 87 92 93 107 108 110 111 114 115 117 119 130 132 135 146 147 **S** Catholic Health Initiatives, Englewood, CO
Primary Contact: Mark Benedum, Chief Executive Officer
CMO: Dennis De Leon, M.D., Associate Chief Medical Officer and Vice President Medical Affairs
CHR: Grace M. Henley, Assistant Administrator Human Resources
CNO: Kim Baisch, R.N., Associate Vice President Patient Care Services
Web address: www.hchnet.org
**Control:** Church–operated, Nongovernment, not–for profit **Service:** General Medical and Surgical

**Staffed Beds:** 128 **Admissions:** 6967 **Census:** 86 **Outpatient Visits:** 116132 **Births:** 941 **Total Expense ($000):** 153448 **Payroll Expense ($000):** 62192 **Personnel:** 886

☐ **REGIONAL HOSPITAL FOR RESPIRATORY AND COMPLEX CARE (502001)**, 16251 Sylvester Road S.W., Zip 98166–3017; tel. 206/248–4548 **A**1 10 **F**1 29 30 50 85 87 130 135 148
Primary Contact: Anne McBride, Executive Vice President and Chief Financial Officer
CMO: Embra Roper, Chief Medical Officer
CHR: Valerie Albano, Director, Human Resources
CNO: Christi Sifri, Chief Nursing Executive
Web address: www.regionalhospital.org
**Control:** Church–operated, Nongovernment, not–for profit **Service:** Long–Term Acute Care hospital

**Staffed Beds:** 26 **Admissions:** 189 **Census:** 21 **Outpatient Visits:** 0 **Births:** 0 **Total Expense ($000):** 17546 **Payroll Expense ($000):** 7229

## CENTRALIA—Lewis County

✠ **PROVIDENCE CENTRALIA HOSPITAL (500019)**, 914 South Scheuber Road, Zip 98531–9027; tel. 360/736–2803 **A**1 3 9 10 20 **F**3 8 11 13 15 30 31 34 35 40 43 45 47 51 57 58 59 64 68 70 75 76 77 78 79 80 81 82 83 84 85 86 87 93 107 108 110 111 114 115 116 117 118 119 120 121 123 124 130 131 132 146 148 **S** Providence Health & Services, Renton, WA
Primary Contact: Medrice Coluccio, R.N., Southwest Region Chief Executive
CFO: Denise Marroni, Chief Financial Officer
CMO: Kevin Caserta, M.D., Chief Medical Officer
CIO: Kerry Miles, Site Director
CHR: Susan Meenk, Vice President Service Area
CNO: Michelle James, Regional Chief Nursing Officer
Web address: www.providence.org
**Control:** Church–operated, Nongovernment, not–for profit **Service:** General Medical and Surgical

**Staffed Beds:** 91 **Admissions:** 5189 **Census:** 45 **Outpatient Visits:** 201190 **Births:** 662 **Total Expense ($000):** 97053 **Payroll Expense ($000):** 45244 **Personnel:** 528

## CHELAN—Chelan County

★ **LAKE CHELAN COMMUNITY HOSPITAL (501334)**, 503 East Highland Avenue, Zip 98816–8631, Mailing Address: P.O. Box 908, Zip 98816–0908; tel. 509/682–3300 **A**9 10 18 **F**4 5 7 8 11 13 15 29 30 32 34 35 36 38 40 41 43 44 45 50 56 57 59 62 63 64 65 66 68 71 74 75 76 77 79 81 84 85 86 87 91 92 93 94 96 97 99 100 101 102 103 104 106 107 108 110 111 119 125 127 130 131 132 133 135 143 144 146 147 148 **P**6
Primary Contact: Kevin Abel, Chief Executive Officer
COO: Brad Hankins, Chief Operating Quality Officer
CFO: Vickie Bodle, Chief Financial Officer
CIO: Ross Hurd, Chief Information Officer
CHR: DeLynn K. Cook, Director Human Resources
CNO: Carol Nunley Velasquez, R.N., Chief Nursing Officer
Web address: www.lakechelancommunityhospital.com
**Control:** Hospital district or authority, Government, nonfederal **Service:** General Medical and Surgical

**Staffed Beds:** 25 **Admissions:** 771 **Census:** 16 **Outpatient Visits:** 27752 **Births:** 91 **Total Expense ($000):** 24020 **Payroll Expense ($000):** 14206 **Personnel:** 224

## CHEWELAH—Stevens County

✠ **PROVIDENCE ST. JOSEPH'S HOSPITAL (501309)**, 500 East Webster Street, Zip 99109–9523; tel. 509/935–8211, (Total facility includes 40 beds in nursing home–type unit) **A**1 9 10 18 **F**3 8 10 11 15 29 30 34 35 40 43 44 45 57 59 65 75 79 81 82 84 87 91 93 107 114 119 128 133 146 148 **P**6 **S** Providence Health & Services, Renton, WA
Primary Contact: Ronald G. Rehn, Chief Executive Officer
CFO: Helen Andrus, Chief Financial Officer
CMO: Jeff Collins, Chief Medical Officer
CNO: Deborah Watson, R.N., Chief Nursing Officer
Web address: www.washington.providence.org/hospitals/st–josephs–hospital/
**Control:** Church–operated, Nongovernment, not–for profit **Service:** General Medical and Surgical

**Staffed Beds:** 65 **Admissions:** 409 **Census:** 44 **Outpatient Visits:** 24999 **Births:** 0 **Total Expense ($000):** 14168 **Payroll Expense ($000):** 8698 **Personnel:** 137

## CLARKSTON—Asotin County

★ ◇ **TRI–STATE MEMORIAL HOSPITAL (501332)**, 1221 Highland Avenue, Zip 99403–2829, Mailing Address: P.O. Box 189, Zip 99403–0189; tel. 509/758–5511, (Nonreporting) **A**9 10 18 21
Primary Contact: Donald Wee, Chief Executive Officer
CFO: Alex Town, Vice President Finance
CMO: Don Greggain, M.D., Physician Network Director
CIO: Joleen Carper, Vice President Quality and Risk
CHR: Regana Davis, Vice President Human Resources
CNO: Rhonda Mason, Vice President of Patient Care Services
Web address: www.tristatehospital.org
**Control:** Other not–for–profit (including NFP Corporation) **Service:** General Medical and Surgical

**Staffed Beds:** 35

## COLFAX—Whitman County

★ **WHITMAN HOSPITAL AND MEDICAL CENTER (501327)**, 1200 West Fairview Street, Zip 99111–9579; tel. 509/397–3435 **A**9 10 18 **F**3 13 15 29 35 40 43 45 50 53 64 75 76 81 84 85 87 93 107 110 114 119 130 133 **S** Providence Health & Services, Renton, WA
Primary Contact: Hank Hanigan, Administrator and Chief Executive Officer
CFO: Jim Heilsberg, Chief Financial Officer and Chief Information Officer
CMO: W. Kimball Mellor, M.D., Chief Medical Officer
CIO: Jim Heilsberg, Chief Financial Officer and Chief Information Officer
CHR: Michelle Ellis, Director Human Resources
CNO: Denise Fowler, R.N., Chief Clinical Officer
Web address: www.whitmanhospital.com
**Control:** Hospital district or authority, Government, nonfederal **Service:** General Medical and Surgical

**Staffed Beds:** 25 **Admissions:** 512 **Census:** 5 **Outpatient Visits:** 15795 **Births:** 54 **Total Expense ($000):** 23215 **Payroll Expense ($000):** 9385 **Personnel:** 169

**WA**

---

## COLVILLE—Stevens County

☒ **PROVIDENCE MOUNT CARMEL HOSPITAL (501326)**, 982 East Columbia Avenue, Zip 99114–3352; tel. 509/685–5100 **A**1 3 9 10 18 **F**3 11 13 15 29 30 34 40 43 44 45 57 59 64 70 75 76 77 79 81 82 84 85 86 87 93 107 108 115 118 119 123 129 131 132 133 135 146 148 **P**6 **S** Providence Health & Services, Renton, WA
Primary Contact: Ronald G. Rehn, Chief Executive Officer
CFO: Helen Andrus, Chief Financial Officer
CMO: Deborah Montowski, M.D., Chief Medical Officer
CHR: Stacey Cloke, Vice President Human Resources
CNO: Deborah Watson, R.N., Senior Director of Nursing and Vice President, Patient Care Services
Web address: www.mtcarmelhospital.org
**Control:** Church–operated, Nongovernment, not–for profit **Service:** General Medical and Surgical

**Staffed Beds:** 25 **Admissions:** 1194 **Census:** 12 **Outpatient Visits:** 66296 **Births:** 269 **Total Expense ($000):** 29366 **Payroll Expense ($000):** 14722 **Personnel:** 220

## COUPEVILLE—Island County

★ **WHIDBEY GENERAL HOSPITAL (501339)**, 101 North Main Street, Zip 98239–3413; tel. 360/678–5151, (Nonreporting) **A**2 9 10 18
Primary Contact: Geri Forbes, Chief Executive Officer
CMO: Gabe Barrio, M.D., Chief of Staff
CNO: Linda Stephens Gipson, MSN, Chief Nursing Officer
Web address: www.whidbeygen.org
**Control:** Hospital district or authority, Government, nonfederal **Service:** General Medical and Surgical

**Staffed Beds:** 25

## DAVENPORT—Lincoln County

★ **LINCOLN HOSPITAL (501305)**, 10 Nicholls Street, Zip 99122–9729; tel. 509/725–7101, (Total facility includes 35 beds in nursing home–type unit) **A**9 10 18 **F**7 10 11 15 29 40 46 54 57 59 64 65 77 81 85 93 97 107 119 128 130 133 135 148
Primary Contact: Thomas J. Martin, Administrator
CFO: Tyson Lacy, Chief Financial Officer
CMO: Fred Reed, M.D., Chief of Staff
CIO: Elliott Donson, Chief Information Specialist
CHR: Becky Bailey, Director Human Resources
CNO: Jennifer Larmer, Chief Clinical Officer
Web address: www.lincolnhospital.org
**Control:** Hospital district or authority, Government, nonfederal **Service:** General Medical and Surgical

**Staffed Beds:** 60 **Admissions:** 505 **Census:** 14 **Outpatient Visits:** 24467

## DAYTON—Columbia County

**COLUMBIA COUNTY HEALTH SYSTEM (501302)**, 1012 South Third Street, Zip 99328–1696; tel. 509/382–2531 **A**9 10 18 **F**11 15 34 35 40 50 57 64 65 68 92 93 97 107 127 133 146 148
Primary Contact: Jon D. Smiley, Interim Chief Executive Officer
COO: Shane McGuire, Chief Operations Officer and Information Technology Director
CFO: Steve Geidl, Chief Financial Officer
CIO: Shane McGuire, Chief Operations Officer and Information Technology Director
CHR: Steven J. Stahl, Director Human Resources
CNO: Stephanie Carpenter, Director of Nursing Services
Web address: www.cchd–wa.org
**Control:** Hospital district or authority, Government, nonfederal **Service:** General Medical and Surgical

**Staffed Beds:** 44 **Admissions:** 237 **Census:** 44 **Outpatient Visits:** 9039 **Births:** 0 **Total Expense ($000):** 12284 **Payroll Expense ($000):** 5639 **Personnel:** 129

## EDMONDS—Snohomish County

**STEVENS HEALTHCARE** See Swedish/Edmonds

☒ **SWEDISH/EDMONDS (500026)**, 21601 76th Avenue West, Zip 98026–7506; tel. 425/640–4000 **A**1 2 9 10 **F**2 3 11 13 15 18 20 22 28 29 30 31 34 35 38 40 41 43 45 49 56 59 60 61 64 65 68 70 73 74 75 76 77 78 79 81 82 84 85 87 92 93 96 98 100 101 102 103 104 105 107 108 111 114 118 119 124 129 130 131 132 135 141 146 147 148 **P**6 **S** Swedish Health Services, Seattle, WA
Primary Contact: Jennifer Graves, R.N., MS, Chief Executive
COO: Sarah Zabel, Vice President, Operations
CMO: Tim Roddy, M.D., Vice President Medical Affairs
CNO: Nancy Wood, R.N., Nurse Executive
Web address: www.swedish.org
**Control:** Other not–for–profit (including NFP Corporation) **Service:** General Medical and Surgical

**Staffed Beds:** 164 **Admissions:** 8341 **Census:** 107 **Outpatient Visits:** 157549 **Births:** 1140 **Total Expense ($000):** 204475 **Payroll Expense ($000):** 84644 **Personnel:** 1060

## ELLENSBURG—Kittitas County

★ **KITTITAS VALLEY HEALTHCARE (501333)**, 603 South Chestnut Street, Zip 98926–3875; tel. 509/962–7302, (Nonreporting) **A**3 9 10 18
Primary Contact: Paul E. Nurick, Chief Executive Officer
COO: Catherine Bambrick, Chief Operating Officer
CFO: Libby Allgood, Chief Financial Officer
CMO: Don Solberg, M.D., Chief Medical Officer
CNO: Rhonda C. Holden, R.N., Chief Nursing Officer
Web address: www.kvhealthcare.org
**Control:** Hospital district or authority, Government, nonfederal **Service:** General Medical and Surgical

**Staffed Beds:** 25

## ELMA—Grays Harbor County

**SUMMIT PACIFIC MEDICAL CENTER (501304)**, 600 East Main Street, Zip 98541–9560; tel. 360/346–2222, (Nonreporting) **A**9 10 18
Primary Contact: Renee K. Jensen, Chief Executive Officer
COO: Tim G. O'Haver, Chief Operating Officer
CFO: William Callicoat, Chief Financial Officer
CMO: William Hurley, M.D., Chief Medical Officer
CIO: Jeff Painter, Manager Information Technology
CHR: Mindy Portchy, Manager Human Resources
CNO: Brenda West, R.N., Chief Nursing Officer
Web address: www.markreed.org
**Control:** Corporation, Investor–owned, for–profit **Service:** General Medical and Surgical

**Staffed Beds:** 6

## ENUMCLAW—King County

★ **ST. ELIZABETH HOSPITAL (501335)**, 1455 Battersby Avenue, Zip 98022–3634, Mailing Address: P.O. Box 218, Zip 98022–0218; tel. 360/802–8800 **A**9 10 18 **F**3 13 15 18 29 30 34 35 38 40 44 45 50 57 64 74 75 76 79 81 85 87 107 108 110 111 115 119 135 146 **S** Catholic Health Initiatives, Englewood, CO
Primary Contact: Anthony McLean, Interim President
COO: Joseph Wilczek, Chief Executive Officer
CFO: Philip Hjembo, Chief Financial Officer
CHR: Jerilyn Ray, Manager Human Resources
Web address: www.fhshealth.org
**Control:** Church–operated, Nongovernment, not–for profit **Service:** General Medical and Surgical

**Staffed Beds:** 25 **Admissions:** 1504 **Census:** 15 **Outpatient Visits:** 29751 **Births:** 304 **Total Expense ($000):** 45056 **Payroll Expense ($000):** 18370 **Personnel:** 225

## EPHRATA—Grant County

★ **COLUMBIA BASIN HOSPITAL (501317)**, 200 Nat Washington Way, Zip 98823–1982; tel. 509/754–4631, (Total facility includes 12 beds in nursing home–type unit) **A**9 10 18 **F**3 10 11 34 40 50 54 56 57 59 64 68 75 87 93 96 97 107 119 127 130 133 135 143 146 148 **P**6
Primary Contact: Rosalinda Kibby, Superintendent and Administrator
CFO: Rhonda Handley, Chief Financial Officer
CMO: Lowell C. Allred, M.D., Chief of Staff
CHR: Suzanne Little, Human Resources Specialist
Web address: www.columbiabasinhospital.org
**Control:** Hospital district or authority, Government, nonfederal **Service:** General Medical and Surgical

**Staffed Beds:** 25 **Admissions:** 295 **Census:** 18 **Outpatient Visits:** 17560 **Births:** 0 **Total Expense ($000):** 16033 **Payroll Expense ($000):** 6800 **Personnel:** 144

**WA**

*Many Facility Codes have changed. Please refer to the AHA Guide Code Chart.* © 2015 AHA Guide

## EVERETT—Snohomish County

⊞ △ **PROVIDENCE REGIONAL MEDICAL CENTER EVERETT (500014)**, 1321 Colby Avenue, Zip 98201–1665, Mailing Address: P.O. Box 1147, Zip 98206–1147; tel. 425/261–2000, (Includes PROVIDENCE EVERETT MEDICAL CENTER – COLBY CAMPUS, 1321 Colby Avenue, Zip 98206, Mailing Address: P.O. Box 1147, Zip 98206; tel. 425/261–2000; PROVIDENCE EVERETT MEDICAL CENTER – PACIFIC CAMPUS, Pacific and Nassau Streets, Zip 98201, Mailing Address: P.O. Box 1067, Zip 98206–1067; tel. 206/258–7123) **A**1 2 3 5 7 9 10 **F**3 4 5 8 11 12 13 15 17 18 20 22 24 26 28 29 30 31 32 34 35 36 38 40 43 44 45 46 47 48 49 50 53 54 55 56 57 58 59 60 61 64 65 66 68 70 72 73 74 75 76 77 78 79 80 81 82 84 85 86 87 89 90 93 94 96 97 100 107 108 109 111 114 115 116 117 118 119 120 121 123 124 126 129 130 131 132 135 144 145 146 147 148 **P**6 8 **S** Providence Health & Services, Renton, WA
Primary Contact: Preston M. Simmons, FACHE, Chief Executive Officer
COO: Kim Williams, R.N., Chief Operating Officer
CFO: Sheri Feeney, Chief Financial Officer
CMO: Joanne Roberts, M.D., Chief Medical Officer
CIO: Matt Wonser, Director, Information Services
CHR: Lori A. Vocca, Vice President Human Resources
CNO: Barbara M. Hyland–Hill, R.N., Chief Nursing Officer
Web address: www.providence.org
**Control:** Church–operated, Nongovernment, not–for profit **Service:** General Medical and Surgical

**Staffed Beds:** 501 **Admissions:** 28687 **Census:** 359 **Outpatient Visits:** 445514 **Births:** 4498 **Total Expense ($000):** 462229 **Payroll Expense ($000):** 203269 **Personnel:** 3418

## FEDERAL WAY—King County

⊞ **ST. FRANCIS HOSPITAL (500141)**, 34515 Ninth Avenue South, Zip 98003–6799; tel. 253/944–8100 **A**1 2 9 10 **F**3 8 11 12 13 15 18 20 22 29 30 31 32 34 35 38 40 44 45 49 50 51 57 59 64 65 70 73 74 75 76 77 78 79 80 81 85 86 87 92 93 107 108 110 111 114 117 119 126 129 130 132 135 146 147 **S** Catholic Health Initiatives, Englewood, CO
Primary Contact: Anthony McLean, President
CFO: Mike Fitzgerald, Chief Financial Officer
CMO: Mark C. Adams, M.D., Chief Medical Officer
CIO: Rand Strobel, Regional Chief Information Officer
CHR: Les Soltis, Director – Human Resources
CNO: Laurie Brown, R.N., Chief Nursing Officer
Web address: www.fhshealth.org
**Control:** Church–operated, Nongovernment, not–for profit **Service:** General Medical and Surgical

**Staffed Beds:** 118 **Admissions:** 9540 **Census:** 83 **Outpatient Visits:** 143600 **Births:** 1172 **Total Expense ($000):** 183774 **Payroll Expense ($000):** 73486 **Personnel:** 915

## FORKS—Clallam County

◇ **FORKS COMMUNITY HOSPITAL (501325)**, 530 Bogachiel Way, Zip 98331–9120; tel. 360/374–6271, (Nonreporting) **A**9 10 18 21
Primary Contact: David B. Selman, FACHE, Administrator
CFO: Tim Cournyer, Chief Financial Officer
CIO: Andrea Perkins–Peppers, Chief Information Officer
CHR: Cindy Paget, Chief Human Resources Officer
CNO: Laura Kripinski, Chief Nursing Officer
Web address: www.forkshospital.org
**Control:** Hospital district or authority, Government, nonfederal **Service:** General Medical and Surgical

**Staffed Beds:** 45

## FRIDAY HARBOR—San Juan County

★ ◇ **PEACEHEALTH PEACE ISLAND MEDICAL CENTER (501340)**, 1117 Spring Street, Zip 98250–9782; tel. 360/378–2141 **A**9 10 18 21 **F**3 11 15 29 30 31 34 35 40 44 45 46 47 48 49 50 57 59 64 65 68 77 78 81 84 85 87 97 102 107 108 110 114 119 130 133 135 146 148 **S** PeaceHealth, Vancouver, WA
Primary Contact: James R. Barnhart, Chief Administrator Officer
CFO: Carolyn Foster, Chief Financial Officer
CMO: Michael Sullivan, M.D., Medical Director Emergency Services
CHR: Lorraine Allison, Human Resource Partner
CNO: Merry Ann Keane, Chief Nursing Officer and Director of Clinical Services
Web address: www.peacehealth.org
**Control:** Other not–for–profit (including NFP Corporation) **Service:** General Medical and Surgical

**Staffed Beds:** 10 **Admissions:** 92 **Census:** 1 **Outpatient Visits:** 9987 **Births:** 0 **Total Expense ($000):** 12720 **Payroll Expense ($000):** 5356 **Personnel:** 50

## GIG HARBOR—Pierce County

⊞ **ST. ANTHONY HOSPITAL (500151)**, 11567 Canterwood Boulevard N.W., Zip 98332–5812; tel. 253/530–2000 **A**1 9 10 **F**3 11 12 15 18 20 22 29 30 31 34 38 40 44 45 49 50 51 57 59 60 64 70 74 75 78 79 81 85 87 92 93 107 108 110 111 115 119 126 129 130 132 135 146 147 **S** Catholic Health Initiatives, Englewood, CO
Primary Contact: David W. Schultz, FACHE, President
Web address: www.fhshealth.org/
**Control:** Church–operated, Nongovernment, not–for profit **Service:** General Medical and Surgical

**Staffed Beds:** 80 **Admissions:** 5014 **Census:** 55 **Outpatient Visits:** 60937 **Births:** 0 **Total Expense ($000):** 108181 **Payroll Expense ($000):** 39733 **Personnel:** 538

## GOLDENDALE—Klickitat County

★ **KLICKITAT VALLEY HEALTH (501316)**, 310 South Roosevelt Avenue, Zip 98620–9201; tel. 509/773–4022 **A**3 9 10 18 **F**3 8 15 18 29 30 34 35 40 43 45 57 59 62 63 64 65 68 75 77 81 83 84 85 97 107 119 127 128 130 133 135 146 148
Primary Contact: Leslie Hiebert, Chief Executive Officer
CFO: Jamie Eldred, Controller
CMO: Rod Krehbiel, M.D., Chief of Staff
CIO: Jonathan Hatfield, Supervisor Information Technology
CHR: Herbert Hill, Director Human Resources
CNO: Gwen Cox, Director Nursing Services
Web address: www.kvhealth.net
**Control:** Hospital district or authority, Government, nonfederal **Service:** General Medical and Surgical

**Staffed Beds:** 17 **Admissions:** 251 **Census:** 5 **Outpatient Visits:** 4458 **Births:** 0 **Total Expense ($000):** 22664 **Payroll Expense ($000):** 9037

## GRAND COULEE—Grant County

**COULEE COMMUNITY HOSPITAL** See Coulee Medical Center
**COULEE MEDICAL CENTER (501308)**, 411 Fortuyn Road, Zip 99133–8718; tel. 509/633–1753, (Total facility includes 20 beds in nursing home–type unit) **A**9 10 18 **F**35 40 46 59 65 76 79 81 85 87 97 107 110 119 128 130 133 147 148
Primary Contact: Debbie Bigelow, Chief Executive Officer
CFO: Paul Babcock, Chief Financial Officer
CMO: Andrew Castrodale, M.D., Chief Medical Officer
CHR: Heather McCleary, Director Human Resources
Web address: www.cmccares.org
**Control:** Hospital district or authority, Government, nonfederal **Service:** General Medical and Surgical

**Staffed Beds:** 45 **Admissions:** 397 **Census:** 18

## ILWACO—Pacific County

★ **OCEAN BEACH HOSPITAL (501314)**, 174 First Avenue North, Zip 98624–9137, Mailing Address: P.O. Box H., Zip 98624–0258; tel. 360/642–3181 **A**9 10 18 **F**3 11 12 15 28 29 30 31 34 35 40 43 45 50 57 59 68 75 77 78 81 85 86 87 93 97 102 107 111 114 119 127 128 130 132 133 135 147 **P**6
Primary Contact: Kendall Sawa, R.N., Chief Executive Officer
CFO: Kathy Hubbard, Controller
CMO: Patty Malone, M.D., Chief Medical Officer
CIO: Julie P. Oakes, R.N., Manager Risk and Quality
CHR: Beth Whitton, Director Human Resources
CNO: Linda Kaino, Chief Nursing Officer
Web address: www.oceanbeachhospital.com
**Control:** Hospital district or authority, Government, nonfederal **Service:** General Medical and Surgical

**Staffed Beds:** 15 **Admissions:** 399 **Census:** 3 **Outpatient Visits:** 24385 **Births:** 0 **Total Expense ($000):** 17414 **Payroll Expense ($000):** 8374 **Personnel:** 43

## ISSAQUAH—King County

★ ◇ **SWEDISH/ISSAQUAH (500152)**, 751 N.E. Blakely Drive, Zip 98029–6201; tel. 425/313–4000 **A**3 9 10 21 **F**3 12 13 15 18 20 22 29 30 31 34 35 37 38 40 41 45 48 49 50 56 57 58 59 60 61 64 65 68 70 73 74 75 76 77 78 79 81 82 85 86 87 89 92 93 96 97 102 107 108 110 111 114 115 119 126 129 130 131 132 134 135 141 143 146 147 148 **P**6 **S** Swedish Health Services, Seattle, WA
Primary Contact: Rayburn Lewis, M.D., Chief Executive Officer
Web address: www.swedish.org/issaquah
**Control:** Other not–for–profit (including NFP Corporation) **Service:** General Medical and Surgical

**Staffed Beds:** 80 **Admissions:** 5992 **Census:** 40 **Outpatient Visits:** 100769 **Births:** 1352 **Total Expense ($000):** 155608 **Payroll Expense ($000):** 45978 **Personnel:** 571

**WA**

---

**Hospital, Medicare Provider Number, Address, Telephone, Approval, Facility, and Physician Codes, Health Care System**

★ American Hospital Association (AHA) membership ○ Healthcare Facilities Accreditation Program ⇑ Center for Improvement in Healthcare Quality Accreditation
□ The Joint Commission accreditation ◇ DNV Healthcare Inc. accreditation △ Commission on Accreditation of Rehabilitation Facilities (CARF) accreditation

## KENNEWICK—Benton County

✠ **TRIOS HEALTH (500053)**, 900 South Auburn Street, Zip 99336–5621, Mailing Address: P.O. Box 6128, Zip 99336–0128; tel. 509/586–6111, (Nonreporting) **A**1 2 9 10 13
Primary Contact: Glen Marshall, Chief Executive Officer
CFO: Tony Sudduth, Chief Financial Officer
CIO: Michael Cloutier, Director Information Services
CHR: Russ Keefer, Chief Human Resources Officer
CNO: Diane M. Sanders, Chief Nursing Officer
Web address: www.trioshealth.org
**Control:** Hospital district or authority, Government, nonfederal **Service:** General Medical and Surgical

> **Staffed Beds:** 111

## KIRKLAND—King County

**EVERGREEN HEALTHCARE** See EvergreenHealth

✠ **EVERGREENHEALTH (500124)**, 12040 N.E. 128th Street, Zip 98034–3013; tel. 425/899–1000 **A**1 2 3 5 9 10 **F**3 11 12 13 15 18 20 22 28 29 30 34 35 37 38 40 42 43 44 45 46 49 50 51 54 55 56 57 59 60 62 63 64 65 68 70 71 72 73 74 75 76 78 79 80 81 82 84 85 86 87 89 90 91 92 93 94 95 96 97 100 102 107 108 110 111 114 115 119 120 121 123 124 126 129 130 131 132 134 135 144 146 147 148 **P**4 6
Primary Contact: Robert H. Malte, Chief Executive Officer
COO: David S. Danielson, Senior Vice President Operations
CFO: Chrissy Yamada, CPA, Senior Vice President Finance
CMO: Mitch Weinberg, M.D., Chief of Staff
CIO: Tom Martin, Vice President and Chief Information Officer
Web address: www.evergreenhealthcare.org
**Control:** Hospital district or authority, Government, nonfederal **Service:** General Medical and Surgical

> **Staffed Beds:** 278 **Admissions:** 14707 **Census:** 150 **Outpatient Visits:** 620222 **Births:** 4654 **Total Expense ($000):** 536139 **Payroll Expense ($000):** 270140 **Personnel:** 3162

☐ **FAIRFAX BEHAVIORAL HEALTH (504002)**, 10200 N.E. 132nd Street, Zip 98034–2899; tel. 425/821–2000, (Includes FAIRFAX BEHAVIORAL HEALTH EVERETT, 916 Pacific Avenue, Everett, Zip 98201–4147; tel. 425/821–2000), (Nonreporting) **A**1 9 10 **S** Universal Health Services, Inc., King of Prussia, PA
Primary Contact: Ron Escarda, Chief Executive Officer
COO: Todd Thama, Chief Operating Officer
CFO: Pam Rhoads, Chief Financial Officer
CMO: Samir Aziz, M.D., Medical Director
CHR: Anne Schreiber, Manager Human Resources
Web address: www.fairfaxhospital.com
**Control:** Corporation, Investor–owned, for–profit **Service:** Psychiatric

> **Staffed Beds:** 157

## LAKEWOOD—Pierce County

✠ △ **ST. CLARE HOSPITAL (500021)**, 11315 Bridgeport Way S.W., Zip 98499–3004; tel. 253/985–1711 **A**1 2 3 7 9 10 **F**3 8 29 30 31 34 35 38 40 44 45 49 50 51 57 59 64 65 70 74 75 77 78 79 81 85 86 87 92 93 107 108 111 114 119 126 129 130 132 135 146 **S** Catholic Health Initiatives, Englewood, CO
Primary Contact: Kathy Bressler, R.N., President
COO: Kathy Bressler, R.N., President
CFO: Mike Fitzgerald, Chief Financial Officer
CIO: Bruce Elkington, Regional Chief Information Officer
CHR: David C. Lawson, Senior Vice President Human Resources
Web address: www.fhshealth.org
**Control:** Church–operated, Nongovernment, not–for profit **Service:** General Medical and Surgical

> **Staffed Beds:** 105 **Admissions:** 6593 **Census:** 79 **Outpatient Visits:** 94553 **Births:** 0 **Total Expense ($000):** 129888 **Payroll Expense ($000):** 52986 **Personnel:** 717

## LEAVENWORTH—Chelan County

★ **CASCADE MEDICAL CENTER (501313)**, 817 Commercial Street, Zip 98826–1316; tel. 509/548–5815, (Nonreporting) **A**5 9 10 18
Primary Contact: Diane Blake, Chief Executive Officer
COO: Amy Webb, Chief Operating Officer
CFO: Jim Hopkins, Chief Financial Officer
CMO: Emily Johnston, M.D., Chief Medical Officer
CHR: Reyne Boik, Director Human Resources
Web address: www.cascademedical.org
**Control:** Hospital district or authority, Government, nonfederal **Service:** General Medical and Surgical

> **Staffed Beds:** 9

## LONGVIEW—Cowlitz County

✠ ◇ **PEACEHEALTH ST. JOHN MEDICAL CENTER (500041)**, 1615 Delaware Street, Zip 98632–2367, Mailing Address: P.O. Box 3002, Zip 98632–0302; tel. 360/414–2000 **A**1 2 9 10 19 21 **F**5 11 13 15 18 20 22 26 28 29 30 31 32 33 34 35 38 40 43 45 46 49 50 51 56 57 59 60 61 63 64 65 68 70 71 74 75 76 77 78 79 80 81 82 84 85 93 94 96 97 98 99 100 101 102 104 107 108 109 111 114 115 117 119 120 121 129 130 144 145 146 147 148 **P**6 **S** PeaceHealth, Vancouver, WA
Primary Contact: Kirk Raboin, Chief Administrative Officer
Web address: www.peacehealth.org
**Control:** Hospital district or authority, Government, nonfederal **Service:** General Medical and Surgical

> **Staffed Beds:** 200 **Admissions:** 7729 **Census:** 87 **Outpatient Visits:** 180302 **Births:** 882 **Total Expense ($000):** 250735 **Payroll Expense ($000):** 102534 **Personnel:** 1299

## MEDICAL LAKE—Spokane County

☐ **EASTERN STATE HOSPITAL (504004)**, Maple Street, Zip 99022–0045, Mailing Address: P.O. Box 800, Zip 99022–0800; tel. 509/565–4705, (Nonreporting) **A**1 3 9 10
Primary Contact: Dorothy Sawyer, Chief Executive Officer
Web address: www.dshs.wa.gov/mhsystems/esh.shtml
**Control:** State–Government, nonfederal **Service:** Psychiatric

> **Staffed Beds:** 319

## MONROE—Snohomish County

★ ◇ **EVERGREENHEALTH MONROE (500084)**, 14701 179th S.E., Zip 98272–1108, Mailing Address: P.O. Box 646, Zip 98272–0646; tel. 360/794–7497, (Nonreporting) **A**9 10 21
Primary Contact: Eric P. Jensen, Chief Executive Officer
CFO: Scott Olander, Chief Financial Officer
CMO: Jack Handley, M.D., Chief Medical Officer
CIO: Scott Crader, Director Information Systems
CHR: Jessika A. Groce, Director Human Resources
CNO: Debbie T. Brown, R.N., Chief Nursing Officer
Web address: www.valleygeneral.com
**Control:** Hospital district or authority, Government, nonfederal **Service:** General Medical and Surgical

> **Staffed Beds:** 68

## MORTON—Lewis County

★ **MORTON GENERAL HOSPITAL (501319)**, 521 Adams Avenue, Zip 98356–9323, Mailing Address: P.O. Box 1138, Zip 98356–0019; tel. 360/496–5112 **A**9 10 18 **F**3 34 40 45 85 87 97 107 110 114 119 127 129 148
Primary Contact: Robert D. Campbell, Jr., Interim Chief Executive Officer
CFO: Geoff Hamilton, Interim Chief Financial Officer
CIO: Randy Nielsen, Director Information Technology
CHR: Shannon Kelly, Director Human Resources
CNO: Heidi Anderson, Chief Nursing Officer
Web address: www.mortongeneral.org
**Control:** Hospital district or authority, Government, nonfederal **Service:** General Medical and Surgical

> **Staffed Beds:** 25 **Admissions:** 224 **Census:** 15

## MOSES LAKE—Grant County

★ **SAMARITAN HEALTHCARE (500033)**, 801 East Wheeler Road, Zip 98837–1899; tel. 509/765–5606 **A**9 10 20 **F**3 8 13 15 29 34 35 40 43 45 50 57 59 64 65 68 70 75 76 79 81 86 87 93 97 107 108 110 111 115 118 119 127 130 132 135 144 146 147
Primary Contact: Theresa Sullivan, Chief Operating Officer
COO: Theresa Sullivan, Chief Operating Officer
CFO: Paul Ishizuka, Chief Financial Officer and Chief Operating Officer
CMO: James Irwin, M.D., Chief Medical Officer
CHR: Lisa A. McDaniel, Chief Human Resources Officer
CNO: Kathryn E. Trumbull, R.N., Chief Nursing Officer and Vice President Patient Care Services
Web address: www.samaritanhealthcare.com
**Control:** Hospital district or authority, Government, nonfederal **Service:** General Medical and Surgical

> **Staffed Beds:** 50 **Admissions:** 2853 **Census:** 22 **Outpatient Visits:** 109252 **Births:** 1024 **Total Expense ($000):** 65800 **Payroll Expense ($000):** 31214 **Personnel:** 450

## MOUNT VERNON—Skagit County

★ ◇ **SKAGIT VALLEY HOSPITAL (500003)**, 1415 East Kincaid Street, Zip 98274–4126, Mailing Address: P.O. Box 1376, Zip 98273–1376; tel. 360/424–4111 **A**2 5 9 10 13 19 21 **F**3 9 11 13 18 20 22 26 28 29 30 31 32 34 35 36 40 41 43 45 47 48 49 50 51 54 56 57 58 59 60 62 63 64 68 70 73 74 77 78 79 80 81 82 84 85 86 87 92 93 97 98 100 102 103 107 108 111 114 115 116 117 118 120 121 123 124 127 129 130 144 146 147 148 **P**6
Primary Contact: Gregg Agustin Davidson, FACHE, Chief Executive Officer
COO: Michael T. Liepman, Chief Operating Officer
CFO: Thomas Litaker, Chief Financial Officer
CMO: Connie L. Davis, M.D., Chief Medical Officer
CIO: John Dwight, Chief Information Officer
CHR: Deborah Martin, Assistant Administrator Human Resources
CNO: Roxanne Olason, R.N., Chief Nursing Officer
Web address: www.skagitvalleyhospital.org
**Control:** Hospital district or authority, Government, nonfederal **Service:** General Medical and Surgical

**Staffed Beds:** 137 **Admissions:** 6950 **Census:** 78 **Outpatient Visits:** 495814 **Births:** 1137 **Total Expense ($000):** 268153 **Payroll Expense ($000):** 112004 **Personnel:** 1686

## NEWPORT—Pend Oreille County

**NEWPORT HOSPITAL AND HEALTH SERVICES (501310)**, 714 West Pine Street, Zip 99156–9046; tel. 509/447–2441, (Nonreporting) **A**9 10 18
Primary Contact: Thomas W. Wilbur, Chief Executive Officer and Superintendent
COO: Shelley Froehlich, R.N., Director Nursing Services
CMO: Jeremy Lewis, Chief Medical Staff
CIO: Walter Price, Director Information Technology
CHR: Joseph Clouse, Chief Administrative Officer
Web address: www.newporthospitalandhealth.org
**Control:** Hospital district or authority, Government, nonfederal **Service:** General Medical and Surgical

**Staffed Beds:** 70

## OAK HARBOR—Island County

✠ **NAVAL HOSPITAL OAK HARBOR**, 3475 North Saratoga Street, Zip 98278–8800; tel. 360/257–9500, (Nonreporting) **A**1 **S** Bureau of Medicine and Surgery, Department of the Navy, Washington, DC
Primary Contact: Commander Frederick Joseph McDonald, Commanding Officer
COO: Lieutenant Michael Bowers, Interim Director for Administration
CFO: Lieutenant Matthew Martin, Director Resource Management
CMO: Lieutenant Commander Catherine Borja, M.D., Chairman Executive Committee Medical Staff
CIO: Gregory Carruth, Head Information Management
CHR: Lieutenant Michael Bowers, Head Human Resources
CNO: Captain Karen Pruett–Baer, Senior Nurse Executive
Web address: www.med.navy.mil/sites/nhoh/Pages/default.aspx
**Control:** Navy, Government, federal **Service:** General Medical and Surgical

**Staffed Beds:** 29

## ODESSA—Lincoln County

★ **ODESSA MEMORIAL HEALTHCARE CENTER (501307)**, 502 East Amende Drive, Zip 99159–7003, Mailing Address: P.O. Box 368, Zip 99159–0368; tel. 509/982–2611 **A**9 10 18 **F**3 7 10 29 30 34 40 43 45 50 57 59 65 77 93 127 128 130 133 **P**6
Primary Contact: Mo P. Sheldon, Chief Executive Officer and Superintendent
CFO: Annette Edwards, Chief Financial Officer
CMO: Linda J. Powel, M.D., Medical Director
CHR: Jodi J. Bailey, Human Resources Director
CNO: Megan Shepard, Director Clinical Services
Web address: www.omhc.org
**Control:** Hospital district or authority, Government, nonfederal **Service:** General Medical and Surgical

**Staffed Beds:** 25 **Admissions:** 36 **Census:** 34 **Total Expense ($000):** 7625 **Payroll Expense ($000):** 3353

## OLYMPIA—Thurston County

□ **CAPITAL MEDICAL CENTER (500139)**, 3900 Capital Mall Drive S.W., Zip 98502–5026, Mailing Address: P.O. Box 19002, Zip 98507–0013; tel. 360/754–5858 **A**1 9 10 **F**3 8 11 12 13 15 22 28 29 30 31 35 37 40 43 59 64 68 72 76 77 78 79 81 82 85 86 87 93 107 108 111 114 118 119 132 146 147 148 **S** Capella Healthcare, Franklin, TN
Primary Contact: Jim Geist, Chief Executive Officer
CFO: Brian Anderson, Chief Financial Officer
CMO: Rojesh Sharangpani, M.D., Chief of Staff
CIO: Renee Crotty, Coordinator Marketing and Public Relations
CHR: Dana Vandewege, Director Human Resources
Web address: www.capitalmedical.com
**Control:** Partnership, Investor–owned, for–profit **Service:** General Medical and Surgical

**Staffed Beds:** 85 **Admissions:** 4288 **Census:** 37 **Births:** 646

✠ △ **PROVIDENCE ST. PETER HOSPITAL (500024)**, 413 Lilly Road N.E., Zip 98506–5166; tel. 360/491–9480 **A**1 3 7 9 10 **F**3 5 11 13 15 17 18 20 22 24 26 28 29 30 34 35 38 40 43 44 45 46 48 49 50 51 53 56 57 58 59 60 61 63 64 66 70 73 74 75 76 77 78 79 80 81 82 83 84 85 86 87 89 90 92 93 96 98 99 100 101 102 104 105 107 108 111 114 115 118 119 129 130 131 132 134 135 143 146 147 148 **S** Providence Health & Services, Renton, WA
Primary Contact: Medrice Coluccio, R.N., Chief Executive Officer
COO: Paul G. Wilkinson, Chief Operating Officer
CFO: Denise Marroni, Chief Financial Officer
CMO: Kevin Caserta, M.D., Chief Medical Officer
CIO: Kerry Miles, Chief Information Officer
CHR: Susan Meenk, Vice President Human Resources
CNO: Michelle James, Chief Nursing Officer
Web address: www.providence.org/swsa/facilities/st_peter_hospital
**Control:** Church–operated, Nongovernment, not–for profit **Service:** General Medical and Surgical

**Staffed Beds:** 347 **Admissions:** 18701 **Census:** 236 **Outpatient Visits:** 312982 **Births:** 2165 **Total Expense ($000):** 272182 **Payroll Expense ($000):** 137499 **Personnel:** 1803

## OMAK—Okanogan County

**MID–VALLEY HOSPITAL (501328)**, 810 Jasmine, Zip 98841–9578, Mailing Address: P.O. Box 793, Zip 98841–0793; tel. 509/826–1760 **A**5 9 10 18 **F**11 13 15 29 34 40 43 45 57 59 64 65 68 70 76 81 82 87 89 93 107 115 119 127 133 135
Primary Contact: Michael D. Billing, Administrator
CFO: Scott Attridge, Chief Financial Officer
CMO: Jennifer Thill, Chief of Staff
CIO: Ethan Harris, Manager Information Systems
CHR: Randy Coffell, Manager Human Resources
CNO: Rebecca Christoph, Director Nursing and Patient Care Services
Web address: www.mvhealth.org
**Control:** Hospital district or authority, Government, nonfederal **Service:** General Medical and Surgical

**Staffed Beds:** 30 **Admissions:** 950 **Census:** 7 **Births:** 230 **Total Expense ($000):** 30149 **Payroll Expense ($000):** 14686

## OTHELLO—Adams County

★ **OTHELLO COMMUNITY HOSPITAL (501318)**, 315 North 14th Avenue, Zip 99344–1297; tel. 509/488–2636, (Nonreporting) **A**9 10 18
Primary Contact: Connie Agenbroad, Chief Executive Officer
CFO: Mark Bunch, Director Finance
CHR: Mindy Gonzales, Chief Human Resources Officer
CNO: Tina Bernsen, Chief Nursing Officer
Web address: www.othellocommunityhospital.org
**Control:** Hospital district or authority, Government, nonfederal **Service:** General Medical and Surgical

**Staffed Beds:** 25

**WA**

### PASCO—Franklin County

☒ △ **LOURDES MEDICAL CENTER (501337)**, 520 North Fourth Avenue, Zip 99301–5257, Mailing Address: P.O. Box 2568, Zip 99302–2568; tel. 509/547–7704 **A**1 7 9 10 18 **F**8 13 15 18 29 30 34 35 37 40 41 42 45 46 50 52 56 57 59 68 70 74 75 76 77 79 80 81 84 90 91 96 97 107 108 110 111 114 118 126 129 130 131 143 144 145 146 147 **S** Ascension Health, Saint Louis, MO
Primary Contact: John Serle, FACHE, President and Chief Executive Officer
CFO: Frank Becker, Chief Financial Officer
CMO: Venkataraman Sambasivan, M.D., Chief Medical Officer
CIO: Deb Carpenter, Director Information Technology
CHR: Barbara Blood, Executive Director Human Resources
CNO: Denise Clapp, Chief Nursing Officer
Web address: www.lourdeshealth.net
**Control:** Church–operated, Nongovernment, not–for profit **Service:** General Medical and Surgical

**Staffed Beds:** 53 **Admissions:** 1816 **Census:** 19 **Total Expense ($000):** 85249 **Payroll Expense ($000):** 28391

### POMEROY—Garfield County

★ **GARFIELD COUNTY PUBLIC HOSPITAL DISTRICT (501301)**, 66 North 6th Street, Zip 99347–9705; tel. 509/843–1591, (Nonreporting) **A**9 10 18
Primary Contact: Jay Pottenger, Chief Executive Officer
CMO: Glenn Houser, M.D., Chief Medical Officer
CIO: Nevelyn Schooler, Health Information Manager
CHR: Alicia Scharnhorst, Human Resources and Business Office Manager
CNO: Susan Morrow, R.N., Chief Nursing Officer
Web address: www.pomeroymd.com
**Control:** Hospital district or authority, Government, nonfederal **Service:** General Medical and Surgical

**Staffed Beds:** 40

### PORT ANGELES—Clallam County

★ ◇ **OLYMPIC MEDICAL CENTER (500072)**, 939 Caroline Street, Zip 98362–3997; tel. 360/417–7000 **A**2 5 9 10 21 **F**3 13 15 18 28 29 31 34 40 45 54 57 59 62 64 70 74 75 76 77 78 79 81 82 85 87 89 91 93 97 107 108 110 111 114 119 121 123 127 129 131 132 144 146 147 148 **P**4
Primary Contact: Eric Lewis, Chief Executive Officer
CFO: Julie Rukstad, Chief Financial Officer
CMO: R. Scott Kennedy, M.D., Chief Medical Officer and Hospital Chief Operating Officer
CHR: Richard Neuman, Chief Human Resources Officer
CNO: Lorraine Wall, Chief Nursing Officer
Web address: www.olympicmedical.org
**Control:** Hospital district or authority, Government, nonfederal **Service:** General Medical and Surgical

**Staffed Beds:** 78 **Admissions:** 4449 **Census:** 39 **Outpatient Visits:** 318105 **Births:** 495 **Total Expense ($000):** 145278 **Payroll Expense ($000):** 69992 **Personnel:** 1000

### PORT TOWNSEND—Jefferson County

★ ◇ **JEFFERSON HEALTHCARE (501323)**, 834 Sheridan Street, Zip 98368–2443; tel. 360/385–2200 **A**9 10 18 21 **F**13 15 18 28 29 31 34 35 40 45 46 50 62 63 65 70 76 81 87 93 107 110 111 114 119 127 129 130 135 146 148
Primary Contact: Mike Glenn, Chief Executive Officer
COO: Paula Dowdle, Chief Operating Officer
CFO: Hilary Whittington, Chief Financial Officer
CMO: Joe Mattern, M.D., Chief Medical Officer
CHR: Heather Bailey, Chief Human Resources Officer
CNO: Joyce Cardinal, Chief Nursing Executive
Web address: www.jeffersonhealthcare.org
**Control:** Hospital district or authority, Government, nonfederal **Service:** General Medical and Surgical

**Staffed Beds:** 25 **Admissions:** 1412 **Census:** 12 **Births:** 112 **Total Expense ($000):** 74172 **Payroll Expense ($000):** 37132

### PROSSER—Benton County

★ **PMH MEDICAL CENTER (501312)**, 723 Memorial Street, Zip 99350–1593; tel. 509/786–2222, (Nonreporting) **A**9 10 18
Primary Contact: Julie Petersen, Chief Executive Officer
CFO: Tim Cooper, Chief Financial Officer
CMO: Keith Butvilas, M.D., Chief Medical Officer
CIO: Dan Harter, Manager Information Systems
CHR: Pamela S. Healea, Director Human Resources
CNO: Tina Glockner, Chief Nursing Officer
Web address: www.pmhmedicalcenter.com/
**Control:** Hospital district or authority, Government, nonfederal **Service:** General Medical and Surgical

**Staffed Beds:** 25

### PULLMAN—Whitman County

◇ **PULLMAN REGIONAL HOSPITAL (501331)**, 835 S.E. Bishop Boulevard, Zip 99163–5512; tel. 509/332–2541 **A**9 10 18 21 **F**3 13 15 28 29 30 34 35 36 37 38 40 43 44 45 47 50 51 53 55 57 59 64 68 70 74 75 76 77 78 79 81 86 87 89 93 98 101 102 104 105 107 108 110 111 114 118 119 126 129 130 131 132 133 144 146 **P**5
Primary Contact: Scott K. Adams, Chief Executive Officer
CFO: Steven Febus, Chief Financial Officer
CMO: Richard Caggiano, M.D., Chief Medical Officer
CHR: Bernadette Berney, Director Human Resources
Web address: www.pullmanhospital.org
**Control:** Hospital district or authority, Government, nonfederal **Service:** General Medical and Surgical

**Staffed Beds:** 25 **Admissions:** 1142 **Census:** 11 **Outpatient Visits:** 71087 **Births:** 424 **Total Expense ($000):** 54242 **Payroll Expense ($000):** 24502

### PUYALLUP—Pierce County

**GOOD SAMARITAN COMMUNITY HEALTHCARE** See MultiCare Good Samaritan Hospital

☐ △ **MULTICARE GOOD SAMARITAN HOSPITAL (500079)**, 401 15th Avenue S.E., Zip 98372–3770, Mailing Address: P.O. Box 1247, Zip 98371–0192; tel. 253/697–4000 **A**1 2 3 7 9 10 13 **F**3 11 13 17 18 20 22 24 28 29 30 31 34 35 38 40 41 43 45 47 48 50 51 55 56 57 58 59 61 64 65 66 68 70 73 74 75 76 78 79 81 82 84 85 87 89 90 91 93 96 97 102 106 107 108 111 114 115 117 118 119 126 129 130 132 146 147 148 **S** MultiCare Health System, Tacoma, WA
Primary Contact: Marcia L. Johnson, R.N., Chief Operating Officer
COO: Marcia L. Johnson, R.N., Chief Operating Officer
CFO: Anna Loomis, Interim Vice President
CMO: David Chen, M.D., Vice President Medical Affairs
CIO: Florence Chang, Executive Vice President
CHR: Sarah Horsman, Vice President Human Resources
CNO: Kate Bechtold, R.N., Senior Vice President and Chief Nurse Executive
Web address: www.goodsamhealth.org
**Control:** Other not–for–profit (including NFP Corporation) **Service:** General Medical and Surgical

**Staffed Beds:** 282 **Admissions:** 15615 **Census:** 197 **Outpatient Visits:** 139003 **Births:** 2340 **Total Expense ($000):** 316867 **Payroll Expense ($000):** 148171 **Personnel:** 1696

### QUINCY—Grant County

★ **QUINCY VALLEY MEDICAL CENTER (501320)**, 908 10th Avenue S.W., Zip 98848–1376; tel. 509/787–3531, (Nonreporting) **A**9 10 18
Primary Contact: Mehdi Merred, Chief Executive Officer
CFO: Dean Taplett, Controller
CMO: Mark Vance, M.D., Chief Medical Officer
CIO: Ruth Vance, Director Information Systems
CHR: Alene Walker, Director Human Resources
Web address: www.quincyhospital.org
**Control:** County–Government, nonfederal **Service:** General Medical and Surgical

**Staffed Beds:** 25

### RENTON—King County

☒ **UW MEDICINE/VALLEY MEDICAL CENTER (500088)**, 400 South 43rd Street, Zip 98055–5714, Mailing Address: P.O. Box 50010, Zip 98058–5010; tel. 425/228–3450 **A**1 2 3 5 9 10 **F**8 11 13 15 18 19 20 22 26 28 29 30 31 32 34 35 36 37 38 40 43 44 45 48 49 50 51 53 54 55 57 58 59 60 64 65 66 68 70 72 74 75 76 77 78 79 81 82 83 84 85 86 87 89 91 92 93 94 96 97 100 101 102 104 107 110 114 115 118 119 120 121 123 124 126 129 130 131 132 135 144 146 147 148 **P**6 **S** UW Medicine, Seattle, WA
Primary Contact: Richard D. Roodman, Chief Executive Officer
CFO: Larry Smith, Senior Vice President and Chief Financial Officer
CMO: Kathryn Beattie, M.D., Senior Vice President and Chief Medical Officer
CHR: Barbara Mitchell, Senior Vice President Marketing and Human Resources
CNO: Scott Alleman, Senior Vice President Patient Care Services and Chief Nursing Officer
Web address: www.valleymed.org
**Control:** Hospital district or authority, Government, nonfederal **Service:** General Medical and Surgical

**Staffed Beds:** 187 **Admissions:** 16693 **Census:** 168 **Outpatient Visits:** 484168 **Births:** 3935 **Total Expense ($000):** 465741 **Payroll Expense ($000):** 209411 **Personnel:** 2450

WA

*Many Facility Codes have changed. Please refer to the AHA Guide Code Chart.* © 2015 AHA Guide

## REPUBLIC—Ferry County

★ **FERRY COUNTY MEMORIAL HOSPITAL (501322)**, 36 Klondike Road,
Zip 99166–9701; tel. 509/775–3333, (Nonreporting) **A**9 10 18
Primary Contact: Brenda Parnell, Chief Executive Officer
CFO: Kelly Leslie, Chief Financial Officer
CMO: Farhad H. Alrashedy, M.D., Chief Medical Officer
CIO: James Davidson, Director of Information Services
CHR: Michelle Loftis, Human Resources Officer
CNO: Thomas Durham, Chief Nursing Officer
Web address: www.fcphd.org
**Control:** Hospital district or authority, Government, nonfederal **Service:** General
Medical and Surgical

| Staffed Beds: 25 |
| --- |

## RICHLAND—Benton County

⊠ △ **KADLEC REGIONAL MEDICAL CENTER (500058)**, 888 Swift Boulevard,
Zip 99352–3514; tel. 509/946–4611 **A**1 2 3 7 9 10 **F**3 11 13 15 18 20 22 24
26 28 29 30 31 34 36 40 42 43 46 47 48 49 50 51 54 55 57 59 64 68 70
72 74 75 77 78 79 81 82 85 86 87 90 93 96 97 107 108 110 111 114 115
116 117 118 119 127 130 144 146 147 148 **P**6 **S** Providence Health &
Services, Renton, WA
Primary Contact: Rand J. Wortman, President and Chief Executive Officer
COO: Rand J. Wortman, Chief Executive Officer
CFO: Julie Meek, Vice President Finance
CMO: Dale Hoekema, M.D., Vice President Medical Affairs and Chief Medical
Officer
CIO: David Roach, Vice President Information Systems
CHR: Jeff Clark, Vice President Human Resources
CNO: Kirk Harper, R.N., Vice President, Nursing
Web address: www.kadlecmed.org
**Control:** Other not–for–profit (including NFP Corporation) **Service:** General
Medical and Surgical

| Staffed Beds: 254 Admissions: 14796 Census: 167 Outpatient Visits: 289696 Births: 2762 Total Expense ($000): 425996 Payroll Expense ($000): 192478 Personnel: 2296 |
| --- |

★ **LOURDES COUNSELING CENTER (504008)**, 1175 Carondelet Drive,
Zip 99354–3300; tel. 509/943–9104 **A**9 10 **F**3 29 30 38 50 64 98 99 100
101 103 104 106 **S** Ascension Health, Saint Louis, MO
Primary Contact: Barbara Mead, Executive Director
CFO: Frank Becker, Chief Financial Officer
CIO: Jared Fleming, Director, Information Services
CHR: Barbara Blood, Director Human Resources
CNO: Denise Clapp, Chief Nursing Officer
Web address: www.lourdeshealth.net
**Control:** Church–operated, Nongovernment, not–for profit **Service:** Psychiatric

| Staffed Beds: 20 Admissions: 571 Census: 15 Births: 0 |
| --- |

## RITZVILLE—Adams County

★ **EAST ADAMS RURAL HOSPITAL (501311)**, 903 South Adams Street,
Zip 99169–2298; tel. 509/659–1200, (Nonreporting) **A**9 10 18
Primary Contact: Gary Bostrom, Chief Executive Officer and Chief Financial Officer
COO: Dina McBride, Chief Operating Officer and Director Human Resources
CFO: Gary Bostrom, Chief Executive Officer and Chief Financial Officer
CMO: Valerie Eckley, M.D., Chief of Staff
CIO: Kellie Ottmar, Manager Information Services
CHR: Dina McBride, Chief Operating Officer and Director Human Resources
CNO: Brenda Herr, Chief Nursing Officer
Web address: www.earh.com
**Control:** Hospital district or authority, Government, nonfederal **Service:** General
Medical and Surgical

| Staffed Beds: 8 |
| --- |

## SEATTLE—King County

◇ **GROUP HEALTH COOPERATIVE CENTRAL HOSPITAL (500052)**, 201 16th
Avenue East, Zip 98112–5226; tel. 206/326–3000, (Nonreporting) **A**3 5 9 10 21
Primary Contact: Carol M. Taylor, R.N., Regional Director Clinical Operations
Web address: www.https://www.ghc.org
**Control:** Corporation, Investor–owned, for–profit **Service:** General Medical and
Surgical

| Staffed Beds: 306 |
| --- |

⊠ **KINDRED HOSPITAL SEATTLE–NORTHGATE (502002)**, 10631 8th Avenue
N.E., Zip 98125–7213; tel. 206/364–2050, (Includes KINDRED HOSPITAL
SEATTLE–FIRST HILL, 1334 Terry Avenue, Zip 98101–2747; tel. 206/682–2661)
**A**1 9 10 **F**1 29 50 60 68 70 75 107 119 148 **S** Kindred Healthcare,
Louisville, KY
Primary Contact: Jean Clark, Administrator
CFO: David Stob, Chief Financial Officer
Web address: www.kindredhospitalseattle.com/
**Control:** Corporation, Investor–owned, for–profit **Service:** General Medical and
Surgical

| Staffed Beds: 80 Admissions: 547 Census: 51 Births: 0 |
| --- |

☐ **NAVOS (504009)**, 2600 S.W. Holden Street, Zip 98126–3505;
tel. 206/933–7299 **A**1 9 10 **F**29 98 99 100 101 102 103 104
Primary Contact: David Johnson, Chief Executive Officer
COO: Cassie Undlin, Chief Administrative Officer
CFO: Cassie Undlin, Chief Administrative Officer
CMO: Carlos Andarsio, M.D., Chief Medical Officer
CIO: Jim Rudnick, Vice President Information Technology
CHR: Judi Mitchell, Vice President Administrative Services
CNO: Terry McInerney, Director of Nursing, Inpatient
Web address: www.navos.org
**Control:** Other not–for–profit (including NFP Corporation) **Service:** Psychiatric

| Staffed Beds: 69 Admissions: 963 Census: 38 Births: 0 |
| --- |

**SCHICK SHADEL HOSPITAL**, 12101 Ambaum Boulevard S.W.,
Zip 98146–2651, Mailing Address: P.O. Box 48149, Zip 98148–0149;
tel. 206/244–8100, (Nonreporting) **A**9
Primary Contact: Bruce Brandler, Administrator
CFO: Troy Cherry, Chief Financial Officer
CMO: Kayyan Danbdala, M.D., Medical Director
CIO: Peter Vermulen, Director Information Technology
CHR: Elaine Oksendahl, Director Human Resources and Risk Management
Web address: www.schickshadel.com
**Control:** Corporation, Investor–owned, for–profit **Service:** Alcoholism and other
chemical dependency

| Staffed Beds: 48 |
| --- |

⊠ **SEATTLE CANCER CARE ALLIANCE (500138)**, 825 Eastlake Avenue East,
Zip 98109–4405, Mailing Address: P.O. Box 19023, Zip 98109–1023;
tel. 206/288–1400 **A**1 2 9 10 **F**3 15 30 31 34 35 39 50 55 57 59 64 68 75
78 80 82 84 86 87 93 107 108 110 111 114 115 116 117 119 120 121 123
124 130 132 135 136 142 143 146 147 148 **P**1
Primary Contact: Norm Hubbard, Executive Vice President
CFO: Jonathan Tingstad, Vice President and Chief Financial Officer
CMO: Marc Stewart, M.D., Vice President and Medical Director
CIO: David Ackerson, Chief Information Officer
CHR: Han Nachtrieb, Vice President Human Resources
Web address: www.seattlecca.org
**Control:** Other not–for–profit (including NFP Corporation) **Service:** Cancer

| Staffed Beds: 20 Admissions: 579 Census: 16 Outpatient Visits: 77177 Births: 0 Total Expense ($000): 408154 Payroll Expense ($000): 79466 Personnel: 1093 |
| --- |

☐ △ ◇ **SEATTLE CHILDREN'S HOSPITAL (503300)**, 4800 Sand Point Way
N.E., Zip 98105–3901, Mailing Address: P.O. Box 5371, Zip 98145–5005;
tel. 206/987–2000 **A**1 2 3 5 7 9 10 21 **F**3 7 8 9 21 23 25 27 29 30 31 32 34
35 36 38 39 40 43 46 53 54 55 57 58 60 61 62 64 65 66 68 71 72 74 75
77 78 79 81 82 84 85 86 87 88 89 90 93 97 98 99 100 102 104 105 107
108 111 115 116 117 119 126 129 130 131 132 134 136 137 138 139 141
142 143 144 146 148
Primary Contact: Jeff Sperring, M.D., Chief Executive Officer
COO: Cindy Gazecki, Senior Vice President, Hospital Operations
CFO: Kelly Wallace, Senior Vice President and Chief Financial Officer
CMO: David Fisher, M.D., Senior Vice President and Chief Medical Officer
CIO: Wes Wright, Senior Vice President and Chief Information Officer
CHR: Steven Hurwitz, Senior Vice President Shared Services
CNO: Susan Heath, R.N., Senior Vice President and Chief Nursing Officer
Web address: www.seattlechildrens.org
**Control:** Other not–for–profit (including NFP Corporation) **Service:** Children's
general

| Staffed Beds: 250 Admissions: 15205 Census: 221 Total Expense ($000): 974596 Payroll Expense ($000): 387872 |
| --- |

WA

---

| **Hospital, Medicare Provider Number, Address, Telephone, Approval, Facility, and Physician Codes, Health Care System** |
| --- |
| ★ American Hospital Association (AHA) membership ○ Healthcare Facilities Accreditation Program ⇑ Center for Improvement in Healthcare Quality Accreditation ☐ The Joint Commission accreditation ◇ DNV Healthcare Inc. accreditation △ Commission on Accreditation of Rehabilitation Facilities (CARF) accreditation |

⊠ △ **SWEDISH MEDICAL CENTER–CHERRY HILL CAMPUS (500025)**, 500 17th Avenue, Zip 98122–5711; tel. 206/320–2000 **A**1 2 3 5 7 9 10 **F**3 8 11 17 18 20 21 22 23 24 26 27 28 29 30 31 34 35 37 38 40 41 45 46 53 57 58 59 60 61 64 65 68 74 75 77 78 79 80 81 82 85 87 90 91 92 93 97 98 100 101 102 107 108 109 111 118 119 124 126 129 130 131 132 135 141 143 146 148 **P**6 **S** Swedish Health Services, Seattle, WA
Primary Contact: June Altaras, R.N., Chief Executive Officer
CFO: Jeffrey Veilleux, Senior Vice President and Chief Financial Officer
CMO: John Vassall, M.D., Chief Medical Officer
CIO: Janice Newell, Chief Information Officer
Web address: www.swedish.org
**Control:** Other not–for–profit (including NFP Corporation) **Service:** General Medical and Surgical

**Staffed Beds:** 198 **Admissions:** 9193 **Census:** 134 **Outpatient Visits:** 138640 **Births:** 0 **Total Expense ($000):** 413139 **Payroll Expense ($000):** 106749 **Personnel:** 1281

⊠ **SWEDISH MEDICAL CENTER–FIRST HILL (500027)**, 747 Broadway, Zip 98122–4307; tel. 206/386–6000, (Includes SWEDISH MEDICAL CENTER–BALLARD, 5300 Tallman Avenue N.W., Zip 98107–3932; tel. 206/782–2700; Jennifer Graves, R.N., MS, Chief Executive) **A**1 2 3 5 9 10 **F**3 4 5 7 8 11 12 13 15 18 19 20 21 22 23 25 26 29 30 31 32 34 35 36 37 38 39 40 41 42 45 46 47 48 49 52 54 55 56 57 58 59 60 61 64 65 66 68 70 71 72 73 74 75 76 77 78 79 80 81 82 83 84 85 86 87 88 89 91 92 93 96 97 100 101 102 104 107 108 109 110 111 114 115 116 117 118 119 120 121 123 126 127 130 131 132 134 135 136 138 139 141 143 144 146 147 148 **P**6 **S** Swedish Health Services, Seattle, WA
Primary Contact: June Altaras, R.N., Chief Executive Officer
CFO: Jeffrey Veilleux, Executive Vice President and Chief Financial Officer
CMO: John Vassall, M.D., Chief Medical Officer
CIO: Janice Newell, Chief Information Officer
Web address: www.swedish.org
**Control:** Other not–for–profit (including NFP Corporation) **Service:** General Medical and Surgical

**Staffed Beds:** 631 **Admissions:** 33241 **Census:** 383 **Outpatient Visits:** 596624 **Births:** 6827 **Total Expense ($000):** 1082770 **Payroll Expense ($000):** 321317 **Personnel:** 3613

⊠ △ **UNIVERSITY OF WASHINGTON MEDICAL CENTER (500008)**, 1959 N.E. Pacific Street, Zip 98195–6151; tel. 206/598–3300 **A**1 2 3 5 7 8 9 10 **F**3 8 9 11 12 13 15 17 18 20 22 24 26 29 30 31 32 34 35 36 40 44 45 46 47 48 49 50 52 54 55 56 57 58 59 60 61 64 65 68 70 72 74 75 76 78 79 81 82 84 85 86 87 90 91 92 93 94 95 97 98 100 101 102 103 104 107 110 111 114 115 116 117 118 119 120 121 123 124 126 130 131 132 136 137 138 139 140 141 142 144 145 146 147 148 **P**6 **S** UW Medicine, Seattle, WA
Primary Contact: Geoff Austin, Interim Executive Director
CFO: Lori J. Mitchell, Chief Financial Officer
CMO: Tom Staiger, M.D., Medical Director
CHR: Jennifer J. Petritz, Director Human Resources
CNO: Grace E. Parker, R.N., Chief Nursing Officer
Web address: www.uwmedicine.org/Patient–Care/Locations/UWMC/Pages/default.aspx
**Control:** State–Government, nonfederal **Service:** General Medical and Surgical

**Staffed Beds:** 428 **Admissions:** 18033 **Census:** 341 **Outpatient Visits:** 320170 **Births:** 1997 **Total Expense ($000):** 971268 **Payroll Expense ($000):** 320482 **Personnel:** 5091

⊠ △ **UW MEDICINE/HARBORVIEW MEDICAL CENTER (500064)**, 325 Ninth Avenue, Zip 98104–2499, Mailing Address: P.O. Box 359717, Zip 98195–9717; tel. 206/744–3000 **A**1 3 5 7 8 9 10 **F**3 5 9 16 17 18 20 22 26 29 30 31 32 34 35 36 37 38 40 41 43 45 46 47 48 49 50 56 58 59 60 61 64 65 66 68 70 72 73 74 75 77 78 79 80 81 82 84 85 86 87 88 89 90 91 92 93 94 96 97 98 100 101 102 103 104 105 107 108 111 114 115 118 119 124 129 130 131 132 135 146 147 148 **P**6 **S** UW Medicine, Seattle, WA
Primary Contact: Paul Hayes, Executive Director
CFO: Kera Dennis, Assistant Administrator, Finance
CMO: J. Richard Goss, M.D., Medical Director
CIO: James Fine, M.D., Chief Information Officer
CHR: Nicki McCraw, Assistant Vice President Human Resources
CNO: Darcy Jaffe, R.N., Chief Nursing Officer
Web address: www.uwmedicine.org/Patient–Care/Locations/HMC/Pages/default.aspx
**Control:** County–Government, nonfederal **Service:** General Medical and Surgical

**Staffed Beds:** 413 **Admissions:** 17176 **Census:** 362 **Outpatient Visits:** 341992 **Births:** 0 **Total Expense ($000):** 825542 **Payroll Expense ($000):** 347055 **Personnel:** 4865

⊠ **UW MEDICINE/NORTHWEST HOSPITAL & MEDICAL CENTER (500001)**, 1550 North 115th Street, Zip 98133–8401; tel. 206/364–0500, (Nonreporting) **A**1 2 3 5 9 10 **S** UW Medicine, Seattle, WA
Primary Contact: Cynthia Hecker, R.N., Executive Director
CFO: Ketty Hsieh, Senior Director Finance
CMO: Greg Schroedl, M.D., Vice President, Medical and Chief Medical Officer
CIO: Eric Neil, Interim Chief Information Officer
CHR: Linda Olmstead, Director, Human Resources
CNO: Susan Manfredi, R.N., Vice President and Chief Nursing Officer
Web address: www.uwmedicine.org/Patient–Care/Locations/nwh/Pages/default.aspx
**Control:** Other not–for–profit (including NFP Corporation) **Service:** General Medical and Surgical

**Staffed Beds:** 176

⊠ △ **VETERANS AFFAIRS PUGET SOUND HEALTH CARE SYSTEM**, 1660 South Columbian Way, Zip 98108–1597; tel. 206/762–1010, (Includes VETERANS AFFAIRS PUGET SOUND HEALTH CARE SYSTEM–AMERICAN LAKE DIVISION, Tacoma, Zip 98493; tel. 253/582–8440), (Nonreporting) **A**1 2 3 5 7 8 9 **S** Department of Veterans Affairs, Washington, DC
Primary Contact: Michael J. Murphy, FACHE, Director
CFO: Kenneth J. Hudson, Chief Financial Officer
CMO: Gordon Starkebaum, M.D., Chief of Staff
CIO: Glenn Zwinger, Manager Information Systems Services
Web address: www.pugetsound.va.gov/
**Control:** Veterans Affairs, Government, federal **Service:** General Medical and Surgical

**Staffed Beds:** 358

⊠ △ **VIRGINIA MASON MEDICAL CENTER (500005)**, 1100 Ninth Avenue, Zip 98101–2756, Mailing Address: P.O. Box 900, Zip 98111–0900; tel. 206/223–6600, (Total facility includes 35 beds in nursing home–type unit) **A**1 2 3 5 7 9 10 **F**3 8 11 12 15 17 18 20 22 24 26 28 29 30 31 34 36 40 44 45 46 47 48 49 50 51 55 56 57 58 59 60 61 63 64 65 68 70 74 75 77 78 79 80 81 82 83 84 85 86 87 90 91 92 93 94 96 97 98 100 101 102 103 104 107 108 110 111 113 114 115 117 118 119 120 121 123 124 126 128 129 130 131 132 135 136 138 141 142 144 146 148 **P**6
Primary Contact: Gary Kaplan, M.D., FACHE, Chairman and Chief Executive Officer
COO: Sarah Patterson, Executive Vice President and Chief Operating Officer
CFO: Sue Anderson, Executive Vice President, Chief Financial Officer and Chief Information Officer
CMO: Michael Glenn, M.D., Chief Medical Officer
CIO: Sue Anderson, Executive Vice President, Chief Financial Officer and Chief Information Officer
CHR: Kathy J. Shingleton, Ed.D., Vice President, Human Resources
CNO: Charleen Tachibana, R.N., Senior Vice President and Chief Nursing Officer
Web address: www.VirginiaMason.org
**Control:** Other not–for–profit (including NFP Corporation) **Service:** General Medical and Surgical

**Staffed Beds:** 286 **Admissions:** 16572 **Census:** 247 **Outpatient Visits:** 900100 **Births:** 0 **Total Expense ($000):** 965652 **Payroll Expense ($000):** 485525 **Personnel:** 4902

**SEDRO–WOOLLEY—Skagit County**

⊠ **PEACEHEALTH UNITED GENERAL MEDICAL CENTER (501329)**, 2000 Hospital Drive, Zip 98284–4327; tel. 360/856–6021, (Data for 91 days) **A**1 2 9 10 18 **F**3 11 15 29 30 31 34 35 40 43 45 50 57 59 64 68 70 75 77 78 79 81 85 89 92 93 107 108 110 114 115 118 119 120 121 123 129 130 133 143 146 **P**6 **S** PeaceHealth, Vancouver, WA
Primary Contact: James R. Barnhart, Chief Administrative Officer
CFO: Michael W. Bonthuis, Chief Financial Officer
CMO: Randy Anderson, DPM, Chief Medical Officer
CHR: Tracie Skrinde, Director Human Resources
Web address: www.peacehealth.org/united–general/Pages/default.aspx
**Control:** Church–operated, Nongovernment, not–for profit **Service:** General Medical and Surgical

**Staffed Beds:** 25 **Admissions:** 181 **Census:** 7 **Outpatient Visits:** 10296 **Births:** 0 **Total Expense ($000):** 9062 **Payroll Expense ($000):** 3054 **Personnel:** 203

**SHELTON—Mason County**

⊠ **MASON GENERAL HOSPITAL (501336)**, 901 Mountain View Drive, Zip 98584–4401, Mailing Address: P.O. Box 1668, Zip 98584–5001; tel. 360/426–1611 **A**1 9 10 18 **F**11 13 15 29 30 40 57 68 70 75 79 81 83 85 107 110 130 132 147
Primary Contact: Eric Moll, Chief Executive Officer
COO: Eileen Branscome, Chief Operating Officer
CFO: Merle Brandt, Chief Financial Officer
CMO: Dean Gushee, M.D., Medical Director
CIO: Tom Hornburg, Director Information Systems
CHR: Claudia Hawley, Director Human Resources
Web address: www.masongeneral.com
**Control:** Hospital district or authority, Government, nonfederal **Service:** General Medical and Surgical

**Staffed Beds:** 25 **Admissions:** 1640 **Census:** 14 **Births:** 244

**WA**

## SNOQUALMIE—King County

**SNOQUALMIE VALLEY HOSPITAL DISTRICT (501338)**, 9575 Ethan Wade Way S.E., Zip 98065–9577, Mailing Address: 9801 Frontier Avenue S.E., Zip 98065–5200; tel. 425/831–2300, (Nonreporting) **A**9 10 18
Primary Contact: Rodger McCollum, Chief Executive Officer
CHR: Kimberly D. Washburn, Director Human Resources
Web address: www.snoqualmiehospital.org/
**Control:** Hospital district or authority, Government, nonfederal **Service:** General Medical and Surgical

**Staffed Beds:** 18

## SOUTH BEND—Pacific County

**WILLAPA HARBOR HOSPITAL (501303)**, 800 Alder Street, Zip 98586–4900, Mailing Address: P.O. Box 438, Zip 98586–0438; tel. 360/875–5526, (Nonreporting) **A**9 10 18
Primary Contact: Carole Halsan, R.N., Chief Executive Officer
CFO: Terry Stone, Chief Financial Officer and Chief Information Officer
CIO: Terry Stone, Chief Financial Officer and Chief Information Officer
CHR: Krisy L. Funkhouser, Manager Human Resources
Web address: www.willapaharborhospital.com
**Control:** Hospital district or authority, Government, nonfederal **Service:** General Medical and Surgical

**Staffed Beds:** 26

## SPOKANE—Spokane County

☒ **DEACONESS HOSPITAL (500044)**, 800 West Fifth Avenue, Zip 99204–2803, Mailing Address: P.O. Box 248, Zip 99210–0248; tel. 509/458–5800 **A**1 2 3 9 10 **F**3 11 12 13 15 17 18 20 22 24 26 28 29 31 40 43 45 46 47 48 49 50 51 56 60 64 68 70 72 73 74 75 76 78 79 81 82 85 86 87 91 92 107 108 110 111 113 114 115 119 124 126 129 130 132 146 147 148 **S** Community Health Systems, Inc., Franklin, TN
Primary Contact: Maurine Cate, Chief Executive Officer
CFO: Rodney Higgins, Chief Financial Officer
CIO: Richard DeRoche, Manager Information Technology
CHR: Melinda Moore, Director Human Resources
CNO: Jennifer Petrik, Interim Chief Nursing Officer
Web address: www.deaconessspokane.com/Deaconess–Hospital/home.aspx
**Control:** Corporation, Investor–owned, for–profit **Service:** General Medical and Surgical

**Staffed Beds:** 352 **Admissions:** 10943 **Census:** 162 **Outpatient Visits:** 70340 **Births:** 1674 **Total Expense ($000):** 247022 **Payroll Expense ($000):** 84293 **Personnel:** 1166

☒ **MANN–GRANDSTAFF VETERANS AFFAIRS MEDICAL CENTER**, 4815 North Assembly Street, Zip 99205–6197; tel. 509/434–7000, (Nonreporting) **A**1 3 5 9 **S** Department of Veterans Affairs, Washington, DC
Primary Contact: Linda K. Reynolds, FACHE, Director
COO: Perry Klein, Chief Engineering
CFO: Michael Stuhlmiller, Chief Financial Officer
CIO: Rob Fortenberry, Chief Information Officer
CHR: Jacqueline Ross, Chief Human Resources Officer
CNO: Nancy Benton, Assistant Director Patient Care Services
Web address: www.spokane.va.gov/
**Control:** Veterans Affairs, Government, federal **Service:** General Medical and Surgical

**Staffed Beds:** 46

☒ △ **PROVIDENCE HOLY FAMILY HOSPITAL (500077)**, 5633 North Lidgerwood Street, Zip 99208–1224; tel. 509/482–0111 **A**1 2 5 7 9 10 **F**3 4 8 11 12 13 15 18 20 22 29 30 31 34 35 37 38 39 40 41 43 45 46 47 48 49 50 53 56 57 58 59 60 61 64 68 70 73 74 75 76 77 78 79 80 81 82 84 85 86 87 89 92 100 107 108 129 130 131 132 135 143 145 146 147 148 **P**6 **S** Providence Health & Services, Renton, WA
Primary Contact: Alex Jackson, Chief Executive
COO: Cathy J. Simchuk, Chief Operating Officer
CIO: Mark Vogelsang, Director Information Services
CHR: Patrick M. Clarry, Vice President Human Resources
Web address: www.providence.org
**Control:** Church–operated, Nongovernment, not–for profit **Service:** General Medical and Surgical

**Staffed Beds:** 191 **Admissions:** 9191 **Census:** 96 **Outpatient Visits:** 109842 **Births:** 1223 **Total Expense ($000):** 186607 **Payroll Expense ($000):** 52358 **Personnel:** 786

☒ **PROVIDENCE SACRED HEART MEDICAL CENTER & CHILDREN'S HOSPITAL (500054)**, 101 West Eighth Avenue, Zip 99204–2364, Mailing Address: P.O. Box 2555, Zip 99220–2555; tel. 509/474–3131, (Includes SACRED HEART CHILDREN'S HOSPITAL, 101 West Eight Avenue, Zip 99204–2307, Mailing Address: PO Box 2555, Zip 99220–2555; tel. 509/474–4841; Alex Jackson, Chief Executive) **A**1 2 3 5 9 10 **F**3 8 13 15 17 18 19 20 21 22 23 24 25 26 27 28 29 30 31 35 36 37 40 41 43 45 46 47 48 56 58 60 64 68 70 71 72 73 74 75 76 78 79 81 82 83 84 85 86 87 88 89 92 98 99 100 101 102 103 104 105 106 107 108 110 111 112 114 115 118 119 120 121 123 124 126 130 132 136 137 138 139 141 142 145 146 147 148 **P**6 **S** Providence Health & Services, Renton, WA
Primary Contact: Alex Jackson, Chief Executive
CFO: Shelby Stokoe, Senior Director Finance
CMO: Dean Martz, Chief Medical Officer
CHR: Mark Smith, Director Human Resources
CNO: Susan Stacey, Chief Nursing Officer
Web address: www.shmc.org
**Control:** Church–operated, Nongovernment, not–for profit **Service:** General Medical and Surgical

**Staffed Beds:** 668 **Admissions:** 28642 **Census:** 422 **Outpatient Visits:** 249016 **Births:** 2987 **Total Expense ($000):** 778046 **Payroll Expense ($000):** 255577 **Personnel:** 3066

☐ **SHRINERS HOSPITALS FOR CHILDREN–SPOKANE (503302)**, 911 West Fifth Avenue, Zip 99204–2901, Mailing Address: P.O. Box 2472, Zip 99210–2472; tel. 509/455–7844, (Nonreporting) **A**1 3 9 10 **S** Shriners Hospitals for Children, Tampa, FL
Primary Contact: Peter G. Brewer, Administrator
CFO: Monica Hickman, Director Fiscal Services
CMO: Paul Caskey, M.D., Chief of Staff
CIO: Mike Allen, Director Information Services
CHR: Kris McHugh Goldman, Director Human Resources
CNO: Lynda Vilanova, Director Patient Care Services
Web address: www.shrinershospitalsforchildren.org/Hospitals/Locations/Spokane.aspx
**Control:** Other not–for–profit (including NFP Corporation) **Service:** Children's orthopedic

**Staffed Beds:** 30

☒ △ **ST. LUKE'S REHABILITATION INSTITUTE (503025)**, 711 South Cowley Street, Zip 99202–1388; tel. 509/473–6000 **A**1 7 9 10 **F**28 29 30 36 38 50 53 58 64 68 74 75 77 79 82 86 87 90 91 92 93 95 96 130 131 132 135 146 **P**6 **S** Providence Health & Services, Renton, WA
Primary Contact: Nancy Vorhees, Chief Administrative Officer
COO: Ulrike Berzau, FACHE, Administrator
CFO: Helen Andrus, Chief Financial Officer
CMO: Stefan Humphries, M.D., Medical Director
CIO: Fred Galusha, Chief Information Officer
CHR: Staci Franz, Director Human Resources
CNO: Ginger Cohen, Chief Nurse Executive
Web address: www.st–lukes.org
**Control:** Other not–for–profit (including NFP Corporation) **Service:** Rehabilitation

**Staffed Beds:** 72 **Admissions:** 1522 **Census:** 56 **Outpatient Visits:** 57185 **Births:** 0 **Total Expense ($000):** 39371 **Payroll Expense ($000):** 23045 **Personnel:** 519

**VETERANS AFFAIRS MEDICAL CENTER** See Mann–Grandstaff Veterans Affairs Medical Center

## SPOKANE VALLEY—Spokane County

☒ **VALLEY HOSPITAL (500119)**, 12606 East Mission Avenue, Zip 99216–1090; tel. 509/924–6650, (Nonreporting) **A**1 2 3 9 10 **S** Community Health Systems, Inc., Franklin, TN
Primary Contact: Gregory Repetti, Interim Chief Executive Officer
COO: David Martin, Assistant Administrator
CFO: Justin Voelker, Chief Financial Officer
Web address: www.valleyhospital.org
**Control:** Corporation, Investor–owned, for–profit **Service:** General Medical and Surgical

**Staffed Beds:** 123

**WA**

---

**Hospital, Medicare Provider Number, Address, Telephone, Approval, Facility, and Physician Codes, Health Care System**

★ American Hospital Association (AHA) membership   ○ Healthcare Facilities Accreditation Program   ⇑ Center for Improvement in Healthcare Quality Accreditation
☐ The Joint Commission accreditation   ◇ DNV Healthcare Inc. accreditation   △ Commission on Accreditation of Rehabilitation Facilities (CARF) accreditation

**SUNNYSIDE—Yakima County**

★ **SUNNYSIDE COMMUNITY HOSPITAL AND CLINICS (501330)**, 1016 Tacoma Avenue, Zip 98944–2263, Mailing Address: P.O. Box 719, Zip 98944–0719; tel. 509/837–1500, (Nonreporting) **A**9 10 18 **S** HealthTech Management Services, Brentwood, TN
Primary Contact: John Gallagher, Chief Executive Officer
CFO: Cary Rowan, Chief Financial Officer
CIO: John Andersen, Manager Information Systems
CHR: Elaina Wagner, Director Human Resources
CNO: Mary Beth Tubbs, Chief Nursing Officer
Web address: www.sunnysidehospital.com
**Control:** Other not–for–profit (including NFP Corporation) **Service:** General Medical and Surgical

| Staffed Beds: 25 |
|---|

**TACOMA—Pierce County**

**ALLENMORE HOSPITAL** See MultiCare Tacoma General Hospital

⊠ **MADIGAN HEALTHCARE SYSTEM**, Fitzsimmons Drive, Building 9040, Zip 98431–1100; tel. 253/968–1110, (Nonreporting) **A**1 2 3 5 **S** Department of the Army, Office of the Surgeon General, Falls Church, VA
Primary Contact: Colonel Ramona Fiorey, MSN, M.P.H., Commander
COO: Colonel R. Neal David, Administrator and Chief of Staff
CFO: Lieutenant Colonel Bryan Longmuir, Chief Resource Management
CIO: Lieutenant Colonel Andrew Smith, Chief Information Management
CHR: David Aiken, Chief Human Resources Officer
Web address: www.mamc.amedd.army.mil
**Control:** Army, Government, federal **Service:** General Medical and Surgical

| Staffed Beds: 227 |
|---|

⊠ **MULTICARE MARY BRIDGE CHILDREN'S HOSPITAL AND HEALTH CENTER (503301)**, 317 Martin Luther King Jr. Way, Zip 98405–4234, Mailing Address: P.O. Box 5299, Zip 98415–0299; tel. 253/403–1400 **A**1 5 9 10 **F**3 7 8 12 19 21 23 25 27 29 30 31 32 34 35 40 41 43 48 50 54 55 57 59 62 63 64 65 66 71 74 75 78 79 81 82 84 85 86 87 88 89 91 92 93 96 97 99 102 104 107 108 110 111 114 115 116 117 119 120 121 123 124 129 130 131 132 134 135 143 144 146 148 **S** MultiCare Health System, Tacoma, WA
Primary Contact: Robert Lenza, Chief Operating Officer and Administrator
CFO: Vince Schmitz, Senior Vice President and Chief Financial Officer
CMO: Lester Reed, M.D., Vice President Medical Affairs and Acute Care
CIO: Florence Chang, Executive Vice President
CHR: Sarah Horsman, Senior Vice President Human Potential
CNO: Kate Bechtold, R.N., Senior Vice President and Chief Nurse Executive
Web address: www.multicare.org/marybridge
**Control:** Other not–for–profit (including NFP Corporation) **Service:** Children's general

| Staffed Beds: 75 Admissions: 2878 Census: 33 Outpatient Visits: 107553 Births: 0 Total Expense ($000): 133667 Payroll Expense ($000): 60309 Personnel: 551 |
|---|

⊠ **MULTICARE TACOMA GENERAL HOSPITAL (500129)**, 315 Martin Luther King Jr. Way, Zip 98405–4234, Mailing Address: P.O. Box 5299, Zip 98415–0299; tel. 253/403–1000, (Includes ALLENMORE HOSPITAL, South 19th and Union Avenue, Zip 98405, Mailing Address: P.O. Box 11414, Zip 98411–0414; tel. 253/403–2323) **A**1 2 3 9 10 **F**2 3 8 13 15 17 18 19 20 21 22 23 24 25 26 27 28 29 30 31 34 35 36 40 42 43 45 46 47 48 49 50 51 54 55 57 58 59 62 63 64 65 70 71 72 73 74 75 76 77 78 79 80 81 82 84 85 86 87 93 97 102 107 108 109 110 111 114 115 116 117 119 120 121 123 124 126 127 129 130 131 132 135 144 146 147 148 **S** MultiCare Health System, Tacoma, WA
Primary Contact: William G. Robertson, President and Chief Executive Officer
COO: Lisa Strom, R.N., Chief Operating Officer
CFO: Anna Loomis, Interim Chief Financial Officer
CMO: Claire Spain–Remy, M.D., Senior Vice President, MultiCare Medical Associates
CIO: Florence Chang, Executive Vice President
CHR: Sarah Horsman, Senior Vice President Human Potential
CNO: Kate Bechtold, R.N., Senior Vice President and Chief Nurse Executive
Web address: www.multicare.org
**Control:** Other not–for–profit (including NFP Corporation) **Service:** General Medical and Surgical

| Staffed Beds: 381 Admissions: 17105 Census: 234 Outpatient Visits: 193814 Births: 3084 Total Expense ($000): 473043 Payroll Expense ($000): 234457 Personnel: 2233 |
|---|

⊠ △ **ST. JOSEPH MEDICAL CENTER (500108)**, 1717 South J Street, Zip 98405–3004, Mailing Address: P.O. Box 2197, Zip 98401–2197; tel. 253/426–4101 **A**1 2 3 7 9 10 **F**3 8 12 13 17 18 20 22 24 26 28 29 30 31 34 35 38 40 43 44 45 46 47 48 49 50 51 55 57 58 59 60 63 64 65 70 72 73 74 75 76 77 78 79 81 82 84 85 86 87 90 92 93 98 102 107 108 111 114 115 119 124 126 130 132 135 145 146 148 **S** Catholic Health Initiatives, Englewood, CO
Primary Contact: Syd Bersante, R.N., President
COO: Syd Bersante, R.N., President
CFO: Mike Fitzgerald, Chief Financial Officer
CIO: Rand Strobel, Vice President Information Technology and Compliance
CHR: Sharon Royne, Interim Senior Vice President Human Resources
Web address: www.fhshealth.org
**Control:** Church–operated, Nongovernment, not–for profit **Service:** General Medical and Surgical

| Staffed Beds: 366 Admissions: 21979 Census: 286 Outpatient Visits: 254140 Births: 4050 Total Expense ($000): 568705 Payroll Expense ($000): 226230 Personnel: 3297 |
|---|

**VETERANS AFFAIRS PUGET SOUND HEALTH CARE SYSTEM–AMERICAN LAKE DIVISION** See Veterans Affairs Puget Sound Health Care System, Seattle

☐ **WESTERN STATE HOSPITAL (504003)**, 9601 Steilacom Boulevard S.W., Zip 98498–7213; tel. 253/582–8900, (Nonreporting) **A**1 5 9 10
Primary Contact: Ron Adler, Superintendent
COO: Dale Thompson, Chief Operating Officer
CFO: Charm Reimer, Chief Financial Officer
CMO: John Chiles, M.D., Medical Director
CHR: Lori Manning, Administrator Human Resources
Web address: www.dshs.wa.gov/mentalhealth/wsh.shtml
**Control:** State–Government, nonfederal **Service:** Psychiatric

| Staffed Beds: 867 |
|---|

**TONASKET—Okanogan County**

★ **NORTH VALLEY HOSPITAL (501321)**, 203 South Western Avenue, Zip 98855–8803; tel. 509/486–2151, (Nonreporting) **A**9 10 18
Primary Contact: Mike Zwicker, Chief Executive Officer
CFO: Helen Verhasselt, Chief Financial Officer
CMO: Paul Lacey, M.D., Chief Medical Staff
CIO: Kelly Cariker, Chief Information Officer
CHR: Jan Gonzales, Director Human Resources
Web address: www.nvhospital.org
**Control:** Hospital district or authority, Government, nonfederal **Service:** General Medical and Surgical

| Staffed Beds: 83 |
|---|

**TOPPENISH—Yakima County**

⊠ **TOPPENISH COMMUNITY HOSPITAL (500037)**, 502 West Fourth Avenue, Zip 98948–1616, Mailing Address: P.O. Box 672, Zip 98948–0672; tel. 509/865–3105 **A**1 3 5 9 10 **F**3 13 15 18 20 28 29 30 34 35 40 43 45 46 50 57 59 68 70 76 79 81 89 107 111 114 119 133 135 **S** Community Health Systems, Inc., Franklin, TN
Primary Contact: Perry Gay, Chief Executive Officer
CFO: Curtis Herrin, Chief Financial Officer
CHR: Rosa Solorzano, Interim Director Human Resources
Web address: www.toppenishhospital.com
**Control:** Corporation, Investor–owned, for–profit **Service:** General Medical and Surgical

| Staffed Beds: 48 Admissions: 1506 Census: 10 Births: 464 Personnel: 208 |
|---|

**TUKWILA—King County**

⊠ **CASCADE BEHAVIORAL HOSPITAL (504011)**, 12844 Military Road South, Zip 98168–3045; tel. 206/244–0180, (Nonreporting) **A**1 3 10 **S** Acadia Healthcare Company, Inc., Franklin, TN
Primary Contact: Michael Uradnik, Chief Executive Officer
CFO: Gregg Terreson, Chief Financial Officer
CHR: Sherry Cochran, Manager Human Resources
Web address: www.cascadebh.com
**Control:** Corporation, Investor–owned, for–profit **Service:** Psychiatric

| Staffed Beds: 63 |
|---|

**VANCOUVER—Clark County**

**LEGACY SALMON CREEK HOSPITAL** See Legacy Salmon Creek Medical Center

**WA**

⊞ **LEGACY SALMON CREEK MEDICAL CENTER (500150)**, 2211 N.E. 139th Street, Zip 98686–2742; tel. 360/487–1000 **A**1 2 5 9 10 **F**3 11 13 15 18 20 26 28 29 30 31 32 34 35 38 39 40 44 45 46 47 50 51 57 59 60 64 65 68 70 72 74 75 76 77 78 79 80 81 82 84 85 87 93 96 97 101 107 108 110 111 114 116 117 118 119 120 121 126 129 130 132 146 147 148 **P**6 **S** Legacy Health, Portland, OR
Primary Contact: Bryce R. Helgerson, Chief Administrative Officer
COO: Michael Newcomb, D.O., Senior Vice President and Chief Operating Officer
CMO: Lewis Low, M.D., Senior Vice President and Chief Medical Officer
CHR: Sonja Steves, Senior Vice President Human Resources
CNO: Carol Bradley, MSN, Senior Vice President and Chief Nursing Officer
Web address: www.legacyhealth.org
**Control:** Other not–for–profit (including NFP Corporation) **Service:** General Medical and Surgical

**Staffed Beds: 214 Admissions: 12455 Census: 124 Outpatient Visits: 202123 Births: 2676 Total Expense ($000): 220099 Payroll Expense ($000): 118322 Personnel: 1577**

★ △ ◇ **PEACEHEALTH SOUTHWEST MEDICAL CENTER (500050)**, 400 N.E. Mother Joseph Place, Zip 98664–3200, Mailing Address: P.O. Box 1600, Zip 98668–1600; tel. 360/256–2000, (Includes VANCOUVER MEMORIAL CAMPUS, 3400 Main Street, Zip 98663; tel. 360/696–5270) **A**2 3 5 7 9 10 21 **F**3 11 12 13 15 17 18 20 24 26 28 29 30 31 34 35 40 43 44 45 46 49 50 51 54 57 58 59 60 61 62 63 64 65 68 70 72 74 75 76 77 78 79 81 82 84 85 86 87 89 90 92 93 96 97 98 100 101 102 103 104 105 107 108 109 110 111 113 114 115 116 119 120 121 122 124 126 129 130 131 132 135 144 145 146 147 148 **S** PeaceHealth, Vancouver, WA
COO: Joanne Owen, Interim Vice President Operations
CFO: Gordon Edwards, System Vice President and Chief Financial Officer, Columbia Network
CMO: Alden Roberts, M.D., Chief Medical Officer
CIO: Don McMillan, Chief Information Officer
CHR: Laurie Lemieux, Vice President People and Culture
Web address: www.swmedicalcenter.org
**Control:** Other not–for–profit (including NFP Corporation) **Service:** General Medical and Surgical

**Staffed Beds: 450 Admissions: 21201 Census: 257 Births: 2208 Total Expense ($000): 544363 Payroll Expense ($000): 190077**

**SOUTHWEST WASHINGTON MEDICAL CENTER** See PeaceHealth Southwest Medical Center

### WALLA WALLA—Walla Walla County

★ **JONATHAN M. WAINWRIGHT MEMORIAL VETERANS AFFAIRS MEDICAL CENTER**, 77 Wainwright Drive, Zip 99362–3994; tel. 509/525–5200, (Nonreporting) **A**9 **S** Department of Veterans Affairs, Washington, DC
Primary Contact: Brian W. Westfield, MSN, Director
CFO: Debra Pearson, Chief Financial Officer
CMO: Charles Beleny, D.O., Chief of Staff
CIO: Gary Ramer, Manager Information Management
CHR: Mary C. Lee, Manager Human Resources
CNO: Diana Nelson, R.N., Associate Director for Patient Care Services/Nurse Executive
Web address: www.wallawalla.va.gov
**Control:** Veterans Affairs, Government, federal **Service:** General Medical and Surgical

**Staffed Beds: 14**

⊞ △ **PROVIDENCE ST. MARY MEDICAL CENTER (500002)**, 401 West Poplar Street, Zip 99362–2846, Mailing Address: P.O. Box 1477, Zip 99362–0312; tel. 509/525–3320 **A**1 2 7 9 10 19 **F**3 13 15 18 20 22 28 29 30 31 34 35 40 43 45 46 49 50 59 62 64 70 73 74 75 76 77 78 79 81 82 85 89 90 93 96 97 107 110 111 114 115 118 119 121 123 129 130 131 135 144 146 147 148 **P**2 **S** Providence Health & Services, Renton, WA
Primary Contact: Steven A. Burdick, Chief Executive Officer
COO: Susan Blackburn, Chief Operating Officer
CMO: Tim Davidson, M.D., Chief Executive Physician Services
CIO: Martin Manny, Director, I.S.
CNO: Yvonne M. Strader, Chief Nursing Officer
Web address: www.washington.providence.org/hospitals/st–mary/
**Control:** Church–operated, Nongovernment, not–for profit **Service:** General Medical and Surgical

**Staffed Beds: 80 Admissions: 4093 Census: 41 Outpatient Visits: 152820 Births: 588 Total Expense ($000): 132045 Payroll Expense ($000): 70428 Personnel: 804**

**STATE PENITENTIARY HOSPITAL**, 1313 North 13th Street, Zip 99362–8817; tel. 509/525–3610, (Nonreporting)
Primary Contact: Karen Forest, Health Care Manager
**Control:** State–Government, nonfederal **Service:** Hospital unit of an institution (prison hospital, college infirmary, etc.)

**Staffed Beds: 36**

⊞ **WALLA WALLA GENERAL HOSPITAL (500049)**, 1025 South Second Avenue, Zip 99362–4116, Mailing Address: P.O. Box 1398, Zip 99362–0309; tel. 509/525–0480 **A**1 9 10 **F**11 13 15 17 18 20 28 29 30 34 35 40 43 45 49 52 57 59 62 64 68 69 70 74 75 76 79 81 87 89 93 97 107 108 110 111 114 118 119 127 129 130 132 133 135 146 147 **S** Adventist Health, Roseville, CA
Primary Contact: Monty E. Knittel, President and Chief Executive Officer
CFO: Duane Meidinger, Vice President Finance
CIO: Gary Dietz, Director Information Technology Services
CHR: Barbara Blood, Director Human Resources
Web address: www.wwgh.com
**Control:** Church–operated, Nongovernment, not–for profit **Service:** General Medical and Surgical

**Staffed Beds: 38 Admissions: 1324 Census: 10 Births: 224**

### WENATCHEE—Chelan County

⊞ **CENTRAL WASHINGTON HOSPITAL (500016)**, 1201 South Miller Street, Zip 98801–3201, Mailing Address: P.O. Box 1887, Zip 98807–1887; tel. 509/662–1511, (Total facility includes 22 beds in nursing home–type unit) **A**1 9 10 19 **F**3 13 17 18 20 22 24 26 28 29 30 31 34 35 40 43 45 46 47 49 50 62 63 64 68 69 70 73 74 75 76 78 79 81 84 85 86 89 91 93 94 95 107 111 114 115 119 128 130 146 148
Primary Contact: Peter Rutherford, M.D., Chief Executive Officer
CFO: John Doyle, Chief Financial Officer
CMO: Stuart Freed, M.D., Chief Medical Officer
CIO: Robert Pageler, Chief Information Officer
CHR: Jim Wood, Chief Administrative Officer
CNO: Tracey A. Kasnic, R.N., Chief Nursing Officer
Web address: www.cwhs.org
**Control:** Other not–for–profit (including NFP Corporation) **Service:** General Medical and Surgical

**Staffed Beds: 198 Admissions: 10668 Census: 127 Outpatient Visits: 148542 Births: 1384 Total Expense ($000): 253569 Payroll Expense ($000): 81459 Personnel: 1204**

△ **WENATCHEE VALLEY MEDICAL CENTER (500148)**, 820 North Chelan Avenue, Zip 98801–2028; tel. 509/663–8711, (Nonreporting) **A**2 7 9 10
Primary Contact: Peter Rutherford, M.D., Chief Executive Officer
COO: Kevin Gilbert, R.N., Vice President
CFO: John Doyle, Chief Financial Officer
CMO: Stuart Freed, M.D., Medical Director
CIO: Robert Pageler, Chief Information Officer
CHR: Jim Wood, Chief Human Resources Officer
CNO: Tracey A. Kasnic, R.N., Chief Nursing Officer
Web address: www.wvmedical.com
**Control:** Partnership, Investor–owned, for–profit **Service:** General Medical and Surgical

**Staffed Beds: 20**

### WHITE SALMON—Klickitat County

**SKYLINE HOSPITAL (501315)**, 211 Skyline Drive, Zip 98672–1918, Mailing Address: P.O. Box 99, Zip 98672–0099; tel. 509/493–1101 **A**9 10 18 **F**34 35 40 43 45 57 64 67 70 74 81 82 87 93 107 111 115 119 128 131 133 146 **P**6
Primary Contact: Robert P. Kimmes, Chief Executive Officer
CFO: Brenda Schneider, Chief Financial Officer
CMO: Christopher Samuels, Chief of Staff
CIO: Steve Opbroek, Manager Information Technology
CHR: Jessie Ramos, Manager Human Resources
CNO: Stefanie Boen, Chief Nursing Officer
Web address: www.skylinehospital.com
**Control:** Hospital district or authority, Government, nonfederal **Service:** General Medical and Surgical

**Staffed Beds: 18 Admissions: 290 Census: 5 Outpatient Visits: 18621 Births: 0 Total Expense ($000): 17095 Payroll Expense ($000): 7516 Personnel: 116**

**WA**

---

**Hospital, Medicare Provider Number, Address, Telephone, Approval, Facility, and Physician Codes, Health Care System**

★ American Hospital Association (AHA) membership  ○ Healthcare Facilities Accreditation Program  ⇧ Center for Improvement in Healthcare Quality Accreditation
☐ The Joint Commission accreditation  ◇ DNV Healthcare Inc. accreditation  △ Commission on Accreditation of Rehabilitation Facilities (CARF) accreditation

WA

**YAKIMA—Yakima County**

✠ △ **YAKIMA REGIONAL MEDICAL AND CARDIAC CENTER (500012)**, 110 South Ninth Avenue, Zip 98902–3315; tel. 509/575–5000 **A**1 2 7 9 10 **F**3 15 17 18 19 20 22 24 26 28 29 30 34 35 37 40 41 43 45 46 49 50 57 58 59 60 62 63 64 65 67 68 70 74 77 78 79 81 82 85 87 89 90 93 96 102 107 108 110 111 115 119 126 130 132 144 145 146 **S** Community Health Systems, Inc., Franklin, TN
Primary Contact: Veronica Knudson, Chief Executive Officer
CMO: Dave Atteberry, M.D., Chief of Staff
CHR: Ralph L. Lundberg, Director Human Resources
Web address: www.yakimaregional.net
**Control:** Corporation, Investor–owned, for–profit **Service:** General Medical and Surgical

**Staffed Beds:** 167 **Admissions:** 4621 **Census:** 56 **Outpatient Visits:** 82509 **Births:** 0 **Total Expense ($000):** 133153 **Payroll Expense ($000):** 36176 **Personnel:** 590

✠ **YAKIMA VALLEY MEMORIAL HOSPITAL (500036)**, 2811 Tieton Drive, Zip 98902–3761; tel. 509/575–8000 **A**1 2 3 5 9 10 **F**3 8 11 13 15 17 18 20 22 26 28 29 30 31 32 34 35 36 40 41 42 43 44 45 46 47 49 50 51 55 57 59 60 62 63 65 68 70 72 73 74 75 76 77 78 79 81 82 84 85 86 87 89 92 93 96 98 100 102 104 107 108 110 111 114 116 117 119 120 121 123 124 129 130 131 132 135 144 146 147 148 **P**4 6 7
Primary Contact: Russ Myers, Chief Executive Officer
COO: James Aberle, Vice President, Hospital Operations
CFO: Tim Reed, Vice President and Chief Financial Officer
CMO: Kevin Sweeny, M.D., Vice President and Chief Medical Officer
CIO: Jeff Yamada, Vice President
CHR: Jolene R. Seda, Administrative Director
CNO: Diane Patterson, Vice President, Chief Clinical Officer
Web address: www.yakimamemorial.org
**Control:** Other not–for–profit (including NFP Corporation) **Service:** General Medical and Surgical

**Staffed Beds:** 226 **Admissions:** 11523 **Census:** 132 **Outpatient Visits:** 339023 **Births:** 2803 **Total Expense ($000):** 341052 **Payroll Expense ($000):** 119742 **Personnel:** 1913

# WEST VIRGINIA

## BECKLEY—Raleigh County

☐ **BECKLEY ARH HOSPITAL (510062)**, 306 Stanaford Road, Zip 25801–3142; tel. 304/255–3000 **A**1 9 10 **F**3 6 11 12 15 17 18 20 28 29 30 31 34 35 39 40 43 44 45 46 47 48 49 50 51 54 56 57 59 60 61 62 64 65 70 74 75 77 78 79 81 82 84 85 86 87 89 92 93 97 98 99 100 101 102 103 105 107 108 109 110 111 114 115 116 118 119 129 130 132 146 148 **P**6 **S** Appalachian Regional Healthcare, Inc., Lexington, KY
Primary Contact: Rocco K. Massey, Community Chief Executive Officer
CMO: Ali Suleiman, M.D., Chief of Staff
CHR: Sue Thomas, Manager Human Resources
CNO: Rosalina Dunford–Boothe, Community Chief Nursing Officer
Web address: www.arh.org
**Control:** Other not–for–profit (including NFP Corporation) **Service:** General Medical and Surgical

**Staffed Beds:** 170 **Admissions:** 6509 **Census:** 106 **Outpatient Visits:** 79759 **Births:** 0 **Total Expense ($000):** 87204 **Payroll Expense ($000):** 25786 **Personnel:** 524

✠ **BECKLEY VETERANS AFFAIRS MEDICAL CENTER**, 200 Veterans Avenue, Zip 25801–6499; tel. 304/255–2121, (Nonreporting) **A**1 **S** Department of Veterans Affairs, Washington, DC
Primary Contact: Karin L. McGraw, MSN, FACHE, Director
CFO: Terry Massey, Chief Fiscal Services
CMO: John David Berryman, M.D., Chief of Staff
CIO: Sherry Gregg, Chief Information Technology Officer
CNO: Debra Lynn Legg, Associate Director Patient Care Services and Nurse Executive
Web address: www.beckley.va.gov/
**Control:** Veterans Affairs, Government, federal **Service:** General Medical and Surgical

**Staffed Beds:** 40

✠ **RALEIGH GENERAL HOSPITAL (510070)**, 1710 Harper Road, Zip 25801–3397; tel. 304/256–4100 **A**1 9 10 19 **F**3 13 15 17 18 20 22 29 30 31 34 35 40 43 45 49 50 57 59 60 64 70 74 75 76 78 79 81 85 87 89 93 107 108 110 111 114 115 117 119 126 130 131 132 146 147 **S** LifePoint Health, Brentwood, TN
Primary Contact: David B. Darden, Chief Executive Officer
CFO: Randy Harrison, Chief Financial Officer
CMO: Syed Siddiqi, M.D., President Medical Staff
CIO: Kevin Sexton, Director Information Systems
CHR: Chris T. Beebe, Director Human Resources
CNO: Alene Lewis, R.N., Chief Nursing Officer
Web address: www.raleighgeneral.com
**Control:** Corporation, Investor–owned, for–profit **Service:** General Medical and Surgical

**Staffed Beds:** 229 **Admissions:** 10894 **Census:** 133 **Outpatient Visits:** 110904 **Births:** 1237 **Total Expense ($000):** 131151 **Payroll Expense ($000):** 44951 **Personnel:** 853

## BERKELEY SPRINGS—Morgan County

★ **WAR MEMORIAL HOSPITAL (511309)**, One Healthy Way, Zip 25411–7463; tel. 304/258–1234, (Total facility includes 16 beds in nursing home–type unit) **A**9 10 18 **F**3 11 15 28 29 30 34 35 40 45 50 53 54 57 59 64 65 77 79 81 85 86 93 97 107 119 129 130 133 **P**6 **S** Valley Health System, Winchester, VA
Primary Contact: Neil R. McLaughlin, R.N., President
CFO: Kathryn Morales, Director of Finance
CMO: Gerald Bechamps, M.D., Vice President Medical Affairs
CHR: Abbey Rembold, Human Resources Senior Generalist
CNO: Heather Sigel, Director of Clinical Services
Web address: www.valleyhealthlink.com/war
**Control:** Other not–for–profit (including NFP Corporation) **Service:** General Medical and Surgical

**Staffed Beds:** 41 **Admissions:** 381 **Census:** 25 **Outpatient Visits:** 42140 **Births:** 0 **Total Expense ($000):** 19267 **Payroll Expense ($000):** 8699 **Personnel:** 177

## BLUEFIELD—Mercer County

✠ **BLUEFIELD REGIONAL MEDICAL CENTER (510071)**, 500 Cherry Street, Zip 24701–3390; tel. 304/327–1100 **A**1 9 10 12 13 19 **F**3 8 13 15 17 18 20 22 28 29 31 34 40 43 45 46 47 49 50 56 57 59 60 64 68 70 74 75 76 77 78 79 81 86 89 96 107 108 110 111 115 118 119 121 124 126 127 129 130 132 144 146 147 **P**8 **S** Community Health Systems, Inc., Franklin, TN
Primary Contact: Gigi Fergus, Interim Chief Executive Officer
CMO: Joel Shor, M.D., Chief of Staff
CIO: Rose Lasker, Director Information Services
CHR: Sandee Cheynet, Vice President Administrative Services
Web address: www.bluefield.org
**Control:** Corporation, Investor–owned, for–profit **Service:** General Medical and Surgical

**Staffed Beds:** 102 **Admissions:** 4345 **Census:** 45 **Outpatient Visits:** 72984 **Births:** 523 **Total Expense ($000):** 84252 **Payroll Expense ($000):** 26880 **Personnel:** 474

## BRIDGEPORT—Harrison County

✠ **UNITED HOSPITAL CENTER (510006)**, 327 Medical Park Drive, Zip 26330–9006; tel. 681/342–1000 **A**1 2 3 5 9 10 12 13 **F**3 5 11 13 15 17 18 20 22 28 29 30 31 34 36 38 39 40 45 46 47 48 49 51 54 57 58 59 60 62 63 64 65 68 70 74 75 76 77 78 79 81 82 84 85 86 87 89 93 97 98 99 100 101 102 103 104 107 108 109 110 111 114 115 116 117 118 119 120 121 123 126 128 129 130 131 132 146 148 **P**6 7 8 **S** West Virginia United Health System, Fairmont, WV
Primary Contact: Michael C. Tillman, President and Chief Executive Officer
CFO: Douglas Coffman, Vice President and Chief Financial Officer
CMO: Eric Radcliffe, M.D., Medical Director
CIO: Brian Cottrill, Chief Information Officer
CHR: Timothy M. Allen, Vice President Human Resources
Web address: www.thenewuhc.com
**Control:** Other not–for–profit (including NFP Corporation) **Service:** General Medical and Surgical

**Staffed Beds:** 264 **Admissions:** 12423 **Census:** 189 **Outpatient Visits:** 458764 **Births:** 1046 **Total Expense ($000):** 253222 **Payroll Expense ($000):** 100478 **Personnel:** 1803

## BUCKEYE—Pocahontas County

★ **POCAHONTAS MEMORIAL HOSPITAL (511314)**, 150 Duncan Road, Zip 24924, Mailing Address: Rural Route 2, Box 52 W, Zip 24924; tel. 304/799–7400 **A**9 10 18 **F**3 7 11 29 30 34 35 40 43 56 57 59 64 65 67 68 77 86 90 93 97 107 119 127 128 132 133 135 144 146
Primary Contact: Barbara Lay, Chief Executive Officer
COO: Terry Wagner, R.N., Chief Operating Officer
CFO: Melissa Kane, Chief Financial Officer
CMO: Frank Puckett, M.D., Chief Medical Officer
CIO: Aaron Vaughan, Coordinator Information Systems
CHR: Katie Brown, Coordinator Human Resources
CNO: Kerrie Ridgeway, R.N., Chief Nursing Officer
Web address: www.pmhwv.org/
**Control:** County–Government, nonfederal **Service:** General Medical and Surgical

**Staffed Beds:** 24 **Admissions:** 231 **Census:** 3 **Outpatient Visits:** 8586 **Births:** 3 **Total Expense ($000):** 11085 **Payroll Expense ($000):** 5546 **Personnel:** 118

**WV**

---

**Hospital, Medicare Provider Number, Address, Telephone, Approval, Facility, and Physician Codes, Health Care System**

★ American Hospital Association (AHA) membership    ◯ Healthcare Facilities Accreditation Program    ⇑ Center for Improvement in Healthcare Quality Accreditation
☐ The Joint Commission accreditation    ◇ DNV Healthcare Inc. accreditation    △ Commission on Accreditation of Rehabilitation Facilities (CARF) accreditation

**BUCKHANNON—Upshur County**

⊞ **ST. JOSEPH'S HOSPITAL OF BUCKHANNON (511321)**, 1 Amalia Drive, Zip 26201–2276; tel. 304/473–2000, (Total facility includes 20 beds in nursing home–type unit) **A**1 9 10 18 **F**3 11 13 15 18 28 29 30 31 34 35 40 43 44 45 50 57 59 64 65 70 75 76 79 81 83 84 85 87 89 107 110 114 119 128 129 130 132 133 135 144 146 147 **P**6 8 **S** Pallottine Health Services, Huntington, WV
Primary Contact: Sue E. Johnson–Phillippe, FACHE, President and Chief Executive Officer
CFO: Renee Hofer, Chief Financial Officer
CMO: Robert Blake, M.D., Chief of Staff
CIO: Brian Williams, Service Leader Corporate Information Systems
CHR: Anissa Hite–Davis, Vice President Human Resources
CNO: Kelle Bari, R.N., Vice President Patient Care Services
Web address: www.stj.net
**Control:** Other not–for–profit (including NFP Corporation) **Service:** General Medical and Surgical

**Staffed Beds:** 51 **Admissions:** 1260 **Census:** 26 **Outpatient Visits:** 94908 **Births:** 311 **Total Expense ($000):** 40088 **Payroll Expense ($000):** 19295 **Personnel:** 349

**CHARLESTON—Kanawha County**

**CAMC MEMORIAL HOSPITAL** See Charleston Area Medical Center

**CAMC WOMEN AND CHILDREN'S HOSPITAL** See Charleston Area Medical Center

★ △ ◇ **CHARLESTON AREA MEDICAL CENTER (510022)**, 501 Morris Street, Zip 25301–1300, Mailing Address: P.O. Box 1547, Zip 25326–1547; tel. 304/388–5432, (Includes CAMC MEMORIAL HOSPITAL, 3200 MacCorkle Avenue S.E., Zip 25304; tel. 304/388–5973; Jeffrey L. Oskin, Vice President and Administrator; CAMC TEAYS VALLEY HOSPITAL, 1400 Hospital Drive, Hurricane, Zip 25526–9202; tel. 304/757–1700; Randall H. Hodges, FACHE, Vice President and Administrator; CAMC WOMEN AND CHILDREN'S HOSPITAL, 800 Pennsylvania Avenue, Zip 25302, Mailing Address: P.O. Box 6669, Zip 25362; tel. 304/388–5432; Andrew Weber, Vice President and Administrator; GENERAL HOSPITAL, 501 Morris Street, Zip 25301, Mailing Address: Box 1393, Zip 25325; tel. 304/388–5432; Michael D. Williams, Vice President and Administrator) **A**2 3 5 7 8 9 10 12 13 21 **F**3 8 11 12 13 15 17 18 19 20 22 24 26 28 29 30 31 32 34 35 38 40 41 43 44 45 46 47 48 49 50 51 52 54 55 56 57 59 60 61 64 65 68 70 72 74 75 76 77 78 79 81 82 84 85 86 88 89 90 92 93 94 96 97 98 99 100 101 102 103 104 107 108 110 111 114 115 116 117 118 119 120 121 123 124 126 129 130 131 132 134 135 138 141 143 144 145 146 147 148 **P**6
Primary Contact: David L. Ramsey, President and Chief Executive Officer
COO: Glenn Crotty, Jr., M.D., Executive Vice President and Chief Operating Officer
CFO: Larry C. Hudson, Executive Vice President and Chief Financial Officer
CMO: T. Pinckney McIlwain, M.D., Vice President and Chief Medical Officer
CHR: Kristi Snyder, Vice President Human Resources
CNO: Ronald E. Moore, R.N., Vice President Professional Practice and Chief Nursing Officer
Web address: www.camc.org
**Control:** Other not–for–profit (including NFP Corporation) **Service:** General Medical and Surgical

**Staffed Beds:** 865 **Admissions:** 37061 **Census:** 552 **Outpatient Visits:** 644148 **Births:** 2896 **Total Expense ($000):** 879285 **Payroll Expense ($000):** 304218 **Personnel:** 6071

▢ **EYE AND EAR CLINIC OF CHARLESTON (510059)**, 1306 Kanawha Boulevard East, Zip 25301–3001, Mailing Address: P.O. Box 2271, Zip 25328–2271; tel. 304/343–4371 **A**1 10 **F**3 45 57 59 75 79 81 107 111 119 141
Primary Contact: Christina Arvon, Administrator and Chief Executive Officer
CMO: James W. Candill, M.D., President Medical Staff
Web address: www.eyeandearclinicwv.org
**Control:** Corporation, Investor–owned, for–profit **Service:** General Medical and Surgical

**Staffed Beds:** 6 **Admissions:** 78 **Census:** 1 **Outpatient Visits:** 9050 **Births:** 0 **Total Expense ($000):** 11559 **Payroll Expense ($000):** 3985 **Personnel:** 125

**GENERAL HOSPITAL** See Charleston Area Medical Center

⊞ **HIGHLAND HOSPITAL (514001)**, 300 56th Street S.E., Zip 25304–2361, Mailing Address: P.O. Box 4107, Zip 25364–4107; tel. 304/926–1600 **A**1 9 10 **F**3 29 34 35 50 57 59 86 87 98 99 101 102 103 130
Primary Contact: Cynthia A. Persily, Ph.D., R.N., President and Chief Executive Officer
COO: Lisa Layden, Chief Operating Officer
CFO: Lisa Layden, Director of Finance
CMO: Kiran Devaraj, Medical Director
CIO: Pearl McWatters, Director Information Services
CNO: Carla Hall, Director of Nursing
Web address: www.highlandhosp.com
**Control:** Other not–for–profit (including NFP Corporation) **Service:** Psychiatric

**Staffed Beds:** 80 **Admissions:** 2304 **Census:** 68 **Outpatient Visits:** 0 **Births:** 0 **Total Expense ($000):** 19116 **Payroll Expense ($000):** 9637 **Personnel:** 245

⊞ **SAINT FRANCIS HOSPITAL (510031)**, 333 Laidley Street, Zip 25301–1628, Mailing Address: P.O. Box 471, Zip 25322–0471; tel. 304/347–6500, (Total facility includes 25 beds in nursing home–type unit) **A**1 9 10 **F**3 11 15 18 20 22 29 30 34 37 40 45 48 49 51 57 58 59 60 64 68 69 70 74 75 79 81 82 84 86 87 93 107 108 110 111 115 119 128 130 131 146 147 148 **S** Thomas Health System, Inc., South Charleston, WV
Primary Contact: Daniel Lauffer, FACHE, President and Chief Executive Officer
COO: Brian Ulery, Senior Vice President and Chief Operating Officer
CFO: Renee Cross, Senior Vice President and Chief Financial Officer
CMO: Matthew Upton, Chief Medical Officer
CIO: Jeremy Taylor, Director Information Services
CHR: Marybeth Smith, Director Human Resources
CNO: Rebecca Brannon, R.N., Senior Vice President and Chief Nursing Officer
Web address: www.stfrancishospital.com
**Control:** Other not–for–profit (including NFP Corporation) **Service:** General Medical and Surgical

**Staffed Beds:** 118 **Admissions:** 3609 **Census:** 47 **Outpatient Visits:** 95544 **Births:** 0 **Total Expense ($000):** 102102 **Payroll Expense ($000):** 30907 **Personnel:** 628

⊞ **SELECT SPECIALTY HOSPITAL–CHARLESTON (512002)**, 333 Laidley Street, 3rd Floor East, Zip 25301–1614; tel. 304/720–7234 **A**1 9 10 **F**1 29 74 75 79 85 130 148 **S** Select Medical Corporation, Mechanicsburg, PA
Primary Contact: Frank Weber, Chief Executive Officer
CHR: Sabrina White, Coordinator Human Resources
Web address: www.selectspecialtyhospitals.com/company/locations/charleston.aspx
**Control:** Corporation, Investor–owned, for–profit **Service:** Long–Term Acute Care hospital

**Staffed Beds:** 32 **Admissions:** 399 **Census:** 30 **Outpatient Visits:** 0 **Births:** 0 **Total Expense ($000):** 16308 **Payroll Expense ($000):** 6083 **Personnel:** 106

**CLARKSBURG—Harrison County**

▢ **HIGHLAND–CLARKSBURG HOSPITAL (514011)**, 3 Hospital Plaza, Zip 26301–9316; tel. 304/969–3100 **A**1 10 **F**4 5 86 87 98 99 101
Primary Contact: James H. Dissen, Chief Executive Officer
COO: Michael Casdorph, Chief Operating Officer
CFO: Shelly Giaguinto, Chief Financial Officer
CMO: Marilou Patalinjug Tyner, M.D., Medical Director
CHR: Cynthia Drury, Coordinator Human Resources
CNO: Paula Herndon, R.N., Nurse Executive
Web address: www.highlandhosp.com
**Control:** Other not–for–profit (including NFP Corporation) **Service:** Psychiatric

**Staffed Beds:** 116 **Admissions:** 607 **Census:** 24 **Outpatient Visits:** 0 **Births:** 0 **Total Expense ($000):** 10956 **Payroll Expense ($000):** 5457 **Personnel:** 134

⊞ **LOUIS A. JOHNSON VETERANS AFFAIRS MEDICAL CENTER**, 1 Medical Center Drive, Zip 26301–4199; tel. 304/623–3461, (Nonreporting) **A**1 2 3 5 **S** Department of Veterans Affairs, Washington, DC
Primary Contact: Glenn R. Snider, M.D., Interim Director
CMO: Glenn R. Snider, M.D., Chief of Staff
CIO: Michael Matthey, Facility Chief Information Officer
CHR: Ian Jacobs, Chief, Human Resource Management Service
Web address: www.clarksburg.va.gov
**Control:** Veterans Affairs, Government, federal **Service:** General Medical and Surgical

**Staffed Beds:** 71

**ELKINS—Randolph County**

⊞ **DAVIS MEDICAL CENTER (510030)**, Gorman Avenue and Reed Street, Zip 26241, Mailing Address: P.O. Box 1484, Zip 26241–1484; tel. 304/636–3300 **A**1 2 9 10 20 **F**11 13 15 28 29 30 31 34 35 40 49 50 51 54 57 59 64 68 69 70 71 75 76 78 79 81 82 84 85 86 87 89 92 107 108 109 110 111 115 116 117 118 119 121 123 129 130 132 135 146 147 148 **P**8 **S** Davis Health System, Elkins, WV
Primary Contact: Vance Jackson, Chief Executive Officer
CFO: Rebecca J. Hammer, Chief Financial Officer
CMO: Charles Kirkland, D.O., Chief Medical Officer
CIO: Steve Crowl, Director of Information Services
CHR: Jon Steen, Director Human Resources
CNO: Diana Patella, R.N., Chief Nursing Officer
Web address: www.davishealthsystem.com
**Control:** Other not–for–profit (including NFP Corporation) **Service:** General Medical and Surgical

**Staffed Beds:** 80 **Admissions:** 3036 **Census:** 28 **Outpatient Visits:** 149070 **Births:** 308 **Total Expense ($000):** 82354 **Payroll Expense ($000):** 38215 **Personnel:** 656

**WV**

*Many Facility Codes have changed. Please refer to the AHA Guide Code Chart.*
© 2015 AHA Guide

## FAIRMONT—Marion County

☒ **FAIRMONT REGIONAL MEDICAL CENTER (510047)**, 1325 Locust Avenue, Zip 26554–1435; tel. 304/367–7100 **A**1 2 9 10 **F**3 11 12 13 14 15 18 20 28 29 30 31 34 35 38 39 40 41 43 44 45 46 47 48 49 50 51 53 54 56 57 59 60 62 64 68 69 70 75 76 77 78 79 81 84 85 86 87 89 91 92 93 98 100 102 103 104 107 108 110 111 114 115 118 119 130 132 135 146 147 148 **P**6
Primary Contact: Margaret C. Coster, R.N., MSN, President and Chief Executive Officer
CFO: Daniel Honerbrink, Vice President Finance and Chief Financial Officer
CMO: Wes Steele, M.D., Chief of Staff
CIO: Mike Wooddell, Director Information Services
CHR: Jim Harris, Vice President Human Resources
CNO: Margaret C. Coster, R.N., Vice President Patient Services
Web address: www.fghi.com
**Control:** Corporation, Investor–owned, for–profit **Service:** General Medical and Surgical

**Staffed Beds:** 140 **Admissions:** 4194 **Census:** 70 **Outpatient Visits:** 156751 **Births:** 265 **Total Expense ($000):** 75273 **Payroll Expense ($000):** 27244 **Personnel:** 612

## GASSAWAY—Braxton County

**BRAXTON COUNTY MEMORIAL HOSPITAL (511308)**, 100 Hoylman Drive, Zip 26624–9318; tel. 304/364–5156 **A**9 10 18 **F**3 8 11 15 30 32 34 35 40 43 45 57 59 62 64 75 81 97 107 108 114 116 127 130 133 146 147 **P**6
Primary Contact: Ben Vincent, FACHE, Chief Executive Officer
CFO: Kimber Knight, Chief Financial Officer
CMO: Russell L. Stewart, D.O., Chief Medical Officer
CNO: Julia Rose, R.N., Director of Nursing
Web address: www.braxtonmemorial.org
**Control:** Other not–for–profit (including NFP Corporation) **Service:** General Medical and Surgical

**Staffed Beds:** 25 **Admissions:** 319 **Census:** 3 **Outpatient Visits:** 44110 **Births:** 0 **Total Expense ($000):** 15869 **Payroll Expense ($000):** 6733 **Personnel:** 157

## GLEN DALE—Marshall County

☒ **REYNOLDS MEMORIAL HOSPITAL (510013)**, 800 Wheeling Avenue, Zip 26038–1697; tel. 304/845–3211, (Total facility includes 20 beds in nursing home–type unit) **A**1 6 9 10 **F**3 11 13 15 18 20 28 30 34 39 40 43 53 56 57 59 62 64 65 70 74 75 76 77 78 79 80 81 82 85 86 89 92 93 107 108 110 111 114 118 119 128 130 132 135 146 148 **P**8
Primary Contact: David F. Hess, M.D., Chief Executive Officer
COO: Kevin Britt, Chief Operating Officer
CFO: William Robert Hunt, Chief Financial Officer
CMO: David F. Hess, M.D., President Medical Staff
CIO: Warren Kelley, Chief Information Officer
CHR: R. Craig Madden, Director Employee Relations
CNO: Carol R. Miller, R.N., Chief Nursing Officer
Web address: www.reynoldsmemorial.com
**Control:** Other not–for–profit (including NFP Corporation) **Service:** General Medical and Surgical

**Staffed Beds:** 99 **Admissions:** 2076 **Census:** 37 **Outpatient Visits:** 80585 **Births:** 0 **Total Expense ($000):** 36046 **Payroll Expense ($000):** 17702 **Personnel:** 340

## GRAFTON—Taylor County

**GRAFTON CITY HOSPITAL (511307)**, 1 Hospital Plaza, Zip 26354–1283; tel. 304/265–0400, (Total facility includes 76 beds in nursing home–type unit) **A**9 10 18 **F**11 15 28 29 30 31 32 34 35 38 39 40 53 54 56 57 59 61 64 65 67 75 77 78 79 81 84 86 87 91 93 97 100 101 103 104 107 108 111 119 127 128 129 130 131 132 133 135 144 146 **P**6
Primary Contact: Patrick D. Shaw, Chief Executive Officer
CFO: Regina Pickens, Chief Financial Officer
CMO: Christopher Villaraza, II, M.D., Chief Medical Staff
CIO: Jim Harris, Director Information Technology
CHR: Missey Kimbrew, Director Human Resources
CNO: Violet Shaw, R.N., Director of Nursing
Web address: www.graftonhospital.com
**Control:** City–Government, nonfederal **Service:** General Medical and Surgical

**Staffed Beds:** 101 **Admissions:** 443 **Census:** 67 **Outpatient Visits:** 39429 **Births:** 0 **Total Expense ($000):** 18643 **Payroll Expense ($000):** 10300 **Personnel:** 231

## GRANTSVILLE—Calhoun County

★ **MINNIE HAMILTON HEALTHCARE CENTER (511303)**, 186 Hospital Drive, Zip 26147–7100; tel. 304/354–9244, (Total facility includes 24 beds in nursing home–type unit) **A**9 10 18 **F**3 7 11 15 28 29 30 32 34 35 36 39 40 41 43 44 50 53 56 57 59 61 64 65 66 68 75 82 84 86 87 93 97 99 101 107 108 119 127 130 132 133 134 135 143 144 146 147 148 **P**6
Primary Contact: Steve Whited, Chief Executive Officer
CFO: Kyle Pierson, Chief Financial Officer
CMO: Suresh Balasubramony, M.D., Chief Medical Officer
CIO: Brent Barr, Chief Information Officer
CHR: Sheila Gherke, Director Human Resources
CNO: Kim Houchin, Chief Nursing Officer
Web address: www.mhhcc.com
**Control:** Other not–for–profit (including NFP Corporation) **Service:** General Medical and Surgical

**Staffed Beds:** 42 **Admissions:** 313 **Census:** 25 **Outpatient Visits:** 60607 **Births:** 0 **Total Expense ($000):** 20260 **Payroll Expense ($000):** 11358 **Personnel:** 262

## HINTON—Summers County

☐ **SUMMERS COUNTY ARH HOSPITAL (511310)**, Terrace Street, Zip 25951–2407, Mailing Address: Drawer 940, Zip 25951–0940; tel. 304/466–1000 **A**1 9 10 18 **F**11 15 29 30 32 34 35 40 43 44 50 54 57 59 62 64 65 71 77 81 82 85 86 87 90 93 97 107 114 119 127 130 133 146 147 148 **P**6 **S** Appalachian Regional Healthcare, Inc., Lexington, KY
Primary Contact: Wesley Dangerfield, Community Chief Executive Officer
CMO: Waheed Khan, M.D., President Medical Staff
CIO: Brent Styer, Chief Information Officer
CHR: Beth Elswick, Administrative Assistant
CNO: Sharon Milburn, Chief Nursing Officer
Web address: www.arh.org
**Control:** Other not–for–profit (including NFP Corporation) **Service:** General Medical and Surgical

**Staffed Beds:** 25 **Admissions:** 585 **Census:** 8 **Outpatient Visits:** 23807 **Births:** 0 **Total Expense ($000):** 11539 **Payroll Expense ($000):** 4689 **Personnel:** 101

## HUNTINGTON—Cabell County

☒ **CABELL HUNTINGTON HOSPITAL (510055)**, 1340 Hal Greer Boulevard, Zip 25701–0195; tel. 304/526–2000, (Includes HOOPS FAMILY CHILDREN'S HOSPITAL, 1340 Hal Greer Boulevard, Zip 25701–3800; tel. 304/526–2000), (Total facility includes 15 beds in nursing home–type unit) **A**1 2 3 5 9 10 **F**3 7 11 12 13 15 16 17 18 20 22 26 28 29 30 31 32 34 35 37 38 39 40 41 43 44 45 46 47 48 49 50 51 52 54 55 56 57 58 59 60 61 62 64 65 66 70 72 73 74 75 76 77 78 79 81 82 84 85 86 87 88 89 92 93 94 96 97 107 108 110 111 114 115 117 118 119 120 121 123 126 128 129 130 131 132 134 135 144 145 146 147 148
Primary Contact: Kevin N. Fowler, President and Chief Executive Officer
CFO: David M. Ward, Chief Financial Officer and Chief Acquisition Officer
CMO: Hoyt J. Burdick, M.D., Vice President Medical Affairs
CIO: Dennis Lee, Vice President and Chief Information Officer
CHR: Barry Tourigny, Vice President Human Resources and Organizational Development
CNO: Joy S. Pelfrey, R.N., Vice President and Chief Nursing Officer
Web address: www.cabellhuntington.org
**Control:** Other not–for–profit (including NFP Corporation) **Service:** General Medical and Surgical

**Staffed Beds:** 303 **Admissions:** 25847 **Census:** 250 **Outpatient Visits:** 531674 **Births:** 2766 **Total Expense ($000):** 434260 **Payroll Expense ($000):** 145516 **Personnel:** 2261

☐ **CORNERSTONE HOSPITAL OF HUNTINGTON (512003)**, 2900 First Avenue, Two East, Zip 25702–1241; tel. 304/399–2600 **A**1 9 10 **F**1 29 148 **S** Cornerstone Healthcare Group, Dallas, TX
Primary Contact: Cynthia Isaacs, Chief Executive Officer
CFO: Frank Carter, Chief Financial Officer
CMO: William Beam, M.D., Chief of Staff
Web address: www.chghospitals.com
**Control:** Corporation, Investor–owned, for–profit **Service:** Long–Term Acute Care hospital

**Staffed Beds:** 25 **Admissions:** 350 **Census:** 24 **Outpatient Visits:** 0 **Births:** 0 **Total Expense ($000):** 10120 **Payroll Expense ($000):** 4324 **Personnel:** 67

**WV**

---

**Hospital, Medicare Provider Number, Address, Telephone, Approval, Facility, and Physician Codes, Health Care System**

★ American Hospital Association (AHA) membership   ○ Healthcare Facilities Accreditation Program   ⇧ Center for Improvement in Healthcare Quality Accreditation
☐ The Joint Commission accreditation   ◇ DNV Healthcare Inc. accreditation   △ Commission on Accreditation of Rehabilitation Facilities (CARF) accreditation

⊞ **HEALTHSOUTH HUNTINGTON REHABILITATION HOSPITAL (513028)**, 6900 West Country Club Drive, Zip 25705–2000; tel. 304/733–1060 **A**1 10 **F**29 34 59 90 95 96 **S** HEALTHSOUTH Corporation, Birmingham, AL
Primary Contact: Michael E. Zuliani, Chief Executive Officer
CHR: Jenny Overcash, Director Human Resources
CNO: Ann Evans, Chief Nursing Officer
Web address: www.healthsouthhuntington.com
**Control:** Corporation, Investor–owned, for–profit **Service:** Rehabilitation

**Staffed Beds:** 50 **Admissions:** 1239 **Census:** 46 **Outpatient Visits:** 0 **Births:** 0 **Total Expense ($000):** 14171 **Payroll Expense ($000):** 7088 **Personnel:** 212

⊞ **HUNTINGTON VETERANS AFFAIRS MEDICAL CENTER**, 1540 Spring Valley Drive, Zip 25704–9300; tel. 304/429–6741 **A**1 3 5 **F**3 12 18 20 29 30 31 35 36 38 39 40 45 46 49 50 53 56 57 58 59 60 61 63 64 65 68 70 74 75 77 78 79 81 82 83 84 85 86 87 93 94 97 100 101 102 103 104 107 108 109 111 114 115 118 119 127 130 132 135 144 146 147 148 **P**1 **S** Department of Veterans Affairs, Washington, DC
Primary Contact: Brian Nimmo, Director
CIO: Gary Henderson, Chief Information Resources Management Services
Web address: www.huntington.va.gov/
**Control:** Veterans Affairs, Government, federal **Service:** General Medical and Surgical

**Staffed Beds:** 80 **Admissions:** 3471 **Census:** 39 **Outpatient Visits:** 444336 **Births:** 0 **Total Expense ($000):** 221143 **Payroll Expense ($000):** 114300 **Personnel:** 1312

☐ **MILDRED MITCHELL–BATEMAN HOSPITAL (514009)**, 1530 Norway Avenue, Zip 25705–1358, Mailing Address: P.O. Box 448, Zip 25709–0448; tel. 304/525–7801 **A**1 3 9 10 **F**3 4 11 30 86 87 97 98 103 106 130 135 143 146 **P**6
Primary Contact: Craig A. Richards, Chief Executive Officer
CFO: Lucille Gedies, Chief Financial Officer
CMO: Shahid Masood, M.D., Clinical Director
CIO: Elias Majdalani, Director Management Information Systems
CHR: Kieth Anne Worden, Director Human Resources
CNO: Patricia Hamilton, R.N., Director of Nursing
Web address: www.batemanhospital.org
**Control:** State–Government, nonfederal **Service:** Psychiatric

**Staffed Beds:** 110 **Admissions:** 450 **Census:** 103 **Outpatient Visits:** 0 **Births:** 0 **Total Expense ($000):** 34547 **Payroll Expense ($000):** 14295 **Personnel:** 394

☐ **RIVER PARK HOSPITAL (514008)**, 1230 Sixth Avenue, Zip 25701–2312, Mailing Address: P.O. Box 1875, Zip 25719–1875; tel. 304/526–9111 **A**1 3 9 10 **F**29 34 35 38 98 99 100 101 102 103 106 130 143 **P**4 5 6 **S** Universal Health Services, Inc., King of Prussia, PA
Primary Contact: Terry A. Stephens, Chief Executive Officer
CFO: Steve Kuhn, Chief Financial Officer
CMO: Mark A. Hughes, M.D., Medical Director
CIO: Tony Radenheimer, Network Administrator
CHR: Mary Stratton, Director Human Resources
CNO: Charles Christopher Whitt, Chief Nursing Officer
Web address: www.riverparkhospital.net
**Control:** Corporation, Investor–owned, for–profit **Service:** Psychiatric

**Staffed Beds:** 173 **Admissions:** 1476 **Census:** 147 **Outpatient Visits:** 0 **Births:** 0 **Total Expense ($000):** 20668 **Payroll Expense ($000):** 11663 **Personnel:** 299

⊞ **ST. MARY'S MEDICAL CENTER (510007)**, 2900 First Avenue, Zip 25702–1272; tel. 304/526–1234, (Total facility includes 19 beds in nursing home–type unit) **A**1 2 3 9 10 **F**3 9 11 12 13 15 17 18 20 22 24 26 28 29 30 31 32 34 35 36 39 40 42 43 44 45 46 47 48 49 50 53 55 57 58 59 60 61 62 64 65 66 67 68 70 74 75 76 77 78 79 81 82 84 85 86 87 89 92 93 96 97 98 100 101 102 103 107 108 110 111 114 115 118 119 120 121 123 124 126 128 129 130 132 133 135 144 145 146 147 148 **P**8 **S** Pallottine Health Services, Huntington, WV
Primary Contact: Michael G. Sellards, President and Chief Executive Officer
COO: Todd Campbell, Senior Vice President and Chief Operating Officer
CFO: Angela Swearingen, Vice President Finance
CMO: Ernest Lee Taylor, M.D., Vice President Medical Affairs
CIO: Michael House, Director Information Systems
CHR: Susan Beth Robinson, Vice President Human Resources
CNO: Elizabeth Bosley, R.N., Vice President Patient Services
Web address: www.st-marys.org
**Control:** Church–operated, Nongovernment, not–for profit **Service:** General Medical and Surgical

**Staffed Beds:** 393 **Admissions:** 16143 **Census:** 268 **Outpatient Visits:** 248845 **Births:** 399 **Total Expense ($000):** 352840 **Payroll Expense ($000):** 120654 **Personnel:** 2445

**KEYSER—Mineral County**

⊞ **POTOMAC VALLEY HOSPITAL (511315)**, 100 Pin Oak Lane, Zip 26726–5908; tel. 304/597–3500 **A**1 9 10 18 **F**3 15 18 28 29 30 34 35 40 44 45 50 57 59 63 64 68 70 71 75 79 81 85 86 87 93 107 108 110 111 112 114 119 127 130 132 133 135 146 **S** West Virginia United Health System, Fairmont, WV
Primary Contact: Linda K. Shroyer, Administrator
CFO: Marian Cardwell, Chief Financial Officer
CMO: Charles Bess, M.D., Medical Director
CIO: Micah Reel, Director of Bio–Med
CHR: Dianne Smith, Director Personnel and Human Resources
CNO: Mary Ann Billings, Director of Nursing
Web address: www.potomacvalleyhospital.com
**Control:** Other not–for–profit (including NFP Corporation) **Service:** General Medical and Surgical

**Staffed Beds:** 25 **Admissions:** 726 **Census:** 8 **Outpatient Visits:** 46093 **Births:** 0 **Total Expense ($000):** 19449 **Payroll Expense ($000):** 7445 **Personnel:** 195

**KINGWOOD—Preston County**

★ **PRESTON MEMORIAL HOSPITAL (511312)**, 150 Memorial Drive, Zip 26537–1495; tel. 304/329–1400 **A**9 10 18 **F**3 12 15 18 29 30 34 35 40 43 45 47 48 50 53 57 59 64 65 70 74 75 76 77 81 92 93 97 107 108 110 111 114 119 129 132 133 135 144 146 147 148 **P**6 **S** Monongalia Health System, Morgantown, WV
Primary Contact: Melissa Lockwood, Chief Executive Officer
CFO: Robert W. Milvet, Jr., Chief Financial Officer
CIO: Beth Horne, System Administrator Information Technology
CHR: Michele Batiste, Director Human Resources
Web address: www.prestonmemorial.org
**Control:** Other not–for–profit (including NFP Corporation) **Service:** General Medical and Surgical

**Staffed Beds:** 25 **Admissions:** 640 **Census:** 6 **Outpatient Visits:** 61968 **Births:** 0 **Total Expense ($000):** 26900 **Payroll Expense ($000):** 12575 **Personnel:** 250

**LOGAN—Logan County**

⊞ **LOGAN REGIONAL MEDICAL CENTER (510048)**, 20 Hospital Drive, Zip 25601–3452; tel. 304/831–1101 **A**1 9 10 20 **F**3 11 13 15 18 20 28 29 31 34 35 40 43 45 49 51 54 57 59 64 65 70 74 75 76 77 78 79 81 82 86 87 89 90 92 93 97 107 108 110 111 114 115 117 118 119 129 130 133 135 146 147 **P**6 **S** LifePoint Health, Brentwood, TN
Primary Contact: Kevin Zachary, Chief Executive Officer
COO: Brian Springate, Interim Chief Operating Officer
CFO: Tim Matney, Chief Financial Officer
CMO: Kathy Harvey, D.O., Chief Medical Officer
CIO: Barry Hensley, Director Information Systems
CHR: Jessica Martin, Director Human Resources
CNO: Karen Barnes, Interim Chief Nursing Officer
Web address: www.loganregionalmedicalcenter.com
**Control:** Corporation, Investor–owned, for–profit **Service:** General Medical and Surgical

**Staffed Beds:** 129 **Admissions:** 4572 **Census:** 62 **Outpatient Visits:** 98235 **Births:** 298 **Total Expense ($000):** 75736 **Payroll Expense ($000):** 24461 **Personnel:** 628

**MADISON—Boone County**

⊞ **BOONE MEMORIAL HOSPITAL (511313)**, 701 Madison Avenue, Zip 25130–1699; tel. 304/369–1230 **A**1 9 10 18 **F**3 11 15 28 34 35 40 43 45 50 53 54 57 59 64 65 75 77 81 87 97 107 108 111 119 127 129 130 131 133 135 146 147
Primary Contact: Virgil Underwood, Chief Executive Officer
CFO: Randy Foxx, Chief Financial Officer
CMO: Ziad Chanaa, M.D., Chief of Staff
CIO: Susan Shreve, Executive Director Information Technology
CHR: Sheliah Cook, Director Human Resources
CNO: Teresa Meade, R.N., Chief Nursing Officer
Web address: www.bmh.org
**Control:** Other not–for–profit (including NFP Corporation) **Service:** General Medical and Surgical

**Staffed Beds:** 25 **Admissions:** 730 **Census:** 13 **Outpatient Visits:** 52852 **Births:** 0 **Total Expense ($000):** 23100 **Payroll Expense ($000):** 8069 **Personnel:** 179

## MARTINSBURG—Berkeley County

✣ **BERKELEY MEDICAL CENTER (510008)**, 2500 Hospital Drive, Zip 25401–3402; tel. 304/264–1000 **A**1 2 3 5 9 10 **F**3 11 12 13 15 17 18 20 22 28 29 30 31 34 35 38 40 43 44 45 47 49 51 53 57 59 62 64 70 72 74 75 76 77 78 79 81 82 85 86 87 89 92 93 98 102 103 107 108 110 111 115 118 119 124 129 130 131 132 135 145 146 148 **S** West Virginia United Health System, Fairmont, WV
Primary Contact: Anthony Zelenka, President and Chief Operating Officer
CFO: Kathleen Quinones, Interim Vice President Finance
CIO: Mark Combs, Interim Director System Information Technology
CHR: Michelle Thomas, Vice President Human Resources
CNO: Donna Clews, Ph.D., Vice President Patient Care Services
Web address: www.cityhospital.org
**Control:** Other not–for–profit (including NFP Corporation) **Service:** General Medical and Surgical

| | |
|---|---|
| **Staffed Beds:** 174 **Admissions:** 7788 **Census:** 99 **Outpatient Visits:** 239978 **Births:** 986 **Total Expense ($000):** 155338 **Payroll Expense ($000):** 59029 **Personnel:** 1281 | |

✣ **MARTINSBURG VETERANS AFFAIRS MEDICAL CENTER**, 510 Butler Avenue, Zip 25405–9990; tel. 304/263–0811, (Total facility includes 121 beds in nursing home–type unit) **A**1 3 5 9 **F**3 4 5 7 10 15 18 22 24 26 29 30 31 33 34 35 38 39 40 45 46 47 48 49 50 53 56 58 59 61 62 63 64 65 66 68 70 74 75 77 78 79 81 82 83 84 85 87 91 92 93 94 97 98 101 102 103 104 105 106 107 108 111 114 115 118 119 127 128 129 130 132 133 135 141 142 143 146 147 148 **S** Department of Veterans Affairs, Washington, DC
Primary Contact: Timothy J. Cooke, Medical Center Director and Chief Executive Officer
COO: Timothy J. Cooke, Medical Center Director and Chief Executive Officer
CMO: Jonathan Fierer, M.D., Chief of Staff
CIO: Mary Ann Creel, Chief Information Resource Management
CHR: Brenda Byrd–Pelaez, Chief Human Resources Management Office
CNO: Susan George, R.N., Associate Director Patient Care Services
Web address: www.martinsburg.va.gov/
**Control:** Veterans Affairs, Government, federal **Service:** General Medical and Surgical

| | |
|---|---|
| **Staffed Beds:** 449 **Admissions:** 3663 **Census:** 277 **Outpatient Visits:** 492424 **Births:** 0 **Total Expense ($000):** 269942 **Payroll Expense ($000):** 123077 **Personnel:** 1788 | |

## MONTGOMERY—Fayette County

✣ **MONTGOMERY GENERAL HOSPITAL (511318)**, 401 Sixth Avenue, Zip 25136–2116, Mailing Address: P.O. Box 270, Zip 25136–0270; tel. 304/442–5151, (Total facility includes 44 beds in nursing home–type unit) **A**1 9 10 18 **F**3 11 15 29 30 34 35 40 45 49 50 53 57 59 64 67 68 77 81 87 93 97 107 111 114 119 128 129 130 131 133 135 146 147 **P**6 8
Primary Contact: Vickie Gay, Chief Executive Officer
CFO: Sherri Murray, Chief Financial Officer
CMO: Traci Acklin, M.D., Chief of Staff
CIO: Denzil Blevins, Director Information Systems
CHR: Kelly D. Frye, Director Human Resources
Web address: www.mghwv.com
**Control:** Other not–for–profit (including NFP Corporation) **Service:** General Medical and Surgical

| | |
|---|---|
| **Staffed Beds:** 69 **Admissions:** 539 **Census:** 44 **Outpatient Visits:** 70318 **Births:** 0 **Total Expense ($000):** 21745 **Payroll Expense ($000):** 10966 **Personnel:** 221 | |

## MORGANTOWN—Monongalia County

**CHESTNUT RIDGE HOSPITAL** See West Virginia University Hospitals

✣ **HEALTHSOUTH MOUNTAINVIEW REGIONAL REHABILITATION HOSPITAL (513030)**, 1160 Van Voorhis Road, Zip 26505–3437; tel. 304/598–1100 **A**1 3 5 10 **F**3 29 34 35 57 59 60 64 74 75 77 79 86 90 91 93 94 95 96 100 103 130 131 132 135 146 148 **S** HEALTHSOUTH Corporation, Birmingham, AL
Primary Contact: Lou Little, Chief Executive Officer
CFO: Jason Gizzi, Controller
CMO: Govind Patel, M.D., Medical Director
CIO: Robin Wherry, Risk Manager and Director Quality Assurance and Health Information Management
CHR: Shannon Hyde, Director Human Resources
CNO: Stacy Jones, Chief Nursing Officer
Web address: www.healthsouthmountainview.com
**Control:** Corporation, Investor–owned, for–profit **Service:** Rehabilitation

| | |
|---|---|
| **Staffed Beds:** 96 **Admissions:** 1907 **Census:** 73 **Outpatient Visits:** 8837 **Births:** 0 **Total Expense ($000):** 26129 **Payroll Expense ($000):** 12405 **Personnel:** 277 | |

✣ **MONONGALIA GENERAL HOSPITAL (510024)**, 1200 J. D. Anderson Drive, Zip 26505–3486; tel. 304/598–1200 **A**1 2 3 9 10 19 **F**3 13 15 17 18 20 22 24 26 28 29 30 31 32 34 35 40 43 45 46 49 50 51 54 57 59 60 64 65 68 70 74 75 76 77 78 79 81 82 84 85 86 87 89 97 107 108 111 114 115 116 118 119 126 129 130 132 135 145 146 147 148 **P**6 8 **S** Monongalia Health System, Morgantown, WV
Primary Contact: Darryl L. Duncan, President and Chief Executive Officer
COO: Linda Neu Ollis, FACHE, Chief Operating Officer
CFO: Daris Rosencrance, Chief Financial Officer
CMO: Mike Ferrebee, M.D., Vice President Medical Affairs
CIO: Linda Allen, Vice President Quality and Information Systems
CHR: Melissa Shreves, Director Human Resources
Web address: www.mongeneral.com
**Control:** Other not–for–profit (including NFP Corporation) **Service:** General Medical and Surgical

| | |
|---|---|
| **Staffed Beds:** 175 **Admissions:** 8466 **Census:** 97 **Outpatient Visits:** 207626 **Births:** 1110 **Total Expense ($000):** 216927 **Payroll Expense ($000):** 73491 **Personnel:** 1278 | |

✣ **WEST VIRGINIA UNIVERSITY HOSPITALS (510001)**, 1 Medical Center Drive, Zip 26506–4749; tel. 304/598–4000, (Includes CHESTNUT RIDGE HOSPITAL, 930 Chestnut Ridge Road, Zip 26505–2854; tel. 304/293–4000; WEST VIRGINIA UNIVERSITY CHILDREN'S HOSPITAL, Medical Center Drive, Zip 26506–8111; tel. 800/982–6277) **A**1 3 5 8 9 10 19 **F**3 4 5 9 11 12 13 15 17 18 19 20 21 22 23 24 25 26 27 28 29 30 31 35 36 37 38 39 40 43 45 46 47 48 49 50 51 54 55 56 57 59 60 61 64 68 70 72 74 75 76 77 78 79 80 81 82 84 85 86 87 88 89 92 98 99 100 101 102 103 105 106 107 108 110 111 114 115 118 119 120 121 123 124 126 129 130 132 136 141 145 146 147 148 **P**6 **S** West Virginia United Health System, Fairmont, WV
Primary Contact: Albert Wright, PharmD, President and Chief Executive Officer
CFO: Mary Jo Shahan, Vice President and Chief Financial Officer
CMO: Michelle Nuss, M.D., Chief Medical Officer
CIO: Rich King, Vice President Information Technology
CHR: Charlotte Bennett, Vice President Human Resources
Web address: www.health.wvu.edu
**Control:** Other not–for–profit (including NFP Corporation) **Service:** General Medical and Surgical

| | |
|---|---|
| **Staffed Beds:** 514 **Admissions:** 25979 **Census:** 426 **Outpatient Visits:** 711439 **Births:** 1493 **Total Expense ($000):** 715569 **Payroll Expense ($000):** 253866 **Personnel:** 4994 | |

## NEW MARTINSVILLE—Wetzel County

✣ **WETZEL COUNTY HOSPITAL (510072)**, 3 East Benjamin Drive, Zip 26155–2758; tel. 304/455–8000 **A**1 9 10 20 **F**3 8 15 28 30 31 34 40 43 45 57 59 64 65 70 75 77 81 85 90 93 94 107 108 114 118 119 127 130 132 133 135 146 148 **P**6
Primary Contact: Brian K. Felici, Chief Executive Officer
CFO: Edwin Szewczyk, Chief Financial Officer
CMO: Donald A. Blum, M.D., Chief of Staff
CIO: Amy Frazier, Supervisor Management Information Systems
CHR: Sarah Boley, Director Human Resources
Web address: www.wetzelcountyhospital.com
**Control:** County–Government, nonfederal **Service:** General Medical and Surgical

| | |
|---|---|
| **Staffed Beds:** 44 **Admissions:** 687 **Census:** 8 **Outpatient Visits:** 85223 **Births:** 0 **Total Expense ($000):** 23839 **Payroll Expense ($000):** 9506 **Personnel:** 199 | |

## OAK HILL—Fayette County

✣ **PLATEAU MEDICAL CENTER (511317)**, 430 Main Street, Zip 25901–3455; tel. 304/469–8600 **A**1 9 10 18 **F**3 8 15 18 29 30 34 35 40 45 46 50 57 59 64 68 70 75 77 79 81 85 87 91 93 97 107 108 110 111 114 119 126 129 146 **S** Community Health Systems, Inc., Franklin, TN
Primary Contact: Derek W. Cimala, Interim Chief Executive Officer
CFO: Heather Hylton, Chief Financial Officer
CMO: Jacob McNeel, D.O., Chief of Staff
CIO: Nick Stover, Director Information Systems
CHR: Tammie Chinn, Director Marketing and Public Relations
CNO: Randell Thompson, Chief Nursing Officer
Web address: www.plateaumedicalcenter.com
**Control:** Corporation, Investor–owned, for–profit **Service:** General Medical and Surgical

| | |
|---|---|
| **Staffed Beds:** 25 **Admissions:** 1196 **Census:** 11 **Outpatient Visits:** 29770 **Births:** 0 **Total Expense ($000):** 30654 **Payroll Expense ($000):** 13013 **Personnel:** 191 | |

| Hospital, Medicare Provider Number, Address, Telephone, Approval, Facility, and Physician Codes, Health Care System | | |
|---|---|---|
| ★ American Hospital Association (AHA) membership | ◯ Healthcare Facilities Accreditation Program | ⇧ Center for Improvement in Healthcare Quality Accreditation |
| ☐ The Joint Commission accreditation | ◇ DNV Healthcare Inc. accreditation | △ Commission on Accreditation of Rehabilitation Facilities (CARF) accreditation |

## PARKERSBURG—Wood County

✠ **CAMDEN CLARK MEDICAL CENTER (510058)**, 800 Garfield Avenue,
Zip 26101–5378, Mailing Address: P.O. Box 718, Zip 26102–0718;
tel. 304/424–2111 **A**1 9 10 13 19 **F**1 3 7 8 11 12 13 15 17 18 20 22 24 28
29 30 31 34 35 40 43 45 50 51 53 54 57 58 59 64 65 66 67 68 70 74 75
76 78 79 81 84 85 86 87 89 92 97 98 100 101 102 107 108 110 111 114
115 116 117 118 119 120 121 123 124 128 129 130 132 135 146 147 148
**P**6 7 8 **S** West Virginia United Health System, Fairmont, WV
Primary Contact: David K. McClure, President and Chief Executive Officer
CFO: Carolyn Allen, Vice President and Chief Financial Officer
CMO: David Gnegy, M.D., Vice President of Medical Affairs
CIO: Josh Woods, Director Information Systems
CHR: Tom Heller, Vice President Human Resources
CNO: Tom L. Mars, R.N., Vice President Patient Care Services and Chief Nursing
Officer
Web address: www.camdenclark.org
**Control:** Other not–for–profit (including NFP Corporation) **Service:** General
Medical and Surgical

> **Staffed Beds:** 240 **Admissions:** 12162 **Census:** 157 **Outpatient Visits:**
> 317255 **Births:** 1465 **Total Expense ($000):** 232058 **Payroll Expense**
> **($000):** 71311 **Personnel:** 1517

✠ **HEALTHSOUTH WESTERN HILLS REGIONAL REHABILITATION HOSPITAL**
**(513027)**, 3 Western Hills Drive, Zip 26105–8122; tel. 304/420–1300 **A**1 10
**F**29 64 90 93 94 96 130 146 148 **S** HEALTHSOUTH Corporation,
Birmingham, AL
Primary Contact: Alvin R. Lawson, JD, FACHE, Chief Executive Officer
CFO: Jessica Walkup, Controller
CMO: Kalapala Rao, M.D., Medical Director
CHR: Julie Swanson, Coordinator Human Resources
CNO: Tanda Hockenberry, Chief Nursing Officer
Web address: www.healthsouthwesternhills.com
**Control:** Corporation, Investor–owned, for–profit **Service:** Rehabilitation

> **Staffed Beds:** 40 **Admissions:** 1010 **Census:** 36 **Outpatient Visits:** 6209
> **Births:** 0 **Total Expense ($000):** 13786 **Payroll Expense ($000):** 6108
> **Personnel:** 100

## PETERSBURG—Grant County

★ **GRANT MEMORIAL HOSPITAL (511316)**, 117 Hospital Drive,
Zip 26847–9566, Mailing Address: P.O. Box 1019, Zip 26847–1019;
tel. 304/257–1026, (Total facility includes 20 beds in nursing home–type unit) **A**9
10 18 **F**3 11 13 15 18 28 29 30 34 35 40 45 50 57 59 64 65 67 68 70 75
76 77 79 81 84 85 86 87 93 102 107 108 110 114 119 128 130 132 133
146 148 **P**6
Primary Contact: Mary Beth Barr, R.N., Chief Executive Officer
CFO: Joe Barnes, Chief Financial Officer
CMO: Bruce W. Leslie, M.D., Chief of Staff
CIO: Derek Nesselrodt, Director Information Systems
CHR: Ronnie Arbaugh, Director Human Resources
CNO: Kimberly Linville, Chief Nursing Officer
Web address: www.grantmemorial.com
**Control:** County–Government, nonfederal **Service:** General Medical and Surgical

> **Staffed Beds:** 45 **Admissions:** 1585 **Census:** 27 **Outpatient Visits:** 46912
> **Births:** 236 **Total Expense ($000):** 31271 **Payroll Expense ($000):** 10571
> **Personnel:** 269

## PHILIPPI—Barbour County

★ **BROADDUS HOSPITAL (511300)**, 1 Healthcare Drive, Zip 26416–9405, Mailing
Address: P.O. Box 930, Zip 26416–0930; tel. 304/457–1760, (Total facility
includes 60 beds in nursing home–type unit) **A**9 10 18 **F**3 15 29 30 34 35 40
50 57 59 64 75 85 87 97 107 110 114 119 128 130 133 143 146 **S** Davis
Health System, Elkins, WV
Primary Contact: Jeffrey A. Powelson, Chief Executive Officer
CFO: Cathy Kalar, Chief Financial Officer
CHR: Penny D. Brown, Director of Human Resources
Web address: www.davishealthsystem.org/
**Control:** Other not–for–profit (including NFP Corporation) **Service:** General
Medical and Surgical

> **Staffed Beds:** 72 **Admissions:** 305 **Census:** 62 **Outpatient Visits:** 23897
> **Births:** 0 **Total Expense ($000):** 15445 **Payroll Expense ($000):** 6671
> **Personnel:** 157

## POINT PLEASANT—Mason County

✠ **PLEASANT VALLEY HOSPITAL (510012)**, 2520 Valley Drive,
Zip 25550–2031; tel. 304/675–4340, (Total facility includes 100 beds in nursing
home–type unit) **A**1 9 10 **F**3 11 13 15 17 18 28 29 30 31 33 34 35 39 40 43
48 50 53 56 57 59 62 63 68 70 74 75 76 77 78 79 81 85 86 87 89 93 107
108 110 111 114 115 116 119 128 129 130 131 132 143 144 146 147
148 **P**6
Primary Contact: Glen A. Washington, Chief Executive Officer
COO: William A. Barker, Jr., Vice President Administration
CFO: Richard Hogan, Chief Financial Officer
CMO: Agnes Enrico–Simon, M.D., President Medical Staff
CIO: Paula Brooker, Director Information Services
CHR: David A. Brown, Director Human Resources and Corporate Compliance
CNO: Amber Findley, Senior Director Nursing Services and NRC Administrator
Web address: www.pvalley.org
**Control:** Other not–for–profit (including NFP Corporation) **Service:** General
Medical and Surgical

> **Staffed Beds:** 201 **Admissions:** 2167 **Census:** 108 **Outpatient Visits:**
> 203684 **Births:** 83 **Total Expense ($000):** 62849 **Payroll Expense ($000):**
> 27041 **Personnel:** 599

## PRINCETON—Mercer County

✠ **HEALTHSOUTH SOUTHERN HILLS REHABILITATION HOSPITAL (513026)**,
120 Twelfth Street, Zip 24740–2352; tel. 304/487–8000 **A**1 10 **F**29 56 57 59
60 74 75 77 79 87 90 93 94 130 132 148 **S** HEALTHSOUTH Corporation,
Birmingham, AL
Primary Contact: Robert Williams, R.N., Chief Executive Officer
CFO: Melinda Fanning, Chief Financial Officer and Controller
CMO: Robert Walker, M.D., Medical Director
CIO: Brian Bales, Director Plant Operations
CHR: Jan Thibodeau, Director Human Resources
CNO: Lisa Lester, Chief Nursing Officer
Web address: www.healthsouthsouthernhills.com
**Control:** Corporation, Investor–owned, for–profit **Service:** Rehabilitation

> **Staffed Beds:** 45 **Admissions:** 884 **Census:** 28 **Outpatient Visits:** 0 **Births:**
> 0 **Personnel:** 101

✠ **PRINCETON COMMUNITY HOSPITAL (510046)**, 122 12th Street,
Zip 24740–2352, Mailing Address: P.O. Box 1369, Zip 24740–1369;
tel. 304/487–7000 **A**1 2 9 10 19 **F**3 11 12 13 15 17 29 30 31 32 34 35 39
40 44 45 46 48 49 50 51 53 57 59 64 65 70 74 75 76 77 78 79 81 85 86
87 89 93 98 100 101 102 103 104 107 108 110 111 114 115 118 119 127
129 130 131 132 135 141 142 144 146 147 **P**1
Primary Contact: Jeff Lilley, Chief Executive Officer
COO: Jeffrey Lilley, CPA, Chief Operating Officer
CFO: Frank J. Sinicrope, Jr., Vice President Financial Services
CMO: Wesley Asbury, M.D., President Medical Staff
CIO: Stephen A. Curry, Director Information Services
CHR: Heather Poff, Director Human Resources
CNO: Rose Morgan, R.N., Vice President Patient Care Services
Web address: www.pchonline.org
**Control:** City–Government, nonfederal **Service:** General Medical and Surgical

> **Staffed Beds:** 210 **Admissions:** 8310 **Census:** 122 **Outpatient Visits:**
> 225211 **Births:** 668 **Total Expense ($000):** 120602 **Payroll Expense**
> **($000):** 45807 **Personnel:** 1032

## RANSON—Jefferson County

✠ **JEFFERSON MEDICAL CENTER (511319)**, 300 South Preston Street,
Zip 25438–1631; tel. 304/728–1600 **A**1 3 5 9 10 18 **F**3 11 13 15 29 30 34
35 38 40 43 44 45 57 59 64 70 74 75 76 77 79 81 82 85 86 87 92 93 107
108 110 111 115 118 119 129 130 132 133 135 146 148 **S** West Virginia
United Health System, Fairmont, WV
Primary Contact: Anthony Zelenka, Chief Executive Officer
CFO: Kathleen Quinones, Interim Vice President Finance
CMO: David A. Baltierra, M.D., President Medical Staff
CIO: Mark Combs, Chief Information Security Officer
CNO: Linda Blanc, R.N., Administrative Director of Nursing
Web address: www.wvuniversityhealthcare.com/locations/Jefferson–Medical–
Center.aspx
**Control:** Other not–for–profit (including NFP Corporation) **Service:** General
Medical and Surgical

> **Staffed Beds:** 25 **Admissions:** 1343 **Census:** 11 **Outpatient Visits:** 73793
> **Births:** 278 **Total Expense ($000):** 47057 **Payroll Expense ($000):** 18151
> **Personnel:** 280

**WV**

*Many Facility Codes have changed. Please refer to the AHA Guide Code Chart.*   © 2015 AHA Guide

## RIPLEY—Jackson County

☐ **JACKSON GENERAL HOSPITAL (511320)**, 122 Pinnell Street,
Zip 25271–9101, Mailing Address: P.O. Box 720, Zip 25271–0720;
tel. 304/372–2731 **A**1 9 10 18 **F**3 11 15 17 29 30 34 35 40 50 57 59 64 68
75 79 81 85 93 107 114 119 127 132 133 **P**6
Primary Contact: Stephanie McCoy, President and Chief Executive Officer
CFO: Angela Frame, Chief Financial Officer
CMO: James G. Gaal, M.D., Chief of Medical Staff
CIO: John Manley, Director Information Systems
CHR: Jeffrey Tabor, Director Human Resources
Web address: www.jacksongeneral.com
**Control:** Other not-for-profit (including NFP Corporation) **Service:** General
Medical and Surgical

**Staffed Beds:** 25 **Admissions:** 1042 **Census:** 12 **Outpatient Visits:** 44654
**Births:** 0 **Total Expense ($000):** 20144 **Payroll Expense ($000):** 9862
**Personnel:** 236

## ROMNEY—Hampshire County

⊠ **HAMPSHIRE MEMORIAL HOSPITAL (511311)**, 363 Sunrise Boulevard,
Zip 26757–4607; tel. 304/822–4561, (Total facility includes 30 beds in nursing
home–type unit) **A**1 9 10 18 **F**3 15 29 30 40 45 54 59 64 65 71 77 79 81 85
93 97 107 119 127 128 129 130 133 148 **P**6 **S** Valley Health System,
Winchester, VA
Primary Contact: Neil R. McLaughlin, R.N., President
CFO: Kathryn Morales, Director of Finance
CMO: Gerald Bechamps, M.D., Vice President of Medical Affairs
CHR: Abbey Rembold, Human Resources Senior Generalist
CNO: Mary Sas, Director of Clinical Services
Web address: www.valleyhealthlink.com/hampshire
**Control:** Other not-for-profit (including NFP Corporation) **Service:** General
Medical and Surgical

**Staffed Beds:** 44 **Admissions:** 437 **Census:** 37 **Outpatient Visits:** 44255
**Total Expense ($000):** 21084 **Payroll Expense ($000):** 7946 **Personnel:**
169

## RONCEVERTE—Greenbrier County

★ ◯ **GREENBRIER VALLEY MEDICAL CENTER (510002)**, 202 Maplewood
Avenue, Zip 24970–1334, Mailing Address: P.O. Box 497, Zip 24970–0497;
tel. 304/647–4411 **A**9 10 11 12 13 19 **F**13 15 18 20 29 31 34 40 45 49 51
57 59 60 68 70 75 76 78 79 81 82 85 86 87 89 107 108 110 111 114 116
119 120 129 133 135 146 **P**6 **S** Community Health Systems, Inc., Franklin, TN
Primary Contact: Robert Calhoun, Chief Executive Officer
CFO: Paige Adkins, Chief Financial Officer
CMO: John Johnson, M.D., Chief of Staff
CIO: Matt Turley, Interim Director Information Systems
CHR: Melissa Wickline, Director Marketing
CNO: Charlene Warren, R.N., Chief Nursing Officer
Web address: www.gvmc.com
**Control:** Corporation, Investor–owned, for–profit **Service:** General Medical and
Surgical

**Staffed Beds:** 113 **Admissions:** 3745 **Census:** 41 **Outpatient Visits:** 57829
**Births:** 489 **Total Expense ($000):** 54494 **Payroll Expense ($000):** 20177
**Personnel:** 415

## SISTERSVILLE—Tyler County

★ **SISTERSVILLE GENERAL HOSPITAL (511304)**, 314 South Wells Street,
Zip 26175–1098; tel. 304/652–2611 **A**9 10 18 **F**3 7 11 15 28 29 30 32 35
40 43 50 53 57 59 63 64 65 79 83 84 87 93 97 107 119 127 129 130 132
133 135 144 146 147 148 **P**6
Primary Contact: John May, Chief Executive Officer
COO: Brandon Chadock, Director of Operations
CFO: Carl Worrell, Chief Financial Officer
CMO: Amanda Nichols, M.D., Chief of Staff
CIO: Casey Tuttle, Director Information Technology
CHR: Marissa Powell, Human Resources Director
CNO: Matthew Childers, Director of Nursing
Web address: www.sistersvillehospital.com
**Control:** City–Government, nonfederal **Service:** General Medical and Surgical

**Staffed Beds:** 12 **Admissions:** 205 **Census:** 2 **Outpatient Visits:** 34560
**Births:** 0 **Total Expense ($000):** 10983 **Payroll Expense ($000):** 6020
**Personnel:** 128

## SOUTH CHARLESTON—Kanawha County

⊠ **THOMAS MEMORIAL HOSPITAL (510029)**, 4605 MacCorkle Avenue S.W.,
Zip 25309–1398; tel. 304/766–3600 **A**1 3 5 9 10 **F**3 5 8 11 13 15 17 18 20
22 29 30 31 32 34 35 38 40 43 45 46 47 48 49 50 53 54 57 59 60 62 64
65 68 69 70 72 74 75 76 77 78 79 81 84 85 86 87 89 92 93 98 99 100
101 102 103 104 105 107 108 110 111 114 115 118 119 120 121 123 124
126 129 130 131 132 143 144 146 147 **S** Thomas Health System, Inc., South
Charleston, WV
Primary Contact: Daniel Lauffer, FACHE, President and Chief Executive Officer
COO: Brian Ulery, Senior Vice President and Chief Operating Officer
CFO: Charles O. Covert, Vice President Finance
CMO: Matthew Upton, Chief Medical Information Officer
CIO: Charles O. Covert, Vice President Finance
CHR: Marybeth Smith, Director Human Resources
CNO: Rebecca Brannon, R.N., Vice President Patient Services
Web address: www.thomaswv.org
**Control:** Other not-for-profit (including NFP Corporation) **Service:** General
Medical and Surgical

**Staffed Beds:** 215 **Admissions:** 9010 **Census:** 124 **Outpatient Visits:**
184291 **Births:** 1158 **Total Expense ($000):** 168859 **Payroll Expense**
**($000):** 57074 **Personnel:** 1009

## SPENCER—Roane County

⊠ **ROANE GENERAL HOSPITAL (511306)**, 200 Hospital Drive, Zip 25276–1050;
tel. 304/927–4444, (Total facility includes 35 beds in nursing home–type unit) **A**1
9 10 18 **F**1 3 15 28 29 34 35 40 43 45 53 57 59 64 65 67 81 89 90 93 97
107 108 114 119 127 128 130 133 148 **P**6
Primary Contact: Douglas E. Bentz, Chief Executive Officer
CFO: Louise Ward, Vice President Financial and Support Services
CMO: Brent Watson, M.D., Chief Medical Staff
CIO: Tony Keaton, Director Information Systems
CHR: Jeff Beane, Director Human Resources
Web address: www.roanegeneralhospital.com
**Control:** Other not-for-profit (including NFP Corporation) **Service:** General
Medical and Surgical

**Staffed Beds:** 60 **Admissions:** 429 **Census:** 43 **Outpatient Visits:** 37455
**Births:** 0 **Total Expense ($000):** 26403 **Payroll Expense ($000):** 12205
**Personnel:** 277

## SUMMERSVILLE—Nicholas County

⊠ **SUMMERSVILLE REGIONAL MEDICAL CENTER (510082)**, 400 Fairview
Heights Road, Zip 26651–9308; tel. 304/872–2891, (Total facility includes 52
beds in nursing home–type unit) **A**1 9 10 20 **F**1 3 13 15 28 30 34 35 40 43 57
59 64 65 67 68 70 75 76 77 79 81 83 84 85 89 91 93 97 107 108 110 111
115 119 127 128 129 130 131 133 135 146 147 148
Primary Contact: Daniel M. Ayres, President and Chief Executive Officer
CFO: Brian Kelbaugh, Chief Financial Officer
CMO: Bandy Mullins, M.D., Chief of Staff
CIO: Mike Ellison, Information Systems Lead
CHR: David M. Henderson, Director Human Resources
CNO: Jennifer McCue, Director Patient Care
Web address: www.https://www.summersvilleregional.org/
**Control:** City–Government, nonfederal **Service:** General Medical and Surgical

**Staffed Beds:** 105 **Admissions:** 1799 **Census:** 74 **Outpatient Visits:** 116009
**Births:** 300 **Total Expense ($000):** 49138 **Payroll Expense ($000):** 24307
**Personnel:** 470

## WEBSTER SPRINGS—Webster County

★ **WEBSTER COUNTY MEMORIAL HOSPITAL (511301)**, 324 Miller Mountain
Drive, Zip 26288–1087, Mailing Address: P.O. Box 312, Zip 26288–0312;
tel. 304/847–5682 **A**9 10 18 **F**7 15 28 30 34 35 40 57 59 64 75 82 87 93
97 107 114 119 127 130 135 146 147 148
Primary Contact: Robert Mace, M.D., Interim Chief Executive Officer
CMO: Robert Mace, M.D., Chief of Staff
CIO: Margaret W. Short, Coordinator Information Technology
CHR: Deborah Bragg, Director Human Resources
Web address: www.wcmhw.com
**Control:** Other not-for-profit (including NFP Corporation) **Service:** General
Medical and Surgical

**Staffed Beds:** 15 **Admissions:** 145 **Census:** 1 **Outpatient Visits:** 42094
**Births:** 0 **Total Expense ($000):** 13852 **Payroll Expense ($000):** 7114
**Personnel:** 134

**WV**

---

**Hospital, Medicare Provider Number, Address, Telephone, Approval, Facility, and Physician Codes, Health Care System**

★ American Hospital Association (AHA) membership  ◯ Healthcare Facilities Accreditation Program  ⇑ Center for Improvement in Healthcare Quality Accreditation
☐ The Joint Commission accreditation  ◇ DNV Healthcare Inc. accreditation  △ Commission on Accreditation of Rehabilitation Facilities (CARF) accreditation

## WEIRTON—Brooke County

✠ **WEIRTON MEDICAL CENTER (510023)**, 601 Colliers Way, Zip 26062–5091; tel. 304/797–6000, (Total facility includes 33 beds in nursing home–type unit) **A**1 9 10 **F**3 5 9 11 13 15 17 18 20 22 26 29 30 32 34 35 37 39 40 41 43 45 46 47 48 49 50 51 53 54 56 57 59 60 61 62 64 68 70 74 75 76 77 78 79 81 82 85 86 89 90 92 93 96 97 99 100 101 102 103 104 107 108 110 111 114 115 116 118 119 124 126 128 129 130 131 132 135 143 145 146 147 148 **P**6
Primary Contact: Charles M. O'Brien, Jr., President and Chief Executive Officer
COO: David S. Artman, Chief Operating Officer
CFO: Gene Trout, Chief Financial Officer
CMO: Eric Balzano, Chief of Staff
CIO: Dave Angalich, Director Information Services
CHR: Barbara Coalter, Director Human Resources
CNO: Denise P. Westwood, Chief Nursing Officer
Web address: www.weirtonmedical.com
**Control:** Other not–for–profit (including NFP Corporation) **Service:** General Medical and Surgical

**Staffed Beds:** 168 **Admissions:** 6090 **Census:** 94 **Outpatient Visits:** 251268 **Births:** 272 **Total Expense ($000):** 121128 **Payroll Expense ($000):** 52548 **Personnel:** 1117

## WELCH—Mcdowell County

**WELCH COMMUNITY HOSPITAL (510086)**, 454 McDowell Street, Zip 24801–2097; tel. 304/436–8461, (Nonreporting) **A**9 10 20
Primary Contact: Walter J. Garrett, Chief Executive Officer
COO: Heather Smith, Chief Operating Officer
CFO: Johnny Brant, Chief Financial Officer
CMO: Chandra Sharma, M.D., Chief of Staff
CHR: Diana Blankenship, Director Human Resources
CNO: Mark Simpson, Director of Nursing
**Control:** State–Government, nonfederal **Service:** General Medical and Surgical

**Staffed Beds:** 108

## WESTON—Lewis County

✠ **STONEWALL JACKSON MEMORIAL HOSPITAL (510038)**, 230 Hospital Plaza, Zip 26452–8558; tel. 304/269–8000 **A**1 9 10 **F**3 11 13 15 28 29 30 31 35 40 43 45 48 50 56 57 59 62 64 68 70 75 76 78 79 81 85 86 87 93 94 97 107 108 111 114 118 119 129 130 131 132 135 145 146 147 148 **P**6
Primary Contact: Avah Stalnaker, Chief Executive Officer
COO: Kevin P. Stalnaker, CPA, Chief Operating Officer
CFO: Dodie Arbogest, Chief Financial Officer
CMO: Jeremy Williams, M.D., President Medical Staff
CIO: Kay Butcher, Director Health Information Management
CHR: Rhonda M. Hager, Director Human Resources
Web address: www.stonewallhospital.com
**Control:** Other not–for–profit (including NFP Corporation) **Service:** General Medical and Surgical

**Staffed Beds:** 70 **Admissions:** 2161 **Census:** 23 **Outpatient Visits:** 89011 **Births:** 269 **Total Expense ($000):** 43400 **Payroll Expense ($000):** 21987 **Personnel:** 426

☐ **WILLIAM R. SHARPE, JR. HOSPITAL (514010)**, 936 Sharpe Hospital Road, Zip 26452–8550; tel. 304/269–1210 **A**1 5 9 10 **F**11 30 53 56 75 86 87 98 100 101 103 130 132 143 146 **P**6
Primary Contact: Parker Haddix, Chief Executive Officer
COO: Terry L. Small, Assistant Chief Executive Officer
CFO: Robert J. Kimble, Chief Financial Officer
CIO: Pam Lewis, Chief Compliance Officer
CNO: Cheryl France, M.D., Chief Medical Officer
Web address: www.wvdhhr.org/sharpe
**Control:** State–Government, nonfederal **Service:** Psychiatric

**Staffed Beds:** 150 **Admissions:** 552 **Census:** 142 **Outpatient Visits:** 0 **Births:** 0 **Total Expense ($000):** 47528 **Payroll Expense ($000):** 14199 **Personnel:** 456

## WHEELING—Ohio County

☐ ○ **OHIO VALLEY MEDICAL CENTER (510039)**, 2000 Eoff Street, Zip 26003–3870; tel. 304/234–0123 **A**1 2 9 10 11 12 13 19 **F**3 5 9 11 13 15 18 20 28 29 30 31 34 35 38 40 43 44 48 49 50 51 53 55 56 57 58 59 60 61 64 65 68 70 74 75 76 77 78 79 81 82 84 85 86 87 89 93 97 98 99 100 101 102 103 104 105 107 108 110 111 114 115 116 117 119 121 123 129 130 131 132 134 135 146 147 148 **P**6 **S** Ohio Valley Health Services and Education Corporation, Wheeling, WV
Primary Contact: Michael J. Caruso, President and Chief Executive Officer
COO: Kelly Bettem, Chief Administrative Officer
CFO: Lisa M. Simon, Senior Vice President and Chief Financial Officer
CIO: Lisa M. Simon, Senior Vice President and Chief Financial Officer
CHR: Robert Wright, Senior Human Resource Advisor
CNO: Patsy George, R.N., Chief Nursing Officer
Web address: www.ovmc-eorh.com
**Control:** Other not–for–profit (including NFP Corporation) **Service:** General Medical and Surgical

**Staffed Beds:** 189 **Admissions:** 6083 **Census:** 90 **Outpatient Visits:** 135193 **Births:** 324 **Total Expense ($000):** 99111 **Payroll Expense ($000):** 37185 **Personnel:** 793

★ **PETERSON REHABILITATION HOSPITAL (513025)**, Homestead Avenue, Zip 26003; tel. 304/234–0500, (Total facility includes 150 beds in nursing home–type unit) **A**10 **F**29 34 50 56 57 59 75 77 86 87 90 93 96 128 130 131 132 143 148
Primary Contact: Diane Miller, Chief Executive Officer
COO: Tom Barr, Director Operational Support Services
CFO: Tammy Parasida, Manager Business Office
CMO: William Mercer, M.D., Director
CIO: Jolene Nagle, Director Medical Records
CHR: Annie Barton, Director Human Resources
Web address: www.weat.com/site6/
**Control:** Corporation, Investor–owned, for–profit **Service:** Rehabilitation

**Staffed Beds:** 172 **Admissions:** 818 **Census:** 153 **Outpatient Visits:** 3111 **Births:** 0 **Total Expense ($000):** 19535 **Payroll Expense ($000):** 6153 **Personnel:** 144

☐ **WHEELING HOSPITAL (510050)**, 1 Medical Park, Zip 26003–6379; tel. 304/243–3000 **A**1 2 3 9 10 13 **F**3 11 13 15 17 18 20 22 24 26 28 29 30 31 32 34 35 36 40 43 44 45 46 49 50 53 54 57 58 59 61 62 64 66 70 74 75 76 77 78 79 81 85 86 87 89 90 92 93 96 97 99 107 108 110 114 115 117 118 119 120 121 123 129 130 131 132 135 143 146 147 148 **P**5
Primary Contact: Ronald L. Violi, Chief Executive Officer
CMO: Angelo Georges, M.D., President Medical and Dental Staff
CIO: David Rapp, Chief Information Officer
CHR: Susan Falbo, Vice President Human Resources
Web address: www.wheelinghospital.org
**Control:** Other not–for–profit (including NFP Corporation) **Service:** General Medical and Surgical

**Staffed Beds:** 238 **Admissions:** 10164 **Census:** 120 **Outpatient Visits:** 575138 **Births:** 1191 **Total Expense ($000):** 268309 **Payroll Expense ($000):** 116451 **Personnel:** 1895

## WILLIAMSON—Mingo County

✠ **WILLIAMSON MEMORIAL HOSPITAL (510077)**, 859 Alderson Street, Zip 25661–3215, Mailing Address: P.O. Box 1980, Zip 25661–1980; tel. 304/235–2500, (Nonreporting) **A**1 9 10 **S** Community Health Systems, Inc., Franklin, TN
Primary Contact: Cindy Segar-Miller, R.N., MS, Interim Chief Executive Officer
CMO: Manuel Angco, M.D., Chief of Staff
CHR: Tina Jackson, Manager Human Resources
Web address: www.williamsonmemorial.net
**Control:** Corporation, Investor–owned, for–profit **Service:** General Medical and Surgical

**Staffed Beds:** 76

**WV**

*Many Facility Codes have changed. Please refer to the AHA Guide Code Chart.*  © 2015 AHA Guide

# WISCONSIN

## AMERY—Polk County

★ **AMERY HOSPITAL AND CLINIC (521308)**, 265 Griffin Street East,
Zip 54001–1439; tel. 715/268–8000 **A**9 10 18 **F**6 11 13 15 28 29 34 36 38
40 53 54 56 64 75 76 77 78 80 81 82 86 87 89 93 98 100 103 104 107
108 111 119 130 131 144 **P**6 **S** HealthPartners, Bloomington, MN
Primary Contact: Debra Rudquist, FACHE, President and Chief Executive Officer
CFO: Scott D. Edin, Chief Financial Officer
CMO: James Quenan, M.D., Chief Medical Officer
CIO: Patrice P. Wolff, Director Management Information Systems
CHR: Joanne Jackson, Administrator Human Resources, Community Relations and
Quality Improvement
Web address: www.amerymedicalcenter.org
**Control:** Other not–for–profit (including NFP Corporation) **Service:** General
Medical and Surgical

**Staffed Beds:** 12 **Admissions:** 1085 **Census:** 12 **Outpatient Visits:** 111667
**Births:** 142 **Total Expense ($000):** 49882 **Payroll Expense ($000):** 16874
**Personnel:** 266

## ANTIGO—Langlade County

☐ **LANGLADE HOSPITAL (521350)**, 112 East Fifth Avenue, Zip 54409–2796;
tel. 715/623–2331 **A**1 9 10 18 **F**2 3 8 10 11 13 15 28 29 30 31 34 35 40 43
46 50 53 54 56 57 59 60 63 64 65 68 69 70 75 76 77 78 79 81 82 84 85
86 87 89 92 93 96 97 107 108 110 111 115 116 118 119 121 127 129 130
131 132 133 144 146
Primary Contact: David R. Schneider, Executive Director
CFO: Pat Tincher, Director Finance
CMO: Renee Smith, M.D., Chief Medical Staff
CHR: Janelle K. Markgraf, Director Human Resources
CNO: Sherry Bunten, Director Patient Care Services
Web address: www.langladehospital.org
**Control:** Church–operated, Nongovernment, not–for profit **Service:** General
Medical and Surgical

**Staffed Beds:** 11 **Admissions:** 1053 **Census:** 9 **Outpatient Visits:** 110072
**Births:** 220 **Total Expense ($000):** 73255 **Payroll Expense ($000):** 32395
**Personnel:** 452

## APPLETON—Outagamie County

☐ **APPLETON MEDICAL CENTER (520160)**, 1818 North Meade Street,
Zip 54911–3496; tel. 920/731–4101 **A**1 3 5 9 10 **F**3 4 8 9 11 13 15 17 18
19 20 21 22 23 24 25 26 28 29 30 31 32 34 35 36 40 43 44 45 46 49 50
51 53 55 56 59 60 64 68 69 70 74 75 76 78 79 80 81 82 85 86 87 88 89
93 107 108 110 111 114 116 117 118 119 120 121 122 123 124 130 132
135 143 144 146 147 148 **S** ThedaCare, Inc., Appleton, WI
Primary Contact: Brian Burmeister, Senior Vice President
COO: MaryJeanne Schaffmeyer, Chief Operating Officer
CFO: Tim Olson, Senior Vice President Finance
CMO: Gregory L. Long, M.D., Chief Medical Officer
CIO: Keith Livingston, Senior Vice President and Chief Information Officer
CHR: Maureen Pistone, Senior Vice President Talent Development and Human
Resources
Web address: www.thedacare.org
**Control:** Other not–for–profit (including NFP Corporation) **Service:** General
Medical and Surgical

**Staffed Beds:** 149 **Admissions:** 8310 **Census:** 87 **Outpatient Visits:** 119664
**Births:** 1210 **Total Expense ($000):** 216366 **Payroll Expense ($000):**
90555 **Personnel:** 1184

✠ **ST. ELIZABETH HOSPITAL (520009)**, 1506 South Oneida Street,
Zip 54915–1305; tel. 920/738–2000 **A**1 2 3 5 9 10 **F**3 4 5 6 8 9 11 13 15 17
18 20 22 24 26 28 29 30 31 32 34 35 36 37 38 40 43 44 45 46 47 48 49
50 56 59 66 68 69 70 72 74 75 76 77 78 79 80 81 82 84 85 86 87 88 93
97 98 99 100 102 103 104 105 106 107 108 110 111 113 114 115 117
118 119 120 121 123 124 126 129 130 131 132 135 144 145 146 147 148
**S** Ascension Health, Saint Louis, MO
Primary Contact: Monica Hilt, President and Chief Executive Officer
CFO: Jeff Badger, Chief Financial Officer
CMO: Lawrence Donatelle, M.D., Vice President Medical Affairs
CIO: Will Weider, Chief Information Officer
CHR: Vince Gallucci, Senior Vice President Human Resources
Web address: www.affinityhealth.org
**Control:** Church–operated, Nongovernment, not–for profit **Service:** General
Medical and Surgical

**Staffed Beds:** 211 **Admissions:** 8084 **Census:** 97 **Outpatient Visits:** 147797
**Births:** 1068 **Total Expense ($000):** 146866 **Payroll Expense ($000):**
62404 **Personnel:** 872

## ASHLAND—Ashland County

✠ **MEMORIAL MEDICAL CENTER – ASHLAND (521359)**, 1615 Maple Lane,
Zip 54806–3689; tel. 715/685–5500 **A**1 9 10 18 **F**3 5 8 13 15 28 30 34 40
41 43 45 46 47 48 49 57 59 64 65 75 76 77 78 79 80 81 82 85 86 87 89
90 93 94 98 99 100 101 102 103 104 105 107 108 110 111 115 118 119
130 132 135 144 145 146 148
Primary Contact: Jason T. Douglas, Chief Executive Officer
COO: Karen Hansen, Vice President and Chief Operating Officer
CFO: Kent Dumonseau, Vice President Finance and Information Services
CIO: Todd Reynolds, Chief Information Officer
CHR: Diane Lulich, Director Human Resources
CNO: Kathryn Tuttle, R.N., Director of Nursing
Web address: www.ashlandmmc.com
**Control:** Other not–for–profit (including NFP Corporation) **Service:** General
Medical and Surgical

**Staffed Beds:** 35 **Admissions:** 2636 **Census:** 17 **Outpatient Visits:** 13036
**Births:** 234 **Total Expense ($000):** 47249 **Payroll Expense ($000):** 21249
**Personnel:** 360

## BALDWIN—St. Croix County

★ **BALDWIN AREA MEDICAL CENTER (521347)**, 730 10th Avenue,
Zip 54002–9416; tel. 715/684–3311 **A**9 10 18 **F**3 11 13 15 17 28 29 31 32
34 35 36 40 41 43 45 48 50 53 57 59 64 65 68 70 75 76 77 78 79 80 81
84 85 86 87 89 90 93 96 97 107 108 110 115 127 129 130 131 132 133
143 144 146 147 148
Primary Contact: Alison Page, Chief Executive Officer
CFO: Brian A. Lovdahl, Chief Financial Officer
CMO: Clint Semrau, Chief of Staff
CIO: Kendra Shaw, Chief Information Officer
CHR: Chris Riba, Director Human Resources
Web address: www.baldwinhospital.com
**Control:** Other not–for–profit (including NFP Corporation) **Service:** General
Medical and Surgical

**Staffed Beds:** 25 **Admissions:** 401 **Census:** 4 **Outpatient Visits:** 30988
**Births:** 42 **Total Expense ($000):** 29894 **Payroll Expense ($000):** 15684
**Personnel:** 221

## BARABOO—Sauk County

✠ **ST. CLARE HOSPITAL (520057)**, 707 14th Street, Zip 53913–1597;
tel. 608/356–1400 **A**1 3 5 10 **F**5 11 12 13 15 28 29 34 36 38 40 56 60 64
69 70 75 76 77 78 80 81 82 86 93 107 108 116 118 119 130 131 144
**S** SSM Health, Saint Louis, MO
Primary Contact: Laura Jelle, President
CFO: Troy Walker, Director Finance
CMO: Maureen Murphy, M.D., Director of Medical Affairs
CIO: Alan Steevens, Director Information Management
CHR: Jason Stelzer, Director Human Resources
CNO: Ginger Selle, Vice President Patient Care Services
Web address: www.stclare.com
**Control:** Church–operated, Nongovernment, not–for profit **Service:** General
Medical and Surgical

**Staffed Beds:** 60 **Admissions:** 2581 **Census:** 18 **Outpatient Visits:** 93806
**Births:** 221 **Total Expense ($000):** 53044 **Payroll Expense ($000):** 20496
**Personnel:** 285

**WI**

| | | |
|---|---|---|
| **Hospital, Medicare Provider Number, Address, Telephone, Approval, Facility, and Physician Codes, Health Care System** | | |
| ★ American Hospital Association (AHA) membership | ○ Healthcare Facilities Accreditation Program | ⇑ Center for Improvement in Healthcare Quality Accreditation |
| ☐ The Joint Commission accreditation | ◇ DNV Healthcare Inc. accreditation | △ Commission on Accreditation of Rehabilitation Facilities (CARF) accreditation |

## BARRON—Barron County

☐ **MAYO CLINIC HEALTH SYSTEM – NORTHLAND IN BARRON (521315)**, 1222 Woodland Avenue, Zip 54812–1798; tel. 715/537–3186, (Total facility includes 20 beds in nursing home–type unit) **A**1 9 10 18 **F**3 6 7 8 10 13 15 18 28 29 30 31 32 34 35 36 40 43 44 45 50 53 54 56 57 59 60 63 64 65 69 75 76 77 78 79 80 81 82 84 85 86 87 89 90 93 97 104 107 110 115 118 125 127 128 130 131 132 133 135 144 145 146 147 148 **P**6 **S** Mayo Clinic, Rochester, MN
Primary Contact: Maurita Sullivan, Vice President
COO: Karolyn Bartlett, Assistant Administrator
CFO: Paul Bammel, Vice President
CMO: Richard Nagler, M.D., Chief of Staff
CIO: Todd Muden, Section Head Information Management
CHR: Blythe Rinaldi, Vice President
CNO: Patricia Keller, MSN, Nurse Administrator
Web address: www.luthermidelfortnorthland.org
**Control:** Other not–for–profit (including NFP Corporation) **Service:** General Medical and Surgical

**Staffed Beds:** 35 **Admissions:** 794 **Census:** 29 **Outpatient Visits:** 55805
**Births:** 103 **Total Expense ($000):** 50291 **Payroll Expense ($000):** 24191
**Personnel:** 338

## BEAVER DAM—Dodge County

✠ **BEAVER DAM COMMUNITY HOSPITALS (520076)**, 707 South University Avenue, Zip 53916–3089; tel. 920/887–7181, (Total facility includes 123 beds in nursing home–type unit) **A**1 9 10 19 **F**3 6 8 10 11 13 15 17 18 26 28 29 31 34 36 37 40 43 44 45 47 48 51 53 56 57 59 62 63 64 65 69 70 74 75 76 77 78 79 80 81 82 85 86 87 89 93 94 96 97 107 108 110 111 114 115 118 119 128 129 130 131 132 135 143 144 146 147 148 **P**6
Primary Contact: Kimberly J. Miller, FACHE, Chief Executive Officer
COO: David Corso, Chief Operating Officer
CFO: Donna Hutchinson, Chief Financial Officer
CMO: Richard Tovar, M.D., Chief of Staff
CHR: Bridget Sheridan, Chief Human Resources Officer
CNO: Mike Murphy, Chief Patient Care Officer
Web address: www.bdch.com
**Control:** Other not–for–profit (including NFP Corporation) **Service:** General Medical and Surgical

**Staffed Beds:** 171 **Admissions:** 2249 **Census:** 121 **Outpatient Visits:** 93557
**Births:** 375 **Total Expense ($000):** 78742 **Payroll Expense ($000):** 29796
**Personnel:** 522

## BELOIT—Rock County

☐ **BELOIT HEALTH SYSTEM (520100)**, 1969 West Hart Road, Zip 53511–2299; tel. 608/364–5011 **A**1 3 9 10 **F**5 6 9 10 11 13 15 17 20 22 24 28 29 36 40 43 51 53 54 56 60 62 70 75 76 77 78 80 81 82 86 87 89 93 99 100 101 102 103 104 108 111 116 118 119 130 131 144 147 **P**1
Primary Contact: Timothy M. McKevett, President
CFO: William E. Groeper, Vice President Finance
CMO: Kenneth Klein, M.D., Vice President Medical Affairs
CHR: Thomas J. McCawley, Vice President Human Resources
CNO: Doris Mulder, Vice President Nursing
Web address: www.beloithealthsystem.org
**Control:** Other not–for–profit (including NFP Corporation) **Service:** General Medical and Surgical

**Staffed Beds:** 103 **Admissions:** 4086 **Census:** 50 **Outpatient Visits:** 341552
**Births:** 533 **Total Expense ($000):** 191666 **Payroll Expense ($000):** 88565
**Personnel:** 1135

## BERLIN—Green Lake County

☐ **BERLIN MEMORIAL HOSPITAL (521355)**, 225 Memorial Drive, Zip 54923–1295; tel. 920/361–1313, (Includes JULIETTE MANOR NURSING HOME, COMMUNITY CLINICS ), (Total facility includes 54 beds in nursing home–type unit) **A**1 9 10 18 **F**3 8 10 11 13 15 17 28 29 34 35 37 40 43 45 51 53 54 56 57 59 62 64 65 66 68 69 70 75 76 77 78 79 80 81 82 83 84 85 86 88 89 91 92 93 94 96 97 107 108 111 116 119 125 128 129 130 131 132 135 144 145 146 147 148 **S** ThedaCare, Inc., Appleton, WI
Primary Contact: John Feeney, President and Chief Executive Officer
CFO: Thomas P. Krystowiak, Chief Financial Officer
Web address: www.chnwi.org
**Control:** Other not–for–profit (including NFP Corporation) **Service:** General Medical and Surgical

**Staffed Beds:** 75 **Admissions:** 1712 **Census:** 46 **Outpatient Visits:** 58800
**Births:** 185 **Total Expense ($000):** 66608 **Payroll Expense ($000):** 33157
**Personnel:** 310

## BLACK RIVER FALLS—Jackson County

☐ **BLACK RIVER MEMORIAL HOSPITAL (521333)**, 711 West Adams Street, Zip 54615–9113; tel. 715/284–5361 **A**1 9 10 18 **F**11 13 29 30 34 35 40 48 50 53 57 62 63 69 75 76 77 80 81 86 87 89 90 93 107 111 112 115 116 118 119 129 130 131 132 133 135 144 146 148
Primary Contact: Mary Beth White–Jacobs, R.N., FACHE, President and Chief Executive Officer
CFO: Robert Daley, Vice President Fiscal and Information Technology Services
CMO: Lea Coville, Chief of Staff
CIO: Robert Daley, Vice President Fiscal and Information Technology Services
CHR: Holly Winn, Vice President Human Resources and Ancillary Services
CNO: Melissa Bergerson, R.N., Vice President Patient Care Services
Web address: www.brmh.net
**Control:** Other not–for–profit (including NFP Corporation) **Service:** General Medical and Surgical

**Staffed Beds:** 25 **Admissions:** 907 **Census:** 7 **Outpatient Visits:** 18755
**Births:** 151 **Total Expense ($000):** 38285 **Payroll Expense ($000):** 17444
**Personnel:** 274

## BLOOMER—Chippewa County

☐ **MAYO CLINIC HEALTH SYSTEM – CHIPPEWA VALLEY IN BLOOMER (521314)**, 1501 Thompson Street, Zip 54724–1299; tel. 715/568–2000, (Total facility includes 35 beds in nursing home–type unit) **A**1 9 10 18 **F**3 8 15 18 28 29 30 31 32 34 35 40 43 44 45 50 53 54 56 57 59 63 64 65 75 77 78 80 81 84 85 86 87 90 93 96 97 107 110 115 119 128 130 132 133 135 144 146 147 148 **P**6 **S** Mayo Clinic, Rochester, MN
Primary Contact: Edward A. Wittrock, Vice President Regional System
Web address: www.bloomermedicalcenter.org
**Control:** Other not–for–profit (including NFP Corporation) **Service:** General Medical and Surgical

**Staffed Beds:** 54 **Admissions:** 470 **Census:** 41 **Outpatient Visits:** 48978
**Births:** 0 **Total Expense ($000):** 31466 **Payroll Expense ($000):** 16114
**Personnel:** 231

## BOSCOBEL—Grant County

**GUNDERSEN BOSCOBEL AREA HOSPITAL AND CLINICS (521344)**, 205 Parker Street, Zip 53805–1698; tel. 608/375–4112 **A**9 10 18 **F**3 8 15 28 29 34 35 38 40 43 56 57 59 62 70 75 77 80 81 82 85 86 87 89 90 93 101 102 107 110 119 127 130 131 133 135 144 148 **P**6
Primary Contact: David Hartberg, Administrator
CFO: Melissa Uselman, Director Finance
CMO: Marilu Bintz, M.D., Chief of Staff
CIO: Scott Pauls, Manager Information Systems
CHR: Jennifer Dax, Director Human Resources
CNO: Theresa Lynn Braudt, Chief Nursing Officer
Web address: www.gundersonhealth.org/boscobel
**Control:** Other not–for–profit (including NFP Corporation) **Service:** General Medical and Surgical

**Staffed Beds:** 7 **Admissions:** 255 **Census:** 3 **Outpatient Visits:** 29382
**Births:** 0 **Total Expense ($000):** 15078 **Payroll Expense ($000):** 5130
**Personnel:** 106

## BROOKFIELD—Waukesha County

★ **WHEATON FRANCISCAN HEALTHCARE – ELMBROOK MEMORIAL (520170)**, 19333 West North Avenue, Zip 53045–4198; tel. 262/785–2000 **A**9 **F**3 4 8 11 12 13 15 17 18 20 22 24 26 28 29 30 31 34 35 36 40 41 43 45 46 47 49 50 54 56 58 59 64 65 68 70 72 74 75 76 77 78 79 80 81 82 84 85 86 87 89 90 91 92 93 97 99 100 107 108 109 110 111 112 114 115 117 118 119 120 121 122 123 124 126 130 131 132 135 143 145 146 147 148 **S** Wheaton Franciscan Healthcare, Wheaton, IL
Primary Contact: Debra K. Standridge, President
CFO: Michael Petitt, Director of Finance
CMO: Rita Hanson, M.D., Vice President Medical Affairs
CIO: Andrew Donovan, Director Information Technology
CHR: Christopher Morris, Director Human Resources
CNO: Sharon Baughman, R.N., Vice President Patient Services and Chief Nursing Officer
Web address: www.wfhealthcare.org
**Control:** Church–operated, Nongovernment, not–for profit **Service:** General Medical and Surgical

**Staffed Beds:** 100 **Admissions:** 4867 **Census:** 54 **Outpatient Visits:** 70339
**Births:** 526 **Total Expense ($000):** 106087 **Payroll Expense ($000):** 35512
**Personnel:** 452

**WI**

## BURLINGTON—Racine County

✠ **AURORA MEMORIAL HOSPITAL OF BURLINGTON (520059)**, 252 McHenry Street, Zip 53105–1828; tel. 262/767–6000 **A**1 2 9 10 **F**11 15 17 20 28 29 34 36 40 51 53 56 70 75 80 81 82 86 87 89 93 107 108 111 116 118 119 130 131 **P**6 **S** Aurora Health Care, Milwaukee, WI
Primary Contact: Lisa Just, President
CFO: Stuart Arnett, Vice President Finance and Chief Financial Officer
CIO: Jean Chase, Regional Manager Information Services
CHR: Gene Krauklis, Regional Vice President Human Resources
Web address: www.aurorahealthcare.org
**Control:** Other not–for–profit (including NFP Corporation) **Service:** General Medical and Surgical

**Staffed Beds:** 55 **Admissions:** 2552 **Census:** 24 **Outpatient Visits:** 82521
**Births:** 0 **Total Expense ($000):** 61660 **Payroll Expense ($000):** 22679
**Personnel:** 382

## CHILTON—Calumet County

✠ **CALUMET MEDICAL CENTER (521317)**, 614 Memorial Drive, Zip 53014–1597; tel. 920/849–2386 **A**1 9 10 18 **F**3 7 11 15 28 29 34 35 40 43 45 54 56 57 59 64 65 75 77 78 79 80 81 82 85 86 87 89 92 93 97 107 110 114 119 127 129 130 131 132 133 144 145 146 148 **S** Ascension Health, Saint Louis, MO
Primary Contact: Timothy Richman, President
CFO: Jeff Badger, Chief Financial Officer
CMO: Mark W. Kehrberg, M.D., Chief Medical Officer
CIO: Will Weider, Chief Information Officer
CHR: Beth O'laire, Manager Human Resources
CNO: Tom Veeser, R.N., Chief Nursing Officer
Web address: www.affinityhealth.org
**Control:** Other not–for–profit (including NFP Corporation) **Service:** General Medical and Surgical

**Staffed Beds:** 15 **Admissions:** 508 **Census:** 6 **Outpatient Visits:** 40430
**Births:** 0 **Total Expense ($000):** 20530 **Payroll Expense ($000):** 8671
**Personnel:** 119

## CHIPPEWA FALLS—Chippewa County

✠ **HSHS ST. JOSEPH'S HOSPITAL (520017)**, 2661 County Highway I., Zip 54729–5407; tel. 715/723–1811 **A**1 9 10 **F**3 4 5 13 15 17 18 28 29 30 34 35 38 40 43 56 59 62 63 64 69 70 75 76 77 79 80 81 82 84 85 86 87 88 89 93 100 101 102 104 105 107 111 115 119 129 130 132 144 145 146 147 148 **P**6 **S** Hospital Sisters Health System, Springfield, IL
Primary Contact: Joan M. Coffman, President and Chief Executive Officer
CFO: David Nelson, FACHE, Division Chief Financial Officer
CIO: Kevin Groskreutz, Division Chief Information Officer
CHR: Denise McMahon, Director People Services
CNO: Stella Clark, MSN, Chief Nursing Officer
Web address: www.stjoeschipfalls.com
**Control:** Other not–for–profit (including NFP Corporation) **Service:** General Medical and Surgical

**Staffed Beds:** 102 **Admissions:** 2994 **Census:** 36 **Outpatient Visits:** 82534
**Births:** 396 **Total Expense ($000):** 63394 **Payroll Expense ($000):** 27025
**Personnel:** 385

## COLUMBUS—Columbia County

✠ **COLUMBUS COMMUNITY HOSPITAL, INC. (521338)**, 1515 Park Avenue, Zip 53925–2402; tel. 920/623–2200 **A**1 9 10 18 **F**3 8 13 15 16 17 18 28 29 34 40 45 47 50 51 54 56 57 58 59 64 70 75 76 77 78 79 80 81 85 86 88 89 91 93 96 110 114 115 118 119 129 130 132 133 135 144 146 147
Primary Contact: John D. Russell, President and Chief Executive Officer
CFO: Phillip G. Roberts, Vice President Finance and Chief Financial Officer
CMO: Samuel G. Poser, M.D., Chief of Staff
CIO: Phillip G. Roberts, Vice President Finance and Chief Financial Officer
CHR: Ann Roundy, Vice President Employee Services
CNO: Jamie Hendrix, Vice President Patient Care Services
Web address: www.cch–inc.com
**Control:** Other not–for–profit (including NFP Corporation) **Service:** General Medical and Surgical

**Staffed Beds:** 9 **Admissions:** 874 **Census:** 9 **Outpatient Visits:** 33648
**Births:** 66 **Total Expense ($000):** 29861 **Payroll Expense ($000):** 11922
**Personnel:** 163

## CUBA CITY—Grant County

**SOUTHWEST HEALTH CENTER NURSING HOME** See Southwest Health Center, Platteville

## CUDAHY—Milwaukee County

**AURORA ST. LUKE'S SOUTH SHORE** See Aurora St. Luke's Medical Center, Milwaukee

## CUMBERLAND—Barron County

☐ **CUMBERLAND MEMORIAL HOSPITAL (521353)**, 1110 Seventh Avenue, Zip 54829–9138; tel. 715/822–2741, (Total facility includes 50 beds in nursing home–type unit) **A**1 9 10 18 **F**11 13 28 29 34 40 43 53 55 56 75 76 77 81 82 86 87 89 93 107 125 128 130 131 144 **P**8
Primary Contact: Michael Gutsch, Chief Executive Officer
COO: Bob Lindberg, Chief Operating Officer
CFO: Angela Martens, Chief Financial Officer
CMO: Tom Lingen, M.D., Chief of Staff
CIO: Jason Morse, Director Information Technology
CHR: Hilary Butzler, Director Human Resources
Web address: www.cumberlandhealthcare.com
**Control:** Other not–for–profit (including NFP Corporation) **Service:** General Medical and Surgical

**Staffed Beds:** 75 **Admissions:** 562 **Census:** 49 **Outpatient Visits:** 10115
**Births:** 34 **Total Expense ($000):** 20192 **Payroll Expense ($000):** 9455
**Personnel:** 177

## DARLINGTON—Lafayette County

**MEMORIAL HOSPITAL OF LAFAYETTE COUNTY (521312)**, 800 Clay Street, Zip 53530–1228, Mailing Address: P.O. Box 70, Zip 53530–0070; tel. 608/776–4466 **A**9 10 18 **F**1 3 11 13 15 18 26 28 29 32 35 40 43 45 46 47 48 54 56 57 64 68 74 75 76 79 80 81 82 86 89 90 93 102 105 107 110 111 114 116 117 119 130 131 133 144
Primary Contact: Julie Chikowski, Administrator
CFO: Marie Wamsley, Chief Financial Officer
Web address: www.memorialhospitaloflafayettecounty.org
**Control:** County–Government, nonfederal **Service:** General Medical and Surgical

**Staffed Beds:** 23 **Admissions:** 401 **Census:** 4 **Outpatient Visits:** 21267
**Births:** 45 **Total Expense ($000):** 13150 **Payroll Expense ($000):** 3938
**Personnel:** 87

## DODGEVILLE—Iowa County

✠ **UPLAND HILLS HEALTH (521352)**, 800 Compassion Way, Zip 53533–1956, Mailing Address: P.O. Box 800, Zip 53533–0800; tel. 608/930–8000, (Total facility includes 44 beds in nursing home–type unit) **A**1 9 10 18 **F**3 11 13 15 17 28 29 31 32 34 35 36 40 43 53 54 56 57 59 60 62 63 64 67 70 75 76 77 78 80 81 82 85 86 87 88 89 90 92 93 96 107 114 119 128 129 130 131 132 133 144 146 147 148 **P**6
Primary Contact: Lisa W. Schnedler, FACHE, President and Chief Executive Officer
CFO: Karl Pustina, Vice President Finance
CIO: Karen Thuli, Coordinator Information Systems
CHR: Troy Marx, Director Human Resources
CNO: Lynn Hebgen, Vice President Nursing
Web address: www.uplandhillshealth.org
**Control:** Other not–for–profit (including NFP Corporation) **Service:** General Medical and Surgical

**Staffed Beds:** 69 **Admissions:** 1121 **Census:** 50 **Outpatient Visits:** 46641
**Births:** 254 **Total Expense ($000):** 36464 **Payroll Expense ($000):** 16210
**Personnel:** 249

## DURAND—Pepin County

★ **CHIPPEWA VALLEY HOSPITAL AND OAKVIEW CARE CENTER (521307)**, 1220 Third Avenue West, Zip 54736–1600, Mailing Address: P.O. Box 224, Zip 54736–0224; tel. 715/672–4211, (Total facility includes 50 beds in nursing home–type unit) **A**9 10 18 **F**8 15 18 28 29 34 35 40 45 50 56 57 59 65 69 71 75 79 81 86 87 97 107 127 128 129 130 133 **S** Adventist Health System Sunbelt Health Care Corporation, Altamonte Springs, FL
Primary Contact: Douglas R. Peterson, President and Chief Executive Officer
Web address: www.chippewavalleyhospital.com/
**Control:** Church–operated, Nongovernment, not–for profit **Service:** General Medical and Surgical

**Staffed Beds:** 75 **Admissions:** 347 **Census:** 43 **Outpatient Visits:** 33052
**Births:** 0 **Total Expense ($000):** 16820 **Payroll Expense ($000):** 7122
**Personnel:** 97

**WI**

---

**Hospital, Medicare Provider Number, Address, Telephone, Approval, Facility, and Physician Codes, Health Care System**

★ American Hospital Association (AHA) membership
☐ The Joint Commission accreditation
○ Healthcare Facilities Accreditation Program
◇ DNV Healthcare Inc. accreditation
⇑ Center for Improvement in Healthcare Quality Accreditation
△ Commission on Accreditation of Rehabilitation Facilities (CARF) accreditation

**EAGLE RIVER—Vilas County**

★ **MINISTRY EAGLE RIVER MEMORIAL HOSPITAL (521300)**, 201 Hospital Road, Zip 54521–8835; tel. 715/479–7411 **A**9 10 18 **F**3 11 15 28 29 30 35 40 45 47 50 57 59 68 75 80 81 82 84 85 86 87 89 93 107 108 110 115 119 130 133 146 148 **S** Ascension Health, Saint Louis, MO
Primary Contact: Sandra L. Anderson, President and Chief Executive Officer
CFO: Cathy Bukowski, Regional Chief Financial Officer
CMO: Richard Brodhead, M.D., President Medical Staff
CIO: Howard Dobizl, Director Information Technology Services
CHR: Michelle Cornelius, Director Human Resources for Northern Region
CNO: Deborah Karow, R.N., Vice President Patient Care Services
Web address: www.ministryhealth.org
**Control:** Church–operated, Nongovernment, not–for profit **Service:** General Medical and Surgical

Staffed Beds: 12 **Admissions:** 414 **Census:** 5 **Outpatient Visits:** 18550 **Births:** 0 **Total Expense ($000):** 13794 **Payroll Expense ($000):** 7039 **Personnel:** 104

**EAU CLAIRE—Eau Claire County**

☐ **MAYO CLINIC HEALTH SYSTEM IN EAU CLAIRE (520070)**, 1221 Whipple Street, Zip 54703–5270, Mailing Address: P.O. Box 4105, Zip 54702–4105; tel. 715/838–3311 **A**1 2 3 5 9 10 **F**3 4 5 8 12 13 15 17 18 20 22 24 26 28 29 30 31 32 34 35 36 37 40 43 44 45 46 48 49 50 53 55 57 58 59 60 63 64 65 68 70 71 72 74 75 76 79 80 81 82 83 84 85 86 87 89 90 92 93 96 97 98 99 100 101 102 103 104 105 107 108 110 111 115 118 119 120 121 124 126 129 130 132 135 144 145 146 147 148 **P**6 **S** Mayo Clinic, Rochester, MN
Primary Contact: Randall L. Linton, M.D., President and Chief Executive Officer
COO: John M. Dickey, Chief Administrative Officer
CFO: Paul Bammel, Vice President
CMO: Robert C. Peck, M.D., Chief Medical Officer
CHR: Blythe Loyd, Vice President
CNO: Pamela K. White, R.N., Chief Nursing Officer
Web address: www.mhs.mayo.edu
**Control:** Other not–for–profit (including NFP Corporation) **Service:** General Medical and Surgical

Staffed Beds: 185 **Admissions:** 9710 **Census:** 116 **Outpatient Visits:** 171315 **Births:** 1035 **Total Expense ($000):** 205695 **Payroll Expense ($000):** 89130 **Personnel:** 1396

☐ **OAKLEAF SURGICAL HOSPITAL (520196)**, 3802 West Oakwood Mall Drive, Zip 54701–3016; tel. 715/831–8130 **A**1 9 10 **F**3 37 45 47 48 51 64 75 80 81 82 85 107 119 130 145 148 **S** National Surgical Healthcare, Chicago, IL
Primary Contact: Anne Hargrave–Thomas, Chief Executive Officer
COO: Erma Radke, Director of Operations
CFO: Denise Freid–Scheppke, Chief Accounting Officer
CHR: Dorothy Conroy, Director Human Resources
CNO: Jacquelyn Maki, Chief Nursing Officer
Web address: www.oakleafmedical.com
**Control:** Corporation, Investor–owned, for–profit **Service:** General Medical and Surgical

Staffed Beds: 13 **Admissions:** 535 **Census:** 4 **Outpatient Visits:** 9611 **Births:** 0 **Total Expense ($000):** 40880 **Payroll Expense ($000):** 10240 **Personnel:** 170

✚ △ **SACRED HEART HOSPITAL (520013)**, 900 West Clairemont Avenue, Zip 54701–6122; tel. 715/717–4121 **A**1 2 3 5 7 9 10 **F**3 6 11 12 13 15 17 18 20 22 24 28 29 30 31 32 34 35 38 40 41 43 44 45 46 47 48 49 50 51 53 56 57 58 59 60 64 69 70 72 74 75 76 78 79 80 81 82 84 85 86 87 88 89 90 91 92 93 94 96 97 98 99 100 101 102 103 104 107 108 110 111 112 114 115 116 117 118 119 120 121 123 124 126 129 130 132 135 141 144 145 146 147 **P**6 **S** Hospital Sisters Health System, Springfield, IL
Primary Contact: Julie Manas, President and Chief Executive Officer
COO: Faye L. Deich, R.N., Senior Vice President Division Operations; Chief Operating Officer
CFO: David Nelson, FACHE, Chief Financial Officer
CMO: Humayun Khan, M.D., Chief Medical Officer
CIO: Kevin Groskreutz, Chief Information Officer
CHR: Craig Brenholt, Division Director People Services
CNO: Amy L. Dwyer, R.N., Chief Nursing Officer
Web address: www.sacredhearteauclaire.org
**Control:** Other not–for–profit (including NFP Corporation) **Service:** General Medical and Surgical

Staffed Beds: 216 **Admissions:** 9334 **Census:** 122 **Outpatient Visits:** 108822 **Births:** 901 **Total Expense ($000):** 185937 **Payroll Expense ($000):** 70562 **Personnel:** 1076

**EDGERTON—Rock County**

✚ **EDGERTON HOSPITAL AND HEALTH SERVICES (521319)**, 11101 North Sherman Road, Zip 53534–9002; tel. 608/884–3441 **A**1 9 10 18 **F**3 8 11 15 18 28 34 40 41 43 45 48 49 59 64 65 75 77 81 85 86 90 92 93 97 107 108 110 111 115 117 119 129 130 132 133 134 135 144 146 148
Primary Contact: Jim Schultz, Interim Chief Executive Officer
CFO: Charles Roader, Vice President Finance
CMO: William West, M.D., Chief of Staff
CIO: Sheryl Rucker, Chief Information Officer
CHR: Brad Olm, Director Human Resources
Web address: www.edgertonhospital.com
**Control:** Other not–for–profit (including NFP Corporation) **Service:** General Medical and Surgical

Staffed Beds: 18 **Admissions:** 301 **Census:** 8 **Outpatient Visits:** 14094 **Births:** 0 **Total Expense ($000):** 18496 **Payroll Expense ($000):** 7286 **Personnel:** 124

**ELKHORN—Walworth County**

✚ △ **AURORA LAKELAND MEDICAL CENTER (520102)**, W3985 County Road NN, Zip 53121–4389; tel. 262/741–2000 **A**1 2 7 9 10 **F**11 13 15 17 29 34 36 40 43 51 56 64 70 75 76 78 80 81 82 86 87 89 90 93 100 107 108 111 116 118 119 130 131 **P**6 **S** Aurora Health Care, Milwaukee, WI
Primary Contact: Lisa Just, President
CFO: Stuart Arnett, Regional Vice President Finance
CMO: Greg Gerber, M.D., Chief Medical Officer
CIO: Jean Chase, Regional Manager Information Services
CHR: Gene Krauklis, Regional Vice President Human Resources
Web address: www.aurorahealthcare.org
**Control:** Other not–for–profit (including NFP Corporation) **Service:** General Medical and Surgical

Staffed Beds: 67 **Admissions:** 3002 **Census:** 29 **Outpatient Visits:** 81067 **Births:** 767 **Total Expense ($000):** 66873 **Payroll Expense ($000):** 20615 **Personnel:** 338

**FOND DU LAC—Fond Du Lac County**

✚ △ **AGNESIAN HEALTHCARE (520088)**, 430 East Division Street, Zip 54935–4560, Mailing Address: P.O. Box 385, Zip 54936–0385; tel. 920/929–2300 **A**1 2 7 9 10 20 **F**2 3 5 6 11 13 15 18 20 22 24 26 28 29 30 31 34 35 36 38 40 42 43 44 45 46 47 48 49 50 51 53 54 55 56 57 59 62 63 64 66 67 68 69 71 74 75 76 77 78 79 80 81 82 83 84 85 86 87 90 92 93 94 96 97 98 99 100 101 102 103 104 105 106 107 108 109 110 111 114 115 117 118 119 120 121 123 124 126 129 130 131 132 134 135 143 144 146 147 148 **P**3 6
Primary Contact: Steven N. Little, President and Chief Executive Officer
COO: James Mugan, Senior Vice President for Clinical Services and Chief Operating Officer
CFO: Bonnie Schmitz, Vice President and Chief Financial Officer
CMO: Derek Colmenares, M.D., Chief Medical Officer
CIO: Nancy Birschbach, Assistant Vice President Information Services
CHR: Sue Edminster, Vice President Human Resources
Web address: www.agnesian.com
**Control:** Church–operated, Nongovernment, not–for profit **Service:** General Medical and Surgical

Staffed Beds: 160 **Admissions:** 6691 **Census:** 74 **Outpatient Visits:** 699534 **Births:** 834 **Total Expense ($000):** 304722 **Payroll Expense ($000):** 111879 **Personnel:** 1320

**FOND DU LAC COUNTY MENTAL HEALTH CENTER (524025)**, 459 East First Street, Zip 54935–4599; tel. 920/929–3502, (Nonreporting) **A**10
Primary Contact: Dr. J.R. Musunuru, M.D., Executive Director
Web address: www.fdlco.wi.gov
**Control:** County–Government, nonfederal **Service:** Psychiatric

Staffed Beds: 25

**FORT ATKINSON—Jefferson County**

✚ **FORT HEALTHCARE (520071)**, 611 East Sherman Avenue, Zip 53538–1998; tel. 920/568–5000 **A**1 9 10 **F**3 11 12 13 15 28 29 34 35 40 47 48 50 53 55 56 57 59 68 75 76 77 79 80 81 85 86 87 89 90 93 94 96 107 108 110 111 115 118 119 124 129 130 132 135 144 145 146 147 **P**1 5
Primary Contact: Michael S. Wallace, President and Chief Executive Officer
CFO: James J. Nelson, Senior Vice President Finance and Strategic Planning
CHR: Nancy Alstad, Director Human Resources
CNO: Renee Clark, R.N., Vice President Nursing Services and Performance Improvement
Web address: www.forthealthcare.com
**Control:** Other not–for–profit (including NFP Corporation) **Service:** General Medical and Surgical

Staffed Beds: 72 **Admissions:** 2148 **Census:** 16 **Outpatient Visits:** 278336 **Births:** 471 **Total Expense ($000):** 114650 **Payroll Expense ($000):** 36892 **Personnel:** 418

**WI**

## FRANKLIN—Milwaukee County

☒ **MIDWEST ORTHOPEDIC SPECIALTY HOSPITAL (520205)**, 10101 South 27th Street, 2nd Floor, Zip 53132–7209; tel. 414/817–5800 **A**1 3 5 9 10 **F**3 29 30 34 50 57 65 68 79 81 82 85 86 91 92 94 96 114 130 131 **S** Wheaton Franciscan Healthcare, Wheaton, IL
Primary Contact: Coreen Dicus–Johnson, President
CFO: Aaron Bridgeland, Director Finance
CMO: Daniel Guehlstorf, M.D., Chief of Staff
CIO: Gregory Smith, Senior Vice President and Chief Information Officer
CHR: Robert Bauer, Vice President Human Resources
CNO: Sheila Gansemer, R.N., Vice President Patient Care Services
Web address: www.mymosh.com/
**Control:** Partnership, Investor–owned, for–profit **Service:** General Medical and Surgical

**Staffed Beds:** 16 **Admissions:** 1354 **Census:** 8 **Outpatient Visits:** 8571
**Births:** 0 **Total Expense ($000):** 40216 **Payroll Expense ($000):** 6603
**Personnel:** 107

☒ **WHEATON FRANCISCAN HEALTHCARE – FRANKLIN (520204)**, 10101 South 27th Street, Zip 53132–7209; tel. 414/325–4700 **A**1 9 10 **F**3 15 18 20 22 26 29 30 31 34 35 40 45 46 47 48 49 50 56 57 64 65 68 70 74 75 77 79 81 82 84 85 86 87 91 92 93 94 96 107 108 110 111 115 119 120 121 122 123 129 130 131 132 144 145 146 147 148 **S** Wheaton Franciscan Healthcare, Wheaton, IL
Primary Contact: Coreen Dicus–Johnson, President
CFO: Aaron Bridgeland, Director Finance
CMO: Michelle Graham, M.D., Vice President Medical Affairs
CIO: Gregory Smith, Senior Vice President and Chief Information Officer
CHR: Robert Bauer, Vice President Human Resources
CNO: Sheila Gansemer, R.N., Vice President Patient Care Services
Web address: www.mywheaton.org/
**Control:** Church–operated, Nongovernment, not–for profit **Service:** General Medical and Surgical

**Staffed Beds:** 37 **Admissions:** 1895 **Census:** 21 **Outpatient Visits:** 83018
**Births:** 0 **Total Expense ($000):** 59768 **Payroll Expense ($000):** 21162
**Personnel:** 346

## FRIENDSHIP—Adams County

**MOUNDVIEW MEMORIAL HOSPITAL & CLINICS (521309)**, 402 West Lake Street, Zip 53934–9699, Mailing Address: P.O. Box 40, Zip 53934–0040; tel. 608/339–3331 **A**9 10 18 **F**6 11 15 18 28 29 31 34 35 36 40 43 50 53 56 57 59 64 77 79 81 82 84 86 87 93 97 107 108 111 115 119 127 129 130 131 133 144 146 **P**6
Primary Contact: Don Heinz, Interim Chief Executive Officer
Web address: www.moundview.org
**Control:** Other not–for–profit (including NFP Corporation) **Service:** General Medical and Surgical

**Staffed Beds:** 25 **Admissions:** 145 **Census:** 2 **Outpatient Visits:** 35849
**Births:** 0 **Total Expense ($000):** 13605 **Payroll Expense ($000):** 6457
**Personnel:** 102

## GLENDALE—Milwaukee County

**ORTHOPAEDIC HOSPITAL OF WISCONSIN – GLENDALE (520194)**, 475 West River Woods Parkway, Zip 53212–1081; tel. 414/961–6800 **A**9 10 **F**29 34 38 53 64 80 81 82 86 93 107 111 119 130 131
Primary Contact: Brian J. Cramer, Chief Executive Officer
CFO: Tom Swiderski, Chief Financial Officer
CMO: Rory Wright, M.D., President Medical Staff
CIO: Todd Heikkinen, Manager Sports Medicine and Rehabilitation Services
CNO: Nanette Johnson, Chief Nursing Officer
Web address: www.ohow.org
**Control:** Partnership, Investor–owned, for–profit **Service:** General Medical and Surgical

**Staffed Beds:** 30 **Admissions:** 1127 **Census:** 8 **Outpatient Visits:** 26014
**Births:** 0 **Total Expense ($000):** 35225 **Payroll Expense ($000):** 11456
**Personnel:** 172

## GRAFTON—Ozaukee County

☒ **AURORA MEDICAL CENTER GRAFTON (520207)**, 975 Port Washington Road, Zip 53024–9201; tel. 262/329–1000 **A**1 2 3 5 9 10 **F**6 13 15 17 20 22 24 28 29 34 36 40 43 51 53 54 56 64 69 70 72 75 76 78 80 81 82 86 87 89 90 93 107 108 111 116 118 119 130 131 **P**6 **S** Aurora Health Care, Milwaukee, WI
Primary Contact: Carrie Killoran, Interim President
CMO: Doug McManus, Chief Medical Officer
CNO: Terry Kabitzke–Groth, R.N., Vice President Nursing
Web address: www.aurorahealthcare.org
**Control:** Other not–for–profit (including NFP Corporation) **Service:** General Medical and Surgical

**Staffed Beds:** 107 **Admissions:** 6572 **Census:** 64 **Outpatient Visits:** 106635
**Births:** 748 **Total Expense ($000):** 155290 **Payroll Expense ($000):** 42350
**Personnel:** 726

## GRANTSBURG—Burnett County

★ **BURNETT MEDICAL CENTER (521331)**, 257 West St. George Avenue, Zip 54840–7827; tel. 715/463–5353, (Total facility includes 50 beds in nursing home–type unit) **A**9 10 18 **F**2 3 13 15 28 29 30 31 34 35 40 43 45 56 57 59 64 68 75 76 77 78 80 81 84 85 86 87 89 90 93 97 107 114 127 128 130 131 132 133 135 144 148 **P**6
Primary Contact: Gordon Lewis, Chief Executive Officer
CFO: Charles J. Faught, Chief Financial Officer
CMO: Hans Rechsteiner, M.D., Chief of Staff
CIO: Andy Douglas, Manager Information Technology
CHR: Sandy Hinrichs, Director Human Resources
Web address: www.burnettmedicalcenter.com
**Control:** Other not–for–profit (including NFP Corporation) **Service:** General Medical and Surgical

**Staffed Beds:** 67 **Admissions:** 522 **Census:** 52 **Outpatient Visits:** 33483
**Births:** 39 **Total Expense ($000):** 14835 **Payroll Expense ($000):** 7106
**Personnel:** 136

## GREEN BAY—Brown County

☒ △ **AURORA BAYCARE MEDICAL CENTER (520193)**, 2845 Greenbrier Road, Zip 54311–6519, Mailing Address: P.O. Box 8900, Zip 54308–8900; tel. 920/288–8000 **A**1 2 7 9 10 **F**12 13 15 17 20 22 24 28 29 34 36 40 43 53 54 64 70 72 75 76 78 80 81 82 86 87 89 90 93 107 108 111 116 118 119 130 131 144 147 **P**6 **S** Aurora Health Care, Milwaukee, WI
Primary Contact: Daniel T. Meyer, President
COO: Daniel T. Meyer, President
CFO: Gwen Christensen, Vice President Finance
CMO: Stephen Brada, Chief of Staff
CIO: Chuck Geurts, Manager Management Information Services
CHR: Elizabeth A. Kirby, Director Human Resources
CNO: Heather Schroeder, R.N., Chief Nurse Executive and Vice President of Nursing
Web address: www.aurorabaycare.com
**Control:** Partnership, Investor–owned, for–profit **Service:** General Medical and Surgical

**Staffed Beds:** 167 **Admissions:** 8416 **Census:** 98 **Outpatient Visits:** 248145
**Births:** 1403 **Total Expense ($000):** 233321 **Payroll Expense ($000):** 76064 **Personnel:** 1159

★ ◇ **BELLIN MEMORIAL HOSPITAL (520049)**, 744 South Webster Avenue, Zip 54301–3581, Mailing Address: P.O. Box 23400, Zip 54305–3400; tel. 920/433–3500 **A**9 10 21 **F**3 12 13 15 17 18 20 22 24 26 28 29 30 31 36 37 40 41 43 44 45 46 47 49 51 53 54 62 64 68 71 74 75 76 77 78 80 81 82 83 84 85 86 87 89 90 91 92 96 97 106 107 108 110 111 115 116 117 118 119 120 121 122 123 124 126 129 130 131 144 146 **P**2 6
Primary Contact: George Kerwin, President
CFO: Jim Dietsche, Chief Financial Officer
CMO: Ed Millermaier, M.D., Chief Medical Officer
CIO: John Rocheleau, Vice President Business Support and Information Technology
CHR: Troy L. Koebke, Director Human Resources Management
CNO: Laura Hieb, R.N., Chief Nursing Officer
Web address: www.bellin.org
**Control:** Church–operated, Nongovernment, not–for profit **Service:** General Medical and Surgical

**Staffed Beds:** 167 **Admissions:** 8433 **Census:** 87 **Outpatient Visits:** 860322
**Births:** 1289 **Total Expense ($000):** 371038 **Payroll Expense ($000):** 169633 **Personnel:** 2271

**WI**

---

**Hospital, Medicare Provider Number, Address, Telephone, Approval, Facility, and Physician Codes, Health Care System**

★ American Hospital Association (AHA) membership    ○ Healthcare Facilities Accreditation Program    ⇑ Center for Improvement in Healthcare Quality Accreditation
□ The Joint Commission accreditation    ◇ DNV Healthcare Inc. accreditation    △ Commission on Accreditation of Rehabilitation Facilities (CARF) accreditation

◇ **BELLIN PSYCHIATRIC CENTER (524038)**, 301 East St. Joseph Street, Zip 54305–3725, Mailing Address: P.O. Box 23725, Zip 54305–3725; tel. 920/433–3630 **A**9 10 21 **F**4 5 6 29 34 36 38 53 54 56 64 75 86 87 98 99 100 101 102 103 104 105 130 **P**2 6
Primary Contact: Sharla Baenen, President
CFO: Kevin McGurk, Controller
CMO: Ed Millermaier, M.D., Chief Medical Officer
CIO: Troy Schiesl, Director Information Services
CHR: Troy L. Koebke, Director Human Resources
CNO: Ray Bork, Team Leader Nursing
Web address: www.bellin.org
**Control:** Church–operated, Nongovernment, not–for profit **Service:** Psychiatric

**Staffed Beds:** 53 **Admissions:** 1302 **Census:** 15 **Outpatient Visits:** 53937 **Births:** 0 **Total Expense ($000):** 15628 **Payroll Expense ($000):** 9716 **Personnel:** 108

**BROWN COUNTY COMMUNITY TREATMENT CENTER (524014)**, 3150 Gershwin Drive, Zip 54311–5899; tel. 920/391–4700 **A**10 **F**98 102 130
Primary Contact: Roberta Morschauser, Administrator
CFO: Margaret Hoff, Account Manager
CMO: Yogesh Pareek, M.D., Clinical Director
CIO: Dawn LaPlant, Manager Health Information Management
CHR: Brent R. Miller, Manager Human Resources
Web address: www.co.brown.wi.us/
**Control:** County–Government, nonfederal **Service:** Psychiatric

**Staffed Beds:** 10 **Admissions:** 965 **Census:** 11 **Outpatient Visits:** 4927 **Births:** 0 **Total Expense ($000):** 4359 **Payroll Expense ($000):** 2498 **Personnel:** 62

**BROWN COUNTY HUMAN SERVICES MENTAL HEALTH CENTER** See Brown County Community Treatment Center

⊠ **ST. MARY'S HOSPITAL MEDICAL CENTER (520097)**, 1726 Shawano Avenue, Zip 54303–3282; tel. 920/498–4200 **A**1 2 9 10 **F**3 13 15 17 18 20 22 26 28 29 30 31 34 35 40 43 44 45 46 47 48 49 50 51 53 55 57 59 64 65 68 69 70 74 75 76 77 78 79 80 81 82 84 85 86 87 92 94 96 102 107 108 110 111 114 115 116 117 118 119 130 132 143 145 146 147 148 **P**2 **S** Hospital Sisters Health System, Springfield, IL
Primary Contact: Therese B. Pandl, President and Chief Executive Officer
COO: Lawrence J. Connors, Chief Operating Officer
CFO: Greg Simia, Chief Financial Officer
CMO: Kenneth Johnson, M.D., Chief Physician Executive
CIO: Shane Miller, Chief Information Officer
CHR: Christine Jensema, Ph.D., Chief People Officer
CNO: Paula Hafeman, R.N., Chief Nursing Officer
Web address: www.stmgb.org
**Control:** Church–operated, Nongovernment, not–for profit **Service:** General Medical and Surgical

**Staffed Beds:** 83 **Admissions:** 4532 **Census:** 39 **Outpatient Visits:** 114749 **Births:** 631 **Total Expense ($000):** 111962 **Payroll Expense ($000):** 35204 **Personnel:** 393

⊠ **ST. VINCENT HOSPITAL (520075)**, 835 South Van Buren Street, Zip 54301–3526, Mailing Address: P.O. Box 13508, Zip 54307–3508; tel. 920/433–0111 **A**1 2 9 10 **F**3 9 11 12 13 15 17 18 20 22 24 29 30 31 34 35 36 40 43 44 45 49 50 51 56 57 58 59 60 62 64 65 68 70 72 74 75 76 77 78 79 80 81 83 84 85 86 87 88 89 90 91 92 94 96 107 108 110 111 114 115 116 117 118 119 120 121 123 124 126 129 130 132 135 143 144 146 147 148 **P**2 **S** Hospital Sisters Health System, Springfield, IL
Primary Contact: Therese B. Pandl, President and Chief Executive Officer
COO: Lawrence J. Connors, Chief Operating Officer
CFO: Greg Simia, Chief Financial Officer
CMO: Kenneth Johnson, M.D., Chief Physician Executive
CIO: Shane Miller, Chief Information Officer
CHR: Christine Jensema, Ph.D., Chief People Officer
CNO: Paula Hafeman, R.N., Chief Nurse Executive
Web address: www.stvincenthospital.org
**Control:** Church–operated, Nongovernment, not–for profit **Service:** General Medical and Surgical

**Staffed Beds:** 255 **Admissions:** 9705 **Census:** 123 **Outpatient Visits:** 128088 **Births:** 878 **Total Expense ($000):** 246362 **Payroll Expense ($000):** 80142 **Personnel:** 1266

GREENFIELD—Milwaukee County

**KINDRED HOSPITAL–MILWAUKEE** See Post Acute Medical Specialty Hospital of Milwaukee

⊠ **POST ACUTE MEDICAL SPECIALTY HOSPITAL OF MILWAUKEE (522004)**, 5017 South 110Th Street, Zip 53228–3131; tel. 414/427–8282 **A**1 9 10 **F**1 3 29 34 65 68 74 75 82 84 85 86 96 97 119 130 148 **S** Post Acute Medical, LLC, Enola, PA
Primary Contact: Christine Ninu, Chief Executive Officer
CMO: Alok Goyal, M.D., Medical Director
CNO: Dorie Petitt, Chief Nursing Officer
Web address: www.postacutemedical.com/
**Control:** Corporation, Investor–owned, for–profit **Service:** Long–Term Acute Care hospital

**Staffed Beds:** 56 **Admissions:** 402 **Census:** 26 **Outpatient Visits:** 0 **Births:** 0 **Total Expense ($000):** 15832 **Payroll Expense ($000):** 7101 **Personnel:** 110

HARTFORD—Washington County

⊠ **AURORA MEDICAL CENTER IN WASHINGTON COUNTY (520038)**, 1032 East Sumner Street, Zip 53027–1698; tel. 262/673–2300 **A**1 2 9 10 **F**2 11 15 29 34 36 40 43 53 54 56 64 70 75 77 80 81 82 86 87 89 90 93 107 111 118 119 130 **P**6 **S** Aurora Health Care, Milwaukee, WI
Primary Contact: Carrie Killoran, Interim President
CIO: John Sipek, Supervisor Client Services
CNO: Terry Kabitzke–Groth, R.N., Chief Nursing Officer
Web address: www.aurorahealthcare.org
**Control:** Other not–for–profit (including NFP Corporation) **Service:** General Medical and Surgical

**Staffed Beds:** 34 **Admissions:** 1657 **Census:** 15 **Outpatient Visits:** 80028 **Births:** 0 **Total Expense ($000):** 50145 **Payroll Expense ($000):** 17783 **Personnel:** 267

HAYWARD—Sawyer County

★ **HAYWARD AREA MEMORIAL HOSPITAL AND NURSING HOME (521336)**, 11040 North State Road 77, Zip 54843–6391; tel. 715/934–4321, (Total facility includes 70 beds in nursing home–type unit) **A**9 10 18 **F**3 8 10 11 13 15 31 34 35 40 43 45 51 64 75 76 77 78 81 82 85 86 93 97 107 111 115 119 128 130 132 133 134 135 145 146 148
Primary Contact: Timothy M. Gullingsrud, Chief Executive Officer
COO: Brad Zeller, Vice President Operations
CFO: Kent Dumonseau, Vice President Finance and Information Services
CHR: Rose Gates, Director Human Resources
Web address: www.hamhnh.com
**Control:** Other not–for–profit (including NFP Corporation) **Service:** General Medical and Surgical

**Staffed Beds:** 75 **Admissions:** 996 **Census:** 75 **Outpatient Visits:** 21749 **Births:** 142 **Total Expense ($000):** 28597 **Payroll Expense ($000):** 12745 **Personnel:** 176

HILLSBORO—Vernon County

★ **GUNDERSEN ST. JOSEPH'S HOSPITAL AND CLINICS (521304)**, 400 Water Avenue, Zip 54634–9054, Mailing Address: P.O. Box 527, Zip 54634–0527; tel. 608/489–8000 **A**9 10 18 **F**3 8 11 15 28 29 30 34 35 40 42 43 50 53 54 56 57 59 64 65 68 69 75 77 80 81 82 85 86 87 89 90 91 92 93 96 97 107 109 110 114 127 129 130 131 132 133 135 144 147 148 **P**6
Primary Contact: Debra Smith, Chief Executive Officer
CFO: Robin Nelson, Chief Financial Officer
CMO: William Cooke, M.D., Chief of Staff
CIO: Danial Phetteplace, Director Information Technology
CHR: Kristie McCoic, Clinic Operations Officer and Director Human Resources
Web address: www.stjhealthcare.org
**Control:** Other not–for–profit (including NFP Corporation) **Service:** General Medical and Surgical

**Staffed Beds:** 14 **Admissions:** 245 **Census:** 2 **Outpatient Visits:** 22273 **Births:** 0 **Total Expense ($000):** 16512 **Payroll Expense ($000):** 6603 **Personnel:** 117

HUDSON—St. Croix County

☐ **HUDSON HOSPITAL AND CLINIC (521335)**, 405 Stageline Road, Zip 54016–7848; tel. 715/531–6000 **A**1 3 9 10 18 **F**3 5 8 13 15 18 28 29 31 34 35 36 37 38 40 43 44 45 46 50 53 56 57 59 64 68 74 75 76 77 78 79 80 81 85 86 87 89 93 94 96 97 107 110 111 115 117 119 129 130 132 133 135 143 146 148 **S** HealthPartners, Bloomington, MN
Primary Contact: Marian M. Furlong, R.N., FACHE, Chief Executive Officer
CFO: Douglas E. Johnson, Interim Vice President Operations and Chief Financial Officer
CMO: Paul Scott, M.D., Chief of Staff
CHR: Scott J. Allen, Director Human Resources
CNO: Robbi Hagelberg, R.N., Vice President Operations and Chief Nursing Officer
Web address: www.hudsonhospital.org
**Control:** Other not–for–profit (including NFP Corporation) **Service:** General Medical and Surgical

**Staffed Beds:** 7 **Admissions:** 1566 **Census:** 7 **Outpatient Visits:** 43132 **Births:** 690 **Total Expense ($000):** 50690 **Payroll Expense ($000):** 19436 **Personnel:** 292

**WI**

## JANESVILLE—Rock County

✠ **MERCY HOSPITAL AND TRAUMA CENTER (520066)**, 1000 Mineral Point Avenue, Zip 53548–2982, Mailing Address: P.O. Box 5003, Zip 53547–5003; tel. 608/756–6000, (Total facility includes 27 beds in nursing home–type unit) **A**1 2 9 10 **F**3 4 5 9 11 12 13 15 17 18 20 22 24 26 28 29 30 31 33 34 35 36 37 38 40 42 43 44 45 49 50 54 55 56 57 58 59 60 61 64 65 66 68 69 70 74 75 76 77 78 79 80 81 82 84 85 86 87 88 89 90 92 93 94 96 97 98 100 101 102 103 104 105 107 108 110 111 114 115 116 118 119 120 121 126 128 129 130 131 132 135 144 146 147 148 **P**6 **S** Mercy Health System, Janesville, WI
Primary Contact: Javon R. Bea, President and Chief Executive Officer
CFO: John Cook, Vice President and Chief Financial Officer
CMO: Mark L. Goelzer, M.D., Director Medical Affairs
CHR: Kathy Harris, Vice President
CNO: Sue Ripsch, R.N., Vice President and Chief Nursing Officer
Web address: www.mercyhealthsystem.org
**Control:** Other not–for–profit (including NFP Corporation) **Service:** General Medical and Surgical

**Staffed Beds:** 132 **Admissions:** 6762 **Census:** 91 **Outpatient Visits:** 1032402 **Births:** 836 **Total Expense ($000):** 378352 **Payroll Expense ($000):** 122254 **Personnel:** 1636

✠ **ST. MARY'S JANESVILLE HOSPITAL (520208)**, 3400 East Racine Steeet, Zip 53546–2344; tel. 608/373–8000 **A**1 10 **F**3 8 11 13 28 29 30 34 35 38 40 44 45 46 47 49 50 57 59 65 68 70 74 75 76 77 79 80 81 82 84 85 86 87 89 90 93 107 108 111 118 119 129 130 132 135 146 **S** SSM Health, Saint Louis, MO
Primary Contact: Kerry Swanson, President
Web address: www.stmarysjanesville.com
**Control:** Church–operated, Nongovernment, not–for profit **Service:** General Medical and Surgical

**Staffed Beds:** 50 **Admissions:** 2784 **Census:** 26 **Outpatient Visits:** 28491 **Births:** 441 **Total Expense ($000):** 56084 **Payroll Expense ($000):** 18310 **Personnel:** 280

## KENOSHA—Kenosha County

✠ **AURORA MEDICAL CENTER (520189)**, 10400 75th Street, Zip 53142–7884; tel. 262/948–5600 **A**1 2 9 10 **F**11 13 15 17 20 28 29 34 36 40 43 51 54 64 70 75 76 80 81 82 86 87 89 93 100 107 108 111 116 118 119 130 131 **P**6 **S** Aurora Health Care, Milwaukee, WI
Primary Contact: Douglas E. Koch, Market President
COO: Linda A. Gump, Chief Clinical Services Officer
CFO: Laurie B. Yake, Vice President Finance
CMO: James Santarelli, M.D., President Medical Staff
CIO: Debora R. Chapdelaine, Manager Information Technology
CHR: Kellie Nelson, Director Human Resources
CNO: Donna F. Jamieson, Chief Nursing Officer
Web address: www.aurorahealthcare.org
**Control:** Other not–for–profit (including NFP Corporation) **Service:** General Medical and Surgical

**Staffed Beds:** 74 **Admissions:** 5026 **Census:** 46 **Outpatient Visits:** 186140 **Births:** 840 **Total Expense ($000):** 115694 **Payroll Expense ($000):** 35269 **Personnel:** 610

☐ **UNITED HOSPITAL SYSTEM–KENOSHA CAMPUS (520021)**, 6308 Eighth Avenue, Zip 53143–5082; tel. 262/656–2011, (Nonreporting) **A**1 2 9 10
Primary Contact: Richard O. Schmidt, Jr., President and Chief Executive Officer
Web address: www.unitedhospitalsystem.org/
**Control:** Other not–for–profit (including NFP Corporation) **Service:** General Medical and Surgical

**Staffed Beds:** 247

## LA CROSSE—La Crosse County

✠ △ **GUNDERSEN HEALTH SYSTEM (520087)**, 1900 South Avenue, Zip 54601–5467; tel. 608/782–7300 **A**1 2 3 5 7 8 9 10 **F**2 3 4 5 6 9 11 13 15 18 19 20 22 24 28 29 30 31 32 34 35 36 38 40 43 45 46 47 48 49 50 51 52 54 55 56 59 61 64 68 72 74 75 76 77 78 79 80 81 82 83 85 86 87 88 89 90 91 92 93 94 96 97 98 99 100 101 102 103 104 105 106 107 108 110 111 114 115 116 117 118 119 120 121 123 124 126 129 130 131 134 144 145 146 147 148
Primary Contact: Jeffrey E. Thompson, M.D., Chief Executive Officer
COO: Kathy Klock, R.N., Senior Vice President Clinical Operations and Human Resources
CFO: Michael Allen, Chief Financial Officer
CMO: Greg Thompson, Chief Medical Officer
CIO: Deb Rislow, Chief Information Officer
CHR: Kathy Klock, R.N., Senior Vice President Clinical Operations and Human Resources
CNO: Mary Lu Gerke, R.N., Vice President Nursing Systems
Web address: www.gundluth.org
**Control:** Other not–for–profit (including NFP Corporation) **Service:** General Medical and Surgical

**Staffed Beds:** 268 **Admissions:** 14200 **Census:** 176 **Outpatient Visits:** 976925 **Births:** 1526 **Total Expense ($000):** 731117 **Payroll Expense ($000):** 271855 **Personnel:** 2470

☐ **MAYO CLINIC HEALTH SYSTEM – FRANCISCAN HEALTHCARE IN LA CROSSE (520004)**, 700 West Avenue South, Zip 54601–4783; tel. 608/785–0940 **A**1 2 3 5 9 10 **F**1 3 4 5 6 8 9 11 13 14 15 16 17 18 19 20 21 22 23 25 26 27 28 29 30 31 32 34 35 36 40 43 44 45 50 52 53 54 55 56 57 58 59 61 64 65 66 68 69 70 71 72 74 75 76 77 78 79 80 81 82 84 85 86 87 88 89 90 93 94 97 98 99 100 101 102 103 104 105 107 108 109 110 111 112 114 115 117 118 119 120 121 123 124 127 129 130 131 132 134 135 143 144 145 146 147 148 **S** Mayo Clinic, Rochester, MN
Primary Contact: Timothy J. Johnson, President and Chief Executive Officer
COO: Joseph J. Kruse, Executive Vice President
CFO: Tom Tiggelaar, Vice President Finance
CMO: David Rushlow, Vice President Medical Affairs
CIO: Neal Sanger, Vice President Information Services
CNO: Diane Holmay, R.N., Vice President and Chief Nursing Officer
Web address: www.franciscanskemp.org
**Control:** Church–operated, Nongovernment, not–for profit **Service:** General Medical and Surgical

**Staffed Beds:** 152 **Admissions:** 7517 **Census:** 76 **Outpatient Visits:** 88964 **Births:** 935 **Total Expense ($000):** 200400 **Payroll Expense ($000):** 91523 **Personnel:** 1552

## LADYSMITH—Rusk County

★ **RUSK COUNTY MEMORIAL HOSPITAL (521328)**, 900 College Avenue West, Zip 54848–2116; tel. 715/532–5561 **A**9 10 18 **F**3 15 28 29 30 34 40 45 50 51 53 56 57 59 64 68 70 76 77 81 85 87 89 90 93 97 107 110 111 115 117 119 133 144 146 147 148
Primary Contact: Charisse S. Oland, FACHE, Chief Executive Officer
CFO: David Kuehn, Chief Financial Officer
CMO: Ganesh Pawar, M.D., Chief of Staff
CHR: Rita Telitz, Chief Administrative Officer
CNO: Debra Frenn, FACHE, Chief Patient Care Officer
Web address: www.ruskhospital.org
**Control:** County–Government, nonfederal **Service:** General Medical and Surgical

**Staffed Beds:** 25 **Admissions:** 444 **Census:** 6 **Outpatient Visits:** 30306 **Births:** 10 **Total Expense ($000):** 18929 **Payroll Expense ($000):** 7806 **Personnel:** 127

## LAKE GENEVA—Walworth County

**MERCY WALWORTH HOSPITAL AND MEDICAL CENTER (521357)**, N2950 State Road 67, Zip 53147–2655; tel. 262/245–0535 **A**9 10 18 **F**3 5 9 11 13 15 18 26 29 31 34 35 40 44 45 50 54 55 57 59 64 65 70 74 75 76 77 78 79 81 82 85 86 92 93 94 96 97 100 101 103 104 107 108 110 111 114 118 119 129 130 131 132 135 144 146 148 **P**6 **S** Mercy Health System, Janesville, WI
Primary Contact: Jennifer Hallatt, Chief Operating Officer
Web address: www.mercyhealthsystem.org
**Control:** Other not–for–profit (including NFP Corporation) **Service:** General Medical and Surgical

**Staffed Beds:** 15 **Admissions:** 1080 **Census:** 9 **Outpatient Visits:** 138045 **Births:** 170 **Total Expense ($000):** 64776 **Payroll Expense ($000):** 16023 **Personnel:** 262

**WI**

**LANCASTER—Grant County**

⊠ **GRANT REGIONAL HEALTH CENTER (521322)**, 507 South Monroe Street, Zip 53813–2054; tel. 608/723–2143 **A**1 9 10 18 **F**3 8 11 13 15 28 29 34 35 36 40 43 44 53 56 57 59 64 65 68 69 75 76 77 78 79 80 81 82 84 85 86 87 89 90 93 97 107 110 119 129 130 131 132 133 135 144 146 148 **P**6 **S** HealthTech Management Services, Brentwood, TN
Primary Contact: Nicole Clapp, R.N., MSN, FACHE, President and Chief Executive Officer
CFO: Dawn Bandy, Chief Financial Officer
CMO: Sheirlie Lamantia, M.D., Chief of Staff
CIO: Ken Kaiser, Coordinator Information Systems
CHR: Stacy L. Martin, Director Human Resources
CNO: Jennifer Rutkowski, R.N., Vice President Professional Services
Web address: www.grantregional.com
**Control:** Other not–for–profit (including NFP Corporation) **Service:** General Medical and Surgical

**Staffed Beds:** 9 **Admissions:** 644 **Census:** 5 **Outpatient Visits:** 27627 **Births:** 163 **Total Expense ($000):** 24403 **Payroll Expense ($000):** 11415 **Personnel:** 155

**MADISON—Dane County**

☐ **MENDOTA MENTAL HEALTH INSTITUTE (524008)**, 301 Troy Drive, Zip 53704–1599; tel. 608/301–1000 **A**1 3 5 9 10 **F**6 29 30 38 44 50 56 68 75 82 86 87 98 100 101 103 104 105 130 143
Primary Contact: Greg Van Rybroek, Chief Executive Officer
CFO: Stacie Schiereck, Director Management Services
CMO: Molli Martha Rolli, M.D., Medical Director
CNO: Jane Walters, Director of Nursing
Web address: www.dhfs.state.wi.us
**Control:** State–Government, nonfederal **Service:** Psychiatric

**Staffed Beds:** 272 **Admissions:** 762 **Census:** 246 **Outpatient Visits:** 0 **Births:** 0 **Total Expense ($000):** 60926 **Payroll Expense ($000):** 38678 **Personnel:** 762

⊠ △ **MERITER UNITYPOINT HEALTH (520089)**, 202 South Park Street, Zip 53715–1507; tel. 608/417–6000 **A**1 3 5 7 9 10 **F**3 4 5 9 11 12 13 15 17 18 20 22 24 26 28 29 30 31 32 34 35 36 37 40 41 43 44 49 50 53 56 57 58 59 64 65 66 68 70 71 72 74 75 76 78 79 80 81 84 85 86 87 90 92 93 96 97 98 99 100 101 102 103 104 105 106 107 108 111 115 117 118 119 126 130 132 135 145 146 147 148 **P**6
Primary Contact: Arthur Nizza, Chief Executive Officer
CFO: Beth Erdman, Chief Financial Officer
CMO: Geoff Priest, M.D., Chief Medical Officer
CIO: Denise Gomez, Assistant Vice President Information Systems
CHR: James Arnett, Vice President Human Resources
CNO: Pat Grunwald, MSN, Chief Nursing Officer
Web address: www.meriter.com
**Control:** Other not–for–profit (including NFP Corporation) **Service:** General Medical and Surgical

**Staffed Beds:** 336 **Admissions:** 15899 **Census:** 193 **Outpatient Visits:** 186863 **Births:** 3850 **Total Expense ($000):** 435555 **Payroll Expense ($000):** 192681 **Personnel:** 2293

⊠ **SELECT SPECIALTY HOSPITAL–MADISON (522008)**, 801 Braxton Place, 2nd Floor, Zip 53715–1415; tel. 608/260–2700 **A**1 10 **F**1 29 34 60 75 86 119 130 **P**2 8 **S** Select Medical Corporation, Mechanicsburg, PA
Primary Contact: Raymond F. Carnevale, Chief Executive Officer
CHR: Mallary Stramowski, Chief Human Resources Officer
CNO: Dana McKinney, Chief Nursing Officer
Web address: www.madison.selectspecialtyhospitals.com
**Control:** Corporation, Investor–owned, for–profit **Service:** Long–Term Acute Care hospital

**Staffed Beds:** 58 **Admissions:** 562 **Census:** 41 **Outpatient Visits:** 0 **Births:** 0 **Total Expense ($000):** 26299 **Payroll Expense ($000):** 10217 **Personnel:** 173

⊠ **ST. MARY'S HOSPITAL (520083)**, 700 South Park Street, Zip 53715–1830; tel. 608/251–6100 **A**1 3 10 **F**2 9 11 13 15 17 20 22 24 28 29 34 40 43 51 53 56 60 64 70 72 75 76 77 78 80 81 86 89 90 98 100 101 102 103 107 108 119 130 141 **S** SSM Health, Saint Louis, MO
Primary Contact: Damond Boatwright, Interim President
COO: Kristin McManmon, Chief Operating Officer
CFO: Steve Caldwell, Vice President Finance and Chief Financial Officer
CHR: Linda Taplin Statz, System Vice President Human Resources
CNO: Ginger Malone, MSN, RN–B, Chief Nursing Officer
Web address: www.stmarysmadison.com
**Control:** Church–operated, Nongovernment, not–for profit **Service:** General Medical and Surgical

**Staffed Beds:** 364 **Admissions:** 20079 **Census:** 247 **Outpatient Visits:** 130946 **Births:** 3480 **Total Expense ($000):** 359173 **Payroll Expense ($000):** 128043 **Personnel:** 1728

⊠ △ **UNIVERSITY OF WISCONSIN HOSPITAL AND CLINICS (520098)**, 600 Highland Avenue, Zip 53792–0002; tel. 608/263–6400, (Includes UNIVERSITY OF WISCONSIN CHILDREN'S HOSPITAL ; AMERICAN FAMILY CHILDREN'S HOSPITAL, 1675 Highland Avenue, Zip 53705; tel. 608/890–5437; Jeffrey S. Poltawsky, Senior Vice President) **A**1 2 3 5 7 8 9 10 13 **F**3 5 6 8 9 12 15 16 17 18 19 20 21 22 23 24 25 26 27 28 29 30 31 32 34 35 36 37 40 41 43 44 45 46 47 48 49 50 51 52 53 54 55 56 57 58 59 60 61 62 64 68 70 72 74 75 77 78 79 80 81 82 83 84 85 86 87 88 89 90 91 92 93 94 95 97 98 100 102 103 104 105 107 108 110 111 112 114 115 116 117 118 119 120 121 123 124 126 129 130 131 132 134 135 136 137 138 139 140 141 142 145 146 147 148 **P**3
Primary Contact: Ron Sliwinski, President and Chief Executive Officer
COO: Timothy Gaillard, Senior Vice President and Chief Operating Officer
CFO: Robert D. O'Keefe, Senior Vice President and Chief Financial Officer
CMO: Christopher Green, M.D., Senior Vice President Medical Affairs and Associate Dean Hospital Affairs
CIO: Jocelyn DeWitt, Ph.D., Vice President and Chief Information Officer
CHR: Elizabeth T. Bolt, Chief Human Resources Officer
CNO: Beth Houlahan, MSN, Senior Vice President and Chief Nursing Officer
Web address: www.uwhealth.org
**Control:** Other not–for–profit (including NFP Corporation) **Service:** General Medical and Surgical

**Staffed Beds:** 544 **Admissions:** 28596 **Census:** 401 **Outpatient Visits:** 912766 **Births:** 0 **Total Expense ($000):** 1251759 **Payroll Expense ($000):** 457109 **Personnel:** 7447

⊠ **WILLIAM S. MIDDLETON MEMORIAL VETERANS HOSPITAL**, 2500 Overlook Terrace, Zip 53705–2286; tel. 608/256–1901, (Nonreporting) **A**1 3 5 **S** Department of Veterans Affairs, Washington, DC
Primary Contact: Judy McKee, FACHE, Director
COO: John J. Rohrer, Associate Director
CFO: Evarista Mikell, Assistant Finance Officer
CMO: Alan J. Bridges, M.D., Chief of Staff
CIO: Randall Margenau, Chief Information Officer
CHR: Stuart Souders, Chief, Human Resources
CNO: Rebecca Kordahl, R.N., Associate Director, Patient Care Services
Web address: www.madison.va.gov
**Control:** Veterans Affairs, Government, federal **Service:** General Medical and Surgical

**Staffed Beds:** 87

**MANITOWOC—Manitowoc County**

⊠ **HOLY FAMILY MEMORIAL (520107)**, 2300 Western Avenue, Zip 54220–3712, Mailing Address: P.O. Box 1450, Zip 54221–1450; tel. 920/320–2011 **A**1 2 9 10 **F**3 4 5 8 11 13 15 17 20 22 26 28 29 30 31 34 36 40 45 46 47 48 49 50 51 53 54 56 57 58 59 62 63 64 65 68 70 74 75 76 77 78 79 80 81 82 84 85 86 89 93 97 99 100 101 102 103 104 107 108 110 111 115 116 118 119 121 129 130 131 132 135 144 146 147 148 **P**6 8 **S** Franciscan Sisters of Christian Charity Sponsored Ministries, Inc., Manitowoc, WI
Primary Contact: Mark P. Herzog, President and Chief Executive Officer
COO: Jane Curran–Meuli, Chief Operating Officer
CFO: Patricia Huettl, Vice President Finance and Chief Financial Officer
CMO: Steve Driggers, M.D., Chief Medical Officer
CIO: Theron Pappas, Director Management Information Systems
CHR: Laura M. Fielding, Administrative Director Organizational Development
CNO: Bonny Range, MSN, Chief Nursing Officer
Web address: www.hfmhealth.org
**Control:** Church–operated, Nongovernment, not–for profit **Service:** General Medical and Surgical

**Staffed Beds:** 67 **Admissions:** 2516 **Census:** 23 **Outpatient Visits:** 225315 **Births:** 234 **Total Expense ($000):** 124199 **Payroll Expense ($000):** 62503 **Personnel:** 728

**MARINETTE—Marinette County**

⊠ **BAY AREA MEDICAL CENTER (520113)**, 3100 Shore Drive, Zip 54143–4242; tel. 715/735–6621 **A**1 9 10 20 **F**3 7 8 11 13 15 17 18 20 22 28 29 30 31 34 40 42 43 45 46 48 50 54 56 57 59 68 70 74 75 76 77 78 79 80 81 85 86 87 89 93 96 107 108 110 111 115 119 130 131 143 146 147 148 **P**8
Primary Contact: Edward A. Harding, FACHE, President and Chief Executive Officer
COO: Bernie VanCourt, Chief Operating Officer
CFO: C. Daniel Carlson, Chief Financial Officer
CMO: Richard Stein, M.D., Chief Medical Officer
CIO: Pete Eisenzoph, Director Information Technology
CHR: Ken Joyner, Vice President of Employee Services
CNO: Rooney Freimund, R.N., Chief Nurse Executive
Web address: www.bamc.org
**Control:** Other not–for–profit (including NFP Corporation) **Service:** General Medical and Surgical

**Staffed Beds:** 34 **Admissions:** 3259 **Census:** 34 **Outpatient Visits:** 58432 **Births:** 318 **Total Expense ($000):** 95523 **Payroll Expense ($000):** 41423 **Personnel:** 475

**WI**

## MARSHFIELD—Wood County

✠ △ **MINISTRY SAINT JOSEPH'S HOSPITAL (520037)**, 611 St. Joseph Avenue, Zip 54449–1898; tel. 715/387–1713, (Includes SAINT JOSEPH'S CHILDEN'S HOSPITAL, 611 Saint Joseph Avenue, Zip 54449–1832; tel. 715/387–1713) **A**1 2 3 5 7 9 10 20 **F**3 5 6 7 9 11 12 13 16 17 18 19 20 22 24 26 27 28 29 30 31 34 35 36 38 40 41 43 44 49 50 56 57 59 61 64 68 69 70 72 74 75 76 77 78 79 80 81 82 83 84 85 86 87 88 89 90 93 96 98 100 101 102 103 108 111 112 116 117 118 119 120 121 123 124 126 130 132 135 136 144 146 147 148 **S** Ascension Health, Saint Louis, MO
Primary Contact: Brian Kief, Regional Vice President Ministry Health Care and President Ministry Saint Joseph's Hospital
CFO: William J. Hinner, Vice President Financial Analysis and Planning Ministry Health Care
CMO: Peter Stamas, M.D., Vice President Medical Affairs
CIO: Will Weider, Chief Information Officer
CHR: Cheryl F. Zima, Vice President Human Resources Ministry Health Care
CNO: Robin Kretschman, MSN, Vice President Patient Care Services
Web address: www.stjosephs–marshfield.org
**Control:** Church–operated, Nongovernment, not–for profit **Service:** General Medical and Surgical

**Staffed Beds:** 319 **Admissions:** 15914 **Census:** 236 **Outpatient Visits:** 52084 **Births:** 986 **Total Expense ($000):** 314051 **Payroll Expense ($000):** 107520 **Personnel:** 1497

**NORWOOD HEALTH CENTER (524019)**, 1600 North Chestnut Avenue, Zip 54449–1499; tel. 715/384–2188, (Total facility includes 24 beds in nursing home–type unit) **A**9 10 **F**3 4 30 34 98 99 100 101 102 103 128 130 143 146 148 **P**6
Primary Contact: Rhonda Kozik, Administrator
CFO: Jo Timmerman, Manager Accounting
CHR: Larry Shear, Administrative Assistant
Web address: www.co.wood.wi.us/norwood/index.htm
**Control:** County–Government, nonfederal **Service:** Psychiatric

**Staffed Beds:** 40 **Admissions:** 620 **Census:** 30 **Outpatient Visits:** 0 **Births:** 0 **Total Expense ($000):** 3096 **Payroll Expense ($000):** 1591 **Personnel:** 37

## MAUSTON—Juneau County

☐ **MILE BLUFF MEDICAL CENTER (520109)**, 1050 Division Street, Zip 53948–1997; tel. 608/847–6161, (Total facility includes 99 beds in nursing home–type unit) **A**1 9 10 20 **F**3 10 11 13 15 18 28 29 30 31 34 35 36 40 43 44 45 46 50 56 57 59 60 62 64 65 66 68 69 71 75 76 77 78 79 80 81 82 85 86 87 89 92 93 94 96 97 107 108 110 111 112 114 115 117 118 119 125 127 128 129 130 131 132 133 143 144 145 146 148
Primary Contact: James M. O'Keefe, President and Chief Executive Officer
Web address: www.milebluff.com
**Control:** Other not–for–profit (including NFP Corporation) **Service:** General Medical and Surgical

**Staffed Beds:** 119 **Admissions:** 1363 **Census:** 119 **Outpatient Visits:** 172508 **Births:** 172 **Total Expense ($000):** 67592 **Payroll Expense ($000):** 36917 **Personnel:** 472

## MEDFORD—Taylor County

✠ **ASPIRUS MEDFORD HOSPITAL (521324)**, 135 South Gibson Street, Zip 54451–1696; tel. 715/748–8100, (Includes MEMORIAL NURSING HOME ), (Total facility includes 109 beds in nursing home–type unit) **A**1 9 10 **F**1 3 8 10 11 13 15 18 28 29 31 32 34 35 36 40 41 43 50 53 55 57 58 59 60 64 65 68 75 76 77 78 81 82 85 86 87 89 90 93 97 107 110 111 115 116 118 119 125 127 128 129 130 131 132 133 135 144 146 147 148 **S** Aspirus, Inc., Wausau, WI
Primary Contact: Gregory A. Olson, President and Chief Executive Officer
COO: Kaaron Keene, Vice President Patient Care Services
CFO: Lori Peck, Vice President Finance
CMO: Alecia Hylton, M.D., Chief of Staff
CIO: Helen Volger, Director of Information Services
CHR: Angela C. Hupf, Vice President Human Resources and Community Relations
CNO: Kaaron Keene, Vice President Patient Care Services
Web address: www.memhc.com
**Control:** Other not–for–profit (including NFP Corporation) **Service:** General Medical and Surgical

**Staffed Beds:** 124 **Admissions:** 873 **Census:** 90 **Outpatient Visits:** 76124 **Births:** 226 **Total Expense ($000):** 50129 **Payroll Expense ($000):** 23895 **Personnel:** 380

## MENOMONEE FALLS—Waukesha County

✠ △ **COMMUNITY MEMORIAL HOSPITAL (520103)**, W180 N8085 Town Hall Road, Zip 53051–3518, Mailing Address: P.O. Box 408, Zip 53052–0408; tel. 262/251–1000 **A**1 2 3 7 9 10 **F**3 4 5 11 13 15 17 18 20 22 24 26 28 29 30 31 34 35 36 38 40 43 44 45 46 47 48 49 50 51 56 57 59 60 64 68 70 72 74 75 76 77 78 79 80 81 82 84 85 86 87 88 89 90 93 98 100 101 102 103 104 107 108 110 111 114 115 116 118 119 120 121 126 129 130 131 132 135 145 146 147 148
Primary Contact: Dennis Pollard, President
COO: Allen Ericson, Chief Operating Officer CHD
CFO: Thomas Knoll, Site Director Finance
CMO: David Goldberg, M.D., Vice President Medical Affairs
CIO: William Showalter, Senior Vice President Information Systems, Chief Information Officer
CHR: Keith Allen, Senior Vice President and Chief Human Resources Officer
CNO: Teri Lux, R.N., Vice President Patient Care Services and Chief Nursing Officer
Web address: www.communitymemorial.com
**Control:** Other not–for–profit (including NFP Corporation) **Service:** General Medical and Surgical

**Staffed Beds:** 198 **Admissions:** 8603 **Census:** 107 **Outpatient Visits:** 90107 **Births:** 978 **Total Expense ($000):** 168031 **Payroll Expense ($000):** 60689 **Personnel:** 960

## MENOMONIE—Dunn County

☐ **MAYO CLINIC HEALTH SYSTEM – RED CEDAR IN MENOMONIE (521340)**, 2321 Stout Road, Zip 54751–2397; tel. 715/235–5531 **A**1 9 10 18 **F**3 8 11 13 15 17 18 28 29 30 31 32 34 35 36 40 43 44 45 50 53 54 55 57 59 60 63 64 65 70 75 76 77 78 79 80 81 82 84 85 86 87 89 90 93 97 99 100 101 102 103 104 107 108 110 111 115 119 127 129 130 131 132 133 135 144 146 147 148 **P**6 **S** Mayo Clinic, Rochester, MN
Primary Contact: Steven Lindberg, Chief Administrative Officer
CFO: Jeanie Lubinsky, Chief Financial Officer
CMO: Mark Deyo Svendsen, M.D., Medical Director
CIO: Frank Wrogg, Director Information Technology
CHR: Leann Wurtzel, Director Human Resources
Web address: www.rcmc–mhs.org
**Control:** Other not–for–profit (including NFP Corporation) **Service:** General Medical and Surgical

**Staffed Beds:** 23 **Admissions:** 1473 **Census:** 15 **Outpatient Visits:** 95662 **Births:** 327 **Total Expense ($000):** 74412 **Payroll Expense ($000):** 37233 **Personnel:** 451

**RED CEDAR MEDICAL CENTER–MAYO HEALTH SYSTEM** See Mayo Clinic Health System – Red Cedar in Menomonie

## MEQUON—Ozaukee County

**COLUMBIA CENTER (520195)**, 13125 North Port Washington Road, Zip 53097–2416; tel. 262/243–7408 **A**9 10 **F**3 8 13 34 35 64 71 76 81 85 86 87 104 133
Primary Contact: Candy J. Casey, R.N., MS, President and Chief Executive Officer
CMO: Daniel Hagerman, M.D., President Medical Staff
Web address: www.columbiacenter.org
**Control:** Other not–for–profit (including NFP Corporation) **Service:** General Medical and Surgical

**Staffed Beds:** 6 **Admissions:** 494 **Census:** 3 **Outpatient Visits:** 248 **Births:** 488 **Total Expense ($000):** 6152 **Payroll Expense ($000):** 2942 **Personnel:** 39

✠ **COLUMBIA ST. MARY'S OZAUKEE HOSPITAL (520027)**, 13111 North Port Washington Road, Zip 53097–2416; tel. 262/243–7300 **A**1 2 9 10 **F**4 5 9 15 17 20 22 24 28 29 34 36 38 40 43 51 53 54 56 64 70 75 77 78 80 81 86 89 90 93 98 100 102 103 107 108 111 116 118 119 130 144 147 **P**6 **S** Ascension Health, Saint Louis, MO
Primary Contact: Travis Andersen, President and Chief Executive Officer
CFO: Rhonda Anderson, Executive Vice President Finance and Chief Financial Officer
CMO: David Shapiro, M.D., Vice President Medical Affairs and Chief Medical Officer
CIO: Mary Paul, Chief Information Officer
CHR: Cheryl Hill, Vice President Human Resources
Web address: www.columbia–stmarys.org
**Control:** Church–operated, Nongovernment, not–for profit **Service:** General Medical and Surgical

**Staffed Beds:** 116 **Admissions:** 4905 **Census:** 55 **Outpatient Visits:** 100795 **Births:** 0 **Total Expense ($000):** 113471 **Payroll Expense ($000):** 30961 **Personnel:** 495

---

**Hospital, Medicare Provider Number, Address, Telephone, Approval, Facility, and Physician Codes, Health Care System**

★ American Hospital Association (AHA) membership
☐ The Joint Commission accreditation
○ Healthcare Facilities Accreditation Program
◇ DNV Healthcare Inc. accreditation
⇑ Center for Improvement in Healthcare Quality Accreditation
△ Commission on Accreditation of Rehabilitation Facilities (CARF) accreditation

WI

## MERRILL—Lincoln County

**GOOD SAMARITAN HEALTH CENTER OF MERRILL** See Ministry Good Samaritan Health Center

⊞ **MINISTRY GOOD SAMARITAN HEALTH CENTER (521339)**, 601 South Center Avenue, Zip 54452–3404; tel. 715/536–5511 **A**1 9 10 18 **F**3 15 18 28 29 30 31 34 35 40 43 44 45 50 56 57 64 68 75 78 79 80 81 82 85 86 87 89 93 107 108 111 115 118 119 130 132 133 144 146 147 **P**2 **S** Ascension Health, Saint Louis, MO
Primary Contact: Mary T. Krueger, President
CFO: David Jirovec, Director Finance
CHR: Nancy Kwiesielewicz, Human Resources Manager
CNO: Kristine McGarigle, R.N., Vice President Patient Care
Web address: www.ministryhealth.org
**Control:** Church–operated, Nongovernment, not–for profit **Service:** General Medical and Surgical

**Staffed Beds:** 10 **Admissions:** 550 **Census:** 4 **Outpatient Visits:** 20976 **Births:** 0 **Total Expense ($000):** 21133 **Payroll Expense ($000):** 11325 **Personnel:** 105

## MILWAUKEE—Milwaukee County

★ △ **AURORA SINAI MEDICAL CENTER (520064)**, 945 North 12th Street, Zip 53233–1337, Mailing Address: P.O. Box 342, Zip 53201–0342; tel. 414/219–2000 **A**2 3 5 7 8 9 **F**1 5 6 11 12 13 15 17 20 22 24 28 29 34 36 38 40 51 54 55 56 64 70 72 75 76 77 78 80 81 82 86 87 89 90 93 102 103 107 108 111 118 119 130 131 144 147 **P**6 **S** Aurora Health Care, Milwaukee, WI
Primary Contact: Carolynn Glocka, R.N., President
CHR: Heidi Grow, Director Human Resources
CNO: Ania Horner, R.N., Vice President and Chief Nurse Executive
Web address: www.aurorahealthcare.org
**Control:** Other not–for–profit (including NFP Corporation) **Service:** General Medical and Surgical

**Staffed Beds:** 177 **Admissions:** 7811 **Census:** 98 **Outpatient Visits:** 321153 **Births:** 2124 **Total Expense ($000):** 187315 **Payroll Expense ($000):** 59379 **Personnel:** 944

⊞ △ **AURORA ST. LUKE'S MEDICAL CENTER (520138)**, 2900 West Oklahoma Avenue, Zip 53215–4330, Mailing Address: P.O. Box 2901, Zip 53201–2901; tel. 414/649–6000, (Includes AURORA ST. LUKE'S SOUTH SHORE, 5900 South Lake Drive, Cudahy, Zip 53110–8903; tel. 414/769–9000) **A**1 2 3 5 7 8 9 10 **F**1 2 4 5 6 11 12 15 17 20 22 24 28 29 34 36 38 40 43 51 54 56 64 69 70 72 75 78 80 81 82 86 87 89 90 93 98 100 101 102 103 104 105 107 108 111 116 118 119 130 136 137 138 140 144 **P**6 **S** Aurora Health Care, Milwaukee, WI
Primary Contact: Marie Golanowski, R.N., MS, President
CFO: Nan Nelson, Senior Vice President Finance
CMO: Jeffrey A. Smith, M.D., Senior Vice President and Chief Medical Officer
CIO: Philip Loftus, Ph.D., Vice President and Chief Information Officer
CHR: Thomas C. Ter Horst, Vice President Human Resources
CNO: Faye Zwieg, Vice President and Chief Nursing Officer
Web address: www.aurorahealthcare.org
**Control:** Other not–for–profit (including NFP Corporation) **Service:** General Medical and Surgical

**Staffed Beds:** 726 **Admissions:** 34671 **Census:** 553 **Outpatient Visits:** 540982 **Births:** 0 **Total Expense ($000):** 983323 **Payroll Expense ($000):** 273199 **Personnel:** 4428

⊞ **CHILDREN'S HOSPITAL OF WISCONSIN (523300)**, 9000 West Wisconsin Avenue, Zip 53226–4810, Mailing Address: P.O. Box 1997, Zip 53201–1997; tel. 414/266–2000 **A**1 3 5 9 10 **F**12 17 20 22 24 28 29 34 36 38 40 43 51 60 61 64 72 75 77 78 81 82 87 88 89 93 99 100 104 107 108 111 116 119 130 131 136 137 138 140 141 **P**2 **S** Children's Hospital and Health System, Milwaukee, WI
Primary Contact: Peggy N. Troy, President and Chief Executive Officer
COO: Cinthia S. Christensen, JD, Executive Vice President and Chief Operating Officer
CMO: Michael Gutzeit, M.D., Chief Medical Officer
CIO: Michael Jones, Vice President and Chief Information Officer
CHR: Peggy Niemer, Vice President Human Resources
Web address: www.chw.org
**Control:** Other not–for–profit (including NFP Corporation) **Service:** Children's general

**Staffed Beds:** 306 **Admissions:** 23356 **Census:** 228 **Outpatient Visits:** 348914 **Births:** 0 **Total Expense ($000):** 529783 **Payroll Expense ($000):** 156183 **Personnel:** 2307

⊞ △ **CLEMENT J. ZABLOCKI VETERANS AFFAIRS MEDICAL CENTER**, 5000 West National Avenue, Zip 53295–0001; tel. 414/384–2000, (Nonreporting) **A**1 2 3 5 7 **S** Department of Veterans Affairs, Washington, DC
Primary Contact: Robert H. Beller, FACHE, Director
COO: James McClain, Deputy Director
CFO: John Lasota, Assistant Finance Officer
CMO: Michael Erdmann, M.D., Chief of Staff
CIO: Bryan Vail, Chief Information Officer
CHR: Kay Schwieger, Chief Human Resources Officer
CNO: Mary E. Brunn, R.N., Acting Associate Director Nursing
Web address: www.milwaukee.va.gov/
**Control:** Veterans Affairs, Government, federal **Service:** General Medical and Surgical

**Staffed Beds:** 637

⊞ **COLUMBIA ST. MARY'S HOSPITAL MILWAUKEE (520051)**, 2301 North Lake Drive, Zip 53211–4508; tel. 414/291–1000, (Includes COLUMBIA ST. MARY'S COLUMBIA HOSPITAL, 2025 East Newport Avenue, Zip 53211–2990; tel. 414/961–3300; COLUMBIA ST. MARY'S MILWAUKEE HOSPITAL, 2323 North Lake Drive, Zip 53211–9682, Mailing Address: P.O. Box 503, Zip 53201–0503; tel. 414/291–1000), (Nonreporting) **A**1 2 3 5 9 10 **S** Ascension Health, Saint Louis, MO
Primary Contact: Travis Andersen, President and Chief Executive Officer
CFO: Rhonda Anderson, Executive Vice President Finance and Chief Financial Officer
CMO: David Shapiro, M.D., Vice President Medical Affairs and Chief Medical Officer
CIO: Mary Paul, Chief Information Officer
CHR: Cheryl Hill, Vice President Human Resources
Web address: www.columbia–stmarys.org
**Control:** Church–operated, Nongovernment, not–for profit **Service:** General Medical and Surgical

**Staffed Beds:** 324

⊞ △ **FROEDTERT MEMORIAL LUTHERAN HOSPITAL (520177)**, 9200 West Wisconsin Avenue, Zip 53226–3596, Mailing Address: P.O. Box 26099, Zip 53226–0099; tel. 414/805–3000 **A**1 2 3 5 7 8 9 10 **F**3 6 12 13 15 17 18 20 22 24 26 29 30 31 34 35 37 38 40 43 44 45 46 47 48 49 50 51 52 54 55 56 57 58 59 60 61 64 68 70 74 75 76 77 78 79 80 81 84 85 86 87 90 91 92 93 94 95 96 97 98 100 107 108 110 111 113 114 115 116 117 118 119 120 121 123 124 126 129 130 131 132 134 135 136 137 138 139 140 141 142 145 146 147 148
Primary Contact: Catherine Buck, President
CFO: Scott Hawig, Chief Financial Officer and Senior Vice President Finance and Treasurer
CMO: Lee Biblo, M.D., Chief Medical Officer
CIO: Robert DeGrand, Chief Information Officer
CHR: Keith Allen, Senior Vice President and Chief Human Resources Officer
CNO: Kathleen Bechtel, MSN, Vice President Patient Care Services and Chief Nursing Officer
Web address: www.froedtert.com
**Control:** Other not–for–profit (including NFP Corporation) **Service:** General Medical and Surgical

**Staffed Beds:** 516 **Admissions:** 26112 **Census:** 384 **Outpatient Visits:** 736450 **Births:** 2119 **Total Expense ($000):** 973656 **Payroll Expense ($000):** 274793 **Personnel:** 4506

★ **MILWAUKEE COUNTY BEHAVIORAL HEALTH DIVISION (524001)**, 9455 Watertown Plank Road, Zip 53226–3559; tel. 414/257–6995, (Total facility includes 29 beds in nursing home–type unit) **A**3 5 10 **F**87 98 99 100 102 103 104 105 128 130 **P**3 6
Primary Contact: Patricia S. Schroeder, MSN, R.N., Administrator
COO: Steve Delgado, Operations Coordinator
CFO: Randy Oleszak, Director Fiscal Services
CMO: John Schneider, M.D., Medical Director
CIO: Chris Lindberg, Chief Information Officer
CHR: Ara Garcia, Manager Human Resources
CNO: Nancy Ann Marigomen, R.N., Director of Nursing
Web address: www.milwaukeecounty.org
**Control:** County–Government, nonfederal **Service:** Psychiatric

**Staffed Beds:** 111 **Admissions:** 2047 **Census:** 111 **Outpatient Visits:** 11888 **Births:** 0 **Total Expense ($000):** 148460 **Payroll Expense ($000):** 34073 **Personnel:** 597

⊞ △ **SACRED HEART REHABILITATION INSTITUTE (523025)**, 2323 North Lake Drive, Zip 53211–4508; tel. 414/298–6750 **A**1 7 9 10 **F**9 29 34 54 64 75 77 86 90 93 100 102 103 130 131 **P**6 **S** Ascension Health, Saint Louis, MO
Primary Contact: Allan M. Spooner, President
CFO: Rhonda Anderson, Executive Vice President Finance and Chief Financial Officer
CMO: David Shapiro, M.D., Vice President Medical Affairs and Chief Medical Officer
CIO: Mary Paul, Vice President and Chief Information Officer
CHR: Cheryl Hill, Vice President Human Resources
Web address: www.columbia–stmarys.org/SHRI
**Control:** Church–operated, Nongovernment, not–for profit **Service:** Rehabilitation

**Staffed Beds:** 31 **Admissions:** 315 **Census:** 15 **Outpatient Visits:** 8871 **Births:** 0 **Total Expense ($000):** 12642 **Payroll Expense ($000):** 5263 **Personnel:** 79

*Many Facility Codes have changed. Please refer to the AHA Guide Code Chart.* © 2015 AHA Guide

⊠ **SELECT SPECIALTY HOSPITAL–MILWAUKEE (522006)**, 8901 West Lincoln Avenue, 2nd Floor, Zip 53227–2409; tel. 414/328–7700 **A**1 9 10 **F**1 29 60 78 100 130 **S** Select Medical Corporation, Mechanicsburg, PA
Primary Contact: Richard Keddington, Chief Executive Officer
CMO: Matt Mathai, M.D., Medical Director
CHR: Chris Froh, Senior Coordinator Human Resources
CNO: Jane Cerra, Market Nurse Executive and Chief Nursing Officer
Web address: www.selectspecialtyhospitals.com/company/locations/milwaukee.aspx
**Control:** Corporation, Investor–owned, for–profit **Service:** Long–Term Acute Care hospital

**Staffed Beds:** 34 **Admissions:** 384 **Census:** 31 **Outpatient Visits:** 0 **Births:** 0 **Total Expense ($000):** 17304 **Payroll Expense ($000):** 6147 **Personnel:** 109

⊠ **WHEATON FRANCISCAN HEALTHCARE – ST. FRANCIS (520078)**, 3237 South 16th Street, Zip 53215–4592; tel. 414/647–5000 **A**1 2 9 10 **F**3 9 13 15 18 20 22 24 26 28 29 30 31 34 35 38 40 45 46 47 48 49 50 54 56 57 64 65 68 72 74 75 76 77 78 79 80 81 82 84 85 86 87 91 92 93 94 96 98 100 101 102 103 104 107 108 110 111 115 118 119 120 121 122 123 129 130 131 132 144 145 146 147 148 **S** Wheaton Franciscan Healthcare, Wheaton, IL
Primary Contact: Coreen Dicus–Johnson, President
CFO: Aaron Bridgeland, Director Finance
CMO: Michelle Graham, M.D., Vice President Medical Affairs
CIO: Gregory Smith, Senior Vice President and Chief Information Officer
CHR: Robert Bauer, Vice President Human Resources
CNO: Marilyn Spenner, R.N., Vice President Patient Care Services
Web address: www.mywheaton.org/stfrancis
**Control:** Church–operated, Nongovernment, not–for profit **Service:** General Medical and Surgical

**Staffed Beds:** 177 **Admissions:** 8012 **Census:** 108 **Outpatient Visits:** 174578 **Births:** 1164 **Total Expense ($000):** 168482 **Payroll Expense ($000):** 64396 **Personnel:** 941

⊠ **WHEATON FRANCISCAN HEALTHCARE – ST. JOSEPH'S (520136)**, 5000 West Chambers Street, Zip 53210–1650; tel. 414/447–2000 **A**1 2 9 10 **F**3 6 8 11 13 15 17 18 20 22 24 26 28 29 30 31 33 34 35 37 40 41 43 45 46 48 49 50 53 54 56 57 58 59 64 65 68 70 72 74 75 76 77 78 79 80 81 82 83 84 85 87 89 90 91 92 93 94 95 96 97 107 108 109 110 111 112 113 114 115 116 117 118 119 129 130 131 135 143 144 145 146 147 148 **P**6 **S** Wheaton Franciscan Healthcare, Wheaton, IL
Primary Contact: Debra K. Standridge, President
CFO: Michael Petitt, Director of Finance
CMO: Rita Hanson, M.D., Vice President Medical Affairs
CIO: Andrew Donovan, Regional Director Information Services
CHR: Christopher Morris, Vice President Human Resources
CNO: Sharon Baughman, R.N., Senior Vice President Patient Services and Chief Nursing Officer
Web address: www.mywheaton.org/stjoseph
**Control:** Church–operated, Nongovernment, not–for profit **Service:** General Medical and Surgical

**Staffed Beds:** 189 **Admissions:** 9623 **Census:** 118 **Outpatient Visits:** 422368 **Births:** 2527 **Total Expense ($000):** 249419 **Payroll Expense ($000):** 93346 **Personnel:** 1419

☐ **MONROE CLINIC (520028)**, 515 22nd Avenue, Zip 53566–1598; tel. 608/324–1000 **A**1 3 9 10 13 **F**3 5 6 8 9 11 13 15 17 18 20 22 26 28 29 30 31 32 34 35 37 38 40 43 44 45 46 49 50 55 56 57 59 63 65 68 70 74 75 76 77 79 80 81 82 84 85 86 87 90 93 96 97 99 100 101 102 103 104 107 108 110 111 112 115 117 119 126 129 130 131 132 135 144 145 146 147 148 **P**6
Primary Contact: Michael B. Sanders, President and Chief Executive Officer
COO: Julie Wilke, Vice President
CFO: Jim Nemeth, Chief Financial Officer
CMO: Mark Thompson, M.D., Chief Medical Officer
CIO: Carrie Blum, Chief Information Officer
CHR: Jane Monahan, Vice President Ministry and Human Resources
CNO: Paula Elmer, R.N., Vice President and Chief Nursing Officer
Web address: www.monroeclinic.org
**Control:** Other not–for–profit (including NFP Corporation) **Service:** General Medical and Surgical

**Staffed Beds:** 54 **Admissions:** 2676 **Census:** 24 **Outpatient Visits:** 268956 **Births:** 481 **Total Expense ($000):** 159076 **Payroll Expense ($000):** 79955 **Personnel:** 1008

☐ **CHILDREN'S HOSPITAL OF WISCONSIN–FOX VALLEY (523302)**, 130 Second Avenue, 3rd Floor South, Zip 54956–2883; tel. 920/969–7900 **A**1 9 10 **F**29 34 38 72 75 86 89 93 100 130 **P**2 6 **S** Children's Hospital and Health System, Milwaukee, WI
Primary Contact: Peggy N. Troy, President and Chief Executive Officer
COO: Tim Klunk, Executive Director
CMO: Paul Myers, M.D., Neonatologist and Chief Medical Officer
Web address: www.chw.org
**Control:** Other not–for–profit (including NFP Corporation) **Service:** Children's general

**Staffed Beds:** 42 **Admissions:** 1851 **Census:** 20 **Outpatient Visits:** 10146 **Births:** 0 **Total Expense ($000):** 23170 **Payroll Expense ($000):** 8655 **Personnel:** 114

☐ **THEDA CLARK MEDICAL CENTER (520045)**, 130 Second Street, Zip 54956–2883, Mailing Address: P.O. Box 2021, Zip 54957–2021; tel. 920/729–3100 **A**1 2 3 9 10 **F**3 4 5 7 8 9 11 12 13 15 17 18 19 20 21 22 23 25 28 29 30 31 32 34 35 36 40 43 44 45 46 47 48 49 50 51 53 55 56 59 60 64 68 69 70 74 75 76 78 79 80 82 84 85 86 87 88 90 93 98 99 101 102 103 104 105 106 107 108 110 111 112 113 114 115 118 119 126 130 132 134 135 144 146 147 148 **S** ThedaCare, Inc., Appleton, WI
Primary Contact: Brian Burmeister, Senior Vice President, ThedaCare Hospitals
COO: MaryJeanne Schaffmeyer, Chief Operating Officer
CFO: Tim Olson, Senior Vice President Finance
CMO: Gregory L. Long, M.D., Chief Medical Officer
CIO: Keith Livingston, Senior Vice President and Chief Information Officer
CHR: Maureen Pistone, Senior Vice President Human Resources
Web address: www.thedacare.org
**Control:** Other not–for–profit (including NFP Corporation) **Service:** General Medical and Surgical

**Staffed Beds:** 151 **Admissions:** 7558 **Census:** 83 **Outpatient Visits:** 90990 **Births:** 1275 **Total Expense ($000):** 161629 **Payroll Expense ($000):** 64674 **Personnel:** 817

★ **MEMORIAL MEDICAL CENTER – NEILLSVILLE (521323)**, 216 Sunset Place, Zip 54456–1799; tel. 715/743–3101, (Includes NEILLSVILLE MEMORIAL HOME ) **A**9 10 18 **F**3 6 13 15 28 29 34 40 41 43 50 54 55 56 59 64 66 75 76 77 79 80 81 82 85 86 89 93 96 97 107 108 110 111 119 125 127 130 131 132 133 144 146 147 **P**6
Primary Contact: Ryan T. Neville, FACHE, President and Chief Executive Officer
CFO: Roger Sneath, Chief Financial Officer
CMO: Timothy Meyer, M.D., Chief of Staff
CIO: Derrick Longdo, Director Information Systems
CHR: Tamie Zarak, Director Human Resources
Web address: www.memorialmedcenter.org
**Control:** Other not–for–profit (including NFP Corporation) **Service:** General Medical and Surgical

**Staffed Beds:** 23 **Admissions:** 280 **Census:** 16 **Outpatient Visits:** 24980 **Births:** 2 **Total Expense ($000):** 22232 **Payroll Expense ($000):** 12018 **Personnel:** 198

☐ **NEW LONDON FAMILY MEDICAL CENTER (521326)**, 1405 Mill Street, Zip 54961–2155, Mailing Address: P.O. Box 307, Zip 54961–0307; tel. 920/531–2000 **A**1 9 10 18 **F**7 11 13 15 28 29 34 40 43 56 64 75 76 80 81 82 86 87 89 90 93 107 108 111 119 131 141 **S** ThedaCare, Inc., Appleton, WI
Primary Contact: William Schmidt, President and Chief Executive Officer
CFO: Kerry Lee Blanke, Vice President Finance
CMO: Paul Hoell, M.D., President Medical Staff
Web address: www.thedacare.org
**Control:** Other not–for–profit (including NFP Corporation) **Service:** General Medical and Surgical

**Staffed Beds:** 25 **Admissions:** 808 **Census:** 12 **Outpatient Visits:** 31976 **Births:** 105 **Total Expense ($000):** 27814 **Payroll Expense ($000):** 13130 **Personnel:** 148

**WI**

---

**Hospital, Medicare Provider Number, Address, Telephone, Approval, Facility, and Physician Codes, Health Care System**

★ American Hospital Association (AHA) membership
☐ The Joint Commission accreditation
◯ Healthcare Facilities Accreditation Program
◇ DNV Healthcare Inc. accreditation
⇑ Center for Improvement in Healthcare Quality Accreditation
△ Commission on Accreditation of Rehabilitation Facilities (CARF) accreditation

## NEW RICHMOND—St. Croix County

★ **WESTFIELDS HOSPITAL (521345)**, 535 Hospital Road, Zip 54017–1449; tel. 715/243–2600 **A**9 10 18 **F**1 3 8 13 15 28 29 30 38 40 42 43 50 56 57 59 64 65 70 75 76 77 78 80 81 82 85 86 87 89 90 93 94 97 104 107 109 110 111 114 115 119 129 130 131 132 133 143 146 148 **S** HealthPartners, Bloomington, MN
Primary Contact: Steven Massey, President and Chief Executive Officer
CFO: Jason J. Luhrs, Vice President Fiscal Services
CMO: David O. DeGear, M.D., Vice President Medical Affairs
CIO: Patrice P. Wolff, Director Information Services
CHR: Chad P. Engstrom, Director Human Resources
Web address: www.westfieldshospital.com
**Control:** Other not–for–profit (including NFP Corporation) **Service:** General Medical and Surgical

**Staffed Beds:** 25 **Admissions:** 921 **Census:** 8 **Outpatient Visits:** 78763 **Births:** 136 **Total Expense ($000):** 46866 **Payroll Expense ($000):** 16261 **Personnel:** 274

## OCONOMOWOC—Waukesha County

⊠ **OCONOMOWOC MEMORIAL HOSPITAL (520062)**, 791 Summit Avenue, Zip 53066–3896; tel. 262/569–9400 **A**1 2 9 10 **F**3 11 13 15 18 20 22 28 29 30 31 35 37 40 45 46 47 48 49 64 74 75 76 78 79 80 81 82 84 85 87 89 92 93 107 108 110 111 114 115 118 119 120 121 126 130 132 135 146 147 148 **S** ProHealth Care, Inc., Waukesha, WI
Primary Contact: John R. Robertstad, FACHE, President
COO: Mary Jo O'Malley, R.N., Vice President Diagnostics and Support Services
CMO: Brian Lipman, M.D., Medical Director and Medical Staff Services
CIO: Christine Bessler, Vice President Information Services
CHR: Edward Malindzak, Chief Human Resources Officer
CNO: Catherine Rapp, R.N., Vice President Nursing
Web address: www.prohealthcare.org/locations/locations–v2–detail/?id=1123
**Control:** Other not–for–profit (including NFP Corporation) **Service:** General Medical and Surgical

**Staffed Beds:** 58 **Admissions:** 3060 **Census:** 25 **Outpatient Visits:** 70071 **Births:** 401 **Total Expense ($000):** 91475 **Payroll Expense ($000):** 22007 **Personnel:** 327

⊠ **ROGERS MEMORIAL HOSPITAL (524018)**, 34700 Valley Road, Zip 53066–4599; tel. 262/646–4411, (Includes ROGERS MEMORIAL HOSPITAL–BROWN DEER, 4600 West Schroeder Drive, Brown Deer, Zip 53223; tel. 414/865–2500; Jim Kubicek, Vice President, Operations; ROGERS MEMORIAL HOSPITAL–WEST ALLIS, 11101 West Lincoln Avenue, West Allis, Zip 53227; tel. 414/327–3000; T. Orvin Fillman, Dr.PH, Vice President, Operations) **A**1 3 9 10 **F**5 29 34 38 75 86 87 98 99 100 101 102 103 104 105 130
Primary Contact: Paul A. Mueller, Chief Executive Officer
COO: Paul A. Mueller, Chief Operating Officer
CFO: Gerald A. Noll, Chief Financial Officer
CMO: Peter M. Lake, M.D., Chief Medical Officer
CIO: Wayne Mattson, Management Information Systems Specialist
CHR: Renee A. Patterson, Vice President Employment and Training Services
CNO: Teresa L. Schultz, R.N., Vice President of Patient Care
Web address: www.rogershospital.org
**Control:** Other not–for–profit (including NFP Corporation) **Service:** Psychiatric

**Staffed Beds:** 71 **Admissions:** 2393 **Census:** 48 **Outpatient Visits:** 48099 **Births:** 0 **Total Expense ($000):** 54791 **Payroll Expense ($000):** 30464 **Personnel:** 570

## OCONTO—Oconto County

◇ **BELLIN HEALTH OCONTO HOSPITAL (521356)**, 820 Arbutus Avenue, Zip 54153–2004, Mailing Address: P.O. Box 357, Zip 54153–0357; tel. 920/835–1100 **A**9 10 18 21 **F**3 8 15 18 29 31 32 34 35 40 43 44 45 46 47 51 59 62 64 65 68 71 78 79 80 81 85 92 97 99 100 101 104 107 111 115 119 127 129 135 144 147 **P**8
Primary Contact: Laura Cormier, Director
Web address: www.bellin.org/facilities_amenities/oconto_hospital_medical_center/
**Control:** Other not–for–profit (including NFP Corporation) **Service:** General Medical and Surgical

**Staffed Beds:** 10 **Admissions:** 169 **Census:** 1 **Outpatient Visits:** 12819 **Births:** 0 **Total Expense ($000):** 11036 **Payroll Expense ($000):** 4212 **Personnel:** 65

## OCONTO FALLS—Oconto County

★ **HSHS ST. CLARE MEMORIAL HOSPITAL (521310)**, 855 South Main Street, Zip 54154–1296; tel. 920/846–3444 **A**9 10 18 **F**3 11 15 28 29 30 34 40 41 43 50 56 57 59 64 65 75 77 79 80 81 85 86 87 89 90 93 96 97 107 108 110 111 114 119 127 132 133 144 145 146 147 148 **P**4 5 6
Primary Contact: Daniel DeGroot, Chief Executive Officer
CFO: Michele Miller–Campbell, Chief Financial Officer
CMO: Isaias Cupino, Chief of Staff
CIO: Jared Alfson, Chief Information Officer
CHR: Laura Majewski, Director Human Resources
CNO: Kay Baranczyk, R.N., Chief Nursing Officer
Web address: www.cmhospital.org
**Control:** Other not–for–profit (including NFP Corporation) **Service:** General Medical and Surgical

**Staffed Beds:** 9 **Admissions:** 675 **Census:** 8 **Outpatient Visits:** 27028 **Births:** 0 **Total Expense ($000):** 33778 **Payroll Expense ($000):** 14739 **Personnel:** 227

## OSCEOLA—Polk County

**OSCEOLA MEDICAL CENTER (521318)**, 2600 65th Avenue, Zip 54020–4370, Mailing Address: P.O. Box 218, Zip 54020–0218; tel. 715/294–2111 **A**9 10 18 **F**11 13 15 28 29 34 40 43 53 56 64 70 75 76 77 78 81 86 87 89 93 107 111 119 144 **P**6
Primary Contact: Tom G. Geskermann, Chief Executive Officer
CMO: Rene Milner, Chief Medical Officer
CIO: Shawn Kammerud, Manager Information Services
CHR: Margie Evenson, Manager Human Resources
Web address: www.osceolamedicalcenter.com
**Control:** Other not–for–profit (including NFP Corporation) **Service:** General Medical and Surgical

**Staffed Beds:** 18 **Admissions:** 497 **Census:** 4 **Outpatient Visits:** 16035 **Births:** 82 **Total Expense ($000):** 29318 **Payroll Expense ($000):** 10444 **Personnel:** 206

## OSHKOSH—Winnebago County

⊠ **AURORA MEDICAL CENTER OF OSHKOSH (520198)**, 855 North Westhaven Drive, Zip 54904–7668; tel. 920/456–6000, (Nonreporting) **A**1 2 9 10 **S** Aurora Health Care, Milwaukee, WI
Primary Contact: Jeffrey Bard, President
CFO: Sandra Ewald, Vice President Finance
CMO: Bruce L. Van Cleave, M.D., Senior Vice President and Chief Medical Officer
CIO: Philip Loftus, Ph.D., Vice President and Chief Information Officer
CHR: Linda Mingus, Director Human Resources
CNO: Mary Beth Kingston, R.N., Executive Vice President and Chief Nursing Officer
Web address: www.aurorahealthcare.com
**Control:** Other not–for–profit (including NFP Corporation) **Service:** General Medical and Surgical

**Staffed Beds:** 61

⊠ △ **MERCY MEDICAL CENTER (520048)**, 500 South Oakwood Road, Zip 54904–7944; tel. 920/223–2000 **A**1 2 7 9 10 **F**4 5 11 13 15 16 17 20 22 28 29 34 38 40 43 51 53 56 64 70 75 76 78 80 81 82 86 87 88 89 90 93 98 103 104 107 108 111 119 130 131 144 147 **S** Ascension Health, Saint Louis, MO
Primary Contact: Jeremy Normington–Slay, FACHE, Chief Executive Officer
CFO: Jeff Badger, Chief Financial Officer
CMO: Mark W. Kehrberg, M.D., Senior Vice President and Chief Medical Officer
CIO: Will Weider, Chief Information Officer
CHR: Vince Gallucci, Senior Vice President Human Resources
Web address: www.affinityhealth.org
**Control:** Church–operated, Nongovernment, not–for profit **Service:** General Medical and Surgical

**Staffed Beds:** 120 **Admissions:** 4928 **Census:** 52 **Outpatient Visits:** 84497 **Births:** 603 **Total Expense ($000):** 98658 **Payroll Expense ($000):** 38946 **Personnel:** 508

## OSSEO—Trempealeau County

☐ **MAYO CLINIC HEALTH SYSTEM – OAKRIDGE IN OSSEO (521302)**, 13025 Eighth Street, Zip 54758–7634, Mailing Address: P.O. Box 70, Zip 54758–0070; tel. 715/597–3121, (Total facility includes 35 beds in nursing home–type unit) **A**1 9 10 18 **F**3 7 10 15 18 28 29 30 32 34 35 40 43 44 45 50 54 56 57 59 63 64 65 75 77 80 84 85 86 87 90 93 97 107 110 115 125 128 130 132 133 135 143 144 146 148 **P**6 **S** Mayo Clinic, Rochester, MN
Primary Contact: Dean Eide, Vice President
Web address: www.mayoclinichealthsystem.org/locations/osseo
**Control:** Other not–for–profit (including NFP Corporation) **Service:** General Medical and Surgical

**Staffed Beds:** 39 **Admissions:** 347 **Census:** 39 **Outpatient Visits:** 26069 **Births:** 0 **Total Expense ($000):** 19838 **Payroll Expense ($000):** 10571 **Personnel:** 164

**WI**

*Many Facility Codes have changed. Please refer to the AHA Guide Code Chart.* © 2015 AHA Guide

## PARK FALLS—Price County

★ **FLAMBEAU HOSPITAL (521325)**, 98 Sherry Avenue, Zip 54552–1467, Mailing Address: P.O. Box 310, Zip 54552–0310; tel. 715/762–2484 **A**9 10 18 **F**3 11 15 17 28 29 30 31 34 35 40 44 45 50 53 56 57 59 62 63 64 65 68 69 70 75 77 79 80 81 82 84 85 86 87 89 90 93 96 97 107 108 110 119 130 131 132 133 143 146 148 **S** Ascension Health, Saint Louis, MO
Primary Contact: David A. Grundstrom, Chief Administrative Officer
CFO: James R. Braun, Chief Financial Officer
CMO: Yusuf Kasirye, M.D., Chief of Staff
CHR: Elizabeth Harrop, Director, Human Resources
CNO: Elizabeth Schreiber, R.N., Director Patient Care Services
Web address: www.flambeauhospital.org
**Control:** Other not–for–profit (including NFP Corporation) **Service:** General Medical and Surgical

**Staffed Beds:** 25 **Admissions:** 588 **Census:** 5 **Outpatient Visits:** 27707 **Births:** 0 **Total Expense ($000):** 18823 **Payroll Expense ($000):** 8233 **Personnel:** 171

## PEWAUKEE—Waukesha County

⊠ **LIFECARE HOSPITALS OF WISCONSIN (522007)**, 2400 Golf Road, Zip 53072–5590; tel. 262/524–2600 **A**1 9 10 **F**1 3 29 77 86 90 96 107 130 148 **P**5 **S** LifeCare Management Services, Plano, TX
Primary Contact: Gayla Campbell, Interim Chief Executive Officer
CMO: John Daniels, M.D., Medical Director
CHR: Stephanie Matter, Manager Human Resources
CNO: Angela Osowski, Chief Nursing Officer
Web address: www.lifecare–hospitals.com
**Control:** Corporation, Investor–owned, for–profit **Service:** Long–Term Acute Care hospital

**Staffed Beds:** 30 **Admissions:** 375 **Census:** 29 **Outpatient Visits:** 0 **Births:** 0 **Total Expense ($000):** 19187 **Payroll Expense ($000):** 8271 **Personnel:** 104

## PLATTEVILLE—Grant County

⊠ **SOUTHWEST HEALTH CENTER (521354)**, 1400 Eastside Road, Zip 53818–9800; tel. 608/348–2331, (Includes SOUTHWEST HEALTH CENTER NURSING HOME, 808 South Washington Street, Cuba City, Zip 53807; tel. 608/744–2161), (Total facility includes 84 beds in nursing home–type unit) **A**1 9 10 18 **F**2 3 6 8 13 15 28 29 34 40 43 45 46 47 48 49 50 56 57 58 59 64 74 75 76 77 79 81 82 83 84 85 86 87 93 96 97 98 100 101 102 103 104 105 106 107 110 111 112 115 119 128 129 130 132 133 143 144 146 148
Primary Contact: Dan D. Rohrbach, President and Chief Executive Officer
CFO: Matthew Streeter, Chief Financial Officer
CMO: Andrew Klann, D.O., Chief of Staff
CIO: Todd Lull, Director Information Technology
CHR: Holly Beehn, Director Human Resources
CNO: Suzi Okey, Director of Nursing
Web address: www.southwesthealth.org
**Control:** Other not–for–profit (including NFP Corporation) **Service:** General Medical and Surgical

**Staffed Beds:** 119 **Admissions:** 857 **Census:** 85 **Outpatient Visits:** 39247 **Births:** 138 **Total Expense ($000):** 27990 **Payroll Expense ($000):** 10809 **Personnel:** 205

## PLEASANT PRAIRIE—Kenosha County

★ **UNITED HOSPITAL SYSTEM, ST. CATHERINE'S MEDICAL CENTER CAMPUS**, 9555 76th Street, Zip 53158–1984; tel. 262/656–2011, (Nonreporting) **A**2 9 **S** Wheaton Franciscan Healthcare, Wheaton, IL
Primary Contact: Richard O. Schmidt, Jr., President and Chief Executive Officer
Web address: www.uhsi.org
**Control:** Other not–for–profit (including NFP Corporation) **Service:** General Medical and Surgical

**Staffed Beds:** 202

## PORTAGE—Columbia County

☐ **DIVINE SAVIOR HEALTHCARE (520041)**, 2817 New Pinery Road, Zip 53901–9240, Mailing Address: P.O. Box 387, Zip 53901–0387; tel. 608/742–4131, (Total facility includes 123 beds in nursing–type unit) **A**1 9 10 **F**3 4 7 11 12 13 15 28 30 31 34 35 36 40 43 44 45 48 50 54 55 57 59 60 62 64 68 69 70 74 75 76 77 78 79 80 81 82 85 86 87 89 90 91 92 93 94 96 97 107 108 110 111 115 117 118 119 128 129 130 131 132 133 143 144 145 146 147 148 **P**6
Primary Contact: Michael Decker, President and Chief Executive Officer
CFO: Marlin Pete Nelson, Vice President Fiscal Services
CMO: Elizabeth Strabel, M.D., Chief Medical Staff
CHR: Carol J. Bank, Vice President Human Resources
Web address: www.dshealthcare.com
**Control:** Church–operated, Nongovernment, not–for profit **Service:** General Medical and Surgical

**Staffed Beds:** 133 **Admissions:** 1735 **Census:** 108 **Outpatient Visits:** 152167 **Births:** 236 **Total Expense ($000):** 67120 **Payroll Expense ($000):** 36763 **Personnel:** 573

## PRAIRIE DU CHIEN—Crawford County

⊠ **PRAIRIE DU CHIEN MEMORIAL HOSPITAL (521330)**, 705 East Taylor Street, Zip 53821–2196; tel. 608/357–2000 **A**1 9 10 18 **F**1 10 11 13 15 17 28 29 34 36 40 53 56 62 63 64 69 70 75 76 77 80 81 82 86 87 93 107 108 119 130 131 144 147
Primary Contact: William P. Sexton, Chief Executive Officer
CFO: Dave Breitbach, Chief Financial Officer
CMO: Steven Bush, Chief Medical Officer
CIO: John Daane, Information Systems Officer
CHR: Gabriel Oosthuysen, Director Human Resources
Web address: www.pdcmemorialhospital.org
**Control:** Other not–for–profit (including NFP Corporation) **Service:** General Medical and Surgical

**Staffed Beds:** 23 **Admissions:** 941 **Census:** 10 **Outpatient Visits:** 10143 **Births:** 102 **Total Expense ($000):** 36108 **Payroll Expense ($000):** 17306 **Personnel:** 275

## PRAIRIE DU SAC—Sauk County

★ ○ **SAUK PRAIRIE HEALTHCARE (520095)**, 260 26th Street, Zip 53578–1599; tel. 608/643–3311 **A**3 9 10 11 **F**3 11 13 15 29 34 35 36 40 43 45 47 48 53 54 56 57 64 68 69 70 75 76 78 79 80 81 82 85 86 90 92 93 96 107 108 110 111 115 118 119 127 129 130 131 132 133 144 146 148 **P**7
Primary Contact: Larry Schroeder, Chief Executive Officer
CFO: Carol May, Chief Financial Officer, Vice President Finance and Operations and Chief Financial Officer
CMO: John McAuliffe, M.D., Medical Director
CIO: Marybeth Bay, Director Information Technology
CHR: Robbi E. Bos, Vice President Human Resources
CNO: Denise Marie Cole–Ouzounian, Vice President Patient Services
Web address: www.saukprairiehealthcare.org/
**Control:** Other not–for–profit (including NFP Corporation) **Service:** General Medical and Surgical

**Staffed Beds:** 36 **Admissions:** 1717 **Census:** 11 **Outpatient Visits:** 103806 **Births:** 316 **Total Expense ($000):** 75586 **Payroll Expense ($000):** 34482 **Personnel:** 429

## RACINE—Racine County

⊠ △ **WHEATON FRANCISCAN HEALTHCARE – ALL SAINTS (520096)**, 3801 Spring Street, Zip 53405–1690; tel. 262/687–4011, (Total facility includes 50 beds in nursing home–type unit) **A**1 2 7 9 10 **F**3 4 5 6 13 15 17 18 20 22 24 26 28 29 30 31 33 34 35 38 40 44 45 46 48 49 50 51 53 55 56 57 58 59 64 65 68 70 72 74 75 76 77 78 79 80 81 82 85 86 87 89 90 91 92 93 96 97 98 99 100 101 102 103 104 105 107 108 110 111 112 115 116 118 119 120 121 123 124 126 128 129 130 131 132 134 135 146 147 148 **P**6 **S** Wheaton Franciscan Healthcare, Wheaton, IL
Primary Contact: Susan Boland, R.N., MSN, President and Chief Executive Officer
CFO: Jeanne Gramza, Director Finance
CMO: Jerry Hardacre, M.D., Chief of Staff
CIO: Joanne Bisterfeldt, Chief Information Officer
CHR: Mary Jo Wodicka, Vice President Human Resources
CNO: Mary Elizabeth Ouimet, MSN, Senior Vice President and Chief Nursing Officer
Web address: www.allsaintshealth.com
**Control:** Church–operated, Nongovernment, not–for profit **Service:** General Medical and Surgical

**Staffed Beds:** 405 **Admissions:** 14741 **Census:** 240 **Outpatient Visits:** 428783 **Births:** 1596 **Total Expense ($000):** 310512 **Payroll Expense ($000):** 111336 **Personnel:** 2384

**WI**

---

**Hospital, Medicare Provider Number, Address, Telephone, Approval, Facility, and Physician Codes, Health Care System**

★ American Hospital Association (AHA) membership
☐ The Joint Commission accreditation
○ Healthcare Facilities Accreditation Program
◇ DNV Healthcare Inc. accreditation
⇑ Center for Improvement in Healthcare Quality Accreditation
△ Commission on Accreditation of Rehabilitation Facilities (CARF) accreditation

**REEDSBURG—Sauk County**

✠ **REEDSBURG AREA MEDICAL CENTER (521351)**, 2000 North Dewey Street, Zip 53959–1097; tel. 608/524–6487 **A**1 9 10 18 **F**11 13 15 17 28 29 34 40 43 53 54 64 70 75 76 77 78 80 81 82 86 87 88 89 93 107 111 130 131 144 147
Primary Contact: Robert Van Meeteren, President and Chief Executive Officer
COO: Dale Turner, Chief Operating Officer
CFO: Barry Borchert, Vice President Finance
CNO: Dena Jarog, R.N., Vice President Patient Care
Web address: www.ramchealth.com
**Control:** Other not–for–profit (including NFP Corporation) **Service:** General Medical and Surgical

**Staffed Beds: 25 Admissions:** 1301 **Census:** 13 **Outpatient Visits:** 58925
**Births:** 281 **Total Expense ($000):** 54186 **Payroll Expense ($000):** 21448
**Personnel:** 424

**RHINELANDER—Oneida County**

✠ **MINISTRY SAINT MARY'S HOSPITALS (520019)**, 2251 North Shore Drive, Zip 54501–6710; tel. 715/361–2000, (Includes ST. MARY'S HOSPITAL, 1044 Kabel Avenue, Zip 54501; tel. 715/369–6600) **A**1 9 10 20 **F**3 4 5 13 15 18 28 29 30 31 34 35 40 44 45 49 50 54 57 59 64 65 68 69 74 75 76 77 78 79 80 81 82 84 85 86 87 89 91 92 93 94 96 98 99 100 101 103 104 107 108 110 111 115 116 117 119 120 121 123 130 131 132 144 146 148 **S** Ascension Health, Saint Louis, MO
Primary Contact: Sandra L. Anderson, President and Chief Executive Officer
COO: Laurie Oungst, Vice President and Chief Operating Officer
CFO: Cathy Bukowski, Regional Chief Financial Officer
CMO: Dean Pollnow, M.D., President Medical Staff
CIO: Howard Dobizl, Director Information Services for the Northern Region
CHR: Michelle Cornelius, Director Human Resources for the Northern Region
CNO: Ann Zenk, Vice President Patient Care Services
Web address: www.ministryhealth.org
**Control:** Church–operated, Nongovernment, not–for profit **Service:** General Medical and Surgical

**Staffed Beds: 64 Admissions:** 3064 **Census:** 29 **Outpatient Visits:** 123810
**Births:** 322 **Total Expense ($000):** 119598 **Payroll Expense ($000):** 65486
**Personnel:** 565

**RICE LAKE—Barron County**

✠ **LAKEVIEW MEDICAL CENTER (520011)**, 1700 West Stout Street, Zip 54868–5000; tel. 715/234–1515 **A**1 9 10 20 **F**7 11 13 15 28 29 34 36 40 43 51 53 54 56 60 62 63 64 69 70 75 76 77 78 80 81 82 86 87 89 93 107 111 119 130 147
Primary Contact: Edward H. Wolf, President and Chief Executive Officer
COO: Cindy Arts–Strenke, R.N., Chief Operating Officer and Chief Nursing Officer
CFO: Jacqueline Klein, Chief Financial Officer
CMO: John L. Olson, M.D., Medical Director
CIO: Brad Gerrits, Director Information Systems
CHR: Kathy Mitchell, Director Human Resources
Web address: www.lakeviewmedical.com
**Control:** Other not–for–profit (including NFP Corporation) **Service:** General Medical and Surgical

**Staffed Beds: 40 Admissions:** 2174 **Census:** 16 **Outpatient Visits:** 145281
**Births:** 480 **Total Expense ($000):** 56403 **Payroll Expense ($000):** 20986
**Personnel:** 384

**RICHLAND CENTER—Richland County**

✠ **RICHLAND HOSPITAL (521341)**, 333 East Second Street, Zip 53581–1914; tel. 608/647–6321 **A**1 9 10 18 **F**2 8 12 13 15 18 28 30 31 34 35 40 43 45 46 50 56 57 58 59 64 65 66 70 74 76 77 78 79 80 81 86 89 93 97 107 110 112 115 119 127 129 130 131 132 133 143 144 146 148
Primary Contact: Bruce E. Roesler, FACHE, Chief Executive Officer
CFO: Karen Traynor, Chief Financial Officer
CMO: Kay M. Balink, M.D., Chief of Staff
CIO: Jerry Cooper, Manager Data Processing
CHR: Rhonda Sutton, Director Human Resources
Web address: www.richlandhospital.com
**Control:** Other not–for–profit (including NFP Corporation) **Service:** General Medical and Surgical

**Staffed Beds: 25 Admissions:** 1149 **Census:** 11 **Outpatient Visits:** 37508
**Births:** 192 **Total Expense ($000):** 35844 **Payroll Expense ($000):** 14705
**Personnel:** 243

**RIPON—Fond Du Lac County**

☐ **RIPON MEDICAL CENTER (521321)**, 845 Parkside Street, Zip 54971–8505, Mailing Address: P.O. Box 390, Zip 54971–0390; tel. 920/748–3101 **A**1 9 10 18 **F**3 8 11 13 15 17 26 28 29 30 32 34 35 36 37 40 43 45 46 49 51 53 57 59 68 69 70 74 75 76 77 79 80 81 82 85 86 87 88 89 93 96 97 107 108 110 114 118 119 130 131 132 133 135 144 146 147 148 **P**6
Primary Contact: Katherine Vergos, Chief Operating Officer
COO: Katherine Vergos, Chief Operating Officer
CFO: Bonnie Schmitz, Chief Financial Officer
CIO: Nancy Birschbach, Vice President and Chief Information Officer
CHR: Sue Edminster, Vice President Human Resources
Web address: www.agnesian.com
**Control:** Church–operated, Nongovernment, not–for profit **Service:** General Medical and Surgical

**Staffed Beds: 25 Admissions:** 526 **Census:** 5 **Outpatient Visits:** 25703
**Births:** 11 **Total Expense ($000):** 20549 **Payroll Expense ($000):** 9244
**Personnel:** 116

**RIVER FALLS—St. Croix County**

✠ **RIVER FALLS AREA HOSPITAL (521349)**, 1629 East Division Street, Zip 54022–1571; tel. 715/425–6155 **A**1 2 9 10 18 **F**3 13 15 28 29 31 34 35 40 41 43 44 45 50 53 64 68 76 77 78 79 80 81 82 84 86 87 89 90 91 93 94 107 114 117 119 126 129 130 131 133 146 147 148 **S** Allina Health, Minneapolis, MN
Primary Contact: David R. Miller, President
COO: William Frommelt, Director Operations and Finance
CFO: William Frommelt, Director Operations and Finance
CHR: Kristen Novak, Manager Human Resources
Web address: www.allina.com
**Control:** Other not–for–profit (including NFP Corporation) **Service:** General Medical and Surgical

**Staffed Beds: 12 Admissions:** 897 **Census:** 8 **Outpatient Visits:** 22143
**Births:** 174 **Total Expense ($000):** 33891 **Payroll Expense ($000):** 12887
**Personnel:** 168

**SHAWANO—Shawano County**

✠ **SHAWANO MEDICAL CENTER (521346)**, 309 North Bartlette Street, Zip 54166–2127; tel. 715/526–2111 **A**1 9 10 18 **F**11 13 28 29 34 40 53 56 64 75 76 77 80 81 82 86 87 90 93 102 107 108 111 119 131 **P**5 **S** ThedaCare, Inc., Appleton, WI
Primary Contact: Dorothy Erdmann, Chief Executive Officer
CFO: Kerry Lee Blanke, Chief Financial Officer
CMO: Mindy Frimodig, D.O., President Medical Staff ThedaCare Physicians Shawano
CIO: Jennifer Quinn, Quality and Safety Coordinator
CNO: Patricia A. Angelucci, MS, Director Patient Care Services
Web address: www.shawanomed.org
**Control:** Other not–for–profit (including NFP Corporation) **Service:** General Medical and Surgical

**Staffed Beds: 25 Admissions:** 1543 **Census:** 13 **Outpatient Visits:** 43410
**Births:** 293 **Total Expense ($000):** 33266 **Payroll Expense ($000):** 16846
**Personnel:** 222

**SHEBOYGAN—Sheboygan County**

✠ **AURORA SHEBOYGAN MEMORIAL MEDICAL CENTER (520035)**, 2629 North Seventh Street, Zip 53083–4998; tel. 920/451–5000 **A**1 2 9 10 **F**4 13 17 20 22 28 29 34 36 40 43 53 54 56 64 70 72 75 76 78 80 81 82 86 87 89 90 93 98 99 100 102 103 105 107 108 111 118 119 130 131 147 **P**6 **S** Aurora Health Care, Milwaukee, WI
Primary Contact: David Graebner, President
CFO: Pamela Ott, Vice President Finance
CMO: Andrea Gavin, M.D., Chief Medical officer
CIO: Steve Serketich, Manager Information Services
CHR: Stacie A. Schneider, Director Human Resources
CNO: Lori Knitt, Chief Nursing Officer
Web address: www.aurorahealthcare.org
**Control:** Other not–for–profit (including NFP Corporation) **Service:** General Medical and Surgical

**Staffed Beds: 136 Admissions:** 5407 **Census:** 53 **Outpatient Visits:** 94892
**Births:** 791 **Total Expense ($000):** 111539 **Payroll Expense ($000):** 33471
**Personnel:** 562

**WI**

*Many Facility Codes have changed. Please refer to the AHA Guide Code Chart.* © 2015 AHA Guide

✠ **ST. NICHOLAS HOSPITAL (520044)**, 3100 Superior Avenue, Zip 53081–1948;
tel. 920/459–8300 **A**1 2 9 10 **F**3 8 11 13 15 17 18 20 22 28 29 30 31 34 35
36 38 40 43 44 47 48 49 50 53 57 59 60 62 63 64 65 68 70 71 74 75 76
79 80 81 84 85 86 87 89 90 93 107 108 110 111 115 116 117 118 119
120 121 123 129 130 132 134 146 **P**2 5 **S** Hospital Sisters Health System,
Springfield, IL
Primary Contact: Andrew Bagnall, President and Chief Executive Officer
CFO: Greg Simia, Chief Financial Officer
CMO: Jeffrey Herold, M.D., President Medical Staff
CIO: Shane Miller, Chief Information Officer
CHR: Christine Jensema, Ph.D., Chief People Officer
CNO: Mary Martin, MSN, Chief Nursing Officer
Web address: www.stnicholashospital.org
**Control:** Church–operated, Nongovernment, not–for profit **Service:** General
Medical and Surgical

**Staffed Beds: 53 Admissions: 2741 Census: 26 Outpatient Visits: 69070
Births: 274 Total Expense ($000): 71603 Payroll Expense ($000): 20864
Personnel: 299**

## SHELL LAKE—Washburn County

☐ **INDIANHEAD MEDICAL CENTER (521342)**, 113 Fourth Avenue,
Zip 54871–4457, Mailing Address: P.O. Box 300, Zip 54871–0300;
tel. 715/468–7833 **A**1 9 10 18 **F**3 15 17 18 28 31 34 35 40 43 45 47 48 50
56 57 59 62 64 65 66 70 76 80 81 83 84 85 86 89 93 96 97 107 114 119
127 130 133 143 144 148 **P**5
Primary Contact: Paul Naglosky, Administrator
CFO: Michael Elliott, Controller
CMO: Allan Haesemeyer, M.D., Chief of Staff
CHR: Gwen Nielsen, Manager Human Resources
Web address: www.indianheadmedicalcenter.com
**Control:** Corporation, Investor–owned, for–profit **Service:** General Medical and
Surgical

**Staffed Beds: 25 Admissions: 316 Census: 4 Outpatient Visits: 9146
Births: 5 Total Expense ($000): 6562 Payroll Expense ($000): 2712
Personnel: 67**

## SPARTA—Monroe County

**MAYO CLINIC HEALTH SYSTEM – FRANCISCAN HEALTHCARE IN SPARTA
(521305)**, 310 West Main Street, Zip 54656–2171; tel. 608/269–2132 **A**9 10
18 **F**5 11 14 15 28 29 30 34 35 40 43 53 56 57 59 64 65 66 68 75 77 80
81 85 86 87 93 97 107 108 119 127 130 132 133 143 144 146 **S** Mayo
Clinic, Rochester, MN
Primary Contact: Kimberly Hawthorne, Administrator
COO: Joseph J. Kruse, Chief Administrative Officer
CFO: Tom Tiggelaar, Vice President Finance ad Chief Financial Officer
CMO: Tracy Warsing, M.D., Site Leader Chief of Staff
CHR: Mike J. Hesch, Regional Administrator Human Resources
CNO: Diane Holmay, R.N., Chief Nursing Officer
Web address: www.mayoclinichealthsystem.org
**Control:** Church–operated, Nongovernment, not–for profit **Service:** General
Medical and Surgical

**Staffed Beds: 10 Admissions: 314 Census: 9 Outpatient Visits: 22434
Births: 0 Total Expense ($000): 14712 Payroll Expense ($000): 8489
Personnel: 126**

## SPOONER—Washburn County

★ **SPOONER HEALTH SYSTEM (521332)**, 819 Ash Street, Zip 54801–1299;
tel. 715/635–2111 **A**9 10 18 **F**3 13 15 17 29 31 34 35 40 43 45 50 56 57
59 62 63 64 65 68 70 76 78 80 81 85 86 87 89 90 93 107 111 115 119
130 132 133 135 146 148 **S** HealthTech Management Services, Brentwood, TN
Primary Contact: Michael Schafer, Chief Executive Officer and Administrator
CFO: Rebecca Busch, Chief Financial Officer
CHR: Cindy Rouzer, Director Human Resources
Web address: www.spoonerhealthsystem.com
**Control:** Other not–for–profit (including NFP Corporation) **Service:** General
Medical and Surgical

**Staffed Beds: 25 Admissions: 497 Census: 7 Outpatient Visits: 21211
Births: 53 Total Expense ($000): 14713 Payroll Expense ($000): 6822
Personnel: 109**

## ST. CROIX FALLS—Polk County

**ST. CROIX REGIONAL MEDICAL CENTER (521337)**, 235 State Street,
Zip 54024–4117; tel. 715/483–3261 **A**9 10 18 **F**6 11 13 15 28 29 34 36 40
43 51 53 55 56 64 70 75 76 77 78 80 81 82 86 87 93 99 100 101 104 107
108 111 116 118 119 131 **P**5 6
Primary Contact: Dave Dobosenski, Chief Executive Officer
CFO: John Tremble, Chief Financial Officer
CMO: Jeffrey Hall, DPM, Chief Medical Officer
CIO: Brent McCurdy, Director Management Information
CHR: Lee Ann Vitalis, Executive Director Human Resources
CNO: Laura J. Jensen, Vice President Patient Care Services
Web address: www.scrmc.org
**Control:** Other not–for–profit (including NFP Corporation) **Service:** General
Medical and Surgical

**Staffed Beds: 25 Admissions: 1524 Census: 14 Outpatient Visits: 189035
Births: 262 Total Expense ($000): 62360 Payroll Expense ($000): 24636
Personnel: 415**

## STANLEY—Chippewa County

★ **MINISTRY OUR LADY OF VICTORY HOSPITAL (521311)**, 1120 Pine Street,
Zip 54768–1297; tel. 715/644–5571 **A**9 10 18 **F**3 15 29 30 34 35 40 41 43
45 50 56 59 65 77 80 81 84 85 86 87 89 90 93 94 96 97 107 109 110 114
127 130 131 133 144 146 148 **S** Ascension Health, Saint Louis, MO
Primary Contact: Vanessa Freitag, President
CFO: Terri Lewandowski, Director Financial Services
Web address: www.ministryhealth.org
**Control:** Other not–for–profit (including NFP Corporation) **Service:** General
Medical and Surgical

**Staffed Beds: 5 Admissions: 291 Census: 5 Outpatient Visits: 22021
Births: 0 Total Expense ($000): 16459 Payroll Expense ($000): 8009
Personnel: 562**

## STEVENS POINT—Portage County

✠ **MINISTRY SAINT MICHAEL'S HOSPITAL (520002)**, 900 Illinois Avenue,
Zip 54481–3196; tel. 715/346–5000, (Nonreporting) **A**1 9 10 19 **S** Ascension
Health, Saint Louis, MO
Primary Contact: Jeffrey L. Martin, President
CFO: William J. Hinner, Vice President Financial Analysis and Planning
CIO: Will Weider, Chief Information Officer
CHR: Cheryl F. Zima, Vice President Human Resources
Web address: www.ministryhealth.org/SMH/home.nws
**Control:** Church–operated, Nongovernment, not–for profit **Service:** General
Medical and Surgical

**Staffed Beds: 51**

**SAINT MICHAEL'S HOSPITAL** See Ministry Saint Michael's Hospital

## STOUGHTON—Dane County

☐ **STOUGHTON HOSPITAL ASSOCIATION (521343)**, 900 Ridge Street,
Zip 53589–1864; tel. 608/873–6611 **A**1 9 10 18 **F**3 4 6 8 15 18 26 28 29 30
34 35 36 40 44 45 50 53 54 56 57 59 62 64 65 66 68 70 71 75 77 79 80
81 85 86 87 89 90 93 96 97 98 100 103 106 107 115 129 130 131 132
133 144 146 147 148
Primary Contact: Terrence Brenny, President and Chief Executive Officer
CFO: Karen Myers, Vice President Financial Services
CMO: Dean Kresge, M.D., Chief of Staff
CIO: Karen Myers, Vice President Financial Services
CHR: Christopher Schmitz, Director Human Resources
Web address: www.stoughtonhospital.com
**Control:** Other not–for–profit (including NFP Corporation) **Service:** General
Medical and Surgical

**Staffed Beds: 32 Admissions: 889 Census: 15 Outpatient Visits: 50968
Births: 0 Total Expense ($000): 37126 Payroll Expense ($000): 14778
Personnel: 266**

## STURGEON BAY—Door County

**DOOR COUNTY MEMORIAL HOSPITAL** See Ministry Door County Medical
Center

**WI**

---

**Hospital, Medicare Provider Number, Address, Telephone, Approval, Facility, and Physician Codes, Health Care System**

★ American Hospital Association (AHA) membership    ○ Healthcare Facilities Accreditation Program    ⇑ Center for Improvement in Healthcare Quality Accreditation
☐ The Joint Commission accreditation    ◇ DNV Healthcare Inc. accreditation    △ Commission on Accreditation of Rehabilitation Facilities (CARF) accreditation

© 2015 AHA Guide     *Many Facility Codes have changed. Please refer to the AHA Guide Code Chart.*     Hospitals **A711**

★ **MINISTRY DOOR COUNTY MEDICAL CENTER (521358)**, 323 South 18th Avenue, Zip 54235–1495; tel. 920/743–5566, (Total facility includes 30 beds in nursing home–type unit) **A**9 10 18 **F**2 3 11 13 15 17 28 29 30 31 32 34 35 36 40 43 55 56 57 59 61 64 65 66 68 70 75 76 77 78 79 80 81 82 84 85 86 87 89 90 93 107 108 110 111 115 118 119 127 128 129 130 132 133 135 144 145 147 148 **P**6 **S** Ascension Health, Saint Louis, MO
Primary Contact: Gerald M. Worrick, President and Chief Executive Officer
CFO: Brian Stephens, Chief Financial Officer
CIO: Mary Lopas, Chief Information Officer
CHR: Kelli Bowling, Chief Culture Officer
CNO: Jody Boes, Vice President Patient Care Services
Web address: www.ministryhealth.org
**Control:** Church–operated, Nongovernment, not–for profit **Service:** General Medical and Surgical

**Staffed Beds:** 55 **Admissions:** 1499 **Census:** 36 **Outpatient Visits:** 76743 **Births:** 141 **Total Expense ($000):** 64457 **Payroll Expense ($000):** 34425 **Personnel:** 477

### SUMMIT—Waukesha County

✠ **AURORA MEDICAL CENTER SUMMIT (520206)**, 36500 Aurora Drive, Zip 53066–4899; tel. 262/434–1000 **A**1 2 9 10 **F**11 12 13 15 17 20 22 24 28 29 34 36 40 43 53 54 55 64 70 72 75 76 80 81 82 86 87 89 90 93 107 108 111 116 118 119 130 131 147 **P**6 **S** Aurora Health Care, Milwaukee, WI
Primary Contact: Michael Bergmann, President
Web address: www.aurorahealthcare.org
**Control:** Other not–for–profit (including NFP Corporation) **Service:** General Medical and Surgical

**Staffed Beds:** 85 **Admissions:** 2796 **Census:** 30 **Outpatient Visits:** 90007 **Births:** 420 **Total Expense ($000):** 99088 **Payroll Expense ($000):** 27930 **Personnel:** 452

### SUPERIOR—Douglas County

✠ **ESSENTIA HEALTH ST. MARY'S HOSPITAL OF SUPERIOR (521329)**, 3500 Tower Avenue, Zip 54880–5395; tel. 715/817–7000 **A**1 9 10 18 **F**3 11 15 28 29 30 40 41 42 56 59 64 65 75 77 78 80 81 82 86 87 90 93 96 97 107 110 111 119 130 133 135 142 146 148 **S** Essentia Health, Duluth, MN
Primary Contact: Terry Jacobson, Administrator and Chief Executive Officer
Web address: www.essentiahealth.org/ EssentiaHealthStMarysHospitalofSuperiorFoundation/overview.aspx
**Control:** Other not–for–profit (including NFP Corporation) **Service:** General Medical and Surgical

**Staffed Beds:** 25 **Admissions:** 487 **Census:** 8 **Outpatient Visits:** 50951 **Births:** 0 **Total Expense ($000):** 30047 **Payroll Expense ($000):** 16426 **Personnel:** 191

### TOMAH—Monroe County

✠ **TOMAH MEMORIAL HOSPITAL (521320)**, 321 Butts Avenue, Zip 54660–1412; tel. 608/372–2181 **A**1 9 10 18 **F**3 8 11 12 13 28 31 34 35 40 42 43 45 50 56 57 59 63 64 68 76 77 79 80 81 82 84 85 86 87 89 90 93 94 107 111 115 119 130 132 133 135 143 144 **P**5 6 **S** HealthTech Management Services, Brentwood, TN
Primary Contact: Philip J. Stuart, Administrator and Chief Executive Officer
CFO: Joseph Zeps, Vice President Finance
CIO: LaVonne Smith, Director Health Information Technology
CHR: Brenda Reinert, Director Human Resources
CNO: Tracy Myhre, R.N., Chief Nursing Officer
Web address: www.tomahhospital.org
**Control:** Other not–for–profit (including NFP Corporation) **Service:** General Medical and Surgical

**Staffed Beds:** 25 **Admissions:** 965 **Census:** 8 **Outpatient Visits:** 30883 **Births:** 293 **Total Expense ($000):** 35053 **Payroll Expense ($000):** 15590 **Personnel:** 207

✠ **TOMAH VETERANS AFFAIRS MEDICAL CENTER**, 500 East Veterans Street, Zip 54660–3105; tel. 608/372–3971, (Nonreporting) **A**1 **S** Department of Veterans Affairs, Washington, DC
Primary Contact: John J. Rohrer, Acting Director
CFO: Jane Mashak–Ekern, Fiscal Officer
CMO: David Houlihan, M.D., Chief of Staff
CIO: Edward Hensel, Chief Information Officer
CHR: David Dechant, Chief Human Resources Officer
Web address: www.tomah.va.gov
**Control:** Veterans Affairs, Government, federal **Service:** General Medical and Surgical

**Staffed Beds:** 71

### TOMAHAWK—Lincoln County

★ **MINISTRY SACRED HEART HOSPITAL (521313)**, 401 West Mohawk Drive, Zip 54487–2274; tel. 715/453–7700 **A**9 10 18 **F**3 5 15 28 29 30 34 35 40 45 49 50 57 59 65 68 75 77 80 81 84 86 87 89 91 92 93 96 99 100 101 104 107 109 115 119 130 131 133 146 **S** Ascension Health, Saint Louis, MO
Primary Contact: Sandra L. Anderson, President and Chief Executive Officer
Web address: www.ministryhealth.org
**Control:** Church–operated, Nongovernment, not–for profit **Service:** General Medical and Surgical

**Staffed Beds:** 8 **Admissions:** 361 **Census:** 3 **Outpatient Visits:** 24203 **Births:** 0 **Total Expense ($000):** 12356 **Payroll Expense ($000):** 7939 **Personnel:** 83

### TWO RIVERS—Manitowoc County

✠ **AURORA MEDICAL CENTER – MANITOWOC COUNTY (520034)**, 5000 Memorial Drive, Zip 54241–3900; tel. 920/794–5000 **A**1 2 9 10 **F**11 13 28 29 34 36 40 43 56 64 75 76 78 80 81 86 87 93 107 108 111 119 130 147 **P**6 **S** Aurora Health Care, Milwaukee, WI
Primary Contact: Cathie A. Kocourek, President
COO: Carrie L. Penovich, Chief Clinical Services Officer
CFO: Sandra Ewald, Vice President Finance
CMO: Paul Mihalakakos, M.D., Chief of Staff
CIO: Sony Jacob, Chief Information Officer
CHR: Stacie A. Schneider, Director Human Resources
CNO: Betsy Benz, R.N., Chief Nursing Officer
Web address: www.aurorahealthcare.org
**Control:** Other not–for–profit (including NFP Corporation) **Service:** General Medical and Surgical

**Staffed Beds:** 63 **Admissions:** 2222 **Census:** 18 **Outpatient Visits:** 82774 **Births:** 410 **Total Expense ($000):** 53758 **Payroll Expense ($000):** 17366 **Personnel:** 318

### VIROQUA—Vernon County

**VERNON MEMORIAL HEALTHCARE (521348)**, 507 South Main Street, Zip 54665–2096; tel. 608/637–2101 **A**9 10 18 **F**3 5 13 15 28 29 34 35 36 37 40 43 45 53 56 57 59 62 63 68 75 76 77 80 81 82 85 86 87 89 93 97 107 110 127 130 131 132 133 135 144 146 148 **P**6
Primary Contact: Kyle Bakkum, Chief Executive Officer and Administrator
COO: Kristy Wiltrout, R.N., Chief Operating Officer
CFO: Mary Koenig, Chief Financial Officer
CIO: Scott Adkins, Manager Information Technology
CHR: Kay Starr, Manager Human Resources
Web address: www.vmh.org
**Control:** Other not–for–profit (including NFP Corporation) **Service:** General Medical and Surgical

**Staffed Beds:** 25 **Admissions:** 1210 **Census:** 8 **Outpatient Visits:** 118231 **Births:** 173 **Total Expense ($000):** 59115 **Payroll Expense ($000):** 24878 **Personnel:** 361

### WATERFORD—Racine County

☐ △ **LAKEVIEW SPECIALTY HOSPITAL AND REHABILITATION CENTER (522005)**, 1701 Sharp Road, Zip 53185–5214; tel. 262/534–7297 **A**1 7 9 10 **F**1 12 28 29 30 34 36 38 53 62 64 75 82 85 86 87 90 91 92 93 94 97 99 100 101 104 106 127 128 130 143 148 **P**6
Primary Contact: Christopher Slover, Chief Executive Officer
Web address: www.lakeviewsystem.com
**Control:** Corporation, Investor–owned, for–profit **Service:** Long–Term Acute Care hospital

**Staffed Beds:** 48 **Admissions:** 261 **Census:** 23 **Outpatient Visits:** 9761 **Births:** 0 **Total Expense ($000):** 12353 **Payroll Expense ($000):** 5326 **Personnel:** 152

### WATERTOWN—Dodge County

✠ **WATERTOWN REGIONAL MEDICAL CENTER (520116)**, 125 Hospital Drive, Zip 53098–3303; tel. 920/261–4210 **A**1 9 10 **F**3 8 10 11 13 15 18 20 22 26 27 28 29 34 35 36 40 41 42 44 45 46 47 48 50 53 54 56 57 59 64 65 66 68 69 74 75 76 77 78 79 80 81 82 85 86 87 89 90 93 94 96 97 104 107 108 110 111 114 118 119 125 129 130 131 132 135 144 146 147 **P**8
Primary Contact: John P. Kosanovich, President
COO: John P. Kosanovich, President
CFO: John Graf, Senior Vice President
CIO: Jennifer Laughlin, Chief Information Officer
CHR: Duane Floyd, Vice President Human Resources and Professional Services
CNO: Mary Kay Diderrich, Vice President Patient Services
Web address: www.uwphwatertown.com
**Control:** Other not–for–profit (including NFP Corporation) **Service:** General Medical and Surgical

**Staffed Beds:** 55 **Admissions:** 1681 **Census:** 15 **Outpatient Visits:** 190390 **Births:** 248 **Total Expense ($000):** 89773 **Payroll Expense ($000):** 40618 **Personnel:** 597

*Many Facility Codes have changed. Please refer to the AHA Guide Code Chart.*

## WAUKESHA—Waukesha County

☐ **REHABILITATION HOSPITAL OF WISCONSIN (523027)**, 1625 Coldwater Creek Drive, Zip 53188–8028; tel. 262/521–8800 **A**1 9 10 **F**3 29 34 35 57 64 65 74 75 79 86 90 91 93 96 97 130 148 **S** Kindred Healthcare, Louisville, KY
Primary Contact: Linda Newberry–Ferguson, Chief Executive Officer
CMO: Tim McAvoy, M.D., Medical Director
CHR: Jenny Franke, Director Human Resources
CNO: Sharon Behrens, R.N., Director of Nursing
Web address: www.rehabhospitalwi.com
**Control:** Partnership, Investor–owned, for–profit **Service:** Rehabilitation

**Staffed Beds: 40 Admissions: 697 Census: 28 Outpatient Visits:** 4635 **Births:** 0 **Total Expense ($000):** 12739 **Payroll Expense ($000):** 6467 **Personnel:** 113

**WAUKESHA COUNTY MENTAL HEALTH CENTER (524026)**, 2501 Airport Road, Zip 53188; tel. 262/548–7950 **A**10 **F**4 98 130
Primary Contact: Jeff Lewis, Administrator
Web address: www.waukeshacounty.gov/
**Control:** County–Government, nonfederal **Service:** Psychiatric

**Staffed Beds: 28 Admissions: 753 Census: 16 Outpatient Visits:** 0 **Births:** 0 **Total Expense ($000):** 6461 **Payroll Expense ($000):** 3355 **Personnel:** 47

⊞ **WAUKESHA MEMORIAL HOSPITAL (520008)**, 725 American Avenue, Zip 53188–5099; tel. 262/928–1000 **A**1 2 3 5 9 10 **F**3 4 5 6 11 12 13 15 18 20 22 24 28 29 30 31 34 35 37 40 44 45 46 47 49 50 56 57 58 59 64 68 72 74 75 76 78 79 80 81 82 84 85 87 89 92 93 97 98 100 101 102 103 105 107 108 110 111 114 115 116 117 118 119 120 121 123 124 126 129 130 132 135 146 147 148 **S** ProHealth Care, Inc., Waukesha, WI
Primary Contact: John R. Robertstad, FACHE, President
CMO: James D. Gardner, M.D., Vice President and Chief Medical Officer
CIO: Rodney Dykehouse, Senior Vice President Information Services
CHR: Nadine T. Guirl, Senior Vice President Human Resources
Web address: www.prohealthcare.org/locations/locations-v2-detail/?id=1119
**Control:** Other not–for–profit (including NFP Corporation) **Service:** General Medical and Surgical

**Staffed Beds: 287 Admissions: 13939 Census: 160 Outpatient Visits:** 289227 **Births:** 1748 **Total Expense ($000):** 388819 **Payroll Expense ($000):** 102234 **Personnel:** 1689

## WAUPACA—Waupaca County

☐ **RIVERSIDE MEDICAL CENTER (521334)**, 800 Riverside Drive, Zip 54981–1999; tel. 715/258–1000 **A**1 9 10 18 **F**11 13 17 28 29 34 40 70 75 76 78 80 81 82 86 87 88 89 90 107 111 119 130 144 147 **S** ThedaCare, Inc., Appleton, WI
Primary Contact: Craig A. Kantos, Chief Executive Officer
CFO: Kerry Lee Blanke, Director Financial Services
CMO: James Williams, M.D., Chief of Staff
CHR: Kevin Gossens, Director Human Resources
Web address: www.riversidemedical.org
**Control:** Other not–for–profit (including NFP Corporation) **Service:** General Medical and Surgical

**Staffed Beds: 25 Admissions: 1000 Census: 11 Outpatient Visits:** 39913 **Births:** 146 **Total Expense ($000):** 30442 **Payroll Expense ($000):** 16310 **Personnel:** 198

## WAUPUN—Dodge County

☐ **WAUPUN MEMORIAL HOSPITAL (521327)**, 620 West Brown Street, Zip 53963–1799; tel. 920/324–5581 **A**1 9 10 18 **F**3 11 13 15 28 29 30 31 34 35 36 40 43 44 50 51 57 59 60 64 66 68 69 70 71 74 75 76 77 78 79 81 82 84 85 86 87 93 97 107 108 110 114 118 119 130 131 132 133 134 143 144 146 147 148 **P**6
Primary Contact: DeAnn Thurmer, Chief Operating Officer
COO: DeAnn Thurmer, Chief Operating Officer
CFO: Bonnie Schmitz, Chief Financial Officer
CMO: Derek Colmenares, M.D., Chief Medical Officer
CIO: Nancy Birschbach, Vice President and Chief Information Officer
CHR: Sue Edminster, Vice President Human Resources
CNO: DeAnn Thurmer, Chief Nursing Officer
Web address: www.agnesian.com
**Control:** Church–operated, Nongovernment, not–for profit **Service:** General Medical and Surgical

**Staffed Beds: 25 Admissions: 858 Census: 7 Outpatient Visits:** 54625 **Births:** 132 **Total Expense ($000):** 32189 **Payroll Expense ($000):** 14334 **Personnel:** 159

## WAUSAU—Marathon County

⊞ △ **ASPIRUS WAUSAU HOSPITAL (520030)**, 333 Pine Ridge Boulevard, Zip 54401–4187; tel. 715/847–2121 **A**1 2 3 5 7 9 10 **F**3 5 6 7 8 11 12 13 15 17 18 20 22 24 26 28 29 30 31 34 35 36 40 43 44 45 46 47 49 50 51 54 55 56 58 59 60 62 63 64 65 68 69 70 71 72 74 75 76 78 79 80 81 82 83 84 85 86 87 89 90 92 93 96 97 100 102 103 104 107 108 110 111 114 115 116 117 118 119 120 121 123 124 126 129 130 132 135 143 144 145 146 147 148 **P**8 **S** Aspirus, Inc., Wausau, WI
Primary Contact: Darrell Lentz, President
COO: Marita Hattem, Interim President and Chief Operating Officer
CFO: Sidney C. Sczygelski, Senior Vice President Finance and Chief Financial Officer
CHR: Roger V. Lucas, Vice President, Human Resources
Web address: www.aspirus.org
**Control:** Other not–for–profit (including NFP Corporation) **Service:** General Medical and Surgical

**Staffed Beds: 229 Admissions: 11669 Census: 130 Outpatient Visits:** 104662 **Births:** 1306 **Total Expense ($000):** 330676 **Payroll Expense ($000):** 113707 **Personnel:** 1948

**NORTH CENTRAL HEALTH CARE (524017)**, 1100 Lake View Drive, Zip 54403–6785; tel. 715/848–4600, (Total facility includes 207 beds in nursing home–type unit) **A**9 10 **F**3 5 6 29 34 35 38 50 56 57 59 64 66 75 87 93 98 99 100 101 102 103 104 105 106 128 130 132 134 135 146
Primary Contact: Gary Bezucha, FACHE, Chief Executive Officer
CFO: Brenda Glodowski, Chief Financial Officer
CHR: Michael Loy, Director Human Resources
Web address: www.norcen.org
**Control:** County–Government, nonfederal **Service:** Psychiatric

**Staffed Beds: 221 Admissions: 1289 Census: 221 Outpatient Visits:** 137713 **Births:** 0 **Total Expense ($000):** 28907 **Payroll Expense ($000):** 14943 **Personnel:** 220

**NORTH CENTRAL HEALTH CARE FACILITIES** See North Central Health Care

## WAUWATOSA—Milwaukee County

⊞ **AURORA PSYCHIATRIC HOSPITAL (524000)**, 1220 Dewey Avenue, Zip 53213–2598; tel. 414/454–6600 **A**1 3 5 9 10 **F**4 5 29 34 38 54 64 75 86 87 98 99 100 101 102 104 105 130 **P**6 **S** Aurora Health Care, Milwaukee, WI
Primary Contact: Peter Carlson, Administrator
CFO: Susan Dwyer, Vice President Finance
CMO: Anthony Meyer, M.D., Medical Director
CIO: Philip Loftus, Ph.D., Vice President and Chief Information Officer
CHR: Pamela Gamb, Manager Human Resources
CNO: Jamie Lewiston, R.N., Chief Nursing Officer
Web address: www.aurorahealthcare.org
**Control:** Other not–for–profit (including NFP Corporation) **Service:** Psychiatric

**Staffed Beds: 81 Admissions: 3803 Census: 53 Outpatient Visits:** 51755 **Births:** 0 **Total Expense ($000):** 26386 **Payroll Expense ($000):** 14274 **Personnel:** 263

★ **WHEATON FRANCISCAN HEALTHCARE – THE WISCONSIN HEART HOSPITAL (520199)**, 10000 West Bluemound Road, Zip 53226–4321; tel. 414/778–7800, (Nonreporting) **A**9 **S** Wheaton Franciscan Healthcare, Wheaton, IL
Primary Contact: Coreen Dicus–Johnson, President
CFO: Michael Petitt, Director of Finance
CMO: Rita Hanson, M.D., Vice President Medical Affairs
CIO: Gregory Smith, Senior Vice President and Chief Information Officer
CHR: Christopher Morris, Director Human Resources
CNO: Sharon Baughman, R.N., Vice President Patient Services and Chief Nursing Officer
Web address: www.mywheaton.org/hearthospital
**Control:** Church–operated, Nongovernment, not–for profit **Service:** Heart

**Staffed Beds: 30**

**WI**

---

**Hospital, Medicare Provider Number, Address, Telephone, Approval, Facility, and Physician Codes, Health Care System**

★ American Hospital Association (AHA) membership    ◯ Healthcare Facilities Accreditation Program    ⇧ Center for Improvement in Healthcare Quality Accreditation
☐ The Joint Commission accreditation    ◇ DNV Healthcare Inc. accreditation    △ Commission on Accreditation of Rehabilitation Facilities (CARF) accreditation

## WEST ALLIS—Milwaukee County

⊞ **AURORA WEST ALLIS MEDICAL CENTER (520139)**, 8901 West Lincoln Avenue, Zip 53227–2409, Mailing Address: P.O. Box 27901, Zip 53227–0901; tel. 414/328–6000 **A**1 3 9 10 **F**2 11 12 13 15 29 34 38 40 43 52 54 55 56 64 70 72 75 76 78 80 81 82 86 87 93 107 108 111 116 118 119 130 147 **P**6 **S** Aurora Health Care, Milwaukee, WI
Primary Contact: Richard A. Kellar, President
COO: Gerard Colman, Chief Operating Officer
CFO: Chris Hemmer, Director Finance
CMO: Andrew McDonagh, M.D., Chief Medical Officer
CIO: Philip Loftus, Ph.D., Chief Information Officer
CHR: Shannon Christenson, Director Human Resources
CNO: Kathy Becker, Ph.D., Vice President and Chief Nursing Officer
Web address: www.aurorahealthcare.org
**Control:** Other not–for–profit (including NFP Corporation) **Service:** General Medical and Surgical

**Staffed Beds:** 218 **Admissions:** 12749 **Census:** 148 **Outpatient Visits:** 170013 **Births:** 3342 **Total Expense ($000):** 195634 **Payroll Expense ($000):** 61557 **Personnel:** 1040

## WEST BEND—Washington County

⊞ **ST. JOSEPH'S HOSPITAL (520063)**, 3200 Pleasant Valley Road, Zip 53095–9274; tel. 262/334–5533 **A**1 2 3 5 9 10 **F**3 4 8 13 15 17 28 29 30 31 34 35 40 43 44 45 47 48 49 50 56 57 59 60 63 64 68 70 74 75 76 77 78 79 80 81 85 86 87 89 90 98 100 101 107 108 110 111 114 115 116 118 119 120 121 129 130 132 135 145 146 147 148
Primary Contact: Allen Ericson, President
CFO: Scott Hawig, Chief Financial Officer
CMO: Patrick Gardner, M.D., Vice President Medical Affairs
CIO: Will Showalter, Senior Vice President, Chief Information Officer
CHR: Keith Allen, Senior Vice President Human Resources
CNO: Teri Lux, R.N., Vice President Patient Care Services and Chief Nursing Officer
Web address: www.froedtert.com
**Control:** Other not–for–profit (including NFP Corporation) **Service:** General Medical and Surgical

**Staffed Beds:** 78 **Admissions:** 3727 **Census:** 44 **Outpatient Visits:** 78909 **Births:** 770 **Total Expense ($000):** 87793 **Payroll Expense ($000):** 30051 **Personnel:** 451

## WESTON—Marathon County

⊞ **MINISTRY SAINT CLARE'S HOSPITAL (520202)**, 3400 Ministry Parkway, Zip 54476–5220; tel. 715/393–3000 **A**1 9 10 **F**3 11 13 17 18 20 22 24 26 29 30 31 34 35 37 40 43 44 50 51 57 59 64 68 70 72 74 75 76 78 79 80 81 82 84 85 86 87 89 126 130 132 135 143 146 148 **S** Ascension Health, Saint Louis, MO
Primary Contact: Mary T. Krueger, President
CFO: Charlotte Esselman, Director Finance
CMO: Heong P'ng, M.D., Interim Chief Medical Officer
CIO: Tammy Hawkey, Manager Information Technology Client Services
CHR: Nancy Kwiesielewicz, Human Resources Manager
CNO: Kristine McGarigle, R.N., Vice President Patient Care
Web address: www.ministryhealth.org
**Control:** Church–operated, Nongovernment, not–for profit **Service:** General Medical and Surgical

**Staffed Beds:** 90 **Admissions:** 5338 **Census:** 49 **Outpatient Visits:** 18148 **Births:** 626 **Total Expense ($000):** 89212 **Payroll Expense ($000):** 33983 **Personnel:** 373

## WHITEHALL—Trempealeau County

★ **GUNDERSEN TRI–COUNTY HOSPITAL AND CLINICS (521316)**, 18601 Lincoln Street, Zip 54773–8605; tel. 715/538–4361, (Total facility includes 47 beds in nursing home–type unit) **A**9 10 18 **F**7 10 11 15 28 34 40 43 53 56 64 69 75 81 82 86 90 93 107 108 128 130 144
Primary Contact: Brian Theiler, President and Chief Executive Officer
COO: Brian Theiler, President and Chief Executive Officer
CFO: Vince Studer, Director Finance
CMO: Katrina Hammel, M.D., Chief Medical Officer
CIO: John Waldera, Director Information Technology
CHR: Jill Wesener Dieck, Director Human Resources
CNO: Emily Anderson, Director of Nursing Emergency Room
Web address: www.gundersenhealth.org/tri–county
**Control:** Other not–for–profit (including NFP Corporation) **Service:** General Medical and Surgical

**Staffed Beds:** 50 **Admissions:** 319 **Census:** 46 **Outpatient Visits:** 29205 **Births:** 0 **Total Expense ($000):** 15936 **Payroll Expense ($000):** 7460 **Personnel:** 152

## WILD ROSE—Waushara County

**WILD ROSE COMMUNITY MEMORIAL HOSPITAL (521303)**, 601 Grove Avenue, Zip 54984–6903, Mailing Address: P.O. Box 243, Zip 54984–0243; tel. 920/622–3257 **A**9 10 18 **F**11 15 28 29 34 40 43 56 64 75 77 80 81 86 87 89 90 93 99 100 101 102 103 104 107 111 119 131 144 147 **P**7 **S** ThedaCare, Inc., Appleton, WI
Primary Contact: Dawn Schuman, President
CFO: Thomas P. Krystowiak, Vice President Finance
CMO: Reginaldo Arboleda, M.D., Chief of Staff
CHR: Karen M. West, Administrator Support Services
Web address: www.wildrosehospital.org
**Control:** Other not–for–profit (including NFP Corporation) **Service:** General Medical and Surgical

**Staffed Beds:** 25 **Admissions:** 409 **Census:** 2 **Outpatient Visits:** 7875 **Births:** 0 **Total Expense ($000):** 12536 **Payroll Expense ($000):** 5284 **Personnel:** 120

## WINNEBAGO—Winnebago County

☐ **WINNEBAGO MENTAL HEALTH INSTITUTE (524002)**, 1300 South Drive, Zip 54985, Mailing Address: Box 9, Zip 54985–0009; tel. 920/235–4910 **A**1 5 9 10 **F**3 4 5 29 75 82 87 92 98 99 103 130 143 146 **P**7
Primary Contact: Thomas Speech, Ph.D., Director
COO: Chris Craggs, Deputy Director
CFO: Lisa Spanbauer, Financial Program Supervisor
CMO: Randy Kerswill, M.D., Medical Director
CIO: Terrance J. Sweet, Director Information Technology
CHR: Mary Howard, Director Human Resources
CNO: Lori Monroe, Director of Nursing
Web address: www.dhfs.state.wi.us/mh_winnebago
**Control:** State–Government, nonfederal **Service:** Psychiatric

**Staffed Beds:** 184 **Admissions:** 2389 **Census:** 184 **Outpatient Visits:** 0 **Births:** 0 **Total Expense ($000):** 47758 **Payroll Expense ($000):** 30475 **Personnel:** 615

## WISCONSIN RAPIDS—Wood County

⊞ **ASPIRUS RIVERVIEW HOSPITAL AND CLINICS, INC. (520033)**, 410 Dewey Street, Zip 54494–4715, Mailing Address: P.O. Box 8080, Zip 54495–8080; tel. 715/423–6060 **A**1 2 9 10 **F**3 4 8 13 14 15 17 28 30 31 34 35 40 43 45 50 56 59 64 65 68 69 70 74 75 76 77 78 79 80 81 84 85 86 88 89 90 93 97 98 100 107 108 110 111 115 118 119 120 121 124 127 129 130 131 132 135 146 148 **S** Aspirus, Inc., Wausau, WI
Primary Contact: Rick Nevers, Interim Chief Executive Officer
CFO: Michael Bovee, Vice President Finance
CMO: Timothy K. Huebner, M.D., President Medical Affairs
CIO: Marjorie Tell, Vice President Information Technology
Web address: www.riverviewhospital.org
**Control:** Other not–for–profit (including NFP Corporation) **Service:** General Medical and Surgical

**Staffed Beds:** 69 **Admissions:** 2595 **Census:** 22 **Outpatient Visits:** 49770 **Births:** 400 **Total Expense ($000):** 84974 **Payroll Expense ($000):** 35171 **Personnel:** 485

## WOODRUFF—Oneida County

⊞ **HOWARD YOUNG MEDICAL CENTER (520091)**, 240 Maple Street, Zip 54568–9190, Mailing Address: P.O. Box 470, Zip 54568–0470; tel. 715/356–8000 **A**1 5 9 10 20 **F**3 8 11 13 15 18 28 29 30 35 40 43 45 47 48 49 50 57 59 68 75 76 77 80 81 82 84 85 86 87 88 89 93 96 107 108 110 115 119 126 129 130 133 146 148 **P**6 **S** Ascension Health, Saint Louis, MO
Primary Contact: Sandra L. Anderson, President and Chief Executive Officer
CFO: Cathy Bukowski, Chief Financial Officer
CMO: Mark Rassier, M.D., President Howard Young Medical Center Staff
CIO: Howard Dobizl, Director Information Technology Services
CHR: Michelle Cornelius, Director Human Resources
CNO: Deborah Karow, R.N., Vice President Patient Care Services
Web address: www.ministryhealth.org
**Control:** Church–operated, Nongovernment, not–for profit **Service:** General Medical and Surgical

**Staffed Beds:** 44 **Admissions:** 2720 **Census:** 27 **Outpatient Visits:** 36734 **Births:** 272 **Total Expense ($000):** 49285 **Payroll Expense ($000):** 24324 **Personnel:** 335

**WI**

# WYOMING

## AFTON—Lincoln County

★ **STAR VALLEY MEDICAL CENTER (531313)**, 901 Adams Street,
Zip 83110–9621, Mailing Address: P.O. Box 579, Zip 83110–0579;
tel. 307/885–5800, (Total facility includes 24 beds in nursing home–type unit) **A**9
10 18 **F**3 7 11 12 13 15 29 31 34 40 43 45 50 57 59 64 65 67 74 75 77 78
79 81 82 85 86 87 93 97 102 107 110 111 114 118 119 129 130 131 132
133 135 144 146 147 148 **P**6
Primary Contact: Charlie A. Button, President and Chief Executive Officer
CFO: Chad Turner, Chief Financial Officer
CMO: Christian Morgan, M.D., Chief of Staff
CIO: Denise Wheeler, Chief Information Officer
CHR: Trevor Merritt, Director Human Resources
CNO: Dave Dunn, Director of Nursing
Web address: www.svmcwy.org
**Control:** Hospital district or authority, Government, nonfederal **Service:** General
Medical and Surgical

**Staffed Beds: 44 Admissions: 697 Census: 32 Outpatient Visits: 24600
Births: 110 Total Expense ($000): 28749 Payroll Expense ($000): 13347
Personnel: 247**

## BASIN—Big Horn County

**SOUTH BIG HORN COUNTY HOSPITAL (531301)**, 388 South U.S. Highway
20, Zip 82410–8902; tel. 307/568–3311, (Total facility includes 37 beds in
nursing home–type unit) **A**9 10 18 **F**32 34 35 40 56 57 59 64 82 93 97 107
110 119 127 128 130 133 **P**4
Primary Contact: Jackie Claudson, Administrator
Web address: www.midwayclinic.com
**Control:** Hospital district or authority, Government, nonfederal **Service:** General
Medical and Surgical

**Staffed Beds: 43 Admissions: 138 Census: 36 Outpatient Visits: 4860
Births: 1 Total Expense ($000): 6428 Payroll Expense ($000): 3249
Personnel: 94**

## BUFFALO—Johnson County

★ **JOHNSON COUNTY HEALTHCARE CENTER (531308)**, 497 West Lott Street,
Zip 82834–1691; tel. 307/684–5521, (Total facility includes 48 beds in nursing
home–type unit) **A**9 10 18 **F**11 13 15 28 31 40 57 62 63 67 70 76 78 79 81
89 93 107 119 130 133
Primary Contact: Sandy Ward, Administrator
CFO: Sandy Ward, Administrator
CMO: Brian Darnell, D.O., Chief of Staff
CIO: Laurie Hansen, Director Administrative Services
CHR: Karen Ferguson, Director Human Resources
CNO: Mary Whaley, Director of Acute Care
Web address: www.jchealthcare.com
**Control:** Hospital district or authority, Government, nonfederal **Service:** General
Medical and Surgical

**Staffed Beds: 59 Admissions: 474 Census: 46 Outpatient Visits: 17876
Births: 47 Total Expense ($000): 18512 Payroll Expense ($000): 10249
Personnel: 173**

## CASPER—Natrona County

☐ **ELKHORN VALLEY REHABILITATION HOSPITAL (533027)**, 5715 East 2nd
Street, Zip 82609–4322; tel. 307/265–0005, (Nonreporting) **A**1 10 **S** Ernest
Health, Inc., Albuquerque, NM
Primary Contact: Michael Phillips, Chief Executive Officer
Web address: www.evrh.ernesthealth.com/
**Control:** Corporation, Investor–owned, for–profit **Service:** Rehabilitation

**Staffed Beds: 40**

○ **MOUNTAIN VIEW REGIONAL HOSPITAL (530033)**, 6550 East Second Street,
Zip 82609–4321, Mailing Address: P.O. Box 51888, Zip 82605–1888;
tel. 307/995–8100, (Nonreporting) **A**10 11 **S** National Surgical Healthcare,
Chicago, IL
Primary Contact: Jeff Van Horn, Chief Executive Officer
Web address: www.mountainviewregionalhospital.com
**Control:** Partnership, Investor–owned, for–profit **Service:** Surgical

**Staffed Beds: 23**

☐ **WYOMING BEHAVIORAL INSTITUTE (534004)**, 2521 East 15th Street,
Zip 82609–4126; tel. 307/237–7444, (Nonreporting) **A**1 10 **S** Universal Health
Services, Inc., King of Prussia, PA
Primary Contact: Joseph Gallagher, Chief Executive Officer
CFO: Carmel Bickford, Chief Financial Officer
CMO: Steven Brown, M.D., Medical Director
CHR: Jon Barra, Director Human Resources
Web address: www.wbihelp.com
**Control:** Corporation, Investor–owned, for–profit **Service:** Psychiatric

**Staffed Beds: 130**

⊞ **WYOMING MEDICAL CENTER (530012)**, 1233 East Second Street,
Zip 82601–2988; tel. 307/577–7201 **A**1 3 9 10 **F**3 7 11 12 13 18 20 22 24
28 29 30 31 34 35 40 41 43 45 46 48 49 50 51 57 59 60 61 68 70 74 76
79 81 82 85 86 87 89 97 102 107 108 114 118 119 120 121 123 124 126
129 130 132 135 144 146 147 148 **P**6
Primary Contact: Vickie L. Diamond, R.N., MS, President and Chief Executive
Officer
COO: Chad Pew, Chief Operating Officer and Senior Vice President
CFO: Yvonne Wigington, Vice President, Chief Financial Officer
CMO: Carol M. Solie, M.D., Chief Medical Officer
CIO: Rob Pettigrew, Director Information Technology
CNO: Jan Sternberg, MS, Senior Vice President Patient Care Services and Chief
Nursing Officer
Web address: www.wmcnet.org
**Control:** Other not–for–profit (including NFP Corporation) **Service:** General
Medical and Surgical

**Staffed Beds: 191 Admissions: 8807 Census: 91 Outpatient Visits: 84961
Births: 1205 Total Expense ($000): 190911 Payroll Expense ($000):
67589 Personnel: 1050**

## CHEYENNE—Laramie County

⊞ △ **CHEYENNE REGIONAL MEDICAL CENTER (530014)**, 214 East 23rd
Street, Zip 82001–3790; tel. 307/634–2273 **A**1 2 3 5 7 9 10 20 **F**3 5 11 12
13 15 18 20 22 24 26 28 29 30 31 34 35 37 38 40 43 44 45 46 47 48 49
50 51 57 59 60 62 63 64 65 66 68 69 70 71 73 74 75 76 77 78 79 81 82
83 84 85 86 87 89 90 93 94 96 97 98 99 100 101 102 103 104 107 108
110 111 114 116 117 118 119 120 121 123 124 128 129 130 131 132 135
143 144 146 147 148 **P**4 6
Primary Contact: Margo Karsten, Ph.D., MSN, Chief Executive Officer
COO: Jason Shenefield, Chief Operating Officer
CFO: Kerry Warburton, Chief Financial Officer
CMO: David Lind, M.D., Chief Medical Officer
CIO: Ashutosh Goel, M.D., Chief Information Technology Officer
CHR: Craig Luzinski, MSN, Chief Human Resources Officer
CNO: Constance Schmidt, R.N., Chief Nursing Officer
Web address: www.cheyenneregional.org/
**Control:** County–Government, nonfederal **Service:** General Medical and Surgical

**Staffed Beds: 238 Admissions: 9558 Census: 126 Outpatient Visits:
168532 Births: 1193 Total Expense ($000): 255860 Payroll Expense
($000): 105495 Personnel: 1853**

⊞ **CHEYENNE VETERANS AFFAIRS MEDICAL CENTER**, 2360 East Pershing
Boulevard, Zip 82001–5392; tel. 307/778–7550, (Total facility includes 42 beds
in nursing home–type unit) **A**1 9 **F**3 5 8 18 29 30 31 34 35 38 39 40 44 45 51
54 56 59 61 62 63 64 65 68 70 71 74 75 77 78 79 81 82 84 85 86 87 91
92 93 94 97 100 101 102 103 104 107 108 109 111 115 119 128 129 130
132 135 143 144 146 147 148 **P**6 **S** Department of Veterans Affairs,
Washington, DC
Primary Contact: Cynthia McCormack, MS, Director
CFO: Melvin Cranford, Chief Fiscal Services
CMO: Roger Johnson, M.D., Chief of Staff
CIO: Liz McCulloch, Chief Information Resource Management Systems
CHR: Ron Lester, Chief Human Resources
Web address: www.cheyenne.va.gov/
**Control:** Veterans Affairs, Government, federal **Service:** General Medical and
Surgical

**Staffed Beds: 61 Admissions: 1082 Census: 45 Outpatient Visits: 257952
Births: 0 Total Expense ($000): 166435 Payroll Expense ($000): 47973**

---

**Hospital, Medicare Provider Number, Address, Telephone, Approval, Facility, and Physician Codes, Health Care System**

★ American Hospital Association (AHA) membership
☐ The Joint Commission accreditation
○ Healthcare Facilities Accreditation Program
◇ DNV Healthcare Inc. accreditation
⇑ Center for Improvement in Healthcare Quality Accreditation
△ Commission on Accreditation of Rehabilitation Facilities (CARF) accreditation

## CODY—Park County

★ **WEST PARK HOSPITAL (531312)**, 707 Sheridan Avenue, Zip 82414–3409; tel. 307/527–7501, (Total facility includes 87 beds in nursing home–type unit) **A**9 10 18 **F**3 4 5 6 7 11 13 15 18 24 26 28 29 30 31 34 35 36 38 40 43 45 46 50 56 57 59 62 63 64 65 68 70 75 76 78 79 81 84 85 86 87 93 97 99 100 102 103 104 105 107 108 110 111 114 119 120 124 128 130 131 132 133 135 143 144 145 146 147 148 **S** QHR, Brentwood, TN
Primary Contact: Douglas A. McMillan, Administrator and Chief Executive Officer
CFO: Patrick G. McConnell, Chief Financial Officer
CHR: Dick Smith, Director Human Resources
Web address: www.westparkhospital.org
**Control:** Hospital district or authority, Government, nonfederal **Service:** General Medical and Surgical

**Staffed Beds:** 112 **Admissions:** 1664 **Census:** 88 **Outpatient Visits:** 67848 **Births:** 277 **Total Expense ($000):** 73560 **Payroll Expense ($000):** 30460 **Personnel:** 492

## DOUGLAS—Converse County

★ **MEMORIAL HOSPITAL OF CONVERSE COUNTY (531302)**, 111 South Fifth Street, Zip 82633–2434, Mailing Address: P.O. Box 1450, Zip 82633–1450; tel. 307/358–2122 **A**10 18 **F**3 7 8 13 15 28 29 32 34 35 40 43 45 46 50 57 59 64 70 74 75 76 79 81 82 85 86 87 89 94 107 110 111 115 119 126 127 128 129 131 133 135 144 146 147 148 **P**6
Primary Contact: Ryan K. Smith, Chief Executive Officer
COO: Karl Edward Hertz, Assistant Administrator
CFO: Curtis R. Dugger, Chief Financial Officer
CMO: James Morgan, M.D., Chief Medical Officer
CIO: Dave Patterson, Chief Information Officer
CHR: Linda York, Director Human Resource
CNO: Christy Dicklich-Cobb, Chief Nursing Officer
Web address: www.conversehospital.com
**Control:** County–Government, nonfederal **Service:** General Medical and Surgical

**Staffed Beds:** 25 **Admissions:** 759 **Census:** 6 **Outpatient Visits:** 31044 **Births:** 165 **Total Expense ($000):** 47354 **Payroll Expense ($000):** 23508 **Personnel:** 339

## EVANSTON—Uinta County

☒ **EVANSTON REGIONAL HOSPITAL (530032)**, 190 Arrowhead Drive, Zip 82930–9266; tel. 307/789–3636 **A**1 9 10 20 **F**3 11 13 15 29 34 35 40 43 45 48 60 65 70 74 75 76 77 79 81 82 85 86 87 89 93 107 108 111 114 119 128 129 131 134 146 **P**6 **S** Community Health Systems, Inc., Franklin, TN
Primary Contact: George Winn, Chief Executive Officer
CFO: Paul Selivanoff, Chief Financial Officer
CHR: Joshua Jones, Director of Human Resources
CNO: Cheri Willard, R.N., Chief Nursing Officer
Web address: www.evanstonregionalhospital.com
**Control:** Corporation, Investor–owned, for–profit **Service:** General Medical and Surgical

**Staffed Beds:** 42 **Admissions:** 965 **Census:** 5 **Outpatient Visits:** 25780 **Births:** 259 **Total Expense ($000):** 23104 **Payroll Expense ($000):** 14159 **Personnel:** 163

**WYOMING STATE HOSPITAL (534001)**, 830 Highway 150 South, Zip 82931–5341, Mailing Address: P.O. Box 177, Zip 82931–0177; tel. 307/789–3464 **A**9 10 **F**29 30 50 56 77 98 100 101 102 103 130 132 135 143 **P**6
Primary Contact: William J. Sexton, Administrator
CFO: Paul Mullenax, Business Manager
CIO: Steve Baldwin, Manager Information Technology
Web address: www.health.wyo.gov/statehospital/index.html
**Control:** State–Government, nonfederal **Service:** Psychiatric

**Staffed Beds:** 103 **Admissions:** 210 **Census:** 91 **Outpatient Visits:** 0 **Births:** 0 **Personnel:** 383

## GILLETTE—Campbell County

★ ◇ **CAMPBELL COUNTY MEMORIAL HOSPITAL (530002)**, 501 South Burma Avenue, Zip 82716–3426, Mailing Address: P.O. Box 3011, Zip 82717–3011; tel. 307/682–8811, (Total facility includes 125 beds in nursing home–type unit) **A**9 10 20 21 **F**3 5 6 7 11 13 15 18 20 22 26 28 29 30 31 34 35 38 40 43 45 50 51 53 54 56 59 60 62 63 64 65 66 68 70 71 73 74 75 76 77 78 79 81 82 84 85 86 87 88 93 94 96 97 98 99 100 101 102 103 104 105 107 108 109 110 111 114 115 116 118 119 120 121 125 129 130 131 132 133 134 135 143 144 146 147 148 **P**6
Primary Contact: Andy Fitzgerald, Chief Executive Officer
CFO: Dalton Huber, Chief Financial Officer
CIO: Chris Harrison, Manager Information Systems
CHR: John A. Fitch, Vice President Human Resources
CNO: Deb L. Tonn, Vice President Patient Care
Web address: www.ccmh.net
**Control:** Hospital district or authority, Government, nonfederal **Service:** General Medical and Surgical

**Staffed Beds:** 196 **Admissions:** 2961 **Census:** 140 **Outpatient Visits:** 263654 **Births:** 759 **Total Expense ($000):** 149813 **Payroll Expense ($000):** 76547 **Personnel:** 1023

## JACKSON—Teton County

☒ **ST. JOHN'S MEDICAL CENTER AND LIVING CENTER (530015)**, 625 East Broadway Street, Zip 83001–8642, Mailing Address: P.O. Box 428, Zip 83001–0428; tel. 307/733–3636, (Total facility includes 60 beds in nursing home–type unit) **A**1 5 9 10 20 **F**3 11 13 15 29 30 31 34 35 40 43 44 45 46 51 53 54 57 59 62 63 67 68 70 74 75 76 77 78 81 82 84 86 87 97 107 108 110 111 115 119 129 130 132 133 135 144 145 146 148 **P**5
Primary Contact: Lou Hochheiser, M.D., Chief Executive Officer
COO: Gary Tauner, Chief Operating Officer
CFO: John Kren, Chief Financial Officer
CIO: David Witton, Manager Information Systems
CNO: Lynn Kirman, R.N., Chief Nursing Officer
Web address: www.tetonhospital.org
**Control:** Hospital district or authority, Government, nonfederal **Service:** General Medical and Surgical

**Staffed Beds:** 106 **Admissions:** 2023 **Census:** 64 **Outpatient Visits:** 69071 **Births:** 442 **Total Expense ($000):** 84201 **Payroll Expense ($000):** 33522 **Personnel:** 556

## KEMMERER—Lincoln County

★ **SOUTH LINCOLN MEDICAL CENTER (531315)**, 711 Onyx Street, Zip 83101–3214; tel. 307/877–4401, (Total facility includes 24 beds in nursing home–type unit) **A**9 10 18 **F**3 7 13 15 31 32 34 35 40 43 57 59 65 68 75 76 77 79 81 93 97 107 111 114 119 128 129 130 133 135 146 148 **P**6
Primary Contact: Kenneth W. Archer, Chief Executive Officer
CFO: Curtis Nielson, Chief Financial Officer
CMO: G. Christopher Krell, M.D., Chief of Staff
CIO: Kristin Housley, Chief Information Officer
CNO: Kathi Parks, Director of Nursing
Web address: www.southlincolnmedical.com
**Control:** Hospital district or authority, Government, nonfederal **Service:** General Medical and Surgical

**Staffed Beds:** 38 **Admissions:** 128 **Census:** 20 **Outpatient Visits:** 22149 **Births:** 48 **Total Expense ($000):** 13190 **Payroll Expense ($000):** 7066 **Personnel:** 125

## LARAMIE—Albany County

☒ **IVINSON MEMORIAL HOSPITAL (530025)**, 255 North 30th Street, Zip 82072–5140; tel. 307/742–2141, (Total facility includes 9 beds in nursing home–type unit) **A**1 10 20 **F**3 11 13 15 28 29 30 31 34 38 40 45 50 56 57 59 60 64 70 73 75 77 78 79 81 85 87 93 96 98 99 102 103 107 108 110 111 115 118 119 120 121 123 132 133 146 147 148 **P**8
Primary Contact: Doug Faus, FACHE, Chief Executive Officer
COO: Holly Zajic, Chief Operating Officer
CFO: Bryan Chalmers, Chief Financial Officer
CMO: John Byers, M.D., Chief of Staff
CIO: Brandon Lewis, Director of Information Technology
CHR: Becky Kosach, Director Human Resources
CNO: Sharon Gern, R.N., Chief Nursing Officer
Web address: www.ivinsonhospital.org
**Control:** Hospital district or authority, Government, nonfederal **Service:** General Medical and Surgical

**Staffed Beds:** 99 **Admissions:** 1928 **Census:** 20 **Outpatient Visits:** 39950 **Total Expense ($000):** 61752 **Payroll Expense ($000):** 22633 **Personnel:** 391

## LOVELL—Big Horn County

★ **NORTH BIG HORN HOSPITAL DISTRICT (531309)**, 1115 Lane 12, Zip 82431–9537; tel. 307/548–5203, (Total facility includes 85 beds in nursing home–type unit) **A**9 10 18 **F**3 6 7 10 15 28 29 30 34 35 36 40 41 45 50 56 57 59 62 64 65 66 68 71 75 79 81 82 85 86 87 93 97 107 110 114 119 127 128 130 131 132 133 135 143 146 147 148 **P**3 8
Primary Contact: Rick Schroeder, Chief Executive Officer
CFO: Lori Smith, Chief Financial Officer
CMO: Richard Jay, D.O., Chief of Staff
CIO: Lisa Strom, Director Information Systems
CHR: Barbara Shumway, Director Human Resources
CNO: Tina Toner, Director of Nursing
Web address: www.nbhh.com
**Control:** Hospital district or authority, Government, nonfederal **Service:** General Medical and Surgical

**Staffed Beds:** 100 **Admissions:** 283 **Census:** 80 **Outpatient Visits:** 21711 **Births:** 0 **Total Expense ($000):** 15712 **Payroll Expense ($000):** 8921 **Personnel:** 181

## LUSK—Niobrara County

★ **NIOBRARA HEALTH AND LIFE CENTER (531314)**, 921 Ballencee Avenue, Zip 82225, Mailing Address: P.O. Box 780, Zip 82225–0780; tel. 307/334–4000 **A**9 10 18 **F**3 40 41 82 91 107 119 127 128 133 135 148 **P**6
Primary Contact: Chris Smolik, Chief Executive Officer
Web address: www.niobrarahospital.com
**Control:** County–Government, nonfederal **Service:** General Medical and Surgical

**Staffed Beds:** 24 **Admissions:** 48 **Census:** 1 **Outpatient Visits:** 6914 **Births:** 0 **Total Expense ($000):** 6421 **Payroll Expense ($000):** 3068 **Personnel:** 90

## NEWCASTLE—Weston County

★ **WESTON COUNTY HEALTH SERVICES (531303)**, 1124 Washington Boulevard, Zip 82701–2972; tel. 307/746–4491, (Total facility includes 54 beds in nursing home–type unit) **A**9 10 18 **F**28 29 40 41 56 57 59 62 64 77 91 93 107 119 130 133
Primary Contact: Maureen K. Cadwell, Chief Executive Officer
CFO: Lynn Moller, Chief Financial Officer
CMO: Chuck Franklin, M.D., Chief Medical Staff
CIO: Terri Frye, Information Technology Officer
CHR: Julie A. Sindlinger, Director of Human Resources
Web address: www.wchs–wy.org
**Control:** Hospital district or authority, Government, nonfederal **Service:** General Medical and Surgical

**Staffed Beds:** 75 **Admissions:** 200 **Census:** 60 **Outpatient Visits:** 8275 **Births:** 0 **Total Expense ($000):** 12526 **Payroll Expense ($000):** 5681 **Personnel:** 136

## POWELL—Park County

★ **POWELL VALLEY HEALTHCARE (531310)**, 777 Avenue H, Zip 82435–2296; tel. 307/754–2267, (Total facility includes 100 beds in nursing home–type unit) **A**9 10 18 **F**3 7 10 11 13 15 18 28 29 34 35 36 40 43 45 50 56 57 59 62 63 64 65 67 68 70 75 76 79 81 82 84 85 87 97 107 110 111 115 119 125 130 131 132 133 135 144 146 147 148 **P**1 6 **S** HealthTech Management Services, Brentwood, TN
Primary Contact: Terry Odom, Chief Executive Officer
CFO: Mike Long, Chief Financial Officer
CMO: Valerie Lengfelder, M.D., Chief of Staff
CIO: Joshua Baxter, Director, Information Systems
CHR: Cassie Tinsley, Director, Human Resources
CNO: Arleen Campeau, R.N., Vice President of Patient Care Services, Chief Nursing Officer
Web address: www.pvhc.org
**Control:** Other not–for–profit (including NFP Corporation) **Service:** General Medical and Surgical

**Staffed Beds:** 125 **Admissions:** 637 **Census:** 89 **Outpatient Visits:** 36225 **Births:** 149 **Total Expense ($000):** 44053 **Payroll Expense ($000):** 21194 **Personnel:** 341

## RAWLINS—Carbon County

★ **MEMORIAL HOSPITAL OF CARBON COUNTY (531316)**, 2221 West Elm Street, Zip 82301–5108, Mailing Address: P.O. Box 460, Zip 82301–0460; tel. 307/324–2221 **A**9 10 18 **F**7 11 13 15 29 31 34 35 40 45 50 57 59 65 68 70 79 81 85 93 107 110 111 114 119 129 133 135 146 147 **S** QHR, Brentwood, TN
Primary Contact: Dana Barnett, Chief Executive Officer
CFO: David Pike, Interim Chief Financial Officer
CMO: David Cesko, M.D., Chief of Staff
CIO: Toby Schaef, Director Information Technology
CNO: Amber Green, R.N., Chief Clinical Officer
Web address: www.imhcc.com
**Control:** County–Government, nonfederal **Service:** General Medical and Surgical

**Staffed Beds:** 25 **Admissions:** 719 **Census:** 6 **Outpatient Visits:** 27183 **Births:** 102 **Total Expense ($000):** 21901 **Payroll Expense ($000):** 9985 **Personnel:** 144

## RIVERTON—Fremont County

⊞ **SAGEWEST HEALTH CARE AT RIVERTON (530008)**, 2100 West Sunset Drive, Zip 82501–2274; tel. 307/856–4161, (Includes SAGEWEST HEALTH CARE AT LANDER, 1320 Bishop Randall Drive, Lander, Zip 82520–3996; tel. 307/332–4420; Stephen M. Erixon, Chief Executive Officer) **A**1 9 10 20 **F**3 11 12 13 15 28 29 34 35 38 39 40 43 50 57 59 70 74 75 76 77 79 81 82 85 87 90 93 97 98 103 106 107 108 110 111 114 115 119 129 130 131 132 145 146 147 148 **P**7 **S** LifePoint Health, Brentwood, TN
Primary Contact: Stephen M. Erixon, Chief Executive Officer
COO: Derrick Brumfield, Chief Operating Officer
CFO: Jennifer Hamilton, Chief Financial Officer
CMO: Cielette Karn, M.D., Chief of Staff
CIO: Linda Tice, Director Information Systems
CHR: Dawn Nelson, Director Human Resources
CNO: Karen A. Lund, R.N., Chief Nursing Officer
Web address: www.sagewesthealthcare.com
**Control:** Corporation, Investor–owned, for–profit **Service:** General Medical and Surgical

**Staffed Beds:** 71 **Admissions:** 3228 **Census:** 37 **Outpatient Visits:** 63830 **Births:** 557 **Total Expense ($000):** 60867 **Payroll Expense ($000):** 20060 **Personnel:** 366

## ROCK SPRINGS—Sweetwater County

⊞ **MEMORIAL HOSPITAL OF SWEETWATER COUNTY (530011)**, 1200 College Drive, Zip 82901–5868, Mailing Address: P.O. Box 1359, Zip 82902–1359; tel. 307/362–3711 **A**1 9 10 20 **F**3 5 8 11 13 15 28 29 30 31 34 35 40 43 48 57 59 60 64 70 75 76 77 78 79 81 82 87 93 97 99 100 102 103 104 105 107 110 111 114 115 116 118 119 123 129 130 131 132 135 146 147
Primary Contact: Gerard D. Klein, Chief Executive Officer
CFO: Irene Richardson, Chief Financial Officer
CMO: Melinda Poyer, D.O., President, Medical Staff
CHR: Keri Chorazewitz, Vice President Compliance and Employee Relations
CNO: Deborah L. Gaspar, R.N., Chief Nursing Officer
Web address: www.sweetwatermedicalcenter.com
**Control:** County–Government, nonfederal **Service:** General Medical and Surgical

**Staffed Beds:** 58 **Admissions:** 1989 **Census:** 16 **Outpatient Visits:** 124646 **Births:** 508 **Total Expense ($000):** 67977 **Payroll Expense ($000):** 28507 **Personnel:** 390

## SHERIDAN—Sheridan County

⊞ **SHERIDAN MEMORIAL HOSPITAL (530006)**, 1401 West Fifth Street, Zip 82801–2799; tel. 307/672–1000, (Nonreporting) **A**1 9 10 20
Primary Contact: Michael McCafferty, Chief Executive Officer
CFO: Charlotte Marie Mather, R.N., Chief Nursing Officer
CMO: John Addlesperger, D.O., Chief Medical Officer
CIO: Nyle Morgan, Chief Information Officer
CHR: Len Gross, Chief Human Resources Officer
Web address: www.sheridanhospital.org
**Control:** County–Government, nonfederal **Service:** General Medical and Surgical

**Staffed Beds:** 88

⊞ **SHERIDAN VETERANS AFFAIRS MEDICAL CENTER**, 1898 Fort Road, Zip 82801–8320; tel. 307/672–3473, (Total facility includes 30 beds in nursing home–type unit) **A**1 9 **F**29 30 38 39 45 50 53 56 59 62 63 64 65 75 77 82 83 84 85 86 87 93 94 97 98 100 103 106 107 111 119 127 129 130 132 135 143 146 147 148 **S** Department of Veterans Affairs, Washington, DC
Primary Contact: Kathy Berger, R.N., Acting Director
COO: Chandra Lake, Associate Director
CFO: Donna Fuerstenberg, Fiscal Chief
CMO: Wendell Robison, M.D., Chief of Staff
CIO: Anthony Giljum, Chief Information Officer
CHR: James Hardin, Human Resources Officer
CNO: Kathy Berger, R.N., Associate Director, Nursing and Patient Support Services
Web address: www.sheridan.va.gov/
**Control:** Veterans Affairs, Government, federal **Service:** Psychiatric

**Staffed Beds:** 185 **Admissions:** 1098 **Census:** 152 **Outpatient Visits:** 122289 **Births:** 0 **Total Expense ($000):** 103080 **Payroll Expense ($000):** 36644 **Personnel:** 584

## SUNDANCE—Crook County

★ **CROOK COUNTY MEDICAL SERVICES DISTRICT (531311)**, 713 Oak Street, Zip 82729, Mailing Address: P.O. Box 517, Zip 82729–0517; tel. 307/283–3501, (Total facility includes 32 beds in nursing home–type unit) **A**9 10 18 **F**7 32 38 40 41 44 57 59 64 65 67 68 75 89 90 91 107 127 128 130 133 143 147 148 **P**6 7
Primary Contact: Jeff Mengenhausen, Chief Executive Officer
CFO: Betty Meyers, Chief Financial Officer
CMO: Jeremi Villano, M.D., Chief of Staff
CHR: Patricia Feist, Manager Human Resources
Web address: www.crookcountymedical.com
**Control:** Hospital district or authority, Government, nonfederal **Service:** General Medical and Surgical

**Staffed Beds:** 48 **Admissions:** 55 **Census:** 11 **Outpatient Visits:** 1133 **Births:** 0 **Total Expense ($000):** 7034 **Payroll Expense ($000):** 3975 **Personnel:** 37

## THERMOPOLIS—Hot Springs County

★ **HOT SPRINGS COUNTY MEMORIAL HOSPITAL (531304)**, 150 East Arapahoe Street, Zip 82443–2498; tel. 307/864–3121, (Nonreporting) **A**10 18 **S** HealthTech Management Services, Brentwood, TN
Primary Contact: Robin Roling, Chief Executive Officer
CFO: Shelly Larson, Chief Financial Officer
CHR: Patti Jeunehomme, Director Human Resources
CNO: Glennda Grier, Chief Nursing Officer
Web address: www.hscmh.org
**Control:** County–Government, nonfederal **Service:** General Medical and Surgical

**Staffed Beds:** 25

---

**Hospital, Medicare Provider Number, Address, Telephone, Approval, Facility, and Physician Codes, Health Care System**

★ American Hospital Association (AHA) membership
□ The Joint Commission accreditation
○ Healthcare Facilities Accreditation Program
◇ DNV Healthcare Inc. accreditation
⇧ Center for Improvement in Healthcare Quality Accreditation
△ Commission on Accreditation of Rehabilitation Facilities (CARF) accreditation

**WY**

### TORRINGTON—Goshen County

★ **COMMUNITY HOSPITAL (531307)**, 2000 Campbell Drive, Zip 82240–1597;
tel. 307/532–4181 **A**9 10 18 **F**3 11 13 15 28 29 31 35 40 43 45 57 59 64
70 75 78 81 85 87 93 107 110 111 114 119 128 129 131 133 146 147 148
**P**6 **S** Banner Health, Phoenix, AZ
Primary Contact: Shelby Nelson, Interim Chief Executive Officer
CMO: Bonnie Randolph, M.D., Chief of Staff
CIO: Rod Miller, Chief Information Technology
Web address: www.bannerhealth.com/Locations/Wyoming/Community+Hospital/
**Control:** Other not–for–profit (including NFP Corporation) **Service:** General
Medical and Surgical

> **Staffed Beds:** 20 **Admissions:** 624 **Census:** 6 **Outpatient Visits:** 17535
> **Births:** 79 **Total Expense ($000):** 18607 **Payroll Expense ($000):** 7639
> **Personnel:** 141

### WHEATLAND—Platte County

☒ **PLATTE COUNTY MEMORIAL HOSPITAL (531305)**, 201 14th Street,
Zip 82201–3201, Mailing Address: P.O. Box 848, Zip 82201–0848;
tel. 307/322–3636 **A**1 9 10 18 **F**3 13 14 15 29 30 34 40 45 50 57 59 68 70
76 78 79 81 82 85 87 107 114 119 133 147 148 **S** Banner Health,
Phoenix, AZ
Primary Contact: Shelby Nelson, Chief Executive Officer
CFO: James Cussins, Chief Financial Officer
CMO: Lauri Palmer, M.D., Chief of Staff
CIO: Robin May, Director Information Systems
CHR: Sandy Dugger, Chief Human Resources Officer
Web address: www.bannerhealth.com/Locations/Wyoming/Platte+County+
Memorial+Hospital
**Control:** Other not–for–profit (including NFP Corporation) **Service:** General
Medical and Surgical

> **Staffed Beds:** 25 **Admissions:** 425 **Census:** 4 **Outpatient Visits:** 13514
> **Births:** 52 **Total Expense ($000):** 15135 **Payroll Expense ($000):** 7152
> **Personnel:** 109

### WORLAND—Washakie County

★ **WASHAKIE MEDICAL CENTER (531306)**, 400 South 15th Street,
Zip 82401–3531, Mailing Address: P.O. Box 700, Zip 82401–0700;
tel. 307/347–3221 **A**9 10 18 **F**2 3 11 13 15 28 29 31 34 40 43 45 53 57 59
64 70 75 76 77 79 81 82 85 87 89 93 97 107 111 114 119 147 **P**6
**S** Banner Health, Phoenix, AZ
Primary Contact: Jay Stallings, Chief Executive Officer
CFO: Jennifer Montgomery, Chief Financial Officer
CMO: Ryan Clifford, M.D., Chief of Staff
CHR: Jerry Clipp, Manager Human Resources
Web address: www.washakiemedicalcenter.com
**Control:** Other not–for–profit (including NFP Corporation) **Service:** General
Medical and Surgical

> **Staffed Beds:** 25 **Admissions:** 521 **Census:** 5 **Births:** 44 **Total Expense
> ($000):** 17979 **Payroll Expense ($000):** 7811 **Personnel:** 98

**Other Associated Areas**

## AMERICAN SAMOA

### PAGO PAGO— County

**LYNDON B. JOHNSON TROPICAL MEDICAL CENTER (640001)**, Faga'alu Village, Zip 96799, Mailing Address: P.O. Box LBJ, Zip 96799; tel. 684/633–1222, (Nonreporting) **A**10
Primary Contact: Patricia Tindall, Chief Executive Officer
Web address: www.asmca.org
**Control:** State–Government, nonfederal **Service:** General Medical and Surgical

**Staffed Beds:** 125

## GUAM

### AGANA—Guam County

✠ **U. S. NAVAL HOSPITAL GUAM**, Zip 96910; Mailing Address: FPO, tel. 671/344–9340, (Nonreporting) **A**1 **S** Bureau of Medicine and Surgery, Department of the Navy, Washington, DC
Primary Contact: Lieutenant Commander Rona Green
Web address: www.med.navy.mil/sites/usnhguam/Pages/default.aspx
**Control:** Navy, Government, federal **Service:** General Medical and Surgical

**Staffed Beds:** 55

### TAMUNING—Guam County

✠ **GUAM MEMORIAL HOSPITAL AUTHORITY (650001)**, 850 Governor Carlos G. Camacho Road, Zip 96913; tel. 671/647–2108, (Nonreporting) **A**1 10
Primary Contact: Joseph P. Verga, FACHE, Chief Executive Officer
CFO: Alan Ulrich, Chief Financial Officer
CMO: James J. Stadler, M.D., Associate Administrator Medical Services
CIO: Vince Quichocho, Manager Information Systems
CHR: Elizabeth Claros, Administrator Personnel Services
Web address: www.gmha.org
**Control:** Hospital district or authority, Government, nonfederal **Service:** General Medical and Surgical

**Staffed Beds:** 104

## MARSHALL ISLANDS

### KWAJALEIN ISLAND— County

**KWAJALEIN HOSPITAL**, U.S. Army Kwajalein Atoll, Zip 96960, Mailing Address: Box 1702, APO, UNIT, Zip 96555–5000; tel. 805/355–2225, (Nonreporting) **S** Department of the Army, Office of the Surgeon General, Falls Church, VA
Primary Contact: Elaine McMahon, Administrator
**Control:** Army, Government, federal **Service:** General Medical and Surgical

**Staffed Beds:** 14

## PUERTO RICO

### AGUADILLA—Aguadilla County

✠ **HOSPITAL BUEN SAMARITANO (400079)**, Carr #2 Km 141–1 Avenue Severiano Cuevas, Zip 603, Mailing Address: P.O. Box 4055, Zip 00605–4055; tel. 787/658–0000, (Nonreporting) **A**1 5 9 10
Primary Contact: Sarah I. Villanueva Cabrera, Interim Executive Director
CFO: Edwin Orama Acevedo, Financial Supervisor
CMO: Arturo Cedeno Llorens, M.D., Medical Director
CHR: Jose Garcia Rivera, Director Human Resources
CNO: Eneida Alicea Perez, Interim Nursing Director
Web address: www.hbspr.org
**Control:** Other not–for–profit (including NFP Corporation) **Service:** General Medical and Surgical

**Staffed Beds:** 150

### AIBONITO—Aibonito County

✠ **CENTRO DE SALUD CONDUCTUAL MENONITA–CIMA (404009)**, Carretera Estatal 14 Interior, Zip 705, Mailing Address: PO Box 871, Zip 705; tel. 787/714–2462, (Nonreporting) **A**1 9 10
Primary Contact: Pedro Melendez, Chief Executive Officer
**Control:** Other not–for–profit (including NFP Corporation) **Service:** Psychiatric

**Staffed Beds:** 20

✠ **MENNONITE GENERAL HOSPITAL (400018)**, Calle Jose C. Vasquez, Zip 705, Mailing Address: P.O. Box 372800, Cayey, Zip 00737–2800; tel. 787/535–1001 **A**1 9 10 **F**7 8 13 15 29 30 31 34 35 40 41 42 46 47 57 59 62 63 64 65 68 70 75 76 78 79 81 82 89 107 111 114 115 119 124 130 143 144 145 146 147 148 **P**5
Primary Contact: Pedro Melendez, Chief Executive Officer
COO: Marta R Mercado Suro, Chief Operating Officer
CFO: Jose E. Solivan, Chief Financial Officer
CMO: Victor Hernandez Miranda, M.D., Chief of Staff
CIO: Daniza Morales, Manager Information System
CHR: Evelyn Padilla Ortiz, Director Human Resources
CNO: Gloria Mercado, Director of Nursing
Web address: www.hospitalmenonita.com
**Control:** Other not–for–profit (including NFP Corporation) **Service:** General Medical and Surgical

**Staffed Beds:** 143 **Admissions:** 9031 **Census:** 99 **Outpatient Visits:** 66107 **Births:** 656 **Total Expense ($000):** 68247 **Payroll Expense ($000):** 23096 **Personnel:** 860

### ARECIBO—Arecibo County

✠ **HOSPITAL DR. CAYETANO COLL Y TOSTE (400087)**, 129 San Luis Avenue, Zip 612, Mailing Address: P.O. Box 659, Zip 613; tel. 787/650–7272 **A**1 3 9 10 **F**1 3 8 14 15 17 29 30 40 41 43 45 46 60 61 65 72 73 74 75 76 79 80 81 91 97 100 102 107 108 110 111 112 114 115 118 119 129 130 141 147 148
Primary Contact: Homar Perez, Chief Executive Officer and Vice President Administration
COO: Jamie Rivera, Chief Financial Officer
CFO: Agustin Gonzalez, Director Finance
CMO: Antoine Pavia, M.D., Medical Director
CIO: David Valle, Chief Information Officer
CHR: Yesenia Natal, Coordinator Human Resources
CNO: Iris Toledo, Chief Nursing Officer
Web address: www.cayetano@xsn.net
**Control:** Corporation, Investor–owned, for–profit **Service:** General Medical and Surgical

**Staffed Beds:** 202 **Admissions:** 9592 **Census:** 138 **Outpatient Visits:** 41505 **Births:** 988 **Total Expense ($000):** 50414 **Payroll Expense ($000):** 14716 **Personnel:** 597

---

**Hospital, Medicare Provider Number, Address, Telephone, Approval, Facility, and Physician Codes, Health Care System**

★ American Hospital Association (AHA) membership
□ The Joint Commission accreditation
○ Healthcare Facilities Accreditation Program
◇ DNV Healthcare Inc. accreditation
⇧ Center for Improvement in Healthcare Quality
△ Commission on Accreditation of Rehabilitation Facilities (CARF) accreditation

★ **HOSPITAL METROPOLITANO DR. SUSONI (400117)**, Calle Palma #55,
Zip 612, Mailing Address: P.O. Box 145200, Zip 614; tel. 787/650–1030 **A**9 10
**F**3 7 15 29 40 41 45 49 51 64 70 74 75 77 79 81 87 107 110 111 114 119
130 148
Primary Contact: Astrid J. Abreu, Executive Director
CFO: Hector Ortiz, Financial Director
CMO: Ada S. Miranda, M.D., Medical Director
CIO: Mayra Montano, Director Information Systems
CHR: Janiva Hernandez, Coordinator Human Resources
CNO: Carmen G. Fuster, Nursing Director
Web address: www.metropavia.com/DrSusoni.cfm
**Control:** Corporation, Investor–owned, for–profit **Service:** General Medical and
Surgical

**Staffed Beds:** 134 **Admissions:** 8078 **Census:** 108 **Outpatient Visits:** 63626
**Births:** 0 **Total Expense ($000):** 40594 **Payroll Expense ($000):** 12939

### ARROYO—Arroyo County

★ **LAFAYETTE HOSPITAL (400026)**, Central Lafayette, Zip 714, Mailing Address:
P.O. Box 207, Zip 714; tel. 787/839–3232, (Nonreporting) **A**9 10
Primary Contact: Ruth M. Ortiz Vargas, Administrator
CMO: Jose L. Pimentel Fernandez, Medical Director
**Control:** Corporation, Investor–owned, for–profit **Service:** General Medical and
Surgical

**Staffed Beds:** 38

### BAYAMON—Bayamon County

★ **DOCTOR'S CENTER OF BAYAMON (400102)**, Extension Hermanas Davila,
Zip 960, Mailing Address: P.O. Box 2957, Zip 960; tel. 787/622–5420,
(Nonreporting) **A**10
Primary Contact: Carlos Blanco, M.D., Administrator
**Control:** Corporation, Investor–owned, for–profit **Service:** General Medical and
Surgical

**Staffed Beds:** 91

☒ **HOSPITAL HERMANOS MELENDEZ (400032)**, Route 2, KM 11–7, Zip 960,
Mailing Address: P.O. Box 306, Zip 960; tel. 787/620–8181, (Includes PUERTO
RICO CHILDREN'S HOSPITAL, P.O. Box 1999, Zip 00960; tel. 787/474–1378;
Tania Conde, Administrator), (Nonreporting) **A**1 3 9 10
Primary Contact: Maria T. Machado, Administrator
CFO: Luz D. Medina, Controller
CMO: Norma Ortiz, M.D., Medical Director
CIO: Leticia Santana, Administrator Medical Records
Web address: www.hospitalhermanosmelendez.net
**Control:** Corporation, Investor–owned, for–profit **Service:** General Medical and
Surgical

**Staffed Beds:** 211

☒ **HOSPITAL SAN PABLO (400109)**, Calle Santa Cruz 70, Zip 00961–7020,
Mailing Address: P.O. Box 236, Zip 00960–0236; tel. 787/740–4747 **A**1 3 5 9
10 **F**3 8 13 17 18 19 20 22 24 26 29 30 31 34 40 41 45 46 47 49 51 59 70
72 73 74 75 76 78 79 80 81 86 87 88 89 92 93 107 110 111 114 115 119
126 130 145 146 148 **P**1
Primary Contact: Jose E. Carballo, Chief Executive Officer and Managing Director
Web address: www.sanpablo.com
**Control:** Corporation, Investor–owned, for–profit **Service:** General Medical and
Surgical

**Staffed Beds:** 394 **Admissions:** 16704 **Census:** 328 **Outpatient Visits:**
64646 **Births:** 1358 **Total Expense ($000):** 146153 **Payroll Expense**
**($000):** 53823 **Personnel:** 1668

☒ **HOSPITAL UNIVERSITARIO DR. RAMON RUIZ ARNAU (400105)**, Avenue
Laurel, Santa Juanita, Zip 956; tel. 787/787–5151, (Nonreporting) **A**1 3 5 10
**S** Puerto Rico Department of Health, San Juan, PR
Primary Contact: Humberto M. Monserrate, Chief Executive Officer
CFO: Elsie Morales, Chief Financial Officer
CMO: Hector Cintron Principe, M.D., Director
CIO: Irma Duprey, Administrator Medical Records
CHR: Aurea De Leon, Chief Human Resources Officer
**Control:** State–Government, nonfederal **Service:** General Medical and Surgical

**Staffed Beds:** 101

### CABO ROJO—Cabo Rojo County

☒ **HOSPITAL PSIQUIATRICO METROPOLITANO (404007)**, 108 Munoz Rivera
Street, Zip 00623–4060, Mailing Address: P.O. Box 910, Zip 00623–0910;
tel. 787/851–2025 **A**1 9 10 **F**2 40 98 101 102 103 105
Primary Contact: Elizabeth De Santiago, Director
**Control:** Hospital district or authority, Government, nonfederal **Service:**
Psychiatric

**Staffed Beds:** 80 **Admissions:** 2114 **Census:** 29 **Births:** 0 **Total Expense**
**($000):** 4166 **Payroll Expense ($000):** 2955 **Personnel:** 52

### CAGUAS—Caguas County

☒ **HOSPITAL HIMA SAN PABLO CAGUAS (400120)**, Avenida Munoz Marin,
Zip 726, Mailing Address: P.O. Box 4980, Zip 726; tel. 787/653–3434 **A**1 2 3 5
9 10 **F**3 8 13 15 16 20 22 26 29 30 31 40 41 42 43 54 57 58 68 70 72 74
75 76 78 80 81 88 89 92 93 107 108 111 114 115 116 117 118 119 124
126 130 136 141 142 145 146 147 **P**8
Primary Contact: Claudia V. Guzman, Executive Director
CFO: Luis A. Arroyo, Chief Financial Officer
CMO: Ivan E. Del Toro, M.D., Medical Director
CIO: Giovanni Piereschi, Vice President Enterprise Information and Chief
Information Officer
CHR: Elena Robinson, Chief Human Resources Officer
CNO: Elenia Berrios, Chief Nursing Officer
**Control:** Corporation, Investor–owned, for–profit **Service:** General Medical and
Surgical

**Staffed Beds:** 415 **Admissions:** 19515 **Census:** 345 **Outpatient Visits:**
57763 **Births:** 2036

☐ **HOSPITAL MENONITA DE CAGUAS (400104)**, P.O. Box 6660,
Zip 00726–6660; tel. 787/653–0550, (Nonreporting) **A**1 5 10
Primary Contact: Rogelio Diaz, Administrator
**Control:** Other not–for–profit (including NFP Corporation) **Service:** General
Medical and Surgical

**Staffed Beds:** 25

### CAROLINA—Carolina County

☒ **HOSPITAL DE LA UNIVERSIDAD DE PUERTO RICO/DR. FEDERICO TRILLA
(400112)**, 65th Infanteria, KM 8 3, Zip 984, Mailing Address: P.O. Box 6021,
Zip 984; tel. 787/757–1800, (Nonreporting) **A**1 3 5 9 10
Primary Contact: Diraida Maldonado, Chief Executive Officer
COO: Diraida Maldonado, Chief Executive Officer
CFO: Yolanda Quinonez, Chief Financial Officer
CMO: Marina Roman, M.D., Medical Director
CIO: Francisco Perez, Manager Management Information Systems
CHR: Betzaida Jimenez, Director Human Resources
Web address: www.hospitalupr.org
**Control:** Corporation, Investor–owned, for–profit **Service:** General Medical and
Surgical

**Staffed Beds:** 250

### CASTANER—Lares County

★ **CASTANER GENERAL HOSPITAL (400010)**, KM 64–2, Route 135, Zip 631,
Mailing Address: P.O. Box 1003, Zip 631; tel. 787/829–5010, (Nonreporting) **A**3
5 10
Primary Contact: Domingo Monroig, Executive Director
COO: Agustin Ponce, Supervisor Maintenance
CFO: Guillermo Jimenez, Director Finance
CMO: Jose O. Rodriguez, M.D., Medical Director
CIO: Domingo Monroig, Executive Director
CHR: Nydimar Salcedo, Chief Human Resources Officer
CNO: Margarita Rentas, R.N., Nursing Director
**Control:** Other not–for–profit (including NFP Corporation) **Service:** General
Medical and Surgical

**Staffed Beds:** 24

### CAYEY—Cayey County

☒ **HOSPITAL MENONITA DE CAYEY (400013)**, 4 H. Mendoza Street,
Zip 00736–3801, Mailing Address: P.O. Box 373130, Zip 00737–3130;
tel. 787/263–1001, (Nonreporting) **A**1 5 9 10
Primary Contact: Pedro Melendez, Chief Executive Director
COO: Leda Marta R Mercado, Chief Operating Officer
CFO: Jose E. Solivan, Chief Financial Officer
CMO: Luis J Rodriquez Saenz, M.D., Medical Director
CIO: Daniza Morales, Chief Information Officer
CHR: Evelyn Padilla Ortiz, Director Human Resources
Web address: www.hospitalmenonita.com
**Control:** Other not–for–profit (including NFP Corporation) **Service:** General
Medical and Surgical

**Staffed Beds:** 208

### CIDRA—Cidra County

☒ **FIRST HOSPITAL PANAMERICANO (404004)**, State Road 787 KM 1 5,
Zip 739, Mailing Address: P.O. Box 1400, Zip 739; tel. 787/739–5555,
(Nonreporting) **A**1 3 5 9 10 **S** Universal Health Services, Inc., King of Prussia, PA
Primary Contact: Astro Munoz, Executive Director
COO: Tim McCarthy, President Puerto Rico Division
CFO: Arthur Fernandez, Chief Financial Officer
CMO: Arlene Martinez-Nieto, M.D., Chief Medical Officer
CIO: Tomas Rodriguez, Chief Information Technology Officer
CHR: Shirley Ayala, Director Human Resources
Web address: www.hospitalpanamericano.com
**Control:** Corporation, Investor–owned, for–profit **Service:** Psychiatric

**Staffed Beds:** 153

*Many Facility Codes have changed. Please refer to the AHA Guide Code Chart.* © 2015 AHA Guide

## COTO LAUREL—Ponce County

★ **HOSPITAL SAN CRISTOBAL (400113)**, 506 Carr Road, Zip 780; tel. 787/848–2100, (Nonreporting) **A**3 5 9 10
Primary Contact: Pedro L. Benetti–Loyola, Administrator
COO: Pedro L. Benetti–Loyola, Senior Executive and Vice President
CFO: Marian Collazo, Director Finance
CMO: Ramon Rodriguez Rivas, M.D., Medical Director
CIO: Ramon Acevedo, Supervisor Information Systems
CHR: Candie Rodriguez, Director Human Resources
Web address: www.hospitalsancristobal.com
**Control:** Corporation, Investor–owned, for–profit **Service:** Other specialty

**Staffed Beds:** 103

## FAJARDO—Fajardo County

★ **CARIBBEAN MEDICAL CENTER (400131)**, 151 Avenue Osvaldo Molina, Zip 00738–4013, Mailing Address: Call Box 70006, Zip 00738–7006; tel. 787/801–0081, (Nonreporting) **A**9 10
Primary Contact: Eduardo Sotomayor, Executive Director
CMO: Miguel Rodriguez, Medical Director
**Control:** Other not–for–profit (including NFP Corporation) **Service:** General Medical and Surgical

**Staffed Beds:** 45

✠ **HOSPITAL SAN PABLO DEL ESTE (400125)**, Avenida General Valero, 404, Zip 738, Mailing Address: P.O. Box 1028, Zip 00738–1028; tel. 787/863–0505, (Nonreporting) **A**1 9 10
Primary Contact: Aixa Irizarry, Executive Director
CFO: Luis A. Arroyo, Chief Financial Officer
CMO: Manuel Navas, M.D., Medical Director
CHR: Vilma Rodriguez, Director Human Resources
Web address: www.sanpablo.com
**Control:** Corporation, Investor–owned, for–profit **Service:** General Medical and Surgical

**Staffed Beds:** 145

## GUAYAMA—Guayama County

✠ **HOSPITAL EPISCOPAL SAN LUCAS GUAYAMA (400048)**, Avenue Pedro Albizu Campos, Zip 784, Mailing Address: PO Box 10011, Zip 00785–1006; tel. 787/864–4300, (Nonreporting) **A**1 3 5 9 10
Primary Contact: Julio Colon, CPA, Chief Executive Officer
COO: Arnaldo Rodriguez Sanchez, M.D., Chief Operating Officer
CFO: Rosemary De La Cruz, Chief Financial Officer
CMO: Gerson Jimenez, M.D., Medical Director
CHR: Ivette Lacot, Director Human Resources
Web address: www.ssepr.com
**Control:** Church–operated, Nongovernment, not–for profit **Service:** General Medical and Surgical

**Staffed Beds:** 115

★ **HOSPITAL SANTA ROSA (400009)**, Veterans Avenue, Zip 784, Mailing Address: P.O. Box 10008, Zip 785; tel. 787/864–0101 **A**9 10 **F**18 20 40 42 45 46 70 76 81 89 107 111 119 130
Primary Contact: Gloria Diaz, Executive Director
CFO: Edwin De Jesus, Comptroller
CMO: Ausberto Alejandro, M.D., President
CIO: Waleska Rolon, Manager
**Control:** Other not–for–profit (including NFP Corporation) **Service:** General Medical and Surgical

**Staffed Beds:** 89 **Admissions:** 2980 **Census:** 29 **Outpatient Visits:** 24551 **Births:** 171 **Total Expense ($000):** 13308 **Payroll Expense ($000):** 3607 **Personnel:** 131

## GUAYNABO—Guaynabo County

**PROFESSIONAL HOSPITAL GUAYNABO (400122)**, Carretera 199 Km 1.2 Avenue, Zip 969, Mailing Address: PO Box 1609, Zip 970; tel. 787/708–6560, (Nonreporting) **A**3 10
Primary Contact: Leonardo Valentin, Chief Executive Officer
Web address: www.professionalhospital.com
**Control:** Other not–for–profit (including NFP Corporation) **Service:** Psychiatric

**Staffed Beds:** 54

## HATO REY—San Juan County, See San Juan

## HUMACAO—Humacao County

**HOSPITAL DR. DOMINGUEZ** See Hospital Oriente

✠ **HOSPITAL HMA DE HUMACAO (400005)**, 3 Font Martelo Street, Zip 00791–3342, Mailing Address: P.O. Box 639, Zip 00792–0639; tel. 787/656–2424, (Nonreporting) **A**1 9 10
Primary Contact: Aixa Irizarry, Executive Director
COO: Carlos M. Pineiro, President
CFO: Luis A. Arroyo, Chief Financial Officer
CMO: Francisco R. Carballo, M.D., Medical Director
CIO: Giovanni Piereschi, Vice President Management Information Systems
CHR: Iris Abreu, Supervisor Human Resources
**Control:** Corporation, Investor–owned, for–profit **Service:** General Medical and Surgical

**Staffed Beds:** 64

★ **HOSPITAL ORIENTE (400011)**, 300 Font Martelo Street, Zip 00791–3230, Mailing Address: P.O. Box 699, Zip 00792–0699; tel. 787/852–0505, (Nonreporting) **A**9 10
Primary Contact: Juan Carlos Latorre, Administrator
CFO: Ivonne Rivera, Director Finance
CMO: Carmelo Herrero, M.D., Medical Director
CHR: Ivonne Lopez, Director Human Resources
**Control:** Corporation, Investor–owned, for–profit **Service:** General Medical and Surgical

**Staffed Beds:** 60

★ **RYDER MEMORIAL HOSPITAL (400007)**, 355 Font Martelo Street, Zip 00791–3249, Mailing Address: P.O. Box 859, Zip 00792–0859; tel. 787/852–0768, (Total facility includes 62 beds in nursing home–type unit) **A**9 10 **F**3 6 8 10 13 15 20 26 30 31 34 35 39 40 41 42 54 56 57 59 61 62 63 64 65 68 70 72 75 76 77 78 81 87 89 93 94 107 110 111 115 119 124 125 128 130 144 146 147 **P**5 8
Primary Contact: Jose R. Feliciano, Chief Executive Officer
CFO: Jose O. Ortiz, Chief Financial Officer
CMO: Raul Ramos Pereira, M.D., Medical Director
CIO: Joseph V. Cruz, Chief Information Officer
CHR: Maria Figueroa, Director Human Resources
CNO: Aurelis Burgus, Nursing Director
Web address: www.hryder@prtc.net
**Control:** Other not–for–profit (including NFP Corporation) **Service:** General Medical and Surgical

**Staffed Beds:** 165 **Admissions:** 6697 **Census:** 103 **Outpatient Visits:** 103929 **Births:** 978 **Total Expense ($000):** 56081 **Payroll Expense ($000):** 21580 **Personnel:** 873

## MANATI—Manati County

✠ **DOCTORS CENTER (400118)**, KM 47–7, Zip 674, Mailing Address: P.O. Box 30532, Zip 674; tel. 787/854–3322, (Nonreporting) **A**1 9 10
Primary Contact: Carlos Blanco, M.D., Administrator
**Control:** Corporation, Investor–owned, for–profit **Service:** General Medical and Surgical

**Staffed Beds:** 150

★ **HEALTHSOUTH HOSPITAL OF MANATI (403026)**, Carretera 2, Kilometro 47 7, Zip 674; tel. 787/621–3800 **A**9 10 **F**3 72 80 90 91 96 130 **P**1
**S** HEALTHSOUTH Corporation, Birmingham, AL
Primary Contact: Enrique A. Vicens–Rivera, Jr., JD, Chief Executive Officer
CFO: Jesus M. Corazon, Controller
CMO: Jamie L. Marrero, M.D., Medical Director
CHR: Erika Landrau, Director Human Resources
CNO: Evelyn Diaz, R.N., Chief Nursing Officer
Web address: www.healthsouth.com
**Control:** Corporation, Investor–owned, for–profit **Service:** Rehabilitation

**Staffed Beds:** 40 **Admissions:** 1099 **Census:** 37 **Outpatient Visits:** 0 **Births:** 0 **Total Expense ($000):** 7190 **Payroll Expense ($000):** 3517

✠ **HOSPITAL MANATI MEDICAL CENTER (400114)**, Calle Hernandez, Carrion 668, Zip 674, Mailing Address: P.O. Box 1142, Zip 00674–1142; tel. 787/621–3700 **A**1 3 5 9 10 **F**3 8 13 14 15 17 18 19 20 22 26 29 30 34 40 41 45 46 47 48 49 51 60 69 70 73 74 75 76 78 79 80 87 89 93 107 110 111 113 114 115 119 130 145 146 **P**8
Primary Contact: Alfonso Vazquez, Executive Director
CFO: Noriselle Rivera–Pol, Vice President Finance
CMO: Luis R. Rosa–Toledo, M.D., Medical Director
CIO: Alberto Medina, Information Technology Senior Consultant
CHR: Nilda Paravisini, Director Human Resources
Web address: www.manatimedical.com
**Control:** Corporation, Investor–owned, for–profit **Service:** General Medical and Surgical

**Staffed Beds:** 235 **Admissions:** 16908 **Census:** 226 **Births:** 1869

---

**Hospital, Medicare Provider Number, Address, Telephone, Approval, Facility, and Physician Codes, Health Care System**

★ American Hospital Association (AHA) membership  ○ Healthcare Facilities Accreditation Program  ⇑ Center for Improvement in Healthcare Quality Accreditation
☐ The Joint Commission accreditation  ◇ DNV Healthcare Inc. accreditation  △ Commission on Accreditation of Rehabilitation Facilities (CARF) accreditation

## MAYAGUEZ—Mayaguez County

☒ **BELLA VISTA HOSPITAL (400014)**, State Road 349, Zip 680, Mailing Address: P.O. Box 1750, Zip 681; tel. 787/834–6000, (Nonreporting) **A**1 3 5 9 10
Primary Contact: Jesus Nieves, Chief Executive Officer
CFO: Enrique Rivera, Chief Financial Officer
CMO: Miguel Cruz, M.D., Medical Director
CHR: Benjamin Astacio, Director Human Resources
Web address: www.bvhpr.org
**Control:** Church–operated, Nongovernment, not–for profit **Service:** General Medical and Surgical

**Staffed Beds: 157**

☒ **DR. RAMON E. BETANCES HOSPITAL–MAYAGUEZ MEDICAL CENTER BRANCH (400103)**, 410 Hostos Avenue, Zip 00680–1501, Mailing Address: P.O. Box 600, Zip 00681–0600; tel. 787/652–9200, (Nonreporting) **A**1 3 5 9 10
Primary Contact: Jaime Maestre, Chief Executive Officer
CMO: Milton D. Carrero, M.D., Medical Director
CHR: Betsmari Medina, Director Human Resources
**Control:** State–Government, nonfederal **Service:** General Medical and Surgical

**Staffed Beds: 144**

★ **HOSPITAL PEREA (400123)**, 15 Basora Street, Zip 681, Mailing Address: P.O. Box 170, Zip 681; tel. 787/834–0101, (Nonreporting) **A**3 10 **S** United Medical Corporation, Windermere, FL
Primary Contact: Jorge I. Martinez, Executive Director
CFO: Joannie Garcia, CPA, Director Finance
CMO: Humberto Olivencia, M.D., Medical Director
Web address: www.paviahealth.com/perea_hospital.htm
**Control:** Corporation, Investor–owned, for–profit **Service:** General Medical and Surgical

**Staffed Beds: 103**

**HOSPITAL SAN ANTONIO (018487)**, Calle Drive Ramon Emeterio Betances N. #18, Zip 680; tel. 787/834–0050, (Nonreporting) **A**3 5
Primary Contact: Francisco Martinez, Executive Director
**Control:** Other not–for–profit (including NFP Corporation) **Service:** General Medical and Surgical

**Staffed Beds: 25**

## MOCA— County

**CENTRO DE TRAUMA (400127)**, Calle Menlo Miranda, Zip 676; tel. 787/777–3535, (Nonreporting)
**Control:** Other not–for–profit (including NFP Corporation) **Service:** General Medical and Surgical

**Staffed Beds: 25**

★ **HOSPITAL SAN CARLOS BORROMEO (400111)**, 550 Concepcion Vera Ayala, Zip 676; tel. 787/877–8000 **A**9 10 **F**8 15 29 30 34 40 45 65 70 74 75 76 79 81 89 107 111 115 119 130 133 145 146 148 **P**8
Primary Contact: Rosaida M. Crespo, Executive Director
COO: Rosaida M. Crespo, Executive Director
CFO: Irma Cabrera, Finance Director
CMO: Erick Nieves, M.D., Medical Director
CIO: Juan Carlos Soto, Director Information Systems
CHR: Migdalia Ortiz, Director Human Resources
CNO: Luz M. Velez, Director–Administration of Nursing Services
Web address: www.hscbpr.org
**Control:** Other not–for–profit (including NFP Corporation) **Service:** General Medical and Surgical

**Staffed Beds: 106 Admissions: 5151 Census: 68 Outpatient Visits: 35056 Births: 736**

## PONCE—Ponce County

☒ **DR. PILA'S HOSPITAL (400003)**, Avenida Las Americas, Zip 731, Mailing Address: P.O. Box 1910, Zip 00733–1910; tel. 787/848–5600 **A**1 3 5 9 10 **F**3 8 13 29 30 34 35 36 37 40 41 45 49 50 51 57 59 60 62 64 65 70 72 75 76 77 79 81 87 89 100 107 111 114 119 130 146 148
Primary Contact: Rafael Alvarado, Chief Executive Officer
Web address: www.drpila.com
**Control:** Corporation, Investor–owned, for–profit **Service:** General Medical and Surgical

**Staffed Beds: 143 Admissions: 7229 Census: 86 Outpatient Visits: 71438 Births: 535 Total Expense ($000): 41721 Payroll Expense ($000): 11948 Personnel: 361**

☒ **HOSPITAL DE DAMAS (400022)**, Ponce by Pass, Zip 731; tel. 787/840–8686, (Nonreporting) **A**1 3 5 9 10
Primary Contact: Edwin Sueiro, Administrator
CFO: Julio Colon, Financial Director
CMO: Pedro Benitez, M.D., Medical Director
CIO: Bienvenido Ortiz, Coordinator Information Systems
CHR: Gilberto Cuevas, Director Human Resources
CNO: Sandra Dominicci, Nursing Director
Web address: www.hospitaldamas.com
**Control:** Other not–for–profit (including NFP Corporation) **Service:** General Medical and Surgical

**Staffed Beds: 251**

**HOSPITAL DE PSIQUIATRIA FORENSE**, Road 14, Zip 731; tel. 787/844–0210, (Nonreporting)
Web address: www.bestmentalhealthfacilities.com/hospital–psiquiatria–forenseponce–in–ponce–pr–731/
**Control:** State–Government, nonfederal **Service:** Psychiatric

**Staffed Beds: 25**

★ **HOSPITAL ONCOLOGICO ANDRES GRILLASCA (400028)**, Centro Medico De Ponce, Zip 733, Mailing Address: P.O. Box 331324, Zip 00733–1324; tel. 787/848–0800, (Nonreporting) **A**3 5 9
Primary Contact: Manuel J. Vazquez, Executive Administrator
CMO: Roberto Velasquez, M.D., Medical Director
CIO: Maria T. Teissonniere, Director Public Relations
CHR: Carlos T. Santiago, Director Human Resources
**Control:** Other not–for–profit (including NFP Corporation) **Service:** Cancer

**Staffed Beds: 49**

★ **INSPIRA PONCE (404008)**, Calle Guadalupe, #184, Piso2, Zip 730; tel. 787/709–4130, (Nonreporting) **A**10
Primary Contact: Alberto M. Varela, M.D., President
Web address: www.inspirapr.com
**Control:** Corporation, Investor–owned, for–profit **Service:** Psychiatric

**Staffed Beds: 30**

☒ **ST. LUKE'S EPISCOPAL HOSPITAL (400044)**, 917 Tito Castro Avenue, Zip 00731–4717, Mailing Address: P.O. Box 336810, Zip 00733–6810; tel. 787/844–2080 **A**1 3 5 9 10 **F**3 8 13 14 15 17 18 20 22 24 26 28 29 30 34 40 41 42 43 45 46 49 50 57 59 67 70 72 73 74 75 76 79 81 85 86 87 88 89 91 92 93 107 110 111 113 114 115 118 119 128 130 144 148
Primary Contact: Julio Colon, Interim President and Chief Executive Officer
CFO: Julio Colon, Chief Financial Officer
CMO: Jenaro Scarano, M.D., Medical Director
CHR: Juan Salazar, Director Human Resources
Web address: www.sanlucaspr.com
**Control:** Church–operated, Nongovernment, not–for profit **Service:** General Medical and Surgical

**Staffed Beds: 334 Admissions: 16791 Census: 275 Outpatient Visits: 94147 Births: 2085 Total Expense ($000): 107747 Payroll Expense ($000): 32427 Personnel: 1146**

## RIO PIEDRAS—San Juan County, See San Juan

## SAN GERMAN—San German County

☒ **HOSPITAL DE LA CONCEPCION (400021)**, Carr 2, Km 173, Bo Cain Alto, Zip 00683–3920, Mailing Address: P.O. Box 285, Zip 00683–0285; tel. 787/892–1860, (Nonreporting) **A**1 3 5 9 10
Primary Contact: Felicita Bonilla, Administrator
COO: Gustavo Almodovar, Executive Director
CFO: Lizmari Calderon, Director Finance
CMO: Ivan Acosta, M.D., Medical Director
CIO: Daniel Ferreira, Director Management Information Systems
CHR: Ada Bermudez, Director Human Resources
CNO: Amanda Caraballo, Nursing Director
Web address: www.hospitalconcepcion.org
**Control:** Church–operated, Nongovernment, not–for profit **Service:** General Medical and Surgical

**Staffed Beds: 167**

★ **HOSPITAL METROPOLITANO SAN GERMAN (400126)**, Calle Javilla Al Costado Parque de Bombas, Zip 683; tel. 787/892–5300, (Nonreporting) **A**9 10
Primary Contact: Nannete Acosta, Chief Executive Officer
**Control:** Corporation, Investor–owned, for–profit **Service:** Other specialty

**Staffed Beds: 40**

**SAN JUAN—San Juan County**
**(Mailing Addresses - Hato Rey, Rio Piedras)**

✴ **ASHFORD PRESBYTERIAN COMMUNITY HOSPITAL (400001)**, 1451 Avenue Ashford, Zip 00907–1511, Mailing Address: P.O. Box 9020032, Zip 00902–0032; tel. 787/721–2160 **A**1 5 9 10 **F**3 8 11 13 15 17 18 30 40 41 43 45 46 49 51 53 59 65 70 72 75 76 79 80 81 82 87 88 89 91 93 97 107 110 111 114 119 130 131 146 147 148 **P**5
Primary Contact: Pedro J. Gonzalez, FACHE, Chief Executive Officer
COO: Obdulia Medina, MSN, Associate Director for Administrative Support, Clinical Management and Ambulatory Care
CFO: Mayra Torres, Chief Financial Officer
CMO: Francisco de Torres, M.D., Medical Director
CIO: Gerald Lopez, Chief Information Officer
CHR: Irma Carrillo, Director Human Resources
CNO: Itza Soto, MSN, Nursing Executive
Web address: www.presbypr.com
**Control:** Other not–for–profit (including NFP Corporation) **Service:** General Medical and Surgical

**Staffed Beds:** 191 **Admissions:** 10737 **Census:** 137 **Outpatient Visits:** 56696 **Births:** 3351 **Total Expense ($000):** 77420 **Payroll Expense ($000):** 26511 **Personnel:** 771

✴ **AUXILIO MUTUO HOSPITAL (400016)**, Ponce De Leon Avenue, Zip 00918–1000, Mailing Address: P.O. Box 191227, Zip 00919–1227; tel. 787/758–2000, (Nonreporting) **A**1 3 5 9 10
Primary Contact: Jorge L. Matta Serrano, Administrator
COO: Carmen Martin, Associate Administrator
CFO: Maria L. Marti, Director Fiscal Services
CMO: Jose Isado, M.D., Medical Director
CIO: Edgardo Rodriguez, Director Management Information Systems
CHR: Maria Vega, Director Human Resources
Web address: www.auxiliomutuo.com
**Control:** Other not–for–profit (including NFP Corporation) **Service:** General Medical and Surgical

**Staffed Beds:** 483

✴ **CARDIOVASCULAR CENTER OF PUERTO RICO AND THE CARIBBEAN (400124)**, Americo Miranda Centro Medico, Zip 936, Mailing Address: P.O. Box 366528, Zip 00936–6528; tel. 787/754–8500, (Nonreporting) **A**1 3 5 10 **S** Puerto Rico Department of Health, San Juan, PR
Primary Contact: Waleska Crespo, Executive Director
COO: Wilfredo Rabelo Millan, Chief Operating Officer
CFO: Arthur J. Fernandez del Valle, Chief Financial Officer
CMO: Jose E. Novoa Loyola, M.D., Medical Director
CIO: Eugenio Torres Ayala, Director Information Systems
CHR: Myriam T. Rodriguez Schmidt, Director Human Resources
CNO: Pedro Laureano Cantre, Chief Nursing Officer
Web address: www.cardiovascular.gobierno.pr
**Control:** State–Government, nonfederal **Service:** General Medical and Surgical

**Staffed Beds:** 146

★ **DOCTORS' CENTER HOSPITAL SAN JUAN (400006)**, 1395 San Rafael Street, Zip 00909–2518, Mailing Address: Box 11338, Santurce Station, Zip 00910–3428; tel. 787/999–7620 **A**9 10 **F**29 40 41 45 46 70 74 76 77 78 81 89 107 119 130 148
Primary Contact: Norma Marrero, Executive Administrator
COO: Norma Marrero, Executive Administrator
CFO: Alejandro Santiago, Director Finance
CMO: Ubaldo Santiago, M.D., Chairman
CIO: Luis Alicea, Chief Information Officer
CHR: Carmen Perez, Director Human Resources
CNO: Lesbia Lopez, Chief Nursing Officer
Web address: www.tuhospitalfamiliar.com
**Control:** Corporation, Investor–owned, for–profit **Service:** General Medical and Surgical

**Staffed Beds:** 125 **Admissions:** 6431 **Census:** 115 **Outpatient Visits:** 36015 **Births:** 260 **Total Expense ($000):** 34703 **Payroll Expense ($000):** 9939 **Personnel:** 451

★ **HEALTHSOUTH REHABILITATION HOSPITAL OF SAN JUAN (403025)**, University Hospital, 3rd Floor, Zip 923, Mailing Address: P.O. Box 70344, Zip 923; tel. 787/274–5100 **A**3 5 9 10 **F**7 29 77 90 93 **P**1 **S** HEALTHSOUTH Corporation, Birmingham, AL
Primary Contact: Daniel Del Castillo, Chief Executive Officer
CFO: Jesus M. Corazon, Controller
CMO: Eduardo Ramos, M.D., Medical Director
CHR: Frances Fuentes, Coordinator Human Resources
CNO: Zamarys Rivera, R.N., Chief Nursing Officer
Web address: www.healthsouthsanjuan.com
**Control:** Corporation, Investor–owned, for–profit **Service:** Rehabilitation

**Staffed Beds:** 32 **Admissions:** 892 **Census:** 32 **Outpatient Visits:** 5405 **Births:** 0 **Total Expense ($000):** 7076 **Payroll Expense ($000):** 3424 **Personnel:** 100

★ **HOSPITAL DE PSIQUIATRIA (404006)**, Dr. Ramon Fernandez Marina, P.O. Box 2100, Zip 936; tel. 787/766–4646, (Nonreporting) **A**3 5
Primary Contact: Miguel J. Bustelo, Executive Director
CMO: Brunilda Vazquez, Medical Director
CHR: Idalia Garcia, Chief Human Resources Officer
**Control:** State–Government, nonfederal **Service:** Psychiatric

**Staffed Beds:** 153

✴ **HOSPITAL DEL MAESTRO (400004)**, 550 Sergio Cuevas, Zip 00918–3741, Mailing Address: P.O. Box 364708, Zip 00936–4708; tel. 787/758–8383, (Nonreporting) **A**1 9 10
Primary Contact: Jorge Torres Otero, Executive Director
CFO: Marisol Vargas, Director Finance
CMO: Jose Montalvo, M.D., Medical Director
CIO: Laura Rodriguez, Director Medical Records
CHR: Orlando Santiago, Human Resources Officer
**Control:** Corporation, Investor–owned, for–profit **Service:** General Medical and Surgical

**Staffed Beds:** 250

✴ **HOSPITAL METROPOLITAN (400106)**, 1785 Carr 21, Zip 00921–3399, Mailing Address: P.O. Box 11981, Zip 922; tel. 787/782–9999, (Nonreporting) **A**1 9 10
Primary Contact: Jose Rosado, Chief Executive Officer
CFO: Maritza Rodriguez, Chief Financial Officer
CMO: Maria de los Angeles Correa, M.D., Medical Director
CIO: Manuel Santiago, Chief Information Officer
**Control:** Corporation, Investor–owned, for–profit **Service:** General Medical and Surgical

**Staffed Beds:** 127

✴ **HOSPITAL PAVIA–HATO REY (400128)**, 435 Ponce De Leon Avenue, Zip 00917–3428; tel. 787/641–2323, (Nonreporting) **A**1 3 5 9 10 **S** United Medical Corporation, Windermere, FL
Primary Contact: Guillermo Pastrana, Executive Director
Web address: www.paviahealth.com
**Control:** Corporation, Investor–owned, for–profit **Service:** General Medical and Surgical

**Staffed Beds:** 180

✴ **HOSPITAL PAVIA–SANTURCE (400019)**, 1462 Asia Street, Zip 00909–2143, Mailing Address: Box 11137, Santurce Station, Zip 00910–1137; tel. 787/727–6060 **A**1 10 **F**3 7 8 13 15 17 18 19 20 22 24 26 29 30 34 35 38 40 45 46 47 48 49 56 57 58 59 60 64 65 68 70 72 73 74 75 76 78 79 81 82 86 87 92 94 100 107 108 109 110 111 112 114 115 119 130 135 **S** United Medical Corporation, Windermere, FL
Primary Contact: Jose Luis Rodriguez, Chief Executive Officer
CFO: Francisco Espina, Director Finance
Web address: www.paviahealth.com
**Control:** Corporation, Investor–owned, for–profit **Service:** General Medical and Surgical

**Staffed Beds:** 198 **Admissions:** 9159 **Census:** 169 **Outpatient Visits:** 32996 **Births:** 1015 **Total Expense ($000):** 83577 **Payroll Expense ($000):** 24379 **Personnel:** 861

✴ **HOSPITAL PSIQUIATRICO CORRECCIONAL**, PMB 302 P.O. Box 70344, Zip 936; tel. 787/774–3344, (Nonreporting)
Primary Contact: Felicita E. Alvarado, Administrator
**Control:** State–Government, nonfederal **Service:** General Medical and Surgical

**Staffed Beds:** 25

| Hospital, Medicare Provider Number, Address, Telephone, Approval, Facility, and Physician Codes, Health Care System |
| --- |

★ American Hospital Association (AHA) membership
☐ The Joint Commission accreditation
○ Healthcare Facilities Accreditation Program
◇ DNV Healthcare Inc. accreditation
⇑ Center for Improvement in Healthcare Quality Accreditation
△ Commission on Accreditation of Rehabilitation Facilities (CARF) accreditation

⊞ **HOSPITAL SAN FRANCISCO (400098)**, 371 Avenida De Diego, Zip 00923–1711, Mailing Address: P.O. Box 29025, Zip 00929–0025; tel. 787/767–5100 **A**1 10 **F**3 8 30 40 41 42 45 46 54 60 65 70 79 81 88 89 107 110 111 119 146 147 **P**5
Primary Contact: Marcos Aguila, Chief Executive Officer
CFO: Lizzette Rodriguez, Director Finance
CMO: Hector L. Cotto, M.D., Medical Director
CIO: Deborah Nieves, Director Management Information Systems
CHR: Sugehi Santiago, Director
Web address: www.sanpablo.com
**Control:** Corporation, Investor–owned, for–profit **Service:** General Medical and Surgical

| Staffed Beds: 148 Admissions: 7402 Census: 109 Births: 0 |

★ **HOSPITAL SAN GERARDO (400121)**, 138 Avenue Winston Churchill, Zip 00926–6013; tel. 787/761–8383, (Nonreporting) **A**9 10
Primary Contact: Henry Ruberte, Administrator
**Control:** Other not–for–profit (including NFP Corporation) **Service:** Chronic disease

| Staffed Beds: 60 |

⊞ **I. GONZALEZ MARTINEZ ONCOLOGIC HOSPITAL (400012)**, Puerto Rico Medical Center, Hato Rey, Zip 935, Mailing Address: P.O. Box 191811, Zip 00919–1811; tel. 787/765–2382 **A**1 2 3 5 10 **F**3 8 15 18 29 30 31 34 35 45 54 57 58 59 63 64 65 66 70 75 77 78 79 81 86 87 93 100 107 110 111 114 119 130 132 136 141 146 148 **P**5
Primary Contact: Jorge De Jesus, Executive Director
COO: Felix Ortiz Baez, Administrator
CFO: Yolanda Quinones, Director Finance
CMO: Carlos Chevere, M.D., Medical Director
CHR: Luz Maria Hernandez, Director Human Resources
**Control:** Other not–for–profit (including NFP Corporation) **Service:** Cancer

| Staffed Beds: 57 Admissions: 1140 Census: 17 Outpatient Visits: 21252 Births: 0 Total Expense ($000): 14131 Payroll Expense ($000): 5258 Personnel: 146 |

★ **INDUSTRIAL HOSPITAL**, Puerto Rico Medical Center, Zip 936, Mailing Address: P.O. Box 365028, Zip 936; tel. 787/754–2525, (Nonreporting) **A**9
Primary Contact: Carlos Cabrera, Executive Director
CFO: Robert Bernier Casanova, Chief Financial Officer
CMO: Carmen Carrasquillo, M.D., Medical Director
CHR: Sonia M. Lebron, Human Resources Specialist
**Control:** State–Government, nonfederal **Service:** General Medical and Surgical

| Staffed Beds: 108 |

⊞ **SAN JORGE CHILDREN'S HOSPITAL**, 252 San Jorge Street, Santurce, Zip 00912–3310; tel. 787/727–1000, (Nonreporting) **A**1 3 5 9 **S** United Medical Corporation, Windermere, FL
Primary Contact: Domingo Cruz, Senior Vice President Operations
CFO: Jose Marrero, Director Finance
CMO: Luis Clavell, M.D., Medical Director
CIO: Rogelio Caballero, Chief Information Systems
CHR: Odette Burgos, Supervisor Human Resources
CNO: Leticia Fuentes, Nursing Director
Web address: www.sanjorgechildrenshospital.com
**Control:** Corporation, Investor–owned, for–profit **Service:** Children's general

| Staffed Beds: 125 |

⊞ **SAN JUAN CAPESTRANO HOSPITAL (404005)**, Rural Route 2, Box 11, Zip 926; tel. 787/625–2900, (Nonreporting) **A**1 9 10
Primary Contact: Marta Rivera Plaza, Chief Executive Officer and Managing Director
CFO: Julia Cruz, Chief Financial Officer
CMO: Jose' Alonso, M.D., Medical Director
CIO: Ana Morandeira, Director Marketing
CHR: Luis Rivera, Director Human Resources
Web address: www.sjcapestrano.com
**Control:** Corporation, Investor–owned, for–profit **Service:** Psychiatric

| Staffed Beds: 108 |

⊞ **SAN JUAN CITY HOSPITAL (400015)**, Puerto Rico Medical Center, Zip 928, Mailing Address: PMB 79, P.O. Box 70344, Zip 00936–8344; tel. 787/766–2222, (Nonreporting) **A**1 3 5 10
Primary Contact: Ramon Lopez Maldonado, Executive Director
COO: Norma Marcano, Chief Operating Officer
CFO: Jaime Rodriguez, Chief Financial Officer
CMO: Raul Reyes, M.D., Medical Director
CIO: Gustavo Mesa, Chief Information Officer
CHR: Jose Garcia, Chief Human Resources Officer
Web address: www.massalud.com
**Control:** City–Government, nonfederal **Service:** General Medical and Surgical

| Staffed Beds: 267 |

★ **UNIVERSITY HOSPITAL (400061)**, Nineyas 869 Rio Piedras, Zip 922, Mailing Address: P.O. Box 2116, Zip 922; tel. 787/754–0101, (Nonreporting) **A**3 5 9 10 **S** Puerto Rico Department of Health, San Juan, PR
Primary Contact: Jorge Matta Gonzalez, Executive Director
CFO: Janet Baez, Director
CMO: Ricardo Moscoso, M.D., Medical Director
CIO: Josue Martinez, Coordinator Information Systems
CHR: Ramomita Navarro, Director Human Resources
**Control:** State–Government, nonfederal **Service:** General Medical and Surgical

| Staffed Beds: 262 |

⊞ **UNIVERSITY PEDIATRIC HOSPITAL (403301)**, Barrio Monacenno, Carretera 22, Rio Piedras, Zip 935, Mailing Address: P.O. Box 191079, San Juan, Zip 00910–1070; tel. 787/777–3535, (Nonreporting) **A**1 3 5 9 10 **S** Puerto Rico Department of Health, San Juan, PR
Primary Contact: Gloria Hernandez, Executive Director
CMO: Myrna Quinones Feliciano, M.D., Medical Director
Web address: www.md.rcm.upr.edu/pediatrics/university_pediatric_hospital.php
**Control:** State–Government, nonfederal **Service:** Children's general

| Staffed Beds: 145 |

⊞ △ **VETERANS AFFAIRS CARIBBEAN HEALTHCARE SYSTEM**, 10 Casia Street, Zip 00921–3201; tel. 787/641–7582, (Nonreporting) **A**1 2 3 5 7 8 9 **S** Department of Veterans Affairs, Washington, DC
Primary Contact: DeWayne Hamlin, Director
CFO: Oscar Rodriguez, Chief Fiscal Officer
CMO: Antonio Sanchez, M.D., Chief of Staff
CIO: Manuel Negron, Chief Information Technology Service
CHR: Omar Ahmed, Acting Manager Human Resources
CNO: Kathleen Ruiz, M.D., Associate Director Patient Care Services
Web address: www.caribbean.va.gov/
**Control:** Veterans Affairs, Government, federal **Service:** General Medical and Surgical

| Staffed Beds: 330 |

**UTUADO— County**

★ **METROPOLITANO DE LA MONTANA (400130)**, Calle Issac Gonzalez, Zip 641, Mailing Address: P.O. Box 2600, Zip 641; tel. 787/933–1100, (Nonreporting) **A**10
Primary Contact: Waleska Marrero, Administrator
**Control:** Corporation, Investor–owned, for–profit **Service:** General Medical and Surgical

| Staffed Beds: 25 |

**VEGA BAJA—Vega Alta County**

★ **WILMA N. VAZQUEZ MEDICAL CENTER (400115)**, KM 39 1/2 Road 2, Call Box 7001, Zip 694; tel. 787/858–1580, (Nonreporting) **A**9 10
Primary Contact: Ramon J. Vilar, Administrator
COO: Jose O. Pabon, Director Operations
CFO: Youdie Reynolds–Gossette, Controller
CMO: Jorge Feria, M.D., President Medical Staff
CIO: Miguel Aponte, Supervisor Management Information Systems
CHR: Aymette Garcia, Manager Human Resources
**Control:** Corporation, Investor–owned, for–profit **Service:** General Medical and Surgical

| Staffed Beds: 150 |

**YAUCO—Yauco County**

⊞ **HOSPITAL METROPOLITANO DR. TITO MATTEI (400110)**, Carretera 128 KM 1, Zip 698, Mailing Address: P.O. Box 5643, Zip 698; tel. 787/856–1000 **A**1 5 9 10 **F**2 3 8 13 15 18 26 29 34 37 38 40 41 44 45 46 49 60 62 67 68 74 75 79 81 92 93 98 102 103 105 107 108 110 111 114 115 119 127 144 145 148 **P**8
Primary Contact: Marco Reyes, Vice President of Operations
CFO: Elizabeth Gonzalez, Chief Financial Officer
CMO: Manuel Ramirez Soto, M.D., Medical Director
CIO: Edson Ortiz, Chief Information Officer
Web address: www.hmyauco.com
**Control:** Public Health Service, Government, federal **Service:** Hospital unit within a facility for persons with intellectual disabilities

| Staffed Beds: 114 Admissions: 5641 Census: 73 Outpatient Visits: 39586 Births: 307 Total Expense ($000): 28405 Payroll Expense ($000): 8184 Personnel: 309 |

# VIRGIN ISLANDS

## CHRISTIANSTED—St. Croix County

✠ **GOVERNOR JUAN F. LUIS HOSPITAL (480002)**, 4007 Estate Diamond Ruby, Zip 00820–4421; tel. 340/778–6311, (Nonreporting) **A**1 9 10
Primary Contact: Darice S. Plaskett, R.N., FACHE, Interim Chief Executive Officer
CFO: Rosalie Javois, Chief Financial Officer
CMO: Robert Centeno, M.D., Chief Medical Officer
CIO: Reuben D. Molloy, Chief Information Officer
CHR: Joan Jean–Baptiste, Vice President Human Resources
Web address: www.jflusvi.org
**Control:** State–Government, nonfederal **Service:** General Medical and Surgical

**Staffed Beds:** 165

## SAINT THOMAS—St. Thomas County

✠ **SCHNEIDER REGIONAL MEDICAL CENTER (480001)**, 9048 Sugar Estate, Charlotte Amalie, Zip 802; tel. 340/776–8311 **A**1 10 **F**3 8 13 15 18 20 22 26 29 30 31 34 40 41 45 46 49 50 55 56 57 59 60 64 65 68 70 72 74 75 76 77 78 79 81 85 86 87 89 92 93 94 97 98 100 101 102 107 108 114 119 121 130 132 148 **P**5
Primary Contact: Bernard Wheatley, FACHE, Chief Executive Officer
CMO: Thelma Ruth Watson, M.D., Medical Director
CIO: J. C. Creque, Director Management Information Systems
CHR: Marlene J. Adams, Director Human Resources
Web address: www.rlshospital.org
**Control:** Hospital district or authority, Government, nonfederal **Service:** General Medical and Surgical

**Staffed Beds:** 86 **Admissions:** 2571 **Census:** 60 **Outpatient Visits:** 69730 **Births:** 696 **Total Expense ($000):** 88772 **Payroll Expense ($000):** 37092 **Personnel:** 493

---

**Hospital, Medicare Provider Number, Address, Telephone, Approval, Facility, and Physician Codes, Health Care System**

★ American Hospital Association (AHA) membership
□ The Joint Commission accreditation
○ Healthcare Facilities Accreditation Program
◇ DNV Healthcare Inc. accreditation
⇑ Center for Improvement in Healthcare Quality Accreditation
△ Commission on Accreditation of Rehabilitation Facilities (CARF) accreditation

# U.S. Government Hospitals
## Outside the United States, by Area

**GERMANY**

**Heidelberg:** ★ Heidelberg Army Community Hospital, APO, CMR 242, AE 09042

**Landstuhl:** ★ Landstuhl Army Regional Medical Center, APO, CMR 402, AE 09180

**Wuerzburg:** ★ Wuerzburg Army Community Hospital, APO, USAMEDDAC Wuerzburg, Ut 26610, AE 09244

**ITALY**

**Naples:** ★ U. S. Naval Hospital, FPO, none, AE 09619

**JAPAN**

**Yokosuka:** ★ U. S. Naval Hospital, Box 1487, UNIT 96350

**SOUTH KOREA**

**Seoul:** ★ Brian Allgood Army Community Hospital, 121st General Hospital, UNIT 96205

**Yongsan: Medcom 18th Commander, Facilities Division Eamc L EM, UNIT 96205**

**SPAIN**

**Rota:** ★ U. S. Naval Hospital, Rota, FPO, PSC 819, Box 18, AE 09645–2500

**TAIWAN**

**Taipei:** ★ U. S. Naval Hospital Taipei, No 300 Shin–Pai Road, Sec 2

This section is an index of all hospitals in alphabetical order by hospital name, followed by the city, state, and page reference to the hospital's listing in Section A.

## A

A. WEBB ROBERTS HOSPITAL, DALLAS, TEXAS (see BAYLOR UNIVERSITY MEDICAL CENTER), p. A604
ABBEVILLE AREA MEDICAL CENTER, ABBEVILLE, SC, p. A557
ABBEVILLE GENERAL HOSPITAL, ABBEVILLE, LA, p. A268
ABBOTT NORTHWESTERN HOSPITAL, MINNEAPOLIS, MN, p. A342
ABILENE BEHAVIORAL HEALTH, ABILENE, TX, p. A590
ABILENE REGIONAL MEDICAL CENTER, ABILENE, TX, p. A590
ABINGTON HEALTH LANSDALE HOSPITAL, LANSDALE, PA, p. A538
ABINGTON MEMORIAL HOSPITAL, ABINGTON, PA, p. A528
ABRAHAM LINCOLN MEMORIAL HOSPITAL, LINCOLN, IL, p. A193
ABRAZO MARYVALE CAMPUS, PHOENIX, AZ, p. A34
ABRAZO SCOTTSDALE CAMPUS, PHOENIX, AZ, p. A34
ABROM KAPLAN MEMORIAL HOSPITAL, KAPLAN, LA, p. A276
ACADIA GENERAL HOSPITAL, CROWLEY, LA, p. A272
ACADIA OPTIMA HOSPITAL, LAFAYETTE, LA, p. A277
ACADIA VERMILION HOSPITAL, LAFAYETTE, LA, p. A277
ACADIA–ST. LANDRY HOSPITAL, CHURCH POINT, LA, p. A271
ACADIAN MEDICAL CENTER, EUNICE, LOUISIANA (see MERCY REGIONAL MEDICAL CENTER), p. A286
ACCESS HOSPITAL DAYTON, DAYTON, OH, p. A487
ACMH HOSPITAL, KITTANNING, PA, p. A537
ACOMA-CANONCITO-LAGUNA HOSPITAL, ACOMA, NM, p. A422
ACUITY HOSPITAL OF SOUTH TEXAS, SAN ANTONIO, TX, p. A640
ACUITY SPECIALTY HOSPITAL OF ARIZONA AT MESA, MESA, AZ, p. A
ACUITY SPECIALTY HOSPITAL OF NEW JERSEY, ATLANTIC CITY, NJ, p. A409
ACUITY SPECIALTY HOSPITAL OF SUN CITY, SUN CITY, AZ, p. A
ACUITY SPECIALTY HOSPITALS OHIO VALLEY, STEUBENVILLE, OH, p. A498
ACUITY SPECIALTY HOSPITALS OHIO VALLEY AT BELMONT, BELLAIRE, OHIO (see ACUITY SPECIALTY HOSPITALS OHIO VALLEY), p. A498
ACUTE GENERAL HOSPITAL, MERWICK UNIT–EXTENDED CARE AND REHABILITATION, PRINCETON HOUSE UNIT–COMMUNITY MENTAL HEALTH AND SUBSTANCE ABUSE (see UNIVERSITY MEDICAL CENTER OF PRINCETON AT PLAINSBORO), p. A417
ADAIR COUNTY MEMORIAL HOSPITAL, GREENFIELD, IA, p. A228
ADAMS COUNTY REGIONAL MEDICAL CENTER, SEAMAN, OH, p. A497
ADAMS MEMORIAL HOSPITAL, DECATUR, IN, p. A207
ADCARE HOSPITAL OF WORCESTER, WORCESTER, MA, p. A313
ADDISON GILBERT HOSPITAL, GLOUCESTER, MASSACHUSETTS (see BEVERLY HOSPITAL), p. A302
ADENA GREENFIELD MEDICAL CENTER, GREENFIELD, OH, p. A490
ADENA MEDICAL CENTER, CHILLICOTHE, OH, p. A482
ADENA PIKE MEDICAL CENTER, WAVERLY, OH, p. A500
ADIRONDACK MEDICAL CENTER, SARANAC LAKE, NY, p. A450
ADVANCED CARE HOSPITAL OF MONTANA, BILLINGS, MT, p. A381
ADVANCED CARE HOSPITAL OF SOUTHERN NEW MEXICO, LAS CRUCES, NM, p. A424
ADVANCED CARE HOSPITAL OF WHITE COUNTY, SEARCY, AR, p. A50
ADVANCED SPECIALTY HOSPITAL OF TOLEDO, TOLEDO, OH, p. A498
ADVANCED SURGICAL HOSPITAL, WASHINGTON, PA, p. A552
ADVENTIST BEHAVIORAL HEALTH ROCKVILLE, ROCKVILLE, MD, p. A299
ADVENTIST BOLINGBROOK HOSPITAL, BOLINGBROOK, IL, p. A180
ADVENTIST HINSDALE HOSPITAL, HINSDALE, IL, p. A191
ADVENTIST LA GRANGE MEMORIAL HOSPITAL, LA GRANGE, IL, p. A192
ADVENTIST MEDICAL CENTER – HANFORD, HANFORD, CA, p. A64
ADVENTIST MEDICAL CENTER–PORTLAND, PORTLAND, OR, p. A524
ADVENTIST MEDICAL CENTER–REEDLEY, REEDLEY, CA, p. A83

ADVENTIST MEDICAL CENTER–SELMA, SELMA, CALIFORNIA (see ADVENTIST MEDICAL CENTER – HANFORD), p. A64
ADVENTIST REHABILITATION HOSPITAL OF MARYLAND, ROCKVILLE, MD, p. A300
ADVOCATE BROMENN MEDICAL CENTER, NORMAL, IL, p. A196
ADVOCATE CHRIST MEDICAL CENTER, OAK LAWN, IL, p. A196
ADVOCATE CONDELL MEDICAL CENTER, LIBERTYVILLE, IL, p. A192
ADVOCATE EUREKA HOSPITAL, EUREKA, IL, p. A187
ADVOCATE GOOD SAMARITAN HOSPITAL, DOWNERS GROVE, IL, p. A186
ADVOCATE GOOD SHEPHERD HOSPITAL, BARRINGTON, IL, p. A179
ADVOCATE HOPE CHILDREN'S HOSPITAL, OAK LAWN, ILLINOIS (see ADVOCATE CHRIST MEDICAL CENTER), p. A196
ADVOCATE ILLINOIS MASONIC MEDICAL CENTER, CHICAGO, IL, p. A181
ADVOCATE LUTHERAN GENERAL HOSPITAL, PARK RIDGE, IL, p. A197
ADVOCATE SHERMAN HOSPITAL, ELGIN, IL, p. A187
ADVOCATE SOUTH SUBURBAN HOSPITAL, HAZEL CREST, IL, p. A190
ADVOCATE TRINITY HOSPITAL, CHICAGO, IL, p. A181
AFFINITY MEDICAL CENTER, MASSILLON, OH, p. A493
AGNESIAN HEALTHCARE, FOND DU LAC, WI, p. A700
AHMC ANAHEIM REGIONAL MEDICAL CENTER, ANAHEIM, CA, p. A53
AIKEN REGIONAL MEDICAL CENTERS, AIKEN, SC, p. A557
AKRON CHILDREN'S HOSPITAL, AKRON, OH, p. A478
AKRON GENERAL MEDICAL CENTER, AKRON, OH, p. A478
ALAMANCE REGIONAL MEDICAL CENTER, BURLINGTON, NC, p. A456
ALAMEDA HOSPITAL, ALAMEDA, CA, p. A53
ALASKA NATIVE MEDICAL CENTER, ANCHORAGE, AK, p. A27
ALASKA PSYCHIATRIC INSTITUTE, ANCHORAGE, AK, p. A27
ALASKA REGIONAL HOSPITAL, ANCHORAGE, AK, p. A27
ALBANY MEDICAL CENTER, ALBANY, NY, p. A428
ALBANY MEDICAL CENTER SOUTH–CLINICAL CAMPUS, ALBANY, NEW YORK (see ALBANY MEDICAL CENTER), p. A428
ALBANY MEMORIAL HOSPITAL, ALBANY, NY, p. A428
ALBANY STRATTON VETERANS AFFAIRS MEDICAL CENTER, ALBANY, NY, p. A428
ALBERT J. SOLNIT PSYCHIATRIC CENTER – SOUTH CAMPUS, MIDDLETOWN, CT, p. A113
ALEDA E. LUTZ VETERANS AFFAIRS MEDICAL CENTER, SAGINAW, MI, p. A329
ALEXANDRIA VETERANS AFFAIRS HEALTH CARE SYSTEM, PINEVILLE, LA, p. A283
ALEXIAN BROTHERS BEHAVIORAL HEALTH HOSPITAL, HOFFMAN ESTATES, IL, p. A191
ALEXIAN BROTHERS MEDICAL CENTER, ELK GROVE VILLAGE, IL, p. A187
ALEXIAN BROTHERS WOMEN & CHILDREN'S HOSPITAL, HOFFMAN ESTATES, ILLINOIS (see ALEXIAN BROTHERS MEDICAL CENTER), p. A187
ALEXIAN REHABILITATION HOSPITAL, ELK GROVE VILLAGE, ILLINOIS (see ALEXIAN BROTHERS MEDICAL CENTER), p. A187
ALFRED AND NORMA LERNER TOWER, BOLWELL HEALTH CENTER, HANNA PAVILION, LAKESIDE HOSPITAL, SAMUEL MATHER PAVILION, HANNA HOUSE SKILLED NURSING FACILITY, CLEVELAND, OHIO (see UNIVERSITY HOSPITALS CASE MEDICAL CENTER), p. A485
RAINBOW BABIES AND CHILDREN'S HOSPITAL, CLEVELAND, OHIO (see UNIVERSITY HOSPITALS CASE MEDICAL CENTER), p. A485
UNIVERSITY MACDONALD WOMEN'S HOSPITAL, CLEVELAND, OHIO (see UNIVERSITY HOSPITALS CASE MEDICAL CENTER), p. A485
ALFRED I. DUPONT HOSPITAL FOR CHILDREN, WILMINGTON, DE, p. A118
ALHAMBRA HOSPITAL MEDICAL CENTER, ALHAMBRA, CA, p. A53
ALICE HYDE MEDICAL CENTER, MALONE, NY, p. A436
ALICE PECK DAY MEMORIAL HOSPITAL, LEBANON, NH, p. A406
ALL CHILDREN'S HOSPITAL JOHNS HOPKINS MEDICINE, SAINT PETERSBURG, FL, p. A141
ALLEGAN GENERAL HOSPITAL, ALLEGAN, MI, p. A314
ALLEGHANY MEMORIAL HOSPITAL, SPARTA, NC, p. A469

ALLEGHENY GENERAL HOSPITAL, PITTSBURGH, PA, p. A546
ALLEGHENY VALLEY HOSPITAL, NATRONA HEIGHTS, PA, p. A541
ALLEGIANCE BEHAVIORAL HEALTH CENTER OF PLAINVIEW, PLAINVIEW, TX, p. A636
ALLEGIANCE HEALTH, JACKSON, MI, p. A323
ALLEGIANCE HEALTH CENTER OF RUSTON, RUSTON, LA, p. A284
ALLEGIANCE SPECIALTY HOSPITAL OF GREENVILLE, GREENVILLE, MS, p. A353
ALLEGIANCE SPECIALTY HOSPITAL OF KILGORE, KILGORE, TX, p. A626
ALLEN COUNTY REGIONAL HOSPITAL, IOLA, KS, p. A242
ALLEN PARISH HOSPITAL, KINDER, LA, p. A276
ALLENDALE COUNTY HOSPITAL, FAIRFAX, SC, p. A560
ALLENMORE HOSPITAL, TACOMA, WASHINGTON (see MULTICARE TACOMA GENERAL HOSPITAL), p. A686
ALLIANCE COMMUNITY HOSPITAL, ALLIANCE, OH, p. A478
ALLIANCE HEALTH CENTER, MERIDIAN, MS, p. A357
ALLIANCE HEALTHCARE SYSTEM, HOLLY SPRINGS, MS, p. A354
ALLIANCEHEALTH BLACKWELL, BLACKWELL, OK, p. A504
ALLIANCEHEALTH CLINTON, CLINTON, OK, p. A505
ALLIANCEHEALTH DEACONESS, OKLAHOMA CITY, OK, p. A511
ALLIANCEHEALTH DURANT, DURANT, OK, p. A506
ALLIANCEHEALTH MADILL, MADILL, OK, p. A509
ALLIANCEHEALTH MIDWEST, MIDWEST CITY, OK, p. A510
ALLIANCEHEALTH PONCA CITY, PONCA CITY, OK, p. A514
ALLIANCEHEALTH PRYOR, PRYOR, OK, p. A514
ALLIANCEHEALTH SEMINOLE, SEMINOLE, OK, p. A514
ALLIANCEHEALTH WOODWARD, WOODWARD, OK, p. A518
ALLIED SERVICES REHABILITATION HOSPITAL, SCRANTON, PA, p. A549
ALPENA REGIONAL MEDICAL CENTER, ALPENA, MI, p. A314
ALTA BATES MEDICAL CENTER–HERRICK CAMPUS, BERKELEY, CALIFORNIA (see ALTA BATES SUMMIT MEDICAL CENTER), p. A56
ALTA BATES SUMMIT MEDICAL CENTER, BERKELEY, CA, p. A56
ALTA BATES SUMMIT MEDICAL CENTER – SUMMIT CAMPUS, OAKLAND, CA, p. A78
ALTA VIEW HOSPITAL, SANDY, UT, p. A659
ALTA VISTA REGIONAL HOSPITAL, LAS VEGAS, NM, p. A425
ALTON MEMORIAL HOSPITAL, ALTON, IL, p. A178
ALTON MENTAL HEALTH CENTER, ALTON, IL, p. A178
ALTRU HEALTH SYSTEM, GRAND FORKS, ND, p. A474
ALTRU HOSPITAL, GRAND FORKS, NORTH DAKOTA (see ALTRU HEALTH SYSTEM), p. A474
ALTRU REHABILITATION CENTER, GRAND FORKS, NORTH DAKOTA (see ALTRU HEALTH SYSTEM), p. A474
ALVARADO HOSPITAL MEDICAL CENTER, SAN DIEGO, CA, p. A86
ALVARADO PARKWAY INSTITUTE BEHAVIORAL HEALTH SYSTEM, LA MESA, CA, p. A66
ALVIN C. YORK CAMPUS, MURFREESBORO, TENNESSEE (see TENNESSEE VALLEY HEALTHCARE SYSTEM), p. A586
ALVIN DIAGNOSTIC AND URGENT CARE CENTER, ALVIN, TEXAS (see CLEAR LAKE REGIONAL MEDICAL CENTER), p. A651
AMARILLO VETERANS AFFAIRS HEALTH CARE SYSTEM, AMARILLO, TX, p. A591
AMERICAN FORK HOSPITAL, AMERICAN FORK, UT, p. A654
AMERY HOSPITAL AND CLINIC, AMERY, WI, p. A697
AMG SPECIALTY HOSPITAL – LAS VEGAS, LAS VEGAS, NV, p. A401
AMG SPECIALTY HOSPITAL – MUNCIE, MUNCIE, IN, p. A216
AMG SPECIALTY HOSPITAL–ALBUQUERQUE, ALBUQUERQUE, NM, p. A422
AMG SPECIALTY HOSPITAL–DENHAM SPRINGS, DENHAM SPRINGS, LA, p. A273
AMG SPECIALTY HOSPITAL–EDMOND, EDMOND, OK, p. A506
AMG SPECIALTY HOSPITAL–FELICIANA, CLINTON, LA, p. A271
AMG SPECIALTY HOSPITAL–GREENWOOD, GREENWOOD, MS, p. A353
AMG SPECIALTY HOSPITAL–HOUMA, HOUMA, LA, p. A275
AMG SPECIALTY HOSPITAL–LAFAYETTE, LAFAYETTE, LA, p. A277
AMG SPECIALTY HOSPITAL–SLIDELL, SLIDELL, LA, p. A285
AMG SPECIALTY HOSPITAL–TULSA, TULSA, OK, p. A516
AMG SPECIALTY HOSPITAL–WICHITA, WICHITA, KS, p. A252
AMITA HEALTH ADVENTIST GLENOAKS HOSPITAL, GLENDALE HEIGHTS, IL, p. A189

ANCHOR HOSPITAL, ATLANTA, GA, p. A149

ANCORA PSYCHIATRIC HOSPITAL, HAMMONTON, NJ, p. A412

ANDALUSIA REGIONAL HOSPITAL, ANDALUSIA, AL, p. A15

ANDERSON COUNTY HOSPITAL, GARNETT, KS, p. A240

ANDERSON HOSPITAL, MARYVILLE, IL, p. A193

ANDERSON REGIONAL MEDICAL CENTER, MERIDIAN, MS, p. A357

ANDERSON REGIONAL MEDICAL CENTER–SOUTH CAMPUS, MERIDIAN, MS, p. A357

ANDREW MCFARLAND MENTAL HEALTH CENTER, SPRINGFIELD, IL, p. A201

ANDROSCOGGIN VALLEY HOSPITAL, BERLIN, NH, p. A405

ANDRUS PAVILION, YONKERS, NEW YORK (see ST. JOHN'S RIVERSIDE HOSPITAL), p. A454

ANGEL MEDICAL CENTER, FRANKLIN, NC, p. A460

ANGLETON DANBURY CAMPUS, ANGLETON, TEXAS (see UNIVERSITY OF TEXAS MEDICAL BRANCH), p. A615

ANIMAS SURGICAL HOSPITAL, DURANGO, CO, p. A102

ANMED HEALTH MEDICAL CENTER, ANDERSON, SC, p. A557

ANMED HEALTH REHABILITATION HOSPITAL, ANDERSON, SC, p. A557

ANMED HEALTH WOMEN'S AND CHILDREN'S HOSPITAL, ANDERSON, SOUTH CAROLINA (see ANMED HEALTH MEDICAL CENTER), p. A557

ANN & ROBERT H. LURIE CHILDREN'S HOSPITAL OF CHICAGO, CHICAGO, IL, p. A181

ANNA JAQUES HOSPITAL, NEWBURYPORT, MA, p. A309

ANNE ARUNDEL MEDICAL CENTER, ANNAPOLIS, MD, p. A293

ANNIE JEFFREY MEMORIAL COUNTY HEALTH CENTER, OSCEOLA, NE, p. A397

ANNIE PENN HOSPITAL, REIDSVILLE, NORTH CAROLINA (see MOSES H. CONE MEMORIAL HOSPITAL), p. A461

ANOKA–METROPOLITAN REGIONAL TREATMENT CENTER, ANOKA, MN, p. A334

ANSON GENERAL HOSPITAL, ANSON, TX, p. A592

ANTELOPE MEMORIAL HOSPITAL, NELIGH, NE, p. A394

ANTELOPE VALLEY HOSPITAL, LANCASTER, CA, p. A67

ANTHONY MEDICAL CENTER, ANTHONY, KS, p. A237

APPALACHIAN BEHAVIORAL HEALTHCARE, ATHENS, OH, p. A479

APPLETON AREA HEALTH SERVICES, APPLETON, MN, p. A334

APPLETON MEDICAL CENTER, APPLETON, WI, p. A697

APPLING HEALTHCARE SYSTEM, BAXLEY, GA, p. A152

ARBOUR H. R. I. HOSPITAL, BROOKLINE, MA, p. A305

ARBOUR HOSPITAL, BOSTON, MA, p. A302

ARBOUR–FULLER HOSPITAL, ATTLEBORO, MA, p. A302

ARBUCKLE MEMORIAL HOSPITAL, SULPHUR, OK, p. A515

ARCHBOLD HOSPITAL, ARCHBOLD, OHIO (see COMMUNITY HOSPITALS AND WELLNESS CENTERS), p. A480

ARIA HEALTH, PHILADELPHIA, PA, p. A542

ARISE AUSTIN MEDICAL CENTER, AUSTIN, TX, p. A593

ARIZONA CHILDREN'S CENTER, PHOENIX, ARIZONA (see MARICOPA INTEGRATED HEALTH SYSTEM), p. A35

ARIZONA HEART HOSPITAL, PHOENIX, ARIZONA (see PHOENIX BAPTIST HOSPITAL), p. A35

ARIZONA ORTHOPEDIC SURGICAL HOSPITAL, CHANDLER, AZ, p. A30

ARIZONA SPINE AND JOINT HOSPITAL, MESA, AZ, p. A33

ARIZONA STATE HOSPITAL, PHOENIX, AZ, p. A34

ARKANSAS CHILDREN'S HOSPITAL, LITTLE ROCK, AR, p. A46

ARKANSAS DEPARTMENT OF CORRECTION HOSPITAL, PINE BLUFF, AR, p. A49

ARKANSAS HEART HOSPITAL, LITTLE ROCK, AR, p. A47

ARKANSAS METHODIST MEDICAL CENTER, PARAGOULD, AR, p. A49

ARKANSAS STATE HOSPITAL, LITTLE ROCK, AR, p. A47

ARKANSAS SURGICAL HOSPITAL, NORTH LITTLE ROCK, AR, p. A49

ARKANSAS VALLEY REGIONAL MEDICAL CENTER, LA JUNTA, CO, p. A105

ARMS ACRES, CARMEL, NY, p. A431

ARNOLD PALMER CHILDREN'S HOSPITAL, ORLANDO, FLORIDA (see ORLANDO REGIONAL MEDICAL CENTER), p. A138

ARNOT OGDEN MEDICAL CENTER, ELMIRA, NY, p. A433

AROOSTOOK HEALTH CENTER, MARS HILL, MAINE (see THE AROOSTOOK MEDICAL CENTER), p. A292

ARROWHEAD BEHAVIORAL HEALTH HOSPITAL, MAUMEE, OH, p. A494

ARROWHEAD HOSPITAL, GLENDALE, AZ, p. A32

ARROWHEAD REGIONAL MEDICAL CENTER, COLTON, CA, p. A58

ARROYO GRANDE COMMUNITY HOSPITAL, ARROYO GRANDE, CA, p. A54

ARTESIA GENERAL HOSPITAL, ARTESIA, NM, p. A423

ARTHUR R. GOULD MEMORIAL HOSPITAL, PRESQUE ISLE, MAINE (see THE AROOSTOOK MEDICAL CENTER), p. A292

ASANTE ASHLAND COMMUNITY HOSPITAL, ASHLAND, OR, p. A519

ASANTE ROGUE REGIONAL MEDICAL CENTER, MEDFORD, OR, p. A523

ASANTE THREE RIVERS MEDICAL CENTER, GRANTS PASS, OR, p. A521

ASHE MEMORIAL HOSPITAL, JEFFERSON, NC, p. A463

ASHEVILLE SPECIALTY HOSPITAL, ASHEVILLE, NC, p. A455

ASHFORD PRESBYTERIAN COMMUNITY HOSPITAL, SAN JUAN, PR, p. A723

ASHLAND HEALTH CENTER, ASHLAND, KS, p. A237

ASHLEY COUNTY MEDICAL CENTER, CROSSETT, AR, p. A42

ASHLEY MEDICAL CENTER, ASHLEY, ND, p. A472

ASHLEY REGIONAL MEDICAL CENTER, VERNAL, UT, p. A659

ASHTABULA COUNTY MEDICAL CENTER, ASHTABULA, OH, p. A478

ASPEN VALLEY HOSPITAL DISTRICT, ASPEN, CO, p. A99

ASPIRE HEALTH PARTNERS, ORLANDO, FL, p. A137

ASPIRE HOSPITAL, CONROE, TX, p. A602

ASPIRUS GRAND VIEW, IRONWOOD, MI, p. A323

ASPIRUS IRON RIVER HOSPITALS AND CLINICS, IRON RIVER, MI, p. A323

ASPIRUS KEWEENAW HOSPITAL, LAURIUM, MI, p. A324

ASPIRUS MEDFORD HOSPITAL, MEDFORD, WI, p. A705

ASPIRUS ONTONAGON HOSPITAL, ONTONAGON, MI, p. A327

ASPIRUS RIVERVIEW HOSPITAL AND CLINICS, INC., WISCONSIN RAPIDS, WI, p. A714

ASPIRUS WAUSAU HOSPITAL, WAUSAU, WI, p. A713

ASSUMPTION COMMUNITY HOSPITAL, NAPOLEONVILLE, LA, p. A281

ATASCADERO STATE HOSPITAL, ATASCADERO, CA, p. A54

ATCHISON HOSPITAL, ATCHISON, KS, p. A237

ATHENS REGIONAL MEDICAL CENTER, ATHENS, GA, p. A149

ATHENS–LIMESTONE HOSPITAL, ATHENS, AL, p. A15

ATHOL MEMORIAL HOSPITAL, ATHOL, MA, p. A302

ATLANTA MEDICAL CENTER, ATLANTA, GA, p. A150

ATLANTA MEDICAL CENTER – SOUTH CAMPUS, ATLANTA, GEORGIA (see ATLANTA MEDICAL CENTER), p. A150

ATLANTA VETERANS AFFAIRS MEDICAL CENTER, DECATUR, GA, p. A155

ATLANTIC GENERAL HOSPITAL, BERLIN, MD, p. A295

ATLANTIC SHORES HOSPITAL, FORT LAUDERDALE, FL, p. A126

ATLANTICARE REGIONAL MEDICAL CENTER, ATLANTIC CITY, NJ, p. A409

ATLANTICARE REGIONAL MEDICAL CENTER–MAINLAND DIVISION, POMONA, NEW JERSEY (see ATLANTICARE REGIONAL MEDICAL CENTER), p. A409

ATMORE COMMUNITY HOSPITAL, ATMORE, AL, p. A16

ATOKA COUNTY MEDICAL CENTER, ATOKA, OK, p. A504

ATRIUM MEDICAL CENTER, MIDDLETOWN, OH, p. A494

ATRIUM MEDICAL CENTER, STAFFORD, TX, p. A645

ATRIUM MEDICAL CENTER OF CORINTH, CORINTH, TX, p. A602

AUBURN COMMUNITY HOSPITAL, AUBURN, NY, p. A429

AUDUBON COUNTY MEMORIAL HOSPITAL, AUDUBON, IA, p. A222

AUGUSTA HEALTH, FISHERSVILLE, VA, p. A664

AULTMAN HOSPITAL, CANTON, OH, p. A481

AULTMAN HOSPITAL PEDIATRIC SERVICES, CANTON, OHIO (see AULTMAN HOSPITAL), p. A481

AULTMAN ORRVILLE HOSPITAL, ORRVILLE, OH, p. A496

AULTMAN SPECIALTY HOSPITAL, CANTON, OH, p. A481

AURELIA OSBORN FOX MEMORIAL HOSPITAL, ONEONTA, NY, p. A446

AURORA BAYCARE MEDICAL CENTER, GREEN BAY, WI, p. A701

AURORA BEHAVIORAL HEALTH SYSTEM EAST, TEMPE, AZ, p. A38

AURORA BEHAVIORAL HEALTH SYSTEM WEST, GLENDALE, AZ, p. A32

AURORA CHARTER OAK HOSPITAL, COVINA, CA, p. A59

AURORA LAKELAND MEDICAL CENTER, ELKHORN, WI, p. A700

AURORA MEDICAL CENTER, KENOSHA, WI, p. A703

AURORA MEDICAL CENTER – MANITOWOC COUNTY, TWO RIVERS, WI, p. A712

AURORA MEDICAL CENTER GRAFTON, GRAFTON, WI, p. A701

AURORA MEDICAL CENTER IN WASHINGTON COUNTY, HARTFORD, WI, p. A702

AURORA MEDICAL CENTER OF OSHKOSH, OSHKOSH, WI, p. A708

AURORA MEDICAL CENTER SUMMIT, SUMMIT, WI, p. A712

AURORA MEMORIAL HOSPITAL OF BURLINGTON, BURLINGTON, WI, p. A699

AURORA PAVILION, AIKEN, SOUTH CAROLINA (see AIKEN REGIONAL MEDICAL CENTERS), p. A557

AURORA PSYCHIATRIC HOSPITAL, WAUWATOSA, WI, p. A713

AURORA SAN DIEGO HOSPITAL, SAN DIEGO, CA, p. A86

AURORA SHEBOYGAN MEMORIAL MEDICAL CENTER, SHEBOYGAN, WI, p. A710

AURORA SINAI MEDICAL CENTER, MILWAUKEE, WI, p. A706

AURORA ST. LUKE'S MEDICAL CENTER, MILWAUKEE, WI, p. A706

AURORA ST. LUKE'S SOUTH SHORE, CUDAHY, WISCONSIN (see AURORA ST. LUKE'S MEDICAL CENTER), p. A706

AURORA WEST ALLIS MEDICAL CENTER, WEST ALLIS, WI, p. A714

AUSTEN RIGGS CENTER, STOCKBRIDGE, MA, p. A312

AUSTIN LAKES HOSPITAL, AUSTIN, TX, p. A593

AUSTIN OAKS HOSPITAL, AUSTIN, TX, p. A593

AUSTIN STATE HOSPITAL, AUSTIN, TX, p. A594

AUXILIO MUTUO HOSPITAL, SAN JUAN, PR, p. A723

AVENTURA HOSPITAL AND MEDICAL CENTER, AVENTURA, FL, p. A121

AVERA BEHAVIORAL HEALTH CENTER, SIOUX FALLS, SOUTH DAKOTA (see AVERA MCKENNAN HOSPITAL AND UNIVERSITY HEALTH CENTER), p. A571

AVERA CHILDREN'S HOSPITAL, SIOUX FALLS, SOUTH DAKOTA (see AVERA MCKENNAN HOSPITAL AND UNIVERSITY HEALTH CENTER), p. A571

AVERA CREIGHTON HOSPITAL, CREIGHTON, NE, p. A391

AVERA DE SMET MEMORIAL HOSPITAL, DE SMET, SD, p. A568

AVERA DELLS AREA HOSPITAL, DELL RAPIDS, SD, p. A568

AVERA FLANDREAU HOSPITAL, FLANDREAU, SD, p. A568

AVERA GETTYSBURG HOSPITAL, GETTYSBURG, SD, p. A569

AVERA GREGORY HOSPITAL, GREGORY, SD, p. A569

AVERA HAND COUNTY MEMORIAL HOSPITAL, MILLER, SD, p. A569

AVERA HEART HOSPITAL OF SOUTH DAKOTA, SIOUX FALLS, SD, p. A571

AVERA HOLY FAMILY HOSPITAL, ESTHERVILLE, IA, p. A227

AVERA MARSHALL REGIONAL MEDICAL CENTER, MARSHALL, MN, p. A342

AVERA MCKENNAN HOSPITAL AND UNIVERSITY HEALTH CENTER, SIOUX FALLS, SD, p. A571

AVERA QUEEN OF PEACE HOSPITAL, MITCHELL, SD, p. A570

AVERA SACRED HEART HOSPITAL, YANKTON, SD, p. A573

AVERA ST. ANTHONY'S HOSPITAL, O'NEILL, NE, p. A395

AVERA ST. BENEDICT HEALTH CENTER, PARKSTON, SD, p. A570

AVERA ST. LUKE'S HOSPITAL, ABERDEEN, SD, p. A567

AVERA ST. MARY'S HOSPITAL, PIERRE, SD, p. A570

AVERA WESKOTA MEMORIAL HOSPITAL, WESSINGTON SPRINGS, SD, p. A573

AVISTA ADVENTIST HOSPITAL, LOUISVILLE, CO, p. A107

AVITA GALION HOSPITAL, GALION, OH, p. A490

AVOYELLES HOSPITAL, MARKSVILLE, LA, p. A279

# B

BACHARACH INSTITUTE FOR REHABILITATION, POMONA, NJ, p. A417

BACON COUNTY HOSPITAL AND HEALTH SYSTEM, ALMA, GA, p. A149

BAILEY MEDICAL CENTER, OWASSO, OK, p. A513

BAKERSFIELD HEART HOSPITAL, BAKERSFIELD, CA, p. A54

BAKERSFIELD MEMORIAL HOSPITAL, BAKERSFIELD, CA, p. A55

BALDPATE HOSPITAL, HAVERHILL, MA, p. A307

BALDWIN AREA MEDICAL CENTER, BALDWIN, WI, p. A697

BALLARD REHABILITATION HOSPITAL, SAN BERNARDINO, CA, p. A86

BALLINGER MEMORIAL HOSPITAL, BALLINGER, TX, p. A595

BANNER – UNIVERSITY MEDICAL CENTER SOUTH, TUCSON, AZ, p. A39

BANNER – UNIVERSITY MEDICAL CENTER TUCSON, TUCSON, AZ, p. A39

BANNER BAYWOOD MEDICAL CENTER, MESA, AZ, p. A33

BANNER BEHAVIORAL HEALTH CENTER–THUNDERBIRD CAMPUS, GLENDALE, ARIZONA (see BANNER THUNDERBIRD MEDICAL CENTER), p. A32

BANNER BEHAVIORAL HEALTH HOSPITAL – SCOTTSDALE, SCOTTSDALE, AZ, p. A37

BANNER BOSWELL MEDICAL CENTER, SUN CITY, AZ, p. A38

BANNER CASA GRANDE MEDICAL CENTER, CASA GRANDE, AZ, p. A30

BANNER CHURCHILL COMMUNITY HOSPITAL, FALLON, NV, p. A400

BANNER DEL E. WEBB MEDICAL CENTER, SUN CITY WEST, AZ, p. A38

BANNER DESERT MEDICAL CENTER, MESA, AZ, p. A33

BANNER ESTRELLA MEDICAL CENTER, PHOENIX, AZ, p. A34

BANNER FORT COLLINS MEDICAL CENTER, FORT COLLINS, CO, p. A103

BANNER GATEWAY MEDICAL CENTER, GILBERT, AZ, p. A31

BANNER GOLDFIELD MEDICAL CENTER, APACHE JUNCTION, AZ, p. A30

BANNER GOOD SAMARITAN MEDICAL CENTER, PHOENIX, AZ, p. A34

BANNER HEART HOSPITAL, MESA, AZ, p. A33

BANNER IRONWOOD MEDICAL CENTER, SAN TAN VALLEY, AZ, p. A37

BANNER LASSEN MEDICAL CENTER, SUSANVILLE, CA, p. A93

BANNER THUNDERBIRD MEDICAL CENTER, GLENDALE, AZ, p. A32

BROOKS REHABILITATION HOSPITAL, JACKSONVILLE, FL, p. A129
BROOKWOOD MEDICAL CENTER, BIRMINGHAM, AL, p. A16
BROUGHTON HOSPITAL, MORGANTON, NC, p. A465
BROWARD HEALTH CORAL SPRINGS, CORAL SPRINGS, FL, p. A124
BROWARD HEALTH IMPERIAL POINT, FORT LAUDERDALE, FL, p. A126
BROWARD HEALTH MEDICAL CENTER, FORT LAUDERDALE, FL, p. A126
BROWARD HEALTH NORTH, DEERFIELD BEACH, FL, p. A125
BROWN COUNTY COMMUNITY TREATMENT CENTER, GREEN BAY, WI, p. A702
BROWN COUNTY HOSPITAL, AINSWORTH, NE, p. A389
BROWNFIELD REGIONAL MEDICAL CENTER, BROWNFIELD, TX, p. A598
BROWNWOOD REGIONAL MEDICAL CENTER, BROWNWOOD, TX, p. A599
BRUNSWICK PSYCH CENTER, AMITYVILLE, NY, p. A428
BRYAN HOSPITAL, BRYAN, OHIO (see COMMUNITY HOSPITALS AND WELLNESS CENTERS), p. A480
BRYAN MEDICAL CENTER, LINCOLN, NE, p. A393
BRYAN MEDICAL CENTER–EAST, LINCOLN, NEBRASKA (see BRYAN MEDICAL CENTER), p. A393
BRYAN MEDICAL CENTER–WEST, LINCOLN, NEBRASKA (see BRYAN MEDICAL CENTER), p. A393
BRYAN W. WHITFIELD MEMORIAL HOSPITAL, DEMOPOLIS, AL, p. A18
BRYCE HOSPITAL, TUSCALOOSA, AL, p. A25
BRYLIN HOSPITALS, BUFFALO, NY, p. A430
BRYN MAWR HOSPITAL, BRYN MAWR, PA, p. A530
BRYN MAWR REHABILITATION HOSPITAL, MALVERN, PA, p. A539
BRYNN MARR HOSPITAL, JACKSONVILLE, NC, p. A463
BUCHANAN COUNTY HEALTH CENTER, INDEPENDENCE, IA, p. A229
BUCHANAN GENERAL HOSPITAL, GRUNDY, VA, p. A665
BUCKS COUNTY CAMPUS, LANGHORNE, PENNSYLVANIA (see ARIA HEALTH), p. A542
BUCKTAIL MEDICAL CENTER, RENOVO, PA, p. A548
BUCYRUS COMMUNITY HOSPITAL, BUCYRUS, OH, p. A480
BUENA VISTA REGIONAL MEDICAL CENTER, STORM LAKE, IA, p. A235
BUFFALO HOSPITAL, BUFFALO, MN, p. A336
BUFFALO PSYCHIATRIC CENTER, BUFFALO, NY, p. A430
BULLOCK COUNTY HOSPITAL, UNION SPRINGS, AL, p. A26
BUNKIE GENERAL HOSPITAL, BUNKIE, LA, p. A271
BURGESS HEALTH CENTER, ONAWA, IA, p. A232
BURKE MEDICAL CENTER, WAYNESBORO, GA, p. A167
BURKE REHABILITATION HOSPITAL, WHITE PLAINS, NY, p. A454
BURLESON ST. JOSEPH HEALTH CENTER, CALDWELL, TX, p. A599
BURNETT MEDICAL CENTER, GRANTSBURG, WI, p. A701
BUTLER COUNTY HEALTH CARE CENTER, DAVID CITY, NE, p. A391
BUTLER HEALTH SYSTEM, BUTLER, PA, p. A530
BUTLER HOSPITAL, PROVIDENCE, RI, p. A555
BYRD REGIONAL HOSPITAL, LEESVILLE, LA, p. A279

# C

C. S. MOTT CHILDREN'S HOSPITAL, ANN ARBOR, MICHIGAN (see UNIVERSITY OF MICHIGAN HOSPITALS AND HEALTH CENTERS), p. A314
CABELL HUNTINGTON HOSPITAL, HUNTINGTON, WV, p. A691
CABINET PEAKS MEDICAL CENTER, LIBBY, MT, p. A385
CACHE VALLEY HOSPITAL, NORTH LOGAN, UT, p. A656
CALAIS REGIONAL HOSPITAL, CALAIS, ME, p. A289
CALCASIEU OAKS GERIATRIC PSYCHIATRIC HOSPITAL, LAKE CHARLES, LA, p. A278
CALDWELL MEDICAL CENTER, PRINCETON, KY, p. A265
CALDWELL MEMORIAL HOSPITAL, COLUMBIA, LA, p. A271
CALDWELL MEMORIAL HOSPITAL, LENOIR, NC, p. A464
CALHOUN HEALTH SERVICES, CALHOUN CITY, MS, p. A351
CALHOUN–LIBERTY HOSPITAL, BLOUNTSTOWN, FL, p. A121
CALIFORNIA HOSPITAL MEDICAL CENTER, LOS ANGELES, CA, p. A69
CALIFORNIA MEDICAL FACILITY, VACAVILLE, CA, p. A95
CALIFORNIA MENS COLONY CORRECTIONAL TREATMENT CENTER, SAN LUIS OBISPO, CA, p. A90
CALIFORNIA PACIFIC MEDICAL CENTER, SAN FRANCISCO, CA, p. A88
CALIFORNIA PACIFIC MEDICAL CENTER–DAVIES CAMPUS, SAN FRANCISCO, CALIFORNIA (see CALIFORNIA PACIFIC MEDICAL CENTER), p. A88
CALLAWAY DISTRICT HOSPITAL, CALLAWAY, NE, p. A390
CALUMET MEDICAL CENTER, CHILTON, WI, p. A699

CALVARY HOSPITAL,, NY, p. A439
CALVERT MEMORIAL HOSPITAL, PRINCE FREDERICK, MD, p. A299
CAMBRIDGE HEALTH ALLIANCE, CAMBRIDGE, MA, p. A305
CAMBRIDGE HOSPITAL, CAMBRIDGE, MASSACHUSETTS (see CAMBRIDGE HEALTH ALLIANCE), p. A305
CAMBRIDGE HOSPITAL IN HOUSTON, HOUSTON, TX, p. A619
CAMBRIDGE MEDICAL CENTER, CAMBRIDGE, MN, p. A336
CAMC MEMORIAL HOSPITAL, CHARLESTON, WEST VIRGINIA (see CHARLESTON AREA MEDICAL CENTER), p. A690
CAMC TEAYS VALLEY HOSPITAL, HURRICANE, WEST VIRGINIA (see CHARLESTON AREA MEDICAL CENTER), p. A690
CAMC WOMEN AND CHILDREN'S HOSPITAL, CHARLESTON, WEST VIRGINIA (see CHARLESTON AREA MEDICAL CENTER), p. A690
CAMDEN CLARK MEDICAL CENTER, PARKERSBURG, WV, p. A694
CAMDEN GENERAL HOSPITAL, CAMDEN, TN, p. A574
CAMERON MEMORIAL COMMUNITY HOSPITAL, ANGOLA, IN, p. A204
CAMERON REGIONAL MEDICAL CENTER, CAMERON, MO, p. A364
CAMPBELL COUNTY MEMORIAL HOSPITAL, GILLETTE, WY, p. A716
CAMPBELLTON GRACEVILLE HOSPITAL, GRACEVILLE, FL, p. A128
CANANDAIGUA VETERANS AFFAIRS MEDICAL CENTER, CANANDAIGUA, NY, p. A431
CANDLER COUNTY HOSPITAL, METTER, GA, p. A161
CANDLER HOSPITAL, SAVANNAH, GA, p. A164
CANNON MEMORIAL HOSPITAL, PICKENS, SC, p. A564
CANONSBURG GENERAL HOSPITAL, CANONSBURG, PA, p. A530
CANTON–POTSDAM HOSPITAL, POTSDAM, NY, p. A448
CANYON RIDGE HOSPITAL, CHINO, CA, p. A57
CANYON VISTA MEDICAL CENTER, SIERRA VISTA, AZ, p. A38
CAPE COD & ISLAND COMMUNITY MENTAL HEALTH CENTER, POCASSET, MA, p. A310
CAPE COD HOSPITAL, HYANNIS, MA, p. A307
CAPE CORAL HOSPITAL, CAPE CORAL, FL, p. A123
CAPE FEAR HOSPITAL, WILMINGTON, NORTH CAROLINA (see NEW HANOVER REGIONAL MEDICAL CENTER), p. A470
CAPE FEAR VALLEY – BLADEN COUNTY HOSPITAL, ELIZABETHTOWN, NC, p. A460
CAPE FEAR VALLEY MEDICAL CENTER, FAYETTEVILLE, NC, p. A460
CAPE REGIONAL MEDICAL CENTER, CAPE MAY COURT HOUSE, NJ, p. A410
CAPITAL DISTRICT PSYCHIATRIC CENTER, ALBANY, NY, p. A428
CAPITAL HEALTH MEDICAL CENTER–HOPEWELL, PENNINGTON, NJ, p. A416
CAPITAL HEALTH REGIONAL MEDICAL CENTER, TRENTON, NJ, p. A419
CAPITAL HOSPICE, ARLINGTON, VA, p. A662
CAPITAL MEDICAL CENTER, OLYMPIA, WA, p. A681
CAPITAL REGION MEDICAL CENTER, JEFFERSON CITY, MO, p. A368
CAPITAL REGIONAL MEDICAL CENTER, TALLAHASSEE, FL, p. A144
CAPTAIN JAMES A. LOVELL FEDERAL HEALTH CARE CENTER, NORTH CHICAGO, IL, p. A196
CARDINAL HILL REHABILITATION HOSPITAL, LEXINGTON, KY, p. A259
CARDIOVASCULAR CENTER OF PUERTO RICO AND THE CARIBBEAN, SAN JUAN, PR, p. A723
CARDON CHILDREN'S MEDICAL CENTER, MESA, ARIZONA (see BANNER DESERT MEDICAL CENTER), p. A33
CARE ONE AT RARITAN BAY MEDICAL CENTER, PERTH AMBOY, NJ, p. A416
CARE REGIONAL MEDICAL CENTER, ARANSAS PASS, TX, p. A592
CARELINK OF JACKSON, JACKSON, MI, p. A323
CAREPARTNERS HEALTH SERVICES, ASHEVILLE, NC, p. A455
CARIBBEAN MEDICAL CENTER, FAJARDO, PR, p. A721
CARIBOU MEMORIAL HOSPITAL AND LIVING CENTER, SODA SPRINGS, ID, p. A176
CARILION CLINIC CHILDREN'S HOSPITAL, ROANOKE, VIRGINIA (see CARILION ROANOKE MEMORIAL HOSPITAL), p. A672
CARILION CLINIC SAINT ALBANS HOSPITAL, CHRISTIANSBURG, VIRGINIA (see CARILION NEW RIVER VALLEY MEDICAL CENTER), p. A663
CARILION FRANKLIN MEMORIAL HOSPITAL, ROCKY MOUNT, VA, p. A672
CARILION GILES COMMUNITY HOSPITAL, PEARISBURG, VA, p. A670
CARILION NEW RIVER VALLEY MEDICAL CENTER, CHRISTIANSBURG, VA, p. A663

CARILION ROANOKE COMMUNITY HOSPITAL, ROANOKE, VIRGINIA (see CARILION ROANOKE MEMORIAL HOSPITAL), p. A672
CARILION ROANOKE MEMORIAL HOSPITAL, ROANOKE, VA, p. A672
CARILION STONEWALL JACKSON HOSPITAL, LEXINGTON, VA, p. A667
CARILION TAZEWELL COMMUNITY HOSPITAL, TAZEWELL, VA, p. A673
CARL ALBERT COMMUNITY MENTAL HEALTH CENTER, MCALESTER, OK, p. A509
CARL R. DARNALL ARMY MEDICAL CENTER, FORT HOOD, TX, p. A612
CARL VINSON VETERANS AFFAIRS MEDICAL CENTER, DUBLIN, GA, p. A156
CARLE FOUNDATION HOSPITAL, URBANA, IL, p. A202
CARLE HOOPESTON REGIONAL HEALTH CENTER, HOOPESTON, IL, p. A191
CARLINVILLE AREA HOSPITAL, CARLINVILLE, IL, p. A180
CARLISLE REGIONAL MEDICAL CENTER, CARLISLE, PA, p. A531
CARLSBAD MEDICAL CENTER, CARLSBAD, NM, p. A423
CARNEGIE TRI–COUNTY MUNICIPAL HOSPITAL, CARNEGIE, OK, p. A504
CARNEY HOSPITAL, BOSTON, MA, p. A303
CARO CENTER, CARO, MI, p. A316
CARO COMMUNITY HOSPITAL, CARO, MI, p. A316
CAROLINA CENTER FOR BEHAVIORAL HEALTH, GREER, SC, p. A562
CAROLINA PINES REGIONAL MEDICAL CENTER, HARTSVILLE, SC, p. A562
CAROLINAEAST HEALTH SYSTEM, NEW BERN, NC, p. A466
CAROLINAS CONTINUECARE HOSPITAL AT KINGS MOUNTAIN, KINGS MOUNTAIN, NC, p. A463
CAROLINAS CONTINUECARE HOSPITAL AT PINEVILLE, CHARLOTTE, NC, p. A457
CAROLINAS HEALTHCARE SYSTEM ANSON, WADESBORO, NC, p. A470
CAROLINAS HEALTHCARE SYSTEM LINCOLN, LINCOLNTON, NC, p. A464
CAROLINAS HEALTHCARE SYSTEM NORTHEAST, CONCORD, NC, p. A458
CAROLINAS HEALTHCARE SYSTEM PINEVILLE, CHARLOTTE, NC, p. A457
CAROLINAS HEALTHCARE SYSTEM UNION, MONROE, NC, p. A465
CAROLINAS HOSPITAL SYSTEM, FLORENCE, SC, p. A560
CAROLINAS HOSPITAL SYSTEM MARION, MULLINS, SC, p. A563
CAROLINAS MEDICAL CENTER, CHARLOTTE, NC, p. A457
CAROLINAS MEDICAL CENTER–MERCY, CHARLOTTE, NORTH CAROLINA (see CAROLINAS MEDICAL CENTER), p. A457
CAROLINAS MEDICAL CENTER–UNIVERSITY, CHARLOTTE, NC, p. A457
CAROLINAS REHABILITATION, CHARLOTTE, NC, p. A457
CAROMONT REGIONAL MEDICAL CENTER, GASTONIA, NC, p. A460
CARONDELET HOLY CROSS HOSPITAL, NOGALES, AZ, p. A33
CARONDELET ST. JOSEPH'S HOSPITAL, TUCSON, AZ, p. A39
CARONDELET ST. MARY'S HOSPITAL, TUCSON, AZ, p. A39
CARRIE TINGLEY HOSPITAL, ALBUQUERQUE, NEW MEXICO (see UNIVERSITY OF NEW MEXICO HOSPITALS), p. A423
CARRIER CLINIC, BELLE MEAD, NJ, p. A409
CARRINGTON HEALTH CENTER, CARRINGTON, ND, p. A472
CARROLL COUNTY MEMORIAL HOSPITAL, CARROLLTON, KY, p. A255
CARROLL COUNTY MEMORIAL HOSPITAL, CARROLLTON, MO, p. A365
CARROLL HOSPITAL CENTER, WESTMINSTER, MD, p. A301
CARROLLTON SPRINGS, CARROLLTON, TX, p. A600
CARRUS REHABILITATION HOSPITAL, SHERMAN, TX, p. A643
CARRUS SPECIALTY HOSPITAL, SHERMAN, TX, p. A644
CARSON TAHOE CONTINUING CARE HOSPITAL, CARSON CITY, NV, p. A400
CARSON TAHOE HEALTH, CARSON CITY, NV, p. A400
CARSON VALLEY MEDICAL CENTER, GARDNERVILLE, NV, p. A400
CARTERET HEALTH CARE, MOREHEAD CITY, NC, p. A465
CARTERSVILLE MEDICAL CENTER, CARTERSVILLE, GA, p. A153
CARTHAGE AREA HOSPITAL, CARTHAGE, NY, p. A431
CARY MEDICAL CENTER, CARIBOU, ME, p. A289
CASA COLINA HOSPITAL AND HEALTH SYSTEMS, POMONA, CA, p. A81
CASCADE BEHAVIORAL HOSPITAL, TUKWILA, WA, p. A686
CASCADE MEDICAL CENTER, CASCADE, ID, p. A173
CASCADE MEDICAL CENTER, LEAVENWORTH, WA, p. A680
CASCADE VALLEY HOSPITAL AND CLINICS, ARLINGTON, WA, p. A676
CASEY COUNTY HOSPITAL, LIBERTY, KY, p. A260
CASS COUNTY MEMORIAL HOSPITAL, ATLANTIC, IA, p. A222
CASS REGIONAL MEDICAL CENTER, HARRISONVILLE, MO, p. A368

CASSIA REGIONAL MEDICAL CENTER, BURLEY, ID, p. A173
CASTANER GENERAL HOSPITAL, CASTANER, PR, p. A720
CASTLE MANOR (see FALL RIVER HOSPITAL), p. A569
CASTLE MEDICAL CENTER, KAILUA, HI, p. A169
CASTLE ROCK ADVENTIST HOSPITAL, CASTLE ROCK, CO, p. A100
CASTLEVIEW HOSPITAL, PRICE, UT, p. A657
CATALINA ISLAND MEDICAL CENTER, AVALON, CA, p. A54
CATAWBA HOSPITAL, CATAWBA, VA, p. A663
CATAWBA VALLEY MEDICAL CENTER, HICKORY, NC, p. A462
CATHOLIC MEDICAL CENTER, MANCHESTER, NH, p. A407
CATSKILL REGIONAL MEDICAL CENTER, HARRIS, NY, p. A435
CAVALIER COUNTY MEMORIAL HOSPITAL, LANGDON, ND, p. A475
CAVERNA MEMORIAL HOSPITAL, HORSE CAVE, KY, p. A258
CAYUGA MEDICAL CENTER AT ITHACA, ITHACA, NY, p. A435
CCC AT PINEVIEW HOSPITAL, LAKESIDE, AZ, p. A32
CEDAR COUNTY MEMORIAL HOSPITAL, EL DORADO SPRINGS, MO, p. A366
CEDAR CREST HOSPITAL AND RESIDENTIAL TREATMENT CENTER, BELTON, TX, p. A597
CEDAR HILLS HOSPITAL, PORTLAND, OR, p. A524
CEDAR PARK REGIONAL MEDICAL CENTER, CEDAR PARK, TX, p. A600
CEDAR RIDGE HOSPITAL, OKLAHOMA CITY, OK, p. A511
CEDAR SPRINGS HOSPITAL, COLORADO SPRINGS, CO, p. A100
CEDARS–SINAI MEDICAL CENTER, LOS ANGELES, CA, p. A69
CENTEGRA HOSPITAL – MCHENRY, MCHENRY, IL, p. A194
CENTEGRA HOSPITAL – WOODSTOCK, WOODSTOCK, IL, p. A203
CENTENNIAL HILLS HOSPITAL MEDICAL CENTER, LAS VEGAS, NV, p. A401
CENTENNIAL MEDICAL CENTER, FRISCO, TX, p. A615
CENTENNIAL PEAKS HOSPITAL, LOUISVILLE, CO, p. A107
CENTER FOR BEHAVIORAL MEDICINE, KANSAS CITY, MO, p. A369
CENTER FOR DISABILITIES AND DEVELOPMENT, IOWA CITY, IOWA (see UNIVERSITY OF IOWA HOSPITALS AND CLINICS), p. A230
CENTER FOR FORENSIC PSYCHIATRY, SALINE, MI, p. A330
CENTER FOR RESTORATIVE CARE AND REHABILITATION, LYNCHBURG, VA, p. A667
CENTERPOINT MEDICAL CENTER, INDEPENDENCE, MO, p. A368
CENTERPOINTE HOSPITAL, SAINT CHARLES, MO, p. A375
CENTINELA HOSPITAL MEDICAL CENTER, INGLEWOOD, CA, p. A65
CENTRA LYNCHBURG GENERAL HOSPITAL, LYNCHBURG, VA, p. A667
CENTRA SOUTHSIDE COMMUNITY HOSPITAL, FARMVILLE, VA, p. A664
CENTRA VIRGINIA BAPTIST HOSPITAL, LYNCHBURG, VIRGINIA (see CENTRA LYNCHBURG GENERAL HOSPITAL), p. A667
CENTRACARE HEALTH–LONG PRAIRIE, LONG PRAIRIE, MN, p. A341
CENTRACARE HEALTH–MELROSE, MELROSE, MN, p. A342
CENTRACARE HEALTH–MONTICELLO, MONTICELLO, MN, p. A343
CENTRACARE HEALTH–PAYNESVILLE, PAYNESVILLE, MN, p. A344
CENTRACARE HEALTH–SAUK CENTRE, SAUK CENTRE, MN, p. A347
CENTRAL ALABAMA VETERANS HEALTH CARE SYSTEM, MONTGOMERY, AL, p. A23
CENTRAL ARKANSAS VETERANS HEALTHCARE SYSTEM, LITTLE ROCK, AR, p. A47
CENTRAL CAROLINA HOSPITAL, SANFORD, NC, p. A468
CENTRAL COMMUNITY HOSPITAL, ELKADER, IA, p. A227
CENTRAL FLORIDA BEHAVIORAL HOSPITAL, ORLANDO, FL, p. A137
CENTRAL FLORIDA REGIONAL HOSPITAL, SANFORD, FL, p. A142
CENTRAL HARTNETT HOSPITAL, LILLINGTON, NORTH CAROLINA (see HARNETT HEALTH SYSTEM), p. A459
CENTRAL IOWA HEALTHCARE, MARSHALLTOWN, IA, p. A231
CENTRAL LOUISIANA STATE HOSPITAL, PINEVILLE, LA, p. A283
CENTRAL LOUISIANA SURGICAL HOSPITAL, ALEXANDRIA, LA, p. A268
CENTRAL MAINE MEDICAL CENTER, LEWISTON, ME, p. A290
CENTRAL MONTANA MEDICAL CENTER, LEWISTOWN, MT, p. A385
CENTRAL NEW YORK PSYCHIATRIC CENTER, MARCY, NY, p. A437
CENTRAL PENINSULA GENERAL HOSPITAL, SOLDOTNA, AK, p. A29
CENTRAL PRISON HOSPITAL, RALEIGH, NC, p. A466
CENTRAL REGIONAL HOSPITAL, BUTNER, NC, p. A456
CENTRAL STATE HOSPITAL, MILLEDGEVILLE, GA, p. A161
CENTRAL STATE HOSPITAL, LOUISVILLE, KY, p. A261
CENTRAL STATE HOSPITAL, PETERSBURG, VA, p. A670

CENTRAL TEXAS MEDICAL CENTER, SAN MARCOS, TX, p. A643
CENTRAL TEXAS REHABILITATION HOSPITAL, AUSTIN, TX, p. A594
CENTRAL TEXAS VETERANS AFFAIRS HEALTH CARE SYSTEM, OLIN E. TEAGUE VETERANS CENTER, TEMPLE, TEXAS (see CENTRAL TEXAS VETERANS HEALTH CARE SYSTEM), p. A646
CENTRAL TEXAS VETERANS HEALTH CARE SYSTEM, TEMPLE, TX, p. A646
CENTRAL VALLEY GENERAL HOSPITAL, HANFORD, CA, p. A64
CENTRAL VALLEY MEDICAL CENTER, NEPHI, UT, p. A656
CENTRAL VALLEY SPECIALTY HOSPITAL, MODESTO, CA, p. A75
CENTRAL VIRGINIA TRAINING CENTER, MADISON HEIGHTS, VA, p. A667
CENTRAL WASHINGTON HOSPITAL, WENATCHEE, WA, p. A687
CENTRASTATE HEALTHCARE SYSTEM, FREEHOLD, NJ, p. A412
CENTRO DE SALUD CONDUCTUAL MENONITA–CIMA, AIBONITO, PR, p. A719
CENTRO DE TRAUMA, MOCA, PR, p. A722
CGH MEDICAL CENTER, STERLING, IL, p. A201
CHADRON COMMUNITY HOSPITAL AND HEALTH SERVICES, CHADRON, NE, p. A391
CHAMBERS COUNTY PUBLIC HOSPITAL DISTRICT 1, ANAHUAC, TX, p. A592
CHAMBERS MEMORIAL HOSPITAL, DANVILLE, AR, p. A42
CHAMBERSBURG HOSPITAL, CHAMBERSBURG, PA, p. A531
CHANDLER REGIONAL MEDICAL CENTER, CHANDLER, AZ, p. A30
CHAPMAN MEDICAL CENTER, ORANGE, CA, p. A79
CHARLES A. CANNON MEMORIAL HOSPITAL, LINVILLE, NC, p. A464
CHARLES A. DEAN MEMORIAL HOSPITAL, GREENVILLE, ME, p. A290
CHARLES GEORGE VETERANS AFFAIRS MEDICAL CENTER, ASHEVILLE, NC, p. A455
CHARLESTON AREA MEDICAL CENTER, CHARLESTON, WV, p. A690
CHARLEVOIX AREA HOSPITAL, CHARLEVOIX, MI, p. A316
CHARLIE NORWOOD VETERANS AFFAIRS MEDICAL CENTER, AUGUSTA, GA, p. A151
CHARLTON MEMORIAL HOSPITAL, FALL RIVER, MASSACHUSETTS (see SOUTHCOAST HOSPITALS GROUP), p. A306
CHASE COUNTY COMMUNITY HOSPITAL, IMPERIAL, NE, p. A393
CHATHAM HOSPITAL, SILER CITY, NC, p. A468
CHATUGE REGIONAL HOSPITAL AND NURSING HOME, HIAWASSEE, GA, p. A158
CHEMICAL DEPENDENCY CENTER, IOWA CITY, IOWA (see UNIVERSITY OF IOWA HOSPITALS AND CLINICS), p. A230
CHENANGO MEMORIAL HOSPITAL, NORWICH, NY, p. A446
CHEROKEE INDIAN HOSPITAL, CHEROKEE, NC, p. A458
CHEROKEE MEDICAL CENTER, CENTRE, AL, p. A18
CHEROKEE NATION W.W. HASTINGS INDIAN HOSPITAL, TAHLEQUAH, OK, p. A515
CHEROKEE REGIONAL MEDICAL CENTER, CHEROKEE, IA, p. A224
CHERRY COUNTY HOSPITAL, VALENTINE, NE, p. A398
CHERRY HOSPITAL, GOLDSBORO, NC, p. A461
CHESAPEAKE REGIONAL MEDICAL CENTER, CHESAPEAKE, VA, p. A663
CHESHIRE MEDICAL CENTER, KEENE, NH, p. A406
CHESTATEE REGIONAL HOSPITAL, DAHLONEGA, GA, p. A155
CHESTER MENTAL HEALTH CENTER, CHESTER, IL, p. A181
CHESTER REGIONAL MEDICAL CENTER, CHESTER, SC, p. A558
CHESTNUT HILL HOSPITAL, PHILADELPHIA, PA, p. A542
CHESTNUT RIDGE HOSPITAL, MORGANTOWN, WEST VIRGINIA (see WEST VIRGINIA UNIVERSITY HOSPITALS), p. A693
CHEYENNE COUNTY HOSPITAL, SAINT FRANCIS, KS, p. A249
CHEYENNE REGIONAL MEDICAL CENTER, CHEYENNE, WY, p. A715
CHEYENNE VETERANS AFFAIRS MEDICAL CENTER, CHEYENNE, WY, p. A715
CHI ALBANY AREA HEALTH, ALBANY, MN, p. A334
CHI HEALTH BERGAN MERCY, OMAHA, NE, p. A395
CHI HEALTH CREIGHTON UNIVERSITY MEDICAL CENTER, OMAHA, NE, p. A395
CHI HEALTH GOOD SAMARITAN, KEARNEY, NE, p. A393
CHI HEALTH IMMANUEL, OMAHA, NE, p. A396
CHI HEALTH LAKESIDE, OMAHA, NE, p. A396
CHI HEALTH MERCY CORNING, CORNING, IA, p. A225
CHI HEALTH MERCY COUNCIL BLUFFS, COUNCIL BLUFFS, IA, p. A225
CHI HEALTH MIDLANDS, PAPILLION, NE, p. A397
CHI HEALTH MISSOURI VALLEY, MISSOURI VALLEY, IA, p. A231
CHI HEALTH NEBRASKA HEART, LINCOLN, NE, p. A393
CHI HEALTH PLAINVIEW, PLAINVIEW, NE, p. A397
CHI HEALTH SAINT FRANCIS, GRAND ISLAND, NE, p. A392
CHI HEALTH SCHUYLER, SCHUYLER, NE, p. A398
CHI HEALTH ST ELIZABETH, LINCOLN, NE, p. A393

CHI HEALTH ST. MARY'S, NEBRASKA CITY, NE, p. A394
CHI LAKEWOOD HEALTH, BAUDETTE, MN, p. A335
CHI LISBON HEALTH, LISBON, ND, p. A475
CHI MEMORIAL, CHATTANOOGA, TN, p. A575
CHI MERCY HOSPITAL, DEVILS LAKE, ND, p. A473
CHI OAKES HOSPITAL, OAKES, ND, p. A476
CHI ST. ALEXIUS HEALTH, BISMARCK, ND, p. A472
CHI ST. ANTHONY HOSPITAL, PENDLETON, OR, p. A523
CHI ST. FRANCIS HEALTH, BRECKENRIDGE, MN, p. A336
CHI ST. GABRIEL'S HEALTH, LITTLE FALLS, MN, p. A341
CHI ST. JOSEPH'S HEALTH, PARK RAPIDS, MN, p. A344
CHI ST. LUKE'S HEALTH MEMORIAL LIVINGSTON, LIVINGSTON, TX, p. A628
CHI ST. LUKE'S HEALTH MEMORIAL LUFKIN, LUFKIN, TX, p. A630
CHI ST. LUKE'S HEALTH MEMORIAL SAN AUGUSTINE, SAN AUGUSTINE, TX, p. A643
CHI ST. LUKE'S HEALTH MEMORIAL SPECIALTY HOSPITAL, LUFKIN, TX, p. A630
CHI ST. VINCENT HOT SPRINGS, HOT SPRINGS, AR, p. A45
CHI ST. VINCENT INFIRMARY MEDICAL CENTER, LITTLE ROCK, AR, p. A47
CHI ST. VINCENT MEDICAL CENTER–NORTH, SHERWOOD, AR, p. A50
CHICAGO LAKESHORE HOSPITAL, CHICAGO, IL, p. A181
CHICAGO LYING–IN HOSPITAL, CHICAGO, ILLINOIS (see UNIVERSITY OF CHICAGO MEDICAL CENTER), p. A185
CHICAGO–READ MENTAL HEALTH CENTER, CHICAGO, IL, p. A181
CHICKASAW NATION MEDICAL CENTER, ADA, OK, p. A503
CHICOT MEMORIAL MEDICAL CENTER, LAKE VILLAGE, AR, p. A46
CHILD AND ADOLESCENT BEHAVIORAL HEALTH SERVICES, WILLMAR, MN, p. A349
CHILDEN'S REGIONAL HOSPITAL AT COOPER, CAMDEN, NEW JERSEY (see COOPER UNIVERSITY HEALTH CARE), p. A410
CHILDREN AT PROVIDENCE ST. VINCENT, PORTLAND, OREGON (see PROVIDENCE ST. VINCENT MEDICAL CENTER), p. A524
CHILDREN'S HEALTH CENTER, PHOENIX, ARIZONA (see ST. JOSEPH'S HOSPITAL AND MEDICAL CENTER), p. A36
CHILDREN'S HEALTH SYSTEM OF TEXAS, DALLAS, TX, p. A604
CHILDREN'S HEALTHCARE OF ATLANTA, ATLANTA, GA, p. A150
CHILDREN'S HEALTHCARE OF ATLANTA AT EGLESTON, ATLANTA, GEORGIA (see CHILDREN'S HEALTHCARE OF ATLANTA), p. A150
CHILDREN'S HEALTHCARE OF ATLANTA AT HUGHES SPALDING, ATLANTA, GEORGIA (see CHILDREN'S HEALTHCARE OF ATLANTA), p. A150
CHILDREN'S HEALTHCARE OF ATLANTA AT SCOTTISH RITE, ATLANTA, GEORGIA (see CHILDREN'S HEALTHCARE OF ATLANTA), p. A150
CHILDREN'S HEALTHCARE OF MISSISSIPPI, JACKSON, MISSISSIPPI (see UNIVERSITY HOSPITAL), p. A355
CHILDREN'S HOSPITAL, NEW ORLEANS, LA, p. A281
CHILDREN'S HOSPITAL, GREENVILLE, SOUTH CAROLINA (see GREENVILLE MEMORIAL HOSPITAL), p. A561
CHILDREN'S HOSPITAL, MACON, GEORGIA (see MEDICAL CENTER, NAVICENT HEALTH), p. A160
CHILDREN'S HOSPITAL AND MEDICAL CENTER, OMAHA, NE, p. A396
CHILDREN'S HOSPITAL AND RESEARCH CENTER OAKLAND, OAKLAND, CA, p. A78
CHILDREN'S HOSPITAL AT BRONSON, KALAMAZOO, MICHIGAN (see BRONSON METHODIST HOSPITAL), p. A323
CHILDREN'S HOSPITAL AT DARTMOUTH, LEBANON, NEW HAMPSHIRE (see DARTMOUTH–HITCHCOCK MEDICAL CENTER), p. A407
CHILDREN'S HOSPITAL AT MONMOUTH MEDICAL CENTER, LONG BRANCH, NEW JERSEY (see MONMOUTH MEDICAL CENTER, LONG BRANCH CAMPUS), p. A413
CHILDREN'S HOSPITAL AT PROVIDENCE, ANCHORAGE, ALASKA (see PROVIDENCE ALASKA MEDICAL CENTER), p. A27
CHILDREN'S HOSPITAL AT SAINT FRANCIS, TULSA, OKLAHOMA (see SAINT FRANCIS HOSPITAL), p. A517
CHILDREN'S HOSPITAL COLORADO, AURORA, CO, p. A99
CHILDREN'S HOSPITAL OF COLORADO AT MEMORIAL, COLORADO SPRINGS, COLORADO (see CHILDREN'S HOSPITAL COLORADO), p. A99
CHILDREN'S HOSPITAL OF GEORGIA, AUGUSTA, GEORGIA (see GEORGIA REGENTS MEDICAL CENTER), p. A151
CHILDREN'S HOSPITAL OF ILLINOIS, PEORIA, ILLINOIS (see OSF SAINT FRANCIS MEDICAL CENTER), p. A198
CHILDREN'S HOSPITAL OF MICHIGAN, DETROIT, MI, p. A317
CHILDREN'S HOSPITAL OF MONTEFIORE,, NEW YORK (see MONTEFIORE MEDICAL CENTER), p. A442
CHILDREN'S HOSPITAL OF NEVADA AT UMC, LAS VEGAS, NEVADA (see UNIVERSITY MEDICAL CENTER), p. A403

CHILDREN'S HOSPITAL LOS ANGELES, LOS ANGELES, CA, p. A69

CHILDREN'S HOSPITAL OF NEW JERSEY, NEWARK, NEW JERSEY (see NEWARK BETH ISRAEL MEDICAL CENTER), p. A415

CHILDREN'S HOSPITAL OF OKLAHOMA, OKLAHOMA CITY, OKLAHOMA (see OU MEDICAL CENTER), p. A512

CHILDREN'S HOSPITAL OF ORANGE COUNTY, ORANGE, CA, p. A79

CHILDREN'S HOSPITAL OF PHILADELPHIA, PHILADELPHIA, PA, p. A543

CHILDREN'S HOSPITAL OF PITTSBURGH OF UPMC, PITTSBURGH, PA, p. A546

CHILDREN'S HOSPITAL OF RICHMOND AT VCU–BROOK ROAD CAMPUS, RICHMOND, VA, p. A671

CHILDREN'S HOSPITAL OF SAN ANTONIO, SAN ANTONIO, TEXAS (see CHRISTUS SANTA ROSA HEALTH SYSTEM), p. A640

CHILDREN'S HOSPITAL OF SHREVEPORT, SHREVEPORT, LOUISIANA (see UNIVERSITY HEALTH SHREVEPORT), p. A285

CHILDREN'S HOSPITAL OF SOUTH CAROLINA AT MUSC, CHARLESTON, SOUTH CAROLINA (see MUSC MEDICAL CENTER OF MEDICAL UNIVERSITY OF SOUTH CAROLINA), p. A558

CHILDREN'S HOSPITAL OF SOUTHWEST FLORIDA, FORT MYERS, FLORIDA (see LEE MEMORIAL HOSPITAL), p. A127

CHILDREN'S HOSPITAL OF THE KING'S DAUGHTERS, NORFOLK, VA, p. A669

CHILDREN'S HOSPITAL OF WISCONSIN, MILWAUKEE, WI, p. A706

CHILDREN'S HOSPITAL OF WISCONSIN–FOX VALLEY, NEENAH, WI, p. A707

CHILDREN'S HOSPITALS AND CLINICS OF MINNESOTA, MINNEAPOLIS, MN, p. A342

CHILDREN'S HOSPITALS AND CLINICS OF MINNESOTA, SAINT PAUL, MINNESOTA (see CHILDREN'S HOSPITALS AND CLINICS OF MINNESOTA), p. A342

CHILDREN'S INN AT NIH, BETHESDA, MARYLAND (see NATIONAL INSTITUTES OF HEALTH CLINICAL CENTER), p. A296

CHILDREN'S MEDICAL CENTER, DAYTON, OH, p. A487

CHILDREN'S MEDICAL CENTER, MINEOLA, NEW YORK (see WINTHROP–UNIVERSITY HOSPITAL), p. A437

CHILDREN'S MEDICAL CENTER PLANO, PLANO, TX, p. A637

CHILDREN'S MEMORIAL HERMANN HOSPITAL, HOUSTON, TEXAS (see MEMORIAL HERMANN – TEXAS MEDICAL CENTER), p. A620

CHILDREN'S MERCY HOSPITALS AND CLINICS, KANSAS CITY, MO, p. A369

CHILDREN'S MERCY SOUTH, OVERLAND PARK, KS, p. A248

CHILDREN'S NATIONAL MEDICAL CENTER, WASHINGTON, DC, p. A119

CHILDREN'S OF ALABAMA, BIRMINGHAM, AL, p. A16

CHILDREN'S SPECIALIZED HOSPITAL, MOUNTAINSIDE, NEW JERSEY (see CHILDREN'S SPECIALIZED HOSPITAL–PSE&G), p. A415

CHILDREN'S SPECIALIZED HOSPITAL–PSE&G, NEW BRUNSWICK, NJ, p. A415

CHILDRENS CARE HOSPITAL AND SCHOOL, SIOUX FALLS, SD, p. A571

CHILDRESS REGIONAL MEDICAL CENTER, CHILDRESS, TX, p. A600

CHILLICOTHE HOSPITAL DISTRICT, CHILLICOTHE, TX, p. A600

CHILLICOTHE VETERANS AFFAIRS MEDICAL CENTER, CHILLICOTHE, OH, p. A482

CHILTON MEDICAL CENTER, POMPTON PLAINS, NJ, p. A417

CHINESE HOSPITAL, SAN FRANCISCO, CA, p. A88

CHINLE COMPREHENSIVE HEALTH CARE FACILITY, CHINLE, AZ, p. A30

CHINO VALLEY MEDICAL CENTER, CHINO, CA, p. A57

CHIPPENHAM HOSPITAL, RICHMOND, VA, p. A671

CHIPPENHAM MEDICAL CENTER, RICHMOND, VIRGINIA (see CHIPPENHAM HOSPITAL), p. A671

CHIPPEWA COUNTY–MONTEVIDEO HOSPITAL, MONTEVIDEO, MN, p. A343

CHIPPEWA VALLEY HOSPITAL AND OAKVIEW CARE CENTER, DURAND, WI, p. A699

CHOATE MENTAL HEALTH CENTER, ANNA, IL, p. A178

CHOC CHILDREN'S AT MISSION HOSPITAL, MISSION VIEJO, CA, p. A75

CHOCTAW GENERAL HOSPITAL, BUTLER, AL, p. A17

CHOCTAW HEALTH CENTER, PHILADELPHIA, MS, p. A359

CHOCTAW MEMORIAL HOSPITAL, HUGO, OK, p. A508

CHOCTAW NATION HEALTH CARE CENTER, TALIHINA, OK, p. A516

CHOCTAW REGIONAL MEDICAL CENTER, ACKERMAN, MS, p. A350

CHRIS EVERT CHILDRENS HOSPITAL, FORT LAUDERDALE, FLORIDA (see BROWARD HEALTH MEDICAL CENTER), p. A126

CHRIST HOSPITAL, JERSEY CITY, NJ, p. A413

CHRIST HOSPITAL, CINCINNATI, OH, p. A482

CHRISTIAN HEALTH CARE CENTER, WYCKOFF, NJ, p. A421

CHRISTIAN HOSPITAL, SAINT LOUIS, MO, p. A376

CHRISTIANA CARE HEALTH SYSTEM, NEWARK, DE, p. A117

CHRISTIANA HOSPITAL, WILMINGTON, DELAWARE (see CHRISTIANA CARE HEALTH SYSTEM), p. A117

CHRISTUS COUSHATTA HEALTH CARE CENTER, COUSHATTA, LA, p. A272

CHRISTUS DUBUIS HOSPITAL OF ALEXANDRIA, ALEXANDRIA, LA, p. A268

CHRISTUS DUBUIS HOSPITAL OF BEAUMONT, BEAUMONT, TX, p. A596

CHRISTUS DUBUIS HOSPITAL OF BRYAN, BRYAN, TX, p. A599

CHRISTUS DUBUIS HOSPITAL OF FORT SMITH, FORT SMITH, AR, p. A44

CHRISTUS DUBUIS HOSPITAL OF HOT SPRINGS, HOT SPRINGS NATIONAL PARK, AR, p. A46

CHRISTUS DUBUIS HOSPITAL OF PARIS, PARIS, TX, p. A635

CHRISTUS DUBUIS HOSPITAL OF PORT ARTHUR, PORT ARTHUR, TX, p. A637

CHRISTUS HEALTH SHREVEPORT–BOSSIER, SHREVEPORT, LA, p. A284

CHRISTUS HIGHLAND MEDICAL CENTER, SHREVEPORT, LOUISIANA (see CHRISTUS HEALTH SHREVEPORT–BOSSIER), p. A284

CHRISTUS HOSPITAL–ST. ELIZABETH, BEAUMONT, TX, p. A596

CHRISTUS HOSPITAL–ST. MARY, PORT ARTHUR, TEXAS (see CHRISTUS HOSPITAL–ST. ELIZABETH), p. A596

CHRISTUS JASPER MEMORIAL HOSPITAL, JASPER, TX, p. A624

CHRISTUS SANTA ROSA HEALTH SYSTEM, SAN ANTONIO, TX, p. A640

CHRISTUS SANTA ROSA HOSPITAL – NEW BRAUNFELS, NEW BRAUNFELS, TEXAS (see CHRISTUS SANTA ROSA HEALTH SYSTEM), p. A640

CHRISTUS SANTA ROSA–MEDICAL CENTER, SAN ANTONIO, TEXAS (see CHRISTUS SANTA ROSA HEALTH SYSTEM), p. A640

CHRISTUS SPOHN HOSPITAL ALICE, ALICE, TX, p. A590

CHRISTUS SPOHN HOSPITAL BEEVILLE, BEEVILLE, TX, p. A597

CHRISTUS SPOHN HOSPITAL CORPUS CHRISTI MEMORIAL, CORPUS CHRISTI, TX, p. A602

CHRISTUS SPOHN HOSPITAL CORPUS CHRISTI SHORELINE, CORPUS CHRISTI, TEXAS (see CHRISTUS SPOHN HOSPITAL CORPUS CHRISTI MEMORIAL), p. A602

CHRISTUS SPOHN HOSPITAL CORPUS CHRISTI SOUTH, CORPUS CHRISTI, TEXAS (see CHRISTUS SPOHN HOSPITAL CORPUS CHRISTI MEMORIAL), p. A602

CHRISTUS SPOHN HOSPITAL KLEBERG, KINGSVILLE, TX, p. A626

CHRISTUS ST. FRANCES CABRINI HOSPITAL, ALEXANDRIA, LA, p. A268

CHRISTUS ST. MICHAEL HEALTH SYSTEM, TEXARKANA, TX, p. A647

CHRISTUS ST. MICHAEL HOSPITAL–ATLANTA, ATLANTA, TEXAS (see CHRISTUS ST. MICHAEL HEALTH SYSTEM), p. A647

CHRISTUS ST. MICHAEL REHABILITATION HOSPITAL, TEXARKANA, TX, p. A647

CHRISTUS ST. PATRICK HOSPITAL OF LAKE CHARLES, LAKE CHARLES, LA, p. A278

CHRISTUS ST. VINCENT PHYSICIANS MEDICAL CENTER, SANTA FE, NEW MEXICO (see CHRISTUS ST. VINCENT REGIONAL MEDICAL CENTER), p. A426

CHRISTUS ST. VINCENT REGIONAL MEDICAL CENTER, SANTA FE, NM, p. A426

CIBOLA GENERAL HOSPITAL, GRANTS, NM, p. A424

CIMARRON MEMORIAL HOSPITAL, BOISE CITY, OK, p. A504

CINCINNATI CHILDREN'S HOSPITAL MEDICAL CENTER, CINCINNATI, OH, p. A482

CINCINNATI VETERANS AFFAIRS MEDICAL CENTER, CINCINNATI, OH, p. A482

CIRCLES OF CARE, MELBOURNE, FL, p. A133

CITIZENS BAPTIST MEDICAL CENTER, TALLADEGA, AL, p. A25

CITIZENS MEDICAL CENTER, COLBY, KS, p. A238

CITIZENS MEDICAL CENTER, COLUMBIA, LA, p. A271

CITIZENS MEDICAL CENTER, VICTORIA, TX, p. A650

CITIZENS MEMORIAL HOSPITAL, BOLIVAR, MO, p. A363

CITRUS MEMORIAL HEALTH SYSTEM, INVERNESS, FL, p. A129

CITRUS VALLEY MEDICAL CENTER–INTER COMMUNITY CAMPUS, COVINA, CA, p. A59

CITRUS VALLEY MEDICAL CENTER–INTER–COMMUNITY CAMPUS, COVINA, CALIFORNIA (see CITRUS VALLEY MEDICAL CENTER–INTER COMMUNITY CAMPUS), p. A59

CITRUS VALLEY MEDICAL CENTER–QUEEN OF THE VALLEY CAMPUS, WEST COVINA, CALIFORNIA (see CITRUS VALLEY MEDICAL CENTER–INTER COMMUNITY CAMPUS), p. A59

CITY OF HOPE'S HELFORD CLINICAL RESEARCH HOSPITAL, DUARTE, CA, p. A60

CLAIBORNE COUNTY MEDICAL CENTER, PORT GIBSON, MS, p. A359

CLAIBORNE MEDICAL CENTER, TAZEWELL, TN, p. A588

CLAIBORNE MEMORIAL MEDICAL CENTER, HOMER, LA, p. A275

CLARA BARTON HOSPITAL, HOISINGTON, KS, p. A241

CLARA MAASS MEDICAL CENTER, BELLEVILLE, NJ, p. A409

CLAREMORE INDIAN HOSPITAL, CLAREMORE, OK, p. A505

CLARENDON MEMORIAL HOSPITAL, MANNING, SC, p. A563

CLARINDA REGIONAL HEALTH CENTER, CLARINDA, IA, p. A224

CLARION HOSPITAL, CLARION, PA, p. A531

CLARION PSYCHIATRIC CENTER, CLARION, PA, p. A531

CLARITY CHILD GUIDANCE CENTER, SAN ANTONIO, TX, p. A640

CLARK FORK VALLEY HOSPITAL, PLAINS, MT, p. A386

CLARK MEMORIAL HOSPITAL, JEFFERSONVILLE, IN, p. A213

CLARK REGIONAL MEDICAL CENTER, WINCHESTER, KY, p. A267

CLARKE COUNTY HOSPITAL, OSCEOLA, IA, p. A232

CLARKS SUMMIT STATE HOSPITAL, CLARKS SUMMIT, PA, p. A531

CLAXTON–HEPBURN MEDICAL CENTER, OGDENSBURG, NY, p. A446

CLAY COUNTY HOSPITAL, ASHLAND, AL, p. A15

CLAY COUNTY HOSPITAL, FLORA, IL, p. A188

CLAY COUNTY MEDICAL CENTER, CLAY CENTER, KS, p. A238

CLAY COUNTY MEMORIAL HOSPITAL, HENRIETTA, TX, p. A618

CLEAR BROOK LODGE, SHICKSHINNY, PA, p. A550

CLEAR BROOK MANOR, WILKES-BARRE, PA, p. A553

CLEAR LAKE REGIONAL MEDICAL CENTER, WEBSTER, TX, p. A651

CLEARVIEW REGIONAL MEDICAL CENTER, MONROE, GA, p. A161

CLEARWATER VALLEY HOSPITAL AND CLINICS, OROFINO, ID, p. A175

CLEMENT J. ZABLOCKI VETERANS AFFAIRS MEDICAL CENTER, MILWAUKEE, WI, p. A706

CLEO WALLACE CENTERS HOSPITAL, WESTMINSTER, CO, p. A109

CLEVELAND AREA HOSPITAL, CLEVELAND, OK, p. A505

CLEVELAND CAMPUS, CLEVELAND, OHIO (see NORTHCOAST BEHAVIORAL HEALTHCARE SYSTEM), p. A495

CLEVELAND CLINIC, CLEVELAND, OH, p. A484

CLEVELAND CLINIC CHILDREN'S HOSPITAL, CLEVELAND, OHIO (see CLEVELAND CLINIC), p. A484

CLEVELAND CLINIC CHILDREN'S HOSPITAL FOR REHABILITATION, CLEVELAND, OH, p. A484

CLEVELAND CLINIC FLORIDA, WESTON, FL, p. A147

CLEVELAND REGIONAL MEDICAL CENTER, SHELBY, NC, p. A468

CLIFTON SPRINGS HOSPITAL AND CLINIC, CLIFTON SPRINGS, NY, p. A431

CLIFTON T. PERKINS HOSPITAL CENTER, JESSUP, MD, p. A298

CLIFTON–FINE HOSPITAL, STAR LAKE, NY, p. A450

CLINCH MEMORIAL HOSPITAL, HOMERVILLE, GA, p. A159

CLINCH VALLEY MEDICAL CENTER, RICHLANDS, VA, p. A671

CLINTON COUNTY HOSPITAL, ALBANY, KY, p. A254

CLINTON HOSPITAL, CLINTON, MA, p. A306

CLINTON MEMORIAL HOSPITAL, WILMINGTON, OH, p. A501

CLOUD COUNTY HEALTH CENTER, CONCORDIA, KS, p. A238

CLOVIS COMMUNITY MEDICAL CENTER, CLOVIS, CA, p. A58

COAL COUNTY GENERAL HOSPITAL, COALGATE, OK, p. A505

COALINGA REGIONAL MEDICAL CENTER, COALINGA, CA, p. A58

COAST PLAZA HOSPITAL, NORWALK, CA, p. A78

COASTAL CAROLINA HOSPITAL, HARDEEVILLE, SC, p. A562

COASTAL COMMUNITIES HOSPITAL, SANTA ANA, CA, p. A90

COASTAL HARBOR TREATMENT CENTER, SAVANNAH, GA, p. A164

COATESVILLE VETERANS AFFAIRS MEDICAL CENTER, COATESVILLE, PA, p. A532

COBLESKILL REGIONAL HOSPITAL, COBLESKILL, NY, p. A432

COBRE VALLEY REGIONAL MEDICAL CENTER, GLOBE, AZ, p. A32

COCHRAN MEMORIAL HOSPITAL, MORTON, TX, p. A633

COFFEE REGIONAL MEDICAL CENTER, DOUGLAS, GA, p. A156

COFFEY COUNTY HOSPITAL, BURLINGTON, KS, p. A238

COFFEYVILLE REGIONAL MEDICAL CENTER, COFFEYVILLE, KS, p. A238

COGDELL MEMORIAL HOSPITAL, SNYDER, TX, p. A644

COLE MEMORIAL, COUDERSPORT, PA, p. A532

COLEMAN COUNTY MEDICAL CENTER, COLEMAN, TX, p. A601

COLER MEMORIAL HOSPITAL, NEW YORK, NEW YORK (see HENRY J. CARTER SPECIALTY HOSPITAL AND NURSING FACILITY), p. A440

COLISEUM CENTER FOR BEHAVIORAL HEALTH, MACON, GEORGIA (see COLISEUM MEDICAL CENTERS), p. A160

COLISEUM MEDICAL CENTERS, MACON, GA, p. A160

COLISEUM NORTHSIDE HOSPITAL, MACON, GA, p. A160

COLLEGE HOSPITAL CERRITOS, CERRITOS, CA, p. A57

COLLEGE HOSPITAL COSTA MESA, COSTA MESA, CA, p. A59

COLLEGE MEDICAL CENTER, LONG BEACH, CA, p. A68

COLLEGE STATION MEDICAL CENTER, COLLEGE STATION, TX, p. A601

COLLETON MEDICAL CENTER, WALTERBORO, SC, p. A565

COTTAGE CHILDREN'S HOSPITAL, SANTA BARBARA, CALIFORNIA (*see* SANTA BARBARA COTTAGE HOSPITAL), p. A91
COTTAGE HOSPITAL, WOODSVILLE, NH, p. A408
COTTAGE REHABILITATION HOSPITAL, SANTA BARBARA, CALIFORNIA (*see* SANTA BARBARA COTTAGE HOSPITAL), p. A91
COULEE MEDICAL CENTER, GRAND COULEE, WA, A679
COVENANT CHILDREN'S HOSPITAL, LUBBOCK, TX, p. A629
COVENANT HEALTHCARE, SAGINAW, MI, p. A329
COVENANT HOSPITAL PLAINVIEW, PLAINVIEW, TX, p. A636
COVENANT HOSPITAL–LEVELLAND, LEVELLAND, TX, p. A628
COVENANT MEDICAL CENTER, WATERLOO, IA, p. A235
COVENANT MEDICAL CENTER, LUBBOCK, TX, p. A629
COVENANT MEDICAL CENTER–COOPER, SAGINAW, MICHIGAN (*see* COVENANT HEALTHCARE), p. A329
COVENANT MEDICAL CENTER–HARRISON, SAGINAW, MICHIGAN (*see* COVENANT HEALTHCARE), p. A329
COVENANT MEDICAL CENTER–LAKESIDE, LUBBOCK, TEXAS (*see* COVENANT MEDICAL CENTER), p. A629
COVENANT SPECIALTY HOSPITAL, LUBBOCK, TX, p. A629
COVINGTON COUNTY HOSPITAL, COLLINS, MS, p. A352
COX MEDICAL CENTER BRANSON, BRANSON, MO, p. A364
COX MEDICAL CENTER NORTH, SPRINGFIELD, MISSOURI (*see* COX MEDICAL CENTERS), p. A378
COX MEDICAL CENTER SOUTH, SPRINGFIELD, MISSOURI (*see* COX MEDICAL CENTERS), p. A378
COX MEDICAL CENTERS, SPRINGFIELD, MO, p. A378
COX MONETT, MONETT, MO, p. A373
COZAD COMMUNITY HOSPITAL, COZAD, NE, p. A391
CRAIG GENERAL HOSPITAL, VINITA, OK, p. A517
CRAIG HOSPITAL, ENGLEWOOD, CO, p. A103
CRANE MEMORIAL HOSPITAL, CRANE, TX, p. A603
CRAWFORD COUNTY MEMORIAL HOSPITAL, DENISON, IA, p. A226
CRAWFORD MEMORIAL HOSPITAL, ROBINSON, IL, p. A199
CREEDMOOR PSYCHIATRIC CENTER,, NY, p. A439
CREEK NATION COMMUNITY HOSPITAL, OKEMAH, OK, p. A511
CRENSHAW COMMUNITY HOSPITAL, LUVERNE, AL, p. A21
CRESCENT MEDICAL CENTER LANCASTER, LANCASTER, TX, p. A627
CRESTWOOD MEDICAL CENTER, HUNTSVILLE, AL, p. A21
CRETE AREA MEDICAL CENTER, CRETE, NE, p. A391
CRISP REGIONAL HOSPITAL, CORDELE, GA, p. A155
CRITTENDEN COUNTY HOSPITAL, MARION, KY, p. A262
CRITTENTON CHILDREN'S CENTER, KANSAS CITY, MO, p. A369
CRITTENTON HOSPITAL MEDICAL CENTER, ROCHESTER, MI, p. A328
CROOK COUNTY MEDICAL SERVICES DISTRICT, SUNDANCE, WY, p. A717
CROSBYTON CLINIC HOSPITAL, CROSBYTON, TX, p. A603
CROSSRIDGE COMMUNITY HOSPITAL, WYNNE, AR, p. A52
CROSSROADS COMMUNITY HOSPITAL, MOUNT VERNON, IL, p. A195
CROTCHED MOUNTAIN REHABILITATION CENTER, GREENFIELD, NH, p. A406
CROUSE HOSPITAL, SYRACUSE, NY, p. A451
CROW/NORTHERN CHEYENNE HOSPITAL, CROW AGENCY, MT, p. A382
CROZER–CHESTER MEDICAL CENTER, UPLAND, PA, p. A551
CUBA MEMORIAL HOSPITAL, CUBA, NY, p. A432
CUERO COMMUNITY HOSPITAL, CUERO, TX, p. A603
CULBERSON HOSPITAL, VAN HORN, TX, p. A649
CULLMAN REGIONAL MEDICAL CENTER, CULLMAN, AL, p. A18
CUMBERLAND COUNTY HOSPITAL, BURKESVILLE, KY, p. A255
CUMBERLAND HALL HOSPITAL, HOPKINSVILLE, KY, p. A258
CUMBERLAND HOSPITAL, NEW KENT, VA, p. A668
CUMBERLAND MEDICAL CENTER, CROSSVILLE, TN, p. A577
CUMBERLAND MEMORIAL HOSPITAL, CUMBERLAND, WI, p. A699
CUMBERLAND RIVER HOSPITAL, CELINA, TN, p. A574
CURRY GENERAL HOSPITAL, GOLD BEACH, OR, p. A521
CUSTER REGIONAL HOSPITAL, CUSTER, SD, p. A568
CUYUNA REGIONAL MEDICAL CENTER, CROSBY, MN, p. A337
CYPRESS CREEK HOSPITAL, HOUSTON, TX, p. A619
CYPRESS FAIRBANKS MEDICAL CENTER, HOUSTON, TX, p. A619
CYPRESS POINTE SURGICAL HOSPITAL, HAMMOND, LA, p. A274

# D

D. W. MCMILLAN MEMORIAL HOSPITAL, BREWTON, AL, p. A17
DAHL MEMORIAL HEALTHCARE ASSOCIATION, EKALAKA, MT, p. A383
DAKOTA PLAINS SURGICAL CENTER, ABERDEEN, SD, p. A567
DALE MEDICAL CENTER, OZARK, AL, p. A24

DALLAS BEHAVIORAL HEALTHCARE HOSPITAL, DESOTO, TX, p. A608
DALLAS COUNTY HOSPITAL, PERRY, IA, p. A233
DALLAS COUNTY MEDICAL CENTER, FORDYCE, AR, p. A44
DALLAS MEDICAL CENTER, DALLAS, TX, p. A604
DALLAS REGIONAL MEDICAL CENTER, MESQUITE, TX, p. A632
DAMERON HOSPITAL, STOCKTON, CA, p. A93
DANA–FARBER CANCER INSTITUTE, BOSTON, MA, p. A303
DANBURY HOSPITAL, DANBURY, CT, p. A111
DANIEL DRAKE CENTER FOR POST ACUTE CARE, CINCINNATI, OH, p. A482
DANIELS MEMORIAL HEALTHCARE CENTER, SCOBEY, MT, p. A387
DANVILLE REGIONAL MEDICAL CENTER, DANVILLE, VA, p. A664
DANVILLE STATE HOSPITAL, DANVILLE, PA, p. A532
DARTMOUTH–HITCHCOCK MEDICAL CENTER, LEBANON, NH, p. A407
DAUTERIVE HOSPITAL, NEW IBERIA, LA, p. A281
DAVID GRANT USAF MEDICAL CENTER, TRAVIS AFB, CA, p. A94
DAVIESS COMMUNITY HOSPITAL, WASHINGTON, IN, p. A221
DAVIS COUNTY HOSPITAL, BLOOMFIELD, IA, p. A223
DAVIS HOSPITAL AND MEDICAL CENTER, LAYTON, UT, p. A655
DAVIS MEDICAL CENTER, ELKINS, WV, p. A690
DAVIS REGIONAL MEDICAL CENTER, STATESVILLE, NC, p. A469
DAY KIMBALL HOSPITAL, PUTNAM, CT, p. A114
DAYTON REHABILITATION INSTITUTE, DAYTON, OH, p. A487
DAYTON VETERANS AFFAIRS MEDICAL CENTER, DAYTON, OH, p. A488
DCH REGIONAL MEDICAL CENTER, TUSCALOOSA, AL, p. A25
DE GRAFF MEMORIAL HOSPITAL, NORTH TONAWANDA, NEW YORK (*see* KALEIDA HEALTH), p. A430
DE POO HOSPITAL, KEY WEST, FLORIDA (*see* LOWER KEYS MEDICAL CENTER), p. A130
DE QUEEN MEDICAL CENTER, DE QUEEN, AR, p. A43
DE SOTO REGIONAL HEALTH SYSTEM, MANSFIELD, LA, p. A279
DEACONESS CROSS POINTE CENTER, EVANSVILLE, INDIANA (*see* DEACONESS HOSPITAL), p. A208
DEACONESS HOSPITAL, EVANSVILLE, IN, p. A208
DEACONESS HOSPITAL, SPOKANE, WA, p. A685
DEARBORN COUNTY HOSPITAL, LAWRENCEBURG, IN, p. A214
DEBORAH HEART AND LUNG CENTER, BROWNS MILLS, NJ, p. A410
DECATUR COUNTY GENERAL HOSPITAL, PARSONS, TN, p. A587
DECATUR COUNTY HOSPITAL, LEON, IA, p. A231
DECATUR COUNTY MEMORIAL HOSPITAL, GREENSBURG, IN, p. A210
DECATUR HEALTH SYSTEMS, OBERLIN, KS, p. A247
DECATUR MEMORIAL HOSPITAL, DECATUR, IL, p. A186
DECATUR MORGAN HOSPITAL, DECATUR, AL, p. A18
DECATUR MORGAN HOSPITAL PARKWAY CAMPUS, DECATUR, ALABAMA (*see* DECATUR MORGAN HOSPITAL), p. A18
DECATUR MORGAN HOSPITAL–WEST, DECATUR, ALABAMA (*see* DECATUR MORGAN HOSPITAL), p. A18
DECKERVILLE COMMUNITY HOSPITAL, DECKERVILLE, MI, p. A317
DEER LODGE MEDICAL CENTER, DEER LODGE, MT, p. A382
DEER'S HEAD HOSPITAL CENTER, SALISBURY, MD, p. A300
DEKALB HEALTH, AUBURN, IN, p. A204
DEKALB MEDICAL AT DOWNTOWN DECATUR, DECATUR, GA, p. A155
DEKALB MEDICAL AT HILLANDALE, LITHONIA, GA, p. A160
DEKALB MEDICAL AT NORTH DECATUR, DECATUR, GA, p. A156
DEKALB REGIONAL MEDICAL CENTER, FORT PAYNE, AL, p. A20
DEL AMO HOSPITAL, TORRANCE, CA, p. A94
DEL SOL MEDICAL CENTER, EL PASO, TEXAS (*see* LAS PALMAS MEDICAL CENTER), p. A611
DELANO REGIONAL MEDICAL CENTER, DELANO, CA, p. A59
DELAWARE COUNTY MEMORIAL HOSPITAL, DREXEL HILL, PA, p. A533
DELAWARE PSYCHIATRIC CENTER, NEW CASTLE, DE, p. A117
DELAWARE VALLEY HOSPITAL, WALTON, NY, p. A453
DELL CHILDREN'S MEDICAL CENTER OF CENTRAL TEXAS, AUSTIN, TX, p. A594
DELRAY MEDICAL CENTER, DELRAY BEACH, FL, p. A125
DELTA COMMUNITY MEDICAL CENTER, DELTA, UT, p. A654
DELTA COUNTY MEMORIAL HOSPITAL, DELTA, CO, p. A101
DELTA MEDICAL CENTER, MEMPHIS, TN, p. A583
DELTA MEMORIAL HOSPITAL, DUMAS, AR, p. A43
DELTA REGIONAL MEDICAL CENTER, GREENVILLE, MS, p. A353
DENTON REGIONAL MEDICAL CENTER, DENTON, TX, p. A608
DENVER HEALTH, DENVER, CO, p. A101
DEPAUL CENTER, WACO, TEXAS (*see* PROVIDENCE HEALTHCARE NETWORK), p. A650
DEQUINCY MEMORIAL HOSPITAL, DEQUINCY, LA, p. A273
DES MOINES DIVISION, DES MOINES, IOWA (*see* VETERANS AFFAIRS CENTRAL IOWA HEALTH CARE SYSTEM), p. A227
DES PERES HOSPITAL, SAINT LOUIS, MO, p. A376

DESERT REGIONAL MEDICAL CENTER, PALM SPRINGS, CA, p. A80
DESERT SPRINGS HOSPITAL MEDICAL CENTER, LAS VEGAS, NV, p. A401
DESERT VALLEY HOSPITAL, VICTORVILLE, CA, p. A96
DESERT VIEW HOSPITAL, PAHRUMP, NV, p. A403
DESERT WILLOW TREATMENT CENTER, LAS VEGAS, NV, p. A401
DESOTO MEMORIAL HOSPITAL, ARCADIA, FL, p. A121
DETAR HEALTHCARE SYSTEM, VICTORIA, TX, p. A650
DETAR HOSPITAL NORTH, VICTORIA, TEXAS (*see* DETAR HEALTHCARE SYSTEM), p. A650
DETROIT RECEIVING HOSPITAL/UNIVERSITY HEALTH CENTER, DETROIT, MI, p. A317
DETTMER HOSPITAL, TROY, OHIO (*see* UPPER VALLEY MEDICAL CENTER), p. A499
DEVEREUX CHILDREN'S BEHAVIORAL HEALTH CENTER, MALVERN, PA, p. A539
DEVEREUX GEORGIA TREATMENT NETWORK, KENNESAW, GA, p. A159
DEVEREUX HOSPITAL AND CHILDREN'S CENTER OF FLORIDA, MELBOURNE, FL, p. A133
DEVEREUX TEXAS TREATMENT NETWORK, LEAGUE CITY, TX, p. A628
DEWITT HOSPITAL, DE WITT, AR, p. A43
DIAMOND CHILDREN'S HOSPITAL, TUCSON, ARIZONA (*see* BANNER – UNIVERSITY MEDICAL CENTER TUCSON), p. A39
DICKENSON COMMUNITY HOSPITAL, CLINTWOOD, VA, p. A663
DICKINSON COUNTY HEALTHCARE SYSTEM, IRON MOUNTAIN, MI, p. A322
DIGNITY HEALTH ARIZONA GENERAL HOSPITAL, LAVEEN, AZ, p. A33
DILEY RIDGE MEDICAL CENTER, CANAL WINCHESTER, OH, p. A482
DIMMIT REGIONAL HOSPITAL, CARRIZO SPRINGS, TX, p. A600
DISTRICT ONE HOSPITAL, FARIBAULT, MN, p. A338
DIVINE PROVIDENCE HOSPITAL, WILLIAMSPORT, PA, p. A553
DIVINE SAVIOR HEALTHCARE, PORTAGE, WI, p. A709
DIVISION OF ADOLESCENT MEDICINE, CINCINNATI CENTER FOR DEVELOPMENTAL DISORDERS, AND CONVALESCENT HOSPITAL FOR CHILDREN, CHILDREN'S HOSPITAL, CINCINNATI, OHIO (*see* CINCINNATI CHILDREN'S HOSPITAL MEDICAL CENTER), p. A482
DIXIE REGIONAL MEDICAL CENTER, SAINT GEORGE, UT, p. A658
DIXIE REGIONAL MEDICAL CENTER, ST. GEORGE, UTAH (*see* DIXIE REGIONAL MEDICAL CENTER), p. A658
DMC HARPER UNIVERSITY HOSPITAL, DETROIT, MI, p. A317
DMC HURON VALLEY–SINAI HOSPITAL, COMMERCE TOWNSHIP, MI, p. A317
DOCTOR'S CENTER OF BAYAMON, BAYAMON, PR, p. A720
DOCTOR'S HOSPITAL, LEAWOOD, KS, p. A244
DOCTOR'S HOSPITAL – TIDWELL, HOUSTON, TX, p. A619
DOCTOR'S HOSPITAL AT RENAISSANCE, EDINBURG, TX, p. A610
DOCTOR'S HOSPITAL OF DEER CREEK, LEESVILLE, LA, p. A279
DOCTOR'S MEMORIAL HOSPITAL, PERRY, FL, p. A140
DOCTORS CENTER, MANATI, PR, p. A721
DOCTORS COMMUNITY HOSPITAL, LANHAM, MD, p. A298
DOCTORS HOSPITAL, AUGUSTA, GA, p. A151
DOCTORS HOSPITAL AT WHITE ROCK LAKE, DALLAS, TX, p. A605
DOCTORS HOSPITAL OF JEFFERSON, METAIRIE, LOUISIANA (*see* EAST JEFFERSON GENERAL HOSPITAL), p. A280
DOCTORS HOSPITAL OF LAREDO, LAREDO, TX, p. A627
DOCTORS HOSPITAL OF MANTECA, MANTECA, CA, p. A74
DOCTORS HOSPITAL OF SARASOTA, SARASOTA, FL, p. A142
DOCTORS HOSPITAL OF WEST COVINA, WEST COVINA, CA, p. A97
DOCTORS HOSPITAL PARKWAY, HOUSTON, TEXAS (*see* DOCTOR'S HOSPITAL – TIDWELL), p. A619
DOCTORS MEDICAL CENTER, MODESTO, CA, p. A75
DOCTORS MEMORIAL HOSPITAL, BONIFAY, FL, p. A122
DOCTORS NEUROMEDICAL HOSPITAL, BREMEN, IN, p. A205
DOCTORS NEUROPSYCHIATRIC HOSPITAL AND RESEARCH INSTITUTE, BREMEN, IN, p. A205
DOCTORS' CENTER HOSPITAL SAN JUAN, SAN JUAN, PR, p. A723
DOCTORS' HOSPITAL OF MICHIGAN, PONTIAC, MI, p. A328
DODGE COUNTY HOSPITAL, EASTMAN, GA, p. A157
DOERNBECHER CHILDREN'S HOSPITAL, PORTLAND, OREGON (*see* OHSU HOSPITAL), p. A524
DOMINICAN HOSPITAL, SANTA CRUZ, CA, p. A91
DOMINION HOSPITAL, FALLS CHURCH, VA, p. A664
DONALSONVILLE HOSPITAL, DONALSONVILLE, GA, p. A156
DORMINY MEDICAL CENTER, FITZGERALD, GA, p. A157
DOROTHEA DIX PSYCHIATRIC CENTER, BANGOR, ME, p. A288
DOUGLAS COUNTY COMMUNITY MENTAL HEALTH CENTER, OMAHA, NE, p. A396
DOUGLAS COUNTY HOSPITAL, ALEXANDRIA, MN, p. A334

DOUGLAS COUNTY MEMORIAL HOSPITAL, ARMOUR, SD, p. A567

DOVER BEHAVIORAL HEALTH SYSTEM, DOVER, DE, p. A117

DOWN EAST COMMUNITY HOSPITAL, MACHIAS, ME, p. A291

DOYLESTOWN HOSPITAL, DOYLESTOWN, PA, p. A533

DR. DAN C. TRIGG MEMORIAL HOSPITAL, TUCUMCARI, NM, p. A427

DR. J. CORRIGAN MENTAL HEALTH CENTER, FALL RIVER, MA, p. A306

DR. JOHN WARNER HOSPITAL, CLINTON, IL, p. A185

DR. PILA'S HOSPITAL, PONCE, PR, p. A722

DR. RAMON E. BETANCES HOSPITAL–MAYAGUEZ MEDICAL CENTER BRANCH, MAYAGUEZ, PR, p. A722

DR. SOLOMON CARTER FULLER MENTAL HEALTH CENTER, BOSTON, MA, p. A303

DREW MEMORIAL HOSPITAL, MONTICELLO, AR, p. A48

DRISCOLL CHILDREN'S HOSPITAL, CORPUS CHRISTI, TX, p. A602

DRUMRIGHT REGIONAL HOSPITAL, DRUMRIGHT, OK, p. A505

DUANE L. WATERS HOSPITAL, JACKSON, MI, p. A323

DUBLIN SPRINGS, DUBLIN, OH, p. A489

DUKE CHILDREN'S HOSPITAL & HEALTH CENTER, DURHAM, NORTH CAROLINA (see DUKE UNIVERSITY HOSPITAL), p. A459

DUKE RALEIGH HOSPITAL, RALEIGH, NC, p. A466

DUKE REGIONAL HOSPITAL, DURHAM, NC, p. A459

DUKE UNIVERSITY HOSPITAL, DURHAM, NC, p. A459

DUKES MEMORIAL HOSPITAL, PERU, IN, p. A218

DUNCAN REGIONAL HOSPITAL, DUNCAN, OK, p. A505

DUNDY COUNTY HOSPITAL, BENKELMAN, NE, p. A390

DUPONT HOSPITAL, FORT WAYNE, IN, p. A208

DURHAM VETERANS AFFAIRS MEDICAL CENTER, DURHAM, NC, p. A459

DWIGHT DAVID EISENHOWER ARMY MEDICAL CENTER, FORT GORDON, GA, p. A157

# E

EAGLEVILLE HOSPITAL, EAGLEVILLE, PA, p. A533

EARLE E. MORRIS ALCOHOL AND DRUG TREATMENT CENTER, COLUMBIA, SC, p. A559

EAST ADAMS RURAL HOSPITAL, RITZVILLE, WA, p. A683

EAST ALABAMA MEDICAL CENTER, OPELIKA, AL, p. A23

EAST ALABAMA MEDICAL CENTER–LANIER, VALLEY, ALABAMA (see EAST ALABAMA MEDICAL CENTER), p. A23

EAST CAMPUS, NORFOLK, NEBRASKA (see FAITH REGIONAL HEALTH SERVICES), p. A395

EAST CARROLL PARISH HOSPITAL, LAKE PROVIDENCE, LA, p. A278

EAST CENTRAL REGIONAL HOSPITAL, AUGUSTA, GA, p. A151

EAST CENTRAL REGIONAL HOSPITAL, GRACEWOOD, GEORGIA (see EAST CENTRAL REGIONAL HOSPITAL), p. A151

EAST COOPER MEDICAL CENTER, MOUNT PLEASANT, SC, p. A563

EAST GEORGIA REGIONAL MEDICAL CENTER, STATESBORO, GA, p. A165

EAST HOUSTON REGIONAL MEDICAL CENTER, HOUSTON, TEXAS (see BAYSHORE MEDICAL CENTER), p. A635

EAST JEFFERSON GENERAL HOSPITAL, METAIRIE, LA, p. A280

EAST LIVERPOOL CITY HOSPITAL, EAST LIVERPOOL, OH, p. A489

EAST LOS ANGELES DOCTORS HOSPITAL, LOS ANGELES, CA, p. A69

EAST MISSISSIPPI STATE HOSPITAL, MERIDIAN, MS, p. A357

EAST MORGAN COUNTY HOSPITAL, BRUSH, CO, p. A100

EAST MOUNTAIN HOSPITAL, BELLE MEAD, NJ, p. A409

EAST OHIO REGIONAL HOSPITAL, MARTINS FERRY, OH, p. A493

EAST ORANGE DIVISION, EAST ORANGE, NEW JERSEY (see VETERANS AFFAIRS NEW JERSEY HEALTH CARE SYSTEM), p. A411

EAST ORANGE GENERAL HOSPITAL, EAST ORANGE, NJ, p. A411

EAST RIDGE HOSPITAL, EAST RIDGE, TENNESSEE (see PARKRIDGE MEDICAL CENTER), p. A575

EAST TENNESSEE CHILDREN'S HOSPITAL, KNOXVILLE, TN, p. A580

EAST TEXAS MEDICAL CENTER ATHENS, ATHENS, TX, p. A593

EAST TEXAS MEDICAL CENTER BEHAVIORAL HEALTH CENTER, TYLER, TEXAS (see EAST TEXAS MEDICAL CENTER TYLER), p. A649

EAST TEXAS MEDICAL CENTER CARTHAGE, CARTHAGE, TX, p. A600

EAST TEXAS MEDICAL CENTER FAIRFIELD, FAIRFIELD, TX, p. A612

EAST TEXAS MEDICAL CENTER HENDERSON, HENDERSON, TX, p. A618

EAST TEXAS MEDICAL CENTER JACKSONVILLE, JACKSONVILLE, TX, p. A624

EAST TEXAS MEDICAL CENTER PITTSBURG, PITTSBURG, TX, p. A636

EAST TEXAS MEDICAL CENTER REHABILITATION HOSPITAL, TYLER, TX, p. A648

EAST TEXAS MEDICAL CENTER SPECIALTY HOSPITAL, TYLER, TX, p. A648

EAST TEXAS MEDICAL CENTER TRINITY, TRINITY, TX, p. A648

EAST TEXAS MEDICAL CENTER TYLER, TYLER, TX, p. A649

EAST TEXAS MEDICAL CENTER–QUITMAN, QUITMAN, TX, p. A638

EASTAR HEALTH SYSTEM, MUSKOGEE, OK, p. A510

EASTAR HEALTH SYSTEM, EAST CAMPUS, MUSKOGEE, OKLAHOMA (see EASTAR HEALTH SYSTEM), p. A510

EASTERN IDAHO REGIONAL MEDICAL CENTER, IDAHO FALLS, ID, p. A174

EASTERN LONG ISLAND HOSPITAL, GREENPORT, NY, p. A434

EASTERN LOUISIANA MENTAL HEALTH SYSTEM, JACKSON, LA, p. A275

EASTERN MAINE MEDICAL CENTER, BANGOR, ME, p. A288

EASTERN NEW MEXICO MEDICAL CENTER, ROSWELL, NM, p. A426

EASTERN NIAGARA HOSPITAL, LOCKPORT, NY, p. A436

EASTERN NIAGARA HOSPITAL LOCKPORT, LOCKPORT, NEW YORK (see EASTERN NIAGARA HOSPITAL), p. A436

EASTERN NIAGARA HOSPITAL NEWFANE, NEWFANE, NEW YORK (see EASTERN NIAGARA HOSPITAL), p. A436

EASTERN OKLAHOMA MEDICAL CENTER, POTEAU, OK, p. A514

EASTERN PLUMAS HEALTH CARE, PORTOLA, CA, p. A81

EASTERN REGIONAL MEDICAL CENTER, PHILADELPHIA, PA, p. A543

EASTERN SHORE HOSPITAL CENTER, CAMBRIDGE, MD, p. A296

EASTERN STATE HOSPITAL, LEXINGTON, KY, p. A259

EASTERN STATE HOSPITAL, WILLIAMSBURG, VA, p. A674

EASTERN STATE HOSPITAL, MEDICAL LAKE, WA, p. A680

EASTLAND MEMORIAL HOSPITAL, EASTLAND, TX, p. A609

EASTON HOSPITAL, EASTON, PA, p. A533

EASTPOINTE HOSPITAL, DAPHNE, AL, p. A18

EASTSIDE MEDICAL CENTER, SNELLVILLE, GA, p. A164

EASTSIDE PSYCHIATRIC HOSPITAL, TALLAHASSEE, FL, p. A144

EATON RAPIDS MEDICAL CENTER, EATON RAPIDS, MI, p. A319

ED FRASER MEMORIAL HOSPITAL AND BAKER COMMUNITY HEALTH CENTER, MACCLENNY, FL, p. A132

EDEN MEDICAL CENTER, CASTRO VALLEY, CA, p. A57

EDGEFIELD COUNTY HOSPITAL, EDGEFIELD, SC, p. A560

EDGERTON HOSPITAL AND HEALTH SERVICES, EDGERTON, WI, p. A700

EDGEWOOD SURGICAL HOSPITAL, TRANSFER, PA, p. A551

EDINBURG CHILDREN'S HOSPITAL, EDINBURG, TEXAS (see SOUTH TEXAS HEALTH SYSTEM), p. A610

EDINBURG REGIONAL MEDICAL CENTER, EDINBURG, TEXAS (see SOUTH TEXAS HEALTH SYSTEM), p. A610

EDWARD HINES, JR. VETERANS AFFAIRS HOSPITAL, HINES, IL, p. A190

EDWARD HOSPITAL, NAPERVILLE, IL, p. A195

EDWARDS COUNTY HOSPITAL AND HEALTHCARE CENTER, KINSLEY, KS, p. A243

EDWIN SHAW REHAB, CUYAHOGA FALLS, OH, p. A487

EFFINGHAM HOSPITAL, SPRINGFIELD, GA, p. A165

EINSTEIN MEDICAL CENTER ELKINS PARK, ELKINS PARK, PENNSYLVANIA (see EINSTEIN MEDICAL CENTER PHILADELPHIA), p. A543

EINSTEIN MEDICAL CENTER MONTGOMERY, EAST NORRITON, PA, p. A533

EINSTEIN MEDICAL CENTER PHILADELPHIA, PHILADELPHIA, PA, p. A543

EISENHOWER MEDICAL CENTER, RANCHO MIRAGE, CA, p. A82

EL CAMINO HOSPITAL, MOUNTAIN VIEW, CA, p. A77

EL CAMINO HOSPITAL LOS GATOS, LOS GATOS, CALIFORNIA (see EL CAMINO HOSPITAL), p. A77

EL CAMPO MEMORIAL HOSPITAL, EL CAMPO, TX, p. A610

EL CENTRO REGIONAL MEDICAL CENTER, EL CENTRO, CA, p. A60

EL PASO CHILDREN'S HOSPITAL, EL PASO, TX, p. A610

EL PASO LTAC HOSPITAL, EL PASO, TX, p. A610

EL PASO PSYCHIATRIC CENTER, EL PASO, TX, p. A610

EL PASO SPECIALTY HOSPITAL, EL PASO, TX, p. A610

ELBERT MEMORIAL HOSPITAL, ELBERTON, GA, p. A157

ELEANOR SLATER HOSPITAL, CRANSTON, RI, p. A555

ELECTRA MEMORIAL HOSPITAL, ELECTRA, TX, p. A612

ELGIN MENTAL HEALTH CENTER, ELGIN, IL, p. A187

ELIZA COFFEE MEMORIAL HOSPITAL, FLORENCE, AL, p. A19

ELKHART GENERAL HEALTHCARE SYSTEM, ELKHART, IN, p. A207

ELKHORN VALLEY REHABILITATION HOSPITAL, CASPER, WY, p. A715

ELKVIEW GENERAL HOSPITAL, HOBART, OK, p. A508

ELLENVILLE REGIONAL HOSPITAL, ELLENVILLE, NY, p. A433

ELLETT MEMORIAL HOSPITAL, APPLETON CITY, MO, p. A363

ELLINWOOD DISTRICT HOSPITAL, ELLINWOOD, KS, p. A239

ELLIOT HOSPITAL, MANCHESTER, NH, p. A407

ELLIS FISCHEL CANCER CENTER, COLUMBIA, MISSOURI (see UNIVERSITY OF MISSOURI HOSPITALS AND CLINICS), p. A366

ELLIS HOSPITAL, SCHENECTADY, NY, p. A450

ELLIS HOSPITAL HEALTH CENTER, SCHENECTADY, NEW YORK (see ELLIS HOSPITAL), p. A450

ELLSWORTH COUNTY MEDICAL CENTER, ELLSWORTH, KS, p. A239

ELLWOOD CITY HOSPITAL, ELLWOOD CITY, PA, p. A533

ELMHURST HOSPITAL CENTER,, NY, p. A439

ELMHURST MEMORIAL HOSPITAL,, IL, p. A187

ELMIRA PSYCHIATRIC CENTER, ELMIRA, NY, p. A433

ELMORE COMMUNITY HOSPITAL, WETUMPKA, AL, p. A26

ELMWOOD HEALTHCARE CENTER AT THE SPRINGS, GREEN SPRINGS, OH, p. A490

ELY–BLOOMENSON COMMUNITY HOSPITAL, ELY, MN, p. A338

EMANUEL MEDICAL CENTER, TURLOCK, CA, p. A95

EMANUEL MEDICAL CENTER, SWAINSBORO, GA, p. A165

EMERALD COAST BEHAVIORAL HOSPITAL, PANAMA CITY, FL, p. A139

EMERSON HOSPITAL, CONCORD, MA, p. A306

EMERUS, SUGAR LAND, TX, p. A645

EMMA PENDLETON BRADLEY HOSPITAL, EAST PROVIDENCE, RI, p. A555

EMORY JOHNS CREEK HOSPITAL, JOHNS CREEK, GA, p. A159

EMORY REHABILITATION HOSPITAL, ATLANTA, GA, p. A150

EMORY SAINT JOSEPH'S HOSPITAL OF ATLANTA, ATLANTA, GA, p. A150

EMORY UNIVERSITY HOSPITAL, ATLANTA, GA, p. A150

EMORY UNIVERSITY HOSPITAL MIDTOWN, ATLANTA, GA, p. A150

EMORY UNIVERSITY ORTHOPAEDIC AND SPINE HOSPITAL, TUCKER, GEORGIA (see EMORY UNIVERSITY HOSPITAL), p. A150

EMORY WESLEY WOODS GERIATRIC HOSPITAL, ATLANTA, GEORGIA (see EMORY UNIVERSITY HOSPITAL), p. A150

ENCINO HOSPITAL MEDICAL CENTER,, CA, p. A69

ENDLESS MOUNTAIN HEALTH SYSTEMS, MONTROSE, PA, p. A541

ENGLEWOOD COMMUNITY HOSPITAL, ENGLEWOOD, FL, p. A126

ENGLEWOOD HOSPITAL AND MEDICAL CENTER, ENGLEWOOD, NJ, p. A412

ENLOE MEDICAL CENTER, CHICO, CA, p. A57

ENLOE MEDICAL CENTER–COHASSET, CHICO, CALIFORNIA (see ENLOE MEDICAL CENTER), p. A57

ENNIS REGIONAL MEDICAL CENTER, ENNIS, TX, p. A612

EPHRAIM MCDOWELL FORT LOGAN HOSPITAL, STANFORD, KY, p. A266

EPHRAIM MCDOWELL REGIONAL MEDICAL CENTER, DANVILLE, KY, p. A256

EPHRATA COMMUNITY HOSPITAL, EPHRATA, PA, p. A534

EPIC MEDICAL CENTER, EUFAULA, OK, p. A506

ERIE COUNTY MEDICAL CENTER, BUFFALO, NY, p. A430

ERIE VETERANS AFFAIRS MEDICAL CENTER, ERIE, PA, p. A534

ERIK AND MARGARET JONSSON HOSPITAL, DALLAS, TEXAS (see BAYLOR UNIVERSITY MEDICAL CENTER), p. A604

ERLANGER BLEDSOE HOSPITAL, PIKEVILLE, TN, p. A587

ERLANGER EAST HOSPITAL, CHATTANOOGA, TENNESSEE (see ERLANGER MEDICAL CENTER), p. A575

ERLANGER MEDICAL CENTER, CHATTANOOGA, TN, p. A575

ERLANGER NORTH HOSPITAL, CHATTANOOGA, TENNESSEE (see ERLANGER MEDICAL CENTER), p. A575

ESKENAZI HEALTH, INDIANAPOLIS, IN, p. A211

ESSENTIA HEALTH ADA, ADA, MN, p. A334

ESSENTIA HEALTH DULUTH, DULUTH, MN, p. A337

ESSENTIA HEALTH FARGO, FARGO, ND, p. A473

ESSENTIA HEALTH FOSSTON, FOSSTON, MN, p. A339

ESSENTIA HEALTH NORTHERN PINES MEDICAL CENTER, AURORA, MN, p. A335

ESSENTIA HEALTH SANDSTONE, SANDSTONE, MN, p. A347

ESSENTIA HEALTH ST. JOSEPH'S MEDICAL CENTER, BRAINERD, MN, p. A336

ESSENTIA HEALTH ST. MARY'S – DETROIT LAKES, DETROIT LAKES, MN, p. A337

ESSENTIA HEALTH ST. MARY'S HOSPITAL OF SUPERIOR, SUPERIOR, WI, p. A712

ESSENTIA HEALTH ST. MARY'S MEDICAL CENTER, DULUTH, MN, p. A338

ESSENTIA HEALTH–DEER RIVER, DEER RIVER, MN, p. A337

ESSENTIA HEALTH–GRACEVILLE, GRACEVILLE, MN, p. A339

ESSENTIA HEALTH–VIRGINIA, VIRGINIA, MN, p. A348

ESSEX COUNTY HOSPITAL CENTER, CEDAR GROVE, NJ, p. A410

ESTES PARK MEDICAL CENTER, ESTES PARK, CO, p. A103

ETHICUS HOSPITAL – GRAPEVINE, GRAPEVINE, TX, p. A617

EUCLID HOSPITAL, EUCLID, OH, p. A489

# F

FRANCISCAN ST. JAMES HOSPITAL AND HEALTH CENTERS, OLYMPIA FIELDS, IL, p. A197

FRANCISCAN ST. MARGARET HEALTH – DYER, DYER, INDIANA (see FRANCISCAN ST. MARGARET HEALTH – HAMMOND), p. A210

FRANCISCAN ST. MARGARET HEALTH – HAMMOND, HAMMOND, IN, p. A210

FRANK R. HOWARD MEMORIAL HOSPITAL, WILLITS, CA, p. A98

FRANKFORD CAMPUS, PHILADELPHIA, PENNSYLVANIA (see ARIA HEALTH), p. A542

FRANKFORT REGIONAL MEDICAL CENTER, FRANKFORT, KY, p. A257

FRANKLIN COUNTY MEDICAL CENTER, PRESTON, ID, p. A176

FRANKLIN COUNTY MEMORIAL HOSPITAL, MEADVILLE, MS, p. A357

FRANKLIN COUNTY MEMORIAL HOSPITAL, FRANKLIN, NE, p. A391

FRANKLIN FOUNDATION HOSPITAL, FRANKLIN, LA, p. A274

FRANKLIN GENERAL HOSPITAL, HAMPTON, IA, p. A228

FRANKLIN HOSPITAL, VALLEY STREAM, NY, p. A452

FRANKLIN HOSPITAL DISTRICT, BENTON, IL, p. A179

FRANKLIN MEDICAL CENTER, WINNSBORO, LA, p. A287

FRANKLIN MEMORIAL HOSPITAL, FARMINGTON, ME, p. A290

FRANKLIN REGIONAL HOSPITAL, FRANKLIN, NH, p. A406

FRANKLIN WOODS COMMUNITY HOSPITAL, JOHNSON CITY, TN, p. A579

FRAZIER REHAB INSTITUTE, LOUISVILLE, KY, p. A261

FREDERICK MEMORIAL HOSPITAL, FREDERICK, MD, p. A298

FREDONIA REGIONAL HOSPITAL, FREDONIA, KS, p. A240

FREEDOM PAIN HOSPITAL, SCOTTSDALE, AZ, p. A37

FREEMAN HOSPITAL EAST, JOPLIN, MISSOURI (see FREEMAN HOSPITAL WEST), p. A369

FREEMAN HOSPITAL WEST, JOPLIN, MO, p. A369

FREEMAN NEOSHO HOSPITAL, NEOSHO, MO, p. A373

FREEMAN REGIONAL HEALTH SERVICES, FREEMAN, SD, p. A569

FREMONT HEALTH, FREMONT, NE, p. A391

FREMONT HOSPITAL, FREMONT, CA, p. A62

FREMONT MEDICAL CENTER, FREMONT, CA, p. A62

FREMONT MEDICAL CENTER, YUBA CITY, CALIFORNIA (see RIDEOUT MEMORIAL HOSPITAL), p. A75

FRENCH HOSPITAL MEDICAL CENTER, SAN LUIS OBISPO, CA, p. A90

FRESNO HEART AND SURGICAL HOSPITAL, FRESNO, CA, p. A62

FRESNO SURGICAL HOSPITAL, FRESNO, CA, p. A62

FRIENDS HOSPITAL, PHILADELPHIA, PA, p. A543

FRIO REGIONAL HOSPITAL, PEARSALL, TX, p. A636

FRISBIE MEMORIAL HOSPITAL, ROCHESTER, NH, p. A408

FROEDTERT MEMORIAL LUTHERAN HOSPITAL, MILWAUKEE, WI, p. A706

FRYE REGIONAL MEDICAL CENTER, HICKORY, NC, p. A462

FRYE REGIONAL MEDICAL CENTER–SOUTH CAMPUS, HICKORY, NORTH CAROLINA (see FRYE REGIONAL MEDICAL CENTER), p. A462

FULTON COUNTY HEALTH CENTER, WAUSEON, OH, p. A500

FULTON COUNTY HOSPITAL, SALEM, AR, p. A50

FULTON COUNTY MEDICAL CENTER, MC CONNELLSBURG, PA, p. A539

FULTON DIVISION,, NEW YORK (see BRONX–LEBANON HOSPITAL CENTER HEALTH CARE SYSTEM), p. A438

FULTON MEDICAL CENTER, FULTON, MO, p. A368

FULTON STATE HOSPITAL, FULTON, MO, p. A368

# G

G. WERBER BRYAN PSYCHIATRIC HOSPITAL, COLUMBIA, SC, p. A559

G.V. (SONNY) MONTGOMERY VETERANS AFFAIRS MEDICAL CENTER, JACKSON, MS, p. A355

GADSDEN REGIONAL MEDICAL CENTER, GADSDEN, AL, p. A20

GAINESVILLE VETERANS AFFAIRS MEDICAL CENTER, GAINESVILLE, FLORIDA (see NORTH FLORIDA/SOUTH GEORGIA VETERAN'S HEALTH SYSTEM), p. A127

GALESBURG COTTAGE HOSPITAL, GALESBURG, IL, p. A188

GALICHIA HEART HOSPITAL, WICHITA, KANSAS (see WESLEY MEDICAL CENTER), p. A253

GALLUP INDIAN MEDICAL CENTER, GALLUP, NM, p. A424

GARDEN CITY HOSPITAL, GARDEN CITY, MI, p. A320

GARDEN GROVE HOSPITAL AND MEDICAL CENTER, GARDEN GROVE, CA, p. A63

GARDEN PARK MEDICAL CENTER, GULFPORT, MS, p. A353

GARDENS REGIONAL HOSPITAL AND MEDICAL CENTER, HAWAIIAN GARDENS, CA, p. A64

GARDENVIEW NURSING HOME (see MINNESOTA VALLEY HEALTH CENTER), p. A341

GARFIELD COUNTY HEALTH CENTER, JORDAN, MT, p. A384

GARFIELD COUNTY PUBLIC HOSPITAL DISTRICT, POMEROY, WA, p. A682

GARFIELD MEDICAL CENTER, MONTEREY PARK, CA, p. A76

GARFIELD MEMORIAL HOSPITAL AND CLINICS, PANGUITCH, UT, p. A657

GARFIELD PARK HOSPITAL, CHICAGO, IL, p. A182

GARRETT COUNTY MEMORIAL HOSPITAL, OAKLAND, MD, p. A299

GARRISON MEMORIAL HOSPITAL, GARRISON, ND, p. A474

GATEWAY MEDICAL CENTER, CLARKSVILLE, TN, p. A576

GATEWAY REGIONAL MEDICAL CENTER, GRANITE CITY, IL, p. A189

GATEWAY REHABILITATION HOSPITAL, FLORENCE, KY, p. A256

GATEWAYS HOSPITAL AND MENTAL HEALTH CENTER, LOS ANGELES, CA, p. A69

GAYLORD HOSPITAL, WALLINGFORD, CT, p. A115

GEARY COMMUNITY HOSPITAL, JUNCTION CITY, KS, p. A243

GEISINGER HEALTHSOUTH REHABILITATION HOSPITAL, DANVILLE, PA, p. A532

GEISINGER MEDICAL CENTER, DANVILLE, PA, p. A532

GEISINGER WYOMING VALLEY MEDICAL CENTER, WILKES BARRE, PA, p. A553

GEISINGER–BLOOMSBURG HOSPITAL, BLOOMSBURG, PA, p. A529

GEISINGER–COMMUNITY MEDICAL CENTER, SCRANTON, PA, p. A549

GEISINGER–LEWISTOWN HOSPITAL, LEWISTOWN, PA, p. A539

GEISINGER–SHAMOKIN AREA COMMUNITY HOSPITAL, COAL TOWNSHIP, PENNSYLVANIA (see GEISINGER MEDICAL CENTER), p. A532

GENERAL HOSPITAL, CHARLESTON, WEST VIRGINIA (see CHARLESTON AREA MEDICAL CENTER), p. A690

GENERAL HOSPITAL, LOS ANGELES, CALIFORNIA (see LAC/UNIVERSITY OF SOUTHERN CALIFORNIA MEDICAL CENTER), p. A71

GENERAL HOSPITAL, EUREKA, CALIFORNIA (see ST. JOSEPH HOSPITAL), p. A60

GENERAL JOHN J. PERSHING MEMORIAL HOSPITAL, BROOKFIELD, MO, p. A364

GENERAL LEONARD WOOD ARMY COMMUNITY HOSPITAL, FORT LEONARD WOOD, MO, p. A367

GENESIS BEHAVIORAL HOSPITAL, BREAUX BRIDGE, LA, p. A271

GENESIS HEALTHCARE SYSTEM, ZANESVILLE, OH, p. A502

GENESIS MEDICAL CENTER, DEWITT, DE WITT, IA, p. A226

GENESIS MEDICAL CENTER, ILLINI CAMPUS, SILVIS, IL, p. A200

GENESIS MEDICAL CENTER–ALEDO, ALEDO, IL, p. A178

GENESIS MEDICAL CENTER–DAVENPORT, DAVENPORT, IA, p. A225

GENESIS MEDICAL CENTER–EAST CAMPUS, DAVENPORT, IOWA (see GENESIS MEDICAL CENTER–DAVENPORT), p. A225

GENESIS MEDICAL CENTER–WEST CAMPUS, DAVENPORT, IOWA (see GENESIS MEDICAL CENTER–DAVENPORT), p. A225

GENESYS REGIONAL MEDICAL CENTER, GRAND BLANC, MI, p. A320

GENEVA GENERAL HOSPITAL, GENEVA, NY, p. A434

GENOA MEDICAL FACILITIES, GENOA, NE, p. A392

GEORGE C GRAPE COMMUNITY HOSPITAL, HAMBURG, IA, p. A228

GEORGE E. WEEMS MEMORIAL HOSPITAL, APALACHICOLA, FL, p. A121

GEORGE REGIONAL HOSPITAL, LUCEDALE, MS, p. A356

GEORGE W. TRUETT MEMORIAL HOSPITAL, DALLAS, TEXAS (see BAYLOR UNIVERSITY MEDICAL CENTER), p. A604

GEORGE WASHINGTON UNIVERSITY HOSPITAL, WASHINGTON, DC, p. A119

GEORGETOWN BEHAVIORAL HEALTH INSTITUTE, GEORGETOWN, TX, p. A616

GEORGETOWN COMMUNITY HOSPITAL, GEORGETOWN, KY, p. A257

GEORGIA REGENTS MEDICAL CENTER, AUGUSTA, GA, p. A151

GEORGIA REGIONAL HOSPITAL AT ATLANTA, DECATUR, GA, p. A156

GEORGIA REGIONAL HOSPITAL AT SAVANNAH, SAVANNAH, GA, p. A164

GEORGIANA HOSPITAL, GEORGIANA, AL, p. A20

GERALD CHAMPION REGIONAL MEDICAL CENTER, ALAMOGORDO, NM, p. A422

GETTYSBURG HOSPITAL, GETTYSBURG, PA, p. A534

GHS – LAURENS COUNTY MEMORIAL HOSPITAL, CLINTON, SOUTH CAROLINA (see GREENVILLE HEALTH SYSTEM – LAURENS COUNTY MEMORIAL HOSPITAL), p. A559

GIBSON AREA HOSPITAL AND HEALTH SERVICES, GIBSON CITY, IL, p. A189

GIBSON COMMUNITY HOSPITAL NURSING HOME (see GIBSON AREA HOSPITAL AND HEALTH SERVICES), p. A189

GIBSON GENERAL HOSPITAL, PRINCETON, IN, p. A218

GIFFORD MEDICAL CENTER, RANDOLPH, VT, p. A661

GILA REGIONAL MEDICAL CENTER, SILVER CITY, NM, p. A427

GILBERT HOSPITAL, GILBERT, AZ, p. A31

GILLETTE CHILDREN'S SPECIALTY HEALTHCARE, SAINT PAUL, MN, p. A346

GIRARD MEDICAL CENTER, GIRARD, KS, p. A240

GIRARD MEDICAL CENTER, PHILADELPHIA, PENNSYLVANIA (see NORTH PHILADELPHIA HEALTH SYSTEM), p. A544

GLACIAL RIDGE HEALTH SYSTEM, GLENWOOD, MN, p. A339

GLADYS SPELLMAN SPECIALTY HOSPITAL AND NURSING CENTER, CHEVERLY, MD, p. A296

GLEN COVE HOSPITAL, GLEN COVE, NY, p. A434

GLEN OAKS HOSPITAL, GREENVILLE, TX, p. A617

GLEN ROSE MEDICAL CENTER, GLEN ROSE, TX, p. A616

GLENBEIGH HOSPITAL AND OUTPATIENT CENTERS, ROCK CREEK, OH, p. A497

GLENCOE REGIONAL HEALTH SERVICES, GLENCOE, MN, p. A339

GLENDALE ADVENTIST MEDICAL CENTER, GLENDALE, CA, p. A63

GLENDALE MEMORIAL HOSPITAL AND HEALTH CENTER, GLENDALE, CA, p. A63

GLENDIVE MEDICAL CENTER, GLENDIVE, MT, p. A383

GLENDORA COMMUNITY HOSPITAL, GLENDORA, CA, p. A64

GLENN MEDICAL CENTER, WILLOWS, CA, p. A98

GLENS FALLS HOSPITAL, GLENS FALLS, NY, p. A434

GLENWOOD REGIONAL MEDICAL CENTER, WEST MONROE, LA, p. A286

GNADEN HUETTEN MEMORIAL HOSPITAL, LEHIGHTON, PA, p. A538

GOLDEN OURS CONVALESCENT HOME (see PERKINS COUNTY HEALTH SERVICES), p. A392

GOLDEN PLAINS COMMUNITY HOSPITAL, BORGER, TX, p. A598

GOLDEN VALLEY MEMORIAL HEALTHCARE, CLINTON, MO, p. A365

GOLDWATER MEMORIAL HOSPITAL, NEW YORK, NEW YORK (see HENRY J. CARTER SPECIALTY HOSPITAL AND NURSING FACILITY), p. A440

GOLETA VALLEY COTTAGE HOSPITAL, SANTA BARBARA, CA, p. A91

GOLISANO CHILDREN'S HOSPITAL, ROCHESTER, NEW YORK (see STRONG MEMORIAL HOSPITAL OF THE UNIVERSITY OF ROCHESTER), p. A449

GOLISANO CHILDREN'S HOSPITAL, SYRACUSE, NEW YORK (see UPSTATE UNIVERSITY HOSPITAL), p. A451

GOOD SAMARITAN HOSPITAL, BAKERSFIELD, CA, p. A55

GOOD SAMARITAN HOSPITAL, LOS ANGELES, CA, p. A70

GOOD SAMARITAN HOSPITAL, SAN JOSE, CA, p. A89

GOOD SAMARITAN HOSPITAL, VINCENNES, IN, p. A221

GOOD SAMARITAN HOSPITAL, SUFFERN, NY, p. A451

GOOD SAMARITAN HOSPITAL, CINCINNATI, OH, p. A483

GOOD SAMARITAN HOSPITAL, DAYTON, OH, p. A488

GOOD SAMARITAN HOSPITAL AND MEDICAL CENTER, PORTLAND, OREGON (see LEGACY GOOD SAMARITAN HOSPITAL AND MEDICAL CENTER), p. A524

GOOD SAMARITAN HOSPITAL MEDICAL CENTER, WEST ISLIP, NY, p. A453

GOOD SAMARITAN MEDICAL AND REHABILITATION CENTER, ZANESVILLE, OHIO (see GENESIS HEALTHCARE SYSTEM), p. A502

GOOD SAMARITAN MEDICAL CENTER, JOHNSTOWN, PENNSYLVANIA (see CONEMAUGH MEMORIAL MEDICAL CENTER), p. A537

GOOD SAMARITAN MEDICAL CENTER, LAFAYETTE, CO, p. A106

GOOD SAMARITAN MEDICAL CENTER, WEST PALM BEACH, FL, p. A147

GOOD SAMARITAN MEDICAL CENTER, BROCKTON, MA, p. A305

GOOD SAMARITAN MEDICAL CENTER – CUSHING CAMPUS, BROCKTON, MASSACHUSETTS (see GOOD SAMARITAN MEDICAL CENTER), p. A305

GOOD SAMARITAN REGIONAL HEALTH CENTER, MOUNT VERNON, IL, p. A195

GOOD SAMARITAN REGIONAL MEDICAL CENTER, CORVALLIS, OR, p. A520

GOOD SHEPHERD CAMPUS, WICHITA, KANSAS (see VIA CHRISTI HOSPITAL ON ST. FRANCIS), p. A253

GOOD SHEPHERD HEALTH CARE SYSTEM, HERMISTON, OR, p. A521

GOOD SHEPHERD MEDICAL CENTER, LONGVIEW, TX, p. A629

GOOD SHEPHERD MEDICAL CENTER–MARSHALL, MARSHALL, TX, p. A631

GOOD SHEPHERD PENN PARTNERS SPECIALTY HOSPITAL AT RITTENHOUSE, PHILADELPHIA, PA, p. A543

GOOD SHEPHERD REHABILITATION HOSPITAL, ALLENTOWN, PA, p. A528

GOOD SHEPHERD SPECIALTY HOSPITAL, BETHLEHEM, PA, p. A529

GOODALL–WITCHER HOSPITAL AUTHORITY, CLIFTON, TX, p. A601

GOODLAND REGIONAL MEDICAL CENTER, GOODLAND, KS, p. A240

GORDON HOSPITAL, CALHOUN, GA, p. A153

GORDON MEMORIAL HOSPITAL, GORDON, NE, p. A392

GOTHENBURG MEMORIAL HOSPITAL, GOTHENBURG, NE, p. A392

GOTTLIEB MEMORIAL HOSPITAL, MELROSE PARK, IL, p. A194

GOUVERNEUR HOSPITAL, GOUVERNEUR, NY, p. A434

GOVE COUNTY MEDICAL CENTER, QUINTER, KS, p. A249

GOVERNOR JUAN F. LUIS HOSPITAL, CHRISTIANSTED, VI, p. A725

GRACE COTTAGE HOSPITAL, TOWNSHEND, VT, p. A661

GRACE HOSPITAL, MORGANTON, NORTH CAROLINA (see BLUE RIDGE HEALTHCARE HOSPITALS), p. A465

GRACE HOSPITAL, CLEVELAND, OH, p. A484

GRACE MEDICAL CENTER, LUBBOCK, TX, p. A629

GRACIE SQUARE HOSPITAL, NEW YORK, NY, p. A439

GRADY GENERAL HOSPITAL, CAIRO, GA, p. A153

GRADY MEMORIAL HOSPITAL, ATLANTA, GA, p. A150

GRADY MEMORIAL HOSPITAL, CHICKASHA, OK, p. A505

GRAFTON CITY HOSPITAL, GRAFTON, WV, p. A691

GRAHAM COUNTY HOSPITAL, HILL CITY, KS, p. A241

GRAHAM HOSPITAL, CANTON, IL, p. A180

GRAHAM REGIONAL MEDICAL CENTER, GRAHAM, TX, p. A616

GRAND ITASCA CLINIC AND HOSPITAL, GRAND RAPIDS, MN, p. A339

GRAND JUNCTION VETERANS HEALTH CARE SYSTEM, GRAND JUNCTION, CO, p. A104

GRAND RIVER HOSPITAL DISTRICT, RIFLE, CO, p. A108

GRAND STRAND REGIONAL MEDICAL CENTER, MYRTLE BEACH, SC, p. A564

GRAND VIEW HEALTH, SELLERSVILLE, PA, p. A549

GRANDE RONDE HOSPITAL, LA GRANDE, OR, p. A522

GRANDVIEW MEDICAL CENTER, BIRMINGHAM, AL, p. A17

GRANDVIEW MEDICAL CENTER, DAYTON, OH, p. A488

GRANITE COUNTY MEDICAL CENTER, PHILIPSBURG, MT, p. A386

GRANITE FALLS MUNICIPAL HOSPITAL AND MANOR, GRANITE FALLS, MN, p. A340

GRANT MEMORIAL HOSPITAL, PETERSBURG, WV, p. A694

GRANT REGIONAL HEALTH CENTER, LANCASTER, WI, p. A704

GRANT–BLACKFORD MENTAL HEALTH CENTER, MARION, IN, p. A215

GRANVILLE HEALTH SYSTEM, OXFORD, NC, p. A466

GRAYS HARBOR COMMUNITY HOSPITAL, ABERDEEN, WA, p. A676

GREAT BEND REGIONAL HOSPITAL, GREAT BEND, KS, p. A240

GREAT FALLS CLINIC MEDICAL CENTER, GREAT FALLS, MT, p. A384

GREAT LAKES SPECIALTY HOSPITAL–GRAND RAPIDS, GRAND RAPIDS, MI, p. A320

GREAT LAKES SPECIALTY HOSPITAL–MUSKEGON, MUSKEGON, MI, p. A326

GREAT PLAINS HEALTH, NORTH PLATTE, NE, p. A395

GREAT PLAINS REGIONAL MEDICAL CENTER, ELK CITY, OK, p. A506

GREAT RIVER MEDICAL CENTER, BLYTHEVILLE, AR, p. A41

GREAT RIVER MEDICAL CENTER, WEST BURLINGTON, IA, p. A236

GREATER BALTIMORE MEDICAL CENTER, BALTIMORE, MD, p. A293

GREATER BINGHAMTON HEALTH CENTER, BINGHAMTON, NY, p. A429

GREATER EL MONTE COMMUNITY HOSPITAL, SOUTH EL MONTE, CA, p. A93

GREATER REGIONAL MEDICAL CENTER, CRESTON, IA, p. A225

GREELEY COUNTY HEALTH SERVICES, TRIBUNE, KS, p. A251

GREEN CLINIC SURGICAL HOSPITAL, RUSTON, LOUISIANA (see NORTHERN LOUISIANA MEDICAL CENTER), p. A284

GREEN OAKS HOSPITAL, DALLAS, TX, p. A605

GREENBRIER VALLEY MEDICAL CENTER, RONCEVERTE, WV, p. A695

GREENE COUNTY GENERAL HOSPITAL, LINTON, IN, p. A215

GREENE COUNTY HEALTH SYSTEM, EUTAW, AL, p. A19

GREENE COUNTY HOSPITAL, LEAKESVILLE, MS, p. A356

GREENE COUNTY MEDICAL CENTER, JEFFERSON, IA, p. A230

GREENE MEMORIAL HOSPITAL, XENIA, OH, p. A501

GREENLEAF CENTER, VALDOSTA, GA, p. A166

GREENVILLE CAMPUS, GREENVILLE, PENNSYLVANIA (see UPMC HORIZON), p. A535

GREENVILLE HEALTH SYSTEM – LAURENS COUNTY MEMORIAL HOSPITAL, CLINTON, SC, p. A559

GREENVILLE MEMORIAL HOSPITAL, GREENVILLE, SC, p. A561

GREENVILLE REGIONAL HOSPITAL, GREENVILLE, IL, p. A189

GREENWICH HOSPITAL, GREENWICH, CT, p. A112

GREENWOOD COUNTY HOSPITAL, EUREKA, KS, p. A239

GREENWOOD LEFLORE HOSPITAL, GREENWOOD, MS, p. A353

GREENWOOD REGIONAL REHABILITATION HOSPITAL, GREENWOOD, SC, p. A562

GREER MEMORIAL HOSPITAL, GREER, SC, p. A562

GREYSTONE PARK PSYCHIATRIC HOSPITAL, MORRIS PLAINS, NJ, p. A414

GRIFFIN HOSPITAL, DERBY, CT, p. A112

GRIFFIN MEMORIAL HOSPITAL, NORMAN, OK, p. A510

GRIMES ST. JOSEPH HEALTH CENTER, NAVASOTA, TX, p. A634

GRINNELL REGIONAL MEDICAL CENTER, GRINNELL, IA, p. A228

GRISELL MEMORIAL HOSPITAL DISTRICT ONE, RANSOM, KS, p. A249

GRITMAN MEDICAL CENTER, MOSCOW, ID, p. A175

GROUP HEALTH COOPERATIVE CENTRAL HOSPITAL, SEATTLE, WA, p. A683

GROVE CITY MEDICAL CENTER, GROVE CITY, PA, p. A535

GROVE HILL MEMORIAL HOSPITAL, GROVE HILL, AL, p. A20

GROVER C. DILS MEDICAL CENTER, CALIENTE, NV, p. A400

GROVER M. HERMANN HOSPITAL, CALLICOON, NY, p. A431

GRUNDY COUNTY MEMORIAL HOSPITAL, GRUNDY CENTER, IA, p. A228

GUADALUPE COUNTY HOSPITAL, SANTA ROSA, NM, p. A426

GUADALUPE REGIONAL MEDICAL CENTER, SEGUIN, TX, p. A643

GUAM MEMORIAL HOSPITAL AUTHORITY, TAMUNING, GU, p. A719

GUIDANCE CENTER, FLAGSTAFF, AZ, p. A31

GULF BREEZE HOSPITAL, GULF BREEZE, FL, p. A128

GULF COAST MEDICAL CENTER, FORT MYERS, FL, p. A127

GULF COAST MEDICAL CENTER, WHARTON, TX, p. A651

GULF COAST REGIONAL MEDICAL CENTER, PANAMA CITY, FL, p. A139

GUNDERSEN BOSCOBEL AREA HOSPITAL AND CLINICS, BOSCOBEL, WI, p. A698

GUNDERSEN HEALTH SYSTEM, LA CROSSE, WI, p. A703

GUNDERSEN ST. JOSEPH'S HOSPITAL AND CLINICS, HILLSBORO, WI, p. A702

GUNDERSEN TRI–COUNTY HOSPITAL AND CLINICS, WHITEHALL, WI, p. A714

GUNNISON VALLEY HOSPITAL, GUNNISON, CO, p. A104

GUNNISON VALLEY HOSPITAL, GUNNISON, UT, p. A655

GUTHRIE COUNTY HOSPITAL, GUTHRIE CENTER, IA, p. A228

GUTHRIE TOWANDA MEMORIAL HOSPITAL, TOWANDA, PA, p. A551

GUTTENBERG MUNICIPAL HOSPITAL, GUTTENBERG, IA, p. A228

GWINNETT HOSPITAL SYSTEM, LAWRENCEVILLE, GA, p. A160

GWINNETT MEDICAL CENTER, LAWRENCEVILLE, GEORGIA (see GWINNETT HOSPITAL SYSTEM), p. A160

GWINNETT MEDICAL CENTER–DULUTH, DULUTH, GEORGIA (see GWINNETT HOSPITAL SYSTEM), p. A160

# H

H. C. WATKINS MEMORIAL HOSPITAL, QUITMAN, MS, p. A360

H. LEE MOFFITT CANCER CENTER AND RESEARCH INSTITUTE, TAMPA, FL, p. A144

HABERSHAM MEDICAL CENTER, DEMOREST, GA, p. A156

HACKENSACK UNIVERSITY MEDICAL CENTER, HACKENSACK, NJ, p. A412

HACKENSACK UNIVERSITY MEDICAL CENTER AT PASCACK VALLEY, WESTWOOD, NJ, p. A420

HACKENSACK UNIVERSITY MEDICAL CENTER MOUNTAINSIDE, MONTCLAIR, NJ, p. A414

HACKETTSTOWN REGIONAL MEDICAL CENTER, HACKETTSTOWN, NJ, p. A412

HAHNEMANN CAMPUS, WORCESTER, MASSACHUSETTS (see UMASS MEMORIAL MEDICAL CENTER), p. A313

HAHNEMANN UNIVERSITY HOSPITAL, PHILADELPHIA, PA, p. A543

HALE COUNTY HOSPITAL, GREENSBORO, AL, p. A20

HALE HO'OLA HAMAKUA, HONOKAA, HI, p. A168

HALIFAX BEHAVIORAL SERVICES, DAYTONA BEACH, FLORIDA (see HALIFAX HEALTH MEDICAL CENTER OF DAYTONA BEACH), p. A125

HALIFAX HEALTH MEDICAL CENTER OF DAYTONA BEACH, DAYTONA BEACH, FL, p. A125

HALIFAX HEALTH MEDICAL CENTER OF PORT ORANGE, PORT ORANGE, FLORIDA (see HALIFAX HEALTH MEDICAL CENTER OF DAYTONA BEACH), p. A125

HALIFAX REGIONAL MEDICAL CENTER, ROANOKE RAPIDS, NC, p. A467

HALLMARK HEALTH SYSTEM, MELROSE, MA, p. A308

HALLMARK YOUTHCARE – RICHMOND, RICHMOND, VA, p. A671

HAMILTON CENTER, TERRE HAUTE, IN, p. A220

HAMILTON COUNTY HOSPITAL, SYRACUSE, KS, p. A251

HAMILTON GENERAL HOSPITAL, HAMILTON, TX, p. A617

HAMILTON HOSPITAL, OLNEY, TX, p. A635

HAMILTON MEDICAL CENTER, DALTON, GA, p. A155

HAMILTON MEMORIAL HOSPITAL DISTRICT, MCLEANSBORO, IL, p. A194

HAMLIN MEMORIAL HOSPITAL, HAMLIN, TX, p. A617

HAMMOND–HENRY HOSPITAL, GENESEO, IL, p. A189

HAMPSHIRE MEMORIAL HOSPITAL, ROMNEY, WV, p. A695

HAMPSTEAD HOSPITAL, HAMPSTEAD, NH, p. A406

HAMPTON BEHAVIORAL HEALTH CENTER, WESTAMPTON, NJ, p. A420

HAMPTON REGIONAL MEDICAL CENTER, VARNVILLE, SC, p. A565

HAMPTON ROADS SPECIALTY HOSPITAL, NEWPORT NEWS, VA, p. A668

HAMPTON VETERANS AFFAIRS MEDICAL CENTER, HAMPTON, VA, p. A666

HANCOCK COUNTY HEALTH SYSTEM, BRITT, IA, p. A223

HANCOCK MEDICAL CENTER, BAY SAINT LOUIS, MS, p. A350

HANCOCK REGIONAL HOSPITAL, GREENFIELD, IN, p. A210

HANNIBAL REGIONAL HOSPITAL, HANNIBAL, MO, p. A368

HANOVER HOSPITAL, HANOVER, KS, p. A241

HANOVER HOSPITAL, HANOVER, PA, p. A535

HANSEN FAMILY HOSPITAL, IOWA FALLS, IA, p. A230

HANSFORD HOSPITAL, SPEARMAN, TX, p. A644

HARBOR BEACH COMMUNITY HOSPITAL, HARBOR BEACH, MI, p. A322

HARBOR HOSPITAL OF SOUTHEAST TEXAS, BEAUMONT, TX, p. A596

HARBOR OAKS HOSPITAL, NEW BALTIMORE, MI, p. A326

HARBOR–UCLA MEDICAL CENTER, TORRANCE, CA, p. A94

HARDEMAN COUNTY MEMORIAL HOSPITAL, QUANAH, TX, p. A638

HARDIN COUNTY GENERAL HOSPITAL, ROSICLARE, IL, p. A200

HARDIN MEDICAL CENTER, SAVANNAH, TN, p. A587

HARDIN MEMORIAL HOSPITAL, ELIZABETHTOWN, KY, p. A256

HARDTNER MEDICAL CENTER, OLLA, LA, p. A283

HARDY WILSON MEMORIAL HOSPITAL, HAZLEHURST, MS, p. A354

HARLAN ARH HOSPITAL, HARLAN, KY, p. A258

HARLAN COUNTY HEALTH SYSTEM, ALMA, NE, p. A389

HARLEM GENERAL CARE UNIT AND HARLEM PSYCHIATRIC UNIT (see HARLEM HOSPITAL CENTER), p. A439

HARLEM HOSPITAL CENTER, NEW YORK, NY, p. A439

HARLINGEN MEDICAL CENTER, HARLINGEN, TX, p. A617

HARMON MEDICAL AND REHABILITATION HOSPITAL, LAS VEGAS, NV, p. A401

HARMON MEMORIAL HOSPITAL, HOLLIS, OK, p. A508

HARNETT HEALTH SYSTEM, DUNN, NC, p. A459

HARNEY DISTRICT HOSPITAL, BURNS, OR, p. A519

HARPER COUNTY COMMUNITY HOSPITAL, BUFFALO, OK, p. A504

HARPER HOSPITAL DISTRICT FIVE, HARPER, KS, p. A241

HARRINGTON MEMORIAL HOSPITAL, SOUTHBRIDGE, MA, p. A311

HARRIS HEALTH SYSTEM, HOUSTON, TX, p. A619

HARRIS REGIONAL HOSPITAL, SYLVA, NC, p. A469

HARRISBURG HOSPITAL, HARRISBURG, PENNSYLVANIA (see PINNACLE HEALTH SYSTEM), p. A535

HARRISBURG MEDICAL CENTER, HARRISBURG, IL, p. A189

HARRISON COMMUNITY HOSPITAL, CADIZ, OH, p. A480

HARRISON COUNTY COMMUNITY HOSPITAL, BETHANY, MO, p. A363

HARRISON COUNTY HOSPITAL, CORYDON, IN, p. A206

HARRISON MEDICAL CENTER, BREMERTON, WA, p. A676

HARRISON MEMORIAL HOSPITAL, CYNTHIANA, KY, p. A256

HARRY S. TRUMAN MEMORIAL VETERANS HOSPITAL, COLUMBIA, MO, p. A366

HARSHA BEHAVIORAL CENTER, TERRE HAUTE, IN, p. A220

HARTFORD HOSPITAL, HARTFORD, CT, p. A112

HARTGROVE HOSPITAL, CHICAGO, IL, p. A182

HARTON REGIONAL MEDICAL CENTER, TULLAHOMA, TN, p. A588

HASBRO CHILDREN'S HOSPITAL, PROVIDENCE, RHODE ISLAND (see RHODE ISLAND HOSPITAL), p. A556

HASKELL COUNTY COMMUNITY HOSPITAL, STIGLER, OK, p. A515

HASKELL MEMORIAL HOSPITAL, HASKELL, TX, p. A618

HAVASU REGIONAL MEDICAL CENTER, LAKE HAVASU CITY, AZ, p. A32

HAVEN BEHAVIORAL HEALTH OF EASTERN PENNSYLVANIA, READING, PA, p. A548

HAVEN BEHAVIORAL HOSPITAL OF FRISCO, FRISCO, TX, p. A615

HAVEN BEHAVIORAL SENIOR CARE OF ALBUQUERQUE, ALBUQUERQUE, NM, p. A422

HAVEN BEHAVIORAL SENIOR CARE OF DAYTON, DAYTON, OH, p. A488

HAVEN BEHAVIORAL WAR HEROES HOSPITAL, PUEBLO, CO, p. A108

HAVEN SENIOR HORIZONS, PHOENIX, AZ, p. A35

HAVENWYCK HOSPITAL, AUBURN HILLS, MI, p. A314

HAWAII STATE HOSPITAL, KANEOHE, HI, p. A170

HAWARDEN REGIONAL HEALTHCARE, HAWARDEN, IA, p. A229

HAWTHORN CENTER, NORTHVILLE, MI, p. A327

HAWTHORN CHILDREN PSYCHIATRIC HOSPITAL, SAINT LOUIS, MO, p. A376

HAXTUN HOSPITAL DISTRICT, HAXTUN, CO, p. A105

HAYES GREEN BEACH MEMORIAL HOSPITAL, CHARLOTTE, MI, p. A316

HAYS MEDICAL CENTER, HAYS, KS, p. A241

HAYWARD AREA MEMORIAL HOSPITAL AND NURSING HOME, HAYWARD, WI, p. A702

HAYWOOD REGIONAL MEDICAL CENTER, CLYDE, NC, p. A458

HAZARD ARH REGIONAL MEDICAL CENTER, HAZARD, KY, p. A258

HAZEL HAWKINS MEMORIAL HOSPITAL, HOLLISTER, CA, p. A65

HCMC DEPARTMENT OF PEDIATRICS, MINNEAPOLIS, MINNESOTA (see HENNEPIN COUNTY MEDICAL CENTER), p. A342

HEALDSBURG DISTRICT HOSPITAL, HEALDSBURG, CA, p. A64

HEALTH ALLIANCE HOSPITAL – BROADWAY CAMPUS, KINGSTON, NY, p. A436

HEALTH ALLIANCE HOSPITAL – MARY'S AVENUE CAMPUS, KINGSTON, NY, p. A436

HEALTH CENTRAL HOSPITAL, OCOEE, FL, p. A137

HEALTH FIRST CAPE CANAVERAL HOSPITAL, COCOA BEACH, FL, p. A124

HEALTH FIRST HOLMES REGIONAL MEDICAL CENTER, MELBOURNE, FL, p. A133

HEALTH FIRST PALM BAY HOSPITAL, PALM BAY, FL, p. A138

HEALTH FIRST VIERA HOSPITAL, MELBOURNE, FL, p. A133

HEALTHALLIANCE HOSPITALS, LEOMINSTER, MA, p. A308

HEALTHBRIDGE CHILDREN'S HOSPITAL, ORANGE, CA, p. A79

HEALTHBRIDGE CHILDREN'S HOSPITAL OF HOUSTON, HOUSTON, TX, p. A619

HEALTHMARK REGIONAL MEDICAL CENTER, DEFUNIAK SPRINGS, FL, p. A125

HEALTHPARK, OWENSBORO, KENTUCKY (see OWENSBORO HEALTH REGIONAL HOSPITAL), p. A264

HEALTHPARK HOSPITAL, HOT SPRINGS NATIONAL PARK, ARKANSAS (see CHI ST. VINCENT HOT SPRINGS), p. A45

HEALTHPARK MEDICAL CENTER, FORT MYERS, FLORIDA (see LEE MEMORIAL HOSPITAL), p. A127

HEALTHSOURCE SAGINAW, INC., SAGINAW, MI, p. A329

HEALTHSOUTH BAKERSFIELD REHABILITATION HOSPITAL, BAKERSFIELD, CA, p. A55

HEALTHSOUTH CANE CREEK REHABILITATION HOSPITAL, MARTIN, TN, p. A582

HEALTHSOUTH CHATTANOOGA REHABILITATION HOSPITAL, CHATTANOOGA, TN, p. A575

HEALTHSOUTH CHESAPEAKE REHABILITATION HOSPITAL, SALISBURY, MD, p. A300

HEALTHSOUTH CITY VIEW REHABILITATION HOSPITAL, FORT WORTH, TX, p. A613

HEALTHSOUTH DEACONESS REHABILITATION HOSPITAL, EVANSVILLE, IN, p. A208

HEALTHSOUTH DESERT CANYON REHABILITATION HOSPITAL, LAS VEGAS, NV, p. A402

HEALTHSOUTH EAST VALLEY REHABILITATION HOSPITAL, MESA, AZ, p. A33

HEALTHSOUTH EMERALD COAST REHABILITATION HOSPITAL, PANAMA CITY, FL, p. A139

HEALTHSOUTH HARMARVILLE REHABILITATION HOSPITAL, PITTSBURGH, PA, p. A546

HEALTHSOUTH HOSPITAL OF MANATI, MANATI, PR, p. A721

HEALTHSOUTH HUNTINGTON REHABILITATION HOSPITAL, HUNTINGTON, WV, p. A692

HEALTHSOUTH LAKESHORE REHABILITATION HOSPITAL, BIRMINGHAM, AL, p. A16

HEALTHSOUTH LAKEVIEW REHABILITATION HOSPITAL, ELIZABETHTOWN, KY, p. A256

HEALTHSOUTH MOUNTAINVIEW REGIONAL REHABILITATION HOSPITAL, MORGANTOWN, WV, p. A693

HEALTHSOUTH NITTANY VALLEY REHABILITATION HOSPITAL, PLEASANT GAP, PA, p. A547

HEALTHSOUTH NORTHERN KENTUCKY REHABILITATION HOSPITAL, EDGEWOOD, KY, p. A256

HEALTHSOUTH PLANO REHABILITATION HOSPITAL, PLANO, TX, p. A637

HEALTHSOUTH READING REHABILITATION HOSPITAL, READING, PA, p. A548

HEALTHSOUTH REHABILITATION HOSPITAL, DOTHAN, AL, p. A18

HEALTHSOUTH REHABILITATION HOSPITAL, FAYETTEVILLE, AR, p. A43

HEALTHSOUTH REHABILITATION HOSPITAL, LARGO, FL, p. A131

HEALTHSOUTH REHABILITATION HOSPITAL, CONCORD, NH, p. A405

HEALTHSOUTH REHABILITATION HOSPITAL, ALBUQUERQUE, NM, p. A422

HEALTHSOUTH REHABILITATION HOSPITAL, KINGSPORT, TN, p. A580

HEALTHSOUTH REHABILITATION HOSPITAL – HENDERSON, HENDERSON, NV, p. A401

HEALTHSOUTH REHABILITATION HOSPITAL AT DRAKE, CINCINNATI, OH, p. A483

HEALTHSOUTH REHABILITATION HOSPITAL AT MARTIN HEALTH, STUART, FL, p. A143

HEALTHSOUTH REHABILITATION HOSPITAL MEMPHIS–NORTH, MEMPHIS, TN, p. A583

HEALTHSOUTH REHABILITATION HOSPITAL MIDLAND–ODESSA, MIDLAND, TX, p. A632

HEALTHSOUTH REHABILITATION HOSPITAL OF ALEXANDRIA, ALEXANDRIA, LA, p. A268

HEALTHSOUTH REHABILITATION HOSPITAL OF ALTAMONTE SPRINGS, ALTAMONTE SPRINGS, FL, p. A121

HEALTHSOUTH REHABILITATION HOSPITAL OF ALTOONA, ALTOONA, PA, p. A528

HEALTHSOUTH REHABILITATION HOSPITAL OF ARLINGTON, ARLINGTON, TX, p. A592

HEALTHSOUTH REHABILITATION HOSPITAL OF AUSTIN, AUSTIN, TX, p. A594

HEALTHSOUTH REHABILITATION HOSPITAL OF BEAUMONT, BEAUMONT, TX, p. A596

HEALTHSOUTH REHABILITATION HOSPITAL OF CHARLESTON, CHARLESTON, SC, p. A558

HEALTHSOUTH REHABILITATION HOSPITAL OF COLORADO SPRINGS, COLORADO SPRINGS, CO, p. A100

HEALTHSOUTH REHABILITATION HOSPITAL OF COLUMBIA, COLUMBIA, SC, p. A559

HEALTHSOUTH REHABILITATION HOSPITAL OF CYPRESS, HOUSTON, TX, p. A620

HEALTHSOUTH REHABILITATION HOSPITAL OF DENVER, LITTLETON, CO, p. A106

HEALTHSOUTH REHABILITATION HOSPITAL OF ERIE, ERIE, PA, p. A534

HEALTHSOUTH REHABILITATION HOSPITAL OF FLORENCE, FLORENCE, SC, p. A560

HEALTHSOUTH REHABILITATION HOSPITAL OF FORT SMITH, FORT SMITH, AR, p. A44

HEALTHSOUTH REHABILITATION HOSPITAL OF FORT WORTH, FORT WORTH, TX, p. A613

HEALTHSOUTH REHABILITATION HOSPITAL OF FREDERICKSBURG, FREDERICKSBURG, VA, p. A665

HEALTHSOUTH REHABILITATION HOSPITAL OF HUMBLE, LLC, HUMBLE, TX, p. A623

HEALTHSOUTH REHABILITATION HOSPITAL OF JONESBORO, JONESBORO, AR, p. A46

HEALTHSOUTH REHABILITATION HOSPITAL OF MECHANICSBURG, MECHANICSBURG, PA, p. A540

HEALTHSOUTH REHABILITATION HOSPITAL OF MEMPHIS, MEMPHIS, TN, p. A583

HEALTHSOUTH REHABILITATION HOSPITAL OF MIAMI, CUTLER BAY, FL, p. A124

HEALTHSOUTH REHABILITATION HOSPITAL OF MONTGOMERY, MONTGOMERY, AL, p. A23

HEALTHSOUTH REHABILITATION HOSPITAL OF NORTH ALABAMA, HUNTSVILLE, AL, p. A21

HEALTHSOUTH REHABILITATION HOSPITAL OF NORTHERN VIRGINIA, ALDIE, VA, p. A662

HEALTHSOUTH REHABILITATION HOSPITAL OF OCALA, OCALA, FL, p. A136

HEALTHSOUTH REHABILITATION HOSPITAL OF PETERSBURG, PETERSBURG, VA, p. A670

HEALTHSOUTH REHABILITATION HOSPITAL OF ROCK HILL, ROCK HILL, SC, p. A564

HEALTHSOUTH REHABILITATION HOSPITAL OF SAN JUAN, SAN JUAN, PR, p. A723

HEALTHSOUTH REHABILITATION HOSPITAL OF SARASOTA, SARASOTA, FL, p. A142

HEALTHSOUTH REHABILITATION HOSPITAL OF SEWICKLEY, SEWICKLEY, PA, p. A550

HEALTHSOUTH REHABILITATION HOSPITAL OF SOUTHERN ARIZONA, TUCSON, AZ, p. A39

HEALTHSOUTH REHABILITATION HOSPITAL OF SPRING HILL, BROOKSVILLE, FL, p. A123

HEALTHSOUTH REHABILITATION HOSPITAL OF TALLAHASSEE, TALLAHASSEE, FL, p. A144

HEALTHSOUTH REHABILITATION HOSPITAL OF TEXARKANA, TEXARKANA, TX, p. A647

HEALTHSOUTH REHABILITATION HOSPITAL OF TOMS RIVER, TOMS RIVER, NJ, p. A419

HEALTHSOUTH REHABILITATION HOSPITAL OF UTAH, SANDY, UT, p. A659

HEALTHSOUTH REHABILITATION HOSPITAL OF VINELAND, VINELAND, NJ, p. A419

HEALTHSOUTH REHABILITATION HOSPITAL OF VIRGINIA, RICHMOND, VA, p. A671

HEALTHSOUTH REHABILITATION HOSPITAL OF WESTERN MASSACHUSETTS, LUDLOW, MA, p. A308

HEALTHSOUTH REHABILITATION HOSPITAL OF YORK, YORK, PA, p. A554

HEALTHSOUTH REHABILITATION HOSPITAL THE WOODLANDS, CONROE, TX, p. A602

HEALTHSOUTH REHABILITATION HOSPITAL–LAS VEGAS, LAS VEGAS, NV, p. A402

HEALTHSOUTH REHABILITATION HOSPITAL–WICHITA FALLS, WICHITA FALLS, TX, p. A652

HEALTHSOUTH REHABILITATION INSTITUTE OF SAN ANTONIO, SAN ANTONIO, TX, p. A640

HEALTHSOUTH REHABILITATION INSTITUTE OF TUCSON, TUCSON, AZ, p. A39

HEALTHSOUTH REHABILITATION OF GADSDEN, GADSDEN, AL, p. A20

HEALTHSOUTH SCOTTSDALE REHABILITATION HOSPITAL, SCOTTSDALE, AZ, p. A37

HEALTHSOUTH SEA PINES REHABILITATION HOSPITAL, MELBOURNE, FL, p. A133

HEALTHSOUTH SOUTHERN HILLS REHABILITATION HOSPITAL, PRINCETON, WV, p. A694

HEALTHSOUTH SUGAR LAND REHABILITATION HOSPITAL, SUGAR LAND, TX, p. A645

HEALTHSOUTH SUNRISE REHABILITATION HOSPITAL, SUNRISE, FL, p. A143

HEALTHSOUTH TREASURE COAST REHABILITATION HOSPITAL, VERO BEACH, FL, p. A146

HEALTHSOUTH TUSTIN REHABILITATION HOSPITAL, TUSTIN, CA, p. A95

HEALTHSOUTH VALLEY OF THE SUN REHABILITATION HOSPITAL, GLENDALE, AZ, p. A32

HEALTHSOUTH WALTON REHABILITATION HOSPITAL, AUGUSTA, GA, p. A151

HEALTHSOUTH WESTERN HILLS REGIONAL REHABILITATION HOSPITAL, PARKERSBURG, WV, p. A694

HEART HOSPITAL OF AUSTIN, AUSTIN, TEXAS (see ST. DAVID'S MEDICAL CENTER), p. A595

HEART HOSPITAL OF LAFAYETTE, LAFAYETTE, LA, p. A277

HEART HOSPITAL OF NEW MEXICO, ALBUQUERQUE, NEW MEXICO (see LOVELACE MEDICAL CENTER), p. A422

HEART OF AMERICA MEDICAL CENTER, RUGBY, ND, p. A476

HEART OF FLORIDA REGIONAL MEDICAL CENTER, DAVENPORT, FL, p. A125

HEART OF LANCASTER REGIONAL MEDICAL CENTER, LITITZ, PA, p. A539

HEART OF TEXAS MEMORIAL HOSPITAL, BRADY, TX, p. A598

HEART OF THE ROCKIES REGIONAL MEDICAL CENTER, SALIDA, CO, p. A108

HEARTLAND BEHAVIORAL HEALTH SERVICES, NEVADA, MO, p. A373

HEARTLAND BEHAVIORAL HEALTHCARE, MASSILLON, OH, p. A493

HEARTLAND REGIONAL MEDICAL CENTER, MARION, IL, p. A193

HEATHERHILL CARE COMMUNITIES, CHARDON, OH, p. A481

HEBER VALLEY MEDICAL CENTER, HEBER CITY, UT, p. A655

HEBREW REHABILITATION CENTER, BOSTON, MA, p. A303

HEDRICK MEDICAL CENTER, CHILLICOTHE, MO, p. A365

HEGG MEMORIAL HEALTH CENTER AVERA, ROCK VALLEY, IA, p. A234

HELEN DEVOS CHILDREN'S HOSPITAL, GRAND RAPIDS, MICHIGAN (see SPECTRUM HEALTH – BUTTERWORTH HOSPITAL), p. A321

HELEN HAYES HOSPITAL, WEST HAVERSTRAW, NY, p. A453

HELEN KELLER HOSPITAL, SHEFFIELD, AL, p. A25

HELEN M. SIMPSON REHABILITATION HOSPITAL, HARRISBURG, PA, p. A535

HELEN NEWBERRY JOY HOSPITAL, NEWBERRY, MI, p. A327

HELEN NEWBERRY JOY HOSPITAL ANNEX (see HELEN NEWBERRY JOY HOSPITAL), p. A327

HELENA REGIONAL MEDICAL CENTER, HELENA, AR, p. A45

HEMET VALLEY MEDICAL CENTER, HEMET, CA, p. A65

HEMPHILL COUNTY HOSPITAL, CANADIAN, TX, p. A600

HENDERSON COUNTY COMMUNITY HOSPITAL, LEXINGTON, TN, p. A581

HENDERSON HEALTH CARE SERVICES, HENDERSON, NE, p. A392

HENDRICK HEALTH SYSTEM, ABILENE, TX, p. A590

HENDRICKS COMMUNITY HOSPITAL ASSOCIATION, HENDRICKS, MN, p. A340

HENDRICKS REGIONAL HEALTH, DANVILLE, IN, p. A207

HENDRY REGIONAL MEDICAL CENTER, CLEWISTON, FL, p. A124

HENNEPIN COUNTY MEDICAL CENTER, MINNEAPOLIS, MN, p. A342

HENRICO DOCTORS' HOSPITAL, RICHMOND, VA, p. A672

HENRICO DOCTORS' HOSPITAL – FOREST, RICHMOND, VIRGINIA (see HENRICO DOCTORS' HOSPITAL), p. A672

HENRICO DOCTORS' HOSPITAL – PARHAM, RICHMOND, VIRGINIA (see HENRICO DOCTORS' HOSPITAL), p. A672

HENRICO DOCTORS' HOSPITAL – RETREAT CAMPUS, RICHMOND, VIRGINIA (see HENRICO DOCTORS' HOSPITAL), p. A672

HENRY COUNTY HEALTH CENTER, MOUNT PLEASANT, IA, p. A232

HENRY COUNTY HOSPITAL, NEW CASTLE, IN, p. A217

HENRY COUNTY HOSPITAL, NAPOLEON, OH, p. A495

HENRY COUNTY MEDICAL CENTER, PARIS, TN, p. A587

HUNTINGTON VETERANS AFFAIRS MEDICAL CENTER, HUNTINGTON, WV, p. A692
HUNTSVILLE HOSPITAL, HUNTSVILLE, AL, p. A21
HUNTSVILLE HOSPITAL FOR WOMEN AND CHILDREN, HUNTSVILLE, ALABAMA (see HUNTSVILLE HOSPITAL), p. A21
HUNTSVILLE MEMORIAL HOSPITAL, HUNTSVILLE, TX, p. A623
HURLEY CHILDREN'S HOSPITAL, FLINT, MICHIGAN (see HURLEY MEDICAL CENTER), p. A319
HURLEY MEDICAL CENTER, FLINT, MI, p. A319
HURON MEDICAL CENTER, BAD AXE, MI, p. A314
HURON REGIONAL MEDICAL CENTER, HURON, SD, p. A569
HUTCHESON MEDICAL CENTER, FORT OGLETHORPE, GA, p. A158
HUTCHINSON HEALTH, HUTCHINSON, MN, p. A340
HUTCHINSON REGIONAL MEDICAL CENTER, HUTCHINSON, KS, p. A242

# I

I-70 COMMUNITY HOSPITAL, SWEET SPRINGS, MO, p. A379
I. GONZALEZ MARTINEZ ONCOLOGIC HOSPITAL,, PR, p. A724
IBERIA EXTENDED CARE HOSPITAL, NEW IBERIA, LOUISIANA (see LOUISIANA EXTENDED CARE HOSPITAL OF LAFAYETTE), p. A277
IBERIA MEDICAL CENTER, NEW IBERIA, LA, p. A281
IBERIA REHABILITATION HOSPITAL, NEW IBERIA, LA, p. A281
ICON HOSPITAL, HUMBLE, TX, p. A623
ILLINI COMMUNITY HOSPITAL, PITTSFIELD, IL, p. A198
ILLINOIS VALLEY COMMUNITY HOSPITAL, PERU, IL, p. A198
INCLINE VILLAGE COMMUNITY HOSPITAL, INCLINE VILLAGE, NV, p. A401
INDIAN HEALTH SERVICE – QUENTIN N. BURDICK MEMORIAL HEALTH CARE FACILITY, BELCOURT, ND, p. A472
INDIAN HEALTH SERVICE HOSPITAL, RAPID CITY, SD, p. A570
INDIAN PATH MEDICAL CENTER, KINGSPORT, TN, p. A580
INDIAN RIVER MEDICAL CENTER, VERO BEACH, FL, p. A146
INDIANA ORTHOPAEDIC HOSPITAL, INDIANAPOLIS, IN, p. A211
INDIANA REGIONAL MEDICAL CENTER, INDIANA, PA, p. A536
INDIANA UNIVERSITY HEALTH ARNETT HOSPITAL, LAFAYETTE, IN, p. A214
INDIANA UNIVERSITY HEALTH BALL MEMORIAL HOSPITAL, MUNCIE, IN, p. A216
INDIANA UNIVERSITY HEALTH BEDFORD HOSPITAL, BEDFORD, IN, p. A204
INDIANA UNIVERSITY HEALTH BLACKFORD HOSPITAL, HARTFORD CITY, IN, p. A210
INDIANA UNIVERSITY HEALTH BLOOMINGTON HOSPITAL, BLOOMINGTON, IN, p. A205
INDIANA UNIVERSITY HEALTH GOSHEN HOSPITAL, GOSHEN, IN, p. A210
INDIANA UNIVERSITY HEALTH LA PORTE HOSPITAL, LA PORTE, IN, p. A214
INDIANA UNIVERSITY HEALTH METHODIST HOSPITAL, INDIANAPOLIS, INDIANA (see INDIANA UNIVERSITY HEALTH UNIVERSITY HOSPITAL), p. A212
INDIANA UNIVERSITY HEALTH NORTH HOSPITAL, CARMEL, IN, p. A206
INDIANA UNIVERSITY HEALTH PAOLI HOSPITAL, PAOLI, IN, p. A218
INDIANA UNIVERSITY HEALTH STARKE HOSPITAL, KNOX, IN, p. A213
INDIANA UNIVERSITY HEALTH TIPTON HOSPITAL, TIPTON, IN, p. A220
INDIANA UNIVERSITY HEALTH UNIVERSITY HOSPITAL, INDIANAPOLIS, IN, p. A212
INDIANA UNIVERSITY HEALTH WEST HOSPITAL, AVON, IN, p. A204
INDIANA UNIVERSITY HEALTH WHITE MEMORIAL HOSPITAL, MONTICELLO, IN, p. A216
INDIANA UNIVERSITY HOSPITAL, INDIANAPOLIS, INDIANA (see INDIANA UNIVERSITY HEALTH UNIVERSITY HOSPITAL), p. A212
INDIANHEAD MEDICAL CENTER, SHELL LAKE, WI, p. A711
INDUSTRIAL HOSPITAL, SAN JUAN, PR, p. A724
INFIRMARY LONG TERM ACUTE CARE HOSPITAL, MOBILE, AL, p. A22
INGALLS MEMORIAL HOSPITAL, HARVEY, IL, p. A190
INGHAM REGIONAL MEDICAL CENTER, GREENLAWN CAMPUS, LANSING, MICHIGAN (see MCLAREN GREATER LANSING), p. A324
INLAND HOSPITAL, WATERVILLE, ME, p. A292
INLAND VALLEY MEDICAL CENTER, WILDOMAR, CALIFORNIA (see SOUTHWEST HEALTHCARE SYSTEM), p. A77
INOVA ALEXANDRIA HOSPITAL, ALEXANDRIA, VA, p. A662
INOVA FAIR OAKS HOSPITAL, FAIRFAX, VA, p. A664
INOVA FAIRFAX HOSPITAL, FALLS CHURCH, VA, p. A664

INOVA FAIRFAX HOSPITAL FOR CHILDREN, FALLS CHURCH, VIRGINIA (see INOVA FAIRFAX HOSPITAL), p. A664
INOVA LOUDOUN HOSPITAL, LEESBURG, VA, p. A667
INOVA MOUNT VERNON HOSPITAL, ALEXANDRIA, VA, p. A662
INSPIRA MEDICAL CENTER–ELMER, ELMER, NJ, p. A411
INSPIRA MEDICAL CENTER–VINELAND, VINELAND, NJ, p. A420
INSPIRA MEDICAL CENTER–WOODBURY, WOODBURY, NJ, p. A420
INSPIRA PONCE, PONCE, PR, p. A722
INSTITUTE FOR ORTHOPAEDIC SURGERY, LIMA, OH, p. A492
INSTITUTE OF LIVING, HARTFORD, CONNECTICUT (see HARTFORD HOSPITAL), p. A112
INTEGRIS BAPTIST MEDICAL CENTER, OKLAHOMA CITY, OK, p. A511
INTEGRIS BAPTIST REGIONAL HEALTH CENTER, MIAMI, OK, p. A509
INTEGRIS BASS BAPTIST HEALTH CENTER, ENID, OK, p. A506
INTEGRIS BASS PAVILION, ENID, OK, p. A506
INTEGRIS CANADIAN VALLEY HOSPITAL, YUKON, OK, p. A518
INTEGRIS GROVE HOSPITAL, GROVE, OK, p. A507
INTEGRIS HEALTH EDMOND, EDMOND, OK, p. A506
INTEGRIS MENTAL HEALTH SYSTEM–SPENCER, SPENCER, OKLAHOMA (see INTEGRIS BAPTIST MEDICAL CENTER), p. A511
INTEGRIS SOUTHWEST MEDICAL CENTER, OKLAHOMA CITY, OK, p. A511
INTEGRITY TRANSITIONAL HOSPITAL, DENTON, TX, p. A608
INTERFAITH MEDICAL CENTER,, NY, p. A440
INTERIM LSU PUBLIC HOSPITAL, NEW ORLEANS, LA, p. A282
INTERMEDICAL HOSPITAL OF SOUTH CAROLINA, COLUMBIA, SC, p. A559
INTERMOUNTAIN HOSPITAL, BOISE, ID, p. A172
INTERMOUNTAIN MEDICAL CENTER, MURRAY, UT, p. A656
INTRACARE NORTH HOSPITAL, HOUSTON, TX, p. A620
IOWA CITY VETERANS AFFAIRS HEALTH CARE SYSTEM, IOWA CITY, IA, p. A229
IOWA MEDICAL AND CLASSIFICATION CENTER, CORALVILLE, IA, p. A224
IOWA SPECIALTY HOSPITAL–BELMOND, BELMOND, IA, p. A222
IOWA SPECIALTY HOSPITAL–CLARION, CLARION, IA, p. A224
IRA DAVENPORT MEMORIAL HOSPITAL, BATH, NY, p. A429
IRAAN GENERAL HOSPITAL, IRAAN, TX, p. A624
IREDELL MEMORIAL HOSPITAL, STATESVILLE, NC, p. A469
IRELAND ARMY COMMUNITY HOSPITAL, FORT KNOX, KY, p. A257
IRON COUNTY MEDICAL CENTER, PILOT KNOB, MO, p. A374
IROQUOIS MEMORIAL HOSPITAL AND RESIDENT HOME, WATSEKA, IL, p. A202
IRVING COPPELL SURGICAL HOSPITAL, IRVING, TX, p. A624
IRWIN ARMY COMMUNITY HOSPITAL, JUNCTION CITY, KS, p. A243
IRWIN COUNTY HOSPITAL, OCILLA, GA, p. A162
ISLAND HOSPITAL, ANACORTES, WA, p. A676
IU HEALTH SAXONY HOSPITAL, FISHERS, INDIANA (see INDIANA UNIVERSITY HEALTH UNIVERSITY HOSPITAL), p. A212
IVINSON MEMORIAL HOSPITAL, LARAMIE, WY, p. A716

# J

J. ARTHUR DOSHER MEMORIAL HOSPITAL, SOUTHPORT, NC, p. A468
J. C. BLAIR MEMORIAL HOSPITAL, HUNTINGDON, PA, p. A536
J. D. MCCARTY CENTER FOR CHILDREN WITH DEVELOPMENTAL DISABILITIES, NORMAN, OK, p. A510
J. PAUL JONES HOSPITAL, CAMDEN, AL, p. A17
JACK C. MONTGOMERY VETERANS AFFAIRS MEDICAL CENTER, MUSKOGEE, OK, p. A510
JACK D WEILER HOSPITAL OF ALBERT EINSTEIN COLLEGE OF MEDICINE,, NEW YORK (see MONTEFIORE MEDICAL CENTER), p. A442
JACK HUGHSTON MEMORIAL HOSPITAL, PHENIX CITY, AL, p. A24
JACKSON COUNTY HOSPITAL DISTRICT, EDNA, TX, p. A610
JACKSON COUNTY MEMORIAL HOSPITAL, ALTUS, OK, p. A503
JACKSON COUNTY REGIONAL HEALTH CENTER, MAQUOKETA, IA, p. A231
JACKSON GENERAL HOSPITAL, RIPLEY, WV, p. A695
JACKSON HEALTH SYSTEM, MIAMI, FL, p. A134
JACKSON HOSPITAL, MARIANNA, FL, p. A133
JACKSON HOSPITAL AND CLINIC, MONTGOMERY, AL, p. A23
JACKSON MEDICAL CENTER, JACKSON, AL, p. A21
JACKSON MEMORIAL HOSPITAL, MIAMI, FLORIDA (see JACKSON HEALTH SYSTEM), p. A134
JACKSON NORTH MEDICAL CENTER, NORTH MIAMI BEACH, FLORIDA (see JACKSON HEALTH SYSTEM), p. A134
JACKSON PARISH HOSPITAL, JONESBORO, LA, p. A276

JACKSON PARK HOSPITAL AND MEDICAL CENTER, CHICAGO, IL, p. A182
JACKSON PURCHASE MEDICAL CENTER, MAYFIELD, KY, p. A262
JACKSON SOUTH COMMUNITY HOSPITAL, MIAMI, FLORIDA (see JACKSON HEALTH SYSTEM), p. A134
JACKSON–MADISON COUNTY GENERAL HOSPITAL, JACKSON, TN, p. A579
JACOBI MEDICAL CENTER,, NY, p. A440
JACOBSON MEMORIAL HOSPITAL CARE CENTER, ELGIN, ND, p. A473
JAMAICA HOSPITAL MEDICAL CENTER,, NY, p. A440
JAMES A. HALEY VETERANS' HOSPITAL–TAMPA, TAMPA, FL, p. A144
JAMES AND CONNIE MAYNARD CHILDREN'S HOSPITAL, GREENVILLE, NORTH CAROLINA (see VIDANT MEDICAL CENTER), p. A461
JAMES B. HAGGIN MEMORIAL HOSPITAL, HARRODSBURG, KY, p. A258
JAMES CANCER HOSPITAL AND SOLOVE RESEARCH INSTITUTE, COLUMBUS, OH, p. A485
JAMES E. VAN ZANDT VETERANS AFFAIRS MEDICAL CENTER, ALTOONA, PA, p. A528
JAMES H. QUILLEN VETERANS AFFAIRS MEDICAL CENTER, MOUNTAIN HOME, TN, p. A585
JAMES J. PETERS VETERANS AFFAIRS MEDICAL CENTER,, NY, p. A440
JAMESON HOSPITAL, NEW CASTLE, PA, p. A541
JAMESTOWN REGIONAL MEDICAL CENTER, JAMESTOWN, ND, p. A475
JAMESTOWN REGIONAL MEDICAL CENTER, JAMESTOWN, TN, p. A579
JANE PHILLIPS MEDICAL CENTER, BARTLESVILLE, OK, p. A504
JANE PHILLIPS NOWATA HEALTH CENTER, NOWATA, OK, p. A510
JANE TODD CRAWFORD HOSPITAL, GREENSBURG, KY, p. A257
JASPER COUNTY NURSING HOME (see JASPER GENERAL HOSPITAL), p. A350
JASPER GENERAL HOSPITAL, BAY SPRINGS, MS, p. A350
JASPER MEMORIAL HOSPITAL, MONTICELLO, GA, p. A162
JAY COUNTY HOSPITAL, PORTLAND, IN, p. A218
JAY HOSPITAL, JAY, FL, p. A130
JEANES HOSPITAL, PHILADELPHIA, PA, p. A544
JEFF DAVIS HOSPITAL, HAZLEHURST, GA, p. A158
JEFFERSON COMMUNITY HEALTH CENTER, FAIRBURY, NE, p. A391
JEFFERSON COUNTY HEALTH CENTER, FAIRFIELD, IA, p. A227
JEFFERSON COUNTY HOSPITAL, FAYETTE, MS, p. A352
JEFFERSON COUNTY HOSPITAL, WAURIKA, OK, p. A518
JEFFERSON DAVIS COMMUNITY HOSPITAL, PRENTISS, MS, p. A359
JEFFERSON HEALTHCARE, PORT TOWNSEND, WA, p. A682
JEFFERSON HOSPITAL, LOUISVILLE, GA, p. A160
JEFFERSON HOSPITAL, JEFFERSON HILLS, PA, p. A536
JEFFERSON MEDICAL CENTER, RANSON, WV, p. A694
JEFFERSON REGIONAL MEDICAL CENTER, PINE BLUFF, AR, p. A50
JELLICO COMMUNITY HOSPITAL, JELLICO, TN, p. A579
JENNERSVILLE REGIONAL HOSPITAL, WEST GROVE, PA, p. A552
JENNIE M. MELHAM MEMORIAL MEDICAL CENTER, BROKEN BOW, NE, p. A390
JENNIE STUART MEDICAL CENTER, HOPKINSVILLE, KY, p. A258
JENNINGS AMERICAN LEGION HOSPITAL, JENNINGS, LA, p. A275
JENNINGS SENIOR CARE HOSPITAL, JENNINGS, LA, p. A276
JEROLD PHELPS COMMUNITY HOSPITAL, GARBERVILLE, CA, p. A63
JEROME GOLDEN CENTER FOR BEHAVIORAL HEALTH, INC., WEST PALM BEACH, FL, p. A147
JERSEY CITY MEDICAL CENTER, JERSEY CITY, NJ, p. A413
JERSEY COMMUNITY HOSPITAL, JERSEYVILLE, IL, p. A191
JERSEY SHORE HOSPITAL, JERSEY SHORE, PA, p. A536
JERSEY SHORE UNIVERSITY MEDICAL CENTER, NEPTUNE, NJ, p. A414
JESSE BROWN VETERANS AFFAIRS MEDICAL CENTER, CHICAGO, IL, p. A182
JEWELL COUNTY HOSPITAL, MANKATO, KS, p. A245
JEWISH HOME OF SAN FRANCISCO, SAN FRANCISCO, CA, p. A88
JEWISH HOSPITAL, LOUISVILLE, KY, p. A261
JEWISH HOSPITAL–SHELBYVILLE, SHELBYVILLE, KY, p. A266
JFK JOHNSON REHABILITATION INSTITUTE, EDISON, NJ, p. A411
JFK MEDICAL CENTER, ATLANTIS, FL, p. A121
JFK MEDICAL CENTER, EDISON, NJ, p. A411
JIM TALIAFERRO COMMUNITY MENTAL HEALTH, LAWTON, OK, p. A508
JOE DIMAGGIO CHILDREN'S HOSPITAL,, FLORIDA (see MEMORIAL REGIONAL HOSPITAL), p. A128

JOHN C. FREMONT HEALTHCARE DISTRICT, MARIPOSA, CA, p. A74

JOHN C. STENNIS MEMORIAL HOSPITAL, DE KALB, MS, p. A352

JOHN D. ARCHBOLD MEMORIAL HOSPITAL, THOMASVILLE, GA, p. A166

JOHN D. DINGELL VETERANS AFFAIRS MEDICAL CENTER, DETROIT, MI, p. A318

JOHN F. KENNEDY MEMORIAL HOSPITAL, INDIO, CA, p. A65

JOHN GEORGE PSYCHIATRIC HOSPITAL, SAN LEANDRO, CALIFORNIA (see HIGHLAND HOSPITAL), p. A78

JOHN H. STROGER JR. HOSPITAL OF COOK COUNTY, CHICAGO, IL, p. A182

JOHN HEINZ INSTITUTE OF REHABILITATION MEDICINE, WILKES–BARRE, PA, p. A553

JOHN J. MADDEN MENTAL HEALTH CENTER, HINES, IL, p. A190

JOHN J. PERSHING VETERANS AFFAIRS MEDICAL CENTER, POPLAR BLUFF, MO, p. A374

JOHN MUIR BEHAVIORAL HEALTH CENTER, CONCORD, CA, p. A58

JOHN MUIR MEDICAL CENTER, CONCORD, CONCORD, CA, p. A58

JOHN MUIR MEDICAL CENTER, WALNUT CREEK, WALNUT CREEK, CA, p. A97

JOHN PETER SMITH HOSPITAL, FORT WORTH, TEXAS (see JPS HEALTH NETWORK), p. A613

JOHN RANDOLPH MEDICAL CENTER, HOPEWELL, VA, p. A666

JOHN T. MATHER MEMORIAL HOSPITAL, PORT JEFFERSON, NY, p. A447

JOHNS HOPKINS BAYVIEW MEDICAL CENTER, BALTIMORE, MD, p. A293

JOHNS HOPKINS CHILDREN'S CENTER, BALTIMORE, MARYLAND (see JOHNS HOPKINS HOSPITAL), p. A293

JOHNS HOPKINS HOSPITAL, BALTIMORE, MD, p. A293

JOHNSON CITY MEDICAL CENTER, JOHNSON CITY, TN, p. A580

JOHNSON COUNTY COMMUNITY HOSPITAL, MOUNTAIN CITY, TN, p. A584

JOHNSON COUNTY HEALTHCARE CENTER, BUFFALO, WY, p. A715

JOHNSON COUNTY HOSPITAL, TECUMSEH, NE, p. A398

JOHNSON MEMORIAL HEALTH SERVICES, DAWSON, MN, p. A337

JOHNSON MEMORIAL HOSPITAL, FRANKLIN, IN, p. A209

JOHNSON MEMORIAL MEDICAL CENTER, STAFFORD SPRINGS, CT, p. A115

JOHNSON REGIONAL MEDICAL CENTER, CLARKSVILLE, AR, p. A42

JOHNSTON HEALTH, SMITHFIELD, NC, p. A468

JOHNSTON MEMORIAL HOSPITAL, ABINGDON, VA, p. A662

JOHNSTON R. BOWMAN HEALTH CENTER, CHICAGO, ILLINOIS (see RUSH UNIVERSITY MEDICAL CENTER), p. A184

JOHNSTON–WILLIS HOSPITAL, RICHMOND, VIRGINIA (see CHIPPENHAM HOSPITAL), p. A671

JOINT TOWNSHIP DISTRICT MEMORIAL HOSPITAL, SAINT MARYS, OH, p. A497

JONATHAN M. WAINWRIGHT MEMORIAL VETERANS AFFAIRS MEDICAL CENTER, WALLA WALLA, WA, p. A687

JONES MEMORIAL HOSPITAL, WELLSVILLE, NY, p. A453

JORDAN VALLEY MEDICAL CENTER, WEST JORDAN, UT, p. A659

JORDAN VALLEY MEDICAL CENTER–WVC CAMPUS, WEST VALLEY CITY, UT, p. A659

JOYCE EISENBERG–KEEFER MEDICAL CENTER, RESEDA, CA, p. A83

JPS HEALTH NETWORK, FORT WORTH, TX, p. A613

JULIAN F. KEITH ALCOHOL AND DRUG ABUSE TREATMENT CENTER, BLACK MOUNTAIN, NC, p. A455

JULIETTE MANOR NURSING HOME, COMMUNITY CLINICS (see BERLIN MEMORIAL HOSPITAL), p. A698

JUPITER MEDICAL CENTER, JUPITER, FL, p. A130

# K

K. HOVNANIAN CHILDREN'S HOSPITAL, NEPTUNE, NEW JERSEY (see JERSEY SHORE UNIVERSITY MEDICAL CENTER), p. A414

KAATERSKILL CARE, CATSKILL, NEW YORK (see COLUMBIA MEMORIAL HOSPITAL), p. A435

KADLEC REGIONAL MEDICAL CENTER, RICHLAND, WA, p. A683

KAHI MOHALA BEHAVIORAL HEALTH, EWA BEACH, HI, p. A168

KAHUKU MEDICAL CENTER, KAHUKU, HI, p. A169

KAISER FOUNDATION HOSPITAL, MARTINEZ, CALIFORNIA (see KAISER PERMANENTE WALNUT CREEK MEDICAL CENTER), p. A97

KAISER FOUNDATION HOSPITAL WESTSIDE MEDICAL CENTER, HILLSBORO, OR, p. A521

KAISER FOUNDATION MENTAL HEALTH CENTER, LOS ANGELES, CALIFORNIA (see KAISER PERMANENTE LOS ANGELES MEDICAL CENTER), p. A70

KAISER PERMANENTE ANTIOCH MEDICAL CENTER, ANTIOCH, CA, p. A53

KAISER PERMANENTE BALDWIN PARK MEDICAL CENTER, BALDWIN PARK, CA, p. A55

KAISER PERMANENTE DOWNEY MEDICAL CENTER, DOWNEY, CA, p. A60

KAISER PERMANENTE FONTANA MEDICAL CENTER, FONTANA, CA, p. A61

KAISER PERMANENTE FRESNO MEDICAL CENTER, FRESNO, CA, p. A62

KAISER PERMANENTE LOS ANGELES MEDICAL CENTER, LOS ANGELES, CA, p. A70

KAISER PERMANENTE MANTECA MEDICAL CENTER, MANTECA, CA, p. A74

KAISER PERMANENTE MEDICAL CENTER, HONOLULU, HI, p. A168

KAISER PERMANENTE MORENO VALLEY MEDICAL CENTER, MORENO VALLEY, CA, p. A76

KAISER PERMANENTE OAKLAND MEDICAL CENTER, OAKLAND, CA, p. A78

KAISER PERMANENTE ONTARIO MEDICAL CENTER, ONTARIO, CALIFORNIA (see KAISER PERMANENTE FONTANA MEDICAL CENTER), p. A61

KAISER PERMANENTE ORANGE COUNTY ANAHEIM MEDICAL CENTER, ANAHEIM, CA, p. A53

KAISER PERMANENTE PANORAMA CITY MEDICAL CENTER,, CA, p. A70

KAISER PERMANENTE REDWOOD CITY MEDICAL CENTER, REDWOOD CITY, CA, p. A83

KAISER PERMANENTE RICHMOND MEDICAL CENTER, RICHMOND, CALIFORNIA (see KAISER PERMANENTE OAKLAND MEDICAL CENTER), p. A78

KAISER PERMANENTE RIVERSIDE MEDICAL CENTER, RIVERSIDE, CA, p. A83

KAISER PERMANENTE ROSEVILLE MEDICAL CENTER, ROSEVILLE, CA, p. A84

KAISER PERMANENTE SACRAMENTO MEDICAL CENTER, SACRAMENTO, CA, p. A84

KAISER PERMANENTE SAN DIEGO MEDICAL CENTER, SAN DIEGO, CA, p. A86

KAISER PERMANENTE SAN FRANCISCO MEDICAL CENTER, SAN FRANCISCO, CA, p. A88

KAISER PERMANENTE SAN JOSE MEDICAL CENTER, SAN JOSE, CA, p. A89

KAISER PERMANENTE SAN LEANDRO MEDICAL CENTER, SAN LEANDRO, CA, p. A89

KAISER PERMANENTE SAN RAFAEL MEDICAL CENTER, SAN RAFAEL, CA, p. A90

KAISER PERMANENTE SANTA CLARA MEDICAL CENTER, SANTA CLARA, CA, p. A91

KAISER PERMANENTE SANTA ROSA MEDICAL CENTER, SANTA ROSA, CA, p. A92

KAISER PERMANENTE SOUTH BAY MEDICAL CENTER,, CA, p. A70

KAISER PERMANENTE SOUTH SACRAMENTO MEDICAL CENTER, SACRAMENTO, CA, p. A84

KAISER PERMANENTE SOUTH SAN FRANCISCO, SOUTH SAN FRANCISCO, CA, p. A93

KAISER PERMANENTE SUNNYSIDE MEDICAL CENTER, CLACKAMAS, OR, p. A520

KAISER PERMANENTE VACAVILLE MEDICAL CENTER, VACAVILLE, CA, p. A95

KAISER PERMANENTE VALLEJO MEDICAL CENTER, VALLEJO, CA, p. A96

KAISER PERMANENTE WALNUT CREEK MEDICAL CENTER, WALNUT CREEK, CA, p. A97

KAISER PERMANENTE WEST LOS ANGELES MEDICAL CENTER, LOS ANGELES, CA, p. A70

KAISER PERMANENTE WOODLAND HILLS MEDICAL CENTER,, CA, p. A70

KALAMAZOO PSYCHIATRIC HOSPITAL, KALAMAZOO, MI, p. A323

KALEIDA HEALTH, BUFFALO, NY, p. A430

KALISPELL REGIONAL MEDICAL CENTER, KALISPELL, MT, p. A385

KALKASKA MEMORIAL HEALTH CENTER, KALKASKA, MI, p. A324

KANE COMMUNITY HOSPITAL, KANE, PA, p. A537

KANE COUNTY HOSPITAL, KANAB, UT, p. A655

KANSAS CITY ORTHOPAEDIC INSTITUTE, LEAWOOD, KS, p. A244

KANSAS CITY VETERANS AFFAIRS MEDICAL CENTER, KANSAS CITY, MO, p. A369

KANSAS HEART HOSPITAL, WICHITA, KS, p. A252

KANSAS MEDICAL CENTER, ANDOVER, KS, p. A237

KANSAS NEUROLOGICAL INSTITUTE, TOPEKA, KS, p. A251

KANSAS REHABILITATION HOSPITAL, TOPEKA, KS, p. A251

KANSAS SPINE AND SPECIALTY HOSPITAL, WICHITA, KS, p. A252

KANSAS SURGERY AND RECOVERY CENTER, WICHITA, KS, p. A252

KAPIOLANI MEDICAL CENTER FOR WOMEN & CHILDREN, HONOLULU, HI, p. A168

KARL AND ESTHER HOBLITZELLE MEMORIAL HOSPITAL, DALLAS, TEXAS (see BAYLOR UNIVERSITY MEDICAL CENTER), p. A604

KARMANOS CANCER CENTER, DETROIT, MI, p. A318

KATHERINE SHAW BETHEA HOSPITAL, DIXON, IL, p. A186

KAU HOSPITAL, PAHALA, HI, p. A170

KAUAI VETERANS MEMORIAL HOSPITAL, WAIMEA, HI, p. A171

KAWEAH DELTA MEDICAL CENTER, VISALIA, CA, p. A97

KEARNEY COUNTY HEALTH SERVICES, MINDEN, NE, p. A394

KEARNEY REGIONAL MEDICAL CENTER, KEARNEY, NE, p. A393

KEARNY COUNTY HOSPITAL, LAKIN, KS, p. A244

KECK HOSPITAL OF USC, LOS ANGELES, CA, p. A70

KEDREN COMMUNITY MENTAL HEALTH CENTER, LOS ANGELES, CA, p. A70

KEEFE MEMORIAL HOSPITAL, CHEYENNE WELLS, CO, p. A100

KELL WEST REGIONAL HOSPITAL, WICHITA FALLS, TX, p. A652

KELLER ARMY COMMUNITY HOSPITAL, WEST POINT, NY, p. A453

KEMPSVILLE CENTER FOR BEHAVIORAL HEALTH, NORFOLK, VA, p. A669

KENDALL REGIONAL MEDICAL CENTER, MIAMI, FL, p. A134

KENMARE COMMUNITY HOSPITAL, KENMARE, ND, p. A475

KENMORE MERCY HOSPITAL, KENMORE, NY, p. A436

KENNEDY HEALTH SYSTEM, CHERRY HILL, NJ, p. A410

KENNEDY KRIEGER INSTITUTE, BALTIMORE, MD, p. A293

KENNEDY UNIVERSITY HOSPITAL – STRATFORD, STRATFORD, NEW JERSEY (see KENNEDY HEALTH SYSTEM), p. A410

KENNEDY UNIVERSITY HOSPITAL – WASHINGTON TOWNSHIP, TURNERSVILLE, NEW JERSEY (see KENNEDY HEALTH SYSTEM), p. A410

KENSINGTON HOSPITAL, PHILADELPHIA, PA, p. A544

KENT COUNTY MEMORIAL HOSPITAL, WARWICK, RI, p. A556

KENTFIELD REHABILITATION AND SPECIALTY HOSPITAL, KENTFIELD, CA, p. A65

KENTUCKIANA MEDICAL CENTER, CLARKSVILLE, IN, p. A206

KENTUCKY CHILDREN'S HOSPITAL, LEXINGTON, KENTUCKY (see UNIVERSITY OF KENTUCKY ALBERT B. CHANDLER HOSPITAL), p. A260

KENTUCKY RIVER MEDICAL CENTER, JACKSON, KY, p. A259

KEOKUK AREA HOSPITAL, KEOKUK, IA, p. A230

KEOKUK COUNTY HEALTH CENTER, SIGOURNEY, IA, p. A234

KERN MEDICAL CENTER, BAKERSFIELD, CA, p. A55

KERN VALLEY HEALTHCARE DISTRICT, LAKE ISABELLA, CA, p. A67

KERNERSVILLE MEDICAL CENTER, KERNERSVILLE, NORTH CAROLINA (see NOVANT HEALTH FORSYTH MEDICAL CENTER), p. A471

KERRVILLE DIVISION, KERRVILLE, TEXAS (see SOUTH TEXAS VETERANS HEALTH CARE SYSTEM), p. A642

KERRVILLE STATE HOSPITAL, KERRVILLE, TX, p. A626

KERSHAWHEALTH, CAMDEN, SC, p. A557

KESSLER INSTITUTE FOR REHABILITATION, WEST ORANGE, NJ, p. A420

KESSLER INSTITUTE FOR REHABILITATION, CHESTER, NEW JERSEY (see KESSLER INSTITUTE FOR REHABILITATION), p. A420

KESSLER INSTITUTE FOR REHABILITATION, SADDLE BROOK, NEW JERSEY (see KESSLER INSTITUTE FOR REHABILITATION), p. A420

KESSLER INSTITUTE FOR REHABILITATION, WEST ORANGE, NEW JERSEY (see KESSLER INSTITUTE FOR REHABILITATION), p. A420

KETTERING MEDICAL CENTER, KETTERING, OH, p. A491

KEYSTONE NEWPORT NEWS, NEWPORT NEWS, VA, p. A668

KIDSPEACE CHILDREN'S HOSPITAL, OREFIELD, PA, p. A542

KIMBALL HEALTH SERVICES, KIMBALL, NE, p. A393

KIMBALL–RIDGE CENTER, WATERLOO, IOWA (see COVENANT MEDICAL CENTER), p. A235

KIMBLE HOSPITAL, JUNCTION, TX, p. A625

KINDRED CHICAGO LAKESHORE, CHICAGO, ILLINOIS (see KINDRED CHICAGO–CENTRAL HOSPITAL), p. A182

KINDRED CHICAGO–CENTRAL HOSPITAL, CHICAGO, IL, p. A182

KINDRED HOSPITAL ARIZONA–NORTHWEST PHOENIX, PEORIA, ARIZONA (see KINDRED HOSPITAL ARIZONA–PHOENIX), p. A35

KINDRED HOSPITAL ARIZONA–PHOENIX, PHOENIX, AZ, p. A35

KINDRED HOSPITAL BAY AREA–TAMPA, TAMPA, FL, p. A145

KINDRED HOSPITAL BAYTOWN, BAYTOWN, TEXAS (see KINDRED HOSPITAL CLEAR LAKE), p. A651

KINDRED HOSPITAL BOSTON–NORTH SHORE, PEABODY, MA, p. A310

KINDRED HOSPITAL CENTRAL TAMPA, TAMPA, FL, p. A145

KINDRED HOSPITAL CHICAGO NORTH, CHICAGO, ILLINOIS (see KINDRED CHICAGO–CENTRAL HOSPITAL), p. A182

KINDRED HOSPITAL CHICAGO–NORTHLAKE, NORTHLAKE, IL, p. A196
KINDRED HOSPITAL CLEAR LAKE, WEBSTER, TX, p. A651
KINDRED HOSPITAL CLEVELAND–GATEWAY, CLEVELAND, OH, p. A484
KINDRED HOSPITAL DALLAS CENTRAL, DALLAS, TX, p. A605
KINDRED HOSPITAL DALLAS–WALNUT HILL, DALLAS, TEXAS (see KINDRED HOSPITAL–DALLAS), p. A605
KINDRED HOSPITAL DETROIT, DETROIT, MI, p. A318
KINDRED HOSPITAL EL PASO, EL PASO, TX, p. A611
KINDRED HOSPITAL INDIANAPOLIS SOUTH, GREENWOOD, IN, p. A210
KINDRED HOSPITAL KANSAS CITY, KANSAS CITY, MO, p. A369
KINDRED HOSPITAL LAS VEGAS, DESERT SPRINGS CAMPUS, LAS VEGAS, NEVADA (see KINDRED HOSPITAL LAS VEGAS–SAHARA), p. A402
KINDRED HOSPITAL LAS VEGAS–SAHARA, LAS VEGAS, NV, p. A402
KINDRED HOSPITAL LIMA, LIMA, OH, p. A492
KINDRED HOSPITAL LOUISVILLE AT JEWISH HOSPITAL, LOUISVILLE, KENTUCKY (see KINDRED HOSPITAL–LOUISVILLE), p. A261
KINDRED HOSPITAL MELBOURNE, MELBOURNE, FL, p. A133
KINDRED HOSPITAL NEW JERSEY – RAHWAY, RAHWAY, NEW JERSEY (see KINDRED HOSPITAL–NEW JERSEY MORRIS COUNTY), p. A411
KINDRED HOSPITAL NEW JERSEY – WAYNE, WAYNE, NEW JERSEY (see KINDRED HOSPITAL–NEW JERSEY MORRIS COUNTY), p. A411
KINDRED HOSPITAL NORTH FLORIDA, GREEN COVE SPRINGS, FL, p. A128
KINDRED HOSPITAL NORTHEAST–STOUGHTON, STOUGHTON, MA, p. A312
KINDRED HOSPITAL NORTHLAND, KANSAS CITY, MO, p. A370
KINDRED HOSPITAL NORTHWEST INDIANA, HAMMOND, IN, p. A210
KINDRED HOSPITAL OCALA, OCALA, FL, p. A137
KINDRED HOSPITAL OF CENTRAL OHIO, MANSFIELD, OH, p. A492
KINDRED HOSPITAL OF CLEVELAND, CLEVELAND, OHIO (see KINDRED HOSPITAL CLEVELAND–GATEWAY), p. A484
KINDRED HOSPITAL OF NORTHERN INDIANA, MISHAWAKA, IN, p. A216
KINDRED HOSPITAL PEORIA, PEORIA, IL, p. A198
KINDRED HOSPITAL PHILADELPHIA – HAVERTOWN, HAVERTOWN, PENNSYLVANIA (see KINDRED HOSPITAL–PHILADELPHIA), p. A544
KINDRED HOSPITAL RANCHO, RANCHO CUCAMONGA, CA, p. A82
KINDRED HOSPITAL RIVERSIDE, PERRIS, CA, p. A81
KINDRED HOSPITAL ROME, ROME, GA, p. A163
KINDRED HOSPITAL SAN GABRIEL VALLEY, WEST COVINA, CALIFORNIA (see KINDRED HOSPITAL–LA MIRADA), p. A66
KINDRED HOSPITAL SANTA ANA, SANTA ANA, CALIFORNIA (see KINDRED HOSPITAL–LA MIRADA), p. A66
KINDRED HOSPITAL SEATTLE–FIRST HILL, SEATTLE, WASHINGTON (see KINDRED HOSPITAL SEATTLE–NORTHGATE), p. A683
KINDRED HOSPITAL SEATTLE–NORTHGATE, SEATTLE, WA, p. A683
KINDRED HOSPITAL SOUTH BAY, GARDENA, CA, p. A63
KINDRED HOSPITAL SOUTH FLORIDA–CORAL GABLES, CORAL GABLES, FLORIDA (see KINDRED HOSPITAL SOUTH FLORIDA–FORT LAUDERDALE), p. A127
KINDRED HOSPITAL SOUTH FLORIDA–FORT LAUDERDALE, FORT LAUDERDALE, FL, p. A127
KINDRED HOSPITAL SOUTH FLORIDA–HOLLYWOOD,, FLORIDA (see KINDRED HOSPITAL SOUTH FLORIDA–FORT LAUDERDALE), p. A127
KINDRED HOSPITAL SOUTH PHILADELPHIA, PHILADELPHIA, PA, p. A544
KINDRED HOSPITAL SPRING, HOUSTON, TEXAS (see KINDRED HOSPITAL TOMBALL), p. A648
KINDRED HOSPITAL ST. LOUIS–ST. ANTHONY'S, SAINT LOUIS, MISSOURI (see KINDRED HOSPITAL–ST. LOUIS), p. A376
KINDRED HOSPITAL SUGAR LAND, SUGAR LAND, TX, p. A645
KINDRED HOSPITAL TARRANT COUNTY–ARLINGTON, ARLINGTON, TX, p. A592
KINDRED HOSPITAL TARRANT COUNTY–FORT WORTH SOUTHWEST, FORT WORTH, TEXAS (see KINDRED HOSPITAL–FORT WORTH), p. A613
KINDRED HOSPITAL THE PALM BEACHES, RIVIERA BEACH, FL, p. A141
KINDRED HOSPITAL TOMBALL, TOMBALL, TX, p. A648
KINDRED HOSPITAL– OKLAHOMA CITY, OKLAHOMA CITY, OK, p. A511
KINDRED HOSPITAL–ALBUQUERQUE, ALBUQUERQUE, NM, p. A422
KINDRED HOSPITAL–ATLANTA, ATLANTA, GA, p. A150
KINDRED HOSPITAL–AURORA, AURORA, CO, p. A99

KINDRED HOSPITAL–BALDWIN PARK, BALDWIN PARK, CA, p. A55
KINDRED HOSPITAL–BAY AREA, PASADENA, TX, p. A636
KINDRED HOSPITAL–BAY AREA ST. PETERSBURG, SAINT PETERSBURG, FLORIDA (see KINDRED HOSPITAL BAY AREA–TAMPA), p. A145
KINDRED HOSPITAL–BOSTON, BRIGHTON, MA, p. A304
KINDRED HOSPITAL–BREA, BREA, CA, p. A56
KINDRED HOSPITAL–CHATTANOOGA, CHATTANOOGA, TN, p. A575
KINDRED HOSPITAL–DALLAS, DALLAS, TX, p. A605
KINDRED HOSPITAL–DAYTON, DAYTON, OH, p. A488
KINDRED HOSPITAL–DENVER, DENVER, CO, p. A102
KINDRED HOSPITAL–FLAMINGO, LAS VEGAS, NEVADA (see KINDRED HOSPITAL LAS VEGAS–SAHARA), p. A402
KINDRED HOSPITAL–FORT WORTH, FORT WORTH, TX, p. A613
KINDRED HOSPITAL–GREENSBORO, GREENSBORO, NC, p. A461
KINDRED HOSPITAL–HERITAGE VALLEY, BEAVER, PA, p. A529
KINDRED HOSPITAL–HOUSTON, HOUSTON, TX, p. A620
KINDRED HOSPITAL–HOUSTON NORTHWEST, HOUSTON, TX, p. A620
KINDRED HOSPITAL–INDIANAPOLIS, INDIANAPOLIS, IN, p. A212
KINDRED HOSPITAL–LA MIRADA, LA MIRADA, CA, p. A66
KINDRED HOSPITAL–LOS ANGELES, LOS ANGELES, CA, p. A70
KINDRED HOSPITAL–LOUISVILLE, LOUISVILLE, KY, p. A261
KINDRED HOSPITAL–MANSFIELD, MANSFIELD, TX, p. A631
KINDRED HOSPITAL–NASHVILLE, NASHVILLE, TN, p. A585
KINDRED HOSPITAL–NEW JERSEY MORRIS COUNTY, DOVER, NJ, p. A411
KINDRED HOSPITAL–NEW ORLEANS, NEW ORLEANS, LA, p. A282
KINDRED HOSPITAL–OKLAHOMA CITY SOUTH, OKLAHOMA CITY, OKLAHOMA (see KINDRED HOSPITAL– OKLAHOMA CITY), p. A511
KINDRED HOSPITAL–ONTARIO, ONTARIO, CA, p. A79
KINDRED HOSPITAL–PHILADELPHIA, PHILADELPHIA, PA, p. A544
KINDRED HOSPITAL–PITTSBURGH, OAKDALE, PA, p. A542
KINDRED HOSPITAL–SAN ANTONIO, SAN ANTONIO, TX, p. A641
KINDRED HOSPITAL–SAN DIEGO, SAN DIEGO, CA, p. A86
KINDRED HOSPITAL–SAN FRANCISCO BAY AREA, SAN LEANDRO, CA, p. A90
KINDRED HOSPITAL–ST. LOUIS, SAINT LOUIS, MO, p. A376
KINDRED HOSPITAL–ST. LOUIS AT MERCY, SAINT LOUIS, MO, p. A376
KINDRED HOSPITAL–SYCAMORE, SYCAMORE, IL, p. A202
KINDRED HOSPITAL–TUCSON, TUCSON, AZ, p. A39
KINDRED HOSPITAL–WESTMINSTER, WESTMINSTER, CA, p. A97
KINDRED HOSPITAL–WHITE ROCK, DALLAS, TX, p. A605
KINDRED REHABILITATION HOSPITAL ARLINGTON, ARLINGTON, TX, p. A592
KINDRED REHABILITATION HOSPITAL CLEAR LAKE, WEBSTER, TX, p. A651
KINDRED REHABILITATION HOSPITAL NORTHEAST HOUSTON, HUMBLE, TX, p. A623
KING'S DAUGHTERS MEDICAL CENTER, ASHLAND, KY, p. A254
KING'S DAUGHTERS MEDICAL CENTER, BROOKHAVEN, MS, p. A351
KING'S DAUGHTERS' HEALTH, MADISON, IN, p. A215
KINGMAN COMMUNITY HOSPITAL, KINGMAN, KS, p. A243
KINGMAN REGIONAL MEDICAL CENTER, KINGMAN, AZ, p. A32
KINGS COUNTY HOSPITAL CENTER,, NY, p. A440
KINGS MOUNTAIN HOSPITAL, KINGS MOUNTAIN, NC, p. A463
KINGSBORO PSYCHIATRIC CENTER,, NY, p. A440
KINGSBROOK JEWISH MEDICAL CENTER,, NY, p. A441
KINGWOOD MEDICAL CENTER, KINGWOOD, TX, p. A626
KINGWOOD PINES HOSPITAL, KINGWOOD, TX, p. A626
KIOWA COUNTY MEMORIAL HOSPITAL, GREENSBURG, KS, p. A241
KIOWA DISTRICT HOSPITAL AND MANOR, KIOWA, KS, p. A244
KIRBY MEDICAL CENTER, MONTICELLO, IL, p. A194
KIRKBRIDE CENTER, PHILADELPHIA, PA, p. A544
KISHWAUKEE HOSPITAL, DEKALB, IL, p. A186
KIT CARSON COUNTY HEALTH SERVICE DISTRICT, BURLINGTON, CO, p. A100
KITTITAS VALLEY HEALTHCARE, ELLENSBURG, WA, p. A678
KITTSON MEMORIAL HEALTHCARE CENTER, HALLOCK, MN, p. A340
KLICKITAT VALLEY HEALTH, GOLDENDALE, WA, p. A679
KNAPP MEDICAL CENTER, WESLACO, TX, p. A651
KNOX COMMUNITY HOSPITAL, MOUNT VERNON, OH, p. A495
KNOX COUNTY HOSPITAL, BARBOURVILLE, KY, p. A254
KNOX COUNTY HOSPITAL, KNOX CITY, TX, p. A626
KNOXVILLE DIVISION, KNOXVILLE, IOWA (see VETERANS AFFAIRS CENTRAL IOWA HEALTH CARE SYSTEM), p. A227
KNOXVILLE HOSPITAL & CLINICS, KNOXVILLE, IA, p. A230
KOHALA HOSPITAL, KOHALA, HI, p. A170
KONA COMMUNITY HOSPITAL, KEALAKEKUA, HI, p. A170

KOOTENAI BEHAVIORAL HEALTH, COEUR D'ALENE, IDAHO (see KOOTENAI HEALTH), p. A173
KOOTENAI HEALTH, COEUR D'ALENE, ID, p. A173
KOSAIR CHILDREN'S HOSPITAL, LOUISVILLE, KY, p. A261
KOSCIUSKO COMMUNITY HOSPITAL, WARSAW, IN, p. A221
KOSSUTH REGIONAL HEALTH CENTER, ALGONA, IA, p. A222
KRAVIS CHILDREN'S HOSPITAL, NEW YORK, NEW YORK (see MOUNT SINAI HOSPITAL), p. A442
KUAKINI MEDICAL CENTER, HONOLULU, HI, p. A168
KULA HOSPITAL, KULA, HI, p. A170
KVC PRAIRIE RIDGE PSYCHIATRIC HOSPITAL, KANSAS CITY, KS, p. A243
KWAJALEIN HOSPITAL, KWAJALEIN ISLAND, MH, p. A719

# L

L. V. STABLER MEMORIAL HOSPITAL, GREENVILLE, AL, p. A20
LA PALMA INTERCOMMUNITY HOSPITAL, LA PALMA, CA, p. A66
LA PAZ REGIONAL HOSPITAL, PARKER, AZ, p. A34
LA RABIDA CHILDREN'S HOSPITAL, CHICAGO, IL, p. A182
LABETTE HEALTH, PARSONS, KS, p. A248
LAC–OLIVE VIEW–UCLA MEDICAL CENTER,, CA, p. A71
LAC/UNIVERSITY OF SOUTHERN CALIFORNIA MEDICAL CENTER, LOS ANGELES, CA, p. A71
LACKEY MEMORIAL HOSPITAL, FOREST, MS, p. A353
LADY OF THE SEA GENERAL HOSPITAL, CUT OFF, LA, p. A272
LAFAYETTE BEHAVIORAL HEALTH, LAFAYETTE, LOUISIANA (see LAFAYETTE GENERAL MEDICAL CENTER), p. A277
LAFAYETTE GENERAL MEDICAL CENTER, LAFAYETTE, LA, p. A277
LAFAYETTE GENERAL SURGICAL HOSPITAL, LAFAYETTE, LA, p. A277
LAFAYETTE HOSPITAL, ARROYO, PR, p. A720
LAFAYETTE PHYSICAL REHABILITATION HOSPITAL, LAFAYETTE, LA, p. A277
LAFAYETTE REGIONAL HEALTH CENTER, LEXINGTON, MO, p. A372
LAFAYETTE REGIONAL REHABILITATION HOSPITAL, LAFAYETTE, IN, p. A214
LAFAYETTE SURGICAL SPECIALTY HOSPITAL, LAFAYETTE, LA, p. A277
LAGUNA HONDA HOSPITAL AND REHABILITATION CENTER, SAN FRANCISCO, CA, p. A88
LAHEY HOSPITAL & MEDICAL CENTER, BURLINGTON, BURLINGTON, MA, p. A305
LAHEY MEDICAL CENTER, PEABODY, PEABODY, MASSACHUSETTS (see LAHEY HOSPITAL & MEDICAL CENTER, BURLINGTON), p. A305
LAIRD HOSPITAL, UNION, MS, p. A361
LAKE AREA MEDICAL CENTER, LAKE CHARLES, LA, p. A278
LAKE BUTLER HOSPITAL HAND SURGERY CENTER, LAKE BUTLER, FL, p. A131
LAKE CHARLES MEMORIAL HOSPITAL, LAKE CHARLES, LA, p. A278
LAKE CHARLES MEMORIAL HOSPITAL FOR WOMEN, LAKE CHARLES, LOUISIANA (see LAKE CHARLES MEMORIAL HOSPITAL), p. A278
LAKE CHELAN COMMUNITY HOSPITAL, CHELAN, WA, p. A677
LAKE CITY COMMUNITY HOSPITAL, LAKE CITY, SC, p. A563
LAKE CITY MEDICAL CENTER, LAKE CITY, FL, p. A131
LAKE CITY VETERANS AFFAIRS MEDICAL CENTER, LAKE CITY, FLORIDA (see NORTH FLORIDA/SOUTH GEORGIA VETERAN'S HEALTH SYSTEM), p. A127
LAKE CUMBERLAND REGIONAL HOSPITAL, SOMERSET, KY, p. A266
LAKE DISTRICT HOSPITAL, LAKEVIEW, OR, p. A522
LAKE GRANBURY MEDICAL CENTER, GRANBURY, TX, p. A616
LAKE HEALTH, CONCORD TOWNSHIP, OH, p. A487
LAKE MARTIN COMMUNITY HOSPITAL, DADEVILLE, AL, p. A18
LAKE NORMAN REGIONAL MEDICAL CENTER, MOORESVILLE, NC, p. A465
LAKE POINTE MEDICAL CENTER, ROWLETT, TX, p. A639
LAKE REGION HEALTHCARE, FERGUS FALLS, MN, p. A338
LAKE REGIONAL HEALTH SYSTEM, OSAGE BEACH, MO, p. A374
LAKE TAYLOR TRANSITIONAL CARE HOSPITAL, NORFOLK, VA, p. A669
LAKE VIEW MEMORIAL HOSPITAL, TWO HARBORS, MN, p. A348
LAKE WALES MEDICAL CENTER, LAKE WALES, FL, p. A131
LAKE WHITNEY MEDICAL CENTER, WHITNEY, TX, p. A652
LAKELAND BEHAVIORAL HEALTH SYSTEM, SPRINGFIELD, MO, p. A378
LAKELAND COMMUNITY HOSPITAL, HALEYVILLE, AL, p. A21
LAKELAND HOSPITAL, NILES, NILES, MICHIGAN (see LAKELAND MEDICAL CENTER, ST. JOSEPH), p. A329
LAKELAND HOSPITAL, WATERVLIET, WATERVLIET, MI, p. A332

LODI MEMORIAL HOSPITAL WEST, LODI, CALIFORNIA (see LODI MEMORIAL HOSPITAL), p. A67

LOGAN COUNTY HOSPITAL, OAKLEY, KS, p. A247

LOGAN MEMORIAL HOSPITAL, RUSSELLVILLE, KY, p. A265

LOGAN REGIONAL HOSPITAL, LOGAN, UT, p. A655

LOGAN REGIONAL MEDICAL CENTER, LOGAN, WV, p. A692

LOGANSPORT MEMORIAL HOSPITAL, LOGANSPORT, IN, p. A215

LOGANSPORT STATE HOSPITAL, LOGANSPORT, IN, p. A215

LOMA LINDA UNIVERSITY BEHAVIORAL MEDICINE CENTER, REDLANDS, CA, p. A82

LOMA LINDA UNIVERSITY CHILDREN'S HOSPITAL, LOMA LINDA, CALIFORNIA (see LOMA LINDA UNIVERSITY MEDICAL CENTER), p. A67

LOMA LINDA UNIVERSITY EAST CAMPUS HOSPITAL, LOMA LINDA, CALIFORNIA (see LOMA LINDA UNIVERSITY MEDICAL CENTER), p. A67

LOMA LINDA UNIVERSITY HEART & SURGICAL HOSPITAL, LOMA LINDA, CALIFORNIA (see LOMA LINDA UNIVERSITY MEDICAL CENTER), p. A67

LOMA LINDA UNIVERSITY MEDICAL CENTER, LOMA LINDA, CA, p. A67

LOMA LINDA UNIVERSITY MEDICAL CENTER–MURRIETA, MURRIETA, CA, p. A77

LOMPOC VALLEY MEDICAL CENTER, LOMPOC, CA, p. A68

LONE PEAK HOSPITAL, DRAPER, UT, p. A654

LONE STAR BEHAVIORAL HEALTH, CYPRESS, TX, p. A603

LONG BEACH MEMORIAL MEDICAL CENTER, LONG BEACH, CA, p. A68

LONG ISLAND JEWISH MEDICAL CENTER,, NY, p. A441

LONG TERM CARE CENTER (see NORTHFIELD HOSPITAL), p. A344

LONG–TERM ACUTE CARE HOSPITAL, MOSAIC LIFE CARE AT ST. JOSEPH, SAINT JOSEPH, MO, p. A375

LONGLEAF HOSPITAL, ALEXANDRIA, LA, p. A268

LONGMONT UNITED HOSPITAL, LONGMONT, CO, p. A107

LONGVIEW REGIONAL MEDICAL CENTER, LONGVIEW, TX, p. A629

LORETTO HOSPITAL, CHICAGO, IL, p. A182

LORING HOSPITAL, SAC CITY, IA, p. A234

LOS ALAMITOS MEDICAL CENTER, LOS ALAMITOS, CA, p. A68

LOS ALAMOS MEDICAL CENTER, LOS ALAMOS, NM, p. A425

LOS ANGELES COMMUNITY HOSPITAL AT LOS ANGELES, LOS ANGELES, CA, p. A71

LOS ANGELES COMMUNITY HOSPITAL OF NORWALK, NORWALK, CALIFORNIA (see LOS ANGELES COMMUNITY HOSPITAL AT LOS ANGELES), p. A71

LOS ANGELES COUNTY CENTRAL JAIL HOSPITAL, LOS ANGELES, CA, p. A71

LOS NINOS HOSPITAL, PHOENIX, AZ, p. A35

LOS ROBLES HOSPITAL AND MEDICAL CENTER, THOUSAND OAKS, CA, p. A94

LOST RIVERS MEDICAL CENTER, ARCO, ID, p. A172

LOUIS & PEACHES OWEN HEART HOSPITAL, TYLER, TEXAS (see MOTHER FRANCES HOSPITAL – TYLER), p. A649

LOUIS A. JOHNSON VETERANS AFFAIRS MEDICAL CENTER, CLARKSBURG, WV, p. A690

LOUIS A. WEISS MEMORIAL HOSPITAL, CHICAGO, IL, p. A182

LOUIS STOKES CLEVELAND VETERANS AFFAIRS MEDICAL CENTER, CLEVELAND, OH, p. A484

LOUISIANA CONTINUING CARE HOSPITAL, MARRERO, LA, p. A280

LOUISIANA EXTENDED CARE HOSPITAL OF LAFAYETTE, LAFAYETTE, LA, p. A277

LOUISIANA EXTENDED CARE HOSPITAL OF NATCHITOCHES, NATCHITOCHES, LA, p. A281

LOUISIANA EXTENDED CARE HOSPITAL WEST MONROE, WEST MONROE, LA, p. A287

LOUISIANA HEART HOSPITAL, LACOMBE, LA, p. A277

LOURDES COUNSELING CENTER, RICHLAND, WA, p. A683

LOURDES HOSPITAL, PADUCAH, KY, p. A264

LOURDES MEDICAL CENTER, PASCO, WA, p. A682

LOURDES MEDICAL CENTER OF BURLINGTON COUNTY, WILLINGBORO, NJ, p. A420

LOURDES SPECIALTY HOSPITAL OF SOUTHERN NEW JERSEY, WILLINGBORO, NJ, p. A420

LOVELACE MEDICAL CENTER, ALBUQUERQUE, NM, p. A422

LOVELACE REGIONAL HOSPITAL – ROSWELL, ROSWELL, NM, p. A426

LOVELACE REHABILITATION HOSPITAL, ALBUQUERQUE, NM, p. A422

LOVELACE WESTSIDE HOSPITAL, ALBUQUERQUE, NM, p. A422

LOVELACE WOMEN'S HOSPITAL, ALBUQUERQUE, NM, p. A422

LOWELL GENERAL HOSPITAL, LOWELL, MA, p. A308

LOWELL GENERAL HOSPITAL, SAINTS CAMPUS, LOWELL, MASSACHUSETTS (see LOWELL GENERAL HOSPITAL), p. A308

LOWER BUCKS HOSPITAL, BRISTOL, PA, p. A530

LOWER KEYS MEDICAL CENTER, KEY WEST, FL, p. A130

LOWER UMPQUA HOSPITAL DISTRICT, REEDSPORT, OR, p. A525

LOYOLA UNIVERSITY MEDICAL CENTER, MAYWOOD, IL, p. A193

LUBBOCK HEART HOSPITAL, LUBBOCK, TX, p. A629

LUCAS COUNTY HEALTH CENTER, CHARITON, IA, p. A224

LUCILE SALTER PACKARD CHILDREN'S HOSPITAL STANFORD, PALO ALTO, CA, p. A80

LUTHERAN HOSPITAL, CLEVELAND, OH, p. A485

LUTHERAN HOSPITAL OF INDIANA, FORT WAYNE, IN, p. A208

LUTHERAN MEDICAL CENTER, WHEAT RIDGE, CO, p. A109

LUTZ WING CONVALESCENT AND NURSING CARE UNIT (see MAYO CLINIC HEALTH SYSTEM IN FAIRMONT), p. A338

LYNCHBURG GENERAL HOSPITAL, LYNCHBURG, VIRGINIA (see CENTRA LYNCHBURG GENERAL HOSPITAL), p. A667

LYNDON B JOHNSON GENERAL HOSPITAL, HOUSTON, TEXAS (see HARRIS HEALTH SYSTEM), p. A619

LYNDON B. JOHNSON TROPICAL MEDICAL CENTER, PAGO PAGO, AS, p. A719

LYNN COUNTY HOSPITAL DISTRICT, TAHOKA, TX, p. A646

LYONS DIVISION, LYONS, NEW JERSEY (see VETERANS AFFAIRS NEW JERSEY HEALTH CARE SYSTEM), p. A411

# M

MACKINAC STRAITS HEALTH SYSTEM, INC., SAINT IGNACE, MI, p. A329

MACNEAL HOSPITAL, BERWYN, IL, p. A179

MACON COUNTY GENERAL HOSPITAL, LAFAYETTE, TN, p. A581

MAD RIVER COMMUNITY HOSPITAL, ARCATA, CA, p. A54

MADELIA COMMUNITY HOSPITAL, MADELIA, MN, p. A341

MADERA COMMUNITY HOSPITAL, MADERA, CA, p. A74

MADIGAN HEALTHCARE SYSTEM, TACOMA, WA, p. A686

MADISON COMMUNITY HOSPITAL, MADISON, SD, p. A569

MADISON COUNTY HEALTH CARE SYSTEM, WINTERSET, IA, p. A236

MADISON COUNTY MEMORIAL HOSPITAL, MADISON, FL, p. A132

MADISON HEALTH, LONDON, OH, p. A492

MADISON HOSPITAL, MADISON, ALABAMA (see HUNTSVILLE HOSPITAL), p. A21

MADISON HOSPITAL, MADISON, MN, p. A341

MADISON MEDICAL CENTER, FREDERICKTOWN, MO, p. A367

MADISON MEMORIAL HOSPITAL, REXBURG, ID, p. A176

MADISON PARISH HOSPITAL, TALLULAH, LA, p. A286

MERIT HEALTH MADISON, CANTON, MS, p. A351

MADISON ST. JOSEPH HEALTH CENTER, MADISONVILLE, TX, p. A630

MADISON STATE HOSPITAL, MADISON, IN, p. A215

MADISON VALLEY MEDICAL CENTER, ENNIS, MT, p. A383

MADONNA REHABILITATION HOSPITAL, LINCOLN, NE, p. A394

MADONNA REHABILITATION HOSPITAL, LINCOLN, NE, p. A394

MADONNA REHABILITATION SPECIALTY HOSPITAL, BELLEVUE, NE, p. A390

MAGEE GENERAL HOSPITAL, MAGEE, MS, p. A356

MAGEE REHABILITATION HOSPITAL, PHILADELPHIA, PA, p. A544

MAGEE–WOMENS HOSPITAL OF UPMC, PITTSBURGH, PA, p. A546

MAGNOLIA REGIONAL HEALTH CENTER, CORINTH, MS, p. A352

MAGNOLIA REGIONAL MEDICAL CENTER, MAGNOLIA, AR, p. A48

MAGRUDER MEMORIAL HOSPITAL, PORT CLINTON, OH, p. A496

MAHASKA HEALTH PARTNERSHIP, OSKALOOSA, IA, p. A233

MAHNOMEN HEALTH CENTER, MAHNOMEN, MN, p. A341

MAIMONIDES INFANTS AND CHILDREN'S HOSPITAL OF BROOKLYN,, NEW YORK (see MAIMONIDES MEDICAL CENTER), p. A441

MAIMONIDES MEDICAL CENTER,, NY, p. A441

MAIN CAMPUS, BATTLE CREEK, MICHIGAN (see BRONSON BATTLE CREEK), p. A315

MAINE COAST MEMORIAL HOSPITAL, ELLSWORTH, ME, p. A290

MAINE MEDICAL CENTER, PORTLAND, ME, p. A291

MAINE MEDICAL CENTER, BRIGHTON CAMPUS, PORTLAND, MAINE (see MAINE MEDICAL CENTER), p. A291

MAINE VETERANS AFFAIRS MEDICAL CENTER, AUGUSTA, ME, p. A288

MAINEGENERAL MEDICAL CENTER, AUGUSTA, ME, p. A288

MAINEGENERAL MEDICAL CENTER–AUGUSTA CAMPUS, AUGUSTA, MAINE (see MAINEGENERAL MEDICAL CENTER), p. A288

MAINLAND MEDICAL CENTER, TEXAS CITY, TEXAS (see CLEAR LAKE REGIONAL MEDICAL CENTER), p. A651

MAJOR HOSPITAL, SHELBYVILLE, IN, p. A220

MALVERN INSTITUTE, MALVERN, PA, p. A539

MAMMOTH HOSPITAL, MAMMOTH LAKES, CA, p. A74

MANATEE GLENS HOSPITAL AND ADDICTION CENTER, BRADENTON, FL, p. A122

MANATEE MEMORIAL HOSPITAL, BRADENTON, FL, p. A122

MANCHESTER MEMORIAL HOSPITAL, MANCHESTER, CT, p. A112

MANCHESTER MEMORIAL HOSPITAL, MANCHESTER, KY, p. A262

MANCHESTER VETERANS AFFAIRS MEDICAL CENTER, MANCHESTER, NH, p. A407

MANHASSET AMBULATORY CARE PAVILION, MANHASSET, NEW YORK (see LONG ISLAND JEWISH MEDICAL CENTER), p. A441

MANHATTAN EYE, EAR AND THROAT HOSPITAL, NEW YORK, NEW YORK (see LENOX HILL HOSPITAL), p. A441

MANHATTAN PSYCHIATRIC CENTER–WARD'S ISLAND, NEW YORK, NY, p. A441

MANHATTAN SURGICAL,, KS, p. A245

MANIILAQ HEALTH CENTER, KOTZEBUE, AK, p. A28

MANN–GRANDSTAFF VETERANS AFFAIRS MEDICAL CENTER, SPOKANE, WA, p. A685

MANNING REGIONAL HEALTHCARE CENTER, MANNING, IA, p. A231

MANSFIELD HOSPITAL, MANSFIELD, OHIO (see OHIOHEALTH MEDCENTRAL MANSFIELD HOSPITAL), p. A493

MAPLE GROVE HOSPITAL, MAPLE GROVE, MN, p. A342

MARCUM AND WALLACE MEMORIAL HOSPITAL, IRVINE, KY, p. A259

MARCUS DALY MEMORIAL HOSPITAL, HAMILTON, MT, p. A384

MARENGO MEMORIAL HOSPITAL, UNITYPOINT HEALTH, MARENGO, IA, p. A231

MARGARET MARY HEALTH, BATESVILLE, IN, p. A204

MARGARET R. PARDEE MEMORIAL HOSPITAL, HENDERSONVILLE, NC, p. A462

MARGARETVILLE HOSPITAL, MARGARETVILLE, NY, p. A437

MARIA FARERI CHILDREN'S HOSPITAL, VALHALLA, NEW YORK (see WESTCHESTER MEDICAL CENTER), p. A452

MARIA PARHAM MEDICAL CENTER, HENDERSON, NC, p. A462

MARIAN CENTER, SALT LAKE CITY, UT, p. A658

MARIAN REGIONAL MEDICAL CENTER, SANTA MARIA, CA, p. A91

MARIANJOY REHABILITATION HOSPITAL, WHEATON, IL, p. A203

MARIAS MEDICAL CENTER, SHELBY, MT, p. A387

MARICOPA INTEGRATED HEALTH SYSTEM, PHOENIX, AZ, p. A35

MARIETTA MEMORIAL HOSPITAL, MARIETTA, OH, p. A493

MARIN GENERAL HOSPITAL, GREENBRAE, CA, p. A64

MARINA DEL REY HOSPITAL, MARINA DEL REY, CA, p. A74

MARION GENERAL HOSPITAL, MARION, IN, p. A215

MARION GENERAL HOSPITAL, COLUMBIA, MS, p. A352

MARION REGIONAL MEDICAL CENTER, HAMILTON, AL, p. A21

MARION VETERANS AFFAIRS MEDICAL CENTER, MARION, IL, p. A193

MARK TWAIN MEDICAL CENTER, SAN ANDREAS, CA, p. A85

MARLETTE REGIONAL HOSPITAL, MARLETTE, MI, p. A325

MARLTON REHABILITATION HOSPITAL, MARLTON, NJ, p. A414

MARSHALL BROWNING HOSPITAL, DU QUOIN, IL, p. A186

MARSHALL COUNTY HEALTHCARE CENTER AVERA, BRITTON, SD, p. A567

MARSHALL COUNTY HOSPITAL, BENTON, KY, p. A254

MARSHALL I. PICKENS HOSPITAL, GREENVILLE, SOUTH CAROLINA (see GREENVILLE MEMORIAL HOSPITAL), p. A561

MARSHALL MEDICAL CENTER, PLACERVILLE, CA, p. A81

MARSHALL MEDICAL CENTER, LEWISBURG, TN, p. A581

MARSHALL MEDICAL CENTER NORTH, GUNTERSVILLE, AL, p. A20

MARSHALL MEDICAL CENTER SOUTH, BOAZ, AL, p. A17

MARTHA JEFFERSON HOSPITAL, CHARLOTTESVILLE, VA, p. A663

MARTHA'S VINEYARD HOSPITAL, OAK BLUFFS, MA, p. A310

MARTIN ARMY COMMUNITY HOSPITAL, FORT BENNING, GA, p. A157

MARTIN COUNTY HOSPITAL DISTRICT, STANTON, TX, p. A645

MARTIN GENERAL HOSPITAL, WILLIAMSTON, NC, p. A470

MARTIN HEALTH SYSTEM, STUART, FL, p. A143

MARTIN LUTHER KING, JR. COMMUNITY HOSPITAL, LOS ANGELES, CA, p. A71

MARTIN MEMORIAL HOSPITAL SOUTH, STUART, FLORIDA (see MARTIN HEALTH SYSTEM), p. A143

MARTINSBURG VETERANS AFFAIRS MEDICAL CENTER, MARTINSBURG, WV, p. A693

MARY BLACK HEALTH SYSTEM – GAFFNEY, GAFFNEY, SC, p. A561

MARY BLACK HEALTH SYSTEM – SPARTANBURG, SPARTANBURG, SC, p. A565

MARY BRECKINRIDGE ARH HOSPITAL, HYDEN, KY, p. A258

MARY FREE BED REHABILITATION HOSPITAL, GRAND RAPIDS, MI, p. A320

MARY GREELEY MEDICAL CENTER, AMES, IA, p. A222

MARY IMMACULATE HOSPITAL, NEWPORT NEWS, VA, p. A669

MARY LANNING HEALTHCARE, HASTINGS, NE, p. A392

MARY RUTAN HOSPITAL, BELLEFONTAINE, OH, p. A479

MARY S HARPER GERIATRIC PSYCHIATRY CENTER, TUSCALOOSA, AL, p. A25

MARY WASHINGTON HOSPITAL, FREDERICKSBURG, VA, p. A665

MARYMOUNT HOSPITAL, GARFIELD HEIGHTS, OH, p. A490

MASON DISTRICT HOSPITAL, HAVANA, IL, p. A190
MASON GENERAL HOSPITAL, SHELTON, WA, p. A684
MASONICARE HEALTH CENTER, WALLINGFORD, CT, p. A115
MASSAC MEMORIAL HOSPITAL, METROPOLIS, IL, p. A194
MASSACHUSETTS EYE AND EAR INFIRMARY, BOSTON, MA, p. A304
MASSACHUSETTS GENERAL HOSPITAL, BOSTON, MA, p. A304
MASSACHUSETTS HOSPITAL SCHOOL, CANTON, MA, p. A306
MASSENA MEMORIAL HOSPITAL, MASSENA, NY, p. A437
MASSGENERAL FOR CHILDREN AT NEWTON–WELLESLEY HOSPITAL, NEWTON, MASSACHUSETTS (see NEWTON–WELLESLEY HOSPITAL), p. A309
MASSGENERAL FOR CHILDREN AT NORTH SHORE MEDICAL CENTER, SALEM, MASSACHUSETTS (see NORTH SHORE MEDICAL CENTER), p. A310
MASSGENERAL HOSPITAL FOR CHILDREN, BOSTON, MASSACHUSETTS (see MASSACHUSETTS GENERAL HOSPITAL), p. A304
MAT–SU REGIONAL MEDICAL CENTER, PALMER, AK, p. A29
MATAGORDA REGIONAL MEDICAL CENTER, BAY CITY, TX, p. A596
MATHENY MEDICAL AND EDUCATIONAL CENTER, PEAPACK, NJ, p. A416
MATTEL CHILDREN'S HOSPITAL, LOS ANGELES, CALIFORNIA (see RONALD REAGAN UCLA MEDICAL CENTER), p. A72
MAUI MEMORIAL MEDICAL CENTER, WAILUKU, HI, p. A170
MAURY REGIONAL HOSPITAL, COLUMBIA, TN, p. A576
MAYERS MEMORIAL HOSPITAL DISTRICT, FALL RIVER MILLS, CA, p. A61
MAYHILL HOSPITAL, DENTON, TX, p. A608
MAYO CLINIC – SAINT MARYS HOSPITAL, ROCHESTER, MINNESOTA (see MAYO CLINIC HOSPITAL – ROCHESTER), p. A345
MAYO CLINIC HEALTH SYSTEM – CHIPPEWA VALLEY IN BLOOMER, BLOOMER, WI, p. A698
MAYO CLINIC HEALTH SYSTEM – FRANCISCAN HEALTHCARE IN LA CROSSE, LA CROSSE, WI, p. A703
MAYO CLINIC HEALTH SYSTEM – FRANCISCAN HEALTHCARE IN SPARTA, SPARTA, WI, p. A711
MAYO CLINIC HEALTH SYSTEM – NORTHLAND IN BARRON, BARRON, WI, p. A698
MAYO CLINIC HEALTH SYSTEM – OAKRIDGE IN OSSEO, OSSEO, WI, p. A708
MAYO CLINIC HEALTH SYSTEM – RED CEDAR IN MENOMONIE, MENOMONIE, WI, p. A705
MAYO CLINIC HEALTH SYSTEM IN ALBERT LEA, ALBERT LEA, MN, p. A334
MAYO CLINIC HEALTH SYSTEM IN CANNON FALLS, CANNON FALLS, MN, p. A336
MAYO CLINIC HEALTH SYSTEM IN EAU CLAIRE, EAU CLAIRE, WI, p. A700
MAYO CLINIC HEALTH SYSTEM IN FAIRMONT, FAIRMONT, MN, p. A338
MAYO CLINIC HEALTH SYSTEM IN LAKE CITY, LAKE CITY, MN, p. A340
MAYO CLINIC HEALTH SYSTEM IN MANKATO, MANKATO, MN, p. A341
MAYO CLINIC HEALTH SYSTEM IN NEW PRAGUE, NEW PRAGUE, MN, p. A343
MAYO CLINIC HEALTH SYSTEM IN RED WING, RED WING, MN, p. A345
MAYO CLINIC HEALTH SYSTEM IN SAINT JAMES, SAINT JAMES, MN, p. A346
MAYO CLINIC HEALTH SYSTEM IN SPRINGFIELD, SPRINGFIELD, MN, p. A347
MAYO CLINIC HEALTH SYSTEM IN WASECA, WASECA, MN, p. A348
MAYO CLINIC HEALTH SYSTEM IN WAYCROSS, WAYCROSS, GA, p. A167
MAYO CLINIC HEALTH SYSTEM–ALBERT LEA AND AUSTIN, AUSTIN, MN, p. A335
MAYO CLINIC HOSPITAL, PHOENIX, AZ, p. A35
MAYO CLINIC HOSPITAL – ROCHESTER, ROCHESTER, MN, p. A345
MAYO CLINIC JACKSONVILLE, JACKSONVILLE, FL, p. A129
MAYO REGIONAL HOSPITAL, DOVER–FOXCROFT, ME, p. A290
MCALESTER REGIONAL HEALTH CENTER, MCALESTER, OK, p. A509
MCALLEN HEART HOSPITAL, MCALLEN, TEXAS (see SOUTH TEXAS HEALTH SYSTEM), p. A610
MCALLEN MEDICAL CENTER, MCALLEN, TEXAS (see SOUTH TEXAS HEALTH SYSTEM), p. A610
MCBRIDE CLINIC ORTHOPEDIC HOSPITAL, OKLAHOMA CITY, OK, p. A512
MCCAMEY COUNTY HOSPITAL DISTRICT, MCCAMEY, TX, p. A631
MCCONE COUNTY HEALTH CENTER, CIRCLE, MT, p. A382
MCCREADY FOUNDATION, CRISFIELD, MD, p. A297
MCCULLOUGH–HYDE MEMORIAL HOSPITAL/TRIHEALTH, OXFORD, OH, p. A496

MCCURTAIN MEMORIAL HOSPITAL, IDABEL, OK, p. A508
MCDONOUGH DISTRICT HOSPITAL, MACOMB, IL, p. A193
MCDOWELL ARH HOSPITAL, MCDOWELL, KY, p. A263
MCDOWELL HOSPITAL, MARION, NC, p. A464
MCFARLAND SPECIALTY HOSPITAL, LEBANON, TENNESSEE (see UNIVERSITY MEDICAL CENTER), p. A581
MCGEHEE–DESHA COUNTY HOSPITAL, MCGEHEE, AR, p. A48
MCKAY–DEE MEDICAL CENTER, OGDEN, UT, p. A656
MCKEE MEDICAL CENTER, LOVELAND, CO, p. A107
MCKENZIE COUNTY HEALTHCARE SYSTEM, WATFORD CITY, ND, p. A477
MCKENZIE HEALTH SYSTEM, SANDUSKY, MI, p. A330
MCKENZIE REGIONAL HOSPITAL, MCKENZIE, TN, p. A582
MCKENZIE–WILLAMETTE MEDICAL CENTER, SPRINGFIELD, OR, p. A526
MCLANE CHILDREN'S HOSPITAL SCOTT & WHITE, TEMPLE, TEXAS (see SCOTT & WHITE MEMORIAL HOSPITAL), p. A647
MCLANE CHILDREN'S HOSPITAL SCOTT & WHITE, TEMPLE, TEXAS (see SCOTT & WHITE MEMORIAL HOSPITAL), p. A647
MCLAREN BAY REGION, BAY CITY, MI, p. A315
MCLAREN BAY SPECIAL CARE, BAY CITY, MI, p. A315
MCLAREN CENTRAL MICHIGAN, MOUNT PLEASANT, MI, p. A326
MCLAREN FLINT, FLINT, MI, p. A319
MCLAREN GREATER LANSING, LANSING, MI, p. A324
MCLAREN LAPEER REGION, LAPEER, MI, p. A324
MCLAREN MACOMB, MOUNT CLEMENS, MI, p. A326
MCLAREN NORTHERN MICHIGAN, PETOSKEY, MI, p. A327
MCLAREN OAKLAND, PONTIAC, MI, p. A328
MCLAREN ORTHOPEDIC HOSPITAL, LANSING, MICHIGAN (see MCLAREN GREATER LANSING), p. A324
MCLAREN PORT HURON, PORT HURON, MI, p. A328
MCLEAN HOSPITAL, BELMONT, MA, p. A302
MCLEOD HEALTH CHERAW, CHERAW, SC, p. A558
MCLEOD LORIS SEACOAST HOSPITAL, LORIS, SC, p. A563
MCLEOD MEDICAL CENTER DILLON, DILLON, SC, p. A560
MCLEOD MEDICAL CENTER–DARLINGTON, DARLINGTON, SC, p. A560
MCLEOD REGIONAL MEDICAL CENTER, FLORENCE, SC, p. A561
MCLEOD SEACOAST, LITTLE RIVER, SOUTH CAROLINA (see MCLEOD LORIS SEACOAST HOSPITAL), p. A563
MCREYNOLDS HALL (see OTSEGO MEMORIAL HOSPITAL), p. A320
MEADE DISTRICT HOSPITAL, MEADE, KS, p. A246
MEADOW WOOD BEHAVIORAL HEALTH SYSTEM, NEW CASTLE, DE, p. A117
MEADOWBROOK REHABILITATION HOSPITAL, GARDNER, KS, p. A240
MEADOWLANDS HOSPITAL MEDICAL CENTER, SECAUCUS, NJ, p. A418
MEADOWS PSYCHIATRIC CENTER, CENTRE HALL, PA, p. A531
MEADOWS REGIONAL MEDICAL CENTER, VIDALIA, GA, p. A166
MEADOWVIEW REGIONAL MEDICAL CENTER, MAYSVILLE, KY, p. A263
MEADVILLE MEDICAL CENTER, MEADVILLE, PA, p. A540
MEASE COUNTRYSIDE HOSPITAL, SAFETY HARBOR, FL, p. A141
MEASE DUNEDIN HOSPITAL, DUNEDIN, FL, p. A126
MEDICAL ARTS HOSPITAL, LAMESA, TX, p. A627
MEDICAL CENTER ALLIANCE, TARANT, TX, p. A613
MEDICAL CENTER ARLINGTON, ARLINGTON, TX, p. A592
MEDICAL CENTER AT BOWLING GREEN, BOWLING GREEN, KY, p. A254
MEDICAL CENTER AT FRANKLIN, FRANKLIN, KY, p. A257
MEDICAL CENTER AT SCOTTSVILLE, SCOTTSVILLE, KY, p. A266
MEDICAL CENTER BARBOUR, EUFAULA, AL, p. A19
MEDICAL CENTER ENTERPRISE, ENTERPRISE, AL, p. A19
MEDICAL CENTER HEALTH SYSTEM, ODESSA, TX, p. A634
MEDICAL CENTER HOSPITAL CAMPUS, BURLINGTON, VERMONT (see THE UNIVERSITY OF VERMONT HEALTH NETWORK UNIVERSITY OF VERMONT MEDICAL CENTER), p. A660
MEDICAL CENTER OF AURORA, AURORA, CO, p. A99
MEDICAL CENTER OF AURORA NORTH, AURORA, COLORADO (see MEDICAL CENTER OF AURORA), p. A99
MEDICAL CENTER OF LEWISVILLE, LEWISVILLE, TX, p. A628
MEDICAL CENTER OF MANCHESTER, MANCHESTER, TN, p. A582
MEDICAL CENTER OF MCKINNEY, MCKINNEY, TX, p. A632
MEDICAL CENTER OF PEACH COUNTY, NAVICENT HEALTH, FORT VALLEY, GA, p. A158
MEDICAL CENTER OF PLANO, PLANO, TX, p. A637
MEDICAL CENTER OF SOUTH ARKANSAS, EL DORADO, AR, p. A43
MEDICAL CENTER OF THE ROCKIES, LOVELAND, CO, p. A107
MEDICAL CENTER OF TRINITY, TRINITY, FL, p. A146
MEDICAL CENTER, NAVICENT HEALTH, MACON, GA, p. A160
MEDICAL CITY CHILDREN'S HOSPITAL, DALLAS, TEXAS (see MEDICAL CITY DALLAS HOSPITAL), p. A605
MEDICAL CITY DALLAS HOSPITAL, DALLAS, TX, p. A605

MEDICAL WEST, BESSEMER, AL, p. A16
MEDICINE LODGE MEMORIAL HOSPITAL, MEDICINE LODGE, KS, p. A246
MEDINA HOSPITAL, MEDINA, OH, p. A494
MEDINA MEMORIAL HOSPITAL, MEDINA, NY, p. A437
MEDINA REGIONAL HOSPITAL, HONDO, TX, p. A618
MEDSTAR FRANKLIN SQUARE MEDICAL CENTER, BALTIMORE, MD, p. A294
MEDSTAR GEORGETOWN UNIVERSITY HOSPITAL, WASHINGTON, DC, p. A119
MEDSTAR GOOD SAMARITAN HOSPITAL, BALTIMORE, MD, p. A294
MEDSTAR HARBOR HOSPITAL, BALTIMORE, MD, p. A294
MEDSTAR MONTGOMERY MEDICAL CENTER, OLNEY, MD, p. A299
MEDSTAR NATIONAL REHABILITATION HOSPITAL, WASHINGTON, DC, p. A119
MEDSTAR SOUTHERN MARYLAND HOSPITAL CENTER, CLINTON, MD, p. A297
MEDSTAR ST. MARY'S HOSPITAL, LEONARDTOWN, MD, p. A299
MEDSTAR UNION MEMORIAL HOSPITAL, BALTIMORE, MD, p. A294
MEDSTAR WASHINGTON HOSPITAL CENTER, WASHINGTON, DC, p. A119
MEE MEMORIAL HOSPITAL, KING CITY, CA, p. A66
MEEKER MEMORIAL HOSPITAL, LITCHFIELD, MN, p. A341
MELISSA MEMORIAL HOSPITAL, HOLYOKE, CO, p. A105
MELROSE–WAKEFIELD HOSPITAL, MELROSE, MASSACHUSETTS (see HALLMARK HEALTH SYSTEM), p. A308
MEMORIAL BEHAVIORAL HEALTH, GULFPORT, MISSISSIPPI (see MEMORIAL HOSPITAL AT GULFPORT), p. A353
MEMORIAL CAMPUS, WORCESTER, MASSACHUSETTS (see UMASS MEMORIAL MEDICAL CENTER), p. A313
MEMORIAL CHILDREN'S HOSPITAL, SAVANNAH, GEORGIA (see MEMORIAL HEALTH), p. A164
MEMORIAL CHILDREN'S HOSPITAL, SOUTH BEND, INDIANA (see MEMORIAL HOSPITAL OF SOUTH BEND), p. A220
MEMORIAL COMMUNITY HEALTH, AURORA, NE, p. A389
MEMORIAL COMMUNITY HOSPITAL AND HEALTH SYSTEM, BLAIR, NE, p. A390
MEMORIAL HEALTH, SAVANNAH, GA, p. A164
MEMORIAL HEALTH, MARYSVILLE, OH, p. A493
MEMORIAL HEALTH CARE SYSTEMS, SEWARD, NE, p. A398
MEMORIAL HEALTH SYSTEM, ABILENE, KS, p. A237
MEMORIAL HEALTHCARE, OWOSSO, MI, p. A327
MEMORIAL HERMANN – TEXAS MEDICAL CENTER, HOUSTON, TX, p. A620
MEMORIAL HERMANN KATY HOSPITAL, KATY, TX, p. A625
MEMORIAL HERMANN MEMORIAL CITY MEDICAL CENTER, HOUSTON, TX, p. A621
MEMORIAL HERMANN NORTHEAST, HUMBLE, TX, p. A623
MEMORIAL HERMANN NORTHWEST HOSPITAL, HOUSTON, TX, p. A621
MEMORIAL HERMANN REHABILITATION HOSPITAL – KATY, KATY, TX, p. A625
MEMORIAL HERMANN SOUTHEAST HOSPITAL, HOUSTON, TEXAS (see MEMORIAL HERMANN NORTHWEST HOSPITAL), p. A621
MEMORIAL HERMANN SOUTHWEST HOSPITAL, HOUSTON, TEXAS (see MEMORIAL HERMANN NORTHWEST HOSPITAL), p. A621
MEMORIAL HERMANN SUGAR LAND HOSPITAL, SUGAR LAND, TX, p. A645
MEMORIAL HERMANN SURGICAL HOSPITAL KINGWOOD, KINGWOOD, TX, p. A626
MEMORIAL HERMANN SURGICAL HOSPITAL‰FIRST COLONY, SUGAR LAND, TX, p. A645
MEMORIAL HERMANN THE WOODLANDS HOSPITAL, THE WOODLANDS, TEXAS (see MEMORIAL HERMANN NORTHWEST HOSPITAL), p. A621
MEMORIAL HOSPITAL, COLORADO SPRINGS, CO, p. A100
MEMORIAL HOSPITAL, BELLEVILLE, IL, p. A179
MEMORIAL HOSPITAL, CARTHAGE, IL, p. A180
MEMORIAL HOSPITAL, CHESTER, IL, p. A181
MEMORIAL HOSPITAL, NORTH CONWAY, NH, p. A408
MEMORIAL HOSPITAL, FREMONT, OH, p. A490
MEMORIAL HOSPITAL, STILWELL, OK, p. A515
MEMORIAL HOSPITAL, YORK, PA, p. A554
MEMORIAL HOSPITAL, GONZALES, TX, p. A616
MEMORIAL HOSPITAL, SEMINOLE, TX, p. A643
MEMORIAL HOSPITAL, MARTINSVILLE, VA, p. A668
MEMORIAL HOSPITAL AND HEALTH CARE CENTER, JASPER, IN, p. A213
MEMORIAL HOSPITAL AND MANOR, BAINBRIDGE, GA, p. A152
MEMORIAL HOSPITAL AND PHYSICIAN GROUP, FREDERICK, OK, p. A507
MEMORIAL HOSPITAL AT GULFPORT, GULFPORT, MS, p. A353
MEMORIAL HOSPITAL HIXSON, HIXSON, TENNESSEE (see CHI MEMORIAL), p. A575

METHODIST LE BONHEUR GERMANTOWN HOSPITAL, GERMANTOWN, TENNESSEE (see METHODIST HEALTHCARE MEMPHIS HOSPITALS), p. A584
METHODIST MANSFIELD MEDICAL CENTER, MANSFIELD, TX, p. A631
METHODIST MCKINNEY HOSPITAL, MCKINNEY, TX, p. A632
METHODIST MEDICAL CENTER OF OAK RIDGE, OAK RIDGE, TN, p. A586
METHODIST OLIVE BRANCH HOSPITAL, OLIVE BRANCH, MS, p. A358
METHODIST REHABILITATION CENTER, JACKSON, MS, p. A355
METHODIST REHABILITATION HOSPITAL, DALLAS, TX, p. A606
METHODIST RICHARDSON MEDICAL CENTER, RICHARDSON, TX, p. A638
METHODIST SPECIALTY AND TRANSPLANT HOSPITAL, SAN ANTONIO, TEXAS (see METHODIST HOSPITAL), p. A641
METHODIST STONE OAK HOSPITAL, SAN ANTONIO, TX, p. A641
METHODIST TEXSAN HOSPITAL, SAN ANTONIO, TEXAS (see METHODIST HOSPITAL), p. A641
METHODIST WOMEN'S HOSPITAL, ELKHORN, NEBRASKA (see NEBRASKA METHODIST HOSPITAL), p. A396
METRO HEALTH HOSPITAL, WYOMING, MI, p. A333
METROHEALTH MEDICAL CENTER, CLEVELAND, OH, p. A485
METROPLEX ADVENTIST HOSPITAL, KILLEEN, TX, p. A626
METROPOLITAN GENERAL CARE UNIT, METROPOLITAN DRUG DETOXIFICATION AND METROPOLITAN PSYCHIATRIC UNIT (see METROPOLITAN HOSPITAL CENTER), p. A441
METROPOLITAN HOSPITAL CENTER, NEW YORK, NY, p. A441
METROPOLITAN METHODIST HOSPITAL, SAN ANTONIO, TEXAS (see METHODIST HOSPITAL), p. A641
METROPOLITAN ST. LOUIS PSYCHIATRIC CENTER, SAINT LOUIS, MO, p. A376
METROPOLITAN STATE HOSPITAL, NORWALK, CA, p. A78
METROPOLITANO DE LA MONTANA, UTUADO, PR, p. A724
METROSOUTH MEDICAL CENTER, BLUE ISLAND, IL, p. A180
METROWEST MEDICAL CENTER, FRAMINGHAM, MA, p. A307
MIAMI COUNTY MEDICAL CENTER, PAOLA, KS, p. A248
MIAMI HEART CAMPUS AT MOUNT SINAI MEDICAL CENTER, MIAMI BEACH, FLORIDA (see MOUNT SINAI MEDICAL CENTER), p. A135
MIAMI JEWISH HOME AND HOSPITAL FOR AGED, MIAMI, FL, p. A134
MIAMI VALLEY HOSPITAL, DAYTON, OH, p. A488
MIAMI VALLEY HOSPITAL SOUTH, CENTERVILLE, OHIO (see MIAMI VALLEY HOSPITAL), p. A488
MIAMI VETERANS AFFAIRS HEALTHCARE SYSTEM, MIAMI, FL, p. A134
MICHAEL E. DEBAKEY VETERANS AFFAIRS MEDICAL CENTER, HOUSTON, TX, p. A621
MICHIANA BEHAVIORAL HEALTH CENTER, PLYMOUTH, IN, p. A218
MID COAST HOSPITAL, BRUNSWICK, ME, p. A289
MID-AMERICA REHABILITATION HOSPITAL, SHAWNEE MISSION, KS, p. A250
MID-COLUMBIA MEDICAL CENTER, THE DALLES, OR, p. A526
MID-HUDSON FORENSIC PSYCHIATRIC CENTER, NEW HAMPTON, NY, p. A438
MID-JEFFERSON EXTENDED CARE HOSPITAL, NEDERLAND, TX, p. A634
MID-VALLEY HOSPITAL, OMAK, WA, p. A681
MIDDLE PARK MEDICAL CENTER-KREMMLING, KREMMLING, CO, p. A105
MIDDLE TENNESSEE MENTAL HEALTH INSTITUTE, NASHVILLE, TN, p. A585
MIDDLESBORO ARH HOSPITAL, MIDDLESBORO, KY, p. A263
MIDDLESEX HOSPITAL, MIDDLETOWN, CT, p. A113
MIDHUDSON REGIONAL HOSPITAL OF WESTCHESTER MEDICAL CENTER, POUGHKEEPSIE, NEW YORK (see WESTCHESTER MEDICAL CENTER), p. A452
MIDLAND MEMORIAL HOSPITAL, MIDLAND, TX, p. A632
MIDLAND MEMORIAL HOSPITAL, MIDLAND, TEXAS (see MIDLAND MEMORIAL HOSPITAL), p. A632
MIDMICHIGAN MEDICAL CENTER-CLARE, CLARE, MI, p. A316
MIDMICHIGAN MEDICAL CENTER-GLADWIN, GLADWIN, MI, p. A320
MIDMICHIGAN MEDICAL CENTER-GRATIOT, ALMA, MI, p. A314
MIDMICHIGAN MEDICAL CENTER-MIDLAND, MIDLAND, MI, p. A325
MIDSTATE MEDICAL CENTER, MERIDEN, CT, p. A113
MIDTOWN MEDICAL CENTER WEST, COLUMBUS, GA, p. A154
MIDWEST MEDICAL CENTER, GALENA, IL, p. A188
MIDWEST ORTHOPEDIC SPECIALTY HOSPITAL, FRANKLIN, WI, p. A701
MIDWEST SURGICAL HOSPITAL, OMAHA, NE, p. A396
MIDWESTERN REGIONAL MEDICAL CENTER, ZION, IL, p. A203
MIKE O'CALLAGHAN FEDERAL HOSPITAL, NELLIS AFB, NV, p. A403
MILAN GENERAL HOSPITAL, MILAN, TN, p. A584
MILBANK AREA HOSPITAL AVERA, MILBANK, SD, p. A569

MILDRED MITCHELL-BATEMAN HOSPITAL, HUNTINGTON, WV, p. A692
MILE BLUFF MEDICAL CENTER, MAUSTON, WI, p. A705
MILFORD HOSPITAL, MILFORD, CT, p. A113
MILFORD REGIONAL MEDICAL CENTER, MILFORD, MA, p. A309
MILFORD VALLEY MEMORIAL HOSPITAL, MILFORD, UT, p. A655
MILLARD FILLMORE SUBURBAN HOSPITAL, WILLIAMSVILLE, NEW YORK (see KALEIDA HEALTH), p. A430
MILLCREEK COMMUNITY HOSPITAL, ERIE, PA, p. A534
MILLE LACS HEALTH SYSTEM, ONAMIA, MN, p. A344
MILLER CHILDREN'S & WOMEN'S HOSPITAL LONG BEACH, LONG BEACH, CA, p. A68
MILLER COUNTY HOSPITAL, COLQUITT, GA, p. A154
MILLINOCKET REGIONAL HOSPITAL, MILLINOCKET, ME, p. A291
MILLS HEALTH CENTER, SAN MATEO, CALIFORNIA (see MILLS-PENINSULA HEALTH SERVICES), p. A56
MILLS-PENINSULA HEALTH SERVICES, BURLINGAME, CA, p. A56
MILLS-PENINSULA MEDICAL CENTER, BURLINGAME, CALIFORNIA (see MILLS-PENINSULA HEALTH SERVICES), p. A56
MILLWOOD HOSPITAL, ARLINGTON, TX, p. A592
MILWAUKEE COUNTY BEHAVIORAL HEALTH DIVISION, MILWAUKEE, WI, p. A706
MIMBRES MEMORIAL HOSPITAL, DEMING, NM, p. A424
MINDEN MEDICAL CENTER, MINDEN, LA, p. A280
MINERAL COMMUNITY HOSPITAL, SUPERIOR, MT, p. A387
MINERS' COLFAX MEDICAL CENTER, RATON, NM, p. A425
MINERS' HOSPITAL OF NEW MEXICO, RATON, NEW MEXICO (see MINERS' COLFAX MEDICAL CENTER), p. A425
MINIDOKA MEMORIAL HOSPITAL, RUPERT, ID, p. A176
MINIMALLY INVASIVE SURGERY CENTER, LENEXA, KS, p. A245
MINISTRY DOOR COUNTY MEDICAL CENTER, STURGEON BAY, WI, p. A712
MINISTRY EAGLE RIVER MEMORIAL HOSPITAL, EAGLE RIVER, WI, p. A700
MINISTRY GOOD SAMARITAN HEALTH CENTER, MERRILL, WI, p. A706
MINISTRY OUR LADY OF VICTORY HOSPITAL, STANLEY, WI, p. A711
MINISTRY SACRED HEART HOSPITAL, TOMAHAWK, WI, p. A712
MINISTRY SAINT CLARE'S HOSPITAL, WESTON, WI, p. A714
MINISTRY SAINT JOSEPH'S HOSPITAL, MARSHFIELD, WI, p. A705
MINISTRY SAINT MARY'S HOSPITALS, RHINELANDER, WI, p. A710
MINISTRY SAINT MICHAEL'S HOSPITAL, STEVENS POINT, WI, p. A711
MINNEAPOLIS VETERANS AFFAIRS HEALTH CARE SYSTEM, MINNEAPOLIS, MN, p. A342
MINNEOLA DISTRICT HOSPITAL, MINNEOLA, KS, p. A246
MINNESOTA VALLEY HEALTH CENTER, LE SUEUR, MN, p. A341
MINNIE HAMILTON HEALTHCARE CENTER, GRANTSVILLE, WV, p. A691
MIRACLE MILE MEDICAL CENTER, LOS ANGELES, CA, p. A71
MIRIAM HOSPITAL, PROVIDENCE, RI, p. A555
MISSION CHILDREN'S HOSPITAL, ASHEVILLE, NORTH CAROLINA (see MISSION HOSPITAL), p. A455
MISSION COMMUNITY HOSPITAL,, CA, p. A71
MISSION HOSPITAL, MISSION VIEJO, CA, p. A75
MISSION HOSPITAL, ASHEVILLE, NC, p. A455
MISSION HOSPITAL LAGUNA BEACH, LAGUNA BEACH, CALIFORNIA (see MISSION HOSPITAL), p. A75
MISSION REGIONAL MEDICAL CENTER, MISSION, TX, p. A633
MISSION TRAIL BAPTIST HOSPITAL, SAN ANTONIO, TEXAS (see BAPTIST MEDICAL CENTER), p. A640
MISSISSIPPI BAPTIST MEDICAL CENTER, JACKSON, MS, p. A355
MISSISSIPPI HOSPITAL FOR RESTORATIVE CARE, JACKSON, MS, p. A355
MISSISSIPPI STATE HOSPITAL, WHITFIELD, MS, p. A361
MISSOURI BAPTIST MEDICAL CENTER, SAINT LOUIS, MO, p. A377
MISSOURI BAPTIST SULLIVAN HOSPITAL, SULLIVAN, MO, p. A379
MISSOURI DELTA MEDICAL CENTER, SIKESTON, MO, p. A378
MISSOURI RIVER MEDICAL CENTER, FORT BENTON, MT, p. A383
MITCHELL COUNTY HOSPITAL, CAMILLA, GA, p. A153
MITCHELL COUNTY HOSPITAL, COLORADO CITY, TX, p. A601
MITCHELL COUNTY HOSPITAL HEALTH SYSTEMS, BELOIT, KS, p. A238
MITCHELL COUNTY REGIONAL HEALTH CENTER, OSAGE, IA, p. A232
MIZELL MEMORIAL HOSPITAL, OPP, AL, p. A24
MMO GREENBRIER HOSPITAL, COVINGTON, LA, p. A272
MMO REHABILITATION AND WELLNESS CENTER, PLAQUEMINE, LA, p. A283
MMO WESTEND HOSPITAL, JENNINGS, LA, p. A276
MOAB REGIONAL HOSPITAL, MOAB, UT, p. A655

MOBERLY REGIONAL MEDICAL CENTER, MOBERLY, MO, p. A373
MOBILE INFIRMARY MEDICAL CENTER, MOBILE, AL, p. A22
MOBRIDGE REGIONAL HOSPITAL, MOBRIDGE, SD, p. A570
MOCCASIN BEND MENTAL HEALTH INSTITUTE, CHATTANOOGA, TN, p. A575
MODESTO MEDICAL CENTER, MODESTO, CALIFORNIA (see KAISER PERMANENTE MANTECA MEDICAL CENTER), p. A74
MODOC MEDICAL CENTER, ALTURAS, CA, p. A53
MOHAWK VALLEY PSYCHIATRIC CENTER, UTICA, NY, p. A452
MOLOKAI GENERAL HOSPITAL, KAUNAKAKAI, HI, p. A170
MONADNOCK COMMUNITY HOSPITAL, PETERBOROUGH, NH, p. A408
MONCKS CORNER MEDICAL CENTER, MONCKS CORNER, SOUTH CAROLINA (see TRIDENT MEDICAL CENTER), p. A558
MONCRIEF ARMY COMMUNITY HOSPITAL, FORT JACKSON, SC, p. A561
MONMOUTH MEDICAL CENTER, LONG BRANCH CAMPUS, LONG BRANCH, NJ, p. A413
MONMOUTH MEDICAL CENTER, SOUTHERN CAMPUS, LAKEWOOD, NJ, p. A413
MONONGAHELA VALLEY HOSPITAL, MONONGAHELA, PA, p. A540
MONONGALIA GENERAL HOSPITAL, MORGANTOWN, WV, p. A693
MONROE CARELL JR. CHILDREN'S HOSPITAL AT VANDERBILT, NASHVILLE, TENNESSEE (see VANDERBILT HOSPITAL AND CLINICS), p. A586
MONROE CLINIC, MONROE, WI, p. A707
MONROE COUNTY HOSPITAL, MONROEVILLE, AL, p. A22
MONROE COUNTY HOSPITAL, FORSYTH, GA, p. A157
MONROE COUNTY HOSPITAL AND CLINICS, ALBIA, IA, p. A222
MONROE COUNTY MEDICAL CENTER, TOMPKINSVILLE, KY, p. A266
MONROE HOSPITAL, BLOOMFIELD, IN, p. A205
MONROE SURGICAL HOSPITAL, MONROE, LA, p. A280
MONROVIA MEMORIAL HOSPITAL, MONROVIA, CA, p. A76
MONTANA STATE HOSPITAL, WARM SPRINGS, MT, p. A387
MONTCLAIR HOSPITAL MEDICAL CENTER, MONTCLAIR, CA, p. A76
MONTEFIORE MEDICAL CENTER,, NY, p. A442
MONTEFIORE MEDICAL CENTER – NORTH DIVISION,, NEW YORK (see MONTEFIORE MEDICAL CENTER), p. A442
MONTEFIORE MOUNT VERNON, MOUNT VERNON, NY, p. A438
MONTEFIORE NEW ROCHELLE, NEW ROCHELLE, NY, p. A438
MONTEREY PARK HOSPITAL, MONTEREY PARK, CA, p. A76
MONTEVISTA HOSPITAL, LAS VEGAS, NV, p. A402
MONTGOMERY COUNTY EMERGENCY SERVICE, NORRISTOWN, PA, p. A541
MONTGOMERY COUNTY MEMORIAL HOSPITAL, RED OAK, IA, p. A233
MONTGOMERY DIVISION, MONTGOMERY, ALABAMA (see CENTRAL ALABAMA VETERANS HEALTH CARE SYSTEM), p. A23
MONTGOMERY GENERAL HOSPITAL, MONTGOMERY, WV, p. A693
MONTPELIER HOSPITAL, MONTPELIER, OHIO (see COMMUNITY HOSPITALS AND WELLNESS CENTERS), p. A480
MONTROSE MEMORIAL HOSPITAL, MONTROSE, CO, p. A107
MOORE COUNTY HOSPITAL DISTRICT, DUMAS, TX, p. A609
MOORE MEDICAL CENTER, MOORE, OKLAHOMA (see NORMAN REGIONAL HEALTH SYSTEM), p. A510
MOREHEAD MEMORIAL HOSPITAL, EDEN, NC, p. A459
MOREHOUSE GENERAL HOSPITAL, BASTROP, LA, p. A269
MORGAN COUNTY ARH HOSPITAL, WEST LIBERTY, KY, p. A266
MORGAN MEMORIAL HOSPITAL, MADISON, GA, p. A161
MORGAN STANLEY CHILDREN'S HOSPITAL OF NEW YORK-PRESBYTERIAN, NEW YORK, NEW YORK (see NEW YORK-PRESBYTERIAN HOSPITAL), p. A443
MORRILL COUNTY COMMUNITY HOSPITAL, BRIDGEPORT, NE, p. A390
MORRIS COUNTY HOSPITAL, COUNCIL GROVE, KS, p. A239
MORRIS HOSPITAL & HEALTHCARE CENTERS, MORRIS, IL, p. A195
MORRISON COMMUNITY HOSPITAL, MORRISON, IL, p. A195
MORRISTOWN MEDICAL CENTER, MORRISTOWN, NJ, p. A414
MORRISTOWN-HAMBLEN HEALTHCARE SYSTEM, MORRISTOWN, TN, p. A584
MORROW COUNTY HOSPITAL, MOUNT GILEAD, OH, p. A495
MORTON COUNTY HEALTH SYSTEM, ELKHART, KS, p. A239
MORTON GENERAL HOSPITAL, MORTON, WA, p. A680
MORTON HOSPITAL AND MEDICAL CENTER, TAUNTON, MA, p. A312
MORTON PLANT HOSPITAL, CLEARWATER, FL, p. A123
MORTON PLANT NORTH BAY HOSPITAL, NEW PORT RICHEY, FL, p. A136
MOSAIC LIFE CARE AT ST. JOSEPH, SAINT JOSEPH, MO, p. A375
MOSES H. CONE MEMORIAL HOSPITAL, GREENSBORO, NC, p. A461

MOSES H. CONE MEMORIAL HOSPITAL, GREENSBORO, NORTH CAROLINA (see MOSES H. CONE MEMORIAL HOSPITAL), p.A461
MOSES LUDINGTON HOSPITAL, TICONDEROGA, NY, p. A452
MOSES TAYLOR HOSPITAL, SCRANTON, PA, p. A549
MOTHER FRANCES HOSPITAL – JACKSONVILLE, JACKSONVILLE, TX, p. A624
MOTHER FRANCES HOSPITAL – TYLER, TYLER, TX, p. A649
MOTHER FRANCES HOSPITAL – WINNSBORO, WINNSBORO, TX, p. A652
MOTION PICTURE AND TELEVISION FUND HOSPITAL AND RESIDENTIAL SERVICES,, CA, p. A71
MOUNDVIEW MEMORIAL HOSPITAL & CLINICS, FRIENDSHIP, WI, p. A701
MOUNT AUBURN HOSPITAL, CAMBRIDGE, MA, p. A305
MOUNT CARMEL, COLUMBUS, OH, p. A486
MOUNT CARMEL EAST HOSPITAL, COLUMBUS, OHIO (see MOUNT CARMEL), p. A486
MOUNT CARMEL NEW ALBANY SURGICAL HOSPITAL, NEW ALBANY, OH, p. A495
MOUNT CARMEL ST. ANN'S, WESTERVILLE, OH, p. A500
MOUNT CARMEL WEST HOSPITAL, COLUMBUS, OHIO (see MOUNT CARMEL), p. A486
MOUNT DESERT ISLAND HOSPITAL, BAR HARBOR, ME, p. A288
MOUNT GRANT GENERAL HOSPITAL, HAWTHORNE, NV, p. A401
MOUNT NITTANY MEDICAL CENTER, STATE COLLEGE, PA, p. A550
MOUNT SINAI BETH ISRAEL, NEW YORK, NY, p. A442
MOUNT SINAI BETH ISRAEL BROOKLYN,, NEW YORK (see MOUNT SINAI BETH ISRAEL), p. A442
MOUNT SINAI HOSPITAL, CHICAGO, IL, p. A183
MOUNT SINAI HOSPITAL, NEW YORK, NY, p. A442
MOUNT SINAI MEDICAL CENTER, MIAMI BEACH, FL, p. A135
MOUNT SINAI QUEENS,, NEW YORK (see MOUNT SINAI HOSPITAL), p. A442
MOUNT SINAI REHABILITATION HOSPITAL, HARTFORD, CT, p. A112
MOUNT SINAI ROOSEVELT HOSPITAL, NEW YORK, NEW YORK (see MOUNT SINAI ST. LUKE'S – ROOSEVELT), p. A442
MOUNT SINAI ST. LUKE'S – ROOSEVELT, NEW YORK, NY, p. A442
MOUNT ST. MARY'S HOSPITAL AND HEALTH CENTER, LEWISTON, NY, p. A436
MOUNTAIN CREST HOSPITAL, FORT COLLINS, COLORADO (see POUDRE VALLEY HOSPITAL), p. A103
MOUNTAIN LAKES MEDICAL CENTER, CLAYTON, GA, p. A154
MOUNTAIN POINT MEDICAL CENTER, LEHII, UTAH (see JORDAN VALLEY MEDICAL CENTER), p. A659
MOUNTAIN RIVER BIRTHING AND SURGERY CENTER, BLACKFOOT, ID, p. A172
MOUNTAIN VALLEY REGIONAL REHABILITATION HOSPITAL, PRESCOTT VALLEY, AZ, p. A36
MOUNTAIN VIEW HOSPITAL, GADSDEN, AL, p. A20
MOUNTAIN VIEW HOSPITAL, IDAHO FALLS, ID, p. A174
MOUNTAIN VIEW HOSPITAL, PAYSON, UT, p. A657
MOUNTAIN VIEW REGIONAL HOSPITAL, CASPER, WY, p. A715
MOUNTAIN VIEW REGIONAL MEDICAL CENTER, NORTON, VA, p. A670
MOUNTAIN VISTA MEDICAL CENTER, MESA, AZ, p. A33
MOUNTAIN WEST MEDICAL CENTER, TOOELE, UT, p. A659
MOUNTAINVIEW HOSPITAL, LAS VEGAS, NV, p. A402
MOUNTAINVIEW MEDICAL CENTER, WHITE SULPHUR SPRINGS, MT, p. A387
MOUNTAINVIEW REGIONAL MEDICAL CENTER, LAS CRUCES, NM, p. A425
MOUNTRAIL COUNTY MEDICAL CENTER, STANLEY, ND, p. A476
MT. ASCUTNEY HOSPITAL AND HEALTH CENTER, WINDSOR, VT, p. A661
MT. GRAHAM REGIONAL MEDICAL CENTER, SAFFORD, AZ, p. A37
MT. SAN RAFAEL HOSPITAL, TRINIDAD, CO, p. A109
MT. WASHINGTON PEDIATRIC HOSPITAL, BALTIMORE, MD, p. A294
MUENSTER MEMORIAL HOSPITAL, MUENSTER, TX, p. A633
MULESHOE AREA MEDICAL CENTER, MULESHOE, TX, p. A633
MULTICARE AUBURN MEDICAL CENTER, AUBURN, WA, p. A676
MULTICARE GOOD SAMARITAN HOSPITAL, PUYALLUP, WA, p. A682
MULTICARE MARY BRIDGE CHILDREN'S HOSPITAL AND HEALTH CENTER, TACOMA, WA, p. A686
MULTICARE TACOMA GENERAL HOSPITAL, TACOMA, WA, p. A686
MUNCY VALLEY HOSPITAL, MUNCY, PA, p. A541
MUNISING MEMORIAL HOSPITAL, MUNISING, MI, p. A326
MUNROE REGIONAL MEDICAL CENTER, OCALA, FL, p. A137
MUNSON HEALTHCARE CADILLAC HOSPITAL, CADILLAC, MI, p. A315
MUNSON HEALTHCARE GRAYLING HOSPITAL, GRAYLING, MI, p. A321

MUNSON MEDICAL CENTER, TRAVERSE CITY, MI, p. A331
MURPHY MEDICAL CENTER, MURPHY, NC, p. A465
MURRAY COUNTY MEDICAL CENTER, SLAYTON, MN, p. A347
MURRAY MEDICAL CENTER, CHATSWORTH, GA, p. A153
MURRAY–CALLOWAY COUNTY HOSPITAL, MURRAY, KY, p. A264
MUSC MEDICAL CENTER OF MEDICAL UNIVERSITY OF SOUTH CAROLINA, CHARLESTON, SC, p. A558
MUSCOGEE CREEK NATION MEDICAL CENTER, OKMULGEE, OK, p. A513
MUSCOGEE CREEK NATION PHYSICAL REHABILITATION CENTER, OKMULGEE, OK, p. A513
MYRTUE MEDICAL CENTER, HARLAN, IA, p. A229

# N

NACOGDOCHES MEDICAL CENTER, NACOGDOCHES, TX, p. A633
NACOGDOCHES MEMORIAL HOSPITAL, NACOGDOCHES, TX, p. A633
NANTICOKE MEMORIAL HOSPITAL, SEAFORD, DE, p. A117
NANTUCKET COTTAGE HOSPITAL, NANTUCKET, MA, p. A309
NAPA STATE HOSPITAL, NAPA, CA, p. A77
NASH HEALTH CARE SYSTEMS, ROCKY MOUNT, NC, p. A467
NASHOBA VALLEY MEDICAL CENTER, AYER, MA, p. A302
NASHVILLE CAMPUS, NASHVILLE, TENNESSEE (see TENNESSEE VALLEY HEALTHCARE SYSTEM), p.A586
NASHVILLE GENERAL HOSPITAL, NASHVILLE, TN, p.A585
NASON HOSPITAL, ROARING SPRING, PA, p. A549
NASSAU UNIVERSITY MEDICAL CENTER, EAST MEADOW, NY, p. A433
NATCHAUG HOSPITAL, MANSFIELD CENTER, CT, p. A113
NATCHEZ COMMUNITY HOSPITAL, NATCHEZ, MS, p. A358
NATCHITOCHES REGIONAL MEDICAL CENTER, NATCHITOCHES, LA, p. A281
NATHAN LITTAUER HOSPITAL AND NURSING HOME, GLOVERSVILLE, NY, p. A434
NATIONAL INSTITUTES OF HEALTH CLINICAL CENTER, BETHESDA, MD, p. A296
NATIONAL JEWISH HEALTH, DENVER, CO, p. A102
NATIONAL PARK MEDICAL CENTER, HOT SPRINGS, AR, p. A45
NATIONWIDE CHILDREN'S HOSPITAL, COLUMBUS, OH, p. A486
NATIVIDAD MEDICAL CENTER, SALINAS, CA, p. A85
NAVAL HOSPITAL BEAUFORT, BEAUFORT, SC, p. A557
NAVAL HOSPITAL BREMERTON, BREMERTON, WA, p. A676
NAVAL HOSPITAL CAMP LEJEUNE, CAMP LEJEUNE, NC, p. A456
NAVAL HOSPITAL CAMP PENDLETON, CAMP PENDLETON, CA, p. A57
NAVAL HOSPITAL JACKSONVILLE, JACKSONVILLE, FL, p. A129
NAVAL HOSPITAL LEMOORE, PORTSMITH, VA, p. A670
NAVAL HOSPITAL OAK HARBOR, OAK HARBOR, WA, p. A681
NAVAL HOSPITAL PENSACOLA, PENSACOLA, FL, p. A139
NAVAL MEDICAL CENTER, PORTSMOUTH, VA, p. A670
NAVAL MEDICAL CENTER SAN DIEGO, SAN DIEGO, CA, p. A86
NAVARRO REGIONAL HOSPITAL, CORSICANA, TX, p. A603
NAVOS, SEATTLE, WA, p. A683
NAZARETH HOSPITAL, PHILADELPHIA, PA, p. A544
NCH DOWNTOWN NAPLES HOSPITAL, NAPLES, FL, p. A136
NCH NORTH NAPLES HOSPITAL, NAPLES, FLORIDA (see NCH DOWNTOWN NAPLES HOSPITAL), p. A136
NEA BAPTIST MEMORIAL HOSPITAL, JONESBORO, AR, p. A46
NEBRASKA MEDICINE – BELLEVUE, BELLEVUE, NE, p. A390
NEBRASKA MEDICINE – NEBRASKA MEDICAL CENTER, OMAHA, NE, p. A396
NEBRASKA METHODIST HOSPITAL, OMAHA, NE, p. A396
NEBRASKA ORTHOPAEDIC HOSPITAL, OMAHA, NE, p. A396
NEBRASKA PENAL AND CORRECTIONAL HOSPITAL, LINCOLN, NE, p. A394
NEBRASKA SPINE HOSPITAL, OMAHA, NE, p. A396
NEILLSVILLE MEMORIAL HOME (see MEMORIAL MEDICAL CENTER – NEILLSVILLE), p. A707
NELL J. REDFIELD MEMORIAL HOSPITAL, MALAD CITY, ID, p. A174
NELSON COUNTY HEALTH SYSTEM, MCVILLE, ND, p. A476
NEMAHA COUNTY HOSPITAL, AUBURN, NE, p. A389
NEMAHA VALLEY COMMUNITY HOSPITAL, SENECA, KS, p. A250
NEMOURS CHILDREN'S HOSPITAL, ORLANDO, FL, p. A138
NEOSHO MEMORIAL REGIONAL MEDICAL CENTER, CHANUTE, KS, p. A238
NESHOBA COUNTY GENERAL HOSPITAL, PHILADELPHIA, MS, p. A359
NESS COUNTY HOSPITAL, NESS CITY, KS, p. A246
NEVADA REGIONAL MEDICAL CENTER, NEVADA, MO, p. A373
NEW BEDFORD REHABILITATION HOSPITAL, NEW BEDFORD, MA, p. A309
NEW BRAUNFELS REGIONAL REHABILITATION HOSPITAL, NEW BRAUNFELS, TX, p. A634

NEW BRITAIN GENERAL, NEW BRITAIN, CONNECTICUT (see THE HOSPITAL OF CENTRAL CONNECTICUT), p. A113
NEW ENGLAND BAPTIST HOSPITAL, BOSTON, MA, p. A304
NEW ENGLAND REHABILITATION HOSPITAL, WOBURN, MA, p. A313
NEW ENGLAND REHABILITATION HOSPITAL OF PORTLAND, PORTLAND, ME, p. A292
NEW ENGLAND SINAI HOSPITAL AND REHABILITATION CENTER, STOUGHTON, MA, p. A312
NEW HAMPSHIRE HOSPITAL, CONCORD, NH, p. A405
NEW HANOVER REGIONAL MEDICAL CENTER, WILMINGTON, NC, p. A470
NEW HORIZONS HEALTH SYSTEMS, OWENTON, KY, p. A264
NEW LONDON FAMILY MEDICAL CENTER, NEW LONDON, WI, p. A707
NEW LONDON HOSPITAL, NEW LONDON, NH, p. A408
NEW MEXICO BEHAVIORAL HEALTH INSTITUTE AT LAS VEGAS, LAS VEGAS, NM, p. A425
NEW MEXICO REHABILITATION CENTER, ROSWELL, NM, p. A426
NEW MEXICO VETERANS AFFAIRS HEALTH CARE SYSTEM – RAYMOND G. MURPHY MEDICAL CENTER, ALBUQUERQUE, NM, p. A422
NEW MILFORD HOSPITAL, NEW MILFORD, CONNECTICUT (see DANBURY HOSPITAL), p. A111
NEW ORLEANS EAST HOSPITAL, NEW ORLEANS, LA, p. A282
NEW ULM MEDICAL CENTER, NEW ULM, MN, p. A344
NEW YORK CITY CHILDREN'S CENTER,, NY, p. A442
NEW YORK COMMUNITY HOSPITAL,, NY, p. A442
NEW YORK EYE AND EAR INFIRMARY OF MOUNT SINAI, NEW YORK, NY, p. A442
NEW YORK METHODIST HOSPITAL,, NY, p. A443
NEW YORK PRESBYTERIAN LOWER MANHATTAN HOSPITAL, NEW YORK, NEW YORK (see NEW YORK–PRESBYTERIAN HOSPITAL), p. A443
NEW YORK STATE PSYCHIATRIC INSTITUTE, NEW YORK, NY, p. A443
NEW YORK–PRESBYTERIAN HOSPITAL, NEW YORK, NY, p. A443
NEW YORK–PRESBYTERIAN HOSPITAL, WESTCHESTER DIVISION, WHITE PLAINS, NEW YORK (see NEW YORK–PRESBYTERIAN HOSPITAL), p. A443
NEW YORK–PRESBYTERIAN HOSPITAL/WEILL CORNELL MEDICAL CENTER, NEW YORK, NEW YORK (see NEW YORK–PRESBYTERIAN HOSPITAL), p. A443
NEW YORK–PRESBYTERIAN/COLUMBIA UNIVERSITY MEDICAL CENTER, NEW YORK, NEW YORK (see NEW YORK–PRESBYTERIAN HOSPITAL), p. A443
NEW YORK–PRESBYTERIAN/HUDSON VALLEY HOSPITAL, CORTLANDT MANOR, NY, p. A432
NEW YORK–PRESBYTERIAN/LAWRENCE HOSPITAL, BRONXVILLE, NY, p. A430
NEW YORK–PRESBYTERIAN/QUEENS,, NY, p. A443
NEWARK BETH ISRAEL MEDICAL CENTER, NEWARK, NJ, p. A415
NEWARK–WAYNE COMMUNITY HOSPITAL, NEWARK, NY, p. A445
NEWBERRY COUNTY MEMORIAL HOSPITAL, NEWBERRY, SC, p. A564
NEWMAN MEMORIAL HOSPITAL, SHATTUCK, OK, p. A514
NEWMAN REGIONAL HEALTH, EMPORIA, KS, p. A239
NEWPORT BAY HOSPITAL, NEWPORT BEACH, CA, p. A78
NEWPORT HOSPITAL, NEWPORT, RI, p. A555
NEWPORT HOSPITAL AND HEALTH SERVICES, NEWPORT, WA, p. A681
NEWPORT SPECIALTY HOSPITAL, TUSTIN, CA, p. A95
NEWTON MEDICAL CENTER, COVINGTON, GA, p. A155
NEWTON MEDICAL CENTER, NEWTON, KS, p. A246
NEWTON MEDICAL CENTER, NEWTON, NJ, p. A416
NEWTON–WELLESLEY HOSPITAL, NEWTON LOWER FALLS, MA, p. A309
NEXUS SPECIALTY HOSPITAL, SHENANDOAH, TX, p. A643
NEXUS SPECIALTY HOSPITAL THE WOODLANDS, SPRING, TX, p. A644
NIAGARA FALLS MEMORIAL MEDICAL CENTER, NIAGARA FALLS, NY, p. A445
NICHOLAS H. NOYES MEMORIAL HOSPITAL, DANSVILLE, NY, p. A432
NICKLAUS CHILDREN'S HOSPITAL, MIAMI, FL, p. A134
NIOBRARA HEALTH AND LIFE CENTER, LUSK, WY, p. A716
NIOBRARA VALLEY HOSPITAL, LYNCH, NE, p. A394
NISWONGER CHILDREN'S HOSPITAL, JOHNSON CITY, TENNESSEE (see JOHNSON CITY MEDICAL CENTER), p. A580
NIX COMMUNITY GENERAL HOSPITAL, DILLEY, TX, p. A609
NIX HEALTH CARE SYSTEM, SAN ANTONIO, TX, p. A641
NOCONA GENERAL HOSPITAL, NOCONA, TX, p. A634
NOLAND HOSPITAL ANNISTON, ANNISTON, AL, p. A15
NOLAND HOSPITAL BIRMINGHAM, BIRMINGHAM, AL, p. A16
NOLAND HOSPITAL DOTHAN, DOTHAN, AL, p. A19
NOLAND HOSPITAL MONTGOMERY, MONTGOMERY, AL, p. A23

NOLAND HOSPITAL SHELBY, ALABASTER, AL, p. A15
NOLAND HOSPITAL TUSCALOOSA, TUSCALOOSA, AL, p. A25
NOR–LEA GENERAL HOSPITAL, LOVINGTON, NM, p. A425
NORMAN REGIONAL HEALTH SYSTEM, NORMAN, OK, p. A510
NORMAN REGIONAL HOSPITAL, NORMAN, OKLAHOMA (see NORMAN REGIONAL HEALTH SYSTEM), p. A510
NORMAN SPECIALTY HOSPITAL, NORMAN, OK, p. A510
NORRISTOWN STATE HOSPITAL, NORRISTOWN, PA, p. A542
NORTH ARKANSAS REGIONAL MEDICAL CENTER, HARRISON, AR, p. A45
NORTH BALDWIN INFIRMARY, BAY MINETTE, AL, p. A16
NORTH BIG HORN HOSPITAL DISTRICT, LOVELL, WY, p. A716
NORTH CADDO MEDICAL CENTER, VIVIAN, LA, p. A286
NORTH CANYON MEDICAL CENTER, GOODING, ID, p. A174
NORTH CAROLINA CHILDREN'S AND WOMEN'S HOSPITAL, N.C. WOMEN'S HOSPITAL, CHAPEL HILL, NORTH CAROLINA (see UNIVERSITY OF NORTH CAROLINA HOSPITALS), p. A457
NORTH CAROLINA CHILDREN'S HOSPITAL, CHAPEL HILL, NORTH CAROLINA (see UNIVERSITY OF NORTH CAROLINA HOSPITALS), p. A457
NORTH CAROLINA NEUROSCIENCES HOSPITAL, CHAPEL HILL, NORTH CAROLINA (see UNIVERSITY OF NORTH CAROLINA HOSPITALS), p. A457
UNC LINEBERGER COMPREHENSIVE CANCER CENTER, CHAPEL HILL, NORTH CAROLINA (see UNIVERSITY OF NORTH CAROLINA HOSPITALS), p. A457
NORTH CAROLINA SPECIALTY HOSPITAL, DURHAM, NC, p. A459
NORTH CENTRAL BAPTIST HOSPITAL, SAN ANTONIO, TEXAS (see BAPTIST MEDICAL CENTER), p. A640
NORTH CENTRAL BRONX HOSPITAL,, NY, p. A443
NORTH CENTRAL HEALTH CARE, WAUSAU, WI, p. A713
NORTH CENTRAL SURGICAL CENTER, DALLAS, TX, p. A606
NORTH COLORADO MEDICAL CENTER, GREELEY, CO, p. A104
NORTH COUNTRY HOSPITAL AND HEALTH CENTER, NEWPORT, VT, p. A660
NORTH CYPRESS MEDICAL CENTER, CYPRESS, TX, p. A603
NORTH DAKOTA STATE HOSPITAL, JAMESTOWN, ND, p. A475
NORTH FLORIDA REGIONAL MEDICAL CENTER, GAINESVILLE, FL, p. A127
NORTH FLORIDA/SOUTH GEORGIA VETERAN'S HEALTH SYSTEM, GAINESVILLE, FL, p. A127
NORTH FULTON REGIONAL HOSPITAL, ROSWELL, GA, p. A163
NORTH GEORGIA MEDICAL CENTER, ELLIJAY, GA, p. A157
NORTH GREENVILLE HOSPITAL, TRAVELERS REST, SC, p. A565
NORTH HAWAII COMMUNITY HOSPITAL, KAMUELA, HI, p. A169
NORTH HILLS HOSPITAL, NORTH RICHLAND HILLS, TX, p. A634
NORTH KANSAS CITY HOSPITAL, NORTH KANSAS CITY, MO, p. A373
NORTH LITTLE ROCK DIVISION, NORTH LITTLE ROCK, ARKANSAS (see CENTRAL ARKANSAS VETERANS HEALTHCARE SYSTEM), p. A47
NORTH MEMORIAL MEDICAL CENTER, ROBBINSDALE, MN, p. A345
NORTH METRO MEDICAL CENTER, JACKSONVILLE, AR, p. A46
NORTH MISSISSIPPI MEDICAL CENTER – TUPELO, TUPELO, MS, p. A360
NORTH MISSISSIPPI MEDICAL CENTER–EUPORA, EUPORA, MS, p. A352
NORTH MISSISSIPPI MEDICAL CENTER–PONTOTOC, PONTOTOC, MS, p. A359
NORTH MISSISSIPPI MEDICAL CENTER–WEST POINT, WEST POINT, MS, p. A361
NORTH MISSISSIPPI STATE HOSPITAL, TUPELO, MS, p. A361
NORTH OAK REGIONAL MEDICAL CENTER, SENATOBIA, MS, p. A360
NORTH OAKS MEDICAL CENTER, HAMMOND, LA, p. A274
NORTH OAKS REHABILITATION HOSPITAL, HAMMOND, LA, p. A274
NORTH OKALOOSA MEDICAL CENTER, CRESTVIEW, FL, p. A124
NORTH OTTAWA COMMUNITY HOSPITAL, GRAND HAVEN, MI, p. A320
NORTH PHILADELPHIA HEALTH SYSTEM, PHILADELPHIA, PA, p. A544
NORTH RUNNELS HOSPITAL, WINTERS, TX, p. A652
NORTH SHORE MEDICAL CENTER, MIAMI, FL, p. A134
NORTH SHORE MEDICAL CENTER, SALEM, MA, p. A310
NORTH SHORE UNIVERSITY HOSPITAL, MANHASSET, NY, p. A437
NORTH STAR BEHAVIORAL HEALTH, ANCHORAGE, ALASKA (see NORTH STAR BEHAVIORAL HEALTH SYSTEM), p. A27
NORTH STAR BEHAVIORAL HEALTH SYSTEM, ANCHORAGE, AK, p. A27
NORTH SUBURBAN MEDICAL CENTER, THORNTON, CO, p. A109
NORTH SUNFLOWER MEDICAL CENTER, RULEVILLE, MS, p. A360
NORTH TAMPA BEHAVIORAL HEALTH, WESLEY CHAPEL, FL, p. A147
NORTH TEXAS MEDICAL CENTER, GAINESVILLE, TX, p. A615

NORTH TEXAS STATE HOSPITAL, VERNON, TX, p. A649
NORTH TEXAS STATE HOSPITAL, WICHITA FALLS CAMPUS, WICHITA FALLS, TX, p. A652
NORTH VALLEY HEALTH CENTER, WARREN, MN, p. A348
NORTH VALLEY HOSPITAL, WHITEFISH, MT, p. A388
NORTH VALLEY HOSPITAL, TONASKET, WA, p. A686
NORTH VISTA HOSPITAL, NORTH LAS VEGAS, NV, p. A403
NORTHBAY MEDICAL CENTER, FAIRFIELD, CA, p. A61
NORTHBAY VACAVALLEY HOSPITAL, VACAVILLE, CALIFORNIA (see NORTHBAY MEDICAL CENTER), p. A61
NORTHCOAST BEHAVIORAL HEALTHCARE SYSTEM, NORTHFIELD, OH, p. A495
NORTHCREST MEDICAL CENTER, SPRINGFIELD, TN, p. A588
NORTHEAST ALABAMA REGIONAL MEDICAL CENTER, ANNISTON, AL, p. A15
NORTHEAST BAPTIST HOSPITAL, SAN ANTONIO, TEXAS (see BAPTIST MEDICAL CENTER), p. A640
NORTHEAST GEORGIA MEDICAL CENTER, GAINESVILLE, GA, p. A158
NORTHEAST GEORGIA MEDICAL CENTER BRASELTON, BRASELTON, GA, p. A152
NORTHEAST METHODIST HOSPITAL, LIVE OAK, TEXAS (see METHODIST HOSPITAL), p. A641
NORTHEAST REGIONAL MEDICAL CENTER, KIRKSVILLE, MO, p. A371
NORTHEAST REHABILITATION HOSPITAL, SALEM, NH, p. A408
NORTHEASTERN CENTER, AUBURN, IN, p. A204
NORTHEASTERN HEALTH SYSTEM, TAHLEQUAH, OK, p. A515
NORTHEASTERN NEVADA REGIONAL HOSPITAL, ELKO, NV, p. A400
NORTHEASTERN VERMONT REGIONAL HOSPITAL, SAINT JOHNSBURY, VT, p. A661
NORTHERN ARIZONA VETERANS AFFAIRS HEALTH CARE SYSTEM, PRESCOTT, AZ, p. A36
NORTHERN COCHISE COMMUNITY HOSPITAL, WILLCOX, AZ, p. A40
NORTHERN COLORADO LONG TERM ACUTE HOSPITAL, JOHNSTOWN, CO, p. A105
NORTHERN COLORADO REHABILITATION HOSPITAL, JOHNSTOWN, CO, p. A105
NORTHERN DUTCHESS HOSPITAL, RHINEBECK, NY, p. A448
NORTHERN HOSPITAL OF SURRY COUNTY, MOUNT AIRY, NC, p. A465
NORTHERN IDAHO ADVANCED CARE HOSPITAL, POST FALLS, ID, p. A176
NORTHERN INYO HOSPITAL, BISHOP, CA, p. A56
NORTHERN LOUISIANA MEDICAL CENTER, RUSTON, LA, p. A284
NORTHERN MAINE MEDICAL CENTER, FORT KENT, ME, p. A290
NORTHERN MONTANA HOSPITAL, HAVRE, MT, p. A384
NORTHERN NAVAJO MEDICAL CENTER, SHIPROCK, NM, p. A426
NORTHERN NEVADA ADULT MENTAL HEALTH SERVICES, SPARKS, NV, p. A404
NORTHERN NEVADA MEDICAL CENTER, SPARKS, NV, p. A404
NORTHERN ROCKIES MEDICAL CENTER, CUT BANK, MT, p. A382
NORTHERN VIRGINIA MENTAL HEALTH INSTITUTE, FALLS CHURCH, VA, p. A664
NORTHERN WESTCHESTER HOSPITAL, MOUNT KISCO, NY, p. A438
NORTHFIELD CAMPUS, NORTHFIELD, OHIO (see NORTHCOAST BEHAVIORAL HEALTHCARE SYSTEM), p. A495
NORTHFIELD HOSPITAL, NORTHFIELD, MN, p. A344
NORTHKEY COMMUNITY CARE, COVINGTON, KY, p. A255
NORTHLAKE BEHAVIORAL HOSPITAL, MANDEVILLE, LA, p. A279
NORTHPORT MEDICAL CENTER, NORTHPORT, AL, p. A23
NORTHPORT VETERANS AFFAIRS MEDICAL CENTER, NORTHPORT, NY, p. A445
NORTHRIDGE HOSPITAL MEDICAL CENTER,, CA, p. A71
NORTHRIDGE MEDICAL CENTER, COMMERCE, GA, p. A154
NORTHSHORE EVANSTON HOSPITAL, EVANSTON, ILLINOIS (see NORTHSHORE UNIVERSITY HEALTH SYSTEM), p. A187
NORTHSHORE GLENBROOK HOSPITAL, GLENVIEW, ILLINOIS (see NORTHSHORE UNIVERSITY HEALTH SYSTEM), p. A187
NORTHSHORE HIGHLAND PARK HOSPITAL, HIGHLAND PARK, ILLINOIS (see NORTHSHORE UNIVERSITY HEALTH SYSTEM), p. A187
NORTHSHORE SKOKIE HOSPITAL, SKOKIE, ILLINOIS (see NORTHSHORE UNIVERSITY HEALTH SYSTEM), p. A187
NORTHSHORE UNIVERSITY HEALTH SYSTEM, EVANSTON, IL, p. A187
NORTHSIDE HOSPITAL, SAINT PETERSBURG, FL, p. A142
NORTHSIDE HOSPITAL, ATLANTA, GA, p. A150
NORTHSIDE HOSPITAL–CHEROKEE, CANTON, GA, p. A153
NORTHSIDE HOSPITAL–FORSYTH, CUMMING, GA, p. A155
NORTHSIDE MEDICAL CENTER, COLUMBUS, GA, p. A154
NORTHSIDE MEDICAL CENTER, YOUNGSTOWN, OH, p. A501
NORTHSIDE MEDICAL CENTER, YOUNGSTOWN, OHIO (see NORTHSIDE MEDICAL CENTER), p. A501

NORTHWEST CENTER FOR BEHAVIORAL HEALTH, FORT SUPPLY, OK, p. A507
NORTHWEST CHILDREN'S HOSPITAL, AMARILLO, TEXAS (see NORTHWEST TEXAS HEALTHCARE SYSTEM), p. A591
NORTHWEST COMMUNITY HOSPITAL, ARLINGTON HEIGHTS, IL, p. A178
NORTHWEST FLORIDA COMMUNITY HOSPITAL, CHIPLEY, FL, p. A123
NORTHWEST HILLS SURGICAL HOSPITAL, AUSTIN, TX, p. A594
NORTHWEST HOSPITAL, RANDALLSTOWN, MD, p. A299
NORTHWEST MEDICAL CENTER, WINFIELD, AL, p. A26
NORTHWEST MEDICAL CENTER, TUCSON, AZ, p. A39
NORTHWEST MEDICAL CENTER, MARGATE, FL, p. A133
NORTHWEST MEDICAL CENTER, ALBANY, MO, p. A363
NORTHWEST MEDICAL CENTER – BENTONVILLE, BENTONVILLE, ARKANSAS (see NORTHWEST MEDICAL CENTER – SPRINGDALE), p. A51
NORTHWEST MEDICAL CENTER – SPRINGDALE, SPRINGDALE, AR, p. A51
NORTHWEST MISSOURI PSYCHIATRIC REHABILITATION CENTER, SAINT JOSEPH, MO, p. A375
NORTHWEST OHIO PSYCHIATRIC HOSPITAL, TOLEDO, OH, p. A498
NORTHWEST PAVILION, AMARILLO, TEXAS (see NORTHWEST TEXAS HEALTHCARE SYSTEM), p. A591
NORTHWEST SPECIALTY HOSPITAL, POST FALLS, ID, p. A176
NORTHWEST SURGICAL HOSPITAL, OKLAHOMA CITY, OK, p. A512
NORTHWEST TEXAS HEALTHCARE SYSTEM, AMARILLO, TX, p. A591
NORTHWEST TEXAS SURGERY CENTER, AMARILLO, TX, p. A591
NORTHWESTERN LAKE FOREST HOSPITAL, LAKE FOREST, IL, p. A192
NORTHWESTERN MEDICAL CENTER, SAINT ALBANS, VT, p. A661
NORTHWESTERN MEDICINE CENTRAL DUPAGE HOSPITAL, WINFIELD, IL, p. A203
NORTHWESTERN MEDICINE DELNOR HOSPITAL, GENEVA, IL, p. A189
NORTHWESTERN MEMORIAL HOSPITAL, CHICAGO, IL, p. A183
NORTHWOOD DEACONESS HEALTH CENTER, NORTHWOOD, ND, p. A476
NORTON AUDUBON HOSPITAL, LOUISVILLE, KY, p. A261
NORTON BROWNSBORO HOSPITAL, LOUISVILLE, KY, p. A261
NORTON COMMUNITY HOSPITAL, NORTON, VA, p. A670
NORTON COUNTY HOSPITAL, NORTON, KS, p. A247
NORTON HEALTHCARE PAVILION, LOUISVILLE, KENTUCKY (see NORTON HOSPITAL), p. A261
NORTON HOSPITAL, LOUISVILLE, KY, p. A261
NORTON SOUND REGIONAL HOSPITAL, NOME, AK, p. A28
NORTON WOMEN'S AND KOSAIR CHILDREN'S HOSPITAL, LOUISVILLE, KY, p. A261
NORWALK HOSPITAL, NORWALK, CT, p. A114
NORWEGIAN AMERICAN HOSPITAL, CHICAGO, IL, p. A183
NORWOOD HEALTH CENTER, MARSHFIELD, WI, p. A705
NORWOOD HOSPITAL, NORWOOD, MA, p. A310
NOVANT HEALTH BRUNSWICK MEDICAL CENTER, BOLIVIA, NC, p. A456
NOVANT HEALTH CHARLOTTE ORTHOPAEDIC HOSPITAL, CHARLOTTE, NC, p. A457
NOVANT HEALTH FORSYTH MEDICAL CENTER, WINSTON–SALEM, NC, p. A471
NOVANT HEALTH FRANKLIN MEDICAL CENTER, LOUISBURG, NC, p. A464
NOVANT HEALTH HAYMARKET MEDICAL CENTER, HAYMARKET, VA, p. A666
NOVANT HEALTH HUNTERSVILLE MEDICAL CENTER, HUNTERSVILLE, NC, p. A462
NOVANT HEALTH MATTHEWS MEDICAL CENTER, MATTHEWS, NC, p. A464
NOVANT HEALTH MEDICAL PARK HOSPITAL, WINSTON–SALEM, NC, p. A471
NOVANT HEALTH PRESBYTERIAN MEDICAL CENTER, CHARLOTTE, NC, p. A458
NOVANT HEALTH PRINCE WILLIAM MEDICAL CENTER, MANASSAS, VA, p. A667
NOVANT HEALTH ROWAN MEDICAL CENTER, SALISBURY, NC, p. A468
NOVANT HEALTH THOMASVILLE MEDICAL CENTER, THOMASVILLE, NC, p. A469
NOVATO COMMUNITY HOSPITAL, NOVATO, CA, p. A78
NOXUBEE GENERAL HOSPITAL, MACON, MS, p. A356
NYACK HOSPITAL, NYACK, NY, p. A446
NYU CHILDREN'S HOSPITAL, NEW YORK, NEW YORK (see NYU LANGONE MEDICAL CENTER), p. A443
NYU LANGONE MEDICAL CENTER, NEW YORK, NY, p. A443

# O

# P

PROVIDENCE HOOD RIVER MEMORIAL HOSPITAL, HOOD RIVER, OR, p. A521
PROVIDENCE HOSPITAL, MOBILE, AL, p. A22
PROVIDENCE HOSPITAL, WASHINGTON, DC, p. A120
PROVIDENCE HOSPITAL, COLUMBIA, SC, p. A559
PROVIDENCE HOSPITAL NORTHEAST, COLUMBIA, SOUTH CAROLINA (see PROVIDENCE HOSPITAL), p. A559
PROVIDENCE KODIAK ISLAND MEDICAL CENTER, KODIAK, AK, p. A28
PROVIDENCE LITTLE COMPANY OF MARY MEDICAL CENTER – TORRANCE, TORRANCE, CA, p. A94
PROVIDENCE LITTLE COMPANY OF MARY MEDICAL CENTER SAN PEDRO,, CA, p. A72
PROVIDENCE MEDFORD MEDICAL CENTER, MEDFORD, OR, p. A523
PROVIDENCE MEDICAL CENTER, KANSAS CITY, KS, p. A243
PROVIDENCE MEDICAL CENTER, WAYNE, NE, p. A399
PROVIDENCE MILWAUKIE HOSPITAL, MILWAUKIE, OR, p. A523
PROVIDENCE MOUNT CARMEL HOSPITAL, COLVILLE, WA, p. A678
PROVIDENCE NEWBERG MEDICAL CENTER, NEWBERG, OR, p. A523
PROVIDENCE PORTLAND MEDICAL CENTER, PORTLAND, OR, p. A524
PROVIDENCE REGIONAL MEDICAL CENTER EVERETT, EVERETT, WA, p. A679
PROVIDENCE SACRED HEART MEDICAL CENTER & CHILDREN'S HOSPITAL, SPOKANE, WA, p. A685
PROVIDENCE SAINT JOSEPH MEDICAL CENTER, BURBANK, CA, p. A56
PROVIDENCE SEASIDE HOSPITAL, SEASIDE, OR, p. A526
PROVIDENCE SEWARD MEDICAL CENTER, SEWARD, AK, p. A29
PROVIDENCE ST. JOSEPH MEDICAL CENTER, POLSON, MT, p. A386
PROVIDENCE ST. JOSEPH'S HOSPITAL, CHEWELAH, WA, p. A677
PROVIDENCE ST. MARY MEDICAL CENTER, WALLA WALLA, WA, p. A687
PROVIDENCE ST. PETER HOSPITAL, OLYMPIA, WA, p. A681
PROVIDENCE ST. VINCENT MEDICAL CENTER, PORTLAND, OR, p. A524
PROVIDENCE TARZANA MEDICAL CENTER,, CA, p. A72
PROVIDENCE VALDEZ MEDICAL CENTER, VALDEZ, AK, p. A29
PROVIDENCE VETERANS AFFAIRS MEDICAL CENTER, PROVIDENCE, RI, p. A556
PROVIDENCE WILLAMETTE FALLS MEDICAL CENTER, OREGON CITY, OR, p. A523
PROVIDENT HOSPITAL OF COOK COUNTY, CHICAGO, IL, p. A184
PROVO CANYON BEHAVIORAL HOSPITAL, OREM, UT, p. A656
PROWERS MEDICAL CENTER, LAMAR, CO, p. A106
PSYCHIATRIC INSTITUTE OF WASHINGTON, WASHINGTON, DC, p. A120
PSYCHIATRIC MEDICINE CENTER, SALEM, OREGON (see SALEM HOSPITAL), p. A526
PUERTO RICO CHILDREN'S HOSPITAL, BAYAMON, PUERTO RICO (see HOSPITAL HERMANOS MELENDEZ), p. A720
PULASKI MEMORIAL HOSPITAL, WINAMAC, IN, p. A221
PULLMAN REGIONAL HOSPITAL, PULLMAN, WA, p. A682
PUNXSUTAWNEY AREA HOSPITAL, PUNXSUTAWNEY, PA, p. A548
PURCELL MUNICIPAL HOSPITAL, PURCELL, OK, p. A514
PUSHMATAHA HOSPITAL & HOME HEALTH, ANTLERS, OK, p. A503
PUTNAM COMMUNITY MEDICAL CENTER, PALATKA, FL, p. A138
PUTNAM COUNTY HOSPITAL, GREENCASTLE, IN, p. A210
PUTNAM COUNTY MEMORIAL HOSPITAL, UNIONVILLE, MO, p. A380
PUTNAM GENERAL HOSPITAL, EATONTON, GA, p. A157
PUTNAM HOSPITAL CENTER, CARMEL, NY, p. A431

## Q

QUARTZ MOUNTAIN MEDICAL CENTER, MANGUM, OK, p. A509
QUEEN OF THE VALLEY MEDICAL CENTER, NAPA, CA, p. A77
QUEEN'S MEDICAL CENTER, HONOLULU, HI, p. A169
QUEEN'S MEDICAL CENTER – WEST OAHU, EWA BEACH, HAWAII (see QUEEN'S MEDICAL CENTER), p. A169
QUEENS HOSPITAL CENTER,, NY, p. A444
QUENTIN MEASE HOSPITAL, HOUSTON, TEXAS (see HARRIS HEALTH SYSTEM), p. A619
QUILLEN REHABILITATION HOSPITAL, JOHNSON CITY, TN, p. A580
QUINCY VALLEY MEDICAL CENTER, QUINCY, WA, p. A682
QUITMAN COUNTY HOSPITAL, MARKS, MS, p. A356

## R

RADY CHILDREN'S HOSPITAL – SAN DIEGO, SAN DIEGO, CA, p. A86
RAINBOW MENTAL HEALTH FACILITY, KANSAS CITY, KS, p. A243
RAINY LAKE MEDICAL CENTER, INTERNATIONAL FALLS, MN, p. A340
RALEIGH GENERAL HOSPITAL, BECKLEY, WV, p. A689
RALPH H. JOHNSON VETERANS AFFAIRS MEDICAL CENTER, CHARLESTON, SC, p. A558
RANCHO LOS AMIGOS NATIONAL REHABILITATION CENTER, DOWNEY, CA, p. A60
RANCHO SPRINGS MEDICAL CENTER, MURRIETA, CALIFORNIA (see SOUTHWEST HEALTHCARE SYSTEM), p. A77
RANDALL CHILDREN'S HOSPITAL, PORTLAND, OREGON (see LEGACY EMANUEL HOSPITAL AND HEALTH CENTER), p. A524
RANDOLPH HOSPITAL, ASHEBORO, NC, p. A455
RANGE REGIONAL HEALTH SERVICES, HIBBING, MN, p. A340
RANGELY DISTRICT HOSPITAL, RANGELY, CO, p. A108
RANKEN JORDAN PEDIATRIC BRIDGE HOSPITAL, MARYLAND HEIGHTS, MO, p. A372
RANKIN HOSPITAL DISTRICT, RANKIN, TX, p. A638
RANSOM MEMORIAL HOSPITAL, OTTAWA, KS, p. A247
RAPID CITY REGIONAL HOSPITAL, RAPID CITY, SD, p. A570
RAPIDES REGIONAL MEDICAL CENTER, ALEXANDRIA, LA, p. A268
RAPPAHANNOCK GENERAL HOSPITAL, KILMARNOCK, VA, p. A666
RARITAN BAY MEDICAL CENTER, PERTH AMBOY, NJ, p. A417
RAULERSON HOSPITAL, OKEECHOBEE, FL, p. A137
RAWLINS COUNTY HEALTH CENTER, ATWOOD, KS, p. A237
RAY COUNTY MEMORIAL HOSPITAL, RICHMOND, MO, p. A375
RAYMOND BLANK MEMORIAL HOSPITAL FOR CHILDREN, DES MOINES, IOWA (see UNITYPOINT HEALTH – IOWA METHODIST MEDICAL CENTER), p. A226
RC HOSPITAL AND CLINICS, OLIVIA, MN, p. A344
READING HOSPITAL, WEST READING, PA, p. A553
REAGAN MEMORIAL HOSPITAL, BIG LAKE, TX, p. A597
RECEPTION AND MEDICAL CENTER, LAKE BUTLER, FL, p. A131
RED BAY HOSPITAL, RED BAY, AL, p. A24
RED BUD REGIONAL HOSPITAL, RED BUD, IL, p. A199
RED LAKE INDIAN HEALTH SERVICE HOSPITAL, RED LAKE, MN, p. A345
RED RIVER BEHAVIORAL CENTER, BOSSIER CITY, LA, p. A271
RED RIVER HOSPITAL, LLC, WICHITA FALLS, TX, p. A652
RED ROCK BEHAVIORAL HOSPITAL, LAS VEGAS, NV, p. A402
REDINGTON–FAIRVIEW GENERAL HOSPITAL, SKOWHEGAN, ME, p. A292
REDLANDS COMMUNITY HOSPITAL, REDLANDS, CA, p. A83
REDMOND REGIONAL MEDICAL CENTER, ROME, GA, p. A163
REDWOOD AREA HOSPITAL, REDWOOD FALLS, MN, p. A345
REDWOOD MEMORIAL HOSPITAL, FORTUNA, CA, p. A61
REEDSBURG AREA MEDICAL CENTER, REEDSBURG, WI, p. A710
REEVES COUNTY HOSPITAL, PECOS, TX, p. A636
REEVES MEMORIAL MEDICAL CENTER, BERNICE, LA, p. A270
REFUGIO COUNTY MEMORIAL HOSPITAL, REFUGIO, TX, p. A638
REGENCY HOSPITAL CLEVELAND EAST, WARRENSVILLE HEIGHTS, OH, p. A500
REGENCY HOSPITAL OF CENTRAL GEORGIA, MACON, GA, p. A161
REGENCY HOSPITAL OF CLEVELAND – WEST, MIDDLEBURG HEIGHTS, OHIO (see REGENCY HOSPITAL CLEVELAND EAST), p. A500
REGENCY HOSPITAL OF COLUMBUS, COLUMBUS, OH, p. A486
REGENCY HOSPITAL OF COVINGTON, COVINGTON, LA, p. A272
REGENCY HOSPITAL OF FLORENCE, FLORENCE, SC, p. A561
REGENCY HOSPITAL OF FORT WORTH, FORT WORTH, TX, p. A614
REGENCY HOSPITAL OF GREENVILLE, GREENVILLE, SC, p. A561
REGENCY HOSPITAL OF HATTIESBURG, HATTIESBURG, MS, p. A354
REGENCY HOSPITAL OF JACKSON, JACKSON, MS, p. A355
REGENCY HOSPITAL OF MERIDIAN, MERIDIAN, MS, p. A357
REGENCY HOSPITAL OF MINNEAPOLIS, GOLDEN VALLEY, MN, p. A339
REGENCY HOSPITAL OF NORTHWEST ARKANSAS – SPRINGDALE, SPRINGDALE, AR, p. A51
REGENCY HOSPITAL OF NORTHWEST INDIANA, EAST CHICAGO, IN, p. A207
REGENCY HOSPITAL OF PORTER COUNTY, PORTAGE, INDIANA (see REGENCY HOSPITAL OF NORTHWEST INDIANA), p. A207
REGENCY HOSPITAL OF SOUTH ATLANTA, EAST POINT, GA, p. A156

REGENCY HOSPITAL OF TOLEDO, SYLVANIA, OH, p. A498
REGINA HOSPITAL, HASTINGS, MN, p. A340
REGIONAL GENERAL HOSPITAL, WILLISTON, FL, p. A147
REGIONAL HEALTH SERVICES OF HOWARD COUNTY, CRESCO, IA, p. A225
REGIONAL HOSPITAL FOR RESPIRATORY AND COMPLEX CARE, BURIEN, WA, p. A677
REGIONAL HOSPITAL OF SCRANTON, SCRANTON, PA, p. A549
REGIONAL MEDICAL CENTER, MANCHESTER, IA, p. A231
REGIONAL MEDICAL CENTER, ORANGEBURG, SC, p. A564
REGIONAL MEDICAL CENTER BAYONET POINT, HUDSON, FL, p. A129
REGIONAL MEDICAL CENTER OF ACADIANA, LAFAYETTE, LA, p. A278
REGIONAL MEDICAL CENTER OF SAN JOSE, SAN JOSE, CA, p. A89
REGIONAL MENTAL HEALTH CENTER, MERRILLVILLE, IN, p. A215
REGIONAL ONE HEALTH, MEMPHIS, TN, p. A584
REGIONAL ONE HEALTH EXTENDED CARE HOSPITAL, MEMPHIS, TN, p. A584
REGIONAL REHABILITATION CENTER, SALEM, OREGON (see SALEM HOSPITAL), p. A526
REGIONAL REHABILITATION HOSPITAL, PHENIX CITY, AL, p. A24
REGIONAL WEST GARDEN COUNTY, OSHKOSH, NE, p. A397
REGIONAL WEST MEDICAL CENTER, SCOTTSBLUFF, NE, p. A398
REGIONS HOSPITAL, SAINT PAUL, MN, p. A346
REHABILITATION HOSPITAL OF FORT WAYNE, FORT WAYNE, IN, p. A209
REHABILITATION HOSPITAL OF INDIANA, INDIANAPOLIS, IN, p. A212
REHABILITATION HOSPITAL OF JENNINGS, JENNINGS, LA, p. A276
REHABILITATION HOSPITAL OF RHODE ISLAND, NORTH SMITHFIELD, RI, p. A555
REHABILITATION HOSPITAL OF SOUTHERN NEW MEXICO, LAS CRUCES, NM, p. A425
REHABILITATION HOSPITAL OF SOUTHWEST VIRGINIA, BRISTOL, VA, p. A662
REHABILITATION HOSPITAL OF THE PACIFIC, HONOLULU, HI, p. A169
REHABILITATION HOSPITAL OF TINTON FALLS, TINTON FALLS, NJ, p. A419
REHABILITATION HOSPITAL OF WISCONSIN, WAUKESHA, WI, p. A713
REHABILITATION HOSPITAL, NAVICENT HEALTH, MACON, GA, p. A161
REHABILITATION INSTITUTE AT THE MOUNT KEMBLE DIVISION, GORYEB CHILDREN'S HOSPITAL, MORRISTOWN, NEW JERSEY (see MORRISTOWN MEDICAL CENTER), p. A414
REHABILITATION INSTITUTE OF CHICAGO, CHICAGO, IL, p. A184
REHABILITATION INSTITUTE OF MICHIGAN, DETROIT, MI, p. A318
REHABILITATION INSTITUTE OF OREGON, PORTLAND, OREGON (see LEGACY GOOD SAMARITAN HOSPITAL AND MEDICAL CENTER), p. A524
REHABILITATION INSTITUTE OF WEST FLORIDA, PENSACOLA, FLORIDA (see WEST FLORIDA HOSPITAL), p. A140
REHOBOTH MCKINLEY CHRISTIAN HEALTH CARE SERVICES, GALLUP, NM, p. A424
REID HEALTH, RICHMOND, IN, p. A219
REISCH MEMORIAL NURSING HOME (see THOMAS H. BOYD MEMORIAL HOSPITAL), p. A180
RELIANT AUSTIN, AUSTIN, TX, p. A594
RELIANT NORTHWEST HOUSTON, HOUSTON, TX, p. A621
RELIANT REHABILITATION HOSPITAL ABILENE, ABILENE, TX, p. A590
RELIANT REHABILITATION HOSPITAL CENTRAL TEXAS, ROUND ROCK, TX, p. A639
RELIANT REHABILITATION HOSPITAL DALLAS, DALLAS, TX, p. A606
RELIANT REHABILITATION HOSPITAL MID–CITIES, BEDFORD, TX, p. A596
RELIANT REHABILITATION HOSPITAL NORTH HOUSTON, SHENANDOAH, TX, p. A643
RELIANT REHABILITATION HOSPITAL NORTH TEXAS, RICHARDSON, TX, p. A638
RENOWN CHILDREN'S HOSPITAL, RENO, NEVADA (see RENOWN REGIONAL MEDICAL CENTER), p. A403
RENOWN REGIONAL MEDICAL CENTER, RENO, NV, p. A403
RENOWN REHABILITATION HOSPITAL, RENO, NV, p. A404
RENOWN SOUTH MEADOWS MEDICAL CENTER, RENO, NV, p. A404
REPUBLIC COUNTY HOSPITAL, BELLEVILLE, KS, p. A237
RESEARCH MEDICAL CENTER, KANSAS CITY, MO, p. A370
RESEARCH PSYCHIATRIC CENTER, KANSAS CITY, MISSOURI (see RESEARCH MEDICAL CENTER), p. A370
RESOLUTE HEALTH, NEW BRAUNFELS, TX, p. A634
RESTON HOSPITAL CENTER, RESTON, VA, p. A671

## S

SAINT ALPHONSUS MEDICAL CENTER – ONTARIO, ONTARIO, OR, p. A523
SAINT ALPHONSUS REGIONAL MEDICAL CENTER, BOISE, ID, p. A172
SAINT ANNE'S HOSPITAL, FALL RIVER, MA, p. A306
SAINT ANTHONY HOSPITAL, CHICAGO, IL, p. A184
SAINT BARNABAS MEDICAL CENTER, LIVINGSTON, NJ, p. A413
SAINT CLARE'S HEALTH CENTER AT SUSSEX, SUSSEX, NEW JERSEY (see SAINT CLARE'S HEALTH SYSTEM), p. A411
SAINT CLARE'S HEALTH SYSTEM, DENVILLE, NJ, p. A411
SAINT CLARE'S HOSPITAL/BOONTON TOWNSHIP, BOONTON TOWNSHIP, NEW JERSEY (see SAINT CLARE'S HEALTH SYSTEM), p. A411
SAINT CLARE'S HOSPITAL/DENVILLE, DENVILLE, NEW JERSEY (see SAINT CLARE'S HEALTH SYSTEM), p. A411
SAINT CLARE'S HOSPITAL/DOVER, DOVER, NEW JERSEY (see SAINT CLARE'S HEALTH SYSTEM), p. A411
SAINT ELIZABETH'S MEDICAL CENTER, WABASHA, MN, p. A348
SAINT ELIZABETHS HOSPITAL, WASHINGTON, DC, p. A120
SAINT FRANCIS HEART HOSPITAL, TULSA, OKLAHOMA (see SAINT FRANCIS HOSPITAL), p. A517
SAINT FRANCIS HOSPITAL, TULSA, OK, p. A517
SAINT FRANCIS HOSPITAL, MEMPHIS, TN, p. A584
SAINT FRANCIS HOSPITAL, CHARLESTON, WV, p. A690
SAINT FRANCIS HOSPITAL AND MEDICAL CENTER, HARTFORD, CT, p. A112
SAINT FRANCIS HOSPITAL SOUTH, TULSA, OK, p. A517
SAINT FRANCIS HOSPITAL–BARTLETT, BARTLETT, TN, p. A574
SAINT FRANCIS MEDICAL CENTER, CAPE GIRARDEAU, MO, p. A364
SAINT FRANCIS MEMORIAL HOSPITAL, SAN FRANCISCO, CA, p. A88
SAINT JOHN HOSPITAL, LEAVENWORTH, KS, p. A244
SAINT JOHN'S HEALTH CENTER, SANTA MONICA, CA, p. A91
SAINT JOSEPH – LONDON, LONDON, KY, p. A260
SAINT JOSEPH – MARTIN, MARTIN, KY, p. A262
SAINT JOSEPH BEREA, BEREA, KY, p. A254
SAINT JOSEPH EAST, LEXINGTON, KY, p. A260
SAINT JOSEPH HOSPITAL, DENVER, CO, p. A102
SAINT JOSEPH HOSPITAL, LEXINGTON, KY, p. A260
SAINT JOSEPH MOUNT STERLING, MOUNT STERLING, KY, p. A263
SAINT JOSEPH REGIONAL MEDICAL CENTER, MISHAWAKA, IN, p. A216
SAINT JOSEPH REGIONAL MEDICAL CENTER–PLYMOUTH CAMPUS, PLYMOUTH, IN, p. A218
SAINT JOSEPH'S CHILDEN'S HOSPITAL, MARSHFIELD, WISCONSIN (see MINISTRY SAINT JOSEPH'S HOSPITAL), p. A705
SAINT LOUISE REGIONAL HOSPITAL, GILROY, CA, p. A63
SAINT LUKE INSTITUTE, SILVER SPRING, MD, p. A300
SAINT LUKE'S CUSHING HOSPITAL, LEAVENWORTH, KS, p. A244
SAINT LUKE'S EAST HOSPITAL, LEE'S SUMMIT, MO, p. A371
SAINT LUKE'S HOSPITAL OF KANSAS CITY, KANSAS CITY, MO, p. A370
SAINT LUKE'S NORTH HOSPITAL – BARRY ROAD, KANSAS CITY, MO, p. A370
SAINT LUKE'S NORTH HOSPITAL–SMITHVILLE CAMPUS, SMITHVILLE, MISSOURI (see SAINT LUKE'S NORTH HOSPITAL – BARRY ROAD), p. A370
SAINT LUKE'S SOUTH HOSPITAL, OVERLAND PARK, KS, p. A248
SAINT MARGARET MERCY HEALTHCARE CENTERS–NORTH CAMPUS, HAMMOND, INDIANA (see FRANCISCAN ST. MARGARET HEALTH – HAMMOND), p. A210
SAINT MARY'S HOSPITAL, WATERBURY, CT, p. A115
SAINT MARY'S REGIONAL MEDICAL CENTER, RUSSELLVILLE, AR, p. A50
SAINT MARY'S REGIONAL MEDICAL CENTER, RENO, NV, p. A404
SAINT MICHAEL'S MEDICAL CENTER, NEWARK, NJ, p. A415
SAINT PETER'S UNIVERSITY HOSPITAL, NEW BRUNSWICK, NJ, p. A415
SAINT SIMONS BY–THE–SEA HOSPITAL, SAINT SIMONS ISLAND, GA, p. A163
SAINT THOMAS DEKALB HOSPITAL, SMITHVILLE, TN, p. A588
SAINT THOMAS HICKMAN HOSPITAL, CENTERVILLE, TN, p. A575
SAINT THOMAS HIGHLANDS HOSPITAL, SPARTA, TN, p. A588
SAINT THOMAS HOSPITAL FOR SPINAL SURGERY, NASHVILLE, TN, p. A585
SAINT THOMAS MIDTOWN HOSPITAL, NASHVILLE, TN, p. A585
SAINT THOMAS RIVER PARK HOSPITAL, MC MINNVILLE, TN, p. A582
SAINT THOMAS RUTHERFORD HOSPITAL, MURFREESBORO, TN, p. A585
SAINT THOMAS STONES RIVER HOSPITAL, WOODBURY, TN, p. A589
SAINT THOMAS WEST HOSPITAL, NASHVILLE, TN, p. A585

SAINT VINCENT HEALTH CENTER, ERIE, PA, p. A534
SAINT VINCENT HOSPITAL, WORCESTER, MA, p. A313
SAKAKAWEA MEDICAL CENTER, HAZEN, ND, p. A474
SALEM CAMPUS, SALEM, MASSACHUSETTS (see NORTH SHORE MEDICAL CENTER), p. A310
SALEM HOSPITAL, SALEM, OR, p. A526
SALEM MEMORIAL DISTRICT HOSPITAL, SALEM, MO, p. A378
SALEM REGIONAL MEDICAL CENTER, SALEM, OH, p. A497
SALEM TOWNSHIP HOSPITAL, SALEM, IL, p. A200
SALEM VETERANS AFFAIRS MEDICAL CENTER, SALEM, VA, p. A672
SALINA REGIONAL HEALTH CENTER, SALINA, KS, p. A250
SALINA REGIONAL HEALTH CENTER– PENN CAMPUS, SALINA, KANSAS (see SALINA REGIONAL HEALTH CENTER), p. A250
SALINA REGIONAL HEALTH CENTER–SANTA FE CAMPUS, SALINA, KANSAS (see SALINA REGIONAL HEALTH CENTER), p. A250
SALINA SURGICAL HOSPITAL, SALINA, KS, p. A250
SALINAS VALLEY MEMORIAL HEALTHCARE SYSTEM, SALINAS, CA, p. A85
SALINE MEMORIAL HOSPITAL, BENTON, AR, p. A41
SALT LAKE BEHAVIORAL HEALTH, SALT LAKE CITY, UT, p. A658
SALT LAKE REGIONAL MEDICAL CENTER, SALT LAKE CITY, UT, p. A658
SAM RAYBURN MEMORIAL VETERANS CENTER, BONHAM, TEXAS (see VETERANS AFFAIRS NORTH TEXAS HEALTH CARE SYSTEM), p. A607
SAMARITAN ALBANY GENERAL HOSPITAL, ALBANY, OR, p. A519
SAMARITAN BEHAVIORAL HEALTH CENTER–DESERT SAMARITAN MEDICAL CENTER, MESA, ARIZONA (see BANNER DESERT MEDICAL CENTER), p. A33
SAMARITAN HEALTHCARE, MOSES LAKE, WA, p. A680
SAMARITAN HOSPITAL, TROY, NY, p. A452
SAMARITAN LEBANON COMMUNITY HOSPITAL, LEBANON, OR, p. A522
SAMARITAN MEDICAL CENTER, WATERTOWN, NY, p. A453
SAMARITAN MEMORIAL HOSPITAL, MACON, MO, p. A372
SAMARITAN NORTH LINCOLN HOSPITAL, LINCOLN CITY, OR, p. A522
SAMARITAN PACIFIC COMMUNITIES HOSPITAL, NEWPORT, OR, p. A523
SAMARITAN REGIONAL HEALTH SYSTEM, ASHLAND, OH, p. A478
SAME DAY SURGERY CENTER, RAPID CITY, SD, p. A571
SAMPSON REGIONAL MEDICAL CENTER, CLINTON, NC, p. A458
SAMUEL MAHELONA MEMORIAL HOSPITAL, KAPAA, HI, p. A170
SAMUEL SIMMONDS MEMORIAL HOSPITAL, BARROW, AK, p. A27
SAN ANGELO COMMUNITY MEDICAL CENTER, SAN ANGELO, TX, p. A640
SAN ANTONIO COMMUNITY HOSPITAL, UPLAND, CA, p. A95
SAN ANTONIO DIVISION, SAN ANTONIO, TEXAS (see SOUTH TEXAS VETERANS HEALTH CARE SYSTEM), p. A642
SAN ANTONIO STATE HOSPITAL, SAN ANTONIO, TX, p. A642
SAN BERNARDINO MOUNTAINS COMMUNITY HOSPITAL DISTRICT, LAKE ARROWHEAD, CA, p. A67
SAN DIEGO COUNTY PSYCHIATRIC HOSPITAL, SAN DIEGO, CA, p. A87
SAN DIMAS COMMUNITY HOSPITAL, SAN DIMAS, CA, p. A87
SAN FRANCISCO GENERAL HOSPITAL AND TRAUMA CENTER, SAN FRANCISCO, CA, p. A88
SAN FRANCISCO VA MEDICAL CENTER, SAN FRANCISCO, CA, p. A88
SAN GABRIEL VALLEY MEDICAL CENTER, SAN GABRIEL, CA, p. A89
SAN GORGONIO MEMORIAL HOSPITAL, BANNING, CA, p. A55
SAN JOAQUIN COMMUNITY HOSPITAL, BAKERSFIELD, CA, p. A55
SAN JOAQUIN GENERAL HOSPITAL, FRENCH CAMP, CA, p. A62
SAN JOAQUIN VALLEY REHABILITATION HOSPITAL, FRESNO, CA, p. A62
SAN JORGE CHILDREN'S HOSPITAL, SAN JUAN, PR, p. A724
SAN JUAN CAPESTRANO HOSPITAL, SAN JUAN, PR, p. A724
SAN JUAN CITY HOSPITAL, SAN JUAN, PR, p. A724
SAN JUAN HOSPITAL, MONTICELLO, UT, p. A655
SAN JUAN REGIONAL MEDICAL CENTER, FARMINGTON, NM, p. A424
SAN JUAN REGIONAL MEDICAL CENTER REHABILITATION HOSPITAL, FARMINGTON, NEW MEXICO (see SAN JUAN REGIONAL MEDICAL CENTER), p. A424
SAN LEANDRO HOSPITAL, SAN LEANDRO, CA, p. A90
SAN LUIS VALLEY HEALTH, ALAMOSA, CO, p. A99
SAN LUIS VALLEY HEALTH CONEJOS COUNTY HOSPITAL, LA JARA, CO, p. A105
SAN MATEO MEDICAL CENTER, SAN MATEO, CA, p. A90
SAN RAMON REGIONAL MEDICAL CENTER, SAN RAMON, CA, p. A90

SANDHILLS REGIONAL MEDICAL CENTER, HAMLET, NC, p. A461
SANFORD ABERDEEN MEDICAL CENTER, ABERDEEN, SD, p. A567
SANFORD BAGLEY MEDICAL CENTER, BAGLEY, MN, p. A335
SANFORD BEMIDJI MEDICAL CENTER, BEMIDJI, MN, p. A335
SANFORD BISMARCK, BISMARCK, ND, p. A472
SANFORD CANBY MEDICAL CENTER, CANBY, MN, p. A336
SANFORD CANTON–INWOOD MEDICAL CENTER, CANTON, SD, p. A567
SANFORD CHAMBERLAIN MEDICAL CENTER, CHAMBERLAIN, SD, p. A567
SANFORD CHILDREN'S HOSPITAL, SIOUX FALLS, SOUTH DAKOTA (see SANFORD USD MEDICAL CENTER), p. A571
SANFORD CLEAR LAKE MEDICAL CENTER, CLEAR LAKE, SD, p. A568
SANFORD HILLSBORO MEDICAL CENTER, HILLSBORO, ND, p. A475
SANFORD JACKSON MEDICAL CENTER, JACKSON, MN, p. A340
SANFORD LUVERNE MEDICAL CENTER, LUVERNE, MN, p. A341
SANFORD MAYVILLE MEDICAL CENTER, MAYVILLE, ND, p. A475
SANFORD MEDICAL CENTER FARGO, FARGO, ND, p. A474
SANFORD ROCK RAPIDS MEDICAL CENTER, ROCK RAPIDS, IA, p. A233
SANFORD SHELDON MEDICAL CENTER, SHELDON, IA, p. A234
SANFORD SOUTH UNIVERSITY, FARGO, NORTH DAKOTA (see SANFORD MEDICAL CENTER FARGO), p. A474
SANFORD THIEF RIVER FALLS MEDICAL CENTER, THIEF RIVER FALLS, MN, p. A348
SANFORD TRACY MEDICAL CENTER, TRACY, MN, p. A348
SANFORD USD MEDICAL CENTER, SIOUX FALLS, SD, p. A571
SANFORD VERMILLION MEDICAL CENTER, VERMILLION, SD, p. A572
SANFORD WEBSTER MEDICAL CENTER, WEBSTER, SD, p. A573
SANFORD WESTBROOK MEDICAL CENTER, WESTBROOK, MN, p. A349
SANFORD WHEATON MEDICAL CENTER, WHEATON, MN, p. A349
SANFORD WORTHINGTON MEDICAL CENTER, WORTHINGTON, MN, p. A349
SANPETE VALLEY HOSPITAL, MOUNT PLEASANT, UT, p. A656
SANTA BARBARA COTTAGE HOSPITAL, SANTA BARBARA, CA, p. A91
SANTA BARBARA COUNTY PSYCHIATRIC HEALTH FACILITY, SANTA BARBARA, CA, p. A91
SANTA CLARA VALLEY MEDICAL CENTER, SAN JOSE, CA, p. A89
SANTA MONICA–UCLA MEDICAL CENTER AND ORTHOPAEDIC HOSPITAL, SANTA MONICA, CA, p. A92
SANTA ROSA MEDICAL CENTER, MILTON, FL, p. A135
SANTA ROSA MEMORIAL HOSPITAL, SANTA ROSA, CA, p. A92
SANTA YNEZ VALLEY COTTAGE HOSPITAL, SOLVANG, CA, p. A92
SANTIAM MEMORIAL HOSPITAL, STAYTON, OR, p. A526
SARAH BUSH LINCOLN HEALTH CENTER, MATTOON, IL, p. A193
SARAH D. CULBERTSON MEMORIAL HOSPITAL, RUSHVILLE, IL, p. A200
SARASOTA MEMORIAL HEALTH CARE SYSTEM, SARASOTA, FL, p. A142
SARATOGA HOSPITAL, SARATOGA SPRINGS, NY, p. A450
SARTORI MEMORIAL HOSPITAL, CEDAR FALLS, IA, p. A223
SATANTA DISTRICT HOSPITAL AND LONG TERM CARE, SATANTA, KS, p. A250
SAUK PRAIRIE HEALTHCARE, PRAIRIE DU SAC, WI, p. A709
SAUNDERS MEDICAL CENTER, WAHOO, NE, p. A398
SAVOY MEDICAL CENTER, MAMOU, LA, p. A279
SAYRE MEMORIAL HOSPITAL, SAYRE, OK, p. A514
SCENIC MOUNTAIN MEDICAL CENTER, BIG SPRING, TX, p. A597
SCHEURER HOSPITAL, PIGEON, MI, p. A327
SCHICK SHADEL HOSPITAL, SEATTLE, WA, p. A683
SCHLEICHER COUNTY MEDICAL CENTER, ELDORADO, TX, p. A612
SCHNECK MEDICAL CENTER, SEYMOUR, IN, p. A219
SCHNEIDER REGIONAL MEDICAL CENTER, SAINT THOMAS, VI, p. A725
SCHOOLCRAFT MEMORIAL HOSPITAL, MANISTIQUE, MI, p. A325
SCHUYLER HOSPITAL, MONTOUR FALLS, NY, p. A437
SCHUYLKILL MEDICAL CENTER – EAST NORWEGIAN STREET, POTTSVILLE, PA, p. A548
SCHUYLKILL MEDICAL CENTER – SOUTH JACKSON STREET, POTTSVILLE, PA, p. A548
SCHWAB REHABILITATION HOSPITAL, CHICAGO, IL, p. A184
SCOTLAND COUNTY HOSPITAL, MEMPHIS, MO, p. A372
SCOTLAND HEALTH CARE SYSTEM, LAURINBURG, NC, p. A463
SCOTT & WHITE EMERGENCY HOSPITAL– CEDAR PARK, CEDAR PARK, TX, p. A600
SCOTT & WHITE HOSPITAL – BRENHAM, BRENHAM, TX, p. A598

ST. CHARLES SURGICAL HOSPITAL, NEW ORLEANS, LA, p. A282

ST. CHRISTOPHER'S HOSPITAL FOR CHILDREN, PHILADELPHIA, PA, p. A545

ST. CLAIR HOSPITAL, PITTSBURGH, PA, p. A546

ST. CLAIRE REGIONAL MEDICAL CENTER, MOREHEAD, KY, p. A263

ST. CLARE HOSPITAL, LAKEWOOD, WA, p. A680

ST. CLARE HOSPITAL, BARABOO, WI, p. A697

ST. CLOUD HOSPITAL, SAINT CLOUD, MN, p. A345

ST. CLOUD REGIONAL MEDICAL CENTER, SAINT CLOUD, FL, p. A141

ST. CLOUD VETERANS AFFAIRS HEALTH CARE SYSTEM, SAINT CLOUD, MN, p. A346

ST. CROIX REGIONAL MEDICAL CENTER, ST. CROIX FALLS, WI, p. A711

ST. DAVID'S GEORGETOWN HOSPITAL, GEORGETOWN, TEXAS (see ST. DAVID'S MEDICAL CENTER), p. A595

ST. DAVID'S MEDICAL CENTER, AUSTIN, TX, p. A595

ST. DAVID'S NORTH AUSTIN MEDICAL CENTER, AUSTIN, TX, p. A595

ST. DAVID'S REHABILITATION CENTER, AUSTIN, TEXAS (see ST. DAVID'S MEDICAL CENTER), p. A595

ST. DAVID'S ROUND ROCK MEDICAL CENTER, ROUND ROCK, TX, p. A639

ST. DAVID'S SOUTH AUSTIN MEDICAL CENTER, AUSTIN, TX, p. A595

ST. DOMINIC–JACKSON MEMORIAL HOSPITAL, JACKSON, MS, p. A355

ST. ELIAS SPECIALTY HOSPITAL, ANCHORAGE, AK, p. A27

ST. ELIZABETH BOARDMAN HEALTH CENTER, BOARDMAN, OH, p. A480

ST. ELIZABETH COMMUNITY HOSPITAL, RED BLUFF, CA, p. A82

ST. ELIZABETH COVINGTON, COVINGTON, KENTUCKY (see ST. ELIZABETH EDGEWOOD), p. A256

ST. ELIZABETH EDGEWOOD, EDGEWOOD, KY, p. A256

ST. ELIZABETH FLORENCE, FLORENCE, KY, p. A256

ST. ELIZABETH FORT THOMAS, FORT THOMAS, KY, p. A257

ST. ELIZABETH GRANT, WILLIAMSTOWN, KY, p. A267

ST. ELIZABETH HEALTH CENTER, YOUNGSTOWN, OH, p. A501

ST. ELIZABETH HOSPITAL, GONZALES, LA, p. A274

ST. ELIZABETH HOSPITAL, ENUMCLAW, WA, p. A678

ST. ELIZABETH HOSPITAL, APPLETON, WI, p. A697

ST. ELIZABETH MEDICAL CENTER, UTICA, NY, p. A452

ST. ELIZABETH'S MEDICAL CENTER, BRIGHTON, MA, p. A305

ST. FRANCIS CAMPUS, WICHITA, KANSAS (see VIA CHRISTI HOSPITAL ON ST. FRANCIS), p. A253

ST. FRANCIS EASTSIDE, GREENVILLE, SOUTH CAROLINA (see BON SECOURS ST. FRANCIS HEALTH SYSTEM), p. A561

ST. FRANCIS HEALTH, TOPEKA, KS, p. A251

ST. FRANCIS HOSPITAL, WILMINGTON, DE, p. A118

ST. FRANCIS HOSPITAL, COLUMBUS, GA, p. A154

ST. FRANCIS HOSPITAL, ROSLYN, NY, p. A449

ST. FRANCIS HOSPITAL, FEDERAL WAY, WA, p. A679

ST. FRANCIS MEDICAL CENTER, COLORADO SPRINGS, COLORADO (see PENROSE–ST. FRANCIS HEALTH SERVICES), p. A101

ST. FRANCIS MEDICAL CENTER, LYNWOOD, CA, p. A74

ST. FRANCIS MEDICAL CENTER, MONROE, LA, p. A280

ST. FRANCIS MEDICAL CENTER, TRENTON, NJ, p. A419

ST. FRANCIS MEDICAL PLAZA, GRAND ISLAND, NEBRASKA (see CHI HEALTH SAINT FRANCIS), p. A392

ST. FRANCIS MEMORIAL HOSPITAL, WEST POINT, NE, p. A399

ST. FRANCIS NORTH HOSPITAL, MONROE, LOUISIANA (see ST. FRANCIS MEDICAL CENTER), p. A280

ST. FRANCIS NURSING CENTER (see MARY IMMACULATE HOSPITAL), p. A669

ST. FRANCIS REGIONAL MEDICAL CENTER, SHAKOPEE, MN, p. A347

ST. HELENA HOSPITAL CLEAR LAKE, CLEARLAKE, CA, p. A58

ST. HELENA HOSPITAL NAPA VALLEY, SAINT HELENA, CA, p. A85

ST. HELENA HOSPITAL–CENTER FOR BEHAVIORAL HEALTH, VALLEJO, CA, p. A96

ST. HELENA PARISH HOSPITAL, GREENSBURG, LA, p. A274

ST. JAMES BEHAVIORAL HEALTH HOSPITAL, GONZALES, LA, p. A274

ST. JAMES HEALTHCARE, BUTTE, MT, p. A382

ST. JAMES HOSPITAL AND HEALTH CENTERS – CHICAGO HEIGHTS CAMPUS, CHICAGO HEIGHTS, ILLINOIS (see FRANCISCAN ST. JAMES HOSPITAL AND HEALTH CENTERS), p. A197

ST. JAMES HOSPITALS AND HEALTH CENTERS – OLYMPIA FIELDS CAMPUS, OLYMPIA FIELDS, ILLINOIS (see FRANCISCAN ST. JAMES HOSPITAL AND HEALTH CENTERS), p. A197

ST. JAMES MERCY HEALTH SYSTEM, HORNELL, NY, p. A435

ST. JAMES PARISH HOSPITAL, LUTCHER, LA, p. A279

ST. JOHN BROKEN ARROW, BROKEN ARROW, OK, p. A504

ST. JOHN HOSPITAL AND MEDICAL CENTER, DETROIT, MI, p. A318

ST. JOHN MACOMB–OAKLAND HOSPITAL, WARREN, MI, p. A332

ST. JOHN MACOMB–OAKLAND HOSPITAL, MADISON HEIGHTS CAMPUS, MADISON HEIGHTS, MICHIGAN (see ST. JOHN MACOMB–OAKLAND HOSPITAL), p. A332

ST. JOHN MACOMB–OAKLAND HOSPITAL, WARREN CAMPUS, WARREN, MICHIGAN (see ST. JOHN MACOMB–OAKLAND HOSPITAL), p. A332

ST. JOHN MEDICAL CENTER, WESTLAKE, OH, p. A500

ST. JOHN MEDICAL CENTER, TULSA, OK, p. A517

ST. JOHN OWASSO, OWASSO, OK, p. A513

ST. JOHN RIVER DISTRICT HOSPITAL, EAST CHINA, MI, p. A318

ST. JOHN SAPULPA, SAPULPA, OK, p. A514

ST. JOHN VIANNEY HOSPITAL, DOWNINGTOWN, PA, p. A532

ST. JOHN'S RIVERSIDE HOSPITAL – PARK CARE PAVILION, YONKERS, NEW YORK (see ST. JOHN'S RIVERSIDE HOSPITAL), p. A454

ST. JOHN'S CHILDREN'S HOSPITAL, SPRINGFIELD, ILLINOIS (see ST. JOHN'S HOSPITAL), p. A201

ST. JOHN'S EPISCOPAL HOSPITAL–SOUTH SHORE,, NY, p. A444

ST. JOHN'S HOSPITAL, SPRINGFIELD, IL, p. A201

ST. JOHN'S HOSPITAL, MAPLEWOOD, MN, p. A342

ST. JOHN'S MEDICAL CENTER AND LIVING CENTER, JACKSON, WY, p. A716

ST. JOHN'S PLEASANT VALLEY HOSPITAL, CAMARILLO, CA, p. A57

ST. JOHN'S REGIONAL MEDICAL CENTER, OXNARD, CA, p. A79

ST. JOHN'S REHABILITATION CENTER, JOPLIN, MISSOURI (see MERCY HOSPITAL JOPLIN), p. A369

ST. JOHN'S RIVERSIDE HOSPITAL, YONKERS, NY, p. A454

ST. JOHN'S RIVERSIDE HOSPITAL – DOBBS FERRY PAVILION, DOBBS FERRY, NEW YORK (see ST. JOHN'S RIVERSIDE HOSPITAL), p. A454

ST. JOSEPH CAMPUS, WICHITA, KANSAS (see VIA CHRISTI HOSPITAL ON ST. FRANCIS), p. A253

ST. JOSEPH HEALTH CENTER, WARREN, OH, p. A499

ST. JOSEPH HEALTH SERVICES OF RHODE ISLAND, NORTH PROVIDENCE, RI, p. A555

ST. JOSEPH HEALTH SYSTEM, TAWAS CITY, MI, p. A331

ST. JOSEPH HOSPITAL, EUREKA, CA, p. A60

ST. JOSEPH HOSPITAL, ORANGE, CA, p. A79

ST. JOSEPH HOSPITAL, FORT WAYNE, IN, p. A209

ST. JOSEPH HOSPITAL, BANGOR, ME, p. A288

ST. JOSEPH HOSPITAL, NASHUA, NH, p. A407

ST. JOSEPH HOSPITAL, BETHPAGE, NY, p. A429

ST. JOSEPH HOSPITAL & HEALTH CENTER, KOKOMO, IN, p. A214

ST. JOSEPH HOSPITAL FOR SPECIALTY CARE, PROVIDENCE, RHODE ISLAND (see ST. JOSEPH HEALTH SERVICES OF RHODE ISLAND), p. A555

ST. JOSEPH MEDICAL CENTER, KANSAS CITY, MO, p. A370

ST. JOSEPH MEDICAL CENTER, HOUSTON, TX, p. A622

ST. JOSEPH MEDICAL CENTER, TACOMA, WA, p. A686

ST. JOSEPH MEDICAL CENTER–DOWNTOWN READING, READING, PENNSYLVANIA (see ST. JOSEPH REGIONAL HEALTH NETWORK), p. A548

ST. JOSEPH MEMORIAL HOSPITAL, MURPHYSBORO, IL, p. A195

ST. JOSEPH MERCY ANN ARBOR, YPSILANTI, MI, p. A333

ST. JOSEPH MERCY CHELSEA, CHELSEA, MI, p. A316

ST. JOSEPH MERCY LIVINGSTON HOSPITAL, HOWELL, MI, p. A322

ST. JOSEPH MERCY OAKLAND, PONTIAC, MI, p. A328

ST. JOSEPH MERCY PORT HURON, PORT HURON, MI, p. A328

ST. JOSEPH REGIONAL HEALTH CENTER, BRYAN, TX, p. A599

ST. JOSEPH REGIONAL HEALTH NETWORK, READING, PA, p. A548

ST. JOSEPH REGIONAL MEDICAL CENTER, LEWISTON, ID, p. A174

ST. JOSEPH'S BEHAVIORAL HEALTH CENTER, STOCKTON, CA, p. A93

ST. JOSEPH'S CHILDREN'S HOSPITAL, TAMPA, FLORIDA (see ST. JOSEPH'S HOSPITAL), p. A145

ST. JOSEPH'S CHILDREN'S HOSPITAL, PATERSON, NEW JERSEY (see ST. JOSEPH'S REGIONAL MEDICAL CENTER), p. A416

ST. JOSEPH'S HOSPITAL, ASHEVILLE, NORTH CAROLINA (see MISSION HOSPITAL), p. A455

ST. JOSEPH'S HOSPITAL, PHILADELPHIA, PENNSYLVANIA (see NORTH PHILADELPHIA HEALTH SYSTEM), p. A544

ST. JOSEPH'S HOSPITAL, TAMPA, FL, p. A145

ST. JOSEPH'S HOSPITAL, SAVANNAH, GA, p. A164

ST. JOSEPH'S HOSPITAL, SAINT PAUL, MN, p. A346

ST. JOSEPH'S HOSPITAL, ELMIRA, NY, p. A433

ST. JOSEPH'S HOSPITAL, WEST BEND, WI, p. A714

ST. JOSEPH'S HOSPITAL – NORTH, LUTZ, FLORIDA (see ST. JOSEPH'S HOSPITAL), p. A145

ST. JOSEPH'S HOSPITAL AND HEALTH CENTER, DICKINSON, ND, p. A473

ST. JOSEPH'S HOSPITAL AND MEDICAL CENTER, PHOENIX, AZ, p. A36

ST. JOSEPH'S HOSPITAL BEHAVIORAL HEALTH CENTER, TAMPA, FLORIDA (see ST. JOSEPH'S HOSPITAL), p. A145

ST. JOSEPH'S HOSPITAL HEALTH CENTER, SYRACUSE, NY, p. A451

ST. JOSEPH'S HOSPITAL OF BUCKHANNON, BUCKHANNON, WV, p. A690

ST. JOSEPH'S HOSPITAL–SOUTH, RIVERVIEW, FLORIDA (see ST. JOSEPH'S HOSPITAL), p. A145

ST. JOSEPH'S MEDICAL CENTER, STOCKTON, CA, p. A93

ST. JOSEPH'S MEDICAL CENTER, YONKERS, NY, p. A454

ST. JOSEPH'S MERCY HOSPITAL–WEST, CLINTON TOWNSHIP, MICHIGAN (see HENRY FORD MACOMB HOSPITALS), p. A316

ST. JOSEPH'S MERCY–NORTH, ROMEO, MICHIGAN (see HENRY FORD MACOMB HOSPITALS), p. A316

ST. JOSEPH'S REGIONAL MEDICAL CENTER, PATERSON, NJ, p. A416

ST. JOSEPH'S WAYNE HOSPITAL, WAYNE, NEW JERSEY (see ST. JOSEPH'S REGIONAL MEDICAL CENTER), p. A416

ST. JOSEPH'S WOMEN'S HOSPITAL, TAMPA, FLORIDA (see ST. JOSEPH'S HOSPITAL), p. A145

ST. JUDE CHILDREN'S RESEARCH HOSPITAL, MEMPHIS, TN, p. A584

ST. JUDE MEDICAL CENTER, FULLERTON, CA, p. A63

ST. LANDRY EXTENDED CARE HOSPITAL, OPELOUSAS, LA, p. A283

ST. LAWRENCE PSYCHIATRIC CENTER, OGDENSBURG, NY, p. A446

ST. LAWRENCE REHABILITATION CENTER, LAWRENCEVILLE, NJ, p. A413

ST. LOUIS CHILDREN'S HOSPITAL, SAINT LOUIS, MO, p. A377

ST. LOUIS PSYCHIATRIC REHABILITATION CENTER, SAINT LOUIS, MO, p. A378

ST. LUCIE MEDICAL CENTER, PORT ST. LUCIE, FL, p. A141

ST. LUKE COMMUNITY HEALTHCARE, RONAN, MT, p. A386

ST. LUKE HOSPITAL AND LIVING CENTER, MARION, KS, p. A245

ST. LUKE'S BAPTIST HOSPITAL, SAN ANTONIO, TEXAS (see BAPTIST MEDICAL CENTER), p. A640

ST. LUKE'S BEHAVIORAL HEALTH CENTER, PHOENIX, AZ, p. A36

ST. LUKE'S CAMPUS, UTICA, NEW YORK (see FAXTON–ST. LUKE'S HEALTHCARE), p. A452

ST. LUKE'S CHILDREN'S HOSPITAL, BOISE, IDAHO (see ST. LUKE'S REGIONAL MEDICAL CENTER), p. A173

ST. LUKE'S CORNWALL HOSPITAL, NEWBURGH, NY, p. A445

ST. LUKE'S CORNWALL HOSPITAL – CORNWALL CAMPUS, CORNWALL, NEW YORK (see ST. LUKE'S CORNWALL HOSPITAL), p. A445

ST. LUKE'S CORNWALL HOSPITAL – NEWBURGH CAMPUS, NEWBURGH, NEW YORK (see ST. LUKE'S CORNWALL HOSPITAL), p. A445

ST. LUKE'S ELMORE, MOUNTAIN HOME, ID, p. A175

ST. LUKE'S EPISCOPAL HOSPITAL, PONCE, PR, p. A722

ST. LUKE'S HOSPITAL, NEW BEDFORD, MASSACHUSETTS (see SOUTHCOAST HOSPITALS GROUP), p. A306

ST. LUKE'S HOSPITAL, SAN FRANCISCO, CA, p. A88

ST. LUKE'S HOSPITAL, DULUTH, MN, p. A338

ST. LUKE'S HOSPITAL, CHESTERFIELD, MO, p. A365

ST. LUKE'S HOSPITAL, COLUMBUS, NC, p. A458

ST. LUKE'S HOSPITAL – ANDERSON CAMPUS, EASTON, PA, p. A533

ST. LUKE'S HOSPITAL – MINERS CAMPUS, COALDALE, PA, p. A531

ST. LUKE'S HOSPITAL – QUAKERTOWN CAMPUS, QUAKERTOWN, PA, p. A548

ST. LUKE'S HOSPITAL – THE VINTAGE HOSPITAL, HOUSTON, TX, p. A622

ST. LUKE'S HOSPITAL – WARREN CAMPUS, PHILLIPSBURG, NJ, p. A417

ST. LUKE'S JEROME, JEROME, ID, p. A174

ST. LUKE'S LAKESIDE HOSPITAL, THE WOODLANDS, TX, p. A647

ST. LUKE'S MAGIC VALLEY MEDICAL CENTER, TWIN FALLS, ID, p. A176

ST. LUKE'S MCCALL, MCCALL, ID, p. A175

ST. LUKE'S MEDICAL CENTER, CROSBY, ND, p. A473

ST. LUKE'S MEDICAL CENTER, PHOENIX, AZ, p. A36

ST. LUKE'S MERIDIAN MEDICAL CENTER, MERIDIAN, IDAHO (see ST. LUKE'S REGIONAL MEDICAL CENTER), p. A173

ST. LUKE'S PATIENTS MEDICAL CENTER, PASADENA, TX, p. A636

ST. LUKE'S REGIONAL MEDICAL CENTER, BOISE, ID, p. A173

ST. LUKE'S REHABILITATION HOSPITAL, BOISE, ID, p. A173

ST. LUKE'S REHABILITATION HOSPITAL, CHESTERFIELD, MO, p. A365

ST. LUKE'S REHABILITATION INSTITUTE, SPOKANE, WA, p. A685

ST. LUKE'S SUGAR LAND HOSPITAL, SUGAR LAND, TX, p. A646

ST. LUKE'S THE WOODLANDS HOSPITAL, THE WOODLANDS, TX, p. A648

ST. LUKE'S UNIVERSITY HOSPITAL – BETHLEHEM CAMPUS, BETHLEHEM, PA, p. A529

ST. LUKE'S WOOD RIVER MEDICAL CENTER, KETCHUM, ID, p. A174

ST. MARGARET'S HOSPITAL, SPRING VALLEY, IL, p. A201

ST. MARK'S HOSPITAL, SALT LAKE CITY, UT, p. A658

ST. MARK'S MEDICAL CENTER, LA GRANGE, TX, p. A627

ST. MARTIN HOSPITAL, BREAUX BRIDGE, LA, p. A271

ST. MARY MEDICAL CENTER, APPLE VALLEY, CA, p. A54

ST. MARY MEDICAL CENTER, LONG BEACH, CA, p. A68

ST. MARY MEDICAL CENTER, HOBART, IN, p. A211

ST. MARY MEDICAL CENTER, LANGHORNE, PA, p. A538

ST. MARY MERCY HOSPITAL, LIVONIA, MI, p. A325

ST. MARY'S WARRICK HOSPITAL, BOONVILLE, IN, p. A205

ST. MARY'S CHILDREN'S HOSPITAL, DULUTH, MINNESOTA (see ESSENTIA HEALTH ST. MARY'S MEDICAL CENTER), p. A338

ST. MARY'S GENERAL HOSPITAL, PASSAIC, NJ, p. A416

ST. MARY'S GOOD SAMARITAN HOSPITAL, GREENSBORO, GA, p. A158

ST. MARY'S HEALTH CARE SYSTEM, ATHENS, GA, p. A149

ST. MARY'S HEALTHCARE, AMSTERDAM, NY, p. A428

ST. MARY'S HEALTHCARE, AMSTERDAM, NEW YORK (see ST. MARY'S HEALTHCARE), p. A428

ST. MARY'S HOSPITAL, RHINELANDER, WISCONSIN (see MINISTRY SAINT MARY'S HOSPITALS), p. A710

ST. MARY'S HOSPITAL, COTTONWOOD, ID, p. A174

ST. MARY'S HOSPITAL, CENTRALIA, IL, p. A180

ST. MARY'S HOSPITAL, TROY, NY, p. A452

ST. MARY'S HOSPITAL, MADISON, WI, p. A704

ST. MARY'S HOSPITAL AND REHABILITATION CENTER, MINNEAPOLIS, MINNESOTA (see UNIVERSITY OF MINNESOTA MEDICAL CENTER, FAIRVIEW), p. A343

ST. MARY'S HOSPITAL MEDICAL CENTER, GREEN BAY, WI, p. A702

ST. MARY'S JANESVILLE HOSPITAL, JANESVILLE, WI, p. A703

ST. MARY'S MEDICAL CENTER, SAN FRANCISCO, CA, p. A88

ST. MARY'S MEDICAL CENTER, GRAND JUNCTION, CO, p. A104

ST. MARY'S MEDICAL CENTER, WEST PALM BEACH, FL, p. A147

ST. MARY'S MEDICAL CENTER, BLUE SPRINGS, MO, p. A363

ST. MARY'S MEDICAL CENTER, HUNTINGTON, WV, p. A692

ST. MARY'S MEDICAL CENTER OF EVANSVILLE, EVANSVILLE, IN, p. A208

ST. MARY'S OF MICHIGAN, SAGINAW, MI, p. A329

ST. MARY'S OF MICHIGAN STANDISH HOSPITAL, STANDISH, MI, p. A330

ST. MARY'S REGIONAL MEDICAL CENTER, LEWISTON, ME, p. A291

ST. MARY'S REGIONAL MEDICAL CENTER, ENID, OK, p. A506

ST. MARY'S SACRED HEART HOSPITAL, LAVONIA, GA, p. A160

ST. MARY-CORWIN MEDICAL CENTER, PUEBLO, CO, p. A108

ST. MICHAEL'S HOSPITAL AVERA, TYNDALL, SD, p. A572

ST. NICHOLAS HOSPITAL, SHEBOYGAN, WI, p. A711

ST. PATRICK HOSPITAL, MISSOULA, MT, p. A386

ST. PETER'S HOSPITAL, HELENA, MT, p. A384

ST. PETER'S HOSPITAL, ALBANY, NY, p. A428

ST. PETERSBURG GENERAL HOSPITAL, SAINT PETERSBURG, FL, p. A142

ST. RITA'S MEDICAL CENTER, LIMA, OH, p. A492

ST. ROSE DOMINICAN HOSPITALS – ROSE DE LIMA CAMPUS, HENDERSON, NV, p. A401

ST. ROSE DOMINICAN HOSPITALS – SAN MARTIN CAMPUS, LAS VEGAS, NV, p. A402

ST. ROSE DOMINICAN HOSPITALS – SIENA CAMPUS, HENDERSON, NV, p. A401

ST. ROSE HOSPITAL, HAYWARD, CA, p. A64

ST. TAMMANY PARISH HOSPITAL, COVINGTON, LA, p. A272

ST. THERESA SPECIALTY HOSPITAL, KENNER, LA, p. A276

ST. THOMAS MORE HOSPITAL, CANON CITY, CO, p. A100

ST. VINCENT ANDERSON REGIONAL HOSPITAL, ANDERSON, IN, p. A204

ST. VINCENT CARMEL HOSPITAL, CARMEL, IN, p. A206

ST. VINCENT CHARITY MEDICAL CENTER, CLEVELAND, OH, p. A485

ST. VINCENT CLAY HOSPITAL, BRAZIL, IN, p. A205

ST. VINCENT DUNN HOSPITAL, BEDFORD, IN, p. A204

ST. VINCENT FISHERS HOSPITAL, FISHERS, IN, p. A208

ST. VINCENT FRANKFORT HOSPITAL, FRANKFORT, IN, p. A209

ST. VINCENT GENERAL HOSPITAL DISTRICT, LEADVILLE, CO, p. A106

ST. VINCENT HEALTHCARE, BILLINGS, MT, p. A381

ST. VINCENT HEART CENTER, INDIANAPOLIS, IN, p. A212

ST. VINCENT HOSPITAL, GREEN BAY, WI, p. A702

ST. VINCENT INDIANAPOLIS HOSPITAL, INDIANAPOLIS, IN, p. A212

ST. VINCENT JENNINGS HOSPITAL, NORTH VERNON, IN, p. A218

ST. VINCENT MEDICAL CENTER, LOS ANGELES, CA, p. A73

ST. VINCENT MERCY HOSPITAL, ELWOOD, IN, p. A207

ST. VINCENT MORRILTON, MORRILTON, AR, p. A48

ST. VINCENT RANDOLPH HOSPITAL, WINCHESTER, IN, p. A221

ST. VINCENT REHABILITATION HOSPITAL, SHERWOOD, AR, p. A50

ST. VINCENT SALEM HOSPITAL, SALEM, IN, p. A219

ST. VINCENT SETON SPECIALTY HOSPITAL, INDIANAPOLIS, IN, p. A213

ST. VINCENT STRESS CENTER, INDIANAPOLIS, INDIANA (see ST. VINCENT INDIANAPOLIS HOSPITAL), p. A212

ST. VINCENT WILLIAMSPORT HOSPITAL, WILLIAMSPORT, IN, p. A221

ST. VINCENT WOMEN'S HOSPITAL, INDIANAPOLIS, INDIANA (see ST. VINCENT INDIANAPOLIS HOSPITAL), p. A212

ST. VINCENT'S BEHAVIORAL HEALTH, WESTPORT, CONNECTICUT (see ST. VINCENT'S MEDICAL CENTER), p. A111

ST. VINCENT'S BIRMINGHAM, BIRMINGHAM, AL, p. A17

ST. VINCENT'S BLOUNT, ONEONTA, AL, p. A23

ST. VINCENT'S EAST, BIRMINGHAM, AL, p. A17

ST. VINCENT'S MEDICAL CENTER, BRIDGEPORT, CT, p. A111

ST. VINCENT'S MEDICAL CENTER CLAY COUNTY, MIDDLEBURG, FL, p. A135

ST. VINCENT'S MEDICAL CENTER RIVERSIDE, JACKSONVILLE, FL, p. A130

ST. VINCENT'S MEDICAL CENTER SOUTHSIDE, JACKSONVILLE, FL, p. A130

ST. VINCENT'S ST. CLAIR, PELL CITY, AL, p. A24

ST. WILLIAM HOME FOR THE AGED (see MILBANK AREA HOSPITAL AVERA), p. A569

STAFFORD COUNTY HOSPITAL, STAFFORD, KS, p. A250

STAFFORD HOSPITAL, STAFFORD, VA, p. A673

STAMFORD HOSPITAL, STAMFORD, CT, p. A115

STAMFORD MEMORIAL HOSPITAL, STAMFORD, TX, p. A645

STANDING ROCK SERVICE UNIT, FORT YATES HOSPITAL, INDIAN HEALTH SERVICE, DHHS, FORT YATES, ND, p. A474

STANFORD HEALTH CARE, PALO ALTO, CA, p. A80

STANFORD HEALTH CARE – VALLEYCARE, PLEASANTON, CA, p. A81

STANISLAUS SURGICAL HOSPITAL, MODESTO, CA, p. A76

STANLY REGIONAL MEDICAL CENTER, ALBEMARLE, NC, p. A455

STANTON COUNTY HOSPITAL, JOHNSON, KS, p. A242

STAR VALLEY MEDICAL CENTER, AFTON, WY, p. A715

STARR COUNTY MEMORIAL HOSPITAL, RIO GRANDE CITY, TX, p. A638

STARR REGIONAL MEDICAL CENTER, ATHENS, TN, p. A574

STATE CORRECTIONAL INSTITUTION AT CAMP HILL, CAMP HILL, PA, p. A530

STATE HOSPITAL NORTH, OROFINO, ID, p. A175

STATE HOSPITAL SOUTH, BLACKFOOT, ID, p. A172

STATE PENITENTIARY HOSPITAL, WALLA WALLA, WA, p. A687

STATE PSYCHIATRIC HOSPITAL, IOWA CITY, IOWA (see UNIVERSITY OF IOWA HOSPITALS AND CLINICS), p. A230

STATEN ISLAND UNIVERSITY HOSPITAL,, NY, p. A444

STE. GENEVIEVE COUNTY MEMORIAL HOSPITAL, STE. GENEVIEVE, MO, p. A379

STEELE MEMORIAL MEDICAL CENTER, SALMON, ID, p. A176

STEPHENS COUNTY HOSPITAL, TOCCOA, GA, p. A166

STEPHENS MEMORIAL HOSPITAL, NORWAY, ME, p. A291

STEPHENS MEMORIAL HOSPITAL, BRECKENRIDGE, TX, p. A598

STERLING REGIONAL MEDCENTER, STERLING, CO, p. A109

STERLING SURGICAL HOSPITAL, SLIDELL, LA, p. A285

STERLINGTON REHABILITATION HOSPITAL, BASTROP, LA, p. A269

STEVEN AND ALEXANDRA COHEN CHILDREN'S MEDICAL CENTER OF NEW YORK,, NEW YORK (see LONG ISLAND JEWISH MEDICAL CENTER), p. A441

STEVENS COMMUNITY MEDICAL CENTER, MORRIS, MN, p. A343

STEVENS COUNTY HOSPITAL, HUGOTON, KS, p. A242

STEWART & LYNDA RESNICK NEUROPSYCHIATRIC HOSPITAL AT UCLA, LOS ANGELES, CA, p. A73

STEWART MEMORIAL COMMUNITY HOSPITAL, LAKE CITY, IA, p. A230

STILLWATER COMMUNITY HOSPITAL, COLUMBUS, MT, p. A382

STILLWATER MEDICAL CENTER, STILLWATER, OK, p. A515

STONE COUNTY HOSPITAL, WIGGINS, MS, p. A361

STONE COUNTY MEDICAL CENTER, MOUNTAIN VIEW, AR, p. A48

STONE INSTITUTE OF PSYCHIATRY, CHICAGO, ILLINOIS (see NORTHWESTERN MEMORIAL HOSPITAL), p. A183

STONECREST CENTER, DETROIT, MI, p. A318

STONEWALL JACKSON MEMORIAL HOSPITAL, WESTON, WV, p. A696

STONEWALL MEMORIAL HOSPITAL, ASPERMONT, TX, p. A593

STONY BROOK CHILDREN'S HOSPITAL, STONY BROOK, NEW YORK (see STONY BROOK UNIVERSITY MEDICAL CENTER), p. A451

STONY BROOK UNIVERSITY MEDICAL CENTER, STONY BROOK, NY, p. A451

STORMONT–VAIL HEALTHCARE, TOPEKA, KS, p. A251

STORY COUNTY MEDICAL CENTER, NEVADA, IA, p. A232

STOUGHTON HOSPITAL ASSOCIATION, STOUGHTON, WI, p. A711

STRAITH HOSPITAL FOR SPECIAL SURGERY, SOUTHFIELD, MI, p. A330

STRATEGIC BEHAVIORAL HEALTH – CHARLOTTE, CHARLOTTE, NC, p. A458

STRATEGIC BEHAVIORAL HEALTH – RALEIGH, GARNER, NC, p. A460

STRATEGIC BEHAVIORAL HEALTH – WILMINGTON, LELAND, NC, p. A463

STRAUB CLINIC & HOSPITAL, HONOLULU, HI, p. A169

STREAMWOOD BEHAVIORAL HEALTH CENTER, STREAMWOOD, IL, p. A202

STRINGFELLOW MEMORIAL HOSPITAL, ANNISTON, AL, p. A15

STRONG MEMORIAL HOSPITAL OF THE UNIVERSITY OF ROCHESTER, ROCHESTER, NY, p. A449

STROUD REGIONAL MEDICAL CENTER, STROUD, OK, p. A515

STS. MARY & ELIZABETH HOSPITAL, LOUISVILLE, KY, p. A262

STURDY MEMORIAL HOSPITAL, ATTLEBORO, MA, p. A302

STURGIS HOSPITAL, STURGIS, MI, p. A331

STURGIS REGIONAL HOSPITAL, STURGIS, SD, p. A572

SUBURBAN HOSPITAL, BETHESDA, MD, p. A296

SULLIVAN COUNTY COMMUNITY HOSPITAL, SULLIVAN, IN, p. A220

SULLIVAN COUNTY MEMORIAL HOSPITAL, MILAN, MO, p. A373

SUMMA AKRON CITY HOSPITAL, AKRON, OH, p. A478

SUMMA AKRON CITY HOSPITAL, AKRON, OHIO (see SUMMA AKRON CITY HOSPITAL), p. A478

SUMMA BARBERTON CITIZENS HOSPITAL, BARBERTON, OH, p. A479

SUMMA REHAB HOSPITAL, AKRON, OH, p. A478

SUMMA SAINT THOMAS HOSPITAL, AKRON, OHIO (see SUMMA AKRON CITY HOSPITAL), p. A478

SUMMA WESTERN RESERVE HOSPITAL, CUYAHOGA FALLS, OH, p. A487

SUMMERLIN HOSPITAL MEDICAL CENTER, LAS VEGAS, NV, p. A402

SUMMERS COUNTY ARH HOSPITAL, HINTON, WV, p. A691

SUMMERSVILLE REGIONAL MEDICAL CENTER, SUMMERSVILLE, WV, p. A695

SUMMERVILLE MEDICAL CENTER, SUMMERVILLE, SOUTH CAROLINA (see TRIDENT MEDICAL CENTER), p. A558

SUMMIT BEHAVIORAL HEALTHCARE, CINCINNATI, OH, p. A483

SUMMIT HEALTHCARE REGIONAL MEDICAL CENTER, SHOW LOW, AZ, p. A38

SUMMIT MEDICAL CENTER, EDMOND, OK, p. A506

SUMMIT OAKS HOSPITAL, SUMMIT, NJ, p. A418

SUMMIT PACIFIC MEDICAL CENTER, ELMA, WA, p. A678

SUMMIT PARK HOSPITAL AND NURSING CARE CENTER, POMONA, NY, p. A447

SUMMIT SURGICAL, HUTCHINSON, KS, p. A242

SUMMITRIDGE HOSPITAL, LAWRENCEVILLE, GA, p. A160

SUMNER COUNTY HOSPITAL DISTRICT ONE, CALDWELL, KS, p. A238

SUMNER REGIONAL MEDICAL CENTER, WELLINGTON, KS, p. A252

SUMNER REGIONAL MEDICAL CENTER, GALLATIN, TN, p. A578

SUNBURY COMMUNITY HOSPITAL AND OUTPATIENT CENTER, SUNBURY, PA, p. A550

SUNCOAST BEHAVIORAL HEALTH CENTER, BRADENTON, FL, p. A122

SUNDANCE HOSPITAL, ARLINGTON, TX, p. A592

SUNNYSIDE COMMUNITY HOSPITAL AND CLINICS, SUNNYSIDE, WA, p. A686

SUNNYVIEW REHABILITATION HOSPITAL, SCHENECTADY, NY, p. A450

SUNRISE CANYON HOSPITAL, LUBBOCK, TX, p. A629

SUNRISE CHILDREN'S HOSPITAL (see SUNRISE HOSPITAL AND MEDICAL CENTER), p. A403

SUNRISE HOSPITAL AND MEDICAL CENTER, LAS VEGAS, NV, p. A403

SUNY DOWNSTATE MEDICAL CENTER UNIVERSITY HOSPITAL,, NY, p. A444

SURGERY SPECIALTY HOSPITALS OF AMERICA, PASADENA, TX, p. A636

SURGICAL HOSPITAL AT SOUTHWOODS, YOUNGSTOWN, OH, p. A502

SURGICAL HOSPITAL OF OKLAHOMA, OKLAHOMA CITY, OK, p. A513

SURGICAL INSTITUTE OF READING, WYOMISSING, PA, p. A554

SURGICAL SPECIALTY CENTER AT COORDINATED HEALTH, ALLENTOWN, PA, p. A528

# T

# U

UNIVERSITY OF TEXAS MEDICAL BRANCH, GALVESTON, TX, p. A615

UNIVERSITY OF TEXAS SOUTHWESTERN MEDICAL CENTER, DALLAS, TX, p. A607

UNIVERSITY OF TEXAS SOUTHWESTERN MEDICAL CENTER – ST. PAUL, DALLAS, TEXAS (see UNIVERSITY OF TEXAS SOUTHWESTERN MEDICAL CENTER), p. A607

UNIVERSITY OF TEXAS SOUTHWESTERN MEDICAL CENTER – ZALE LIPSHY, DALLAS, TEXAS (see UNIVERSITY OF TEXAS SOUTHWESTERN MEDICAL CENTER), p. A607

UNIVERSITY OF UTAH HEALTH CARE – HOSPITAL AND CLINICS, SALT LAKE CITY, UT, p. A659

UNIVERSITY OF UTAH NEUROPSYCHIATRIC INSTITUTE, SALT LAKE CITY, UT, p. A659

UNIVERSITY OF VIRGINIA CHILDREN'S HOSPITAL, CHARLOTTESVILLE, VIRGINIA (see UNIVERSITY OF VIRGINIA MEDICAL CENTER), p. A663

UNIVERSITY OF VIRGINIA MEDICAL CENTER, CHARLOTTESVILLE, VA, p. A663

UNIVERSITY OF WASHINGTON MEDICAL CENTER, SEATTLE, WA, p. A684

UNIVERSITY OF WISCONSIN CHILDREN'S HOSPITAL, AMERICAN FAMILY CHILDREN'S HOSPITAL, MADISON, WISCONSIN (see UNIVERSITY OF WISCONSIN HOSPITAL AND CLINICS), p. A704

UNIVERSITY OF WISCONSIN HOSPITAL AND CLINICS, MADISON, WI, p. A704

UNIVERSITY PAVILION, TAMARAC, FLORIDA (see UNIVERSITY HOSPITAL AND MEDICAL CENTER), p. A144

UNIVERSITY PEDIATRIC HOSPITAL,, PR, p. A724

UNM CHILDREN'S HOSPITAL, ALBUQUERQUE, NEW MEXICO (see UNIVERSITY OF NEW MEXICO HOSPITALS), p. A423

UNM SANDOVAL REGIONAL MEDICAL CENTER, RIO RANCHO, NM, p. A426

UP HEALTH SYSTEM–BELL, ISHPEMING, MI, p. A323

UP HEALTH SYSTEM–MARQUETTE, MARQUETTE, MI, p. A325

UP HEALTH SYSTEM–PORTAGE, HANCOCK, MI, p. A322

UPLAND HILLS HEALTH, DODGEVILLE, WI, p. A699

UPMC ALTOONA, ALTOONA, PA, p. A528

UPMC BEDFORD MEMORIAL, EVERETT, PA, p. A534

UPMC EAST, MONROEVILLE, PA, p. A540

UPMC HAMOT, ERIE, PA, p. A534

UPMC HORIZON, GREENVILLE, PA, p. A535

UPMC MCKEESPORT, MCKEESPORT, PA, p. A539

UPMC MERCY, PITTSBURGH, PA, p. A547

UPMC MONTEFIORE, PITTSBURGH, PENNSYLVANIA (see UPMC PRESBYTERIAN SHADYSIDE), p. A547

UPMC NORTHWEST, SENECA, PA, p. A550

UPMC PASSAVANT, PITTSBURGH, PA, p. A547

UPMC PASSAVANT CRANBERRY, CRANBERRY, PENNSYLVANIA (see UPMC PASSAVANT), p. A547

UPMC PRESBYTERIAN HOSPITAL, PITTSBURGH, PENNSYLVANIA (see UPMC PRESBYTERIAN SHADYSIDE), p. A547

UPMC PRESBYTERIAN SHADYSIDE, PITTSBURGH, PA, p. A547

UPMC SHADYSIDE, PITTSBURGH, PENNSYLVANIA (see UPMC PRESBYTERIAN SHADYSIDE), p. A547

UPMC ST. MARGARET, PITTSBURGH, PA, p. A547

UPPER CONNECTICUT VALLEY HOSPITAL, COLEBROOK, NH, p. A405

UPPER VALLEY MEDICAL CENTER, TROY, OH, p. A499

UPSON REGIONAL MEDICAL CENTER, THOMASTON, GA, p. A165

UPSTATE UNIVERSITY HOSPITAL, SYRACUSE, NY, p. A451

UPSTATE UNIVERSITY HOSPITAL AT COMMUNITY GENERAL, SYRACUSE, NEW YORK (see UPSTATE UNIVERSITY HOSPITAL), p. A451

USC VERDUGO HILLS HOSPITAL, GLENDALE, CA, p. A64

USMD HOSPITAL AT ARLINGTON, ARLINGTON, TX, p. A593

USMD HOSPITAL AT FORT WORTH, FORT WORTH, TX, p. A614

UTAH STATE HOSPITAL, PROVO, UT, p. A657

UTAH VALLEY REGIONAL MEDICAL CENTER, PROVO, UT, p. A657

UTAH VALLEY SPECIALTY HOSPITAL, PROVO, UT, p. A657

UVA CULPEPER HOSPITAL, CULPEPER, VA, p. A664

UVA TRANSITIONAL CARE HOSPITAL, CHARLOTTESVILLE, VA, p. A663

UVA–HEALTHSOUTH REHABILITATION HOSPITAL, CHARLOTTESVILLE, VA, p. A663

UVALDE COUNTY HOSPITAL AUTHORITY, UVALDE, TX, p. A649

UW MEDICINE/HARBORVIEW MEDICAL CENTER, SEATTLE, WA, p. A684

UW MEDICINE/NORTHWEST HOSPITAL & MEDICAL CENTER, SEATTLE, WA, p. A684

UW MEDICINE/VALLEY MEDICAL CENTER, RENTON, WA, p. A682

# V

VA GREATER LOS ANGELES HEALTHCARE SYSTEM, LOS ANGELES, CA, p. A73

VA LONG BEACH HEALTHCARE SYSTEM, LONG BEACH, CA, p. A68

VA PALO ALTO HEALTH CARE SYSTEM, PALO ALTO, CA, p. A80

VA SAN DIEGO HEALTHCARE SYSTEM, SAN DIEGO, CA, p. A87

VAIL VALLEY MEDICAL CENTER, VAIL, CO, p. A109

VAL VERDE REGIONAL MEDICAL CENTER, DEL RIO, TX, p. A607

VALDESE GENERAL HOSPITAL, VALDESE, NORTH CAROLINA (see BLUE RIDGE HEALTHCARE HOSPITALS), p. A465

VALIR REHABILITATION HOSPITAL, OKLAHOMA CITY, OK, p. A513

VALLE VISTA HOSPITAL, GREENWOOD, IN, p. A210

VALLEY BAPTIST MEDICAL CENTER–BROWNSVILLE, BROWNSVILLE, TX, p. A599

VALLEY BAPTIST MEDICAL CENTER–HARLINGEN, HARLINGEN, TX, p. A618

VALLEY BEHAVIORAL HEALTH SYSTEM, BARLING, AR, p. A41

VALLEY CHILDREN'S HOSPITAL, MADERA, CA, p. A74

VALLEY COUNTY HEALTH SYSTEM, ORD, NE, p. A397

VALLEY FORGE MEDICAL CENTER AND HOSPITAL, NORRISTOWN, PA, p. A542

VALLEY HOSPITAL, RIDGEWOOD, NJ, p. A418

VALLEY HOSPITAL, SPOKANE VALLEY, WA, p. A685

VALLEY HOSPITAL MEDICAL CENTER, LAS VEGAS, NV, p. A403

VALLEY HOSPITAL PHOENIX, PHOENIX, AZ, p. A36

VALLEY MEMORIAL, LIVERMORE, CALIFORNIA (see STANFORD HEALTH CARE – VALLEYCARE), p. A81

VALLEY PRESBYTERIAN HOSPITAL,, CA, p. A73

VALLEY REGIONAL HOSPITAL, CLAREMONT, NH, p. A405

VALLEY REGIONAL MEDICAL CENTER, BROWNSVILLE, TX, p. A599

VALLEY VIEW HOSPITAL, GLENWOOD SPRINGS, CO, p. A104

VALLEY VIEW MEDICAL CENTER, FORT MOHAVE, AZ, p. A31

VALLEY VIEW MEDICAL CENTER, CEDAR CITY, UT, p. A654

VALLEY WEST HOSPITAL, SANDWICH, IL, p. A200

VALOR HEALTH, EMMETT, ID, p. A174

VAN BUREN COUNTY HOSPITAL, KEOSAUQUA, IA, p. A230

VAN DIEST MEDICAL CENTER, WEBSTER CITY, IA, p. A236

VAN MATRE HEALTHSOUTH REHABILITATION HOSPITAL, ROCKFORD, IL, p. A200

VAN WERT COUNTY HOSPITAL, VAN WERT, OH, p. A499

VANCOUVER MEMORIAL CAMPUS, VANCOUVER, WASHINGTON (see PEACEHEALTH SOUTHWEST MEDICAL CENTER), p. A687

VANDERBILT HOSPITAL AND CLINICS, NASHVILLE, TN, p. A586

VANDERBILT PSYCHIATRIC HOSPITAL, NASHVILLE, TENNESSEE (see VANDERBILT HOSPITAL AND CLINICS), p. A586

VANDERBILT STALLWORTH REHABILITATION HOSPITAL, NASHVILLE, TN, p. A586

VANTAGE POINT OF NORTHWEST ARKANSAS, FAYETTEVILLE, AR, p. A44

VASSAR BROTHERS MEDICAL CENTER, POUGHKEEPSIE, NY, p. A448

VAUGHAN REGIONAL MEDICAL CENTER, SELMA, AL, p. A24

VCU COMMUNITY MEMORIAL HOSPITAL, SOUTH HILL, VA, p. A673

VCU HEALTH SYSTEM CHILDREN'S MEDICAL CENTER, RICHMOND, VIRGINIA (see VCU MEDICAL CENTER), p. A672

VCU MEDICAL CENTER, RICHMOND, VA, p. A672

VENICE REGIONAL BAYFRONT HEALTH, VENICE, FL, p. A146

VENTURA COUNTY MEDICAL CENTER, VENTURA, CA, p. A96

VERDE VALLEY MEDICAL CENTER, COTTONWOOD, AZ, p. A30

VERMONT CHILDREN'S HOSPITAL, BURLINGTON, VERMONT (see THE UNIVERSITY OF VERMONT HEALTH NETWORK UNIVERSITY OF VERMONT MEDICAL CENTER), p. A660

VERNON MEMORIAL HEALTHCARE, VIROQUA, WI, p. A712

VETERAN AFFAIRS HUDSON VALLEY HEALTH CARE SYSTEM–CASTLE POINT CAMPUS, WAPPINGERS, NEW YORK (see VETERANS AFFAIRS HUDSON VALLEY HEALTH CARE SYSTEM), p. A438

VETERANS AFFAIRS ANN ARBOR HEALTHCARE SYSTEM, ANN ARBOR, MI, p. A314

VETERANS AFFAIRS BLACK HILLS HEALTH CARE SYSTEM, FORT MEADE, SD, p. A568

VETERANS AFFAIRS BOSTON HEALTHCARE SYSTEM, BOSTON, MA, p. A304

VETERANS AFFAIRS BOSTON HEALTHCARE SYSTEM BROCKTON DIVISION, BROCKTON, MA, p. A305

VETERANS AFFAIRS CARIBBEAN HEALTHCARE SYSTEM, SAN JUAN, PR, p. A724

VETERANS AFFAIRS CENTRAL CALIFORNIA HEALTH CARE SYSTEM, FRESNO, CA, p. A63

VETERANS AFFAIRS CENTRAL IOWA HEALTH CARE SYSTEM, DES MOINES, IA, p. A227

VETERANS AFFAIRS CENTRAL WESTERN MASSACHUSETTS HEALTHCARE SYSTEM, LEEDS, MA, p. A308

VETERANS AFFAIRS CONNECTICUT HEALTHCARE SYSTEM, WEST HAVEN, CT, p. A116

VETERANS AFFAIRS EASTERN COLORADO HEALTH CARE SYSTEM, DENVER, CO, p. A102

VETERANS AFFAIRS EASTERN KANSAS HEALTH CARE SYSTEM, TOPEKA, KS, p. A251

VETERANS AFFAIRS EASTERN KANSAS HEALTH CARE SYSTEM–COLMERY–O'NEIL VETERANS AFFAIRS MEDICAL CENTER, TOPEKA, KANSAS (see VETERANS AFFAIRS EASTERN KANSAS HEALTH CARE SYSTEM), p. A251

VETERANS AFFAIRS EASTERN KANSAS HEALTH CARE SYSTEM–DWIGHT D. EISENHOWER VETERANS AFFAIRS MEDICAL CENTER, LEAVENWORTH, KANSAS (see VETERANS AFFAIRS EASTERN KANSAS HEALTH CARE SYSTEM), p. A251

VETERANS AFFAIRS GULF COAST VETERANS HEALTH CARE SYSTEM, BILOXI, MS, p. A350

VETERANS AFFAIRS HUDSON VALLEY HEALTH CARE SYSTEM, MONTROSE, NY, p. A438

VETERANS AFFAIRS HUDSON VALLEY HEALTH CARE SYSTEM–MONTROSE CAMPUS, MONTROSE, NEW YORK (see VETERANS AFFAIRS HUDSON VALLEY HEALTH CARE SYSTEM), p. A438

VETERANS AFFAIRS ILLIANA HEALTH CARE SYSTEM, DANVILLE, IL, p. A185

VETERANS AFFAIRS LOMA LINDA HEALTHCARE SYSTEM, LOMA LINDA, CA, p. A68

VETERANS AFFAIRS MARYLAND HEALTH CARE SYSTEM–BALTIMORE DIVISION, BALTIMORE, MD, p. A295

VETERANS AFFAIRS MARYLAND HEALTH CARE SYSTEM–PERRY POINT DIVISION, PERRY POINT, MARYLAND (see VETERANS AFFAIRS MARYLAND HEALTH CARE SYSTEM–BALTIMORE DIVISION), p. A295

VETERANS AFFAIRS MEDICAL CENTER, PITTSBURGH, PENNSYLVANIA (see VETERANS AFFAIRS PITTSBURGH HEALTHCARE SYSTEM), p. A547

VETERANS AFFAIRS MEDICAL CENTER, PITTSBURGH, PENNSYLVANIA (see VETERANS AFFAIRS PITTSBURGH HEALTHCARE SYSTEM), p. A547

VETERANS AFFAIRS MEDICAL CENTER HOT SPRINGS CAMPUS, HOT SPRINGS, SOUTH DAKOTA (see VETERANS AFFAIRS BLACK HILLS HEALTH CARE SYSTEM), p. A568

VETERANS AFFAIRS MEDICAL CENTER WEST ROXBURY DIVISION, WEST ROXBURY, MASSACHUSETTS (see VETERANS AFFAIRS BOSTON HEALTHCARE SYSTEM BROCKTON DIVISION), p. A305

VETERANS AFFAIRS MONTANA HEALTH CARE SYSTEM, FORT HARRISON, MT, p. A383

VETERANS AFFAIRS NEBRASKA–WESTERN IOWA HEALTH CARE SYSTEM, OMAHA, NE, p. A397

VETERANS AFFAIRS NEBRASKA–WESTERN IOWA HEALTH CARE SYSTEM – LINCOLN, LINCOLN, NE, p. A394

VETERANS AFFAIRS NEW JERSEY HEALTH CARE SYSTEM, EAST ORANGE, NJ, p. A411

VETERANS AFFAIRS NEW YORK HARBOR HEALTHCARE SYSTEM,, NY, p. A445

VETERANS AFFAIRS NEW YORK HARBOR HEALTHCARE SYSTEM – MANHATTAN CAMPUS, NEW YORK, NEW YORK (see VETERANS AFFAIRS NEW YORK HARBOR HEALTHCARE SYSTEM), p. A445

VETERANS AFFAIRS NORTH TEXAS HEALTH CARE SYSTEM, DALLAS, TX, p. A607

VETERANS AFFAIRS NORTHERN INDIANA HEALTH CARE SYSTEM, FORT WAYNE, IN, p. A209

VETERANS AFFAIRS NORTHERN INDIANA HEALTH CARE SYSTEM–MARION CAMPUS, MARION, INDIANA (see VETERANS AFFAIRS NORTHERN INDIANA HEALTH CARE SYSTEM), p. A209

VETERANS AFFAIRS PACIFIC ISLANDS HEALTH CARE SYSTEM, HONOLULU, HI, p. A169

VETERANS AFFAIRS PALO ALTO HEALTH CARE SYSTEM, LIVERMORE DIVISION, LIVERMORE, CALIFORNIA (see VA PALO ALTO HEALTH CARE SYSTEM), p. A80

VETERANS AFFAIRS PITTSBURGH HEALTHCARE SYSTEM, PITTSBURGH, PA, p. A547

VETERANS AFFAIRS PUGET SOUND HEALTH CARE SYSTEM, SEATTLE, WA, p. A684

VETERANS AFFAIRS PUGET SOUND HEALTH CARE SYSTEM–AMERICAN LAKE DIVISION, TACOMA, WASHINGTON (see VETERANS AFFAIRS PUGET SOUND HEALTH CARE SYSTEM), p. A684

VETERANS AFFAIRS ROSEBURG HEALTHCARE SYSTEM, ROSEBURG, OR, p. A525

VETERANS AFFAIRS SALT LAKE CITY HEALTH CARE SYSTEM, SALT LAKE CITY, UT, p. A659

VETERANS AFFAIRS SIERRA NEVADA HEALTH CARE SYSTEM, RENO, NV, p. A404

VETERANS AFFAIRS SOUTHERN NEVADA HEALTHCARE SYSTEM, NORTH LAS VEGAS, NV, p. A403

# W

WRANGELL MEDICAL CENTER, WRANGELL, AK, p. A29
WRAY COMMUNITY DISTRICT HOSPITAL, WRAY, CO, p. A110
WRIGHT MEMORIAL HOSPITAL, TRENTON, MO, p. A379
WRIGHT PATTERSON MEDICAL CENTER, WRIGHT–PATTERSON AFB, OH, p. A501
WUESTHOFF MEDICAL CENTER – MELBOURNE, MELBOURNE, FL, p. A133
WUESTHOFF MEDICAL CENTER – ROCKLEDGE, ROCKLEDGE, FL, p. A141
WYANDOT MEMORIAL HOSPITAL, UPPER SANDUSKY, OH, p. A499
WYCKOFF HEIGHTS MEDICAL CENTER,, NY, p. A445
WYOMING BEHAVIORAL INSTITUTE, CASPER, WY, p. A715
WYOMING COUNTY COMMUNITY HOSPITAL, WARSAW, NY, p. A453
WYOMING MEDICAL CENTER, CASPER, WY, p. A715
WYOMING STATE HOSPITAL, EVANSTON, WY, p. A716
WYSONG CAMPUS, MCKINNEY, TEXAS (see MEDICAL CENTER OF MCKINNEY), p. A632
WYTHE COUNTY COMMUNITY HOSPITAL, WYTHEVILLE, VA, p. A675

# Y

YAKIMA REGIONAL MEDICAL AND CARDIAC CENTER, YAKIMA, WA, p. A688

YAKIMA VALLEY MEMORIAL HOSPITAL, YAKIMA, WA, p. A688
YALE–NEW HAVEN CHILDREN'S HOSPITAL, NEW HAVEN, CONNECTICUT (see YALE–NEW HAVEN HOSPITAL), p. A114
YALE–NEW HAVEN HOSPITAL, NEW HAVEN, CT, p. A114
YALE–NEW HAVEN HOSPITAL–SAINT RAPHAEL CAMPUS, NEW HAVEN, CONNECTICUT (see YALE–NEW HAVEN HOSPITAL), p. A114
YALE–NEW HAVEN PSYCHIATRIC HOSPITAL, NEW HAVEN, CONNECTICUT (see YALE–NEW HAVEN HOSPITAL), p. A114
YALOBUSHA GENERAL HOSPITAL, WATER VALLEY, MS, p. A361
YAMPA VALLEY MEDICAL CENTER, STEAMBOAT SPRINGS, CO, p. A108
YAVAPAI REGIONAL  MEDICAL CENTER – EAST, PRESCOTT VALLEY, AZ, p. A36
YAVAPAI REGIONAL MEDICAL CENTER, PRESCOTT, AZ, p. A36
YOAKUM COMMUNITY HOSPITAL, YOAKUM, TX, p. A653
YOAKUM COUNTY HOSPITAL, DENVER CITY, TX, p. A608
YORK GENERAL HOSPITAL, YORK, NE, p. A399
YORK HOSPITAL, YORK, ME, p. A292
YORK HOSPITAL, YORK, PA, p. A554
YOUNKER MEMORIAL REHABILITATION CENTER, DES MOINES, IOWA (see UNITYPOINT HEALTH – IOWA METHODIST MEDICAL CENTER), p. A226
YOUTH VILLAGES INNER HARBOUR CAMPUS, DOUGLASVILLE, GA, p. A156
YUKON–KUSKOKWIM DELTA REGIONAL HOSPITAL, BETHEL, AK, p. A27
YUMA DISTRICT HOSPITAL, YUMA, CO, p. A110
YUMA REGIONAL MEDICAL CENTER, YUMA, AZ, p. A40
YUMA REHABILITATION HOSPITAL, YUMA, AZ, p. A40

# Z

ZUCKER HILLSIDE HOSPITAL,, NEW YORK (see LONG ISLAND JEWISH MEDICAL CENTER), p. A441

# Index of Health
# Care Professionals

*This section is an index of the key health care professionals for the hospitals and/or health care systems listed in this publication. The index is in alphabetical order, by individual, followed by the title, institutional affiliation, city, state and page reference to the hospital and/or health care system listing in section A and/or B.*

## A

AAGARD, Kim, Chief Financial Officer, Tri–County Hospital, Wadena, MN, p. A348

ABAIR, Cynthia, Associate Director, VA San Diego Healthcare System, San Diego, CA, p. A87

ABANG, Toni, M.D. Medical Director, HEALTHSOUTH Lakeview Rehabilitation Hospital, Elizabethtown, KY, p. A256

ABBATIELLO, Michael, Chief Financial Officer, Spring Harbor Hospital, Westbrook, ME, p. A292

ABBOTT, Jody, Senior Vice President and Chief Operating Officer, North Kansas City Hospital, North Kansas City, MO, p. A373

ABBOTT, Joe, Director Information Systems, North Ottawa Community Hospital, Grand Haven, MI, p. A320

ABBOTT, Justin, M.D. Medical Director, Sevier Valley Medical Center, Richfield, UT, p. A657

ABBOTT, Lisa, Chief Human Resources Officer, Penn State Milton S. Hershey Medical Center, Hershey, PA, p. A536

ABBOTT, Peggy L., President and Chief Executive Officer, Ouachita County Medical Center, Camden, AR, p. A42

ABDA, William, Chief Human Resources Officer, Clarks Summit State Hospital, Clarks Summit, PA, p. A531

ABDELNASER, Mohammad, Chief Nursing Officer, Centinela Hospital Medical Center, Inglewood, CA, p. A65

ABE, Ann, Administrator and Chief Operating Officer, Orange County Global Medical Center, Inc., Santa Ana, CA, p. A90

ABEL, Barbara J., Vice President Human Resources, Heart of the Rockies Regional Medical Center, Salida, CO, p. A108

ABEL, Jeffrey, M.D. Chief Medical Officer, Ogden Regional Medical Center, Ogden, UT, p. A656

ABEL, Kevin, Chief Executive Officer, Lake Chelan Community Hospital, Chelan, WA, p. A677

ABEL, Stacy L., Director Human Resources, Craig Hospital, Englewood, CO, p. A103

ABELLERA, Roland, Chief Quality Officer and Vice President Clinical Operations, St. Bernard Hospital and Health Care Center, Chicago, IL, p. A184

ABELSON, David, M.D., President and Chief Executive Officer, Park Nicollet Methodist Hospital, Saint Louis Park, MN, p. A346

ABELY, Susan Cerrone
Vice President and Chief Information Officer, Roger Williams Medical Center, Providence, RI, p. A556
Chief Information Officer, St. Joseph Health Services of Rhode Island, North Providence, RI, p. A555

ABERCROMBIE, David E., Chief Executive Officer, Montgomery County Memorial Hospital, Red Oak, IA, p. A233

ABERCROMBIE, Zach, Chief Financial Officer, Citizens Baptist Medical Center, Talladega, AL, p. A25

ABERLE, James, Vice President, Hospital Operations, Yakima Valley Memorial Hospital, Yakima, WA, p. A688

ABERNATHY, Clint, Interim Chief Executive Officer, Texas Health Harris Methodist Hospital Alliance, Fort Worth, TX, p. A614

ABEYTA, Mary Anna, R.N. Chief Nursing/Clinical Services Officer, Holy Cross Hospital, Taos, NM, p. A427

ABINSAY, Alvin, M.D. Chief Medical Staff, Carolinas Hospital System Marion, Mullins, SC, p. A563

ABNEY, Stuart, Controller, Jasper Memorial Hospital, Monticello, GA, p. A162

ABOUD, Al, Chief Financial Officer, East Orange General Hospital, East Orange, NJ, p. A411

ABRAHAM, Akram, M.D. Chief of Staff, Harmon Memorial Hospital, Hollis, OK, p. A508

ABRAHAM, Brian, Chief Operating Officer, Mesquite Rehabilitation Institute, Mesquite, TX, p. A632

ABRAHAM, JiJi, Chief Financial Officer, Kaiser Permanente Riverside Medical Center, Riverside, CA, p. A83

ABRAHAMSON–BATY, Sherri, Director Patient Care Services, Cambridge Medical Center, Cambridge, MN, p. A336

ABRAHAMY, Ran, M.D. Chief of Staff, University Hospital and Medical Center, Tamarac, FL, p. A144

ABRAMS, Danielle, Manager Human Resources, Marketing and Executive Assistant, St. Vincent Clay Hospital, Brazil, IN, p. A205

ABRAMS, David, Vice President Human Resources, North Memorial Medical Center, Robbinsdale, MN, p. A345

ABRAMS, Denise, Human Resources, Mother Frances Hospital – Jacksonville, Jacksonville, TX, p. A624

ABREU, Astrid J., Executive Director, Hospital Metropolitano Dr. Susoni, Arecibo, PR, p. A720

ABREU, Iris, Supervisor Human Resources, Hospital HMA de Humacao, Humacao, PR, p. A721

ABREU, John, Vice President and Chief Financial Officer, Portneuf Medical Center, Pocatello, ID, p. A175

ABRINA, Sofia, Administrator and Chief Nursing Officer, Huntington Beach Hospital, Huntington Beach, CA, p. A65

ABROMOVICH, Sari, Chief Executive Officer, Harbor Oaks Hospital, New Baltimore, MI, p. A326

ABRUTZ Jr., Joseph F., Administrator, Cameron Regional Medical Center, Cameron, MO, p. A364

ABUNDO, Manuel, M.D. Chief of Staff, Wahiawa General Hospital, Wahiawa, HI, p. A170

ABY, Sherry, Director Information Management, Carlisle Regional Medical Center, Carlisle, PA, p. A531

ACCASHIAN, Chris, Chief Executive Officer, Parkland Medical Center, Derry, NH, p. A405

ACETO, Anthony, Vice President Human Resources, Norwalk Hospital, Norwalk, CT, p. A114

ACEVEDO, Edwin Orama, Financial Supervisor, Hospital Buen Samaritano, Aguadilla, PR, p. A719

ACEVEDO, Jose, M.D., President and Chief Executive Officer, Finger Lakes Health, Geneva, NY, p. B56

ACEVEDO, Jose, M.D.,
President and Chief Executive Officer, Geneva General Hospital, Geneva, NY, p. A434
President and Chief Executive Officer, Soldiers and Sailors Memorial Hospital of Yates County, Penn Yan, NY, p. A447

ACEVEDO, Ramon, Supervisor Information Systems, Hospital San Cristobal, Coto Laurel, PR, p. A721

ACHARYA, Ganesh, Chief Executive Officer, Good Samaritan Hospital, Bakersfield, CA, p. A55

ACHEBE, James Bob, M.D. President Medical Staff, South Shore Hospital, Chicago, IL, p. A184

ACHTER, Dick, Chief Financial Officer, Barrett Hospital & HealthCare, Dillon, MT, p. A383

ACKER, Carmen, Chief Financial Officer, Morton Hospital and Medical Center, Taunton, MA, p. A312

ACKER, David B., FACHE, President and CEO, Canton–Potsdam Hospital, Potsdam, NY, p. A448

ACKER, David B., FACHE, President and CEO, St. Lawrence Health System, Potsdam, NY, p. B127

ACKER, Peter W., President and Chief Executive Officer, Carolinas HealthCare System Lincoln, Lincolnton, NC, p. A464

ACKERMAN, F. Kenneth, Chair, Hospital Operations, Mayo Clinic Hospital – Rochester, Rochester, MN, p. A345

ACKERMAN, S. Jeffrey, M.D., Chief Executive Officer, Citizens Medical Center, Victoria, TX, p. A650

ACKERMAN, Sigurd H., M.D., President and Chief Executive Officer, Silver Hill Hospital, New Canaan, CT, p. A114

ACKERSON, David, Chief Information Officer, Seattle Cancer Care Alliance, Seattle, WA, p. A683

ACKERT, Sara, Associate Director, Sioux Falls Veterans Affairs Health Care System, Sioux Falls, SD, p. A572

ACKLAND, Jeanne, Director of Finance, Fillmore County Hospital, Geneva, NE, p. A392

ACKLEY, Michael
Chief Financial Officer, Kentucky River Medical Center, Jackson, KY, p. A259
Chief Financial Officer, Three Rivers Medical Center, Louisa, KY, p. A260

ACKLIN, Traci, M.D. Chief of Staff, Montgomery General Hospital, Montgomery, WV, p. A693

ACKMAN, Jeffrey D., M.D. Chief of Staff, Shriners Hospitals for Children–Chicago, Chicago, IL, p. A184

ACKMAN, Laura, Chief Operating Officer and Administrator, Essentia Health Northern Pines Medical Center, Aurora, MN, p. A335

ACOSTA, Ivan, M.D. Medical Director, Hospital De La Concepcion, San German, PR, p. A722

ACOSTA, Jose' A., USN, Commanding Officer, Naval Medical Center San Diego, San Diego, CA, p. A86

ACOSTA, Louis, M.D. Chief of Staff, Silver Lake Medical Center, Los Angeles, CA, p. A72

ACOSTA, Nannete, Chief Executive Officer, Hospital Metropolitano San German, San German, PR, p. A722

ACOSTA–CARLSON, Francisca, M.D. Chief of Staff, Lexington Regional Health Center, Lexington, NE, p. A393

ACOSTA–CRUZ, Maridel, Chief Executive Officer, Eastern New Mexico Medical Center, Roswell, NM, p. A426

ACREE, Charis, Senior Vice President, West Georgia Health, Lagrange, GA, p. A160

ADAIR, Dale K., M.D. Chief Medical Officer, Wernersville State Hospital, Wernersville, PA, p. A552

ADAIR, Julie, Interim Corporate Chief Human Resources Officer, Fresno Heart and Surgical Hospital, Fresno, CA, p. A62

ADAM, Sheryl, Chief Financial Officer, Hanover Hospital, Hanover, KS, p. A241

ADAMO, James D., M.D. Medical Director, Harbor Oaks Hospital, New Baltimore, MI, p. A326

ADAMO, Peter J.
Chief Executive Officer, Lower Bucks Hospital, Bristol, PA, p. A530
Chief Executive Officer, Roxborough Memorial Hospital, Philadelphia, PA, p. A545

ADAMS, Alan L., President, Memorial Hospital, Stilwell, OK, p. A515

ADAMS, Amy B.
Executive Director Human Resources, Laureate Psychiatric Clinic and Hospital, Tulsa, OK, p. A516
Executive Director Human Resources, Saint Francis Hospital, Tulsa, OK, p. A517
Executive Director Human Resources, Saint Francis Hospital South, Tulsa, OK, p. A517

ADAMS, Bob, Director Information Services, Bay Area Hospital, Coos Bay, OR, p. A520

ADAMS, Brian
President and Chief Executive Officer, Florida Hospital at Connerton Long Term Acute Care, Land O'Lakes, FL, p. A131
President and CEO, Florida Hospital Tampa, Tampa, FL, p. A144

ADAMS, Carla A., Chief Nursing Officer and Chief Operating Officer, French Hospital Medical Center, San Luis Obispo, CA, p. A90

ADAMS, Cathleen, Chief Nursing Officer, CarePartners Health Services, Asheville, NC, p. A455

ADAMS, Charlotte, Director Associate Resources, Carolina Pines Regional Medical Center, Hartsville, SC, p. A562

ADAMS, Chris, Vice President Patient Care Services, Good Samaritan Regional Health Center, Mount Vernon, IL, p. A195

ADAMS, Cynthia, Vice President Human Resources, TriStar StoneCrest Medical Center, Smyrna, TN, p. A588

ADAMS, Earl, Chief Information Officer, Indiana University Health La Porte Hospital, La Porte, IN, p. A214

ADAMS, Emmy, Chief Financial Officer, Mayhill Hospital, Denton, TX, p. A608

ADAMS, Essie, Director of Nursing, Kedren Community Mental Health Center, Los Angeles, CA, p. A70

ADAMS, Gini, Director Employee and Public Relations, Yuma District Hospital, Yuma, CO, p. A110

ADAMS, J'Dee, Chief Operating Officer, North Canyon Medical Center, Gooding, ID, p. A174

ADAMS, Jason, Chief Operating Officer, CHRISTUS St. Vincent Regional Medical Center, Santa Fe, NM, p. A426

ADAMS, Jason, M.D. Medical Staff President, Forest Health Medical Center, Ypsilanti, MI, p. A333

ADAMS, Jennifer B., Chief Operating Officer and Chief Financial Officer, Lake City Medical Center, Lake City, FL, p. A131

ADAMS, Jo, Director Human Resources, Donalsonville Hospital, Donalsonville, GA, p. A156

ADAMS, Karen, Vice President Human Resources, Baxter Regional Medical Center, Mountain Home, AR, p. A48

ADAMS, Kelly H., Chief Executive Officer, Desert View Hospital, Pahrump, NV, p. A403

ADAMS, Kimberly, Manager Human Resources, Carroll County Memorial Hospital, Carrollton, KY, p. A255

ADAMS, Leslie, Chief Nursing Executive, Saint Joseph Berea, Berea, KY, p. A254

ADAMS, Mark A., President and Chief Executive Officer, Methodist Rehabilitation Center, Jackson, MS, p. A355

Index of Health Care Professionals / Akin

ADAMS, Mark B., Chief Executive Officer, Ogden Regional Medical Center, Ogden, UT, p. A656
ADAMS, Mark C., M.D. Chief Medical Officer, St. Francis Hospital, Federal Way, WA, p. A679
ADAMS, Marlene J., Director Human Resources, Schneider Regional Medical Center, Saint Thomas, VI, p. A725
ADAMS, Marsha, Interim Director Human Resources, Texas Health Harris Methodist Hospital Cleburne, Cleburne, TX, p. A601
ADAMS, Mary Jane, R.N. Senior Vice President and Chief Nursing Officer, University of Louisville Hospital, Louisville, KY, p. A262
ADAMS, Michael, Chief Operating Officer, Freedom Pain Hospital, Scottsdale, AZ, p. A37
ADAMS, Mike, M.D. Chief Medical Officer, Gateway Regional Medical Center, Granite City, IL, p. A189
ADAMS, Nancy D., R.N. Senior Vice President Chief Operating Officer and Chief Nurse Executive, Western Maryland Regional Medical Center, Cumberland, MD, p. A297
ADAMS, Norma, Director Human Resources, Southern Regional Medical Center, Riverdale, GA, p. A163
ADAMS, Patricia, Chief Executive Officer, Select Specialty Hospital–Flint, Flint, MI, p. A319
ADAMS, Patsy, Vice President Human Resources, Redmond Regional Medical Center, Rome, GA, p. A163
ADAMS, Renee, Director Information Technology, Windber Medical Center, Windber, PA, p. A553
ADAMS, Robert H., Vice President Operations, Jersey Shore University Medical Center, Neptune, NJ, p. A414
ADAMS, Robin, Director Human Resources, Reeves Memorial Medical Center, Bernice, LA, p. A270
ADAMS, Scott K., Chief Executive Officer, Pullman Regional Hospital, Pullman, WA, p. A682
ADAMS, Shannon, Chief Financial Officer, Avera Holy Family Hospital, Estherville, IA, p. A227
ADAMS, Sharon, R.N. Senior Vice President Patient Care Services and Chief Quality Officer, Mercy Medical Center, Springfield, MA, p. A311
ADAMS, Shaun, Chief Financial Officer, Harton Regional Medical Center, Tullahoma, TN, p. A588
ADAMS, Shawn, Chief Financial Officer, CHRISTUS Hospital–St. Elizabeth, Beaumont, TX, p. A596
ADAMS, Shelah, Chief Executive Officer, Timberlawn Mental Health System, Dallas, TX, p. A607
ADAMS, Stanley
  Chief Financial Officer, Banner Baywood Medical Center, Mesa, AZ, p. A33
  Chief Financial Officer, Banner Heart Hospital, Mesa, AZ, p. A33
ADAMS, Stephen D., Executive Vice President and Chief Information Officer, UPMC Mercy, Pittsburgh, PA, p. A547
ADAMS, William D., Chief Executive Officer, Knapp Medical Center, Weslaco, TX, p. A651
ADAMSKI, Joseph, Chief Nursing Officer, HEALTHSOUTH Rehabilitation Hospital, Concord, NH, p. A405
ADAMSON, James, Chief Executive Officer, Mountain View Hospital, Idaho Falls, ID, p. A174
ADAMSON, Kandi, R.N. Chief Nursing Officer, Indiana University Health Blackford Hospital, Hartford City, IN, p. A210
ADAMSON, Nancy, R.N. Chief Nursing Officer, Banner Estrella Medical Center, Phoenix, AZ, p. A34
ADCOCK, Robert S., Chief Executive Officer, Kindred Hospital–St. Louis at Mercy, Saint Louis, MO, p. A376
ADCOCK, William, Chief Financial Officer, Union General Hospital, Farmerville, LA, p. A273
ADDINGTON, Tom, Chief Information Officer, Saint Michael's Medical Center, Newark, NJ, p. A415
ADDISON, Holland M., M.D. Medical Director, Mississippi Hospital for Restorative Care, Jackson, MS, p. A355
ADDISON, Lenora, Vice President Patient Care and Nursing, MedStar Harbor Hospital, Baltimore, MD, p. A294
ADDISON, Lewis C., Senior Vice President and Chief Financial Officer, Centra Lynchburg General Hospital, Lynchburg, VA, p. A667
ADDLESPERGER, John, D.O. Chief Medical Officer, Sheridan Memorial Hospital, Sheridan, WY, p. A717
ADDO–SAMUELS, Deborah, Chief Executive Officer, Inova Mount Vernon Hospital, Alexandria, VA, p. A662
ADEDOKUN, Ade, M.D. Medical Director, Baylor Institute for Rehabilitation at Fort Worth, Fort Worth, TX, p. A613
ADELMAN, Michael, M.D., Medical Center Director, Wilkes–Barre Veterans Affairs Medical Center, Wilkes–Barre, PA, p. A553
ADEN, Susie, Director of IP Services, Pocahontas Community Hospital, Pocahontas, IA, p. A233
ADER, Michael H., M.D. Vice President Medical Affairs, Hanover Hospital, Hanover, PA, p. A535
ADERHOLD, Pat, Director Human Resources, J. Arthur Dosher Memorial Hospital, Southport, NC, p. A468
ADERHOLDT, Elizabeth
  President and Chief Executive Officer, Genesys Regional Medical Center, Grand Blanc, MI, p. A320
  President and Chief Executive Officer, St. Mary's of Michigan, Saginaw, MI, p. A329
  President and Chief Executive Officer, St. Mary's of Michigan Standish Hospital, Standish, MI, p. A330
ADKINS, Gary W., Chief Executive Officer, Parkview Noble Hospital, Kendallville, IN, p. A213
ADKINS, Kedrick D., Chief Financial Officer, Mayo Clinic Hospital – Rochester, Rochester, MN, p. A345
ADKINS, Kevin, Director Human Resources, Green Oaks Hospital, Dallas, TX, p. A605
ADKINS, Paige, Chief Financial Officer, Greenbrier Valley Medical Center, Ronceverte, WV, p. A695
ADKINS, Raymond, Chief Information Officer, Peninsula Regional Medical Center, Salisbury, MD, p. A300
ADKINS, Scott, Manager Information Technology, Vernon Memorial Healthcare, Viroqua, WI, p. A712
ADKINSON, Jessica, Administrator, MMO WestEnd Hospital, Jennings, LA, p. A276
ADLER, Cal, Director of of Information Technology, Rock County Hospital, Bassett, NE, p. A389
ADLER, Josh, M.D. Chief Medical Officer, UCSF Medical Center, San Francisco, CA, p. A89
ADLER, Kenneth, M.D. Medical Director, Arrowhead Behavioral Health Hospital, Maumee, OH, p. A494
ADLER, Maurita, Director Information Services, Gottlieb Memorial Hospital, Melrose Park, IL, p. A194
ADLER, Ron, Superintendent, Western State Hospital, Tacoma, WA, p. A686
ADLER–MARKS, Cathy
  Director Information Technology, Vista Medical Center East, Waukegan, IL, p. A203
  Director Information Technology, Vista Medical Center West, Waukegan, IL, p. A203
ADMA, Vishal, M.D. Medical Director, KVC Prairie Ridge Psychiatric Hospital, Kansas City, KS, p. A243
ADORNATO, Sara F., Executive Director, Barnes–Kasson County Hospital, Susquehanna, PA, p. A550
ADRIAANSE, Steven W., Vice President and Chief Human Resources Officer, Tallahassee Memorial HealthCare, Tallahassee, FL, p. A144
ADVEY, Linda, Manager Information Systems, Glenbeigh Hospital and Outpatient Centers, Rock Creek, OH, p. A497
AFANEH, Bassam, M.D. Chief of Staff, Deckerville Community Hospital, Deckerville, MI, p. A317
AFENYA, Kenneth, M.D. Chief of Staff, Baptist Memorial Hospital–Tipton, Covington, TN, p. A576
AFLAK, Ziba, Chief Financial Officer, Kindred Hospital–San Francisco Bay Area, San Leandro, CA, p. A90
AFZAL, Muhammed, M.D. Chief of Staff, Sutter Medical Center, Sacramento, Sacramento, CA, p. A85
AGANA, Ben, M.D. Medical Director, HEALTHSOUTH Rehabilitation Hospital The Woodlands, Conroe, TX, p. A602
AGBA, C. Okey, Senior Vice President, Chief Financial Officer and Treasurer, Tufts Medical Center, Boston, MA, p. A304
AGEE, Joan, Vice President Patient Care Services, St. Joseph Regional Medical Center, Lewiston, ID, p. A174
AGEE, Nancy Howell, President and Chief Executive Officer, Carilion Clinic, Roanoke, VA, p. B27
AGENBROAD, Connie, Chief Executive Officer, Othello Community Hospital, Othello, WA, p. A681
AGLIECO, Fabio, D.O. Chief of Staff, Sweeny Community Hospital, Sweeny, TX, p. A646
AGLOINGA, Roy, Chief Administrative Officer, Norton Sound Regional Hospital, Nome, AK, p. A28
AGNEW, Claire, Chief Financial Officer, Banner Gateway Medical Center, Gilbert, AZ, p. A31
AGNEW, Deborah, M.D., Chief Executive Officer, Beartooth Billings Clinic, Red Lodge, MT, p. A386
AGNEW, Mary Christine, R.N. Vice President and Chief Nursing Officer, Reading Hospital, West Reading, PA, p. A553
AGOSTINI, Scott, Director, Magee Rehabilitation Hospital, Philadelphia, PA, p. A544
AGOSTO, Paula M., R.N. Senior Vice President and Chief Nursing Officer, Children's Hospital of Philadelphia, Philadelphia, PA, p. A543
AGRAWAL, Abha, M.D. Chief Operating Officer and Chief Medical Officer, Norwegian American Hospital, Chicago, IL, p. A183
AGRESTI, Katie, R.N. Director Patient Care Services, Millcreek Community Hospital, Erie, PA, p. A534
AGUAS, Hugo, Vice President Human Resources, Inova Alexandria Hospital, Alexandria, VA, p. A662
AGUIAR–OLSEN, Rinely, M.D. Medical Director, Yuma Rehabilitation Hospital, Yuma, AZ, p. A40
AGUILA, Marcos, Chief Executive Officer, Hospital San Francisco, San Juan, PR, p. A724
AGUILAR, Gretchen, Director Patient Care and Chief Nursing Officer, Three Rivers Hospital, Brewster, WA, p. A677
AGUILAR, Marisa, Chief Operating Officer, Valley Baptist Medical Center–Brownsville, Brownsville, TX, p. A599
AGUILERA, Louie, Director Information Technology, Foundation Surgical Hospital of El Paso, El Paso, TX, p. A610
AGUINAGA, Miguel, M.D. Medical Director, Advanced Care Hospital of White County, Searcy, AR, p. A50
AGUIRRE, Jose, M.D. Medical Director, Carson Tahoe Continuing Care Hospital, Carson City, NV, p. A400
AHAINE, Israel, Chief Nursing Officer, West Oaks Hospital, Houston, TX, p. A623
AHEARN, Patrick, Chief Operating Officer and Senior Vice President, Saint Barnabas Medical Center, Livingston, NJ, p. A413
AHL, Dennis, Director Information Technology, Jefferson Community Health Center, Fairbury, NE, p. A391
AHLBERG, Suzanne, Director of Nursing, Clay County Medical Center, Clay Center, KS, p. A238
AHLERS, Timothy, FACHE, Chief Executive Officer, Story County Medical Center, Nevada, IA, p. A232
AHMAD, Yousuf, Divisional Senior Vice President and Chief Network Transformation Officer, Mercy Health – Fairfield Hospital, Fairfield, OH, p. A489
AHMED, Ashraf, M.D. Senior Vice President Physician and Hospital Services, Alliance Community Hospital, Alliance, OH, p. A478
AHMED, Imtiaz, Chief of Staff, Mercy Hospital Ada, Ada, OK, p. A503
AHMED, Mohammed Shafeeq, M.D. Chief Operating Officer and Chief Medical Officer, Baystate Mary Lane Hospital, Ware, MA, p. A312
AHMED, Omar, Acting Manager Human Resources, Veterans Affairs Caribbean Healthcare System, San Juan, PR, p. A724
AHMED, Sajid, Chief Information and Innovation Officer, Martin Luther King, Jr. Community Hospital, Los Angeles, CA, p. A71
AHMED, Shabeer A., M.D. Clinical Director, Community Behavioral Health Hospital – Annandale, Annandale, MN, p. A334
AHNER, Dawn, Chief Financial Officer, Renown Rehabilitation Hospital, Reno, NV, p. A404
AIELLO, Joseph, M.D. Chief of Staff, Asheville Specialty Hospital, Asheville, NC, p. A455
AIELLO, Louis
  Senior Vice President and Chief Financial Officer, Faxton–St. Luke's Healthcare, Utica, NY, p. A452
  Chief Financial Officer, St. Elizabeth Medical Center, Utica, NY, p. A452
AIKEN, David, Chief Human Resources Officer, Madigan Healthcare System, Tacoma, WA, p. A686
AIKEN, Richard, M.D. Medical Director, Lakeland Behavioral Health System, Springfield, MO, p. A378
AILOR, Lorie, Chief Executive Officer, Orthopaedic Hospital of Lutheran Health Network, Fort Wayne, IN, p. A208
AINSLEY, Howard N., Chief Executive Officer, Morehead Memorial Hospital, Eden, NC, p. A459
AINTABLIAN, Susan, Chief Information Officer, LAC–Olive View–UCLA Medical Center, CA, p. A71
AIONA, Michael, M.D. Chief of Staff, Shriners Hospitals for Children–Portland, Portland, OR, p. A525
AIRHART, Steven, Chief Executive Officer, Hartgrove Hospital, Chicago, IL, p. A182
AIROSUS, Diane, Chief Financial Officer, Pembroke Hospital, Pembroke, MA, p. A310
AISEN, Mindy, M.D. Chief Medical Officer, Rancho Los Amigos National Rehabilitation Center, Downey, CA, p. A60
AISENBREY, Lisa, Administrator Human Resources and Support Services, Sidney Health Center, Sidney, MT, p. A387
AITI, Tamer, M.D. Chief of Staff, Union County Hospital, Anna, IL, p. A178
AJANAH, Muhammed, M.D. Clinical Director, Clifton T. Perkins Hospital Center, Jessup, MD, p. A298
AJMAL, Farooq, Vice President and Chief Information Officer, Nassau University Medical Center, East Meadow, NY, p. A433
AKBARIAN, M., M.D. Medical Director, Kindred Hospital Boston–North Shore, Peabody, MA, p. A310
AKENS, Rick, Director Human Resources and Labor Relations, Methodist Medical Center of Oak Ridge, Oak Ridge, TN, p. A586
AKERS, Earl, Supervisor Information Technology, Salina Surgical Hospital, Salina, KS, p. A250
AKERS, Sandra, Bureau Director, Public Health Hospitals, Massachusetts Department of Public Health, Boston, MA, p. B86
AKHRAS, Omar, M.D. Chief of Staff, Putnam General Hospital, Eatonton, GA, p. A157
AKIN, Pam, Interim Chief Nursing Officer, Wilbarger General Hospital, Vernon, TX, p. A650
AKIN, Terry, President and Chief Executive Officer, Cone Health, Greensboro, NC, p. B41
AKIN, Terry, President and Chief Operating Officer, Moses H. Cone Memorial Hospital, Greensboro, NC, p. A461

Index of Health Care Professionals

Index of Health Care Professionals

Index of Health Care Professionals / Akins

AKINS, Tina, Director Human Resources, Lost Rivers Medical Center, Arco, ID, p. A172
AKOPYAN, George, Director Human Resources, Centinela Hospital Medical Center, Inglewood, CA, p. A65
AL-HASHMI, Samer, M.D. Chief Medical Staff, Stevens County Hospital, Hugoton, KS, p. A242
AL-KHOURI, Samir, M.D. Medical Director, Specialty Hospital of Washington-Hadley, Washington, DC, p. A120
ALAGAR, Ravi, M.D. Medical Director, Kindred Hospital-Pittsburgh, Oakdale, PA, p. A542
ALASZEWSKI, Lydia, Chief Nursing Officer, Select Specialty Hospital-Macomb County, Mount Clemens, MI, p. A326
ALBANO, Valerie, Director, Human Resources, Regional Hospital for Respiratory and Complex Care, Burien, WA, p. A677
ALBANY, Karen, Chief Information Officer, Naval Medical Center, Portsmouth, VA, p. A670
ALBARANO, Francis G.
Administrator, St. Vincent Mercy Hospital, Elwood, IN, p. A207
Administrator, St. Vincent Randolph Hospital, Winchester, IN, p. A221
ALBAUGH, Jolene, R.N. Vice President and Chief Nursing Officer, Adventist Bolingbrook Hospital, Bolingbrook, IL, p. A180
ALBAUM, Michael, M.D. Senior Vice President and Chief Medical Officer, Southern Maine Health Care – Biddeford Medical Center, Biddeford, ME, p. A289
ALBERG, Ellen, Director Human Resources, Johnson Memorial Health Services, Dawson, MN, p. A337
ALBERT, Debra, MSN Senior Vice President Patient Care and Chief Nursing Officer, University of Chicago Medical Center, Chicago, IL, p. A185
ALBERT, Todd, M.D. Surgeon-in-Chief and Medical Director, Hospital for Special Surgery, New York, NY, p. A440
ALBERTI, Harry, M.D. Chief Medical Officer and Vice President Medical Affairs, Verde Valley Medical Center, Cottonwood, AZ, p. A30
ALBERTINI, Bernie, Chief Administrative Officer, East Ohio Regional Hospital, Martins Ferry, OH, p. A493
ALBERTS, Patrick J., Senior Vice President and Chief Operating Officer, Monongahela Valley Hospital, Monongahela, PA, p. A540
ALBERTS, W. Michael, M.D. Vice President Medical Affairs, H. Lee Moffitt Cancer Center and Research Institute, Tampa, FL, p. A144
ALBERTSON, Robert, M.D. Chief Medical Officer, CareLink of Jackson, Jackson, MI, p. A323
ALBIN, James, Chief Information Officer, Baylor St. Luke's Medical Center, Houston, TX, p. A619
ALBOSTA, Kevin, Vice President, Chief Financial Officer, Covenant Healthcare, Saginaw, MI, p. A329
ALBRECHT, David L., President, Owatonna Hospital, Owatonna, MN, p. A344
ALBRECHTSEN, Bradley C., Chief Executive Officer and Administrator, Marian Center, Salt Lake City, UT, p. A658
ALBRIGHT, Bill, Director Human Resources, Stewart Memorial Community Hospital, Lake City, IA, p. A230
ALBRIGHT, Leslie, Vice President Information Systems, Bethesda Hospital East, Boynton Beach, FL, p. A122
ALBRIGHT, Sara Z., Vice President Human Resources, Bassett Medical Center, Cooperstown, NY, p. A432
ALBRIGHT, Tammy, Chief Nursing Officer, Takoma Regional Hospital, Greeneville, TN, p. A578
ALBRIGHT, Tina, Director Human Resources, National Park Medical Center, Hot Springs, AR, p. A45
ALCOCER, Deborah, Chief Information Officer, South Texas Rehabilitation Hospital, Brownsville, TX, p. A598
ALDANA, Eladio, Manager Information Systems, College Hospital Costa Mesa, Costa Mesa, CA, p. A59
ALDERFER, Jennifer, Chief Executive Officer, North Suburban Medical Center, Thornton, CO, p. A109
ALDERSON, Charles, Chief Financial Officer, Summa Barberton Citizens Hospital, Barberton, OH, p. A479
ALDIS, Karen, Director of Nursing, Harper Hospital District Five, Harper, KS, p. A241
ALDRED, Linda W., Senior Vice President, Texas Children's Hospital, Houston, TX, p. A622
ALDREDGE, Sarah, M.D. Chief Medical Officer, Essentia Health Sandstone, Sandstone, MN, p. A347
ALDRICH, Alan, Chief Financial Officer, Central Montana Medical Center, Lewistown, MT, p. A385
ALDRIDGE, Kenneth, M.D
Vice President Medical Affairs, DCH Regional Medical Center, Tuscaloosa, AL, p. A25
Vice President Medical Affairs, Northport Medical Center, Northport, AL, p. A23
ALEEM, Asaf, M.D. Medical Director, Peachford Behavioral Health System, Atlanta, GA, p. A150
ALEJANDRO, Ausberto, M.D. President, Hospital Santa Rosa, Guayama, PR, p. A721
ALEMAN, Ralph A., President and Chief Executive Officer, Citrus Memorial Health System, Inverness, FL, p. A129
ALEXAITIS, Irene, MSN Vice President Nursing and Chief Nursing Officer, UF Health Shands Hospital, Gainesville, FL, p. A128
ALEXANDA, Lisa, M.D. Vice President Medical Affairs, Parrish Medical Center, Titusville, FL, p. A146
ALEXANDER, Alan B., Chief Executive Officer, Caverna Memorial Hospital, Horse Cave, KY, p. A258
ALEXANDER, Angie, Chief Executive Officer, Allegiance Behavioral Health Center of Plainview, Plainview, TX, p. A636
ALEXANDER, April, Director Human Resources, Metropolitan Hospital Center, New York, NY, p. A441
ALEXANDER, Bobby, R.N. Chief Nursing Officer, Pinnacle Pointe Hospital, Little Rock, AR, p. A47
ALEXANDER, Brian, Chief Administrative Officer, Novato Community Hospital, Novato, CA, p. A78
ALEXANDER, Craig, Fiscal Specialist, Thomas B. Finan Center, Cumberland, MD, p. A297
ALEXANDER, David, Chief Financial Officer, St. Joseph's Regional Medical Center, Paterson, NJ, p. A416
ALEXANDER, Debra, Chief Information Officer, Safe Haven Hospital of Treasure Valley, Boise, ID, p. A172
ALEXANDER, Fred, M.D. Medical Director, Kaiser Permanente West Los Angeles Medical Center, Los Angeles, CA, p. A70
ALEXANDER, Jack, M.D. Chief Medical Officer, Mayo Clinic Health System in Red Wing, Red Wing, MN, p. A345
ALEXANDER, Jane, Director Facility Administrative Services, Sagamore Children's Psychiatric Center, Dix Hills, NY, p. A432
ALEXANDER, Jason P., FACHE, Chief Executive Officer, East Cooper Medical Center, Mount Pleasant, SC, p. A563
ALEXANDER, Jeffrey, Chief Executive Officer, Select Specialty Hospital-Western Missouri, Kansas City, MO, p. A370
ALEXANDER, Jerry, Chief Executive Officer, Regency Hospital of Northwest Arkansas – Springdale, Springdale, AR, p. A51
ALEXANDER, Jr., John, M.D. Chief of Staff, Magnolia Regional Medical Center, Magnolia, AR, p. A48
ALEXANDER, Mary, Interim Chief Executive Officer, Promise Hospital of Dallas, Dallas, TX, p. A606
ALEXANDER, Michael D., MS,
Administrator, Higgins General Hospital, Bremen, GA, p. A152
Administrator, Wedowee Hospital, Wedowee, AL, p. A26
ALEXANDER, Pam, R.N. Chief Nursing Officer, Bowie Memorial Hospital, Bowie, TX, p. A598
ALEXANDER, Peter H., Administrator, St. Vincent Seton Specialty Hospital, Indianapolis, IN, p. A213
ALEXANDER, Richmond, M.D. President Medical Staff, Specialty Hospital of Meridian, Meridian, MS, p. A358
ALEXANDER, Steven, Executive Director, Bellevue Hospital Center, New York, NY, p. A438
ALEXANDER, Thomas, Chief Executive Officer, Vibra Specialty Hospital at DeSoto, Desoto, TX, p. A608
ALEXANDER, Wendy F., Director Human Resources, Louisiana Heart Hospital, Lacombe, LA, p. A277
ALEXANDER-HINES, Joyce, R.N. Associate Director, Patient Care Services, Fayetteville Veterans Affairs Medical Center, Fayetteville, NC, p. A460
ALEXANDER-LANE, Victoria, Chief Executive Officer, Northern Inyo Hospital, Bishop, CA, p. A56
ALEXIADES, Nik, Chief Financial Officer, Clara Maass Medical Center, Belleville, NJ, p. A409
ALFANO, Anthony, Vice President Executive Director, Montefiore New Rochelle, New Rochelle, NY, p. A438
ALFONSO, Eduardo, M.D. Chairman Ophthalmology, Bascom Palmer Eye Institute-Anne Bates Leach Eye Hospital, Miami, FL, p. A134
ALFORD, Charles
Vice President Finance, Vidant Beaufort Hospital, Washington, NC, p. A470
Vice President Financial Services, Vidant Edgecombe Hospital, Tarboro, NC, p. A469
ALFORD, Karla, Chief Information Officer, Greater Regional Medical Center, Creston, IA, p. A225
ALFORD, Michelle, R.N. Director of Nursing, Washington County Hospital, Chatom, AL, p. A18
ALFRED, Lorrie, Director Human Resources, Southern Surgical Hospital, Slidell, LA, p. A285
ALFSON, Jared, Chief Information Officer, HSHS St. Clare Memorial Hospital, Oconto Falls, WI, p. A708
ALGER, Steve, Senior Vice President and Chief Financial Officer, Lakes Regional Healthcare, Spirit Lake, IA, p. A235
ALHADEFF, Joseph, M.D., President and Chief Executive Officer, OSS Orthopaedic Hospital, York, PA, p. A554
ALI, Irfan, Director Information Services, Saint Agnes Medical Center, Fresno, CA, p. A62
ALI, Mirza Z., M.D. Chief of Staff, Wilkes-Barre Veterans Affairs Medical Center, Wilkes-Barre, PA, p. A553
ALI, Muhammad, M.D. Chief Medical Officer, Sanford Tracy Medical Center, Tracy, MN, p. A348
ALI, Solomon, M.D. Chief of Staff, Fairview Regional Medical Center, Fairview, OK, p. A507
ALI-KHAN, Mir, M.D. Medical Director, Canyon Ridge Hospital, Chino, CA, p. A57
ALICE, Patricia, Chief Executive Officer, Arizona Orthopedic Surgical Hospital, Chandler, AZ, p. A30
ALICEA, Luis, Chief Information Officer, Doctors' Center Hospital San Juan, San Juan, PR, p. A723
ALICEA PEREZ, Eneida, Interim Nursing Director, Hospital Buen Samaritano, Aguadilla, PR, p. A719
ALIFF, Sarah, Vice President Patient Care Service and Chief Nursing Officer, CHI Mercy Hospital, Devils Lake, ND, p. A473
ALKHOULI, Hassan, M.D
Chief Medical Officer, Garden Grove Hospital and Medical Center, Garden Grove, CA, p. A63
Medical Director, Huntington Beach Hospital, Huntington Beach, CA, p. A65
Chief Medical Officer, West Anaheim Medical Center, Anaheim, CA, p. A53
ALLA, Vamseedhar, M.D. Director Medical Staff, Connecticut Veterans Home and Hospital, Rocky Hill, CT, p. A114
ALLAN, John, Chief of Staff, Davis Regional Medical Center, Statesville, NC, p. A469
ALLARD, Joan, Director Human Resources, Heart of Florida Regional Medical Center, Davenport, FL, p. A125
ALLATT, Richard, M.D. Medical Director, HEALTHSOUTH Nittany Valley Rehabilitation Hospital, Pleasant Gap, PA, p. A547
ALLBEE, Roger, Chief Executive Officer and Administrator, Grace Cottage Hospital, Townshend, VT, p. A661
ALLBRITTON, James, Chief Financial Officer, Morehouse General Hospital, Bastrop, LA, p. A269
ALLBRITTON, Jim, nterim Chief Executive Officer and Chief Financial Officer, Morehouse General Hospital, Bastrop, LA, p. A269
ALLDREDGE, Kim, Director Human Resources, Lawrence County Memorial Hospital, Lawrenceville, IL, p. A192
ALLEE, Erin, R.N. Director of Nursing, Royal Oaks Hospital, Windsor, MO, p. A380
ALLEMAN, Scott, Senior Vice President Patient Care Services and Chief Nursing Officer, UW Medicine/Valley Medical Center, Renton, WA, p. A682
ALLEN, Audrey, Coordinator Benefits, Dallas County Medical Center, Fordyce, AR, p. A44
ALLEN, Brian, M.D. President Medical Staff, Georgetown Community Hospital, Georgetown, KY, p. A257
ALLEN, Carolyn, Vice President and Chief Financial Officer, Camden Clark Medical Center, Parkersburg, WV, p. A694
ALLEN, David B., Chief Executive Officer, Richland Memorial Hospital, Olney, IL, p. A197
ALLEN, Dawn, R.N. Chief Clinical Officer, Redwood Area Hospital, Redwood Falls, MN, p. A345
ALLEN, Devon, M.D. Chief of Medical Staff, Samuel Simmonds Memorial Hospital, Barrow, AK, p. A27
ALLEN, Donald, Chief Operating Officer, Unity Medical & Surgical Hospital, Mishawaka, IN, p. A216
ALLEN, Douglas H., Senior Vice President Human Resources, Cooper University Health Care, Camden, NJ, p. A410
ALLEN, Elms, M.D
Senior Vice President Medical Affairs, Novant Health Forsyth Medical Center, Winston-Salem, NC, p. A471
Senior Vice President Medical Affairs, Novant Health Medical Park Hospital, Winston-Salem, NC, p. A471
ALLEN, Jason, Director Patient Care Services, Brook Lane Health Services, Hagerstown, MD, p. A298
ALLEN, Jennifer, Vice President Human Resources, Plantation General Hospital, Plantation, FL, p. A140
ALLEN, John, Chief Information Officer, Holzer Medical Center, Gallipolis, OH, p. A490
ALLEN, John P., Chief Executive Officer, Titus Regional Medical Center, Mount Pleasant, TX, p. A633
ALLEN, Judy, Human Resource Specialist, Carl Albert Community Mental Health Center, McAlester, OK, p. A509
ALLEN, Kandice K., R.N., Chief Executive Officer, Share Medical Center, Alva, OK, p. A503
ALLEN, Karen A., R.N. Chief Nursing Officer, Butler Health System, Butler, PA, p. A530
ALLEN, Keith
Senior Vice President and Chief Human Resources Officer, Community Memorial Hospital, Menomonee Falls, WI, p. A705
Senior Vice President and Chief Human Resources Officer, Froedtert Memorial Lutheran Hospital, Milwaukee, WI, p. A706
Senior Vice President Human Resources, St. Joseph's Hospital, West Bend, WI, p. A714
ALLEN, Kent, Director Human Resources, West Branch Regional Medical Center, West Branch, MI, p. A332
ALLEN, Laura, Chief Financial Officer, Mena Regional Health System, Mena, AR, p. A48

A772 Index of Health Care Professionals

Index of Health Care Professionals / Amerson

Index of Health Care Professionals

ALLEN, Linda, Vice President Quality and Information Systems, Monongalia General Hospital, Morgantown, WV, p. A693
ALLEN, Linda M., Vice President Human Resources, The Children's Institute of Pittsburgh, Pittsburgh, PA, p. A546
ALLEN, Lori, Chief Financial Officer, Anthony Medical Center, Anthony, KS, p. A237
ALLEN, Mary Beth, Vice President Human Resources, Emory University Hospital, atlanta, GA, p. A150
ALLEN, Michael, Chief Financial Officer, Gundersen Health System, La Crosse, WI, p. A703
ALLEN, Mike
Director Information Services, Shawnee Mission Medical Center, Shawnee Mission, KS, p. A250
Director Information Technology, Shriners Hospitals for Children–Salt Lake City, Salt Lake City, UT, p. A658
Director Information Services, Shriners Hospitals for Children–Spokane, Spokane, WA, p. A685
ALLEN, Myrna, R.N. Chief Operating and Nursing Officer, Martin Luther King, Jr. Community Hospital, Los Angeles, CA, p. A71
ALLEN, Nancy, R.N. Director, Patient Services and Chief Nursing Executive, Advocate Eureka Hospital, Eureka, IL, p. A187
ALLEN, Nikki, Patient Care Executive, Sutter Amador Hospital, Jackson, CA, p. A65
ALLEN, Patty, St. John's Vice President Finance, St. John's Hospital, Springfield, IL, p. A201
ALLEN, R. Keith, Senior Vice President Human Resources, University of Maryland Medical Center, Baltimore, MD, p. A295
ALLEN, Richard
Chief Executive Officer, Palmdale Regional Medical Center, Palmdale, CA, p. A80
Chief Executive Officer, Warren General Hospital, Warren, PA, p. A551
ALLEN, Rob, Chief Executive Officer, Sitka Community Hospital, Sitka, AK, p. A29
ALLEN, Robert
Chief Financial Officer, Keck Hospital of USC, Los Angeles, CA, p. A70
Chief Financial Officer, University of Southern California–Norris Cancer Hospital, Los Angeles, CA, p. A73
ALLEN, Scott J., Director Human Resources, Hudson Hospital and Clinic, Hudson, WI, p. A702
ALLEN, Steve, M.D., Chief Executive Officer, Nationwide Children's Hospital, Columbus, OH, p. A486
ALLEN, Timothy J., FACHE,
Chief Executive Officer, Leonard J. Chabert Medical Center, Houma, LA, p. A275
Chief Executive Officer, Ochsner St. Anne General Hospital, Raceland, LA, p. A284
ALLEN, Timothy M., Vice President Human Resources, United Hospital Center, Bridgeport, WV, p. A689
ALLEN, Tracey, Controller, Central Texas Rehabilitation Hospital, Austin, TX, p. A594
ALLEN, Vicki, Chief Financial Officer, Chicot Memorial Medical Center, Lake Village, AR, p. A46
ALLEN, Vicki, R.N. Vice President Patient Care Services and Chief Nursing Officer, Harnett Health System, Dunn, NC, p. A459
ALLEN, Wain, M.D. Medical Director, Park City Medical Center, Park City, UT, p. A657
ALLEN, Wayne
Acting Chief Operating Officer, Brooklyn Hospital Center, NY, p. A439
Chief Financial Officer, Mendocino Coast District Hospital, Fort Bragg, CA, p. A61
ALLEN, Zac, CPA Chief Financial Officer, Cherokee Medical Center, Centre, AL, p. A18
ALLEN–JOHNSON, Angela, Director Information Services, Ephraim McDowell Regional Medical Center, Danville, KY, p. A256
ALLENSWORTH, Ed, M.D. Medical Director, Craig General Hospital, Vinita, OK, p. A517
ALLEY, David, Chief Financial Officer, Starr Regional Medical Center, Athens, TN, p. A574
ALLEY, John L., Chief Executive Officer, Woodlawn Hospital, Rochester, IN, p. A219
ALLEY, Steve B., M.D. Chief of Staff, Crosbyton Clinic Hospital, Crosbyton, TX, p. A603
ALLGEIER, Patricia, R.N. Chief Nursing Officer, Boys Town National Research Hospital, Omaha, NE, p. A395
ALLGOOD, Libby, Chief Financial Officer, Kittitas Valley Healthcare, Ellensburg, WA, p. A678
ALLICON, Keary T., Vice President Finance and Chief Financial Officer, Baystate Wing Hospital, Palmer, MA, p. A310
ALLIES, Karla, Director Human Resources, Rosebud Health Care Center, Forsyth, MT, p. A383
ALLINSON, Randy, R.N. Patient Care Services Director, Central Valley Medical Center, Nephi, UT, p. A656
ALLISON, David G., President and Chief Executive Officer, University Medical Center, Lubbock, TX, p. A630
ALLISON, Joel T., Chief Executive Officer, Baylor Scott & White Health, Dallas, TX, p. B22
ALLISON, Lorraine, Human Resource Partner, PeaceHealth Peace Island Medical Center, Friday Harbor, WA, p. A679
ALLISON, Shannon, Chief Financial Officer, Houston County Community Hospital, Erin, TN, p. A577
ALLISON, Steve, Director Human Resources, Logan County Hospital, Oakley, KS, p. A247
ALLMAN, Rex, M.D. President Medical Staff, Pulaski Memorial Hospital, Winamac, IN, p. A221
ALLORE, Gary
Chief Financial Officer, Mercy Health Hackley Campus, Muskegon, MI, p. A326
Chief Financial Officer, Mercy Health, Mercy Campus, Muskegon, MI, p. A326
ALLOWAY, Cindy
President, CHI Health Lakeside, Omaha, NE, p. A396
President, CHI Health Midlands, Papillion, NE, p. A397
ALLPHIN, Allan, M.D. Chief of Staff, Mercy Hospital Springfield, Springfield, MO, p. A379
ALLPORT, Jeff, Vice President, Chief Information Officer, Valley Presbyterian Hospital, CA, p. A73
ALLRED, Al W., Chief Financial Officer, Bert Fish Medical Center, New Smyrna Beach, FL, p. A136
ALLRED, B. Dee, M.D. President Medical Staff, Jordan Valley Medical Center, West Jordan, UT, p. A659
ALLRED, Lowell C., M.D. Chief of Staff, Columbia Basin Hospital, Ephrata, WA, p. A678
ALLRED, William, M.D. Vice President Medical Affairs, St. John Medical Center, Tulsa, OK, p. A517
ALLSOP, Brian, Director Human Resources, Central Valley Medical Center, Nephi, UT, p. A656
ALLSTOTT, Patti, Administrative Coordinator Human Resources and Grant Writer, Pioneer Memorial Hospital, Heppner, OR, p. A521
ALLSTROM, Sheree, Director Human Resources, Acuity Hospital of South Texas, San Antonio, TX, p. A640
ALLUMS, Allyson, Director Medical Records, North Caddo Medical Center, Vivian, LA, p. A286
ALMANZOR, Michael, Chief Financial Officer, Hollywood Presbyterian Medical Center, Los Angeles, CA, p. A70
ALMAUHY, Deborah, R.N. Chief Nursing Officer, Emory Rehabilitation Hospital, Atlanta, GA, p. A150
ALMEIDA, Sergio, Director Information Systems, West Houston Medical Center, Houston, TX, p. A623
ALMEIDA–SUAREZ, Mario, M.D. Chief of Staff, Larkin Community Hospital, South Miami, FL, p. A143
ALMENDINGER, J. Todd, President and Chief Executive Officer, Magruder Memorial Hospital, Port Clinton, OH, p. A496
ALMODOVAR, Gustavo, Executive Director, Hospital De La Concepcion, San German, PR, p. A722
ALMOHAMMED, Salah, Chief of Staff, East Texas Medical Center Carthage, Carthage, TX, p. A600
ALO, Kathleen, R.N. Chief Nursing Officer, Mammoth Hospital, Mammoth Lakes, CA, p. A74
ALONSO, Gwen, Chief Nursing Officer, Florida Hospital Zephyrhills, Zephyrhills, FL, p. A148
ALONSO, Jose', M.D. Medical Director, San Juan Capestrano Hospital, San Juan, PR, p. A724
ALONZO, Patti, Manager Human Resources, Pacifica Hospital of the Valley, CA, p. A72
ALPERT, Jeffrey, M.D. Medical Director, Wichita County Health Center, Leoti, KS, p. A245
ALPERT, Len, Director Human Resources, Larkin Behavioral Health Services, FL, p. A128
ALRASHEDY, Farhad H., M.D. Chief Medical Officer, Ferry County Memorial Hospital, Republic, WA, p. A683
ALREDGE, Will, Administrator, Genesis Behavioral Hospital, Breaux Bridge, LA, p. A271
ALSIP, Bryan, M.D. Executive Vice President, Chief Medical Officer, University Health System, San Antonio, TX, p. A642
ALSTAD, Nancy, Director Human Resources, Fort HealthCare, Fort Atkinson, WI, p. A700
ALSTON, Dorie, Manager Human Resources, Victory Medical Center Craig Ranch, McKinney, TX, p. A632
ALT, Melinda, Chief Financial Officer, Guthrie County Hospital, Guthrie Center, IA, p. A228
ALTARAS, June, R.N.,
Chief Executive Officer, Swedish Medical Center–Cherry Hill Campus, Seattle, WA, p. A684
Chief Executive Officer, Swedish Medical Center–First Hill, Seattle, WA, p. A684
ALTEBARMAKIAN, Varouj, M.D. Physician in Chief, Kaiser Permanente Fresno Medical Center, Fresno, CA, p. A62
ALTENBURGER, Andy, Chief Information Officer, Marietta Memorial Hospital, Marietta, OH, p. A493
ALTENDORF, Amanda, Chief Human Resources and Quality Management, Richard P. Stadter Psychiatric Center, Grand Forks, ND, p. A474
ALTHOEN, David, Director Financial Planning and Analysis, Forest Health Medical Center, Ypsilanti, MI, p. A333
ALTHOUSE, Douglas, Chief Medical Staff, Kearney County Health Services, Minden, NE, p. A394
ALTMAN, III, Alexander B., Chief Financial Officer, Union County General Hospital, Clayton, NM, p. A423
ALTMAN, Angela, Market Human Resources Director, Shands Live Oak Regional Medical Center, Live Oak, FL, p. A132
ALTMAN, Deana, Chief Nursing Officer, Harney District Hospital, Burns, OR, p. A519
ALTMAN, Harold, M.D. Chief Medical Officer, ACMH Hospital, Kittanning, PA, p. A537
ALTMILLER, Steve, President and Chief Executive Officer, Good Shepherd Health System, Longview, TX, p. B59
ALTMILLER, Steve, President and Chief Executive Officer, Good Shepherd Medical Center, Longview, TX, p. A629
ALTOE, Ann, Senior Director Information Systems and Security Officer, Alfred I. duPont Hospital for Children, Wilmington, DE, p. A118
ALTOM, Andy, Chief Executive Officer, Methodist Behavioral Hospital of Arkansas, Maumelle, AR, p. A48
ALTON, Aaron K., President and Chief Executive Officer, Sisters of Mary of the Presentation Health System, Fargo, ND, p. B124
ALTOSE, Murray, M.D. Chief of Staff, Louis Stokes Cleveland Veterans Affairs Medical Center, Cleveland, OH, p. A484
ALTSHULER, Keith, President and Chief Administrative Officer, Fort Sanders Regional Medical Center, Knoxville, TN, p. A580
ALUISE, Tony, Chief Executive Officer, Three Gables Surgery Center, Proctorville, OH, p. A496
ALVARADO, Felicita E., Administrator, Hospital Psiquiatrico Correccional, San Juan, PR, p. A723
ALVARADO, Rafael, Chief Executive Officer, Dr. Pila's Hospital, Ponce, PR, p. A722
ALVARADO, Ramona, Interim Manager Human Resources, Adventist Medical Center–Reedley, Reedley, CA, p. A83
ALVAREZ, Dena C., R.N. COO & Chief Compliance Officer, Brodstone Memorial Hospital, Superior, NE, p. A398
ALVAREZ, Janie, Accounting Director, Cornerstone Regional Hospital, Edinburg, TX, p. A609
ALVAREZ, Jose, M.D. Chief Medical Staff, Circles of Care, Melbourne, FL, p. A133
ALVAREZ, Maria Charlotte, M.D. Chief of Staff, Sheridan Community Hospital, Sheridan, MI, p. A330
ALVAREZ, Mike, M.D. Chief Medical Officer, Dauterive Hospital, New Iberia, LA, p. A281
ALVAREZ, Valerie, Executive Assistant, Adventist Medical Center–Reedley, Reedley, CA, p. A83
ALVERSON, Tammy S., M.D. Chief of Staff, Coshocton County Memorial Hospital, Coshocton, OH, p. A487
ALVES, Richard, Chief Financial Officer, Kaiser Permanente Fresno Medical Center, Fresno, CA, p. A62
ALVEY, Raymond, Chief Financial Officer, SSM Health Saint Louis University Hospital, Saint Louis, MO, p. A377
ALWARD, Dale, Chief Executive Officer, Englewood Community Hospital, Englewood, FL, p. A126
ALWINE, Steven, Chief Executive Officer, HEALTHSOUTH Rehabilitation Hospital of York, York, PA, p. A554
ALZEIN, Bashar, M.D. President Medical Staff, Illini Community Hospital, Pittsfield, IL, p. A198
AMADO, Mitchell, Senior Vice President Finance and Chief Financial Officer, Glens Falls Hospital, Glens Falls, NY, p. A434
AMANTEA, Paul, Director Finance, University Hospitals Geauga Medical Center, Chardon, OH, p. A481
AMAR Jr., Eugene, Administrator, Kohala Hospital, Kohala, HI, p. A170
AMATO, James, Interim Chief Operating Officer, University of Virginia Medical Center, Charlottesville, VA, p. A663
AMBACHER, Linda, Interim Chief Nursing Officer, Hackettstown Regional Medical Center, Hackettstown, NJ, p. A412
AMBRIZ, Debra, Director Human Resources, Torrance Memorial Medical Center, Torrance, CA, p. A94
AMBROSE, Sherie, Vice President Patient Care Services, Mercy Medical Center Mount Shasta, Mount Shasta, CA, p. A76
AMBROSIANI, Michael, Chief Financial Officer, Knox Community Hospital, Mount Vernon, OH, p. A495
AMBROSINI, Joseph, Director Human Resources, Olympia Medical Center, Los Angeles, CA, p. A71
AMDUR, Deborah, Director, White River Junction Veterans Affairs Medical Center, White River Junction, VT, p. A661
AMEEN, David J., President and Chief Executive Officer, Logansport Memorial Hospital, Logansport, IN, p. A215
AMENT, Rick, Chief Executive Officer, Select Specialty Hospital–Indianapolis, Indianapolis, IN, p. A212
AMERSON, Jeff, Director Information System, West Florida Hospital, Pensacola, FL, p. A140

© 2015 AHA Guide Index of Health Care Professionals **A773**

Index of Health Care Professionals

Index of Health Care Professionals / Ames

AMES, Becky, Chief Executive Officer, Victory Medical Center Beaumont, Beaumont, TX, p. A596
AMES, Laura, Chief Executive Officer, Arbour Hospital, Boston, MA, p. A302
AMEY, Mark, Chief Information Officer, Keck Hospital of USC, Los Angeles, CA, p. A70
AMIN, Yogesh, M.D. Medical Director, Select Specialty Hospital–Fort Wayne, Fort Wayne, IN, p. A209
AMIRNENI, Vamsee, M.D. Chief of Staff, Mercy Allen Hospital, Oberlin, OH, p. A495
AMMAZZALORSO, Michael, M.D. Chief Medical Officer, Winthrop–University Hospital, Mineola, NY, p. A437
AMMONS, Eric, President, Mercy Hospital Jefferson, Crystal City, MO, p. A366
AMODO, Mitch, Vice President and Chief Financial Officer, Orange Regional Medical Center, Middletown, NY, p. A437
AMONS, Gene, Administrator and Chief Executive Officer, Beacham Memorial Hospital, Magnolia, MS, p. A356
AMOROSE, Carl, Vice President Finance, Norton Hospital, Louisville, KY, p. A261
AMOROSO, Mitze, Chief Information Officer, Terence Cardinal Cooke Health Care Center, New York, NY, p. A444
AMOS, John
Chief Executive Officer, Yavapai Regional Medical Center – East, Prescott Valley, AZ, p. A36
President and Chief Executive Officer, Yavapai Regional Medical Center, Prescott, AZ, p. A36
AMOS, Robert, Vice President and Chief Financial Officer, Winchester Medical Center, Winchester, VA, p. A674
AMROM, George, M.D. Vice President Medical Affairs, Hahnemann University Hospital, Philadelphia, PA, p. A543
AMSBERRY, Shelly, Director of Nursing, Jennie M. Melham Memorial Medical Center, Broken Bow, NE, p. A390
AMYX, Maleigha, Chief Information Officer, Rockcastle Regional Hospital and Respiratory Care Center, Mount Vernon, KY, p. A263
ANASTASI, Frank, Chief Financial Officer, Pennsylvania Hospital, Philadelphia, PA, p. A545
ANAYA, Sandra J., R.N., Chief Executive Officer, Palo Verde Hospital, Blythe, CA, p. A56
ANCHONDO, Laura, Administrator Human Resources, Kindred Hospital El Paso, El Paso, TX, p. A611
ANDARSIO, Carlos, M.D. Chief Medical Officer, Navos, Seattle, WA, p. A683
ANDERMAN, Steven, Chief Operating Officer, Bronx–Lebanon Hospital Center Health Care System, NY, p. A438
ANDERS, Anna, Vice President and Chief Nursing Officer, Carson Tahoe Health, Carson City, NV, p. A400
ANDERS, Jr., James M., Administrator and Chief Operating Officer, Kennedy Krieger Institute, Baltimore, MD, p. A293
ANDERS, Mark, Administrator, Villa Feliciana Medical Complex, Jackson, LA, p. A275
ANDERS, Robert, Chief Financial Officer, Ouachita County Medical Center, Camden, AR, p. A42
ANDERSEN, Donia L., Director of Nursing, Centennial Peaks Hospital, Louisville, CO, p. A107
ANDERSEN, John, Manager Information Systems, Sunnyside Community Hospital and Clinics, Sunnyside, WA, p. A686
ANDERSEN, Sue
Chief Financial Officer, French Hospital Medical Center, San Luis Obispo, CA, p. A90
Vice President and Service Area and Chief Financial Officer, Marian Regional Medical Center, Santa Maria, CA, p. A91
ANDERSEN, Toni, R.N. Chief Nurse Executive, Kaiser Permanente Fontana Medical Center, Fontana, CA, p. A61
ANDERSEN, Tracy, Chief Information Officer, St. Mary's Regional Medical Center, Enid, OK, p. A506
ANDERSEN, Travis
President and Chief Executive Officer, Columbia St. Mary's Hospital Milwaukee, Milwaukee, WI, p. A706
President and Chief Executive Officer, Columbia St. Mary's Ozaukee Hospital, Mequon, WI, p. A705
ANDERSEN, Wendy, Director Human Resources, Eastern Idaho Regional Medical Center, Idaho Falls, ID, p. A174
ANDERSON, A. Elizabeth, Administrator, University of South Alabama Medical Center, Mobile, AL, p. A22
ANDERSON, Allen, Interim Chief Executive Officer, Madison Hospital, Madison, MN, p. A341
ANDERSON, Allyson, Chief Administrative Officer, Legacy Meridian Park Medical Center, Tualatin, OR, p. A527
ANDERSON, Angela L., Director Human Resources, Newton Medical Center, Newton, KS, p. A246
ANDERSON, Angie, Director Information Technology, Crawford County Memorial Hospital, Denison, IA, p. A226
ANDERSON, Ashley, Manager Human Resources, Winona Health, Winona, MN, p. A349
ANDERSON, Barbara, Chief Financial Officer, Stanton County Hospital, Johnson, KS, p. A242
ANDERSON, Barbara M., President and Chief Executive Officer, Franciscan St. Anthony Health – Crown Point, Crown Point, IN, p. A207
ANDERSON, Benjamin, Chief Executive Officer and Administrator, Kearny County Hospital, Lakin, KS, p. A244
ANDERSON, Brad, Chief Financial Officer, Community Memorial Hospital, Cloquet, MN, p. A336
ANDERSON, Brian, Chief Financial Officer, Capital Medical Center, Olympia, WA, p. A681
ANDERSON, Charles, M.D. Chief Medical Officer, Desert Regional Medical Center, Palm Springs, CA, p. A80
ANDERSON, Cherri, Chief Nursing Officer, Banner Behavioral Health Hospital – Scottsdale, Scottsdale, AZ, p. A37
ANDERSON, Chris, Chief Executive Officer, Baptist Health Systems, Jackson, MS, p. B20
ANDERSON, Chris, Chief Executive Officer, Mississippi Baptist Medical Center, Jackson, MS, p. A355
ANDERSON, Christine, Chief Nursing Officer and Vice President of Patient Care Services, LincolnHealth, Damariscotta, ME, p. A290
ANDERSON, Conde Nevin, M.D. Chief of Staff, DeTar Healthcare System, Victoria, TX, p. A650
ANDERSON, Craig, Director Management Information Systems, River Bend Hospital, West Lafayette, IN, p. A221
ANDERSON, Dana, Interim Administrator, Long–Term Acute Care Hospital, Mosaic Life Care at St. Joseph, Saint Joseph, MO, p. A375
ANDERSON, Darla, Chief Financial Officer, Ridgeview Sibley Medical Center, Arlington, MN, p. A334
ANDERSON, Dave, FACHE Vice President Administration, Carolinas Healthcare System Union, Monroe, NC, p. A465
ANDERSON, David, Chief Executive Officer, Jackson Purchase Medical Center, Mayfield, KY, p. A262
ANDERSON, Dawn, Chief Nursing Officer, Select Specialty Hospital–Sioux Falls, Sioux Falls, SD, p. A571
ANDERSON, Debra, Manager Patient Financial Services, Norman Specialty Hospital, Norman, OK, p. A510
ANDERSON, Dennis, Administrator and Director of Nursing, Signature Psychiatric Hospital, Kansas City, MO, p. A370
ANDERSON, Dianne J., R.N., President and Chief Executive Officer, Lawrence General Hospital, Lawrence, MA, p. A308
ANDERSON, Donna K., R.N. Chief Nursing Officer, Cannon Memorial Hospital, Pickens, SC, p. A564
ANDERSON, Duke, President and Chief Executive Officer, Hillsdale Community Health Center, Hillsdale, MI, p. A322
ANDERSON, Edward, Chief Financial Officer, Johnson Regional Medical Center, Clarksville, AR, p. A42
ANDERSON, Edwin, M.D. Chief of Staff and Chief Medical Officer, Bigfork Valley Hospital, Bigfork, MN, p. A335
ANDERSON, Emily, Director of Nursing Emergency Room, Gundersen Tri–County Hospital and Clinics, Whitehall, WI, p. A714
ANDERSON, Gaynell, M.D. Medical Director, St. Anthony Shawnee Hospital, Shawnee, OK, p. A515
ANDERSON, Gina
Human Resources Officer, Riverview Regional Medical Center, Carthage, TN, p. A574
Chief Financial Officer, St. Elizabeth Community Hospital, Red Bluff, CA, p. A82
ANDERSON, Greg E., Chief Financial Officer, Emory Health System, Emory University Hospital, atlanta, GA, p. A150
ANDERSON, Heidi, Chief Nursing Officer, Morton General Hospital, Morton, WA, p. A680
ANDERSON, Holly, Supervisor Human Resources, Sanford Rock Rapids Medical Center, Rock Rapids, IA, p. A233
ANDERSON, J. Bryant, Administrator and Chief Executive Officer, Anthony Medical Center, Anthony, KS, p. A237
ANDERSON, Jason, Chief Financial Officer, Mackinac Straits Health System, Inc., Saint Ignace, MI, p. A329
ANDERSON, Jimmy, Director of Information Systems, Regional Hospital of Jackson, Jackson, TN, p. A579
ANDERSON, Joann, President and Chief Executive Officer, Southeastern Health, Lumberton, NC, p. A464
ANDERSON, Jodie, Director Human Resources, Mitchell County Regional Health Center, Osage, IA, p. A232
ANDERSON, John D., FACHE, Administrator, Marshall Medical Center South, Boaz, AL, p. A17
ANDERSON, John G.
Chief Executive Officer, Anderson Regional Medical Center, Meridian, MS, p. A357
Vice President, Administrator, Anderson Regional Medical Center–South Campus, Meridian, MS, p. A357
ANDERSON, Kenneth, M.D. Vice President and Chief Medical Officer, Baptist Health Louisville, Louisville, KY, p. A260
ANDERSON, Kimball, FACHE, Chief Executive Officer, Timpanogos Regional Hospital, Orem, UT, p. A657
ANDERSON, Libby, Chief Financial Officer, Satanta District Hospital and Long Term Care, Satanta, KS, p. A250
ANDERSON, Lisa, Vice President Nursing, Ferrell Hospital, Eldorado, IL, p. A186
ANDERSON, Louis, Chief Financial Officer, McLeod Health Cheraw, Cheraw, SC, p. A558
ANDERSON, Lucia E., Senior Vice President Operations and Chief Nurse Executive, Lake Region Healthcare, Fergus Falls, MN, p. A338
ANDERSON, Mark, Chief Financial Officer, Lane Regional Medical Center, Zachary, LA, p. A287
ANDERSON, Mark T., Chief Financial Officer, Danville Regional Medical Center, Danville, VA, p. A664
ANDERSON, Michael, M.D. Senior Vice President Quality and Chief Medical Officer, Harrison Medical Center, Bremerton, WA, p. A676
ANDERSON, Michael, Ph.D. Chief Operating Officer, Metropolitan St. Louis Psychiatric Center, Saint Louis, MO, p. A376
ANDERSON, Michael, M.D. Chief Medical Officer, University Hospitals Case Medical Center, Cleveland, OH, p. A485
ANDERSON, Patrick, Chief Information Officer, Memorial Medical Center, Modesto, CA, p. A75
ANDERSON, Paula, Administrative Director Human Resources, Endless Mountain Health Systems, Montrose, PA, p. A541
ANDERSON, Randy, DPM Chief Medical Officer, PeaceHealth United General Medical Center, Sedro–Woolley, WA, p. A684
ANDERSON, Rhonda
Executive Vice President Finance and Chief Financial Officer, Columbia St. Mary's Hospital Milwaukee, Milwaukee, WI, p. A706
Executive Vice President Finance and Chief Financial Officer, Columbia St. Mary's Ozaukee Hospital, Mequon, WI, p. A705
Executive Vice President Finance and Chief Financial Officer, Sacred Heart Rehabilitation Institute, Milwaukee, WI, p. A706
ANDERSON, Richard A., President and Chief Executive Officer, St. Luke's University Health Network, Bethlehem, PA, p. B128
ANDERSON, Rick, M.D. Senior Vice President and Chief Medical Officer, TMC Healthcare, Tucson, AZ, p. A40
ANDERSON, Robert C., Interim Chief Financial Officer, Alameda Hospital, Alameda, CA, p. A53
ANDERSON, Rohan, Chief Information Officer, Doctors Memorial Hospital, Bonifay, FL, p. A122
ANDERSON, Roland, M.D., Medical Director, Arkansas Department of Correction Hospital, Pine Bluff, AR, p. A49
ANDERSON, Sandra L.
President and Chief Executive Officer, Howard Young Medical Center, Woodruff, WI, p. A714
President and Chief Executive Officer, Ministry Eagle River Memorial Hospital, Eagle River, WI, p. A700
President and Chief Executive Officer, Ministry Sacred Heart Hospital, Tomahawk, WI, p. A712
President and Chief Executive Officer, Ministry Saint Mary's Hospitals, Rhinelander, WI, p. A710
ANDERSON, Sharla, Chief Executive Officer, Trinity Mother Frances Rehabilitation Hospital, Tyler, TX, p. A649
ANDERSON, Shawn, Chief Operating Officer, Cary Medical Center, Caribou, ME, p. A289
ANDERSON, Sims, Manager Facility Automation, Terrell State Hospital, Terrell, TX, p. A647
ANDERSON, Stephanie, Executive Vice President and Chief Operating Officer, Woman's Hospital, Baton Rouge, LA, p. A270
ANDERSON, Stephen, M.D
Chief Medical Officer, Saint Joseph Regional Medical Center, Mishawaka, IN, p. A216
Chief Medical Officer, Saint Joseph Regional Medical Center–Plymouth Campus, Plymouth, IN, p. A218
ANDERSON, Steven
Chief Executive Officer, Jordan Valley Medical Center, West Jordan, UT, p. A659
Chief Executive Officer, Jordan Valley Medical Center–WVC Campus, West Valley City, UT, p. A659
ANDERSON, Sue, Executive Vice President, Chief Financial Officer and Chief Information Officer, Virginia Mason Medical Center, Seattle, WA, p. A684
ANDERSON, Susan, Director Information Systems, Texas Health Presbyterian Hospital Plano, Plano, TX, p. A637
ANDERSON, Suzanne P., Nurse Administrator, Intermountain Medical Center, Murray, UT, p. A656
ANDERSON, Thomas, M.D. Vice President Medical Affairs, Chambersburg Hospital, Chambersburg, PA, p. A531
ANDERSON, Thomas, Vice President Medical Affairs, Lakeview Hospital, Stillwater, MN, p. A347
ANDERSON, Thomas, M.D
Chief of Staff, Portland Veterans Affairs Medical Center, Portland, OR, p. A524
Vice President Medical Affairs, Waynesboro Hospital, Waynesboro, PA, p. A552
ANDERSON, Tim, Controller, Van Matre HealthSouth Rehabilitation Hospital, Rockford, IL, p. A200
ANDERSON, Jr., Timothy Craig, Chief Nursing Officer, Wellmont Bristol Regional Medical Center, Bristol, TN, p. A574

A774 Index of Health Care Professionals

Index of Health Care Professionals / Arakelian

Index of Health Care Professionals

ANDERSON, Traci, Chief Financial Officer, Memorial Hospital, Seminole, TX, p. A643
ANDERSON, William, M.D. Medical Director, Rosebud Health Care Center, Forsyth, MT, p. A383
ANDERT, Nancy, Director Human Resources, Murray County Medical Center, Slayton, MN, p. A347
ANDERT, Vicki, Chief Nursing Officer, Eureka Springs Hospital, Eureka Springs, AR, p. A43
ANDRADA, Sally, Chief Information Officer, Los Alamitos Medical Center, Los Alamitos, CA, p. A68
ANDRAE, Andrea
Chief Financial Officer, Gnaden Huetten Memorial Hospital, Lehighton, PA, p. A538
Chief Financial Officer, Palmerton Hospital, Palmerton, PA, p. A542
ANDRE, Katelyn, Human Resource Coordinator, Select Specialty Hospital–Macomb County, Mount Clemens, MI, p. A326
ANDREAS, Ginger, Coordinator Personnel and Credentialing, El Campo Memorial Hospital, El Campo, TX, p. A610
ANDREAS, Lori, Director Patient Care Services, Johnson Memorial Health Services, Dawson, MN, p. A337
ANDREASEN, Raymond, M.D. Chief Medical Officer–Inpatient, California Medical Facility, Vacaville, CA, p. A95
ANDRES, Elizabeth, Director Human Resources, Atascadero State Hospital, Atascadero, CA, p. A54
ANDRES, Leonidas, M.D. Chief of Staff, Winnie Community Hospital, Winnie, TX, p. A652
ANDRESEN, Daniel, Chief information Officer, Mercy Medical Center Merced, Merced, CA, p. A75
ANDREWS, Ashleigh
Director Human Resources, Riverside Behavioral Health Center, Hampton, VA, p. A666
Manager Human Resources, Riverside Rehabilitation Institute, Newport News, VA, p. A669
ANDREWS, Brandy, Director Human Resources, Merit Health Northwest Mississippi, Clarksdale, MS, p. A351
ANDREWS, Callie, Chief Operating Officer, Eastside Medical Center, Snellville, GA, p. A164
ANDREWS, Carolle, Interim Chief Human Resources Officer, University of Connecticut Health Center, John Dempsey Hospital, Farmington, CT, p. A112
ANDREWS, David, Manager Information Systems, Chicot Memorial Medical Center, Lake Village, AR, p. A46
ANDREWS, Fred J., Director of Nursing and Ancillary Services, Baylor Institute for Rehabilitation at Fort Worth, Fort Worth, TX, p. A613
ANDREWS, Jim, Chief Financial Officer, North Okaloosa Medical Center, Crestview, FL, p. A124
ANDREWS, John, M.D. Chief of Staff, East Texas Medical Center Tyler, Tyler, TX, p. A649
ANDREWS, Lisa, Director Human Resources, Lancaster Rehabilitation Hospital, Lancaster, PA, p. A537
ANDREWS, Maria R., Director, Charlie Norwood Veterans Affairs Medical Center, Augusta, GA, p. A151
ANDREWS, Michael, Coordinator Information Systems, Harlan County Health System, Alma, NE, p. A389
ANDREWS, Michele, Chief Clinical Officer, Integrity Transitional Hospital, Denton, TX, p. A608
ANDREWS, Mike, Associate Administrator and Chief Operating Officer, OCH Regional Medical Center, Starkville, MS, p. A360
ANDREWS, Paul
Chief Executive Officer, The Brook at Dupont, Louisville, KY, p. A262
Chief Executive Officer, The Brook Hospital – KMI, Louisville, KY, p. A262
ANDREWS, Rebecca, Chief Financial Officer, Vibra Hospital of Northern California, Redding, CA, p. A82
ANDREWS, Steve, Chief Financial Officer, Three Rivers Health, Three Rivers, MI, p. A331
ANDREWS, Sue E., Chief Financial Officer, O'Connor Hospital, Delhi, NY, p. A432
ANDREWS, Susan E., Chief Executive Officer, Touro Infirmary, New Orleans, LA, p. A282
ANDREWS, Terri, Director Information Technology, Alamance Regional Medical Center, Burlington, NC, p. A456
ANDREWS, Terry, Manager Information Technology, Aultman Orrville Hospital, Orrville, OH, p. A496
ANDRITSCH, Scott, Chief Financial Officer, Sullivan County Community Hospital, Sullivan, IN, p. A220
ANDRO, Ronald J., President and Chief Executive Officer, West Penn Hospital, Pittsburgh, PA, p. A547
ANDRUS, Helen
Chief Financial Officer, Providence Mount Carmel Hospital, Colville, WA, p. A678
Chief Financial Officer, Providence St. Joseph's Hospital, Chewelah, WA, p. A677
Chief Financial Officer, St. Luke's Rehabilitation Institute, Spokane, WA, p. A685
ANDRUS, Jonathon, Chief Executive Officer, Fairchild Medical Center, Yreka, CA, p. A98
ANDRUS, Terry W., President, East Alabama Medical Center, Opelika, AL, p. A23
ANDURSKY, John, Chief Financial Officer, Highlands Hospital, Connellsville, PA, p. A532
ANFINSON, Julie, Director Human Resources, Mercy Medical Center–Sioux City, Sioux City, IA, p. A234
ANGALICH, Dave, Director Information Services, Weirton Medical Center, Weirton, WV, p. A696
ANGCO, Manuel, M.D. Chief of Staff, Williamson Memorial Hospital, Williamson, WV, p. A696
ANGELL, Nancy, Associate Administrator Personnel, Sagamore Children's Psychiatric Center, Dix Hills, NY, p. A432
ANGELO, Gregory, Chief Fiscal Program, James J. Peters Veterans Affairs Medical Center, NY, p. A440
ANGELO, Thomas, Chief Executive Officer, Centra Southside Community Hospital, Farmville, VA, p. A664
ANGELUCCI, Patricia A., MS Director Patient Care Services, Shawano Medical Center, Shawano, WI, p. A710
ANGERAMI, Deborah, Chief Operating Officer, Health First Viera Hospital, Melbourne, FL, p. A133
ANGERMEIER, Elizabeth, Director of Nursing, Evansville Psychiatric Children Center, Evansville, IN, p. A208
ANGLE, James L., FACHE,
Chief Executive Officer, St. Luke's Jerome, Jerome, ID, p. A174
Regional Chief Executive Officer, St. Luke's Magic Valley Medical Center, Twin Falls, ID, p. A176
ANGLE, Mary Ann, R.N. Chief Nursing Officer, TriStar Summit Medical Center, Hermitage, TN, p. A578
ANGLIN, Jason, Chief Executive Officer, Memorial Medical Center, Port Lavaca, TX, p. A638
ANGUS, Jolyn M., R.N. Chief Nursing Officer, Miami Valley Hospital, Dayton, OH, p. A488
ANKIN, Michael G., M.D
Vice President Medical Affairs & Chief Medical Officer, Northwestern Lake Forest Hospital, Lake Forest, IL, p. A192
Vice President Medical Affairs & Chief Medical Officer, Northwestern Memorial Hospital, Chicago, IL, p. A183
ANMUTH, Craig, M.D. Medical Director, Bacharach Institute for Rehabilitation, Pomona, NJ, p. A417
ANNARINO, Phillip, Vice President Human Resources, Fisher–Titus Medical Center, Norwalk, OH, p. A495
ANNECHARICO, Mary Alice
Chief Information Officer, Henry Ford Hospital, Detroit, MI, p. A317
Senior VP and CIO, Henry Ford Health System, Henry Ford Wyandotte Hospital, Wyandotte, MI, p. A332
ANNESSER, Sue
Chief Information Officer, Freeman Hospital West, Joplin, MO, p. A369
Director Information Systems, Freeman Neosho Hospital, Neosho, MO, p. A373
ANNIS, Donald E., Chief Executive Officer, Crawford Memorial Hospital, Robinson, IL, p. A199
ANOLIK, Adam, Chief Financial Officer, Highland Hospital of Rochester, Rochester, NY, p. A448
ANSELL, David A., M.D. Senior Vice President Clinical Affairs and Chief Medical Officer, Rush University Medical Center, Chicago, IL, p. A184
ANSELL, L. V., M.D. Medical Director, Houston Orthopedic and Spine Hospital, Bellaire, TX, p. A597
ANSELMA, M., Chief Operating Officer, OSF Saint Anthony's Health Center, Alton, IL, p. A178
ANSI, Azena, Manager Health Information Management, Horizon Specialty Hospital, Las Vegas, NV, p. A402
ANSLEY, Pamela, Director Finance, Sutter Center for Psychiatry, Sacramento, CA, p. A85
ANSON, Ashley, Chief Executive Officer, Victory Medical Center Craig Ranch, McKinney, TX, p. A632
ANSON, Crystal, Director Health Information, Fairlawn Rehabilitation Hospital, Worcester, MA, p. A313
ANTCZAK, Kenneth, Vice President Human Resources, St. Mary Mercy Hospital, Livonia, MI, p. A325
ANTES, John, President, Missouri Baptist Medical Center, Saint Louis, MO, p. A377
ANTHONY, Anne, FACHE President and Chief Executive Officer, Willow Crest Hospital, Miami, OK, p. A509
ANTHONY, Jean, R.N., President and Chief Executive Officer, Hills & Dales General Hospital, Cass City, MI, p. A316
ANTHONY, Kim, Director Human Resources, Burke Medical Center, Waynesboro, GA, p. A167
ANTHONY, Mark, Executive Vice President and Chief Operating Officer, Borgess Medical Center, Kalamazoo, MI, p. A323
ANTHONY, Michelle, Chief Nursing Officer, HEALTHSOUTH Rehabilitation Hospital of Virginia, Richmond, VA, p. A671
ANTHONY, Paula
Vice President Information Services, East Texas Medical Center Pittsburg, Pittsburg, TX, p. A636
Vice President Information Services, East Texas Medical Center Rehabilitation Hospital, Tyler, TX, p. A648
Vice President Information Services, East Texas Medical Center Specialty Hospital, Tyler, TX, p. A648
Vice President Information Services, East Texas Medical Center Tyler, Tyler, TX, p. A649
ANTHONY, Sharon, Interim Chief Executive Officer, Select Specialty Hospital–Phoenix, Phoenix, AZ, p. A35
ANTINELLI, Mark, Manager Human Resources, Syracuse Veterans Affairs Medical Center, Syracuse, NY, p. A451
ANTINORI, James, M.D. Chief of Staff, Mountain West Medical Center, Tooele, UT, p. A659
ANTOINE, Greg, M.D. Chief of Staff, Fayetteville Veterans Affairs Medical Center, Fayetteville, NC, p. A460
ANTON, Lourdes, Director Human Resources, Palm Springs General Hospital, Hialeah, FL, p. A128
ANTONACCI, Amy, MSN Vice President Nursing Services, Alliance Community Hospital, Alliance, OH, p. A478
ANTONECCHIA, Paul, M.D. Vice President Medical Affairs and Chief Medical Officer, St. John's Riverside Hospital, Yonkers, NY, p. A454
ANTONIADES, Michael A., Executive Vice President and Chief Operating Officer, Robert Wood Johnson University Hospital, New Brunswick, NJ, p. A415
ANTONSON, Pete, Chief Executive Officer, Northwood Deaconess Health Center, Northwood, ND, p. A476
ANTONUCCI, Lawrence, M.D
Chief Operating Officer, Cape Coral Hospital, Cape Coral, FL, p. A123
Chief Operating Officer, Gulf Coast Medical Center, Fort Myers, FL, p. A127
Chief Operating Officer, Lee Memorial Hospital, Fort Myers, FL, p. A127
ANTRUM, Sheila, R.N. Chief Nursing Officer, Director Patient Care Services, UCSF Medical Center, San Francisco, CA, p. A89
ANWAR, Muhammad, M.D. Chief Medical Officer, Encino Hospital Medical Center, CA, p. A69
ANYASO, Vanessa, Chief Human Resources, Tomball Regional Medical Center, Tomball, TX, p. A648
APIKI, Zessica L., Accountant, Molokai General Hospital, Kaunakakai, HI, p. A170
APLAND, Wendy
Regional Vice President of Finance/Chief Financial Officer, PeaceHealth Sacred Heart Medical Center at RiverBend, Springfield, OR, p. A526
Interim Chief Financial Officer, PeaceHealth Sacred Heart Medical Center University District, Eugene, OR, p. A520
APOLINAR, Adam, Chief Clinical Officer, Victory Medical Center – Southcross, San Antonio, TX, p. A642
APOLIONA, Nicole, M.D. Medical Director, Kula Hospital, Kula, HI, p. A170
APONTE, Miguel, Supervisor Management Information Systems, Wilma N. Vazquez Medical Center, Vega Baja, PR, p. A724
APPEL, Sheryl, Chief Executive Officer, HEALTHSOUTH Rehabilitation Hospital of Arlington, Arlington, TX, p. A592
APPENHEIMER, A. Timothy, M.D. Vice President and Chief Medical Officer, Katherine Shaw Bethea Hospital, Dixon, IL, p. A186
APPLE, Donald L., Chief Financial Officer, St. Vincent Anderson Regional Hospital, Anderson, IN, p. A204
APPLEBAUM, Jon D., Chief Executive Officer, Twin County Regional Healthcare, Galax, VA, p. A665
APPLEGATE, Mary Jane, Chief Nursing Officer, Knoxville Hospital & Clinics, Knoxville, IA, p. A230
APPLETON, Joe, M.D. Chief of Surgery, Milan General Hospital, Milan, TN, p. A584
APPLEWOOD, David, Controller, HealthSouth Rehabilitation Hospital of Tallahassee, Tallahassee, FL, p. A144
APRILE, Patricia, Chief Operating Officer, Southern Maine Health Care – Biddeford Medical Center, Biddeford, ME, p. A289
AQUILINA, Joanne, Vice President Finance and Chief Financial Officer, Bethesda Hospital East, Boynton Beach, FL, p. A122
ARAD, Lana
Chief Financial Officer, Good Samaritan Hospital, San Jose, CA, p. A89
Chief Financial Officer, MountainView Hospital, Las Vegas, NV, p. A402
ARAGON, Juliette, Finance Director, Turquoise Lodge Hospital, Albuquerque, NM, p. A423
ARAGON, Liz, R.N. Vice President, Chief Nursing Officer, San Antonio Community Hospital, Upland, CA, p. A95
ARAIR, Sohaib, M.D. Chairman of Medical Staff, Pioneer Community Hospital of Newton, Newton, MS, p. A358
ARAKELIAN, Armen, Chief Information Officer, Fulton County Medical Center, Mc Connellsburg, PA, p. A539

Index of Health Care Professionals

Index of Health Care Professionals / Arambula


ARAMBULA, Frank, Chief Financial Officer, Arrowhead Regional Medical Center, Colton, CA, p. A58
ARAN, Peter P., M.D
Senior Vice President and Chief Medical Officer, Saint Francis Hospital, Tulsa, OK, p. A517
Senior Vice President and Chief Medical Officer, Saint Francis Hospital South, Tulsa, OK, p. A517
ARANDA, Heather R., R.N. Chief Nursing Officer, F. W. Huston Medical Center, Winchester, KS, p. A253
ARANIO, Lani, Regional Director Human Resources, Samuel Mahelona Memorial Hospital, Kapaa, HI, p. A170
ARATOW, Michael, M.D. Chief Information Officer, San Mateo Medical Center, San Mateo, CA, p. A90
ARAUJO, Marianne D., R.N. Vice President Nursing and Chief Nurse Executive, Advocate Good Shepherd Hospital, Barrington, IL, p. A179
ARAUJO, Markeeta, Chief Nursing Officer, Desert View Hospital, Pahrump, NV, p. A403
ARBAUGH, Ronnie, Director Human Resources, Grant Memorial Hospital, Petersburg, WV, p. A694
ARBOGEST, Dodie, Chief Financial Officer, Stonewall Jackson Memorial Hospital, Weston, WV, p. A696
ARBOLEDA, Reginaldo, M.D. Chief of Staff, Wild Rose Community Memorial Hospital, Wild Rose, WI, p. A714
ARBON, Don, Vice President Finance, Mid–Columbia Medical Center, The Dalles, OR, p. A526
ARBON, Terron, R.N. Chief Nursing Officer, Salt Lake Regional Medical Center, Salt Lake City, UT, p. A658
ARBONEAUX, Jane, Chief Financial Officer, Prevost Memorial Hospital, Donaldsonville, LA, p. A273
ARBONEAUX, Wayne M., Chief Executive Officer, Assumption Community Hospital, Napoleonville, LA, p. A281
ARBUCKLE, Barry S., Ph.D., President and Chief Executive Officer, MemorialCare, Fountain Valley, CA, p. B89
ARBUTHNOT, Rena, Director Human Resources, Shriners Hospitals for Children–Shreveport, Shreveport, LA, p. A285
ARCANGELI, Barbara J., Vice President Human Resources, Newport Hospital, Newport, RI, p. A555
ARCE, Daisy, Chief of Medical Staff, Weslaco Rehabilitation Hospital, Weslaco, TX, p. A651
ARCENEAUX, Larrie, Chief Clinical Officer, Promise Hospital Baton Rouge – Main Campus, Baton Rouge, LA, p. A270
ARCENEAUX, Susan, R.N. Coordinator Information Technology, Leonard J. Chabert Medical Center, Houma, LA, p. A275
ARCENEAUX, Trina, Assistant Chief Financial Officer, Promise Hospital Baton Rouge – Main Campus, Baton Rouge, LA, p. A270
ARCH, Chrissy, Chief Financial Officer, Cherokee Indian Hospital, Cherokee, NC, p. A458
ARCH, John K., FACHE, Director, Boys Town National Research Hospital, Omaha, NE, p. A395
ARCHAMBAULT, Jennifer, Vice President Human Resources and Compliance, Copley Hospital, Morrisville, VT, p. A660
ARCHAMBEAULT, Shirley, Chief Information Officer, Medical Center of Lewisville, Lewisville, TX, p. A628
ARCHER, David, Director Information Systems, Tristar Ashland City Medical Center, Ashland City, TN, p. A574
ARCHER, David L., Chief Executive Officer, Saint Francis Hospital, Memphis, TN, p. A584
ARCHER, Doug, Assistant Administrator, Sutter Tracy Community Hospital, Tracy, CA, p. A94
ARCHER, Joe, Chief Information Officer, Victor Valley Global Medical Center, Victorville, CA, p. A96
ARCHER, Kenneth W., Chief Executive Officer, South Lincoln Medical Center, Kemmerer, WY, p. A716
ARCHER–DUSTE, Helen, Chief Operating Officer, Kaiser Permanente San Francisco Medical Center, San Francisco, CA, p. A88
ARCHEY, Eugene, Chief Information Technology, VA Greater Los Angeles Healthcare System, Los Angeles, CA, p. A73
ARCHIBOLD, Robert, Director, Human Resources, St. Anthony North Health Campus, Westminster, CO, p. A109
ARCHULETA, Michael, Chief Information Technology Officer, Mt. San Rafael Hospital, Trinidad, CO, p. A109
ARCIDI, Alfred J., M.D.,
Senior Vice President, Whittier Rehabilitation Hospital, Bradford, MA, p. A304
Senior Vice President, Whittier Rehabilitation Hospital, Westborough, MA, p. A312
ARCIDI, Alfred L., M.D., President, Whittier Health Network, Haverhill, MA, p. B154
ARCIDI, Alfred L., M.D., Chief Executive Officer, Whittier Pavilion, Haverhill, MA, p. A307
ARCILLA, Jelden, R.N. Vice President and Chief Nursing Officer, HonorHealth John C. Lincoln Medical Center, Phoenix, AZ, p. A35
ARD, Sheila, Chief Nursing Officer, Huntsville Memorial Hospital, Huntsville, TX, p. A623
ARDABELL, Toni R., R.N., Chief Executive Officer, Bon Secours St. Mary's Hospital, Richmond, VA, p. A671
ARDEMAGNI, Jeff, Chief Financial Officer, Medical Center Arlington, Arlington, TX, p. A592
ARDION, Doug, M.D. Chief Medical Officer, NCH Downtown Naples Hospital, Naples, FL, p. A136
ARDOIN, Cody, Director Human Resources, Mercy Regional Medical Center, Ville Platte, LA, p. A286
ARDOIN, Stan, M.D. Medical Director, Griffin Memorial Hospital, Norman, OK, p. A510
ARELLANO, Edgar Alejandro, Chief Information Technologist, Three Rivers Hospital, Brewster, WA, p. A677
ARGIRO, Donald V., Vice President, Human Resources, Summa Barberton Citizens Hospital, Barberton, OH, p. A479
ARGUETA, David
Chief Executive Officer, St. Luke's Lakeside Hospital, The Woodlands, TX, p. A647
President, St. Luke's The Woodlands Hospital, The Woodlands, TX, p. A648
ARGYROS, Gregory J., M.D. Senior Vice President, Medical Affairs & Chief Medical Officer, MedStar Washington Hospital Center, Washington, DC, p. A119
ARIAS, Taffy J., Chief Executive Officer, Martin General Hospital, Williamston, NC, p. A470
ARISPE, Joe, Director Information Systems, Wise Regional Health System, Decatur, TX, p. A607
ARIZPE, Robert C., Superintendent, San Antonio State Hospital, San Antonio, TX, p. A642
ARKFELD, Diane, R.N. Vice President, Clinical Nursing, Crawford County Memorial Hospital, Denison, IA, p. A226
ARLEDGE, Denton
Vice President and Chief Information Officer, WakeMed Cary Hospital, Cary, NC, p. A456
Vice President and Chief Information Officer, WakeMed Raleigh Campus, Raleigh, NC, p. A467
ARLIEN, Dana, M.D. Chief Medical Officer, Willow Springs Center, Reno, NV, p. A404
ARMADA, Anthony A., Senior Vice President, Chief Executive Officer of Swedish Health Services and Providence Health and Services, Swedish Health Services, Seattle, WA, p. B130
ARMATO, Carl S., President and Chief Executive Officer, Novant Health, Winston Salem, NC, p. B99
ARMBRUSTER, Kent A W, M.D. Vice President Medical Affairs, Little Company of Mary Hospital and Health Care Centers, Evergreen Park, IL, p. A188
ARMENDARIZ, Elias, Chief Operating Officer and Chief Nursing Officer, El Paso Children's Hospital, El Paso, TX, p. A610
ARMENTROUT, Rich, Chief Financial Officer, Meadows Psychiatric Center, Centre Hall, PA, p. A531
ARMFIELD, Ben, Chief Financial Officer, Fresno Heart and Surgical Hospital, Fresno, CA, p. A62
ARMISTEAD, Russell, Chief Executive Officer, UF Health Jacksonville, Jacksonville, FL, p. A130
ARMOUR, John, Chief Financial Officer, Bayshore Medical Center, Pasadena, TX, p. A635
ARMSTEAD, Cori, MSN Vice President, Chief Nursing Officer, Midland Memorial Hospital, Midland, TX, p. A632
ARMSTRONG, Alan, M.D. Chief Medical Officer, Pine Rest Christian Mental Health Services, Grand Rapids, MI, p. A321
ARMSTRONG, Deborah, Chief Executive Officer, Rockdale Medical Center, Conyers, GA, p. A154
ARMSTRONG, Evelyn, Chief Nursing Officer, HEALTHSOUTH Rehabilitation Hospital of Erie, Erie, PA, p. A534
ARMSTRONG, Gary, Executive Vice President, Methodist Rehabilitation Center, Jackson, MS, p. A355
ARMSTRONG, James, Manager Information Technology, Delaware Valley Hospital, Walton, NY, p. A453
ARMSTRONG, Jeffery, CPA Chief Financial Officer, Granville Health System, Oxford, NC, p. A466
ARMSTRONG, Jeremy, FACHE, Chief Executive Officer, Mitchell County Hospital Health Systems, Beloit, KS, p. A238
ARMSTRONG, Kim, Chief Financial Officer, Windom Area Hospital, Windom, MN, p. A349
ARMSTRONG, Kyle E., Administrator and Chief Executive Officer, Baptist Memorial Hospital–Collierville, Collierville, TN, p. A576
ARMSTRONG, Mark, M.D. Medical Director, Baylor Medical Center at Uptown, Dallas, TX, p. A604
ARMSTRONG, Neil G., FACHE Vice President and Chief Operating Officer, Divine Providence Hospital, Williamsport, PA, p. A553
ARMSTRONG, Robert, Senior Vice President and Chief Operating Officer, Lima Memorial Health System, Lima, OH, p. A492
ARMSTRONG, Roger
Interim Chief Financial Officer, Pioneers Memorial Healthcare District, Brawley, CA, p. A56
Vice President Finance and Chief Financial Officer, UnityPoint Health–Proctor, Peoria, IL, p. A198
ARMSTRONG, Sandra, Chief Information Officer, University of Connecticut Health Center, John Dempsey Hospital, Farmington, CT, p. A112
ARMSTRONG, William C.
Senior Vice President and Chief Financial Officer, Mercy Medical Center, Rockville Centre, NY, p. A449
Vice President and Chief Financial Officer, St. Francis Hospital, Roslyn, NY, p. A449
ARMSTRONG–HUFF, Glenda, Assistant Superintendent, Texas Center for Infectious Disease, San Antonio, TX, p. A642
ARNAU, Barbara, R.N. Chief Nursing Officer, Chestatee Regional Hospital, Dahlonega, GA, p. A155
ARNAU, Dede, R.N. Chief Nursing Officer, Elbert Memorial Hospital, Elberton, GA, p. A157
ARNDELL, Scott, Chief Financial Officer, Twin Lakes Regional Medical Center, Leitchfield, KY, p. A259
ARNER, Steven C.
Chief Operating Officer, Carilion Franklin Memorial Hospital, Rocky Mount, VA, p. A672
President, Carilion Roanoke Memorial Hospital, Roanoke, VA, p. A672
President, Carilion Roanoke Memorial Hospital, Roanoke, VA, p. A672
ARNESON, Brenda, Administrative Assistant, St. Andrew's Health Center, Bottineau, ND, p. A472
ARNESON, Garrett, Chief Executive Officer, LifeCare Hospitals of Chester County, West Chester, PA, p. A552
ARNETT, Jacob, Chief Information Technology Officer, Lakeside Behavioral Health System, Memphis, TN, p. A583
ARNETT, James, Vice President Human Resources, Meriter UnityPoint Health, Madison, WI, p. A704
ARNETT, Randal M., President and Chief Executive Officer, Southern Ohio Medical Center, Portsmouth, OH, p. A496
ARNETT, Sallie, Vice President Information Systems, Licking Memorial Hospital, Newark, OH, p. A495
ARNETT, Stuart
Regional Vice President Finance, Aurora Lakeland Medical Center, Elkhorn, WI, p. A700
Vice President Finance and Chief Financial Officer, Aurora Memorial Hospital of Burlington, Burlington, WI, p. A699
ARNHART, Carol, Vice President and Chief Financial Officer, Siskin Hospital for Physical Rehabilitation, Chattanooga, TN, p. A575
ARNOLD, Ann, M.D. Medical Director, Medical Center of Plano, Plano, TX, p. A637
ARNOLD, Bill, Chief Operating Officer, Monmouth Medical Center, Long Branch Campus, Long Branch, NJ, p. A413
ARNOLD, Bobby, President and Chief Executive Officer, Jackson–Madison County General Hospital, Jackson, TN, p. A579
ARNOLD, Bobby, President and Chief Executive Officer, West Tennessee Healthcare, Jackson, TN, p. B153
ARNOLD, Dustin, D.O. Chief Medical Officer, UnityPoint Health – St. Luke's Hospital, Cedar Rapids, IA, p. A223
ARNOLD, Jeffrey, M.D. Chief Medical Officer, Santa Clara Valley Medical Center, San Jose, CA, p. A89
ARNOLD, Kimberly N., R.N. Chief Nursing Officer and Interim Chief Quality Officer, AllianceHealth Woodward, Woodward, OK, p. A518
ARNOLD, Leslie, Chief Executive Officer and Administrator, St. Vincent Morrilton, Morrilton, AR, p. A48
ARNOLD, Paul, M.D. Chief of Medical Staff, Florida Hospital North Pinellas, Tarpon Springs, FL, p. A145
ARNOLD, Pauline, MSN Chief Nursing and Quality Officer and Vice President Clinical Operations, Indiana University Health La Porte Hospital, La Porte, IN, p. A214
ARNOLD, Scott, Senior Vice President Information Systems, Tampa General Hospital, Tampa, FL, p. A145
ARNOLD, Thomas, Chief Financial Officer, Piedmont Hospital, Atlanta, GA, p. A151
ARNOW, Debra, R.N. VP Patient Care & Chief Nursing Officer, Children's Hospital and Medical Center, Omaha, NE, p. A396
ARNSTON, Hanz, R.N., Chief Executive Officer, Garfield County Health Center, Jordan, MT, p. A384
ARNTZ, Mary, Manager Business Office and Executive Assistant, Physicians' Medical Center, New Albany, IN, p. A217
AROCHO, Jacqueline, Administrator, BayCare Alliant Hospital, Dunedin, FL, p. A126
ARONS, Bernard, M.D. Director Medical Affairs, Saint Elizabeths Hospital, Washington, DC, p. A120
ARORA, Gaurau, M.D. Chief Medical Officer, Indiana University Health Tipton Hospital, Tipton, IN, p. A220
ARORA, Pamela, Senior Vice President Information Systems, Children's Health System of Texas, Dallas, TX, p. A604
ARORA, Sat, M.D. President Medical and Dental Staff, Crozer–Chester Medical Center, Upland, PA, p. A551
ARRINGTON, Rex, Chief Information Officer, Laughlin Memorial Hospital, Greeneville, TN, p. A578
ARROWOOD, Al, Chief Financial Officer, Washington County Hospital, Plymouth, NC, p. A466


A776 Index of Health Care Professionals 

Index of Health Care Professionals / Austerlitz

Index of Health Care Professionals


ARROYO, Luis A.
Chief Financial Officer, Hospital HIMA San Pablo Caguas, Caguas, PR, p. A720
Chief Financial Officer, Hospital HMA de Humacao, Humacao, PR, p. A721
Chief Financial Officer, Hospital San Pablo Del Este, Fajardo, PR, p. A721
ARSENAULT, Donna, Director Human Resources, Baystate Mary Lane Hospital, Ware, MA, p. A312
ARSENAULT, Lisa, Vice President Human Resources and Compliance, Millinocket Regional Hospital, Millinocket, ME, p. A291
ARSENAULT, Rebecca L., MS, President and Chief Executive Officer, Franklin Memorial Hospital, Farmington, ME, p. A290
ARSLANPAY, Robin, Director Human Resources, LifeCare Hospitals of Pittsburgh, Pittsburgh, PA, p. A546
ARSURA, Edward, M.D. Chief Medical Officer, Richmond University Medical Center, NY, p. A444
ART, Steve, Senior Vice President and Chief Information Officer, NYU Lutheran, NY, p. A444
ARTERBURN, Catherine T., R.N. Vice President Human Resources, Sidney Regional Medical Center, Sidney, NE, p. A398
ARTHUR, John
Chief Financial Officer, St. Vincent Mercy Hospital, Elwood, IN, p. A207
Chief Financial Officer, St. Vincent Randolph Hospital, Winchester, IN, p. A221
ARTHUR, Lawrence J., President, Rural Community Hospitals of America, Kansas City, MO, p. B114
ARTHUR, Rita K., Director Human Resources, Littleton Adventist Hospital, Littleton, CO, p. A106
ARTIS, Cornelius, M.D. Chief Medical Officer, Our Community Hospital, Scotland Neck, NC, p. A468
ARTMAN, David S., Chief Operating Officer, Weirton Medical Center, Weirton, WV, p. A696
ARTS–STRENKE, Cindy, R.N. Chief Operating Officer and Chief Nursing Officer, Lakeview Medical Center, Rice Lake, WI, p. A710
ARUNAMATA, Peti, Interim Area Director Information Technology, Kaiser Permanente San Francisco Medical Center, San Francisco, CA, p. A88
ARVIDSON, Betty, Chief Financial Officer, RiverView Health, Crookston, MN, p. A337
ARVIN, Jon A., M.D. Chief Medical Officer, Rockcastle Regional Hospital and Respiratory Care Center, Mount Vernon, KY, p. A263
ARVON, Christina, Administrator and Chief Executive Officer, Eye and Ear Clinic of Charleston, Charleston, WV, p. A690
ARZE, Steven, M.D. Chief Medical Officer and Vice President Medical Affairs, Baylor Medical Center at Garland, Garland, TX, p. A616
ASADA, Bonnie, Director of Nursing, Alvarado Parkway Institute Behavioral Health System, La Mesa, CA, p. A66
ASAFTEI, Laura, Administrative Director, Florida Hospital Zephyrhills, Zephyrhills, FL, p. A148
ASAOKA, Danny, Executive Director Information Systems, Long Beach Memorial Medical Center, Long Beach, CA, p. A68
ASBERRY, James
Chief Financial Officer, Post Acute/Warm Springs Rehabilitation Hospital of San Antonio, San Antonio, TX, p. A642
Chief Financial Officer, Post Acute/Warm Springs Specialty Hospital of Luling, Luling, TX, p. A630
Chief Financial Officer, Post Acute/Warm Springs Specialty Hospital of Victoria, Victoria, TX, p. A650
ASBURY, Wesley, M.D. President Medical Staff, Princeton Community Hospital, Princeton, WV, p. A694
ASCHOFF, Jodi, Chief Financial Officer, Osmond General Hospital, Osmond, NE, p. A397
ASH, Michael A., Chief Transformation Officer, Nebraska Medicine – Nebraska Medical Center, Omaha, NE, p. A396
ASH, Richard M., Chief Executive Officer, United Hospital District, Blue Earth, MN, p. A335
ASHBY, F. Michael, M.D. Vice President and Medical Director, Martha Jefferson Hospital, Charlottesville, VA, p. A663
ASHBY, Fred, Director Information Technology, Fort Washington Medical Center, Oxen Hill, MD, p. A299
ASHBY, Pamela, Vice President Human Resources, MedStar National Rehabilitation Hospital, Washington, DC, p. A119
ASHCOM, Thomas L., Ph.D., Chief Executive Officer, Kansas Heart Hospital, Wichita, KS, p. A252
ASHENFELTER, Kathy, Chief Financial Officer, Swedish Medical Center, Englewood, CO, p. A103
ASHFORD, Michael, Administrator, DeQuincy Memorial Hospital, DeQuincy, LA, p. A273
ASHLEY, Clint, Director, South Mississippi State Hospital, Purvis, MS, p. A360
ASHLEY, Dennis H.
Vice President Human Resources, Montefiore Mount Vernon, Mount Vernon, NY, p. A438
Vice President Human Resources, Montefiore New Rochelle, New Rochelle, NY, p. A438
ASHLEY, Sharon, MSN Chief Nursing Officer, Adams County Regional Medical Center, Seaman, OH, p. A497
ASHLEY, Stanley, M.D. Chief Medical Officer, Brigham and Women's Hospital, Boston, MA, p. A303
ASHRAF, Mirza, M.D. Medical Director, Carthage Area Hospital, Carthage, NY, p. A431
ASHWORTH, Fred, Chief Financial Officer, Orange Park Medical Center, Orange Park, FL, p. A137
ASHWORTH, John W., Interim President and Chief Executive Officer, University of Maryland Medical Center Midtown Campus, Baltimore, MD, p. A295
ASKARI, Hasan, M.D. Chief of Staff, Sunbury Community Hospital and Outpatient Center, Sunbury, PA, p. A550
ASKEW, Pam, R.N. Vice President Patient Care Services, UnityPoint Health – Trinity Muscatine, Muscatine, IA, p. A232
ASKEY, Raymond C., CPA Vice President Fiscal Services, Nason Hospital, Roaring Spring, PA, p. A549
ASKINAZI, Murray, Senior Vice President and Chief Financial Officer, New York–Presbyterian/Lawrence Hospital, Bronxville, NY, p. A430
ASKINS, Stephen, M.D. Chief of Staff, Lake City Community Hospital, Lake City, SC, p. A563
ASLIN, Judy, MSN Vice President and Chief Nursing Officer, Southeast Hospital, Cape Girardeau, MO, p. A365
ASPEREN, Jayne Van, Acting Director of Nursing, Crete Area Medical Center, Crete, NE, p. A391
ASPLUND, David, Chief Operating Officer, Motion Picture and Television Fund Hospital and Residential Services, CA, p. A71
ASSAAD, Haney, Vice President Medical Affairs, North Ottawa Community Hospital, Grand Haven, MI, p. A320
ASSAVAPISITKUL, Colleen, Chief Nursing Officer, St. Helena Hospital Clear Lake, Clearlake, CA, p. A58
ASSESSOR, Peggy, Director Information Services, St. Joseph Mercy Port Huron, Port Huron, MI, p. A328
ASTACIO, Benjamin, Director Human Resources, Bella Vista Hospital, Mayaguez, PR, p. A722
ASTLEFORD, Daniel, Vice President Operations, Lafayette Regional Health Center, Lexington, MO, p. A372
ASTON, Brian W., Chief Operating Officer, Mission Hospital, Asheville, NC, p. A455
ATADERO, Robyn, R.N. Chief Nursing Officer, Pioneers Memorial Healthcare District, Brawley, CA, p. A56
ATCHLEY, Mark, Vice President and Chief Financial Officer, Medical City Dallas Hospital, Dallas, TX, p. A605
ATEIA, Nashat, M.D. Chief of Staff, Doctors Hospital of West Covina, West Covina, CA, p. A97
ATEN, Byron, Interim Chief Executive Officer, HEALTHSOUTH Rehabilitation Hospital, Albuquerque, NM, p. A422
ATHENAIS, Dierdre, Director Human Resources, Colusa Regional Medical Center, Colusa, CA, p. A58
ATHERTON, Dorie, Manager Human Resources, University Behavioral Health of Denton, Denton, TX, p. A608
ATKIN, Suzanne, M.D. Chief of Staff and Associate Dean Clinical Affairs, University Hospital, Newark, NJ, p. A415
ATKINS, Christa, Administrator, Commonwealth Regional Specialty Hospital, Bowling Green, KY, p. A254
ATKINS, James, Chief Operating Officer, Rockdale Medical Center, Conyers, GA, p. A154
ATKINS, Jim, Director Employee Services, St. Luke's Rehabilitation Hospital, Boise, ID, p. A173
ATKINS, Jodi, Human Resources Specialist, Baptist Medical Center Nassau, Fernandina Beach, FL, p. A126
ATKINS, Melissa, CPA, Chief Executive Officer, Graham County Hospital, Hill City, KS, p. A241
ATKINS, Tracy, Chief Operating and Nursing Officer, Orchard Hospital, Gridley, CA, p. A64
ATKINS–GUIDRY, Stephanie, Administrator and Chief Nursing Officer, USMD Hospital at Fort Worth, Fort Worth, TX, p. A614
ATKINSON, James, M.D., Interim President, Ronald Reagan UCLA Medical Center, Los Angeles, CA, p. A72
ATKINSON, James, M.D. Medical Director, Santa Monica–UCLA Medical Center and Orthopaedic Hospital, Santa Monica, CA, p. A92
ATKINSON, Jodi, President and Chief Executive Officer, St. Andrew's Health Center, Bottineau, ND, p. A472
ATKINSON, Johnie M., Chief Human Resources Officer, Saint Vincent Health Center, Erie, PA, p. A534
ATTEBERRY, Dave, M.D. Chief of Staff, Yakima Regional Medical and Cardiac Center, Yakima, WA, p. A688
ATTEBERY, Tim, Chief Executive Officer, Wellmont Holston Valley Medical Center, Kingsport, TN, p. A580
ATTEBURY, Mary, Chief Operating Officer, Northwest Missouri Psychiatric Rehabilitation Center, Saint Joseph, MO, p. A375
ATTERBERG, Linda, Chief Information Officer, Keokuk Area Hospital, Keokuk, IA, p. A230
ATTLESEY–PRIES, Jacqueline M., R.N. Chief Nursing Officer, Vice President, Boulder Community Health, Boulder, CO, p. A99
ATTRIDGE, Scott, Chief Financial Officer, Mid–Valley Hospital, Omak, WA, p. A681
ATTY, James, Chief Executive Officer, Waverly Health Center, Waverly, IA, p. A236
ATWAL, Money
Chief Financial Officer, Hilo Medical Center, Hilo, HI, p. A168
Chief Financial Officer, Kau Hospital, Pahala, HI, p. A170
ATWELL, Denaye, Manager Human Resources, Muscogee Creek Nation Physical Rehabilitation Center, Okmulgee, OK, p. A513
ATWOOD, Julie, Director Human Resources, San Bernardino Mountains Community Hospital District, Lake Arrowhead, CA, p. A67
AUBE–WARREN, Robin C., Director, Wilmington Veterans Affairs Medical Center, Wilmington, DE, p. A118
AUBEL, Eugenia, President, St. Elizabeth Boardman Health Center, Boardman, OH, p. A480
AUBEL, James, Chief Financial Officer, Jameson Hospital, New Castle, PA, p. A541
AUBRY, Michael, Director Information Systems, Adventist Medical Center – Hanford, Hanford, CA, p. A64
AUBUCHON, Christy, Director Personnel, Washington County Memorial Hospital, Potosi, MO, p. A374
AUCKER, Kendra A., President and Chief Executive Officer, Evangelical Community Hospital, Lewisburg, PA, p. A538
AUCKERMAN, Graydon Todd, Chief Nursing Officer, OhioHealth Rehabilitation Hospital, Columbus, OH, p. A486
AUDET, Stefanie, Director Human Resources, Florida Hospital DeLand, DeLand, FL, p. A125
AUDETT, John R., M.D. Medical Director Clinical Affairs, Overlook Medical Center, Summit, NJ, p. A418
AUDIRSCH, Lanell, Administrative Assistant, North Caddo Medical Center, Vivian, LA, p. A286
AUER, Kenneth E., Director Human Resources, Unity Hospital, Fridley, MN, p. A339
AUERBACH, Bruce S., M.D., President and Chief Executive Officer, Sturdy Memorial Hospital, Attleboro, MA, p. A302
AUERBACH, Jeffrey, D.O. Medical Director, Bon Secours Community Hospital, Port Jervis, NY, p. A448
AUERBACH, Lorraine P., FACHE, President and Chief Executive Officer, Dameron Hospital, Stockton, CA, p. A93
AUGSBURGER, Marc, R.N., President and Chief Executive Officer, Caro Community Hospital, Caro, MI, p. A316
AUGSBURGER, Tod, FACHE, President and Chief Executive Officer, Lexington Medical Center, West Columbia, SC, p. A566
AUGSBURGER, Tod, Senior Vice President and Chief Operating Officer, Lexington Medical Center, West Columbia, SC, p. A566
AUGUST, Brad, Director Information Systems, Fairfield Memorial Hospital, Fairfield, IL, p. A188
AUGUST, Prudence, Chief Information Officer, Palomar Medical Center, Escondido, CA, p. A60
AUGUSTIN, Robert, Director Human Resources, Southern Tennessee Regional Health System–Lawrenceburg, Lawrenceburg, TN, p. A581
AUGUSTIN, III, W. Walter, CPA Vice President Financial Services and Chief Financial Officer, University of Maryland Rehabilitation & Orthopaedic Institute, Baltimore, MD, p. A295
AUGUSTINE, David, Chief Executive Officer, Trego County–Lemke Memorial Hospital, Wakeeney, KS, p. A252
AUGUSTUS, Richard, M.D. Chief Medical Officer, West Valley Medical Center, Caldwell, ID, p. A173
AUGUSTYNIAK, Becky, Director Human Resources, Northside Medical Center, Columbus, GA, p. A154
AUJLA, Surinder, M.D. Chief of Staff, Bowie Memorial Hospital, Bowie, TX, p. A598
AUKES, Amy, Human Resources Analyst, Avera Flandreau Hospital, Flandreau, SD, p. A568
AUL, Christopher T., M.D. Chief Medical Officer, Cape Fear Valley Medical Center, Fayetteville, NC, p. A460
AUMAN, Patrick A., Ph.D., Interim President and Chief Executive Officer, Susan B. Allen Memorial Hospital, El Dorado, KS, p. A239
AUNAN, II, Milton E., CPA Senior Vice President and Chief Financial Officer, UnityPoint Health – St. Luke's Hospital, Cedar Rapids, IA, p. A223
AURILIO, Lisa, R.N. Vice President Patient Services and Chief Nursing Officer, Akron Children's Hospital, Akron, OH, p. A478
AUSMAN, Dan F., President and Chief Executive Officer, Methodist Hospital of Southern California, Arcadia, CA, p. A54
AUSTELLI, Oscar, Chief Information Officer, LAC/University of Southern California Medical Center, Los Angeles, CA, p. A71
AUSTERLITZ, Michael, M.D. Chief of Staff, East Los Angeles Doctors Hospital, Los Angeles, CA, p. A69

AUSTIN, Aaron A., Vice President Human Resources, Schwab Rehabilitation Hospital, Chicago, IL, p. A184

AUSTIN, Arthur, M.D. Vice President Medical Affairs, Gerald Champion Regional Medical Center, Alamogordo, NM, p. A422

AUSTIN, Dan, Manager Data Processing, Ashley County Medical Center, Crossett, AR, p. A42

AUSTIN, Debbie W., MSN Vice President Patient Care Services, P & S Surgical Hospital, Monroe, LA, p. A280

AUSTIN, Deborah, Chief People Officer, Physicians' Specialty Hospital, Fayetteville, AR, p. A43

AUSTIN, Geoff, Interim Executive Director, University of Washington Medical Center, Seattle, WA, p. A684

AUSTIN, Joe, Executive Vice President and Chief Operating Officer, Phoebe Putney Memorial Hospital, Albany, GA, p. A149

AUSTIN, Judy, Director Human Resources, Campbellton Graceville Hospital, Graceville, FL, p. A128

AUSTIN, Laura, Chief Financial Officer and Chief Operating Officer, Community Hospital of Anaconda, Anaconda, MT, p. A381

AUSTIN, Robert, Chief Executive Officer, Moab Regional Hospital, Moab, UT, p. A655

AUSTIN, Jr., W. William
Senior Vice President Finance, Riverside Behavioral Health Center, Hampton, VA, p. A666
Senior Vice President Finance, Riverside Shore Memorial Hospital, Nassawadox, VA, p. A668

AUSTIN, Warren, M.D. Vice President Medical Affairs, Bon Secours Maryview Medical Center, Portsmouth, VA, p. A670

AUSTIN–MOORE, Gale, Director Area Technology, Kaiser Permanente Vallejo Medical Center, Vallejo, CA, p. A96

AUTREY, Pamela Spencer, R.N. Chief Nursing Officer, Medical West, Bessemer, AL, p. A16

AUTRY, Paula R., FACHE, Chief Executive Officer, Sinai–Grace Hospital, Detroit, MI, p. A318

AVANT, Andre, Facility Automation Manager, Texas Center for Infectious Disease, San Antonio, TX, p. A642

AVATO, Rich, Director, St. Mary's Medical Center, West Palm Beach, FL, p. A147

AVELINO, Joseph, Chief Executive Officer, College Medical Center, Long Beach, CA, p. A68

AVENEL, William, Assistant Vice President Information Services, Medical Center, Navicent Health, Macon, GA, p. A160

AVERETT, Elaine, Chief Financial Officer, Grove Hill Memorial Hospital, Grove Hill, AL, p. A20

AVERILL, Clark, Director Information Technology, St. Luke's Hospital, Duluth, MN, p. A338

AVERNA, Russell
Director Human Resources, Spaulding Rehabilitation Hospital, Charlestown, MA, p. A306
Vice President of Human Resources, Spaulding Rehabilitation Hospital Cape Cod, East Sandwich, MA, p. A306

AVERY, Baret H., Chief Information Officer, Siskin Hospital for Physical Rehabilitation, Chattanooga, TN, p. A575

AVERY, Danny, Chief Financial Officer and Chief Operating Officer, Quartz Mountain Medical Center, Mangum, OK, p. A509

AVERY, Donald R., FACHE, President and Chief Executive Officer, Fairview Park Hospital, Dublin, GA, p. A156

AVERY III, John B., Administrator, Perry Community Hospital, Linden, TN, p. A581

AVERY, Jonathan, Chief Administrative Officer, Legacy Good Samaritan Hospital and Medical Center, Portland, OR, p. A524

AVERY, Scott B., Commander, Martin Army Community Hospital, Fort Benning, GA, p. A157

AVIADO, Gail, Chief Nursing Officer, Montclair Hospital Medical Center, Montclair, CA, p. A76

AVILA, Brandi, Chief Nursing Officer, Martin County Hospital District, Stanton, TX, p. A645

AVVISATO, Michael, Senior Vice President and Chief Financial Officer, Allied Services Rehabilitation Hospital, Scranton, PA, p. A549

AVVISATO, Mike, Vice President and Chief Financial Officer, John Heinz Institute of Rehabilitation Medicine, Wilkes-Barre, PA, p. A553

AWALD, Tamara, Chief Nursing Officer and Chief Operating Officer, Saint Joseph Regional Medical Center–Plymouth Campus, Plymouth, IN, p. A218

AWALT, Scott, Chief Financial Officer, Sanford Hillsboro Medical Center, Hillsboro, ND, p. A475

AWAN, Naveed, FACHE, Chief Executive Officer, St. Helena Parish Hospital, Greensburg, LA, p. A274

AWOLOWO, Yinusa, Business Officer, Kingsboro Psychiatric Center, NY, p. A440

AWWAD, Emad, Director Care Delivery Sites Information Systems and Technology, Lakeview Hospital, Stillwater, MN, p. A347

AXTELL, Vicki, Director Human Resources, Livingston HealthCare, Livingston, MT, p. A385

AYALA, Jose L., M.D. Chief Medical Officer, Valley Baptist Medical Center–Brownsville, Brownsville, TX, p. A599

AYALA, Lisa, R.N. Director Human Resources, Specialty Hospital Jacksonville, Jacksonville, FL, p. A130

AYALA, Shirley, Director Human Resources, First Hospital Panamericano, Cidra, PR, p. A720

AYCOCK, Jean, President and Chief Executive Officer, Oconee Regional Health Systems, Milledgeville, GA, p. B100

AYCOCK, Mark, Chief Operating Officer, Spartanburg Regional Medical Center, Spartanburg, SC, p. A565

AYERS, James G., Chief Financial Officer, Piedmont Geriatric Hospital, Burkeville, VA, p. A663

AYERS, Jessi, Chief Financial Officer, Person Memorial Hospital, Roxboro, NC, p. A467

AYERS, Matthew, Chief Administrative Officer, Norton Hospital, Louisville, KY, p. A261

AYKUL, Nikki, Manager Business Office, LifeCare Hospitals of Pittsburgh, Pittsburgh, PA, p. A546

AYRES, Daniel M., President and Chief Executive Officer, Summersville Regional Medical Center, Summersville, WV, p. A695

AYRES, Michael, Senior Vice President and Chief Financial Officer, Maricopa Integrated Health System, Phoenix, AZ, p. A35

AYRES, Robert, Director Information Systems, Firelands Regional Health System, Sandusky, OH, p. A497

AYRES, Shane, Chief Financial Officer, Sanford Wheaton Medical Center, Wheaton, MN, p. A349

AYSCUE, Charles F., Senior Vice President Finance and Chief Financial Officer, Mission Hospital, Asheville, NC, p. A455

AZAR, Jennifer, Director Human Resources, Turning Point Hospital, Moultrie, GA, p. A162

AZCONA, Alain, Director Business Development, Aurora San Diego Hospital, San Diego, CA, p. A86

AZEVEDO, Michael, M.D. Medical Director, San Joaquin Valley Rehabilitation Hospital, Fresno, CA, p. A62

AZIZ, Samir, M.D. Medical Director, Fairfax Behavioral Health, Kirkland, WA, p. A680

AZURE, Vernon, Clinical Director, Indian Health Service – Quentin N. Burdick Memorial Health Care Facility, Belcourt, ND, p. A472

# B

BAACKE, II, George C., M.D. Acting Clinical Director, Northern Navajo Medical Center, Shiprock, NM, p. A426

BAAS, Daniel, R.N. Chief Nursing Officer, Baylor Emergency Medical Center at Aubrey, Aubrey, TX, p. A593

BAAS, Dina, Director Financial Services, Orange City Area Health System, Orange City, IA, p. A232

BABAKANIAN, Ed, Chief Information Officer, UC San Diego Health, San Diego, CA, p. A87

BABB, Cindy, Executive Director Human Resources and Organizational Effectiveness, St. Joseph Hospital & Health Center, Kokomo, IN, p. A214

BABB, Donald J., Chief Executive Officer, Citizens Memorial Hospital, Bolivar, MO, p. A363

BABB, Kathy, Manager Human Resources, Clifton Springs Hospital and Clinic, Clifton Springs, NY, p. A431

BABCOCK, Daniel, Chief Executive Officer, Marlette Regional Hospital, Marlette, MI, p. A325

BABCOCK, Janet, Director of Nursing, Dorothea Dix Psychiatric Center, Bangor, ME, p. A288

BABCOCK, Kimberly, Administrative Director of Operations, Kalkaska Memorial Health Center, Kalkaska, MI, p. A324

BABCOCK, Paul, Chief Financial Officer, Coulee Medical Center, Grand Coulee, WA, p. A679

BABCOCK, Robert, M.D. Chief of Staff, Canandaigua Veterans Affairs Medical Center, Canandaigua, NY, p. A431

BABER, Jonathan, Director Information Technology, Central State Hospital, Petersburg, VA, p. A670

BABICH, Eli, Chief Nursing Officer, Select Specialty Hospital–Pittsburgh/UPMC, Pittsburgh, PA, p. A546

BABINEAU, Timothy J., M.D., President and Chief Executive Officer, Lifespan Corporation, Providence, RI, p. B85

BABINEAU, Timothy J., M.D., President and Chief Executive Officer, Rhode Island Hospital, Providence, RI, p. A556

BABUSCIO, Cathy, Director Human Resources, Mat–Su Regional Medical Center, Palmer, AK, p. A29

BACA, Modesto, Chief Information Officer, Amarillo Veterans Affairs Health Care System, Amarillo, TX, p. A591

BACH, Dawn M., MS Chief Clinical Officer, Buena Vista Regional Medical Center, Storm Lake, IA, p. A235

BACHA, Fadi, M.D. Chief Medical Officer, Select Specialty Hospital–Lexington, Lexington, KY, p. A260

BACHE–WIIG, Ben, M.D., President, Abbott Northwestern Hospital, Minneapolis, MN, p. A342

BACHELDOR, H. Lee, D.O. Medical Director, St. John River District Hospital, East China, MI, p. A318

BACHER, Beth, Chief Executive Officer, HEALTHSOUTH Valley of the Sun Rehabilitation Hospital, Glendale, AZ, p. A32

BACHER, Katherine, Interim Senior Vice President and Chief Financial Officer, Vassar Brothers Medical Center, Poughkeepsie, NY, p. A448

BACHMAN, John Page, Corporate Vice President, St. John Medical Center, Tulsa, OK, p. A517

BACHMAN, Judith Lynn
Chief Operating Officer, Fox Chase Cancer Center–American Oncologic Hospital, Philadelphia, PA, p. A543
Chief Operating Officer, Jeanes Hospital, Philadelphia, PA, p. A544

BACHMAN, Roberta, Director Human Resources, Riverview Behavioral Health, Texarkana, AR, p. A51

BACHMEIER, Susan T., R.N. Chief Nursing Officer, Wake Forest Baptist Health–Davie Medical Center, Mocksville, NC, p. A465

BACK, Barbara, Manager Human Resources, Encino Hospital Medical Center, CA, p. A69

BACK, Bill, M.D. Chief of Staff, Mercy Willard Hospital, Willard, OH, p. A500

BACKER, Jacqueline Ann, Vice President of Human Resources, Providence Medical Center, Wayne, NE, p. A399

BACON, James S., Director Team Resources, St. Anthony's Hospital, Saint Petersburg, FL, p. A142

BACON, Jeff, D.O. Medical Director, Sterling Regional MedCenter, Sterling, CO, p. A109

BACON, Ken J., President and Chief Executive Officer, Shawnee Mission Medical Center, Shawnee Mission, KS, p. A250

BACUS, Randy B., FACHE, Chief Executive Officer, North Texas Medical Center, Gainesville, TX, p. A615

BADALIAN, B. Joseph, Chief Executive Officer, Fountain Valley Regional Hospital and Medical Center, Fountain Valley, CA, p. A61

BADEN, Robert M., Chief Financial Officer, Lompoc Valley Medical Center, Lompoc, CA, p. A68

BADEN, Jr., Thomas, Chief Information Officer, Community Behavioral Health Hospital – Rochester, Rochester, MN, p. A345

BADGER, Jeff
Chief Financial Officer, Calumet Medical Center, Chilton, WI, p. A699
Chief Financial Officer, Mercy Medical Center, Oshkosh, WI, p. A708
Chief Financial Officer, St. Elizabeth Hospital, Appleton, WI, p. A697

BADILLO, Linda, M.D. Chief of Medical Staff, Medical Center of Trinity, Trinity, FL, p. A146

BADINGER, Sandy, Chief Financial Officer, Slidell Memorial Hospital, Slidell, LA, p. A285

BADR, Safwan, M.D. Executive Vice President and Chief Medical Officer, Detroit Receiving Hospital/University Health Center, Detroit, MI, p. A317

BAECHLE, Christopher, Chief Executive Officer, St. Luke's Rehabilitation Hospital, Chesterfield, MO, p. A365

BAEHSER, Deborah, Vice President Patient Care Services, Cape Regional Medical Center, Cape May Court House, NJ, p. A410

BAENEN, Sharla, President, Bellin Psychiatric Center, Green Bay, WI, p. A702

BAER, Douglas M., Chief Executive Officer, Brooks Rehabilitation Hospital, Jacksonville, FL, p. A129

BAER, James E., FACHE, President and Chief Executive Officer, Highland District Hospital, Hillsboro, OH, p. A491

BAEZ, Janet, Director, University Hospital, San Juan, PR, p. A724

BAEZ, Juan, M.D. President Medical Staff, Robert Wood Johnson University Hospital Rahway, Rahway, NJ, p. A417

BAGCHI, Sam, Chief Medical Officer, Methodist Mansfield Medical Center, Mansfield, TX, p. A631

BAGGERLY, Karen, Chief Nursing Officer and Vice President, Covenant Medical Center, Lubbock, TX, p. A629

BAGGETT, Al, M.D. Interim Chief of Staff, Taylor Regional Hospital, Hawkinsville, GA, p. A158

BAGGETT, Margarita, MSN Interim Chief Operating Officer, UC San Diego Health, San Diego, CA, p. A87

BAGLEY, Brenda, Director Human Resources, TMC Bonham Hospital, Bonham, TX, p. A598

BAGLEY, Peter, M.D. Medical Director, Fairlawn Rehabilitation Hospital, Worcester, MA, p. A313

BAGNALL, Andrew, President and Chief Executive Officer, St. Nicholas Hospital, Sheboygan, WI, p. A711

BAGNELL, Kelly, M.D. Chief of Staff, Providence St. Joseph Medical Center, Polson, MT, p. A386

BAHL, Barry I., Director, St. Cloud Veterans Affairs Health Care System, Saint Cloud, MN, p. A346

BAHLS, Fredrick, M.D. Chief of Staff, Veterans Affairs Central Iowa Health Care System, Des Moines, IA, p. A227

Index of Health Care Professionals / Baldwin

Index of Health Care Professionals


BAHNLEIN, Carl, Executive Vice President and Chief Operating Officer, Virginia Hospital Center – Arlington, Arlington, VA, p. A662
BAIDA–FRAGOSO, Nicolas, M.D. Clinical Director, El Paso Psychiatric Center, El Paso, TX, p. A610
BAIER, Roger, Chief Executive Officer, Sanford Mayville Medical Center, Mayville, ND, p. A475
BAILEY, Amy, Director Information Systems, Texas Scottish Rite Hospital for Children, Dallas, TX, p. A607
BAILEY, Ann, Assistant Director Administration, Central State Hospital, Petersburg, VA, p. A670
BAILEY, Becky, R.N. Director Nursing, Kansas Surgery and Recovery Center, Wichita, KS, p. A252
BAILEY, Becky, Director Human Resources, Lincoln Hospital, Davenport, WA, p. A678
BAILEY, Brenda, Assistant Administrator, Windsor–Laurelwood Center for Behavioral Medicine, Willoughby, OH, p. A501
BAILEY, Cheryl, R.N. Chief Nursing Officer Vice President Patient Care Services, Cullman Regional Medical Center, Cullman, AL, p. A18
BAILEY, Cindy, R.N. Chief Nursing Officer, Richland Memorial Hospital, Olney, IL, p. A197
BAILEY, Cori, Accountant, Tyler Holmes Memorial Hospital, Winona, MS, p. A362
BAILEY, Craig, MS, Administrator, Colorado Acute Long Term Hospital, Denver, CO, p. A101
BAILEY, Dan, Director Information Systems, Norton Sound Regional Hospital, Nome, AK, p. A28
BAILEY, Dan, M.D. Vice President Medical Affairs and Chief Medical Officer, Upper Valley Medical Center, Troy, OH, p. A499
BAILEY, David, FACHE, Chief Executive Officer, Community Hospital of Bremen, Bremen, IN, p. A205
BAILEY, David J., M.D., President and Chief Executive Officer, Nemours, Jacksonville, FL, p. B95
BAILEY, Dawn A., R.N. Vice President Nursing and Chief Nursing Officer, Euclid Hospital, Euclid, OH, p. A489
BAILEY, Dianne, Chief Information Officer, Pana Community Hospital, Pana, IL, p. A197
BAILEY, Heather, Chief Human Resources Officer, Jefferson Healthcare, Port Townsend, WA, p. A682
BAILEY, Jim, M.D. Chief Medical Officer, Northeast Georgia Medical Center, Gainesville, GA, p. A158
BAILEY, Jodi J., Human Resources Director, Odessa Memorial Healthcare Center, Odessa, WA, p. A681
BAILEY, John E., Chief Financial Officer, Moore County Hospital District, Dumas, TX, p. A609
BAILEY, Jonathan D., Chief Executive Officer and Administrator, Hansford Hospital, Spearman, TX, p. A644
BAILEY, Joy, Director Information Technology, Sutter Amador Hospital, Jackson, CA, p. A65
BAILEY, Kathy C., FACHE, President and Chief Executive Officer, Blue Ridge Healthcare Hospitals, Morganton, NC, p. A465
BAILEY, Kelly, Administrator, Kindred Hospital–White Rock, Dallas, TX, p. A605
BAILEY, Larry, Chief Executive Officer, Indiana University Health Paoli Hospital, Paoli, IN, p. A218
BAILEY, Leisa, M.D. Chief of Staff, Doctors Memorial Hospital, Bonifay, FL, p. A122
BAILEY, Marquita, Chief Nursing Officer, DeKalb Regional Medical Center, Fort Payne, AL, p. A20
BAILEY, Matthew D., FACHE, President and Chief Executive Officer, Indiana University Health West Hospital, Avon, IN, p. A204
BAILEY, Mikeana, Director Human Resources, Brownwood Regional Medical Center, Brownwood, TX, p. A599
BAILEY, Owen, FACHE Administrator, University of South Alabama Children's and Women's Hospital, Mobile, AL, p. A22
BAILEY, Robert W., Chief Information Officer, Hawthorn Center, Northville, MI, p. A327
BAILEY, Ron, Chief Financial Officer, Franklin Foundation Hospital, Franklin, LA, p. A274
BAILEY, Russell, Chief Executive Officer, Texas Rehabilitation Hospital of Fort Worth, Fort Worth, TX, p. A614
BAILEY, Scott, Chief Financial Officer, EASTAR Health System, Muskogee, OK, p. A510
BAILEY, Susan P., R.N., Chief Executive Officer, Specialty Hospital of Washington, Washington, DC, p. A120
BAILEY, Travis A., Vice President Administration, St. Claire Regional Medical Center, Morehead, KY, p. A263
BAILEY–DELEEUW, Sandra, Chief Executive Officer, Methodist Extended Care Hospital, Memphis, TN, p. A583
BAILEY–NEWELL, Susan, Vice President Human Resources, Baylor St. Luke's Medical Center, Houston, TX, p. A619
BAILEY–OETKER, Jessica, Director Quality and Medical Staff, Providence Willamette Falls Medical Center, Oregon City, OR, p. A523
BAIN, Brad, Information Systems Leader, Kaiser Permanente Fresno Medical Center, Fresno, CA, p. A62
BAIN, Holly, Chief Nursing Officer, AllianceHealth Madill, Madill, OK, p. A509
BAIN, Joel, Director Information Services, TriStar Summit Medical Center, Hermitage, TN, p. A578
BAIN, Mark, Chief Human Resources, Veterans Affairs Connecticut Healthcare System, West Haven, CT, p. A116
BAIN, Pat, Chief Nursing Officer, Lower Bucks Hospital, Bristol, PA, p. A530
BAIOCCO, Jeffrey D., Chief Financial Officer, Eastern Idaho Regional Medical Center, Idaho Falls, ID, p. A174
BAIR, Ada, Chief Executive Officer, Memorial Hospital, Carthage, IL, p. A180
BAIR, Connie, Human Resources Assistant, Pike County Memorial Hospital, Louisiana, MO, p. A372
BAIRD, Brenda
Senior Vice President and Chief Nursing Officer, CHI St. Vincent Infirmary Medical Center, Little Rock, AR, p. A47
Senior Vice President and Chief Nursing Officer, CHI St. Vincent Medical Center–North, Sherwood, AR, p. A50
BAIRD, David
Director of Information Systems, Intermountain Medical Center, Murray, UT, p. A656
Chief Information Officer, LDS Hospital, Salt Lake City, UT, p. A658
Chief Information Officer, The Orthopedic Specialty Hospital, Murray, UT, p. A656
BAIRD, Donna, Vice President Corporate Services, Bay Medical Center Sacred Heart Health System, Panama City, FL, p. A139
BAISCH, Kim, R.N. Associate Vice President Patient Care Services, Highline Medical Center, Burien, WA, p. A677
BAISDEN, Monica, Director Human Resources, Memorial Hermann Northeast, Humble, TX, p. A623
BAJARI, Pamela R., R.N., Interim Administrator, Community Behavioral Health Hospital – Annandale, Annandale, MN, p. A334
BAJARI, Pamela R., R.N. Nurse Executive MHSATS, Community Behavioral Health Hospital – Rochester, Rochester, MN, p. A345
BAKAR, Anne L.
President and Chief Executive Officer, Telecare Heritage Psychiatric Health Center, Oakland, CA, p. A78
President and Chief Executive Officer, Willow Rock Center, San Leandro, CA, p. A90
BAKER, Bonnie, Vice President Finance and Chief Financial Officer, Butler Hospital, Providence, RI, p. A555
BAKER, Bonnie, M.D. Chief Medical Services, Veterans Health Care System of the Ozarks, Fayetteville, AR, p. A44
BAKER, Brenda, Chief Financial Officer, Riverview Hospital, Noblesville, IN, p. A218
BAKER, Chuck, R.N. Chief Operating Officer and Chief Nursing Officer, Fulton Medical Center, Fulton, MO, p. A368
BAKER, Damon, D.O. Chief Medical Officer, Oklahoma State University Medical Center, Tulsa, OK, p. A516
BAKER, Deborah, Vice President, Patient Care Services, Mount Auburn Hospital, Cambridge, MA, p. A305
BAKER, Denis, Chief Information Officer, Sarasota Memorial Health Care System, Sarasota, FL, p. A142
BAKER, Dennis, Chief Executive Officer, Select Specialty Hospital–Longview, Longview, TX, p. A629
BAKER, Frank, Chief Information Officer, Mary Breckinridge ARH Hospital, Hyden, KY, p. A258
BAKER, Gary E., Senior Vice President and Chief Executive Officer, HonorHealth Scottsdale Shea Medical Center, Scottsdale, AZ, p. A37
BAKER, Harlan T., Department Leader Information Systems, McDonough District Hospital, Macomb, IL, p. A193
BAKER, J. Matthew, M.D. President Medical Staff, Bertrand Chaffee Hospital, Springville, NY, p. A450
BAKER, Joann, Administrator, Doctors Memorial Hospital, Bonifay, FL, p. A122
BAKER, Joel, D.O. Chief Medical Officer, Wayne County Hospital, Corydon, IA, p. A225
BAKER, John, Interim Chief Executive Officer, Haven Behavioral Health of Eastern Pennsylvania, Reading, PA, p. A548
BAKER, Judy, Chief Financial Officer, Kindred Hospital–Mansfield, Mansfield, TX, p. A631
BAKER, Linda, Director Human Resources, St. Alexius Medical Center, Hoffman Estates, IL, p. A191
BAKER, Maia, MSN Chief Nurse Executive, Rio Grande State Center/South Texas Health Care System, Harlingen, TX, p. A618
BAKER, Mark A., Chief Executive Officer, Jack Hughston Memorial Hospital, Phenix City, AL, p. A24
BAKER, Meredith, Business Manager, Mental Health Institute, Clarinda, IA, p. A224
BAKER, Michael, D.O. Chief of Staff, Daviess Community Hospital, Washington, IN, p. A221
BAKER, Michelle, Director Information Systems, Indiana University Health White Memorial Hospital, Monticello, IN, p. A216
BAKER, Nichelle A., Chair Human Resources, Mayo Clinic Hospital, Phoenix, AZ, p. A35
BAKER, Patrick, R.N. Vice President, Chief Nursing Officer, West Chester Hospital, West Chester, OH, p. A500
BAKER, Paula F., President and Chief Executive Officer, Freeman Health System, Joplin, MO, p. B58
BAKER, Paula F.
President and Chief Executive Officer, Freeman Hospital West, Joplin, MO, p. A369
President and Chief Executive Officer, Freeman Neosho Hospital, Neosho, MO, p. A373
BAKER, Phillip, Vice President and Chief Financial Officer, Fawcett Memorial Hospital, Port Charlotte, FL, p. A140
BAKER, R. Hal, M.D. Vice President and Chief Information Officer, York Hospital, York, PA, p. A554
BAKER, Reese, Director Information Systems, Crittenden County Hospital, Marion, KY, p. A262
BAKER, Reta K., President, Mercy Hospital Fort Scott, Fort Scott, KS, p. A240
BAKER, Rodger H., President and Chief Executive Officer, Fauquier Hospital, Warrenton, VA, p. A674
BAKER, Ronald L., Chief Executive Officer, Saint Luke's East Hospital, Lee's Summit, MO, p. A371
BAKER, Roni, Director of Nursing, Herington Municipal Hospital, Herington, KS, p. A241
BAKER, Shari
Director Human Resources, Orange City Area Health System, Orange City, IA, p. A232
Chief Executive Officer, Palmetto Lowcountry Behavioral Health, Charleston, SC, p. A558
BAKER, Sharon, Director Support Services, Fairbanks, Indianapolis, IN, p. A211
BAKER, Shawna, M.D. Chief of Staff, Community Hospital of Anaconda, Anaconda, MT, p. A381
BAKER, Steve, Chief Information Officer, East Jefferson General Hospital, Metairie, LA, p. A280
BAKER, Vanya, Director, Wilkes Regional Medical Center, North Wilkesboro, NC, p. A466
BAKER, W. Douglas, Director, Julian F. Keith Alcohol and Drug Abuse Treatment Center, Black Mountain, NC, p. A455
BAKER Jr., Wendell H., President, Vidant Edgecombe Hospital, Tarboro, NC, p. A469
BAKHTIER, Hasan, M.D. Medical Director, Community Mental Health Center, Lawrenceburg, IN, p. A214
BAKICH, Sandy, Director Information Management, Delano Regional Medical Center, Delano, CA, p. A59
BAKKEN, Mary, Executive Vice President and Chief Operating Officer, Silver Cross Hospital, New Lenox, IL, p. A196
BAKKUM, Kyle, Chief Executive Officer and Administrator, Vernon Memorial Healthcare, Viroqua, WI, p. A712
BALASUBRAMONY, Suresh, M.D. Chief Medical Officer, Minnie Hamilton HealthCare Center, Grantsville, WV, p. A691
BALAZY, Thomas E., M.D. Medical Director, Craig Hospital, Englewood, CO, p. A103
BALCAVAGE, Thomas, Vice President Information Systems and Chief Information Officer Technology, Kennedy Health System, Cherry Hill, NJ, p. A410
BALCITIS, Judith, MSN Vice President, Nursing and Chief Nursing Officer, Advocate Sherman Hospital, Elgin, IL, p. A187
BALDAUF, Robb, Coordinator Information Systems, Lodi Community Hospital, Lodi, OH, p. A492
BALDERRAMA, Jose, Vice President Human Resources, Valley Hospital, Ridgewood, NJ, p. A418
BALDOSARO, Thomas
Chief Financial Officer, Inspira Medical Center–Elmer, Elmer, NJ, p. A411
Chief Financial Officer, Inspira Medical Center–Vineland, Vineland, NJ, p. A420
BALDRICA, Joyce, Chief Executive Officer, Kindred Hospital Melbourne, Melbourne, FL, p. A133
BALDRIDGE, Dava, R.N. Chief Nursing Officer, Hillcrest Hospital – South, Tulsa, OK, p. A516
BALDWIN, Barbara, Chief Information Officer, Anne Arundel Medical Center, Annapolis, MD, p. A293
BALDWIN, Bruce A., Chief Executive Officer, Newberry County Memorial Hospital, Newberry, SC, p. A564
BALDWIN, David, Chief Information Officer, UH Robinson Medical Center, Ravenna, OH, p. A496
BALDWIN, Ellen, R.N. Chief Nursing Officer, Texas Health Center for Diagnostic & Surgery, Plano, TX, p. A637
BALDWIN, Erin, M.P.H. Chief Operating Officer, Mahaska Health Partnership, Oskaloosa, IA, p. A233
BALDWIN, Genny, R.N. Chief Nursing Officer, Santiam Memorial Hospital, Stayton, OR, p. A526
BALDWIN, Gilda, Chief Executive Officer, Westchester General Hospital, Miami, FL, p. A135

Index of Health Care Professionals

Index of Health Care Professionals / Baldwin

BALDWIN, Gregory D., Vice President Human Resources, Pioneer Community Hospital of Patrick, Stuart, VA, p. A673
BALDWIN, Nathan, M.D. President Medical Staff, Baptist Memorial Hospital–Booneville, Booneville, MS, p. A351
BALDWIN, Steve
Vice President Finance, The Willough at Naples, Naples, FL, p. A136
Manager Information Technology, Wyoming State Hospital, Evanston, WY, p. A716
BALDWIN, William, Chief Information Officer, Ashe Memorial Hospital, Jefferson, NC, p. A463
BALES, Brian, Director Plant Operations, HEALTHSOUTH Southern Hills Rehabilitation Hospital, Princeton, WV, p. A694
BALES, Correen, Executive Director Human Resources, UNM Sandoval Regional Medical Center, Rio Rancho, NM, p. A426
BALES, Glenn, Chief Financial Officer, Providence Saint Joseph Medical Center, Burbank, CA, p. A56
BALES–CHUBB, Denyse, Chief Executive Officer, Florida Hospital Wesley Chapel, Wesley Chapel, FL, p. A146
BALFOUR, Ann M., R.N., President, St. Joseph Health System, Tawas City, MI, p. A331
BALINK, Kay M., M.D. Chief of Staff, Richland Hospital, Richland Center, WI, p. A710
BALKO, Tom, Manager Information Systems, Redwood Area Hospital, Redwood Falls, MN, p. A345
BALL, Cassie, Chief Financial Officer, Hilton Head Hospital, Hilton Head Island, SC, p. A562
BALL, Charlie, Chief Operating Officer, Specialty Rehabilitation Hospital of Coushatta, Coushatta, LA, p. A272
BALL, Clifford, D.O. Medical Director Emergency Room, Wickenburg Community Hospital, Wickenburg, AZ, p. A40
BALL, Connie, Chief Financial Officer, Specialty Rehabilitation Hospital of Coushatta, Coushatta, LA, p. A272
BALL, Jim, Chief Operating Officer, St. Catherine's Rehabilitation Hospital, North Miami, FL, p. A136
BALL, III, Johnny Percy, Assistant Administrator Human Resources, South Georgia Medical Center, Valdosta, GA, p. A166
BALL, Marlon, Chief Information Officer, Ralph H. Johnson Veterans Affairs Medical Center, Charleston, SC, p. A558
BALL, Rodney, Vice President Finance, Carolinas HealthCare System NorthEast, Concord, NC, p. A458
BALLA, Matt, Chief Executive Officer, St. Vincent Dunn Hospital, Bedford, IN, p. A204
BALLANCE, William, M.D. Chief of Medical Staff, Vidant Bertie Hospital, Windsor, NC, p. A470
BALLARD, Annette, Director Information Systems, Murray–Calloway County Hospital, Murray, KY, p. A264
BALLARD, Bryan M., Interim Chief Executive Officer, Catalina Island Medical Center, Avalon, CA, p. A54
BALLARD, Christine A.
Vice President Human Resources, Muncy Valley Hospital, Muncy, PA, p. A541
Vice President Human Resources, Soldiers and Sailors Memorial Hospital, Wellsboro, PA, p. A552
Senior Vice President Human Resources, Williamsport Regional Medical Center, Williamsport, PA, p. A553
BALLARD, Jacque, Vice President Human Resources, St. Bernards Medical Center, Jonesboro, AR, p. A46
BALLARD, Jerry, Director Information Systems, Central Florida Regional Hospital, Sanford, FL, p. A142
BALLARD, John, Ph.D., Chief Executive Officer, Kentucky River Medical Center, Jackson, KY, p. A259
BALLARD, Lorraine L., Director Human Resources, St. Helena Parish Hospital, Greensburg, LA, p. A274
BALLARD, Richard R., Chief Executive Officer and Administrator, University of Miami Hospital and Clinics, Miami, FL, p. A135
BALLARD, Terri, Chief Nursing Officer, HEALTHSOUTH Northern Kentucky Rehabilitation Hospital, Edgewood, KY, p. A256
BALLESTERO, Susan, Vice President and Chief Human Resources Officer, Saint Peter's University Hospital, New Brunswick, NJ, p. A415
BALLIETT, Matt, Chief Information Officer, Coal County General Hospital, Coalgate, OK, p. A505
BALLINGHOFF, James R., MSN Chief Nursing Officer and Associate Executive Director, Penn Presbyterian Medical Center, Philadelphia, PA, p. A544
BALLMAN, Patricia, Director, Westfield Memorial Hospital, Westfield, NY, p. A454
BALLOU, Michele, M.D. Chief Medical Staff, LewisGale Hospital Alleghany, Low Moor, VA, p. A667
BALOGA–ALTIERI, Bonnie, Ph.D. Chief Nursing Officer, Children's Specialized Hospital–PSE&G, New Brunswick, NJ, p. A415
BALON, Stanley, M.D. President Medical Staff, Landmark Medical Center, Woonsocket, RI, p. A556
BALSANO, Tony, Vice President Finance, Saint Francis Medical Center, Cape Girardeau, MO, p. A364
BALT, David, D.O. Chief Medical Officer, Avera Queen of Peace Hospital, Mitchell, SD, p. A570
BALTIERRA, David A., M.D. President Medical Staff, Jefferson Medical Center, Ranson, WV, p. A694
BALUTANSKI, Brian, CPA Chief Financial Officer, Chestnut Hill Hospital, Philadelphia, PA, p. A542
BALZANO, Eric, Chief of Staff, Weirton Medical Center, Weirton, WV, p. A696
BALZANO, Janice, Chief Executive Officer, St. Petersburg General Hospital, Saint Petersburg, FL, p. A142
BAMAN, Raj, D.O. President Medical Staff, Samaritan North Lincoln Hospital, Lincoln City, OR, p. A522
BAMBRICK, Catherine, Chief Operating Officer, Kittitas Valley Healthcare, Ellensburg, WA, p. A678
BAMMEL, Paul
Vice President, Mayo Clinic Health System – Northland in Barron, Barron, WI, p. A698
Vice President, Mayo Clinic Health System in Eau Claire, Eau Claire, WI, p. A700
BANBURY, Brian, Director Site Information Systems, Advocate Christ Medical Center, Oak Lawn, IL, p. A196
BANCO, Leonard, M.D. Senior Vice President and Chief Medical Officer, Bristol Hospital, Bristol, CT, p. A111
BANDA, Venkat, M.D. President Medical Staff, Promise Hospital of Baton Rouge – Ochsner Campus, Baton Rouge, LA, p. A270
BANDLA, H., M.D. Chief Clinical Affairs, Walter P. Reuther Psychiatric Hospital, Westland, MI, p. A332
BANDY, Dawn, Chief Financial Officer, Grant Regional Health Center, Lancaster, WI, p. A704
BANDY, Don, Director Information Technology, AllianceHealth Deaconess, Oklahoma City, OK, p. A511
BANDY, P. Ross, M.D. Chief Medical Officer and Chief of Staff, Levi Hospital, Hot Springs National Park, AR, p. A46
BANE, William, Chief Financial Officer, Inova Loudoun Hospital, Leesburg, VA, p. A667
BANG, W. J., M.D. Chief of Staff, Reeves County Hospital, Pecos, TX, p. A636
BANIEWICZ, John, M.D. Chief Medical Officer, Lake Health, Concord Township, OH, p. A487
BANIGAN, Elisa, Chief Financial Officer, Forest Park Medical Center Frisco, Frisco, TX, p. A615
BANK, Carol J., Vice President Human Resources, Divine Savior Healthcare, Portage, WI, p. A709
BANKER, Julie G., R.N. Chief Nursing Officer, Lehigh Regional Medical Center, Lehigh Acres, FL, p. A132
BANKERS, Diane, Director of Nursing, FirstLight Health System, Mora, MN, p. A343
BANKS, Chester, Director Human Resources, East Orange General Hospital, East Orange, NJ, p. A411
BANKS, Donald, Chief Medical Officer, Miami County Medical Center, Paola, KS, p. A248
BANKS, Elizabeth, Chief Executive Officer, Summit Behavioral Healthcare, Cincinnati, OH, p. A483
BANKS, Matthew, Chief Operating Officer, Lake Norman Regional Medical Center, Mooresville, NC, p. A465
BANKS, Maureen, FACHE,
President, Spaulding Hospital for Continuing Medical Care North Shore, Salem, MA, p. A311
President, Spaulding Hospital for Continuing Medical Care Cambridge, Cambridge, MA, p. A306
BANKS, Maureen, R.N. Chief Operating Officer, Spaulding Rehabilitation Hospital, Charlestown, MA, p. A306
BANKS, Maureen, FACHE, President, Spaulding Rehabilitation Hospital Cape Cod, East Sandwich, MA, p. A306
BANKS, Robbi, Executive Director Human Resources, Medical Center Health System, Odessa, TX, p. A634
BANKS, Scott, Chief Financial Officer, Salt Lake Regional Medical Center, Salt Lake City, UT, p. A658
BANKS, Walter, Director Human Resources, Baptist Memorial Hospital–Desoto, Southaven, MS, p. A360
BANKTSON, Julie, Manager Human Resources, Paul Oliver Memorial Hospital, Frankfort, MI, p. A319
BANNER, Fred, Chief Information Officer, Shore Medical Center, Somers Point, NJ, p. A418
BANUEDOS, Jorge, Director Human Resources, Metropolitan State Hospital, Norwalk, CA, p. A78
BANVILLE, Carol Anne, Chief Nursing Officer, HEALTHSOUTH Rehabilitation Hospital of Denver, Littleton, CO, p. A106
BAPTISTE, Ernest, Executive Director, Kings County Hospital Center, NY, p. A440
BAQUET, Shawn, Chief of Staff, Iberia Medical Center, New Iberia, LA, p. A281
BARANCZYK, Kay, R.N. Chief Nursing Officer, HSHS St. Clare Memorial Hospital, Oconto Falls, WI, p. A708
BARANSKI, David J., Vice President Human Resources, Phoebe Putney Memorial Hospital, Albany, GA, p. A149
BARANSKI, Kenneth, Chief Financial Officer, Hills & Dales General Hospital, Cass City, MI, p. A316
BARBA, James J., President and Chief Executive Officer, Albany Medical Center, Albany, NY, p. A428
BARBADIAN, John, Vice President Human Resources, Tulare Regional Medical Center, Tulare, CA, p. A95
BARBAGLIA, J. Joseph, Vice President Financial Services, Columbus Community Hospital, Columbus, NE, p. A391
BARBAREE, Jerry, Director Human Resources, Baptist Memorial Hospital – Memphis, Memphis, TN, p. A583
BARBARIN, LaSharndra
Chief Executive Officer and Chief Operating Officer, Medical Center of Lewisville, Lewisville, TX, p. A628
Chief Operating Officer, Medical Center of McKinney, McKinney, TX, p. A632
BARBAROTTA, Ann Marie, Executive Director, Creedmoor Psychiatric Center, NY, p. A439
BARBEE, Daniel, Vice President Clinical Affairs, The University of Toledo Medical Center, Toledo, OH, p. A499
BARBER, Chris B., FACHE, President and Chief Executive Officer, St. Bernards Medical Center, Jonesboro, AR, p. A46
BARBER, Eric A., FACHE, President and Chief Executive Officer, Mary Lanning Healthcare, Hastings, NE, p. A392
BARBER, Jack W., M.D., Director, Western State Hospital, Staunton, VA, p. A673
BARBER, Karen, R.N., Chief Executive Officer, Yoakum Community Hospital, Yoakum, TX, p. A653
BARBER, Michael, Chief Operating Officer, Penn Medicine Chester County Hospital, West Chester, PA, p. A552
BARBER, Richard, M.D. Chief Medical Officer, Wilkes Regional Medical Center, North Wilkesboro, NC, p. A466
BARBER, Scott, Chief Executive Officer, Decatur County General Hospital, Parsons, TN, p. A587
BARBER, Teresa Rini, Vice President Support Services, Southwest General Health Center, Middleburg Heights, OH, p. A494
BARBER, Wendi, Vice President Finance and Chief Financial Officer, Park Ridge Health, Hendersonville, NC, p. A462
BARBINI, Gerald J., President and Chief Executive Officer, Allegan General Hospital, Allegan, MI, p. A314
BARBO, Steve, R.N., Administrator, Citizens Medical Center, Columbia, LA, p. A271
BARBOUR, Alexis, Director Finance, Dublin Springs, Dublin, OH, p. A489
BARBUAT, James P., Chief Financial Officer, Gunnison Valley Hospital, Gunnison, CO, p. A104
BARCHI, Daniel
Senior Vice President, Technical Services and Chief Information Officer, Bridgeport Hospital, Bridgeport, CT, p. A111
Senior Vice President Information Systems and Chief Information Officer, Yale–New Haven Hospital, New Haven, CT, p. A114
BARCLAY, Duane, D.O. Chief Medical Officer, DeKalb Medical at Hillandale, Lithonia, GA, p. A160
BARCLAY, Emily, Vice President Human Resources, Dana–Farber Cancer Institute, Boston, MA, p. A303
BARCLAY, Rick, Vice President Support Services, Mercy Hospital Rogers, Rogers, AR, p. A50
BARCLIFT, Larry, Chief Financial Officer, Yuma Rehabilitation Hospital, Yuma, AZ, p. A40
BARD, Jeffrey, President, Aurora Medical Center of Oshkosh, Oshkosh, WI, p. A708
BARDEN, Sean
Executive Vice President and Chief Financial Officer, Mary Washington Hospital, Fredericksburg, VA, p. A665
Executive Vice President and Chief Financial Officer, Stafford Hospital, Stafford, VA, p. A673
BARDIER, Catherine, Vice President, Human Resources, Elliot Hospital, Manchester, NH, p. A407
BARDWELL, Carol A., R.N. Chief Nurse Executive, Martha's Vineyard Hospital, Oak Bluffs, MA, p. A310
BARDWELL, Jean, Vice President and Chief Financial Officer, Ranken Jordan Pediatric Bridge Hospital, Maryland Heights, MO, p. A372
BARDWELL, Sheila, Director Information Systems, Baptist Memorial Hospital–Golden Triangle, Columbus, MS, p. A352
BARDWELL, Tom, Vice President Human Resources, Hills & Dales General Hospital, Cass City, MI, p. A316
BAREFOOT, Denise, Director Health Information Systems, Carolina Pines Regional Medical Center, Hartsville, SC, p. A562
BAREIS, Charles, M.D. Medical Director, MacNeal Hospital, Berwyn, IL, p. A179
BARELA, Barbara, Director Human Resources, Gila Regional Medical Center, Silver City, NM, p. A427
BARFIELD, Donna, Chief Nursing Officer, Tennova Healthcare – Volunteer Community Hospital, Martin, TN, p. A582
BARGINERE, Cynthia, MSN Vice President Clinical Nursing and Chief Nursing Officer, Rush University Medical Center, Chicago, IL, p. A184
BARI, Kelle, R.N. Vice President Patient Care Services, St. Joseph's Hospital of Buckhannon, Buckhannon, WV, p. A690

A780 Index of Health Care Professionals 

Index of Health Care Professionals / Barrow

Index of Health Care Professionals

BARIOLA, Christopher L.
Chief Executive Officer, Eureka Springs Hospital, Eureka Springs, AR, p. A43
Chief Executive Officer, River Valley Medical Center, Dardanelle, AR, p. A43
BARISANO, Nancy, Chief Information Officer, Monadnock Community Hospital, Peterborough, NH, p. A408
BARKEMA, Annette, Chief Financial Officer, Portland Veterans Affairs Medical Center, Portland, OR, p. A524
BARKER, Alanna, Director Human Resources, MetroSouth Medical Center, Blue Island, IL, p. A180
BARKER, Alex, Vice President Human Resources and Compliance and Privacy Officer, Winchester Hospital, Winchester, MA, p. A313
BARKER, Jaime, M.D. Medical Director, Suncoast Behavioral Health Center, Bradenton, FL, p. A122
BARKER, James, Chief Executive Officer, West Shore Medical Center, Manistee, MI, p. A325
BARKER, Karen, Vice President and Chief Information Officer, Sinai Hospital of Baltimore, Baltimore, MD, p. A295
BARKER, Kathryn L., Chief Human Resources Management, Veterans Health Care System of the Ozarks, Fayetteville, AR, p. A44
BARKER, Larry, Chief Operating Officer, Clearwater Valley Hospital and Clinics, Orofino, ID, p. A175
BARKER, Louise, R.N., Chief Executive Officer, Central Louisiana Surgical Hospital, Alexandria, LA, p. A268
BARKER, Richard, Administrator, Mercy Health Love County, Marietta, OK, p. A509
BARKER, Russell
Community Chief Executive Officer, McDowell ARH Hospital, McDowell, KY, p. A263
Information Officer, U. S. Public Health Service Indian Hospital–Whiteriver, Whiteriver, AZ, p. A40
BARKER, Thomas, Director Information, Southeast Health Center of Reynolds County, Ellington, MO, p. A366
BARKER, Jr., William A., Vice President Administration, Pleasant Valley Hospital, Point Pleasant, WV, p. A694
BARKHYMER, Mary C., R.N. Vice President Patient Care Services and Chief Nursing Officer, UPMC St. Margaret, Pittsburgh, PA, p. A547
BARKMAN, Joseph, Vice President Financial Services, Oaklawn Psychiatric Center, Goshen, IN, p. A210
BARKSDALE, Mary, Director Human Resources, Person Memorial Hospital, Roxboro, NC, p. A467
BARKSDALE, Vickie, Manager Human Resources, North Oak Regional Medical Center, Senatobia, MS, p. A360
BARLAGE, Seth, Associate Medical Center Director, John J. Pershing Veterans Affairs Medical Center, Poplar Bluff, MO, p. A374
BARLEY, Leonard, M.D. Chief Medical Officer, Windsor–Laurelwood Center for Behavioral Medicine, Willoughby, OH, p. A501
BARLEY, Tammy, Director, Human Resources, HEALTHSOUTH Rehabilitation Hospital of Jonesboro, Jonesboro, AR, p. A46
BARLOW, Mark, M.D. Chief Medical Officer and President Medical Staff, Cornerstone Hospital of Houston at Clearlake, Webster, TX, p. A651
BARLOW, Teresa, Medical Records Administrator, Mental Health Institute, Clarinda, IA, p. A224
BARMECHA, Jitendra, M.D. Senior Vice President and Chief Information Officer, St. Barnabas Hospital, NY, p. A444
BARNARD, Jeanna, Chief Executive Officer, Bayshore Medical Center, Pasadena, TX, p. A635
BARNARD, Kerri, Director Human Resources, Larned State Hospital, Larned, KS, p. A244
BARNARD, Lawrence, President and Chief Executive Officer, St. Rose Dominican Hospitals – San Martin Campus, Las Vegas, NV, p. A402
BARNARD, Ryan, Chief Executive Officer, Swisher Memorial Hospital District, Tulia, TX, p. A648
BARNCORD, Sharon
Business Partner Human Resources, Kaiser Permanente Redwood City Medical Center, Redwood City, CA, p. A83
Human Resource Business Partner, Kaiser Permanente South San Francisco, South San Francisco, CA, p. A93
BARNELL, Phil, Chief Medical Officer, HSHS St. Mary's Hospital, Decatur, IL, p. A186
BARNES, Alan, Chief Financial Officer, North Star Behavioral Health System, Anchorage, AK, p. A27
BARNES, Becky, Chief Operating Officer, Rapides Regional Medical Center, Alexandria, LA, p. A268
BARNES, Deborah, Vice President and Chief Information Officer, Children's Hospital of The King's Daughters, Norfolk, VA, p. A669
BARNES, Donald K., Chief Human Resources Officer, Duke Raleigh Hospital, Raleigh, NC, p. A466
BARNES, Douglas A., M.D. Chief of Staff, Shriners Hospitals for Children–Houston, Houston, TX, p. A622
BARNES, Gary, Chief Information Officer, Medical Center Health System, Odessa, TX, p. A634
BARNES, George, M.D. Medical Director, Lakeview Regional Medical Center, Covington, LA, p. A272
BARNES, Gloria V., MSN Assistant Vice President Patient Care Services, Southeastern Regional Medical Center, Newnan, GA, p. A162
BARNES, Jacqueline, Manager Health Information, Select Specialty Hospital–Jackson, Jackson, MS, p. A355
BARNES, Jeff, Director Information Technology, Girard Medical Center, Girard, KS, p. A240
BARNES, Joe, Chief Financial Officer, Grant Memorial Hospital, Petersburg, WV, p. A694
BARNES, John, Administrative Director Human Resources, Beverly Hospital, Montebello, CA, p. A76
BARNES, Karen, Interim Chief Nursing Officer, Logan Regional Medical Center, Logan, WV, p. A692
BARNES, Larry, Vice President Information Technology, Salina Regional Health Center, Salina, KS, p. A250
BARNES, Laura P., MSN Vice President Patient Care Services and Chief Nursing Officer, East Tennessee Children's Hospital, Knoxville, TN, p. A580
BARNES, Leslie, Chief Financial Officer, Parkview Medical Center, Pueblo, CO, p. A108
BARNES, Marla, Director of Nursing, Pushmataha Hospital & Home Health, Antlers, OK, p. A503
BARNES, Maryann, M
Vice President and Chief Nursing Officer East Region, St. John Hospital and Medical Center, Detroit, MI, p. A318
Chief Nursing Officer, St. John Macomb–Oakland Hospital, Warren, MI, p. A332
BARNES, Michael, Chief Information Officer, North Valley Hospital, Whitefish, MT, p. A388
BARNES, P. Marie, Director, Human Resources, North Mississippi Medical Center–Pontotoc, Pontotoc, MS, p. A359
BARNES, Sherry, Director Health Information and Quality Management, Rolling Hills Hospital, Ada, OK, p. A503
BARNES, William H., Administrator, Sweeny Community Hospital, Sweeny, TX, p. A646
BARNETT, Barbara, M.D. Medical Director, Glen Cove Hospital, Glen Cove, NY, p. A434
BARNETT, Carol, Chief Human Resources Officer, Fairbanks Memorial Hospital, Fairbanks, AK, p. A28
BARNETT, Dana, Chief Executive Officer, Memorial Hospital of Carbon County, Rawlins, WY, p. A717
BARNETT, Frederick, M.D. Chief of Staff, Metroplex Adventist Hospital, Killeen, TX, p. A626
BARNETT, Julia, Chief Nursing Officer, Union General Hospital, Blairsville, GA, p. A152
BARNETT, Kelly, Human Resource Officer, Brownfield Regional Medical Center, Brownfield, TX, p. A598
BARNETT, Laura, Executive Director, Human Resources, Brigham and Women's Faulkner Hospital, Boston, MA, p. A303
BARNETT, Lori, R.N. Chief Nursing Officer, Troy Community Hospital, Troy, PA, p. A551
BARNETT, Shawn, Vice President and Chief Financial Officer, CHRISTUS Santa Rosa Health System, San Antonio, TX, p. A640
BARNETT, Steve, MS, President and Chief Executive Officer, McKenzie Health System, Sandusky, MI, p. A330
BARNHARDT, Bonnie, Executive Director Human Resources, Minnesota Valley Health Center, Le Sueur, MN, p. A341
BARNHART, Ann, Chief Executive Officer, Heart of Florida Regional Medical Center, Davenport, FL, p. A125
BARNHART, Cody, Chief Executive Officer, St. Luke's Medical Center, Crosby, ND, p. A473
BARNHART, David, Director Information Systems, Wuesthoff Medical Center – Rockledge, Rockledge, FL, p. A141
BARNHART, James R.
Chief Administrator Officer, PeaceHealth Peace Island Medical Center, Friday Harbor, WA, p. A679
Chief Administrative Officer, PeaceHealth United General Medical Center, Sedro–Woolley, WA, p. A684
BARNHART, Jeff
Chief Executive Officer, Lynn County Hospital District, Tahoka, TX, p. A646
Administrator, Northwest Texas Surgery Center, Amarillo, TX, p. A591
BARNHART, Roger, Chief Executive Officer, Ashland Health Center, Ashland, KS, p. A237
BARONE, Nancy, Vice President and Executive Director Operations and Strategic Planning, University of Cincinnati Medical Center, Cincinnati, OH, p. A484
BARONE, Richard, M.D. Medical Director, Montefiore New Rochelle, New Rochelle, NY, p. A438
BARONOFF, Peter R.
Chief Executive Officer, Promise Healthcare, Boca Raton, FL, p. B108
President and Chief Executive Officer, Success Healthcare, Boca Raton, FL, p. B129
BARR, Ann, Chief Information Officer, Sutter Health Bay Area, Sutter Maternity and Surgery Center of Santa Cruz, Santa Cruz, CA, p. A91
BARR, Brant, M.D. Chief Medical Officer, District One Hospital, Faribault, MN, p. A338
BARR, Brent, Chief Information Officer, Minnie Hamilton HealthCare Center, Grantsville, WV, p. A691
BARR, Bret, Vice President Fiscal Services, Conway Medical Center, Conway, SC, p. A560
BARR, Catherine, Senior Vice President and President, Bethesda Hospital, Bethesda Hospital, Saint Paul, MN, p. A346
BARR, Francine, R.N. Vice President and Chief Operating Officer, Bon Secours St. Mary's Hospital, Richmond, VA, p. A671
BARR, Kristine, Vice President Communication Services, O'Bleness Memorial Hospital, Athens, OH, p. A479
BARR, Laurie C.
Vice President Human Resources, Salem Hospital, Salem, OR, p. A526
Vice President Human Resources, West Valley Hospital, Dallas, OR, p. A520
BARR, Mary Beth, R.N., Chief Executive Officer, Grant Memorial Hospital, Petersburg, WV, p. A694
BARR, Tom, Director Operational Support Services, Peterson Rehabilitation Hospital, Wheeling, WV, p. A696
BARR, Vivian C.
Director Human Resources, Higgins General Hospital, Bremen, GA, p. A152
Director Human Resources, Tanner Medical Center–Carrollton, Carrollton, GA, p. A153
BARRA, Jon, Director Human Resources, Wyoming Behavioral Institute, Casper, WY, p. A715
BARRAGY, Susan, Chief Executive Officer, Houston Physicians Hospital, Webster, TX, p. A651
BARRALL, Audrey, Director Human Resources, St. Helena Hospital Clear Lake, Clearlake, CA, p. A58
BARRAMEDA, Maricar, Chief Information Officer, Lincoln Medical and Mental Health Center, NY, p. A441
BARREIRO, Maggie E., Administrator, Weslaco Rehabilitation Hospital, Weslaco, TX, p. A651
BARRERA, Edward, Director Communications, Encino Hospital Medical Center, CA, p. A69
BARRERE, Davie Ann, Coordinator Information Technology, Dahl Memorial Healthcare Association, Ekalaka, MT, p. A383
BARRETT, Anne J., Associate Executive Director Human Resources, Southside Hospital, Bay Shore, NY, p. A429
BARRETT, Cindy, Administrative Assistant, Patton State Hospital, Patton, CA, p. A80
BARRETT, Heather, Chief Executive Officer, Kindred Hospital Rancho, Rancho Cucamonga, CA, p. A82
BARRETT Jr., James W., Chief Executive Officer, Richardson Medical Center, Rayville, LA, p. A284
BARRETT, Jason P., Chief Operating Officer, Flagler Hospital, Saint Augustine, FL, p. A141
BARRETT, John, Regional Director Human Resources, Franciscan St. Anthony Health – Michigan City, Michigan City, IN, p. A216
BARRETT III, John E., Chief Executive Officer, Bon Secours–DePaul Medical Center, Norfolk, VA, p. A669
BARRETT, Kerry Flynn, Vice President Human Resources, Northern Westchester Hospital, Mount Kisco, NY, p. A438
BARRETT, Linda, Vice President of Information Services, Community Hospital of Bremen, Bremen, IN, p. A205
BARRETT, Lynn, Chief Nursing Officer, Centerpoint Medical Center, Independence, MO, p. A368
BARRETT, Pam, Human Resources Director, Colorado River Medical Center, Needles, CA, p. A77
BARRETT, Peggy, R.N., Chief Executive Officer, Central Texas Rehabilitation Hospital, Austin, TX, p. A594
BARRETT, T. Marc, M.D. Senior Vice President and Chief Medical Officer, Providence Healthcare Network, Waco, TX, p. A650
BARRICK, Lisa, Controller, HEALTHSOUTH Scottsdale Rehabilitation Hospital, Scottsdale, AZ, p. A37
BARRILLEAUX, Scott G., FACHE, Chief Executive Officer, Drew Memorial Hospital, Monticello, AR, p. A48
BARRIO, Gabe, M.D. Chief of Staff, Whidbey General Hospital, Coupeville, WA, p. A678
BARROCAS, Albert, M.D. Chief Medical Officer, Atlanta Medical Center, Atlanta, GA, p. A150
BARRON, Lee, Chief Executive Officer, Southern Inyo Healthcare District, Lone Pine, CA, p. A68
BARROW, Robert, Chief Executive Officer, Doctors' Hospital of Michigan, Pontiac, MI, p. A328

Index of Health Care Professionals

Index of Health Care Professionals / Barrow


BARROW II, William F., President and Chief Executive Officer, Our Lady of Lourdes Regional Medical Center, Lafayette, LA, p. A278
BARROWS, Cheryl, Vice President Human Resources, Sturdy Memorial Hospital, Attleboro, MA, p. A302
BARRY, Amy C., Senior Vice President and Chief Human Resources Officer, Lakeland Regional Health, Lakeland, FL, p. A131
BARRY, Anne, Deputy Commissioner, Minnesota Department of Human Services, Saint Paul, MN, p. B92
BARRY, Rick, Director Information Systems, Baylor Medical Center at Frisco, Frisco, TX, p. A615
BARRY, Thomas, Chief Executive Officer, Pulaski Memorial Hospital, Winamac, IN, p. A221
BARSOM, Michael, M.D., Executive Director, Metropolitan State Hospital, Norwalk, CA, p. A78
BARSOUM, Wael, Interim Chief Executive Officer, Cleveland Clinic Florida, Weston, FL, p. A147
BARSTAD, Stacy
Chief Executive Officer, Sanford Tracy Medical Center, Tracy, MN, p. A348
Chief Executive Officer, Sanford Westbrook Medical Center, Westbrook, MN, p. A349
BARTAL, Ely, M.D., Chief Executive Officer, Kansas Surgery and Recovery Center, Wichita, KS, p. A252
BARTELL, Michael, CEO, Regional Rehabilitation Hospital, Phenix City, AL, p. A24
BARTELS, Jennifer, Director Human Resources, Pawnee County Memorial Hospital and Rural Health Clinic, Pawnee City, NE, p. A397
BARTH, Marci, Chief Nursing Officer, Fayette County Hospital, Vandalia, IL, p. A202
BARTHEL, Gayle, Coordinator Human Resources, Select Specialty Hospital–Flint, Flint, MI, p. A319
BARTHOLOMEW, Brenda, Chief Nursing Officer, Gunnison Valley Hospital, Gunnison, UT, p. A655
BARTHOLOMEW, K. A., M.D. Medical Director, Faulkton Area Medical Center, Faulkton, SD, p. A568
BARTHOLOMEW, Shelley, Director Human Resources, Decatur County General Hospital, Parsons, TN, p. A587
BARTILSON, Jim, Manager Information Systems, South Peninsula Hospital, Homer, AK, p. A28
BARTINGALE, Robert, Administrator, Mayo Clinic Health System in Fairmont, Fairmont, MN, p. A338
BARTLETT, Beth, MSN Vice President Nursing, CHI Health Saint Francis, Grand Island, NE, p. A392
BARTLETT, James, Chief Financial Officer, Faith Community Hospital, Jacksboro, TX, p. A624
BARTLETT, Jonathan L., Chief Executive Officer, Lewis–Gale Medical Center, Salem, VA, p. A672
BARTLETT, Karolyn, Assistant Administrator, Mayo Clinic Health System – Northland in Barron, Barron, WI, p. A698
BARTLETT, Regina, Chief Executive Officer, TriStar Hendersonville Medical Center, Hendersonville, TN, p. A578
BARTLETT, Richard, M.D. Chief Medical Officer, Basin Healthcare Center, Odessa, TX, p. A634
BARTLETT, Ronald E., Chief Financial Officer, Boston Medical Center, Boston, MA, p. A303
BARTLETT, Taci, Chief Financial Officer, Gothenburg Memorial Hospital, Gothenburg, NE, p. A392
BARTLETT III, Thomas G., Administrator, Laird Hospital, Union, MS, p. A361
BARTLETT, Wayne, Director Information Systems, Alvarado Hospital Medical Center, San Diego, CA, p. A86
BARTLEY, Tracy, Manager Information Technology, Bath Community Hospital, Hot Springs, VA, p. A666
BARTO Jr., John K., President and Chief Executive Officer, New Hanover Regional Medical Center, Wilmington, NC, p. A470
BARTO Jr., John K., President and Chief Executive Officer, New Hanover Regional Medical Center, Wilmington, NC, p. B96
BARTOLOTTA, Carmen J., Chief Nursing Officer, Missouri Baptist Sullivan Hospital, Sullivan, MO, p. A379
BARTON, Annie, Director Human Resources, Peterson Rehabilitation Hospital, Wheeling, WV, p. A696
BARTON, Cheryl, R.N. Chief Executive Officer, Southeast Health Center of Reynolds County, Ellington, MO, p. A366
BARTON, Cheryl, R.N., Chief Executive Officer, Southeast Health Center of Ripley County, Doniphan, MO, p. A366
BARTON, Gratia, Chief Financial Officer, Sequoia Hospital, Redwood City, CA, p. A83
BARTON, Rod, Administrator, Cassia Regional Medical Center, Burley, ID, p. A173
BARTON, Thomas, M.D. Medical Director, TOPS Surgical Specialty Hospital, Houston, TX, p. A622
BARTON, Vikki, R.N. Chief Nursing Officer, Collingsworth General Hospital, Wellington, TX, p. A651
BARTON–JOE, Roberta, Chief Operations Officer, Spotsylvania Regional Medical Center, Fredericksburg, VA, p. A665
BARTOS, John M., Chief Executive Officer, Marcus Daly Memorial Hospital, Hamilton, MT, p. A384
BARTS, Dennis, Chief Executive Officer, Avista Adventist Hospital, Louisville, CO, p. A107
BARTZ, Ryan, D.O. Chief of Staff, Tennova Healthcare – McNairy Regional Hospital, Selmer, TN, p. A587
BARWICK, Kim, Vice President Human Resources, Anthony Medical Center, Anthony, KS, p. A237
BARWIS, Kurt A., FACHE, President and Chief Executive Officer, Bristol Hospital, Bristol, CT, p. A111
BASA, Rhea, Director Human Resources, Morrill County Community Hospital, Bridgeport, NE, p. A390
BASA–REYES, Fiona, Chief Executive Officer, Kindred Hospital–Baldwin Park, Baldwin Park, CA, p. A55
BASCOM, Steven, M.D. Chief Medical Officer, Guthrie County Hospital, Guthrie Center, IA, p. A228
BASELGA, Jose, M.D. Physician–in–Chief, Memorial Sloan–Kettering Cancer Center, New York, NY, p. A441
BASEY, Marjorie, Chief Financial Officer, Rehabilitation Hospital of Indiana, Indianapolis, IN, p. A212
BASH, Camille, Chief Financial Officer, Doctors Community Hospital, Lanham, MD, p. A298
BASLER, Cyndi, Chief Operating Officer, Iron County Medical Center, Pilot Knob, MO, p. A374
BASQUILL, Debra, Director Human Resources, Jennersville Regional Hospital, West Grove, PA, p. A552
BASRIA, Deborah, Human Resources Payroll Administrator, Kindred Hospital Bay Area–Tampa, Tampa, FL, p. A145
BASS, Andrew C., M.D. Medical Director, Shands Live Oak Regional Medical Center, Live Oak, FL, p. A132
BASS, Darren, President, Cox Monett, Monett, MO, p. A373
BASS, Gordon B., Chief Operating Officer, Ann & Robert H. Lurie Children's Hospital of Chicago, Chicago, IL, p. A181
BASS, Louis A., Chief Executive Officer, Northeast Alabama Regional Medical Center, Anniston, AL, p. A15
BASS, Sonya, MS Chief Nursing Officer, Colorado Plains Medical Center, Fort Morgan, CO, p. A103
BASSETT, Annie, Director Finance, McBride Clinic Orthopedic Hospital, Oklahoma City, OK, p. A512
BASSETT, Kimberly S., R.N.,
President, Morton Hospital and Medical Center, Taunton, MA, p. A312
Interim President, Norwood Hospital, Norwood, MA, p. A310
BASSO, Amanda J., President, Clay County Hospital, Flora, IL, p. A188
BASSO, Marty
Chief Financial Officer, Sibley Memorial Hospital, Washington, DC, p. A120
Senior Vice President Finance, Suburban Hospital, Bethesda, MD, p. A296
BASTIANELLO, Carol, Director Employee Services, Aspirus Iron River Hospitals and Clinics, Iron River, MI, p. A323
BASTIEN IV, Samuel A., Ph.D., Chief Executive Officer, Four Winds Hospital, Saratoga Springs, NY, p. A450
BASTING, Gregory, M.D
Vice President Medical Affairs, Allied Services Rehabilitation Hospital, Scranton, PA, p. A549
Vice President Medical Affairs, John Heinz Institute of Rehabilitation Medicine, Wilkes–Barre, PA, p. A553
BASTONE, Peter F., Chief Executive Officer, Chesapeake Regional Medical Center, Chesapeake, VA, p. A663
BATA, Katie
Vice President Human Resources, Advocate Illinois Masonic Medical Center, Chicago, IL, p. A181
Vice President Human Resources, Advocate Lutheran General Hospital, Park Ridge, IL, p. A197
BATAL, Lucille M., Administrator, Baldpate Hospital, Haverhill, MA, p. A307
BATCHELOR, Cheryl, Chief Financial Officer, Coffeyville Regional Medical Center, Coffeyville, KS, p. A238
BATCHELOR, Dale, M.D. Chief Medical Officer, Saint Thomas West Hospital, Nashville, TN, p. A585
BATCHELOR, Daniela, Director Human Resources, Springhill Memorial Hospital, Mobile, AL, p. A22
BATCHELOR, Diana, Chief Nursing Officer, UnityPoint Health – Finley Hospital, Dubuque, IA, p. A227
BATCHELOR, Michael, Chief Executive Officer, Baptist Easley Hospital, Easley, SC, p. A560
BATCHLOR, Elaine, M.P.H., Chief Executive Officer, Martin Luther King, Jr. Community Hospital, Los Angeles, CA, p. A71
BATEMAN, Bryan S., Chief Executive Officer, Lake Area Medical Center, Lake Charles, LA, p. A278
BATEMAN, Jana, R.N. Chief Nursing Officer, East Texas Medical Center Jacksonville, Jacksonville, TX, p. A624
BATEMAN, Kenneth, CPA, Chief Executive Officer, Southeast Hospital, Cape Girardeau, MO, p. A365
BATEMAN, Kenneth, CPA, Chief Executive Officer, SoutheastHEALTH, Cape Girardeau, MO, p. B124
BATEMAN, Mark T., Interim Chief Operating Officer, Saint Agnes Medical Center, Fresno, CA, p. A62
BATEMAN, Steven B., Chief Executive Officer, St. Mark's Hospital, Salt Lake City, UT, p. A658
BATES, Beth, Chief Nursing Officer, Shoshone Medical Center, Kellogg, ID, p. A174
BATES, Don, President and Chief Executive Officer, Cloud County Health Center, Concordia, KS, p. A238
BATES, Donald, Chief Executive Officer, Sayre Memorial Hospital, Sayre, OK, p. A514
BATES, Earl, Director Information Technology, Western Mental Health Institute, Bolivar, TN, p. A574
BATES, Joe, M.D. Clinical Director, Rusk State Hospital, Rusk, TX, p. A639
BATES, Leslie, Manager Human Resources, Alta View Hospital, Sandy, UT, p. A659
BATES, Margaret, Chief of Staff, Good Samaritan Hospital, Los Angeles, CA, p. A70
BATES, Mary, Director Human Resources, Bowie Memorial Hospital, Bowie, TX, p. A598
BATES, Ondrea, Senior Vice President Patient Care Continuum and Chief Nursing Officer, Allegiance Health, Jackson, MI, p. A323
BATES, Peter, M.D. Vice President Medical Affairs and Chief Medical Officer, Maine Medical Center, Portland, ME, p. A291
BATES, Richard, Vice President of Medical Affairs, Alpena Regional Medical Center, Alpena, MI, p. A314
BATES, Robert A., Executive Director Finance and Chief Financial Officer, St. Vincent Carmel Hospital, Carmel, IN, p. A206
BATH, Harneet, M.D. Vice President, Chief Medicine Officer, OSF Saint Anthony Medical Center, Rockford, IL, p. A199
BATISTA, David J., Chief Executive Officer, Garfield Medical Center, Monterey Park, CA, p. A76
BATISTE, Michele, Director Human Resources, Preston Memorial Hospital, Kingwood, WV, p. A692
BATORY, Robert J., Vice President Human Resources, York Hospital, York, PA, p. A554
BATRASH, Ahmad, Chief of Staff, Kansas City Veterans Affairs Medical Center, Kansas City, MO, p. A369
BATSHAW, Mark L., M.D. Physician–in–Chief, Executive Vice President and Chief Academic Officer, Children's National Medical Center, Washington, DC, p. A119
BATTISTA, Edward
Vice President Human Resources, Good Samaritan Hospital, San Jose, CA, p. A89
Vice President Human Resources, West Hills Hospital and Medical Center, CA, p. A73
BATTLE, Joe, Director, G.V. (Sonny) Montgomery Veterans Affairs Medical Center, Jackson, MS, p. A355
BATTY, Jill I., Chief Financial Officer, Cambridge Health Alliance, Cambridge, MA, p. A305
BATTY, Mark, Chief Executive Officer, Rochelle Community Hospital, Rochelle, IL, p. A199
BATULIS, Scott, President and Chief Executive Officer, Greater Hudson Valley Health System, Middletown, NY, p. B60
BATULIS, Scott, President and Chief Executive Officer, Orange Regional Medical Center, Middletown, NY, p. A437
BATY, Grace, Director Human Resources, Sweeny Community Hospital, Sweeny, TX, p. A646
BATY, Krista, R.N. Chief Nursing Officer, Cedar Park Regional Medical Center, Cedar Park, TX, p. A600
BATZEL, Linnane, M.D. Senior Vice President Quality and Medical Affairs and Chief Medical Officer, UPMC Altoona, Altoona, PA, p. A528
BAUER, Brian
Chief Executive Officer, Lutheran Hospital of Indiana, Fort Wayne, IN, p. A208
Chief Executive Officer, Rehabilitation Hospital of Fort Wayne, Fort Wayne, IN, p. A209
BAUER, John, Chief Operating Officer, Post Acute Northshore Specialty Hospital, Covington, LA, p. A272
BAUER, Jonathan, Director Information Systems, Somerset Hospital, Somerset, PA, p. A550
BAUER, Kyle, Chief Financial Officer, Cuyuna Regional Medical Center, Crosby, MN, p. A337
BAUER, Richard, M.D. Chief of Staff, South Texas Veterans Health Care System, San Antonio, TX, p. A642
BAUER, Robert
Vice President Human Resources, Midwest Orthopedic Specialty Hospital, Franklin, WI, p. A701
Vice President Human Resources, Wheaton Franciscan Healthcare – Franklin, Franklin, WI, p. A701
Vice President Human Resources, Wheaton Franciscan Healthcare – St. Francis, Milwaukee, WI, p. A707
BAUER, Roberta, M.D. Acting Chair Medical Staff, Cleveland Clinic Children's Hospital for Rehabilitation, Cleveland, OH, p. A484
BAUER, Sandra A., Director Human Resources, Jefferson Community Health Center, Fairbury, NE, p. A391
BAUER, Shar, Executive Secretary, Wishek Community Hospital and Clinics, Wishek, ND, p. A477
BAUER, Tracy, Chief Executive Officer, Midwest Medical Center, Galena, IL, p. A188


A782 Index of Health Care Professionals 

Index of Health Care Professionals / Beck

Index of Health Care Professionals


BAUER, William, Vice President Finance and Chief Financial Officer, Lehigh Valley Hospital – Hazleton, Hazleton, PA, p. A536
BAUER, William, M.D. Medical Director, Montevista Hospital, Las Vegas, NV, p. A402
BAUGHMAN, Sharon, R.N
Vice President Patient Services and Chief Nursing Officer, Wheaton Franciscan Healthcare – Elmbrook Memorial, Brookfield, WI, p. A698
Senior Vice President Patient Services and Chief Nursing Officer, Wheaton Franciscan Healthcare – St. Joseph's, Milwaukee, WI, p. A707
Vice President Patient Services and Chief Nursing Officer, Wheaton Franciscan Healthcare – The Wisconsin Heart Hospital, Wauwatosa, WI, p. A713
BAUM, David, M.D. Senior Vice President Medical Services, F. F. Thompson Hospital, Canandaigua, NY, p. A431
BAUM, Judy, Chief Executive Officer, Mountain Valley Regional Rehabilitation Hospital, Prescott Valley, AZ, p. A36
BAUMAN, Chris, Director of Nursing, Ballard Rehabilitation Hospital, San Bernardino, CA, p. A86
BAUMAN, Jonathan, M.D. Chief Medical Officer, Four Winds Hospital, Katonah, NY, p. A435
BAUMBERGER, David, Chief Medical Officer, Decatur Memorial Hospital, Decatur, IL, p. A186
BAUMEIER, Mark, M.D. Chief of Staff, St. Joseph Mercy Livingston Hospital, Howell, MI, p. A322
BAUMERT, Steven P., President and Chief Executive Officer, Methodist Jennie Edmundson Hospital, Council Bluffs, IA, p. A225
BAUMGARDNER, Brian, Chief Executive Officer, West Florida Hospital, Pensacola, FL, p. A140
BAUMGARDNER, Charles J., President and Chief Executive Officer, Psychiatric Institute of Washington, Washington, DC, p. A120
BAUMGARDNER, David, Director Information Management, Union Hospital, Dover, OH, p. A489
BAUMGARTNER, Jennifer, Chief Information Officer, Perkins County Health Services, Grant, NE, p. A392
BAUMGARTNER, Michael A., President, SSM Health St. Francis Hospital – Maryville, Maryville, MO, p. A372
BAUNCHALK, James M., Deputy Chief Clinical Services, Dwight David Eisenhower Army Medical Center, Fort Gordon, GA, p. A157
BAUR, Heidi, R.N. Chief Nursing Officer, St. Christopher's Hospital for Children, Philadelphia, PA, p. A545
BAUSCHKA, Martha F., R.N. Vice President and Chief Nursing Officer, Southwest General Health Center, Middleburg Heights, OH, p. A494
BAUTE, Corey
Vice President Human Resources, Franciscan St. Francis Health – Indianapolis, Indianapolis, IN, p. A211
Vice President of Human Resource, Franciscan St. Francis Health–Carmel, Carmel, IN, p. A206
BAVA, Michele, Director Human Resources, Doctors Medical Center, Modesto, CA, p. A75
BAVERSO, Lou, Vice President Operations, Magee–Womens Hospital of UPMC, Pittsburgh, PA, p. A546
BAW, Joseph, Director Human Resources, Riveredge Hospital, Forest Park, IL, p. A188
BAWA, Balraj, M.D. Assistant Director Medical Services, Central Virginia Training Center, Madison Heights, VA, p. A667
BAXLEY, Russell, Chief Executive Officer, Lancaster Regional Medical Center, Lancaster, PA, p. A537
BAXTER, Greg, M.D. Senior Vice President Medical Affairs and Chief Medical Officer, Elliot Hospital, Manchester, NH, p. A407
BAXTER, Joshua, Director, Information Systems, Powell Valley Healthcare, Powell, WY, p. A717
BAXTER, Michael T., Chief Executive Officer, Parkview Medical Center, Pueblo, CO, p. A108
BAXTER, Robert O., President and Chief Executive Officer, St. Rita's Medical Center, Lima, OH, p. A492
BAY, Marybeth, Director Information Technology, Sauk Prairie Healthcare, Prairie Du Sac, WI, p. A709
BAYARDO, Fernando, M.D. Chief Medical Officer, Presbyterian Espanola Hospital, Espanola, NM, p. A424
BAYER, Brian, Information Technology Site Leader, Kalamazoo Psychiatric Hospital, Kalamazoo, MI, p. A323
BAYLESS, Victoria, President and Chief Executive Officer, Anne Arundel Medical Center, Annapolis, MD, p. A293
BAYTOS, David G., Chief Executive Officer, Methodist Olive Branch Hospital, Olive Branch, MS, p. A358
BAYUS, Robin, Chief Financial Officer, Rancho Los Amigos National Rehabilitation Center, Downey, CA, p. A60
BAZELEY, Stephen, M.D. Vice President Medical Affairs, ProMedica St. Luke's Hospital, Maumee, OH, p. A494
BAZEMORE, Webster Carl, M.D. Interim Chief of Staff, Charles George Veterans Affairs Medical Center, Asheville, NC, p. A455
BEA, Javon R., Chief Executive Officer, Mercy Harvard Hospital, Harvard, IL, p. A189
BEA, Javon R., President and Chief Executive Officer, Mercy Health System, Janesville, WI, p. B91
BEA, Javon R., President and Chief Executive Officer, Mercy Hospital and Trauma Center, Janesville, WI, p. A703
BEACH, David, Vice President Human Resources, Spectrum Health – Butterworth Hospital, Grand Rapids, MI, p. A321
BEACH, Karrie, Vice President of Finance, Community Memorial Hospital, Syracuse, NE, p. A398
BEACH, Sarah, Director of Nursing, Jerold Phelps Community Hospital, Garberville, CA, p. A63
BEACHMAN, Michelle, Chief Financial Officer, Twin Rivers Regional Medical Center, Kennett, MO, p. A371
BEADLE, Walter, Chief Information Officer, Physicians' Specialty Hospital, Fayetteville, AR, p. A43
BEADMAN, Cindi, Director Medical Records, Harper Hospital District Five, Harper, KS, p. A241
BEAL, Christopher, M.D. Chief of Staff, Sparrow Clinton Hospital, Saint Johns, MI, p. A329
BEAL, Dwight, Chief Fiscal Services, Jack C. Montgomery Veterans Affairs Medical Center, Muskogee, OK, p. A510
BEAM, William, M.D. Chief of Staff, Cornerstone Hospital of Huntington, Huntington, WV, p. A691
BEAMAN Jr., Charles D., Chief Executive Officer, Palmetto Health, Columbia, SC, p. B103
BEAMAN, Frank, Administrator, Faith Community Hospital, Jacksboro, TX, p. A624
BEAN, Howard, M.D. Chief Medical Officer, Mary Black Health System – Spartanburg, Spartanburg, SC, p. A565
BEAN, Roberta, R.N
Associate Chief Nursing Officer, Banner Fort Collins Medical Center, Fort Collins, CO, p. A103
Interim Chief Nursing Officer, East Morgan County Hospital, Brush, CO, p. A100
BEANE, Jeff, Director Human Resources, Roane General Hospital, Spencer, WV, p. A695
BEAR, John, Hospital Administrator Officer and Supervisor Human Resources, Lawton Indian Hospital, Lawton, OK, p. A508
BEARD, Angie, Chief Nursing Officer, Northcrest Medical Center, Springfield, TN, p. A588
BEARD, Bert, Chief Operating Officer, Wilson Medical Center, Wilson, NC, p. A470
BEARD, Bradley, Regional President, Fairview Southdale Hospital, Edina, MN, p. A338
BEARD, Edward L., R.N. Chief Operating Officer and Chief Nursing Officer, Catawba Valley Medical Center, Hickory, NC, p. A462
BEARD, Gerald C., Chief Operating Officer, Healthmark Regional Medical Center, DeFuniak Springs, FL, p. A125
BEARD, Joan, Chief Nursing Officer, Northwest Florida Community Hospital, Chipley, FL, p. A123
BEARD, Pat, Director Human Resources, Clinton County Hospital, Albany, KY, p. A254
BEARD, Rhonda
Director Human Resources, Palestine Regional Medical Center, Palestine, TX, p. A635
Director Human Resources, Palestine Regional Medical Center–East, Palestine, TX, p. A635
BEARD, Robert, Chief Clinical Officer, Vibra Hospital of Northwestern Indiana, Crown Point, IN, p. A207
BEARD, Tim, Chief Executive Officer, Cimarron Memorial Hospital, Boise City, OK, p. A504
BEARDEN, Amy, R.N. Vice President Patient Care Services and Chief Nursing Officer, St. Luke's Magic Valley Medical Center, Twin Falls, ID, p. A176
BEASLEY, Carla, Director of Nursing, Mitchell County Hospital, Camilla, GA, p. A153
BEASLEY, Ruth, Director Human Resources, Vanderbilt Stallworth Rehabilitation Hospital, Nashville, TN, p. A586
BEASLEY, Tareka, Director Human Resources, RiverWoods Behavioral Health System, Riverdale, GA, p. A163
BEASLEY, Terry, R.N. Chief Nursing Officer, Columbus Regional Healthcare System, Whiteville, NC, p. A470
BEATTIE, Kathryn, M.D. Senior Vice President and Chief Medical Officer, UW Medicine/Valley Medical Center, Renton, WA, p. A682
BEATTIE, Mac, Computer Network Specialist, Deer's Head Hospital Center, Salisbury, MD, p. A300
BEATTY, Alan L., Vice President Human Resources, Shore Medical Center, Somers Point, NJ, p. A418
BEATTY, Ann, Director Human Resources, Fairview Hospital, Cleveland, OH, p. A484
BEATTY, Jim, Chief Operating Officer, Overland Park Regional Medical Center, Overland Park, KS, p. A248
BEATTY, John, Vice President Human Resources, Barnes–Jewish Hospital, Saint Louis, MO, p. A376
BEATTY, Talia, Director Human Resources, Sunbury Community Hospital and Outpatient Center, Sunbury, PA, p. A550
BEATY, Holly, Chief Financial Officer, South Central Kansas Medical Center, Arkansas City, KS, p. A237
BEATY, Ralph E., Chief Executive Officer, Great River Medical Center, Blytheville, AR, p. A41
BEATY, Ralph E., Chief Executive Officer, Mississippi County Hospital System, Blytheville, AR, p. B93
BEATY, Ralph E., Chief Executive Officer, South Mississippi County Regional Medical Center, Osceola, AR, p. A49
BEATY, Shannon, Nursing Director, Ten Broeck Tennessee Treatment Facility, Cookeville, TN, p. A576
BEAUBIEN, Troy, Director Information Services, Manatee Memorial Hospital, Bradenton, FL, p. A122
BEAUCHAMP, Bill, Chief Financial Officer, St. Luke's Sugar Land Hospital, Sugar Land, TX, p. A646
BEAUDOIN, Dale, Vice President Human Resources, Lewis–Gale Medical Center, Salem, VA, p. A672
BEAUDOIN, Paul
Senior Vice President Finance and Chief Financial Officer, Kent County Memorial Hospital, Warwick, RI, p. A556
Senior Vice President Finance, Memorial Hospital of Rhode Island, Pawtucket, RI, p. A555
BEAUDRY, Lisa, M.P.H. Director, Patient Care, Baystate Mary Lane Hospital, Ware, MA, p. A312
BEAULAC, Gary, Chief Operating Officer, Henry Ford Macomb Hospitals, Clinton Township, MI, p. A316
BEAULIEU, Lynn, R.N. Chief Nursing Officer, HEALTHSOUTH Walton Rehabilitation Hospital, Augusta, GA, p. A151
BEAUPRE, Paul, M.D., Chief Executive Officer, Good Samaritan Hospital, San Jose, CA, p. A89
BEAUVAIS, Richard E., Ph.D., Chief Executive Officer, Wellspring Foundation, Bethlehem, CT, p. A111
BEAVEN, Stacey, R.N. Chief Nursing Officer, Saint Thomas Rutherford Hospital, Murfreesboro, TN, p. A585
BEAVER, Patrick, Chief Nursing Officer, North Shore Medical Center, Miami, FL, p. A134
BEAVER, Randy, Chief Information Officer, Palo Alto County Health System, Emmetsburg, IA, p. A227
BEAVER, Rhonda, Chief Operating Officer, Creek Nation Community Hospital, Okemah, OK, p. A511
BEAZLEY, Gary, Coordinator Information Systems, Baylor Medical Center at Waxahachie, Waxahachie, TX, p. A650
BEBOW, Gary, FACHE, Administrator and Chief Executive Officer, White River Health System, Batesville, AR, p. B154
BEBOW, Gary, FACHE, Administrator and Chief Executive Officer, White River Medical Center, Batesville, AR, p. A41
BECHAMPS, Gerald, M.D
Vice President of Medical Affairs, Hampshire Memorial Hospital, Romney, WV, p. A695
Vice President Medical Affairs, War Memorial Hospital, Berkeley Springs, WV, p. A689
BECHTEL, Kathleen, MSN Vice President Patient Care Services and Chief Nursing Officer, Froedtert Memorial Lutheran Hospital, Milwaukee, WI, p. A706
BECHTLE, Mavis, MSN Senior Vice President and Chief Nursing Officer, MetroHealth Medical Center, Cleveland, OH, p. A485
BECHTOLD, Kate, R.N
Senior Vice President and Chief Nurse Executive, MultiCare Good Samaritan Hospital, Puyallup, WA, p. A682
Senior Vice President and Chief Nurse Executive, MultiCare Mary Bridge Children's Hospital and Health Center, Tacoma, WA, p. A686
Senior Vice President and Chief Nurse Executive, MultiCare Tacoma General Hospital, Tacoma, WA, p. A686
BECK, Allan, Chief Executive Officer, Baylor Orthopedic and Spine Hospital at Arlington, Arlington, TX, p. A592
BECK, Ann
Vice President and Chief Financial Officer, Carson Tahoe Continuing Care Hospital, Carson City, NV, p. A400
Vice President Finance, Carson Tahoe Health, Carson City, NV, p. A400
BECK, David, Chief Operating Officer and Director Human Resources, Lane Regional Medical Center, Zachary, LA, p. A287
BECK, Gary E., Administrator, Sevier Valley Medical Center, Richfield, UT, p. A657
BECK, Howard, M.D. Chief of Staff, Grace Medical Center, Lubbock, TX, p. A629
BECK, J. Christopher, D.O. President Medical Staff, Aspen Valley Hospital District, Aspen, CO, p. A99
BECK, J. Robert, M.D. Chief Medical Officer, Fox Chase Cancer Center–American Oncologic Hospital, Philadelphia, PA, p. A543
BECK, James, Interim Chief Executive Officer, Loring Hospital, Sac City, IA, p. A234
BECK, Michael D., Vice President Operations, Mission Hospital, Mission Viejo, CA, p. A75
BECK, Paul, Chief Medical Officer, St. Joseph Hospital, Orange, CA, p. A79


© 2015 AHA Guide Index of Health Care Professionals A783

Index of Health Care Professionals

Index of Health Care Professionals / Beck


BECK, Rebecca
President, Wellmont Hancock County Hospital, Sneedville, TN, p. A588
President, Wellmont Hawkins County Memorial Hospital, Rogersville, TN, p. A587
BECK, Steve, MS Manager Human Resources, Kearney Regional Medical Center, Kearney, NE, p. A393
BECK, Walter G., Chief Executive Officer, Colusa Regional Medical Center, Colusa, CA, p. A58
BECK,PHR,MHROD, Brian, Vice President Human Resources, Oak Valley Hospital District, Oakdale, CA, p. A78
BECKER, Bernard H., Vice President and Chief Human Resources Officer, Stormont–Vail HealthCare, Topeka, KS, p. A251
BECKER, Bruce, M.D. Chief Medical Officer, Medical Center Health System, Odessa, TX, p. A634
BECKER, Cindy, Vice President and Chief Operating Officer, Highland Hospital of Rochester, Rochester, NY, p. A448
BECKER, Eric, Chief Operating Officer, Research Medical Center, Kansas City, MO, p. A370
BECKER, Frank
Chief Financial Officer, Lourdes Counseling Center, Richland, WA, p. A683
Chief Financial Officer, Lourdes Medical Center, Pasco, WA, p. A682
BECKER, Kathleen R., MPH, JD President, SSM Health Saint Louis University Hospital, Saint Louis, MO, p. A377
BECKER, Kathy, Ph.D. Vice President and Chief Nursing Officer, Aurora West Allis Medical Center, West Allis, WI, p. A714
BECKER, Kelly, Administrative Coordinator Human Resources, Select Specialty Hospital–Indianapolis, Indianapolis, IN, p. A212
BECKER, Preston, Chief Financial Officer, Gritman Medical Center, Moscow, ID, p. A175
BECKER, Ralph W., Vice President, Chief Financial Officer, Saint Mary's Hospital, Waterbury, CT, p. A115
BECKES, Hap, Director Information Systems, Sullivan County Community Hospital, Sullivan, IN, p. A220
BECKETT, Jason, Director Information Services, San Dimas Community Hospital, San Dimas, CA, p. A87
BECKETT, Tedi, Director of Nursing, Kalamazoo Psychiatric Hospital, Kalamazoo, MI, p. A323
BECKHAM, Steve, Director Human Resources, Magee General Hospital, Magee, MS, p. A356
BECKMAN, Beth P., R.N. Chief Nursing Officer, Baylor Regional Medical Center at Grapevine, Grapevine, TX, p. A616
BECKMANN, Gregory, Finance Controller, Avera Creighton Hospital, Creighton, NE, p. A391
BECKNER, Jana, Director Human Resources, LewisGale Hospital Pulaski, Pulaski, VA, p. A671
BECKSVOORT, Jennifer F., Senior Human Resource Business Partner, Spectrum Health Zeeland Community Hospital, Zeeland, MI, p. A333
BEDARD, Lori, Chief Executive Officer, HEALTHSOUTH Rehabilitation Hospital of Spring Hill, Brooksville, FL, p. A123
BEDDOE, Chris, Chief Executive Officer, Sabine Medical Center, Many, LA, p. A279
BEDELL, Diane, R.N., Chief Executive Officer, Cedar Ridge Hospital, Oklahoma City, OK, p. A511
BEDELL, Mikael, M.D. Medical Director, Cascade Medical Center, Cascade, ID, p. A173
BEDFORD, Jeff, Executive Vice President and Chief Financial Officer, Merit Health Woman's Hospital, Flowood, MS, p. A352
BEDFORD, Tim, Chief Executive Officer, Emerald Coast Behavioral Hospital, Panama City, FL, p. A139
BEDGER, Kathy, Chief Nursing Officer, Penn Highlands Clearfield, Clearfield, PA, p. A531
BEDI, Andrew, Chief Operating Officer, TriStar Greenview Regional Hospital, Bowling Green, KY, p. A255
BEDICK, Jennifer L., Deputy Commander Nursing, Tripler Army Medical Center, Honolulu, HI, p. A169
BEDINGFIELD, Lance, Director Information Services, Dixie Regional Medical Center, Saint George, UT, p. A658
BEDSOLE, Jessica, Director, Human Resources, WellStar Paulding Hospital, Hiram, GA, p. A159
BEDZYK, J. Paul, Deputy Director Administration, Elmira Psychiatric Center, Elmira, NY, p. A433
BEEBE, Chris T., Director Human Resources, Raleigh General Hospital, Beckley, WV, p. A689
BEEBY, Lori, Director Information Systems, Community Hospital, McCook, NE, p. A394
BEECHLER, Jane, Director Healthcare Information Systems, Wyoming County Community Hospital, Warsaw, NY, p. A453
BEECHY, Andrew, Manager Information Technology Systems, Lee's Summit Medical Center, Lee's Summit, MO, p. A371
BEED, Donna E., Chief Information Management Division, Tripler Army Medical Center, Honolulu, HI, p. A169
BEEDLE, Chester
Chief Financial Officer, Kern Valley Healthcare District, Lake Isabella, CA, p. A67
Interim Chief Financial Officer, Tehachapi Valley Healthcare District, Tehachapi, CA, p. A94
BEEDY, Scott, Chief Financial Officer, Hansford Hospital, Spearman, TX, p. A644
BEEG, Gregg, Chief Financial Officer, McLaren Central Michigan, Mount Pleasant, MI, p. A326
BEEG, Gregg M., FACHE Chief Financial Officer, Oaklawn Hospital, Marshall, MI, p. A325
BEEHLER, Darryl, D.O. Chief of Staff, CHI St. Joseph's Health, Park Rapids, MN, p. A344
BEEHLER, Janelle E., Human Resource Manager, Baraga County Memorial Hospital, L'Anse, MI, p. A324
BEEHN, Holly, Director Human Resources, Southwest Health Center, Platteville, WI, p. A709
BEENE, Nikia, Assistant Chief Executive Officer, AllianceHealth Ponca City, Ponca City, OK, p. A514
BEER, Ronald R., FACHE, Vice President, Clinical Operations, Geisinger Wyoming Valley Medical Center, Wilkes Barre, PA, p. A553
BEESON, John C., M.D. Chief Medical Officer, CHRISTUS St. Vincent Regional Medical Center, Santa Fe, NM, p. A426
BEGALSKE, Kathy, Chief Nursing Officer, Palmer Lutheran Health Center, West Union, IA, p. A236
BEGAY, Trudy, Human Resources Specialist, Hopi Health Care Center, Keams Canyon, AZ, p. A32
BEGGANE, Thomas, Manager Human Resources, LAC–Olive View–UCLA Medical Center, CA, p. A71
BEGGS, Shaun, Interim Administrator, Pawhuska Hospital, Pawhuska, OK, p. A513
BEGLEY, Bruce D., Executive Director, Methodist Hospital, Henderson, KY, p. A258
BEGLEY, Robyn, R.N. Chief Nursing Officer, AtlantiCare Regional Medical Center, Atlantic City, NJ, p. A409
BEHAN, Lawrence, Vice President Administration and Finance, Chief Financial Officer, Walden Psychiatric Care, Waltham, MA, p. A312
BEHAR, Robert, M.D., Chief Executive Officer, North Cypress Medical Center, Cypress, TX, p. A603
BEHL, Mark, Chief Executive Officer, Renown South Meadows Medical Center, Reno, NV, p. A404
BEHM, Anthony, D.O. Chief of Staff, Erie Veterans Affairs Medical Center, Erie, PA, p. A534
BEHNE, Carl P., Administrator and Chief Executive Officer, Greene County Medical Center, Jefferson, IA, p. A230
BEHNER, Bruce M., Chief Operating Officer, Knox Community Hospital, Mount Vernon, OH, p. A495
BEHNKEN, Nick, Supervisor Information Technology, Red Bud Regional Hospital, Red Bud, IL, p. A199
BEHR, Richard A., Deputy Commander for Health Services, Reynolds Army Community Hospital, Fort Sill, OK, p. A507
BEHRENDT, Darcy, R.N. Vice President, Patient Care Services, CHI Health Missouri Valley, Missouri Valley, IA, p. A231
BEHRENDT, William, Ph.D. Vice President Human Resources, University of Texas Southwestern Medical Center, Dallas, TX, p. A607
BEHRENDTSEN, Ole, M.D. Medical Director, Santa Barbara County Psychiatric Health Facility, Santa Barbara, CA, p. A91
BEHRENS, Colleen, Director Information Technology, Community Memorial Healthcare, Marysville, KS, p. A246
BEHRENS, Karen, Director Technology Services, Perry Memorial Hospital, Princeton, IL, p. A198
BEHRENS, Sharon, R.N. Director of Nursing, Rehabilitation Hospital of Wisconsin, Waukesha, WI, p. A713
BEIDELSCHIES, Sandra, MSN Vice President Patient Services, Wood County Hospital, Bowling Green, OH, p. A480
BEIERMAN, Jennifer, Director Human Resources, Boone County Health Center, Albion, NE, p. A389
BEIFUS, Donna, Chief Executive Officer, HEALTHSOUTH Rehabilitation Hospital of Southern Arizona, Tucson, AZ, p. A39
BEIGHLE, John, Flight Chief Medical Information Systems, Wright Patterson Medical Center, Wright–Patterson AFB, OH, p. A501
BEILER, Jeffrey, Associate Director, Philadelphia Veterans Affairs Medical Center, Philadelphia, PA, p. A545
BEINDIT, Dawn, Director Work Life Services, St. John River District Hospital, East China, MI, p. A318
BEIRNE, Frank T., FACHE,
Senior Vice President and Area Manager, Kaiser Permanente Redwood City Medical Center, Redwood City, CA, p. A83
Senior Vice President and Area Manager, Kaiser Permanente South San Francisco, South San Francisco, CA, p. A93
BEISSEL, Debbie, Chief Executive Officer, Surgical Institute of Reading, Wyomissing, PA, p. A554
BEISWENGER, Joel, Chief Executive Officer, Tri–County Hospital, Wadena, MN, p. A348
BEITCHER, Bob, Chief Executive Officer, Motion Picture and Television Fund Hospital and Residential Services, CA, p. A71
BEITER, Amy, M.D., President and Chief Executive Officer, Carondelet St. Mary's Hospital, Tucson, AZ, p. A39
BEITER, Donna M., MSN, Director, VA Greater Los Angeles Healthcare System, Los Angeles, CA, p. A73
BEITING, Mark, Vice President Human Resources, Alta Bates Summit Medical Center – Summit Campus, Oakland, CA, p. A78
BEITZEL, Mark, Director Information Systems, Advocate Lutheran General Hospital, Park Ridge, IL, p. A197
BEJARANO, Nick, Regional Marketing Manager, Frank R. Howard Memorial Hospital, Willits, CA, p. A98
BEJNAR, Darla, M.D. Chief Medical Officer, Socorro General Hospital, Socorro, NM, p. A427
BELAIR, Norman, Senior Vice President and Chief Financial Officer, Southern Maine Health Care – Biddeford Medical Center, Biddeford, ME, p. A289
BELBECK, Michael, President and Chief Administrative Officer, Methodist Medical Center of Oak Ridge, Oak Ridge, TN, p. A586
BELCHER, Debbie, Director Human Resources, HEALTHSOUTH Rehabilitation Hospital of Austin, Austin, TX, p. A594
BELDECOS, Athena, M.D. Medical Director, Vibra Hospital of Charleston, Mt. Pleasant, SC, p. A563
BELENY, Charles, D.O. Chief of Staff, Jonathan M. Wainwright Memorial Veterans Affairs Medical Center, Walla Walla, WA, p. A687
BELGARDE, Donna, Human Resources Specialist, Indian Health Service – Quentin N. Burdick Memorial Health Care Facility, Belcourt, ND, p. A472
BELHASEN, F. K., M.D. Medical Director, Paul B. Hall Regional Medical Center, Paintsville, KY, p. A264
BELJIN, Dawn, R.N., Chief Operating Officer, Forest Park Medical Center–Southlake, Southlake, TX, p. A644
BELKOSKI, Dave, Chief Financial Officer, University Hospital McDuffie, Thomson, GA, p. A166
BELKOSKI, David, Executive Vice President and Chief Financial Officer, University Hospital, Augusta, GA, p. A152
BELL, Brian, Associate Administrator and Chief Operating Officer, National Park Medical Center, Hot Springs, AR, p. A45
BELL, Cindy, Director Finance, Willow Crest Hospital, Miami, OK, p. A509
BELL, David C., Chief Executive Officer, Brentwood Meadows, Newburgh, IN, p. A217
BELL, Gordon, M.D. Chief of Staff, Frances Mahon Deaconess Hospital, Glasgow, MT, p. A383
BELL, Heath
Chief Information Officer, Kishwaukee Hospital, DeKalb, IL, p. A186
Chief Information Officer, Valley West Hospital, Sandwich, IL, p. A200
BELL, Hollis, M.D. Medical Director, Mercy Rehabilition Hospital Springfield, Springfield, MO, p. A379
BELL, Julie, Director of Nursing, Covenant Specialty Hospital, Lubbock, TX, p. A629
BELL, Kae, Chief Financial Officer, Brentwood Hospital, Shreveport, LA, p. A284
BELL, Kristen, Director Human Resources, UPMC Mercy, Pittsburgh, PA, p. A547
BELL, Lorraine, Vice President Operations Human Resources, Scott & White Memorial Hospital, Temple, TX, p. A647
BELL, Madeline, Chief Executive Officer, Children's Hospital of Philadelphia, Philadelphia, PA, p. A543
BELL, Pam, Vice President Patient Care Services and Chief Nursing Officer, Presence Resurrection Medical Center, Chicago, IL, p. A183
BELL, Randall C., M.D. Medical Director, LifeCare Hospitals of San Antonio, San Antonio, TX, p. A641
BELL, Roderick, Chief Financial Officer, College Hospital Cerritos, Cerritos, CA, p. A57
BELL, Rodric, M.D. Medical Director, HEALTHSOUTH Tustin Rehabilitation Hospital, Tustin, CA, p. A95
BELL, Roni Sue, Director Nursing Services, Ohio Valley Hospital, McKees Rocks, PA, p. A539
BELL, Roseanna, Nurse Executive, MultiCare Auburn Medical Center, Auburn, WA, p. A676
BELL, Jr., Sammie, Chief Financial Officer, Tallahatchie General Hospital, Charleston, MS, p. A351
BELL, Scot, Chief Medical Officer, Anderson Regional Medical Center, Meridian, MS, p. A357
BELL, Sonja, Coordinator Human Resources, Sedgwick County Health Center, Julesburg, CO, p. A105
BELL, Stuart, M.D. Vice President Medical Affairs, MedStar Union Memorial Hospital, Baltimore, MD, p. A294
BELL, Talana, Chief Financial Officer, Flowers Hospital, Dothan, AL, p. A18


A784 Index of Health Care Professionals 

Index of Health Care Professionals / Berges

Index of Health Care Professionals


BELL, Tammie
Director Human Resources, McKenzie Regional Hospital, McKenzie, TN, p. A582
Director Human Resources, Tennova Healthcare – Volunteer Community Hospital, Martin, TN, p. A582
BELL, Tanya, Public Information Officer, Penrose–St. Francis Health Services, Colorado Springs, CO, p. A101
BELL, Tony, Manager Personnel, Tippah County Hospital, Ripley, MS, p. A360
BELL, W. Scot, M.D. Chief Medical Officer, Rush Foundation Hospital, Meridian, MS, p. A357
BELLAMY, David, Chief Financial Officer, McLaren Northern Michigan, Petoskey, MI, p. A327
BELLAND, Patrick, President and Chief Executive Officer, Fairview Ridges Hospital, Burnsville, MN, p. A336
BELLEAU, Christopher, M.D. Medical Director, Sage Rehabilitation Hospital, Baton Rouge, LA, p. A270
BELLEAU, Donella, Director Human Resources, Graham County Hospital, Hill City, KS, p. A241
BELLER, Robert H., FACHE, Director, Clement J. Zablocki Veterans Affairs Medical Center, Milwaukee, WI, p. A706
BELLUCCI, Alessandro, M.D., Executive Director, North Shore University Hospital, Manhasset, NY, p. A437
BELLWAY, Regina, Vice President Human Resources, Bethesda Hospital East, Boynton Beach, FL, p. A122
BELMONT, Chris, Chief Information Officer and Vice President, University of Texas M.D. Anderson Cancer Center, Houston, TX, p. A622
BELMONT, James, Associate Director, Northern Arizona Veterans Affairs Health Care System, Prescott, AZ, p. A36
BELMONT, Terry A., Chief Executive Officer, UC Irvine Medical Center, Orange, CA, p. A79
BELT, Katrina, Chief Financial Officer, Baptist Medical Center East, Montgomery, AL, p. A22
BELTRAN, Grace, Director Human Resources, Foundation Surgical Hospital of El Paso, El Paso, TX, p. A610
BELTZ, John, Chief Financial Officer, Hendry Regional Medical Center, Clewiston, FL, p. A124
BELVINS, Pam, Director Information Technology Member Hospitals Mission, McDowell Hospital, Marion, NC, p. A464
BELYEU, Peggy, Controller, Vanderbilt Stallworth Rehabilitation Hospital, Nashville, TN, p. A586
BELZER, Michael, M.D. Medical Director, Hennepin County Medical Center, Minneapolis, MN, p. A342
BEMENT, Douglas J., Chief Financial Officer, Kosciusko Community Hospital, Warsaw, IN, p. A221
BEN, Sabrina, Director Human Resources, North Star Behavioral Health System, Anchorage, AK, p. A27
BENAVIDES, Christina, Director Employee Services, Otto Kaiser Memorial Hospital, Kenedy, TX, p. A625
BENCITO ACA–AC, Norie Lee Reyes, R.N. Director of Nursing, Loma Linda University Behavioral Medicine Center, Redlands, CA, p. A82
BENCOMO, Dionisio, Chief Executive Officer, Select Specialty Hospital–Miami, Miami, FL, p. A135
BENDER, Brad, M.D. Chief of Staff, North Florida/South Georgia Veteran's Health System, Gainesville, FL, p. A127
BENDER, Janette, Chief Financial Officer, Arkansas Valley Regional Medical Center, La Junta, CO, p. A105
BENDER, Robert, Chief Financial Officer, Banner Casa Grande Medical Center, Casa Grande, AZ, p. A30
BENDER, Steve, Chief Financial Officer, Wuesthoff Medical Center – Melbourne, Melbourne, FL, p. A133
BENDINELLI, Emily, Director of Nurses, Ashley County Medical Center, Crossett, AR, p. A42
BENEDICT, Eva, R.N., President and Chief Executive Officer, Jones Memorial Hospital, Wellsville, NY, p. A453
BENEDICT, Joy M., Director Human Resources, Baptist Health Richmond, Richmond, KY, p. A265
BENEDUM, Mark, Chief Executive Officer, Highline Medical Center, Burien, WA, p. A677
BENEFIELD, Marlene, Director Human Resources, Cherokee Medical Center, Centre, AL, p. A18
BENEPAL, Jaspreet, Chief Nursing Officer, Contra Costa Regional Medical Center, Martinez, CA, p. A74
BENETTI–LOYOLA, Pedro L., Administrator, Hospital San Cristobal, Coto Laurel, PR, p. A721
BENFIELD, Ronald K., Chief Operating Officer, Adventist Medical Center–Portland, Portland, OR, p. A524
BENGALI, Abdul, Chief Information Officer, Via Christi Hospital on St. Francis, Wichita, KS, p. A253
BENGSTON, Jennifer, M.D. Chief Medical Officer, Valley County Health System, Ord, NE, p. A397
BENGTSON, Paul R., Chief Executive Officer, Northeastern Vermont Regional Hospital, Saint Johnsbury, VT, p. A661
BENINK, Eric, M.D. Chief Medical Officer, Northwest Community Hospital, Arlington Heights, IL, p. A178
BENITEZ, Pedro, M.D. Medical Director, Hospital De Damas, Ponce, PR, p. A722
BENJAMIN, Christian, MC, Commander, Mike O'Callaghan Federal Hospital, Nellis AFB, NV, p. A403
BENJAMIN, Kathleen, R.N. Chief Nursing Officer, MacNeal Hospital, Berwyn, IL, p. A179
BENJAMIN, Sunny J., Chief Human Resources Officer, Oklahoma State University Medical Center, Tulsa, OK, p. A516
BENNER, Brenda, Director Human Resources, HEALTHSOUTH Rehabilitation Hospital of Sarasota, Sarasota, FL, p. A142
BENNETT, Anthony, M.D. Chief Clinical Affairs, Baptist Health Medical Center–Little Rock, Little Rock, AR, p. A47
BENNETT, Bart, Chief Financial Officer, Springbrook Behavioral Health System, Travelers Rest, SC, p. A565
BENNETT, Charlotte, Vice President Human Resources, West Virginia University Hospitals, Morgantown, WV, p. A693
BENNETT, Dan, Director Operations, Waldo County General Hospital, Belfast, ME, p. A289
BENNETT, Darnell, Director Finance, Horizon Specialty Hospital, Las Vegas, NV, p. A402
BENNETT, E. Kyle, President and Chief Executive Officer, Memorial Hospital and Health Care Center, Jasper, IN, p. A213
BENNETT, Edwin, Controller, Turning Point Hospital, Moultrie, GA, p. A162
BENNETT, Fay, Vice President Employee Services, Guadalupe Regional Medical Center, Seguin, TX, p. A643
BENNETT, Kay
Vice President Human Resources, Baptist Medical Center East, Montgomery, AL, p. A22
System Director Human Resources, Baptist Medical Center South, Montgomery, AL, p. A22
BENNETT, Kimberly, Director Patient Care, CHRISTUS Dubuis Hospital of Alexandria, Alexandria, LA, p. A268
BENNETT, Kris, Chief Operating Officer, Lutheran Hospital, Cleveland, OH, p. A485
BENNETT, Laurie, Director Human Resources, Sarasota Memorial Health Care System, Sarasota, FL, p. A142
BENNETT, Lee W., Chief Financial Officer, Sitka Community Hospital, Sitka, AK, p. A29
BENNETT, Leo, M.D. Deputy Commander Clinical Services, Bassett Army Community Hospital, Fort Wainwright, AK, p. A28
BENNETT, Lisa, Chief Financial Officer, Waverly Health Center, Waverly, IA, p. A236
BENNETT, Mary Ann, Chief Nursing Officer, Glendora Community Hospital, Glendora, CA, p. A64
BENNETT, Mary Ann, R.N. Chief Operating Officer and Chief Nursing Officer, Springbrook Behavioral Health System, Travelers Rest, SC, p. A565
BENNETT, Melissa, Chief Nursing Officer, Trumbull Memorial Hospital, Warren, OH, p. A499
BENNETT, Nathan, M.D. Chief Medical Officer, Mercy Hospital Waldron, Waldron, AR, p. A51
BENNETT, Patti, Chief Nursing Officer and Senior Vice President, Good Shepherd Medical Center, Longview, TX, p. A629
BENNETT, Randall, Assistant Administrator, Uintah Basin Medical Center, Roosevelt, UT, p. A658
BENNETT, Richard G., M.D., President, Johns Hopkins Bayview Medical Center, Baltimore, MD, p. A293
BENNETT, Richard I., Senior Vice President and Chief Financial Officer, Delaware County Memorial Hospital, Drexel Hill, PA, p. A533
BENNETT, Rick, Administrator, St. James Behavioral Health Hospital, Gonzales, LA, p. A274
BENNETT, Robert, M.D. Medical Director, Millwood Hospital, Arlington, TX, p. A592
BENNETT, Ron, Chief Financial Officer, Abilene Regional Medical Center, Abilene, TX, p. A590
BENNETT, Sharon, Manager Information Systems, Cobre Valley Regional Medical Center, Globe, AZ, p. A32
BENNETT, Sheila, R.N. Vice President & Chief Nursing Officer, Floyd Medical Center, Rome, GA, p. A163
BENNETT, Tony N., Chief Executive Officer, HEALTHSOUTH Emerald Coast Rehabilitation Hospital, Panama City, FL, p. A139
BENNETT, W. Bradley, President and Chief Executive Officer, Fundamental Long Term Care Holdings, LLC, Sparks Glencoe, MD, p. B58
BENNETT, Wayne, Chief Financial Officer, Franklin Memorial Hospital, Farmington, ME, p. A290
BENOIT, Paul, Associate Administrator, Central Louisiana State Hospital, Pineville, LA, p. A283
BENOIT, Rebecca, R.N. Chief Nursing Officer, Lafayette General Medical Center, Lafayette, LA, p. A277
BENSEMA, David, Chief Information Officer, Baptist Health La Grange, La Grange, KY, p. A259
BENSON, Cheryl, Chief Operating Officer, Wernersville State Hospital, Wernersville, PA, p. A552
BENSON, Chris, Chief Financial Officer, DeKalb Regional Medical Center, Fort Payne, AL, p. A20
BENSON, Eric, Vice President Human Resources & Wellness, Sarah Bush Lincoln Health Center, Mattoon, IL, p. A193
BENSON, Kathryn, Human Resource and Marketing Partner, Avera St. Anthony's Hospital, O'Neill, NE, p. A395
BENSON, Kevin, Interim Chief Executive Officer, Ortonville Area Health Services, Ortonville, MN, p. A344
BENTLEY, Scott, Chief Financial Officer, Woman's Hospital of Texas, Houston, TX, p. A623
BENTON, Dennis C., Executive Director, Kaiser Permanente Panorama City Medical Center, CA, p. A70
BENTON, Edred, Chief Exeutive Officer and Chief Operating Officer, Cleveland Area Hospital, Cleveland, OK, p. A505
BENTON, Nancy, Assistant Director Patient Care Services, Mann–Grandstaff Veterans Affairs Medical Center, Spokane, WA, p. A685
BENTZ, Douglas E., Chief Executive Officer, Roane General Hospital, Spencer, WV, p. A695
BENVENUTTI, Cathy, Human Resource Director, Hancock Medical Center, Bay Saint Louis, MS, p. A350
BENWARE, Joel, Vice President Information Technology and Compliance, Northwestern Medical Center, Saint Albans, VT, p. A661
BENYI, Elizabeth, D.O. Chief of Staff, Aspirus Keweenaw Hospital, Laurium, MI, p. A324
BENZ, Betsy, R.N. Chief Nursing Officer, Aurora Medical Center – Manitowoc County, Two Rivers, WI, p. A712
BENZ Jr., Edward J., M.D., President and Chief Executive Officer, Dana–Farber Cancer Institute, Boston, MA, p. A303
BENZEL, Cindy, Manager Human Resources, Sanford Vermillion Medical Center, Vermillion, SD, p. A572
BEPLER, Gerold, Ph.D., President and Chief Executive Officer, Karmanos Cancer Center, Detroit, MI, p. A318
BERARDI, Paula, Manager Human Resources, Bournewood Health Systems, Brookline, MA, p. A305
BERCHER, Richard, M.D. Chief Medical Officer, Paris Regional Medical Center, Paris, TX, p. A635
BERCI, Haya, Executive Director of Nursing, Joyce Eisenberg–Keefer Medical Center, Reseda, CA, p. A83
BERDAN, Barclay E., FACHE, Chief Executive Officer, Texas Health Resources, Arlington, TX, p. B134
BERENS, Jeff, MS Chief Nursing Officer, Sanford Vermillion Medical Center, Vermillion, SD, p. A572
BERENTES, Amy, R.N. Vice President Patient Care Services, Mercy Medical Center–Clinton, Clinton, IA, p. A224
BERETTA, Dante, M.D. Chief of Staff, CentraCare Health–Melrose, Melrose, MN, p. A342
BERG, Gary L., D.O. Chief Medical Officer, St. John Macomb–Oakland Hospital, Warren, MI, p. A332
BERG, James, FACHE, President, Texas Health Presbyterian Hospital Dallas, Dallas, TX, p. A606
BERG, Jon, M.D. Chief of Staff, Northwood Deaconess Health Center, Northwood, ND, p. A476
BERG, Tony L., M.D. Chief of Staff, Winner Regional Healthcare Center, Winner, SD, p. A573
BERG, William, Chief Information Officer, Naval Hospital Pensacola, Pensacola, FL, p. A139
BERGE, Ron, Executive Vice President and Chief Operating Officer, National Jewish Health, Denver, CO, p. A102
BERGEAUX, Scott, M.D. Chief Medical Staff, Abrom Kaplan Memorial Hospital, Kaplan, LA, p. A276
BERGEMANN, John, Director Human Resources, Crouse Hospital, Syracuse, NY, p. A451
BERGEN, Jan L., President and Chief Executive Officer, Lancaster General Health, Lancaster, PA, p. A537
BERGENFELD, Joel M.
Chief Hospital Executive Officer, Hemet Valley Medical Center, Hemet, CA, p. A65
Chief Hospital Executive Officer, Menifee Valley Medical Center, Sun City, CA, p. A93
BERGENFELD, Joel M., Chief Executive Officer, Physicians for Healthy Hospitals, Hemet, CA, p. B104
BERGER, George, Controller, HEALTHSOUTH Rehabilitation Hospital of Altoona, Altoona, PA, p. A528
BERGER, Jeffrey, M.D. Chief Medical Officer, Brighton Center for Recovery, Brighton, MI, p. A315
BERGER, Kathy, R.N., Acting Director, Sheridan Veterans Affairs Medical Center, Sheridan, WY, p. A717
BERGERON, Johnny, Chief Information Officer, Bunkie General Hospital, Bunkie, LA, p. A271
BERGERON, Pierre, Director Information Services, Wellington Regional Medical Center, West Palm Beach, FL, p. A147
BERGERON, Timothy, Deputy Commander, Administration, Bassett Army Community Hospital, Fort Wainwright, AK, p. A28
BERGERSON, Melissa, R.N. Vice President Patient Care Services, Black River Memorial Hospital, Black River Falls, WI, p. A698
BERGES, Iris, Chief Executive Officer, Larkin Behavioral Health Services, FL, p. A128

BERGFORT, Joe, Chief Information Officer, UCSF Medical Center, San Francisco, CA, p. A89

BERGH, Roger, Director Human Resources, Helen Newberry Joy Hospital, Newberry, MI, p. A327

BERGHERM, Bruce, Chief Executive Officer, Florida Hospital North Pinellas, Tarpon Springs, FL, p. A145

BERGHOLM, Brenda, MSN Chief Nursing Officer, Caribou Memorial Hospital and Living Center, Soda Springs, ID, p. A176

BERGLING, Richard Q., Interim Chief Executive Officer, Morton County Health System, Elkhart, KS, p. A239

BERGMAN, Angela, Director Health Information Management, Van Matre HealthSouth Rehabilitation Hospital, Rockford, IL, p. A200

BERGMAN, Chris, Chief Financial Officer, Christ Hospital, Cincinnati, OH, p. A482

BERGMAN, Jim, Director Human Resources, Northeast Regional Medical Center, Kirksville, MO, p. A371

BERGMANN, Michael, President, Aurora Medical Center Summit, Summit, WI, p. A712

BERGMANN, Peter U., President and Chief Executive Officer, Sisters of Charity Hospital of Buffalo, Buffalo, NY, p. A431

BERGQUIST, Susan, Human Resources Generalist, Kindred Hospital–La Mirada, La Mirada, CA, p. A66

BERGSENG, John H., D.O. Vice President Medical Affairs, Glencoe Regional Health Services, Glencoe, MN, p. A339

BERGSTEDT, Sharon, Director of Nursing, Alaska Psychiatric Institute, Anchorage, AK, p. A27

BERGSTROM, Jenny, Project Manager Information Technology, Cloud County Health Center, Concordia, KS, p. A238

BERKLEY, William, Director Human Resources, Arrowhead Regional Medical Center, Colton, CA, p. A58

BERKOWITZ, David J., Vice President and Chief Operating Officer, Palisades Medical Center, North Bergen, NJ, p. A416

BERKRAM, Treasure, Chief Financial Officer, Northern Rockies Medical Center, Cut Bank, MT, p. A382

BERLINGHOFF, Kathleen, Director Human Resources, Sharon Hospital, Sharon, CT, p. A114

BERLOT, Alvin, M.D. Medical Director, Bucktail Medical Center, Renovo, PA, p. A548

BERLOWITZ, Dan, M.D. Acting Chief of Staff, Bedford Veterans Affairs Medical Center, Edith Nourse Rogers Memorial Veterans Hospital, Bedford, MA, p. A302

BERLUCCHI, Scott A., FACHE, President and Chief Executive Officer, Auburn Community Hospital, Auburn, NY, p. A429

BERLYN, Maria, Assistant Vice President Nursing Services, John Heinz Institute of Rehabilitation Medicine, Wilkes–Barre, PA, p. A553

BERMAN, Manuel S., President and Chief Executive Officer, Tuality Healthcare, Hillsboro, OR, p. A521

BERMAN, Ronald, M.D. Chief of Staff, Mad River Community Hospital, Arcata, CA, p. A54

BERMUDEZ, Ada, Director Human Resources, Hospital De La Concepcion, San German, PR, p. A722

BERMUDEZ, Armand, M.D. Medical Director, Select Specialty Hospital of Southeast Ohio, Zanesville, OH, p. A502

BERMUDEZ, Yuri, M.D. Chief of Staff, South Texas Health System, Edinburg, TX, p. A610

BERNAL, Hector, Chief Executive Officer, Post Acute Medical Specialty Hospital of Corpus Christi, Corpus Christi, TX, p. A603

BERNAL, Leroy, Chief Operating Officer, Victory Medical Center – Southcross, San Antonio, TX, p. A642

BERNARD, David P., Administrator, Houston Methodist San Jacinto Hospital, Baytown, TX, p. A596

BERNARD, Donald P., Chief Financial Officer, Kaiser Permanente Fontana Medical Center, Fontana, CA, p. A61

BERNARD, Doug, M.D. Chief Medical Officer, White River Medical Center, Batesville, AR, p. A41

BERNARD, Joseph, Chief Executive Officer, Highlands Regional Medical Center, Sebring, FL, p. A143

BERNARD, Mark L., Chief Executive Officer, St. Joseph Medical Center, Houston, TX, p. A622

BERNARD, Peter J., Chief Executive Officer, Bon Secours St. Francis Medical Center, Midlothian, VA, p. A668

BERNARD, Robert, M.D. Chief of Staff, Alexandria Veterans Affairs Health Care System, Pineville, LA, p. A283

BERNARD, Traci, President, Texas Health Harris Methodist Hospital Southlake, Southlake, TX, p. A644

BERNARDI, Barbara, R.N. Nurse Executive, Jameson Hospital, New Castle, PA, p. A541

BERNARDO, Maria, M.D. Chief of Staff, Bullock County Hospital, Union Springs, AL, p. A26

BERNASEK, Robert, M.D. Chief Medical Officer, Coastal Carolina Hospital, Hardeeville, SC, p. A562

BERNATIS, Terry D., Director Human Resources, Community HealthCare System, Onaga, KS, p. A247

BERND, David L., Chief Executive Officer, Sentara Healthcare, Norfolk, VA, p. B122

BERND, Jason, Vice President, Novant Health Charlotte Orthopaedic Hospital, Charlotte, NC, p. A457

BERNDT, Julia L., Chief Financial Officer, Logansport Memorial Hospital, Logansport, IN, p. A215

BERNERT–YAP, Kellie, Director Human Resources, Vibra Specialty Hospital of Portland, Portland, OR, p. A525

BERNEY, Bernadette, Director Human Resources, Pullman Regional Hospital, Pullman, WA, p. A682

BERNHARDT–KADLEC, Peggy, Chief Human Resources Officer, SEARHC MT. Edgecumbe Hospital, Sitka, AK, p. A29

BERNICK, Michael, Executive Vice President and Chief Financial Officer, Clarity Child Guidance Center, San Antonio, TX, p. A640

BERNINI, A. Susan, Chief Operating Officer, Einstein Medical Center Philadelphia, Philadelphia, PA, p. A543

BERNOSKY, Matt, Manager Human Resources, OhioHealth Rehabilitation Hospital, Columbus, OH, p. A486

BERNS, Erin, Director Human Resources, Veterans Memorial Hospital, Waukon, IA, p. A236

BERNSEN, Tina, Chief Nursing Officer, Othello Community Hospital, Othello, WA, p. A681

BERNSTEIN, Lee
  Regional Executive Vice President and Chief Operating Officer, SSM St. Clare Health Center, Fenton, MO, p. A367
  Regional Executive Vice President and Chief Operating Officer, SSM St. Joseph Health Center, Saint Charles, MO, p. A375

BERNSTEIN, Les, Chief Information Officer, Cookeville Regional Medical Center, Cookeville, TN, p. A576

BERNSTEIN, Michael, Chief Financial Officer, Tulare Regional Medical Center, Tulare, CA, p. A95

BERNSTEIN, Paul E., M.D. Area Medical Director, Kaiser Permanente San Diego Medical Center, San Diego, CA, p. A86

BERRIGAN, Mary, Chief Operating Officer, Medical Center of Aurora, Aurora, CO, p. A99

BERRIOS, Elenia, Chief Nursing Officer, Hospital HIMA San Pablo Caguas, Caguas, PR, p. A720

BERRONG, Barbara, R.N. Chief Nursing Officer, Parkland Health Center – Liberty Street, Farmington, MO, p. A367

BERRY, Carlos E., M.D. Acting Chief of Staff, Tuscaloosa Veterans Affairs Medical Center, Tuscaloosa, AL, p. A25

BERRY, Cheryl Furdge, Chief Nursing Officer, Baptist Memorial Hospital–Tipton, Covington, TN, p. A576

BERRY, David, Senior Vice President and Chief Operating Officer, Arkansas Children's Hospital, Little Rock, AR, p. A46

BERRY, Deborah, Director of Operations, Greene County Hospital, Leakesville, MS, p. A356

BERRY, Dennis, Chief Executive Officer, Tennessee Health Management, Parsons, TN, p. B133

BERRY, Eilleen, Manager Information Technology, Webster County Community Hospital, Red Cloud, NE, p. A397

BERRY, Greg, Chief Financial Officer, Doctors Medical Center, Modesto, CA, p. A75

BERRY, Linda, Vice President Human Resources, Guthrie Towanda Memorial Hospital, Towanda, PA, p. A551

BERRY, Lisa, Director, Saint Anne's Hospital, Fall River, MA, p. A306

BERRY, Rebecca
  Senior Director Human Resources, Pioneer Memorial Hospital, Prineville, OR, p. A525
  Senior Director Human Resources, St. Charles Bend, Bend, OR, p. A519
  Senior Director Human Resources, St. Charles Redmond, Redmond, OR, p. A525

BERRY, Robert F., Chief Executive Officer, Lane Frost Health and Rehabilitation Center, Hugo, OK, p. A508

BERRYMAN, John David, M.D. Chief of Staff, Beckley Veterans Affairs Medical Center, Beckley, WV, p. A689

BERRYMAN, William R., M.D. Chief of Staff, Grand Junction Veterans Health Care System, Grand Junction, CO, p. A104

BERSANTE, Syd, R.N., President, St. Joseph Medical Center, Tacoma, WA, p. A686

BERSHAD, Joshua M., M.D. Senior Vice President Medical Affairs and Chief Medical Officer, Robert Wood Johnson University Hospital, New Brunswick, NJ, p. A415

BERSINGER, David, M.D. Chief of Staff, McLeod Health Cheraw, Cheraw, SC, p. A558

BERSTLER, Michael T., Chief Medical Officer, Waverly Health Center, Waverly, IA, p. A236

BERT, Alisa, Chief Financial Officer, Aventura Hospital and Medical Center, Aventura, FL, p. A121

BERTHIL, Emmanuel, Chief Clinical Officer, New Bedford Rehabilitation Hospital, New Bedford, MA, p. A309

BERTKE, Bradley J., Chief Executive Officer, Mercy St. Anne Hospital, Toledo, OH, p. A498

BERTRAND, Joan L., Vice President Human Resources, Adcare Hospital of Worcester, Worcester, MA, p. A313

BERTRAND, Neil W., Chief Financial Officer, Longmont United Hospital, Longmont, CO, p. A107

BERTSCH, Darrold, Chief Executive Officer, Sakakawea Medical Center, Hazen, ND, p. A474

BERZ, Derek, Chief Operating Officer, Kaiser Permanente Los Angeles Medical Center, Los Angeles, CA, p. A70

BERZAU, Ulrike, FACHE Administrator, St. Luke's Rehabilitation Institute, Spokane, WA, p. A685

BESCOE, Bradley, Chief Financial Officer, Straith Hospital for Special Surgery, Southfield, MI, p. A330

BESHEL, Michael, R.N. Vice President Patient Care and Chief Nursing Officer, Nazareth Hospital, Philadelphia, PA, p. A544

BESIO, Adam, Chief Information Officer, Memorial Medical Center, Port Lavaca, TX, p. A638

BESPALEC, Jason, M.D. Chief of Staff, Fillmore County Hospital, Geneva, NE, p. A392

BESS, Amy, Chief Financial Officer, Mizell Memorial Hospital, Opp, AL, p. A24

BESS, Charles, M.D. Medical Director, Potomac Valley Hospital, Keyser, WV, p. A692

BESS, Timothy A., Chief Executive Officer, Lake Cumberland Regional Hospital, Somerset, KY, p. A266

BESSE, Kim, Senior Vice President and Chief Human Resource Officer, Children's Health System of Texas, Dallas, TX, p. A604

BESSET, Kerry, Senior Vice President Human Resources, Memorial Sloan–Kettering Cancer Center, New York, NY, p. A441

BESSLER, Christine, Vice President Information Services, Oconomowoc Memorial Hospital, Oconomowoc, WI, p. A708

BESSLER, September, Manager Human Resources, Brookings Health System, Brookings, SD, p. A567

BESSON, Kathleen, Executive Vice President and Chief Operating Officer, CaroMont Regional Medical Center, Gastonia, NC, p. A460

BESST, Kara, President and Chief Executive Officer, Gritman Medical Center, Moscow, ID, p. A175

BEST, Rosa, Chief Nursing Officer, Rolling Plains Memorial Hospital, Sweetwater, TX, p. A646

BESTEN, Robert, Chief Financial Officer, Mary Breckinridge ARH Hospital, Hyden, KY, p. A258

BESTGEN, Pat, Manager Human Resources, Cameron Regional Medical Center, Cameron, MO, p. A364

BESWICK, Elizabeth, Vice President Human Resources and Public Relations, Carteret Health Care, Morehead City, NC, p. A465

BETANCOURT, Erika, Coordinator Human Resources, Cornerstone Regional Hospital, Edinburg, TX, p. A609

BETHELL, Mark, Chief Executive Officer, Springwoods Behavioral Health Hospital, Fayetteville, AR, p. A43

BETHON, Celeste Ann, MS Chief Nursing Officer, Nyack Hospital, Nyack, NY, p. A446

BETKE–MENA, Rachel, Director Health Information Management, Colusa Regional Medical Center, Colusa, CA, p. A58

BETTCHER, Sue, R.N. Vice President of Nursing Services, Community Hospital of Bremen, Bremen, IN, p. A205

BETTEM, Kelly, Chief Administrative Officer, Ohio Valley Medical Center, Wheeling, WV, p. A696

BETTS, Brooks, Director Information Systems and Chief Information Officer, Pen Bay Medical Center, Rockport, ME, p. A292

BETTS, Crystal
  Chief Financial Officer, Incline Village Community Hospital, Incline Village, NV, p. A401
  Chief Financial Officer, Tahoe Forest Hospital District, Truckee, CA, p. A95

BETTS, Nicholas, Director Information Technology, Grundy County Memorial Hospital, Grundy Center, IA, p. A228

BETTS, Tracy, Chief Financial Officer, Hardeman County Memorial Hospital, Quanah, TX, p. A638

BETZ, Paul, FACHE Chief Operating Officer and Senior Vice President, Maury Regional Hospital, Columbia, TN, p. A576

BEUS, Lance, Chief Executive Officer, CHRISTUS Jasper Memorial Hospital, Jasper, TX, p. A624

BEUTKE, Kenneth, President, OSF Saint Elizabeth Medical Center, Ottawa, IL, p. A197

BEVARD, Julie, Director Human Resources, Perkins County Health Services, Grant, NE, p. A392

BEVEL, John, Manager Information Systems, Shriners Hospitals for Children–Northern California, Sacramento, CA, p. A84

BEVELACQUA, Timothy J., R.N., Chief Executive Officer, Woodlands Specialty Hospital, Spring, TX, p. A644

BEVERLEY, Tracey, M.D. Chief Medical Staff, Sweetwater Hospital, Sweetwater, TN, p. A588

BEVERLY, Douglas H., Chief Executive Officer, HEALTHSOUTH Rehabilitation Hospital of North Alabama, Huntsville, AL, p. A21

BEVERLY, Esther, Vice President Human Resources, Tri–City Medical Center, Oceanside, CA, p. A79

BEVERS, Donald, Chief Financial Officer, Memorial Hospital of Salem County, Salem, NJ, p. A418

Index of Health Care Professionals / Birkhofer

Index of Health Care Professionals

BEYER, Jim, Director Human Resources, Norman Regional Health System, Norman, OK, p. A510
BEYER, Laurie, Senior Vice President and Chief Financial Officer, Union Hospital, Elkton, MD, p. A297
BEYER, Teri, Chief Information Officer, Quality, Rice Memorial Hospital, Willmar, MN, p. A349
BEZUCHA, Gary, FACHE, Chief Executive Officer, North Central Health Care, Wausau, WI, p. A713
BHAMBI, Brijesh, M.D. Chief Medical Officer, Bakersfield Heart Hospital, Bakersfield, CA, p. A54
BHAMBRA, Jody, Chief Nursing Officer, Hartgrove Hospital, Chicago, IL, p. A182
BHANDARI, Raj, M.D. Physician–in–Chief, Kaiser Permanente San Jose Medical Center, San Jose, CA, p. A89
BHATEJA, Renu, M.D. President Medical Staff, Ridgeview Psychiatric Hospital and Center, Oak Ridge, TN, p. A587
BHATIA, Sanjay, Chief Medical Officer, Lower Bucks Hospital, Bristol, PA, p. A530
BHAYANI, Sam B., M.D. Chief Medical Officer, Barnes–Jewish West County Hospital, Saint Louis, MO, p. A376
BHOORASINGH, Merlene, Administrator, Kindred Hospital Ocala, Ocala, FL, p. A137
BHUCHAR, Subodh, M.D. Chief of Staff, Kindred Hospital Sugar Land, Sugar Land, TX, p. A645
BIAGIONI, Donna K., R.N. Director of Nursing, Maniilaq Health Center, Kotzebue, AK, p. A28
BIANCAMANO, John, Chief Financial Officer, University of Connecticut Health Center, John Dempsey Hospital, Farmington, CT, p. A112
BIANCHI, Cynthia, Chief Information Officer, Woodhull Medical and Mental Health Center, NY, p. A445
BIANCHI, Patty, Chief Executive Officer, Pershing General Hospital, Lovelock, NV, p. A403
BIAS, Richard R., Chief Operating Officer, Lahey Hospital & Medical Center, Burlington, Burlington, MA, p. A305
BIBAL, Antoinette, Director Human Resources, Kindred Hospital–Baldwin Park, Baldwin Park, CA, p. A55
BIBB, Jeff, Chief Operating Officer, Oklahoma Center for Orthopedic and Multi–Specialty Surgery, Oklahoma City, OK, p. A512
BIBB, Lisa, Director Human Resources, San Angelo Community Medical Center, San Angelo, TX, p. A640
BIBBO, Karen, R.N. Chief Nursing Officer, Aventura Hospital and Medical Center, Aventura, FL, p. A121
BIBBY, John, Vice President Human Resources, Los Robles Hospital and Medical Center, Thousand Oaks, CA, p. A94
BIBEAU, Roland R., FACHE, President, Novant Health Matthews Medical Center, Matthews, NC, p. A464
BIBER, Carl, Chief Financial Officer, Columbus Regional Healthcare System, Whiteville, NC, p. A470
BIBLO, Lee, M.D. Chief Medical Officer, Froedtert Memorial Lutheran Hospital, Milwaukee, WI, p. A706
BIBY, Thom, Chief Financial Officer, Tulsa Spine and Specialty Hospital, Tulsa, OK, p. A517
BICE, Rodney, R.N. Chief Nursing Officer, Pikes Peak Regional Hospital, Woodland Park, CO, p. A109
BICHIMER, Michael, Acting Vice President of Finance, OhioHealth MedCentral Mansfield Hospital, Mansfield, OH, p. A493
BICKEL, George, Director, Information Systems, Merit Health Biloxi, Biloxi, MS, p. A350
BICKEL, James, Chief Executive Officer, Columbus Regional Hospital, Columbus, IN, p. A206
BICKFORD, Carmel, Chief Financial Officer, Wyoming Behavioral Institute, Casper, WY, p. A715
BICKFORD, David, Chief Information Officer, Melissa Memorial Hospital, Holyoke, CO, p. A105
BIDDLE, Kenneth, Controller, Kensington Hospital, Philadelphia, PA, p. A544
BIDES, Adrienne, Assistant Chief Financial Officer and Budget Analyst, Big Spring State Hospital, Big Spring, TX, p. A597
BIDLEMAN, Angela, R.N. Chief Nursing Officer, Integris Grove Hospital, Grove, OK, p. A507
BIE, Gary E., CPA Chief Financial Officer, Stony Brook University Medical Center, Stony Brook, NY, p. A451
BIEBER, Courtney, Director Information Systems, Mercy Regional Medical Center, Ville Platte, LA, p. A286
BIEBER, Eric, M.D., President and Chief Executive Officer, Rochester Regional Health, Rochester, NY, p. B114
BIEBER, Judi, Senior Vice President Human Resources, Beth Israel Deaconess Medical Center, Boston, MA, p. A302
BIEBER, Martin A., Interim President and Chief Executive Officer, East Orange General Hospital, East Orange, NJ, p. A411
BIEDIGER, Daniel F., Vice President Human Resources, FirstHealth Moore Regional Hospital, Pinehurst, NC, p. A466
BIEDRON, Janet, R.N., Chief Executive Officer, Vibra Hospital of Sacramento, Folsom, CA, p. A61
BIEGANSKI, Gary, Interim Chief Executive Officer, Pawnee County Memorial Hospital and Rural Health Clinic, Pawnee City, NE, p. A397
BIEGERT, Dara, Vice President Human Resources, Medical Center of Lewisville, Lewisville, TX, p. A628
BIEGLER, Elizabeth Anne, R.N
  Chief Nursing Officer, OhioHealth Dublin Methodist Hospital, Dublin, OH, p. A489
  Chief Nursing Officer, OhioHealth Grady Memorial Hospital, Delaware, OH, p. A488
BIEHL, Albert, M.D. Vice President Medical Affairs, Bethesda Hospital East, Boynton Beach, FL, p. A122
BIEL, Christopher, Chief Information Officer, Goodland Regional Medical Center, Goodland, KS, p. A240
BIELECKI, Thomas A., Chief Financial Officer, Geisinger Wyoming Valley Medical Center, Wilkes Barre, PA, p. A553
BIEN, Jim, M.D. Vice President Quality and Patient Safety, Indiana University Health Arnett Hospital, Lafayette, IN, p. A214
BIEN, John, Vice President Finance, United Hospital, Saint Paul, MN, p. A346
BIER, Alan, M.D. Executive Vice President and Chief Medical Officer, Gwinnett Hospital System, Lawrenceville, GA, p. A160
BIERI, Bryan, Manager Finance, Kansas City Veterans Affairs Medical Center, Kansas City, MO, p. A369
BIERLE, Dennis, Chief Operating Officer, Nebraska Medicine – Nebraska Medical Center, Omaha, NE, p. A396
BIERMAN, Debra, Associate Executive Director Human Resources, North Shore University Hospital, Manhasset, NY, p. A437
BIERMAN, Joan, Vice President Finance, Cherokee Regional Medical Center, Cherokee, IA, p. A224
BIERMAN, Marcia, M.D. Chief of Staff, North Shore Medical Center, Miami, FL, p. A134
BIERMAN, Ronald L., Chief Executive Officer, Affinity Medical Center, Massillon, OH, p. A493
BIERSCHENK, Kevin, Chief Executive Officer, Dodge County Hospital, Eastman, GA, p. A157
BIERUT, Barbara, Chief Financial Officer, HEALTHSOUTH Rehabilitation Hospital of Sarasota, Sarasota, FL, p. A142
BIFFLE, Sandra, Personnel Clerk, Quitman County Hospital, Marks, MS, p. A356
BIGELOW, Barbara
  Administrator, Providence Kodiak Island Medical Center, Kodiak, AK, p. A28
  Administrator, Providence Valdez Medical Center, Valdez, AK, p. A29
BIGELOW, David C., PharmD, Chief Executive Officer, Samaritan Pacific Communities Hospital, Newport, OR, p. A523
BIGELOW, Debbie, Chief Executive Officer, Coulee Medical Center, Grand Coulee, WA, p. A679
BIGELOW, Timothy, Director Human Resources, Butler Hospital, Providence, RI, p. A555
BIGGINS RN, Lillie, R.N., President, Texas Health Harris Methodist Hospital Fort Worth, Fort Worth, TX, p. A614
BIGGS, Daniel, Director Human Resources, Valley View Hospital, Glenwood Springs, CO, p. A104
BIGGS, Jeremy, President and Chief Administrative Officer, Cumberland Medical Center, Crossville, TN, p. A577
BIGGS, Kelly, M.D. Chief Medical Officer, Tyrone Hospital, Tyrone, PA, p. A551
BIGHAM, Laurie S., R.N. Chief Nursing Officer, Lovelace Medical Center, Albuquerque, NM, p. A422
BIGLER, Nathan, Vice President Human Relations, Riverside Community Hospital, Riverside, CA, p. A84
BIGLER, Pamela, R.N. Senior Vice President Chief Nursing Officer, Carle Foundation Hospital, Urbana, IL, p. A202
BIGLEY, John, M.D. Medical Director, Kaiser Permanente Baldwin Park Medical Center, Baldwin Park, CA, p. A55
BIGLEY, Robert F., President and Chief Executive Officer, East Georgia Regional Medical Center, Statesboro, GA, p. A165
BIGNAULT, Jon, M.D. Chief of Staff, Athens–Limestone Hospital, Athens, AL, p. A15
BIGONEY, Rebecca, M.D
  Executive Vice President and Chief Medical Officer, Mary Washington Hospital, Fredericksburg, VA, p. A665
  Executive Vice President and Chief Medical Officer, Stafford Hospital, Stafford, VA, p. A673
BIGOS, Ardelle, R.N. Chief Nursing Officer and Vice President Patient Care Services, Maine Coast Memorial Hospital, Ellsworth, ME, p. A290
BIHUNIAK, Peter, Vice President Finance, Robert Wood Johnson University Hospital Rahway, Rahway, NJ, p. A417
BIITTNER, Sallie, Vice President Human Resources, St. Joseph's Hospital Health Center, Syracuse, NY, p. A451
BIK, Lymar, M.D. Medical Director, Coalinga Regional Medical Center, Coalinga, CA, p. A58
BILBREY, Mickey, President and Chief Executive Officer, QHR, Brentwood, TN, p. B110
BILL, Charles E., Chief Executive Officer, Bartlett Regional Hospital, Juneau, AK, p. A28
BILLECI, Theresa, Executive Director, Porterville Developmental Center, Porterville, CA, p. A81
BILLIG, Samantha, Chief Executive Officer, HEALTHSOUTH Rehabilitation Hospital – Henderson, Henderson, NV, p. A401
BILLING, Michael D., Administrator, Mid–Valley Hospital, Omak, WA, p. A681
BILLINGS, Mary Ann, Director of Nursing, Potomac Valley Hospital, Keyser, WV, p. A692
BILLINGS, Robert E., Chief Financial Officer, Largo Medical Center, Largo, FL, p. A132
BILLINGSLEA, Anidra, Health Insurance Management, HEALTHSOUTH Rehabilitation Hospital of Montgomery, Montgomery, AL, p. A23
BILLINGSLEY, Angela, Director Human Resources, Intermountain Hospital, Boise, ID, p. A172
BILLINGSLEY, Margaret, R.N. Chief Nursing Officer, T. J. Samson Community Hospital, Glasgow, KY, p. A257
BILLINGSLEY, Richard A., MSN Chief Operating Officer and Chief Nursing Officer, Mena Regional Health System, Mena, AR, p. A48
BILLINGTON, Carole, R.N. Vice President Patient Care Services, Saint Anne's Hospital, Fall River, MA, p. A306
BILLMEYER, Joe, Director, Information Services, Mercy Medical Center–Dubuque, Dubuque, IA, p. A227
BILLS, James, Chief Executive Officer, Logan Memorial Hospital, Russellville, KY, p. A265
BILLY, Frank, Chief Financial Officer, Kindred Hospital Bay Area–Tampa, Tampa, FL, p. A145
BILUNKA, Dianne C., Director Human Resources, Clarion Psychiatric Center, Clarion, PA, p. A531
BINDER, Buzz, Vice President Finance, Saint Joseph Hospital, Denver, CO, p. A102
BINDERMAN, Judi, Chief Information Technology Officer and Chief Medical Informatics Officer, St. Francis Medical Center, Lynwood, CA, p. A74
BINDRA, Pavel, M.D. Chief Medical Officer and Chief Information Officer, Citrus Valley Medical Center–Inter Community Campus, Covina, CA, p. A59
BINGHAM, Julie, IT Supervisor, San Juan Hospital, Monticello, UT, p. A655
BINGHAM, Leslie, Senior Vice President and Chief Executive Officer, Valley Baptist Medical Center–Brownsville, Brownsville, TX, p. A599
BINGHAM, Roxane, Director Marketing, Baton Rouge Rehabilitation Hospital, Baton Rouge, LA, p. A269
BINGMAN, Ryan, Director Operations, Grundy County Memorial Hospital, Grundy Center, IA, p. A228
BINKLEY, Sharon, Director Human Resources, Fairfax Community Hospital, Fairfax, OK, p. A507
BINTZ, Marilu, M.D. Chief of Staff, Gundersen Boscobel Area Hospital and Clinics, Boscobel, WI, p. A698
BIRCH, Misty, Director Human Resources, Castleview Hospital, Price, UT, p. A657
BIRCHMEIER, Kevin, Director Human Resources, Covenant Healthcare, Saginaw, MI, p. A329
BIRD, Alan, Chief Executive Officer, Franklin County Medical Center, Preston, ID, p. A176
BIRD, Chris, Chief Operating Officer, Phoenix Baptist Hospital, Phoenix, AZ, p. A35
BIRD, Gregory A., R.N. Interim Chief Nursing Officer, York Hospital, York, ME, p. A292
BIRD, Jace, M.D. Chief Medical Officer, Missouri River Medical Center, Fort Benton, MT, p. A383
BIRD, Jeffrey C., M.D. Chief Operating Officer and Chief Medical Officer, Indiana University Health Ball Memorial Hospital, Muncie, IN, p. A216
BIRD, Lindsay, Director Finance, South Pointe Hospital, Warrensville Heights, OH, p. A500
BIRD, Michele
  Chief Human Resources Officer, Hemet Valley Medical Center, Hemet, CA, p. A65
  Chief Human Resources Officer, Menifee Valley Medical Center, Sun City, CA, p. A93
BIRD, Suzanne C., R.N. Chief Nursing Officer, Mobile Infirmary Medical Center, Mobile, AL, p. A22
BIRDZELL, JoAnn, Chief Executive Officer and Administrator, St. Catherine Hospital, East Chicago, IN, p. A207
BIREN, David, Chief Financial Officer, Mayo Clinic Health System in Lake City, Lake City, MN, p. A340
BIRENBERG, Allan, Vice President Medical Affairs, MedStar Harbor Hospital, Baltimore, MD, p. A294
BIRK, Deborah L., Ph.D. Vice President Patient Care Services, OSF Saint Anthony's Health Center, Alton, IL, p. A178
BIRKEL, Sue M., R.N. Director of Nursing, Butler County Health Care Center, David City, NE, p. A391
BIRKENSTOCK, Timothy L., Chief Financial Officer, Nicklaus Children's Hospital, Miami, FL, p. A134
BIRKHOFER, Colleen, Chief Nursing Officer, Trenton Psychiatric Hospital, Trenton, NJ, p. A419

Index of Health Care Professionals

Index of Health Care Professionals / Birmingham

BIRMINGHAM, Karen, Director Human Resources, West Springs Hospital, Grand Junction, CO, p. A104
BIRNBAUM, Bernard, M.D. Senior Vice President, Vice Dean and Chief Hospital Operations, NYU Langone Medical Center, New York, NY, p. A443
BIRSCHBACH, Nancy
Assistant Vice President Information Services, Agnesian HealthCare, Fond Du Lac, WI, p. A700
Vice President and Chief Information Officer, Ripon Medical Center, Ripon, WI, p. A710
Vice President and Chief Information Officer, Waupun Memorial Hospital, Waupun, WI, p. A713
BISCONE, Mark A.
Chief Executive Officer, Pen Bay Medical Center, Rockport, ME, p. A292
Chief Executive Officer, Waldo County General Hospital, Belfast, ME, p. A289
BISDORF, Jonathan, Director Information Technology, Ohio Valley Surgical Hospital, Springfield, OH, p. A497
BISH, Carol, Human Resources Coordinator, North Greenville Hospital, Travelers Rest, SC, p. A565
BISHARA, Reemon, M.D. Medical Director, Coastal Harbor Treatment Center, Savannah, GA, p. A164
BISHOP, Amy Leigh, Director Human Resources, Red Bay Hospital, Red Bay, AL, p. A24
BISHOP, Bill, Chief Information Officer, Colquitt Regional Medical Center, Moultrie, GA, p. A162
BISHOP, Bryan, Chief Financial Officer, Heartland Behavioral Health Services, Nevada, MO, p. A373
BISHOP, Clint, Program Manager, Marion Veterans Affairs Medical Center, Marion, IL, p. A193
BISHOP, Elizabeth, Manager Business Office, Salina Surgical Hospital, Salina, KS, p. A250
BISHOP, Janice E., R.N. Chief Nursing Officer, Tewksbury Hospital, Tewksbury, MA, p. A312
BISHOP, John
Chief Financial Officer, Long Beach Memorial Medical Center, Long Beach, CA, p. A68
Chief Executive Officer and Chief Financial Officer, Madison Valley Medical Center, Ennis, MT, p. A383
Chief Executive Officer and Chief Financial Officer, Madison Valley Medical Center, Ennis, MT, p. A383
BISHOP, Steve, Chief Financial Officer, UP Health System–Portage, Hancock, MI, p. A322
BISIGNANI, Thomas, Chief Financial Officer, Moses Taylor Hospital, Scranton, PA, p. A549
BISSEL, Jane, Chief Financial Officer, Parkview Wabash County Hospital, Wabash, IN, p. A221
BISSELL, John, Chief Information Officer, Hutchinson Regional Medical Center, Hutchinson, KS, p. A242
BISSENDEN, Chris, Director Human Resources, Ogden Regional Medical Center, Ogden, UT, p. A656
BISSONETTE, Christine, R.N. Service Line Director for Acute Services, Kalkaska Memorial Health Center, Kalkaska, MI, p. A324
BISSONNETTE, Andre, Chief Financial Officer, North Country Hospital and Health Center, Newport, VT, p. A660
BISTERFELDT, Joanne, Chief Information Officer, Wheaton Franciscan Healthcare – All Saints, Racine, WI, p. A709
BITAR, Adib, M.D. Medical Director, Aurora Charter Oak Hospital, Covina, CA, p. A59
BITAR, Ali, M.D. Vice President Medical Affairs, Rehabilitation Institute of Michigan, Detroit, MI, p. A318
BITHER, Dean, Chief Financial Officer, Inland Hospital, Waterville, ME, p. A292
BITNER, Janet
Chief Operating Officer, Texas NeuroRehab Center, Austin, TX, p. A595
Chief Operating Officer, Texas Star Recovery, Austin, TX, p. A595
BITSILLY, Christina, Human Resource Specialist, U. S. Public Health Service Indian Hospital, Crownpoint, NM, p. A424
BITSOLI, Deborah, Chief Operating Officer, Saint Vincent Hospital, Worcester, MA, p. A313
BITTNER, Augustine, Chief Information Officer, Robley Rex Veterans Affairs Medical Center, Louisville, KY, p. A262
BITTNER, David, Chief Financial Officer, Mount Sinai Rehabilitation Hospital, Hartford, CT, p. A112
BIUSO, Joseph, M.D. Vice President and Chief of Medical Affairs, Floyd Medical Center, Rome, GA, p. A163
BIVIN, Richard, M.D. President Medical Staff, Abraham Lincoln Memorial Hospital, Lincoln, IL, p. A193
BIXLER, David, Chief Executive Officer, Daviess Community Hospital, Washington, IN, p. A221
BIXLER, Jacquelyn, Vice President Human Resources, BryLin Hospitals, Buffalo, NY, p. A430
BJARNASON, Dana, R.N. Vice President and Chief Nursing Officer, OHSU Hospital, Portland, OR, p. A524
BJELICH, Steven C., President and Chief Executive Officer, Saint Francis Medical Center, Cape Girardeau, MO, p. A364
BJELLA, Karmon T., Chief Executive Officer, Alpena Regional Medical Center, Alpena, MI, p. A314
BJERKE, Carolyn, Director Human Resources, Mercy Hospital Kingfisher, Kingfisher, OK, p. A508
BJERKNES, Dan, Director Human Resources, Mercy Medical Center, Williston, ND, p. A477
BJORDAHL, Kevin, M.D. Chief Medical Officer, Milbank Area Hospital Avera, Milbank, SD, p. A569
BJORK, David, M.D. Chief Medical Officer, Prairie Ridge Hospital and Health Services, Elbow Lake, MN, p. A338
BJORNBERG, Christopher R., Chief Executive Officer, Warren Memorial Hospital, Friend, NE, p. A392
BJORNSTAD, Brad, M.D. Vice President and Chief Medical Officer, Florida Hospital Tampa, Tampa, FL, p. A144
BLACK, Amy, Risk Manager/PI Director, Brynn Marr Hospital, Jacksonville, NC, p. A463
BLACK, Amy, R.N. Chief Operating Officer, Martha Jefferson Hospital, Charlottesville, VA, p. A663
BLACK, Chad, Director Information Technology, Crossroads Community Hospital, Mount Vernon, IL, p. A195
BLACK, Jr., Charles, Chief Financial Officer, Rockcastle Regional Hospital and Respiratory Care Center, Mount Vernon, KY, p. A263
BLACK, Douglas, President, Barnes–Jewish West County Hospital, Saint Louis, MO, p. A376
BLACK, Gary E., President and Chief Executive Officer, Lenoir Memorial Hospital, Kinston, NC, p. A463
BLACK, Marcey, Chief Financial Officer, Northwest Florida Community Hospital, Chipley, FL, p. A123
BLACK, Maria, MSN Nurse Administrator, American Fork Hospital, American Fork, UT, p. A654
BLACK, Marilynn
Chief Information Officer and Vice President, Flagstaff Medical Center, Flagstaff, AZ, p. A31
Chief Information Officer, Verde Valley Medical Center, Cottonwood, AZ, p. A30
BLACK, Michael, Director Human Resources, East Georgia Regional Medical Center, Statesboro, GA, p. A165
BLACK, Paul S.
Controller, H. C. Watkins Memorial Hospital, Quitman, MS, p. A360
Chief Financial Officer, Scott Regional Hospital, Morton, MS, p. A358
Interim Administrator, Winston Medical Center, Louisville, MS, p. A356
BLACK, Robert O., Chief Executive Officer, Linton Hospital, Linton, ND, p. A475
BLACK, Ronald, M.D. Chief of Staff, Clark Fork Valley Hospital, Plains, MT, p. A386
BLACK, Terri, Network Manager, Lucas County Health Center, Chariton, IA, p. A224
BLACK, Tim, Director Human Resources, Timpanogos Regional Hospital, Orem, UT, p. A657
BLACKBEAR, Annabelle, Human Resources Specialist, U. S. Public Health Service Indian Hospital, Pine Ridge, SD, p. A570
BLACKBURN, Lisa R., Director Human Resources, St. Margaret's Hospital, Spring Valley, IL, p. A201
BLACKBURN, Mary, Vice President Operations and Chief Practice Officer, Hugh Chatham Memorial Hospital, Elkin, NC, p. A460
BLACKBURN, Susan, Chief Operating Officer, Providence St. Mary Medical Center, Walla Walla, WA, p. A687
BLACKFORD, Nate, Chief Operating Officer, Northwest Medical Center, Albany, MO, p. A363
BLACKHAM, Cami, R.N. Nurse Administrator, Sevier Valley Medical Center, Richfield, UT, p. A657
BLACKHURST, Kristi, Interim Vice President Operations, Asante Rogue Regional Medical Center, Medford, OR, p. A523
BLACKMAN, Jay H., Senior Vice President and Chief Operating Officer, Howard County General Hospital, Columbia, MD, p. A297
BLACKMON, Jenean
Assistant Vice President and Chief Information Officer, McLeod Medical Center Dillon, Dillon, SC, p. A560
Associate Vice President and Chief Information Officer, McLeod Regional Medical Center, Florence, SC, p. A561
BLACKWELL, Dawn, R.N. VP, Patient Care Services, Memorial Healthcare, Owosso, MI, p. A327
BLACKWELL, Jack, Chief Financial Officer, Highlands Regional Medical Center, Prestonsburg, KY, p. A265
BLACKWELL, James, Chief Executive Officer, Clara Barton Hospital, Hoisington, KS, p. A241
BLACKWELL, Lenore, Director Human Resources, Harton Regional Medical Center, Tullahoma, TN, p. A588
BLACKWELL, Timothy, Manager Human Resources, Rolling Hills Hospital, Ada, OK, p. A503
BLACKWOOD, Jim, Chief Executive Officer, Tallahatchie General Hospital, Charleston, MS, p. A351
BLAD, Nathan, Chief Executive Officer, RC Hospital and Clinics, Olivia, MN, p. A344
BLADEN, Anthony M., Vice President Human Resources, Calvert Memorial Hospital, Prince Frederick, MD, p. A299
BLAHA, Bill, Manager Information Technology, Tri–County Hospital, Wadena, MN, p. A348
BLAHA, John E., Vice President Finance and Chief Financial Officer, Brattleboro Retreat, Brattleboro, VT, p. A660
BLAHNIK, David, Chief Operating Officer, Twin Valley Behavioral Healthcare, Columbus, OH, p. A487
BLAIN, Brenda K., FACHE Chief Nursing Officer and Chief Operating Officer, Baylor Medical Center at Irving, Irving, TX, p. A624
BLAIR, Betsy, R.N. Chief Operating Officer, Chippenham Hospital, Richmond, VA, p. A671
BLAIR, Brenda, Vice President Human Resources, Alice Peck Day Memorial Hospital, Lebanon, NH, p. A406
BLAIR, Diane, Human Resources and Admissions, CHI Health Plainview, Plainview, NE, p. A397
BLAIR, Heidi L., Vice President Administration, Manatee Glens Hospital and Addiction Center, Bradenton, FL, p. A122
BLAIR, Jan, Director Human Resources, Clinton Memorial Hospital, Wilmington, OH, p. A501
BLAIR, Judy, Senior Vice President Clinical Services and Chief Nursing Officer, Glendale Adventist Medical Center, Glendale, CA, p. A63
BLAIR, Mark, M.D. Medical Director, Dublin Springs, Dublin, OH, p. A489
BLAIR, Jr., Raymond W., M.D. Chief of Staff, Ennis Regional Medical Center, Ennis, TX, p. A612
BLAIR, Robert D., Chief Executive Officer, Spine Hospital of Louisiana (formally the NeuroMedical Center Surgical Hospital), Baton Rouge, LA, p. A270
BLAKE, Alan, M.D. President Medical Staff, Samaritan Lebanon Community Hospital, Lebanon, OR, p. A522
BLAKE, Daphne, R.N. Chief Nursing Officer, Guadalupe Regional Medical Center, Seguin, TX, p. A643
BLAKE, Diane, Chief Executive Officer, Cascade Medical Center, Leavenworth, WA, p. A680
BLAKE, Kelly, Chief Executive Officer, Select Specialty Hospital–Johnstown, Johnstown, PA, p. A537
BLAKE, Robert, Chief Human Resources Officer Southwest Market, Memorial Hermann Sugar Land Hospital, Sugar Land, TX, p. A645
BLAKE, Robert, M.D
Chief of Staff, St. Joseph's Hospital of Buckhannon, Buckhannon, WV, p. A690
Chief Medical Officer, The HSC Pediatric Center, Washington, DC, p. A120
BLAKE, Sheryl Lewis, FACHE, President, Spectrum Health Pennock, Hastings, MI, p. A322
BLAKE, Skylier, R.N. Director of Nursing, El Paso LTAC Hospital, El Paso, TX, p. A610
BLAKELY, Michelle, Associate Director, Jesse Brown Veterans Affairs Medical Center, Chicago, IL, p. A182
BLAKEMORE, Chris, Interim Chief Information Officer, Good Shepherd Medical Center, Longview, TX, p. A629
BLAKENEY, Dell, Vice President and Chief Information Officer, South Central Regional Medical Center, Laurel, MS, p. A356
BLAKEY GORMAN, Mary, Director Human Resources, Northwest Missouri Psychiatric Rehabilitation Center, Saint Joseph, MO, p. A375
BLALOCK, Andy, M.D. Physician Executive, Our Lady of Lourdes Regional Medical Center, Lafayette, LA, p. A278
BLALOCK, Cam, Senior Vice President Corporate Services, Nash Health Care Systems, Rocky Mount, NC, p. A467
BLALOCK, Tracey, Chief Nursing Officer, Medical Center, Navicent Health, Macon, GA, p. A160
BLANC, Linda, R.N. Administrative Director of Nursing, Jefferson Medical Center, Ranson, WV, p. A694
BLANCHARD, Timothy D., Chief Financial Officer, Kingman Regional Medical Center, Kingman, AZ, p. A32
BLANCHARD, Wayne D., Chief Executive Officer, Kindred Hospital–Louisville, Louisville, KY, p. A261
BLANCHARD, William R., Chief Executive Officer, DeTar Healthcare System, Victoria, TX, p. A650
BLANCHETTE, Edward A., M.D., Director, Connecticut Department of Correction's Hospital, Somers, CT, p. A115
BLANCO, Andres, Director Management Information Systems, Westside Regional Medical Center, Plantation, FL, p. A140
BLANCO, Carlos, M.D.,
Administrator, Doctor's Center of Bayamon, Bayamon, PR, p. A720
Administrator, Doctors Center, Manati, PR, p. A721
BLAND, David, Chief Executive Officer, South Davis Community Hospital, Bountiful, UT, p. A654
BLAND, Douglas, Manager Information Services, Spring View Hospital, Lebanon, KY, p. A259
BLAND, James G., M.D. Chief of Staff, Jane Todd Crawford Hospital, Greensburg, KY, p. A257
BLANDING, Carlene, Commander, Bayne–Jones Army Community Hospital, Fort Polk, LA, p. A273

A788 Index of Health Care Professionals 

Index of Health Care Professionals / Boerschel

Index of Health Care Professionals

BLANK, Arthur J., President and Chief Executive Officer, Mount Desert Island Hospital, Bar Harbor, ME, p. A288
BLANKE, Kerry Lee
Vice President Finance, New London Family Medical Center, New London, WI, p. A707
Director Financial Services, Riverside Medical Center, Waupaca, WI, p. A713
Chief Financial Officer, Shawano Medical Center, Shawano, WI, p. A710
BLANKENSHIP, Beth, Coordinator Human Resources, Norman Specialty Hospital, Norman, OK, p. A510
BLANKENSHIP, Diana, Director Human Resources, Welch Community Hospital, Welch, WV, p. A696
BLANKENSHIP, Jeff, CP
Vice President and Chief Financial Officer, Jackson–Madison County General Hospital, Jackson, TN, p. A579
Chief Financial Officer, Pathways of Tennessee, Jackson, TN, p. A579
BLANKENSHIP, Stacy, Chief Nursing Officer, Mercy Hospital Washington, Washington, MO, p. A380
BLANTON, Christina, Administrative Assistant and Human Resources Coordinator, Select Specialty Hospital–Knoxville, Knoxville, TN, p. A580
BLANTON, Forest
Senior VP and Chief Information Officer, Memorial Hospital Miramar, Miramar, FL, p. A136
Chief Information Officer, Memorial Hospital Pembroke, Pembroke Pines, FL, p. A139
Chief Information Officer, Memorial Hospital West, Pembroke Pines, FL, p. A139
Administrator Process Engineering, Memorial Regional Hospital, FL, p. A128
BLANTON, James
Chief Financial Officer, East Texas Medical Center Rehabilitation Hospital, Tyler, TX, p. A648
Chief Financial Officer, East Texas Medical Center Specialty Hospital, Tyler, TX, p. A648
BLANTON, Kevin, D.O. Chief of Staff, Goodall–Witcher Hospital Authority, Clifton, TX, p. A601
BLANTON, Marion, Chief Financial Officer, Minneola District Hospital, Minneola, KS, p. A246
BLANTON, Ron, Chief Fiscal Services, Boise Veterans Affairs Medical Center, Boise, ID, p. A172
BLAS, Phil, Chief Information Officer, John C. Fremont Healthcare District, Mariposa, CA, p. A74
BLASER, Karla, Director Human Resources, UnityPoint Health – Trinity Muscatine, Muscatine, IA, p. A232
BLASINGAME, Billy, Administrator and Chief Executive Officer, Norman Specialty Hospital, Norman, OK, p. A510
BLASIUS, Rita, Assistant Administrator and Chief Financial Officer, Avera St. Benedict Health Center, Parkston, SD, p. A570
BLASKO, Edward, Chief of Staff, Carolinas HealthCare System Anson, Wadesboro, NC, p. A470
BLAUER, Michael, Administrator, St. Luke's Elmore, Mountain Home, ID, p. A175
BLAUWET, Judy, M.P.H. Senior Vice President Operations and Chief Nursing Officer, Avera McKennan Hospital and University Health Center, Sioux Falls, SD, p. A571
BLAYLOCK, Darrell, Chief Executive Officer, Tennova Healthcare – Volunteer Community Hospital, Martin, TN, p. A582
BLAYLOCK, Kevin, Chief Executive Officer, Oklahoma Spine Hospital, Oklahoma City, OK, p. A512
BLAYLOCK, L. Dwayne, Chief Executive Officer, Merit Health River Oaks, Flowood, MS, p. A352
BLAZAKIS, Shelly, Director Human Resources Services, Scripps Memorial Hospital–La Jolla, La Jolla, CA, p. A66
BLAZEK, Dennis, Chief Information Officer, Clarke County Hospital, Osceola, IA, p. A232
BLAZIER, Patty, Chief Nursing Officer, Hamilton Memorial Hospital District, McLeansboro, IL, p. A194
BLEAK, Jason, Administrator and Chief Executive Officer, Grover C. Dils Medical Center, Caliente, NV, p. A400
BLECHA, Timothy, M.D. Medical Director, Brodstone Memorial Hospital, Superior, NE, p. A398
BLEDSOE, Cindy, Chief Executive Officer, Forest Park Medical Center, Dallas, TX, p. A605
BLEDSOE, Kristi, R.N., Administrator, St. Vincent Frankfort Hospital, Frankfort, IN, p. A209
BLEDSOE, Richard, Director Information Systems, Mary Black Health System – Gaffney, Gaffney, SC, p. A561
BLESI, Michael, Director Information Technology, Rainy Lake Medical Center, International Falls, MN, p. A340
BLESSING, Brian, Chief Financial Officer, Texas Health Harris Methodist Hospital Azle, Azle, TX, p. A595
BLEVINS, Denzil, Director Information Systems, Montgomery General Hospital, Montgomery, WV, p. A693
BLEVINS, Heather, Director Human Resources, HEALTHSOUTH Rehabilitation of Gadsden, Gadsden, AL, p. A20
BLEVINS, Matthew H., Chief Operating Officer, Gateway Regional Medical Center, Granite City, IL, p. A189
BLEVINS, Pam, R.N. Director, Clinical Informatics, Blue Ridge Regional Hospital, Spruce Pine, NC, p. A469
BLIGHTON, Gordon, Director Resource Management, Naval Hospital Camp Pendleton, Camp Pendleton, CA, p. A57
BLINCO, Lynne, Associate Vice President, Edwin Shaw Rehab, Cuyahoga Falls, OH, p. A487
BLIVEN, Donna, Vice President Patient Care Services and Chief Nursing Officer, Jones Memorial Hospital, Wellsville, NY, p. A453
BLOB, Burchkhard, Manager Human Resources, Central Virginia Training Center, Madison Heights, VA, p. A667
BLOCHLINGER, Pamela, Acting Vice President Finance, Cloud County Health Center, Concordia, KS, p. A238
BLOCK, Annie, Director Human Resources, Poplar Community Hospital, Poplar, MT, p. A386
BLOCK, Deborah, Vice President Nursing and Chief Nursing Officer, Oconee Regional Medical Center, Milledgeville, GA, p. A161
BLOCK, Sherri, Chief Operating Officer, Vista Del Mar Hospital, Ventura, CA, p. A96
BLODGETT, Debbie, Director of Fiscal Services, Ochiltree General Hospital, Perryton, TX, p. A636
BLOEMER, Brad, Vice President Finance and Chief Financial Officer, Arkansas Methodist Medical Center, Paragould, AR, p. A49
BLOEMKER, Jeff, Chief Executive Officer, I–70 Community Hospital, Sweet Springs, MO, p. A379
BLOM, David P., President and Chief Executive Officer, OhioHealth, Columbus, OH, p. B101
BLOMELEY, Geoff, Interim Chief Financial Officer, AllianceHealth Ponca City, Ponca City, OK, p. A514
BLOMQUIST, David, Director Information Technology, McKenzie–Willamette Medical Center, Springfield, OR, p. A526
BLOMSTEDT, Jason, Chief of Staff, Community Hospital, McCook, NE, p. A394
BLOND, Carl, M.D. Chief of Staff, Connally Memorial Medical Center, Floresville, TX, p. A612
BLOOD, Barbara
Director Human Resources, Lourdes Counseling Center, Richland, WA, p. A683
Executive Director Human Resources, Lourdes Medical Center, Pasco, WA, p. A682
Director Human Resources, Walla Walla General Hospital, Walla Walla, WA, p. A687
BLOOM, Jane, Ph.D. Chief Nursing Officer, Austen Riggs Center, Stockbridge, MA, p. A312
BLOOM, Laura, Director Human Resources, Coffee Regional Medical Center, Douglas, GA, p. A156
BLOUGH Jr., Daniel D., Chief Executive Officer, Punxsutawney Area Hospital, Punxsutawney, PA, p. A548
BLUE, Gaea, R.N., Administrator and Chief Executive Officer, Avera Weskota Memorial Hospital, Wessington Springs, SD, p. A573
BLUE, Jan L., Vice President Human Resources, Hoag Memorial Hospital Presbyterian, Newport Beach, CA, p. A77
BLUE, Lawrence, Administrator and Chief Executive Officer, Cavalier County Memorial Hospital, Langdon, ND, p. A475
BLUE, Lee Ann, MSN Chief Nursing Officer and Executive Vice President Patient Care Services, Eskenazi Health, Indianapolis, IN, p. A211
BLUE, Yvonne, Chief Operations Officer, Moore County Hospital District, Dumas, TX, p. A609
BLUHM, Tom, Director Information Systems, Island Hospital, Anacortes, WA, p. A676
BLUM, Carrie, Chief Information Officer, Monroe Clinic, Monroe, WI, p. A707
BLUM, Daniel, President, Phelps Memorial Hospital Center, Sleepy Hollow, NY, p. A450
BLUM, Donald A., M.D. Chief of Staff, Wetzel County Hospital, New Martinsville, WV, p. A693
BLUM, Walter B., M.D. Chief of Staff, McLeod Medical Center Dillon, Dillon, SC, p. A560
BLUNK, Jim, D.O. Chief Medical Officer, Sumner County Hospital District One, Caldwell, KS, p. A238
BLURTON, Cheri
Director Human Resources, HIPAA Privacy Officer, Great River Medical Center, Blytheville, AR, p. A41
Director Human Resources, South Mississippi County Regional Medical Center, Osceola, AR, p. A49
BLYTHE, Thomas W.
System Vice President Human Resources, Good Samaritan Regional Health Center, Mount Vernon, IL, p. A195
Vice President Human Resources, St. Mary's Hospital, Centralia, IL, p. A180
BOAL, Jeremy, M.D
Executive Vice President and Chief Medical Officer, Mount Sinai Beth Israel, New York, NY, p. A442
Executive Vice President and Chief Medical Officer, Mount Sinai St. Luke's – Roosevelt, New York, NY, p. A442
Executive Vice President and Chief Medical Officer, New York Eye and Ear Infirmary of Mount Sinai, New York, NY, p. A442
BOARD, Gloria, Director Human Resources, Liberty Healthcare Systems, Bastrop, LA, p. A269
BOARD, Patricia, Vice President Human Resources, Community Hospital of Bremen, Bremen, IN, p. A205
BOARDMAN, Debra K., FACHE, President and Chief Executive Officer, Range Regional Health Services, Hibbing, MN, p. A340
BOAS, Erik, Vice President Finance, University of Maryland Charles Regional Medical Center, La Plata, MD, p. A298
BOATMAN, Robert, Director Information Technology, Richmond State Hospital, Richmond, IN, p. A219
BOATRIGHT, Donna, MSN, Administrator, Rolling Plains Memorial Hospital, Sweetwater, TX, p. A646
BOATWRIGHT, Damond, Interim President, St. Mary's Hospital, Madison, WI, p. A704
BOBBITT, James, Vice President Human Resources, Saint Agnes Hospital, Baltimore, MD, p. A294
BOBBS, Kathy, FACHE, President and Chief Executive Officer, Regional Medical Center of Acadiana, Lafayette, LA, p. A278
BOBO, Matt, Chief Information Officer, Meade District Hospital, Meade, KS, p. A246
BOBSEINE, Shannon, Manager Human Resources, TLC Health Network – Lake Shore Hospital, Irving, NY, p. A435
BOCCELLATO, Judy, R.N. Chief Nursing Officer, Specialty Hospital of Central Jersey, Lakewood, NJ, p. A413
BOCHATON, Philippe, Chief Executive Officer, Lakeway Regional Medical Center, Lakeway, TX, p. A627
BOCKENEK, William, M.D. Chief Medical Officer, Carolinas Rehabilitation, Charlotte, NC, p. A457
BOCKMANN, Rick, Chief Executive Officer, Frank R. Howard Memorial Hospital, Willits, CA, p. A98
BOCKNEK, Marc, D.O. Vice President Medical Affairs, DMC Huron Valley–Sinai Hospital, Commerce Township, MI, p. A317
BODENHAM, Steve, Senior Manager Clinical Engineering, Indiana University Health North Hospital, Carmel, IN, p. A206
BODENMANN, Linda, Chief Operating Officer, Southcoast Hospitals Group, Fall River, MA, p. A306
BODENNER, Nancy, Director Human Resources, St. Joseph Health System, Tawas City, MI, p. A331
BODENSTEINER, Kim, Chief Financial Officer, Essentia Health Fosston, Fosston, MN, p. A339
BODIN, Donna L., Vice President, Woman's Hospital, Baton Rouge, LA, p. A270
BODINE, Maureen, Chief Clinical Officer, Kindred Hospital–San Diego, San Diego, CA, p. A86
BODLE, Vickie, Chief Financial Officer, Lake Chelan Community Hospital, Chelan, WA, p. A677
BODLOVIC, Kirk
Vice President and Chief Financial Officer, Providence St. Joseph Medical Center, Polson, MT, p. A386
Regional Chief Financial Officer, St. Patrick Hospital, Missoula, MT, p. A386
BODNAR, Darrell, Director Information, Weeks Medical Center, Lancaster, NH, p. A406
BODWELL, Amy, Vice President Finance, Methodist Richardson Medical Center, Richardson, TX, p. A638
BOECKMANN, Patricia, R.N. Vice President Operations and Chief Nursing Officer, Straub Clinic & Hospital, Honolulu, HI, p. A169
BOEHLER, Richard, M.D., President and Chief Executive Officer, St. Joseph Hospital, Nashua, NH, p. A407
BOEHM, Scott D., Executive Vice President Human Resources and Facilities, Sanford Bismarck, Bismarck, ND, p. A472
BOEHMER, Bernard, M.D. Medical Director, Cassia Regional Medical Center, Burley, ID, p. A173
BOEHNKE, Winnie, Director Human Resources, Timberlawn Mental Health System, Dallas, TX, p. A607
BOEMER, Sally Mason
Senior Vice President Finance, Massachusetts General Hospital, Boston, MA, p. A304
Chief Financial Officer, North Shore Medical Center, Salem, MA, p. A310
BOEMMEL, Michael, Vice President and Chief Financial Officer, MedStar National Rehabilitation Hospital, Washington, DC, p. A119
BOEN, Stefanie, Chief Nursing Officer, Skyline Hospital, White Salmon, WA, p. A687
BOER, Jeff, Director Information Technology, Pulaski Memorial Hospital, Winamac, IN, p. A221
BOERSCHEL, Viva, Director of Nursing, Floyd County Medical Center, Charles City, IA, p. A224

BOES, Jody, Vice President Patient Care Services, Ministry Door County Medical Center, Sturgeon Bay, WI, p. A712

BOESE, Chris, Vice President and Chief Nursing Officer, Regions Hospital, Saint Paul, MN, p. A346

BOGAN, James, FACHE, Interim Chief Executive Officer, UP Health System–Marquette, Marquette, MI, p. A325

BOGARD, Tim, Manager Information Technology, Highland District Hospital, Hillsboro, OH, p. A491

BOGEDAIN, Carol, FACHE, Director, Veterans Affairs Roseburg Healthcare System, Roseburg, OR, p. A525

BOGEN, Mark A., Senior Vice President and Chief Financial Officer, South Nassau Communities Hospital, Oceanside, NY, p. A446

BOGERS, Christina, Chief Clinical Officer, North Valley Hospital, Whitefish, MT, p. A388

BOGGAN Jr., Daniel, Interim Chief Executive Officer, Alameda Health System, San Leandro, CA, p. B8

BOGGESS, Carrie
    Human Resource Generalist, Carilion Giles Community Hospital, Pearisburg, VA, p. A670
    Human Resources Generalist, Carilion Tazewell Community Hospital, Tazewell, VA, p. A673

BOGGESS, Jack, Chief Executive Officer, Reliant Austin, Austin, TX, p. A594

BOGGS, Danny L., President and Chief Executive Officer, Samaritan Regional Health System, Ashland, OH, p. A478

BOGGS, Lynn Ingram, Chief Executive Officer, Porter Medical Center, Middlebury, VT, p. A660

BOGGS, Michael S., Chief Executive Officer, Regency Hospital of Central Georgia, Macon, GA, p. A161

BOGGUS, Bradley, Chief Financial Officer, Clinton Memorial Hospital, Wilmington, OH, p. A501

BOGLE, William J., Director Information Systems, North Arkansas Regional Medical Center, Harrison, AR, p. A45

BOGOLIN, Loretta, MSN Chief Nursing Officer and Vice President Care Services, Vassar Brothers Medical Center, Poughkeepsie, NY, p. A448

BOHALL, Karen, Director Human Resources, Woman's Christian Association Hospital, Jamestown, NY, p. A435

BOHATY, Richard, Director Information Technology, CHI Health St Elizabeth, Lincoln, NE, p. A393

BOHLMANN, Charles, Chief Executive Officer, Iroquois Memorial Hospital and Resident Home, Watseka, IL, p. A202

BOHNEN, Christa N., Director Human Resources, Ellsworth County Medical Center, Ellsworth, KS, p. A239

BOHNENKAMP, Russ, Chief Financial Officer, Chadron Community Hospital and Health Services, Chadron, NE, p. A391

BOICE, Sheila, Director Human Resources, Barton County Memorial Hospital, Lamar, MO, p. A371

BOIK, Reyne, Director Human Resources, Cascade Medical Center, Leavenworth, WA, p. A680

BOIKE, Darlene, Chief Financial Officer, Chippewa County–Montevideo Hospital, Montevideo, MN, p. A343

BOILEAU, Michel, M.D
    Chief Clinical Officer, Pioneer Memorial Hospital, Prineville, OR, p. A525
    Chief Clinical Officer, St. Charles Bend, Bend, OR, p. A519
    Chief Clinical Officer, St. Charles Redmond, Redmond, OR, p. A525

BOILY, Cindy, MSN Senior Vice President and Chief Nursing Officer, WakeMed Cary Hospital, Cary, NC, p. A456

BOIS, Alain, R.N. Director of Nursing, Northern Maine Medical Center, Fort Kent, ME, p. A290

BOISVERT, Gerald J., Vice President and Chief Financial Officer, Connecticut Children's Medical Center, Hartford, CT, p. A112

BOJO, Rolland, R.N. Chief Nursing Officer, Administrator Patient Care and Services, Catskill Regional Medical Center, Harris, NY, p. A435

BOJO, Rolland, R.N., Administrator, Grover M. Hermann Hospital, Callicoon, NY, p. A431

BOKA, Darin, Chief Information Officer, McLaren Oakland, Pontiac, MI, p. A328

BOKERN, Bob, Director Human Resources, St. Mary Medical Center, Long Beach, CA, p. A68

BOKHARI, Syed, M.D. Chief Medical Officer, Presence St. Mary's Hospital, Kankakee, IL, p. A192

BOKOVITZ, Beverly, R.N. Chief Nursing Officer, St. Anthony's Medical Center, Saint Louis, MO, p. A377

BOLAND, E. Kay, R.N. Vice President and Chief Nursing Officer, United Health Services Hospitals–Binghamton, Binghamton, NY, p. A430

BOLAND, Susan, MSN, President and Chief Executive Officer, Wheaton Franciscan Healthcare – All Saints, Racine, WI, p. A709

BOLANDER, Patrick C., Chief Financial Officer, Georgetown Community Hospital, Georgetown, KY, p. A257

BOLANO, Odette, R.N., Senior Vice President and Area Manager, Kaiser Permanente Oakland Medical Center, Oakland, CA, p. A78

BOLCAVAGE, Ted, Vice President Division Controller, Inpatient, OhioHealth Rehabilitation Hospital, Columbus, OH, p. A486

BOLDA, Craig, Chief Operating Officer, St. Catherine Hospital, East Chicago, IN, p. A207

BOLDING, Kay, R.N. Vice President Patient Care Services and Chief Nursing Officer, Jackson County Memorial Hospital, Altus, OK, p. A503

BOLDUC, Tiana, Chief Information Officer, Mercy Hospital Ozark, Ozark, AR, p. A49

BOLEN, David, Vice President and Chief Financial Officer, Passavant Area Hospital, Jacksonville, IL, p. A191

BOLEN, Shannon, Director Human Resources, Baptist Memorial Hospital–Booneville, Booneville, MS, p. A351

BOLES, Bonnie, M.D., Administrator, Tanner Medical Center–Villa Rica, Villa Rica, GA, p. A166

BOLES, Glen
    Vice President and Chief Financial Officer, CHRISTUS St. Michael Health System, Texarkana, TX, p. A647
    Vice President and Chief Financial Officer, CHRISTUS St. Michael Rehabilitation Hospital, Texarkana, TX, p. A647

BOLES, Lee, Assistant Administrator and Chief Financial Officer, Hunt Regional Medical Center, Greenville, TX, p. A617

BOLES, Mark D., Chief Executive Officer, Baylor Institute for Rehabilitation at Frisco, Frisco, TX, p. A615

BOLEWARE, Mike, Administrator, Franklin County Memorial Hospital, Meadville, MS, p. A357

BOLEY, Jason, M.D. Medical Director, Rock Prairie Behavioral Health, College Station, TX, p. A601

BOLEY, Sarah, Director Human Resources, Wetzel County Hospital, New Martinsville, WV, p. A693

BOLGER, Thomas, Chief Financial Officer, Chinese Hospital, San Francisco, CA, p. A88

BOLIN, Angie, Executive Administrative Assistant and Human Resources Manager, Black River Medical Center, Poplar Bluff, MO, p. A374

BOLIN, Cris, Chief Executive Officer, Delta Memorial Hospital, Dumas, AR, p. A43

BOLIN, Kerry F., Chief Nursing Officer, Mother Frances Hospital – Jacksonville, Jacksonville, TX, p. A624

BOLIN, Paul, Vice President Human Resources, The Acadia Hospital, Bangor, ME, p. A288

BOLINGER, John, M.D. Vice President Medical Affairs, Union Hospital, Terre Haute, IN, p. A220

BOLLARD, Robert, Chief Financial Officer, HEALTHSOUTH Rehabilitation Hospital – Henderson, Henderson, NV, p. A401

BOLLICH, Mary, Director of Nurses, AMG Specialty Hospital–Lafayette, Lafayette, LA, p. A277

BOLLIER, Sheila A., Chief Executive Officer, HEALTHSOUTH Rehabilitation Hospital of Cypress, Houston, TX, p. A620

BOLLINGER, Bill, Chief Information Officer, Carroll County Memorial Hospital, Carrollton, MO, p. A365

BOLLINGER, Bruce, M.D. Medical Director, Baylor Surgical Hospital at Fort Worth, Fort Worth, TX, p. A613

BOLLINGER, Candace, Director of Nursing, Mercy Hospital Booneville, Booneville, AR, p. A42

BOLLMANN, Brett, Administrator, Memorial Hospital, Chester, IL, p. A181

BOLLONE, Ann M., Vice President Human Resources, Flagstaff Medical Center, Flagstaff, AZ, p. A31

BOLOGNANI, Laurie, Human Resources Officer, Speare Memorial Hospital, Plymouth, NH, p. A408

BOLOR, Erlinda, R.N. Chief Nursing Officer, San Joaquin General Hospital, French Camp, CA, p. A62

BOLT, Elizabeth T., Chief Human Resources Officer, University of Wisconsin Hospital and Clinics, Madison, WI, p. A704

BOLTER, Cindy, Chief Nursing and Operations Officer, John Muir Behavioral Health Center, Concord, CA, p. A58

BOLTON, Jeffrey W., Chief Administrative Officer, Mayo Clinic Hospital – Rochester, Rochester, MN, p. A345

BOMAR, Jacob, Director Information Technology, Hardin Medical Center, Savannah, TN, p. A587

BOMBA, Douglas, Chief Financial Officer, Cameron Memorial Community Hospital, Angola, IN, p. A204

BOMERSBACH, Karen, Chief Financial Officer, Dallas Medical Center, Dallas, TX, p. A604

BOMSTAD, Heather, R.N. Chief Nursing Officer, OSF Saint Paul Medical Center, Mendota, IL, p. A194

BONACQUISTI, Gary, M.D. Chief Medical Officer, Texas Health Presbyterian Hospital of Rockwall, Rockwall, TX, p. A639

BONAR, Carrie, Chief Information Officer, Southern California Hospital at Culver City, Culver City, CA, p. A59

BONAR, Lynette, Chief Executive Officer, Tuba City Regional Health Care Corporation, Tuba City, AZ, p. A38

BONAR Jr., Robert, Chief Executive Officer, Children's Hospitals and Clinics of Minnesota, Minneapolis, MN, p. A342

BONAR Jr., Robert I., Chief Executive Officer, Dell Children's Medical Center of Central Texas, Austin, TX, p. A594

BONCZEK, Mary Ellen, R.N. Chief Nursing Executive, New Hanover Regional Medical Center, Wilmington, NC, p. A470

BOND, Lee, Chief Financial Officer, Singing River Health System, Pascagoula, MS, p. A359

BOND, Rodney, Director Information Technology, Northern Hospital of Surry County, Mount Airy, NC, p. A465

BOND, Sharon, Director Human Resources, College Station Medical Center, College Station, TX, p. A601

BONDI, Blaise, Chief Financial Officer, Centennial Medical Center, Frisco, TX, p. A615

BONDS, Cyrillia, Administrator, United Medical Rehabilitation Hospital, Hammond, LA, p. A274

BONDURANT, Barry, Administrator and Chief Executive Officer, Baptist Memorial Hospital–Union City, Union City, TN, p. A589

BONDURANT, Charles, Chief Information Officer, Meadows Regional Medical Center, Vidalia, GA, p. A166

BONECUTTER, Dane, Director Human Resources, Connally Memorial Medical Center, Floresville, TX, p. A612

BONFILIO, Nicholas, M.D. Chief of Staff, Great Falls Clinic Medical Center, Great Falls, MT, p. A384

BONI, Shirley M., Administrative Officer, U. S. Public Health Service Indian Hospital, San Carlos, AZ, p. A37

BONILLA, Felicita, Administrator, Hospital De La Concepcion, San German, PR, p. A722

BONILLA, Tony, Chief Executive Officer, Healthbridge Children's Hospital of Houston, Houston, TX, p. A619

BONIN, Stephanie, Administrator, Acadia Optima Hospital, Lafayette, LA, p. A277

BONK, Daniel J., Chief Executive Officer, Aspen Valley Hospital District, Aspen, CO, p. A99

BONNELL, Jay, Controller, Beaumont Hospital – Wayne, Wayne, MI, p. A332

BONNER, Gwen, Chief Operating Officer, Saint Francis Hospital–Bartlett, Bartlett, TN, p. A574

BONNER, Lauren, Director Human Resources, Cumberland Hospital, New Kent, VA, p. A668

BONNER, Lenne
    Interim President, Clearwater Valley Hospital and Clinics, Orofino, ID, p. A175
    Chief Financial Officer, Clearwater Valley Hospital and Clinics, Orofino, ID, p. A175
    Interim President, St. Mary's Hospital, Cottonwood, ID, p. A174
    Chief Financial Officer, St. Mary's Hospital, Cottonwood, ID, p. A174

BONNER, Robert
    Chief Financial Officer, Glendora Community Hospital, Glendora, CA, p. A64
    Chief Financial Officer, Montclair Hospital Medical Center, Montclair, CA, p. A76
    Chief Financial Officer, San Dimas Community Hospital, San Dimas, CA, p. A87

BONNETTE, James C., M.D. Chief Clinical Officer, Genesys Regional Medical Center, Grand Blanc, MI, p. A320

BONNICHSEN, Daniel G., Deputy Commander for Administration, Irwin Army Community Hospital, Junction City, KS, p. A243

BONO, Jenny, Chief Financial Officer, Allen Parish Hospital, Kinder, LA, p. A276

BONOMO, Carrie, M.D. Chief of Staff, Riverland Medical Center, Ferriday, LA, p. A273

BONSER, Kathleen, R.N. Vice President Nursing and Chief Nursing Officer, SSM DePaul Health Center, Bridgeton, MO, p. A364

BONTHUIS, Michael W., Chief Financial Officer, PeaceHealth United General Medical Center, Sedro–Woolley, WA, p. A684

BONZO, Kelly, Director, Baptist Health Richmond, Richmond, KY, p. A265

BOO, Thomas, M.D. Chief of Staff, Northern Inyo Hospital, Bishop, CA, p. A56

BOOHER, Terresa O., Vice President of Patient Care Services, Highlands Regional Medical Center, Prestonsburg, KY, p. A265

BOOKER, Angela, Director of Nursing Services, Teton Valley Health Care, Driggs, ID, p. A174

BOOM, Marc L., M.D., Chief Executive Officer, Houston Methodist, Houston, TX, p. B71

BOONE, Bradley, M.D. Chief Medical Staff, Anderson Regional Medical Center–South Campus, Meridian, MS, p. A357

BOONE, David J., Senior Vice President, Finance, Catawba Valley Medical Center, Hickory, NC, p. A462

BOONE, Donna, R.N. Chief Nursing Officer, Weatherford Regional Medical Center, Weatherford, TX, p. A650

BOONE III, Elwood Bernard, FACHE, President, Sentara Virginia Beach General Hospital, Virginia Beach, VA, p. A674

BOONE, Margie, Registered Health Information Technician, Cumberland River Hospital, Celina, TN, p. A574

BOONE, Richard, Chief Financial Officer, Johnson City Medical Center, Johnson City, TN, p. A580

Index of Health Care Professionals

Index of Health Care Professionals / Bowers

BOWERS, Melodee, Director Human Resources, Carle Hoopeston Regional Health Center, Hoopeston, IL, p. A191
BOWERS, Michael, Interim Director for Administration, Naval Hospital Oak Harbor, Oak Harbor, WA, p. A681
BOWERS, Michael E., President, SSM St. Joseph Health Center, Saint Charles, MO, p. A375
BOWERS, Sharon, R.N. Manager of Community, Public and Employee Relations, Sheridan Community Hospital, Sheridan, MI, p. A330
BOWERS, Shelby, Director Marketing and Public Relations, Peninsula Hospital, Louisville, TN, p. A582
BOWERS, Tracy, Director Human Resources, Novant Health Prince William Medical Center, Manassas, VA, p. A667
BOWERSOX, Bruce D., Chief Executive Officer, Nelson County Health System, Mcville, ND, p. A476
BOWES, Arthur, Senior Vice President Human Resources, North Shore Medical Center, Salem, MA, p. A310
BOWES, William, Chief Financial Officer, UAMS Medical Center, Little Rock, AR, p. A47
BOWIE, Joshua, Chief Executive Officer, Yuma Rehabilitation Hospital, Yuma, AZ, p. A40
BOWLEG, Teresa, R.N. Chief Nursing Officer, Murphy Medical Center, Murphy, NC, p. A465
BOWLES, Patrica, R.N. Chief Nursing Officer, Franklin County Medical Center, Preston, ID, p. A176
BOWLES, Tara, Employee Relations Director, Rawlins County Health Center, Atwood, KS, p. A237
BOWLING, Donald, M.D. Chief Medical Staff, Southampton Memorial Hospital, Franklin, VA, p. A665
BOWLING, Judy, Director Human Resources, Southeast Health Center of Stoddard County, Dexter, MO, p. A366
BOWLING, Kay, Chief Executive Officer, Center for Restorative Care and Rehabilitation, Lynchburg, VA, p. A667
BOWLING, Kelli, Chief Culture Officer, Ministry Door County Medical Center, Sturgeon Bay, WI, p. A712
BOWLING, Nancy, Director Human Resources, Shoals Hospital, Muscle Shoals, AL, p. A23
BOWMAN, Barbara, Chief Human Resource Officer, Ann & Robert H. Lurie Children's Hospital of Chicago, Chicago, IL, p. A181
BOWMAN, Dyan, Director Human Resources, Newberry County Memorial Hospital, Newberry, SC, p. A564
BOWMAN, Joseph E., Chief Financial Officer, TriStar StoneCrest Medical Center, Smyrna, TN, p. A588
BOWMAN, Ken, Chief Executive Officer, Van Matre HealthSouth Rehabilitation Hospital, Rockford, IL, p. A200
BOWMAN, Mark, M.D. President Medical Staff, Tillamook Regional Medical Center, Tillamook, OR, p. A526
BOWMAN, Maureen, Vice President of Nursing and Chief Nursing Officer, Beaumont Hospital – Royal Oak, Royal Oak, MI, p. A328
BOWMAN, Scott, Administrator, Sweetwater Hospital, Sweetwater, TN, p. A588
BOWMAN, William, M.D. Vice President Medical Affairs, Moses H. Cone Memorial Hospital, Greensboro, NC, p. A461
BOWMER, Carolyn,Lawrence Memorial Hospital, Lawrence, KS, p. A244
BOWSER, John, Vice President, Chief Financial Officer, OSF Saint Luke Medical Center, Kewanee, IL, p. A192
BOX, Darrel, Chief Executive Officer, Lafayette Regional Health Center, Lexington, MO, p. A372
BOX, Tom, CPA Chief Financial Officer, HEALTHSOUTH Rehabilitation Hospital–Wichita Falls, Wichita Falls, TX, p. A652
BOXELL, Shelley, R.N. Interim Chief Operating Officer, Rehabilitation Hospital of Fort Wayne, Fort Wayne, IN, p. A209
BOYCE, Charlotte, Chief Nursing Officer, HEALTHSOUTH Rehabilitation Hospital Memphis–North, Memphis, TN, p. A583
BOYCE, Joe, M.D. Chief Technology Officer and Chief Medical Information Officer, Mosaic Life Care at St. Joseph, Saint Joseph, MO, p. A375
BOYD, Amy, Information Systems Manager, Vidant Beaufort Hospital, Washington, NC, p. A470
BOYD, Cathy, Chief Nursing Officer, Select Specialty Hospital–Pontiac, Pontiac, MI, p. A328
BOYD, Christopher L., Senior Vice President and Area Manager, Kaiser Permanente Santa Clara Medical Center, Santa Clara, CA, p. A91
BOYD, Dennis, Chief Financial Officer, St. Mark's Medical Center, La Grange, TX, p. A627
BOYD, Diana, Vice President Nursing, Union Hospital, Dover, OH, p. A489
BOYD, Ellen, Director Human Resources, Emanuel Medical Center, Swainsboro, GA, p. A165
BOYD, John W., PsyD,
 Chief Administrative Officer, Sutter Center for Psychiatry, Sacramento, CA, p. A85
 Chief Executive Officer, Sutter Solano Medical Center, Vallejo, CA, p. A96
BOYD Jr., Kenneth, President and Chief Executive Officer, McDonough District Hospital, Macomb, IL, p. A193
BOYD, Kim, Chief Financial Officer, Buchanan General Hospital, Grundy, VA, p. A665
BOYD, Larry, M.D. Chief of Staff, Pecos County Memorial Hospital, Fort Stockton, TX, p. A612
BOYD, Steven, R.N. Nurse Executive, Levi Hospital, Hot Springs National Park, AR, p. A46
BOYD, Travis, Manager, Information Technology, Mercy Hospital Lincoln, Troy, MO, p. A379
BOYER, Aurelia, Senior Vice President and Chief Information Officer, New York–Presbyterian Hospital, New York, NY, p. A443
BOYER, Charlene, Chief Nursing Officer, Kaiser Permanente Oakland Medical Center, Oakland, CA, p. A78
BOYER, Cheryl T.
 Vice President Human Resources, Levindale Hebrew Geriatric Center and Hospital, Baltimore, MD, p. A293
 Vice President Human Resources, Sinai Hospital of Baltimore, Baltimore, MD, p. A295
BOYER, Craig, Vice President Finance, Sanford Bemidji Medical Center, Bemidji, MN, p. A335
BOYER, Diana, Chief Information Officer, Columbus Regional Hospital, Columbus, IN, p. A206
BOYER, Jeanne, R.N. Director of Nurses, Parkland Health Center–Bonne Terre, Bonne Terre, MO, p. A363
BOYER, Jim, Vice President Information Technology and Chief Information Officer, Rush Memorial Hospital, Rushville, IN, p. A219
BOYER, Roderick, M.D. Medical Director, Select Specialty Hospital–Downriver, Wyandotte, MI, p. A332
BOYER, William, Chief Financial Officer, Community Memorial Hospital, Redfield, SD, p. A571
BOYKIN, Doyle, MSN, Administrator, Presbyterian Kaseman Hospital, Albuquerque, NM, p. A423
BOYLE, Donna, Director, West Palm Hospital, West Palm Beach, FL, p. A147
BOYLE, James W., M.D. Chief Medical Officer, UPMC Passavant, Pittsburgh, PA, p. A547
BOYLE, Kathy, R.N. Chief Nursing Officer, Denver Health, Denver, CO, p. A101
BOYLE, Lisa, M.D. Vice President Medical Affairs and Medical Director, MedStar Georgetown University Hospital, Washington, DC, p. A119
BOYLE, Patrick R.
 Vice President Human Resources, Geneva General Hospital, Geneva, NY, p. A434
 Vice President Human Resources, Soldiers and Sailors Memorial Hospital of Yates County, Penn Yan, NY, p. A447
BOYLE, Thomas W., Chief Financial Officer, St. Lawrence Rehabilitation Center, Lawrenceville, NJ, p. A413
BOYLES, Clay
 Director Human Resources, Peachford Behavioral Health System, Atlanta, GA, p. A150
 Executive Director, Human Resources, Piedmont Newnan Hospital, Newnan, GA, p. A162
BOYLES, George, Senior Vice President of Finance and Chief Financial Officer, Mercer Health, Coldwater, OH, p. A485
BOYLES, Lee, President, CHI St. Gabriel's Health, Little Falls, MN, p. A341
BOYLES, Mary Gen, Chief Nursing Officer, HEALTHSOUTH Rehabilitation Hospital of Altoona, Altoona, PA, p. A528
BOYNE, Barbara, Executive Director, Operations, Bethesda North Hospital, Cincinnati, OH, p. A482
BOYNTON, Jr., James P., Chief Financial Officer, Carolina Center for Behavioral Health, Greer, SC, p. A562
BOYNTON, Kimberly, President and Chief Executive Officer, Crouse Hospital, Syracuse, NY, p. A451
BOYNTON, Stephanie, Administrator, Erlanger Bledsoe Hospital, Pikeville, TN, p. A587
BOYSEN, Doug, Chief Legal Counsel and Vice President Human Resources, Good Samaritan Regional Medical Center, Corvallis, OR, p. A520
BOYSEN, James, M.D. Executive Medical Director, Texas NeuroRehab Center, Austin, TX, p. A595
BOYSEN, Joan, Chief Operating Officer, District One Hospital, Faribault, MN, p. A338
BOZELL, Jerry, Vice President, Human Resources, Jay County Hospital, Portland, IN, p. A218
BOZZUTO, Elizabeth, R.N. Chief Nursing Officer and Vice President, Saint Mary's Hospital, Waterbury, CT, p. A115
BRA, Nancy, Director Human Resources, Community Memorial Hospital, Syracuse, NE, p. A398
BRAAM, Richard, Vice President Finance, MedStar St. Mary's Hospital, Leonardtown, MD, p. A299
BRAASCH, David A., President, Alton Memorial Hospital, Alton, IL, p. A178
BRABAND, Jon D., FACHE, President and Chief Executive Officer, Glencoe Regional Health Services, Glencoe, MN, p. A339
BRACEY, Donny, Director Information Services, Marion General Hospital, Columbia, MS, p. A352
BRACK, Nancy, Vice President of Human Resources, Community Memorial Hospital, Syracuse, NE, p. A398
BRACKEN, Thomas H., M.D. Vice President Medical Affairs, Mille Lacs Health System, Onamia, MN, p. A344
BRACKETT, Lori, Director Human Resources, HEALTHSOUTH Bakersfield Rehabilitation Hospital, Bakersfield, CA, p. A55
BRACKLEY, Donna, R.N. Senior Vice President Patient Care Services, John Muir Medical Center, Concord, Concord, CA, p. A58
BRACKS, Adam, Chief Executive Officer, Southeast Health Center of Stoddard County, Dexter, MO, p. A366
BRACY, Dale, Chief Financial Officer, College Hospital Costa Mesa, Costa Mesa, CA, p. A59
BRADA, Stephen, Chief of Staff, Aurora BayCare Medical Center, Green Bay, WI, p. A701
BRADBURY, Monica, Chief Executive Officer, Clarks Summit State Hospital, Clarks Summit, PA, p. A531
BRADDOCK, Mary B., Director Human Resources, Palo Pinto General Hospital, Mineral Wells, TX, p. A632
BRADEN, III, Terence, D.O. Medical Director, HEALTHSOUTH Rehabilitation Hospital of Jonesboro, Jonesboro, AR, p. A46
BRADEY, Sarah, Vice President Finance, CHI St. Vincent Hot Springs, Hot Springs, AR, p. A45
BRADFORD, Anna, R.N. Chief Nursing Officer, Crosbyton Clinic Hospital, Crosbyton, TX, p. A603
BRADFORD, Beth, Director Human Resources, Floyd Medical Center, Rome, GA, p. A163
BRADFORD, Randy L., Chief Executive Officer, Eastern Shore Hospital Center, Cambridge, MD, p. A296
BRADFORD, Scot, Chief Information Officer, Baylor Medical Center at Trophy Club, Trophy Club, TX, p. A648
BRADFORD, Susan, Director Nursing, Kansas Heart Hospital, Wichita, KS, p. A252
BRADICK, Joe, Chief Financial Officer, Willow Springs Center, Reno, NV, p. A404
BRADLEY, Berninia, Director, Human Resources, Corona Regional Medical Center, Corona, CA, p. A58
BRADLEY, Betsy, Coordinator Performance Improvement, Central State Hospital, Milledgeville, GA, p. A161
BRADLEY, Carol, MS
 Senior Vice President and Chief Nursing Officer, Legacy Meridian Park Medical Center, Tualatin, OR, p. A527
 Senior Vice President and Chief Nursing Officer, Legacy Salmon Creek Medical Center, Vancouver, WA, p. A687
BRADLEY, Connie, R.N
 Chief Nursing Officer, Health First Cape Canaveral Hospital, Cocoa Beach, FL, p. A124
 Senior Vice President and Chief Nursing Officer, Health First Palm Bay Hospital, Palm Bay, FL, p. A138
 Senior Vice President and Chief Nursing Officer, Health First Viera Hospital, Melbourne, FL, p. A133
BRADLEY, Deidre, Vice President Human Resources, Clark Regional Medical Center, Winchester, KY, p. A267
BRADLEY, Douglas, M.D. Chief Medical Officer, Belton Regional Medical Center, Belton, MO, p. A363
BRADLEY, Eric, Director Computer Information Services, Summit Behavioral Healthcare, Cincinnati, OH, p. A483
BRADLEY Jr., J. Lindsey, FACHE, President, Trinity Mother Frances Hospitals and Clinics, Tyler, TX, p. B137
BRADLEY, Linda, Chief Executive Officer, Centinela Hospital Medical Center, Inglewood, CA, p. A65
BRADLEY, Louis, Chief Executive Officer, Mesquite Specialty Hospital, Mesquite, TX, p. A632
BRADLEY, Melody, Chief Nursing Officer, Miracle Mile Medical Center, Los Angeles, CA, p. A71
BRADLEY, Michelle, Director Health Information Management, AMG Specialty Hospital–Wichita, Wichita, KS, p. A252
BRADLEY, Sam, M.D. Chief of Staff, Russell County Hospital, Russell Springs, KY, p. A265
BRADLEY, Sara, Chief Financial Officer, Oklahoma State University Medical Center, Tulsa, OK, p. A516
BRADLEY, Scott, Interim Chief Executive Officer, Houston County Community Hospital, Erin, TN, p. A577
BRADLEY, Stacye, R.N. Chief Nursing Officer, Union County General Hospital, Clayton, NM, p. A423
BRADLEY, Terri, CPA Vice President Financial Services and Chief Financial Officer, Western Missouri Medical Center, Warrensburg, MO, p. A380
BRADLEY, Virginia D., Chief Information Officer, Breckinridge Memorial Hospital, Hardinsburg, KY, p. A257
BRADLEY, William L., President and Chief Executive Officer, Washington Regional Medical Center, Fayetteville, AR, p. A44
BRADSHAW, Benjamin, M.D. President Medical Staff, Texas Health Presbyterian Hospital Kaufman, Kaufman, TX, p. A625

A792 Index of Health Care Professionals 

Index of Health Care Professionals / Breitenbach

Index of Health Care Professionals


BRADSHAW, David
Chief Information Officer, Memorial Hermann – Texas Medical Center, Houston, TX, p. A620
Chief Information, Planning and Marketing Officer, Memorial Hermann Memorial City Medical Center, Houston, TX, p. A621
Chief Information Officer, Memorial Hermann Northwest Hospital, Houston, TX, p. A621
Chief Information Officer, Memorial Hermann Rehabilitation Hospital – Katy, Katy, TX, p. A625
BRADSHAW, Rita, Director Human Resources, Chatuge Regional Hospital and Nursing Home, Hiawassee, GA, p. A158
BRADSHAW, Thomas A., Vice President Operations, Wayne Memorial Hospital, Goldsboro, NC, p. A461
BRADY, James, Area Information Officer, Kaiser Permanente Orange County Anaheim Medical Center, Anaheim, CA, p. A53
BRADY, Jeff
Director Information Systems, Hazard ARH Regional Medical Center, Hazard, KY, p. A258
Director Information Systems, McDowell ARH Hospital, McDowell, KY, p. A263
Director Information Systems, Morgan County ARH Hospital, West Liberty, KY, p. A266
Chief Information Officer, Tug Valley ARH Regional Medical Center, South Williamson, KY, p. A266
BRADY, John, Vice President Physician Services and Organizational Planning, Marianjoy Rehabilitation Hospital, Wheaton, IL, p. A203
BRADY, Karen, Chief Operating Officer and Chief Nursing Officer, Silverton Hospital, Silverton, OR, p. A526
BRADY, Kit, Vice President Human Resources, Gillette Children's Specialty Healthcare, Saint Paul, MN, p. A346
BRADY, Linda, M.D., President and Chief Executive Officer, Kingsbrook Jewish Medical Center, NY, p. A441
BRADY, Patrick R., Chief Executive Officer, Sutter Roseville Medical Center, Roseville, CA, p. A84
BRADY, Tim, Director Information Systems, Mt. Washington Pediatric Hospital, Baltimore, MD, p. A294
BRAGDON, Carol, Director Human Resources, Saint Thomas Rutherford Hospital, Murfreesboro, TN, p. A585
BRAGG, Craig, Chief Executive Officer, TrustPoint Hospital, Lubbock, TX, p. A630
BRAGG, Deborah, Director Human Resources, Webster County Memorial Hospital, Webster Springs, WV, p. A695
BRAGG, Lisa, Vice President Human Resources, Knox Community Hospital, Mount Vernon, OH, p. A495
BRAGG, Shelly, Director Human Resources, Valley Regional Hospital, Claremont, NH, p. A405
BRAILSFORD, Tammie McMann, Interim Chief Executive Officer, Long Beach Memorial Medical Center, Long Beach, CA, p. A68
BRAINERD, Mary K., President and Chief Executive Officer, HealthPartners, Bloomington, MN, p. B66
BRAINSTEIN, Paul, M.D. Interim Chief Medical Officer, Chesapeake Regional Medical Center, Chesapeake, VA, p. A663
BRAITHWAITE, Robert, President and Chief Executive Officer, Hoag Memorial Hospital Presbyterian, Newport Beach, CA, p. A77
BRAKE, Joe, Director Information Services, Fishermen's Hospital, Marathon, FL, p. A132
BRAKENHOFF, Jason, Director Information Services, Presbyterian–St. Luke's Medical Center, Denver, CO, p. A102
BRANAN, Annette, Chief Nursing Officer and Vice President Patient Care Services, Select Specialty Hospital – Northeast Atlanta, Atlanta, GA, p. A151
BRANCATO, Joyce A., Chief Executive Officer, Seven Rivers Regional Medical Center, Crystal River, FL, p. A124
BRANCEL, Dale, D.O. Chief of Staff, Victory Medical Center Mid–Cities, Hurst, TX, p. A624
BRANCH, Terrance, Chief Information Management, Fort Belvoir Community Hospital, Fort Belvoir, VA, p. A665
BRANCHICK, James, MS, Executive Director, Kaiser Permanente Downey Medical Center, Downey, CA, p. A60
BRAND, Debbie, Chief Nursing Officer, Carolina Pines Regional Medical Center, Hartsville, SC, p. A562
BRANDECKER, John A., Director, Hunter Holmes McGuire Veterans Affairs Medical Center–Richmond, Richmond, VA, p. A672
BRANDENBURG, Valerie, Director Human Resources, Northwest Hospital, Randallstown, MD, p. A299
BRANDIS, Destin, Chief Information Officer, William Bee Ririe Hospital, Ely, NV, p. A400
BRANDLER, Bruce, Administrator, Schick Shadel Hospital, Seattle, WA, p. A683
BRANDNER, Nicholas R., Chief Executive Officer, Freeman Regional Health Services, Freeman, SD, p. A569
BRANDON, David R., President and Chief Executive Officer, UnityPoint Health – Finley Hospital, Dubuque, IA, p. A227
BRANDON, Deborah, Director Total Quality Management, Eastern Louisiana Mental Health System, Jackson, LA, p. A275
BRANDON, Wendy H., Chief Executive Officer, Central Florida Regional Hospital, Sanford, FL, p. A142
BRANDSTATER, Ronda, Vice President Patient Care, Grandview Medical Center, Dayton, OH, p. A488
BRANDT, Debbie, Director Human Resources, Community Hospital, Munster, IN, p. A217
BRANDT, Matthew, Chief Financial Officer, St. Alexius Hospital – Broadway Campus, Saint Louis, MO, p. A377
BRANDT, Merle, Chief Financial Officer, Mason General Hospital, Shelton, WA, p. A684
BRANDT, Rob, Chief Executive Officer, Mountainview Medical Center, White Sulphur Springs, MT, p. A387
BRANDT, Steve, M.D. Chief of Staff, Dale Medical Center, Ozark, AL, p. A24
BRANN, Terry, Chief Financial Officer, MaineGeneral Medical Center, Augusta, ME, p. A288
BRANNAN, Debbie
Chief Financial Officer, George Regional Hospital, Lucedale, MS, p. A356
Chief Financial Officer, Greene County Hospital, Leakesville, MS, p. A356
BRANNEN, Charles C., Senior Vice President and Chief Operating Officer, Southeast Alabama Medical Center, Dothan, AL, p. A19
BRANNEN, Judy, M.D. Interim Chief of Staff, Hunter Holmes McGuire Veterans Affairs Medical Center–Richmond, Richmond, VA, p. A672
BRANNMAN, Brian G., President and Chief Executive Officer, St. Rose Dominican Hospitals – Siena Campus, Henderson, NV, p. A401
BRANNON, Jeffrey M., Chief Executive Officer, Monroe County Hospital, Monroeville, AL, p. A22
BRANNON, Jim, Vice President Human Resources, Atlantic General Hospital, Berlin, MD, p. A295
BRANNON, Linda, Vice President Human Resources, Circles of Care, Melbourne, FL, p. A133
BRANNON, Rebecca, R.N
Senior Vice President and Chief Nursing Officer, Saint Francis Hospital, Charleston, WV, p. A690
Vice President Patient Services, Thomas Memorial Hospital, South Charleston, WV, p. A695
BRANSCOME, Eileen, Chief Operating Officer, Mason General Hospital, Shelton, WA, p. A684
BRANSCUM, Suzette, Director of Nursing, Vantage Point of Northwest Arkansas, Fayetteville, AR, p. A44
BRANSON, Brett, M.D. Chief of Staff, TriStar Hendersonville Medical Center, Hendersonville, TN, p. A578
BRANT, Johnny, Chief Financial Officer, Welch Community Hospital, Welch, WV, p. A696
BRANT, Mick, FACHE, Chief Executive Officer, Gothenburg Memorial Hospital, Gothenburg, NE, p. A392
BRANTZ, Jerry, Chief Executive Officer, Shoshone Medical Center, Kellogg, ID, p. A174
BRASEL, James, Chief Financial Officer, Jane Phillips Medical Center, Bartlesville, OK, p. A504
BRASHER, Tanya, Administrator, Marion Regional Medical Center, Hamilton, AL, p. A21
BRASSER, Brian, President, Spectrum Health United Hospital, Greenville, MI, p. A321
BRASSINGER, Cindy, Chief Operating Officer, Vibra Hospital of Southeastern Michigan, LLC, Lincoln Park, MI, p. A324
BRASWELL, Gingie, Director Human Resources, Saint Thomas DeKalb Hospital, Smithville, TN, p. A588
BRATCHER, Tammy
System Information Technology Director, Great River Medical Center, Blytheville, AR, p. A41
Director Information Technology, South Mississippi County Regional Medical Center, Osceola, AR, p. A49
BRATTON, Michael J., R.N. Chief Nurse Executive and Vice President Patient Care Services, Bon Secours–DePaul Medical Center, Norfolk, VA, p. A669
BRATTVET, William W., Chief Executive Officer, Haven Behavioral Hospital of Frisco, Frisco, TX, p. A615
BRAUDT, Theresa Lynn, Chief Nursing Officer, Gundersen Boscobel Area Hospital and Clinics, Boscobel, WI, p. A698
BRAUN, James R., Chief Financial Officer, Flambeau Hospital, Park Falls, WI, p. A709
BRAUN, Matthew, Executive Director Information Systems, UNM Sandoval Regional Medical Center, Rio Rancho, NM, p. A426
BRAUN, Norma, Vice President Human Resources, Hollywood Presbyterian Medical Center, Los Angeles, CA, p. A70
BRAUN, Peggy, R.N. Vice President Patient Care Services and Chief Nurse Executive, Sentara Virginia Beach General Hospital, Virginia Beach, VA, p. A674
BRAUN, Jr., Richard G., CP
Senior Vice President and Chief Financial Officer, Bradford Regional Medical Center, Bradford, PA, p. A530
Senior Vice President and Chief Financial Officer, Olean General Hospital, Olean, NY, p. A446
BRAVO, Arturo, M.D. Chief of Staff, Cypress Fairbanks Medical Center, Houston, TX, p. A619
BRAVO, Stacey, Vice President Human Resources, Denton Regional Medical Center, Denton, TX, p. A608
BRAWLEY, Carrie, Administrator, Behavioral HealthCare Center at Martin, Martin, TN, p. A582
BRAXTON, Edwin R., Director Human Resources, Lompoc Valley Medical Center, Lompoc, CA, p. A68
BRAY, Bob, Chief Information Officer, Jersey Community Hospital, Jerseyville, IL, p. A191
BRAY, Delnita, Administrator, Promise Hospital of Wichita Falls, Wichita Falls, TX, p. A652
BRAY, John, M.D. Medical Director, Select Specialty Hospital–Pensacola, Pensacola, FL, p. A140
BRAY, Karen A., R.N. Vice President Patient Care Services, Washington Hospital, Washington, PA, p. A552
BRAY, Pam, Director of Nursing and Director Inpatient Services, Kane Community Hospital, Kane, PA, p. A537
BRAYFORD, Amy, Chief Human Resources Officer, Geisinger Medical Center, Danville, PA, p. A532
BRAYTON, Jackie, Vice President Human Resources, Portsmouth Regional Hospital, Portsmouth, NH, p. A408
BRAYTON, Ranee C., MSN, Chief Executive Officer, Northeast Regional Medical Center, Kirksville, MO, p. A371
BRAZ, Marcus, Chief Executive Officer, HEALTHSOUTH Rehabilitation Hospital of Sarasota, Sarasota, FL, p. A142
BRAZASKI, Karrie, R.N. Chief Operating Officer and Chief Nursing Officer, Lovelace Westside Hospital, Albuquerque, NM, p. A422
BRAZEL, Gary, M.D
Chief Medical Officer, St. Vincent Mercy Hospital, Elwood, IN, p. A207
Chief Medical Officer, St. Vincent Randolph Hospital, Winchester, IN, p. A221
BRAZIL, Bob, Chief Operating Officer, Memorial Health System, Abilene, KS, p. A237
BRAZIL, Wendy, Chief Operating Officer, Neosho Memorial Regional Medical Center, Chanute, KS, p. A238
BREA, Christie, Manager Human Resources, Promise Hospital of Phoenix, Mesa, AZ, p. A33
BREADY, Sharon, R.N., Chief Executive Officer, Care One at Raritan Bay Medical Center, Perth Amboy, NJ, p. A416
BREAKWELL, Michael, R.N. Nurse Executive, Twin Valley Behavioral Healthcare, Columbus, OH, p. A487
BREAZEALE, Scott, Chief Nursing Officer, Neshoba County General Hospital, Philadelphia, MS, p. A359
BREEDEN, Patricia, M.D. Chief of Staff, Lexington Veterans Affairs Medical Center, Lexington, KY, p. A260
BREEDEN, Susan M., Administrator and Chief Executive Officer, Baptist Memorial Hospital–Huntingdon, Huntingdon, TN, p. A579
BREEDLOVE, Jean Ann
Chief Information Officer, Children's Mercy Hospitals and Clinics, Kansas City, MO, p. A369
Chief Information Officer, Children's Mercy South, Overland Park, KS, p. A248
BREEDLOVE, Kelly, Vice President of Nursing, Health First Holmes Regional Medical Center, Melbourne, FL, p. A133
BREEDLOVE, Linda, Vice President of Patient Care Services and Chief Nursing Officer, UH Robinson Medical Center, Ravenna, OH, p. A496
BREEDVELD, Stacey, R.N. Associate Director for Patient Care, Veterans Affairs Ann Arbor Healthcare System, Ann Arbor, MI, p. A314
BREEN, Charles J., M.D. Medical Director, Sanford Hillsboro Medical Center, Hillsboro, ND, p. A475
BREEN, Thomas, Vice President and Chief Financial Officer, South County Hospital, Wakefield, RI, p. A556
BREHM, Robert, President, Kessler Institute for Rehabilitation, West Orange, NJ, p. A420
BREHMER, Jennifer, Director of Patient Care, New Ulm Medical Center, New Ulm, MN, p. A344
BREIDSTER, Cara, Chief Financial Officer, Indiana University Health Arnett Hospital, Lafayette, IN, p. A214
BREIER, Benjamin, Chief Executive Officer, Kindred Healthcare, Louisville, KY, p. B77
BREILAND, Keith, M.D. Medical Director, Seven Hills Hospital, Henderson, NV, p. A401
BREITBACH, Dave, Chief Financial Officer, Prairie du Chien Memorial Hospital, Prairie Du Chien, WI, p. A709
BREITENBACH, Karl L., M.D. Chief of Staff, Ashley Regional Medical Center, Vernal, UT, p. A659
BREITENBACH, Ray, M.D. Chief of Staff, Doctors' Hospital of Michigan, Pontiac, MI, p. A328

BREITFELDER, Michelle
Chief Operating Officer, Northside Medical Center, Columbus, GA, p. A154
Chief Nursing Officer, Piedmont Mountainside Hospital, Jasper, GA, p. A159

BREITLING, Bryan, Administrator, Avera Hand County Memorial Hospital, Miller, SD, p. A569

BREKKE, Erin, Director Human Resources, Burgess Health Center, Onawa, IA, p. A232

BRELAND, Kelly R., CPA Director Support Services, Mississippi State Hospital, Whitfield, MS, p. A361

BREMER, David, D.O. Chief of Staff, MidMichigan Medical Center–Clare, Clare, MI, p. A316

BRENAN, Kevin, Chief Financial Officer, Emory Saint Joseph's Hospital of Atlanta, Atlanta, GA, p. A150

BRENDLE, Judi, Vice President Clinical Support and Chief Nursing Officer, Bassett Medical Center, Cooperstown, NY, p. A432

BRENDLER, Stephen, Director Information Systems, Hilton Head Hospital, Hilton Head Island, SC, p. A562

BRENHOLT, Craig, Division Director People Services, Sacred Heart Hospital, Eau Claire, WI, p. A700

BRENKLE, George, Chief Information Officer, UMass Memorial Medical Center, Worcester, MA, p. A313

BRENN, Andrea, R.N. Chief Nursing Officer, Texoma Medical Center, Denison, TX, p. A607

BRENNAN, Angela, M.D. Chief of Staff, Howard County Medical Center, Saint Paul, NE, p. A398

BRENNAN, John A., M.P.H., President and Chief Executive Officer, Newark Beth Israel Medical Center, Newark, NJ, p. A415

BRENNAN, Kevin F., CPA Executive Vice President and Chief Financial Officer, Geisinger Medical Center, Danville, PA, p. A532

BRENNAN, Maria, R.N. Vice President and Chief Nursing Officer, St. Joseph's Regional Medical Center, Paterson, NJ, p. A416

BRENNAN, Patrick, Director Information System Technology, SSM Health Saint Louis University Hospital, Saint Louis, MO, p. A377

BRENNAN, Patrick J., M.D. Senior Vice President and Chief Medical Officer, Hospital of the University of Pennsylvania, Philadelphia, PA, p. A544

BRENNAN, Theresa, M.D. Chief Medical Officer, University of Iowa Hospitals and Clinics, Iowa City, IA, p. A230

BRENNER, Lawrence, M.D. Chief of Staff, Corpus Christi Medical Center, Corpus Christi, TX, p. A602

BRENNER, Pattie, R.N. Chief Nursing Officer, HEALTHSOUTH Rehabilitation Hospital, Largo, FL, p. A131

BRENNER, William
Chief Financial Officer, Kindred Hospital Indianapolis South, Greenwood, IN, p. A210
Chief Financial Officer, Kindred Hospital–Indianapolis, Indianapolis, IN, p. A212

BRENNY, Terrence, President and Chief Executive Officer, Stoughton Hospital Association, Stoughton, WI, p. A711

BRENTANO, Gregory
Chief Financial Officer, Chino Valley Medical Center, Chino, CA, p. A57
Chief Executive Officer, Montclair Hospital Medical Center, Montclair, CA, p. A76
Chief Executive Officer, San Dimas Community Hospital, San Dimas, CA, p. A87

BREON, Richard C., President and Chief Executive Officer, Spectrum Health, Grand Rapids, MI, p. B126

BRES, Thomas, Senior Vice President and Chief Administrative Officer, Sparrow Hospital, Lansing, MI, p. A324

BRESCIA, Michael J., M.D. Executive Medical Director, Calvary Hospital, NY, p. A439

BRESLIN, Susan, R.N. Vice President Patient Care Services and Chief Nursing Officer, DeKalb Medical at North Decatur, Decatur, GA, p. A156

BRESNAHAN, Jacky, Director Human Resources, Mahaska Health Partnership, Oskaloosa, IA, p. A233

BRESNAHAN, Patti, Director Human Resources, Mercy Medical Center, Canton, OH, p. A481

BRESSLER, Kathy, R.N., President, St. Clare Hospital, Lakewood, WA, p. A680

BRETTNER, Eric, Vice President and Chief Financial Officer, St. Mary's Medical Center, San Francisco, CA, p. A88

BREUDER, Andrew, M.D. Chief of Staff, Manchester Veterans Affairs Medical Center, Manchester, NH, p. A407

BREUER, Rick, Chief Executive Officer and Administrator, Community Memorial Hospital, Cloquet, MN, p. A336

BREUM, Linda G., R.N. Chief Nursing Officer, Bert Fish Medical Center, New Smyrna Beach, FL, p. A136

BREVING, Robert, M.D. Chief of Staff, National Park Medical Center, Hot Springs, AR, p. A45

BREWER, Becca, Chief Operations Officer, Falls Community Hospital and Clinic, Marlin, TX, p. A631

BREWER, David, Chief Financial Officer, Memorial Hospital, Fremont, OH, p. A490

BREWER, Douglas, Chief Operating Officer, Atlanta Medical Center, Atlanta, GA, p. A150

BREWER, Gary L., Chief Executive Officer, Valley View Hospital, Glenwood Springs, CO, p. A104

BREWER, Jennifer, R.N. Chief Nursing Officer and Vice President Nursing Services, Verde Valley Medical Center, Cottonwood, AZ, p. A30

BREWER, Jennifer Lynn, Chief Executive Officer, HEALTHSOUTH Plano Rehabilitation Hospital, Plano, TX, p. A637

BREWER, Jim, M.P.H. Chief Financial Officer, Healthmark Regional Medical Center, DeFuniak Springs, FL, p. A125

BREWER, Kaye, Vice President Human Resources, Maury Regional Hospital, Columbia, TN, p. A576

BREWER, Kelley, MSN, President, Lakeside Women's Hospital, Oklahoma City, OK, p. A511

BREWER, Peter G., Administrator, Shriners Hospitals for Children–Spokane, Spokane, WA, p. A685

BREWER, RN, Ruby, Senior Vice President and Chief Quality Officer, East Jefferson General Hospital, Metairie, LA, p. A280

BREWINGTON, Yvonne, Director Human Resources, Belton Regional Medical Center, Belton, MO, p. A363

BREXLER, James L., President and Chief Executive Officer, Doylestown Hospital, Doylestown, PA, p. A533

BREYFOGLE, Cynthia, FACHE, Director, Charles George Veterans Affairs Medical Center, Asheville, NC, p. A455

BREZA, Lisa, R.N. Vice President and Chief Nursing Officer, Robert Wood Johnson University Hospital at Hamilton, Hamilton, NJ, p. A412

BREZNY, Angie, Director Human Resources, Prague Community Hospital, Prague, OK, p. A514

BRIAN, David
Chief Information Officer, Shriners Hospitals for Children–Cincinnati Burns Hospital, Cincinnati, OH, p. A483
Director Information Services, Shriners Hospitals for Children–Lexington, Lexington, KY, p. A260

BRICHER, Joan
Senior Vice President Finance and Chief Financial Officer, Goleta Valley Cottage Hospital, Santa Barbara, CA, p. A91
Senior Vice President Finance and Chief Financial Officer, Santa Barbara Cottage Hospital, Santa Barbara, CA, p. A91
Senior Vice President Finance and Chief Financial Officer, Santa Ynez Valley Cottage Hospital, Solvang, CA, p. A92

BRICKER, Tim
President and Chief Executive Officer, Chandler Regional Medical Center, Chandler, AZ, p. A30
President and Chief Executive Officer, Mercy Gilbert Medical Center, Gilbert, AZ, p. A31

BRICKMAN, Jeffrey, FACHE, President and Chief Executive Officer, St. Anthony Hospital, Lakewood, CO, p. A106

BRICKNER, Derek, President Medical Staff, Jamestown Regional Medical Center, Jamestown, ND, p. A475

BRIDEAU, Donald, M.D. Chief Medical Officer, Inova Mount Vernon Hospital, Alexandria, VA, p. A662

BRIDEN, David, Chief Information Officer, Exeter Hospital, Exeter, NH, p. A406

BRIDGE, Lauren M., R.N. Chief Nursing Officer, Kaiser Permanente Sunnyside Medical Center, Clackamas, OR, p. A520

BRIDGELAND, Aaron
Director Finance, Midwest Orthopedic Specialty Hospital, Franklin, WI, p. A701
Director Finance, Wheaton Franciscan Healthcare – Franklin, Franklin, WI, p. A701
Director Finance, Wheaton Franciscan Healthcare – St. Francis, Milwaukee, WI, p. A707

BRIDGES, Alan J., M.D. Chief of Staff, William S. Middleton Memorial Veterans Hospital, Madison, WI, p. A704

BRIDGES, James M., Executive Vice President and Chief Operating Officer, Palmetto Health Baptist, Columbia, SC, p. A559

BRIDGES, Jane Ann, Chief Financial Officer, Nacogdoches Memorial Hospital, Nacogdoches, TX, p. A633

BRIDGES, Mary, Director Human Resources, Ouachita County Medical Center, Camden, AR, p. A42

BRIDGES, Richard, M.D. Chief of Staff, Hood Memorial Hospital, Amite, LA, p. A268

BRIDGES, Stephanie, Chief Executive Officer, Kindred Hospital–St. Louis, Saint Louis, MO, p. A376

BRIDGES–KEE, Lorinnsa, Chief Human Resources Officer, Doctors Hospital at White Rock Lake, Dallas, TX, p. A605

BRIDGEWATER, Melinda, Director, Information Services, Montana State Hospital, Warm Springs, MT, p. A387

BRIER, Pamela S., President and Chief Executive Officer, Maimonides Medical Center, NY, p. A441

BRIESEMEISTER, Eric, Chief Executive Officer, UnityPoint Health – Jones Regional Medical Center, Anamosa, IA, p. A222

BRIETE, Mark, M.D. Vice President Medical Affairs, Mercy Hospital Jefferson, Crystal City, MO, p. A366

BRIGGS, Deborah, Vice President Human Resources, Marketing, Volunteer Services and Community Relations, Ellenville Regional Hospital, Ellenville, NY, p. A433

BRIGGS, Gary, Vice President Human Resources, TriStar Southern Hills Medical Center, Nashville, TN, p. A586

BRIGGS, Michael, M.D. Chief Medical Officer, Essentia Health Fargo, Fargo, ND, p. A473

BRIGGS, Paul
Executive Vice President and Chief Operating Officer, Presbyterian Hospital, Albuquerque, NM, p. A423
Executive VP/Chief Operating Officer, Presbyterian Kaseman Hospital, Albuquerque, NM, p. A423

BRIGGS, Thomas, Chief Financial Officer, AllianceHealth Madill, Madill, OK, p. A509

BRIGHAM, Randy, Director Human Resources, Haxtun Hospital District, Haxtun, CO, p. A105

BRIGHT, Kim, M.D. Clinical Director, Springfield Hospital Center, Sykesville, MD, p. A300

BRILEY, Jay, President, Vidant Duplin Hospital, Kenansville, NC, p. A463

BRILL, Beth K., Senior Director Human Resources, Barnesville Hospital, Barnesville, OH, p. A479

BRILL, Elizabeth, M.D. Chief Operating Officer, OhioHealth Riverside Methodist Hospital, Columbus, OH, p. A486

BRILL, Karen, R.N. Chief Nursing Officer, Vice President Care, Gillette Children's Specialty Healthcare, Saint Paul, MN, p. A346

BRILLANTES, Dorothy, Senior Vice President Human Resources, Howard County General Hospital, Columbia, MD, p. A297

BRILLI, Richard, M.D. Chief Medical Officer, Nationwide Children's Hospital, Columbus, OH, p. A486

BRILLIANT, Patrick D., President and Chief Executive Officer, Riverside Community Hospital, Riverside, CA, p. A84

BRILLIANT, Steven, M.D. Chief of Staff, Veterans Affairs Sierra Nevada Health Care System, Reno, NV, p. A404

BRINDLE, Charles B., M.D. Chief Medical Staff, Iowa Specialty Hospital–Belmond, Belmond, IA, p. A222

BRINER, Junior, Chief Operating Officer, Lawrence Memorial Hospital, Walnut Ridge, AR, p. A51

BRINK, Jr., Bruce, D.O. Chief of Staff, Gibson General Hospital, Princeton, IN, p. A218

BRINKERHOFF, Cindy H., Director Human Resources, South Peninsula Hospital, Homer, AK, p. A28

BRINKERHOFF, Douglas, M.D. Clinical Director, U. S. Public Health Service Indian Hospital, San Carlos, AZ, p. A37

BRINKHAUS, Theresa, Chief Financial Officer, St. Helena Parish Hospital, Greensburg, LA, p. A274

BRINKLEY, Charlie, Chief Financial Officer, Clearview Regional Medical Center, Monroe, GA, p. A161

BRINKLEY, Terry, Vice President Finance, Paris Community Hospital, Paris, IL, p. A197

BRINKMAN, Dan, R.N., Interim Chief Executive Officer, Hilo Medical Center, Hilo, HI, p. A168

BRINKMAN, Janet, Director Human Resources, Colorado Plains Medical Center, Fort Morgan, CO, p. A103

BRINSON, David, Director Information Technology, Parkview Wabash County Hospital, Wabash, IN, p. A221

BRINSON, Pam, Nurse Executive, South Mississippi State Hospital, Purvis, MS, p. A360

BRIONES, Melba, M.D. Medical Director, Evansville State Hospital, Evansville, IN, p. A208

BRISBOE, Mark
VP and Chief Financial Officer, Sparrow Clinton Hospital, Saint Johns, MI, p. A329
VP and Chief Financial Officer, Sparrow Ionia Hospital, Ionia, MI, p. A322

BRISCOE, Betsy, Chief Executive Officer, Memorial Hospital, Seminole, TX, p. A643

BRISCOE, Mary Beth, Chief Financial Officer, University of Alabama Hospital, Birmingham, AL, p. A17

BRISENDINE, Chad
Vice President and Chief Information Officer, St. Luke's Hospital – Miners Campus, Coaldale, PA, p. A531
Chief Information Officer, St. Luke's Hospital – Quakertown Campus, Quakertown, PA, p. A548
Chief Information Officer, St. Luke's University Hospital – Bethlehem Campus, Bethlehem, PA, p. A529

BRISSE, Thomas M., President and Chief Executive Officer, McLaren Macomb, Mount Clemens, MI, p. A326

BRISTER, Kim, Director Human Resources, Gettysburg Hospital, Gettysburg, PA, p. A534

BRISTER, Marilyn, M.D. Chief of Staff, Texas Health Harris Methodist Hospital Stephenville, Stephenville, TX, p. A645

BRISTO, Cathie, Director Human Resources, Wilbarger General Hospital, Vernon, TX, p. A650

BRISTOL, Michelle, Director of Nursing, Clifton–Fine Hospital, Star Lake, NY, p. A450

Index of Health Care Professionals / Brown

Index of Health Care Professionals

BRISTOLL, Holly L.
President, ProMedica Bay Park Hospital, Oregon, OH, p. A496
President, ProMedica Fostoria Community Hospital, Fostoria, OH, p. A490
BRITT, Kevin, Chief Operating Officer, Reynolds Memorial Hospital, Glen Dale, WV, p. A691
BRITT, Key, Associate Director, Greenwood Leflore Hospital, Greenwood, MS, p. A353
BRITT, Linda, Director Information Systems, Baptist Memorial Hospital–North Mississippi, Oxford, MS, p. A359
BRITT, Suzanne, Director Human Resources, Samaritan Memorial Hospital, Macon, MO, p. A372
BRITT, Tommy, Vice President of Human Resources, West Georgia Health, Lagrange, GA, p. A160
BRITTAIN, Libby, Director Human Resources, Steele Memorial Medical Center, Salmon, ID, p. A176
BRITTON, David, Interim Chief Financial Officer, Medina Memorial Hospital, Medina, NY, p. A437
BRITTON, John, Vice President Information Services, Fisher–Titus Medical Center, Norwalk, OH, p. A495
BRITTON, Lynn, President and Chief Executive Officer, Mercy Health, Chesterfield, MO, p. B90
BRITTON, Natalie, Director Human Resources, Silverton Hospital, Silverton, OR, p. A526
BRITTON, William N., Associate Administrator Finance, Alfred I. duPont Hospital for Children, Wilmington, DE, p. A118
BROACH, Keith, Chief Executive Officer, Abilene Behavioral Health, Abilene, TX, p. A590
BROADUS, Ronald, Assistant Administrator Human Resources, Interim LSU Public Hospital, New Orleans, LA, p. A282
BROADWATER, Gary W., Chief Financial Officer, McCready Foundation, Crisfield, MD, p. A297
BROADWAY, Brenda, Chief Nursing Officer, CHI St. Luke's Health Memorial Specialty Hospital, Lufkin, TX, p. A630
BROADWAY, Chris, Manager Information Technology, Mayers Memorial Hospital District, Fall River Mills, CA, p. A61
BROBBEY, Andrew, M.D. Chief of Staff, Euclid Hospital, Euclid, OH, p. A489
BROBERG, John R., FACHE, Senior Administrator, Via Christi Hospital Manhattan, Inc., KS, p. A245
BROBST, Mary, R.N. Senior Vice President Patient Care Services and Chief Nursing Officer, Mercy Medical Center–Cedar Rapids, Cedar Rapids, IA, p. A223
BROCK, Berna, Vice President Human Resources, Adena Pike Medical Center, Waverly, OH, p. A500
BROCK, Jamie, Director Human Resources, Windber Medical Center, Windber, PA, p. A553
BROCK, Kyle, Vice President Human Resources, Glens Falls Hospital, Glens Falls, NY, p. A434
BROCK, Lisa M., Chief Human Resource Officer, Overlake Medical Center, Bellevue, WA, p. A676
BROCK, Melinda, Director Human Resources, AllianceHealth Woodward, Woodward, OK, p. A518
BROCK, Nancy, Chief Financial Officer, Houston Methodist St. Catherine Hospital, Katy, TX, p. A625
BROCK, Robert
Chief Financial Officer and Vice President, Rollins–Brook Community Hospital, Lampasas, TX, p. A627
Vice President Finance, Saint Joseph – Martin, Martin, KY, p. A262
BROCK, Steve, Chief Financial Officer, Lynn County Hospital District, Tahoka, TX, p. A646
BROCK, Theresa, Vice President Nursing, Good Shepherd Health Care System, Hermiston, OR, p. A521
BROCK, William, Chief Information Officer, Atlanta Veterans Affairs Medical Center, Decatur, GA, p. A155
BROCKERT, Nicholas, President, Saint Luke's Cushing Hospital, Leavenworth, KS, p. A244
BROCKETTE, Darby, Chief Executive Officer, Ernest Health, Inc., Albuquerque, NM, p. B54
BROCKHAUS, Jennifer, Chief Information Officer, Sidney Regional Medical Center, Sidney, NE, p. A398
BROCKHOUSE, Dena M., Director Human Resources, Mercy Iowa City, Iowa City, IA, p. A229
BROCKMEYER, Heather, Human Resource Administrative Officer, Nevada Regional Medical Center, Nevada, MO, p. A373
BROCKMEYER, JoEllyn, Director Human Resources, Indiana University Health White Memorial Hospital, Monticello, IN, p. A216
BROCKUS, Harry, Chief Executive Officer, Carle Hoopeston Regional Health Center, Hoopeston, IL, p. A191
BROCKWELL, Linda, Chief Nursing Officer, Wickenburg Community Hospital, Wickenburg, AZ, p. A40
BRODBECK, MSN, RN–, Kathleen, Chief Nursing Officer, St. James Mercy Health System, Hornell, NY, p. A435
BRODBECK, Lisa, Chief Financial Officer, Medical Center of Lewisville, Lewisville, TX, p. A628
BRODERICK, John, M.D. Chief Medical Officer, Adirondack Medical Center, Saranac Lake, NY, p. A450
BRODEUR, Mark S., FACHE, Chief Executive Officer, Select Specialty Hospital–Springfield, Springfield, MO, p. A379
BRODHEAD, Richard, M.D. President Medical Staff, Ministry Eagle River Memorial Hospital, Eagle River, WI, p. A700
BRODHEAD, Richard Ross, Director Human Resources, St. Vincent Randolph Hospital, Winchester, IN, p. A221
BRODHEAD, Ross, Manager Human Resources, St. Vincent Mercy Hospital, Elwood, IN, p. A207
BRODIAN, Craig R., Vice President Human Resources, Johns Hopkins Bayview Medical Center, Baltimore, MD, p. A293
BRODRICK, Theresa M., R.N
Chief Nursing Officer, Alamance Regional Medical Center, Burlington, NC, p. A456
Executive Vice President and Chief Nursing Officer, Moses H. Cone Memorial Hospital, Greensboro, NC, p. A461
BRODY, Anne Marie, Director Information Systems Customer Service, Providence Saint Joseph Medical Center, Burbank, CA, p. A56
BROEKHUIS, Arlyn
Chief Information Officer, Sanford Medical Center Fargo, Fargo, ND, p. A474
Vice President and Chief Information Officer, Sanford USD Medical Center, Sioux Falls, SD, p. A571
BROEMELING, Richard, Information Systems Flight Commander, U. S. Air Force Clinic, Mountain Home AFB, ID, p. A175
BROERMANN, Robert
Senior Vice President and Chief Financial Officer, Sentara Leigh Hospital, Norfolk, VA, p. A669
Senior Vice President and Chief Financial Officer, Sentara Norfolk General Hospital, Norfolk, VA, p. A669
Senior Vice President and Chief Financial Officer, Sentara Princess Anne Hospital, Virginia Beach, VA, p. A674
BROGAN Jr., Gerard, M.D., Executive Director, Huntington Hospital, Huntington, NY, p. A435
BROGGER, Portlyn
Chief Executive Officer, Post Acute Medical Specialty Hospital of Victoria, Victoria, TX, p. A650
Chief Executive Officer, Post Acute/Warm Springs Specialty Hospital of Victoria, Victoria, TX, p. A650
BROHAWN, Bill, Chief of Staff, Trace Regional Hospital, Houston, MS, p. A354
BROKAW, Sara, Vice President Patient Care Services, Bellevue Hospital, Bellevue, OH, p. A480
BROKENSHIRE, Shelia Kay, Vice President of Nursing, Van Wert County Hospital, Van Wert, OH, p. A499
BROMAN, Craig J., FACHE, President, St. Cloud Hospital, Saint Cloud, MN, p. A345
BROMLEY, Trudy, Vice President Human Resources, JFK Medical Center, Atlantis, FL, p. A121
BRONER, Eloise, President and Chief Executive Officer, Good Samaritan Hospital, Dayton, OH, p. A488
BRONHARD, John, Interim Chief Financial Officer, HealthAlliance Hospitals, Leominster, MA, p. A308
BROOCKS, Kelli C., Director Human Resources, Public Relations and Physician Recruitment, Beauregard Memorial Hospital, De Ridder, LA, p. A273
BROOKE, Teresa, Chief Nursing Officer, Dominion Hospital, Falls Church, VA, p. A664
BROOKE, William R., M.D. President Medical Staff, Pickens County Medical Center, Carrollton, AL, p. A17
BROOKER, Brian, Chief Executive Officer, Cypress Creek Hospital, Houston, TX, p. A619
BROOKER, Paula, Director Information Services, Pleasant Valley Hospital, Point Pleasant, WV, p. A694
BROOKER, Susan E., R.N. Chief Clinical Officer, Vibra Specialty Hospital of Portland, Portland, OR, p. A525
BROOKES, Jeffrey, M.D
Chief Medical Officer, Parkview LaGrange Hospital, LaGrange, IN, p. A214
Medical Director, Parkview Whitley Hospital, Columbia City, IN, p. A206
BROOKHYSER, Joan, M.D. Medical Center Director and Chief Executive Officer, University Medical Center, Las Vegas, NV, p. A403
BROOKMAN, Mark, Chief Information Officer, Medical Center at Bowling Green, Bowling Green, KY, p. A254
BROOKS, Albert, M.D. Chief Medical Staff Services, Washington Hospital Healthcare System, Fremont, CA, p. A62
BROOKS, Ann Marie T., R.N. Vice President, Nursing, Riddle Hospital, Media, PA, p. A540
BROOKS, Anthony, Chief Information Officer, Miami Veterans Affairs Healthcare System, Miami, FL, p. A134
BROOKS, April, Chief Nursing Officer, HEALTHSOUTH Rehabilitation Hospital of Columbia, Columbia, SC, p. A559
BROOKS, Harris W., Administrator and Chief Executive Officer, Palo Pinto General Hospital, Mineral Wells, TX, p. A632
BROOKS, Janet, Chief Nursing Officer, USC Verdugo Hills Hospital, Glendale, CA, p. A64
BROOKS, Janet, R.N. Vice President and Chief Nursing Officer, West Hills Hospital and Medical Center, CA, p. A73
BROOKS, Jeffrey, M.D. Medical Director, Parkview Huntington Hospital, Huntington, IN, p. A211
BROOKS, Jerome M., Chief Operating Officer, South Texas Health System, Edinburg, TX, p. A610
BROOKS, Joe, Chief Financial Officer, Keystone Newport News, Newport News, VA, p. A668
BROOKS, Lisa, Chief Financial Officer, Comanche County Hospital, Coldwater, KS, p. A238
BROOKS, Lori, Director Human Resources, Red Bud Regional Hospital, Red Bud, IL, p. A199
BROOKS, Nick, Director of Information Systems, Citrus Memorial Health System, Inverness, FL, p. A129
BROOKS, Patrice Gay, Chief Executive Officer, Cumberland Hospital, New Kent, VA, p. A668
BROOKS, Patti, Director Information Systems, Avera Queen of Peace Hospital, Mitchell, SD, p. A570
BROOKS, Robert E., FACHE Executive Vice President and Chief Operating Officer, Erlanger Medical Center, Chattanooga, TN, p. A575
BROOKS, Scott, Information Technology, Boulder City Hospital, Boulder City, NV, p. A400
BROOKS, Steven Michael, Vice President Human Resources, Southeastern Ohio Regional Medical Center, Cambridge, OH, p. A481
BROOKS, Troy, Assistant Administrator Fiscal Services, Newton Medical Center, Covington, GA, p. A155
BROOKS–WILLIAMS, Denise, President and Chief Executive Officer, Henry Ford Wyandotte Hospital, Wyandotte, MI, p. A332
BROOKSHIRE–HEAVIN, Keri S., Chief Nurse Executive, Phelps County Regional Medical Center, Rolla, MO, p. A375
BROPHY, Beth, Interim VP for Human Resources, Hurley Medical Center, Flint, MI, p. A319
BROSIUS, William, Vice President and Chief Financial Officer, Baylor St. Luke's Medical Center, Houston, TX, p. A619
BROSKEY, Steven, Associate Director, Veterans Affairs Roseburg Healthcare System, Roseburg, OR, p. A525
BROSNAHAN, Jan, Chief Financial Officer, Winona Health, Winona, MN, p. A349
BROSNAN, Kimberly, Director Human Resources, Norwood Hospital, Norwood, MA, p. A310
BROSS, James B., President, Angel Medical Center, Franklin, NC, p. A460
BROST, Michelle, Financial Officer, Victory Medical Center Mid–Cities, Hurst, TX, p. A624
BROTEN, Kurt, Chief Financial Officer, Palmdale Regional Medical Center, Palmdale, CA, p. A80
BROTHMAN, Joe, Assistant Vice President, Information Systems, MedStar Washington Hospital Center, Washington, DC, p. A119
BROUGHMAN, Robin, R.N. Chief Nursing Officer, LewisGale Hospital Alleghany, Low Moor, VA, p. A667
BROUGHMAN, Wade
Chief Operating Officer, Riverside Behavioral Health Center, Hampton, VA, p. A666
Executive Vice President and Chief Financial Officer, Riverside Regional Medical Center, Newport News, VA, p. A669
Executive Vice President and Chief Financial Officer, Riverside Rehabilitation Institute, Newport News, VA, p. A669
BROUSSARD, Clifford M., FACHE, Administrator, WK Bossier Health Center, Bossier City, LA, p. A271
BROUWER, Heath, Administrator, Douglas County Memorial Hospital, Armour, SD, p. A567
BROWDER, Renate, R.N. Director of Nursing, Lake City Community Hospital, Lake City, SC, p. A563
BROWER, Fred B., President and Chief Executive Officer, Trinity Health System, Steubenville, OH, p. A498
BROWER, Laura E., R.N. Chief Nursing Officer, Georgia Regents Medical Center, Augusta, GA, p. A151
BROWN, Angel
Director Human Resources, Morton Plant Hospital, Clearwater, FL, p. A123
Director Team Resources, Morton Plant North Bay Hospital, New Port Richey, FL, p. A136
BROWN, Ann R., FACHE, Director, Jesse Brown Veterans Affairs Medical Center, Chicago, IL, p. A182
BROWN, Austin, Chief Operating Officer, Seven Rivers Regional Medical Center, Crystal River, FL, p. A124
BROWN, B. Blaine, Vice President and General Counsel, Prattville Baptist Hospital, Prattville, AL, p. A24
BROWN, Barbara, D.O. Chief of Staff, Osborne County Memorial Hospital, Osborne, KS, p. A247
BROWN, Bryan
Director Information Services and Technology, Corpus Christi Medical Center, Corpus Christi, TX, p. A602
Executive Director, Mercy Hospital Fort Smith, Fort Smith, AR, p. A44
BROWN, Chad J., M.P.H., President, Wake Forest Baptist Health–Davie Medical Center, Mocksville, NC, p. A465

BROWN, Cheryl, Administrator, Henderson Health Care Services, Henderson, NE, p. A392

BROWN, Chistiane, Assistant Vice President, MedStar Montgomery Medical Center, Olney, MD, p. A299

BROWN, Christi, Director Human Resources, Our Lady of the Angels Hospital, Bogalusa, LA, p. A270

BROWN, Christopher, M.D. Chief of Staff, Ellinwood District Hospital, Ellinwood, KS, p. A239

BROWN, Crystal, M.D. Medical Director, Medical Center of Peach County, Navicent Health, Fort Valley, GA, p. A158

BROWN, Cynthia, Director of Nursing, Hill Hospital of Sumter County, York, AL, p. A26

BROWN, Damon, Chief Executive Officer, AllianceHealth Midwest, Midwest City, OK, p. A510

BROWN, Darin, Vice President Finance, Henry County Hospital, New Castle, IN, p. A217

BROWN, David A., Director Human Resources and Corporate Compliance, Pleasant Valley Hospital, Point Pleasant, WV, p. A694

BROWN, Deana, Director Administrative Services, Franciscan Health Rensselear, Rensselaer, IN, p. A219

BROWN, Debbie T., R.N. Chief Nursing Officer, EvergreenHealth Monroe, Monroe, WA, p. A680

BROWN, Debra L., Area Financial Officer, Kaiser Permanente Manteca Medical Center, Manteca, CA, p. A74

BROWN, Denise, Vice President Human Resources, Presence Saint Joseph Hospital, Chicago, IL, p. A183

BROWN, Derek, Chief Information Officer, Jellico Community Hospital, Jellico, TN, p. A579

BROWN, Eric, M.D. Physician Executive, Palmetto Health Richland, Columbia, SC, p. A559

BROWN, Geoffrey
Chief Information Officer, Inova Fair Oaks Hospital, Fairfax, VA, p. A664
Vice President Information Systems, Inova Fairfax Hospital, Falls Church, VA, p. A664
Chief Information Officer, Piedmont Mountainside Hospital, Jasper, GA, p. A159

BROWN, George J., M.D., President and Chief Executive Officer, Legacy Health, Portland, OR, p. B81

BROWN, Greg, Chief Executive Officer, Clinch Memorial Hospital, Homerville, GA, p. A159

BROWN, Howard, Chief Financial Officer, North Shore Medical Center, Miami, FL, p. A134

BROWN, James H., Chief Financial Officer, Centerpoint Medical Center, Independence, MO, p. A368

BROWN, Janice, Chief Financial Officer, Coosa Valley Medical Center, Sylacauga, AL, p. A25

BROWN, Jason, Director Information Systems, Sanford Sheldon Medical Center, Sheldon, IA, p. A234

BROWN, Jay
Vice President and Chief Information Officer, University of Cincinnati Medical Center, Cincinnati, OH, p. A484
Senior Vice President, Chief Information Officer, West Chester Hospital, West Chester, OH, p. A500

BROWN, Jeffrey L., Director Information Systems, Lawrence General Hospital, Lawrence, MA, p. A308

BROWN, Jill, Chief Financial Officer, Miller County Hospital, Colquitt, GA, p. A154

BROWN, Jim, Director Information Technology, Lynn County Hospital District, Tahoka, TX, p. A646

BROWN, John D., Director Information Systems, Pacific Alliance Medical Center, Los Angeles, CA, p. A71

BROWN, Joni, Director Human Resources, Rehabilitation Hospital of Indiana, Indianapolis, IN, p. A212

BROWN, Joseph, Vice President Operations, Baylor Regional Medical Center at Plano, Plano, TX, p. A636

BROWN, Judy, Executive Vice President and Chief Operating Officer, East Jefferson General Hospital, Metairie, LA, p. A280

BROWN, Karen, Manager Information Technology, Guthrie Towanda Memorial Hospital, Towanda, PA, p. A551

BROWN, Karen C., Vice President Chief Operating Officer, OSF Saint Anthony Medical Center, Rockford, IL, p. A199

BROWN, Katie, Coordinator Human Resources, Pocahontas Memorial Hospital, Buckeye, WV, p. A689

BROWN, Ken, Vice President and Chief Human Resource Officer, Pratt Regional Medical Center, Pratt, KS, p. A249

BROWN, Kendra, Job Requisition Coordinator, Rusk State Hospital, Rusk, TX, p. A639

BROWN, Kevin, President and Chief Executive Officer, Piedmont Healthcare, Atlanta, GA, p. B104

BROWN, Kris, Associate Director, Bay Pines Veterans Affairs Healthcare System, Bay Pines, FL, p. A121

BROWN, Laurie, R.N. Chief Nursing Officer, St. Francis Hospital, Federal Way, WA, p. A679

BROWN, Lewis, Director Information Technology, Baptist St. Anthony Health System, Amarillo, TX, p. A591

BROWN, Lisa, Director of Nursing, Pearl River County Hospital, Poplarville, MS, p. A359

BROWN, Liz, Manager Human Resources, Gunnison Valley Hospital, Gunnison, UT, p. A655

BROWN, Lori, Chief Nursing Officer, Baptist Memorial Hospital–Union City, Union City, TN, p. A589

BROWN, Lori J., MSN Chief Nursing Officer, Sunrise Hospital and Medical Center, Las Vegas, NV, p. A403

BROWN, Margaret, Director Medical Records, Vantage Point of Northwest Arkansas, Fayetteville, AR, p. A44

BROWN, Markham, M.D. Chief Medical Staff, Mike O'Callaghan Federal Hospital, Nellis AFB, NV, p. A403

BROWN, Martin, Vice President Information Services and Chief Information Officer, Nathan Littauer Hospital and Nursing Home, Gloversville, NY, p. A434

BROWN, Mary Beth, Director Human Resources, Bertrand Chaffee Hospital, Springville, NY, p. A450

BROWN, Mary J., R.N. Vice President and Chief Nursing Officer, Mercy Medical Center–Des Moines, Des Moines, IA, p. A226

BROWN, Mary W., Senior Vice President Operations, St. Joseph's Hospital Health Center, Syracuse, NY, p. A451

BROWN, Michael, D.O. Chief of Staff, TMC Bonham Hospital, Bonham, TX, p. A598

BROWN, Michael L.
Regional President and Chief Executive Officer, Presence Mercy Medical Center, Aurora, IL, p. A178
Regional President and Chief Executive Officer, Presence Saint Joseph Hospital, Elgin, IL, p. A187

BROWN, Mike, Chief Financial Officer, Carlinville Area Hospital, Carlinville, IL, p. A180

BROWN, Molly B., Chief Operating Officer, University of Mississippi Medical Center Grenada, Grenada, MS, p. A353

BROWN, Nancy, R.N. Vice President Patient Care Services and Chief Nursing Officer, Norman Regional Health System, Norman, OK, p. A510

BROWN, Natalie, Chief Human Resources Management Services, Memphis Veterans Affairs Medical Center, Memphis, TN, p. A583

BROWN, Pam, Human Resources Manager, Behavioral HealthCare Center at Columbia, Columbia, TN, p. A576

BROWN, Pat, R.N. Chief Nursing Officer, San Gorgonio Memorial Hospital, Banning, CA, p. A55

BROWN, Patsy, Site Coordinator Human Resources, Erlanger Bledsoe Hospital, Pikeville, TN, p. A587

BROWN, Patti, M.D. Medical Director, HEALTHSOUTH Reading Rehabilitation Hospital, Reading, PA, p. A548

BROWN, Paulette, Chief Operating Officer, Indiana University Health Goshen Hospital, Goshen, IN, p. A210

BROWN, Penny D., Director of Human Resources, Broaddus Hospital, Philippi, WV, p. A694

BROWN, Philip, D.O. Vice President Medical Affairs, The University of Vermont Health Network Central Vermont Medical Center, Berlin, VT, p. A660

BROWN, Phyllis, Chief Executive Officer, Marshall Medical Center, Lewisburg, TN, p. A581

BROWN, Randal, M.D. Chief of Staff, Guadalupe County Hospital, Santa Rosa, NM, p. A426

BROWN, Regenia, Vice President Human Resources, Magnolia Regional Health Center, Corinth, MS, p. A352

BROWN, Rex H., President and Chief Executive Officer, Hillsboro Area Hospital, Hillsboro, IL, p. A190

BROWN, Richard L., Interim Chief Executive Officer, St. John's Episcopal Hospital–South Shore, NY, p. A444

BROWN, Rickie F., Chief Financial Officer, Monroe County Medical Center, Tompkinsville, KY, p. A266

BROWN, Rita, Director Human Resources, Richardson Medical Center, Rayville, LA, p. A284

BROWN, Robert, M.D. Chief Medical Officer, Park Plaza Hospital, Houston, TX, p. A621

BROWN, Robert, Chief Operating Officer, Parkview Community Hospital Medical Center, Riverside, CA, p. A83

BROWN, Roberta, Chief Nursing Officer, Community Memorial Hospital, Staunton, IL, p. A201

BROWN, Robin
Chief Executive, Senior Vice President, Scripps Green Hospital, La Jolla, CA, p. A66
Chief Information Officer and Compliance Officer, St. Joseph Medical Center, Houston, TX, p. A622

BROWN, Rodger, Vice President Human Resources, North Mississippi Medical Center – Tupelo, Tupelo, MS, p. A360

BROWN, Rodney, Chief Executive Officer, Landmark Hospital of Cape Girardeau, Cape Girardeau, MO, p. A364

BROWN, Scott, Chief Financial Officer, Valir Rehabilitation Hospital, Oklahoma City, OK, p. A513

BROWN, Shane, Vice President and Chief Human Resources Officer, CGH Medical Center, Sterling, IL, p. A201

BROWN, Shannon, Chief Executive Officer, Huntsville Memorial Hospital, Huntsville, TX, p. A623

BROWN, Sharon, Vice President Human Resources, Sierra View Medical Center, Porterville, CA, p. A81

BROWN, Sharon, R.N. Vice President Patient Care and Chief Nursing Officer, St. Mary Medical Center, Langhorne, PA, p. A538

BROWN, Sharon, Deputy Commander Nursing, Winn Army Community Hospital, Hinesville, GA, p. A159

BROWN, Sherry, Director Human Resources, Cleveland Area Hospital, Cleveland, OK, p. A505

BROWN, Stephen A., Chief Financial Officer, Grace Cottage Hospital, Townshend, VT, p. A661

BROWN, Steve, M.D. Chief Quality Officer, Saint Alphonsus Regional Medical Center, Boise, ID, p. A172

BROWN, Steve
Director Information Systems, Spalding Regional Medical Center, Griffin, GA, p. A158
Chief Information Officer, Sylvan Grove Hospital, Jackson, GA, p. A159

BROWN, Steven, Vice President Fiscal Affairs, Mary Rutan Hospital, Bellefontaine, OH, p. A479

BROWN, Steven, M.D. Medical Director, Wyoming Behavioral Institute, Casper, WY, p. A715

BROWN, Steven E., FACHE, President and Chief Executive Officer, Mount Nittany Medical Center, State College, PA, p. A550

BROWN, Sue, Administrator Human Resources, South Lake Hospital, Clermont, FL, p. A123

BROWN, Susan
Chief Human Resources Officer, North Fulton Regional Hospital, Roswell, GA, p. A163
Chief Nursing Officer, University Behavioral Health of El Paso, El Paso, TX, p. A611

BROWN, Susan E., R.N. Sr. Vice President, Chief Nursing Officer, Blue Ridge Healthcare Hospitals, Morganton, NC, p. A465

BROWN, Theodore, Chief Operating Officer, Community Howard Regional Health, Kokomo, IN, p. A213

BROWN, Todd A., M.D. Medical Director, Logan Regional Hospital, Logan, UT, p. A655

BROWN, Tom, M.D. President Medical Staff, Wayne Hospital, Greenville, OH, p. A491

BROWN, Towanda, Director Standards and Regulatory Compliance, Cumberland Hospital, New Kent, VA, p. A668

BROWN, Traci, Human Resources Generalist, Medical Arts Hospital, Lamesa, TX, p. A627

BROWN, Vance, M.D., President and Chief Executive Officer, Bassett Healthcare Network, Cooperstown, NY, p. B22

BROWN, Vance, M.D., President and Chief Executive Officer, Bassett Medical Center, Cooperstown, NY, p. A432

BROWN, Wendy W., M.D. Chief of Staff, Jesse Brown Veterans Affairs Medical Center, Chicago, IL, p. A182

BROWN, William A., FACHE, President and CEO, Baptist Health Paducah, Paducah, KY, p. A264

BROWN, William V., Chief Executive Officer, Audubon Behavioral Healthcare, Longview, TX, p. B16

BROWN, Willie, Director Administration, Naval Hospital Beaufort, Beaufort, SC, p. A557

BROWN, Winfield S., FACHE,
President and Chief Executive Officer, Athol Memorial Hospital, Athol, MA, p. A302
President and Chief Executive Officer, Heywood Hospital, Gardner, MA, p. A307

BROWN–ROBERTS, Bonita, Director Information Systems, Advocate Trinity Hospital, Chicago, IL, p. A181

BROWN–TEZERA, Belina, MSN Associate Director Patient Care Services, John D. Dingell Veterans Affairs Medical Center, Detroit, MI, p. A318

BROWNE, J. Timothy, FACHE, Chief Executive Officer, Carolina Pines Regional Medical Center, Hartsville, SC, p. A562

BROWNE, John
Senior Chief Financial Officer, Kindred Hospital Riverside, Perris, CA, p. A81
Assistant Administrator Finance, Kindred Hospital–Brea, Brea, CA, p. A56

BROWNE, Mark, M.D
Covenant Health, Senior Vice President and Chief Medical Officer, Methodist Medical Center of Oak Ridge, Oak Ridge, TN, p. A586
Chief Medical Officer, Roane Medical Center, Harriman, TN, p. A578

BROWNER, Warren S., M.P.H.,
Chief Executive Officer, California Pacific Medical Center, San Francisco, CA, p. A88
Chief Executive Officer, St. Luke's Hospital, San Francisco, CA, p. A88

BROWNEWELL, Victoria, Chief Nursing Officer, Houston Methodist West Hospital, Houston, TX, p. A620

BROWNFIELD, Mona, M.D. Chief Medical Staff, Cooper County Memorial Hospital, Boonville, MO, p. A364

Index of Health Care Professionals / Buckley

Index of Health Care Professionals

BROWNING, Douglas
Chief Financial Officer, Texas Health Center for Diagnostic & Surgery, Plano, TX, p. A637
Group Financial Officer, Texas Health Harris Methodist Hospital Southlake, Southlake, TX, p. A644
BROWNING, Michael, Chief Financial Officer, Madison Health, London, OH, p. A492
BROWNING, Susan, Executive Director, Forest Hills Hospital, NY, p. A439
BROWNSTEIN, Gregory, Chief Executive Officer, Westwood Lodge Hospital, Westwood, MA, p. A313
BROWNSWORTH, Ray, Interim Chief Executive Officer, Van Buren County Hospital, Keosauqua, IA, p. A230
BROYHILL, David, Chief Information Management, Brooke Army Medical Center, Fort Sam Houston, TX, p. A612
BROYLES, Jim, Chief Executive Officer and Chief Nursing Officer, Benewah Community Hospital, Saint Maries, ID, p. A176
BROYLES, Susan, Director Human Resources and Safety, Unicoi County Memorial Hospital, Erwin, TN, p. A577
BRUBAKER, Kathy M., R.N. Vice President and Chief Nursing Officer, St. Joseph Mercy Chelsea, Chelsea, MI, p. A316
BRUBAKER, Margaret M., Senior Vice President Human Resources, Brookdale Hospital Medical Center, NY, p. A439
BRUCE, Bill, FACHE, Chief Executive Officer, Crawford County Memorial Hospital, Denison, IA, p. A226
BRUCE, Karen, Director of Nursing, Keystone Newport News, Newport News, VA, p. A668
BRUCE, Michael D., Chief Executive Officer, Lake Martin Community Hospital, Dadeville, AL, p. A18
BRUCE, Mike, Chief Financial Officer, Elmore Community Hospital, Wetumpka, AL, p. A26
BRUCE, Paul, Chief Nursing Officer, HEALTHSOUTH Rehabilitation Hospital of Austin, Austin, TX, p. A594
BRUCE, Sandra B., FACHE, President and Chief Executive Officer, Presence Health, Chicago, IL, p. B106
BRUCE, Scott, Vice President Operations, St. Mary's Healthcare, Amsterdam, NY, p. A428
BRUCE, Sheila, Director Information System, Baptist Health Madisonville, Madisonville, KY, p. A262
BRUCK, Paul, Administrator, East Central Regional Hospital, Augusta, GA, p. A151
BRUCKNER, Alison, Chief Operating Officer, Cass County Memorial Hospital, Atlantic, IA, p. A222
BRUDNICKI, Gary F., Senior Executive Vice President, Chief Operating Officer and Chief Financial Officer, Westchester Medical Center, Valhalla, NY, p. A452
BRUELS, Raymond, Manager Information Technology, Natchitoches Regional Medical Center, Natchitoches, LA, p. A281
BRUENS, Dennis, Vice President Operations, St. Thomas More Hospital, Canon City, CO, p. A100
BRUFF, Edward, President and Chief Executive Officer, Covenant Healthcare, Saginaw, MI, p. A329
BRUGGEMAN, Chris, Chief Operating Officer, RiverView Health, Crookston, MN, p. A337
BRUHL, Lisa G., Chief Operating Officer, Lallie Kemp Medical Center, Independence, LA, p. A275
BRUHN, Julie, R.N. Associate Director Patient Care and Nurse Executive, Fargo Veterans Affairs Health Care System, Fargo, ND, p. A473
BRUI, Thomas M., Director Resource Management, Naval Hospital Lemoore, Portsmith, VA, p. A670
BRUMFIELD, Derrick, Chief Operating Officer, SageWest Health Care at Riverton, Riverton, WY, p. A717
BRUMFIELD, Rita, R.N. Chief Nursing Officer, Ste. Genevieve County Memorial Hospital, Ste. Genevieve, MO, p. A379
BRUMMETT, Vince, Director Administrative Services, Merit Health Batesville, Batesville, MS, p. A350
BRUMSTED, John R., M.D., President and Chief Executive Officer, The University of Vermont Health Network University of Vermont Medical Center, Burlington, VT, p. A660
BRUNDISE, Cynthia, Vice President Human Resources, St. Anthony Hospital, Oklahoma City, OK, p. A513
BRUNELLE, Diane, MSN Director Patient Care Services and Chief Nursing Officer, Shriners Hospitals for Children–Springfield, Springfield, MA, p. A311
BRUNER, Deborah, Chief Executive Officer and Administrator, Minneola District Hospital, Minneola, KS, p. A246
BRUNING, Troy, Director Information Technology, Meeker Memorial Hospital, Litchfield, MN, p. A341
BRUNKE, Renea, Vice President Human Resources, Chandler Regional Medical Center, Chandler, AZ, p. A30
BRUNN, Mary E., R.N. Acting Associate Director Nursing, Clement J. Zablocki Veterans Affairs Medical Center, Milwaukee, WI, p. A706
BRUNO, Catherine, FACHE Chief Information Officer, Eastern Maine Medical Center, Bangor, ME, p. A288
BRUNO, John P., Vice President Human Resources, St. Joseph's Regional Medical Center, Paterson, NJ, p. A416
BRUNO, Judy, R.N. Vice President, Clinical Operations, The Outer Banks Hospital, Nags Head, NC, p. A466
BRUNO, Steve, Manager Business, Central Regional Hospital, Butner, NC, p. A456
BRUNO, Yolanda, M.D. Medical Director, Henry J. Carter Specialty Hospital and Nursing Facility, New York, NY, p. A440
BRUNSON, Pam, Director Human Resources, South Baldwin Regional Medical Center, Foley, AL, p. A19
BRUNT, C. Hal, M.D. Medical Director, Lakeside Behavioral Health System, Memphis, TN, p. A583
BRUNTON, Hope, Chief Manpower Branch, Irwin Army Community Hospital, Junction City, KS, p. A243
BRUNTZ, Troy, Vice President Finance and Chief Financial Officer, Community Hospital, McCook, NE, p. A394
BRUS, Sarah, Director Human Resources, Doctor's Memorial Hospital, Perry, FL, p. A140
BRUSSEAU, Margie, R.N. Chief Nursing Officer, Starr Regional Medical Center, Athens, TN, p. A574
BRUTON, Jeff, Director Human Resources, Fairview Park Hospital, Dublin, GA, p. A156
BRUUN, Edward, President and Chief Executive Officer, Sparrow Clinton Hospital, Saint Johns, MI, p. A329
BRVENIK, Richard A., FACHE, President, Carteret Health Care, Morehead City, NC, p. A465
BRYAN, Darlene, R.N. Chief Nursing Officer, Humboldt General Hospital, Winnemucca, NV, p. A404
BRYAN, Douglas, President, Medical Staff, Mercy Harvard Hospital, Harvard, IL, p. A189
BRYAN, Jason, Director Human Resources, Middle Park Medical Center–Kremmling, Kremmling, CO, p. A105
BRYAN, Jay, President and Chief Executive Officer, Mercy Health, Lakeshore Campus, Shelby, MI, p. A330
BRYAN, Kenneth E., FACHE President and Chief Executive Officer, Harnett Health System, Dunn, NC, p. A459
BRYAN, Lynda, Vice President Human Resources, Northwest Medical Center, Margate, FL, p. A133
BRYAN, Margaret, Administrator, Shriners Hospitals for Children–Northern California, Sacramento, CA, p. A84
BRYAN, Mark, Chief Executive Officer, Delray Medical Center, Delray Beach, FL, p. A125
BRYAN, Sarah, Manager Human Resources, The Heart Hospital at Deaconess Gateway, Newburgh, IN, p. A217
BRYAN–SMITH, Lissa, Chief Administrative Officer, Geisinger–Bloomsburg Hospital, Bloomsburg, PA, p. A529
BRYANT, Amy, Chief Financial Officer, Cornerstone Hospital of Southwest Louisiana, Sulphur, LA, p. A286
BRYANT, Dawn L., Senior Vice President and Chief Human Resource Officer, Saint Francis Hospital and Medical Center, Hartford, CT, p. A112
BRYANT, Gayla, R.N., Administrator, Sage Rehabilitation Hospital, Baton Rouge, LA, p. A270
BRYANT, Gerald W., R.N. Chief Nursing Officer, Scott & White Memorial Hospital, Temple, TX, p. A647
BRYANT, Karen, Chief Support Services Officer, Prowers Medical Center, Lamar, CO, p. A106
BRYANT, Kay, Executive Director Human Resources, Saint Clare's Health System, Denville, NJ, p. A411
BRYANT, Kim, Chief Executive Officer, Highlands Medical Center, Scottsboro, AL, p. A24
BRYANT, Lisa G., Director Human Resources, Cannon Memorial Hospital, Pickens, SC, p. A564
BRYANT, Maureen A., FACHE, President, Northwestern Medicine Delnor Hospital, Geneva, IL, p. A189
BRYANT, Pam, Director Human Resources, Helen Keller Hospital, Sheffield, AL, p. A25
BRYANT, Ronald, President, Baystate Noble Hospital, Westfield, MA, p. A312
BRYANT, Rusty, Director Information Technology, Drew Memorial Hospital, Monticello, AR, p. A48
BRYANT, Valerie, Chief Financial Officer, Deckerville Community Hospital, Deckerville, MI, p. A317
BRYANT, William, Chief Executive Officer, LifeCare Hospital of Dayton, Miamisburg, OH, p. A494
BRYANT–MOBLEY, Phyllis, M.D. Director Medical Services, William S. Hall Psychiatric Institute, Columbia, SC, p. A560
BRYCE, Keith, Vice President Finance and Chief Financial Officer, Mt. Graham Regional Medical Center, Safford, AZ, p. A37
BRYCE, Lance, M.D. Chief Medical Officer, Brigham City Community Hospital, Brigham City, UT, p. A654
BRYDON, Paul, Chief Financial Officer, Antelope Valley Hospital, Lancaster, CA, p. A67
BRYER, Alex, Director Information Management, Los Robles Hospital and Medical Center, Thousand Oaks, CA, p. A94
BRYNER, Jennifer, Director Nursing, Petersburg Medical Center, Petersburg, AK, p. A29
BRYSON, Brent J., Chief Executive Officer, Pacific Grove Hospital, Riverside, CA, p. A83
BRYSON, Kellie, Director Human Resources, The Hospital at Westlake Medical Center, Austin, TX, p. A595
BUBENIK, Oldrich, M.D. Chief of Staff, Rush County Memorial Hospital, La Crosse, KS, p. A244
BUCCI, Annette, Senior Administrator Human Resources, Burke Rehabilitation Hospital, White Plains, NY, p. A454
BUCCI, Barbara A., R.N. Vice President Patient Care and Chief Nursing Officer, Mount St. Mary's Hospital and Health Center, Lewiston, NY, p. A436
BUCCIARELLI, Brant, Chief Information Officer, Riverview Hospital, Noblesville, IN, p. A218
BUCCOLO, Martin A., Ph.D., Chief Executive Officer, Four Winds Hospital, Katonah, NY, p. A435
BUCCULATO, Vito, Chief Operating Officer, Coney Island Hospital, NY, p. A439
BUCH, David, M.D. Chief Medical Officer, Carrier Clinic, Belle Mead, NJ, p. A409
BUCH, Naishadh, Chief Operating Officer, Lompoc Valley Medical Center, Lompoc, CA, p. A68
BUCHANAN, Dennis, Vice President Human Resources, New York Methodist Hospital, NY, p. A443
BUCHANAN, Donald E., Interim Chief Executive Officer, Haskell County Community Hospital, Stigler, OK, p. A515
BUCHANAN, Donna, Director Nursing, Stroud Regional Medical Center, Stroud, OK, p. A515
BUCHANAN, Herbert, President, Indiana University Health University Hospital, Indianapolis, IN, p. A212
BUCHANAN, Jean, Director Human Resources, Broughton Hospital, Morganton, NC, p. A465
BUCHANAN, Kevin, Chief Information Officer, Wake Forest Baptist Health–Lexington Medical Center, Lexington, NC, p. A464
BUCHANAN, Kyle, Chief Executive Officer, Lawrence Medical Center, Moulton, AL, p. A23
BUCHANAN, Robert, Chief Information Officer, Anna Jaques Hospital, Newburyport, MA, p. A309
BUCHANAN, Ron, Director Information Services, West Central Georgia Regional Hospital, Columbus, GA, p. A154
BUCHANAN, Toni, Chief Financial Officer, Unicoi County Memorial Hospital, Erwin, TN, p. A577
BUCHANAN, Tracy, Chief Executive Officer / President, CarePartners Health Services, Asheville, NC, p. A455
BUCHART, Phyllis, Chief Operating Officer, Marina Del Rey Hospital, Marina Del Rey, CA, p. A74
BUCHELE, Paula, Chief Human Resources, Bay Pines Veterans Affairs Healthcare System, Bay Pines, FL, p. A121
BUCHERT, Charles, Director Human Resources, Lake Area Medical Center, Lake Charles, LA, p. A278
BUCHHEIT, Anne, Coordinator Mental Health Local Information Systems, Buffalo Psychiatric Center, Buffalo, NY, p. A430
BUCHHEIT, Joe, Chief Financial Officer, Our Lady of Bellefonte Hospital, Ashland, KY, p. A254
BUCHHOLZ, Kari, Director Health Information Management, Wishek Community Hospital and Clinics, Wishek, ND, p. A477
BUCHHOLZ, Thomas, M.D. Physician–in–Chief and Executive Vice President, University of Texas M.D. Anderson Cancer Center, Houston, TX, p. A622
BUCHNESS, Michael P., M.D. Director Medical, Deer's Head Hospital Center, Salisbury, MD, p. A300
BUCIENSKI, Jennifer C., Vice President Human Resources, Hayes Green Beach Memorial Hospital, Charlotte, MI, p. A316
BUCK, Catherine, President, Froedtert Memorial Lutheran Hospital, Milwaukee, WI, p. A706
BUCK, Cindy D., Chief Executive Officer, Rutherford Regional Health System, Rutherfordton, NC, p. A468
BUCK, Gwen, R.N. Chief Nursing Officer, Greater Regional Medical Center, Creston, IA, p. A225
BUCK, Linda K., Vice President Human Resources, UnityPoint Health–Proctor, Peoria, IL, p. A198
BUCK, Nathan, R.N. Nursing Manager, Mountain River Birthing and Surgery Center, Blackfoot, ID, p. A172
BUCK, Phylis, Controller, HEALTHSOUTH Rehabilitation Hospital of Texarkana, Texarkana, TX, p. A647
BUCK, Tavia
Chief Nursing Officer, Roper St. Francis Mount Pleasant Hospital, Mount Pleasant, SC, p. A563
Interim Chief Executive Officer, Roper St. Francis Mount Pleasant Hospital, Mount Pleasant, SC, p. A563
BUCK, William, Chief of Staff, Horton Community Hospital, Horton, KS, p. A242
BUCKELEW, Rick, Chief Executive Officer, Austin Lakes Hospital, Austin, TX, p. A593
BUCKHOY, Sandra, Chief Clinical Officer, Kindred Hospital Chicago–Northlake, Northlake, IL, p. A196
BUCKLEY, David, Acting Chief Information Management Services, Oklahoma City Veterans Affairs Medical Center, Oklahoma City, OK, p. A512
BUCKLEY, John, M.D. President Medical Staff, Vibra Hospital of Denver, Thornton, CO, p. A109

Index of Health Care Professionals

Index of Health Care Professionals / Buckley


BUCKLEY, Kalvin, Director Information Systems, Woodland Heights Medical Center, Lufkin, TX, p. A630
BUCKLEY, Karen L., R.N. Chief Nursing Officer, Community Behavioral Health Center, Fresno, CA, p. A62
BUCKLEY, Patrick, Vice President Human Resources, St. Elizabeth Medical Center, Utica, NY, p. A452
BUCKLEY, Peter, M.D., Interim Chief Executive Officer, Georgia Regents Medical Center, Augusta, GA, p. A151
BUCKLEY, William, M.D. Chief of Staff, Elkhart General Healthcare System, Elkhart, IN, p. A207
BUCKMINSTER, Joe, Manager Information Technology, Community Medical Center, Falls City, NE, p. A391
BUCKNER Jr., James E., FACHE, Chief Executive Officer, Dimmit Regional Hospital, Carrizo Springs, TX, p. A600
BUCKNER, Marlys, Chief Nursing Officer, Barton County Memorial Hospital, Lamar, MO, p. A371
BUCKNER, Terry, Chief Executive Officer, Pikes Peak Regional Hospital, Woodland Park, CO, p. A109
BUCKNER, Twila, Chief Nursing Officer, Cass Regional Medical Center, Harrisonville, MO, p. A368
BUCKWORTH, Albert Bennett, Director Human Resources, Primary Children's Hospital, Salt Lake City, UT, p. A658
BUDA, Jeff, Chief Information Officer, Floyd Medical Center, Rome, GA, p. A163
BUDD, Edward, President and Chief Executive Officer, Thorek Memorial Hospital, Chicago, IL, p. A185
BUDDE, Rex P., President and Chief Executive Officer, Southern Illinois Hospital Services, Carbondale, IL, p. B124
BUDIG, Aletha, R.N. Director Nursing, Ellinwood District Hospital, Ellinwood, KS, p. A239
BUDINGER, David P., Associate Director, Hunter Holmes McGuire Veterans Affairs Medical Center–Richmond, Richmond, VA, p. A672
BUDNICK, Michael J., FACHE Chief Operating Officer, Franklin Hospital District, Benton, IL, p. A179
BUDZINSKY, Chris, R.N. Vice President Nursing/CNO Alexian Brothers Acute Care Ministries, St. Alexius Medical Center, Hoffman Estates, IL, p. A191
BUE, Cheryl, Health Information Transcriptionist, Faulkton Area Medical Center, Faulkton, SD, p. A568
BUEHLER, Bonnie, Chief Information Officer, St. Mary Medical Center, Langhorne, PA, p. A538
BUELL, Jack, Director Information Services, Sutter Lakeside Hospital, Lakeport, CA, p. A67
BUENVENIDA, Brenda, Director, Hiram W. Davis Medical Center, Petersburg, VA, p. A670
BUER, Shane, Vice President, Human Resources, Mercy Medical Center–Clinton, Clinton, IA, p. A224
BUFFENBARGER, Andrew, Director of Human Resources, Compliance and Risk Management, Kirby Medical Center, Monticello, IL, p. A194
BUFFINGTON, John, Chief Operating Officer, San Juan Regional Medical Center, Farmington, NM, p. A424
BUFFINGTON, Mike, Manager Information Technology, Kansas Medical Center, Andover, KS, p. A237
BUGAYONG, Carol, Human Resources Director, HealthSouth Rehabilitation Hospital of Tallahassee, Tallahassee, FL, p. A144
BUGG, Robert, Chief Financial Officer, Broward Health North, Deerfield Beach, FL, p. A125
BUGNA, Eric, M.D. Chief of Staff, Eastern Plumas Health Care, Portola, CA, p. A81
BUHLKE, Brian, M.D. Medical Director, Genoa Medical Facilities, Genoa, NE, p. A392
BUIT, Timothy, Executive Vice President and Chief Financial Officer, Bellevue Hospital, Bellevue, OH, p. A480
BUKOWSKI, Cathy
Chief Financial Officer, Howard Young Medical Center, Woodruff, WI, p. A714
Regional Chief Financial Officer, Ministry Eagle River Memorial Hospital, Eagle River, WI, p. A700
Regional Chief Financial Officer, Ministry Saint Mary's Hospitals, Rhinelander, WI, p. A710
BULAU, Chris, Manager Information Technology, Ridgeview Sibley Medical Center, Arlington, MN, p. A334
BULEN, Susan, M.D. Medical Director, HEALTHSOUTH Rehabilitation Hospital of Southern Arizona, Tucson, AZ, p. A39
BULFIN, Joey, R.N., Interim Chief Executive Officer, St. Mary's Medical Center, West Palm Beach, FL, p. A147
BULLARD, Brandon
Chief Financial Officer, AllianceHealth Midwest, Midwest City, OK, p. A510
Chief Financial Officer, Bailey Medical Center, Owasso, OK, p. A513
Chief Financial Officer, Hillcrest Hospital Claremore, Claremore, OK, p. A505
BULLARD, Elizabeth, Chief Operating Officer, Northern Colorado Rehabilitation Hospital, Johnstown, CO, p. A105
BULLARD, John, Director Information Technology, St. Mary's Medical Center, Grand Junction, CO, p. A104
BULLARD, Patrick, Chief Financial Officer, Fayetteville Veterans Affairs Medical Center, Fayetteville, NC, p. A460
BULLARD, Timothy, M.D. Chief of Staff, Orlando Regional Medical Center, Orlando, FL, p. A138
BULLINGTON, Benjamin P., M.D. Chief of Staff, Pioneer Medical Center, Big Timber, MT, p. A381
BULLINGTON, Gina, Chief Nursing Officer, TriStar Horizon Medical Center, Dickson, TN, p. A577
BULLITT, Michael L., Chief Executive Officer, HEALTHSOUTH Rehabilitation Hospital–Wichita Falls, Wichita Falls, TX, p. A652
BULLOCK, David, Director Information Services, Northwest Medical Center, Tucson, AZ, p. A39
BULLOCK, Lance, M.D. Medical Director, St. James Behavioral Health Hospital, Gonzales, LA, p. A274
BULLOCK, Scott, Director Information Systems, Barstow Community Hospital, Barstow, CA, p. A56
BULMAN, Laurie, Director Human Resources, Winneshiek Medical Center, Decorah, IA, p. A226
BULMASH, Jack, M.D. Chief of Staff, Edward Hines, Jr. Veterans Affairs Hospital, Hines, IL, p. A190
BUMAN, Karen, Chief Nursing Executive, Myrtue Medical Center, Harlan, IA, p. A229
BUMANN, Tim, D.O. Chief of Staff, Abilene Regional Medical Center, Abilene, TX, p. A590
BUMBAUGH, Christopher
Executive Human Resources, Meritus Medical Center, Hagerstown, MD, p. A298
Corporate Director, Human Resources, Western Maryland Regional Medical Center, Cumberland, MD, p. A297
BUMGARDNER, Chuck
Director Information Systems, Southeast Georgia Health System Brunswick Campus, Brunswick, GA, p. A152
Director, Southeast Georgia Health System Camden Campus, Saint Marys, GA, p. A163
BUMGARNER, William J., President, Spencer Hospital, Spencer, IA, p. A235
BUMP, Cathy, R.N. Chief Nursing Officer, Methodist Ambulatory Surgery Hospital – Northwest, San Antonio, TX, p. A641
BUNCH, David V., Chief Executive Officer, Heritage Medical Center, Shelbyville, TN, p. A588
BUNCH, Elicia, Chief Executive Officer, Centennial Peaks Hospital, Louisville, CO, p. A107
BUNCH, Jimm, President and Chief Executive Officer, Park Ridge Health, Hendersonville, NC, p. A462
BUNCH, Kim, Director Information Technology, Marshall Medical Center North, Guntersville, AL, p. A20
BUNCH, Mark, Director Finance, Othello Community Hospital, Othello, WA, p. A681
BUNCH, Mike, Executive Vice President, Chief Operating Officer and Chief Financial Officer, KershawHealth, Camden, SC, p. A557
BUNCH, Terri, R.N. Chief Nursing Officer, Hopkins County Memorial Hospital, Sulphur Springs, TX, p. A646
BUND, Linda, Chief Information Officer and Director Education, James J. Peters Veterans Affairs Medical Center, NY, p. A440
BUNGER, Mary, R.N. Director Nursing Services, Kearney County Health Services, Minden, NE, p. A394
BUNKER, Marla, Vice President Nursing and Chief Operating Officer, War Memorial Hospital, Sault Sainte Marie, MI, p. A330
BUNN, Barry, M.D. Chief of Staff, Vidant Edgecombe Hospital, Tarboro, NC, p. A469
BUNNER, Blake, Chief Executive Officer, HEALTHSOUTH Deaconess Rehabilitation Hospital, Evansville, IN, p. A208
BUNSELMEYER, Becky, Director Information Services, Memorial Hospital, Chester, IL, p. A181
BUNTEN, Sherry, Director Patient Care Services, Langlade Hospital, Antigo, WI, p. A697
BUNTING, Katherine, Chief Executive Officer, Fairfield Memorial Hospital, Fairfield, IL, p. A188
BUNTON, William Ralph, Supervisor Information Technology, Marshall Browning Hospital, Du Quoin, IL, p. A186
BUNTYN, Diane, MSN Vice President Patient Care Services, Southeast Alabama Medical Center, Dothan, AL, p. A19
BUNYARD, Steve
President, OhioHealth Dublin Methodist Hospital, Dublin, OH, p. A489
President, OhioHealth Grady Memorial Hospital, Delaware, OH, p. A488
BUONGIORNO, Michael J.
Executive Vice President Finance and Chief Financial Officer, Bryn Mawr Hospital, Bryn Mawr, PA, p. A530
Vice President Finance, Lankenau Medical Center, Wynnewood, PA, p. A554
BUPP, Steven, M.D. Medical Director, Sonora Behavioral Health Hospital, Tucson, AZ, p. A40
BURASCO, Carmen, Director Human Resources, Siloam Springs Regional Hospital, Siloam Springs, AR, p. A50
BURBANK, Jimmy, Chief Information Officer, U. S. Public Health Service Indian Hospital, Crownpoint, NM, p. A424
BURCH, Debra, Chief Nursing Officer, Burke Medical Center, Waynesboro, GA, p. A167
BURCH, Eric, Chief Executive Officer, Lewis County General Hospital, Lowville, NY, p. A436
BURCH, Lee, Director Management Information Systems, Bayfront Health Brooksville, Brooksville, FL, p. A123
BURCHAM Sr., Michael G., FACHE, Chief Executive Officer, Thayer County Health Services, Hebron, NE, p. A392
BURCHELL, Pam, Director Human Resources, Lawnwood Regional Medical Center & Heart Institute, Fort Pierce, FL, p. A127
BURCHETT, Claudia L., R.N. Vice President of Patient Services, Southern Ohio Medical Center, Portsmouth, OH, p. A496
BURCHETT, Travis, Troop Commander Human Resources, Colonel Florence A. Blanchfield Army Community Hospital, Fort Campbell, KY, p. A256
BURCHILL, Kevin, Chief Executive Officer, Arbour–Fuller Hospital, Attleboro, MA, p. A302
BURCZEUSKI, Jason
Controller, Arms Acres, Carmel, NY, p. A431
Controller, Conifer Park, Glenville, NY, p. A434
BURD, Vanessa, R.N. Chief Nursing Officer, Caverna Memorial Hospital, Horse Cave, KY, p. A258
BURDEN, Jennifer, Human Resources Director, TriStar Centennial Medical Center, Nashville, TN, p. A586
BURDICK, Ginny
Senior Vice President and Chief Human Resources Officer, Clovis Community Medical Center, Clovis, CA, p. A58
Vice President Human Resources, Community Behavioral Health Center, Fresno, CA, p. A62
Vice President Human Resources, Community Regional Medical Center, Fresno, CA, p. A62
BURDICK, Hoyt J., M.D. Vice President Medical Affairs, Cabell Huntington Hospital, Huntington, WV, p. A691
BURDICK, Steven A., Chief Executive Officer, Providence St. Mary Medical Center, Walla Walla, WA, p. A687
BURG, Andrew, M.D. Chief of Staff, St. Mary Medical Center, Long Beach, CA, p. A68
BURGER, Janice, Chief Executive, Providence St. Vincent Medical Center, Portland, OR, p. A524
BURGESS, Angela, Chief Information Officer, Randolph Hospital, Asheboro, NC, p. A455
BURGESS, Daniel, Chief Information Officer, MaineGeneral Medical Center, Augusta, ME, p. A288
BURGESS, John, Director Information Services, Hocking Valley Community Hospital, Logan, OH, p. A492
BURGESS, Robert L., President and Chief Executive Officer, St. Elizabeth Hospital, Gonzales, LA, p. A274
BURGESS, Steven, Administrator Human Resources, Henrico Doctors' Hospital, Richmond, VA, p. A672
BURGIN, Kelli, Director Information Technology, Audubon County Memorial Hospital, Audubon, IA, p. A222
BURGOS, Odette, Supervisor Human Resources, San Jorge Children's Hospital, San Juan, PR, p. A724
BURGUILLOS, Richard, Chief Financial Officer, Care One at Raritan Bay Medical Center, Perth Amboy, NJ, p. A416
BURGUS, Aurelis, Nursing Director, Ryder Memorial Hospital, Humacao, PR, p. A721
BURICK, Adam, M.D. Chief Medical Officer, Post Acute Northshore Specialty Hospital, Covington, LA, p. A272
BURICK, Marsha, Chief Financial Officer, Central Florida Behavioral Hospital, Orlando, FL, p. A137
BURINGRUD, Duane, M.D. Chief Medical and Quality Officer, Palomar Medical Center, Escondido, CA, p. A60
BURISH, Brent, Chief Executive Officer, St. Cloud Regional Medical Center, Saint Cloud, FL, p. A141
BURK, Thomas J., Chief Operating Officer, Danville State Hospital, Danville, PA, p. A532
BURKE, Brian, M.D. President Medical Staff, Fairview Hospital, Great Barrington, MA, p. A307
BURKE, Christopher D., Director, Colorado Mental Health Institute at Fort Logan, Denver, CO, p. A101
BURKE, David J., Director Finance and Chief Financial Officer, Nantucket Cottage Hospital, Nantucket, MA, p. A309
BURKE, Dennis E., President and Chief Executive Officer, Good Shepherd Health Care System, Hermiston, OR, p. A521
BURKE, Dorothy, Chief Financial Officer, Southeast Colorado Hospital District, Springfield, CO, p. A108
BURKE, Ed, Chief Financial Officer, Interim LSU Public Hospital, New Orleans, LA, p. A282
BURKE, Greg, M.D. Medical Director, Geisinger HEALTHSOUTH Rehabilitation Hospital, Danville, PA, p. A532
BURKE, Jack J., R.N., Interim Chief Executive Officer, Antelope Valley Hospital, Lancaster, CA, p. A67


A798 Index of Health Care Professionals 

Index of Health Care Professionals / Burton

BURKE, James, M.D
Senior Vice President and Chief Medical Officer, HonorHealth Scottsdale Osborn Medical Center, Scottsdale, AZ, p. A37
Senior Vice President and Chief Medical Officer, HonorHealth Scottsdale Shea Medical Center, Scottsdale, AZ, p. A37
Senior Vice President and Chief Medical Officer, HonorHealth Scottsdale Thompson Peak Medical Center, Scottsdale, AZ, p. A37
BURKE, James B., Chief Operating Officer, Hahnemann University Hospital, Philadelphia, PA, p. A543
BURKE, Jeff, Chief Information Officer, Bon Secours–Richmond Community Hospital, Richmond, VA, p. A671
BURKE, John, Chief Financial Officer, Nyack Hospital, Nyack, NY, p. A446
BURKE, Julie, Director Human Resources, New England Sinai Hospital and Rehabilitation Center, Stoughton, MA, p. A312
BURKE, Kaye, Administrator, Noland Hospital Dothan, Dothan, AL, p. A19
BURKE, Marsha, Senior Vice President and Chief Financial Officer, WellStar Windy Hill Hospital, Marietta, GA, p. A161
BURKE, Michael, Senior Vice President and Corporate Chief Financial Officer, NYU Langone Medical Center, New York, NY, p. A443
BURKE, Paul, Administrator, Schleicher County Medical Center, Eldorado, TX, p. A612
BURKE, Rebecca, R.N. Senior Vice President and Chief Nursing Officer, Kent County Memorial Hospital, Warwick, RI, p. A556
BURKE, Rose, Associate Director Patient Care Services, Marion Veterans Affairs Medical Center, Marion, IL, p. A193
BURKE, Timothy, Chief Executive Officer, AMG Specialty Hospital–Slidell, Slidell, LA, p. A285
BURKE, Timothy, M.D. Medical Director, The Brook Hospital – KMI, Louisville, KY, p. A262
BURKEL, Gregory, Chief Financial Officer, Mitchell County Regional Health Center, Osage, IA, p. A232
BURKET, Mark, Chief Executive Officer, Platte Health Center Avera, Platte, SD, p. A570
BURKETT, Doug, Manager Information Technology, L. V. Stabler Memorial Hospital, Greenville, AL, p. A20
BURKETT, Eric, M.D. Vice President Medical Affairs, Monmouth Medical Center, Long Branch Campus, Long Branch, NJ, p. A413
BURKETT, Evan, Chief Human Resource Officer, Sanford USD Medical Center, Sioux Falls, SD, p. A571
BURKEY, Brent, M.D. Chief Medical Officer, Fairview Hospital, Cleveland, OH, p. A484
BURKEY, Kathleen, R.N. Vice President of Nursing, Grand View Health, Sellersville, PA, p. A549
BURKHARDT, Minnie, Administrator, AllianceHealth Madill, Madill, OK, p. A509
BURKHARDT, Raye, Chief Nursing Officer, St. John's Pleasant Valley Hospital, Camarillo, CA, p. A57
BURKHART, Brad, Assistant Administrator, Harlan ARH Hospital, Harlan, KY, p. A258
BURKHART, James R., FACHE, President and Chief Executive Officer, Tampa General Hospital, Tampa, FL, p. A145
BURKHART, Steven, M.D. Chief Medical Officer, Crittenden County Hospital, Marion, KY, p. A262
BURKHART, Tracy, Vice President Information Services, Sacred Heart Hospital, Allentown, PA, p. A528
BURKHOLDER, Adrienne, Director Human Resources, AMG Specialty Hospital–Wichita, Wichita, KS, p. A252
BURKHOLDER–MCNUTT, Kim, Chief Executive Officer, Advanced Specialty Hospital of Toledo, Toledo, OH, p. A498
BURKITT, David, Director Fiscal Services, Shriners Hospitals for Children–Los Angeles, Los Angeles, CA, p. A72
BURKS, Felicia, Chief Financial Officer, U. S. Air Force Regional Hospital, Elmendorf AFB, AK, p. A28
BURKS, Matt, Director Information Technology, United Regional Medical Center, Manchester, TN, p. A582
BURKS, Mel, Chief Executive Officer, Hamilton Center, Terre Haute, IN, p. A220
BURKS, Tami
Chief Fiscal Services, Iraan General Hospital, Iraan, TX, p. A624
Comptroller, Rankin Hospital District, Rankin, TX, p. A638
BURLESON, Linda, Administrative Secretary, Clay County Memorial Hospital, Henrietta, TX, p. A618
BURLESON, Stan, M.D. Chief Medical Staff, DeWitt Hospital, De Witt, AR, p. A43
BURLING, Chris, M.D. Chief of Staff, Titus Regional Medical Center, Mount Pleasant, TX, p. A633
BURMAN, Don
Director, Veterans Affairs Nebraska–Western Iowa Health Care System, Omaha, NE, p. A397
Director, Veterans Affairs Nebraska–Western Iowa Health Care System – Lincoln, Lincoln, NE, p. A394
BURMEISTER, Brian
Senior Vice President, Appleton Medical Center, Appleton, WI, p. A697
Senior Vice President, ThedaCare Hospitals, Theda Clark Medical Center, Neenah, WI, p. A707
BURMEISTER, Geraldine F., FACHE, Chief Executive Officer, Windom Area Hospital, Windom, MN, p. A349
BURMESTER, Mark A., Vice President Strategy and Communications, Kaiser Permanente Sunnyside Medical Center, Clackamas, OR, p. A520
BURNAM, Gregg, Chief Information Officer and Manager Business Office, Quartz Mountain Medical Center, Mangum, OK, p. A509
BURNELL, Lori, R.N. Senior Vice President and Chief Nursing Officer, Valley Presbyterian Hospital, CA, p. A73
BURNES BOLTON, Linda, R.N. Vice President and Chief Nursing Officer, Cedars–Sinai Medical Center, Los Angeles, CA, p. A69
BURNETT, Anthony, M.D. Medical Director, Julian F. Keith Alcohol and Drug Abuse Treatment Center, Black Mountain, NC, p. A455
BURNETT, Brad, Chief Financial Officer, Heart of Texas Memorial Hospital, Brady, TX, p. A598
BURNETT, Cindi, Chief Human Resources Officer, Madison County Memorial Hospital, Madison, FL, p. A132
BURNETT, Mark, President and Chief Executive Officer, Scott County Hospital, Scott City, KS, p. A250
BURNETT, Michael, Chief Executive Officer, Piedmont Fayette Hospital, Fayetteville, GA, p. A157
BURNETT, Rob, Director Human Resources, Jordan Valley Medical Center–WVC Campus, West Valley City, UT, p. A659
BURNETT, Tasha, Director of Nursing, Falls Community Hospital and Clinic, Marlin, TX, p. A631
BURNETTE, Linda, R.N. Chief Nursing Officer, Southern Virginia Regional Medical Center, Emporia, VA, p. A664
BURNETTE, Peg, Chief Financial Officer, Denver Health, Denver, CO, p. A101
BURNETTE, Sheri, R.N., Chief Executive Officer and Administrator, Cornerstone Hospital of Bossier City, Bossier City, LA, p. A270
BURNETTE, W. Scott, Chief Executive Officer, VCU Community Memorial Hospital, South Hill, VA, p. A673
BURNEY, Sibte, M.D. Senior Vice President Medical Affairs and Chief Medical Officer, Kingsbrook Jewish Medical Center, NY, p. A441
BURNHAM, Sharon, Director of Nursing, Simpson General Hospital, Mendenhall, MS, p. A357
BURNS, Barry, Vice President, Methodist Ambulatory Surgery Hospital – Northwest, San Antonio, TX, p. A641
BURNS, Becky L., Manager Health Information Management, Ellinwood District Hospital, Ellinwood, KS, p. A239
BURNS, Bruce R., Chief Financial Officer, Concord Hospital, Concord, NH, p. A405
BURNS, Christal, R.N. Chief Nursing Officer, Care Regional Medical Center, Aransas Pass, TX, p. A592
BURNS, Coreg, Human Resources Lead, West Central Georgia Regional Hospital, Columbus, GA, p. A154
BURNS, Darlene A., R.N., Interim Chief Executive Officer, Rome Memorial Hospital, Rome, NY, p. A449
BURNS, Helen K., Ph.D
Senior Vice President and Chief Nursing Officer, Excela Frick Hospital, Mount Pleasant, PA, p. A541
Senior Vice President and Chief Nursing Officer, Excela Health Westmoreland Hospital, Greensburg, PA, p. A535
Senior Vice President and Chief Nursing Officer, Excela Latrobe Area Hospital, Latrobe, PA, p. A538
BURNS, Helene M., MSN Chief Nursing Executive, Kennedy Health System, Cherry Hill, NJ, p. A410
BURNS, Jared, Coordinator Human Resources, Regency Hospital of Hattiesburg, Hattiesburg, MS, p. A354
BURNS, Jeff, Manager of Information Technology, Mary Free Bed Rehabilitation Hospital, Grand Rapids, MI, p. A320
BURNS, Jon P.
Chief Information Officer, University of Maryland Medical Center, Baltimore, MD, p. A295
Senior Vice President and Chief Information Officer, University of Maryland Medical Center Midtown Campus, Baltimore, MD, p. A295
BURNS, Katherine, Vice President Human Resources, High Point Regional Health System, High Point, NC, p. A462
BURNS, Kathryn I., R.N. Director of Nursing, Medicine Lodge Memorial Hospital, Medicine Lodge, KS, p. A246
BURNS, Jr., Larry P., Chief Operating Officer, Yavapai Regional Medical Center, Prescott, AZ, p. A36
BURNS, Patrick, Vice President Finance, ACMH Hospital, Kittanning, PA, p. A537
BURNS, Rhonda, Director Human Resources, Caldwell Medical Center, Princeton, KY, p. A265
BURNS, Sonda, Chief Executive Officer, Select Specialty Hospital–Akron, Akron, OH, p. A478
BURNS, Steven, Director Fiscal Services, Summit Behavioral Healthcare, Cincinnati, OH, p. A483
BURNS, Terry M.
President, Greene Memorial Hospital, Xenia, OH, p. A501
Administrator, Senior Vice President of KHN, Soin Medical Center, Beavercreek, OH, p. A479
BURNS, Tom, M.D. Chief of Staff, The Hospital at Westlake Medical Center, Austin, TX, p. A595
BURNS–TISDALE, Susan, Senior Vice President Clinical Operations, Interim CNO, Exeter Hospital, Exeter, NH, p. A406
BURNSIDE, Brian D., FACHE, Chief Executive Officer, Connally Memorial Medical Center, Floresville, TX, p. A612
BURPEE, Scott, President, Safe Haven Health Care, Pocatello, ID, p. B115
BURRAGE, Chris, Manager Information Technology, Coalinga Regional Medical Center, Coalinga, CA, p. A58
BURRELL, Carol H., President and Chief Executive Officer, Northeast Georgia Medical Center, Gainesville, GA, p. A158
BURRESS, Lori, Vice President Patient Services and Chief Nursing Officer, Mt. Graham Regional Medical Center, Safford, AZ, p. A37
BURRIS, Bradley D., Chief Executive Officer, Pipestone County Medical Center Avera, Pipestone, MN, p. A344
BURRIS, Don, Chief Executive Officer, Foundation Surgical Hospital of El Paso, El Paso, TX, p. A610
BURRIS, J. Michael
Vice President Corporate Services and Chief Financial Officer, Martha Jefferson Hospital, Charlottesville, VA, p. A663
Chief Financial Officer, Sentara RMH Medical Center, Harrisonburg, VA, p. A666
BURRIS, Lisa
Manager Human Resources, Frazier Rehab Institute, Louisville, KY, p. A261
Director Human Resources, Southern Indiana Rehabilitation Hospital, New Albany, IN, p. A217
BURRISS, Jessica, Chief Financial Officer, HEALTHSOUTH Rehabilitation Hospital of Columbia, Columbia, SC, p. A559
BURRISS, Steve W., Interim President, Rex Healthcare, Raleigh, NC, p. A467
BURRISS, Tracie, Chief Financial Officer, Wills Memorial Hospital, Washington, GA, p. A167
BURROUGHS, James, Chief Executive Officer, Kingwood Pines Hospital, Kingwood, TX, p. A626
BURROUGHS, Michael R., FACHE, Chief Executive Officer, Western Plains Medical Complex, Dodge City, KS, p. A239
BURROUGHS, Steven, Chief Financial Officer, Palms West Hospital, Loxahatchee, FL, p. A132
BURROUGHS, Valentine, M.D. Chief Medical Officer, East Orange General Hospital, East Orange, NJ, p. A411
BURROW, Debbie, R.N. Chief Nursing Officer, Saline Memorial Hospital, Benton, AR, p. A41
BURROWS, Susan M., Vice President Human Resources, Martin Luther King, Jr. Community Hospital, Los Angeles, CA, p. A71
BURRUS, Gary, Director Information Technology, Winner Regional Healthcare Center, Winner, SD, p. A573
BURT, Alan, Director Information Services, Sunrise Hospital and Medical Center, Las Vegas, NV, p. A403
BURT, Gregory, M.D. Chief Medical Officer, Colusa Regional Medical Center, Colusa, CA, p. A58
BURT, Keith, Director Marketing, Woodrow Wilson Rehabilitation Center, Fishersville, VA, p. A665
BURT, Linda K.
Corporate Vice President Finance, Methodist Jennie Edmundson Hospital, Council Bluffs, IA, p. A225
Corporate Vice President Finance, Nebraska Methodist Hospital, Omaha, NE, p. A396
BURT, Noel F., Ph.D. Chief Human Resources Officer, Moses H. Cone Memorial Hospital, Greensboro, NC, p. A461
BURT, Wilton M., Chief Executive Officer, Vibrant Healthcare, Dallas, TX, p. B150
BURTCH, Gloria, Director Human Resources, Cornerstone of Medical Arts Center Hospital, Fresh Meadows, NY, p. A433
BURTCHELL, Scott, Director Information Systems, Maine Coast Memorial Hospital, Ellsworth, ME, p. A290
BURTHAY, Darcy, MSN Chief Nursing Officer and Chief Operating Officer, St. Vincent Indianapolis Hospital, Indianapolis, IN, p. A212
BURTON, Angela, Privacy Officer, Wayne County Hospital, Monticello, KY, p. A263
BURTON, Carmella, Chief Nursing Officer, AnMed Health Rehabilitation Hospital, Anderson, SC, p. A557
BURTON, Charles, Chief Human Resources, Carl R. Darnall Army Medical Center, Fort Hood, TX, p. A612
BURTON, Cynthia, R.N. Chief Nursing Officer, Rockcastle Regional Hospital and Respiratory Care Center, Mount Vernon, KY, p. A263
BURTON, Faye, Director Health Information Management, Edgefield County Hospital, Edgefield, SC, p. A560

Index of Health Care Professionals

Index of Health Care Professionals

Index of Health Care Professionals / Burton

BURTON, James, Vice President and Chief Information Officer, Valley Health, Shenandoah Memorial Hospital, Woodstock, VA, p. A675
BURTON, Luanne, Director Human Resources, HEALTHSOUTH Rehabilitation Hospital of Columbia, Columbia, SC, p. A559
BURTON, Robert, Manager Finance, Utah State Hospital, Provo, UT, p. A657
BURTON, Stacey R., Director Human Resources, Muscogee Creek Nation Medical Center, Okmulgee, OK, p. A513
BURTRON, Sandra, MS Chief Nursing Officer, Crawford Memorial Hospital, Robinson, IL, p. A199
BURY, Peter, Vice President Finance, OhioHealth Riverside Methodist Hospital, Columbus, OH, p. A486
BURZYNSKI, Cheryl A., President, McLaren Bay Special Care, Bay City, MI, p. A315
BUSBEE, Cathy L., Chief Nursing Officer, Woodland Heights Medical Center, Lufkin, TX, p. A630
BUSBY, Jay, M.D. President Medical Staff, Franklin Medical Center, Winnsboro, LA, p. A287
BUSBY, Kathy, Medical Record Technician, Chillicothe Hospital District, Chillicothe, TX, p. A600
BUSCH, Michael D.
Executive Vice President and Chief Operating Officer, Excela Frick Hospital, Mount Pleasant, PA, p. A541
Executive Vice President and Chief Operating Officer, Excela Health Westmoreland Hospital, Greensburg, PA, p. A535
Executive Vice President and Chief Operating Officer, Excela Latrobe Area Hospital, Latrobe, PA, p. A538
Executive Vice President and Chief Operating Officer, Excela Latrobe Area Hospital, Latrobe, PA, p. A538
BUSCH, Rebecca, Chief Financial Officer, Spooner Health System, Spooner, WI, p. A711
BUSCH, Steve, Chief Operating Officer, Midwest Medical Center, Galena, IL, p. A188
BUSH, Amy, Vice President Operations, UPMC McKeesport, McKeesport, PA, p. A539
BUSH, Bruce A., M.D. Senior Vice President Medical Affairs, Indiana Regional Medical Center, Indiana, PA, p. A536
BUSH, Linda, Director of Finance, Franklin County Memorial Hospital, Franklin, NE, p. A391
BUSH, Mark E., Chief Executive Officer, Northwest Florida Community Hospital, Chipley, FL, p. A123
BUSH, Michael, M.D. Chief Medical Officer, Holy Rosary Healthcare, Miles City, MT, p. A385
BUSH, Stephen, Chief Financial Officer, TMC Healthcare, Tucson, AZ, p. A40
BUSH, Steven, Chief Medical Officer, Prairie du Chien Memorial Hospital, Prairie Du Chien, WI, p. A709
BUSH, William B., CP
Chief Financial Officer, University of South Alabama Children's and Women's Hospital, Mobile, AL, p. A22
Chief Financial Officer, University of South Alabama Medical Center, Mobile, AL, p. A22
BUSHART, Phyllis, R.N. Chief Operating Officer, Providence Tarzana Medical Center, CA, p. A72
BUSHART, Stephanie, Chief Financial Officer, Ochsner Medical Center–Baton Rouge, Baton Rouge, LA, p. A269
BUSHELL, Michael, Vice President Finance, Business Development and Support Services, Saint Anne's Hospital, Fall River, MA, p. A306
BUSHEY, Dale, Chief Financial Officer, OSS Orthopaedic Hospital, York, PA, p. A554
BUSHMAN, Jerry, Chief Nursing Officer, Brigham City Community Hospital, Brigham City, UT, p. A654
BUSHNELL, Kim, R.N. Chief Nursing Officer, Mercy Medical Center, Baltimore, MD, p. A294
BUSINELLE, Denise, Chief Financial Officer, Fairway Medical Center, Covington, LA, p. A272
BUSKEY, Irene, Director Human Resources, Southside Regional Medical Center, Petersburg, VA, p. A670
BUSS, Georganna, Chief Executive Officer, Harper County Community Hospital, Buffalo, OK, p. A504
BUSS, Theresa L., Regional Vice President Human Resources, Windham Hospital, Willimantic, CT, p. A116
BUSSELL, Walter, Chief Financial Officer, Memorial Hospital West, Pembroke Pines, FL, p. A139
BUSSIERE, Mark, Administrator Human Resources, New Hampshire Hospital, Concord, NH, p. A405
BUSSLER, David, Chief Information Officer, Sheridan Community Hospital, Sheridan, MI, p. A330
BUSTELO, Miguel J., Executive Director, Hospital de Psiquiatria, San Juan, PR, p. A723
BUTCHER, Kay, Director Health Information Management, Stonewall Jackson Memorial Hospital, Weston, WV, p. A696
BUTCHER, Scott, Chief Executive Officer, HEALTHSOUTH Rehabilitation Institute of San Antonio, San Antonio, TX, p. A640
BUTE, Phil, Manager Information Technology, Clay County Hospital, Flora, IL, p. A188
BUTERBAUGH, Roger W., Chief Human Resources Officer, Charlie Norwood Veterans Affairs Medical Center, Augusta, GA, p. A151
BUTERBAUGH, William, Director Support Services, Fulton County Medical Center, Mc Connellsburg, PA, p. A539
BUTIKOFER, Lon D., Ph.D., Chief Executive Officer, Regional Medical Center, Manchester, IA, p. A231
BUTKER, Jeff, Chief Information Officer, Memorial Hospital, Martinsville, VA, p. A668
BUTLER, Anita M., Chief Executive Officer, Spartanburg Hospital for Restorative Care, Spartanburg, SC, p. A565
BUTLER, Brad, Network Administrator, Barton County Memorial Hospital, Lamar, MO, p. A371
BUTLER, Carol A., R.N. VP Patient Care Services & Operations, St. Anthony North Health Campus, Westminster, CO, p. A109
BUTLER, Catherine, M.D. Chief Medical Staff, Hancock County Health System, Britt, IA, p. A223
BUTLER, Chris, Chief Information Officer, Monmouth Medical Center, Long Branch Campus, Long Branch, NJ, p. A413
BUTLER, Dana, M.D. Medical Director, Sunrise Canyon Hospital, Lubbock, TX, p. A629
BUTLER, David, President and Chief Executive Officer, Tillamook Regional Medical Center, Tillamook, OR, p. A526
BUTLER, David K., M.D. Chief Medical Officer, Dignity Health Arizona General Hospital, Laveen, AZ, p. A33
BUTLER, Debby
Director Human Resources, Wadley Regional Medical Center, Texarkana, TX, p. A647
Director Human Resources, Wadley Regional Medical Center at Hope, Hope, AR, p. A45
BUTLER, Everett A., Interim Chief Executive Officer, Pembina County Memorial Hospital and Wedgewood Manor, Cavalier, ND, p. A473
BUTLER, Keith L., Administrator, Reagan Memorial Hospital, Big Lake, TX, p. A597
BUTLER, Linda H., M.D. Chief Medical Officer, Rex Healthcare, Raleigh, NC, p. A467
BUTLER, Margaret, Vice President Human Resources, Abbott Northwestern Hospital, Minneapolis, MN, p. A342
BUTLER, Michael K., M.D. Executive Vice President and Chief Medical Officer, Jackson Health System, Miami, FL, p. A134
BUTLER, Peter W., President and Chief Operating Officer, Rush University Medical Center, Chicago, IL, p. A184
BUTLER, Randy, Chief Financial Officer, West Florida Hospital, Pensacola, FL, p. A140
BUTLER, Rosemary M., R.N. Chief Nurse Executive, Kaiser Permanente Riverside Medical Center, Riverside, CA, p. A83
BUTLER, Stuart, Director Information Technology, Sweeny Community Hospital, Sweeny, TX, p. A646
BUTRYN, Judith
Chief Executive Officer, Nexus Specialty Hospital, Shenandoah, TX, p. A643
Chief Executive Officer, Nexus Specialty Hospital The Woodlands, Spring, TX, p. A644
BUTT, Qasim, M.D. Chief Medical Officer, Acuity Hospital of South Texas, San Antonio, TX, p. A640
BUTTELL, Christine, Chief Operating Officer, Knoxville Hospital & Clinics, Knoxville, IA, p. A230
BUTTELL, Phil, Chief Operating Officer, Centerpoint Medical Center, Independence, MO, p. A368
BUTTER, Hazel, Manager Human Resources, Hammond–Henry Hospital, Geneseo, IL, p. A189
BUTTERFIELD, Jon
Chief Operating Officer, Jordan Valley Medical Center, West Jordan, UT, p. A659
Administrator and Chief Operating Officer, Jordan Valley Medical Center–WVC Campus, West Valley City, UT, p. A659
BUTTERFIELD, Scott, Chief Executive Officer, Select Specialty Hospital – Lincoln, Lincoln, NE, p. A394
BUTTERMORE, Bruce
Director Human Resources, Parkview LaGrange Hospital, LaGrange, IN, p. A214
Manager Human Resources, Parkview Noble Hospital, Kendallville, IN, p. A213
BUTTON, Charlie A., President and Chief Executive Officer, Star Valley Medical Center, Afton, WY, p. A715
BUTTS, Kim, System Nurse Executive, Anchor Hospital, Atlanta, GA, p. A149
BUTTS, Ursula N., FACHE Vice President of Patient Care Services, VCU Community Memorial Hospital, South Hill, VA, p. A673
BUTVILAS, Keith, M.D. Chief Medical Officer, PMH Medical Center, Prosser, WA, p. A682
BUTZER, John, M.D. Medical Director, Mary Free Bed Rehabilitation Hospital, Grand Rapids, MI, p. A320
BUTZLER, Hilary, Director Human Resources, Cumberland Memorial Hospital, Cumberland, WI, p. A699
BUUCK, Brian, Chief Executive Officer, Ridgeview Psychiatric Hospital and Center, Oak Ridge, TN, p. A587
BUXTON, Barton, Ed.D., President and Chief Executive Officer, McLaren Lapeer Region, Lapeer, MI, p. A324
BUYOK, Tammy K., Vice President Support Services, St. Peter's Hospital, Helena, MT, p. A384
BUZACHERO, Victor, Corporate Senior Vice President for Innovation, Human Resources and Performance Management, Scripps Green Hospital, La Jolla, CA, p. A66
BUZZANGA, Terra, Chief Nurse Executive, St. Louis Psychiatric Rehabilitation Center, Saint Louis, MO, p. A378
BYARS, Stephanie, Chief Nursing Officer, United Regional Medical Center, Manchester, TN, p. A582
BYBERG, Jeff, Manager Human Resources, Mammoth Hospital, Mammoth Lakes, CA, p. A74
BYDA, Jeff, Vice President Information Technology, Mercy Fitzgerald Hospital, Darby, PA, p. A532
BYDALEK, Julie, Director of Nursing, Franklin County Memorial Hospital, Franklin, NE, p. A391
BYERS, John, M.D
Chief of Staff, Ivinson Memorial Hospital, Laramie, WY, p. A716
Medical Director, Select Specialty Hospital–Tri Cities, Bristol, TN, p. A574
BYERS, Suzann, Director of Nursing, Southern Indiana Rehabilitation Hospital, New Albany, IN, p. A217
BYERS, William, Chief Technology Officer, Western Maryland Regional Medical Center, Cumberland, MD, p. A297
BYLER, Karen, Information Technology Generalist, Warren State Hospital, Warren, PA, p. A552
BYNUM, Chigger, Chief Financial Officer, John Randolph Medical Center, Hopewell, VA, p. A666
BYNUM, Dennis T., Interim Chief Financial Officer, Watsonville Community Hospital, Watsonville, CA, p. A97
BYNUM, Justin, Chief Financial Officer, Saint Anthony Hospital, Chicago, IL, p. A184
BYRD, Catherine, Vice President Patient Services, Parkview Noble Hospital, Kendallville, IN, p. A213
BYRD, David, Chief Financial Officer, The Hospitals of Providence Sierra Campus, El Paso, TX, p. A611
BYRD, Greg, Vice President Medical Affairs, Shenandoah Memorial Hospital, Woodstock, VA, p. A675
BYRD, Lisa, Interim President, Cape Fear Valley – Bladen County Hospital, Elizabethtown, NC, p. A460
BYRD, Lu, R.N. Vice President Hospital Operations and Chief Nursing Officer, Billings Clinic, Billings, MT, p. A381
BYRD, O. Wayne, M.D. Chief of Staff, H. C. Watkins Memorial Hospital, Quitman, MS, p. A360
BYRD–PELAEZ, Brenda, Chief Human Resources Management Office, Martinsburg Veterans Affairs Medical Center, Martinsburg, WV, p. A693
BYRNE, Bobbie, M.D
Vice President Chief Information Officer, Edward Hospital, Naperville, IL, p. A195
Vice President Information Systems and Chief Information Officer, Elmhurst Memorial Hospital, IL, p. A187
BYRNE, Frank J., Vice President Finance, Newport Hospital, Newport, RI, p. A555
BYRNES, Matthew C., M.D. Chief Medical Officer, St. Catherine Hospital, Garden City, KS, p. A240
BYROM, David, Chief Executive Officer, Coryell Memorial Hospital, Gatesville, TX, p. A616

## C

CAAMANO, Tero, Director Information Technology, Saint Clare's Health System, Denville, NJ, p. A411
CABALLERO, Rogelio, Chief Information Systems, San Jorge Children's Hospital, San Juan, PR, p. A724
CABANA, David, Director Management Information Systems, Southwest Memorial Hospital, Cortez, CO, p. A101
CABANAS, Deborah, R.N. Chief Nursing Officer, HEALTHSOUTH Rehabilitation Hospital of Western Massachusetts, Ludlow, MA, p. A308
CABEZZAS, Noel, Chief Operating Officer, Good Samaritan Hospital, Bakersfield, CA, p. A55
CABIGAO, Edwin, Chief Nursing Officer, Jewish Home of San Francisco, San Francisco, CA, p. A88
CABRAL, Joseph, Chief Human Resources Officer, Cleveland Clinic, Cleveland, OH, p. A484
CABRERA, Carlos, Executive Director, Industrial Hospital, San Juan, PR, p. A724
CABRERA, Daniel, Chief Nursing Officer, Doctors Hospital of Laredo, Laredo, TX, p. A627
CABRERA, Irma, Finance Director, Hospital San Carlos Borromeo, Moca, PR, p. A722
CABRERA, Sheelah, Chief Information Officer, La Rabida Children's Hospital, Chicago, IL, p. A182

A800 Index of Health Care Professionals

Index of Health Care Professionals / Cammenga

CACCIAMANI, John D., M.D., Chief Executive Officer, Chestnut Hill Hospital, Philadelphia, PA, p. A542
CACERES, Janet L., Chief Financial Officer, Paradise Valley Hospital, National City, CA, p. A77
CADE, Paul, Administrator and Chief Executive Officer, Baptist Memorial Hospital–Golden Triangle, Columbus, MS, p. A352
CADIGAN, Elizabeth, R.N. Senior Vice President Patient Care Services and Chief Nursing Officer, Cambridge Health Alliance, Cambridge, MA, p. A305
CADOGAN, David, Chief Medical Officer, Alaska Regional Hospital, Anchorage, AK, p. A27
CADORETTE, Brenda E., R.N. Chief Nursing Officer, Berkshire Medical Center, Pittsfield, MA, p. A310
CADWELL, Carrie, M.D. Chief Clinical Officer, Four County Counseling Center, Logansport, IN, p. A215
CADWELL, Maureen K., Chief Executive Officer, Weston County Health Services, Newcastle, WY, p. A717
CADY, Kathy, Coordinator Human Resources, Accounts Payable and Payroll, Safe Haven Hospital of Treasure Valley, Boise, ID, p. A172
CADY, Thomas, Vice President Human Resources, Heywood Hospital, Gardner, MA, p. A307
CADY, Tina, Controller, The Women's Hospital, Newburgh, IN, p. A217
CAFASSO, Michael, Vice President Operations, St. Mary–Corwin Medical Center, Pueblo, CO, p. A108
CAGGIANO, Richard, M.D. Chief Medical Officer, Pullman Regional Hospital, Pullman, WA, p. A682
CAGLE, Jennifer, Director of Nursing, Marion Regional Medical Center, Hamilton, AL, p. A21
CAGLE, Karen, Chief Nursing Officer, Select Specialty Hospital–Nashville, Nashville, TN, p. A585
CAGNA, Ralph A.
Director Information Technology Operations, Cleveland Clinic Health System South Market, Marymount Hospital, Garfield Heights, OH, p. A490
Director Information Technology, South Pointe Hospital, Warrensville Heights, OH, p. A500
CAHALAN, Jay P., Chief Executive Officer, Columbia Memorial Hospital, Hudson, NY, p. A435
CAHILL, Donna, Vice President Human Resources, Palisades Medical Center, North Bergen, NJ, p. A416
CAHILL, Joseph, President and Chief Operating Officer, South Shore Hospital, South Weymouth, MA, p. A311
CAHILL, Marty, Chief Executive Officer, Samaritan North Lincoln Hospital, Lincoln City, OR, p. A522
CAHO–MOONEY, Linda, Chief Financial Officer, Claiborne County Medical Center, Port Gibson, MS, p. A359
CAHOJ, Lindsey, Chief Nursing Officer, Select Specialty Hospital–Wichita, Wichita, KS, p. A252
CAIN, Amy, District Director Human Resources, Kindred Hospital South Philadelphia, Philadelphia, PA, p. A544
CAIN, Donna, Director Information Systems Department, Cypress Fairbanks Medical Center, Houston, TX, p. A619
CAIN, Heather L., Chief Executive Officer, Stewart Memorial Community Hospital, Lake City, IA, p. A230
CAIN, Julie, Administrator, Stone County Hospital, Wiggins, MS, p. A361
CAIN, Mark, Chief Executive Officer, Tennova Healthcare–LaFollette Medical Center, La Follette, TN, p. A581
CAIN, Roxie, Chief Financial Officer, Big Horn County Memorial Hospital, Hardin, MT, p. A384
CAIN, William, Controller, Penn Highlands Clearfield, Clearfield, PA, p. A531
CAINE, Claudia, President and Chief Operating Officer, NYU Lutheran, NY, p. A444
CAIRNS, Craig, M.D. Vice President Medical Affairs, Licking Memorial Hospital, Newark, OH, p. A495
CALABRESE, Joan L., Director Human Resources, Putnam Hospital Center, Carmel, NY, p. A431
CALABRESE, Steve, Vice President and Chief Financial Officer, Canyon Vista Medical Center, Sierra Vista, AZ, p. A38
CALAIS, C. Matthew, Senior Vice President and Chief Information Officer, Legacy Good Samaritan Hospital and Medical Center, Portland, OR, p. A524
CALAMARI, Frank A., President and Chief Executive Officer, Calvary Hospital, NY, p. A439
CALAMARI, Jacquelyn, MSN Vice President and Chief Nursing Officer, Middlesex Hospital, Middletown, CT, p. A113
CALANDRELLA, Paul, Chief Operating Officer, Mt. Ascutney Hospital and Health Center, Windsor, VT, p. A661
CALANDRIELLO, John, Vice President and Chief Financial Officer, Palisades Medical Center, North Bergen, NJ, p. A416
CALAWAY, Shearmaine, Director Human Resources, East Mississippi State Hospital, Meridian, MS, p. A357
CALBONE, Angelo G., President and Chief Executive Officer, Saratoga Hospital, Saratoga Springs, NY, p. A450
CALBY, Elizabeth, Vice President Human Resources, Advocate Good Samaritan Hospital, Downers Grove, IL, p. A186
CALDARI, Patricia, Vice President, Richmond University Medical Center, NY, p. A444
CALDAS, James, President, Putnam Hospital Center, Carmel, NY, p. A431
CALDAS, Robert, D.O. Chief Medical Officer, Southcoast Hospitals Group, Fall River, MA, p. A306
CALDEIRA, Amy, Director Information Technology and Systems, Fort Walton Beach Medical Center, Fort Walton Beach, FL, p. A127
CALDERA, Ken, Director Human Resources, Kessler Institute for Rehabilitation, West Orange, NJ, p. A420
CALDERON, Lizmari, Director Finance, Hospital De La Concepcion, San German, PR, p. A722
CALDERONE, John A., Ph.D., Chief Executive Officer, Olympia Medical Center, Los Angeles, CA, p. A71
CALDWELL, Bettie, Director Finance, Indiana University Health Blackford Hospital, Hartford City, IN, p. A210
CALDWELL, Carolyn P., Chief Executive Officer, Desert Regional Medical Center, Palm Springs, CA, p. A80
CALDWELL, Dari, FACHE, President and Chief Operating Officer, Novant Health Rowan Medical Center, Salisbury, NC, p. A468
CALDWELL, Eric, Director Finance, Northside Hospital–Forsyth, Cumming, GA, p. A155
CALDWELL, James, R.N. Chief Nursing Officer, Henry County Medical Center, Paris, TN, p. A587
CALDWELL, Matthew T., Chief Executive Officer, University Medical Center, Lebanon, TN, p. A581
CALDWELL, Paul, Facility Coordinator Information Technology Customer Relations, Page Hospital, Page, AZ, p. A34
CALDWELL, Steve, Vice President Finance and Chief Financial Officer, St. Mary's Hospital, Madison, WI, p. A704
CALDWELL Jr., William E., Chief Executive Officer, Wilson Medical Center, Wilson, NC, p. A470
CALEY, Carl, Chief Financial Officer, Spring Valley Hospital Medical Center, Las Vegas, NV, p. A402
CALHOUN, Cathy, Director Human Resources, River Point Behavioral Health, Jacksonville, FL, p. A129
CALHOUN, Joshua, M.D. Medical Director, Hawthorn Children Psychiatric Hospital, Saint Louis, MO, p. A376
CALHOUN, Kevin P., Chief Executive Officer, Munising Memorial Hospital, Munising, MI, p. A326
CALHOUN, Kirk A., M.D., President, University of Texas Health Northeast, Tyler, TX, p. A649
CALHOUN, Robert, Chief Executive Officer, Greenbrier Valley Medical Center, Ronceverte, WV, p. A695
CALHOUN, Timothy
Vice President Finance, Chief Financial Officer, Lakeland Hospital, Watervliet, Watervliet, MI, p. A332
Vice President Finance and Chief Financial Officer, Lakeland Medical Center, St. Joseph, Saint Joseph, MI, p. A329
CALHOUN, William
President, Community Hospitals, Health First Cape Canaveral Hospital, Cocoa Beach, FL, p. A124
President, Community Hospitals, Health First Palm Bay Hospital, Palm Bay, FL, p. A138
President, Community Hospitals, Health First Viera Hospital, Melbourne, FL, p. A133
CALIA, Christopher, Director Human Resources, Brazosport Regional Health System, Lake Jackson, TX, p. A627
CALIFORNIA, Randy, Chief Operating Officer, Warren General Hospital, Warren, PA, p. A551
CALIGIURI, Michael, Chief Executive Officer, James Cancer Hospital and Solove Research Institute, Columbus, OH, p. A485
CALIVA, Todd, Chief Executive Officer, West Houston Medical Center, Houston, TX, p. A623
CALKIN, Steven, D.O. Vice President Medical Affairs, McLaren Oakland, Pontiac, MI, p. A328
CALKINS, Paul, M.D. Chief Medical Officer, Indiana University Health North Hospital, Carmel, IN, p. A206
CALL, Brett, D.O. Chief of Staff, Berger Health System, Circleville, OH, p. A484
CALL, Carie, Computer Support, Cassia Regional Medical Center, Burley, ID, p. A173
CALL, Dave, M.D. Medical Director, Select Long Term Care Hospital – Colorado Springs, Colorado Springs, CO, p. A101
CALL, Stacie, R.N. Vice President Patient Care and Chief Nursing Officer, East Liverpool City Hospital, East Liverpool, OH, p. A489
CALLAGHAN, Barbara, Interim Chief Executive Officer, Atrium Medical Center of Corinth, Corinth, TX, p. A602
CALLAGHAN III, James, M.D., President and Chief Executive Officer, Franciscan St. Francis Health – Indianapolis, Indianapolis, IN, p. A211
CALLAHAN, Ame, Acting Manager Resource Management Service, Northern Arizona Veterans Affairs Health Care System, Prescott, AZ, p. A36
CALLAHAN, Charles D., Ph.D. Executive Vice President and Chief Operating Officer, Memorial Medical Center, Springfield, IL, p. A201
CALLAHAN, Christopher M., Vice President Human Resources, Exeter Hospital, Exeter, NH, p. A406
CALLAHAN, Deanna, Director Information Systems, Titusville Area Hospital, Titusville, PA, p. A550
CALLAHAN, Kelly, Public Information Officer, Elgin Mental Health Center, Elgin, IL, p. A187
CALLAHAN, Kevin J., President and Chief Executive Officer, Exeter Hospital, Exeter, NH, p. A406
CALLAHAN, Larry A., Senior Vice President Human Resources, Grady Memorial Hospital, Atlanta, GA, p. A150
CALLAHAN, Mark, Chief Operating Officer, Mary Lanning Healthcare, Hastings, NE, p. A392
CALLAHAN, Mary Beth, Chief Financial Officer, McLaren Lapeer Region, Lapeer, MI, p. A324
CALLAHAN, Neil, Chief Executive Officer, Brooke Glen Behavioral Hospital, Fort Washington, PA, p. A534
CALLAHAN Jr., Robert W., Director, Lebanon Veterans Affairs Medical Center, Lebanon, PA, p. A538
CALLAHAN, Shannon, Director Human Resources, Sitka Community Hospital, Sitka, AK, p. A29
CALLAHAN, Teresa, MSN, Chief Executive Officer, Iraan General Hospital, Iraan, TX, p. A624
CALLAHAN, William, Chief Information Management Division, Bayne–Jones Army Community Hospital, Fort Polk, LA, p. A273
CALLAN, C. M., M.D. Chief of Staff, Fisher County Hospital District, Rotan, TX, p. A639
CALLANAN, Patrick, Vice President Patient Care Services, Mercy Hospital Fort Scott, Fort Scott, KS, p. A240
CALLAS, Robin B., R.N. Vice President Human Resources, Rutherford Regional Health System, Rutherfordton, NC, p. A468
CALLECOD, David L., FACHE, President and CEO, Lafayette General Health, Lafayette, LA, p. B80
CALLENS, Don, M.D. Chief Medical Officer, Liberty Dayton Regional Medical Center, Liberty, TX, p. A628
CALLENS, Paul A., Ph.D., Director, North Mississippi State Hospital, Tupelo, MS, p. A361
CALLICOAT, William, Chief Financial Officer, Summit Pacific Medical Center, Elma, WA, p. A678
CALLISTE, Gregory, PHD Acting Executive Director, North Central Bronx Hospital, NY, p. A443
CALLISTER, T. Brian, M.D. Chief Medical Officer, Tahoe Pacific Hospitals, Sparks, NV, p. A404
CALLOWAY, Jennifer, Human Resources Coordinator, Asheville Specialty Hospital, Asheville, NC, p. A455
CALLOWAY, Maria, R.N. Chief Nursing Officer, Central Florida Regional Hospital, Sanford, FL, p. A142
CALMAN, Kurt, Chief Information Officer, United Memorial Medical Center, Batavia, NY, p. A429
CALUBAQUIB, Evelyn, Chief Nursing Officer, Greater El Monte Community Hospital, South El Monte, CA, p. A93
CALVARUSO, Gaspare, President, Capital Region Medical Center, Jefferson City, MO, p. A368
CALVERT, Mandy, Director Information Systems, Southern Coos Hospital and Health Center, Bandon, OR, p. A519
CALVERT, Regina, Chief Nursing Executive, Shelby Memorial Hospital, Shelbyville, IL, p. A200
CALVERT, Sarah, Chief Nursing Officer, McGehee–Desha County Hospital, McGehee, AR, p. A48
CALVIN, Jeff, Chief Financial Officer, Michiana Behavioral Health Center, Plymouth, IN, p. A218
CAMA, Joseph, M.D. President Medical Staff, Guthrie Towanda Memorial Hospital, Towanda, PA, p. A551
CAMACHO, Jose, Director Information Technology, Spanish Peaks Regional Health Center, Walsenburg, CO, p. A109
CAMARA, Robert, M.D. Chief Medical Officer, St. Joseph Mercy Port Huron, Port Huron, MI, p. A328
CAMARDELLO, Heidi, Vice President Patient Care Services and Chief Nursing Officer, Little Falls Hospital, Little Falls, NY, p. A436
CAMERON, Carl, Director Information Systems, Holyoke Medical Center, Holyoke, MA, p. A307
CAMERON, Don, Chief Operating Officer, Allegiance Behavioral Health Center of Plainview, Plainview, TX, p. A636
CAMERON, Kim, Manager Health Information Services, Patients' Hospital of Redding, Redding, CA, p. A82
CAMERON, Lana, Chief Nursing Officer, Central Texas Medical Center, San Marcos, TX, p. A643
CAMIRE, Patricia M., MS Senior Vice President Clinical Services and Chief Nursing Officer, Southern Maine Health Care – Biddeford Medical Center, Biddeford, ME, p. A289
CAMMACK, Geri, R.N. Director of Nursing, Lost Rivers Medical Center, Arco, ID, p. A172
CAMMENGA, Randall, M.D. Vice President Medical Affairs, Indiana University Health Goshen Hospital, Goshen, IN, p. A210

Index of Health Care Professionals

Index of Health Care Professionals

Index of Health Care Professionals / Camp

CAMP III, Claude E. Chip", FACHE, Chief Executive Officer, Brownwood Regional Medical Center, Brownwood, TX, p. A599
CAMP, David, Director Human Resources, Nor–Lea General Hospital, Lovington, NM, p. A425
CAMP, Julie A., R.N., Chief Executive Officer, Forest Park Medical Center Frisco, Frisco, TX, p. A615
CAMP, Lea Ann, R.N. Chief Nursing Officer, Greene County General Hospital, Linton, IN, p. A215
CAMPA, Melissa, Controller, Kindred Hospital El Paso, El Paso, TX, p. A611
CAMPANA, Thomas, M.D. Chief of Staff, Spectrum Health Reed City Hospital, Reed City, MI, p. A328
CAMPANELLA, Alfred, Chief Information Officer, Virtua Voorhees, Voorhees, NJ, p. A420
CAMPAS, Janice, Chief Financial Officer, Wichita County Health Center, Leoti, KS, p. A245
CAMPBELL, Amy, Chief Financial Officer, Community Hospital North, Indianapolis, IN, p. A211
CAMPBELL, April, Director Human Resources, Broadwater Health Center, Townsend, MT, p. A387
CAMPBELL, Belinda H., Director Human Resources, Legal Compliance and Risk Management, University Hospital McDuffie, Thomson, GA, p. A166
CAMPBELL, Bernard M., Administrator Human Resources, LewisGale Hospital Alleghany, Low Moor, VA, p. A667
CAMPBELL, Brian, Director Professional Services, U. S. Public Health Service Indian Hospital–Whiteriver, Whiteriver, AZ, p. A40
CAMPBELL, Carla, R.N. Chief Nurse Officer, Mercy Hospital and Medical Center, Chicago, IL, p. A183
CAMPBELL, Chad, Chief Executive Officer, McKenzie–Willamette Medical Center, Springfield, OR, p. A526
CAMPBELL, David, Administrator, Perry Hospital, Perry, GA, p. A162
CAMPBELL, David J., Executive Vice President Operations Systems Strategy and Growth, Beaumont Hospital – Trenton, Trenton, MI, p. A331
CAMPBELL, Dean, Vice President Information Services and Chief Information Officer, Good Samaritan Hospital, Los Angeles, CA, p. A70
CAMPBELL, Deborah, Administrator, Thomas H. Boyd Memorial Hospital, Carrollton, IL, p. A180
CAMPBELL, Debra, R.N., Administrator, Riverside Behavioral Health Center, Hampton, VA, p. A666
CAMPBELL, Emily, Senior Director Human Resources, Alice Hyde Medical Center, Malone, NY, p. A436
CAMPBELL, Eric, Chief Financial Officer, Oswego Hospital, Oswego, NY, p. A447
CAMPBELL, Gayla, Interim Chief Executive Officer, LifeCare Hospitals of Wisconsin, Pewaukee, WI, p. A709
CAMPBELL, Gina, R.N. Chief Operating Officer, Baystate Franklin Medical Center, Greenfield, MA, p. A307
CAMPBELL, Ivy, Director of Nursing, Community Medical Center, Falls City, NE, p. A391
CAMPBELL, John
  Chief Medical Officer, South Baldwin Regional Medical Center, Foley, AL, p. A19
  Director Information Systems, Spaulding Hospital for Continuing Medical Care Cambridge, Cambridge, MA, p. A306
  Director Management Information Systems, Spaulding Rehabilitation Hospital, Charlestown, MA, p. A306
  Chief Information Officer, Spaulding Rehabilitation Hospital Cape Cod, East Sandwich, MA, p. A306
CAMPBELL, Kathy, R.N. Interim Director of Nursing, Siskin Hospital for Physical Rehabilitation, Chattanooga, TN, p. A575
CAMPBELL, Kathy, Interim Chief Nursing Officer, Wellmont Holston Valley Medical Center, Kingsport, TN, p. A580
CAMPBELL, Kyle D., Commander, Brooke Army Medical Center, Fort Sam Houston, TX, p. A612
CAMPBELL, Melissa, Controller, Mercy Rehabilition Hospital Springfield, Springfield, MO, p. A379
CAMPBELL, Melvin, M.D. Medical Staff Chairman, Brown County Hospital, Ainsworth, NE, p. A389
CAMPBELL, Pamela, M.D. Medical Director, Lincoln Prairie Behavioral Health Center, Springfield, IL, p. A201
CAMPBELL Jr., Robert D., Interim Chief Executive Officer, Morton General Hospital, Morton, WA, p. A680
CAMPBELL, Rose, R.N., President, Penn Highlands Elk, Saint Marys, PA, p. A549
CAMPBELL, Sandra M., R.N. Chief Nursing Officer, Dodge County Hospital, Eastman, GA, p. A157
CAMPBELL, Stephen J., Chief Operating Officer, Pioneers Memorial Healthcare District, Brawley, CA, p. A56
CAMPBELL, Susie, Chief Executive Officer, Community Memorial Hospital, Staunton, IL, p. A201
CAMPBELL, Teresa, R.N. Chief Nursing Executive, Sutter Lakeside Hospital, Lakeport, CA, p. A67
CAMPBELL, Todd, Senior Vice President and Chief Operating Officer, St. Mary's Medical Center, Huntington, WV, p. A692
CAMPEAU, Arleen, R.N. Vice President of Patient Care Services, Chief Nursing Officer, Powell Valley Healthcare, Powell, WY, p. A717
CAMPION, John, Administrator, Essentia Health–Graceville, Graceville, MN, p. A339
CAMPO, Mary Beth, MS Director of Nursing, Eastern Niagara Hospital, Lockport, NY, p. A436
CAMPOS, Christina, Administrator, Guadalupe County Hospital, Santa Rosa, NM, p. A426
CAMPOS–DIAZ, Evelyn, Director Human Resources, MedStar St. Mary's Hospital, Leonardtown, MD, p. A299
CAMPS, Lourdes, R.N. Chief Nursing Officer, Hialeah Hospital, Hialeah, FL, p. A128
CANADY, Carolyn, Chief Financial Officer, Sierra Nevada Memorial Hospital, Grass Valley, CA, p. A64
CANADY, Ray B., Chief Executive Officer and Administrator, Knox County Hospital, Barbourville, KY, p. A254
CANALE, Joseph, Business Manager, Trenton Psychiatric Hospital, Trenton, NJ, p. A419
CANALEJO, Donald, Director Human Resources, Lower Keys Medical Center, Key West, FL, p. A130
CANALES, Joe
  Director Human Resources, Seton Edgar B. Davis Hospital, Luling, TX, p. A630
  Director Human Resources, Seton Shoal Creek Hospital, Austin, TX, p. A594
  Vice President Human Resources, University Medical Center at Brackenridge, Austin, TX, p. A595
CANARD, R. Shannon, Chief Executive Officer, Regency Hospital of Jackson, Jackson, MS, p. A355
CANARIOS, Mike, Vice President and Chief Financial Officer, St. Jude Children's Research Hospital, Memphis, TN, p. A584
CANCEL, Diana, Director Human Resources, Glendora Community Hospital, Glendora, CA, p. A64
CANCILLA, Deborah, Chief Information Officer, Grady Memorial Hospital, Atlanta, GA, p. A150
CANDIA, Gary R., FACHE, Chief Administrative Officer, Abington Health Lansdale Hospital, Lansdale, PA, p. A538
CANDILL, James W., M.D. President Medical Staff, Eye and Ear Clinic of Charleston, Charleston, WV, p. A690
CANDIO, Christine, President and Chief Executive Officer, St. Luke's Hospital, Chesterfield, MO, p. A365
CANDULLO, Carl, Chief Information Officer, Munroe Regional Medical Center, Ocala, FL, p. A137
CANEDO, Jim, Chief Financial Officer, College Medical Center, Long Beach, CA, p. A68
CANFIELD, Brian, Chief Operating Officer, FirstHealth Moore Regional Hospital, Pinehurst, NC, p. A466
CANIZARO, Tom, Vice President and Chief Financial Officer, South Central Regional Medical Center, Laurel, MS, p. A356
CANNIDA, Ieesha, Director Human Resources, Reliant Rehabilitation Hospital Dallas, Dallas, TX, p. A606
CANNIFF, Christopher, Executive Director, Human Resources, Harrington Memorial Hospital, Southbridge, MA, p. A311
CANNING, John, Chief Financial Officer, Blythedale Children's Hospital, Valhalla, NY, p. A452
CANNINGTON, H. D., Administrator, Campbellton Graceville Hospital, Graceville, FL, p. A128
CANNON, Brenda, R.N. Director of Nursing, Laughlin Memorial Hospital, Greeneville, TN, p. A578
CANNON, Gayle, Director Human Resources, Childress Regional Medical Center, Childress, TX, p. A600
CANNON, Linda, Chief Medical Records Services, San Diego County Psychiatric Hospital, San Diego, CA, p. A87
CANNON, Matt, Chief Executive Officer, Regency Hospital of Toledo, Sylvania, OH, p. A498
CANNON, Matthew, Chief Executive Officer, Select Specialty Hospital–Saginaw, Saginaw, MI, p. A329
CANNON, Pam
  Chief Human Resources Officer, Banner Baywood Medical Center, Mesa, AZ, p. A33
  Chief Human Resources Officer, Banner Heart Hospital, Mesa, AZ, p. A33
CANNON, Robert W., President, Barnes–Jewish Hospital, Saint Louis, MO, p. A376
CANO, Daniel, M.D. Chief Medical Officer, Citizens Medical Center, Victoria, TX, p. A650
CANTLEY, J. Scott, President and Chief Executive Officer, Marietta Memorial Hospital, Marietta, OH, p. A493
CANTRE, Pedro Laureano, Chief Nursing Officer, Cardiovascular Center of Puerto Rico and the Caribbean, San Juan, PR, p. A723
CANTRELL, Dedra
  Chief Information Officer, Emory Saint Joseph's Hospital of Atlanta, Atlanta, GA, p. A150
  Chief Information Officer, Emory University Hospital, atlanta, GA, p. A150
  Chief Information Officer, Emory University Hospital Midtown, Atlanta, GA, p. A150
CANTRELL, Eric, Chief Executive Officer, Kindred Hospital Tomball, Tomball, TX, p. A648
CANTRELL, Tara, Director Human Resources, Davis Hospital and Medical Center, Layton, UT, p. A655
CANTU, Janie, Director Human Resources, Crosbyton Clinic Hospital, Crosbyton, TX, p. A603
CAPANNARI, Margaret, Director Information Systems, Advocate Illinois Masonic Medical Center, Chicago, IL, p. A181
CAPECE Jr., Vincent G., President and Chief Executive Officer, Middlesex Hospital, Middletown, CT, p. A113
CAPILI, Anthony, M.D. Chief of Staff, Chambers County Public Hospital District 1, Anahuac, TX, p. A592
CAPIOLA, Richard, M.D. Chief Medical Officer, Baton Rouge Behavioral Hospital, Baton Rouge, LA, p. A269
CAPITELLI, Robert, M.D. Senior Vice President and Chief Medical Officer, St. Tammany Parish Hospital, Covington, LA, p. A272
CAPITULO, Kathleen, Ph.D. Chief Nurse Executive, James J. Peters Veterans Affairs Medical Center, NY, p. A440
CAPLAN, Margaret B., Director, Veterans Affairs Hudson Valley Health Care System, Montrose, NY, p. A438
CAPLER, Glenda, Interim Director of Nursing, Gordon Memorial Hospital, Gordon, NE, p. A392
CAPLES, Greg, Chief Operating Officer, TriStar Summit Medical Center, Hermitage, TN, p. A578
CAPOTE, Henry, Interim Chief Financial Officer, Coral Gables Hospital, Coral Gables, FL, p. A124
CAPOZELLO Jr., Fred, Chief Executive Officer, Valley View Medical Center, Fort Mohave, AZ, p. A31
CAPPEL, Blaine, Director Information Systems, Memorial Health System, Abilene, KS, p. A237
CAPPS, Kim, Chief Financial Officer, Hayes Green Beach Memorial Hospital, Charlotte, MI, p. A316
CAPPS, Melissa, Site Leader Information Technology, St. Luke's Magic Valley Medical Center, Twin Falls, ID, p. A176
CAPPS, Rick, Chief Financial Officer, Cumberland County Hospital, Burkesville, KY, p. A255
CAPUANO, Terry Ann, R.N
  Chief Operating Officer, Lehigh Valley Hospital, Allentown, PA, p. A528
  Chief Operating Officer, Lehigh Valley Hospital–Muhlenberg, Bethlehem, PA, p. A529
CAPUTO, Becky, Interim Director Human Resources, Cleveland Clinic Florida, Weston, FL, p. A147
CAPUTO, Louis, Chief Executive Officer, TriStar StoneCrest Medical Center, Smyrna, TN, p. A588
CARABALLO, Amanda, Nursing Director, Hospital De La Concepcion, San German, PR, p. A722
CARACCIOLO, Kevin, Chief Human Resources Officer, Palm Beach Gardens Medical Center, Palm Beach Gardens, FL, p. A138
CARACCIOLO, Mary Jo, Director Human Resources, Wellington Regional Medical Center, West Palm Beach, FL, p. A147
CARAMANICA, Laura J., Ph.D. Vice President and Chief Nursing Officer, WellStar Kennestone Hospital, Marietta, GA, p. A161
CARBALLO, Francisco R., M.D. Medical Director, Hospital HMA de Humacao, Humacao, PR, p. A721
CARBALLO, Jose E., Chief Executive Officer and Managing Director, Hospital San Pablo, Bayamon, PR, p. A720
CARBONE, Dominick, M.D. Chief of Staff, Hugh Chatham Memorial Hospital, Elkin, NC, p. A460
CARBONEL MASON, Wilma, Chief Nursing Officer, Fort Duncan Regional Medical Center, Eagle Pass, TX, p. A609
CARD, Dean, Chief Financial Officer, Kindred Hospital South Florida–Fort Lauderdale, Fort Lauderdale, FL, p. A127
CARDA, Greg, Vice President Finance, Missouri Delta Medical Center, Sikeston, MO, p. A378
CARDALI, Paul, M.D. Chief of Staff, Lakeway Regional Hospital, Morristown, TN, p. A584
CARDELL, Melinda H.
  Interim Vice President and Chief Information Officer, Roper Hospital, Charleston, SC, p. A558
  Interim Chief Information Officer, Roper St. Francis Mount Pleasant Hospital, Mount Pleasant, SC, p. A563
CARDEN, Lamar, M.D. Chief Medical Officer, Jack Hughston Memorial Hospital, Phenix City, AL, p. A24
CARDENAS, Al, M.D. President Medical Staff, Wilson N. Jones Regional Medical Center, Sherman, TX, p. A644
CARDENAS, Lydia, Director Human Resources, River Crest Hospital, San Angelo, TX, p. A640
CARDENAS, Mark, Director Plant Operations, Vibra Hospital of Northern California, Redding, CA, p. A82

A802 Index of Health Care Professionals 

Index of Health Care Professionals / Carrillo

Index of Health Care Professionals


CARDENAS, Mitzi
Chief Information Officer, Truman Medical Center–Hospital Hill, Kansas City, MO, p. A370
Chief Information Officer, Truman Medical Center–Lakewood, Kansas City, MO, p. A370
CARDENAS, Noel J., FACHE, Commander and Chief Executive Officer, Reynolds Army Community Hospital, Fort Sill, OK, p. A507
CARDILE, Eileen K., MS, Executive Vice President, Inspira Health Network and President and Chief Executive Officer, Inspira, Inspira Medical Center–Woodbury, Woodbury, NJ, p. A420
CARDIN, Deborah, MS, Chief Executive Officer, Jefferson County Health Center, Fairfield, IA, p. A227
CARDINAL, Joyce, Chief Nursing Executive, Jefferson Healthcare, Port Townsend, WA, p. A682
CARDLE, Lori, Senior Vice President, Chief Financial Officer, Valley Presbyterian Hospital, CA, p. A73
CARDWELL, Marian, Chief Financial Officer, Potomac Valley Hospital, Keyser, WV, p. A692
CAREY, Ann, Vice President and Chief Information Officer, St. Vincent's Medical Center Riverside, Jacksonville, FL, p. A130
CAREY, Bruce, Chief Executive Officer, Kindred Chicago–Central Hospital, Chicago, IL, p. A182
CAREY, Dorothy, Senior Vice President and Chief Nursing Officer, Olathe Medical Center, Olathe, KS, p. A247
CAREY, Eric R., Vice President Information Systems and Chief Information Officer, Valley Hospital, Ridgewood, NJ, p. A418
CAREY, Jeannie, R.N. Director Patient Care, Perry Memorial Hospital, Perry, OK, p. A513
CAREY, John, M.D. Chief Medical Director, Hamilton County Hospital, Syracuse, KS, p. A251
CAREY, Michele, Vice President Patient Care and Chief Nursing Officer, McLaren Oakland, Pontiac, MI, p. A328
CARGILL, Kevin, Chief Financial Officer, Trinity Hospital of Augusta, Augusta, GA, p. A151
CARGONARA, Douglas, Ph.D. Chief Information Officer, Pilgrim Psychiatric Center, Brentwood, NY, p. A430
CARIGSON, John, Chief Financial Officer, Covenant Specialty Hospital, Lubbock, TX, p. A629
CARIKER, Kelly, Chief Information Officer, North Valley Hospital, Tonasket, WA, p. A686
CARISSIMI, Derek, Vice President Human Resources, OHSU Hospital, Portland, OR, p. A524
CARLE, Chris, Senior Vice President and Chief Operating Officer, St. Elizabeth Florence, Florence, KY, p. A256
CARLETON, David
Chief Information Officer, Heritage Valley Health System, Beaver, PA, p. A529
Chief Information Officer, Sewickley Valley Hospital, (A Division of Valley Medical Facilities), Sewickley, PA, p. A550
CARLINO, James, Vice President Human Resources, Deborah Heart and Lung Center, Browns Mills, NJ, p. A410
CARLINO, Tracy, R.N. Chief Nursing Officer, Virtua Marlton, Marlton, NJ, p. A414
CARLISLE, Brenda H., R.N. Chief Operating Officer, Brookwood Medical Center, Birmingham, AL, p. A16
CARLISLE, Charles, Director, East Mississippi State Hospital, Meridian, MS, p. A357
CARLISLE, Sandy, Manager Human Resources, Holzer Medical Center – Jackson, Jackson, OH, p. A491
CARLOCK, Carey, Chief Executive Officer, Riveredge Hospital, Forest Park, IL, p. A188
CARLOS, Ilona, M.D. President Medical Staff, Thorek Memorial Hospital, Chicago, IL, p. A185
CARLSON, Andrew, M.D. Vice President Medical Staff Services, Phoebe Sumter Medical Center, Americus, GA, p. A149
CARLSON, Bev, Chief Financial Officer, Delta County Memorial Hospital, Delta, CO, p. A101
CARLSON, Brian J., FACHE, Chief Executive Officer, Sanford Thief River Falls Medical Center, Thief River Falls, MN, p. A348
CARLSON, C. Daniel, Chief Financial Officer, Bay Area Medical Center, Marinette, WI, p. A704
CARLSON, Carol, Director Community Relations, Memorial Health Care Systems, Seward, NE, p. A398
CARLSON, Daniel, M.D. Chief Medical Officer, Wellmont Holston Valley Medical Center, Kingsport, TN, p. A580
CARLSON, Kellie, Director Human Resources, Coastal Harbor Treatment Center, Savannah, GA, p. A164
CARLSON, Kim
Director Human Resources, Essentia Health Northern Pines Medical Center, Aurora, MN, p. A335
Senior Vice President Human Resources, FirstLight Health System, Mora, MN, p. A343
CARLSON, Kurt, Chief Executive Officer, Otis R. Bowen Center for Human Services, Warsaw, IN, p. A221
CARLSON, Niti, M.D. Chief of Staff, Trinity Hospital of Augusta, Augusta, GA, p. A151
CARLSON, Pam, Senior Vice President and Chief Nursing Officer, Phoenix Children's Hospital, Phoenix, AZ, p. A35
CARLSON, Peter, Administrator, Aurora Psychiatric Hospital, Wauwatosa, WI, p. A713
CARLSON, Richard, Chief Financial Officer, Crawford Memorial Hospital, Robinson, IL, p. A199
CARLSON, Sandee, Director of Nursing, Essentia Health Duluth, Duluth, MN, p. A337
CARLSON, Sarah, Director Human Resources, Essentia Health St. Joseph's Medical Center, Brainerd, MN, p. A336
CARLSON, Scott, Director, Mary Greeley Medical Center, Ames, IA, p. A222
CARLSON, Wendie, Vice President, Human Resources, Jackson–Madison County General Hospital, Jackson, TN, p. A579
CARLSON, Wendy, Director Human Resources, Pathways of Tennessee, Jackson, TN, p. A579
CARLTON, Terrie, R.N. Vice President & Chief Nursing Officer, Tuomey Healthcare System, Sumter, SC, p. A565
CARLYLE, Dave, Director Human Resources, Wayne County Hospital, Corydon, IA, p. A225
CARMAN, Thomas H., President and Chief Executive Officer, Samaritan Medical Center, Watertown, NY, p. A453
CARMELLINI, Tracy, M.D. Chief of Staff, Jennersville Regional Hospital, West Grove, PA, p. A552
CARMEN, Lee, Associate Vice President Health Care Information Systems, University of Iowa Hospitals and Clinics, Iowa City, IA, p. A230
CARMICHAEL, Craig, Vice President, Operations, University of Maryland St. Joseph Medical Center, Towson, MD, p. A300
CARMODY, James, Vice President Human Resources, Wilkes–Barre General Hospital, Wilkes–Barre, PA, p. A553
CARMODY, Jane, R.N
Vice President and System Chief Nursing Officer, CHI Health Bergan Mercy, Omaha, NE, p. A395
Chief Nursing Officer, CHI Health Immanuel, Omaha, NE, p. A396
Chief Nursing Officer, CHI Health Lakeside, Omaha, NE, p. A396
Vice President and System Chief Nursing Officer, CHI Health Mercy Corning, Corning, IA, p. A225
Vice President and System Chief Nursing Officer, CHI Health Mercy Council Bluffs, Council Bluffs, IA, p. A225
Chief Nursing Officer, CHI Health Midlands, Papillion, NE, p. A397
Vice President and System Chief Nursing Officer, CHI Health Schuyler, Schuyler, NE, p. A398
CARMONA, Mariaelena, Chief Executive Officer, Highlands Regional Rehabilitation Hospital, El Paso, TX, p. A610
CARNAHAN, II, Robert H., Chief Nursing Officer, Banner Churchill Community Hospital, Fallon, NV, p. A400
CARNES, Ruth, Manager Human Resources, Jennings American Legion Hospital, Jennings, LA, p. A275
CARNEVALE, Raymond F., Chief Executive Officer, Select Specialty Hospital–Madison, Madison, WI, p. A704
CARNEY, Adrienne, R.N. Director Nursing and Surgical Services, Kearney Regional Medical Center, Kearney, NE, p. A393
CARNEY, Glenn, Chief Operating Officer, Central Florida Regional Hospital, Sanford, FL, p. A142
CARNEY, Judi, M.D. President Medical Staff, Baptist Memorial Hospital for Women, Memphis, TN, p. A583
CARNEY, Kevin, Senior Information Systems Analyst, Pine Creek Medical Center, Dallas, TX, p. A606
CARNEY, Michael J., Chief Executive Officer, Brentwood Behavioral HealthCare of Mississippi, Jackson, MS, p. A354
CARNEY, Mike, Chief Executive Officer, Select Specialty Hospital–Evansville, Evansville, IN, p. A208
CARNEY, William, M.D. Interim Chief Medical Officer, Conemaugh Memorial Medical Center, Johnstown, PA, p. A537
CARO, Vique, Chief Information Officer, Cincinnati Veterans Affairs Medical Center, Cincinnati, OH, p. A482
CAROL, Karin, Chief Operating Officer, Atlantic Shores Hospital, Fort Lauderdale, FL, p. A126
CAROLINA, Dorinda, Chief Human Resources Officer, Aria Health, Philadelphia, PA, p. A542
CAROLUS, Rhonda, Director of Nursing Operations, Northern Colorado Rehabilitation Hospital, Johnstown, CO, p. A105
CARON, Jacqueline, Chief Human Resources, Birmingham Veterans Affairs Medical Center, Birmingham, AL, p. A16
CARON, Phillip A.
Chief Financial Officer, East Texas Medical Center Carthage, Carthage, TX, p. A600
Chief Financial Officer, East Texas Medical Center Henderson, Henderson, TX, p. A618
Chief Financial Officer, East Texas Medical Center Jacksonville, Jacksonville, TX, p. A624
CARON Jr., William L., President, MaineHealth, Portland, ME, p. B86
CAROTHERS, Jonathan, Chief Operating Officer, Ochsner St. Anne General Hospital, Raceland, LA, p. A284
CAROZZA, Sally, Director Human Resources, West Penn Hospital, Pittsburgh, PA, p. A547
CARPEL, Emmett, M.D. Medical Director and Chief of Staff, Phillips Eye Institute, Minneapolis, MN, p. A343
CARPENTER, Curt, Manager Information Technology, Coquille Valley Hospital, Coquille, OR, p. A520
CARPENTER, Dan
Chief Financial Officer, UnityPoint Health – Allen Hospital, Waterloo, IA, p. A236
Chief Financial Officer, UnityPoint Health – Finley Hospital, Dubuque, IA, p. A227
CARPENTER, Deb, Director Information Technology, Lourdes Medical Center, Pasco, WA, p. A682
CARPENTER, Jackie, Office Manager, Rock County Hospital, Bassett, NE, p. A389
CARPENTER, Leah A., Administrator and Chief Executive Officer, Memorial Hospital Miramar, Miramar, FL, p. A136
CARPENTER, Posie, R.N. Chief Administrative Officer, Santa Monica–UCLA Medical Center and Orthopaedic Hospital, Santa Monica, CA, p. A92
CARPENTER, Stephanie, Director of Nursing Services, Columbia County Health System, Dayton, WA, p. A678
CARPENTER III, William F., Chairman and Chief Executive Officer, LifePoint Health, Brentwood, TN, p. B83
CARPER, Joleen, Vice President Quality and Risk, Tri–State Memorial Hospital, Clarkston, WA, p. A677
CARR, Ann, R.N. Chief Nursing Officer, Craig General Hospital, Vinita, OK, p. A517
CARR, Cathy, MSN Chief Nursing Officer, Venice Regional Bayfront Health, Venice, FL, p. A146
CARR, Charles E., Vice President and Administrator, Carilion Stonewall Jackson Hospital, Lexington, VA, p. A667
CARR, David, M.D. Physician Medical Director, The Rehabilitation Institute of St. Louis, Saint Louis, MO, p. A378
CARR, Deborah, Vice President Human Resources, Orange Regional Medical Center, Middletown, NY, p. A437
CARR, Diane
Chief Information Officer, Jacobi Medical Center, NY, p. A440
Chief Information Officer, North Central Bronx Hospital, NY, p. A443
CARR, George, Chief Information Officer, Bryan Medical Center, Lincoln, NE, p. A393
CARR, Mark, Chief Information Resource Management, Jack C. Montgomery Veterans Affairs Medical Center, Muskogee, OK, p. A510
CARR, Randall
Director Human Resources, Parkwest Medical Center, Knoxville, TN, p. A580
Director Human Resources, Roane Medical Center, Harriman, TN, p. A578
CARR, Sheila, Chief Executive Officer, Wekiva Springs, Jacksonville, FL, p. A130
CARR, Tim, Chief Financial Officer, Methodist Ambulatory Surgery Hospital – Northwest, San Antonio, TX, p. A641
CARRANZA, Diana, Interim Director, Veterans Affairs Illiana Health Care System, Danville, IL, p. A185
CARRASCO, Anthony, Director Information Systems, Gardens Regional Hospital and Medical Center, Hawaiian Gardens, CA, p. A64
CARRASCO, Michelle, Director Human Resources, Palo Verde Mental Health Services, Tucson, AZ, p. A39
CARRASQUILLO, Carmen, M.D. Medical Director, Industrial Hospital, San Juan, PR, p. A724
CARRELLI, Bobbie, Director Human Resources, Summit Behavioral Healthcare, Cincinnati, OH, p. A483
CARRERA, Lavern H., Senior Vice President Human Resources, Northside Medical Center, Youngstown, OH, p. A501
CARRERO, Milton D., M.D. Medical Director, Dr. Ramon E. Betances Hospital–Mayaguez Medical Center Branch, Mayaguez, PR, p. A722
CARRIER, Jeffrey, R.N. Chief Clinical Officer, Freeman Hospital West, Joplin, MO, p. A369
CARRIER, Lynn, Associate Director Administration and Support, VA Greater Los Angeles Healthcare System, Los Angeles, CA, p. A73
CARRIGG, John, Executive Vice President and Chief Operating Officer, United Health Services Hospitals–Binghamton, Binghamton, NY, p. A430
CARRILLO, Irma, Director Human Resources, Ashford Presbyterian Community Hospital, San Juan, PR, p. A723
CARRILLO, Todd, Chief Information Officer, Yoakum County Hospital, Denver City, TX, p. A608
CARRILLO, Zulema, Superintendent, El Paso Psychiatric Center, El Paso, TX, p. A610

Index of Health Care Professionals

Index of Health Care Professionals / Carringer


CARRINGER, Rick
Vice President Finance and Support Services, LeConte Medical Center, Sevierville, TN, p. A588
Vice President and Chief Financial Officer, Methodist Medical Center of Oak Ridge, Oak Ridge, TN, p. A586
CARRINGTON, Paul Henry, Chief Nursing Officer, Pawnee Valley Community Hospital, Larned, KS, p. A244
CARROCINO, Joanne, FACHE, President and Chief Executive Officer, Cape Regional Medical Center, Cape May Court House, NJ, p. A410
CARROLL, Allen P., Senior Vice President and Chief Executive Officer, Bon Secours St. Francis Xavier Hospital, Charleston, SC, p. A558
CARROLL, Candice R., Chief Nursing Officer, Coliseum Medical Centers, Macon, GA, p. A160
CARROLL, Dale, M.D. Senior Vice President Medical Affairs and Performance Improvement, Sentara RMH Medical Center, Harrisonburg, VA, p. A666
CARROLL, Eric, Chief Executive Officer, Unicoi County Memorial Hospital, Erwin, TN, p. A577
CARROLL, Jack, Senior Director Human Resources, Spaulding Hospital for Continuing Medical Care Cambridge, Cambridge, MA, p. A306
CARROLL, Jack A., Ph.D., President and Chief Executive Officer, Magee Rehabilitation Hospital, Philadelphia, PA, p. A544
CARROLL, Jacqueline, Director Human Resources, Los Alamos Medical Center, Los Alamos, NM, p. A425
CARROLL, Jaime, Department Head, Walter Reed National Military Medical Center, Bethesda, MD, p. A296
CARROLL, James H., Chief Information Officer, St. John Medical Center, Westlake, OH, p. A500
CARROLL, John, M.D. Chief Medical Officer, St. James Mercy Health System, Hornell, NY, p. A435
CARROLL, Karen, MSN Vice President and Chief Nursing Officer, Beaufort Memorial Hospital, Beaufort, SC, p. A557
CARROLL, Marsha
Director of Fiscal Services, Optim Medical Center – Jenkins, Millen, GA, p. A161
Director Financial Services, Optim Medical Center – Screven, Sylvania, GA, p. A165
CARROLL, Michael W., Administrator, Richland Parish Hospital, Delhi, LA, p. A273
CARROLL, Peggy, Chief Information Officer, Palos Community Hospital, Palos Heights, IL, p. A197
CARROLL, Richard, M.D
Chief Medical officer, Adventist Bolingbrook Hospital, Bolingbrook, IL, p. A180
Chief Medical Officer, AMITA Health Adventist GlenOaks Hospital, Glendale Heights, IL, p. A189
CARROLL, Susan, Chief Executive Officer, Inova Alexandria Hospital, Alexandria, VA, p. A662
CARROLL, Terrence, Ph.D. Vice President, Information Services, Dartmouth–Hitchcock Medical Center, Lebanon, NH, p. A407
CARROLL, Terri L., Vice President Financial Services, Hillsboro Area Hospital, Hillsboro, IL, p. A190
CARROLL, Velma, Chief Information Officer, Augusta Health, Fishersville, VA, p. A664
CARROLL, William, M.D. Chief Medical Executive, Sutter Santa Rosa Regional Hospital, Santa Rosa, CA, p. A92
CARRON, Patrick E., FACHE, President and Chief Executive Officer, Perry County Memorial Hospital, Perryville, MO, p. A374
CARRUTH, Gregory, Head Information Management, Naval Hospital Oak Harbor, Oak Harbor, WA, p. A681
CARRUTH, Keith, Chief Executive Officer, AMG Specialty Hospital–Houma, Houma, LA, p. A275
CARSON, Carole, Director of Nursing Operations, Rehabilitation Hospital of Southern New Mexico, Las Cruces, NM, p. A425
CARSON, Debbie, Director Human Resources, Promise Hospital of Vicksburg, Vicksburg, MS, p. A361
CARSON, Gregory W., Administrator, U. S. Air Force Clinic, Mountain Home AFB, ID, p. A175
CARSON, Joe, Director Human Resources, Glen Oaks Hospital, Greenville, TX, p. A617
CARSON, Kara Jo, Chief Financial Officer, Pinckneyville Community Hospital, Pinckneyville, IL, p. A198
CARSON, Mitchell C., President and Chief Executive Officer, Longmont United Hospital, Longmont, CO, p. A107
CARSTENSEN, Karla, Director Patient Care, Avera Dells Area Hospital, Dell Rapids, SD, p. A568
CARTAGENA, Maria, M.D. Chief Medical Officer, BryLin Hospitals, Buffalo, NY, p. A430
CARTER, Barbara, Chief Nursing Officer, Cimarron Memorial Hospital, Boise City, OK, p. A504
CARTER, Billie, Chief Operating Officer and Assistant Administrator, Stonewall Memorial Hospital, Aspermont, TX, p. A593
CARTER, Charla, Human Resource Officer, Uvalde County Hospital Authority, Uvalde, TX, p. A649
CARTER, Christen, Director Public Relations, Roosevelt Warm Springs Rehabilitation and Specialty Hospitals – Rehab, Warm Springs, GA, p. A167
CARTER, Cindy, Chief Nursing Officer, Northeast Regional Medical Center, Kirksville, MO, p. A371
CARTER, D. Montez, President, St. Mary's Good Samaritan Hospital, Greensboro, GA, p. A158
CARTER, Dennis, M.D. Chief of Staff, Eastern Oklahoma Medical Center, Poteau, OK, p. A514
CARTER, Donna, Director Human Resources, Lawrence Memorial Hospital, Walnut Ridge, AR, p. A51
CARTER, Donna, MSN Chief Nursing Officer, Minden Medical Center, Minden, LA, p. A280
CARTER, Doug, Chief Financial Officer, Brookwood Medical Center, Birmingham, AL, p. A16
CARTER, Douglas S., M.D. Vice President and Chief Medical Officer, Major Hospital, Shelbyville, IN, p. A220
CARTER, Frank, Chief Financial Officer, Cornerstone Hospital of Huntington, Huntington, WV, p. A691
CARTER, Gary L., M.D. Vice President and Chief Medical Officer, North Kansas City Hospital, North Kansas City, MO, p. A373
CARTER, Jr., James R., Chief Operating Officer, Methodist Healthcare Memphis Hospitals, Memphis, TN, p. A584
CARTER, Jessica Y., Chief Financial Officer, Crisp Regional Hospital, Cordele, GA, p. A155
CARTER, Jim, Chief Operating Officer, Grady General Hospital, Cairo, GA, p. A153
CARTER, Leonard M., Vice President Human Resources, FHN Memorial Hospital, Freeport, IL, p. A188
CARTER, Leslia, Administrator, North Mississippi Medical Center–Pontotoc, Pontotoc, MS, p. A359
CARTER, Malinda Yvonne, Vice President Human Resources, Saint Anthony Hospital, Chicago, IL, p. A184
CARTER, Marcia, Director Human Resources, Bluegrass Community Hospital, Versailles, KY, p. A266
CARTER, Michael, Administrator Information Technology, Northwest Ohio Psychiatric Hospital, Toledo, OH, p. A498
CARTER, Michael C., Executive Director, Kaiser Permanente Woodland Hills Medical Center, CA, p. A70
CARTER, Michael J., Chief Executive Officer, Eastern Oklahoma Medical Center, Poteau, OK, p. A514
CARTER, Misty, Director Human Resources and Chief Operating Officer, Great Plains Regional Medical Center, Elk City, OK, p. A506
CARTER, Priscilla, Chief Financial Officer, Mesa Hills Specialty Hospital, El Paso, TX, p. A611
CARTER, Rebecca W., FACHE, Chief Executive Officer and Chief Nursing Officer, Blue Ridge Regional Hospital, Spruce Pine, NC, p. A469
CARTER, Richard, Chief Executive Officer, Hunt Regional Healthcare, Greenville, TX, p. B72
CARTER, Richard, District Chief Executive Officer, Hunt Regional Medical Center, Greenville, TX, p. A617
CARTER, Richard, M.D. Chief of Staff, Tennova Healthcare–Jefferson Memorial Hospital, Jefferson City, TN, p. A579
CARTER, Shanti, Chief Executive Officer, Carrollton Springs, Carrollton, TX, p. A600
CARTER, Teresa, Vice President Patient Care Services, OneCore Health, Oklahoma City, OK, p. A512
CARTER, Theodora, Administrative Director Human Resources, Hackensack University Medical Center at Pascack Valley, Westwood, NJ, p. A420
CARTER, Vickie, Information Systems Director, Sumner Regional Medical Center, Gallatin, TN, p. A578
CARTER–ROBERTSON, Kira, FACHE, President and Chief Executive Officer, Sparrow Specialty Hospital, Lansing, MI, p. A324
CARTWRIGHT, Bryan, Chief Information Technology Officer, Missouri River Medical Center, Fort Benton, MT, p. A383
CARTWRIGHT, David, Director Management Information Systems, Danville Regional Medical Center, Danville, VA, p. A664
CARTWRIGHT, David A., Vice President Finance and Support Services, Advocate Condell Medical Center, Libertyville, IL, p. A192
CARTWRIGHT, Debra
Chief Financial Officer, St. Francis Health, Topeka, KS, p. A251
Chief Financial Officer, St. Joseph Medical Center, Kansas City, MO, p. A370
CARTWRIGHT, Kay B., R.N. Vice President and Chief Nursing Officer, Reid Health, Richmond, IN, p. A219
CARUCCI, Dean, Interim Chief Executive Officer, Portsmouth Regional Hospital, Portsmouth, NH, p. A408
CARUGATI, Diane, Chief Operating Officer, Friends Hospital, Philadelphia, PA, p. A543
CARUSO, Diane M., MSN Chief Nursing Officer, HEALTHSOUTH Scottsdale Rehabilitation Hospital, Scottsdale, AZ, p. A37
CARUSO, Don, President and Chief Executive Officer, Cheshire Medical Center, Keene, NH, p. A406
CARUSO, Don, M.D. Chief Medical Officer, Cheshire Medical Center, Keene, NH, p. A406
CARUSO, Michael J., President and Chief Executive Officer, East Ohio Regional Hospital, Martins Ferry, OH, p. A493
CARUSO, Michael J., President and Chief Executive Officer, Ohio Valley Health Services and Education Corporation, Wheeling, WV, p. B101
CARUSO, Michael J., President and Chief Executive Officer, Ohio Valley Medical Center, Wheeling, WV, p. A696
CARVER, Carol, MSN Vice President Patient Services, Clarity Child Guidance Center, San Antonio, TX, p. A640
CARVER, Deborah, R.N. Vice President Patient Care Services, Yuma Regional Medical Center, Yuma, AZ, p. A40
CARVETH, Barbara, Chief Financial Officer, University of Colorado Hospital, Aurora, CO, p. A99
CARVOLTH, Richard, M.D. Chief Medical Officer, Santa Rosa Memorial Hospital, Santa Rosa, CA, p. A92
CARYNSKI, Paula A., R.N., President, OSF Saint Anthony Medical Center, Rockford, IL, p. A199
CASABONA, Nicholas, Chief Information Officer, Winthrop–University Hospital, Mineola, NY, p. A437
CASADAY, Thomas E., Chief Executive Officer, Atlanta Medical Center, Atlanta, GA, p. A150
CASALOU, Robert F.
President and Chief Executive Officer, St. Joseph Mercy Ann Arbor, Ypsilanti, MI, p. A333
President and Chief Executive Officer, St. Joseph Mercy Livingston Hospital, Howell, MI, p. A322
CASALS, Patricia, MSN Chief Nursing Officer, Tyler Memorial Hospital, Tunkhannock, PA, p. A551
CASANOVA, Robert Bernier, Chief Financial Officer, Industrial Hospital, San Juan, PR, p. A724
CASAREZ, Margaret, Chief Financial Officer, San Joaquin Valley Rehabilitation Hospital, Fresno, CA, p. A62
CASAREZ, Teresa, Director Human Resources, New Mexico Rehabilitation Center, Roswell, NM, p. A426
CASAS, Miguel, R.N. Chief Clinical Officer, East Texas Medical Center Henderson, Henderson, TX, p. A618
CASCIO, Richard C., Interim Chief Executive Officer, University Health System, Shreveport, LA, p. B145
CASDORPH, Michael, Chief Operating Officer, Highland–Clarksburg Hospital, Clarksburg, WV, p. A690
CASE, Cliff, Chief Financial Officer, Mineral Community Hospital, Superior, MT, p. A387
CASE, Ed, Executive Vice President and Chief Financial Officer, Rehabilitation Institute of Chicago, Chicago, IL, p. A184
CASE, Harvey, President, Vidant Beaufort Hospital, Washington, NC, p. A470
CASE, Matthew, USN, Director For Administration, Naval Medical Center, Portsmouth, VA, p. A670
CASERTA, Kevin, M.D
Chief Medical Officer, Providence Centralia Hospital, Centralia, WA, p. A677
Chief Medical Officer, Providence St. Peter Hospital, Olympia, WA, p. A681
CASEY, Candy J., MS, President and Chief Executive Officer, Columbia Center, Mequon, WI, p. A705
CASEY, Dina, Human Resources Officer, Lane County Hospital, Dighton, KS, p. A239
CASEY, John P., Administrator, Shodair Children's Hospital, Helena, MT, p. A384
CASEY, Joseph, Chief Financial Officer, Sturdy Memorial Hospital, Attleboro, MA, p. A302
CASEY, Rick, M.D. Chief Medical Staff, Cedar County Memorial Hospital, El Dorado Springs, MO, p. A366
CASH, Jeff, Senior Vice President and Chief Information Officer, Mercy Medical Center–Cedar Rapids, Cedar Rapids, IA, p. A223
CASH, Jimmie, R.N. Executive Director and Patient Care, Saint Francis Hospital South, Tulsa, OK, p. A517
CASH, Jordan, President, Integris Baptist Regional Health Center, Miami, OK, p. A509
CASH, Judy, MSN Chief Nursing Officer, Baylor Institute for Rehabilitation at Northwest Dallas, Dallas, TX, p. A604
CASHWELL, David, Chief Executive Officer, HEALTHSOUTH Rehabilitation Hospital of Virginia, Richmond, VA, p. A671
CASIANO, Manuel, M.D. Senior Vice President Medical Affairs, Frederick Memorial Hospital, Frederick, MD, p. A298
CASIANO, Sonia V., R.N. Interim Chief Nursing Officer, Norwegian American Hospital, Chicago, IL, p. A183
CASILLAS, Rosalind, Director of Nursing, Lawrence Memorial Hospital, Walnut Ridge, AR, p. A51
CASKEY, Paul, M.D. Chief of Staff, Shriners Hospitals for Children–Spokane, Spokane, WA, p. A685
CASNER, Trina, President and Chief Executive Officer, Pana Community Hospital, Pana, IL, p. A197
CASOLA, Frances, Senior Vice President Operations, St. Joseph's Medical Center, Yonkers, NY, p. A454


A804 Index of Health Care Professionals 

Index of Health Care Professionals / Cecil

Index of Health Care Professionals


CASON, Diane, Chief Information Officer, Controller and Director Human Resources, Lake Butler Hospital Hand Surgery Center, Lake Butler, FL, p. A131
CASON, Randall R., FACHE, Senior Administrator, Via Christi Hospital Pittsburg, Pittsburg, KS, p. A249
CASON, Steven, Chief Information Officer, Putnam General Hospital, Eatonton, GA, p. A157
CASON, Will, Vice President Human Resources, St. Rita's Medical Center, Lima, OH, p. A492
CASPER, Rylee, R.N. Chief Nursing Officer, Newman Memorial Hospital, Shattuck, OK, p. A514
CASPERSON, William, M.D. Vice President Medical Affairs, Memorial Hospital, Belleville, IL, p. A179
CASS, Jinilinn, Director Medical Records, Lakeview Regional Medical Center, Covington, LA, p. A272
CASS, Julene J., R.N. Director of Nursing, Community Memorial Hospital, Redfield, SD, p. A571
CASS, Paul, D.O. Chief Medical & Clinical Integration Officer, Wentworth–Douglass Hospital, Dover, NH, p. A406
CASSADY, Craig, Director of Nursing, Wiregrass Medical Center, Geneva, AL, p. A20
CASSADY, Perry, M.D. Medical Director, Physicians' Medical Center, New Albany, IN, p. A217
CASSAGNE, Nancy R., FACHE, Chief Executive Officer, West Jefferson Medical Center, Marrero, LA, p. A280
CASSEDY, Ryan, Chief Executive Officer, Vibra Hospital of Fort Wayne, Fort Wayne, IN, p. A209
CASSEL, Asenath, Chief Nursing Officer, Wellington Regional Medical Center, West Palm Beach, FL, p. A147
CASSEL, Kari
Senior Vice President and Chief Information Officer, UF Health Jacksonville, Jacksonville, FL, p. A130
Senior Vice President and Chief Information Officer, UF Health Shands Hospital, Gainesville, FL, p. A128
CASSELL, Sally, Manager Human Resources, Ozark Health Medical Center, Clinton, AR, p. A42
CASSELS, William H., Administrator, DCH Regional Medical Center, Tuscaloosa, AL, p. A25
CASSIDAY, Cheryl, R.N. Director of Nursing, Chadron Community Hospital and Health Services, Chadron, NE, p. A391
CASSIDY, Donna, Chief Nursing Executive, South Haven Health System, South Haven, MI, p. A330
CASSIDY, Doris B., Associate Director, Veterans Health Care System of the Ozarks, Fayetteville, AR, p. A44
CASSIDY, John W., M.D., President, Chief Executive Officer and Chief Medical Officer, Nexus Health Systems, Houston, TX, p. B97
CASSIDY, Joseph J., Vice President and Chief Human Resources Officer, Holy Redeemer Hospital, Meadowbrook, PA, p. A540
CASSIDY, Louise, Chief Executive Officer, Cornerstone Hospital of SouthEast Arizona, Tucson, AZ, p. A39
CASSLE, Susie, R.N. Assistant Vice President Nursing Services, Hendrick Health System, Abilene, TX, p. A590
CASTANEDA, Edmundo
President, Mercy General Hospital, Sacramento, CA, p. A84
President, Mercy Hospital of Folsom, Folsom, CA, p. A61
CASTANEDA, Marissa, Chief Operating Officer and Director Marketing, Doctor's Hospital at Renaissance, Edinburg, TX, p. A610
CASTANEDA, Trevor, Chief Executive Officer, Tennova Newport Medical Center, Newport, TN, p. A586
CASTEEL, Brian, Information Technology Technician, Hardin County General Hospital, Rosiclare, IL, p. A200
CASTEEL, Karen, Director Human Resources, Palms of Pasadena Hospital, Saint Petersburg, FL, p. A142
CASTEEL, Lisa, Assistant Administrator and Chief Financial Officer, Henry County Medical Center, Paris, TN, p. A587
CASTEEL, Rick
Vice President Management Information Systems and Chief Information Officer, University of Maryland Harford Memorial Hospital, Havre De Grace, MD, p. A298
Vice President Management Information Systems and Chief Information Officer, University of Maryland Upper Chesapeake Medical Center, Bel Air, MD, p. A295
CASTELLO, Fred, M.D. Chief Medical Officer, Augusta Health, Fishersville, VA, p. A664
CASTER, Patrick, Chief Operating Officer, John F. Kennedy Memorial Hospital, Indio, CA, p. A65
CASTILLO, Carol, Medical Director, Sonoma Developmental Center, Eldridge, CA, p. A60
CASTILLO, Dan, Chief Executive Officer, LAC/University of Southern California Medical Center, Los Angeles, CA, p. A71
CASTILLO, Edgar, Chief Financial Officer, Larkin Community Hospital, South Miami, FL, p. A143
CASTILLO, Paul, Chief Financial Officer, University of Michigan Hospitals and Health Centers, Ann Arbor, MI, p. A314
CASTILLO, Ralph A., CPA, Chief Executive Officer, Morgan Memorial Hospital, Madison, GA, p. A161
CASTILLO, Randall, Vice President, Operations, Mercy Hospital of Folsom, Folsom, CA, p. A61
CASTILLO, Renee, Chief Nursing Officer, Plains Memorial Hospital, Dimmitt, TX, p. A609
CASTILLO, Rita S., R.N. Chief Quality Officer and Risk Management, South Texas Regional Medical Center, Jourdanton, TX, p. A625
CASTLE, Dorothy, Director Human Resources, North Mississippi Medical Center–Eupora, Eupora, MS, p. A352
CASTLE, Eric, Director Information Services, Lawnwood Regional Medical Center & Heart Institute, Fort Pierce, FL, p. A127
CASTLE, Kenneth, Chief Information Officer, Easton Hospital, Easton, PA, p. A533
CASTLE, Samantha, Chief Operating Officer, Ridge Behavioral Health System, Lexington, KY, p. A260
CASTLEBERRY, David L., FACHE, Chief Executive Officer, Upson Regional Medical Center, Thomaston, GA, p. A165
CASTLEBERRY, Ginger, Corporate Risk Manager, Quality and Patient Safety, Valir Rehabilitation Hospital, Oklahoma City, OK, p. A513
CASTLEMAN, Pam, MSN Chief Nursing Officer, Regional One Health, Memphis, TN, p. A584
CASTLEY, Karen, Medical Director, Summit Park Hospital and Nursing Care Center, Pomona, NY, p. A447
CASTON, David, Chief Executive Officer, Reeves Memorial Medical Center, Bernice, LA, p. A270
CASTOR, Susan, Chief Nursing Officer, HEALTHSOUTH Rehabilitation Hospital of Toms River, Toms River, NJ, p. A419
CASTRO, Ana, Director Information Services and Clinical Information Services, Gerald Champion Regional Medical Center, Alamogordo, NM, p. A422
CASTRO, Craig
Chief Executive Officer, Clovis Community Medical Center, Clovis, CA, p. A58
Chief Information Officer, Community Regional Medical Center, Fresno, CA, p. A62
CASTRO, Darcy, Director, Human Resources, Orange County Global Medical Center, Inc., Santa Ana, CA, p. A90
CASTRO, Jill, M.D. Medical Director, HEALTHSOUTH Rehabilitation Hospital of Denver, Littleton, CO, p. A106
CASTRO, Pete, D.O. Chief of Staff, Heart of Texas Memorial Hospital, Brady, TX, p. A598
CASTRO, Richard, Chief Executive Officer, Whittier Hospital Medical Center, Whittier, CA, p. A97
CASTRODALE, Andrew, M.D. Chief Medical Officer, Coulee Medical Center, Grand Coulee, WA, p. A679
CASTROMAN, Nellie, Chief Executive Officer, Select Specialty Hospital–Orlando, Orlando, FL, p. A138
CASTRONUEVO, Joseph, Director Information Management, St. Lawrence Rehabilitation Center, Lawrenceville, NJ, p. A413
CASWELL, Lori, Director Information Technology, Good Samaritan Medical Center, Brockton, MA, p. A305
CASWELL, Penny, Director of Nursing, Bloomington Meadows Hospital, Bloomington, IN, p. A205
CATALA, Lucy, Vice President Finance, Baylor All Saints Medical Center at Fort Worth, Fort Worth, TX, p. A613
CATALDO, Linda, Human Resources Secretary, Prevost Memorial Hospital, Donaldsonville, LA, p. A273
CATALIOTTI, Palmira, Senior Vice President, Chief Financial Officer and Treasurer, Winthrop–University Hospital, Mineola, NY, p. A437
CATANIA, Joseph M., President and Chief Executive Officer, Catholic Health Services, Lauderdale Lakes, FL, p. B31
CATANIA, Joseph M., Chief Executive Officer, St. Anthony's Rehabilitation Hospital, Lauderdale Lakes, FL, p. A132
CATAUDELLA, Mary, Corporate Director Human Resources, Jersey City Medical Center, Jersey City, NJ, p. A413
CATE, Maurine, Chief Executive Officer, Deaconess Hospital, Spokane, WA, p. A685
CATENA, Cornelio R., President and Chief Executive Officer, Wilkes–Barre General Hospital, Wilkes–Barre, PA, p. A553
CATES, Jessica, Fiscal Manager, Western State Hospital, Hopkinsville, KY, p. A258
CATES, Rodney, Senior Vice President Human Resources, Covenant Children's Hospital, Lubbock, TX, p. A629
CATHEY, Michele, Interim Chief Financial officer, Martin County Hospital District, Stanton, TX, p. A645
CATHEY, Walt, Chief Executive Officer, Covenant Medical Center, Lubbock, TX, p. A629
CATINO, Anne, R.N. Vice President and Chief Nursing Officer, Holy Redeemer Hospital, Meadowbrook, PA, p. A540
CATLIN, Rexford, Chief Executive Officer, Endless Mountain Health Systems, Montrose, PA, p. A541
CATT, Robbin K., Chief Nursing Officer, Jackson Hospital, Marianna, FL, p. A133
CATTALANI, Mark, M.D. Clinical Director, Richard H. Hutchings Psychiatric Center, Syracuse, NY, p. A451
CATTELL, JoAnne, Chief Nursing Officer, St. Petersburg General Hospital, Saint Petersburg, FL, p. A142
CATTELL, Nancy E., Vice President Human Resources, Liberty Hospital, Liberty, MO, p. A372
CATTON, Jane, R.N. Chief Operating Officer and Chief Nursing Officer, Northwestern Medical Center, Saint Albans, VT, p. A661
CATUCCI, Paul, Administrative Director Human Resources, Bon Secours St. Francis Medical Center, Midlothian, VA, p. A668
CAUBLE, David, Chief Financial Officer, St. Vincent's Blount, Oneonta, AL, p. A23
CAUDEL, Katie, Controller, Southeast Health Center of Reynolds County, Ellington, MO, p. A366
CAUDILL, Allan, M.D. Chief of Staff, South Haven Health System, South Haven, MI, p. A330
CAUDILL, David
Administrator, Grisell Memorial Hospital District One, Ransom, KS, p. A249
Director Human Resources, Rush County Memorial Hospital, La Crosse, KS, p. A244
CAUGHELL, David, M.D. Chief of Staff, Jane Phillips Nowata Health Center, Nowata, OK, p. A510
CAUGHEY, Michelle, M.D. Physician In Chief, Kaiser Permanente South San Francisco, South San Francisco, CA, p. A93
CAUSEY, Cynthia, Associate Administrator Human and Mission Services, McLeod Medical Center Dillon, Dillon, SC, p. A560
CAUSEY, Jack M., Chief Executive Officer, Leesville Rehabilitation Hospital, Leesville, LA, p. A279
CAUSEY, Jennifer, Chief Executive Officer, Select Specialty Hospital–Nashville, Nashville, TN, p. A585
CAUWENBERG, Jude, M.D. Chief of Staff, Ashtabula County Medical Center, Ashtabula, OH, p. A478
CAVA, Anthony V., Chief Operating Officer, Bayshore Community Hospital, Holmdel, NJ, p. A413
CAVAGNARO III, Charles E., M.D.,
President, Baystate Mary Lane Hospital, Ware, MA, p. A312
President and Chief Executive Officer, Baystate Wing Hospital, Palmer, MA, p. A310
CAVANAUGH, Paul, Director Human Resources, Friends Hospital, Philadelphia, PA, p. A543
CAVE, Rogelio, M.D. Medical Director, Roseland Community Hospital, Chicago, IL, p. A184
CAVELL, Richard, M.D. Medical Director, University Health Conway, Monroe, LA, p. A281
CAVEN, Tom, M.D. Vice President Medical Affairs, University Medical Center at Brackenridge, Austin, TX, p. A595
CAVENEY, Timothy, President, South Shore Hospital, Chicago, IL, p. A184
CAVERNO, John
Chief Human Resources Officer, Excela Frick Hospital, Mount Pleasant, PA, p. A541
Chief Human Resources Officer, Excela Health Westmoreland Hospital, Greensburg, PA, p. A535
CAWLEY, Karen, Chief Executive Officer, Kindred Hospital Arizona–Phoenix, Phoenix, AZ, p. A35
CAWLEY, Patrick J., M.D., FACHE Chief Executive Officer and Vice President for Clinical Operations, MUSC Medical Center of Medical University of South Carolina, Charleston, SC, p. A558
CAWOOD, Marina, Administrative Assistant, Middlesboro ARH Hospital, Middlesboro, KY, p. A263
CAYER, Gerald, Executive Vice President and Chief Operating Officer, Franklin Memorial Hospital, Farmington, ME, p. A290
CAZARES, Erik, Interim Chief Nursing Officer, The Hospitals of Providence Sierra Campus, El Paso, TX, p. A611
CAZAYOUX, John, Chief Financial Officer, Pointe Coupee General Hospital, New Roads, LA, p. A283
CAZES, Anna Leah, Chief Nursing Officer, Baton Rouge General Medical Center, Baton Rouge, LA, p. A269
CEBALLOS, Gloria Alicia, MSN Chief Nursing Officer, AllianceHealth Midwest, Midwest City, OK, p. A510
CEBULA, Scott, Interim Chief Information Officer, UC Irvine Medical Center, Orange, CA, p. A79
CECCONI, Thomas E., President and Chief Executive Officer, Mercy Medical Center, Canton, OH, p. A481
CECH, Bob, Regional Finance Officer, Presence Saints Mary & Elizabeth Medical Center, Chicago, IL, p. A183
CECIL, Bruce, Chief Financial Officer, Fresno Surgical Hospital, Fresno, CA, p. A62
CECIL, Janell, R.N. Senior Vice President and Chief Nursing Officer, University of Tennessee Medical Center, Knoxville, TN, p. A581
CECIL, Jason, Chief Information Officer, Capital Region Medical Center, Jefferson City, MO, p. A368

Index of Health Care Professionals

Index of Health Care Professionals / Cecil

CECIL, Jon C.
Chief Human Resource Officer, Cape Coral Hospital, Cape Coral, FL, p. A123
Chief Human Resource Officer, Gulf Coast Medical Center, Fort Myers, FL, p. A127
Chief Human Resource Officer, Lee Memorial Hospital, Fort Myers, FL, p. A127
CEDENO LLORENS, Arturo, M.D. Medical Director, Hospital Buen Samaritano, Aguadilla, PR, p. A719
CEDOTAL, Kiley P., Chief Executive Officer, Promise Hospital Baton Rouge – Main Campus, Baton Rouge, LA, p. A270
CEHELYK, Bohdan, M.D. Chief Medical Officer, East Mountain Hospital, Belle Mead, NJ, p. A409
CEKALLA, Bernie, Manager Human Resources, CHI Albany Area Health, Albany, MN, p. A334
CELANO, Julie, Vice President Human Resources, Brigham and Women's Hospital, Boston, MA, p. A303
CELLA, Ann S., R.N. Senior Vice President, Patient Care Services, St. Francis Hospital, Roslyn, NY, p. A449
CELLA, Robert, M.D
Chief Medical Officer, Albany Memorial Hospital, Albany, NY, p. A428
Vice President Medical Affairs, Berkshire Medical Center, Pittsfield, MA, p. A310
Chief Medical Officer, St. Peter's Hospital, Albany, NY, p. A428
CELSOR, Reba, Chief Executive Officer, Tennova Healthcare – Dyersburg Regional Hospital, Dyersburg, TN, p. A577
CELUCH, Paul
Corporate Human Resources Director, Community Hospital of Huntington Park, Huntington Park, CA, p. A65
Chief Human Resource Officer, East Los Angeles Doctors Hospital, Los Angeles, CA, p. A69
CEMATE, David D., FACHE Senior Vice President and Chief Operating Officer, Mercy Medical Center, Canton, OH, p. A481
CEMENO, Michael J., Chief Information Officer, Waterbury Hospital, Waterbury, CT, p. A116
CENTENO, Robert, M.D. Chief Medical Officer, Governor Juan F. Luis Hospital, Christiansted, VI, p. A725
CEPERO, Jesus, Ph.D. Chief Operating Officer and Chief Nursing Officer, Meritus Medical Center, Hagerstown, MD, p. A298
CERCEO, Richard, Executive Vice President and Chief Operating Officer, Mercy Hospital and Medical Center, Chicago, IL, p. A183
CERIMELE, Leeann, Vice President Human Resources, UPMC Passavant, Pittsburgh, PA, p. A547
CERISE, Fred, M.D., Chief Executive Officer, Parkland Health & Hospital System, Dallas, TX, p. A606
CERNAVA, Joanne, Director Human Resources, Marlton Rehabilitation Hospital, Marlton, NJ, p. A414
CERNOCH, Desiree, Director of Nurses, El Campo Memorial Hospital, El Campo, TX, p. A610
CERONE, Shane, President, Beaumont Hospital – Royal Oak, Royal Oak, MI, p. A328
CERRA, Jane, Market Nurse Executive and Chief Nursing Officer, Select Specialty Hospital–Milwaukee, Milwaukee, WI, p. A707
CERVANTES, Jason
Corporate Chief Information Officer, Community Hospital of Huntington Park, Huntington Park, CA, p. A65
Chief Information Officer, East Los Angeles Doctors Hospital, Los Angeles, CA, p. A69
CERVANTES, Mary Ann, District Director Management Information Systems, Matagorda Regional Medical Center, Bay City, TX, p. A596
CERVINO, Noel A., President and Chief Executive Officer, University of Maryland Charles Regional Medical Center, La Plata, MD, p. A298
CESAREZ, Margaret, Chief Financial Officer, Gateway Rehabilitation Hospital, Florence, KY, p. A256
CESCA, Ken, Vice President Human Resources, MidState Medical Center, Meriden, CT, p. A113
CESKO, David, M.D. Chief of Staff, Memorial Hospital of Carbon County, Rawlins, WY, p. A717
CHA BRIDIER, Vicky, Chief Operating Officer, College Station Medical Center, College Station, TX, p. A601
CHABALOWSKI, Edward, Chief Financial Officer, Geisinger–Community Medical Center, Scranton, PA, p. A549
CHACKO, Benson, Chief Operating Officer, The Hospitals of Providence Sierra Campus, El Paso, TX, p. A611
CHADEK, Richard, M.D. Clinical Director, Lawton Indian Hospital, Lawton, OK, p. A508
CHADHA, Beenu, Chief Financial Officer, San Ramon Regional Medical Center, San Ramon, CA, p. A90
CHADOCK, Brandon, Director of Operations, Sistersville General Hospital, Sistersville, WV, p. A695
CHADWICK, Maureen C., R.N. Chief Nursing Officer, Saint Vincent Health Center, Erie, PA, p. A534
CHADWICK, Sharon M., Director Human Resources, Arrowhead Hospital, Glendale, AZ, p. A32
CHAFFIN, Angela, Administrative Director Human Resources, Siskin Hospital for Physical Rehabilitation, Chattanooga, TN, p. A575
CHAFFIN, Linda, Director Medical Review, Baptist Memorial Hospital–Booneville, Booneville, MS, p. A351
CHAHANOVICH, Jen, President and Chief Executive Officer, Wilcox Memorial Hospital, Lihue, HI, p. A170
CHAILDIN, Roberta, Manager Human Resources, Parrish Medical Center, Titusville, FL, p. A146
CHALFANT, Cathie, Director Human Resources, Harrison County Community Hospital, Bethany, MO, p. A363
CHALIAN, Christopher, M.D. Medical Director, Casa Colina Hospital and Health Systems, Pomona, CA, p. A81
CHALK, Jackie, Director Human Resources, HEALTHSOUTH Rehabilitation Hospital, Largo, FL, p. A131
CHALKE, Dennis, Senior Vice President, Finance and Community Hospitals, Chief Financial Officer and Treasurer, Baystate Medical Center, Springfield, MA, p. A311
CHALMERS, Bryan, Chief Financial Officer, Ivinson Memorial Hospital, Laramie, WY, p. A716
CHALONER, Robert S., President and Chief Executive Officer, Southampton Hospital, Southampton, NY, p. A450
CHALPHANT, Steve, Director Information Management Service Line, Wm. Jennings Bryan Dorn Veterans Affairs Medical Center, Columbia, SC, p. A560
CHALTRY, Richard, M.D. Director Medical Staff, Aspirus Ontonagon Hospital, Ontonagon, MI, p. A327
CHAMBERLIN, Kim, Vice President Patient Services and Chief Nursing Officer, Mercy Medical Center–North Iowa, Mason City, IA, p. A231
CHAMBERS, Bradley
President and Chief Executive Officer, MedStar Good Samaritan Hospital, Baltimore, MD, p. A294
President, MedStar Union Memorial Hospital, Baltimore, MD, p. A294
CHAMBERS, Erin, M.D. Chief Medical Officer, Houston County Community Hospital, Erin, TN, p. A577
CHAMBERS, Gwen, Executive Director Human Resources, Methodist Hospital of Southern California, Arcadia, CA, p. A54
CHAMBERS, Matthew
Chief Information Officer, Scott & White Hospital at Round Rock, Round Rock, TX, p. A639
Chief Information Officer, Scott & White Memorial Hospital, Temple, TX, p. A647
CHAMBERS, Regina, Vice President Human Resource, Rome Memorial Hospital, Rome, NY, p. A449
CHAMBLEE, Jane, Manager Human Resources, Tishomingo Health Services, Iuka, MS, p. A354
CHAMBLESS, Lesley
Assistant Vice President Human Resources, Carolinas HealthCare System Lincoln, Lincolnton, NC, p. A464
Assistant Vice President Workforce Relations, Carolinas HealthCare System NorthEast, Concord, NC, p. A458
CHAMBLISS, Robert, M.D. Chief Medical Officer, Breckinridge Memorial Hospital, Hardinsburg, KY, p. A257
CHAMPAGNE, Charles, Chief Financial Officer, Northeast Rehabilitation Hospital, Salem, NH, p. A408
CHAMPAGNE, Laurie, Controller, Kindred Hospital–New Orleans, New Orleans, LA, p. A282
CHAMPAVANNARATH, Vilakon, Director Information Systems, Bartow Regional Medical Center, Bartow, FL, p. A121
CHAMPION, Joshua I., Director, Florida Hospital–Flagler, Palm Coast, FL, p. A138
CHAN, Eric, Chief Executive Officer, Surgery Specialty Hospitals of America, Pasadena, TX, p. A636
CHAN, Fred, Chief Financial Officer, Intracare North Hospital, Houston, TX, p. A620
CHAN, Joyce, Chief Human Resources Officer, CentraCare Health–Melrose, Melrose, MN, p. A342
CHAN, Thomas T., Chief Financial Officer, Meritus Medical Center, Hagerstown, MD, p. A298
CHANAA, Ziad, M.D. Chief of Staff, Boone Memorial Hospital, Madison, WV, p. A692
CHANAGA, Luis, Chief Financial Officer, Grandview Medical Center, Dayton, OH, p. A488
CHANCE, Tammara, D.O. Chief of Staff, Boone County Hospital, Boone, IA, p. A223
CHANCELLOR, Jayme, Chief Operating Officer, Northside Hospital, Saint Petersburg, FL, p. A142
CHAND, Parveen, Chief Operating Officer, Eskenazi Health, Indianapolis, IN, p. A211
CHANDLER, Aileen
Director of Nursing, Ogallala Community Hospital, Ogallala, NE, p. A395
Interim Chief Executive Officer, Ogallala Community Hospital, Ogallala, NE, p. A395
CHANDLER, Christopher, Chief Executive Officer, Pioneer Community Hospital of Aberdeen, Aberdeen, MS, p. A350
CHANDLER, Laurie, Financial Officer, Prairie Community Hospital, Terry, MT, p. A387
CHANDLER, Loren, President, Mount Sinai Hospital, Chicago, IL, p. A183
CHANDLER, Ryan
Chief Executive Officer, Midtown Medical Center West, Columbus, GA, p. A154
President and Chief Executive Officer, The Medical Center, Columbus, GA, p. A154
CHANDLER, Vincent, Director Information Services, Porterville Developmental Center, Porterville, CA, p. A81
CHANDY, Joseph, Administrator, Methodist Hospital of Chicago, Chicago, IL, p. A183
CHANEZ, Adolfo, Vice President Finance and Chief Financial Officer, Saddleback Memorial Medical Center, Laguna Hills, CA, p. A66
CHANG, Alex, Chief Operating Officer, Englewood Community Hospital, Englewood, FL, p. A126
CHANG, Florence
Executive Vice President, MultiCare Good Samaritan Hospital, Puyallup, WA, p. A682
Executive Vice President, MultiCare Mary Bridge Children's Hospital and Health Center, Tacoma, WA, p. A686
Executive Vice President, MultiCare Tacoma General Hospital, Tacoma, WA, p. A686
CHANG, Jason, M.D. Chief Medical Director, Rehabilitation Hospital of the Pacific, Honolulu, HI, p. A169
CHANG, Myrna, Chief Nursing Executive, Sutter Davis Hospital, Davis, CA, p. A59
CHANG, Sang–ick, M.D. Chief Medical Officer, Highland Hospital, Oakland, CA, p. A78
CHANNELL, Lesley
Vice President Human Resources, Dominion Hospital, Falls Church, VA, p. A664
Vice President Human Resources, Reston Hospital Center, Reston, VA, p. A671
CHANSKI, Jared, Administrator, Culberson Hospital, Van Horn, TX, p. A649
CHAPARRO, Natalia, Manager Human Resources, El Paso Children's Hospital, El Paso, TX, p. A610
CHAPDELAINE, Debora R., Manager Information Technology, Aurora Medical Center, Kenosha, WI, p. A703
CHAPLIN, Steven, M.D. Medical Director, Kahi Mohala Behavioral Health, Ewa Beach, HI, p. A168
CHAPMAN, Cully, Chief Financial Officer, Lutheran Hospital of Indiana, Fort Wayne, IN, p. A208
CHAPMAN, Glen, M.D. Medical Director, Moses Ludington Hospital, Ticonderoga, NY, p. A452
CHAPMAN, Judy, Interim Director Information Systems, Lock Haven Hospital, Lock Haven, PA, p. A539
CHAPMAN, Karen, Director Human Resources, Chester Regional Medical Center, Chester, SC, p. A558
CHAPMAN, Kathy, Chief Clinical Officer and Vice President of Patient Services, Allegan General Hospital, Allegan, MI, p. A314
CHAPMAN, Patrick, Assistant Vice President Operations, West Palm Hospital, West Palm Beach, FL, p. A147
CHAPMAN, Rachel, Nurse Manager, Noland Hospital Birmingham, Birmingham, AL, p. A16
CHAPMAN, Rick, Chief Information Officer, Kindred Hospital North Florida, Green Cove Springs, FL, p. A128
CHAPMAN, Roland, Chief Information Officer, Northern Navajo Medical Center, Shiprock, NM, p. A426
CHAPMAN, Scott, Administrator, Manhattan Surgical, KS, p. A245
CHAPMAN, Teresa, Vice President Human Resources, Marianjoy Rehabilitation Hospital, Wheaton, IL, p. A203
CHAPPELL, Brandee, Director of Nursing, LifeCare Hospitals of North Carolina, Rocky Mount, NC, p. A467
CHAPPELL, Robert, M.D. Chief Medical Officer and Chief Quality Officer, Huntsville Hospital, Huntsville, AL, p. A21
CHAPPELL, Teresa, Chief Information Officer, Johnston Health, Smithfield, NC, p. A468
CHAPPLE, Albert J., R.N. Chief Clinical Officer, Kindred Rehabilitation Hospital Northeast Houston, Humble, TX, p. A623
CHAPPLE, Scott, Chief Operating Officer, Oroville Hospital, Oroville, CA, p. A79
CHAPRNKA, Karen, Senior Vice President and Chief Operating Officer, Allegiance Health, Jackson, MI, p. A323
CHARDAVOYNE, Alan, Controller, The University of Vermont Health Network Elizabethtown Community Hospital, Elizabethtown, NY, p. A433
CHAREST, Richard
President, Landmark Medical Center, Woonsocket, RI, p. A556
Chief Executive Officer, Rehabilitation Hospital of Rhode Island, North Smithfield, RI, p. A555
CHARETTE, Deborah, Director of Nursing, East Mountain Hospital, Belle Mead, NJ, p. A409
CHARLAT, Richard A., Chief of Staff, Iowa City Veterans Affairs Health Care System, Iowa City, IA, p. A229

A806 Index of Health Care Professionals

Index of Health Care Professionals / Chilcott

Index of Health Care Professionals


CHARLES, Charlotte, Director Acute Patient Services, Madison Community Hospital, Madison, SD, p. A569
CHARLES, Sally, Coordinator Human Resources, Grace Medical Center, Lubbock, TX, p. A629
CHARLES, Timothy L., President and Chief Executive Officer, Mercy Medical Center–Cedar Rapids, Cedar Rapids, IA, p. A223
CHARLTON, Jr., Francis, M.D. Chief Medical Staff, St. Mary's Medical Center, San Francisco, CA, p. A88
CHARMEL, Patrick, President and Chief Executive Officer, Griffin Hospital, Derby, CT, p. A112
CHARRON, Robert M., Chief Executive Officer, Beauregard Memorial Hospital, De Ridder, LA, p. A273
CHARTIER, Bridgett, Director of Nursing, Beartooth Billings Clinic, Red Lodge, MT, p. A386
CHARTIER, Terry
Director, Information Systems, Mercy Medical Center–New Hampton, New Hampton, IA, p. A232
Director, Information Systems, Mercy Medical Center–North Iowa, Mason City, IA, p. A231
CHASE, Brenda, Chief Operating Officer, Mercy Hospital Rogers, Rogers, AR, p. A50
CHASE, Jean
Regional Manager Information Services, Aurora Lakeland Medical Center, Elkhorn, WI, p. A700
Regional Manager Information Services, Aurora Memorial Hospital of Burlington, Burlington, WI, p. A699
CHASE, Kyle, Chief Financial Officer, Glacial Ridge Health System, Glenwood, MN, p. A339
CHASE, Layla, Chief Financial Officer, Springhill Medical Center, Springhill, LA, p. A286
CHASE, Pansy, Director Human Resources, Vidant Duplin Hospital, Kenansville, NC, p. A463
CHASE, Robert, M.D
Chief Medical Officer, West Suburban Medical Center, Oak Park, IL, p. A196
Chief Medical Officer, Westlake Hospital, Melrose Park, IL, p. A194
CHASE, Susan, Vice President, Carolinas Rehabilitation, Charlotte, NC, p. A457
CHASIN, Marc, M.D. Chief Information Officer, St. Luke's Regional Medical Center, Boise, ID, p. A173
CHASON, Robert E., Interim Chief Executive Officer, Rideout Memorial Hospital, Marysville, CA, p. A75
CHASSE, Floyd, Vice President Human Resources, McLaren Greater Lansing, Lansing, MI, p. A324
CHASTAIN, James G., FACHE, Director, Mississippi State Hospital, Whitfield, MS, p. A361
CHASTAIN, Katherine L., R.N. Chief Nursing Officer, Sacred Heart Hospital on the Gulf, Port St. Joe, FL, p. A140
CHASTAIN, Stephen L., M.D. Chief Medical Officer, HEALTHSOUTH Rehabilitation Hospital at Martin Health, Stuart, FL, p. A143
CHASTANT, Lee, M.D., Chief Executive Officer, West Feliciana Parish Hospital, Saint Francisville, LA, p. A284
CHATANI, Kumar
Senior Vice President and Chief Information Officer Mount Sinai Health System, Mount Sinai Beth Israel, New York, NY, p. A442
Senior Vice President and Chief Information Officer Mount Sinai Health System, Mount Sinai Hospital, New York, NY, p. A442
Chief Information Officer, Mount Sinai Health System, Mount Sinai St. Luke's – Roosevelt, New York, NY, p. A442
Chief Information Officer, Mount Sinai Health System, New York Eye and Ear Infirmary of Mount Sinai, New York, NY, p. A442
CHATELAIN, Alicia, Director Human Resource, Hood Memorial Hospital, Amite, LA, p. A268
CHATELAIN, Vincent, Director Business Development, River Oaks Hospital, New Orleans, LA, p. A282
CHATLEY, Alice M., R.N. Vice President Acute Care Services, SSM Health St. Mary's Hospital – Jefferson City, Jefferson City, MO, p. A369
CHATMAN, Hubert, Chief Civilian Personnel, Wright Patterson Medical Center, Wright–Patterson AFB, OH, p. A501
CHATMAN, Jim, Chief Financial Officer, Maria Parham Medical Center, Henderson, NC, p. A462
CHATMAN, Mary, Ph.D. Senior Vice President, Chief Operating Officer and Chief Nursing Officer, Memorial Health, Savannah, GA, p. A164
CHATTERJEE, Kanan, M.D. Chief of Staff, Lebanon Veterans Affairs Medical Center, Lebanon, PA, p. A538
CHATTERTON, Bryan, Chief Executive Officer, Kindred Hospital–Indianapolis, Indianapolis, IN, p. A212
CHAUDHARY, Shahid, M.D. Chief Medical Officer, Avera St. Luke's Hospital, Aberdeen, SD, p. A567
CHAUDHRY, Deepak
Vice President Information Technology, Nexus Specialty Hospital, Shenandoah, TX, p. A643
Vice President Information Technology, Nexus Specialty Hospital The Woodlands, Spring, TX, p. A644
CHAUSSARD, David, Chief Executive Officer, Hillcrest Hospital Claremore, Claremore, OK, p. A505
CHAVEZ, Irene, Senior Vice President and Area Manager, Kaiser Permanente San Jose Medical Center, San Jose, CA, p. A89
CHAVEZ, Shari, Chief Nursing Officer, Swedish Medical Center, Englewood, CO, p. A103
CHAVEZ, Steven
Vice President Finance and Operations, Kettering Medical Center, Kettering, OH, p. A491
Vice President Finance and Operations, Sycamore Medical Center, Miamisburg, OH, p. A494
CHAVEZ, Virgil, Director Information Technology, Tsehootsooi Medical Center, Fort Defiance, AZ, p. A31
CHAVIS, Anthony D., M.D. Vice President Enterprise Medical Officer, Community Hospital Foundation, Community Hospital of the Monterey Peninsula, Monterey, CA, p. A76
CHAWLA, Nikki, M.D. Medical Director, AllianceHealth Seminole, Seminole, OK, p. A514
CHAYER, Olivia, Lead Human Resources, York Hospital, York, ME, p. A292
CHEANEY, Theresa, Controller, Chambers County Public Hospital District 1, Anahuac, TX, p. A592
CHEATWOOD, Elizabeth, Human Resource Director and Administrative Assistant, Jackson Parish Hospital, Jonesboro, LA, p. A276
CHECK, Arthur, M.D. Chief Medical Officer, Story County Medical Center, Nevada, IA, p. A232
CHECKETTS, Lannie
Interim Assistant Chief Financial Officer, Saint Alphonsus Medical Center – Nampa, Nampa, ID, p. A175
Vice President Finance and Operations, Saint Alphonsus Medical Center – Ontario, Ontario, OR, p. A523
CHEEMA, Linde, Vice President Human Resources, Sequoia Hospital, Redwood City, CA, p. A83
CHEESEMAN, Karen, Executive Vice President, Mackinac Straits Health System, Inc., Saint Ignace, MI, p. A329
CHEEVER, Liz, Administrator, Miracle Mile Medical Center, Los Angeles, CA, p. A71
CHEKOURAS, Christopher, President and Chief Executive Officer, St. Mary's Regional Medical Center, Lewiston, ME, p. A291
CHEKURU, Naidu, M.D. Chief Medical Officer, Covenant Specialty Hospital, Lubbock, TX, p. A629
CHELLAPPA, Sheila, M.D. Chief of Staff, Coatesville Veterans Affairs Medical Center, Coatesville, PA, p. A532
CHEN, David, M.D. Vice President Medical Affairs, MultiCare Good Samaritan Hospital, Puyallup, WA, p. A682
CHEN, Helen, M.D. Chief Medical Officer, Hebrew Rehabilitation Center, Boston, MA, p. A303
CHEN, Stephen, M.D. Chief Medicare, Alhambra Hospital Medical Center, Alhambra, CA, p. A53
CHEN, Van, M.D. Medical Director, Ballard Rehabilitation Hospital, San Bernardino, CA, p. A86
CHENEY, David, Chief Executive Officer, Banner Boswell Medical Center, Sun City, AZ, p. A38
CHENG, Alice, President and Chief Executive Officer, Beverly Hospital, Montebello, CA, p. A76
CHENG, Rebecca
Chief Financial Officer, California Hospital Medical Center, Los Angeles, CA, p. A69
Chief Financial Officer, Glendale Memorial Hospital and Health Center, Glendale, CA, p. A63
CHENG, Ringo, Director Information Technology, Surgery Specialty Hospitals of America, Pasadena, TX, p. A636
CHENNAULT, Paula, Administrator, Behavioral HealthCare Center at Columbia, Columbia, TN, p. A576
CHENNAULT, Scott, M.D. Chief of Staff, Burleson St. Joseph Health Center, Caldwell, TX, p. A599
CHENOWETH, Judy, Chief Nursing Officer, Russell County Hospital, Russell Springs, KY, p. A265
CHEPAK, Lois, R.N. Chief Clinical Officer, Eagleville Hospital, Eagleville, PA, p. A533
CHERAMIE, Bennett, Vice President Information Technology, Baton Rouge General Medical Center, Baton Rouge, LA, p. A269
CHERMSIDE, Paula L., Chief Operating Officer, Aspirus Grand View, Ironwood, MI, p. A323
CHERNOW, David S., President and Chief Executive Officer, Select Medical Corporation, Mechanicsburg, PA, p. B118
CHERONE, Nancy, Executive Director and Administrator, Nazareth Hospital, Philadelphia, PA, p. A544
CHERRINGTON, Steven B., M.D. Chief of Staff, Timpanogos Regional Hospital, Orem, UT, p. A657
CHERRNAY, Jennifer, Director Human Resources, Texas Institute for Surgery at Texas Health Presbyterian Dallas, Dallas, TX, p. A606
CHERRY, Jean
Executive Vice President, Commonwealth Regional Specialty Hospital, Bowling Green, KY, p. A254
Executive Vice President & Chief Information Officer, Medical Center at Franklin, Franklin, KY, p. A257
Chief Information Officer, Medical Center at Scottsville, Scottsville, KY, p. A266
CHERRY, Jonathan M., President and Chief Executive Officer, LifeStream Behavioral Center, Leesburg, FL, p. A132
CHERRY, Kris, Chief Nursing Officer, Saint Francis Hospital–Bartlett, Bartlett, TN, p. A574
CHERRY, Robert, M.D. Chief Medical Officer, Loyola University Medical Center, Maywood, IL, p. A193
CHERRY, Troy, Chief Financial Officer, Schick Shadel Hospital, Seattle, WA, p. A683
CHESLEY, Jeanine, Chief Executive Officer, New England Rehabilitation Hospital of Portland, Portland, ME, p. A292
CHESLEY, Stephen, Chief of Staff, Sanford Luverne Medical Center, Luverne, MN, p. A341
CHESLEY, Walter, Vice President Human Resources, Hennepin County Medical Center, Minneapolis, MN, p. A342
CHESNOS, Richard C., Senior Vice President Finance and Chief Financial Officer, St. Clair Hospital, Pittsburgh, PA, p. A546
CHESSARE, John B., FACHE, President and Chief Executive Officer, Greater Baltimore Medical Center, Baltimore, MD, p. A293
CHESSIN, Neil A., Vice President, Jameson Hospital, New Castle, PA, p. A541
CHESSUM, George
Senior Vice President and Chief Information Officer, Community First Medical Center, Chicago, IL, p. A181
Vice President Information Systems, Presence Saint Francis Hospital, Evanston, IL, p. A188
Senior Vice President Information Systems and Chief Information Officer, Presence Saint Joseph Hospital, Chicago, IL, p. A183
CHESTER, Julie, Vice President Human Resources, University Hospitals Case Medical Center, Cleveland, OH, p. A485
CHESTER, Linnes L., USAF Administrator, Mike O'Callaghan Federal Hospital, Nellis AFB, NV, p. A403
CHESTER, William, Manager Human Resources, Grand Junction Veterans Health Care System, Grand Junction, CO, p. A104
CHESTNUT–RAULS, Monica, Vice President Human Resources, Peconic Bay Medical Center, Riverhead, NY, p. A448
CHEUNG, Alan, M.D. Vice President Medical Affairs, Castle Medical Center, Kailua, HI, p. A169
CHEUNG, Anna, President, St. Mary's Medical Center, San Francisco, CA, p. A88
CHEUNG, Marilou, Assistant Administrator Finance, Kaiser Permanente Woodland Hills Medical Center, CA, p. A70
CHEVERE, Carlos, M.D. Medical Director, I. Gonzalez Martinez Oncologic Hospital, PR, p. A724
CHEW, Brian, Human Resources Officer, Holy Cross Hospital, Taos, NM, p. A427
CHEW, Roy G., Ph.D., President, Kettering Medical Center, Kettering, OH, p. A491
CHEWNING III, Larry H., President and Chief Executive Officer, Nash Health Care Systems, Rocky Mount, NC, p. A467
CHEYNET, Sandee, Vice President Administrative Services, Bluefield Regional Medical Center, Bluefield, WV, p. A689
CHHABRA, Ankit
Director Finance, Fairview Hospital, Cleveland, OH, p. A484
Director Finance, Lakewood Hospital, Lakewood, OH, p. A491
CHIACCHIARO, Peter, Vice President Human Resources, St. Joseph Hospital, Bethpage, NY, p. A429
CHIANESE, Chuck, Chief Information Officer, Children's Specialized Hospital–PSE&G, New Brunswick, NJ, p. A415
CHIANTELLA, Christopher, M.D. Chief Medical Officer, Inova Loudoun Hospital, Leesburg, VA, p. A667
CHIANTELLO, Charmaine, Chief Financial Officer, Aspirus Grand View, Ironwood, MI, p. A323
CHIARCHIARO, Martha, Vice President Human Resources, Clinton Hospital, Clinton, MA, p. A306
CHIAVETTA, Robert, Vice President Finance, United Memorial Medical Center, Batavia, NY, p. A429
CHICK, Melanie, Chief Executive Officer, Baylor Medical Center at Trophy Club, Trophy Club, TX, p. A648
CHICKEN, Kurt, Director Support Services, Palmer Lutheran Health Center, West Union, IA, p. A236
CHIEFFO, Ron, Chief Information Officer, Colorado River Medical Center, Needles, CA, p. A77
CHIKOWSKI, Julie, Administrator, Memorial Hospital of Lafayette County, Darlington, WI, p. A699
CHILCOTT, Stephen, Associate Director Human Resources, University of California, Davis Medical Center, Sacramento, CA, p. A85


 Index of Health Care Professionals A807

Index of Health Care Professionals

Index of Health Care Professionals / Child

CHILD, Clint L., R.N. Chief Nursing Officer, Saint Alphonsus Medical Center – Nampa, Nampa, ID, p. A175
CHILDERS, Bethany, Director Human Resources, Fremont Health, Fremont, NE, p. A391
CHILDERS, Christy, Director Information Technology, P & S Surgical Hospital, Monroe, LA, p. A280
CHILDERS, Linda, Director Human Resources, Wallowa Memorial Hospital, Enterprise, OR, p. A520
CHILDERS, Matthew, Director of Nursing, Sistersville General Hospital, Sistersville, WV, p. A695
CHILDRE Jr., Jimmy, Interim Chief Executive Officer, Washington County Regional Medical Center, Sandersville, GA, p. A164
CHILDS, Joe, M.D. Vice President Medical Services, East Tennessee Children's Hospital, Knoxville, TN, p. A580
CHILDS, Michelle B., Senior Administrative Director Human Resources, Salinas Valley Memorial Healthcare System, Salinas, CA, p. A85
CHILES, John, M.D. Medical Director, Western State Hospital, Tacoma, WA, p. A686
CHILES, Kevin, Vice President Human Resources, Hutchinson Regional Medical Center, Hutchinson, KS, p. A242
CHILES, Morton, M.D. Chief Medical Officer, UVA Culpeper Hospital, Culpeper, VA, p. A664
CHILESKI, Andy, Chief Information Officer and Vice President Facilities, Berger Health System, Circleville, OH, p. A484
CHILL, Martha O'Regan, Interim Chief Information Officer, Wellmont Hancock County Hospital, Sneedville, TN, p. A588
CHILSON, Terrance, Chief of Staff, Tyler Memorial Hospital, Tunkhannock, PA, p. A551
CHILTON, Bryan, Director Information Systems, Navarro Regional Hospital, Corsicana, TX, p. A603
CHIN, Ellyn, Vice President Finance, Gottlieb Memorial Hospital, Melrose Park, IL, p. A194
CHINBURG, Paul, M.D. Medical Director, Lane County Hospital, Dighton, KS, p. A239
CHING, Angelica, Director Information Systems, Monterey Park Hospital, Monterey Park, CA, p. A76
CHING, Geraldine, Assistant General Minister, Sisters of Saint Francis, Syracuse, NY, p. B124
CHINN, Tammie, Director Marketing and Public Relations, Plateau Medical Center, Oak Hill, WV, p. A693
CHINN, Terri, Vice President Finance, St. Mary's Medical Center, Grand Junction, CO, p. A104
CHINNOCK, Rachel, Chief Human Resources Officer, Latimer County General Hospital, Wilburton, OK, p. A518
CHIOLO, Denise, Chief Human Resources Officer, Phoenixville Hospital, Phoenixville, PA, p. A545
CHIPMAN, Kim, Chief Clinical Officer, Kindred Hospital–White Rock, Dallas, TX, p. A605
CHIRICHELLA, Joseph, President and Chief Executive Officer, Deborah Heart and Lung Center, Browns Mills, NJ, p. A410
CHISHOLM, Donna, Interim Director of Nursing Services, Cedar Crest Hospital and Residential Treatment Center, Belton, TX, p. A597
CHISHOLM, Ken, Director Human Resources, Martha's Vineyard Hospital, Oak Bluffs, MA, p. A310
CHISHOLM, Sharon, Entity Human Resource Officer, Texas Health Presbyterian Hospital Allen, Allen, TX, p. A590
CHISSELL, Herbert G., M.D. Chief Medical Officer, Torrance State Hospital, Torrance, PA, p. A551
CHITAYAT, Ron, M.D. Chief Medical Staff, West Hills Hospital and Medical Center, CA, p. A73
CHITTENDEN, Michael D., President, St. Vincent Carmel Hospital, Carmel, IN, p. A206
CHIVERS, John, Senior Vice President Finance, Sierra View Medical Center, Porterville, CA, p. A81
CHIZEK, Chris, Chief Executive Officer, Solara Hospital McAllen, McAllen, TX, p. A631
CHMIELEWSKI, Linda A., R.N. Vice President Operations, St. Cloud Hospital, Saint Cloud, MN, p. A345
CHMURA, David, Chief Information Officer, Copper Queen Community Hospital, Bisbee, AZ, p. A30
CHOATE, Charlotte, Director Information Systems, Trinity Hospital of Augusta, Augusta, GA, p. A151
CHODKOWSKI, Paul J., Chief Executive Officer, St. Anthony Summit Medical Center, Frisco, CO, p. A104
CHOINKA, Keith A., Vice President Information Systems and Chief Information Officer, St. Joseph Hospital, Nashua, NH, p. A407
CHOKSHI, Sushil, M.D. Chief Medical Officer, Faith Community Hospital, Jacksboro, TX, p. A624
CHOLGER, Dave, Chief Financial Officer, Woodlawn Hospital, Rochester, IN, p. A219
CHONG, Johnnette, Chief Financial Officer, Los Angeles Community Hospital at Los Angeles, Los Angeles, CA, p. A71
CHOPIN, Candice, Vice President Human Resources, Regional Medical Center of Acadiana, Lafayette, LA, p. A278
CHOPRA, Praveen, Executive Vice President and Chief Information and Transformation Innovative Environment Officer, Thomas Jefferson University Hospitals, Philadelphia, PA, p. A545
CHORAZEWITZ, Keri, Vice President Compliance and Employee Relations, Memorial Hospital of Sweetwater County, Rock Springs, WY, p. A717
CHORD, Ginger, Coordinator Human Resources, Sturgis Regional Hospital, Sturgis, SD, p. A572
CHOREY, Raymond M., President and Chief Executive Officer, Southeastern Ohio Regional Medical Center, Cambridge, OH, p. A481
CHOU, Rebecca
Directory Information Systems, Palestine Regional Medical Center, Palestine, TX, p. A635
Director Information Systems, Palestine Regional Medical Center–East, Palestine, TX, p. A635
CHOUDHURY, Seleem, R.N. Chief Nursing Officer, Northeastern Vermont Regional Hospital, Saint Johnsbury, VT, p. A661
CHOY, Ann N., Manager Human Resources and Payroll, Kuakini Medical Center, Honolulu, HI, p. A168
CHOY, Rose, Chief Financial Officer, Kahi Mohala Behavioral Health, Ewa Beach, HI, p. A168
CHOZINSKI, Joseph P., M.D. Deputy Commander Clinical Services, Brooke Army Medical Center, Fort Sam Houston, TX, p. A612
CHRENCIK, Robert A., President and Chief Executive Officer, University of Maryland Medical System, Baltimore, MD, p. B146
CHRISTENSEN, Carl (Jim), Chief Executive Officer, Comanche County Medical Center, Comanche, TX, p. A601
CHRISTENSEN, Cinthia S., JD Executive Vice President and Chief Operating Officer, Children's Hospital of Wisconsin, Milwaukee, WI, p. A706
CHRISTENSEN, Claudia, Director, Human Resources, Mills–Peninsula Health Services, Burlingame, CA, p. A56
CHRISTENSEN, Connie, Chief Financial Officer, Morrill County Community Hospital, Bridgeport, NE, p. A390
CHRISTENSEN, David, M.D. Senior Vice President and Chief Medical Officer, Valley Children's Hospital, Madera, CA, p. A74
CHRISTENSEN, Earlene, Director Human Resources, Fayette County Memorial Hospital, Washington Court House, OH, p. A500
CHRISTENSEN, Elizabeth B., Director Human Resources, Mercy Hospital of Portland, Portland, ME, p. A291
CHRISTENSEN, G. N., M.D. Chief Medical Officer, William Bee Ririe Hospital, Ely, NV, p. A400
CHRISTENSEN, Gwen, Vice President Finance, Aurora BayCare Medical Center, Green Bay, WI, p. A701
CHRISTENSEN, Jay, FACHE, Administrator, Mahaska Health Partnership, Oskaloosa, IA, p. A233
CHRISTENSEN, Jeffrey, Chief Executive Officer, HEALTHSOUTH Rehabilitation Institute of Tucson, Tucson, AZ, p. A39
CHRISTENSEN, Kim, Interim Chief Nursing Executive, Sheridan Community Hospital, Sheridan, MI, p. A330
CHRISTENSEN, Marilyn, Director Information Technology, Milford Hospital, Milford, CT, p. A113
CHRISTENSEN, Mark, Director, Finance, Cassia Regional Medical Center, Burley, ID, p. A173
CHRISTENSEN, Marti, Director of Psychiatric Nursing, Douglas County Community Mental Health Center, Omaha, NE, p. A396
CHRISTENSEN, Sandra, Chief Financial Officer, Dallas County Hospital, Perry, IA, p. A233
CHRISTENSEN, Scott, Chief Executive Officer, Delta Regional Medical Center, Greenville, MS, p. A353
CHRISTENSEN, Todd, Chief Financial Officer, Kittson Memorial Healthcare Center, Hallock, MN, p. A340
CHRISTENSEN, Troy, Chief Financial Officer, Madison Memorial Hospital, Rexburg, ID, p. A176
CHRISTENSEN, W. R., M.D. Chief of Staff, East Texas Medical Center Pittsburg, Pittsburg, TX, p. A636
CHRISTENSEN–MORES, Donna, Director Human Resources, Myrtue Medical Center, Harlan, IA, p. A229
CHRISTENSON, Ann, Executive Vice President Human Resources and Support Services, Sanford Medical Center Fargo, Fargo, ND, p. A474
CHRISTENSON, Paul, Chief Financial Officer, Pampa Regional Medical Center, Pampa, TX, p. A635
CHRISTENSON, Ron, Chief Financial Officer, Morris County Hospital, Council Grove, KS, p. A239
CHRISTENSON, Shannon, Director Human Resources, Aurora West Allis Medical Center, West Allis, WI, p. A714
CHRISTIAN, Bruce C., Chief Executive Officer, AMITA Health Adventist GlenOaks Hospital, Glendale Heights, IL, p. A189
CHRISTIAN, Chuck, Vice President Chief Information Officer, St. Francis Hospital, Columbus, GA, p. A154
CHRISTIAN, Glenn, Administrator, Mayo Clinic Health System in Cannon Falls, Cannon Falls, MN, p. A336
CHRISTIAN, Greg, Executive Director, Kaiser Permanente Fontana Medical Center, Fontana, CA, p. A61
CHRISTIAN, Karolyne, Director Human Resources, Byrd Regional Hospital, Leesville, LA, p. A279
CHRISTIANO, Barbara, Vice President, Patient Care Services and Chief Nursing Officer, University Medical Center of Princeton at Plainsboro, Plainsboro, NJ, p. A417
CHRISTIANSEN, Anne, Chief Financial Officer, Pioneer Memorial Hospital and Health Services, Viborg, SD, p. A572
CHRISTIANSEN, Hilary, Chief Financial Officer, George C Grape Community Hospital, Hamburg, IA, p. A228
CHRISTIANSEN, Keith, Chief Nursing Officer, Select Specialty Hospital–Erie, Erie, PA, p. A534
CHRISTIANSEN, Patrick, Ph.D., Chief Executive Officer, Inova Fairfax Hospital, Falls Church, VA, p. A664
CHRISTIANSEN, Sara, Interim Director Human Resources, Ridgeview Sibley Medical Center, Arlington, MN, p. A334
CHRISTIANSON, Clinton J., FACHE, President and Chief Executive Officer, Mercy Medical Center–Centerville, Centerville, IA, p. A224
CHRISTIANSON, Delano, Administrator, CentraCare Health–Sauk Centre, Sauk Centre, MN, p. A347
CHRISTIE, Janet L., Senior Vice President Human Resources, UF Health Shands Hospital, Gainesville, FL, p. A128
CHRISTINE, Gerald, Chief Financial Officer, Lakewood Ranch Medical Center, Bradenton, FL, p. A122
CHRISTION, Lydia, Director Human Resources, HEALTHSOUTH Rehabilitation Hospital, Dothan, AL, p. A18
CHRISTISON, George, M.D. Medical Director, Patton State Hospital, Patton, CA, p. A80
CHRISTMAN, Lawrence, Chief Financial Officer and Chief Operating Officer, Riverview Hospital, Noblesville, IN, p. A218
CHRISTMAN, Thomas C., Director Plant Operations, Kindred Hospital–St. Louis, Saint Louis, MO, p. A376
CHRISTMANN, Linda, M.D. Chief of Staff, Manatee Memorial Hospital, Bradenton, FL, p. A122
CHRISTOPH, Rebecca, Director Nursing and Patient Care Services, Mid–Valley Hospital, Omak, WA, p. A681
CHRISTOPHEL, Randal, President and Chief Executive Officer, Indiana University Health Goshen Hospital, Goshen, IN, p. A210
CHROBAK, Jeffrey, Vice President Finance and Chief Financial Officer, Sharon Regional Health System, Sharon, PA, p. A550
CHU, Edward, Chief Financial Officer, Leahi Hospital, Honolulu, HI, p. A168
CHUA, Jesus, M.D. Chief of Staff, Franklin Foundation Hospital, Franklin, LA, p. A274
CHUE, Bevins, M.D. Medical Director, HEALTHSOUTH Desert Canyon Rehabilitation Hospital, Las Vegas, NV, p. A402
CHUGHTAI, Omar, Vice President and Chief Operating Officer, West Hills Hospital and Medical Center, CA, p. A73
CHULI, Judith, R.N. Chief Nursing Officer, Fairlawn Rehabilitation Hospital, Worcester, MA, p. A313
CHUN, Leslie, M.D. Vice President Medical Staff and Chief Quality Officer, Queen's Medical Center, Honolulu, HI, p. A169
CHUN, MiRhee, Chief Financial Officer, Seven Hills Hospital, Henderson, NV, p. A401
CHUN, Ryan, Information Resources Management, San Francisco VA Medical Center, San Francisco, CA, p. A88
CHUNG, Maria, CPA Director Fiscal Services, Shriners Hospitals for Children–Boston, Boston, MA, p. A304
CHUNG, Michael
Chief Financial Officer, AHMC Anaheim Regional Medical Center, Anaheim, CA, p. A53
Chief Financial Officer, Greater El Monte Community Hospital, South El Monte, CA, p. A93
CHUNG, Raymond, M.D. Chief of Staff, Phoenix Veterans Affairs Health Care System, Phoenix, AZ, p. A35
CHUNG, William, M.D. Chief of Staff, Chinese Hospital, San Francisco, CA, p. A88
CHUNN, Ashley, Director of Nursing, Atmore Community Hospital, Atmore, AL, p. A16
CHUNN, Debbie, Director Medical Records, Bastrop Rehabilitation Hospital, Monroe, LA, p. A280
CHURCH, Kim
Manager Human Resources, G. Werber Bryan Psychiatric Hospital, Columbia, SC, p. A559
Manager Human Resources, William S. Hall Psychiatric Institute, Columbia, SC, p. A560
CHURCHILL, Brigitte, Director of Human Resources, Mayo Clinic Health System in Waycross, Waycross, GA, p. A167
CHURCHILL, Julie, Chief Financial Officer, Victory Medical Center – Southcross, San Antonio, TX, p. A642
CHURCHILL, Larry, Director Information Services, AllianceHealth Woodward, Woodward, OK, p. A518
CHURCHILL, Sandi, Vice President Business Development and Operations, Professional Services, Advocate Good Samaritan Hospital, Downers Grove, IL, p. A186
CHURCHILL, Timothy A., President, Stephens Memorial Hospital, Norway, ME, p. A291

A808 Index of Health Care Professionals © 2015 AHA Guide

Index of Health Care Professionals

Index of Health Care Professionals / Claudson

CLAUDSON, Jackie, Administrator, South Big Horn County Hospital, Basin, WY, p. A715
CLAUDY, Frank, M.D. Vice President Medical Staff Affairs, Genesis Medical Center–Davenport, Davenport, IA, p. A225
CLAUNCH, Jeremy, Chief Financial Officer, Power County Hospital District, American Falls, ID, p. A172
CLAUSEN, Patricia J., R.N. Chief Nurse Executive, Kaiser Permanente Downey Medical Center, Downey, CA, p. A60
CLAUSSEN, Denise, R.N. Chief Nursing Officer, Texas Health Presbyterian Hospital Kaufman, Kaufman, TX, p. A625
CLAUSSEN, Tammy, Human Resources Executive, Tri Valley Health System, Cambridge, NE, p. A390
CLAVELL, Luis, M.D. Medical Director, San Jorge Children's Hospital, San Juan, PR, p. A724
CLAVELLE, Joanne T., R.N. Senior Vice President and Chief Clinical Officer, HonorHealth Scottsdale Shea Medical Center, Scottsdale, AZ, p. A37
CLAWSON, Tonya, Manager Human Resources, Mercy Medical Center–Centerville, Centerville, IA, p. A224
CLAXTON, Anthony, M.D. Clinical Director, Terrell State Hospital, Terrell, TX, p. A647
CLAXTON, Tracey
Chief Financial Officer, Chester Regional Medical Center, Chester, SC, p. A558
Chief Financial Officer, Jennersville Regional Hospital, West Grove, PA, p. A552
CLAY, David, Chief Executive Officer, Sandhills Regional Medical Center, Hamlet, NC, p. A461
CLAYMORE, Krystal, Chief Financial Officer, Great Plains Health, North Platte, NE, p. A395
CLAYPOOL, Blain, President, St. Vincent's Medical Center Clay County, Middleburg, FL, p. A135
CLAYTON, Edward, Chief Financial Officer, Phelps County Regional Medical Center, Rolla, MO, p. A375
CLAYTON, Julie, R.N. Chief Nursing Officer and Vice President Patient Care Services, Overlake Medical Center, Bellevue, WA, p. A676
CLAYTON, Kent G., Chief Executive Officer, Los Alamitos Medical Center, Los Alamitos, CA, p. A68
CLAYTON, Philip A., President and Chief Executive Officer, Conway Medical Center, Conway, SC, p. A560
CLEARY, Mary Elizabeth, Chief Financial Officer, MacNeal Hospital, Berwyn, IL, p. A179
CLEARY, Steven R., Vice President Finance, St. Mary's Medical Center, Blue Springs, MO, p. A363
CLEAVER, Chuck, Vice President and Chief Financial Officer, Martin Health System, Stuart, FL, p. A143
CLECKLER, Jason, Chief Executive Officer, Delta County Memorial Hospital, Delta, CO, p. A101
CLELAND, Dub, Chief Financial Officer, Oklahoma Surgical Hospital, Tulsa, OK, p. A516
CLELAND, Richard C., FACHE, President and Chief Operating Officer and Interim Chief Executive Officer, Erie County Medical Center, Buffalo, NY, p. A430
CLELAND, William H., M.D. Chief Medical Officer, University of Mississippi Medical Center, Jackson, MS, p. A355
CLEMEN, Linda, R.N. Vice President and Chief Nursing Officer, Katherine Shaw Bethea Hospital, Dixon, IL, p. A186
CLEMENS, Brian L.
President and Chief Executive Officer, Community Hospital, Oklahoma City, OK, p. A511
Chief Executive Officer, Northwest Surgical Hospital, Oklahoma City, OK, p. A512
CLEMENS, Dennis, Chief of Staff, Northern Hospital of Surry County, Mount Airy, NC, p. A465
CLEMENT, Bernie, Chief Information Officer, Thibodaux Regional Medical Center, Thibodaux, LA, p. A286
CLEMENT, Bruce, Chief Operating Officer, Slidell Memorial Hospital, Slidell, LA, p. A285
CLEMENT, Charles, Chief Executive Officer, SEARHC MT. Edgecumbe Hospital, Sitka, AK, p. A29
CLEMENT, Kevin J., Chief Executive Officer, Landmark Hospital of Joplin, Joplin, MO, p. A369
CLEMENT, Michelle, Executive Assistant/Human Resources Director, Roundup Memorial Healthcare, Roundup, MT, p. A386
CLEMENTS, James, Chief Executive Officer, Cullman Regional Medical Center, Cullman, AL, p. A18
CLEMENTS, John R., Chief Financial Officer, McCullough–Hyde Memorial Hospital/TriHealth, Oxford, OH, p. A496
CLEMENTS, Lynn, Director Human Resources, Shriners Hospitals for Children–Houston, Houston, TX, p. A622
CLEMMENSEN, J. Scott
Vice President Human Resources and Leadership Enhancement, Capital Health Medical Center–Hopewell, Pennington, NJ, p. A416
Vice President Human Resources and Leadership Enhancement, Capital Health Regional Medical Center, Trenton, NJ, p. A419
CLEMMER, Deb, Vice President Human Resources, Bothwell Regional Health Center, Sedalia, MO, p. A378
CLEMONS, Deneace, Chief Operating Officer, Twin Lakes Regional Medical Center, Leitchfield, KY, p. A259
CLERE, Trevor, Director Information Technology, Mercy Medical Center, Canton, OH, p. A481
CLEVELAND, Austin B., Chief Executive Officer, Vibra Hospital of Denver, Thornton, CO, p. A109
CLEVELAND, Cynthia, Ph.D. Associate Director for Patient Care Services and Nurse Executive, Birmingham Veterans Affairs Medical Center, Birmingham, AL, p. A16
CLEVENGER, Erin R., Chief Nursing Officer and Director of Quality, Memorial Medical Center, Port Lavaca, TX, p. A638
CLEWS, Donna, Ph.D. Vice President Patient Care Services, Berkeley Medical Center, Martinsburg, WV, p. A693
CLICK, Glenn, Chief Financial Officer, Sequoyah Memorial Hospital, Sallisaw, OK, p. A514
CLICK, Mike, Administrator, Brownfield Regional Medical Center, Brownfield, TX, p. A598
CLIFFE, Peggy, Chief Executive Officer, Select Specialty Hospital–Wichita, Wichita, KS, p. A252
CLIFFORD, Michael J., Director Finance, Wayne Memorial Hospital, Honesdale, PA, p. A536
CLIFFORD, Ryan, M.D. Chief of Staff, Washakie Medical Center, Worland, WY, p. A718
CLIFTON, Mark, Interim Chief Financial Officer, CHI St. Luke's Health Memorial Livingston, Livingston, TX, p. A628
CLINE, Richard, D.O. Chief of Staff, Lincoln County Health System, Fayetteville, TN, p. A577
CLINE, Vickie, Director Human Resources, Northwest Medical Center, Albany, MO, p. A363
CLINGENPEEL, Jeremy, Administrator, Satanta District Hospital and Long Term Care, Satanta, KS, p. A250
CLINGER, Dallas, Administrator, Power County Hospital District, American Falls, ID, p. A172
CLINITE, Ed, D.O. Chief of Staff, Sonora Regional Medical Center, Sonora, CA, p. A92
CLINTON, Lee, FACHE Vice President Operations, Perry County Memorial Hospital, Perryville, MO, p. A374
CLINTON, Lori, Chief Nursing Officer, Sparta Community Hospital, Sparta, IL, p. A200
CLIPP, Jerry, Manager Human Resources, Washakie Medical Center, Worland, WY, p. A718
CLISTER, Martha L., Director Human Resources, Canonsburg General Hospital, Canonsburg, PA, p. A530
CLOHSEY, Maria, Director of Nursing, Shore Rehabilitation Institute, Brick, NJ, p. A409
CLOKE, Stacey, Vice President Human Resources, Providence Mount Carmel Hospital, Colville, WA, p. A678
CLONTS, Jolene, Director Human Resources, Logan Regional Hospital, Logan, UT, p. A655
CLOSE, Debra, Chief Executive Officer, Dukes Memorial Hospital, Peru, IN, p. A218
CLOUD, Avery, Vice President and Chief Information Officer, New Hanover Regional Medical Center, Wilmington, NC, p. A470
CLOUD, Sylvia, Director Human Resources, Silver Lake Medical Center, Los Angeles, CA, p. A72
CLOUGH, Jeanette G., President and Chief Executive Officer, Mount Auburn Hospital, Cambridge, MA, p. A305
CLOUGH, Sheila, Chief Executive Officer, Asante Ashland Community Hospital, Ashland, OR, p. A519
CLOUGH–BERRY, Cherie, Vice President, Finance, Hampstead Hospital, Hampstead, NH, p. A406
CLOUSE, Joseph, Chief Administrative Officer, Newport Hospital and Health Services, Newport, WA, p. A681
CLOUSE DAY, Sherry, Vice President Finance, Mercy Hospital Berryville, Berryville, AR, p. A41
CLOUTIER, Mary, Director Human Resources, Adventist Behavioral Health Rockville, Rockville, MD, p. A299
CLOUTIER, Michael, Director Information Services, Trios Health, Kennewick, WA, p. A680
CLOVER, Robert, Superintendent and Chief Executive Officer, Logansport State Hospital, Logansport, IN, p. A215
CLOWARD, Laura, Human Resources Coordinator, Cordova Community Medical Center, Cordova, AK, p. A27
CLOWES, Jennifer, Chief Financial Officer, Broadwater Health Center, Townsend, MT, p. A387
CLOYD, Elizabeth, R.N. Chief Nurse Executive and Executive Vice President, Harris Health System, Houston, TX, p. A619
CLUCK, Robert N., M.D. Vice President and Medical Director, Texas Health Arlington Memorial Hospital, Arlington, TX, p. A593
CLUFF, Ben, Chief Executive Officer, Ashley Regional Medical Center, Vernal, UT, p. A659
CLUNE, T. Patrick, Chief Financial Officer, Florence Hospital at Anthem, Florence, AZ, p. A31
CLUNN, Amy, M.D. Medical Director, HEALTHSOUTH Rehabilitation Hospital of Ocala, Ocala, FL, p. A136
CLUTTS, Kathaleen, Chief Human Resources Officer, Des Peres Hospital, Saint Louis, MO, p. A376
CLYNE, Andrea, R.N. Chief Nursing Officer, Palms of Pasadena Hospital, Saint Petersburg, FL, p. A142
CLYNE, Mary Ellen, R.N., President and Chief Executive Officer, Clara Maass Medical Center, Belleville, NJ, p. A409
CMIEL, Peggy, R.N. Chief Nursing Officer, Chinese Hospital, San Francisco, CA, p. A88
COALTER, Barbara, Director Human Resources, Weirton Medical Center, Weirton, WV, p. A696
COATE, Mark, M.D. Chief of Staff, Madison Health, London, OH, p. A492
COATES, Janet E., R.N., President and Chief Executive Officer, Mother Frances Hospital – Winnsboro, Winnsboro, TX, p. A652
COATES, Jennifer, Coordinator Information Technology, Purcell Municipal Hospital, Purcell, OK, p. A514
COATS, Daniel J., Vice President Operations, Mercy Hospital Ada, Ada, OK, p. A503
COATS, John, M.D. Chief Medical Staff, Morehouse General Hospital, Bastrop, LA, p. A269
COATS, Kevin, Chief Operating Officer and Chief Financial Officer, Baylor Medical Center at Frisco, Frisco, TX, p. A615
COBARRUBIAS, Samuel, M.D. Chief of Staff, Clinch Memorial Hospital, Homerville, GA, p. A159
COBB, April, Chief Nursing Officer, HEALTHSOUTH Lakeshore Rehabilitation Hospital, Birmingham, AL, p. A16
COBB, Heidi, R.N. Chief Nursing Officer, Medical Arts Hospital, Lamesa, TX, p. A627
COBB, Janice M., R.N. Chief Nursing Officer, Tennessee Valley Healthcare System, Nashville, TN, p. A586
COBB, Jason E., FACHE, Chief Executive Officer, Rapides Regional Medical Center, Alexandria, LA, p. A268
COBB, Jeff, Information Technologist, Guthrie County Hospital, Guthrie Center, IA, p. A228
COBB, Maura, R.N. Chief Nursing Officer, Northridge Medical Center, Commerce, GA, p. A154
COBB, Tammy, Chief Financial Officer, Northeast Regional Medical Center, Kirksville, MO, p. A371
COBBLE, Emlyn, Vice President and Chief Support Officer, Parkwest Medical Center, Knoxville, TN, p. A580
COBBS, Wendy, Director of Human Resources, Promise Hospital of Baton Rouge – Ochsner Campus, Baton Rouge, LA, p. A270
COBLE, Hal, Administrator, Murray Medical Center, Chatsworth, GA, p. A153
COBURN, Nate, Chief Financial Officer, Weiser Memorial Hospital, Weiser, ID, p. A177
COBURN, Paul, Chief Financial Officer, Liberty Healthcare Systems, Bastrop, LA, p. A269
COCCA, Lisa, Chief Executive Officer, Belmont Pines Hospital, Youngstown, OH, p. A501
COCCHI, Dean, Chief Financial Officer, Kindred Hospital Ocala, Ocala, FL, p. A137
COCHENNET, Bradley, Chief Executive Officer, Pagosa Springs Medical Center, Pagosa Springs, CO, p. A107
COCHRAN, Dan
Chief Operating Officer, Bingham Memorial Hospital, Blackfoot, ID, p. A172
Chief Operating Officer, Mountain River Birthing and Surgery Center, Blackfoot, ID, p. A172
COCHRAN, Daniel, Vice President and Chief Financial Officer, Shady Grove Adventist Hospital, Rockville, MD, p. A300
COCHRAN, Janice, R.N. Director of Patient Care, CHRISTUS Dubuis Hospital of Paris, Paris, TX, p. A635
COCHRAN, Kenneth, FACHE, President and Chief Executive Officer, East Liverpool City Hospital, East Liverpool, OH, p. A489
COCHRAN, Kenneth, President and Chief Executive Officer, Opelousas General Health System, Opelousas, LA, p. A283
COCHRAN, Sherry, Manager Human Resources, Cascade Behavioral Hospital, Tukwila, WA, p. A686
COCHRAN, Jr., Willie, M.D. Chief of Staff, Southern Regional Medical Center, Riverdale, GA, p. A163
COCHRANE, Andrew S., Chief Executive Officer, Maple Grove Hospital, Maple Grove, MN, p. A342
COCHRANE, Donna, Interim Chief Executive Officer, Liberty Regional Medical Center, Hinesville, GA, p. A158
COCHRANE, Robert K., Interim Vice President, Finance, Cheshire Medical Center, Keene, NH, p. A406
COCKING, Kathy, R.N. Vice President Operations, Barton Memorial Hospital, South Lake Tahoe, CA, p. A93
COCKRELL, Christopher, Executive Director Human Resources, Providence Hospital, Mobile, AL, p. A22
COCKRELL, Dennis, Director Human Resources, Gritman Medical Center, Moscow, ID, p. A175
COCKRELL, Tim, Chief Executive Officer, Patients Choice Medical Center of Smith County, Raleigh, MS, p. A360
CODER, Charles, Chief Financial Officer, Southside Regional Medical Center, Petersburg, VA, p. A670

A810 Index of Health Care Professionals

Index of Health Care Professionals / Collins

Index of Health Care Professionals


CODER, Denise, Chief Human Resource Officer, Cass County Memorial Hospital, Atlantic, IA, p. A222
CODY, James, Director, Syracuse Veterans Affairs Medical Center, Syracuse, NY, p. A451
CODY, Kyllan, Chief Executive Officer, Cook Children's Northeast Hospital, Hurst, TX, p. A624
COE, Jason, M.D. Medical Director, MMO Greenbrier Hospital, Covington, LA, p. A272
COE, Jason C., President and Chief Executive Officer, Hackettstown Regional Medical Center, Hackettstown, NJ, p. A412
COE, Susan
Vice President Human Resources, University of Maryland Shore Medical Center at Chestertown, Chestertown, MD, p. A296
Regional Vice President Human Resources, University of Maryland Shore Medical Center at Dorchester, Cambridge, MD, p. A296
Regional Vice President Human Resources, University of Maryland Shore Medical Center at Easton, Easton, MD, p. A297
COELLO, Jennifer, Chief Operating Officer, Clinch Valley Medical Center, Richlands, VA, p. A671
COEN, Vickie, Chief Clinical Officer and Nurse Executive, Pana Community Hospital, Pana, IL, p. A197
COFFEE, Heidi Malez, Chief Nursing Officer, East Georgia Regional Medical Center, Statesboro, GA, p. A165
COFFEE, Paula, Director Human Resources, St. Mary's of Michigan, Saginaw, MI, p. A329
COFFEE, Robert, Chief Information Officer, Creek Nation Community Hospital, Okemah, OK, p. A511
COFFELL, Randy, Manager Human Resources, Mid–Valley Hospital, Omak, WA, p. A681
COFFEY, C. Edward, M.D., President, Menninger Clinic, Houston, TX, p. A621
COFFEY, Daniel B., President and Chief Executive Officer, The Acadia Hospital, Bangor, ME, p. A288
COFFEY, Douglas W., R.N. Chief Nursing Officer, St. Mary's Regional Medical Center, Enid, OK, p. A506
COFFEY, Glenna, R.N., Chief Operating Officer, Bridgewell Hospital of Cincinnati, Cincinnati, OH, p. A482
COFFEY, Joseph, Director Facility Administration, Rochester Psychiatric Center, Rochester, NY, p. A449
COFFEY, Judy, R.N., Senior Vice President and Area Manager, Kaiser Permanente San Rafael Medical Center, San Rafael, CA, p. A90
COFFEY, Judy, R.N. Senior Vice President and Area Manager, Kaiser Permanente San Rafael Medical Center, San Rafael, CA, p. A90
COFFEY, Judy, R.N., Senior Vice President and Area Manager, Kaiser Permanente Santa Rosa Medical Center, Santa Rosa, CA, p. A92
COFFEY, Kevin, Chief Executive Officer, Winner Regional Healthcare Center, Winner, SD, p. A573
COFFEY, Timothy O., Senior Vice President Operations, Lake Charles Memorial Hospital, Lake Charles, LA, p. A278
COFFING, Sylvia K., R.N. Chief Nursing and Compliance Officer, Unity Medical & Surgical Hospital, Mishawaka, IN, p. A216
COFFMAN, Brian, Director Information System, National Park Medical Center, Hot Springs, AR, p. A45
COFFMAN, Courtney, Chief Financial Officer, Lower Bucks Hospital, Bristol, PA, p. A530
COFFMAN, Douglas, Vice President and Chief Financial Officer, United Hospital Center, Bridgeport, WV, p. A689
COFFMAN, Joan M., President and Chief Executive Officer, HSHS St. Joseph's Hospital, Chippewa Falls, WI, p. A699
COFFMAN BARNES, Julie, M.D. Chief Medical Officer, Redmond Regional Medical Center, Rome, GA, p. A163
COFINAS, Rebecca, Vice President and Chief Operating Executive Operations, Scripps Memorial Hospital–Encinitas, Encinitas, CA, p. A60
COGGINS, Parkes, Interim Chief Executive Officer, Carolinas Hospital System Marion, Mullins, SC, p. A563
COHEE, Jonathan, Chief Executive Officer, Kindred Hospital–New Jersey Morris County, Dover, NJ, p. A411
COHEN, Cindy, Director Human Resources, Stewart & Lynda Resnick Neuropsychiatric Hospital at UCLA, Los Angeles, CA, p. A73
COHEN, Ginger, Chief Nurse Executive, St. Luke's Rehabilitation Institute, Spokane, WA, p. A685
COHEN, Kathleena, Director of Nursing, Hampton Behavioral Health Center, Westampton, NJ, p. A420
COHEN, Mark, M.D. Chief Medical Officer, Piedmont Hospital, Atlanta, GA, p. A151
COHEN, Philip A., Chief Executive Officer, Monterey Park Hospital, Monterey Park, CA, p. A76
COHEN, Robert, M.D. Chief Medical Officer, Sonoma Valley Hospital, Sonoma, CA, p. A92
COHICK, Jim, Chief Executive Officer, Kindred Hospital–Sycamore, Sycamore, IL, p. A202
COKER, Cindy, M.P.H. Vice President, Patient Care Services, Vidant Chowan Hospital, Edenton, NC, p. A459
COLADONATO, Angela, MSN Chief Nursing Officer, Penn Medicine Chester County Hospital, West Chester, PA, p. A552
COLAGUORI, Ronald J., Vice President Operations, St. Anthony's Hospital, Saint Petersburg, FL, p. A142
COLAMARIA, James, Director of Nursing, Four Winds Hospital, Saratoga Springs, NY, p. A450
COLANGELO, Nicholas, Ph.D., Chief Executive Officer, Clear Brook Lodge, Shickshinny, PA, p. A550
COLAS, Chuck, M.D. Medical Director, Surprise Valley Health Care District, Cedarville, CA, p. A57
COLBURN, Douglas, Chief Information Officer, Northside Medical Center, Columbus, GA, p. A154
COLBURN, Timothy D., President and Chief Executive Officer, Berger Health System, Circleville, OH, p. A484
COLBY, Dennis, M.D. Chief of Staff, Iowa Specialty Hospital–Clarion, Clarion, IA, p. A224
COLCHER, Marian W., President and Chief Executive Officer, Valley Forge Medical Center and Hospital, Norristown, PA, p. A542
COLE, Annette E., R.N. Vice President and Chief Nursing Officer, Sky Lakes Medical Center, Klamath Falls, OR, p. A522
COLE, Bernadette Green, R.N. Chief Nursing Officer, Charlevoix Area Hospital, Charlevoix, MI, p. A316
COLE, Beth, Director Information Services, Lewis–Gale Medical Center, Salem, VA, p. A672
COLE, Cal, Director Information Systems, Winter Haven Hospital, Winter Haven, FL, p. A148
COLE, Carlene, Manager Human Resources, Kittson Memorial Healthcare Center, Hallock, MN, p. A340
COLE, Eric, Director Information Technology, Coffey County Hospital, Burlington, KS, p. A238
COLE, F. Sessions, M.D. Chief Medical Officer, St. Louis Children's Hospital, Saint Louis, MO, p. A377
COLE, Georgeanne, Chief Executive Officer, Rehabilitation Hospital of Southwest Virginia, Bristol, VA, p. A662
COLE Jr., Harry, Administrator, Georgiana Hospital, Georgiana, AL, p. A20
COLE, James B., Chief Executive Officer, Virginia Hospital Center – Arlington, Arlington, VA, p. A662
COLE, Jason
Director Finance, Scott & White Hospital – Llano, Llano, TX, p. A628
Senior Director Finance, Scott & White Hospital at Round Rock, Round Rock, TX, p. A639
Senior Director, Management Information Systems, Suburban Hospital, Bethesda, MD, p. A296
COLE, Karen S., FACHE, Chief Executive Officer, Shenandoah Medical Center, Shenandoah, IA, p. A234
COLE, Kirk, Interim Commissioner, Texas Department of State Health Services, Austin, TX, p. B133
COLE, Lori, Director Information Technology, Wayne Memorial Hospital, Goldsboro, NC, p. A461
COLE, Missy, Director Human Resources, HEALTHSOUTH Rehabilitation Hospital, Fayetteville, AR, p. A43
COLE, Robert, Chief Operating Officer, Connecticut Mental Health Center, New Haven, CT, p. A114
COLE, Shawn, Chief Clinical Officer, Tri Valley Health System, Cambridge, NE, p. A390
COLE–OUZOUNIAN, Denise Marie, Vice President Patient Services, Sauk Prairie Healthcare, Prairie Du Sac, WI, p. A709
COLECCHI, Stephen, President and Chief Executive Officer, UH Robinson Medical Center, Ravenna, OH, p. A496
COLEMAN, Alice, Blessing Corporate Controller, Illini Community Hospital, Pittsfield, IL, p. A198
COLEMAN, Alisa, Chief Executive Officer, Ferrell Hospital, Eldorado, IL, p. A186
COLEMAN, Amy, Director Human Resources, Loretto Hospital, Chicago, IL, p. A182
COLEMAN, Andrea C., Chief Operating Officer, Penrose–St. Francis Health Services, Colorado Springs, CO, p. A101
COLEMAN, Curt, FACHE,
Chief Executive Officer, Genesis Medical Center, DeWitt, De Witt, IA, p. A226
Administrator, Jackson County Regional Health Center, Maquoketa, IA, p. A231
COLEMAN, D. Scott, Medical Director, Livingston HealthCare, Livingston, MT, p. A385
COLEMAN, Donna, Coordinator Human Resources, Jackson County Hospital District, Edna, TX, p. A610
COLEMAN, Jr., Jim L., Chief Operating Officer, Parkridge Medical Center, Chattanooga, TN, p. A575
COLEMAN, Judy, Chief Financial Officer, Indiana University Health Ball Memorial Hospital, Muncie, IN, p. A216
COLEMAN, Karen, Director of Nursing, Grove Hill Memorial Hospital, Grove Hill, AL, p. A20
COLEMAN, Keith T., Chief Financial Officer, Mount Carmel, Columbus, OH, p. A486
COLEMAN, Melissa, Director Human Resources, HEALTHSOUTH Rehabilitation Hospital of Sewickley, Sewickley, PA, p. A550
COLEMAN, Richard, Interim Administrator, Memorial Hospital and Physician Group, Frederick, OK, p. A507
COLENDA, Christopher, M.P.H., President and Chief Executive Officer, West Virginia United Health System, Fairmont, WV, p. B153
COLERICK, Steven, Chief Executive Officer, Buena Vista Regional Medical Center, Storm Lake, IA, p. A235
COLETTA, Antonio
Vice President Human Resources, Advocate BroMenn Medical Center, Normal, IL, p. A196
Vice President Human Resources, Advocate Eureka Hospital, Eureka, IL, p. A187
COLETTA, Diane, Director Human Resources, Royal Oaks Hospital, Windsor, MO, p. A380
COLETTI, Edmund, Chief Executive Officer, Helen Hayes Hospital, West Haverstraw, NY, p. A453
COLEY, Brenda
Executive Director, Metroplex Adventist Hospital, Killeen, TX, p. A626
Executive Director, Rollins–Brook Community Hospital, Lampasas, TX, p. A627
COLGAN, Teresa, VP of Nursing, Great River Medical Center, West Burlington, IA, p. A236
COLINERI, Lori, MSN Senior Vice President Nursing and Chief Nursing Officer, Robert Wood Johnson University Hospital, New Brunswick, NJ, p. A415
COLLAZO, Marian, Director Finance, Hospital San Cristobal, Coto Laurel, PR, p. A721
COLLETT, John, Vice President and Chief Financial Officer, Cayuga Medical Center at Ithaca, Ithaca, NY, p. A435
COLLETT, Josh, Director Human Resources, Pineville Community Hospital Association, Pineville, KY, p. A265
COLLETTI, Teresa, Director Patient Services, South Florida Baptist Hospital, Plant City, FL, p. A140
COLLEY, Sarah, Senior Vice President Human Resources, Regional One Health, Memphis, TN, p. A584
COLLIER, Betty, Director Human Resources, Johnson Regional Medical Center, Clarksville, AR, p. A42
COLLIER, Brad, Director, Newton Medical Center, Covington, GA, p. A155
COLLIER, Jack, M.D. Chief of Staff, MountainView Hospital, Las Vegas, NV, p. A402
COLLIER, Russell J., FACHE, President and Chief Executive Officer, Good Shepherd Medical Center–Marshall, Marshall, TX, p. A631
COLLIER, Scarlet, Chief Information Officer, Lane Regional Medical Center, Zachary, LA, p. A287
COLLIER, Shari
Chief Financial Officer, Overland Park Regional Medical Center, Overland Park, KS, p. A248
Chief Financial Officer, Presbyterian–St. Luke's Medical Center, Denver, CO, p. A102
COLLIER, Tammy, R.N. Vice President Patient Services, Texas Health Huguley Hospital Fort Worth South, Fort Worth, TX, p. A614
COLLINI, M. Patrick, M.D. President Medical Staff, USMD Hospital at Arlington, Arlington, TX, p. A593
COLLINS, Alesha Danielle, MSN Chief Nursing Officer, Howard Memorial Hospital, Nashville, AR, p. A48
COLLINS, Andrea, Acting Director, Oscar G. Johnson Veterans Affairs Medical Center, Iron Mountain, MI, p. A322
COLLINS, Bobby
Director Human Resources, Mountain View Regional Medical Center, Norton, VA, p. A670
Director Human Resources, Wellmont Lonesome Pine Hospital, Big Stone Gap, VA, p. A662
COLLINS, Chauncey, Director Operations and Finance, Austen Riggs Center, Stockbridge, MA, p. A312
COLLINS, Dennis, Chief Financial Officer, The Brook Hospital – KMI, Louisville, KY, p. A262
COLLINS, Edmund, Chief Information Officer, Martin Health System, Stuart, FL, p. A143
COLLINS, Frances, Director of Nursing, Andrew McFarland Mental Health Center, Springfield, IL, p. A201
COLLINS, Harold E., JD Chief Financial Officer, Franciscan Healthcare – Munster, Munster, IN, p. A217
COLLINS, James M., President and Chief Executive Officer, St. Clair Hospital, Pittsburgh, PA, p. A546
COLLINS, Jeff, Chief Medical Officer, Providence St. Joseph's Hospital, Chewelah, WA, p. A677
COLLINS, Jeffrey A., M.D., Senior Vice President and Area Manager, Kaiser Permanente Roseville Medical Center, Roseville, CA, p. A84
COLLINS, John, Chief Financial Officer, Orange County Global Medical Center, Inc., Santa Ana, CA, p. A90
COLLINS, John F., President and Chief Executive Officer, Winthrop–University Hospital, Mineola, NY, p. A437


© 2015 AHA Guide Index of Health Care Professionals **A811**

COLLINS, John P., Medical Center Director, Veterans Affairs Central Western Massachusetts Healthcare System, Leeds, MA, p. A308

COLLINS, John R., Chief Financial Officer, Hemet Valley Medical Center, Hemet, CA, p. A65

COLLINS, Karen S., R.N., Chief Executive Officer, Lady of the Sea General Hospital, Cut Off, LA, p. A272

COLLINS, Kathleen, M.D. Chief Medical Officer, Presence Covenant Medical Center, Urbana, IL, p. A202

COLLINS, Kevin J., M.D. Medical Director, St. Vincent Rehabilitation Hospital, Sherwood, AR, p. A50

COLLINS, Leonora, Chief Nursing Officer, Nashville General Hospital, Nashville, TN, p. A585

COLLINS, Pam, Director Human Resources, Fairway Medical Center, Covington, LA, p. A272

COLLINS, Pamela, Vice President Chief Patient Services Officer, McCullough–Hyde Memorial Hospital/TriHealth, Oxford, OH, p. A496

COLLINS, Richard F., M.D. Executive Vice President and Chief Medical Officer, Jefferson Hospital, Jefferson Hills, PA, p. A536

COLLINS, Ricky M., M.D. Chief of Staff, Whitesburg ARH Hospital, Whitesburg, KY, p. A266

COLLINS, Ron, Chief Financial Officer, Victory Medical Center Craig Ranch, McKinney, TX, p. A632

COLLINS, Rudy
Human Resources Business Partner, Kaiser Permanente San Rafael Medical Center, San Rafael, CA, p. A90
Human Resources Business Partner, Kaiser Permanente Santa Rosa Medical Center, Santa Rosa, CA, p. A92

COLLINS, Sandra, Chief Clinical Officer, Kindred Hospital–Philadelphia, Philadelphia, PA, p. A544

COLLINS, Sharon
Director Human Resources and Chief Operating Officer, Russell Regional Hospital, Russell, KS, p. A249
Chief Information Officer, Salem Veterans Affairs Medical Center, Salem, VA, p. A672

COLLINS, Shaw, Director Information Technology, Methodist Hospitals, Gary, IN, p. A209

COLLINS, Teresa L., Chief Nursing Officer, Spotsylvania Regional Medical Center, Fredericksburg, VA, p. A665

COLLINS, Terry, Chief Financial Officer, Aspen Valley Hospital District, Aspen, CO, p. A99

COLLINS, Thomas M., President, Chairman and Chief Executive Officer, Green Oaks Hospital, Dallas, TX, p. A605

COLLIPP, Dan, M.D. Chief of Staff, Wayne Memorial Hospital, Jesup, GA, p. A159

COLLISON, June, President, Community Hospital of San Bernardino, San Bernardino, CA, p. A86

COLLOM, Bobbie, Nursing Director, North Runnels Hospital, Winters, TX, p. A652

COLLOTTA, Sharon
Director Human Resources, Mease Countryside Hospital, Safety Harbor, FL, p. A141
Director Human Resources, Mease Dunedin Hospital, Dunedin, FL, p. A126

COLMAN, Gerard, Chief Operating Officer, Aurora West Allis Medical Center, West Allis, WI, p. A714

COLMENARES, Derek, M.D
Chief Medical Officer, Agnesian HealthCare, Fond Du Lac, WI, p. A700
Chief Medical Officer, Waupun Memorial Hospital, Waupun, WI, p. A713

COLOMBO, Armando, Chief Executive Officer, Intermedical Hospital of South Carolina, Columbia, SC, p. A559

COLOMBO, Lisa, R.N. Senior Vice President and Chief Nursing Officer, Lahey Hospital & Medical Center, Burlington, Burlington, MA, p. A305

COLON, Julio, Financial Director, Hospital De Damas, Ponce, PR, p. A722

COLON, Julio, CPA, Chief Executive Officer, Hospital Episcopal San Lucas Guayama, Guayama, PR, p. A721

COLON, Julio
Interim President and Chief Executive Officer, St. Luke's Episcopal Hospital, Ponce, PR, p. A722
Chief Financial Officer, St. Luke's Episcopal Hospital, Ponce, PR, p. A722

COLON, Omar, M.D. Medical Director, HEALTHSOUTH Plano Rehabilitation Hospital, Plano, TX, p. A637

COLONES, Robert L., President and Chief Executive Officer, McLeod Health, Florence, SC, p. B88

COLONES, Robert L., President and Chief Executive Officer, McLeod Regional Medical Center, Florence, SC, p. A561

COLORADO, Judy, R.N. Chief Nursing Officer, Monmouth Medical Center, Southern Campus, Lakewood, NJ, p. A413

COLPITTS, Robert, Chief Human Resource Service, Bedford Veterans Affairs Medical Center, Edith Nourse Rogers Memorial Veterans Hospital, Bedford, MA, p. A302

COLSON, Wayne, Chief Financial Officer, Southwestern Medical Center, Lawton, OK, p. A509

COLTHARP, Missy, Director, Baptist Memorial Hospital–Union County, New Albany, MS, p. A358

COLTON, Jan, M.D. Acting Clinical Director, U. S. Public Health Service Indian Hospital, Pine Ridge, SD, p. A570

COLTRAIN, Penny, Director Human Resources, Vidant Beaufort Hospital, Washington, NC, p. A470

COLUCCI, Eugene, Vice President Finance, Greenwich Hospital, Greenwich, CT, p. A112

COLUCCIO, Medrice, R.N.,
Southwest Region Chief Executive, Providence Centralia Hospital, Centralia, WA, p. A677
Chief Executive Officer, Providence St. Peter Hospital, Olympia, WA, p. A681

COLVARD, Dusty, Manager Information Technology, Tehachapi Valley Healthcare District, Tehachapi, CA, p. A94

COLVERT, Richard, Chief Information Officer, Royal Oaks Hospital, Windsor, MO, p. A380

COLVIN, Garren
Chief Executive Officer, St. Elizabeth Edgewood, Edgewood, KY, p. A256
Chief Executive Officer, St. Elizabeth Florence, Florence, KY, p. A256
Chief Executive Officer, St. Elizabeth Fort Thomas, Fort Thomas, KY, p. A257
Chief Executive Officer, St. Elizabeth Grant, Williamstown, KY, p. A267

COLVIN, Garren, Chief Executive Officer, St. Elizabeth Healthcare, Edgewood, KY, p. B127

COLVIN, Robert L., Administrator, Ouachita Community Hospital, West Monroe, LA, p. A287

COLVIN, William, Human Resources Officer, Claiborne Memorial Medical Center, Homer, LA, p. A275

COLWELL, Dean, D.O. Vice President Medical Affairs, OhioHealth Doctors Hospital, Columbus, OH, p. A486

COLYER, Valeri J.
Director Human Resources, Dickenson Community Hospital, Clintwood, VA, p. A663
Director Human Resources, Norton Community Hospital, Norton, VA, p. A670

COMAIANNI, Sheri, Vice President Human Resources, Bakersfield Memorial Hospital, Bakersfield, CA, p. A55

COMBEST, Felton, M.D. Vice President Medical Affairs, Magnolia Regional Health Center, Corinth, MS, p. A352

COMBS, Mark
Interim Director System Information Technology, Berkeley Medical Center, Martinsburg, WV, p. A693
Chief Information Security Officer, Jefferson Medical Center, Ranson, WV, p. A694

COMBS, Meri, R.N. Vice President and Chief Nursing Officer, Madera Community Hospital, Madera, CA, p. A74

COMBS, Mike, Manager Information Technology, Holdenville General Hospital, Holdenville, OK, p. A508

COMBS, Will, Director Information Technology, Harrison Community Hospital, Cadiz, OH, p. A480

COMER, Fannessa, Chief Executive Officer, Northern Navajo Medical Center, Shiprock, NM, p. A426

COMER, Jennifer, M.D. Medical Director, Valle Vista Hospital, Greenwood, IN, p. A210

COMER, Randy, Chief Operating Officer, Athens–Limestone Hospital, Athens, AL, p. A15

COMER, Scott, Director Administrative Services, Marshall Medical Center, Placerville, CA, p. A81

COMERFORD, Jennifer, Manager Information Services, MidState Medical Center, Meriden, CT, p. A113

COMFORT, Jeff, Vice President Administration, Northcoast Behavioral Healthcare System, Northfield, OH, p. A495

COMITTO, Judy, Vice President Information Services and Chief Information Officer, Trinitas Regional Medical Center, Elizabeth, NJ, p. A411

COMPTON, Brenda, Manager Information Technology, Plumas District Hospital, Quincy, CA, p. A82

COMPTON, Mark, Chief Financial Officer, Laughlin Memorial Hospital, Greeneville, TN, p. A578

COMPTON, Ty, Chief Nursing Officer, Horton Community Hospital, Horton, KS, p. A242

COMPTON–OGLE, Carri, Administrative Officer, Heartland Behavioral Health Services, Nevada, MO, p. A373

COMSTOCK, John M., Chief Executive Officer, Cherokee Regional Medical Center, Cherokee, IA, p. A224

CONALLEN, Kathryn
Chief Executive Officer, Mercy Fitzgerald Hospital, Darby, PA, p. A532
Interim Chief Executive Officer, Mercy Suburban Hospital, Norristown, PA, p. A541

CONANT, Cathy, Chief Human Resources and Personnel, Eastern Plumas Health Care, Portola, CA, p. A81

CONANT, Merrill, M.D. Chief of Staff, Western Plains Medical Complex, Dodge City, KS, p. A239

CONANT, Sonya, Senior Director Human Resources, Alaska Native Medical Center, Anchorage, AK, p. A27

CONATY, Robert B., Executive Vice President Operations, Montefiore Medical Center, NY, p. A442

CONAWAY, E. Edwin, M.D. Vice President Medical Affairs and Chief Medical Officer, Southeastern Ohio Regional Medical Center, Cambridge, OH, p. A481

CONAWAY, Keith, M.D. Chief Medical Officer, Cornerstone Hospital of Oklahoma–Shawnee, Shawnee, OK, p. A515

CONCANNON, Laura, M.D. Regional Chief Medical Officer, Presence Saints Mary & Elizabeth Medical Center, Chicago, IL, p. A183

CONCEPCION, Walter, Chief Executive Officer, West Gables Rehabilitation Hospital, Miami, FL, p. A135

CONCORDIA, Elizabeth B., President and Chief Executive Officer, University of Colorado Health, Fort Collins, CO, p. B146

CONCORDIA, Elizabeth B., Interim President and Chief Executive Officer, University of Colorado Hospital, Aurora, CO, p. A99

CONDIT, Brian, Vice President Chief Medical Officer, Virginia Operations Medical Staff Services, Russell County Medical Center, Lebanon, VA, p. A666

CONDIT, Edward, President and Chief Executive Officer, St. Mary's General Hospital, Passaic, NJ, p. A416

CONDOLUCI, David, M.D. Senior Vice President and Chief Medical Officer, Kennedy Health System, Cherry Hill, NJ, p. A410

CONDON, Joseph
Entity Human Resources Officer, Texas Health Harris Methodist Hospital Fort Worth, Fort Worth, TX, p. A614
Director Human Resources, Texas Health Specialty Hospital, Fort Worth, TX, p. A614

CONDRY, Donna, Director Human Resources, UnityPoint Health – Jones Regional Medical Center, Anamosa, IA, p. A222

CONE, Maryann, Chief Operating Officer, Sharp Grossmont Hospital, La Mesa, CA, p. A66

CONEJO, David, Chief Executive Officer, Rehoboth McKinley Christian Health Care Services, Gallup, NM, p. A424

CONFALONE, Daniel, Chief Financial Officer and Vice President Finance, St. Mary Medical Center, Langhorne, PA, p. A538

CONFER, James, Manager Information Systems, Clarion Hospital, Clarion, PA, p. A531

CONGDON, James B., M.D. Medical Director, Horsham Clinic, Ambler, PA, p. A528

CONGER, Rex D., FACHE, President and Chief Executive Officer, Perry Memorial Hospital, Princeton, IL, p. A198

CONGER, Sue, Chief Operating Officer, Eastside Psychiatric Hospital, Tallahassee, FL, p. A144

CONKERTON, Lawrence, Administrator, Seaside Health System, Baton Rouge, LA, p. A270

CONKLIN, Maggie C., Interim Vice President, Patient Care Services, Northern Montana Hospital, Havre, MT, p. A384

CONKLIN, Jr., Michael E., Chief Financial Officer, St. Joseph Health Services of Rhode Island, North Providence, RI, p. A555

CONKLIN, Robin, R.N. Chief Nursing Officer, Carondelet St. Joseph's Hospital, Tucson, AZ, p. A39

CONKLING, Victoria, Vice President Patient Care Services and Chief Nursing Officer, Delaware Valley Hospital, Walton, NY, p. A453

CONLEY, David, Chief Administrative Officer, SUNY Downstate Medical Center University Hospital, NY, p. A444

CONLEY, Joanna J., FACHE, Chief Executive Officer, Poinciana Medical Center, Kissimmee, FL, p. A131

CONLEY, Karen A., R.N. Chief Nursing Officer and Senior Vice President Patient Care Services, Newton–Wellesley Hospital, Newton Lower Falls, MA, p. A309

CONLEY, Kenneth, Controller, Calhoun Health Services, Calhoun City, MS, p. A351

CONLEY, Marcus, Chief Financial Officer, Lake Norman Regional Medical Center, Mooresville, NC, p. A465

CONLEY, Melissa, Director Human Resources, Midwest Medical Center, Galena, IL, p. A188

CONLEY, Michelle E., R.N. Chief Nursing Officer, Aria Health, Philadelphia, PA, p. A542

CONLEY, Susan
Chief Executive Officer, Saint Thomas DeKalb Hospital, Smithville, TN, p. A588
Chief Executive Officer, Saint Thomas Stones River Hospital, Woodbury, TN, p. A589

CONLEY, Teressa
President and Chief Executive Officer, St. Rose Dominican Hospitals – Rose de Lima Campus, Henderson, NV, p. A401
Chief Operating Officer, St. Rose Dominican Hospitals – Siena Campus, Henderson, NV, p. A401

CONLEY, Theresa, Manager Human Resources, Cherokee Regional Medical Center, Cherokee, IA, p. A224

CONLEY, Thomas C., Vice President, Human Resources and Organizational Development, Northwestern Medical Center, Saint Albans, VT, p. A661

Index of Health Care Professionals / Cooney

Index of Health Care Professionals


CONNAWAY, Jessica, Director Human Resources, Crossroads Community Hospital, Mount Vernon, IL, p. A195
CONNEL, Lorene, Chief Human Resources Management Service, Veterans Affairs Eastern Colorado Health Care System, Denver, CO, p. A102
CONNELL, Faith, Director of Nursing, Turning Point Hospital, Moultrie, GA, p. A162
CONNELL, Pam, Manager Human Resources, Windsor–Laurelwood Center for Behavioral Medicine, Willoughby, OH, p. A501
CONNELLEY, Bertha Mary, Director Human Resources, Austen Riggs Center, Stockbridge, MA, p. A312
CONNELLY, Jac, Chief Financial Officer, Rose Medical Center, Denver, CO, p. A102
CONNELLY, Kathryn, Manager Information Technology, Connecticut Valley Hospital, Middletown, CT, p. A113
CONNELLY, Michael, President, Huggins Hospital, Wolfeboro, NH, p. A408
CONNELLY, Michael D., President and Chief Executive Officer, Mercy Health, Cincinnati, OH, p. B89
CONNELLY, Steven, M.D. Chief Medical Officer, Park Nicollet Methodist Hospital, Saint Louis Park, MN, p. A346
CONNER, Gary F.
Chief Financial Officer, City of Hope's Helford Clinical Research Hospital, Duarte, CA, p. A60
Chief Financial Officer, Southcoast Hospitals Group, Fall River, MA, p. A306
CONNER, Jeff, M.D. Chief Medical Staff, Loma Linda University Medical Center–Murrieta, Murrieta, CA, p. A77
CONNER, Stacey, Director Personnel, Ed Fraser Memorial Hospital and Baker Community Health Center, MacClenny, FL, p. A132
CONNERS, Stephanie, Senior Executive Vice President Chief Operating Officer and Chief Nursing Officer, Cooper University Health Care, Camden, NJ, p. A410
CONNERTON, Kathryn, Chief Executive Officer, Our Lady of Lourdes Memorial Hospital, Inc., Binghamton, NY, p. A429
CONNOLLY, Christine, M.D. Chief of Staff, Keefe Memorial Hospital, Cheyenne Wells, CO, p. A100
CONNOLLY, James W., President and Chief Executive Officer, Ellis Hospital, Schenectady, NY, p. A450
CONNOLLY, Teresa, R.N. Chief Nursing Officer, Mayo Clinic Hospital, Phoenix, AZ, p. A35
CONNOLLY, Thomas, M.D. Chief Medical Officer, Jersey Shore Hospital, Jersey Shore, PA, p. A536
CONNOLLY ROBBINS, Danielle, Chief Nursing Officer, Select Specialty Hospital–Knoxville, Knoxville, TN, p. A580
CONNOR, Della, Director Human Resource, Sandhills Regional Medical Center, Hamlet, NC, p. A461
CONNOR III, Paul J., President and Chief Executive Officer, Eastern Long Island Hospital, Greenport, NY, p. A434
CONNOR, Starr, Chief Nursing Officer, Fairfield Memorial Hospital, Winnsboro, SC, p. A566
CONNOR, William, Assistant Administrator and Director Human Resources, River Hospital, Alexandria Bay, NY, p. A428
CONNORS, Alfred, M.D. Executive Vice President and Chief Quality Officer and Interim Chief Medical Officer, MetroHealth Medical Center, Cleveland, OH, p. A485
CONNORS, Dennis, Executive Director, Lenox Hill Hospital, New York, NY, p. A441
CONNORS, Lawrence J.
Chief Operating Officer, St. Mary's Hospital Medical Center, Green Bay, WI, p. A702
Chief Operating Officer, St. Vincent Hospital, Green Bay, WI, p. A702
CONNORS, Michael
Senior Vice President and Chief Financial Officer, Cape Cod Hospital, Hyannis, MA, p. A307
Senior Vice President and Chief Financial Officer, Falmouth Hospital, Falmouth, MA, p. A306
CONNOVICH, Ron D.
Chief Financial Officer, Greene Memorial Hospital, Xenia, OH, p. A501
Chief Financial Officer and Chief Operating Officer, Soin Medical Center, Beavercreek, OH, p. A479
CONNY, Sophia, Deputy Administrative Officer, U. S. Public Health Service Indian Hospital, Pine Ridge, SD, p. A570
CONOCENTI, Paul, Chief Information Officer, City of Hope's Helford Clinical Research Hospital, Duarte, CA, p. A60
CONOVER, Jevne, Chief Executive Officer, Great Lakes Specialty Hospital–Grand Rapids, Grand Rapids, MI, p. A320
CONRAD, Daniel S., M.D., President, Phillips Eye Institute, Minneapolis, MN, p. A343
CONRAD, Elizabeth P., Senior Vice President and Chief Human Resource Officer, Lahey Hospital & Medical Center, Burlington, Burlington, MA, p. A305
CONRAD, Heidi, Vice President and Chief Financial Officer, Regions Hospital, Saint Paul, MN, p. A346
CONRATH, Mark, Chief Financial Officer, Drumright Regional Hospital, Drumright, OK, p. A505
CONROW–VERVERIS, Stacy, Director Human Resources, Mineral Community Hospital, Superior, MT, p. A387
CONROY, Carol, R.N. Chief Nursing Officer, Southwestern Vermont Medical Center, Bennington, VT, p. A660
CONROY, Dorothy, Director Human Resources, Oakleaf Surgical Hospital, Eau Claire, WI, p. A700
CONROY, Joanne, M.D., Chief Executive Officer, Lahey Hospital & Medical Center, Burlington, Burlington, MA, p. A305
CONROY, Kevin, Vice President and Chief Information Officer, Brookhaven Memorial Hospital Medical Center, Patchogue, NY, p. A447
CONROY, Mary Ann, Chief Executive Officer, Terre Haute Regional Hospital, Terre Haute, IN, p. A220
CONROY, Michael, Chief Financial Officer, Pine Creek Medical Center, Dallas, TX, p. A606
CONROY, Mike, Chief Financial Officer, Methodist McKinney Hospital, McKinney, TX, p. A632
CONSIDINE, William H., President, Akron Children's Hospital, Akron, OH, p. A478
CONSIGLIO, Gayle, Chief Information Officer, McLaren Lapeer Region, Lapeer, MI, p. A324
CONSIGNEY, Ginger, Vice President Human Resources, Lake Charles Memorial Hospital, Lake Charles, LA, p. A278
CONSTANT, Jean–Charles, Administrator, Dover Behavioral Health System, Dover, DE, p. A117
CONSTANTINO, Chris D., Senior Vice President and Executive Director, Elmhurst Hospital Center, NY, p. A439
CONTE, John D., Director Facility Services, Wayne Memorial Hospital, Honesdale, PA, p. A536
CONTI, John, Director Finance, Shriners Hospitals for Children–Greenville, Greenville, SC, p. A561
CONTRERAS, Marta, Chief Nursing Officer and Chief Operating Officer, Foundation Surgical Hospital of El Paso, El Paso, TX, p. A610
CONWAY, Gerard, Chief Executive Officer, Las Encinas Hospital, Pasadena, CA, p. A80
CONWAY, Jimmy, M.D. President Medical Staff, Northwest Surgical Hospital, Oklahoma City, OK, p. A512
CONWAY, William, Chief Executive Officer, Continuum Rehabilitation Hospital of North Texas, Flower Mound, TX, p. A612
CONWELL, Heather, Chief Nursing Officer, PIH Health Hospital – Downey, Downey, CA, p. A60
CONWILL, Michael, Director Human Resources, Corpus Christi Medical Center, Corpus Christi, TX, p. A602
COOK, Aaron, Director Information Services, Lake Area Medical Center, Lake Charles, LA, p. A278
COOK, Annette, Application Support Specialist, Arkansas Valley Regional Medical Center, La Junta, CO, p. A105
COOK, Brenda, Chief Nursing Officer, Monroe Hospital, Bloomfield, IN, p. A205
COOK, Brian, Chief Executive Officer, North Florida Regional Medical Center, Gainesville, FL, p. A127
COOK, Brooke, Director of Nursing, Strategic Behavioral Health – Wilmington, Leland, NC, p. A463
COOK, Carla, Director of Nursing, Scotland County Hospital, Memphis, MO, p. A372
COOK, David, Manager Information Systems, CHRISTUS Dubuis Hospital of Hot Springs, Hot Springs National Park, AR, p. A46
COOK, David, M.D. Chief Medical Officer, Novant Health Huntersville Medical Center, Huntersville, NC, p. A462
COOK, David, Chief Operating Officer, University Hospitals Parma Medical Center, Parma, OH, p. A496
COOK, David A., Vice President and Chief Financial Officer, University Hospitals Elyria Medical Center, Elyria, OH, p. A489
COOK, DeLynn K., Director Human Resources, Lake Chelan Community Hospital, Chelan, WA, p. A677
COOK, Elizabeth, Chief Information Officer, Mizell Memorial Hospital, Opp, AL, p. A24
COOK, G. Anthony, M.D. Medical Director, Hemphill County Hospital, Canadian, TX, p. A600
COOK, Greg, Chief Financial Officer, Castleview Hospital, Price, UT, p. A657
COOK, Heidi, Chief Nursing Officer, Dr. John Warner Hospital, Clinton, IL, p. A185
COOK, Jaime, Director Human Resources, Riverside Tappahannock Hospital, Tappahannock, VA, p. A673
COOK, Janie, Director Information Systems, Passavant Area Hospital, Jacksonville, IL, p. A191
COOK, Jeffrey A., Chief Executive Officer, Appleton Area Health Services, Appleton, MN, p. A334
COOK, John, Vice President and Chief Financial Officer, Mercy Hospital and Trauma Center, Janesville, WI, p. A703
COOK, Katheryn, R.N. Nurse Executive, Cincinnati Veterans Affairs Medical Center, Cincinnati, OH, p. A482
COOK, Kathy, MSN, President, St. Joseph Health Center, Warren, OH, p. A499
COOK, Kevin S., Chief Executive Officer, University Hospitals and Health System, Jackson, MS, p. B145
COOK, Kevin S., Chief Executive Officer, University of Mississippi Medical Center, Jackson, MS, p. A355
COOK, Kim, Interim Clinical Applications Services Manager, Tri–City Medical Center, Oceanside, CA, p. A79
COOK, LaMont, Administrator, F. W. Huston Medical Center, Winchester, KS, p. A253
COOK, Linda, Vice President Human Resources, St. Joseph Hospital, Eureka, CA, p. A60
COOK, Lottie, Superintendent, Evansville Psychiatric Children Center, Evansville, IN, p. A208
COOK, Marcia, Director Information Technology, Bates County Memorial Hospital, Butler, MO, p. A364
COOK, Mark B., Director Human Resources, Merit Health Central, Jackson, MS, p. A355
COOK, Mary Ann, R.N. Director of Nursing, Red Lake Indian Health Service Hospital, Red Lake, MN, p. A345
COOK, Pamela W., Chief Financial Officer, Trace Regional Hospital, Houston, MS, p. A354
COOK, Patrick, Vice President Support Services, Morgan Memorial Hospital, Madison, GA, p. A161
COOK, Ruth
Administrator, East Texas Medical Center Fairfield, Fairfield, TX, p. A612
Chief Executive Officer and Administrator, East Texas Medical Center Trinity, Trinity, TX, p. A648
COOK, Scott, Chief Information Officer, Johnson Regional Medical Center, Clarksville, AR, p. A42
COOK, Shelia, Director Information Systems, Novant Health Charlotte Orthopaedic Hospital, Charlotte, NC, p. A457
COOK, Sheliah, Director Human Resources, Boone Memorial Hospital, Madison, WV, p. A692
COOK, Sherry P., R.N. Chief Nursing Executive, Merit Health River Oaks, Flowood, MS, p. A352
COOK, Stacey M., MS Director Human Resources, University of Maryland Charles Regional Medical Center, La Plata, MD, p. A298
COOK, Thomas J., Chief Executive Officer, UVA–HEALTHSOUTH Rehabilitation Hospital, Charlottesville, VA, p. A663
COOK, Thomas M., CPA Chief Financial Officer, St. Vincent Indianapolis Hospital, Indianapolis, IN, p. A212
COOK, Timothy W., President and CEO, Florida Hospital DeLand, DeLand, FL, p. A125
COOK, Wendy J., Senior Vice President and Chief Financial Officer, Athens Regional Medical Center, Athens, GA, p. A149
COOK, William
Associate Warden Business Service, California Mens Colony Correctional Treatment Center, San Luis Obispo, CA, p. A90
Director, Southern Virginia Mental Health Institute, Danville, VA, p. A664
COOKE, Barbara
Director Health Information Systems, Montefiore Mount Vernon, Mount Vernon, NY, p. A438
Director Health Information Systems, Montefiore New Rochelle, New Rochelle, NY, p. A438
COOKE, David, Chief Nursing Officer, Sutter Surgical Hospital – North Valley, Yuba City, CA, p. A98
COOKE, Ellen, Chief Operating Officer, Sanford Medical Center Fargo, Fargo, ND, p. A474
COOKE, Jordan, Director Human Resources, Shadow Mountain Behavioral Health System, Tulsa, OK, p. A517
COOKE, Nancy, Chief Financial Officer, Weatherford Regional Medical Center, Weatherford, TX, p. A650
COOKE, Rebecca L., Director Human Resources, Kearney County Health Services, Minden, NE, p. A394
COOKE, Timothy J., Medical Center Director and Chief Executive Officer, Martinsburg Veterans Affairs Medical Center, Martinsburg, WV, p. A693
COOKE, William, M.D. Chief of Staff, Gundersen St. Joseph's Hospital and Clinics, Hillsboro, WI, p. A702
COOKSEY, Jill, Vice President Chief Nursing Officer, University Hospitals Elyria Medical Center, Elyria, OH, p. A489
COOLEY, Elizabeth, Chief Executive Officer, Gateway Rehabilitation Hospital, Florence, KY, p. A256
COOLEY, W. Carl, M.D. Chief Medical Officer, Crotched Mountain Rehabilitation Center, Greenfield, NH, p. A406
COOMBS, James, Chief Executive Officer, Grand River Hospital District, Rifle, CO, p. A108
COOMBS, Teri, R.N. Director Nursing Services, Cascade Medical Center, Cascade, ID, p. A173
COONER, Suzanne, MSN, Chief Executive Officer, Decatur County Hospital, Leon, IA, p. A231
COONEY, Darlene, Director Nursing, Sumner Regional Medical Center, Wellington, KS, p. A252
COONEY, Lauri Ann, Director Nursing, Wheatland Memorial Healthcare, Harlowton, MT, p. A384


 

COOPER, Alisa, Manager Financial Resources, Michael E. DeBakey Veterans Affairs Medical Center, Houston, TX, p. A621

COOPER, Allison, Administrator, Physicians Behavioral Hospital, Shreveport, LA, p. A284

COOPER, Casey, Chief Executive Officer, Cherokee Indian Hospital, Cherokee, NC, p. A458

COOPER, Chad D., Chief Executive Officer, Riverwood Healthcare Center, Aitkin, MN, p. A334

COOPER, Curtis, Manager Information Systems, Pioneers Medical Center, Meeker, CO, p. A107

COOPER, Dena, Chief Financial Officer, Campbellton Graceville Hospital, Graceville, FL, p. A128

COOPER, Donald, Director Information Systems, Harton Regional Medical Center, Tullahoma, TN, p. A588

COOPER, Douglas, M.D. Chief Medical Officer, Grundy County Memorial Hospital, Grundy Center, IA, p. A228

COOPER Jr., Edwin H., MS, President and Chief Executive Officer, AcuityHealthcare, LP, Charlotte, NC, p. B4

COOPER, Hunt, M.D. Chief of Staff, Siloam Springs Regional Hospital, Siloam Springs, AR, p. A50

COOPER, Ian, Chief Executive Officer, Hillside Rehabilitation Hospital, Warren, OH, p. A499

COOPER, Jeff, Chief Operating Officer, Piedmont Henry Hospital, Stockbridge, GA, p. A165

COOPER, Jerry, Manager Data Processing, Richland Hospital, Richland Center, WI, p. A710

COOPER, John C., Chief Executive Officer, Fremont Hospital, Fremont, CA, p. A62

COOPER, Jon, Chief Administrative Officer, Norton Audubon Hospital, Louisville, KY, p. A261

COOPER, Kevin S., R.N., Chief Executive Officer, LifeCare Hospitals of Dallas, Dallas, TX, p. A605

COOPER, Mike, Chief Executive Officer, George E. Weems Memorial Hospital, Apalachicola, FL, p. A121

COOPER, Pamela, Director Finance, Providence Seaside Hospital, Seaside, OR, p. A526

COOPER, Scott, M.D., Chief Executive Officer, St. Barnabas Hospital, NY, p. A444

COOPER, Sheri, Director Human Resources, Union General Hospital, Farmerville, LA, p. A273

COOPER, Tim, Chief Financial Officer, PMH Medical Center, Prosser, WA, p. A682

COOPER-LOHR, Willie, Chief Financial Officer, Barnesville Hospital, Barnesville, OH, p. A479

COOPERMAN, Todd, M.D. Medical Director, Rehabilitation Hospital of Tinton Falls, Tinton Falls, NJ, p. A419

COOPWOOD, Reginald W., M.D., President and Chief Executive Officer, Regional One Health, Memphis, TN, p. A584

COOTS, Aaron, Information Technology Director, Mason District Hospital, Havana, IL, p. A190

COOTS, Lawrence, M.D. Chief Medical Officer, Orange Park Medical Center, Orange Park, FL, p. A137

COPE, Brent A., Chief Executive Officer, Silver Lake Medical Center, Los Angeles, CA, p. A72

COPELAND, Carolyn, Business Administrator, Madison State Hospital, Madison, IN, p. A215

COPELAND, Darlinda, Chief Operating Officer, Florida Hospital Memorial Medical Center, Daytona Beach, FL, p. A125

COPELAND, Gail, Director Management Information Systems, CrossRidge Community Hospital, Wynne, AR, p. A52

COPELAND, Gearline, R.N. Chief Nursing Officer, Saint Thomas Highlands Hospital, Sparta, TN, p. A588

COPELAND, Willie Mae, Chief Financial Officer, Harmon Memorial Hospital, Hollis, OK, p. A508

COPELAND, Yolanda, R.N. Senior Vice President and Chief Nursing Officer, Saint Agnes Hospital, Baltimore, MD, p. A294

COPEN, Greg, Chief Information Officer, Haywood Regional Medical Center, Clyde, NC, p. A458

COPENHAVER, Kathy, Director Human Resources, Haven Behavioral Health of Eastern Pennsylvania, Reading, PA, p. A548

COPES, Tammy, Director Information Systems, St. Mary's of Michigan Standish Hospital, Standish, MI, p. A330

COPPLE, Brad
President, Kishwaukee Hospital, DeKalb, IL, p. A186
President, Kishwaukee Hospital, DeKalb, IL, p. A186
President, Valley West Hospital, Sandwich, IL, p. A200

COPPLE, Robert C., FACHE, President and CEO, Memorial Community Hospital and Health System, Blair, NE, p. A390

COPPOCK, R. Alan, FACHE, President, ContinueCare Hospital at Baptist Health Corbin, Corbin, KY, p. A255

CORAZON, Jesus M.
Controller, HEALTHSOUTH Hospital of Manati, Manati, PR, p. A721
Controller, HEALTHSOUTH Rehabilitation Hospital of San Juan, San Juan, PR, p. A723

CORBET, Mark, Interim Chief Financial Officer, LAC/University of Southern California Medical Center, Los Angeles, CA, p. A71

CORBIN, Michelle, M.D. Chief of Staff, Deer Lodge Medical Center, Deer Lodge, MT, p. A382

CORCIMIGLIA, Michael, Chief Operating Officer, Wyoming County Community Hospital, Warsaw, NY, p. A453

CORCORAN, Joseph C., Chief Medical Officer, Brandon Regional Hospital, Brandon, FL, p. A122

CORCORAN, Kevin, Chief Financial Officer, Westside Regional Medical Center, Plantation, FL, p. A140

CORCORAN, Nancy R., Senior Vice President Human Resources and Quality Service, Hackensack University Medical Center, Hackensack, NJ, p. A412

CORD, David, Director, Erie Veterans Affairs Medical Center, Erie, PA, p. A534

CORD, Jennifer
Assistant Vice President Operations, Presence Covenant Medical Center, Urbana, IL, p. A202
Vice President Operations, Presence United Samaritans Medical Center, Danville, IL, p. A185

CORDDRY, David, Chief Financial Officer, Ten Broeck Tennessee Treatment Facility, Cookeville, TN, p. A576

CORDER, Earline, Chief Fiscal, Charlie Norwood Veterans Affairs Medical Center, Augusta, GA, p. A151

CORDER, Scott, Controller, HEALTHSOUTH Rehabilitation Hospital at Drake, Cincinnati, OH, p. A483

CORDES, Debra, Chief Nursing Officer, Rehabilitation Hospital of Indiana, Indianapolis, IN, p. A212

CORDIA, Jennifer, Vice President and Chief Nursing Executive, Christian Hospital, Saint Louis, MO, p. A376

CORDOLA, Craig, Chief Executive Officer, Memorial Hermann – Texas Medical Center, Houston, TX, p. A620

CORDOVA, Mandelyn, R.N. Director of Nurses, Guadalupe County Hospital, Santa Rosa, NM, p. A426

CORDOVA, Martin, Director Information Services, Centinela Hospital Medical Center, Inglewood, CA, p. A65

CORDOVA, Sheila, Director Clinical Services and Chief Operating Officer, Aurora Charter Oak Hospital, Covina, CA, p. A59

CORDTS, Paul, Commander, Colonel Florence A. Blanchfield Army Community Hospital, Fort Campbell, KY, p. A256

CORDUM, Shelly L., R.N. Administrator and Chief Nursing Executive, Sparks Medical Center – Van Buren, Van Buren, AR, p. A51

CORDY, Roy, M.D. President Medical Staff, Presentation Medical Center, Rolla, ND, p. A476

COREA, Rohan, Director Healthcare Information Technology, College Medical Center, Long Beach, CA, p. A68

COREY, Mark, Chief Financial Officer, Behavioral Center of Michigan, Warren, MI, p. A332

CORFITS, Joe
Senior Vice President Finance, UnityPoint Health – Iowa Methodist Medical Center, Des Moines, IA, p. A226
Chief Financial Officer, UnityPoint Health–Iowa Lutheran Hospital, Des Moines, IA, p. A226

CORK, Ronald J., President and Chief Executive Officer, Avera St. Anthony's Hospital, O'Neill, NE, p. A395

CORKERY, Thomas B., D.O. Chief Medical Officer, Canonsburg General Hospital, Canonsburg, PA, p. A530

CORLEW, Scott, M.D. Chief Medical Officer, Saint Thomas Rutherford Hospital, Murfreesboro, TN, p. A585

CORLEY, Becky, Director Human Resources, Tyler Holmes Memorial Hospital, Winona, MS, p. A362

CORLEY, Janet, Accountant, Malvern Institute, Malvern, PA, p. A539

CORMIER, Laura, Director, Bellin Health Oconto Hospital, Oconto, WI, p. A708

CORMIER, Philip M., Chief Executive Officer, Beverly Hospital, Beverly, MA, p. A302

CORN, Rick, Chief Information Officer, Huntsville Hospital, Huntsville, AL, p. A21

CORNEJO, C. Susan
Senior Vice President Finance and Chief Financial Officer, Providence Hospital, Mobile, AL, p. A22
Chief Financial Officer, Sacred Heart Hospital of Pensacola, Pensacola, FL, p. A140

CORNELIUS, David, Director Information Systems, Parkridge Medical Center, Chattanooga, TN, p. A575

CORNELIUS, Margaret E., Vice President Human Resources, Wyckoff Heights Medical Center, NY, p. A445

CORNELIUS, Michelle
Director Human Resources, Howard Young Medical Center, Woodruff, WI, p. A714
Director Human Resources for Northern Region, Ministry Eagle River Memorial Hospital, Eagle River, WI, p. A700
Director Human Resources for the Northern Region, Ministry Saint Mary's Hospitals, Rhinelander, WI, p. A710

CORNELIUS, Senta, Director Human Resources, West Valley Medical Center, Caldwell, ID, p. A173

CORNELL, John, Vice President Finance, Meadows Regional Medical Center, Vidalia, GA, p. A166

CORNES, Robert, Commander, Ireland Army Community Hospital, Fort Knox, KY, p. A257

CORNETT, Sheila, Manager Human Resources, Hazard ARH Regional Medical Center, Hazard, KY, p. A258

CORNETT, Suzanne, Director Human Resources, Southern Kentucky Rehabilitation Hospital, Bowling Green, KY, p. A255

CORNICELLI, Kari
Chief Financial Officer, Sharp Grossmont Hospital, La Mesa, CA, p. A66
Chief Financial Officer, Sharp Memorial Hospital, San Diego, CA, p. A87
Chief Financial Officer, Sharp Mesa Vista Hospital, San Diego, CA, p. A87

CORNWALL, Thomas, M.D. Medical Director, Holly Hill Hospital, Raleigh, NC, p. A466

CORNWELL, Cheryl, Chief Financial Officer, Great Falls Clinic Medical Center, Great Falls, MT, p. A384

CORNWELL, Cheryl J., Chief Financial Officer, Lake District Hospital, Lakeview, OR, p. A522

CORNWELL, James, M.D. Chief Medical Staff, Effingham Hospital, Springfield, GA, p. A165

CORNWELL, Richard, Chief Executive Officer, Surprise Valley Health Care District, Cedarville, CA, p. A57

CORONEL, Jorge, Chief Information Officer, Regional Hospital of Scranton, Scranton, PA, p. A549

CORPORA, Don, Executive Vice President and Chief Human Resources Officer, Akron General Medical Center, Akron, OH, p. A478

CORRADINO, Richard L., Chief Financial Officer, Spanish Peaks Regional Health Center, Walsenburg, CO, p. A109

CORRADO, Joseph, M.D. Chief of Staff, SSM Health St. Mary's Hospital – Audrain, Mexico, MO, p. A372

CORRADO, Theresa, Director Finance, St. Luke's Hospital – Quakertown Campus, Quakertown, PA, p. A548

CORREA, Elizabeth, Director Information Management, Big Spring State Hospital, Big Spring, TX, p. A597

CORREA, Maria de los Angeles, M.D. Medical Director, Hospital Metropolitan, San Juan, PR, p. A723

CORREA, Omar, Chief Financial Officer, Texas NeuroRehab Center, Austin, TX, p. A595

CORREA, Sharon, Vice President and Chief Information Officer, Glendale Adventist Medical Center, Glendale, CA, p. A63

CORREIA, Antonio, Chief Financial Officer, Holyoke Medical Center, Holyoke, MA, p. A307

CORREIA, Kathryn G., President and Chief Executive Officer, HealthEast Care System, Saint Paul, MN, p. B66

CORRIDON, Fran, Vice President Human Resources and Shared Services, Hackensack University Medical Center Mountainside, Montclair, NJ, p. A414

CORRIGAN, Heidi, Manager Human Resources, Trinity Hospital, Weaverville, CA, p. A97

CORRIGAN, Jeffrey T., Vice President Human Resources, Brattleboro Retreat, Brattleboro, VT, p. A660

CORRIGAN, Paula, Vice President and Chief Financial Officer, OSF Saint James – John W. Albrecht Medical Center, Pontiac, IL, p. A198

CORRIGAN, Thomas L., Senior Vice President Finance, Managed Care and Chief Financial Officer, Christiana Care Health System, Newark, DE, p. A117

CORS, William K., M.D. Vice President and Chief Medical Quality Officer, Pocono Medical Center, East Stroudsburg, PA, p. A533

CORSO, David, Chief Operating Officer, Beaver Dam Community Hospitals, Beaver Dam, WI, p. A698

CORTI, Ronald J., President and Chief Executive Officer, St. John's Riverside Hospital, Yonkers, NY, p. A454

CORUM, Sharon, Chief Financial Officer, Kingwood Pines Hospital, Kingwood, TX, p. A626

CORWIN, Florence, Director for Administration, Pilgrim Psychiatric Center, Brentwood, NY, p. A430

CORWIN, Nancy, Chief Operating Officer, Summit Surgical, Hutchinson, KS, p. A242

CORWIN, R. William, M.D. Vice President and Chief Medical Officer, Miriam Hospital, Providence, RI, p. A555

CORWIN, Steven J., M.D., Chief Executive Officer, New York Presbyterian Healthcare System, New York, NY, p. B96

CORWIN, Steven J., M.D., Chief Executive Officer, New York–Presbyterian Hospital, New York, NY, p. A443

CORZINE, Judy, Administrative Director and Chief Information Officer, Stormont–Vail HealthCare, Topeka, KS, p. A251

COSBY, Dwan, Manager Human Resources, McLaren Oakland, Pontiac, MI, p. A328

COSBY, Ernestine Y., Vice President Clinical Services and Chief Nursing Officer, Sheppard Pratt Health System, Baltimore, MD, p. A294

COSGRAVE, Michael, Director, Information System, Speare Memorial Hospital, Plymouth, NH, p. A408

COSGROVE, Delos, M.D., President and Chief Executive Officer, Cleveland Clinic, Cleveland, OH, p. A484

COSGROVE, Delos, M.D., President and Chief Executive Officer, Cleveland Clinic Health System, Cleveland, OH, p. B34

Index of Health Care Professionals / Coy

Index of Health Care Professionals

COSGROVE, Mila, Manager Human Resources, Bartlett Regional Hospital, Juneau, AK, p. A28
COSTA, Christopher P., M.D. Chief of Staff, Gordon Memorial Hospital, Gordon, NE, p. A392
COSTA, Joe
Chief Financial Officer, Veterans Affairs Boston Healthcare System, Boston, MA, p. A304
Acting Chief Fiscal Officer, Veterans Affairs Boston Healthcare System Brockton Division, Brockton, MA, p. A305
COSTA, Mark E., Executive Director, Kaiser Permanente Orange County Anaheim Medical Center, Anaheim, CA, p. A53
COSTA, Michael G.
Vice President Human Resources, Burleson St. Joseph Health Center, Caldwell, TX, p. A599
Director Human Resources, Grimes St. Joseph Health Center, Navasota, TX, p. A634
Vice President Human Resources, St. Joseph Regional Health Center, Bryan, TX, p. A599
COSTA, Vivian, Director, Barix Clinics of Pennsylvania, Langhorne, PA, p. A537
COSTANTINO, Vincent
Vice President Operations and Human Resources, Raritan Bay Medical Center, Perth Amboy, NJ, p. A417
Chief Administrative Officer, St. Francis Medical Center, Trenton, NJ, p. A419
COSTELLA, Jeane L., Vice President, New York–Presbyterian/Hudson Valley Hospital, Cortlandt Manor, NY, p. A432
COSTELLO, Benny, Chief Executive Officer, Promise Hospital of Miss Lou, Vidalia, LA, p. A286
COSTELLO, Jeff
Chief Financial Officer, Elkhart General Healthcare System, Elkhart, IN, p. A207
Chief Financial Officer, Memorial Hospital of South Bend, South Bend, IN, p. A220
COSTELLO, Susan, Chief Nursing Officer, Lucile Salter Packard Children's Hospital Stanford, Palo Alto, CA, p. A80
COSTER, Margaret C., MSN, President and Chief Executive Officer, Fairmont Regional Medical Center, Fairmont, WV, p. A691
COSTIC, Andrew
Regional Chief Financial Officer, Abraham Lincoln Memorial Hospital, Lincoln, IL, p. A193
Regional Chief Financial Officer, Taylorville Memorial Hospital, Taylorville, IL, p. A202
COSTIE, Glenn A., FACHE, Director, Dayton Veterans Affairs Medical Center, Dayton, OH, p. A488
COTA, Scott, M.D. Director Medical Services, Naval Hospital Lemoore, Portsmith, VA, p. A670
COTE, Gerri, Vice President Operations, Brattleboro Retreat, Brattleboro, VT, p. A660
COTE, Mary, Director Human Resources, New England Rehabilitation Hospital of Portland, Portland, ME, p. A292
COTNOIR, Laurie, Director Nursing and Quality, Upper Connecticut Valley Hospital, Colebrook, NH, p. A405
COTT, Gary, M.D. Executive Vice President Medical and Clinical Services, National Jewish Health, Denver, CO, p. A102
COTTER, Brian, Chief Executive Officer, Healthbridge Children's Hospital, Orange, CA, p. A79
COTTER, Carole
Senior Vice President and Chief Information Officer, Emma Pendleton Bradley Hospital, East Providence, RI, p. A555
Vice President and Chief Information Officer, Miriam Hospital, Providence, RI, p. A555
Senior Vice President and Chief Information Officer, Rhode Island Hospital, Providence, RI, p. A556
COTTERMAN, Rob, Assistant Superintendent Program Services, Moccasin Bend Mental Health Institute, Chattanooga, TN, p. A575
COTTI, Matthew, Chief Financial Officer, Rehabilitation Hospital of Rhode Island, North Smithfield, RI, p. A555
COTTINGHAM, Jerod, Director Information Systems, Carlinville Area Hospital, Carlinville, IL, p. A180
COTTLE, Jeremy, Ph.D., Chief Executive Officer, Provo Canyon Behavioral Hospital, Orem, UT, p. A656
COTTLE, Mike, Chief Information Officer, Newton Medical Center, Newton, KS, p. A246
COTTO, Hector L., M.D. Medical Director, Hospital San Francisco, San Juan, PR, p. A724
COTTON, C. Gerald, Interim Chief Operating Officer, Baptist Medical Center Leake, Carthage, MS, p. A351
COTTON, Michael, Chief Financial Officer, Gadsden Regional Medical Center, Gadsden, AL, p. A20
COTTRELL, Leslie, R.N. Nurse Lead, Iroquois Memorial Hospital and Resident Home, Watseka, IL, p. A202
COTTRILL, Brian, Chief Information Officer, United Hospital Center, Bridgeport, WV, p. A689
COUCH, Beulah, Director Human Resources, Mary Breckinridge ARH Hospital, Hyden, KY, p. A258
COUCH, Bill, Chief Financial Officer, Ashley County Medical Center, Crossett, AR, p. A42
COUCH, Lorie, Assistant Superintendent, Big Spring State Hospital, Big Spring, TX, p. A597
COUCH, Robert J., Chief Executive Officer, Medical Center of Manchester, Manchester, TN, p. A582
COUCHMAN, Diane, Vice President Patient Care Services and Chief Nursing Executive, Calvert Memorial Hospital, Prince Frederick, MD, p. A299
COUGHLIN, Ann, Director Human Resources, Boundary Community Hospital, Bonners Ferry, ID, p. A173
COUGHLIN, Cynthia, MS Chief Nursing Officer, Cheshire Medical Center, Keene, NH, p. A406
COULLIETTE, Edwina, Manager Human Resources, St. Vincent's Medical Center Southside, Jacksonville, FL, p. A130
COULTER, Barbara
Director Information Systems, Franciscan St. Francis Health – Indianapolis, Indianapolis, IN, p. A211
Director Information Systems, Franciscan St. Francis Health – Mooresville, Mooresville, IN, p. A216
COUNTRYMAN, Cory, Chief Executive Officer, Walnut Hill Medical Center, Dallas, TX, p. A607
COUNTS, Virginia, Manager Human Resources, Scott & White Hospital – Brenham, Brenham, TX, p. A598
COUNTY–TEEMER, Vickie, Coordinator Human Resources, Mitchell County Hospital, Camilla, GA, p. A153
COURIS, John D., President and Chief Executive Officer, Jupiter Medical Center, Jupiter, FL, p. A130
COURNYER, Tim, Chief Financial Officer, Forks Community Hospital, Forks, WA, p. A679
COUROUNIS, Glenn, Vice President People and Patient Experience, St. Luke's Cornwall Hospital, Newburgh, NY, p. A445
COURREGE, Chad, Vice President Human Resources, Touro Infirmary, New Orleans, LA, p. A282
COURREGE, Gary, Chief Information Officer, Jennings American Legion Hospital, Jennings, LA, p. A275
COURTNEY, Christine, R.N. Vice President and Chief Nursing Officer, Providence Healthcare Network, Waco, TX, p. A650
COURTOIS, Harold, Chief Executive Officer, Russell Regional Hospital, Russell, KS, p. A249
COURTOIS, Robert, Vice President Finance, Otsego Memorial Hospital, Gaylord, MI, p. A320
COUSAR, Myra, Director Human Resources, Baptist Memorial Hospital–Tipton, Covington, TN, p. A576
COUSINEAU, Cathy, Director Human Resources, Kaiser Permanente Woodland Hills Medical Center, CA, p. A70
COUTURE, Maureen, Chief Nursing Officer and Vice President Nursing, Cardinal Hill Rehabilitation Hospital, Lexington, KY, p. A259
COVA, Charles J., President and Chief Executive Officer, Marian Regional Medical Center, Santa Maria, CA, p. A91
COVAULT, Julie, Vice President Finance, Wilson Memorial Hospital, Sidney, OH, p. A497
COVE, Netty S., R.N. Vice President Patient Services and Chief Nursing Officer, Spectrum Health Big Rapids Hospital, Big Rapids, MI, p. A315
COVELL, Nancy, Director Human Resources, Cameron Memorial Community Hospital, Angola, IN, p. A204
COVELLI, Margaret, R.N. Chief Nursing Officer, Spring Valley Hospital Medical Center, Las Vegas, NV, p. A402
COVER, Barry, M.D. Medical Director, Magruder Memorial Hospital, Port Clinton, OH, p. A496
COVERT, Charles O., Vice President Finance, Thomas Memorial Hospital, South Charleston, WV, p. A695
COVERT, Kathy, Vice President Human Resources, Schneck Medical Center, Seymour, IN, p. A219
COVERT, Michael H., FACHE, President and Chief Executive Officer, Baylor St. Luke's Medical Center, Houston, TX, p. A619
COVERT, Terri, Vice President Human Resources, Mission Hospital, Mission Viejo, CA, p. A75
COVEY, Staci, MS, President, Troy Community Hospital, Troy, PA, p. A551
COVILLE, Lea, Chief of Staff, Black River Memorial Hospital, Black River Falls, WI, p. A698
COVINGTON, Carmen, Chief Nursing Officer, Middle Park Medical Center–Kremmling, Kremmling, CO, p. A105
COVINGTON, Casey, M.D. President Elect, Medical Staff, Jennie Stuart Medical Center, Hopkinsville, KY, p. A258
COVINGTON, Celia, MSN Director of Nursing, St. Mary's Good Samaritan Hospital, Greensboro, GA, p. A158
COVINGTON, Jerome, M.D. Chief Medical Officer, Lower Keys Medical Center, Key West, FL, p. A130
COVONE, Ann Marie, Senior Vice President and Chief Financial Officer, Terence Cardinal Cooke Health Care Center, New York, NY, p. A444
COWAN, J. W., Administrator, Choctaw General Hospital, Butler, AL, p. A17
COWAN, Joshua, Chief Information Officer, St. Helena Hospital Clear Lake, Clearlake, CA, p. A58
COWAN, Ronald M., Vice President Information Systems, Geisinger–Lewistown Hospital, Lewistown, PA, p. A539
COWART, Mark, Chief Information Officer, Carl Vinson Veterans Affairs Medical Center, Dublin, GA, p. A156
COWART, Michelle, R.N. Chief Nursing Officer, HEALTHSOUTH Chattanooga Rehabilitation Hospital, Chattanooga, TN, p. A575
COWART, Timothy, Chief Executive Officer, The Centers, Ocala, FL, p. A137
COWLES, John, Chief Financial Officer, Silver Lake Medical Center, Los Angeles, CA, p. A72
COWLING, Phyllis A., CPA, President and Chief Executive Officer, United Regional Health Care System, Wichita Falls, TX, p. A652
COWPERTHWAIT, Cheri, R.N., Chief Executive Officer, Lourdes Specialty Hospital of Southern New Jersey, Willingboro, NJ, p. A420
COX, Amber, Director Human Resources, East Texas Medical Center Carthage, Carthage, TX, p. A600
COX, Brian, Director Information Systems, Floyd Memorial Hospital and Health Services, New Albany, IN, p. A217
COX, Carla C., Chief Nursing Officer, Indiana University Health Ball Memorial Hospital, Muncie, IN, p. A216
COX, David W., Chief Financial Officer, Marin General Hospital, Greenbrae, CA, p. A64
COX, Debbie D., Administrative Director Human Resources, Central Texas Medical Center, San Marcos, TX, p. A643
COX, Denida A., Chief Nursing Officer, Shoals Hospital, Muscle Shoals, AL, p. A23
COX, Dina, Director Human Resources, Kansas Rehabilitation Hospital, Topeka, KS, p. A251
COX, Dorothy, Manager Information Systems, Hackettstown Regional Medical Center, Hackettstown, NJ, p. A412
COX, Gwen
Director Nursing Services, Klickitat Valley Health, Goldendale, WA, p. A679
Human Resources Coordinator, Select Specialty Hospital–Omaha, Omaha, NE, p. A396
COX, Jack, M.D. Senior Vice President and Chief Quality Officer, Hoag Memorial Hospital Presbyterian, Newport Beach, CA, p. A77
COX, Jason, Chief Executive Officer, Chestatee Regional Hospital, Dahlonega, GA, p. A155
COX, Jeffrey, Chief Information Officer, Glendora Community Hospital, Glendora, CA, p. A64
COX, Jr., John A., M.D. President Medical Staff, Comanche County Memorial Hospital, Lawton, OK, p. A508
COX, Keith, Administrator, LifeCare Hospitals of Shreveport, Shreveport, LA, p. A284
COX, Kenneth, M.D. Chief Medical Officer, Lucile Salter Packard Children's Hospital Stanford, Palo Alto, CA, p. A80
COX, Kenneth, Interim Chief Financial Officer, McKenzie County Healthcare System, Watford City, ND, p. A477
COX, Leigh, Chief Information Officer, WellStar Windy Hill Hospital, Marietta, GA, p. A161
COX, Lisa D., R.N. Chief Nursing Officer, Cypress Fairbanks Medical Center, Houston, TX, p. A619
COX, Lynna B., Director Health Information Services, Anson General Hospital, Anson, TX, p. A592
COX, Randell, Director Data Processing, Bowie Memorial Hospital, Bowie, TX, p. A598
COX, Randy, Vice President and Chief Information Officer, Saint Thomas West Hospital, Nashville, TN, p. A585
COX, Raymond L., M.D. Chief Medical Officer, Providence Hospital, Washington, DC, p. A120
COX, Sandra, Controller, Permian Regional Medical Center, Andrews, TX, p. A592
COX, Sharon K., FACHE, Chief Executive Officer, Rawlins County Health Center, Atwood, KS, p. A237
COX, Sheila, Director Human Resources, Cibola General Hospital, Grants, NM, p. A424
COX, Sherry, Chief Human Resources Officer, Ashe Memorial Hospital, Jefferson, NC, p. A463
COX, Steve, M.D. Chief Medical Officer, Fairfield Medical Center, Lancaster, OH, p. A491
COX, Steven, M.D. Chief Medical Officer, University of Texas Health Northeast, Tyler, TX, p. A649
COX, Walter R., M.D. President Medical Staff, Monongahela Valley Hospital, Monongahela, PA, p. A540
COX–HENLEY, Michelle, R.N. Associate Director for Patient and Nursing Services, Charlie Norwood Veterans Affairs Medical Center, Augusta, GA, p. A151
COY, Nelson, Director Human Resources, Tahoe Pacific Hospitals, Sparks, NV, p. A404

Index of Health Care Professionals

Index of Health Care Professionals / Coye

COYE, Ed
Director Information Technology Mission Health System Hospitals, Angel Medical Center, Franklin, NC, p. A460
Director Information Technology, Transylvania Regional Hospital, Brevard, NC, p. A456
COYLE, Joseph P., President and Chief Executive Officer, Southern Ocean Medical Center, Manahawkin, NJ, p. A414
COYLE, Michael F., Chief Executive Officer, Coteau des Prairies Hospital, Sisseton, SD, p. A572
COYNE, Rose, Interim CFO, Haywood Regional Medical Center, Clyde, NC, p. A458
COZAD, Adam, Director Human Resources, Lima Memorial Health System, Lima, OH, p. A492
COZART, Adrienne, Vice President Human Resources, University Medical Center, Lubbock, TX, p. A630
CRABB, Ian, M.D. Chief Medical Officer, Nebraska Orthopaedic Hospital, Omaha, NE, p. A396
CRABBE, Amy
Vice President People Services, Charles A. Cannon Memorial Hospital, Linville, NC, p. A464
Senior Vice President Human Resources, Watauga Medical Center, Boone, NC, p. A456
CRABDREE, Nathan, Chief Financial Officer, MountainView Regional Medical Center, Las Cruces, NM, p. A425
CRABLE, W. Trent, Chief Executive Officer, Northside Medical Center, Youngstown, OH, p. A501
CRABTREE, Douglas, Chief Executive Officer, Eastern Idaho Regional Medical Center, Idaho Falls, ID, p. A174
CRABTREE, Gordon, Chief Financial Officer, University of Utah Health Care – Hospital and Clinics, Salt Lake City, UT, p. A659
CRABTREE, John D., M.D. Chief of Staff, Harton Regional Medical Center, Tullahoma, TN, p. A588
CRABTREE, Robert, M.D
Chief of Staff and Medical Director, Physicians Surgical Hospital – Panhandle Campus, Amarillo, TX, p. A591
Chief of Staff and Medical Director, Physicians Surgical Hospital – Quail Creek, Amarillo, TX, p. A591
CRABTREE, Susan, Director Human Resources, Glendale Adventist Medical Center, Glendale, CA, p. A63
CRACROFT, Davis, M.D. Senior Director Medical Affairs, Scripps Mercy Hospital, San Diego, CA, p. A87
CRADER, Scott, Director Information Systems, EvergreenHealth Monroe, Monroe, WA, p. A680
CRAFT, Brian, Group Finance Officer, Texas Health Presbyterian Hospital Dallas, Dallas, TX, p. A606
CRAFT, Christina, Director Information Systems, Washington County Hospital, Plymouth, NC, p. A466
CRAFT, Kirby, Chief Information Officer, Magee General Hospital, Magee, MS, p. A356
CRAFTS, Nicholas, Chief Executive Officer, Victory Medical Center Houston, Houston, TX, p. A623
CRAGGS, Chris, Deputy Director, Winnebago Mental Health Institute, Winnebago, WI, p. A714
CRAIG, Alan, M.D. Chief Medical Officer, Princeton Baptist Medical Center, Birmingham, AL, p. A16
CRAIG, Celine, Director Human Resources, King's Daughters Medical Center, Brookhaven, MS, p. A351
CRAIG, Cheniere, Director Human Resources, P & S Surgical Hospital, Monroe, LA, p. A280
CRAIG, Daniel, Warden, Iowa Medical and Classification Center, Coralville, IA, p. A224
CRAIG, Donnette, Director Human Resources, CHRISTUS Coushatta Health Care Center, Coushatta, LA, p. A272
CRAIG, Elizabeth J., MSN Chief Nursing Officer and Vice President Patient Services, Temple University Hospital, Philadelphia, PA, p. A545
CRAIG, Emmett
Director Human Resources, Harlingen Medical Center, Harlingen, TX, p. A617
Chief Human Resources Officer, Knapp Medical Center, Weslaco, TX, p. A651
CRAIG, Glenn L., Chief Operating Officer, Louisiana Heart Hospital, Lacombe, LA, p. A277
CRAIG, Jeff, Chief Human Resource Management, Veterans Affairs Maryland Health Care System–Baltimore Division, Baltimore, MD, p. A295
CRAIG, Julian R., Chief Medical Officer, United Medical Center, Washington, DC, p. A120
CRAIG, Mike, Chief Financial Officer, Indiana University Health Bloomington Hospital, Bloomington, IN, p. A205
CRAIG, Pamela, R.N. Chief Nursing Officer, Seton Medical Center Harker Heights, Harker Heights, TX, p. A617
CRAIG, Patrice, Manager Human Resources, Southern Arizona Veterans Affairs Health Care System, Tucson, AZ, p. A40
CRAIG, Paul A., JD, Interim Chief Executive Officer, Keck Medicine of USC, Los Angeles, CA, p. B77
CRAIG, Paul A., JD, Chief Executive Officer, USC Verdugo Hills Hospital, Glendale, CA, p. A64
CRAIG, Rebecca W., Vice President and Chief Financial Officer, Wayne Memorial Hospital, Goldsboro, NC, p. A461
CRAIG, Scott, M.D. Medical Director, Van Matre HealthSouth Rehabilitation Hospital, Rockford, IL, p. A200
CRAIG, Sherry, Director Human Resources, Trace Regional Hospital, Houston, MS, p. A354
CRAIG, Tracy, Director Human Resources, Novant Health Huntersville Medical Center, Huntersville, NC, p. A462
CRAIG, William J., Chief Financial Officer, Howard Memorial Hospital, Nashville, AR, p. A48
CRAIGER, Lisa, Vice President, Chief Nursing Officer, Jay County Hospital, Portland, IN, p. A218
CRAIGIE, James N., M.D. Vice President Medical Affairs, McLeod Loris Seacoast Hospital, Loris, SC, p. A563
CRAIGIN, Jane, Chief Executive Officer, St. Vincent Williamsport Hospital, Williamsport, IN, p. A221
CRAIN, Doris
Vice President Information Services, Broward Health Medical Center, Fort Lauderdale, FL, p. A126
Vice President and Chief Information Officer, Broward Health North, Deerfield Beach, FL, p. A125
CRAIN, Greg, FACHE, Vice President and Administrator, Baptist Health Medical Center–Little Rock, Little Rock, AR, p. A47
CRAIN, Michelle B., MSN, Administrator and Chief Operating Officer, Heart Hospital of Lafayette, Lafayette, LA, p. A277
CRAMBES, Terry, Manager Finance, Warren State Hospital, Warren, PA, p. A552
CRAMER, Brian J., Chief Executive Officer, Orthopaedic Hospital of Wisconsin – Glendale, Glendale, WI, p. A701
CRAMER, James R.
Vice President and Chief Information Officer, HonorHealth Scottsdale Osborn Medical Center, Scottsdale, AZ, p. A37
Vice President and Chief Information Officer, HonorHealth Scottsdale Shea Medical Center, Scottsdale, AZ, p. A37
Chief Information Officer, HonorHealth Scottsdale Thompson Peak Medical Center, Scottsdale, AZ, p. A37
CRANDALL, Kristin, Director Human Resources, Bon Secours St. Mary's Hospital, Richmond, VA, p. A671
CRANDELL, Kristy, M.D. Medical Staff President, Red Bay Hospital, Red Bay, AL, p. A24
CRANE, David, Chief Executive Officer, National Surgical Healthcare, Chicago, IL, p. B94
CRANE, Margaret W., Chief Executive Officer, Barlow Respiratory Hospital, Los Angeles, CA, p. A69
CRANFORD, Melvin, Chief Fiscal Services, Cheyenne Veterans Affairs Medical Center, Cheyenne, WY, p. A715
CRAPSER, Douglas, Executive Vice President, Harrington Memorial Hospital, Southbridge, MA, p. A311
CRATON, Deborah W., M.D. Chief Medical Officer, St. Vincent Dunn Hospital, Bedford, IN, p. A204
CRAVEN, Darcy, Chief Executive Officer, Carolinas Hospital System, Florence, SC, p. A560
CRAVEN, Denise, Director Information Systems Relationship Management, Springfield Regional Medical Center, Springfield, OH, p. A498
CRAW, David, Coordinator Information Technology, Dundy County Hospital, Benkelman, NE, p. A390
CRAWFORD, Arnita, Director Human Resources, Woman's Hospital of Texas, Houston, TX, p. A623
CRAWFORD, Jeff
Chief Executive Officer, Reliant Northwest Houston, Houston, TX, p. A621
Chief Executive Officer, Reliant Rehabilitation Hospital North Houston, Shenandoah, TX, p. A643
CRAWFORD, Jim, Chief Financial Officer, Lawrence Medical Center, Moulton, AL, p. A23
CRAWFORD, John W.
Chief Financial Officer, Muscogee Creek Nation Medical Center, Okmulgee, OK, p. A513
Chief Financial Officer, St. John Sapulpa, Sapulpa, OK, p. A514
CRAWFORD, Linda, R.N. Chief Nursing Officer, Cookeville Regional Medical Center, Cookeville, TN, p. A576
CRAWFORD, Lucinda, Vice President Financial Services, Vidant Duplin Hospital, Kenansville, NC, p. A463
CRAWFORD, Mark W., Chief Executive Officer, Northwest Texas Healthcare System, Amarillo, TX, p. A591
CRAWFORD, Pam, R.N. Vice President of Nursing and Chief Nursing Officer, OhioHealth MedCentral Mansfield Hospital, Mansfield, OH, p. A493
CRAWFORD, Robin, Vice President and Chief Financial Officer, Susan B. Allen Memorial Hospital, El Dorado, KS, p. A239
CRAWFORD, Ryan, Director Talent, Southwestern Regional Medical Center, Tulsa, OK, p. A517
CRAWFORD, Susan, Manager Human Resources, Fayette County Hospital, Vandalia, IL, p. A202
CRAWFORD, Thomas, Chicago Market Chief Information Officer, Louis A. Weiss Memorial Hospital, Chicago, IL, p. A182
CRAWFORD, Tom
Vice President Human Resources, DeKalb Medical at Downtown Decatur, Decatur, GA, p. A155
Vice President Human Resources, DeKalb Medical at Hillandale, Lithonia, GA, p. A160
Chief Information Officer, Jupiter Medical Center, Jupiter, FL, p. A130
CRAWFORD, Traci, R.N., Commander, Moncrief Army Community Hospital, Fort Jackson, SC, p. A561
CRAYTON, Karen, Administrator, AMG Specialty Hospital–Denham Springs, Denham Springs, LA, p. A273
CREAL, Sharon, Vice President Financial Operations, Scripps Memorial Hospital–Encinitas, Encinitas, CA, p. A60
CREAMER, Ken, Chief Human Resource, Amarillo Veterans Affairs Health Care System, Amarillo, TX, p. A591
CREASMAN, Ginny L., Acting Director, Richard L. Roudebush Veterans Affairs Medical Center, Indianapolis, IN, p. A212
CREEL, James, M.D. Chief Medical Officer, Erlanger Medical Center, Chattanooga, TN, p. A575
CREEL, Keith, Vice President Operations, Good Shepherd Medical Center–Marshall, Marshall, TX, p. A631
CREEL, Mary Ann, Chief Information Resource Management, Martinsburg Veterans Affairs Medical Center, Martinsburg, WV, p. A693
CREIGHTON, Chris, Manager Information Technology, Curry General Hospital, Gold Beach, OR, p. A521
CREIGHTON, Peggy F., R.N. Director of Nursing Services, Methodist Hospital Union County, Morganfield, KY, p. A263
CRENSHAW, Neville, D.O. Chief of Staff, Keokuk Area Hospital, Keokuk, IA, p. A230
CRENSHAW, Rachel H., Chief Operating Officer, Jack Hughston Memorial Hospital, Phenix City, AL, p. A24
CRENSHAW, William, M.D. Chief of Staff, Lady of the Sea General Hospital, Cut Off, LA, p. A272
CREPEAU, Diana, Director Human Resources, HEALTHSOUTH Rehabilitation Hospital of Colorado Springs, Colorado Springs, CO, p. A100
CREPS, Barbara, Director Human Resources and Accounting, Okeene Municipal Hospital, Okeene, OK, p. A511
CREQUE, J. C., Director Management Information Systems, Schneider Regional Medical Center, Saint Thomas, VI, p. A725
CRESPO, Rosaida M., Executive Director, Hospital San Carlos Borromeo, Moca, PR, p. A722
CRESPO, Waleska, Executive Director, Cardiovascular Center of Puerto Rico and the Caribbean, San Juan, PR, p. A723
CRESWELL, Linda, Director Human Resource, Cypress Fairbanks Medical Center, Houston, TX, p. A619
CREVLING, Charles, Senior Vice President and Chief Financial Officer, Vail Valley Medical Center, Vail, CO, p. A109
CREWS, Kimberly, Vice President Finance and Chief Financial Officer, High Point Regional Health System, High Point, NC, p. A462
CRIBBS, Cyndie, Director of Nursing, Nor–Lea General Hospital, Lovington, NM, p. A425
CRIBBS, Sammie, Vice President Patient Care Services, North Arkansas Regional Medical Center, Harrison, AR, p. A45
CRIBBS, Susan, D.O. Chief of Staff, Tehachapi Valley Healthcare District, Tehachapi, CA, p. A94
CRIDER, Terry, Information Technology Site Manager, NEA Baptist Memorial Hospital, Jonesboro, AR, p. A46
CRIGER, Sara J., President, Mercy Hospital, Coon Rapids, MN, p. A337
CRILLY, Tom
Executive Vice President, Chief Financial Officer, Newark–Wayne Community Hospital, Newark, NY, p. A445
Executive Vice President and Chief Financial Officer, Unity Hospital, Rochester, NY, p. A449
CRIM, Marcia, MSN, Chief Executive Officer, USMD Hospital at Arlington, Arlington, TX, p. A593
CRIPE, Kimberly C.
President and Chief Executive Officer, Children's Hospital of Orange County, Orange, CA, p. A79
President and Chief Executive Officer, CHOC Children's at Mission Hospital, Mission Viejo, CA, p. A75
CRIPPS, Hugh Don, M.D. Chief of Staff, Saint Thomas DeKalb Hospital, Smithville, TN, p. A588
CRISANTI, John, M.D. Vice President Medical Affairs, Community Medical Center, Toms River, NJ, p. A419
CRIST, Chris, Director Information Technology, Nevada Regional Medical Center, Nevada, MO, p. A373
CRIST, Kathy, Director of Patient Care Services, Highlands–Cashiers Hospital, Highlands, NC, p. A462
CRISTY, Kirk, Chief Financial Officer, Sanford Bismarck, Bismarck, ND, p. A472
CRISWELL, Jodie, Vice President Fiscal Services, Hammond–Henry Hospital, Geneseo, IL, p. A189

A816 Index of Health Care Professionals 

Index of Health Care Professionals / Culp

Index of Health Care Professionals


CRITCHLEY, Dan
Chief Information Officer, Banner – University Medical Center South, Tucson, AZ, p. A39
Chief Information Officer, Banner – University Medical Center Tucson, Tucson, AZ, p. A39
CRITTENDEN, Shana, Chief Operating Officer, North Shore Medical Center, Miami, FL, p. A134
CRNKOVIC, A. Elaine, Chief Executive Officer, Cedar Springs Hospital, Colorado Springs, CO, p. A100
CROCKER, Daniel, M.D. Chief Medical Officer, LifeCare Hospitals of North Carolina, Rocky Mount, NC, p. A467
CROCKER, Phillip, Accounting Specialist, Black River Medical Center, Poplar Bluff, MO, p. A374
CROCKETT, James Scott, M.D. Chief of Staff, Falls Community Hospital and Clinic, Marlin, TX, p. A631
CROCKETT, Kim, Director Management Information Systems, Shriners Hospitals for Children–Shreveport, Shreveport, LA, p. A285
CROCKETT, Mandy Lee
Director Human Resources, San Luis Valley Health, Alamosa, CO, p. A99
Director Human Resources, San Luis Valley Health Conejos County Hospital, La Jara, CO, p. A105
CROCKETT, Richard, Acting Medical Center Director, Jack C. Montgomery Veterans Affairs Medical Center, Muskogee, OK, p. A510
CROCKETT, Russ, Director Human Resources, Shriners Hospitals for Children–Salt Lake City, Salt Lake City, UT, p. A658
CROFT, Kim, R.N. Executive Director Human Resources, Pomerene Hospital, Millersburg, OH, p. A494
CROFTON, Michael
Senior Vice President and Chief Financial Officer, Bethesda North Hospital, Cincinnati, OH, p. A482
Chief Financial Officer, Good Samaritan Hospital, Cincinnati, OH, p. A483
Chief Financial Officer, TriHealth Evendale Hospital, Cincinnati, OH, p. A483
CROKER, James, Director Information Systems, St. Bernardine Medical Center, San Bernardino, CA, p. A86
CROLEY, John S., Vice President Business Operations, Texas Institute for Surgery at Texas Health Presbyterian Dallas, Dallas, TX, p. A606
CRONER, Robert, Senior Vice President and Chief Human Resources Officer, Children's Hospital of Philadelphia, Philadelphia, PA, p. A543
CRONIN, Annamarie, Director Human Resources, New England Rehabilitation Hospital, Woburn, MA, p. A313
CRONIN, David J., Regional Vice President Human Resources, Good Samaritan Medical Center, Brockton, MA, p. A305
CROOKS, Heidi M., R.N. Senior Associate Director, Outpatient and Patient Care Services, Ronald Reagan UCLA Medical Center, Los Angeles, CA, p. A72
CROOKS, John, Chair Information Services, Mayo Clinic Jacksonville, Jacksonville, FL, p. A129
CROOM, Jon–Paul, Chief Executive Officer, Merit Health Rankin, Brandon, MS, p. A351
CROOM Jr., Kennedy L., Administrator and Chief Executive Officer, Rhea Medical Center, Dayton, TN, p. A577
CROPLEY, Stacey, M.D. Chief Nursing Officer, Moore County Hospital District, Dumas, TX, p. A609
CROPPER, Douglas P., President and Chief Executive Officer, Genesis Health System, Davenport, IA, p. B58
CROPPER, Ronnie, Chief Operating Officer, Warren State Hospital, Warren, PA, p. A552
CROSBIE, John, Director Support Services, Indiana University Health Blackford Hospital, Hartford City, IN, p. A210
CROSBY, Evalie M., CPA Vice President Finance and Chief Financial Officer, Alice Peck Day Memorial Hospital, Lebanon, NH, p. A406
CROSBY, Robert
Chief Financial Officer, Athol Memorial Hospital, Athol, MA, p. A302
Senior Vice President and Chief Financial Officer, Heywood Hospital, Gardner, MA, p. A307
CROSHAW, Diane, Vice President Human Resources, Bacharach Institute for Rehabilitation, Pomona, NJ, p. A417
CROSS, Carol, Director Finance, Texas Health Harris Methodist Hospital Stephenville, Stephenville, TX, p. A645
CROSS, Lynda, R.N. Director of Nurses, Nemaha Valley Community Hospital, Seneca, KS, p. A250
CROSS, Patricia, Chief Executive Officer, Life Line Hospital, Steubenville, OH, p. A498
CROSS, Renee, Senior Vice President and Chief Financial Officer, Saint Francis Hospital, Charleston, WV, p. A690
CROSSAN, Eric, Chief Executive Officer, HEALTHSOUTH Walton Rehabilitation Hospital, Augusta, GA, p. A151
CROSSER, Roxanna, President, OSF St. Mary Medical Center, Galesburg, IL, p. A188
CROSSEY, Robert, D.O. Chief Medical Officer, LifeCare Hospitals of Pittsburgh – Monroeville, Monroeville, PA, p. A540
CROSSLAND, Jeanne, Director of Nursing, Shamrock General Hospital, Shamrock, TX, p. A643
CROSSLEY, Kent, M.D. Acting Chief of Staff, Minneapolis Veterans Affairs Health Care System, Minneapolis, MN, p. A342
CROSSLEY, Rachel, R.N. Chief Patient Care Services, Veterans Affairs Sierra Nevada Health Care System, Reno, NV, p. A404
CROSTON, J. Kevin, M.D., Chief Executive Officer, North Memorial Health Care, Robbinsdale, MN, p. B97
CROSTON, J. Kevin, M.D. Chief Medical Officer, North Memorial Medical Center, Robbinsdale, MN, p. A345
CROTEAU, Christine, MBA Director, Bedford Veterans Affairs Medical Center, Edith Nourse Rogers Memorial Veterans Hospital, Bedford, MA, p. A302
CROTEAU, Gary, Assistant Vice President and Chief Information Officer, South County Hospital, Wakefield, RI, p. A556
CROTTY, Jr., Glenn, M.D. Executive Vice President and Chief Operating Officer, Charleston Area Medical Center, Charleston, WV, p. A690
CROTTY, Renee, Coordinator Marketing and Public Relations, Capital Medical Center, Olympia, WA, p. A681
CROUCH, Amy, Chief Financial Officer, Community Health Center of Branch County, Coldwater, MI, p. A317
CROUCH, Chester, Chief Executive Officer, Reliant Healthcare Partners, Richardson, TX, p. B113
CROUCH, James, Vice President Technical Services, Northwest Medical Center, Albany, MO, p. A363
CROUCH, Kenneth, Chief Executive Officer, Foundation Surgical Hospital of San Antonio, San Antonio, TX, p. A640
CROUCH, Matthew, Chief Executive Officer and Managing Director, Peachford Behavioral Health System, Atlanta, GA, p. A150
CROUCH, Max, M.D. Chief Medical Staff, Mountain View Hospital, Payson, UT, p. A657
CROUT, Tom, MS Director Human Resources, Central Louisiana State Hospital, Pineville, LA, p. A283
CROW, Angie, Director Finance, Saint Thomas Hospital for Spinal Surgery, Nashville, TN, p. A585
CROW, Regina W., R.N. Chief Nursing Officer, Bothwell Regional Health Center, Sedalia, MO, p. A378
CROW, Ruth Ann, Administrator, Lake Whitney Medical Center, Whitney, TX, p. A652
CROWDER, Andy, Senior Vice President, Chief Information Officer, Maine Medical Center, Portland, ME, p. A291
CROWDER, Jerry W., President and Chief Executive Officer, Bradford Health Services, Birmingham, AL, p. B25
CROWDER, Lonna, Director of Nursing, Phillips County Hospital, Malta, MT, p. A385
CROWE, Arthur, Director Information Systems, Peconic Bay Medical Center, Riverhead, NY, p. A448
CROWE, William R., President, Conemaugh Miners Medical Center, Hastings, PA, p. A535
CROWELL, Eric T.
President and Chief Executive Officer, UnityPoint Health – Iowa Methodist Medical Center, Des Moines, IA, p. A226
President and Chief Executive Officer, UnityPoint Health–Iowa Lutheran Hospital, Des Moines, IA, p. A226
CROWELL, Lynn, Chief Executive Officer, Arkansas Valley Regional Medical Center, La Junta, CO, p. A105
CROWELL, Robin, Chief Nursing Officer and Chief Operating Officer, Saint Thomas Hickman Hospital, Centerville, TN, p. A575
CROWL, Heather N., Chief Human Resources Officer, Kingman Regional Medical Center, Kingman, AZ, p. A32
CROWL, Steve, Director of Information Services, Davis Medical Center, Elkins, WV, p. A690
CROWLEY, Thomas, President and Chief Executive Officer, Saint Elizabeth's Medical Center, Wabasha, MN, p. A348
CRUCETTI, Carol, R.N. Chief Nursing Officer, St. Mary's Hospital, Troy, NY, p. A452
CRUDDAS, Brian, Chief Operating Officer, Bayfront Health Port Charlotte, Port Charlotte, FL, p. A140
CRUM, Dennis L., Senior Vice President and Chief Financial Officer, Tift Regional Medical Center, Tifton, GA, p. A166
CRUM Jr., Herbert, Chief Executive Officer, Craig General Hospital, Vinita, OK, p. A517
CRUMB, Dennis, Chief Information Officer, Ellwood City Hospital, Ellwood City, PA, p. A533
CRUMLEY, Vickie L., Vice President Human Resources, Mary Rutan Hospital, Bellefontaine, OH, p. A479
CRUMP, Rick, Chief Financial Officer, Lakeland Behavioral Health System, Springfield, MO, p. A378
CRUMPTON, Patsy Sue, R.N. Chief Nursing Officer, National Park Medical Center, Hot Springs, AR, p. A45
CRUNK, Frances H., Vice President and Chief Financial Officer, Florida Hospital Waterman, Tavares, FL, p. A145
CRUNK, Tommy, M.D. Chief of Staff, Northcrest Medical Center, Springfield, TN, p. A588
CRUSE, Ray, Chief Executive Officer, Lakeland Hospital, Watervliet, Watervliet, MI, p. A332
CRUSON, Jim, Chief Information Officer, Riverview Behavioral Health, Texarkana, AR, p. A51
CRUTHIRDS, Leslie, Chief Human Resource Management Service, South Texas Veterans Health Care System, San Antonio, TX, p. A642
CRUTHIRDS, Richard, Director Information Systems, Peterson Regional Medical Center, Kerrville, TX, p. A626
CRUZ, Arlene, Director, Rush Oak Park Hospital, Oak Park, IL, p. A196
CRUZ, Dihitri, Vice President, Information Technology, Englewood Hospital and Medical Center, Englewood, NJ, p. A412
CRUZ, Domingo, Senior Vice President Operations, San Jorge Children's Hospital, San Juan, PR, p. A724
CRUZ, Joseph V., Chief Information Officer, Ryder Memorial Hospital, Humacao, PR, p. A721
CRUZ, Julia, Chief Financial Officer, San Juan Capestrano Hospital, San Juan, PR, p. A724
CRUZ, Michael, Senior Vice President Operations, Baptist St. Anthony Health System, Amarillo, TX, p. A591
CRUZ, Michael A., M.D., President, OSF Saint Francis Medical Center, Peoria, IL, p. A198
CRUZ, Miguel, M.D. Medical Director, Bella Vista Hospital, Mayaguez, PR, p. A722
CRUZ, Miguel, Medical Staff Credentialing Coordinator, HEALTHSOUTH Rehabilitation Hospital of Miami, Cutler Bay, FL, p. A124
CRYER, Betty, Chief Nursing Officer, Anderson Regional Medical Center–South Campus, Meridian, MS, p. A357
CRYER, Selena, Director Human Resources, Ennis Regional Medical Center, Ennis, TX, p. A612
CSEPKE, Cheryl, Controller, Kindred Rehabilitation Hospital Northeast Houston, Humble, TX, p. A623
CUBELLIS, Guido J.
Chief Operating Officer, Nexus Specialty Hospital, Shenandoah, TX, p. A643
Chief Operating Officer, Nexus Specialty Hospital The Woodlands, Spring, TX, p. A644
CUBRE, Alan, M.D. Medical Director, Vibra Hospital of Sacramento, Folsom, CA, p. A61
CUDWORTH, Craig R., Chief Executive Officer, Franklin Foundation Hospital, Franklin, LA, p. A274
CUELLAR, Eddie, Vice President Information Systems, Methodist Hospital, San Antonio, TX, p. A641
CUELLAR, Jacob, M.D., Chief Executive Officer, Laurel Ridge Treatment Center, San Antonio, TX, p. A641
CUENCA, Derrick, Chief Executive Officer, Lake Granbury Medical Center, Granbury, TX, p. A616
CUERO, Liza, Coordinator Human Resources, Central Texas Rehabilitation Hospital, Austin, TX, p. A594
CUEVAS, Gilberto, Director Human Resources, Hospital De Damas, Ponce, PR, p. A722
CUEVAS, Jacki, Director Health Information Services, Regional Rehabilitation Hospital, Phenix City, AL, p. A24
CULBERSON, David K., Chief Executive Officer, San Joaquin General Hospital, French Camp, CA, p. A62
CULBERT, Devon, Controller, The Hospital at Westlake Medical Center, Austin, TX, p. A595
CULBRETH, David, Administrator, Hale Ho'ola Hamakua, Honokaa, HI, p. A168
CULBRETH, Lucile, Chief Nursing Officer, Abbeville Area Medical Center, Abbeville, SC, p. A557
CULLEN, John, M.D. Chief of Staff and Medical Director Long Term Care, Providence Valdez Medical Center, Valdez, AK, p. A29
CULLEN, John, Assistant Superintendent, Thomas B. Finan Center, Cumberland, MD, p. A297
CULLEN, Mark J., Chief Executive Officer, Compass Health, Crowley, LA, p. B41
CULLEN, Michael, Senior Vice President and Chief Financial Officer, South Shore Hospital, South Weymouth, MA, p. A311
CULLEN, Neil, Director Human Resources, HEALTHSOUTH Rehabilitation Hospital of Southern Arizona, Tucson, AZ, p. A39
CULLEN, Paul T., M.D. Vice President Medical Affairs, Washington Hospital, Washington, PA, p. A552
CULLEN, Scott, Chief Executive Officer, Northwest Hills Surgical Hospital, Austin, TX, p. A594
CULLITON, Gerald F., Medical Center Director, Veterans Affairs Connecticut Healthcare System, West Haven, CT, p. A116
CULLUM, Beth, Chief Operating Officer, Kindred Hospital Boston–North Shore, Peabody, MA, p. A310
CULP, Judy, Chief Financial Officer, Hill Regional Hospital, Hillsboro, TX, p. A618

Index of Health Care Professionals

Index of Health Care Professionals / Culumber

CULUMBER, Janene, Vice President and Chief Financial Officer, H. Lee Moffitt Cancer Center and Research Institute, Tampa, FL, p. A144
CULVER, Douglas, Chief Financial Officer, Mercy Hospital Carthage, Carthage, MO, p. A365
CULVER, Shawna, Director Information Systems, Western Plains Medical Complex, Dodge City, KS, p. A239
CUMBEE, Lib, Director Information Systems, Providence Hospital, Columbia, SC, p. A559
CUMBIE, Dan L., Chief Nursing Officer, Flowers Hospital, Dothan, AL, p. A18
CUMBO, Adam, Chief Financial Officer, Dukes Memorial Hospital, Peru, IN, p. A218
CUMING, Richard, R.N. Vice President and Chief Nurse Executive, Einstein Medical Center Philadelphia, Philadelphia, PA, p. A543
CUMMINGS, Allana, Chief Information Officer, Children's Healthcare of Atlanta, Atlanta, GA, p. A150
CUMMINGS, Brooke, Chief Financial Officer, Our Lady of the Angels Hospital, Bogalusa, LA, p. A270
CUMMINGS, Bruce D., President and Chief Executive Officer, L+M Healthcare, New London, CT, p. B80
CUMMINGS, Bruce D.
President and Chief Executive Officer, Lawrence + Memorial Hospital, New London, CT, p. A114
President and Chief Executive Officer, Westerly Hospital, Westerly, RI, p. A556
CUMMINGS, Cindy, Chief Executive Officer, Putnam County Memorial Hospital, Unionville, MO, p. A380
CUMMINGS, Greg, Chief Financial Officer, Texas Spine & Joint Hospital, Tyler, TX, p. A649
CUMMINGS, Jerry, Chief Operating Officer, Putnam County Memorial Hospital, Unionville, MO, p. A380
CUMMINGS, Kelly, Chief Nursing Officer, Abington Health Lansdale Hospital, Lansdale, PA, p. A538
CUMMINGS, Rae, Chief Operating Officer, Boulder City Hospital, Boulder City, NV, p. A400
CUMMINGS, Steve, M.D. Chief of Medical Staff, Stillwater Medical Center, Stillwater, OK, p. A515
CUMMINGS, Steven, Chief Operating Officer and Chief Information Officer, Baystate Noble Hospital, Westfield, MA, p. A312
CUMMINS, Frank L., Vice President Human Resources, HonorHealth Deer Valley Medical Center, Phoenix, AZ, p. A35
CUMMINS, Thomas H., M.D
Senior Vice President and Chief Medical Officer, CHI St. Vincent Infirmary Medical Center, Little Rock, AR, p. A47
Senior Vice President and Chief Medical Officer, CHI St. Vincent Medical Center–North, Sherwood, AR, p. A50
CUNNIGHAM, James, D.O. Chief of Staff, Audubon County Memorial Hospital, Audubon, IA, p. A222
CUNNINGHAM, Becky, Controller, Salem Memorial District Hospital, Salem, MO, p. A378
CUNNINGHAM, Brian, Interim Chief Executive Officer, Gila Regional Medical Center, Silver City, NM, p. A427
CUNNINGHAM, Gail, Interim Chief Medical Officer, University of Maryland St. Joseph Medical Center, Towson, MD, p. A300
CUNNINGHAM, Gary, Chief Nursing Officer, Dixie Regional Medical Center, Saint George, UT, p. A658
CUNNINGHAM, James C., M.D. Chief Medical Officer, Cook Children's Medical Center, Fort Worth, TX, p. A613
CUNNINGHAM, Julie, Associate Administrator and Chief Human Resources Officer, Pioneers Memorial Healthcare District, Brawley, CA, p. A56
CUNNINGHAM, Keith W., M.D. Medical Director, HEALTHSOUTH Scottsdale Rehabilitation Hospital, Scottsdale, AZ, p. A37
CUNNINGHAM, Larmar, Chief Operating Officer, West Central Georgia Regional Hospital, Columbus, GA, p. A154
CUNNINGHAM, M. Edward, Chief Executive Officer, Gateway Regional Medical Center, Granite City, IL, p. A189
CUNNINGHAM, Michelle P., Chief Executive Officer, Highlands Hospital, Connellsville, PA, p. A532
CUNNINGHAM, Regina, Ph.D. Chief Nurse Executive, Hospital of the University of Pennsylvania, Philadelphia, PA, p. A544
CUPINO, Isaias, Chief of Staff, HSHS St. Clare Memorial Hospital, Oconto Falls, WI, p. A708
CURCURUTO, James J., Senior Vice President Finance, St. Joseph's Medical Center, Yonkers, NY, p. A454
CURD, R. Blake, M.D., Chief Executive Officer, Sioux Falls Specialty Hospital, Sioux Falls, SD, p. A572
CURLEE, Robbin, Controller, RMC Jacksonville, Jacksonville, AL, p. A21
CURLING, Susan, M.D. Chief Medical Officer, Memorial Hermann Northeast, Humble, TX, p. A623
CURNEL, Robin, MSN Chief Operating Officer and Chief Nursing Officer, Crittenden County Hospital, Marion, KY, p. A262
CURNUTT, Ann, Director Information Systems, Garfield Medical Center, Monterey Park, CA, p. A76
CURPHY, Rona, President and Chief Executive Officer, Banner Casa Grande Medical Center, Casa Grande, AZ, p. A30
CURRAN, Dezerae, Director Human Resources, Osawatomie State Hospital, Osawatomie, KS, p. A247
CURRAN, Maria, Vice President Human Resources, VCU Medical Center, Richmond, VA, p. A672
CURRAN–MEULI, Jane, Chief Operating Officer, Holy Family Memorial, Manitowoc, WI, p. A704
CURRANCE, Lana, MSN, Chief Executive Officer, Peak View Behavioral Health, Colorado Springs, CO, p. A100
CURREN, Robert
Director Information Technology, Center for Behavioral Medicine, Kansas City, MO, p. A369
Western Region Chief Information Technology Officer, Northwest Missouri Psychiatric Rehabilitation Center, Saint Joseph, MO, p. A375
CURRIE, Michelle, Chief Financial Officer, Richard P. Stadter Psychiatric Center, Grand Forks, ND, p. A474
CURRIE, Scott D., Vice President and Chief Financial Officer, MidMichigan Medical Center–Midland, Midland, MI, p. A325
CURRIE, Stuart, Chief Medical Officer, Tuality Healthcare, Hillsboro, OR, p. A521
CURRIER, Donald L., Vice President Human Resources, Piedmont Medical Center, Rock Hill, SC, p. A564
CURRY, Cheryl, Chief Financial Officer, Littleton Adventist Hospital, Littleton, CO, p. A106
CURRY, Christopher, Chief Operating Officer, Iroquois Memorial Hospital and Resident Home, Watseka, IL, p. A202
CURRY, Jeffrey T.
Executive Vice President and Chief Financial Officer, Excela Frick Hospital, Mount Pleasant, PA, p. A541
Executive Vice President and Chief Financial Officer, Excela Health Westmoreland Hospital, Greensburg, PA, p. A535
CURRY, Lori, Regional Chief Human Resources Officer, Providence Holy Cross Medical Center, CA, p. A72
CURRY, Robert H., President and Chief Executive Officer, Citrus Valley Health Partners, Covina, CA, p. B33
CURRY, Robert H.
President and Chief Executive Officer, Citrus Valley Medical Center–Inter Community Campus, Covina, CA, p. A59
President and Chief Executive Officer, Foothill Presbyterian Hospital, Glendora, CA, p. A64
CURRY, Stephen A., Director Information Services, Princeton Community Hospital, Princeton, WV, p. A694
CURRY, Steve, Regional Director Human Resources, Four County Counseling Center, Logansport, IN, p. A215
CURRY, Susan
Interim Chief Nursing Officer, Schuylkill Medical Center – East Norwegian Street, Pottsville, PA, p. A548
Interim Chief Nursing Officer, Schuylkill Medical Center – South Jackson Street, Pottsville, PA, p. A548
CURRY, Thomas A., M.D
Vice President Medical Affairs for Clinical Effectiveness and Documentation, Schuylkill Medical Center – East Norwegian Street, Pottsville, PA, p. A548
Vice President Medical Affairs for Clinical Effectiveness and Documentation, Schuylkill Medical Center – South Jackson Street, Pottsville, PA, p. A548
CURRY–PELYAK, Mary Jane, R.N. Vice President and Chief Clinical Officer, The Villages Regional Hospital, The Villages, FL, p. A146
CURTI, Tate, Senior Vice President and Chief Operating Officer, Southern New Hampshire Medical Center, Nashua, NH, p. A407
CURTIN, Jackie, Director of Clinical Services, Aurora Charter Oak Hospital, Covina, CA, p. A59
CURTIN, Sean, Chief Financial Officer, Alice Hyde Medical Center, Malone, NY, p. A436
CURTIS, Edgar J., FACHE, President and Chief Executive Officer, Memorial Health System, Springfield, IL, p. B88
CURTIS, Edgar J., FACHE, President and Chief Executive Officer, Memorial Medical Center, Springfield, IL, p. A201
CURTIS, George
Chief Information Officer, Houston Medical Center, Warner Robins, GA, p. A167
Director Information Systems, Perry Hospital, Perry, GA, p. A162
CURTIS, Janis, Interim Director Information Technology, Duke Raleigh Hospital, Raleigh, NC, p. A466
CURTIS, Joy U., Senior Vice President Human Resources, Cambridge Health Alliance, Cambridge, MA, p. A305
CURTIS, Lorna, Chief Financial Officer, John F. Kennedy Memorial Hospital, Indio, CA, p. A65
CURTIS, Michael, Chief Administrative Officer, McKenzie County Healthcare System, Watford City, ND, p. A477
CURTIS, Scott A., Administrator and Chief Executive Officer, Kossuth Regional Health Center, Algona, IA, p. A222
CURTIS, Tracie, Vice President Human Resources, Medina Hospital, Medina, OH, p. A494
CURVIN, Thomas J., M.D. Chief of Staff, Rankin Hospital District, Rankin, TX, p. A638
CUSA, Philip L., Administrator, EastPointe Hospital, Daphne, AL, p. A18
CUSACK–MCGUIRK, Joan, Interim President and Chief Executive Officer, St. Luke's Cornwall Hospital, Newburgh, NY, p. A445
CUSANO, Susan, Director Human Resources, Four Winds Hospital, Katonah, NY, p. A435
CUSENZ, Bruce J., M.D. Medical Director, Eastern Niagara Hospital, Lockport, NY, p. A436
CUSHING, Heidi, Director Finance, Gordon Memorial Hospital, Gordon, NE, p. A392
CUSHING, Herbert, M.D. Chief Medical Officer, Temple University Hospital, Philadelphia, PA, p. A545
CUSSINS, James, Chief Financial Officer, Platte County Memorial Hospital, Wheatland, WY, p. A718
CUSTER, Cherie, Chief Nursing Officer, Cherry Hospital, Goldsboro, NC, p. A461
CUSTER, Joshua, Director Finance, St. Luke's Magic Valley Medical Center, Twin Falls, ID, p. A176
CUSTER–MITCHELL, Marilyn J., President, Parkview Wabash County Hospital, Wabash, IN, p. A221
CUSTIN, Melinda, Chief Information Officer, JPS Health Network, Fort Worth, TX, p. A613
CUSUMANO, Margaret M., R.N. Vice President Patient Care Services and Chief Nursing Officer, St. Joseph's Medical Center, Yonkers, NY, p. A454
CUTOLO, Jr., Edward, M.D. Chief of Staff, James A. Haley Veterans' Hospital–Tampa, Tampa, FL, p. A144
CUTRIGHT, Bruce E., MS Vice President Human Resources, Mary Lanning Healthcare, Hastings, NE, p. A392
CUTSFORTH, Shawn, Information Systems Officer, Pioneer Memorial Hospital, Heppner, OR, p. A521
CUTTER, Elise, Chief Financial Officer, Island Hospital, Anacortes, WA, p. A676
CUZZOLA, Anthony, Vice President Administrator, JFK Johnson Rehabilitation Institute, Edison, NJ, p. A411
CYTLAK, David
Chief Financial Officer, Blanchard Valley Hospital, Findlay, OH, p. A490
Vice President Finance, Bluffton Hospital, Bluffton, OH, p. A480
CZAJKA, Paul M., Chief Operating Officer, USC Verdugo Hills Hospital, Glendale, CA, p. A64
CZEREW, Jane, Vice President Clinical Services and Quality, Spectrum Health Zeeland Community Hospital, Zeeland, MI, p. A333
CZINCILA, Robert, D.O. Medical Staff President, Einstein Medical Center Montgomery, East Norriton, PA, p. A533
CZYMBOR, Mary, Chief Medical Officer, Milford Regional Medical Center, Milford, MA, p. A309
CZYZ, AnneMarie, R.N. Vice President for Clinical and Educational Services, St. Joseph's Hospital Health Center, Syracuse, NY, p. A451

## D

D'ACCURZIO, Albert, M.D. Medical Director, St. Elizabeth Medical Center, Utica, NY, p. A452
D'AGNES, Michael R., FACHE, President and Chief Executive Officer, Raritan Bay Medical Center, Perth Amboy, NJ, p. A417
D'ALBERTO, Richard E., FACHE, Campus President, Greenville Health System – Laurens County Memorial Hospital, Clinton, SC, p. A559
D'AMBROSIO, Matthew, Director Information Systems, Southwest General Hospital, San Antonio, TX, p. A642
D'AMBROSIO, Paul, Chief Operating Officer, Complex Care Hospital at Tenaya, Las Vegas, NV, p. A401
D'AMICO, Ken, Chief Executive Officer, Landmark Hospital of Salt Lake City, Murray, UT, p. A656
D'AMICO, Paul, M.D. Chief of Staff, Stanly Regional Medical Center, Albemarle, NC, p. A455
D'AMORE, Seanna, Director Human Resources, Penn Highlands Elk, Saint Marys, PA, p. A549
D'ANGELO, Elizabeth, M.D. Chief of Staff, Onslow Memorial Hospital, Jacksonville, NC, p. A463
D'ANGELO, Jennifer, Assistant Vice President Information Services, Christian Health Care Center, Wyckoff, NJ, p. A421
D'ANGINA, Joseph, Area Finance Officer, Kaiser Permanente Vallejo Medical Center, Vallejo, CA, p. A96
D'APOLLO, Julie, R.N. Director of Nursing, Hampstead Hospital, Hampstead, NH, p. A406
D'AQUILA, Richard, President and Chief Operating Officer, Yale–New Haven Hospital, New Haven, CT, p. A114
D'ELIA, Peter, Chief Financial Officer, Saint Vincent Hospital, Worcester, MA, p. A313
D'ETTORRE, Joseph A., Chief Executive Officer, Wyandot Memorial Hospital, Upper Sandusky, OH, p. A499

Index of Health Care Professionals / Danker

D'EVANO, John, Chief Operating Officer, Connecticut Valley Hospital, Middletown, CT, p. A113
D'SOUZA, Carol, Chief Human Resources Officer, Banner Casa Grande Medical Center, Casa Grande, AZ, p. A30
D'SOUZA, Gladys, Chief Nursing Officer, Barlow Respiratory Hospital, Los Angeles, CA, p. A69
DAANE, John, Information Systems Officer, Prairie du Chien Memorial Hospital, Prairie Du Chien, WI, p. A709
DABBS, Mark, MSN Chief Operating Officer, Vibra Hospital of Springfield, Springfield, IL, p. A201
DABNEY, Ann, Manager Human Resources, Spring View Hospital, Lebanon, KY, p. A259
DABNEY, Janice, Chief Executive Officer, Springs Memorial Hospital, Lancaster, SC, p. A563
DACE, Linda, Vice President Finance, McDonough District Hospital, Macomb, IL, p. A193
DACEY, Michael J., MS, President and Chief Operating Officer, Kent County Memorial Hospital, Warwick, RI, p. A556
DACUS, Michael E.
Vice President and Chief Financial Officer, Sheltering Arms Hospital South, Midlothian, VA, p. A668
Vice President and Chief Financial Officer, Sheltering Arms Rehabilitation Hospital, Mechanicsville, VA, p. A668
DADD, Steven, Flight Commander Resource Management, U. S. Air Force Hospital, Hampton, VA, p. A666
DADEY, Mary Lee, R.N. Vice President of Nursing, Windber Medical Center, Windber, PA, p. A553
DADLEZ, Christopher M., President and Chief Executive Officer, Saint Francis Care, Inc., Hartford, CT, p. B115
DADLEZ, Christopher M., President and Chief Executive Officer, Saint Francis Hospital and Medical Center, Hartford, CT, p. A112
DADO, Joseph, Chief Information Officer, Conemaugh Memorial Medical Center, Johnstown, PA, p. A537
DAEGER, Brian, Vice President Financial Services, Margaret Mary Health, Batesville, IN, p. A204
DAFFRON, Eric Allen, Division Director, Information Systems, Southeast Alabama Medical Center, Dothan, AL, p. A19
DAFOE, Joe, R.N. Chief Clinical Officer, Columbia Memorial Hospital, Astoria, OR, p. A519
DAGENBACH, Pete, Chief Financial Officer, Adams County Regional Medical Center, Seaman, OH, p. A497
DAGHER, Michel, D.O. Vice President and Chief Medical Officer, Banner Del E. Webb Medical Center, Sun City West, AZ, p. A38
DAGLIO, Michael
President, Norwalk Hospital, Norwalk, CT, p. A114
President – Norwalk Hospital – SVP, WCHN, Danbury Hospital, Danbury, CT, p. A111
DAHDUL, Adnan, M.D. Medical Director, HEALTHSOUTH Rehabilitation Hospital of Western Massachusetts, Ludlow, MA, p. A308
DAHLBERG, Connie, Director Business and Employee, Sleepy Eye Medical Center, Sleepy Eye, MN, p. A347
DAHLHAUSEN, Daniel J., M.D. President of Medical Staff/Chief Medical Officer, Cannon Memorial Hospital, Pickens, SC, p. A564
DAHLING, James D., President and Chief Executive Officer, Children's Hospital of The King's Daughters, Norfolk, VA, p. A669
DAHLSTRAND, David, Associate Chief of Staff Information Technology, Hunter Holmes McGuire Veterans Affairs Medical Center–Richmond, Richmond, VA, p. A672
DAHLSTROM, Josiah, Administrator, Safe Haven Hospital of Pocatello, Pocatello, ID, p. A176
DAIGLE, Charles D.
Senior Vice President and Chief Operating Officer, Willis–Knighton Medical Center, Shreveport, LA, p. A285
Chief Operating Officer, WK Bossier Health Center, Bossier City, LA, p. A271
DAIGLE, Cindy, Chief Financial Officer, Northern Maine Medical Center, Fort Kent, ME, p. A290
DAIGLE, J. Barry, Manager Information Systems, University Hospital and Clinics, Lafayette, LA, p. A278
DAIGLE, Richard, Director Information Technology, Manchester Memorial Hospital, Manchester, CT, p. A112
DAIKEN, Michael E., Chief Financial Officer, Highlands–Cashiers Hospital, Highlands, NC, p. A462
DAIKER, David, Chief Information Resource Management, Veterans Affairs Nebraska–Western Iowa Health Care System – Lincoln, Lincoln, NE, p. A394
DAILEY, Gina, Chief Financial Officer, Pinnacle Pointe Hospital, Little Rock, AR, p. A47
DAILEY, Jacqueline, Chief Information Officer, West Penn Hospital, Pittsburgh, PA, p. A547
DAILEY, Richard R., D.O. President Medical Staff, Ellett Memorial Hospital, Appleton City, MO, p. A363
DAISLEY, Samuel, D.O. Vice President Medical Affairs, UPMC Horizon, Greenville, PA, p. A535
DAJCZAK, Stanislaw, M.D. Chief of Staff, ProMedica Defiance Regional Hospital, Defiance, OH, p. A488
DALBY, William, Director Fiscal Services, Shriners Hospitals for Children–Northern California, Sacramento, CA, p. A84
DALE, Jackson, Director Management Information Services, Johnston Memorial Hospital, Abingdon, VA, p. A662
DALE, Jae, Chief Executive Officer, Oro Valley Hospital, Oro Valley, AZ, p. A34
DALEBOUT, Kenneth, Administrator and Chief Executive Officer, Arroyo Grande Community Hospital, Arroyo Grande, CA, p. A54
DALEY, Kathy, R.N. Chief Nursing Officer, Doctors Hospital of Manteca, Manteca, CA, p. A74
DALEY, Linda, Vice President Human Resources, Oswego Hospital, Oswego, NY, p. A447
DALEY, Robert, Vice President Fiscal and Information Technology Services, Black River Memorial Hospital, Black River Falls, WI, p. A698
DALGAI, Netrisha, Director of Operations, Sage Memorial Hospital, Ganado, AZ, p. A31
DALL, Jamie, Chief Financial Officer, New Hampshire Hospital, Concord, NH, p. A405
DALLER, Sue, R.N. Assistant Administrator Nursing, Hermann Area District Hospital, Hermann, MO, p. A368
DALLEY, Mark F., Administrator, Gunnison Valley Hospital, Gunnison, UT, p. A655
DALLIS, Donna, R.N. Vice President Patient Care, Northeastern Health System, Tahlequah, OK, p. A515
DALPOAS, Dolan, President and Chief Executive Officer, Abraham Lincoln Memorial Hospital, Lincoln, IL, p. A193
DALTON, Deana, Human Resources, San Juan Hospital, Monticello, UT, p. A655
DALTON, Eric
Chief Financial Officer, Memorial Medical Center, Modesto, CA, p. A75
Chief Financial Officer, Sutter Tracy Community Hospital, Tracy, CA, p. A94
DALTON, John, President and Chief Executive Officer, Inland Hospital, Waterville, ME, p. A292
DALTON, Valerie, R.N., Administrator, Oceans Behavioral Hospital of Baton Rouge, Baton Rouge, LA, p. A269
DALTON, Wayne, Chief Financial Officer, Lakeview Hospital, Bountiful, UT, p. A654
DALY, Cindy, R.N. Director of Nursing, Syringa Hospital and Clinics, Grangeville, ID, p. A174
DALY, Derek, Chief Executive Officer, Liberty Medical Center, Chester, MT, p. A382
DALY, Gail, Chief Nursing Officer and Chief Operating Officer, St. Mary Medical Center, Long Beach, CA, p. A68
DALY, Sheila, MS, President and Chief Executive Officer, Clinton Hospital, Clinton, MA, p. A306
DALY, Thomas M., Chief Financial Officer, University Hospital, Newark, NJ, p. A415
DALY, William, Chief Executive Officer, Pennsylvania Psychiatric Institute, Harrisburg, PA, p. A535
DAMA, Sunil, M.D. Medical Director, Select Specialty Hospital – Cincinnati North, Cincinnati, OH, p. A483
DAMBOISE, Robin, Director Human Resources, Northern Maine Medical Center, Fort Kent, ME, p. A290
DAMICO, Donna, Director Human Resources, Carolinas Hospital System, Florence, SC, p. A560
DAMM, Julie, Chief Financial Officer, Hancock County Health System, Britt, IA, p. A223
DAMMEYER, Matt, Ph.D. Chief Operating Officer, Central Peninsula General Hospital, Soldotna, AK, p. A29
DAMODARAN, A. N., M.D. President Medical Staff, Indiana University Health Starke Hospital, Knox, IN, p. A213
DAMON, Chad, Contractor, St. Vincent Dunn Hospital, Bedford, IN, p. A204
DAMON, Kerry, Director Human Resources, Baystate Franklin Medical Center, Greenfield, MA, p. A307
DAMRON, Greg, Vice President Finance and Chief Financial Officer, Georgia Regents Medical Center, Augusta, GA, p. A151
DAMSCHRODER, Robin
Chief Operating Officer, St. Joseph Mercy Ann Arbor, Ypsilanti, MI, p. A333
Chief Operating Officer, St. Joseph Mercy Livingston Hospital, Howell, MI, p. A322
DANBDALA, Kayyan, M.D. Medical Director, Schick Shadel Hospital, Seattle, WA, p. A683
DANCER, Stephanie, Manager Human Resources, Pauls Valley General Hospital, Pauls Valley, OK, p. A513
DANCH, Stephen M., Chief Financial Officer, UPMC Hamot, Erie, PA, p. A534
DANDRIDGE, Thomas C., FACHE, President and Chief Executive Officer, Regional Medical Center, Orangeburg, SC, p. A564
DANE, Jeff, Executive Vice President and Chief Financial Officer, University Medical Center, Lubbock, TX, p. A630
DANELLO, Sherry, MS
Vice President and Chief Nursing Officer, Candler Hospital, Savannah, GA, p. A164
Vice President and Chief Nursing Officer, St. Joseph's Hospital, Savannah, GA, p. A164
DANG, Cynthia, Vice President Human Resources, North Hills Hospital, North Richland Hills, TX, p. A634
DANG, Minh, Vice President Finance, Robert Packer Hospital, Sayre, PA, p. A549
DANG–DO, Mihn, Chief Financial Officer, Shands Live Oak Regional Medical Center, Live Oak, FL, p. A132
DANGERFIELD, Wesley, Community Chief Executive Officer, Summers County ARH Hospital, Hinton, WV, p. A691
DANIEL, Christopher W., Administrator, Sterling Surgical Hospital, Slidell, LA, p. A285
DANIEL, Dena, Director Information Systems, Jackson County Memorial Hospital, Altus, OK, p. A503
DANIEL, Karen, Chief Executive Officer, Warm Springs Medical Center, Warm Springs, GA, p. A167
DANIEL, Lisa, Chief Executive Officer, Memphis Mental Health Institute, Memphis, TN, p. A583
DANIEL, Patricia, Chief Information Officer, Lake Whitney Medical Center, Whitney, TX, p. A652
DANIEL, Ron, Manager Information Systems, Matheny Medical and Educational Center, Peapack, NJ, p. A416
DANIEL, S., M.D. Chief Medical Officer, Spring Valley Hospital Medical Center, Las Vegas, NV, p. A402
DANIEL, Steven G., Senior Vice President and Chief Operating Officer, CHRISTUS Spohn Hospital Alice, Alice, TX, p. A590
DANIEL, Troy, Chief Human Resources Officer, Forrest General Hospital, Hattiesburg, MS, p. A354
DANIEL, Vera W., Chief Human Resources Officer, SSM Health Saint Louis University Hospital, Saint Louis, MO, p. A377
DANIEL, W. D., D.O. Chief of Staff, Medical Center of Manchester, Manchester, TN, p. A582
DANIELS, Alex, Chief Nurse Executive, U. S. Public Health Service Indian Hospital, Crownpoint, NM, p. A424
DANIELS, Andy
Vice President Non–Clinical Operations and Information Systems, Avita Galion Hospital, Galion, OH, p. A490
Chief Operating Officer, Bucyrus Community Hospital, Bucyrus, OH, p. A480
DANIELS, Anita, Executive Director, New York City Children's Center, NY, p. A442
DANIELS, Betty, M.D. Chief of Staff, St. Bernardine Medical Center, San Bernardino, CA, p. A86
DANIELS, Craig M., Chief Financial Officer, Moab Regional Hospital, Moab, UT, p. A655
DANIELS, Don, M.D. Chief Medical Officer, Rollins–Brook Community Hospital, Lampasas, TX, p. A627
DANIELS, Don, Executive Vice President and Chief Operating Officer, SwedishAmerican Hospital, A Division of UW Health, Rockford, IL, p. A200
DANIELS, Jeff
Chief Financial Officer, Bingham Memorial Hospital, Blackfoot, ID, p. A172
Chief Financial Officer, Mountain River Birthing and Surgery Center, Blackfoot, ID, p. A172
DANIELS, John, M.D. Medical Director, LifeCare Hospitals of Wisconsin, Pewaukee, WI, p. A709
DANIELS, Judy, Vice President Human Resources, Our Lady of Bellefonte Hospital, Ashland, KY, p. A254
DANIELS, Karen, MSN Chief Nursing Officer, Halifax Regional Medical Center, Roanoke Rapids, NC, p. A467
DANIELS, Kristin, Manager Human Resources, Sutter Center for Psychiatry, Sacramento, CA, p. A85
DANIELS, Lee, Chief Financial Officer, Horsham Clinic, Ambler, PA, p. A528
DANIELS, Mark, M.D. Vice President Physician Enterprise, Northwestern Medicine Delnor Hospital, Geneva, IL, p. A189
DANIELS, S. Janette, Director Human Resources, HEALTHSOUTH Rehabilitation Hospital of Fort Smith, Fort Smith, AR, p. A44
DANIELS, Sarah, Vice President, Information Technology, Mayo Clinic Health System in Mankato, Mankato, MN, p. A341
DANIELS, Todd, M.D. Medical Director, HEALTHSOUTH Rehabilitation Hospital of Arlington, Arlington, TX, p. A592
DANIELSEN, Marsha, Director Information Systems, Good Samaritan Hospital, Vincennes, IN, p. A221
DANIELSON, Carol, R.N. Senior Vice President and Chief Nursing Officer, Gwinnett Hospital System, Lawrenceville, GA, p. A160
DANIELSON, David S., Senior Vice President Operations, EvergreenHealth, Kirkland, WA, p. A680
DANKER, Doug, Administrator, Mercy Hospital El Reno, El Reno, OK, p. A506

Index of Health Care Professionals

Index of Health Care Professionals / Dankert


DANKERT, Sheri
Chief Financial Officer, Mayo Clinic Health System in Albert Lea, Albert Lea, MN, p. A334
Vice President Finance, Mayo Clinic Health System–Albert Lea and Austin, Austin, MN, p. A335
DANKO, Douglas, President and Chief Executive Officer, Jameson Hospital, New Castle, PA, p. A541
DANN, Doreen, R.N. Chief Operating Officer, Victor Valley Global Medical Center, Victorville, CA, p. A96
DANNENBERG, Walt, Interim Director, Amarillo Veterans Affairs Health Care System, Amarillo, TX, p. A591
DANOWSKI, Dale G., R.N. Senior Vice President Chief Operating Officer and Chief Nursing Officer, St. Vincent's Medical Center, Bridgeport, CT, p. A111
DANSBY, Tommy, Chief Medical Officer, Liberty Healthcare Systems, Bastrop, LA, p. A269
DANTIS, Gerry, Assistant Vice President Finance, SUNY Downstate Medical Center University Hospital, NY, p. A444
DANUSER, James, Chief Information Officer, Veterans Affairs Central Iowa Health Care System, Des Moines, IA, p. A227
DAOUD, Joudat, M.D. Chief of Staff, Community Health Center of Branch County, Coldwater, MI, p. A317
DAQUIOAG, Francis, Controller, Kahuku Medical Center, Kahuku, HI, p. A169
DARBONNE, Tina, Chief Financial Officer, Central Louisiana State Hospital, Pineville, LA, p. A283
DARBY, Kristin, Chief Information Officer, Eastern Regional Medical Center, Philadelphia, PA, p. A543
DARBY, Sharon, R.N. Vice President, Clinical Operations, Children's Hospital of Richmond at VCU–Brook Road Campus, Richmond, VA, p. A671
DARCEY, Patricia, R.N. Vice President/Chief Nursing Officer, Southampton Hospital, Southampton, NY, p. A450
DARDANO, Anthony, M.D. Chief Medical Officer, Delray Medical Center, Delray Beach, FL, p. A125
DARDEAU, Sean T., FACHE Chief Executive Officer, Mary Black Health System – Spartanburg, Spartanburg, SC, p. A565
DARDEN, David B., Chief Executive Officer, Raleigh General Hospital, Beckley, WV, p. A689
DAREY, Roland, M.D. Medical Director, Wamego Health Center, Wamego, KS, p. A252
DARLING, Cory, Chief Operating Officer, TriStar Hendersonville Medical Center, Hendersonville, TN, p. A578
DARLING, Rudy, Chief Operating Officer, Baxter Regional Medical Center, Mountain Home, AR, p. A48
DARNAUER, Patricia, Medical Center Commander, Carl R. Darnall Army Medical Center, Fort Hood, TX, p. A612
DARNELL, Brian, D.O. Chief of Staff, Johnson County Healthcare Center, Buffalo, WY, p. A715
DARNELL, Don, Chief Information Officer, Hamilton Memorial Hospital District, McLeansboro, IL, p. A194
DARNELL, Gerald K., PsyD, Acting Medical Center Director, Oklahoma City Veterans Affairs Medical Center, Oklahoma City, OK, p. A512
DARNELL, Linda, Director Management Information Systems, King's Daughters' Health, Madison, IN, p. A215
DARNELL, Vicki A., MSN, Chief Executive Officer, Ephraim McDowell Fort Logan Hospital, Stanford, KY, p. A266
DARNELL, Vicki A., MSN, President and Chief Executive Officer, Ephraim McDowell Health, Danville, KY, p. B54
DARNELL, Vicki A., MSN, President and Chief Executive Officer, Ephraim McDowell Regional Medical Center, Danville, KY, p. A256
DARRINGTON, Gilbert, Director Human Resources, Jackson Hospital and Clinic, Montgomery, AL, p. A23
DARVIN, Ken, M.D. Chief of Staff, Stroud Regional Medical Center, Stroud, OK, p. A515
DASARO, Lynda, Director Human Resources, Sutter Roseville Medical Center, Roseville, CA, p. A84
DASCANI, Jimmy, Chief Executive Officer, Landmark Hospital of Southwest Florida, Naples, FL, p. A136
DASCENZO, Douglas R., R.N., Chief Executive Officer, Select Specialty Hospital–Downriver, Wyandotte, MI, p. A332
DASCHER Jr., Norman E.
Chief Executive Officer, Samaritan Hospital, Troy, NY, p. A452
Chief Executive Officer, St. Mary's Hospital, Troy, NY, p. A452
DASHIELD, Luanne G., Personnel Administrator, Deer's Head Hospital Center, Salisbury, MD, p. A300
DASHIELL, Stacy, M.D. Chief of Staff, Hospital District One of Rice County, Lyons, KS, p. A245
DASKALAKIS, Tom G., Chief Operating Officer, West Chester Hospital, West Chester, OH, p. A500
DASS, Karla, Director Human Resources, Regional General Hospital, Williston, FL, p. A147
DASSENKO, Dennis, Chief Information Officer, Essentia Health Duluth, Duluth, MN, p. A337
DAUBERT, Stephanie
Chief Financial Officer, Nebraska Medicine – Bellevue, Bellevue, NE, p. A390
Chief Financial Officer, Nebraska Medicine – Nebraska Medical Center, Omaha, NE, p. A396
DAUBY, Randall W., CPA, Chief Executive Officer, Pinckneyville Community Hospital, Pinckneyville, IL, p. A198
DAUGHDRILL, Diane, Director Human Resources, Jefferson Davis Community Hospital, Prentiss, MS, p. A359
DAUGHERTY, Alan
Interim Chief Executive Officer, Ennis Regional Medical Center, Ennis, TX, p. A612
Interim Chief Executive Officer, Parkview Regional Hospital, Mexia, TX, p. A632
DAUGHERTY, Bart, Interim Administrator, Carnegie Tri–County Municipal Hospital, Carnegie, OK, p. A504
DAUGHERTY, Beth Ann, R.N. Vice President Care Services and Chief Nursing Executive, Sparrow Clinton Hospital, Saint Johns, MI, p. A329
DAUGHERTY, Don, Director Information Systems, Fleming County Hospital, Flemingsburg, KY, p. A256
DAUGHERTY, Marney, Worklife Services Consultant, Brighton Center for Recovery, Brighton, MI, p. A315
DAUGHERTY, Stephen J., Chief Executive Officer, Coliseum Northside Hospital, Macon, GA, p. A160
DAUGHTRY, Kaci, Director Human Resources, Andalusia Regional Hospital, Andalusia, AL, p. A15
DAUM, Karen, R.N. Vice President and Chief Nursing Officer, Passavant Area Hospital, Jacksonville, IL, p. A191
DAUTERIVE, F. Ralph, M.D. Vice President Medical Affairs, Ochsner Medical Center–Baton Rouge, Baton Rouge, LA, p. A269
DAUZ, Urbano, M.D. President Medical Staff, Shelby Memorial Hospital, Shelbyville, IL, p. A200
DAVE, Bhasker J., M.D., Superintendent, Mental Health Institute, Independence, IA, p. A229
DAVE', Rajesh J., M.D. Executive Vice President and Chief Medical Officer, United Health Services Hospitals–Binghamton, Binghamton, NY, p. A430
DAVENPORT, David, Director Human Resources, Washington County Hospital, Nashville, IL, p. A196
DAVENPORT, Douglas
Senior Vice President and Chief Financial Officer, St. John's Hospital, Maplewood, MN, p. A342
Senior Vice President and Chief Financial Officer, St. Joseph's Hospital, Saint Paul, MN, p. A346
Senior Vice President and Chief Financial Officer, Woodwinds Health Campus, Woodbury, MN, p. A349
DAVENPORT, Ginger, Director Human Resources, Promise Hospital of Dallas, Dallas, TX, p. A606
DAVENPORT, Michael, M.D. Vice President Medical Affairs, Methodist Hospitals, Gary, IN, p. A209
DAVENPORT, Paula, Chief Nursing Officer, Princeton Baptist Medical Center, Birmingham, AL, p. A16
DAVENPORT, Polly J., R.N., President, CHI St. Vincent Infirmary, CHI St. Vincent Infirmary Medical Center, Little Rock, AR, p. A47
DAVENPORT, Polly J., FACHE President, CHI St. Vincent Infirmary, CHI St. Vincent Infirmary Medical Center, Little Rock, AR, p. A47
DAVENPORT, Polly J., R.N., President, CHI St. Vincent Medical Center–North, Sherwood, AR, p. A50
DAVENPORT, Sally M., MS Chief Nursing Officer and Chief Operating Officer, Ephraim McDowell Regional Medical Center, Danville, KY, p. A256
DAVES, Ronnie, Chief Executive Officer, North Okaloosa Medical Center, Crestview, FL, p. A124
DAVID, Biff, R.N., Administrator, St. Landry Extended Care Hospital, Opelousas, LA, p. A283
DAVID, Daphne, Chief Operating Officer, Garden Park Medical Center, Gulfport, MS, p. A353
DAVID, Lim, Vice President Finance and Chief Financial Officer, St. Joseph Regional Health Network, Reading, PA, p. A548
DAVID, Michelle, Chief Executive Officer, Valley Hospital Phoenix, Phoenix, AZ, p. A36
DAVID, R. Neal, Administrator and Chief of Staff, Madigan Healthcare System, Tacoma, WA, p. A686
DAVID, Robert G., President, UH Regional Hospitals, Cleveland, OH, p. A485
DAVIDOFF, Ravin, M.D. Chief Medical Officer, Boston Medical Center, Boston, MA, p. A303
DAVIDOW, Daniel N., M.D. Medical Director, Cumberland Hospital, New Kent, VA, p. A668
DAVIDSON, Camille, Director Human Resources, Stanton County Hospital, Johnson, KS, p. A242
DAVIDSON, Craig Val
Chief Executive Officer and Administrator, Beaver Valley Hospital, Beaver, UT, p. A654
Chief Executive Officer, Milford Valley Memorial Hospital, Milford, UT, p. A655
DAVIDSON, Diane, Senior Vice President Human Resources, Essentia Health Duluth, Duluth, MN, p. A337
DAVIDSON, Elizabeth, R.N. Vice President, Patient Care Services, OSF Saint James – John W. Albrecht Medical Center, Pontiac, IL, p. A198
DAVIDSON, Gary, Senior Vice President and Chief Information Officer, Lancaster General Health, Lancaster, PA, p. A537
DAVIDSON, Gary, M.D. Medical Director, Select Specialty Hospital–Johnstown, Johnstown, PA, p. A537
DAVIDSON, Gregg Agustin, FACHE, Chief Executive Officer, Skagit Valley Hospital, Mount Vernon, WA, p. A681
DAVIDSON, James, Director of Information Services, Ferry County Memorial Hospital, Republic, WA, p. A683
DAVIDSON, James F., Chief Operating Officer, EASTAR Health System, Muskogee, OK, p. A510
DAVIDSON, James N., Troop Commander, Tripler Army Medical Center, Honolulu, HI, p. A169
DAVIDSON, John, Vice President Human Resources, Sharon Regional Health System, Sharon, PA, p. A550
DAVIDSON, Nancy, Senior Vice President and Chief Financial Officer, Jackson County Memorial Hospital, Altus, OK, p. A503
DAVIDSON, Paulette, FACHE Chief Experience Officer, Nebraska Medicine – Bellevue, Bellevue, NE, p. A390
DAVIDSON, Rocky, Chief Financial Officer, Larkin Behavioral Health Services, FL, p. A128
DAVIDSON, Rowena, Manager Business Office, AMG Specialty Hospital–Edmond, Edmond, OK, p. A506
DAVIDSON, Sammi, Administrative Director, Sanford Bagley Medical Center, Bagley, MN, p. A335
DAVIDSON, Stephen, Director Human Resources, Lafayette Regional Health Center, Lexington, MO, p. A372
DAVIDSON, Stuart, President Medical Staff, Mount Desert Island Hospital, Bar Harbor, ME, p. A288
DAVIDSON, Tim, M.D. Chief Executive Physician Services, Providence St. Mary Medical Center, Walla Walla, WA, p. A687
DAVIDSON, Tori, R.N. Chief Nursing Officer, Tsehootsooi Medical Center, Fort Defiance, AZ, p. A31
DAVIES, Janie, Chief Financial Officer, New Mexico Rehabilitation Center, Roswell, NM, p. A426
DAVILA, Susan, Chief Executive Officer and Administrator, Carson Valley Medical Center, Gardnerville, NV, p. A400
DAVIN, Joni, Director Information and Business Management Service Line, Veterans Affairs Eastern Kansas Health Care System, Topeka, KS, p. A251
DAVINI, John, Vice President, St. Rose Hospital, Hayward, CA, p. A64
DAVIS, Adam
Director Information Technology, Cornerstone Hospital of SouthEast Arizona, Tucson, AZ, p. A39
Chief Information Officer, Cornerstone Hospital–West Monroe, West Monroe, LA, p. A286
Chief Information Officer, Solara Hospital Harlingen, Harlingen, TX, p. A618
DAVIS, Amelia, Director of Nursing, CrossRidge Community Hospital, Wynne, AR, p. A52
DAVIS, Andrea, Chief Executive Officer, HEALTHSOUTH Desert Canyon Rehabilitation Hospital, Las Vegas, NV, p. A402
DAVIS Jr., Andrew L., Interim Chief Executive Officer, United Medical Center, Washington, DC, p. A120
DAVIS, Anne, Director Human Resources, Mason District Hospital, Havana, IL, p. A190
DAVIS, Astrid, R.N. Chief Nursing Officer, York Hospital, York, PA, p. A554
DAVIS, Autherine, Director Human Resources, D. W. McMillan Memorial Hospital, Brewton, AL, p. A17
DAVIS, Barry L., FACHE, President and Chief Executive Officer, Arkansas Methodist Medical Center, Paragould, AR, p. A49
DAVIS, Betty, Director Administrative Services, Porterville Developmental Center, Porterville, CA, p. A81
DAVIS, Brenda, R.N. Vice President of Patient Services, Indiana University Health Bedford Hospital, Bedford, IN, p. A204
DAVIS, Brent
Human Resources Team Leader, Arkansas Heart Hospital, Little Rock, AR, p. A47
Chief Financial Officer, Avista Adventist Hospital, Louisville, CO, p. A107
Chief Financial Officer, Central Valley Medical Center, Nephi, UT, p. A656
DAVIS, C.J., Chief Executive Officer/ Executive Director, Four County Counseling Center, Logansport, IN, p. A215
DAVIS, Cathy J.
Director Human Resources, ProMedica Bixby Hospital, Adrian, MI, p. A314
Director Human Resources, ProMedica Herrick Hospital, Tecumseh, MI, p. A331
DAVIS, Charlotte C., Director Human Resources, Lincoln Trail Behavioral Health System, Radcliff, KY, p. A265


A820 Index of Health Care Professionals 

DE LEON, Aurea, Chief Human Resources Officer, Hospital Universitario Dr. Ramon Ruiz Arnau, Bayamon, PR, p. A720

DE LEON, Darcy, Executive Director, Human Resources, Frank R. Howard Memorial Hospital, Willits, CA, p. A98

DE LEON, Dennis, M.D. Associate Chief Medical Officer and Vice President Medical Affairs, Highline Medical Center, Burien, WA, p. A677

DE LOS REYES, Jay
Chief Operating Officer, HEALTHSOUTH Sunrise Rehabilitation Hospital, Sunrise, FL, p. A143
Chief Operating Officer, Trumbull Memorial Hospital, Warren, OH, p. A499

DE LOS SANTOS, Conrad, President Medical Staff, Medical West, Bessemer, AL, p. A16

DE ONIS, Luis, Interim Chief Human Resources Officer, Stony Brook University Medical Center, Stony Brook, NY, p. A451

DE PALO, Vera, M.D. Chief Medical Officer, Signature Healthcare Brockton Hospital, Brockton, MA, p. A305

DE PASQUALE, Edward, Chief Financial Officer, Conemaugh Memorial Medical Center, Johnstown, PA, p. A537

DE PIANO, Linda, Ph.D., Chief Executive Officer, Jerome Golden Center for Behavioral Health, Inc., West Palm Beach, FL, p. A147

DE PREZ, Bernadette, Chief Operating Officer, Skyridge Medical Center, Cleveland, TN, p. A576

DE ROSIER, Colleen, Coordinator Human Resource, Spearfish Regional Hospital, Spearfish, SD, p. A572

DE SANTIAGO, Elizabeth, Director, Hospital Psiquiatrico Metropolitano, Cabo Rojo, PR, p. A720

DE TORRES, Francisco, M.D. Medical Director, Ashford Presbyterian Community Hospital, San Juan, PR, p. A723

DEAK, Terry, Chief Financial Officer, Lodi Memorial Hospital, Lodi, CA, p. A67

DEAKYNE, John R., Chief Financial Officer, Saint Mary's Regional Medical Center, Reno, NV, p. A404

DEAL, Jennifer, Chief Financial Officer, Greeley County Health Services, Tribune, KS, p. A251

DEAL, Lisa, Budget Analyst, U. S. Public Health Service Indian Hospital, Eagle Butte, SD, p. A568

DEAN, Amanda, Human Resources Officer, Ralph H. Johnson Veterans Affairs Medical Center, Charleston, SC, p. A558

DEAN, Donna, Chief Financial Officer, Rainbow Mental Health Facility, Kansas City, KS, p. A243

DEAN, Douglas B., Chief Human Resources Officer, Children's of Alabama, Birmingham, AL, p. A16

DEAN, Harrison M., FACHE,
Senior Vice President and Administrator, Baptist Health Medical Center – North Little Rock, North Little Rock, AR, p. A49
Interim Administrator, Baptist Health Medical Center–Stuttgart, Stuttgart, AR, p. A51

DEAN, Joel, Director Information Services, Piedmont Medical Center, Rock Hill, SC, p. A564

DEAN, Laura, Director Human Resources, Wilson Medical Center, Neodesha, KS, p. A246

DEAN, Lloyd H., President and Chief Executive Officer, Dignity Health, San Francisco, CA, p. B50

DEAN, Megan, Director Human Resources, South Bay Hospital, Sun City Center, FL, p. A143

DEAN, Morre
Chief Executive Officer, Parker Adventist Hospital, Parker, CO, p. A107
Chief Executive Officer, Porter Adventist Hospital, Denver, CO, p. A102

DEAN, Thomas, M.D. Chief of Staff, Avera Weskota Memorial Hospital, Wessington Springs, SD, p. A573

DEANE, Leslie, Chief Executive Officer, Select Specialty Hospital–Winston-Salem, Winston-Salem, NC, p. A471

DEANS, Ken, Chief Information Officer, Chesapeake Regional Medical Center, Chesapeake, VA, p. A663

DEAO, Ellen, Director Information Services, CHI Health Creighton University Medical Center, Omaha, NE, p. A395

DEARDORFF, John A., Chief Executive Officer, Reston Hospital Center, Reston, VA, p. A671

DEARMOND, Karl, Director Information Systems, Geary Community Hospital, Junction City, KS, p. A243

DEARY, Shirley, Director Human Resources, Glenbeigh Hospital and Outpatient Centers, Rock Creek, OH, p. A497

DEATER, Gary A., Vice President Administration, Human Resources and Risk Management, Witham Memorial Hospital, Lebanon, IN, p. A215

DEATHERAGE, Karen, Director of Nursing, Russell Regional Hospital, Russell, KS, p. A249

DEATON, David, Chief Executive Officer, Ozark Health Medical Center, Clinton, AR, p. A42

DEATON, Eric, Executive Vice President, Chief Operating Officer and Corporate Operating, Wellmont Hancock County Hospital, Sneedville, TN, p. A588

DEATON, Mike, Chief Financial Officer, Ozark Health Medical Center, Clinton, AR, p. A42

DEATON, Timothy, Chief Executive Officer, Plum Creek Specialty Hospital, Amarillo, TX, p. A591

DEBBAS, Elias, M.D. President Medical Staff, Fort Washington Medical Center, Oxen Hill, MD, p. A299

DEBEVEC, Teresa, Chief Executive Officer, Cook Hospital and Convalescent Nursing Care Unit, Cook, MN, p. A337

DEBLASIS, John, Vice President, Belmont Community Hospital, Bellaire, OH, p. A479

DEBLIEUX, Dawna, Vice President Patient Care Services and Chief Nurse Executive, Natchitoches Regional Medical Center, Natchitoches, LA, p. A281

DEBLOIS, Georgean, M.D. Chairman Medical Staff, Chippenham Hospital, Richmond, VA, p. A671

DEBOER, Cynthia D., Chief Financial Officer, Cedar Springs Hospital, Colorado Springs, CO, p. A100

DEBOER, K. C., President and Chief Executive Officer, Jamestown Regional Medical Center, Jamestown, ND, p. A475

DEBOOY, Ann, R.N. Chief Nursing Officer, Memorial Medical Center, Las Cruces, NM, p. A425

DEBORD, Thomas, Chief Operating Officer, Overlake Medical Center, Bellevue, WA, p. A676

DECELIS, Lori, Director Human Resources, Hampton Behavioral Health Center, Westampton, NJ, p. A420

DECELL, Daniela, Chief Executive Officer, Las Colinas Medical Center, Irving, TX, p. A624

DECHABERT, Rebecca, Acting Director Personnel, New York State Psychiatric Institute, New York, NY, p. A443

DECHAIRO–MARINO, Ann, R.N. Chief Nursing Officer, Providence Holy Cross Medical Center, CA, p. A72

DECHANT, David, Chief Human Resources Officer, Tomah Veterans Affairs Medical Center, Tomah, WI, p. A712

DECKARD, Rick, Chief Fiscal Service, Chillicothe Veterans Affairs Medical Center, Chillicothe, OH, p. A482

DECKARD, Steven D., Vice President Human Resources, Indiana University Health Bloomington Hospital, Bloomington, IN, p. A205

DECKER, Janet, Assistant Vice President, MedStar Union Memorial Hospital, Baltimore, MD, p. A294

DECKER, Jeanine, Manager Human Resources, Arizona State Hospital, Phoenix, AZ, p. A34

DECKER, Kathy, Interim Chief Nursing Officer, Northern Inyo Hospital, Bishop, CA, p. A56

DECKER, Kevin, Chief Executive Officer, Forrest City Medical Center, Forrest City, AR, p. A44

DECKER, Michael, President and Chief Executive Officer, Divine Savior Healthcare, Portage, WI, p. A709

DECORTE, Raymond P., M.D. Chief Medical Officer, East Jefferson General Hospital, Metairie, LA, p. A280

DECOUX, Bobby, Assistant Vice President Human Resources, WellStar Kennestone Hospital, Marietta, GA, p. A161

DECREMER, Dean, Chief Information Officer, Dickinson County Healthcare System, Iron Mountain, MI, p. A322

DEDECKER, Troy, FACHE, Chief Executive Officer, Mid–America Rehabilitation Hospital, Shawnee Mission, KS, p. A250

DEE, Thomas A., Chief Executive Officer, Southwestern Vermont Medical Center, Bennington, VT, p. A660

DEEMER, Miriam, Chief Executive Officer, Select Specialty Hospital–Grosse Pointe, Grosse Pointe, MI, p. A321

DEEN, Cody, Chief of Medical Staff, Chatham Hospital, Siler City, NC, p. A468

DEERING, Linda, R.N., President, Advocate Sherman Hospital, Elgin, IL, p. A187

DEERING, Lisa, Administrator, Heatherhill Care Communities, Chardon, OH, p. A481

DEES, Edith, Vice President Information Services and Chief Information Officer, Holy Spirit – A Geisinger Affiliate, Camp Hill, PA, p. A530

DEFAUW, Thomas D., FACHE, President and Chief Executive Officer, McLaren Port Huron, Port Huron, MI, p. A328

DEFAYE, Yael, Director, Information Technology, Rio Grande Hospital, Del Norte, CO, p. A101

DEFOORE, Richard G., FACHE, Chief Executive Officer, Stamford Memorial Hospital, Stamford, TX, p. A645

DEFORD, Drexel, Chief Information Officer, Scripps Mercy Hospital, San Diego, CA, p. A87

DEFRANCESCO, Anthony, Associate Director, VA Long Beach Healthcare System, Long Beach, CA, p. A68

DEFREECE, Todd, Vice President Operations, CHI Health Creighton University Medical Center, Omaha, NE, p. A395

DEFURIO, Ken, President and Chief Executive Officer, Butler Health System, Butler, PA, p. A530

DEGEAR, David O., M.D. Vice President Medical Affairs, Westfields Hospital, New Richmond, WI, p. A708

DEGENNARO, Vincent, M.D. Chief of Staff, Miami Veterans Affairs Healthcare System, Miami, FL, p. A134

DEGINA, Anthony M., President and Chief Executive Officer, Largo Medical Center, Largo, FL, p. A132

DEGLANDON, Frances, Chief Financial Officer, Bunkie General Hospital, Bunkie, LA, p. A271

DEGRAND, Robert, Chief Information Officer, Froedtert Memorial Lutheran Hospital, Milwaukee, WI, p. A706

DEGRAVELLE, Eric, Director Human Resources, Thibodaux Regional Medical Center, Thibodaux, LA, p. A286

DEGROFF, James, Vice President Technology and Network Services, St. Mary's Healthcare, Amsterdam, NY, p. A428

DEGROOT, Daniel, Chief Executive Officer, HSHS St. Clare Memorial Hospital, Oconto Falls, WI, p. A708

DEGROOT, Randy, President and Chief Executive Officer, Community Health Center of Branch County, Coldwater, MI, p. A317

DEHAVEN, Bryce, Chief Financial Officer, Medical Center of Aurora, Aurora, CO, p. A99

DEHNING, Cielo, M.D. Medical Director, Mid–America Rehabilitation Hospital, Shawnee Mission, KS, p. A250

DEIBEL, Justin, Senior Vice President and Chief Financial Officer, Mercy Medical Center, Baltimore, MD, p. A294

DEICH, Faye L., R.N. Senior Vice President Division Operations; Chief Operating Officer, Sacred Heart Hospital, Eau Claire, WI, p. A700

DEIS, Terrence G., FACHE, Chief Executive Officer, Saint Joseph – London, London, KY, p. A260

DEITERING, Stacey, Administrative Director of Finance, Lima Memorial Health System, Lima, OH, p. A492

DEITRICK, Diana, Director Information Services, Devereux Hospital and Children's Center of Florida, Melbourne, FL, p. A133

DEITZEN, Denise M., Director, Veterans Affairs Northern Indiana Health Care System, Fort Wayne, IN, p. A209

DEJACO, Lynn S., Chief Financial Officer, FirstHealth Moore Regional Hospital, Pinehurst, NC, p. A466

DEJESUS, David, Senior Vice President Human Resources, Southcoast Hospitals Group, Fall River, MA, p. A306

DEJONG, Tyler
Senior Director of Finance, CHI Health Lakeside, Omaha, NE, p. A396
Senior Director of Finance, CHI Health Midlands, Papillion, NE, p. A397

DEKASTLE, Reuben J., Chief Nursing Officer, Weiser Memorial Hospital, Weiser, ID, p. A177

DEKEYZER, Ron, Regional Director Information Systems, CHRISTUS St. Vincent Regional Medical Center, Santa Fe, NM, p. A426

DEKOK, Joni, Chief Nursing Officer, Sanford Sheldon Medical Center, Sheldon, IA, p. A234

DEKONING, Bernard L., M.D. Chief of Staff, Wm. Jennings Bryan Dorn Veterans Affairs Medical Center, Columbia, SC, p. A560

DEKREY, Dale, MS Associate Director Operations and Resources, Fargo Veterans Affairs Health Care System, Fargo, ND, p. A473

DEKREY, Daniel, M.D. Chief of Staff, Sanford Bemidji Medical Center, Bemidji, MN, p. A335

DEKRUSE, Jet L., Administrator, Humboldt County Mental Health, Eureka, CA, p. A60

DEL BOCCIO, Suzanne, MS Chief Nursing Officer and Vice President Patient Care Services, Indiana University Health North Hospital, Carmel, IN, p. A206

DEL CASTILLO, Daniel, Chief Executive Officer, HEALTHSOUTH Rehabilitation Hospital of San Juan, San Juan, PR, p. A723

DEL GAUDIO, Frank J., Administrator, Essex County Hospital Center, Cedar Grove, NJ, p. A410

DEL GUIDICE, Mary Margaret, R.N. Chief Nursing Officer, Pennsylvania Hospital, Philadelphia, PA, p. A545

DEL RIO, R. Maxilimien, M.D. Medical Director, Northern Virginia Mental Health Institute, Falls Church, VA, p. A664

DEL TORO, Gustavo, M.D. Chief Medical Officer, Wyckoff Heights Medical Center, NY, p. A445

DEL TORO, Ivan E., M.D. Medical Director, Hospital HIMA San Pablo Caguas, Caguas, PR, p. A720

DELA TORRE, Victor, Command Legal Officer, Naval Hospital Lemoore, Portsmith, VA, p. A670

DELACROIX, Marc, Chief Information Officer, Signature Healthcare Brockton Hospital, Brockton, MA, p. A305

DELAGARDELLE, Pamela K., President and Chief Executive Officer, UnityPoint Health – Allen Hospital, Waterloo, IA, p. A236

DELANEY, Michael, Chief Financial Officer, Two Rivers Behavioral Health System, Kansas City, MO, p. A371

DELANO, John
Vice President Chief Information Officer, Integris Baptist Medical Center, Oklahoma City, OK, p. A511
Vice President and Chief Information Officer, Integris Southwest Medical Center, Oklahoma City, OK, p. A511

DELATTE, Sandra, Director Human Resources, Villa Feliciana Medical Complex, Jackson, LA, p. A275

DELAVAN, Karen, Interim Director Human Resources, Comanche County Medical Center, Comanche, TX, p. A601

DELELLIS, Terry, R.N. Director of Nursing, Corry Memorial Hospital, Corry, PA, p. A532

Index of Health Care Professionals / Deshpande

Index of Health Care Professionals

DELEON, Arsenio V., M.D. Chief Medical Officer, Select Specialty Hospital–Macomb County, Mount Clemens, MI, p. A326
DELEON, Joseph, President, Texas Health Harris Methodist Hospital Southwest Fort Worth, Fort Worth, TX, p. A614
DELEON, Marcos
Vice President Community Engagement, Truman Medical Center–Hospital Hill, Kansas City, MO, p. A370
Vice President Community Engagement, Truman Medical Center–Lakewood, Kansas City, MO, p. A370
DELFS, Michael, Chief Executive Officer, Mercy Hospital, Moose Lake, MN, p. A343
DELGADO, Eric, Chief Financial Officer, Lakewood Regional Medical Center, Lakewood, CA, p. A67
DELGADO, Pete, President and Chief Executive Officer, Salinas Valley Memorial Healthcare System, Salinas, CA, p. A85
DELGADO, Steve, Operations Coordinator, Milwaukee County Behavioral Health Division, Milwaukee, WI, p. A706
DELGRECO, Trish, Director of Nursing, OhioHealth MedCentral Shelby Hospital, Shelby, OH, p. A497
DELIEN, Rudie, Director Human Resources, Devereux Georgia Treatment Network, Kennesaw, GA, p. A159
DELISE, Donna, Associate Director Patient Care Services, Oklahoma City Veterans Affairs Medical Center, Oklahoma City, OK, p. A512
DELLA FLORA, Thomas, Vice President and Chief Information Officer, Catholic Medical Center, Manchester, NH, p. A407
DELLA LANA, David, M.D. Chief of Staff, Fairchild Medical Center, Yreka, CA, p. A98
DELLASEGA, Dave, President and Chief Executive Officer, Great Plains Health Alliance, Inc., Wichita, KS, p. B59
DELLEA, Eugene A., President, Fairview Hospital, Great Barrington, MA, p. A307
DELLICK, Charles, Director Information Technology, Magruder Memorial Hospital, Port Clinton, OH, p. A496
DELLOCONO, John, Senior Vice President and Chief Financial Officer, CentraState Healthcare System, Freehold, NJ, p. A412
DELONE, Lori
Senior Vice President Support Services and Chief Information Officer, Health First Cape Canaveral Hospital, Cocoa Beach, FL, p. A124
Senior Vice President and Chief Information Officer, Health First Viera Hospital, Melbourne, FL, p. A133
DELONG, Patricia, Chief Nursing Officer, Essentia Health St. Joseph's Medical Center, Brainerd, MN, p. A336
DELORENZO, David, Senior Director Human Resources, Sisters of Charity Hospital of Buffalo, Buffalo, NY, p. A431
DELPHIN–RITTMON, Miriam, Ph.D., Commissioner, Connecticut Department of Mental Health and Addiction Services, Hartford, CT, p. B42
DELPLEACHE, Michael, Specialist Information Technology, Anchor Hospital, Atlanta, GA, p. A149
DELVEAUX, Joe, Manager Information Services, St. Francis Regional Medical Center, Shakopee, MN, p. A347
DEMARCO, Victor, Chief Financial Officer, Bronx–Lebanon Hospital Center Health Care System, NY, p. A438
DEMAREST, Pamela, R.N. Chief Nursing Officer, UNM Sandoval Regional Medical Center, Rio Rancho, NM, p. A426
DEMASIE, Dennis, Vice President Information Systems and Chief Information Officer, Rush–Copley Medical Center, Aurora, IL, p. A179
DEMATTEO, Kathleen, Chief Information Officer, Danbury Hospital, Danbury, CT, p. A111
DEMAY, Paul, Chief Information Officer, Northwest Medical Center – Springdale, Springdale, AR, p. A51
DEMERICH, Lois B., Director Human Resources, Sentara Williamsburg Regional Medical Center, Williamsburg, VA, p. A674
DEMERS, Vickie, Chief Executive Officer, HEALTHSOUTH Lakeshore Rehabilitation Hospital, Birmingham, AL, p. A16
DEMETRIADES, James, Vice President, Operations, University Medical Center of Princeton at Plainsboro, Plainsboro, NJ, p. A417
DEMING, Mark, Controller, Beaumont Hospital – Taylor, Taylor, MI, p. A331
DEMING, Peggy, Executive Vice President and Chief Financial Officer, University Health System, San Antonio, TX, p. A642
DEMING, Terra, Director Human Resources, Otsego Memorial Hospital, Gaylord, MI, p. A320
DEMMEL, Ruth, M.D. Chief Medical Officer, Perkins County Health Services, Grant, NE, p. A392
DEMORLIS, John, M.D. Chief Medical Staff, Salem Memorial District Hospital, Salem, MO, p. A378
DEMORROW, Dawn P., Chief Human Resources Service, Wilkes–Barre Veterans Affairs Medical Center, Wilkes–Barre, PA, p. A553
DEMPSEY, Jeffrey, President and Chief Executive Officer, Mercy St. Charles Hospital, Oregon, OH, p. A495
DEMPSEY, John, Vice President and Chief Financial Officer, Hardin Memorial Hospital, Elizabethtown, KY, p. A256
DEMPSEY, John J., Chief Executive Officer, Little Colorado Medical Center, Winslow, AZ, p. A40
DEMURO, Rob, M.D. President Medical Staff, The University of Vermont Health Network Elizabethtown Community Hospital, Elizabethtown, NY, p. A433
DENBO, John R., Chief Executive Officer, Phelps County Regional Medical Center, Rolla, MO, p. A375
DENCKLAU, Larry, D.O. Chief of Staff, Lake Pointe Medical Center, Rowlett, TX, p. A639
DENEFF, Randall, Vice President Finance, Mary Free Bed Rehabilitation Hospital, Grand Rapids, MI, p. A320
DENEGRI, David, Chief Financial Officer, Parkwood Behavioral Health System, Olive Branch, MS, p. A358
DENEN, Bruce, Manager Data Processing, Fayette County Memorial Hospital, Washington Court House, OH, p. A500
DENG, Mei, Chief Financial Officer, MetroSouth Medical Center, Blue Island, IL, p. A180
DENHAM, Stephanie, Chief Financial Officer and Human Resources Officer, Phillips County Hospital, Malta, MT, p. A385
DENICOLA, Joseph, Chief Executive Officer and Managing Director, Arrowhead Behavioral Health Hospital, Maumee, OH, p. A494
DENIGRIS, Deborah, Chief Nursing Officer, Kingsboro Psychiatric Center, NY, p. A440
DENIO, Arthur E., Vice President and Chief Financial Officer, NorthBay Medical Center, Fairfield, CA, p. A61
DENIRO, Lori, Senior Director Nursing, St. Elizabeth Boardman Health Center, Boardman, OH, p. A480
DENISIENKO, Mary, Vice President Human Resources, Palos Community Hospital, Palos Heights, IL, p. A197
DENISON, Rita, Director of Information Systems, Sturgis Hospital, Sturgis, MI, p. A331
DENKER, Jill, Executive Director Human Resources, Lexington Regional Health Center, Lexington, NE, p. A393
DENMARK, Donald, M.D
Chief Medical Officer, Carondelet St. Joseph's Hospital, Tucson, AZ, p. A39
Chief Medical Officer, Carondelet St. Mary's Hospital, Tucson, AZ, p. A39
DENNETT, Bryan, M.D. Chief of Staff, William Newton Hospital, Winfield, KS, p. A253
DENNEY, Jeff, Administrator, Southern Crescent Hospital for Specialty Care, Riverdale, GA, p. A163
DENNIS, Bradley, M.D. Chief Medical Officer, Brookwood Medical Center, Birmingham, AL, p. A16
DENNIS, Jeanne, Chief Nursing Officer, Abraham Lincoln Memorial Hospital, Lincoln, IL, p. A193
DENNIS, Kera, Assistant Administrator, Finance, UW Medicine/Harborview Medical Center, Seattle, WA, p. A684
DENNIS, Michael, Director, William J. McCord Adolescent and Treatment Center, Orangeburg, SC, p. A564
DENNIS, Ronnie, Chief of Staff, Rolling Plains Memorial Hospital, Sweetwater, TX, p. A646
DENNISON, Cindy, Senior Director Rural Division, Mercy Willard Hospital, Willard, OH, p. A500
DENNO, Charles, Chief Financial Officer, Westwood Lodge Hospital, Westwood, MA, p. A313
DENNSTEDT, Crystal, Chief Information Officer, North Texas State Hospital, Wichita Falls Campus, Wichita Falls, TX, p. A652
DENNY, Donald, M.D. Senior Vice President, Medical Affairs, University Medical Center of Princeton at Plainsboro, Plainsboro, NJ, p. A417
DENO, Mark S., Chief Executive Officer, Spalding Rehabilitation Hospital, Aurora, CO, p. A99
DENO, Mary, Vice President Human Resources, Community Medical Center, Toms River, NJ, p. A419
DENSON, Anna, Human Resources Specialist, Choctaw Health Center, Philadelphia, MS, p. A359
DENSON, Paula Lajean, M.D. President, Tyler County Hospital, Woodville, TX, p. A653
DENT, Bruce
Human Resources Director, Heber Valley Medical Center, Heber City, UT, p. A655
Director Human Resources, Park City Medical Center, Park City, UT, p. A657
DENT, Robert L., R.N. Senior Vice President and Chief Operating Officer, Midland Memorial Hospital, Midland, TX, p. A632
DENTEN, Jane, MSN Vice President Nursing and Chief Nurse Executive, Advocate Lutheran General Hospital, Park Ridge, IL, p. A197
DENTON, Brian, Administrator, Mercy Hospital Kingfisher, Kingfisher, OK, p. A508
DENTON, Christopher, Chief Financial Officer, Henrico Doctors' Hospital, Richmond, VA, p. A672
DENTON, Genise, Manager Human Resources, John J. Pershing Veterans Affairs Medical Center, Poplar Bluff, MO, p. A374
DENTON, Joe, Executive Vice President and Chief Financial Officer, Mobile Infirmary Medical Center, Mobile, AL, p. A22
DENTON, Tony, JD, Acting Chief Executive Officer and Chief Operating Officer, University of Michigan Hospitals and Health Centers, Ann Arbor, MI, p. A314
DENTONI, Terry, Chief Nursing Officer, San Francisco General Hospital and Trauma Center, San Francisco, CA, p. A88
DENUCCI, Alex, Chief Financial Officer, Franciscan Hospital for Children, Boston, MA, p. A303
DEPASQUALE, Joseph, M.D. Interim Chief Medical Officer, Saint Michael's Medical Center, Newark, NJ, p. A415
DEPAULIS, Hugh, Interim Vice President and Chief Financial Officer, Mercy Medical Center–Sioux City, Sioux City, IA, p. A234
DEPINHO, Ronald A., M.D., President, University of Texas M.D. Anderson Cancer Center, Houston, TX, p. A622
DEPKO, Mike, Director Information Technology, Brown County Hospital, Ainsworth, NE, p. A389
DEPOOTER, Stephen, Chief Information Officer, Norwegian American Hospital, Chicago, IL, p. A183
DEPPERMAN, Kristi, Chief Financial Officer, Memphis Veterans Affairs Medical Center, Memphis, TN, p. A583
DEPRATO, Jeremy, Director Information Technology, Spine Hospital of Louisiana (formally the NeuroMedical Center Surgical Hospital), Baton Rouge, LA, p. A270
DEQUARDO, John R., M.D., Superintendent, Colorado Mental Health Institute at Pueblo, Pueblo, CO, p. A108
DERAMUS, Brenda, Manager Human Resources, Sutter Lakeside Hospital, Lakeport, CA, p. A67
DERBY, Richard P., Vice President Finance, Barton Memorial Hospital, South Lake Tahoe, CA, p. A93
DERFLINGER, Terri, Administrator, Mercy Hospital of Franciscan Sisters, Oelwein, IA, p. A232
DERMAN, Nancy, Director Human Resources, Southwest Connecticut Mental Health System, Bridgeport, CT, p. A111
DEROCHE, Richard, Manager Information Technology, Deaconess Hospital, Spokane, WA, p. A685
DERONCEREY, Josiane, Director Human Resources, Christ Hospital, Jersey City, NJ, p. A413
DEROUEN, Jason, Director Management Information Systems, Grace Medical Center, Lubbock, TX, p. A629
DEROUSSE, Jacqueline, Assistant Vice President Talent, Midwestern Regional Medical Center, Zion, IL, p. A203
DERRICO, Patricia, FACHE Chief Nursing Officer, Coliseum Northside Hospital, Macon, GA, p. A160
DERRINGTON, Ken R., Chief Financial Officer, Northern Colorado Rehabilitation Hospital, Johnstown, CO, p. A105
DERSCH, Stephen, M.D. President Medical Staff, Regency Hospital of Florence, Florence, SC, p. A561
DERTZ, Donna, Director Human Resources, St. Bernard Hospital and Health Care Center, Chicago, IL, p. A184
DERUS, Charles, M.D. Vice President Medical Management, Advocate Good Samaritan Hospital, Downers Grove, IL, p. A186
DERUYTER, David N., M.D. President Medical Staff, Kindred Hospital–Atlanta, Atlanta, GA, p. A150
DERYNCK, Dodie, Chief Nursing Officer, Avera Marshall Regional Medical Center, Marshall, MN, p. A342
DESAI, Ankur, Interim Chief Medical officer, Rome Memorial Hospital, Rome, NY, p. A449
DESAI, Nimesh, M.D. Medical Director, Massena Memorial Hospital, Massena, NY, p. A437
DESAI, Shailesh, M.D. Chief of Staff, Baum Harmon Mercy Hospital, Primghar, IA, p. A233
DESALVO, Susan, Manager Human Resources, Bath Veterans Affairs Medical Center, Bath, NY, p. A429
DESANTIS, John
Chief Financial Officer, Glenwood Regional Medical Center, West Monroe, LA, p. A286
Chief Financial Officer, Ouachita Community Hospital, West Monroe, LA, p. A287
DESANTIS, Vincent, Vice President Finance, Phelps Memorial Hospital Center, Sleepy Hollow, NY, p. A450
DESCHAMBEAU, Wayne G., President and Chief Executive Officer, Wayne Hospital, Greenville, OH, p. A491
DESCHENE, Normand E., FACHE, Chief Executive Officer, Lowell General Hospital, Lowell, MA, p. A308
DESCHRYVER, Joseph, Chief Executive Officer, Sierra Vista Regional Medical Center, San Luis Obispo, CA, p. A90
DESEI, Nitin, M.D. Medical Director, Regional Rehabilitation Hospital, Phenix City, AL, p. A24
DESHAZO, Sheri, Chief Operating Officer, Kings Mountain Hospital, Kings Mountain, NC, p. A463
DESHONG, Andre, Administrator, Behavioral Hospital of Longview, Longview, TX, p. A628
DESHPANDE, Jay, M.D. Chief Quality Officer and Chief Medical Officer, Arkansas Children's Hospital, Little Rock, AR, p. A46

Index of Health Care Professionals

Index of Health Care Professionals / Desimone


DESIMONE, Maureen, Chief Operating Officer, Blythedale Children's Hospital, Valhalla, NY, p. A452
DESJEUNES, Carol, Vice President and Chief Operating Officer, Psychiatric Institute of Washington, Washington, DC, p. A120
DESKINS, Juanita, Chief Operating Officer, Pikeville Medical Center, Pikeville, KY, p. A264
DESMARAIS, John, M.D., President and Chief Executive Officer, Fayette County Memorial Hospital, Washington Court House, OH, p. A500
DESMARTEAU, Lisa Jo, Chief Financial Officer, Miami Jewish Home and Hospital for Aged, Miami, FL, p. A134
DESMOND, Debbie, Director Human Resources, Martha Jefferson Hospital, Charlottesville, VA, p. A663
DESMOND, Heather, Chief Financial Officer, Bibb Medical Center, Centreville, AL, p. A18
DESMOND, Jeffrey, M.D. Interim Chief Medical Officer, University of Michigan Hospitals and Health Centers, Ann Arbor, MI, p. A314
DESMOND, P. Craig, Chief Executive Officer, Southwest General Hospital, San Antonio, TX, p. A642
DESOTELLE, Robert C., President and Chief Executive Officer, Asheville Specialty Hospital, Asheville, NC, p. A455
DESOTO, James, M.D
Vice President Medical Affairs, Mercy Medical Center Redding, Redding, CA, p. A82
Vice President Medical Affairs, St. Elizabeth Community Hospital, Red Bluff, CA, p. A82
DESOUZA, Jacqueline, Chief Executive Officer, Research Medical Center, Kansas City, MO, p. A370
DESPRES, Paul J., Chief Executive Officer, Eleanor Slater Hospital, Cranston, RI, p. A555
DESROCHES, Jeff, Manager Information Systems, AHMC Anaheim Regional Medical Center, Anaheim, CA, p. A53
DESSIEUX, Guesly, D.O. Chief Medical Officer, Santiam Memorial Hospital, Stayton, OR, p. A526
DESTEFANO, Geraldine, R.N. Chief Nursing Officer, West Palm Hospital, West Palm Beach, FL, p. A147
DESTEFANO, Jane, R.N. Chief Nursing Officer, Houston Methodist San Jacinto Hospital, Baytown, TX, p. A596
DETANO, Teresa R., M.P.H., Chief Executive Officer, Select Specialty Hospital–Fort Wayne, Fort Wayne, IN, p. A209
DETER, Kevin, Chief Operating Officer, WellStar Cobb Hospital, Austell, GA, p. A152
DETTERMAN, B. Lynn
President, Mercy Tiffin Hospital, Tiffin, OH, p. A498
President and Chief Executive Officer, Mercy Willard Hospital, Willard, OH, p. A500
DETTMER, Brantley, Finance Director, Kaiser Foundation Hospital Westside Medical Center, Hillsboro, OR, p. A521
DETTMER, Robert E., Deputy Commander for Health Services, Irwin Army Community Hospital, Junction City, KS, p. A243
DETWILER, Courtney, R.N., Administrator, Hampton Roads Specialty Hospital, Newport News, VA, p. A668
DETWILER, Eric, Director Information Technology, Barnes–Kasson County Hospital, Susquehanna, PA, p. A550
DEUEL, Teresa L., Chief Executive Officer, Hodgeman County Health Center, Jetmore, KS, p. A242
DEURMIER, Carol, Chief Executive Officer, St. Michael's Hospital Avera, Tyndall, SD, p. A572
DEVANATHAN, Raja, M.D. Chief Medical Officer, Vibra Hospital of Northwestern Indiana, Crown Point, IN, p. A207
DEVANEY, Catherine, Chief Executive Officer, HEALTHSOUTH Rehabilitation Hospital, Concord, NH, p. A405
DEVANSKY, Gary W., Director, Coatesville Veterans Affairs Medical Center, Coatesville, PA, p. A532
DEVARAJ, Kiran, Medical Director, Highland Hospital, Charleston, WV, p. A690
DEVARAJAN, Vadakkipalayam N., Chief Medical Staff, St. Charles Parish Hospital, Luling, LA, p. A279
DEVAUGHN, Michael D.
Executive Vice President and Chief Financial Officer, WakeMed Cary Hospital, Cary, NC, p. A456
Senior Vice President Finance and Chief Financial Officer, WakeMed Raleigh Campus, Raleigh, NC, p. A467
DEVAULT, Jennifer, Vice President Associate Services, F. F. Thompson Hospital, Canandaigua, NY, p. A431
DEVAULT, Rosanne, Chief Financial Officer, McKenzie–Willamette Medical Center, Springfield, OR, p. A526
DEVAULT, Roseann M., Chief Financial Officer, Tennova Healthcare–Jefferson Memorial Hospital, Jefferson City, TN, p. A579
DEVAUX, Sheri, Information Technology Manager, Connecticut Veterans Home and Hospital, Rocky Hill, CT, p. A114
DEVENUTO, Joseph, Vice President and Chief Information Officer, Norton Women's and Kosair Children's Hospital, Louisville, KY, p. A261
DEVILLE, Linda F., Chief Executive Officer, Bunkie General Hospital, Bunkie, LA, p. A271
DEVIN, Brian V., Chief Executive Officer, Massachusetts Hospital School, Canton, MA, p. A306
DEVIN, Joseph, Chief Financial Officer, Boone County Hospital, Boone, IA, p. A223
DEVINE, Joseph W., FACHE, President and Chief Executive Officer, Kennedy Health System, Cherry Hill, NJ, p. A410
DEVINE, Kathryn, Vice President Human Resources, UPMC Presbyterian Shadyside, Pittsburgh, PA, p. A547
DEVITA, James, M.D. Chief Medical Officer, Tewksbury Hospital, Tewksbury, MA, p. A312
DEVITO, Joseph M., Vice President Finance and Chief Operating Officer, Geisinger–Bloomsburg Hospital, Bloomsburg, PA, p. A529
DEVLIN, James, Director Information Systems, St. Cloud Regional Medical Center, Saint Cloud, FL, p. A141
DEVOCELLE, Frank H., President and Chief Executive Officer, Olathe Medical Center, Olathe, KS, p. A247
DEVOE, Andrew, Chief Financial Officer, Aria Health, Philadelphia, PA, p. A542
DEVORE, Kathy, R.N. Director Patient Services, Advanced Care Hospital of White County, Searcy, AR, p. A50
DEVORE, Pam, Financial Manager, Hillcrest Memorial Hospital, Simpsonville, SC, p. A564
DEVORE, Paul A., M.D. Medical Director, Gladys Spellman Specialty Hospital and Nursing Center, Cheverly, MD, p. A296
DEVORSETZ, Marc, Chief Executive Officer, Heritage Park Surgical Hospital, Sherman, TX, p. A644
DEVRIES, Russell, Chief Business Operations, Keller Army Community Hospital, West Point, NY, p. A453
DEW, Douglas, M.D. President Medical Staff, Flagler Hospital, Saint Augustine, FL, p. A141
DEWALSCHE, Diane, R.N. Chief Operating Officer, Community Hospital Long Beach, Long Beach, CA, p. A68
DEWAN, Vijay, M.D. Clinical Director, Lincoln Regional Center, Lincoln, NE, p. A394
DEWANE, Patti, Vice President Finance and Treasurer, SwedishAmerican Hospital, A Division of UW Health, Rockford, IL, p. A200
DEWAR, William, M.D. Chief of Staff, Wayne Memorial Hospital, Honesdale, PA, p. A536
DEWBERRY, Robbie, Chief Executive Officer, Mitchell County Hospital, Colorado City, TX, p. A601
DEWERFF, Mike, President and Chief Executive Officer, UnityPoint Health – Trinity Regional Medical Center, Fort Dodge, IA, p. A228
DEWISPELARE, Cheryl M., Chief Human Resources Officer, Veterans Affairs Nebraska–Western Iowa Health Care System, Omaha, NE, p. A397
DEWITT, Alan Neil, Chief Medical Officer, Summit Healthcare Regional Medical Center, Show Low, AZ, p. A38
DEWITT, Jocelyn, Ph.D. Vice President and Chief Information Officer, University of Wisconsin Hospital and Clinics, Madison, WI, p. A704
DEWORTH, Gerald M., Associate Director, Carl Vinson Veterans Affairs Medical Center, Dublin, GA, p. A156
DEXTER, Sue, Administrative Department Leader Human Resources, McDonough District Hospital, Macomb, IL, p. A193
DEYARMIN, James A., Controller, Children's Hospital of Richmond at VCU–Brook Road Campus, Richmond, VA, p. A671
DHAWAN, Ajay, M.D. Chief of Staff, Veterans Affairs Northern Indiana Health Care System, Fort Wayne, IN, p. A209
DHILLON, Avtar, M.D. Medical Director, Keystone Newport News, Newport News, VA, p. A668
DHINGRA, Ashok, M.D. Executive Medical Director, HEALTHSOUTH Deaconess Rehabilitation Hospital, Evansville, IN, p. A208
DHULIPALA, Vasudeva, M.D. Medical Director, HEALTHSOUTH Rehabilitation Hospital of Alexandria, Alexandria, LA, p. A268
DI BACCO, David J., Chief Operating Officer, Eastern Niagara Hospital, Lockport, NY, p. A436
DI BERNARDO, Deborah, Chief Information Officer, St. Joseph's Medical Center, Yonkers, NY, p. A454
DIAL, Jeffery
President, Vidant Bertie Hospital, Windsor, NC, p. A470
President, Vidant Chowan Hospital, Edenton, NC, p. A459
DIAL, Jody S., Chief Financial Officer, Timpanogos Regional Hospital, Orem, UT, p. A657
DIALTO, Margaret, Vice President Human Resources, Staten Island University Hospital, NY, p. A444
DIAMOND, Anne, JD, Chief Executive Officer, University of Connecticut Health Center, John Dempsey Hospital, Farmington, CT, p. A112
DIAMOND, Gene, Interim President, Franciscan St. Anthony Health – Michigan City, Michigan City, IN, p. A216
DIAMOND, Kevin, M.D. Chief of Staff, Lawrence Memorial Hospital, Walnut Ridge, AR, p. A51
DIAMOND, Lester K., President, St. Dominic–Jackson Memorial Hospital, Jackson, MS, p. A355
DIAMOND, Robert
Senior Vice President and Chief Information Officer, Northern Dutchess Hospital, Rhinebeck, NY, p. A448
Vice President and Chief Information Officer, Putnam Hospital Center, Carmel, NY, p. A431
Chief Information Officer, Vassar Brothers Medical Center, Poughkeepsie, NY, p. A448
DIAMOND, Vickie L., MS, President and Chief Executive Officer, Wyoming Medical Center, Casper, WY, p. A715
DIANGELO, John A., President and Chief Executive Officer, Inspira Health Network, Mullica Hill, NJ, p. B74
DIANGELO, John A.
President and Chief Executive Officer, Inspira Medical Center–Elmer, Elmer, NJ, p. A411
President and Chief Executive Officer, Inspira Medical Center–Vineland, Vineland, NJ, p. A420
DIAZ, Alberto, Chief Financial Officer, Oak Valley Hospital District, Oakdale, CA, p. A78
DIAZ, Evelyn, R.N. Chief Nursing Officer, HEALTHSOUTH Hospital of Manati, Manati, PR, p. A721
DIAZ, Felipe, M.D. Chief of Staff, Bath Veterans Affairs Medical Center, Bath, NY, p. A429
DIAZ, Georgina, Chief Operating Officer, Palmetto General Hospital, Hialeah, FL, p. A128
DIAZ, Gloria, Executive Director, Hospital Santa Rosa, Guayama, PR, p. A721
DIAZ, Janine, Human Resources Manager, Emory Rehabilitation Hospital, Atlanta, GA, p. A150
DIAZ, Jesse, Chief Information Officer, Phoebe Putney Memorial Hospital, Albany, GA, p. A149
DIAZ, Jimmy, Director Information Technology, Odessa Regional Medical Center, Odessa, TX, p. A635
DIAZ, Jose, Director Information Systems, St. Mary's Medical Center of Evansville, Evansville, IN, p. A208
DIAZ, Joseph, M.D. Chief Medical Officer, Memorial Hospital of Rhode Island, Pawtucket, RI, p. A555
DIAZ, Lillian, R.N. Chief Nursing Officer, Metropolitan Hospital Center, New York, NY, p. A441
DIAZ, Rogelio, Administrator, Hospital Menonita De Caguas, Caguas, PR, p. A720
DIAZ, Ron, Manager Operations, Albany Stratton Veterans Affairs Medical Center, Albany, NY, p. A428
DIAZ, Steve, M.D. Chief Medical Officer, MaineGeneral Medical Center, Augusta, ME, p. A288
DIBBLE, Lynn, Vice President Patient Care Services, Guthrie Towanda Memorial Hospital, Towanda, PA, p. A551
DICESARE, Gayle, President and Chief Executive Officer, RiverValley Behavioral Health Hospital, Owensboro, KY, p. A264
DICESARE, Jan, Vice President Financial Operations, St. Vincent's East, Birmingham, AL, p. A17
DICICCO, Marilyn, Director Human Resources, Chestnut Hill Hospital, Philadelphia, PA, p. A542
DICK, Andy, Director Information Services, Saline Memorial Hospital, Benton, AR, p. A41
DICK, David, Chief Executive Officer, Huron Regional Medical Center, Huron, SD, p. A569
DICK, Frances, Chief Executive Officer, Oceans Behavioral Hospital Lufkin, Lufkin, TX, p. A630
DICK, Landon, Chief Information Officer, Claiborne Memorial Medical Center, Homer, LA, p. A275
DICK, Lynette, Director of Support Services, Ellsworth County Medical Center, Ellsworth, KS, p. A239
DICK, Mollie, Coordinator Human Resources, Wayne County Hospital, Monticello, KY, p. A263
DICK, Myra, Manager Business Office, AMG Specialty Hospital–Wichita, Wichita, KS, p. A252
DICKENS, Betty, Director Human Resources, Sierra Tucson, Tucson, AZ, p. A40
DICKENS, Shelby, Director, Patient Care Services, Fort Madison Community Hospital, Fort Madison, IA, p. A228
DICKERSON, Gene, M.D. Vice President Medical Affairs, Tuomey Healthcare System, Sumter, SC, p. A565
DICKERSON, Kathy, Chief Financial Officer, HEALTHSOUTH Rehabilitation Hospital of Arlington, Arlington, TX, p. A592
DICKERSON, Melody Ford, Chief Nursing Officer, Memorial Hermann Northwest Hospital, Houston, TX, p. A621
DICKERSON, Taylor, Chief Information Officer, Lake City Medical Center, Lake City, FL, p. A131
DICKERSON, Toby, Chief Information Resources Management Services, Durham Veterans Affairs Medical Center, Durham, NC, p. A459
DICKEY, John M., Chief Administrative Officer, Mayo Clinic Health System in Eau Claire, Eau Claire, WI, p. A700
DICKEY, Mark, Director Business Development, Valir Rehabilitation Hospital, Oklahoma City, OK, p. A513
DICKEY, Sarah J., Director Human Resources, Marshall Browning Hospital, Du Quoin, IL, p. A186
DICKINSON, Ashley, Chief Operating Officer, Porter Regional Hospital, Valparaiso, IN, p. A220


A824 Index of Health Care Professionals 

Index of Health Care Professionals / Dmello

Index of Health Care Professionals

DICKINSON, Galen, Chief Financial Officer, Cary Medical Center, Caribou, ME, p. A289
DICKINSON, Lani, R.N. Chief Nursing Officer, Doctors Medical Center, Modesto, CA, p. A75
DICKLICH–COBB, Christy, Chief Nursing Officer, Memorial Hospital of Converse County, Douglas, WY, p. A716
DICKMAN, Kathy, Director Information Technology, McCullough–Hyde Memorial Hospital/TriHealth, Oxford, OH, p. A496
DICKREITER, Adrian, Vice President Technology, Nix Health Care System, San Antonio, TX, p. A641
DICKS, Mandy, Director of Nursing, Lake Butler Hospital Hand Surgery Center, Lake Butler, FL, p. A131
DICKSON, Anita, Director Human Resources, Five Rivers Medical Center, Pocahontas, AR, p. A50
DICKSON, Eric, M.D., President and Chief Executive Officer, UMass Memorial Health Care, Inc., Worcester, MA, p. B138
DICKSON, James J., Administrator and Chief Executive Officer, Copper Queen Community Hospital, Bisbee, AZ, p. A30
DICKSON, Lynette, Director Clinical Operations and Director of Nursing, District One Hospital, Faribault, MN, p. A338
DICKSON, Scott, Director Information Technology, Reeves Memorial Medical Center, Bernice, LA, p. A270
DICKSON, Thomas C.
Chief Executive Officer, Banner – University Medical Center Tucson, Tucson, AZ, p. A39
Chief Executive Officer, Banner Thunderbird Medical Center, Glendale, AZ, p. A32
DICKSON, William, Acting Executive Director, Capital District Psychiatric Center, Albany, NY, p. A428
DICUS–JOHNSON, Coreen
President, Midwest Orthopedic Specialty Hospital, Franklin, WI, p. A701
President, Wheaton Franciscan Healthcare – Franklin, Franklin, WI, p. A701
President, Wheaton Franciscan Healthcare – St. Francis, Milwaukee, WI, p. A707
President, Wheaton Franciscan Healthcare – The Wisconsin Heart Hospital, Wauwatosa, WI, p. A713
DIDENKO, Dima, Chief Financial Officer, Florida Hospital Tampa, Tampa, FL, p. A144
DIDERRICH, Mary Kay, Vice President Patient Services, Watertown Regional Medical Center, Watertown, WI, p. A712
DIEBLING, Tara, Chief Executive Officer, The Rehabilitation Institute of St. Louis, Saint Louis, MO, p. A378
DIECKMANN, Holli, Director Health Information, Sabetha Community Hospital, Sabetha, KS, p. A249
DIEDERICH, John A., Senior Vice President Operations and Chief Operating Officer, Rush–Copley Medical Center, Aurora, IL, p. A179
DIEDERICH, Thomas, Senior Vice President Human Resources, Phoenix Children's Hospital, Phoenix, AZ, p. A35
DIEDRICH, Michele, R.N. Chief Nursing Officer, Mercy Hospital Rogers, Rogers, AR, p. A50
DIEFFENBACH, Todd, Chief Financial Officer, Tyrone Hospital, Tyrone, PA, p. A551
DIER, Joy, R.N. Vice President Clinical Services and Chief Nursing Officer, Texas Institute for Surgery at Texas Health Presbyterian Dallas, Dallas, TX, p. A606
DIERKENS, Janelle, Chief Administration Officer, New York State Psychiatric Institute, New York, NY, p. A443
DIERKER, Anne, Vice President Hospital Services, Pekin Hospital, Pekin, IL, p. A197
DIERS, Suzanne, R.N. Director Patient Care Services, Shriners Hospitals for Children–Portland, Portland, OR, p. A525
DIESTEL, Peter, Senior Vice President and Chief Operating Officer, Valley Hospital, Ridgewood, NJ, p. A418
DIETER, Brian, President and Chief Executive Officer, Mary Greeley Medical Center, Ames, IA, p. A222
DIETERICH, Kevin, Director Information Services, Inland Hospital, Waterville, ME, p. A292
DIETLIN, Steve, Chief Financial Officer, Tri–City Medical Center, Oceanside, CA, p. A79
DIETRICH, Brenda, Chief Human Resources Officer, Banner Boswell Medical Center, Sun City, AZ, p. A38
DIETRICK, Brian, Director Information Systems, Wilson Medical Center, Wilson, NC, p. A470
DIETSCH, Barry, Chief Financial Officer, Virginia Gay Hospital, Vinton, IA, p. A235
DIETSCHE, Jim, Chief Financial Officer, Bellin Memorial Hospital, Green Bay, WI, p. A701
DIETZ, Brian E., FACHE, Interim President and Chief Executive officer, St. Francis Hospital, Wilmington, DE, p. A118
DIETZ, Gary, Director Information Technology Services, Walla Walla General Hospital, Walla Walla, WA, p. A687
DIETZ, Mark, Chief Medical Officer, CentraCare Health–Monticello, Monticello, MN, p. A343
DIETZ, Michael, Administrator, U. S. Air Force Hospital, Hampton, VA, p. A666
DIFRANCO, Vincent B., Chief Executive Officer, Plains Regional Medical Center, Clovis, NM, p. A423
DIGEROLAMO, Anthony, MSN, Chief Executive Officer, St. Charles Parish Hospital, Luling, LA, p. A279
DIGGINS, Dana, Chief Financial Officer, Landmark Medical Center, Woonsocket, RI, p. A556
DIIESO, Nicholas T., R.N. Chief Operating Officer, Mount Auburn Hospital, Cambridge, MA, p. A305
DIIORIO, Emil, M.D., Chief Executive Officer, Surgical Specialty Center at Coordinated Health, Allentown, PA, p. A528
DIKE, Charles, M.D. Chief of Staff, Sanford Worthington Medical Center, Worthington, MN, p. A349
DILALLO, Kevin, Chief Executive Officer, Manatee Memorial Hospital, Bradenton, FL, p. A122
DILISI, Jeffrey P., Vice President and Chief Medical Officer, Virginia Hospital Center – Arlington, Arlington, VA, p. A662
DILL, Cathy, R.N. Director Patient Services, Spearfish Regional Hospital, Spearfish, SD, p. A572
DILL, Stephen, M.D. Chief of Staff, LeConte Medical Center, Sevierville, TN, p. A588
DILLARD, Evan S., FACHE, President and Chief Executive Officer, Forrest General Hospital, Hattiesburg, MS, p. A354
DILLARD, Leigh, M.D. Chief of Staff, De Soto Regional Health System, Mansfield, LA, p. A279
DILLEHUNT, David B., Chief Information Officer, FirstHealth Moore Regional Hospital, Pinehurst, NC, p. A466
DILLION, Tim, Vice President of Human Resources, Devereux Hospital and Children's Center of Florida, Melbourne, FL, p. A133
DILLON, Jim, Chief Financial Officer, Rangely District Hospital, Rangely, CO, p. A108
DILLON, Lorie, Chief Executive Officer, Geisinger HEALTHSOUTH Rehabilitation Hospital, Danville, PA, p. A532
DILLON, Mary E., MS Vice President Patient Care Services, Sisters of Charity Hospital of Buffalo, Buffalo, NY, p. A431
DILORENZO, Randolph, M.D. Medical Director, Syosset Hospital, Syosset, NY, p. A451
DILORETO, David, M.D. Executive Vice President and Chief Medical Officer, Presence Saint Francis Hospital, Evanston, IL, p. A188
DIMARCO, Lisa, R.N. Vice President Patient Care Service and Chief Nursing Officer, Little Company of Mary Hospital and Health Care Centers, Evergreen Park, IL, p. A188
DIMARE, John, M.D. Medical Director, Foothill Presbyterian Hospital, Glendora, CA, p. A64
DIMAURO, Cynthia, M.D. Medical Director, Hillside Rehabilitation Hospital, Warren, OH, p. A499
DIMICHELE, Maria, Administrative Assistant, Kensington Hospital, Philadelphia, PA, p. A544
DIMITROVA, Gergana, M.D. Medical Director, Carolina Center for Behavioral Health, Greer, SC, p. A562
DIMMICK, Scott
Senior Vice President Human Resources, St. Elizabeth Boardman Health Center, Boardman, OH, p. A480
Senior Vice President Human Resources, St. Elizabeth Health Center, Youngstown, OH, p. A501
DIMMIG, Thomas, M.D. Medical Director, North Carolina Specialty Hospital, Durham, NC, p. A459
DINGER, Bradley, Chief Financial Officer, UPMC Northwest, Seneca, PA, p. A550
DINGES, Brenda, Director of Nursing, Ness County Hospital, Ness City, KS, p. A246
DINGILIAN, John, M.D. Chief Medical Officer, Simi Valley Hospital, Simi Valley, CA, p. A92
DINGLE, Steve, M.D. Chief Medical Officer, Arizona State Hospital, Phoenix, AZ, p. A34
DINGLER, Chance, M.D. Chief Medical Officer, Nocona General Hospital, Nocona, TX, p. A634
DINGMAN, III, Vincent, Chief Financial Officer, Columbia Memorial Hospital, Hudson, NY, p. A435
DINHAM, Vilma L., R.N. Chief Nursing Officer, Encino Hospital Medical Center, CA, p. A69
DINKHA, Duncan, M.D. Chief of Staff, Morrison Community Hospital, Morrison, IL, p. A195
DINKINS, Vicki, Director Human Resources, South Georgia Medical Center Lanier Campus, Lakeland, GA, p. A160
DINON, Nancy
Vice President Human Resources, Health Central Hospital, Ocoee, FL, p. A137
Vice President Human Resources, Orlando Regional Medical Center, Orlando, FL, p. A138
DINSLAGE, Dennis, Vice President Finance and Chief Financial Officer, St. Francis Memorial Hospital, West Point, NE, p. A399
DION, Jeffrey P.
Vice President Finance and Chief Financial Officer, Newton–Wellesley Hospital, Newton Lower Falls, MA, p. A309
Vice President Finance, St. Elizabeth's Medical Center, Brighton, MA, p. A305
DIONISOPOULOS, Peter, Chief Medical Officer, CHI Health Nebraska Heart, Lincoln, NE, p. A393
DIPALMA, Maureen, Chief Financial Officer, Tewksbury Hospital, Tewksbury, MA, p. A312
DIPAOLO, Daneca Donna, Chief of Staff, Greenwood Leflore Hospital, Greenwood, MS, p. A353
DIPAOLO, Joseph, FACHE, President, Newton Medical Center, Newton, NJ, p. A416
DIPIERO, Annette, Human Resource Director, HEALTHSOUTH Rehabilitation Hospital at Martin Health, Stuart, FL, p. A143
DIPIETRO, Sandra P., Chief Financial Officer, St. Tammany Parish Hospital, Covington, LA, p. A272
DIPILLA, Victor, Vice President and Chief Business Development Officer, Christ Hospital, Cincinnati, OH, p. A482
DISANTO, Larry
Executive Vice President and Chief Operating Officer, Capital Health Medical Center–Hopewell, Pennington, NJ, p. A416
Executive Vice President and Chief Operating Officer, Capital Health Regional Medical Center, Trenton, NJ, p. A419
DISANZO, Frank, Vice President and Chief Information Officer and Chief Strategy Officer, Saint Peter's University Hospital, New Brunswick, NJ, p. A415
DISPOTO, I, Martha, R.N. Chief Nurse Executive, Anaheim Medical Center, Kaiser Permanente Orange County Anaheim Medical Center, Anaheim, CA, p. A53
DISSEN, James H., Chief Executive Officer, Highland–Clarksburg Hospital, Clarksburg, WV, p. A690
DISTASIO, Stephen R., Director, Veterans Affairs Black Hills Health Care System, Fort Meade, SD, p. A568
DISTEFANO, Lisa, M.D. President Medical Staff, SSM Health St. Francis Hospital – Maryville, Maryville, MO, p. A372
DISWOOD, Lavenia, R.N. Chief Nurse Executive, Northern Navajo Medical Center, Shiprock, NM, p. A426
DITMANSON, Paul, M.D. Clinical Director, Red Lake Indian Health Service Hospital, Red Lake, MN, p. A345
DITORO, Michael, Chief Operating Officer, Westlake Hospital, Melrose Park, IL, p. A194
DITTBENNER, Beth, Regional Director, Human Resources, Mayo Clinic Health System in Mankato, Mankato, MN, p. A341
DITTMANN, Jerry, Vice President Human Resources, Mount Nittany Medical Center, State College, PA, p. A550
DITTO, Debbie, CPA Controller, Lincoln Trail Behavioral Health System, Radcliff, KY, p. A265
DITURO, Beth, Divisional Chief Information Officer, Lenox Hill Hospital, New York, NY, p. A441
DITZLER, Andru, Chief Information Officer, Lebanon Veterans Affairs Medical Center, Lebanon, PA, p. A538
DIVELLO, Douglas F., President and Chief Executive Officer, Alice Hyde Medical Center, Malone, NY, p. A436
DIVERSI, Sarah, Chief Financial Officer, Our Community Hospital, Scotland Neck, NC, p. A468
DIVINS, Brooke, Manager Human Resources, Clarion Hospital, Clarion, PA, p. A531
DIVITO, Frank, Manager Information Systems, Jameson Hospital, New Castle, PA, p. A541
DIX, Roger J., Vice President Finance, Hannibal Regional Hospital, Hannibal, MO, p. A368
DIX, Theresa, R.N. Chief Nursing Officer, Wythe County Community Hospital, Wytheville, VA, p. A675
DIXON, Christy, Chief Human Resources Officer, HealthSouth Rehabilitation Hospital of Humble, LLC, Humble, TX, p. A623
DIXON, Debbie, Director Human Resources, Pampa Regional Medical Center, Pampa, TX, p. A635
DIXON, Del, Chief Information Officer, South Shore Hospital, South Weymouth, MA, p. A311
DIXON, Florine, Chief Operating Officer, Memorial Hospital, Carthage, IL, p. A180
DIXON, Gregg, CPA Chief Financial Officer, CarePartners Health Services, Asheville, NC, p. A455
DIXON, Matt, Chief Executive Officer, Pearland Medical Center, Pearland, TX, p. A636
DIXON, Michael, Director Human Resources, Self Regional Healthcare, Greenwood, SC, p. A562
DIXON, Patricia J., R.N. Chief Clinical Officer, Kindred Hospital Kansas City, Kansas City, MO, p. A369
DIXON, Sally J., Chief Executive Officer, Memorial Hospital, York, PA, p. A554
DIXON, Shannon, Manager Business Office, Weisbrod Memorial County Hospital, Eads, CO, p. A103
DIXON, Todd, R.N
Chief Operating Officer, Coliseum Medical Centers, Macon, GA, p. A160
Chief Operating Officer, Coliseum Northside Hospital, Macon, GA, p. A160
DIZNEY, Donald R., Chairman and Chief Executive Officer, United Medical Corporation, Windermere, FL, p. B139
DJOGAN, Djogan, Chief Financial Officer, Muscogee Creek Nation Physical Rehabilitation Center, Okmulgee, OK, p. A513
DMELLO, Artie, Director Case Management, Kindred Hospital Sugar Land, Sugar Land, TX, p. A645

DOAK, Mark, President and Chief Executive Officer, Davis Health System, Elkins, WV, p. B44

DOAN, Angela, Chief Financial Officer, Scott Memorial Hospital, Scottsburg, IN, p. A219

DOANE, Peter, M.D
Chief Medical Officer, Franklin Regional Hospital, Franklin, NH, p. A406
Chief Medical Officer, Lakes Region General Hospital, Laconia, NH, p. A406

DOBALIAN, Derek, M.D. Chief of Staff, Gardens Regional Hospital and Medical Center, Hawaiian Gardens, CA, p. A64

DOBBING, Eileen, R.N. Senior Vice President for Patient Care Services, Memorial Hospital of Rhode Island, Pawtucket, RI, p. A555

DOBBINS, Jim, Vice President Human Resources, Lenoir Memorial Hospital, Kinston, NC, p. A463

DOBBS, Stephanie, Chief Nursing Officer, Sanford Clear Lake Medical Center, Clear Lake, SD, p. A568

DOBIN, Jennifer, Vice President Human Resources, Bayonne Medical Center, Bayonne, NJ, p. A409

DOBIZL, Howard
Director Information Technology Services, Howard Young Medical Center, Woodruff, WI, p. A714
Director Information Technology Services, Ministry Eagle River Memorial Hospital, Eagle River, WI, p. A700
Director Information Services for the Northern Region, Ministry Saint Mary's Hospitals, Rhinelander, WI, p. A710

DOBOSENSKI, Dave, Chief Executive Officer, St. Croix Regional Medical Center, St. Croix Falls, WI, p. A711

DOBOSH, Jr., Joseph J., Vice President and Chief Financial Officer, Children's Specialized Hospital–PSE&G, New Brunswick, NJ, p. A415

DOBRAWA, Stanley
Area Technology Director, Kaiser Permanente San Rafael Medical Center, San Rafael, CA, p. A90
Area Technology Director, Kaiser Permanente Santa Rosa Medical Center, Santa Rosa, CA, p. A92

DOBRINSKI, Sandra, Director of Nursing, Comanche County Hospital, Coldwater, KS, p. A238

DOBROVICH, Michael, M.D. Chief Medical Officer, St. John Medical Center, Westlake, OH, p. A500

DOBSON, Glenda, Vice President Clinical Services, Louisiana Heart Hospital, Lacombe, LA, p. A277

DOBSON, Glenn E., Chief Financial Officer, Aspirus Iron River Hospitals and Clinics, Iron River, MI, p. A323

DOBSON, Trey, M.D. Chief Medical Officer, Southwestern Vermont Medical Center, Bennington, VT, p. A660

DOCIMO, Anne, M.D. Executive Vice President and Chief Medical Officer, Thomas Jefferson University Hospitals, Philadelphia, PA, p. A545

DODD, John, Vice President Human Resources, Central Peninsula General Hospital, Soldotna, AK, p. A29

DODD, Kathy M., Director of Nursing, Southern Virginia Mental Health Institute, Danville, VA, p. A664

DODD, Pam, Chief Operating Officer, Harper County Community Hospital, Buffalo, OK, p. A504

DODDS, Cheryl, M.D. Medical Director, Three Rivers Behavioral Health, West Columbia, SC, p. A566

DODDS, George, M.D. Medical Director, Gouverneur Hospital, Gouverneur, NY, p. A434

DODDS, Sheryl, Chief Clinical Officer, Florida Hospital, Orlando, FL, p. A138

DODERER, Marcella, FACHE, President and Chief Executive Officer, Arkansas Children's Hospital, Little Rock, AR, p. A46

DODGE, Terry, M.D. Chief of Staff, Chester Regional Medical Center, Chester, SC, p. A558

DODSON, Thomas, Executive Director, Buffalo Psychiatric Center, Buffalo, NY, p. A430

DODSWORTH, Richard, Vice President Human Resources, MacNeal Hospital, Berwyn, IL, p. A179

DOEHRING, Christopher, M.D
Vice President Medical Affairs, Franciscan St. Francis Health – Indianapolis, Indianapolis, IN, p. A211
Vice President of Medical Affairs, Franciscan St. Francis Health–Carmel, Carmel, IN, p. A206

DOELING, Mariann, R.N., President, Carrington Health Center, Carrington, ND, p. A472

DOERFLER, Mary P., Chief Human Resources Officer, Central Texas Veterans Health Care System, Temple, TX, p. A646

DOERGE, Jean B., MS Chief Nursing Executive, UnityPoint Health – Trinity Bettendorf, Bettendorf, IA, p. A222

DOERING, Dean, Chief Executive Officer, Central Prison Hospital, Raleigh, NC, p. A466

DOERR, Brian, Chief Information Officer, ContinueCare Hospital at Baptist Health Corbin, Corbin, KY, p. A255

DOGGETT, Geri, Director Business, East Mississippi State Hospital, Meridian, MS, p. A357

DOGGETT, Sherri L., Vice President Patient Services, Mercy Medical Center–Centerville, Centerville, IA, p. A224

DOHERTY, Allison, Chief Financial Officer, Spine Hospital of Louisiana (formally the NeuroMedical Center Surgical Hospital), Baton Rouge, LA, p. A270

DOHERTY, Bryan, Management Information Technology Services I, Sagamore Children's Psychiatric Center, Dix Hills, NY, p. A432

DOHERTY, Donna, R.N. Vice President of Nursing and Chief Nursing Officer, Beth Israel Deaconess Hospital Plymouth, Plymouth, MA, p. A310

DOHERTY, Donnie, Director Information Systems, Fairfield Memorial Hospital, Winnsboro, SC, p. A566

DOHERTY, John, Vice President Finance, University of Minnesota Medical Center, Fairview, Minneapolis, MN, p. A343

DOHERTY, Randy, CPA, Chief Executive Officer, Braintree Rehabilitation Hospital, Braintree, MA, p. A304

DOHERTY, Ray, Director Information Technology, Clinton Memorial Hospital, Wilmington, OH, p. A501

DOHERTY, William J., M.D. Executive Vice President and Chief Operating Officer, Hallmark Health System, Melrose, MA, p. A308

DOHLZEL, Cheryl, Director Information Technology, Marcus Daly Memorial Hospital, Hamilton, MT, p. A384

DOHMANN, Eileen L., R.N
Senior Vice President and Chief Nursing Officer, Mary Washington Hospital, Fredericksburg, VA, p. A665
Senior Vice President and Chief Nursing Officer, Stafford Hospital, Stafford, VA, p. A673

DOI, Kathy, Executive Director Human Resources, AHMC Anaheim Regional Medical Center, Anaheim, CA, p. A53

DOIDGE, John C., Vice President Finance, Glencoe Regional Health Services, Glencoe, MN, p. A339

DOKSUM, Kathryn, Director Finance, Samaritan North Lincoln Hospital, Lincoln City, OR, p. A522

DOLAN, John, Chief Financial Officer, Cimarron Memorial Hospital, Boise City, OK, p. A504

DOLAN, Mary
Regional Director Information Services and HIPAA Security Official, Shriners Hospitals for Children–Boston, Boston, MA, p. A304
Director Information Services, Shriners Hospitals for Children–Springfield, Springfield, MA, p. A311

DOLAN, Patricia R., R.N. Vice President/ Chief Nursing Officer, Florida Hospital Waterman, Tavares, FL, p. A145

DOLAN, Shari, Chief Financial Officer, Liberty Medical Center, Chester, MT, p. A382

DOLAN, Steve, Chief Information Officer, EastPointe Hospital, Daphne, AL, p. A18

DOLBEE, Hilary, Chief Financial Officer, Central Iowa Healthcare, Marshalltown, IA, p. A231

DOLE, Patricia, Vice President Patient Care Services, TLC Health Network – Lake Shore Hospital, Irving, NY, p. A435

DOLEN, Cassie, Vice President Finance and Chief Financial Officer, Hutchinson Regional Medical Center, Hutchinson, KS, p. A242

DOLLINGER, Michael, Chief Operating Officer and Assistant Superintendent, Deer's Head Hospital Center, Salisbury, MD, p. A300

DOLLINS, Gary, Director Management Information Systems, Poplar Bluff Regional Medical Center, Poplar Bluff, MO, p. A374

DOLOHANTY–JOHNSON, Bridget, R.N. Vice President Patient Care Services, Parkview Whitley Hospital, Columbia City, IN, p. A206

DOLORESCO, Laureen, R.N. Associate Director for Patient Care and Nursing Services, James A. Haley Veterans' Hospital–Tampa, Tampa, FL, p. A144

DOMALESKI, Vareen O'Keefe, MS Vice Patient Care Services and Chief Nursing Officer, Emma Pendleton Bradley Hospital, East Providence, RI, p. A555

DOMANICO, Lee, Chief Executive Officer, Marin General Hospital, Greenbrae, CA, p. A64

DOMANN, Debbie, Director of Operations, Fillmore County Hospital, Geneva, NE, p. A392

DOMANSKY, John, Vice President Operations, Rutherford Regional Health System, Rutherfordton, NC, p. A468

DOMBROUSKI, Joyce, R.N. Regional Chief Nursing Officer, St. Patrick Hospital, Missoula, MT, p. A386

DOMEIER, Sandy, Director Patient Care Services, Ridgeview Sibley Medical Center, Arlington, MN, p. A334

DOMIAN, Catherine, R.N. Chief Nursing Officer, South Texas Health System, Edinburg, TX, p. A610

DOMINGO, Connie, M.D. Medical Director, Weisman Children's Rehabilitation Hospital, Marlton, NJ, p. A414

DOMINGO, Ramon, M.D. Chief of Staff, McCamey County Hospital District, McCamey, TX, p. A631

DOMINGUE, Buffy, Chief Executive Officer, Lafayette Surgical Specialty Hospital, Lafayette, LA, p. A277

DOMINGUEZ, Brenda, Director Human Resources, Cypress Creek Hospital, Houston, TX, p. A619

DOMINGUEZ, Ed, President Medical Staff, Vibra Specialty Hospital at DeSoto, Desoto, TX, p. A608

DOMINGUEZ, Isabel, Director Human Resources, Benson Hospital, Benson, AZ, p. A30

DOMINGUEZ, Jerry A., CPA Chief Financial Officer, East Texas Medical Center Trinity, Trinity, TX, p. A648

DOMINICCI, Sandra, Nursing Director, Hospital De Damas, Ponce, PR, p. A722

DOMINO, Laura, R.N. Vice President Patient Care Services, Hammond–Henry Hospital, Geneseo, IL, p. A189

DOMINSKI, Paul, Vice President Human Resources, Park Nicollet Methodist Hospital, Saint Louis Park, MN, p. A346

DOMMER, Matthew, M.D. Chief Medical Officer, Bronson LakeView Hospital, Paw Paw, MI, p. A327

DOMON, Steven, M.D. Medical Director, Arkansas State Hospital, Little Rock, AR, p. A47

DOMRES, Mary Jane, Director Materials Management and Administrator Information Technology, Cavalier County Memorial Hospital, Langdon, ND, p. A475

DONAGHY, Deirdre, M.D. Vice President Medical Affairs, St. Mary Medical Center, Langhorne, PA, p. A538

DONAHEY, Kenneth C., Chief Operating Officer, West Florida Hospital, Pensacola, FL, p. A140

DONAHUE, Debra, Senior Vice President and Chief Operating Officer, The University of Vermont Health Network–Champlain Valley Physicians Hospital, Plattsburgh, NY, p. A447

DONAHUE, Elisabeth, Associate Director Human Resources, Jeanes Hospital, Philadelphia, PA, p. A544

DONAHUE, Leslie A., President and Chief Executive Officer, Piedmont Hospital, Atlanta, GA, p. A151

DONAHUE, Michael, M.D. Medical Director, Select Specialty Hospital–Pittsburgh/UPMC, Pittsburgh, PA, p. A546

DONAHUE, Moreen, R.N. Chief Nursing Executive, Danbury Hospital, Danbury, CT, p. A111

DONAHUE, Patrick, Vice President and Administrator, Methodist Hospital Union County, Morganfield, KY, p. A263

DONAHUE, Ruth, R.N. Chief Nursing Officer, Harrison County Hospital, Corydon, IN, p. A206

DONALD, Steve, M.D. Chief of Staff, Washington County Hospital, Chatom, AL, p. A18

DONALDSON, Brooke G., Assistant Administrator Human Resources, Jackson Hospital, Marianna, FL, p. A133

DONALDSON, Jill, Vice President Operations, MedStar Harbor Hospital, Baltimore, MD, p. A294

DONALDSON, Les, M.D. Chief of Staff, Roosevelt General Hospital, Portales, NM, p. A425

DONALDSON, Lori, Chief Financial Officer, UC San Diego Health, San Diego, CA, p. A87

DONALDSON, Nesha, Chief Financial Officer, Cullman Regional Medical Center, Cullman, AL, p. A18

DONALDSON, Sherry, Director Human Resources, Southern Palmetto Hospital, Barnwell, SC, p. A557

DONALDSON, Tammy, Director of Nursing, Highlands Hospital, Connellsville, PA, p. A532

DONATELLE, Lawrence, M.D. Vice President Medical Affairs, St. Elizabeth Hospital, Appleton, WI, p. A697

DONAWAY, Duane, Director Information Technology, Hendrick Health System, Abilene, TX, p. A590

DONELAN, Matthias B., M.D. Chief of Staff, Shriners Hospitals for Children–Boston, Boston, MA, p. A304

DONENWIRTH, Karl, Vice President Information Services, Northcoast Behavioral Healthcare System, Northfield, OH, p. A495

DONGILLI, Jr., Paul, Ph.D. Executive Vice President and Chief Operating Officer, Madonna Rehabilitation Hospital, Lincoln, NE, p. A394

DONHAM, Guyle, M.D. Chief of Staff, Comanche County Medical Center, Comanche, TX, p. A601

DONICA, Joanna, Director Human Resource, HEALTHSOUTH Rehabilitation Hospital of Beaumont, Beaumont, TX, p. A596

DONLEY, Linda, Vice President Operations, Ira Davenport Memorial Hospital, Bath, NY, p. A429

DONLIN, Bruce, Director Information Services, Mount Desert Island Hospital, Bar Harbor, ME, p. A288

DONLIN, John
Regional Director Human Resources – Boston, Erie, and Springfield, Shriners Hospitals for Children–Boston, Boston, MA, p. A304
Director Human Resources, Shriners Hospitals for Children–Springfield, Springfield, MA, p. A311

DONLIN, Michael T., FACHE, Administrator, Floyd Valley Hospital, Le Mars, IA, p. A230

DONNELLY, Gloria, Director Human Resources, Euclid Hospital, Euclid, OH, p. A489

DONNELLY, James E., Chief Nursing Officer and Vice President Patient Care Services, UPMC Hamot, Erie, PA, p. A534

DONNELLY, Lane, M.D. Chief Medical Officer, Nemours Children's Hospital, Orlando, FL, p. A138

DONNELLY, Sheryl, Human Resources Specialist, State Hospital South, Blackfoot, ID, p. A172

Index of Health Care Professionals

Index of Health Care Professionals / Drabant

DONNER, Larry, Administrator, University Health Conway, Monroe, LA, p. A281
DONOGHUE, Alicia, Director Human Resources, EastPointe Hospital, Daphne, AL, p. A18
DONOHUE, Carolyn Viall, MSN Vice President Nursing, Roper Hospital, Charleston, SC, p. A558
DONOHUE, Mary Ann T., Ph.D. Chief Patient Care Services Officer, Stony Brook University Medical Center, Stony Brook, NY, p. A451
DONOVAN, Andrew
Director Information Technology, Wheaton Franciscan Healthcare – Elmbrook Memorial, Brookfield, WI, p. A698
Regional Director Information Services, Wheaton Franciscan Healthcare – St. Joseph's, Milwaukee, WI, p. A707
DONOVAN, James W., President and Chief Executive Officer, LincolnHealth, Damariscotta, ME, p. A290
DONOVAN, Jenny, Director Human Resources, Wright Memorial Hospital, Trenton, MO, p. A379
DONOVAN, Kevin, Chief Executive Officer, Mt. Ascutney Hospital and Health Center, Windsor, VT, p. A661
DONOVAN, Mary, Controller, HEALTHSOUTH Rehabilitation Institute of Tucson, Tucson, AZ, p. A39
DONOVAN, Mike, Chief Financial Officer, Lemuel Shattuck Hospital, Jamaica Plain, MA, p. A307
DONOVAN, Patrick, M.D. Director Medical Staff, HEALTHSOUTH Rehabilitation Hospital of Fort Worth, Fort Worth, TX, p. A613
DONSON, Elliott, Chief Information Specialist, Lincoln Hospital, Davenport, WA, p. A678
DONZE, Richard D., D.O. Senior Vice President Medical Affairs, Penn Medicine Chester County Hospital, West Chester, PA, p. A552
DOODY, Kris A., R.N., Chief Executive Officer, Cary Medical Center, Caribou, ME, p. A289
DOOKEERAM, David, Chief Operating Officer, Porter Adventist Hospital, Denver, CO, p. A102
DOOLEY, Lisa, Health Information Officer, Middlesboro ARH Hospital, Middlesboro, KY, p. A263
DOOLEY, Mark J., Chief Executive Officer, Wilson Memorial Hospital, Sidney, OH, p. A497
DOOLING, Edward, Vice President, Human Resources, Masonicare Health Center, Wallingford, CT, p. A115
DOOLITTLE, Jon D., President and Chief Executive Officer, Northwest Medical Center, Albany, MO, p. A363
DOORENBOS, Pamela, Medical Director, Medical Affairs, Maple Grove Hospital, Maple Grove, MN, p. A342
DOPLER, Lois, Interim Director Human Resources, Phoenix Baptist Hospital, Phoenix, AZ, p. A35
DORAK, John, Chief Information Officer, Nicholas H. Noyes Memorial Hospital, Dansville, NY, p. A432
DORAN, Judy, R.N. Vice President of Hospital Services and Chief Nurse Executive, Stanly Regional Medical Center, Albemarle, NC, p. A455
DORAN, Ken, Interim Chief Executive Officer, Sierra Surgery Hospital, Carson City, NV, p. A400
DORAN, T., Chief of Staff, Perry Memorial Hospital, Princeton, IL, p. A198
DORF, Jeffrey, M.D. Medical Director, Kindred Hospital–Albuquerque, Albuquerque, NM, p. A422
DORGAN, Amanda, Chief Nursing Officer, Central Regional Hospital, Butner, NC, p. A456
DORITY, Paula, Director Human Resources, Martin County Hospital District, Stanton, TX, p. A645
DORMAN, Christopher, Senior Vice President/Chief Operating Officer, Tift Regional Medical Center, Tifton, GA, p. A166
DORMAN, Stephen, M.D. Chief Medical Officer, New Mexico Rehabilitation Center, Roswell, NM, p. A426
DORNOFF, Edward G., Associate Director, Battle Creek Veterans Affairs Medical Center, Battle Creek, MI, p. A315
DOROGY, Sharon, Director Health Information Management, The Children's Institute of Pittsburgh, Pittsburgh, PA, p. A546
DOROTHY, Jonnie, Senior Director Human Resources, Massena Memorial Hospital, Massena, NY, p. A437
DORR, Amy, Vice President Human Resources, McLaren Lapeer Region, Lapeer, MI, p. A324
DORRIS, Ronald E., Chief Executive Officer, Carrus Hospitals, Sherman, TX, p. B28
DORRIS, Steve, Chief Financial Officer, Poplar Bluff Regional Medical Center, Poplar Bluff, MO, p. A374
DORSCH, Anthony, Chief Financial Officer, Providence Alaska Medical Center, Anchorage, AK, p. A27
DORSEY, John T., M.D. Vice President Clinical Integration and Population Health, Rockford Memorial Hospital, Rockford, IL, p. A199
DORSEY, William, M.D., Board Chairman and Chief Executive Officer, Jackson Park Hospital and Medical Center, Chicago, IL, p. A182
DORST, Jake, Interim Chief Executive Officer, Tahoe Forest Hospital District, Truckee, CA, p. A95
DORTON, Patty, Director of Nursing, Buchanan General Hospital, Grundy, VA, p. A665
DOSCHER, Suzanne C., Chief Executive Officer, Fairfield Memorial Hospital, Winnsboro, SC, p. A566
DOSS, Mounir F.
Executive Vice President and Chief Financial Officer, Flushing Hospital Medical Center, NY, p. A439
Executive Vice President and Chief Financial Officer, Jamaica Hospital Medical Center, NY, p. A440
DOSSETT, Phyllis, Director of Clinical Services, Wellmont Hancock County Hospital, Sneedville, TN, p. A588
DOSSEY, Emily, Director Human Resources, Hamilton General Hospital, Hamilton, TX, p. A617
DOTTS–MCCOOL, Michelle, Chief Nursing Officer, St. Vincent Dunn Hospital, Bedford, IN, p. A204
DOTY, Lisa, Manager Human Resources, Desert View Hospital, Pahrump, NV, p. A403
DOUBLE, Ron
Chief Information Technology Officer, Parkview LaGrange Hospital, LaGrange, IN, p. A214
Chief Information Officer, Parkview Noble Hospital, Kendallville, IN, p. A213
DOUCETTE, Diane, MBA, RN President, Mount Carmel New Albany Surgical Hospital, New Albany, OH, p. A495
DOUCETTE, Elmer H., Chief Financial Officer, Redington–Fairview General Hospital, Skowhegan, ME, p. A292
DOUCETTE, Jeffrey N., R.N. Chief Nursing Officer, Mary Immaculate Hospital, Newport News, VA, p. A669
DOUCETTE, Michael J., Senior Vice President and Administrator, Riverside Regional Medical Center, Newport News, VA, p. A669
DOUD, Tony, Controller, St. Mary's of Michigan Standish Hospital, Standish, MI, p. A330
DOUGHERTY, Christopher J., Chief Executive Officer, Covenant Children's Hospital, Lubbock, TX, p. A629
DOUGHERTY, Chuck, Chief Information Officer, Shenandoah Medical Center, Shenandoah, IA, p. A234
DOUGHERTY, David, Chief Information Management Officer, Irwin Army Community Hospital, Junction City, KS, p. A243
DOUGHERTY, James, Commander, U. S. Air Force Medical Center Keesler, Keesler AFB, MS, p. A355
DOUGHERTY, Terry, Director Human Resources, Bryn Mawr Hospital, Bryn Mawr, PA, p. A530
DOUGHTY, Cathy, Vice President Human Resources, Sheppard Pratt Health System, Baltimore, MD, p. A294
DOUGHTY, Linda, Chief Nursing Officer, Alaska Regional Hospital, Anchorage, AK, p. A27
DOUGHTY, Stephanie
Chief Financial Officer, Medical Center of the Rockies, Loveland, CO, p. A107
Chief Financial Officer, Poudre Valley Hospital, Fort Collins, CO, p. A103
DOUGLAS, Andy, Manager Information Technology, Burnett Medical Center, Grantsburg, WI, p. A701
DOUGLAS, Bill, Senior Vice President and Chief Financial Officer, Riverside Medical Center, Kankakee, IL, p. A192
DOUGLAS, Debbie, Director Human Resources, Putnam County Memorial Hospital, Unionville, MO, p. A380
DOUGLAS, Errol, Director Human Resources, University of Miami Hospital, Miami, FL, p. A135
DOUGLAS, Jason T., Chief Executive Officer, Memorial Medical Center – Ashland, Ashland, WI, p. A697
DOUGLAS, Lesia, R.N. Vice President Patient Care Services and Chief Nurse Executive, Bon Secours Baltimore Health System, Baltimore, MD, p. A293
DOUGLAS, Paul, Vice President Human Resources, Baton Rouge General Medical Center, Baton Rouge, LA, p. A269
DOUGLAS, Phillip B., Chairman and Chief Executive Officer, LifeCare Management Services, Plano, TX, p. B82
DOULAVERIS, Phyllis, MS
Senior Vice President and Chief Nursing Officer, Covenant Medical Center, Waterloo, IA, p. A235
Senior Vice President and Chief Nursing Officer, Mercy Hospital of Franciscan Sisters, Oelwein, IA, p. A232
DOVEL, Melissa, Manager Human Resources, Atrium Medical Center of Corinth, Corinth, TX, p. A602
DOVER, Jerry, Chief Executive Officer, Sullivan County Memorial Hospital, Milan, MO, p. A373
DOVNARSKY, James, M.D. Director Pulmonary Medical, Kindred Hospital South Philadelphia, Philadelphia, PA, p. A544
DOW, Laura, Vice President, Finance, Memorial Health, Savannah, GA, p. A164
DOWDLE, Paula, Chief Operating Officer, Jefferson Healthcare, Port Townsend, WA, p. A682
DOWDY, Kathren, MSN, Regional Hospital Senior Director, Carilion Tazewell Community Hospital, Tazewell, VA, p. A673
DOWELL, James, Administrator and Chief Executive Officer, Little River Memorial Hospital, Ashdown, AR, p. A41
DOWELL, Wade, M.D. Chief of Staff, South Sunflower County Hospital, Indianola, MS, p. A354
DOWERS, Cindy, Chief Nursing Officer, Harsha Behavioral Center, Terre Haute, IN, p. A220
DOWGUN, Richard, Chief Information Officer, St. Francis Medical Center, Trenton, NJ, p. A419
DOWLING, Deanna, R.N. Chief Nursing Officer, Promise Hospital of Wichita Falls, Wichita Falls, TX, p. A652
DOWLING, Lisa, Manager Finance, Mercy Hospital Tishomingo, Tishomingo, OK, p. A516
DOWLING, Michael J., President and Chief Executive Officer, North Shore–Long Island Jewish Health System, Great Neck, NY, p. B98
DOWN, Melanie Falls, Site Manager, Crow/Northern Cheyenne Hospital, Crow Agency, MT, p. A382
DOWN, Philip B., Chief Executive Officer, Doctors Community Hospital, Lanham, MD, p. A298
DOWNARD, Diane, Chief Financial Officer, Coal County General Hospital, Coalgate, OK, p. A505
DOWNES, Patrick, Chief Executive Officer, Coral Gables Hospital, Coral Gables, FL, p. A124
DOWNEY, Brandon W., Chief Executive Officer, Bayfront Health Punta Gorda, Punta Gorda, FL, p. A141
DOWNEY, Daniel, Chief Fiscal Service, Veterans Affairs New York Harbor Healthcare System, NY, p. A445
DOWNEY, Susan, MS, Chief Executive Officer, Kindred Hospital–Boston, Brighton, MA, p. A304
DOWNEY, William B., President and Chief Executive Officer, Riverside Health System, Newport News, VA, p. B113
DOWNEY, William B.
Chief Operating Officer, Riverside Regional Medical Center, Newport News, VA, p. A669
President and Chief Executive Officer, Riverside Rehabilitation Institute, Newport News, VA, p. A669
DOWNIE, Beth, Chief Information Officer, Newton–Wellesley Hospital, Newton Lower Falls, MA, p. A309
DOWNING, James, M.D., Chief Executive Officer, St. Jude Children's Research Hospital, Memphis, TN, p. A584
DOWNING, Jeff, R.N. Chief Nursing Officer, National Jewish Health, Denver, CO, p. A102
DOWNS, Beverly Sue, FACHE,
President, Flaget Memorial Hospital, Bardstown, KY, p. A254
Interim Chief Executive Officer, Saint Joseph Hospital, Lexington, KY, p. A260
DOWNS, Bryan, Director Information Systems, Central Peninsula General Hospital, Soldotna, AK, p. A29
DOWNS, Connie, CPA Vice President, Finance and Chief Financial Officer, Spectrum Health Pennock, Hastings, MI, p. A322
DOWNS, Lisa M., R.N. Chief Nursing Officer, Sarah D. Culbertson Memorial Hospital, Rushville, IL, p. A200
DOWNS, Patricia, Director Human Resources, Northern Nevada Medical Center, Sparks, NV, p. A404
DOWNS, Ray, Senior Staff Accountant, Healthmark Regional Medical Center, DeFuniak Springs, FL, p. A125
DOXTADER, Regina, Corporate Vice President and Chief Financial Officer, Beaumont Hospital – Farmington Hills, Farmington Hills, MI, p. A319
DOYEL, Brenda K., Chief Financial Officer, Sayre Memorial Hospital, Sayre, OK, p. A514
DOYLE, Barbara J., MS, Chief Executive Officer, MetroWest Medical Center, Framingham, MA, p. A307
DOYLE, Ben, R.N. Director of Nursing, Jefferson Hospital, Louisville, GA, p. A160
DOYLE, Christopher, Chief Executive Officer, Physicians Care Surgical Hospital, Royersford, PA, p. A549
DOYLE, Craig, Director and Chief Information Officer, St. Tammany Parish Hospital, Covington, LA, p. A272
DOYLE, Jay, Chief Financial Officer, St. James Healthcare, Butte, MT, p. A382
DOYLE, John
Chief Financial Officer, Central Washington Hospital, Wenatchee, WA, p. A687
Vice President Finance, Paoli Hospital, Paoli, PA, p. A542
Chief Financial Officer, Wenatchee Valley Medical Center, Wenatchee, WA, p. A687
DOYLE, Kelly, Chief Executive Officer, Rothman Specialty Hospital, Bensalem, PA, p. A529
DOYLE, Mark, Chief Executive Officer, Memorial Hospital Pembroke, Pembroke Pines, FL, p. A139
DOYLE, Patricia S., R.N. Chief Nursing Officer, Regional Medical Center, Manchester, IA, p. A231
DOZIER, Carol
President and Chief Executive Officer, King's Daughters' Health, Madison, IN, p. A215
Chief Financial Officer, LifeStream Behavioral Center, Leesburg, FL, p. A132
DOZIER, Mike, Chief Information Officer, Southeast Hospital, Cape Girardeau, MO, p. A365
DRABANT, Leah, Director of Finance, Complex Care Hospital at Ridgelake, Sarasota, FL, p. A142

Index of Health Care Professionals

Index of Health Care Professionals / Draeger


DRAEGER, Anne, Chief Nursing Officer, Owatonna Hospital, Owatonna, MN, p. A344
DRAEGER, Trish, Chief Nursing Officer, HEALTHSOUTH Deaconess Rehabilitation Hospital, Evansville, IN, p. A208
DRAGE, Marcia, R.N. Chief Nursing Officer, Minidoka Memorial Hospital, Rupert, ID, p. A176
DRAGO, Susan, R.N., Chief Executive Officer, Kindred Hospital North Florida, Green Cove Springs, FL, p. A128
DRAKE, Bryan L., D.O. Chief of Staff, Weiser Memorial Hospital, Weiser, ID, p. A177
DRAKE, Carolyn, Director of Nursing, Milan General Hospital, Milan, TN, p. A584
DRAKE, Marian, Chief Financial Officer, Greenwood County Hospital, Eureka, KS, p. A239
DRAKE, Megan, Assistant Administrator, Cedar Park Regional Medical Center, Cedar Park, TX, p. A600
DRAPER, Jason, Chief Financial Officer, Tennova Healthcare – Volunteer Community Hospital, Martin, TN, p. A582
DRAPER, Vivian, Chief Financial Officer, U. S. Public Health Service Indian Hospital–Sells, Sells, AZ, p. A38
DREGNEY, Jim, Chief Financial Officer, Lakewood Health System, Staples, MN, p. A347
DREHER, Craig, Chief Information Officer, Mercy Hospital of Portland, Portland, ME, p. A291
DREHER, Ronald, Finance Officer, Robert J. Dole Veterans Affairs Medical Center, Wichita, KS, p. A252
DREHR, Sammie, Chief Nursing Officer, DeTar Healthcare System, Victoria, TX, p. A650
DRENTH, Nancy E., Director Ancillary Services, Sanford Luverne Medical Center, Luverne, MN, p. A341
DRESSEL, Amy, M.D. Chief of Staff, Bartlett Regional Hospital, Juneau, AK, p. A28
DRESSER, Carol Ann, Vice President Information Services and Chief Information Officer, Hallmark Health System, Melrose, MA, p. A308
DRESSLER, Kaeli, R.N. Chief Nursing Officer, Peterson Regional Medical Center, Kerrville, TX, p. A626
DREUSSI, Rob, Interim Director Information Systems, AllianceHealth Ponca City, Ponca City, OK, p. A514
DREW, Jeff, Fiscal Officer, Aleda E. Lutz Veterans Affairs Medical Center, Saginaw, MI, p. A329
DREW, Jim, Chief Information Officer, Saint Thomas Midtown Hospital, Nashville, TN, p. A585
DREWETTE, Frederick J., Chief Financial Officer, Corona Regional Medical Center, Corona, CA, p. A58
DREXLER, Diane, R.N
  Chief Nursing Officer, Yavapai Regional Medical Center – East, Prescott Valley, AZ, p. A36
  Chief Nursing Officer, Yavapai Regional Medical Center, Prescott, AZ, p. A36
DRIFTMIER, PHR, Tammie, Director Human Resources, Clarinda Regional Health Center, Clarinda, IA, p. A224
DRIGGERS, Gina, Manager Information Technology, Greenville Health System – Laurens County Memorial Hospital, Clinton, SC, p. A559
DRIGGERS, Steve, M.D. Chief Medical Officer, Holy Family Memorial, Manitowoc, WI, p. A704
DRIGGS, Christi, Chief Financial Officer, Phillips County Hospital, Phillipsburg, KS, p. A248
DRINKWATER, Jinia, R.N. Director Patient Care Services, Braintree Rehabilitation Hospital, Braintree, MA, p. A304
DRINKWATER, Linda, Chief Financial Officer, Waldo County General Hospital, Belfast, ME, p. A289
DRINKWITZ, Jeremy, Chief Operating Officer, Sparks Regional Medical Center, Fort Smith, AR, p. A45
DRISCOLL, Angie, Director Human Resources, Los Alamitos Medical Center, Los Alamitos, CA, p. A68
DRISCOLL, Nancy, R.N. Chief Nursing Officer, Longmont United Hospital, Longmont, CO, p. A107
DRIVER, Ramona, Director Human Resources, De Queen Medical Center, De Queen, AR, p. A43
DROEGE, Marie T., President, Robert Packer Hospital, Sayre, PA, p. A549
DRONE, Marilyn, R.N. Vice President, CNO, St. Mary Medical Center, Apple Valley, CA, p. A54
DROTTS, Jennifer, Manager Human Resources, Bigfork Valley Hospital, Bigfork, MN, p. A335
DROZD, Carol, Chief Operating Officer, St. Mark's Medical Center, La Grange, TX, p. A627
DRUCKENMILLER, Carol, R.N. Assistant Administrator and Chief Nursing Officer, University of South Alabama Children's and Women's Hospital, Mobile, AL, p. A22
DRUMMOND, Gregory, Chief Executive Officer, West Oaks Hospital, Houston, TX, p. A623
DRUMMOND, Michael, Chief Financial Officer, Runnells Center for Rehabilitation and Healthcare, Berkeley Heights, NJ, p. A409
DRURY, Cynthia, Coordinator Human Resources, Highland–Clarksburg Hospital, Clarksburg, WV, p. A690
DRURY, Dennis, Director Information Technology, Northern Cochise Community Hospital, Willcox, AZ, p. A40
DRVARIC, David M., M.D. Chief of Staff, Shriners Hospitals for Children–Springfield, Springfield, MA, p. A311
DRYBURGH, Louise, Chief Executive Officer, First Care Health Center, Park River, ND, p. A476
DRYMON, Lisa, Manager, Fairfax Community Hospital, Fairfax, OK, p. A507
DRZEWIECKI–BURGER, Mary Jo, Administrative Manager, Caro Center, Caro, MI, p. A316
DU PONT, Karen, Chief Human Resource Officer, Casa Colina Hospital and Health Systems, Pomona, CA, p. A81
DU RALL, Marty, Executive Director Human Resources, St. Vincent Indianapolis Hospital, Indianapolis, IN, p. A212
DUANE, Paul K.
  Chief Financial Officer and Office of Health Reform, Palmetto Health Baptist, Columbia, SC, p. A559
  Chief Financial Officer and Office of Health Reform, Palmetto Health Richland, Columbia, SC, p. A559
DUARTE, Ray, Director, Information Technology and Services, Monmouth Medical Center, Southern Campus, Lakewood, NJ, p. A413
DUBE, Cynthia, M.D. Medical Director, Mayo Clinic Health System–Albert Lea and Austin, Austin, MN, p. A335
DUBE, Sheri, Chief Operating Officer, St. David's North Austin Medical Center, Austin, TX, p. A595
DUBEN, Julie, Chief Clinical Officer, Kindred Hospital Northland, Kansas City, MO, p. A370
DUBICKI, Robert, Executive Vice President and Chief Operating Officer, Kingsbrook Jewish Medical Center, NY, p. A441
DUBOIS, Brady, Chief Executive Officer, Northern Louisiana Medical Center, Ruston, LA, p. A284
DUBROCA, Darryl S.
  Chief Executive Officer and Managing Director, Spring Mountain Sahara, Las Vegas, NV, p. A402
  Chief Executive Officer and Managing Director, Spring Mountain Treatment Center, Las Vegas, NV, p. A402
DUBROW, Melissa, Chief Operating Officer, Waynesboro Hospital, Waynesboro, PA, p. A552
DUBRUYNE, Sharon, Director Human Resources, College Hospital Costa Mesa, Costa Mesa, CA, p. A59
DUCEY, Ann, Chief Information Officer, Boys Town National Research Hospital, Omaha, NE, p. A395
DUCHARME, Adele, MSN, Chief Executive Officer, Saint Luke's Cushing Hospital, Leavenworth, KS, p. A244
DUCHARME, Maria, R.N. Interim Chief Nursing Officer, Miriam Hospital, Providence, RI, p. A555
DUCHEMIN, MaDena, Assistant Administrator Human Resources, John Randolph Medical Center, Hopewell, VA, p. A666
DUCHENE, Pam, R.N. Vice President Patient Care Services, St. Joseph Hospital, Nashua, NH, p. A407
DUCHESNEAU, Angy, Senior Director Human Resources, Lakeview Hospital, Stillwater, MN, p. A347
DUCHICELA, Jorge, M.D. Chief of Staff, Columbus Community Hospital, Columbus, TX, p. A601
DUCHMAN, Susan, R.N. Vice President and Chief Nursing Officer, Williamsport Regional Medical Center, Williamsport, PA, p. A553
DUCKERT, Jon, Chief Executive Officer, Baylor Medical Center at Uptown, Dallas, TX, p. A604
DUCKOR, Steven, M.D. Chief of Staff, Chapman Medical Center, Orange, CA, p. A79
DUCKWORTH, Allison G., R.N. Chief Operating Officer and Chief Nursing Officer, FirstHealth Richmond Memorial Hospital, Rockingham, NC, p. A467
DUCKWORTH, Bob, Director Information Systems, Medical West, Bessemer, AL, p. A16
DUDA, David, Senior Vice President and Chief Operating Officer, Riverside Medical Center, Kankakee, IL, p. A192
DUDLEY, III, Edward L., Executive Vice President and Chief Financial Officer, Catholic Medical Center, Manchester, NH, p. A407
DUDLEY, Heather, Director Administrative Services, Brookhaven Hospital, Tulsa, OK, p. A516
DUDLEY, James, M.D. Medical Director, Cordova Community Medical Center, Cordova, AK, p. A27
DUDLEY, Sharon, Chief Operating Officer, Comanche County Memorial Hospital, Lawton, OK, p. A508
DUDLEY, W. Steve, CPA Chief Financial Officer, Ed Fraser Memorial Hospital and Baker Community Health Center, MacClenny, FL, p. A132
DUENSING, Kenneth, Chief of Staff, Community Memorial Healthcare, Marysville, KS, p. A246
DUETSCH, Stephen, Vice President Operations and Support, Spencer Hospital, Spencer, IA, p. A235
DUFF, Isabel, MS, Director, Veterans Affairs Southern Nevada Healthcare System, North Las Vegas, NV, p. A403
DUFF, Jim, Chief Financial Officer, Colorado Mental Health Institute at Pueblo, Pueblo, CO, p. A108
DUFF, Mary Claire, CPA Chief Financial Officer, Ridgeview Psychiatric Hospital and Center, Oak Ridge, TN, p. A587
DUFFEE, Patrick, Director Medical Information Systems, Delta Medical Center, Memphis, TN, p. A583
DUFFEY, Pam, MSN Chief Nursing Officer, Texas Health Specialty Hospital, Fort Worth, TX, p. A614
DUFFIELD, Douglas, President and Chief Executive Officer, San Joaquin Community Hospital, Bakersfield, CA, p. A55
DUFFIN, Kelly L., Operations Officer, Intermountain Medical Center, Murray, UT, p. A656
DUFFORD, Shawn, M.D. Vice President Medical Affairs and Chief Medical Officer, Saint Joseph Hospital, Denver, CO, p. A102
DUFFY, Beth, Chief Operating Officer, Einstein Medical Center Montgomery, East Norriton, PA, p. A533
DUFFY, Daniel, D.O. Chief Medical Director, HealthSource Saginaw, Inc., Saginaw, MI, p. A329
DUFFY, Delilah, Interim Chief Nurse Officer, Central Montana Medical Center, Lewistown, MT, p. A385
DUFFY, Kenneth, M.D. Medical Director, Seiling Municipal Hospital, Seiling, OK, p. A514
DUFFY, Marie Theresa, Chief Operating Officer, Christ Hospital, Jersey City, NJ, p. A413
DUFFY, Pam, Vice President Human Resources, South Oaks Hospital, Amityville, NY, p. A428
DUFFY, Pamela
  Vice President Patient Care Services and Chief Nursing Officer, Kishwaukee Hospital, DeKalb, IL, p. A186
  Vice President Patient Services and CNO, Valley West Hospital, Sandwich, IL, p. A200
DUFT, Ryan, R.N. Chief Nursing Officer, Fredonia Regional Hospital, Fredonia, KS, p. A240
DUGAN, Elizabeth, Ph.D. Chief Nursing Officer, Inova Loudoun Hospital, Leesburg, VA, p. A667
DUGAN, Gary, M.D. Vice President Medical Affairs, Penn Highlands DuBois, DuBois, PA, p. A533
DUGAR, Edward, Chief Executive Officer, Hood Memorial Hospital, Amite, LA, p. A268
DUGGAL, Harpreet, M.D. Medical Director, Department of Health and Human Services, Humboldt County Mental Health, Eureka, CA, p. A60
DUGGAN, Daniel, Chief Operating Officer, Bon Secours St. Francis Health System, Greenville, SC, p. A561
DUGGAN, Eileen, M.D. Medical Director, Crittenton Children's Center, Kansas City, MO, p. A369
DUGGAN, James E., Director Human Resources, Western Massachusetts Hospital, Westfield, MA, p. A313
DUGGAN, Margaret M., M.D. Chief Medical Officer, Brigham and Women's Faulkner Hospital, Boston, MA, p. A303
DUGGAN, Stephanie J., M.D. Vice President and Chief Medical Officer, Sacred Heart Hospital of Pensacola, Pensacola, FL, p. A140
DUGGAN, Tonya, Director Human Resources, Northern Louisiana Medical Center, Ruston, LA, p. A284
DUGGAR, Susan, R.N. Vice President Nursing, Spartanburg Regional Medical Center, Spartanburg, SC, p. A565
DUGGER, Curtis R., Chief Financial Officer, Memorial Hospital of Converse County, Douglas, WY, p. A716
DUGGER, Sandy, Chief Human Resources Officer, Platte County Memorial Hospital, Wheatland, WY, p. A718
DUHAIME, Robert A., R.N. Senior Vice President Clinical Operations and Chief Nursing Officer, Catholic Medical Center, Manchester, NH, p. A407
DUHE, Louis, Senior Director Information Technology, George Washington University Hospital, Washington, DC, p. A119
DUHE, Suzette, Chief Financial Officer, Louisiana Heart Hospital, Lacombe, LA, p. A277
DUHON, Thomas, Director Human Resources, Heart Hospital of Lafayette, Lafayette, LA, p. A277
DUKE, II, Lee M., M.D. Senior Vice President and Chief Physician Executive, Lancaster General Health, Lancaster, PA, p. A537
DUKES, Brenda, Director Human Resources, Sonoma Developmental Center, Eldridge, CA, p. A60
DUKOFF, Ruth, M.D. Medical Director, North Star Behavioral Health System, Anchorage, AK, p. A27
DULANEY, Paul, M.D. Chief of Staff, Troy Regional Medical Center, Troy, AL, p. A25
DULANEY, Thomas, M.D. Chief of Staff, St. Anthony Regional Hospital, Carroll, IA, p. A223
DULIT, Alan, M.D. Chief Medical Officer, St. Anthony Summit Medical Center, Frisco, CO, p. A104
DULNY, David
  Chief Financial Officer, Providence Medical Center, Kansas City, KS, p. A243
  Chief Financial Officer, Saint John Hospital, Leavenworth, KS, p. A244
DUMAL, Jennifer, R.N. Chief Operating Officer of Clinical and Chief Nursing Officer, Memorial Hospital at Gulfport, Gulfport, MS, p. A353


**A828** Index of Health Care Professionals 

Index of Health Care Professionals / Dworkin

Index of Health Care Professionals


DUMONSEAU, Kent
Vice President Finance and Information Services, Hayward Area Memorial Hospital and Nursing Home, Hayward, WI, p. A702
Vice President Finance and Information Services, Memorial Medical Center – Ashland, Ashland, WI, p. A697
DUMONT, Frank, Director Human Resources, Eastern Long Island Hospital, Greenport, NY, p. A434
DUMONT, Rene, Vice President Strategic Growth, St. Mary's Regional Medical Center, Lewiston, ME, p. A291
DUNAVAN, Chad, R.N. Chief Nursing Officer, Medical Center Health System, Odessa, TX, p. A634
DUNCAN, Allison, Chief Financial Officer, Arrowhead Behavioral Health Hospital, Maumee, OH, p. A494
DUNCAN, Barbara, Chief Financial Officer, Habersham Medical Center, Demorest, GA, p. A156
DUNCAN, Charles, M.D. Medical Director, Kindred Hospital–San Antonio, San Antonio, TX, p. A641
DUNCAN, Cindy
Manager Human Resources, Plains Regional Medical Center, Clovis, NM, p. A423
Director Human Resources, Roosevelt General Hospital, Portales, NM, p. A425
DUNCAN, Cynthia, Chief Executive Officer, Roger Mills Memorial Hospital, Cheyenne, OK, p. A504
DUNCAN, Darryl L., President and Chief Executive Officer, Monongalia General Hospital, Morgantown, WV, p. A693
DUNCAN, Darryl L., President and Chief Executive Officer, Monongalia Health System, Morgantown, WV, p. B93
DUNCAN, Jeremy, Director Information Systems, Lawrence Medical Center, Moulton, AL, p. A23
DUNCAN, Jimmy, Chief Human Resources Officer, Atlanta Medical Center, Atlanta, GA, p. A150
DUNCAN, Leeann, Director Patient Care Services, Harbor Oaks Hospital, New Baltimore, MI, p. A326
DUNCAN, Linda, Director Human Resources, Lee's Summit Medical Center, Lee's Summit, MO, p. A371
DUNCAN, Lyman, Chief Financial Officer, San Juan Hospital, Monticello, UT, p. A655
DUNCAN, Michael J., President and Chief Executive Officer, Penn Medicine Chester County Hospital, West Chester, PA, p. A552
DUNCAN, Nathan, Chief Executive Officer, Lakeland Behavioral Health System, Springfield, MO, p. A378
DUNCAN, Richard, Vice President and Chief Information Officer, Mount Sinai Hospital, Chicago, IL, p. A183
DUNCAN, Thomas M., Executive Vice President and Chief Financial Officer, Miami Valley Hospital, Dayton, OH, p. A488
DUNFEE, Michael H., Director, Hampton Veterans Affairs Medical Center, Hampton, VA, p. A666
DUNFORD, Ben, Chief Financial Officer, Texas Regional Medical Center at Sunnyvale, Sunnyvale, TX, p. A646
DUNFORD, Bill, Manager, Northside Hospital–Cherokee, Canton, GA, p. A153
DUNFORD–BOOTHE, Rosalina, Community Chief Nursing Officer, Beckley ARH Hospital, Beckley, WV, p. A689
DUNGAN, Janice L., Senior Vice President Clinical Services, Lake Regional Health System, Osage Beach, MO, p. A374
DUNHAM, Shelly, Chief Executive Officer, Okeene Municipal Hospital, Okeene, OK, p. A511
DUNIGAN, Linda, Chief Executive Officer, Claiborne County Medical Center, Port Gibson, MS, p. A359
DUNIO, Gina, Chief Human Resources, James E. Van Zandt Veterans Affairs Medical Center, Altoona, PA, p. A528
DUNKER, Karla, Director Finance, Sedgwick County Health Center, Julesburg, CO, p. A105
DUNKIEL, Barbara, Director Human Resources, HEALTHSOUTH Sunrise Rehabilitation Hospital, Sunrise, FL, p. A143
DUNKIN, Jackie J., Director Human Resources, Platte Valley Medical Center, Brighton, CO, p. A100
DUNLAP, DeeDee, Information Officer, Regional West Garden County, Oshkosh, NE, p. A397
DUNLAP, Mary Lou, Correctional Health Services Administrator, California Medical Facility, Vacaville, CA, p. A95
DUNLAY, Sherry, Chief Nursing Officer, St. Mary's Hospital, Centralia, IL, p. A180
DUNLEY, Pamela L., R.N. Vice President Chief Nursing Officer and Chief Operating Officer, Elmhurst Memorial Hospital, IL, p. A187
DUNLOP, Jr., James H., CP
Executive Vice President and Chief Financial Officer, Kenmore Mercy Hospital, Kenmore, NY, p. A436
Senior Vice President Finance and Chief Financial Officer, Mercy Hospital, Buffalo, NY, p. A430
Chief Financial Officer, Sisters of Charity Hospital of Buffalo, Buffalo, NY, p. A431
DUNMAN, Robyn, Coordinator Human Resources, Kindred Hospital–Nashville, Nashville, TN, p. A585
DUNMYER, Daniel C., Chief Executive Officer, Carolinas ContinueCare Hospital at Pineville, Charlotte, NC, p. A457
DUNN, Christopher, M.D. Vice President Medical Affairs, Sequoia Hospital, Redwood City, CA, p. A83
DUNN, Daniel N., Vice President Operations, Wentworth–Douglass Hospital, Dover, NH, p. A406
DUNN, Dave, Director of Nursing, Star Valley Medical Center, Afton, WY, p. A715
DUNN, E. D., Vice President Human Resources, Virtua Memorial, Mount Holly, NJ, p. A414
DUNN, Edna, Chief Nursing Officer, Western Plains Medical Complex, Dodge City, KS, p. A239
DUNN, Hope, Chief Nursing Officer, HEALTHSOUTH East Valley Rehabilitation Hospital, Mesa, AZ, p. A33
DUNN, Jack, M.D. Chief of Staff, La Paz Regional Hospital, Parker, AZ, p. A34
DUNN, Janice, Chief Financial Officer, Saint Joseph Regional Medical Center–Plymouth Campus, Plymouth, IN, p. A218
DUNN, Leonard, M.D. Chief Medical Officer, BayCare Alliant Hospital, Dunedin, FL, p. A126
DUNN, Marcy
Vice President Information Services and Chief Information Officer, Good Samaritan Hospital Medical Center, West Islip, NY, p. A453
Vice President Information Services and Chief Information Officer, Mercy Medical Center, Rockville Centre, NY, p. A449
Vice President Information Services and Chief Information Officer, St. Francis Hospital, Roslyn, NY, p. A449
DUNN, Margie, Director Human Resources, Middle Tennessee Mental Health Institute, Nashville, TN, p. A585
DUNN, Nicholas, Director Information Systems, Mena Regional Health System, Mena, AR, p. A48
DUNN, Patrick A., R.N. Chief Nursing Officer, Lea Regional Medical Center, Hobbs, NM, p. A424
DUNN, Rosemary, R.N. Chief Nursing Officer, Hahnemann University Hospital, Philadelphia, PA, p. A543
DUNN, Sheila, Assistant Administrator Human Resources, Dale Medical Center, Ozark, AL, p. A24
DUNN, Tandra, Director of Nursing, San Luis Valley Health Conejos County Hospital, La Jara, CO, p. A105
DUNN, Terry, Director Information Technology, Battle Mountain General Hospital, Battle Mountain, NV, p. A400
DUNNAM, Lorie, Superintendent, Big Spring State Hospital, Big Spring, TX, p. A597
DUNNE, Elizabeth, President and Chief Executive Officer, PeaceHealth, Vancouver, WA, p. B104
DUNNE, Elizabeth, Chief Executive, Providence Little Company of Mary Medical Center – Torrance, Torrance, CA, p. A94
DUNNING, David K., Commanding Officer, Tripler Army Medical Center, Honolulu, HI, p. A169
DUNPHY–ALEXANDER, Shannon, Director, Mercy Harvard Hospital, Harvard, IL, p. A189
DUNWOODY, Robert, Chief Financial Officer, Lawnwood Regional Medical Center & Heart Institute, Fort Pierce, FL, p. A127
DUPLAN, Don, M.D. Chief of Staff, The Medical Center of Southeast Texas, Port Arthur, TX, p. A637
DUPPER, Harold, Chief Financial Officer, Platte Valley Medical Center, Brighton, CO, p. A100
DUPPER, Larry L., Chief Financial Officer, Valley View Hospital, Glenwood Springs, CO, p. A104
DUPPSTADT, Edwin, M.D. Chief Medical Officer, Medical Center Arlington, Arlington, TX, p. A592
DUPRE', Charlotte W., Chief Executive Officer, Merit Health Central, Jackson, MS, p. A355
DUPREE, Harry, Director of Nursing, LCMH Specialty Hospital, Lake Charles, LA, p. A278
DUPREE, Lucy G., Director Human Resources, District One Hospital, Faribault, MN, p. A338
DUPREY, Irma, Administrator Medical Records, Hospital Universitario Dr. Ramon Ruiz Arnau, Bayamon, PR, p. A720
DUPUIS, Pamela M., R.N. Senior Vice President Patient Care Services, Montefiore New Rochelle, New Rochelle, NY, p. A438
DUQUETTE, Cathy E., Ph.D. Vice President Nursing and Chief Nursing Officer, Newport Hospital, Newport, RI, p. A555
DUQUETTE, Connie, Director Human Resources, Sharp Memorial Hospital, San Diego, CA, p. A87
DUQUETTE, William M., Chief Executive Officer, Baptist Health South Florida, Homestead Hospital, Homestead, FL, p. A129
DURAN, Jody, Manager Information Systems, Livingston HealthCare, Livingston, MT, p. A385
DURAND, Crista F., President, Newport Hospital, Newport, RI, p. A555
DURAND, Mark, Assistant Administrator Operations, CHRISTUS Jasper Memorial Hospital, Jasper, TX, p. A624
DURBAK, Ivan, Chief Information Officer, Bronx–Lebanon Hospital Center Health Care System, NY, p. A438
DURBIN, Melissa, R.N. Chief Nursing Officer, Boca Raton Regional Hospital, Boca Raton, FL, p. A122
DURDEN, Rhonda, Chief Financial Officer, Emanuel Medical Center, Swainsboro, GA, p. A165
DURGIN, Manal, Network Medical Director, Devereux Hospital and Children's Center of Florida, Melbourne, FL, p. A133
DURHAM, Linda
Director Human Resources, Henderson County Community Hospital, Lexington, TN, p. A581
Director Human Resources, Tennova Healthcare – McNairy Regional Hospital, Selmer, TN, p. A587
DURHAM, Thomas, Chief Nursing Officer, Ferry County Memorial Hospital, Republic, WA, p. A683
DURIS, Deb, Director of Nursing, Northwest Ohio Psychiatric Hospital, Toledo, OH, p. A498
DURNEY, Gerry, Chief Operating Officer, Good Samaritan Hospital, Suffern, NY, p. A451
DURNIOK, Brian
Vice President Human Resources, UPMC Hamot, Erie, PA, p. A534
Vice President Operations, UPMC Northwest, Seneca, PA, p. A550
DURON, Kety, Vice President Human Resources, Stanford Health Care, Palo Alto, CA, p. A80
DUROVICH, Christopher J.
President and Chief Executive Officer, Children's Health System of Texas, Dallas, TX, p. A604
President and Chief Executive, Children's Medical Center Plano, Plano, TX, p. A637
DURR, Amber, Director Human Resources, Community Hospital–Fairfax, Fairfax, MO, p. A367
DURR, Durinda, Vice President Clinical Services and Chief Nursing Officer, Rome Memorial Hospital, Rome, NY, p. A449
DURR, Michele, M.D. Chief of Medical Staff, Harlan County Health System, Alma, NE, p. A389
DURRENCE, Elizabeth, Chief Operating Officer, Kendall Regional Medical Center, Miami, FL, p. A134
DURST, Geoff, Vice President Finance, Avera St. Luke's Hospital, Aberdeen, SD, p. A567
DURST, Sue, R.N. Vice President Plant Operations, McLaren Macomb, Mount Clemens, MI, p. A326
DURSTELER, Courtney, Chief Human Resources Officer, Franklin County Medical Center, Preston, ID, p. A176
DURYEE, Edward E., Director Information Systems, Saint Francis Medical Center, Cape Girardeau, MO, p. A364
DUSANG, Nina
Vice President Finance and Chief Financial Officer, DCH Regional Medical Center, Tuscaloosa, AL, p. A25
Chief Financial Officer, Northport Medical Center, Northport, AL, p. A23
DUSENBERY, Jack, FACHE, President and Chief Executive Officer, Covenant Medical Center, Waterloo, IA, p. A235
DUTCHER, Phillip C., Chief Operating Officer, NCH Downtown Naples Hospital, Naples, FL, p. A136
DUTHE, Robert J., Director Information Systems and Chief Information Officer, Cortland Regional Medical Center, Cortland, NY, p. A432
DUTLA, Nimal, M.D. Chief Medical Staff, Holzer Medical Center – Jackson, Jackson, OH, p. A491
DUTMERS, David, Manager Technology Information System, Spectrum Health United Hospital, Greenville, MI, p. A321
DUTTON, Angela, Chief Human Resources Management Service, Robley Rex Veterans Affairs Medical Center, Louisville, KY, p. A262
DUTTON, Rebecca, Director Human Resources, Larue D. Carter Memorial Hospital, Indianapolis, IN, p. A212
DUTTON, Teresa, R.N. Chief Nursing Officer, Heritage Park Surgical Hospital, Sherman, TX, p. A644
DUVAL, John, Chief Executive Officer, VCU Medical Center, Richmond, VA, p. A672
DUVAL, Rob, Chief Human Resources Officer, Emma Pendleton Bradley Hospital, East Providence, RI, p. A555
DUVALL, Richard, Chief Executive Officer, Carthage Area Hospital, Carthage, NY, p. A431
DUVALL, Wendy, Chief Executive Officer, Barton County Memorial Hospital, Lamar, MO, p. A371
DUVVURI, Vikas, M.D. Medical Director, Fremont Hospital, Fremont, CA, p. A62
DVORAK, Rebecca, Chief Nursing Officer, Two Rivers Behavioral Health System, Kansas City, MO, p. A371
DWIGHT, John, Chief Information Officer, Skagit Valley Hospital, Mount Vernon, WA, p. A681
DWORKIN, Darren, Senior Vice President and Chief Information Officer, Cedars–Sinai Medical Center, Los Angeles, CA, p. A69
DWORKIN, Jack H., M.D. Vice President Medical Affairs and Chief Medical Officer, CentraState Healthcare System, Freehold, NJ, p. A412
DWORKIN, Paul, M.D. Physician–in–Chief, Connecticut Children's Medical Center, Hartford, CT, p. A112

Index of Health Care Professionals

Index of Health Care Professionals / Dwozan

DWOZAN, C. Richard
Administrator, South Georgia Medical Center Berrien Campus, Nashville, GA, p. A162
Administrator, South Georgia Medical Center Lanier Campus, Lakeland, GA, p. A160
DWYER, Amy L., R.N. Chief Nursing Officer, Sacred Heart Hospital, Eau Claire, WI, p. A700
DWYER, Cathy, Senior Administrator Information Systems, Burke Rehabilitation Hospital, White Plains, NY, p. A454
DWYER, James P., D.O
Executive Vice President and Chief Medical Officer, Virtua Memorial, Mount Holly, NJ, p. A414
Executive Vice President and Chief Medical Officer, Virtua Voorhees, Voorhees, NJ, p. A420
DWYER, Karla, R.N. Chief Nursing Officer, HEALTHSOUTH Rehabilitation Hospital–Wichita Falls, Wichita Falls, TX, p. A652
DWYER, Susan, Vice President Finance, Aurora Psychiatric Hospital, Wauwatosa, WI, p. A713
DWYER, William, Vice President Human Resources, Children's Specialized Hospital–PSE&G, New Brunswick, NJ, p. A415
DYCHE, Ginny, Director Community Relations, Aspen Valley Hospital District, Aspen, CO, p. A99
DYCUS, Steve, Director Marketing and Public Relations, Williamson Medical Center, Franklin, TN, p. A578
DYE, Blake A., President, St. Vincent Heart Center, Indianapolis, IN, p. A212
DYE, Chris, Director Information Systems, Saint Joseph – Martin, Martin, KY, p. A262
DYE, Dana, R.N., Vice President, Administrator and Chief Executive Officer, Baptist Memorial Hospital – Memphis, Memphis, TN, p. A583
DYE, Emily, Vice President Human Resources, TriStar Summit Medical Center, Hermitage, TN, p. A578
DYE, Kathy, Interim Administrator, Adena Greenfield Medical Center, Greenfield, OH, p. A490
DYER, Kathleen, Vice President and Chief Information Officer, Adventist Behavioral Health Rockville, Rockville, MD, p. A299
DYKEHOUSE, Rod, Chief Information Officer, Penn State Milton S. Hershey Medical Center, Hershey, PA, p. A536
DYKEHOUSE, Rodney, Senior Vice President Information Services, Waukesha Memorial Hospital, Waukesha, WI, p. A713
DYKENS, Jeff, CPA Chief Operating Officer, Falmouth Hospital, Falmouth, MA, p. A306
DYKES, Bradford W., President and Chief Executive Officer, Indiana University Health Bedford Hospital, Bedford, IN, p. A204
DYKES, Jennifer, Director Human Resources, Russell County Hospital, Russell Springs, KY, p. A265
DYKES, Nichole, Chief Financial Officer, Reliant Rehabilitation Hospital North Texas, Richardson, TX, p. A638
DYKSTERHOUSE, Trevor J., President, Forest Health Medical Center, Ypsilanti, MI, p. A333
DYKSTRA, Janet H., Chief Executive Officer, Osceola Community Hospital, Sibley, IA, p. A234
DYLE, Amanda, Chief Financial Officer, Coastal Carolina Hospital, Hardeeville, SC, p. A562
DYRKACZ, Anna, Chief Financial Officer, Vibra Hospital of Western Massachusetts, Springfield, MA, p. A312
DYSART–CREDEUR, Amy, Administrator, Oceans Behavioral Hospital of Broussard, Broussard, LA, p. A271
DZIEDZICKI, Ron, R.N. Chief Operating Officer, University Hospitals Case Medical Center, Cleveland, OH, p. A485
DZURENKO, Jeanne, R.N. Chief Nursing Officer and Senior Vice President Patient Care, Good Samaritan Hospital Medical Center, West Islip, NY, p. A453

# E

EADIE, Reginald J., M.D., Chief Executive Officer, DMC Harper University Hospital, Detroit, MI, p. A317
EADS, Barry, Chief Nursing Officer, HEALTHSOUTH Rehabilitation of Gadsden, Gadsden, AL, p. A20
EAGEN, Mary K., R.N. Executive Vice President, Chief Nursing Officer, Parkland Health & Hospital System, Dallas, TX, p. A606
EAGER, David, Senior Vice President and Chief Financial Officer, Children's Health System of Texas, Dallas, TX, p. A604
EAGERTON, Gregory S., Ph.D. Nurse Executive, Durham Veterans Affairs Medical Center, Durham, NC, p. A459
EAKS, C. Alan, Chief Executive Officer, Dominion Hospital, Falls Church, VA, p. A664
EARL, Anna, M.D. Chief of Staff, Liberty Medical Center, Chester, MT, p. A382
EARL, Mindy, Health Information Manager, Power County Hospital District, American Falls, ID, p. A172
EARLE, Audra, FACHE, Chief Executive Officer, Watsonville Community Hospital, Watsonville, CA, p. A97
EARLE, Cletis, Vice President and Chief Information Officer, St. Luke's Cornwall Hospital, Newburgh, NY, p. A445
EARLEY, Robert, President and Chief Executive Officer, JPS Health Network, Fort Worth, TX, p. A613
EARLEY, Tom, Chief Financial Officer, AllianceHealth Woodward, Woodward, OK, p. A518
EARLS, Sandra, Chief Financial Officer, Coalinga Regional Medical Center, Coalinga, CA, p. A58
EARLY, Elfie, Manager Data Services, Georgia Regional Hospital at Atlanta, Decatur, GA, p. A156
EARNSHAW, Dallas, Superintendent, Utah State Hospital, Provo, UT, p. A657
EASLEY, Evan, M.D. Chief Medical Officer, Carson Valley Medical Center, Gardnerville, NV, p. A400
EASLEY, Mike, Vice President and Chief Operating Officer, Sabine County Hospital, Hemphill, TX, p. A618
EASON, Laurence, M.D. Chief Medical Officer, Providence Little Company of Mary Medical Center – Torrance, Torrance, CA, p. A94
EASON SMEDLEY, Jessie, Chief Executive Officer, South Texas Rehabilitation Hospital, Brownsville, TX, p. A598
EASTBURG, Mark C., Ph.D., President and Chief Executive Officer, Pine Rest Christian Mental Health Services, Grand Rapids, MI, p. A321
EASTER, Louise, R.N. Chief Operating Officer and Chief Nursing Officer, Wagoner Community Hospital, Wagoner, OK, p. A518
EASTER, Susan, Chief Nursing Officer, Palacios Community Medical Center, Palacios, TX, p. A635
EASTERLING, Jamie, Executive Director, Operations, Good Samaritan Hospital, Cincinnati, OH, p. A483
EASTERWOOD, Diane J., Human Resources Business Partner, Kaiser Permanente San Francisco Medical Center, San Francisco, CA, p. A88
EASTHOPE, Kerry, Area Finance Officer, Kaiser Permanente Antioch Medical Center, Antioch, CA, p. A53
EASTMAN, David, Site Director, Ukiah Valley Medical Center, Ukiah, CA, p. A95
EASTMAN, Joseph F., Director Human Resources, Central Carolina Hospital, Sanford, NC, p. A468
EASTON, Laura J., R.N., President and Chief Executive Officer, Caldwell Memorial Hospital, Lenoir, NC, p. A464
EATHERLY, Theresa, Chief Financial Officer, Doctor's Hospital – Tidwell, Houston, TX, p. A619
EATON, Jim, Chief Financial Officer, Wise Regional Health System, Decatur, TX, p. A607
EATON, Philip, Interim Chief Executive Officer, Mountain West Medical Center, Tooele, UT, p. A659
EAVENSON, Steve, Vice President Finance, Mercy Health Saint Mary's, Grand Rapids, MI, p. A321
EAVES, Clinton, Administrator, H. C. Watkins Memorial Hospital, Quitman, MS, p. A360
EAVES, Dan, Board President and Acting Chief Executive Officer, Marshall Browning Hospital, Du Quoin, IL, p. A186
EBANGIT, Ruth, M.D. Chief of Staff and Medical Officer, Throckmorton County Memorial Hospital, Throckmorton, TX, p. A648
EBAUGH, Matthew T., Area Information Officer, Kaiser Permanente San Diego Medical Center, San Diego, CA, p. A86
EBBETT, Patricia, Chief Human Resources Officer, Catawba Hospital, Catawba, VA, p. A663
EBERSOLE, Nathan, Controller, Calhoun–Liberty Hospital, Blountstown, FL, p. A121
EBERT, Jr., Larry W., Chief Operating Officer and Chief Financial Officer, Northridge Medical Center, Commerce, GA, p. A154
EBERT, Michael, M.D. Chief of Staff, Veterans Affairs Connecticut Healthcare System, West Haven, CT, p. A116
EBERT–LOOMIS, Cynthia, R.N. Chief Nursing Officer, Summit Healthcare Regional Medical Center, Show Low, AZ, p. A38
EBERTH, Denise A., Chief Human Resources Officer, Allegan General Hospital, Allegan, MI, p. A314
EBLIN, Steven E., Chief Executive Officer / President, Randolph Hospital, Asheboro, NC, p. A455
EBNER, Carl, Vice President Finance, UH Robinson Medical Center, Ravenna, OH, p. A496
EBNER, Joseph, M.D. Chief Medical Officer, Speare Memorial Hospital, Plymouth, NH, p. A408
EBRI, Patrick D., Ph.D
Vice President, Human Resources, Southeast Georgia Health System Brunswick Campus, Brunswick, GA, p. A152
Vice President Human Resources, Southeast Georgia Health System Camden Campus, Saint Marys, GA, p. A163
ECCLESTON, Julie, Vice President Human Resources, Hillcrest Medical Center, Tulsa, OK, p. A516
ECHOLS, Jane, Chief Executive Officer, Wills Memorial Hospital, Washington, GA, p. A167
ECKELS, Dan, Chief Financial Officer, Washington Regional Medical Center, Fayetteville, AR, p. A44
ECKENFELS, Susan, Chief Financial Officer, Ste. Genevieve County Memorial Hospital, Ste. Genevieve, MO, p. A379
ECKERT, Mark, Vice President Finance, Ochsner Medical Center – Kenner, Kenner, LA, p. A276
ECKERT, Mary L., President and Chief Executive Officer, Millcreek Community Hospital, Erie, PA, p. A534
ECKERT, Susan E., R.N. Senior Vice President and Chief Nursing Officer, MedStar Washington Hospital Center, Washington, DC, p. A119
ECKES, Chad, Vice President Information Services and Chief Information Officer, Wake Forest Baptist Medical Center, Winston–Salem, NC, p. A471
ECKFORD, Marjorie, Chief Nursing Officer, Menlo Park Surgical Hospital, Menlo Park, CA, p. A75
ECKLEY, Valerie, M.D. Chief of Staff, East Adams Rural Hospital, Ritzville, WA, p. A683
ECKSTEIN, William, Chief Financial Officer, Columbus Specialty Hospital, Columbus, GA, p. A154
EDALATI, David, M.D. Medical Director, Meadowbrook Rehabilitation Hospital, Gardner, KS, p. A240
EDDEY, Gary E., M.D. Medical Director, Matheny Medical and Educational Center, Peapack, NJ, p. A416
EDDINGTON, Tonya, Coordinator Human Resources, Select Specialty Hospital–Springfield, Springfield, MO, p. A379
EDDLEMAN, Patricia, Fiscal Officer, Heartland Behavioral Healthcare, Massillon, OH, p. A493
EDELMAN, Marc D., Vice President Operations, Bristol Hospital, Bristol, CT, p. A111
EDEN, Tina M., Director of Nursing, Virginia Gay Hospital, Vinton, IA, p. A235
EDENFIELD, Janet, Director Financial Services, Georgia Regional Hospital at Savannah, Savannah, GA, p. A164
EDGAR, Joseph H., Senior Vice President Operations, Gettysburg Hospital, Gettysburg, PA, p. A534
EDGAR, Nancy, Vice President Human Resources, Methodist Hospital, San Antonio, TX, p. A641
EDGEWORTH, Mitch, Adult Enterprise Chief Operating Officer, Vanderbilt Hospital and Clinics, Nashville, TN, p. A586
EDIN, Scott D., Chief Financial Officer, Amery Hospital and Clinic, Amery, WI, p. A697
EDLER, Susie, R.N. Chief Nursing Officer, Dallas Behavioral Healthcare Hospital, Desoto, TX, p. A608
EDMINSTER, Sue
Vice President Human Resources, Agnesian HealthCare, Fond Du Lac, WI, p. A700
Vice President Human Resources, Ripon Medical Center, Ripon, WI, p. A710
Vice President Human Resources, Waupun Memorial Hospital, Waupun, WI, p. A713
EDMISTON, Gena, R.N. Chief Nursing Officer, Fairbanks Memorial Hospital, Fairbanks, AK, p. A28
EDMONDS, Kelly, Chief Financial Officer, Western Maryland Hospital Center, Hagerstown, MD, p. A298
EDMONDSON, Bobby, Controller, Regional Rehabilitation Hospital, Phenix City, AL, p. A24
EDMONDSON, James H., Chief Executive Officer, Southern Tennessee Regional Health System–Pulaski, Pulaski, TN, p. A587
EDMONS, Stephenie, Human Resources Clerk, Allegiance Specialty Hospital of Kilgore, Kilgore, TX, p. A626
EDMONSON, Cole, R.N. Vice President and Chief Nursing Officer, Texas Health Presbyterian Hospital Dallas, Dallas, TX, p. A606
EDMUNDS, Liza, Director Human Resources, Gateway Medical Center, Clarksville, TN, p. A576
EDMUNDSON, Reed
Regional Administrator, Grimes St. Joseph Health Center, Navasota, TX, p. A634
Administrator, Madison St. Joseph Health Center, Madisonville, TX, p. A630
EDNEY, Daniel, M.D. Chief of Staff, Promise Hospital of Vicksburg, Vicksburg, MS, p. A361
EDRINGTON, Katherine, R.N. Administrator, Mercy Health – Anderson Hospital, Cincinnati, OH, p. A483
EDSON, Pamela A., Chief Executive Officer, Kindred Hospital of Central Ohio, Mansfield, OH, p. A492
EDWARD, Adolphe
Market Chief Executive Officer, Kindred Hospital–Aurora, Aurora, CO, p. A99
Market Chief Executive Officer, Kindred Hospital–Denver, Denver, CO, p. A102
EDWARD, Virginia, R.N. Administrator and Chief Nursing Officer, West Anaheim Medical Center, Anaheim, CA, p. A53
EDWARDS, Angela Imelda, R.N. Chief Nurse Executive, Woodhull Medical and Mental Health Center, NY, p. A445
EDWARDS, Annette, Chief Financial Officer, Odessa Memorial Healthcare Center, Odessa, WA, p. A681
EDWARDS, Becky, Manager Human Resources, Irwin County Hospital, Ocilla, GA, p. A162

Index of Health Care Professionals / Elegant

Index of Health Care Professionals


EDWARDS Jr., Bob S., FACHE, Chief Executive Officer, Mendocino Coast District Hospital, Fort Bragg, CA, p. A61
EDWARDS, Bruce
Vice President Human Resources, Heritage Valley Health System, Beaver, PA, p. A529
Vice President Human Resources, Sewickley Valley Hospital, (A Division of Valley Medical Facilities), Sewickley, PA, p. A550
EDWARDS, Chris, M.D. Chief Medical Officer, Maury Regional Hospital, Columbia, TN, p. A576
EDWARDS, Dana, Chief Financial Officer, HEALTHSOUTH Sea Pines Rehabilitation Hospital, Melbourne, FL, p. A133
EDWARDS, Danny R., Administrator, Complex Care Hospital at Ridgelake, Sarasota, FL, p. A142
EDWARDS, David, M.D. Chief Medical Officer, Banner Gateway Medical Center, Gilbert, AZ, p. A31
EDWARDS, Dennis, M.D. Vice President Medical Affairs, CHI Health Good Samaritan, Kearney, NE, p. A393
EDWARDS, Frank, M.D. Medical Director, Jones Memorial Hospital, Wellsville, NY, p. A453
EDWARDS, Gordon, System Vice President and Chief Financial Officer, Columbia Network, PeaceHealth Southwest Medical Center, Vancouver, WA, p. A687
EDWARDS, Gregg
Vice President Human Resources, Asante Ashland Community Hospital, Ashland, OR, p. A519
Chief People Officer, Asante Rogue Regional Medical Center, Medford, OR, p. A523
Chief People Officer, Asante Three Rivers Medical Center, Grants Pass, OR, p. A521
EDWARDS, James D., Chief Executive Officer, Howard University Hospital, Washington, DC, p. A119
EDWARDS, Jeff, Manager Information Services, Mendocino Coast District Hospital, Fort Bragg, CA, p. A61
EDWARDS, John R., Administrator and Chief Executive Officer, Pacific Alliance Medical Center, Los Angeles, CA, p. A71
EDWARDS, Kathleen, Manager Information Systems Operation, HEALTHSOUTH Rehabilitation Hospital of Altoona, Altoona, PA, p. A528
EDWARDS, Kristy, M.D. Chief Medical Officer, Lillian M. Hudspeth Memorial Hospital, Sonora, TX, p. A644
EDWARDS, Mark A., Chief Executive Officer, Livingston Hospital and Healthcare Services, Salem, KY, p. A265
EDWARDS, Marti, MS
Chief Nursing Officer, RML Specialty Hospital, Chicago, IL, p. A184
Chief Nursing Officer, RML Specialty Hospital, Hinsdale, IL, p. A191
EDWARDS, Matt, Vice President Nursing Services and Chief Nursing Officer, Anderson Regional Medical Center, Meridian, MS, p. A357
EDWARDS, Michael R., Administrator, Scott Regional Hospital, Morton, MS, p. A358
EDWARDS, Michelle, Executive Vice President Information Technology, Palmetto Health Baptist, Columbia, SC, p. A559
EDWARDS, Nicki E., Ph.D. Interim Chief Nursing Officer, Sierra Vista Regional Medical Center, San Luis Obispo, CA, p. A90
EDWARDS, Rebecca
Chief Nursing Officer, Greenwood Leflore Hospital, Greenwood, MS, p. A353
Director Human Resources, Martin General Hospital, Williamston, NC, p. A470
Chief Human Resources Officer, Penn Highlands Brookville, Brookville, PA, p. A530
EDWARDS, Rick
Vice President and Chief Financial Officer, Hancock Regional Hospital, Greenfield, IN, p. A210
Director Information Systems, Howard County General Hospital, Columbia, MD, p. A297
EDWARDS, Samuel, M.D. Chief of Staff, Florida Hospital DeLand, DeLand, FL, p. A125
EDWARDS, Sondra, Human Resources Supervisor, Epic Medical Center, Eufaula, OK, p. A506
EDWARDS, Steven D., President and Chief Executive Officer, Cox Medical Centers, Springfield, MO, p. A378
EDWARDS, Steven D., President and Chief Executive Officer, CoxHealth, Springfield, MO, p. B43
EDWARDS, Susan, Vice President Human Resources, UVA Culpeper Hospital, Culpeper, VA, p. A664
EDWARDS, Susan A., President and Chief Executive Officer, ProHealth Care, Inc., Waukesha, WI, p. B108
EDWARDS, Teresa L., President and Administrator, Sentara Leigh Hospital, Norfolk, VA, p. A669
EDWARDS, Terry, Controller, Kings Mountain Hospital, Kings Mountain, NC, p. A463
EDWARDS, Todd, Director Information Management Systems, Brazosport Regional Health System, Lake Jackson, TX, p. A627
EDWARDS, William, Information Technology Generalist, Wernersville State Hospital, Wernersville, PA, p. A552
EESLEY, Michael S., Chief Executive Officer, Centegra Health System, Crystal Lake, IL, p. B32
EESLEY, Michael S.
Chief Executive Officer, Centegra Hospital – McHenry, McHenry, IL, p. A194
Chief Executive Officer, Centegra Hospital – Woodstock, Woodstock, IL, p. A203
EGAN, Kim, Executive Director Human Resources, Regions Hospital, Saint Paul, MN, p. A346
EGAN, Timothy, Chief Restructuring Officer and President, Roseland Community Hospital, Chicago, IL, p. A184
EGAN, Timothy C., Director, Human Resources, MountainView Regional Medical Center, Las Cruces, NM, p. A425
EGBERT, Jeff, Interim Chief Operating Officer, Canyon Vista Medical Center, Sierra Vista, AZ, p. A38
EGEN, Carol, R.N. Chief Nursing Officer, Rutland Regional Medical Center, Rutland, VT, p. A661
EGERTON, W. Eugene, M.D. Chief Medical Officer, University of Maryland Medical Center Midtown Campus, Baltimore, MD, p. A295
EGGEN, Caity, Chief Human Resource Officer, Cuyuna Regional Medical Center, Crosby, MN, p. A337
EGGERS, Judy, Manager Human Resources, Alliance HealthCare System, Holly Springs, MS, p. A354
EGGLESTON, Kirk W., Commanding Officer, Winn Army Community Hospital, Hinesville, GA, p. A159
EGGLESTON, Ryan, Chief Financial Officer, Desert View Hospital, Pahrump, NV, p. A403
EGYUD, Amber, Vice President Chief Nursing Officer, Forbes Regional Hospital, Monroeville, PA, p. A540
EHASZ, James, Chief Financial Officer, Copper Queen Community Hospital, Bisbee, AZ, p. A30
EHLER, Phyllis, Director Human Resources, Avera St. Benedict Health Center, Parkston, SD, p. A570
EHLERS, Jeffrey, Chief Financial Officer, Memorial Health, Marysville, OH, p. A493
EHLINGER, Forrest, System Chief Financial Officer, Benefis Hospitals, Great Falls, MT, p. A384
EHLKE, Ranae, Administrative Secretary and Coordinator Risk Management and Human Resources, Kenmare Community Hospital, Kenmare, ND, p. A475
EHLY, Ronda S., R.N. Chief Nursing Officer, Mary Lanning Healthcare, Hastings, NE, p. A392
EHN, Jerry, Chief Operating Officer, Northfield Hospital, Northfield, MN, p. A344
EHRAT, Michael, Chief Executive Officer, Memorial Hospital, Martinsville, VA, p. A668
EHRENBERGER, David, M.D. Chief Medical Officer, Avista Adventist Hospital, Louisville, CO, p. A107
EHRET, Charlene S., FACHE, Director, James H. Quillen Veterans Affairs Medical Center, Mountain Home, TN, p. A585
EHRICH, Laurie, Chief Communications Officer, Wayne County Hospital, Corydon, IA, p. A225
EHRLICH, Frank, M.D
Chief Medical Officer, Health Alliance Hospital – Broadway Campus, Kingston, NY, p. A436
Chief Medical Officer, Health Alliance Hospital – Mary's Avenue Campus, Kingston, NY, p. A436
EHRLICH, Susan P., M.D., Chief Executive Officer, San Mateo Medical Center, San Mateo, CA, p. A90
EHTISHAM, Saad, R.N
Vice President and Chief Operating Officer, Leesburg Regional Medical Center, Leesburg, FL, p. A132
Vice President and Chief Operating Officer, The Villages Regional Hospital, The Villages, FL, p. A146
EICHENAUER, Donald T., Chief Executive Officer, Wyoming County Community Hospital, Warsaw, NY, p. A453
EICHENBERGER, Daniel J., M.D., Interim President and Chief Executive Officer, Floyd Memorial Hospital and Health Services, New Albany, IN, p. A217
EICHNER, John, Vice President Finance, TLC Health Network – Lake Shore Hospital, Irving, NY, p. A435
EIDAM, JoEllen, Chief Executive Officer, Adams Memorial Hospital, Decatur, IN, p. A207
EIDE, Dean, Vice President, Mayo Clinic Health System – Oakridge in Osseo, Osseo, WI, p. A708
EIDE, Tom, Chief Financial Officer, Prairie St. John's, Fargo, ND, p. A473
EIFFERT, Sarah, Director Human Resources, Mercy Rehabilition Hospital Springfield, Springfield, MO, p. A379
EIG, Blair, M.D. Senior Vice President Medical Affairs, Holy Cross Hospital, Silver Spring, MD, p. A300
EIKE, Gail, Chief Financial Officer, Sanford Jackson Medical Center, Jackson, MN, p. A340
EILBRACHT, Hans, Chief Information Officer, Hamilton Center, Terre Haute, IN, p. A220
EIMERS, Katy, Human Resources Officer, Syringa Hospital and Clinics, Grangeville, ID, p. A174
EINSWEILER, Desiree, Chief Executive Officer, Palo Alto County Health System, Emmetsburg, IA, p. A227
EIPE, Joseph, M.D. Chief Medical Officer, Pacifica Hospital of the Valley, CA, p. A72
EISCHEID, Randy, Director Information Systems, St. Anthony Regional Hospital, Carroll, IA, p. A223
EISELE, Karla, M.D. Clinical Director, State Hospital North, Orofino, ID, p. A175
EISEMANN, Bradley, Administrator, Crenshaw Community Hospital, Luverne, AL, p. A21
EISEN, Robert A.
Vice President Human Resources, Northern California Region, Queen of the Valley Medical Center, Napa, CA, p. A77
Vice President Human Resources, Santa Rosa Memorial Hospital, Santa Rosa, CA, p. A92
EISENBERG, Barry, FACHE, Chief Operating Officer and Executive Director, Levindale Hebrew Geriatric Center and Hospital, Baltimore, MD, p. A293
EISENMAN, Edward, Chief Executive Officer, Sunnyview Rehabilitation Hospital, Schenectady, NY, p. A450
EISENMANN, Claudia, Chief Executive Officer, Wilbarger General Hospital, Vernon, TX, p. A650
EISENTRAGER, Steve, President, Ohio Valley Surgical Hospital, Springfield, OH, p. A497
EISENZOPH, Pete, Director Information Technology, Bay Area Medical Center, Marinette, WI, p. A704
EISMAN, Michael, M.D. Medical Director, Schuyler Hospital, Montour Falls, NY, p. A437
EISNER, Nina W., Chief Executive Officer and Managing Director, Ridge Behavioral Health System, Lexington, KY, p. A260
EITZEN, Tamara, Chief Nursing Officer, Fairview Regional Medical Center, Fairview, OK, p. A507
EKEH, Cyril, Interim Director, Central Arkansas Veterans Healthcare System, Little Rock, AR, p. A47
EKENGREN, Francie H., M.D. Chief Medical Officer, Wesley Medical Center, Wichita, KS, p. A253
EKEREN, Douglas R., Regional President and Chief Executive Officer, Avera Sacred Heart Hospital, Yankton, SD, p. A573
EKLOFE, Robert, Chief Executive Officer, Strategic Behavioral Health – Raleigh, Garner, NC, p. A460
EKLUND, Cynda
Interim Chief Human Resources Officer, Ogallala Community Hospital, Ogallala, NE, p. A395
Chief Human Resources Officer, Sterling Regional MedCenter, Sterling, CO, p. A109
EKPO, Felix, Manager, Information Systems, Arrowhead Regional Medical Center, Colton, CA, p. A58
EL KHALILI, Nizar, M.D. Medical Director, Sycamore Springs Hospital, Lafayette, IN, p. A214
EL SANADI, Nabil, M.D., President and Chief Executive Officer, Broward Health, Fort Lauderdale, FL, p. B25
EL–DALATI, Sam, M.D. Chief Medical Officer, Mercy Regional Medical Center, Lorain, OH, p. A492
EL–MELIGI, Christi J., R.N., Chief Executive Officer, Sage Memorial Hospital, Ganado, AZ, p. A31
EL–SOLH, Ali, M.D. Interim Chief of Staff, Veterans Affairs Western New York Healthcare System–Buffalo Division, Buffalo, NY, p. A431
ELAM, Lora, R.N. Chief Nursing Officer, Wayne County Hospital, Monticello, KY, p. A263
ELAM, Moses D., M.D. Physician–in–Chief, Kaiser Permanente Manteca Medical Center, Manteca, CA, p. A74
ELARBEE, Vernon, Director of Human Resources, Florida Hospital North Pinellas, Tarpon Springs, FL, p. A145
ELBERT, Darlene M., R.N. Assistant Administrator and Chief Nursing Officer, Kossuth Regional Health Center, Algona, IA, p. A222
ELDER, Becky, Vice President Clinical Services, Perry County Memorial Hospital, Tell City, IN, p. A220
ELDER, Sonja, Director Information Services, Pikeville Medical Center, Pikeville, KY, p. A264
ELDER, Susie, Interim Chief Executive Officer, Crescent Medical Center Lancaster, Lancaster, TX, p. A627
ELDIDY, Rene, M.D. Chief of Staff, CentraCare Health–Long Prairie, Long Prairie, MN, p. A341
ELDRED, Jamie, Controller, Klickitat Valley Health, Goldendale, WA, p. A679
ELDRIDGE, Janet, Director Human Resources and Personnel, Brooks County Hospital, Quitman, GA, p. A162
ELDRIDGE, Jim, Area Financial Officer, Kaiser Permanente Sacramento Medical Center, Sacramento, CA, p. A84
ELDRIDGE, Laurie, Chief Financial Officer, Marshall Medical Center, Placerville, CA, p. A81
ELDRIDGE, Lisa, Human Resources Officer, Thomas H. Boyd Memorial Hospital, Carrollton, IL, p. A180
ELDRIDGE, Sherry, Vice President Patient Care Services and Chief Nurse Executive, Sequoia Hospital, Redwood City, CA, p. A83
ELEGANT, Bruce M., FACHE, President and Chief Executive Officer, Rush Oak Park Hospital, Oak Park, IL, p. A196

Index of Health Care Professionals

Index of Health Care Professionals / Elenbaas

ELENBAAS, Jerry, Administrator, Post Acute Specialty Hospital of Hammond, Hammond, LA, p. A274
ELFERT, Mike, Director Information Services, Lourdes Medical Center of Burlington County, Willingboro, NJ, p. A420
ELFORD, Dorothy J., Chief Executive Officer, Carrus Rehabilitation Hospital, Sherman, TX, p. A643
ELGARICO, David, Chief Operating Officer, Rio Grande Regional Hospital, McAllen, TX, p. A631
ELI, Bev, Chief Nursing Officer, Cox Monett, Monett, MO, p. A373
ELIAS, Abe, M.D. President Medical Staff, Shodair Children's Hospital, Helena, MT, p. A384
ELICH, Liz, Vice President Human Resources, Frye Regional Medical Center, Hickory, NC, p. A462
ELIE, Charlene, Vice President Patient Care Services, Clinton Hospital, Clinton, MA, p. A306
ELIOT, Jason L., Vice President Human Resources, Integris Baptist Medical Center, Oklahoma City, OK, p. A511
ELKINGTON, Bruce, Regional Chief Information Officer, St. Clare Hospital, Lakewood, WA, p. A680
ELKINGTON, Mark, M.D. Chief Medical Officer, Willow Crest Hospital, Miami, OK, p. A509
ELKINS, Carl, Director Information Technology, Rollins–Brook Community Hospital, Lampasas, TX, p. A627
ELKINS, James N., FACHE, Superintendent, Texas Center for Infectious Disease, San Antonio, TX, p. A642
ELKINS, Wendy, Director Operations, Dundy County Hospital, Benkelman, NE, p. A390
ELLARD, Ellen, Director Human Resources, Putnam General Hospital, Eatonton, GA, p. A157
ELLARD, Sam, Chief Financial Officer, Riverland Medical Center, Ferriday, LA, p. A273
ELLEDGE, David
Controller, Select Specialty Hospital–Knoxville, Knoxville, TN, p. A580
Controller, Select Specialty Hospital–North Knoxville, Powell, TN, p. A587
ELLEN, Jonathan D., M.D. Medical Director, HEALTHSOUTH Rehabilitation Hospital of Memphis, Memphis, TN, p. A583
ELLEN, Jonathan M., M.D., President, All Children's Hospital Johns Hopkins Medicine, Saint Petersburg, FL, p. A141
ELLENBURG, Cynthia, Director Health Information Services, Baptist Easley Hospital, Easley, SC, p. A560
ELLER, Bill, Director Information Technology, El Campo Memorial Hospital, El Campo, TX, p. A610
ELLER, Steven M., Vice President Human Resources, Elkhart General Healthcare System, Elkhart, IN, p. A207
ELLERSON, Thomas, Chief Information Officer, Our Lady of Lourdes Memorial Hospital, Inc., Binghamton, NY, p. A429
ELLEY, Michael, Chief Information Officer, Owensboro Health Regional Hospital, Owensboro, KY, p. A264
ELLINGER, Thomas, Vice President, University Medical Center at Brackenridge, Austin, TX, p. A595
ELLINGTON, Christopher, Executive Vice President and Chief Financial Officer, University of North Carolina Hospitals, Chapel Hill, NC, p. A457
ELLIOTT, Barb, Interim President and Chief Executive Officer, Fairbanks, Indianapolis, IN, p. A211
ELLIOTT, Charles M., M.D. Chief of Staff, Tippah County Hospital, Ripley, MS, p. A360
ELLIOTT Jr., Charles W., Chief Executive Officer, Johnston Health, Smithfield, NC, p. A468
ELLIOTT, Jennifer, Chief Nursing Officer, Saint Thomas West Hospital, Nashville, TN, p. A585
ELLIOTT, Jim
Director Human Resources, Bryce Hospital, Tuscaloosa, AL, p. A25
Director Human Resources, Mary S Harper Geriatric Psychiatry Center, Tuscaloosa, AL, p. A25
ELLIOTT, Laura, Director Human Resources, Northeastern Nevada Regional Hospital, Elko, NV, p. A400
ELLIOTT, Lee Ann, R.N. Director of Nursing, Select Rehabilitation Hospital of Denton, Denton, TX, p. A608
ELLIOTT, Mark, Manager Information Systems, Novant Health Franklin Medical Center, Louisburg, NC, p. A464
ELLIOTT, Marye, Chief Nursing Officer, Eliza Coffee Memorial Hospital, Florence, AL, p. A19
ELLIOTT, Michael, M.D. Chief Medical Officer and Senior Vice President of Medical Affairs, Avera McKennan Hospital and University Health Center, Sioux Falls, SD, p. A571
ELLIOTT, Michael, Controller, Indianhead Medical Center, Shell Lake, WI, p. A711
ELLIOTT, Peyton, Vice President Operations, Houston Methodist West Hospital, Houston, TX, p. A620
ELLIOTT, R. James, Vice President Human Resources, The Charlotte Hungerford Hospital, Torrington, CT, p. A115
ELLIOTT, Rhonda M., Director Information Technology and Meaningful Use, Person Memorial Hospital, Roxboro, NC, p. A467
ELLIOTT, Robin, Personnel Officer, Community Memorial Hospital, Sumner, IA, p. A235
ELLIOTT, Shane, Associate Director Administration, Veterans Affairs Loma Linda Healthcare System, Loma Linda, CA, p. A68
ELLIOTT MSN, Randi, Chief Nursing Officer, Baylor Medical Center at Frisco, Frisco, TX, p. A615
ELLIS, Amanda, Chief Financial Officer, Knox County Hospital, Barbourville, KY, p. A254
ELLIS, Angela, R.N. Chief Nursing Officer, Terre Haute Regional Hospital, Terre Haute, IN, p. A220
ELLIS, Becky, Interim Chief Executive Officer, Ballinger Memorial Hospital, Ballinger, TX, p. A595
ELLIS, Betts, Administrator Institutional Relations, MUSC Medical Center of Medical University of South Carolina, Charleston, SC, p. A558
ELLIS, Bob, Director of Nursing, D. W. McMillan Memorial Hospital, Brewton, AL, p. A17
ELLIS, Deb, Director Human Resources, Perry Memorial Hospital, Perry, OK, p. A513
ELLIS, Elmer G., FACHE, President and Chief Executive Officer, East Texas Medical Center Regional Healthcare System, Tyler, TX, p. B52
ELLIS, Kristin, Vice President Finance, Munson Healthcare Cadillac Hospital, Cadillac, MI, p. A315
ELLIS, Mark, Director Information Technology, Lakeview Hospital, Bountiful, UT, p. A654
ELLIS, Michael J., Chief Executive Officer, Hill Regional Hospital, Hillsboro, TX, p. A618
ELLIS, Michelle, Director Human Resources, Whitman Hospital and Medical Center, Colfax, WA, p. A677
ELLIS, Mike, Chief Financial Officer, Wickenburg Community Hospital, Wickenburg, AZ, p. A40
ELLIS, Rich, Chief Operating Officer, Frye Regional Medical Center, Hickory, NC, p. A462
ELLIS, Richard, Chief Executive Officer, Medical Center Enterprise, Enterprise, AL, p. A19
ELLIS, Scott, D.O. Chief Medical Officer, The Memorial Hospital at Craig, Craig, CO, p. A101
ELLIS, Susan Renee', R.N. Vice President of Human Resources, Highlands Regional Medical Center, Prestonsburg, KY, p. A265
ELLIS, Thomas J., Vice President Human Resources, Mt. Washington Pediatric Hospital, Baltimore, MD, p. A294
ELLIS, Wendel, D.O. Chief Medical Staff, Greeley County Health Services, Tribune, KS, p. A251
ELLISH, Patti M., FACHE, President and Chief Executive Officer, St. Tammany Parish Hospital, Covington, LA, p. A272
ELLISON, Darcy, R.N. Senior Vice President, Chief Nursing Officer and Inpatient Flow, St. Mary's Medical Center of Evansville, Evansville, IN, p. A208
ELLISON, Keith, Chief Nursing Officer, Big Bend Regional Medical Center, Alpine, TX, p. A591
ELLISON, Mike, Information Systems Lead, Summersville Regional Medical Center, Summersville, WV, p. A695
ELLISON, Patricia, Chief Financial Officer, Streamwood Behavioral Health Center, Streamwood, IL, p. A202
ELLISON, Tracey, Vice President Human Resources, Carroll Hospital Center, Westminster, MD, p. A301
ELLSWORTH, Anthon, Director Information Technology, Mt. Graham Regional Medical Center, Safford, AZ, p. A37
ELLWANGER, Dina, R.N. Chief Nursing Officer, Saint Alphonsus Medical Center – Ontario, Ontario, OR, p. A523
ELLZEY, Bob S., FACHE, President, Texas Health Harris Methodist Hospital Azle, Azle, TX, p. A595
ELMER, Paula, R.N. Vice President and Chief Nursing Officer, Monroe Clinic, Monroe, WI, p. A707
ELMORE, Kevin, Chief Information Officer, Covenant Hospital–Levelland, Levelland, TX, p. A628
ELMORE, Nadine, Chief Executive Officer, Dahl Memorial Healthcare Association, Ekalaka, MT, p. A383
ELMORE, Trent, Director Human Resources, Springs Memorial Hospital, Lancaster, SC, p. A563
ELROD, James K., FACHE, President and Chief Executive Officer, Willis–Knighton Health System, Shreveport, LA, p. B154
ELROD, James K., FACHE, Chief Executive Officer, Willis–Knighton Medical Center, Shreveport, LA, p. A285
ELSBERRY, Kevin
Senior Vice President Human Resources, Mercy Medical Center – West Lakes, West Des Moines, IA, p. A236
Senior Vice President Human Resources, Mercy Medical Center–Des Moines, Des Moines, IA, p. A226
ELSBREE, Heidi, Vice President People and Culture, Rockford Memorial Hospital, Rockford, IL, p. A199
ELSE, Ryan, M.D. Vice President Medical Affairs, Mercy Hospital, Coon Rapids, MN, p. A337
ELSWICK, Beth, Administrative Assistant, Summers County ARH Hospital, Hinton, WV, p. A691
ELTON, James, Chief Executive Officer, Vibra Hospital of Boise, Meridian, ID, p. A175
ELWELL, Richard, Senior Vice President and Chief Financial Officer, Elliot Hospital, Manchester, NH, p. A407
ELWELL, Russell, M.D. Medical Director, Westfield Memorial Hospital, Westfield, NY, p. A454
ELY, Thomas L., D.O. Chief Medical Officer, Gateway Medical Center, Clarksville, TN, p. A576
EMAMGHORAISHI, Anna, Human Resources, Specialty Hospital of Midwest City, Midwest City, OK, p. A510
EMANUEL, Kate, Director Human Resources, Clarke County Hospital, Osceola, IA, p. A232
EMBREE, Steve, Chief Financial Officer, UP Health System–Marquette, Marquette, MI, p. A325
EMBREY, Jeffrey, M.D. Vice President Medical Affairs, Baylor Medical Center at Irving, Irving, TX, p. A624
EMBURY, Stuart, M.D. Chief Medical Officer, Phelps Memorial Health Center, Holdrege, NE, p. A393
EMDUR, Larry, D.O
Chief Medical Officer, Alvarado Hospital Medical Center, San Diego, CA, p. A86
Chief of Staff, Promise Hospital of San Diego, San Diego, CA, p. A86
EMEOTT, Sandra, R.N. Chief Nursing Officer, Northwest Medical Center, Margate, FL, p. A133
EMERICK, Ron, M.D. Chief of Staff, Doctor's Memorial Hospital, Perry, FL, p. A140
EMERSON, Leah, Director of Nursing, St. Luke Community Healthcare, Ronan, MT, p. A386
EMERSON, Shelly, President, Texas Health Heart & Vascular Hospital Arlington, Arlington, TX, p. A593
EMERY, Jeff, Chief Financial Officer and Chief Operating Officer, Gateways Hospital and Mental Health Center, Los Angeles, CA, p. A69
EMGE, Joann, Chief Executive Officer, Sparta Community Hospital, Sparta, IL, p. A200
EMIG, Laura, Director Marketing Operations, HEALTHSOUTH Rehabilitation Hospital of York, York, PA, p. A554
EMMINGER, Dianne, Vice President Information Services, ACMH Hospital, Kittanning, PA, p. A537
EMMONS, Michelle, Associate Executive Director, Kings County Hospital Center, NY, p. A440
EMON, Dee, R.N. Vice President and Chief Information Officer, Wake Forest Baptist Health–Davie Medical Center, Mocksville, NC, p. A465
EMORY, Mark L., Director Human Resources, Transylvania Regional Hospital, Brevard, NC, p. A456
EMPEY, Dennis
Chief Financial Officer, Kenmare Community Hospital, Kenmare, ND, p. A475
Chief Financial Officer, Trinity Health, Minot, ND, p. A476
EMTER, David, Chief Operating Officer, Providence Saint Joseph Medical Center, Burbank, CA, p. A56
ENCAPERA, Kimberly, M.D. Medical Director, Rehabilitation Hospital of Southern New Mexico, Las Cruces, NM, p. A425
ENCE, Michael, Computer Specialist, Sanpete Valley Hospital, Mount Pleasant, UT, p. A656
ENCKE, Faye, Director Information Management, HEALTHSOUTH Rehabilitation Hospital of Virginia, Richmond, VA, p. A671
ENDEN, Jay, M.D. Medical Director, Southside Hospital, Bay Shore, NY, p. A429
ENDERS Jr., Robert A., President, Chatham Hospital, Siler City, NC, p. A468
ENDOM, Beth W., R.N. Vice President and Chief Nursing Officer, South Central Regional Medical Center, Laurel, MS, p. A356
ENDRES, Jack R., FACHE, Administrator, East Texas Medical Center Jacksonville, Jacksonville, TX, p. A624
ENG, Bland, Chief Executive Officer, Brandon Regional Hospital, Brandon, FL, p. A122
ENG, Jeffrey, M.D. Medical Director, HEALTHSOUTH Rehabilitation Hospital of Montgomery, Montgomery, AL, p. A23
ENGBRECHT, Chad, Chief Financial Officer, Alvarado Parkway Institute Behavioral Health System, La Mesa, CA, p. A66
ENGEL, David, Chief Executive Officer, Phillips County Hospital, Phillipsburg, KS, p. A248
ENGEL, Dawn M., Chief Nursing Officer, Geary Community Hospital, Junction City, KS, p. A243
ENGEL, Marsha, Director Human Resources, Gothenburg Memorial Hospital, Gothenburg, NE, p. A392
ENGELKE, Brian, Chief Financial Officer, Community Memorial Hospital, Staunton, IL, p. A201
ENGESSER, Edward, Chief Financial Officer and Chief Information Officer, Barlow Respiratory Hospital, Los Angeles, CA, p. A69
ENGFEHR, Tricia A., Chief Human Resources, Selby General Hospital, Marietta, OH, p. A493
ENGLAND, Dave, Director Human Resources, Lakeland Behavioral Health System, Springfield, MO, p. A378

A832 Index of Health Care Professionals 

ESTES, Stephen A., Chief Executive Officer, Rockcastle Regional Hospital and Respiratory Care Center, Mount Vernon, KY, p. A263

ESTEVEZ, Aurora, M.D. Chief Medical Officer, Texas Health Presbyterian Hospital Dallas, Dallas, TX, p. A606

ESTEVEZ, Mercy, Chief Executive Officer, Strategic Behavioral Health – Charlotte, Charlotte, NC, p. A458

ESTRADA, Luis, Director Multifacility Information Systems, North Shore Medical Center, Miami, FL, p. A134

ESTRELLA, Mario B., R.N. Chief Nursing Officer, Nacogdoches Medical Center, Nacogdoches, TX, p. A633

ETCHASON, Barbara, HR Manager, West Gables Rehabilitation Hospital, Miami, FL, p. A135

ETHERIDGE, Darold, Vice President and Chief Financial Officer, WellStar Cobb Hospital, Austell, GA, p. A152

ETHERINGTON, Betty, Chief Financial Officer, Humboldt County Memorial Hospital, Humboldt, IA, p. A229

ETHERINGTON, Rosalie, Superintendent and Chief Executive Officer, North Dakota State Hospital, Jamestown, ND, p. A475

ETHRIDGE, Sandy, Interim Chief Operating Officer, Baptist Medical Center, San Antonio, TX, p. A640

ETIENNE, Gracia, M.D. President Medical Staff, OSS Orthopaedic Hospital, York, PA, p. A554

ETTER, Carl J., Chief Executive and Senior Vice President, Scripps Memorial Hospital–Encinitas, Encinitas, CA, p. A60

ETTESTAD, Donita, R.N. Chief Nursing Officer, Rainy Lake Medical Center, International Falls, MN, p. A340

EUBANKS, Bill, Senior Vice President and Chief Information Officer, University Medical Center, Lubbock, TX, p. A630

EUBANKS, Susan, Chief Nursing Officer, Page Hospital, Page, AZ, p. A34

EULER, Barbara, Director Human Resources, Regional Hospital of Jackson, Jackson, TN, p. A579

EULIARTE, Mary Ann, R.N
Chief Operating Officer, Memorial Hermann Rehabilitation Hospital – Katy, Katy, TX, p. A625
Chief Operating Officer and Chief Nursing Officer, TIRR Memorial Hermann, Houston, TX, p. A622

EURE, Thomas, Vice President Administration, Blue Ridge Healthcare Hospitals, Morganton, NC, p. A465

EUSEBIO, Barbara, Chief Nursing Officer, John F. Kennedy Memorial Hospital, Indio, CA, p. A65

EUSEBIO, Barbara, R.N. Vice President, Chief Nurse Executive, St. Mary's Medical Center, San Francisco, CA, p. A88

EUSTACE, Scott, Director Health Information Technology, Trenton Psychiatric Hospital, Trenton, NJ, p. A419

EVANCHO, Timothy R., Chief Financial Officer, Southeastern Ohio Regional Medical Center, Cambridge, OH, p. A481

EVANDER, Justin, Chief Financial Officer, Kaiser Permanente Sunnyside Medical Center, Clackamas, OR, p. A520

EVANGELISTA, Larry, Supervisor Information Technology, Clay County Memorial Hospital, Henrietta, TX, p. A618

EVANOFF, John, M.D. Vice President Medical Affairs, ProMedica Flower Hospital, Sylvania, OH, p. A498

EVANS, Ann, Chief Nursing Officer, HEALTHSOUTH Huntington Rehabilitation Hospital, Huntington, WV, p. A692

EVANS, Arthur D., Chief Executive Officer and Administrator, Bryan W. Whitfield Memorial Hospital, Demopolis, AL, p. A18

EVANS, Bradford L., Director Human Resources, Regional West Medical Center, Scottsbluff, NE, p. A398

EVANS, Brian, M.D. Chief of Medicine, Sierra Nevada Memorial Hospital, Grass Valley, CA, p. A64

EVANS, Brian G., FACHE, Chief Executive Officer, Clarke County Hospital, Osceola, IA, p. A232

EVANS, Chris, Vice President Operations, CHI Health Bergan Mercy, Omaha, NE, p. A395

EVANS, Cindy, R.N. Chief Nursing Officer, Legacy Good Samaritan Hospital and Medical Center, Portland, OR, p. A524

EVANS Jr., Daniel F., JD, President and Chief Executive Officer, Indiana University Health, Indianapolis, IN, p. B73

EVANS, Dawn, Manager Information Technology, SSM Health St. Mary's Hospital – Audrain, Mexico, MO, p. A372

EVANS, Dwight, M.D. Chief of Staff, Veterans Affairs Loma Linda Healthcare System, Loma Linda, CA, p. A68

EVANS, Eric, Chief Operating Officer, Woman's Hospital of Texas, Houston, TX, p. A623

EVANS, George, Vice President and Chief Information Officer, Candler Hospital, Savannah, GA, p. A164

EVANS, Heath
Chief Operating Officer, East Georgia Regional Medical Center, Statesboro, GA, p. A165
Assistant Chief Executive Officer, North Okaloosa Medical Center, Crestview, FL, p. A124

EVANS, Janice, Chief Financial Officer, John J. Madden Mental Health Center, Hines, IL, p. A190

EVANS, Jeff W., Vice President Information and Technology, Hannibal Regional Hospital, Hannibal, MO, p. A368

EVANS, Jeremy, Vice President Operations, Kootenai Health, Coeur D'Alene, ID, p. A173

EVANS, Kirstie, Chief Financial Officer, Covington County Hospital, Collins, MS, p. A352

EVANS, Lorrie, Director Human Resources, Laurel Oaks Behavioral Health Center, Dothan, AL, p. A19

EVANS, Manuel J., Senior Vice President Finance and Chief Financial Officer, Holy Spirit – A Geisinger Affiliate, Camp Hill, PA, p. A530

EVANS, Melinda S.
Vice President Finance, Saint Joseph East, Lexington, KY, p. A260
Vice President Finance, Saint Joseph Hospital, Lexington, KY, p. A260

EVANS, Mendy, Vice President of Finance, Flaget Memorial Hospital, Bardstown, KY, p. A254

EVANS, Michael C., Chief Executive Officer and Deputy Director of Finance and Administration, Santa Barbara County Psychiatric Health Facility, Santa Barbara, CA, p. A91

EVANS, Michael K., Chief Executive Officer, Park Royal Hospital, Fort Myers, FL, p. A127

EVANS, Myra L., Interim Chief Executive Officer, Kit Carson County Health Service District, Burlington, CO, p. A100

EVANS, Nina, R.N. Vice President and Chief Nursing Officer, St. Mary's Health Care System, Athens, GA, p. A149

EVANS, Patsy, Comptroller, Citizens Medical Center, Colby, KS, p. A238

EVANS, Paulette, MSN, President and Chief Executive Officer, HSHS St. Joseph's Hospital, Breese, IL, p. A180

EVANS, Robert B., Administrator and Chief Executive Officer, East Texas Medical Center Tyler, Tyler, TX, p. A649

EVANS, Rod, Chief Information Officer, Community HealthCare System, Onaga, KS, p. A247

EVANS, S. Lagina, R.N
Assistant Chief Nursing Officer, Optim Medical Center – Jenkins, Millen, GA, p. A161
Assistant Chief Nursing Officer, Optim Medical Center – Screven, Sylvania, GA, p. A165

EVANS, Sam, Chief Human Resources Management, G.V. (Sonny) Montgomery Veterans Affairs Medical Center, Jackson, MS, p. A355

EVANS, Scott, PharmD, Senior Vice President and Chief Executive Officer, Sharp Grossmont Hospital, La Mesa, CA, p. A66

EVANS, Stanley, M.D. Chief of Staff, Denton Regional Medical Center, Denton, TX, p. A608

EVANS, Susan, Chief Nursing Officer, HEALTHSOUTH Nittany Valley Rehabilitation Hospital, Pleasant Gap, PA, p. A547

EVANS, Tim, Assistant Financial Director, Devereux Children's Behavioral Health Center, Malvern, PA, p. A539

EVANS, Timothy, Vice President and Chief Financial Officer, Self Regional Healthcare, Greenwood, SC, p. A562

EVANS–HARRISON, Martina, R.N. Chief Nurse Executive, Methodist Hospital of Sacramento, Sacramento, CA, p. A84

EVE, John R., Vice President Human Resources, Wilson Memorial Hospital, Sidney, OH, p. A497

EVELIUS, Karen, Director Human Resources, MedStar Harbor Hospital, Baltimore, MD, p. A294

EVELYN, David M., M.D. Vice President Medical Affairs, Cayuga Medical Center at Ithaca, Ithaca, NY, p. A435

EVENS, James, Executive Director Human Resources, Cole Memorial, Coudersport, PA, p. A532

EVENS, Richard R., Chief Executive Officer, HEALTHSOUTH Northern Kentucky Rehabilitation Hospital, Edgewood, KY, p. A256

EVENS, Tamara, Director Human Resources, Moses Ludington Hospital, Ticonderoga, NY, p. A452

EVENSON, Carolyn, R.N. Chief Nursing Officer, Gothenburg Memorial Hospital, Gothenburg, NE, p. A392

EVENSON, Margie, Manager Human Resources, Osceola Medical Center, Osceola, WI, p. A708

EVERDING, Dawn, Chief Financial Officer, Community Memorial Hospital, Sumner, IA, p. A235

EVERETT, John, Chief Financial Officer, Cogdell Memorial Hospital, Snyder, TX, p. A644

EVERETT, Michael, Chief Executive Officer, Scott Memorial Hospital, Scottsburg, IN, p. A219

EVERETT, Neil, Vice President Human Resources, UH Robinson Medical Center, Ravenna, OH, p. A496

EVERHART, Carole, Administrative Director Human Resources, PIH Health Hospital – Downey, Downey, CA, p. A60

EVERHART, Martin S., Senior Vice President Human Resources, Robert Wood Johnson University Hospital, New Brunswick, NJ, p. A415

EVERLY, Nanette, Manager Human Resources and Administrative Assistant, Jefferson County Health Center, Fairfield, IA, p. A227

EVERS, Andrea, Director Information Technology, Haxtun Hospital District, Haxtun, CO, p. A105

EVERS, Anthony, Interim Chief Financial Officer, Katherine Shaw Bethea Hospital, Dixon, IL, p. A186

EVERSOLE, Matt, Regional Vice President Information Services, Mercy Health – Anderson Hospital, Cincinnati, OH, p. A483

EVERT, Barbara, M.D
Vice President Medical Affairs, OhioHealth Dublin Methodist Hospital, Dublin, OH, p. A489
Vice President Medical Affairs, OhioHealth Grady Memorial Hospital, Delaware, OH, p. A488

EVINS, Starling C., M.D. Chief of Staff, Williamson Medical Center, Franklin, TN, p. A578

EVISCHI, Deland
Regional Chief Financial Officer, Southern Illinois, Good Samaritan Regional Health Center, Mount Vernon, IL, p. A195
Chief Financial Officer, St. Mary's Hospital, Centralia, IL, p. A180

EVOLGA, Nancy K., Executive Director Human Resources, Bert Fish Medical Center, New Smyrna Beach, FL, p. A136

EWALD, Ronald, Chief Financial Officer, Inova Fairfax Hospital, Falls Church, VA, p. A664

EWALD, Sandra
Vice President Finance, Aurora Medical Center – Manitowoc County, Two Rivers, WI, p. A712
Vice President Finance, Aurora Medical Center of Oshkosh, Oshkosh, WI, p. A708

EWELL, Dorene L., Director Human Resources and Education, Harrisburg Medical Center, Harrisburg, IL, p. A189

EWELL, Sandy, Chief Nursing Officer, Timpanogos Regional Hospital, Orem, UT, p. A657

EWING, Brenda, Chief Nursing Officer, Sandhills Regional Medical Center, Hamlet, NC, p. A461

EWING, Chandler, Chief Executive Officer, Select Specialty Hospital–Jackson, Jackson, MS, p. A355

EWING, Corey, FACHE, Chief Executive Officer, DeKalb Regional Medical Center, Fort Payne, AL, p. A20

EWING, Thomas
Director Information Technology, Sentara CarePlex Hospital, Hampton, VA, p. A666
Director Information Technology, Sentara Northern Virginia Medical Center, Woodbridge, VA, p. A674

EXLINE, Michael
Chief Financial Officer, Carrus Rehabilitation Hospital, Sherman, TX, p. A643
Chief Financial Officer, Carrus Specialty Hospital, Sherman, TX, p. A644

EYE, Jeffrey, R.N. Chief Nursing Officer, Saint Luke's North Hospital – Barry Road, Kansas City, MO, p. A370

EYER, Ron, Manager Information Services, Aspirus Grand View, Ironwood, MI, p. A323

EYLER, Sandra, M
Chief Nursing Officer, Sheltering Arms Hospital South, Midlothian, VA, p. A668
Chief Nursing Officer, Sheltering Arms Rehabilitation Hospital, Mechanicsville, VA, p. A668

# F

FAAS, Michael D., President and Chief Executive Officer, Metro Health Hospital, Wyoming, MI, p. A333

FAAS, Nancy, R.N. Chief Nursing Officer, Reliant Rehabilitation Hospital Dallas, Dallas, TX, p. A606

FABER, Chris, Human Resources Analyst, Stanford Health Care – ValleyCare, Pleasanton, CA, p. A81

FABER, Tammy, Director Human Resources, Hegg Memorial Health Center Avera, Rock Valley, IA, p. A234

FABIAN, Alan J., Chief Executive Officer, LewisGale Hospital Montgomery, Blacksburg, VA, p. A662

FABIANO, Tom, Director Human Resources, Mount Auburn Hospital, Cambridge, MA, p. A305

FABIN, Peggy, Director Human Resources, Phillips County Hospital, Phillipsburg, KS, p. A248

FABRICK, Peter, Vice President Clinical Operations, Mountain View Hospital, Idaho Falls, ID, p. A174

FABRY, Joseph, D.O. Chief of Staff, Sutter Maternity and Surgery Center of Santa Cruz, Santa Cruz, CA, p. A91

FACKRELL, Sherlyn, Finance Controller, Grover C. Dils Medical Center, Caliente, NV, p. A400

FACTEAU, Lorna M., Ph.D. Chief Nursing Officer, University of Virginia Medical Center, Charlottesville, VA, p. A663

FACTEAU, Patrick M., Chief Financial Officer, Massena Memorial Hospital, Massena, NY, p. A437

Index of Health Care Professionals / Faul

Index of Health Care Professionals

FACTOR, David, M.D. Chief of Staff, Ashe Memorial Hospital, Jefferson, NC, p. A463
FADALE, Sean, President and Chief Executive Officer, Community Memorial Hospital, Hamilton, NY, p. A434
FADLER, Jeannie, R.N. Vice President Patient Care Services, Saint Francis Medical Center, Cape Girardeau, MO, p. A364
FAEHNLE, Steve, M.D. Vice President Medical Affairs, Hendrick Health System, Abilene, TX, p. A590
FAGAN, Erin, Manager Human Resources, George Washington University Hospital, Washington, DC, p. A119
FAGAN, Mary, MSN Chief Nursing Officer, Rady Children's Hospital – San Diego, San Diego, CA, p. A86
FAGAN, Michael
 Chief Financial Officer, Huntington Hospital, Huntington, NY, p. A435
 Senior Vice President Finance, New York Methodist Hospital, NY, p. A443
FAGBONGBE, Eniola, M.D. Chief Medical Staff, Grove Hill Memorial Hospital, Grove Hill, AL, p. A20
FAGERBERG, Lesley, Vice President Fiscal Services, Heart of the Rockies Regional Medical Center, Salida, CO, p. A108
FAGERSTROM, Joel, Executive Vice President and Chief Operating Officer, St. Luke's Hospital – Miners Campus, Coaldale, PA, p. A531
FAGG, Cindy, Fiscal Officer, Battle Mountain General Hospital, Battle Mountain, NV, p. A400
FAGIN, Beth, Manager Information Systems, St. Vincent's Medical Center Southside, Jacksonville, FL, p. A130
FAHEY, Dana, Manager Management Information Systems, Santa Barbara County Psychiatric Health Facility, Santa Barbara, CA, p. A91
FAHEY, Linda L., R.N. Vice President and Chief Nurse Executive, Decatur Memorial Hospital, Decatur, IL, p. A186
FAHEY, Patrick, M.D
 Chief Medical Director, RML Specialty Hospital, Chicago, IL, p. A184
 Chief Medical Officer, RML Specialty Hospital, Hinsdale, IL, p. A191
FAHEY, Stephen P., Executive Director, Sierra Tucson, Tucson, AZ, p. A40
FAHEY, Walter, Chief Information Officer, Maimonides Medical Center, NY, p. A441
FAHRLANDER, Jason, FACHE, President, Community Hospital North, Indianapolis, IN, p. A211
FAILE, J. Gene, Chief Executive Officer and President, Wilkes Regional Medical Center, North Wilkesboro, NC, p. A466
FAILLA, Richard, Chief Executive Officer, Montevista Hospital, Las Vegas, NV, p. A402
FAIN, Marilyn, R.N. Chief Operating Officer, Banner Fort Collins Medical Center, Fort Collins, CO, p. A103
FAIN, Nona, Ph.D. Director of Nursing, Belmont Center for Comprehensive Treatment, Philadelphia, PA, p. A542
FAIN, Nona, M.D. Chief Operations Officer, Cambridge Hospital in Houston, Houston, TX, p. A619
FAIRBANKS, Bruce, Vice President and Chief Financial Officer, Southeast Hospital, Cape Girardeau, MO, p. A365
FAIRCHILD, David, M.D. Chief Medical Officer, Tufts Medical Center, Boston, MA, p. A304
FAIRCHILDS, Constance, R.N. Vice President Patient Care Services, Emanuel Medical Center, Turlock, CA, p. A95
FAIRCLOTH, Gerald, FACHE Chief Executive Officer, Twin Rivers Regional Medical Center, Kennett, MO, p. A371
FAIRCLOTH, Karen, Chief Financial Officer, Memorial Hospital and Manor, Bainbridge, GA, p. A152
FAIRFAX, Tom, Director Information Systems, Bothwell Regional Health Center, Sedalia, MO, p. A378
FAIRFAX, Walter, M.D. Chief Medical Officer, Kootenai Health, Coeur D'Alene, ID, p. A173
FAIRLEY, Dawn Ann, M.D. Chief of Staff, Putnam County Memorial Hospital, Unionville, MO, p. A380
FAIZI, Sajid, M.D. Medical Director, Salt Lake Behavioral Health, Salt Lake City, UT, p. A658
FALBO, Susan, Vice President Human Resources, Wheeling Hospital, Wheeling, WV, p. A696
FALCON, Hugo, M.D. Director Medical Services, Piedmont Geriatric Hospital, Burkeville, VA, p. A663
FALIVENA, Richard, D.O. Vice President and Chief Medical Officer, Saratoga Hospital, Saratoga Springs, NY, p. A450
FALK, Chelsie, Chief Nursing Officer, Sanford Wheaton Medical Center, Wheaton, MN, p. A349
FALKENBERRY, Jody, Director Information Systems, Monroe County Hospital, Monroeville, AL, p. A22
FALL, J. Mark, Chief Executive Officer, CareLink of Jackson, Jackson, MI, p. A323
FALLEN, Barbara, FACHE, Director, Veterans Affairs Loma Linda Healthcare System, Loma Linda, CA, p. A68
FALLIS, Susan, Chief Nursing Officer, Buffalo Psychiatric Center, Buffalo, NY, p. A430
FALLON, Jeanne M.
 Senior Vice President and Chief Information Officer, Cape Cod Hospital, Hyannis, MA, p. A307
 Chief Information Officer, Falmouth Hospital, Falmouth, MA, p. A306
FALLON, L. J., Executive Vice President, Chief Legal and Human Resources Officer, Carle Foundation Hospital, Urbana, IL, p. A202
FALSETTI, Domonic F., M.D. Chief of Staff and Medical Director, Mount St. Mary's Hospital and Health Center, Lewiston, NY, p. A436
FALSEY, Fran, Senior Vice President Site Operations, Kent County Memorial Hospital, Warwick, RI, p. A556
FALTERMAN, Jr., James B., M.D. Medical Director, University Hospital and Clinics, Lafayette, LA, p. A278
FAMAKINWA, Abiodun, M.D. Acting Clinical Director, West Central Georgia Regional Hospital, Columbus, GA, p. A154
FAMMARTINO, Gary, Administrator, St. Vincent Fishers Hospital, Fishers, IN, p. A208
FANALE, James E., M.D. Senior Vice President System Development, Beth Israel Deaconess Hospital Plymouth, Plymouth, MA, p. A310
FANALE, James E., M.D., Interim Chief Operating Officer and Chief Medical Officer, Memorial Hospital of Rhode Island, Pawtucket, RI, p. A555
FANCHER, Diana, Chief Nursing Officer, University Medical Center of El Paso, El Paso, TX, p. A611
FANDRICH, Patti, Human Resources Operations Director, Lake Region Healthcare, Fergus Falls, MN, p. A338
FANNIN, Allyson, Director Human Resources, LaSalle General Hospital, Jena, LA, p. A275
FANNIN, Pam, Coordinator Human Resources, LifeCare Hospital of Dayton, Miamisburg, OH, p. A494
FANNING, Melinda, Chief Financial Officer and Controller, HEALTHSOUTH Southern Hills Rehabilitation Hospital, Princeton, WV, p. A694
FANNING, Teresa E., Director of Patient Care, Avera Hand County Memorial Hospital, Miller, SD, p. A569
FANNON, Susan, Chief Nursing Officer, Indian Path Medical Center, Kingsport, TN, p. A580
FANSELAU, Michael G., District Director Human Resources, Vibra Hospital of Sacramento, Folsom, CA, p. A61
FANTANO, Gene, Chief Financial Officer, Aurora San Diego Hospital, San Diego, CA, p. A86
FARAH, Tony, M.D. President Medical Staff, Allegheny General Hospital, Pittsburgh, PA, p. A546
FARBER, Bobbi, M.D. Chief Medical Officer, St. Francis Hospital, Columbus, GA, p. A154
FARBER, Nancy D., Chief Executive Officer, Washington Hospital Healthcare System, Fremont, CA, p. A62
FARBER, Niceta, Chief Executive Officer, Sheridan County Health Complex, Hoxie, KS, p. A242
FARELL, Clay, Chief Operating Officer, Nacogdoches Medical Center, Nacogdoches, TX, p. A633
FARGASON, Crayton A., M.D. Medical Director, Children's of Alabama, Birmingham, AL, p. A16
FARGUSON, Jack, Director Information Technology, TMC Bonham Hospital, Bonham, TX, p. A598
FARIA, Karen, Executive Director, Sonoma Developmental Center, Eldridge, CA, p. A60
FARIA, Mary, Ph.D., Vice President and Chief Operating Officer, Seton Southwest Hospital, Austin, TX, p. A594
FARICY, Patrick O., M.D. Chief Medical Officer, Memorial Hospital, Colorado Springs, CO, p. A100
FARINA, Albert M.
 Chief Financial Officer, Montefiore Mount Vernon, Mount Vernon, NY, p. A438
 Senior Vice President and Chief Financial Officer, Montefiore New Rochelle, New Rochelle, NY, p. A438
FARINA, Jonathan, Chief Information Officer, Brattleboro Memorial Hospital, Brattleboro, VT, p. A660
FARISH, Audra, Vice President Human Resources, Emory Saint Joseph's Hospital of Atlanta, Atlanta, GA, p. A150
FARKAS, Laura, Director Human Resources, Fairview Hospital, Great Barrington, MA, p. A307
FARLEY, H. Fred, FACHE,
 President and Chief Operating Officer, Arnot Ogden Medical Center, Elmira, NY, p. A433
 President and Chief Operating Officer, St. Joseph's Hospital, Elmira, NY, p. A433
FARMER, Carlos, R.N. Director Clinical Operations, RMC Jacksonville, Jacksonville, AL, p. A21
FARMER, Kathleen, Assistant Administrator Finance and Chief Financial Officer, El Centro Regional Medical Center, El Centro, CA, p. A60
FARMER, Pat, Coordinator Human Resources and Safety Officer, Institute for Orthopaedic Surgery, Lima, OH, p. A492
FARMER, William, M.D. Chief of Staff, Evergreen Medical Center, Evergreen, AL, p. A19
FARNHAM, Diane, Acting Director Human Resources, Lallie Kemp Medical Center, Independence, LA, p. A275
FARNHAM, Krista, Chief Operating Officer, Providence Portland Medical Center, Portland, OR, p. A524
FARO, Joan, M.D. Chief Medical Officer, John T. Mather Memorial Hospital, Port Jefferson, NY, p. A447
FARR, Lorraine, Manager Human Resources, Georgia Regional Hospital at Atlanta, Decatur, GA, p. A156
FARR, Ronald, Chief Financial Officer, Jewish Hospital, Louisville, KY, p. A261
FARR, William L., M.D. Chief Medical Officer, University Hospital, Augusta, GA, p. A152
FARRAGE, Jim, M.D. Medical Director, Southern Kentucky Rehabilitation Hospital, Bowling Green, KY, p. A255
FARRAUTO, Joseph, Director Human Resources, Eastern Niagara Hospital, Lockport, NY, p. A436
FARRELL, Brenda, Vice President Finance, Brookhaven Memorial Hospital Medical Center, Patchogue, NY, p. A447
FARRELL, Coleen M., Vice President Human Resources, Mid Coast Hospital, Brunswick, ME, p. A289
FARRELL, Darin, Chief Executive Officer, Arbuckle Memorial Hospital, Sulphur, OK, p. A515
FARRELL, George, M.D
 Chief Medical Officer, Clinch Valley Medical Center, Richlands, VA, p. A671
 Chief of Staff, Wythe County Community Hospital, Wytheville, VA, p. A675
FARRELL, Katie, Chief Operating Officer, Abington Health Lansdale Hospital, Lansdale, PA, p. A538
FARRELL, Roy, M.D. Chief Medical Officer, Carondelet Holy Cross Hospital, Nogales, AZ, p. A33
FARRELL, Steven E., M.D. Chief Medical Officer, Forrest General Hospital, Hattiesburg, MS, p. A354
FARRELL, Terence, Vice President and Administrator, Herrin Hospital, Herrin, IL, p. A190
FARRELL, Teresa, Chief Human Resources Officer, Nacogdoches Medical Center, Nacogdoches, TX, p. A633
FARRELL, Timothy, Executive Director, St. Lawrence Psychiatric Center, Ogdensburg, NY, p. A446
FARRELLY, Irene, Vice President and Chief Information Officer, Brooklyn Hospital Center, NY, p. A439
FARRER, Joe, Interim Administrator, North Metro Medical Center, Jacksonville, AR, p. A46
FARRINGTON, Robyn, Chief Nursing Officer, Broward Health Medical Center, Fort Lauderdale, FL, p. A126
FARRIS, Bain J., President and Chief Executive Officer, Saint Joseph Hospital, Denver, CO, p. A102
FARRIS, James R., FACHE, Chief Executive Officer, Union County Hospital, Anna, IL, p. A178
FARRIS, Jason, Chief Nursing Officer, Specialty Hospital of Midwest City, Midwest City, OK, p. A510
FARROW, Diane, Manager Information Technology and Systems, Willamette Valley Medical Center, McMinnville, OR, p. A522
FARRUGIA, Gianrico, M.D., Vice President and Chief Executive Officer, Mayo Clinic Jacksonville, Jacksonville, FL, p. A129
FARSHAO, Nosratian, M.D. Chief Medical Staff, Memorial Hospital of Gardena, Gardena, CA, p. A63
FARUGIA, Celeste, R.N. Chief Nurse Executive, Kaiser Permanente Panorama City Medical Center, CA, p. A70
FARWELL, Brenda
 Director Human Resources, Providence Medical Center, Kansas City, KS, p. A243
 Director Human Resources, Saint John Hospital, Leavenworth, KS, p. A244
FASANO, Philip, Chief Information Officer, Kaiser Permanente Sacramento Medical Center, Sacramento, CA, p. A84
FASSIO, Deana, Director, Northeast Rehabilitation Hospital, Salem, NH, p. A408
FAST, Gary, M.D. Medical Director, Prairie View, Newton, KS, p. A246
FASTHORSE, Lena, Supervisor Human Resource, U. S. Public Health Service Indian Hospital–Whiteriver, Whiteriver, AZ, p. A40
FATCH, Casey, Chief Operating Officer, Tri–City Medical Center, Oceanside, CA, p. A79
FATTIG, Marty, Chief Executive Officer, Nemaha County Hospital, Auburn, NE, p. A389
FATULA, Suzette, Chief Financial Officer, Winn Parish Medical Center, Winnfield, LA, p. A287
FAUBION, Matthew, M.D. Clinical Director, Kerrville State Hospital, Kerrville, TX, p. A626
FAUCHER, Kimberly, M.D. Chief Medical Officer, Frank R. Howard Memorial Hospital, Willits, CA, p. A98
FAUCHEUX, Lisa, Director Human Resources, St. James Parish Hospital, Lutcher, LA, p. A279
FAUGHT, Charles J., Chief Financial Officer, Burnett Medical Center, Grantsburg, WI, p. A701
FAUL, Jennifer, Chief Operating Officer, Prairie St. John's, Fargo, ND, p. A473

Index of Health Care Professionals

Index of Health Care Professionals / Faulis

FAULIS, Karen, Chief Operating Officer, Palmdale Regional Medical Center, Palmdale, CA, p. A80
FAULK, Gordon, Administrator, Elmore Community Hospital, Wetumpka, AL, p. A26
FAULKNER, Cheryl, Director of Nursing, McKenzie County Healthcare System, Watford City, ND, p. A477
FAULKNER, Cynthia, R.N. Chief Nursing Executive, Pender Memorial Hospital, Burgaw, NC, p. A456
FAULKNER, David, Interim Chief Executive Officer, Bear Valley Community Hospital, Big Bear Lake, CA, p. A56
FAULKNER, Kristi, Director Human Resources, United Regional Health Care System, Wichita Falls, TX, p. A652
FAULKNER, Laura, Chief Human Resource Management Service, Lexington Veterans Affairs Medical Center, Lexington, KY, p. A260
FAULKNER, Mark T., President, Baptist Health Care Corporation, Pensacola, FL, p. B20
FAULKNER, Sharon, Chief Nursing Officer, AMG Specialty Hospital–Denham Springs, Denham Springs, LA, p. A273
FAUS, Doug, FACHE, Chief Executive Officer, Ivinson Memorial Hospital, Laramie, WY, p. A716
FAUST, Bill D., Administrator, Floyd County Medical Center, Charles City, IA, p. A224
FAUST, Bonnie H., R.N. Vice President Chief Nursing Officer, CaroMont Regional Medical Center, Gastonia, NC, p. A460
FAUTHEREE, Greg, M.D. Medical Director, Spine Hospital of Louisiana (formally the NeuroMedical Center Surgical Hospital), Baton Rouge, LA, p. A270
FAVALE, Maria, FACHE Associate Director, Northport Veterans Affairs Medical Center, Northport, NY, p. A445
FAVATA, Valerie, R.N. Chief Nursing Officer, Oswego Hospital, Oswego, NY, p. A447
FAVRET, John M., Director, Eastern State Hospital, Williamsburg, VA, p. A674
FAWLEY, Kimberly, Chief Nursing Officer, Florence Hospital at Anthem, Florence, AZ, p. A31
FAWNS, Bill, Interim Manager Information Systems, Kern Medical Center, Bakersfield, CA, p. A55
FAY, Brian, Director Information Systems, Sidney Health Center, Sidney, MT, p. A387
FAYARD, Jack, Director Information Technology, Louisiana Heart Hospital, Lacombe, LA, p. A277
FAYEN, Edward J., Associate Administrator Operations and Support, Washington Hospital Healthcare System, Fremont, CA, p. A62
FAYRE, Gail, M.D. Medical Director, Anna Jaques Hospital, Newburyport, MA, p. A309
FAZIO, Charles, Chief Health Officer and Medical Director Health Plan, Regions Hospital, Saint Paul, MN, p. A346
FEAK, Christina, Chief Information Officer, Onslow Memorial Hospital, Jacksonville, NC, p. A463
FEAR, Frank, Vice President Ancillary Services and Chief Information Officer, Memorial Healthcare, Owosso, MI, p. A327
FEASEL, Jeff, Chief Executive Officer, Halifax Health Medical Center of Daytona Beach, Daytona Beach, FL, p. A125
FEATHER, Leroy P., Vice President Finance, Community Hospitals and Wellness Centers, Bryan, OH, p. A480
FEAZELL, Kayla, Chief Executive Officer, HEALTHSOUTH Rehabilitation of Gadsden, Gadsden, AL, p. A20
FEBRY, Ricardo, M.D. Medical Director, St. Theresa Specialty Hospital, Kenner, LA, p. A276
FEBUS, Steven, Chief Financial Officer, Pullman Regional Hospital, Pullman, WA, p. A682
FEDELE, Jerry J., President and Chief Executive Officer, Boca Raton Regional Hospital, Boca Raton, FL, p. A122
FEDER, Diane, R.N. Senior Vice President and Chief Operating Officer, Witham Memorial Hospital, Lebanon, IN, p. A215
FEDERICO, Skip, Director Information Systems, Fairway Medical Center, Covington, LA, p. A272
FEDERINKO, David, Chief Information Officer, Allegan General Hospital, Allegan, MI, p. A314
FEDERSPIEL, John C., President and Chief Executive Officer, New York–Presbyterian/Hudson Valley Hospital, Cortlandt Manor, NY, p. A432
FEDORA, Deborah, Director Human Resources, Paoli Hospital, Paoli, PA, p. A542
FEE, Jeff, Chief Executive Officer, St. Patrick Hospital, Missoula, MT, p. A386
FEEMAN, Kimberly, Senior Vice President and Chief Operating Officer, The Good Samaritan Hospital, Lebanon, PA, p. A538
FEENEY, Daniel, M.D. Medical Director, Brentwood Hospital, Shreveport, LA, p. A284
FEENEY, John, President and Chief Executive Officer, Berlin Memorial Hospital, Berlin, WI, p. A698
FEENEY, Sheri, Chief Financial Officer, Providence Regional Medical Center Everett, Everett, WA, p. A679
FEESS, David, President and Chief Executive Officer, Liberty Hospital, Liberty, MO, p. A372
FEGAN, Claudia, M.D. Chief Medical Officer, John H. Stroger Jr. Hospital of Cook County, Chicago, IL, p. A182
FEGAN, Theresa, R.N. Chief Clinical Officer, Tahoe Pacific Hospitals, Sparks, NV, p. A404
FEGHALI, Georges, M.D
Senior Vice President Quality and Chief Medical Officer, Bethesda North Hospital, Cincinnati, OH, p. A482
Senior Vice President Quality and Chief Medical Officer, Good Samaritan Hospital, Cincinnati, OH, p. A483
FEHLINGS, Michele, Controller, Hermann Area District Hospital, Hermann, MO, p. A368
FEHRING, Marcia, Chief Financial Officer, Horn Memorial Hospital, Ida Grove, IA, p. A229
FEIDT, Leslie, Chief Information Officer, Erie County Medical Center, Buffalo, NY, p. A430
FEIKE, Jeffrey, President and Chief Administrative Officer, Fort Loudoun Medical Center, Lenoir City, TN, p. A581
FEIL, Julie, Accountant, Cavalier County Memorial Hospital, Langdon, ND, p. A475
FEILER, Kenneth H., Chief Executive Officer, Rose Medical Center, Denver, CO, p. A102
FEILMEIER, Patricia, R.N. Chief Nurse Executive, Atlanta Medical Center, Atlanta, GA, p. A150
FEILNER, Margaret, Director Information Services, SSM St. Joseph Health Center, Saint Charles, MO, p. A375
FEINBERG, Daniel, M.D. Chief Medical Officer, Pennsylvania Hospital, Philadelphia, PA, p. A545
FEINBERG, David T., M.D., President and Chief Executive Officer, Geisinger Health System, Danville, PA, p. B58
FEINBERG, David T., M.D. Chief Executive Officer, Geisinger–Community Medical Center, Scranton, PA, p. A549
FEINBERG, Jason, M.D
Vice President Medical Affairs and Chief Medical Officer, Geneva General Hospital, Geneva, NY, p. A434
Vice President Medical Affairs and Chief Medical Officer, Soldiers and Sailors Memorial Hospital of Yates County, Penn Yan, NY, p. A447
FEINER, David, M.D. Chief Staff, Calais Regional Hospital, Calais, ME, p. A289
FEIRN, Greg, CPA, President and Chief Executive Officer, LCMC Health, New Orleans, LA, p. B81
FEIST, Patricia, Manager Human Resources, Crook County Medical Services District, Sundance, WY, p. A717
FEISTRITZER, Nancye R., Chief Nursing Officer, Emory University Hospital, atlanta, GA, p. A150
FELBINGER, Richard, Senior Vice President and Chief Financial Officer, Borgess Medical Center, Kalamazoo, MI, p. A323
FELCZAK, Jr., Michael J., Finance Manager, Brighton Center for Recovery, Brighton, MI, p. A315
FELDER, Debra A., Director Human Resources, Shriners Hospitals for Children–Cincinnati Burns Hospital, Cincinnati, OH, p. A483
FELDMAN, David L., Executive Vice President and Treasurer, Circles of Care, Melbourne, FL, p. A133
FELDMAN, Deborah A., President and Chief Executive Officer, Children's Medical Center, Dayton, OH, p. A487
FELDMAN, Joel, M.D., President, St. Vincent Indianapolis Hospital, Indianapolis, IN, p. A212
FELDMAN, Mitchell S., Chief Executive Officer, West Boca Medical Center, Boca Raton, FL, p. A122
FELDMANN, Scott, Director Information Technology, SSM DePaul Health Center, Bridgeton, MO, p. A364
FELDSTEIN, Charles S., M.D. Vice President Medical Affairs, St. Rose Hospital, Hayward, CA, p. A64
FELEGE, Lester, Controller, New England Rehabilitation Hospital, Woburn, MA, p. A313
FELICE, Michael, Chief Financial Officer, Pennsylvania Psychiatric Institute, Harrisburg, PA, p. A535
FELICETTI, Jacqueline, Chief Human Resource Officer, Penn Medicine Chester County Hospital, West Chester, PA, p. A552
FELICI, Brian K., Chief Executive Officer, Wetzel County Hospital, New Martinsville, WV, p. A693
FELICIANO, Jose R., Chief Executive Officer, Ryder Memorial Hospital, Humacao, PR, p. A721
FELICIANO, Myrna Quinones, M.D. Medical Director, University Pediatric Hospital, PR, p. A724
FELICIANO, Pablo, Manager Human Resources, Veterans Affairs Central Western Massachusetts Healthcare System, Leeds, MA, p. A308
FELIZ, Miriam, M.D. Medical Director, St. Catherine's Rehabilitation Hospital, North Miami, FL, p. A136
FELKNER, Joseph G.
Senior Vice President Finance and Chief Financial Officer, Health First Cape Canaveral Hospital, Cocoa Beach, FL, p. A124
Executive Vice President, Finance and Chief Financial Officer, Health First Holmes Regional Medical Center, Melbourne, FL, p. A133
Executive Vice President and Chief Financial Officer, Health First Palm Bay Hospital, Palm Bay, FL, p. A138
Executive Vice President and Chief Financial Officer, Health First Viera Hospital, Melbourne, FL, p. A133
FELL, David, M.D. Chief Medical Officer, Tulsa Spine and Specialty Hospital, Tulsa, OK, p. A517
FELLER, Julie, Director Human Resources, Grays Harbor Community Hospital, Aberdeen, WA, p. A676
FELLOWS, James, M.D. Chief of Staff, Methodist Hospital, Henderson, KY, p. A258
FELLOWS, Steven A.
Executive Vice President and Chief Operating Officer, Goleta Valley Cottage Hospital, Santa Barbara, CA, p. A91
Executive Vice President and Chief Operating Officer, Santa Barbara Cottage Hospital, Santa Barbara, CA, p. A91
Executive Vice President and Chief Operating Officer, Santa Ynez Valley Cottage Hospital, Solvang, CA, p. A92
FELMLEE, Charles, Assistant Director Fiscal Services, Central Virginia Training Center, Madison Heights, VA, p. A667
FELTMAN, Steven, CPA Chief Financial Officer, Essentia Health–Virginia, Virginia, MN, p. A348
FELTON, David
Regional Chief Information Officer, LincolnHealth, Damariscotta, ME, p. A290
Manager Information Systems, Waldo County General Hospital, Belfast, ME, p. A289
FELTS, Dave, Chief Information Systems, Logan Regional Hospital, Logan, UT, p. A655
FELTY, Craig, Chief Executive Officer, Indiana University Health Starke Hospital, Knox, IN, p. A213
FENDER, Tamra, Chief Nursing Officer, Marias Medical Center, Shelby, MT, p. A387
FENDT, Phil, Chief Financial Officer, Memorial Community Health, Aurora, NE, p. A389
FENELLO, Michael A., Administrator, St. Luke's McCall, McCall, ID, p. A175
FENER, Michael
Executive Director, Plainview Hospital, Plainview, NY, p. A447
Executive Director, Syosset Hospital, Syosset, NY, p. A451
FENN, Mark, Director Human Resources, Pulaski Memorial Hospital, Winamac, IN, p. A221
FENNELL, Charles, Vice President Information Management, St. Joseph's Hospital Health Center, Syracuse, NY, p. A451
FENNELL, Colin, M.D. Chief Medical Officer, RiverView Health, Crookston, MN, p. A337
FENNELL, David, M.D. Acting Medical Director, Atascadero State Hospital, Atascadero, CA, p. A54
FENNELL, Dustin, Director Information Systems, Mission Community Hospital, CA, p. A71
FENSKE, Bill, Chief Financial Officer, Rice Memorial Hospital, Willmar, MN, p. A349
FENSKE, Candace, Chief Executive Officer, Madelia Community Hospital, Madelia, MN, p. A341
FENSKE, Mary, Human Resource Business Partner, Spectrum Health United Hospital, Greenville, MI, p. A321
FENTER, Kim, Chief Financial Officer, Wilbarger General Hospital, Vernon, TX, p. A650
FENWICK, Sandra L., M.P.H., President and Chief Executive Officer, Boston Children's Hospital, Boston, MA, p. A303
FEOLA, Ferd, Chief Information Officer, Pocono Medical Center, East Stroudsburg, PA, p. A533
FERBER, Robert, M.D. Chief Clinical Innovation Officer, Nanticoke Memorial Hospital, Seaford, DE, p. A117
FERCH, Wayne
President and Chief Executive Officer, Adventist Medical Center – Hanford, Hanford, CA, p. A64
President and Chief Executive Officer, Adventist Medical Center–Reedley, Reedley, CA, p. A83
President and Chief Executive Officer, Central Valley General Hospital, Hanford, CA, p. A64
FERGUS, Gigi, Interim Chief Executive Officer, Bluefield Regional Medical Center, Bluefield, WV, p. A689
FERGUS, Janie
Director and Chief Information Officer, Saint Joseph East, Lexington, KY, p. A260
Director and Chief Information Officer, Saint Joseph Hospital, Lexington, KY, p. A260
FERGUS, Linda, Manager Information Technology, Allegheny Valley Hospital, Natrona Heights, PA, p. A541
FERGUSON, Allison, Director Human Resources, Avoyelles Hospital, Marksville, LA, p. A279
FERGUSON, Cathy, R.N. Vice President and Chief Nursing Officer, Hamilton Medical Center, Dalton, GA, p. A155

A836 Index of Health Care Professionals 

Index of Health Care Professionals / Finelli

Index of Health Care Professionals

FERGUSON, Cheryl L., Associate Administrator, Sanford Canby Medical Center, Canby, MN, p. A336
FERGUSON, Clifford, Director Information Technology and Systems, Bayshore Medical Center, Pasadena, TX, p. A635
FERGUSON, Deborah, Human Resources Consultant, Sentara Obici Hospital, Suffolk, VA, p. A673
FERGUSON, Denise, Chief Nursing Officer, Baptist Memorial Hospital–Collierville, Collierville, TN, p. A576
FERGUSON, G. Thomas, Senior Vice President and Chief Human Resources Officer, New York–Presbyterian Hospital, New York, NY, p. A443
FERGUSON, Gary W., Executive Vice President and Chief Operating Officer, Christiana Care Health System, Newark, DE, p. A117
FERGUSON, Gordon B., President and Chief Executive Officer, Saint Thomas Rutherford Hospital, Murfreesboro, TN, p. A585
FERGUSON, Karen, Director Human Resources, Johnson County Healthcare Center, Buffalo, WY, p. A715
FERGUSON, Louis D.
Chief Financial Officer, Palestine Regional Medical Center, Palestine, TX, p. A635
Chief Financial Officer, Palestine Regional Medical Center–East, Palestine, TX, p. A635
FERGUSON, Michael, Chief Financial Officer, Harbor Oaks Hospital, New Baltimore, MI, p. A326
FERGUSON, Nina L., Director Human Resources, Little Colorado Medical Center, Winslow, AZ, p. A40
FERGUSON, Randy, Chief Information Officer, Ridgecrest Regional Hospital, Ridgecrest, CA, p. A83
FERGUSON, Rick, Chief Executive Officer, Oklahoma Surgical Hospital, Tulsa, OK, p. A516
FERGUSON, Susan, Chief Nursing Officer, LifeCare Hospitals of Chester County, West Chester, PA, p. A552
FERGUSON, Tonya, Director Human Resources, HEALTHSOUTH Rehabilitation Hospital of Virginia, Richmond, VA, p. A671
FERGUSON, Zeta, Chief Human Resources, Atlanta Veterans Affairs Medical Center, Decatur, GA, p. A155
FERIA, Jorge, M.D. President Medical Staff, Wilma N. Vazquez Medical Center, Vega Baja, PR, p. A724
FERNANDES, Roxanne, R.N. Chief Nursing Officer, Children's Hospitals and Clinics of Minnesota, Minneapolis, MN, p. A342
FERNANDEZ, Alexander, Chief Financial Officer, Broward Health Medical Center, Fort Lauderdale, FL, p. A126
FERNANDEZ, Arthur, Chief Financial Officer, First Hospital Panamericano, Cidra, PR, p. A720
FERNANDEZ, Benigno J., M.D. Executive Medical Director, Laurel Ridge Treatment Center, San Antonio, TX, p. A641
FERNANDEZ, Darlene, Chief Financial Officer, UNM Sandoval Regional Medical Center, Rio Rancho, NM, p. A426
FERNANDEZ, Genaro, M.D. Chief of Staff, Paradise Valley Hospital, National City, CA, p. A77
FERNANDEZ, Jean, Chief Information Officer, Beth Israel Deaconess Hospital–Milton, Milton, MA, p. A309
FERNANDEZ, John R., President and Chief Executive Officer, Massachusetts Eye and Ear Infirmary, Boston, MA, p. A304
FERNANDEZ, Jose L. Pimentel, Medical Director, Lafayette Hospital, Arroyo, PR, p. A720
FERNANDEZ, Mark, M.D. Chief of Staff and President Medical Staff, Illinois Valley Community Hospital, Peru, IL, p. A198
FERNANDEZ, Ruben D., R.N. Vice President and Chief Nursing Officer, Palisades Medical Center, North Bergen, NJ, p. A416
FERNANDEZ, Tracey, Chief Financial Officer, St. Mary Medical Center, Apple Valley, CA, p. A54
FERNANDEZ DEL VALLE, Arthur J., Chief Financial Officer, Cardiovascular Center of Puerto Rico and the Caribbean, San Juan, PR, p. A723
FERNANDEZ–BRAVO, Grisel, R.N. Chief Nursing Officer, Memorial Hospital West, Pembroke Pines, FL, p. A139
FERNIANY, William, Ph.D., Chief Executive Officer, UAB Health System, Birmingham, AL, p. B138
FERRACANE, Tony, Vice President Human Resources, St. Mary Medical Center, Hobart, IN, p. A211
FERRANCE, Randy, M.D. President Medical Staff, Riverside Tappahannock Hospital, Tappahannock, VA, p. A673
FERRANTI, Jeffrey, M.D. Chief Information Officer, Duke University Hospital, Durham, NC, p. A459
FERRAROTTI, Gianna, Director Human Resources North Region, OhioHealth Marion General Hospital, Marion, OH, p. A493
FERREBEE, Mike, M.D. Vice President Medical Affairs, Monongalia General Hospital, Morgantown, WV, p. A693
FERREIRA, Daniel, Director Management Information Systems, Hospital De La Concepcion, San German, PR, p. A722
FERRELL, Angie
Director Human Resources, Mercy Health – Anderson Hospital, Cincinnati, OH, p. A483
Director Human Resources, Mercy Health – Clermont Hospital, Batavia, OH, p. A479
FERRELL, David A., Regional Administrator, Shriners Hospitals for Children–Houston, Houston, TX, p. A622
FERRELL, Eileen Brennan, MS Vice President and Chief Nursing Officer, MedStar Georgetown University Hospital, Washington, DC, p. A119
FERRELL, Jennifer, Chief Nursing Officer, HEALTHSOUTH Rehabilitation Hospital of Memphis, Memphis, TN, p. A583
FERRELL, John, President and Chief Executive Officer, Seton Medical Center, Daly City, CA, p. A59
FERRELL, Ronald, Chief Information Officer, New Mexico Veterans Affairs Health Care System – Raymond G. Murphy Medical Center, Albuquerque, NM, p. A422
FERREN, Alison
Vice President Information Technology and Chief Information Officer, Abington Health Lansdale Hospital, Lansdale, PA, p. A538
Vice President Information Technology and Chief Information Officer, Abington Memorial Hospital, Abington, PA, p. A528
FERRERO, Marcia L., MS Chief Nursing Officer, Heritage Valley Health System, Beaver, PA, p. A529
FERRIS, David, Chief Nursing Officer and Vice President Patient Care Services, Claxton–Hepburn Medical Center, Ogdensburg, NY, p. A446
FERRIS, Joseph, Chief Financial Officer, Veterans Affairs Black Hills Health Care System, Fort Meade, SD, p. A568
FERRIS, Mark, M.D. Medical Director, Kindred Hospital–White Rock, Dallas, TX, p. A605
FERRIS, Michael, M.D. Chief Medical Officer, CHI Health St Elizabeth, Lincoln, NE, p. A393
FERRONI, Karen, M.D. Medical Director, Holyoke Medical Center, Holyoke, MA, p. A307
FERRY, Jane, M.D. Vice President Medical Affairs, Grand View Health, Sellersville, PA, p. A549
FERRY, Thomas, Business Administrator, Oakwood Correctional Facility, Lima, OH, p. A492
FESKO, Donald P., Chief Executive Officer and Administrator, Community Hospital, Munster, IN, p. A217
FETTER, Trevor, President and Chief Executive Officer, TENET Healthcare Corporation, Dallas, TX, p. B131
FETTERLEY, Kathy, Vice President and Chief Human Resources Officer, Hardin Memorial Hospital, Elizabethtown, KY, p. A256
FETTEROLF, Kim, R.N. Chief Clinical Officer, Lourdes Specialty Hospital of Southern New Jersey, Willingboro, NJ, p. A420
FETTERS, Valerie, Chief Financial Officer, Hillsdale Community Health Center, Hillsdale, MI, p. A322
FEUCHT, Jason, Chief Financial Officer, Kossuth Regional Health Center, Algona, IA, p. A222
FEUER, Tammy, Chief Executive Officer, HEALTHSOUTH Rehabilitation Hospital of Vineland, Vineland, NJ, p. A419
FEUNNING, Charles, M.D. President Medical Staff, Summa Western Reserve Hospital, Cuyahoga Falls, OH, p. A487
FICCHI, Adrienne, Vice President Information Management, Philadelphia Veterans Affairs Medical Center, Philadelphia, PA, p. A545
FICICCHY, Teri, R.N. Chief Nursing Officer, Bon Secours St. Francis Health System, Greenville, SC, p. A561
FICKES, Catherine, R.N., President and Chief Executive Officer, St. Vincent Medical Center, Los Angeles, CA, p. A73
FIDLER, Soniya, Chief Human Resources and Compliance Officer, Yampa Valley Medical Center, Steamboat Springs, CO, p. A108
FIDUCIA, Karen A., FACHE, President, Hospital Division, USMD Inc., Irving, TX, p. B148
FIELD, Clifford, M.D. Medical Director, Kau Hospital, Pahala, HI, p. A170
FIELD, Edward, Administrator, Loma Linda University Behavioral Medicine Center, Redlands, CA, p. A82
FIELD, Kori, Director of Nursing, Brodstone Memorial Hospital, Superior, NE, p. A398
FIELD, Laurie, Director Human Resources, Eaton Rapids Medical Center, Eaton Rapids, MI, p. A319
FIELDER, Barb, Vice President Finance, St. Joseph Mercy Chelsea, Chelsea, MI, p. A316
FIELDER, Jaf, Vice President and Administrator, Willis–Knighton Medical Center, Shreveport, LA, p. A285
FIELDING, Colene, Manager Business Office, Baylor Medical Center at Uptown, Dallas, TX, p. A604
FIELDING, Laura M., Administrative Director Organizational Development, Holy Family Memorial, Manitowoc, WI, p. A704
FIELDS, Donald, Community Chief Executive Officer, Harrison Memorial Hospital, Cynthiana, KY, p. A256
FIELDS, Donald R., Senior Community Chief Executive Officer, Hazard ARH Regional Medical Center, Hazard, KY, p. A258
FIELDS, Glenn C., Vice President, Human Resources, St. Vincent Anderson Regional Hospital, Anderson, IN, p. A204
FIELDS, Greg, Director Information Technology, Elbert Memorial Hospital, Elberton, GA, p. A157
FIELDS, Laurie, Director Human Resources, ContinueCARE Hospital at Hendrick Medical Center, Abilene, TX, p. A590
FIERER, Jonathan, M.D. Chief of Staff, Martinsburg Veterans Affairs Medical Center, Martinsburg, WV, p. A693
FIERRO, Barbara, Director, Human Resources, St. Francis Hospital, Roslyn, NY, p. A449
FIFERLICK, Bev, Chief Financial Officer, Community Memorial Healthcare, Marysville, KS, p. A246
FIFIELD, Michael, Vice President Human Resources, Oneida Healthcare, Oneida, NY, p. A446
FIGUEROA, Maria, Director Human Resources, Ryder Memorial Hospital, Humacao, PR, p. A721
FIGUEROA, Roseann, Director Human Resources, Doctors Hospital of Laredo, Laredo, TX, p. A627
FIKE, Ruthita J., Chief Executive Officer, Loma Linda University Behavioral Medicine Center, Redlands, CA, p. A82
FILER, Christine, Director Human Resources, HEALTHSOUTH Rehabilitation Hospital of Altoona, Altoona, PA, p. A528
FILES, Ashley S., Director Human Resources and Public Relations and Marketing, Winn Parish Medical Center, Winnfield, LA, p. A287
FILES, Carol, Chief Financial Officer, Victory Surgical Hospital East Houston, Houston, TX, p. A623
FILIAK, Thomas, Vice President Administration, Auburn Community Hospital, Auburn, NY, p. A429
FILIPINI, Alfred, Manager Human Resources, Ancora Psychiatric Hospital, Hammonton, NJ, p. A412
FILIPOWICZ, Thomas, M.D. Medical Director, St. Luke's Hospital – Quakertown Campus, Quakertown, PA, p. A548
FILLER, Richard, Chief Financial Officer, Berger Health System, Circleville, OH, p. A484
FILLER, Scott, Chief Executive Officer, HEALTHSOUTH Rehabilitation Hospital of Altoona, Altoona, PA, p. A528
FILLINGIM, Jed, Acting Chief Operating Officer and Associate Director, G.V. (Sonny) Montgomery Veterans Affairs Medical Center, Jackson, MS, p. A355
FILLIPO, Brian, M.D. Chief Medical Officer, Robert Packer Hospital, Sayre, PA, p. A549
FILOSA, Frank, Fiscal Manager, Washington DC Veterans Affairs Medical Center, Washington, DC, p. A120
FILPI, Jeanette, Chief Executive Officer, Pioneer Community Hospital of Patrick, Stuart, VA, p. A673
FILSON, Debbie, Chief Financial Officer, Ashland Health Center, Ashland, KS, p. A237
FINAN Jr., John J., FACHE, President and Chief Executive Officer, Franciscan Missionaries of Our Lady Health System, Inc., Baton Rouge, LA, p. B57
FINAN, Timothy J., FACHE,
President and Chief Executive Officer, Bradford Regional Medical Center, Bradford, PA, p. A530
President and Chief Executive Officer, Olean General Hospital, Olean, NY, p. A446
FINAN, Timothy J., FACHE, President and Chief Executive Officer, Upper Allegheny Health System, Olean, NY, p. B148
FINCH, John
Vice President Information Services, Health Alliance Hospital – Broadway Campus, Kingston, NY, p. A436
Chief Information and Community Officer, Health Alliance Hospital – Mary's Avenue Campus, Kingston, NY, p. A436
FINCH, Kenneth A., President and Chief Executive Officer, Texas Health Huguley Hospital Fort Worth South, Fort Worth, TX, p. A614
FINCH, Kim, Chief Nursing Officer, Kosciusko Community Hospital, Warsaw, IN, p. A221
FINCH, Robert D., Vice President Human Resources, Athens Regional Medical Center, Athens, GA, p. A149
FINCH, Roy, Chief Operating Officer, Longview Regional Medical Center, Longview, TX, p. A629
FINCH, Teresa, Chief Financial Officer, Trident Medical Center, Charleston, SC, p. A558
FINCHER, Jodi, Vice President Patient Care Services, Saint John Hospital, Leavenworth, KS, p. A244
FINDLAY, Andrew L., Deputy Commander Clinical Services, Tripler Army Medical Center, Honolulu, HI, p. A169
FINDLAY, Denice C., Director Human Resources, Community Hospital of San Bernardino, San Bernardino, CA, p. A86
FINDLEY, Amber, Senior Director Nursing Services and NRC Administrator, Pleasant Valley Hospital, Point Pleasant, WV, p. A694
FINDLEY, John, Interim Chief Executive Officer, Beatrice Community Hospital and Health Center, Beatrice, NE, p. A390
FINDLEY, John T, M.D. Chief Medical Officer, Beatrice Community Hospital and Health Center, Beatrice, NE, p. A390
FINE, Allan, Chief Operating Officer, New York Eye and Ear Infirmary of Mount Sinai, New York, NY, p. A442
FINE, James, M.D. Chief Information Officer, UW Medicine/Harborview Medical Center, Seattle, WA, p. A684
FINE, Mathew N., M.D. Chief Medical Officer, Oroville Hospital, Oroville, CA, p. A79
FINE, Peter S., FACHE, President and Chief Executive Officer, Banner Health, Phoenix, AZ, p. B18
FINELLI, Frederick, M.D. Vice President Medical Affairs, MedStar Montgomery Medical Center, Olney, MD, p. A299

Index of Health Care Professionals

Index of Health Care Professionals / Finelli


FINELLI, Peter, Chief Financial Officer, Payson Regional Medical Center, Payson, AZ, p. A34
FINETTI, Yoany, R.N. Chief Nursing Officer, Barnes–Jewish West County Hospital, Saint Louis, MO, p. A376
FINK, Andrew, Vice President Medical Affairs, Morton Plant North Bay Hospital, New Port Richey, FL, p. A136
FINK, Daniel, Chief Operating Officer, The Hospitals of Providence Memorial Campus, El Paso, TX, p. A611
FINK, Renee, CPA Chief Financial Officer, Dundy County Hospital, Benkelman, NE, p. A390
FINK, Tom, Vice President Regional Finance Officer, Range Regional Health Services, Hibbing, MN, p. A340
FINKEL, Naomi, Nurse Executive, Montgomery County Emergency Service, Norristown, PA, p. A541
FINLAYSON, Susan D., R.N. Senior Vice President of Operations, Mercy Medical Center, Baltimore, MD, p. A294
FINLEY, Alan, Chief Operating Officer, Conway Regional Medical Center, Conway, AR, p. A42
FINLEY, Cindy, Chief Nursing Officer, Iron County Medical Center, Pilot Knob, MO, p. A374
FINLEY, Delvecchio
Chief Executive Officer, Harbor–UCLA Medical Center, Torrance, CA, p. A94
Chief Executive Officer, Highland Hospital, Oakland, CA, p. A78
FINLEY, E. Jane, Senior Vice President and Executive Director, Kaiser Permanente San Diego Medical Center, San Diego, CA, p. A86
FINLEY, Kevan, Chief Executive Officer, Oklahoma Forensic Center, Vinita, OK, p. A517
FINLEY, Kevin, D.O. Chief of Staff, Knox County Hospital, Knox City, TX, p. A626
FINLEY, Mike, M.D. Chief Medical Officer, CHRISTUS St. Michael Health System, Texarkana, TX, p. A647
FINLEY, Tommy, Chief Information Officer, Rutherford Regional Health System, Rutherfordton, NC, p. A468
FINLEY, Waynea
Senior Vice President Human Resources, Post Acute Medical Specialty Hospital of Lafayette, Lafayette, LA, p. A278
Senior Vice President Human Resources, Post Acute Northshore Specialty Hospital, Covington, LA, p. A272
System Director Human Resources, Post Acute/Warm Springs Rehabilitation Hospital of San Antonio, San Antonio, TX, p. A642
Corporate Director Human Resources, Post Acute/Warm Springs Specialty Hospital of Victoria, Victoria, TX, p. A650
FINLEY–HAZLE, Gabrielle, Chief Executive Officer, Florida Medical Center – A Campus of North Shore, Fort Lauderdale, FL, p. A126
FINN, Barry C., President and Chief Executive Officer, Rush–Copley Medical Center, Aurora, IL, p. A179
FINN, Patti, Chief Executive Officer, Fulton County Health Center, Wauseon, OH, p. A500
FINNEGAN, Jay, Chief Executive Officer, St. Lucie Medical Center, Port St. Lucie, FL, p. A141
FINNEGAN, Patricia, Vice President, Columbia Memorial Hospital, Hudson, NY, p. A435
FINNELL, Ian, Business Manager, Essex County Hospital Center, Cedar Grove, NJ, p. A410
FINNEY, David, R.N. Vice President Nursing, Chenango Memorial Hospital, Norwich, NY, p. A446
FINSTAD, Gary A., M.D. Chief of Staff, Kern Valley Healthcare District, Lake Isabella, CA, p. A67
FIORE–LOPEZ, Nicolette, R.N. Chief Nursing Officer, St. Charles Hospital, Port Jefferson, NY, p. A448
FIORENZO, V. James, President, UPMC Hamot, Erie, PA, p. A534
FIORET, Phil, M.D. Vice President Medical Affairs, King's Daughters Medical Center, Ashland, KY, p. A254
FIOREY, Ramona, M.P.H., Commander, Madigan Healthcare System, Tacoma, WA, p. A686
FIRES, Wiley M., Administrator, Shamrock General Hospital, Shamrock, TX, p. A643
FIRMAN, DNP, Julie, R.N
Vice President and Chief Nursing Officer, Memorial Hospital of Carbondale, Carbondale, IL, p. A180
Chief Nursing Officer, St. Joseph Memorial Hospital, Murphysboro, IL, p. A195
FISCHELS, Diane, Senior Vice President and Chief Operating Officer, Mercy Medical Center–North Iowa, Mason City, IA, p. A231
FISCHER, Angie, Chief Financial Officer, Loring Hospital, Sac City, IA, p. A234
FISCHER, James, R.N. Vice President Patient Care Services/Chief Nursing Officer, Munson Medical Center, Traverse City, MI, p. A331
FISCHER, Jason, Chief Information Officer, PIH Health Hospital–Whittier, Whittier, CA, p. A97
FISCHER, JC, Director Human Resources, Mercy Regional Medical Center, Lorain, OH, p. A492
FISCHER, John, Director Medical Staff, Clay County Hospital, Ashland, AL, p. A15
FISCHER, Linda, Director Information Services, Huntington Hospital, Huntington, NY, p. A435
FISCHER, Lisa, Director Human Resources, Brown County Hospital, Ainsworth, NE, p. A389
FISCHER, Patricia, President and Chief Executive Officer, HSHS St. Francis Hospital, Litchfield, IL, p. A193
FISCHER, Racheal Z., Interim Chief Executive Officer, Regency Hospital of Covington, Covington, LA, p. A272
FISCHER, Robert, M.D. Medical Director, Methodist Hospital for Surgery, Addison, TX, p. A590
FISCHER, Sandra, Director Human Resources, W. G. (Bill) Heffner Veterans Affairs Medical Center, Salisbury, NC, p. A468
FISCHER, Steve, Chief Financial Officer, T. J. Samson Community Hospital, Glasgow, KY, p. A257
FISCHER, Steven P., Chief Financial Officer, Beth Israel Deaconess Medical Center, Boston, MA, p. A302
FISCHER, Tamara, Chief Nursing Officer, Okeene Municipal Hospital, Okeene, OK, p. A511
FISER, David, Vice President and Chief Information Officer, Akron General Medical Center, Akron, OH, p. A478
FISH, Carolyn, Director Human Resources, Mission Community Hospital, CA, p. A71
FISH, Carrie L., Senior Vice President and Chief Operating Officer, Florida Hospital Waterman, Tavares, FL, p. A145
FISH, Elizabeth
Senior Director Site Executive and Information Technology, University of Maryland Shore Medical Center at Chestertown, Chestertown, MD, p. A296
Chief Information Officer, University of Maryland Shore Medical Center at Dorchester, Cambridge, MD, p. A296
Chief Information Officer, University of Maryland Shore Medical Center at Easton, Easton, MD, p. A297
FISHBAIN, Ken, Chief Operating Officer, Gottlieb Memorial Hospital, Melrose Park, IL, p. A194
FISHBAUGHER, David, Chief Medical Information, Mercy Iowa City, Iowa City, IA, p. A229
FISHEL, Stephanie, Vice President Patient Care Services and Chief Nursing Officer, Nathan Littauer Hospital and Nursing Home, Gloversville, NY, p. A434
FISHER, Alan, Chief Executive Officer, Doctors NeuroMedical Hospital, Bremen, IN, p. A205
FISHER, Carol, Director of Nursing, Old Vineyard Behavioral Health Services, Winston–Salem, NC, p. A471
FISHER, Charles, Chief Executive Officer, U. S. Public Health Service Indian Hospital, Eagle Butte, SD, p. A568
FISHER, David, Director Information Systems, Heart of Lancaster Regional Medical Center, Lititz, PA, p. A539
FISHER, David, M.D. Senior Vice President and Chief Medical Officer, Seattle Children's Hospital, Seattle, WA, p. A683
FISHER, David, Vice President Human Resources, Signature Healthcare Brockton Hospital, Brockton, MA, p. A305
FISHER, Diane, R.N. VP, Patient Care Services, Otsego Memorial Hospital, Gaylord, MI, p. A320
FISHER, Donna, R.N. Chief Nursing Officer, St. Mary–Corwin Medical Center, Pueblo, CO, p. A108
FISHER, Ebony, Chief Nurse Executive, Metropolitan St. Louis Psychiatric Center, Saint Louis, MO, p. A376
FISHER, Jacob, Chief Executive Officer, Tampa Community Hospital, Tampa, FL, p. A145
FISHER, Jan E., President, Williamsport Regional Medical Center, Williamsport, PA, p. A553
FISHER, Jennifer A., Manager Human Resources, Henry County Hospital, Napoleon, OH, p. A495
FISHER, John, M.D. Chief Medical Officer, Martin Luther King, Jr. Community Hospital, Los Angeles, CA, p. A71
FISHER, Kenneth, Associate Vice President Finance and Chief Financial Officer, University of Iowa Hospitals and Clinics, Iowa City, IA, p. A230
FISHER, Laura, Director Human Resources, Texas Health Huguley Hospital Fort Worth South, Fort Worth, TX, p. A614
FISHER, Lynn, M.D. Chief of Staff, Rooks County Health Center, Plainville, KS, p. A249
FISHER, Mahana, M.D. Medical Director, Blue Mountain Hospital, Blanding, UT, p. A654
FISHER, Margaret A., Executive Director Human Resources, Specialty Hospital of Washington, Washington, DC, p. A120
FISHER, Mathew, M.D. Medical Director, Springbrook Behavioral Health System, Travelers Rest, SC, p. A565
FISHER, Matt, Vice President Finance, St. Dominic–Jackson Memorial Hospital, Jackson, MS, p. A355
FISHER, Michael, President and Chief Executive Officer, Cincinnati Children's Hospital Medical Center, Cincinnati, OH, p. A482
FISHER, Michael W., Director, VA Long Beach Healthcare System, Long Beach, CA, p. A68
FISHER, Rachael, Chief Executive Officer, Regency Hospital of Hattiesburg, Hattiesburg, MS, p. A354
FISHER, Richard, President and Chief Executive Officer, Fox Chase Cancer Center–American Oncologic Hospital, Philadelphia, PA, p. A543
FISHER, Ryan
Director of Human Resources, Blanchard Valley Hospital, Findlay, OH, p. A490
Director Human Resources, Bluffton Hospital, Bluffton, OH, p. A480
FISHER, Sharon, R.N. Chief Nursing Officer, Tyrone Hospital, Tyrone, PA, p. A551
FISHER, Teresa, R.N. Chief Nursing Officer, Fort Loudoun Medical Center, Lenoir City, TN, p. A581
FISHER, Teresa, Chief Nursing Officer, Lakewood Health System, Staples, MN, p. A347
FISHER, Thomas, Senior Vice President and Chief Financial Officer, University of Tennessee Medical Center, Knoxville, TN, p. A581
FISHER, Vicky, Ph.D. Chief Nurse Executive, Catawba Hospital, Catawba, VA, p. A663
FISHKIN, Edward, M.D. Medical Director, Woodhull Medical and Mental Health Center, NY, p. A445
FISK, Anita, Director Human Resources, Three Rivers Hospital, Brewster, WA, p. A677
FISK, Kathryn M., Chief Human Resources Officer, El Camino Hospital, Mountain View, CA, p. A77
FISK, Kellee J., Chief People Resources Executive, Altru Health System, Grand Forks, ND, p. A474
FISLER, Eileen, Chief Financial Officer, Pacifica Hospital of the Valley, CA, p. A72
FITCH, James A., Director Human Resources, Houston Methodist St. Catherine Hospital, Katy, TX, p. A625
FITCH, John A., Vice President Human Resources, Campbell County Memorial Hospital, Gillette, WY, p. A716
FITE, David, Director Information Technology, Towner County Medical Center, Cando, ND, p. A472
FITE, Theresa, Chief Financial Officer, Logan Memorial Hospital, Russellville, KY, p. A265
FITTON, Lenora, D.O. Chief of Staff, Fayette County Memorial Hospital, Washington Court House, OH, p. A500
FITTS, Barry, Chief Information Officer, Trumbull Memorial Hospital, Warren, OH, p. A499
FITZ–PATRICK, Christina, R.N. Executive Director, Mercy Suburban Hospital, Norristown, PA, p. A541
FITZGERALD, Andy, Chief Executive Officer, Campbell County Memorial Hospital, Gillette, WY, p. A716
FITZGERALD, George, Regional Director Information Systems, LifeCare Hospitals of Pittsburgh, Pittsburgh, PA, p. A546
FITZGERALD, John L., Chief Executive Officer, Inova Fair Oaks Hospital, Fairfax, VA, p. A664
FITZGERALD, Mike
Chief Financial Officer, Harrison Medical Center, Bremerton, WA, p. A676
Chief Financial Officer, St. Clare Hospital, Lakewood, WA, p. A680
Chief Financial Officer, St. Francis Hospital, Federal Way, WA, p. A679
Chief Financial Officer, St. Joseph Medical Center, Tacoma, WA, p. A686
FITZGERALD, Patty, Staff Services, Charlevoix Area Hospital, Charlevoix, MI, p. A316
FITZMAURICE, Dennis, Interim Chief Executive Officer, Community First Medical Center, Chicago, IL, p. A181
FITZPATRICK, Anna, Director Human Resources, St. Anthony Regional Hospital, Carroll, IA, p. A223
FITZPATRICK, Daniel, Director Human Resources, Whitesburg ARH Hospital, Whitesburg, KY, p. A266
FITZPATRICK, James, M.D. Vice President Medical Affairs, Kenmore Mercy Hospital, Kenmore, NY, p. A436
FITZPATRICK, James G., FACHE, Chief Executive Officer, Mercy Medical Center–Sioux City, Sioux City, IA, p. A234
FITZPATRICK, Leigh, Director Human Resources, Arkansas Valley Regional Medical Center, La Junta, CO, p. A105
FITZPATRICK, Leigh Ann, Superintendent, Kerrville State Hospital, Kerrville, TX, p. A626
FITZPATRICK, Sean, Area Finance Officer, Kaiser Permanente Santa Clara Medical Center, Santa Clara, CA, p. A91
FITZSIMMONS, Shawn, Director Information Technology Services, Community Medical Center, Toms River, NJ, p. A419
FITZSIMONS, Patricia Sue, R.N. Senior Vice President Patient Services, Yale–New Haven Hospital, New Haven, CT, p. A114
FIX, Judith A., R.N. Senior Vice President and Chief Nursing Officer, Long Beach Memorial Medical Center, Long Beach, CA, p. A68
FLACH, Shannan, Chief Executive Officer, Wamego Health Center, Wamego, KS, p. A252
FLADER, Steve, Chief Financial Officer, Northwest Medical Center – Springdale, Springdale, AR, p. A51
FLAHERTY, Daniel, M.D. Chief Medical Staff, Prairie Lakes Healthcare System, Watertown, SD, p. A572


**A838** Index of Health Care Professionals

FOJTASEK, Georgia R., Ed.D., President and Chief Executive Officer, Allegiance Health, Jackson, MI, p. A323

FOLEY, Chris, Chief of Medicine, Children's Hospital of The King's Daughters, Norfolk, VA, p. A669

FOLEY, Crystal, Director Human Resources, Little River Rockdale Hospital, Rockdale, TX, p. A638

FOLEY, James T., CPA Vice President and Chief Financial Officer, Shore Medical Center, Somers Point, NJ, p. A418

FOLEY, Jay, Chief Operating Officer, Southwestern Regional Medical Center, Tulsa, OK, p. A517

FOLEY, John, Chief Information Officer, Allegheny General Hospital, Pittsburgh, PA, p. A546

FOLEY, John V., Chief Information Officer, University Hospitals Case Medical Center, Cleveland, OH, p. A485

FOLEY, Michael, M.D. Chief Medical Officer, North Okaloosa Medical Center, Crestview, FL, p. A124

FOLEY, Regina, R.N. Vice President Nursing and Operations, Ocean Medical Center, Brick Township, NJ, p. A410

FOLK, Jeffrey R., M.D. Vice President Medical Affairs and Chief Medical Officer, Piedmont Newnan Hospital, Newnan, GA, p. A162

FOLKENBERG, Todd, Chief Executive Officer, Castle Rock Adventist Hospital, Castle Rock, CO, p. A100

FOLKS, David G., M.D. Chief Medical Officer, New Hampshire Hospital, Concord, NH, p. A405

FOLL, Gary R., Chief Financial Officer, Atchison Hospital, Atchison, KS, p. A237

FOLLARD, Cheyenne, Chief Financial Officer, The University of Vermont Health Network Central Vermont Medical Center, Berlin, VT, p. A660

FOLLETT, Richard, Chief Information Officer, The Good Samaritan Hospital, Lebanon, PA, p. A538

FOLSKE, Lance, Chief Executive Officer, Hickory Trail Hospital, Desoto, TX, p. A608

FOLSOM, Lori S., Assistant Vice President Human Resources, Tift Regional Medical Center, Tifton, GA, p. A166

FOLTZ, JoAnn M., R.N., Chief Executive Officer, Sanford Wheaton Medical Center, Wheaton, MN, p. A349

FONDESSY, Terrence, M.D. Vice President Medical Affairs, ProMedica Fostoria Community Hospital, Fostoria, OH, p. A490

FONG, Joseph, Administrator, Providence Seward Medical Center, Seward, AK, p. A29

FONKEN, Paul, M.D. Chief of Staff, Estes Park Medical Center, Estes Park, CO, p. A103

FONSECA, Jesus, M.D. Chief of Staff, Lea Regional Medical Center, Hobbs, NM, p. A424

FONSECA, Luis, Chief Operating Officer, Salinas Valley Memorial Healthcare System, Salinas, CA, p. A85

FONTAINE, Melissa, Chief Operating Officer, UAMS Medical Center, Little Rock, AR, p. A47

FONTAINE, Tim, Chief Operating Officer, Pioneer Community Hospital of Stokes, Danbury, NC, p. A458

FONTAINE–WESTHART, Mark, Associate Director, Bedford Veterans Affairs Medical Center, Edith Nourse Rogers Memorial Veterans Hospital, Bedford, MA, p. A302

FONTENAULT, Richard, Director Information Systems, Green Oaks Hospital, Dallas, TX, p. A605

FONTENELLE, Mary, Executive Nurse Director, Eastern Louisiana Mental Health System, Jackson, LA, p. A275

FONTENOT, Cathi E., M.D. Medical Director, Interim LSU Public Hospital, New Orleans, LA, p. A282

FONTENOT, H. Jerrel, M.D. Medical Director, Ouachita Community Hospital, West Monroe, LA, p. A287

FONTENOT, Micheal, Chief Financial Officer, Mercy Regional Medical Center, Ville Platte, LA, p. A286

FONTENOT, Teri G., FACHE, President and Chief Executive Officer, Woman's Hospital, Baton Rouge, LA, p. A270

FONTENOT, Theresa, Executive Director, Oceans Behavioral Hospital of Opelousas, Opelousas, LA, p. A283

FONZE, Tony, President and Chief Executive Officer, Carondelet St. Joseph's Hospital, Tucson, AZ, p. A39

FONZIE, Juril, Director Human Resources, Helena Regional Medical Center, Helena, AR, p. A45

FOOKES, Sherman, Interim Administrator, Savoy Medical Center, Mamou, LA, p. A279

FOOTE, Donald E., Fiscal Officer, Wilkes–Barre Veterans Affairs Medical Center, Wilkes–Barre, PA, p. A553

FOOTE, John, Chief Information Officer, Manchester Veterans Affairs Medical Center, Manchester, NH, p. A407

FOOTE, Mark, Chief Financial Officer, Madera Community Hospital, Madera, CA, p. A74

FORAND, Angela, Director, William S. Hall Psychiatric Institute, Columbia, SC, p. A560

FORBES, Brenda, Controller, HEALTHSOUTH Rehabilitation Hospital of Fort Smith, Fort Smith, AR, p. A44

FORBES, Geri, Chief Executive Officer, Whidbey General Hospital, Coupeville, WA, p. A678

FORBES, Jonathan, Director Human Resources, Ashtabula County Medical Center, Ashtabula, OH, p. A478

FORBES, Ronald O., M.D. Medical Director, Central State Hospital, Petersburg, VA, p. A670

FORBES, Vidette J., R.N
Chief Nursing Officer and Chief Operating Officer, Reliant Austin, Austin, TX, p. A594
Chief Nursing Officer and Chief Operating officer, Reliant Rehabilitation Hospital Central Texas, Round Rock, TX, p. A639

FORBORT, Gordy, Chief Financial Officer, FirstLight Health System, Mora, MN, p. A343

FORD, Alisa, Vice President Human Resources, The University of Kansas Hospital, Kansas City, KS, p. A243

FORD, Angelique, Administrator Human Resources, Spring Valley Hospital Medical Center, Las Vegas, NV, p. A402

FORD, Cindy, R.N. Chief Nursing Officer, Harrisburg Medical Center, Harrisburg, IL, p. A189

FORD, Cora, Vice President Human Resources, Our Lady of the Lake Regional Medical Center, Baton Rouge, LA, p. A269

FORD, James, Director Human Resources, Sparks Medical Center – Van Buren, Van Buren, AR, p. A51

FORD, Karen, Chief Nursing Officer, Sabine Medical Center, Many, LA, p. A279

FORD, LeeAnn, Director Human Resources and Imaging, The Physicians Centre Hospital, Bryan, TX, p. A599

FORD, Marcia F., Chief Operating Officer, Hawthorn Children Psychiatric Hospital, Saint Louis, MO, p. A376

FORD, Michael, Vice President Patient Services, Wood County Hospital, Bowling Green, OH, p. A480

FORD, Mike, Vice President Human Resources, Floyd Memorial Hospital and Health Services, New Albany, IN, p. A217

FORD, Timothy R., President and Chief Executive Officer, Springfield Hospital, Springfield, VT, p. A661

FORDE, Steve, Chief Financial Officer, Nelson County Health System, Mcville, ND, p. A476

FORDE, Terry, Interim President and Chief Executive Officer, Adventist HealthCare, Gaithersburg, MD, p. B7

FORDHAM, Karen, President, DMC Huron Valley–Sinai Hospital, Commerce Township, MI, p. A317

FORDYCE, Brian, Director Information Technology, Roosevelt Medical Center, Culbertson, MT, p. A382

FORDYCE, Carol, Director Patient Care Services, Sullivan County Memorial Hospital, Milan, MO, p. A373

FORDYCE, Michael L., President and Chief Executive Officer, Craig Hospital, Englewood, CO, p. A103

FOREMAN, Christopher, Director Human Resources, Santa Rosa Medical Center, Milton, FL, p. A135

FOREMAN, Kim, M.D. Chief of Staff, Texas Spine & Joint Hospital, Tyler, TX, p. A649

FOREMAN, Lee Ann
Vice President Human Resources, Mississippi Baptist Medical Center, Jackson, MS, p. A355
Vice President Human Resources, Mississippi Hospital for Restorative Care, Jackson, MS, p. A355

FOREMAN, Nena, Chief Nursing Officer, Palo Verde Hospital, Blythe, CA, p. A56

FORESE, Joseph, Chief Executive Officer, Mountain Lakes Medical Center, Clayton, GA, p. A154

FORESE, Laura, M.D. Senior Vice President and Chief Medical Officer, New York–Presbyterian Hospital, New York, NY, p. A443

FOREST, Karen, Health Care Manager, State Penitentiary Hospital, Walla Walla, WA, p. A687

FORESYTHE, Brad, Director Information Systems, Emory Johns Creek Hospital, Johns Creek, GA, p. A159

FORET, Chris, M.D. Chief of Staff, Riverside Medical Center, Franklinton, LA, p. A274

FORET, Robert, Chief Financial Officer, Yoakum Community Hospital, Yoakum, TX, p. A653

FORGEY, Warren, FACHE, President and Chief Executive Officer, Schneck Medical Center, Seymour, IN, p. A219

FORKEL, Todd, President and Chief Executive Officer, Avera St. Luke's Hospital, Aberdeen, SD, p. A567

FORKNER, Christine, Executive Vice President and Chief Financial Officer, National Jewish Health, Denver, CO, p. A102

FORMELLA, Nancy A., R.N. Chief Operating Officer, Beth Israel Deaconess Medical Center, Boston, MA, p. A302

FORNERIS, Lori, R.N. Chief Clinical Officer, Loring Hospital, Sac City, IA, p. A234

FORNIER–JOHNSON, Michelle, Group Vice President Human Resources, St. Anthony Hospital, Lakewood, CO, p. A106

FORREST, Brian K.
Director Human Resources, Arnot Ogden Medical Center, Elmira, NY, p. A433
Director Human Resources, Ira Davenport Memorial Hospital, Bath, NY, p. A429
Vice President Human Resources, St. Joseph's Hospital, Elmira, NY, p. A433

FORREST, Mary Helen, R.N. Chief Nursing Officer, UAMS Medical Center, Little Rock, AR, p. A47

FORREST, Molly, President and Chief Executive Officer, Joyce Eisenberg–Keefer Medical Center, Reseda, CA, p. A83

FORRESTER, John M., Director Information Services, Hamilton Medical Center, Dalton, GA, p. A155

FORREY, Ebony, Director of Nursing, Windhaven Psychiatric Hospital, Prescott Valley, AZ, p. A36

FORRY, Bryan, Chief Financial Officer, Houston Northwest Medical Center, Houston, TX, p. A620

FORSCH, Randall T., M.D. Chief Medical Officer, St. Joseph Mercy Chelsea, Chelsea, MI, p. A316

FORSYTH, Beth, Chief Operating Officer, Good Samaritan Medical Center, Lafayette, CO, p. A106

FORSYTH, Larry, Director Information Services, OU Medical Center, Oklahoma City, OK, p. A512

FORT, Claudio D., President and Chief Executive Officer, North Country Hospital and Health Center, Newport, VT, p. A660

FORTENBERRY, Denise, Chief Nursing Officer and Chief Compliance Officer, Cypress Pointe Surgical Hospital, Hammond, LA, p. A274

FORTENBERRY, Doris, Coordinator Human Resources, Delta Memorial Hospital, Dumas, AR, p. A43

FORTENBERRY, Rob, Chief Information Officer, Mann–Grandstaff Veterans Affairs Medical Center, Spokane, WA, p. A685

FORTIER, Jeanne M., R.N. Chief Nursing Officer and Interim Chief Operating Officer, Grace Cottage Hospital, Townshend, VT, p. A661

FORTIN, Amanda, Manager Finance, Decatur Health Systems, Oberlin, KS, p. A247

FORTIN, Laura, R.N. Chief Operating Officer, St. Joseph Medical Center, Houston, TX, p. A622

FORTNEY, John, M.D. Chief Medical Officer, Adena Medical Center, Chillicothe, OH, p. A482

FOSNESS, Nick, Chief Executive Officer, Marshall County Healthcare Center Avera, Britton, SD, p. A567

FOSNOCHT, Kevin, M.D. Chief Medical Officer and Associate Executive Director, Penn Presbyterian Medical Center, Philadelphia, PA, p. A544

FOSS, David, Chief Information Officer, New London Hospital, New London, NH, p. A408

FOSS, R. Coleman, Chief Executive Officer, Skyridge Medical Center, Cleveland, TN, p. A576

FOSSINA, Michael, President and Chief Executive Officer, New York–Presbyterian/Lawrence Hospital, Bronxville, NY, p. A430

FOSSUM, John, Chief Executive Officer, Ely–Bloomenson Community Hospital, Ely, MN, p. A338

FOSTER, Barbara A., Regional Human Resources Director, Select Specialty Hospital–Wilmington, Wilmington, DE, p. A118

FOSTER, Becky
Manager Human Resources, Sanford Tracy Medical Center, Tracy, MN, p. A348
Manager Human Resources, Sanford Westbrook Medical Center, Westbrook, MN, p. A349

FOSTER, Beverly, Chief Executive Officer, Kindred Hospital Chicago–Northlake, Northlake, IL, p. A196

FOSTER, Bob, Chief Information Officer, South Georgia Medical Center, Valdosta, GA, p. A166

FOSTER, Brian, Chief Information Officer, Vail Valley Medical Center, Vail, CO, p. A109

FOSTER, Carolyn, Chief Financial Officer, PeaceHealth Peace Island Medical Center, Friday Harbor, WA, p. A679

FOSTER, Charles, Regional Director Human Resources, CHRISTUS Hospital–St. Elizabeth, Beaumont, TX, p. A596

FOSTER, Chris, Director Health Information Management, Deer Lodge Medical Center, Deer Lodge, MT, p. A382

FOSTER, Daniel J., Chief Financial Officer, South Davis Community Hospital, Bountiful, UT, p. A654

FOSTER, Gary, R.N. Assistant Administrator, Banner Estrella Medical Center, Phoenix, AZ, p. A34

FOSTER, Gary, Vice President and Chief Financial Officer, Saratoga Hospital, Saratoga Springs, NY, p. A450

FOSTER, Joel, Director Human Resources, Massac Memorial Hospital, Metropolis, IL, p. A194

FOSTER, Kennetha, Chief Nursing Officer, Mission Regional Medical Center, Mission, TX, p. A633

FOSTER, Michael, Director Information Systems, East Cooper Medical Center, Mount Pleasant, SC, p. A563

FOSTER, Mickey, President, Moses H. Cone Memorial Hospital, Greensboro, NC, p. A461

FOSTER, Mike, Manager Information Systems, Moab Regional Hospital, Moab, UT, p. A655

FOSTER, Mitzi, Director Information Services, Southern Tennessee Regional Health System–Pulaski, Pulaski, TN, p. A587

FOSTER, Rebecca, Chief Nursing Officer, Cumberland Medical Center, Crossville, TN, p. A577

FOSTER, Robert, Director Human Resources, L. V. Stabler Memorial Hospital, Greenville, AL, p. A20

FOSTER, Stephanie, MSN Chief Nursing Officer, Longview Regional Medical Center, Longview, TX, p. A629

FOSTER, Steven, Chief Executive Officer, Barstow Community Hospital, Barstow, CA, p. A56

FOSTER, Terri, Hospital Finance Officer, Baylor Regional Medical Center at Grapevine, Grapevine, TX, p. A616

FOSTER, Wanda, R.N. Vice President Nursing, McDonough District Hospital, Macomb, IL, p. A193

FOTIADIS, George, M.D. Chief of Staff, Clarke County Hospital, Osceola, IA, p. A232

FOTTER, Robert L., Chief Financial Officer, Littleton Regional Hospital, Littleton, NH, p. A407

FOUGHT, Scott, Vice President Finance, ProMedica Bay Park Hospital, Oregon, OH, p. A496

FOULKE, Elvia, Executive Vice President and Chief Operating Officer, Foothill Presbyterian Hospital, Glendora, CA, p. A64

FOUNTAIN, Aaron, Chief Information Officer, Brandon Regional Hospital, Brandon, FL, p. A122

FOUNTAIN, Wesley D., Chief Financial Officer, St. David's South Austin Medical Center, Austin, TX, p. A595

FOURNIER, Joseph, Chief Human Resources Officer, University of Michigan Hospitals and Health Centers, Ann Arbor, MI, p. A314

FOURRE, Mark, Senior Vice President and Chief Medical Officer, LincolnHealth, Damariscotta, ME, p. A290

FOUSE, Carla, Chief Nursing Officer, St. Vincent Randolph Hospital, Winchester, IN, p. A221

FOUSE, Sarah, Associate Director of Patient Services, Captain James A. Lovell Federal Health Care Center, North Chicago, IL, p. A196

FOUST, Lisa
Senior Vice President Human Resources, John Muir Behavioral Health Center, Concord, CA, p. A58
Senior Vice President Human Resources, John Muir Medical Center, Concord, Concord, CA, p. A58

FOUTS, Phillip, Chief Financial Officer, Fannin Regional Hospital, Blue Ridge, GA, p. A152

FOUTZ, Patricia, Director Human Resources, Bath Community Hospital, Hot Springs, VA, p. A666

FOWLER, Andrew, Vice President Information Services, Atlantic General Hospital, Berlin, MD, p. A295

FOWLER, Andy, Senior Vice President Information Systems, Methodist Healthcare Memphis Hospitals, Memphis, TN, p. A584

FOWLER, Barry, Director Human and System Resources, Clark Fork Valley Hospital, Plains, MT, p. A386

FOWLER, Denise, R.N. Chief Clinical Officer, Whitman Hospital and Medical Center, Colfax, WA, p. A677

FOWLER, Eileen, Clinical Director and Chief Nursing Officer, New Horizons Health Systems, Owenton, KY, p. A264

FOWLER, Gary, M.D. Chief of Staff Family Practice, Northwest Medical Center, Winfield, AL, p. A26

FOWLER, Karen, R.N. Chief Nursing Officer, The Hospitals of Providence Memorial Campus, El Paso, TX, p. A611

FOWLER, Kate, Chief Financial Officer, West Valley Medical Center, Caldwell, ID, p. A173

FOWLER, Kevin, Director Finance, Putnam County Hospital, Greencastle, IN, p. A210

FOWLER, Kevin N., President and Chief Executive Officer, Cabell Huntington Hospital, Huntington, WV, p. A691

FOWLER, Maureen, Director Human Resources, Conifer Park, Glenville, NY, p. A434

FOWLER, Ruth, Senior Vice President and Chief Financial Officer, Children's Healthcare of Atlanta, Atlanta, GA, p. A150

FOWLER, Sean, Chief Executive Officer, Marina Del Rey Hospital, Marina Del Rey, CA, p. A74

FOWLER, Steven, M.D. President Medical Staff, Genesis Medical Center, DeWitt, De Witt, IA, p. A226

FOX, Alan, Chief Financial Officer, Saint Francis Memorial Hospital, San Francisco, CA, p. A88

FOX, Betsy, Director Human Resources, Shepherd Center, Atlanta, GA, p. A151

FOX, Carol J., M.D. Senior Vice President and Chief Medical Officer, Excela Latrobe Area Hospital, Latrobe, PA, p. A538

FOX, David, President, Advocate Good Samaritan Hospital, Downers Grove, IL, p. A186

FOX, Debra, Chief Nursing Officer, University Medical Center, Las Vegas, NV, p. A403

FOX, Devin, M.D. Chief Medical Officer, CHI Health Creighton University Medical Center, Omaha, NE, p. A395

FOX, E. Kay, Director of Nursing, Black River Medical Center, Poplar Bluff, MO, p. A374

FOX, Jay
Chief Executive Officer, Round Rock Region, Scott & White Hospital – Taylor, Taylor, TX, p. A646
Chief Executive Officer, Scott & White Hospital at Round Rock, Round Rock, TX, p. A639

FOX, John, M.D. Medical Director, Vibra Hospital of San Diego, San Diego, CA, p. A87

FOX, John A., Interim Chief of Staff, Shriners Hospitals for Children–Shreveport, Shreveport, LA, p. A285

FOX, John T., President and Chief Executive Officer, Beaumont Health, Royal Oak, MI, p. B23

FOX, Leana, MSN Interim Chief Nurse Executive, Bon Secours Maryview Medical Center, Portsmouth, VA, p. A670

FOX, Leticia, Chief Financial Officer, Pecos County Memorial Hospital, Fort Stockton, TX, p. A612

FOX, Patricia K., President and Chief Executive Officer, Riverview Hospital, Noblesville, IN, p. A218

FOX, Randy, Director Performance Improvement and Risk Management, Lakeland Behavioral Health System, Springfield, MO, p. A378

FOX, Starla, Director of Nursing, Bristol Bay Area Health Corporation, Dillingham, AK, p. A28

FOX, Steve, Chief Executive Officer, Fort Belknap U. S. Public Health Service Indian Hospital, Harlem, MT, p. A384

FOX, Susan, President, White Plains Hospital Center, White Plains, NY, p. A454

FOX, William, Chief Executive Officer and Administrator, Horizon Specialty Hospital, Las Vegas, NV, p. A402

FOXX, Randy, Chief Financial Officer, Boone Memorial Hospital, Madison, WV, p. A692

FOY, Gregory S., Human Resources System Leader, Scheurer Hospital, Pigeon, MI, p. A327

FRABLE, Arthur H., Chief Executive Officer, Bob Wilson Memorial Grant County Hospital, Ulysses, KS, p. A251

FRACHISEUR, Kenny, Chief Information Officer, Ouachita County Medical Center, Camden, AR, p. A42

FRACICA, Phil, M.D. Vice President and Chief Medical Officer, Mercy Gilbert Medical Center, Gilbert, AZ, p. A31

FRACK, RN, Darla, R.N. Vice President, Patient Services, St. Luke's Hospital – Anderson Campus, Easton, PA, p. A533

FRAGGOS, Mary C., R.N. Associate Director of Nursing and Patient Care Services, Ralph H. Johnson Veterans Affairs Medical Center, Charleston, SC, p. A558

FRAIOLA, Anthony, Associate Administrator Administrative and Support Services, Hawaii State Hospital, Kaneohe, HI, p. A170

FRAKER, Steven, Chief Financial Officer, Banner Churchill Community Hospital, Fallon, NV, p. A400

FRALEY, Danny, Chief Clinical Officer, Acuity Hospital of South Texas, San Antonio, TX, p. A640

FRALEY, Janice, IT Entity Director – Information Services Division, Chatham Hospital, Siler City, NC, p. A468

FRAME, Angela, Chief Financial Officer, Jackson General Hospital, Ripley, WV, p. A695

FRAME, Ken, Chief Nursing Officer, Ashtabula County Medical Center, Ashtabula, OH, p. A478

FRANCE, Cheryl, M.D. Chief Medical Officer, William R. Sharpe, Jr. Hospital, Weston, WV, p. A696

FRANCE, James, M.D. Chief of Staff, Conway Regional Medical Center, Conway, AR, p. A42

FRANCETICH, Kane, Chief Information Officer, Gritman Medical Center, Moscow, ID, p. A175

FRANCIK, Tamara, Human Resources Generalist, Thayer County Health Services, Hebron, NE, p. A392

FRANCIOLI, Carl H., Vice President Finance, Johns Hopkins Bayview Medical Center, Baltimore, MD, p. A293

FRANCIS, Carolyn, R.N. Director of Nursing, LaSalle General Hospital, Jena, LA, p. A275

FRANCIS, Christy, Chief Executive Officer, Hemphill County Hospital, Canadian, TX, p. A600

FRANCIS, Duane, President and Chief Executive Officer, Mid–Columbia Medical Center, The Dalles, OR, p. A526

FRANCIS, Lana B., Interim Chief Executive Officer, LaSalle General Hospital, Jena, LA, p. A275

FRANCIS, Mark J., President, Chief Executive Officer and Hospital Administrator, Family Health West, Fruita, CO, p. A104

FRANCIS, Perry, Supervisory Information Technology Specialist, Chinle Comprehensive Health Care Facility, Chinle, AZ, p. A30

FRANCIS, Rebekah, J
Chief Financial Officer, Aurora Behavioral Health System East, Tempe, AZ, p. A38
Chief Financial Officer, Aurora Behavioral Health System West, Glendale, AZ, p. A32

FRANCIS, Stephen, M.D. Vice President Medical Affairs, UH Robinson Medical Center, Ravenna, OH, p. A496

FRANCISCO, Gerard E., M.D. Chief Medical Officer, TIRR Memorial Hermann, Houston, TX, p. A622

FRANCO, Luis, M.D. Medical Director, United Medical Rehabilitation Hospital, Hammond, LA, p. A274

FRANCO, Richard
Chief Financial Officer, Community First Medical Center, Chicago, IL, p. A181
Chief Financial Officer, Presence Resurrection Medical Center, Chicago, IL, p. A183
Chief Financial Officer, West Valley Hospital, Goodyear, AZ, p. A32

FRANCO, Roger, Director Human Resources, St. John's Episcopal Hospital–South Shore, NY, p. A444

FRANDSEN, Jeff, Chief Executive Officer, HEALTHSOUTH Rehabilitation Hospital of Utah, Sandy, UT, p. A659

FRANGESCH, Wayne C.
Vice President Human Resources, Covenant Medical Center, Waterloo, IA, p. A235
Senior Vice President Human Resources, Sartori Memorial Hospital, Cedar Falls, IA, p. A223

FRANK, Barbara, Human Resource Specialist, Caro Center, Caro, MI, p. A316

FRANK, Debra, Chief Financial Officer, Ness County Hospital, Ness City, KS, p. A246

FRANK, Jim, CPA, Chief Executive Officer, Providence Medical Center, Wayne, NE, p. A399

FRANK, Kevin, Administrator, Louisiana Extended Care Hospital of Lafayette, Lafayette, LA, p. A277

FRANK, Kim, Chief Human Resources Officer, Virginia Gay Hospital, Vinton, IA, p. A235

FRANK, Mitchell, Chief Financial Officer, Heritage Medical Center, Shelbyville, TN, p. A588

FRANK, Patricia, Chief Nursing Officer, Henry County Hospital, Napoleon, OH, p. A495

FRANK, Richard, Chief Executive Officer, Wuesthoff Medical Center – Melbourne, Melbourne, FL, p. A133

FRANK, Stanley, Chief Executive Officer, Ohio Hospital for Psychiatry, Columbus, OH, p. A486

FRANK, Thomas, Chief Operating Officer, North Country Hospital and Health Center, Newport, VT, p. A660

FRANKE, Jenny, Director Human Resources, Rehabilitation Hospital of Wisconsin, Waukesha, WI, p. A713

FRANKE, John, Chief Financial Officer, Baptist Health Lexington, Lexington, KY, p. A259

FRANKE, Paul, M.D. Chief Medical Officer, Alaska Native Medical Center, Anchorage, AK, p. A27

FRANKEL, Harris, M.D. Interim Chief Medical Officer, Nebraska Medicine – Nebraska Medical Center, Omaha, NE, p. A396

FRANKEL, Michele, Associate Executive Director Finance, Glen Cove Hospital, Glen Cove, NY, p. A434

FRANKEN, Stephanie, Vice President Operational Finance, St. Joseph's Hospital and Health Center, Dickinson, ND, p. A473

FRANKENSTEIN, Richard, M.D. Vice President and Chief Medical Officer, Henry Mayo Newhall Memorial Hospital, Valencia, CA, p. A96

FRANKL, Angie, Director Human Resources, Adair County Memorial Hospital, Greenfield, IA, p. A228

FRANKLIN, Chuck, M.D. Chief Medical Staff, Weston County Health Services, Newcastle, WY, p. A717

FRANKLIN, Clay, Chief Executive Officer, Plaza Medical Center of Fort Worth, Fort Worth, TX, p. A614

FRANKLIN, Ed, Chief Human Resources Officer, Page Hospital, Page, AZ, p. A34

FRANKLIN, James P., Administrator, Calhoun Health Services, Calhoun City, MS, p. A351

FRANKLIN, Jennifer, R.N. Chief Clinical Officer, Yoakum Community Hospital, Yoakum, TX, p. A653

FRANKLIN, Mary, R.N. Chief Nursing Officer, Merit Health Biloxi, Biloxi, MS, p. A350

FRANKLIN, Michael A., FACHE, President and Chief Executive Officer, Atlantic General Hospital, Berlin, MD, p. A295

FRANKLIN, Michelle, Chief Executive Officer, Sullivan County Community Hospital, Sullivan, IN, p. A220

FRANKLIN, Tammy, Manager Personnel and Marketing, Covenant Hospital–Levelland, Levelland, TX, p. A628

FRANKO, Stephen
Vice President Finance and Chief Financial Officer, Mount St. Mary's Hospital and Health Center, Lewiston, NY, p. A436
Vice President Finance and Chief Financial Officer, Regional Hospital of Scranton, Scranton, PA, p. A549

FRANKS, RN, Cathy, Chief Operating Officer, Community Medical Center of Izard County, Calico Rock, AR, p. A42

FRANKS, Charles, Chief Human Resources, Louis Stokes Cleveland Veterans Affairs Medical Center, Cleveland, OH, p. A484

FRANKS, Dennis, Vice President Operations, Doctors' Hospital of Michigan, Pontiac, MI, p. A328

FRANKS, Dennis, FACHE, Chief Executive Officer, Neosho Memorial Regional Medical Center, Chanute, KS, p. A238

FRANKS, Trudy, Administrator, MMO Greenbrier Hospital, Covington, LA, p. A272

FRANSON, John K., M.D. Chief Medical Staff, Caribou Memorial Hospital and Living Center, Soda Springs, ID, p. A176

FRANTZ, Vincent, M.D. Chief of Staff, Plumas District Hospital, Quincy, CA, p. A82

FRANZ, Eric, Vice President, Finance and Chief Financial Officer, Graham Hospital, Canton, IL, p. A180

FRANZ, Jerome, M.D. Chief Medical Staff, St. Luke's Hospital, San Francisco, CA, p. A88

FRANZ, Staci, Director Human Resources, St. Luke's Rehabilitation Institute, Spokane, WA, p. A685

FRANZ, Thomas, M.D. Medical Director, HEALTHSOUTH Harmarville Rehabilitation Hospital, Pittsburgh, PA, p. A546

Index of Health Care Professionals

Index of Health Care Professionals / Franzblau

FRANZBLAU, David R., M.D. Chief Medical Officer, Presence Saint Joseph Medical Center, Joliet, IL, p. A192
FRANZE, Ingrid, Chief Medical Staff, Buena Vista Regional Medical Center, Storm Lake, IA, p. A235
FRANZEL, Carrie, Chief Nursing Officer, Huron Medical Center, Bad Axe, MI, p. A314
FRANZELLA, Susan, Human Resource Business Partner, Kaiser Permanente San Jose Medical Center, San Jose, CA, p. A89
FRARDO, Virgil, M.D. Medical Director, HEALTHSOUTH Rehabilitation Hospital–Wichita Falls, Wichita Falls, TX, p. A652
FRASCA, Edith, Controller and Chief Financial Officer, The Pavilion, Champaign, IL, p. A181
FRASER, Francis, M.D. Chief of Staff, Byrd Regional Hospital, Leesville, LA, p. A279
FRASER, James, Administrator Finance, Via Christi Hospital Manhattan, Inc., KS, p. A245
FRASER, John M., FACHE, President and Chief Executive Officer, Nebraska Methodist Health System, Inc., Omaha, NE, p. B95
FRASIER, Nora, R.N. Chief Nursing Officer, Methodist Mansfield Medical Center, Mansfield, TX, p. A631
FRATZKE, Mark, R.N. Chief Nursing Officer and Chief Operating Officer, Mayo Clinic Health System in Saint James, Saint James, MN, p. A346
FRAUENHOFER, Chris, Chief Financial Officer, Maine Coast Memorial Hospital, Ellsworth, ME, p. A290
FRAYSER, P. Jay, Chief Executive Officer, Palo Verde Mental Health Services, Tucson, AZ, p. A39
FRAZEE, Kim, R.N. Vice President Physician and Business Development, Southern Ocean Medical Center, Manahawkin, NJ, p. A414
FRAZIER, Amy, Supervisor Management Information Systems, Wetzel County Hospital, New Martinsville, WV, p. A693
FRAZIER, Derrick A., Chief Executive Officer, Claiborne Memorial Medical Center, Homer, LA, p. A275
FRAZIER III, James P., Chief Executive Officer, Teche Regional Medical Center, Morgan City, LA, p. A281
FRAZIER, Joel L., M.D. Medical Director, OneCore Health, Oklahoma City, OK, p. A512
FRAZIER, Kimberly
Chief Nursing Officer, Saint Thomas DeKalb Hospital, Smithville, TN, p. A588
Chief Nursing Officer, Saint Thomas Stones River Hospital, Woodbury, TN, p. A589
FRAZIER, Shane, Chief Executive Officer, Pinnacle Pointe Hospital, Little Rock, AR, p. A47
FREAS, Mary Ann, Senior Vice President and Chief Financial Officer, Southwest General Health Center, Middleburg Heights, OH, p. A494
FRED, Mark, R.N. Chief Operating Officer, Kirby Medical Center, Monticello, IL, p. A194
FREDERICK, Brenda, Director Human Resources, Laurel Ridge Treatment Center, San Antonio, TX, p. A641
FREDERICK, Dessa, Manager Human Resources, St. James Behavioral Health Hospital, Gonzales, LA, p. A274
FREDERICK, Gretchen A., R.N. Director Patient Care Services, Buffalo Hospital, Buffalo, MN, p. A336
FREDERICKS, Raymond F., President and Chief Executive Officer, JFK Health System, Edison, NJ, p. B75
FREDERICKS, Raymond F., President and CEO, JFK Medical Center, Edison, NJ, p. A411
FREDERICKSON, Kathy, Information Systems Site Lead, Sutter Delta Medical Center, Antioch, CA, p. A54
FREDETTE, Beth, Chief Information Officer, Children's Medical Center, Dayton, OH, p. A487
FREDRICH, Nancy, R.N. Chief Clinical Officer, Cooper County Memorial Hospital, Boonville, MO, p. A364
FREDRICK, Joyce, Associate Director, Veterans Affairs Central Western Massachusetts Healthcare System, Leeds, MA, p. A308
FREDRICK, Rick, Director Information Technology, Cottage Hospital, Woodsville, NH, p. A408
FREDRICKSON, Kelley, Director Information Services, Plaza Medical Center of Fort Worth, Fort Worth, TX, p. A614
FREDRICKSON, Mark A., M.D. Medical Director, HEALTHSOUTH Rehabilitation Hospital Midland–Odessa, Midland, TX, p. A632
FREEBERN, Joseph, Executive Director, Mid–Hudson Forensic Psychiatric Center, New Hampton, NY, p. A438
FREEBURG, Rick, Chief Executive Officer, Baptist Health South Florida, Mariners Hospital, Tavernier, FL, p. A146
FREEBURN, Mark, Chief Executive Officer, HEALTHSOUTH Rehabilitation Hospital of Mechanicsburg, Mechanicsburg, PA, p. A540
FREED, Glenn, D.O. Medical Director, St. Luke's Hospital – Miners Campus, Coaldale, PA, p. A531
FREED, Nancy, Chief Financial Officer, Seiling Municipal Hospital, Seiling, OK, p. A514
FREED, Stuart, M.D
Chief Medical Officer, Central Washington Hospital, Wenatchee, WA, p. A687
Medical Director, Wenatchee Valley Medical Center, Wenatchee, WA, p. A687
FREED–SIGURDSSON, Anna, M.D. Medical Director, Reliant Rehabilitation Hospital Dallas, Dallas, TX, p. A606
FREEDMAN, Barry R., President and Chief Executive Officer, Einstein Healthcare Network, Philadelphia, PA, p. B53
FREEDMAN, Barry R., President and Chief Executive Officer, Einstein Medical Center Philadelphia, Philadelphia, PA, p. A543
FREEDMAN, Kenneth, M.D. Chief Medical Officer, Lemuel Shattuck Hospital, Jamaica Plain, MA, p. A307
FREEDMAN, Liz, Director Human Resources, Mercy Health – West Hospital, Cincinnati, OH, p. A483
FREEDMAN, Rick, Commanding Officer, Naval Hospital Camp Lejeune, Camp Lejeune, NC, p. A456
FREEHILL, Sarah, Chief Nursing Officer, Arbuckle Memorial Hospital, Sulphur, OK, p. A515
FREEHOF, Leonard, Chief Executive Officer and Managing Director, Spring Valley Hospital Medical Center, Las Vegas, NV, p. A402
FREELAND, R. Alan, M.D. Chief Clinical Officer, Twin Valley Behavioral Healthcare, Columbus, OH, p. A487
FREEMAN, Amy E., President and Chief Executive Officer, Providence Hospital, Washington, DC, p. A120
FREEMAN, Brian, Vice President of Operations, Stanly Regional Medical Center, Albemarle, NC, p. A455
FREEMAN, Diane, R.N. Assistant Vice President and Chief Nursing Officer, St. Luke's Lakeside Hospital, The Woodlands, TX, p. A647
FREEMAN, Donald, President and Chief Executive Officer, Preferred Management Corporation, Shawnee, OK, p. B106
FREEMAN, Elizabeth Joyce, FACHE, Director, VA Palo Alto Health Care System, Palo Alto, CA, p. A80
FREEMAN, Jerry, Chief, Human Resources Management Services, Durham Veterans Affairs Medical Center, Durham, NC, p. A459
FREEMAN, Kimberlee, R.N. Vice President Patient Care Services and Chief Nursing Officer, Wayne Hospital, Greenville, OH, p. A491
FREEMAN, Marianne, Vice President Human Resources, Rockdale Medical Center, Conyers, GA, p. A154
FREEMAN, Michael
Director Human Resources, Alta Vista Regional Hospital, Las Vegas, NM, p. A425
Director Human Resources, Huhukam Memorial Hospital, Sacaton, AZ, p. A37
FREEMAN, Mike, Director Information Technology, Sentara Williamsburg Regional Medical Center, Williamsburg, VA, p. A674
FREEMAN, Nikki, Vice President Human Resources, Wesley Medical Center, Wichita, KS, p. A253
FREEMAN, Richard, President and Chief Executive Officer, Robert Wood Johnson University Hospital at Hamilton, Hamilton, NJ, p. A412
FREEMAN, Robert, Director Human Resources, Sparks Regional Medical Center, Fort Smith, AR, p. A45
FREER, Carol V., M.D. Chief Medical Officer, Penn State Milton S. Hershey Medical Center, Hershey, PA, p. A536
FREESE–DECKER, Christina, President, Spectrum Health Hospital Group, Spectrum Health – Butterworth Hospital, Grand Rapids, MI, p. A321
FREID–SCHEPPKE, Denise, Chief Accounting Officer, Oakleaf Surgical Hospital, Eau Claire, WI, p. A700
FREIER, Toby, President, New Ulm Medical Center, New Ulm, MN, p. A344
FREIJ, Walid, M.D. Chief of Staff, Vaughan Regional Medical Center, Selma, AL, p. A24
FREILICH, Josh, Vice President and Chief Nurse Executive, Mercy Hospital of Folsom, Folsom, CA, p. A61
FREIMARK, Jeffrey P., Chief Executive Officer, Miami Jewish Home and Hospital for Aged, Miami, FL, p. A134
FREIMUND, Rooney, R.N. Chief Nurse Executive, Bay Area Medical Center, Marinette, WI, p. A704
FREIN, Ethel, Chief Executive Officer, Bennett County Hospital and Nursing Home, Martin, SD, p. A569
FREIS, Leon, Chief Operating Officer, Northern Inyo Hospital, Bishop, CA, p. A56
FREITAG, Donald, M.D. Chief Medical Officer, Lynn County Hospital District, Tahoka, TX, p. A646
FREITAG, Vanessa, President, Ministry Our Lady of Victory Hospital, Stanley, WI, p. A711
FRELING, Eric, M.D. Director Medical Staff Affairs, Memorial Hospital West, Pembroke Pines, FL, p. A139
FRENCH, Dean, M.D., Chief Executive Officer, Canyon Vista Medical Center, Sierra Vista, AZ, p. A38
FRENCH, Dean, M.D. Interim Chief Executive Officer, Community Medical Center, Missoula, MT, p. A385
FRENCH, Dean O., M.D. Chief of Staff, Faith Regional Health Services, Norfolk, NE, p. A395
FRENCH III, George E., FACHE, Chief Executive Officer, Minden Medical Center, Minden, LA, p. A280
FRENCH, Holly, Chief Financial Officer, Newman Regional Health, Emporia, KS, p. A239
FRENCH, Michael, Interim Chief Executive Officer, Providence Hospital, Columbia, SC, p. A559
FRENCH, Tracy
Chief Financial Officer, Banner Goldfield Medical Center, Apache Junction, AZ, p. A30
Chief Financial Officer, Banner Ironwood Medical Center, San Tan Valley, AZ, p. A37
FRENCH, William Chad, Chief Executive Officer, Davis Regional Medical Center, Statesville, NC, p. A469
FRENN, Debra, FACHE Chief Patient Care Officer, Rusk County Memorial Hospital, Ladysmith, WI, p. A703
FRERER, Mary
Chief Human Resources Officer, Freeman Hospital West, Joplin, MO, p. A369
Chief Human Resources Officer, Freeman Neosho Hospital, Neosho, MO, p. A373
FRERICHS, Craig, Chief Information Technology Service, Grand Junction Veterans Health Care System, Grand Junction, CO, p. A104
FRESH, John, Vice President Human Resources, Conemaugh Miners Medical Center, Hastings, PA, p. A535
FRESHOUR, David, Chief Financial Officer, Comanche County Medical Center, Comanche, TX, p. A601
FRESQUEZ, Juan, Chief Operating Officer, Houston Northwest Medical Center, Houston, TX, p. A620
FREUDENBERG, Liz, Chief Financial Officer, HEALTHSOUTH Rehabilitation Hospital of Denver, Littleton, CO, p. A106
FREUDENBERGER, Joe, Chief Executive Officer, OakBend Medical Center, Richmond, TX, p. A638
FREY, Jack, Acting Business Manager, Greystone Park Psychiatric Hospital, Morris Plains, NJ, p. A414
FREY, Jeff, Business Administrator, Andrew McFarland Mental Health Center, Springfield, IL, p. A201
FREY, Paul, Director Information Technology Applications, Indiana Orthopaedic Hospital, Indianapolis, IN, p. A211
FREY, Rachel, Director Human Resources, Athens–Limestone Hospital, Athens, AL, p. A15
FREYER, Mary, Chief Operating Officer, Little Company of Mary Hospital and Health Care Centers, Evergreen Park, IL, p. A188
FREYER, Sharon, Chief Nursing Officer, Baptist Health Paducah, Paducah, KY, p. A264
FREYMULLER, Robert S., Chief Executive Officer, Summerlin Hospital Medical Center, Las Vegas, NV, p. A402
FREYSINGER, Edward E., Chief Executive Officer, Providence Hood River Memorial Hospital, Hood River, OR, p. A521
FREYTAG, Peter, Senior Vice President Finance and Chief Financial Officer, Bristol Hospital, Bristol, CT, p. A111
FRIARTE, Pedro, Director of Physician Services, Coral Gables Hospital, Coral Gables, FL, p. A124
FRIBERG, Deborah G., Interim Senior Vice President and Area Manager, Kaiser Permanente Manteca Medical Center, Manteca, CA, p. A74
FRICK, Mark P., Senior Vice President Human Resources, Somerset Hospital, Somerset, PA, p. A550
FRICK, Mary Jo, Director Finance, St. Catherine's Rehabilitation Hospital, North Miami, FL, p. A136
FRICKE, Rhett D., Chief Financial Officer, Frio Regional Hospital, Pearsall, TX, p. A636
FRICKS, Tom, Interim Senior Vice President of Information Technology, PeaceHealth Sacred Heart Medical Center at RiverBend, Springfield, OR, p. A526
FRIDAY, Jason, M.D. Medical Director, Aurora Behavioral Health System East, Tempe, AZ, p. A38
FRIDKIN, Marjorie, M.D. Chief Medical Officer, Garrett County Memorial Hospital, Oakland, MD, p. A299
FRIED, Guy, M.D. Chief Medical Officer, Magee Rehabilitation Hospital, Philadelphia, PA, p. A544
FRIED, Jeffrey M., FACHE, President and Chief Executive Officer, Beebe Healthcare, Lewes, DE, p. A117
FRIED, Tera, Manager Human Resources, West River Regional Medical Center, Hettinger, ND, p. A474
FRIEDBERG, Robert, President, Vassar Brothers Medical Center, Poughkeepsie, NY, p. A448
FRIEDELL, Benjamin, Vice President Medical Affairs, Aurelia Osborn Fox Memorial Hospital, Oneonta, NY, p. A446
FRIEDEN, Robert
Vice President Information Systems, Genesis Medical Center, Illini Campus, Silvis, IL, p. A200
Vice President Information Systems, Genesis Medical Center–Aledo, Aledo, IL, p. A178
Vice President Information Systems, Genesis Medical Center–Davenport, Davenport, IA, p. A225

**A842** Index of Health Care Professionals

FRIEDENBACH, Daryl, Director Fiscal Services, Floyd Valley Hospital, Le Mars, IA, p. A230

FRIEDLINE, Jennifer, R.N. Director of Nursing, Mercy Rehabilitation Hospital Springfield, Springfield, MO, p. A379

FRIEDLY, Jennifer, Chief Operating Officer and Vice President, UnityPoint Health – Allen Hospital, Waterloo, IA, p. A236

FRIEDMAN, Greg, Director Information Technology, Children's Hospital of Richmond at VCU–Brook Road Campus, Richmond, VA, p. A671

FRIEDMAN, Jonathan, Public Affairs Officer, Captain James A. Lovell Federal Health Care Center, North Chicago, IL, p. A196

FRIEDMAN, Lloyd, M.D. Vice President Medical Affairs and Chief Operating Officer, Milford Hospital, Milford, CT, p. A113

FRIEDMAN, Ross, Chief Operating Officer, Greystone Park Psychiatric Hospital, Morris Plains, NJ, p. A414

FRIEDRICH III, Daniel J., Chief Executive Officer, Blake Medical Center, Bradenton, FL, p. A122

FRIEL, Donald F., Executive Vice President, Holy Redeemer Hospital, Meadowbrook, PA, p. A540

FRIELING, Jeff
  Vice President Information Systems, Camden General Hospital, Camden, TN, p A574
  Vice President and Chief Information Officer, Jackson–Madison County General Hospital, Jackson, TN, p. A579
  Chief Information Officer, Pathways of Tennessee, Jackson, TN, p. A579

FRIELING, Morris J., Chief Financial Officer, UC Irvine Medical Center, Orange, CA, p. A79

FRIEND, Lori
  Director Human Resources, AllianceHealth Madill, Madill, OK, p. A509
  Human Resources Director, AllianceHealth Seminole, Seminole, OK, p. A514

FRIER, Nancy, Chief Financial Officer, Eastern Oklahoma Medical Center, Poteau, OK, p. A514

FRIESEN, Dale L., Chief Financial Officer, CareLink of Jackson, Jackson, MI, p. A323

FRIESEN, Lynette, Manager Human Resources, Henderson Health Care Services, Henderson, NE, p. A392

FRIESEN, Nancy, Chief Financial Officer, CentraCare Health–Monticello, Monticello, MN, p. A343

FRIGEN, Karen, Director Human Resources, Shriners Hospitals for Children–Twin Cities, Minneapolis, MN, p. A343

FRIGO, Dave
  Vice President Financial Planning and Treasury, Akron General Medical Center, Akron, OH, p. A478
  Director Finance and Controller, Lodi Community Hospital, Lodi, OH, p. A492

FRIGON, Shelby, Chief Financial Officer, Saint Luke's South Hospital, Overland Park, KS, p. A248

FRIGY, Alan, M.D. President Medical Staff, Pana Community Hospital, Pana, IL, p. A197

FRIMODIG, Mindy, D.O. President Medical Staff ThedaCare Physicians Shawano, Shawano Medical Center, Shawano, WI, p. A710

FRISBEE, Kent, Director Human Resources, Saint Thomas Highlands Hospital, Sparta, TN, p. A588

FRITSCH, William, M.D. Medical Director, Landmark Hospital of Cape Girardeau, Cape Girardeau, MO, p. A364

FRITSCHEN, James, Chief Executive Officer, Louisiana Continuing Care Hospital, Marrero, LA, p. A280

FRITTON, Amy, Controller, Sierra Tucson, Tucson, AZ, p. A40

FRITTS, Doris, R.N., Executive Director, Same Day Surgery Center, Rapid City, SD, p. A571

FRITTS, Robert G., Chief Financial Officer and Senior Vice President, Blue Ridge Healthcare Hospitals, Morganton, NC, p. A465

FROCHTZWAJG, Stanley, M.D. Chief Medical Officer, Community Memorial Health System, Ventura, CA, p. A96

FROEHLICH, Shelley, R.N. Director Nursing Services, Newport Hospital and Health Services, Newport, WA, p. A681

FROEMKE, Janet, Human Resources Officer, CHI Lisbon Health, Lisbon, ND, p. A475

FROESE, Stacy
  Regional Director Human Resources, Integris Bass Pavilion, Enid, OK, p. A506
  Regional Director Human Resources, Integris Grove Hospital, Grove, OK, p. A507

FROH, Chris, Senior Coordinator Human Resources, Select Specialty Hospital–Milwaukee, Milwaukee, WI, p. A707

FROHNHOFER, Erin J.
  Vice President Human Resources, Ohio Valley Hospital, McKees Rocks, PA, p. A539
  Director Human Resources, Southwood Psychiatric Hospital, Pittsburgh, PA, p. A546

FROIO, Ann M., Interim Chief Executive Officer, Arizona State Hospital, Phoenix, AZ, p. A34

FROISLAND, Jeffrey R., Chief Financial Officer, Mayo Clinic Hospital, Phoenix, AZ, p. A35

FROMHOLD, John A., FACHE, Chief Executive Officer, Hackensack University Medical Center Mountainside, Montclair, NJ, p. A414

FROMM, Robert, M.D. Chief Medical Officer, Maricopa Integrated Health System, Phoenix, AZ, p. A35

FROMME, Chris, Acting Chief Executive Officer, Baylor Surgical Hospital at Fort Worth, Fort Worth, TX, p. A613

FROMME, Pete, Chief Financial Officer, Fayette County Hospital, Vandalia, IL, p. A202

FROMMELT, William, Director Operations and Finance, River Falls Area Hospital, River Falls, WI, p. A710

FRONZA, Sarah, Interim President and Chief Executive Officer, Silverton Hospital, Silverton, OR, p. A526

FROSCH, Kevin, Chief Financial Officer, Medina Regional Hospital, Hondo, TX, p. A618

FROST, Eric, Associate Vice President Human Resources, Upstate University Hospital, Syracuse, NY, p. A451

FROST, Joan, R.N. Chief Operating Officer, Mercy Hospital Washington, Washington, MO, p. A380

FROST, Mark I., M.D. Vice President Medical Staff Affairs, Laureate Psychiatric Clinic and Hospital, Tulsa, OK, p. A516

FROST, Sarah
  Administrator, Banner – University Medical Center South, Tucson, AZ, p. A39
  Chief Operating Officer and Administrator, University of Arizona Medical Center – South Campus, Banner – University Medical Center Tucson, Tucson, AZ, p. A39

FROST–KUNNEN, Jacqueline C., R.N. Senior Vice President Operations, Mercy Medical Center–Des Moines, Des Moines, IA, p. A226

FRUGE, Janie, FACHE, MSN, Chief Executive Officer, West Calcasieu Cameron Hospital, Sulphur, LA, p. A286

FRUM, Judy, R.N. Chief Nursing Officer, Memorial Hospital Pembroke, Pembroke Pines, FL, p. A139

FRUM, R. David
  President, Bridgton Hospital, Bridgton, ME, p. A289
  President, Rumford Hospital, Rumford, ME, p. A292

FRUSH, Wendy, R.N. Nursing Executive, Mackinac Straits Health System, Inc., Saint Ignace, MI, p. A329

FRY, Kenneth, Chief Financial Officer, Saint Alphonsus Regional Medical Center, Boise, ID, p. A172

FRY, Patrick E., President and Chief Executive Officer, Sutter Health, Sacramento, CA, p. B129

FRYE, Charles, Director Human Resources, Estes Park Medical Center, Estes Park, CO, p. A103

FRYE, Kelly D., Director Human Resources, Montgomery General Hospital, Montgomery, WV, p. A693

FRYE, Terri, Information Technology Officer, Weston County Health Services, Newcastle, WY, p. A717

FRYER, Ramona D., Chief Financial Officer, WK Bossier Health Center, Bossier City, LA, p. A271

FUCCI, Thomas, Chief Operating Officer, Saint Vincent Health Center, Erie, PA, p. A534

FUCHS, Jonathan, Chief Information Officer, DeWitt Hospital, De Witt, AR, p. A43

FUCHS, Mary Ann, R.N. Vice President Patient Care and System Chief Nurse Executive, Duke University Hospital, Durham, NC, p. A459

FUCILE, Joanne, R.N. Vice President Operations and Director of Nursing, Spaulding Hospital for Continuing Medical Care Cambridge, Cambridge, MA, p. A306

FUEHRER, Susan, Director, Louis Stokes Cleveland Veterans Affairs Medical Center, Cleveland, OH, p. A484

FUENTES, Frances, Coordinator Human Resources, HEALTHSOUTH Rehabilitation Hospital of San Juan, San Juan, PR, p. A723

FUENTES, Leticia, Nursing Director, San Jorge Children's Hospital, San Juan, PR, p. A724

FUENTES Jr., Miguel A., President and Chief Executive Officer, Bronx–Lebanon Hospital Center Health Care System, NY, p. A438

FUERSTENBERG, Donna, Fiscal Chief, Sheridan Veterans Affairs Medical Center, Sheridan, WY, p. A717

FUGATTE, Cheryl, MSN Vice President and Chief Nursing Officer, Jewish Hospital, Louisville, KY, p. A261

FUGAZY, Chris, Acting Executive Director, Jacobi Medical Center, NY, p. A440

FUGAZY, Christopher, Chief Operating Officer, Jacobi Medical Center, NY, p. A440

FUGLEBERG, Jason, R.N. Vice President Patient Services and Chief Nursing Officer, Millinocket Regional Hospital, Millinocket, ME, p. A291

FUGLER, Shawna, R.N. Chief Nursing Officer, Memorial Hermann Surgical Hospital Kingwood, Kingwood, TX, p. A626

FUHRMAN, Bradley, M.D. Physician in Chief, El Paso Children's Hospital, El Paso, TX, p. A610

FUHRMAN, Dennis, Vice President Finance, Essentia Health Fargo, Fargo, ND, p. A473

FUHRMAN, Geri, Chief Nursing Officer, I–70 Community Hospital, Sweet Springs, MO, p. A379

FUHRMAN, L. Wesley, President and Chief Executive Officer, Warwick Manor Behavioral Health, East New Market, MD, p. A297

FUHRO, Mary, Chief Nursing Officer, Newark Beth Israel Medical Center, Newark, NJ, p. A415

FUHS, Veronica, Chief Executive Officer, Monroe County Hospital and Clinics, Albia, IA, p. A222

FUJINAKA, Jason, Manager Information System, Wahiawa General Hospital, Wahiawa, HI, p. A170

FULCHER, Cathe, Superintendent, Evansville State Hospital, Evansville, IN, p. A208

FULCHER, Kimberly, Chief Human Resources Officer, Halifax Health Medical Center of Daytona Beach, Daytona Beach, FL, p. A125

FULCHER, Martha, MSN Chief Nursing Officer, OCH Regional Medical Center, Starkville, MS, p. A360

FULKERSON, Judy, Director Human Resources, TriStar Greenview Regional Hospital, Bowling Green, KY, p. A255

FULKERSON, Richard, Director Fiscal Services, Shriners Hospitals for Children–Springfield, Springfield, MA, p. A311

FULKS, Chris, Vice President Finance, St. Joseph Mercy Port Huron, Port Huron, MI, p. A328

FULKS, Gerald N., President and Chief Executive Officer, West Georgia Health, Lagrange, GA, p. A160

FULLBRIGHT, Gary D., Comptroller, Citizens Memorial Hospital, Bolivar, MO, p. A363

FULLER, Cara
  Vice President Human Resources, UnityPoint Health – Trinity Bettendorf, Bettendorf, IA, p. A222
  Vice President Human Resources, UnityPoint Health – Trinity Rock Island, Rock Island, IL, p. A199

FULLER, Cheryl, Director Information Resources, Kansas Neurological Institute, Topeka, KS, p. A251

FULLER, Dale, Vice President and Chief Information Officer, UPMC Altoona, Altoona, PA, p. A528

FULLER, David, Director Human Resources, Porter Medical Center, Middlebury, VT, p. A660

FULLER, Debbie, Director Health Information Systems and Chief Information Officer, Doctors Medical Center, Modesto, CA, p. A75

FULLER, Jami, Manager Information Technology, Catalina Island Medical Center, Avalon, CA, p. A54

FULLER, Jeremy, Director Information Systems, Conroe Regional Medical Center, Conroe, TX, p. A602

FULLER, Jill, Ph.D., President and Chief Executive Officer, Prairie Lakes Healthcare System, Watertown, SD, p. A572

FULLER, Lexie, Controller, Specialty Hospital of Meridian, Meridian, MS, p. A358

FULLER, Marion, Chief of Staff, West Shore Medical Center, Manistee, MI, p. A325

FULLER, Robert, Executive Vice President and Chief Operating Officer, PIH Health Hospital – Downey, Downey, CA, p. A60

FULLOP, Julko, M.D. Chief of Staff, Wabash General Hospital, Mount Carmel, IL, p. A195

FULLUM, Jane, Vice President Patient Care Services, East Alabama Medical Center, Opelika, AL, p. A23

FULTON, Diane, R.N. Chief Nursing Officer, Rapides Regional Medical Center, Alexandria, LA, p. A268

FULTON, Lorna, Director Human Resources, Vibra Hospital of Denver, Thornton, CO, p. A109

FULTON, Lynn, President, OSF Saint Luke Medical Center, Kewanee, IL, p. A192

FUNDERBURG, Michelle, Director Human Resources, Stephens Memorial Hospital, Breckenridge, TX, p. A598

FUNDERBURK, Mark, Executive Vice President and Administrator, University Medical Center, Lubbock, TX, p. A630

FUNG, Adrian, Director Information Systems, University Medical Center, Lebanon, TN, p. A581

FUNK, Luann, Administrative Assistant and Manager Human Resources, Pana Community Hospital, Pana, IL, p. A197

FUNKHOUSER, Krisy L., Manager Human Resources, Willapa Harbor Hospital, South Bend, WA, p. A685

FUNKHOUSER, Lana, Vice President Human Resources, Indiana University Health West Hospital, Avon, IN, p. A204

FUQUA, David, Director Human Resources Management, University Health Shreveport, Shreveport, LA, p. A285

FUQUA, David G., Chief Executive Officer, Marshall County Hospital, Benton, KY, p. A254

FUQUA, Leon, Chief Operating Officer, Wise Regional Health System, Decatur, TX, p. A607

FURGURSON, Carol, Chief Operating Officer, Saint Louise Regional Hospital, Gilroy, CA, p. A63

FURLONG, Marian M., FACHE, Chief Executive Officer, Hudson Hospital and Clinic, Hudson, WI, p. A702

FURLOW, Pete, Director Information Technology Services, Northeast Alabama Regional Medical Center, Anniston, AL, p. A15

FURMAN, John, Interim Director Human Resources, DeTar Healthcare System, Victoria, TX, p. A650

FURNAS, David, Chief Information Officer, Gila Regional Medical Center, Silver City, NM, p. A427

FURNEY, June, R.N. Director of Nursing, Brooks County Hospital, Quitman, GA, p. A162

FURNISS, Scott, Senior Vice President and Chief Financial Officer, Saint Agnes Hospital, Baltimore, MD, p. A294

FURR, Robert, Director Information Services, Cannon Memorial Hospital, Pickens, SC, p. A564

FUSCHILLO, Ronald
   Chief Information Officer, Renown Rehabilitation Hospital, Reno, NV, p. A404
   Chief Information Officer, Renown South Meadows Medical Center, Reno, NV, p. A404

FUSCO, Kevin, Chief Operating Officer, Broward Health North, Deerfield Beach, FL, p. A125

FUSELIER, Gerald, Chief Operating Officer, Savoy Medical Center, Mamou, LA, p. A279

FUSELIER, Michael, FACHE Chief Financial Officer, Central Louisiana Surgical Hospital, Alexandria, LA, p. A268

FUSSELL, Eugene, M.D. Chief Medical Officer, St. John's Pleasant Valley Hospital, Camarillo, CA, p. A57

FUSTER, Carmen G., Nursing Director, Hospital Metropolitano Dr. Susoni, Arecibo, PR, p. A720

FUTCH, Margaret A., Chief Executive Officer, HEALTHSOUTH Rehabilitation Hospital, Dothan, AL, p. A18

FUTCH, Sharon
   Interim Vice President Human Resources, Anderson Regional Medical Center, Meridian, MS, p. A357
   Interim Vice President Human Resources, Anderson Regional Medical Center–South Campus, Meridian, MS, p. A357

FUTRAL, Cindy, Director Human Resources, Elmore Community Hospital, Wetumpka, AL, p. A26

FYBEL, Gary G., Chief Executive, Senior Vice President, Scripps Memorial Hospital–La Jolla, La Jolla, CA, p. A66

# G

GAAL, James G., M.D. Chief of Medical Staff, Jackson General Hospital, Ripley, WV, p. A695

GAASCH, Andrew
   Chief Financial Officer, Parker Adventist Hospital, Parker, CO, p. A107
   Chief Financial Officer, Porter Adventist Hospital, Denver, CO, p. A102

GABALDON, Karen, Chief Management Information Systems, West Palm Beach Veterans Affairs Medical Center, West Palm Beach, FL, p. A147

GABEL, Christopher, Chief Operating Officer, Larkin Behavioral Health Services, FL, p. A128

GABEL, Kelly, Chief of Staff, Citizens Medical Center, Colby, KS, p. A238

GABEL, Marcia, Chief Financial Officer, Lane County Hospital, Dighton, KS, p. A239

GABLE, Beth, Administrative Assistant, Jasper General Hospital, Bay Springs, MS, p. A350

GABLENZ, Gordon, Vice President Finance, Ridgeview Medical Center, Waconia, MN, p. A348

GABORIAULT, Randall, Chief Information Officer, Christiana Care Health System, Newark, DE, p. A117

GABRIEL, Kay, R.N. Chief Nursing Officer, Van Buren County Hospital, Keosauqua, IA, p. A230

GABRIEL, Scott F., President, Parkview Whitley Hospital, Columbia City, IN, p. A206

GABRIEL, Shirley, Vice President and Chief Information Officer, University Hospital, Augusta, GA, p. A152

GABRIELE, Joan, Deputy Executive Director, Queens Hospital Center, NY, p. A444

GABRIELLI, MSN, RN–, Melissa, Director of Nursing, River Crest Hospital, San Angelo, TX, p. A640

GABRYEL, Timothy, M.D. Vice President Medical Affairs and Medical Director, Mercy Hospital, Buffalo, NY, p. A430

GADALLAH, Yousri, M.D. Chief Medical Officer, Pershing General Hospital, Lovelock, NV, p. A403

GADDAM, Summa, Chief Information Officer, Butler Hospital, Providence, RI, p. A555

GADDIS, Cathryn H., Director Human Resources, RiverValley Behavioral Health Hospital, Owensboro, KY, p. A264

GADDY, Pam, Director, Patient Care Services and Chief Nursing Officer, FirstHealth Montgomery Memorial Hospital, Troy, NC, p. A469

GADE, Swami P., M.D. Medical Director, Tioga Medical Center, Tioga, ND, p. A476

GADEN, Paul, Chief Executive Officer, Providence Portland Medical Center, Portland, OR, p. A524

GADOMSKI, Veronica, R.N. Chief Nursing Officer, HEALTHSOUTH Rehabilitation Hospital, Albuquerque, NM, p. A422

GAEDE, John, Director Information Systems, El Centro Regional Medical Center, El Centro, CA, p. A60

GAENZLE, Jack, Senior Vice President Finance and Administration, UPMC Mercy, Pittsburgh, PA, p. A547

GAFFOLI, Jill, Director Human Resources, Physicians Regional – Pine Ridge, Naples, FL, p. A136

GAFFORD, Deborah, Chief Financial Officer, Menorah Medical Center, Overland Park, KS, p. A248

GAFFORD, Grady Paul, Chief Financial Officer, Brownfield Regional Medical Center, Brownfield, TX, p. A598

GAGE, Bobby, Director Information Technology, Wabash General Hospital, Mount Carmel, IL, p. A195

GAGE, Eileen, R.N
   Vice President Nursing, Geneva General Hospital, Geneva, NY, p. A434
   Vice President Nursing, Soldiers and Sailors Memorial Hospital of Yates County, Penn Yan, NY, p. A447

GAGE, Kevin, Chief Financial Officer, Stamford Hospital, Stamford, CT, p. A115

GAGE, Mark, D.O. Medical Director, Brookhaven Hospital, Tulsa, OK, p. A516

GAGE, Susan, Financial Manager, Veterans Affairs Western New York Healthcare System–Buffalo Division, Buffalo, NY, p. A431

GAGER, Brian
   Vice President, Acute Care Operations, St. Joseph's Hospital, Saint Paul, MN, p. A346
   Vice President of Operations, Acute Care Hospitals, Woodwinds Health Campus, Woodbury, MN, p. A349

GAGLIARDI, Teresa, R.N. Chief Nursing Officer, Trinity Hospital Twin City, Dennison, OH, p. A489

GAGLIO, Tony, Chief Financial Officer, Henry Ford Kingswood Hospital, Ferndale, MI, p. A319

GAGNON, Andy, Director Information Technology, Via Christi Hospital Manhattan, Inc., KS, p. A245

GAGNON, Lynne, Chief Nursing Officer, Valley Regional Hospital, Claremont, NH, p. A405

GAILLARD, Timothy, Senior Vice President and Chief Operating Officer, University of Wisconsin Hospital and Clinics, Madison, WI, p. A704

GAINER, Rolf B., M.D., Chief Executive Officer and Administrator, Brookhaven Hospital, Tulsa, OK, p. A516

GAINES, Willie, Director Management Information Systems, Southern Virginia Regional Medical Center, Emporia, VA, p. A664

GAIRE, Susan, M.D. President Medical Staff, Frisbie Memorial Hospital, Rochester, NH, p. A408

GAITAN, Alberto, M.D. Medical Director, O'Connor Hospital, Delhi, NY, p. A432

GAITER, Thomas E., M.D. Chief Medical Officer, Howard University Hospital, Washington, DC, p. A119

GAJ, Steve, Facility Chief Information Officer, Louis Stokes Cleveland Veterans Affairs Medical Center, Cleveland, OH, p. A484

GAJEWSKI, Christie, Director Human Resources, Pinckneyville Community Hospital, Pinckneyville, IL, p. A198

GALANDA, Chris, Chief Information Officer, Wilkes–Barre General Hospital, Wilkes–Barre, PA, p. A553

GALANG, Michael, M.D
   Chief Information Officer, Mercy Hospital, Buffalo, NY, p. A430
   Chief Information Officer, Sisters of Charity Hospital of Buffalo, Buffalo, NY, p. A431

GALARNEAU, Ciprian, Director Information Systems, Tri Valley Health System, Cambridge, NE, p. A390

GALARNEAU, Gerard, M.D., Chief Executive Officer and Chief Medical Officer, Catskill Regional Medical Center, Harris, NY, p. A435

GALATI, John P., Chief Executive Officer, TLC Health Network – Lake Shore Hospital, Irving, NY, p. A435

GALATI, Vicki L., Chief Financial Officer, Texas Health Specialty Hospital, Fort Worth, TX, p. A614

GALBRAITH, Kathleen B., President, Duke Regional Hospital, Durham, NC, p. A459

GALDIERI, Lou, R.N.,
   President, Mease Countryside Hospital, Safety Harbor, FL, p. A141
   President, Mease Dunedin Hospital, Dunedin, FL, p. A126

GALE, Brendan, Chief Financial Officer, Middle Park Medical Center–Kremmling, Kremmling, CO, p. A105

GALE, Donald I., M.D. Vice President Medical Affairs, Winter Haven Hospital, Winter Haven, FL, p. A148

GALE, Gabrielle, Chief Financial Officer, Lighthouse Care Center of Conway, Conway, SC, p. A560

GALE, Michael, Chief Financial Officer, Bournewood Health Systems, Brookline, MA, p. A305

GALFANO, Victor J., FACHE, Chief Executive Officer, Select Specialty Hospital–Northern Kentucky, Fort Thomas, KY, p. A257

GALIPEAU, Michelle, Director Human Resources, St. Vincent's Birmingham, Birmingham, AL, p. A17

GALKOWSKI, James, Associate Director for Operations, Fayetteville Veterans Affairs Medical Center, Fayetteville, NC, p. A460

GALLA, Bernie, Interim Director Management Information Systems, Howard University Hospital, Washington, DC, p. A119

GALLAGHER, Chris, M.D. Chief Medical Officer, Hopkins County Memorial Hospital, Sulphur Springs, TX, p. A646

GALLAGHER, Doug, Director Human Resources, Carolinas ContinueCare Hospital at Pineville, Charlotte, NC, p. A457

GALLAGHER, J. P., Chief Operating Officer, NorthShore University Health System, Evanston, IL, p. A187

GALLAGHER, Jeannie
   jeanie.gallagher@bannerhealth.com, McKee Medical Center, Loveland, CO, p. A107
   Chief Human Resource Officer, North Colorado Medical Center, Greeley, CO, p. A104

GALLAGHER, John, Chief Executive Officer, Sunnyside Community Hospital and Clinics, Sunnyside, WA, p. A686

GALLAGHER, Joseph, Chief Executive Officer, Wyoming Behavioral Institute, Casper, WY, p. A715

GALLAGHER, Karen, Vice President Human Resources and Learning, Brooks Rehabilitation Hospital, Jacksonville, FL, p. A129

GALLAGHER, Pamela, Chief Financial Officer, Providence Hospital, Columbia, SC, p. A559

GALLAGHER, Regen, M.D. Chief Medical Officer, Cary Medical Center, Caribou, ME, p. A289

GALLAGHER, Sherry, Director Nursing, Department of Health and Human Services, Humboldt County Mental Health, Eureka, CA, p. A60

GALLAGHER, Thomas E., Chief Financial Officer, Seton Edgar B. Davis Hospital, Luling, TX, p. A630

GALLAHOM, Gerty, Director Human Resources, Maniilaq Health Center, Kotzebue, AK, p. A28

GALLARDO, Kathleen, Chief Nursing Officer, Select Specialty Hospital–Flint, Flint, MI, p. A319

GALLARDO, Ysidro, Associate Administrator Human Resources, Hazel Hawkins Memorial Hospital, Hollister, CA, p. A65

GALLATI, Todd, FACHE, President and Chief Executive Officer, Trident Medical Center, Charleston, SC, p. A558

GALLAY, Emily, Vice President and Chief Information Officer, Lakeland Medical Center, St. Joseph, Saint Joseph, MI, p. A329

GALLEGOS, Colleen, Director Human Resources, Guadalupe County Hospital, Santa Rosa, NM, p. A426

GALLEGOS, Enrique, Chief Executive Officer, Laredo Medical Center, Laredo, TX, p. A627

GALLEGOS, Kelly, Administrator, San Luis Valley Health Conejos County Hospital, La Jara, CO, p. A105

GALLEGOS, Ken, Director Support Services and Information Technology, Medina Regional Hospital, Hondo, TX, p. A618

GALLI, Jodi, Chief Nursing Officer, Eastern Maine Medical Center, Bangor, ME, p. A288

GALLIARDT, Scott, Chief Executive Officer, Cornerstone Hospital of Austin, Austin, TX, p. A594

GALLIART, Mark, Chief Executive Officer, McBride Clinic Orthopedic Hospital, Oklahoma City, OK, p. A512

GALLIK, Becky, Information Systems Manager, FirstLight Health System, Mora, MN, p. A343

GALLIN, John I., M.D., Director, National Institutes of Health Clinical Center, Bethesda, MD, p. A296

GALLO, Ronald, Director Human Resources, Blythedale Children's Hospital, Valhalla, NY, p. A452

GALLOGLY–SIMON, Catherine A., R.N. Chief Nursing Officer, Wyckoff Heights Medical Center, NY, p. A445

GALLUCCI, Kathleen, Chief Human Resources, Highland Hospital of Rochester, Rochester, NY, p. A448

GALLUCCI, Vince
   Senior Vice President Human Resources, Mercy Medical Center, Oshkosh, WI, p. A708
   Senior Vice President Human Resources, St. Elizabeth Hospital, Appleton, WI, p. A697

GALT, Nick
   Chief Financial Officer, Las Colinas Medical Center, Irving, TX, p. A624
   Chief Financial Officer, North Hills Hospital, North Richland Hills, TX, p. A634

GALUSHA, Fred, Chief Information Officer, St. Luke's Rehabilitation Institute, Spokane, WA, p. A685

GALYON, Darlene, Director Human Resources, Choctaw Memorial Hospital, Hugo, OK, p. A508

GAMACHE, Cynde, R.N. Vice President and Chief Nursing Officer, Baptist Hospital, Pensacola, FL, p. A139

GAMB, Pamela, Manager Human Resources, Aurora Psychiatric Hospital, Wauwatosa, WI, p. A713

GAMBLA, Kurt, D.O. Chief Medical Officer, Beaufort Memorial Hospital, Beaufort, SC, p. A557

Index of Health Care Professionals / Garrity

Index of Health Care Professionals


GAMBLE, Allen J., Chief Executive Officer, Pioneer Community Hospital of Early, Blakely, GA, p. A152
GAMBLE, Brian, Chief Financial Officer, Karmanos Cancer Center, Detroit, MI, p. A318
GAMBLE, Kathleen, Fiscal Officer, Patton State Hospital, Patton, CA, p. A80
GAMBLE, Laura, Vice President of Clinical Services, Providence Medical Center, Wayne, NE, p. A399
GAMBLE, Robert, M.D. Chief of Staff, Terrebonne General Medical Center, Houma, LA, p. A275
GAMBLE, Jr., Troy B., M.D. Chief Medical Staff, Williamsburg Regional Hospital, Kingstree, SC, p. A562
GAMBOA, Eileen, Director Human Resources, OakBend Medical Center, Richmond, TX, p. A638
GAMBRELL Jr., Edward C., Administrator, Stephens County Hospital, Toccoa, GA, p. A166
GAMEL, Richard B., President, Regional Hospital, CHI Health Plainview, Plainview, NE, p. A397
GAMET, Nicki, R.N
Vice President and Chief Nursing Officer, Mercy Hospital Aurora, Aurora, MO, p. A363
Chief Nursing Officer, Mercy Hospital Cassville, Cassville, MO, p. A365
GAMEZ, Kriss
Director Human Resources, Baylor Regional Medical Center at Plano, Plano, TX, p. A636
Director Human Resources, The Heart Hospital Baylor Plano, Plano, TX, p. A637
GAMINO, Randall, Director Perot Site, St. Joseph's Medical Center, Stockton, CA, p. A93
GAMMIERE, Thomas A., Chief Executive, Senior Vice President, Scripps Mercy Hospital, San Diego, CA, p. A87
GANDHI, Tejas, Chief Administrative Officer, Medical Center, Navicent Health, Macon, GA, p. A160
GANDY, Patrick W., CPA, Executive Vice President and Chief Executive Officer, Lafayette General Medical Center, Lafayette, LA, p. A277
GANGULY, Indranil, Vice President and Chief Information Officer, JFK Medical Center, Edison, NJ, p. A411
GANLEY, Evan, Manager Human Resources, LifeCare Hospitals of Chester County, West Chester, PA, p. A552
GANN, Lisa, R.N. Chief Nursing Officer, TriStar Hendersonville Medical Center, Hendersonville, TN, p. A578
GANN, Michele, Vice President Patient Services, Mercy Hospital Berryville, Berryville, AR, p. A41
GANNON, Ronnie, Director Information Services, TriStar Southern Hills Medical Center, Nashville, TN, p. A586
GANONG, Richard, M.D. Chief of Staff, Tahoe Forest Hospital District, Truckee, CA, p. A95
GANS, Bruce M., M.D. Executive Vice President and Chief Medical Officer, Kessler Institute for Rehabilitation, West Orange, NJ, p. A420
GANSEMER, Sheila, R.N
Vice President Patient Care Services, Midwest Orthopedic Specialty Hospital, Franklin, WI, p. A701
Vice President Patient Care Services, Wheaton Franciscan Healthcare – Franklin, Franklin, WI, p. A701
GANSKE, Jary, Chief Financial Officer, Methodist Mansfield Medical Center, Mansfield, TX, p. A631
GANTNER, John, Executive Vice President Finance and Partner Company Operations, Jersey Shore University Medical Center, Neptune, NJ, p. A414
GANTT, Marsha, Interim Chief Nursing Officer, Southern Palmetto Hospital, Barnwell, SC, p. A557
GANTZER, Ann M., Ph.D. Vice President Patient Services and Chief Nursing Officer, SwedishAmerican Hospital, A Division of UW Health, Rockford, IL, p. A200
GAPSTUR, Roxanna L., Ph.D. Chief Nursing Officer, Park Nicollet Methodist Hospital, Saint Louis Park, MN, p. A346
GARAY, Kenneth, M.D. Chief Medical Officer, Jersey City Medical Center, Jersey City, NJ, p. A413
GARBANZOS, Del, Director Human Resources, Delano Regional Medical Center, Delano, CA, p. A59
GARBARINO, James, Chief Financial Officer, Clay County Medical Center, Clay Center, KS, p. A238
GARBER, Jennifer Elizabeth, Vice President Human Resources, Emory Johns Creek Hospital, Johns Creek, GA, p. A159
GARBER, Mark E., Director Human Resources, Mary Black Health System – Spartanburg, Spartanburg, SC, p. A565
GARBER, Mary, Vice President Finance, Mercy Hospital Ada, Ada, OK, p. A503
GARCIA, Alex, Chief Executive Officer, Victory Medical Center Landmark, San Antonio, TX, p. A643
GARCIA, Ara, Manager Human Resources, Milwaukee County Behavioral Health Division, Milwaukee, WI, p. A706
GARCIA, Aymette, Manager Human Resources, Wilma N. Vazquez Medical Center, Vega Baja, PR, p. A724
GARCIA, Danette, Director Human Resources, HEALTHSOUTH Valley of the Sun Rehabilitation Hospital, Glendale, AZ, p. A32
GARCIA, Estevan, M.D. Chief Medical Officer, Brookdale Hospital Medical Center, NY, p. A439
GARCIA, Evangeline, M.D. Clinical Director, Eastern Shore Hospital Center, Cambridge, MD, p. A296
GARCIA, Georgina R., R.N., Executive Director, Kaiser Permanente West Los Angeles Medical Center, Los Angeles, CA, p. A70
GARCIA, Gerard, Acting Vice President Human Resources, University Hospital, Newark, NJ, p. A415
GARCIA, Idalia, Chief Human Resources Officer, Hospital de Psiquiatria, San Juan, PR, p. A723
GARCIA, Iris, Director, Information Services, Jerome Golden Center for Behavioral Health, Inc., West Palm Beach, FL, p. A147
GARCIA, Irma, Job Coordinator, Rio Grande State Center/South Texas Health Care System, Harlingen, TX, p. A618
GARCIA, Joanne, Chief Operating Officer, Kindred Chicago–Central Hospital, Chicago, IL, p. A182
GARCIA, Joannie, CPA Director Finance, Hospital Perea, Mayaguez, PR, p. A722
GARCIA, Jose, M.D. Chief Medical Staff, Dundy County Hospital, Benkelman, NE, p. A390
GARCIA, Jose, Chief Human Resources Officer, San Juan City Hospital, San Juan, PR, p. A724
GARCIA, Kathleen, Controller, St. John's Episcopal Hospital–South Shore, NY, p. A444
GARCIA, Louis O., Chief Executive Officer, Victory Medical Center – Southcross, San Antonio, TX, p. A642
GARCIA, Jr., Luis Mario, Director Human Resources, Houston Methodist Sugar Land Hospital, Sugar Land, TX, p. A645
GARCIA, Margaret, Manager Human Resources, Baylor Medical Center at Frisco, Frisco, TX, p. A615
GARCIA, Michael, M.D. Medical Director, Leonard J. Chabert Medical Center, Houma, LA, p. A275
GARCIA, Orlando, M.D. Chief Medical Officer, Hialeah Hospital, Hialeah, FL, p. A128
GARCIA, Robert W., M.D. Chief Medical Officer, Iraan General Hospital, Iraan, TX, p. A624
GARCIA, Roland
Senior Vice President and Chief Information Officer, Baptist Medical Center Beaches, Jacksonville Beach, FL, p. A130
Senior Vice President and Chief Information Officer, Baptist Medical Center Jacksonville, Jacksonville, FL, p. A129
GARCIA, Sharon, Human Resources Representative, Medina Regional Hospital, Hondo, TX, p. A618
GARCIA, Shawn, Manager Human Resources, Memorial Hospital Los Banos, Los Banos, CA, p. A73
GARCIA, Sylvia, Chief Accounting Officer, South Texas Spine and Surgical Hospital, San Antonio, TX, p. A642
GARD, Emily, Chief Clinical Officer, Kindred Hospital–San Francisco Bay Area, San Leandro, CA, p. A90
GARDINER, David, Operations Officer, LDS Hospital, Salt Lake City, UT, p. A658
GARDINER, Greg, Chief Clinical Officer, Ashley Regional Medical Center, Vernal, UT, p. A659
GARDINER, Karen, Human Resources Director, Bayfront Health Port Charlotte, Port Charlotte, FL, p. A140
GARDNER, Carla, Director of Nursing, Munson Healthcare Grayling Hospital, Grayling, MI, p. A321
GARDNER, Debra C., MSN, Administrator, Ten Lakes Center, Dennison, OH, p. A489
GARDNER, Greg, Senior Vice President and Chief Financial Officer, Indian River Medical Center, Vero Beach, FL, p. A146
GARDNER, Jacque, Administrative Assistant, Clinic Manager, Co–Chief Financial Officer and Chief Human Resources, McCone County Health Center, Circle, MT, p. A382
GARDNER, James D., M.D. Vice President and Chief Medical Officer, Waukesha Memorial Hospital, Waukesha, WI, p. A713
GARDNER, John, Chief Executive Officer, Yuma District Hospital, Yuma, CO, p. A110
GARDNER, Jonathan H., FACHE, Director, Southern Arizona Veterans Affairs Health Care System, Tucson, AZ, p. A40
GARDNER, Michelle, M.D. Clinical Director, Dorothea Dix Psychiatric Center, Bangor, ME, p. A288
GARDNER, Patrick, M.D. Vice President Medical Affairs, St. Joseph's Hospital, West Bend, WI, p. A714
GARDNER, Robb, Chief Executive Officer, Henry County Health Center, Mount Pleasant, IA, p. A232
GARDNER, Sharon, Manager Information Systems, SSM St. Joseph Hospital West, Lake Saint Louis, MO, p. A371
GARDNER, Sharon R., Vice President Human Resources, Yuma Regional Medical Center, Yuma, AZ, p. A40
GARDNER, William, Chief Nursing Officer, Bartlett Regional Hospital, Juneau, AK, p. A28
GARDNER, Zoe, Manager Human Resources, Sharp Chula Vista Medical Center, Chula Vista, CA, p. A58
GARES, Donna, MSN, Chief Executive Officer, Select Specialty Hospital–Wilmington, Wilmington, DE, p. A118
GARISON, Jerri, R.N., President, Baylor Regional Medical Center at Plano, Plano, TX, p. A636
GARKO, Michael, Chief Financial Officer, St. Vincent Medical Center, Los Angeles, CA, p. A73
GARLAND, Greg, Interim Chief Executive Officer, Glen Oaks Hospital, Greenville, TX, p. A617
GARLETS, Mary, Director Human Resources, Mayo Clinic Health System in Cannon Falls, Cannon Falls, MN, p. A336
GARMAN, Denise M., Director Human Resources, The Good Samaritan Hospital, Lebanon, PA, p. A538
GARMAN, Mary E., R.N. Chief Operating Officer and Chief Nursing Officer, Good Samaritan Hospital, Dayton, OH, p. A488
GARMAN, Michael, Chief Financial Officer, Avera St. Anthony's Hospital, O'Neill, NE, p. A395
GARNAS, David, Chief Executive Officer, Sedgwick County Health Center, Julesburg, CO, p. A105
GARNER, David, Chief Operating Officer, Yampa Valley Medical Center, Steamboat Springs, CO, p. A108
GARNER, Douglas, Vice President, Thomas Hospital, Fairhope, AL, p. A19
GARNER, Ethnee, R.N. Vice President Nursing Services, Memorial Hospital, North Conway, NH, p. A408
GARNETT, Mark, M.D. Chief of Staff, Hansford Hospital, Spearman, TX, p. A644
GAROFOLA, Aaron, Chief Executive Officer, Bluffton Regional Medical Center, Bluffton, IN, p. A205
GARON, Jack, M.D. Chief Medical Officer, Mount Sinai Hospital, Chicago, IL, p. A183
GARONE, Marlene, M.D. Vice President Medical Affairs and Medical Director, Woman's Christian Association Hospital, Jamestown, NY, p. A435
GARRAMONE, Kathy
Chief Financial Officer, Jacobi Medical Center, NY, p. A440
Chief Financial Officer, North Central Bronx Hospital, NY, p. A443
GARRARD, Michael Eric, Chief Executive Officer, Emory Rehabilitation Hospital, Atlanta, GA, p. A150
GARRED, Sr., John, M.D. Chief Medical Officer, Burgess Health Center, Onawa, IA, p. A232
GARRETT, Alan H., Chief Executive Officer, St. Mary Medical Center, Apple Valley, CA, p. A54
GARRETT, Courtney, CPA Senior Vice President, Chief Financial Officer, Children's Hospital, New Orleans, LA, p. A281
GARRETT, David B.
Chief Information Officer, Novant Health Forsyth Medical Center, Winston–Salem, NC, p. A471
Chief Information Officer, Novant Health Matthews Medical Center, Matthews, NC, p. A464
Senior Vice President Information Technology, Novant Health Presbyterian Medical Center, Charlotte, NC, p. A458
GARRETT, Josh, Chief of Staff, Habersham Medical Center, Demorest, GA, p. A156
GARRETT, Mark, Chief Information Officer, Shriners Hospitals for Children–Los Angeles, Los Angeles, CA, p. A72
GARRETT, Matthew, Director Information Systems, Flowers Hospital, Dothan, AL, p. A18
GARRETT, Nancy, Chief Analytics and Information Technology Officer, Hennepin County Medical Center, Minneapolis, MN, p. A342
GARRETT, Robert C., FACHE, President and Chief Executive Officer, Hackensack University Health Network, Hackensack, NJ, p. B60
GARRETT, Robert C., FACHE, President and Chief Executive Officer, Hackensack University Medical Center, Hackensack, NJ, p. A412
GARRETT, Scott, Director of IS, Ottumwa Regional Health Center, Ottumwa, IA, p. A233
GARRETT, Walter J., Chief Executive Officer, Welch Community Hospital, Welch, WV, p. A696
GARRICK, Renee, M.D. Director, Executive Medical, Westchester Medical Center, Valhalla, NY, p. A452
GARRIDO, Mary, Vice President and Regional Chief Information Officer, Valley Baptist Medical Center–Brownsville, Brownsville, TX, p. A599
GARRISON, Cort, M.D
Chief Information Officer, Salem Hospital, Salem, OR, p. A526
Chief Information Officer, West Valley Hospital, Dallas, OR, p. A520
GARRISON, Julie, System Director Human Resources Operations, Woodwinds Health Campus, Woodbury, MN, p. A349
GARRISON, Tina, Vice President Operations, SSM DePaul Health Center, Bridgeton, MO, p. A364
GARRISON, Wes,St. Luke's Sugar Land Hospital, Sugar Land, TX, p. A646
GARRITY, Elizabeth, Director Human Resources, Meadowlands Hospital Medical Center, Secaucus, NJ, p. A418
GARRITY, Nerissa, Chief Financial Officer, Kula Hospital, Kula, HI, p. A170

Index of Health Care Professionals

Index of Health Care Professionals / Garrow

GARROW, Dina, Chief Nursing Officer and Chief Operating Officer, Kindred Hospital–Baldwin Park, Baldwin Park, CA, p. A55
GARRY, William, Chief Financial Officer, Edgefield County Hospital, Edgefield, SC, p. A560
GARSA, Arebi, Interim Chief Financial Officer, North Valley Hospital, Whitefish, MT, p. A388
GARSKE, Tom, Director Information Systems, Wiregrass Medical Center, Geneva, AL, p. A20
GARTLAND, Bryce, Chief Executive Officer, Emory University Hospital, atlanta, GA, p. A150
GARTMAN, Kathy Degenstein, Chief Nursing Officer, Medical Center of South Arkansas, El Dorado, AR, p. A43
GARTNER, Katie, Director Health Information Management, CHI Health Good Samaritan, Kearney, NE, p. A393
GARVEY, Heather, Chief Financial Officer, Raulerson Hospital, Okeechobee, FL, p. A137
GARVEY, James
Administrator, Essentia Health Duluth, Duluth, MN, p. A337
Executive Vice President, Operations and Administrator, Essentia Health St. Mary's Medical Center, Duluth, MN, p. A338
GARVEY, Rita, Chief Nursing Officer, Lawrence County Memorial Hospital, Lawrenceville, IL, p. A192
GARVEY, Sheila
Vice President Human Resources, Flushing Hospital Medical Center, NY, p. A439
Vice President Human Resources, Jamaica Hospital Medical Center, NY, p. A440
GARVEY, Thomas J., Senior Vice President Operations and Chief Financial Officer, Swedish Covenant Hospital, Chicago, IL, p. A185
GARVIN, David, Chief Executive Officer, Osage Beach Center for Cognitive Disorders, Osage Beach, MO, p. A374
GARVIN, Jan, Vice President Human Resources, Bryan Medical Center, Lincoln, NE, p. A393
GARY, Al, COO, Simpson General Hospital, Mendenhall, MS, p. A357
GARZA, Annette, Controller, Weslaco Rehabilitation Hospital, Weslaco, TX, p. A651
GARZA, Art, Interim Chief Executive Officer, Valley Regional Medical Center, Brownsville, TX, p. A599
GARZA, Ismelda, Director Information Systems, Comanche County Medical Center, Comanche, TX, p. A601
GARZA, Jennifer, Chief Executive Officer, South Texas Health System, Edinburg, TX, p. A610
GARZA, Laura, Director Human Resources, Promise Hospital of Houston, Houston, TX, p. A621
GARZA, Oscar, M.D. Chief Medical Staff, Frio Regional Hospital, Pearsall, TX, p. A636
GARZA, Teri, Director Health Information Services, Knapp Medical Center, Weslaco, TX, p. A651
GARZA, Tom, Director Fiscal and Support, Rio Grande State Center/South Texas Health Care System, Harlingen, TX, p. A618
GASAWAY, Rob, Chief Financial Officer, Galesburg Cottage Hospital, Galesburg, IL, p. A188
GASCHO, Dwight, President and Chief Executive Officer, Scheurer Hospital, Pigeon, MI, p. A327
GASH, Deborah
Vice President and Chief Information Officer, Crittenton Children's Center, Kansas City, MO, p. A369
Chief Information Officer, Saint Luke's Hospital of Kansas City, Kansas City, MO, p. A370
Chief Information Officer, Saint Luke's South Hospital, Overland Park, KS, p. A248
GASKILL, Michelle, R.N., President, Advocate Trinity Hospital, Chicago, IL, p. A181
GASKINS, Michael, Director Information Technology, Lincoln Community Hospital and Nursing Home, Hugo, CO, p. A105
GASKINS, Michael W., Interim President and Chief Executive Officer, Hanover Hospital, Hanover, PA, p. A535
GASPAR, Deborah L., R.N. Chief Nursing Officer, Memorial Hospital of Sweetwater County, Rock Springs, WY, p. A717
GASPARD, H. J., Chief Executive Officer, HEALTHSOUTH Rehabilitation Hospital of Beaumont, Beaumont, TX, p. A596
GASPARINI, Michael L., Vice President Clinical Services and Chief Operating Officer, Western Missouri Medical Center, Warrensburg, MO, p. A380
GASQUE, James, M.D. Chief Hospital Services, U. S. Air Force Medical Center Keesler, Keesler AFB, MS, p. A355
GASS, Angela, Chief Nursing Officer, Stamford Memorial Hospital, Stamford, TX, p. A645
GASTON, Jan, Administrator, Jasper Memorial Hospital, Monticello, GA, p. A162
GASTON, Kathy, Chief Nursing Officer, Baptist Medical Center East, Montgomery, AL, p. A22
GASTON, Tammy, Chief Information Officer, Smith County Memorial Hospital, Smith Center, KS, p. A250
GATES, John
Vice President Finance and Chief Financial Officer, California Pacific Medical Center, San Francisco, CA, p. A88
Chief Financial Officer, St. Luke's Hospital, San Francisco, CA, p. A88
GATES, Robert, Director Information Technology, Hackensack University Medical Center Mountainside, Montclair, NJ, p. A414
GATES, Rose, Director Human Resources, Hayward Area Memorial Hospital and Nursing Home, Hayward, WI, p. A702
GATES, Tracy, Chief Financial Officer, Jones Memorial Hospital, Wellsville, NY, p. A453
GATHERS, Mary
Manager Information Systems, American Fork Hospital, American Fork, UT, p. A654
Director Information Systems, McKay–Dee Hospital Center, Ogden, UT, p. A656
Director Information Systems, Utah Valley Regional Medical Center, Provo, UT, p. A657
GATHRIGHT, Travis, Chief Information and Corporate Compliance Officer, Magee Rehabilitation Hospital, Philadelphia, PA, p. A544
GATIEN, Lionel J., D.O. Chief of Staff, Kindred Hospital North Florida, Green Cove Springs, FL, p. A128
GATMAITAN, Alfonso W., Chief Executive Officer, Indiana University Health Arnett Hospital, Lafayette, IN, p. A214
GATRELL, Kristi, Chief Executive Officer, Big Horn County Memorial Hospital, Hardin, MT, p. A384
GATTMAN, Gregory B., Acute Care Executive, Palmetto Health Baptist, Columbia, SC, p. A559
GATTO, Tony, Director Management Information Systems, Flushing Hospital Medical Center, NY, p. A439
GAU, Kimberley A., FACHE, Chief Executive Officer, Guttenberg Municipal Hospital, Guttenberg, IA, p. A228
GAUBERT, Steve C., Chief Financial Officer, Thibodaux Regional Medical Center, Thibodaux, LA, p. A286
GAUER, Natalie, Administrator, Milbank Area Hospital Avera, Milbank, SD, p. A569
GAUGHAN, Thomas, M.D. Chief Medical Officer, Kingman Regional Medical Center, Kingman, AZ, p. A32
GAUL, Michael, Manager Information Systems, Atchison Hospital, Atchison, KS, p. A237
GAUL, Mike, Director Information Technology, Golden Valley Memorial Healthcare, Clinton, MO, p. A365
GAUL–HOUSER, Kelly, Director Human Resources, Ottumwa Regional Health Center, Ottumwa, IA, p. A233
GAULKE, Becky, Chief Nursing Officer, Ely–Bloomenson Community Hospital, Ely, MN, p. A338
GAURON, Patricia, Director Human Resources, Holy Family Hospital, Methuen, MA, p. A308
GAUTHIER, Bonnie B., President and Chief Executive Officer, The Hospital at Hebrew Health Care, West Hartford, CT, p. A116
GAUTHIER, Paul, Chief Information Resources Management, Veterans Affairs Montana Health Care System, Fort Harrison, MT, p. A383
GAUTNEY, Steven, Chief Executive Officer, Crisp Regional Hospital, Cordele, GA, p. A155
GAVALCHIK, Stephen M., FACHE, Community Chief Executive Officer, Morgan County ARH Hospital, West Liberty, KY, p. A266
GAVENS, Mark R., Senior Vice President Clinical Care Services and Chief Operating Officer, Cedars–Sinai Medical Center, Los Angeles, CA, p. A69
GAVIN, Andrea, M.D. Chief Medical officer, Aurora Sheboygan Memorial Medical Center, Sheboygan, WI, p. A710
GAVIN, Donald, Chief Financial Officer, Southern Tennessee Regional Health System–Pulaski, Pulaski, TN, p. A587
GAVIN, Martin J., President and Chief Executive Officer, Connecticut Children's Medical Center, Hartford, CT, p. A112
GAVIN, Patrick J., President, Crozer–Chester Medical Center, Upland, PA, p. A551
GAVIN, Todd, Chief Medical Officer, Madelia Community Hospital, Madelia, MN, p. A341
GAVINO, Rey, M.D. Chief of Staff, RMC Jacksonville, Jacksonville, AL, p. A21
GAVIS, Patricia, Chief Financial Officer, Ellenville Regional Hospital, Ellenville, NY, p. A433
GAVORA, George, Director Program Evaluation, Kingsboro Psychiatric Center, NY, p. A440
GAVULIC, Melany, President & Chief Executive Officer, Hurley Medical Center, Flint, MI, p. A319
GAWALUCK, David
Vice President and Chief Information Officer, Excela Frick Hospital, Mount Pleasant, PA, p. A541
Vice President and Chief Information Officer, Excela Health Westmoreland Hospital, Greensburg, PA, p. A535
Vice President and Chief Information Officer, Excela Latrobe Area Hospital, Latrobe, PA, p. A538
GAWITH, Marlene, Director of Nursing, Ottawa County Health Center, Minneapolis, KS, p. A246
GAWLER, William, Chief Information Officer, Chillicothe Veterans Affairs Medical Center, Chillicothe, OH, p. A482
GAWNE, Bernard B., M.D. Vice President and Chief Medical Officer, Christ Hospital, Cincinnati, OH, p. A482
GAWORSKI, Mark, Vice President Finance, Chief Financial Officer, Spencer Hospital, Spencer, IA, p. A235
GAY, Christophe, M.D. Chief of Staff, Bellville St. Joseph Health Center, Bellville, TX, p. A597
GAY, Don, Director Human Resources, West Hills Hospital, Reno, NV, p. A404
GAY, Kristi
Chief Financial Officer, CHI St. Luke's Health Memorial Lufkin, Lufkin, TX, p. A630
Chief Financial Officer, CHI St. Luke's Health Memorial San Augustine, San Augustine, TX, p. A643
GAY, Michael, Chief Operating Officer, Habersham Medical Center, Demorest, GA, p. A156
GAY, Perry, Chief Executive Officer, Toppenish Community Hospital, Toppenish, WA, p. A686
GAY, Vickie, Chief Executive Officer, Montgomery General Hospital, Montgomery, WV, p. A693
GAYDUSEK, Lori, Chief Nursing Officer, Goodland Regional Medical Center, Goodland, KS, p. A240
GAYLER, Lisa, Director Human Resources, Select Long Term Care Hospital – Colorado Springs, Colorado Springs, CO, p. A101
GAYLOR, Rosanne, M.D., Acting Executive Director, South Beach Psychiatric Center, NY, p. A444
GAYNE, William, Chief Financial Officer, MedStar Washington Hospital Center, Washington, DC, p. A119
GAYNOR, Sheila, Director Human Resources, Perry County Memorial Hospital, Tell City, IN, p. A220
GAYTKO, Caren, Chief Nursing Officer, Regency Hospital of Minneapolis, Golden Valley, MN, p. A339
GAZECKI, Cindy, Senior Vice President, Hospital Operations, Seattle Children's Hospital, Seattle, WA, p. A683
GEARHARD, Cynthia, Chief Nursing Officer, St. Luke's Regional Medical Center, Boise, ID, p. A173
GEARHART, Danielle, Chief Executive Officer, Cooper County Memorial Hospital, Boonville, MO, p. A364
GEARY, David S., Chief Financial Officer, Cache Valley Hospital, North Logan, UT, p. A656
GEARY, Herb J., R.N. Vice President Patient Care Services and Chief Nursing Officer, Santa Barbara Cottage Hospital, Santa Barbara, CA, p. A91
GEBHARD, Scott, Executive VP and Chief Operating Officer, JFK Medical Center, Edison, NJ, p. A411
GEBHART, Cheryl
Director Human Resources Providence Health Plan and Providence Medical Group, Providence Newberg Medical Center, Newberg, OR, p. A523
Chief Human Resources Officer, Tuality Healthcare, Hillsboro, OR, p. A521
GEBHART Jr., Jim, FACHE, President, Mercy Hospital Oklahoma City, Oklahoma City, OK, p. A512
GEBHART, Ronald J., M.D. Chief of Staff, Veterans Affairs Salt Lake City Health Care System, Salt Lake City, UT, p. A659
GEDDINGS, Toni, Director Human Resources, Cullman Regional Medical Center, Cullman, AL, p. A18
GEDIES, Lucille, Chief Financial Officer, Mildred Mitchell–Bateman Hospital, Huntington, WV, p. A692
GEE, Kyle
Chief Financial Officer, Beartooth Billings Clinic, Red Lodge, MT, p. A386
Chief Financial Officer, Pioneer Medical Center, Big Timber, MT, p. A381
Regional Vice President Financial Operations, Roundup Memorial Healthcare, Roundup, MT, p. A386
GEE, Roland D., Interim Chief Executive Officer, Adams County Regional Medical Center, Seaman, OH, p. A497
GEE, Thomas H., Administrator, Henry County Medical Center, Paris, TN, p. A587
GEERTS, Jodi, Chief Nursing Officer, Henry County Health Center, Mount Pleasant, IA, p. A232
GEHLAUF, Dee Ann, Senior Vice President Business and Organization Development, Marietta Memorial Hospital, Marietta, OH, p. A493
GEHRIG, Ryan
President, Mercy Hospital Fort Smith, Fort Smith, AR, p. A44
President, Mercy Orthopedic Hospital Fort Smith, Fort Smith, AR, p. A44
GEHRING, Jay, Director Information Systems, Kingman Community Hospital, Kingman, KS, p. A243
GEHRING, Mikaela, Chief Operating Officer, Marengo Memorial Hospital, UnityPoint Health, Marengo, IA, p. A231
GEHRING, Sherry, R.N. Vice President and Chief Nursing Officer, Hancock Regional Hospital, Greenfield, IN, p. A210

A846 Index of Health Care Professionals 

Index of Health Care Professionals / Gheringhelli

Index of Health Care Professionals


GEIDL, Steve, Chief Financial Officer, Columbia County Health System, Dayton, WA, p. A678
GEIDT, Steve, Chief Executive Officer, Saddleback Memorial Medical Center, Laguna Hills, CA, p. A66
GEIER, Joyce, Director Nursing, Girard Medical Center, Girard, KS, p. A240
GEIER, Kathy, Director of Nursing, Chase County Community Hospital, Imperial, NE, p. A393
GEIER, Peter E., Chief Executive Officer, Ohio State University Health System, Columbus, OH, p. B101
GEIER, Peter E., Chief Operating Officer, Ohio State University Wexner Medical Center, Columbus, OH, p. A486
GEIGER, Deb, Executive Director of Acute Care, Harbor Beach Community Hospital, Harbor Beach, MI, p. A322
GEIGER, Judy, R.N. Chief Nursing Officer, Primary Children's Hospital, Salt Lake City, UT, p. A658
GEIGER, Ralph, M.D. Chief of Staff, Sebastian River Medical Center, Sebastian, FL, p. A143
GEIGLE, Joseph, Director Human Resources, Fort Hamilton Hospital, Hamilton, OH, p. A491
GEIL, Kristie A., VP, Chief Nursing Officer, CGH Medical Center, Sterling, IL, p. A201
GEIMAN, Robert, Senior Financial Analyst, Maple Grove Hospital, Maple Grove, MN, p. A342
GEISLER, Linda W., R.N. Vice President Patient Services, CentraState Healthcare System, Freehold, NJ, p. A412
GEIST, Jim, Chief Executive Officer, Capital Medical Center, Olympia, WA, p. A681
GEIST, Tammy, Chief Financial Officer, Novant Health Charlotte Orthopaedic Hospital, Charlotte, NC, p. A457
GEISTER, Bennett, Vice President Operations, Integris Grove Hospital, Grove, OK, p. A507
GEITZ, Cheri, Director Human Resources, Hansen Family Hospital, Iowa Falls, IA, p. A230
GEITZ, James, M.D. Chief of Staff, Newman Regional Health, Emporia, KS, p. A239
GEIVER, Betsy, Chief Human Resources Officer, Sioux Falls Veterans Affairs Health Care System, Sioux Falls, SD, p. A572
GELDERS, Albert, M.D. Chief of Staff, Oak Valley Hospital District, Oakdale, CA, p. A78
GELDHOF, Jay
Director Information Systems, Greater El Monte Community Hospital, South El Monte, CA, p. A93
Director Information Systems, Whittier Hospital Medical Center, Whittier, CA, p. A97
GELFAND, Andrew, M.D. Medical Director, Our Children's House at Baylor, Dallas, TX, p. A606
GELL, Michael, Director Human Resources, Boys Town National Research Hospital, Omaha, NE, p. A395
GELLER, Harold S., Chief Executive Officer, CHI St. Anthony Hospital, Pendleton, OR, p. A523
GELLER, Mark, M.D., President and Chief Executive Officer, Nyack Hospital, Nyack, NY, p. A446
GELLER, Robert D., M.D. Vice President Medical Affairs, FHN Memorial Hospital, Freeport, IL, p. A188
GELLER, Warren, President and Chief Executive Officer, Englewood Hospital and Medical Center, Englewood, NJ, p. A412
GELORMINI, Frank, Chief Operating Officer, Community Medical Center, Toms River, NJ, p. A419
GEMBOL, Leslie, MSN Chief Nursing Officer, Scott & White Hospital at Round Rock, Round Rock, TX, p. A639
GEMME, Donna T., R.N. Chief Nursing Officer, MetroWest Medical Center, Framingham, MA, p. A307
GENDER, Aloma, MSN, Administrator and Chief Nursing Officer, CHRISTUS St. Michael Rehabilitation Hospital, Texarkana, TX, p. A647
GENESIO, Sabina, Finance Officer for Institutes, Colorado Mental Health Institute at Fort Logan, Denver, CO, p. A101
GENEVRO, Thomas A., Vice President Human Resources, Butler Health System, Butler, PA, p. A530
GENGLER, Laraine, Chief Financial Officer, Lindsborg Community Hospital, Lindsborg, KS, p. A245
GENNA, Nick, Administrator, Treasure Valley Hospital, Boise, ID, p. A173
GENNARO, John, FACHE, Director, Cincinnati Veterans Affairs Medical Center, Cincinnati, OH, p. A482
GENOVESE, Vincent P., M.D. President Medical Staff, Owensboro Health Muhlenberg Community Hospital, Greenville, KY, p. A257
GENSERT, Kurt, R.N. Vice President Operations, Platte Valley Medical Center, Brighton, CO, p. A100
GENTHNER, Diane, Chief Nursing Officer, HSHS St. Mary's Hospital, Streator, IL, p. A202
GENTILE, John, M.D
Vice President Medical Affairs, Alta Bates Summit Medical Center, Berkeley, CA, p. A56
Vice President Medical Affairs, Alta Bates Summit Medical Center – Summit Campus, Oakland, CA, p. A78
Chief Medical Officer, Hollywood Presbyterian Medical Center, Los Angeles, CA, p. A70
GENTILE, Serge, Director Human Resources, Belmont Community Hospital, Bellaire, OH, p. A479
GENTNER, Rocky, Chief Financial Officer, Newport Bay Hospital, Newport Beach, CA, p. A78
GENTRY, Cheryl G., Chief Executive Officer, Regency Hospital of Northwest Indiana, East Chicago, IN, p. A207
GENTRY, Gregg, Senior Vice President Human Resources, Erlanger Medical Center, Chattanooga, TN, p. A575
GENTRY, Jeanine
Chief Executive Officer, Pioneer Memorial Hospital, Prineville, OR, p. A525
Chief Executive Officer, St. Charles Madras, Madras, OR, p. A522
GENTRY, Jennifer, R.N. Chief Nursing Officer, CHRISTUS Spohn Hospital Corpus Christi Memorial, Corpus Christi, TX, p. A602
GENTRY, Kristen, Chief Operating Officer, Venice Regional Bayfront Health, Venice, FL, p. A146
GENTRY, Lee, FACHE, Vice President and Administrator, Baptist Health Rehabilitation Institute, Little Rock, AR, p. A47
GENTRY, Margie, Controller, T. J. Samson Community Hospital, Glasgow, KY, p. A257
GEORGE, Alan E.
Chief Executive Officer, Palestine Regional Medical Center, Palestine, TX, p. A635
Chief Executive Officer, Palestine Regional Medical Center–East, Palestine, TX, p. A635
GEORGE, Amanda, Assistant Controller, St. Vincent Morrilton, Morrilton, AR, p. A48
GEORGE, Brad, Director Information Systems, Parkland Medical Center, Derry, NH, p. A405
GEORGE, Carol, Chief Nursing Officer, Columbus Specialty Hospital, Columbus, GA, p. A154
GEORGE, Daniel M., Executive Vice President, Operations, Covenant Healthcare, Saginaw, MI, p. A329
GEORGE, Denise, R.N., President, Northern Dutchess Hospital, Rhinebeck, NY, p. A448
GEORGE, Gary
Regional Vice President Human Resources, Mercy St. Anne Hospital, Toledo, OH, p. A498
Regional Vice President Human Resources, Mercy St. Charles Hospital, Oregon, OH, p. A495
Senior Vice President Human Resources, Mercy St. Vincent Medical Center, Toledo, OH, p. A498
GEORGE, P. A., M.D. Chief of Staff, Madison Medical Center, Fredericktown, MO, p. A367
GEORGE, Patsy, R.N. Chief Nursing Officer, Ohio Valley Medical Center, Wheeling, WV, p. A696
GEORGE, Saju, Chief Executive Officer, Garden City Hospital, Garden City, MI, p. A320
GEORGE, Shayne, Chief Executive Officer, Regional Medical Center Bayonet Point, Hudson, FL, p. A129
GEORGE, Susan, R.N. Associate Director Patient Care Services, Martinsburg Veterans Affairs Medical Center, Martinsburg, WV, p. A693
GEORGE, Tracy L., Chief Financial Officer, St. James Parish Hospital, Lutcher, LA, p. A279
GEORGE, William, M.D. Chief of Staff, Beartooth Billings Clinic, Red Lodge, MT, p. A386
GEORGES, Angelo, M.D. President Medical and Dental Staff, Wheeling Hospital, Wheeling, WV, p. A696
GERACI, Jeff, Administrator, Quitman County Hospital, Marks, MS, p. A356
GERBER, Allen, M.D. Chief of Staff, Baptist Health Medical Center–Hot Spring County, Malvern, AR, p. A48
GERBER, Andrew, Ph.D., Medical Director and Chief Executive Officer, Austen Riggs Center, Stockbridge, MA, p. A312
GERBER, Greg, M.D. Chief Medical Officer, Aurora Lakeland Medical Center, Elkhorn, WI, p. A700
GERDTS, Elizabeth, Chief Nursing Officer, North Central Bronx Hospital, NY, p. A443
GERETY, Meghan, M.D. Chief of Staff, New Mexico Veterans Affairs Health Care System – Raymond G. Murphy Medical Center, Albuquerque, NM, p. A422
GERHART, Paul, Chief Financial Officer, Sanford Canton–Inwood Medical Center, Canton, SD, p. A567
GERIG, Stacey L., Chief Executive Officer, Odessa Regional Medical Center, Odessa, TX, p. A635
GERING, Jeffrey T., FACHE, Director, VA San Diego Healthcare System, San Diego, CA, p. A87
GERING, Paul, M.D. Vice President Medical Affairs, Saint Alphonsus Medical Center – Ontario, Ontario, OR, p. A523
GERKE, Daniel, Chief Nursing Officer, Wright Patterson Medical Center, Wright–Patterson AFB, OH, p. A501
GERKE, Mary Lu, R.N. Vice President Nursing Systems, Gundersen Health System, La Crosse, WI, p. A703
GERKE, Sarah, Manager Human Resources, Dr. John Warner Hospital, Clinton, IL, p. A185
GERLACH, George, Chief Executive Officer and Administrator, Granite Falls Municipal Hospital and Manor, Granite Falls, MN, p. A340
GERLACH, Matthew S.
Chief Operating Officer, Children's Hospital of Orange County, Orange, CA, p. A79
Chief Operating Officer, CHOC Children's at Mission Hospital, Mission Viejo, CA, p. A75
GERMAN, Mike, Chief Financial Officer, Cape Coral Hospital, Cape Coral, FL, p. A123
GERMANY, Alan, Interim Chief Financial Officer, Bartlett Regional Hospital, Juneau, AK, p. A28
GERMUSKA, Natalie, MSN, Market Chief Executive Officer, Kindred Hospital–San Diego, San Diego, CA, p. A86
GERN, Sharon, R.N. Chief Nursing Officer, Ivinson Memorial Hospital, Laramie, WY, p. A716
GERNDT, Angie, Human Resources Manager, Central Community Hospital, Elkader, IA, p. A227
GERNHART, Diana, Senior Vice President and Hospital Chief Financial Officer, OHSU Hospital, Portland, OR, p. A524
GERRIOR, Marilyn, R.N. Chief Nursing Executive, Saint Louise Regional Hospital, Gilroy, CA, p. A63
GERRITS, Brad, Director Information Systems, Lakeview Medical Center, Rice Lake, WI, p. A710
GERSCH, Aaron, M.D. Chief of Staff, CHI Albany Area Health, Albany, MN, p. A334
GERSON, Elaine, Chief Clinical Officer and General Counsel, Aspen Valley Hospital District, Aspen, CO, p. A99
GERSTENBERGER, Linda
Vice President Human Resources, St. Rose Dominican Hospitals – San Martin Campus, Las Vegas, NV, p. A402
Vice President Human Resources, St. Rose Dominican Hospitals – Siena Campus, Henderson, NV, p. A401
GERSTNER, Nancy, Manager Human Resources, Robert J. Dole Veterans Affairs Medical Center, Wichita, KS, p. A252
GERTEN, Michael E., Chief Executive Officer, AMG Specialty Hospital–Edmond, Edmond, OK, p. A506
GERTH, Kevin, M.D. Chief of Staff, Spectrum Health Gerber Memorial, Fremont, MI, p. A320
GERVELER, Patrick M., Vice President Finance and Chief Financial Officer, Blessing Hospital, Quincy, IL, p. A199
GESKERMANN, Tom G., Chief Executive Officer, Osceola Medical Center, Osceola, WI, p. A708
GESSEL, Thomas, FACHE, President and Chief Executive Officer, Mercy Regional Medical Center, Durango, CO, p. A102
GESSNER, Christopher, President, Children's Hospital of Pittsburgh of UPMC, Pittsburgh, PA, p. A546
GETMAN, Sylvia, President and Chief Executive Officer, The Aroostook Medical Center, Presque Isle, ME, p. A292
GETSAY, Timothy, Chief Information Officer, Vice President of Performance & Information Mgmt, Gillette Children's Specialty Healthcare, Saint Paul, MN, p. A346
GETTINGER, Thomas
Chief Operating Officer and Executive Vice President, WakeMed Cary Hospital, Cary, NC, p. A456
Executive Vice President and Chief Operating Officer, WakeMed Raleigh Campus, Raleigh, NC, p. A467
GETTINGS, Scott, M.D
Senior Vice President and Chief Medical Officer, Health First Palm Bay Hospital, Palm Bay, FL, p. A138
Senior Vice President and Chief Medical Officer, Health First Viera Hospital, Melbourne, FL, p. A133
GETTYS, Sky, Chief Financial Officer, Fairfield Medical Center, Lancaster, OH, p. A491
GETWOOD, Charles, Assistant Chief Executive Officer, Calcasieu Oaks Geriatric Psychiatric Hospital, Lake Charles, LA, p. A278
GETZ, Liz, Chief Information Officer, Aultman Hospital, Canton, OH, p. A481
GEUDER, Denise, Vice President Patient Care Service and Chief Nursing Officer, Southwestern Regional Medical Center, Tulsa, OK, p. A517
GEURTS, Chuck, Manager Management Information Services, Aurora BayCare Medical Center, Green Bay, WI, p. A701
GEWECKE, Tyler, Information Technology Technician, Fillmore County Hospital, Geneva, NE, p. A392
GFELLER, Michael, Director Information Systems, Medical Center of Plano, Plano, TX, p. A637
GHAEMMAGHAMI, Chris A., M.D. Chief Medical Officer, University of Virginia Medical Center, Charlottesville, VA, p. A663
GHAFFARI, Bahram, President, Delano Regional Medical Center, Delano, CA, p. A59
GHERINGHELLI, Thomas, Chief Financial Officer, New England Baptist Hospital, Boston, MA, p. A304

Index of Health Care Professionals / Glynn


GILLY, Mike, Chief Information Officer, Our Lady of the Angels Hospital, Bogalusa, LA, p. A270
GILMAN, Howard, M.D. Medical Executive, Christian Health Care Center, Wyckoff, NJ, p. A421
GILMAN, Kim
Chief Executive Officer, Phoebe Worth Medical Center, Sylvester, GA, p. A165
Chief Executive Officer and Chief Nursing Officer, Southwest Georgia Regional Medical Center, Cuthbert, GA, p. A155
GILMORE, Hugh V., M.D. Vice President Medical Affairs, Seton Medical Center Williamson, Round Rock, TX, p. A639
GILMORE, Linda, Chief Nursing Officer/Chief Administrative Officer, Littleton Regional Hospital, Littleton, NH, p. A407
GILMORE, Phillip K., FACHE, Chief Executive Officer, Ashley County Medical Center, Crossett, AR, p. A42
GILPIN, Michael W., Vice President Human Resources, Sampson Regional Medical Center, Clinton, NC, p. A458
GILROY, Robert, M.D. Chief of Staff, Jackson–Madison County General Hospital, Jackson, TN, p. A579
GILTNER, Michelle, Interim Chief Nursing Officer, UH Regional Hospitals, Cleveland, OH, p. A485
GIN, Nancy, M.D. Area Associate Medical Director, Kaiser Permanente Orange County Anaheim Medical Center, Anaheim, CA, p. A53
GINGHER, Barbara S., R.N. Assistant Administrator for Patient Care Services, Baptist Medical Center Nassau, Fernandina Beach, FL, p. A126
GINGRAS, Sean, CPA Chief Financial Officer, Manatee Glens Hospital and Addiction Center, Bradenton, FL, p. A122
GINGRICH, Mary, Director Health Care Services, Kansas Neurological Institute, Topeka, KS, p. A251
GINN, Bobby, Chief Operating Officer, Crestwood Medical Center, Huntsville, AL, p. A21
GINN, Doug, Executive Vice President Operations, Peak Behavioral Health Services, Santa Teresa, NM, p. A426
GINNITY, John, Interim Director, Veterans Affairs Montana Health Care System, Fort Harrison, MT, p. A383
GINSBERG, Ronald L., M.D. Vice President Medical Affairs, Northwest Hospital, Randallstown, MD, p. A299
GINSBURG, J. Lawrence, M.D. Vice President Medical Affairs, Evangelical Community Hospital, Lewisburg, PA, p. A538
GINTER, Gary, System Vice President and Chief Information Officer, Miami Valley Hospital, Dayton, OH, p. A488
GINTZIG, Donald R., President and Chief Executive Officer, WakeMed Cary Hospital, Cary, NC, p. A456
GINTZIG, Donald R., President and Chief Executive Officer, WakeMed Health & Hospitals, Raleigh, NC, p. B152
GINTZIG, Donald R., President and Chief Executive Officer, WakeMed Raleigh Campus, Raleigh, NC, p. A467
GIOIA, Anthony, Chief Financial Officer, Indiana Orthopaedic Hospital, Indianapolis, IN, p. A211
GIORDANO, Paul, Vice President Human Resources, South Nassau Communities Hospital, Oceanside, NY, p. A446
GIORDANO, Peter, Senior Director Human Resources, Harrison Community Hospital, Cadiz, OH, p. A480
GIORDANO, Roger, M.D. Medical Director, HEALTHSOUTH Rehabilitation Hospital of Virginia, Richmond, VA, p. A671
GIORDANO, Susan, R.N. Chief Nursing Officer, Hackensack University Medical Center at Pascack Valley, Westwood, NJ, p. A420
GIPP, Jana, Chief Executive Officer, Standing Rock Service Unit, Fort Yates Hospital, Indian Health Service, DHHS, Fort Yates, ND, p. A474
GIPSON, David N., Senior Vice President and Chief Clinical Operations Officer, Union Hospital, Elkton, MD, p. A297
GIPSON, Linda Stephens, MSN Chief Nursing Officer, Whidbey General Hospital, Coupeville, WA, p. A678
GIRALT, Juana, Chief Financial Officer, River Crest Hospital, San Angelo, TX, p. A640
GIRARD, Thomas R.
Vice President Human Resources, LincolnHealth, Damariscotta, ME, p. A290
Vice President Human Resources, Pen Bay Medical Center, Rockport, ME, p. A292
GIRARDIER, Cheryl, Director Information Technology, Millcreek Community Hospital, Erie, PA, p. A534
GIRARDY, James, M.D. Vice President, Chief Surgical Officer, OSF Saint Anthony Medical Center, Rockford, IL, p. A199
GIRTEN, David M., Corporate Director Financial Services, St. Vincent Seton Specialty Hospital, Indianapolis, IN, p. A213
GIRTY, Tara, Director Human Resources, Kiowa District Hospital and Manor, Kiowa, KS, p. A244
GISH, Kevin, Administrator and Vice President, Essentia Health Fosston, Fosston, MN, p. A339
GISLESON, Joni, Director Finance, Palmer Lutheran Health Center, West Union, IA, p. A236
GISSEL, Betty, Vice President Human Resources, University of Tennessee Medical Center, Knoxville, TN, p. A581
GITMAN, Michael, M.D. Medical Director, North Shore University Hospital, Manhasset, NY, p. A437
GITTELMAN, Michael B., Administrator, Bascom Palmer Eye Institute–Anne Bates Leach Eye Hospital, Miami, FL, p. A134
GIUDICE, William A., Vice President and Chief Financial Officer, Tallahassee Memorial HealthCare, Tallahassee, FL, p. A144
GIULIANELLI, Victor, FACHE, President and Chief Executive Officer, St. Mary's Healthcare, Amsterdam, NY, p. A428
GIVENS, Michael K., FACHE Administrator, St. Bernards Medical Center, Jonesboro, AR, p. A46
GIVENS, Stephen K., Assistant Vice President and Administrator, Russell County Medical Center, Lebanon, VA, p. A666
GIZDIC, John H., Chief Operating Officer, New Hanover Regional Medical Center, Wilmington, NC, p. A470
GIZINSKI, Judy, Chief Operating Officer, Health First Palm Bay Hospital, Palm Bay, FL, p. A138
GIZZI, Jason, Controller, HEALTHSOUTH MountainView Regional Rehabilitation Hospital, Morgantown, WV, p. A693
GJOLBERG, Skip, FACHE, Chief Executive Officer, Cuero Community Hospital, Cuero, TX, p. A603
GLADE, James G., Director Human Resources, Penn Highlands Clearfield, Clearfield, PA, p. A531
GLADEN, Tracy, Chief Financial Officer, Twin Valley Behavioral Healthcare, Columbus, OH, p. A487
GLADFELTER, Sharon, Health Information Officer, Brook Lane Health Services, Hagerstown, MD, p. A298
GLADSTONE, Art, R.N.,
President and Chief Executive Officer, Pali Momi Medical Center, Aiea, HI, p. A168
Chief Executive Officer, Straub Clinic & Hospital, Honolulu, HI, p. A169
GLANVILLE, Tristan, Chief Financial Officer, Adirondack Medical Center, Saranac Lake, NY, p. A450
GLANZER, Elgin, Chief Financial Officer, Memorial Health System, Abilene, KS, p. A237
GLASBERG, Michael, Senior Vice President, Chief Operating Officer, Dameron Hospital, Stockton, CA, p. A93
GLASER, Elaine, Chief Executive Officer, Managing Director, Valley Hospital Medical Center, Las Vegas, NV, p. A403
GLASER, Ruth, President, Pender Memorial Hospital, Burgaw, NC, p. A456
GLASNAPP, Sherry L., Director, Douglas County Community Mental Health Center, Omaha, NE, p. A396
GLASS, Debbie, Interim Chief Executive Officer, Providence Seaside Hospital, Seaside, OR, p. A526
GLASS, Ian, M.D. Chief Medical Officer, Tomball Regional Medical Center, Tomball, TX, p. A648
GLASS, Ina Louise, Chief Nursing Officer and Vice President and Interim Administrator, Ephraim McDowell Fort Logan Hospital, Stanford, KY, p. A266
GLASS, Steven, Chief Financial Officer, Cleveland Clinic, Cleveland, OH, p. A484
GLASS, Wendy, Director Human Resources, Colleton Medical Center, Walterboro, SC, p. A565
GLASSBURN, David, Vice President Finance and Chief Financial Officer, Harlingen Medical Center, Harlingen, TX, p. A617
GLASSCOCK, Gary M., President and Chief Executive Officer, Noland Health Services, Inc., Birmingham, AL, p. B97
GLASSCOCK, Sheryl, Chief Nursing Officer, Lake Cumberland Regional Hospital, Somerset, KY, p. A266
GLASSMAN, Kimberly S., Ph.D. Chief Nursing Officer, NYU Langone Medical Center, New York, NY, p. A443
GLATT, Aaron, M.D., Executive Vice President and Chief Administrative Officer, Mercy Medical Center, Rockville Centre, NY, p. A449
GLAVES, Ann, Vice President Human Resources, St. Francis Regional Medical Center, Shakopee, MN, p. A347
GLAVIN, Jolene, R.N. Director Nursing, Salina Surgical Hospital, Salina, KS, p. A250
GLAZIER, Douglas, Interim Chief Financial Officer, Day Kimball Hospital, Putnam, CT, p. A114
GLAZIER, Stephen, Chief Operating Officer, University of Texas Harris County Psychiatric Center, Houston, TX, p. A622
GLEASON, Jeffrey J., M.D. Chief Medical Officer, Cookeville Regional Medical Center, Cookeville, TN, p. A576
GLEASON, Mike, Vice President and Chief Financial Officer, UF Health Jacksonville, Jacksonville, FL, p. A130
GLEASON, Ronald M., Chief Executive Officer, Mineral Community Hospital, Superior, MT, p. A387
GLEASON, Vallerie L., R.N. Chief Nursing Officer, Newton Medical Center, Newton, KS, p. A246
GLECKLER, John, Chief Financial Officer, St. Vincent's Medical Center, Bridgeport, CT, p. A111
GLEESON, Gabrielle, Human Resources, Hermann Area District Hospital, Hermann, MO, p. A368
GLEN, Diane M., Assistant Administrator, Barnes–Jewish West County Hospital, Saint Louis, MO, p. A376
GLEN, Susan, Chief Executive Officer, Select Specialty Hospital – Cincinnati North, Cincinnati, OH, p. A483
GLENN, Gary
Director Information Technology, Carrus Rehabilitation Hospital, Sherman, TX, p. A643
Director Information Technology, Carrus Specialty Hospital, Sherman, TX, p. A644
GLENN, Jeannette, Vice President Human Resources, Education and Training, McLeod Regional Medical Center, Florence, SC, p. A561
GLENN, Maggie, Director Human Resources, North Carolina Specialty Hospital, Durham, NC, p. A459
GLENN, Michael, M.D. Chief Medical Officer, Virginia Mason Medical Center, Seattle, WA, p. A684
GLENN, Mike, Chief Executive Officer, Jefferson Healthcare, Port Townsend, WA, p. A682
GLENN, Wil A., Director Communications, Larry B. Zieverink, Sr. Alcoholism Treatment Center, Raleigh, NC, p. A467
GLENNING, Robert, Executive Vice President Finance and Chief Financial Officer, Hackensack University Medical Center, Hackensack, NJ, p. A412
GLICK, Jennifer, Manager Clinical Informatics, Oaklawn Psychiatric Center, Goshen, IN, p. A210
GLIDDEN, Elizabeth, Chief Nursing Officer, New England Rehabilitation Hospital of Portland, Portland, ME, p. A292
GLIDDEN, Nancy
Chief Financial Officer, Calais Regional Hospital, Calais, ME, p. A289
Chief Financial Officer and Vice President Finance, Mayo Regional Hospital, Dover–Foxcroft, ME, p. A290
GLIDDEN, Weldon, M.D. Chief of Staff, Chillicothe Hospital District, Chillicothe, TX, p. A600
GLIDEWELL Jr., Calvin E., Chief Executive Officer, Broward Health Medical Center, Fort Lauderdale, FL, p. A126
GLIHA, Frank, Vice President of Patient Care, Mary Rutan Hospital, Bellefontaine, OH, p. A479
GLIHA, Jennie, Vice President Human Resources and Clinical Services, Aurelia Osborn Fox Memorial Hospital, Oneonta, NY, p. A446
GLOCKA, Carolynn, R.N., President, Aurora Sinai Medical Center, Milwaukee, WI, p. A706
GLOCKNER, Tina, Chief Nursing Officer, PMH Medical Center, Prosser, WA, p. A682
GLODOWSKI, Brenda, Chief Financial Officer, North Central Health Care, Wausau, WI, p. A713
GLOFF, Vicki, Chief Financial Officer, Goodall–Witcher Hospital Authority, Clifton, TX, p. A601
GLOGGNER, Peter, Chief Human Resources Officer, Jupiter Medical Center, Jupiter, FL, p. A130
GLONER, James, Senior Vice President, North Philadelphia Health System, Philadelphia, PA, p. A544
GLORIA–BARRAZA, Patricia, Coordinator Human Resources, Mayhill Hospital, Denton, TX, p. A608
GLOSS, John, FACHE, Administrator, Shriners Hospitals for Children–St. Louis, Saint Louis, MO, p. A377
GLOTZBACK, Lee, Director Human Resources, Citrus Memorial Health System, Inverness, FL, p. A129
GLOVER, Cynthia, R.N. Vice President and Chief Nursing Officer, Reston Hospital Center, Reston, VA, p. A671
GLOVER, Doug, Controller, William S. Hall Psychiatric Institute, Columbia, SC, p. A560
GLOVER, Leslie, Director Operations, Mary Black Health System – Gaffney, Gaffney, SC, p. A561
GLOWA, Meghan, Director Human Resources, Sunnyview Rehabilitation Hospital, Schenectady, NY, p. A450
GLUBKA, Theresa, R.N., Chief Executive Officer, Eden Medical Center, Castro Valley, CA, p. A57
GLUCHOWSKI, Jeanne, Executive Director, Conifer Park, Glenville, NY, p. A434
GLUCK, Michael, M.D. Medical Director, LifeCare Hospitals of Mechanicsburg, Mechanicsburg, PA, p. A540
GLUECK, Dane, M.D. Chief of Staff, Progress West Hospital, O'Fallon, MO, p. A374
GLUECKERT, John W., Administrator, Montana State Hospital, Warm Springs, MT, p. A387
GLUM, Derrick, Chief Executive Officer, Tahoe Pacific Hospitals, Sparks, NV, p. A404
GLYER, David, Vice President Finance, Community Memorial Health System, Ventura, CA, p. A96
GLYNN, Cindy, Director Human Resources, Regional Rehabilitation Hospital, Phenix City, AL, p. A24
GLYNN, John
Executive Vice President, Chief Information Officer, Newark–Wayne Community Hospital, Newark, NY, p. A445
Senior Vice President and Chief Information Officer, Unity Hospital, Rochester, NY, p. A449
GLYNN, Margaret, M.D. Chief Medical Officer, Tishomingo Health Services, Iuka, MS, p. A354
GLYNN, Shari, Vice President Finance and Chief Financial Officer, Eaton Rapids Medical Center, Eaton Rapids, MI, p. A319

Index of Health Care Professionals

Index of Health Care Professionals / Gnagey


GNAGEY, Keith, Chief Executive Officer, Teton Valley Health Care, Driggs, ID, p. A174

GNAM, Gwen, R.N. Chief Nursing Officer, Henry Ford Hospital, Detroit, MI, p. A317

GNANN, Andrew, Vice President Operations, St. Vincent's East, Birmingham, AL, p. A17

GNEGY, David, M.D. Vice President of Medical Affairs, Camden Clark Medical Center, Parkersburg, WV, p. A694

GOACHER, Brad, Vice President Administration, Alton Memorial Hospital, Alton, IL, p. A178

GOAD, Pat, Director Human Resources, Hillcrest Hospital Claremore, Claremore, OK, p. A505

GOBEL, Bret, Chief Financial Officer, Sierra Vista Hospital, Truth or Consequences, NM, p. A427

GOBELL, James, Chief Financial Officer, UnityPoint Health – St. Luke's, Sioux City, IA, p. A235

GOBER, Kirby, Chief Executive Officer, Throckmorton County Memorial Hospital, Throckmorton, TX, p. A648

GOBLE, Jonathan R., FACHE, President and Chief Executive Officer, Indiana University Health North Hospital, Carmel, IN, p. A206

GOBLE, Mandy C., President and Chief Executive Officer, Mary Rutan Hospital, Bellefontaine, OH, p. A479

GOCHENOUR, Julia, Manager Information Systems, West River Regional Medical Center, Hettinger, ND, p. A474

GODAMUNNE, Karim, M.D. Chief Medical Officer, North Fulton Regional Hospital, Roswell, GA, p. A163

GODDARD, Mark, M.D. Medical Director, HEALTHSOUTH Rehabilitation Hospital at Drake, Cincinnati, OH, p. A483

GODESKY, Susan, Director Information Technology, Nanticoke Memorial Hospital, Seaford, DE, p. A117

GODFREY, Katrina, Director Human Resources, Mercy Hospital Ada, Ada, OK, p. A503

GODFREY, Kristine, Director Human Resources, Skyridge Medical Center, Cleveland, TN, p. A576

GODFREY, Larry, Administrator, Baton Rouge Behavioral Hospital, Baton Rouge, LA, p. A269

GODINEZ, Roxanna M., Chief Executive Officer, Cornerstone Regional Hospital, Edinburg, TX, p. A609

GODLEY, James R., Vice President of Human Resources, Mayo Regional Hospital, Dover–Foxcroft, ME, p. A290

GODLEY, Maria, R.N., Chief Executive Officer, Northern Idaho Advanced Care Hospital, Post Falls, ID, p. A176

GODLEY, Patrick, Chief Financial Officer, Contra Costa Regional Medical Center, Martinez, CA, p. A74

GODWIN, Jr., Herman A., M.D. Senior Vice President and Medical Director, Watauga Medical Center, Boone, NC, p. A456

GOEB–BURKETT, Michele, R.N. Chief Nursing Officer, Florida Hospital Memorial Medical Center, Daytona Beach, FL, p. A125

GOEBEL, Bret, Finance Officer, Guadalupe County Hospital, Santa Rosa, NM, p. A426

GOEBEL, Cecilia B., R.N. Vice President and Chief Nursing Officer, Susan B. Allen Memorial Hospital, El Dorado, KS, p. A239

GOEBEL, Dennis, Chief Executive Officer, Murray County Medical Center, Slayton, MN, p. A347

GOEBEL, Donna, M.D. Chief Nursing Officer, Mitchell County Hospital, Colorado City, TX, p. A601

GOEBEL, Michael
- Vice President and Chief Executive Officer, Adventist Hinsdale Hospital, Hinsdale, IL, p. A191
- Vice President and Chief Executive Officer, Adventist La Grange Memorial Hospital, La Grange, IL, p. A192

GOEHRING, Lawanda, MSN Chief Nursing Officer, Good Shepherd Penn Partners Specialty Hospital at Rittenhouse, Philadelphia, PA, p. A543

GOEL, Amitabh, M.D. Chief Medical Officer, University Hospitals Geneva Medical Center, Geneva, OH, p. A490

GOEL, Ashutosh, M.D. Chief Information Technology Officer, Cheyenne Regional Medical Center, Cheyenne, WY, p. A715

GOEL, Vineet, Chief Medical Officer, Carolinas HealthCare System Lincoln, Lincolnton, NC, p. A464

GOELOE–ALSTON, Hendrina, Assistant Vice President Personnel, SUNY Downstate Medical Center University Hospital, NY, p. A444

GOELZER, Mark L., M.D. Director Medical Affairs, Mercy Hospital and Trauma Center, Janesville, WI, p. A703

GOERINGER, Dawn Marie, Chief Clinical Care Officer, O'Connor Hospital, San Jose, CA, p. A89

GOESER, Stephen L., FACHE, President and Chief Executive Officer, Nebraska Methodist Hospital, Omaha, NE, p. A396

GOETTSCH, Barry, FACHE, Chief Executive Officer, Marengo Memorial Hospital, UnityPoint Health, Marengo, IA, p. A231

GOETZ, Kathy L., Administrator, Mercy Medical Center – West Lakes, West Des Moines, IA, p. A236

GOFF, Gary E., M.D. Medical Director, Promise Hospital of Dallas, Dallas, TX, p. A606

GOGGIN, Daniel
- Senior Vice President and Chief Financial Officer, Burleson St. Joseph Health Center, Caldwell, TX, p. A599
- Senior Vice President and Chief Financial Officer, Grimes St. Joseph Health Center, Navasota, TX, p. A634

GOGGIN, Kathy, Director Administrative Services, Devereux Georgia Treatment Network, Kennesaw, GA, p. A159

GOGIA, Harmohinder, M.D. Chief Medical Officer, Western Medical Center Anaheim, Anaheim, CA, p. A53

GOGLIETTINO, Deborah
- Senior Vice President Human Resources, Manchester Memorial Hospital, Manchester, CT, p. A112
- Senior Vice President Human Resources, Rockville General Hospital, Vernon, CT, p. A115

GOINGS, Harold, Chief Human Resources, VA Greater Los Angeles Healthcare System, Los Angeles, CA, p. A73

GOKLI, Ash, M.D., Chief Executive Officer, Memorial Hospital Los Banos, Los Banos, CA, p. A73

GOLAN, Marc
- Chief Financial Officer, Franciscan St. Anthony Health – Crown Point, Crown Point, IN, p. A207
- Regional Chief Financial Officer, Franciscan St. Anthony Health – Michigan City, Michigan City, IN, p. A216
- Chief Financial Officer, Franciscan St. Margaret Health – Hammond, Hammond, IN, p. A210

GOLANOWSKI, Marie, MS, President, Aurora St. Luke's Medical Center, Milwaukee, WI, p. A706

GOLD, Barbara, M.D. Chief Medical Officer, University of Minnesota Medical Center, Fairview, Minneapolis, MN, p. A343

GOLD, Joseph, M.D. Chief Medical Officer, McLean Hospital, Belmont, MA, p. A302

GOLD, Larry M., Chief Executive Officer, Children's Hospital of Michigan, Detroit, MI, p. A317

GOLD, Neal, Chief Executive Officer, Westlake Regional Hospital, Columbia, KY, p. A255

GOLDAMMER, Kyle, Chief Financial Officer, Sioux Falls Specialty Hospital, Sioux Falls, SD, p. A572

GOLDBERG, Andrew S., Associate Executive Director, Syosset Hospital, Syosset, NY, p. A451

GOLDBERG, David, M.D. Vice President Medical Affairs, Community Memorial Hospital, Menomonee Falls, WI, p. A705

GOLDBERG, Frederick, M.D. Vice President Medical Affairs and Chief Medical Officer, Nathan Littauer Hospital and Nursing Home, Gloversville, NY, p. A434

GOLDBERG, Gary, M.D. Chief Medical Officer, North Hawaii Community Hospital, Kamuela, HI, p. A169

GOLDBERG, Jonathan
- Chief Information Officer, Albany Memorial Hospital, Albany, NY, p. A428
- Vice President and Chief Information Officer, St. Mary's Hospital, Troy, NY, p. A452
- Chief Information Officer, St. Peter's Hospital, Albany, NY, p. A428

GOLDBERG, Larry M., President and Chief Executive Officer, Loyola University Medical Center, Maywood, IL, p. A193

GOLDBERG, Michael, Executive Director, Long Island Jewish Medical Center, NY, p. A441

GOLDBERG, Paul R., Chief Financial Officer, Jersey City Medical Center, Jersey City, NJ, p. A413

GOLDBERG, Richard L., M.D., President, MedStar Georgetown University Hospital, Washington, DC, p. A119

GOLDBERG, Stephanie J., MSN Senior Vice President and Chief Nursing Officer, Hospital for Special Surgery, New York, NY, p. A440

GOLDBERGER, Joseph, M.D
- Chief Medical Officer, Yavapai Regional Medical Center – East, Prescott Valley, AZ, p. A36
- Chief Medical Officer, Yavapai Regional Medical Center, Prescott, AZ, p. A36

GOLDEN, Joy, Chief Executive Officer, Lakeside Behavioral Health System, Memphis, TN, p. A583

GOLDENBERG, Dianne, Chief Executive Officer, Aventura Hospital and Medical Center, Aventura, FL, p. A121

GOLDENSTEIN, Rachel, R.N. Chief Nursing Officer, Buchanan County Health Center, Independence, IA, p. A229

GOLDFARB, I. William, Chief Medical Officer, West Penn Hospital, Pittsburgh, PA, p. A547

GOLDFISHER, Anne M., R.N. Chief Nursing Officer, Kaiser Permanente Santa Clara Medical Center, Santa Clara, CA, p. A91

GOLDHAGEN, Michele, M.D. Chief of Staff, Russell Medical Center, Alexander City, AL, p. A15

GOLDMAN, David, M.D. Vice President Medical Affairs and Education, Prince George's Hospital Center, Cheverly, MD, p. A296

GOLDMAN, Eric, Chief Executive Officer, Palms West Hospital, Loxahatchee, FL, p. A132

GOLDMAN, Kris McHugh, Director Human Resources, Shriners Hospitals for Children–Spokane, Spokane, WA, p. A685

GOLDSCHMID, David, M.D. President Medical Staff, Seton Medical Center, Daly City, CA, p. A59

GOLDSCHMIDT, Pascal J., M.D., Chief Executive Officer, University of Miami Health System, Miami, FL, p. B147

GOLDSMITH, Cheri L.
- Director Financial Services, Parkland Health Center – Liberty Street, Farmington, MO, p. A367
- Director, Financial Services, Parkland Health Center – Weber Road, Farmington, MO, p. A367
- Director Financial Services, Parkland Health Center–Bonne Terre, Bonne Terre, MO, p. A363

GOLDSMITH, Dana L., M.D. Vice President Medical Affairs, Pen Bay Medical Center, Rockport, ME, p. A292

GOLDSMITH, Debra, Chief Executive Officer, CHI Health Mercy Corning, Corning, IA, p. A225

GOLDSTEIN, Allan, M.D. Medical Director and Chief of Staff, Select Specialty Hospital–Birmingham, Birmingham, AL, p. A16

GOLDSTEIN, Brian, M.D. Executive Vice President and Chief Operating Officer, University of North Carolina Hospitals, Chapel Hill, NC, p. A457

GOLDSTEIN, Charles, M.D. President Medical Staff, Riverside Shore Memorial Hospital, Nassawadox, VA, p. A668

GOLDSTEIN, David, M.D. Chief Medical Officer, Contra Costa Regional Medical Center, Martinez, CA, p. A74

GOLDSTEIN, Gary W., M.D., President and Chief Executive Officer, Kennedy Krieger Institute, Baltimore, MD, p. A293

GOLDSTEIN, Gerald, M.D. Senior Vice President and Chief Medical Officer, Western Maryland Regional Medical Center, Cumberland, MD, p. A297

GOLDSTEIN, Lawrence, M.D. Chief Medical Officer, Vibra Hospital of Mahoning Valley, Boardman, OH, p. A480

GOLDSTEIN, Lisa, Executive Vice President and Chief Operating Officer, Hospital for Special Surgery, New York, NY, p. A440

GOLDSTEIN, Mark L., President and Chief Executive Officer, Anna Jaques Hospital, Newburyport, MA, p. A309

GOLDSTEIN, Paul, Vice President Finance and Chief Financial Officer, Orlando Regional Medical Center, Orlando, FL, p. A138

GOLDSTEIN, Steven I.
- President and Chief Executive Officer, Highland Hospital of Rochester, Rochester, NY, p. A448
- President and Chief Executive Officer, Strong Memorial Hospital of the University of Rochester, Rochester, NY, p. A449

GOLDSTEIN, Steven I., General Director and Chief Executive Officer, University of Rochester Medical Center, Rochester, NY, p. B147

GOLDSTEIN, Wendy Z., Chief Executive Officer, NYU Lutheran, NY, p. A444

GOLDSZER, Robert, M.D. Senior Vice President and Chief Medical Officer, Mount Sinai Medical Center, Miami Beach, FL, p. A135

GOLIGHTLY, Beverly, Director Information Technology, St. Vincent's East, Birmingham, AL, p. A17

GOLKE, Rynae, Director Human Resources, Jacobson Memorial Hospital Care Center, Elgin, ND, p. A473

GOLL, Cheri, MSN Chief Nursing Officer, Inova Fair Oaks Hospital, Fairfax, VA, p. A664

GOLLAHER, Jeffrey, Chief Executive Officer, Hendricks Community Hospital Association, Hendricks, MN, p. A340

GOLLINGER, Mary A., MS Director of Nursing, Schwab Rehabilitation Hospital, Chicago, IL, p. A184

GOLOVAN, Ronald, M.D. Vice President Medical Operations, Lutheran Hospital, Cleveland, OH, p. A485

GOMAN, Valerie, M.D. President Medical Staff, Baylor Medical Center at Waxahachie, Waxahachie, TX, p. A650

GOMBAR, Greg A.
- Chief Financial Officer, Carolinas Medical Center, Charlotte, NC, p. A457
- Chief Financial Officer, Carolinas Medical Center–University, Charlotte, NC, p. A457

GOMBERG, Sandra, Chief Operating Officer, Aria Health, Philadelphia, PA, p. A542

GOMES, Carol, FACHE Chief Operating Officer, Stony Brook University Medical Center, Stony Brook, NY, p. A451

GOMES, Robert, FACHE,
- Chief Executive Officer, St. Charles Bend, Bend, OR, p. A519
- Chief Executive Officer, St. Charles Redmond, Redmond, OR, p. A525

GOMEZ, Carmen, Director Human Resources, North Shore Medical Center, Miami, FL, p. A134

GOMEZ, Denise, Assistant Vice President Information Systems, Meriter UnityPoint Health, Madison, WI, p. A704

GOMEZ, Dolores S., R.N. Chief Operating Officer, Mills–Peninsula Health Services, Burlingame, CA, p. A56

GOMEZ, Eddie, Senior Manager Director Information Systems, Environmental Services Laundry, HEALTHSOUTH Deaconess Rehabilitation Hospital, Evansville, IN, p. A208


A850 Index of Health Care Professionals 

Index of Health Care Professionals / Gormsen

Index of Health Care Professionals


GOMEZ, Gloria, M.D. Medical Director, East Mississippi State Hospital, Meridian, MS, p. A357
GOMEZ, Jay Michael, Chief Financial Officer, Memorial Hermann Surgical Hospital Kingwood, Kingwood, TX, p. A626
GOMEZ, Jesse, Vice President Human Resources, University of Texas Health Northeast, Tyler, TX, p. A649
GOMEZ, Mike, Site Manager Medical Information Systems, Our Lady of Bellefonte Hospital, Ashland, KY, p. A254
GOMEZ, Omar, M.D. Chief of Staff, Cornerstone Regional Hospital, Edinburg, TX, p. A609
GOMEZ, Robin, MSN, Administrator, Alvarado Hospital Medical Center, San Diego, CA, p. A86
GOMEZ, Sherry, Chief Nursing Officer, Spanish Peaks Regional Health Center, Walsenburg, CO, p. A109
GOMEZ–LUNA, Sandra, Medical Director, Southwest Connecticut Mental Health System, Bridgeport, CT, p. A111
GOMPF, Shelly, Director Human Resources, Douglas County Hospital, Alexandria, MN, p. A334
GONCZ, Gray, Vice President of Medical Affairs, Trinity Health System, Steubenville, OH, p. A498
GONDER, Christie, Chief Nursing Officer, Salinas Valley Memorial Healthcare System, Salinas, CA, p. A85
GONDRON, Elizabeth, R.N. Vice President and Chief Nursing Officer, Iberia Medical Center, New Iberia, LA, p. A281
GONG, Christopher, M.D. Chief Staff, Huron Medical Center, Bad Axe, MI, p. A314
GONGAWARE, Robert, Senior Vice President Finance, Indiana Regional Medical Center, Indiana, PA, p. A536
GONYEA, Sonja, Director Human Resources, United Memorial Medical Center, Batavia, NY, p. A429
GONZALES, Amy, Director of Human Resources, McKenzie County Healthcare System, Watford City, ND, p. A477
GONZALES, Angela, Manager Human Resources, San Mateo Medical Center, San Mateo, CA, p. A90
GONZALES, D. V., Head Information Technology Management, Naval Medical Center San Diego, San Diego, CA, p. A86
GONZALES, Ed
Vice President Human Resources, Marian Regional Medical Center, Santa Maria, CA, p. A91
Vice President Human Resources, St. John's Pleasant Valley Hospital, Camarillo, CA, p. A57
Vice President Human Resources, St. John's Regional Medical Center, Oxnard, CA, p. A79
GONZALES, Jan, Director Human Resources, North Valley Hospital, Tonasket, WA, p. A686
GONZALES, Mary Ann, M.D. Medical Director, Central Texas Rehabilitation Hospital, Austin, TX, p. A594
GONZALES, Mike, Chief Financial Officer, Vibra Hospital of San Diego, San Diego, CA, p. A87
GONZALES, Mindy, Chief Human Resources Officer, Othello Community Hospital, Othello, WA, p. A681
GONZALES, Pamela, Administrator, Anson General Hospital, Anson, TX, p. A592
GONZALES, Rachel Ann, M.D., Chief Executive Officer, Madison Memorial Hospital, Rexburg, ID, p. A176
GONZALEZ, Agustin, Director Finance, Hospital Dr. Cayetano Coll Y Toste, Arecibo, PR, p. A719
GONZALEZ, Arthur A., FACHE, Chief Executive Officer, Denver Health, Denver, CO, p. A101
GONZALEZ, Aurelio, Chief Financial Officer, University Hospital and Medical Center, Tamarac, FL, p. A144
GONZALEZ, David, M.D. Medical Director, Brook Lane Health Services, Hagerstown, MD, p. A298
GONZALEZ, David, Chief Clinical Officer, Victory Surgical Hospital East Houston, Houston, TX, p. A623
GONZALEZ, Dinah L., Chief Financial Officer, Knapp Medical Center, Weslaco, TX, p. A651
GONZALEZ, Elizabeth, Chief Financial Officer, Hospital Metropolitano Dr. Tito Mattei, Yauco, PR, p. A724
GONZALEZ, Erin, Director Chief Human Resources, Abrazo Maryvale Campus, Phoenix, AZ, p. A34
GONZALEZ, Hugo, M.D. Chief Medical Officer, Sister Emmanuel Hospital, Miami, FL, p. A135
GONZALEZ, Jacqueline, Senior Vice President and Chief Nursing Officer, Nicklaus Children's Hospital, Miami, FL, p. A134
GONZALEZ, Jaime, Administrator, St. Catherine's Rehabilitation Hospital, North Miami, FL, p. A136
GONZALEZ, Joni, Controller, Kindred Hospital Dallas Central, Dallas, TX, p. A605
GONZALEZ, Jorge F., M.D
Chief Medical Officer, Florida Hospital Heartland Medical Center, Sebring, FL, p. A143
Vice President and Chief Nursing Officer, Florida Hospital Wauchula, Wauchula, FL, p. A146
GONZALEZ, Jorge Matta, Executive Director, University Hospital, San Juan, PR, p. A724
GONZALEZ, Laura, Interim Chief Nurse Executive, South Shore Hospital, Chicago, IL, p. A184
GONZALEZ, Pedro J., FACHE, Chief Executive Officer, Ashford Presbyterian Community Hospital, San Juan, PR, p. A723
GONZALEZ, Rainier, Chairman and Chief Executive Officer, Pacer Health Corporation, Miami Lakes, FL, p. B102
GONZALEZ, Richard, Chief Executive Officer, The Medical Center of Southeast Texas, Port Arthur, TX, p. A637
GONZALEZ, Roberto, Executive Director Human Resources, Hoboken University Medical Center, Hoboken, NJ, p. A412
GONZALEZ, Susan, Director of Clinical Services, Stanislaus Surgical Hospital, Modesto, CA, p. A76
GONZALEZ–FAJARDO, Ana, Human Resources Director, Palmetto General Hospital, Hialeah, FL, p. A128
GOOCH, Chris, Information Technology Director, Hermann Area District Hospital, Hermann, MO, p. A368
GOOD, Jo, Director of Nursing, Palmetto Lowcountry Behavioral Health, Charleston, SC, p. A558
GOOD, Scott, Manager Information Services, Kearny County Hospital, Lakin, KS, p. A244
GOOD, Vance A., M.D. Chief Medical Staff, Troy Community Hospital, Troy, PA, p. A551
GOODALL, David, M.D. Chief Medical Staff, Essentia Health–Deer River, Deer River, MN, p. A337
GOODBALIAN, Terry
Vice President Finance and Chief Financial Officer, Henry Ford Macomb Hospitals, Clinton Township, MI, p. A316
Regional Chief Financial Officer, Henry Ford West Bloomfield Hospital, West Bloomfield, MI, p. A332
Vice President, Finance and Chief Financial Officer, Henry Ford Wyandotte Hospital, Wyandotte, MI, p. A332
GOODE, Lori, Director Human Resources, Baptist Memorial Hospital–Union County, New Albany, MS, p. A358
GOODE, Shayne, Administrator, Post Acute/Warm Springs Specialty Hospital of New Braunfels, New Braunfels, TX, p. A634
GOODE, Vicky, Director Human Resources, LifeCare Hospitals of North Carolina, Rocky Mount, NC, p. A467
GOODELL, Thomas, M.D. Chief of Staff, Mt. San Rafael Hospital, Trinidad, CO, p. A109
GOODEMOTE, Patricia, M.D. Chief Medical Officer, Cass County Memorial Hospital, Atlantic, IA, p. A222
GOODENBERY, Jason, Administrative Assistant III, Alaska Psychiatric Institute, Anchorage, AK, p. A27
GOODHAND, Melony W.
Regional Chief Financial Officer, Presence Saint Joseph Medical Center, Joliet, IL, p. A192
Chief Financial Officer, Presence St. Mary's Hospital, Kankakee, IL, p. A192
GOODING, Lari, MBA Chief Executive Officer, Allendale County Hospital, Fairfax, SC, p. A560
GOODISON, Sharon A., R.N. Chief Nursing Officer, Jackson Hospital and Clinic, Montgomery, AL, p. A23
GOODLETT, Lisa, Senior Vice President and Chief Financial Officer, Laurel Regional Hospital, Laurel, MD, p. A299
GOODMAN, Brenda, Chief Nursing Officer, Medical Center of Peach County, Navicent Health, Fort Valley, GA, p. A158
GOODMAN, David M., Ph.D. Chief Information Officer, Veterans Affairs Boston Healthcare System, Boston, MA, p. A304
GOODMAN, Doug, Vice President Human Resources, Brandon Regional Hospital, Brandon, FL, p. A122
GOODMAN, Larry J., M.D., Chief Executive Officer, Rush University Medical Center, Chicago, IL, p. B115
GOODMAN, Larry J., M.D., Chief Executive Officer, Rush University Medical Center, Chicago, IL, p. A184
GOODMAN, Louis, Senior Vice President Human Resources, Monongahela Valley Hospital, Monongahela, PA, p. A540
GOODMAN, Mary Jo, Chief Operating Officer, Park Plaza Hospital, Houston, TX, p. A621
GOODMAN, Steven, Chief Operating Officer, Willow Crest Hospital, Miami, OK, p. A509
GOODMAN, William H., Vice President Medical Affairs, Chief Medical Officer, Catholic Medical Center, Manchester, NH, p. A407
GOODNOW, John H., Chief Executive Officer, Benefis Health System, Great Falls, MT, p. B23
GOODNOW, John H., Chief Executive Officer, Benefis Hospitals, Great Falls, MT, p. A384
GOODPASTER, Amber, Chief Financial Officer, Clark Regional Medical Center, Winchester, KY, p. A267
GOODRICH, C. Harlan, Vice President and Chief Information Officer, MidMichigan Medical Center–Midland, Midland, MI, p. A325
GOODRICH, Zane, Vice President Finance, East Tennessee Children's Hospital, Knoxville, TN, p. A580
GOODROW, Darrin, Chief Information Officer, Alice Hyde Medical Center, Malone, NY, p. A436
GOODSON, Bradley R., Chief Executive Officer, Ochsner Medical Center – North Shore, Slidell, LA, p. A285
GOODSON, David, Chief Executive Officer, Select Specialty Hospital–Pensacola, Pensacola, FL, p. A140
GOODSON, Jacob, Director Information Technology, North Oaks Medical Center, Hammond, LA, p. A274
GOODSPEED, Darwin, Director, Sioux Falls Veterans Affairs Health Care System, Sioux Falls, SD, p. A572
GOODSTEIN, Ruth, Controller, HEALTHSOUTH Sunrise Rehabilitation Hospital, Sunrise, FL, p. A143
GOODWIN, Jeremy, M.D. President, Medical Staff, Monroe County Hospital, Forsyth, GA, p. A157
GOODWIN, Keith D., President and Chief Executive Officer, East Tennessee Children's Hospital, Knoxville, TN, p. A580
GOODWIN, W. Jarrad, M.D. Director, University of Miami Hospital and Clinics, Miami, FL, p. A135
GOOLSBY, Elizabeth, Director, Fayetteville Veterans Affairs Medical Center, Fayetteville, NC, p. A460
GORANSON, Ken, Chief Financial Officer, Benson Hospital, Benson, AZ, p. A30
GORBACH, Debbie, Vice President and Treasurer, Edwin Shaw Rehab, Cuyahoga Falls, OH, p. A487
GORBY, David R., M.D. Vice President Quality and Patient Safety, Nash Health Care Systems, Rocky Mount, NC, p. A467
GORCZYCA, Julie A., R.N. Chief Nursing Officer, Genesys Regional Medical Center, Grand Blanc, MI, p. A320
GORDIAN, Michael, Chief Financial Officer, Western Plains Medical Complex, Dodge City, KS, p. A239
GORDON, Cynthia, R.N., Chief Executive Officer, Shasta Regional Medical Center, Redding, CA, p. A82
GORDON, Dan, Chief Financial Officer, Feather River Hospital, Paradise, CA, p. A80
GORDON, Jackie, Chief Clinical Officer, Kindred Hospital Dallas Central, Dallas, TX, p. A605
GORDON, Jacqueline, R.N. Chief Nursing Officer, CHI St. Luke's Health Memorial Livingston, Livingston, TX, p. A628
GORDON, John Mark, Administrator, Chatuge Regional Hospital and Nursing Home, Hiawassee, GA, p. A158
GORDON, Kevin, M.D. Chief of Staff, AllianceHealth Durant, Durant, OK, p. A506
GORDON, Mark, Chief Nursing Officer, Kern Valley Healthcare District, Lake Isabella, CA, p. A67
GORDON, Mark M., Chief Executive Officer, Bon Secours St. Francis Medical Center, Midlothian, VA, p. A668
GORDON, Nancy Gail, R.N. CNO and VP of Nursing, Baptist Health South Florida, Homestead Hospital, Homestead, FL, p. A129
GORDON, Robert, Manager Information Systems, Halifax Regional Medical Center, Roanoke Rapids, NC, p. A467
GORDON, Steve, Director Human Resources, Lake City Medical Center, Lake City, FL, p. A131
GORDON, Steve, M.D
Chief Medical Officer, Salem Hospital, Salem, OR, p. A526
Chief Medical Officer, West Valley Hospital, Dallas, OR, p. A520
GORDON, Steven R., President and Chief Executive Officer, Brattleboro Memorial Hospital, Brattleboro, VT, p. A660
GORDON, Susan, R.N. Chief Nursing Officer, Memorial Hospital, York, PA, p. A554
GORDON, Thomas, Chief Information Officer, Virtua Marlton, Marlton, NJ, p. A414
GORDON, Wayne
Chief Financial Officer, Memorial Hermann Rehabilitation Hospital – Katy, Katy, TX, p. A625
Chief Financial Officer, TIRR Memorial Hermann, Houston, TX, p. A622
GORDY, Joseph S., President, Flagler Hospital, Saint Augustine, FL, p. A141
GORE, Gary R., Chief Executive Officer, Marshall Health System, Guntersville, AL, p. B86
GORE, Tim, Chief Financial Officer, Rivendell Behavioral Health, Bowling Green, KY, p. A254
GOREAU, Judy, R.N. Director of Nursing, Eastside Psychiatric Hospital, Tallahassee, FL, p. A144
GOREY, Peter, Administrative Coordinator, Rockland Children's Psychiatric Center, Orangeburg, NY, p. A446
GORLEWSKI, Todd, Senior Vice President and Chief Financial Officer, St. Barnabas Hospital, NY, p. A444
GORMAN, Brandon, Controller, Bradley County Medical Center, Warren, AR, p. A51
GORMAN, Jodie, Director Human Resources, Salem Memorial District Hospital, Salem, MO, p. A378
GORMAN, Kathleen, MSN Executive Vice President Patient Care Services and Chief Operating Officer, Children's National Medical Center, Washington, DC, p. A119
GORMAN, Matt, Administrator, Polk Medical Center, Cedartown, GA, p. A153
GORMAN, Patricia, Chief Nurse Executive, Chinle Comprehensive Health Care Facility, Chinle, AZ, p. A30
GORMLEY, Ann H., Vice President Human Resources, Pinnacle Health System, Harrisburg, PA, p. A535
GORMLEY, Maureen E., R.N. Chief Operating Officer, National Institutes of Health Clinical Center, Bethesda, MD, p. A296
GORMSEN, David, D.O. Chief Medical Officer, Mercy Medical Center, Canton, OH, p. A481

Index of Health Care Professionals

Index of Health Care Professionals / Gorn

GORN, Angela, Vice President, Norton Sound Regional Hospital, Nome, AK, p. A28
GORS, Ann, Chief Executive Officer, Kentfield Rehabilitation and Specialty Hospital, Kentfield, CA, p. A65
GORSKI, William R., M.D., President and Chief Executive Officer, SwedishAmerican Hospital, A Division of UW Health, Rockford, IL, p. A200
GORSKI, Yara, M.D. Chief of Staff, Southwest Healthcare System, Murrieta, CA, p. A77
GORY, James, Chief Financial Officer, Northwest Medical Center, Winfield, AL, p. A26
GOSCH, Shawn, Chief Financial Officer, Burgess Health Center, Onawa, IA, p. A232
GOSEY, J., M.D. Medical Director, Southern Surgical Hospital, Slidell, LA, p. A285
GOSHE, Nick, Chief Executive Officer, Rangely District Hospital, Rangely, CO, p. A108
GOSHIA, Rob, Chief Financial Officer, Paulding County Hospital, Paulding, OH, p. A496
GOSLEE, Belle, Chief Nursing Officer, HEALTHSOUTH Chesapeake Rehabilitation Hospital, Salisbury, MD, p. A300
GOSLINE, Peter L., Chief Administrative Officer, Upper Connecticut Valley Hospital, Colebrook, NH, p. A405
GOSNEY, Brett, Chief Executive Officer, Animas Surgical Hospital, Durango, CO, p. A102
GOSS, Darin, Administrator, Mayo Clinic Hospital, Phoenix, AZ, p. A35
GOSS, J. Richard, M.D. Medical Director, UW Medicine/Harborview Medical Center, Seattle, WA, p. A684
GOSS, Norma, R.N. Chief Operating Officer and Chief Nursing Officer, Flaget Memorial Hospital, Bardstown, KY, p. A254
GOSS, Roger, Director, Information Services, North Sunflower Medical Center, Ruleville, MS, p. A360
GOSSENS, Kevin, Director Human Resources, Riverside Medical Center, Waupaca, WI, p. A713
GOSSETT, Lisa, MSN Chief Nursing Officer, OhioHealth Riverside Methodist Hospital, Columbus, OH, p. A486
GOTSOULIAS, Kostas, Interim Chief Executive Officer, Aspire Hospital, Conroe, TX, p. A602
GOTTI, Sreekant, Director Information Systems, Desert Valley Hospital, Victorville, CA, p. A96
GOTTLIEB, Harold, M.D. Chief Medical Officer, Memorial Hermann Memorial City Medical Center, Houston, TX, p. A621
GOTTLIEB, Jonathan, M.D. Senior Vice President and Chief Medical Officer, University of Maryland Medical Center, Baltimore, MD, p. A295
GOUGEON, Michele L., Executive Vice President and Chief Operating Officer, McLean Hospital, Belmont, MA, p. A302
GOUGH, Galal S., M.D. Chief of Staff, Coast Plaza Hospital, Norwalk, CA, p. A78
GOULD, Brian, Director Information System, Carson Valley Medical Center, Gardnerville, NV, p. A400
GOULD, Jacquelyn M., MS Vice President Patient Care Services and Chief Nursing Officer, The Good Samaritan Hospital, Lebanon, PA, p. A538
GOULD, Tamara, R.N. Director of Nursing, Wabash General Hospital, Mount Carmel, IL, p. A195
GOULD, William R., Vice President Human Resources, Saint Joseph Hospital, Denver, CO, p. A102
GOULET, James P., Vice President Operations, Columbus Community Hospital, Columbus, NE, p. A391
GOULSON, Dan, M.D. Chief Medical Officer, Our Lady of Bellefonte Hospital, Ashland, KY, p. A254
GOURLEY, Paul, M.D. Chief Hospital Services, U. S. Air Force Hospital, Hampton, VA, p. A666
GOUSE, Beth, Ph.D., Interim Chief Executive Officer, Saint Elizabeths Hospital, Washington, DC, p. A120
GOVE, Cynthia A., Chief Operating Officer, Hampstead Hospital, Hampstead, NH, p. A406
GOVINDAIAH, Rajesh G., M.D. Chief Medical Officer, Memorial Medical Center, Springfield, IL, p. A201
GOVORCHIN, Pete, Vice President Operations, Midwestern Regional Medical Center, Zion, IL, p. A203
GOWDER, Mike, Chief Executive Officer, Union General Hospital, Blairsville, GA, p. A152
GOWDER, Mike, Chief Executive Officer, Union General Hospital, Inc., Blairsville, GA, p. B139
GOWEN, Tina, System Controller, Westfield Memorial Hospital, Westfield, NY, p. A454
GOWER, Gary, Chief Information Officer, Appling Healthcare System, Baxley, GA, p. A152
GOYAL, Alok, M.D. Medical Director, Post Acute Medical Specialty Hospital of Milwaukee, Greenfield, WI, p. A702
GOYAL, Deepak, M.D. Chief of Staff, Jacobson Memorial Hospital Care Center, Elgin, ND, p. A473
GOYTIA–LEOS, Dina, M.D. Chief of Staff, Nix Health Care System, San Antonio, TX, p. A641
GOZA, Brian, Chief Information Officer, Hemphill County Hospital, Canadian, TX, p. A600
GOZIAH, Vicky, Software Administrator, Select Specialty Hospital – Northeast Atlanta, Atlanta, GA, p. A151
GRABER, Donald, M.D. Medical Director, Richmond State Hospital, Richmond, IN, p. A219
GRABUS, Christina, R.N. Chief Nursing Officer, Novant Health Thomasville Medical Center, Thomasville, NC, p. A469
GRACE, Jeffery, M.D. Clinical Director, Buffalo Psychiatric Center, Buffalo, NY, p. A430
GRACE, Michael, President, UPMC Mercy, Pittsburgh, PA, p. A547
GRACE, Richard, Chief Administrative Officer, Mayo Clinic Health System in Saint James, Saint James, MN, p. A346
GRACE, Terry, Director Information Technology, Logan County Hospital, Oakley, KS, p. A247
GRACE, Walter, Chief Executive Officer and Administrator, Baptist Memorial Hospital–Union County, New Albany, MS, p. A358
GRACER, Erik, M.D. Chief of Staff, San Ramon Regional Medical Center, San Ramon, CA, p. A90
GRACIE, Michael, Chief Information Officer, Veterans Health Care System of the Ozarks, Fayetteville, AR, p. A44
GRADDY, Steve W.
Chief Financial Officer, Freeman Hospital West, Joplin, MO, p. A369
Chief Financial Officer, Freeman Neosho Hospital, Neosho, MO, p. A373
GRADY, John M., Associate Director, Veterans Affairs Hudson Valley Health Care System, Montrose, NY, p. A438
GRADY, Kevin, M.D. Chief Medical Officer, St. John Hospital and Medical Center, Detroit, MI, p. A318
GRADY, Raymond, FACHE, President and Chief Executive Officer, Methodist Hospitals, Gary, IN, p. A209
GRAEBER, Tod
Administrator, Community Memorial Hospital, Turtle Lake, ND, p. A476
Administrator, Garrison Memorial Hospital, Garrison, ND, p. A474
GRAEBNER, David, President, Aurora Sheboygan Memorial Medical Center, Sheboygan, WI, p. A710
GRAEBNER, Nancy Kay, President and Chief Executive Officer, St. Joseph Mercy Chelsea, Chelsea, MI, p. A316
GRAF, John, Senior Vice President, Watertown Regional Medical Center, Watertown, WI, p. A712
GRAFF, Ann, Vice President System Human Resources, Benefis Hospitals, Great Falls, MT, p. A384
GRAGG, Connie, Director Human Resources, Saint Mary's Regional Medical Center, Russellville, AR, p. A50
GRAGNOLATI, Brian A., FACHE, President and Chief Executive Officer, Atlantic Health System, Morristown, NJ, p. B15
GRAH, John A., FACHE, Chief Executive Officer, Des Peres Hospital, Saint Louis, MO, p. A376
GRAHAM, Bill, President, Sequoia Hospital, Redwood City, CA, p. A83
GRAHAM, Bonnie S., Director, San Francisco VA Medical Center, San Francisco, CA, p. A88
GRAHAM, Brenda, Chief Nursing Officer, Knox County Hospital, Barbourville, KY, p. A254
GRAHAM, Brooke, Human Resources Manager, Franklin Woods Community Hospital, Johnson City, TN, p. A579
GRAHAM, C. Scott, D.O. Chief of Staff, Lake District Hospital, Lakeview, OR, p. A522
GRAHAM, Christopher W., Chief Financial Officer, Community Memorial Hospital, Hamilton, NY, p. A434
GRAHAM, Connie, Public Information Officer, Mercy Health Love County, Marietta, OK, p. A509
GRAHAM, David B., M.D. Senior Vice President and Chief Information Officer, Memorial Medical Center, Springfield, IL, p. A201
GRAHAM, Jay, Interim Chief Financial Officer, Brandywine Hospital, Coatesville, PA, p. A531
GRAHAM, Jeff
Market Leader and President, Mercy Health – Anderson Hospital, Cincinnati, OH, p. A483
Market Leader and President, Mercy Health – Clermont Hospital, Batavia, OH, p. A479
GRAHAM, John, M.D. Vice President Medical Affairs, Day Kimball Hospital, Putnam, CT, p. A114
GRAHAM, Jon, Chief Financial Officer, Vidant Roanoke–Chowan Hospital, Ahoskie, NC, p. A455
GRAHAM, Kathryn, Director Communications and Community Relations, Novato Community Hospital, Novato, CA, p. A78
GRAHAM, Kenneth D., FACHE, President, North Hawaii Community Hospital, Kamuela, HI, p. A169
GRAHAM, Kimberley, R.N. Chief Nursing Officer and Chief Operating Officer, Broward Health Coral Springs, Coral Springs, FL, p. A124
GRAHAM, Larry M., FACHE, President and Chief Executive Officer, Lake Charles Memorial Hospital, Lake Charles, LA, p. A278
GRAHAM, Michelle, M.D
Vice President Medical Affairs, Wheaton Franciscan Healthcare – Franklin, Franklin, WI, p. A701
Vice President Medical Affairs, Wheaton Franciscan Healthcare – St. Francis, Milwaukee, WI, p. A707
GRAHAM, Scott, Chief Executive Officer, Three Rivers Hospital, Brewster, WA, p. A677
GRAHAM, Shauna, Director of Professional Services Human Resources, Marketing Foundation, Litzenberg Memorial County Hospital, Central City, NE, p. A390
GRAHAM, Sheri
Director Human Resources and Administrative Services, Parkland Health Center – Liberty Street, Farmington, MO, p. A367
Administrative Director Human Resources and Volunteer Services Associate Ethics and Compliance Officer, Parkland Health Center – Weber Road, Farmington, MO, p. A367
Director Human Resources and Administrative Services, Parkland Health Center–Bonne Terre, Bonne Terre, MO, p. A363
GRAHAM, Sonja, Chief Executive Officer, North Oak Regional Medical Center, Senatobia, MS, p. A360
GRAHAM, Susan, R.N. Nurse Executive, HealthSource Saginaw, Inc., Saginaw, MI, p. A329
GRAHAM, Yolanda, M.D. Medical Director, Devereux Georgia Treatment Network, Kennesaw, GA, p. A159
GRAMBY, Tiffany, Senior Director Information Management and Privacy Officer, Barnesville Hospital, Barnesville, OH, p. A479
GRAMER, Johanna, Director Human Resources, Mimbres Memorial Hospital, Deming, NM, p. A424
GRAMZA, Jeanne, Director Finance, Wheaton Franciscan Healthcare – All Saints, Racine, WI, p. A709
GRANADO–VILLAR, Deise, M.D. Chief Medical Officer and Senior Vice President Medical Affairs, Nicklaus Children's Hospital, Miami, FL, p. A134
GRANATO, Jerome, M.D
Senior Vice President and Chief Medical Officer, Excela Frick Hospital, Mount Pleasant, PA, p. A541
Senior Vice President and Chief Medical Officer, Excela Health Westmoreland Hospital, Greensburg, PA, p. A535
GRAND, Lawrence N., Executive Vice President and Chief Operating Officer, Hunterdon Medical Center, Flemington, NJ, p. A412
GRANDIOSI, Joe, Director Information Technology, Southern Hills Hospital and Medical Center, Las Vegas, NV, p. A402
GRANER, Terry J., R.N. Vice President Patient Care, Abbott Northwestern Hospital, Minneapolis, MN, p. A342
GRANGER, Keith, President and Chief Executive Officer, Trinity Medical Center, Birmingham, AL, p. A17
GRANT, Cathy, R.N. Associate Vice President, Patient Services, DMC Huron Valley–Sinai Hospital, Commerce Township, MI, p. A317
GRANT, Chad M., President and Chief Executive Officer, McLaren Oakland, Pontiac, MI, p. A328
GRANT, Cheryl, Director Information Systems, Coastal Carolina Hospital, Hardeeville, SC, p. A562
GRANT, Debra, R.N. Chief Nursing Officer, Texas Health Harris Methodist Hospital Hurst–Euless–Bedford, Bedford, TX, p. A597
GRANT, Dianna, M.D. Vice President Medical Management, Advocate Trinity Hospital, Chicago, IL, p. A181
GRANT, Gail, Director Human Resources, CHI St. Francis Health, Breckenridge, MN, p. A336
GRANT, Howard R., M.D., President and Chief Executive Officer, Lahey Health, Burlington, MA, p. B80
GRANT, Mikki, Chief Information Officer, Fort Belknap U. S. Public Health Service Indian Hospital, Harlem, MT, p. A384
GRANT, Pauline, FACHE, Chief Executive Officer, Broward Health North, Deerfield Beach, FL, p. A125
GRANT, Samuel, Chief Financial Officer, Stephens Memorial Hospital, Breckenridge, TX, p. A598
GRANT, Tonya, Director Human Resources, Westlake Regional Hospital, Columbia, KY, p. A255
GRANT, Will, Chief Financial Officer, Cannon Memorial Hospital, Pickens, SC, p. A564
GRANTHAM, Charlie, Manager Information Systems, Carolinas Hospital System Marion, Mullins, SC, p. A563
GRANTHAM, James, Administrator and Chief Executive Officer, Baptist Memorial Hospital–Booneville, Booneville, MS, p. A351
GRANVILLE, Brian, Director Information Technology, Buena Vista Regional Medical Center, Storm Lake, IA, p. A235
GRANVILLE, Sabrina M., Senior Vice President and Chief Human Resources Officer, Lowell General Hospital, Lowell, MA, p. A308
GRANZOTTI, Maria, M.D. Chief Physician Executive, Central Illinois Division, HSHS St. Mary's Hospital, Streator, IL, p. A202
GRANZOW, Steven L., Chief Executive Officer, Lincoln County Hospital, Lincoln, KS, p. A245

A852 Index of Health Care Professionals

Index of Health Care Professionals / Gregonis

Index of Health Care Professionals


GRASER, David, Vice President and Chief Information Officer, Hillcrest Hospital – South, Tulsa, OK, p. A516
GRASSER, Tierney Lynn, Senior Vice President and Chief Financial Officer, Olathe Medical Center, Olathe, KS, p. A247
GRATCH, Amie, Director Financial Services, LifeCare Hospitals of Dallas, Dallas, TX, p. A605
GRATZ, Silvia, D.O. Chief Medical Officer, Fairmount Behavioral Health System, Philadelphia, PA, p. A543
GRAU, Leah, Director Human Resources, Tulane Medical Center, New Orleans, LA, p. A282
GRAUER, David, Chief Executive Officer and Administrator, Intermountain Medical Center, Murray, UT, p. A656
GRAUMANN, Julie, Director, AllianceHealth Clinton, Clinton, OK, p. A505
GRAVELY, Sean, D.O. Chief of Staff, Nevada Regional Medical Center, Nevada, MO, p. A373
GRAVES, Amanda, Chief Information Systems, Washington DC Veterans Affairs Medical Center, Washington, DC, p. A120
GRAVES, Bruce, M.D. Chief of Staff, Hale Ho'ola Hamakua, Honokaa, HI, p. A168
GRAVES, Buddy, Chief Information Officer, Southern Surgical Hospital, Slidell, LA, p. A285
GRAVES, Deanna, Chief Executive Officer, Texas Specialty Hospital at Lubbock, Lubbock, TX, p. A630
GRAVES, Jared, Chief Financial Officer, Byrd Regional Hospital, Leesville, LA, p. A279
GRAVES, Jennifer, MS, Chief Executive, Swedish/Edmonds, Edmonds, WA, p. A678
GRAVES, Jimmy, Interim Chief Executive Officer, Jefferson Davis Community Hospital, Prentiss, MS, p. A359
GRAVES, John A., Chief Executive Officer, Lillian M. Hudspeth Memorial Hospital, Sonora, TX, p. A644
GRAY, Albert, Chief Executive Officer, The Children's Center Rehabilitation Hospital, Bethany, OK, p. A504
GRAY, Anthony, Chief Financial Officer, LAC–Olive View–UCLA Medical Center, CA, p. A71
GRAY, Bob, Chief Financial Officer, Aspire Hospital, Conroe, TX, p. A602
GRAY, Carrie, Director of Nursing, Riverview Behavioral Health, Texarkana, AR, p. A51
GRAY, Clarence, Chief Financial Officer, TriStar Horizon Medical Center, Dickson, TN, p. A577
GRAY, David L., FACHE, President, Baptist Health Louisville, Louisville, KY, p. A260
GRAY, Eric, Chief Financial Officer, HEALTHSOUTH Rehabilitation Hospital of Memphis, Memphis, TN, p. A583
GRAY, Gary, D.O., Interim Chief Executive Officer and Chief Medical Officer, Natividad Medical Center, Salinas, CA, p. A85
GRAY, James, M.D. Chief Medical Service, Amarillo Veterans Affairs Health Care System, Amarillo, TX, p. A591
GRAY, Jason, M.D. Chief Medical Officer, Mercy Medical Center, Roseburg, OR, p. A525
GRAY, Jeremy, Chief Operating Officer, Fort Walton Beach Medical Center, Fort Walton Beach, FL, p. A127
GRAY, Jerry, Interim Chief Executive Officer, HEALTHSOUTH East Valley Rehabilitation Hospital, Mesa, AZ, p. A33
GRAY, Judy
Vice President Human Resources, Albany Memorial Hospital, Albany, NY, p. A428
Vice President Human Resources, St. Peter's Hospital, Albany, NY, p. A428
GRAY, Karen D., Director Human Resources, Vibra Hospital of Southeastern Michigan, LLC, Lincoln Park, MI, p. A324
GRAY, Larry, President, Baptist Health Corbin, Corbin, KY, p. A255
GRAY, Marty, R.N. Director of Nursing, Wyandot Memorial Hospital, Upper Sandusky, OH, p. A499
GRAY, Mary, Director Human Resources, Lehigh Regional Medical Center, Lehigh Acres, FL, p. A132
GRAY, Michelle
Nurse Executive, Atrium Medical Center of Corinth, Corinth, TX, p. A602
Vice President and Regional Chief Information Officer, Rex Healthcare, Raleigh, NC, p. A467
GRAY, Mike, Corporate Vice President Human Resources, East Texas Medical Center Tyler, Tyler, TX, p. A649
GRAY, Patricia, Director Health Information Management, Cumberland Hall Hospital, Hopkinsville, KY, p. A258
GRAY, Roshanda, Assistant Administrator, Memorial Medical Center, Port Lavaca, TX, p. A638
GRAY, Sarah, Vice President Information Services, East Alabama Medical Center, Opelika, AL, p. A23
GRAY, Stephen, Chief Administrative Officer, Sutter Maternity and Surgery Center of Santa Cruz, Santa Cruz, CA, p. A91
GRAY, Tami, Chief Financial Officer, Irwin County Hospital, Ocilla, GA, p. A162
GRAY, Teresa, Chief Nursing Officer and Assistant Vice President, INTEGRIS Canadian Valley Hospital, Yukon, OK, p. A518
GRAY, Terry, Vice President Human Resources, Emanuel Medical Center, Turlock, CA, p. A95
GRAY, Thomas, M.D. Medical Director, Montana State Hospital, Warm Springs, MT, p. A387
GRAY, Tracy
Chief Information Officer, Grady General Hospital, Cairo, GA, p. A153
Senior Vice President Information Services, John D. Archbold Memorial Hospital, Thomasville, GA, p. A166
Chief Information Officer, Mitchell County Hospital, Camilla, GA, p. A153
GRAYBEAL, Phillip
Chief Financial Officer, Page Memorial Hospital, Luray, VA, p. A667
Chief Financial Officer, Warren Memorial Hospital, Front Royal, VA, p. A665
GRAYBILL, Matthew P., Chief Operating Officer, Children's Medical Center, Dayton, OH, p. A487
GRAYSON, Barbara, Vice President Human Resources, Mercy Hospital Washington, Washington, MO, p. A380
GREASON, Linda, Vice President Human Resources, Milford Regional Medical Center, Milford, MA, p. A309
GREBOSKY, Jamie, M.D. Vice President of Medical Affairs, Asante Rogue Regional Medical Center, Medford, OR, p. A523
GRECO, Andrew, Chief Financial Officer, Calvary Hospital, NY, p. A439
GRECO, Anthony C., Compliance Officer, Essex County Hospital Center, Cedar Grove, NJ, p. A410
GRECO, Margaret, Chief Human Resources, Keller Army Community Hospital, West Point, NY, p. A453
GREELEY, Donna, Director Human Resources, Spalding Rehabilitation Hospital, Aurora, CO, p. A99
GREEN, Amber, R.N. Chief Clinical Officer, Memorial Hospital of Carbon County, Rawlins, WY, p. A717
GREEN, Arnold, Senior Vice President and Chief Operating Officer, McLeod Loris Seacoast Hospital, Loris, SC, p. A563
GREEN, Babatunde O., Chief Executive Officer, Connecticut Veterans Home and Hospital, Rocky Hill, CT, p. A114
GREEN, Barbara, Director Human Resources, O'Connor Hospital, Delhi, NY, p. A432
GREEN, Calvin, Chief Executive Officer, Oakdale Community Hospital, Oakdale, LA, p. A283
GREEN, Christopher, M.D. Senior Vice President Medical Affairs and Associate Dean Hospital Affairs, University of Wisconsin Hospital and Clinics, Madison, WI, p. A704
GREEN, Darryl, Director Administration, Naval Hospital Jacksonville, Jacksonville, FL, p. A129
GREEN, David, Chief Human Resources, West Palm Beach Veterans Affairs Medical Center, West Palm Beach, FL, p. A147
GREEN, David F., M.D. Chief Medical Officer, Concord Hospital, Concord, NH, p. A405
GREEN, Debra Jane, R.N. Director of Nursing, Turquoise Lodge Hospital, Albuquerque, NM, p. A423
GREEN, Gail P., R.N. Chief Nursing Officer, St. Vincent's Medical Center Riverside, Jacksonville, FL, p. A130
GREEN, Garry Kim, FACHE, Administrator, Shriners Hospitals for Children–Shreveport, Shreveport, LA, p. A285
GREEN, Gene E., M.D., President, Suburban Hospital, Bethesda, MD, p. A296
GREEN, Jack W., Administrator, Antelope Memorial Hospital, Neligh, NE, p. A394
GREEN, Jodie L., Chief Nursing Officer, Select Long Term Care Hospital – Colorado Springs, Colorado Springs, CO, p. A101
GREEN, Jody, Chief Quality Manager, Sanpete Valley Hospital, Mount Pleasant, UT, p. A656
GREEN, John
Vice President Professional Services and Facility Planning, Iredell Memorial Hospital, Statesville, NC, p. A469
Vice President Finance, St. Peter's Hospital, Helena, MT, p. A384
GREEN, Julie, Vice President Human Resources, Cheshire Medical Center, Keene, NH, p. A406
GREEN, Karen, Chief Information Officer, Brooks Rehabilitation Hospital, Jacksonville, FL, p. A129
GREEN, Kaye, FACHE, Director, W. G. (Bill) Heffner Veterans Affairs Medical Center, Salisbury, NC, p. A468
GREEN, Ladonna, Director Human Resources, Glen Rose Medical Center, Glen Rose, TX, p. A616
GREEN Jr., Larry D., Chief Executive Officer, Windhaven Psychiatric Hospital, Prescott Valley, AZ, p. A36
GREEN, Marsha, Chief Executive Officer, Essentia Health–Deer River, Deer River, MN, p. A337
GREEN, Patrick, Chief Operating Officer, St. Anthony Hospital, Lakewood, CO, p. A106
GREEN, Paul, Chief Clinical Officer, Kindred Hospital–Aurora, Aurora, CO, p. A99
GREEN, Ricky, Senior Human Resources Business Partner, Spectrum Health Big Rapids Hospital, Big Rapids, MI, p. A315
GREEN, Rona,U. S. Naval Hospital Guam, Agana, GU, p. A719
GREEN, Ronnie, Director Information Systems, McBride Clinic Orthopedic Hospital, Oklahoma City, OK, p. A512
GREEN, Rose Marie, Director Human Resources, Humboldt General Hospital, Winnemucca, NV, p. A404
GREEN, Steve, Comptroller, Jasper General Hospital, Bay Springs, MS, p. A350
GREEN, Susan, Senior Vice President Finance, Chief Financial Officer, Lowell General Hospital, Lowell, MA, p. A308
GREEN, Tracy V., Chief Financial Officer, Metropolitan Hospital Center, New York, NY, p. A441
GREEN–LORENZEN, Susan, Senior Vice President Operations, Montefiore Mount Vernon, Mount Vernon, NY, p. A438
GREENBERG, Mark, M.D
Chief Medical Officer, Cape Coral Hospital, Cape Coral, FL, p. A123
Medical Director, Gulf Coast Medical Center, Fort Myers, FL, p. A127
GREENBERG, Raymond, M.D., Executive Vice Chancellor, University of Texas System, Austin, TX, p. B148
GREENBLATT, James, M.D. Chief Medical Officer, Vice President Medical Clinical Services, Walden Psychiatric Care, Waltham, MA, p. A312
GREENE, Arthur, M.D. Vice President Medical Affairs, Sentara CarePlex Hospital, Hampton, VA, p. A666
GREENE, Beth, Chief Operating Officer, Cherokee Indian Hospital, Cherokee, NC, p. A458
GREENE, Bradley, Chief Financial Officer, WellStar Douglas Hospital, Douglasville, GA, p. A156
GREENE, Cora, Chief Nursing Officer, Novant Health Rowan Medical Center, Salisbury, NC, p. A468
GREENE, Dustin, Chief Executive Officer, TriStar Horizon Medical Center, Dickson, TN, p. A577
GREENE, Erin, Coordinator Human Resources, Kindred Hospital–San Francisco Bay Area, San Leandro, CA, p. A90
GREENE, Hugh, President and Chief Executive Officer, Baptist Health, Jacksonville, FL, p. B19
GREENE, Kathleen, Director Human Resources, Promise Hospital of San Diego, San Diego, CA, p. A86
GREENE, Melodi, R.N. Chief Nursing Officer, Community Howard Regional Health, Kokomo, IN, p. A213
GREENE, Palmer, R.N. Chief Nursing Officer, Sierra Vista Hospital, Truth or Consequences, NM, p. A427
GREENE, Robert, Director Information Technology, Promise Hospital of Miss Lou, Vidalia, LA, p. A286
GREENE, Scott, Chief Information Officer, Gateway Medical Center, Clarksville, TN, p. A576
GREENE, Todd, Chief Executive Officer, Arizona Spine and Joint Hospital, Mesa, AZ, p. A33
GREENER, Angela, Chief Administrative Officer, West Jefferson Medical Center, Marrero, LA, p. A280
GREENFIELD, Tadd, Chief Nursing Officer, Great Plains Health, North Platte, NE, p. A395
GREENLEE, Kathryn M., R.N
Vice President, Clinical Services/CNO, ProMedica Bixby Hospital, Adrian, MI, p. A314
Vice President, Clinical Services/CNO, ProMedica Herrick Hospital, Tecumseh, MI, p. A331
GREENMAN, Sharon, Director Human Resources, Melissa Memorial Hospital, Holyoke, CO, p. A105
GREENWOOD, Sherri, Chief Nursing Officer, St. John's Hospital, Springfield, IL, p. A201
GREENWOOD, Susan, R.N. Vice President and Chief Nursing Officer, St. Bernards Medical Center, Jonesboro, AR, p. A46
GREER, Nancy, R.N. Vice President Nursing, Asante Three Rivers Medical Center, Grants Pass, OR, p. A521
GREER, Troy, Chief Executive Officer, Lovelace Medical Center, Albuquerque, NM, p. A422
GREEVER, Suzanne, Chief Executive Officer, North Central Surgical Center, Dallas, TX, p. A606
GREGERSEN, Glenn, Director Information Technology, District One Hospital, Faribault, MN, p. A338
GREGERSON, Scott, President and Chief Executive Officer, Stanford Health Care – ValleyCare, Pleasanton, CA, p. A81
GREGG, Richard, M.D. Medical Director, LifeCare Hospital of Dayton, Miamisburg, OH, p. A494
GREGG, Shawna, Director Human Resources, Porterville Developmental Center, Porterville, CA, p. A81
GREGG, Sherry, Chief Information Technology Officer, Beckley Veterans Affairs Medical Center, Beckley, WV, p. A689
GREGG, Thomas, Vice President Human Resources, St. Peter's Hospital, Helena, MT, p. A384
GREGG, Tom, Vice President Human Resources, CHI St. Alexius Health, Bismarck, ND, p. A472
GREGG, Travis, Director Support Services, Kearney Regional Medical Center, Kearney, NE, p. A393
GREGGAIN, Don, M.D. Physician Network Director, Tri–State Memorial Hospital, Clarkston, WA, p. A677
GREGONIS, Michael, Comptroller, Naval Hospital Jacksonville, Jacksonville, FL, p. A129


© 2015 AHA Guide Index of Health Care Professionals **A853**

Index of Health Care Professionals

Index of Health Care Professionals / Gregor


GREGOR, Brian, Manager Information Technology Operations, Glendale Memorial Hospital and Health Center, Glendale, CA, p. A63

GREGORIAN, Myra, Vice President and Chief Human Resources Officer, Children's Hospital Los Angeles, Los Angeles, CA, p. A69

GREGORICH, Miki, Director Human Resources, Pioneer Medical Center, Big Timber, MT, p. A381

GREGORIO, Felipe, Chief Nursing Officer, HEALTHSOUTH Rehabilitation Institute of San Antonio, San Antonio, TX, p. A640

GREGORY, Adina, Chief Operating Officer, Great Bend Regional Hospital, Great Bend, KS, p. A240

GREGORY, Audrey, MSN, Chief Executive Officer, Placentia–Linda Hospital, Placentia, CA, p. A81

GREGORY, Ben, Director, Walter B. Jones Alcohol and Drug Abuse Treatment Center, Greenville, NC, p. A461

GREGORY, Jan, Chief of Human Resources, Crittenden County Hospital, Marion, KY, p. A262

GREGORY, Jay, M.D. Chief Medical Officer, EASTAR Health System, Muskogee, OK, p. A510

GREGORY, Jim, Controller, Methodist Hospital of Chicago, Chicago, IL, p. A183

GREGORY, Sean, President, Health First Holmes Regional Medical Center, Melbourne, FL, p. A133

GREGORY, Shawn
- Chief Financial Officer, South Bay Hospital, Sun City Center, FL, p. A143
- Chief Financial Officer, St. Petersburg General Hospital, Saint Petersburg, FL, p. A142

GREGORY, Trip, Senior Vice President Human Resources, Palmetto Health Baptist, Columbia, SC, p. A559

GREGOS, Ruth, Director Finance, Shriners Hospitals for Children–Tampa, Tampa, FL, p. A145

GREIMAN, Alan W., Chief Executive Officer and President, Royal Oaks Hospital, Windsor, MO, p. A380

GREINER, Walter, Chief Financial Officer, AtlantiCare Regional Medical Center, Atlantic City, NJ, p. A409

GREINER, William, M.D. Chief of Staff, F. W. Huston Medical Center, Winchester, KS, p. A253

GREMILLION, Karen, R.N. Chief Nursing Officer, Opelousas General Health System, Opelousas, LA, p. A283

GRENALDO, Paul, Executive Vice President and Chief Operating Officer, Doctors Community Hospital, Lanham, MD, p. A298

GRENDON, M. Todd, M.D. President Medical Staff, Presence Saint Joseph Hospital, Chicago, IL, p. A183

GRENIER, Raymond, Chief Financial Officer, Memorial Medical Center, Las Cruces, NM, p. A425

GRENNAN, Jr., M. Joseph, M.D. Senior Vice President and Chief Medical Officer, Reading Hospital, West Reading, PA, p. A553

GRESKOVICH, William, Chief Information Officer, Saint Agnes Hospital, Baltimore, MD, p. A294

GRESLA, Mark S., M.D. Chief of Staff, Adams Memorial Hospital, Decatur, IN, p. A207

GRESSLE, Charles, Chief Executive Officer, Medical Center of Plano, Plano, TX, p. A637

GREW, Kate, MSN Vice President/Chief Nurse Executive, Carolinas HealthCare System NorthEast, Concord, NC, p. A458

GREW, Terry, Chief Business Office, Hampton Veterans Affairs Medical Center, Hampton, VA, p. A666

GREY, Curtis E., M.D. Chief of Staff, East Texas Medical Center Athens, Athens, TX, p. A593

GREY, Mitzi, Chief Operating Officer, Bath Community Hospital, Hot Springs, VA, p. A666

GRIBBIN, John, FACHE, President and Chief Executive Officer, CentraState Healthcare System, Freehold, NJ, p. A412

GRICE, William N., Executive Director, Kaiser Permanente Los Angeles Medical Center, Los Angeles, CA, p. A70

GRICUS, Peggy, R.N. Vice President, Patient Care Services and Chief Nursing Officer, Silver Cross Hospital, New Lenox, IL, p. A196

GRIDLEY, Mark, FACHE Executive Vice President and Chief Operating Officer, FHN Memorial Hospital, Freeport, IL, p. A188

GRIEB, Paula, R.N
- Vice President Patient Care Service and Chief Nursing Officer, ProMedica Bay Park Hospital, Oregon, OH, p. A496
- Chief Nursing Officer, ProMedica Fostoria Community Hospital, Fostoria, OH, p. A490

GRIEP, John, M.D. Chief Medical Director, St. Catherine Hospital, East Chicago, IN, p. A207

GRIER, Glennda, Chief Nursing Officer, Hot Springs County Memorial Hospital, Thermopolis, WY, p. A717

GRIESHEIM, Glen, Chief Executive Officer, Select Specialty Hospital–Des Moines, Des Moines, IA, p. A226

GRIESS, Dan, FACHE, Chief Executive Officer, Box Butte General Hospital, Alliance, NE, p. A389

GRIEST, Mary, Vice President Finance and Chief Financial Officer, Samaritan Regional Health System, Ashland, OH, p. A478

GRIFFEE, James, M.D. Chief Medical Officer, Slidell Memorial Hospital, Slidell, LA, p. A285

GRIFFES, Carol, Administrator, Duane L. Waters Hospital, Jackson, MI, p. A323

GRIFFES, John M., Chief Executive Officer, Select Specialty Hospital–Dallas, Carrollton, TX, p. A600

GRIFFIE, Lametria, Interim Chief Nursing Officer, HEALTHSOUTH Rehabilitation Hospital of Texarkana, Texarkana, TX, p. A647

GRIFFIN, Amy, Vice President Patient Care Services, John D. Archbold Memorial Hospital, Thomasville, GA, p. A166

GRIFFIN, Betty, Interim Chief Nursing Officer, Chester Regional Medical Center, Chester, SC, p. A558

GRIFFIN, Brad, Chief Executive Officer, Colleton Medical Center, Walterboro, SC, p. A565

GRIFFIN, Breanne, R.N. Executive Director, Nursing, Mercy Hospital Lincoln, Troy, MO, p. A379

GRIFFIN, Brian, Director Information Services, Springhill Medical Center, Springhill, LA, p. A286

GRIFFIN, Caleigh, Vice President Human Resources, Ferrell Hospital, Eldorado, IL, p. A186

GRIFFIN, Charles, Director of Nursing, Clay County Hospital, Ashland, AL, p. A15

GRIFFIN, Christopher B., Chief Executive Officer, D. W. McMillan Memorial Hospital, Brewton, AL, p. A17

GRIFFIN, Cindy
- Chief Nursing Officer, Liberty Dayton Regional Medical Center, Liberty, TX, p. A628
- Director Human Resources, Medical Center Barbour, Eufaula, AL, p. A19

GRIFFIN, Donald, CPA Chief Financial Officer, New London Hospital, New London, NH, p. A408

GRIFFIN, Holly, R.N. Chief Nursing Officer, Lady of the Sea General Hospital, Cut Off, LA, p. A272

GRIFFIN, James, Manager Information Systems, Martin General Hospital, Williamston, NC, p. A470

GRIFFIN, Jeannine, M.D. Chief of Staff, Memorial Medical Center, Port Lavaca, TX, p. A638

GRIFFIN, Jeff, Assistant Vice President Finance, Carolinas HealthCare System Anson, Wadesboro, NC, p. A470

GRIFFIN, Laura Jane, M.D. Chief Nursing Executive, Kindred Hospital Sugar Land, Sugar Land, TX, p. A645

GRIFFIN, Margaret Elizabeth, Chief Executive Officer, HonorHealth John C. Lincoln Medical Center, Phoenix, AZ, p. A35

GRIFFIN, Matthew, M.D. Vice President Medical Affairs, Sinai–Grace Hospital, Detroit, MI, p. A318

GRIFFIN, Paulette
- Vice President Human Resources, Detroit Receiving Hospital/University Health Center, Detroit, MI, p. A317
- Director Human Resources, Sinai–Grace Hospital, Detroit, MI, p. A318

GRIFFIN–JONES, Christie, R.N. Chief Nursing Officer, HealthSouth Rehabilitation Hospital of Humble, LLC, Humble, TX, p. A623

GRIFFIN–MAHON, Selena, Assistant Vice President Human Resources, Bronx–Lebanon Hospital Center Health Care System, NY, p. A438

GRIFFIS, Daniel, M.D. Chief Medical Officer, Syringa Hospital and Clinics, Grangeville, ID, p. A174

GRIFFITH, Barbara, M.D. Chief Medical Officer, Duke Regional Hospital, Durham, NC, p. A459

GRIFFITH, David, M.D. Medical Director, Texas Center for Infectious Disease, San Antonio, TX, p. A642

GRIFFITH, Dusty, Director Information Systems, Bolivar Medical Center, Cleveland, MS, p. A352

GRIFFITH, James D., Interim Chief Executive Officer, Tanner Medical Center–Carrollton, Carrollton, GA, p. A153

GRIFFITH, Jeanne, Chief Nursing Officer, Coryell Memorial Hospital, Gatesville, TX, p. A616

GRIFFITH, John H., Ph.D., President & Chief Executive Officer, Kedren Community Mental Health Center, Los Angeles, CA, p. A70

GRIFFITH, Patti, R.N. Chief Nursing Officer, Methodist Hospital for Surgery, Addison, TX, p. A590

GRIFFITH, Susan M., Chief Operations Officer, Eastern State Hospital, Lexington, KY, p. A259

GRIFFITH, Wes
- Director Information Technology, Hancock Medical Center, Bay Saint Louis, MS, p. A350
- Chief Financial Officer, Tennova Healthcare–LaFollette Medical Center, La Follette, TN, p. A581

GRIFFITHS, David, Senior Vice President and Chief Financial Officer, Regional West Medical Center, Scottsbluff, NE, p. A398

GRIFFITHS, Elaine, R.N. Chief Nursing Officer, Chesapeake Regional Medical Center, Chesapeake, VA, p. A663

GRIFFITHS, Mark
- Director Management Information Systems, Incline Village Community Hospital, Incline Village, NV, p. A401
- Chief Systems Innovation Officer, Tahoe Forest Hospital District, Truckee, CA, p. A95

GRIGG, Dan, Chief Executive Officer, Harney District Hospital, Burns, OR, p. A519

GRIGG, William E., Senior Vice President and Chief Financial Officer, Methodist Hospital of Southern California, Arcadia, CA, p. A54

GRIGGS, Stacie, MIS Analyst, North Mississippi Medical Center–West Point, West Point, MS, p. A361

GRIGSBY, Jan, Vice President and Chief Financial Officer, Springhill Memorial Hospital, Mobile, AL, p. A22

GRIGSON, John A., Vice President and Chief Financial Officer, Covenant Medical Center, Lubbock, TX, p. A629

GRILL, Laura D., R.N. Executive Vice President and Administrator, East Alabama Medical Center, Opelika, AL, p. A23

GRILLO, Jorge C., Chief Information Officer, Canton–Potsdam Hospital, Potsdam, NY, p. A448

GRIM, Andrew, Chief Financial Officer, San Gabriel Valley Medical Center, San Gabriel, CA, p. A89

GRIMALDI, Richard, President Medical Staff, Highlands Hospital, Connellsville, PA, p. A532

GRIMER, Ginny, Director Human Resources, George E. Weems Memorial Hospital, Apalachicola, FL, p. A121

GRIMES, Pam, Director Human Resources, AMG Specialty Hospital–Edmond, Edmond, OK, p. A506

GRIMES, Paula, R.N. Chief Nursing Officer, NEA Baptist Memorial Hospital, Jonesboro, AR, p. A46

GRIMES, Teresa G., Chief Executive Officer, Troy Regional Medical Center, Troy, AL, p. A25

GRIMES, Walter, Director Information Technology, Good Shepherd Medical Center–Marshall, Marshall, TX, p. A631

GRIMLEY, Karen A., R.N. Chief Nursing Officer, UC Irvine Medical Center, Orange, CA, p. A79

GRIMM, Tamara, R.N. Chief Clinical Officer and Chief Nursing Officer, Cornerstone Hospital of Bossier City, Bossier City, LA, p. A270

GRIMM, William, Director, Information Services, Marengo Memorial Hospital, UnityPoint Health, Marengo, IA, p. A231

GRIMMER, Michael, Chief Operating Officer, Athol Memorial Hospital, Athol, MA, p. A302

GRIMMETT, Teresa, Chief Executive Officer, Wayne Medical Center, Waynesboro, TN, p. A589

GRIMSHAW, Bruce P., FACHE, Chief Executive Officer, Southern California Hospital at Hollywood, Los Angeles, CA, p. A72

GRIMSHAW, Matthew, President, Mercy Medical Center, Williston, ND, p. A477

GRIMSLEY, Denise, Administrator, Florida Hospital Wauchula, Wauchula, FL, p. A146

GRINNELL, Steven, Chief Executive Officer, Lourdes Hospital, Paducah, KY, p. A264

GRINNEY, Jay F., President and Chief Executive Officer, HEALTHSOUTH Corporation, Birmingham, AL, p. B67

GRIPPEN, Glen W., Interim Medical Center Director, Phoenix Veterans Affairs Health Care System, Phoenix, AZ, p. A35

GRIPPI, Michael, M.D. Chief Medical Officer, Good Shepherd Penn Partners Specialty Hospital at Rittenhouse, Philadelphia, PA, p. A543

GRISH, John, Chief Financial Officer, Johnson Memorial Medical Center, Stafford Springs, CT, p. A115

GRISIER, Douglas, D.O. Medical Director, HEALTHSOUTH Rehabilitation Hospital of Erie, Erie, PA, p. A534

GRISNAK, Karen, R.N. Chief Operating Officer and Assistant Administrator Quality Services, Kaiser Permanente Vallejo Medical Center, Vallejo, CA, p. A96

GRISNER, Margaret, Chief Executive Officer, Kiowa District Hospital and Manor, Kiowa, KS, p. A244

GRISPINO, Frank, Vice President Operations, SSM Health St. Francis Hospital – Maryville, Maryville, MO, p. A372

GRISSINGER, Matthew, Site Manager Information Systems, Indian Path Medical Center, Kingsport, TN, p. A580

GRISSLER, Brian G., President and Chief Executive Officer, Stamford Hospital, Stamford, CT, p. A115

GRISSOM, Robyn, Director Employee Relations, OSF Saint Anthony's Health Center, Alton, IL, p. A178

GRISSOM, Tina, Chief Information Technology Officer, Arkansas State Hospital, Little Rock, AR, p. A47

GRISWOLD, Barbara, Chief Nursing Officer, Washington County Hospital and Clinics, Washington, IA, p. A235

GROCE, Jessika A., Director Human Resources, EvergreenHealth Monroe, Monroe, WA, p. A680

GROCE, Vicky, Chief Nursing Officer, Lincoln County Health System, Fayetteville, TN, p. A577


**A854** Index of Health Care Professionals 

GULRICH, Erica, Chief Executive Officer, Northwest Medical Center, Margate, FL, p. A133

GUM, Gary, R.N. Chief Nursing Officer, Kindred Hospital–Albuquerque, Albuquerque, NM, p. A422

GUMBINER, Carl H., M.D. Senior Vice President Medical Affairs and Chief Medical Officer, Children's Hospital and Medical Center, Omaha, NE, p. A396

GUMBS, Milton A., M.D. Vice President and Medical Director, Bronx–Lebanon Hospital Center Health Care System, NY, p. A438

GUMMADI, Subhaker, M.D
  Chief Medical Staff, Promise Hospital Baton Rouge – Main Campus, Baton Rouge, LA, p. A270
  President Medical Staff, Promise Hospital of Baton Rouge – Mid–City Campus, Baton Rouge, LA, p. A270

GUMP, Linda A., Chief Clinical Services Officer, Aurora Medical Center, Kenosha, WI, p. A703

GUNABALAN, Ryan, Chief Executive Officer, Behavioral Center of Michigan, Warren, MI, p. A332

GUNASEKARAN, Suresh, Assistant Vice President Information Resources, University of Texas Southwestern Medical Center, Dallas, TX, p. A607

GUNDERSEN, Robert A., Market Chief Executive Officer, Kindred Hospital Northeast–Stoughton, Stoughton, MA, p. A312

GUNDLAPALLI, Madhu, M.D. Clinical Director, Utah State Hospital, Provo, UT, p. A657

GUNDT, Kristin, Chief Nursing Officer, Community Hospital, Grand Junction, CO, p. A104

GUNKEL, Jeff, Chief Information Officer, Jamestown Regional Medical Center, Jamestown, ND, p. A475

GUNN, Deborah, Chief Information Officer, W. G. (Bill) Heffner Veterans Affairs Medical Center, Salisbury, NC, p. A468

GUNN, Elizabeth, R.N. Vice President, Patient Care Services, Southeast Georgia Health System Brunswick Campus, Brunswick, GA, p. A152

GUNN, John R., Executive Vice President and Chief Operating Officer, Memorial Sloan–Kettering Cancer Center, New York, NY, p. A441

GUNN, Terry, FACHE Chief Executive Officer, KershawHealth, Camden, SC, p. A557

GUNNELL, Nancy
  Chief Human Resource Officer, West Suburban Medical Center, Oak Park, IL, p. A196
  Chief Human Resource Officer, Westlake Hospital, Melrose Park, IL, p. A194

GUNNERSEN, Nils, Administrator, Bertrand Chaffee Hospital, Springville, NY, p. A450

GUNTHER, DNP, Anne, R.N. Chief Nursing Officer, Aultman Hospital, Canton, OH, p. A481

GUNUKULA, Srinivas, M.D. Chief of Staff, Dallas Regional Medical Center, Mesquite, TX, p. A632

GUOYAVATIN, Kora
  Chief Financial Officer, Garden Grove Hospital and Medical Center, Garden Grove, CA, p. A63
  Chief Financial Officer, West Anaheim Medical Center, Anaheim, CA, p. A53

GUPTA, Anil, M.D. Chief of Staff, Kindred Hospital–Baldwin Park, Baldwin Park, CA, p. A55

GUPTA, Arun, M.D. Vice President Medical Affairs, South Pointe Hospital, Warrensville Heights, OH, p. A500

GUPTA, Ashok K., M.D. Chief of Staff, Eaton Rapids Medical Center, Eaton Rapids, MI, p. A319

GUPTA, Vijay D., M.D. President and Chief Executive Officer, Franciscan Healthcare – Munster, Munster, IN, p. A217

GURR, Lory, Chief Human Resources Division, Evans U. S. Army Community Hospital, Fort Carson, CO, p. A103

GURRI, Joseph Albert, Vice President of Medical Affairs, Health First Holmes Regional Medical Center, Melbourne, FL, p. A133

GURTO, Barbara
  Manager Human Resources, University Hospitals Conneaut Medical Center, Conneaut, OH, p. A487
  Manager Human Resources, University Hospitals Geneva Medical Center, Geneva, OH, p. A490

GURULE, Eric, Chief Information Officer, Turquoise Lodge Hospital, Albuquerque, NM, p. A423

GURUNG, Anju, M.D. Chief Medical Officer, Mahnomen Health Center, Mahnomen, MN, p. A341

GUSHEE, Dean, M.D. Medical Director, Mason General Hospital, Shelton, WA, p. A684

GUSHO, Michael, Chief Financial Officer, St. Joseph Mercy Oakland, Pontiac, MI, p. A328

GUSSERT, Jeff, Director Operations, Dickinson County Healthcare System, Iron Mountain, MI, p. A322

GUSTAFSON, Brian, Chief Financial Officer, Veterans Affairs Montana Health Care System, Fort Harrison, MT, p. A383

GUSTAFSON, Connie, Director of Nursing, Jacobson Memorial Hospital Care Center, Elgin, ND, p. A473

GUSTAFSON, Michael, M.D., President, Brigham and Women's Faulkner Hospital, Boston, MA, p. A303

GUSTAFSON, Sarah S., Vice President of Finance, Grand Itasca Clinic and Hospital, Grand Rapids, MN, p. A339

GUSTER, Cherie M., R.N. Senior Vice President and Chief Nursing Officer, Akron General Medical Center, Akron, OH, p. A478

GUSTILO, Maria, M.D
  Medical Director, Osawatomie State Hospital, Osawatomie, KS, p. A247
  Medical Director, Rainbow Mental Health Facility, Kansas City, KS, p. A243

GUTHMILLER, Martin W., Chief Executive Officer, Orange City Area Health System, Orange City, IA, p. A232

GUTHRIE, Pamela A., Chief Human Resources Officer, AllianceHealth Pryor, Pryor, OK, p. A514

GUTIERREZ, Albert, FACHE, President and Chief Executive Officer, Saint Joseph Regional Medical Center, Mishawaka, IN, p. A216

GUTIERREZ, Doris, Director Human Resources, Holy Cross Hospital, Chicago, IL, p. A182

GUTIERREZ, Eugene, Vice President Finance, Huntington Memorial Hospital, Pasadena, CA, p. A80

GUTIERREZ, Lori, Chief Financial Officer, Rochelle Community Hospital, Rochelle, IL, p. A199

GUTIERREZ, Michelle, Executive Director Human Resources, Orange Coast Memorial Medical Center, Fountain Valley, CA, p. A62

GUTIERREZ, Noe, Chief Financial Officer, Lake Granbury Medical Center, Granbury, TX, p. A616

GUTIERREZ, Vickie, Director of Patient Care, Dr. Dan C. Trigg Memorial Hospital, Tucumcari, NM, p. A427

GUTIERREZ, Victor A., M.D. Medical Director, Allegiance Behavioral Health Center of Plainview, Plainview, TX, p. A636

GUTJAHR, Susan, Reimbursement Specialist, Sparta Community Hospital, Sparta, IL, p. A200

GUTKIN, Marty, Vice President Finance and Chief Financial Officer, WellStar Kennestone Hospital, Marietta, GA, p. A161

GUTMAN, Luisa, Senior Vice President and Chief Operating Officer, Holy Cross Hospital, Fort Lauderdale, FL, p. A126

GUTNICK, Michael, Senior Vice President Finance, Memorial Sloan–Kettering Cancer Center, New York, NY, p. A441

GUTOW, Andrew, M.D. Medical Director, Menlo Park Surgical Hospital, Menlo Park, CA, p. A75

GUTSCH, Michael, Chief Executive Officer, Cumberland Memorial Hospital, Cumberland, WI, p. A699

GUTSCHENRITTER, John, Chief Financial Officer, Wilson Medical Center, Neodesha, KS, p. A246

GUTTENBERG, Ellen, Chief Operating Officer, Frances Mahon Deaconess Hospital, Glasgow, MT, p. A383

GUTTIN, Enrique, M.D. Chief of Staff, Wilmington Veterans Affairs Medical Center, Wilmington, DE, p. A118

GUTTMACHER, Laurence, M.D. Clinical Director, Rochester Psychiatric Center, Rochester, NY, p. A449

GUTZEIT, Michael, M.D. Chief Medical Officer, Children's Hospital of Wisconsin, Milwaukee, WI, p. A706

GUYETTE, William, M.D. President Medical Staff, Livingston Hospital and Healthcare Services, Salem, KY, p. A265

GUZ, Andrew, Chief Executive Officer, Jennersville Regional Hospital, West Grove, PA, p. A552

GUZMAN, Claudia V., Executive Director, Hospital HIMA San Pablo Caguas, Caguas, PR, p. A720

GUZMAN, Elizabeth, Chief Operating Officer, Metropolitan Hospital Center, New York, NY, p. A441

GUZMAN, Lisa, Director Human Resources, California Hospital Medical Center, Los Angeles, CA, p. A69

GUZMAN, Sarah, M.D. Medical Director, Cedar Crest Hospital and Residential Treatment Center, Belton, TX, p. A597

GWATKIN, Betty Ann, Vice President Human Resources, Northeastern Vermont Regional Hospital, Saint Johnsbury, VT, p. A661

GWYN, Brian
  President and Chief Executive Officer, Cleveland Regional Medical Center, Shelby, NC, p. A468
  President Chief Operating Officer, Cleveland Regional Medical Center, Shelby, NC, p. A468
  President and Chief Executive Officer, Kings Mountain Hospital, Kings Mountain, NC, p. A463

GYNTHER, Tracy, R.N. Vice President and Chief Nursing Officer, West Georgia Health, Lagrange, GA, p. A160

GYROS, Guy, Chief Financial Officer, Huntsville Memorial Hospital, Huntsville, TX, p. A623

# H

HAACK, Wanda, MSN Chief Nursing Officer, Genesis Medical Center, DeWitt, De Witt, IA, p. A226

HAAGENSON, Deb, R.N. Vice President of Patient Care, CHI St. Joseph's Health, Park Rapids, MN, p. A344

HAAK, Karen S., R.N. Chief Nursing Officer, Good Samaritan Hospital, Vincennes, IN, p. A221

HAAK, Thelma, Manager Health Information, Avera Dells Area Hospital, Dell Rapids, SD, p. A568

HAAR, Clare A., Chief Executive Officer, Eastern Niagara Hospital, Lockport, NY, p. A436

HAAS, Christine, Chief Information Officer, Jersey Shore Hospital, Jersey Shore, PA, p. A536

HAAS, Lorin, Chief Financial Officer, Rush County Memorial Hospital, La Crosse, KS, p. A244

HAAS, Robert, M.D. Chief Medical Officer, Liberty Hospital, Liberty, MO, p. A372

HAAS, Scott A., M.D. Chief Medical Officer, Eastern State Hospital, Lexington, KY, p. A259

HAAS, Steven J.
  Chief Financial Officer, Health Alliance Hospital – Broadway Campus, Kingston, NY, p. A436
  Chief Financial Officer, Health Alliance Hospital – Mary's Avenue Campus, Kingston, NY, p. A436

HAAS, Susan, Director Human Resources, Aurora San Diego Hospital, San Diego, CA, p. A86

HAASE, Patricia, Director Information Technology and Communications, Marian Regional Medical Center, Santa Maria, CA, p. A91

HAASKEN, Timothy W., Chief Financial Officer, LewisGale Hospital Montgomery, Blacksburg, VA, p. A662

HABASHY, Hany Mounir, M.D. Chief Medical Director, Methodist Extended Care Hospital, Memphis, TN, p. A583

HABIB, Noel, M.D. Chief Medical Officer, Huhukam Memorial Hospital, Sacaton, AZ, p. A37

HABOWSKI, Michael J., President and Chief Executive Officer, Ashtabula County Medical Center, Ashtabula, OH, p. A478

HACHENBERG, Dennis A., FACHE, Chief Executive Officer, Anderson County Hospital, Garnett, KS, p. A240

HACHEY, Michael
  Senior Vice President and Chief Financial Officer, Emerson Hospital, Concord, MA, p. A306
  Senior Vice President and Chief Financial Officer, Mercy Hospital of Portland, Portland, ME, p. A291

HACKBARTH, John, CPA Senior Vice President Finance and Chief Financial Officer, Owensboro Health Regional Hospital, Owensboro, KY, p. A264

HACKER, Leanne, Chief Financial Officer, Eastern New Mexico Medical Center, Roswell, NM, p. A426

HACKER, Mary Dee, R.N. Vice President, Patient Care Services and Chief Nursing Officer, Children's Hospital Los Angeles, Los Angeles, CA, p. A69

HACKER, Phillip, Chief Financial Officer, White River Medical Center, Batesville, AR, p. A41

HACKER, Tina, Director Human Resources, Advanced Specialty Hospital of Toledo, Toledo, OH, p. A498

HACKETT, Leslie, Chief Nursing Officer, Covenant Hospital Plainview, Plainview, TX, p. A636

HACKETT, Sylvia D., Vice President Human Resources, Rex Healthcare, Raleigh, NC, p. A467

HACKNEY, Hannah, Director Accounting and Human Resources, DeWitt Hospital, De Witt, AR, p. A43

HACKSTEDDE, Anita, M.D., President and Chief Executive Officer, Salem Regional Medical Center, Salem, OH, p. A497

HADDADIN, Maen, M.D. President Medical Staff, CHI Health Mercy Corning, Corning, IA, p. A225

HADDICAN, James, Chief Financial Officer, Vice President Finance, Gillette Children's Specialty Healthcare, Saint Paul, MN, p. A346

HADDIX, Parker, Chief Executive Officer, William R. Sharpe, Jr. Hospital, Weston, WV, p. A696

HADDOX, Melissa, Controller, HEALTHSOUTH Rehabilitation Hospital of Cypress, Houston, TX, p. A620

HADLEY, David R., Managing Director and Chief Financial Officer, Integris Baptist Medical Center, Oklahoma City, OK, p. A511

HADLEY, H. Roger, M.D. Vice President, Medical Affairs, Loma Linda University Medical Center, Loma Linda, CA, p. A67

HADLEY, Steven N., Chief Financial Officer, Kansas Medical Center, Andover, KS, p. A237

HADZEGA, Angela, Chief Financial Officer, Kane Community Hospital, Kane, PA, p. A537

HAEHN, Debra, Chief Financial Officer, Clay County Memorial Hospital, Henrietta, TX, p. A618

HAENELT, Michael, Chief Information Management, Weed Army Community Hospital, Fort Irwin, CA, p. A61

HAESEMEYER, Allan, M.D. Chief of Staff, Indianhead Medical Center, Shell Lake, WI, p. A711

HAESEMEYER, Christa, Chief Nursing Officer, Lincoln County Hospital, Lincoln, KS, p. A245

HAFEMAN, Paula, R.N
  Chief Nursing Officer, St. Mary's Hospital Medical Center, Green Bay, WI, p. A702
  Chief Nurse Executive, St. Vincent Hospital, Green Bay, WI, p. A702

HALLIDAY, Lisa, Director Accounting Services, Taylor Regional Hospital, Hawkinsville, GA, p. A158

HALLISEY, Thomas, Chief Information Officer, United Medical Center, Washington, DC, p. A120

HALLIWILL, Donald B.
Chief Financial Officer, Carilion Franklin Memorial Hospital, Rocky Mount, VA, p. A672
Executive Vice President and Chief Financial Officer, Carilion Roanoke Memorial Hospital, Roanoke, VA, p. A672

HALLMARK, Todd, Chief Executive Officer, Choctaw Nation Health Care Center, Talihina, OK, p. A516

HALPIN, Jean
President, OhioHealth MedCentral Mansfield Hospital, Mansfield, OH, p. A493
President, OhioHealth MedCentral Shelby Hospital, Shelby, OH, p. A497

HALPIN, Kim, Director Human Resources, Arms Acres, Carmel, NY, p. A431

HALSAN, Carole, R.N., Chief Executive Officer, Willapa Harbor Hospital, South Bend, WA, p. A685

HALSELL, David, Senior Vice President and Chief Financial Officer, Lake Regional Health System, Osage Beach, MO, p. A374

HALSTEAD, Lisa, Chief Nursing Officer, Integris Baptist Regional Health Center, Miami, OK, p. A509

HALTER, Bev, Director Human Resources and Payroll, Liberty Medical Center, Chester, MT, p. A382

HALTER, Kevin, Chief Executive Officer, Our Lady of Bellefonte Hospital, Ashland, KY, p. A254

HALTER, Michael P., Chief Executive Officer, Hahnemann University Hospital, Philadelphia, PA, p. A543

HALVORSEN, Lisa, Chief Nurse Executive, Providence Milwaukie Hospital, Milwaukie, OR, p. A523

HALVORSON, Marla, Director Human Resources, St. Luke's Hospital, Duluth, MN, p. A338

HAM, Michael, Chief Executive Officer, North Tampa Behavioral Health, Wesley Chapel, FL, p. A147

HAMAM, Hisham, M.D. Chief of Staff, Northern Cochise Community Hospital, Willcox, AZ, p. A40

HAMB, Aaron, M.D. Chief Medical Officer, Provident Hospital of Cook County, Chicago, IL, p. A184

HAMBLIN, James, Chief Financial Officer, White Mountain Regional Medical Center, Springerville, AZ, p. A38

HAMEL, Loren, M.D., President and Chief Executive Officer, Lakeland Health, Saint Joseph, MI, p. B80

HAMEL, Loren, M.D., President and Chief Executive Officer, Lakeland Medical Center, St. Joseph, Saint Joseph, MI, p. A329

HAMEL, Susan, Chief Nursing Officer, St. Luke's Hospital, Duluth, MN, p. A338

HAMILL, Dave H., President and Chief Executive Officer, Hampton Regional Medical Center, Varnville, SC, p. A565

HAMILTON, Aggie, Chief Human Resources, Veterans Affairs Montana Health Care System, Fort Harrison, MT, p. A383

HAMILTON, Brandy, Chief Executive Officer, Suncoast Behavioral Health Center, Bradenton, FL, p. A122

HAMILTON, Catherine, Chief Nursing Officer, Hedrick Medical Center, Chillicothe, MO, p. A365

HAMILTON, Chanda, Chief Information Officer, Clifton T. Perkins Hospital Center, Jessup, MD, p. A298

HAMILTON, Crystal, R.N., Chief Executive Officer, Abrazo Maryvale Campus, Phoenix, AZ, p. A34

HAMILTON, Dan, Director Inpatient Services, Nor–Lea General Hospital, Lovington, NM, p. A425

HAMILTON, Geoff, Interim Chief Financial Officer, Morton General Hospital, Morton, WA, p. A680

HAMILTON, Jennifer, Chief Financial Officer, SageWest Health Care at Riverton, Riverton, WY, p. A717

HAMILTON, Kay A., MS, Chief Administrative Officer, Geisinger–Lewistown Hospital, Lewistown, PA, p. A539

HAMILTON, Marci, Chief Nursing Officer, Orthopaedic Hospital of Lutheran Health Network, Fort Wayne, IN, p. A208

HAMILTON, Marilyn, Director Human Resources, Promise Hospital Baton Rouge – Main Campus, Baton Rouge, LA, p. A270

HAMILTON, Nancy, Chief Human and Learning Resources, Veterans Affairs New Jersey Health Care System, East Orange, NJ, p. A411

HAMILTON, Neal C., Chief Human Resources, James A. Haley Veterans' Hospital–Tampa, Tampa, FL, p. A144

HAMILTON, Patricia, R.N. Director of Nursing, Mildred Mitchell–Bateman Hospital, Huntington, WV, p. A692

HAMILTON, Phil, R.N., Chief Executive Officer, General John J. Pershing Memorial Hospital, Brookfield, MO, p. A364

HAMILTON, Randal S., Chief Executive Officer, Select Specialty Hospital–Panama City, Panama City, FL, p. A139

HAMILTON, Scott
Vice President and Chief Financial Officer, Parkwest Medical Center, Knoxville, TN, p. A580
Chief Financial Officer, Peninsula Hospital, Louisville, TN, p. A582

HAMILTON, Sharon, Chief Nursing Officer, HEALTHSOUTH Emerald Coast Rehabilitation Hospital, Panama City, FL, p. A139

HAMILTON, Terry, President, St. John Macomb–Oakland Hospital, Warren, MI, p. A332

HAMILTON, Thomas, D.O. Chief Medical Officer, St. Francis Health, Topeka, KS, p. A251

HAMILTON, Toby, Chief Executive Officer, Emerus, The Woodlands, TX, p. B54

HAMILTON, Tom, M.D. Chief of Staff, Decatur County General Hospital, Parsons, TN, p. A587

HAMILTON, William L., M.D
Urban Central Region Medical Director, Intermountain Medical Center, Murray, UT, p. A656
Chief Medical Officer, LDS Hospital, Salt Lake City, UT, p. A658

HAMILTON–BEYER, Maggie, Chief Financial Officer, Knoxville Hospital & Clinics, Knoxville, IA, p. A230

HAMLIN, David, Chief Patient Care Services, Catalina Island Medical Center, Avalon, CA, p. A54

HAMLIN, DeWayne, Director, Veterans Affairs Caribbean Healthcare System, San Juan, PR, p. A724

HAMLIN, Faye, Manager Human Resources, Julian F. Keith Alcohol and Drug Abuse Treatment Center, Black Mountain, NC, p. A455

HAMLIN, Scott J., Chief Financial Officer, Cincinnati Children's Hospital Medical Center, Cincinnati, OH, p. A482

HAMM, David, President and Chief Executive Officer, Good Samaritan Medical Center, Lafayette, CO, p. A106

HAMM, Jay, R.N., FACHE Chief Acute Care Executive, Palmetto Health Richland, Columbia, SC, p. A559

HAMMACK, Stanley K., Chief Executive Officer, University of South Alabama Hospitals, Mobile, AL, p. B147

HAMMAKER, Barry, M.D. Chief Medical Officer and Chief Clinical Officer, Vail Valley Medical Center, Vail, CO, p. A109

HAMMEL, Katrina, M.D. Chief Medical Officer, Gundersen Tri–County Hospital and Clinics, Whitehall, WI, p. A714

HAMMEL, Leah, Acting Administrator, Chester Mental Health Center, Chester, IL, p. A181

HAMMER, Michael, Chief Executive Officer, Sanford Worthington Medical Center, Worthington, MN, p. A349

HAMMER, Rebecca J., Chief Financial Officer, Davis Medical Center, Elkins, WV, p. A690

HAMMES, Paul, Chief Executive Officer, Hugh Chatham Memorial Hospital, Elkin, NC, p. A460

HAMMETT, Doran, Chief Financial Officer, Petersburg Medical Center, Petersburg, AK, p. A29

HAMMETT, George, Director Human Resources, Carolina Center for Behavioral Health, Greer, SC, p. A562

HAMMETT, Ron, M.D. Chief of Staff, Glenwood Regional Medical Center, West Monroe, LA, p. A286

HAMMETT, Troy, Vice President and Chief Financial Officer, OhioHealth Doctors Hospital, Columbus, OH, p. A486

HAMMOCK, Preston W., President and Chief Executive Officer, Alamance Regional Medical Center, Burlington, NC, p. A456

HAMMON, Selene Q., Chief Executive Officer, Dallas Behavioral Healthcare Hospital, Desoto, TX, p. A608

HAMMOND, Flora, M.D. Chief Medical Affairs, Rehabilitation Hospital of Indiana, Indianapolis, IN, p. A212

HAMMOND, Michael
Chief Financial Officer, Lourdes Medical Center of Burlington County, Willingboro, NJ, p. A420
Chief Financial Officer, Our Lady of Lourdes Medical Center, Camden, NJ, p. A410

HAMMOND, Patti, Chief Operating Officer, Adirondack Medical Center, Saranac Lake, NY, p. A450

HAMMOND, Reed, Chief Operating Officer, Centennial Medical Center, Frisco, TX, p. A615

HAMMONDS, Janie, Human Resources Officer, Columbus Community Hospital, Columbus, TX, p. A601

HAMMONDS, Laura, Assistant Administrator, Jasper Memorial Hospital, Monticello, GA, p. A162

HAMNER, Candy, Vice President and Chief Nursing Officer, Levindale Hebrew Geriatric Center and Hospital, Baltimore, MD, p. A293

HAMON, Eric, Chief Financial Officer, Driscoll Children's Hospital, Corpus Christi, TX, p. A602

HAMP, Matthew, Chief Operating Officer, Sisters of Charity Hospital of Buffalo, Buffalo, NY, p. A431

HAMPF, Carl, M.D. Chief Medical Officer, Saint Thomas Hospital for Spinal Surgery, Nashville, TN, p. A585

HAMPSHIRE, Misty, Chief Financial Officer, Ozarks Community Hospital, Springfield, MO, p. A379

HAMPTON, Angie, Director Human Resources, Porter Regional Hospital, Valparaiso, IN, p. A220

HAMPTON, David, M.D. Chief Medical Staff, Pampa Regional Medical Center, Pampa, TX, p. A635

HAMPTON, Jeff, Director Information Systems, Lehigh Regional Medical Center, Lehigh Acres, FL, p. A132

HAMPTON, Mary Ann, R.N. Chief Nursing Officer, Des Peres Hospital, Saint Louis, MO, p. A376

HAMRICK, Jan, Chief Financial Officer, Dodge County Hospital, Eastman, GA, p. A157

HAMSTRA, Nancy, Interim President and Chief Executive Officer, University Hospital, Newark, NJ, p. A415

HAN, Ba, M.D. Clinical Director, Big Spring State Hospital, Big Spring, TX, p. A597

HAN, Kevin, Vice President and Chief Financial Officer, Stormont–Vail HealthCare, Topeka, KS, p. A251

HANCOCK, J. Brian, M.D. Chief of Staff, Fargo Veterans Affairs Health Care System, Fargo, ND, p. A473

HANCOCK, Katherine, R.N. Executive Chief Nursing Officer, Cleveland Clinic, Cleveland, OH, p. A484

HANCOCK, Kerry, Director Human Resources, Bacon County Hospital and Health System, Alma, GA, p. A149

HANCOCK, Lori, Chief Business Officer, West Palm Beach Veterans Affairs Medical Center, West Palm Beach, FL, p. A147

HANCOCK, Melinda, Interim Chief Financial Officer, Good Samaritan Hospital, Suffern, NY, p. A451

HANCOCK, Myrna, Director Financial Services, Choctaw Health Center, Philadelphia, MS, p. A359

HANCOCK, Paul, M.D. Chief Medical Officer, Swedish Medical Center, Englewood, CO, p. A103

HANCOCK, Shannon L., Director, Patient Services, Morton Plant North Bay Hospital, New Port Richey, FL, p. A136

HANCOCK, Sharon, Chief Human Resources Officer, McCullough–Hyde Memorial Hospital/TriHealth, Oxford, OH, p. A496

HANCOCK, Todd, Senior Vice President and Chief Operating Officer, Mother Frances Hospital – Tyler, Tyler, TX, p. A649

HANDEL, Daniel, M.D. Chief Medical Officer, MUSC Medical Center of Medical University of South Carolina, Charleston, SC, p. A558

HANDLER, Michael, M.D. Vice President Medical Administration, SSM St. Joseph Hospital West, Lake Saint Louis, MO, p. A371

HANDLEY, Charles, Chief Financial Officer, The Hospitals of Providence Memorial Campus, El Paso, TX, p. A611

HANDLEY, Charles R., Chief Financial Officer, Plaza Specialty Hospital, Houston, TX, p. A621

HANDLEY, Jack, M.D. Chief Medical Officer, EvergreenHealth Monroe, Monroe, WA, p. A680

HANDLEY, Rhonda, Chief Financial Officer, Columbia Basin Hospital, Ephrata, WA, p. A678

HANDOL, Nelson, M.D. Medical Director, Laurel Oaks Behavioral Health Center, Dothan, AL, p. A19

HANDY, Steven P., CPA, Chief Executive Officer, Uniontown Hospital, Uniontown, PA, p. A551

HANEFELD, Darlene, Chief Human Resources Officer, Banner Churchill Community Hospital, Fallon, NV, p. A400

HANENBURG, Thomas S., Senior Vice President and Area Manager, Kaiser Permanente San Leandro Medical Center, San Leandro, CA, p. A89

HANEY, Kathryn, Controller, HEALTHSOUTH Valley of the Sun Rehabilitation Hospital, Glendale, AZ, p. A32

HANEY, Mark, President, WellStar Paulding Hospital, Hiram, GA, p. A159

HANGER, Kelvin, Chief Executive Officer, TriHealth Evendale Hospital, Cincinnati, OH, p. A483

HANIGAN, Hank, Administrator and Chief Executive Officer, Whitman Hospital and Medical Center, Colfax, WA, p. A677

HANISCH, Denise, M.D. Chief of Staff, Avera St. Mary's Hospital, Pierre, SD, p. A570

HANKINS, Brad, Chief Operating Quality Officer, Lake Chelan Community Hospital, Chelan, WA, p. A677

HANKS, Claire H., R.N. Vice President and Chief Nursing Officer, Glendale Memorial Hospital and Health Center, Glendale, CA, p. A63

HANKS, John, Director Information Systems, East Tennessee Children's Hospital, Knoxville, TN, p. A580

HANKS, Tammy, Director Human Resources, Minidoka Memorial Hospital, Rupert, ID, p. A176

HANLEY, Darlene S., FACHE, President and Chief Executive Officer, St. Lawrence Rehabilitation Center, Lawrenceville, NJ, p. A413

HANLEY, Robert, Chief Human Resources Officer, University of Chicago Medical Center, Chicago, IL, p. A185

HANLON, Jerad, Chief Operating Officer, Southside Regional Medical Center, Petersburg, VA, p. A670

HANNA, Mitchell J.
Chief Executive Officer, Sutter Auburn Faith Hospital, Auburn, CA, p. A54
Interim Chief Executive Officer, Sutter Coast Hospital, Crescent City, CA, p. A59

Index of Health Care Professionals / Harkleroad

HANNA, Philip S., Administrator and Chief Executive Officer, Battle Mountain General Hospital, Battle Mountain, NV, p. A400
HANNA, Robb, Executive Director Information Technology, Lexington Regional Health Center, Lexington, NE, p. A393
HANNAH, Jill, Director Human Resources, James Cancer Hospital and Solove Research Institute, Columbus, OH, p. A485
HANNAH, Steven, Chief Executive Officer, Montrose Memorial Hospital, Montrose, CO, p. A107
HANNAN, Barbara E., R.N., Chief Executive Officer, Select Specialty Hospital–Northeast New Jersey, Rochelle Park, NJ, p. A418
HANNERS, Brandy, Chief Financial Officer, Memorial Hospital, Martinsville, VA, p. A668
HANNERS, Rodney
Chief Executive Officer, Keck Hospital of USC, Los Angeles, CA, p. A70
Chief Executive Officer, University of Southern California–Norris Cancer Hospital, Los Angeles, CA, p. A73
HANNON, Edward J., Chief Executive Officer, Bates County Memorial Hospital, Butler, MO, p. A364
HANNON, Jennifer, Director Human Resources, Madison County Health Care System, Winterset, IA, p. A236
HANNON, Kay, Director Information Systems, Des Peres Hospital, Saint Louis, MO, p. A376
HANNON, Trish, FACHE, President and Chief Executive Officer, New England Baptist Hospital, Boston, MA, p. A304
HANS, Christopher, Chief Financial Officer, Riverside County Regional Medical Center, Moreno Valley, CA, p. A76
HANSART, Bed K., Administrator, North Baldwin Infirmary, Bay Minette, AL, p. A16
HANSCOME, Joyce
Senior Vice President and Chief Information Officer, Mary Washington Hospital, Fredericksburg, VA, p. A665
Senior Vice President and Chief Information Officer, Stafford Hospital, Stafford, VA, p. A673
HANSEL, Jimmie W., Ph.D., Chief Executive Officer, Edwards County Hospital and Healthcare Center, Kinsley, KS, p. A243
HANSEN, Becky, Chief Executive Officer, Southwest Healthcare Services, Bowman, ND, p. A472
HANSEN, Carolyn, Chief Nursing Officer, Bingham Memorial Hospital, Blackfoot, ID, p. A172
HANSEN, Chris, Senior Vice President Ambulatory Services and Chief Information Officer, The University of Kansas Hospital, Kansas City, KS, p. A243
HANSEN, Gayle B., R.N
Chief Operating Officer, Mayo Clinic Health System in Fairmont, Fairmont, MN, p. A338
Chief Integration Officer, Mayo Clinic Health System in Saint James, Saint James, MN, p. A346
HANSEN, Jay, Director Information Services, Oconee Memorial Hospital, Seneca, SC, p. A564
HANSEN, Karen, Vice President and Chief Operating Officer, Memorial Medical Center – Ashland, Ashland, WI, p. A697
HANSEN, Kristy, Chief Financial Officer, Myrtue Medical Center, Harlan, IA, p. A229
HANSEN, Kyle, Corporate Director Information Systems, Riverside Medical Center, Kankakee, IL, p. A192
HANSEN, Kyle A., Chief Executive Officer, Logan Regional Hospital, Logan, UT, p. A655
HANSEN, Laurie
Associate Administrator, Emory Johns Creek Hospital, Johns Creek, GA, p. A159
Director Administrative Services, Johnson County Healthcare Center, Buffalo, WY, p. A715
HANSEN, Linda, Director Human Resources, Bakersfield Heart Hospital, Bakersfield, CA, p. A54
HANSEN, Maggie, R.N. Chief Nursing Officer, Memorial Regional Hospital, FL, p. A128
HANSEN, Marcia A., R.N. Vice President Operations and Chief Nursing Officer, Ephrata Community Hospital, Ephrata, PA, p. A534
HANSEN, Michael T., FACHE, President and Chief Executive Officer, Columbus Community Hospital, Columbus, NE, p. A391
HANSEN, Misty
Chief Financial Officer, Banner – University Medical Center South, Tucson, AZ, p. A39
Chief Financial Officer, Banner – University Medical Center Tucson, Tucson, AZ, p. A39
HANSEN, Paul, Administrator, Maniilaq Health Center, Kotzebue, AK, p. A28
HANSEN, Steven, Director Information Technology, Healdsburg District Hospital, Healdsburg, CA, p. A64
HANSON, Brent, Chief Executive Officer and HIPAA Security and Compliance Officer, Great Bend Regional Hospital, Great Bend, KS, p. A240
HANSON, Carl, Administrator, Minidoka Memorial Hospital, Rupert, ID, p. A176
HANSON, Denise, Information Technology Specialist, St. Cloud Veterans Affairs Health Care System, Saint Cloud, MN, p. A346
HANSON, Emily, M.D. President, Medical Staff, St. Joseph Memorial Hospital, Murphysboro, IL, p. A195
HANSON, Gregory S., M.D., Chief Executive Officer, Clark Fork Valley Hospital, Plains, MT, p. A386
HANSON, Jane E., R.N. Chief Operating Officer, Mercy Gilbert Medical Center, Gilbert, AZ, p. A31
HANSON, Jennifer, R.N., President and Chief Administrative Officer, LeConte Medical Center, Sevierville, TN, p. A588
HANSON, Jesica, Vice President and Chief Financial Officer, Bakersfield Memorial Hospital, Bakersfield, CA, p. A55
HANSON, Mary Ann, Director Personnel, Mental Health Institute, Cherokee, IA, p. A224
HANSON, Paul A., FACHE, President, Sanford USD Medical Center, Sioux Falls, SD, p. A571
HANSON, Rhonda, Director Human Resources, Huron Regional Medical Center, Huron, SD, p. A569
HANSON, Rita, M.D
Vice President Medical Affairs, Wheaton Franciscan Healthcare – Elmbrook Memorial, Brookfield, WI, p. A698
Vice President Medical Affairs, Wheaton Franciscan Healthcare – St. Joseph's, Milwaukee, WI, p. A707
Vice President Medical Affairs, Wheaton Franciscan Healthcare – The Wisconsin Heart Hospital, Wauwatosa, WI, p. A713
HANSON, Samantha, Chief Human Resources Officer, Children's Hospitals and Clinics of Minnesota, Minneapolis, MN, p. A342
HANSON, Stephen C., Chief Executive Officer, Baptist Health, Louisville, KY, p. B19
HANTOOT, Mark, M.D. Medical Director, Gateways Hospital and Mental Health Center, Los Angeles, CA, p. A69
HANYAK, Diana C., Chief Executive Officer, HEALTHSOUTH Tustin Rehabilitation Hospital, Tustin, CA, p. A95
HAPNEY, Sherry, Chief Financial Officer, HEALTHSOUTH Rehabilitation Hospital of Fort Worth, Fort Worth, TX, p. A613
HAPPEL, Terry J., M.D. Vice President and Chief Medical Officer, Chandler Regional Medical Center, Chandler, AZ, p. A30
HAQQANI, Rahim, M.D. Medical Director, Dallas Behavioral Healthcare Hospital, Desoto, TX, p. A608
HAQUE, Haroon, M.D. Medical Director, Cornerstone Hospital of SouthEast Arizona, Tucson, AZ, p. A39
HARA, Karen, Personnel Management Specialist, Hawaii State Hospital, Kaneohe, HI, p. A170
HARALDSON, Richard, Chief Executive Officer, Sidney Health Center, Sidney, MT, p. A387
HARALSON, Gregory
Chief Executive Officer, Memorial Hermann Sugar Land Hospital, Sugar Land, TX, p. A645
Chief Operating Officer, Plaza Medical Center of Fort Worth, Fort Worth, TX, p. A614
HARALSON, Robert, Chief Financial Officer, Breckinridge Memorial Hospital, Hardinsburg, KY, p. A257
HARARI, Jack L., M.D. Chief Medical Officer, West Boca Medical Center, Boca Raton, FL, p. A122
HARBAUGH, Charles, Director Human Resources, Mountain Lakes Medical Center, Clayton, GA, p. A154
HARBAUGH, Ken, Vice President and Chief Financial Officer, OSF Saint Francis Medical Center, Peoria, IL, p. A198
HARBERT, Jim, Chief Technology Officer, Anthony Medical Center, Anthony, KS, p. A237
HARBERTS, Jerry, Information Technologist, Madison Hospital, Madison, MN, p. A341
HARBISON, Damon R., MBA, Interim Chief Executive Officer, SSM Cardinal Glennon Children's Medical Center, Saint Louis, MO, p. A377
HARBISON, Linda, Chief Nursing Officer, Red Bud Regional Hospital, Red Bud, IL, p. A199
HARCHENKO, Vern, M.D. Chief of Staff, Garrison Memorial Hospital, Garrison, ND, p. A474
HARCLERODE, Tim, Chief Operating Officer, Maria Parham Medical Center, Henderson, NC, p. A462
HARCOURT, Jenifer, Chief Operating Officer, RiverWoods Behavioral Health System, Riverdale, GA, p. A163
HARCUP, Craig, M.D. Hospital Medical Director, Complex Care Hospital at Ridgelake, Sarasota, FL, p. A142
HARDACRE, Jerry, M.D. Chief of Staff, Wheaton Franciscan Healthcare – All Saints, Racine, WI, p. A709
HARDAN, Terry, Director Human Resources, Longview Regional Medical Center, Longview, TX, p. A629
HARDCASTLE, Brad, Chief Financial Officer, South Baldwin Regional Medical Center, Foley, AL, p. A19
HARDCASTLE, Kathy, Director Human Resources, Texas Health Presbyterian Hospital Denton, Denton, TX, p. A608
HARDEE, Gary R., M.D. Medical Director, Plains Memorial Hospital, Dimmitt, TX, p. A609
HARDEMAN, Diane, Director Personnel, Stephens County Hospital, Toccoa, GA, p. A166
HARDEN, Diane P.
Chief Financial Officer, Leesburg Regional Medical Center, Leesburg, FL, p. A132
Senior Vice President and Chief Financial Officer, The Villages Regional Hospital, The Villages, FL, p. A146
HARDESTY, Keith, Chief Financial Officer, Springfield Hospital Center, Sykesville, MD, p. A300
HARDIN, Cecil, CPA Chief Financial Officer, Catawba Hospital, Catawba, VA, p. A663
HARDIN, James, Human Resources Officer, Sheridan Veterans Affairs Medical Center, Sheridan, WY, p. A717
HARDIN, Leslie, Chief Executive Officer and Chief Financial Officer, Seymour Hospital, Seymour, TX, p. A643
HARDIN, Mark, M.D. Medical Director, Ed Fraser Memorial Hospital and Baker Community Health Center, MacClenny, FL, p. A132
HARDIN, Nicholas, Chief Executive Officer, HEALTHSOUTH Sugar Land Rehabilitation Hospital, Sugar Land, TX, p. A645
HARDING, Cathy, Chief Clinical Officer, Vibra Hospital of Springfield, Springfield, IL, p. A201
HARDING, Christina, Vice President Finance, Mount Desert Island Hospital, Bar Harbor, ME, p. A288
HARDING, Denise, Director Human Resources, Plumas District Hospital, Quincy, CA, p. A82
HARDING, Edward A., FACHE, President and Chief Executive Officer, Bay Area Medical Center, Marinette, WI, p. A704
HARDING, Geoff, Chief Clinical Officer, Promise Hospital of Salt Lake, Salt Lake City, UT, p. A658
HARDING, Gwen, Site Manager Information Systems, Bon Secours Memorial Regional Medical Center, Mechanicsville, VA, p. A668
HARDING, John, Interim Chief Executive Officer, Lincoln County Health System, Fayetteville, TN, p. A577
HARDING, John P., Chief Operating Officer, Children's Hospital of The King's Daughters, Norfolk, VA, p. A669
HARDING, Rick, Chief Executive Officer, Sundance Hospital, Arlington, TX, p. A592
HARDOBY, Greg, Director Personnel, Runnells Center for Rehabilitation and Healthcare, Berkeley Heights, NJ, p. A409
HARDWICK, Garry, R.N. Chief Operating Officer, Newport Bay Hospital, Newport Beach, CA, p. A78
HARDY, Bob, Chief Operating Officer, Opelousas General Health System, Opelousas, LA, p. A283
HARDY, Eric S., Chief Financial Officer, Mesa View Regional Hospital, Mesquite, NV, p. A403
HARDY, James, D.O. Chief of Staff, Dayton Veterans Affairs Medical Center, Dayton, OH, p. A488
HARDY, Janice, Chief Human Resource Management Service, Central Alabama Veterans Health Care System, Montgomery, AL, p. A23
HARDY, Kevin, Chief Financial Officer, HEALTHSOUTH Treasure Coast Rehabilitation Hospital, Vero Beach, FL, p. A146
HARDY, Melanie, D.O. Chief of Staff, Marias Medical Center, Shelby, MT, p. A387
HARDY, Tammie H., Chief Executive Officer, Lauderdale Community Hospital, Ripley, TN, p. A587
HARDY, Valonia, Chief Healthy Living Officer, Tsehootsooi Medical Center, Fort Defiance, AZ, p. A31
HARGER, Anita, Director Human Resources, Mercy Gilbert Medical Center, Gilbert, AZ, p. A31
HARGETT, Stephen, Administrator Finance and Support Services, MUSC Medical Center of Medical University of South Carolina, Charleston, SC, p. A558
HARGETT, Stephen A., Senior Vice President and Chief Financial Officer, Marina Del Rey Hospital, Marina Del Rey, CA, p. A74
HARGIS, Bryan J., FACHE, Chief Executive Officer, Gilbert Hospital, Gilbert, AZ, p. A31
HARGIS, Chris, Manager Finance, Alta View Hospital, Sandy, UT, p. A659
HARGRAVE–THOMAS, Anne, Chief Executive Officer, Oakleaf Surgical Hospital, Eau Claire, WI, p. A700
HARGRODER, Ty, M.D. Chief of Staff, Acadia–St. Landry Hospital, Church Point, LA, p. A271
HARGROVE, Ben, Human Resources Director, LifeStream Behavioral Center, Leesburg, FL, p. A132
HARGROVE, Jeno, R.N. Director of Nursing, Columbus Community Hospital, Columbus, TX, p. A601
HARGROVE, Tressa B., Director Human Resources, Jackson Purchase Medical Center, Mayfield, KY, p. A262
HARIHARAN, Parma, M.D. Chief of Staff, Mercy Health – Clermont Hospital, Batavia, OH, p. A479
HARKEY, Shirley S., R.N. Vice President, Patient Services, Wayne Memorial Hospital, Goldsboro, NC, p. A461
HARKINS, Shelly, M.D. Chief Medical Officer, HSHS St. Elizabeth's Hospital, Belleville, IL, p. A179
HARKLEROAD, Rod, R.N.,
Administrator, Riverview Regional Medical Center, Carthage, TN, p. A574
Chief Executive Officer, Trousdale Medical Center, Hartsville, TN, p. A578

Index of Health Care Professionals

Index of Health Care Professionals

Index of Health Care Professionals / Hatiras

HARRIS, Vena, Director Human Resources, Minneola District Hospital, Minneola, KS, p. A246
HARRIS, William R., Chief Information Officer, Lawton Indian Hospital, Lawton, OK, p. A508
HARRIS–BREKEL, Donna
Director Human Resources, Hawthorn Children Psychiatric Hospital, Saint Louis, MO, p. A376
Director Human Resources, Metropolitan St. Louis Psychiatric Center, Saint Louis, MO, p. A376
Director Human Resources, St. Louis Psychiatric Rehabilitation Center, Saint Louis, MO, p. A378
HARRISON, Alicia, Data Management Officer, Excelsior Springs Hospital, Excelsior Springs, MO, p. A367
HARRISON, Allen, Chief Executive Officer, St. David's North Austin Medical Center, Austin, TX, p. A595
HARRISON, Ann, R.N. Director of Nursing, Wills Memorial Hospital, Washington, GA, p. A167
HARRISON, Charles, Chief Executive Officer, San Bernardino Mountains Community Hospital District, Lake Arrowhead, CA, p. A67
HARRISON, Chris, Manager Information Systems, Campbell County Memorial Hospital, Gillette, WY, p. A716
HARRISON, Dean M., President and Chief Executive Officer, Northwestern Memorial Healthcare, Chicago, IL, p. B99
HARRISON, Dean M., President and Chief Executive Officer, Northwestern Memorial Hospital, Chicago, IL, p. A183
HARRISON, Debra, MS Chief Nursing Officer, Mayo Clinic Jacksonville, Jacksonville, FL, p. A129
HARRISON, Denise, Associate Director, Veterans Affairs Nebraska–Western Iowa Health Care System, Omaha, NE, p. A397
HARRISON, Dyan, Manager Health Information, Ochiltree General Hospital, Perryton, TX, p. A636
HARRISON, Jo L., Vice President of Patient Care Services, Southwest Medical Center, Liberal, KS, p. A245
HARRISON, Marva, R.N. Vice President and Chief Nursing Officer, Integris Southwest Medical Center, Oklahoma City, OK, p. A511
HARRISON, Randy, Chief Financial Officer, Raleigh General Hospital, Beckley, WV, p. A689
HARROD, Tracy, Director of Nursing, Greenwood County Hospital, Eureka, KS, p. A239
HARRON, Rick, Chief Financial Officer, Dominican Hospital, Santa Cruz, CA, p. A91
HARROP, Elizabeth, Director, Human Resources, Flambeau Hospital, Park Falls, WI, p. A709
HARROP, Phil, Executive Director Operations, Saint Alphonsus Medical Center – Nampa, Nampa, ID, p. A175
HARRYMAN, John D., Chief Administrative Officer, Norton Brownsboro Hospital, Louisville, KY, p. A261
HARSHAWAT, Paras, M.D. Medical Director, Harsha Behavioral Center, Terre Haute, IN, p. A220
HARSHBARGER, Catherine S., R.N., Chief Executive Officer, Banner Lassen Medical Center, Susanville, CA, p. A93
HARSY, Brice, Chief Financial Officer, Marshall Browning Hospital, Du Quoin, IL, p. A186
HART, Amy, Chief Operating Officer, Cuyuna Regional Medical Center, Crosby, MN, p. A337
HART, Chet, Vice President Operations, Sentara CarePlex Hospital, Hampton, VA, p. A666
HART, Deborah, Chief Financial Officer, North Suburban Medical Center, Thornton, CO, p. A109
HART, Denise, Director Human Resources, Sullivan County Community Hospital, Sullivan, IN, p. A220
HART, Donna, Chief Information Officer, Provident Hospital of Cook County, Chicago, IL, p. A184
HART, Gary, M.D. Chief Medical Officer, Claxton–Hepburn Medical Center, Ogdensburg, NY, p. A446
HART, John, Chief Executive Officer, Fredonia Regional Hospital, Fredonia, KS, p. A240
HART, Joline, Vice President Human Resources, Franklin Memorial Hospital, Farmington, ME, p. A290
HART, Ken, Vice President Operations, Saint Alphonsus Medical Center – Ontario, Ontario, OR, p. A523
HART, Linda, Vice President Finance, Grady Memorial Hospital, Chickasha, OK, p. A505
HART, Lisa, Chief Executive Officer, Elkview General Hospital, Hobart, OK, p. A508
HART, Michael, M.D. Medical Director, Stamford Memorial Hospital, Stamford, TX, p. A645
HART, Monique, Chief Financial Officer, Baptist Memorial Hospital–Tipton, Covington, TN, p. A576
HART, Pat, Director Human Resources, Three Rivers Medical Center, Louisa, KY, p. A260
HART, Richard, Chief Financial Officer, Stanislaus Surgical Hospital, Modesto, CA, p. A76
HART, Richard H., M.D., President and Chief Executive Officer, Loma Linda University Adventist Health Sciences Center, Loma Linda, CA, p. B85
HART, Scott, Controller, HEALTHSOUTH Lakeview Rehabilitation Hospital, Elizabethtown, KY, p. A256
HART, Steve, Controller, Kindred Hospital North Florida, Green Cove Springs, FL, p. A128
HART–FLYNN, Wilma, Ph.D. Vice President Patient Care Services and Chief Nursing Officer, Illinois Valley Community Hospital, Peru, IL, p. A198
HARTBERG, David, Administrator, Gundersen Boscobel Area Hospital and Clinics, Boscobel, WI, p. A698
HARTE, Brian J., M.D., President, Hillcrest Hospital, Cleveland, OH, p. A484
HARTER, Dan, Manager Information Systems, PMH Medical Center, Prosser, WA, p. A682
HARTGRAVES, Steve L., President and Chief Executive Officer, Jackson County Memorial Hospital, Altus, OK, p. A503
HARTKE, Michael, Executive Vice President, Chief Operating Officer, Northwest Community Hospital, Arlington Heights, IL, p. A178
HARTLE, Christopher L., President, Seton Medical Center Hays, Kyle, TX, p. A626
HARTLEY, Diane L., R.N. Director of Patient Care Services, Beaumont Hospital – Wayne, Wayne, MI, p. A332
HARTLEY, Melinda D., R.N. Vice President Patient Care Services, Perry Hospital, Perry, GA, p. A162
HARTLEY, Michael, MS Chief Nursing Officer, Holly Hill Hospital, Raleigh, NC, p. A466
HARTLEY, Michael Ward, Director Human Resources, AllianceHealth Midwest, Midwest City, OK, p. A510
HARTLEY, Norma, Director Human Resources, Power County Hospital District, American Falls, ID, p. A172
HARTLEY, Shauna, Hospital Administrator, Turquoise Lodge Hospital, Albuquerque, NM, p. A423
HARTLEY, Shawn, Chief Financial Officer, Crossroads Community Hospital, Mount Vernon, IL, p. A195
HARTLEY, Wannah, Controller, Winkler County Memorial Hospital, Kermit, TX, p. A625
HARTLEY, William, FACHE, Interim Chief Executive Officer, Marias Medical Center, Shelby, MT, p. A387
HARTMAN, Daphne, Director Information Systems, College Station Medical Center, College Station, TX, p. A601
HARTMAN, Dennis, Chief Financial Officer, Excelsior Springs Hospital, Excelsior Springs, MO, p. A367
HARTMAN, Don, Director Human Resources, Sutter Davis Hospital, Davis, CA, p. A59
HARTMAN, Kathleen, Chief Nursing Officer, MetroSouth Medical Center, Blue Island, IL, p. A180
HARTMAN, Sally, Senior Vice President, Riverside Regional Medical Center, Newport News, VA, p. A669
HARTMAN, Susan, Chief Executive Officer, HEALTHSOUTH Nittany Valley Rehabilitation Hospital, Pleasant Gap, PA, p. A547
HARTMANN, Doreen, Chief Financial Officer, St. Joseph's Behavioral Health Center, Stockton, CA, p. A93
HARTMANN, Margot, Ph.D., President and Chief Executive Officer, Nantucket Cottage Hospital, Nantucket, MA, p. A309
HARTMANN, Peter M., M.D. Vice President Medical Affairs, York Hospital, York, PA, p. A554
HARTMANN, Rob, Assistant Director Human Resources Management, University Health Conway, Monroe, LA, p. A281
HARTNETT, Tammy, Employee Relations Manager, UnityPoint Health – St. Luke's, Sioux City, IA, p. A235
HARTSELL, Scott, Chief Operating Officer, Bayfront Health Brooksville, Brooksville, FL, p. A123
HARTTER, Lynn, Director Human Resources, Nemaha Valley Community Hospital, Seneca, KS, p. A250
HARTUNG, Andy, Director Information Systems, Self Regional Healthcare, Greenwood, SC, p. A562
HARTWICK, Bryan
Vice President Human Resources, Alton Memorial Hospital, Alton, IL, p. A178
Vice President Human Resources, Christian Hospital, Saint Louis, MO, p. A376
HARTWIG, Michael, M.D. Chief of Staff, Perry Memorial Hospital, Perry, OK, p. A513
HARVEY, Alice, Director of Nursing, Heatherhill Care Communities, Chardon, OH, p. A481
HARVEY, Anne, MSN Chief Nursing Officer, El Paso Specialty Hospital, El Paso, TX, p. A610
HARVEY, John, M.D., President and Chief Executive Officer, Oklahoma Heart Hospital, Oklahoma City, OK, p. A512
HARVEY, John, M.D. President and Chief Executive Officer, Oklahoma Heart Hospital, Oklahoma City, OK, p. A512
HARVEY, John, M.D., President and Chief Executive Officer, Oklahoma Heart Hospital South Campus, Oklahoma City, OK, p. A512
HARVEY, Kathy, D.O. Chief Medical Officer, Logan Regional Medical Center, Logan, WV, p. A692
HARVEY, Kevin, Chief Financial Officer, McKenzie Regional Hospital, McKenzie, TN, p. A582
HARVEY, Laurie, Controller, El Campo Memorial Hospital, El Campo, TX, p. A610
HARVEY, Linda, Chief Financial Officer, West Feliciana Parish Hospital, Saint Francisville, LA, p. A284
HARVEY, Michael, FACHE President and Chief Executive Officer, Community Memorial Hospital, Syracuse, NE, p. A398
HARVILL, Brian
Vice President Financial Services, Vidant Bertie Hospital, Windsor, NC, p. A470
Vice President Financial Services, Vidant Chowan Hospital, Edenton, NC, p. A459
HARYASZ, Sandy, R.N., Chief Executive Officer, Page Hospital, Page, AZ, p. A34
HASBROUCK, Matthew Steven, Chief Operating Officer, Fairview Park Hospital, Dublin, GA, p. A156
HASELTON, David, Chief Medical Officer, Riverton Hospital, Riverton, UT, p. A657
HASHMI, Mubashir, Chief Information Officer, Pacifica Hospital of the Valley, CA, p. A72
HASHMI, Suleman, President and Chief Executive Officer, Texas General Hospital, Grand Prairie, TX, p. A616
HASKELL, Jeffrey, M.D. Chief Medical Staff, Lost Rivers Medical Center, Arco, ID, p. A172
HASKINS, Don, Administrative Director Human Resources, Southwest Mississippi Regional Medical Center, McComb, MS, p. A357
HASLER, Marge, R.N. Vice President Patient Care Services and Chief Nursing Officer, Beaumont Hospital – Farmington Hills, Farmington Hills, MI, p. A319
HASNI, Kamran, M.D. Chief of Medical Staff, Knox County Hospital, Barbourville, KY, p. A254
HASS, Brian, M.D. Chief of Staff, St. Francis Memorial Hospital, West Point, NE, p. A399
HASS, Roxanne, Director of Nursing, Madison St. Joseph Health Center, Madisonville, TX, p. A630
HASSAN, Tariq, M.D. Associate Director of Patient Care, Captain James A. Lovell Federal Health Care Center, North Chicago, IL, p. A196
HASSANI, Dahlia, Vice President of Medical Affairs, Baylor All Saints Medical Center at Fort Worth, Fort Worth, TX, p. A613
HASSELBARTH, William C., Chief Financial Officer, Albany Medical Center, Albany, NY, p. A428
HASSELBRACK, Jeni, Director Human Resources, Gordon Hospital, Calhoun, GA, p. A153
HASSLER, Robert, M.D. Director Medical Affairs, Novant Health Brunswick Medical Center, Bolivia, NC, p. A456
HAST, Anne S., R.N., Chief Executive Officer, Advanced Surgical Hospital, Washington, PA, p. A552
HASTIN, Kathy, Administrative Assistant Human Resources, River Valley Medical Center, Dardanelle, AR, p. A43
HASTINGS, Bryan J., Interim Chief Executive Officer, Florence Hospital at Anthem, Florence, AZ, p. A31
HASTINGS, Clare, R.N. Chief Nurse Officer, National Institutes of Health Clinical Center, Bethesda, MD, p. A296
HASTINGS, James E., M.D., Director, Veterans Affairs Pacific Islands Health Care System, Honolulu, HI, p. A169
HASTINGS, Sarah M., Executive Director, Ridgeview Medical Center, Waconia, MN, p. A348
HASTINGS–SMITH, Julie, Chief Financial Officer, Abrazo Maryvale Campus, Phoenix, AZ, p. A34
HATA, Marilynn, Vice President Finance and Operations, North Hawaii Community Hospital, Kamuela, HI, p. A169
HATALA, Alexander J., FACHE, President and Chief Executive Officer, Our Lady of Lourdes Medical Center, Camden, NJ, p. A410
HATCH, Tammy, Manager, Sebasticook Valley Health, Pittsfield, ME, p. A291
HATCHEL, Kimberly Kay, Chief Nursing Officer, Medical Center of McKinney, McKinney, TX, p. A632
HATCHER, Amy, Chief Financial Officer, Children's Hospital and Medical Center, Omaha, NE, p. A396
HATCHER, Julie, Vice President Human Resources, O'Connor Hospital, San Jose, CA, p. A89
HATFIELD, Chad, Chief Executive Officer, Barrow Regional Medical Center, Winder, GA, p. A167
HATFIELD, Jonathan, Supervisor Information Technology, Klickitat Valley Health, Goldendale, WA, p. A679
HATFIELD, Timothy A., Community Chief Executive Officer, Tug Valley ARH Regional Medical Center, South Williamson, KY, p. A266
HATHAWAY, William, M.D. Chief Medical Officer, Mission Hospital, Asheville, NC, p. A455
HATHCOCK, Claudette
Administrative Director Human Resources, University of Mississippi Medical Center Grenada, Grenada, MS, p. A353
Human Resources Director, University of Mississippi Medical Center Holmes County, Lexington, MS, p. A356
HATIRAS, Spiros, FACHE, President and Chief Executive Officer, Holyoke Medical Center, Holyoke, MA, p. A307

© 2015 AHA Guide Index of Health Care Professionals **A861**

Index of Health Care Professionals

Index of Health Care Professionals / Hatlestad

HATLESTAD, Jill, Vice President Human Resources and Marketing, Glencoe Regional Health Services, Glencoe, MN, p. A339
HATSFELT, Annette Wyble, Chief Nursing Officer, Oakdale Community Hospital, Oakdale, LA, p. A283
HATTEM, Marita, Interim President and Chief Operating Officer, Aspirus Wausau Hospital, Wausau, WI, p. A713
HATTERER–HOAG, Dawn, Director Human Resources, Psychiatric Institute of Washington, Washington, DC, p. A120
HATTON, Julia
  Chief Financial Officer, Nexus Specialty Hospital, Shenandoah, TX, p. A643
  Chief Financial Officer, Nexus Specialty Hospital The Woodlands, Spring, TX, p. A644
HATTON, Tad, Chief Operating Officer, St. David's Round Rock Medical Center, Round Rock, TX, p. A639
HAUBL, Eileen, Senior Vice President and Chief Financial Officer, Mission Hospital, Mission Viejo, CA, p. A75
HAUG, Darin L., D.O., President and Chief Executive Officer, Fitzgibbon Hospital, Marshall, MO, p. A372
HAUGE, Meri, R.N. Associate Director of Patient Care Services and Nurse Executive, St. Cloud Veterans Affairs Health Care System, Saint Cloud, MN, p. A346
HAUGEN, O. G., Director Resources, Naval Medical Center San Diego, San Diego, CA, p. A86
HAUGH, William, Administrator, Georgetown Community Hospital, Georgetown, KY, p. A257
HAUN, Richard, Chief Financial Officer, Wuesthoff Medical Center – Rockledge, Rockledge, FL, p. A141
HAUPERT, John M., FACHE, Chief Executive Officer, Grady Memorial Hospital, Atlanta, GA, p. A150
HAUSAUER, Patricia K., Director Finance, Baptist Medical Center Nassau, Fernandina Beach, FL, p. A126
HAUSE, Eileen, Chief Executive Officer, Kensington Hospital, Philadelphia, PA, p. A544
HAUSER, Mark J., M.D. Chief Medical Officer, Baptist Health South Florida, Baptist Hospital of Miami, Miami, FL, p. A133
HAUSER, Megan, Director Human Resources, Shriners Hospitals for Children–Philadelphia, Philadelphia, PA, p. A545
HAUSHALTER, Richard L., Senior Vice President Operations and Chief Operating Officer, Sentara RMH Medical Center, Harrisonburg, VA, p. A666
HAUSMANN, Jena, President and Chief Executive Officer, Children's Hospital Colorado, Aurora, CO, p. A99
HAUSMANN, Sherry, Senior Administrator, Via Christi Hospital on St. Francis, Wichita, KS, p. A253
HAUSWIRTH, Michael
  Chief Operating Officer, Aspirus Keweenaw Hospital, Laurium, MI, p. A324
  Chief Operating Officer, Aspirus Keweenaw Hospital, Laurium, MI, p. A324
  Chief Operating Officer, Aspirus Ontonagon Hospital, Ontonagon, MI, p. A327
  Chief Operating Officer, Aspirus Ontonagon Hospital, Ontonagon, MI, p. A327
HAUSWIRTH, Renay, Chief Financial Officer, Palo Alto County Health System, Emmetsburg, IA, p. A227
HAVARD, Greg, Administrator, George Regional Hospital, Lucedale, MS, p. A356
HAVEN, Adrian C., Site Manager, Gallup Indian Medical Center, Gallup, NM, p. A424
HAVENS, Jennifer, Director of Nursing and Chief Executive Officer, Grundy County Memorial Hospital, Grundy Center, IA, p. A228
HAVERSTOCK, Loren, Manager Human Resources, Harrison County Hospital, Corydon, IN, p. A206
HAVRILLA, David A., Chief Financial Officer, MedStar Montgomery Medical Center, Olney, MD, p. A299
HAWIG, Scott
  Chief Financial Officer and Senior Vice President Finance and Treasurer, Froedtert Memorial Lutheran Hospital, Milwaukee, WI, p. A706
  Chief Financial Officer, St. Joseph's Hospital, West Bend, WI, p. A714
HAWK, Kevin, Chief Executive Officer, Hillcrest Hospital Cushing, Cushing, OK, p. A505
HAWKES, Reed, Chief Information Officer, Wills Memorial Hospital, Washington, GA, p. A167
HAWKEY, Tammy, Manager Information Technology Client Services, Ministry Saint Clare's Hospital, Weston, WI, p. A714
HAWKINS, Brian A., Director, Washington DC Veterans Affairs Medical Center, Washington, DC, p. A120
HAWKINS, Bryan, Controller, FirstHealth Montgomery Memorial Hospital, Troy, NC, p. A469
HAWKINS, Carl, M.D. Chief of Staff, Mackinac Straits Health System, Inc., Saint Ignace, MI, p. A329
HAWKINS, Ellis, President, SSM St. Clare Health Center, Fenton, MO, p. A367
HAWKINS, Erick, Chief Financial Officer, Rex Healthcare, Raleigh, NC, p. A467
HAWKINS, Hillary, M.D. Medical Director, Sheltering Arms Rehabilitation Hospital, Mechanicsville, VA, p. A668
HAWKINS, Janine, R.N. Vice President Patient Care Services and Chief Nursing Officer, Dameron Hospital, Stockton, CA, p. A93
HAWKINS, Jason F.
  President and Chief Executive Officer, Fulton County Medical Center, Mc Connellsburg, PA, p. A539
  President and Chief Executive Officer, J. C. Blair Memorial Hospital, Huntingdon, PA, p. A536
HAWKINS, Sheri, Chief Nursing Officer, Shawnee Mission Medical Center, Shawnee Mission, KS, p. A250
HAWKINS, Tami, R.N. Vice President Patient Care and Chief Nursing Officer, Texas Health Presbyterian Hospital of Rockwall, Rockwall, TX, p. A639
HAWKINSON, Curtis R., Chief Executive Officer, Community Memorial Healthcare, Marysville, KS, p. A246
HAWLEY, Candice, Chief Nursing Executive, Washington County Hospital, Nashville, IL, p. A196
HAWLEY, Claudia, Director Human Resources, Mason General Hospital, Shelton, WA, p. A684
HAWLEY, Jason, Manager Information Services, Yuma District Hospital, Yuma, CO, p. A110
HAWTHORNE, Kimberly, Administrator, Mayo Clinic Health System – Franciscan Healthcare in Sparta, Sparta, WI, p. A711
HAWTOF, Jeffrey, M.D. Vice President Medical Operations and Informatics, Beebe Healthcare, Lewes, DE, p. A117
HAXTON, Rita K., R.N. Vice President Patient Care Nursing, Rapid City Regional Hospital, Rapid City, SD, p. A570
HAY, Morgan, Chief Financial Officer, Gerald Champion Regional Medical Center, Alamogordo, NM, p. A422
HAYDEN, Crystal, MSN Chief Nursing Officer, Onslow Memorial Hospital, Jacksonville, NC, p. A463
HAYDEN, James, M.D. Chief Medical Officer, J. C. Blair Memorial Hospital, Huntingdon, PA, p. A536
HAYDEN, Jamie, Chief Financial Officer, Eastland Memorial Hospital, Eastland, TX, p. A609
HAYDEN, John
  Senior Vice President and Human Resources Officer, Bronson Battle Creek, Battle Creek, MI, p. A315
  Senior Vice President and Chief Human Resources Officer, Bronson LakeView Hospital, Paw Paw, MI, p. A327
  Vice President and Chief Human Resources Officer, Bronson Methodist Hospital, Kalamazoo, MI, p. A323
HAYDEN, Karen, Director Health Information Services, Performance Improvement and Risk Management, Valle Vista Hospital, Greenwood, IN, p. A210
HAYDEN, Sheryl, Chief Financial Officer, Sierra Surgery Hospital, Carson City, NV, p. A400
HAYDEN–PUGH, Beverly P., R.N. Senior Vice President and Chief Nursing Officer, Valley Children's Hospital, Madera, CA, p. A74
HAYEK, Anthony, D.O. Medical Director, Edwin Shaw Rehab, Cuyahoga Falls, OH, p. A487
HAYES, Brian T., Commander, David Grant USAF Medical Center, Travis AFB, CA, p. A94
HAYES, Cheryl, Vice President Patient Care Services, Kenmore Mercy Hospital, Kenmore, NY, p. A436
HAYES, David R., Chief Financial Officer, Westlake Regional Hospital, Columbia, KY, p. A255
HAYES, Deborah Marie, R.N. Chief Hospital Officer and Chief Nursing Officer, Christ Hospital, Cincinnati, OH, p. A482
HAYES, Di, Chief Executive Officer, Hallmark Youthcare – Richmond, Richmond, VA, p. A671
HAYES, Donna, Controller, Decatur County General Hospital, Parsons, TN, p. A587
HAYES, Elaine, Controller, Sts. Mary & Elizabeth Hospital, Louisville, KY, p. A262
HAYES, Farrell, President and Chief Executive Officer, Hutcheson Medical Center, Fort Oglethorpe, GA, p. A158
HAYES, George E., FACHE, President and Chief Executive Officer, Memorial Hospital, Colorado Springs, CO, p. A100
HAYES, James L., Director Human Resources, Western State Hospital, Hopkinsville, KY, p. A258
HAYES, James M., Chief Executive Officer, UnityPoint Health – Trinity Muscatine, Muscatine, IA, p. A232
HAYES, Jo, Chief Nursing Officer, Horn Memorial Hospital, Ida Grove, IA, p. A229
HAYES, Judy M., R.N. Vice President Nursing and Chief Nursing Officer, Brigham and Women's Faulkner Hospital, Boston, MA, p. A303
HAYES, June, Chief Financial Officer, Harrisburg Medical Center, Harrisburg, IL, p. A189
HAYES, Kathe, Executive Director, Western New York Children's Psychiatric Center, West Seneca, NY, p. A454
HAYES, Kelly
  Chief Financial Officer, Methodist Hospital for Surgery, Addison, TX, p. A590
  Chief Financial Officer, North Texas Medical Center, Gainesville, TX, p. A615
HAYES, Kevin, M.D. Chief of Staff, Pioneer Community Hospital of Aberdeen, Aberdeen, MS, p. A350
HAYES, Kim, Director Human Resources, Bibb Medical Center, Centreville, AL, p. A18
HAYES, Paul, Executive Director, UW Medicine/Harborview Medical Center, Seattle, WA, p. A684
HAYES, Sharon, Chief Executive Officer, Palms of Pasadena Hospital, Saint Petersburg, FL, p. A142
HAYES, Stacy, R.N. Chief Nursing Officer, Arizona Spine and Joint Hospital, Mesa, AZ, p. A33
HAYES, Susan, Director Human Resources, Southeastern Health, Lumberton, NC, p. A464
HAYES, Tammy A., R.N. Chief Nurse Executive and Long Term Care Administrator, Northfield Hospital, Northfield, MN, p. A344
HAYES, Thomas P., Chief Executive Officer, Eastern Plumas Health Care, Portola, CA, p. A81
HAYES, Warren, Chief of Staff, Montgomery County Memorial Hospital, Red Oak, IA, p. A233
HAYES, William M., Chief Executive Officer, Northside Hospital–Cherokee, Canton, GA, p. A153
HAYGOOD, Rachel Joy, Director Information Technology, Tyler County Hospital, Woodville, TX, p. A653
HAYHURST, Leslie, Director Information Systems, Washington Health System Greene, Waynesburg, PA, p. A552
HAYMON, Beverly, Chief Financial Officer, Princeton Baptist Medical Center, Birmingham, AL, p. A16
HAYNES, Apryl, R.N., Vice President, Chief Operating Officer, Chief Nursing Officer and Administrator, Seton Edgar B. Davis Hospital, Luling, TX, p. A630
HAYNES, Christopher, Chief Executive Officer, Kindred Hospital–Greensboro, Greensboro, NC, p. A461
HAYNES, Deatosha D., Interim Associates Director for Patient, Veterans Affairs Gulf Coast Veterans Health Care System, Biloxi, MS, p. A350
HAYNES, Elaine S., R.N. Vice President Patient Services and Chief Nursing Executive, Carolinas HealthCare System Lincoln, Lincolnton, NC, p. A464
HAYNES, Jamil, Regional Director Human Resources, Integris Baptist Regional Health Center, Miami, OK, p. A509
HAYNES, Jerry, President and Chief Executive Officer, Appalachian Regional Healthcare, Inc., Lexington, KY, p. B11
HAYNES, Jill, Financial Coach, Bath Veterans Affairs Medical Center, Bath, NY, p. A429
HAYNES, Jr., John H., M.D. Chief of Medical Staff, North Caddo Medical Center, Vivian, LA, p. A286
HAYNES, Ken, President and Chief Executive Officer, CHRISTUS Santa Rosa Health System, San Antonio, TX, p. A640
HAYNES, Laurie, Chief Financial Officer, Gulf Coast Regional Medical Center, Panama City, FL, p. A139
HAYNES, Mark, M.D. Chief of Staff, Claiborne Memorial Medical Center, Homer, LA, p. A275
HAYNES, Robert, FACHE, Chief Executive Officer, Guadalupe Regional Medical Center, Seguin, TX, p. A643
HAYNES, William, Director Information Technology, Central Louisiana State Hospital, Pineville, LA, p. A283
HAYS, Cheryl M., FACHE, Administrator, Marshall Medical Center North, Guntersville, AL, p. A20
HAYS, Chuck, President and Chief Executive Officer, MaineGeneral Medical Center, Augusta, ME, p. A288
HAYS, Larry, Director Information Technology, Southern Virginia Mental Health Institute, Danville, VA, p. A664
HAYS, Richard, M.D. Chief of Staff, Wellington Regional Medical Center, West Palm Beach, FL, p. A147
HAYS, Richard O., Chief Fiscal Service, Veterans Affairs Southern Nevada Healthcare System, North Las Vegas, NV, p. A403
HAYS, Timothy A., Vice President Human Resources, Johnston Health, Smithfield, NC, p. A468
HAYTAIAN, Mike, Head Director Information Resources Management, Naval Hospital Jacksonville, Jacksonville, FL, p. A129
HAYTON, Gregg, Vice President Finance and Chief Financial Officer, Our Lady of Lourdes Memorial Hospital, Inc., Binghamton, NY, p. A429
HAYWARD, Ernest, M.D. Chief of Staff, Saddleback Memorial Medical Center, Laguna Hills, CA, p. A66
HAYWOOD, Nancy
  Chief Financial Officer, Genesys Regional Medical Center, Grand Blanc, MI, p. A320
  Chief Financial Officer, St. Mary's of Michigan, Saginaw, MI, p. A329
HAYWOOD, Stephanie, Director Human Resources, Southern Virginia Mental Health Institute, Danville, VA, p. A664

HAZELBAKER, Matthew, M.D. President Medical Staff, Memorial Health, Marysville, OH, p. A493

HAZZARD, Aaron R., Interim Chief Executive Officer, MetroSouth Medical Center, Blue Island, IL, p. A180

HEAD, David, M.D. Chief Medical Staff, Norton Sound Regional Hospital, Nome, AK, p. A28

HEADLAND, Mark
Chief Information Officer, Children's Hospital of Orange County, Orange, CA, p. A79
Chief Information Officer, CHOC Children's at Mission Hospital, Mission Viejo, CA, p. A75

HEALD, Robin R., Vice President Human Resources, Brattleboro Memorial Hospital, Brattleboro, VT, p. A660

HEALEA, Pamela S., Director Human Resources, PMH Medical Center, Prosser, WA, p. A682

HEALY, John, Manager Information Technology, Friends Hospital, Philadelphia, PA, p. A543

HEALY, Peter J., Chief Executive Officer, Beth Israel Deaconess Hospital–Milton, Milton, MA, p. A309

HEALY, Stan, Administrator, North Greenville Hospital, Travelers Rest, SC, p. A565

HEALY, Victoria, Chief Executive Officer, HEALTHSOUTH Rehabilitation Hospital of Western Massachusetts, Ludlow, MA, p. A308

HEARD, Alex, Chief Medical Officer, Falmouth Hospital, Falmouth, MA, p. A306

HEARD, Heather, Director Human Resources, Holdenville General Hospital, Holdenville, OK, p. A508

HEARD, John E., Chief Executive Officer, McGehee–Desha County Hospital, McGehee, AR, p. A48

HEARD, M. Denise, Director Business Services, North Mississippi Medical Center–Pontotoc, Pontotoc, MS, p. A359

HEARN, Gregory K., Chief Executive Officer, Ty Cobb Healthcare System, Inc., Royston, GA, p. B

HEARNE, Diane, Director Human Resources, Arizona Spine and Joint Hospital, Mesa, AZ, p. A33

HEARNSBERGER, John, M.D. Chief of Staff, Howard Memorial Hospital, Nashville, AR, p. A48

HEARTSILL, Keith
Vice President of Finance, Anderson Regional Medical Center, Meridian, MS, p. A357
Vice President Finance, Anderson Regional Medical Center–South Campus, Meridian, MS, p. A357

HEATER, Floyd
President, Shenandoah Memorial Hospital, Woodstock, VA, p. A675
Interim President and Chief Executive Officer, Warren Memorial Hospital, Front Royal, VA, p. A665

HEATH, Benjamin, Interim Chief Executive Officer, AllianceHealth Seminole, Seminole, OK, p. A514

HEATH, Ed, Chief Executive Officer, Owensboro Health Muhlenberg Community Hospital, Greenville, KY, p. A257

HEATH, Susan, R.N. Senior Vice President and Chief Nursing Officer, Seattle Children's Hospital, Seattle, WA, p. A683

HEATHERLY, John
Assistant Administrator Support Services, Hunt Regional Community Hospital, Commerce, TX, p. A602
Assistant Administrator Support Services, Hunt Regional Medical Center, Greenville, TX, p. A617

HEATHERLY, Neil, Interim Chief Executive Officer, Tennova Physicians Regional Medical Center, Knoxville, TN, p. A580

HEATHERLY, Steve
Chief Executive Officer, Harris Regional Hospital, Sylva, NC, p. A469
Chief Executive Officer, Swain Community Hospital, Bryson City, NC, p. A456

HEATHERLY–LLOYD, Sara, Chief Operating Officer, Tennova Healthcare–LaFollette Medical Center, La Follette, TN, p. A581

HEATON, Crystal, Director of Finance, St. Mary's Warrick Hospital, Boonville, IN, p. A205

HEATON, John, M.D. Senior Vice President and Medical Director, Children's Hospital, New Orleans, LA, p. A281

HEBBERD, Hilda, R.N. Senior Director Clinical Services, Marlette Regional Hospital, Marlette, MI, p. A325

HEBEL, Barbara, Vice President Human Resources, Doylestown Hospital, Doylestown, PA, p. A533

HEBERT, Jr., Bernie, Chief Financial Officer, Doctors NeuroMedical Hospital, Bremen, IN, p. A205

HEBERT, Bryan, Director Information Systems, The Medical Center of Southeast Texas, Port Arthur, TX, p. A637

HEBERT, Gerard, Chief Financial Officer, Texoma Medical Center, Denison, TX, p. A607

HEBERT, Jeff, Interim Vice President Finance, Gifford Medical Center, Randolph, VT, p. A661

HEBERT, Katherine D., Chief Operating Officer, University Hospital and Clinics, Lafayette, LA, p. A278

HEBERT, Mark, M.D. President Medical Staff, Medical City Dallas Hospital, Dallas, TX, p. A605

HEBERT, Rachel, Chief Financial Officer, Heart Hospital of Lafayette, Lafayette, LA, p. A277

HEBERT, Raquel, Business Manager, Memorial Hermann Surgical HospitalG‰(First Colony, Sugar Land, TX, p. A645

HEBERT, Timothy, Director Human Resources, Teche Regional Medical Center, Morgan City, LA, p. A281

HEBGEN, Lynn, Vice President Nursing, Upland Hills Health, Dodgeville, WI, p. A699

HECHLER, Tracy, Healthcare Director Information Services, Chippenham Hospital, Richmond, VA, p. A671

HECHT, David, M.D. Chief of Staff, James H. Quillen Veterans Affairs Medical Center, Mountain Home, TN, p. A585

HECKATHORNE, Daniel R.
System Chief Financial Officer, East Los Angeles Doctors Hospital, Los Angeles, CA, p. A69
Chief Financial Officer, Memorial Hospital of Gardena, Gardena, CA, p. A63

HECKER, Cynthia, R.N., Executive Director, UW Medicine/Northwest Hospital & Medical Center, Seattle, WA, p. A684

HECKER, Lisa, Director Human Resources, Hedrick Medical Center, Chillicothe, MO, p. A365

HECKERMAN, Ray, Chief Executive Officer and Managing Director, Coastal Harbor Treatment Center, Savannah, GA, p. A164

HECKERT Jr., Robert J., Chief Executive Officer, Gerald Champion Regional Medical Center, Alamogordo, NM, p. A422

HECKLER, Edward, Administrator, Riverside Rehabilitation Institute, Newport News, VA, p. A669

HEDBERG, Beth, R.N. Director Nursing, Lindsborg Community Hospital, Lindsborg, KS, p. A245

HEDDE, Charles C., M.D. Chief Medical Officer, Good Samaritan Hospital, Vincennes, IN, p. A221

HEDDEN, Elizabeth A., Chief Financial Officer, Johnson Memorial Hospital, Franklin, IN, p. A209

HEDDERMAN, Michael, Senior Vice President Finance and Chief Financial Officer, Marianjoy Rehabilitation Hospital, Wheaton, IL, p. A203

HEDGES, David, Chief Financial Officer, Southwestern Regional Medical Center, Tulsa, OK, p. A517

HEDIGER, Joseph, Chief Financial Officer, Fox Chase Cancer Center–American Oncologic Hospital, Philadelphia, PA, p. A543

HEDLEY, Kristen, Controller, Huron Medical Center, Bad Axe, MI, p. A314

HEDLUND, Chris, Director Information Systems, Community Hospital–Fairfax, Fairfax, MO, p. A367

HEDRIX, Michael D., Administrator and President, Essentia Health Sandstone, Sandstone, MN, p. A347

HEEMANN, John, Chief Information Officer, Aspire Hospital, Conroe, TX, p. A602

HEETER, Eric, Superintendent, Larue D. Carter Memorial Hospital, Indianapolis, IN, p. A212

HEFFERNAN, Paul F., Vice President Human Resources, Women & Infants Hospital of Rhode Island, Providence, RI, p. A556

HEFFERNAN, Rebecca, Director Human Resources, MetroWest Medical Center, Framingham, MA, p. A307

HEFFERS, Margaret, Assistant Vice President Human Resources, Geisinger Wyoming Valley Medical Center, Wilkes Barre, PA, p. A553

HEFFLINGER, Larry, Director Information Systems, Fulton County Health Center, Wauseon, OH, p. A500

HEFLIN, Clyde, M.D. Chief Medical Officer, Kindred Hospital–Nashville, Nashville, TN, p. A585

HEFNER, Donna J., R.N., President and Chief Executive Officer, Sierra View Medical Center, Porterville, CA, p. A81

HEFNER, Kathy, Chief Nursing Officer, McDowell Hospital, Marion, NC, p. A464

HEGGEM, Mark, M.D. Chief Medical Officer, Riverwood Healthcare Center, Aitkin, MN, p. A334

HEGGEN, Karra, R.N. Vice President Nursing, Elkhart General Healthcare System, Elkhart, IN, p. A207

HEGGEN, Steve, Administrative Director Human Resources, St. Joseph Hospital, Fort Wayne, IN, p. A209

HEGGER, John, Director Information Systems, Union County Hospital, Anna, IL, p. A178

HEGLAND, Sandra, Chief Executive Officer, HEALTHSOUTH Rehabilitation Hospital of Austin, Austin, TX, p. A594

HEGWOOD, Wayne, Chief Financial Officer, Acuity Hospital of South Texas, San Antonio, TX, p. A640

HEHEMANN, Bryan D., President and Chief Executive Officer, McCullough–Hyde Memorial Hospital/TriHealth, Oxford, OH, p. A496

HEICHERT, Susan
Senior Vice President and Chief Information Officer, Abbott Northwestern Hospital, Minneapolis, MN, p. A342
Chief Information Officer, Mercy Hospital, Coon Rapids, MN, p. A337
Senior Vice President, United Hospital, Saint Paul, MN, p. A346
Chief Information Officer, Unity Hospital, Fridley, MN, p. A339

HEIDER, John R., Vice President Finance, Augusta Health, Fishersville, VA, p. A664

HEIDT, Robert, Director Information Systems, Pembina County Memorial Hospital and Wedgewood Manor, Cavalier, ND, p. A473

HEIFNER, Bruce, Chief Financial Officer, Pella Regional Health Center, Pella, IA, p. A233

HEIFNER, Robert A., Chief Executive Officer, St. Luke's Sugar Land Hospital, Sugar Land, TX, p. A646

HEIGHES, Brenna, Manager Information Technology, Mt. Ascutney Hospital and Health Center, Windsor, VT, p. A661

HEIKKINEN, Todd, Manager Sports Medicine and Rehabilitation Services, Orthopaedic Hospital of Wisconsin – Glendale, Glendale, WI, p. A701

HEILSBERG, Jim, Chief Financial Officer and Chief Information Officer, Whitman Hospital and Medical Center, Colfax, WA, p. A677

HEIM, Nicole, Chief Information Officer, Milford Regional Medical Center, Milford, MA, p. A309

HEIM, Richard, President, Advocate South Suburban Hospital, Hazel Crest, IL, p. A190

HEIM, Tonya, R.N. Vice President Patient Services and Chief Nursing Officer, Memorial Hospital and Health Care Center, Jasper, IN, p. A213

HEIMALL, Michael S., Commander, William Beaumont Army Medical Center, El Paso, TX, p. A611

HEIMAN, Thomas, Vice President Information Services and Chief Information Officer, John T. Mather Memorial Hospital, Port Jefferson, NY, p. A447

HEINECK, Susan, M.D. President Professional Staff, Providence Seaside Hospital, Seaside, OR, p. A526

HEINEMANN, Don, Administrator and Chief Executive Officer, Blount Memorial Hospital, Maryville, TN, p. A582

HEINEMEIER, Robert
Chief Financial Officer, Chapman Medical Center, Orange, CA, p. A79
Chief Financial Officer, Coastal Communities Hospital, Santa Ana, CA, p. A90

HEINISCH, Sheri, Compliance Officer, CHI Lisbon Health, Lisbon, ND, p. A475

HEINRICH, Bill, Chief Financial Officer, Florida Hospital Zephyrhills, Zephyrhills, FL, p. A148

HEINRICH, Kerry, JD, Chief Executive Officer, Loma Linda University Medical Center, Loma Linda, CA, p. A67

HEINRICH, Michael G., Executive Vice President and Chief Financial Officer, Mercy Iowa City, Iowa City, IA, p. A229

HEINRICHS, Alice, CPA Chief Financial Officer, Van Diest Medical Center, Webster City, IA, p. A236

HEINS, Patrick, Vice President Patient Care Services, Vidant Edgecombe Hospital, Tarboro, NC, p. A469

HEINSOHN, Carmel, M.D. Medical Director, Bournewood Health Systems, Brookline, MA, p. A305

HEINTZ, Shirley, R.N. Vice President Patient Care, Liberty Hospital, Liberty, MO, p. A372

HEINTZELMAN, Gayle, R.N. Site Administrator and Chief Nursing Officer, Mercy Health – Clermont Hospital, Batavia, OH, p. A479

HEINZ, Don, Interim Chief Executive Officer, Moundview Memorial Hospital & Clinics, Friendship, WI, p. A701

HEINZE, Kyle, Coordinator Information Technology, Riveredge Hospital, Forest Park, IL, p. A188

HEINZMAN, Jerry, Senior Vice President and Chief Financial Officer, Sampson Regional Medical Center, Clinton, NC, p. A458

HEINZMANN, Bill, Director Human Resources, Texoma Medical Center, Denison, TX, p. A607

HEISE, Rosemarie, Vice President Finance, Indiana University Health Starke Hospital, Knox, IN, p. A213

HEISE, Teresa, Coordinator Management Information Systems, Pender Community Hospital, Pender, NE, p. A397

HEISER, Eric, Chief Information Resource Management, Sioux Falls Veterans Affairs Health Care System, Sioux Falls, SD, p. A572

HEISMEYER, Joyce, Chief Operating Officer, Kansas Heart Hospital, Wichita, KS, p. A252

HEISSER, Randy, M.D. Medical Director, Kindred Hospital–Chattanooga, Chattanooga, TN, p. A575

HEIT, Ryan, Chief Financial Officer, Northern Nevada Medical Center, Sparks, NV, p. A404

HEITMAN, Susan, Chief Nursing Officer, Winneshiek Medical Center, Decorah, IA, p. A226

Index of Health Care Professionals

Index of Health Care Professionals / Heitzenrater

HEITZENRATER, James, Chief Executive Officer, Jefferson Hospital, Louisville, GA, p. A160
HEITZMAN, Cynthia, R.N. Chief Nursing Officer, Seven Rivers Regional Medical Center, Crystal River, FL, p. A124
HELDRETH, Karen, Director Data Processing, Mercy Hospital El Reno, El Reno, OK, p. A506
HELDT, Katie, Chief Nursing Officer, Greene County Medical Center, Jefferson, IA, p. A230
HELFER, Cassandra, Chief Financial Officer, Ralph H. Johnson Veterans Affairs Medical Center, Charleston, SC, p. A558
HELFER, David, President, Texas Institute for Surgery at Texas Health Presbyterian Dallas, Dallas, TX, p. A606
HELGERSON, Bryce R., Chief Administrative Officer, Legacy Salmon Creek Medical Center, Vancouver, WA, p. A687
HELGESEN, Roald, Chief Executive Officer, Alaska Native Medical Center, Anchorage, AK, p. A27
HELGESON, Heidi E., M.D. Chief Medical Officer, Rio Grande Hospital, Del Norte, CO, p. A101
HELGET, Peggy, R.N. Vice President Patient Services and Chief Nursing Officer, Methodist Jennie Edmundson Hospital, Council Bluffs, IA, p. A225
HELLA, Timothy, Chief Information Officer, Otsego Memorial Hospital, Gaylord, MI, p. A320
HELLAND, Don, M.D. Chief Medical Officer, Roosevelt Medical Center, Culbertson, MT, p. A382
HELLE, Dan, Human Resources Officer, Iowa City Veterans Affairs Health Care System, Iowa City, IA, p. A229
HELLELAND, Brian, Executive Vice President and Chief Operating Officer, St. Jude Medical Center, Fullerton, CA, p. A63
HELLER, Corey, Corporate Vice President and Chief Human Resources Officer, Baptist Health South Florida, Homestead Hospital, Homestead, FL, p. A129
HELLER, Michael, Chief Financial Officer, Corry Memorial Hospital, Corry, PA, p. A532
HELLER, Tom, Vice President Human Resources, Camden Clark Medical Center, Parkersburg, WV, p. A694
HELLINGER, Jeffrey, Interim Chief Financial Officer, Lewis County General Hospital, Lowville, NY, p. A436
HELLYER, Nancy R., FACHE, Chief Executive Officer, CHRISTUS St. Frances Cabrini Hospital, Alexandria, LA, p. A268
HELM, Carrie, Chief Executive Officer, Arkansas Surgical Hospital, North Little Rock, AR, p. A49
HELM, Pamela E., Executive Director, Devereux Texas Treatment Network, League City, TX, p. A628
HELMANDOLLAR, Billy, Director Information Services, Union Medical Center, Union, SC, p. A565
HELMICH, Cynthia, R.N
Chief Nursing Officer, Banner Baywood Medical Center, Mesa, AZ, p. A33
Chief Nursing Officer, Banner Heart Hospital, Mesa, AZ, p. A33
HELMS, Candace, Director Information Services, Good Samaritan Medical Center, West Palm Beach, FL, p. A147
HELMS, Joseph, Director Information Systems, DeKalb Regional Medical Center, Fort Payne, AL, p. A20
HELMS Jr., Robert N., Board Chair, President and Chief Executive Officer, Victory Healthcare, The Woodlands, TX, p. B150
HELPER, Mark A., Vice President, Chief Financial Officer, Munson Medical Center, Traverse City, MI, p. A331
HELSEL, David S., M.D., Chief Executive Officer, Spring Grove Hospital Center, Baltimore, MD, p. A295
HELSPER, Richard S., Chief Operating Officer, Genesis HealthCare System, Zanesville, OH, p. A502
HELTON, Deirdre, Director Human Resources, Lakeway Regional Hospital, Morristown, TN, p. A584
HELTON, Fay, Director Medical Records, Red River Hospital, LLC, Wichita Falls, TX, p. A652
HELTON, Michelle, Director Human Resources, Union Medical Center, Union, SC, p. A565
HELTON, R.J, D.O. Chief of Staff, Coal County General Hospital, Coalgate, OK, p. A505
HELTON, Stephanie, Chief Financial Officer, Weatherford Regional Hospital, Weatherford, OK, p. A518
HELWIG, Kent, Chief Executive Officer, Select Long Term Care Hospital – Colorado Springs, Colorado Springs, CO, p. A101
HEMATILLAKE, M. Ganga, M.D. Chief of Staff, White River Junction Veterans Affairs Medical Center, White River Junction, VT, p. A661
HEMEON, Frank, Interim Chief Financial Officer, Catskill Regional Medical Center, Harris, NY, p. A435
HEMKER, Debbie, Senior Vice President and Area Manager, Kaiser Permanente Fresno Medical Center, Fresno, CA, p. A62
HEMKER, Robert, President and Chief Executive Officer, Palomar Health, Escondido, CA, p. B103
HEMMER, Chris, Director Finance, Aurora West Allis Medical Center, West Allis, WI, p. A714
HEMMING, Stuart, Chief Operating Officer, Portsmouth Regional Hospital, Portsmouth, NH, p. A408
HEMPEL, Stephen, M.D. President Medical Staff, Lakeland Medical Center, St. Joseph, Saint Joseph, MI, p. A329
HEMPHILL, Dana, Manager Human Resources, Shoshone Medical Center, Kellogg, ID, p. A174
HEMPHILL, Robyn, Interim Chief Executive Officer and Chief Nursing Officer, Monroe Surgical Hospital, Monroe, LA, p. A280
HEMPLER, Shannan, Director Human Resources, Norton County Hospital, Norton, KS, p. A247
HENDEE, Daniel, Director, Philadelphia Veterans Affairs Medical Center, Philadelphia, PA, p. A545
HENDEL, Dawna, R.N. Chief Nursing Officer and Vice President Patient Care Services, Saint John's Health Center, Santa Monica, CA, p. A91
HENDEL, Diana, PharmD,
Chief Executive Officer, Community Hospital Long Beach, Long Beach, CA, p. A68
Chief Executive Officer, Miller Children's & Women's Hospital Long Beach, Long Beach, CA, p. A68
HENDERSON, Carol
Senior Vice President, Chief Talent Officer, HonorHealth John C. Lincoln Medical Center, Phoenix, AZ, p. A35
Vice President Human Resources, HonorHealth Scottsdale Osborn Medical Center, Scottsdale, AZ, p. A37
Senior Vice President and Chief Talent Officer, HonorHealth Scottsdale Shea Medical Center, Scottsdale, AZ, p. A37
Vice President Human Resources, HonorHealth Scottsdale Thompson Peak Medical Center, Scottsdale, AZ, p. A37
HENDERSON, Claudia, Chief Human Resources, St. Elizabeth's Medical Center, Brighton, MA, p. A305
HENDERSON, David K., M.D. Deputy Director Clinical Care, National Institutes of Health Clinical Center, Bethesda, MD, p. A296
HENDERSON, David M., Director Human Resources, Summersville Regional Medical Center, Summersville, WV, p. A695
HENDERSON, Deborah, Acting Chief Financial Officer, Harry S. Truman Memorial Veterans Hospital, Columbia, MO, p. A366
HENDERSON, Donald G., FACHE, Chief Executive Officer, Central Florida Health Alliance, Leesburg, FL, p. B32
HENDERSON, Donald G., FACHE,
President and Chief Executive Officer, Leesburg Regional Medical Center, Leesburg, FL, p. A132
President and Chief Executive Officer, The Villages Regional Hospital, The Villages, FL, p. A146
HENDERSON, Gary, Chief Information Resources Management Services, Huntington Veterans Affairs Medical Center, Huntington, WV, p. A692
HENDERSON, Jace, Chief Financial Officer, Parkview Hospital, Wheeler, TX, p. A652
HENDERSON, Jessica, Employee Relations Specialist, Fitzgibbon Hospital, Marshall, MO, p. A372
HENDERSON, John
Chief Executive Officer, Childress Regional Medical Center, Childress, TX, p. A600
Chief Human Resources Management, James H. Quillen Veterans Affairs Medical Center, Mountain Home, TN, p. A585
HENDERSON, John, M.D. Chief Medical Officer, Unity Health White County Medical Center, Searcy, AR, p. A50
HENDERSON, Katherine, Chief Executive Officer, Seton Medical Center Austin, Austin, TX, p. A594
HENDERSON, Kathy, Director Human Resources, Willow Crest Hospital, Miami, OK, p. A509
HENDERSON, Larry, M.D. Medical Director, Greene County Hospital, Leakesville, MS, p. A356
HENDERSON, Lisa, Chief Operating Officer, Palacios Community Medical Center, Palacios, TX, p. A635
HENDERSON, Lori, Chief Nursing Officer, Vice President Clinical, Family Health West, Fruita, CO, p. A104
HENDERSON, Lorrie, Ph.D., Chief Executive Officer, Huhukam Memorial Hospital, Sacaton, AZ, p. A37
HENDERSON, Maryanne, D.O. Chief Medical Officer, The Children's Institute of Pittsburgh, Pittsburgh, PA, p. A546
HENDERSON, Melody, R.N. Chief Operating Officer and Chief Nursing Officer, Golden Plains Community Hospital, Borger, TX, p. A598
HENDERSON, Mike, Director Human Resources, Forest View Psychiatric Hospital, Grand Rapids, MI, p. A320
HENDERSON, Pamela S., Vice President Human Resources, Memorial Hospital of Carbondale, Carbondale, IL, p. A180
HENDERSON, Patricia, R.N. Vice President Nursing and Clinical Services, Glencoe Regional Health Services, Glencoe, MN, p. A339
HENDERSON, Paula
Vice President Human Resources, University of Maryland Medical Center Midtown Campus, Baltimore, MD, p. A295
Vice President Human Resources, University of Maryland Rehabilitation & Orthopaedic Institute, Baltimore, MD, p. A295
HENDERSON, Peggy, Director Health Information, Stringfellow Memorial Hospital, Anniston, AL, p. A15
HENDERSON, Rex, M.D. Chief of Staff, McDowell Hospital, Marion, NC, p. A464
HENDERSON, Sherry, Chief Financial Officer, Piedmont Henry Hospital, Stockbridge, GA, p. A165
HENDERSON, Sue, Human Resource Manager, Smyth County Community Hospital, Marion, VA, p. A667
HENDERSON, Teto E., Director Human Resources, Geary Community Hospital, Junction City, KS, p. A243
HENDERSON, Travis, M.D. Chief of Staff, Mobridge Regional Hospital, Mobridge, SD, p. A570
HENDERSON, Volante, Director Human Resources, HEALTHSOUTH Walton Rehabilitation Hospital, Augusta, GA, p. A151
HENDLER, Robert S., M.D. Regional Chief Medical Officer, Centennial Medical Center, Frisco, TX, p. A615
HENDREN, Karen, Vice President of Finance and Operations, Mercy Hospital Ardmore, Ardmore, OK, p. A503
HENDRICK, Kirk, Director Information Systems, Northside Hospital, Saint Petersburg, FL, p. A142
HENDRICKS, Barbara A., Vice President, Human Resources, Nanticoke Memorial Hospital, Seaford, DE, p. A117
HENDRICKS, Marcia, FACHE, Chief Executive Officer, Madison County Health Care System, Winterset, IA, p. A236
HENDRICKSEN, Sherry, R.N. Chief Nursing Officer, ContinueCARE Hospital at Hendrick Medical Center, Abilene, TX, p. A590
HENDRICKSON, Leslie, Director Human Resources, Coteau des Prairies Hospital, Sisseton, SD, p. A572
HENDRICKSON, Roman, M.D. Medical Director, Ruby Valley Hospital, Sheridan, MT, p. A387
HENDRIX, Angie, Director of Nursing, Evergreen Medical Center, Evergreen, AL, p. A19
HENDRIX, Billie, R.N. Director of Nursing, W. J. Mangold Memorial Hospital, Lockney, TX, p. A628
HENDRIX, Jamie, Vice President Patient Care Services, Columbus Community Hospital, Inc., Columbus, WI, p. A699
HENDRIX, Jr., Michael A., Chief Financial Officer, St. Joseph Hospital, Bangor, ME, p. A288
HENDRIX, Ricky, M.D. Chief of Staff, Winn Parish Medical Center, Winnfield, LA, p. A287
HENDRIXSON, Mark, M.D. Chief Medical Officer, Jamestown Regional Medical Center, Jamestown, TN, p. A579
HENES, MSN, RN–, Jean M., R.N. Director of Nursing, Avera Creighton Hospital, Creighton, NE, p. A391
HENESSEE, Nolan, Vice President and Chief Information Officer, St. Joseph's Hospital, Savannah, GA, p. A164
HENINGER, Bev, Director of Nursing, Kenmare Community Hospital, Kenmare, ND, p. A475
HENKEL, Robert J., FACHE, President and Chief Executive Officer, Ascension Health, Saint Louis, MO, p. B12
HENKENIUS, Jim, Chief Financial Officer, Stewart Memorial Community Hospital, Lake City, IA, p. A230
HENLEY, Donald, Vice President Human Resources and Social Services, Grove City Medical Center, Grove City, PA, p. A535
HENLEY, Grace M., Assistant Administrator Human Resources, Highline Medical Center, Burien, WA, p. A677
HENNEBOLD, Julie, R.N. Interim Chief Nursing Officer, Winner Regional Healthcare Center, Winner, SD, p. A573
HENNEMAN, Diane, Chief Executive Officer, Havenwyck Hospital, Auburn Hills, MI, p. A314
HENNENBERG, Shayla, Director Human Resources, Essentia Health Ada, Ada, MN, p. A334
HENNESSEY, Ruth, Executive Vice President and Chief Administrative Officer, St. Francis Hospital, Roslyn, NY, p. A449
HENNIGAN, Michael, M.D. Medical Director, HEALTHSOUTH Emerald Coast Rehabilitation Hospital, Panama City, FL, p. A139
HENNIKE, Michael, Chief Executive Officer, Central Regional Hospital, Butner, NC, p. A456
HENNING, Cindy, R.N. Chief Nursing Officer, Houston Northwest Medical Center, Houston, TX, p. A620
HENNING, William C., Administrator and Chief Executive Officer, Baptist Memorial Hospital–North Mississippi, Oxford, MS, p. A359
HENNIS, Michelle, Administrative Director Financial Services, Grace Hospital, Cleveland, OH, p. A484
HENOCH, Malcolm S., M.D. Chief Medical Officer, Beaumont Hospital–Dearborn, Dearborn, MI, p. A317
HENRICH, Christy, Controller, Kindred Hospital of Northern Indiana, Mishawaka, IN, p. A216

**A864** Index of Health Care Professionals

Index of Health Care Professionals / Hertel

Index of Health Care Professionals

HENRICI, Michael, Associate Administrator, Roxborough Memorial Hospital, Philadelphia, PA, p. A545
HENRICKS, William, ice President and Chief Financial Officer, Seton Shoal Creek Hospital, Austin, TX, p. A594
HENRIKSON, Mary L., Chief Nursing Officer and Chief Operating Officer, St. Anthony Summit Medical Center, Frisco, CO, p. A104
HENRY, Aden, R.N. Vice President, Patient Care, La Rabida Children's Hospital, Chicago, IL, p. A182
HENRY, Andrea, Director of Nursing, Sweetwater Hospital, Sweetwater, TN, p. A588
HENRY, Anna, Chief Information Officer, Kimble Hospital, Junction, TX, p. A625
HENRY, Ashley, Director Information Systems, Clearview Regional Medical Center, Monroe, GA, p. A161
HENRY, Chris, Associate Administrator and Chief Financial Officer, Washington Hospital Healthcare System, Fremont, CA, p. A62
HENRY, Dane, Executive Vice President and Chief Operating Officer, DeKalb Medical at North Decatur, Decatur, GA, p. A156
HENRY, David, President and Chief Executive Officer, Northern Montana Hospital, Havre, MT, p. A384
HENRY, Debbie, Vice President Financial Services, North Arkansas Regional Medical Center, Harrison, AR, p. A45
HENRY, Donna, Vice President of Nursing Services, Four County Counseling Center, Logansport, IN, p. A215
HENRY, Heather, Manager Information Systems, Hammond–Henry Hospital, Geneseo, IL, p. A189
HENRY Jr., Jake, President and Chief Executive Officer, Saint Francis Health System, Tulsa, OK, p. B115
HENRY, James L., Director Human Resources, HEALTHSOUTH Sea Pines Rehabilitation Hospital, Melbourne, FL, p. A133
HENRY, Joy, R.N. Director Nurses, Faith Community Hospital, Jacksboro, TX, p. A624
HENRY, Joyce, Controller, HEALTHSOUTH Rehabilitation Hospital of York, York, PA, p. A554
HENRY, Peter, M.D. Chief Medical Officer, Essentia Health St. Joseph's Medical Center, Brainerd, MN, p. A336
HENRY, Peter P., FACHE, Interim Director, Alexandria Veterans Affairs Health Care System, Pineville, LA, p. A283
HENRY, Roshonda, Chief Nursing Officer, HEALTHSOUTH Rehabilitation Hospital of Cypress, Houston, TX, p. A620
HENRY, Tim, Accountant, Chatuge Regional Hospital and Nursing Home, Hiawassee, GA, p. A158
HENRY, William
Director Human Resources, East Texas Medical Center Henderson, Henderson, TX, p. A618
Director Human Resources, East Texas Medical Center–Quitman, Quitman, TX, p. A638
HENSEL, David, Director Financial Operations, OhioHealth Grady Memorial Hospital, Delaware, OH, p. A488
HENSEL, Edward, Chief Information Officer, Tomah Veterans Affairs Medical Center, Tomah, WI, p. A712
HENSLEY, Anna, Chief Operating Officer, OhioHealth Grady Memorial Hospital, Delaware, OH, p. A488
HENSLEY, Barry, Director Information Systems, Logan Regional Medical Center, Logan, WV, p. A692
HENSLEY, Kristy, Director Human Resources, Indiana Orthopaedic Hospital, Indianapolis, IN, p. A211
HENSON, Judith, R.N. Chief Nursing Officer, Adena Medical Center, Chillicothe, OH, p. A482
HENSON, Maureen, Vice President Human Resources, Rapid City Regional Hospital, Rapid City, SD, p. A570
HENSON, Pam, Executive Director, Pathways of Tennessee, Jackson, TN, p. A579
HENSON, Steve, Chief Executive Officer, Arkansas State Hospital, Little Rock, AR, p. A47
HENTHORN, Cheryl, Chief Executive Officer, Summa Rehab Hospital, Akron, OH, p. A478
HENTON, Thomas, Chief Executive Officer, Sumner County Hospital District One, Caldwell, KS, p. A238
HENTZEN PAGE, Ann, M.D., Chief Executive Officer, Summit Surgical, Hutchinson, KS, p. A242
HENZE, Mary Kay, Chief Nursing Officer, Hutchinson Health, Hutchinson, MN, p. A340
HENZE, Michael E., Chief Executive Officer, Lake Regional Health System, Osage Beach, MO, p. A374
HENZE, Rick, Vice President, Finance, St. Mary's Healthcare, Amsterdam, NY, p. A428
HEPKER, Wendy J., FACHE, Director, Chillicothe Veterans Affairs Medical Center, Chillicothe, OH, p. A482
HEPNER, Tim, M.D. Medical Director, St. John Owasso, Owasso, OK, p. A513
HERALD, Kathleen R., Vice President and Chief Information Officer, Lexington Medical Center, West Columbia, SC, p. A566
HERBECK, Marilyn, Coordinator Human Resources, Community Memorial Hospital, Staunton, IL, p. A201
HERBEK, Gary J., Chief Executive Officer, HEALTHSOUTH Rehabilitation Hospital of Fredericksburg, Fredericksburg, VA, p. A665
HERBER, Matt, M.D. Chief of Staff, Avera Dells Area Hospital, Dell Rapids, SD, p. A568
HERBER, Steven, FACS, President and Chief Executive Officer, St. Helena Hospital Napa Valley, Saint Helena, CA, p. A85
HERBERGER, Eva, Administrator Human Resources, USC Verdugo Hills Hospital, Glendale, CA, p. A64
HERBERS, Mark C., Chief Executive Officer, El Paso Children's Hospital, El Paso, TX, p. A610
HERBERT, Daniel, M.D. Medical Administrative Officer, Millinocket Regional Hospital, Millinocket, ME, p. A291
HERBERT, Janet, R.N. Chief Operating Officer, McKenzie Health System, Sandusky, MI, p. A330
HERBERT, Janet, Vice President Operations and Chief Nursing Officer, St. Joseph Mercy Port Huron, Port Huron, MI, p. A328
HERBERT, Laurie, Vice President Operations, Three Rivers Health, Three Rivers, MI, p. A331
HERBERT, Peter N., M.D. Senior Vice President Medical Affairs and Chief of Staff, Yale–New Haven Hospital, New Haven, CT, p. A114
HERBOLD, Charlotte, Manager Business Officer, Garfield County Health Center, Jordan, MT, p. A384
HERBST, Gary, Senior Vice President and Chief Financial Officer, Kaweah Delta Medical Center, Visalia, CA, p. A97
HERDENER, Tony, Vice President Systems and Finance, Northeast Georgia Medical Center, Gainesville, GA, p. A158
HERDER, Debbie, Controller, Promise Hospital of Wichita Falls, Wichita Falls, TX, p. A652
HEREDIA, Paul, Chief Human Resources Officer, Citrus Valley Medical Center–Inter Community Campus, Covina, CA, p. A59
HEREFORD, James, Chief Operating Officer, Stanford Health Care, Palo Alto, CA, p. A80
HEREFORD, Michelle, Chief, UVA Transitional Care Hospital, Charlottesville, VA, p. A663
HERFINDAHL, Gary, M.D. Chief of Staff, Mercy Medical Center Mount Shasta, Mount Shasta, CA, p. A76
HERFORT, Oliver, M.D. Chief Medical Officer, Valley Regional Hospital, Claremont, NH, p. A405
HERGET, Jordan, Chief Operating Officer, Good Samaritan Hospital, San Jose, CA, p. A89
HERING, Kristine, R.N. Chief Nursing Officer, Speare Memorial Hospital, Plymouth, NH, p. A408
HERINGER, Mark, Interim Director Information Systems, St. Helena Hospital Napa Valley, Saint Helena, CA, p. A85
HERMAN, David C., M.D., Chief Executive Officer, Essentia Health, Duluth, MN, p. B55
HERMAN, Jeff, Chief Executive Officer, Prairie St. John's, Fargo, ND, p. A473
HERMAN, John J., Chief Operating Officer, Mercy Hospital, Buffalo, NY, p. A430
HERMAN, John W.
Chief Executive Officer, Fairview Lakes Health Services, Wyoming, MN, p. A349
Chief Executive Officer, Fairview Northland Medical Center, Princeton, MN, p. A345
HERMAN, Michael, Chief Operating Officer, Sumner Regional Medical Center, Gallatin, TN, p. A578
HERMANN, Terri, R.N. Chief Nursing Officer, Franklin Hospital District, Benton, IL, p. A179
HERMANN, Tom, Chief of Staff, Sturgis Regional Hospital, Sturgis, SD, p. A572
HERMOSA, Mercy, Director of Information System, Coral Gables Hospital, Coral Gables, FL, p. A124
HERNANDEZ, Ashley, Chief Information Technology Officer, Pender Memorial Hospital, Burgaw, NC, p. A456
HERNANDEZ, Bernadette, R.N. Chief Nursing Officer, Texas Specialty Hospital at Lubbock, Lubbock, TX, p. A630
HERNANDEZ, Debra T., R.N. Vice President Chief Operating Officer, University Medical Center at Brackenridge, Austin, TX, p. A595
HERNANDEZ Jr., George B., President and Chief Executive Officer, University Health System, San Antonio, TX, p. A642
HERNANDEZ, Gloria, Executive Director, University Pediatric Hospital, PR, p. A724
HERNANDEZ, Jaime, Chief Executive Officer, Kempsville Center for Behavioral Health, Norfolk, VA, p. A669
HERNANDEZ, Janiva, Coordinator Human Resources, Hospital Metropolitano Dr. Susoni, Arecibo, PR, p. A720
HERNANDEZ, Kim
Chief Human Resources Officer, AMG Specialty Hospital–Denham Springs, Denham Springs, LA, p. A273
Director Human Resources, AMG Specialty Hospital–Slidell, Slidell, LA, p. A285
HERNANDEZ, Kristen, Director Human Resources, HEALTHSOUTH Rehabilitation Hospital, Albuquerque, NM, p. A422
HERNANDEZ, Leonard, President and Chief Executive Officer, Coffey County Hospital, Burlington, KS, p. A238
HERNANDEZ, Luz Maria, Director Human Resources, I. Gonzalez Martinez Oncologic Hospital, PR, p. A724
HERNANDEZ, Reyna, Chief Financial Officer, HEALTHSOUTH Rehabilitation Hospital of Miami, Cutler Bay, FL, p. A124
HERNANDEZ, Sandi, Controller, Lafayette General Surgical Hospital, Lafayette, LA, p. A277
HERNANDEZ, Susan, R.N. Chief Nursing Officer, Rice Medical Center, Eagle Lake, TX, p. A609
HERNANDEZ, Susan, Chief Nursing Officer, University of Texas Southwestern Medical Center, Dallas, TX, p. A607
HERNANDEZ, Tony, Director Information Technology, Fort Duncan Regional Medical Center, Eagle Pass, TX, p. A609
HERNANDEZ–KEEBLE, Sonia, Superintendent, Rio Grande State Center/South Texas Health Care System, Harlingen, TX, p. A618
HERNANDEZ–LICHTL, Javier, Chief Executive Officer, Baptist Health South Florida, West Kendall Baptist Hospital, Miami, FL, p. A134
HERNDON, Amy, Director Finance, Morristown–Hamblen Healthcare System, Morristown, TN, p. A584
HERNDON, David N., M.D. Chief of Staff, Shriners Hospitals for Children–Galveston, Galveston, TX, p. A615
HERNDON, Lori, R.N., President and Chief Executive Officer, AtlantiCare Regional Medical Center, Atlantic City, NJ, p. A409
HERNDON, Paula, R.N. Nurse Executive, Highland–Clarksburg Hospital, Clarksburg, WV, p. A690
HERNDON, Scott, Chief Financial Officer, Kendall Regional Medical Center, Miami, FL, p. A134
HEROLD, Jeffrey, M.D. President Medical Staff, St. Nicholas Hospital, Sheboygan, WI, p. A711
HEROLD, Mary, Director Human Resources, Share Medical Center, Alva, OK, p. A503
HERR, Brenda, Chief Nursing Officer, East Adams Rural Hospital, Ritzville, WA, p. A683
HERRARA, Espie, Chief Financial Officer, Peak Behavioral Health Services, Santa Teresa, NM, p. A426
HERREN, Richenda Dawn, M.D. Chief of Staff, Mercy Hospital Independence, Independence, KS, p. A242
HERRERA, Jocelyn A., Director Human Resources, Kaiser Permanente Orange County Anaheim Medical Center, Anaheim, CA, p. A53
HERRERA, Veronica, Director Human Resources, Las Encinas Hospital, Pasadena, CA, p. A80
HERRERA, Yamila, Director Human Resources, Hialeah Hospital, Hialeah, FL, p. A128
HERRERO, Carmelo, M.D. Medical Director, Hospital Oriente, Humacao, PR, p. A721
HERRICK, Stephen M., Ph.D., Director, Piedmont Geriatric Hospital, Burkeville, VA, p. A663
HERRIN, Curtis, Chief Financial Officer, Toppenish Community Hospital, Toppenish, WA, p. A686
HERRING, Donnette, Chief Information Officer, Vidant Medical Center, Greenville, NC, p. A461
HERRING, Randy, M.D. Chief of Staff, Coon Memorial Hospital, Dalhart, TX, p. A604
HERRINGTON, Bruce, M.D. Chief Medical Officer, South Georgia Medical Center Lanier Campus, Lakeland, GA, p. A160
HERRIOTT, Sue A., Executive Director Support Services, OSF St. Joseph Medical Center, Bloomington, IL, p. A179
HERRMAN, Edward, FACHE,
President, Integris Bass Baptist Health Center, Enid, OK, p. A506
President, Integris Bass Pavilion, Enid, OK, p. A506
HERRMANN, Deborah, M.D. Chief of Staff, I–70 Community Hospital, Sweet Springs, MO, p. A379
HERRMANN, Lee, Chief Healthcare Technology Officer, Santa Clara Valley Medical Center, San Jose, CA, p. A89
HERRMANN, Marty, M.D. Medical Director, Mayo Clinic Health System in New Prague, New Prague, MN, p. A343
HERRMANN, Tim, R.N., Administrator, PeaceHealth Cottage Grove Community Medical Center, Cottage Grove, OR, p. A520
HERRON, Katherine, Director Human Resources, Richard H. Hutchings Psychiatric Center, Syracuse, NY, p. A451
HERRON, Mary Beth, Director of Human Resources, Illinois Valley Community Hospital, Peru, IL, p. A198
HERSEY, Robert, Chief Financial Officer, Northeastern Vermont Regional Hospital, Saint Johnsbury, VT, p. A661
HERSHBERGER, Scott, Acting Chief Information Management Services, Battle Creek Veterans Affairs Medical Center, Battle Creek, MI, p. A315
HERSOM, Deborah, Director Human Resources, HEALTHSOUTH Chattanooga Rehabilitation Hospital, Chattanooga, TN, p. A575
HERTEL, Cheryl, Coordinator Human Resources, Stamford Memorial Hospital, Stamford, TX, p. A645

© 2015 AHA Guide Index of Health Care Professionals **A865**

Index of Health Care Professionals

Index of Health Care Professionals / Hertel

HERTEL, Holly, Director Nursing, Larned State Hospital, Larned, KS, p. A244
HERTZ, Karl Edward, Assistant Administrator, Memorial Hospital of Converse County, Douglas, WY, p. A716
HERWIG, Brian J., Chief Executive Officer, Estes Park Medical Center, Estes Park, CO, p. A103
HERZBERG, Deborah L., FACHE, Chief Executive Officer, Tri Valley Health System, Cambridge, NE, p. A390
HERZBERG, Joseph W., Assistant Vice President Human Resources, WellStar Cobb Hospital, Austell, GA, p. A152
HERZOG, Dean, Chief Financial Officer, Kona Community Hospital, Kealakekua, HI, p. A170
HERZOG, Mark P., President and Chief Executive Officer, Holy Family Memorial, Manitowoc, WI, p. A704
HERZOG, Paul F., Chief Operating Officer, University of New Mexico Hospitals, Albuquerque, NM, p. A423
HERZOG, Vernail, Chief Executive Officer, Allegiance Specialty Hospital of Greenville, Greenville, MS, p. A353
HESCH, Dennis, Executive Vice President Finance and Chief Financial Officer, Carle Foundation Hospital, Urbana, IL, p. A202
HESCH, Mike J., Regional Administrator Human Resources, Mayo Clinic Health System – Franciscan Healthcare in Sparta, Sparta, WI, p. A711
HESS, Bob, Chief Information Officer, Bonner General Hospital, Sandpoint, ID, p. A176
HESS, Brian, Chief Financial Officer, Venice Regional Bayfront Health, Venice, FL, p. A146
HESS, David F., M.D., Chief Executive Officer, Reynolds Memorial Hospital, Glen Dale, WV, p. A691
HESS, Heidi, Chief Nursing Officer, Genesis Medical Center–Aledo, Aledo, IL, p. A178
HESS, Jim, Chief Operations Officer, Salt Lake Behavioral Health, Salt Lake City, UT, p. A658
HESS, Michael, M.D. Chief Medical Officer, Lakeview Hospital, Bountiful, UT, p. A654
HESS, Pamela, Chief Financial Officer, St. Joseph Hospital, Fort Wayne, IN, p. A209
HESS, Phil, Chief Executive Officer, Philhaven, Mount Gretna, PA, p. A541
HESS, Steve
Vice President & Chief Information Officer, Medical Center of the Rockies, Loveland, CO, p. A107
Vice President Information Services and Chief Information Officer, University of Colorado Hospital, Aurora, CO, p. A99
HESSE, Fred, M.D. Medical Director, Arms Acres, Carmel, NY, p. A431
HESSE, Nancy, R.N. Senior Vice President Patient Care Services, Eastern Regional Medical Center, Philadelphia, PA, p. A543
HESSELRODE, Renee, Director Health Information Management, Landmark Hospital of Cape Girardeau, Cape Girardeau, MO, p. A364
HESSER, Jason, M.D. Chief of Staff, Crete Area Medical Center, Crete, NE, p. A391
HESSHEIMER, Susan, Director Human Resources, Johnson County Hospital, Tecumseh, NE, p. A398
HESSING, Jeffrey, M.D. Medical Director, Treasure Valley Hospital, Boise, ID, p. A173
HESSMAN, Mary Pat, Chief Fiscal, Northport Veterans Affairs Medical Center, Northport, NY, p. A445
HESTER, Amber, Chief Executive Officer, Kindred Hospital Boston–North Shore, Peabody, MA, p. A310
HESTER, Janet, R.N. Chief Nurse Executive, Massac Memorial Hospital, Metropolis, IL, p. A194
HESTER, Josh, Chief Operating Officer, Troy Regional Medical Center, Troy, AL, p. A25
HESTER, Joyce, CPA Senior Vice President and Chief Financial Officer, Mother Frances Hospital – Tyler, Tyler, TX, p. A649
HESTER, Kathy, Chief Nursing Officer, Orange Park Medical Center, Orange Park, FL, p. A137
HESTER, Steven, M.D. Vice President Medical Affairs, Norton Women's and Kosair Children's Hospital, Louisville, KY, p. A261
HESTON, Thomas, M.D. Chief of Staff, Shoshone Medical Center, Kellogg, ID, p. A174
HETHERINGTON, Ray, Network Administrator, Wheatland Memorial Healthcare, Harlowton, MT, p. A384
HETHERINGTON, Thomas, M.D. Chief of Staff, Capital Region Medical Center, Jefferson City, MO, p. A368
HETLAGE, C. Kennon, FACHE, Administrator and Chief Executive Officer, Memorial Hospital West, Pembroke Pines, FL, p. A139
HETLETVED, Beth, Director of Nurses, Garrison Memorial Hospital, Garrison, ND, p. A474
HETRICK, Robert G., Vice President Finance and Chief Financial Officer, Morehead Memorial Hospital, Eden, NC, p. A459
HETT, Samantha, Manager Human Resources, Satanta District Hospital and Long Term Care, Satanta, KS, p. A250
HETTICH, E. Paul, Chief Financial Officer, BryLin Hospitals, Buffalo, NY, p. A430
HETTINGER, JoAnn, R.N. Director of Patient Care Services, Avera Weskota Memorial Hospital, Wessington Springs, SD, p. A573
HETTINGER, MaryLou, Director Quality Management, Devereux Children's Behavioral Health Center, Malvern, PA, p. A539
HETTINGER, Tiffany Erin, Associate Chief Nursing Officer, North Colorado Medical Center, Greeley, CO, p. A104
HETU, Maureen, Chief Information Officer, Our Lady of Lourdes Medical Center, Camden, NJ, p. A410
HETZ, Mark
Chief Information Officer, Asante Ashland Community Hospital, Ashland, OR, p. A519
Chief Information Officer, Asante Rogue Regional Medical Center, Medford, OR, p. A523
Chief Information Officer, Asante Three Rivers Medical Center, Grants Pass, OR, p. A521
HEURING, Ron, Director Information Systems, Perry County Memorial Hospital, Perryville, MO, p. A374
HEURTIN, John, Chief Financial Officer, Lee's Summit Medical Center, Lee's Summit, MO, p. A371
HEUSER, Keith E., President, CHI Mercy Health, Valley City, ND, p. A476
HEVER, Susan C., Director Human Resources, Brookhaven Memorial Hospital Medical Center, Patchogue, NY, p. A447
HEYDON, Larry, President and Chief Executive Officer, Johnson Memorial Hospital, Franklin, IN, p. A209
HEYN, Matthew M., Chief Executive Officer, Ransom Memorial Hospital, Ottawa, KS, p. A247
HEYWOOD, Matthew, Chief Executive Officer, Aspirus, Inc., Wausau, WI, p. B15
HIATT, Tim, Chief Information Officer, Brodstone Memorial Hospital, Superior, NE, p. A398
HIBBARD, Carrie, Human Resource Business Partner, Adventist Rehabilitation Hospital of Maryland, Rockville, MD, p. A300
HIBBS, Cathy, Chief Executive Officer, Carlsbad Medical Center, Carlsbad, NM, p. A423
HIBEN, Daniel, Chief Executive Officer, Oswego Community Hospital, Oswego, KS, p. A247
HIBSCHMAN, Kimberly, Chief Financial Officer, Riverview Behavioral Health, Texarkana, AR, p. A51
HICKEY, Conner, Chief Operating Officer, Woodland Heights Medical Center, Lufkin, TX, p. A630
HICKEY, Mairead, Ph.D. Executive Vice President and Chief Operating Officer, Brigham and Women's Hospital, Boston, MA, p. A303
HICKEY, Marcia H., Senior Vice President Operations, The Hospital at Hebrew Health Care, West Hartford, CT, p. A116
HICKEY, Thomas P., Chief Executive Officer and Managing Director, Pembroke Hospital, Pembroke, MA, p. A310
HICKEY–BOYNTON, Meg, Director Human Resources and Marketing, Community Hospital of Anaconda, Anaconda, MT, p. A381
HICKLING, Andrea, Vice President Finance and Chief Finance Officer, Northern Hospital of Surry County, Mount Airy, NC, p. A465
HICKLING, Karen, Director Human Resources, Palmdale Regional Medical Center, Palmdale, CA, p. A80
HICKMAN, George, Executive Vice President and Chief Information Officer, Albany Medical Center, Albany, NY, p. A428
HICKMAN, Louise, R.N. Vice President of Patient Care Services, Jefferson Regional Medical Center, Pine Bluff, AR, p. A50
HICKMAN, Monica, Director Fiscal Services, Shriners Hospitals for Children–Spokane, Spokane, WA, p. A685
HICKMAN, Sherie C., Vice President Operations and Chief Operating Officer, Sequoia Hospital, Redwood City, CA, p. A83
HICKMAN, Troy, Director Human Resources, Harper Hospital District Five, Harper, KS, p. A241
HICKS, Christia, Vice President Human Resources, Eskenazi Health, Indianapolis, IN, p. A211
HICKS, Crystal, R.N. Chief Nursing Officer, Harrison County Community Hospital, Bethany, MO, p. A363
HICKS, Dana, Director of Nursing, Community Medical Center of Izard County, Calico Rock, AR, p. A42
HICKS, Janelle, R.N. Vice President Patient Services, Hocking Valley Community Hospital, Logan, OH, p. A492
HICKS, Joan, Chief Information Officer, University of Alabama Hospital, Birmingham, AL, p. A17
HICKS, Joe, President and Chief Executive Officer, Barnabas Health Behavioral Health Center, Toms River, NJ, p. A419
HICKS, John R., President and Chief Executive Officer, Platte Valley Medical Center, Brighton, CO, p. A100
HICKS, Kevin J., President and CEO, Overland Park Regional Medical Center, Overland Park, KS, p. A248
HICKS, Scott, Vice President, Clark Memorial Hospital, Jeffersonville, IN, p. A213
HICKS, Shawnee, Director Human Resources, Magnolia Regional Medical Center, Magnolia, AR, p. A48
HICKS, Susan, Chief Executive Officer, Sky Ridge Medical Center, Lone Tree, CO, p. A106
HICKS, Terri, Chief Operating Officer and Chief Financial Officer, P & S Surgical Hospital, Monroe, LA, p. A280
HICKS, William, Chief Operating Officer, Bellevue Hospital Center, New York, NY, p. A438
HICKSON, Stan, FACHE, Chief Executive Officer, Northside Medical Center, Columbus, GA, p. A154
HIDAY, Holly, Director Human Resources, Kalamazoo Psychiatric Hospital, Kalamazoo, MI, p. A323
HIEB, Dorothy, Director Human Resources, Sanford Chamberlain Medical Center, Chamberlain, SD, p. A567
HIEB, Laura, R.N. Chief Nursing Officer, Bellin Memorial Hospital, Green Bay, WI, p. A701
HIEBERT, Leslie, Chief Executive Officer, Klickitat Valley Health, Goldendale, WA, p. A679
HIGA, Russel, JD Regional Director Human Resources, Leahi Hospital, Honolulu, HI, p. A168
HIGDON, Karen, R.N. Vice President and Chief Nursing Officer, Baptist Health La Grange, La Grange, KY, p. A259
HIGGINBOTHAM, G. Douglas, President and Chief Executive Officer, South Central Regional Medical Center, Laurel, MS, p. A356
HIGGINBOTHAM, Michael, Chief Executive Officer, Cornerstone Hospital–Medical Center of Houston, Houston, TX, p. A619
HIGGINS, Alana
Regional Information Management Executive, CHRISTUS St. Michael Health System, Texarkana, TX, p. A647
Regional Information Management Executive, CHRISTUS St. Michael Rehabilitation Hospital, Texarkana, TX, p. A647
HIGGINS, JoAnn, Chief Nursing Officer and Assistant Administrator, Palo Alto County Health System, Emmetsburg, IA, p. A227
HIGGINS, John, Vice President and Chief Financial Officer, Good Samaritan Medical Center, Lafayette, CO, p. A106
HIGGINS, Kevin A., Chief Financial Officer, Olmsted Medical Center, Rochester, MN, p. A345
HIGGINS, Larry, Vice President Human Resources, King's Daughters Medical Center, Ashland, KY, p. A254
HIGGINS, Rodney, Chief Financial Officer, Deaconess Hospital, Spokane, WA, p. A685
HIGGINS, Thomas, M.D., Interim President and Chief Executive Officer, Baystate Franklin Medical Center, Greenfield, MA, p. A307
HIGGINS, William, M.D. Vice President Medical Affairs, New York–Presbyterian/Hudson Valley Hospital, Cortlandt Manor, NY, p. A432
HIGGINS BOWERS, Shirley, Senior Vice President Human Resources, JFK Medical Center, Edison, NJ, p. A411
HIGGINSON, David, Senior Vice President and Chief Information Officer, Phoenix Children's Hospital, Phoenix, AZ, p. A35
HIGH, Kim, Chief Financial Officer, Baptist Memorial Hospital–Union County, New Albany, MS, p. A358
HIGHSMITH, Cameron, Chief Executive Officer, Washington County Hospital, Plymouth, NC, p. A466
HIGHTOWER, Bernita, Chief Human Resources, Martin Army Community Hospital, Fort Benning, GA, p. A157
HIGHTOWER, Skip
Chief Financial Officer, Brooks County Hospital, Quitman, GA, p. A162
Chief Financial Officer, Grady General Hospital, Cairo, GA, p. A153
Senior Vice President and Chief Financial Officer, John D. Archbold Memorial Hospital, Thomasville, GA, p. A166
Senior Vice President and Chief Financial Officer, Mitchell County Hospital, Camilla, GA, p. A153
HIGHTOWER, Thomas, R.N. Chief Operating Officer, Grays Harbor Community Hospital, Aberdeen, WA, p. A676
HIJECK, Thomas W., R.N. Vice President Nursing Services and Chief Nursing Officer, Harrington Memorial Hospital, Southbridge, MA, p. A311
HILAMAN, Brad L., M.D. Chief of Staff, J. Arthur Dosher Memorial Hospital, Southport, NC, p. A468
HILBERT, Frank, Senior Vice President and Chief Information Officer, McAlester Regional Health Center, McAlester, OK, p. A509
HILDEBRAND, Randall, M.D. Chief Medical Officer, Great Bend Regional Hospital, Great Bend, KS, p. A240
HILDEBRANDT, James, D.O. Vice President Medical Affairs, Sarah Bush Lincoln Health Center, Mattoon, IL, p. A193
HILDEN, Michael, M.D. President Medical Staff, Carlisle Regional Medical Center, Carlisle, PA, p. A531
HILDRETH, Beth, Vice President Human Resources, OhioHealth MedCentral Mansfield Hospital, Mansfield, OH, p. A493
HILDRETH, Joe, Director Information Technology, Three Rivers Hospital, Waverly, TN, p. A589
HILDWEIN, Robin, Chief Information Officer, Boca Raton Regional Hospital, Boca Raton, FL, p. A122

A866 Index of Health Care Professionals 

Index of Health Care Professionals / Hobbs

Index of Health Care Professionals

HILFIGER, Janie, President, Soldiers and Sailors Memorial Hospital, Wellsboro, PA, p. A552
HILL, Beth, Director Human Resources, Russell County Medical Center, Lebanon, VA, p. A666
HILL, Bettie, Chief Financial Officer, Poplar Springs Hospital, Petersburg, VA, p. A670
HILL, Cheryl
Vice President Human Resources, Columbia St. Mary's Hospital Milwaukee, Milwaukee, WI, p. A706
Vice President Human Resources, Columbia St. Mary's Ozaukee Hospital, Mequon, WI, p. A705
Vice President Human Resources, Sacred Heart Rehabilitation Institute, Milwaukee, WI, p. A706
HILL, Christopher, Chief Executive Officer, St. Luke's Medical Center, Phoenix, AZ, p. A36
HILL, David, Regional Administrator, Mercy Hospital Booneville, Booneville, AR, p. A42
HILL, Duane N., Chief Executive Officer, Beaumont Bone and Joint Institute, Beaumont, TX, p. A596
HILL, Herbert, Director Human Resources, Klickitat Valley Health, Goldendale, WA, p. A679
HILL, Jack, Chief Operating Officer and Administrator, The Jewish Hospital – Mercy Health, Cincinnati, OH, p. A483
HILL, James P., Senior Vice President Administrative Services, MedStar Washington Hospital Center, Washington, DC, p. A119
HILL, Janice, R.N.,
Administrator, Baptist Memorial Restorative Care Hospital, Memphis, TN, p. A583
President and Chief Executive Officer, Baptist Rehabilitation–Germantown, Germantown, TN, p. A578
HILL, Jason, M.D. Chief Medical Officer, Choctaw Nation Health Care Center, Talihina, OK, p. A516
HILL, Jean, Chief Nursing Officer and Chief Clinical Officer, St. Charles Parish Hospital, Luling, LA, p. A279
HILL, Jeff, Chief Executive Officer, Steele Memorial Medical Center, Salmon, ID, p. A176
HILL, Jessica, Vice President, Chief Nursing Officer, Texas Health Harris Methodist Hospital Southlake, Southlake, TX, p. A644
HILL, Jill, Director Information Technology, Utah State Hospital, Provo, UT, p. A657
HILL, Jr., Joe B., Vice President Human Resources, Trident Medical Center, Charleston, SC, p. A558
HILL, Karen, Director Human Resources, Baylor Institute for Rehabilitation, Dallas, TX, p. A604
HILL, Karen S., R.N. Chief Operating Officer and Chief Nursing Officer, Baptist Health Lexington, Lexington, KY, p. A259
HILL, Kerry
Chief Financial Officer, Vista Medical Center East, Waukegan, IL, p. A203
Chief Financial Officer, Vista Medical Center West, Waukegan, IL, p. A203
HILL, Leo, Chief Information Officer, Massachusetts Eye and Ear Infirmary, Boston, MA, p. A304
HILL, Nancy L., R.N. Chief Operating Officer, North Hills Hospital, North Richland Hills, TX, p. A634
HILL, Ned, President and Chief Executive Officer, Northern Hospital of Surry County, Mount Airy, NC, p. A465
HILL, Pam, Director Human Resources, Baptist Rehabilitation–Germantown, Germantown, TN, p. A578
HILL, Patricia, Senior Director Nurse Executive, Sentara Northern Virginia Medical Center, Woodbridge, VA, p. A674
HILL, Phillip, Chief Executive Officer, Calhoun–Liberty Hospital, Blountstown, FL, p. A121
HILL, Robert, M.D
Vice President Medical Staff Affairs, Borgess Medical Center, Kalamazoo, MI, p. A323
Chief Medical Officer, Borgess–Lee Memorial Hospital, Dowagiac, MI, p. A318
HILL, Ryan
Chief Executive Officer, Essentia Health Ada, Ada, MN, p. A334
Chief Financial Officer, Essentia Health St. Mary's – Detroit Lakes, Detroit Lakes, MN, p. A337
HILL, Scott, Chief Executive Officer, Columbus Regional Healthcare System, Columbus, GA, p. B34
HILL, Stephen, Vice President and Chief Nursing Officer, Valley Baptist Medical Center–Harlingen, Harlingen, TX, p. A618
HILL, Stuart, Vice President and Treasurer, Unity Health White County Medical Center, Searcy, AR, p. A50
HILL, Susan, R.N. Director of Nursing, Marcus Daly Memorial Hospital, Hamilton, MT, p. A384
HILL, Terri L., Vice President and Administrator, Union Hospital Clinton, Clinton, IN, p. A206
HILL, Todd, D.O. Medical Director, Signature Psychiatric Hospital, Kansas City, MO, p. A370
HILL–DAVIS, Nancy L., Vice President Human Resources and Risk Management, Mercy Hospital and Medical Center, Chicago, IL, p. A183
HILLARD, Mary, R.N. Vice President Patient Care Services and Clinical Operations, Chief Nursing Executive, Advocate Condell Medical Center, Libertyville, IL, p. A192
HILLARY, Maureen, Chief Nursing Officer, Hayes Green Beach Memorial Hospital, Charlotte, MI, p. A316
HILLEGASS, Bonnie Essex, Chief Executive Officer, Harmon Medical and Rehabilitation Hospital, Las Vegas, NV, p. A401
HILLEMEIER, A. Craig, M.D., Chief Executive Officer, Penn State Milton S. Hershey Medical Center, Hershey, PA, p. A536
HILLESTAD, Tammy, Chief Nursing Officer, Brookings Health System, Brookings, SD, p. A567
HILLIARD, David J., D.O. Chief of Staff, Barnesville Hospital, Barnesville, OH, p. A479
HILLIS, David W., Chairman and Chief Executive Officer, Adcare Hospital of Worcester, Worcester, MA, p. A313
HILLMAN, Annette, Director Human Resources, Doctor's Hospital of Deer Creek, Leesville, LA, p. A279
HILLS, Cindi, Director Human Resources, Riverwood Healthcare Center, Aitkin, MN, p. A334
HILT, Monica, President and Chief Executive Officer, St. Elizabeth Hospital, Appleton, WI, p. A697
HILTON, Craig, Chief Executive Officer, Hampton Behavioral Health Center, Westampton, NJ, p. A420
HILTON, Lois, Director Human Resources, DeSoto Memorial Hospital, Arcadia, FL, p. A121
HILTON, Richard G., Administrator and Chief Executive Officer, OCH Regional Medical Center, Starkville, MS, p. A360
HILTUNEN, Theresa, Entity Information Officer, Penn Presbyterian Medical Center, Philadelphia, PA, p. A544
HILTZ, Paul C., FACHE, Market President and Chief Executive Officer, Springfield Regional Medical Center, Springfield, OH, p. A498
HINCHEY, Paul P.
President and Chief Executive Officer, Candler Hospital, Savannah, GA, p. A164
President and Chief Executive Officer, St. Joseph's Hospital, Savannah, GA, p. A164
HINCKLEY, Fran X., Chief Information Officer, North Shore Medical Center, Salem, MA, p. A310
HINDMAN, Robbie, Vice President Patient Care Services and Chief Nursing Officer, Walker Baptist Medical Center, Jasper, AL, p. A21
HINDS, Bob, Executive Director, Bradford Health Services at Huntsville, Madison, AL, p. A21
HINDS, Nigel, Chief Financial Officer, Florida Hospital DeLand, DeLand, FL, p. A125
HINE, Rhonda, R.N. Interim Chief Nursing Executive, Mason District Hospital, Havana, IL, p. A190
HINEMAN, Elizabeth, M.D. Chief Medical Staff, Scott County Hospital, Scott City, KS, p. A250
HINER, Jill, Vice President and Chief Financial Officer, Summa Western Reserve Hospital, Cuyahoga Falls, OH, p. A487
HINER, Peggy, Director Human Resources, Wheatland Memorial Healthcare, Harlowton, MT, p. A384
HINES, Frederick W., President and Chief Executive Officer, Clarity Child Guidance Center, San Antonio, TX, p. A640
HINES, John, M.D. Chief of Staff, Arkansas Methodist Medical Center, Paragould, AR, p. A49
HINES, Linda, Vice President Information Technology and Information Systems, University of Maryland Rehabilitation & Orthopaedic Institute, Baltimore, MD, p. A295
HINES, Lisa, Director Nursing, Eastern Shore Hospital Center, Cambridge, MD, p. A296
HINES, Mary Beth, D.O. Chief Medical Officer, UP Health System–Portage, Hancock, MI, p. A322
HINESLEY, Jay, Chief Executive Officer, Stringfellow Memorial Hospital, Anniston, AL, p. A15
HINKLE, David, Senior Vice President and Chief Information Officer, Nash Health Care Systems, Rocky Mount, NC, p. A467
HINKLE, Stacey, Director Information Technology, Banner Desert Medical Center, Mesa, AZ, p. A33
HINNER, William J.
Vice President Financial Analysis and Planning Ministry Health Care, Ministry Saint Joseph's Hospital, Marshfield, WI, p. A705
Vice President Financial Analysis and Planning, Ministry Saint Michael's Hospital, Stevens Point, WI, p. A711
HINOJOSA, Anna, MSN Interim Chief Nursing Officer, Knapp Medical Center, Weslaco, TX, p. A651
HINOJOSA, Jose Luis, Chief of Staff, Stanton County Hospital, Johnson, KS, p. A242
HINOJOZA, Rebecca, Chief Nursing Officer, Medina Regional Hospital, Hondo, TX, p. A618
HINRICHS, Becky, Vice President Human Resources, Riverside Medical Center, Kankakee, IL, p. A192
HINRICHS, Sandy, Director Human Resources, Burnett Medical Center, Grantsburg, WI, p. A701
HINSHAW, Bruce, Director Human Resources, Artesia General Hospital, Artesia, NM, p. A423
HINTON, James H., President and Chief Executive Officer, Presbyterian Healthcare Services, Albuquerque, NM, p. B106
HINTON, Tommye, R.N. Chief Nursing Officer, Highland Hospital of Rochester, Rochester, NY, p. A448
HINTZ, Lori, Coordinator Information Systems, Rochester Psychiatric Center, Rochester, NY, p. A449
HINTZE, Hart, Chief Nursing Officer, Payson Regional Medical Center, Payson, AZ, p. A34
HINTZE, Paul, M.D. Vice President Medical Affairs, Mercy Hospital St. Louis, Saint Louis, MO, p. A376
HIOTT, III, Jimmy O., Chief Financial Officer, Colleton Medical Center, Walterboro, SC, p. A565
HIPKISS, Tom, Vice President Finance, Forbes Regional Hospital, Monroeville, PA, p. A540
HIRKALER, Kim, Director Human Resources, Bon Secours Community Hospital, Port Jervis, NY, p. A448
HIROSE, Mivic, Executive Administrator, Laguna Honda Hospital and Rehabilitation Center, San Francisco, CA, p. A88
HIRSCH, Ted W., Senior Executive Director, Kalispell Regional Medical Center, Kalispell, MT, p. A385
HIRSCHBERG, Paula, R.N. Director of Nursing, Timberlawn Mental Health System, Dallas, TX, p. A607
HIRSHBERG, Mark I., Chief Operating Officer, Bothwell Regional Health Center, Sedalia, MO, p. A378
HIRST, Barb, Vice President Human Resources and Chief Nursing Officer, Salem Regional Medical Center, Salem, OH, p. A497
HISE, Landon, Chief Executive Officer, Cordell Memorial Hospital, Cordell, OK, p. A505
HISERODT, James, Senior Vice President Operations, Geneva General Hospital, Geneva, NY, p. A434
HISEY, Commie, D.O. Chief of Staff, Memorial Hospital, Gonzales, TX, p. A616
HITE–DAVIS, Anissa, Vice President Human Resources, St. Joseph's Hospital of Buckhannon, Buckhannon, WV, p. A690
HITT, Patricia A., Associate Director, Grand Junction Veterans Health Care System, Grand Junction, CO, p. A104
HIXENBAUGH, Cynthia, Director Human Resources, Pershing General Hospital, Lovelock, NV, p. A403
HIXSON, Kim, Vice President of Financial Officer and Chief Financial Officer, Providence Medical Center, Wayne, NE, p. A399
HJEMBO, Philip, Chief Financial Officer, St. Elizabeth Hospital, Enumclaw, WA, p. A678
HLAHOL, Jan, Manager Human Resources, Cleveland Clinic Children's Hospital for Rehabilitation, Cleveland, OH, p. A484
HLUCHY, Nicholas, Business Analyst, Support Services Manager, Baton Rouge Rehabilitation Hospital, Baton Rouge, LA, p. A269
HO, David, Senior Vice President and Chief Financial Officer, White Plains Hospital Center, White Plains, NY, p. A454
HO, Sylvia, Director Health Information Systems, Grady Memorial Hospital, Chickasha, OK, p. A505
HO–SHING, Viodelda, Deputy Director Administration, Creedmoor Psychiatric Center, NY, p. A439
HOAG, Linda, Director Human Resources, St. Mary's Regional Medical Center, Enid, OK, p. A506
HOAGBIN, Joseph, M.D
Chief Medical Officer, CHI Health Immanuel, Omaha, NE, p. A396
Chief Quality Officer, CHI Health Mercy Council Bluffs, Council Bluffs, IA, p. A225
HOAGLAND, Jason, M.D. President, Medical Staff, Davis Hospital and Medical Center, Layton, UT, p. A655
HOAR, Brad, Director Information and Technology, Cedar Park Regional Medical Center, Cedar Park, TX, p. A600
HOAR, Tanya, Chief Executive Officer and Chief Financial Officer, Schoolcraft Memorial Hospital, Manistique, MI, p. A325
HOARD, Kaylee S., Chief Financial Officer, Cook Hospital and Convalescent Nursing Care Unit, Cook, MN, p. A337
HOARD, RN, Shelly, Director of Nursing, Liberty Healthcare Systems, Bastrop, LA, p. A269
HOBACK, Kim, Supervisor Information Systems, Athens–Limestone Hospital, Athens, AL, p. A15
HOBAN, Donna, M.D. Senior Vice President and Physician–in–Chief, Beaumont Hospital Grosse Pointe, Grosse Pointe, MI, p. A321
HOBAN, Douglas M., Vice President and Chief Financial Officer, Mercy Hospital Lebanon, Lebanon, MO, p. A371
HOBAN, Robert E., Chief Executive Officer, St. John Hospital and Medical Center, Detroit, MI, p. A318
HOBART, Robert, Director Management Information Systems, Heartland Behavioral Healthcare, Massillon, OH, p. A493
HOBBS, Donna, Nurse Executive, U. S. Public Health Service Indian Hospital–Sells, Sells, AZ, p. A38
HOBBS, Ed, Director Information Services, DeKalb Health, Auburn, IN, p. A204
HOBBS, Emilie, Director Human Resources, Woodland Heights Medical Center, Lufkin, TX, p. A630

Index of Health Care Professionals

Index of Health Care Professionals / Hobbs

HOBBS, Joey, Chief Information Officer, Community Hospital of Anderson and Madison County, Anderson, IN, p. A204
HOBBS, Mike, Chief Financial Officer, Clay County Hospital, Flora, IL, p. A188
HOBBS, Steve E.
Chief Financial Officer, Eliza Coffee Memorial Hospital, Florence, AL, p. A19
Chief Financial Officer, Shoals Hospital, Muscle Shoals, AL, p. A23
HOBBS, Tommy, Chief Executive Officer, Illinois Valley Community Hospital, Peru, IL, p. A198
HOBGOOD, Lisa, Chief Information Officer, The Heart Hospital at Deaconess Gateway, Newburgh, IN, p. A217
HOBGOOD, Marcus, Director Information Services, University Health Shreveport, Shreveport, LA, p. A285
HOBSON, Christopher, Chief Operating Officer, Wellmont Bristol Regional Medical Center, Bristol, TN, p. A574
HOBSON, James M., Chief Executive Officer, CHI Memorial, Chattanooga, TN, p. A575
HOCATE, Crispin P., Professional and Support Services Officer, Texas Health Presbyterian Hospital Allen, Allen, TX, p. A590
HOCE, N. Kristopher, President, Morton Plant Hospital, Clearwater, FL, p. A123
HOCHENBERG, Paul S., Senior Vice President Human Resources, Westchester Medical Center, Valhalla, NY, p. A452
HOCHHEISER, Lou, M.D., Chief Executive Officer, St. John's Medical Center and Living Center, Jackson, WY, p. A716
HOCHMAN, Rodney F., M.D., President and Chief Executive Officer, Providence Health & Services, Renton, WA, p. B109
HOCHSTETLER, Amy, Chief Financial Officer, Orthopaedic Hospital of Lutheran Health Network, Fort Wayne, IN, p. A208
HOCK, Douglas G., President and Chief Operating Officer, Children's Medical Center, Children's Health System of Texas, Dallas, TX, p. A604
HOCKENBERRY, Michael A., Vice President Operations, Hanover Hospital, Hanover, PA, p. A535
HOCKENBERRY, Tanda, Chief Nursing Officer, HEALTHSOUTH Western Hills Regional Rehabilitation Hospital, Parkersburg, WV, p. A694
HOCKENBURY, Debbie, Assistant Administrator and Chief Financial Officer, William Newton Hospital, Winfield, KS, p. A253
HOCKERT, Steve, Chief Executive Officer, OneCore Health, Oklahoma City, OK, p. A512
HOCKING, Dale E., Chief Financial Officer, Jupiter Medical Center, Jupiter, FL, p. A130
HOCKING, Patrick
Chief Financial Officer, Asante Ashland Community Hospital, Ashland, OR, p. A519
Chief Financial Officer, Asante Rogue Regional Medical Center, Medford, OR, p. A523
Chief Financial Officer, Asante Three Rivers Medical Center, Grants Pass, OR, p. A521
HOCUM, Timothy, Chief Financial Officer, Providence Kodiak Island Medical Center, Kodiak, AK, p. A28
HODGE, Pamela, R.N. Chief Nursing Officer and Coordinator Performance Improvement, Jellico Community Hospital, Jellico, TN, p. A579
HODGES, Alan, Chief Executive Officer, Hancock Medical Center, Bay Saint Louis, MS, p. A350
HODGES, Dawn, Director Human Resources, Grand River Hospital District, Rifle, CO, p. A108
HODGES, Jay, Chief Financial Officer, TMC Bonham Hospital, Bonham, TX, p. A598
HODGES, Leisha, Human Resources Officer, Eastland Memorial Hospital, Eastland, TX, p. A609
HODGIN, Robin, R.N. Vice President Patient Services and Chief Nursing Officer, Northern Hospital of Surry County, Mount Airy, NC, p. A465
HODGKINSON, Kimberly
Chief Financial Officer, St. Vincent's Medical Center Riverside, Jacksonville, FL, p. A130
Chief Financial Officer, St. Vincent's Medical Center Southside, Jacksonville, FL, p. A130
HODGSON, Judith Ann, Chief Nursing Officer, Cheyenne County Hospital, Saint Francis, KS, p. A249
HODGSON, Susan M., R.N. Vice President Patient Care Services and Chief Nursing Officer, Canton–Potsdam Hospital, Potsdam, NY, p. A448
HODNETT, Laura, Interim Chief Nursing Officer, Glen Rose Medical Center, Glen Rose, TX, p. A616
HODSON, Don, M.D. Chief Medical Officer, St. Luke Hospital and Living Center, Marion, KS, p. A245
HODZEDA, Angela, Chief Financial Officer, Jack Hughston Memorial Hospital, Phenix City, AL, p. A24
HOEFER, Robert William, FACHE Chief Operating Officer, SSM Health Saint Louis University Hospital, Saint Louis, MO, p. A377
HOEFS, Dennis, Manager Information Technology, New Mexico Rehabilitation Center, Roswell, NM, p. A426
HOEKEMA, Dale, M.D. Vice President Medical Affairs and Chief Medical Officer, Kadlec Regional Medical Center, Richland, WA, p. A683
HOELL, Paul, M.D. President Medical Staff, New London Family Medical Center, New London, WI, p. A707
HOELSCHER, Steven C., Chief Operating Officer, Valley Regional Medical Center, Brownsville, TX, p. A599
HOERTZ, Joanne, Vice President of Nursing, Brooks Rehabilitation Hospital, Jacksonville, FL, p. A129
HOETH, Richard, Interim Chief Executive Officer and Administrator, Ochiltree General Hospital, Perryton, TX, p. A636
HOEY, Amy J., R.N. Executive Vice President and Chief Operating Officer, Lowell General Hospital, Lowell, MA, p. A308
HOFELICH, Kurt T., President, Sentara Norfolk General Hospital, Norfolk, VA, p. A669
HOFER, Maggie, Human Resources Representative, Hawarden Regional Healthcare, Hawarden, IA, p. A229
HOFER, Renee, Chief Financial Officer, St. Joseph's Hospital of Buckhannon, Buckhannon, WV, p. A690
HOFF, David L., Chief Executive Officer, Wayne Memorial Hospital, Honesdale, PA, p. A536
HOFF, Deanna, R.N. Director of Nursing, Bacon County Hospital and Health System, Alma, GA, p. A149
HOFF, Irv, Director Information Systems, Corona Regional Medical Center, Corona, CA, p. A58
HOFF, Linda, Senior Vice President and Chief Financial Officer, Legacy Mount Hood Medical Center, Gresham, OR, p. A521
HOFF, Margaret, Account Manager, Brown County Community Treatment Center, Green Bay, WI, p. A702
HOFFBERGER, Darren, D.O. Chief of Staff, Broward Health North, Deerfield Beach, FL, p. A125
HOFFELD, Thomas, M.D. Chief of Staff, Spanish Peaks Regional Health Center, Walsenburg, CO, p. A109
HOFFER, Nolan, Senior Director, St. Luke's Rehabilitation Hospital, Boise, ID, p. A173
HOFFMAN, Barbara, M.D. Chief Medical Officer, St. Christopher's Hospital for Children, Philadelphia, PA, p. A545
HOFFMAN, Brad, Administrative Director Human Resources, Shawnee Mission Medical Center, Shawnee Mission, KS, p. A250
HOFFMAN, Brian, Director Human Resources, Lancaster Regional Medical Center, Lancaster, PA, p. A537
HOFFMAN, Brian, M.D. Chief Medical Services, Veterans Affairs Boston Healthcare System, Boston, MA, p. A304
HOFFMAN, Carole, Vice President, Parkridge Medical Center, Chattanooga, TN, p. A575
HOFFMAN, Chris, Chief Operating Officer, Highlands Regional Medical Center, Prestonsburg, KY, p. A265
HOFFMAN, Daniel, M.D. Administrative Medical Director, Good Samaritan Regional Health Center, Mount Vernon, IL, p. A195
HOFFMAN, Debbie, Vice President Patient Services, SSM Health St. Francis Hospital – Maryville, Maryville, MO, p. A372
HOFFMAN, Debra, Manager Human Resources, Kern Valley Healthcare District, Lake Isabella, CA, p. A67
HOFFMAN, Howard, M.D. Medical Director, Psychiatric Institute of Washington, Washington, DC, p. A120
HOFFMAN, Jeff, M.D. Chief Medical Officer, Atrium Medical Center, Middletown, OH, p. A494
HOFFMAN, Jerry, Chief Financial Officer, Platte Health Center Avera, Platte, SD, p. A570
HOFFMAN, III, Joseph E.
Executive Vice President and Chief Financial Officer, University of Maryland Harford Memorial Hospital, Havre De Grace, MD, p. A298
Executive Vice President and Chief Financial Officer, University of Maryland Upper Chesapeake Medical Center, Bel Air, MD, p. A295
HOFFMAN, Julie, Vice President Patient Care Services and Chief Nursing Officer, Mercy Gilbert Medical Center, Gilbert, AZ, p. A31
HOFFMAN, Marcus, Area Chief Financial Officer, Kaiser Permanente Orange County Anaheim Medical Center, Anaheim, CA, p. A53
HOFFMAN, Mary, Chief Administrative Officer and Chief Financial Officer, Mayo Clinic Health System in Waycross, Waycross, GA, p. A167
HOFFMAN, Pamela S., Director of Human Resources, Monroe Hospital, Bloomfield, IN, p. A205
HOFFMAN, Robert P., Vice President and Director Patient Care Services, Wilkes–Barre General Hospital, Wilkes–Barre, PA, p. A553
HOFFMAN, Todd, M.D. Medical Director, St. John Broken Arrow, Broken Arrow, OK, p. A504
HOFFMAN, Tom, Manager Information Systems, Wayne Memorial Hospital, Honesdale, PA, p. A536
HOFFMAN, Trudy, Executive Director, Northwest Center for Behavioral Health, Fort Supply, OK, p. A507
HOFFMAN, Val, Chief Financial Officer, Granite Falls Municipal Hospital and Manor, Granite Falls, MN, p. A340
HOFFMANN, Wanda, Director Human Resources, River Oaks Hospital, New Orleans, LA, p. A282
HOFFNER, Amy, Administrator, Kindred Rehabilitation Hospital Arlington, Arlington, TX, p. A592
HOFIUS, Chuck, Chief Executive Officer, Perham Health, Perham, MN, p. A344
HOFLER, Linda D., Ph.D. Senior Vice President, Nurse Executive, Vidant Medical Center, Greenville, NC, p. A461
HOFMAN, William, Manager Information Technology, Wilkes Regional Medical Center, North Wilkesboro, NC, p. A466
HOFMANN, Bill, M.D. Chief Medical Staff, Grays Harbor Community Hospital, Aberdeen, WA, p. A676
HOFSTETTER, Peter A., Chief Executive Officer, Willamette Valley Medical Center, McMinnville, OR, p. A522
HOGAN, Brian, Chief Executive Officer and Administrator, Baptist Memorial Rehabilitation Hospital, Germantown, TN, p. A578
HOGAN, Dan, Chief Financial Officer, DeSoto Memorial Hospital, Arcadia, FL, p. A121
HOGAN, Judith, Comptroller and Director Resources and Logistics, Naval Hospital Bremerton, Bremerton, WA, p. A676
HOGAN, Michael, Chief Resource Management, General Leonard Wood Army Community Hospital, Fort Leonard Wood, MO, p. A367
HOGAN, Richard, Chief Financial Officer, Pleasant Valley Hospital, Point Pleasant, WV, p. A694
HOGAN, Richard H., CPA Chief Financial Officer, Landmark Hospital of Cape Girardeau, Cape Girardeau, MO, p. A364
HOGAN, Ronald E.
Chief Financial Officer, Our Lady of Lourdes Regional Medical Center, Lafayette, LA, p. A278
Regional Chief Financial Officer, St. Francis Medical Center, Monroe, LA, p. A280
HOGAN, Sean, President, SSM DePaul Health Center, Bridgeton, MO, p. A364
HOGAN, Timothy J., FACHE,
Regional President, Bayshore Community Hospital, Holmdel, NJ, p. A413
Regional President, Riverview Medical Center, Red Bank, NJ, p. A418
HOGDSON, Judy, R.N. Chief Nursing Officer, Hospital District One of Rice County, Lyons, KS, p. A245
HOGG, Donna, Supervisor Medical Records, Monroe County Hospital, Forsyth, GA, p. A157
HOGGARD GREEN, Jill, Ph.D., President, Mission Hospital, Asheville, NC, p. A455
HOGUE, Vicky, R.N. Vice President Patient Services and Chief Nursing Officer, WellStar Paulding Hospital, Hiram, GA, p. A159
HOHENSHELL, Valerie, Director of Clinical Services, Memorial Hospital, Gonzales, TX, p. A616
HOHMAN, Jennifer, M.D. President Medical Staff, Van Wert County Hospital, Van Wert, OH, p. A499
HOLBERT, Brandon, Director, Information Services, Ocala Regional Medical Center, Ocala, FL, p. A137
HOLBROOK, Chip, M.D. Chief of Staff, Simpson General Hospital, Mendenhall, MS, p. A357
HOLBROOK, Curtis, M.D. Chief Medical Officer, Heritage Park Surgical Hospital, Sherman, TX, p. A644
HOLCOMB, Holly, R.N. Chief Operating Officer, Childress Regional Medical Center, Childress, TX, p. A600
HOLCOMB, Sheila, M.D. President Medical Staff, Floyd Valley Hospital, Le Mars, IA, p. A230
HOLCOMBE, Sheryl, Administrative Assistant, Brownfield Regional Medical Center, Brownfield, TX, p. A598
HOLDEMAN, Royce, Chief Financial Officer, Mercy Hospital, Moundridge, KS, p. A246
HOLDEN, Carol E., M.D., Director, Center for Forensic Psychiatry, Saline, MI, p. A330
HOLDEN, Jay T.
Senior Vice President Chief Human Resources Officer, Beaumont Hospital – Royal Oak, Royal Oak, MI, p. A328
Vice President, Human Resources, Beaumont Hospital Grosse Pointe, Grosse Pointe, MI, p. A321
HOLDEN, Patricia, Chief Executive Officer, Mesa View Regional Hospital, Mesquite, NV, p. A403
HOLDEN, Peter J., President and Chief Executive Officer, Beth Israel Deaconess Hospital Plymouth, Plymouth, MA, p. A310
HOLDEN, Rhonda C., R.N. Chief Nursing Officer, Kittitas Valley Healthcare, Ellensburg, WA, p. A678
HOLDEN, Teal A., Chief Executive Officer, Memorial Hermann Surgical Hospital Kingwood, Kingwood, TX, p. A626

**A868** Index of Health Care Professionals 

Index of Health Care Professionals

Index of Health Care Professionals / Hood

HOLDER, Hal
Director Finance, SSM DePaul Health Center, Bridgeton, MO, p. A364
Regional Chief Financial Officer–Hospital Operations, SSM St. Clare Health Center, Fenton, MO, p. A367
Director Finance, SSM St. Joseph Hospital West, Lake Saint Louis, MO, p. A371
HOLDER, Joanna, Director Human Resources, Novant Health Franklin Medical Center, Louisburg, NC, p. A464
HOLDER, Virgil, Human Resources Business Partner, Piedmont Henry Hospital, Stockbridge, GA, p. A165
HOLDERMAN, Wanda, R.N., Chief Executive Officer, Fresno Heart and Surgical Hospital, Fresno, CA, p. A62
HOLEKAMP, Nicholas, M.D. Chief Medical Officer, Ranken Jordan Pediatric Bridge Hospital, Maryland Heights, MO, p. A372
HOLGUIN, Brenda, Manager Human Resources, University Behavioral Health of El Paso, El Paso, TX, p. A611
HOLGUIN, Mindee, Manager Human Resources, Sierra Vista Hospital, Truth or Consequences, NM, p. A427
HOLINER, Joel, M.D. Executive Medical Director, Green Oaks Hospital, Dallas, TX, p. A605
HOLLAND, Baxter C., M.D. Chief Medical Officer, Rutland Regional Medical Center, Rutland, VT, p. A661
HOLLAND, Brad D., Chief Executive Officer, Cedar Park Regional Medical Center, Cedar Park, TX, p. A600
HOLLAND, Charles, President and Chief Executive Officer, St. Bernard Hospital and Health Care Center, Chicago, IL, p. A184
HOLLAND, David
Chief Information Officer, Herrin Hospital, Herrin, IL, p. A190
Vice President Chief Innovation Officer, Memorial Hospital of Carbondale, Carbondale, IL, p. A180
Vice President Information Services, St. Joseph Memorial Hospital, Murphysboro, IL, p. A195
HOLLAND, Gabrielle, Chief Financial Officer, Irving Coppell Surgical Hospital, Irving, TX, p. A624
HOLLAND, John F., Chief Executive Officer, LHP Hospital Group, Plano, TX, p. B82
HOLLAND, Kevin, Chief Executive Officer, Singing River Health System, Pascagoula, MS, p. A359
HOLLAND, Kim, Senior Director Nursing Services, Comanche County Memorial Hospital, Lawton, OK, p. A508
HOLLAND, Kwi, Vice President Information Services, Knox Community Hospital, Mount Vernon, OH, p. A495
HOLLAND, Michael, M.D., Chief Executive Officer, Rehabilitation Hospital of Jennings, Jennings, LA, p. A276
HOLLAND, Penny, Associate Director for Patient Care Services, Aleda E. Lutz Veterans Affairs Medical Center, Saginaw, MI, p. A329
HOLLAND, Shannon S., R.N. Vice President of Patient Care Service, St. James Healthcare, Butte, MT, p. A382
HOLLAND, Sharron, Chief Financial Officer, Baptist Memorial Hospital–Huntingdon, Huntingdon, TN, p. A579
HOLLAND, Stace, Administrator, Pineville Community Hospital Association, Pineville, KY, p. A265
HOLLAND, Stephen, M.D. Vice President Chief Medical Officer and Medical Director, Gaylord Hospital, Wallingford, CT, p. A115
HOLLAND, Tiffany, Chief Nursing Officer, Bradley County Medical Center, Warren, AR, p. A51
HOLLAND, William
Chief Executive Officer, Drumright Regional Hospital, Drumright, OK, p. A505
Chief Executive Officer, Prague Community Hospital, Prague, OK, p. A514
HOLLEMAN, Ivan, Chief Financial Officer, Baxter Regional Medical Center, Mountain Home, AR, p. A48
HOLLEMAN, James, M.D. Chief of Staff, St. Luke's Hospital, Columbus, NC, p. A458
HOLLEMAN, Stephen B., Chief Financial Officer, Shepherd Center, Atlanta, GA, p. A151
HOLLIDAY, Jonathan, Manager Information Technology, Central Community Hospital, Elkader, IA, p. A227
HOLLIDAY, Michael T., Vice President Fiscal and Administrative Services, Van Wert County Hospital, Van Wert, OH, p. A499
HOLLIMAN, Emily L., Chief Executive Officer, Hackensack University Medical Center at Pascack Valley, Westwood, NJ, p. A420
HOLLINGER, Brad, Chairman and Chief Executive Officer, Vibra Healthcare, Mechanicsburg, PA, p. B149
HOLLINGER, Lori, Manager Human Resources, Fulton State Hospital, Fulton, MO, p. A368
HOLLINGSWORTH, Carl, Chief Financial Officer, Artesia General Hospital, Artesia, NM, p. A423
HOLLINGSWORTH, Christine, Chief Financial Officer, Phoenix Veterans Affairs Health Care System, Phoenix, AZ, p. A35
HOLLINGSWORTH, Nancy, MSN, President and Chief Executive Officer, Saint Agnes Medical Center, Fresno, CA, p. A62
HOLLINGSWORTH, Sherri, Chief Human Resources Officer, PIH Health Hospital–Whittier, Whittier, CA, p. A97
HOLLIS, Carla, President and Chief Executive Officer, Columbus Regional Healthcare System, Whiteville, NC, p. A470
HOLLIS, Gary W., Comptroller, Arkansas State Hospital, Little Rock, AR, p. A47
HOLLIS, Tom, Chief Executive Officer, Ellett Memorial Hospital, Appleton City, MO, p. A363
HOLLISTER, Jerry, Chief Executive Officer, NorthEastern Center, Auburn, IN, p. A204
HOLLISTER, Richard, President of Medical Staff, Exeter Hospital, Exeter, NH, p. A406
HOLLON, Kim Norton, FACHE, President and Chief Executive Officer, Signature Healthcare Brockton Hospital, Brockton, MA, p. A305
HOLLOWAY, Basil, Director Information Services, Medical Center Arlington, Arlington, TX, p. A592
HOLLOWAY, Kristina, Chief Human Resources Officer, Healdsburg District Hospital, Healdsburg, CA, p. A64
HOLLOWAY, Myra, Director Human Resources Management, Central State Hospital, Milledgeville, GA, p. A161
HOLLOWAY, Walter R., Chief Medical Officer, Ozarks Medical Center, West Plains, MO, p. A380
HOLLOWAY, Whitney, Chief Financial Officer, Berwick Hospital Center, Berwick, PA, p. A529
HOLM, Mary Ann, Office Clerk, Tioga Medical Center, Tioga, ND, p. A476
HOLM, Stan V., FACHE, Chief Executive Officer, West Valley Hospital, Goodyear, AZ, p. A32
HOLMAN, Joel, Chief of Staff, Central Valley Medical Center, Nephi, UT, p. A656
HOLMAN, Steve M., Chief Executive Officer, Union Hospital, Terre Haute, IN, p. A220
HOLMAY, Diane, R.N
Vice President and Chief Nursing Officer, Mayo Clinic Health System – Franciscan Healthcare in La Crosse, La Crosse, WI, p. A703
Chief Nursing Officer, Mayo Clinic Health System – Franciscan Healthcare in Sparta, Sparta, WI, p. A711
HOLMBERG, Daniel, M.D. Director of Medical Affairs, New Ulm Medical Center, New Ulm, MN, p. A344
HOLMEN, Kenneth D., M.D., President and Chief Executive Officer, CentraCare Health, Saint Cloud, MN, p. B32
HOLMES, Dawne, Chief Financial Officer, Greenwood Leflore Hospital, Greenwood, MS, p. A353
HOLMES, Heather, Director Health Information Systems, Merit Health Rankin, Brandon, MS, p. A351
HOLMES, Heidi, Chief Information Officer, Oklahoma State University Medical Center, Tulsa, OK, p. A516
HOLMES Jr., James M., President and Chief Executive Officer, Rappahannock General Hospital, Kilmarnock, VA, p. A666
HOLMES, James R., President and Chief Executive Officer, Redlands Community Hospital, Redlands, CA, p. A83
HOLMES, Jeremy, D.O. Chief of Staff, Kalkaska Memorial Health Center, Kalkaska, MI, p. A324
HOLMES, John, Business Manager, Ancora Psychiatric Hospital, Hammonton, NJ, p. A412
HOLMES, Mardy, Director Information Technology, Arkansas Methodist Medical Center, Paragould, AR, p. A49
HOLMES, Terry R., M.D. Clinical Director, Moccasin Bend Mental Health Institute, Chattanooga, TN, p. A575
HOLMES, Troy, Director Finance, Advanced Specialty Hospital of Toledo, Toledo, OH, p. A498
HOLOM, Randall G., Chief Executive Officer, Frances Mahon Deaconess Hospital, Glasgow, MT, p. A383
HOLSAPPLE, Kim, Human Resource Specialist, Chester Mental Health Center, Chester, IL, p. A181
HOLSCHBACH, Dennis, Chief Financial Officer and Director Human Resources, Ruby Valley Hospital, Sheridan, MT, p. A387
HOLSON, Debbie C., R.N. Vice President Patient Care Services and Chief Nursing Officer, The HSC Pediatric Center, Washington, DC, p. A120
HOLST, Ken, Chief Financial Officer, Borgess–Lee Memorial Hospital, Dowagiac, MI, p. A318
HOLSTEN, Robyn, Human Resources Director, Salt Lake Behavioral Health, Salt Lake City, UT, p. A658
HOLSTIEN, Bruce, President and Chief Executive Officer, Spartanburg Regional Healthcare System, Spartanburg, SC, p. B125
HOLSTIEN, Bruce, President and Chief Executive Officer, Spartanburg Regional Medical Center, Spartanburg, SC, p. A565
HOLSTON, James, M.D. Vice President and Chief Quality Officer, South Central Regional Medical Center, Laurel, MS, p. A356
HOLT, Bebe, Vice President Chief Operating Officer, Novant Health Prince William Medical Center, Manassas, VA, p. A667
HOLT, Brian, Chief Executive Officer, Post Acute Medical Specialty Hospital of Lafayette, Lafayette, LA, p. A278
HOLT, Clayton, Chief Executive Officer, San Juan Hospital, Monticello, UT, p. A655
HOLT, Kory
Division Controller Network Operations, Avera Dells Area Hospital, Dell Rapids, SD, p. A568
Assistant Vice President for Financial Integration, Avera Flandreau Hospital, Flandreau, SD, p. A568
HOLT, Mari J., R.N. Vice President Patient Care Services, Unity Hospital, Fridley, MN, p. A339
HOLT, Peter, M.D. Director Medical Affairs, Saint Luke's Hospital of Kansas City, Kansas City, MO, p. A370
HOLT, Richard, R.N. Associate Director Patient Care Services, Veterans Affairs St. Louis Health Care System, Saint Louis, MO, p. A378
HOLT, Sherry, Director Human Resources, United Regional Medical Center, Manchester, TN, p. A582
HOLT, Stephen R., M.D., Director, Captain James A. Lovell Federal Health Care Center, North Chicago, IL, p. A196
HOLT, Thomas A., Chief Financial Officer, Conroe Regional Medical Center, Conroe, TX, p. A602
HOLT, Will, Director Information Technology, Harrison County Community Hospital, Bethany, MO, p. A363
HOLTHAUS, Julie K., Director Human Resources, Sabetha Community Hospital, Sabetha, KS, p. A249
HOLTHAUS, Monica, Chief Financial Officer, Community HealthCare System, Onaga, KS, p. A247
HOLTZ, George, Director Human Resources, Sharp Grossmont Hospital, La Mesa, CA, p. A66
HOLTZ, Keith, Chief Human Resources Officer, Cook Children's Medical Center, Fort Worth, TX, p. A613
HOLTZ, Mark
Chief Operating Officer, Coordinated Health–Bethlehem, Bethlehem, PA, p. A529
Senior Vice President Operations and Chief Operating Officer, Glens Falls Hospital, Glens Falls, NY, p. A434
HOLTZ, Noel, M.D. Chief Medical Officer, WellStar Douglas Hospital, Douglasville, GA, p. A156
HOLTZMAN, Michael, M.D. Medical Director, Kindred Hospital–St. Louis, Saint Louis, MO, p. A376
HOLUBEK, William, M.D. Chief Medical Officer, Christ Hospital, Jersey City, NJ, p. A413
HOLYFIELD, Linda S., MSN, President and Chief Executive Officer, P & S Surgical Hospital, Monroe, LA, p. A280
HOLYOAK, Mark, Chief Executive Officer, Castleview Hospital, Price, UT, p. A657
HOLZER, Traci, Chief Human Resources Officer, Doctors Hospital of Manteca, Manteca, CA, p. A74
HOMA, Jim, Chief Executive Officer, Heatherhill Care Communities, Chardon, OH, p. A481
HOMAN, Cheryl, Administrative Director, Lima Memorial Health System, Lima, OH, p. A492
HOMER, Kenneth, M.D. Chief Medical Officer, Holy Cross Hospital, Fort Lauderdale, FL, p. A126
HOMER, Margie, President, Southern Plains Medical Group, Oklahoma City, OK, p. B125
HOMYK, David, Vice President Human Resources, Beaufort Memorial Hospital, Beaufort, SC, p. A557
HOMYK, Linda, Chief Nursing Officer, Sewickley Valley Hospital, (A Division of Valley Medical Facilities), Sewickley, PA, p. A550
HONAKER, Linda, Vice President Financial Operations, Scripps Memorial Hospital–La Jolla, La Jolla, CA, p. A66
HONEA, Bert, M.D
Associate Chief Medical Officer Northern Colorado, Banner Fort Collins Medical Center, Fort Collins, CO, p. A103
Medical Director, McKee Medical Center, Loveland, CO, p. A107
HONEA, Bruce, Director Information Services, CHRISTUS Coushatta Health Care Center, Coushatta, LA, p. A272
HONEA, Michael, Chief Financial Officer, Glen Rose Medical Center, Glen Rose, TX, p. A616
HONERBRINK, Daniel, Vice President Finance and Chief Financial Officer, Fairmont Regional Medical Center, Fairmont, WV, p. A691
HONEYCUTT, Cynthia, Director Human Resources, Moccasin Bend Mental Health Institute, Chattanooga, TN, p. A575
HONEYCUTT, Robert C., Chief Executive Officer, Dignity Health Arizona General Hospital, Laveen, AZ, p. A33
HONEYCUTT, Tammy, R.N. Director of Nursing, Jasper Memorial Hospital, Monticello, GA, p. A162
HONSINGER, Melissa, Chief Operating Officer, St. Luke's Rehabilitation Hospital, Boise, ID, p. A173
HONTS, Gary, Chief Executive Officer, John F. Kennedy Memorial Hospital, Indio, CA, p. A65
HOOD, Cliff, Chief Operating Officer, Central Regional Hospital, Butner, NC, p. A456
HOOD, Kathy, Administrative Assistant Human Resources, Union General Hospital, Blairsville, GA, p. A152

Index of Health Care Professionals

Index of Health Care Professionals / Hood


HOOD, M. Michelle, FACHE, President and Chief Executive Officer, Eastern Maine Healthcare Systems, Brewer, ME, p. B53
HOOD, Ron, M.D. Chief of Staff, Sutter Amador Hospital, Jackson, CA, p. A65
HOOD, Sam, Director Human Resources, Heartland Regional Medical Center, Marion, IL, p. A193
HOOD, Tom, Chief Operating Officer, King's Daughters Medical Center, Brookhaven, MS, p. A351
HOOFMAN, Kevin, Director Management Information, Unity Health White County Medical Center, Searcy, AR, p. A50
HOOK, Diane, Chief Financial Officer, Wayne County Hospital, Corydon, IA, p. A225
HOOKER, Melvin, Chief Human Resources, New Mexico Veterans Affairs Health Care System – Raymond G. Murphy Medical Center, Albuquerque, NM, p. A422
HOOKER, Rita, Administrative Director Information Services, Bon Secours St. Francis Health System, Greenville, SC, p. A561
HOOKS, Al, Senior Vice President and Chief Financial Officer, Nash Health Care Systems, Rocky Mount, NC, p. A467
HOOKS Jr., Dwayne, R.N., Chief Executive Officer, Select Specialty Hospital–Atlanta, Atlanta, GA, p. A151
HOOLAHAN, Susan E., R.N. Vice President Patient Care Services and Chief Nursing Officer, UPMC Passavant, Pittsburgh, PA, p. A547
HOOP, Heather, Human Resources Generalist, Adams County Regional Medical Center, Seaman, OH, p. A497
HOOPER, Joseph, President and Chief Executive Officer, Community Howard Regional Health, Kokomo, IN, p. A213
HOOPER, Robert A.
Director Human Resources, TriStar Skyline Madison Campus, Madison, TN, p. A582
Director Human Resources, TriStar Skyline Medical Center, Nashville, TN, p. A586
HOOVER, Alvin, FACHE, Chief Executive Officer, King's Daughters Medical Center, Brookhaven, MS, p. A351
HOOVER, Garrett W., FACHE, Senior Vice President, President and Chief Operating Officer, Corning Hospital, Corning, NY, p. A432
HOOVER, Jeremy Steven, Chief Information Officer, Kiowa County Memorial Hospital, Greensburg, KS, p. A241
HOOVER, Leon, Director Information Systems, Hendry Regional Medical Center, Clewiston, FL, p. A124
HOOVER, Randy, Interim President and Chief Executive Officer, Oconee Regional Medical Center, Milledgeville, GA, p. A161
HOPE, Joseph D., D.O. President Medical Staff, Riddle Hospital, Media, PA, p. A540
HOPE, Lisa R., Director Human Resources, Owensboro Health Muhlenberg Community Hospital, Greenville, KY, p. A257
HOPE, Steve, Vice President Corporate Services, Methodist Rehabilitation Center, Jackson, MS, p. A355
HOPE, IV, William, M.D. Chief of Medical Staff, Vidant Chowan Hospital, Edenton, NC, p. A459
HOPKINS, Denver, Director of Human Resources, Aventura Hospital and Medical Center, Aventura, FL, p. A121
HOPKINS, Frances F., Chief Financial Officer, Sabine Medical Center, Many, LA, p. A279
HOPKINS, Jason, Director, Human Resources, Hamilton Medical Center, Dalton, GA, p. A155
HOPKINS, Jim, Chief Financial Officer, Cascade Medical Center, Leavenworth, WA, p. A680
HOPKINS, Joy, Vice President Patient Care Services, OSF St. Francis Hospital and Medical Group, Escanaba, MI, p. A319
HOPKINS, Kelli, Director Human Resources, Baptist Health Medical Center–Hot Spring County, Malvern, AR, p. A48
HOPKINS, Ken, Vice President Finance and Chief Financial Officer, Norman Regional Health System, Norman, OK, p. A510
HOPKINS, Kevin, Vice President of Operations, Hutcheson Medical Center, Fort Oglethorpe, GA, p. A158
HOPKINS, Ronald, D.O. Chief of Staff, Nor–Lea General Hospital, Lovington, NM, p. A425
HOPKINS, William, Director Finance, Carolinas Rehabilitation, Charlotte, NC, p. A457
HOPP, Eva, Chief Nurse Executive, Pinckneyville Community Hospital, Pinckneyville, IL, p. A198
HOPPE, Janice
Vice President Information Technology System, Banner Baywood Medical Center, Mesa, AZ, p. A33
Vice President, Information Technology System, Banner Heart Hospital, Mesa, AZ, p. A33
HOPPEN, Claudine N., MSN Interim Chief Nursing Officer, Children's Hospital of Michigan, Detroit, MI, p. A317
HOPPS, Deborah, Chief Executive Officer, Vibra Rehabilitation Hospital Lake Travis, Lakeway, TX, p. A627
HOPSON, W. Briggs, M.D. Clinical Medical Director, Merit Health River Region, Vicksburg, MS, p. A361
HOPSTAD, Kyle, Chief Executive Officer, Broadwater Health Center, Townsend, MT, p. A387
HOPWOOD, James, Chief Financial Officer, Promise Hospital of Miss Lou, Vidalia, LA, p. A286
HORAN, Gary S., FACHE, President and Chief Executive Officer, Trinitas Regional Medical Center, Elizabeth, NJ, p. A411
HORAN, Sandra A., Executive Director, Margaretville Hospital, Margaretville, NY, p. A437
HORATH, Kevin, Vice President Human Resources, Decatur Memorial Hospital, Decatur, IL, p. A186
HORECKA, Richard, Chief Medical Officer, Swift County–Benson Hospital, Benson, MN, p. A335
HORN, Jeff, Vice President, Information and Support Services, Jay County Hospital, Portland, IN, p. A218
HORN, LeeAnn, Chief Nurse Executive, Providence Kodiak Island Medical Center, Kodiak, AK, p. A28
HORN, Sarah
Chief Nursing Officer, Salem Hospital, Salem, OR, p. A526
Chief Nursing Officer, West Valley Hospital, Dallas, OR, p. A520
HORN, Syndi, Director Information Systems, Memorial Hospital, Carthage, IL, p. A180
HORNBURG, Tom, Director Information Systems, Mason General Hospital, Shelton, WA, p. A684
HORNE, Beth, System Administrator Information Technology, Preston Memorial Hospital, Kingwood, WV, p. A692
HORNE, Eilene, Manager Human Resources, Mountain View Hospital, Idaho Falls, ID, p. A174
HORNE, Harry, D.O. Chief of Staff, Cumberland River Hospital, Celina, TN, p. A574
HORNE, J. Mark, Senior Vice President and Chief Operating Officer, Grand View Health, Sellersville, PA, p. A549
HORNE, Theresa, MS Vice President Patient Care Services, St. Dominic–Jackson Memorial Hospital, Jackson, MS, p. A355
HORNER, Ania, R.N. Vice President and Chief Nurse Executive, Aurora Sinai Medical Center, Milwaukee, WI, p. A706
HORNER, Bryan, President and Chief Executive Officer, Shannon Medical Center, San Angelo, TX, p. A640
HORNER, Cheryl, Supervisor Data Processing, Community Memorial Hospital, Staunton, IL, p. A201
HORNER, Eva, Assistant Executive Director Operations, Devereux Hospital and Children's Center of Florida, Melbourne, FL, p. A133
HORNER, James, Chief Information Officer, Portland Veterans Affairs Medical Center, Portland, OR, p. A524
HORNER, John M., President and Chief Executive Officer, Major Hospital, Shelbyville, IN, p. A220
HORNICK, Greg, Chief Nursing Officer, Martin General Hospital, Williamston, NC, p. A470
HORNSBY, Donny, Director Fiscal Services, Memphis Mental Health Institute, Memphis, TN, p. A583
HORNUNG, Dona, Director Information and Technology Services, Doctors Hospital, Augusta, GA, p. A151
HORNUNG, Kurt, Director, Medical Center of Trinity, Trinity, FL, p. A146
HOROWITZ, Ira, M.D. Chief Medical Officer, Emory University Hospital, atlanta, GA, p. A150
HORRIGAN, Timothy, M.D. Chief Quality Officer, UnityPoint Health – Allen Hospital, Waterloo, IA, p. A236
HORSLEY, Steve, Vice President and Chief Information Officer, Moses H. Cone Memorial Hospital, Greensboro, NC, p. A461
HORSMAN, Sarah
Vice President Human Resources, MultiCare Good Samaritan Hospital, Puyallup, WA, p. A682
Senior Vice President Human Potential, MultiCare Mary Bridge Children's Hospital and Health Center, Tacoma, WA, p. A686
Senior Vice President Human Potential, MultiCare Tacoma General Hospital, Tacoma, WA, p. A686
HORST, Brad, Director Human Resources, Clear Lake Regional Medical Center, Webster, TX, p. A651
HORSTMAN, Jennifer M., R.N. Chief Nursing Officer and Chief Information Officer, Fairbanks, Indianapolis, IN, p. A211
HORTILLOSA, Maria, M.D. Chief of Staff, Middlesboro ARH Hospital, Middlesboro, KY, p. A263
HORTON, Eileen M.
Vice President Patient Services and Chief Nursing Officer, Capital Health Medical Center–Hopewell, Pennington, NJ, p. A416
Vice President, Patient Services/Chief Nursing Officer, Capital Health Regional Medical Center, Trenton, NJ, p. A419
HORTON, Greg, Director Support Services, State Hospital South, Blackfoot, ID, p. A172
HORTON, Jim, Chief Executive Officer, Rankin Hospital District, Rankin, TX, p. A638
HORTON, Kenny, Director Information Systems, Walker Baptist Medical Center, Jasper, AL, p. A21
HORTON, Landon, Director of Nursing, Valley Behavioral Health System, Barling, AR, p. A41
HORTON, Marie, Director Associate Relations, Bartow Regional Medical Center, Bartow, FL, p. A121
HORTON, Melanie Paige, Chief Nursing Officer, Russell County Medical Center, Lebanon, VA, p. A666
HORTON, Warren, Information Technologist, Baptist Health Medical Center–Stuttgart, Stuttgart, AR, p. A51
HORVAT, Kami, Chief Financial Officer, Doctors Hospital of West Covina, West Covina, CA, p. A97
HOSKINS, Mary, Chief Executive Officer, Kindred Hospital Detroit, Detroit, MI, p. A318
HOSKINS, Pearly Graham, M.D. President Medical Staff, Cape Fear Valley – Bladen County Hospital, Elizabethtown, NC, p. A460
HOSKINS, Shirley, Chief Operating Officer, Meadows Regional Medical Center, Vidalia, GA, p. A166
HOSLER, Stephan, Vice President Human Resources, Mercy Medical Center Redding, Redding, CA, p. A82
HOSTEENEZ, Vivie, Chief Financial Officer, U. S. Public Health Service Indian Hospital, San Carlos, AZ, p. A37
HOSTETTER, Lynne, Vice President Human Resources, The HSC Pediatric Center, Washington, DC, p. A120
HOTA, Bala, Interim Chief Information Officer, John H. Stroger Jr. Hospital of Cook County, Chicago, IL, p. A182
HOTALING, Andrew, Chief Executive Officer, Forest View Psychiatric Hospital, Grand Rapids, MI, p. A320
HOTCHKISS, Kaleigh, Controller, HEALTHSOUTH Rehabilitation Hospital of Southern Arizona, Tucson, AZ, p. A39
HOTES, Lawrence S., M.D. Chief Medical Officer, New England Sinai Hospital and Rehabilitation Center, Stoughton, MA, p. A312
HOTT, Judith, Chief Executive Officer, Thomas B. Finan Center, Cumberland, MD, p. A297
HOTTENDORF, Catherine, MS, Executive Director, Franklin Hospital, Valley Stream, NY, p. A452
HOUCHIN, Kim, Chief Nursing Officer, Minnie Hamilton HealthCare Center, Grantsville, WV, p. A691
HOUGH, Jason, Medical Staff President, Spencer Hospital, Spencer, IA, p. A235
HOUGHTON, Roxan, Director Human Resources, Promise Hospital of Miss Lou, Vidalia, LA, p. A286
HOULAHAN, Beth, MSN Senior Vice President and Chief Nursing Officer, University of Wisconsin Hospital and Clinics, Madison, WI, p. A704
HOULE, David, Executive Vice President and Chief Financial Officer, The Hospital at Hebrew Health Care, West Hartford, CT, p. A116
HOULIHAN, David, M.D. Chief of Staff, Tomah Veterans Affairs Medical Center, Tomah, WI, p. A712
HOULIHAN, James, Chief Financial Officer, Warren Memorial Hospital, Friend, NE, p. A392
HOUMANN, Lars D., President, Florida Hospital, Orlando, FL, p. A138
HOURANY, Joseph, Chief Medical Officer, Montclair Hospital Medical Center, Montclair, CA, p. A76
HOUSAND, Jill, Director Human Resources, Mesa Springs, Fort Worth, TX, p. A613
HOUSE, Alan, Chief Financial Officer, Margaret R. Pardee Memorial Hospital, Hendersonville, NC, p. A462
HOUSE, David
Vice President, Baptist Health Extended Care Hospital, Little Rock, AR, p. A47
Vice President and Chief Information Officer, Baptist Health Medical Center – North Little Rock, North Little Rock, AR, p. A49
Vice President and Chief Information Officer, Baptist Health Medical Center–Arkadelphia, Arkadelphia, AR, p. A41
Vice President and Chief Information Officer, Baptist Health Medical Center–Little Rock, Little Rock, AR, p. A47
Vice President and Chief Information Officer, Baptist Health Rehabilitation Institute, Little Rock, AR, p. A47
HOUSE, Jennifer R., Chief Operations and Readiness, Reynolds Army Community Hospital, Fort Sill, OK, p. A507
HOUSE, Michael, Director Information Systems, St. Mary's Medical Center, Huntington, WV, p. A692
HOUSER, David, M.D. Vice President Medical Affairs, Rapid City Regional Hospital, Rapid City, SD, p. A570
HOUSER, Glenn, M.D. Chief Medical Officer, Garfield County Public Hospital District, Pomeroy, WA, p. A682
HOUSER, James P., Interim Chief Executive Officer, Saint Francis Memorial Hospital, San Francisco, CA, p. A88
HOUSER, Kurt, Chief Operating Officer, University Medical Center, Las Vegas, NV, p. A403
HOUSER, Sara, Chief Nursing Officer, Ashe Memorial Hospital, Jefferson, NC, p. A463
HOUSER–HANFELDER, Sallie, FACHE, Director, Central Texas Veterans Health Care System, Temple, TX, p. A646
HOUSH, Joe, District Director Human Resources, Kindred Hospital–Indianapolis, Indianapolis, IN, p. A212
HOUSLEY, Kristin, Chief Information Officer, South Lincoln Medical Center, Kemmerer, WY, p. A716
HOUSMAN, Bradley W., M.D. Chief Medical Officer, Baptist Health Paducah, Paducah, KY, p. A264


**A870** Index of Health Care Professionals 

HOUSTON, Anthony, President, CHI St. Vincent Hot Springs, Hot Springs, AR, p. A45

HOUSTON, Jerry, Director Information Systems, Jennie Stuart Medical Center, Hopkinsville, KY, p. A258

HOUSTON, Sally, M.D. Executive Vice President and Chief Medical Officer, Tampa General Hospital, Tampa, FL, p. A145

HOUSTON, William J., M.D. Chief Medical Officer, Indiana University Health La Porte Hospital, La Porte, IN, p. A214

HOVAN, Keith A., R.N., President and Chief Executive Officer, Southcoast Hospitals Group, Fall River, MA, p. A306

HOVDENES, Jodi Lynn, Vice President of Patient Care, Carrington Health Center, Carrington, ND, p. A472

HOVE, Barton A., President and Chief Executive Officer, Wellmont Health System, Kingsport, TN, p. B152

HOVENS, Michael R., M.D. Chief Medical Officer, Merit Health Batesville, Batesville, MS, p. A350

HOWALT, Lyra, Chief Financial Officer, North Fulton Regional Hospital, Roswell, GA, p. A163

HOWARD, Andrew, Interim Chief Executive Officer, Lake Wales Medical Center, Lake Wales, FL, p. A131

HOWARD, Ben, D.O. Chief of Staff, Salt Lake Regional Medical Center, Salt Lake City, UT, p. A658

HOWARD, Catherine, Director Human Resources, Sentara Halifax Regional Hospital, South Boston, VA, p. A673

HOWARD, Charles, M.D. Chief of Staff, St. Vincent Morrilton, Morrilton, AR, p. A48

HOWARD, Cindy, Director Financial Services, Nell J. Redfield Memorial Hospital, Malad City, ID, p. A174

HOWARD, Daniel, Chief Financial Officer, Maine Veterans Affairs Medical Center, Augusta, ME, p. A288

HOWARD, Eddie L.
Vice President and Chief Operating Officer, East Texas Medical Center Rehabilitation Hospital, Tyler, TX, p. A648
Chief Operating Officer, East Texas Medical Center Rehabilitation Hospital, Tyler, TX, p. A648
Vice President and Chief Operating Officer, East Texas Medical Center Specialty Hospital, Tyler, TX, p. A648

HOWARD, Gary L., Senior Vice President and Chief Financial Officer, Hamilton Medical Center, Dalton, GA, p. A155

HOWARD, Greg M.
Director Human Resource, Health Alliance Hospital – Broadway Campus, Kingston, NY, p. A436
Vice President Human Resources, Health Alliance Hospital – Mary's Avenue Campus, Kingston, NY, p. A436

HOWARD, Gwenyth, Vice President Finance, St. Thomas More Hospital, Canon City, CO, p. A100

HOWARD, Jill, R.N. Chief Operating Officer, TriStar Skyline Madison Campus, Madison, TN, p. A582

HOWARD, Kari, Interim Director of Nursing, Pauls Valley General Hospital, Pauls Valley, OK, p. A513

HOWARD, Lisa M., Acting Director, Veterans Affairs Sierra Nevada Health Care System, Reno, NV, p. A404

HOWARD, Loy M., President and Chief Executive Officer, Tanner Health System, Carrollton, GA, p. B131

HOWARD, Mary, Director Human Resources, Winnebago Mental Health Institute, Winnebago, WI, p. A714

HOWARD, Mike, Associate Administrator, Eliza Coffee Memorial Hospital, Florence, AL, p. A19

HOWARD, Opal R., Executive Director Human Resources, Florida Hospital Memorial Medical Center, Daytona Beach, FL, p. A125

HOWARD, Pamela B., R.N., Chief Executive Officer, Administrator and Risk Manager, Lake Butler Hospital Hand Surgery Center, Lake Butler, FL, p. A131

HOWARD, Roger, M.D. Senior Vice President and Medical Director, Beaumont Hospital – Troy, Troy, MI, p. A331

HOWARD, Roger, President and Chief Executive Officer, Dearborn County Hospital, Lawrenceburg, IN, p. A214

HOWARD, Ron, Chief Financial Officer, Holly Hill Hospital, Raleigh, NC, p. A466

HOWARD, Sabra, Manager Human Resources, Harlan ARH Hospital, Harlan, KY, p. A258

HOWARD, Teresa, Manager Human Resources, Yoakum County Hospital, Denver City, TX, p. A608

HOWARD, Tim
Chief Human Resources Officer, Fountain Valley Regional Hospital and Medical Center, Fountain Valley, CA, p. A61
Interim Chief Financial Officer, The Memorial Hospital at Craig, Craig, CO, p. A101

HOWARD, Tom, Chief Financial Officer, Texas Health Presbyterian Hospital Flower Mound, Flower Mound, TX, p. A612

HOWARD, Win, Chief Executive Officer, Asante Three Rivers Medical Center, Grants Pass, OR, p. A521

HOWARD–CROW, Dallis, Chief Human Resources Officer, Emory University Hospital Midtown, Atlanta, GA, p. A150

HOWAT, Greg, Vice President Human Resources, Eastern Maine Medical Center, Bangor, ME, p. A288

HOWDEN, William, Vice President Nursing, Good Samaritan Regional Medical Center, Corvallis, OR, p. A520

HOWE, Debbie, Chief Executive Officer, Weatherford Regional Hospital, Weatherford, OK, p. A518

HOWE, James L., Director Human Resources, Pinnacle Pointe Hospital, Little Rock, AR, p. A47

HOWE, Mary Lenzini, Vice President Human Resources, Geisinger–Bloomsburg Hospital, Bloomsburg, PA, p. A529

HOWE, Scott W., Chief Executive Officer, Weeks Medical Center, Lancaster, NH, p. A406

HOWE, Vicki, Health Information Management, Ness County Hospital, Ness City, KS, p. A246

HOWELL, Amy M., Director Human Resources, St. Luke's Behavioral Health Center, Phoenix, AZ, p. A36

HOWELL, Bradley, Chief Executive Officer, Roundup Memorial Healthcare, Roundup, MT, p. A386

HOWELL, Carrie, Chief Financial Officer, Barstow Community Hospital, Barstow, CA, p. A56

HOWELL, Diana, Director Human Resources, Conroe Regional Medical Center, Conroe, TX, p. A602

HOWELL, Jill, Clinical Director and Chief Nursing Officer, St. Luke's Jerome, Jerome, ID, p. A174

HOWELL, Kathy A., Vice President Human Resources, Lexington Medical Center, West Columbia, SC, p. A566

HOWELL, Kristie, System Information Technology Director, Southampton Memorial Hospital, Franklin, VA, p. A665

HOWELL, Nathan, President and Chief Executive Officer, Claxton–Hepburn Medical Center, Ogdensburg, NY, p. A446

HOWELL, Pat, Chief Nursing Officer, Community Memorial Hospital, Syracuse, NE, p. A398

HOWELL, R. Edward, Vice President and Chief Executive Officer, UVA Health System, Charlottesville, VA, p. B148

HOWELL, Ronene, Director Health Information Management, Bryce Hospital, Tuscaloosa, AL, p. A25

HOWELL, Sheri, Deputy Commander Nursing, Brooke Army Medical Center, Fort Sam Houston, TX, p. A612

HOWELLS, Stephen, Chief Financial Officer, Kane County Hospital, Kanab, UT, p. A655

HOWERTER, Mark, M.D. President Medical Staff, Columbus Community Hospital, Columbus, NE, p. A391

HOWERTON, Russell M., M.D. Chief Medical Officer, Wake Forest Baptist Medical Center, Winston–Salem, NC, p. A471

HOWERTON, Shawn, M.D., Chief Executive Officer and President, Medical Staff, Sampson Regional Medical Center, Clinton, NC, p. A458

HOWES, Julie, Director Finance, Carson Valley Medical Center, Gardnerville, NV, p. A400

HOWLAND, Carol, Chief Nursing Officer, Twin Cities Community Hospital, Templeton, CA, p. A94

HOY, Jonathan B., Chief Financial Officer, Duke Regional Hospital, Durham, NC, p. A459

HOYE, Kelly, M.D. Vice President Medical Affairs, Morton Hospital and Medical Center, Taunton, MA, p. A312

HOYER, Sara, Director Administrative Services, Kansas Neurological Institute, Topeka, KS, p. A251

HOYER, Scott, M.D. Vice President Quality and Chief Medical Officer, United Regional Health Care System, Wichita Falls, TX, p. A652

HOYES, Garry W., Chief Executive Officer, Dublin Springs, Dublin, OH, p. A489

HOYLE, Lisa, R.N. Chief Nursing Officer, Kingwood Medical Center, Kingwood, TX, p. A626

HOYOS, Kent, Chief Information Officer, Pomona Valley Hospital Medical Center, Pomona, CA, p. A81

HOYT, Nancy, R.N. Vice President Operations/Clinical and Chief Nursing Officer, Mercy Regional Medical Center, Durango, CO, p. A102

HRITZ, Diane, Chief Financial Officer, Advanced Surgical Hospital, Washington, PA, p. A552

HRON, Janine, Chief Executive Officer, Crittenton Children's Center, Kansas City, MO, p. A369

HRUBIAK, Dan, Associate Computer Program Analyst, Western New York Children's Psychiatric Center, West Seneca, NY, p. A454

HRUBY, Deidre, Director of Patient Care, Madelia Community Hospital, Madelia, MN, p. A341

HSIEH, Ketty, Senior Director Finance, UW Medicine/Northwest Hospital & Medical Center, Seattle, WA, p. A684

HSING, Shirley, Senior Vice President and Chief Financial Officer, North Oaks Medical Center, Hammond, LA, p. A274

HSU, Wah Chung, Senior Vice President Finance, San Antonio Community Hospital, Upland, CA, p. A95

HUANG, Joseph, M.D. Chief Medical and Quality Officer, Silverton Hospital, Silverton, OR, p. A526

HUBBARD, Bill, Vice President, Operations, Carolinas HealthCare System NorthEast, Concord, NC, p. A458

HUBBARD, Blake W., FACH
Senior Vice President and Chief Operating Officer Medical Surgical Operations and Human Resources, Nix Community General Hospital, Dilley, TX, p. A609
Senior Vice President and Chief Operating Officer, Nix Health Care System, San Antonio, TX, p. A641

HUBBARD, Brent
Chief Operating Officer, Mercy Hospital Fort Smith, Fort Smith, AR, p. A44
Chief Operating Officer, Mercy Hospital Ozark, Ozark, AR, p. A49
Chief Operating Officer, Mercy Hospital Paris, Paris, AR, p. A49
Chief Operating Officer, Mercy Hospital Waldron, Waldron, AR, p. A51

HUBBARD, Daniel, Chief Financial Officer, Sioux Falls Veterans Affairs Health Care System, Sioux Falls, SD, p. A572

HUBBARD, David, Chief Executive Officer, Daniels Memorial Healthcare Center, Scobey, MT, p. A387

HUBBARD, Gwen, Director of Nursing, Sierra Vista Hospital, Sacramento, CA, p. A85

HUBBARD, Kathy
Manager Human Resources, Nell J. Redfield Memorial Hospital, Malad City, ID, p. A174
Controller, Ocean Beach Hospital, Ilwaco, WA, p. A679

HUBBARD, Lynn, R.N. Vice President and Chief Nursing Officer, Indian River Medical Center, Vero Beach, FL, p. A146

HUBBARD, Mark, Vice President Risk Management, Loma Linda University Behavioral Medicine Center, Redlands, CA, p. A82

HUBBARD, Norm, Executive Vice President, Seattle Cancer Care Alliance, Seattle, WA, p. A683

HUBBARD, Tyson, Director Human Resources, Stanislaus Surgical Hospital, Modesto, CA, p. A76

HUBBS III, Olas A., FACHE, President and Chief Executive Officer, Memorial Health, Marysville, OH, p. A493

HUBER, Dalton, Chief Financial Officer, Campbell County Memorial Hospital, Gillette, WY, p. A716

HUBER, Timothy, Manager Financial Support, Mercy Hospital of Franciscan Sisters, Oelwein, IA, p. A232

HUBER, Vicki Lynn, R.N. Chief Nursing Officer, Abrazo Scottsdale Campus, Phoenix, AZ, p. A34

HUBERT, Michael F., Vice President Human Resources, J. C. Blair Memorial Hospital, Huntingdon, PA, p. A536

HUBL, Bryan, M.D. Chief of Staff, Thayer County Health Services, Hebron, NE, p. A392

HUBLEY, Grover, M.D. President Medical Staff, Madison St. Joseph Health Center, Madisonville, TX, p. A630

HUBSCHMAN, Gary
Administrative Director Finance, Sutter Auburn Faith Hospital, Auburn, CA, p. A54
Administrative Director Finance, Sutter Roseville Medical Center, Roseville, CA, p. A84

HUCK, Karma, Chief Operating Officer, Scott County Hospital, Scott City, KS, p. A250

HUCKABEE, Mike, Network Administrator, Coryell Memorial Hospital, Gatesville, TX, p. A616

HUCKABY, Don, Chief Information Management Service, Veterans Affairs Eastern Colorado Health Care System, Denver, CO, p. A102

HUCKABY, Kenneth, Senior Director Information Technology Systems Operations, Texas Health Presbyterian Hospital of Rockwall, Rockwall, TX, p. A639

HUDA, Edith, Director Human Resources, Daniels Memorial Healthcare Center, Scobey, MT, p. A387

HUDAK, Corey, Director Human Resources, Memorial Hospital, York, PA, p. A554

HUDDLESTON, Tina, Chief Nursing Officer, Baylor Medical Center at Trophy Club, Trophy Club, TX, p. A648

HUDGENS, Roselyn, Director Human Resources, Ballinger Memorial Hospital, Ballinger, TX, p. A595

HUDGINS, Paul
Associate Vice President Human Resources, Bascom Palmer Eye Institute–Anne Bates Leach Eye Hospital, Miami, FL, p. A134
Associate Vice President Human Resources, University of Miami Hospital and Clinics, Miami, FL, p. A135

HUDNELL, Sharon, R.N. Chief Nursing Officer, WK Bossier Health Center, Bossier City, LA, p. A271

HUDSON, Beth, Chief Nursing Officer, Baylor Institute for Rehabilitation, Dallas, TX, p. A604

HUDSON, C. R., Senior Vice President and Chief Financial Officer, Henry Mayo Newhall Memorial Hospital, Valencia, CA, p. A96

HUDSON, Gary Mikeal, Administrator, East Texas Medical Center Carthage, Carthage, TX, p. A600

HUDSON, Janell, M.D. Chief Clinical Officer, Sanford Thief River Falls Medical Center, Thief River Falls, MN, p. A348

HUDSON, Kayce H., Executive Director Human Resources, Saddleback Memorial Medical Center, Laguna Hills, CA, p. A66

HUDSON, Kenneth J., Chief Financial Officer, Veterans Affairs Puget Sound Health Care System, Seattle, WA, p. A684

HUDSON, Kent, Chief Financial Officer, Kingman Community Hospital, Kingman, KS, p. A243

HUDSON, Larry C., Executive Vice President and Chief Financial Officer, Charleston Area Medical Center, Charleston, WV, p. A690

HUDSON, Lowell K., Chief Financial Officer, Glen Oaks Hospital, Greenville, TX, p. A617

HUDSON, Maggie, Chief Financial and Operations Officer, Santiam Memorial Hospital, Stayton, OR, p. A526

HUDSON, MeKinzie, Chief Financial Officer, Stafford County Hospital, Stafford, KS, p. A250

HUDSON, Mike, Administrator, Federal Correctional Institute Hospital, Littleton, CO, p. A106

HUDSON, Pamela, M.D., Chief Executive Officer, Crestwood Medical Center, Huntsville, AL, p. A21

HUDSON, Robbi, Chief Financial Officer, HEALTHSOUTH Rehabilitation Hospital, Fayetteville, AR, p. A43

HUDSON, Skip, Manager Information Technology, Community Mental Health Center, Lawrenceburg, IN, p. A214

HUDSON–JINKS, Therese M., R.N. Chief Nursing Officer, Tufts Medical Center, Boston, MA, p. A304

HUDSPETH, Todd R., FACHE, Chief Executive Officer and President, Cass County Memorial Hospital, Atlantic, IA, p. A222

HUEBNER, Thomas W., President, Rutland Regional Medical Center, Rutland, VT, p. A661

HUEBNER, Timothy K., M.D. President Medical Affairs, Aspirus Riverview Hospital and Clinics, Inc., Wisconsin Rapids, WI, p. A714

HUENERGARDT, Sam, President and Chief Executive Officer, Central Texas Medical Center, San Marcos, TX, p. A643

HUERTA, Brad, Chief Executive Officer and Administrator, Lost Rivers Medical Center, Arco, ID, p. A172

HUERTA, Guillermo, M.D. Chief Medical Officer, Select Specialty Hospital–Omaha, Omaha, NE, p. A396

HUERTER, Holly
Vice President Human Resources, Methodist Jennie Edmundson Hospital, Council Bluffs, IA, p. A225
Vice President Human Resources, Nebraska Methodist Hospital, Omaha, NE, p. A396

HUETTL, Patricia, Vice President Finance and Chief Financial Officer, Holy Family Memorial, Manitowoc, WI, p. A704

HUEY, Peggy, Chief Nursing Officer, Red River Hospital, LLC, Wichita Falls, TX, p. A652

HUFF, Donnie, M.D. Chief Medical Officer, Livingston Regional Hospital, Livingston, TN, p. A581

HUFF, Jeff, Assistant Administrator Finance, Fayette Medical Center, Fayette, AL, p. A19

HUFF, Michael H., Chief Executive Officer, Hamilton Hospital, Olney, TX, p. A635

HUFF, Shelly E., Manager Human Resources, Indiana University Health Tipton Hospital, Tipton, IN, p. A220

HUFFMAN, David, Vice President and Controller, Select Specialty Hospital–Wilmington, Wilmington, DE, p. A118

HUFFMAN, James, Chief Executive Officer and Administrator, Baptist Memorial Hospital–Desoto, Southaven, MS, p. A360

HUFFMAN, Sherry
Administrator Human Resources, Beaumont Hospital – Taylor, Taylor, MI, p. A331
Administrator Human Resources, Beaumont Hospital–Dearborn, Dearborn, MI, p. A317

HUFFMAN, Steve
Chief Information Officer, Elkhart General Healthcare System, Elkhart, IN, p. A207
Chief Information Officer, Memorial Hospital of South Bend, South Bend, IN, p. A220

HUFFNER, William, M.D
Vice President Medical Affairs, Arnot Ogden Medical Center, Elmira, NY, p. A433
Chief Medical Officer and Senior Vice President Medical Affairs, St. Joseph's Hospital, Elmira, NY, p. A433
Chief Medical Officer, University of Maryland Shore Medical Center at Chestertown, Chestertown, MD, p. A296
Vice President Medical Affairs, University of Maryland Shore Medical Center at Dorchester, Cambridge, MD, p. A296
Chief Medical Officer, University of Maryland Shore Medical Center at Easton, Easton, MD, p. A297

HUFFORD, Dustin, Chief Information Officer, Memorial Hospital, Fremont, OH, p. A490

HUFFSTUTLER, Brandon, Chief Information Officer, Electra Memorial Hospital, Electra, TX, p. A612

HUFNAGEL, Keith, Director Human Resources, Stillwater Medical Center, Stillwater, OK, p. A515

HUGGINS, Lois, Chief Human Resources Officer and Senior Vice President Human Resources, Rehabilitation Institute of Chicago, Chicago, IL, p. A184

HUGGINS, Michael C., Administrator Network System, Eastern Oklahoma Medical Center, Poteau, OK, p. A514

HUGHES, April, Chief Financial Officer, Peachford Behavioral Health System, Atlanta, GA, p. A150

HUGHES, Beverly, R.N. Vice President Nursing, Fayette County Memorial Hospital, Washington Court House, OH, p. A500

HUGHES, Bill, Chief Nursing Officer, Granville Health System, Oxford, NC, p. A466

HUGHES, Chad, Information Officer, North Texas State Hospital, Vernon, TX, p. A649

HUGHES, Constance, Director of Nursing, West Gables Rehabilitation Hospital, Miami, FL, p. A135

HUGHES, David S., Chief Financial Officer, Vidant Medical Center, Greenville, NC, p. A461

HUGHES, Dustan, M.D. Vice President Medical Affairs, Saint Alphonsus Medical Center – Nampa, Nampa, ID, p. A175

HUGHES, Edith M., R.N., President, Beaumont Hospital – Trenton, Trenton, MI, p. A331

HUGHES, James, Director Human Resources, Lake Cumberland Regional Hospital, Somerset, KY, p. A266

HUGHES, Jessica, Director Finance, Hawarden Regional Healthcare, Hawarden, IA, p. A229

HUGHES, John, FACHE, President and Chief Executive Officer, Central Iowa Healthcare, Marshalltown, IA, p. A231

HUGHES, John, Administrator, Pawnee Valley Community Hospital, Larned, KS, p. A244

HUGHES, Katherine, R.N. Chief Nursing Officer, Colusa Regional Medical Center, Colusa, CA, p. A58

HUGHES, Lee, R.N. Chief Nursing Officer, Flint River Community Hospital, Montezuma, GA, p. A162

HUGHES, Leigh Ann, Chief Financial Officer, Hardin Medical Center, Savannah, TN, p. A587

HUGHES, Lori, R.N. Chief Nursing Officer, Vice President Operations and Patient Care Services, Cottage Hospital, Woodsville, NH, p. A408

HUGHES, Mark A., M.D. Medical Director, River Park Hospital, Huntington, WV, p. A692

HUGHES, Michelle, Director Health Information Management, Merit Health Madison, Canton, MS, p. A351

HUGHES, Robert K., Executive Director, Henry J. Carter Specialty Hospital and Nursing Facility, New York, NY, p. A440

HUGHES, Sandra, Chief Financial Officer, Clinch Memorial Hospital, Homerville, GA, p. A159

HUGHES, Susan, Interim Director Human Resources, Winner Regional Healthcare Center, Winner, SD, p. A573

HUGHES, Terry, Director Information Systems, Nantucket Cottage Hospital, Nantucket, MA, p. A309

HUGHES, Thomas, President, St. Joseph Health Services of Rhode Island, North Providence, RI, p. A555

HUGHES, Veronica, Chief Nursing Officer, Mesilla Valley Hospital, Las Cruces, NM, p. A425

HUGHS, Julie, Administrative Operations Support Analyst, North Oaks Health System, Hammond, LA, p. B98

HUGHS, Mary, Chief Human Resources Officer, Our Lady of Lourdes Memorial Hospital, Inc., Binghamton, NY, p. A429

HUGHSON, John, Chief Executive Officer, Big Bend Regional Medical Center, Alpine, TX, p. A591

HUGLE, Dana, Administrator, Latimer County General Hospital, Wilburton, OK, p. A518

HUGUELEY, Sandra, Assistant Administrator and Chief Nursing Officer, Methodist Extended Care Hospital, Memphis, TN, p. A583

HULBERT, Kim, R.N. Chief Clinical Officer, Madison County Health Care System, Winterset, IA, p. A236

HULETT, Rachelle, Vice President Human Resources, McLaren Flint, Flint, MI, p. A319

HULETT, Wendi, Chief Nursing Officer, Artesia General Hospital, Artesia, NM, p. A423

HULL, Brad, Chief Financial Officer, Dale Medical Center, Ozark, AL, p. A24

HULL, Debbie, Chief Financial Officer, Fisher County Hospital District, Rotan, TX, p. A639

HULL, Kathy, President and Chief Executive Officer, Illini Community Hospital, Pittsfield, IL, p. A198

HULL, Ken, Director Human Resources, Inova Fairfax Hospital, Falls Church, VA, p. A664

HULSE, Mark, Vice President and Chief Information Officer, H. Lee Moffitt Cancer Center and Research Institute, Tampa, FL, p. A144

HULSEY, Cathy, Manager of Human Resources, Hutcheson Medical Center, Fort Oglethorpe, GA, p. A158

HULSEY, Grant, Director Information Technology, Heritage Park Surgical Hospital, Sherman, TX, p. A644

HULSEY, Kelly, Chief Nursing Officer, Piedmont Hospital, Atlanta, GA, p. A151

HULSMAN, Laurie, M.D. Chief of Staff, El Campo Memorial Hospital, El Campo, TX, p. A610

HUMBLE, Kathryn G., Chief Human Resources Officer, Beatrice Community Hospital and Health Center, Beatrice, NE, p. A390

HUMBLE, Linnea, Director of Finance, Sutter Lakeside Hospital, Lakeport, CA, p. A67

HUME, Craig P., Chief Executive Officer, Surgical Specialty Center of Baton Rouge, Baton Rouge, LA, p. A270

HUME, Diana, Manager Human Resources, Methodist McKinney Hospital, McKinney, TX, p. A632

HUMES, Ronny, President and Chief Executive Officer, Magnolia Regional Health Center, Corinth, MS, p. A352

HUMME, Sarah, MSN Chief Operating Officer, Southwest General Hospital, San Antonio, TX, p. A642

HUMMEL, Angela, Vice President Human Resources, Evangelical Community Hospital, Lewisburg, PA, p. A538

HUMMELKE, Arlita, Manager Human Resources, Mercy Hospital Tishomingo, Tishomingo, OK, p. A516

HUMMER, Christopher R., President, Carolinas Healthcare System Pineville, Charlotte, NC, p. A457

HUMMER, Denise, R.N. Vice President Administrative Services, Community Memorial Hospital, Hamilton, NY, p. A434

HUMPHREY, Dale, Chief Executive Officer, Henderson County Community Hospital, Lexington, TN, p. A581

HUMPHREY, James, Vice President Talent Resources and Human Resources for South Side Operating Group, Penrose–St. Francis Health Services, Colorado Springs, CO, p. A101

HUMPHREY, Randy, Chief Financial Officer, Merit Health Wesley, Hattiesburg, MS, p. A354

HUMPHREYS, Lynn, Director Human Resources, Henry County Health Center, Mount Pleasant, IA, p. A232

HUMPHRIES, Stefan, M.D. Medical Director, St. Luke's Rehabilitation Institute, Spokane, WA, p. A685

HUMPHRIES, Vickie Witcher
Director Human Resources, Bon Secours Maryview Medical Center, Portsmouth, VA, p. A670
Vice President Human Resources, Bon Secours–DePaul Medical Center, Norfolk, VA, p. A669
Vice President Human Resources, Mary Immaculate Hospital, Newport News, VA, p. A669

HUNDAL, Ranjit, M.D. Chief Medical Executive, Mills–Peninsula Health Services, Burlingame, CA, p. A56

HUNGER, Dennis, Chief Executive Officer, Washington County Hospital and Clinics, Washington, IA, p. A235

HUNKINS, Theresa, R.N., Chief Executive Officer, Select Specialty Hospital–Durham, Durham, NC, p. A459

HUNSBERGER, Tom, Director Human Resources, Olmsted Medical Center, Rochester, MN, p. A345

HUNSICKER, Elizabeth, Chief Executive Officer, West Valley Medical Center, Caldwell, ID, p. A173

HUNT, Amy, Director Human Resources, Menorah Medical Center, Overland Park, KS, p. A248

HUNT, Cheri, R.N. Vice President Patient Care Services and Chief Nursing Officer, Children's Mercy Hospitals and Clinics, Kansas City, MO, p. A369

HUNT, D. Deann, Director Human Resources, Gibson General Hospital, Princeton, IN, p. A218

HUNT, Deloris, Corporate Vice President Human Resources, DMC Harper University Hospital, Detroit, MI, p. A317

HUNT, Don, M.D. Vice President Patient Centered Care and Chief Nursing Officer, University of Texas Health Northeast, Tyler, TX, p. A649

HUNT, Julie, R.N. Chief Nursing Officer, Oro Valley Hospital, Oro Valley, AZ, p. A34

HUNT, Karen, Executive Director, Harsha Behavioral Center, Terre Haute, IN, p. A220

HUNT, Kathy, Chief Executive Officer, Elmwood Healthcare Center at the Springs, Green Springs, OH, p. A490

HUNT, Lynelle, Director of Nursing, Indian Health Service – Quentin N. Burdick Memorial Health Care Facility, Belcourt, ND, p. A472

HUNT, Mary Miles, Chief Executive Officer, Ballard Rehabilitation Hospital, San Bernardino, CA, p. A86

HUNT, Reta, Director of Nursing, Scott & White Hospital – Llano, Llano, TX, p. A628

HUNT, Richard, M.D. Chief Operating Officer, Kaiser Permanente Sunnyside Medical Center, Clackamas, OR, p. A520

HUNT, Ronald, Chief Executive Officer, Harbor Hospital of Southeast Texas, Beaumont, TX, p. A596

HUNT, W. Jeffrey, Chief Executive Officer, Brandywine Hospital, Coatesville, PA, p. A531

HUNT, William Robert, Chief Financial Officer, Reynolds Memorial Hospital, Glen Dale, WV, p. A691

HUNTER, Becky, R.N. Chief Nursing Officer, Baptist Memorial Hospital – Memphis, Memphis, TN, p. A583

HUNTER, Bridgette, Chief Operating Officer, Acuity Specialty Hospital of Arizona at Mesa, Mesa, AZ, p. A

HUNTER, Byron, Vice President Human Resources, Cape Regional Medical Center, Cape May Court House, NJ, p. A410

HUNTER, Diana, Director of Nursing, Fort Belknap U. S. Public Health Service Indian Hospital, Harlem, MT, p. A384

HUNTER, Fred, R.N., Chief Executive Officer, Desert Valley Hospital, Victorville, CA, p. A96

HUNTER, Jerry, Vice President, Information Technology, Crotched Mountain Rehabilitation Center, Greenfield, NH, p. A406

HUNTER, Ken, R.N., Chief Executive Officer, Kimball Health Services, Kimball, NE, p. A393

Index of Health Care Professionals / Ingram

Index of Health Care Professionals


HUNTER, Linda, Chief Nursing Officer, Spring View Hospital, Lebanon, KY, p. A259
HUNTER, Mary Ann, Director Nursing Services, Baptist Easley Hospital, Easley, SC, p. A560
HUNTER, Shelly
Chief Financial Officer, Mercy Hospital Fort Scott, Fort Scott, KS, p. A240
Chief Financial Officer, Mercy Hospital Independence, Independence, KS, p. A242
Chief Financial Officer, Mercy Hospital Joplin, Joplin, MO, p. A369
HUNTER, Stephanie, Chief Human Resources Officer, Veterans Affairs Ann Arbor Healthcare System, Ann Arbor, MI, p. A314
HUNTER, Terri Lynn, Nurse Administrator, The Orthopedic Specialty Hospital, Murray, UT, p. A656
HUNTER, Tracy, Chief Human Resources Officer, East Cooper Medical Center, Mount Pleasant, SC, p. A563
HUNTLEY, Adrienne, Director Human Resources, HEALTHSOUTH Rehabilitation Hospital Memphis–North, Memphis, TN, p. A583
HUNTLEY, Devin, Vice President Operations, Community Medical Center, Missoula, MT, p. A385
HUNTON, David, M.D. Chief Medical Officer, Mercy Hospital Fort Smith, Fort Smith, AR, p. A44
HUPF, Angela C., Vice President Human Resources and Community Relations, Aspirus Medford Hospital, Medford, WI, p. A705
HUPP, Diane, R.N. Vice President Patient Care Services and Chief Nursing Officer, Children's Hospital of Pittsburgh of UPMC, Pittsburgh, PA, p. A546
HURD, Debra J., R.N
Vice President Nursing Acute Care, St. John's Hospital, Maplewood, MN, p. A342
Vice President Nursing, St. Joseph's Hospital, Saint Paul, MN, p. A346
Vice President of Nursing, Acute Care Hospitals, Woodwinds Health Campus, Woodbury, MN, p. A349
HURD, Ross, Chief Information Officer, Lake Chelan Community Hospital, Chelan, WA, p. A677
HURFORD, Bill, Chief Medical Officer, University of Cincinnati Medical Center, Cincinnati, OH, p. A484
HURLBUT, Marty, M.D. Medical Director, HEALTHSOUTH Rehabilitation Hospital, Fayetteville, AR, p. A43
HURLBUTT, Nichole, Director Human Resources, OSF St. Mary Medical Center, Galesburg, IL, p. A188
HURLEY, Al, Clinic Chief Operating Officer, Sanford Bismarck, Bismarck, ND, p. A472
HURLEY, Jeff, Vice President Human Resources, Flagler Hospital, Saint Augustine, FL, p. A141
HURLEY, Sandra, MS Chief Nursing Officer, Valley View Hospital, Glenwood Springs, CO, p. A104
HURLEY, William, M.D. Chief Medical Officer, Summit Pacific Medical Center, Elma, WA, p. A678
HUROWITZ, Marc P., D.O., President and Chief Executive Officer, Jeanes Hospital, Philadelphia, PA, p. A544
HURSH, John, Vice President Human Resources, Cox Medical Centers, Springfield, MO, p. A378
HURST, Steve, Information Technology Specialist, Haskell County Community Hospital, Stigler, OK, p. A515
HURT, Christie, M.D. Chief of Staff and Medical Director, Mercy Hospital Aurora, Aurora, MO, p. A363
HURT, Kelly, Chief Human Resources Officer Northern Colorado and Western Region, Banner Fort Collins Medical Center, Fort Collins, CO, p. A103
HURT, Todd, Administrator, State Hospital North, Orofino, ID, p. A175
HURT–DEITCH, Sally A., FACHE, Chief Executive Officer, The Hospitals of Providence Memorial Campus, El Paso, TX, p. A611
HURTADO, Xochy, Chief Executive Officer, Val Verde Regional Medical Center, Del Rio, TX, p. A607
HURWITZ, Steven, Senior Vice President Shared Services, Seattle Children's Hospital, Seattle, WA, p. A683
HURZELER, Rosemary Johnson, President and Chief Executive Officer, The Connecticut Hospice, Branford, CT, p. A111
HUSAIN, Syed Arshad, M.D. Executive Vice President and Chief Medical Officer, Royal Oaks Hospital, Windsor, MO, p. A380
HUSEBY, Custer, Chief Executive Officer, Vibra Hospital of Fargo, Fargo, ND, p. A474
HUSHER, Phil, Chief Financial Officer, Winner Regional Healthcare Center, Winner, SD, p. A573
HUSKEY, Jeff, Chief Executive Officer and Administrator, Clay County Memorial Hospital, Henrietta, TX, p. A618
HUSSAIN, Hamid, M.D. Medical Director, Our Lady of the Angels Hospital, Bogalusa, LA, p. A270
HUSSAIN, Iftikhar, Chief Financial Officer, El Camino Hospital, Mountain View, CA, p. A77
HUSTEDT, Dale, Administrator, Avera Holy Family Hospital, Estherville, IA, p. A227
HUSTON, Gary, D.O. Chief Medical Officer, University Hospitals Conneaut Medical Center, Conneaut, OH, p. A487
HUSTON, William R., Senior Vice President and Chief Financial Officer, Texas Scottish Rite Hospital for Children, Dallas, TX, p. A607
HUTCHENRIDER, E. Kenneth, President and Chief Executive Officer, Methodist Richardson Medical Center, Richardson, TX, p. A638
HUTCHENS, Zachary, M.D. Chief Medical Officer, Saint Thomas Hickman Hospital, Centerville, TN, p. A575
HUTCHES, Trampas, Chief Operating Officer, Middle Park Medical Center–Kremmling, Kremmling, CO, p. A105
HUTCHESON, Lou Ellen, M.D. Chief of Staff, Bacon County Hospital and Health System, Alma, GA, p. A149
HUTCHINS, Anne, M.D. Chief of Staff, Salem Veterans Affairs Medical Center, Salem, VA, p. A672
HUTCHINS, Michael T., Administrator, Jay Hospital, Jay, FL, p. A130
HUTCHINS, Sheri, Director Health Information Management, Muenster Memorial Hospital, Muenster, TX, p. A633
HUTCHINS–OTERO, Kathy, Chief Clinical Officer, Kindred Rehabilitation Hospital Clear Lake, Webster, TX, p. A651
HUTCHINSON, Donna, Chief Financial Officer, Beaver Dam Community Hospitals, Beaver Dam, WI, p. A698
HUTCHINSON, James, CPA Chief Financial Officer, Affinity Medical Center, Massillon, OH, p. A493
HUTCHISON, Barbra, Director Medical Records, Richland Parish Hospital, Delhi, LA, p. A273
HUTCHISON, Florence N., M.D. Chief of Staff, Ralph H. Johnson Veterans Affairs Medical Center, Charleston, SC, p. A558
HUTCHISON, Harry, Vice President Fiscal Services, St. Bernards Medical Center, Jonesboro, AR, p. A46
HUTCHISON, Lewis, Vice President Operations and Quality, Ashtabula County Medical Center, Ashtabula, OH, p. A478
HUTH, Michael, Chief Financial Officer, Sycamore Springs Hospital, Lafayette, IN, p. A214
HUTH, Richard, Chief Executive Officer, Shands Live Oak Regional Medical Center, Live Oak, FL, p. A132
HUTH, Thomas, M.D. Vice President Medical Affairs, Reid Health, Richmond, IN, p. A219
HUTSELL, Dick, Vice President Information Technology Services, Saint Louise Regional Hospital, Gilroy, CA, p. A63
HUTSELL, Richard, Vice President and Chief Information Officer, Daughters of Charity Health System, O'Connor Hospital, San Jose, CA, p. A89
HUTSON, Donald, Director, Marion Veterans Affairs Medical Center, Marion, IL, p. A193
HUTSON, Joy M., Director Human Resources, Merit Health Rankin, Brandon, MS, p. A351
HUTSON, Mark S., Chief Information Officer, Greenwood Leflore Hospital, Greenwood, MS, p. A353
HUTSON, Marty, Chief Financial Officer, St. Mary's Health Care System, Athens, GA, p. A149
HUTSON, Wayne
Executive Vice President and Chief Financial Officer, Union Hospital, Terre Haute, IN, p. A220
Chief Financial Officer, Union Hospital Clinton, Clinton, IN, p. A206
HUTT, Si, Administrator, Park City Medical Center, Park City, UT, p. A657
HUTTER, Elizabeth, Chief Executive Officer, Cedar Hills Hospital, Portland, OR, p. A524
HUTTER, George, M.D
Chief of Staff, Palms of Pasadena Hospital, Saint Petersburg, FL, p. A142
Chief Medical Officer, St. Petersburg General Hospital, Saint Petersburg, FL, p. A142
HUVAL, Shadelle, Director Finance, St. Martin Hospital, Breaux Bridge, LA, p. A271
HUYCKE, Mark, M.D. Chief of Staff, Oklahoma City Veterans Affairs Medical Center, Oklahoma City, OK, p. A512
HYATT, Charlotte, MSN Chief Operating Officer and Chief Nursing Officer, CareLink of Jackson, Jackson, MI, p. A323
HYATT, David W., Chief Executive Officer, Jay County Hospital, Portland, IN, p. A218
HYATT, Robert, M.D. Senior Vice President Medical Affairs, Lake Regional Health System, Osage Beach, MO, p. A374
HYATT, Ronnie, Senior Vice President Finance and Chief Financial Officer, Bon Secours St. Francis Health System, Greenville, SC, p. A561
HYBERGER, Trey, Director Information Technology, Hardin Memorial Hospital, Elizabethtown, KY, p. A256
HYDE, Devon, Chief Executive Officer, AllianceHealth Deaconess, Oklahoma City, OK, p. A511
HYDE, Jane E., President, Gettysburg Hospital, Gettysburg, PA, p. A534
HYDE, Keith, Chief Executive Officer, Providence Milwaukie Hospital, Milwaukie, OR, p. A523
HYDE, Robert, Human Resources Business Partner, Kaiser Permanente Santa Clara Medical Center, Santa Clara, CA, p. A91
HYDE, Shannon, Director Human Resources, HEALTHSOUTH MountainView Regional Rehabilitation Hospital, Morgantown, WV, p. A693
HYDE, Stephanie, Chief Executive Officer, Tyler Continuecare Hospital at Mother Frances, Tyler, TX, p. A649
HYDE, Stephen O., FACHE, Chief Executive Officer, Southwestern Medical Center, Lawton, OK, p. A509
HYDER, LouAnn, Director Information Integrity Management, Cardinal Hill Rehabilitation Hospital, Lexington, KY, p. A259
HYDER, Shiraz, M.D. Director Medical Affairs, CHI St. Alexius Health, Bismarck, ND, p. A472
HYLAND, Donna W., President and Chief Executive Officer, Children's Healthcare of Atlanta, Atlanta, GA, p. A150
HYLAND–HILL, Barbara M., R.N. Chief Nursing Officer, Providence Regional Medical Center Everett, Everett, WA, p. A679
HYLTON, Alecia, M.D. Chief of Staff, Aspirus Medford Hospital, Medford, WI, p. A705
HYLTON, Heather, Chief Financial Officer, Plateau Medical Center, Oak Hill, WV, p. A693
HYMAN, Bruce, M.D. Vice President Clinical Performance, Advocate Sherman Hospital, Elgin, IL, p. A187
HYMBAUGH, Mitzi, Chief Personnel, Ringgold County Hospital, Mount Ayr, IA, p. A232
HYMER, DNP, RN, CENP, Regina J., MSN Vice President Patient Care Services and Chief Nursing Officer, Norton Brownsboro Hospital, Louisville, KY, p. A261
HYNES, Kristi, Director Human Resources, Georgetown Behavioral Health Institute, Georgetown, TX, p. A616
HYNOSKI, Michael, Chief Information Resource Management, James E. Van Zandt Veterans Affairs Medical Center, Altoona, PA, p. A528


# I


IBRAHIM, Tajudeen, Interim Business Administrator, Elgin Mental Health Center, Elgin, IL, p. A187
IBRAHIM, Tommy, M.D
Chief Physician Office, Mercy Medical Center – West Lakes, West Des Moines, IA, p. A236
Chief Physician Officer, Mercy Medical Center–Des Moines, Des Moines, IA, p. A226
ICENHOWER, Jeremy, Administrator and Chief Executive Officer, De Queen Medical Center, De Queen, AR, p. A43
ICKOWSKI, Michael F., Chief Financial Officer, Eastern Niagara Hospital, Lockport, NY, p. A436
IDBEIS, Badr, M.D., Chief Executive Officer, Kansas Medical Center, Andover, KS, p. A237
IDEUS, Emily, Manager Business Office, Johnson County Hospital, Tecumseh, NE, p. A398
IDSTEIN, Mary, Chief Financial Officer, Porter–Starke Services, Valparaiso, IN, p. A221
IERARDI, Joseph P., Chief Executive Officer, Wayne Memorial Hospital, Jesup, GA, p. A159
IERO, Tony, Director Management Information Systems, North Philadelphia Health System, Philadelphia, PA, p. A544
IFTINIUK, Alan, Chief Executive Officer, French Hospital Medical Center, San Luis Obispo, CA, p. A90
IGNAS, Ann, R.N. Chief Nurse Executive, Fairfield Memorial Hospital, Fairfield, IL, p. A188
IMBIMBO, Richard, Chief Financial Officer, Hahnemann University Hospital, Philadelphia, PA, p. A543
IMHOFF, Sarah, Business Administrator, Chester Mental Health Center, Chester, IL, p. A181
IMLAY, Ralph, M.D. Chief of Staff, Harper Hospital District Five, Harper, KS, p. A241
IMLER, James R., Director Human Resources, Kimball Health Services, Kimball, NE, p. A393
IMSEIS, Mikhail, M.D. Chief of Staff, Ness County Hospital, Ness City, KS, p. A246
IN, Henry, Director Human Resources, Dallas Behavioral Healthcare Hospital, Desoto, TX, p. A608
INCARNATI, Philip A., President and Chief Executive Officer, McLaren Health Care Corporation, Flint, MI, p. B87
INGALLS, Dawn, Regional Manager Human Resources, Avera Dells Area Hospital, Dell Rapids, SD, p. A568
INGE, Ray, Vice President Human Resources, Pomona Valley Hospital Medical Center, Pomona, CA, p. A81
INGHAM, Raymond V., Ph.D., President and Chief Executive Officer, Witham Memorial Hospital, Lebanon, IN, p. A215
INGLIS, Suzanne, MSN Senior Vice President Nursing Services, Fisher–Titus Medical Center, Norwalk, OH, p. A495
INGRAM, David, Director Management Information Systems, Medina Hospital, Medina, OH, p. A494



Index of Health Care Professionals A873

Index of Health Care Professionals

Index of Health Care Professionals / Ingram

INGRAM, Karen, Director Human Resources, Baptist Memorial Hospital for Women, Memphis, TN, p. A583
INGRAM, Nathan Daniel, Chief Executive Officer and Owner, Lone Star Behavioral Health, Cypress, TX, p. A603
INGRAM, Peter X., Chief Information Officer, Hebrew Rehabilitation Center, Boston, MA, p. A303
INGWERSON, Connie, Chief Financial Officer, Nemaha Valley Community Hospital, Seneca, KS, p. A250
INHOFE, Kyle, Chief Human Resources Officer, Oklahoma City Veterans Affairs Medical Center, Oklahoma City, OK, p. A512
INKLEY, Kevin, Acting Medical Center Director, Kansas City Veterans Affairs Medical Center, Kansas City, MO, p. A369
INMAN, Debbie
Chief Nursing Officer, Physicians Surgical Hospital – Panhandle Campus, Amarillo, TX, p. A591
Chief Nursing Officer, Physicians Surgical Hospital – Quail Creek, Amarillo, TX, p. A591
INMAN, Joanne, Vice President Operations, Sentara Virginia Beach General Hospital, Virginia Beach, VA, p. A674
INMAN, Julie, Regional Executive Officer, Southeast Missouri Mental Health Center, Farmington, MO, p. A367
INNOCENTI Sr., John, President and Chief Executive Officer, UPMC Presbyterian Shadyside, Pittsburgh, PA, p. A547
INO, Alan, Chief Financial Officer, Good Samaritan Hospital, Los Angeles, CA, p. A70
INOUYE, Valerie, Chief Financial Officer, San Francisco General Hospital and Trauma Center, San Francisco, CA, p. A88
INSCHO, Kimberly, Vice President Community Relations and Human Resources, Margaret Mary Health, Batesville, IN, p. A204
INSERRA, Toni A., Interim Administrator, South Lyon Medical Center, Yerington, NV, p. A404
INSKEEP, Johnathan, Chief Information Officer, Caribou Memorial Hospital and Living Center, Soda Springs, ID, p. A176
INZANA, Lou, Senior Vice President and Chief Financial Officer, Maine Medical Center, Portland, ME, p. A291
INZANA, Lugene A., Vice President and Chief Financial and Support Services Officer, Lawrence + Memorial Hospital, New London, CT, p. A114
IPSAN, Charlotte, Chief Administrative Officer, Norton Women's and Kosair Children's Hospital, Louisville, KY, p. A261
IQBAL, Nayyar, M.D. Director Medical Staff, Western State Hospital, Hopkinsville, KY, p. A258
IRELAND, Amy, Chief Financial Officer, Carroll County Memorial Hospital, Carrollton, MO, p. A365
IRELAND, Daniel P., FACHE, President, United Memorial Medical Center, Batavia, NY, p. A429
IRISH, Kevin
Chief Information Officer, Franklin Regional Hospital, Franklin, NH, p. A406
Chief Information Officer, Lakes Region General Hospital, Laconia, NH, p. A406
IRISH–CLARDY, Katherine, M.D. Chief Medical Officer, Sparks Regional Medical Center, Fort Smith, AR, p. A45
IRIZARRI, David, Director Information Technology, Northwest Medical Center, Margate, FL, p. A133
IRIZARRY, Aixa
Executive Director, Hospital HMA de Humacao, Humacao, PR, p. A721
Executive Director, Hospital San Pablo Del Este, Fajardo, PR, p. A721
IRIZARRY, Lourdes, M.D. Chief of Staff, Albany Stratton Veterans Affairs Medical Center, Albany, NY, p. A428
IRUEGAS, Javier, FACHE, Chief Executive Officer, Mission Regional Medical Center, Mission, TX, p. A633
IRVIN, Debbie, Director Health Information Management, BHC Alhambra Hospital, Rosemead, CA, p. A84
IRVIN, Donna
Director Human Resources, Baylor Medical Center at Trophy Club, Trophy Club, TX, p. A648
Director Human Resources, Victory Medical Center Mid–Cities, Hurst, TX, p. A624
IRVIN, Mary, R.N. Senior Vice President and Chief Nursing Officer, Bethesda North Hospital, Cincinnati, OH, p. A482
IRVIN, Miriam, CNO, HEALTHSOUTH Rehabilitation Hospital, Fayetteville, AR, p. A43
IRVIN, Thomas M., Administrator Human Resources, Ranken Jordan Pediatric Bridge Hospital, Maryland Heights, MO, p. A372
IRVING, Edith E., R.N. Chief Nursing Officer, West Valley Medical Center, Caldwell, ID, p. A173
IRVING, MSN, RN–, Kelly Ann, Associate Director for Patient Care Services, Michael E. DeBakey Veterans Affairs Medical Center, Houston, TX, p. A621
IRVING, Mark, Manager Management Information Systems, OSF St. Francis Hospital and Medical Group, Escanaba, MI, p. A319
IRWIN, James, M.D. Chief Medical Officer, Samaritan Healthcare, Moses Lake, WA, p. A680
IRWIN, Robert G., Vice President Information Systems, Robert Wood Johnson University Hospital, New Brunswick, NJ, p. A415
IRWIN, Ruth, Associate Director Clinical Operations, Stewart & Lynda Resnick Neuropsychiatric Hospital at UCLA, Los Angeles, CA, p. A73
IRWIN, Vivian, Chief Financial Officer and Controller, HEALTHSOUTH Rehabilitation Hospital Midland–Odessa, Midland, TX, p. A632
ISAAC, Regina, Director of Nursing, Choctaw Health Center, Philadelphia, MS, p. A359
ISAACKS, Scott R., FACHE, Interim Director, Ralph H. Johnson Veterans Affairs Medical Center, Charleston, SC, p. A558
ISAACS, Cynthia, Chief Executive Officer, Cornerstone Hospital of Huntington, Huntington, WV, p. A691
ISAACS, Diane, Director of Nursing, Ouachita County Medical Center, Camden, AR, p. A42
ISAACS, Linda, Vice President Human Resources, St. Luke's Hospital, San Francisco, CA, p. A88
ISAACS, Michael R.
Vice President Human Resources, Vista Medical Center East, Waukegan, IL, p. A203
Vice President Human Resources, Vista Medical Center West, Waukegan, IL, p. A203
ISAACSON, Todd, M.D. Chief Medical Officer, Shenandoah Medical Center, Shenandoah, IA, p. A234
ISADO, Jose, M.D. Medical Director, Auxilio Mutuo Hospital, San Juan, PR, p. A723
ISBELL, Gina, Administrator, Oceans Behavioral Hospital of Kentwood, Kentwood, LA, p. A276
ISBELL, Samantha, R.N. Chief Nursing Officer, Hamilton Hospital, Olney, TX, p. A635
ISBELL, Sherri, Chief Information Officer, Virginia Gay Hospital, Vinton, IA, p. A235
ISEKE, Richard, M.D. Vice President Medical Affairs, Winchester Hospital, Winchester, MA, p. A313
ISEMANN, William R., President and Chief Executive Officer, KidsPeace Children's Hospital, Orefield, PA, p. A542
ISENMANN, Debra, Human Resources Generalist, Cox Monett, Monett, MO, p. A373
ISHAQUE, Saleem, M.D. Executive Medical Director, Alvarado Parkway Institute Behavioral Health System, La Mesa, CA, p. A66
ISHIZUKA, Paul, Chief Financial Officer and Chief Operating Officer, Samaritan Healthcare, Moses Lake, WA, p. A680
ISHKANIAN, Gary, M.D. Vice President Medical Affairs, Montefiore Mount Vernon, Mount Vernon, NY, p. A438
ISKANDAR, Said, M.D. Chief Medical Officer, Sentara Halifax Regional Hospital, South Boston, VA, p. A673
ISLAM, Asad, M.D. Chief Medical Officer, Mayhill Hospital, Denton, TX, p. A608
ISLEY, L. Lee, FACHE, Chief Executive Officer, Granville Health System, Oxford, NC, p. A466
ISMAIL, Asad, M.D. Medical Director, Wellstone Regional Hospital, Jeffersonville, IN, p. A213
ISMAIL, Hummayun, M.D. Medical Director, Select Specialty Hospital–Wilmington, Wilmington, DE, p. A118
ISOM, Julie, Director Human Resources, Lakeview Hospital, Bountiful, UT, p. A654
ISON, Tamara
Chief Operating Officer, Spalding Regional Medical Center, Griffin, GA, p. A158
Chief Financial Officer, Sylvan Grove Hospital, Jackson, GA, p. A159
ISON, William G., Human Resources Manager, Select Specialty Hospital–Tri Cities, Bristol, TN, p. A574
ISRAEL, Corry, Director Human Resources, Western Plains Medical Complex, Dodge City, KS, p. A239
ISRAEL, Michael D., President and Chief Executive Officer, Westchester Medical Center, Valhalla, NY, p. A452
ISSAI, Alice H.
Business Strategy and Finance Leader, Kaiser Permanente West Los Angeles Medical Center, Los Angeles, CA, p. A70
Chief Operating Officer, UC Irvine Medical Center, Orange, CA, p. A79
ISSAI, Robert, President and Chief Executive Officer, Daughters of Charity Health System, Los Altos Hills, CA, p. B44
ISTAS, Deborah, Chief Operating Officer, Madonna Rehabilitation Specialty Hospital, Bellevue, NE, p. A390
ISTRE, Tony, Director Information Technology Services, Regional Medical Center of Acadiana, Lafayette, LA, p. A278
ITAGAKI, Brian, M.D. Chief of Staff, St. Vincent Medical Center, Los Angeles, CA, p. A73
ITEN, Tess, Director of Nursing and Chief Nursing Officer, Deer's Head Hospital Center, Salisbury, MD, p. A300
ITO, Derek, Director Human Resources, Shriners Hospitals for Children–Honolulu, Honolulu, HI, p. A169
IVES, Matthew, Administrator and Chief Financial Officer, Keokuk County Health Center, Sigourney, IA, p. A234
IVES, Sheri, R.N. Vice President Patient Care Services, Mountain View Regional Medical Center, Norton, VA, p. A670
IVES ERICKSON, Jeanette R., MS Senior Vice President Patient Care and Chief Nurse, Massachusetts General Hospital, Boston, MA, p. A304
IVEY, Bobbie, Director Human Resources, Chicot Memorial Medical Center, Lake Village, AR, p. A46
IVEY, Mark J., M.D. Medical Director, Great Lakes Specialty Hospital–Grand Rapids, Grand Rapids, MI, p. A320
IVIE, Brian K.
President, Mercy San Juan Medical Center, Carmichael, CA, p. A57
President and Chief Executive Officer, Methodist Hospital of Sacramento, Sacramento, CA, p. A84
IVIE, Jack, President, Glendale Memorial Hospital and Health Center, Glendale, CA, p. A63
IVORY, Brenda, Chief Executive Officer, Harlingen Medical Center, Harlingen, TX, p. A617
IVY, Michael, M.D. Senior Vice President for Medical Affairs and Chief Medical Officer, Bridgeport Hospital, Bridgeport, CT, p. A111
IWEIMRIN, Salvatore, R.N., Chief Executive Officer, Select Specialty Hospital–Battle Creek, Battle Creek, MI, p. A315
IYER, Raju, Chief Financial Officer, Regional Medical Center of San Jose, San Jose, CA, p. A89
IZAKOVIC, Martin, M.D. Vice President Medical Staff Affairs and Chief Medical Officer, Mercy Iowa City, Iowa City, IA, p. A229
IZQUIERDO, Elizabeth L., CPA, Chief Executive Officer, HEALTHSOUTH Rehabilitation Hospital of Miami, Cutler Bay, FL, p. A124
IZZI, Denine, Site Manager Information Systems, Robert Wood Johnson University Hospital Rahway, Rahway, NJ, p. A417
IZZO, Carolyn, President and Chief Executive Officer, Ellwood City Hospital, Ellwood City, PA, p. A533

## J

JABBARPOUR, Yad, M.D. Chief of Staff, Catawba Hospital, Catawba, VA, p. A663
JABLONSKI, Kevin, Chief Nursing Officer, Mother Frances Hospital – Winnsboro, Winnsboro, TX, p. A652
JABLONSKI, Kevin M., Chief Nursing Officer, East Texas Medical Center Athens, Athens, TX, p. A593
JABLONSKI, Mark, Vice President Mission Integration, St. Jude Medical Center, Fullerton, CA, p. A63
JABOUR, Leon John, Regional Chief Information Officer, Ephrata Community Hospital, Ephrata, PA, p. A534
JACK, Claudia L., Director Associate Relations, Bayfront Health Brooksville, Brooksville, FL, p. A123
JACKES, Frederick D., Assistant Administrator and Director Human Resources, Valley Forge Medical Center and Hospital, Norristown, PA, p. A542
JACKLIN, Bonnie, R.N. Chief Nursing Officer, McKay–Dee Hospital Center, Ogden, UT, p. A656
JACKMAN, Andrew, Director Information Technology, Corry Memorial Hospital, Corry, PA, p. A532
JACKS, Anthony, Director Human Resources, Howard University Hospital, Washington, DC, p. A119
JACKSON, Alex
Chief Executive, Providence Holy Family Hospital, Spokane, WA, p. A685
Chief Executive, Providence Sacred Heart Medical Center & Children's Hospital, Spokane, WA, p. A685
JACKSON, Barbara, Acting Facility Director, Taylor Hardin Secure Medical Facility, Tuscaloosa, AL, p. A25
JACKSON, Bryan G., Vice President and Chief Financial Officer, Jefferson Regional Medical Center, Pine Bluff, AR, p. A50
JACKSON, Carolyn, Chief Operating Officer, Hospital of the University of Pennsylvania, Philadelphia, PA, p. A544
JACKSON, Cindy, Director Human Resources, Phelps Memorial Health Center, Holdrege, NE, p. A393
JACKSON, Collette, R.N. Director of Clinical Services, St. Theresa Specialty Hospital, Kenner, LA, p. A276
JACKSON, Courtney, Director Human Resources, Logan Memorial Hospital, Russellville, KY, p. A265
JACKSON, Darryl, D.O. Chief of Staff, Prague Community Hospital, Prague, OK, p. A514
JACKSON, David, Chief Financial Officer, Baptist Medical Center Leake, Carthage, MS, p. A351
JACKSON, Eileen, M.D. President Medical Staff, Sanpete Valley Hospital, Mount Pleasant, UT, p. A656
JACKSON, III, Frank D., Facility Chief Information Officer, Veterans Affairs Illiana Health Care System, Danville, IL, p. A185
JACKSON, Gary, D.O. Medical Director, Lincoln County Medical Center, Ruidoso, NM, p. A426

A874 Index of Health Care Professionals

Index of Health Care Professionals

Index of Health Care Professionals / James

JAMES, Michelle
Regional Chief Nursing Officer, Providence Centralia Hospital, Centralia, WA, p. A677
Chief Nursing Officer, Providence St. Peter Hospital, Olympia, WA, p. A681
JAMES, Robert L., Director Human Resources, Beaumont Hospital – Wayne, Wayne, MI, p. A332
JAMES, Shelia, Director of Nursing, Riverland Medical Center, Ferriday, LA, p. A273
JAMES, Sherrie, R.N. Director of Nursing, The BridgeWay, North Little Rock, AR, p. A49
JAMES, Stephanie, Chief Executive Officer, Regency Hospital of Greenville, Greenville, SC, p. A561
JAMES, Taya, Director, Mercy Hospital Berryville, Berryville, AR, p. A41
JAMES, Teri, Chief Financial Officer, Lafayette Regional Health Center, Lexington, MO, p. A372
JAMES, Thomas L., M.D. Chief Medical Officer, Trumbull Memorial Hospital, Warren, OH, p. A499
JAMES, William B., FACHE, Chief Executive Officer, Wake Forest Baptist Health–Lexington Medical Center, Lexington, NC, p. A464
JAMESON, David, M.D. Chief of Staff, Annie Jeffrey Memorial County Health Center, Osceola, NE, p. A397
JAMIESON, Donna F., Chief Nursing Officer, Aurora Medical Center, Kenosha, WI, p. A703
JAMIESON, Pamela, Vice President Patient Care Services and Chief Nursing Officer, University of Maryland St. Joseph Medical Center, Towson, MD, p. A300
JAMIN, David, Chief Financial Officer, St. Mary's Regional Medical Center, Enid, OK, p. A506
JANATKA, Lucille A.
President and Chief Executive Officer, Hartford HealthCare Central Region, MidState Medical Center, Meriden, CT, p. A113
President and Chief Executive Officer, Hartford HealthCare Central Region, The Hospital of Central Connecticut, New Britain, CT, p. A113
JANEK, James D., Chief Executive Officer, Rice Medical Center, Eagle Lake, TX, p. A609
JANERELLA, Wendy, Controller, Bucktail Medical Center, Renovo, PA, p. A548
JANICAK, Dan, Chief Financial Officer, University of Mississippi Medical Center, Jackson, MS, p. A355
JANIS, Terry, Assistant Vice President, Park Plaza Hospital, Houston, TX, p. A621
JANKE, Paul, FACHE, President and Chief Executive Officer, Bay Area Hospital, Coos Bay, OR, p. A520
JANKOWSKI, Stan, Vice President and Chief Information Officer, Hospital for Special Care, New Britain, CT, p. A113
JANLOO, Arman, M.D. Chief Medical Staff, Fairfax Community Hospital, Fairfax, OK, p. A507
JANOSO, John R., Chief Executive Officer, Fairfield Medical Center, Lancaster, OH, p. A491
JANOWSKI, Kenneth, M.D. Chief Medical Officer, Hackettstown Regional Medical Center, Hackettstown, NJ, p. A412
JANOYAN, Jano, M.D. Medical Director, Select Specialty Hospital–Knoxville, Knoxville, TN, p. A580
JANSEN, David, Vice President Human Resources, Karmanos Cancer Center, Detroit, MI, p. A318
JANSEN, Eric, Director Information Systems, Clifton Springs Hospital and Clinic, Clifton Springs, NY, p. A431
JANSEN, John, Management Information Specialist, Hawaii State Hospital, Kaneohe, HI, p. A170
JANSSEN, Kathy, Director Medical Records, Mountrail County Medical Center, Stanley, ND, p. A476
JANSSEN, Paul, President and Chief Executive Officer, Henry County Hospital, New Castle, IN, p. A217
JANSSEN, Thomas, M.D. Chief of Staff, McBride Clinic Orthopedic Hospital, Oklahoma City, OK, p. A512
JANTZEN, Daniel, Senior Vice President and Chief Operating Officer, Dartmouth–Hitchcock Medical Center, Lebanon, NH, p. A407
JANUS, Tammy, Senior Vice President Human Resources, Mercy Medical Center, Baltimore, MD, p. A294
JANZEN, Wes, Chief Information Officer, Wamego Health Center, Wamego, KS, p. A252
JAQUEZ, Jason, Director Human Resources, Greater El Monte Community Hospital, South El Monte, CA, p. A93
JARBOE, Joe, Director Human Resources, Kosciusko Community Hospital, Warsaw, IN, p. A221
JARBOE, Lori, Chief Executive Officer, HEALTHSOUTH Lakeview Rehabilitation Hospital, Elizabethtown, KY, p. A256
JARM, Timothy L., President and Chief Executive Officer, Alliant Management Services, Louisville, KY, p. B8
JARMAN, Amy, Director Human Resources, Mena Regional Health System, Mena, AR, p. A48
JAROG, Dena, R.N. Vice President Patient Care, Reedsburg Area Medical Center, Reedsburg, WI, p. A710
JAROPILLO, Erwin, Director Information Systems, Lake Wales Medical Center, Lake Wales, FL, p. A131
JARREAU, Jeff, Senior Vice President Human Resources, North Oaks Medical Center, Hammond, LA, p. A274
JARREAU, Valerie S., RN Chief Nursing Officer, Pointe Coupee General Hospital, New Roads, LA, p. A283
JARRELL, Lindsey, Vice President Information Services, St. Joseph's Hospital, Tampa, FL, p. A145
JARRETT, Adam D., M.D. Executive Vice President and Chief Medical Officer, Holy Name Medical Center, Teaneck, NJ, p. A419
JARRETT, Brenda, Chief Financial Officer, Putnam General Hospital, Eatonton, GA, p. A157
JARRETT, Mark, M.D. Chief Medical Officer, Staten Island University Hospital, NY, p. A444
JARRY, Jacques, Administrator, Bullock County Hospital, Union Springs, AL, p. A26
JARRY, Patricia, Manager Human Resources, Crenshaw Community Hospital, Luverne, AL, p. A21
JARVIS, Dinah, Director of Nursing, Pineville Community Hospital Association, Pineville, KY, p. A265
JARVIS, Keith, Director Information Systems, Longview Regional Medical Center, Longview, TX, p. A629
JASPER, Harry, Administrator, Jerold Phelps Community Hospital, Garberville, CA, p. A63
JASPER, Jerry
Chief Executive Officer and Administrator, Southeast Colorado Hospital District, Springfield, CO, p. A108
Chief Executive Officer, Vibra Hospital of Amarillo, Amarillo, TX, p. A591
Chief Executive Officer, Vibra Rehabilitation Hospital of Amarillo, Amarillo, TX, p. A591
JASTREMSKI, Michael S., M.D. Vice President Medical Affairs and Director Emergency Services, Community Memorial Hospital, Hamilton, NY, p. A434
JATCZAK, Tracy E., CPA Chief Financial Officer, Box Butte General Hospital, Alliance, NE, p. A389
JAUERSACK, Dawn, Vice President and Chief Financial Officer, Boca Raton Regional Hospital, Boca Raton, FL, p. A122
JAVOIS, Laurent D.
Regional Executive Officer, Hawthorn Children Psychiatric Hospital, Saint Louis, MO, p. A376
Regional Executive Officer, Metropolitan St. Louis Psychiatric Center, Saint Louis, MO, p. A376
Chief Executive Officer, St. Louis Psychiatric Rehabilitation Center, Saint Louis, MO, p. A378
JAVOIS, Rosalie, Chief Financial Officer, Governor Juan F. Luis Hospital, Christiansted, VI, p. A725
JAY, Richard, D.O. Chief of Staff, North Big Horn Hospital District, Lovell, WY, p. A716
JEAN–BAPTISTE, Joan, Vice President Human Resources, Governor Juan F. Luis Hospital, Christiansted, VI, p. A725
JEAN–LOUIS, Marie S., R.N. Chief Nursing Officer, Creedmoor Psychiatric Center, NY, p. A439
JEAN–MARIE, Jonathan, Administrator and Chief Executive Officer, Kindred Hospital Riverside, Perris, CA, p. A81
JEANNETTE, Joanie, MSN, Chief Executive Officer, Lehigh Regional Medical Center, Lehigh Acres, FL, p. A132
JEANSONNE, Corey, Chief Nursing Officer, Bunkie General Hospital, Bunkie, LA, p. A271
JEANTY, Johanne, Director Human Resources, Chicago Lakeshore Hospital, Chicago, IL, p. A181
JEDLICKA, Colleen, R.N. Chief Nursing Officer, Comanche County Medical Center, Comanche, TX, p. A601
JEFFERIES, Michael, Vice President Information Systems, Longmont United Hospital, Longmont, CO, p. A107
JEFFERSON, Candace, Manager Human Resources, CHRISTUS Spohn Hospital Kleberg, Kingsville, TX, p. A626
JEFFERSON, Kelly, Vice President, Operations, OSF St. Francis Hospital and Medical Group, Escanaba, MI, p. A319
JEFFERSON, Terrie, R.N. Chief Nursing Officer, South Bay Hospital, Sun City Center, FL, p. A143
JEFFRAS, Charles, Executive Director Human Resources, St. Vincent Carmel Hospital, Carmel, IN, p. A206
JEFFRESS, Chuck, Vice President Fiscal Services, Brazosport Regional Health System, Lake Jackson, TX, p. A627
JEFFREY, Roberta, Chief Executive Officer, Holdenville General Hospital, Holdenville, OK, p. A508
JEFFRIES, John, Director Finance, HSHS St. Joseph's Hospital, Breese, IL, p. A180
JEHAN, Sayed, M.D. Interim Medical Director, Larned State Hospital, Larned, KS, p. A244
JELALIAN, Christine, M.D. Medical Director, St. Luke's Cornwall Hospital, Newburgh, NY, p. A445
JELDEN, Dennis, M.D. Chief of Staff, Melissa Memorial Hospital, Holyoke, CO, p. A105
JELKS, Kim, Fiscal Officer, Villa Feliciana Medical Complex, Jackson, LA, p. A275
JELLE, Laura, President, St. Clare Hospital, Baraboo, WI, p. A697
JEMJEMIAN, Norair, Chief Operating Officer, Los Robles Hospital and Medical Center, Thousand Oaks, CA, p. A94
JENE, Suzanne, Chief Operating Officer, Tennessee Valley Healthcare System, Nashville, TN, p. A586
JENEY, Martie, Director Human Resources, Fulton Medical Center, Fulton, MO, p. A368
JENKINS, Bonnie, Chief Financial Officer, Methodist Hospital of Sacramento, Sacramento, CA, p. A84
JENKINS, Brian, Director Human Resources, Arbour–Fuller Hospital, Attleboro, MA, p. A302
JENKINS, Debbie, Chief Human Resources Management Service, Veterans Affairs Sierra Nevada Health Care System, Reno, NV, p. A404
JENKINS, Denise, Chief Clinical Officer, Kindred Hospital–Brea, Brea, CA, p. A56
JENKINS, Jason, Senior Director of Nursing, Novant Health Haymarket Medical Center, Haymarket, VA, p. A666
JENKINS, Keith, Director, Human Resources, Grandview Medical Center, Dayton, OH, p. A488
JENKINS, Laura, Director Operations Finance and Business Development, Buffalo Hospital, Buffalo, MN, p. A336
JENKINS, Linda, R.N. Vice President Patient Care Services, St. Jude Medical Center, Fullerton, CA, p. A63
JENKINS, Maynard, Regional Vice President Human Resources, Sutter Maternity and Surgery Center of Santa Cruz, Santa Cruz, CA, p. A91
JENKINS, Michelle, M.D. President Medical Staff, Herrin Hospital, Herrin, IL, p. A190
JENKINS, Rebecca, Director Human Resources Management, Harrison Memorial Hospital, Cynthiana, KY, p. A256
JENKINS, Roger T., Chief Executive Officer, Ethicus Hospital – Grapevine, Grapevine, TX, p. A617
JENKINS, Ruth, Chief Financial Officer, Ridgeview Institute, Smyrna, GA, p. A164
JENKINS, Scott, Administrator, Cheyenne County Hospital, Saint Francis, KS, p. A249
JENKS, Lyn, Chief Executive Officer, Charlevoix Area Hospital, Charlevoix, MI, p. A316
JENNER, Jody J., President and Chief Executive Officer, Broadlawns Medical Center, Des Moines, IA, p. A226
JENNETTE, Brian, Chief Financial Officer, Northside Hospital–Cherokee, Canton, GA, p. A153
JENNINGS, Candice, FACHE President, SSM St. Mary's Health Center, Saint Louis, MO, p. A377
JENNINGS, D. Arlo, Ph.D. Chief Information Officer, Mission Hospital, Asheville, NC, p. A455
JENNINGS, Jason, Chief Executive Officer, Scott & White Hospital – College Station, College Station, TX, p. A601
JENNINGS, Jeff, FACHE, Chief Executive Officer, Shoals Hospital, Muscle Shoals, AL, p. A23
JENNINGS, Keith, Chief Information Officer, Massachusetts General Hospital, Boston, MA, p. A304
JENNINGS, Marilyn, Director Human Resources, Arise Austin Medical Center, Austin, TX, p. A593
JENNINGS, Mark
Director Information Systems, Northeast Georgia Medical Center, Gainesville, GA, p. A158
Chief Information Officer, Saint Anthony Hospital, Chicago, IL, p. A184
JENNINGS, Reynold J., Chief Executive Officer, WellStar Health System, Marietta, GA, p. B152
JENNINGS, Shayla, Human Resources Director, Montgomery County Memorial Hospital, Red Oak, IA, p. A233
JENNINGS, William M., President and Chief Executive Officer, Bridgeport Hospital, Bridgeport, CT, p. A111
JENSEMA, Christine, Ph.D
Chief People Officer, St. Mary's Hospital Medical Center, Green Bay, WI, p. A702
Chief People Officer, St. Nicholas Hospital, Sheboygan, WI, p. A711
Chief People Officer, St. Vincent Hospital, Green Bay, WI, p. A702
JENSEN, Alice J., Chief Operating Officer, Geary Community Hospital, Junction City, KS, p. A243
JENSEN, Amy, Director Human Resources, Community Health Center of Branch County, Coldwater, MI, p. A317
JENSEN, Annelise, Chief Nursing Officer, Methodist Olive Branch Hospital, Olive Branch, MS, p. A358
JENSEN, Beth, Director Clinic Operations, Mobridge Regional Hospital, Mobridge, SD, p. A570
JENSEN, Christopher, Chief Financial Officer, Three Rivers Behavioral Health, West Columbia, SC, p. A566
JENSEN, Dave, Director Human Resources, Performance Improvement and Risk Management, Mountain View Hospital, Gadsden, AL, p. A20
JENSEN, Eric P., Chief Executive Officer, EvergreenHealth Monroe, Monroe, WA, p. A680
JENSEN, Gail, Chief Financial Officer, Trego County–Lemke Memorial Hospital, Wakeeney, KS, p. A252

A876 Index of Health Care Professionals 

Index of Health Care Professionals / Johnson

Index of Health Care Professionals


JENSEN, Janette, Manager Human Resources, Avera Holy Family Hospital, Estherville, IA, p. A227
JENSEN, Jeff, Finance Director, Intermountain Medical Center, Murray, UT, p. A656
JENSEN, Jeff, D.O. Vice President, Medical Affairs, Morton Plant Hospital, Clearwater, FL, p. A123
JENSEN, Laura J., Vice President Patient Care Services, St. Croix Regional Medical Center, St. Croix Falls, WI, p. A711
JENSEN, Leanna, Vice President Finance and Chief Financial Officer, Cobleskill Regional Hospital, Cobleskill, NY, p. A432
JENSEN, Mary, Controller, Mountain View Hospital, Gadsden, AL, p. A20
JENSEN, Michael E., Chief Executive Officer, Davis Hospital and Medical Center, Layton, UT, p. A655
JENSEN, Neal, Chief Executive Officer, Cobre Valley Regional Medical Center, Globe, AZ, p. A32
JENSEN, Pamela, FACHE, President, Memorial Hospital, Fremont, OH, p. A490
JENSEN, Paul, M.D. Chief of Staff, Regional Health Services of Howard County, Cresco, IA, p. A225
JENSEN, Renee K., Chief Executive Officer, Summit Pacific Medical Center, Elma, WA, p. A678
JENSEN, Ron, D.O. Chief Medical Officer and Vice President, Baylor Regional Medical Center at Grapevine, Grapevine, TX, p. A616
JENSEN, Ryan, Chief Executive Officer, Memorial Hospital of Salem County, Salem, NJ, p. A418
JENSEN, Sherry, Chief Financial Officer, Halifax Regional Medical Center, Roanoke Rapids, NC, p. A467
JENSEN, Tom, Chief Executive Officer, Grays Harbor Community Hospital, Aberdeen, WA, p. A676
JENSEN, Troy, Director Human Resources, HEALTHSOUTH Rehabilitation Hospital of Utah, Sandy, UT, p. A659
JENSEN, Twyla, Director Human Resources, Pioneers Medical Center, Meeker, CO, p. A107
JENTZ, Amy, M.D. Chief of Staff, Sparrow Ionia Hospital, Ionia, MI, p. A322
JEPPESEN, Kelly, Chief Medical Officer, San Juan Hospital, Monticello, UT, p. A655
JEPSEN, Christinia, R.N., Administrator, Parkland Health Center–Bonne Terre, Bonne Terre, MO, p. A363
JEPSON, Brian, President, OhioHealth Riverside Methodist Hospital, Columbus, OH, p. A486
JEPSON, Jeanne, Director Human Resources, Hackettstown Regional Medical Center, Hackettstown, NJ, p. A412
JEPSON, Mark, Vice President, Silver Cross Hospital, New Lenox, IL, p. A196
JERGER, Greg, Chief Financial Officer, Memorial Health Care Systems, Seward, NE, p. A398
JERINA, Anthony T., Chief Nursing Officer, Hereford Regional Medical Center, Hereford, TX, p. A618
JERNIGAN, Donald L., Ph.D., President and Chief Executive Officer, Adventist Health System Sunbelt Health Care Corporation, Altamonte Springs, FL, p. B5
JERNIGAN, Pam, Chief Financial Officer, United Regional Medical Center, Manchester, TN, p. A582
JESCH, Doug, Director Human Resources, Indiana University Health Starke Hospital, Knox, IN, p. A213
JESIOLOWSKI, Craig A., FACHE, President, Saint Anne's Hospital, Fall River, MA, p. A306
JESSUP, Daniel, Chief Financial Officer, Silverton Hospital, Silverton, OR, p. A526
JESTER, Denise, Chief Financial Officer, Nanticoke Memorial Hospital, Seaford, DE, p. A117
JESTILA–PELTOLA, Gail, Chief Financial Officer, Baraga County Memorial Hospital, L'Anse, MI, p. A324
JESURASA, Jebashini, Vice President, Chief Information Technology Officer, Wyckoff Heights Medical Center, NY, p. A445
JETER, John
  Assistant Administrator and Chief Financial Officer, Johnston Memorial Hospital, Abingdon, VA, p. A662
  Chief Financial Officer, Russell County Medical Center, Lebanon, VA, p. A666
  Assistant Vice President and Chief Financial Officer, Smyth County Community Hospital, Marion, VA, p. A667
JETER, John H., M.D., President and Chief Executive Officer, Hays Medical Center, Hays, KS, p. A241
JETT, Heather, Director Patient Care Services, Peninsula Hospital, Louisville, TN, p. A582
JETTERGREN, Tess, Director Clinical Informatics, Essentia Health St. Mary's Medical Center, Duluth, MN, p. A338
JETTON, Dana, Chief Information Officer, AMG Specialty Hospital–Tulsa, Tulsa, OK, p. A516
JEUNEHOMME, Patti, Director Human Resources, Hot Springs County Memorial Hospital, Thermopolis, WY, p. A717
JEWELL, Bryan, Director Human Resources, Forest Park Medical Center Frisco, Frisco, TX, p. A615
JEWELL, Keith, President, St. Mary's Medical Center of Evansville, Evansville, IN, p. A208
JEWETT, Lori, Vice President of Nursing, Falmouth Hospital, Falmouth, MA, p. A306
JEWETT, Sherri R., Chief Executive Officer, Valle Vista Hospital, Greenwood, IN, p. A210
JEYAKUMAR, Panch, M.D. Chief of Staff, Olympia Medical Center, Los Angeles, CA, p. A71
JEZIORSKE, John J., Director Human Resources, Abilene Regional Medical Center, Abilene, TX, p. A590
JEZSU, Peggy, Chief Nursing Officer, Alvarado Hospital Medical Center, San Diego, CA, p. A86
JILEK, Lea, Director Finance, Bethesda Hospital, Saint Paul, MN, p. A346
JIMENEZ, Betzaida, Director Human Resources, Hospital de la Universidad de Puerto Rico/Dr. Federico Trilla, Carolina, PR, p. A720
JIMENEZ, Cristina, Chief Operating Officer, Coral Gables Hospital, Coral Gables, FL, p. A124
JIMENEZ, Edward, Chief Executive Officer, UF Health Shands, Gainesville, FL, p. B138
JIMENEZ, Edward, Chief Executive Officer, UF Health Shands Hospital, Gainesville, FL, p. A128
JIMENEZ, Gerson, M.D. Medical Director, Hospital Episcopal San Lucas Guayama, Guayama, PR, p. A721
JIMENEZ, Guillermo, Director Finance, Castaner General Hospital, Castaner, PR, p. A720
JIMENEZ, Ron, M.D. Chief Medical Officer, Florida Hospital Memorial Medical Center, Daytona Beach, FL, p. A125
JIMESON, Jean–Marie, Manager Human Resources, Kansas Spine and Specialty Hospital, Wichita, KS, p. A252
JIMMERSON, Kevin, Business Manager, Mental Health Institute, Independence, IA, p. A229
JIN, Marvin, M.D. Medical Director, Parkside Psychiatric Hospital and Clinic, Tulsa, OK, p. A516
JIRON, Feliciano, Chief Executive Officer, Los Alamos Medical Center, Los Alamos, NM, p. A425
JIROVEC, David, Director Finance, Ministry Good Samaritan Health Center, Merrill, WI, p. A706
JITH, Gayathri S., M.P.H. Senior Vice President Strategy and Operations, Valley Presbyterian Hospital, CA, p. A73
JOBBITT, Patty, Vice President Operations, Rehabilitation Institute of Michigan, Detroit, MI, p. A318
JOBE, Kathy, R.N. Chief Nursing Officer and Vice President Patient Care Services, Summa Barberton Citizens Hospital, Barberton, OH, p. A479
JOBE, Kenneth Lynn, Director Human Resources, Tyler County Hospital, Woodville, TX, p. A653
JOCHIM, Steven, Administrator, Cape Cod & Island Community Mental Health Center, Pocasset, MA, p. A310
JODWAY, Timothy, Chief Financial Officer, Garden City Hospital, Garden City, MI, p. A320
JOEL, Linda, Vice President Operations, Spectrum Health Special Care Hospital, Grand Rapids, MI, p. A321
JOHE, David, M.D. President Medical Staff, Penn Highlands Elk, Saint Marys, PA, p. A549
JOHLMAN, Ed, Chief Financial Officer, Grand River Hospital District, Rifle, CO, p. A108
JOHN, Aleyamma, R.N. Director of Nursing, Kensington Hospital, Philadelphia, PA, p. A544
JOHN, Julian, Chief Financial Officer, Kings County Hospital Center, NY, p. A440
JOHN, M. Joseph, M.D. Chief of Staff, Berwick Hospital Center, Berwick, PA, p. A529
JOHNS, Dale, Chief Executive Officer, Salt Lake Regional Medical Center, Salt Lake City, UT, p. A658
JOHNS, Dawn, Director Human Resources, Colquitt Regional Medical Center, Moultrie, GA, p. A162
JOHNS, Jeffery, M.D. Medical Director, Vanderbilt Stallworth Rehabilitation Hospital, Nashville, TN, p. A586
JOHNS, Paul, Chief Operating Officer, South Lake Hospital, Clermont, FL, p. A123
JOHNS, Thomas Bradford, M.D. Medical Director, Ridgeview Institute, Smyrna, GA, p. A164
JOHNS, Timothy, M.D. Chief Medical Officer, Gilbert Hospital, Gilbert, AZ, p. A31
JOHNSEN, Timothy J., MS, President, Integris Baptist Medical Center, Oklahoma City, OK, p. A511
JOHNSON, Alan, Chief Information Officer, Doctors Community Hospital, Lanham, MD, p. A298
JOHNSON, Allen
  Chief Financial Officer, Truman Medical Center–Hospital Hill, Kansas City, MO, p. A370
  Chief Financial Officer, Truman Medical Center–Lakewood, Kansas City, MO, p. A370
JOHNSON, Amy, M.D. Chief of Staff, Longmont United Hospital, Longmont, CO, p. A107
JOHNSON, Arlan D., ACHE, Chief Executive Officer, Howard County Medical Center, Saint Paul, NE, p. A398
JOHNSON, Barbara A.
  Vice President Human Resources, Good Samaritan Hospital, Dayton, OH, p. A488
  Vice President Human Resources, Miami Valley Hospital, Dayton, OH, p. A488
JOHNSON, Becky, Director Human Resources, Oakdale Community Hospital, Oakdale, LA, p. A283
JOHNSON, Belinda, R.N. Chief Nursing Officer/Chief Clinical Officer, Russellville Hospital, Russellville, AL, p. A24
JOHNSON, Betty, Associate Administrator, University Health Shreveport, Shreveport, LA, p. A285
JOHNSON, Beverly, Vice President Human Resources, North Kansas City Hospital, North Kansas City, MO, p. A373
JOHNSON, Billy, Chief Executive Officer, Coal County General Hospital, Coalgate, OK, p. A505
JOHNSON, Bonnie, R.N. Vice President of Patient Services, Perham Health, Perham, MN, p. A344
JOHNSON, Brandi, Site Manager Technology Information Systems, Spectrum Health Reed City Hospital, Reed City, MI, p. A328
JOHNSON, Brenda
  Director Human Resources, Baptist Memorial Hospital–Collierville, Collierville, TN, p. A576
  Director Human Resources, North Mississippi Medical Center–West Point, West Point, MS, p. A361
JOHNSON, Bret
  Chief Financial Officer, Bon Secours St. Francis Xavier Hospital, Charleston, SC, p. A558
  Chief Financial Officer, Mount Pleasant Hospital, Mount Pleasant, SC, p. A563
  Chief Financial Officer, Roper Hospital, Charleston, SC, p. A558
JOHNSON, Bryan L., Administrator, Alta View Hospital, Sandy, UT, p. A659
JOHNSON, III, C. Thomas, Vice President Finance and Chief Financial Officer, Southeastern Health, Lumberton, NC, p. A464
JOHNSON, Candace, Ph.D., President and Chief Executive Officer, Roswell Park Cancer Institute, Buffalo, NY, p. A430
JOHNSON, Casey R., Chief Financial Officer, Sanford Thief River Falls Medical Center, Thief River Falls, MN, p. A348
JOHNSON, Charles, M.D. Chief of Staff, Renown Regional Medical Center, Reno, NV, p. A403
JOHNSON, Cheryl, Regional Chief Information Officer, St. Joseph Medical Center, Kansas City, MO, p. A370
JOHNSON, Chris, R.N. Chief Nursing Officer, Davis Hospital and Medical Center, Layton, UT, p. A655
JOHNSON, Chris, M.D. Chief of Staff, Mercy Hospital Rogers, Rogers, AR, p. A50
JOHNSON, Christina, M.D. Vice President and Chief Clinical and Quality Officer, Lutheran Medical Center, Wheat Ridge, CO, p. A109
JOHNSON, Craig, D.O. Medical Director, St. Vincent Clay Hospital, Brazil, IN, p. A205
JOHNSON, Craig A., Chief Executive Officer, Boundary Community Hospital, Bonners Ferry, ID, p. A173
JOHNSON, Cynthia J., R.N. Chief Nursing Officer, Los Robles Hospital and Medical Center, Thousand Oaks, CA, p. A94
JOHNSON, Danielle, Chief Operating Officer, Florida Hospital Fish Memorial, Orange City, FL, p. A137
JOHNSON, Darren, M.D. Chief of Staff, Tennova Healthcare – Dyersburg Regional Hospital, Dyersburg, TN, p. A577
JOHNSON, David
  Chief Executive Officer, Navos, Seattle, WA, p. A683
  Manager Information Services, Providence Kodiak Island Medical Center, Kodiak, AK, p. A28
JOHNSON, Deborah Carey, R.N., President and Chief Executive Officer, Eastern Maine Medical Center, Bangor, ME, p. A288
JOHNSON, Deeann, Director Human Resources, Saint Thomas River Park Hospital, Mc Minnville, TN, p. A582
JOHNSON, Denise, M.D. Medical Director, Meadville Medical Center, Meadville, PA, p. A540
JOHNSON, Dennis B., President & CEO, Hardin Memorial Hospital, Elizabethtown, KY, p. A256
JOHNSON, Derek, Chief Executive Officer, Laurel Oaks Behavioral Health Center, Dothan, AL, p. A19
JOHNSON, Dian I., MSN Chief Nurse Executive, Staten Island University Hospital, NY, p. A444
JOHNSON, Diana G., Acting Chief Human Resources Officer, Novato Community Hospital, Novato, CA, p. A78
JOHNSON, Diane, R.N. Vice President Patient Care Services and Chief Nursing Officer, Sinai Hospital of Baltimore, Baltimore, MD, p. A295
JOHNSON, Dominica, Executive Administrative Assistant and Executive Assistant Human Resources and Payroll, Pioneer Community Hospital of Newton, Newton, MS, p. A358


© 2015 AHA Guide Index of Health Care Professionals A877

Index of Health Care Professionals

Index of Health Care Professionals / Johnson

JOHNSON, Douglas E.
Interim Vice President Operations and Chief Financial Officer, Hudson Hospital and Clinic, Hudson, WI, p. A702
Chief Financial Officer, Lakeview Hospital, Stillwater, MN, p. A347
JOHNSON, Douglas V., Chief Executive Officer, Stanislaus Surgical Hospital, Modesto, CA, p. A76
JOHNSON, Doyle K., Administrator, Mercy Hospital, Moundridge, KS, p. A246
JOHNSON, Drew, Chief Financial Officer, Holdenville General Hospital, Holdenville, OK, p. A508
JOHNSON, Earle, Area Information Officer, Kaiser Permanente Panorama City Medical Center, CA, p. A70
JOHNSON, Eddie, Chief Information Technology Officer, Kansas City Veterans Affairs Medical Center, Kansas City, MO, p. A369
JOHNSON, Eunice, M.D. Chief Medical Staff, Kentucky River Medical Center, Jackson, KY, p. A259
JOHNSON, Gigi, Interim Chief Executive Officer, Kindred Hospital–Chattanooga, Chattanooga, TN, p. A575
JOHNSON, Greg, IT Coordinator, Cook County North Shore Hospital, Grand Marais, MN, p. A339
JOHNSON, Gregory, D.D.S. Medical Director, Fairbanks Memorial Hospital, Fairbanks, AK, p. A28
JOHNSON, Helen, R.N. Vice President Patient Services, Spectrum Health Ludington Hospital, Ludington, MI, p. A325
JOHNSON, J. David, M.D. Chief of Staff, East Texas Medical Center Specialty Hospital, Tyler, TX, p. A648
JOHNSON, Jack, Chief Nursing Officer, Sanford Rock Rapids Medical Center, Rock Rapids, IA, p. A233
JOHNSON, Jackie, Executive Vice President Human Resources, United Medical Center, Washington, DC, p. A120
JOHNSON, James, Chief Financial Officer, HSHS St. Joseph's Hospital, Highland, IL, p. A190
JOHNSON, Jamie, R.N. Vice President Nursing, Community Hospital of Anaconda, Anaconda, MT, p. A381
JOHNSON, Jamie, Director Human Resources, Miners' Colfax Medical Center, Raton, NM, p. A425
JOHNSON, Jan, R.N. Chief Nursing Officer, Northside Hospital–Cherokee, Canton, GA, p. A153
JOHNSON, Jani L., MSN, Chief Executive Officer, Saint Luke's Hospital of Kansas City, Kansas City, MO, p. A370
JOHNSON, Jason, Controller, F. W. Huston Medical Center, Winchester, KS, p. A253
JOHNSON, Jay, Chief Financial Officer, AllianceHealth Clinton, Clinton, OK, p. A505
JOHNSON, Jay R., FACHE, President and Chief Executive Officer, Duncan Regional Hospital, Duncan, OK, p. A505
JOHNSON, Jayne, Director of Human Resources, Great Plains Health, North Platte, NE, p. A395
JOHNSON, Jeff, Director Information Systems, Saint Thomas River Park Hospital, Mc Minnville, TN, p. A582
JOHNSON, Jeffrey, Vice President, Memorial Hospital, Colorado Springs, CO, p. A100
JOHNSON, Jeremy, Director of Information Technology, OSF Saint Luke Medical Center, Kewanee, IL, p. A192
JOHNSON, Jimmy, Chief Financial Officer, Blue Mountain Hospital, Blanding, UT, p. A654
JOHNSON, Joe, Chief Executive Officer, Florida Hospital Carrollwood, Tampa, FL, p. A144
JOHNSON, Joel, M.D. Chief Medical Staff, First Care Health Center, Park River, ND, p. A476
JOHNSON, John, M.D
Chief of Staff, Greenbrier Valley Medical Center, Ronceverte, WV, p. A695
Clinical Director, U. S. Public Health Service Indian Hospital, Crownpoint, NM, p. A424
JOHNSON, Jolene M., R.N. Acting Chief Nursing Officer, Warren General Hospital, Warren, PA, p. A551
JOHNSON, Juantina, Chief of Staff, Choctaw Health Center, Philadelphia, MS, p. A359
JOHNSON, Judith, Controller, HEALTHSOUTH Rehabilitation Hospital, Largo, FL, p. A131
JOHNSON, Juli, R.N., President, Parkview Huntington Hospital, Huntington, IN, p. A211
JOHNSON, Kathie A., Ph.D., Chief Executive Officer, Novant Health Thomasville Medical Center, Thomasville, NC, p. A469
JOHNSON, Kathryn
Chief Nursing Officer, Casa Colina Hospital and Health Systems, Pomona, CA, p. A81
Manager Human Resources, Marketing and Public Relations, St. Vincent Jennings Hospital, North Vernon, IN, p. A218
JOHNSON, Kathy, Chief Executive Officer and Administrator, Johnson Memorial Health Services, Dawson, MN, p. A337
JOHNSON, Kawanda, Director of Nursing, Specialty Hospital of Meridian, Meridian, MS, p. A358
JOHNSON, Kay, M.D. Chief of Staff, Bluffton Regional Medical Center, Bluffton, IN, p. A205
JOHNSON, Kayla, R.N. Vice President Patient Care Services and Chief Nursing Officer, St. Francis Medical Center, Monroe, LA, p. A280
JOHNSON, Keenan, Director Information Systems, Castleview Hospital, Price, UT, p. A657
JOHNSON, Kelly, R.N. Chief Nursing Officer, St. John Sapulpa, Sapulpa, OK, p. A514
JOHNSON, Kelly Marie, R.N. Senior Vice President Patience Care Services and Chief Nursing Officer, Children's Hospital Colorado, Aurora, CO, p. A99
JOHNSON, Ken, Interim President and Chief Executive Officer, Hutchinson Regional Medical Center, Hutchinson, KS, p. A242
JOHNSON, Kendall, Chief Financial Officer, Baton Rouge General Medical Center, Baton Rouge, LA, p. A269
JOHNSON, Kenneth, M.D
Chief Physician Executive, St. Mary's Hospital Medical Center, Green Bay, WI, p. A702
Chief Physician Executive, St. Vincent Hospital, Green Bay, WI, p. A702
JOHNSON, Kenneth, Vice President, Sts. Mary & Elizabeth Hospital, Louisville, KY, p. A262
JOHNSON, Kirby, Chief Executive Officer, Davis County Hospital, Bloomfield, IA, p. A223
JOHNSON, Kristen, Chief Nursing Officer, Southwest Healthcare System, Murrieta, CA, p. A77
JOHNSON, Kurt, M.D. Chief of Staff, Ogallala Community Hospital, Ogallala, NE, p. A395
JOHNSON, Kurt E., President and Chief Executive Officer, Ingalls Memorial Hospital, Harvey, IL, p. A190
JOHNSON, Kyle
Vice President Finance, East Liverpool City Hospital, East Liverpool, OH, p. A489
Chief Information Officer, The Aroostook Medical Center, Presque Isle, ME, p. A292
JOHNSON, Larry C., M.D. Medical Director Rural Health Clinic, New Horizons Health Systems, Owenton, KY, p. A264
JOHNSON, Laurie, Director – Human Resources, Via Christi Hospital Pittsburg, Pittsburg, KS, p. A249
JOHNSON, Linda, R.N
Vice President, Patient Services and Chief Nursing Officer, Heart of the Rockies Regional Medical Center, Salida, CO, p. A108
Chief Clinical Officer, Mission Hospital, Mission Viejo, CA, p. A75
JOHNSON, Lisa, Vice President Human Resources, Hillside Rehabilitation Hospital, Warren, OH, p. A499
JOHNSON, Lisa, R.N. Chief Nursing Executive, Morton Plant Hospital, Clearwater, FL, p. A123
JOHNSON, Lois, Administrator Fiscal Services, Ridgecrest Regional Hospital, Ridgecrest, CA, p. A83
JOHNSON, Lowell W., LFACHE, Chief Executive Officer, Presence Resurrection Medical Center, Chicago, IL, p. A183
JOHNSON, Ludwig, Vice President Information Technology, Middlesex Hospital, Middletown, CT, p. A113
JOHNSON, Marcia L., R.N., Chief Operating Officer, MultiCare Good Samaritan Hospital, Puyallup, WA, p. A682
JOHNSON, Margaret M., Interim President, St. Joseph Hospital & Health Center, Kokomo, IN, p. A214
JOHNSON, Marianne, Chief Nursing Officer, Trace Regional Hospital, Houston, MS, p. A354
JOHNSON, Marie
Chief Nursing Officer, Carrus Rehabilitation Hospital, Sherman, TX, p. A643
Chief Nursing Officer, Carrus Specialty Hospital, Sherman, TX, p. A644
JOHNSON, Marisa, M.D. Vice President Medical Affairs, CHRISTUS Health Shreveport–Bossier, Shreveport, LA, p. A284
JOHNSON, Mark, M.D. Chief Medical Officer, Mercy Hospital Oklahoma City, Oklahoma City, OK, p. A512
JOHNSON, Mark
Chief Financial Officer, Norwood Hospital, Norwood, MA, p. A310
Chief Information Officer, West Holt Memorial Hospital, Atkinson, NE, p. A389
JOHNSON, Melissa, Chief Financial Officer, Baptist Medical Center South, Montgomery, AL, p. A22
JOHNSON, Michael, M.D. Medical Director, Salina Surgical Hospital, Salina, KS, p. A250
JOHNSON, Michael A., M.D. Chief of Staff, Bucyrus Community Hospital, Bucyrus, OH, p. A480
JOHNSON, Michael T., FACHE, President and Chief Executive Officer, Regional Medical Center of San Jose, San Jose, CA, p. A89
JOHNSON, Mike
Vice President, Chief Information Officer, CaroMont Regional Medical Center, Gastonia, NC, p. A460
Chief Financial Officer, Lancaster Regional Medical Center, Lancaster, PA, p. A537
JOHNSON, Nancy, Chief Nursing Officer, Select Specialty Hospital–North Knoxville, Powell, TN, p. A587
JOHNSON, Nanette, Chief Nursing Officer, Orthopaedic Hospital of Wisconsin – Glendale, Glendale, WI, p. A701
JOHNSON, Nate, Chief Information Officer, Highlands Regional Medical Center, Sebring, FL, p. A143
JOHNSON, Nikki, Interim Chief Executive Officer, Cooperstown Medical Center, Cooperstown, ND, p. A473
JOHNSON, Pam, R.N. Chief Nursing Officer, McCurtain Memorial Hospital, Idabel, OK, p. A508
JOHNSON, Pamela
Treasurer and Chief Financial Officer, Geneva General Hospital, Geneva, NY, p. A434
Treasurer and Chief Financial Officer, Soldiers and Sailors Memorial Hospital of Yates County, Penn Yan, NY, p. A447
JOHNSON, Pamela O., MS Chief Nursing Officer, Mayo Clinic Hospital – Rochester, Rochester, MN, p. A345
JOHNSON, Patricia, R.N. Senior Vice President, Woman's Hospital, Baton Rouge, LA, p. A270
JOHNSON, Patrick, Director Human Resources, Pondera Medical Center, Conrad, MT, p. A382
JOHNSON, Paul F., President, Greenville Memorial Hospital, Greenville, SC, p. A561
JOHNSON, Penny
Chief Financial Officer, Metroplex Adventist Hospital, Killeen, TX, p. A626
Chief Financial Officer, Texas Health Huguley Hospital Fort Worth South, Fort Worth, TX, p. A614
JOHNSON, R. Milton, President and Chief Executive Officer, HCA, Nashville, TN, p. B61
JOHNSON, Ralph
Chief Information Officer, Franklin Memorial Hospital, Farmington, ME, p. A290
Interim Chief Information Officer, Southern Maine Health Care – Biddeford Medical Center, Biddeford, ME, p. A289
JOHNSON, Ric, Associate Administrator, Mountain View Hospital, Payson, UT, p. A657
JOHNSON, Richard F., Senior Vice President and Chief Information Officer, Indiana University Health University Hospital, Indianapolis, IN, p. A212
JOHNSON, Robb, Director Operations, Hamilton Center, Terre Haute, IN, p. A220
JOHNSON, Roger, M.D. Chief of Staff, Cheyenne Veterans Affairs Medical Center, Cheyenne, WY, p. A715
JOHNSON, Ronald W., FACHE, President and Chief Executive Officer, Shore Medical Center, Somers Point, NJ, p. A418
JOHNSON, Ryan K., Vice President Finance, Spectrum Health United Hospital, Greenville, MI, p. A321
JOHNSON, Samuel, Chief Executive Officer, Wiregrass Medical Center, Geneva, AL, p. A20
JOHNSON, Sarah, Chief Human Resources Officer, Pennsylvania Hospital, Philadelphia, PA, p. A545
JOHNSON, Scott, Vice President Finance, St. Luke's Hospital, Chesterfield, MO, p. A365
JOHNSON, Sean, Chief Executive Officer, Baptist Medical Center Yazoo, Yazoo City, MS, p. A362
JOHNSON, Sharon, Director Health Information Management, Western State Hospital, Staunton, VA, p. A673
JOHNSON, Sheryl, Chief Information Officer, SwedishAmerican Hospital, A Division of UW Health, Rockford, IL, p. A200
JOHNSON, Shrea, Director Human Resources, Alliance Health Center, Meridian, MS, p. A357
JOHNSON, Steven P., Ph.D., President and Chief Executive Officer, Health First, Inc., Rockledge, FL, p. B66
JOHNSON, Steven P., FACHE, President and Chief Executive Officer, Susquehanna Health System, Williamsport, PA, p. B129
JOHNSON, Sy
Executive Vice President, Chief Operating Officer, Renown Regional Medical Center, Reno, NV, p. A403
Executive Vice President, Chief Operating Officer, Renown South Meadows Medical Center, Reno, NV, p. A404
JOHNSON, Talicia, Director Human Resources, Brentwood Hospital, Shreveport, LA, p. A284
JOHNSON, Tamatha, Director Human Resources, Stringfellow Memorial Hospital, Anniston, AL, p. A15
JOHNSON, Tammy Dawn, Vice President Human Resources, Wilson N. Jones Regional Medical Center, Sherman, TX, p. A644
JOHNSON, Thomas, Director Information Systems, Penn Highlands Brookville, Brookville, PA, p. A530
JOHNSON, Timothy, President and Chief Executive Officer, Eaton Rapids Medical Center, Eaton Rapids, MI, p. A319
JOHNSON, Timothy J., President and Chief Executive Officer, Mayo Clinic Health System – Franciscan Healthcare in La Crosse, La Crosse, WI, p. A703
JOHNSON, Todd, Chief Financial Officer, Longview Regional Medical Center, Longview, TX, p. A629
JOHNSON, Tommy, Chief Executive Officer, Muleshoe Area Medical Center, Muleshoe, TX, p. A633

A878 Index of Health Care Professionals

Index of Health Care Professionals / Jones

Index of Health Care Professionals

JOHNSON, RN, Trudy, R.N. Chief Nursing Officer, Santa Clara Valley Medical Center, San Jose, CA, p. A89
JOHNSON, Vern, Director Information Technology, Sullivan County Memorial Hospital, Milan, MO, p. A373
JOHNSON, Vernon, Administrator, Dale Medical Center, Ozark, AL, p. A24
JOHNSON, Victoria, R.N. Nursing Director of Surgical and Medical Services, The HealthCenter, Kalispell, MT, p. A385
JOHNSON, Vincent, Chief Operating Officer, University of California, Davis Medical Center, Sacramento, CA, p. A85
JOHNSON, Wade C., FACHE, Chief Executive Officer, Valor Health, Emmett, ID, p. A174
JOHNSON Jr., Walter E., President and Chief Executive Officer, Jefferson Regional Medical Center, Pine Bluff, AR, p. A50
JOHNSON, William
Director Information Systems, Eliza Coffee Memorial Hospital, Florence, AL, p. A19
Director Information Systems, Shoals Hospital, Muscle Shoals, AL, p. A23
JOHNSON–HATCHER, Dawn, Chief Financial Officer, Lake Area Medical Center, Lake Charles, LA, p. A278
JOHNSON–MEKOTA, Judith, Director, Iowa City Veterans Affairs Health Care System, Iowa City, IA, p. A229
JOHNSON–PHILLIPPE, Sue E., FACHE, President and Chief Executive Officer, St. Joseph's Hospital of Buckhannon, Buckhannon, WV, p. A690
JOHNSON–POYNTER, Vicki, MSN Vice President Nursing Services and Chief Nursing Officer, Schneck Medical Center, Seymour, IN, p. A219
JOHNSRUD, Carolyn, Manager Human Resources, Missouri River Medical Center, Fort Benton, MT, p. A383
JOHNSRUD, Jill, Director of Nursing, Essentia Health–Graceville, Graceville, MN, p. A339
JOHNSTON, Charles W., Chief Executive Officer, Southern Coos Hospital and Health Center, Bandon, OR, p. A519
JOHNSTON, Diann, R.N. Vice President of Patient Care Services, Monmouth Medical Center, Long Branch Campus, Long Branch, NJ, p. A413
JOHNSTON, Don, Chief Information Officer, San Joaquin General Hospital, French Camp, CA, p. A62
JOHNSTON, Emily, M.D. Chief Medical Officer, Cascade Medical Center, Leavenworth, WA, p. A680
JOHNSTON, Jeffrey A., President, Mercy Hospital St. Louis, Saint Louis, MO, p. A376
JOHNSTON, Michael V., M.D. Chief Medical Officer and Senior Vice President Medical Programs, Kennedy Krieger Institute, Baltimore, MD, p. A293
JOHNSTON, Mike, Director Facilities Operations, Union General Hospital, Blairsville, GA, p. A152
JOHNSTON, Monte, Manager Human Resources, Coquille Valley Hospital, Coquille, OR, p. A520
JOHNSTON, Patricia, Vice President Information Services, Texas Health Harris Methodist Hospital Azle, Azle, TX, p. A595
JOHNSTON, Phyllis, Vice President, Catawba Valley Medical Center, Hickory, NC, p. A462
JOHNSTON, Susan, Vice President Human Resources, East Alabama Medical Center, Opelika, AL, p. A23
JOHNSTON, Susanne, Manager Human Resources, Lincoln County Medical Center, Ruidoso, NM, p. A426
JOHNSTON, William C., Interim Vice President, Information System, Brigham and Women's Hospital, Boston, MA, p. A303
JOHNSTON, Word, Medical Director, Covington County Hospital, Collins, MS, p. A352
JOHNSTONE, Jennifer, Chief Clinical Officer, Kindred Hospital Rome, Rome, GA, p. A163
JOICE, Jason, M.D. Chief Medical Staff, AllianceHealth Pryor, Pryor, OK, p. A514
JOLLEY, Colby, D.O. Acting Chief of Staff, Haxtun Hospital District, Haxtun, CO, p. A105
JOLLEY, Sherry, Chief Clinical Officer, Lawrence Medical Center, Moulton, AL, p. A23
JOLLY, Gaye, FACHE, President/Chief Administrative Officer, Roane Medical Center, Harriman, TN, p. A578
JONAS, Stanley W., Chief Executive Officer, Alliance Community Hospital, Alliance, OH, p. A478
JONASON, Anna, Ph.D. Chief Nursing Officer, Colleton Medical Center, Walterboro, SC, p. A565
JONES, Adrienne, Director Human Resources, Creedmoor Psychiatric Center, NY, p. A439
JONES, Alesia, Chief Human Resources Officer, University of Alabama Hospital, Birmingham, AL, p. A17
JONES, Allan, Controller, HEALTHSOUTH Rehabilitation Hospital of Jonesboro, Jonesboro, AR, p. A46
JONES, Amelia, Chief Operating Officer and Acting Chief Executive Officer, Oakland Regional Hospital, Southfield, MI, p. A330
JONES, Austin, CP
Chief Financial Officer, Physicians Surgical Hospital – Panhandle Campus, Amarillo, TX, p. A591
Chief Financial Officer, Physicians Surgical Hospital – Quail Creek, Amarillo, TX, p. A591
JONES, B. Konard, President, Hospital Division, NorthBay Medical Center, Fairfield, CA, p. A61
JONES, Beth, Chief Operating Officer, Reeves Memorial Medical Center, Bernice, LA, p. A270
JONES, Bill, Chief Executive Officer, Jackson County Hospital District, Edna, TX, p. A610
JONES, Bob, Interim Chief Executive Officer, Trace Regional Hospital, Houston, MS, p. A354
JONES, Brian, Interim Chief Executive Officer, Select Specialty Hospital–Kansas City, Kansas City, KS, p. A243
JONES, Carol, Controller and Manager Business Office, Coryell Memorial Hospital, Gatesville, TX, p. A616
JONES, Carolyn, R.N. Chief Nursing Officer, Box Butte General Hospital, Alliance, NE, p. A389
JONES, Catherine, Chief Nursing Officer, Ancora Psychiatric Hospital, Hammonton, NJ, p. A412
JONES, Cheryl L., Vice President Human Resources and Organizational Development, Baptist St. Anthony Health System, Amarillo, TX, p. A591
JONES, Chris, Chief Executive Officer, Vibra Hospital of Northern California, Redding, CA, p. A82
JONES, Clay, Regional Director of Human Resources, Phoebe Worth Medical Center, Sylvester, GA, p. A165
JONES, Connie, Director Human Resources, Community Behavioral Health Hospital – Rochester, Rochester, MN, p. A345
JONES, Dale, Administrator, Noland Hospital Tuscaloosa, Tuscaloosa, AL, p. A25
JONES, Dana, R.N. Chief Nursing Officer, Springhill Medical Center, Springhill, LA, p. A286
JONES Jr., Danny L., FACHE, Chief Executive Officer, Phoenix Baptist Hospital, Phoenix, AZ, p. A35
JONES, David
Chief Financial Officer, Alexian Brothers Behavioral Health Hospital, Hoffman Estates, IL, p. A191
Chief Nursing Officer, HEALTHSOUTH Rehabilitation Hospital of Arlington, Arlington, TX, p. A592
JONES, David C., Administrator, North Caddo Medical Center, Vivian, LA, p. A286
JONES, Deborah, Controller, Houston Hospital for Specialized Surgery, Houston, TX, p. A620
JONES, Derrick, Chief Executive Officer, Lovelace Rehabilitation Hospital, Albuquerque, NM, p. A422
JONES, Donald J., FACHE, Administrator, Fayette Medical Center, Fayette, AL, p. A19
JONES, Douglas A., Chief Operating Officer, Forrest General Hospital, Hattiesburg, MS, p. A354
JONES, Elaine, M.D. President Medical Staff, Roger Williams Medical Center, Providence, RI, p. A556
JONES, Evan, Chief Financial Officer, Lakeland Regional Health, Lakeland, FL, p. A131
JONES, Evelyn, Director Human Resources, Choctaw Nation Health Care Center, Talihina, OK, p. A516
JONES, Evelyn, R.N. Vice President Nursing Services, St. Bernard Hospital and Health Care Center, Chicago, IL, p. A184
JONES, G.R. Sonny, Senior Vice President Finance and Chief Financial Officer, St. Claire Regional Medical Center, Morehead, KY, p. A263
JONES, Glen M., FACHE Administrator, Red Bay Hospital, Red Bay, AL, p. A24
JONES, Greg, Chief Financial Officer, Wayne Memorial Hospital, Jesup, GA, p. A159
JONES, H. Roger, Chief Executive Officer, Straith Hospital for Special Surgery, Southfield, MI, p. A330
JONES, Holly A., Administrative Director Nursing Services, Illini Community Hospital, Pittsfield, IL, p. A198
JONES, J. Stephen, M.D. Chief of Staff, Muenster Memorial Hospital, Muenster, TX, p. A633
JONES, Jacqueline V., Chief Civilian Personnel Branch, Reynolds Army Community Hospital, Fort Sill, OK, p. A507
JONES, Jason L., R.N. Chief Nursing Officer, Fannin Regional Hospital, Blue Ridge, GA, p. A152
JONES, Jeff, Director Human Resources, Greene Memorial Hospital, Xenia, OH, p. A501
JONES, Jeffrey, Chief Financial Officer, Moses H. Cone Memorial Hospital, Greensboro, NC, p. A461
JONES, Jeremy A., Administrator, Mercy Hospital Healdton, Healdton, OK, p. A507
JONES, John, Chief Nursing Officer, Logan Memorial Hospital, Russellville, KY, p. A265
JONES, John, M.D. Chief Medical Staff, Sanford Chamberlain Medical Center, Chamberlain, SD, p. A567
JONES, Joshua, Director of Human Resources, Evanston Regional Hospital, Evanston, WY, p. A716
JONES, Joyce, Director Human Resources, HEALTHSOUTH Rehabilitation Hospital, Kingsport, TN, p. A580
JONES, Judy, Chief Clinical Officer, Arkansas Surgical Hospital, North Little Rock, AR, p. A49
JONES, Julie L., R.N. Chief Nursing Officer, Beatrice Community Hospital and Health Center, Beatrice, NE, p. A390
JONES, Karen, Administrative Director Human Resources, Marion General Hospital, Marion, IN, p. A215
JONES, Karin, Chief Nursing Officer, HEALTHSOUTH Rehabilitation Hospital of Alexandria, Alexandria, LA, p. A268
JONES, Karol, Chief Nursing Officer, Huntsville Hospital, Huntsville, AL, p. A21
JONES, Kathy, Director Human Resources, Jackson Medical Center, Jackson, AL, p. A21
JONES, Ken M., Chief Operating Officer, UCSF Medical Center, San Francisco, CA, p. A89
JONES, Kenneth, Chief Executive Officer, St. Joseph Hospital, Fort Wayne, IN, p. A209
JONES, Kimberly, Director Human Resources, Spine Hospital of Louisiana (formally the NeuroMedical Center Surgical Hospital), Baton Rouge, LA, p. A270
JONES, Kyle, Controller, Marshall Medical Center, Lewisburg, TN, p. A581
JONES, Lance, Chief Executive Officer, Coliseum Medical Centers, Macon, GA, p. A160
JONES, Liston, M.D. Medical Director, Springhill Memorial Hospital, Mobile, AL, p. A22
JONES, Lorrie Rickman, Ph.D., Director, Division of Mental Health, Department of Human Services, Springfield, IL, p. B52
JONES, Louis, Director Management Information Systems, Heart of Florida Regional Medical Center, Davenport, FL, p. A125
JONES, M. Steven
President, University Hospitals Conneaut Medical Center, Conneaut, OH, p. A487
President, University Hospitals Geauga Medical Center, Chardon, OH, p. A481
President, University Hospitals Geauga Medical Center, Chardon, OH, p. A481
President, University Hospitals Geneva Medical Center, Geneva, OH, p. A490
JONES, Mark, Chief Financial Officer, Hill Country Memorial Hospital, Fredericksburg, TX, p. A614
JONES, Mark A., President, Orlando Regional Medical Center, Orlando, FL, p. A138
JONES, Marsha, R.N. Director Nursing, Baptist Medical Center Yazoo, Yazoo City, MS, p. A362
JONES, Marshall, Senior Vice President Human Resources, Maricopa Integrated Health System, Phoenix, AZ, p. A35
JONES, Mary Jane, R.N. Vice President Nursing Operations, Northridge Hospital Medical Center, CA, p. A71
JONES, Matthew, Senior Director Support Services and Facilities, Alice Hyde Medical Center, Malone, NY, p. A436
JONES, Maud, Manager Medical Records, TOPS Surgical Specialty Hospital, Houston, TX, p. A622
JONES, MaxAnne, Director Human Resources, Rock Prairie Behavioral Health, College Station, TX, p. A601
JONES, Melinda, R.N. Chief Nursing Officer, Morehouse General Hospital, Bastrop, LA, p. A269
JONES, Meredith, Chief Financial Officer, Tennova Healthcare – McNairy Regional Hospital, Selmer, TN, p. A587
JONES, Michael, Vice President and Chief Information Officer, Children's Hospital of Wisconsin, Milwaukee, WI, p. A706
JONES, Michael L., Ph.D. Chief Information Officer, Shepherd Center, Atlanta, GA, p. A151
JONES, Mike, Director Information Services, Marshall Medical Center, Placerville, CA, p. A81
JONES, Mitchell, Director Information Technology, Little River Memorial Hospital, Ashdown, AR, p. A41
JONES, Pam, MSN Associate Hospital Director and Chief Nursing Officer, Vanderbilt Hospital and Clinics, Nashville, TN, p. A586
JONES, Pat, Director Information Systems, Merit Health River Oaks, Flowood, MS, p. A352
JONES, Patrice I., R.N. Vice President and Chief Nursing Officer, UF Health Jacksonville, Jacksonville, FL, p. A130
JONES, Percy E., M.D. Chief of Staff, Kindred Hospital–Greensboro, Greensboro, NC, p. A461
JONES, Philip L., Chief Financial Officer, Kindred Hospital–Nashville, Nashville, TN, p. A585
JONES, Phyllis, Chief Human Resources, Wm. Jennings Bryan Dorn Veterans Affairs Medical Center, Columbia, SC, p. A560
JONES, Ransom, Information Technology Director, Covington County Hospital, Collins, MS, p. A352
JONES, Reginald
Interim President and Chief Executive Officer, Fort Washington Medical Center, Oxen Hill, MD, p. A299
Business Manager, Georgia Regional Hospital at Atlanta, Decatur, GA, p. A156

Index of Health Care Professionals

Index of Health Care Professionals / Jones

JONES, Rex, Chief Executive Officer, Bradley County Medical Center, Warren, AR, p. A51
JONES, Richard, Chief Financial Officer, Bon Secours Baltimore Health System, Baltimore, MD, p. A293
JONES, Richard, M.D. Medical Director, Reliant Rehabilitation Hospital North Texas, Richardson, TX, p. A638
JONES, Richard W., Chief Financial Officer, Reading Hospital, West Reading, PA, p. A553
JONES, Rita A., Chief Executive Officer, Dundy County Hospital, Benkelman, NE, p. A390
JONES, Rob, Chief Nursing Officer, Physicians' Medical Center, New Albany, IN, p. A217
JONES, Robert, Director Management Information Systems, St. Joseph Mercy Oakland, Pontiac, MI, p. A328
JONES, Roger, M.D. Interim Chief of Staff, Tennessee Valley Healthcare System, Nashville, TN, p. A586
JONES, Ruth, Chief Clinical Officer, Regency Hospital of Northwest Arkansas – Springdale, Springdale, AR, p. A51
JONES, Scott, President and Chief Executive Officer, Midwestern Regional Medical Center, Zion, IL, p. A203
JONES, Shannon, M.D. Medical Director and Attending Psychiatrist, Evansville Psychiatric Children Center, Evansville, IN, p. A208
JONES, Sharon, Chief Financial Officer, Evergreen Medical Center, Evergreen, AL, p. A19
JONES, Sherry J., Chief Financial Officer, Crestwood Medical Center, Huntsville, AL, p. A21
JONES, Staci, R.N. Chief Nursing Officer, Methodist McKinney Hospital, McKinney, TX, p. A632
JONES, Stacy, Chief Nursing Officer, HEALTHSOUTH MountainView Regional Rehabilitation Hospital, Morgantown, WV, p. A693
JONES, Stephen K., FACHE, President and Chief Executive Officer, Robert Wood Johnson Health System & Network, New Brunswick, NJ, p. B114
JONES, Stephen K., FACHE, President and Chief Executive Officer, Robert Wood Johnson University Hospital, New Brunswick, NJ, p. A415
JONES, Stephen K., M.D. Vice President Medical Staff Affairs, St. Rose Dominican Hospitals – Rose de Lima Campus, Henderson, NV, p. A401
JONES Jr., Stephen K., FACHE, Chief Executive Officer, Clear Lake Regional Medical Center, Webster, TX, p. A651
JONES, Steven K., M.D. Medical Director, Advocate Eureka Hospital, Eureka, IL, p. A187
JONES, Tammie R., R.N. Chief Nursing Officer, St. Mary Medical Center, Hobart, IN, p. A211
JONES, Theresa, Manager Human Resources, St. Luke Community Healthcare, Ronan, MT, p. A386
JONES, Tim, Chief Executive Officer, Heart of Texas Memorial Hospital, Brady, TX, p. A598
JONES, Timothy P., Chief Operating Officer, Concord Hospital, Concord, NH, p. A405
JONES, Todd, President, Baptist Health Richmond, Richmond, KY, p. A265
JONES, Tom, D.O. Chief Medical Officer, Doctors Hospital at White Rock Lake, Dallas, TX, p. A605
JONES, Tom, Chief Information Officer, Fitzgibbon Hospital, Marshall, MO, p. A372
JONES, Tonya A., Vice President Human Resources, Maria Parham Medical Center, Henderson, NC, p. A462
JONES, Tracey, Director Human Resources, Jackson Park Hospital and Medical Center, Chicago, IL, p. A182
JONES, Trennis, Senior Vice President and Chief Administrative Officer, Seton Northwest Hospital, Austin, TX, p. A594
JONES, Vernita, Site Manager, PHS Santa Fe Indian Hospital, Santa Fe, NM, p. A426
JONES, W. Clark, Superintendent and Administrator, Cascade Valley Hospital and Clinics, Arlington, WA, p. A676
JONES, Wendy, Interim Chief Financial Officer, Blue Hill Memorial Hospital, Blue Hill, ME, p. A289
JONES, Yameeka, Chief Executive Officer, Vibra Hospital of San Diego, San Diego, CA, p. A87
JONES, Yvette A., HIM Director, Putnam Community Medical Center, Palatka, FL, p. A138
JONES MONNETT, Anna, MS Associate Director Patient Care Services, Dayton Veterans Affairs Medical Center, Dayton, OH, p. A488
JONES–BENDEL, Trish, R.N. Chief Nursing Officer, Linden Oaks Hospital, Naperville, IL, p. A195
JONES–BROWNING, Debbie, Vice President Operations and Physician Services and Chief Operating Officer, Rush Memorial Hospital, Rushville, IN, p. A219
JONTZ, Doug, Senior Vice President Human Resources, Mercy Medical Center–Cedar Rapids, Cedar Rapids, IA, p. A223
JORDAN, Amy, Chief Nursing Officer/Vice President of Nursing, Gordon Hospital, Calhoun, GA, p. A153
JORDAN, Andrew, M.D. Chief of Staff, University Medical Center, Lebanon, TN, p. A581
JORDAN, Bobby G., Chief Executive Officer, Jackson Parish Hospital, Jonesboro, LA, p. A276
JORDAN, Gary W., FACHE, Chief Executive Officer, Wright Memorial Hospital, Trenton, MO, p. A379
JORDAN, Jill, Chief Executive Officer, Healthsouth Rehabilitation Hospital of Altamonte Springs, Altamonte Springs, FL, p. A121
JORDAN, Ken, Chief Financial Officer, Fountain Valley Regional Hospital and Medical Center, Fountain Valley, CA, p. A61
JORDAN, Linda U., Administrator, Clay County Hospital, Ashland, AL, p. A15
JORDAN, Lori, Executive Director, Griffin Memorial Hospital, Norman, OK, p. A510
JORDAN, Michelle J., Administrator, Lewis and Clark Specialty Hospital, Yankton, SD, p. A573
JORDAN, Quincy, M.D. Chief of Staff, Flint River Community Hospital, Montezuma, GA, p. A162
JORDAN, Rhonda R., Chief Human Resources Officer, Virtua Marlton, Marlton, NJ, p. A414
JORDAN, Terry, M.D. Chief of Staff, Alliance Health Center, Meridian, MS, p. A357
JORDEN BEST, Rosemary, Director Human Resources, Tyrone Hospital, Tyrone, PA, p. A551
JORE, Bernie, Chief Nursing Officer, St. Mary's of Michigan, Saginaw, MI, p. A329
JORGENSEN, Deanna, Coordinator Human Resources, Regency Hospital of Covington, Covington, LA, p. A272
JOSEHART, Carl E.
Chief Executive Officer, Memorial Hermann Rehabilitation Hospital – Katy, Katy, TX, p. A625
Chief Executive Officer, TIRR Memorial Hermann, Houston, TX, p. A622
JOSEPH, Elliot T., President and Chief Executive Officer, Hartford HealthCare, Hartford, CT, p. B60
JOSEPH, James, M.D. President Medical Staff, Geisinger–Bloomsburg Hospital, Bloomsburg, PA, p. A529
JOSEPH, Kevin, M.D., Chief Executive Officer, West Chester Hospital, West Chester, OH, p. A500
JOSEPH–TAYLOR, Terri, Chief Human Resource Manager, Ochsner Medical Center – North Shore, Slidell, LA, p. A285
JOSHI, Nirmal, M.D. Senior Vice President Medical Affairs and Chief Medical Officer, Pinnacle Health System, Harrisburg, PA, p. A535
JOSLIN, Tim A., President and Chief Executive Officer, Community Medical Centers, Fresno, CA, p. B41
JOSLYN, E. Allen, M.D. Chief Medical Officer, Bedford Memorial Hospital, Bedford, VA, p. A662
JOSLYN, J. Scott, Senior Vice President and Chief Information Officer, Saddleback Memorial Medical Center, Laguna Hills, CA, p. A66
JOUD, Mohammad A., M.D. Chief of Staff, Bayfront Health Brooksville, Brooksville, FL, p. A123
JOUDEH, Jalal, M.D
Chief of Staff, DeQuincy Memorial Hospital, DeQuincy, LA, p. A273
Chief Medical Officer, Specialty Rehabilitation Hospital of Coushatta, Coushatta, LA, p. A272
JOURDEN, Marti, FACHE Chief Quality Officer, St. Anthony Hospital, Oklahoma City, OK, p. A513
JOY, Mike, Administrator, Finance, Via Christi Hospital Pittsburg, Pittsburg, KS, p. A249
JOY, Jr., Roland Eugene, Vice President and Chief Nursing Officer, The Aroostook Medical Center, Presque Isle, ME, p. A292
JOYAL, Shirley, Director Information Systems, Regional Medical Center of San Jose, San Jose, CA, p. A89
JOYCE, Allyson, Vice President Human Resources, Caro Community Hospital, Caro, MI, p. A316
JOYCE, Jodi S., R.N. Interim Chief Nursing Officer, University of Illinois Hospital & Health Sciences System, Chicago, IL, p. A185
JOYCE, Maria, Chief Financial Officer, National Institutes of Health Clinical Center, Bethesda, MD, p. A296
JOYCE, William F., Chief of Staff, Bates County Memorial Hospital, Butler, MO, p. A364
JOYNER, Ken, Vice President of Employee Services, Bay Area Medical Center, Marinette, WI, p. A704
JOYNER, Thomas, Chief Financial Officer, Lakeside Behavioral Health System, Memphis, TN, p. A583
JUAREZ, Edward, M.D. Chief Medical Officer, Kindred Hospital El Paso, El Paso, TX, p. A611
JUAREZ, Elizabeth, M.D. Chief Medical Officer, Harlingen Medical Center, Harlingen, TX, p. A617
JUAREZ, Rose, Chief Civilian Personnel Branch, Brooke Army Medical Center, Fort Sam Houston, TX, p. A612
JUCHNOWICZ, Jean E., Director Human Resources, Merit Health Natchez, Natchez, MS, p. A358
JUDD, Martin H., Regional President and Chief Executive Officer, Presence Saints Mary & Elizabeth Medical Center, Chicago, IL, p. A183
JUDD, Russell V., Chief Executive Officer, Kern Medical Center, Bakersfield, CA, p. A55
JUDGE, Leigh Ann, Manager Human Resources, Guttenberg Municipal Hospital, Guttenberg, IA, p. A228
JUDLIN, Karen Ann, Director Human Resources, St. Charles Parish Hospital, Luling, LA, p. A279
JUDYCKI–CREPEAULT, Christine, Chief Financial Officer, Adcare Hospital of Worcester, Worcester, MA, p. A313
JUENGER, Jacqueline, R.N. Chief Nursing Officer, HEALTHSOUTH Rehabilitation Hospital of Sarasota, Sarasota, FL, p. A142
JUHASZ, Robert S., D.O., President, South Pointe Hospital, Warrensville Heights, OH, p. A500
JUHL, Gregory, M.D. Medical Director, Norton Brownsboro Hospital, Louisville, KY, p. A261
JUHL, Stephanie, Administrator, Community Behavioral Health Hospital – Rochester, Rochester, MN, p. A345
JUHL, Valerie, Director of Health, Madelia Community Hospital, Madelia, MN, p. A341
JULES, Dena, Administrator, Oceans Behavioral Hospital of Lake Charles, Lake Charles, LA, p. A278
JULIAN, Bell, Associate Executive Director and Chief Financial Officer, James Cancer Hospital and Solove Research Institute, Columbus, OH, p. A485
JULIAN, Steve, M.D., President, Sentara Obici Hospital, Suffolk, VA, p. A673
JULIANA, Rich, Director Human Resources, Silver Hill Hospital, New Canaan, CT, p. A114
JULIE, Janet, Chief Nursing Officer, Kaiser Permanente Antioch Medical Center, Antioch, CA, p. A53
JUMP, Beth, Chief Information Officer, Logansport Memorial Hospital, Logansport, IN, p. A215
JUMPING EAGLE, Sara, Clinical Director, Standing Rock Service Unit, Fort Yates Hospital, Indian Health Service, DHHS, Fort Yates, ND, p. A474
JUNEAU, Cindy K., Chief Nursing Officer, Avoyelles Hospital, Marksville, LA, p. A279
JUNEAU, James B., Chief Financial Officer, Opelousas General Health System, Opelousas, LA, p. A283
JUNEAU, Tina Louise, Director Human Resources, Bunkie General Hospital, Bunkie, LA, p. A271
JUNG, Darra, Director of Nursing, Union General Hospital, Farmerville, LA, p. A273
JUNGELS, Trisha, Chief Nursing Officer and Vice President Clinical Services, Jamestown Regional Medical Center, Jamestown, ND, p. A475
JUNGWIRTH, Scott, Chief Human Resources Officer, Providence Alaska Medical Center, Anchorage, AK, p. A27
JUNIS, Jennifer, MSN Vice President Chief Nursing Officer, OSF Saint Luke Medical Center, Kewanee, IL, p. A192
JUNIS, Jennifer, R.N., President, OSF Saint Paul Medical Center, Mendota, IL, p. A194
JUNKINS, Curt M., Assistant Chief Executive Officer, Brownwood Regional Medical Center, Brownwood, TX, p. A599
JUNO, Russell, M.D. Chief of Staff, St. Mark's Medical Center, La Grange, TX, p. A627
JURCZYK, John A., FACHE, Interim President, Good Samaritan Medical Center, Brockton, MA, p. A305
JUREK, Chuck, Interim Administrator and Chief Operating Officer, Specialty Hospital of Winnfield, Winnfield, LA, p. A287
JURGENS, Chad, Chief Executive Officer, Jefferson Community Health Center, Fairbury, NE, p. A391
JURICA, John, M.D. Vice President Medical Affairs, Riverside Medical Center, Kankakee, IL, p. A192
JURIS, Susan V., President, University Hospitals Ahuja Medical Center, Beachwood, OH, p. A479
JURKUS, Patti
Chief Executive Officer, Bedford Memorial Hospital, Bedford, VA, p. A662
Director Human Resources, Carilion New River Valley Medical Center, Christiansburg, VA, p. A663
JURY, Tina M., MSN Executive Vice President Hospital Operations and Chief Nursing Officer, AnMed Health Medical Center, Anderson, SC, p. A557
JUST, Lisa
President, Aurora Lakeland Medical Center, Elkhorn, WI, p. A700
President, Aurora Memorial Hospital of Burlington, Burlington, WI, p. A699
JUST, Paula
Vice President Human Resources, Health First Cape Canaveral Hospital, Cocoa Beach, FL, p. A124
Chief Human Resources Officer, Health First Holmes Regional Medical Center, Melbourne, FL, p. A133
Chief Human Resources Officer, Health First Palm Bay Hospital, Palm Bay, FL, p. A138
Chief Human Resources Officer, Health First Viera Hospital, Melbourne, FL, p. A133
JUSTESEN, Scott, M.D. Chief of Staff, Castleview Hospital, Price, UT, p. A657

A880 Index of Health Care Professionals 

Index of Health Care Professionals / Karn

Index of Health Care Professionals

JUSTICE, Kim, Vice President Planning and Operations, Atlantic General Hospital, Berlin, MD, p. A295
JUSTUS, Jason, Vice President Finance and Chief Financial Officer, Pomerene Hospital, Millersburg, OH, p. A494
JUTILA, Kathy, M.D. Chief of Staff, Wheatland Memorial Healthcare, Harlowton, MT, p. A384
JYRKAS, Wade A., Director Computer Information Systems, Lake Region Healthcare, Fergus Falls, MN, p. A338

# K

KA'AKIMAKA, Holly, Director Human Resources, Hilo Medical Center, Hilo, HI, p. A168
KABITZKE–GROTH, Terry, R.N
Vice President Nursing, Aurora Medical Center Grafton, Grafton, WI, p. A701
Chief Nursing Officer, Aurora Medical Center in Washington County, Hartford, WI, p. A702
KABLE, Mary Ellen, Chief Executive Officer, LifeCare Hospitals of Mechanicsburg, Mechanicsburg, PA, p. A540
KACHIGION, Claudia, M.D. Medical Director, Alton Mental Health Center, Alton, IL, p. A178
KADDOURI, Sami, M.D. Medical Director, Cornerstone of Medical Arts Center Hospital, Fresh Meadows, NY, p. A433
KADLICK, Pamela, Vice President Nursing, Mercy St. Anne Hospital, Toledo, OH, p. A498
KAELIN, Darryl, M.D. Medical Director, Frazier Rehab Institute, Louisville, KY, p. A261
KAEMS, Amanda, Manager Information Systems, Paradise Valley Hospital, National City, CA, p. A77
KAFKA, Rich, M.D. Chief Medical Officer, Avera Gregory Hospital, Gregory, SD, p. A569
KAHL, Vicky, Director Human Resources, Valley Regional Medical Center, Brownsville, TX, p. A599
KAHLE, Ty, Director Human Resources, Methodist Hospital, Henderson, KY, p. A258
KAHLER, Ralph, M.D. Medical Director, Regency Hospital of Hattiesburg, Hattiesburg, MS, p. A354
KAHLY–MCMAHON, Heidi
Vice President Human Resources, Genesis Medical Center, Illini Campus, Silvis, IL, p. A200
Interim Vice President Human Resources, Genesis Medical Center–Davenport, Davenport, IA, p. A225
KAHN, Jalil, M.D. Chief of Staff, Atrium Medical Center of Corinth, Corinth, TX, p. A602
KAHN, Maureen A., R.N., President and Chief Executive Officer, Blessing Hospital, Quincy, IL, p. A199
KAINO, Linda, Chief Nursing Officer, Ocean Beach Hospital, Ilwaco, WA, p. A679
KAISER, Brenda, Director Human Resources, Great Bend Regional Hospital, Great Bend, KS, p. A240
KAISER, Janet, R.N. Chief Nursing Officer, Kansas Medical Center, Andover, KS, p. A237
KAISER, Ken, Coordinator Information Systems, Grant Regional Health Center, Lancaster, WI, p. A704
KAISER, Larry, M.D., President and Chief Executive Officer, Temple University Health System, Philadelphia, PA, p. B131
KAJIWARA, Gary K., President and Chief Executive Officer, Kuakini Medical Center, Honolulu, HI, p. A168
KAKAVAS, Connie, Chief Human Resources Officer, Summit Healthcare Regional Medical Center, Show Low, AZ, p. A38
KAKI, Karim, M.D. Chief Medical Director, Hendry Regional Medical Center, Clewiston, FL, p. A124
KAKUDA, James, M.D. Chief of Staff, Pali Momi Medical Center, Aiea, HI, p. A168
KALAJAINEN, Kimberly, Vice President Operations and Chief Information Officer, Lawrence + Memorial Hospital, New London, CT, p. A114
KALANIHUIA, Janice, President, Molokai General Hospital, Kaunakakai, HI, p. A170
KALAR, Cathy, Chief Financial Officer, Broaddus Hospital, Philippi, WV, p. A694
KALAVAR, Jagadeesh S., M.D. Chief of Staff, Michael E. DeBakey Veterans Affairs Medical Center, Houston, TX, p. A621
KALCHIK, Kevin, Chief Financial Officer, War Memorial Hospital, Sault Sainte Marie, MI, p. A330
KALE, Debra
Vice President Human Resources, Cleveland Regional Medical Center, Shelby, NC, p. A468
Director Human Resources, Kings Mountain Hospital, Kings Mountain, NC, p. A463
KALEEL, Reza, Executive Vice President and Chief Operating Officer, St. Mary's Medical Center, Grand Junction, CO, p. A104
KALINA, Andrea, Vice President External Affairs and Chief Human Resources Officer, St. Clair Hospital, Pittsburgh, PA, p. A546
KALINOWSKI, Christopher, Chief Nursing Officer, The Memorial Hospital at Craig, Craig, CO, p. A101
KALINSKI, Cami, Director Financial Services, Frances Mahon Deaconess Hospital, Glasgow, MT, p. A383
KALKA, Gina, R.N. Chief Nursing Officer, Pecos County Memorial Hospital, Fort Stockton, TX, p. A612
KALKOWSKI, Kelly, Chief Executive Officer, Niobrara Valley Hospital, Lynch, NE, p. A394
KALKUT, Gary, M.D. Senior Vice President and Chief Medical Officer, Montefiore Medical Center, NY, p. A442
KALL, Greg, Chief Information Officer, Summa Akron City Hospital, Akron, OH, p. A478
KALLAL, Catherine, M.D. Chief Medical Officer, Holy Cross Hospital, Chicago, IL, p. A182
KALLAS, Diane, Vice President of Nursing Services, McLaren Flint, Flint, MI, p. A319
KALLEVIG, Daryl, Chief Information Officer, Riverwood Healthcare Center, Aitkin, MN, p. A334
KALSMAN, Stephen L., Area Finance Officer, Kaiser Permanente San Jose Medical Center, San Jose, CA, p. A89
KALTENBACH, Gretchen, R.N. Chief Operating Officer, Genesis Behavioral Hospital, Breaux Bridge, LA, p. A271
KALUA, Patricia, Chief Nurse Executive, Kona Community Hospital, Kealakekua, HI, p. A170
KAMBEROS, Peter N., Chief Operating Officer, Thorek Memorial Hospital, Chicago, IL, p. A185
KAMBIC, Phillip M., President and Chief Executive Officer, Riverside Medical Center, Kankakee, IL, p. A192
KAMBOJ, Pradeep, M.D. Chief Medical Staff, Tulare Regional Medical Center, Tulare, CA, p. A95
KAMERMAYER, Angela K., MS Chief Nursing Officer, INTEGRIS Health Edmond, Edmond, OK, p. A506
KAMGUIA, Rebecca, Administrative Director Human Resources, Bon Secours Memorial Regional Medical Center, Mechanicsville, VA, p. A668
KAMIKAWA, Cynthia, R.N. Vice President Nursing Emergency Department and Trauma and Chief Nursing Officer, Queen's Medical Center, Honolulu, HI, p. A169
KAMINSKI, Gene, Vice President Human Resources, McLaren Northern Michigan, Petoskey, MI, p. A327
KAMINSKI, Tammy, Director Human Resources, Alaska Regional Hospital, Anchorage, AK, p. A27
KAMINSKI, Toni, Director Human Resources, Medical Center Enterprise, Enterprise, AL, p. A19
KAMINSKY, Kathy, R.N. Chief Quality Officer and Interim Chief Nursing Officer, Englewood Hospital and Medical Center, Englewood, NJ, p. A412
KAMMERER, James M., Vice President Support Services, Great River Medical Center, West Burlington, IA, p. A236
KAMMERUD, Shawn, Manager Information Services, Osceola Medical Center, Osceola, WI, p. A708
KAMMIRE, Gordon, M.D. Chief of Staff, Wake Forest Baptist Health–Lexington Medical Center, Lexington, NC, p. A464
KAMOWSKI, David, Vice President and Chief Information Officer, Temple University Hospital, Philadelphia, PA, p. A545
KAMPHUIS, Jan, Ph.D. Executive Vice President and Chief Nurse Executive, Sanford Bismarck, Bismarck, ND, p. A472
KAMPSCHNIEDER, Carol, Vice President Clinical and Regulatory Services, St. Francis Memorial Hospital, West Point, NE, p. A399
KAMPWERTH, Dennis, Director Management Information Systems, Gateway Regional Medical Center, Granite City, IL, p. A189
KAMRAN, Khurram, M.D. Vice President Medical Affairs, ProMedica Toledo Hospital, Toledo, OH, p. A499
KANE, Addy, Chief Financial Officer, Roger Williams Medical Center, Providence, RI, p. A556
KANE, Audrey, Interim Chief Financial Officer, Prowers Medical Center, Lamar, CO, p. A106
KANE, Kelli R., Director of Finance, Barnes–Kasson County Hospital, Susquehanna, PA, p. A550
KANE, Melissa, Chief Financial Officer, Pocahontas Memorial Hospital, Buckeye, WV, p. A689
KANE, Nancy, Assistant Vice President Finance LifeBridge Health, Northwest Hospital, Randallstown, MD, p. A299
KANE, Robert E., President, Divine Providence Hospital, Williamsport, PA, p. A553
KANE, Steve, Director Information Technology, Lower Bucks Hospital, Bristol, PA, p. A530
KANE, Terri, Chief Executive Officer, Dixie Regional Medical Center, Saint George, UT, p. A658
KANE, Thomas, R.N. Vice President Patient Services and Chief Nursing Officer, West Shore Medical Center, Manistee, MI, p. A325
KANESHIRO, Shela, Chief Nursing Officer, Orange County Global Medical Center, Inc., Santa Ana, CA, p. A90
KANIA, Kathy, Chief Information Officer, Staten Island University Hospital, NY, p. A444
KANKEL, LeAnne, Vice President Human Relations, Barton Memorial Hospital, South Lake Tahoe, CA, p. A93
KANNADAY, Colleen, FACHE,
President, Advocate BroMenn Medical Center, Normal, IL, p. A196
President, Advocate Eureka Hospital, Eureka, IL, p. A187
KANSGEN, Mike, Director Information Services, Community Hospital, Grand Junction, CO, p. A104
KANTHILAL, S. K., M.D. President Medical Staff, Sarah D. Culbertson Memorial Hospital, Rushville, IL, p. A200
KANTO, William, M.D. Senior Vice President and Chief Medical Officer, Georgia Regents Medical Center, Augusta, GA, p. A151
KANTOS, Craig A., Chief Executive Officer, Riverside Medical Center, Waupaca, WI, p. A713
KANUCH, James A.
Vice President Finance, Allegheny Valley Hospital, Natrona Heights, PA, p. A541
Vice President Finance, West Penn Hospital, Pittsburgh, PA, p. A547
KANWAL, Neeraj, M.D., President, ProMedica Flower Hospital, Sylvania, OH, p. A498
KAPASKA, David, D.O., Regional President and Chief Executive Officer, Avera McKennan Hospital and University Health Center, Sioux Falls, SD, p. A571
KAPHINGS, Mary, Director Human Resources, Fairview Ridges Hospital, Burnsville, MN, p. A336
KAPLAN, Gary, FACHE, Chairman and Chief Executive Officer, Virginia Mason Medical Center, Seattle, WA, p. A684
KAPLAN, Ronald, Chief Financial Officer, North Philadelphia Health System, Philadelphia, PA, p. A544
KAPLAN, Tamra, Chief Operating Officer, Long Beach Memorial Medical Center, Long Beach, CA, p. A68
KAPLANIS, Gene, Director Information Technology, Alaska Regional Hospital, Anchorage, AK, p. A27
KAPP III, William K., M.D., President and Chief Executive Officer, Landmark Hospitals, Cape Girardeau, MO, p. B80
KAPRE, Sheela, M.D. Chief Medical Officer, San Joaquin General Hospital, French Camp, CA, p. A62
KAPUR, Karun
Chief Information Officer, CHI Health Bergan Mercy, Omaha, NE, p. A395
Regional Chief Information Officer, CHI Health Lakeside, Omaha, NE, p. A396
Senior Vice President and Chief Information Officer, CHI Health Mercy Council Bluffs, Council Bluffs, IA, p. A225
Regional Chief Information Officer, CHI Health Midlands, Papillion, NE, p. A397
KARA, Amynah, M.D. Chief Medical Officer, Baylor Emergency Medical Center at Aubrey, Aubrey, TX, p. A593
KARAM, Annah, Director Human Resources, San Gorgonio Memorial Hospital, Banning, CA, p. A55
KARAM, Chris, President and Chief Executive Officer, CHRISTUS St. Michael Health System, Texarkana, TX, p. A647
KARAM, Christopher J., Chief Operating Officer, Saint Joseph Regional Medical Center, Mishawaka, IN, p. A216
KARANJAI, Rajohn, M.D. Chief Medical Officer, Sidney Health Center, Sidney, MT, p. A387
KARAS, Cecelia, Director of Nursing, Walter B. Jones Alcohol and Drug Abuse Treatment Center, Greenville, NC, p. A461
KARDOW, Vivian
Chief Human Resources Officer, Memorial Hermann – Texas Medical Center, Houston, TX, p. A620
Chief Human Resources Officer, TIRR Memorial Hermann, Houston, TX, p. A622
KAREL, Thomas L., Vice President Organization and Talent Effectiveness, Mercy Health Saint Mary's, Grand Rapids, MI, p. A321
KARIM, Parvez, M.D. Chief Medical Officer, Allegiance Specialty Hospital of Greenville, Greenville, MS, p. A353
KARL, Don, Interim Chief Executive Officer, Las Palmas Medical Center, El Paso, TX, p. A611
KARL, Peter J., President and Chief Executive Officer, Eastern Connecticut Health Network, Manchester, CT, p. B53
KARL, Peter J.
President and Chief Executive Officer, Manchester Memorial Hospital, Manchester, CT, p. A112
President and Chief Executive Officer, Rockville General Hospital, Vernon, CT, p. A115
KARL, Thomas P., President, Parkland Health Center – Liberty Street, Farmington, MO, p. A367
KARMACH, Izabela, R.N., Administrator, San Diego County Psychiatric Hospital, San Diego, CA, p. A87
KARN, Cielette, M.D. Chief of Staff, SageWest Health Care at Riverton, Riverton, WY, p. A717
KARN, Deborah, Chief Executive Officer, Kindred Hospital South Philadelphia, Philadelphia, PA, p. A544

Index of Health Care Professionals

Index of Health Care Professionals / Karner

KARNER, Diana M., R.N. Chief Nursing Officer, California Pacific Medical Center, San Francisco, CA, p. A88
KARNS, Kris, FACHE, Chief Executive Officer, Acuity Hospital of South Texas, San Antonio, TX, p. A640
KAROW, Deborah, R.N
Vice President Patient Care Services, Howard Young Medical Center, Woodruff, WI, p. A714
Vice President Patient Care Services, Ministry Eagle River Memorial Hospital, Eagle River, WI, p. A700
KARPF, Michael, M.D., Executive Vice President of Health Affairs, University of Kentucky Albert B. Chandler Hospital, Lexington, KY, p. A260
KARSOS, Felicia, R.N., President and Chief Executive Officer, Meadowlands Hospital Medical Center, Secaucus, NJ, p. A418
KARSTEN, Margo, MSN, Chief Executive Officer, Cheyenne Regional Medical Center, Cheyenne, WY, p. A715
KARSTEN, Paul H., Vice President Finance and Chief Financial Officer, Pine Rest Christian Mental Health Services, Grand Rapids, MI, p. A321
KASABIAN, Carolyn, Chief Financial Officer, St. Mary's Regional Medical Center, Lewiston, ME, p. A291
KASAI, Darren
Assistant Administrator, Kula Hospital, Kula, HI, p. A170
Assistant Administrator, Lanai Community Hospital, Lanai City, HI, p. A170
KASBERGER, John, Vice President and Chief Financial Officer, Mercy Medical Center, Roseburg, OR, p. A525
KASIRYE, Yusuf, M.D. Chief of Staff, Flambeau Hospital, Park Falls, WI, p. A709
KASITZ, Todd, Vice President Finance, Newton Medical Center, Newton, KS, p. A246
KASNIC, Tracey A., R.N
Chief Nursing Officer, Central Washington Hospital, Wenatchee, WA, p. A687
Chief Nursing Officer, Wenatchee Valley Medical Center, Wenatchee, WA, p. A687
KASPER, Keith, Chief Financial Officer, Hospital of the University of Pennsylvania, Philadelphia, PA, p. A544
KASPER, Yobi, Chief Information Officer, Victory Surgical Hospital East Houston, Houston, TX, p. A623
KASPER–COPE, Shelly, M.D. Chief of Staff, Tri Valley Health System, Cambridge, NE, p. A390
KASPERSKI, Joyce, Director Nursing, St. John River District Hospital, East China, MI, p. A318
KASS, Andrew J A, M.D. Assistant Superintendent, Albert J. Solnit Psychiatric Center – South Campus, Middletown, CT, p. A113
KASSAB, Jerry, President and Chief Executive Officer, Aspire Health Partners, Orlando, FL, p. A137
KASSAHN, Kristine, Chief Executive Officer, Fresno Surgical Hospital, Fresno, CA, p. A62
KASSER, Michael
Chief Financial Officer, Herrin Hospital, Herrin, IL, p. A190
Vice President Chief Financial Officer and Treasurer, Memorial Hospital of Carbondale, Carbondale, IL, p. A180
KASSIS, Charles, President, Mercy Medical Center Merced, Merced, CA, p. A75
KASSIS, Maher, M.D. Chief Medical Staff, Marcum and Wallace Memorial Hospital, Irvine, KY, p. A259
KASTANIS, John N., Chief Executive Officer, Temple University Hospital, Philadelphia, PA, p. A545
KASTNER, Gregory, M.D. Chief of Staff, Crawford Memorial Hospital, Robinson, IL, p. A199
KATES, Josh, Information Technology Analyst, Andrew McFarland Mental Health Center, Springfield, IL, p. A201
KATES, Kenneth P., Chief Executive Officer, University of Iowa Hospitals and Clinics, Iowa City, IA, p. A230
KATHRINS, PH.D, Richard J., President and Chief Executive Officer, Bacharach Institute for Rehabilitation, Pomona, NJ, p. A417
KATIGBAK, Michael, Chief Financial Officer, Sage Memorial Hospital, Ganado, AZ, p. A31
KATNENI, Jitendra P., M.D. Medical Director, Select Specialty Hospital–Flint, Flint, MI, p. A319
KATO, Laura, Vice President Human Resources, St. Francis Medical Center, Lynwood, CA, p. A74
KATSCHKE, Jr., R. William, M.D. Medical Director, Grover C. Dils Medical Center, Caliente, NV, p. A400
KATSIANIS, John, Senior Vice President and Chief Financial Officer, DeKalb Medical at North Decatur, Decatur, GA, p. A156
KATZ, Bonnie B., Vice President, Business Development and Support Operations, Sheppard Pratt Health System, Baltimore, MD, p. A294
KATZ, Jeffrey, M.D. Chief Medical Officer, Memorial Hermann – Texas Medical Center, Houston, TX, p. A620
KATZ, Michelle, Director Human Resources, HEALTHSOUTH Nittany Valley Rehabilitation Hospital, Pleasant Gap, PA, p. A547
KATZ, Mike, Director Information Systems, Logan Memorial Hospital, Russellville, KY, p. A265
KATZ, Mitchell H., M.D., Director, Los Angeles County–Department of Health Services, Los Angeles, CA, p. B85
KATZ, Richard, M.D. Vice President Medical Affairs, Mt. Washington Pediatric Hospital, Baltimore, MD, p. A294
KATZ, Robert, M.D. Vice President Clinical Affairs, University of New Mexico Hospitals, Albuquerque, NM, p. A423
KAUFFMAN, Angie, MSN, Chief Executive Officer, Westside Surgical Hospital, Houston, TX, p. A623
KAUFMAN, Cheryl
Director Health Information Management, Bayfront Health Dade City, Dade City, FL, p. A124
Information Technology Technician, Coteau des Prairies Hospital, Sisseton, SD, p. A572
KAUFMAN, Dan, Director Information Services, Paulding County Hospital, Paulding, OH, p. A496
KAUFMAN, Irvin A., M.D. Chief Medical Officer, Rady Children's Hospital – San Diego, San Diego, CA, p. A86
KAUFMAN, Robert
Director Financial Services, Central State Hospital, Petersburg, VA, p. A670
Fiscal Officer, Hiram W. Davis Medical Center, Petersburg, VA, p. A670
KAUFMAN, Ronald L., M.D. Chief Medical Officer, Lakewood Regional Medical Center, Lakewood, CA, p. A67
KAUFMAN, Samuel, Chief Executive Officer and Managing Director, Desert Springs Hospital Medical Center, Las Vegas, NV, p. A401
KAUPA, Michael, Executive Vice President and Chief Operating Officer, Park Nicollet Methodist Hospital, Saint Louis Park, MN, p. A346
KAUPAS, Bill, Chief Executive Officer, Post Acute/Warm Springs Rehabilitation Hospital of Allen, Allen, TX, p. A590
KAUTZ, Terri, Manager Human Resources, Weiser Memorial Hospital, Weiser, ID, p. A177
KAUZLARICH, Sidney A., M.D. Medical Director, Douglas County Community Mental Health Center, Omaha, NE, p. A396
KAVALIER, MaryJo, Administrator, Sartori Memorial Hospital, Cedar Falls, IA, p. A223
KAVANAGH, Darina, R.N. Chief Nursing Officer, Good Samaritan Hospital, San Jose, CA, p. A89
KAVANAGH, Sean, Supervisor Information Technology and Information Systems, Pondera Medical Center, Conrad, MT, p. A382
KAVANAUGH, Paul B., President and Chief Executive Officer, Community Care Hospital, New Orleans, LA, p. A281
KAVANAUGH, Samantha, Chief Financial Officer, Riverview Psychiatric Center, Augusta, ME, p. A288
KAVTARADZE, David, M.D. Chief of Staff, Crisp Regional Hospital, Cordele, GA, p. A155
KAY, Kirk, Chief Financial Officer, Veterans Affairs Nebraska–Western Iowa Health Care System, Omaha, NE, p. A397
KAY, Robert W., Senior Vice President and Chief Financial Officer, Memorial Medical Center, Springfield, IL, p. A201
KAYE, Jessie, Chief Executive Officer, Prairie View, Newton, KS, p. A246
KAYGA, Alicia R., R.N. Chief Nursing Officer, Brownwood Regional Medical Center, Brownwood, TX, p. A599
KAYSER, Sonya, Human Resources Officer, Avera Marshall Regional Medical Center, Marshall, MN, p. A342
KAZA, Sunil, M.D
President Medical Staff, TriStar Skyline Madison Campus, Madison, TN, p. A582
President Medical Staff, TriStar Skyline Medical Center, Nashville, TN, p. A586
KAZMIERCZAK, Sara Marie, R.N. Director of Nursing, North Valley Health Center, Warren, MN, p. A348
KAZMIERCZAK, Stanley, Controller, Presence Saint Joseph Hospital, Chicago, IL, p. A183
KEANE, Dennis M., Vice President Finance and Chief Financial Officer, St. John's Riverside Hospital, Yonkers, NY, p. A454
KEANE, Fran, Vice President Human Resources, CentraState Healthcare System, Freehold, NJ, p. A412
KEANE, Merry Ann, Chief Nursing Officer and Director of Clinical Services, PeaceHealth Peace Island Medical Center, Friday Harbor, WA, p. A679
KEANE, Valerie E., FACHE Vice President Operations, Sentara Northern Virginia Medical Center, Woodbridge, VA, p. A674
KEARNEY, Karen
Vice President Inpatient Rehabilitation Services, Allied Services Rehabilitation Hospital, Scranton, PA, p. A549
Vice President Inpatient Rehabilitation Services, John Heinz Institute of Rehabilitation Medicine, Wilkes–Barre, PA, p. A553
KEARNEY, M. Clark, Vice President Human Resources, Saint Mary's Hospital, Waterbury, CT, p. A115
KEARNS, Donald, M.D., President and Chief Executive Officer, Rady Children's Hospital – San Diego, San Diego, CA, p. A86
KEARNS, Peggy W., FACHE, Medical Center Director, Aleda E. Lutz Veterans Affairs Medical Center, Saginaw, MI, p. A329
KEATING, Michael, President and Chief Executive Officer, Christ Hospital, Cincinnati, OH, p. A482
KEATING, Todd, Chief Financial Officer, The University of Vermont Health Network University of Vermont Medical Center, Burlington, VT, p. A660
KEATON, Tony, Director Information Systems, Roane General Hospital, Spencer, WV, p. A695
KEATON, William A., Chief Executive Officer, Baylor Medical Center at Frisco, Frisco, TX, p. A615
KEAVENEY, Margaret
President and Chief Executive Officer, O'Connor Hospital, San Jose, CA, p. A89
Chief Executive Officer, Saint Louise Regional Hospital, Gilroy, CA, p. A63
KECK, Paul, M.D., President and Chief Executive Officer, Lindner Center of HOPE, Mason, OH, p. A493
KEDALIS, Bob, Director Business Development, Michiana Behavioral Health Center, Plymouth, IN, p. A218
KEDDINGTON, Richard, Chief Executive Officer, Select Specialty Hospital–Milwaukee, Milwaukee, WI, p. A707
KEE, Agnes, Financial Manager, Gallup Indian Medical Center, Gallup, NM, p. A424
KEE, Robert, Chief Information Officer, Coney Island Hospital, NY, p. A439
KEEF, Shaun, Chief Financial Officer, Central Peninsula General Hospital, Soldotna, AK, p. A29
KEEFE, Dennis D., President and Chief Executive Officer, Care New England Health System, Providence, RI, p. B27
KEEFE, Eileen, Chief Nursing Officer, Parkland Medical Center, Derry, NH, p. A405
KEEFER, Russ, Chief Human Resources Officer, Trios Health, Kennewick, WA, p. A680
KEEGAN, Julie, Vice President Finance, Craig Hospital, Englewood, CO, p. A103
KEEGAN, Justin, Director Support Services, Avera Gregory Hospital, Gregory, SD, p. A569
KEEL, Barry L., Chief Executive Officer, North Mississippi Medical Center–West Point, West Point, MS, p. A361
KEEL, Deborah C., Chief Executive Officer, North Fulton Regional Hospital, Roswell, GA, p. A163
KEEL, Teri, Vice President Chief Clinical Officer, Leesburg Regional Medical Center, Leesburg, FL, p. A132
KEELAN, John E., Administrator and Chief Executive Officer, Brodstone Memorial Hospital, Superior, NE, p. A398
KEELE, Paula
Manager Information Systems, Presence Covenant Medical Center, Urbana, IL, p. A202
Manager Information Systems, Presence United Samaritans Medical Center, Danville, IL, p. A185
KEELER, Dave, Chief Financial Officer, Pipestone County Medical Center Avera, Pipestone, MN, p. A344
KEELER, Jason, Executive Vice President and Chief Operating Officer, University of Chicago Medical Center, Chicago, IL, p. A185
KEELER, Jean M., President and Chief Executive Officer, Grand View Health, Sellersville, PA, p. A549
KEELER, Karl
Chief Executive Officer, Saint Alphonsus Medical Center – Nampa, Nampa, ID, p. A175
Chief Executive Officer, Saint Alphonsus Medical Center – Ontario, Ontario, OR, p. A523
KEELEY, Brian E., President and Chief Executive Officer, Baptist Health South Florida, Coral Gables, FL, p. B20
KEELEY, Katherine, M.D. Chief of Staff, Sunrise Hospital and Medical Center, Las Vegas, NV, p. A403
KEELING, Kevin, Chief Financial Officer, St. Lucie Medical Center, Port St. Lucie, FL, p. A141
KEELING, Terri, Vice President Information Systems, UPMC McKeesport, McKeesport, PA, p. A539
KEEN, Michael, Senior Vice President and Chief Financial Officer, Grand View Health, Sellersville, PA, p. A549
KEEN, Scott R., Chief Executive Officer, HonorHealth Rehabilitation Hospital, Scottsdale, AZ, p. A37
KEENAN, Harold, M.D. Chief Medical Officer, Regional West Garden County, Oshkosh, NE, p. A397
KEENAN, Nancy C., R.N. Chief Nursing Officer, CHRISTUS St. Michael Health System, Texarkana, TX, p. A647
KEENAN, Richard, Senior Vice President Finance and Chief Financial Officer, Valley Hospital, Ridgewood, NJ, p. A418
KEENE, Kaaron, Vice President Patient Care Services, Aspirus Medford Hospital, Medford, WI, p. A705
KEENE, Russell G., Chief Executive Officer, Androscoggin Valley Hospital, Berlin, NH, p. A405
KEENER, Vicki, Administrative Assistant and Director Human Resources, Little River Memorial Hospital, Ashdown, AR, p. A41

**A882** Index of Health Care Professionals 

Index of Health Care Professionals

Index of Health Care Professionals / Kempf


KEENUM, Patricia, Health Information Management Systems Officer, Merit Health Northwest Mississippi, Clarksdale, MS, p. A351
KEEPSEAGLE, Joelle, Director of Nursing, Standing Rock Service Unit, Fort Yates Hospital, Indian Health Service, DHHS, Fort Yates, ND, p. A474
KEEVER, Jerry, Administrator, Sharkey–Issaquena Community Hospital, Rolling Fork, MS, p. A360
KEFALAS, George, Chief Medical Officer, Aultman Specialty Hospital, Canton, OH, p. A481
KEGLEY, Carl J., System Director Information Technology, Fairbanks Memorial Hospital, Fairbanks, AK, p. A28
KEGLEY, Glen, Chief Operating Officer, Hutchinson Health, Hutchinson, MN, p. A340
KEGLEY, Shawn, Director Information Services, Research Medical Center, Kansas City, MO, p. A370
KEGLEY, Sue, Director Human Resources, Onslow Memorial Hospital, Jacksonville, NC, p. A463
KEHIAYAN, Nancy, Director of Nursing, Colorado Mental Health Institute at Fort Logan, Denver, CO, p. A101
KEHRBERG, Mark W., M.D
Chief Medical Officer, Calumet Medical Center, Chilton, WI, p. A699
Senior Vice President and Chief Medical Officer, Mercy Medical Center, Oshkosh, WI, p. A708
KEHUS, Frank, Associate Director for Operations, Marion Veterans Affairs Medical Center, Marion, IL, p. A193
KEILER, Susan, Chief Operating Officer, St. Mary's Regional Medical Center, Lewiston, ME, p. A291
KEIM, Thomas, Chief Executive Officer, Ste. Genevieve County Memorial Hospital, Ste. Genevieve, MO, p. A379
KEIRNS, Melody, Manager Human Resources, F. W. Huston Medical Center, Winchester, KS, p. A253
KEISER, Trish, Comptroller, Avera Gregory Hospital, Gregory, SD, p. A569
KEISTER, Catharine L., Chief Nursing Officer, Sunbury Community Hospital and Outpatient Center, Sunbury, PA, p. A550
KEITEL, SPHR, Kal, Executive Director Human Resources, Baptist Health Paducah, Paducah, KY, p. A264
KEITH, Bridgette, Director Human Resources, HEALTHSOUTH Northern Kentucky Rehabilitation Hospital, Edgewood, KY, p. A256
KEITH, Darlene, Chief Information Systems, Alleghany Memorial Hospital, Sparta, NC, p. A469
KEITH, David N., FACHE, President and Chief Executive Officer, McAlester Regional Health Center, McAlester, OK, p. A509
KEITH, Leesa–Lee, R.N. Chief Nursing Officer, Baystate Franklin Medical Center, Greenfield, MA, p. A307
KEITH, Lorraine, FACHE Chief Nursing Officer, St. Vincent's Medical Center Southside, Jacksonville, FL, p. A130
KELBAUGH, Brian, Chief Financial Officer, Summersville Regional Medical Center, Summersville, WV, p. A695
KELBLY, Kevin, Senior Vice President Finance and Corporate Fiscal Affairs, Carroll Hospital Center, Westminster, MD, p. A301
KELL, Douglas B., Chief Financial Officer, Freedom Pain Hospital, Scottsdale, AZ, p. A37
KELLAR, Mark, R.N. Interim Chief Nursing Officer, Our Lady of the Angels Hospital, Bogalusa, LA, p. A270
KELLAR, Richard A., President, Aurora West Allis Medical Center, West Allis, WI, p. A714
KELLEHER, Cynthia, M.P.H., President and Chief Executive Officer, University of Maryland Rehabilitation & Orthopaedic Institute, Baltimore, MD, p. A295
KELLEHER, John, Vice President Information Technology and Chief Information Officer, Glens Falls Hospital, Glens Falls, NY, p. A434
KELLEHER, Mary, Vice President Human Resources, Holyoke Medical Center, Holyoke, MA, p. A307
KELLEHER, Mary Lou, R.N. Vice President, Nursing, Franciscan Hospital for Children, Boston, MA, p. A303
KELLEHER, Michael, Chief Medical Officer, Ann & Robert H. Lurie Children's Hospital of Chicago, Chicago, IL, p. A181
KELLEHER, Patrick, M.D. Chief Medical Staff, Saint Joseph Berea, Berea, KY, p. A254
KELLENBARGER, Lance, Site Director Information Systems, St. Catherine Hospital, Garden City, KS, p. A240
KELLER, Allen, Director Human Resources, Sumner Regional Medical Center, Wellington, KS, p. A252
KELLER, Anita M., R.N. Chief Nursing Officer, Johnson Memorial Hospital, Franklin, IN, p. A209
KELLER, Ann, Supervisor Health Information Management, HEALTHSOUTH Walton Rehabilitation Hospital, Augusta, GA, p. A151
KELLER, Christine, Chief Administrative Officer, Bluffton Hospital, Bluffton, OH, p. A480
KELLER, Diane R., Chief Executive Officer, Memorial Community Health, Aurora, NE, p. A389
KELLER, Gretchen, Director Health Information, Neosho Memorial Regional Medical Center, Chanute, KS, p. A238
KELLER, J. Michael, Vice President Operations, Newton Medical Center, Newton, KS, p. A246
KELLER, Jack M., Chief Executive Officer, Saint Thomas Hickman Hospital, Centerville, TN, p. A575
KELLER, James, Director Human Resources, NEA Baptist Memorial Hospital, Jonesboro, AR, p. A46
KELLER, Jane, R.N., Chief Executive Officer, Indiana Orthopaedic Hospital, Indianapolis, IN, p. A211
KELLER, Jill, R.N. Vice President for Nursing Services, Quality and Risk Management, Waynesboro Hospital, Waynesboro, PA, p. A552
KELLER, Jim, Site Director Information Services, Mercy Health Saint Mary's, Grand Rapids, MI, p. A321
KELLER, Justin, Chief Information Officer, Murray County Medical Center, Slayton, MN, p. A347
KELLER, Marsha, Director Human Resources, Kane Community Hospital, Kane, PA, p. A537
KELLER, Maryalice, Vice President Brand and Talent Management, Unity Hospital, Rochester, NY, p. A449
KELLER, Patricia, MSN Nurse Administrator, Mayo Clinic Health System – Northland in Barron, Barron, WI, p. A698
KELLER, Ruey, Acting Chief Information Officer, VA San Diego Healthcare System, San Diego, CA, p. A87
KELLER, Stewart, M.D. Medical Director, Mesa Springs, Fort Worth, TX, p. A613
KELLER, Thomas, President and Chief Executive Officer, Ozarks Medical Center, West Plains, MO, p. A380
KELLER, Wendy, Director Health Information Management, Atrium Medical Center of Corinth, Corinth, TX, p. A602
KELLERMAN, Laurie, MSN Chief Nursing Officer, Marshall Browning Hospital, Du Quoin, IL, p. A186
KELLERMAN, Scott, Chief Financial Officer, Ely–Bloomenson Community Hospital, Ely, MN, p. A338
KELLEY, Brent, Director Information Technology, Nor–Lea General Hospital, Lovington, NM, p. A425
KELLEY, Jalinda, Secretary of Interior Services, Chickasaw Nation Medical Center, Ada, OK, p. A503
KELLEY, Janice, Chief Financial Officer, Marshall County Hospital, Benton, KY, p. A254
KELLEY, Jim, Vice President Finance, Advocate Lutheran General Hospital, Park Ridge, IL, p. A197
KELLEY, Lewis, Chief Operating Officer, Union General Hospital, Blairsville, GA, p. A152
KELLEY, Mary, Director Human Resources, The Outer Banks Hospital, Nags Head, NC, p. A466
KELLEY, Neal, Vice President and Chief Operating Officer, Seton Medical Center Hays, Kyle, TX, p. A626
KELLEY, Patti, MSN Chief Nursing Officer, SSM St. Mary's Health Center, Saint Louis, MO, p. A377
KELLEY, Randall L., FACHE, Interim Chief Executive Officer, Hi–Desert Medical Center, Joshua Tree, CA, p. A65
KELLEY, Sarah Jo, Director Human Resources, Ste. Genevieve County Memorial Hospital, Ste. Genevieve, MO, p. A379
KELLEY, Sharon, Chief Financial Officer, Clifton Springs Hospital and Clinic, Clifton Springs, NY, p. A431
KELLEY, Steven L., President and Chief Executive Officer, Ellenville Regional Hospital, Ellenville, NY, p. A433
KELLEY, Sue, Chief Financial Officer, Cordell Memorial Hospital, Cordell, OK, p. A505
KELLEY, Suzanne, Director Human Resources, North Suburban Medical Center, Thornton, CO, p. A109
KELLEY, Vicky, Chief Financial Officer, DeQuincy Memorial Hospital, DeQuincy, LA, p. A273
KELLEY, Warren, Chief Information Officer, Reynolds Memorial Hospital, Glen Dale, WV, p. A691
KELLOGG, Brewster, D.O. Chief Medical Officer, Rawlins County Health Center, Atwood, KS, p. A237
KELLOGG, Jason, M.D. Chief of Staff, Newport Bay Hospital, Newport Beach, CA, p. A78
KELLOGG, Susan, Administrator Patient Care Services, Carthage Area Hospital, Carthage, NY, p. A431
KELLS, Anne, Interim Chief Financial Officer, Appleton Area Health Services, Appleton, MN, p. A334
KELLUM, Craig, Director Management Information Systems, Cape Fear Valley – Bladen County Hospital, Elizabethtown, NC, p. A460
KELLY, Ann Marie, Chief Nursing Officer, Ellenville Regional Hospital, Ellenville, NY, p. A433
KELLY, Brian
Vice President Finance, Advocate South Suburban Hospital, Hazel Crest, IL, p. A190
Acting Chief Fiscal Service, San Francisco VA Medical Center, San Francisco, CA, p. A88
KELLY, Brian E., M.D. President Medical Staff, Saint Elizabeth's Medical Center, Wabasha, MN, p. A348
KELLY, Bruce, Chief Information Officer, ProMedica Monroe Regional Hospital, Monroe, MI, p. A326
KELLY, Charlene, Chief Nursing Officer, Kane County Hospital, Kanab, UT, p. A655
KELLY, Charles, D.O. Vice President Medical Affairs and Chief Medical Officer, Henry Ford Macomb Hospitals, Clinton Township, MI, p. A316
KELLY, Colan, Chief Financial Officer, Pineville Community Hospital Association, Pineville, KY, p. A265
KELLY, Dan, R.N. Chief Nursing Officer, Memorial Hermann Memorial City Medical Center, Houston, TX, p. A621
KELLY, Daniel J., ACHE President, CHI Health St. Mary's, Nebraska City, NE, p. A394
KELLY, Daniel R., Chief Executive Officer, McKenzie County Healthcare System, Watford City, ND, p. A477
KELLY, Debbie, Chief Executive Officer, South Texas Spine and Surgical Hospital, San Antonio, TX, p. A642
KELLY, Dennis, Chief Executive Officer, CarePoint Health, Jersey City, NJ, p. B27
KELLY, Derek J., M.D. Vice President Transformation and Chief Medical Information Officer, Swedish Covenant Hospital, Chicago, IL, p. A185
KELLY, Diane, R.N. Chief Operating Officer, Berkshire Medical Center, Pittsfield, MA, p. A310
KELLY, Jr., James J., Interim Senior Vice President and Chief Financial Officer, UF Health Shands Hospital, Gainesville, FL, p. A128
KELLY, Jim, Chief Operating Officer, Nantucket Cottage Hospital, Nantucket, MA, p. A309
KELLY, John, Chief Nursing Officer and Chief Operating Officer, UMass Memorial–Marlborough Hospital, Marlborough, MA, p. A308
KELLY, John J., M.D. Chief of Staff, Abington Memorial Hospital, Abington, PA, p. A528
KELLY, Laurence E., President and Chief Executive Officer, Nathan Littauer Hospital and Nursing Home, Gloversville, NY, p. A434
KELLY, Leo, M.D. Vice President Medical Management, Advocate Lutheran General Hospital, Park Ridge, IL, p. A197
KELLY, Lynn, Vice President Human Resources, San Antonio Community Hospital, Upland, CA, p. A95
KELLY, Mark
Administrator, Regional One Health Extended Care Hospital, Memphis, TN, p. A584
Vice President Finance, St. Francis Medical Center, Trenton, NJ, p. A419
KELLY, Mary L., R.N. Chief Nursing Officer, New Orleans East Hospital, New Orleans, LA, p. A282
KELLY, Maura, Vice President Fiscal Services, Pen Bay Medical Center, Rockport, ME, p. A292
KELLY, Maureen, R.N. Chief Nursing Officer, Roswell Park Cancer Institute, Buffalo, NY, p. A430
KELLY, Melissa, Administrator, Pender Community Hospital, Pender, NE, p. A397
KELLY, Michael, Vice President, Christian Hospital, Saint Louis, MO, p. A376
KELLY, Patrick J., FACHE, Director, Minneapolis Veterans Affairs Health Care System, Minneapolis, MN, p. A342
KELLY, Raymond, R.N. Chief Nursing Officer, Texas Health Presbyterian Hospital Plano, Plano, TX, p. A637
KELLY, Roy, Facility Director, Hawthorn Center, Northville, MI, p. A327
KELLY, Scott A., Chief Executive Officer, Asante Rogue Regional Medical Center, Medford, OR, p. A523
KELLY, Shannon, Director Human Resources, Morton General Hospital, Morton, WA, p. A680
KELLY, Stephen, M.D. Chief Medical Officer, SSM St. Mary's Health Center, Saint Louis, MO, p. A377
KELLY, Steve, Interim Chief Executive Officer, Austin Oaks Hospital, Austin, TX, p. A593
KELLY, Steven G., President and Chief Executive Officer, Newton Medical Center, Newton, KS, p. A246
KELLY, Teresa M., MSN Chief Nursing Officer, Chestnut Hill Hospital, Philadelphia, PA, p. A542
KELLY, Vicky, Chief Financial Officer, De Queen Medical Center, De Queen, AR, p. A43
KELLY, Virginia, Chief Financial Officer, Eastside Psychiatric Hospital, Tallahassee, FL, p. A144
KEM, Mark, Vice President Finance and Chief Financial Officer, Chandler Regional Medical Center, Chandler, AZ, p. A30
KEMKA, Joseph, Chief Financial Officer, St. Bernard Parish Hospital, Chalmette, LA, p. A271
KEMKER, S. E., M.D. President Medical Staff, St. Vincent Salem Hospital, Salem, IN, p. A219
KEMMERER, Jan, Director of Nursing, Mitchell County Hospital Health Systems, Beloit, KS, p. A238
KEMP, Thomas, Chief Information Officer, New York–Presbyterian/Queens, NY, p. A443
KEMPF, Gary L., R.N., Administrator, Houston Methodist St. Catherine Hospital, Katy, TX, p. A625

Index of Health Care Professionals

Index of Health Care Professionals / Kempiak


KEMPIAK, Matthew, Director Human Resources and Administrative Services, Memorial Hospital of Gardena, Gardena, CA, p. A63
KEMPINSKI, Paul D., Chief Operating Officer, Alfred I. duPont Hospital for Children, Wilmington, DE, p. A118
KEMPT, Brooke, Corporate Nursing Director, Hamilton Center, Terre Haute, IN, p. A220
KEMPTON, Matthew, Chief Executive Officer and Administrator, Stephens Memorial Hospital, Breckenridge, TX, p. A598
KENAGY, John Jay, Ph.D
Senior Vice President and Chief Information Officer, Legacy Meridian Park Medical Center, Tualatin, OR, p. A527
Senior Vice President and Chief Information Officer, Legacy Mount Hood Medical Center, Gresham, OR, p. A521
KENDALL, Abigail, Chief Nursing Officer, Lake Granbury Medical Center, Granbury, TX, p. A616
KENDALL, Anthony
Vice President Human Resources, Baptist Health Extended Care Hospital, Little Rock, AR, p. A47
Vice President Human Resources, Baptist Health Medical Center – North Little Rock, North Little Rock, AR, p. A49
Vice President Human Resources, Baptist Health Medical Center–Arkadelphia, Arkadelphia, AR, p. A41
Vice President Human Resources, Baptist Health Medical Center–Little Rock, Little Rock, AR, p. A47
Vice President Human Resources, Baptist Health Rehabilitation Institute, Little Rock, AR, p. A47
KENDALL, Clint, R.N. Chief Nursing Officer, Clinch Valley Medical Center, Richlands, VA, p. A671
KENDLE, Melinda
Manager Business Office, Evansville Psychiatric Children Center, Evansville, IN, p. A208
Director Fiscal Management, Evansville State Hospital, Evansville, IN, p. A208
KENDLER, Lisa
Chief Financial Officer, Memorial Hermann Memorial City Medical Center, Houston, TX, p. A621
Chief Financial Officer, Memorial Hermann Sugar Land Hospital, Sugar Land, TX, p. A645
KENDRICK, Donovan, M.D. Chief Medical Officer, Baptist Medical Center South, Montgomery, AL, p. A22
KENDRICK, Jim R., Chief Executive Officer, Longview Regional Medical Center, Longview, TX, p. A629
KENDRICK, Ray
Chief Human Resources Officer, Memorial Hospital Miramar, Miramar, FL, p. A136
Chief Human Resources Officer, Memorial Regional Hospital, FL, p. A128
KENDRICK, Robert, Chief Nursing Officer, Madison Memorial Hospital, Rexburg, ID, p. A176
KENNEDY, Anita J., Vice President Operations, Methodist Hospital of Sacramento, Sacramento, CA, p. A84
KENNEDY, Brad, Chief Executive Officer, HEALTHSOUTH Rehabilitation Hospital at Drake, Cincinnati, OH, p. A483
KENNEDY, Bruce, M.D. Chief Medical Officer, Houston Methodist San Jacinto Hospital, Baytown, TX, p. A596
KENNEDY, Carol, Chief Clinical Officer, Barrett Hospital & HealthCare, Dillon, MT, p. A383
KENNEDY, Connie, Director Human Resources, Marlette Regional Hospital, Marlette, MI, p. A325
KENNEDY, Darla, Chief Information Officer, Newport Specialty Hospital, Tustin, CA, p. A95
KENNEDY, Diana, Director Human Resources, Meadowview Regional Medical Center, Maysville, KY, p. A263
KENNEDY, Elizabeth M., Administrator, J. Paul Jones Hospital, Camden, AL, p. A17
KENNEDY, Eric, Chief Executive Officer, Acadia Vermilion Hospital, Lafayette, LA, p. A277
KENNEDY, Jack L., Vice President and Chief Nursing Officer, Pratt Regional Medical Center, Pratt, KS, p. A249
KENNEDY, Jill M., R.N. Vice President Patient Care Services and Chief Nursing Officer, Bon Secours Memorial Regional Medical Center, Mechanicsville, VA, p. A668
KENNEDY, John, M.D. Vice President Medical Affairs, Mercy Health – Fairfield Hospital, Fairfield, OH, p. A489
KENNEDY, Kimberly, Manager Human Resources, OSF Saint Paul Medical Center, Mendota, IL, p. A194
KENNEDY, Mary, R.N. Chief Nursing Officer, Medina Hospital, Medina, OH, p. A494
KENNEDY, Pam
Vice President Regional Human Resources and Organizational Department, CHRISTUS St. Michael Health System, Texarkana, TX, p. A647
Director Human Resources, CHRISTUS St. Michael Rehabilitation Hospital, Texarkana, TX, p. A647
KENNEDY, Peggy S., R.N. Vice President and Chief Nurse Executive, Fremont Health, Fremont, NE, p. A391
KENNEDY, R. Scott, M.D. Chief Medical Officer and Hospital Chief Operating Officer, Olympic Medical Center, Port Angeles, WA, p. A682
KENNEDY, ReChelle, Chief Financial Officer, Kearny County Hospital, Lakin, KS, p. A244
KENNEDY, Ryan
Chief Financial Officer, Holy Name Medical Center, Teaneck, NJ, p. A419
Chief Operating Officer, Kingman Regional Medical Center, Kingman, AZ, p. A32
KENNEDY, Susan, Manager Human Resources, Novant Health Matthews Medical Center, Matthews, NC, p. A464
KENNEDY, Terris, Ph.D. Chief Nursing Officer, Riverside Behavioral Health Center, Hampton, VA, p. A666
KENNEDY, Timea, Director Human Resources, St. Mary–Corwin Medical Center, Pueblo, CO, p. A108
KENNEDY, Todd, President and Chief Executive Officer, Providence Hospital, Mobile, AL, p. A22
KENNEDY, Todd S., Executive Vice President and Chief Operating Officer, Providence Hospital, Mobile, AL, p. A22
KENNETH, Ron, M.D. Chief Medical Officer, West Valley Hospital, Goodyear, AZ, p. A32
KENNETT, Jerry, M.D. Chief Medical Officer, Boone Hospital Center, Columbia, MO, p. A366
KENNEY, Catherine, Chief Nursing Officer, Pampa Regional Medical Center, Pampa, TX, p. A635
KENNEY, Mary Ellen, Chief Human Services, Manchester Veterans Affairs Medical Center, Manchester, NH, p. A407
KENNINGTON, Lynn, Chief Financial Officer, Alaska Regional Hospital, Anchorage, AK, p. A27
KENNISON, Barbara, Director Clinical Services, Aurora San Diego Hospital, San Diego, CA, p. A86
KENNY, Carolyn, Executive Vice President Clinical Care, Children's Healthcare of Atlanta, Atlanta, GA, p. A150
KENNY, Virginia, Interim Chief Nursing Officer, Hancock Medical Center, Bay Saint Louis, MS, p. A350
KENT, Alan, Chief Executive Officer, Meadows Regional Medical Center, Vidalia, GA, p. A166
KENT, Blair, Administrator, Riverton Hospital, Riverton, UT, p. A657
KENT, David, Director Human Resources, Bolivar Medical Center, Cleveland, MS, p. A352
KENT, David, M.D. Chief Medical Officer, Safe Haven Hospital of Treasure Valley, Boise, ID, p. A172
KENT, David, Chief Operating Officer, Southeastern Regional Medical Center, Newnan, GA, p. A162
KENT, Robert, D.O., President and Chief Executive Officer, Summa Western Reserve Hospital, Cuyahoga Falls, OH, p. A487
KENTERA, Amy, Chief Information Officer, Conifer Park, Glenville, NY, p. A434
KENTFIELD, Melinda Johanna, Chief Nursing Officer, Warren Memorial Hospital, Friend, NE, p. A392
KENTON, Bart, Chief Financial Officer, Holton Community Hospital, Holton, KS, p. A242
KENWOOD, Linda S., R.N. Chief Nursing Officer and Chief Operating Officer, Shore Medical Center, Somers Point, NJ, p. A418
KEOWN, Janet, Vice President Human Resources, Behavioral Health Network, Natchaug Hospital, Mansfield Center, CT, p. A113
KEPLER, Andrea, Chief Executive Officer, Wernersville State Hospital, Wernersville, PA, p. A552
KEPLER, Terry W., Chief Executive Officer, CHRISTUS Dubuis Hospital of Bryan, Bryan, TX, p. A599
KEPLINGER, Ron, Chief Information Officer, Western Maryland Hospital Center, Hagerstown, MD, p. A298
KEPNER, Donald L., Chief Financial Officer, Ashtabula County Medical Center, Ashtabula, OH, p. A478
KEPPLE, Jeffrey, M.D., Chief Executive Officer, Plumas District Hospital, Quincy, CA, p. A82
KEPPLER, Edward L., M.D. Chief Medical Officer, Marion General Hospital, Marion, IN, p. A215
KEPPLER, Matthew, Market Chief Executive Officer, Kindred Hospital Indianapolis South, Greenwood, IN, p. A210
KERBS, Curtis, Vice President Information Services, Memorial Hospital, North Conway, NH, p. A408
KERCHENSKI, Marlene, Chief Nurse, U. S. Air Force Hospital, Hampton, VA, p. A666
KERCHER, Eugene, M.D. Chief Medical Officer, Kern Medical Center, Bakersfield, CA, p. A55
KERDEL, Francisco, M.D. President Medical Staff, University of Miami Hospital, Miami, FL, p. A135
KERI, Alison, Director Human Resources, Hiawatha Community Hospital, Hiawatha, KS, p. A241
KERIN, Doug, M.D. Chief of Staff, Saint Mary's Regional Medical Center, Russellville, AR, p. A50
KERKORIAN, Patti
Interim Chief Nursing Officer, Vista Medical Center East, Waukegan, IL, p. A203
Chief Nursing Officer, Vista Medical Center West, Waukegan, IL, p. A203
KERLIN, Kerry, Vice President Information Technology, Roswell Park Cancer Institute, Buffalo, NY, p. A430
KERMEN, John, D.O. Chief Medical Staff, Mendocino Coast District Hospital, Fort Bragg, CA, p. A61
KERN, Daniel, Chief Executive Officer, Strategic Behavioral Health – Wilmington, Leland, NC, p. A463
KERN, Douglas W., Chief Executive Officer, Northcoast Behavioral Healthcare System, Northfield, OH, p. A495
KERN, Gordon, M.D. Medical Director, Oswego Community Hospital, Oswego, KS, p. A247
KERN, Howard P.
President and Chief Operating Officer, Sentara Leigh Hospital, Norfolk, VA, p. A669
Chief Operating Officer, Sentara Princess Anne Hospital, Virginia Beach, VA, p. A674
KERNELL, Shane, Chief Executive Officer, St. Mark's Medical Center, La Grange, TX, p. A627
KERNIZAN, Lorna, Chief Operating Officer, Aventura Hospital and Medical Center, Aventura, FL, p. A121
KERNS, Elizabeth, Chief Information Officer, Lakeland Regional Health, Lakeland, FL, p. A131
KEROACK, Mark A., M.D., President and Chief Executive Officer, Baystate Health, Inc., Springfield, MA, p. B23
KEROACK, Mark A., M.D., M.P.H. President and Chief Executive Officer, Baystate Medical Center, Springfield, MA, p. A311
KERR, Jeff, M.D. Chief Medical Officer, Baylor Medical Center at McKinney, McKinney, TX, p. A631
KERR, Karen, R.N., President and Chief Executive Officer, South Florida Baptist Hospital, Plant City, FL, p. A140
KERR, Mark, Chief Executive Officer, Presentation Medical Center, Rolla, ND, p. A476
KERR, Michael D., Chief Executive Officer, Promise Hospital of East Los Angeles, Los Angeles, CA, p. A72
KERR, Rand, Chief Executive Officer, Lakeview Hospital, Bountiful, UT, p. A654
KERRINS, David, Vice President Information Services and Chief Information Officer, Dameron Hospital, Stockton, CA, p. A93
KERSCHEN, Susan, MS Vice President and Chief Nursing Officer, Good Samaritan Medical Center, Lafayette, CO, p. A106
KERSEY, Jerry, Director Employee Relations, Eastern State Hospital, Lexington, KY, p. A259
KERSTETTER, Kathleen, R.N. Chief Clinical Officer, Acuity Specialty Hospital of New Jersey, Atlantic City, NJ, p. A409
KERSWILL, Randy, M.D. Medical Director, Winnebago Mental Health Institute, Winnebago, WI, p. A714
KERTIS, Robert, Vice President Finance, Calvert Memorial Hospital, Prince Frederick, MD, p. A299
KERWIN, George, President, Bellin Memorial Hospital, Green Bay, WI, p. A701
KERWOOD, Christine, Chief Nursing Officer, East Ohio Regional Hospital, Martins Ferry, OH, p. A493
KERWOOD, Lori A., Director Human Resources, Cooley Dickinson Hospital, Northampton, MA, p. A309
KERWOOD, Patrick, Chief Executive Officer, Siloam Springs Regional Hospital, Siloam Springs, AR, p. A50
KESSEL, Jennifer, Director Human Resources, Aultman Orrville Hospital, Orrville, OH, p. A496
KESSEL–FOX, Teri, Director Clinical Services, Regency Hospital of Covington, Covington, LA, p. A272
KESSLER, Alexander, M.D. Chief of Staff, Northside Hospital–Cherokee, Canton, GA, p. A153
KESSLER, David, M.D. Clinical Director, U. S. Public Health Service Indian Hospital, Zuni, NM, p. A427
KESSLER, Dawn
Senior Vice President Human Resources, St. John's Hospital, Maplewood, MN, p. A342
Senior Vice President Human Resources, St. Joseph's Hospital, Saint Paul, MN, p. A346
KESSLER, Jeffrey R., Vice President Information Services, Dana–Farber Cancer Institute, Boston, MA, p. A303
KESSLER, John E., President and Chief Executive Officer, Salem Township Hospital, Salem, IL, p. A200
KESSLER, Joseph, Executive Vice President and Chief Financial Officer, KALEIDA Health, Buffalo, NY, p. A430
KESSLER, Renee A., Chief Operating Officer, Saint Thomas Midtown Hospital, Nashville, TN, p. A585
KESSLER, Terrence, Interim President and Chief Executive Officer, Sisters of Charity Health System, Cleveland, OH, p. B124
KESSNER, Jennifer, Financial Director, Roosevelt Medical Center, Culbertson, MT, p. A382
KESTER, Bonnie J., R.N. Vice President Patient Care Services and Chief Nursing Officer, Nantucket Cottage Hospital, Nantucket, MA, p. A309
KESTERSON, Matt
Director Information Services, Wadley Regional Medical Center, Texarkana, TX, p. A647
Director Information Services, Wadley Regional Medical Center at Hope, Hope, AR, p. A45


A884 Index of Health Care Professionals 

Index of Health Care Professionals / King

Index of Health Care Professionals


KETCH, Lynn
Human Resources Recruiter Generalist, INTEGRIS Canadian Valley Hospital, Yukon, OK, p. A518
Director, Integris Southwest Medical Center, Oklahoma City, OK, p. A511
KETCHAM, Krista, Chief Financial Officer, Buena Vista Regional Medical Center, Storm Lake, IA, p. A235
KETCHEM, Tami, Human Resource Director, UP Health System–Bell, Ishpeming, MI, p. A323
KETCHER, Greg, Administrator, Lawton Indian Hospital, Lawton, OK, p. A508
KETTELLE, John, M.D. Chief Medical Officer, Banner – University Medical Center South, Tucson, AZ, p. A39
KETTERHAGEN, James P., M.D. Senior Vice President and Chief Medical Officer, Jewish Hospital, Louisville, KY, p. A261
KETTERLING, Kimberly A., Vice President of Nursing, CHI Oakes Hospital, Oakes, ND, p. A476
KETTERMAN, Patricia P., R.N., President and Chief Administrative Officer, Claiborne Medical Center, Tazewell, TN, p. A588
KETTLER, Paul, M.D. Vice President Medical Affairs, Unity Hospital, Fridley, MN, p. A339
KEUTER, Mary Beth, Director Patient Care, Continuing Care Hospital at St. Luke's, Cedar Rapids, IA, p. A223
KEY, Lora, Chief Executive Officer, Sabetha Community Hospital, Sabetha, KS, p. A249
KEY, Mark, M.D. Chief of Staff, Medical Arts Hospital, Lamesa, TX, p. A627
KEYS, Janice Colleen, MSN Chief Nurse Executive, Erlanger Medical Center, Chattanooga, TN, p. A575
KHADE, Kashmira, Coordinator Non–Clinical Services, Behavioral Center of Michigan, Warren, MI, p. A332
KHALIQUE, Tania, Director Human Resources, Vibra Hospital of San Diego, San Diego, CA, p. A87
KHAN, Atique, M.D. Medical Director, University Behavioral Health of Denton, Denton, TX, p. A608
KHAN, Behram, M.D. Medical Director, Post Acute/Warm Springs Specialty Hospital of Victoria, Victoria, TX, p. A650
KHAN, Dan, M.D. Chief Medical Officer, Yoakum County Hospital, Denver City, TX, p. A608
KHAN, Humayun, M.D. Chief Medical Officer, Sacred Heart Hospital, Eau Claire, WI, p. A700
KHAN, Sarfraz, Medical Director, Meridian Health Services, Muncie, IN, p. A216
KHAN, Shahbaz, M.D. Medical Director, Two Rivers Behavioral Health System, Kansas City, MO, p. A371
KHAN, Waheed, M.D. President Medical Staff, Summers County ARH Hospital, Hinton, WV, p. A691
KHANCHANDANI, Ashok, Chief Financial Officer, Oroville Hospital, Oroville, CA, p. A79
KHANNA, Rajive, Chief Executive Officer, Grace Hospital, Cleveland, OH, p. A484
KHANNA, Vijay, M.D. Chief of Staff, Beaumont Hospital – Taylor, Taylor, MI, p. A331
KHATAMI, Manoochehr, M.D. Medical Director, Hickory Trail Hospital, Desoto, TX, p. A608
KHDOUR, Adel, M.D. Chief Medical Officer, Indiana University Health White Memorial Hospital, Monticello, IN, p. A216
KHEMKA, Hemant, Chief Operating Officer, Surgery Specialty Hospitals of America, Pasadena, TX, p. A636
KHIM FUGATE, Guay, Chief Operations Officer, Kindred Hospital Riverside, Perris, CA, p. A81
KHOERL, Thomas, Vice President Finance, Spectrum Health Big Rapids Hospital, Big Rapids, MI, p. A315
KHOO, Alex, Interim Area Finance Officer, Kaiser Permanente San Francisco Medical Center, San Francisco, CA, p. A88
KHOURY, Anwar, M.D. Chief of Staff, Geary Community Hospital, Junction City, KS, p. A243
KHOW, Vida J., Chief Executive Officer, Gallup Indian Medical Center, Gallup, NM, p. A424
KIBAR, Nizar, M.D. Chief Medical Staff, Kiowa County Memorial Hospital, Greensburg, KS, p. A241
KIBBY, Rosalinda, Superintendent and Administrator, Columbia Basin Hospital, Ephrata, WA, p. A678
KIBORT, Phillip M., M.D. Vice President Medical Affairs and Chief Medical Officer, Children's Hospitals and Clinics of Minnesota, Minneapolis, MN, p. A342
KIDD, David, Manager Human Resources, Sentara CarePlex Hospital, Hampton, VA, p. A666
KIDD, Larry R., R.N. Vice President and Chief Nursing Officer, Henry Mayo Newhall Memorial Hospital, Valencia, CA, p. A96
KIDD, Monica, MSN, Administrator, Parkview Hospital, Wheeler, TX, p. A652
KIDD, Scott, Director Human Resources, Mendocino Coast District Hospital, Fort Bragg, CA, p. A61
KIDD, Sue, Chief Financial Officer, Horton Community Hospital, Horton, KS, p. A242
KIDD, Thomas J., Assistant Administrator and Chief Financial Officer, Macon County General Hospital, Lafayette, TN, p. A581
KIDDER, Allison, Administrator, Compass Behavioral Center of Crowley, Crowley, LA, p. A272
KIDDER, David M., D.O. Chief Medical Officer, Garfield County Health Center, Jordan, MT, p. A384
KIDDER, Suzanne F., Director Human Resources, Opelousas General Health System, Opelousas, LA, p. A283
KIEBZAK, Stanley F., R.N. Chief Nursing Officer, Reliant Northwest Houston, Houston, TX, p. A621
KIEDROWSKI, Brian, M.D. Chief Medical Director, Miami Jewish Home and Hospital for Aged, Miami, FL, p. A134
KIEF, Brian, Regional Vice President Ministry Health Care and President Ministry Saint Joseph's Hospital, Ministry Saint Joseph's Hospital, Marshfield, WI, p. A705
KIEFER, William
Chief Operating Officer, Rehoboth McKinley Christian Health Care Services, Gallup, NM, p. A424
Chief Nursing Officer, TMC Bonham Hospital, Bonham, TX, p. A598
KIEFFER, Kelley, Chief Nursing Officer, Banner Casa Grande Medical Center, Casa Grande, AZ, p. A30
KIEHLE, Jessica, R.N. Chief Nursing Officer, Abilene Regional Medical Center, Abilene, TX, p. A590
KIELY, Sharon, M.D. Senior Vice President Medical Affairs and Chief Medical Officer, Stamford Hospital, Stamford, CT, p. A115
KIERNAN, Richard, Vice President Human Resources, Monmouth Medical Center, Long Branch Campus, Long Branch, NJ, p. A413
KIFER, Debbie, Chief Nursing Officer, EASTAR Health System, Muskogee, OK, p. A510
KIGER, Tom, Director Information Systems, Trinity Health System, Steubenville, OH, p. A498
KIGHT, Sheila, Director Human Resources, TriStar Horizon Medical Center, Dickson, TN, p. A577
KILARSKI, David J., Chief Executive Officer, FirstHealth Moore Regional Hospital, Pinehurst, NC, p. A466
KILARSKI, David J., Chief Executive Officer, FirstHealth of the Carolinas, Pinehurst, NC, p. B56
KILBORN, Mark, Director Information Systems, Springhill Memorial Hospital, Mobile, AL, p. A22
KILDAY, Dennis P., Chief Financial Officer, Golden Plains Community Hospital, Borger, TX, p. A598
KILDAY, Kevin, Vice President Finance, Holy Family Hospital, Methuen, MA, p. A308
KILE, Steven E., Director Human Resources, Springfield Regional Medical Center, Springfield, OH, p. A498
KILEY, Dennis, Interim Chief Executive Officer, Takoma Regional Hospital, Greeneville, TN, p. A578
KILFEATHER–MACKEY, Robin F., Chief Financial Officer, Dartmouth–Hitchcock Medical Center, Lebanon, NH, p. A407
KILGORE, Jeremie, Director Information Technology, Galesburg Cottage Hospital, Galesburg, IL, p. A188
KILGORE, Sherry, Chief Financial Management Service, John D. Dingell Veterans Affairs Medical Center, Detroit, MI, p. A318
KILLINGSWORTH, Meri, Chief Operating Officer, Hereford Regional Medical Center, Hereford, TX, p. A618
KILLION, Rosie, R.N. Chief Nursing Officer, DeWitt Hospital, De Witt, AR, p. A43
KILLORAN, Carrie
Interim President, Aurora Medical Center Grafton, Grafton, WI, p. A701
Interim President, Aurora Medical Center in Washington County, Hartford, WI, p. A702
KILO, Charles M., M.D. Chief Medical Officer, OHSU Hospital, Portland, OR, p. A524
KILPATRICK, Von, Chief Nursing Officer, St. Vincent General Hospital District, Leadville, CO, p. A106
KIM, Dong, M.D. Chief of Staff, Parkview Community Hospital Medical Center, Riverside, CA, p. A83
KIM, Eric, Chief Information Officer, Las Encinas Hospital, Pasadena, CA, p. A80
KIM, Soon K., M.D., President and Chief Executive Officer, Signature Healthcare Services, Corona, CA, p. B123
KIMBALL, Amy, D.O. Chief of Staff, Madison County Health Care System, Winterset, IA, p. A236
KIMBLE, D. Gay, Director Human Resources, Susan B. Allen Memorial Hospital, El Dorado, KS, p. A239
KIMBLE, Robert J., Chief Financial Officer, William R. Sharpe, Jr. Hospital, Weston, WV, p. A696
KIMBREW, Missey, Director Human Resources, Grafton City Hospital, Grafton, WV, p. A691
KIMBRO, George, Vice President Finance, Angel Medical Center, Franklin, NC, p. A460
KIMBROUGH, Pam, M.D. Vice President Medical Affairs, Mercy Hospital Ardmore, Ardmore, OK, p. A503
KIMMEL, Arnold, Chief Executive Officer, Franciscan St. James Hospital and Health Centers, Olympia Fields, IL, p. A197
KIMMEL, Edra, M.D. Chief of Staff, Merit Health Woman's Hospital, Flowood, MS, p. A352
KIMMEL, Kyle, Chief Financial Officer, Bacon County Hospital and Health System, Alma, GA, p. A149
KIMMEL, Stephen, Chief Financial Officer, Cook Children's Medical Center, Fort Worth, TX, p. A613
KIMMES, Robert P., Chief Executive Officer, Skyline Hospital, White Salmon, WA, p. A687
KIMMY, Sharon, Coordinator Human Resources, Corry Memorial Hospital, Corry, PA, p. A532
KIMPLE, Robin, Director Information Services, Gettysburg Hospital, Gettysburg, PA, p. A534
KIMZEY, Mike, Chief Executive Officer and Administrator, Oklahoma Center for Orthopedic and Multi–Specialty Surgery, Oklahoma City, OK, p. A512
KINCAID, Kevin, Chief Executive Officer, Knoxville Hospital & Clinics, Knoxville, IA, p. A230
KINDER, Barbara, R.N. Chief Clinical Officer, Clark Regional Medical Center, Winchester, KY, p. A267
KINDERED, Deanne, Vice President Finance, Baylor Regional Medical Center at Plano, Plano, TX, p. A636
KINDRED, Bill, Chief Executive Officer, Russell County Hospital, Russell Springs, KY, p. A265
KINDRED, Bryan N., FACHE, President and Chief Executive Officer, DCH Health System, Tuscaloosa, AL, p. B44
KING, Abner, Chief Operating Officer, Steele Memorial Medical Center, Salmon, ID, p. A176
KING, Amber, Director Human Resources, Northcrest Medical Center, Springfield, TN, p. A588
KING, Beth, Chief Financial Officer, Jersey Community Hospital, Jerseyville, IL, p. A191
KING, Brent R., Chief Medical Officer and Chief Physician, Alfred I. duPont Hospital for Children, Wilmington, DE, p. A118
KING, Bruce, President and Chief Executive Officer, New London Hospital, New London, NH, p. A408
KING, Chris, Director Information Services, OhioHealth Marion General Hospital, Marion, OH, p. A493
KING, Christopher, Director Operations and Administrative Services, Matheny Medical and Educational Center, Peapack, NJ, p. A416
KING, Craig, Coordinator Human Resources, Kindred Hospital Sugar Land, Sugar Land, TX, p. A645
KING, Don
Chief Executive Officer, Saint Thomas Midtown Hospital, Nashville, TN, p. A585
Chief Executive Officer, Saint Thomas West Hospital, Nashville, TN, p. A585
KING, Donna, R.N. Vice President Clinical Operations and Chief Nursing Executive, Advocate Illinois Masonic Medical Center, Chicago, IL, p. A181
KING, Doug, M.D. Director Clinical Services, Western Mental Health Institute, Bolivar, TN, p. A574
KING, Ed, Chief Financial Officer, PIH Health Hospital – Downey, Downey, CA, p. A60
KING, Elizabeth, Director, White Plains Hospital Center, White Plains, NY, p. A454
KING, Glenn, R.N
Vice President, Chief Nursing Officer, MidMichigan Medical Center–Clare, Clare, MI, p. A316
Vice President and Chief Nursing Officer, MidMichigan Medical Center–Gladwin, Gladwin, MI, p. A320
KING, Grace, Regional Director Human Resources, Broward Health North, Deerfield Beach, FL, p. A125
KING, Heath
Chief Financial Officer, Coliseum Medical Centers, Macon, GA, p. A160
Chief Financial Officer, Coliseum Northside Hospital, Macon, GA, p. A160
KING, James E., Corporate Director Information Technology, Reliant Rehabilitation Hospital Dallas, Dallas, TX, p. A606
KING, Jason, Chief Information Officer, RiverView Health, Crookston, MN, p. A337
KING, Jay, Vice President Human Resources, Mercy Hospitals of Bakersfield, Bakersfield, CA, p. A55
KING, Jim, Executive Vice President and Chief Operating Officer, Jackson County Memorial Hospital, Altus, OK, p. A503
KING, Joanie, Chief Financial Officer, Carteret Health Care, Morehead City, NC, p. A465
KING, Kim, Director Human Resources and Public Relations, Baptist Memorial Hospital–Huntingdon, Huntingdon, TN, p. A579
KING, Lenetra S., Chief Operating Officer, Menorah Medical Center, Overland Park, KS, p. A248
KING, Louie
President, Harry Bold Nursing Home Administrator, Missouri River Medical Center, Fort Benton, MT, p. A383
Chief Executive Officer, Teton Medical Center, Choteau, MT, p. A382
KING, Mike, Chief Operating Officer, Doctors Medical Center, Modesto, CA, p. A75
KING, Patrick, Director of Nursing, University Health Conway, Monroe, LA, p. A281

Index of Health Care Professionals

Index of Health Care Professionals / King

KING, Paul, M.D. Medical Director, Parkwood Behavioral Health System, Olive Branch, MS, p. A358
KING, Ray, M.D. Senior Vice President and Chief Medical Officer, Allegiance Health, Jackson, MI, p. A323
KING, Rich, Vice President Information Technology, West Virginia University Hospitals, Morgantown, WV, p. A693
KING, Sam, Chief Financial Officer, Renown Regional Medical Center, Reno, NV, p. A403
KING, Sammy, Controller, HEALTHSOUTH Rehabilitation Hospital of Ocala, Ocala, FL, p. A136
KING, Sandra, Chief Nursing Officer, Sagamore Children's Psychiatric Center, Dix Hills, NY, p. A432
KING, Tamara, R.N. Chief Nurse Executive, Shepherd Center, Atlanta, GA, p. A151
KING, Val, Chief Information Officer, Val Verde Regional Medical Center, Del Rio, TX, p. A607
KING ROBINSON, Jan, Vice President, Operations, Sentara Albemarle Medical Center, Elizabeth City, NC, p. A459
KINGHAM, Darrell L., CPA Vice President Finance, Beauregard Memorial Hospital, De Ridder, LA, p. A273
KINGSLEY, Christi, Director Human Resources, West Calcasieu Cameron Hospital, Sulphur, LA, p. A286
KINGSTON, Eileen M., R.N. Nurse Executive, Associate Director Patient Care, Veterans Affairs Nebraska–Western Iowa Health Care System, Omaha, NE, p. A397
KINGSTON, Mary
  Chief Executive Officer, Promise Hospital of San Diego, San Diego, CA, p. A86
  Chief Executive Officer, Providence Little Company of Mary Medical Center San Pedro, CA, p. A72
KINGSTON, Mary Beth, R.N. Executive Vice President and Chief Nursing Officer, Aurora Medical Center of Oshkosh, Oshkosh, WI, p. A708
KINGSTON, Peggy, Chief Executive Officer, Select Specialty Hospital–Pontiac, Pontiac, MI, p. A328
KINI, M. Narendra, M.D., President and Chief Executive Officer, Nicklaus Children's Hospital, Miami, FL, p. A134
KINKAID, Steve
  Director Information Systems, Gnaden Huetten Memorial Hospital, Lehighton, PA, p. A538
  Director Information Systems, Palmerton Hospital, Palmerton, PA, p. A542
KINLEN, Thomas, Superintendent, Larned State Hospital, Larned, KS, p. A244
KINMAN, Amanda, Director of Finance, Saint Joseph Mount Sterling, Mount Sterling, KY, p. A263
KINMAN, Brett, Chief Operating Officer, Tomball Regional Medical Center, Tomball, TX, p. A648
KINNEER, James W., Vice President Organizational Development, Indiana Regional Medical Center, Indiana, PA, p. A536
KINNEMAN, Mary, R.N. Chief Nursing Officer, Vice President Patient Care Services, Norwood Hospital, Norwood, MA, p. A310
KINNEY, Janet, Chief Operating Officer, Northwest Florida Community Hospital, Chipley, FL, p. A123
KINSALA, Edeli, Chief Executive Officer, Sonora Behavioral Health Hospital, Tucson, AZ, p. A40
KINSEL, Mike, Controller, Federal Medical Center, Lexington, KY, p. A259
KINSELLA, Daniel F.
  Vice President and Chief Information Officer, Northwestern Medicine Central DuPage Hospital, Winfield, IL, p. A203
  Executive Vice President Information Technology, Northwestern Medicine Delnor Hospital, Geneva, IL, p. A189
KINSEY, Daniel, M.D. Medical Director, Oaklawn Psychiatric Center, Goshen, IN, p. A210
KINSEY, Wayne, Chief Executive Officer, Promise Hospital of Salt Lake, Salt Lake City, UT, p. A658
KINSLOW, Kathleen, Ed.D., President and Chief Executive Officer, Aria Health, Philadelphia, PA, p. A542
KINTZ, Ronald J.
  Vice President and Treasurer, Arnot Ogden Medical Center, Elmira, NY, p. A433
  Chief Financial Officer, Ira Davenport Memorial Hospital, Bath, NY, p. A429
  Senior Vice President Finance and Chief Financial Officer, St. Joseph's Hospital, Elmira, NY, p. A433
KINYON, Craig C., President, Reid Health, Richmond, IN, p. A219
KINYON, David, Vice President of Operations and Outpatient Services, Asante Three Rivers Medical Center, Grants Pass, OR, p. A521
KINZIC, Elizabeth, M.D. Chief of Staff, Share Medical Center, Alva, OK, p. A503
KINZIE, Wesley, M.D. Chief of Staff, Stanislaus Surgical Hospital, Modesto, CA, p. A76
KIO, Kenneth, Manager Human Resources, Albany Stratton Veterans Affairs Medical Center, Albany, NY, p. A428
KIPER, Valerie, MSN Chief Nursing Officer, Northwest Texas Healthcare System, Amarillo, TX, p. A591
KIPFER, Debra, Chief Financial Officer, Community Hospital of Bremen, Bremen, IN, p. A205
KIPREOS, Nicholas, M.D. Chief Medical Staff, Pioneer Community Hospital of Patrick, Stuart, VA, p. A673
KIRACOFE, Darin, Director Information Resource Management, Broughton Hospital, Morganton, NC, p. A465
KIRBOW, Keith, R.N. Vice President and Chief Nursing Officer, Good Shepherd Medical Center–Marshall, Marshall, TX, p. A631
KIRBY, Adrienne, FACHE, President and Chief Executive Officer, Cooper University Health Care, Camden, NJ, p. A410
KIRBY, Brendan, M.D. Medical Director, Riverview Psychiatric Center, Augusta, ME, p. A288
KIRBY, Cheryl, Chief Nursing Officer, Palo Pinto General Hospital, Mineral Wells, TX, p. A632
KIRBY, Elizabeth A., Director Human Resources, Aurora BayCare Medical Center, Green Bay, WI, p. A701
KIRBY II, James M., President and Chief Executive Officer, Margaret R. Pardee Memorial Hospital, Hendersonville, NC, p. A462
KIRBY, Juliana Kay, R.N. Chief Nursing Officer, Tehachapi Valley Healthcare District, Tehachapi, CA, p. A94
KIRBY, Len, Chief Executive Officer, Garfield Park Hospital, Chicago, IL, p. A182
KIRBY, Penny V., MSN Chief Nursing Officer, McKenzie Regional Hospital, McKenzie, TN, p. A582
KIRBY, Ruby, Administrator, Bolivar General Hospital, Bolivar, TN, p. A574
KIRBY, Sarah, FACHE, Acute Care Executive, Palmetto Health Baptist Parkridge, Columbia, SC, p. A559
KIRCH, Cyndi
  Vice President Human Resources, Mercy General Hospital, Sacramento, CA, p. A84
  Vice President Human Resources, Methodist Hospital of Sacramento, Sacramento, CA, p. A84
KIRCHER, Janelle, R.N. Vice President Patient Care Services and Chief Nursing Officer, Community Hospital, McCook, NE, p. A394
KIRCHER, Mark, Associate Vice President Finance, Norton Women's and Kosair Children's Hospital, Louisville, KY, p. A261
KIRCHHOFF, Stacy, Coordinator Human Resources, Warren Memorial Hospital, Friend, NE, p. A392
KIRCHNER, Doris, Chief Executive Officer, Vail Valley Medical Center, Vail, CO, p. A109
KIRCHNER, Kent, M.D. Chief of Staff, G.V. (Sonny) Montgomery Veterans Affairs Medical Center, Jackson, MS, p. A355
KIRCHNER, Susan M., Director Human Resources, Four Winds Hospital, Saratoga Springs, NY, p. A450
KIRISITS, Christopher, Chief Nursing Officer, Rochester Psychiatric Center, Rochester, NY, p. A449
KIRITANI, Tracy, Vice President and Chief Financial Officer, Clovis Community Medical Center, Clovis, CA, p. A58
KIRK, Brian T., Vice President Finance, University Hospital and Clinics, Lafayette, LA, p. A278
KIRK, Darlene, Manager Finance, U. S. Public Health Service Indian Hospital, Crownpoint, NM, p. A424
KIRK Jr., H. Lee, FACHE, Administrator, Shriners Hospitals for Children–Springfield, Springfield, MA, p. A311
KIRK, J. Douglas, M.D. Chief Medical Officer, University of California, Davis Medical Center, Sacramento, CA, p. A85
KIRK, Jean, Chief Financial Officer, Bennett County Hospital and Nursing Home, Martin, SD, p. A569
KIRK, Paul, Vice President, Woman's Hospital, Baton Rouge, LA, p. A270
KIRK, Peggy, Senior Vice President Clinical Operations, Rehabilitation Institute of Chicago, Chicago, IL, p. A184
KIRK, Roger L., President and Chief Executive Officer, Bethesda Hospital East, Boynton Beach, FL, p. A122
KIRK, Stephanie, Chief Financial Officer, Iberia Medical Center, New Iberia, LA, p. A281
KIRK, Vanessa, Director of Nursing, Kiowa County Memorial Hospital, Greensburg, KS, p. A241
KIRK, Warren J., Chief Executive Officer, Doctors Medical Center, Modesto, CA, p. A75
KIRKER, Lynda I., Chief Financial Officer, Flagler Hospital, Saint Augustine, FL, p. A141
KIRKER NEA–BC, Donna, R.N. Vice President Patient Services and Chief Nursing Officer, Glens Falls Hospital, Glens Falls, NY, p. A434
KIRKHAM, Brett, Chief Operating Officer, AllianceHealth Deaconess, Oklahoma City, OK, p. A511
KIRKHAM, Paul, Chief Executive Officer, Keystone Newport News, Newport News, VA, p. A668
KIRKLAND, Charles, D.O. Chief Medical Officer, Davis Medical Center, Elkins, WV, p. A690
KIRKLAND–ROSE, Tina, Coordinator Human Resources, Select Specialty Hospital–Lexington, Lexington, KY, p. A260
KIRKS, Linda, Chief Financial Officer, Baptist Medical Center, San Antonio, TX, p. A640
KIRMAN, Lynn, R.N. Chief Nursing Officer, St. John's Medical Center and Living Center, Jackson, WY, p. A716
KIROLLOS, Alan, M.D. President Medical Staff, Lenoir Memorial Hospital, Kinston, NC, p. A463
KIRSHNER, Arthur N., Chief Information Management, Winn Army Community Hospital, Hinesville, GA, p. A159
KIRSTEIN, Susan N., R.N. Chief Nursing Officer, Broadlawns Medical Center, Des Moines, IA, p. A226
KISACKY, Christina A., Vice President, Operations, Chenango Memorial Hospital, Norwich, NY, p. A446
KISER, Greg, Chief Executive Officer, Three Rivers Medical Center, Louisa, KY, p. A260
KISER, Harrison, Interim Chief Executive Officer, Northwest Medical Center – Springdale, Springdale, AR, p. A51
KISER II, James R., Chief Executive Officer, Providence St. Joseph Medical Center, Polson, MT, p. A386
KISER, Pamela, R.N. Chief Nursing Executive and Vice President of Nursing, St. John Medical Center, Tulsa, OK, p. A517
KISER, Terry L.
  Vice President and Chief Financial Officer, Tidelands Georgetown Memorial Hospital, Georgetown, SC, p. A561
  Chief Financial Officer, Tidelands Waccamaw Community Hospital, Murrells Inlet, SC, p. A564
KISKADDON, Robert, M.D. Chief Medical Officer, Margaret R. Pardee Memorial Hospital, Hendersonville, NC, p. A462
KISNER, Angela, Director Human Resources and Coordinator Medical Staff, Landmark Hospital of Cape Girardeau, Cape Girardeau, MO, p. A364
KISSNER, Michael, Chief Executive Officer, HEALTHSOUTH Treasure Coast Rehabilitation Hospital, Vero Beach, FL, p. A146
KISTLER, Beckie, Director of Finance, Our Lady of Peace, Louisville, KY, p. A261
KISTLER, Mike, Chief Executive Officer, Shadow Mountain Behavioral Health System, Tulsa, OK, p. A517
KISTNER, Kasondra, Chief Executive Officer, Post Acute/Warm Springs Rehabilitation Hospital of San Antonio, San Antonio, TX, p. A642
KITCHEN, Randy J., Chief Executive Officer, Dayton Rehabilitation Institute, Dayton, OH, p. A487
KITTELL, Elisabeth, Chief Financial Officer, Syracuse Veterans Affairs Medical Center, Syracuse, NY, p. A451
KITTNER, Bonnie, R.N. Chief Nursing Officer, Mendocino Coast District Hospital, Fort Bragg, CA, p. A61
KITTOE, Michael, Chief Financial Officer, Lake Health, Concord Township, OH, p. A487
KITZKE, Kristopher, Chief Executive Officer, Select Specialty Hospital–Gainesville, Gainesville, FL, p. A128
KJERGAARD, Holly, Chief Nursing Officer, Audubon County Memorial Hospital, Audubon, IA, p. A222
KLANN, Andrew, D.O. Chief of Staff, Southwest Health Center, Platteville, WI, p. A709
KLASEK, Chance, CPA Chief Financial Officer, Jefferson Community Health Center, Fairbury, NE, p. A391
KLASKO, Stephen K., M.D., Chief Executive Officer, Jefferson Health, Radnor, PA, p. B75
KLASSEN, Brad, Information Technology Coordinator, Sanford Worthington Medical Center, Worthington, MN, p. A349
KLASSEN, Karen, Controller, HEALTHSOUTH Chattanooga Rehabilitation Hospital, Chattanooga, TN, p. A575
KLASSEN, Susan K., Chief Executive Officer, Mahnomen Health Center, Mahnomen, MN, p. A341
KLAUKA, Floyd, Chief Financial Officer, Brook Lane Health Services, Hagerstown, MD, p. A298
KLAUSTERMEIER, Lisa, R.N. Chief Nursing Officer, Anderson Hospital, Maryville, IL, p. A193
KLAWITTER, Kyle, Vice President Human Resources, Summa Akron City Hospital, Akron, OH, p. A478
KLEAS, Tara, Director Human Resources, HEALTHSOUTH Rehabilitation Hospital of Fort Worth, Fort Worth, TX, p. A613
KLECKNER, Megan, Vice President and Administrator, Riverside Walter Reed Hospital, Gloucester, VA, p. A665
KLEEN, Kathy, Chief Nursing Officer, Tri–County Hospital, Wadena, MN, p. A348
KLEHN, Paul, Chief Information Technology Officer, Liberty Hospital, Liberty, MO, p. A372
KLEIN, Aron
  Vice President Finance, Advocate BroMenn Medical Center, Normal, IL, p. A196
  Vice President of Finance, Advocate Eureka Hospital, Eureka, IL, p. A187
KLEIN, Barbara, R.N. Director of Nursing, Arms Acres, Carmel, NY, p. A431
KLEIN, Bernard, M.D., Chief Executive, Providence Holy Cross Medical Center, CA, p. A72
KLEIN, Cindy, Chief Financial Officer, Lamb Healthcare Center, Littlefield, TX, p. A628

A886 Index of Health Care Professionals

KNUDSON, Jenny, Controller, Hiawatha Community Hospital, Hiawatha, KS, p. A241

KNUDSON, Veronica, Chief Executive Officer, Yakima Regional Medical and Cardiac Center, Yakima, WA, p. A688

KNUTH, Kerry, Chief Operating Officer, Mercy Hospital of Defiance, Defiance, OH, p. A488

KNUTSON, Holly, Manager Information Technology, Kittson Memorial Healthcare Center, Hallock, MN, p. A340

KNUTSON, John P., M.D. Chief Medical Staff, Delta County Memorial Hospital, Delta, CO, p. A101

KNUTSON, Larry, Director Finance, CentraCare Health–Long Prairie, Long Prairie, MN, p. A341

KNUTSON, Ruth, Chief Financial Officer, AMG Specialty Hospital – Las Vegas, Las Vegas, NV, p. A401

KO, Tommy, M.D. Chief Medical Officer, St. Joseph Medical Center, Kansas City, MO, p. A370

KOBIS, David A., Vice President Operations and Chief Operating Officer, Cortland Regional Medical Center, Cortland, NY, p. A432

KOBY, Lori, R.N. Director of Nursing, Livingston HealthCare, Livingston, MT, p. A385

KOCH, Carol, Manager Human Resources, Callaway District Hospital, Callaway, NE, p. A390

KOCH, Douglas E., Market President, Aurora Medical Center, Kenosha, WI, p. A703

KOCH, Holly, Chief Financial Officer, Girard Medical Center, Girard, KS, p. A240

KOCH, Jamie, R.N. Director of Nursing, Thayer County Health Services, Hebron, NE, p. A392

KOCH, Joseph G., Chief Executive Officer, Bourbon Community Hospital, Paris, KY, p. A264

KOCH, Melanie, R.N. Chief Nursing Officer, Union County Hospital, Anna, IL, p. A178

KOCHEVAR, Vanessa, Chief Financial Officer, St. Mary–Corwin Medical Center, Pueblo, CO, p. A108

KOCHIE, Daniel A., CP
Chief Financial Officer, Samaritan Hospital, Troy, NY, p. A452
Chief Financial Officer, St. Mary's Hospital, Troy, NY, p. A452

KOCHIS, Mary Ellen, Administrator Nursing Operations, Beaumont Hospital–Dearborn, Dearborn, MI, p. A317

KOCIOLA, Matthew, Senior Vice President and Chief Financial Officer, Somerset Hospital, Somerset, PA, p. A550

KOCOUREK, Cathie A., President, Aurora Medical Center – Manitowoc County, Two Rivers, WI, p. A712

KOCSIS, Dana, R.N. Vice President Nursing and Operations, Lodi Community Hospital, Lodi, OH, p. A492

KOCSIS, Violet, Chief Human Resources Officer, Hunterdon Medical Center, Flemington, NJ, p. A412

KOCZENT, Kurt, Executive Vice President and Chief Operating Officer, F. F. Thompson Hospital, Canandaigua, NY, p. A431

KOEBKE, Troy L.
Director Human Resources Management, Bellin Memorial Hospital, Green Bay, WI, p. A701
Director Human Resources, Bellin Psychiatric Center, Green Bay, WI, p. A702

KOEBNICK, Dale, Director Management Information Systems and Patient Access, Metroplex Adventist Hospital, Killeen, TX, p. A626

KOEHLER, Amy, Director Human Resources, Shelby Memorial Hospital, Shelbyville, IL, p. A200

KOEHLER, Maggie, Senior Vice President and Chief Financial Officer, Wilkes–Barre General Hospital, Wilkes–Barre, PA, p. A553

KOEHLER, Mike, Interim Chief Information Officer, Athens Regional Medical Center, Athens, GA, p. A149

KOELE, Craig, Chief Executive Officer, Cornerstone Hospital of Oklahoma–Muskogee, Muskogee, OK, p. A510

KOENIG, Jr., Donald E., Executive Vice President and Chief Operating Officer, St. Elizabeth Health Center, Youngstown, OH, p. A501

KOENIG, Harris F., President and Chief Executive Officer, San Antonio Community Hospital, Upland, CA, p. A95

KOENIG, Mary, Chief Financial Officer, Vernon Memorial Healthcare, Viroqua, WI, p. A712

KOEPKE, Eldon, Chief Financial Officer, Mitchell County Hospital Health Systems, Beloit, KS, p. A238

KOERNER, Jill, Manager Employee Relations, Weisman Children's Rehabilitation Hospital, Marlton, NJ, p. A414

KOESSL, Brenda, R.N. Director of Nursing Services, Frances Mahon Deaconess Hospital, Glasgow, MT, p. A383

KOESTER, Jean, Manager Human Resources, Limestone Medical Center, Groesbeck, TX, p. A617

KOESTERER, Susan, Regional Director Finance, Alton Memorial Hospital, Alton, IL, p. A178

KOETTING, Edward, Chief Financial Officer, Bedford Veterans Affairs Medical Center, Edith Nourse Rogers Memorial Veterans Hospital, Bedford, MA, p. A302

KOHANKE, Crystal H., Vice President Human Resources, CHRISTUS Santa Rosa Health System, San Antonio, TX, p. A640

KOHL, Randy T., M.D., Deputy Director, Health Services, Nebraska Penal and Correctional Hospital, Lincoln, NE, p. A394

KOHLBRENNER, Janis, R.N. Vice President Clinical Services and Chief Nursing Officer, Oneida Healthcare, Oneida, NY, p. A446

KOHLENBERG, Chris, Chief Financial Officer, Jennings American Legion Hospital, Jennings, LA, p. A275

KOHLENBERG, Darnell, R.N. Director of Nursing, Abrom Kaplan Memorial Hospital, Kaplan, LA, p. A276

KOHLER, Douglas, M.D. Vice President Medical Operations, Marymount Hospital, Garfield Heights, OH, p. A490

KOHLER, Mike, Chief Executive Officer, Emerus, Sugar Land, TX, p. A645

KOHRER, Tammy, Director of Nursing–Acute, Wahiawa General Hospital, Wahiawa, HI, p. A170

KOINZAN, Leigh Jean, Director Finance, Boys Town National Research Hospital, Omaha, NE, p. A395

KOKJOHN, Bradley J., Chief Financial Officer, Fort Madison Community Hospital, Fort Madison, IA, p. A228

KOLACZ, Nicole, Vice President Patient Services, Pomerene Hospital, Millersburg, OH, p. A494

KOLAR, Stephen J., M.D
Vice President Medical Affairs, Bethesda Hospital, Saint Paul, MN, p. A346
Vice President Medical Affairs, St. John's Hospital, Maplewood, MN, p. A342
Senior Vice President – Chief Medical Officer, St. Joseph's Hospital, Saint Paul, MN, p. A346
Senior Vice President and Chief Medical Officer, Woodwinds Health Campus, Woodbury, MN, p. A349

KOLB, Andy, Chief Executive Officer, Stonewall Memorial Hospital, Aspermont, TX, p. A593

KOLB, Edward, M.D. Medical Director, Boys Town National Research Hospital, Omaha, NE, p. A395

KOLB, Pat, Manager Information Technology, Clarendon Memorial Hospital, Manning, SC, p. A563

KOLHEDE, Deborah, Vice President and Chief Operating Officer, St. Mary's Medical Center, San Francisco, CA, p. A88

KOLLMEYER, Sherry, Vice President Human Resources, Youth Villages Inner Harbour Campus, Douglasville, GA, p. A156

KOLMAN, Bret G., FACHE, Chief Executive Officer, Lakeview Regional Medical Center, Covington, LA, p. A272

KOLODZIEJCYK, Wanda S., Director Human Resources, Cuero Community Hospital, Cuero, TX, p. A603

KOLODZIEJCZYK, Clayton, Chief Financial Officer, Meadowview Regional Medical Center, Maysville, KY, p. A263

KOLOSKY, John A., Executive Vice President and Chief Operating Officer, H. Lee Moffitt Cancer Center and Research Institute, Tampa, FL, p. A144

KOLSETH, Shelley V., Chief Financial Officer, Memorial Hospital of Tampa, Tampa, FL, p. A145

KOMAN, Stuart, Ph.D., President and Chief Executive Officer, Walden Psychiatric Care, Waltham, MA, p. A312

KOMANDURI, Ramanujam, M.D. Chief of Staff, Veterans Affairs Southern Nevada Healthcare System, North Las Vegas, NV, p. A403

KOMAR, Ellen M., R.N. Vice President Patient Care Services, Stamford Hospital, Stamford, CT, p. A115

KOME, Hunter, Campus President, Oconee Memorial Hospital, Seneca, SC, p. A564

KOMENDA, John, Chief Financial Officer, Hendricks Regional Health, Danville, IN, p. A207

KOMINS, Jeff, M.D. Chief Medical Officer, Mercy Fitzgerald Hospital, Darby, PA, p. A532

KOMORNIK, Jeffrey, Director Human Resources, Milford Hospital, Milford, CT, p. A113

KOMOROSKI, Patrice L., R.N., Chief Executive Officer, Select Specialty Hospital–St. Louis, Saint Charles, MO, p. A375

KONARSKI, Debbie, Interim Chief Financial Officer, Pottstown Memorial Medical Center, Pottstown, PA, p. A548

KONDASH, Dennis, D.O
Vice President Medical Affairs, Gnaden Huetten Memorial Hospital, Lehighton, PA, p. A538
Vice President Medical Affairs, Palmerton Hospital, Palmerton, PA, p. A542

KONDO, Reid, Interim Chief Executive Officer, Leahi Hospital, Honolulu, HI, p. A168

KONECNE, Robin, Manager Human Resources, Kit Carson County Health Service District, Burlington, CO, p. A100

KONGARA, Rama, Chief Financial Officer, St. James Behavioral Health Hospital, Gonzales, LA, p. A274

KONIECZEK, Raymond, Chief Human Resources Officer, John F. Kennedy Memorial Hospital, Indio, CA, p. A65

KONKEL, Robert, Manager Finance, James A. Haley Veterans' Hospital–Tampa, Tampa, FL, p. A144

KONOPKO, Stan, Chief Financial Officer, St. James Mercy Health System, Hornell, NY, p. A435

KONSAVAGE, Christian, M.D. Chief of Staff, Cumberland County Hospital, Burkesville, KY, p. A255

KOOIMAN, Thomas, Chief Executive Officer, Prairie Ridge Hospital and Health Services, Elbow Lake, MN, p. A338

KOON, Rion, Chief Information Management Division, William Beaumont Army Medical Center, El Paso, TX, p. A611

KOOP, Steven, M.D. Medical Director, Gillette Children's Specialty Healthcare, Saint Paul, MN, p. A346

KOOY, Donald C., President and Chief Executive Officer, McLaren Flint, Flint, MI, p. A319

KOPEL, Samuel, M.D. Medical Director, Maimonides Medical Center, NY, p. A441

KOPFLE, Sue, Chief Human Resources Officer, University of Missouri Hospitals and Clinics, Columbia, MO, p. A366

KOPINSKI, Donna, Chief Financial Officer, Crittenton Hospital Medical Center, Rochester, MI, p. A328

KOPPELMAN, Benjamin
Interim President, CHI LakeWood Health, Baudette, MN, p. A335
President, CHI St. Joseph's Health, Park Rapids, MN, p. A344

KOPPELMAN, Catherine S., MSN Chief Nursing Officer, University Hospitals Case Medical Center, Cleveland, OH, p. A485

KOPPERUD, Gordon, Director Operations, Sanford Westbrook Medical Center, Westbrook, MN, p. A349

KORBEL, Tamara, Director Management Information Systems, Ridgeview Medical Center, Waconia, MN, p. A348

KORDAHL, Rebecca, R.N. Associate Director, Patient Care Services, William S. Middleton Memorial Veterans Hospital, Madison, WI, p. A704

KORDUCKI, Stanley R., President, Wood County Hospital, Bowling Green, OH, p. A480

KORDUPEL, Maureen
Director Relationship Manager, St. Elizabeth Boardman Health Center, Boardman, OH, p. A480
Director Relationship Manager, St. Elizabeth Health Center, Youngstown, OH, p. A501

KORICH, Frank, Vice President and Site Administrator, Soldiers and Sailors Memorial Hospital of Yates County, Penn Yan, NY, p. A447

KORKMAS, Ross, Assistant Chief Executive Officer, Medical Center of South Arkansas, El Dorado, AR, p. A43

KORN, Larry, Manager Finance, Southern Arizona Veterans Affairs Health Care System, Tucson, AZ, p. A40

KORN, Roy, M.D. Medical Director, Cobleskill Regional Hospital, Cobleskill, NY, p. A432

KORNBLATT, Lynne R.
Chief Human Resources Officer, Einstein Medical Center Montgomery, East Norriton, PA, p. A533
Chief Human Resources Officer, Einstein Medical Center Philadelphia, Philadelphia, PA, p. A543

KORNFIELD, Lee, M.D. Medical Director, St. Luke's Rehabilitation Hospital, Boise, ID, p. A173

KOROLY, Marla, M.D. Chief Medical Officer and Senior Vice President Medical Affairs, Northern Westchester Hospital, Mount Kisco, NY, p. A438

KORPELA, Donita, R.N. Director of Patient Care Services, Mercy Hospital, Moose Lake, MN, p. A343

KORPIEL, Michael, FACH
President, St. Vincent's Blount, Oneonta, AL, p. A23
President and Chief Operating Officer, St. Vincent's East, Birmingham, AL, p. A17

KORPIEL, Michael, President, St. Vincent's St. Clair, Pell City, AL, p. A24

KORTE, Fred, Chief Financial Officer, McLaren Oakland, Pontiac, MI, p. A328

KORTEMEYER, Jay, Chief Executive Officer, Brynn Marr Hospital, Jacksonville, NC, p. A463

KORTH, Mark D., President, Mercy Medical Center Redding, Redding, CA, p. A82

KORTH, Paul, Chief Executive Officer, Cookeville Regional Medical Center, Cookeville, TN, p. A576

KORTH–WHITE, Kirsten, Vice President Physician Network and Ambulatory Service, Munson Healthcare Grayling Hospital, Grayling, MI, p. A321

KOSACH, Becky, Director Human Resources, Ivinson Memorial Hospital, Laramie, WY, p. A716

KOSANOVICH, John, M.D. Vice President Covenant Healthcare and Chief Executive Officer Covenant Medical Group, Covenant Healthcare, Saginaw, MI, p. A329

KOSANOVICH, John P., President, Watertown Regional Medical Center, Watertown, WI, p. A712

KOSE, William H., M.D
Chief Quality Officer, Blanchard Valley Hospital, Findlay, OH, p. A490
Vice President Quality and Medical Affairs, Bluffton Hospital, Bluffton, OH, p. A480

KOSEK, Kevin, Associate Director Operations, Iowa City Veterans Affairs Health Care System, Iowa City, IA, p. A229

KOSIER, Douglas D., Chief Operating Officer, Mason District Hospital, Havana, IL, p. A190

Index of Health Care Professionals / Kristel

Index of Health Care Professionals

KOSLOW, Howard B., President and Chief Executive Officer, Promise Hospital of Miss Lou, Vidalia, LA, p. A286
KOSNOSKY, David, M.D. Chief Medical Officer, University Hospitals Geauga Medical Center, Chardon, OH, p. A481
KOSSEFF, Christopher O., President and Chief Executive Officer, University Behavioral Healthcare, Piscataway, NJ, p. A417
KOSTER, Tracy, Director Human Resources, Carlinville Area Hospital, Carlinville, IL, p. A180
KOSTERS, Gregory J., D.O. Chief Medical Officer, Osceola Community Hospital, Sibley, IA, p. A234
KOSTOK, Barbara, Manager Human Resources, Punxsutawney Area Hospital, Punxsutawney, PA, p. A548
KOSTURKO, MaryEllen, R.N. Senior Vice President Patient Care Operations and Chief Nursing Officer, Bridgeport Hospital, Bridgeport, CT, p. A111
KOSYLA, Gail, Chief Financial Officer, Hunterdon Medical Center, Flemington, NJ, p. A412
KOSZTYO, Carol, R.N. Vice President, Patient Care Services, Carrier Clinic, Belle Mead, NJ, p. A409
KOTIL, Drew, Director Information Technology, Crete Area Medical Center, Crete, NE, p. A391
KOTIN, Kathy, Chief Financial Officer, Banner Good Samaritan Medical Center, Phoenix, AZ, p. A34
KOTRBA, Mitchell, Chief Financial Officer, North Valley Health Center, Warren, MN, p. A348
KOTSONIS, Robert, Chief Operating Officer, Northeast Rehabilitation Hospital, Salem, NH, p. A408
KOTTENBROOK, Susan, Chief Executive Officer, Red River Behavioral Center, Bossier City, LA, p. A271
KOTZEN, Michael S., Vice President and Chief Operating Officer, Virtua Voorhees, Voorhees, NJ, p. A420
KOUKOS, Dean, M.D. Chief Medical Staff, Southern Palmetto Hospital, Barnwell, SC, p. A557
KOULOVATOS, James E.
Chief Executive Officer, Liberty Dayton Regional Medical Center, Liberty, TX, p. A628
Interim Chief Executive Officer, Pecos County Memorial Hospital, Fort Stockton, TX, p. A612
KOUNS, Nicholas, D.O. Chief of Staff, Clark Regional Medical Center, Winchester, KY, p. A267
KOUNTZ, David, M.D. Senior Vice President Medical Affairs, Jersey Shore University Medical Center, Neptune, NJ, p. A414
KOUSKOLEKAS, Anthony, FACHE, President, Pelham Medical Center, Greer, SC, p. A562
KOUTOUZOS, Connie L., MSN, Chief Executive Officer and President, Aspirus Iron River Hospitals and Clinics, Iron River, MI, p. A323
KOVAC, John, Facility Chief Information Officer, Veterans Affairs Pittsburgh Healthcare System, Pittsburgh, PA, p. A547
KOVACH, Andrew L.
Vice President Human Resources and Chief Administrative Officer, Morristown Medical Center, Morristown, NJ, p. A414
Vice President Human Resources and Chief Administrative Officer, Newton Medical Center, Newton, NJ, p. A416
Vice President Human Resources and Chief Administrative Officer, Overlook Medical Center, Summit, NJ, p. A418
KOVACS, Amber R., Chief Human Resources Officer, Banner Gateway Medical Center, Gilbert, AZ, p. A31
KOVACS, Tina, Chief Financial Officer, Saint Francis Hospital–Bartlett, Bartlett, TN, p. A574
KOVALSKI, Jerry, Director Information Systems, Madera Community Hospital, Madera, CA, p. A74
KOVASZNAY, Beatrice, M.D. Clinical Director, Capital District Psychiatric Center, Albany, NY, p. A428
KOVICH, Lynn, Assistant Commissioner, Division of Mental Health and Addiction Services, Department of Human Services, State of New Jersey, Trenton, NJ, p. B51
KOWALOFF, Harvey, M.D. Vice President Medical Affairs, Saint Anne's Hospital, Fall River, MA, p. A306
KOWALSKI, Patrick A., Chief Financial Officer, Mercy Health – Anderson Hospital, Cincinnati, OH, p. A483
KOWNACKI, Dawn, Director Human Resources, Brooke Glen Behavioral Hospital, Fort Washington, PA, p. A534
KOZAI, Gerald T., President and Chief Executive Officer, St. Francis Medical Center, Lynwood, CA, p. A74
KOZAR, Michael A., Chief Executive Officer, Carroll County Memorial Hospital, Carrollton, KY, p. A255
KOZEL, Kenneth D., FACHE,
President and Chief Executive Officer, University of Maryland Shore Medical Center at Chestertown, Chestertown, MD, p. A296
President and Chief Executive Officer, University of Maryland Shore Medical Center at Dorchester, Cambridge, MD, p. A296
President and Chief Executive Officer, University of Maryland Shore Medical Center at Easton, Easton, MD, p. A297
KOZEL, Mary Ann, Chief Fiscal, Wilmington Veterans Affairs Medical Center, Wilmington, DE, p. A118
KOZIK, Rhonda, Administrator, Norwood Health Center, Marshfield, WI, p. A705
KOZIKUSKI, Courtney, Chief Financial Officer, Perry Memorial Hospital, Perry, OK, p. A513
KOZIN, Scott, M.D. Chief of Staff, Shriners Hospitals for Children–Philadelphia, Philadelphia, PA, p. A545
KOZOROSKY, Laurie, Chief Executive Officer, Select Specialty Hospital–Laurel Highlands, Latrobe, PA, p. A538
KRABBENHOFT, Kelby K., President and Chief Executive Officer, Sanford Health, Sioux Falls, SD, p. B116
KRABILL, Emma, Interim Chief Executive Officer, Scenic Mountain Medical Center, Big Spring, TX, p. A597
KRABLIN, Brett, M.D. Chief of Staff, Mercy Hospital Kingfisher, Kingfisher, OK, p. A508
KRAFT, Chris, Director Information Systems, York General Hospital, York, NE, p. A399
KRAHNERT, John F., M.D. Chief Medical Officer, FirstHealth Moore Regional Hospital, Pinehurst, NC, p. A466
KRAJEWSKI, David, Senior Vice President and Chief Financial Officer, Sinai Hospital of Baltimore, Baltimore, MD, p. A295
KRAMER, Blake, Chief Executive Officer, Franklin Medical Center, Winnsboro, LA, p. A287
KRAMER, Chad, Chief Operating Officer, Berwick Hospital Center, Berwick, PA, p. A529
KRAMER, Danette, Chief Financial Officer, Regional Medical Center, Manchester, IA, p. A231
KRAMER, Janie, Chief Operating Officer, Sharp Memorial Hospital, San Diego, CA, p. A87
KRAMER, Karen, R.N. Vice President and System Chief Nursing Officer, Cox Medical Centers, Springfield, MO, p. A378
KRAMER, Kathryn, M.D. President Medical Staff, Pekin Hospital, Pekin, IL, p. A197
KRAMER, Kevin, Chief Executive Officer, Modoc Medical Center, Alturas, CA, p. A53
KRAMER, Lynette, M.D. Chief Medical Officer, Boone County Health Center, Albion, NE, p. A389
KRAMER, Michael, Chief Operating Officer, Mercy Health – West Hospital, Cincinnati, OH, p. A483
KRAMER, Richard, Interim Chief Executive Officer, Northlake Behavioral Hospital, Mandeville, LA, p. A279
KRAMER, Susan, Director of Human Resources, Levi Hospital, Hot Springs National Park, AR, p. A46
KRAML, Louis D., FACHE,
Chief Executive Officer, Bingham Memorial Hospital, Blackfoot, ID, p. A172
Chief Executive Officer, Mountain River Birthing and Surgery Center, Blackfoot, ID, p. A172
KRAMPITS, Carrie, Director Human Resources, McKenzie Health System, Sandusky, MI, p. A330
KRASON, Jane E., R.N., Chief Executive Officer, Appalachian Behavioral Healthcare, Athens, OH, p. A479
KRASS, Todd, Chief Executive Officer, Belton Regional Medical Center, Belton, MO, p. A363
KRAUKLIS, Gene
Regional Vice President Human Resources, Aurora Lakeland Medical Center, Elkhorn, WI, p. A700
Regional Vice President Human Resources, Aurora Memorial Hospital of Burlington, Burlington, WI, p. A699
KRAUS, Jason, Director Human Resources, Magruder Memorial Hospital, Port Clinton, OH, p. A496
KRAUS, John, M.D. Chief Medical Officer, Bryn Mawr Rehabilitation Hospital, Malvern, PA, p. A539
KRAUSE, Donna, Chief Information Officer, Harry S. Truman Memorial Veterans Hospital, Columbia, MO, p. A366
KRAUSE, Jill A., Director, Kalamazoo Psychiatric Hospital, Kalamazoo, MI, p. A323
KRAUSE, Kim, Director Human Resources, Baylor Jack and Jane Hamilton Heart and Vascular Hospital, Dallas, TX, p. A604
KRAUSE, Steven, Manager Information Technology, Franciscan Healthcare – Munster, Munster, IN, p. A217
KRAUSS, James D., President, Sentara RMH Medical Center, Harrisonburg, VA, p. A666
KRAUTSCHEID, Steven P., Ancillary Services Administrator, Tuality Healthcare, Hillsboro, OR, p. A521
KRAVETZ, Michael, M.D. Medical Director, HEALTHSOUTH Valley of the Sun Rehabilitation Hospital, Glendale, AZ, p. A32
KREATSOULAS, Nicholas, M.D
Vice President Medical Affairs and Chief Quality Officer, St. Elizabeth Boardman Health Center, Boardman, OH, p. A480
Senior Vice President and Chief Medical Officer and Chief Quality Officer, St. Elizabeth Health Center, Youngstown, OH, p. A501
Vice President Medical Affairs, St. Joseph Health Center, Warren, OH, p. A499
KREBS, Anne, Chief Financial Officer, Butler Health System, Butler, PA, p. A530
KREBS, Cindy, District Director Human Resources, Matagorda Regional Medical Center, Bay City, TX, p. A596
KREBS, George, M.D. Chief Medical Officer, Broughton Hospital, Morganton, NC, p. A465
KREBS, Mary Jane, Chief Executive Officer, Spring Harbor Hospital, Westbrook, ME, p. A292
KREBS, Teresa, Director Human Resources, North Texas Medical Center, Gainesville, TX, p. A615
KREBSBACH, Mayla, Chief Executive Officer, Vista Del Mar Hospital, Ventura, CA, p. A96
KREELEY, Chris, Director Nursing, Marlton Rehabilitation Hospital, Marlton, NJ, p. A414
KREHBIEL, Rod, M.D. Chief of Staff, Klickitat Valley Health, Goldendale, WA, p. A679
KREIDER, David, Controller, Ephrata Community Hospital, Ephrata, PA, p. A534
KREIDER, Robert Q., President and Chief Executive Officer, Devereux, Villanova, PA, p. B50
KREIDLER, Marlene, Executive Director Human Resources, San Joaquin Community Hospital, Bakersfield, CA, p. A55
KREIS, Katherine, Chief Clinical Officer, Kindred Rehabilitation Hospital Arlington, Arlington, TX, p. A592
KREITINGER, Tate J., Chief Executive Officer, The HealthCenter, Kalispell, MT, p. A385
KREITZ, Don
Chief Executive Officer, Chapman Medical Center, Orange, CA, p. A79
Interim Chief Executive Officer, Coastal Communities Hospital, Santa Ana, CA, p. A90
KREITZER, Teri, Director Human Resources, Saint Francis Medical Center, Cape Girardeau, MO, p. A364
KRELL, G. Christopher, M.D. Chief of Staff, South Lincoln Medical Center, Kemmerer, WY, p. A716
KRELSTEIN, Michael, M.D. Medical Director, San Diego County Psychiatric Hospital, San Diego, CA, p. A87
KREMER, Ruth, Director Information Services, CentraCare Health–Monticello, Monticello, MN, p. A343
KREN, John, Chief Financial Officer, St. John's Medical Center and Living Center, Jackson, WY, p. A716
KRENOS, Lori L., R.N. Chief Nursing Officer, Bay Area Hospital, Coos Bay, OR, p. A520
KREPPS, John, Senior Vice President Finance, Silver Cross Hospital, New Lenox, IL, p. A196
KRESGE, Dean, M.D. Chief of Staff, Stoughton Hospital Association, Stoughton, WI, p. A711
KRESSE, Gregory, M.D. Chairman Medical Staff, Eureka Springs Hospital, Eureka Springs, AR, p. A43
KRETSCHMAN, Robin, MSN Vice President Patient Care Services, Ministry Saint Joseph's Hospital, Marshfield, WI, p. A705
KRETSCHMER, Suzanne, Interim Hospital Administrator, Solara Hospital Conroe, Conroe, TX, p. A602
KRETZ, Blake, President, Texas Health Arlington Memorial Hospital, Arlington, TX, p. A593
KRETZINGER, Curt, Chief Operating Officer, Mosaic Life Care at St. Joseph, Saint Joseph, MO, p. A375
KREUTNER, Ron, Chief Financial Officer, San Joaquin General Hospital, French Camp, CA, p. A62
KREUTZER, Kevin, Chief Financial Officer, Russell Regional Hospital, Russell, KS, p. A249
KREUZ, Betsy, Chief Financial Officer, UPMC Altoona, Altoona, PA, p. A528
KREUZER, Jay E., FACHE, Chief Executive Officer, Kona Community Hospital, Kealakekua, HI, p. A170
KREYE, David, Chief Executive Officer, First Surgical Hospital, Bellaire, TX, p. A597
KRIEGER, Cathy, Human Resources Director, Greene County Medical Center, Jefferson, IA, p. A230
KRIEGER, Mark, Vice President and Chief Financial Officer, Barnes–Jewish Hospital, Saint Louis, MO, p. A376
KRIEGER, Robert M., Chief Executive Officer, Osceola Regional Medical Center, Kissimmee, FL, p. A130
KRIEGER, Tim, Director Information Systems, Harnett Health System, Dunn, NC, p. A459
KRILICH, Chad, M.D. Physician Executive, MultiCare Auburn Medical Center, Auburn, WA, p. A676
KRINKE, Susan, Chief Executive Officer, Kindred Hospital Lima, Lima, OH, p. A492
KRIPAKARAN, Kasturi, M.D. Medical Director, Andrew McFarland Mental Health Center, Springfield, IL, p. A201
KRIPINSKI, Laura, Chief Nursing Officer, Forks Community Hospital, Forks, WA, p. A679
KRISHNAN, Radha, M.D. Chief Medical Officer, Antelope Valley Hospital, Lancaster, CA, p. A67
KRISHNAN, Suresh, Vice President and Chief Information Officer, Loretto Hospital, Chicago, IL, p. A182
KRISHNASWAMY, Jaikumar, Chief Executive Officer, Doctors Hospital at White Rock Lake, Dallas, TX, p. A605
KRISTEL, John, President and Chief Executive Officer, Good Shepherd Rehabilitation Hospital, Allentown, PA, p. A528
KRISTEL, John, President and Chief Executive Officer, Good Shepherd Rehabilitation Network, Allentown, PA, p. B59

KRISTEL, John, President and Chief Executive Officer, Good Shepherd Specialty Hospital, Bethlehem, PA, p. A529

KRITZ, Howard
Director Human Resources, Bellevue Hospital Center, New York, NY, p. A438
Director, Henry J. Carter Specialty Hospital and Nursing Facility, New York, NY, p. A440

KRITZER, Tammy, Vice President Clinic Operations, Mayo Clinic Health System–Albert Lea and Austin, Austin, MN, p. A335

KRIVENKO, Chuck, M.D. Chief Medical Officer, Clinical and Quality Services, Lee Memorial Hospital, Fort Myers, FL, p. A127

KRMPOTIC, Debra J., R.N., Chief Executive Officer, Banner Estrella Medical Center, Phoenix, AZ, p. A34

KRODEL, Scott, Vice President Information Systems, Johnson Memorial Hospital, Franklin, IN, p. A209

KROESE, Robert D., FACHE, Chief Executive Officer, Pella Regional Health Center, Pella, IA, p. A233

KROGSTAD, Karen, M.D. Chief Medical Officer, Greater Regional Medical Center, Creston, IA, p. A225

KROHN, Karl, M.D. President Medical Staff, CHI St. Luke's Health Memorial Specialty Hospital, Lufkin, TX, p. A630

KROK, Stan, Chief Information Officer, Ann & Robert H. Lurie Children's Hospital of Chicago, Chicago, IL, p. A181

KROLL, Ronald, Chief Financial Officer, Mercy General Hospital, Sacramento, CA, p. A84

KROPP, Richard P., Vice President Human Resources, Lourdes Medical Center of Burlington County, Willingboro, NJ, p. A420

KROSOFF, Mary June, Chief Human Resources Officer, Highlands Hospital, Connellsville, PA, p. A532

KROUSE, Donald, M.D. Chief of Staff, Trinity Hospital, Weaverville, CA, p. A97

KROUSE, Michael
Chief Information Officer, OhioHealth Doctors Hospital, Columbus, OH, p. A486
Senior Vice President Chief Information Officer, OhioHealth Dublin Methodist Hospital, Dublin, OH, p. A489
Chief Information Officer Information Services, OhioHealth Grady Memorial Hospital, Delaware, OH, p. A488
Chief Information Officer, OhioHealth Grant Medical Center, Columbus, OH, p. A486
Chief Information Officer, OhioHealth Riverside Methodist Hospital, Columbus, OH, p. A486

KROUSE, Stephen W., Chief Human Resource Officer, St. Christopher's Hospital for Children, Philadelphia, PA, p. A545

KRUCZEK, Richard, Chief Executive Officer, HEALTHSOUTH Reading Rehabilitation Hospital, Reading, PA, p. A548

KRUEGER, Albert, M.D. Chief of Staff, Pioneers Medical Center, Meeker, CO, p. A107

KRUEGER, Christine, M.D. Chief of Staff, Munising Memorial Hospital, Munising, MI, p. A326

KRUEGER, David, Associate Director, Bath Veterans Affairs Medical Center, Bath, NY, p. A429

KRUEGER, Ellen, Director Human Resources, Chadron Community Hospital and Health Services, Chadron, NE, p. A391

KRUEGER, Eric, Chief Financial Officer, Mercy Hospital and Medical Center, Chicago, IL, p. A183

KRUEGER Jr., Harold L., Chief Executive Officer, Chadron Community Hospital and Health Services, Chadron, NE, p. A391

KRUEGER, James G., Ph.D., Chief Executive Officer, Rockefeller University Hospital, New York, NY, p. A444

KRUEGER, Justin, Chief Operating Officer, Aiken Regional Medical Centers, Aiken, SC, p. A557

KRUEGER, Mary T.
President, Ministry Good Samaritan Health Center, Merrill, WI, p. A706
President, Ministry Saint Clare's Hospital, Weston, WI, p. A714

KRUEGER, Pete, Director Human Resources, Borgess–Lee Memorial Hospital, Dowagiac, MI, p. A318

KRUEGER, Tammy A., Acting Director, Manchester Veterans Affairs Medical Center, Manchester, NH, p. A407

KRUG, Robert J., M.D., Chief Executive Officer, Mount Sinai Rehabilitation Hospital, Hartford, CT, p. A112

KRUGEL, Gary M., Chief Financial Officer, Norwegian American Hospital, Chicago, IL, p. A183

KRUGER, Cory, Interim Chief Executive Officer, Nebraska Spine Hospital, Omaha, NE, p. A396

KRUGER, Dale K., Chief Executive Officer and Chief Financial Officer, Tyler Healthcare Center Avera, Tyler, MN, p. A348

KRUMBERGER, Joanne, FACHE, Director, Portland Veterans Affairs Medical Center, Portland, OR, p. A524

KRUMMEL, Dere, Director Information Systems, Ochsner Medical Center – Kenner, Kenner, LA, p. A276

KRUMREY, Arthur J., Chief Information Officer, Loyola University Medical Center, Maywood, IL, p. A193

KRUMWIED, Robert D., President and Chief Executive Officer, Regional Mental Health Center, Merrillville, IN, p. A215

KRUPALA, Judith, R.N. Chief Nursing Officer, Cuero Community Hospital, Cuero, TX, p. A603

KRUSE, Joseph J.
Executive Vice President, Mayo Clinic Health System – Franciscan Healthcare in La Crosse, La Crosse, WI, p. A703
Chief Administrative Officer, Mayo Clinic Health System – Franciscan Healthcare in Sparta, Sparta, WI, p. A711

KRUSE, Marcia, R.N. Director Nursing, Logan County Hospital, Oakley, KS, p. A247

KRUSE, Victoria, Manager Human Resources, Franklin General Hospital, Hampton, IA, p. A228

KRUSH, Leanne, Chief Financial Officer, Phoenix Baptist Hospital, Phoenix, AZ, p. A35

KRUSIE, Kathleen R., FACHE, Chief Executive Officer, St. Joseph Regional Health Center, Bryan, TX, p. A599

KRUYER–COLLINS, Emyle
Director Human Resources, Doctors NeuroMedical Hospital, Bremen, IN, p. A205
Chief Human Resources Officer, Unity Medical & Surgical Hospital, Mishawaka, IN, p. A216

KRUZEL, Janet, Business Office Manager, CentraCare Health–Melrose, Melrose, MN, p. A342

KRUZICK, Michael, Acting Chief Financial Officer, Norwalk Hospital, Norwalk, CT, p. A114

KRYSTOWIAK, Thomas P.
Chief Financial Officer, Berlin Memorial Hospital, Berlin, WI, p. A698
Vice President Finance, Wild Rose Community Memorial Hospital, Wild Rose, WI, p. A714

KRYZANIAK, Larry, Chief Financial Officer, Hennepin County Medical Center, Minneapolis, MN, p. A342

KRZASTEK, Sue, Vice President Human Resources, Augusta Health, Fishersville, VA, p. A664

KU, Evelyn, Chief Nursing Officer, Monterey Park Hospital, Monterey Park, CA, p. A76

KUANGPARICHAT, Manoch, M.D. President Medical Staff, Excelsior Springs Hospital, Excelsior Springs, MO, p. A367

KUBACKI, Clayton, Interim Controller, Kindred Hospital Detroit, Detroit, MI, p. A318

KUBALA, Joseph
Chief Financial Officer, St. Vincent Jennings Hospital, North Vernon, IN, p. A218
Director Financial and Support Services, St. Vincent Salem Hospital, Salem, IN, p. A219

KUBALL, Lana, Director Administrative Services, Lucas County Health Center, Chariton, IA, p. A224

KUBE, Don, M.D. Chief of Staff, Dickinson County Healthcare System, Iron Mountain, MI, p. A322

KUBIAK, Phillip J., President, Hampstead Hospital, Hampstead, NH, p. A406

KUBIAK, Richard, M.D. Vice President Medical Affairs, Peconic Bay Medical Center, Riverhead, NY, p. A448

KUBOTA, Andrea, R.N. Director Patient Care Services, Shriners Hospitals for Children–Honolulu, Honolulu, HI, p. A169

KUBOUSHEK, David, Chief, Fiscal Service, Durham Veterans Affairs Medical Center, Durham, NC, p. A459

KUCERA, Kim, Chief Operating Officer, Mille Lacs Health System, Onamia, MN, p. A344

KUCHARSKI, Kathy, Director Management Information Systems, Brooks Memorial Hospital, Dunkirk, NY, p. A433

KUCKEWICH, Mike, Director Information Systems, Terre Haute Regional Hospital, Terre Haute, IN, p. A220

KUCZORA, Paul, Chief Executive Officer, Grant–Blackford Mental Health Center, Marion, IN, p. A215

KUEHLER, Sheila, R.N. Director of Nursing, Knox County Hospital, Knox City, TX, p. A626

KUEHN, David, Chief Financial Officer, Rusk County Memorial Hospital, Ladysmith, WI, p. A703

KUEHNEMUND, Bonnie, Comptroller, Heart of America Medical Center, Rugby, ND, p. A476

KUESTERSTEFFEN, Vicki, Chief Executive Officer, J. D. McCarty Center for Children With Developmental Disabilities, Norman, OK, p. A510

KUGHN, Yvonne, Chief Executive Officer, Southeast Michigan Surgical Hospital, Warren, MI, p. A332

KUHAR, Peggy A., R.N. Chief Nursing Officer, University Hospitals Geauga Medical Center, Chardon, OH, p. A481

KUHLMAN, Ian, Manager Information Technology, Shelby Memorial Hospital, Shelbyville, IL, p. A200

KUHN, Anita, Controller, Texas County Memorial Hospital, Houston, MO, p. A368

KUHN, Brenda, Ph.D
Chief Nursing Officer, Fort Hamilton Hospital, Hamilton, OH, p. A491
Chief Nursing Officer, Greene Memorial Hospital, Xenia, OH, p. A501
Chief Nursing Officer, Kettering Medical Center, Kettering, OH, p. A491
Chief Nursing Officer, Sycamore Medical Center, Miamisburg, OH, p. A494

KUHN, Keith, Chief Executive Officer, Haven Behavioral Senior Care of Dayton, Dayton, OH, p. A488

KUHN, Margueritte, M.D. Vice President Medical Affairs, MidMichigan Medical Center–Midland, Midland, MI, p. A325

KUHN, Steve, Chief Financial Officer, River Park Hospital, Huntington, WV, p. A692

KUHNS, Jay, Vice President Human Resources, All Children's Hospital Johns Hopkins Medicine, Saint Petersburg, FL, p. A141

KUKELHAN, Alison, Manager Human Resources, Adams Memorial Hospital, Decatur, IN, p. A207

KULHANEK, Linda, Chief Financial Officer, Memorial Hermann Katy Hospital, Katy, TX, p. A625

KULICK, Daniel, M.D. Chief of Staff, Marlette Regional Hospital, Marlette, MI, p. A325

KULIK, Alec G., Administrator, Cleveland Clinic Children's Hospital for Rehabilitation, Cleveland, OH, p. A484

KULISZ, Michael, D.O
Chief Medical Officer, Kishwaukee Hospital, DeKalb, IL, p. A186
Chief Medical Officer, Valley West Hospital, Sandwich, IL, p. A200

KULLMAN, Betsy, R.N. Executive Vice President and Chief Nursing Officer, Medical Center at Bowling Green, Bowling Green, KY, p. A254

KULMA, Mariarose, R.N. Vice President Patient Services, East Texas Medical Center Tyler, Tyler, TX, p. A649

KUMAR, Daryn J., Chief Executive Officer, Memorial Medical Center, Modesto, CA, p. A75

KUMAR, Nanda, M.D. Chief of Staff, Vibra Hospital of Northern California, Redding, CA, p. A82

KUMAR, Raji
Chief Executive Officer, Dallas Medical Center, Dallas, TX, p. A604
Regional Chief Executive Officer, Dallas Regional Medical Center, Mesquite, TX, p. A632

KUMMER, Margaret, Chief Human Resource Officer, Citizens Medical Center, Colby, KS, p. A238

KUNERT, Alicia, Executive Director, Conway Regional Rehab Hospital, Conway, AR, p. A42

KUNES, Courtney, Director Human Resources, Lock Haven Hospital, Lock Haven, PA, p. A539

KUNKEL, Stephanie, Vice President of Human Resources, Tampa Community Hospital, Tampa, FL, p. A145

KUNKLE, David, Chief Financial Officer, Havenwyck Hospital, Auburn Hills, MI, p. A314

KUNNAPPILLY, Chester, M.D. Chief Medical Officer and Chief Quality Officer, San Mateo Medical Center, San Mateo, CA, p. A90

KUNSTLING, Ted, M.D. Chief Medical Officer, Duke Raleigh Hospital, Raleigh, NC, p. A466

KUNTZ, Alicia, Nurse Manager, LifeCare Hospitals of Mechanicsburg, Mechanicsburg, PA, p. A540

KUNZ, Donna
Director Human Resources, Saint Luke's Cushing Hospital, Leavenworth, KS, p. A244
Director Human Resources, Saint Luke's North Hospital – Barry Road, Kansas City, MO, p. A370
Manager Human Resources, Saint Luke's South Hospital, Overland Park, KS, p. A248

KUNZA, Mary Kay, Manager Human Resources, Mercy Hospital Lincoln, Troy, MO, p. A379

KUNZE, Gloria A., R.N. Interim Chief Operating Officer, St. Joseph's Regional Medical Center, Paterson, NJ, p. A416

KUPER, Kandi, Chief Nursing Officer, Kit Carson County Health Service District, Burlington, CO, p. A100

KUPFERSTEIN, Ron, Chief Executive Officer, Monrovia Memorial Hospital, Monrovia, CA, p. A76

KUPLEN, Carol, R.N. Chief Operating Officer and Chief Nursing Officer, St. Luke's University Hospital – Bethlehem Campus, Bethlehem, PA, p. A529

KUPLER, Carol R., President and Chief Executive Officer, St. Luke's University Hospital – Bethlehem Campus, Bethlehem, PA, p. A529

KURAITIS, Kestutis V., M.D. Chief of Staff, Pioneers Memorial Healthcare District, Brawley, CA, p. A56

KURCAB, Jeff, Chief Financial Officer, LewisGale Hospital Pulaski, Pulaski, VA, p. A671

KURESKA, Kirk, Chief Executive Officer, RiverWoods Behavioral Health System, Riverdale, GA, p. A163

Index of Health Care Professionals / Lamanteer

Index of Health Care Professionals

KURIAN, Santha, M.D. Chief of Staff, James E. Van Zandt Veterans Affairs Medical Center, Altoona, PA, p. A528
KURLE, Janet, Chief Financial Officer, Community Memorial Hospital, Turtle Lake, ND, p. A476
KURRA, Shankar, M.D. Senior Vice President Medical Affairs, Fisher–Titus Medical Center, Norwalk, OH, p. A495
KURTZ, Kris, Controller, Metro Health Hospital, Wyoming, MI, p. A333
KURTZ, Maria
Director Human Resources, Lutheran Hospital of Indiana, Fort Wayne, IN, p. A208
Director Human Resources, Orthopaedic Hospital of Lutheran Health Network, Fort Wayne, IN, p. A208
KURTZ, Marvin A., Chief Financial Officer, Florida Hospital Carrollwood, Tampa, FL, p. A144
KURTZ, Jr., Thomas F., Chief Operating Officer, Georgia Regional Hospital at Savannah, Savannah, GA, p. A164
KURTZ, Thomas M., President and Chief Executive Officer, Windber Medical Center, Windber, PA, p. A553
KURZ, Kenneth R., M.D. Chief of Staff, MidState Medical Center, Meriden, CT, p. A113
KURZ, Sharon H., Ph.D., Chief Executive Officer, St. Elias Specialty Hospital, Anchorage, AK, p. A27
KURZENDOERFER, Laura, R.N. Chief Nursing Officer, Great Plains Regional Medical Center, Elk City, OK, p. A506
KUSHNER, Michael S., Senior Vice President and Chief Talent Officer, Nicklaus Children's Hospital, Miami, FL, p. A134
KUSLER, Julie, Manager Information Services, Avera St. Luke's Hospital, Aberdeen, SD, p. A567
KUSNIERZ, William J., Vice President and Chief Financial Officer, Springfield Regional Medical Center, Springfield, OH, p. A498
KUTA, Daniel, R.N. Director of Nursing, Power County Hospital District, American Falls, ID, p. A172
KUTCH, John M., President, Trinity Health, Minot, ND, p. A476
KUTCHER, Gregory, M.D., President and Chief Executive Officer, Mayo Clinic Health System in Mankato, Mankato, MN, p. A341
KUTILEK, Richard J., Chief Operating Officer, Calvary Hospital, NY, p. A439
KUTNER, Jean, M.D. Chief Medical Officer, University of Colorado Hospital, Aurora, CO, p. A99
KUYKENDALL, Jana, Chief Executive Officer, Post Acute/Warm Springs Specialty Hospital of Luling, Luling, TX, p. A630
KUZAS, Betsy, Executive Vice President and Chief Operating Officer, Phoenix Children's Hospital, Phoenix, AZ, p. A35
KUZEE, Ann, Executive Director Human Resources, Riverview Hospital, Noblesville, IN, p. A218
KUZMA, Gregory, Vice President and Chief Financial Officer, Verde Valley Medical Center, Cottonwood, AZ, p. A30
KWATER, Sherry M., R.N. Chief Nursing Officer, Penn State Milton S. Hershey Medical Center, Hershey, PA, p. A536
KWIATEK, Susan, R.N., Executive Director, Glen Cove Hospital, Glen Cove, NY, p. A434
KWIESIELEWICZ, Nancy
Human Resources Manager, Ministry Good Samaritan Health Center, Merrill, WI, p. A706
Human Resources Manager, Ministry Saint Clare's Hospital, Weston, WI, p. A714
KYHNELL, Koreen H., Vice President Human Resources, Indiana University Health Arnett Hospital, Lafayette, IN, p. A214
KYLER, Yvonne
Director Human Resources, Texas Health Arlington Memorial Hospital, Arlington, TX, p. A593
Director Human Resources, Texas Health Heart & Vascular Hospital Arlington, Arlington, TX, p. A593
KYRIACOU, George M., President and Chief Executive Officer, Gaylord Hospital, Wallingford, CT, p. A115
KYWI, Alberto
Chief Information Officer, Goleta Valley Cottage Hospital, Santa Barbara, CA, p. A91
Chief Information Officer, Santa Barbara Cottage Hospital, Santa Barbara, CA, p. A91
Chief Information Officer, Santa Ynez Valley Cottage Hospital, Solvang, CA, p. A92

## L

L'HEUREUX, Dennis P., Chief Information Officer, Rockford Memorial Hospital, Rockford, IL, p. A199
L'ITALIEN, Mark, Director Information Services, Salem Regional Medical Center, Salem, OH, p. A497
LA CAVA, Joseph, Chief Nursing Officer and Director Of Anesthesia, DeSoto Memorial Hospital, Arcadia, FL, p. A121
LA CROIX, Kent, Supervisor Information Technology, Schoolcraft Memorial Hospital, Manistique, MI, p. A325
LA PORTE, Todd
Chief Financial Officer, HonorHealth John C. Lincoln Medical Center, Phoenix, AZ, p. A35
Senior Vice President and Chief Financial Officer, HonorHealth Scottsdale Osborn Medical Center, Scottsdale, AZ, p. A37
Senior Vice President and Chief Financial Officer, HonorHealth Scottsdale Shea Medical Center, Scottsdale, AZ, p. A37
Chief Financial Officer, HonorHealth Scottsdale Thompson Peak Medical Center, Scottsdale, AZ, p. A37
LABAGNARA, James, M.D. Vice President Medical Affairs, St. Joseph's Regional Medical Center, Paterson, NJ, p. A416
LABAND, Andrew, Chief Information Officer, McLean Hospital, Belmont, MA, p. A302
LABARGE, Robert J., President and Chief Executive Officer, Sturgis Hospital, Sturgis, MI, p. A331
LABELLE, Douglas, M.D. Chief Medical Officer, UP Health System–Bell, Ishpeming, MI, p. A323
LABELLE, James, M.D
Chief Medical Officer, Scripps Green Hospital, La Jolla, CA, p. A66
Chief Medical Officer, Scripps Memorial Hospital–La Jolla, La Jolla, CA, p. A66
LABER, Susan, R.N. Chief Nursing Officer, Tampa Community Hospital, Tampa, FL, p. A145
LABIAGA, Kimberly, Human Resources Leader, Kaiser Permanente Fontana Medical Center, Fontana, CA, p. A61
LABINE, Lance C., Administrator, Dr. Dan C. Trigg Memorial Hospital, Tucumcari, NM, p. A427
LABONTE, Robin, Leader Financial Care, York Hospital, York, ME, p. A292
LABORANTI, Sarah M., Interim Director Human Resources, Tennova Physicians Regional Medical Center, Knoxville, TN, p. A580
LABORIE, Sheree, Director Human Resources, Lakewood Hospital, Lakewood, OH, p. A491
LABOWITZ, Robert, Chief Nursing Officer, Cornerstone Hospital of SouthEast Arizona, Tucson, AZ, p. A39
LABRIOLA, Terri, Human Resources Officer, Sierra Nevada Memorial Hospital, Grass Valley, CA, p. A64
LABRUM, Chad, Chief Financial Officer, Ashley Regional Medical Center, Vernal, UT, p. A659
LACASSE, Paul E., M.P.H., President and Chief Executive Officer, Beaumont Hospital – Farmington Hills, Farmington Hills, MI, p. A319
LACAZE, Todd, Chief Financial Officer, Tulane Medical Center, New Orleans, LA, p. A282
LACEFIELD, Gayla, Director Human Resources, Howard Memorial Hospital, Nashville, AR, p. A48
LACEY, Carmen, R.N., President, Charles A. Cannon Memorial Hospital, Linville, NC, p. A464
LACEY, III, John W., M.D. Senior Vice President and Chief Medical Officer, University of Tennessee Medical Center, Knoxville, TN, p. A581
LACEY, Paul, M.D. Chief Medical Staff, North Valley Hospital, Tonasket, WA, p. A686
LACHANCE, Eric, Chief Financial Officer, Munroe Regional Medical Center, Ocala, FL, p. A137
LACHAPELLE, Diana, Controller, HEALTHSOUTH Rehabilitation Hospital, Concord, NH, p. A405
LACHER, Paula A., MSN Chief Nursing Officer, West Penn Hospital, Pittsburgh, PA, p. A547
LACHINA, Ignazio, M.D. Medical Director, HEALTHSOUTH Rehabilitation Hospital of Cypress, Houston, TX, p. A620
LACHNEY, Cheryl, Chief Executive Officer, Longleaf Hospital, Alexandria, LA, p. A268
LACHOWSKY, John, M.D. Chief Medical Officer, Mercy Hospital Ozark, Ozark, AR, p. A49
LACHTERMAN, Bruce, M.D. Chief of Medical Staff, St. Luke's Lakeside Hospital, The Woodlands, TX, p. A647
LACKEY, Lori, Chief Financial Officer, Sabetha Community Hospital, Sabetha, KS, p. A249
LACKNEY, Christopher J., Director Human Resources, Grace Cottage Hospital, Townshend, VT, p. A661
LACOT, Ivette, Director Human Resources, Hospital Episcopal San Lucas Guayama, Guayama, PR, p. A721
LACY, Albert, Associate Director of Information Technology, Tampa Community Hospital, Tampa, FL, p. A145
LACY, Angela, Director of Nursing, Bolivar General Hospital, Bolivar, TN, p. A574
LACY, Dwight A., Chief Executive Officer, Millwood Hospital, Arlington, TX, p. A592
LACY, Edward L., FACHE, Vice President and Administrator, Baptist Health Medical Center–Heber Springs, Heber Springs, AR, p. A45
LACY, Tyson, Chief Financial Officer, Lincoln Hospital, Davenport, WA, p. A678
LADAROLA, Sandra, Chief Nursing Officer, Waterbury Hospital, Waterbury, CT, p. A116
LADD, Bill, Director Information Services, Western Missouri Medical Center, Warrensburg, MO, p. A380
LADWIG, Michael, M.D. Chief of Staff, Marion Veterans Affairs Medical Center, Marion, IL, p. A193
LAEL, Marielle, R.N. Chief Nursing Officer, Select Specialty Hospital–Fort Wayne, Fort Wayne, IN, p. A209
LAFERNEY, Jimmy, M.D. Vice President Medical Staff Affairs, Baylor Medical Center at Frisco, Frisco, TX, p. A615
LAFFERTY, Aline, Vice President Human Resources, ProMedica Monroe Regional Hospital, Monroe, MI, p. A326
LAFFEY, Leah, R.N., Chief Executive Officer, HEALTHSOUTH Rehabilitation Hospital of Sewickley, Sewickley, PA, p. A550
LAFLAMME, Christine, R.N. Chief Nursing Officer, Seton Smithville Regional Hospital, Smithville, TX, p. A644
LAFLEUR, Cindy, Senior Administrator, Via Christi Rehabilitation Hospital, Wichita, KS, p. A253
LAFLEUR, Phillip, M.D. Medical Director, MMO WestEnd Hospital, Jennings, LA, p. A276
LAFRANCOIS, Mary, Vice President Human Resources, CHRISTUS Spohn Hospital Corpus Christi Memorial, Corpus Christi, TX, p. A602
LAGASSE, David A., Senior Vice President Fiscal Affairs, McLean Hospital, Belmont, MA, p. A302
LAGNESE, John, M.D. Vice President Medical Affairs, UPMC St. Margaret, Pittsburgh, PA, p. A547
LAGROU, Robert, D.O. Medical Director, Henry Ford Kingswood Hospital, Ferndale, MI, p. A319
LAHASKY, Douglas, Chief Financial Officer, Avoyelles Hospital, Marksville, LA, p. A279
LAHAYE, Daniel, Manager, Savoy Medical Center, Mamou, LA, p. A279
LAHOUT, Brenda, Chief Nurse Executive, Danville State Hospital, Danville, PA, p. A532
LAHTI, Molly, Director Human Resources, Parkland Medical Center, Derry, NH, p. A405
LAI, Daniel, Controller, HEALTHSOUTH Rehabilitation Hospital–Las Vegas, Las Vegas, NV, p. A402
LAI, Iris, Chief Executive Officer, Alhambra Hospital Medical Center, Alhambra, CA, p. A53
LAIBINIS, Walter, M.D. Chief Medical Officer, Soldiers and Sailors Memorial Hospital, Wellsboro, PA, p. A552
LAIGN, Michael B., President and Chief Executive Officer, Holy Redeemer Hospital, Meadowbrook, PA, p. A540
LAIOSA, Sarah, M.D. Chief Medical Staff, Harney District Hospital, Burns, OR, p. A519
LAIRD, Carol, R.N. Chief Nursing Officer, Southern Tennessee Regional Health System–Lawrenceburg, Lawrenceburg, TN, p. A581
LAIRD, Charles, Chief Executive Officer, Menorah Medical Center, Overland Park, KS, p. A248
LAIRD, Jeff, Controller, Stephens County Hospital, Toccoa, GA, p. A166
LAIRD, Patrick
Chief Clinical Officer, Nexus Specialty Hospital, Shenandoah, TX, p. A643
Chief Clinical Officer, Nexus Specialty Hospital The Woodlands, Spring, TX, p. A644
LAIRD, Shaw, Chief Information Officer, Chester Regional Medical Center, Chester, SC, p. A558
LAISTER, Judy K., Director, Human Resources, Methodist Mansfield Medical Center, Mansfield, TX, p. A631
LAKE, Chandra, Associate Director, Sheridan Veterans Affairs Medical Center, Sheridan, WY, p. A717
LAKE, Nathan, Vice President Human Resources, Prairie Lakes Healthcare System, Watertown, SD, p. A572
LAKE, Peter M., M.D. Chief Medical Officer, Rogers Memorial Hospital, Oconomowoc, WI, p. A708
LAKE, Ryan, Director Medical Imaging and Information Technology, Glencoe Regional Health Services, Glencoe, MN, p. A339
LAKEY, Travis, Chief Financial Officer, Mayers Memorial Hospital District, Fall River Mills, CA, p. A61
LAKHANI, Ushma, Interim Director Human Resources, Shriners Hospitals for Children–Galveston, Galveston, TX, p. A615
LAKINS, Tom, Director Information Systems, Tennova Physicians Regional Medical Center, Knoxville, TN, p. A580
LAKSHMANAN, Rekha, M.D. Medical Director, Kindred Hospital–St. Louis at Mercy, Saint Louis, MO, p. A376
LAKSHMANAN, S., M.D. Chief of Staff, Salem Township Hospital, Salem, IL, p. A200
LALIBERTE, John, Chief Information Officer, St. Vincent's Blount, Oneonta, AL, p. A23
LALLY, James M., D.O., President and Chief Medical Officer, Chino Valley Medical Center, Chino, CA, p. A57
LALLY, Jr., Robert P., Vice President Finance, MedStar Franklin Square Medical Center, Baltimore, MD, p. A294
LAM, Shiva, M.D. Executive Medical Director, Austin Lakes Hospital, Austin, TX, p. A593
LAMADELEINE, Joseph, Chief Financial Officer, Veterans Affairs Connecticut Healthcare System, West Haven, CT, p. A116
LAMANTEER, Mike, M.D. Senior Vice President Medical Affairs, Baptist St. Anthony Health System, Amarillo, TX, p. A591

 Index of Health Care Professionals A891

LAMANTIA, Sheirlie, M.D. Chief of Staff, Grant Regional Health Center, Lancaster, WI, p. A704

LAMARCHE, Heather, Manager Human Resources, AMG Specialty Hospital–Lafayette, Lafayette, LA, p. A277

LAMARCHE, Marie, Executive Director, Human Resources, Organizational Development, Employee Health, Harrison Medical Center, Bremerton, WA, p. A676

LAMARCHE, Maximo, M.D. Chief Medical Officer, AMG Specialty Hospital–Lafayette, Lafayette, LA, p. A277

LAMB, Andrew, M.D. Chief of Staff, Alamance Regional Medical Center, Burlington, NC, p. A456

LAMB, Cindy, Director Human Resources, Marias Medical Center, Shelby, MT, p. A387

LAMB, Hope, Manager Human Resources, Kimble Hospital, Junction, TX, p. A625

LAMB, Thomas, Director Information Systems, Monongahela Valley Hospital, Monongahela, PA, p. A540

LAMB–PAGONE, Jerilynn, Nurse Executive, Connecticut Valley Hospital, Middletown, CT, p. A113

LAMBERT, Amand, Director Human Resources, Allen Parish Hospital, Kinder, LA, p. A276

LAMBERT, Barbara, Director Healthcare Compliance, Eastern State Hospital, Williamsburg, VA, p. A674

LAMBERT, Cheryl, Chief Financial Officer, Acuity Specialty Hospital of New Jersey, Atlantic City, NJ, p. A409

LAMBERT, Karen A., President, Advocate Good Shepherd Hospital, Barrington, IL, p. A179

LAMBERT, Lynn, Chief Financial Officer, Harnett Health System, Dunn, NC, p. A459

LAMBERT, Paul, M.D. Chief of Staff, Boise Veterans Affairs Medical Center, Boise, ID, p. A172

LAMBERT, Robert K., FACHE, President and Chief Executive Officer, Arnot Health, Elmira, NY, p. B12

LAMBERT, Suzanne, R.N. Regional Chief Nursing Officer and Support Services, Presence Saints Mary & Elizabeth Medical Center, Chicago, IL, p. A183

LAMBERTON, Natalie D., Chief Executive Officer, Regency Hospital of Fort Worth, Fort Worth, TX, p. A614

LAMBETH, Laura, Chief Executive Officer, Ashe Memorial Hospital, Jefferson, NC, p. A463

LAMBKE, Michael, M.D. Medical Director, Redington–Fairview General Hospital, Skowhegan, ME, p. A292

LAMBRECHT, Craig, M.D., President, Sanford Bismarck, Bismarck, ND, p. A472

LAMEBULL, Charlotte, Administrative Officer, Fort Belknap U. S. Public Health Service Indian Hospital, Harlem, MT, p. A384

LAMEN, Drake M., M.D., President and Chief Executive Officer, Chenango Memorial Hospital, Norwich, NY, p. A446

LAMEY, Mark, Commander, U. S. Air Force Regional Hospital, Elmendorf AFB, AK, p. A28

LAMEY, Rebecca, Vice President Human Resources, MaineGeneral Medical Center, Augusta, ME, p. A288

LAMLE, Sandra, Chief Financial Officer, Okeene Municipal Hospital, Okeene, OK, p. A511

LAMMERS, Brent R., Chief Executive Officer, Alleghany Memorial Hospital, Sparta, NC, p. A469

LAMMERS, Sandra, Coordinator Human Resources and Finance, CHI Health Mercy Corning, Corning, IA, p. A225

LAMONT, Jennifer, Chief Financial Officer, Westlake Hospital, Melrose Park, IL, p. A194

LAMORELLA, Vincent M., Chief Financial Officer, Clarion Hospital, Clarion, PA, p. A531

LAMOUREUX, John P., Commander, Dwight David Eisenhower Army Medical Center, Fort Gordon, GA, p. A157

LAMOUREUX, Laurie, Director of Finance, Cooley Dickinson Hospital, Northampton, MA, p. A309

LAMPE, Michael, M.D. Chief of Staff, Kossuth Regional Health Center, Algona, IA, p. A222

LAMPE, Tammy K., Director Human Resources, Edwards County Hospital and Healthcare Center, Kinsley, KS, p. A243

LAMPLEY, Danny, Chief Operating Officer, Harrisburg Medical Center, Harrisburg, IL, p. A189

LAMPTON, Lucius, M.D. Medical Director, Beacham Memorial Hospital, Magnolia, MS, p. A356

LANCASTER, Penny, Controller, Cascade Medical Center, Cascade, ID, p. A173

LANCASTER, Tim, FACHE, President and Chief Executive Officer, Hendrick Health System, Abilene, TX, p. A590

LANCEY, Katie, Chief Nursing Officer, North Georgia Medical Center, Ellijay, GA, p. A157

LAND, David, D.O. Chief Medical Staff, Fort Duncan Regional Medical Center, Eagle Pass, TX, p. A609

LAND, Susann, M.D. Chief Medical Officer, Texas Health Harris Methodist Hospital Hurst–Euless–Bedford, Bedford, TX, p. A597

LANDAU, Kenneth G., Chief Operating Officer, Curry General Hospital, Gold Beach, OR, p. A521

LANDENBERGER, Jason, Director of Nursing, Community Memorial Hospital, Turtle Lake, ND, p. A476

LANDERS, Alice, Administrative Director Operations, Texas Health Harris Methodist Hospital Hurst–Euless–Bedford, Bedford, TX, p. A597

LANDERS, Kimberly A., MS Vice President Patient Care Services, Morris Hospital & Healthcare Centers, Morris, IL, p. A195

LANDERS, LaLah, BSN, RN CNO, Saunders Medical Center, Crete, NE, p. A391

LANDGARTEN, Steven, M.D. Chief Medical Officer, Hillcrest Medical Center, Tulsa, OK, p. A516

LANDIS, Bradlee, Chief Information Officer, Faith Community Hospital, Jacksboro, TX, p. A624

LANDIS, Catherine, R.N., President and Chief Nursing Officer, Transylvania Regional Hospital, Brevard, NC, p. A456

LANDMAN, Paul, Director Human Resources, Ellwood City Hospital, Ellwood City, PA, p. A533

LANDRAU, Erika, Director Human Resources, HEALTHSOUTH Hospital of Manati, Manati, PR, p. A721

LANDRENEAU, Derrick, Director of Nursing, Baton Rouge Rehabilitation Hospital, Baton Rouge, LA, p. A269

LANDRETH, Kathy, Interim Chief Executive Officer, Bath Community Hospital, Hot Springs, VA, p. A666

LANDRETH, Sandy, Director Human Resources, Seiling Municipal Hospital, Seiling, OK, p. A514

LANDRETH, Shannan, Information Systems, Livingston Hospital and Healthcare Services, Salem, KY, p. A265

LANDRUM, David, Chief Police Services, Atascadero State Hospital, Atascadero, CA, p. A54

LANDRUM, Scott M., Interim Administrator, Graham Regional Medical Center, Graham, TX, p. A616

LANDRY, Adam, Coordinator Computer Systems, Northern Maine Medical Center, Fort Kent, ME, p. A290

LANDRY, Candy, Chief Human Resource Officer, Eastside Psychiatric Hospital, Tallahassee, FL, p. A144

LANDRY, Donna F., Chief Operating Officer, Our Lady of Lourdes Regional Medical Center, Lafayette, LA, p. A278

LANDRY, Lisa G., Human Resources Director, Redington–Fairview General Hospital, Skowhegan, ME, p. A292

LANDRY, Ray A., Chief Executive Officer, Abbeville General Hospital, Abbeville, LA, p. A268

LANDRY NUNEZ, Lexis, Chief Executive Officer, St. Catherine Memorial Hospital, New Orleans, LA, p. A282

LANDSMAN, Joseph, President and Chief Executive Officer, University of Tennessee Medical Center, Knoxville, TN, p. A581

LANDSTROM, Gay L., Ph.D. Chief Nursing Officer, Dartmouth–Hitchcock Medical Center, Lebanon, NH, p. A407

LANDSTROM, John
Vice President Human Resources and Operations, RML Specialty Hospital, Chicago, IL, p. A184
Director Human Resources, RML Specialty Hospital, Hinsdale, IL, p. A191

LANE, Diron
Director Information Systems, LewisGale Hospital Montgomery, Blacksburg, VA, p. A662
Director Information Systems, LewisGale Hospital Pulaski, Pulaski, VA, p. A671

LANE, Kevin, D.O. Chief of Staff, Hardeman County Memorial Hospital, Quanah, TX, p. A638

LANE, Kevin, Vice President Information Systems, Silver Cross Hospital, New Lenox, IL, p. A196

LANE, Kim, Chief Fiscal Service, Overton Brooks Veterans Affairs Medical Center, Shreveport, LA, p. A284

LANE, Mike, Chief Operating Officer, Twin Cities Community Hospital, Templeton, CA, p. A94

LANE, Richard, Chief Financial Officer, Mid–America Rehabilitation Hospital, Shawnee Mission, KS, p. A250

LANE, Stacey
Executive Assistant Human Resources, Chambers Memorial Hospital, Danville, AR, p. A42
Director Human Resources, Hunt Regional Community Hospital, Commerce, TX, p. A602

LANEAUX, Eleanor, Director Information Systems, Placentia–Linda Hospital, Placentia, CA, p. A81

LANER, Jr., Richard, Manager Information Systems, Miners' Colfax Medical Center, Raton, NM, p. A425

LANEY, Samuel Mark, M.D., President and Chief Executive Officer, Mosaic Life Care at St. Joseph, Saint Joseph, MO, p. A375

LANG, Cyndi, Director Information Services, French Hospital Medical Center, San Luis Obispo, CA, p. A90

LANG, David, Vice President Human Resources, Baptist Health Madisonville, Madisonville, KY, p. A262

LANG, Gordon, M.D. Chief of Staff, Trego County–Lemke Memorial Hospital, Wakeeney, KS, p. A252

LANG, Heidi, M.D. Chief Medical Officer, Rehabilitation Hospital of Fort Wayne, Fort Wayne, IN, p. A209

LANG, Jeff, President, UP Health System–Portage, Hancock, MI, p. A322

LANG, John Christopher, Chief Executive Officer, Cass Regional Medical Center, Harrisonville, MO, p. A368

LANG, Jordan, Director Human Resources, Brigham City Community Hospital, Brigham City, UT, p. A654

LANG, Joseph, M.D. Chief of Staff, Carolinas ContinueCare Hospital at Pineville, Charlotte, NC, p. A457

LANG, Linda, Chief Human Resources Officer, Marin General Hospital, Greenbrae, CA, p. A64

LANG, Nicholas P., M.D. Chief Medical Officer, UAMS Medical Center, Little Rock, AR, p. A47

LANG, Richard, Ed.D. Vice President and Chief Information Officer, Doylestown Hospital, Doylestown, PA, p. A533

LANG, Richard T., Chief Financial Officer, Gouverneur Hospital, Gouverneur, NY, p. A434

LANGBEHN, Cody, Administrator, St. Luke's Wood River Medical Center, Ketchum, ID, p. A174

LANGBEHN, Jennifer, Medical Director, Mayo Clinic Health System in Saint James, Saint James, MN, p. A346

LANGBERG, Michael L., M.D. Senior Vice President Medical Affairs and Chief Medical Officer, Cedars–Sinai Medical Center, Los Angeles, CA, p. A69

LANGDON, Ashlee, Controller, Yalobusha General Hospital, Water Valley, MS, p. A361

LANGE, Connie, R.N. Vice President of Patient Care Services, Lakes Regional Healthcare, Spirit Lake, IA, p. A235

LANGENBERG, Shannon, Director Human Resources, Jackson County Regional Health Center, Maquoketa, IA, p. A231

LANGFELDER, Richard, Executive Vice President and Chief Financial Officer, NYU Lutheran, NY, p. A444

LANGFORD, Terrie, Director Human Resources, Heritage Park Surgical Hospital, Sherman, TX, p. A644

LANGHOFF, Erik, Ph.D., Director, James J. Peters Veterans Affairs Medical Center, NY, p. A440

LANGLITZ, Sara, Controller, Kindred Hospital–Houston, Houston, TX, p. A620

LANGLOIS, John, Chief Financial Officer, Walker Baptist Medical Center, Jasper, AL, p. A21

LANGMEAD, Paula A., Chief Executive Officer, Springfield Hospital Center, Sykesville, MD, p. A300

LANGOSCH, Richard, President and Chief Executive Officer, Flagstaff Medical Center, Flagstaff, AZ, p. A31

LANGSTON, David L.
Corporate Vice President Human Resources, East Texas Medical Center Rehabilitation Hospital, Tyler, TX, p. A648
Corporate Vice President Human Resources, East Texas Medical Center Specialty Hospital, Tyler, TX, p. A648

LANGSTON, Kimberly K., R.N., Chief Executive Officer, Scott and White Continuing Care Hospital, Temple, TX, p. A647

LANGSTON, Roxann, Chief Nursing Officer, East Texas Medical Center Trinity, Trinity, TX, p. A648

LANGSTON, Sheila, Administrator, Oceans Behavioral Hospital of De Ridder, Deridder, LA, p. A273

LANHAM, Gary, Chief Medical Officer, Parkridge Medical Center, Chattanooga, TN, p. A575

LANIER, Donna, R.N. Chief Nursing Officer, Delta Medical Center, Memphis, TN, p. A583

LANIG, Indria S., M.D. Medical Director, Northern Colorado Rehabilitation Hospital, Johnstown, CO, p. A105

LANKFORD, Deanna, Business Office Manager, Plano Specialty Hospital, Plano, TX, p. A637

LANKOWICZ, Andrew, President, CHI Mercy Hospital, Devils Lake, ND, p. A473

LANNOYE, Craig, Vice President Operations, Wilson Memorial Hospital, Sidney, OH, p. A497

LANOUE, Cheryl, Chief Financial Officer, Ottawa County Health Center, Minneapolis, KS, p. A246

LANS, Sue, Comptroller, Harlan County Health System, Alma, NE, p. A389

LANSDOWNE, Lynn M., Vice President Human Resources, Pocono Medical Center, East Stroudsburg, PA, p. A533

LANSFORD, Georgene, Director Information Systems, HSHS St. Mary's Hospital, Streator, IL, p. A202

LANTOS, Phyllis R., Executive Vice President, Corporate Chief Financial Officer and Treasurer, New York–Presbyterian Hospital, New York, NY, p. A443

LANTZY, William, Vice President Finance, DMC Huron Valley–Sinai Hospital, Commerce Township, MI, p. A317

LANZA, Nicholas, Controller, St. Mary's General Hospital, Passaic, NJ, p. A416

LANZA, Raymond, D.O. Medical Director, Runnells Center for Rehabilitation and Healthcare, Berkeley Heights, NJ, p. A409

LAPERLE, Linda M., Vice President Administrative Services, Androscoggin Valley Hospital, Berlin, NH, p. A405

LAPEROUSE, Bryan, Interim Administrator, St. Martin Hospital, Breaux Bridge, LA, p. A271

LAPHAM, Lisa, President and Chief Executive Officer, HealthSource Saginaw, Inc., Saginaw, MI, p. A329

LAPLANT, Dawn, Manager Health Information Management, Brown County Community Treatment Center, Green Bay, WI, p. A702

Index of Health Care Professionals / Law


LAPOSTA, Mary Jo, Ph.D. Senior Vice President Patient Care and Organizational Excellence, Saratoga Hospital, Saratoga Springs, NY, p. A450
LAPUZ, Miguel H., M.D., Director, Salem Veterans Affairs Medical Center, Salem, VA, p. A672
LARA, Anne, Chief Information Officer, Union Hospital, Elkton, MD, p. A297
LARA, Sergio, M.D. Chief Medical Officer, Covenant Hospital Plainview, Plainview, TX, p. A636
LARAMIE, Robert, Chief Information Officer, Beverly Hospital, Beverly, MA, p. A302
LARAMIE, Wayne, Vice President Nursing, SSM St. Clare Health Center, Fenton, MO, p. A367
LARCAS, John, M.D. Acting Medical Director, Choate Mental Health Center, Anna, IL, p. A178
LARCEN, Stephen W., Ph.D., President and Chief Executive Officer, Natchaug Hospital, Mansfield Center, CT, p. A113
LAREAU, Daniel, Executive Director Operations and Information, St. Vincent Carmel Hospital, Carmel, IN, p. A206
LAREAU, Kim, Vice President and Chief Information Officer, Regions Hospital, Saint Paul, MN, p. A346
LARET, Mark R., Chief Executive Officer, UCSF Medical Center, San Francisco, CA, p. A89
LARIMER, Cynthia, M.D. Chief of Staff, Lake Butler Hospital Hand Surgery Center, Lake Butler, FL, p. A131
LARIMORE, Rhonda, Vice President Human Resources, Magee–Womens Hospital of UPMC, Pittsburgh, PA, p. A546
LARISCY, Robin Barton, M.D. Medical Director, Mary S Harper Geriatric Psychiatry Center, Tuscaloosa, AL, p. A25
LARIVEE, Theresa M., Executive Director, Pennsylvania Hospital, Philadelphia, PA, p. A545
LARIVIERE, Beckye, Controller, HEALTHSOUTH Rehabilitation Hospital of Charleston, Charleston, SC, p. A558
LARKIN, Kevin, Regional Chief Financial Officer, Presence Saint Joseph Hospital, Elgin, IL, p. A187
LARKIN, Kim, Chief Information Officer, Washington County Hospital, Nashville, IL, p. A196
LARKINS, Gloria, Vice President Finance, Detroit Receiving Hospital/University Health Center, Detroit, MI, p. A317
LARMER, Jennifer, Chief Clinical Officer, Lincoln Hospital, Davenport, WA, p. A678
LARMON, Mary Jane, Chief Clinical Officer, Vibra Hospital of Mahoning Valley, Boardman, OH, p. A480
LARNER, Cheryl, Chief Financial Officer, Sentara CarePlex Hospital, Hampton, VA, p. A666
LAROCHELLE, Albert, Chief Executive Officer, Reeves County Hospital, Pecos, TX, p. A636
LARRISON Jr., Robert G., President, Carolinas Rehabilitation, Charlotte, NC, p. A457
LARSEN, Bill, Vice President Human Resources, Driscoll Children's Hospital, Corpus Christi, TX, p. A602
LARSEN, Catherine M., Director Marketing, Sutter Tracy Community Hospital, Tracy, CA, p. A94
LARSEN, Dave M., Chief Financial Officer, LDS Hospital, Salt Lake City, UT, p. A658
LARSEN, Donald, M.D
Chief Medical Officer, Keck Hospital of USC, Los Angeles, CA, p. A70
Chief Medical Officer, USC Verdugo Hills Hospital, Glendale, CA, p. A64
LARSEN, Michael, Director Information Systems, Baylor Medical Center at Garland, Garland, TX, p. A616
LARSEN, Ryan C., FACHE, Chief Executive Officer, Community Medical Center, Falls City, NE, p. A391
LARSON, Alan, Chief Executive Officer, Danville Regional Medical Center, Danville, VA, p. A664
LARSON, Barbara, R.N. Vice President and Chief Nursing Officer, Ottumwa Regional Health Center, Ottumwa, IA, p. A233
LARSON, Bill, Chief Financial Officer, Torrance Memorial Medical Center, Torrance, CA, p. A94
LARSON, Eric, Director Human Resources, HEALTHSOUTH Harmarville Rehabilitation Hospital, Pittsburgh, PA, p. A546
LARSON, Erick, Vice President and Chief Information Officer, Mid–Columbia Medical Center, The Dalles, OR, p. A526
LARSON, Jennifer, M.D. Chief of Staff, Blue Ridge Regional Hospital, Spruce Pine, NC, p. A469
LARSON, Jon, M.D. Medical Director, HEALTHSOUTH Rehabilitation Institute of Tucson, Tucson, AZ, p. A39
LARSON, Karla, Director Human Resources, Stevens Community Medical Center, Morris, MN, p. A343
LARSON, Kay, R.N. Chief Nursing Officer, Essentia Health St. Mary's – Detroit Lakes, Detroit Lakes, MN, p. A337
LARSON, Kirk, Chief Information Officer, Natividad Medical Center, Salinas, CA, p. A85
LARSON, Michael, Vice President Chief Information Officer, MidMichigan Medical Center–Clare, Clare, MI, p. A316
LARSON, Mike, Chief Operating Officer, Essentia Health St. Joseph's Medical Center, Brainerd, MN, p. A336
LARSON, Pamela, Division Director Financial Services, Hutchinson Health, Hutchinson, MN, p. A340
LARSON, Rodney, M.D. Medical Director, Fall River Hospital, Hot Springs, SD, p. A569
LARSON, Ronald, Chief Financial Officer, VA San Diego Healthcare System, San Diego, CA, p. A87
LARSON, Sandra, Interim Chief Executive Officer, Kindred Hospital–Philadelphia, Philadelphia, PA, p. A544
LARSON, Scott, M.D. Vice President Medical Affairs and Chief Medical Officer, Bronson Methodist Hospital, Kalamazoo, MI, p. A323
LARSON, Scott C., Chief Executive Officer, Sanford Canton–Inwood Medical Center, Canton, SD, p. A567
LARSON, Shelly, Chief Financial Officer, Hot Springs County Memorial Hospital, Thermopolis, WY, p. A717
LARSON, Steve, M.D. Director Information Systems, Mercy Medical Center–Sioux City, Sioux City, IA, p. A234
LARSON, Tammy, Chief Financial Officer, Towner County Medical Center, Cando, ND, p. A472
LARSON, Tracy, MS Vice President Patient Care Services and Chief Nursing Officer, Mercy Medical Center–Sioux City, Sioux City, IA, p. A234
LARSON, Walt, Vice President Finance, Tillamook Regional Medical Center, Tillamook, OR, p. A526
LARSON, Wendy, Chief Clinical Officer, Promise Hospital of Phoenix, Mesa, AZ, p. A33
LASALA, Frank, M.D. President Medical Staff, OSF Holy Family Medical Center, Monmouth, IL, p. A194
LASCANO, Terrance, Administrative Officer, U. S. Public Health Service Indian Hospital, Cass Lake, MN, p. A336
LASECKI, Matt, Interim Vice President Human Resources, Providence Hospital, Washington, DC, p. A120
LASH, Lashaunda, Manager Human Resources, Pioneer Community Hospital of Stokes, Danbury, NC, p. A458
LASHER, Karen, Chief Nursing Officer, Vanderbilt Stallworth Rehabilitation Hospital, Nashville, TN, p. A586
LASKER, Rose, Director Information Services, Bluefield Regional Medical Center, Bluefield, WV, p. A689
LASKOWSKI, Rose, R.N., Director, Caro Center, Caro, MI, p. A316
LASKY, John, Vice President and Chief Human Resources Officer, Temple University Hospital, Philadelphia, PA, p. A545
LASOTA, John, Assistant Finance Officer, Clement J. Zablocki Veterans Affairs Medical Center, Milwaukee, WI, p. A706
LASSITER, Rick, President and Chief Administrative Officer, Parkwest Medical Center, Knoxville, TN, p. A580
LASSITER, Susan S., FACHE, President and Chief Executive Officer, Vidant Roanoke–Chowan Hospital, Ahoskie, NC, p. A455
LASTER, Charles, Director Information Management, WK Bossier Health Center, Bossier City, LA, p. A271
LATER, Elizabeth B., R.N. Chief Nursing Officer, Ogden Regional Medical Center, Ogden, UT, p. A656
LATIBEAUDIERE, Jorge, Chief Financial Officer, Lea Regional Medical Center, Hobbs, NM, p. A424
LATIMER, Timothy, Chief Financial Officer, Great Bend Regional Hospital, Great Bend, KS, p. A240
LATIOLAIS, Ryan J., Director Information Systems, Our Lady of Lourdes Regional Medical Center, Lafayette, LA, p. A278
LATORRE, Juan Carlos, Administrator, Hospital Oriente, Humacao, PR, p. A721
LATREILLE, William, M.D. Chief Medical Officer, Alice Hyde Medical Center, Malone, NY, p. A436
LATT, Laura, Vice President of Operations, North Memorial Medical Center, Robbinsdale, MN, p. A345
LATTERNER, Renee, Director Human Resources, Lake Wales Medical Center, Lake Wales, FL, p. A131
LATTIMORE, Justin, Chief Financial Officer, Iron County Medical Center, Pilot Knob, MO, p. A374
LATTIN, Gary, M.D. Vice President, Medical Affairs, St. Joseph Regional Health Network, Reading, PA, p. A548
LATTO, Janet B., Chief Nursing Officer and Disaster Officer, Pacifica Hospital of the Valley, CA, p. A72
LATUCHIE, Richard, Vice President Business Development, Rapid City Regional Hospital, Rapid City, SD, p. A570
LATULIPPE, Steve, President Medical Staff, East Liverpool City Hospital, East Liverpool, OH, p. A489
LAUBENTHAL, Sherrie L., R.N. Chief Nursing Officer, Clarinda Regional Health Center, Clarinda, IA, p. A224
LAUDON, Larry A., Administrator, Community Behavioral Health Hospital – Bemidji, Bemidji, MN, p. A335
LAUE, Edward, M.D. Chief Medical Officer, Texas Health Huguley Hospital Fort Worth South, Fort Worth, TX, p. A614
LAUE, Jerry, Administrator, St. Vincent Clay Hospital, Brazil, IN, p. A205
LAUER, Ann, Director Finance, River's Edge Hospital and Clinic, Saint Peter, MN, p. A347
LAUER, Bill, Chief Information Officer, Morris County Hospital, Council Grove, KS, p. A239
LAUF, Michael K., President and Chief Executive Officer, Cape Cod Healthcare, Inc., Hyannis, MA, p. B26
LAUF, Michael K.
President and Chief Executive Officer, Cape Cod Hospital, Hyannis, MA, p. A307
President and Chief Executive Officer, Falmouth Hospital, Falmouth, MA, p. A306
LAUFFER, Daniel, FACHE, President and Chief Executive Officer, Saint Francis Hospital, Charleston, WV, p. A690
LAUFFER, Daniel, FACHE, President and Chief Executive Officer, Thomas Health System, Inc., South Charleston, WV, p. B134
LAUFFER, Daniel, FACHE, President and Chief Executive Officer, Thomas Memorial Hospital, South Charleston, WV, p. A695
LAUFLE, Chuck, Director of Information Services, San Luis Valley Health, Alamosa, CO, p. A99
LAUGHLIN, Jennifer, Chief Information Officer, Watertown Regional Medical Center, Watertown, WI, p. A712
LAUGHLIN, Nancy, R.N. Chief Nursing Officer, Nebraska Orthopaedic Hospital, Omaha, NE, p. A396
LAUGHLIN, Warren, Vice President Human Resources, Longmont United Hospital, Longmont, CO, p. A107
LAUKAITIS, Fran, R.N., Interim Chief Executive Officer and Chief Nursing Officer, Methodist Charlton Medical Center, Dallas, TX, p. A605
LAUNIUS, Billie, Director Business Finance, Dallas County Medical Center, Fordyce, AR, p. A44
LAURENT, Merrill, M.D. Medical Director, Regency Hospital of Covington, Covington, LA, p. A272
LAURENTS, W. Robert, CPA Chief Financial Officer, Madison Parish Hospital, Tallulah, LA, p. A286
LAURETO, Rose Ann
Corporate Vice President Information Resources, ProMedica Bay Park Hospital, Oregon, OH, p. A496
Chief Information Officer, ProMedica Flower Hospital, Sylvania, OH, p. A498
Chief Information Officer, ProMedica Fostoria Community Hospital, Fostoria, OH, p. A490
Chief Information Officer, ProMedica Toledo Hospital, Toledo, OH, p. A499
LAURIN, George M., Interim Director Human Resources, Crisp Regional Hospital, Cordele, GA, p. A155
LAUTER, Keith A.
Vice President Finance, Franciscan St. Elizabeth Health – Crawfordsville, Crawfordsville, IN, p. A206
Regional Chief Financial Officer, Franciscan St. Francis Health – Indianapolis, Indianapolis, IN, p. A211
Chief Financial Officer, Franciscan St. Francis Health–Carmel, Carmel, IN, p. A206
LAUTEREN, Mark
Chief Information Officer, University of South Alabama Children's and Women's Hospital, Mobile, AL, p. A22
Chief Information Officer, University of South Alabama Medical Center, Mobile, AL, p. A22
LAUTERMILCH, Karen, Chief Executive Officer, Coquille Valley Hospital, Coquille, OR, p. A520
LAUTNER, Marty, Vice President Finance and Chief Financial Officer, Cardinal Hill Rehabilitation Hospital, Lexington, KY, p. A259
LAUVE, Lisa R., R.N. Regional Chief Nursing Executive and Chief Operating Officer, CHRISTUS St. Frances Cabrini Hospital, Alexandria, LA, p. A268
LAUVER, David, M.D. Chief Division Hospital Based Care, Central Maine Medical Center, Lewiston, ME, p. A290
LAUZAU, Paul, Controller, Beaumont Hospital – Trenton, Trenton, MI, p. A331
LAVALLEY, Marlinda L., Chief Executive Officer, Gouverneur Hospital, Gouverneur, NY, p. A434
LAVELLE, John P., M.D. Chief Medical Officer, Parkview Hospital, Wheeler, TX, p. A652
LAVELY, Patricia A., FACHE Senior Vice President and Chief Information Officer, Gwinnett Hospital System, Lawrenceville, GA, p. A160
LAVER, Joseph H., M.D. Chief Medical Officer, Stony Brook University Medical Center, Stony Brook, NY, p. A451
LAVERDIERE, Dana, Director Human Resources, St. Anthony Summit Medical Center, Frisco, CO, p. A104
LAVERY FRASCA, Denise Anne, MSN Vice President Patient Care Services and Chief Nursing Officer, Jeanes Hospital, Philadelphia, PA, p. A544
LAVIGNETTE, Brooke, Director of Nursing, Sycamore Springs Hospital, Lafayette, IN, p. A214
LAVIOLETTE, Judy, M.D
Chief Medical Officer, Texas Health Harris Methodist Hospital Azle, Azle, TX, p. A595
Chief Medical Officer, Texas Health Harris Methodist Hospital Cleburne, Cleburne, TX, p. A601
LAVOIE, Brad, Chief Financial Officer, Coastal Harbor Treatment Center, Savannah, GA, p. A164
LAW, Charles, Ph.D. Chief Operating Officer, Catawba Hospital, Catawba, VA, p. A663


Index of Health Care Professionals

LAW, Johnny, Area Information Officer, Kaiser Permanente Oakland Medical Center, Oakland, CA, p. A78

LAWHORN, Renee, Director Medical Records, East Texas Medical Center Carthage, Carthage, TX, p. A600

LAWHORNE, Thomas, Chief Financial Officer, Regional Medical Center Bayonet Point, Hudson, FL, p. A129

LAWLER, Anne, Director Human Resources, Marion Regional Medical Center, Hamilton, AL, p. A21

LAWLER, Kay, Business Office Manager, North Mississippi Medical Center–West Point, West Point, MS, p. A361

LAWLER, Patrick, Chief Executive Officer, Youth Villages Inner Harbour Campus, Douglasville, GA, p. A156

LAWLESS, JoBeth, Chief Nursing Officer, Nursing Services and Director Emergency Management Services, Lucas County Health Center, Chariton, IA, p. A224

LAWLESS, Rosalie, Director Human Resources, Fairlawn Rehabilitation Hospital, Worcester, MA, p. A313

LAWLEY, Richard W., Vice President Human Resources, TMC Healthcare, Tucson, AZ, p. A40

LAWONN, Kenneth
Senior Vice President and Chief Information Officer, CHI Health Mercy Corning, Corning, IA, p. A225
Senior Vice President and Chief Information Officer, CHI Health Schuyler, Schuyler, NE, p. A398
Senior Vice President and Chief Information Officer, Sharp Grossmont Hospital, La Mesa, CA, p. A66
Senior Vice President and Chief Information Officer, Sharp Memorial Hospital, San Diego, CA, p. A87
Senior Vice President Information Systems, Sharp Mesa Vista Hospital, San Diego, CA, p. A87

LAWRASON, Jock, M.D. Chief Medical Officer, Nantucket Cottage Hospital, Nantucket, MA, p. A309

LAWRENCE, Bruce, President and Chief Executive Officer, INTEGRIS Health, Oklahoma City, OK, p. B74

LAWRENCE, Jeffrey T., Chief Operating Officer, Denton Regional Medical Center, Denton, TX, p. A608

LAWRENCE, Kathy, Interim Vice President of Patient Care Services, Sentara Albemarle Medical Center, Elizabeth City, NC, p. A459

LAWRENCE, Mark, Director Information Systems, Saint Francis Hospital–Bartlett, Bartlett, TN, p. A574

LAWRENCE, Paige, Assistant Administrator, University of Mississippi Medical Center Holmes County, Lexington, MS, p. A356

LAWRENCE, Rita, Director of Nursing, Doctors Hospital of West Covina, West Covina, CA, p. A97

LAWRENCE, Sandra A J
Executive Vice President and Chief Financial Officer, Children's Mercy Hospitals and Clinics, Kansas City, MO, p. A369
Executive Vice President and Chief Financial Officer, Children's Mercy South, Overland Park, KS, p. A248

LAWRENCE, Stephanie
Chief Financial Officer, Kentfield Rehabilitation and Specialty Hospital, Kentfield, CA, p. A65
Chief Financial Officer, Vibra Specialty Hospital of Portland, Portland, OR, p. A525

LAWRENCE, Tiffany, Chief Financial Officer, Sanford Medical Center Fargo, Fargo, ND, p. A474

LAWRENCE, Ursula, MSN Chief Nursing Officer, Piedmont Medical Center, Rock Hill, SC, p. A564

LAWRENCE, William P., President and Chief Executive Officer, McLaren Central Michigan, Mount Pleasant, MI, p. A326

LAWRENSON, Victoria
Chief Operating Officer, Bullock County Hospital, Union Springs, AL, p. A26
Chief Operating Officer, Crenshaw Community Hospital, Luverne, AL, p. A21

LAWSON, Alvin R., FACHE, Chief Executive Officer, HEALTHSOUTH Western Hills Regional Rehabilitation Hospital, Parkersburg, WV, p. A694

LAWSON, David C., Senior Vice President Human Resources, St. Clare Hospital, Lakewood, WA, p. A680

LAWSON, Doug, Chief Operating Officer, Baylor University Medical Center, Dallas, TX, p. A604

LAWSON, Judy, Director Information Services, Norton Community Hospital, Norton, VA, p. A670

LAWSON, Kamilah, Health Information Management Services Director, HealthSouth Rehabilitation Hospital of Tallahassee, Tallahassee, FL, p. A144

LAWSON, Kelly, Chief Nursing Officer, Williamsburg Regional Hospital, Kingstree, SC, p. A562

LAWSON, Michael, President and Chief Operating Officer, OhioHealth Grant Medical Center, Columbus, OH, p. A486

LAWSON, Ralph E., Executive Vice President and Chief Financial Officer, Baptist Health South Florida, Baptist Hospital of Miami, Miami, FL, p. A133

LAWSON, Sandra K., Interim Director Fiscal Services, Shriners Hospitals for Children–St. Louis, Saint Louis, MO, p. A377

LAWSON, West, M.D
Chief Medical Officer, WakeMed Cary Hospital, Cary, NC, p. A456
Chief Medical Officer, WakeMed Raleigh Campus, Raleigh, NC, p. A467

LAWTON, Geoff, Vice President Operations, Littleton Adventist Hospital, Littleton, CO, p. A106

LAY, Jr., A. K., M.D. Chief Medical Officer, Jasper General Hospital, Bay Springs, MS, p. A350

LAY, Barbara, Chief Executive Officer, Pocahontas Memorial Hospital, Buckeye, WV, p. A689

LAYDEN, Lisa, Chief Operating Officer, Highland Hospital, Charleston, WV, p. A690

LAYFIELD, Michael, Chief Executive Officer, Jeff Davis Hospital, Hazlehurst, GA, p. A158

LAYMAN, Linda, Director Human Resources, MedStar Union Memorial Hospital, Baltimore, MD, p. A294

LAYNE, Kristine, R.N. Chief Nursing Officer, Riverwood Healthcare Center, Aitkin, MN, p. A334

LAYTON, Ann, M.D. Chief of Staff, North Metro Medical Center, Jacksonville, AR, p. A46

LAYTON, Rochelle, Finance Manager, Providence Hood River Memorial Hospital, Hood River, OR, p. A521

LAYUGAN, Melvin, Director Human Resources, Horizon Specialty Hospital, Las Vegas, NV, p. A402

LAZARUS, David, M.D. Medical Director Clinical Affairs, Newton Medical Center, Newton, NJ, p. A416

LAZATIN, Lou, Administrator, Shriners Hospitals for Children–Los Angeles, Los Angeles, CA, p. A72

LAZO, Nelson, Chief Executive Officer, Baptist Health South Florida, Doctors Hospital, Coral Gables, FL, p. A124

LAZROFF, Gary, Vice President Human Resources, St. John Medical Center, Westlake, OH, p. A500

LAZURE, Lee A., Director Civil Service Commission, Douglas County Community Mental Health Center, Omaha, NE, p. A396

LAZZARO, III, Frank A., Chief Human Resources Officer, Phelps County Regional Medical Center, Rolla, MO, p. A375

LE, Emily, Director Information Technology and Services, Woman's Hospital of Texas, Houston, TX, p. A623

LE, Jennifer, Chief Financial Officer, Southern Hills Hospital and Medical Center, Las Vegas, NV, p. A402

LEA, Hampton P. S., Acting Chief Executive Officer, Eastern Louisiana Mental Health System, Jackson, LA, p. A275

LEA, Randy, M.D. Vice President and Chief Medical Officer, Alice Peck Day Memorial Hospital, Lebanon, NH, p. A406

LEA, Rich, Vice President Operations, Euclid Hospital, Euclid, OH, p. A489

LEACH, Craig, President and Chief Executive Officer, Torrance Memorial Medical Center, Torrance, CA, p. A94

LEACH, Deonca, Director, Human Resources, Carolinas Rehabilitation, Charlotte, NC, p. A457

LEACH, Leslie, Administrator, CHI St. Luke's Health Memorial Specialty Hospital, Lufkin, TX, p. A630

LEACH, Mary Anne, Vice President and Chief Information Officer, Children's Hospital Colorado, Aurora, CO, p. A99

LEACH, Ryan, Chief Information Officer, St. John's Hospital, Springfield, IL, p. A201

LEACH, Steven, M.D. Chief Medical Officer, University of Texas Southwestern Medical Center, Dallas, TX, p. A607

LEACH, Thomas J., Administrator, Lakeside Medical Center, Belle Glade, FL, p. A121

LEACH, Todd, Vice President and Chief Information Officer, University of Texas Medical Branch, Galveston, TX, p. A615

LEADBETTER, Dan, Information Technology Systems Site Lead, CHI LakeWood Health, Baudette, MN, p. A335

LEADBETTER, Jr., Raymond J., Revenue Cycle Consultant, Appling Healthcare System, Baxley, GA, p. A152

LEADER, Skip, Chief Information Officer, Choctaw Nation Health Care Center, Talihina, OK, p. A516

LEAHY, Kevin D., President and Chief Executive Officer, Franciscan Alliance, Mishawaka, IN, p. B57

LEAHY, Mary, M.D., Chief Executive Officer, Good Samaritan Hospital, Suffern, NY, p. A451

LEAHY, Mary P., Vice President Human Resources, St. Joseph Hospital, Orange, CA, p. A79

LEAHY, Rosanne, Vice President Nursing Services, CarolinaEast Health System, New Bern, NC, p. A466

LEAKE, Jeanne E., R.N. Chief Nursing Officer, Uvalde County Hospital Authority, Uvalde, TX, p. A649

LEAKE, Neta F., Administrative Assistant Human Resources, West Feliciana Parish Hospital, Saint Francisville, LA, p. A284

LEAKE, Sandy, MSN Associate Director, Nursing and Patient Care Services, Atlanta Veterans Affairs Medical Center, Decatur, GA, p. A155

LEAKEY, Kim, R.N. Chief Nursing Officer, Lafayette Regional Health Center, Lexington, MO, p. A372

LEAL, Carlos, Director Information Technology, Valley Regional Medical Center, Brownsville, TX, p. A599

LEAL, Jr., Joseph M., M.D. Chief of Staff, Glendive Medical Center, Glendive, MT, p. A383

LEAMING, Larry E., FACHE, Chief Executive Officer, Roosevelt General Hospital, Portales, NM, p. A425

LEAMON, Jim, Chief Financial Officer, JFK Medical Center, Atlantis, FL, p. A121

LEAR, Richard
Director Information Systems, St. David's Medical Center, Austin, TX, p. A595
Director Information Systems, St. David's South Austin Medical Center, Austin, TX, p. A595

LEARSON, Jerome, Manager Information Technology and Chief Security Officer, Palo Verde Hospital, Blythe, CA, p. A56

LEARY, Edward B., Chief Executive Officer, New Bedford Rehabilitation Hospital, New Bedford, MA, p. A309

LEARY, Matt, Chief Financial Officer, Wesley Medical Center, Wichita, KS, p. A253

LEASE, Faye, Director of Nursing, Reeves County Hospital, Pecos, TX, p. A636

LEASE–HOMEYER, Cheryl, Lead Information Technology Business Partner, Mercy Hospital Carthage, Carthage, MO, p. A365

LEASURE, Sandie, Senior Vice President Human Resources, O'Bleness Memorial Hospital, Athens, OH, p. A479

LEATHERS, Cynthia, R.N
Chief Nursing Officer, Integris Bass Baptist Health Center, Enid, OK, p. A506
Chief Nursing Officer, Integris Bass Pavilion, Enid, OK, p. A506

LEAVER, William B., President and Chief Executive Officer, UnityPoint Health, West Des Moines, IA, p. B140

LEAZER, Ronald, Chief Financial Officer, Gateway Regional Medical Center, Granite City, IL, p. A189

LEBEAU, Michelle, Vice President Human Resources, The University of Vermont Health Network–Champlain Valley Physicians Hospital, Plattsburgh, NY, p. A447

LEBER, Ian, M.D. Chief Medical Officer, Bayshore Community Hospital, Holmdel, NJ, p. A413

LEBLANC, Ed, M.D. Vice President Medical Affairs, Seton Northwest Hospital, Austin, TX, p. A594

LEBLANC, Karen, Director, Applications, Samaritan Hospital, Troy, NY, p. A452

LEBOWITZ, Howard, M.D. Chief Medical Officer, Specialty Hospital of Central Jersey, Lakewood, NJ, p. A413

LEBRON, Juan, M.D. Medical Director, HEALTHSOUTH Sea Pines Rehabilitation Hospital, Melbourne, FL, p. A133

LEBRON, Sonia M., Human Resources Specialist, Industrial Hospital, San Juan, PR, p. A724

LEBRUN, James, Chief Executive Officer, Perkins County Health Services, Grant, NE, p. A392

LECATES, William W., M.D. Medical Director, Bassett Medical Center, Cooperstown, NY, p. A432

LECHICH, Anthony, M.D. Chief Medical Officer, Terence Cardinal Cooke Health Care Center, New York, NY, p. A444

LECHNER, David, M.D. Chief Medical Officer and Vice President Innovation, Community Medical Center, Missoula, MT, p. A385

LECHOCO, Bing, Director Human Resources, Specialty Hospital of Washington–Hadley, Washington, DC, p. A120

LECHUGA, Mario, Director Human Resources, Turquoise Lodge Hospital, Albuquerque, NM, p. A423

LECKELT, Mitchell D., Chief Executive Officer, UP Health System–Bell, Ishpeming, MI, p. A323

LECKER, Marijo, Vice President, Martha Jefferson Hospital, Charlottesville, VA, p. A663

LECKEY, Scott
Chief Financial Officer, Banner Desert Medical Center, Mesa, AZ, p. A33
Vice President Finance, Baptist Health Paducah, Paducah, KY, p. A264

LEDBETTER, Joy, Vice President Employee and Patient Experience and Chief Human Resources Officer, UnityPoint Health – Methodist Proctor, Peoria, IL, p. A198

LEDDEN, Edwin L., Assistant Administrator and Director Human Resources, Henry County Medical Center, Paris, TN, p. A587

LEDELL, Michelle, Director Human Resources, Fairview Southdale Hospital, Edina, MN, p. A338

LEDERER, Jane, R.N. Vice President and Chief Nursing Officer, Kingsbrook Jewish Medical Center, NY, p. A441

LEDERMAN, Joel, Director Information Systems, Community Health Center of Branch County, Coldwater, MI, p. A317

LEDERMAN, Mark, Chief Information Officer, Interfaith Medical Center, NY, p. A440

LEDFORD, Keith, M.D. Chief of Staff, Scenic Mountain Medical Center, Big Spring, TX, p. A597

LEDOUX, Roger C., Chief Executive Officer, Byrd Regional Hospital, Leesville, LA, p. A279

LEDYARD, Robin, M.P.H., President, Community Hospital East, Indianapolis, IN, p. A211

LEE, Brett D., Chief Executive Officer, Lake Pointe Medical Center, Rowlett, TX, p. A639

Index of Health Care Professionals / Lemmons

Index of Health Care Professionals

LEE, Byong, Manager Information Technology and PACS Administrator, Limestone Medical Center, Groesbeck, TX, p. A617
LEE, Charles, Director Clinical Operations, Brentwood Hospital, Shreveport, LA, p. A284
LEE, Cheryl, Director Human Resources, Eliza Coffee Memorial Hospital, Florence, AL, p. A19
LEE, Cheryl D., R.N. Vice President of Patient Care Services and Chief Nursing Officer, University of Maryland Rehabilitation & Orthopaedic Institute, Baltimore, MD, p. A295
LEE, Darren W.
President and Chief Executive Officer, St. John's Pleasant Valley Hospital, Camarillo, CA, p. A57
President and Chief Executive Officer, St. John's Regional Medical Center, Oxnard, CA, p. A79
LEE, David, Chief Executive Officer, Otto Kaiser Memorial Hospital, Kenedy, TX, p. A625
LEE, Dennis, Vice President and Chief Information Officer, Cabell Huntington Hospital, Huntington, WV, p. A691
LEE, Elaine, Manager Human Resources, San Francisco General Hospital and Trauma Center, San Francisco, CA, p. A88
LEE, Eric A., President and Chief Executive Officer, Jennie Stuart Medical Center, Hopkinsville, KY, p. A258
LEE, Gina, Chief Financial Officer, Fort Lauderdale Hospital, Fort Lauderdale, FL, p. A126
LEE, James Y., Executive Vice President and Chief Operating Officer, New York–Presbyterian/Lawrence Hospital, Bronxville, NY, p. A430
LEE, Jeannie, Director Human Resources, Marshall County Hospital, Benton, KY, p. A254
LEE, Jenny, Human Resources Generalist, Essentia Health–Graceville, Graceville, MN, p. A339
LEE, John Paul, M.D. Chief of Staff, Lackey Memorial Hospital, Forest, MS, p. A353
LEE, John R., Chief Executive Officer, Mat–Su Regional Medical Center, Palmer, AK, p. A29
LEE, Joshua, Chief Information Officer, University of Southern California–Norris Cancer Hospital, Los Angeles, CA, p. A73
LEE, Karen, MSN Chief Nursing Officer, Belton Regional Medical Center, Belton, MO, p. A363
LEE, Karen, Director Human Resources, Gallup Indian Medical Center, Gallup, NM, p. A424
LEE, Kayleen R., Chief Executive Officer, Sioux Center Health, Sioux Center, IA, p. A234
LEE, Kevin D., Director and Chief Executive Officer, Polaris Hospital Company, Brentwood, TN, p. B105
LEE, Kim, Chief Financial Officer, Bowie Memorial Hospital, Bowie, TX, p. A598
LEE, Larry, Chief Financial Officer, United Hospital District, Blue Earth, MN, p. A335
LEE, Lori L., Assistant Vice President Nursing, Nanticoke Memorial Hospital, Seaford, DE, p. A117
LEE, Mary C., Manager Human Resources, Jonathan M. Wainwright Memorial Veterans Affairs Medical Center, Walla Walla, WA, p. A687
LEE, Michael D., Chief Human Resources Officer, Adirondack Medical Center, Saranac Lake, NY, p. A450
LEE, Mihi, Chief Financial Officer, Coast Plaza Hospital, Norwalk, CA, p. A78
LEE, Mike, R.N. Chief Nursing Officer, Matagorda Regional Medical Center, Bay City, TX, p. A596
LEE, Nancy, Chief Nursing Officer, Sharp Coronado Hospital and Healthcare Center, Coronado, CA, p. A59
LEE, Nancy, R.N. Vice President Patient Care Services and Chief Nursing Officer, Stanford Health Care, Palo Alto, CA, p. A80
LEE, Nathan W., Chief Executive Officer, Mary Breckinridge ARH Hospital, Hyden, KY, p. A258
LEE, Pamela R., Executive Vice President Operations and Chief Quality Officer, United Medical Center, Washington, DC, p. A120
LEE, Randall, Vice President and Chief Operating Officer, Baptist Health South Florida, Baptist Hospital of Miami, Miami, FL, p. A133
LEE, Robbin, Chief Executive Officer, Wellington Regional Medical Center, West Palm Beach, FL, p. A147
LEE, Robert H., President, Raulerson Hospital, Okeechobee, FL, p. A137
LEE, Sherry, Chief Nurse Executive, Fulton State Hospital, Fulton, MO, p. A368
LEE, Stephen, FACHE, President, Baptist Medical Center Nassau, Fernandina Beach, FL, p. A126
LEE, Terry, M.D. Chief of Staff, Garfield Medical Center, Monterey Park, CA, p. A76
LEE, Thomas G., Chief Financial Officer, Medicine Lodge Memorial Hospital, Medicine Lodge, KS, p. A246
LEE, Victor N., FACHE, President and Chief Executive Officer, Boone County Health Center, Albion, NE, p. A389
LEE, Wayne, Director of Nursing, Clinch Memorial Hospital, Homerville, GA, p. A159
LEE, Wendy, Chief Nursing Officer, Regional Rehabilitation Hospital, Phenix City, AL, p. A24
LEEGSTRA, Ruurd, Chief Financial Officer, Silver Hill Hospital, New Canaan, CT, p. A114
LEEK, Dustin, Vice President of Enterprise Technical Services, Health First Holmes Regional Medical Center, Melbourne, FL, p. A133
LEEKA, Andrew B., President and Chief Executive Officer, Good Samaritan Hospital, Los Angeles, CA, p. A70
LEEMING, Rosemary, M.D. Chief Medical Officer, UH Regional Hospitals, Cleveland, OH, p. A485
LEEPER, Kevin, Chief Executive Officer, Nevada Regional Medical Center, Nevada, MO, p. A373
LEESMAN, Keenan, Director Information Systems, Abraham Lincoln Memorial Hospital, Lincoln, IL, p. A193
LEFEVRE, Denise, Chief Information Officer, Oroville Hospital, Oroville, CA, p. A79
LEFEVRE, Steve, Chief Executive Officer and Administrator, Fisher County Hospital District, Rotan, TX, p. A639
LEFF, Marc, Vice President Human Resources, St. John's Riverside Hospital, Yonkers, NY, p. A454
LEFFLER, Stephen, Chief Medical Officer, The University of Vermont Health Network University of Vermont Medical Center, Burlington, VT, p. A660
LEFKOW, Frances, Director Human Resources, La Rabida Children's Hospital, Chicago, IL, p. A182
LEFTWICH, Hal W., FACHE, Chief Executive Officer, Fishermen's Hospital, Marathon, FL, p. A132
LEGASPI, Johnson, Director Information Systems, Alhambra Hospital Medical Center, Alhambra, CA, p. A53
LEGAULT, Matt, Chief Financial Administrator, Beaumont Hospital–Dearborn, Dearborn, MI, p. A317
LEGER, Lynn, Director Information Systems, Ridgeview Institute, Smyrna, GA, p. A164
LEGERE, Tina, President, Central Maine Medical Center, Lewiston, ME, p. A290
LEGG, Alyce, Vice President Human Resources, Samaritan Regional Health System, Ashland, OH, p. A478
LEGG, Debra Lynn, Associate Director Patient Care Services and Nurse Executive, Beckley Veterans Affairs Medical Center, Beckley, WV, p. A689
LEGG, Susan E., Interim Administrator, Noland Hospital Montgomery, Montgomery, AL, p. A23
LEGGETT III, G. Raymond, President and Chief Executive Officer, CarolinaEast Health System, New Bern, NC, p. A466
LEGGETT, Sandra, R.N. Chief Nursing Officer, Atchison Hospital, Atchison, KS, p. A237
LEGLEITER, Brenda, R.N., Chief Executive Officer, Rush County Memorial Hospital, La Crosse, KS, p. A244
LEGRAND, Daniel, M.D. Chief Medical Officer, St. Vincent Indianapolis Hospital, Indianapolis, IN, p. A212
LEGRAND III, Edwin C., Executive Director, Mississippi State Department of Mental Health, Jackson, MS, p. B93
LEGRAND, Kila, Chief Nursing Officer, Sanford Aberdeen Medical Center, Aberdeen, SD, p. A567
LEHMAN, Andy
Senior Vice President Technology and Analytics, Fort Hamilton Hospital, Hamilton, OH, p. A491
Senior Vice President Technology and Analytics, Grandview Medical Center, Dayton, OH, p. A488
Senior Vice President Technology & Analytics, Greene Memorial Hospital, Xenia, OH, p. A501
Senior Vice President Technology and Analytics, Kettering Medical Center, Kettering, OH, p. A491
Vice President Information Systems, Soin Medical Center, Beavercreek, OH, p. A479
Senior Vice President Technology and Analytics, Sycamore Medical Center, Miamisburg, OH, p. A494
LEHMAN, James A., M.D
Vice President Medical Affairs, Covenant Medical Center, Waterloo, IA, p. A235
Vice President Medical Affairs, Mercy Hospital of Franciscan Sisters, Oelwein, IA, p. A232
LEHMAN, Sandi, Chief Financial Officer, Humboldt General Hospital, Winnemucca, NV, p. A404
LEHN, Matt, Chief Operating Officer, Bluffton Regional Medical Center, Bluffton, IN, p. A205
LEHN, Toby, Director of Nurses, Concho County Hospital, Eden, TX, p. A609
LEHNHOF–WATTS, Laurie
Assistant Administrator Patient Services, East Texas Medical Center Rehabilitation Hospital, Tyler, TX, p. A648
Assistant Administrator Risk Management Performance Improvement and Education, East Texas Medical Center Specialty Hospital, Tyler, TX, p. A648
LEHRACH, Christopher, M.D. Chief Transformation Officer for Interim Operations, Westerly Hospital, Westerly, RI, p. A556
LEIBMAN, Maurice, M.D. Chief Medical Officer, Memorial Hermann Northwest Hospital, Houston, TX, p. A621
LEICHMAN, Ann Marie, R.N. Vice President Patient Care Services and Chief Nursing Officer, Valley Hospital, Ridgewood, NJ, p. A418
LEIDY, R. Grant, Vice President Finance, Deborah Heart and Lung Center, Browns Mills, NJ, p. A410
LEIF, Sue, R.N. Director Human Resources, Annie Jeffrey Memorial County Health Center, Osceola, NE, p. A397
LEIGH, Jordan, Chief Financial Officer, Boundary Community Hospital, Bonners Ferry, ID, p. A173
LEIGHTON, Heather, Director, Revenue Cycle and Privacy Officer, Upper Connecticut Valley Hospital, Colebrook, NH, p. A405
LEIGHTON, Marc
Vice President Human Resources, Nexus Specialty Hospital, Shenandoah, TX, p. A643
Vice President Human Resources, Nexus Specialty Hospital The Woodlands, Spring, TX, p. A644
LEIGHTON, Richard, Financial Application Analyst, Unity Medical & Surgical Hospital, Mishawaka, IN, p. A216
LEINEN, Rick J., Chief Financial Officer, Montgomery County Memorial Hospital, Red Oak, IA, p. A233
LEINTZ, Marsha, Patient Care Manager, Sanford Bagley Medical Center, Bagley, MN, p. A335
LEISE, Karen, Coordinator Human Resources, Saunders Medical Center, Wahoo, NE, p. A398
LEISHER, George, Chief Human Resources Officer, Antelope Valley Hospital, Lancaster, CA, p. A67
LEISHER, Karla, Business Office Manager, Beaver County Memorial Hospital, Beaver, OK, p. A504
LEIST, Vincent, President and Chief Executive Officer, North Arkansas Regional Medical Center, Harrison, AR, p. A45
LEITE, Dolores
Chief Human Resource Executive, Jacobi Medical Center, NY, p. A440
Chief Human Resource Executive, North Central Bronx Hospital, NY, p. A443
LEITNER, Mark, Administrator, East Texas Medical Center Henderson, Henderson, TX, p. A618
LEJSEK, Shari, Administrator, Patients' Hospital of Redding, Redding, CA, p. A82
LELAND, Joni, Director Human Resources, Memorial Hospital, Gonzales, TX, p. A616
LEM, Alan
Vice President Finance, Fairview Ridges Hospital, Burnsville, MN, p. A336
Vice President Finance, Fairview Southdale Hospital, Edina, MN, p. A338
LEMAIRE, Joseph, Executive Vice President Finance, Riverview Medical Center, Red Bank, NJ, p. A418
LEMAIRE, Joseph M.
Executive Vice President Finance and Partner Company Operations, Bayshore Community Hospital, Holmdel, NJ, p. A413
Executive Vice President, Southern Ocean Medical Center, Manahawkin, NJ, p. A414
LEMAIRE, Suzanne, Manager Health Information Management Services and Corporate Compliance Officer, Scheurer Hospital, Pigeon, MI, p. A327
LEMAISTRE, Collin, Chief Executive Officer, Texas Regional Medical Center at Sunnyvale, Sunnyvale, TX, p. A646
LEMANSKI, Dennis R., D.O. Senior Vice President Medical Affairs and Medical Education/CMO, Henry Ford Wyandotte Hospital, Wyandotte, MI, p. A332
LEMASTER, Dennis P., Commander, Evans U. S. Army Community Hospital, Fort Carson, CO, p. A103
LEMASTERS, Debra J., Director Human Resources, Woodlawn Hospital, Rochester, IN, p. A219
LEMAY, Catherine, Vice President Finance, Millinocket Regional Hospital, Millinocket, ME, p. A291
LEMAY, Robert Raymond, R.N. Chief Nursing Officer, The Physicians Centre Hospital, Bryan, TX, p. A599
LEMBCKE, Brad, M.D. Vice President Medical Staff Affairs, Baylor University Medical Center, Dallas, TX, p. A604
LEMEL, Mark, Chief of Staff, Transylvania Regional Hospital, Brevard, NC, p. A456
LEMIEUX, Harry, Chief Information Officer, Harrington Memorial Hospital, Southbridge, MA, p. A311
LEMIEUX, Kandie, Administrative Assistant and Director Human Resources, Northern Rockies Medical Center, Cut Bank, MT, p. A382
LEMIEUX, Laurie, Vice President People and Culture, PeaceHealth Southwest Medical Center, Vancouver, WA, p. A687
LEMMER, Donn J., Chief Financial Officer and Chief Operating Officer, West Shore Medical Center, Manistee, MI, p. A325
LEMMERMAN, Deborah, Vice President, Human Resources, Hebrew Rehabilitation Center, Boston, MA, p. A303
LEMMONS, Joe, D.O. Chief of Staff, Lehigh Regional Medical Center, Lehigh Acres, FL, p. A132

LEMOINE, Kirk, Chief Operating Officer, Bienville Medical Center, Arcadia, LA, p. A268

LEMON, Brian J., President, Northwestern Medicine Central DuPage Hospital, Winfield, IL, p. A203

LEMON, Donna, Director Human Resources, Ward Memorial Hospital, Monahans, TX, p. A633

LEMON, Marc, Chief Executive Officer, Kindred Hospital–Tucson, Tucson, AZ, p. A39

LEMON, Rita, Director Human Resources, Avera Queen of Peace Hospital, Mitchell, SD, p. A570

LEMON, Thomas R., Chief Executive Officer, Otsego Memorial Hospital, Gaylord, MI, p. A320

LEMONS, Elizabeth, Chief Operating Officer, Saint Thomas Rutherford Hospital, Murfreesboro, TN, p. A585

LEMONTE, David, Vice President and Chief Operating Officer, CHRISTUS Spohn Hospital Kleberg, Kingsville, TX, p. A626

LENAHAN, Kevin
   Vice President Finance and Chief Financial Officer, Morristown Medical Center, Morristown, NJ, p. A414
   Director Corporate Accounting, Budgets, Grants and Reimbursements, Newton Medical Center, Newton, NJ, p. A416
   Vice President Finance and Chief Financial Officer, Overlook Medical Center, Summit, NJ, p. A418

LENAMOND, Kevin, Information Management Service Line Executive, Michael E. DeBakey Veterans Affairs Medical Center, Houston, TX, p. A621

LENARD, Gary, Director Human Resources, Hendricks Regional Health, Danville, IN, p. A207

LENCIONI, Kathi, Senior Vice President and Chief Executive Officer, Sharp Mesa Vista Hospital, San Diego, CA, p. A87

LENDARIS, Nia, Regional Vice President Patient Care, St. Helena Hospital Napa Valley, Saint Helena, CA, p. A85

LENFANT, Rodney, Chief Financial Officer, OakBend Medical Center, Richmond, TX, p. A638

LENGFELDER, Valerie, M.D. Chief of Staff, Powell Valley Healthcare, Powell, WY, p. A717

LENKOWSKI, Thomas, Chief Financial Officer, Speare Memorial Hospital, Plymouth, NH, p. A408

LENNARTZ, Randal P., Vice President Finance, Highland District Hospital, Hillsboro, OH, p. A491

LENNEN, Anthony B., President, Community Hospital South, Indianapolis, IN, p. A211

LENNON, Roslyn J., R.N. Chief Nursing Officer, West Suburban Medical Center, Oak Park, IL, p. A196

LENTENBRINK, Laura, Vice President, Human Resources, Borgess Medical Center, Kalamazoo, MI, p. A323

LENTZ, Darrell, Interim President, Aspirus Wausau Hospital, Wausau, WI, p. A713

LENTZ, Matt, R.N. Director of Patient Services, Brown County Hospital, Ainsworth, NE, p. A389

LENZ, Jan, Chief Nursing Officer, Athens–Limestone Hospital, Athens, AL, p. A15

LENZA, Robert, Chief Operating Officer and Administrator, MultiCare Mary Bridge Children's Hospital and Health Center, Tacoma, WA, p. A686

LENZO, Julie, Director Business Office, AMG Specialty Hospital–Albuquerque, Albuquerque, NM, p. A422

LEO, Elizabeth, Chief Human Resources Officer, Moses Taylor Hospital, Scranton, PA, p. A549

LEON, Daniel, Chief Financial Officer, Sherman Oaks Hospital, CA, p. A72

LEON, Luis, Chief Operating Officer, Desert Valley Hospital, Victorville, CA, p. A96

LEONARD, Anne, R.N. Chief Nursing Officer, TriStar Greenview Regional Hospital, Bowling Green, KY, p. A255

LEONARD, Bruce, M.D. Medical Director and Chief of Psychiatry, Colorado Mental Health Institute at Fort Logan, Denver, CO, p. A101

LEONARD, Donavan, Chief Financial Officer, Baptist Memorial Hospital–Booneville, Booneville, MS, p. A351

LEONARD, Edward F., Executive Vice President and Chief Operating Officer, White Plains Hospital Center, White Plains, NY, p. A454

LEONARD, James C., M.D., President and Chief Executive Officer, Carle Foundation, Urbana, IL, p. B27

LEONARD, James C., M.D., President and Chief Executive Officer, Carle Foundation Hospital, Urbana, IL, p. A202

LEONARD, Leland, Ph.D., Chief Executive Officer, Tsehootsooi Medical Center, Fort Defiance, AZ, p. A31

LEONARD, Mark, Vice President Finance, Beaumont Hospital – Troy, Troy, MI, p. A331

LEONARD, Mark T.
   Chief Executive Officer, Dickenson Community Hospital, Clintwood, VA, p. A663
   Chief Executive Officer, Norton Community Hospital, Norton, VA, p. A670

LEONARD, Mike, Vice President Operations and Imaging Director, Northern Hospital of Surry County, Mount Airy, NC, p. A465

LEONARD, Robert, Director Information Services, Sierra Vista Regional Medical Center, San Luis Obispo, CA, p. A90

LEONARD, Wes, Chief Executive Officer, Whitten Center, Clinton, SC, p. A559

LEONARD, William H., President, Carolinas Medical Center–University, Charlotte, NC, p. A457

LEONDAR, Kimberly, Director Human Resources, Texas Health Harris Methodist Hospital Stephenville, Stephenville, TX, p. A645

LEONE, Ellen, R.N. Chief Nursing Officer, University of Connecticut Health Center, John Dempsey Hospital, Farmington, CT, p. A112

LEONELIS, Lisa, Chief Information Officer, Veterans Affairs Salt Lake City Health Care System, Salt Lake City, UT, p. A659

LEONHARDT, Darrell, Senior Vice President Information Systems, Arkansas Children's Hospital, Little Rock, AR, p. A46

LEOPARD, Erik, Manager Human Resource, Methodist Hospital for Surgery, Addison, TX, p. A590

LEOPARD, Jimmy, FACHE, Chief Executive Officer, Wagoner Community Hospital, Wagoner, OK, p. A518

LEPAK, Jason, M.D. Medical Director, St. John Sapulpa, Sapulpa, OK, p. A514

LEPE, Patti, Chief Financial Officer, Parkview Community Hospital Medical Center, Riverside, CA, p. A83

LEPP, Jerry, Chief Executive Officer, Ashley Medical Center, Ashley, ND, p. A472

LEPPER, Dale, Interim Chief Information Officer, Antelope Valley Hospital, Lancaster, CA, p. A67

LEPPKE, Ben, Chief Information Officer, Satanta District Hospital and Long Term Care, Satanta, KS, p. A250

LEQUEUX, Veronica, Vice President Human Resources, Blake Medical Center, Bradenton, FL, p. A122

LERCH, Gail, R.N
   Vice President, Kapiolani Medical Center for Women & Children, Honolulu, HI, p. A168
   Vice President Human Resources, Pali Momi Medical Center, Aiea, HI, p. A168
   Executive Vice President Human Resources, Straub Clinic & Hospital, Honolulu, HI, p. A169

LERCH, Shawn, Chief Executive Officer, Miners' Colfax Medical Center, Raton, NM, p. A425

LERNER, Jerome, M.D. Medical Director, Sierra Tucson, Tucson, AZ, p. A40

LEROY, Michael
   Senior Vice President and Chief Information Officer, Detroit Receiving Hospital/University Health Center, Detroit, MI, p. A317
   Senior Vice President and Chief Information Officer, DMC Harper University Hospital, Detroit, MI, p. A317

LESCH, Jason, Chief Financial Officer, Auburn Community Hospital, Auburn, NY, p. A429

LESCHER, Mary, Interim Chief Executive Officer, Doctor's Memorial Hospital, Perry, FL, p. A140

LESHER, Jennifer, Chief Financial Officer, Lock Haven Hospital, Lock Haven, PA, p. A539

LESIAK, Cindy, Vice President Patient Care Services and Director of Nursing, Boone County Health Center, Albion, NE, p. A389

LESINS, Ross, Chief Information Officer, Casa Colina Hospital and Health Systems, Pomona, CA, p. A81

LESLIE, Andrea M., MSN Chief Nursing Officer, Spectrum Health United Hospital, Greenville, MI, p. A321

LESLIE, Bruce W., M.D. Chief of Staff, Grant Memorial Hospital, Petersburg, WV, p. A694

LESLIE, Desdemona, Finance Officer, U. S. Public Health Service Indian Hospital–Whiteriver, Whiteriver, AZ, p. A40

LESLIE, Donald P., M.D. Medical Director, Shepherd Center, Atlanta, GA, p. A151

LESLIE, Frank, Vice President Operations, Highlands–Cashiers Hospital, Highlands, NC, p. A462

LESLIE, Jeff, Director Information Technology, Berwick Hospital Center, Berwick, PA, p. A529

LESLIE, Kelly, Chief Financial Officer, Ferry County Memorial Hospital, Republic, WA, p. A683

LESNIAK, Jacklynn, R.N. Vice President Patient Care Services and Chief Nursing Officer, Midwestern Regional Medical Center, Zion, IL, p. A203

LESNICK, Kelly, Resource Manager Flight Commander, Wright Patterson Medical Center, Wright–Patterson AFB, OH, p. A501

LESNIEWSKI, Amy, Associate Director Patient Care Services, Alexandria Veterans Affairs Health Care System, Pineville, LA, p. A283

LESTER, Lisa, Chief Nursing Officer, HEALTHSOUTH Southern Hills Rehabilitation Hospital, Princeton, WV, p. A694

LESTER, Ron, Chief Human Resources, Cheyenne Veterans Affairs Medical Center, Cheyenne, WY, p. A715

LESTER, Wade K., Chief Nursing and Operations Officer, Mid–Jefferson Extended Care Hospital, Nederland, TX, p. A634

LESTER, William, M.D. Vice President Medical Affairs, Cardinal Hill Rehabilitation Hospital, Lexington, KY, p. A259

LETCHWORTH, Mike, Manager Information Systems, Cherry Hospital, Goldsboro, NC, p. A461

LETSON, Robert F., FACHE, Chief Executive Officer, South Peninsula Hospital, Homer, AK, p. A28

LETT, Tammy, R.N. Chief Nursing Officer, Greenville Regional Hospital, Greenville, IL, p. A189

LETTOW, Bonnie, Chief Financial Officer, Franklin General Hospital, Hampton, IA, p. A228

LEU, Christopher, President, Texas Health Harris Methodist Hospital Stephenville, Stephenville, TX, p. A645

LEUNG, Lawrence, M.D. Chief of Staff, VA Palo Alto Health Care System, Palo Alto, CA, p. A80

LEVANGER, Nathan, M.D. Chief of Staff, Teton Valley Health Care, Driggs, ID, p. A174

LEVECK, Dianna, Chief Human Resources Officer, Genesis HealthCare System, Zanesville, OH, p. A502

LEVEILLEE, Mary, Senior Vice President Patient Care Services and Chief Nursing Officer, Butler Hospital, Providence, RI, p. A555

LEVELING, Jim, Director Information Technology, Kansas City Orthopaedic Institute, Leawood, KS, p. A244

LEVER, Roger, M.D. President Medical Staff, The Outer Banks Hospital, Nags Head, NC, p. A466

LEVERICH, Karen, Chief Executive Officer, Promise Hospital of Overland Park, Overland Park, KS, p. A248

LEVERING, Theresa, Director Human Resources, Doctors Hospital of Sarasota, Sarasota, FL, p. A142

LEVESQUE, David, Director, Information Systems, New Hampshire Hospital, Concord, NH, p. A405

LEVI, John, Director Human Resources, St. Lawrence Rehabilitation Center, Lawrenceville, NJ, p. A413

LEVINE, Alan M., President and Chief Executive Officer, Mountain States Health Alliance, Johnson City, TN, p. B94

LEVINE, Alexandra, M.D. Chief Medical Officer, City of Hope's Helford Clinical Research Hospital, Duarte, CA, p. A60

LEVINE, Larry L., President and Chief Executive Officer, Blythedale Children's Hospital, Valhalla, NY, p. A452

LEVINE, Peter H., M.D. Executive Medical Director Behavioral Health Services, Adventist Behavioral Health Rockville, Rockville, MD, p. A299

LEVINE, Robert V., Executive Vice President and Chief Operating Officer, Flushing Hospital Medical Center, NY, p. A439

LEVINSON, Adam, Associate Director, Information Services, University Behavioral Healthcare, Piscataway, NJ, p. A417

LEVISON, Julie, Director Human Resources, Providence Medford Medical Center, Medford, OR, p. A523

LEVITAN, Kenneth
   Vice President and Chief Information Officer, Einstein Medical Center Montgomery, East Norriton, PA, p. A533
   Vice President and Chief Information Officer, Einstein Medical Center Philadelphia, Philadelphia, PA, p. A543

LEVITZ, Michele, Director Finance, St. Luke's Hospital – Miners Campus, Coaldale, PA, p. A531

LEVY, Becky, Chief Operating Officer, Shasta Regional Medical Center, Redding, CA, p. A82

LEVY, Brian, M.D. Medical Director, AMG Specialty Hospital–Edmond, Edmond, OK, p. A506

LEVY, Scott S., M.D. Vice President and Chief Medical Officer, Doylestown Hospital, Doylestown, PA, p. A533

LEVY, Susan M., M.D. Vice President Medical Affairs, Levindale Hebrew Geriatric Center and Hospital, Baltimore, MD, p. A293

LEWANDOWSKI, Jim, Interim Director of Human Resources, Carson Tahoe Health, Carson City, NV, p. A400

LEWANDOWSKI, Terri, Director Financial Services, Ministry Our Lady of Victory Hospital, Stanley, WI, p. A711

LEWELLEN, Thomas, D.O. Chief of Staff, Delta Memorial Hospital, Dumas, AR, p. A43

LEWERKE, Jane, Manager Human Resources, Northern Arizona Veterans Affairs Health Care System, Prescott, AZ, p. A36

LEWGOOD, Tony, Administrator, Shriners Hospitals for Children–Lexington, Lexington, KY, p. A260

LEWIS, Alene, R.N. Chief Nursing Officer, Raleigh General Hospital, Beckley, WV, p. A689

LEWIS, Angel
   Senior Vice President Administration, Cookeville Regional Medical Center, Cookeville, TN, p. A576
   Senior Vice President, Cumberland River Hospital, Celina, TN, p. A574

LEWIS, Barbara, Chief Nursing Officer, AllianceHealth Seminole, Seminole, OK, p. A514

LEWIS, Brandon, Director of Information Technology, Ivinson Memorial Hospital, Laramie, WY, p. A716

LEWIS, Cameron, Chief Executive Officer, AllianceHealth Clinton, Clinton, OK, p. A505

Index of Health Care Professionals
Index of Health Care Professionals / Lindell

LEWIS, III, Carlisle, Senior Vice President Legal and Human Resources, Sharp Mesa Vista Hospital, San Diego, CA, p. A87
LEWIS, Colleen, Director Human Resources, Texas NeuroRehab Center, Austin, TX, p. A595
LEWIS, Craig, Interim Chief Financial Officer, Sentara Albemarle Medical Center, Elizabeth City, NC, p. A459
LEWIS, Curtis, M.D. Chief of Staff, Grady Memorial Hospital, Atlanta, GA, p. A150
LEWIS, Cynthia, Chief Nursing Officer, Canyon Vista Medical Center, Sierra Vista, AZ, p. A38
LEWIS, Dana, Director Clinical Services, Southern Kentucky Rehabilitation Hospital, Bowling Green, KY, p. A255
LEWIS, Daniel
Executive Vice President and Chief Operating Officer, MetroHealth Medical Center, Cleveland, OH, p. A485
Chief Medical Officer, Takoma Regional Hospital, Greeneville, TN, p. A578
LEWIS, Darlene, Vice President Human Resources, Canton–Potsdam Hospital, Potsdam, NY, p. A448
LEWIS, Dave, Director Information Services, SSM Health St. Francis Hospital – Maryville, Maryville, MO, p. A372
LEWIS, Jr., Donald C., Vice President and Chief Financial Officer, Coffee Regional Medical Center, Douglas, GA, p. A156
LEWIS, Doug
Chief Financial Officer, St. Luke's Rehabilitation Hospital, Boise, ID, p. A173
Chief Financial Officer, Wheatland Memorial Healthcare, Harlowton, MT, p. A384
LEWIS, Douglas, Chief Financial Officer, Boulder City Hospital, Boulder City, NV, p. A400
LEWIS, Eric, Chief Executive Officer, Olympic Medical Center, Port Angeles, WA, p. A682
LEWIS, Gerry
Chief Information Officer, Seton Highland Lakes, Burnet, TX, p. A599
Chief Information Officer, Seton Medical Center Austin, Austin, TX, p. A594
Chief Information Officer, Seton Medical Center Williamson, Round Rock, TX, p. A639
Chief Information Officer, Seton Northwest Hospital, Austin, TX, p. A594
Chief Information Officer, Seton Shoal Creek Hospital, Austin, TX, p. A594
LEWIS, Gordon, Chief Executive Officer, Burnett Medical Center, Grantsburg, WI, p. A701
LEWIS, Irvan Wick, Vice President Human Resources, Mt. Graham Regional Medical Center, Safford, AZ, p. A37
LEWIS, J. Steve, Director Finance, Youth Villages Inner Harbour Campus, Douglasville, GA, p. A156
LEWIS, Jacob, Chief Financial Officer, Mark Twain Medical Center, San Andreas, CA, p. A85
LEWIS, Jeff, Administrator, Waukesha County Mental Health Center, Waukesha, WI, p. A713
LEWIS, Jeremy, Chief Medical Staff, Newport Hospital and Health Services, Newport, WA, p. A681
LEWIS, John I., President and Chief Executive Officer, ACMH Hospital, Kittanning, PA, p. A537
LEWIS, Kathy, Chief Nursing Officer and Vice President Clinical Services, Riverview Regional Medical Center, Carthage, TN, p. A574
LEWIS, Kenneth S., JD, President and Chief Executive Officer, Union Hospital, Elkton, MD, p. A297
LEWIS, Kent, Director Information Services, Southwestern Medical Center, Lawton, OK, p. A509
LEWIS, Kevin, M.D. Chief Medical Officer, CHI Memorial, Chattanooga, TN, p. A575
LEWIS, Kim, R.N. Director of Nursing Hospital, Minnesota Valley Health Center, Le Sueur, MN, p. A341
LEWIS, Lawrence E., Chief Executive Officer, Pioneers Memorial Healthcare District, Brawley, CA, p. A56
LEWIS, Lisa F., MSN Vice President and Chief Nursing Officer, Holy Spirit – A Geisinger Affiliate, Camp Hill, PA, p. A530
LEWIS, Luther J., FACHE, Chief Executive Officer, Five Rivers Medical Center, Pocahontas, AR, p. A50
LEWIS, Marie, Human Resources Liaison, Veterans Affairs St. Louis Health Care System, Saint Louis, MO, p. A378
LEWIS, Michael, Chief Operating Officer, Mother Frances Hospital – Jacksonville, Jacksonville, TX, p. A624
LEWIS, Nannette M., Chief Executive Officer, Three Rivers Behavioral Health, West Columbia, SC, p. A566
LEWIS, Nicholas P., Chief Executive Officer, Hardin Medical Center, Savannah, TN, p. A587
LEWIS, Pam, Chief Compliance Officer, William R. Sharpe, Jr. Hospital, Weston, WV, p. A696
LEWIS, Paul, Chief Executive Officer, Holy Rosary Healthcare, Miles City, MT, p. A385
LEWIS, Paula, Interim Chief Nursing Officer, Five Rivers Medical Center, Pocahontas, AR, p. A50
LEWIS, Rayburn, M.D., Chief Executive Officer, Swedish/Issaquah, Issaquah, WA, p. A679
LEWIS, Robin, Chief Financial Officer, Kiowa District Hospital and Manor, Kiowa, KS, p. A244
LEWIS, Ron, President, Spectrum Health Zeeland Community Hospital, Zeeland, MI, p. A333
LEWIS, Rosalind, R.N. Chief Nursing Officer, Community HealthCare System, Onaga, KS, p. A247
LEWIS, Sharon, Director Information Systems, Forbes Regional Hospital, Monroeville, PA, p. A540
LEWIS, Sheila, Administrator, Harmon Memorial Hospital, Hollis, OK, p. A508
LEWIS, Sherlyn, Manager Finance, The Orthopedic Specialty Hospital, Murray, UT, p. A656
LEWIS, Shirley, Administrative Officer, Chinle Comprehensive Health Care Facility, Chinle, AZ, p. A30
LEWIS, Stephe, Chief Financial Officer, Chase County Community Hospital, Imperial, NE, p. A393
LEWIS, Stephen, Chief Executive Officer, Chase County Community Hospital, Imperial, NE, p. A393
LEWIS, Thomas D., Acting Chief Executive Officer, Clifton T. Perkins Hospital Center, Jessup, MD, p. A298
LEWIS, Vicki, FACHE, President and Chief Executive Officer, Coffee Regional Medical Center, Douglas, GA, p. A156
LEWIS, Vickie, Chief Executive Officer, Central Florida Behavioral Hospital, Orlando, FL, p. A137
LEWIS, Winifred, R.N. Chief Nursing Officer, Roseland Community Hospital, Chicago, IL, p. A184
LEWISTON, Jamie, R.N. Chief Nursing Officer, Aurora Psychiatric Hospital, Wauwatosa, WI, p. A713
LEWKOWSKI, William, Executive Vice President Information Services and Chief Information Officer, Metro Health Hospital, Wyoming, MI, p. A333
LI, Ronald, Vice President Management Information Systems, Bergen Regional Medical Center, Paramus, NJ, p. A416
LI, Stephen, Vice President Management Information Systems, Jersey City Medical Center, Jersey City, NJ, p. A413
LI, Xiao H., M.D. Chief of Staff, Surgery Specialty Hospitals of America, Pasadena, TX, p. A636
LIAGRE, Ruthann, Vice President Human Resources, Memorial Healthcare, Owosso, MI, p. A327
LIANG, Bonnie, Divisional Finance Officer, Sutter Maternity and Surgery Center of Santa Cruz, Santa Cruz, CA, p. A91
LIBBY, David, Vice President Operations, Winter Haven Hospital, Winter Haven, FL, p. A148
LIBBY, Kenneth, Vice President Finance, VCU Community Memorial Hospital, South Hill, VA, p. A673
LIBCKE, Julia, R.N. VP Patient Care Services, Rehabilitation Institute of Michigan, Detroit, MI, p. A318
LIBERATORE, Kristi, Vice President and Chief Financial Officer, St. Joseph Hospital, Orange, CA, p. A79
LICHIUS, Sylvia Marie, R.N. Chief Nursing Officer, Morrill County Community Hospital, Bridgeport, NE, p. A390
LICHTENFELS, Suellen, Vice President and Chief Nursing Officer, Somerset Hospital, Somerset, PA, p. A550
LICHTENWALNER, Tom, Vice President Finance, St. Luke's University Hospital – Bethlehem Campus, Bethlehem, PA, p. A529
LICHTY, Scott, M.D. Physician, Sanford Sheldon Medical Center, Sheldon, IA, p. A234
LICINA, Leonard, Chief Executive Officer, Kahi Mohala Behavioral Health, Ewa Beach, HI, p. A168
LICKTEIG, Teri, Director Human Resources, Pella Regional Health Center, Pella, IA, p. A233
LIDDELL, Sean, Manager Regional Service Information Technology, UnityPoint Health – Trinity Muscatine, Muscatine, IA, p. A232
LIDHOLM, Helen, Chief Executive Officer, Saint Mary's Regional Medical Center, Reno, NV, p. A404
LIEBER, Alan, Interim President and Chief Executive Officer, Chilton Medical Center, Pompton Plains, NJ, p. A417
LIEBER, Alan R., President, Overlook Medical Center, Summit, NJ, p. A418
LIEBERMAN, Jeffrey A., M.D., Executive Director, New York State Psychiatric Institute, New York, NY, p. A443
LIEBERMAN, Steven L., M.D. Chief of Staff, Veterans Affairs New Jersey Health Care System, East Orange, NJ, p. A411
LIEBERS, David, M.D. Chief Medical Officer and Vice President Medical Affairs, Ellis Hospital, Schenectady, NY, p. A450
LIEBOVICH, Kevin, M.D
President Medical Staff, Vista Medical Center East, Waukegan, IL, p. A203
President Medical Staff, Vista Medical Center West, Waukegan, IL, p. A203
LIEBSACK, David, Chief Operating Officer, Cherokee Regional Medical Center, Cherokee, IA, p. A224
LIECK, Amy, Chief Nursing Officer, Nix Community General Hospital, Dilley, TX, p. A609
LIEFER, Alan, M.D. President Medical Staff, Memorial Hospital, Chester, IL, p. A181
LIEN, Ann, R.N. Chief Nursing Officer, Meeker Memorial Hospital, Litchfield, MN, p. A341
LIEPMAN, Michael T., Chief Operating Officer, Skagit Valley Hospital, Mount Vernon, WA, p. A681
LIESMANN, George, M.D. Chief Medical Officer, Blessing Hospital, Quincy, IL, p. A199
LIGHT, Gary, Vice President and Chief Information Officer, Memorial Hospital and Health Care Center, Jasper, IN, p. A213
LIGHT, Laura, Director Human Resources, St. David's North Austin Medical Center, Austin, TX, p. A595
LIGHTBOURNE, Olieth, Chief Nursing Officer, Streamwood Behavioral Health Center, Streamwood, IL, p. A202
LIGHTCAP, Deb, Director Human Resources, Mercy Medical Center, Roseburg, OR, p. A525
LIGHTFOOT, William M., M.D. Vice President Medical Services, Providence Hospital, Mobile, AL, p. A22
LIGHTNER, Becky, Director Information Systems, Phoebe Sumter Medical Center, Americus, GA, p. A149
LIGON, Kim
Director Information Services, DCH Regional Medical Center, Tuscaloosa, AL, p. A25
Director Information Services, Northport Medical Center, Northport, AL, p. A23
LIGON, Lynda, Chief Nursing Officer, Warm Springs Medical Center, Warm Springs, GA, p. A167
LILES, Jerry, D.O.CHRISTUS Spohn Hospital Alice, Alice, TX, p. A590
LILES, Richard A., M.D. Medical Director, HEALTHSOUTH Rehabilitation Hospital, Largo, FL, p. A131
LILIK, Dennis
Chief Information Officer, Gladys Spellman Specialty Hospital and Nursing Center, Cheverly, MD, p. A296
Chief Information Officer, Prince George's Hospital Center, Cheverly, MD, p. A296
LILLEBOE, Linda, R.N. Director Operations, Carson Valley Medical Center, Gardnerville, NV, p. A400
LILLEY, Jeff, Chief Executive Officer, Princeton Community Hospital, Princeton, WV, p. A694
LILLEY, Jeffrey, CPA Chief Operating Officer, Princeton Community Hospital, Princeton, WV, p. A694
LILLY, Brian, Director Information Systems, Nason Hospital, Roaring Spring, PA, p. A549
LILLY, Ryan S., Director, Maine Veterans Affairs Medical Center, Augusta, ME, p. A288
LILLY, Spencer, President, Carolinas Medical Center, Charlotte, NC, p. A457
LIMA, Robert, Director Information Systems, Massachusetts Hospital School, Canton, MA, p. A306
LIMBAGA, Aries, R.N. Chief Nursing Officer, Rancho Los Amigos National Rehabilitation Center, Downey, CA, p. A60
LIMBOCKER, Jeff, Chief Financial Officer, Our Lady of the Lake Regional Medical Center, Baton Rouge, LA, p. A269
LIN, Dean Q., FACHE, President, Ocean Medical Center, Brick Township, NJ, p. A410
LIN, George, M.D. Physician Advisor, Hackensack University Medical Center at Pascack Valley, Westwood, NJ, p. A420
LIN, James Y., D.O. Chief of Staff, Millcreek Community Hospital, Erie, PA, p. A534
LINAFELTER, Robb, Chief Executive Officer, Lincoln Surgical Hospital, Lincoln, NE, p. A394
LINARES, Manuel, Chief Executive Officer, North Shore Medical Center, Miami, FL, p. A134
LINCKS, Brad, R.N. Chief Nursing Officer and Vice President, Our Lady of Peace, Louisville, KY, p. A261
LINCOLN, David R., FACHE, President and Chief Executive Officer, Covenant Health, Tewksbury, MA, p. B43
LINCOLN, Wendy, Chief Nursing Officer, Northside Hospital, Saint Petersburg, FL, p. A142
LIND, David, M.D. Chief Medical Officer, Cheyenne Regional Medical Center, Cheyenne, WY, p. A715
LIND, Mark, Director Information Technology, Mammoth Hospital, Mammoth Lakes, CA, p. A74
LIND, Sharon, FACHE, Interim Chief Executive Officer, Sterling Regional MedCenter, Sterling, CO, p. A109
LIND, Trent, Chief Executive Officer, Texas Orthopedic Hospital, Houston, TX, p. A622
LINDBERG, Bob, Chief Operating Officer, Cumberland Memorial Hospital, Cumberland, WI, p. A699
LINDBERG, Bonita N., Director Human Resources, Cortland Regional Medical Center, Cortland, NY, p. A432
LINDBERG, Chris, Chief Information Officer, Milwaukee County Behavioral Health Division, Milwaukee, WI, p. A706
LINDBERG, Randy, Director Fiscal Services, Shriners Hospitals for Children–Salt Lake City, Salt Lake City, UT, p. A658
LINDBERG, Steven, Chief Administrative Officer, Mayo Clinic Health System – Red Cedar in Menomonie, Menomonie, WI, p. A705
LINDELL, Charles, Chief Executive Officer, St. Bernard Parish Hospital, Chalmette, LA, p. A271

Index of Health Care Professionals

Index of Health Care Professionals / Lindell

LINDELL, Jonathan, Director Information Technology, Miracle Mile Medical Center, Los Angeles, CA, p. A71
LINDEMAN, Annette, Chief Clinical Officer, Kindred Hospital–Tucson, Tucson, AZ, p. A39
LINDEMAN, Barry K., Director Human Resources, Cardinal Hill Rehabilitation Hospital, Lexington, KY, p. A259
LINDEMANN, Fran, Director Finance, Kell West Regional Hospital, Wichita Falls, TX, p. A652
LINDEMANN, Steve, Chief Financial Officer, Brookings Health System, Brookings, SD, p. A567
LINDEMOEN, Pamela, Chief Operating Officer, Kaiser Permanente Santa Clara Medical Center, Santa Clara, CA, p. A91
LINDEN, Kelly, Senior Vice President, Chief Operating Officer, St. Mary Medical Center, Apple Valley, CA, p. A54
LINDEN, Todd C., President and Chief Executive Officer, Grinnell Regional Medical Center, Grinnell, IA, p. A228
LINDENBOOM, Kristen, Chief Operating Officer, Plantation General Hospital, Plantation, FL, p. A140
LINDER, Lawrence, M.D. Senior Vice President and Chief Medical Officer, University of Maryland Baltimore Washington Medical Center, Glen Burnie, MD, p. A298
LINDLEY, Michael, Chief Executive Officer, Haven Behavioral Healthcare, Nashville, TN, p. B61
LINDQUIST, Gina, Director Human Resources, Schoolcraft Memorial Hospital, Manistique, MI, p. A325
LINDQUIST, James, R.N. Chief Nursing Officer, JFK Medical Center, Edison, NJ, p. A411
LINDQUIST, Molly, Interim Chief Financial Officer, Chestatee Regional Hospital, Dahlonega, GA, p. A155
LINDQUIST, Peter, Vice President and Chief Nursing Officer, Providence Hospital, Mobile, AL, p. A22
LINDSEY, Craig, R.N. Vice President Clinical Services/Chief Nursing Officer, Park Ridge Health, Hendersonville, NC, p. A462
LINDSEY, Don, Vice President and Chief Information Officer, Tallahassee Memorial HealthCare, Tallahassee, FL, p. A144
LINDSEY, Hugh, M.D. Chief Medical Officer, Hayes Green Beach Memorial Hospital, Charlotte, MI, p. A316
LINDSEY, Jay, Chief Executive Officer, Plano Specialty Hospital, Plano, TX, p. A637
LINDSEY, Kim, Chief Human Resources Officer, Lourdes Hospital, Paducah, KY, p. A264
LINDSEY, Jr., Rob, Vice President Human Resources, Allegiance Behavioral Health Center of Plainview, Plainview, TX, p. A636
LINDSEY, Robbie, Chief Information Officer, Twin Lakes Regional Medical Center, Leitchfield, KY, p. A259
LINDSEY, Tony, M.D. Chief of Staff, University of North Carolina Hospitals, Chapel Hill, NC, p. A457
LINDSTROM, David, M.D. Vice President Medical Affairs, ProMedica Bay Park Hospital, Oregon, OH, p. A496
LINES, Brian, Chief Operating Officer, Ogden Regional Medical Center, Ogden, UT, p. A656
LING, Lori, Information Technician, Windom Area Hospital, Windom, MN, p. A349
LINGEN, Tom, M.D. Chief of Staff, Cumberland Memorial Hospital, Cumberland, WI, p. A699
LINGERFELT, Jeff, Chief Executive Officer, Heart of America Medical Center, Rugby, ND, p. A476
LINGO, Jessica, Human Resource Generalist, Story County Medical Center, Nevada, IA, p. A232
LINK, Nate, M.D. Medical Director, Bellevue Hospital Center, New York, NY, p. A438
LINKENHOKER, Ellen, Chief Nursing Officer, LewisGale Hospital Montgomery, Blacksburg, VA, p. A662
LINN, Steven C., M.D
Chief Medical Officer, Inspira Medical Center–Elmer, Elmer, NJ, p. A411
Chief Medical Officer, Inspira Medical Center–Vineland, Vineland, NJ, p. A420
LINNA, Gina, Manager Human Resources, Aspirus Ontonagon Hospital, Ontonagon, MI, p. A327
LINNINGTON, Darryl, Chief Financial Officer, McAlester Regional Health Center, McAlester, OK, p. A509
LINSCHEID, Carol, Vice President Human Resources, Enloe Medical Center, Chico, CA, p. A57
LINSE, Margaret, Administrative Secretary and Director Human Resources, West Holt Memorial Hospital, Atkinson, NE, p. A389
LINSIN, Amy, Chief Human Resources Officer, Good Samaritan Medical Center, West Palm Beach, FL, p. A147
LINSTROM, Joseph, Vice President Operations, Suburban Hospital, Bethesda, MD, p. A296
LINTON, Dwight, Director Human Resources, Scenic Mountain Medical Center, Big Spring, TX, p. A597
LINTON, Randall L., M.D., President and Chief Executive Officer, Mayo Clinic Health System in Eau Claire, Eau Claire, WI, p. A700
LINTZ, Gordon, Chief Administrative Officer, Morristown–Hamblen Healthcare System, Morristown, TN, p. A584
LINVILLE, Kimberly, Chief Nursing Officer, Grant Memorial Hospital, Petersburg, WV, p. A694
LINZMAN, Rob, D.O. Chief of Staff, Jefferson County Hospital, Waurika, OK, p. A518
LIPARI, Cheryl, Manager Information Systems, Teche Regional Medical Center, Morgan City, LA, p. A281
LIPE, Curt, Vice President, Chief Financial Officer, OSF St. Mary Medical Center, Galesburg, IL, p. A188
LIPHAM, Mary Sue
Chief Financial Officer, St. Luke's Lakeside Hospital, The Woodlands, TX, p. A647
Controller, St. Luke's The Woodlands Hospital, The Woodlands, TX, p. A648
LIPINSKI, Gary, M.D
Regional Vice President and Chief Medical Officer, Adventist Hinsdale Hospital, Hinsdale, IL, p. A191
Regional Vice President and Chief Medical Officer, Adventist La Grange Memorial Hospital, La Grange, IL, p. A192
LIPMAN, Brian, M.D. Medical Director and Medical Staff Services, Oconomowoc Memorial Hospital, Oconomowoc, WI, p. A708
LIPMAN, Henry D., Senior Vice President, Financial Strategy and External Relations, Lakes Region General Hospital, Laconia, NH, p. A406
LIPNER, Zach, Vice President Human Resources, Newark Beth Israel Medical Center, Newark, NJ, p. A415
LIPPERT, Brandt, Vice President Human Resources, Adena Greenfield Medical Center, Greenfield, OH, p. A490
LIPPINCOTT, Ken, M.D. Chief of Staff, North Mississippi State Hospital, Tupelo, MS, p. A361
LIPSCOMB, Teresa, Director Human Resources, Springbrook Behavioral Health System, Travelers Rest, SC, p. A565
LIPSCOMB, Tracy, Vice President Financial Services and Chief Financial Officer, Garrett County Memorial Hospital, Oakland, MD, p. A299
LIPSEY, Prentice, Chief Executive Officer, Kindred Hospital Cleveland–Gateway, Cleveland, OH, p. A484
LIPSKY, Janice G., R.N. System Vice President Human Resources and Organizational Development, St. Vincent's Medical Center Riverside, Jacksonville, FL, p. A130
LIPSKY, Richard, M.D., Chief Executive Officer, Columbus Hospital LTACH, Newark, NJ, p. A415
LIPSTEIN, Steven H., President and Chief Executive Officer, BJC HealthCare, Saint Louis, MO, p. B23
LIPTAK, Valenda M., Chief Executive Officer, Western Massachusetts Hospital, Westfield, MA, p. A313
LIRAKIS, Kathy, R.N. Chief Nursing Officer, Blue Hill Memorial Hospital, Blue Hill, ME, p. A289
LIRIO, Ruel R., M.D. Clinical Physician Advisor, Spectrum Health Zeeland Community Hospital, Zeeland, MI, p. A333
LISA, Mark P., FACHE, Chief Executive Officer, Twin Cities Community Hospital, Templeton, CA, p. A94
LISENBY, Michael, M.D. Vice President and Chief Medical Officer, East Alabama Medical Center, Opelika, AL, p. A23
LISKA, Lee Ann, President and Chief Executive Officer, University of Cincinnati Medical Center, Cincinnati, OH, p. A484
LISKE, Thomas, M.D. Chief Medical Officer, Kindred Hospital–Sycamore, Sycamore, IL, p. A202
LISKO, J. Stuart, Regional Director Operations, Critical Access Hospital Operations, Mercy Hospital Booneville, Booneville, AR, p. A42
LISKO, Stuart, Vice President, Chief Financial Officer and Compliance Officer, Levi Hospital, Hot Springs National Park, AR, p. A46
LISKOV, David, M.D. Medical Director, First Hospital Wyoming Valley, Kingston, PA, p. A537
LISONBEE, Rod, Chief Financial Officer, Utah Valley Regional Medical Center, Provo, UT, p. A657
LIST, Alan F., M.D., President and Chief Executive Officer, H. Lee Moffitt Cancer Center and Research Institute, Tampa, FL, p. A144
LISTER, Jack, Director Human Resources, Takoma Regional Hospital, Greeneville, TN, p. A578
LISTI, Daniel, Chief Operating Officer, Valley Baptist Medical Center–Harlingen, Harlingen, TX, p. A618
LISTON, John, Chief Financial Officer, McLaren Port Huron, Port Huron, MI, p. A328
LITAKER, Thomas, Chief Financial Officer, Skagit Valley Hospital, Mount Vernon, WA, p. A681
LITKA, Calvin, R.N. Director of Nursing, Horsham Clinic, Ambler, PA, p. A528
LITOVITZ, Gary, M.D. Medical Director, Dominion Hospital, Falls Church, VA, p. A664
LITSINGER, Jim, Chief Financial Officer, Adventist Rehabilitation Hospital of Maryland, Rockville, MD, p. A300
LITTERER, Karen, MSN, Administrator and Chief Operating Officer, Seton Highland Lakes, Burnet, TX, p. A599
LITTERER, Karen, R.N. Administrator and Chief Operating Officer, Seton Highland Lakes, Burnet, TX, p. A599
LITTERER, Karen, MSN, Administrator and Chief Operating Officer, Seton Northwest Hospital, Austin, TX, p. A594
LITTERER, Karen, R.N. Administrator and Chief Operating Officer, Seton Northwest Hospital, Austin, TX, p. A594
LITTLE, Bridget, Deputy Commander Nursing, Bayne–Jones Army Community Hospital, Fort Polk, LA, p. A273
LITTLE, Christopher M., Vice President and Chief Financial Officer, Ellwood City Hospital, Ellwood City, PA, p. A533
LITTLE, Denise, Director Human Resources, St. Elizabeth Community Hospital, Red Bluff, CA, p. A82
LITTLE, Gary, M.D. Medical Director, George Washington University Hospital, Washington, DC, p. A119
LITTLE, James E., Chief Financial Officer, Siloam Springs Regional Hospital, Siloam Springs, AR, p. A50
LITTLE, James P., M.D. Medical Director, HEALTHSOUTH Rehabilitation Hospital, Kingsport, TN, p. A580
LITTLE, Jason, President and Chief Executive Officer, Baptist Memorial Health Care Corporation, Memphis, TN, p. B21
LITTLE, Lou, Chief Executive Officer, HEALTHSOUTH MountainView Regional Rehabilitation Hospital, Morgantown, WV, p. A693
LITTLE, Marlene, Senior Director, Little Falls Hospital, Little Falls, NY, p. A436
LITTLE, Monica, Coordinator Human Resources, Kindred Rehabilitation Hospital Clear Lake, Webster, TX, p. A651
LITTLE, Steven N., President and Chief Executive Officer, Agnesian HealthCare, Fond Du Lac, WI, p. A700
LITTLE, Suzanne, Human Resources Specialist, Columbia Basin Hospital, Ephrata, WA, p. A678
LITTLE, Vicky, Director Human Resources, Effingham Hospital, Springfield, GA, p. A165
LITTLE, William, Chief Executive Officer, Saint Thomas Highlands Hospital, Sparta, TN, p. A588
LITTLEDEER, Lenora, R.N. Director of Nursing, Lawton Indian Hospital, Lawton, OK, p. A508
LITTLEFIELD, Karen, Manager Human Resources, Waldo County General Hospital, Belfast, ME, p. A289
LITTRELL, Angy, Chief Financial Officer and Chief Operating Officer, Fitzgibbon Hospital, Marshall, MO, p. A372
LITTRELL, Jeremy, Director Human Resources, Brodstone Memorial Hospital, Superior, NE, p. A398
LITTRELL, Mark, Chief Executive Officer, Lincoln Prairie Behavioral Health Center, Springfield, IL, p. A201
LIU, Marsha, Executive Vice President and Chief Financial Officer, Northwest Community Hospital, Arlington Heights, IL, p. A178
LIUZZA, Jed M., Chief Human Resources Officer, OU Medical Center, Oklahoma City, OK, p. A512
LIUZZO, Gary, Director Information Systems, Scotland Health Care System, Laurinburg, NC, p. A463
LIVELY, Corey, Chief Executive Officer, Great Plains Regional Medical Center, Elk City, OK, p. A506
LIVENGOOD, Annette, Vice President Human Resources, Garrett County Memorial Hospital, Oakland, MD, p. A299
LIVERMAN, Brett, Chief Financial Officer, Alleghany Memorial Hospital, Sparta, NC, p. A469
LIVERSAGE, Lavonne
Director, Fargo Veterans Affairs Health Care System, Fargo, ND, p. A473
Acting Director, Veterans Affairs Central Iowa Health Care System, Des Moines, IA, p. A227
LIVESAY, Jr., William, D.O. Medical Director, HEALTHSOUTH Rehabilitation Hospital of Charleston, Charleston, SC, p. A558
LIVIN, Lee
Chief Financial Officer, Yavapai Regional Medical Center – East, Prescott Valley, AZ, p. A36
Chief Financial Officer, Yavapai Regional Medical Center, Prescott, AZ, p. A36
LIVINGSTON, Carolyn, Director Human Resources, Salt Lake Regional Medical Center, Salt Lake City, UT, p. A658
LIVINGSTON, Charles
Administrator, Dakota Plains Surgical Center, Aberdeen, SD, p. A567
Chief Executive Officer, Midwest Surgical Hospital, Omaha, NE, p. A396
LIVINGSTON, Keith
Senior Vice President and Chief Information Officer, Appleton Medical Center, Appleton, WI, p. A697
Senior Vice President and Chief Information Officer, Theda Clark Medical Center, Neenah, WI, p. A707
LIVINGSTON, Richard, M.D. Medical Director, Valley Behavioral Health System, Barling, AR, p. A41
LIVINGSTON, Sam, Information Resource Consultant, G. Werber Bryan Psychiatric Hospital, Columbia, SC, p. A559
LIVINGSTONE, Marie, R.N. Chief Nursing Officer, Effingham Hospital, Springfield, GA, p. A165

**A898** Index of Health Care Professionals

Index of Health Care Professionals / Longnecker

Index of Health Care Professionals


LIVSEY, Don, Vice President and Chief Information Officer, Children's Hospital and Research Center Oakland, Oakland, CA, p. A78
LIVVIX, Susan, R.N. Vice President Nursing Services, Paris Community Hospital, Paris, IL, p. A197
LIZZA, Beth, Chief Nursing Officer, Ohio Valley Surgical Hospital, Springfield, OH, p. A497
LJUNGQUIST, Diane, MS, Chief Executive Officer, Tyler Memorial Hospital, Tunkhannock, PA, p. A551
LLANO, Manuel R.
Chief Executive Officer, Atlantic Shores Hospital, Fort Lauderdale, FL, p. A126
Chief Executive Officer, Fort Lauderdale Hospital, Fort Lauderdale, FL, p. A126
LLEWELLYN, Michael R., Chief Operating Officer, Laguna Honda Hospital and Rehabilitation Center, San Francisco, CA, p. A88
LLOYD, Davie, FACHE, Chief Executive Officer, Regional General Hospital, Williston, FL, p. A147
LLOYD II, Donald H., Administrator, CHRISTUS St. Patrick Hospital of Lake Charles, Lake Charles, LA, p. A278
LLOYD, John K., President and Chief Executive Officer, Meridian Health, Neptune, NJ, p. B91
LLOYD, Richard, D.O. Chief of Staff, Harbor Beach Community Hospital, Harbor Beach, MI, p. A322
LO, Eric, M.D. Chief Medical Staff, Bert Fish Medical Center, New Smyrna Beach, FL, p. A136
LO, Wesley, Regional Chief Executive Officer, Maui Memorial Medical Center, Wailuku, HI, p. A170
LOBBAN, Victoria, Vice President Finance, New England Sinai Hospital and Rehabilitation Center, Stoughton, MA, p. A312
LOBECK, Charles C., Administrator, Shriners Hospitals for Children–Twin Cities, Minneapolis, MN, p. A343
LOCEY, Vicky, R.N. Chief Operating and Chief Nursing Officer, Kaiser Permanente Santa Rosa Medical Center, Santa Rosa, CA, p. A92
LOCHRIDGE, Angela, Director Human Resources, Bradley County Medical Center, Warren, AR, p. A51
LOCKARD, Dennis, Vice President Fiscal Services and Chief Financial Officer, Wayne Hospital, Greenville, OH, p. A491
LOCKCUFF, Todd, Chief Financial Officer, Inova Alexandria Hospital, Alexandria, VA, p. A662
LOCKE, Cheryl, Vice President and Chief Human Resource Officer, Wake Forest Baptist Medical Center, Winston–Salem, NC, p. A471
LOCKE, Christopher, Chief Executive Officer, Saint Francis Hospital–Bartlett, Bartlett, TN, p. A574
LOCKE, Marianne, R.N. Associate Director Patient Care Services, Edward Hines, Jr. Veterans Affairs Hospital, Hines, IL, p. A190
LOCKE, Stuart, Chief Executive Officer, Southern Kentucky Rehabilitation Hospital, Bowling Green, KY, p. A255
LOCKERD, Marie Paul, M.D. Chief Medical Officer, Sanford Jackson Medical Center, Jackson, MN, p. A340
LOCKETT, Kevin, Interim Chief Financial Officer, Mayo Clinic Jacksonville, Jacksonville, FL, p. A129
LOCKHART, Jimmy Wayne, M.D. Medical Director, HEALTHSOUTH Treasure Coast Rehabilitation Hospital, Vero Beach, FL, p. A146
LOCKLEAR, Ann, Vice President, Human Resources, Scotland Health Care System, Laurinburg, NC, p. A463
LOCKWOOD, Melissa, Chief Executive Officer, Preston Memorial Hospital, Kingwood, WV, p. A692
LODGE, Dale M., Chief Executive Officer, Winchester Hospital, Winchester, MA, p. A313
LOE, Cindy, R.N. Director of Nursing, Essentia Health Northern Pines Medical Center, Aurora, MN, p. A335
LOEB, Katherine, R.N. Interim Vice President, Patient Care Services, Holy Cross Hospital, Chicago, IL, p. A182
LOEFFELHOLZ, Tim, Account Executive Information Technology, UnityPoint Health – Finley Hospital, Dubuque, IA, p. A227
LOELIGER, Eric, Vice President of Medical Affairs, Asante Three Rivers Medical Center, Grants Pass, OR, p. A521
LOEPP Jr., Robert A., FACHE, Chief Executive Officer, AMG Specialty Hospital–Wichita, Wichita, KS, p. A252
LOERA, Arnold, M.D. Clinical Director, Bristol Bay Area Health Corporation, Dillingham, AK, p. A28
LOERINC, Albert, M.D. Medical Director, New Bedford Rehabilitation Hospital, New Bedford, MA, p. A309
LOEWENSTEIN, Howard, Chief Information Resource Management Services, Jesse Brown Veterans Affairs Medical Center, Chicago, IL, p. A182
LOFF, Thomas, Chief Financial Officer, East Morgan County Hospital, Brush, CO, p. A100
LOFFING, David, Chief Operating Officer, University of Illinois Hospital & Health Sciences System, Chicago, IL, p. A185
LOFGREN, Richard P., M.P.H., President and CEO, UC Health, Cincinnati, OH, p. B138
LOFTIS, Michelle, Human Resources Officer, Ferry County Memorial Hospital, Republic, WA, p. A683
LOFTON, Jason, M.D. Medical Director, De Queen Medical Center, De Queen, AR, p. A43
LOFTON, Kevin E., FACHE, Chief Executive Officer, Catholic Health Initiatives, Englewood, CO, p. B28
LOFTON, Veronica, Acting Chief Executive Officer, Twin Valley Behavioral Healthcare, Columbus, OH, p. A487
LOFTUS, Dennis, Senior Vice President and Chief Information Officer, Riverside Regional Medical Center, Newport News, VA, p. A669
LOFTUS, John, M.D. Chief of Staff, Kaiser Permanente Oakland Medical Center, Oakland, CA, p. A78
LOFTUS, Philip, Ph.D
Vice President and Chief Information Officer, Aurora Medical Center of Oshkosh, Oshkosh, WI, p. A708
Vice President and Chief Information Officer, Aurora Psychiatric Hospital, Wauwatosa, WI, p. A713
Vice President and Chief Information Officer, Aurora St. Luke's Medical Center, Milwaukee, WI, p. A706
Chief Information Officer, Aurora West Allis Medical Center, West Allis, WI, p. A714
LOFURNO, Justin A., Director Human Resources, Providence Hospital, Columbia, SC, p. A559
LOGAN, Ann P., Ph.D., Chief Operating Officer, Hoboken University Medical Center, Hoboken, NJ, p. A412
LOGAN, Bradley
Chief Financial Officer, Franklin Woods Community Hospital, Johnson City, TN, p. A579
Chief Financial Officer, Sycamore Shoals Hospital, Elizabethton, TN, p. A577
LOGAN, Denise, Director Human Resources, Specialty Rehabilitation Hospital of Coushatta, Coushatta, LA, p. A272
LOGAN, Heather, Assistant Administrator Diagnostic and Support Services, Cascade Valley Hospital and Clinics, Arlington, WA, p. A676
LOGAN, Michael, Chief Financial Officer, Russell County Hospital, Russell Springs, KY, p. A265
LOGAN, Renee, Chief Financial Officer, Murray County Medical Center, Slayton, MN, p. A347
LOGAN–OWENS, Michelle, M.D. Interim Chief Executive Officer and President, Tuomey Healthcare System, Sumter, SC, p. A565
LOGAR, Michael, Assistant Superintendent, Larue D. Carter Memorial Hospital, Indianapolis, IN, p. A212
LOGDSON, David, Chief Nursing Officer, Twin Lakes Regional Medical Center, Leitchfield, KY, p. A259
LOGSDON, Diane, Vice President Planning and Development, Hardin Memorial Hospital, Elizabethtown, KY, p. A256
LOGSDON, Terri, Chief Financial Officer, Hickory Trail Hospital, Desoto, TX, p. A608
LOH, Marcel C., FACHE, Chief Executive Officer, Saint John's Health Center, Santa Monica, CA, p. A91
LOHMAN, Eric, M.D. Chief of Staff, Meadowview Regional Medical Center, Maysville, KY, p. A263
LOHMEIER, Justin, M.D. Chief of Staff, Baptist Memorial Hospital–Union County, New Albany, MS, p. A358
LOHN, Eric
Chief Financial Officer, Lake View Memorial Hospital, Two Harbors, MN, p. A348
Vice President and Chief Financial Officer, St. Luke's Hospital, Duluth, MN, p. A338
LOHR, Daniel E.
Regional Vice President Finance, The William W. Backus Hospital, Norwich, CT, p. A114
Regional Vice President Finance, Windham Hospital, Willimantic, CT, p. A116
LOHRMAN, Joseph W., ACHE, Chief Executive Officer, Annie Jeffrey Memorial County Health Center, Osceola, NE, p. A397
LOHSTRETER, Thomas, M.D. Chief of Staff, Kittson Memorial Healthcare Center, Hallock, MN, p. A340
LOKIE, Mike, Project Director, Bon Secours St. Francis Medical Center, Midlothian, VA, p. A668
LOKKEN, Christine, Manager of Finance, Bigfork Valley Hospital, Bigfork, MN, p. A335
LOLLIS, Sylvia, Director Human Resources, Osceola Regional Medical Center, Kissimmee, FL, p. A130
LOMAN, Sarah, Director Human Resources, Penobscot Valley Hospital, Lincoln, ME, p. A291
LOMBA, Maria R., Medical Director, New Braunfels Regional Rehabilitation Hospital, New Braunfels, TX, p. A634
LOMBARD, Scott, Acting Chief Nursing Officer, Spectrum Health Reed City Hospital, Reed City, MI, p. A328
LOMEO, Jody, Chief Executive Officer, KALEIDA Health, Buffalo, NY, p. A430
LOMMEL, Marsha, FACHE,
President and Chief Executive Officer, Madonna Rehabilitation Hospital, Lincoln, NE, p. A394
President and Chief Executive Officer, Madonna Rehabilitation Hospital, Lincoln, NE, p. A394
LONERGAN, Araceli
Chief Executive Officer, Community Hospital of Huntington Park, Huntington Park, CA, p. A65
Chief Executive Officer, East Los Angeles Doctors Hospital, Los Angeles, CA, p. A69
LONEY, Chris, Director Personnel, Thomas B. Finan Center, Cumberland, MD, p. A297
LONG, Adrian, M.D. Executive Vice President and Chief Medical Officer, Saint Agnes Hospital, Baltimore, MD, p. A294
LONG, Angela S., Vice President Clinical Services and Chief Nursing Officer, Southeastern Ohio Regional Medical Center, Cambridge, OH, p. A481
LONG, Brian, FACHE, President and Chief Executive Officer, Memorial Healthcare, Owosso, MI, p. A327
LONG, Dennis, Director Human Resources, Western Missouri Medical Center, Warrensburg, MO, p. A380
LONG, Douglas, President and Chief Executive Officer, West Hills Hospital and Medical Center, CA, p. A73
LONG, Erik
Controller, Baptist Health South Florida, Homestead Hospital, Homestead, FL, p. A129
Controller, Baptist Health South Florida, Mariners Hospital, Tavernier, FL, p. A146
LONG, Gary L., Senior Vice President Population Management, Virtua Marlton, Marlton, NJ, p. A414
LONG, Gregory L., M.D
Chief Medical Officer, Appleton Medical Center, Appleton, WI, p. A697
Chief Medical Officer, Theda Clark Medical Center, Neenah, WI, p. A707
LONG, Hilda, Chief Executive Officer, ICON Hospital, Humble, TX, p. A623
LONG, James K., CPA, Administrator and Chief Executive Officer, West River Regional Medical Center, Hettinger, ND, p. A474
LONG, Jeremy, Manager Information Systems, St. Vincent Salem Hospital, Salem, IN, p. A219
LONG, John, Chief Information Officer & Chief Analytics Officer, MUSC Medical Center of Medical University of South Carolina, Charleston, SC, p. A558
LONG, Jonathan Ray, M.D. Chief of Staff, Weatherford Regional Hospital, Weatherford, OK, p. A518
LONG, Judy M., R.N
Chief Nursing Officer and Chief Operating Officer, Appling Healthcare System, Baxley, GA, p. A152
Chief Nursing Officer and Vice President Patient Care Services, Piedmont Fayette Hospital, Fayetteville, GA, p. A157
LONG, Karen, R.N. Vice President Nursing, Bayfront Health St. Petersburg, Saint Petersburg, FL, p. A142
LONG, Michelle
Human Resources Business Partner, Abraham Lincoln Memorial Hospital, Lincoln, IL, p. A193
Regional Human Resource Manager, Taylorville Memorial Hospital, Taylorville, IL, p. A202
LONG, Mike, Chief Financial Officer, Powell Valley Healthcare, Powell, WY, p. A717
LONG, Richard, M.D. Chief Medical Officer, UPMC Hamot, Erie, PA, p. A534
LONG, Stephanie, President and Chief Executive Officer, River Bend Hospital, West Lafayette, IN, p. A221
LONG, Steven V., FACHE, President and Chief Executive Officer, Hancock Regional Hospital, Greenfield, IN, p. A210
LONG, Terry, Chief Executive Officer, Cherokee Medical Center, Centre, AL, p. A18
LONG, Theresa, Chief Executive Officer, Danville State Hospital, Danville, PA, p. A532
LONGACRE, Mark E., FACHE Chief Operating Officer, Nebraska Orthopaedic Hospital, Omaha, NE, p. A396
LONGBRAKE, Jeffery, President and Chief Executive Officer, Huron Medical Center, Bad Axe, MI, p. A314
LONGDO, Derrick, Director Information Systems, Memorial Medical Center – Neillsville, Neillsville, WI, p. A707
LONGEST, Bruce, M.D. President Medical Staff, Calhoun Health Services, Calhoun City, MS, p. A351
LONGEST, Sarah, Chief Information Officer, University of Mississippi Medical Center Grenada, Grenada, MS, p. A353
LONGEST, Sonya, M.D. Clinical Director, Walter B. Jones Alcohol and Drug Abuse Treatment Center, Greenville, NC, p. A461
LONGINO, III, Steve B., Director Information Systems, Hopkins County Memorial Hospital, Sulphur Springs, TX, p. A646
LONGMORE, David, Chief Information Officer, Wilkes–Barre Veterans Affairs Medical Center, Wilkes–Barre, PA, p. A553
LONGMUIR, Bryan, Chief Resource Management, Madigan Healthcare System, Tacoma, WA, p. A686
LONGMUIR, Marla, M.D. Chief Medical Officer, Mountrail County Medical Center, Stanley, ND, p. A476
LONGNECKER, Stacy, Chief of Staff, Ortonville Area Health Services, Ortonville, MN, p. A344

LONGO, Marybeth, Manager Human Resources, Trenton Psychiatric Hospital, Trenton, NJ, p. A419

LONGO, Robert J., FACHE, President and Chief Executive Officer, The Good Samaritan Hospital, Lebanon, PA, p. A538

LONGPRE, Donald J., Vice President Finance and Chief Financial Officer, North Ottawa Community Hospital, Grand Haven, MI, p. A320

LONGTIN, Brett, Chief Financial Officer, Lake Region Healthcare, Fergus Falls, MN, p. A338

LONIS, Robert, Interim Chief Financial Officer, Nashville General Hospital, Nashville, TN, p. A585

LOOMIS, Anna
    Interim Vice President, MultiCare Good Samaritan Hospital, Puyallup, WA, p. A682
    Interim Chief Financial Officer, MultiCare Tacoma General Hospital, Tacoma, WA, p. A686

LOOMIS, Greg
    President, Mercy Health Hackley Campus, Muskegon, MI, p. A326
    President, Mercy Health, Mercy Campus, Muskegon, MI, p. A326

LOOMIS, Randy, Chief Financial Officer, Adair County Memorial Hospital, Greenfield, IA, p. A228

LOONEY, Zane, Chief Information Officer, St. Bernard Parish Hospital, Chalmette, LA, p. A271

LOOPER, Eric N., Chief Executive Officer, Scott & White Hospital – Llano, Llano, TX, p. A628

LOOPER, Gary N., Chief Executive Officer, CHI St. Luke's Health Memorial Lufkin, Lufkin, TX, p. A630

LOOPER, Jeanne M., Chief Operating Officer, Ozarks Medical Center, West Plains, MO, p. A380

LOOSBROCK, Tammy
    Chief Executive Officer, Sanford Luverne Medical Center, Luverne, MN, p. A341
    Chief Executive Officer, Sanford Rock Rapids Medical Center, Rock Rapids, IA, p. A233

LOOSEMORE, Tim
    Director, Franciscan St. Anthony Health – Crown Point, Crown Point, IN, p. A207
    Regional Director Information Systems, Franciscan St. Anthony Health – Michigan City, Michigan City, IN, p. A216

LOPACHIN, Vicki, M.D. Chief Medical Officer, Mount Sinai Hospital, New York, NY, p. A442

LOPAS, Mary, Chief Information Officer, Ministry Door County Medical Center, Sturgeon Bay, WI, p. A712

LOPEZ, Amparo, Region Executive Director, Elgin Mental Health Center, Elgin, IL, p. A187

LOPEZ, Augustine, Chief Financial Officer, Salinas Valley Memorial Healthcare System, Salinas, CA, p. A85

LOPEZ, Cesar, R.N. Director of Nurses, Grimes St. Joseph Health Center, Navasota, TX, p. A634

LOPEZ, Enrique, M.D. Medical Director, Larry B. Zieverink, Sr. Alcoholism Treatment Center, Raleigh, NC, p. A467

LOPEZ, Ericca, Director Human Resources, Canyon Ridge Hospital, Chino, CA, p. A57

LOPEZ, Gerald, Chief Information Officer, Ashford Presbyterian Community Hospital, San Juan, PR, p. A723

LOPEZ, Ivonne, Director Human Resources, Hospital Oriente, Humacao, PR, p. A721

LOPEZ, Leonard H., Chief Operating Officer, Hopi Health Care Center, Keams Canyon, AZ, p. A32

LOPEZ, Leonardo, President Medical Staff, OSF Saint Paul Medical Center, Mendota, IL, p. A194

LOPEZ, Lesbia, Chief Nursing Officer, Doctors' Center Hospital San Juan, San Juan, PR, p. A723

LOPEZ, Lisa M., Director Human Resources, San Joaquin General Hospital, French Camp, CA, p. A62

LOPEZ, Lucia, Manager Human Resources, Coalinga Regional Medical Center, Coalinga, CA, p. A58

LOPEZ, Maria Rose, R.N. Chief of Nursing, Nix Health Care System, San Antonio, TX, p. A641

LOPEZ, Maritza, M.D. Chief of Staff, Sanford Canby Medical Center, Canby, MN, p. A336

LOPEZ, Rene, Chief Executive Officer, Doctors Hospital of Laredo, Laredo, TX, p. A627

LOPEZ, Robert, Chief Medical Officer, Highland Community Hospital, Picayune, MS, p. A359

LOPEZ, Rosalio J., M.D. Senior Vice President and Chief Medical Officer, PIH Health Hospital–Whittier, Whittier, CA, p. A97

LOPEZ, Steve, Chief Executive Officer, Colorado River Medical Center, Needles, CA, p. A77

LOPEZ, Steven, M.D. Chief Medical Officer, Palmetto Lowcountry Behavioral Health, Charleston, SC, p. A558

LOPEZ, Susan Nordstrom, President, Advocate Illinois Masonic Medical Center, Chicago, IL, p. A181

LOPEZ, Tony, Vice President and Chief Financial Officer, West Hills Hospital and Medical Center, CA, p. A73

LOPEZ, Valerie, CPA Chief Financial Officer, Uvalde County Hospital Authority, Uvalde, TX, p. A649

LORD, David, President, OSF St. Francis Hospital and Medical Group, Escanaba, MI, p. A319

LORD, Gregory D., M.D
    Medical Director, Doctor's Hospital of Deer Creek, Leesville, LA, p. A279
    Chief Medical Officer, Leesville Rehabilitation Hospital, Leesville, LA, p. A279

LORD, Jeff, Director of Nursing, Connecticut Veterans Home and Hospital, Rocky Hill, CT, p. A114

LORD, Jill, MS Director Patient Care Services, Mt. Ascutney Hospital and Health Center, Windsor, VT, p. A661

LORD, Robert L., JD Senior Vice President and Chief Operating Officer, Martin Health System, Stuart, FL, p. A143

LORENTZ, Derick, Interim Chief Financial Officer, Perkins County Health Services, Grant, NE, p. A392

LORENZ, Holly, R.N. Chief Nurse Executive, UPMC Presbyterian Shadyside, Pittsburgh, PA, p. A547

LORENZ, Pat, Chief Operating Officer, Okeene Municipal Hospital, Okeene, OK, p. A511

LORENZ, Paul E., Chief Executive Officer, Santa Clara Valley Medical Center, San Jose, CA, p. A89

LORENZEN, Shelli, Chief Human Resources Officer, Manning Regional Healthcare Center, Manning, IA, p. A231

LORENZO, Heather, M.D. Vice President and Chief Medical Officer, Meritus Medical Center, Hagerstown, MD, p. A298

LORIMER, IV, Lee, Regional Director Human Resources, McKay–Dee Hospital Center, Ogden, UT, p. A656

LORING, Rosemary C., Vice President Human Resources, Maine Coast Memorial Hospital, Ellsworth, ME, p. A290

LORMAN, William J., Ph.D. Clinical Director, Livengrin Foundation, Bensalem, PA, p. A529

LORMAND, Jared, Vice President Information Technology, Opelousas General Health System, Opelousas, LA, p. A283

LORTON, Donald E., Executive Vice President, Bedford Memorial Hospital, Bedford, VA, p. A662

LORY, Marc H., Chief Executive Officer, Schuylkill Health System, Pottsville, PA, p. B118

LORY, Mark H.
    Chief Executive Officer, Schuylkill Medical Center – East Norwegian Street, Pottsville, PA, p. A548
    Chief Executive Officer, Schuylkill Medical Center – South Jackson Street, Pottsville, PA, p. A548

LOSADA, Marcus, Controller, The Surgical Hospital of Phoenix, Phoenix, AZ, p. A36

LOSASSO, Greg, President, Elkhart General Healthcare System, Elkhart, IN, p. A207

LOSITO, Glenna, R.N. Chief Nursing Officer, Cibola General Hospital, Grants, NM, p. A424

LOTHE, Eric L., Vice President and Administrator, UnityPoint Health–Iowa Lutheran Hospital, Des Moines, IA, p. A226

LOTHIAN, Nancy, Chief Operating Officer and Chief Information Officer, The University of Vermont Health Network Central Vermont Medical Center, Berlin, VT, p. A660

LOTT, Andrea, Vice President Information Services, Northeastern Vermont Regional Hospital, Saint Johnsbury, VT, p. A661

LOTT, Ben, Vice President of Clinical Services, Riverside Medical Center, Franklinton, LA, p. A274

LOTT, Cynthia, Director Human Resources, Northern Virginia Mental Health Institute, Falls Church, VA, p. A664

LOTT, Jeff, Director Information Services, Touro Infirmary, New Orleans, LA, p. A282

LOTT, Laura, Administrative Director, Eastern Louisiana Mental Health System, Jackson, LA, p. A275

LOTT, Rodney, Director Management Information Systems and Facility Operations, Scott & White Hospital – Llano, Llano, TX, p. A628

LOTZE, Eberhard, M.D. Chief Medical Officer, Woman's Hospital of Texas, Houston, TX, p. A623

LOUBERT, Cheryl, M.D. Chief Medical Staff, MidMichigan Medical Center–Gladwin, Gladwin, MI, p. A320

LOUDEN CORBETT, Jeanette L., Chief Human Resources Officer, Highland Hospital, Oakland, CA, p. A78

LOUDERMILK, Kerry, Senior Vice President and Chief Financial Officer, Phoebe Putney Memorial Hospital, Albany, GA, p. A149

LOUGHERY, Vicki, R.N. Chief Nursing Officer, Monadnock Community Hospital, Peterborough, NH, p. A408

LOUGHRAN, Lisa, Chief Nursing Officer, Gunnison Valley Hospital, Gunnison, CO, p. A104

LOUGHRAN, Michael, Vice President Human Resources, Kennedy Krieger Institute, Baltimore, MD, p. A293

LOUIS, Alfred, M.D. Chief Medical Staff, Promise Hospital of Houston, Houston, TX, p. A621

LOUK, Rodney, Vice President Information Systems, Washington Hospital, Washington, PA, p. A552

LOUKATOS, George, M.D. President Medical Staff Affairs, Merit Health Biloxi, Biloxi, MS, p. A350

LOVATO, Anthony, Director Information Technology, Coon Memorial Hospital, Dalhart, TX, p. A604

LOVDAHL, Brian A., Chief Financial Officer, Baldwin Area Medical Center, Baldwin, WI, p. A697

LOVE, Alex, Acting Manager Human Resources, Alexandria Veterans Affairs Health Care System, Pineville, LA, p. A283

LOVE, Bianca, Assistant Administrator Human Resources, Trinity Hospital Twin City, Dennison, OH, p. A489

LOVE, E. Clifford, Director Fiscal Services, Eastern State Hospital, Williamsburg, VA, p. A674

LOVE, Glenn Neil, M.D. Medical Director, Hilton Head Hospital, Hilton Head Island, SC, p. A562

LOVE, Jodi, R.N. Chief Nursing Officer, Helena Regional Medical Center, Helena, AR, p. A45

LOVE, Matt
    Senior Vice President Finance, St. Elizabeth Boardman Health Center, Boardman, OH, p. A480
    Senior Vice President Finance, St. Elizabeth Health Center, Youngstown, OH, p. A501

LOVE, Matthew, Chief Executive Officer, Options Behavioral Health System, Indianapolis, IN, p. A212

LOVE, Tammy, Chief Nursing Officer, Crossroads Community Hospital, Mount Vernon, IL, p. A195

LOVE, Tim, Director Information Services, Reid Health, Richmond, IN, p. A219

LOVE, Valerie, Manager Business Office, Heatherhill Care Communities, Chardon, OH, p. A481

LOVE–WATLER, Meylan, Chief Operating Officer, Lower Keys Medical Center, Key West, FL, p. A130

LOVEJOY, David, Chief Operations Officer, Riverview Psychiatric Center, Augusta, ME, p. A288

LOVEJOY, Leslie, R.N. Chief Nursing and Quality Officer, Sonoma Valley Hospital, Sonoma, CA, p. A92

LOVEJOY, Rob, Chief Operating Officer, Sanford Thief River Falls Medical Center, Thief River Falls, MN, p. A348

LOVELACE, Alan, Vice President and Chief Financial Officer, Stillwater Medical Center, Stillwater, OK, p. A515

LOVELACE, Christina, Director Human Resources, Gunnison Valley Hospital, Gunnison, CO, p. A104

LOVELACE, Donald, Chief Financial Officer, Bluffton Regional Medical Center, Bluffton, IN, p. A205

LOVELESS, Craig, Chief Executive Officer, Prowers Medical Center, Lamar, CO, p. A106

LOVELESS, Jane Doll, Vice President Information Services, Grand View Health, Sellersville, PA, p. A549

LOVELESS, Kurt, Chief Financial Officer, Summit Healthcare Regional Medical Center, Show Low, AZ, p. A38

LOVELESS, Steve, President and Chief Executive Officer, St. Vincent Healthcare, Billings, MT, p. A381

LOVELL Jr., Charles D., FACHE, President and Chief Executive Officer, Caldwell Medical Center, Princeton, KY, p. A265

LOVELL, Mark, Vice President and Chief Financial Officer, Tuomey Healthcare System, Sumter, SC, p. A565

LOVELL, Stephanie, Vice President and General Counsel, Boston Medical Center, Boston, MA, p. A303

LOVELL, Terrence, Vice President Human Resources, Union Hospital, Elkton, MD, p. A297

LOVELLETTE, Teresa A., Manager Human Resources, Herrin Hospital, Herrin, IL, p. A190

LOVERA, Carlos, Director Information Systems, Montrose Memorial Hospital, Montrose, CO, p. A107

LOVERING, Keith, Information Technician, Miller County Hospital, Colquitt, GA, p. A154

LOVERING, Richard, Corporate Vice President Human Resources and Organizational Development, AtlantiCare Regional Medical Center, Atlantic City, NJ, p. A409

LOVERN, Ed, Chief Operating Officer, Piedmont Hospital, Atlanta, GA, p. A151

LOVERSO, Felice L., Ph.D., President and Chief Executive Officer, Casa Colina Hospital and Health Systems, Pomona, CA, p. A81

LOVETT, Chad, Chief Executive Officer, Kindred Hospital Rome, Rome, GA, p. A163

LOVING, David E., Chief Executive Officer, Central Carolina Hospital, Sanford, NC, p. A468

LOVINGOOD, Toni, Chief Operating Officer, Murphy Medical Center, Murphy, NC, p. A465

LOVRICH, John
    Chief Financial Officer, Catalina Island Medical Center, Avalon, CA, p. A54
    Chief Financial Officer, Glenn Medical Center, Willows, CA, p. A98

LOVSHIN, Alex, Chief Operating Officer, Des Peres Hospital, Saint Louis, MO, p. A376

LOW, Kern, M.D. Chief Medical Officer, St. Thomas More Hospital, Canon City, CO, p. A100

Index of Health Care Professionals

Index of Health Care Professionals / Lusterio

LUSTERIO, Efren, Director of Nursing, Behavioral Center of Michigan, Warren, MI, p. A332
LUTES, Adrianne, Chief Executive Officer, Select Specialty Hospital Daytona Beach, Daytona Beach, FL, p. A125
LUTES, Michael
President, Carolinas HealthCare System Anson, Wadesboro, NC, p. A470
President, Carolinas Healthcare System Union, Monroe, NC, p. A465
LUTHER, Vera, M.D. Chief of Staff, Sabine County Hospital, Hemphill, TX, p. A618
LUTTON, Lorraine, President, St. Joseph's Hospital, Tampa, FL, p. A145
LUTZ, Denise, Chief Human Resources Officer, St. Joseph's Hospital and Health Center, Dickinson, ND, p. A473
LUTZ, Don, Chief Information Officer, Bayonne Medical Center, Bayonne, NJ, p. A409
LUTZ, Terry, Chief Financial Officer, Scheurer Hospital, Pigeon, MI, p. A327
LUX, Teri, R.N
Vice President Patient Care Services and Chief Nursing Officer, Community Memorial Hospital, Menomonee Falls, WI, p. A705
Vice President Patient Care Services and Chief Nursing Officer, St. Joseph's Hospital, West Bend, WI, p. A714
LUZINSKI, Craig, MSN Chief Human Resources Officer, Cheyenne Regional Medical Center, Cheyenne, WY, p. A715
LYDE, Shawna Martin, Director Human Resources, Fairfield Memorial Hospital, Winnsboro, SC, p. A566
LYDICK, Bryan, Chief Executive Officer, Redwood Area Hospital, Redwood Falls, MN, p. A345
LYLE, Janet, Chief Human Resources and Allied Health Services, Springfield Hospital, Springfield, VT, p. A661
LYMAN, Jeremy, Chief Executive Officer, Blue Mountain Hospital, Blanding, UT, p. A654
LYNCE, Danialle, Manager Human Resources, University Hospitals Geauga Medical Center, Chardon, OH, p. A481
LYNCH, Becky, Manager Business Entity Management and Information Systems, OSF St. Mary Medical Center, Galesburg, IL, p. A188
LYNCH, Cecelia, R.N. Vice President Patient Care Services and Chief Nursing Officer, Lowell General Hospital, Lowell, MA, p. A308
LYNCH, Danile, Chief Operating Officer, Saint Luke Institute, Silver Spring, MD, p. A300
LYNCH, David, Regional Director Information Systems, Summa Barberton Citizens Hospital, Barberton, OH, p. A479
LYNCH, Elizabeth A., Vice President Human Resources, The Hospital of Central Connecticut, New Britain, CT, p. A113
LYNCH III, Ernest C., President and Chief Executive Officer, Medical Center of McKinney, McKinney, TX, p. A632
LYNCH, G. Michael, M.D. Chief Medical Officer, Inova Fair Oaks Hospital, Fairfax, VA, p. A664
LYNCH, Heather, M.D. Chief of Staff, Purcell Municipal Hospital, Purcell, OK, p. A514
LYNCH, Jim, Chief Financial Officer, Fairbanks Memorial Hospital, Fairbanks, AK, p. A28
LYNCH, John, M.D. Vice President and Chief Medical Officer, Barnes-Jewish Hospital, Saint Louis, MO, p. A376
LYNCH, John, Vice President Chief Information Officer, Catskill Regional Medical Center, Harris, NY, p. A435
LYNCH, Marc, D.O. Chief of Staff, Kindred Hospital-Ontario, Ontario, CA, p. A79
LYNCH, Timothy, Vice President Operations, Spaulding Hospital for Continuing Medical Care Cambridge, Cambridge, MA, p. A306
LYNCH, Torie A., Manager Human Resources, Central Montana Medical Center, Lewistown, MT, p. A385
LYNCH, William, Executive Vice President and Chief Operating Officer, Jamaica Hospital Medical Center, NY, p. A440
LYNCH-KILIC, Cathy, Vice President Human Resources, St. Mary's General Hospital, Passaic, NJ, p. A416
LYND, Samuel, Administrator and Chief Executive Officer, Baptist Memorial Hospital-Tipton, Covington, TN, p. A576
LYNN, Jason, Director Finance, St. Vincent's St. Clair, Pell City, AL, p. A24
LYNN, Samuel, Director Human Resources, Northwest Texas Healthcare System, Amarillo, TX, p. A591
LYNSKEY, Jeanne, Vice President and Chief Financial Officer, Milford Regional Medical Center, Milford, MA, p. A309
LYON, Beverly, R.N. Vice President Nursing, Milford Hospital, Milford, CT, p. A113
LYON, David, M.D. Chief Medical Officer, Easton Hospital, Easton, PA, p. A533
LYON, Robert J., Chief Executive Officer, PHS Santa Fe Indian Hospital, Santa Fe, NM, p. A426
LYON, Tami, Director Human Resources, Community Memorial Hospital, Burke, SD, p. A567
LYONS, Althea C., Vice President Human Resources and Development, Beverly Hospital, Beverly, MA, p. A302
LYONS, Jan, Regional Director Health Improvement Management, Ringgold County Hospital, Mount Ayr, IA, p. A232
LYONS, Jim, Chief Clinic Officer, Hutchinson Health, Hutchinson, MN, p. A340
LYONS, Lenny
Administrator, Delta Community Medical Center, Delta, UT, p. A654
Administrator, Fillmore Community Medical Center, Fillmore, UT, p. A654
LYSAGHT, Marcia C., R.N. Associate Director Patient Care Services, Miami Veterans Affairs Healthcare System, Miami, FL, p. A134
LYSAGHT, William, Chief Financial Officer, Kindred Hospital Las Vegas-Sahara, Las Vegas, NV, p. A402
LYTLE, John, M.D. Chief of Staff, Jefferson Regional Medical Center, Pine Bluff, AR, p. A50
LYTOLLIS, William, M.D. Chief of Staff, Barrow Regional Medical Center, Winder, GA, p. A167

# M

MAALIKI, Hikmat A., M.D. Chief of Staff, St. Luke Community Healthcare, Ronan, MT, p. A386
MAAS, Vernon, M.D. Vice President, Medical Affairs, St. Mary's Medical Center of Evansville, Evansville, IN, p. A208
MABRY, Bradley, Chief Executive Officer, Dauterive Hospital, New Iberia, LA, p. A281
MABRY, Jerry D., FACHE, Chief Executive Officer, National Park Medical Center, Hot Springs, AR, p. A45
MACAFEE, Francis M., Vice President Finance and Chief Financial Officer, Corning Hospital, Corning, NY, p. A432
MACALEER, Cara, Chief Executive Officer/Managing Director, Two Rivers Behavioral Health System, Kansas City, MO, p. A371
MACARONAS, Thomas, Chief Financial Officer, Labette Health, Parsons, KS, p. A248
MACATOL, Matthew, M.D. President Medical Staff, Marietta Memorial Hospital, Marietta, OH, p. A493
MACBRIDE, Samuel, M.D. Chief Medical Officer, Rehoboth McKinley Christian Health Care Services, Gallup, NM, p. A424
MACDONALD, Alan G., President and Chief Executive Officer, Hallmark Health System, Melrose, MA, p. A308
MACDONALD, Laurie, Vice President Finance, Penn Highlands Elk, Saint Marys, PA, p. A549
MACDONALD, Neil, Vice President Operations, MedStar Union Memorial Hospital, Baltimore, MD, p. A294
MACDOUGALL, David, Chief Financial Officer, United Health Services Hospitals-Binghamton, Binghamton, NY, p. A430
MACE, Rick, Chief Executive Officer, Adventist Bolingbrook Hospital, Bolingbrook, IL, p. A180
MACE, Robert, M.D., Interim Chief Executive Officer, Webster County Memorial Hospital, Webster Springs, WV, p. A695
MACE, T. Paul, Chief Medical Officer, Garden Park Medical Center, Gulfport, MS, p. A353
MACFADYEN, James, M.D. Medical Director, St. John Vianney Hospital, Downingtown, PA, p. A532
MACGREGOR, Nancy, Chief Financial Officer, Salt Lake Behavioral Health, Salt Lake City, UT, p. A658
MACHADO, James, Chief Executive Officer, Clearview Regional Medical Center, Monroe, GA, p. A161
MACHADO, Maria T., Administrator, Hospital Hermanos Melendez, Bayamon, PR, p. A720
MACHULSKY, RN, BSN, Janet, Director of Nursing, St. Lawrence Rehabilitation Center, Lawrenceville, NJ, p. A413
MACIAS, Susan, Chief Human Resources Officer, Rehoboth McKinley Christian Health Care Services, Gallup, NM, p. A424
MACIEL, Maureen, M.D. Chief of Staff, Shriners Hospitals for Children-Tampa, Tampa, FL, p. A145
MACIOCE, Gary, President, Penn Highlands Clearfield, Clearfield, PA, p. A531
MACK, Charles, Vice President Finance and Chief Financial Officer, Merit Health Natchez, Natchez, MS, p. A358
MACK, Edward, M.D. Chief of Staff, Northport Veterans Affairs Medical Center, Northport, NY, p. A445
MACKENROTH, Robin D., Chief Operating Officer, Kaiser Permanente Riverside Medical Center, Riverside, CA, p. A83
MACKENZIE, Julie, Manager Human Resources, Presbyterian Espanola Hospital, Espanola, NM, p. A424
MACKENZIE, Susan, Director, Providence Veterans Affairs Medical Center, Providence, RI, p. A556
MACKENZIE, Thomas, M.D. Medical Director, Chief of Clinical Operations, Denver Health, Denver, CO, p. A101
MACKETT, Charles, M.D. Senior Vice President and Chief Medical Officer, Indian River Medical Center, Vero Beach, FL, p. A146
MACKEY Jr., Bruce J., President and Chief Executive Officer, Five Star Quality Care, Newton, MA, p. B56
MACKINNON, Paul, MS Senior Vice President Patient Care Services and Chief Nursing Officer, HealthAlliance Hospitals, Leominster, MA, p. A308
MACKSOOD, Dan
Regional Senior Vice President and Chief Financial Officer, Good Samaritan Hospital Medical Center, West Islip, NY, p. A453
Regional Vice President and Chief Financial Officer, St. Catherine of Siena Medical Center, Smithtown, NY, p. A450
MACLAUCHLAN, Steven, President and CEO, Saint Vincent Hospital, Worcester, MA, p. A313
MACLAUGHLIN, Jeremy, Director Human Resources, Citizens Memorial Hospital, Bolivar, MO, p. A363
MACLEOD, Deborah, MS Vice President Nursing and Patient Care Services, Mid Coast Hospital, Brunswick, ME, p. A289
MACLEOD, Robert J., Chief Executive Officer, New Hampshire Hospital, Concord, NH, p. A405
MACMILLAN, Carllene, Vice President, Patient Care Services, Our Lady of Lourdes Regional Medical Center, Lafayette, LA, p. A278
MACNEILL, Bruce, Chief Financial Officer, Vibra Hospital of Sacramento, Folsom, CA, p. A61
MACPHEE, Alan, Chief Executive Officer, John C. Fremont Healthcare District, Mariposa, CA, p. A74
MACPHERSON, Bonne S., Director Human Resources, Florida Hospital Fish Memorial, Orange City, FL, p. A137
MACPHERSON, David S., M.P.H., Acting Director, Veterans Affairs Pittsburgh Healthcare System, Pittsburgh, PA, p. A547
MACRI, Fredrick, Executive Vice President, Rhode Island Hospital, Providence, RI, p. A556
MACRI, William P., Chief Executive Officer, Kindred Hospital-Nashville, Nashville, TN, p. A585
MACUGA, Paul, Chief Human Resources Officer, The University of Vermont Health Network University of Vermont Medical Center, Burlington, VT, p. A660
MADDEN, R. Craig, Director Employee Relations, Reynolds Memorial Hospital, Glen Dale, WV, p. A691
MADDOX, Dale, Chief Financial Officer, Medical Center of South Arkansas, El Dorado, AR, p. A43
MADER, Elaine, M.D. Chief of Staff, Integris Baptist Regional Health Center, Miami, OK, p. A509
MADER, Frank, Director Information Services, East Liverpool City Hospital, East Liverpool, OH, p. A489
MADER, Vikki, Director Health Information Services, Pratt Regional Medical Center, Pratt, KS, p. A249
MADISON, Jeffrey, Chief Executive Officer, Little River Rockdale Hospital, Rockdale, TX, p. A638
MADKINS, Catrina, Controller and Chief Financial Officer, HEALTHSOUTH Plano Rehabilitation Hospital, Plano, TX, p. A637
MADRID, Melissa, R.N. Chief Nursing Officer, Harper County Community Hospital, Buffalo, OK, p. A504
MADRID, Stephanie, Chief Executive Officer, Kindred Hospital Dallas Central, Dallas, TX, p. A605
MADSEN, Greg T., Chief Executive Officer, Spotsylvania Regional Medical Center, Fredericksburg, VA, p. A665
MAEKAWA, Steve, Chief Financial Officer, Garfield Medical Center, Monterey Park, CA, p. A76
MAENIUS, Linda, Chief Financial Officer, Laurel Ridge Treatment Center, San Antonio, TX, p. A641
MAERTENS, Mary B., FACHE, President and Chief Executive Officer, Avera Marshall Regional Medical Center, Marshall, MN, p. A342
MAES, Jillian, Director Marketing and Public Relations, St. Thomas More Hospital, Canon City, CO, p. A100
MAES, Stephen, Director Information Systems, Franciscan St. James Hospital and Health Centers, Olympia Fields, IL, p. A197
MAESE, John, M.D. Chief Medical Officer, Coney Island Hospital, NY, p. A439
MAESTRE, Jaime, Chief Executive Officer, Dr. Ramon E. Betances Hospital-Mayaguez Medical Center Branch, Mayaguez, PR, p. A722
MAGALLANES, Diana Zamora, Chief Executive Officer, Arise Austin Medical Center, Austin, TX, p. A593
MAGDANGAL, Connie, Executive Vice President and Chief Financial Officer, Bergen Regional Medical Center, Paramus, NJ, p. A416
MAGEE, Becky, Chief Information Officer, Washington Regional Medical Center, Fayetteville, AR, p. A44
MAGEE, James L., Executive Director, Piggott Community Hospital, Piggott, AR, p. A49
MAGEE, Kyle, M.D., Chief Executive Officer, Riverside Medical Center, Franklinton, LA, p. A274
MAGEE, William F., Chief Financial Officer, Alliance HealthCare System, Holly Springs, MS, p. A354
MAGESKI, Denise, MSN Chief Nurse Executive, Northwestern Lake Forest Hospital, Lake Forest, IL, p. A192

A902 Index of Health Care Professionals

Index of Health Care Professionals / Malone

MAGHAZEHE, Al, FACHE, Chief Executive Officer, Capital Health, Trenton, NJ, p. B27
MAGHAZEHE, Al, FACHE,
President and Chief Executive Officer, Capital Health Medical Center–Hopewell, Pennington, NJ, p. A416
President and Chief Executive Officer, Capital Health Regional Medical Center, Trenton, NJ, p. A419
MAGID, Philip, Director Fiscal Services, Shriners Hospitals for Children–Chicago, Chicago, IL, p. A184
MAGILL, Marc, Medical Center Director, Grand Junction Veterans Health Care System, Grand Junction, CO, p. A104
MAGNER, Johanna, Interim Chief Nursing Officer, Saint Michael's Medical Center, Newark, NJ, p. A415
MAGNER, Kile, Administrator, Ellinwood District Hospital, Ellinwood, KS, p. A239
MAGNUSON, Johna, Director Nursing, Hillsboro Community Hospital, Hillsboro, KS, p. A241
MAGNUSON, Robert, Business Operations Flight Chief, U. S. Air Force Clinic, Mountain Home AFB, ID, p. A175
MAGOON, Patrick M., President and Chief Executive Officer, Ann & Robert H. Lurie Children's Hospital of Chicago, Chicago, IL, p. A181
MAGRO, Michael, M.D. Chief Medical Officer, Mercy Suburban Hospital, Norristown, PA, p. A541
MAGRUDER, Joan, President, St. Louis Children's Hospital, Saint Louis, MO, p. A377
MAGUIRE, David L., M.D. Vice President Medical Affairs, Baystate Wing Hospital, Palmer, MA, p. A310
MAGUIRE, Kimberly, R.N
Chief Nursing Officer, Mercy Health Hackley Campus, Muskegon, MI, p. A326
Chief Nursing Officer, Mercy Health, Mercy Campus, Muskegon, MI, p. A326
MAGUREAN, Vickie, Chief Financial Officer, Seven Rivers Regional Medical Center, Crystal River, FL, p. A124
MAGUTA, Sam, Coordinator Information Systems, Devereux Georgia Treatment Network, Kennesaw, GA, p. A159
MAHAJAN, Sumit, M.D. Chief Medical Staff, Hi–Desert Medical Center, Joshua Tree, CA, p. A65
MAHAN, Michael, M.D. Chief Medical Staff, Granville Health System, Oxford, NC, p. A466
MAHAN, Michelle K., Senior Vice President and Chief Financial Officer, Frederick Memorial Hospital, Frederick, MD, p. A298
MAHAN, Vic
Chief Information Officer, Chino Valley Medical Center, Chino, CA, p. A57
Director Information Systems, Garden Grove Hospital and Medical Center, Garden Grove, CA, p. A63
Director Information Technology, La Palma Intercommunity Hospital, La Palma, CA, p. A66
Director Information Technology, West Anaheim Medical Center, Anaheim, CA, p. A53
MAHAR, Priscilla, Chief Clinical Officer, Spectrum Health United Hospital, Greenville, MI, p. A321
MAHER, Donna, R.N. Chief Operating Officer, Morton Hospital and Medical Center, Taunton, MA, p. A312
MAHER, James M., Senior Vice President and Chief Financial Officer, Robert Wood Johnson University Hospital at Hamilton, Hamilton, NJ, p. A412
MAHER, Jennifer, Chief Executive Officer, Sutter Davis Hospital, Davis, CA, p. A59
MAHER, John P., Executive Vice President and Chief Financial Officer, Nassau University Medical Center, East Meadow, NY, p. A433
MAHER, Sean, Director Human Resources, Devereux Children's Behavioral Health Center, Malvern, PA, p. A539
MAHER, Thomas, Chief Executive Officer and Administrator, Boulder City Hospital, Boulder City, NV, p. A400
MAHERA, Tina, M.D. Chief Medical Officer, Garfield Park Hospital, Chicago, IL, p. A182
MAHEUX, Diane, Vice President Finance, Memorial Hospital, North Conway, NH, p. A408
MAHL, Morgan G., Director Human Resources, St. Luke's Hospital – Warren Campus, Phillipsburg, NJ, p. A417
MAHMOOD, Ahsan, M.D. Chief Medical Officer, Hamilton Center, Terre Haute, IN, p. A220
MAHMOOD, K. Alec, Chief Financial Officer, Children's Hospitals and Clinics of Minnesota, Minneapolis, MN, p. A342
MAHMOOD, Tariq, Chief Executive Officer, Lake Whitney Medical Center, Whitney, TX, p. A652
MAHONE, William, President and Chief Executive Officer, Halifax Regional Medical Center, Roanoke Rapids, NC, p. A467
MAHONEY, James, Chief Information Officer, Memorial Hospital, York, PA, p. A554
MAHONEY, Marie, M.D. Chief Medical Officer, AMG Specialty Hospital–Slidell, Slidell, LA, p. A285
MAHONEY, Mark, Manager Information Systems, Meadville Medical Center, Meadville, PA, p. A540
MAHONEY, Nicole, Interim Chief Executive Officer, Pioneer Memorial Hospital, Heppner, OR, p. A521
MAHONEY, Theresa, Director Human Resources, Fairmount Behavioral Health System, Philadelphia, PA, p. A543
MAHONEY, William K., President and Chief Executive Officer, Cox Medical Center Branson, Branson, MO, p. A364
MAHONY, Mary A., Commanding Officer, Naval Hospital Lemoore, Portsmith, VA, p. A670
MAHR–CHAN, Lydia, Director of Human Resources, Chinese Hospital, San Francisco, CA, p. A88
MAIDEN, Phillip, M.D. Medical Director, Belmont Pines Hospital, Youngstown, OH, p. A501
MAIDEN, Susanne, Interim Administrator, Verde Valley Medical Center, Cottonwood, AZ, p. A30
MAIETTA, Carol
Vice President and Talent Resource Officer Human Resources and Learning, St. Vincent's Blount, Oneonta, AL, p. A23
Vice President Human Resources and Chief Learning Officer, St. Vincent's East, Birmingham, AL, p. A17
MAIJALA, Jussi, Vice President, Human Resources, Phelps Memorial Hospital Center, Sleepy Hollow, NY, p. A450
MAINARDI, Carlo, M.D. Vice President Medical Affairs and Chief Medical Officer, Park Ridge Health, Hendersonville, NC, p. A462
MAINE, MSN, RN–, Cathy L., Chief Nursing Officer and Assistant Administrator, Smyth County Community Hospital, Marion, VA, p. A667
MAINIERI, Kathy, Human Resource Specialist, Sister Emmanuel Hospital, Miami, FL, p. A135
MAISH, Elizabeth, R.N. Vice President and Chief Nursing Officer, TMC Healthcare, Tucson, AZ, p. A40
MAIZE, Makyla, Director Information Services, Washington County Hospital and Clinics, Washington, IA, p. A235
MAJCHRZAK, John, Chief Financial Officer, Touchette Regional Hospitals, Centreville, IL, p. A181
MAJDALANI, Elias, Director Management Information Systems, Mildred Mitchell–Bateman Hospital, Huntington, WV, p. A692
MAJETICH, Stephen D., CPA Chief Financial Officer, Southwestern Vermont Medical Center, Bennington, VT, p. A660
MAJEWSKI, Laura, Director Human Resources, HSHS St. Clare Memorial Hospital, Oconto Falls, WI, p. A708
MAJHAIL, Ruby, Chief Financial Officer, St. Luke's Behavioral Health Center, Phoenix, AZ, p. A36
MAJKA, Andrew, Chief Financial Officer, Springfield Hospital, Springfield, VT, p. A661
MAJOR, Aprille, Director Human Resources, Newport Specialty Hospital, Tustin, CA, p. A95
MAJOR, Kerry, R.N. Chief Nursing Officer, Cleveland Clinic Florida, Weston, FL, p. A147
MAJOR, Pattie, Chief Financial Officer, Paul B. Hall Regional Medical Center, Paintsville, KY, p. A264
MAJORS, Valerie, Director Information Services, Western State Hospital, Hopkinsville, KY, p. A258
MAJURE, Thomas K., Administrator, Our Community Hospital, Scotland Neck, NC, p. A468
MAKAROFF, Jason, Chief Operating Officer and Associate Vice President, Adventist Rehabilitation Hospital of Maryland, Rockville, MD, p. A300
MAKELA, Taylor, Director Information Technology, Baraga County Memorial Hospital, L'Anse, MI, p. A324
MAKEPEACE, Anne, Director Human Resources, New Ulm Medical Center, New Ulm, MN, p. A344
MAKI, Jacquelyn, Chief Nursing Officer, Oakleaf Surgical Hospital, Eau Claire, WI, p. A700
MAKI, Richard, R.N. Vice President Nursing and Chief Nursing Officer, Anna Jaques Hospital, Newburyport, MA, p. A309
MAKIEVSKY, Inna, FACHE Chief Nursing Officer, St. Cloud Regional Medical Center, Saint Cloud, FL, p. A141
MAKORO, Leslie, Director Information management Systems, Merit Health Natchez, Natchez, MS, p. A358
MAKSOUD, Jane, R.N
Senior Vice President Human Resources and Labor Relations, Mount Sinai Health System, Mount Sinai Beth Israel, New York, NY, p. A442
Senior Vice President Human Resources and Labor Relations, Mount Sinai Hospital, New York, NY, p. A442
Senior Vice President Human Resources and Labor Relations, Mount Sinai Health System, Mount Sinai St. Luke's – Roosevelt, New York, NY, p. A442
Senior Vice President Human Resources and Labor Relations, Mount Sinai Health System, New York Eye and Ear Infirmary of Mount Sinai, New York, NY, p. A442
MAKSYMOW, Michael, Vice President Information Systems, Beebe Healthcare, Lewes, DE, p. A117
MAKUNDA, Beejadi, M.D. Chief Medical Officer, Heatherhill Care Communities, Chardon, OH, p. A481
MALAER, Gary
Chief Operating Officer, South Bay Hospital, Sun City Center, FL, p. A143
Interim Chief Executive Officer, Wuesthoff Medical Center – Rockledge, Rockledge, FL, p. A141
MALAKOFF, Stacey, Executive Vice President and Chief Financial Officer, Hospital for Special Surgery, New York, NY, p. A440
MALAMED, Michael, M.D. Chief of Staff, Sherman Oaks Hospital, CA, p. A72
MALAN, Glen, Vice President Information Technology and Chief Information Officer, Northwest Community Hospital, Arlington Heights, IL, p. A178
MALANEY, Scott C., President and Chief Executive Officer, Blanchard Valley Health System, Findlay, OH, p. B24
MALANEY, Scott C., President and Chief Executive Officer, Blanchard Valley Hospital, Findlay, OH, p. A490
MALANOWSKI, John S., Chief Human Resources Officer, Dartmouth–Hitchcock Medical Center, Lebanon, NH, p. A407
MALATEK, Jennifer, Chief Executive Officer, New Braunfels Regional Rehabilitation Hospital, New Braunfels, TX, p. A634
MALBROUGH, Christie, Director of Nursing, Pioneer Community Hospital of Newton, Newton, MS, p. A358
MALCOLMSON, James F., M.D. Chief of Staff, Sierra Vista Hospital, Truth or Consequences, NM, p. A427
MALDONADO, Diraida, Chief Executive Officer, Hospital de la Universidad de Puerto Rico/Dr. Federico Trilla, Carolina, PR, p. A720
MALDONADO, Ramon Lopez, Executive Director, San Juan City Hospital, San Juan, PR, p. A724
MALEK, Frank
Chief Financial Officer, Nacogdoches Medical Center, Nacogdoches, TX, p. A633
Chief Financial Officer, Northern Louisiana Medical Center, Ruston, LA, p. A284
MALENSEK, Frank, M.D. Chief Medical Officer, St. Vincent's East, Birmingham, AL, p. A17
MALEY, Shelley, Director Human Resources, St. Luke's Hospital – Quakertown Campus, Quakertown, PA, p. A548
MALIK, Amir, M.D. Cardiologist, Plaza Medical Center of Fort Worth, Fort Worth, TX, p. A614
MALIK, Azfar, M.D., Chief Executive Officer and Chief Medical Officer, CenterPointe Hospital, Saint Charles, MO, p. A375
MALIK, Chuck
Director, Site Information System, Advocate Condell Medical Center, Libertyville, IL, p. A192
Director Information Systems, Advocate Good Shepherd Hospital, Barrington, IL, p. A179
MALIK, Tariq F., CP
Acting Chief Financial Officer, CenterPointe Hospital, Saint Charles, MO, p. A375
Chief Financial Officer, Signature Psychiatric Hospital, Kansas City, MO, p. A370
MALIN, Seth, M.D. President Medical and Dental Staff, Delaware County Memorial Hospital, Drexel Hill, PA, p. A533
MALINA, Joanne J., M.D. Chief of Staff, Veterans Affairs Hudson Valley Health Care System, Montrose, NY, p. A438
MALINDZAK, Edward, Chief Human Resources Officer, Oconomowoc Memorial Hospital, Oconomowoc, WI, p. A708
MALJOVEC, John, M.D. Medical Director, Warren General Hospital, Warren, PA, p. A551
MALLEK, Brent J., Chief Human Resources Officer, Conemaugh Memorial Medical Center, Johnstown, PA, p. A537
MALLERY, Edwina, Assistant Vice President Information Systems, Lafayette General Medical Center, Lafayette, LA, p. A277
MALLETT, Belinda, R.N. Vice President, Patient Care and Clinical Services, Soin Medical Center, Beavercreek, OH, p. A479
MALLETT, Teresa, Chief Financial Officer, Madison Community Hospital, Madison, SD, p. A569
MALLING, Timothy, M.D. Chief of Staff, CentraCare Health–Paynesville, Paynesville, MN, p. A344
MALLONEE, Teresa, Director Human Resources, Angel Medical Center, Franklin, NC, p. A460
MALLOONEE, Teresa, Director Human Resources, Highlands–Cashiers Hospital, Highlands, NC, p. A462
MALLORY, Brenda, M.D. Medical Director, Penn State Hershey Rehabilitation Hospital, Hummelstown, PA, p. A536
MALLOY, Peter, Chief Information Officer, Cheshire Medical Center, Keene, NH, p. A406
MALM, Brad, Director Human Resources and Education, Lindsborg Community Hospital, Lindsborg, KS, p. A245
MALMSTROM, Ron, Information Research Specialist, Parsons State Hospital and Training Center, Parsons, KS, p. A248
MALONE, Donald, M.D., President, Lutheran Hospital, Cleveland, OH, p. A485
MALONE, MSN, RN–, Ginger, Chief Nursing Officer, St. Mary's Hospital, Madison, WI, p. A704
MALONE, Meredith, Chief Financial Officer, Tennova Healthcare – Dyersburg Regional Hospital, Dyersburg, TN, p. A577
MALONE, Michael, Vice President and Chief Human Resources Officer, Virginia Hospital Center – Arlington, Arlington, VA, p. A662
MALONE, Patty, M.D. Chief Medical Officer, Ocean Beach Hospital, Ilwaco, WA, p. A679

Index of Health Care Professionals

MARDY, Paul, Chief Information Technology Officer, Tennessee Valley Healthcare System, Nashville, TN, p. A586

MAREK, Kyle, Manager Information Services, Carteret Health Care, Morehead City, NC, p. A465

MAREK, Rick, Vice President Medical Information Systems, Post Acute/Warm Springs Rehabilitation Hospital of San Antonio, San Antonio, TX, p. A642

MARGENAU, Randall, Chief Information Officer, William S. Middleton Memorial Veterans Hospital, Madison, WI, p. A704

MARGER, Brian, Chief Operating Officer, Tristar Ashland City Medical Center, Ashland City, TN, p. A574

MARGOLIS, Marilyn, Chief Executive Officer, Emory Johns Creek Hospital, Johns Creek, GA, p. A159

MARGOLIS, Ron, Chief Information Officer, University of New Mexico Hospitals, Albuquerque, NM, p. A423

MARGOT, Skip, Vice President Patient Care Services and Chief Nurse Executive, Shady Grove Adventist Hospital, Rockville, MD, p. A300

MARGULIS, Richard T., President and Chief Executive Officer, Brookhaven Memorial Hospital Medical Center, Patchogue, NY, p. A447

MARIANI, Julia, Vice President Business Operations, Northern Montana Hospital, Havre, MT, p. A384

MARIANI, Marilyn, R.N. Chief Nursing Officer, Lakeview Hospital, Bountiful, UT, p. A654

MARICN, Tanya, Interim Vice President Human Resources, Mercy Hospital Springfield, Springfield, MO, p. A379

MARIETTA, John, M.D. Chief Medical Officer, St. David's Medical Center, Austin, TX, p. A595

MARIETTA, Megan, Chief Operating Officer, Kingwood Medical Center, Kingwood, TX, p. A626

MARIETTA, Richard, M.D. Medical Director, Clear Lake Regional Medical Center, Webster, TX, p. A651

MARIGOMEN, Nancy Ann, R.N. Director of Nursing, Milwaukee County Behavioral Health Division, Milwaukee, WI, p. A706

MARIN, Loyman, Chief Human Resources, Miami Veterans Affairs Healthcare System, Miami, FL, p. A134

MARINELLO, Anthony, Chief Executive Officer, Mountain Vista Medical Center, Mesa, AZ, p. A33

MARINI, Frank, Vice President and Chief Information Officer, TMC Healthcare, Tucson, AZ, p. A40

MARINICH, Patsy, Chief Nursing Officer, Cumberland River Hospital, Celina, TN, p. A574

MARINO, A. Michael, M.D. Senior Vice President Medical Administration, Greenwich Hospital, Greenwich, CT, p. A112

MARINO, Christopher, M.D. Chief of Staff, Memphis Veterans Affairs Medical Center, Memphis, TN, p. A583

MARINO, Joseph, M.D. Medical Director, Franklin Hospital, Valley Stream, NY, p. A452

MARINO, Marchita H., Vice President Human Resources, Wuesthoff Medical Center – Rockledge, Rockledge, FL, p. A141

MARINOFF, Peter, President, Paul Oliver Memorial Hospital, Frankfort, MI, p. A319

MARION, Ben, Chief Executive Officer and Managing Director, Turning Point Hospital, Moultrie, GA, p. A162

MARION, Kristie, Chief Nurse Executive, Memorial Hospital Los Banos, Los Banos, CA, p. A73

MARION, Sue, Manager Business Office, Knox County Hospital, Knox City, TX, p. A626

MARIOTTI, Denise, Chief Human Resource Officer, Hospital of the University of Pennsylvania, Philadelphia, PA, p. A544

MARIOTTI, Nadine A., R.N. Chief Nursing Officer, East Los Angeles Doctors Hospital, Los Angeles, CA, p. A69

MARKENSON, David, M.D. Chief Medical Officer, Sky Ridge Medical Center, Lone Tree, CO, p. A106

MARKER, Jason, M.D. Chief Medical Officer, Community Hospital of Bremen, Bremen, IN, p. A205

MARKER, John, Chief Nursing Officer, Regional Medical Center of Acadiana, Lafayette, LA, p. A278

MARKESINO, Patricia A., FACHE Chief Nurse Executive and Chief Operating Officer, Providence Willamette Falls Medical Center, Oregon City, OR, p. A523

MARKETTI, Dean M., Vice President Finance, Morris Hospital & Healthcare Centers, Morris, IL, p. A195

MARKGRAF, Janelle K., Director Human Resources, Langlade Hospital, Antigo, WI, p. A697

MARKHAM, Barbara, Chief Financial Officer, Glendive Medical Center, Glendive, MT, p. A383

MARKHAM, Kevin, Chief Financial Officer, EastPointe Hospital, Daphne, AL, p. A18

MARKOS, Dennis R., Chief Executive Officer, Ed Fraser Memorial Hospital and Baker Community Health Center, MacClenny, FL, p. A132

MARKOWITZ, Bruce J., President and Chief Executive Officer, Palisades Medical Center, North Bergen, NJ, p. A416

MARKOWITZ, Stuart, M.D., President, Hartford Hospital, Hartford, CT, p. A112

MARKOWSKI, Stan, Chief Financial Officer, Palmetto Lowcountry Behavioral Health, Charleston, SC, p. A558

MARKS, Craig J., FACHE, President, Mark Twain Medical Center, San Andreas, CA, p. A85

MARKS, Jerry, Vice President Finance, Decatur County Memorial Hospital, Greensburg, IN, p. A210

MARKS, Kimberly W., Interim Chief Executive Officer, Southampton Memorial Hospital, Franklin, VA, p. A665

MARKS, Marie, Chief Nursing Officer, Lake Norman Regional Medical Center, Mooresville, NC, p. A465

MARKS, Michael, M.D. Chief of Staff, Norwalk Hospital, Norwalk, CT, p. A114

MARKS, Stanley, M.D
 Chief Medical Officer, Memorial Hospital Miramar, Miramar, FL, p. A136
 Chief Medical Officer, Memorial Hospital Pembroke, Pembroke Pines, FL, p. A139
 Chief Medical Officer, Memorial Regional Hospital, FL, p. A128

MARKSTROM, Susan, M.D. Chief of Staff, St. Cloud Veterans Affairs Health Care System, Saint Cloud, MN, p. A346

MARLATT, Pam, Business Systems Director, Essentia Health St. Joseph's Medical Center, Brainerd, MN, p. A336

MARLER, Ruth, Chief Nursing Officer and Chief Operating Officer, Johnston Health, Smithfield, NC, p. A468

MARLER, Steven R., Assistant Administrator, Parkland Health Center – Liberty Street, Farmington, MO, p. A367

MARLEY, Charles, D.O. Vice President Medical Affairs, Gettysburg Hospital, Gettysburg, PA, p. A534

MARLEY, Lee
 VP/Information Services Chief Application Officer, Presbyterian Hospital, Albuquerque, NM, p. A423
 VP/Information Services Chief Application Officer, Presbyterian Kaseman Hospital, Albuquerque, NM, p. A423

MARLEY, Michael, Chief Information Officer, Veterans Affairs Central Western Massachusetts Healthcare System, Leeds, MA, p. A308

MARLIN, Chris, Director Human Resources, Orange Park Medical Center, Orange Park, FL, p. A137

MARLOW, Gary P., Chief Financial Officer, Beverly Hospital, Beverly, MA, p. A302

MARMANDE, Susanne, Administrator, Infirmary Long Term Acute Care Hospital, Mobile, AL, p. A22

MARNEY, Terri A., R.N. Director of Nursing, Plains Regional Medical Center, Clovis, NM, p. A423

MARON, Michael, President and Chief Executive Officer, Holy Name Medical Center, Teaneck, NJ, p. A419

MARONEY, Gerry, Chief Information Officer and Security Officer, Gaylord Hospital, Wallingford, CT, p. A115

MAROSTICA, Tony, Director Human Resources, Spanish Peaks Regional Health Center, Walsenburg, CO, p. A109

MAROTTA, Diane, Vice President Human Resources, John T. Mather Memorial Hospital, Port Jefferson, NY, p. A447

MAROUN, Christiane, M.D. Chief of Staff, Childrens Care Hospital and School, Sioux Falls, SD, p. A571

MARPLE, Richard, M.D. Chief Medical Officer, Baptist Medical Center, San Antonio, TX, p. A640

MARQUES, John
 Vice President Chief Human Resources Officer, Banner – University Medical Center South, Tucson, AZ, p. A39
 Vice President Human Resources, Banner – University Medical Center Tucson, Tucson, AZ, p. A39

MARQUES, Tony, Director Information Systems, Grace Cottage Hospital, Townshend, VT, p. A661

MARQUSEE, Joanne, President and Chief Executive Officer, Cooley Dickinson Hospital, Northampton, MA, p. A309

MARR, Debbie, Administrative Assistant and Director Human Resources, Fredonia Regional Hospital, Fredonia, KS, p. A240

MARRERO, Jamie L., M.D. Medical Director, HEALTHSOUTH Hospital of Manati, Manati, PR, p. A721

MARRERO, Jose, Director Finance, San Jorge Children's Hospital, San Juan, PR, p. A724

MARRERO, Norma, Executive Administrator, Doctors' Center Hospital San Juan, San Juan, PR, p. A723

MARRERO, Waleska, Administrator, Metropolitano De La Montana, Utuado, PR, p. A724

MARRONI, Denise
 Chief Financial Officer, Providence Centralia Hospital, Centralia, WA, p. A677
 Chief Financial Officer, Providence St. Peter Hospital, Olympia, WA, p. A681

MARRUFO, Gabriel, Chief Financial Officer, Methodist Stone Oak Hospital, San Antonio, TX, p. A641

MARS, Tom L., R.N. Vice President Patient Care Services and Chief Nursing Officer, Camden Clark Medical Center, Parkersburg, WV, p. A694

MARSEE, DeWayne, Director of Information Systems and Chief Information Officer, Mercer Health, Coldwater, OH, p. A485

MARSH, J. Michael, President and Chief Executive Officer, Overlake Medical Center, Bellevue, WA, p. A676

MARSH, Leslie, ACHE, Chief Executive Officer, Lexington Regional Health Center, Lexington, NE, p. A393

MARSH, Linda, Vice President Financial Services and Chief Financial Officer, Alhambra Hospital Medical Center, Alhambra, CA, p. A53

MARSH, Mark A., Chief Executive Officer, Gateway Medical Center, Clarksville, TN, p. A576

MARSH, Mitch, Interim Executive Director, Terence Cardinal Cooke Health Care Center, New York, NY, p. A444

MARSH, Rob, Chief Executive Officer, Cedar Crest Hospital and Residential Treatment Center, Belton, TX, p. A597

MARSHAK, Glenn, M.D. Chief of Staff, Mission Community Hospital, CA, p. A71

MARSHALL, David R., JD Chief Nursing and Patient Care Services Officer, University of Texas Medical Branch, Galveston, TX, p. A615

MARSHALL, Deborah K., Vice President Public Relations, Good Samaritan Hospital, Suffern, NY, p. A451

MARSHALL, Glen, Chief Executive Officer, Trios Health, Kennewick, WA, p. A680

MARSHALL, James I., President and Chief Executive Officer, Uintah Basin Medical Center, Roosevelt, UT, p. A658

MARSHALL, Jerry, Director Information Services, Information Technology Security Officer, United Regional Health Care System, Wichita Falls, TX, p. A652

MARSHALL, Jim, Chief Executive Officer, Prattville Baptist Hospital, Prattville, AL, p. A24

MARSHALL, Julie, Chief Nursing Officer, Alice Hyde Medical Center, Malone, NY, p. A436

MARSHALL, Ken, M.D. Chief Medical Officer, Indiana University Health Bloomington Hospital, Bloomington, IN, p. A205

MARSHALL, Kenneth P., President, University of Louisville Hospital, Louisville, KY, p. A262

MARSHALL, Michael, Vice President Finance and Chief Financial Officer, Anderson Hospital, Maryville, IL, p. A193

MARSHALL, Patricia, Assistant Administrator Human Resources, Washington Health System Greene, Waynesburg, PA, p. A552

MARSHALL, Penny, Chief Nursing Officer, Bear River Valley Hospital, Tremonton, UT, p. A659

MARSHALL Jr., Robert L., FACHE, Chief Executive Officer, Bolivar Medical Center, Cleveland, MS, p. A352

MARSHALL, Thomas, Chief Financial Officer, Lakeway Regional Medical Center, Lakeway, TX, p. A627

MARSICO, Nick, Vice President and Chief Operating Officer, Magruder Memorial Hospital, Port Clinton, OH, p. A496

MARSO, Paul, Vice President Human Resources, Avera St. Mary's Hospital, Pierre, SD, p. A570

MARSTON, Shawn, Director Human Resources, Keystone Newport News, Newport News, VA, p. A668

MARTANIUK, Jean, Director Human Resources, Mt. Ascutney Hospital and Health Center, Windsor, VT, p. A661

MARTENS, Angela, Chief Financial Officer, Cumberland Memorial Hospital, Cumberland, WI, p. A699

MARTENS, Troy, Chief Operating Officer, UnityPoint Health – Trinity Regional Medical Center, Fort Dodge, IA, p. A228

MARTHONE, Frances, R.N. Chief Nursing Officer, Piedmont Henry Hospital, Stockbridge, GA, p. A165

MARTI, Maria L., Director Fiscal Services, Auxilio Mutuo Hospital, San Juan, PR, p. A723

MARTIN, Adam, Chief Financial Officer, Terre Haute Regional Hospital, Terre Haute, IN, p. A220

MARTIN, Amanda, Manager Human Resources, Ohio Valley Surgical Hospital, Springfield, OH, p. A497

MARTIN, Angelia, M.D. Chief of Staff, Northwest Medical Center, Albany, MO, p. A363

MARTIN, Barbara, Chief Nursing Officer, Mercy St. Vincent Medical Center, Toledo, OH, p. A498

MARTIN, Barbara J., R.N.,
 President and Chief Executive Officer, Vista Medical Center East, Waukegan, IL, p. A203
 President and Chief Executive Officer, Vista Medical Center West, Waukegan, IL, p. A203

MARTIN, Brent, Administrator, LifeCare Specialty Hospital of North Louisiana, Ruston, LA, p. A284

MARTIN, Bruce A., Vice President Human Resources, CarolinaEast Health System, New Bern, NC, p. A466

MARTIN, C. Gregory, M.D. Chief Medical Officer, Emerson Hospital, Concord, MA, p. A306

MARTIN, Carmen, Associate Administrator, Auxilio Mutuo Hospital, San Juan, PR, p. A723

MARTIN, Cary, Chief Executive Officer, Houston Healthcare System, Warner Robins, GA, p. B71

MARTIN, Cary, Chief Executive Officer, Houston Medical Center, Warner Robins, GA, p. A167

MARTIN, Cherie, FACHE, Chief Executive Officer, Banner Behavioral Health Hospital – Scottsdale, Scottsdale, AZ, p. A37

MARTIN, Cheryl
 Manager Human Resources, Columbia Memorial Hospital, Astoria, OR, p. A519
 Chief Information Officer, Tuomey Healthcare System, Sumter, SC, p. A565

MARTIN, Christine M., Vice President and Chief Financial Officer, Cleveland Regional Medical Center, Shelby, NC, p. A468

MARTIN, Connie
Vice President and Chief Support Officer, Methodist Medical Center of Oak Ridge, Oak Ridge, TN, p. A586
Chief Executive Officer and Administrator, Physicians Medical Center, Houma, LA, p. A275

MARTIN, Corey, M.D. Director Medical Affairs, Buffalo Hospital, Buffalo, MN, p. A336

MARTIN, Cyndie, Director, Coal County General Hospital, Coalgate, OK, p. A505

MARTIN, David, Assistant Administrator, Valley Hospital, Spokane Valley, WA, p. A685

MARTIN, David T., President, UPMC Passavant, Pittsburgh, PA, p. A547

MARTIN, Deanna, Chief Executive Officer, HEALTHSOUTH Rehabilitation Hospital of Rock Hill, Rock Hill, SC, p. A564

MARTIN, Deborah, Assistant Administrator Human Resources, Skagit Valley Hospital, Mount Vernon, WA, p. A681

MARTIN, Debra, Director of Nursing, Hamilton General Hospital, Hamilton, TX, p. A617

MARTIN, Garland, M.D. Chief of Staff, Appling Healthcare System, Baxley, GA, p. A152

MARTIN, Garry, Chief Fiscal, Veterans Affairs North Texas Health Care System, Dallas, TX, p. A607

MARTIN, Gregg
Manager Management Information Systems, Arnot Ogden Medical Center, Elmira, NY, p. A433
Chief Information Officer, Ira Davenport Memorial Hospital, Bath, NY, p. A429
Chief Information Officer, St. Joseph's Hospital, Elmira, NY, p. A433

MARTIN, Harvey C., M.D. Medical Director, Red River Hospital, LLC, Wichita Falls, TX, p. A652

MARTIN, Holly, Human Resources Leader, Iowa Specialty Hospital–Clarion, Clarion, IA, p. A224

MARTIN, James C., M.D. Vice President and Chief Medical Officer, CHRISTUS Santa Rosa Health System, San Antonio, TX, p. A640

MARTIN, James D.
Chief Financial Officer, Hawthorn Children Psychiatric Hospital, Saint Louis, MO, p. A376
Chief Financial Officer, Metropolitan St. Louis Psychiatric Center, Saint Louis, MO, p. A376
Chief Financial Officer, St. Louis Psychiatric Rehabilitation Center, Saint Louis, MO, p. A378

MARTIN, Janice S., R.N. Chief Nursing Officer, Davis Regional Medical Center, Statesville, NC, p. A469

MARTIN, Jeanene R., M.P.H
Senior Vice President Human Resources, WakeMed Cary Hospital, Cary, NC, p. A456
Senior Vice President Human Resources, WakeMed Raleigh Campus, Raleigh, NC, p. A467

MARTIN, Jeffrey H., M.D. Chief of Staff, Murphy Medical Center, Murphy, NC, p. A465

MARTIN, Jeffrey L., President, Ministry Saint Michael's Hospital, Stevens Point, WI, p. A711

MARTIN, Jeremy, Chief Support Services Officer, St. James Parish Hospital, Lutcher, LA, p. A279

MARTIN, Jessica, Director Human Resources, Logan Regional Medical Center, Logan, WV, p. A692

MARTIN, Karen, R.N. Chief Nursing Officer, Marshall Medical Center, Lewisburg, TN, p. A581

MARTIN, Karen, Chief Nursing Officer, Springs Memorial Hospital, Lancaster, SC, p. A563

MARTIN, Kathy, Vice President Patient Care, Baptist Health Medical Center – North Little Rock, North Little Rock, AR, p. A49

MARTIN, Keith, M.D. Vice President and Medical Director, CGH Medical Center, Sterling, IL, p. A201

MARTIN, Kelly, Chief Financial Officer, Fairchild Medical Center, Yreka, CA, p. A98

MARTIN, Kelly K., Human Resource Officer, Texas Health Presbyterian Hospital Plano, Plano, TX, p. A637

MARTIN, Kenneth A., M.D. Chief of Staff, Arkansas Surgical Hospital, North Little Rock, AR, p. A49

MARTIN, Kevin, R.N., Administrator, Shriners Hospitals for Children–Salt Lake City, Salt Lake City, UT, p. A658

MARTIN, Kevin P., M.D. Chief Medical Officer, Four Winds Hospital, Saratoga Springs, NY, p. A450

MARTIN, Konnie, Chief Executive Officer, San Luis Valley Health, Alamosa, CO, p. A99

MARTIN, Konnie, Chief Executive Officer, San Luis Valley Health, Alamosa, CO, p. B116

MARTIN, Kory Lann, M.D. Chief of Staff, Seymour Hospital, Seymour, TX, p. A643

MARTIN, Leslee, Manager Information Technology, HSHS St. Elizabeth's Hospital, Belleville, IL, p. A179

MARTIN, Marlana, Director Human Resources, Benewah Community Hospital, Saint Maries, ID, p. A176

MARTIN, Mary, MSN Chief Nursing Officer, St. Nicholas Hospital, Sheboygan, WI, p. A711

MARTIN, Matthew, Director Resource Management, Naval Hospital Oak Harbor, Oak Harbor, WA, p. A681

MARTIN, Nick, Chief Information Officer, Minidoka Memorial Hospital, Rupert, ID, p. A176

MARTIN, Nikki, Chief Financial Officer, CHRISTUS Jasper Memorial Hospital, Jasper, TX, p. A624

MARTIN, Patrick, Director Information Systems, Calvary Hospital, NY, p. A439

MARTIN, Patrick, M.D. Medical Director, Wilmington Treatment Center, Wilmington, NC, p. A470

MARTIN, Patsy, Manager Human Resources, Select Rehabilitation Hospital of Denton, Denton, TX, p. A608

MARTIN, Paul, Chief Medical Officer, Grandview Medical Center, Dayton, OH, p. A488

MARTIN, Paul J., Director Human Resources, Kaiser Permanente Los Angeles Medical Center, Los Angeles, CA, p. A70

MARTIN, Ric, Information Specialist, Madison State Hospital, Madison, IN, p. A215

MARTIN, Richard A., MSN Senior Vice President and Chief Nursing Officer, Hoag Memorial Hospital Presbyterian, Newport Beach, CA, p. A77

MARTIN, Sabrina, Chief Executive Officer, Rehabilitation Hospital of Southern New Mexico, Las Cruces, NM, p. A425

MARTIN, Sharon E., M.D. President Medical Staff, Fulton County Medical Center, Mc Connellsburg, PA, p. A539

MARTIN, Sheila, Chief Nursing Officer, Clinton Memorial Hospital, Wilmington, OH, p. A501

MARTIN, Sherri, M.D. President Medical Staff, Shawnee Mission Medical Center, Shawnee Mission, KS, p. A250

MARTIN, Stacy L., Director Human Resources, Grant Regional Health Center, Lancaster, WI, p. A704

MARTIN, Susan, Vice President Finance, Middlesex Hospital, Middletown, CT, p. A113

MARTIN, Thomas J., Administrator, Lincoln Hospital, Davenport, WA, p. A678

MARTIN, Tom, Vice President and Chief Information Officer, EvergreenHealth, Kirkland, WA, p. A680

MARTIN, Tracie, M.D. Chief Medical Officer, Oakland Mercy Hospital, Oakland, NE, p. A395

MARTIN, Val, Director Financial Management Services Center, Veterans Affairs Salt Lake City Health Care System, Salt Lake City, UT, p. A659

MARTIN, Valene J., Administrative Director Human Resources, Community Hospital Long Beach, Long Beach, CA, p. A68

MARTIN, W. Carl, Chief Operating Officer, Providence Hospital, Columbia, SC, p. A559

MARTIN–FORMAN, Marty Ann, Chief Operating Officer, Fulton State Hospital, Fulton, MO, p. A368

MARTIN–PRATT, Diane, Director Information Systems, Niagara Falls Memorial Medical Center, Niagara Falls, NY, p. A445

MARTINEAU, Loraine, Chief Financial Officer, Prairie Ridge Hospital and Health Services, Elbow Lake, MN, p. A338

MARTINEK, Jacquelyn, R.N. Chief Nursing Officer, Brookwood Medical Center, Birmingham, AL, p. A16

MARTINEZ, Albino
Director Budget and Finance, Miners' Colfax Medical Center, Raton, NM, p. A425
Director Finance and Budget, New Mexico Behavioral Health Institute at Las Vegas, Las Vegas, NM, p. A425

MARTINEZ, RN, BSN, Angel, Director Patient Care Services, Shriners Hospitals for Children–Galveston, Galveston, TX, p. A615

MARTINEZ, Beverly, Director of Nursing, Rio Grande Hospital, Del Norte, CO, p. A101

MARTINEZ, Carlos J., Director Resource Management, Naval Medical Center, Portsmouth, VA, p. A670

MARTINEZ, Eddie, Chief Executive Officer, El Paso LTAC Hospital, El Paso, TX, p. A610

MARTINEZ, Edward, Chief Information Officer, Nicklaus Children's Hospital, Miami, FL, p. A134

MARTINEZ, Eleanor, Chief Nursing Officer, Alhambra Hospital Medical Center, Alhambra, CA, p. A53

MARTINEZ, Enrique, M.D
Chief Medical Officer, The Hospitals of Providence Memorial Campus, El Paso, TX, p. A611
Chief Medical Officer, The Hospitals of Providence Sierra Campus, El Paso, TX, p. A611

MARTINEZ, Fernando
Vice President and Chief Information Officer, Jackson Health System, Miami, FL, p. A134
Senior Vice President and Chief Information Officer, Parkland Health & Hospital System, Dallas, TX, p. A606

MARTINEZ, Francisco, Executive Director, Hospital San Antonio, Mayaguez, PR, p. A722

MARTINEZ, Frank
Senior Vice President Human Resources, East Jefferson General Hospital, Metairie, LA, p. A280
Vice President Human Resources, West Jefferson Medical Center, Marrero, LA, p. A280

MARTINEZ, Jason, Director Information Technology, West Valley Medical Center, Caldwell, ID, p. A173

MARTINEZ, Jorge I., Executive Director, Hospital Perea, Mayaguez, PR, p. A722

MARTINEZ, Jose, M.D. Chief Medical Officer, Northwest Medical Center, Margate, FL, p. A133

MARTINEZ, Josue, Coordinator Information Systems, University Hospital, San Juan, PR, p. A724

MARTINEZ, Katherine, Chief Nursing Officer, North Central Surgical Center, Dallas, TX, p. A606

MARTINEZ, Kathryn J., Chief Nursing Officer, FHN Memorial Hospital, Freeport, IL, p. A188

MARTINEZ, Lee, Chief Information Officer, Cooley Dickinson Hospital, Northampton, MA, p. A309

MARTINEZ, Louisa, Director of Nursing, Frio Regional Hospital, Pearsall, TX, p. A636

MARTINEZ, Michelle, Chief Executive Officer, U. S. Public Health Service Indian Hospital–Whiteriver, Whiteriver, AZ, p. A40

MARTINEZ, Regina M., Director Human Resources, La Paz Regional Hospital, Parker, AZ, p. A34

MARTINEZ, Roberto, Chief Human Resources Officer, Banner Lassen Medical Center, Susanville, CA, p. A93

MARTINEZ, Rosette, Acting Chief Executive Officer, Lemuel Shattuck Hospital, Jamaica Plain, MA, p. A307

MARTINEZ, Steve, Executive Director and Administrator, New Mexico Behavioral Health Institute at Las Vegas, Las Vegas, NM, p. A425

MARTINEZ, Suzanne, Director Human Resources, Centennial Peaks Hospital, Louisville, CO, p. A107

MARTINEZ, Terri, Chief Financial Officer, Plains Memorial Hospital, Dimmitt, TX, p. A609

MARTINEZ, Tina, Director Human Resources, J. D. McCarty Center for Children With Developmental Disabilities, Norman, OK, p. A510

MARTINEZ, Virginia, Director of Human Resources, Copper Queen Community Hospital, Bisbee, AZ, p. A30

MARTINEZ, Yolanda, Chief Fiscal Services, Edward Hines, Jr. Veterans Affairs Hospital, Hines, IL, p. A190

MARTINEZ, Yvette, Director Human Resources, Sutter Auburn Faith Hospital, Auburn, CA, p. A54

MARTINEZ–NIETO, Arlene, M.D. Chief Medical Officer, First Hospital Panamericano, Cidra, PR, p. A720

MARTING, Bill, Senior Vice President and Chief Financial Officer, The University of Kansas Hospital, Kansas City, KS, p. A243

MARTINO, Anthony, Chief Executive Officer, Select Specialty Hospital–Scottsdale, Scottsdale, AZ, p. A38

MARTINSON, Erling, M.D. Medical Director, Nelson County Health System, Mcville, ND, p. A476

MARTINSON, Tiffany, Director Human Resources, Norton Sound Regional Hospital, Nome, AK, p. A28

MARTOCCIO, Debora, R.N. Chief Operating Officer, Florida Hospital at Connerton Long Term Acute Care, Land O'Lakes, FL, p. A131

MARTORANO, Ann, Chief Operating Officer, Halifax Health Medical Center of Daytona Beach, Daytona Beach, FL, p. A125

MARTUCCI, Kathleen, Chief Operating Officer, Helen Hayes Hospital, West Haverstraw, NY, p. A453

MARTZ, Dean, Chief Medical Officer, Providence Sacred Heart Medical Center & Children's Hospital, Spokane, WA, p. A685

MARVIN, Ryan, Support Services Director, Rawlins County Health Center, Atwood, KS, p. A237

MARX, Kenneth, Chief Executive Officer, Washington County Memorial Hospital, Potosi, MO, p. A374

MARX, Tomasine
Chief Financial Officer, St. John Hospital and Medical Center, Detroit, MI, p. A318
Chief Financial Officer, St. John Macomb–Oakland Hospital, Warren, MI, p. A332

MARX, Troy, Director Human Resources, Upland Hills Health, Dodgeville, WI, p. A699

MARX, William, M.D. Chief of Staff, Syracuse Veterans Affairs Medical Center, Syracuse, NY, p. A451

MARZINZIK, John A., President and Chief Executive Officer, Frisbie Memorial Hospital, Rochester, NH, p. A408

MARZOLF, Steve, R.N. Vice President Patient Care Services, Spectrum Health Pennock, Hastings, MI, p. A322

MASE, Kerin, R.N. Chief Operating Officer and Chief Nursing Officer, Marian Regional Medical Center, Santa Maria, CA, p. A91

MASHAK–EKERN, Jane, Fiscal Officer, Tomah Veterans Affairs Medical Center, Tomah, WI, p. A712

MASI, George V., Chief Executive Officer, Harris Health System, Houston, TX, p. A619

Index of Health Care Professionals / Mattison

Index of Health Care Professionals

MASKELL, Denise, Chief Information Officer, Springfield Hospital Center, Sykesville, MD, p. A300
MASLYN, Jay T., Chief Financial Officer, Nicholas H. Noyes Memorial Hospital, Dansville, NY, p. A432
MASON, Bill A., Chief Executive Officer, Meadow Wood Behavioral Health System, New Castle, DE, p. A117
MASON, Cheryl S., Chief Financial Officer, Regional Medical Center, Orangeburg, SC, p. A564
MASON, Drew, Chief Operating Officer, Trinity Medical Center, Birmingham, AL, p. A17
MASON, Jill K., MS Chief Nursing Officer, Blessing Hospital, Quincy, IL, p. A199
MASON, Kathy, Chief Operating Officer, Atrium Medical Center of Corinth, Corinth, TX, p. A602
MASON, Kathy, R.N. Chief Nursing Officer, LifeCare Hospitals of Dallas, Dallas, TX, p. A605
MASON, Kay, Chief Financial Officer, Texas Health Heart & Vascular Hospital Arlington, Arlington, TX, p. A593
MASON, Keith, Chief Executive Officer, Bailey Medical Center, Owasso, OK, p. A513
MASON, Philip A., Chief Executive Officer, Bournewood Health Systems, Brookline, MA, p. A305
MASON, Phyllis, M.D. Chief Medical Officer, Natchitoches Regional Medical Center, Natchitoches, LA, p. A281
MASON, Rhonda, Vice President of Patient Care Services, Tri–State Memorial Hospital, Clarkston, WA, p. A677
MASON, Sally, Director Human Resources, Golden Plains Community Hospital, Borger, TX, p. A598
MASON, Sandra, MSN Director Nursing Services and Senior Nurse Executive, Robert E. Bush Naval Hospital, Twentynine Palms, CA, p. A95
MASON, Steve, Assistant Superintendent and Chief Operating Officer, Clifton T. Perkins Hospital Center, Jessup, MD, p. A298
MASON, William R., Chief Operating Officer, Brooke Glen Behavioral Hospital, Fort Washington, PA, p. A534
MASON–JONES, Taryn, Chief Nurse Executive, Norristown State Hospital, Norristown, PA, p. A542
MASON–WILLIAMS, Lois, Director of Human Resources, Northwest Ohio Psychiatric Hospital, Toledo, OH, p. A498
MASOOD, Shahid, M.D. Clinical Director, Mildred Mitchell–Bateman Hospital, Huntington, WV, p. A692
MASSA, Rhonda, Director of Nursing, Clarion Psychiatric Center, Clarion, PA, p. A531
MASSE, Roger A., FACHE, Chief Executive Officer, Ellsworth County Medical Center, Ellsworth, KS, p. A239
MASSELLA, Joan, Administrative Vice President and Chief Nursing Officer, St. Clair Hospital, Pittsburgh, PA, p. A546
MASSENGILL, Leigh, Chief Executive Officer, Medical Center of Trinity, Trinity, FL, p. A146
MASSEY, Gina, Vice President Human Resources, Clarity Child Guidance Center, San Antonio, TX, p. A640
MASSEY, Linda, R.N. Nurse Manager, Norman Specialty Hospital, Norman, OK, p. A510
MASSEY, Rocco K., Community Chief Executive Officer, Beckley ARH Hospital, Beckley, WV, p. A689
MASSEY, Steven, President and Chief Executive Officer, Westfields Hospital, New Richmond, WI, p. A708
MASSEY, Terry, Chief Fiscal Services, Beckley Veterans Affairs Medical Center, Beckley, WV, p. A689
MASSIELLO, Martin, Executive Vice President and Chief Operating Officer, Eisenhower Medical Center, Rancho Mirage, CA, p. A82
MASSIET, Jill, R.N. Vice President Patient Care, Baptist Health Medical Center–Little Rock, Little Rock, AR, p. A47
MASSIMILLA, John P., FACHE Vice President Administration and Chief Operating Officer, Chambersburg Hospital, Chambersburg, PA, p. A531
MASSINGALE, David, Chief Financial Officer, Methodist Hospital Union County, Morganfield, KY, p. A263
MASSMAN, Patty, Director of Nursing, Granite Falls Municipal Hospital and Manor, Granite Falls, MN, p. A340
MAST, Dave, Chief Financial Officer, Providence Holy Cross Medical Center, CA, p. A72
MAST, Delvin, R.N. Director of Nursing, Weatherford Regional Hospital, Weatherford, OK, p. A518
MAST, Duane, M.D. Medical Director, Hocking Valley Community Hospital, Logan, OH, p. A492
MAST, Joelle, Ph.D. Chief Medical Officer, Blythedale Children's Hospital, Valhalla, NY, p. A452
MASTERS, Andrea, Chief Nursing Officer, Decatur County Hospital, Leon, IA, p. A231
MASTERS, David, M.D. Chief of Staff, Caldwell Memorial Hospital, Lenoir, NC, p. A464
MASTERS, Emily, Director Human Resources and Marketing, Windom Area Hospital, Windom, MN, p. A349
MASTERS, Ken, Director Information Technology, Chambers Memorial Hospital, Danville, AR, p. A42
MASTERS, Kim, M.D. Medical Director, Saint Simons by–the–Sea Hospital, Saint Simons Island, GA, p. A163
MASTERS, Regina, R.N. Director of Nursing, Continuing Care Hospital, Lexington, KY, p. A259
MASTERSON, David J., President, Sentara Williamsburg Regional Medical Center, Williamsburg, VA, p. A674
MASTERSON, Paul, Chief Financial Officer, Genesis HealthCare System, Zanesville, OH, p. A502
MASTERSON, Sammie, Chief Human Resources Officer, Harney District Hospital, Burns, OR, p. A519
MASTERTON, Melissa, Vice President, Novant Health Presbyterian Medical Center, Charlotte, NC, p. A458
MASTERTON, William, Chief Executive Officer, Piedmont Medical Center, Rock Hill, SC, p. A564
MASTIN, Michelle, Chief Clinical Officer, Kindred Hospital Boston–North Shore, Peabody, MA, p. A310
MASTRO, Mary Lou, President and Chief Executive Officer, Elmhurst Memorial Hospital, IL, p. A187
MASTROIANNI, Thomas, Administrative Director of Human Resources, Halifax Regional Medical Center, Roanoke Rapids, NC, p. A467
MASTROIANNI, Tom, Vice President Human Resources, New York–Presbyterian/Lawrence Hospital, Bronxville, NY, p. A430
MASTROPIETRO, N. A., M.D. Medical Director, Lancaster Regional Medical Center, Lancaster, PA, p. A537
MATA, Maribel, Director Information Services, Doctors Hospital of Laredo, Laredo, TX, p. A627
MATA–GUERRERO, Rita, Nurse Director, Weslaco Rehabilitation Hospital, Weslaco, TX, p. A651
MATAMOROS, Mary L., R.N., Chief Executive Officer, SeaSide Behavioral Center, New Orleans, LA, p. A282
MATEJKA, Cheryl
Chief Financial Officer, Mercy Hospital St. Louis, Saint Louis, MO, p. A376
Chief Financial Officer, Mercy Hospital Washington, Washington, MO, p. A380
MATENS, Brett, Chief Operating Officer, St. David's South Austin Medical Center, Austin, TX, p. A595
MATHAI, George, M.D. Chief of Staff, Three Rivers Hospital, Waverly, TN, p. A589
MATHAI, Matt, M.D. Medical Director, Select Specialty Hospital–Milwaukee, Milwaukee, WI, p. A707
MATHEIS, Tracey, Chief Financial Officer, Moberly Regional Medical Center, Moberly, MO, p. A373
MATHER, Charlotte Marie, R.N. Chief Nursing Officer, Sheridan Memorial Hospital, Sheridan, WY, p. A717
MATHER, Kelly, Chief Executive Officer, Sonoma Valley Hospital, Sonoma, CA, p. A92
MATHER, Martha S., Chief Operating Officer and Vice President, Our Lady of Peace, Louisville, KY, p. A261
MATHERS, Larry, M.D. Chief of Staff, Tennova Newport Medical Center, Newport, TN, p. A586
MATHES, Lisa L., Human Resources Director, Southwest Medical Center, Liberal, KS, p. A245
MATHEW, Bob, Director Finance, Griffin Memorial Hospital, Norman, OK, p. A510
MATHEW, Finny, Chief Executive Officer, Crossroads Community Hospital, Mount Vernon, IL, p. A195
MATHEW, Mammen, M.D. Chief Rehabilitation Medicine, Woodrow Wilson Rehabilitation Center, Fishersville, VA, p. A665
MATHEW, Toby T., Medical Center Director, Overton Brooks Veterans Affairs Medical Center, Shreveport, LA, p. A284
MATHEWS, Christine W., R.N. Vice President Nursing Services, Geisinger–Lewistown Hospital, Lewistown, PA, p. A539
MATHEWS, Gary, M.D. Medical Doctor, Beaver County Memorial Hospital, Beaver, OK, p. A504
MATHEWS, Hilary G., MS Administrator, Mayo Clinic Jacksonville, Jacksonville, FL, p. A129
MATHEWS, Nimmy, Acting Director Quality Management, U. S. Public Health Service Indian Hospital, San Carlos, AZ, p. A37
MATHEWS, Paul G., CPA, Administrator, Hardtner Medical Center, Olla, LA, p. A283
MATHEWS, Steve, Vice President and Chief Information Officer, Regional West Medical Center, Scottsbluff, NE, p. A398
MATHEWSON, John, Interim Chief Operating Officer, The HSC Pediatric Center, Washington, DC, p. A120
MATHEWSON, Patricia, Chief Nursing Officer, Tulare Regional Medical Center, Tulare, CA, p. A95
MATHIAS, Matt, Chief Operating Officer, LewisGale Hospital Montgomery, Blacksburg, VA, p. A662
MATHIEU, Angie, System Director Information Technology and Regional Chief Information Officer, The William W. Backus Hospital, Norwich, CT, p. A114
MATHIS, Ashley, Privacy Officer, Columbus Community Hospital, Columbus, TX, p. A601
MATHIS, Jane, Chief Financial Officer, Baylor Surgical Hospital at Fort Worth, Fort Worth, TX, p. A613
MATHIS, Rebecca
Vice President and Chief Financial Officer, Adventist Hinsdale Hospital, Hinsdale, IL, p. A191
Chief Financial Officer, Adventist La Grange Memorial Hospital, La Grange, IL, p. A192
MATHIS, Robin, Director of Human Resources, Methodist Olive Branch Hospital, Olive Branch, MS, p. A358
MATHIS, Susan, R.N
Chief Operating Officer and Chief Nurse Executive, CenterPointe Hospital, Saint Charles, MO, p. A375
Chief Operating Officer and Chief Nurse Executive, Signature Psychiatric Hospital, Kansas City, MO, p. A370
MATHURIN, Jr., Emile, M.D. Medical Director, HealthSouth Rehabilitation Hospital of Humble, LLC, Humble, TX, p. A623
MATHURIN, Venra, Vice President Human Resources, Interfaith Medical Center, NY, p. A440
MATLACK, Victoria L.
Director and Human Resources Business Partner, OhioHealth Dublin Methodist Hospital, Dublin, OH, p. A489
Director and Human Resources Business Partner, OhioHealth Grady Memorial Hospital, Delaware, OH, p. A488
MATNEY, James L., President and Chief Executive Officer, Colquitt Regional Medical Center, Moultrie, GA, p. A162
MATNEY, Patty, Human Resources Consultant, Saint Thomas Hickman Hospital, Centerville, TN, p. A575
MATNEY, Tim, Chief Financial Officer, Logan Regional Medical Center, Logan, WV, p. A692
MATRELLA, Sandra, Manager Finance, Buffalo Hospital, Buffalo, MN, p. A336
MATSINGER, John, D.O. Chief Medical Officer, Virtua Marlton, Marlton, NJ, p. A414
MATT, Robert Lawrence, Vice President and Chief Operating Officer, Hancock Regional Hospital, Greenfield, IN, p. A210
MATTER, Stephanie, Manager Human Resources, LifeCare Hospitals of Wisconsin, Pewaukee, WI, p. A709
MATTERN, Bonnie, Director Human Resources, CHI Mercy Hospital, Devils Lake, ND, p. A473
MATTERN, Joe, M.D. Chief Medical Officer, Jefferson Healthcare, Port Townsend, WA, p. A682
MATTES, Bryan, Associate Administrator, CrossRidge Community Hospital, Wynne, AR, p. A52
MATTES, James A., President and Chief Executive Officer, Grande Ronde Hospital, La Grande, OR, p. A522
MATTES, Mark David, R.N. Assistant Administrator/Patient Care Services, Golden Valley Memorial Healthcare, Clinton, MO, p. A365
MATTEUCCI, Dolly, Executive Director, Napa State Hospital, Napa, CA, p. A77
MATTHEI, Ruth, R.N. Chief Nursing Officer, Westlake Hospital, Melrose Park, IL, p. A194
MATTHEW, Mathew, M.D. Chief Medical Officer, Nazareth Hospital, Philadelphia, PA, p. A544
MATTHEWS, Adora, M.D. Medical Director, HEALTHSOUTH Rehabilitation Hospital of Florence, Florence, SC, p. A560
MATTHEWS, Carol, Director Human Resources, Saline Memorial Hospital, Benton, AR, p. A41
MATTHEWS, Clinton, President and Chief Executive Officer, Reading Hospital, West Reading, PA, p. A553
MATTHEWS, Gwen, MSN, Chief Executive Officer, Ukiah Valley Medical Center, Ukiah, CA, p. A95
MATTHEWS, Melissa, Director Human Resources, Dahl Memorial Healthcare Association, Ekalaka, MT, p. A383
MATTHEWS, Michael, Vice President Human Resources, Holland Hospital, Holland, MI, p. A322
MATTHEWS, Oliver, M.D. Chief Medical Officer, Eliza Coffee Memorial Hospital, Florence, AL, p. A19
MATTHEWS, Paul, M.D. President of Medical Staff, Palo Alto County Health System, Emmetsburg, IA, p. A227
MATTHEWS, Ted, Chief Executive Officer, Eastland Memorial Hospital, Eastland, TX, p. A609
MATTHEY, Michael, Facility Chief Information Officer, Louis A. Johnson Veterans Affairs Medical Center, Clarksburg, WV, p. A690
MATTHIAS, Mark, M.D. Vice President of Medical Affairs, St. Cloud Hospital, Saint Cloud, MN, p. A345
MATTHIAS, Pam, Vice President of Patient Care Services, J. C. Blair Memorial Hospital, Huntingdon, PA, p. A536
MATTHIESSEN, Matthew, Chief Financial Officer, John C. Fremont Healthcare District, Mariposa, CA, p. A74
MATTHYS, Crystal, Director Human Resources, South Texas Surgical Hospital, Corpus Christi, TX, p. A603
MATTICE, Gloria, R.N. Director Patient Care, George C Grape Community Hospital, Hamburg, IA, p. A228
MATTINGLY, Marty, Chief Human Resources Officer, St. Mary's Medical Center of Evansville, Evansville, IN, p. A208
MATTIS, Paul, Vice President Finance, Titusville Area Hospital, Titusville, PA, p. A550
MATTISON, Kenneth R., Chief Executive Officer, Florida Hospital–Flagler, Palm Coast, FL, p. A138

MATTKE, Roger, Chief Financial Officer, Lafayette General Medical Center, Lafayette, LA, p. A277

MATTLY, Sheila, Chief Nursing Officer, Wayne County Hospital, Corydon, IA, p. A225

MATTSON, Jodi, Director of Nursing, Cedar Springs Hospital, Colorado Springs, CO, p. A100

MATTSON, Wayne, Management Information Systems Specialist, Rogers Memorial Hospital, Oconomowoc, WI, p. A708

MATUS, Jose, M.D. Director Medical, Carrus Rehabilitation Hospital, Sherman, TX, p. A643

MATUSZKIEWICZ, Marcin, M.D. Chief of Staff and Medical Director, Jerold Phelps Community Hospital, Garberville, CA, p. A63

MATZENBACHER, Elaine, Chief Financial Officer, Washington County Hospital, Nashville, IL, p. A196

MATZIGKEIT, Linda, Senior Vice President Human Resources, Children's Healthcare of Atlanta, Atlanta, GA, p. A150

MAUCK, Jan, R.N. Chief Nursing Officer, Sarasota Memorial Health Care System, Sarasota, FL, p. A142

MAUCK, Lynn, R.N. Chief Operating Officer and Chief Nursing Officer, Fishermen's Hospital, Marathon, FL, p. A132

MAUL, Jim, Chief Information Officer and Director Information Services, Southampton Hospital, Southampton, NY, p. A450

MAURER, Gregory L., Chief Executive Officer, Sheridan Memorial Hospital, Plentywood, MT, p. A386

MAURER, Jackie, Fiscal Officer, Julian F. Keith Alcohol and Drug Abuse Treatment Center, Black Mountain, NC, p. A455

MAURER, Linda, Vice President Patient Care Services, Wilson Memorial Hospital, Sidney, OH, p. A497

MAURER, Marjorie A., MSN Vice President Operations, Patient Care Services and Chief Nursing Executive, Advocate Good Samaritan Hospital, Downers Grove, IL, p. A186

MAURER, Marsha L., R.N. Chief Nursing Officer Patient Care Services, Beth Israel Deaconess Medical Center, Boston, MA, p. A302

MAURICE, Timothy, Chief Financial Officer, University of California, Davis Medical Center, Sacramento, CA, p. A85

MAURIN, Michael J., Chief Financial Officer, Southern Surgical Hospital, Slidell, LA, p. A285

MAUST, Richard, Chief Information Officer, RMC Jacksonville, Jacksonville, AL, p. A21

MAVROMATIS, Lou, Vice President Data Processing, MedStar Southern Maryland Hospital Center, Clinton, MD, p. A297

MAWYER, David, Chief Financial Officer, Western State Hospital, Staunton, VA, p. A673

MAXEY, Matt, R.N. Director of Nursing, Brookhaven Hospital, Tulsa, OK, p. A516

MAXFIELD, Matt T., FACHE, Chief Executive Officer, Seton Medical Center Harker Heights, Harker Heights, TX, p. A617

MAXIE, Bryan K.

Administrator, Marion General Hospital, Columbia, MS, p. A352

Administrator, Walthall County General Hospital, Tylertown, MS, p. A361

MAXSON, Diana, Director Human Resources, Trinity Hospital of Augusta, Augusta, GA, p. A151

MAXSON, Lorna, R.N. Chief Nursing Officer, Phoenix Baptist Hospital, Phoenix, AZ, p. A35

MAXWELL, Dale

Executive Vice President and Chief Financial Officer, Presbyterian Hospital, Albuquerque, NM, p. A423

Senior VP Chief Financial Officer, Presbyterian Kaseman Hospital, Albuquerque, NM, p. A423

MAXWELL, David, Vice President Operations, St. Vincent Anderson Regional Hospital, Anderson, IN, p. A204

MAXWELL, Jody, Manager Business Office, Smith County Memorial Hospital, Smith Center, KS, p. A250

MAXWELL, John, Chief Operating Officer, Memorial Hospital, Martinsville, VA, p. A668

MAXWELL, Lora, Chief Nursing Officer, Curry General Hospital, Gold Beach, OR, p. A521

MAXWELL, Phillip, Administrator, Compass Behavioral Center of Alexandria, Alexandria, LA, p. A268

MAXWELL, Ronnie, Director Information Systems, Glenwood Regional Medical Center, West Monroe, LA, p. A286

MAY, Carol, Chief Financial Officer, Vice President Finance and Operations and Chief Financial Officer, Sauk Prairie Healthcare, Prairie Du Sac, WI, p. A709

MAY, Frank, Chief Executive Officer, Yampa Valley Medical Center, Steamboat Springs, CO, p. A108

MAY, John, Chief Executive Officer, Sistersville General Hospital, Sistersville, WV, p. A695

MAY, Kevin B.

System Director Finance, Charles A. Cannon Memorial Hospital, Linville, NC, p. A464

Chief Financial Officer, Watauga Medical Center, Boone, NC, p. A456

MAY, Perry, Executive Director, Cleo Wallace Centers Hospital, Westminster, CO, p. A109

MAY, Robin, Director Information Systems, Platte County Memorial Hospital, Wheatland, WY, p. A718

MAY, Ronald B., M.D. Vice President Medical Affairs, CarolinaEast Health System, New Bern, NC, p. A466

MAY, Scott, Area Director Technology, Kaiser Permanente Santa Clara Medical Center, Santa Clara, CA, p. A91

MAY, Sonja, Director Human Resources, Morton County Health System, Elkhart, KS, p. A239

MAY, Todd, M.D. Chief Medical Officer, San Francisco General Hospital and Trauma Center, San Francisco, CA, p. A88

MAY, Troy, Chief Information Officer, University of Louisville Hospital, Louisville, KY, p. A262

MAY, Walter E., President and Chief Executive Officer, Pikeville Medical Center, Pikeville, KY, p. A264

MAY, William J., Administrator, Hawaii State Hospital, Kaneohe, HI, p. A170

MAYBEN, Casey, Chief Nursing Officer, East Texas Medical Center Pittsburg, Pittsburg, TX, p. A636

MAYER, David, Chief of Staff, Wayne County Hospital, Monticello, KY, p. A263

MAYER, Karen, R.N. Senior Vice President Patient Care Services, Rush Oak Park Hospital, Oak Park, IL, p. A196

MAYER, Peter, Director Information Systems, Bakersfield Heart Hospital, Bakersfield, CA, p. A54

MAYER, William, M.D. Vice President Medical Staff Services, St. Mary's Healthcare, Amsterdam, NY, p. A428

MAYEUX, Michael, Chief Financial Officer, Teche Regional Medical Center, Morgan City, LA, p. A281

MAYEUX–HEBERT, Angela, Vice President Medical Affairs, Lafayette General Medical Center, Lafayette, LA, p. A277

MAYEWSKI, Raymond, M.D

Chief Medical Officer, Highland Hospital of Rochester, Rochester, NY, p. A448

Chief Medical Officer, Strong Memorial Hospital of the University of Rochester, Rochester, NY, p. A449

MAYFIELD, Michael Bradley, M.D. Chief of Staff, Chicot Memorial Medical Center, Lake Village, AR, p. A46

MAYFIELD, William, M.D. Chief of Staff, TriStar StoneCrest Medical Center, Smyrna, TN, p. A588

MAYHLE, Douglas, M.D. Medical Director, Nicholas H. Noyes Memorial Hospital, Dansville, NY, p. A432

MAYLE, Connie, Vice President Administrative Services, UPMC Horizon, Greenville, PA, p. A535

MAYNARD, Amy, Acting Chief Finance Service, Central Texas Veterans Health Care System, Temple, TX, p. A646

MAYNARD, Bob, Chief Information Officer, Fairview Regional Medical Center, Fairview, OK, p. A507

MAYNARD, Rhonda, Chief Financial Officer, Tennova Physicians Regional Medical Center, Knoxville, TN, p. A580

MAYO, Andrew, Ph.D., Chief Executive Officer and Managing Director, North Star Behavioral Health System, Anchorage, AK, p. A27

MAYO, Cindy, FACHE, Chief Executive Officer, Providence Medford Medical Center, Medford, OR, p. A523

MAYO, Hal, Chief Financial Officer, Liberty Dayton Regional Medical Center, Liberty, TX, p. A628

MAYO, Jim, M.D. Clinical Director, Cherry Hospital, Goldsboro, NC, p. A461

MAYO, Michael A., FACHE, President, Baptist Medical Center Jacksonville, Jacksonville, FL, p. A129

MAYO, Randy, Director Information Technology, William Newton Hospital, Winfield, KS, p. A253

MAYO, Robert, M.D

Executive Vice President, Chief Medical Officer, Newark–Wayne Community Hospital, Newark, NY, p. A445

Chief Medical Officer, Rochester General Hospital, Rochester, NY, p. A448

MAYO, Sarah, Vice President Financial and Information Services, Lenoir Memorial Hospital, Kinston, NC, p. A463

MAYORAL, Jorge, M.D. Medical Director, Rehabilitation Hospital of Rhode Island, North Smithfield, RI, p. A555

MAYS, Christine, R.N

Chief Operating Officer and Chief Nurse Executive, Saint Joseph East, Lexington, KY, p. A260

Chief Operating Officer and Chief Nurse Executive, Saint Joseph Hospital, Lexington, KY, p. A260

MAYS, Dawn, Chief Nursing Officer, Scott Memorial Hospital, Scottsburg, IN, p. A219

MAYS, Raymond, M.D. Medical Director, River Crest Hospital, San Angelo, TX, p. A640

MAYSENT, Patty, Interim Chief Executive Officer, UC San Diego Health, San Diego, CA, p. A87

MAYSILLES, Nancy, R.N. Chief Nursing Officer, Medical Center of Trinity, Trinity, FL, p. A146

MAYSON, Mark J., M.D. Medical Director, Palmetto Health Baptist, Columbia, SC, p. A559

MAZANEC, Lori, Chief Operating Officer, Box Butte General Hospital, Alliance, NE, p. A389

MAZOUR, Linda, M.D. President, Franklin County Memorial Hospital, Franklin, NE, p. A391

MAZUR, Robert, Vice President Human Resources, Capital Region Medical Center, Jefferson City, MO, p. A368

MAZZA, Mary, Director Human Resources, HEALTHSOUTH Rehabilitation Hospital of Western Massachusetts, Ludlow, MA, p. A308

MAZZARELLA, Frank, M.D. Chief Medical Officer, Clara Maass Medical Center, Belleville, NJ, p. A409

MAZZARELLI, Anthony J., M.D. Senior Executive Vice President Chief Physician Executive and Chief Medical Officer, Cooper University Health Care, Camden, NJ, p. A410

MAZZO, Joe, Chief Operating Officer, Lakeview Hospital, Bountiful, UT, p. A654

MAZZO, Joseph, Chief Operating Officer, Saint Thomas River Park Hospital, Mc Minnville, TN, p. A582

MAZZOLA, Joe, D.O. Senior Vice President Medical Affairs and Chief Medical Officer, Blue Ridge Healthcare Hospitals, Morganton, NC, p. A465

MAZZUCA, Darryl, Director Management Information Systems, Little Company of Mary Hospital and Health Care Centers, Evergreen Park, IL, p. A188

MBENGA, Saul, Manager Information Technology, Alliance HealthCare System, Holly Springs, MS, p. A354

MC BRIDE, Brian, Chief Financial Officer, Rice Medical Center, Eagle Lake, TX, p. A609

MC KELLAR, Grey, Chief Operating Officer and Director of Performance Improvement and Risk, Kingwood Pines Hospital, Kingwood, TX, p. A626

MCADAMS, David, Chief Financial Officer, Lindner Center of HOPE, Mason, OH, p. A493

MCAFEE, Thomas J., President, North Market, Northwestern Lake Forest Hospital, Lake Forest, IL, p. A192

MCALLISTER, Guy, Vice President and Chief Information Officer, Tift Regional Medical Center, Tifton, GA, p. A166

MCALLISTER, Kimberlie, Chief Administrative Officer, Beaumont Hospital–Dearborn, Dearborn, MI, p. A317

MCALLISTER, Ric, Chief Executive Officer, Windsor–Laurelwood Center for Behavioral Medicine, Willoughby, OH, p. A501

MCALLISTER, Yvonne, Senior Director Human Resources, Southern Maine Health Care – Biddeford Medical Center, Biddeford, ME, p. A289

MCALLITER, Mike, Interim Chief Executive Officer, Baylor Medical Center at Carrollton, Carrollton, TX, p. A600

MCALOON, Richard, Vice President Human Resources, Hartford Hospital, Hartford, CT, p. A112

MCANALLY, Eileen, Senior Vice President Human Resources, Lankenau Medical Center, Wynnewood, PA, p. A554

MCANDREW, Michael, Chief Executive Officer, Hopkins County Memorial Hospital, Sulphur Springs, TX, p. A646

MCARTHUR, Ronald L., Chief Executive Officer, Summit Healthcare Regional Medical Center, Show Low, AZ, p. A38

MCARTOR, Dana, R.N. Director of Nursing, Perkins County Health Services, Grant, NE, p. A392

MCAULIFFE, Gregory, M.D

Chief Medical Officer, San Luis Valley Health, Alamosa, CO, p. A99

Chief Medical Officer, San Luis Valley Health Conejos County Hospital, La Jara, CO, p. A105

MCAULIFFE, John, M.D. Medical Director, Sauk Prairie Healthcare, Prairie Du Sac, WI, p. A709

MCAVOY, Tim, M.D. Medical Director, Rehabilitation Hospital of Wisconsin, Waukesha, WI, p. A713

MCBEE, Gala, Administrator, Muscogee Creek Nation Physical Rehabilitation Center, Okmulgee, OK, p. A513

MCBREARTY, Michael, M.D. Vice President Medical Affairs, Thomas Hospital, Fairhope, AL, p. A19

MCBRIDE, Anne, Executive Vice President and Chief Financial Officer, Regional Hospital for Respiratory and Complex Care, Burien, WA, p. A677

MCBRIDE, Brandon, Operations Officer, Logan Regional Hospital, Logan, UT, p. A655

MCBRIDE, Dina, Chief Operating Officer and Director Human Resources, East Adams Rural Hospital, Ritzville, WA, p. A683

MCBRIDE, Kate, Chief Operating Officer, Poplar Springs Hospital, Petersburg, VA, p. A670

MCBRIDE, Lamar, Chief Operating Officer, Northern Colorado Long Term Acute Hospital, Johnstown, CO, p. A105

MCBRIDE, Michael J., FACHE, President and Chief Executive Officer, St. Mary's Medical Center, Grand Junction, CO, p. A104

MCBRIDE, III, Thomas Y., Executive Vice President and Chief Financial Officer, Gwinnett Hospital System, Lawrenceville, GA, p. A160

MCBROOM, Robert, M.D. Medical Director, Promise Hospital of Wichita Falls, Wichita Falls, TX, p. A652

MCBRYDE, Robin, Chief Information Officer, Alexandria Veterans Affairs Health Care System, Pineville, LA, p. A283

MCCAA, Karen, R.N. Vice President Patient Care Services and Chief Nursing Officer, Baptist Medical Center South, Montgomery, AL, p. A22

Index of Health Care Professionals / McCraw

Index of Health Care Professionals


MCCABE, John B., M.D., Chief Executive Officer, Upstate University Hospital, Syracuse, NY, p. A451
MCCABE, John P., Executive Vice President, Shriners Hospitals for Children, Tampa, FL, p. B122
MCCABE, Mary, Chief Financial Officer, North Colorado Medical Center, Greeley, CO, p. A104
MCCABE, Patrick, Senior Vice President Finance and Chief Financial Officer, Bridgeport Hospital, Bridgeport, CT, p. A111
MCCABE Jr., Patrick G., FACHE, President and Chief Executive Officer, Levi Hospital, Hot Springs National Park, AR, p. A46
MCCABE, Rhonda, Chief Executive Officer, Physicians' Specialty Hospital, Fayetteville, AR, p. A43
MCCABE, Steve, Chief Executive Officer, Hill Crest Behavioral Health Services, Birmingham, AL, p. A16
MCCAFFERTY, Michael, Chief Executive Officer, Sheridan Memorial Hospital, Sheridan, WY, p. A717
MCCAHILL, Connie, R.N., President and Chief Executive Officer, Cameron Memorial Community Hospital, Angola, IN, p. A204
MCCAHILL, Mary, Chief Nursing Officer, Thorek Memorial Hospital, Chicago, IL, p. A185
MCCAIN, Rebecca, Chief Executive Officer, Electra Memorial Hospital, Electra, TX, p. A612
MCCALL, Brad
President and Chief Executive Officer, Physicians Surgical Hospital – Panhandle Campus, Amarillo, TX, p. A591
President and Chief Executive Officer, Physicians Surgical Hospital – Quail Creek, Amarillo, TX, p. A591
MCCALL, Debbie, Director Human Resources, WK Bossier Health Center, Bossier City, LA, p. A271
MCCALL, Harlo, Chief Executive Officer, HEALTHSOUTH Rehabilitation Hospital of Texarkana, Texarkana, TX, p. A647
MCCALL Jr., Lee, Chief Executive Officer, Neshoba County General Hospital, Philadelphia, MS, p. A359
MCCALL, Pam, Director Human Resources, Heatherhill Care Communities, Chardon, OH, p. A481
MCCALLISTER, Bob, Director Human Resources, Baptist Memorial Hospital–Golden Triangle, Columbus, MS, p. A352
MCCALLISTER, Darla, Chief Financial Officer, Lakeside Women's Hospital, Oklahoma City, OK, p. A511
MCCALLISTER, Dianne, M.D. Chief Medical Officer, Medical Center of Aurora, Aurora, CO, p. A99
MCCAMPBELL, Kellie, Coordinator Human Resources, Kindred Hospital–Chattanooga, Chattanooga, TN, p. A575
MCCAMPBELL, Marcia, M.D. Chief Medical Officer, Shasta Regional Medical Center, Redding, CA, p. A82
MCCANCE, Dan, D.O. Chief of Staff, Hillsdale Community Health Center, Hillsdale, MI, p. A322
MCCANDLESS, Barbara, Vice President Human Resources, St. Mary's Hospital, Troy, NY, p. A452
MCCANDLESS, David, Vice President Medical Affairs, UPMC Northwest, Seneca, PA, p. A550
MCCANN, Barbara, Director Human Resources, Sunrise Canyon Hospital, Lubbock, TX, p. A629
MCCANN, Kyle, Chief Operating Officer, St. Joseph's Hospital, Savannah, GA, p. A164
MCCANN, Lew, Director Management Information Systems, OSF Holy Family Medical Center, Monmouth, IL, p. A194
MCCANNA, Peter J., Executive Vice President Administration and Chief Financial Officer, Northwestern Memorial Hospital, Chicago, IL, p. A183
MCCARTAN, Mary E., Manager Human Resources, VA Long Beach Healthcare System, Long Beach, CA, p. A68
MCCARTER, Alyssa, Chief Financial Officer, W. J. Mangold Memorial Hospital, Lockney, TX, p. A628
MCCARTER, Scott, Chief Information Officer, Karmanos Cancer Center, Detroit, MI, p. A318
MCCARTER, Jr., Thomas G., M.D. Chief Medical Officer, Lankenau Medical Center, Wynnewood, PA, p. A554
MCCARTHY, Barbara, Chief Executive Officer, Specialty Hospital Jacksonville, Jacksonville, FL, p. A130
MCCARTHY, Brian, Director Information Systems, Memorial Hospital of Salem County, Salem, NJ, p. A418
MCCARTHY, Cynthia L., R.N. Chief Nursing Officer, Texas Health Harris Methodist Hospital Stephenville, Stephenville, TX, p. A645
MCCARTHY, Linda M., R.N. VP/ Chief Nursing Officer, Citrus Memorial Health System, Inverness, FL, p. A129
MCCARTHY, Rick, Chief Information Officer, St. Vincent's Medical Center, Bridgeport, CT, p. A111
MCCARTHY, Robert R., Vice President Finance and Chief Financial Officer, Chenango Memorial Hospital, Norwich, NY, p. A446
MCCARTHY, Tim, President Puerto Rico Division, First Hospital Panamericano, Cidra, PR, p. A720
MCCARTY, Daniel P., Chief Operating Officer, Orange City Area Health System, Orange City, IA, p. A232
MCCARTY, Jacob M., Chief Executive Officer, Kindred Hospital–San Francisco Bay Area, San Leandro, CA, p. A90
MCCARTY, Maryland, Director Information Systems, Atlanta Medical Center, Atlanta, GA, p. A150
MCCARTY, Melany, R.N. Chief Clinical Officer, Vibra Hospital of Amarillo, Amarillo, TX, p. A591
MCCARTY, Tim, Chief Information Officer, OakBend Medical Center, Richmond, TX, p. A638
MCCARTY, Wendy, Director Human Resources, Hillsboro Community Hospital, Hillsboro, KS, p. A241
MCCARY, Steve C., Administrator, Riverside Doctors' Hospital, Williamsburg, VA, p. A674
MCCASLIN, Anna, Chief Financial Officer, Nebraska Orthopaedic Hospital, Omaha, NE, p. A396
MCCASLIN, Jami, Director Human Resources, Providence Hood River Memorial Hospital, Hood River, OR, p. A521
MCCAUGHEY, James, Chief Strategy Officer, Lucile Salter Packard Children's Hospital Stanford, Palo Alto, CA, p. A80
MCCAULEY, Cynthia, Chief Financial Officer, Good Samaritan Medical Center, West Palm Beach, FL, p. A147
MCCAULEY, Dudley, Controller, Lincoln County Medical Center, Ruidoso, NM, p. A426
MCCAULEY, Lauren, Marketing Director, West Boca Medical Center, Boca Raton, FL, p. A122
MCCAULEY, Sue E., Director Finance, Baum Harmon Mercy Hospital, Primghar, IA, p. A233
MCCAWLEY, Thomas J., Vice President Human Resources, Beloit Health System, Beloit, WI, p. A698
MCCHESNEY, Lisa D., R.N. Senior Director Information Systems, UPMC Hamot, Erie, PA, p. A534
MCCLAIN, April, R.N. Director, Inpatient Nursing, Shenandoah Memorial Hospital, Woodstock, VA, p. A675
MCCLAIN, Barbara, Human Resources, Horton Community Hospital, Horton, KS, p. A242
MCCLAIN, James, Deputy Director, Clement J. Zablocki Veterans Affairs Medical Center, Milwaukee, WI, p. A706
MCCLAIN, Richard, M.D. Chief Medical Officer, Chickasaw Nation Medical Center, Ada, OK, p. A503
MCCLANAHAN, Gary, Chief Information Officer, Sequoyah Memorial Hospital, Sallisaw, OK, p. A514
MCCLARIGAN, Linda, R.N. Chief Nursing Officer, Adirondack Medical Center, Saranac Lake, NY, p. A450
MCCLASKEY, Cynthia, Ph.D., Director, Southwestern Virginia Mental Health Institute, Marion, VA, p. A668
MCCLEARY, Heather, Director Human Resources, Coulee Medical Center, Grand Coulee, WA, p. A679
MCCLEESE, Randy, Vice President Information Services and Chief Information Officer, St. Claire Regional Medical Center, Morehead, KY, p. A263
MCCLELLAN, Ashley, Chief Executive Officer, Woman's Hospital of Texas, Houston, TX, p. A623
MCCLELLAN, Kathryn, Vice President and Chief Information Officer, Memorial Health, Savannah, GA, p. A164
MCCLELLAND, Michele
Vice President Human Resources, Kishwaukee Hospital, DeKalb, IL, p. A186
Vice President Human Resources, Valley West Hospital, Sandwich, IL, p. A200
MCCLELLAND, Patricia, Director Human Resources, South Texas Health System, Edinburg, TX, p. A610
MCCLENDON, Pat, MSN Chief Nursing Officer, Palmdale Regional Medical Center, Palmdale, CA, p. A80
MCCLINTIC, James, M.D. Vice President Medical Affairs, St. Anthony's Hospital, Saint Petersburg, FL, p. A142
MCCLINTICK, Cliff, Chief Information Officer, Lindner Center of HOPE, Mason, OH, p. A493
MCCLOSKEY, Louis, Chief Human Resources, Wilmington Veterans Affairs Medical Center, Wilmington, DE, p. A118
MCCLUNG, David
Chief Financial Officer, Monmouth Medical Center, Long Branch Campus, Long Branch, NJ, p. A413
Chief Financial Officer, Monmouth Medical Center, Southern Campus, Lakewood, NJ, p. A413
MCCLUNG, James W., Chief Executive Officer, HEALTHSOUTH Rehabilitation Hospital of Alexandria, Alexandria, LA, p. A268
MCCLUNG, Lyle, M.D. Chief of Staff, Carilion Stonewall Jackson Hospital, Lexington, VA, p. A667
MCCLURE, David K., President and Chief Executive Officer, Camden Clark Medical Center, Parkersburg, WV, p. A694
MCCLURE, Kenneth, M.D. Chief of Staff, Longview Regional Medical Center, Longview, TX, p. A629
MCCLURE, Thomas, M.D. Vice President Medical Affairs and Chief Medical Officer, Allegheny Valley Hospital, Natrona Heights, PA, p. A541
MCCLURG, Cathy, Director Human Resources, William Newton Hospital, Winfield, KS, p. A253
MCCLURG, Melissa, Human Resources Leader, SSM Health St. Francis Hospital – Maryville, Maryville, MO, p. A372
MCCLURKAN, Mac, Chief Information Officer, Bethesda Hospital, Saint Paul, MN, p. A346
MCCLUSKEY, Tabb, M.D. Chief Medical Officer, Hendricks Community Hospital Association, Hendricks, MN, p. A340
MCCLUSKY, Derek, M.D. Chief of Staff, Northern Louisiana Medical Center, Ruston, LA, p. A284
MCCLYMONT, Troy, Chief Information Technology Officer, Sheridan Memorial Hospital, Plentywood, MT, p. A386
MCCOBB, David, Chief Information Officer, Foothill Presbyterian Hospital, Glendora, CA, p. A64
MCCOIC, Kristie, Clinic Operations Officer and Director Human Resources, Gundersen St. Joseph's Hospital and Clinics, Hillsboro, WI, p. A702
MCCOLLUM, Kathleen, Senior Vice President, Clinical Integration and Chief Operating Officer, University of Maryland Baltimore Washington Medical Center, Glen Burnie, MD, p. A298
MCCOLLUM, Ken, Vice President, Human Resources, NorthBay Medical Center, Fairfield, CA, p. A61
MCCOLLUM, Rodger, Chief Executive Officer, Snoqualmie Valley Hospital District, Snoqualmie, WA, p. A685
MCCOLM, Denni, Chief Information Officer, Citizens Memorial Hospital, Bolivar, MO, p. A363
MCCOMB, Canise A., Director Human Resources, Graham Hospital, Canton, IL, p. A180
MCCONLOGUE, Lisa, Ph.D. Managing Director, Fairmount Behavioral Health System, Philadelphia, PA, p. A543
MCCONNELL, George, Director, Earle E. Morris Alcohol and Drug Treatment Center, Columbia, SC, p. A559
MCCONNELL, John D., M.D., Chief Executive Officer, Wake Forest Baptist Health, Winston–Salem, NC, p. B152
MCCONNELL, John D., M.D., Chief Executive Officer, Wake Forest Baptist Medical Center, Winston–Salem, NC, p. A471
MCCONNELL, Linda M., R.N. Associate Medical Center Director Patient Care Services, James H. Quillen Veterans Affairs Medical Center, Mountain Home, TN, p. A585
MCCONNELL, Patrick G., Chief Financial Officer, West Park Hospital, Cody, WY, p. A716
MCCONNELL, Ron, Chief Operating Officer, UPMC Altoona, Altoona, PA, p. A528
MCCONNELL, William, Ph.D. Vice President Operations and Strategic Outreach, Mercy Regional Medical Center, Durango, CO, p. A102
MCCORD, Sam, Chief Nursing Officer, Willow Springs Center, Reno, NV, p. A404
MCCORMACK, Cynthia, MS, Director, Cheyenne Veterans Affairs Medical Center, Cheyenne, WY, p. A715
MCCORMACK, Jane, R.N. Vice President, Chief Nursing Officer and Nursing and Patient Care Services, Unity Hospital, Rochester, NY, p. A449
MCCORMICK, Brad, Chief Financial Officer, Natchitoches Regional Medical Center, Natchitoches, LA, p. A281
MCCORMICK, Daniel, M.D. Vice President Medical Staff Affairs, Franciscan St. Anthony Health – Crown Point, Crown Point, IN, p. A207
MCCORMICK, Dee Dawn, Director Personnel and Human Resources, Coon Memorial Hospital, Dalhart, TX, p. A604
MCCORMICK, Jayne, M.D
Chief Medical Officer CDS, Presbyterian Hospital, Albuquerque, NM, p. A423
Chief Medical Officer CDS, Presbyterian Kaseman Hospital, Albuquerque, NM, p. A423
MCCORMICK, John, President and Chief Executive Officer, Oak Valley Hospital District, Oakdale, CA, p. A78
MCCORMICK, Martha, Chief Executive Officer, United Regional Medical Center, Manchester, TN, p. A582
MCCORMICK, Pam, Director Human Resources, Permian Regional Medical Center, Andrews, TX, p. A592
MCCOWN, Fran, Administrator, Haskell Memorial Hospital, Haskell, TX, p. A618
MCCOY, Andrea C.S., M.D. Chief Medical Officer, Cape Regional Medical Center, Cape May Court House, NJ, p. A410
MCCOY, Craig
Chief Executive Officer, Bon Secours St. Francis Health System, Greenville, SC, p. A561
Chief Executive Officer, Emory Saint Joseph's Hospital of Atlanta, Atlanta, GA, p. A150
MCCOY, Doug, Chief Executive Officer, Kindred Hospital Las Vegas–Sahara, Las Vegas, NV, p. A402
MCCOY, Janice M., MS Chief Clinical Officer, Promise Hospital of Florida at The Villages, Oxford, FL, p. A138
MCCOY, Jessica, Director Human Resources, Cedar Springs Hospital, Colorado Springs, CO, p. A100
MCCOY, Mike, Interim Chief Executive Officer, Saint Mary's Regional Medical Center, Russellville, AR, p. A50
MCCOY, Shawn W., Chief Administrative Officer, Deaconess Hospital, Evansville, IN, p. A208
MCCOY, Stephanie, President and Chief Executive Officer, Jackson General Hospital, Ripley, WV, p. A695
MCCRANIE, Robbie, Director Human Resources, Plano Specialty Hospital, Plano, TX, p. A637
MCCRAW, Elizabeth, Vice President, Human Resources, CaroMont Regional Medical Center, Gastonia, NC, p. A460
MCCRAW, Nicki, Assistant Vice President Human Resources, UW Medicine/Harborview Medical Center, Seattle, WA, p. A684

Index of Health Care Professionals
Index of Health Care Professionals / McCrea

MCCREA, Kim, Chief Human Resources Officer, Ortonville Area Health Services, Ortonville, MN, p. A344
MCCREA, Yvette, Chief Human Resources, Winn Army Community Hospital, Hinesville, GA, p. A159
MCCREARY, Michael, Chief of Services, Mercy Hospital Washington, Washington, MO, p. A380
MCCRIMMON, Scott, Manager Information Technology, Northern Arizona Veterans Affairs Health Care System, Prescott, AZ, p. A36
MCCROSKEY, Mark, Vice President Operations, Northeastern Health System, Tahlequah, OK, p. A515
MCCUE, Jennifer, Director Patient Care, Summersville Regional Medical Center, Summersville, WV, p. A695
MCCUE, Raymond, M.D. Chief Medical Officer, Bon Secours–DePaul Medical Center, Norfolk, VA, p. A669
MCCUE, Robert N., Vice President Finance, Mid Coast Hospital, Brunswick, ME, p. A289
MCCUE, Steven
Chief Financial Officer, Clinton Hospital, Clinton, MA, p. A306
Chief Financial Officer, UMass Memorial–Marlborough Hospital, Marlborough, MA, p. A308
MCCULLEY, Becky, Chief Operating Officer, University of Texas Southwestern Medical Center, Dallas, TX, p. A607
MCCULLEY, Larry W., President and Chief Executive Officer, Touchette Regional Hospitals, Centreville, IL, p. A181
MCCULLOCH, Greg, CPA Vice President of Finance and Chief Financial Officer, Sonora Regional Medical Center, Sonora, CA, p. A92
MCCULLOCH, Liz, Chief Information Resource Management Systems, Cheyenne Veterans Affairs Medical Center, Cheyenne, WY, p. A715
MCCULLOUGH, Barbara A., Vice President Human Resources, Washington Hospital, Washington, PA, p. A552
MCCULLOUGH, Bobby, Chief Operating Officer, Memorial Hospital Jacksonville, Jacksonville, FL, p. A129
MCCULLOUGH, Mary Kelly, Associate Director Patient Care Services, Lexington Veterans Affairs Medical Center, Lexington, KY, p. A260
MCCULLOUGH, Patrick, M.D. Chief Medical Services, Summit Behavioral Healthcare, Cincinnati, OH, p. A483
MCCULLOUGH, Wadra, Chief Nursing Officer, Spalding Regional Medical Center, Griffin, GA, p. A158
MCCUNE, Anne, Chief Operating Officer, Lucile Salter Packard Children's Hospital Stanford, Palo Alto, CA, p. A80
MCCUNE, Becky, Director Human Resources, Community Relations and Education, Coffeyville Regional Medical Center, Coffeyville, KS, p. A238
MCCURDY, Brent, Director Management Information, St. Croix Regional Medical Center, St. Croix Falls, WI, p. A711
MCCURDY, Judy, R.N. Vice President and Chief Nursing Officer, St. Vincent Medical Center, Los Angeles, CA, p. A73
MCCUTCHAN, Matt, Chief Financial Officer, Greater Regional Medical Center, Creston, IA, p. A225
MCCUTCHEON, Edna I.
Chief Executive Officer, Norristown State Hospital, Norristown, PA, p. A542
Chief Executive Officer, Torrance State Hospital, Torrance, PA, p. A551
MCCUTCHEON Jr., Henry, Chief Executive Officer, Lake City Community Hospital, Lake City, SC, p. A563
MCDADE, E., R.N.Walter P. Reuther Psychiatric Hospital, Westland, MI, p. A332
MCDANALD, Matt, M.D. Chief Medical Officer, Baptist Health La Grange, La Grange, KY, p. A259
MCDANEL, Joyce
Vice President Human Resources and Education, UnityPoint Health – Iowa Methodist Medical Center, Des Moines, IA, p. A226
Vice President Human Resources and Education, UnityPoint Health–Iowa Lutheran Hospital, Des Moines, IA, p. A226
MCDANIEL, Amy, Administrator and Chief Executive Officer, Iowa Specialty Hospital–Belmond, Belmond, IA, p. A222
MCDANIEL, Burton, M.D. Medical Director, Roosevelt Warm Springs Rehabilitation and Specialty Hospitals – Rehab, Warm Springs, GA, p. A167
MCDANIEL, Graciela, Chief Financial Officer, Philadelphia Veterans Affairs Medical Center, Philadelphia, PA, p. A545
MCDANIEL, Kim, Director Human Resources, HEALTHSOUTH Rehabilitation Hospital of Montgomery, Montgomery, AL, p. A23
MCDANIEL, LaDonna, Financial Manager, Prattville Baptist Hospital, Prattville, AL, p. A24
MCDANIEL, Lisa A., Chief Human Resources Officer, Samaritan Healthcare, Moses Lake, WA, p. A680
MCDANIEL, Suzie Q., Chief Human Resource Officer, Bay Area Hospital, Coos Bay, OR, p. A520
MCDANIEL, Jr., W. Burton, M.D. Physician Executive, Roosevelt Warm Springs Rehabilitation and Specialty Hospitals – LTAC, Warm Springs, GA, p. A166
MCDAVID, Clarence, Vice President Human Resources, Rose Medical Center, Denver, CO, p. A102
MCDERMOTT, James, M.D. Chief of Staff, Sedan City Hospital, Sedan, KS, p. A250
MCDERMOTT, Mary, Vice President Nursing, Phelps Memorial Hospital Center, Sleepy Hollow, NY, p. A450
MCDERMOTT, Michael, M.D., President and Chief Executive Officer, Mary Washington Healthcare, Fredericksburg, VA, p. B86
MCDERMOTT, Michael, M.D.,
President and Chief Executive Officer, Mary Washington Hospital, Fredericksburg, VA, p. A665
President and Chief Executive Officer, Stafford Hospital, Stafford, VA, p. A673
MCDERMOTT, Suzan, Director, Human Resources, Gouverneur Hospital, Gouverneur, NY, p. A434
MCDERMOTT, Thomas, Vice President Finance, Fayette County Memorial Hospital, Washington Court House, OH, p. A500
MCDERMOTT, Vincent, Vice President, Finance and Real Estate, Brigham and Women's Faulkner Hospital, Boston, MA, p. A303
MCDERMOTT–LORD, Sheila, Chief Executive Officer, Georgetown Behavioral Health Institute, Georgetown, TX, p. A616
MCDEVITT, Mike, Chief Information Officer, Children's of Alabama, Birmingham, AL, p. A16
MCDEVITT, Robert J., M.D. Chief of Staff, Wilson Memorial Hospital, Sidney, OH, p. A497
MCDIVITT, Robert P., FACHE, Director, Veterans Affairs Ann Arbor Healthcare System, Ann Arbor, MI, p. A314
MCDONAGH, Andrew, M.D. Chief Medical Officer, Aurora West Allis Medical Center, West Allis, WI, p. A714
MCDONALD, Buck, Chief Financial Officer, St. Helena Hospital Clear Lake, Clearlake, CA, p. A58
MCDONALD, Carl, Regional Director Human Resources, Broward Health Imperial Point, Fort Lauderdale, FL, p. A126
MCDONALD, Connie, Chief Financial Officer, Marion Veterans Affairs Medical Center, Marion, IL, p. A193
MCDONALD, Douglas, M.D. Vice President Medical Affairs, University Hospitals Elyria Medical Center, Elyria, OH, p. A489
MCDONALD, Edward A., Chief Financial Officer, St. Helena Hospital–Center for Behavioral Health, Vallejo, CA, p. A96
MCDONALD, Elizabeth, Director Human Resources, Wayne Memorial Hospital, Honesdale, PA, p. A536
MCDONALD, Frederick Joseph, Commanding Officer, Naval Hospital Oak Harbor, Oak Harbor, WA, p. A681
MCDONALD, Gary
Associate Administrator Human Resources, Stone County Medical Center, Mountain View, AR, p. A48
Associate Administrator Human Resources, White River Medical Center, Batesville, AR, p. A41
MCDONALD, Gregory, Vice President Finance and Chief Financial Officer, Roswell Park Cancer Institute, Buffalo, NY, p. A430
MCDONALD, Harold E., Deputy Executive Director and Senior Vice President Administration, Nassau University Medical Center, East Meadow, NY, p. A433
MCDONALD, Jeff
Chief Executive Officer, Canyon Ridge Hospital, Chino, CA, p. A57
Information Technology Manager, Florida Hospital Wauchula, Wauchula, FL, p. A146
MCDONALD, John, M.D. Chief Medical Officer, North Hills Hospital, North Richland Hills, TX, p. A634
MCDONALD, John, Chief Operating Officer, Northwest Texas Healthcare System, Amarillo, TX, p. A591
MCDONALD, Joseph D., President and Chief Executive Officer, Catholic Health System, Buffalo, NY, p. B31
MCDONALD, Larry, Director Human Resources, Miami Jewish Home and Hospital for Aged, Miami, FL, p. A134
MCDONALD, Mark, M.D., President and Chief Executive Officer, Institute for Orthopaedic Surgery, Lima, OH, p. A492
MCDONALD Jr., Michael S., Chief Executive Officer, Holly Hill Hospital, Raleigh, NC, p. A466
MCDONALD, Robert A., Secretary, Veterans Affairs, Department of Veterans Affairs, Washington, DC, p. B46
MCDONALD, Shelly, Chief Human Resources Officer, Ness County Hospital, Ness City, KS, p. A246
MCDONALD, Stanton B., M.D. Medical Director, Heber Valley Medical Center, Heber City, UT, p. A655
MCDONALD, Stuart, M.D. President Medical Staff, Kindred Hospital–Fort Worth, Fort Worth, TX, p. A613
MCDONALD, Susan, M.D. Vice President, St. Joseph's Medical Center, Stockton, CA, p. A93
MCDONALD, Tedd, M.D. Chief Medical Officer, Banner Churchill Community Hospital, Fallon, NV, p. A400
MCDONALD–UPTON, Ann, Chief Nursing Officer, St. Joseph Mercy Oakland, Pontiac, MI, p. A328
MCDONNELL, M. Therese, M.D. Interim Vice President Patient Safety, Quality and Medical Affairs, Sibley Memorial Hospital, Washington, DC, p. A120
MCDONNELL, Michael, M.D. Chief Medical Officer, Mercy Hospital and Medical Center, Chicago, IL, p. A183
MCDONNELL, Nancy, Manager Information Systems, Illinois Valley Community Hospital, Peru, IL, p. A198
MCDONOUGH, Jeffrey, Vice President Human Resources, Vassar Brothers Medical Center, Poughkeepsie, NY, p. A448
MCDOUGLE, Mark, Executive Vice President and Chief Operating Officer, Maimonides Medical Center, NY, p. A441
MCDOWELL, III, Arthur V., M.D. Vice President Clinical Affairs, Middlesex Hospital, Middletown, CT, p. A113
MCDOWELL, Jean, Chief Financial Officer, Kindred Hospital–Dallas, Dallas, TX, p. A605
MCDOWELL, Paul L., Vice President Finance and Chief Financial Officer, King's Daughters Medical Center, Ashland, KY, p. A254
MCDOWELL, Richard, M.D. Medical Director, Kona Community Hospital, Kealakekua, HI, p. A170
MCDOWELL, Richard, Chief Financial Officer, Ridge Behavioral Health System, Lexington, KY, p. A260
MCDOWELL, Wendy, R.N. Director of Nursing, Weisbrod Memorial County Hospital, Eads, CO, p. A103
MCDOWN, Missy, Director Information Systems, Via Christi Hospital Pittsburg, Pittsburg, KS, p. A249
MCDRURY, Martha M., R.N. Chief Operating Officer and Chief Nursing Officer, Holy Family Hospital, Methuen, MA, p. A308
MCEACHERN, John, Controller, Sebastian River Medical Center, Sebastian, FL, p. A143
MCEACHERN, Michael L., Chief Executive Officer, Bowie Memorial Hospital, Bowie, TX, p. A598
MCELDOWNEY, Erin, Manager Human Resources, Haven Senior Horizons, Phoenix, AZ, p. A35
MCELLIGOTT, Daniel P., FACHE, President, CHI Health Saint Francis, Grand Island, NE, p. A392
MCELMURRAY, Charles D., M.D. Chief Medical Officer, Fairfield Memorial Hospital, Winnsboro, SC, p. A566
MCELMURRAY, Dodie, Chief Operating Officer, Greenwood Leflore Hospital, Greenwood, MS, p. A353
MCELRATH, Matthew
Chief Human Resources Officer, Keck Hospital of USC, Los Angeles, CA, p. A70
Chief Human Resources Officer, University of Southern California–Norris Cancer Hospital, Los Angeles, CA, p. A73
MCELROY, Sherry, Director Health Information Management, Osceola Community Hospital, Sibley, IA, p. A234
MCELROY, Wayne, Administrator, Pickens County Medical Center, Carrollton, AL, p. A17
MCENTEE, Chris, Network Specialist, Van Buren County Hospital, Keosauqua, IA, p. A230
MCENTIRE, Ann, MSN Chief Nursing Officer, Citizens Baptist Medical Center, Talladega, AL, p. A25
MCEUEN, Jacqueline, Coordinator Human Resources, Bellville St. Joseph Health Center, Bellville, TX, p. A597
MCEWEN, Michelle, President and Chief Executive Officer, Speare Memorial Hospital, Plymouth, NH, p. A408
MCFADDEN, Mary T., MSN Chief Nurse Executive, Providence Portland Medical Center, Portland, OR, p. A524
MCFALL, Cathy, Human Resources Manager, Kiowa County Memorial Hospital, Greensburg, KS, p. A241
MCFALL, Michael, Chief Financial Officer, Kindred Rehabilitation Hospital Clear Lake, Webster, TX, p. A651
MCFALL, Vicky, Chief Executive Officer, Monroe County Medical Center, Tompkinsville, KY, p. A266
MCFALL–ROBERTS, Ebuni
Director Human Resources, Anchor Hospital, Atlanta, GA, p. A149
Director Human Resources, Holly Hill Hospital, Raleigh, NC, p. A466
MCFARLAND, Kenneth D., President and Chief Executive Officer, Mission Hospital, Mission Viejo, CA, p. A75
MCFARLAND, Nita, Director of Nursing, Kingman Community Hospital, Kingman, KS, p. A243
MCFARLAND, Rhonda
Director Human Resources, Carolinas HealthCare System Anson, Wadesboro, NC, p. A470
Director Human Resources, Carolinas Healthcare System Union, Monroe, NC, p. A465
MCFARLAND, Rodney, M.D. Medical Director, Freeman Neosho Hospital, Neosho, MO, p. A373
MCFARLAND, Tracee, Chief Financial Officer, Claiborne Medical Center, Tazewell, TN, p. A588
MCFAUL, Joan, Senior Vice President and Chief Information Officer, Southcoast Hospitals Group, Fall River, MA, p. A306
MCFERRAN, Virginia
Chief Information Officer, Ronald Reagan UCLA Medical Center, Los Angeles, CA, p. A72
Chief Information Officer, Santa Monica–UCLA Medical Center and Orthopaedic Hospital, Santa Monica, CA, p. A92
MCGAHEY, Nikki, Information Officer, Jefferson County Hospital, Waurika, OK, p. A518

A910 Index of Health Care Professionals 

Index of Health Care Professionals / McKenzie

Index of Health Care Professionals


MCGANN, Robert, M.D. President Medical Staff, Jameson Hospital, New Castle, PA, p. A541

MCGARIGLE, Kristine, R.N
Vice President Patient Care, Ministry Good Samaritan Health Center, Merrill, WI, p. A706
Vice President Patient Care, Ministry Saint Clare's Hospital, Weston, WI, p. A714

MCGARVEY, Missy, Chief Information Officer, Twin Valley Behavioral Healthcare, Columbus, OH, p. A487

MCGEACHEY, Edward J., President and Chief Executive Officer, Southern Maine Health Care – Biddeford Medical Center, Biddeford, ME, p. A289

MCGEE, Genemarie, R.N. Chief Nursing Officer, Sentara Leigh Hospital, Norfolk, VA, p. A669

MCGEE, Jessica
Chief Financial Officer, AMG Specialty Hospital–Denham Springs, Denham Springs, LA, p. A273
Chief Financial Officer, AMG Specialty Hospital–Lafayette, Lafayette, LA, p. A277
Chief Financial Officer, AMG Specialty Hospital–Slidell, Slidell, LA, p. A285

MCGEE, Kevin, Chief Executive Officer, River Point Behavioral Health, Jacksonville, FL, p. A129

MCGEE, Mark F., M.D. Chief Clinical Officer, Appalachian Behavioral Healthcare, Athens, OH, p. A479

MCGEE, Terry, Chief Operations Officer, Central State Hospital, Milledgeville, GA, p. A161

MCGEEHAN, Paul, M.D. Chief Medical Staff, Corry Memorial Hospital, Corry, PA, p. A532

MCGETTIGAN, Ryan, Chief Information Officer, Coatesville Veterans Affairs Medical Center, Coatesville, PA, p. A532

MCGHEE, Michael, M.D. Medical Director, Behavioral HealthCare Center at Clarksville, Clarksville, TN, p. A575

MCGIBBON, Monica, Chief Nursing Officer, Terence Cardinal Cooke Health Care Center, New York, NY, p. A444

MCGILL, Cindy, Senior Vice President Human Resources, Presbyterian Kaseman Hospital, Albuquerque, NM, p. A423

MCGILL, Martha, Executive Vice President and Chief Operating Officer, Nicklaus Children's Hospital, Miami, FL, p. A134

MCGILL, Rusty, System Director Information Technology, Indiana University Health Arnett Hospital, Lafayette, IN, p. A214

MCGILL, Steve, Chief Financial Officer, Wabash General Hospital, Mount Carmel, IL, p. A195

MCGILL, Timothy W., Chief Executive Officer, Saint Thomas River Park Hospital, Mc Minnville, TN, p. A582

MCGILVRAY, Greg, Chief Financial Officer, Medical Center Enterprise, Enterprise, AL, p. A19

MCGIMSEY, Erika, Controller, Jewish Hospital–Shelbyville, Shelbyville, KY, p. A266

MCGINLEY, Mary Ann, Senior Vice President, Patient Services and Chief Nursing Officer, Thomas Jefferson University Hospitals, Philadelphia, PA, p. A545

MCGINNIS, Christina, Director Information Technology, Menorah Medical Center, Overland Park, KS, p. A248

MCGINNIS, Jeff, M.D. President Medical Staff, Saint Joseph Mount Sterling, Mount Sterling, KY, p. A263

MCGIRL, John, Chief Human Resources Officer, NCH Downtown Naples Hospital, Naples, FL, p. A136

MCGLADE, James, Director Human Resources, United Hospital, Saint Paul, MN, p. A346

MCGLEW, Timothy, Chief Executive Officer, Kern Valley Healthcare District, Lake Isabella, CA, p. A67

MCGLON, Tracy, Director Human Resources, Gulf Coast Regional Medical Center, Panama City, FL, p. A139

MCGLORY, Joyce, Vice President Human Resources, Methodist Hospitals, Gary, IN, p. A209

MCGLOTHLIN, Wylie, M.D. Chief Medical Officer, Henry County Hospital, New Castle, IN, p. A217

MCGLYNN, Mia, Director Management Information Systems, Plantation General Hospital, Plantation, FL, p. A140

MCGOLDRICK, Margaret M., President, Abington Memorial Hospital, Abington, PA, p. A528

MCGONNELL, James, Interim Chief Financial Officer, Fleming County Hospital, Flemingsburg, KY, p. A256

MCGOVERN, Julia, Vice President Human Resources, Chilton Medical Center, Pompton Plains, NJ, p. A417

MCGOVERN, Julie, Vice President Human Resources, Anne Arundel Medical Center, Annapolis, MD, p. A293

MCGOVERN, Pam, Director Technology, Huggins Hospital, Wolfeboro, NH, p. A408

MCGOVERN, Sandra, Chief Nursing Officer, UP Health System–Bell, Ishpeming, MI, p. A323

MCGOWAN, Donna, Administrator, Lane County Hospital, Dighton, KS, p. A239

MCGOWAN, Gloria, Chief Financial Officer, Wiregrass Medical Center, Geneva, AL, p. A20

MCGOWEN, Bernard A., M.D. Medical Director, Kindred Hospital Tarrant County–Arlington, Arlington, TX, p. A592

MCGOWIN, III, Norman F., M.D. Chief of Staff, L. V. Stabler Memorial Hospital, Greenville, AL, p. A20

MCGRAIL, David, Vice President Finance, Carney Hospital, Boston, MA, p. A303

MCGRAIL, Robert, Interim Chief Executive Officer, West Branch Regional Medical Center, West Branch, MI, p. A332

MCGRATH, Bradley, Administrator, New Mexico Rehabilitation Center, Roswell, NM, p. A426

MCGRATH, Denise B., Chief Executive Officer, HEALTHSOUTH Sea Pines Rehabilitation Hospital, Melbourne, FL, p. A133

MCGRATH, Lynn, M.D. Vice President Medical Affairs, Deborah Heart and Lung Center, Browns Mills, NJ, p. A410

MCGRATH, Michael
Manager Finance, University Hospitals Conneaut Medical Center, Conneaut, OH, p. A487
Manager Finance, University Hospitals Geneva Medical Center, Geneva, OH, p. A490

MCGRAW, Belinda
Director Human Resources, Boulder City Hospital, Boulder City, NV, p. A400
Director Human Resources, Complex Care Hospital at Tenaya, Las Vegas, NV, p. A401

MCGRAW, Karin L., FACHE, Director, Beckley Veterans Affairs Medical Center, Beckley, WV, p. A689

MCGRAW, Kathleen, M.D. Chief Medical Officer, Brattleboro Memorial Hospital, Brattleboro, VT, p. A660

MCGRAW, Scott, M.D. Medical Director, Irving Coppell Surgical Hospital, Irving, TX, p. A624

MCGREAHAM, David S., M.D. Vice President Medical Affairs and Chief Medical Officer, Munson Medical Center, Traverse City, MI, p. A331

MCGREEVY, John, Chief Executive Officer, Mother Frances Hospital – Tyler, Tyler, TX, p. A649

MCGREGOR, Julie
Vice President and Chief People Officer, Jewish Hospital, Louisville, KY, p. A261
Director Human Resources, Sts. Mary & Elizabeth Hospital, Louisville, KY, p. A262

MCGREGOR, Robert, M.D. Chief Medical Officer, Akron Children's Hospital, Akron, OH, p. A478

MCGREW, David S., Chief Financial Officer, San Mateo Medical Center, San Mateo, CA, p. A90

MCGREW, Deborah A., Vice President and Chief Operating Officer, University of Texas Medical Branch, Galveston, TX, p. A615

MCGREW, Diane, Chief Nurse Executive, Montgomery County Memorial Hospital, Red Oak, IA, p. A233

MCGRIFF, Marchelle M., Chief Nursing Executive, Sutter Medical Center, Sacramento, Sacramento, CA, p. A85

MCGUCKEN, Holly, R.N. Chief Nursing Officer, Fort Walton Beach Medical Center, Fort Walton Beach, FL, p. A127

MCGUE, Lisa, Controller, HEALTHSOUTH Northern Kentucky Rehabilitation Hospital, Edgewood, KY, p. A256

MCGUE, Thomas E., M.D. Vice President Medical Affairs and Chief Medical Officer, Newport Hospital, Newport, RI, p. A555

MCGUFFIN, Patty, R.N. Chief Nursing Officer, Allen County Regional Hospital, Iola, KS, p. A242

MCGUIGAN, Kevin, M.D. Medical Director, St. Lawrence Rehabilitation Center, Lawrenceville, NJ, p. A413

MCGUILL, Gail, R.N. Chief Nursing Officer and Administrative Director of Patient Care Services, Shriners Hospitals for Children–Salt Lake City, Salt Lake City, UT, p. A658

MCGUINNESS, Luke, President and CEO, Health Quest Systems, Inc., LaGrangeville, NY, p. B66

MCGUINNESS, Patrick, Chief Information Management, Keller Army Community Hospital, West Point, NY, p. A453

MCGUIRE, Ann M., Vice President Human Resources, Indiana University Health Ball Memorial Hospital, Muncie, IN, p. A216

MCGUIRE, Cynthia, Chief Executive Officer, Monadnock Community Hospital, Peterborough, NH, p. A408

MCGUIRE, Karen, Chief Financial Officer, Audubon County Memorial Hospital, Audubon, IA, p. A222

MCGUIRE, Lee, Chief Nurse Executive, Kerrville State Hospital, Kerrville, TX, p. A626

MCGUIRE, Matthew, President and Chief Executive Officer, Western Regional Medical Center, Goodyear, AZ, p. A32

MCGUIRE, Shane, Chief Operations Officer and Information Technology Director, Columbia County Health System, Dayton, WA, p. A678

MCGUIRK, Christina, Chief Nursing Officer, Health Central Hospital, Ocoee, FL, p. A137

MCGUIRL, Mary, Director Information Systems, Oneida Healthcare, Oneida, NY, p. A446

MCGURK, Kevin, Controller, Bellin Psychiatric Center, Green Bay, WI, p. A702

MCHANEY, Tracy, Director Human Resources, Cedar Crest Hospital and Residential Treatment Center, Belton, TX, p. A597

MCHARDY, Bryson, M.D. President Medical Staff, Hannibal Regional Hospital, Hannibal, MO, p. A368

MCHUGH, Matthew, Director Information Services, Vaughan Regional Medical Center, Selma, AL, p. A24

MCHUGH, Michael J., M.D., Medical Director, Cleveland Clinic Children's Hospital for Rehabilitation, Cleveland, OH, p. A484

MCHUGH, William, M.D. Medical Director and Chief Medical Officer, Trinitas Regional Medical Center, Elizabeth, NJ, p. A411

MCILROY, Gail, Director Medical Records, Promise Hospital of Wichita Falls, Wichita Falls, TX, p. A652

MCILWAIN, T. Pinckney, M.D. Vice President and Chief Medical Officer, Charleston Area Medical Center, Charleston, WV, p. A690

MCINERNEY, Terry, Director of Nursing, Inpatient, Navos, Seattle, WA, p. A683

MCINTOSH, Craig, Chief Information Officer, Northwest Specialty Hospital, Post Falls, ID, p. A176

MCINTOSH, Ernasha, Interim Director of Nursing, Sage Memorial Hospital, Ganado, AZ, p. A31

MCINTOSH, Joe, Director Management Information Systems, Logansport State Hospital, Logansport, IN, p. A215

MCINTOSH, Tyler, Chief Financial Officer, Creek Nation Community Hospital, Okemah, OK, p. A511

MCINTYRE, Cindy, R.N. Administrative Director Clinical Services, Magee General Hospital, Magee, MS, p. A356

MCINTYRE, Daniel J., President and Chief Executive Officer, The Charlotte Hungerford Hospital, Torrington, CT, p. A115

MCINTYRE, Kathleen, Province Leader, American Province of Little Company of Mary Sisters, Evergreen Park, IL, p. B10

MCIWAIN, John, Director Human Resources, Wayne Memorial Hospital, Jesup, GA, p. A159

MCKALE, Brigitte, MSN Vice President and Chief Nurse Executive, Pali Momi Medical Center, Aiea, HI, p. A168

MCKAY, Amy, Chief Nursing Officer, Mid–America Rehabilitation Hospital, Shawnee Mission, KS, p. A250

MCKAY, Daniel E.
Chief Executive Officer, Sparks Medical Center – Van Buren, Van Buren, AR, p. A51
Chief Executive Officer, Sparks Regional Medical Center, Fort Smith, AR, p. A45

MCKAY, Danny H., Administrator, Noxubee General Hospital, Macon, MS, p. A356

MCKAY, Michael, Chief Information Officer, Wickenburg Community Hospital, Wickenburg, AZ, p. A40

MCKAY, Ronda, R.N. Vice President Patient Care Services, Chief Nursing Officer, Community Hospital, Munster, IN, p. A217

MCKEAN, Kathy, M.P.H. Vice President, Chief Nursing Executive, Riverview Medical Center, Red Bank, NJ, p. A418

MCKEE, Debra, R.N. Chief Nursing Officer, Joint Township District Memorial Hospital, Saint Marys, OH, p. A497

MCKEE, Judy, FACHE, Director, William S. Middleton Memorial Veterans Hospital, Madison, WI, p. A704

MCKEE, Laurie, Vice President Patient Care Services, Avera Sacred Heart Hospital, Yankton, SD, p. A573

MCKEE, Michele, Vice President and Chief Financial Officer, St. Louis Children's Hospital, Saint Louis, MO, p. A377

MCKEE, Robert J., Vice President Human Resources, Penn Highlands DuBois, DuBois, PA, p. A533

MCKEE, Jr., Willis P., M.D. Chief Medical Officer, Frankfort Regional Medical Center, Frankfort, KY, p. A257

MCKEEBY, Jon W., Chief Information Officer, National Institutes of Health Clinical Center, Bethesda, MD, p. A296

MCKEEN, Marcia, Director Human Resources, Twin Valley Behavioral Healthcare, Columbus, OH, p. A487

MCKELDIN, Pat, Human Resource Business Partner, Kaiser Permanente Manteca Medical Center, Manteca, CA, p. A74

MCKENNA, Dennis, M.D. Interim Vice President Medical Affairs, Albany Medical Center, Albany, NY, p. A428

MCKENNA, Donald, President and Chief Executive Officer, St. Mary's Health Care System, Athens, GA, p. A149

MCKENNA, John F., Chief Executive Officer and Managing Director, Rockford Center, Newark, DE, p. A117

MCKENNA, Kathleen, Public Affairs Leader, Kaiser Permanente South Sacramento Medical Center, Sacramento, CA, p. A84

MCKENNA, Quinn, Chief Operating Officer, University of Utah Health Care – Hospital and Clinics, Salt Lake City, UT, p. A659

MCKENNEY, Jennifer, M.D. Chief Medical Officer, Fredonia Regional Hospital, Fredonia, KS, p. A240

MCKENZIE, Christine, Director Human Resources, Davis Regional Medical Center, Statesville, NC, p. A469

MCKENZIE, Jackie, Director Administrative Services, Beacham Memorial Hospital, Magnolia, MS, p. A356

MCKENZIE, Kimberly, R.N. Chief Nursing Officer and Chief Operations Officer, Harbor–UCLA Medical Center, Torrance, CA, p. A94

MCKENZIE, Nancy J., Chief Executive Officer, Greenwood County Hospital, Eureka, KS, p. A239

MCKENZIE, Sandra D., Executive Vice President and Chief Operating Officer, Hamilton Medical Center, Dalton, GA, p. A155

MCKENZIE, William G., President, Chief Executive Officer and Chairman, Gilliard Health Services, Montgomery, AL, p. B58


© 2015 AHA Guide Index of Health Care Professionals **A911**

MCKEON, John, Vice President Human Resources, Kingsbrook Jewish Medical Center, NY, p. A441

MCKEON, Sean, Director, Information Technology, Franciscan Hospital for Children, Boston, MA, p. A303

MCKEOWN, Colleen, Senior Vice President and Area Manager, Kaiser Permanente Walnut Creek Medical Center, Walnut Creek, CA, p. A97

MCKERNAN, James E., Chief Operating Officer, Bronson Battle Creek, Battle Creek, MI, p. A315

MCKERNAN, Kathleen S., Director Information Systems, Pioneers Memorial Healthcare District, Brawley, CA, p. A56

MCKERNAN, Stephen W., Chief Executive Officer, University of New Mexico Hospitals, Albuquerque, NM, p. B147

MCKERNAN, Stephen W., Chief Executive Officer, University of New Mexico Hospitals, Albuquerque, NM, p. A423

MCKEVETT, Timothy M., President, Beloit Health System, Beloit, WI, p. A698

MCKIBBEN, Leeanna, R.N
Vice President Patient Services and Chief Nursing Officer, UPMC McKeesport, McKeesport, PA, p. A539
Vice President Patient Services and Chief Nursing Officer, UPMC Mercy, Pittsburgh, PA, p. A547

MCKIBBEN, Sean, President and Chief Operating Officer, Mount Carmel, Columbus, OH, p. A486

MCKIDDY, Paul, Director Information Technology, Monroe County Medical Center, Tompkinsville, KY, p. A266

MCKIE, Kathy, Director Human Resources, Montrose Memorial Hospital, Montrose, CO, p. A107

MCKILLIP, Ed, Director of Finance, Riddle Hospital, Media, PA, p. A540

MCKIMMY, Doyle L., FACHE, Chief Executive Officer, Jewell County Hospital, Mankato, KS, p. A245

MCKINLEY, Bryan, Chief Financial Officer, St. Mark's Hospital, Salt Lake City, UT, p. A658

MCKINLEY, Ernie, Chief Information Officer, University Medical Center, Las Vegas, NV, p. A403

MCKINLEY, Ivy
Regional Human Resources Officer, Community First Medical Center, Chicago, IL, p. A181
Director Human Resources, Presence Holy Family Medical Center, Des Plaines, IL, p. A186
Regional Lead Human Resources, Presence Resurrection Medical Center, Chicago, IL, p. A183

MCKINLEY, Katie, Assistant Administrator/Nursing, Southwest Mississippi Regional Medical Center, McComb, MS, p. A357

MCKINLEY, Mike, Information Security Officer, West Texas Veterans Affairs Health Care System, Big Spring, TX, p. A597

MCKINLEY, Ronald, Ph.D. Vice President Human Resources and Employee Services, University of Texas Medical Branch, Galveston, TX, p. A615

MCKINLEY, Jr., Rudolph, Vice President Operations and Chief Operating Officer, East Tennessee Children's Hospital, Knoxville, TN, p. A580

MCKINNEY, Brenda, Chief Financial Officer, Reeves County Hospital, Pecos, TX, p. A636

MCKINNEY, Bruce, Business Officer, Administrative Services, Central Prison Hospital, Raleigh, NC, p. A466

MCKINNEY, Dan, Administrator, Hermann Area District Hospital, Hermann, MO, p. A368

MCKINNEY, Dana, Chief Nursing Officer, Select Specialty Hospital–Madison, Madison, WI, p. A704

MCKINNEY, Diane, R.N. Vice President Patient Care Service, Decatur County Memorial Hospital, Greensburg, IN, p. A210

MCKINNEY, Paul, Chief Executive Officer, Martin County Hospital District, Stanton, TX, p. A645

MCKINNON, Bert, M.D. Interim Chief Medical Officer, Flagstaff Medical Center, Flagstaff, AZ, p. A31

MCKINNON, Mark, M.D. Chief of Staff, North Runnels Hospital, Winters, TX, p. A652

MCKINNON, Scott, President and Chief Executive Officer, Memorial Hospital, North Conway, NH, p. A408

MCKINNON, Shauna, Chief Executive Officer, Bayfront Health Dade City, Dade City, FL, p. A124

MCKNIGHT, Craig L., Senior Vice President and Chief Financial Officer, Phoenix Children's Hospital, Phoenix, AZ, p. A35

MCKNIGHT, Richard B., Senior Vice President and Chief Information Officer, Novant Health Huntersville Medical Center, Huntersville, NC, p. A462

MCKNIGHT, Tim, M.D. Chief of Staff, Trinity Hospital Twin City, Dennison, OH, p. A489

MCKOY, Lori, Business Partner, Pender Memorial Hospital, Burgaw, NC, p. A456

MCKULA, Tim, Vice President Information Systems and Chief Information Officer, Rehabilitation Institute of Chicago, Chicago, IL, p. A184

MCKUNE, Jeff, Director Information Technology, Phelps County Regional Medical Center, Rolla, MO, p. A375

MCLAIN, Allen, M.D. Chief of Staff, Grisell Memorial Hospital District One, Ransom, KS, p. A249

MCLAIN, Cindy, Chief Executive Officer, Select Specialty Hospital–Fort Smith, Fort Smith, AR, p. A44

MCLAIN, Jerry, M.D. Chief of Staff, Chadron Community Hospital and Health Services, Chadron, NE, p. A391

MCLAIN, Kathy, Chief Financial Officer, Childress Regional Medical Center, Childress, TX, p. A600

MCLAIN, Terri L., FACHE, President, Mercy Hospital Washington, Washington, MO, p. A380

MCLARIN, Benita, Chief Operating Officer, Santa Clara Valley Medical Center, San Jose, CA, p. A89

MCLARTY, Walter L.
Chief Human Resources Officer, Bethesda North Hospital, Cincinnati, OH, p. A482
Chief Human Resources Officer, Good Samaritan Hospital, Cincinnati, OH, p. A483

MCLAUGHLIN, Anna, Acting Financial Management Officer, Standing Rock Service Unit, Fort Yates Hospital, Indian Health Service, DHHS, Fort Yates, ND, p. A474

MCLAUGHLIN, Dan C., Vice President Professional Services, Good Samaritan Hospital, Los Angeles, CA, p. A70

MCLAUGHLIN, Gary, Executive Vice President Finance and Chief Financial Officer, Overlake Medical Center, Bellevue, WA, p. A676

MCLAUGHLIN, Kathryn, Chief Nursing Officer, Hemet Valley Medical Center, Hemet, CA, p. A65

MCLAUGHLIN, Maribeth, R.N. Vice President Patient Care Services, Magee–Womens Hospital of UPMC, Pittsburgh, PA, p. A546

MCLAUGHLIN, Neil R., R.N.,
President, Hampshire Memorial Hospital, Romney, WV, p. A695
President, War Memorial Hospital, Berkeley Springs, WV, p. A689

MCLAUGHLIN, Pamela, Chief Financial Officer, HEALTHSOUTH Rehabilitation Hospital of Austin, Austin, TX, p. A594

MCLAUGHLIN, Sherry, Director Human Resources, Forrest City Medical Center, Forrest City, AR, p. A44

MCLAURIN, Monty E., President and Chief Executive Officer, Indian Path Medical Center, Kingsport, TN, p. A580

MCLAWS, Douglas, D.O. Chief Medical Officer, Manning Regional Healthcare Center, Manning, IA, p. A231

MCLEAN, Anthony
Interim President, St. Elizabeth Hospital, Enumclaw, WA, p. A678
President, St. Francis Hospital, Federal Way, WA, p. A679

MCLEAN, Chris J., Chief Financial Officer, Methodist Healthcare Memphis Hospitals, Memphis, TN, p. A584

MCLEAN, Cindy J., R.N. Director of Nursing, Central Prison Hospital, Raleigh, NC, p. A466

MCLEAN, Georgia, Director Human Resources, Mount Sinai Medical Center, Miami Beach, FL, p. A135

MCLENDON, Carla
Director Human Resources, Appling Healthcare System, Baxley, GA, p. A152
Director Information Resource Management Services, Charles George Veterans Affairs Medical Center, Asheville, NC, p. A455

MCLENDON, Connie, Director Human Resources, Piedmont Mountainside Hospital, Jasper, GA, p. A159

MCLENDON, John, Senior Vice President and Chief Information Officer, Adventist Bolingbrook Hospital, Bolingbrook, IL, p. A180

MCLENDON, Tom, Administrator, Evergreen Medical Center, Evergreen, AL, p. A19

MCLENNAN, Marlene, Controller, Monroe County Hospital, Forsyth, GA, p. A157

MCLEOD, Les, Director of Nursing Services, Blue Mountain Hospital, John Day, OR, p. A522

MCLEOD, Margie, Director Information Technology, North Canyon Medical Center, Gooding, ID, p. A174

MCLEOD, Michael, M.D. Chief Medical Officer, Cuero Community Hospital, Cuero, TX, p. A603

MCLEOD, Sheldon, Chief Operating Officer, North Central Bronx Hospital, NY, p. A443

MCLIN, Robert D., President and Chief Executive Officer, Good Samaritan Hospital, Vincennes, IN, p. A221

MCLOONE, J. Mark, FACHE, Chief Executive Officer, St. Christopher's Hospital for Children, Philadelphia, PA, p. A545

MCLOONE, Paul, M.D
Chief Medical Officer, UnityPoint Health – Trinity Bettendorf, Bettendorf, IA, p. A222
Chief Medical Officer, UnityPoint Health – Trinity Rock Island, Rock Island, IL, p. A199

MCMAHAN, Mike, Chief Executive Officer, St. Francis Regional Medical Center, Shakopee, MN, p. A347

MCMAHON, Alisha, Director Human Resources, Mountrail County Medical Center, Stanley, ND, p. A476

MCMAHON, Andrew, Chief Fiscal Officer, Veterans Affairs Central Western Massachusetts Healthcare System, Leeds, MA, p. A308

MCMAHON, Chris, Chief Operating Officer, The Medical Center of Southeast Texas, Port Arthur, TX, p. A637

MCMAHON, Denise, Director People Services, HSHS St. Joseph's Hospital, Chippewa Falls, WI, p. A699

MCMAHON, Elaine, Administrator, Kwajalein Hospital, Kwajalein Island, MH, p. A719

MCMAHON, Leigh, MS Senior Vice President Patient Care Services and Chief Nursing Officer, White Plains Hospital Center, White Plains, NY, p. A454

MCMAHON, Nancy, Vice President Human Resources, Miriam Hospital, Providence, RI, p. A555

MCMANMON, Kristin, Chief Operating Officer, St. Mary's Hospital, Madison, WI, p. A704

MCMANUS, Doug, Chief Medical Officer, Aurora Medical Center Grafton, Grafton, WI, p. A701

MCMANUS, Michael T., Chief Operating Officer, Memorial Hospital, Belleville, IL, p. A179

MCMANUS, Ronald, Senior Vice President Clinical Services and Business Entities, Peconic Bay Medical Center, Riverhead, NY, p. A448

MCMANUS, Tim, President and Chief Executive Officer, Chippenham Hospital, Richmond, VA, p. A671

MCMASTER, Sandra
Regional Chief Information Officer, Kauai Veterans Memorial Hospital, Waimea, HI, p. A171
Regional Chief Information Officer, Samuel Mahelona Memorial Hospital, Kapaa, HI, p. A170

MCMATH, Mark W., Chief Information Officer, Indiana University Health Bloomington Hospital, Bloomington, IN, p. A205

MCMENAMIN, Anneliese, Vice President Human Resources, Kennedy Health System, Cherry Hill, NJ, p. A410

MCMICHEN, Diane, Director Human Resources, DeKalb Regional Medical Center, Fort Payne, AL, p. A20

MCMILLAN, Deborah, Director Human Resources, Glenn Medical Center, Willows, CA, p. A98

MCMILLAN, Don
Chief Information Officer, PeaceHealth Sacred Heart Medical Center University District, Eugene, OR, p. A520
Chief Information Officer, PeaceHealth Southwest Medical Center, Vancouver, WA, p. A687

MCMILLAN, Douglas A., Administrator and Chief Executive Officer, West Park Hospital, Cody, WY, p. A716

MCMILLAN, Jon R., Chief Financial Officer, Banner Lassen Medical Center, Susanville, CA, p. A93

MCMILLAN, Sheila, Chief Financial Officer, Park Nicollet Methodist Hospital, Saint Louis Park, MN, p. A346

MCMILLEN, Eric, Chief Executive Officer, Ochsner Medical Center–Baton Rouge, Baton Rouge, LA, p. A269

MCMINN, Ken, Director Information Technology, Scotland County Hospital, Memphis, MO, p. A372

MCMINN, Melvin, Director Human Resources, Wernersville State Hospital, Wernersville, PA, p. A552

MCMULLAN, Heidi, R.N. Chief Nursing Officer, Philhaven, Mount Gretna, PA, p. A541

MCMULLEN, Ronald B., President, Christian Hospital, Saint Louis, MO, p. A376

MCMULLEN, Thomas A., Chief Financial Officer, Kindred Hospital–Philadelphia, Philadelphia, PA, p. A544

MCMULLIN, John, Chief Financial Officer, Rehoboth McKinley Christian Health Care Services, Gallup, NM, p. A424

MCMURRAY, Sean S., FACHE, Vice President and Chief Executive Officer, Johnston Memorial Hospital, Abingdon, VA, p. A662

MCMURREY, Jean Ann, R.N. Chief Nursing Officer, RMC Jacksonville, Jacksonville, AL, p. A21

MCMURRY, Timothy, Director, Wm. Jennings Bryan Dorn Veterans Affairs Medical Center, Columbia, SC, p. A560

MCNABB, Dana, Human Resources Manager, Field Memorial Community Hospital, Centreville, MS, p. A351

MCNABB, Teresita, R.N. Vice President Nursing Services, Terrebonne General Medical Center, Houma, LA, p. A275

MCNAIR, Lisa, CPA Senior Vice President and Chief Financial Officer, St. Joseph Regional Health Center, Bryan, TX, p. A599

MCNAIR, Scott, Chief Financial Officer, Neshoba County General Hospital, Philadelphia, MS, p. A359

MCNALLY, Joseph, M.D. Medical Director, Streamwood Behavioral Health Center, Streamwood, IL, p. A202

MCNALLY, Kathy, Chief Nursing Officer, HEALTHSOUTH Rehabilitation Hospital at Drake, Cincinnati, OH, p. A483

MCNALLY, Lou-Ann, Director Human Resources, Claxton–Hepburn Medical Center, Ogdensburg, NY, p. A446

MCNALLY, Michael, Vice President Human Resources, United Health Services Hospitals–Binghamton, Binghamton, NY, p. A430

MCNAMARA, John, M.D. Chief Medical Officer, Torrance Memorial Medical Center, Torrance, CA, p. A94

MCNAMARA, Marilyn, M.D. Vice President Medical Affairs, Southwest General Health Center, Middleburg Heights, OH, p. A494

Index of Health Care Professionals / Meeker

Index of Health Care Professionals


MCNAMARA, Mike, Chief Information Officer, Mee Memorial Hospital, King City, CA, p. A66
MCNAMARA, Steve, Chief Financial Officer, Orange Coast Memorial Medical Center, Fountain Valley, CA, p. A62
MCNAMARA, Thomas, D.O. Vice President Medical Affairs, WellStar Cobb Hospital, Austell, GA, p. A152
MCNAMARA, Timothy M.
Senior Vice President Human Resources, Bradford Regional Medical Center, Bradford, PA, p. A530
Senior Vice President Human Resources, Olean General Hospital, Olean, NY, p. A446
MCNAMEE, Hugar, D.O. Chief Medical Officer, Florida Hospital Zephyrhills, Zephyrhills, FL, p. A148
MCNATT, James, Chief Financial Officer, Baylor Medical Center at Carrollton, Carrollton, TX, p. A600
MCNAUGHTON, Richard, Chief Information Management Service, Maine Veterans Affairs Medical Center, Augusta, ME, p. A288
MCNEA, Melvin, Chief Executive Officer, Great Plains Health, North Platte, NE, p. A395
MCNEAR, Michael, M.D. Chief Medical Officer, Jersey Community Hospital, Jerseyville, IL, p. A191
MCNEECE, Steve, Chief Executive Officer, Community Hospital of Anaconda, Anaconda, MT, p. A381
MCNEEL, Jacob, D.O. Chief of Staff, Plateau Medical Center, Oak Hill, WV, p. A693
MCNEEL, Wakelin, M.D. Medical Director, BHC Alhambra Hospital, Rosemead, CA, p. A84
MCNEIL, Ane, Vice President Human Resources, St. Joseph Mercy Oakland, Pontiac, MI, p. A328
MCNEIL, Greg R., Chief Executive Officer, Crittenden County Hospital, Marion, KY, p. A262
MCNEIL, John, President and Chief Executive Officer, Eastern Regional Medical Center, Philadelphia, PA, p. A543
MCNEIL, Karen
Chief Nursing Officer, University Hospitals Conneaut Medical Center, Conneaut, OH, p. A487
Chief Nursing Officer, University Hospitals Geneva Medical Center, Geneva, OH, p. A490
MCNEILL, Michael, Chief Financial Management, New Mexico Veterans Affairs Health Care System – Raymond G. Murphy Medical Center, Albuquerque, NM, p. A422
MCNELIS, John, M.D. Acting Medical Director, Jacobi Medical Center, NY, p. A440
MCNEY, Jim, Senior Vice President Finance and Chief Financial Officer, North Kansas City Hospital, North Kansas City, MO, p. A373
MCNULTY III, Joseph S., President and Chief Executive Officer, Pioneer Health Services, Magee, MS, p. B105
MCNULTY, Stephanie, Chief Operating Officer, St. Petersburg General Hospital, Saint Petersburg, FL, p. A142
MCNULTY, Timothy, Director Human Resources, Spring Harbor Hospital, Westbrook, ME, p. A292
MCNUTT, Mike, Assistant Administrator, Covenant Hospital Plainview, Plainview, TX, p. A636
MCNUTT, Pamela
Vice President Information Systems, Methodist Charlton Medical Center, Dallas, TX, p. A605
Senior Vice President and Chief Information Officer, Methodist Dallas Medical Center, Dallas, TX, p. A606
Senior Vice President and Chief Information Officer, Methodist Mansfield Medical Center, Mansfield, TX, p. A631
MCPEAK, Sara, Chief Nursing Officer, Carlinville Area Hospital, Carlinville, IL, p. A180
MCPHERSON, Brian, Chief Information Officer, Beaumont Hospital – Farmington Hills, Farmington Hills, MI, p. A319
MCPHERSON, Jason, Chief Executive Officer and Managing Director, Anchor Hospital, Atlanta, GA, p. A149
MCPHERSON, Lon, M.D. Senior Vice President Medical Affairs and Chief Quality Officer, Munroe Regional Medical Center, Ocala, FL, p. A137
MCPHERSON, Rhonda, Vice President Human Resources, Fayette Regional Health System, Connersville, IN, p. A206
MCPHERSON, Stephen B., President and Chief Executive Officer, Masonicare Health Center, Wallingford, CT, p. A115
MCQUAIDE, Teresa A., Chief Executive Officer, Trenton Psychiatric Hospital, Trenton, NJ, p. A419
MCQUEEN, Elbert T., President and Chief Executive Officer, Rehabilitation Hospital, Navicent Health, Macon, GA, p. A161
MCQUILLEN, Paul, M.D. Chief Medical Officer, Jane Phillips Medical Center, Bartlesville, OK, p. A504
MCQUISTAN, Bob, Vice President Finance, York General Hospital, York, NE, p. A399
MCQUISTON, Mike, Administrative Director Human Resources, Wise Regional Health System, Decatur, TX, p. A607
MCRAE, Colin, Chief Executive Officer, Tennova Healthcare–Jefferson Memorial Hospital, Jefferson City, TN, p. A579
MCRIMMON, Dana, Chief Financial Officer, Mesilla Valley Hospital, Las Cruces, NM, p. A425
MCROBERTS, Kevin G., FACHE Senior Vice President of Operations, Lake Regional Health System, Osage Beach, MO, p. A374
MCROBERTS, Susan, R.N
Vice President and Chief Nursing Officer, Franciscan St. Francis Health – Indianapolis, Indianapolis, IN, p. A211
Chief Nursing Officer, Franciscan St. Francis Health–Carmel, Carmel, IN, p. A206
MCSHANE, Brian, IT Manager, Lakes Regional Healthcare, Spirit Lake, IA, p. A235
MCTAGGART, Jac, Chief Executive Officer, Sanford Hillsboro Medical Center, Hillsboro, ND, p. A475
MCTIGRIT, Chris, Manager Information Technology, Delta Memorial Hospital, Dumas, AR, p. A43
MCTIGUE, Mary, Vice President Patient Care Services and Chief Nursing Officer, Trinitas Regional Medical Center, Elizabeth, NJ, p. A411
MCTIGUE, Michael
Chief Information Officer, Clara Maass Medical Center, Belleville, NJ, p. A409
Chief Information Officer, Saint Barnabas Medical Center, Livingston, NJ, p. A413
MCVAY, Randy, Chief Executive Officer, Ocala Regional Medical Center, Ocala, FL, p. A137
MCVEIGH, Kevin
Interim Chief Human Resources Officer, Banner Behavioral Health Hospital – Scottsdale, Scottsdale, AZ, p. A37
Chief Human Resources Officer, Banner Desert Medical Center, Mesa, AZ, p. A33
MCVEY, Eric A., M.D. Vice President and Chief Medical Officer, Mississippi Baptist Medical Center, Jackson, MS, p. A355
MCVEY, Lynn, Chief Operating Officer, Meadowlands Hospital Medical Center, Secaucus, NJ, p. A418
MCVEY, Marian, Chief Nursing Officer, North Greenville Hospital, Travelers Rest, SC, p. A565
MCVEY, Patrick, Chief Executive Officer, Select Specialty Hospital–Savannah, Savannah, GA, p. A164
MCVEY, Timothy J., Chief Financial Officer, Mission Regional Medical Center, Mission, TX, p. A633
MCVICKER, Sandra I., MSN, President and Chief Nursing Officer, University Hospital McDuffie, Thomson, GA, p. A166
MCWATTERS, Pearl, Director Information Services, Highland Hospital, Charleston, WV, p. A690
MCWAY, Jacob, Senior Vice President and Chief Financial Officer, Cox Medical Centers, Springfield, MO, p. A378
MCWEY, Russ, M.D. Vice President and Chief Information Officer, Virginia Hospital Center – Arlington, Arlington, VA, p. A662
MCWHERTER, Joe, Chief Financial Officer, Baptist Memorial Hospital–Desoto, Southaven, MS, p. A360
MCWHORTER III, John B., President, Baylor University Medical Center, Dallas, TX, p. A604
MCWILLIAMS, Jill, Chief Nursing Officer, Sierra Nevada Memorial Hospital, Grass Valley, CA, p. A64
MEACHAM, Byanka, Director Human Resources, Montgomery County Emergency Service, Norristown, PA, p. A541
MEACHAM, Sherry, Coordinator Human Resources, Select Specialty Hospital–Winston–Salem, Winston–Salem, NC, p. A471
MEACHAM, Steve, Vice President Finance, King's Daughters' Health, Madison, IN, p. A215
MEACHEM, Michelle, Director Human Resources, The University of Vermont Health Network Elizabethtown Community Hospital, Elizabethtown, NY, p. A433
MEAD, Barbara, Executive Director, Lourdes Counseling Center, Richland, WA, p. A683
MEAD, Linda, Director Human Resources, Margaretville Hospital, Margaretville, NY, p. A437
MEAD, Richard, Senior Director Human Resources, Saint Francis Memorial Hospital, San Francisco, CA, p. A88
MEAD, Rick, Human Resources Leader, Kaiser Permanente Oakland Medical Center, Oakland, CA, p. A78
MEADE, Robert C., Chief Executive Officer, Doctors Hospital of Sarasota, Sarasota, FL, p. A142
MEADE, Stephanie, R.N. Chief Nursing Officer, Mercy Health – West Hospital, Cincinnati, OH, p. A483
MEADE, Teresa, R.N. Chief Nursing Officer, Boone Memorial Hospital, Madison, WV, p. A692
MEADOWS, Barbara, Chief Financial Manager, Captain James A. Lovell Federal Health Care Center, North Chicago, IL, p. A196
MEADOWS, Bethany, Director Human Resources, St. Cloud Regional Medical Center, Saint Cloud, FL, p. A141
MEADOWS, Cheryl, Executive Assistant to the President, TMC Healthcare, Tucson, AZ, p. A40
MEADOWS, Danny, M.D. Medical Director, Logansport State Hospital, Logansport, IN, p. A215
MEADOWS, Hal, M.D. Chief Medical Officer, Banner Lassen Medical Center, Susanville, CA, p. A93
MEADOWS, Mark, Chief Executive Officer, Lone Peak Hospital, Draper, UT, p. A654
MEADOWS, Nancy, Chief Financial Officer, Methodist Hospital, San Antonio, TX, p. A641
MEADOWS, Peri, Director Human Resources, Rhea Medical Center, Dayton, TN, p. A577
MEADOWS, Theresa, Chief Information Officer, Cook Children's Medical Center, Fort Worth, TX, p. A613
MEANS, Dennis, M.D. Vice President Medical Affairs, Carilion New River Valley Medical Center, Christiansburg, VA, p. A663
MEARNS, Stephanie, Vice President Patient Care Services and Chief Nurse Executive, Seton Medical Center, Daly City, CA, p. A59
MEARS, Terry, Director Information Systems, Duke Regional Hospital, Durham, NC, p. A459
MECHAM, Cindy, Health Information Director, Mountain View Hospital, Payson, UT, p. A657
MEDAGLIA, Guy A., President and Chief Executive Officer, Saint Anthony Hospital, Chicago, IL, p. A184
MEDCIROS, Ron, Director Applied Information Technology, Worcester Recovery Center and Hospital, Worcester, MA, p. A313
MEDEIROS, Katherine A., President and Chief Executive Officer, Sierra Nevada Memorial Hospital, Grass Valley, CA, p. A64
MEDEROS, Ana J., Chief Executive Officer, Palmetto General Hospital, Hialeah, FL, p. A128
MEDINA, Alberto, Information Technology Senior Consultant, Hospital Manati Medical Center, Manati, PR, p. A721
MEDINA, Betsmari, Director Human Resources, Dr. Ramon E. Betances Hospital–Mayaguez Medical Center Branch, Mayaguez, PR, p. A722
MEDINA, Ed, M.D. Medical Director, Phillips County Hospital, Malta, MT, p. A385
MEDINA, Eleanor, M.D. Chief Medical Officer, Behavioral Center of Michigan, Warren, MI, p. A332
MEDINA, Luz D., Controller, Hospital Hermanos Melendez, Bayamon, PR, p. A720
MEDINA, Marco, Chief Information Officer, Stanton County Hospital, Johnson, KS, p. A242
MEDINA, Obdulia, MSN Associate Director for Administrative Support, Clinical Management and Ambulatory Care, Ashford Presbyterian Community Hospital, San Juan, PR, p. A723
MEDINA, Patricia, Service Unit Director, U. S. Public Health Service Indian Hospital, Winnebago, NE, p. A399
MEDINA, Shelby, Chief Administrative Officer, Buchanan County Health Center, Independence, IA, p. A229
MEDLAND, Jacqueline, MS Regional Chief Nursing Officer, Presence St. Mary's Hospital, Kankakee, IL, p. A192
MEDLEY, Adron, M.D. Chief Medical Staff, Northern Rockies Medical Center, Cut Bank, MT, p. A382
MEDLEY, Barry, Director Information Systems, Cook Medical Center–A Campus of Tift Regional Medical Center, Adel, GA, p. A149
MEDLEY, Dennis, Administrator, Physicians' Medical Center, New Albany, IN, p. A217
MEDLEY, Wathen, M.D. Chief Medical Officer, Owensboro Health Regional Hospital, Owensboro, KY, p. A264
MEDLIN, John, Chief Nursing Officer, North Carolina Specialty Hospital, Durham, NC, p. A459
MEDLIN, Marsha, Senior Vice President of Clinical and Operations, Post Acute Northshore Specialty Hospital, Covington, LA, p. A272
MEDLOCK, Beth, Manager Information Technology, Jackson Hospital, Marianna, FL, p. A133
MEDLOCK, Darci, Manager Human Resources, St. Vincent Dunn Hospital, Bedford, IN, p. A204
MEDOVICH, Lisa, Chief Financial Officer, Peterson Regional Medical Center, Kerrville, TX, p. A626
MEDUNA, Leo L., M.D. Chief Medical Officer, Saunders Medical Center, Wahoo, NE, p. A398
MEE, Randall L., FACHE, Chief Executive Officer, Blue Mountain Hospital, John Day, OR, p. A522
MEE, Thomas, R.N
Chief Operating Officer, McLaren Greater Lansing, Lansing, MI, p. A324
Vice President Operations, McLaren Lapeer Region, Lapeer, MI, p. A324
MEEHAN, Kenneth L., Interim Chief Operating Officer, Saint John's Health Center, Santa Monica, CA, p. A91
MEEHAN, Neil S., D.O. Chief Medical Officer and Chief Medical Information Officer, Lawrence General Hospital, Lawrence, MA, p. A308
MEEK, Julie, Vice President Finance, Kadlec Regional Medical Center, Richland, WA, p. A683
MEEK, Kevin Lee, R.N. Chief Nursing Officer, Dignity Health Arizona General Hospital, Laveen, AZ, p. A33
MEEKER, Brian, D.O. President Medical Staff, Virginia Gay Hospital, Vinton, IA, p. A235
MEEKER, Chris, M.D. Chief Medical Officer, Sanford Bismarck, Bismarck, ND, p. A472
MEEKER, Christina, Director Human Resources, Strategic Behavioral Health – Raleigh, Garner, NC, p. A460

Index of Health Care Professionals

Index of Health Care Professionals / Meeker


MEEKER, Larry, Chief Executive Officer, Howard A. Rusk Rehabilitation Center, Columbia, MO, p. A366
MEEKER, Mark, D.O. Medical Staff President, OSF St. Mary Medical Center, Galesburg, IL, p. A188
MEEKINS, Lance, Administrator, Nocona General Hospital, Nocona, TX, p. A634
MEEKINS, Michelle, Manager Human Resources, Sentara Virginia Beach General Hospital, Virginia Beach, VA, p. A674
MEEKS, Barbara, MSN Chief Nurse Executive, Nemours Children's Hospital, Orlando, FL, p. A138
MEEKS, Deborah, Chief Nursing Officer, Harlingen Medical Center, Harlingen, TX, p. A617
MEEKS, Derek, D.O. Chief of Staff, Boulder City Hospital, Boulder City, NV, p. A400
MEEKS, Julia M., Chief Operating Officer, Specialty Hospital of Lorain, Amherst, OH, p. A478
MEEKS, Shane, Manager Technology Information Systems, Spectrum Health Gerber Memorial, Fremont, MI, p. A320
MEEKS, Teresa, Chief Nursing Officer, East Texas Medical Center–Quitman, Quitman, TX, p. A638
MEENK, Susan
Vice President Service Area, Providence Centralia Hospital, Centralia, WA, p. A677
Vice President Human Resources, Providence St. Peter Hospital, Olympia, WA, p. A681
MEERT, Tiffany, Chief Operating Officer, Northern Nevada Medical Center, Sparks, NV, p. A404
MEESE, Larry, Chief Executive Officer, Jackson Hospital, Marianna, FL, p. A133
MEESIG, Deborah, M.D. Chief of Staff, Chillicothe Veterans Affairs Medical Center, Chillicothe, OH, p. A482
MEGEHEE, Mark, Vice President and Chief Information Officer, Decatur Morgan Hospital, Decatur, AL, p. A18
MEGGERS, Marla, R.N. Chief Nursing Officer, Gilbert Hospital, Gilbert, AZ, p. A31
MEGLI, Cami, Controller, Morrison Community Hospital, Morrison, IL, p. A195
MEGLIOLA, Donna M., Assistant Vice President, Johnson Memorial Medical Center, Stafford Springs, CT, p. A115
MEGOW, Kimberly, M.D. Chief Medical Officer, South Georgia Medical Center, Valdosta, GA, p. A166
MEGUESS, Kyle, Chief Financial Officer, River Oaks Hospital, New Orleans, LA, p. A282
MEGUIAR, Ramon V., M.D. Chief Medical Officer, Memorial Health, Savannah, GA, p. A164
MEHAFFEY, M. Beth, Vice President Human Resources, Baptist Medical Center Jacksonville, Jacksonville, FL, p. A129
MEHARG, John, Director Health Information Technology, Norman Regional Health System, Norman, OK, p. A510
MEHINDRU, Vinay, M.D
Vice President/Chief Medical Officer, Florida Hospital Waterman, Tavares, FL, p. A145
Medical Director, Wuesthoff Medical Center – Rockledge, Rockledge, FL, p. A141
MEHTA, Kalpana, Chief Fiscal Services, Jesse Brown Veterans Affairs Medical Center, Chicago, IL, p. A182
MEHTA, Sanjiv, Chief of Staff, Flaget Memorial Hospital, Bardstown, KY, p. A254
MEHTA, Sonia, M.D., Chief Executive Officer and Chief Medical Officer, Loretto Hospital, Chicago, IL, p. A182
MEHTA, Steven, M.D. Chief Medical Officer, Canyon Vista Medical Center, Sierra Vista, AZ, p. A38
MEIAR, Cindy, Human Resources and Payroll Coordinator, Trego County–Lemke Memorial Hospital, Wakeeney, KS, p. A252
MEIDINGER, Duane, Vice President Finance, Walla Walla General Hospital, Walla Walla, WA, p. A687
MEIDINGER, Sue, Manager Business Office, Linton Hospital, Linton, ND, p. A475
MEIER, Suzanne S., System Director, Compensation and Human Resources Technology, Memorial Hermann Memorial City Medical Center, Houston, TX, p. A621
MEIERGERD, Jean, Chief Information Officer, St. Francis Memorial Hospital, West Point, NE, p. A399
MEIERS, Dawn, Coordinator Medical Staff and Personnel Services, Southeast Michigan Surgical Hospital, Warren, MI, p. A332
MEIGS, Jeffrey L., Chief Financial Officer, Louis A. Weiss Memorial Hospital, Chicago, IL, p. A182
MEIGS, Jr., John, M.D. Chief of Staff, Bibb Medical Center, Centreville, AL, p. A18
MEINDEL, Nympha, R.N. Chief Information Officer, North Shore University Hospital, Manhasset, NY, p. A437
MEINHART, Richard, Manager Information Systems, Daviess Community Hospital, Washington, IN, p. A221
MEINKE, Kenneth, Senior Vice President Administrative Services, Finance and Chief Financial Officer, Spartanburg Regional Medical Center, Spartanburg, SC, p. A565
MEINKE, Victor E., Chief Financial Officer, Jewish Home of San Francisco, San Francisco, CA, p. A88
MEINKOTH, Jennifer, Chief Information Officer, Memorial Hospital, Belleville, IL, p. A179
MEIS, Fred J., Chief Executive Officer, Kearney County Health Services, Minden, NE, p. A394
MEISINGER, Alan, Chief Financial Officer, Herington Municipal Hospital, Herington, KS, p. A241
MEISNER, Anne, MSN, President and Chief Executive Officer, Southeastern Regional Medical Center, Newnan, GA, p. A162
MEITZ, Mary
Senior Vice President and Chief Financial Officer, Bronson Battle Creek, Battle Creek, MI, p. A315
Vice President Finance, Bronson Methodist Hospital, Kalamazoo, MI, p. A323
MEKHAEL, Hani, M.D. Chief Staff, Havenwyck Hospital, Auburn Hills, MI, p. A314
MELAHN, Will L., M.D. Vice President Medical Affairs and Chief Medical Officer, St. Claire Regional Medical Center, Morehead, KY, p. A263
MELANCON, Eric, Chief of Staff, Teche Regional Medical Center, Morgan City, LA, p. A281
MELANCON, Mary, Chief Financial Officer, Abrom Kaplan Memorial Hospital, Kaplan, LA, p. A276
MELAND, Jeff, M.D. Vice President, Chief Medical Officer, Northfield Hospital, Northfield, MN, p. A344
MELARAGNO, Robert, Vice President Finance, O'Bleness Memorial Hospital, Athens, OH, p. A479
MELBOURNE, John, M.D. Medical Director, Conifer Park, Glenville, NY, p. A434
MELBY, Gina, Chief Executive Officer, JFK Medical Center, Atlantis, FL, p. A121
MELBY, Larry, Chief Executive Officer, Select Specialty Hospital–Palm Beach, Lake Worth, FL, p. A131
MELBY, Rachel, Controller, Crawford County Memorial Hospital, Denison, IA, p. A226
MELCHER, Nancy, Chief Nursing Officer, North Fulton Regional Hospital, Roswell, GA, p. A163
MELCHIODE, Joseph D., Chief Executive Officer, University Hospital and Medical Center, Tamarac, FL, p. A144
MELCHIOR, Eric L., Executive Vice President and Chief Financial Officer, Greater Baltimore Medical Center, Baltimore, MD, p. A293
MELENDEZ, Alma, Controller, Dimmit Regional Hospital, Carrizo Springs, TX, p. A600
MELENDEZ, Pedro
Chief Executive Officer, Centro De Salud Conductual Menonita–CIMA, Aibonito, PR, p. A719
Chief Executive Director, Hospital Menonita De Cayey, Cayey, PR, p. A720
Chief Executive Officer, Mennonite General Hospital, Aibonito, PR, p. A719
MELINE, Brenda, Manager Human Resources, Patients' Hospital of Redding, Redding, CA, p. A82
MELL, Kevin, Vice President Operations, MedStar Montgomery Medical Center, Olney, MD, p. A299
MELLETT, David, Chief Financial Officer, Harrison Memorial Hospital, Cynthiana, KY, p. A256
MELLO, Brett, Chief Information Officer, Cayuga Medical Center at Ithaca, Ithaca, NY, p. A435
MELLO, Paul, Manager Data Processing, Metropolitan State Hospital, Norwalk, CA, p. A78
MELLON, Monte, M.D. Chief of Staff, Catalina Island Medical Center, Avalon, CA, p. A54
MELLON, Stacy, Manager Human Resource, Hillsdale Community Health Center, Hillsdale, MI, p. A322
MELLOR, W. Kimball, M.D. Chief Medical Officer, Whitman Hospital and Medical Center, Colfax, WA, p. A677
MELNIKOFF, Jean, Vice President Human Resources, Kaiser Permanente Medical Center, Honolulu, HI, p. A168
MELSON, Benjamin B., CPA Executive Vice President and Chief Financial Officer, Texas Children's Hospital, Houston, TX, p. A622
MELTON, Anne, Chief Nursing Officer, Sumner Regional Medical Center, Gallatin, TN, p. A578
MELTON, Chad, Chief Executive Officer, Wythe County Community Hospital, Wytheville, VA, p. A675
MELTON, Josh, Chief Information Officer, St. Bernards Medical Center, Jonesboro, AR, p. A46
MELTON, Linda Dickey, Vice President Human Resources, North Arkansas Regional Medical Center, Harrison, AR, p. A45
MELTVEDT, Jr., Robert, M.D. Vice President Medical Affairs, Warren Memorial Hospital, Front Royal, VA, p. A665
MELTZER, David B., Chief Financial Officer, Texas Health Presbyterian Hospital Denton, Denton, TX, p. A608
MELTZER, Neil M., President and Chief Executive Officer, LifeBridge Health, Baltimore, MD, p. B82
MELVILLE, Carol, Director Human Resources, West Houston Medical Center, Houston, TX, p. A623
MELVIN, Daryl, Chief Executive Officer, Hopi Health Care Center, Keams Canyon, AZ, p. A32
MELVIN, Susan, D.O. Chief Medical Officer, Long Beach Memorial Medical Center, Long Beach, CA, p. A68
MENDELOWITZ, Susan, FACHE, President, Administrator and Chief Operating Officer, Bergen Regional Medical Center, Paramus, NJ, p. A416
MENDEZ, Alex A., Executive Vice President of Operations and Chief Financial Officer, Mount Sinai Medical Center, Miami Beach, FL, p. A135
MENDEZ, James, Chief Executive Officer, Kindred Hospital–Dallas, Dallas, TX, p. A605
MENDEZ, Kim K., Ed.D. Chief Nurse Officer, Bellevue Hospital Center, New York, NY, p. A438
MENDEZ, Lincoln S., Chief Executive Officer, Baptist Health South Florida, South Miami Hospital, Miami, FL, p. A134
MENDEZ, Samantha, Human Resources, Freedom Pain Hospital, Scottsdale, AZ, p. A37
MENDIOLA–BALDERAS, Rosie L., Director Information Systems, South Texas Health System, Edinburg, TX, p. A610
MENDIZABAL, Oscar, Chief Nursing Officer, Highlands Regional Rehabilitation Hospital, El Paso, TX, p. A610
MENDOZA, Aniceta, R.N. Chief Nursing Officer, Valley Baptist Medical Center–Brownsville, Brownsville, TX, p. A599
MENDOZA, Carlos, Controller, Baptist Memorial Rehabilitation Hospital, Germantown, TN, p. A578
MENDOZA, Dana, Chief Information Officer, Maui Memorial Medical Center, Wailuku, HI, p. A170
MENDOZA, Jackie, Chief Nursing Officer, CHI Health Nebraska Heart, Lincoln, NE, p. A393
MENDOZA, Joseph
Chief Financial Officer, Hillcrest Hospital Cushing, Cushing, OK, p. A505
Chief Financial Officer, Hillcrest Hospital Henryetta, Henryetta, OK, p. A508
MENDOZA, Joseph, M.D. Medical Director, Porterville Developmental Center, Porterville, CA, p. A81
MENDOZA, Yolanda, Director Human Resources, Rehabilitation Hospital of Southern New Mexico, Las Cruces, NM, p. A425
MENDYKA, Nick, Chief Financial Officer, University of Virginia Medical Center, Charlottesville, VA, p. A663
MENEFEE, Jason J., Chief Financial Officer, McCamey County Hospital District, McCamey, TX, p. A631
MENGE, Penny A., MSN Chief Nursing Officer and Vice President Patient Care Services, Touro Infirmary, New Orleans, LA, p. A282
MENGENHAUSEN, Jeff, Chief Executive Officer, Crook County Medical Services District, Sundance, WY, p. A717
MENGLE, Scott, Vice President Human Resources, St. Joseph Regional Health Network, Reading, PA, p. A548
MENNINGA, Cathy, R.N. Chief Nursing Officer, Ellett Memorial Hospital, Appleton City, MO, p. A363
MENNONNA, Guy, Senior Vice President Human Resources, Bergen Regional Medical Center, Paramus, NJ, p. A416
MENON, Rema, M.D. Clinical Director, Parsons State Hospital and Training Center, Parsons, KS, p. A248
MENOR, Peter, Vice President Operations, Chandler Regional Medical Center, Chandler, AZ, p. A30
MENSCH, Alan, M.D. Senior Vice President Medical Affairs, Plainview Hospital, Plainview, NY, p. A447
MENSEN, Amy, Chief Administrative Officer, Regional Medical Center, Manchester, IA, p. A231
MENTGEN, John, FACHE, President and Chief Executive Officer, Regional West Medical Center, Scottsbluff, NE, p. A398
MENTHCOAST, Lynn, Chief Fiscal Service, Tennessee Valley Healthcare System, Nashville, TN, p. A586
MENTINK, Terri, Chief Financial Officer, Oakland Mercy Hospital, Oakland, NE, p. A395
MENTON, Timothy P., Interim Chief Executive Officer, Lakewood Regional Medical Center, Lakewood, CA, p. A67
MENTZER, Larry, Chief Human Resources Officer, Veterans Affairs Roseburg Healthcare System, Roseburg, OR, p. A525
MENZIE, Sue, R.N. Director Patient Care, Sierra Tucson, Tucson, AZ, p. A40
MERCADO, Gloria, Director of Nursing, Mennonite General Hospital, Aibonito, PR, p. A719
MERCADO, Leda Marta R, Chief Operating Officer, Hospital Menonita De Cayey, Cayey, PR, p. A720
MERCER, David, Coordinator Information Systems, Baptist Memorial Hospital–Union City, Union City, TN, p. A589
MERCER, Shawna, Director Human Resources, Kansas Neurological Institute, Topeka, KS, p. A251
MERCHANT, Deven, M.D. Chief Medical Executive, Sutter Davis Hospital, Davis, CA, p. A59
MERCURI, Ralph, Vice President and Chief Financial Officer, Major Hospital, Shelbyville, IN, p. A220
MEREDITH, James, M.D. Chief of Staff, Forrest City Medical Center, Forrest City, AR, p. A44
MEREDITH, Katie, Chief Nursing Officer, Select Specialty Hospital–Lexington, Lexington, KY, p. A260
MEREDITH, Keith, Chief Operating Officer, Salem Regional Medical Center, Salem, OH, p. A497


**A914** Index of Health Care Professionals 

Index of Health Care Professionals / Miccoli

Index of Health Care Professionals

MEREDITH, Linda, MSN Chief Operating Officer, Scott & White Hospital – Llano, Llano, TX, p. A628
MEREK, Gloria, Director of Nursing, Springfield Hospital Center, Sykesville, MD, p. A300
MERGEN, Lynn M., Chief Executive Officer, Hillcrest Hospital – South, Tulsa, OK, p. A516
MERIDA, Andy, Director Management Information Systems, Fayette Regional Health System, Connersville, IN, p. A206
MERILL, Doug, M.D. Chief Medical Officer, UC Irvine Medical Center, Orange, CA, p. A79
MERILLO, Myra, Supervisor Health Information Management, HEALTHSOUTH Rehabilitation Hospital of Spring Hill, Brooksville, FL, p. A123
MERINGOLO, Francis, Vice President Human Resources, UMass Memorial–Marlborough Hospital, Marlborough, MA, p. A308
MERIWETHER, Wayne, Chief Executive Officer, Twin Lakes Regional Medical Center, Leitchfield, KY, p. A259
MERK, Richard, Executive Vice President, Allegiance Behavioral Health Center of Plainview, Plainview, TX, p. A636
MERKEL, Earl, M.D. Chief of Staff, Russell Regional Hospital, Russell, KS, p. A249
MERKEL, Rebecca, Privacy Officer, Franciscan St. Francis Health–Carmel, Carmel, IN, p. A206
MERKLE, Greg, Director Information Systems, Sheppard Pratt Health System, Baltimore, MD, p. A294
MERKLE, John F.
Deputy Director, Louis Stokes Cleveland Veterans Affairs Medical Center, Cleveland, OH, p. A484
Acting Medical Center Director, Tuscaloosa Veterans Affairs Medical Center, Tuscaloosa, AL, p. A25
MERKLE, Scott, Chief Financial Officer, Fishermen's Hospital, Marathon, FL, p. A132
MERKLER, Michael, Chief of Staff, McKenzie Health System, Sandusky, MI, p. A330
MERKLEY, Jason R., Chief Executive Officer, Brookings Health System, Brookings, SD, p. A567
MERKLIN, Paul, Vice President Finance and Chief Financial Officer, Manchester Memorial Hospital, Manchester, KY, p. A262
MERRED, Mehdi, Chief Executive Officer, Quincy Valley Medical Center, Quincy, WA, p. A682
MERRELL, Angie K., R.N. Chief Nursing Officer, Navarro Regional Hospital, Corsicana, TX, p. A603
MERRENS, Edward J., M.D. Medical Director, Dartmouth–Hitchcock Medical Center, Lebanon, NH, p. A407
MERRIGAN, Mary C., Manager Public Relations, Sanford Vermillion Medical Center, Vermillion, SD, p. A572
MERRILL, Chuck, M.D. Vice President Medical Affairs, Marian Regional Medical Center, Santa Maria, CA, p. A91
MERRILL, Mark H., President and Chief Executive Officer, Valley Health System, Winchester, VA, p. B149
MERRILL, Mark H., President, Winchester Medical Center, Winchester, VA, p. A674
MERRILL, Michael, M.D. Interim Vice President Medical Affairs, United Memorial Medical Center, Batavia, NY, p. A429
MERRILL, Rick W., President and Chief Executive Officer, Cook Children's Medical Center, Fort Worth, TX, p. A613
MERRILL, Stacie, Chief Nursing Officer, Baylor Surgical Hospital at Fort Worth, Fort Worth, TX, p. A613
MERRILL, Stephanie, Chief Financial Officer, University Medical Center, Las Vegas, NV, p. A403
MERRITT, Becky A., Director Human Resources, Houston Methodist St. John Hospital, Nassau Bay, TX, p. A633
MERRITT, Belinda, M.D. Medical Director, HEALTHSOUTH Cane Creek Rehabilitation Hospital, Martin, TN, p. A582
MERRITT, Bradley, M.D. Medical Director, Trinity Mother Frances Rehabilitation Hospital, Tyler, TX, p. A649
MERRITT, Janet, Chief Financial Officer, St. Vincent Williamsport Hospital, Williamsport, IN, p. A221
MERRITT, Tim, Chief Executive Officer, Saint Simons by–the–Sea Hospital, Saint Simons Island, GA, p. A163
MERRITT, Trevor, Director Human Resources, Star Valley Medical Center, Afton, WY, p. A715
MERRY, Duane, Chief Information Officer, Little Falls Hospital, Little Falls, NY, p. A436
MERRYMAN, Angela, Chief Executive Officer, Select Specialty Hospital–McKeesport, McKeesport, PA, p. A539
MERRYMAN, Mary, Regional Director Information Management, CHRISTUS Health Shreveport–Bossier, Shreveport, LA, p. A284
MERRYMAN, Scott
Chief Financial Officer, CHRISTUS Coushatta Health Care Center, Coushatta, LA, p. A272
Chief Financial Officer, CHRISTUS Health Shreveport–Bossier, Shreveport, LA, p. A284
MERRYWELL, Paul, Chief Information Officer, Sycamore Shoals Hospital, Elizabethton, TN, p. A577
MERSON, John, M.D. Chief of Staff, John Muir Medical Center, Concord, Concord, CA, p. A58
MERSON, Wendy, Chief Executive Officer, Windmoor Healthcare of Clearwater, Clearwater, FL, p. A123
MERTZ, John, Chief Information Officer, South Nassau Communities Hospital, Oceanside, NY, p. A446
MESA, Gustavo, Chief Information Officer, San Juan City Hospital, San Juan, PR, p. A724
MESIC, John, M.D. Chief Medical Officer, Sutter Auburn Faith Hospital, Auburn, CA, p. A54
MESKAN, Paula, Director of Nursing, River's Edge Hospital and Clinic, Saint Peter, MN, p. A347
MESORAS, Amber, Chief Human Resources Officer, Veterans Affairs Pittsburgh Healthcare System, Pittsburgh, PA, p. A547
MESSELT, Mary Jo
Senior Human Resources Manager, Mercy Hospital Logan County, Guthrie, OK, p. A507
Manager Human Resources, Mercy Hospital Watonga, Watonga, OK, p. A518
MESSER, Kelly, Director of Finance, Devereux Hospital and Children's Center of Florida, Melbourne, FL, p. A133
MESSERSMITH, Darrell, Director Information Systems, Platte Valley Medical Center, Brighton, CO, p. A100
MESSERSMITH, Scott E., Director Human Resources, Columbus Community Hospital, Columbus, NE, p. A391
MESSINA, Arlene, R.N. Director of Nursing, Riverside Doctors' Hospital, Williamsburg, VA, p. A674
MESSINA, Daniel J., FACHE, President and Chief Executive Officer, Richmond University Medical Center, NY, p. A444
MESSMAN, Catherine, Chief Financial Officer, Mills–Peninsula Health Services, Burlingame, CA, p. A56
MESTAS, Lisa, Chief Nursing Officer and Assistant Administrator Clinical Services, University of South Alabama Medical Center, Mobile, AL, p. A22
MESTER, Sulynn, R.N. Chief Nursing Officer, Childress Regional Medical Center, Childress, TX, p. A600
MESZLER, Lori A., Chief Financial Officer, Helen Hayes Hospital, West Haverstraw, NY, p. A453
METCALF, Angie L., Vice President and Chief Human Resource Officer, Martin Health System, Stuart, FL, p. A143
METCALF, Chris, Director of Nursing, Utah State Hospital, Provo, UT, p. A657
METCALF, Emma, R.N., Director, Lexington Veterans Affairs Medical Center, Lexington, KY, p. A260
METCALF, Kathleen, Chief Information Officer, Samaritan Regional Health System, Ashland, OH, p. A478
METCALF, Peter, M.D. President Medical Staff, Genesis Medical Center, Illini Campus, Silvis, IL, p. A200
METCALFE, Kevan, Chief Executive Officer, Huntington Beach Hospital, Huntington Beach, CA, p. A65
METHE, Joan, Chief Information Officer, Mercy Medical Center, Springfield, MA, p. A311
METHVEN, Jeffrey M., Vice President Ambulatory Services and Chief Human Resources Officer, Saratoga Hospital, Saratoga Springs, NY, p. A450
METHVIN, Jeff, Manager Information Technology, St. Luke Hospital and Living Center, Marion, KS, p. A245
METIKO, Olushola, M.D. Medical Director, Central Prison Hospital, Raleigh, NC, p. A466
METIVIER, Roberta, Vice President Human Resources and Administrator, Western Main Nursing Home, Stephens Memorial Hospital, Norway, ME, p. A291
METRO, Michelle, Vice President Nursing, Cloud County Health Center, Concordia, KS, p. A238
METTEAUER, Ken, Chief Financial Officer, Redmond Regional Medical Center, Rome, GA, p. A163
METZ, Amy, Chief Executive Officer, Regency Hospital of Florence, Florence, SC, p. A561
METZ, Bruce, Ph.D. Senior Vice President and Chief Information Officer, Lahey Hospital & Medical Center, Burlington, Burlington, MA, p. A305
METZ, Carl
Vice President, Ephraim McDowell Fort Logan Hospital, Stanford, KY, p. A266
Vice President Human Resources, Ephraim McDowell Regional Medical Center, Danville, KY, p. A256
METZGER, Alysha, Director Human Resources, Hill Country Memorial Hospital, Fredericksburg, TX, p. A614
METZGER, Cynthia, Chief Nursing and Operations Officer, Little River Memorial Hospital, Ashdown, AR, p. A41
METZGER, Jane, Ph.D. Chief Nursing Officer, Morton Hospital and Medical Center, Taunton, MA, p. A312
METZGER, John, Controller, NorthKey Community Care, Covington, KY, p. A255
MEUER, Lynn, Interim Chief Nursing Officer, Sibley Memorial Hospital, Washington, DC, p. A120
MEURER, Bryan, Director Information Systems, Mat–Su Regional Medical Center, Palmer, AK, p. A29
MEWHIRTER, Michael
Chief Financial Officer, Florida Hospital North Pinellas, Tarpon Springs, FL, p. A145
Vice President Finance and Operations, Fort Hamilton Hospital, Hamilton, OH, p. A491
MEYER, Anthony, M.D. Medical Director, Aurora Psychiatric Hospital, Wauwatosa, WI, p. A713
MEYER, Cameron, Chief Financial Officer, Thayer County Health Services, Hebron, NE, p. A392
MEYER, Cheryl, MSN Director of Nursing, Haven Behavioral Senior Care of Dayton, Dayton, OH, p. A488
MEYER, Cheryl, Director Human Resources, Palmer Lutheran Health Center, West Union, IA, p. A236
MEYER, Chirstopher, D.O. Chief Executive Officer, Holzer Medical Center, Gallipolis, OH, p. A490
MEYER, Christopher, D.O. Chief Executive Officer, Holzer Medical Center – Jackson, Jackson, OH, p. A491
MEYER, Daniel T., President, Aurora BayCare Medical Center, Green Bay, WI, p. A701
MEYER, Eugene W., President and Chief Executive Officer, Lawrence Memorial Hospital, Lawrence, KS, p. A244
MEYER, Francis, Vice President Information Systems Technology, KALEIDA Health, Buffalo, NY, p. A430
MEYER, Gary, M.D. Chief Medical Officer, Grand River Hospital District, Rifle, CO, p. A108
MEYER, Gordon, Director Human Resources, Oakland Regional Hospital, Southfield, MI, p. A330
MEYER, Joe S., Chief Financial Officer, Scott County Hospital, Scott City, KS, p. A250
MEYER, June, MSN Vice President Chief Nursing Officer, Laurel Regional Hospital, Laurel, MD, p. A299
MEYER, Karen, Vice President Finance and Chief Financial Officer, Rush Memorial Hospital, Rushville, IN, p. A219
MEYER, Kurt A.
Chief Human Resource Officer, Saint Joseph Regional Medical Center, Mishawaka, IN, p. A216
Chief Human Resources Officer, Saint Joseph Regional Medical Center–Plymouth Campus, Plymouth, IN, p. A218
MEYER, Lori, Interim Chief Financial Officer, South Peninsula Hospital, Homer, AK, p. A28
MEYER, Mark, Chief Financial Officer, Grady Memorial Hospital, Atlanta, GA, p. A150
MEYER, Morgan, Chief Financial Officer, Howard County Medical Center, Saint Paul, NE, p. A398
MEYER, Nate, Director Finance, Douglas County Hospital, Alexandria, MN, p. A334
MEYER, Philip A., Vice President, Finance, Dearborn County Hospital, Lawrenceburg, IN, p. A214
MEYER, Richard A., Chief Financial Officer, Mary Black Health System – Spartanburg, Spartanburg, SC, p. A565
MEYER, Robert L., President and Chief Executive Officer, Phoenix Children's Hospital, Phoenix, AZ, p. A35
MEYER, Roger, M.D. Chief of Staff, Warren Memorial Hospital, Friend, NE, p. A392
MEYER, Timothy, M.D. Chief of Staff, Memorial Medical Center – Neillsville, Neillsville, WI, p. A707
MEYER, Traci, Director Human Resources and Public Relations Officer, Canyon Vista Medical Center, Sierra Vista, AZ, p. A38
MEYER, Wessel H., M.D., Acting Director, Veterans Affairs Central California Health Care System, Fresno, CA, p. A63
MEYERHOEFER, Todd, M.D. Vice President Medical Affairs, Union Hospital, Dover, OH, p. A489
MEYERS, Audrey, FACHE, President and Chief Executive Officer, Valley Hospital, Ridgewood, NJ, p. A418
MEYERS, Betty, Chief Financial Officer, Crook County Medical Services District, Sundance, WY, p. A717
MEYERS, Larry, Chief Information Officer, Wilson Memorial Hospital, Sidney, OH, p. A497
MEYERS, Mark S., M.D. Chief of Staff, Battle Mountain General Hospital, Battle Mountain, NV, p. A400
MEYERS, Russell, President and Chief Executive Officer, Midland Memorial Hospital, Midland, TX, p. A632
MEYERS, Steve, Director Human Resources, New York Community Hospital, NY, p. A442
MEYERS, William, Chief Information Officer, St. Luke's Hospital, Chesterfield, MO, p. A365
MEZA, Eduardo, M.D. Medical Director, Prairie St. John's, Fargo, ND, p. A473
MEZA, Lourdes, Coordinator Human Resources, Doctors Hospital of West Covina, West Covina, CA, p. A97
MEZOFF, Adam, M.D. Vice President and Chief Medical Officer, Children's Medical Center, Dayton, OH, p. A487
MHERABI, Nader, Senior Vice President and Vice Dean, Chief Information Officer, NYU Langone Medical Center, New York, NY, p. A443
MIANO, Christena, Human Resources Director, Medical Center of Trinity, Trinity, FL, p. A146
MICCOLI, Vinny, Executive Director, Manhattan Psychiatric Center–Ward's Island, New York, NY, p. A441

Index of Health Care Professionals

Index of Health Care Professionals / Michael


MICHAEL, Amy J., Chief Operating Officer, Sullivan County Memorial Hospital, Milan, MO, p. A373
MICHAEL, Don, Vice President, Chief Financial Officer, Jay County Hospital, Portland, IN, p. A218
MICHAEL, Elizabeth, R.N. Vice President Patient Care Services and Chief Nursing Officer, Stillwater Medical Center, Stillwater, OK, p. A515
MICHAELS, Bonnie, R.N. Vice President and Chief Nursing Officer, Hackensack University Medical Center Mountainside, Montclair, NJ, p. A414
MICHAELS, Stephen T., M.D. Chief Operating Officer and Chief Medical Officer, MedStar St. Mary's Hospital, Leonardtown, MD, p. A299
MICHAELSON, Linda, Director Human Resources, Lake District Hospital, Lakeview, OR, p. A522
MICHALEK, Debra, Chief Financial Officer, Fayette Regional Health System, Connersville, IN, p. A206
MICHALSKI, Carrie, President and Chief Executive Officer, RiverView Health, Crookston, MN, p. A337
MICHAUD, Thomas A., Chief Executive Officer, Foundation Surgical Hospital Affiliates, Oklahoma City, OK, p. B57
MICHEL, Diane, Senior Vice President, Chief Nursing Officer, Children's Hospital, New Orleans, LA, p. A281
MICHEL, George J., Chief Operating Officer, Larkin Community Hospital, South Miami, FL, p. A143
MICHEL, Randall, M.D. Chief of Staff, Lompoc Valley Medical Center, Lompoc, CA, p. A68
MICHEL–OGBORN, Deborah, Chief Information Resource Management, North Florida/South Georgia Veteran's Health System, Gainesville, FL, p. A127
MICHELE, Margorie, Chief Human Resources Officer, Penn Presbyterian Medical Center, Philadelphia, PA, p. A544
MICHELEN, Jeannith
Associate Executive Director, Elmhurst Hospital Center, NY, p. A439
Senior Associate Executive Director, Lincoln Medical and Mental Health Center, NY, p. A441
Senior Associate Executive Director, Queens Hospital Center, NY, p. A444
MICHELETTI, Denise D., R.N., Director, Central Virginia Training Center, Madison Heights, VA, p. A667
MICHELETTI, Susan C., Chief Executive Officer, Emanuel Medical Center, Turlock, CA, p. A95
MICHELL, Pamela W., R.N. Vice President, Chief Nursing Officer, Munroe Regional Medical Center, Ocala, FL, p. A137
MICHELSON, Soad, M.D. Senior Medical Director, Clarity Child Guidance Center, San Antonio, TX, p. A640
MICHL, Michelle, Director Human Resources, Mercy Medical Center Mount Shasta, Mount Shasta, CA, p. A76
MICINSKI, Bob, Chief Executive Officer, Middle Tennessee Mental Health Institute, Nashville, TN, p. A585
MICKENS, Walt, FACHE, President and Chief Executive Officer, Queen of the Valley Medical Center, Napa, CA, p. A77
MICKEY, Lauren Jane, M.D. Chief of Staff, P & S Surgical Hospital, Monroe, LA, p. A280
MICKIEWICZ, Nanette, M.D., President, Dominican Hospital, Santa Cruz, CA, p. A91
MIDDENDORF, Bruce, M.D. Chief Medical Officer, St. Mary's Health Care System, Athens, GA, p. A149
MIDDLEBROOKS, Mark, M.D. Medical Director, Noland Hospital Birmingham, Birmingham, AL, p. A16
MIDDLETON, Frank, M.D. Interim Chief Medical Officer, Phoebe Putney Memorial Hospital, Albany, GA, p. A149
MIDDLETON, Jackie, Vice President Human Resources, Methodist Dallas Medical Center, Dallas, TX, p. A606
MIDDLETON, James, MSN Chief Nursing Officer, Knox Community Hospital, Mount Vernon, OH, p. A495
MIDGETT, Steve, R.N. Chief Nursing Officer, HEALTHSOUTH Sugar Land Rehabilitation Hospital, Sugar Land, TX, p. A645
MIDKIFF, Rodney, Chief Executive Officer, AMG Specialty Hospital – Muncie, Muncie, IN, p. A216
MIDKIFF, Stephen L., Chief Executive Officer, Lake Norman Regional Medical Center, Mooresville, NC, p. A465
MIEDLER, Michael, M.D. Chief Medical Officer, Continuing Care Hospital, Lexington, KY, p. A259
MIER, David, Chief Financial Officer, El Paso Children's Hospital, El Paso, TX, p. A610
MIESNER, Gail, Chief Financial Officer, Memorial Hospital, Chester, IL, p. A181
MIGOYA, Carlos A., President and Chief Executive Officer, Jackson Health System, Miami, FL, p. A134
MIHALAKAKOS, Paul, M.D. Chief of Staff, Aurora Medical Center – Manitowoc County, Two Rivers, WI, p. A712
MIKELL, Evarista, Assistant Finance Officer, William S. Middleton Memorial Veterans Hospital, Madison, WI, p. A704
MIKELL, Jeffrey, M.D. Chief Medical Officer, Select Specialty Hospital – Northeast Atlanta, Atlanta, GA, p. A151
MIKHAIL, Ashraf, M.D. Medical Director, Brynn Marr Hospital, Jacksonville, NC, p. A463
MIKI, Nobuyuki, M.D. Vice President Medical Services and Chief Medical Officer, Kuakini Medical Center, Honolulu, HI, p. A168
MIKITARIAN Jr., George, Chief Executive Officer, Parrish Medical Center, Titusville, FL, p. A146
MIKITKA, Joseph, Vice President Human Resources, Sacred Heart Hospital, Allentown, PA, p. A528
MIKKELSON, Tom, M.D. Interim Chief Operating Officer, Touchette Regional Hospitals, Centreville, IL, p. A181
MIKLAVIC, Kirk
Director Human Resources, Bridgton Hospital, Bridgton, ME, p. A289
Director, Human Resources, Central Maine Medical Center, Lewiston, ME, p. A290
MIKLOS, Maggie, Director Human Resources, Northside Hospital, Saint Petersburg, FL, p. A142
MIKULA, Joan, Interim Commissioner, Massachusetts Department of Mental Health, Boston, MA, p. B86
MIKULIC, Jeannie
Director Human Resources, Providence Milwaukie Hospital, Milwaukie, OR, p. A523
Director Human Resources, Providence Portland Medical Center, Portland, OR, p. A524
MIKUTOWSKI, Melody, Chief Human Resources Management, Portland Veterans Affairs Medical Center, Portland, OR, p. A524
MILAM, Wendy, Chief Nursing Officer, HEALTHSOUTH Rehabilitation Hospital of Ocala, Ocala, FL, p. A136
MILAN, Isabel, R.N. Chief Nursing Officer, LAC/University of Southern California Medical Center, Los Angeles, CA, p. A71
MILAND, Shelly
Group Finance Officer, Texas Health Harris Methodist Hospital Cleburne, Cleburne, TX, p. A601
Group Financial Officer, Texas Health Harris Methodist Hospital Fort Worth, Fort Worth, TX, p. A614
MILANES, Carlos R., Interim Chief Executive Officer, Edgefield County Hospital, Edgefield, SC, p. A560
MILANO, Arthur D., Vice President Human Resources, Berkshire Medical Center, Pittsfield, MA, p. A310
MILATOVICH, Natasha, Association Vice President Human Resources, White Memorial Medical Center, Los Angeles, CA, p. A73
MILAZZO, John, Chief Financial Officer, Merit Health River Region, Vicksburg, MS, p. A361
MILBRANDT, David, M.D. Vice President Medical Affairs, Fairview Lakes Health Services, Wyoming, MN, p. A349
MILBRIDGE, Daniel, Administrator and Chief Operating Officer, Essentia Health–Virginia, Virginia, MN, p. A348
MILBURN, Sandra, Director Human Resources, HEALTHSOUTH Rehabilitation Hospital of Memphis, Memphis, TN, p. A583
MILBURN, Sharon, Chief Nursing Officer, Summers County ARH Hospital, Hinton, WV, p. A691
MILES, Ben, President, Parkview Regional Medical Center, Fort Wayne, IN, p. A209
MILES, Dana, Chief Nursing Officer and Chief Clinical Officer, Delta Memorial Hospital, Dumas, AR, p. A43
MILES, David K., President and Chief Executive Officer, The Children's Institute of Pittsburgh, Pittsburgh, PA, p. A546
MILES, John, Chief Financial Officer, Piedmont Newnan Hospital, Newnan, GA, p. A162
MILES, Karen, M.D. Medical Director, Strategic Behavioral Health – Raleigh, Garner, NC, p. A460
MILES, Kerry
Site Director, Providence Centralia Hospital, Centralia, WA, p. A677
Chief Information Officer, Providence St. Peter Hospital, Olympia, WA, p. A681
MILES, Lee Ann, Chief Financial Officer, Harrison County Community Hospital, Bethany, MO, p. A363
MILES, Paul V.
Interim Community Chief Executive Officer, Harlan ARH Hospital, Harlan, KY, p. A258
Chief Operating Officer, Morgan County ARH Hospital, West Liberty, KY, p. A266
Vice President Administration, Whitesburg ARH Hospital, Whitesburg, KY, p. A266
MILES, Senta, Director Human Resources, Medical Center of McKinney, McKinney, TX, p. A632
MILETO, Dottie, Chief Nursing Officer, Heart of Florida Regional Medical Center, Davenport, FL, p. A125
MILEY, Dennis C., Administrator, CentraCare Health–Paynesville, Paynesville, MN, p. A344
MILIAN, Tony, Chief Financial Officer, Palm Springs General Hospital, Hialeah, FL, p. A128
MILICEVIC, Heather, Director Human Resources, Summa Western Reserve Hospital, Cuyahoga Falls, OH, p. A487
MILIUS, Hank A., Chief Executive Officer, Meridian Health Services, Muncie, IN, p. A216
MILLAN, Wilfredo Rabelo, Chief Operating Officer, Cardiovascular Center of Puerto Rico and the Caribbean, San Juan, PR, p. A723
MILLARD, James M., President and Chief Executive Officer, Kenmore Mercy Hospital, Kenmore, NY, p. A436
MILLEN, Peter S., Chief Medical Officer MHSATS, Community Behavioral Health Hospital – Rochester, Rochester, MN, p. A345
MILLER, Alan B., Chairman and Chief Executive Officer, Universal Health Services, Inc., King of Prussia, PA, p. B141
MILLER, Alicia, Director Human Resources, Aspen Valley Hospital District, Aspen, CO, p. A99
MILLER, Andy, Chief Financial Officer, Memorial Hospital Jacksonville, Jacksonville, FL, p. A129
MILLER, Barbara, Manager Business Office, Regional General Hospital, Williston, FL, p. A147
MILLER, Ben, Chief Executive Officer, AMG Specialty Hospital–Lafayette, Lafayette, LA, p. A277
MILLER, Blaine K., Administrator, Republic County Hospital, Belleville, KS, p. A237
MILLER, Brent R., Manager Human Resources, Brown County Community Treatment Center, Green Bay, WI, p. A702
MILLER, Carol R., R.N. Chief Nursing Officer, Reynolds Memorial Hospital, Glen Dale, WV, p. A691
MILLER, Carrie, Director Human Resources, ProMedica Defiance Regional Hospital, Defiance, OH, p. A488
MILLER, Chad, Chief Financial Officer, Bolivar Medical Center, Cleveland, MS, p. A352
MILLER, Chad J., President and Chief Executive Officer, Morrow County Hospital, Mount Gilead, OH, p. A495
MILLER, Charles F., Chief Executive Officer, Regional Hospital of Jackson, Jackson, TN, p. A579
MILLER, Christine
General Counsel and Vice President Human Resources, Hanover Hospital, Hanover, PA, p. A535
Chief Human Resources Management Services, Maine Veterans Affairs Medical Center, Augusta, ME, p. A288
MILLER, Connie, Vice President Human Resources, Overland Park Regional Medical Center, Overland Park, KS, p. A248
MILLER, Daniel
Chief Operating Officer, Swedish Medical Center, Englewood, CO, p. A103
Vice President Human Resources, University Hospitals Elyria Medical Center, Elyria, OH, p. A489
Vice President Human Resources, University Hospitals Parma Medical Center, Parma, OH, p. A496
MILLER, David L., Chief Information Officer, UAMS Medical Center, Little Rock, AR, p. A47
MILLER, David R., President, River Falls Area Hospital, River Falls, WI, p. A710
MILLER, David T., Vice President and Chief Financial Officer, Children's Medical Center, Dayton, OH, p. A487
MILLER, Debra, Administrator, Crosbyton Clinic Hospital, Crosbyton, TX, p. A603
MILLER, Denise K., M.D. Chief Medical Officer, Menorah Medical Center, Overland Park, KS, p. A248
MILLER, Derek, Senior Vice President and Chief Financial Officer, Southeast Alabama Medical Center, Dothan, AL, p. A19
MILLER, Diane, Chief Executive Officer, Peterson Rehabilitation Hospital, Wheeling, WV, p. A696
MILLER, Dionne, Chief Operating Officer, Sutter Roseville Medical Center, Roseville, CA, p. A84
MILLER, Donald L., FACHE Vice President, Operations, St. Luke's Hospital, Chesterfield, MO, p. A365
MILLER, Douglas, M.D. Chief of Medical Staff, Clearview Regional Medical Center, Monroe, GA, p. A161
MILLER, Duane
Chief Financial Officer, Integris Bass Baptist Health Center, Enid, OK, p. A506
Chief Financial Officer, Integris Bass Pavilion, Enid, OK, p. A506
MILLER, Eileen, Director Human Resources, Northern Dutchess Hospital, Rhinebeck, NY, p. A448
MILLER, Elaine G., Director of Nursing, Oaklawn Psychiatric Center, Goshen, IN, p. A210
MILLER, Elizabeth, CPA Chief Financial Officer, Stamford Memorial Hospital, Stamford, TX, p. A645
MILLER, Gary L.
Senior Director Information Systems, Saint Joseph Regional Medical Center, Mishawaka, IN, p. A216
Regional Director Information Systems, Saint Joseph Regional Medical Center–Plymouth Campus, Plymouth, IN, p. A218
MILLER, Greg, Senior Vice President Operations, UF Health Jacksonville, Jacksonville, FL, p. A130
MILLER, Harvey, Director, G. Werber Bryan Psychiatric Hospital, Columbia, SC, p. A559


A916 Index of Health Care Professionals 

Index of Health Care Professionals / Mims

Index of Health Care Professionals

MILLER, J. D., M.D
Chief Medical Officer, Hazard ARH Regional Medical Center, Hazard, KY, p. A258
Vice President Medical Affairs, Morgan County ARH Hospital, West Liberty, KY, p. A266
Vice President Medical Affairs, Tug Valley ARH Regional Medical Center, South Williamson, KY, p. A266
MILLER, J. Todd, Vice President and Chief Operating Officer, Alice Peck Day Memorial Hospital, Lebanon, NH, p. A406
MILLER, James, Interim Chief Executive Officer, Alliance Health Center, Meridian, MS, p. A357
MILLER, James, CPA Chief Financial Officer, Regional Medical Center of Acadiana, Lafayette, LA, p. A278
MILLER, James L., Chief Financial Officer, Baptist Medical Center Yazoo, Yazoo City, MS, p. A362
MILLER, Jane E.
Director Human Resources, Avera Creighton Hospital, Creighton, NE, p. A391
Human Resources Officer, Avera Sacred Heart Hospital, Yankton, SD, p. A573
MILLER, Jason, M.P.H., Chief Executive Officer, The BridgeWay, North Little Rock, AR, p. A49
MILLER, Jason R., Chief Financial Officer, The Medical Center of Southeast Texas, Port Arthur, TX, p. A637
MILLER, Jeff, Chief Operating Officer, Citizens Memorial Hospital, Bolivar, MO, p. A363
MILLER, Jeff, M.D. Chief of Staff, Parkview Wabash County Hospital, Wabash, IN, p. A221
MILLER, Jeri, M.D. President Medical Staff, Fairview Park Hospital, Dublin, GA, p. A156
MILLER, John, Director Human Resources, Day Kimball Hospital, Putnam, CT, p. A114
MILLER, Jon, Director Accounting and Information Services, Hancock Regional Hospital, Greenfield, IN, p. A210
MILLER, Joshua, Director Information Systems, Joint Township District Memorial Hospital, Saint Marys, OH, p. A497
MILLER, Joy, Chief Nursing Officer, Cornerstone Hospital of North Little Rock, Jacksonville, AR, p. A46
MILLER, Julie, Chief Operating Officer, Williamson Medical Center, Franklin, TN, p. A578
MILLER, Ken
Chief Financial Officer, CHI St. Luke's Health Memorial Livingston, Livingston, TX, p. A628
Chief Financial Officer, CHI St. Luke's Health Memorial Specialty Hospital, Lufkin, TX, p. A630
MILLER, Kimberly J., FACHE, Chief Executive Officer, Beaver Dam Community Hospitals, Beaver Dam, WI, p. A698
MILLER, Kris, Senior Human Resources Business Partner, Spectrum Health Reed City Hospital, Reed City, MI, p. A328
MILLER, Laura L., MSN Chief Nursing Officer, Lakeway Regional Medical Center, Lakeway, TX, p. A627
MILLER, Laurie, Administrative Assistant, Sakakawea Medical Center, Hazen, ND, p. A474
MILLER, Leanne R., Director Human Resources, Community Hospital, McCook, NE, p. A394
MILLER, Linda, R.N. Senior Vice President Operations and Chief Nursing Officer, Our Lady of Lourdes Memorial Hospital, Inc., Binghamton, NY, p. A429
MILLER, Lisa, Director Human Resources, Hendry Regional Medical Center, Clewiston, FL, p. A124
MILLER, Lisa, R.N. Director of Nursing, North Sunflower Medical Center, Ruleville, MS, p. A360
MILLER, Mark, Chief Financial Officer, Freeman Regional Health Services, Freeman, SD, p. A569
MILLER, Mark, FACHE, Chief Executive Officer, Lake City Medical Center, Lake City, FL, p. A131
MILLER, Mark, Director Information Systems, Perry County Memorial Hospital, Tell City, IN, p. A220
MILLER, Mark A., FACHE, Chief Executive Officer, Memorial Health System, Abilene, KS, p. A237
MILLER, Mary, Vice President Finance and Business Development, Mt. Washington Pediatric Hospital, Baltimore, MD, p. A294
MILLER, Mary Beth, M.D. Chief of Staff, Cheyenne County Hospital, Saint Francis, KS, p. A249
MILLER, Mathew, M.D. Vice President and Chief Medical Officer, St. Joseph Hospital, Eureka, CA, p. A60
MILLER, Matthew, M.D. Chief Medical Officer – WCHN, Danbury Hospital, Danbury, CT, p. A111
MILLER, Melissa, Director Human Resources, St. Elizabeth Hospital, Gonzales, LA, p. A274
MILLER, Michael J.
Director Human Resources, Barnes–Jewish St. Peters Hospital, Saint Peters, MO, p. A378
Director Human Resources, Progress West Hospital, O'Fallon, MO, p. A374
MILLER, Michele A., R.N. Vice President, Acute and Nursing Services, University Behavioral Healthcare, Piscataway, NJ, p. A417
MILLER, Nancy, R.N. Chief Nursing Officer, Van Matre HealthSouth Rehabilitation Hospital, Rockford, IL, p. A200
MILLER, Nicole, Director Human Resources, Riverside Shore Memorial Hospital, Nassawadox, VA, p. A668
MILLER, Patrick, Technology Coordinator, San Bernardino Mountains Community Hospital District, Lake Arrowhead, CA, p. A67
MILLER, Paul, Director of Operations, Sanford Chamberlain Medical Center, Chamberlain, SD, p. A567
MILLER, Peter, Interim Chief Executive Officer, Vibra Hospital of Richmond, Richmond, VA, p. A672
MILLER, Redonda G., M.D. Vice President Medical Affairs, Johns Hopkins Hospital, Baltimore, MD, p. A293
MILLER, Richard, Administrator Finance, Banner Thunderbird Medical Center, Glendale, AZ, p. A32
MILLER, Richard P., Chief Executive Officer, Virtua Health, Marlton, NJ, p. B151
MILLER, Rick
Chief Financial Officer, District One Hospital, Faribault, MN, p. A338
President and Chief Operating Officer, Nationwide Children's Hospital, Columbus, OH, p. A486
MILLER, Rip, Chief Executive Officer, The Hospital at Westlake Medical Center, Austin, TX, p. A595
MILLER, II, Robert R., Chief Operating Officer, Kings County Hospital Center, NY, p. A440
MILLER, Rod, Chief Information Technology, Community Hospital, Torrington, WY, p. A718
MILLER, Ronald, M.D. Chief Medical Officer, North Valley Hospital, Whitefish, MT, p. A388
MILLER, Sam, Chief Executive Officer, North Sunflower Medical Center, Ruleville, MS, p. A360
MILLER, Scott
Director Information Services, Forrest City Medical Center, Forrest City, AR, p. A44
Chief Financial Officer, West Springs Hospital, Grand Junction, CO, p. A104
MILLER, Shane
Chief Information Officer, St. Mary's Hospital Medical Center, Green Bay, WI, p. A702
Chief Information Officer, St. Nicholas Hospital, Sheboygan, WI, p. A711
Chief Information Officer, St. Vincent Hospital, Green Bay, WI, p. A702
MILLER, Stacy, Entity Human Resources Officer, Texas Health Presbyterian Hospital Dallas, Dallas, TX, p. A606
MILLER, Steve
Director Information Systems, Baptist Medical Center South, Montgomery, AL, p. A22
Chief Information Officer, Oklahoma Heart Hospital, Oklahoma City, OK, p. A512
MILLER, Steven, Chief Financial Officer, Takoma Regional Hospital, Greeneville, TN, p. A578
MILLER, Susan, Financial Administrator, Faulkton Area Medical Center, Faulkton, SD, p. A568
MILLER, Suzanne, R.N. Senior Director Patient Care Services and Nursing, St. Luke's Wood River Medical Center, Ketchum, ID, p. A174
MILLER, Tamara, R.N., Administrator, Madison Community Hospital, Madison, SD, p. A569
MILLER, Ted, Chief Financial Officer, Floyd Memorial Hospital and Health Services, New Albany, IN, p. A217
MILLER, Thomas, M.D
Chief Medical Officer, Cameron Memorial Community Hospital, Angola, IN, p. A204
Medical Director, University of Utah Health Care – Hospital and Clinics, Salt Lake City, UT, p. A659
MILLER, Tim C., M.D. Vice President, Chief Medical Officer and Director Academy Affairs, OSF Saint Francis Medical Center, Peoria, IL, p. A198
MILLER, Trey, Chief Executive Officer, Cambridge Hospital in Houston, Houston, TX, p. A619
MILLER, Valerie L., MSN Director of Nursing, Major Hospital, Shelbyville, IN, p. A220
MILLER, Wanda, R.N. Director of Clinical Services, Asheville Specialty Hospital, Asheville, NC, p. A455
MILLER, William, Coordinator Management Information Systems, Livengrin Foundation, Bensalem, PA, p. A529
MILLER–BALFOUR, Pam, Director Human Resources, Socorro General Hospital, Socorro, NM, p. A427
MILLER–CAMPBELL, Michele, Chief Financial Officer, HSHS St. Clare Memorial Hospital, Oconto Falls, WI, p. A708
MILLER–COLLETTE, Melody M., Director Human Resources, North Okaloosa Medical Center, Crestview, FL, p. A124
MILLERMAIER, Ed, M.D
Chief Medical Officer, Bellin Memorial Hospital, Green Bay, WI, p. A701
Chief Medical Officer, Bellin Psychiatric Center, Green Bay, WI, p. A702
MILLIGAN, Jan, Chief Nursing Officer, Cook Children's Northeast Hospital, Hurst, TX, p. A624
MILLIGAN, Jeffrey, Director, Veterans Affairs North Texas Health Care System, Dallas, TX, p. A607
MILLIGAN, John D., Vice President Finance and Chief Financial Officer, Oneida Healthcare, Oneida, NY, p. A446
MILLIS, David, M.D. Clinical Director, Thomas B. Finan Center, Cumberland, MD, p. A297
MILLS, Bryan A., President and Chief Executive Officer, Community Health Network, Indianapolis, IN, p. B34
MILLS, Craig
Chief Financial Officer, Heber Valley Medical Center, Heber City, UT, p. A655
Senior Financial Advisor, Park City Medical Center, Park City, UT, p. A657
Regional Vice President Culture and People, PeaceHealth Sacred Heart Medical Center at RiverBend, Springfield, OR, p. A526
Vice President Human Resources, PeaceHealth Sacred Heart Medical Center University District, Eugene, OR, p. A520
MILLS, Dennis, Director Human Resources, San Ramon Regional Medical Center, San Ramon, CA, p. A90
MILLS, Gene, Director Information Technology, Scenic Mountain Medical Center, Big Spring, TX, p. A597
MILLS, Jerry, Chief Human Resources Management Services, San Francisco VA Medical Center, San Francisco, CA, p. A88
MILLS, Jim, Regional Director Information Technology, Sutter Medical Center, Sacramento, Sacramento, CA, p. A85
MILLS, John C., Senior Vice President Operations, Fairview Hospital, Cleveland, OH, p. A484
MILLS, John E.H., President and Chief Executive Officer, United Medical Healthwest–New Orleans, Gretna, LA, p. A274
MILLS, John E.H., President & Chief Executive Officer, United Medical Rehabilitation Hospitals, Gretna, LA, p. B139
MILLS, Marianne, R.N. Chairperson, Stanton County Hospital, Johnson, KS, p. A242
MILLS, Nikki, Director Human Resources and Operations, Buffalo Hospital, Buffalo, MN, p. A336
MILLS, Scott, M.D. Vice President Medical Staff Administration and Chief Medical Officer, Mid Coast Hospital, Brunswick, ME, p. A289
MILLS, Sean, Chief Financial Officer, Samaritan Medical Center, Watertown, NY, p. A453
MILLS, Stephen S., President and Chief Executive Officer, New York–Presbyterian/Queens, NY, p. A443
MILLS, Vicki L., Chief Financial Officer, Anderson County Hospital, Garnett, KS, p. A240
MILLS, William, M.D
Senior Vice President Quality and Professional Affairs, Bradford Regional Medical Center, Bradford, PA, p. A530
Senior Vice President Quality and Professional Affairs, Olean General Hospital, Olean, NY, p. A446
MILLS, William H., Director, James E. Van Zandt Veterans Affairs Medical Center, Altoona, PA, p. A528
MILLS–MATHEWS, Marcy, Director Human Resources, Palms West Hospital, Loxahatchee, FL, p. A132
MILLSAPS, Janet
Chief Human Resources Officer, Harris Regional Hospital, Sylva, NC, p. A469
Vice President Human Resources, Haywood Regional Medical Center, Clyde, NC, p. A458
MILLSTEAD, Bart, Administrator, Memorial Hospital of Carbondale, Carbondale, IL, p. A180
MILLWOOD, Barbara, Chief Executive Officer, Victory Medical Center Mid–Cities, Hurst, TX, p. A624
MILNE, C. Dean, D.O. Medical Director, Complex Care Hospital at Tenaya, Las Vegas, NV, p. A401
MILNER, Rene, Chief Medical Officer, Osceola Medical Center, Osceola, WI, p. A708
MILONE, Sheri, Chief Executive Officer and Administrator, Lovelace Women's Hospital, Albuquerque, NM, p. A422
MILOVICH, David, Vice President Human Resources, Saint Mary's Regional Medical Center, Reno, NV, p. A404
MILSTIEN, Kim S., Chief Executive Officer, Ventura County Medical Center, Ventura, CA, p. A96
MILTON, Kerry K., R.N. Chief Nursing Officer, St. Tammany Parish Hospital, Covington, LA, p. A272
MILTON, Paul A., Executive Vice President and Chief Operating Officer, Ellis Hospital, Schenectady, NY, p. A450
MILTON, S. Byron, M.D. Medical Director, Emory Rehabilitation Hospital, Atlanta, GA, p. A150
MILUS, Lori, R.N. Director of Nursing, Aurora Behavioral Health System West, Glendale, AZ, p. A32
MILVET, Jr., Robert W., Chief Financial Officer, Preston Memorial Hospital, Kingwood, WV, p. A692
MIMOSO, Michael, FACHE, Interim Chief Executive Officer, Community Medical Center, Toms River, NJ, p. A419
MIMS, Staci, Chief Nursing Officer, Dorminy Medical Center, Fitzgerald, GA, p. A157

© 2015 AHA Guide Index of Health Care Professionals A917

Index of Health Care Professionals

Index of Health Care Professionals / Mims

MIMS, Tammy, Chief Operating Officer, Effingham Hospital, Springfield, GA, p. A165
MINARD, Keith, Chief Information Officer, Chinese Hospital, San Francisco, CA, p. A88
MINCY, Lowney, Director Information Services, Southside Hospital, Bay Shore, NY, p. A429
MINDEN, Philip, Chief Executive Officer, Bartow Regional Medical Center, Bartow, FL, p. A121
MINDER, Cindy, Coordinator Information Systems, Wagner Community Memorial Hospital Avera, Wagner, SD, p. A572
MINEAR, Michael N., Chief Information Officer, University of California, Davis Medical Center, Sacramento, CA, p. A85
MINEAU, Francine, Chief Nursing Officer, Baton Rouge Behavioral Hospital, Baton Rouge, LA, p. A269
MINER, Edwina A., R.N. Chief Nursing Officer, Ennis Regional Medical Center, Ennis, TX, p. A612
MINER, Greg, Administrator, Siouxland Surgery Center, Dakota Dunes, SD, p. A568
MINER, John, Chief Financial Officer, Kindred Hospital Central Tampa, Tampa, FL, p. A145
MINGLE, Regina, Senior Vice President and Chief Leadership Officer, Lancaster General Health, Lancaster, PA, p. A537
MINGS, William, M.D. Medical Director, Carl Albert Community Mental Health Center, McAlester, OK, p. A509
MINGUS, Linda, Director Human Resources, Aurora Medical Center of Oshkosh, Oshkosh, WI, p. A708
MINICK, Mark J., President and Chief Executive Officer, Van Wert County Hospital, Van Wert, OH, p. A499
MINIER, Mary, Vice President Operations, Indiana University Health White Memorial Hospital, Monticello, IN, p. A216
MINIOR, Devin, M.D
Chief Medical Officer, Banner Casa Grande Medical Center, Casa Grande, AZ, p. A30
Interim Chief Medical Officer, Banner Goldfield Medical Center, Apache Junction, AZ, p. A30
MINISSALE, Joseph, President, Methodist McKinney Hospital, McKinney, TX, p. A632
MINKOFF, Daniel B., Interim Chief Executive Officer, Lucas County Health Center, Chariton, IA, p. A224
MINKS, Mike, Chief Information Officer, Seton Edgar B. Davis Hospital, Luling, TX, p. A630
MINNICK, Paul E., MSN, Chief Operating Officer, Bayonne Medical Center, Bayonne, NJ, p. A409
MINNICK, Peggy, R.N., Chief Executive Officer, BHC Alhambra Hospital, Rosemead, CA, p. A84
MINNIS, Rosanne, Business Officer, Rochester Psychiatric Center, Rochester, NY, p. A449
MINON, Maria, M.D
Vice President Medical Affairs and Chief Medical Officer, Children's Hospital of Orange County, Orange, CA, p. A79
Vice President Medical Affairs and Chief Medical Officer, CHOC Children's at Mission Hospital, Mission Viejo, CA, p. A75
MINOR, Amy, Chief Nursing Officer, Troy Regional Medical Center, Troy, AL, p. A25
MINOR, Athena, Chief Nursing Officer, Ohio County Hospital, Hartford, KY, p. A258
MINOR, Beverly, Chief Human Resources, Schleicher County Medical Center, Eldorado, TX, p. A612
MINOR, Blaine, M.D. Chief of Staff, Murray Medical Center, Chatsworth, GA, p. A153
MINOR, Denise, R.N. Chief Nursing Officer, Lutheran Hospital, Cleveland, OH, p. A485
MINSINGER, Linda, Vice President Hospital Division, Gifford Medical Center, Randolph, VT, p. A661
MINTON, Tamra, R.N. Vice President Patient Care Services and Chief Nursing Officer, UPMC East, Monroeville, PA, p. A540
MINTONYE, Traci, Chief Financial Officer, River Hospital, Alexandria Bay, NY, p. A428
MINTZ, Michael, M.D. Chief Medical Officer, South Texas Surgical Hospital, Corpus Christi, TX, p. A603
MIR, Sidney, M.D. Vice President Medical Affairs and Chief Medical Officer, Bon Secours Baltimore Health System, Baltimore, MD, p. A293
MIRABELLA, Ilene, Director Human Resources, New Bedford Rehabilitation Hospital, New Bedford, MA, p. A309
MIRANDA, A. Greg, D.O. President Medical Staff, HSHS St. Joseph's Hospital, Highland, IL, p. A190
MIRANDA, Ada S., M.D. Medical Director, Hospital Metropolitano Dr. Susoni, Arecibo, PR, p. A720
MIRANDA, Ivette, Chief Executive Officer, HEALTHSOUTH Rehabilitation Hospital at Martin Health, Stuart, FL, p. A143
MIRANDA, Juliet, Chief Nursing Officer, Gardens Regional Hospital and Medical Center, Hawaiian Gardens, CA, p. A64
MIRANDA, Kimberly
Chief Financial Officer, Mercy Medical Center Mount Shasta, Mount Shasta, CA, p. A76
Regional Vice President Finance and Chief Financial Officer, Mercy Medical Center Redding, Redding, CA, p. A82
MIRANDA, Michael, Chief of Staff, Mercy Hospital Booneville, Booneville, AR, p. A42
MIRANDA, Vicki, Vice President Human Resources, Dominican Hospital, Santa Cruz, CA, p. A91
MIRANDA, Victor Hernandez, M.D. Chief of Staff, Mennonite General Hospital, Aibonito, PR, p. A719
MIRDITA, Anthony, Chief Financial Officer, Putnam Hospital Center, Carmel, NY, p. A431
MIRISOLA, Virginia, Fiscal Director, Spaulding Hospital for Continuing Medical Care North Shore, Salem, MA, p. A311
MIRZA, Irfan, Chief Financial Officer, Plantation General Hospital, Plantation, FL, p. A140
MIRZABEGIAN, Edward
Chief Executive Officer, Garden Grove Hospital and Medical Center, Garden Grove, CA, p. A63
Chief Executive Officer, Glendora Community Hospital, Glendora, CA, p. A64
MISERENDINO, Carole, MS
Vice President Patient Care Services and Chief Nursing Officer, Community First Medical Center, Chicago, IL, p. A181
Chief Nursing Officer, Presence Holy Family Medical Center, Des Plaines, IL, p. A186
MISHKIND, Steven, M.D. Chief of Staff, DeSoto Memorial Hospital, Arcadia, FL, p. A121
MISHRA, Sanjeeb, M.D. Chief of Staff, University of Maryland Charles Regional Medical Center, La Plata, MD, p. A298
MISITANO, Anthony F., President and Chief Executive Officer, Post Acute Medical, LLC, Enola, PA, p. B105
MISITI, Joseph, M.D. President Medical Staff, Medina Memorial Hospital, Medina, NY, p. A437
MISKIMEN, Theresa, M.D. Vice President Medical Services, University Behavioral Healthcare, Piscataway, NJ, p. A417
MISKO, Michael, M.D. Chief Medical Officer, Citizens Memorial Hospital, Bolivar, MO, p. A363
MISLAN, Tim, MS Vice President and Chief Nurse Executive, Missouri Baptist Medical Center, Saint Louis, MO, p. A377
MISSERITTI, Colomba, Director Human Resources, Rochester Psychiatric Center, Rochester, NY, p. A449
MISTRETTA, Mike, Vice President and Chief Information Officer, Kaweah Delta Medical Center, Visalia, CA, p. A97
MITCHAM, Debbie, Chief Financial Officer, Northside Hospital, Atlanta, GA, p. A150
MITCHEL, David M., Chief Executive Officer, Avoyelles Hospital, Marksville, LA, p. A279
MITCHELL, Adonna, Director Fiscal Services, North Mississippi Medical Center–Eupora, Eupora, MS, p. A352
MITCHELL, Andrew J., President and Chief Executive Officer, Peconic Bay Medical Center, Riverhead, NY, p. A448
MITCHELL, Barbara, Senior Vice President Marketing and Human Resources, UW Medicine/Valley Medical Center, Renton, WA, p. A682
MITCHELL, Bill, Administrator, Noland Hospital Anniston, Anniston, AL, p. A15
MITCHELL, Daniel, Chief Executive Officer, Vibra Hospital of Western Massachusetts, Springfield, MA, p. A312
MITCHELL, Debbie, Director Human Resources, Woodrow Wilson Rehabilitation Center, Fishersville, VA, p. A665
MITCHELL, Elizabeth C., Vice President and Administrator, Specialty Hospital of Meridian, Meridian, MS, p. A358
MITCHELL, Errol
Chief Financial Officer, INTEGRIS Canadian Valley Hospital, Yukon, OK, p. A518
Vice President, Integris Southwest Medical Center, Oklahoma City, OK, p. A511
MITCHELL, Eulala, Interim Director of Nursing, Pawnee County Memorial Hospital and Rural Health Clinic, Pawnee City, NE, p. A397
MITCHELL, Heath, Chief Operating Officer, Memorial Hospital, Seminole, TX, p. A643
MITCHELL, Ivan, Chief Executive Officer, Towner County Medical Center, Cando, ND, p. A472
MITCHELL, Jack C., FACHE, Chief Executive Officer, HEALTHSOUTH Rehabilitation Hospital, Fayetteville, AR, p. A43
MITCHELL, Jenifer, R.N. Director of Nursing Services, Mineral Community Hospital, Superior, MT, p. A387
MITCHELL, Jodie, Facility Financial Director, Sturgis Regional Hospital, Sturgis, SD, p. A572
MITCHELL, Joni K., Vice President Nursing, Lakes Regional Healthcare, Spirit Lake, IA, p. A235
MITCHELL, Joseph J., President, Trinity Hospital Twin City, Dennison, OH, p. A489
MITCHELL, Judi, Vice President Administrative Services, Navos, Seattle, WA, p. A683
MITCHELL, Karen, Vice President Patient Care Services, Children's Hospital of The King's Daughters, Norfolk, VA, p. A669
MITCHELL, Kathy, R.N. Chief Nursing Officer, Doctors Hospital of Sarasota, Sarasota, FL, p. A142
MITCHELL, Kathy
Director Human Resources, Lakeview Medical Center, Rice Lake, WI, p. A710
Chief Nursing Officer, Owensboro Health Muhlenberg Community Hospital, Greenville, KY, p. A257
MITCHELL, Kenneth W., M.D. Medical Director, St. David's North Austin Medical Center, Austin, TX, p. A595
MITCHELL, Kent, Chief Financial Officer, Hamilton Memorial Hospital District, McLeansboro, IL, p. A194
MITCHELL, Lori J., Chief Financial Officer, University of Washington Medical Center, Seattle, WA, p. A684
MITCHELL, Marsha, Director Human Resources, Fleming County Hospital, Flemingsburg, KY, p. A256
MITCHELL, Mary S., Chief Resource Management Services, Birmingham Veterans Affairs Medical Center, Birmingham, AL, p. A16
MITCHELL, Morris, Director Human Resources, Poplar Springs Hospital, Petersburg, VA, p. A670
MITCHELL, Naomi, Director Human Resources, Kentucky River Medical Center, Jackson, KY, p. A259
MITCHELL, Perry, M.D. Chief of Staff, Little Colorado Medical Center, Winslow, AZ, p. A40
MITCHELL, Rebekah, Chief Financial Officer, Madison County Health Care System, Winterset, IA, p. A236
MITCHELL, Richard R., Director Information Technology, Eagleville Hospital, Eagleville, PA, p. A533
MITCHELL, Sarah, Director Finance, Mary S Harper Geriatric Psychiatry Center, Tuscaloosa, AL, p. A25
MITCHELL, Steve, Chief Operating Officer, Memorial Medical Center, Modesto, CA, p. A75
MITCHELL, Susan
System Executive Vice President Human Resources, Edward Hospital, Naperville, IL, p. A195
Senior Vice President Human Resources, Elmhurst Memorial Hospital, IL, p. A187
Vice President Patient Care Services, Vidant Roanoke–Chowan Hospital, Ahoskie, NC, p. A455
MITCHELL, Timothy, R.N. Chief Nursing Officer, Complex Care Hospital at Ridgelake, Sarasota, FL, p. A142
MITCHELL, Timothy, Chief Financial Officer, Fairfield Memorial Hospital, Winnsboro, SC, p. A566
MITCHELL, Vernadine, R.N. Chief Nursing Officer, De Soto Regional Health System, Mansfield, LA, p. A279
MITCHELL III, Walton F., Director, Catawba Hospital, Catawba, VA, p. A663
MITHUN, Robert, M.D. Physician in Chief, Kaiser Permanente San Francisco Medical Center, San Francisco, CA, p. A88
MITRICK, Joseph M., FACHE, President, Baptist Medical Center Beaches, Jacksonville Beach, FL, p. A130
MITRY, Norman F., President and Chief Executive Officer, Heritage Valley Health System, Beaver, PA, p. B70
MITRY, Norman F.
President and Chief Executive Officer, Heritage Valley Health System, Beaver, PA, p. A529
President and Chief Executive Officer, Sewickley Valley Hospital, (A Division of Valley Medical Facilities), Sewickley, PA, p. A550
MITTAL, Vikrant, M.D. Chief Medical Officer, Danville State Hospital, Danville, PA, p. A532
MITTY, Roger, Interim Chief Executive Officer, St. Elizabeth's Medical Center, Brighton, MA, p. A305
MITZNER, Jennifer C., Senior Vice President Finance and Chief Financial Officer, Hoag Memorial Hospital Presbyterian, Newport Beach, CA, p. A77
MIYAMOTO, Faye, Vice President Human Resources, Rehabilitation Hospital of the Pacific, Honolulu, HI, p. A169
MIYASAWA, Patricia, CPA Director Fiscal Service, Shriners Hospitals for Children–Honolulu, Honolulu, HI, p. A169
MIYAUCHI, Kimberly, R.N. Chief Nursing Officer, Kingman Regional Medical Center, Kingman, AZ, p. A32
MIZE, William D., Chief Operating Officer, Trousdale Medical Center, Hartsville, TN, p. A578
MIZELL, Philip L., M.D. Medical Director, The BridgeWay, North Little Rock, AR, p. A49
MIZER, Alison, Chief Financial Officer, St. Anthony North Health Campus, Westminster, CO, p. A109
MIZIA, Robert, Director Information Systems and Chief Information Officer, Inspira Medical Center–Woodbury, Woodbury, NJ, p. A420
MIZONO, Gary, M.D. Physician–in–Chief, Kaiser Permanente San Rafael Medical Center, San Rafael, CA, p. A90
MIZRACH, Kenneth H., Director, Veterans Affairs New Jersey Health Care System, East Orange, NJ, p. A411
MMEJE, Ike, Chief Operating Officer, Sierra Vista Regional Medical Center, San Luis Obispo, CA, p. A90
MOAD, Harold, Chief Operating Officer, Elkview General Hospital, Hobart, OK, p. A508
MOAK, Jennifer, Business Office Manager, Lawrence County Hospital, Monticello, MS, p. A358

A918 Index of Health Care Professionals 

Index of Health Care Professionals / Monvesky

Index of Health Care Professionals


MOAK, Mike, Chief Information Officer, Southwest Mississippi Regional Medical Center, McComb, MS, p. A357
MOAKLER, Thomas J., Chief Executive Officer, Houlton Regional Hospital, Houlton, ME, p. A290
MOALLEMIAN, Patrick, Chief Executive Officer, Chicago Lakeshore Hospital, Chicago, IL, p. A181
MOATS, Susan, R.N. Vice President of Patient Care Services and Chief Nursing Officer, The Heart Hospital Baylor Plano, Plano, TX, p. A637
MOBLEY, Cheryl, FACHE, President, Texas Health Specialty Hospital, Fort Worth, TX, p. A614
MOBLEY, Dana, Chief Information Officer, Our Community Hospital, Scotland Neck, NC, p. A468
MOCK, Presley, M.D. Chief of Staff, Texas Institute for Surgery at Texas Health Presbyterian Dallas, Dallas, TX, p. A606
MOCKLIN, Kevin, M.D. Director Medical Staff, Lake Charles Memorial Hospital, Lake Charles, LA, p. A278
MODLIN, Stacy, Chief Executive Officer, HEALTHSOUTH Sunrise Rehabilitation Hospital, Sunrise, FL, p. A143
MOE, Jonathan, Chief Executive Officer, Landmann–Jungman Memorial Hospital Avera, Scotland, SD, p. A571
MOEEN, Farida, M.D., Interim Administrator, Doctor's Hospital – Tidwell, Houston, TX, p. A619
MOELLER, Deborah A., R.N. Chief Operating Officer, Lake Pointe Medical Center, Rowlett, TX, p. A639
MOELLER, Jerry G., FACHE, President and Chief Executive Officer, Stillwater Medical Center, Stillwater, OK, p. A515
MOEN, Belinda, R.N. Interim Director of Nursing, Mountrail County Medical Center, Stanley, ND, p. A476
MOEN, Daniel P., President and Chief Executive Officer, Mercy Medical Center, Springfield, MA, p. A311
MOEN, Larry, Chief Financial Officer, Coteau des Prairies Hospital, Sisseton, SD, p. A572
MOEN, Nellie, Coordinator Human Resources, Kindred Hospital–Bay Area, Pasadena, TX, p. A636
MOFFAT, Jeanne, Manager Information Technology, Keefe Memorial Hospital, Cheyenne Wells, CO, p. A100
MOFFAT, Jennifer, Staff Accountant, Regional West Garden County, Oshkosh, NE, p. A397
MOFFATT, Dan, Chief Information Officer, Sanford Bemidji Medical Center, Bemidji, MN, p. A335
MOFFET, Chris, Director Information Services, Bob Wilson Memorial Grant County Hospital, Ulysses, KS, p. A251
MOFFITT, Brenda L., Chief Nursing Officer, Memorial Health System, Abilene, KS, p. A237
MOFFITT SOD, Rhonda, Interim Chief Executive Officer, First Hospital Wyoming Valley, Kingston, PA, p. A537
MOGG, Cassie, Chief Financial Officer, Covenant Hospital Plainview, Plainview, TX, p. A636
MOHAMED, Antonia, Acting Chief Information Officer, Birmingham Veterans Affairs Medical Center, Birmingham, AL, p. A16
MOHAMMED, Ehtaisham, M.D. Chief Medical Officer, Ridgeview Sibley Medical Center, Arlington, MN, p. A334
MOHAN, Amit, Executive Director, Shore Rehabilitation Institute, Brick, NJ, p. A409
MOHLER, Brittany, Director Human Resources, Essentia Health–Deer River, Deer River, MN, p. A337
MOHNK, Richard, Vice President Corporate Services, Bayhealth Medical Center, Dover, DE, p. A117
MOHNKERN, Pearl, Vice President and Director Human Resources, CHRISTUS St. Vincent Regional Medical Center, Santa Fe, NM, p. A426
MOHR, Amy, Coordinator Human Resources, Forest Health Medical Center, Ypsilanti, MI, p. A333
MOHR, Angela, R.N. Vice President Nursing and Chief Operating Officer, St. Anthony Shawnee Hospital, Shawnee, OK, p. A515
MOHR, Steve
  Senior Vice President Finance and Chief Financial Officer, Loma Linda University Behavioral Medicine Center, Redlands, CA, p. A82
  Senior Vice President Finance and Chief Financial Officer, Loma Linda University Medical Center, Loma Linda, CA, p. A67
MOISAN, Terrence, M.D., Chief Executive Officer, Palos Community Hospital, Palos Heights, IL, p. A197
MOK, Michelle
  Chief Financial Officer, Redlands Community Hospital, Redlands, CA, p. A83
  Chief Financial Officer, Saint John's Health Center, Santa Monica, CA, p. A91
MOKFI, Shaya, M.D. Medical Director and President Medical Staff, Kindred Hospital of Northern Indiana, Mishawaka, IN, p. A216
MOLACEK, Shane, Chief Information Officer, Valley County Health System, Ord, NE, p. A397
MOLELUS, Elena, Manager Human Resources, Santa Barbara County Psychiatric Health Facility, Santa Barbara, CA, p. A91
MOLINA, Isabel, M.D. Chief Medical Officer, Lamb Healthcare Center, Littlefield, TX, p. A628
MOLINA, Luis
  Vice President Finance and Chief Financial Officer, Community Hospital, Munster, IN, p. A217
  Chief Financial Officer, St. Catherine Hospital, East Chicago, IN, p. A207
MOLINA, Ricky, Director Marketing and Business Development, Rehabilitation Hospital of Southern New Mexico, Las Cruces, NM, p. A425
MOLINARO, Frank L., Chief Executive Officer, Arrowhead Hospital, Glendale, AZ, p. A32
MOLL, Ben, Assistant Chief Financial Officer, Nashoba Valley Medical Center, Ayer, MA, p. A302
MOLL, Eric, Chief Executive Officer, Mason General Hospital, Shelton, WA, p. A684
MOLL, Jeffrey, M.D. Medical Director, Clarion Psychiatric Center, Clarion, PA, p. A531
MOLLER, Dan, M.D. Chief Medical Officer, Willis–Knighton Medical Center, Shreveport, LA, p. A285
MOLLER, Lynn, Chief Financial Officer, Weston County Health Services, Newcastle, WY, p. A717
MOLLOHAN, Joan, Vice President Human Resources, Ochsner Medical Center, New Orleans, LA, p. A282
MOLLOY, Kevin
  Senior Vice President and Chief Operating Officer, Mount Sinai Beth Israel, New York, NY, p. A442
  Senior Vice President and Chief Operating Officer, Mount Sinai St. Luke's – Roosevelt, New York, NY, p. A442
MOLLOY, Laurel, Vice President Nursing Services, Lenoir Memorial Hospital, Kinston, NC, p. A463
MOLLOY, Reuben D., Chief Information Officer, Governor Juan F. Luis Hospital, Christiansted, VI, p. A725
MOLMEN, David R., Chief Executive Officer, Altru Health System, Grand Forks, ND, p. A474
MOLONEY, Ellen, Chief Operating Officer, Newton–Wellesley Hospital, Newton Lower Falls, MA, p. A309
MOLSBERGER, Shawn, Chief Operating Officer, Gateway Medical Center, Clarksville, TN, p. A576
MOLYNEUX, Phyllis, Associate Administrator Human Resources and Education, Williamson Medical Center, Franklin, TN, p. A578
MOMEYER, Polly, Manager Human Resources, Millcreek Community Hospital, Erie, PA, p. A534
MONAHAN, Jane, Vice President Ministry and Human Resources, Monroe Clinic, Monroe, WI, p. A707
MONASTERIO, Eugene A., M.D. Medical Director, Children's Hospital of Richmond at VCU–Brook Road Campus, Richmond, VA, p. A671
MONCHER, Daniel J., Vice President and Chief Financial Officer, Firelands Regional Health System, Sandusky, OH, p. A497
MONCRIEF, William
  Director Information Systems, Garden City Hospital, Garden City, MI, p. A320
  ORH IT Client Executive, Oakland Regional Hospital, Southfield, MI, p. A330
MONCRIEF–WELLS, Angela, Coordinator Human Resources, Kindred Hospital Detroit, Detroit, MI, p. A318
MONCZEWSKI, Patricia, Chief Operating Officer, Mercy General Hospital, Sacramento, CA, p. A84
MONCZEWSKI, Patti, Interim Chief Executive Officer, Paris Regional Medical Center, Paris, TX, p. A635
MONCZEWSKI, Ted, Vice President Human Resources, St. Vincent Charity Medical Center, Cleveland, OH, p. A485
MONDA, Cam, D.O. Medical Director, Greenwood Regional Rehabilitation Hospital, Greenwood, SC, p. A562
MONEY, Lourene, R.N., Interim Chief Executive Officer, Kindred Hospital South Bay, Gardena, CA, p. A63
MONGE, Peter W., President, MedStar Montgomery Medical Center, Olney, MD, p. A299
MONGELL, Mitchell P., FACHE, Chief Executive Officer, Fort Walton Beach Medical Center, Fort Walton Beach, FL, p. A127
MONGER, Shelton, Director Information Technology, Wayne Hospital, Greenville, OH, p. A491
MONIACI, Cathy, Chief Operating Officer, Shriners Hospitals for Children–Houston, Houston, TX, p. A622
MONJE, Mary Anne, Chief Financial Officer and Chief Operating Officer, Whittier Hospital Medical Center, Whittier, CA, p. A97
MONKRES, Paula, Administrative Assistant and Director Human Resources, Nocona General Hospital, Nocona, TX, p. A634
MONROE, Ame, Director Human Resources, Rolling Plains Memorial Hospital, Sweetwater, TX, p. A646
MONROE, Janet J., R.N., Chief Executive Officer, Greystone Park Psychiatric Hospital, Morris Plains, NJ, p. A414
MONROE, Lori, Director of Nursing, Winnebago Mental Health Institute, Winnebago, WI, p. A714
MONROE, Temple, Director of Nursing Operations, Wilson Medical Center, Neodesha, KS, p. A246
MONROIG, Domingo, Executive Director, Castaner General Hospital, Castaner, PR, p. A720
MONROY–MILLER, Cherry, M.D. Acting Medical Director, Greystone Park Psychiatric Hospital, Morris Plains, NJ, p. A414
MONSANTO, Monte, Chief Information Systems, Russell County Hospital, Russell Springs, KY, p. A265
MONSERRATE, Humberto M., Chief Executive Officer, Hospital Universitario Dr. Ramon Ruiz Arnau, Bayamon, PR, p. A720
MONSON, Amy, Chief Financial Officer, Manning Regional Healthcare Center, Manning, IA, p. A231
MONSRUD, Michele, Director Human Resources, Clearview Regional Medical Center, Monroe, GA, p. A161
MONTAG, Kathy, Administrator Health Care, State Correctional Institution at Camp Hill, Camp Hill, PA, p. A530
MONTAGNESE, Robert A., President and Chief Executive Officer, Licking Memorial Hospital, Newark, OH, p. A495
MONTALBO, Tripp, Chief Operating Officer, Conroe Regional Medical Center, Conroe, TX, p. A602
MONTALVO, Cary L., Chief Executive Officer, Solara Hospital Harlingen, Harlingen, TX, p. A618
MONTALVO, Jose, M.D. Medical Director, Hospital Del Maestro, San Juan, PR, p. A723
MONTANA–RHODES, Lou, Vice President of Patient Care Services, Vidant Beaufort Hospital, Washington, NC, p. A470
MONTANEZ, Edwin, R.N. Chief Nursing Officer, HEALTHSOUTH Rehabilitation Hospital of Spring Hill, Brooksville, FL, p. A123
MONTANO, Mayra, Director Information Systems, Hospital Metropolitano Dr. Susoni, Arecibo, PR, p. A720
MONTANTE, Carl, Director Information Systems and Information Technology, Shriners Hospitals for Children–Portland, Portland, OR, p. A525
MONTANYE, Richard, Director Information Systems, Hunt Regional Medical Center, Greenville, TX, p. A617
MONTANYE–IRELAND, Cherelle, Chief Executive Officer, Hansen Family Hospital, Iowa Falls, IA, p. A230
MONTEL, Janet, Chief Financial Officer, Paris Regional Medical Center, Paris, TX, p. A635
MONTENEGRO, Diana, Director Human Resources, Baptist Health South Florida, South Miami Hospital, Miami, FL, p. A134
MONTENEGRO, Robert, M.D. Chief of Staff, Glacial Ridge Health System, Glenwood, MN, p. A339
MONTEROS, Christopher, Director of Nursing, Seven Hills Hospital, Henderson, NV, p. A401
MONTES, Lisa K., Chief Executive Officer, Del Amo Hospital, Torrance, CA, p. A94
MONTGOMERY, Charles, M.D. Medical Director, Logansport Memorial Hospital, Logansport, IN, p. A215
MONTGOMERY, Jennifer, R.N. Vice President, Nursing, McLaren Port Huron, Port Huron, MI, p. A328
MONTGOMERY, Jennifer
  Chief Nursing Officer, Rochelle Community Hospital, Rochelle, IL, p. A199
  Chief Financial Officer, Washakie Medical Center, Worland, WY, p. A718
MONTGOMERY, Lee Anne, Administrator, Beacon Children's Hospital, Luverne, AL, p. A21
MONTGOMERY, Lee Anne, R.N. Chief Nursing Officer, HEALTHSOUTH Rehabilitation Hospital of Montgomery, Montgomery, AL, p. A23
MONTGOMERY, Margaret, Chief Nursing Officer, HEALTHSOUTH Reading Rehabilitation Hospital, Reading, PA, p. A548
MONTGOMERY, Mark, M.D. Chief Medical Officer, Texas Health Harris Methodist Hospital Southwest Fort Worth, Fort Worth, TX, p. A614
MONTGOMERY, Mary Jim, R.N. Chief Operating Officer, Crisp Regional Hospital, Cordele, GA, p. A155
MONTGOMERY, Peggy, Director Medical Records, Arrowhead Behavioral Health Hospital, Maumee, OH, p. A494
MONTGOMERY II, Raymond W., FACHE, President and Chief Executive Officer, Unity Health White County Medical Center, Searcy, AR, p. A50
MONTGOMERY, Robert, Chief Financial Officer, Shriners Hospitals for Children–Lexington, Lexington, KY, p. A260
MONTGOMERY, Susan, Chief Nursing Officer, Asante Ashland Community Hospital, Ashland, OR, p. A519
MONTGOMERY, Tina, Chief Financial Officer, Sidney Health Center, Sidney, MT, p. A387
MONTGOMERY, Vicki, Director and Chief Executive Officer, Central State Hospital, Petersburg, VA, p. A670
MONTOIS, John D., Interim Chief Financial Officer, Highlands Regional Medical Center, Sebring, FL, p. A143
MONTOUR, Vina, Director Information Technology, U. S. Public Health Service Phoenix Indian Medical Center, Phoenix, AZ, p. A36
MONTOWSKI, Deborah, M.D. Chief Medical Officer, Providence Mount Carmel Hospital, Colville, WA, p. A678
MONTOYA, Brooke, Director Human Resources, Lake Granbury Medical Center, Granbury, TX, p. A616
MONVESKY, Kimberly, Chief Financial Officer, Pikes Peak Regional Hospital, Woodland Park, CO, p. A109

Index of Health Care Professionals

Index of Health Care Professionals / Monzingo


MONZINGO, Ashley, Human Resources, Accounts Payable and Payroll, TOPS Surgical Specialty Hospital, Houston, TX, p. A622
MOODY, Crystal R., Director Human Resources, Community Medical Center of Izard County, Calico Rock, AR, p. A42
MOODY, David, Vice President Human Resources, Salina Regional Health Center, Salina, KS, p. A250
MOODY, Heather, Chief Human Resource Management, Hunter Holmes McGuire Veterans Affairs Medical Center–Richmond, Richmond, VA, p. A672
MOODY, James, Chief Financial Officer, Donalsonville Hospital, Donalsonville, GA, p. A156
MOODY, Michael
  Senior Vice President and Chief Financial Officer, John Muir Behavioral Health Center, Concord, CA, p. A58
  Senior Vice President and Chief Financial Officer, John Muir Medical Center, Walnut Creek, Walnut Creek, CA, p. A97
MOODY, Vicky, Director Human Resources, Houlton Regional Hospital, Houlton, ME, p. A290
MOOERS, Margaret, R.N. Chief Operating Officer and Chief Nursing Officer, OSS Orthopaedic Hospital, York, PA, p. A554
MOOG, Darlene, Director Human Resources, HEALTHSOUTH Deaconess Rehabilitation Hospital, Evansville, IN, p. A208
MOON, Bob, Chief Financial Officer, CHRISTUS St. Vincent Regional Medical Center, Santa Fe, NM, p. A426
MOON, Jr., David, Director Information Systems, Lake City Community Hospital, Lake City, SC, p. A563
MOON, James, Chief Financial Officer, Pana Community Hospital, Pana, IL, p. A197
MOON, John, Associate Director, Veterans Affairs Eastern Kansas Health Care System, Topeka, KS, p. A251
MOON, Robert, Chief Financial Officer, Mercy St. Anne Hospital, Toledo, OH, p. A498
MOONEY, Robert W., M.D. Medical Director, Willingway Hospital, Statesboro, GA, p. A165
MOONEY, Susan E., MS, President and Chief Executive Officer, Alice Peck Day Memorial Hospital, Lebanon, NH, p. A406
MOORE, Alison, Chief Financial Officer, Methodist Extended Care Hospital, Memphis, TN, p. A583
MOORE, Amy, Human Resources, Hamilton Hospital, Olney, TX, p. A635
MOORE III, Ben, President and Chief Executive Officer, River Hospital, Alexandria Bay, NY, p. A428
MOORE, Betty, Business Manager, Tishomingo Health Services, Iuka, MS, p. A354
MOORE, Bill, Chief Human Resources, El Centro Regional Medical Center, El Centro, CA, p. A60
MOORE, Bob, FACHE, Chief Executive Officer, Munroe Regional Medical Center, Ocala, FL, p. A137
MOORE, Brandon, Administrator and Chief Executive Officer, Park Place Surgical Hospital, Lafayette, LA, p. A278
MOORE, Brett, CPA Assistant Administrator Finance, Sutter Amador Hospital, Jackson, CA, p. A65
MOORE, Brett, Chief Financial Officer, Sutter Davis Hospital, Davis, CA, p. A59
MOORE, Brian, President and Chief Executive Officer, St. Mary–Corwin Medical Center, Pueblo, CO, p. A108
MOORE, C. Thomas, Chief Financial Officer, Delta Regional Medical Center, Greenville, MS, p. A353
MOORE, Carrie, Director Human Resources, Meadowbrook Rehabilitation Hospital, Gardner, KS, p. A240
MOORE, Cathy, Chief Nursing Officer, St. Luke's Hospital, Columbus, NC, p. A458
MOORE, Cecelia B., CPA Associate Vice Chancellor Finance, Vanderbilt Hospital and Clinics, Nashville, TN, p. A586
MOORE, Christie, Director Human Resources, Reliant Rehabilitation Hospital Mid–Cities, Bedford, TX, p. A596
MOORE, Dana
  Senior Vice President Information Services, St. Anthony Hospital, Lakewood, CO, p. A106
  Senior Vice President Information Services, St. Anthony North Health Campus, Westminster, CO, p. A109
MOORE, Darrell W., Chief Executive Officer, Parkridge Medical Center, Chattanooga, TN, p. A575
MOORE, Deborah, Director Human Resources, Walter P. Reuther Psychiatric Hospital, Westland, MI, p. A332
MOORE, Debra, Chief Executive Officer, Parkside Psychiatric Hospital and Clinic, Tulsa, OK, p. A516
MOORE, Diane, Chief Financial Officer, Big Bend Regional Medical Center, Alpine, TX, p. A591
MOORE, Edward H., President and Chief Executive Officer, Harrington Memorial Hospital, Southbridge, MA, p. A311
MOORE, Elizabeth, Chief Operating Officer, Silver Hill Hospital, New Canaan, CT, p. A114
MOORE, Emily, Director Human Resources and Information Technology, Haskell Memorial Hospital, Haskell, TX, p. A618
MOORE, Ethel L., M.D. Director of Medical Affairs, Fort Belknap U. S. Public Health Service Indian Hospital, Harlem, MT, p. A384
MOORE, Harold, Chief Information Technology Officer, Spartanburg Regional Medical Center, Spartanburg, SC, p. A565
MOORE, James D., FACHE, President, Integris Southwest Medical Center, Oklahoma City, OK, p. A511
MOORE, James L., M.D. Senior Vice President and Chief Medical Officer, Athens Regional Medical Center, Athens, GA, p. A149
MOORE, Jane, Director, Fiscal Services, Quitman County Hospital, Marks, MS, p. A356
MOORE, Jason H., Vice President and Chief Operating Officer, Tallahassee Memorial HealthCare, Tallahassee, FL, p. A144
MOORE, Jeffrey Steve, Chief Financial Officer, Fort Walton Beach Medical Center, Fort Walton Beach, FL, p. A127
MOORE, Jennifer, Interim Chief Information Officer, Carroll Hospital Center, Westminster, MD, p. A301
MOORE, Jody Dewen, District Director Human Resources, Kindred Hospital–San Diego, San Diego, CA, p. A86
MOORE, John, M.D. Medical Director, Granite County Medical Center, Philipsburg, MT, p. A386
MOORE, John
  Administrator, Hiawatha Community Hospital, Hiawatha, KS, p. A241
  President, South Lake Hospital, Clermont, FL, p. A123
MOORE, John, M.D. Vice President Medical Affairs, SSM DePaul Health Center, Bridgeton, MO, p. A364
MOORE, John G., Vice President and Chief Financial Officer, Carolinas Healthcare System Union, Monroe, NC, p. A465
MOORE, Kadie, Director Human Resources, Vidant Edgecombe Hospital, Tarboro, NC, p. A469
MOORE, Kandi, Administrator, Specialists Hospital – Shreveport, Shreveport, LA, p. A285
MOORE, Karen, Vice President Information Technology and Chief Information Officer, Southern Regional Medical Center, Riverdale, GA, p. A163
MOORE, Kathy D., Chief Executive Officer, St. Luke's Regional Medical Center, Boise, ID, p. A173
MOORE, Keri, Vice President Human Resources and Support Services, Presbyterian–St. Luke's Medical Center, Denver, CO, p. A102
MOORE, Kermit, R.N. Chief Operating Officer and Chief Nursing Officer, Nemaha County Hospital, Auburn, NE, p. A389
MOORE, Kerry, M.D. Chief of Staff, Carilion Tazewell Community Hospital, Tazewell, VA, p. A673
MOORE, Kim S., FACHE, President, CHI Health St Elizabeth, Lincoln, NE, p. A393
MOORE, Kyna, R.N. Director of Nursing, Bath Community Hospital, Hot Springs, VA, p. A666
MOORE, Larry E., Executive Vice President and Chief Operating Officer and Chief Financial Officer, Cumberland Medical Center, Crossville, TN, p. A577
MOORE, Lauralinda, Manager Finance, CHRISTUS Spohn Hospital Kleberg, Kingsville, TX, p. A626
MOORE, Leigh, Administrative Assistant Human Resources, H. C. Watkins Memorial Hospital, Quitman, MS, p. A360
MOORE, Linda, Manager Human Resources, Seymour Hospital, Seymour, TX, p. A643
MOORE, Margaret, Director Business Office, Sabine County Hospital, Hemphill, TX, p. A618
MOORE, Mark E., President and Chief Executive Officer, Indiana University Health Bloomington Hospital, Bloomington, IN, p. A205
MOORE, Mary Ann, Director of Nursing, KidsPeace Children's Hospital, Orefield, PA, p. A542
MOORE, Matthew, Executive Vice President and Chief Integration Officer, St. Francis Hospital, Columbus, GA, p. A154
MOORE, Mayzelle, Director Human Resources, Methodist Extended Care Hospital, Memphis, TN, p. A583
MOORE, Melinda, Director Human Resources, Deaconess Hospital, Spokane, WA, p. A685
MOORE, Michael, Ph.D., Acting Medical Center Director, John J. Pershing Veterans Affairs Medical Center, Poplar Bluff, MO, p. A374
MOORE, Michael, Director Information Systems, Troy Regional Medical Center, Troy, AL, p. A25
MOORE, Mike, President and Chief Operating Officer, Jane Phillips Medical Center, Bartlesville, OK, p. A504
MOORE, Mindy S., Chief Executive Officer, Landmark Hospital of Columbia, Columbia, MO, p. A366
MOORE, Neil J., President and Chief Executive Officer, Dimensions Healthcare System, Cheverly, MD, p. B51
MOORE, Nelda, Director Data Processing, Memorial Hospital and Manor, Bainbridge, GA, p. A152
MOORE, Nickie, Chief Financial Officer, North Sunflower Medical Center, Ruleville, MS, p. A360
MOORE, Patricia J., Director Human Resource, Valley Behavioral Health System, Barling, AR, p. A41
MOORE, Paul, Chief Information Officer, Connecticut Mental Health Center, New Haven, CT, p. A114
MOORE, Paula, R.N. Chief Clinical Officer, Hugh Chatham Memorial Hospital, Elkin, NC, p. A460
MOORE, Rick
  Chief Information Officer, Bethesda North Hospital, Cincinnati, OH, p. A482
  Chief Information Officer, Good Samaritan Hospital, Cincinnati, OH, p. A483
MOORE, Robin A., Vice President Human Resources, Concord Hospital, Concord, NH, p. A405
MOORE, Ronald E., R.N. Vice President Professional Practice and Chief Nursing Officer, Charleston Area Medical Center, Charleston, WV, p. A690
MOORE, Sandee, Chief Operating Officer, Eastern Idaho Regional Medical Center, Idaho Falls, ID, p. A174
MOORE, Saunya, Chief Financial Officer, Parkside Psychiatric Hospital and Clinic, Tulsa, OK, p. A516
MOORE, Scott, Chief of Staff, Jay Hospital, Jay, FL, p. A130
MOORE, Steve, Chief Financial Officer, Southern Tennessee Regional Health System–Winchester, Winchester, TN, p. A589
MOORE, Sylvia, Vice President and Chief Operating Officer, Southeast Hospital, Cape Girardeau, MO, p. A365
MOORE, Tim, Chief Accounting Officer and Vice President Ancillary Services and Finance, Blessing Hospital, Quincy, IL, p. A199
MOORE, Tim, R.N. Senior Vice President and Chief Information Officer, Hoag Memorial Hospital Presbyterian, Newport Beach, CA, p. A77
MOORE, Vernon, Senior Vice President Chief Business and Finance, University of Texas Health Northeast, Tyler, TX, p. A649
MOORE, Warren E., Executive Vice President and Chief Operating Officer, Children's Specialized Hospital–PSE&G, New Brunswick, NJ, p. A415
MOORE, William, Chief Information Officer, Parrish Medical Center, Titusville, FL, p. A146
MOORE–CONNELLY, Marci, M.D. Vice President Chief Medical Officer, Memorial Hospital of Carbondale, Carbondale, IL, p. A180
MOORE–HARDY, Cynthia, FACHE, President and Chief Executive Officer, Lake Health, Concord Township, OH, p. A487
MOOREHOUSE, Brett, FACHE Vice President and Chief Operating Officer, Ranken Jordan Pediatric Bridge Hospital, Maryland Heights, MO, p. A372
MOORER, Thad, Chief Information Officer, Eastside Psychiatric Hospital, Tallahassee, FL, p. A144
MOORHEAD, David, M.D. Chief Medical Officer, Florida Hospital, Orlando, FL, p. A138
MOORMAN, Gary L., D.O. Chief Medical Officer and Senior Vice President Medical Affairs, ProMedica Monroe Regional Hospital, Monroe, MI, p. A326
MORACA, Lynn, Director Human Resources, Lodi Community Hospital, Lodi, OH, p. A492
MORAHAN, John, Vice President Finance, St. Joseph Hospital, Bethpage, NY, p. A429
MORAHAN, John R., FACHE, President and Chief Executive Officer, St. Joseph Regional Health Network, Reading, PA, p. A548
MORALES, Anthony, M.D. Medical Director, Louisiana Heart Hospital, Lacombe, LA, p. A277
MORALES, Autumn, Chief Medical Staff Officer, Clarinda Regional Health Center, Clarinda, IA, p. A224
MORALES, Carmela, M.D. Chief of Staff, University Medical Center of El Paso, El Paso, TX, p. A611
MORALES, Daniza
  Chief Information Officer, Hospital Menonita De Cayey, Cayey, PR, p. A720
  Manager Information System, Mennonite General Hospital, Aibonito, PR, p. A719
MORALES, Elsie, Chief Financial Officer, Hospital Universitario Dr. Ramon Ruiz Arnau, Bayamon, PR, p. A720
MORALES, Joel, Chief Financial Officer, Fort Duncan Regional Medical Center, Eagle Pass, TX, p. A609
MORALES, John R., Chief Financial Officer, John H. Stroger Jr. Hospital of Cook County, Chicago, IL, p. A182
MORALES, Juan A., MSN, Health System Director, Tennessee Valley Healthcare System, Nashville, TN, p. A586
MORALES, Kathryn
  Director of Finance, Hampshire Memorial Hospital, Romney, WV, p. A695
  Director of Finance, War Memorial Hospital, Berkeley Springs, WV, p. A689
MORALES, Trish, Director Human Resources, Lakewood Ranch Medical Center, Bradenton, FL, p. A122
MORAN, Alina, Chief Financial Officer, Elmhurst Hospital Center, NY, p. A439
MORAN, Barbara, R.N. Director Patient Care Services and Chief Nursing Officer, Grace Hospital, Cleveland, OH, p. A484
MORAN, Colleen M., Director Human Resources, Spaulding Hospital for Continuing Medical Care North Shore, Salem, MA, p. A311


A920 Index of Health Care Professionals 

Index of Health Care Professionals

Index of Health Care Professionals / Morrison


MORAN, Debbie, Executive Director, Carl Albert Community Mental Health Center, McAlester, OK, p. A509
MORAN, Timothy M., Chief Executive Officer, Tri–City Medical Center, Oceanside, CA, p. A79
MORANDEIRA, Ana, Director Marketing, San Juan Capestrano Hospital, San Juan, PR, p. A724
MORASKO, Jerome, President and Chief Executive Officer, Avita Galion Hospital, Galion, OH, p. A490
MORASKO, Jerome, President and Chief Executive Officer, Avita Health System, Galion, OH, p. B18
MORASKO, Jerome, Chief Executive Officer, Bucyrus Community Hospital, Bucyrus, OH, p. A480
MORASKO, Robert A., Chief Executive Officer, Heart of the Rockies Regional Medical Center, Salida, CO, p. A108
MORAVICK, Donna, MSN, Executive Director, Southside Hospital, Bay Shore, NY, p. A429
MORDACH, John P., Senior Vice President and Chief Financial Officer, Rush University Medical Center, Chicago, IL, p. A184
MORDECAI, Steve, Director Human Resources, Griffin Hospital, Derby, CT, p. A112
MORDUE, Leslie, Chief Nursing Officer, Pioneer Community Hospital of Patrick, Stuart, VA, p. A673
MOREAU, Steven C., President and Chief Executive Officer, St. Joseph Hospital, Orange, CA, p. A79
MOREFIELD, Terri, Deputy Chief Human Resources Division, Bassett Army Community Hospital, Fort Wainwright, AK, p. A28
MOREIN, Sandy, Chief Nursing Officer, Mercy Regional Medical Center, Ville Platte, LA, p. A286
MORELAND, John, M.D. Chief Medical Officer, Marcus Daly Memorial Hospital, Hamilton, MT, p. A384
MORELAND, Tresha, M
  Regional Vice President Human Resources, Dameron Hospital, Stockton, CA, p. A93
  Vice President Human Resources, Rideout Memorial Hospital, Marysville, CA, p. A75
MORELL, Ixel, Director Business Development, Sierra Vista Hospital, Sacramento, CA, p. A85
MORELLI, Gerald, Director Human Resources, Philadelphia Veterans Affairs Medical Center, Philadelphia, PA, p. A545
MORENO, Debbie, Chief Nursing Officer, Lodi Memorial Hospital, Lodi, CA, p. A67
MORENO, Jorge, Director Information Technology Operations, Canyon Vista Medical Center, Sierra Vista, AZ, p. A38
MORENO–COOK, Shannon, Chief Nursing Officer, St. Vincent Rehabilitation Hospital, Sherwood, AR, p. A50
MORESI, Randy, Chief Executive Officer, North Hills Hospital, North Richland Hills, TX, p. A634
MORETTE, Joseph M., Executive Vice President, Methodist Rehabilitation Center, Jackson, MS, p. A355
MOREY, Scott, Chief Nursing Officer, Abrazo Maryvale Campus, Phoenix, AZ, p. A34
MORGAN, Bradley, Vice President of Operations, The Heart Hospital Baylor Denton, Denton, TX, p. A608
MORGAN, Charlene, Chief Nursing Officer, Henderson County Community Hospital, Lexington, TN, p. A581
MORGAN, Christian, M.D. Chief of Staff, Star Valley Medical Center, Afton, WY, p. A715
MORGAN, Christopher, M.D. Chief of Staff, Baptist Health Medical Center–Stuttgart, Stuttgart, AR, p. A51
MORGAN, David, Vice President and Chief Financial Officer, Bristol Bay Area Health Corporation, Dillingham, AK, p. A28
MORGAN, Dennis P., Chief of Staff, Baptist Memorial Hospital–North Mississippi, Oxford, MS, p. A359
MORGAN, Derek
  Vice President Human Resources, Kettering Medical Center, Kettering, OH, p. A491
  Vice President Human Resources, Sycamore Medical Center, Miamisburg, OH, p. A494
MORGAN, Dirk, Vice President, Murray–Calloway County Hospital, Murray, KY, p. A264
MORGAN, James, M.D. Chief Medical Officer, Memorial Hospital of Converse County, Douglas, WY, p. A716
MORGAN, Janelle, Interim Director of Nursing, Howard County Medical Center, Saint Paul, NE, p. A398
MORGAN, Jeff, Director Information Systems, Northeastern Nevada Regional Hospital, Elko, NV, p. A400
MORGAN, Jodi, Chief Nursing Officer, St. Bernard Parish Hospital, Chalmette, LA, p. A271
MORGAN, Jon, M.D. Chief Medical Officer, Regional West Medical Center, Scottsbluff, NE, p. A398
MORGAN, Kelly C., President and Chief Executive Officer, Mercy Medical Center, Roseburg, OR, p. A525
MORGAN, Lisa, R.N. Vice President Patient Services, King's Daughters' Health, Madison, IN, p. A215
MORGAN, Lois, R.N. Vice President and Chief Nursing Officer, Methodist Hospital, Henderson, KY, p. A258
MORGAN, Lori, M.D., Chief Administrative Officer, Legacy Emanuel Hospital and Health Center, Portland, OR, p. A524
MORGAN, Mace, Director Information Systems, Minden Medical Center, Minden, LA, p. A280
MORGAN, Matthew, Associate Administrator, Hillcrest Hospital – South, Tulsa, OK, p. A516
MORGAN, Melody, Chief Financial Officer, Fairfield Memorial Hospital, Fairfield, IL, p. A188
MORGAN, Norma J., Chief Executive Officer, Effingham Hospital, Springfield, GA, p. A165
MORGAN, Nyle, Chief Information Officer, Sheridan Memorial Hospital, Sheridan, WY, p. A717
MORGAN, Rose, R.N. Vice President Patient Care Services, Princeton Community Hospital, Princeton, WV, p. A694
MORGAN, Sandra, Chief Executive Officer, Kindred Hospital Bay Area–Tampa, Tampa, FL, p. A145
MORGAN, Shawn, Acting Finance Officer, Northern Navajo Medical Center, Shiprock, NM, p. A426
MORGAN, Susan, Director of Nursing Services, Prairie Community Hospital, Terry, MT, p. A387
MORGAN, Suzanne M., Chief Clinical Officer, Kindred Hospital of Northern Indiana, Mishawaka, IN, p. A216
MORGAN, Teresa
  Chief Financial Officer, McGehee–Desha County Hospital, McGehee, AR, p. A48
  Assistant Vice President Human Resources, Shannon Medical Center, San Angelo, TX, p. A640
MORGAN, W. Hugh, M.D. Chief Medical Staff, Edgefield County Hospital, Edgefield, SC, p. A560
MORGAN–FINE, Richard, IT Director, Clarinda Regional Health Center, Clarinda, IA, p. A224
MORGESE, Vincent, M.D. Executive Vice President, Chief Operating Officer and Chief Medical Officer, Queen of the Valley Medical Center, Napa, CA, p. A77
MORIARTY, Sharon J., Chief Operating Officer, St. Mary's Hospital, Cottonwood, ID, p. A174
MORIMOTO, Scott, Director Clinical Informatics, Rehabilitation Hospital of the Pacific, Honolulu, HI, p. A169
MORIN, Linda, Director of Nursing, Copper Queen Community Hospital, Bisbee, AZ, p. A30
MORIN, Robert J., Vice President Finance and Chief Financial Officer, Sturgis Hospital, Sturgis, MI, p. A331
MORIN–SCRIBNER, Nicole, Director Human Resources, St. Mary's Regional Medical Center, Lewiston, ME, p. A291
MORISCO, Antonietta, M.D. Medical Director, Chairman Anesthesiology, Jamaica Hospital Medical Center, NY, p. A440
MORISSETTE, Philip
  Chief Financial Officer, Bridgton Hospital, Bridgton, ME, p. A289
  Chief Financial Officer, Central Maine Medical Center, Lewiston, ME, p. A290
MORITZ, Mary, Administrator Human Resources, Humboldt County Memorial Hospital, Humboldt, IA, p. A229
MORK Jr., David L., FACHE,
  Chief Executive Officer, Roosevelt Warm Springs Rehabilitation and Specialty Hospitals – LTAC, Warm Springs, GA, p. A166
  Executive Director and Chief Operating Officer, Roosevelt Warm Springs Rehabilitation and Specialty Hospitals – Rehab, Warm Springs, GA, p. A167
MORKEL, Derek, Chief Executive Officer, HealthTech Management Services, Brentwood, TN, p. B70
MORKRID, Shirley, Chief Nursing Officer, Liberty Medical Center, Chester, MT, p. A382
MORLEY, Denise M., Director Human Resources, Wyoming County Community Hospital, Warsaw, NY, p. A453
MORLEY, Michael, M.D. Chief of Staff, Arkansas Valley Regional Medical Center, La Junta, CO, p. A105
MORLOCK, David, Chief Executive Officer, The University of Toledo Medical Center, Toledo, OH, p. A499
MORLOCK, Paul J., FACHE Vice President Human Resources, Children's Hospital of The King's Daughters, Norfolk, VA, p. A669
MORON, David, M.D. Clinical Director, Rio Grande State Center/South Texas Health Care System, Harlingen, TX, p. A618
MORONY, David, Chief Financial Officer, Casa Colina Hospital and Health Systems, Pomona, CA, p. A81
MORQUECHO, Adam, Director Information Technology, Huntington Beach Hospital, Huntington Beach, CA, p. A65
MORREALE, Daniel, Vice President and Chief Information Officer, Kingsbrook Jewish Medical Center, NY, p. A441
MORREALE, Gene, President and Chief Executive Officer, Oneida Healthcare, Oneida, NY, p. A446
MORRELL, Dan, Manager Information Systems, Sierra Vista Hospital, Truth or Consequences, NM, p. A427
MORRELL, Jeffrey F., Chief Executive Officer, Intermountain Hospital, Boise, ID, p. A172
MORRICAL, Michael G., Chief Executive Officer, McKenzie Regional Hospital, McKenzie, TN, p. A582
MORRIONE, Thomas, Medical Director, New England Rehabilitation Hospital of Portland, Portland, ME, p. A292
MORRIS, Alexander, Corporate Director Human Resources, Fort Washington Medical Center, Oxen Hill, MD, p. A299
MORRIS, Barbara, R.N. Chief Nursing Officer, HEALTHSOUTH Rehabilitation Hospital of Beaumont, Beaumont, TX, p. A596
MORRIS, Christi, Director of Nursing, Chambers County Public Hospital District 1, Anahuac, TX, p. A592
MORRIS, Christopher
  Director Human Resources, Wheaton Franciscan Healthcare – Elmbrook Memorial, Brookfield, WI, p. A698
  Vice President Human Resources, Wheaton Franciscan Healthcare – St. Joseph's, Milwaukee, WI, p. A707
  Director Human Resources, Wheaton Franciscan Healthcare – The Wisconsin Heart Hospital, Wauwatosa, WI, p. A713
MORRIS, David W., Chief Executive Officer, University Behavioral Health of El Paso, El Paso, TX, p. A611
MORRIS, Debbie M., Director Human Resources, Marcus Daly Memorial Hospital, Hamilton, MT, p. A384
MORRIS, Dennis, Area Finance Officer, Kaiser Permanente Oakland Medical Center, Oakland, CA, p. A78
MORRIS, Donald
  System Vice President Human Resources, CHI St. Luke's Health Memorial Livingston, Livingston, TX, p. A628
  Vice President Human Resources, CHI St. Luke's Health Memorial Specialty Hospital, Lufkin, TX, p. A630
MORRIS, Douglas
  Chief Financial Officer, Elmwood Healthcare Center at the Springs, Green Springs, OH, p. A490
  Chief Financial Officer, Vibra Hospital of Northwestern Indiana, Crown Point, IN, p. A207
  Chief Financial Officer, Vibra Hospital of Southeastern Michigan, LLC, Lincoln Park, MI, p. A324
MORRIS, Janet, Director Human Resources, HEALTHSOUTH Lakeview Rehabilitation Hospital, Elizabethtown, KY, p. A256
MORRIS, Janice, Accountant, CrossRidge Community Hospital, Wynne, AR, p. A52
MORRIS, Jarrett L., Controller, Carolinas HealthCare System Lincoln, Lincolnton, NC, p. A464
MORRIS, Jeffrey, M.D. Medical Director, Summa Barberton Citizens Hospital, Barberton, OH, p. A479
MORRIS, Jennifer C., Vice President Human Resources, Medical Center Arlington, Arlington, TX, p. A592
MORRIS, Jim
  Vice President Finance, Baptist Health La Grange, La Grange, KY, p. A259
  Vice President Finance, Baptist Health Louisville, Louisville, KY, p. A260
MORRIS, Jody, President and Chief Operating Officer, Novant Health Franklin Medical Center, Louisburg, NC, p. A464
MORRIS, Jonathan B., M.D
  Senior Vice President and Chief Information Officer, WellStar Cobb Hospital, Austell, GA, p. A152
  Senior Vice President and Chief Information Officer, WellStar Kennestone Hospital, Marietta, GA, p. A161
MORRIS, Lisa, Vice President Human Resources, Swedish Medical Center, Englewood, CO, p. A103
MORRIS, Luke P.
  Regional Director Human Resources, American Fork Hospital, American Fork, UT, p. A654
  Regional Director Human Resources, Utah Valley Regional Medical Center, Provo, UT, p. A657
MORRIS, Marsha, Manager Information Services, Fairview Park Hospital, Dublin, GA, p. A156
MORRIS, Michael, Interim Chief Executive Officer, Lavaca Medical Center, Hallettsville, TX, p. A617
MORRIS, R. Randall, Administrator, West Carroll Memorial Hospital, Oak Grove, LA, p. A283
MORRIS, Rosanna D., R.N.,
  Interim Chief Executive Officer, Nebraska Medicine – Bellevue, Bellevue, NE, p. A390
  Interim Chief Executive Officer, Nebraska Medicine – Nebraska Medical Center, Omaha, NE, p. A396
MORRIS, Shawna, Senior Vice President Operations and Chief Operating Officer, Menninger Clinic, Houston, TX, p. A621
MORRIS, Terri, Director Information Systems, Methodist Richardson Medical Center, Richardson, TX, p. A638
MORRIS, Tony, Business Manager, Mental Health Institute, Cherokee, IA, p. A224
MORRIS, Will, Director Information Technology, Merit Health Batesville, Batesville, MS, p. A350
MORRISON, Christopher, Deputy Chief Executive Officer, Trenton Psychiatric Hospital, Trenton, NJ, p. A419
MORRISON, Deane, Chief Information Officer, Concord Hospital, Concord, NH, p. A405
MORRISON, Devin, Director Administration, Naval Hospital Pensacola, Pensacola, FL, p. A139
MORRISON, Dianne, Director Human Resources, Mizell Memorial Hospital, Opp, AL, p. A24

Index of Health Care Professionals

Index of Health Care Professionals / Morrison

MORRISON, Greg, M.D. Vice President Medical Affairs, OhioHealth Grant Medical Center, Columbus, OH, p. A486
MORRISON, J. E., M.D. Chief Medical Officer, Baylor Scott & White Hillcrest Medical Center, Waco, TX, p. A650
MORRISON, Kathy E., Executive Director Human Resources, St. Catherine Hospital, Garden City, KS, p. A240
MORRISON, Kevin, Chief Financial Officer, Dickenson Community Hospital, Clintwood, VA, p. A663
MORRISON, Maureen, Vice President Financial Services, Advocate Trinity Hospital, Chicago, IL, p. A181
MORRISON, Michael, Chief Financial Officer, TriStar Hendersonville Medical Center, Hendersonville, TN, p. A578
MORRISON, Ron, Chief Human Resources Officer, Lakeway Regional Medical Center, Lakeway, TX, p. A627
MORRISON, Sarah, Vice President Clinical Services, Shepherd Center, Atlanta, GA, p. A151
MORRISSETT, Barbara, Vice President Human Resources, St. Mary's Medical Center, San Francisco, CA, p. A88
MORRISSETTE, Daniel, Chief Financial Officer, Stanford Health Care, Palo Alto, CA, p. A80
MORRISSEY, Moira, Chief Operating Officer and General Counsel, Four Winds Hospital, Katonah, NY, p. A435
MORRISSEY, Una E., R.N. Senior Vice President Chief Operating Officer and Chief Nursing Officer, New York Community Hospital, NY, p. A442
MORRO, Maryalice, Director, Carl Vinson Veterans Affairs Medical Center, Dublin, GA, p. A156
MORROW, Charles, M.D. Chief Medical Officer, Spartanburg Regional Medical Center, Spartanburg, SC, p. A565
MORROW, Ginger
 Executive Vice President Human Resources, Good Shepherd Medical Center, Longview, TX, p. A629
 Executive Vice President Human Resources, Good Shepherd Medical Center–Marshall, Marshall, TX, p. A631
MORROW, Jeffrey, Chief Executive Officer, Doctor's Hospital of Deer Creek, Leesville, LA, p. A279
MORROW, Jennifer, Director Human Resources, San Joaquin Valley Rehabilitation Hospital, Fresno, CA, p. A62
MORROW, Pat, Director Human Resources, Walker Baptist Medical Center, Jasper, AL, p. A21
MORROW, Randy, Vice President and Chief Operating Officer, Boone Hospital Center, Columbia, MO, p. A366
MORROW, Shawn, Administrator, Heber Valley Medical Center, Heber City, UT, p. A655
MORROW, Susan, R.N. Chief Nursing Officer, Garfield County Public Hospital District, Pomeroy, WA, p. A682
MORROW, W. Robert, M.D. Executive Vice President and Chief Medical Officer, Children's Health System of Texas, Dallas, TX, p. A604
MORSCHAUSER, Roberta, Administrator, Brown County Community Treatment Center, Green Bay, WI, p. A702
MORSE, Brad S., Chief Executive Officer, Pampa Regional Medical Center, Pampa, TX, p. A635
MORSE, Craig, Chief Financial Officer, Carlsbad Medical Center, Carlsbad, NM, p. A423
MORSE, Jason, Director Information Technology, Cumberland Memorial Hospital, Cumberland, WI, p. A699
MORSE, Larry, Interim Chief Executive Officer, DeWitt Hospital, De Witt, AR, p. A43
MORSE, Patrick, M.D. President Medical Staff, West Branch Regional Medical Center, West Branch, MI, p. A332
MORSI, Nagy, Chief of Staff, TriStar Greenview Regional Hospital, Bowling Green, KY, p. A255
MORSTAD, Joan, Director Information Systems, Coliseum Medical Centers, Macon, GA, p. A160
MORTENSEN, Lorrie, R.N. Chief Patient Services, Murray County Medical Center, Slayton, MN, p. A347
MORTENSEN, Scott, Administrator, Orem Community Hospital, Orem, UT, p. A656
MORTENSEN, Shane
 Chief Financial Officer, San Luis Valley Health, Alamosa, CO, p. A99
 Chief Financial Officer, San Luis Valley Health Conejos County Hospital, La Jara, CO, p. A105
MORTENSSON, Marcie, Chief Human Resources Officer, Tahoe Forest Hospital District, Truckee, CA, p. A95
MORTHLAND, Tim, Chief of Staff, Franklin Hospital District, Benton, IL, p. A179
MORTINSEN, Roy, M.D. Chief of Staff, Sanford Vermillion Medical Center, Vermillion, SD, p. A572
MORTON, David, M.D. Chief Medical Officer, St. Anthony's Medical Center, Saint Louis, MO, p. A377
MORTON, Lauren, Chief Operating Officer, The Hospitals of Sierra Providence East Campus, El Paso, TX, p. A611
MORTON, Leslie, Manager Human Resources, Riverview Regional Medical Center, Gadsden, AL, p. A20
MORTON, Robert, M.D. Medical Director, Rolling Hills Hospital, Ada, OK, p. A503
MORTON, Stan C., FACHE, President, Texas Health Presbyterian Hospital Denton, Denton, TX, p. A608
MORTON, Stephanie, Chief Information Officer, Providence Alaska Medical Center, Anchorage, AK, p. A27
MORTON, Steve, M.D. Chief Medical Officer, ContinueCare Hospital at Baptist Health Corbin, Corbin, KY, p. A255
MORTOZA, Angela, Administrator, Adair County Memorial Hospital, Greenfield, IA, p. A228
MORVANT, Stephanie, Chief Executive Officer, Post Acute Northshore Specialty Hospital, Covington, LA, p. A272
MOSBY, Charmaine T., Area Director Health Information Management, Promise Hospital Baton Rouge – Main Campus, Baton Rouge, LA, p. A270
MOSBY HENRY, Nita, Vice President Human Resources, Children's Hospital Colorado, Aurora, CO, p. A99
MOSCATO, Mary K., FACHE, President, Hebrew Rehabilitation Center, Boston, MA, p. A303
MOSCHITTA, Philip C., Director, Northport Veterans Affairs Medical Center, Northport, NY, p. A445
MOSCHKAU, Don, Senior Director Human Resources, University of Minnesota Medical Center, Fairview, Minneapolis, MN, p. A343
MOSCOSO, Ricardo, M.D. Medical Director, University Hospital, San Juan, PR, p. A724
MOSEBAR, Anjanette, Director Human Resources, Poudre Valley Hospital, Fort Collins, CO, p. A103
MOSEL, Lindy, Director of Nursing, Memorial Community Health, Aurora, NE, p. A389
MOSELY, Chisty, Director Information Management, Saint Simons by–the–Sea Hospital, Saint Simons Island, GA, p. A163
MOSER, Brenda, Vice President Finance, Regional Health Services of Howard County, Cresco, IA, p. A225
MOSER, Cindy, Director Human Resources, Allegheny Valley Hospital, Natrona Heights, PA, p. A541
MOSER, Neal, M.D. Medical Director, HEALTHSOUTH Northern Kentucky Rehabilitation Hospital, Edgewood, KY, p. A256
MOSER, Stan, Vice President Information Systems, Community Medical Center, Missoula, MT, p. A385
MOSER, Tracy, Director Human Resources, Upper Valley Medical Center, Troy, OH, p. A499
MOSESIAN, Robert, Controller, HEALTHSOUTH Bakersfield Rehabilitation Hospital, Bakersfield, CA, p. A55
MOSHIER, John, Director Human Resources, Clara Barton Hospital, Hoisington, KS, p. A241
MOSHIRPUR, Jasmin, M.D
 Dean and Medical Director, Elmhurst Hospital Center, NY, p. A439
 Chief Medical Officer, Queens Hospital Center, NY, p. A444
MOSHOFSKY, Bill, M.D. Chief of Staff, PeaceHealth Sacred Heart Medical Center University District, Eugene, OR, p. A520
MOSIER, Dawn, Director Human Resources, HEALTHSOUTH Rehabilitation Institute of Tucson, Tucson, AZ, p. A39
MOSIER, John, D.O. Chief of Staff, Herington Municipal Hospital, Herington, KS, p. A241
MOSKOWITZ, Samuel E., President, MedStar Franklin Square Medical Center, Baltimore, MD, p. A294
MOSLEY, Christopher J.
 Chief Operating Officer, Orange Park Medical Center, Orange Park, FL, p. A137
 Chief Executive Officer, Putnam Community Medical Center, Palatka, FL, p. A138
MOSLEY, Christopher R., FACHE Chief Operating Officer, Grady Memorial Hospital, Atlanta, GA, p. A150
MOSLEY, Tonja, Chief Financial Officer, Heart of Florida Regional Medical Center, Davenport, FL, p. A125
MOSMEYER, Kathleen C., Director Human Resources, Citizens Medical Center, Victoria, TX, p. A650
MOSS, Austin, Vice President Human Resources, Jennie Stuart Medical Center, Hopkinsville, KY, p. A258
MOSS, Barry, Assistant Chief Executive Officer, Flowers Hospital, Dothan, AL, p. A18
MOSS, Bradley, Administrator, Behavioral Healthcare Center at Huntsville, Huntsville, AL, p. A21
MOSS, C. Renee, M.D. Chief Medical Officer, Riverside Rehabilitation Institute, Newport News, VA, p. A669
MOSS, Jennifer, MS Chief Clinical Officer, Kirby Medical Center, Monticello, IL, p. A194
MOSS, Misty, Director Business Administration, Logansport State Hospital, Logansport, IN, p. A215
MOSS, Stuart, Chief Financial Officer, Marlton Rehabilitation Hospital, Marlton, NJ, p. A414
MOSSER, Kevin H., M.D., President and Chief Executive Officer, WellSpan Health, York, PA, p. B152
MOSSOFF, Alan, Chief Financial Officer, Northern Dutchess Hospital, Rhinebeck, NY, p. A448
MOST, Kevin, D.O. Vice President Medical Affairs, Northwestern Medicine Central DuPage Hospital, Winfield, IL, p. A203
MOSTAFFA, Cindy, Chief Executive Officer, Texas NeuroRehab Center, Austin, TX, p. A595
MOSTOFI, Ann R., MSN Vice President Patient Care and Chief Nursing Officer, Eisenhower Medical Center, Rancho Mirage, CA, p. A82
MOTAKEF, Shahin, Chief Executive Officer, Scott & White Memorial Hospital, Temple, TX, p. A647
MOTEJZIK, Thomas, Director Information Systems, Carlsbad Medical Center, Carlsbad, NM, p. A423
MOTONAGA, Gregg, M.D. Chief of Staff, Central Peninsula General Hospital, Soldotna, AK, p. A29
MOTTE, Michael J., Chief Executive Officer, St. Alexius Hospital – Broadway Campus, Saint Louis, MO, p. A377
MOUGHAN, Jennifer L., Chief Human Resources Officer, Our Lady of Lourdes Medical Center, Camden, NJ, p. A410
MOUISSET, Rena B., Director Human Resources and Contract Compliance, St. Martin Hospital, Breaux Bridge, LA, p. A271
MOULTON, Susan, Interim Director Health Information Management, Spring Harbor Hospital, Westbrook, ME, p. A292
MOUNIE, Mike, Director Finance, Sentara Obici Hospital, Suffolk, VA, p. A673
MOUNTAIN, J. Michael, Chief Financial Officer, RiverValley Behavioral Health Hospital, Owensboro, KY, p. A264
MOUSA, Ayman, Ph.D., Chief Executive Officer, Pacifica Hospital of the Valley, CA, p. A72
MOUSA, Cindy, Senior Director Human Resources, New Orleans East Hospital, New Orleans, LA, p. A282
MOUSTAKAKIS, John, Senior Vice President Information Systems and Chief Information Officer, Westchester Medical Center, Valhalla, NY, p. A452
MOVSESIAN, Gregory, M.D. Acting Chief of Staff, Aleda E. Lutz Veterans Affairs Medical Center, Saginaw, MI, p. A329
MOWAN, Chris, Chief Executive Officer, MountainView Hospital, Las Vegas, NV, p. A402
MOWDER, Kristan, Director Administration and Patient Care Services, Eastern State Hospital, Lexington, KY, p. A259
MOYA, Linda, Director Human Resources, Mesilla Valley Hospital, Las Cruces, NM, p. A425
MOYER, Dale, Vice President Information Systems, Evangelical Community Hospital, Lewisburg, PA, p. A538
MOYER, Douglas J., Chief Executive Officer, Southside Regional Medical Center, Petersburg, VA, p. A670
MOYER, Karen W., R.N. Senior Vice President and Chief Nursing Officer, Mount Sinai Medical Center, Miami Beach, FL, p. A135
MOYER, William E., President, St. Luke's Hospital – Miners Campus, Coaldale, PA, p. A531
MRAMOR, Joann, Director Human Resources, Seven Rivers Regional Medical Center, Crystal River, FL, p. A124
MUDEN, Todd, Section Head Information Management, Mayo Clinic Health System – Northland in Barron, Barron, WI, p. A698
MUDRY, Janel, Chief Operating Officer, Washington Health System Greene, Waynesburg, PA, p. A552
MUELLER, Arthur, Director Management Information Systems, Cuero Community Hospital, Cuero, TX, p. A603
MUELLER, Charles, M.D. Chief of Staff, Texas County Memorial Hospital, Houston, MO, p. A368
MUELLER, Eric, Chief Executive Officer, Reliant Rehabilitation Hospital Central Texas, Round Rock, TX, p. A639
MUELLER, Jeff T., M.D. Chief Medical Officer, Medical Director, Mayo Clinic Hospital, Phoenix, AZ, p. A35
MUELLER, Karen, R.N. Chief Nursing Officer, Mount Desert Island Hospital, Bar Harbor, ME, p. A288
MUELLER, Michael E., Chief Financial Officer, Health Central Hospital, Ocoee, FL, p. A137
MUELLER, Paul, Chief Financial Officer, Sparta Community Hospital, Sparta, IL, p. A200
MUELLER, Paul A., Chief Executive Officer, Rogers Memorial Hospital, Oconomowoc, WI, p. A708
MUELLER, Scarlott, Chief Nursing Officer, North Florida Regional Medical Center, Gainesville, FL, p. A127
MUGAN, James, Senior Vice President for Clinical Services and Chief Operating Officer, Agnesian HealthCare, Fond Du Lac, WI, p. A700
MUHAMMAD, Mark, Manager Human Resources, Michael E. DeBakey Veterans Affairs Medical Center, Houston, TX, p. A621
MUHS, David, Chief Financial Officer, Henry County Health Center, Mount Pleasant, IA, p. A232
MUILENBURG, Jeff, Chief of Staff, Memorial Community Health, Aurora, NE, p. A389
MUIR, Brian, Chief of Staff, Minidoka Memorial Hospital, Rupert, ID, p. A176
MULDER, Dale R., Chief Executive Officer, Kindred Rehabilitation Hospital Clear Lake, Webster, TX, p. A651
MULDER, Doris, Vice President Nursing, Beloit Health System, Beloit, WI, p. A698
MULDER, Steven, M.D., President and Chief Executive Officer, Hutchinson Health, Hutchinson, MN, p. A340

**A922** Index of Health Care Professionals

Index of Health Care Professionals / Murphy–Frobish

Index of Health Care Professionals


MULDERIG, Marsha L., R.N. Chief Nursing Officer, Crisp Regional Hospital, Cordele, GA, p. A155
MULDOON, Patrick L., FACHE, President and CEO, UMass Memorial Medical Center, Worcester, MA, p. A313
MULDOON, Sean R., M.D. Senior Vice President and Chief Medical Officer–Kindred Healthcare, Hospital Division, Kindred Hospital Northland, Kansas City, MO, p. A370
MULIS, Becky, Director of Health Information Management Systems, Four County Counseling Center, Logansport, IN, p. A215
MULKERRIN, Maureen, R.N. Chief Information Officer, Vice President Innovation and Technology, New England Baptist Hospital, Boston, MA, p. A304
MULKEY, Peter, Chief Executive Officer, Clinch Valley Medical Center, Richlands, VA, p. A671
MULLANEY, Ruth, Personnel Officer, Dorothea Dix Psychiatric Center, Bangor, ME, p. A288
MULLEN, Thomas R., President and Chief Executive Officer, Mercy Medical Center, Baltimore, MD, p. A294
MULLENAX, Paul, Business Manager, Wyoming State Hospital, Evanston, WY, p. A716
MULLENDER, Monica, Director of Nursing, Osborne County Memorial Hospital, Osborne, KS, p. A247
MULLENS, Allen, M.D. Chief Medical Staff, Norton Community Hospital, Norton, VA, p. A670
MULLER, Lynn, Chief Financial Officer, North Metro Medical Center, Jacksonville, AR, p. A46
MULLER, Oz, Director Human Resources, Porter Adventist Hospital, Denver, CO, p. A102
MULLER, Ralph W., President and Chief Executive Officer, University of Pennsylvania Health System, Philadelphia, PA, p. B147
MULLERY, Barbara M., Vice President Administration, Robert Wood Johnson University Hospital Rahway, Rahway, NJ, p. A417
MULLIGAN, Lisa, Commanding Officer, Naval Hospital Camp Pendleton, Camp Pendleton, CA, p. A57
MULLIGAN, Marie, R.N. Vice President Nursing, John T. Mather Memorial Hospital, Port Jefferson, NY, p. A447
MULLIN, Tom, Chief Executive Officer, Select Specialty Hospital–Central Pennsylvania, Camp Hill, PA, p. A530
MULLINGS, Donna, Director of Nursing, Assumption Community Hospital, Napoleonville, LA, p. A281
MULLINGS, Paul, Chief Operating Officer, Howard University Hospital, Washington, DC, p. A119
MULLINS, Bandy, M.D. Chief of Staff, Summersville Regional Medical Center, Summersville, WV, p. A695
MULLINS, Brad, Director Information Technology, Gove County Medical Center, Quinter, KS, p. A249
MULLINS, Cindy, Director Information Technology, Saint Mary's Regional Medical Center, Reno, NV, p. A404
MULLINS, Dustin, Chief Resource Management, Bayne–Jones Army Community Hospital, Fort Polk, LA, p. A273
MULLINS, Erin, D.O. Chief Medical Staff, Dickenson Community Hospital, Clintwood, VA, p. A663
MULLINS Jr., John David, Administrator, Clinton County Hospital, Albany, KY, p. A254
MULLINS, Kem, FACHE,
Senior Vice President and Hospital President, WellStar Cobb Hospital, Austell, GA, p. A152
President, WellStar Windy Hill Hospital, Marietta, GA, p. A161
MULLINS, Larry, Chief Executive Officer and Administrator, W. J. Mangold Memorial Hospital, Lockney, TX, p. A628
MULLINS, Larry A., FACHE, Chief Executive Officer, Good Samaritan Regional Medical Center, Corvallis, OR, p. A520
MULLINS, Larry A., FACHE, President and Chief Executive Officer, Samaritan Health Services, Corvallis, OR, p. B116
MULLIS, Jeffrey, Interim Chief Financial Officer, Bayfront Health Port Charlotte, Port Charlotte, FL, p. A140
MULROONEY, JoAnn M., R.N. Chief Operating Officer, Trinity Health System, Steubenville, OH, p. A498
MULROY, Kevin, D.O. Chief Operating Officer and Chief Quality Officer, Cape Cod Hospital, Hyannis, MA, p. A307
MULTACK, Richard, D.O. Vice President Medical Management, Advocate South Suburban Hospital, Hazel Crest, IL, p. A190
MULVEY, Lee, Human Resource Officer, Texas Health Harris Methodist Hospital Hurst–Euless–Bedford, Bedford, TX, p. A597
MULVIHILL, Jody, Vice President Finance, The Children's Institute of Pittsburgh, Pittsburgh, PA, p. A546
MUMOLIE, Gina, Senior Vice President and Chief Nurse Executive, Inspira Medical Center–Woodbury, Woodbury, NJ, p. A420
MUMPOWER, Rebecca, Director Marketing, Mesilla Valley Hospital, Las Cruces, NM, p. A425
MUNCHEL, Bryan, Senior Vice President and Chief Information Officer, Post Acute Northshore Specialty Hospital, Covington, LA, p. A272
MUNDY, Mark J., President and Chief Executive Officer, New York Methodist Hospital, NY, p. A443
MUNDY, Stephens M., President and Chief Executive Officer, The University of Vermont Health Network–Champlain Valley Physicians Hospital, Plattsburgh, NY, p. A447
MUNFORD, Thedosia, Senior Vice President and Chief Nursing Officer, Providence Hospital, Washington, DC, p. A120
MUNGER, Richard, Administrator, Mount Grant General Hospital, Hawthorne, NV, p. A401
MUNGOVAN, Sandy, Chief Information Officer, Harbor–UCLA Medical Center, Torrance, CA, p. A94
MUNHOLLAND, Cleta
Administrator, Louisiana Extended Care Hospital West Monroe, West Monroe, LA, p. A287
Administrator, Specialty Hospital, Monroe, LA, p. A280
MUNIR, Amjad, M.D. Medical Director, HEALTHSOUTH Chattanooga Rehabilitation Hospital, Chattanooga, TN, p. A575
MUNOZ, Astro, Executive Director, First Hospital Panamericano, Cidra, PR, p. A720
MUNOZ, Thalia H., MS, Chief Executive Officer, Starr County Memorial Hospital, Rio Grande City, TX, p. A638
MUNSON, Bill, Vice President and Chief Financial Officer, Boulder Community Health, Boulder, CO, p. A99
MUNSON, Jennifer, Chief Financial Officer, Three Rivers Hospital, Brewster, WA, p. A677
MUNSON, Joan, Manager Information Systems, Fairchild Medical Center, Yreka, CA, p. A98
MUNSON, John, Vice President and Chief Financial Officer, St. Anthony Regional Hospital, Carroll, IA, p. A223
MUNSON, Kris, Director Human Resources, Arbour H. R. I. Hospital, Brookline, MA, p. A305
MUNTEFERING, Denise, Vice President Patient Care Services, Avera St. Benedict Health Center, Parkston, SD, p. A570
MUNTZ, Dana M., Chief Executive Officer, St. Vincent Salem Hospital, Salem, IN, p. A219
MUNTZ, Tim, President and Chief Executive Officer, St. Margaret's Hospital, Spring Valley, IL, p. A201
MUNYAN, Lori, Director, Human Resources, HEALTHSOUTH Rehabilitation Hospital of Toms River, Toms River, NJ, p. A419
MURANSKY, Ed, Owner, Surgical Hospital at Southwoods, Youngstown, OH, p. A502
MURCHISON, Sandra, Director Medical Records, Coosa Valley Medical Center, Sylacauga, AL, p. A25
MURDOCH, William, M.D. Medical Director, Loma Linda University Behavioral Medicine Center, Redlands, CA, p. A82
MURDOCK, Guy, Vice President Human Resources, Healthbridge Children's Hospital of Houston, Houston, TX, p. A619
MURDOCK, Holly, Human Resources Coordinator, Kindred Hospital Rome, Rome, GA, p. A163
MURDOCK, Mark, Associate Director, Dayton Veterans Affairs Medical Center, Dayton, OH, p. A488
MURDOCK–LANGAN, Patricia, M.D
Chief Medical Officer, CHI Health Lakeside, Omaha, NE, p. A396
Chief Medical Officer, CHI Health Midlands, Papillion, NE, p. A397
MURDY, James B., Chief Financial Officer, Belmont Community Hospital, Bellaire, OH, p. A479
MURFEE, Patrick, Chief Operating Officer, Hemphill County Hospital, Canadian, TX, p. A600
MURILLO, Jeremias, M.D. Chief Medical Officer, Newark Beth Israel Medical Center, Newark, NJ, p. A415
MURIN, William J., Chief Human Resources Officer, UC San Diego Health, San Diego, CA, p. A87
MURPHY, Bruce, M.D., President and Chief Executive Officer, Arkansas Heart Hospital, Little Rock, AR, p. A47
MURPHY, Charles J., Associate Vice President Human Resources, Strong Memorial Hospital of the University of Rochester, Rochester, NY, p. A449
MURPHY, Christine, MS, Administrator, Liberty Healthcare Systems, Bastrop, LA, p. A269
MURPHY, Colleen, M.D. Chief of Staff, Clay County Hospital, Flora, IL, p. A188
MURPHY, David, Interim Chief Executive Officer, Fairview Health Services, Minneapolis, MN, p. B56
MURPHY, Dennis M., Chief Operating Officer, Indiana University Health University Hospital, Indianapolis, IN, p. A212
MURPHY, Elizabeth A., R.N. Vice President for Patient Care Services, Mercy Health Saint Mary's, Grand Rapids, MI, p. A321
MURPHY, Evelyn, R.N. Chief Nursing Officer, St. Mary's Sacred Heart Hospital, Lavonia, GA, p. A160
MURPHY, J. Patrick, Chief Financial Officer, North Baldwin Infirmary, Bay Minette, AL, p. A16
MURPHY, James, Chief Executive Officer, South Texas Surgical Hospital, Corpus Christi, TX, p. A603
MURPHY, James M., M.D. Chief Medical Officer Regional Development and Outpatient Services, New London Hospital, New London, NH, p. A408
MURPHY, Jim, Interim Chief Executive Officer, Melissa Memorial Hospital, Holyoke, CO, p. A105
MURPHY, John B., M.D. Vice President Medical Affairs and Chief Medical Officer, Rhode Island Hospital, Providence, RI, p. A556
MURPHY, John M., M.D., President and Chief Executive Officer, Western Connecticut Health Network, Danbury Hospital, Danbury, CT, p. A111
MURPHY, John M., M.D., President, Western Connecticut Health Network, Danbury, CT, p. B153
MURPHY, Judy, Vice President Human Resources, Southwest General Health Center, Middleburg Heights, OH, p. A494
MURPHY, Julie
Chief Financial Officer, Saint Luke's Cushing Hospital, Leavenworth, KS, p. A244
Chief Financial Officer, Saint Luke's North Hospital – Barry Road, Kansas City, MO, p. A370
MURPHY, Kathryn, Chief Operating Officer and Chief Nursing Officer, Forest Park Medical Center Frisco, Frisco, TX, p. A615
MURPHY, Kathy, Site Manager, Mescalero Public Health Service Indian Hospital, Mescalero, NM, p. A425
MURPHY, Kelly, Director Human Resources, Family Health West, Fruita, CO, p. A104
MURPHY, Kevin, Director, Information Technology Services, Bayfront Health St. Petersburg, Saint Petersburg, FL, p. A142
MURPHY, Kyle, Director Information Technology, Mayhill Hospital, Denton, TX, p. A608
MURPHY, Linda, Chief Financial Officer, Osborne County Memorial Hospital, Osborne, KS, p. A247
MURPHY, Lionel
Chief Executive Officer and Administrator, Bethesda Rehabilitation Hospital, Baton Rouge, LA, p. A269
Chief Executive Officer, Southeast Regional Medical Center, Kentwood, LA, p. A276
MURPHY, Lynda J., Vice President Human Resources, Logansport Memorial Hospital, Logansport, IN, p. A215
MURPHY, Mary S., R.N. Regional Chief Nursing Officer, Adventist La Grange Memorial Hospital, La Grange, IL, p. A192
MURPHY, Marybeth, Director Human Resources, Madison St. Joseph Health Center, Madisonville, TX, p. A630
MURPHY, Matthew, Chief Financial Officer, Marengo Memorial Hospital, UnityPoint Health, Marengo, IA, p. A231
MURPHY, Maureen, M.D. Director of Medical Affairs, St. Clare Hospital, Baraboo, WI, p. A697
MURPHY, Michael, M.D. Chief Medical Officer, Sharp Grossmont Hospital, La Mesa, CA, p. A66
MURPHY, Michael, CPA, President & Chief Executive Officer, Sharp HealthCare, San Diego, CA, p. B122
MURPHY, Michael D., Chief Executive Officer, Abilene Regional Medical Center, Abilene, TX, p. A590
MURPHY, Michael J., FACHE, Director, Veterans Affairs Puget Sound Health Care System, Seattle, WA, p. A684
MURPHY, Mike, Chief Patient Care Officer, Beaver Dam Community Hospitals, Beaver Dam, WI, p. A698
MURPHY, Nancy, Vice President, Human Resources, Franciscan Hospital for Children, Boston, MA, p. A303
MURPHY, Peter J., Senior Vice President and Chief Operating Officer, Franciscan St. Francis Health – Mooresville, Mooresville, IN, p. A216
MURPHY, Richard J., President and Chief Executive Officer, South Nassau Communities Hospital, Oceanside, NY, p. A446
MURPHY, Rita, Director Human Resources, Cobre Valley Regional Medical Center, Globe, AZ, p. A32
MURPHY, Steve
FM–East Region IS, Good Samaritan Regional Health Center, Mount Vernon, IL, p. A195
Director Information Systems, St. Mary's Hospital, Centralia, IL, p. A180
MURPHY, Steven, Executive Director, Devereux Hospital and Children's Center of Florida, Melbourne, FL, p. A133
MURPHY, Terry
President and Chief Executive Officer, Bayhealth Medical Center, Dover, DE, p. A117
Director Information Services, Phoenixville Hospital, Phoenixville, PA, p. A545
MURPHY, Timothy, R.N. Chief Nursing Officer, HEALTHSOUTH Desert Canyon Rehabilitation Hospital, Las Vegas, NV, p. A402
MURPHY, Timothy
Vice President Human Resources, Mercy Hospital Fort Scott, Fort Scott, KS, p. A240
Vice President Human Resources, Mercy Hospital Joplin, Joplin, MO, p. A369
MURPHY, Tom, Chief Executive Officer, Weiser Memorial Hospital, Weiser, ID, p. A177
MURPHY–FROBISH, Erin, Vice President Human Resources, Morris Hospital & Healthcare Centers, Morris, IL, p. A195

Index of Health Care Professionals

Index of Health Care Professionals / Murray

MURRAY, Alexander, Interim Associate Director, Veterans Affairs Gulf Coast Veterans Health Care System, Biloxi, MS, p. A350
MURRAY, Brian, M.D. Medical Director, Erie County Medical Center, Buffalo, NY, p. A430
MURRAY, Brian, Chief Financial Officer, Gunnison Valley Hospital, Gunnison, UT, p. A655
MURRAY, Cindy, R.N. Chief Nursing Officer and Chief Operating Officer, Baylor Medical Center at Waxahachie, Waxahachie, TX, p. A650
MURRAY, Denise R., Chief Executive Officer, Carolinas ContinueCARE Hospital at Kings Mountain, Kings Mountain, NC, p. A463
MURRAY, Diana, Director Information Systems, Grand River Hospital District, Rifle, CO, p. A108
MURRAY, Geno, President and Chief Executive Officer, Charles A. Dean Memorial Hospital, Greenville, ME, p. A290
MURRAY, Gerald
President, UPMC Altoona, Altoona, PA, p. A528
President, UPMC Bedford Memorial, Everett, PA, p. A534
MURRAY, James Patrick, FACHE, President and Chief Executive Officer, Peterson Regional Medical Center, Kerrville, TX, p. A626
MURRAY, Julie, Chief Executive Officer, Litzenberg Memorial County Hospital, Central City, NE, p. A390
MURRAY, Kent, M.D. Chief of Staff, Robert J. Dole Veterans Affairs Medical Center, Wichita, KS, p. A252
MURRAY, Kevin, M.D. Director Medical Services, Lake Taylor Transitional Care Hospital, Norfolk, VA, p. A669
MURRAY, Kevin J., Senior Vice President, John T. Mather Memorial Hospital, Port Jefferson, NY, p. A447
MURRAY, Patricia M., Information Officer, Southern Inyo Healthcare District, Lone Pine, CA, p. A68
MURRAY, Sherri, Chief Financial Officer, Montgomery General Hospital, Montgomery, WV, p. A693
MURRAY, Susan, Director Information Services, Trident Medical Center, Charleston, SC, p. A558
MURRAY, Wesley E., Chief Executive Officer, Texas County Memorial Hospital, Houston, MO, p. A368
MURRELL, Joseph, Chief Executive Officer, Wayne County Hospital, Monticello, KY, p. A263
MURRILL, Mike, Vice President and Chief Financial Officer, Adventist Bolingbrook Hospital, Bolingbrook, IL, p. A180
MURROW, Carol, Vice President Business Development, Cox Medical Center Branson, Branson, MO, p. A364
MURRY, Jim, Chief Information Officer, Stony Brook University Medical Center, Stony Brook, NY, p. A451
MURT, Mary Lou, R.N. Senior Vice President Nursing, Monongahela Valley Hospital, Monongahela, PA, p. A540
MURTHY, Bangalore, M.D. Director Medical Staff, Jackson Park Hospital and Medical Center, Chicago, IL, p. A182
MUSACK, Scott, Chief Information Officer, Silver Lake Medical Center, Los Angeles, CA, p. A72
MUSGRAVE, Chelsea, Director of Human Resources, Clay County Hospital, Flora, IL, p. A188
MUSOIU, Robert, Director Human Resources, Fairfield Memorial Hospital, Fairfield, IL, p. A188
MUSSI, Natalie, President and Chief Executive Officer, Los Robles Hospital and Medical Center, Thousand Oaks, CA, p. A94
MUSSMAN, Rebekah, Chief Executive Officer, Crete Area Medical Center, Crete, NE, p. A391
MUSSO, Lewis C., Vice President Human Resources, Trinity Health System, Steubenville, OH, p. A498
MUSTARD, Ruth W., R.N. Associate Director Nursing and Patient Services, Wm. Jennings Bryan Dorn Veterans Affairs Medical Center, Columbia, SC, p. A560
MUSTIAN, J. Perry, President, Archbold Medical Center, Thomasville, GA, p. B11
MUSTIAN, J. Perry, President and Chief Executive Officer, John D. Archbold Memorial Hospital, Thomasville, GA, p. A166
MUSUNURU, J.R., M.D. Executive Director, Fond Du Lac County Mental Health Center, Fond Du Lax, WI, p. A700
MUTZIGER, John, M.D. Chief Medical Officer, Laird Hospital, Union, MS, p. A361
MWANIKI, Mary
Chief Financial Officer, Reliant Rehabilitation Hospital Dallas, Dallas, TX, p. A606
Chief Financial Officer, Reliant Rehabilitation Hospital Mid–Cities, Bedford, TX, p. A596
MWEBE, David, M.D. Chief of Staff, Osmond General Hospital, Osmond, NE, p. A397
MYATT, Kevin A., Senior Vice President Human Resources, Yale–New Haven Hospital, New Haven, CT, p. A114
MYDLER, Todd, M.D. Vice President and Chief Medical Officer, Good Samaritan Medical Center, Lafayette, CO, p. A106
MYER, Amber, Director Medical Technology, Throckmorton County Memorial Hospital, Throckmorton, TX, p. A648
MYERS, April, Administrator, Kindred Hospital–La Mirada, La Mirada, CA, p. A66
MYERS, Becky, Human Resources Specialist, Illini Community Hospital, Pittsfield, IL, p. A198
MYERS, Carl, M.D. Vice President Medical Affairs and Chief Medical Officer, Yuma Regional Medical Center, Yuma, AZ, p. A40
MYERS, Chrissy, R.N. Director of Nursing, Behavioral HealthCare Center at Clarksville, Clarksville, TN, p. A575
MYERS, Doug, Senior Vice President and Chief Financial Officer, Children's Hospital and Research Center Oakland, Oakland, CA, p. A78
MYERS, Douglas, Executive Vice President and Chief Financial Officer, Children's National Medical Center, Washington, DC, p. A119
MYERS, Ed, Administrator, Shriners Hospitals for Children–Philadelphia, Philadelphia, PA, p. A545
MYERS, Gabby, Human Resources Director, Victory Surgical Hospital East Houston, Houston, TX, p. A623
MYERS, Gary, Chief Executive Officer, Mammoth Hospital, Mammoth Lakes, CA, p. A74
MYERS, Grace, MSN Vice President, Nurse Executive, Sentara Princess Anne Hospital, Virginia Beach, VA, p. A674
MYERS, Jeffrey D., President and Chief Executive Officer, Hamilton Medical Center, Dalton, GA, p. A155
MYERS, Jerry, M.D., Chief Executive Officer, Kell West Regional Hospital, Wichita Falls, TX, p. A652
MYERS, Karen, Vice President Financial Services, Stoughton Hospital Association, Stoughton, WI, p. A711
MYERS, Karen K., MSN Vice President and Chief Nursing Officer, Baylor St. Luke's Medical Center, Houston, TX, p. A619
MYERS, Kathy R., MS Chief Nursing Officer, Tennova Healthcare–LaFollette Medical Center, La Follette, TN, p. A581
MYERS, Keith G., Chairman and Chief Executive Officer, LHC Group, Lafayette, LA, p. B82
MYERS, Kevin, Director Information Systems, Lake Granbury Medical Center, Granbury, TX, p. A616
MYERS, Kimberly, Director Human Resources, Guthrie County Hospital, Guthrie Center, IA, p. A228
MYERS, Lisa, Director Human Resources, Heritage Oaks Hospital, Sacramento, CA, p. A84
MYERS, Loretta, MS Director, Patient Care, Floyd Valley Hospital, Le Mars, IA, p. A230
MYERS, Lynn, Controller, Kindred Hospital–Tucson, Tucson, AZ, p. A39
MYERS, Mark, M.D. Chief Medical Officer, AMG Specialty Hospital–Tulsa, Tulsa, OK, p. A516
MYERS, Mary, R.N. Chief Nursing Officer, St. Vincent Indianapolis Hospital, Indianapolis, IN, p. A212
MYERS, Michael D., R.N., Chief Executive Officer, Veterans Memorial Hospital, Waukon, IA, p. A236
MYERS, Michelle F., Director Human Resources, Florida Hospital Wauchula, Wauchula, FL, p. A146
MYERS, Paul, M.D. Neonatologist and Chief Medical Officer, Children's Hospital of Wisconsin–Fox Valley, Neenah, WI, p. A707
MYERS, Philip, M.D. Vice President Medical Affairs, Samaritan Regional Health System, Ashland, OH, p. A478
MYERS, Randy, Chief Information Officer, Information Technology, Mitchell County Hospital, Colorado City, TX, p. A601
MYERS, Robert T., President, Parkview LaGrange Hospital, LaGrange, IN, p. A214
MYERS, Russ, Chief Executive Officer, Yakima Valley Memorial Hospital, Yakima, WA, p. A688
MYERS, Shane P., Chief Operating Officer, Iberia Medical Center, New Iberia, LA, p. A281
MYERS, Sheri, Vice President Patient Care Services, McLaren Central Michigan, Mount Pleasant, MI, p. A326
MYERS, Steve, Assistant Administrator, Southeast Health Center of Reynolds County, Ellington, MO, p. A366
MYERS, Tara, Director Human Resources, AnMed Health Rehabilitation Hospital, Anderson, SC, p. A557
MYERS, William, Chief Operating Officer, Montgomery County Emergency Service, Norristown, PA, p. A541
MYHRE, Tracy, R.N. Chief Nursing Officer, Tomah Memorial Hospital, Tomah, WI, p. A712
MYSTER, Jennifer, President, Buffalo Hospital, Buffalo, MN, p. A336

## N

NABEL, Elizabeth, M.D., President, Brigham and Women's Hospital, Boston, MA, p. A303
NABORS, Teresa, Director of Nursing, Greenwood Regional Rehabilitation Hospital, Greenwood, SC, p. A562
NACEY, Marley, Director Finance, Sentara Virginia Beach General Hospital, Virginia Beach, VA, p. A674
NACHIMUTHU, Anbu, Chief Financial Officer, Atrium Medical Center of Corinth, Corinth, TX, p. A602
NACHTIGAL, Amy, Chief Financial Officer, Saint Luke's Hospital of Kansas City, Kansas City, MO, p. A370
NACHTRIEB, Han, Vice President Human Resources, Seattle Cancer Care Alliance, Seattle, WA, p. A683
NACION, Glenn, Vice President Human Resources, Trinitas Regional Medical Center, Elizabeth, NJ, p. A411
NADEAU, Barbara, Chief Human Resources Management Service, White River Junction Veterans Affairs Medical Center, White River Junction, VT, p. A661
NADEAU, Colleen, Vice President Patient Care Operations, Maple Grove Hospital, Maple Grove, MN, p. A342
NADEAU, Steve, Senior Vice President Human Resources, Gwinnett Hospital System, Lawrenceville, GA, p. A160
NADER, Daniel, D.O. Chief of Staff, Southwestern Regional Medical Center, Tulsa, OK, p. A517
NADER, Keoni, Director Human Resources, Louis A. Weiss Memorial Hospital, Chicago, IL, p. A182
NADER, Mary, Director Information Technology, Spectrum Health Special Care Hospital, Grand Rapids, MI, p. A321
NADER, Rick Lee, Chief Financial Officer, Haxtun Hospital District, Haxtun, CO, p. A105
NADKARNI, Manasi, M.D. Vice President Medical Affairs, UnityPoint Health – Trinity Muscatine, Muscatine, IA, p. A232
NADLE, Patricia A., R.N. Chief Nursing Officer, St. Joseph Health Services of Rhode Island, North Providence, RI, p. A555
NADLER, Tammy R., Chief Financial Officer, Golden Valley Memorial Healthcare, Clinton, MO, p. A365
NADOLNY, Stephanie, Vice President of Hospital Operations, Spaulding Rehabilitation Hospital Cape Cod, East Sandwich, MA, p. A306
NADONE, John, Chief Financial Officer, Southwest Memorial Hospital, Cortez, CO, p. A101
NAEVE, Clayton, Vice President and Chief Information Officer, St. Jude Children's Research Hospital, Memphis, TN, p. A584
NAFZIGER, Laurie N., President and Chief Executive Officer, Oaklawn Psychiatric Center, Goshen, IN, p. A210
NAFZIGER, Steve, M.D. Vice President Medical Affairs, Parkview Medical Center, Pueblo, CO, p. A108
NAGARAJ, Alaka, M.D. Medical Director, Regency Hospital of Minneapolis, Golden Valley, MN, p. A339
NAGEL, Donna, Director Human Resources, AMG Specialty Hospital–Tulsa, Tulsa, OK, p. A516
NAGEL, Melody, Chief Executive Officer, Select Specialty Hospital – Dallas Downtown, Dallas, TX, p. A606
NAGLE, Jolene, Director Medical Records, Peterson Rehabilitation Hospital, Wheeling, WV, p. A696
NAGLER, Richard, M.D. Chief of Staff, Mayo Clinic Health System – Northland in Barron, Barron, WI, p. A698
NAGLOSKY, Paul, Administrator, Indianhead Medical Center, Shell Lake, WI, p. A711
NAGOWSKI, Michael, President and Chief Executive Officer, Cape Fear Valley Health System, Fayetteville, NC, p. B26
NAGOWSKI, Michael, Chief Executive Officer, Cape Fear Valley Medical Center, Fayetteville, NC, p. A460
NAGY, Jeff, Chief Financial Officer, River Bend Hospital, West Lafayette, IN, p. A221
NAGY, Kimberly, R.N. Executive Vice President, Patient Services and Chief Nursing Officer, Northwest Community Hospital, Arlington Heights, IL, p. A178
NAGY, Linda J., MSN Chief Nursing Officer, Brattleboro Retreat, Brattleboro, VT, p. A660
NAHAPETIAN, Arby, M.D. Vice President Medical Affairs and Quality, Glendale Adventist Medical Center, Glendale, CA, p. A63
NAHMENSEN, Rob, Chief Executive Officer, Hamilton County Hospital, Syracuse, KS, p. A251
NAIBERK, Donald T., Administrator, Butler County Health Care Center, David City, NE, p. A391
NAIR, Chand, M.D. Medical Director, Brooke Glen Behavioral Hospital, Fort Washington, PA, p. A534
NAIR, Vijayachandran, M.D. Chief of Staff, John J. Pershing Veterans Affairs Medical Center, Poplar Bluff, MO, p. A374
NAJIEB, LaDonna, Service Area Director Human Resources, Providence Saint Joseph Medical Center, Burbank, CA, p. A56
NAJJAR, Maher, M.D. Medical Director, Kindred Hospital Chicago–Northlake, Northlake, IL, p. A196
NAJJAR, Milad, Information Technology, Freedom Pain Hospital, Scottsdale, AZ, p. A37
NAKAGAWA, Marc, Regional Director Finance, Transylvania Regional Hospital, Brevard, NC, p. A456
NAKAMOTO, Kenneth, M.D. Vice President Medical Affairs, Pomona Valley Hospital Medical Center, Pomona, CA, p. A81
NAKAMURA, Bridget, Director Information Systems, Simi Valley Hospital, Simi Valley, CA, p. A92

Index of Health Care Professionals

Index of Health Care Professionals / Nell

NAKASUJI, Jody, Chief Financial Officer, Harbor–UCLA Medical Center, Torrance, CA, p. A94
NALDI, Robert, Chief Financial Officer, Maimonides Medical Center, NY, p. A441
NALEPPA, Margaret, Ph.D., President and Chief Executive Officer, Peninsula Regional Medical Center, Salisbury, MD, p. A300
NALL, Brian, President and Chief Executive Officer, Greenville Regional Hospital, Greenville, IL, p. A189
NALL, Wes, Chief Financial Officer, Monroe County Hospital, Monroeville, AL, p. A22
NALLE, Tambara, Chief Financial Officer, Eastern State Hospital, Lexington, KY, p. A259
NALLEY, Leanna W., Director Human Resources, Texas Health Harris Methodist Hospital Southwest Fort Worth, Fort Worth, TX, p. A614
NANAYAKKARA, Nalin, M.D. Chief of Staff, Corona Regional Medical Center, Corona, CA, p. A58
NANCE, Christi, R.N. Chief Nursing Officer, Northwest Specialty Hospital, Post Falls, ID, p. A176
NANCE, Sally S., Chief Executive Officer, Excelsior Springs Hospital, Excelsior Springs, MO, p. A367
NANIA, James A., System Vice President and Chief Financial Officer, Hallmark Health System, Melrose, MA, p. A308
NAPIER, Frank, Interim Chief Financial Officer, Cobre Valley Regional Medical Center, Globe, AZ, p. A32
NAPIER, Michelle, Director of Nursing, Central State Hospital, Louisville, KY, p. A261
NAPIER, Pamela, R.N. Chief Nursing Officer, Mercy Willard Hospital, Willard, OH, p. A500
NAPIER, Randy L.
President, Frazier Rehab Institute, Louisville, KY, p. A261
President, Southern Indiana Rehabilitation Hospital, New Albany, IN, p. A217
NAPIERKOWSKI, Daniel, M.D. Chief Executive Officer, Euclid Hospital, Euclid, OH, p. A489
NAPOLITANO, Mary Pat, Director Human Resources, Specialty Hospital of Central Jersey, Lakewood, NJ, p. A413
NAPP, Marc L., M.D. Vice President Medical Affairs, Lenox Hill Hospital, New York, NY, p. A441
NAPPS, Greg, Chief Executive Officer, UVA Culpeper Hospital, Culpeper, VA, p. A664
NAQVI, Al, Chief Financial Officer, Decatur Memorial Hospital, Decatur, IL, p. A186
NARAMORE, G. Harold, M.D. Chief Medical Officer and In house Legal Counsel, Blount Memorial Hospital, Maryville, TN, p. A582
NARANG, Steve, M.D., Chief Executive Officer, Banner Good Samaritan Medical Center, Phoenix, AZ, p. A34
NARANJO, Maria, Director Human Resources, Memorial Hospital West, Pembroke Pines, FL, p. A139
NARBUTAS, Virgis
Chief Executive Officer, La Palma Intercommunity Hospital, La Palma, CA, p. A66
Chief Executive Officer, West Anaheim Medical Center, Anaheim, CA, p. A53
NAREMORE, Bruce, Senior Vice President and Chief Financial Officer, East Jefferson General Hospital, Metairie, LA, p. A280
NARROW, Ann, Director of Nursing, River Hospital, Alexandria Bay, NY, p. A428
NARY, Ed, Director Information Technology and Chief Compliance Officer, Wilbarger General Hospital, Vernon, TX, p. A650
NASET–PAYNE, Janet, R.N. Chief Nursing Officer, Van Diest Medical Center, Webster City, IA, p. A236
NASH, Gayle, R.N. Chief Nursing Officer, MountainView Regional Medical Center, Las Cruces, NM, p. A425
NASH, Jan, Ph.D. Vice President Patient Services and Chief Nursing Officer, Paoli Hospital, Paoli, PA, p. A542
NASH, Jeff, Director Information Technology and Services, Mary Black Health System – Spartanburg, Spartanburg, SC, p. A565
NASH, John D., FACHE, President and Chief Executive Officer, Franciscan Hospital for Children, Boston, MA, p. A303
NASH, Mary G., Ph.D. Chief Nursing Officer, Ohio State University Wexner Medical Center, Columbus, OH, p. A486
NASH, Rhonda, Director Health Information Management, Dallas Behavioral Healthcare Hospital, Desoto, TX, p. A608
NASH, Robert, M.D. Chief of Staff, Richland Memorial Hospital, Olney, IL, p. A197
NASH, Sandra, Chief Fiscal Service, James H. Quillen Veterans Affairs Medical Center, Mountain Home, TN, p. A585
NASH, Tim, M.D. Chief of Staff, Marshall Medical Center, Lewisburg, TN, p. A581
NASHID, Nadia, M.D. Chief of Staff, Windham Hospital, Willimantic, CT, p. A116
NASIR, Iqbal, M.D. Chief of Staff, Beaumont Hospital – Trenton, Trenton, MI, p. A331
NASLUND, Kevin, Manager Information Technology, Cherokee Regional Medical Center, Cherokee, IA, p. A224
NASR, Anthony, M.D. Chief Medical Staff, Feather River Hospital, Paradise, CA, p. A80
NASRALLA, Anthony J., FACHE, President and Chief Executive Officer, Titusville Area Hospital, Titusville, PA, p. A550
NASRALLAH, Fadi, M.D. Vice President Medical Affairs, Mother Frances Hospital – Tyler, Tyler, TX, p. A649
NASSIEF, Raymond, Senior Vice President Operations and Clinical Transformation, John Muir Medical Center, Walnut Creek, Walnut Creek, CA, p. A97
NASSTROM, Jeff, D.O. Chief of Staff, Mitchell County Regional Health Center, Osage, IA, p. A232
NATAL, Yesenia, Coordinator Human Resources, Hospital Dr. Cayetano Coll Y Toste, Arecibo, PR, p. A719
NATALONI, Tom, Senior Director Information Technology, Hahnemann University Hospital, Philadelphia, PA, p. A543
NATCHER, Charles, Chief Financial Officer, Kindred Hospital–Los Angeles, Los Angeles, CA, p. A70
NATELSON, Richard, M.D. Chief of Staff, Steele Memorial Medical Center, Salmon, ID, p. A176
NATEMAN, Barry, Manager Human Resources, French Hospital Medical Center, San Luis Obispo, CA, p. A90
NATH, Pravene, Chief Information Officer, Stanford Health Care, Palo Alto, CA, p. A80
NATHAN, James R.
President and Chief Executive Officer, Cape Coral Hospital, Cape Coral, FL, p. A123
President and Chief Executive Officer, Gulf Coast Medical Center, Fort Myers, FL, p. A127
NATHAN, James R., President and Chief Executive Officer, Lee Memorial Health System, Fort Myers, FL, p. B81
NATHAN, James R., President and Chief Executive Officer, Lee Memorial Hospital, Fort Myers, FL, p. A127
NATHAN, Matthew L., Surgeon General, Bureau of Medicine and Surgery, Department of the Navy, Washington, DC, p. B25
NATHANSON, Andrea, Director Finance, Baystate Franklin Medical Center, Greenfield, MA, p. A307
NATHEM, Joanne, MSN Chief Clinical and Nursing Officer, Waverly Health Center, Waverly, IA, p. A236
NATOLI, Joseph B., Senior Vice President Business and Finance and Chief Financial Officer, University of Miami Hospital and Clinics, Miami, FL, p. A135
NATRAJAN, Sunil, M.D. Medical Director, Kindred Hospital–Tucson, Tucson, AZ, p. A39
NAU, James, Manager Computer and Applications Support, Delaware Psychiatric Center, New Castle, DE, p. A117
NAVA, Madeline, Chief Operating Officer, Palms West Hospital, Loxahatchee, FL, p. A132
NAVARRO, Israel, Chief Executive Officer, Integrity Transitional Hospital, Denton, TX, p. A608
NAVARRO, Ramomita, Director Human Resources, University Hospital, San Juan, PR, p. A724
NAVARRO, Tess, Chief Financial Officer, Laguna Honda Hospital and Rehabilitation Center, San Francisco, CA, p. A88
NAVAS, Manuel, M.D. Medical Director, Hospital San Pablo Del Este, Fajardo, PR, p. A721
NAWROCKI, Bernie
Administrative Director Finance, ProMedica Bixby Hospital, Adrian, MI, p. A314
Administrative Director Finance, ProMedica Herrick Hospital, Tecumseh, MI, p. A331
NAWROCKI, Edward, President, St. Luke's Hospital – Anderson Campus, Easton, PA, p. A533
NAZ, Haroon, Chief Executive Officer, Pinnacle Hospital, Crown Point, IN, p. A207
NAZARIAN, Alexander, CPA Chief Financial Officer, Kirby Medical Center, Monticello, IL, p. A194
NAZE, Jesse, Chief Financial Officer, Fall River Hospital, Hot Springs, SD, p. A569
NAZEERI–SIMMONS, Iman, Chief Operating Officer, San Francisco General Hospital and Trauma Center, San Francisco, CA, p. A88
NDOW, Emmanuel, Chief Information Officer, Marion General Hospital, Marion, IN, p. A215
NEAL, Bob, Information Technology, Sparrow Ionia Hospital, Ionia, MI, p. A322
NEAL, Greg, President, Wellmont Bristol Regional Medical Center, Bristol, TN, p. A574
NEAL, Robert, Manager Information Technology Services, Newman Memorial Hospital, Shattuck, OK, p. A514
NEAL, Roger, Vice President and Chief Information Officer, Duncan Regional Hospital, Duncan, OK, p. A505
NEAL, Terri, Director Human Resources, Crittenton Children's Center, Kansas City, MO, p. A369
NEALE, Debra, R.N. Chief Nursing Officer, O'Connor Hospital, Delhi, NY, p. A432
NEALON, Matthew, Vice President, Chief Financial Officer, University of Cincinnati Medical Center, Cincinnati, OH, p. A484
NEAPOLITAN, David, Chief Financial Officer, Emanuel Medical Center, Turlock, CA, p. A95
NEAR, Holly, Chief Administrative Officer, Harsha Behavioral Center, Terre Haute, IN, p. A220
NEAT, Gary, Director Information Systems, Ephraim McDowell Fort Logan Hospital, Stanford, KY, p. A266
NECAS, Kevin, Chief Financial Officer, University of Missouri Hospitals and Clinics, Columbia, MO, p. A366
NECHANICKY, Jeff, Assistant Director, Richard L. Roudebush Veterans Affairs Medical Center, Indianapolis, IN, p. A212
NEEB, Verette, R.N. Chief Nursing Officer, Baylor Medical Center at Uptown, Dallas, TX, p. A604
NEECE, Patrick, Chief Information Officer, Jefferson Regional Medical Center, Pine Bluff, AR, p. A50
NEEDHAM, Kim
Assistant Chief Executive Officer, Vista Medical Center East, Waukegan, IL, p. A203
Assistant Chief Executive Officer, Vista Medical Center West, Waukegan, IL, p. A203
NEEDHAM, Tammy, Chief Nursing Officer, Chatham Hospital, Siler City, NC, p. A468
NEEDLES, Kim, Manager Business Office, Patients' Hospital of Redding, Redding, CA, p. A82
NEELAGARU, Narasimhulu, M.D. Chief of Staff, Northridge Medical Center, Commerce, GA, p. A154
NEELEY, Scott, M.D. Chief Medical Officer, St. Alexius Medical Center, Hoffman Estates, IL, p. A191
NEELY, Cindy, Administrator, Mercy Maude Norton Hospital, Columbus, KS, p. A238
NEELY, Denise, R.N. Vice President and Chief Nursing Officer, Bronson Methodist Hospital, Kalamazoo, MI, p. A323
NEELY, K. Dale, FACHE, Chief Executive Officer, HealthSouth Rehabilitation Hospital of Tallahassee, Tallahassee, FL, p. A144
NEELY, Randall, Chief Executive Officer, Simpson General Hospital, Mendenhall, MS, p. A357
NEERGHEEN, Chabilal, M.D. Medical Director, Western Massachusetts Hospital, Westfield, MA, p. A313
NEESEN, Cindy, Director of Information Technology, Butler County Health Care Center, David City, NE, p. A391
NEET, Bradley D., FACHE, Chief Executive Officer, Southwest Healthcare System, Murrieta, CA, p. A77
NEFCY, Christine, M.D. Chief Medical Officer, McKay–Dee Hospital Center, Ogden, UT, p. A656
NEFF, Brenda, MSN Vice President Patient Care Services and Chief Nursing Officer, North Country Hospital and Health Center, Newport, VT, p. A660
NEFF, Mark J., FACHE, President and Chief Executive Officer, St. Claire Regional Medical Center, Morehead, KY, p. A263
NEFF, William, M.D
Chief Medical Officer, Medical Center of the Rockies, Loveland, CO, p. A107
Chief Medical Officer, Poudre Valley Hospital, Fort Collins, CO, p. A103
NEGOSHIAN, Carol, MSN Chief Nursing Officer, Putnam Community Medical Center, Palatka, FL, p. A138
NEGRON, Manuel, Chief Information Technology Service, Veterans Affairs Caribbean Healthcare System, San Juan, PR, p. A724
NEIKIRK, Richard, Chief Executive Officer, Cumberland County Hospital, Burkesville, KY, p. A255
NEIL, Eric, Interim Chief Information Officer, UW Medicine/Northwest Hospital & Medical Center, Seattle, WA, p. A684
NEIL, William, Vice President and Chief Information Officer, Indian River Medical Center, Vero Beach, FL, p. A146
NEILSON, Carol, CPA Controller, HEALTHSOUTH Sugar Land Rehabilitation Hospital, Sugar Land, TX, p. A645
NEILSON, Richard, Director of Information Services, Timpanogos Regional Hospital, Orem, UT, p. A657
NEIMAN, Carla, Chief Financial Officer, Clark Fork Valley Hospital, Plains, MT, p. A386
NEISWONGER, Randy, Chief Executive Officer, Select Specialty Hospital–Erie, Erie, PA, p. A534
NEITZEL, Monte, Chief Executive Officer, Greater Regional Medical Center, Creston, IA, p. A225
NELK, Gretchen, Director Human Resources, Caverna Memorial Hospital, Horse Cave, KY, p. A258
NELKIN MCCORMICK, Elizabeth, MSN Chief Nursing Officer, Memorial Sloan–Kettering Cancer Center, New York, NY, p. A441
NELL, Rocio, M.D., Chief Executive Officer, Montgomery County Emergency Service, Norristown, PA, p. A541
NELL, Sergio, Director Information Systems, Watsonville Community Hospital, Watsonville, CA, p. A97

NELSON, Allison
Chief Financial Officer, Sanford Canby Medical Center, Canby, MN, p. A336
Chief Financial Officer, Sanford Clear Lake Medical Center, Clear Lake, SD, p. A568

NELSON, Barbara J., Ph.D. Chief Nursing Executive, Sutter Roseville Medical Center, Roseville, CA, p. A84

NELSON, Bill, Chief Executive Officer, Mille Lacs Health System, Onamia, MN, p. A344

NELSON, Carol, Director Human Resources, Montevista Hospital, Las Vegas, NV, p. A402

NELSON, Cheryl, Chief Nursing Officer, HEALTHSOUTH Rehabilitation Hospital of Southern Arizona, Tucson, AZ, p. A39

NELSON, David, M.D. Medical Director, Barlow Respiratory Hospital, Los Angeles, CA, p. A69

NELSON, David, FACH
Division Chief Financial Officer, HSHS St. Joseph's Hospital, Chippewa Falls, WI, p. A699
Chief Financial Officer, Sacred Heart Hospital, Eau Claire, WI, p. A700

NELSON, David A., President, CHI St. Francis Health, Breckenridge, MN, p. A336

NELSON, Dawn, Director Human Resources, SageWest Health Care at Riverton, Riverton, WY, p. A717

NELSON, Deana, FACHE Executive Vice President and Chief Operating Officer, Tampa General Hospital, Tampa, FL, p. A145

NELSON, Diana, R.N. Associate Director for Patient Care Services/Nurse Executive, Jonathan M. Wainwright Memorial Veterans Affairs Medical Center, Walla Walla, WA, p. A687

NELSON, Elaine, R.N. Chief Nursing Officer, Texas Health Harris Methodist Hospital Fort Worth, Fort Worth, TX, p. A614

NELSON, Frederick, Administrator, Ochsner Extended Care Hospital of Kenner, Kenner, LA, p. A276

NELSON, Gina, Chief Financial Officer, Renown South Meadows Medical Center, Reno, NV, p. A404

NELSON, Jackie, Director Human Resources, Hansford Hospital, Spearman, TX, p. A644

NELSON, James, MSN Director of Nursing, Saunders Medical Center, Wahoo, NE, p. A398

NELSON, James J., Senior Vice President Finance and Strategic Planning, Fort HealthCare, Fort Atkinson, WI, p. A700

NELSON, Jamie, Vice President and Chief Information Officer, Hospital for Special Surgery, New York, NY, p. A440

NELSON, Jeri, Chief Financial Officer, Eastern Plumas Health Care, Portola, CA, p. A81

NELSON, Joseph, M.D. President Medical Staff, Lewis–Gale Medical Center, Salem, VA, p. A672

NELSON, Julia, Vice President Human Resources, Northern Hospital of Surry County, Mount Airy, NC, p. A465

NELSON, Katey, Director Human Resources, Sevier Valley Medical Center, Richfield, UT, p. A657

NELSON, Kathleen, R.N. Chief Nursing Officer, Eastern Idaho Regional Medical Center, Idaho Falls, ID, p. A174

NELSON, Kathy
Chief Financial Officer, Marshall Medical Center North, Guntersville, AL, p. A20
Chief Financial Officer, Marshall Medical Center South, Boaz, AL, p. A17

NELSON, Kellie, Director Human Resources, Aurora Medical Center, Kenosha, WI, p. A703

NELSON, Kenneth W., Superintendent, Bridgewater State Hospital, Bridgewater, MA, p. A304

NELSON, Kerri, Chief Financial Officer, Spectrum Health Ludington Hospital, Ludington, MI, p. A325

NELSON, Linda M., R.N. Director of Nursing Services, Chippewa County–Montevideo Hospital, Montevideo, MN, p. A343

NELSON, Lucy, Director Finance, Vice President, Maniilaq Health Center, Kotzebue, AK, p. A28

NELSON, Lynn M., R.N. Chief Nursing Officer and Chief Operating Officer, St. John's Riverside Hospital, Yonkers, NY, p. A454

NELSON, Marlin Pete, Vice President Fiscal Services, Divine Savior Healthcare, Portage, WI, p. A709

NELSON, Martha
Chief Financial Officer, Antelope Memorial Hospital, Neligh, NE, p. A394
Chief Financial Officer, Niobrara Valley Hospital, Lynch, NE, p. A394

NELSON, Melissa, Assistant Administrator, Baptist Memorial Hospital for Women, Memphis, TN, p. A583

NELSON, Meredith, Chief Financial Officer, Willamette Valley Medical Center, McMinnville, OR, p. A522

NELSON, Michael
Chief Financial Officer, Kindred Hospital–Atlanta, Atlanta, GA, p. A150
Executive Vice President and Chief Financial Officer, Pomona Valley Hospital Medical Center, Pomona, CA, p. A81

NELSON, Michael E., Chief Financial Officer, Riveredge Hospital, Forest Park, IL, p. A188

NELSON, Mike, Chief Financial Officer, OSF Saint Anthony's Health Center, Alton, IL, p. A178

NELSON, Nan, Senior Vice President Finance, Aurora St. Luke's Medical Center, Milwaukee, WI, p. A706

NELSON, Nick, Director Support Services, Adams Memorial Hospital, Decatur, IN, p. A207

NELSON, Raymond, Acting Chief Information Resource Management, Fargo Veterans Affairs Health Care System, Fargo, ND, p. A473

NELSON, Rhonda, Chief Nursing Officer, Forrest City Medical Center, Forrest City, AR, p. A44

NELSON, Richard, Chief of Human Resources Management Services, Central Arkansas Veterans Healthcare System, Little Rock, AR, p. A47

NELSON, Robin, Chief Financial Officer, Gundersen St. Joseph's Hospital and Clinics, Hillsboro, WI, p. A702

NELSON, Rodney M., Chief Executive Officer, Mackinac Straits Health System, Inc., Saint Ignace, MI, p. A329

NELSON, Selena, Chief Financial Officer, Fallon Medical Complex, Baker, MT, p. A381

NELSON, Shelby
Interim Chief Executive Officer, Community Hospital, Torrington, WY, p. A718
Chief Executive Officer, Platte County Memorial Hospital, Wheatland, WY, p. A718

NELSON, Sherry, JD Chief Nursing Officer, Springfield Regional Medical Center, Springfield, OH, p. A498

NELSON, Siri, Chief Administrative Officer, Sutter Lakeside Hospital, Lakeport, CA, p. A67

NELSON, II, Stacy, Director Human Resources, St. Helena Hospital Napa Valley, Saint Helena, CA, p. A85

NELSON, Stewart R., Chief Financial Officer, Sentara Halifax Regional Hospital, South Boston, VA, p. A673

NELSON, RN, Suzanne, Director of Nursing, Salt Lake Behavioral Health, Salt Lake City, UT, p. A658

NELSON, Tricia, Chief Financial Officer, RiverWoods Behavioral Health System, Riverdale, GA, p. A163

NELSON–JONES, Susan, Director Human Resources, Tehachapi Valley Healthcare District, Tehachapi, CA, p. A94

NEMAZIE, Siamack, M.D. Medical Director, Patient Safety Officer, Flushing Hospital Medical Center, NY, p. A439

NEMETH, James, R.N. Chief Nursing Officer, Borgess–Lee Memorial Hospital, Dowagiac, MI, p. A318

NEMETH, Jim, Chief Financial Officer, Monroe Clinic, Monroe, WI, p. A707

NEMI, Neil, Administrator Facility Information Center, Richard H. Hutchings Psychiatric Center, Syracuse, NY, p. A451

NEONAKIS, Stephanie W., Manager Human Resources, UH Regional Hospitals, Cleveland, OH, p. A485

NERO, Theresa R., R.N. Chief Nursing Officer, Kaiser Permanente San Jose Medical Center, San Jose, CA, p. A89

NESBITT, William, M.D. President Medical Staff, Texas Health Heart & Vascular Hospital Arlington, Arlington, TX, p. A593

NESMITH, Nikki, Interim Chief Operating Officer, Evans Memorial Hospital, Claxton, GA, p. A153

NESPOLI, John L., Chief Executive Officer, Sacred Heart Hospital, Allentown, PA, p. A528

NESS, David L., Vice President Operations, Grinnell Regional Medical Center, Grinnell, IA, p. A228

NESS, Edwin, President and Chief Executive Officer, Munson Healthcare, Traverse City, MI, p. B94

NESS, Jon, Chief Executive Officer, Kootenai Health, Coeur D'Alene, ID, p. A173

NESSEL, Mark
Executive Vice President and Chief Operating Officer, Lourdes Medical Center of Burlington County, Willingboro, NJ, p. A420
Chief Operating Officer, Our Lady of Lourdes Medical Center, Camden, NJ, p. A410

NESSELRODT, Derek, Director Information Systems, Grant Memorial Hospital, Petersburg, WV, p. A694

NESTER, Brian, D.O., President and Chief Executive Officer, Lehigh Valley Health Network, Allentown, PA, p. B81

NESTER, Brian, D.O.,
Interim President and Chief Executive Officer, Lehigh Valley Hospital, Allentown, PA, p. A528
Interim President and Chief Executive Officer, Lehigh Valley Hospital–Muhlenberg, Bethlehem, PA, p. A529

NESTER, Darlene
Market Chief Human Resources Officer, Coastal Carolina Hospital, Hardeeville, SC, p. A562
Chief Human Resources Officer, Hilton Head Hospital, Hilton Head Island, SC, p. A562

NESTER, Michael, Administrator, John C. Stennis Memorial Hospital, De Kalb, MS, p. A352

NESTER WOLFE, Cheryl R., R.N
Senior Vice President Operations, Salem Hospital, Salem, OR, p. A526
Chief Operating Officer, West Valley Hospital, Dallas, OR, p. A520

NETH, Marvin, Chief Executive Officer, Callaway District Hospital, Callaway, NE, p. A390

NETTERVILLE, Chad, Administrator, Field Memorial Community Hospital, Centreville, MS, p. A351

NETTLES, Angela F., Director Human Resources, KershawHealth, Camden, SC, p. A557

NETTLES, Robert, Director Human Resources, MountainView Hospital, Las Vegas, NV, p. A402

NETZER, Craig, M.D. President Medical Staff, Wilcox Memorial Hospital, Lihue, HI, p. A170

NEUBAUER, Brian G., Chief Executive Officer, North Valley Health Center, Warren, MN, p. A348

NEUBERT, Todd, Nurse Administrator, LDS Hospital, Salt Lake City, UT, p. A658

NEUENDORF, Deborah, Vice President Administration, New York–Presbyterian/Hudson Valley Hospital, Cortlandt Manor, NY, p. A432

NEUENDORF, James, M.D. Medical Director, St. Joseph's Medical Center, Yonkers, NY, p. A454

NEUENDORF, Michael, Chief Executive Officer, Merit Health Wesley, Hattiesburg, MS, p. A354

NEUGENT, Kevin, Chief Information Officer, Hayes Green Beach Memorial Hospital, Charlotte, MI, p. A316

NEUHAUS, Joan E.
Senior Vice President Chief Operating Officer, CHI Health Lakeside, Omaha, NE, p. A396
Senior Vice President, Chief Operating Officer, CHI Health Midlands, Papillion, NE, p. A397

NEUMAN, Keith A.
Chief Information Officer, Dupont Hospital, Fort Wayne, IN, p. A208
Chief Information Officer, Lutheran Hospital of Indiana, Fort Wayne, IN, p. A208
Chief Information Officer, Orthopaedic Hospital of Lutheran Health Network, Fort Wayne, IN, p. A208
Chief Information Officer, Rehabilitation Hospital of Fort Wayne, Fort Wayne, IN, p. A209

NEUMAN, Michael J., Vice President Finance, Kennedy Krieger Institute, Baltimore, MD, p. A293

NEUMAN, Richard, Chief Human Resources Officer, Olympic Medical Center, Port Angeles, WA, p. A682

NEUMANN, Jamie, Director Human Resources, Iroquois Memorial Hospital and Resident Home, Watseka, IL, p. A202

NEUMEISTER, Daniel P., Chief Operating Officer, SEARHC MT. Edgecumbe Hospital, Sitka, AK, p. A29

NEUNER, Kathy, R.N. Chief Nursing Officer, Clark Memorial Hospital, Jeffersonville, IN, p. A213

NEUVIRTH, Stephanie, Chief Human Resource and Diversity Officer, City of Hope's Helford Clinical Research Hospital, Duarte, CA, p. A60

NEVERS, Rick, Interim Chief Executive Officer, Aspirus Riverview Hospital and Clinics, Inc., Wisconsin Rapids, WI, p. A714

NEVILLE, Bette, R.N. Vice President and Chief Nursing Officer, Mercy Hospital of Portland, Portland, ME, p. A291

NEVILLE, Ryan T., FACHE, President and Chief Executive Officer, Memorial Medical Center – Neillsville, Neillsville, WI, p. A707

NEVIN, James, M.D. Vice President Medical Management, Advocate BroMenn Medical Center, Normal, IL, p. A196

NEVIN, Janice E., M.P.H., Chief Executive Officer, Christiana Care Health System, Wilmington, DE, p. B33

NEVIN, Janice E., M.P.H., Chief Executive Officer, Christiana Care Health System, Newark, DE, p. A117

NEVINS, Michael R.
Chief Financial Officer, St. John Broken Arrow, Broken Arrow, OK, p. A504
Chief Financial Officer, St. John Owasso, Owasso, OK, p. A513

NEVINS, Norm, Manager Human Resources, Kansas Medical Center, Andover, KS, p. A237

NEVINSKI, Lois, Manager Information Services, Buffalo Hospital, Buffalo, MN, p. A336

NEWBERRY-FERGUSON, Linda, Chief Executive Officer, Rehabilitation Hospital of Wisconsin, Waukesha, WI, p. A713

NEWBOLD, Philip A., Chief Executive Officer, Beacon Health System, South Bend, IN, p. B23

NEWBY, Doug, Chief Information Officer, Highlands Medical Center, Scottsboro, AL, p. A24

NEWBY, Nancy M., FACHE, President and Chief Executive Officer, Washington County Hospital, Nashville, IL, p. A196

NEWCOMB, James, M.D. Vice President Medical, Ochsner Medical Center – North Shore, Slidell, LA, p. A285

Index of Health Care Professionals / Nieves

Index of Health Care Professionals


NEWCOMB, Michael, D.O
Senior Vice President and Chief Operating Officer, Legacy Meridian Park Medical Center, Tualatin, OR, p. A527
Senior Vice President and Chief Operating Officer, Legacy Mount Hood Medical Center, Gresham, OR, p. A521
Senior Vice President and Chief Operating Officer, Legacy Salmon Creek Medical Center, Vancouver, WA, p. A687
NEWCOMER, Jeremy, Director Information Services, Elmira Psychiatric Center, Elmira, NY, p. A433
NEWELL, Dan, Chief Financial Officer, Highlands Medical Center, Scottsboro, AL, p. A24
NEWELL, Janice
Chief Information Officer, Swedish Medical Center–Cherry Hill Campus, Seattle, WA, p. A684
Chief Information Officer, Swedish Medical Center–First Hill, Seattle, WA, p. A684
NEWELL, Rich, Chief Executive Officer, Pottstown Memorial Medical Center, Pottstown, PA, p. A548
NEWEY, Mark, D.O. Chief of Staff, Mercy Hospital Healdton, Healdton, OK, p. A507
NEWHOUSE, Paul R., Chief Executive Officer, Union Medical Center, Union, SC, p. A565
NEWLAND, Judy, R.N., Chief Nursing Officer, Incline Village Community Hospital, Incline Village, NV, p. A401
NEWMAN, Billy, Department Head, Naval Hospital Lemoore, Portsmith, VA, p. A670
NEWMAN, Cynthia, Manager Human Resources, Petersburg Medical Center, Petersburg, AK, p. A29
NEWMAN, Dan, Chief Executive Officer, Houston Methodist St. John Hospital, Nassau Bay, TX, p. A633
NEWMAN, Diane, FACHE, Administrator, Johnson County Hospital, Tecumseh, NE, p. A398
NEWMAN, Edith, Interim Administrator, John J. Madden Mental Health Center, Hines, IL, p. A190
NEWMAN, Karen, Ed.D. Vice President and Chief Nursing Officer, Baptist Health Louisville, Louisville, KY, p. A260
NEWMAN, Kurt, M.D., President and Chief Executive Officer, Children's National Medical Center, Washington, DC, p. A119
NEWMAN, Sonya, R.N. Chief Nursing Officer, Blount Memorial Hospital, Maryville, TN, p. A582
NEWMAN, Thomas M.
Chief Financial Officer, UPMC Passavant, Pittsburgh, PA, p. A547
Vice President Finance, UPMC St. Margaret, Pittsburgh, PA, p. A547
NEWMILLER, Vicki, Chief Operating Officer, Great Falls Clinic Medical Center, Great Falls, MT, p. A384
NEWMYER, Joyce, President and Chief Executive Officer, Adventist Medical Center–Portland, Portland, OR, p. A524
NEWPOWER, Nicole, Coordinator Human Resources, Kindred Hospital–Fort Worth, Fort Worth, TX, p. A613
NEWQUIST, Dennis, Director Information Systems, Abilene Regional Medical Center, Abilene, TX, p. A590
NEWSOM, Paul, Chief Operating Officer, Kentuckiana Medical Center, Clarksville, IN, p. A206
NEWSOME, Samuel C., M.D. Chief of Staff, Pioneer Community Hospital of Stokes, Danbury, NC, p. A458
NEWTON, Gail, R.N. Vice President Patient Care Services, St. Luke's Hospital – Warren Campus, Phillipsburg, NJ, p. A417
NEWTON, Harold, Chief Operating Officer, California Hospital Medical Center, Los Angeles, CA, p. A69
NEWTON, James R., Facility Director, Northern Virginia Mental Health Institute, Falls Church, VA, p. A664
NEWTON, Jennifer, R.N. Chief Nursing Officer, Neosho Memorial Regional Medical Center, Chanute, KS, p. A238
NEWTON, Keith, Chief Executive Officer, South Baldwin Regional Medical Center, Foley, AL, p. A19
NEWTON, Mark, President and Chief Executive Officer, Swedish Covenant Hospital, Chicago, IL, p. A185
NEWTON, Milissa, Supervisor Human Resources, Good Samaritan Hospital, Bakersfield, CA, p. A55
NEWTON, Steven R., President, Baylor Regional Medical Center at Grapevine, Grapevine, TX, p. A616
NEWTON, Susan, Chief Financial Officer, Broward Health Imperial Point, Fort Lauderdale, FL, p. A126
NEWTON, Terri, Chief Nursing Officer, Lakewood Regional Medical Center, Lakewood, CA, p. A67
NEWTON, Wilma, Executive Vice President and Chief Financial Officer, St. Vincent's Birmingham, Birmingham, AL, p. A17
NEZBETH, Jacqueline, Human Resources Officer, Select Specialty Hospital of Southeast Ohio, Zanesville, OH, p. A502
NG, Anthony, M.D. Vice President and Chief Medical Officer, The Acadia Hospital, Bangor, ME, p. A288
NG, Thomas T., Chief Information Officer, Collingsworth General Hospital, Wellington, TX, p. A651
NG, Vincent
Director, Veterans Affairs Boston Healthcare System, Boston, MA, p. A304
Interim Director, Veterans Affairs Boston Healthcare System Brockton Division, Brockton, MA, p. A305
NGUYEN, Abby, R.N. Chief Nursing Officer, Genesis HealthCare System, Zanesville, OH, p. A502
NGUYEN, Anhtai H., M.D. Vice President Medical Affairs and Chief Medical Officer, Fauquier Hospital, Warrenton, VA, p. A674
NGUYEN, Bach, Director Information Systems, Northwest Texas Healthcare System, Amarillo, TX, p. A591
NGUYEN, Dat, M.D. Chief of Staff, Stanford Health Care – ValleyCare, Pleasanton, CA, p. A81
NGUYEN, Harry, Medical Director, The Woods at Parkside, Gahanna, OH, p. A490
NGUYEN, Nga, Manager Human Resources and Organizational Development, Glendale Memorial Hospital and Health Center, Glendale, CA, p. A63
NGUYEN, Son, M.D. President of Medical Staff, Integris Southwest Medical Center, Oklahoma City, OK, p. A511
NGUYEN, Vicki, Chief Financial Officer, Good Samaritan Hospital, Bakersfield, CA, p. A55
NIBLOCK, Christine, Chief Financial Officer, Sheridan County Health Complex, Hoxie, KS, p. A242
NIBLOCK, Jenny, Chief Nursing Officer, Citizens Medical Center, Colby, KS, p. A238
NICAUD, Kent, Chief Operating Officer, Memorial Hospital at Gulfport, Gulfport, MS, p. A353
NICEWONGER, David, Chief Operating Officer, MultiCare Auburn Medical Center, Auburn, WA, p. A676
NICHELSON, Kathleen, Director Human Resources, Horsham Clinic, Ambler, PA, p. A528
NICHOLS, Amanda, M.D. Chief of Staff, Sistersville General Hospital, Sistersville, WV, p. A695
NICHOLS, Barbara, R.N., President and Chief Executive Officer, Corry Memorial Hospital, Corry, PA, p. A532
NICHOLS, Bryan, Chief Financial Officer, The Heart Hospital Baylor Plano, Plano, TX, p. A637
NICHOLS, Christopher, Chief Executive Officer, Horn Memorial Hospital, Ida Grove, IA, p. A229
NICHOLS, Cynthia, MSN, Chief Executive Officer, Lakeland Community Hospital, Haleyville, AL, p. A21
NICHOLS, Dia, Chief Executive Officer, Northside Hospital, Saint Petersburg, FL, p. A142
NICHOLS, Donna, R.N. Chief Nursing Officer, Goodall–Witcher Hospital Authority, Clifton, TX, p. A601
NICHOLS, Gretchen, R.N., Chief Administrative Officer, Legacy Mount Hood Medical Center, Gresham, OR, p. A521
NICHOLS, Laura L., Director Human Resources, Hancock Regional Hospital, Greenfield, IN, p. A210
NICHOLS, Mark, FACHE, Chief Executive Officer, Starr Regional Medical Center, Athens, TN, p. A574
NICHOLS, Michael, Chief Information Officer, Masonicare Health Center, Wallingford, CT, p. A115
NICHOLS, Owen, PsyD, President and Chief Executive Officer, NorthKey Community Care, Covington, KY, p. A255
NICHOLS, Randy
Chief Financial Officer, Great River Medical Center, Blytheville, AR, p. A41
Chief Financial Officer, South Mississippi County Regional Medical Center, Osceola, AR, p. A49
NICHOLS, Robert R., M.D. Vice President Medical Affairs, Mercy Hospital Fort Scott, Fort Scott, KS, p. A240
NICHOLS, Robin, Chief Financial Officer, Coshocton County Memorial Hospital, Coshocton, OH, p. A487
NICHOLS, Suzanne, Director Human Resources, Muleshoe Area Medical Center, Muleshoe, TX, p. A633
NICHOLS, Terry, Chief Executive Officer, Iron County Medical Center, Pilot Knob, MO, p. A374
NICHOLSON, Britain, M.D. Chief Medical Officer, Massachusetts General Hospital, Boston, MA, p. A304
NICHOLSON, Chrissy, Vice President Human Resources, Delta Regional Medical Center, Greenville, MS, p. A353
NICHOLSON, Cindy, Director Human Resources, Shelby Baptist Medical Center, Alabaster, AL, p. A15
NICHOLSON, Debra, Manager Finance, Central Alabama Veterans Health Care System, Montgomery, AL, p. A23
NICHOLSON, Donna, Chief Nursing Officer, Gadsden Regional Medical Center, Gadsden, AL, p. A20
NICHOLSON, Kristin, Coordinator Human Resources, Genesis Medical Center, DeWitt, De Witt, IA, p. A226
NICHOLSON, Molly, R.N
Chief Nurse Executive, Presence Covenant Medical Center, Urbana, IL, p. A202
Vice President of Patient Care/Chief Nurse Executive, Presence United Samaritans Medical Center, Danville, IL, p. A185
NICHOLSON, Tim, Chief Executive Officer, Encore Healthcare, Columbia, MD, p. B54
NICKEL, Kathleen, Director Communications, Mercy Medical Center, Roseburg, OR, p. A525
NICKELL, Jerry, Vice President Human Resource and Mission, Saint Alphonsus Medical Center – Baker City, Baker City, OR, p. A519
NICKELS, John, M.D. President Medical Staff, Grace Hospital, Cleveland, OH, p. A484
NICKENS, Wesley, M.D. Chief of Staff, Collingsworth General Hospital, Wellington, TX, p. A651
NICKERSON, Jeff, Site Manager Information Systems, Midwestern Regional Medical Center, Zion, IL, p. A203
NICKRAND, Tami, Director Information Technology, Harbor Beach Community Hospital, Harbor Beach, MI, p. A322
NICKS, Bret, M.D. Chief Medical Officer and Chief of Staff, Wake Forest Baptist Health–Davie Medical Center, Mocksville, NC, p. A465
NICODEMUS, Lowell, Director Information Systems, Hendricks Regional Health, Danville, IN, p. A207
NICOLAY, Donald, M.D. Chief Medical Officer, Community Hospital, Grand Junction, CO, p. A104
NICOLL, C. Diana, M.D. Chief of Staff, San Francisco VA Medical Center, San Francisco, CA, p. A88
NICOLSON, Lynne T., M.D. Medical Director, Sunnyview Rehabilitation Hospital, Schenectady, NY, p. A450
NICOSIA, Chris, Chief Financial Officer, Corpus Christi Medical Center, Corpus Christi, TX, p. A602
NIECE, Pamela S.
Chief Human Resources Officer, LDS Hospital, Salt Lake City, UT, p. A658
Director Human Resources, Orem Community Hospital, Orem, UT, p. A656
NIEDERPRUEM, Mark L., FACHE, Administrator, Shriners Hospitals for Children–Chicago, Chicago, IL, p. A184
NIEHAUS, Jason, Senior Vice President Operations and Administrator, Summa Barberton Citizens Hospital, Barberton, OH, p. A479
NIELSEN, Colleen, Director Operations, Providence St. Joseph Medical Center, Polson, MT, p. A386
NIELSEN, Gregory A., FACHE, Chief Executive Officer, Clinton Memorial Hospital, Wilmington, OH, p. A501
NIELSEN, Gwen, Manager Human Resources, Indianhead Medical Center, Shell Lake, WI, p. A711
NIELSEN, Helen V.
Director Human Resources, Lovelace Medical Center, Albuquerque, NM, p. A422
Director Human Resources, Lovelace Rehabilitation Hospital, Albuquerque, NM, p. A422
NIELSEN, Kristine, Manager Human Resources, Memorial Community Hospital and Health System, Blair, NE, p. A390
NIELSEN, Peter, M.D., Commander, General Leonard Wood Army Community Hospital, Fort Leonard Wood, MO, p. A367
NIELSEN, Randy, Director Information Technology, Morton General Hospital, Morton, WA, p. A680
NIELSEN, Wayne, Director Human Resources, Ocala Regional Medical Center, Ocala, FL, p. A137
NIELSON, Curtis, Chief Financial Officer, South Lincoln Medical Center, Kemmerer, WY, p. A716
NIELSON, Lars, M.D. Chief Medical Officer, Weeks Medical Center, Lancaster, NH, p. A406
NIELSON, P. Douglas, M.D. Chief of Staff, Kahuku Medical Center, Kahuku, HI, p. A169
NIELSON, Yvonne, Chief Nursing Officer, Director Quality Management and Regulatory Compliance, Mountain West Medical Center, Tooele, UT, p. A659
NIEMANN, Lynne, Director Nurses and Patient Care, Community Memorial Hospital, Sumner, IA, p. A235
NIEMEIER, Mark, Director Human Resources, Twin Rivers Regional Medical Center, Kennett, MO, p. A371
NIEMER, Peggy, Vice President Human Resources, Children's Hospital of Wisconsin, Milwaukee, WI, p. A706
NIEMEYER, Romaine, President and Chief Executive Officer, Holy Spirit – A Geisinger Affiliate, Camp Hill, PA, p. A530
NIEMUTH, Trisha, Director of Finance, LifeCare Hospitals of Mechanicsburg, Mechanicsburg, PA, p. A540
NIERMAN, Peter, M.D. Chief Medical Officer, Chicago Lakeshore Hospital, Chicago, IL, p. A181
NIERMAN, Stephen A., President, Winter Haven Hospital, Winter Haven, FL, p. A148
NIERMANN, Michelle, Senior Vice President and Chief Operating Officer, UnityPoint Health – St. Luke's Hospital, Cedar Rapids, IA, p. A223
NIES, Lynn, Human Resources Officer, Erie Veterans Affairs Medical Center, Erie, PA, p. A534
NIESE, Mel, Chief Fiscal Service, VA Palo Alto Health Care System, Palo Alto, CA, p. A80
NIESSINK, Henry
Regional Director Information Technology Services, Mercy Medical Center Redding, Redding, CA, p. A82
Senior Manager Information Technology Systems, St. Elizabeth Community Hospital, Red Bluff, CA, p. A82
NIEVES, Deborah, Director Management Information Systems, Hospital San Francisco, San Juan, PR, p. A724
NIEVES, Erick, M.D. Medical Director, Hospital San Carlos Borromeo, Moca, PR, p. A722

Index of Health Care Professionals

Index of Health Care Professionals / Nieves

NIEVES, Jesus, Chief Executive Officer, Bella Vista Hospital, Mayaguez, PR, p. A722
NIGH, Andrew, M.D. Chief of Staff, Indiana University Health West Hospital, Avon, IN, p. A204
NIGHMAN, Mike, Facility Coordinator Information Systems, Shelby Baptist Medical Center, Alabaster, AL, p. A15
NIGHTENGALE, Randy, Chief Financial Officer, Pondera Medical Center, Conrad, MT, p. A382
NIGHTINGALE, Judi, R.N. Chief Nursing Officer, Riverside County Regional Medical Center, Moreno Valley, CA, p. A76
NIGRIN, Daniel, M.D. Vice President Information Services and Chief Information Officer, Boston Children's Hospital, Boston, MA, p. A303
NIHALANI, Sunil, M.D. Chief Medical Staff, Lake Wales Medical Center, Lake Wales, FL, p. A131
NIKOLIC, Srbo, Chief Financial Officer, Hartgrove Hospital, Chicago, IL, p. A182
NILES, Heather, Director Human Resources Operations, Mercy Harvard Hospital, Harvard, IL, p. A189
NILSSON, Keith, Chief Financial Officer, Cleveland Clinic Florida, Weston, FL, p. A147
NIMCHAN, Ralph, M.D. Chief of Staff, Doctors Hospital of Laredo, Laredo, TX, p. A627
NIMMO, Ben, M.D. Medical Director, Pinnacle Pointe Hospital, Little Rock, AR, p. A47
NIMMO, Brian, Director, Huntington Veterans Affairs Medical Center, Huntington, WV, p. A692
NIMS, Carrie, Director of Nursing, Post Acute/Warm Springs Specialty Hospital of San Antonio, San Antonio, TX, p. A642
NINNEMAN, David, Associate Director, Cincinnati Veterans Affairs Medical Center, Cincinnati, OH, p. A482
NINU, Christine, Chief Executive Officer, Post Acute Medical Specialty Hospital of Milwaukee, Greenfield, WI, p. A702
NIPPER, Nathan, Vice President and Chief Operating Officer, Piedmont Newnan Hospital, Newnan, GA, p. A162
NIPPERT, Kathi, Acting Chief Human Resources Officer, Kansas City Veterans Affairs Medical Center, Kansas City, MO, p. A369
NISKANEN, Grant, M.D. Vice President Medical Affairs, Sky Lakes Medical Center, Klamath Falls, OR, p. A522
NISSEN, Beth, Director Human Resources, Troy Regional Medical Center, Troy, AL, p. A25
NISTED, Karissa, Interim Chief Executive Officer, Guidance Center, Flagstaff, AZ, p. A31
NIX, Bo, Chief Information Officer, Madison Valley Medical Center, Ennis, MT, p. A383
NIX, D. Mark, President and Chief Executive Officer, Infirmary Health System, Mobile, AL, p. B73
NIXDORF, David L., Director Support Services, Frances Mahon Deaconess Hospital, Glasgow, MT, p. A383
NIXON, Myra, Director Human Resources, HEALTHSOUTH Rehabilitation Hospital, Concord, NH, p. A405
NIZZA, Arthur, Chief Executive Officer, Meriter UnityPoint Health, Madison, WI, p. A704
NNAJI, Felix, Chief Medical Staff, Bolivar General Hospital, Bolivar, TN, p. A574
NOAK, Amy, Director Human Resources, St. David's Round Rock Medical Center, Round Rock, TX, p. A639
NOAKES, Timothy J., Chief Financial Officer, Memorial Hospital Los Banos, Los Banos, CA, p. A73
NOBLE, Damien, Director Information Technology and System, Colleton Medical Center, Walterboro, SC, p. A565
NOBLE, James D., Chief Executive Officer, Horton Community Hospital, Horton, KS, p. A242
NOBLE, James S., Chief Operating Officer, Huntington Memorial Hospital, Pasadena, CA, p. A80
NOBLE, Kerry L., Chief Executive Officer, Pemiscot Memorial Health System, Hayti, MO, p. A368
NOBLE, Mallie S., Administrator, Mary Breckinridge ARH Hospital, Hyden, KY, p. A258
NOBLE, Paula, Chief Financial Officer and Treasurer, Ann & Robert H. Lurie Children's Hospital of Chicago, Chicago, IL, p. A181
NOBLE, Stacy, Administrator, Southeast Rehabilitation Hospital, Lake Village, AR, p. A46
NOBLES, Diane, Nurse Executive, East Mississippi State Hospital, Meridian, MS, p. A357
NOBLES, Sharon, Interim Chief Financial Officer, Baptist Hospital, Pensacola, FL, p. A139
NOBLIN, Jeff, FACHE, Chief Executive Officer, Southern Tennessee Regional Health System–Lawrenceburg, Lawrenceburg, TN, p. A581
NOBRIGA, Robert, Executive Vice President and Chief Financial Officer, Queen's Medical Center, Honolulu, HI, p. A169
NOCITA, Suzanne, Interim Vice President Human Resources, Children's Hospital and Medical Center, Omaha, NE, p. A396
NOCKOWITZ, Richard, M.D. Medical Director, Ohio Hospital for Psychiatry, Columbus, OH, p. A486
NOEL, Bill, Chief Operating Officer, Grand River Hospital District, Rifle, CO, p. A108
NOEL, Denise, Chief Nursing Officer, Abbeville General Hospital, Abbeville, LA, p. A268
NOEL III, Philip J., Chief Executive Officer, Ottumwa Regional Health Center, Ottumwa, IA, p. A233
NOEL, Vicki, Vice President Human Resources, Southern Ohio Medical Center, Portsmouth, OH, p. A496
NOFFSINGER, Sandy, Executive Assistant, Risk Manager and Director Marketing, Dundy County Hospital, Benkelman, NE, p. A390
NOGLER, Wendy, Director Human Resources, Lincoln County Health System, Fayetteville, TN, p. A577
NOHELTY, Susan, R.N. Vice President Patient Services, Cayuga Medical Center at Ithaca, Ithaca, NY, p. A435
NOKELS, Kevin J., FACHE, President, CHI Health Creighton University Medical Center, Omaha, NE, p. A395
NOKES, Gregory, Vice President Human Resources, Middlesex Hospital, Middletown, CT, p. A113
NOLAN, Douglas, M.D. Medical Director, Cherokee Nation W.W. Hastings Indian Hospital, Tahlequah, OK, p. A515
NOLAN, Heather, Director Information Services, Northern Louisiana Medical Center, Ruston, LA, p. A284
NOLAN, Jennifer
  President, Our Lady of Peace, Louisville, KY, p. A261
  President, Sts. Mary & Elizabeth Hospital, Louisville, KY, p. A262
NOLAN, Joe, Chief Operating Officer, Saint Clare's Health System, Denville, NJ, p. A411
NOLAN, Matthew, Director Facilities and Operations, The University of Vermont Health Network Elizabethtown Community Hospital, Elizabethtown, NY, p. A433
NOLAN, Michael J.
  Area Chief Operating Officer and Safety, Promise Hospital of Baton Rouge – Mid–City Campus, Baton Rouge, LA, p. A270
  Area Safety Director, Promise Hospital of Baton Rouge – Ochsner Campus, Baton Rouge, LA, p. A270
NOLAN, Patrick B., Chief Operating Officer, Inspira Medical Center–Woodbury, Woodbury, NJ, p. A420
NOLAN, Rosemary, R.N. Chief Operating Officer, Temple University Hospital, Philadelphia, PA, p. A545
NOLAND, Christopher, Interim Chief Executive Officer, Central Montana Medical Center, Lewistown, MT, p. A385
NOLAND, Pam, Director of Nursing, Northern Cochise Community Hospital, Willcox, AZ, p. A40
NOLD, Pam, Chief Nurse Executive, Northwest Missouri Psychiatric Rehabilitation Center, Saint Joseph, MO, p. A375
NOLEN, Benny, President, Saint Joseph Mount Sterling, Mount Sterling, KY, p. A263
NOLES, Coy, Chief Financial Officer Consultant, Hamilton Hospital, Olney, TX, p. A635
NOLL, Gerald, Vice President and Chief Financial Officer, Sheppard Pratt Health System, Baltimore, MD, p. A294
NOLL, Gerald A., Chief Financial Officer, Rogers Memorial Hospital, Oconomowoc, WI, p. A708
NOLL, Keith D., President, York Hospital, York, PA, p. A554
NOLLETTE, Karen, Chief Financial Officer, West Holt Memorial Hospital, Atkinson, NE, p. A389
NOLT, Lori, Director Information Technology, Philhaven, Mount Gretna, PA, p. A541
NOLTE, Darlene R., Chief Human Resource Officer, Craig General Hospital, Vinita, OK, p. A517
NOLTING, Evelyn, Chief Executive Officer and Managing Director, River Oaks Hospital, New Orleans, LA, p. A282
NONNEMAN, Lisa, Interim Director Information Technology Services, Mary Lanning Healthcare, Hastings, NE, p. A392
NOONAN, Cindy, Chief Operating Officer, Stanford Health Care – ValleyCare, Pleasanton, CA, p. A81
NOONAN, Kathryn, Director Information Management, Lemuel Shattuck Hospital, Jamaica Plain, MA, p. A307
NOONE, Thomas, M.D. Chief Medical Officer, Bayfront Health Port Charlotte, Port Charlotte, FL, p. A140
NORBURY, Denise
  Chief Executive Officer, Center for Behavioral Medicine, Kansas City, MO, p. A369
  Regional Executive Officer, Northwest Missouri Psychiatric Rehabilitation Center, Saint Joseph, MO, p. A375
NORBY, Michael, Chief Financial Officer, Harris Health System, Houston, TX, p. A619
NORD, Gay, Chief Executive Officer, Methodist Hospital, San Antonio, TX, p. A641
NORD, Stanley K., Chief Financial Officer, West Houston Medical Center, Houston, TX, p. A623
NORDAHL, Richard E., Chief Executive Officer, Sanford Sheldon Medical Center, Sheldon, IA, p. A234
NORDBERG, Traci, Chief Human Resources Officer, Vanderbilt Hospital and Clinics, Nashville, TN, p. A586
NORDBY, Shawn A., Chief Financial Officer, Mary Lanning Healthcare, Hastings, NE, p. A392
NORDING, Rodney, Vice President Organizational Support, Mayo Clinic Health System–Albert Lea and Austin, Austin, MN, p. A335
NORDLUND, Judy, R.N. Chief Nursing Officer, Trinity Hospital, Weaverville, CA, p. A97
NORDLUND, Sarah, Director of Nursing, Garfield County Health Center, Jordan, MT, p. A384
NORDMARK, Gary, Administrator and Vice President Operations, Bethesda Hospital East, Boynton Beach, FL, p. A122
NORDSTROM, Janice, Director Human Resources, Landmark Hospital of Joplin, Joplin, MO, p. A369
NORDSTROM, Katie, Director Human Resources, Beartooth Billings Clinic, Red Lodge, MT, p. A386
NORDWICK, Thomas, Chief Executive Officer, Uvalde County Hospital Authority, Uvalde, TX, p. A649
NORDYKE, Charles
  Interim Chief Executive Officer, Vibra Hospital of Northwestern Indiana, Crown Point, IN, p. A207
  Chief Executive Officer, Vibra Hospital of Springfield, Springfield, IL, p. A201
NORDYKE, Melissa, Chief Financial Officer, Seton Smithville Regional Hospital, Smithville, TX, p. A644
NOREEN, James, M.D. Chief Medical Officer, Regina Hospital, Hastings, MN, p. A340
NORELDIN, Mohsen, M.D. President Medical Staff, Athol Memorial Hospital, Athol, MA, p. A302
NOREM, Ashley, Chief Information Systems, Indiana University Health Starke Hospital, Knox, IN, p. A213
NOREN, Tom, M.D. Chief Medical Officer, UP Health System–Marquette, Marquette, MI, p. A325
NORGAARD, Margaret B.
  Chief Executive Officer, Poplar Community Hospital, Poplar, MT, p. A386
  Chief Executive Officer, Trinity Hospital, Wolf Point, MT, p. A388
NORICK, Laurence, M.D. Clinical Director, U. S. Public Health Service Indian Hospital, Parker, AZ, p. A34
NORIEGA, Donna, Chief Operating Officer, Arizona State Hospital, Phoenix, AZ, p. A34
NORMAN, Daniel, Regional Service Manager, UnityPoint Health – Allen Hospital, Waterloo, IA, p. A236
NORMAN, Debbie, Director Human Resources, Central Louisiana Surgical Hospital, Alexandria, LA, p. A268
NORMAN, Jimmy, Chief Financial Officer, Mountain Lakes Medical Center, Clayton, GA, p. A154
NORMAN, Kasey, Chief Executive Officer, Reliant Rehabilitation Hospital Dallas, Dallas, TX, p. A606
NORMAN, Laura, Chief Development and Information Officer, Windhaven Psychiatric Hospital, Prescott Valley, AZ, p. A36
NORMAN, Lori, Chief Financial Officer, HEALTHSOUTH Rehabilitation of Gadsden, Gadsden, AL, p. A20
NORMAN, Mark, Administrator, Pioneer Community Hospital of Newton, Newton, MS, p. A358
NORMAN, Mary, R.N. Chief Nursing Officer, Bear Valley Community Hospital, Big Bear Lake, CA, p. A56
NORMAN, Michael L., Executive Vice President and Chief Operating Officer, Landmark Hospital of Cape Girardeau, Cape Girardeau, MO, p. A364
NORMAN, Robin, Senior Vice President and Chief Financial Officer, Virginia Hospital Center – Arlington, Arlington, VA, p. A662
NORMAND, Lorrie, R.N., Interim Chief Executive Officer, Texas Health Harris Methodist Hospital Cleburne, Cleburne, TX, p. A601
NORMINGTON–SLAY, Jeremy, FACHE, Chief Executive Officer, Mercy Medical Center, Oshkosh, WI, p. A708
NORO, Sharon
  Interim Chief Executive Officer, Select Specialty Hospital – Youngstown, Boardman, OH, p. A480
  Chief Executive Officer, Select Specialty Hospital–Youngstown, Youngstown, OH, p. A501
NORONHA, Augusto A., Vice President Finance and Chief Financial Officer, Missouri Baptist Medical Center, Saint Louis, MO, p. A377
NORQUEST, Cathy, Director Human Resources, York General Hospital, York, NE, p. A399
NORR–MCPHILLIPS, Karina, Associate Executive Director Human Resources, Franklin Hospital, Valley Stream, NY, p. A452
NORRIS, Charles, Chief Executive Officer, Memorial Hospital, Gonzales, TX, p. A616
NORRIS, John, M.D. Vice President Medical Affairs, Johnson Memorial Hospital, Franklin, IN, p. A209
NORRIS, Kathy, Director Human Resources, Bear Valley Community Hospital, Big Bear Lake, CA, p. A56
NORRIS, Ron, Chief Executive Officer, Select Specialty Hospital – Dallas Garland, Garland, TX, p. A616

A928 Index of Health Care Professionals

NORTH, Scott L., FACHE,
Senior Vice President and President, Acute Care Hospitals, St. John's Hospital, Maplewood, MN, p. A342
Senior Vice President and President, Acute Care Hospitals, St. Joseph's Hospital, Saint Paul, MN, p. A346
Senior Vice President and President, Acute Care Hospitals, Woodwinds Health Campus, Woodbury, MN, p. A349

NORTHCUTT, Lynn, Chief Information Officer, Carolinas Hospital System, Florence, SC, p. A560

NORTHERN, Gail M., Director Human Resources, Blue Mountain Hospital, Blanding, UT, p. A654

NORTHUP, Carol, R.N. Chief Nursing Officer, J. Arthur Dosher Memorial Hospital, Southport, NC, p. A468

NORTHUP, Jeffrey, D.O. Chief Medical Officer, Knox Community Hospital, Mount Vernon, OH, p. A495

NORTON, Andrew J., M.D
Chief Medical Officer, Bryn Mawr Hospital, Bryn Mawr, PA, p. A530
Chief Medical Officer, Paoli Hospital, Paoli, PA, p. A542

NORTON, Debbie, Chief Financial Officer, Medical Center Barbour, Eufaula, AL, p. A19

NORTON, Julie, Chief Financial Officer, Avera McKennan Hospital and University Health Center, Sioux Falls, SD, p. A571

NORTON, Lizette O., Vice President Human Resources, Parkview Community Hospital Medical Center, Riverside, CA, p. A83

NORTON, Meg, Executive Vice President and Chief Administrative Officer, Rady Children's Hospital – San Diego, San Diego, CA, p. A86

NORTON, Robert G., President, North Shore Medical Center, Salem, MA, p. A310

NORTON, Sam, System Chief Information Officer, Benefis Hospitals, Great Falls, MT, p. A384

NORTON, Susan, Vice President Human Resources, Georgia Regents Medical Center, Augusta, GA, p. A151

NORVILLE, Amy, Vice President Support Services, St. Luke's Hospital, Columbus, NC, p. A458

NORWOOD, Lyle, M.D. Chief of Staff, Northside Medical Center, Columbus, GA, p. A154

NOSACKA, David, Chief Financial Officer, HSHS St. Elizabeth's Hospital, Belleville, IL, p. A179

NOSACKA, Mark, Chief Executive Officer, Good Samaritan Medical Center, West Palm Beach, FL, p. A147

NOSBISCH, Don, Director Human Resources, Floyd County Medical Center, Charles City, IA, p. A224

NOSEWORTHY, Ed, President and Chief Executive Officer, Florida Hospital Fish Memorial, Orange City, FL, p. A137

NOSEWORTHY, MD, John H., M.D., President and Chief Executive Officer, Mayo Clinic, Rochester, MN, p. B87

NOTEMAN, Laurali, Director Human Resources, Kane County Hospital, Kanab, UT, p. A655

NOTTEBART, Cathy, Acting Superintendent, Austin State Hospital, Austin, TX, p. A594

NOTTER, Pat, R.N. Chief Nursing Officer and Director Quality, Melissa Memorial Hospital, Holyoke, CO, p. A105

NOTTINGHAM, Cheryl, Chief Financial Officer, Atlantic General Hospital, Berlin, MD, p. A295

NOUNA, Nabil, M.D. Chief of Staff, Allegan General Hospital, Allegan, MI, p. A314

NOVAK, Christopher, Chief Operating Officer, Alexian Brothers Behavioral Health Hospital, Hoffman Estates, IL, p. A191

NOVAK, Georgene, Director Human Resources, Littleton Regional Hospital, Littleton, NH, p. A407

NOVAK, James, Vice President, Human Resources, St. Francis Medical Center, Monroe, LA, p. A280

NOVAK, Kristen, Manager Human Resources, River Falls Area Hospital, River Falls, WI, p. A710

NOVAK, Michael, Vice President, Operations and Chief Information Officer, Saint Mary's Hospital, Waterbury, CT, p. A115

NOVAK, Sharon, CPA Vice President Finance, Adena Pike Medical Center, Waverly, OH, p. A500

NOVELLO, Regina, R.N. Chief Operating Officer, Healdsburg District Hospital, Healdsburg, CA, p. A64

NOVICK, Peggy, Vice President, Clinical Support and Outpatient Services, Milford Regional Medical Center, Milford, MA, p. A309

NOVOA LOYOLA, Jose E., M.D. Medical Director, Cardiovascular Center of Puerto Rico and the Caribbean, San Juan, PR, p. A723

NOVOTNY, Mark, M.D. Chief Medical Officer, Cooley Dickinson Hospital, Northampton, MA, p. A309

NOWACHEK, Debra S., Director Human Resources, Grinnell Regional Medical Center, Grinnell, IA, p. A228

NOWICKI, Becky, Director Human Resources, Michiana Behavioral Health Center, Plymouth, IN, p. A218

NOWICKI, Michelle, R.N. Chief Nurse Executive, Kaiser Permanente Baldwin Park Medical Center, Baldwin Park, CA, p. A55

NOWLIN, Angela, R.N. Senior VP, Operations, Magnolia Regional Health Center, Corinth, MS, p. A352

NOWLIN, Jeffrey D., President and Chief Operating Officer, St. John Medical Center, Tulsa, OK, p. A517

NOWLIN, Patricia, Director Accounting, Cooper County Memorial Hospital, Boonville, MO, p. A364

NOWLING, Tara, Director Human Resources, Monroe County Hospital, Monroeville, AL, p. A22

NOYES, Debra, Chief Financial Officer, Putnam Community Medical Center, Palatka, FL, p. A138

NUAKO, Kofi, M.D. President Medical Staff, Baptist Memorial Hospital–Union City, Union City, TN, p. A589

NUDD, Brandon M., Chief Operating Officer, Gordon Hospital, Calhoun, GA, p. A153

NUDO, Patrick, Finance Director, HSHS St. Francis Hospital, Litchfield, IL, p. A193

NUESSLEIN, Cindy
Chief Executive Officer, Interim LSU Public Hospital, New Orleans, LA, p. A282
Interim Chief Executive Officer, University Campus, New Orleans, LA, p. A283

NUNEZ, Michael, Chief Financial Officer, University Medical Center of El Paso, El Paso, TX, p. A611

NUNEZ, Milton, Executive Director, Lincoln Medical and Mental Health Center, NY, p. A441

NUNEZ, Sheila, Director Human Resources, Eastern New Mexico Medical Center, Roswell, NM, p. A426

NUNEZ, Stephanie, Interim Chief Executive Officer, Tri Parish Rehabilitation Hospital, Leesville, LA, p. A279

NUNLEY, Julie, R.N.,
Chief Executive Officer, Banner Goldfield Medical Center, Apache Junction, AZ, p. A30
Chief Executive Officer, Banner Ironwood Medical Center, San Tan Valley, AZ, p. A37

NUNN, Brian, R.N. Chief Nursing Officer, Mary Black Health System – Gaffney, Gaffney, SC, p. A561

NUNN, Chalmers, M.D. Chief Medical Officer and Senior Vice President, Centra Lynchburg General Hospital, Lynchburg, VA, p. A667

NUNNELLY, Sarah, Chief Operating Officer, Princeton Baptist Medical Center, Birmingham, AL, p. A16

NURICK, Paul E., Chief Executive Officer, Kittitas Valley Healthcare, Ellensburg, WA, p. A678

NURU, Betty, Director Human Resources, Millwood Hospital, Arlington, TX, p. A592

NURY, Alex, Chief Information Officer, Providence Tarzana Medical Center, CA, p. A72

NUSBAUM, Neil, M.D. Chief of Staff, Veterans Affairs Central Western Massachusetts Healthcare System, Leeds, MA, p. A308

NUSS, Michelle, M.D. Chief Medical Officer, West Virginia University Hospitals, Morgantown, WV, p. A693

NUSS, Suzanne Langan, M.D. Chief Nursing Officer, Nebraska Medicine – Nebraska Medical Center, Omaha, NE, p. A396

NUSSBAUM, Joseph, M.D. Chief of Staff, California Hospital Medical Center, Los Angeles, CA, p. A69

NUSSBAUM, Mark, Vice President Operations, Marymount Hospital, Garfield Heights, OH, p. A490

NUTTER, Robert, Chief Operating Officer, Vice President of Human Resources and Support Services, Mercy Hospital of Portland, Portland, ME, p. A291

NWANGBURUKA, Okechukwu, M.D. Medical Director, Sierra Vista Hospital, Sacramento, CA, p. A85

NYAMU, Samuel, M.D. Chief Medical Officer, Sanford Aberdeen Medical Center, Aberdeen, SD, p. A567

NYBERG, Becky T., Chief Financial Officer, Bloomington Meadows Hospital, Bloomington, IN, p. A205

NYIKES, Debra, Director Finance and Chief Financial Officer, Cleveland Clinic Children's Hospital for Rehabilitation, Cleveland, OH, p. A484

NYKAMP, Robert, Vice President and Chief Operating Officer, Pine Rest Christian Mental Health Services, Grand Rapids, MI, p. A321

NYLUND, Barbara, M.D. Chief of Staff, Novato Community Hospital, Novato, CA, p. A78

NYMOEN, Gary, Chief Financial Officer, Hialeah Hospital, Hialeah, FL, p. A128

NYP, Randall G., FACHE,
Chief Executive Officer, Providence Medical Center, Kansas City, KS, p. A243
President and Chief Executive Officer, Saint John Hospital, Leavenworth, KS, p. A244

NYSTROM, Dale, M.D. Chief Medical Officer, Physician, Hawarden Regional Healthcare, Hawarden, IA, p. A229

NZERUE, Chike, M.D. Chief Medical Officer, Nashville General Hospital, Nashville, TN, p. A585

# O

O'BAR, Dorothy, R.N., Administrator, Mercy Hospital Waldron, Waldron, AR, p. A51

O'BRIEN Jr., Charles M., President and Chief Executive Officer, Weirton Medical Center, Weirton, WV, p. A696

O'BRIEN, David, Chief Nursing Officer, Coral Gables Hospital, Coral Gables, FL, p. A124

O'BRIEN, David, M.D.,
President, Redwood Memorial Hospital, Fortuna, CA, p. A61
President, St. Joseph Hospital, Eureka, CA, p. A60

O'BRIEN, Eileen, Director Human Resources, Broward Health Coral Springs, Coral Springs, FL, p. A124

O'BRIEN, Elizabeth, Chief Financial Officer, Northern Nevada Adult Mental Health Services, Sparks, NV, p. A404

O'BRIEN, Gracie, Chief Information Officer, Sequoia Hospital, Redwood City, CA, p. A83

O'BRIEN, Jane E., M.D. Medical Director, Franciscan Hospital for Children, Boston, MA, p. A303

O'BRIEN, John, Chief Executive Officer, Manning Regional Healthcare Center, Manning, IA, p. A231

O'BRIEN, Karen, Director Human Resources, Gerald Champion Regional Medical Center, Alamogordo, NM, p. A422

O'BRIEN, Kelly, Chief Operating Officer, Riverview Medical Center, Red Bank, NJ, p. A418

O'BRIEN, Kevin, Chief Financial Officer, Share Medical Center, Alva, OK, p. A503

O'BRIEN, Laureen, Chief Information Officer, Providence Newberg Medical Center, Newberg, OR, p. A523

O'BRIEN, Maureen, Chief Operating Officer, Kaiser Permanente Redwood City Medical Center, Redwood City, CA, p. A83

O'BRIEN, Renee, Director Human Resources, Greater Binghamton Health Center, Binghamton, NY, p. A429

O'BRIEN–EVANS, Yvonne M., MS Chief of Nursing, Pella Regional Health Center, Pella, IA, p. A233

O'BRIEN–PARADIS, Katie, M.D. Chief Medical Officer, CHI Oakes Hospital, Oakes, ND, p. A476

O'BRYANT, G. Mark, President and Chief Executive Officer, Tallahassee Memorial HealthCare, Tallahassee, FL, p. A144

O'CONNELL, Brian, Director Information Services, North Star Behavioral Health System, Anchorage, AK, p. A27

O'CONNELL, Kimberly, President, Roger Williams Medical Center, Providence, RI, p. A556

O'CONNELL, Melody M., Director Human Resources, St. Bernard Parish Hospital, Chalmette, LA, p. A271

O'CONNOR, Colleen, Director Human Resources, Manatee Glens Hospital and Addiction Center, Bradenton, FL, p. A122

O'CONNOR, David, Executive Vice President and Chief Financial Officer, CaroMont Regional Medical Center, Gastonia, NC, p. A460

O'CONNOR, Dennis, M.D. Medical Director, Ira Davenport Memorial Hospital, Bath, NY, p. A429

O'CONNOR, Ellen, Chief Nursing Officer, Jacobi Medical Center, NY, p. A440

O'CONNOR, J. T., M.D. Medical Director, Mercy Health Love County, Marietta, OK, p. A509

O'CONNOR, James, Executive Vice President and Chief Administrative Officer, St. Charles Hospital, Port Jefferson, NY, p. A448

O'CONNOR, Kathy
Vice President Finance, St. Joseph Mercy Ann Arbor, Ypsilanti, MI, p. A333
Vice President Finance and Controller, St. Joseph Mercy Livingston Hospital, Howell, MI, p. A322

O'CONNOR, Kevin, D.O. President Medical Staff, Spectrum Health United Hospital, Greenville, MI, p. A321

O'CONNOR, Marcia, Chief Executive Officer, Choctaw Memorial Hospital, Hugo, OK, p. A508

O'CONNOR, Michael F., Senior Vice President Finance, York Hospital, York, PA, p. A554

O'CONNOR, Nicholas, Vice President and Chief Information Officer, Plainview Hospital, Plainview, NY, p. A447

O'CONNOR, Patrick, Chief Operating Officer, Morris Hospital & Healthcare Centers, Morris, IL, p. A195

O'CONNOR, Steve, Manager Human Resources, Kern Medical Center, Bakersfield, CA, p. A55

O'CONNOR, Thomas, President, United Hospital, Saint Paul, MN, p. A346

O'CONNOR, Tim, Area Finance Officer, Kaiser Permanente Redwood City Medical Center, Redwood City, CA, p. A83

O'CONNOR, Timothy P., Executive Vice President and Chief Financial Officer, Lahey Hospital & Medical Center, Burlington, Burlington, MA, p. A305

O'CONNOR–SNYDER, Judy, Chief Nursing Officer, Mercy Hospital Lebanon, Lebanon, MO, p. A371

O'DEA, Edward
Vice President and Chief Financial Officer, Lehigh Valley Hospital, Allentown, PA, p. A528
Chief Financial Officer, Lehigh Valley Hospital–Muhlenberg, Bethlehem, PA, p. A529

O'DELL, Darrell, Director Information Services, Good Samaritan Hospital, San Jose, CA, p. A89

O'DONNELL, James, Physician in Chief, Kaiser Permanente Redwood City Medical Center, Redwood City, CA, p. A83

O'DONNELL, Jan, Chief Nursing Officer, South Texas Surgical Hospital, Corpus Christi, TX, p. A603

O'DONNELL, Michael, Chief Financial Officer, Peconic Bay Medical Center, Riverhead, NY, p. A448

O'DONNELL, Patrick W., CPA, President and Chief Executive Officer, Chambersburg Hospital, Chambersburg, PA, p. A531

O'DONNELL, Patrick W., CPA, President and Chief Executive Officer, Summit Health, Chambersburg, PA, p. B129

O'DONNELL, Randall L., Ph.D.,
President and Chief Executive Officer, Children's Mercy Hospitals and Clinics, Kansas City, MO, p. A369
President and Chief Executive Officer, Children's Mercy South, Overland Park, KS, p. A248

O'FLANAGAN, Jayne, Director Human Resources, Incline Village Community Hospital, Incline Village, NV, p. A401

O'GORMAN, Brenda, R.N. Interim Chief Nursing Officer, Select Specialty Hospital–Omaha, Omaha, NE, p. A396

O'GORMAN, Victoria, Administrator, Fremont Medical Center, Fremont, CA, p. A62

O'HARA, Denise, Vice President Human Resources, Wilson Medical Center, Wilson, NC, p. A470

O'HARA, Gene L., Interim Chief Executive Officer, Colorado Plains Medical Center, Fort Morgan, CO, p. A103

O'HARA, Kathleen, Vice President Human Resources, Erie County Medical Center, Buffalo, NY, p. A430

O'HARA, Michael
Senior Executive Director Human Resources, Houston Medical Center, Warner Robins, GA, p. A167
Senior Executive Director, Perry Hospital, Perry, GA, p. A162

O'HARE, Rose Ann, R.N. Senior Vice President Patient Services, New York–Presbyterian/Lawrence Hospital, Bronxville, NY, p. A430

O'HAVER, Tim G., Chief Operating Officer, Summit Pacific Medical Center, Elma, WA, p. A678

O'HEARN, Brian, Vice President Patient Care Services and Chief Nursing Officer, Samaritan Medical Center, Watertown, NY, p. A453

O'KEEFE, James, Chief Financial Officer, Westerly Hospital, Westerly, RI, p. A556

O'KEEFE, James M., President and Chief Executive Officer, Mile Bluff Medical Center, Mauston, WI, p. A705

O'KEEFE, John, Chief Executive Officer, Select Specialty Hospital–Gulfport, Gulfport, MS, p. A354

O'KEEFE, Kathy
Executive Director, Pilgrim Psychiatric Center, Brentwood, NY, p. A430
Interim Executive Director, Sagamore Children's Psychiatric Center, Dix Hills, NY, p. A432

O'KEEFE, Michael, Interim Chief Executive Officer, Community Memorial Hospital, Redfield, SD, p. A571

O'KEEFE, Robert D., Senior Vice President and Chief Financial Officer, University of Wisconsin Hospital and Clinics, Madison, WI, p. A704

O'KEEFE, Sharon L., R.N., President, University of Chicago Medical Center, Chicago, IL, p. A185

O'KEEFE, Trish, MSN, Interim President, Morristown Medical Center, Morristown, NJ, p. A414

O'KEEFFE, SPHR, CHHR, Maureen, Vice President and Chief Human Resource Officer, St. Luke's Regional Medical Center, Boise, ID, p. A173

O'LAIRE, Beth, Manager Human Resources, Calumet Medical Center, Chilton, WI, p. A699

O'LEARY, Bill, Chief Executive Officer, Pondera Medical Center, Conrad, MT, p. A382

O'LEARY, Daniel H., M.D. Chief Medical Officer, HealthAlliance Hospitals, Leominster, MA, p. A308

O'LEARY, Kevin J., Senior Vice President and Chief Financial Officer, Exeter Hospital, Exeter, NH, p. A406

O'LEARY, Megan A., Vice President Human Resources and Rehabilitation Services, McKenzie–Willamette Medical Center, Springfield, OR, p. A526

O'LEARY, Rand
Chief Executive Officer, PeaceHealth Sacred Heart Medical Center University District, Eugene, OR, p. A520
Chief Administrative Officer, PeaceHealth Sacred Heart Medical Center at RiverBend, Springfield, OR, p. A526

O'LOUGHLIN, James F., President and Chief Executive Officer, Memorial Hospital Jacksonville, Jacksonville, FL, p. A129

O'MALLEY, John F., FACHE, Chief Executive Officer, Select Specialty Hospital–Ann Arbor, Ypsilanti, MI, p. A333

O'MALLEY, Jon P., Chief Executive Officer, Select Specialty Hospital–Macomb County, Mount Clemens, MI, p. A326

O'MALLEY, Mary Jo, R.N. Vice President Diagnostics and Support Services, Oconomowoc Memorial Hospital, Oconomowoc, WI, p. A708

O'MALLEY, Trevor, Site Manager, Presence Saint Joseph Hospital, Elgin, IL, p. A187

O'NEAL, Charlotte, Vice President Human Resources, Research Medical Center, Kansas City, MO, p. A370

O'NEAL, Lewis Stephen, R.N. Chief Nursing Officer, Saint Joseph – London, London, KY, p. A260

O'NEAL, Michael, Administrator and Chief Executive Officer, George C Grape Community Hospital, Hamburg, IA, p. A228

O'NEIL, Alan, Chief Executive Officer, Unity Medical Center, Grafton, ND, p. A474

O'NEIL, Jeremy, Manager Finance, Providence Valdez Medical Center, Valdez, AK, p. A29

O'NEIL, Linda B., R.N., Chief Executive Officer, Hospital for Extended Recovery, Norfolk, VA, p. A669

O'NEIL, Terry, Chief Information Technology, Nazareth Hospital, Philadelphia, PA, p. A544

O'NEILL, Beth, Chief Nursing Officer, Morgan Memorial Hospital, Madison, GA, p. A161

O'NEILL, Bonnie, Vice President Employee Services, Northern Montana Hospital, Havre, MT, p. A384

O'NEILL, Colene, Associate Director Patient Nursing Services, Syracuse Veterans Affairs Medical Center, Syracuse, NY, p. A451

O'NEILL, Jennifer A., R.N. Vice President Patient Care Services, Saint Barnabas Medical Center, Livingston, NJ, p. A413

O'NEILL, John Patrick, Administrator, Shriners Hospitals for Children–Boston, Boston, MA, p. A304

O'NEILL, Joseph J., M.D. Vice President Medical Affairs, South County Hospital, Wakefield, RI, p. A556

O'NEILL, Lynn, R.N. Chief Nursing Officer, Medical Center of Lewisville, Lewisville, TX, p. A628

O'NEILL, Melissa, Vice President Human Resources, Advocate Sherman Hospital, Elgin, IL, p. A187

O'NEILL, Michael, M.D. Chief Medical Officer, Eastside Medical Center, Snellville, GA, p. A164

O'NEILL, Stephan, Vice President Information Services, Hartford Hospital, Hartford, CT, p. A112

O'REAR, Caleb F., Chief Executive Officer, Denton Regional Medical Center, Denton, TX, p. A608

O'ROURKE, Jane, R.N. Chief Nursing Officer, Vice President Operations, St. Peter's Hospital, Albany, NY, p. A428

O'ROURKE, Michael, Regional Human Resources Lead, Presence Saint Joseph Hospital, Elgin, IL, p. A187

O'SHEA, James, Chief Operating Officer, Baton Rouge Behavioral Hospital, Baton Rouge, LA, p. A269

O'SHEA, James E.
Administrator, Springbrook Hospital, Brooksville, FL, p. A123
Administrator, The Willough at Naples, Naples, FL, p. A136

O'SHEA, Kristen, R.N. Vice President Patient Care Services, Gettysburg Hospital, Gettysburg, PA, p. A534

O'SHIELDS, Hugh, M.D. President Medical Staff, Trinity Medical Center, Birmingham, AL, p. A17

O'STEEN, Neil, Director Information Technology, Bacon County Hospital and Health System, Alma, GA, p. A149

O'SULLIVAN, Barbara, M.D. Medical Director, Rockefeller University Hospital, New York, NY, p. A444

O'SULLIVAN, Paul, Chief Executive Officer, Memorial Hermann Memorial City Medical Center, Houston, TX, p. A621

O. CONNOR, Joyce, Chief Operating Officer, Taunton State Hospital, Taunton, MA, p. A312

OAKES, Julie P., R.N. Manager Risk and Quality, Ocean Beach Hospital, Ilwaco, WA, p. A679

OAKES FERRUCCI, Susan, MS Vice President Patient Services and Chief Nursing Officer, Cobleskill Regional Hospital, Cobleskill, NY, p. A432

OAKLEY, Lisa, Chief Financial Officer, Harper County Community Hospital, Buffalo, OK, p. A504

OAKLEY, Sarah G., Vice President Nursing, North Kansas City Hospital, North Kansas City, MO, p. A373

OAKS, Dana, Chief Executive Officer, West Palm Hospital, West Palm Beach, FL, p. A147

OATES, John
Director Information Systems, Geneva General Hospital, Geneva, NY, p. A434
Director Information Systems, Soldiers and Sailors Memorial Hospital of Yates County, Penn Yan, NY, p. A447

OAXACA, Norma, Director Human Resources, Peak Behavioral Health Services, Santa Teresa, NM, p. A426

OBER, Tammy L., Chief Executive Officer, Lancaster Rehabilitation Hospital, Lancaster, PA, p. A537

OBERHEU, Todd, Chief Executive Officer, Spanish Peaks Regional Health Center, Walsenburg, CO, p. A109

OBERMIER, Jenny, VP, Director of Nursing, York General Hospital, York, NE, p. A399

OBERST, Larry, Vice President Finance, Spectrum Health Special Care Hospital, Grand Rapids, MI, p. A321

OBEY, Bianca A., Chief Financial Officer, Alexandria Veterans Affairs Health Care System, Pineville, LA, p. A283

OCASIO, J. Manuel, Vice President Human Resources, Holy Cross Hospital, Silver Spring, MD, p. A300

OCHOA, Mark S., M.D. Deputy Commander, Clinical Services, Irwin Army Community Hospital, Junction City, KS, p. A243

OCHOA, Nikki, Interim Chief Financial Officer, St. Joseph's Medical Center, Stockton, CA, p. A93

OCHSENDORF, Derrick, Manager Information Technology and Systems, Johnson Memorial Health Services, Dawson, MN, p. A337

OCKER, Danielle, Director, Littleton Regional Hospital, Littleton, NH, p. A407

ODATO, David, Chief Administrative and Chief Human Resources Officer, UCSF Medical Center, San Francisco, CA, p. A89

ODDIS, Joseph M., Chief Executive Officer, Bon Secours Maryview Medical Center, Portsmouth, VA, p. A670

ODEGAARD, Daniel, FACHE, Chief Executive Officer, Rainy Lake Medical Center, International Falls, MN, p. A340

ODELL, Cheryl, R.N. Chief Nursing Officer, Sharp Mesa Vista Hospital, San Diego, CA, p. A87

ODELL, JoAnn, Chief People Resource Officer, Banner Estrella Medical Center, Phoenix, AZ, p. A34

ODEN, Ryan, M.D. Chief of Staff, Arbuckle Memorial Hospital, Sulphur, OK, p. A515

ODETOYINBO, Adedapo, M.D. Chief Medical Office, Emory Johns Creek Hospital, Johns Creek, GA, p. A159

ODLE, Susan, Administrator, St. Joseph Memorial Hospital, Murphysboro, IL, p. A195

ODOM, David, Chief Information Officer, Rehoboth McKinley Christian Health Care Services, Gallup, NM, p. A424

ODOM, Jennifer, Interim Director Human Resources, Flowers Hospital, Dothan, AL, p. A18

ODOM, Lee Ann, Division President, Beaumont Hospital – Taylor, Taylor, MI, p. A331

ODOM, Robbin, R.N. Chief Nursing Officer, Lake Area Medical Center, Lake Charles, LA, p. A278

ODOM, Terry, Chief Executive Officer, Powell Valley Healthcare, Powell, WY, p. A717

ODUWOLE, Adedapo, M.D. Medical Director, Lighthouse Care Center of Conway, Conway, SC, p. A560

OEHLKE, Tammy, Director Human Resources, St. Mark's Medical Center, La Grange, TX, p. A627

OERTLI, Stuart, Executive Director, Covenant Specialty Hospital, Lubbock, TX, p. A629

OESTREICH, Pearl, Director Human Resources, Scott & White Hospital – Llano, Llano, TX, p. A628

OETTING, Phyllis, Director Human Resources, Mitchell County Hospital Health Systems, Beloit, KS, p. A238

OETZEL, Gerald P., Chief Financial Officer, Temple University Hospital, Philadelphia, PA, p. A545

OFFUTT, Dan, Manager Finance, Knox County Hospital, Knox City, TX, p. A626

OFNER, Lori, Vice President Human Resources, Easton Hospital, Easton, PA, p. A533

OFSTEDAL, Jeff, Director Information Technology, St. Andrew's Health Center, Bottineau, ND, p. A472

OGASAWARA, Keith, M.D. Associate Medical Director and Professional Chief of Staff, Kaiser Permanente Medical Center, Honolulu, HI, p. A168

OGAWA, Quin, Vice President Finance and Chief Financial Officer, Kuakini Medical Center, Honolulu, HI, p. A168

OGBURN, J. Anthony, M.D. Chief Medical Officer, UNM Sandoval Regional Medical Center, Rio Rancho, NM, p. A426

OGDEN, Judy, Director Information Technology, Franklin Medical Center, Winnsboro, LA, p. A287

OGDEN, Lesley, M.D. Chief Operating Officer, Samaritan North Lincoln Hospital, Lincoln City, OR, p. A522

OGDEN, Michael L., President and Chief Executive Officer, Little Falls Hospital, Little Falls, NY, p. A436

OGG, Tom, Vice President Information Services and Chief Information Officer, Akron Children's Hospital, Akron, OH, p. A478

OGILVIE, Richard, Chief Information Officer, Southwestern Vermont Medical Center, Bennington, VT, p. A660

OGLESBY, Darrell M., Administrator, Putnam General Hospital, Eatonton, GA, p. A157

OGORZALEK, Ed, Chief Financial Officer, Rutland Regional Medical Center, Rutland, VT, p. A661

OGRINC, Mary L., R.N. Chief Nursing Officer, Senior Vice President Patient Care Services, Lake Health, Concord Township, OH, p. A487

OGROD, Eugene, M.D. Chief Medical Officer, Kingwood Medical Center, Kingwood, TX, p. A626

OHASHI, Curtis, Chief Executive Officer, Select Specialty Hospital–Cincinnati, Cincinnati, OH, p. A483

OHE, Gregory P., President, Health Central Hospital, Ocoee, FL, p. A137

ONOFRE, Bonnie J., MS Vice President and Chief Nursing Officer, Robert Packer Hospital, Sayre, PA, p. A549

OOSTHUYSEN, Gabriel, Director Human Resources, Prairie du Chien Memorial Hospital, Prairie Du Chien, WI, p. A709

OOSTRA, Randall D., FACHE, President and Chief Executive Officer, ProMedica Health System, Toledo, OH, p. B108

OPBROEK, Steve, Manager Information Technology, Skyline Hospital, White Salmon, WA, p. A687

OPHEIKENS, Robyn, Assistant Administrator Human Resources, St. Mark's Hospital, Salt Lake City, UT, p. A658

OPPEGARD, Stanley C., Chief Executive Officer, Trinity Hospital, Weaverville, CA, p. A97

OPRANDI, Allison, M.D. Chief Medical Officer, Aultman Hospital, Canton, OH, p. A481

OPRISKO, Judy P.
Vice President, Allied Services Rehabilitation Hospital, Scranton, PA, p. A549
Vice President Human Resources, John Heinz Institute of Rehabilitation Medicine, Wilkes–Barre, PA, p. A553

OPSTEDAHL, DeeAnna, Vice President Patient Care Services, St. Joseph's Hospital and Health Center, Dickinson, ND, p. A473

OPSUT, Jennifer, Interim Chief Operating Officer, West Valley Medical Center, Caldwell, ID, p. A173

ORAZINE, Jay, Director Information Services, Baptist Health Paducah, Paducah, KY, p. A264

ORCUTT, David, Chief Executive Officer, Weatherford Regional Medical Center, Weatherford, TX, p. A650

ORDYNA, Daniel, Chief Executive Officer, Portneuf Medical Center, Pocatello, ID, p. A175

ORE, Ruta, Director Human Resources, Pottstown Memorial Medical Center, Pottstown, PA, p. A548

OREAR, Kathy, Director Human Resources, Newman Regional Health, Emporia, KS, p. A239

OREGEL, Omar, Controller, Kindred Hospital–Ontario, Ontario, CA, p. A79

ORELLANA, Feliipe, Chief Medical Officer, Barnes–Jewish St. Peters Hospital, Saint Peters, MO, p. A378

OREOL, Harry, Acting Chief Executive Officer, Patton State Hospital, Patton, CA, p. A80

ORIOL, Albert, Vice President Information Management and Chief Information Officer, Rady Children's Hospital – San Diego, San Diego, CA, p. A86

ORLANDI, Mary, Manager Human Resources, Carney Hospital, Boston, MA, p. A303

ORLANDO, Anthony T., Senior Vice President Finance, Englewood Hospital and Medical Center, Englewood, NJ, p. A412

ORLANDO, Lorraine, Vice President Human Resources, New York–Presbyterian/Queens, NY, p. A443

ORMAN Jr., Bernard A., Administrator, Samaritan Memorial Hospital, Macon, MO, p. A372

ORMOND, Evalyn, Chief Executive Officer, Union General Hospital, Farmerville, LA, p. A273

ORMOND, Jack, Chief Financial Officer, Cuba Memorial Hospital, Cuba, NY, p. A432

ORMSBY, Joan, Vice President, West Suburban Medical Center, Oak Park, IL, p. A196

ORNELAS, Henry, Chief Operating Officer, LAC/University of Southern California Medical Center, Los Angeles, CA, p. A71

ORONA, Rene, M.D. Chief of Staff, Marshall Medical Center, Placerville, CA, p. A81

OROZCO, Jorge, Chief Executive Officer, Rancho Los Amigos National Rehabilitation Center, Downey, CA, p. A60

ORR, Karen, Chief Nursing Officer, Providence Medical Center, Kansas City, KS, p. A243

ORR, Natassia, Chief Operating Officer, Broward Health Medical Center, Fort Lauderdale, FL, p. A126

ORR, Stephanie, R.N. Chief Nursing Officer, Steele Memorial Medical Center, Salmon, ID, p. A176

ORRELL, Linda, Interim Chief Nursing Officer, Drew Memorial Hospital, Monticello, AR, p. A48

ORRICK, Charles H., Administrator, Donalsonville Hospital, Donalsonville, GA, p. A156

ORSINI, John
Executive Vice President and Chief Financial Officer, Northwestern Medicine Central DuPage Hospital, Winfield, IL, p. A203
Executive Vice President and Chief Financial Officer, Northwestern Medicine Delnor Hospital, Geneva, IL, p. A189

ORSINI, Thomas J., President and Chief Executive Officer, Lake Taylor Transitional Care Hospital, Norfolk, VA, p. A669

ORT, Linda, Chief Financial Officer, Piggott Community Hospital, Piggott, AR, p. A49

ORTEGA, Becky, Director Human Resources, Avista Adventist Hospital, Louisville, CO, p. A107

ORTEGA, Cesar, M.D. Chief of Staff, Doctor's Hospital – Tidwell, Houston, TX, p. A619

ORTEGA, Debbie, Chief Human Resource Officer and Vice President Administrative Services, Huntington Memorial Hospital, Pasadena, CA, p. A80

ORTEGA, Jose, Chief Operating Officer, Greater El Monte Community Hospital, South El Monte, CA, p. A93

ORTEGO, Ashley, Director Human Resources and Marketing, Springhill Medical Center, Springhill, LA, p. A286

ORTH, Charam, Director Human Resources, Frances Mahon Deaconess Hospital, Glasgow, MT, p. A383

ORTHAUS, Denis, Director Human Resources, Philhaven, Mount Gretna, PA, p. A541

ORTIZ, Bienvenido, Coordinator Information Systems, Hospital De Damas, Ponce, PR, p. A722

ORTIZ, Jr., Blas, Assistant Superintendent and Public Information Officer, Rio Grande State Center/South Texas Health Care System, Harlingen, TX, p. A618

ORTIZ, Edson, Chief Information Officer, Hospital Metropolitano Dr. Tito Mattei, Yauco, PR, p. A724

ORTIZ, Evelyn Padilla
Director Human Resources, Hospital Menonita De Cayey, Cayey, PR, p. A720
Director Human Resources, Mennonite General Hospital, Aibonito, PR, p. A719

ORTIZ, Francisco, M.D. Chief of Staff, Jackson County Hospital District, Edna, TX, p. A610

ORTIZ, Hector, Financial Director, Hospital Metropolitano Dr. Susoni, Arecibo, PR, p. A720

ORTIZ, Jose O., Chief Financial Officer, Ryder Memorial Hospital, Humacao, PR, p. A721

ORTIZ, Migdalia, Director Human Resources, Hospital San Carlos Borromeo, Moca, PR, p. A722

ORTIZ, Nancy, Director Human Resource and Marketing, Frio Regional Hospital, Pearsall, TX, p. A636

ORTIZ, Norma, M.D. Medical Director, Hospital Hermanos Melendez, Bayamon, PR, p. A720

ORTIZ BAEZ, Felix, Administrator, I. Gonzalez Martinez Oncologic Hospital, PR, p. A724

ORTIZ VARGAS, Ruth M., Administrator, Lafayette Hospital, Arroyo, PR, p. A720

ORTIZ–BITNER, Olivia, Acting Chief Financial Officer, VA Greater Los Angeles Healthcare System, Los Angeles, CA, p. A73

ORTO, Victoria K., R.N. Chief Nursing and Patient Care Services Officer, Duke Regional Hospital, Durham, NC, p. A459

ORTOLANI, Philip A., Vice President Operations, Mid Coast Hospital, Brunswick, ME, p. A289

ORTON, Wendy, Chief Nursing Officer, Alleghany Memorial Hospital, Sparta, NC, p. A469

OSANTOSKI, Tina, Director Human Resources, Harbor Beach Community Hospital, Harbor Beach, MI, p. A322

OSARIO, Cesar, Specialist Information Technology, Cedar Crest Hospital and Residential Treatment Center, Belton, TX, p. A597

OSBAHR, Leah, M.P.H., Chief Executive Officer, Helena Regional Medical Center, Helena, AR, p. A45

OSBERG, Art, M.D. Chief Medical Officer, Ocala Regional Medical Center, Ocala, FL, p. A137

OSBORN, Mary Ann, R.N. Senior Vice President and Chief Care Coordinator Officer, UnityPoint Health – St. Luke's Hospital, Cedar Rapids, IA, p. A223

OSBORN, Melodie
Chief Nursing Officer, Renown Rehabilitation Hospital, Reno, NV, p. A404
Chief Nursing Officer, Renown South Meadows Medical Center, Reno, NV, p. A404

OSBORN, Tom, D.O. Chief Medical Staff, Holdenville General Hospital, Holdenville, OK, p. A508

OSBORNE, Anna, Chief Human Resources Management Service, West Texas Veterans Affairs Health Care System, Big Spring, TX, p. A597

OSBORNE, Jay, M.D. Senior Vice President Medical Affairs, Northside Medical Center, Youngstown, OH, p. A501

OSBORNE, Phil, Director Information Technology, Bourbon Community Hospital, Paris, KY, p. A264

OSBURN, Jerry, Chief Executive Officer, Yoakum County Hospital, Denver City, TX, p. A608

OSBURNE, Theresa, Human Resources Strategic Partners, Providence Seaside Hospital, Seaside, OR, p. A526

OSCADAL, Martin
Vice President Human Resources, St. Elizabeth Edgewood, Edgewood, KY, p. A256
Senior Vice President Human Resources, St. Elizabeth Florence, Florence, KY, p. A256
Senior Vice President Human Resources, St. Elizabeth Fort Thomas, Fort Thomas, KY, p. A257

OSEGARD, Jeff, Chief Information Officer, Cass County Memorial Hospital, Atlantic, IA, p. A222

OSEHOBO, Philip, M.D. Chief Medical Officer, Spalding Regional Medical Center, Griffin, GA, p. A158

OSER, William F., M.D. Senior Vice President and Chief Medical Officer, JFK Medical Center, Edison, NJ, p. A411

OSINOWO, Thomas, M.D. Chief Clinical Officer, Northwest Ohio Psychiatric Hospital, Toledo, OH, p. A498

OSINSKI, Kathleen, Chief Human Resources Service, John D. Dingell Veterans Affairs Medical Center, Detroit, MI, p. A318

OSLIN, Dave, M.D. Chief of Staff, Philadelphia Veterans Affairs Medical Center, Philadelphia, PA, p. A545

OSMUS, Richard D., Chief Executive Officer, Abbeville Area Medical Center, Abbeville, SC, p. A557

OSOWSKI, Angela, Chief Nursing Officer, LifeCare Hospitals of Wisconsin, Pewaukee, WI, p. A709

OSSELLO, Susan, Chief Financial Officer, Granite County Medical Center, Philipsburg, MT, p. A386

OSTASZEWSKI, Patricia, MS, Chief Executive Officer, HEALTHSOUTH Rehabilitation Hospital of Toms River, Toms River, NJ, p. A419

OSTBERG, Melissa, Chief Financial Officer, Marias Medical Center, Shelby, MT, p. A387

OSTBLOOM, Jan, Human Resources Consultant, Our Lady of Peace, Louisville, KY, p. A261

OSTEEN, Tom J., Director Area Technology, Kaiser Permanente Manteca Medical Center, Manteca, CA, p. A74

OSTENDORF, Todd, Chief Financial Officer, North Memorial Medical Center, Robbinsdale, MN, p. A345

OSTENSON, Scott, Chief Financial Officer, Jacobson Memorial Hospital Care Center, Elgin, ND, p. A473

OSTER, Kurt, Human Resources Officer, Carl Vinson Veterans Affairs Medical Center, Dublin, GA, p. A156

OSTERBERG, Valerie, Chief Financial Officer, Sanford Vermillion Medical Center, Vermillion, SD, p. A572

OSTERHOLM, Tim
Senior Vice President and Chief People Officer, CHI St. Vincent Infirmary Medical Center, Little Rock, AR, p. A47
Senior Vice President and Chief People Officer, CHI St. Vincent Medical Center–North, Sherwood, AR, p. A50

OSTERHOUT, David, Assistant Superintendent and Chief Financial Officer, El Paso Psychiatric Center, El Paso, TX, p. A610

OSTERLY, Eric, Chief Financial Officer, Florida Hospital Fish Memorial, Orange City, FL, p. A137

OSTLIG, Jane, Chief Medical Officer, Sanford Mayville Medical Center, Mayville, ND, p. A475

OSTRANDER, Maria DC, R.N. Chief Nurse Executive, San Antonio State Hospital, San Antonio, TX, p. A642

OSTRANDER, Mark, Vice President Financial Services, Community Medical Center, Toms River, NJ, p. A419

OSTRANDER, Michael, Chief Financial Officer, Nathan Littauer Hospital and Nursing Home, Gloversville, NY, p. A434

OSTROWSKY, Barry, President and Chief Executive Officer, Barnabas Health, West Orange, NJ, p. B21

OSWALD, Kathy, Senior Vice President and Chief Human Resources Officer, Henry Ford Hospital, Detroit, MI, p. A317

OSWALD, Traci L., Vice President Human Resources, Avita Galion Hospital, Galion, OH, p. A490

OTERO, Jorge Torres, Executive Director, Hospital Del Maestro, San Juan, PR, p. A723

OTHOLE, Jean, Chief Executive Officer, U. S. Public Health Service Indian Hospital, Zuni, NM, p. A427

OTOTIBO, Brenda, Executive Director, Jim Taliaferro Community Mental Health, Lawton, OK, p. A508

OTOTT, Kelly, R.N. Chief Nursing Officer, Washington County Hospital, Washington, KS, p. A252

OTREMBIAK, Robert J., Director of People Services, HSHS St. Joseph's Hospital, Breese, IL, p. A180

OTT, Darin, D.O. Chief of Staff, Kane County Hospital, Kanab, UT, p. A655

OTT, Laurie, Vice President Human Resources and President University Health Care Foundation, University Hospital, Augusta, GA, p. A152

OTT, Lynne, MSN Vice President Patient Care Services and Chief Nursing Officer, Fitzgibbon Hospital, Marshall, MO, p. A372

OTT, Pamela, Vice President Finance, Aurora Sheboygan Memorial Medical Center, Sheboygan, WI, p. A710

OTT, Ronald H.
President, Excela Frick Hospital, Mount Pleasant, PA, p. A541
President, Excela Health Westmoreland Hospital, Greensburg, PA, p. A535

OTTATI, David, Chief Executive Officer, Florida Hospital Waterman, Tavares, FL, p. A145

OTTE, Elaine, Chief Operating Officer, Clarinda Regional Health Center, Clarinda, IA, p. A224

OTTEN, Sharon A., Vice President Nursing, Advocate South Suburban Hospital, Hazel Crest, IL, p. A190

OTTENBACHER, John, Chief of Staff, Bowdle Hospital, Bowdle, SD, p. A567

OTTENS, Mark, Chief Nursing Officer, Baptist Memorial Hospital–North Mississippi, Oxford, MS, p. A359

OTTMAR, Kellie, Manager Information Services, East Adams Rural Hospital, Ritzville, WA, p. A683

Index of Health Care Professionals / Paine

Index of Health Care Professionals


OTTO, Sara, Chief Compliance Officer, North Canyon Medical Center, Gooding, ID, p. A174

OTTO, Steve
- Chief Executive Officer, TriStar Skyline Madison Campus, Madison, TN, p. A582
- Chief Executive Officer, TriStar Skyline Medical Center, Nashville, TN, p. A586

OUBRE, Chris, Information Technology Director, Garden Park Medical Center, Gulfport, MS, p. A353

OUELETTE, Lisa, Director Human Resources, Beaumont Hospital – Troy, Troy, MI, p. A331

OUELLETTE, Demetra, Chief Operating Officer, Rehabilitation Hospital of Rhode Island, North Smithfield, RI, p. A555

OUIMET, Mary Elizabeth, MSN Senior Vice President and Chief Nursing Officer, Wheaton Franciscan Healthcare – All Saints, Racine, WI, p. A709

OUNGST, Laurie, Vice President and Chief Operating Officer, Ministry Saint Mary's Hospitals, Rhinelander, WI, p. A710

OURS, Matt, Chief Executive Officer and Managing Director, Rivendell Behavioral Health, Bowling Green, KY, p. A254

OUSEY, Tracy, Director Human Resources, Washington County Hospital and Clinics, Washington, IA, p. A235

OUTHIER, Amy, Director Health Information Management, Weatherford Regional Hospital, Weatherford, OK, p. A518

OUTLAW, Debbie, R.N. Director Patient Care Services, Riverside Rehabilitation Institute, Newport News, VA, p. A669

OUZTS, Carey, Director of Nursing, Brentwood Hospital, Shreveport, LA, p. A284

OVANDO, Benjamin, Chief Operations Officer, Rancho Los Amigos National Rehabilitation Center, Downey, CA, p. A60

OVERBEY, William J., Chief Executive Officer, Kansas Rehabilitation Hospital, Topeka, KS, p. A251

OVERBY, Roger, Executive Director Information Systems, Greene County Medical Center, Jefferson, IA, p. A230

OVERCASH, Jenny, Director Human Resources, HEALTHSOUTH Huntington Rehabilitation Hospital, Huntington, WV, p. A692

OVEREEM, Mark, Chief Financial Officer, USC Verdugo Hills Hospital, Glendale, CA, p. A64

OVERMAN, David S., President and Chief Operating Officer, Children's Hospitals and Clinics of Minnesota, Minneapolis, MN, p. A342

OVERSTREET, Alyson, Chief Financial Officer, Washington County Hospital, Chatom, AL, p. A18

OVERSTREET, Amy, Director Human Resources, Trousdale Medical Center, Hartsville, TN, p. A578

OVERTON, Deana, Director Human Resources, Mitchell County Hospital, Colorado City, TX, p. A601

OVWIGHO, Godfrey, Vice President Information Technology and Chief Information Officer, The University of Toledo Medical Center, Toledo, OH, p. A499

OWEN, Joanne, Interim Vice President Operations, PeaceHealth Southwest Medical Center, Vancouver, WA, p. A687

OWEN, Ronald S., FACHE, Chief Executive Officer, Southeast Alabama Medical Center, Dothan, AL, p. A19

OWEN, Sabrina, Human Resources Officer, Veterans Affairs Central Iowa Health Care System, Des Moines, IA, p. A227

OWEN, Sandra, Director Fiscal and Accounting, Harper Hospital District Five, Harper, KS, p. A241

OWEN–PLIETZ, Carrie, Chief Executive Officer, Sutter Medical Center, Sacramento, Sacramento, CA, p. A85

OWENS, Beverly, Controller, Rehabilitation Hospital, Navicent Health, Macon, GA, p. A161

OWENS, Brian, Chief Operating Officer, Lindner Center of HOPE, Mason, OH, p. A493

OWENS, Craig A., President, WellStar Douglas Hospital, Douglasville, GA, p. A156

OWENS, Daniel, Chief Executive Officer, Emory University Hospital Midtown, Atlanta, GA, p. A150

OWENS, Johnathan, Chief Executive Officer, Decatur Health Systems, Oberlin, KS, p. A247

OWENS, Kevin, Chief Executive Officer, Quartz Mountain Medical Center, Mangum, OK, p. A509

OWENS, Mark, M.D. Vice President Medical Affairs, Mercy San Juan Medical Center, Carmichael, CA, p. A57

OWENS, Maxwell, FACHE Chief Financial Officer, New Orleans East Hospital, New Orleans, LA, p. A282

OWENS, Pamela, Director Health Information Management, Hanover Hospital, Hanover, PA, p. A535

OWENS, Rick, Chief Financial Officer, D. W. McMillan Memorial Hospital, Brewton, AL, p. A17

OWENS, Stephanie, Manager Human Resources, McDowell ARH Hospital, McDowell, KY, p. A263

OWENS, RN, Steven Vance, Chief Nursing Officer, Southwestern Medical Center, Lawton, OK, p. A509

OWENSBY, Karen, R.N. Chief Clinical Officer, Florida Hospital North Pinellas, Tarpon Springs, FL, p. A145

OWREY, Donald R., President, UPMC Horizon, Greenville, PA, p. A535

OWSLEY, Lindsay, Manager Human Resources, Ellinwood District Hospital, Ellinwood, KS, p. A239

OWUSU, Frederick K., Chief Human Resources Officer, Desert Regional Medical Center, Palm Springs, CA, p. A80

OXENDALE, Roger A., Chief Executive Officer, Nemours Children's Hospital, Orlando, FL, p. A138

OXENDALE, Sharon, Chief Operating Officer, MacNeal Hospital, Berwyn, IL, p. A179

OXFORD, Michelle, Chief Operating Officer, Acting Chief Executive Officer, Bakersfield Heart Hospital, Bakersfield, CA, p. A54

OXFORD, Tammy, Director Human Resources, Bob Wilson Memorial Grant County Hospital, Ulysses, KS, p. A251

OXLER, Karen Flaherty, R.N. President, Lancaster General Hospital and Chief Nursing Officer, Lancaster General Health, Lancaster, PA, p. A537

OXLEY, Dawn, R.N. Associate Director Patient Care Services and Nurse Executive, Iowa City Veterans Affairs Health Care System, Iowa City, IA, p. A229

OXLEY, James, D.O. Vice President Medical Affairs, Orange Regional Medical Center, Middletown, NY, p. A437

OXLEY, Stephen, M.D. Chief Medical Officer, Central Regional Hospital, Butner, NC, p. A456

OXTON, Alice, Director Information Technology, Sentara Obici Hospital, Suffolk, VA, p. A673

OZBURN, Thomas H., Chief Executive Officer, TriStar Southern Hills Medical Center, Nashville, TN, p. A586

OZEL, A. Deniz, M.D
- Medical Director, New England Rehabilitation Hospital, Woburn, MA, p. A313
- Chief Medical Director, Northeast Rehabilitation Hospital, Salem, NH, p. A408

OZMENT, Mary, Chief Nursing Officer, AllianceHealth Pryor, Pryor, OK, p. A514


# P


P'NG, Heong, M.D. Interim Chief Medical Officer, Ministry Saint Clare's Hospital, Weston, WI, p. A714

PAARLBERG, Ted, Chief Executive Officer, Kindred Hospital Peoria, Peoria, IL, p. A198

PAASCH, Michael
- Regional Vice President and Chief Information Officer, SSM Cardinal Glennon Children's Medical Center, Saint Louis, MO, p. A377
- Regional Chief Information Officer, SSM St. Mary's Health Center, Saint Louis, MO, p. A377

PAASCH, Mike, Vice President, Regional Chief Information Officer, SSM St. Clare Health Center, Fenton, MO, p. A367

PABLO, Gary M., M.D. Chief Medical Officer, Sacred Heart Hospital on the Emerald Coast, Miramar Beach, FL, p. A136

PABON, Jose O., Director Operations, Wilma N. Vazquez Medical Center, Vega Baja, PR, p. A724

PABON–RAMIREZ, Felix, Chief Information Officer, St. Charles Hospital, Port Jefferson, NY, p. A448

PACCAPANICCIA, Dominic, Chief Operating Officer, Indiana Regional Medical Center, Indiana, PA, p. A536

PACE, Debbie, Chief Operating Officer, Vaughan Regional Medical Center, Selma, AL, p. A24

PACE, Dewane, Chief of Ancillary Operations, Valley View Hospital, Glenwood Springs, CO, p. A104

PACE, Kathleen, MS
- Chief Nursing Officer, Englewood Community Hospital, Englewood, FL, p. A126
- Vice President and Chief Nursing Officer, Fawcett Memorial Hospital, Port Charlotte, FL, p. A140

PACE, Kelly, Director Human Resource, Strategic Behavioral Health – Wilmington, Leland, NC, p. A463

PACE, Matt, Information Technology Director, Lakeway Regional Medical Center, Lakeway, TX, p. A627

PACEK, Thomas
- Vice President Information Systems and Chief Information Officer, Inspira Medical Center–Elmer, Elmer, NJ, p. A411
- Vice President Information Systems and Chief Information Officer, Inspira Medical Center–Vineland, Vineland, NJ, p. A420

PACEY, Amy, Vice President Human Resources, Good Samaritan Medical Center, Lafayette, CO, p. A106

PACHECO, Robert W., Vice President Finance, Women & Infants Hospital of Rhode Island, Providence, RI, p. A556

PACHUCKI, Jr., James J., Chief Financial Officer, Sunbury Community Hospital and Outpatient Center, Sunbury, PA, p. A550

PACINI, Jenna, Human Resources Specialist, Belmont Center for Comprehensive Treatment, Philadelphia, PA, p. A542

PACK, Kathy, Manager Human Resources, Copper Basin Medical Center, Copperhill, TN, p. A576

PACK, Natalie, Chief Financial Officer, St. David's North Austin Medical Center, Austin, TX, p. A595

PACK, William, Chief Financial Officer, Memorial Hermann – Texas Medical Center, Houston, TX, p. A620

PACK–HOOKFIN, Sherre, Administrator, Lallie Kemp Medical Center, Independence, LA, p. A275

PACKER, Eric, Administrator, Bear River Valley Hospital, Tremonton, UT, p. A659

PACKER, Lee, Administrator, South Florida State Hospital, FL, p. A128

PACKER, Steven J., M.D., President and Chief Executive Officer, Community Hospital of the Monterey Peninsula, Monterey, CA, p. A76

PACKNETT, Michael J., President and Chief Executive Officer, Parkview Health, Fort Wayne, IN, p. B103

PACURA, Lori, MSN, President, Holy Cross Hospital, Chicago, IL, p. A182

PACZKOWSKI, Rick, Chief Operating Officer, Timberlawn Mental Health System, Dallas, TX, p. A607

PADDEN, Ernest C., Chief Financial Officer, Bon Secours Maryview Medical Center, Portsmouth, VA, p. A670

PADEN, Carolyn, Associate Administrator Surgical Services, Mosaic Life Care at St. Joseph, Saint Joseph, MO, p. A375

PADEN, Tawnya, Director Human Resources, Weatherford Regional Hospital, Weatherford, OK, p. A518

PADGETT, Martin, President and Chief Executive Officer, Clark Memorial Hospital, Jeffersonville, IN, p. A213

PADGETT, Randal, Manager Information Systems, Southern Palmetto Hospital, Barnwell, SC, p. A557

PADGETT, Shirley, Director Human Resources, Cook Medical Center–A Campus of Tift Regional Medical Center, Adel, GA, p. A149

PADILLA, Ami, Director Human Resources, Arroyo Grande Community Hospital, Arroyo Grande, CA, p. A54

PADILLA, Julieta M., Chief Nursing Officer, Hollywood Presbyterian Medical Center, Los Angeles, CA, p. A70

PADILLA, Rafael, R.N. Chief Nursing Officer, Florida Hospital at Connerton Long Term Acute Care, Land O'Lakes, FL, p. A131

PAFFORD, Roger, M.D. Medical Director, Mineral Community Hospital, Superior, MT, p. A387

PAGANELLI, Deborah, President, Texas Health Harris Methodist Hospital Hurst–Euless–Bedford, Bedford, TX, p. A597

PAGE, Alison, Chief Executive Officer, Baldwin Area Medical Center, Baldwin, WI, p. A697

PAGE, Bob, Chief Executive Officer, The University of Kansas Hospital, Kansas City, KS, p. A243

PAGE, Deborah, Chief Human Resources Officer, Duke University Hospital, Durham, NC, p. A459

PAGE, Keith Allen, President and Chief Executive Officer, Anderson Hospital, Maryville, IL, p. A193

PAGE, Linda, Chief Nursing Officer, Mary Free Bed Rehabilitation Hospital, Grand Rapids, MI, p. A320

PAGE, Nancy E., MS Interim Chief Nursing Officer, Upstate University Hospital, Syracuse, NY, p. A451

PAGE, Pattie, Director Marketing and Public Relations, Eastside Medical Center, Snellville, GA, p. A164

PAGE, III, Robert, Chief Information and Technology Officer, Memphis Veterans Affairs Medical Center, Memphis, TN, p. A583

PAGE, Sue, Director Human Resources, Monroe County Medical Center, Tompkinsville, KY, p. A266

PAGE, Susan M., President and Chief Executive Officer, Pratt Regional Medical Center, Pratt, KS, p. A249

PAGE, Timothy, Chief Executive Officer, Kindred Hospital the Palm Beaches, Riviera Beach, FL, p. A141

PAGELER, Robert
- Chief Information Officer, Central Washington Hospital, Wenatchee, WA, p. A687
- Chief Information Officer, Wenatchee Valley Medical Center, Wenatchee, WA, p. A687

PAGET, Cindy, Chief Human Resources Officer, Forks Community Hospital, Forks, WA, p. A679

PAGLIUZZA, Greg
- Chief Financial Officer, UnityPoint Health – Trinity Bettendorf, Bettendorf, IA, p. A222
- Chief Financial Officer, UnityPoint Health – Trinity Muscatine, Muscatine, IA, p. A232
- Chief Financial Officer, UnityPoint Health – Trinity Rock Island, Rock Island, IL, p. A199

PAGNANELLI, David, M.D. Chief of Staff, Southwestern Medical Center, Lawton, OK, p. A509

PAGNINI, Janie, Administrator Accounting, Atascadero State Hospital, Atascadero, CA, p. A54

PAGUAGA, Ana, Director of Human Resources, Coral Gables Hospital, Coral Gables, FL, p. A124

PAHE, Gary, Manager Human Resources, Sage Memorial Hospital, Ganado, AZ, p. A31

PAIER–MULLAN, Nicole, M.D. Medical Director, Upper Connecticut Valley Hospital, Colebrook, NH, p. A405

PAINE, Lincoln, M.D. Medical Director, River Oaks Hospital, New Orleans, LA, p. A282

Index of Health Care Professionals

Index of Health Care Professionals / Paine

PAINE, Russ, Human Resources Officer, Murphy Medical Center, Murphy, NC, p. A465
PAINTER, Jeff, Manager Information Technology, Summit Pacific Medical Center, Elma, WA, p. A678
PAIS, Roshan, M.D. Chief of Staff, Baptist Health Richmond, Richmond, KY, p. A265
PAKKALA, Mark, Director Human Resources, Spectrum Health Special Care Hospital, Grand Rapids, MI, p. A321
PALADINO, James, Controller, New England Rehabilitation Hospital of Portland, Portland, ME, p. A292
PALAGI, Richard L., Chief Executive Officer, Northeastern Nevada Regional Hospital, Elko, NV, p. A400
PALANGE, Kathleen, R.N., Chief Administrative Officer, Menlo Park Surgical Hospital, Menlo Park, CA, p. A75
PALAZZOLO, Christopher, Senior Vice President and Chief Operating Officer, Genesys Regional Medical Center, Grand Blanc, MI, p. A320
PALERMO, Robert, Vice President Finance, Ocean Medical Center, Brick Township, NJ, p. A410
PALETTA, Lisa A., R.N. Chief Nursing Officer, Utah Valley Regional Medical Center, Provo, UT, p. A657
PALETZ, Amanda, Director Marketing and Public Relations, LeConte Medical Center, Sevierville, TN, p. A588
PALICKA, Martha, Interim Manager Information Systems, Bartlett Regional Hospital, Juneau, AK, p. A28
PALIGO, Terry, Chief Financial Officer, Union County Hospital, Anna, IL, p. A178
PALIS, Adar, Executive Vice President and Chief Operating Officer, Harrison Medical Center, Bremerton, WA, p. A676
PALKOWSKI, Chris, M.D. Physician in Chief, Kaiser Permanente Sacramento Medical Center, Sacramento, CA, p. A84
PALLAS, Drew, Executive Vice President and Chief Administrative Officer, St. Joseph Hospital, Bethpage, NY, p. A429
PALLIN, Angel, Senior Vice President of Operations, Mount Sinai Medical Center, Miami Beach, FL, p. A135
PALMBERG, Kent, M.D. Senior Vice President and Chief Medical Officer, Stormont–Vail HealthCare, Topeka, KS, p. A251
PALMER, Barbara, Corporate Vice President Human Resources, Beaumont Hospital – Farmington Hills, Farmington Hills, MI, p. A319
PALMER, Debra L., MS Chief Human Resources Officer and Corporate Compliance Officer, Fairfield Medical Center, Lancaster, OH, p. A491
PALMER, Greg, Administrator Information Technology Network, Care Regional Medical Center, Aransas Pass, TX, p. A592
PALMER, Isaac, Chief Executive Officer, CHRISTUS Health Shreveport–Bossier, Shreveport, LA, p. A284
PALMER, Janel M., Director Human Resources, Greenwood County Hospital, Eureka, KS, p. A239
PALMER, Katie, Manager Human Resources, Sanford Aberdeen Medical Center, Aberdeen, SD, p. A567
PALMER, Keith, Assistant Administrator, Winkler County Memorial Hospital, Kermit, TX, p. A625
PALMER, Kelly, D.O. Medical Director, State Hospital South, Blackfoot, ID, p. A172
PALMER, Lauri, M.D. Chief of Staff, Platte County Memorial Hospital, Wheatland, WY, p. A718
PALMER, Linda, Coordinator Medical Records, San Gorgonio Memorial Hospital, Banning, CA, p. A55
PALMER, Stephanie, Chief Nursing Officer, HEALTHSOUTH Valley of the Sun Rehabilitation Hospital, Glendale, AZ, p. A32
PALMER, Trisha, Director, St. James Healthcare, Butte, MT, p. A382
PALMIER, Michael L., Chief Human Resources Management, Overton Brooks Veterans Affairs Medical Center, Shreveport, LA, p. A284
PALO, Alan, Chief Financial Officer, Sarah D. Culbertson Memorial Hospital, Rushville, IL, p. A200
PALSROK, Jerri, Manager Business Office, Osceola Community Hospital, Sibley, IA, p. A234
PALUMBO, Denise S., MSN Executive Vice President and Chief Operating Officer, Lawrence General Hospital, Lawrence, MA, p. A308
PALUMBO, Michael, D.O. Vice President Medical Affairs and Chief Education, Inland Hospital, Waterville, ME, p. A292
PALUMBO, Michael, M.D. Executive Vice President and Medical Director, White Plains Hospital Center, White Plains, NY, p. A454
PAM, Brower, Chief Financial Officer, CHRISTUS Spohn Hospital Corpus Christi Memorial, Corpus Christi, TX, p. A602
PAMPERIEN, Linda, Chief Financial Officer, Texas County Memorial Hospital, Houston, MO, p. A368
PANCOAST, James R., President and Chief Executive Officer, Premier Health, Dayton, OH, p. B106
PANDL, Therese B.
  President and Chief Executive Officer, St. Mary's Hospital Medical Center, Green Bay, WI, p. A702
  President and Chief Executive Officer, St. Vincent Hospital, Green Bay, WI, p. A702
PANDOLFINI, Paul, Chief Financial Officer, Coney Island Hospital, NY, p. A439
PANDOLPH, Philip, Chief Executive Officer, Meadville Medical Center, Meadville, PA, p. A540
PANDYA, Kamel, Director Information Services, San Antonio Community Hospital, Upland, CA, p. A95
PANDYA, Sherrie, Administrator, Kane County Hospital, Kanab, UT, p. A655
PANICUCCI, Michele
  Senior Vice President and Chief Financial Officer, Covenant Medical Center, Waterloo, IA, p. A235
  Chief Financial Officer, Sartori Memorial Hospital, Cedar Falls, IA, p. A223
PANIK, Anne, M
  Senior Vice President Patient Care Services and Chief Nursing Officer, Lehigh Valley Hospital, Allentown, PA, p. A528
  Senior Vice President Patient Care Services and Chief Nursing Officer, Lehigh Valley Hospital–Muhlenberg, Bethlehem, PA, p. A529
PANKEY, Susan Kay, Chief Nursing Officer, Davis County Hospital, Bloomfield, IA, p. A223
PANKOW, Thomas, Chief Information Officer, Jackson Park Hospital and Medical Center, Chicago, IL, p. A182
PANKOWSKI, Charles, Manager Human Resources, Select Specialty Hospital–Columbus, Columbus, OH, p. A487
PANLASIGUI, Bonnie, Chief Administrative Officer, Alameda Hospital, Alameda, CA, p. A53
PANNELL, Ken, Chief Financial Officer, College Station Medical Center, College Station, TX, p. A601
PANNULLO, Ava, M.D. Vice President Medical Services and Physician in Chief, The Hospital at Hebrew Health Care, West Hartford, CT, p. A116
PANSA, Leonard F., Senior Vice President Human Resources and Administrative Services, Mercy Medical Center, Springfield, MA, p. A311
PANTANO, Jane, R.N. Chief Nursing Officer, Pioneer Community Hospital of Stokes, Danbury, NC, p. A458
PANZA Jr., Louis J., President and Chief Executive Officer, Monongahela Valley Hospital, Monongahela, PA, p. A540
PAOLMELLI, Karen, Chief Operating Officer, Madera Community Hospital, Madera, CA, p. A74
PAOLUCCI, Benjamin, D.O. Chief of Staff, Southeast Michigan Surgical Hospital, Warren, MI, p. A332
PAPA, Alan
  President, Akron General Medical Center, Akron, OH, p. A478
  President and Chief Operating Officer, Lodi Community Hospital, Lodi, OH, p. A492
PAPA, AnnMarie, R.N. Vice President and Chief Nursing Officer, Einstein Medical Center Montgomery, East Norriton, PA, p. A533
PAPACOSTAS, Arthur C., M.D. Vice President and Chief Information Officer, Jeanes Hospital, Philadelphia, PA, p. A544
PAPADAKOS, James, Chief Financial Officer, Signature Healthcare Brockton Hospital, Brockton, MA, p. A305
PAPALIA, Fern, Vice President, Patient Care Services, Community Medical Center, Toms River, NJ, p. A419
PAPALIA, John, Chief Executive Officer, HEALTHSOUTH Rehabilitation Hospital of Erie, Erie, PA, p. A534
PAPANIA, Barry A., Interim Administrator, Jewish Hospital–Shelbyville, Shelbyville, KY, p. A266
PAPE, Becky A., R.N. Chief Operating Officer, Good Samaritan Regional Medical Center, Corvallis, OR, p. A520
PAPE, Becky A., R.N., Chief Executive Officer, Samaritan Lebanon Community Hospital, Lebanon, OR, p. A522
PAPKA, Lauren, Chief Administrative Officer, St. Mary's Sacred Heart Hospital, Lavonia, GA, p. A160
PAPPAN, Clayton, Director Human Resources and Marketing, South Central Kansas Medical Center, Arkansas City, KS, p. A237
PAPPAS, Charles, M.D. Chief Operating Officer, Bascom Palmer Eye Institute–Anne Bates Leach Eye Hospital, Miami, FL, p. A134
PAPPAS, Kirk, M.D. Physician–in–Chief, Kaiser Permanente Santa Rosa Medical Center, Santa Rosa, CA, p. A92
PAPPAS, Michael, Chief Fiscal Service Officer, Louis Stokes Cleveland Veterans Affairs Medical Center, Cleveland, OH, p. A484
PAPPAS, Nick, Chief Information Officer, PIH Health Hospital – Downey, Downey, CA, p. A60
PAPPAS, Sharon H., Ph.D. Chief Nursing Officer, Porter Adventist Hospital, Denver, CO, p. A102
PAPPAS, Sheryl L., Chief Financial Officer, Sanford Webster Medical Center, Webster, SD, p. A573
PAPPAS, Theron, Director Management Information Systems, Holy Family Memorial, Manitowoc, WI, p. A704
PARADIS, Brian, Chief Operating Officer, Florida Hospital, Orlando, FL, p. A138
PARADIS, James, President, Paoli Hospital, Paoli, PA, p. A542
PARADIS, Jeanne, Director Information Services, The Acadia Hospital, Bangor, ME, p. A288
PARASIDA, Tammy, Manager Business Office, Peterson Rehabilitation Hospital, Wheeling, WV, p. A696
PARAUDA, Martina A., Director, Veterans Affairs New York Harbor Healthcare System, NY, p. A445
PARAVISINI, Nilda, Director Human Resources, Hospital Manati Medical Center, Manati, PR, p. A721
PARCEL, Jim, Director Information Technology, Maury Regional Hospital, Columbia, TN, p. A576
PARCHMENT, Deborah, Executive Director, Kingsboro Psychiatric Center, NY, p. A440
PARDUE, Helen, Interim Chief Nursing Officer, Johnson County Community Hospital, Mountain City, TN, p. A584
PAREEK, Yogesh, M.D. Clinical Director, Brown County Community Treatment Center, Green Bay, WI, p. A702
PARENT, Charlotte, R.N., Interim Chief Executive Officer, New Orleans East Hospital, New Orleans, LA, p. A282
PARENT, Paula A., R.N. Director Human Resources and Nursing Administration, Cary Medical Center, Caribou, ME, p. A289
PARETI, Donna, Business Unit Chief Financial Officer, Presence Holy Family Medical Center, Des Plaines, IL, p. A186
PARHAM, Eva, R.N. Chief Nurse Executive, Central State Hospital, Petersburg, VA, p. A670
PARHAM, Tracy, MSNUniversity of North Carolina Hospitals, Chapel Hill, NC, p. A457
PARIGI, II, John S., Interim Chief Financial Officer, Healdsburg District Hospital, Healdsburg, CA, p. A64
PARILLE, Susan
  Director Human Resources, Blue Ridge Regional Hospital, Spruce Pine, NC, p. A469
  Director Human Resources Affiliate Mission Health System, McDowell Hospital, Marion, NC, p. A464
PARIS, Cynthia K., R.N., President and Chief Executive Officer, Texas Health Presbyterian Hospital of Rockwall, Rockwall, TX, p. A639
PARIS, David, Chief Executive Officer, Perry County General Hospital, Richton, MS, p. A360
PARIS, Dominic, Chief Financial Officer, Jerome Golden Center for Behavioral Health, Inc., West Palm Beach, FL, p. A147
PARIS, John, M.D. Chief Medical Officer, Riverview Hospital, Noblesville, IN, p. A218
PARIS, Karen, Controller, Crittenden County Hospital, Marion, KY, p. A262
PARIS, Sherri, Chief Operating Officer, Providence Milwaukie Hospital, Milwaukie, OR, p. A523
PARIS, Trevor, M.D. Medical Director, Brooks Rehabilitation Hospital, Jacksonville, FL, p. A129
PARISI, James, Chief Executive Officer, Memorial Hermann Katy Hospital, Katy, TX, p. A625
PARK, Bockhi
  Chief Executive Officer, Encino Hospital Medical Center, CA, p. A69
  Chief Executive Officer, Sherman Oaks Hospital, CA, p. A72
PARK, David B., Chief Operating Officer and General Counsel, Methodist Hospital, Henderson, KY, p. A258
PARK, Denten, Chief Executive Officer, MountainView Regional Medical Center, Las Cruces, NM, p. A425
PARK, Gary L., President, University of North Carolina Hospitals, Chapel Hill, NC, p. A457
PARK, Jessica, Director Accounting, Penn Highlands Brookville, Brookville, PA, p. A530
PARKER, Audrey, Budget Analyst, U. S. Public Health Service Indian Hospital, Winnebago, NE, p. A399
PARKER, Brandon, Vice President, St. Helena Hospital Napa Valley, Saint Helena, CA, p. A85
PARKER, Christopher J., R.N
  Senior Vice President Patient Care Services and Chief Nursing Officer, University of Maryland Shore Medical Center at Chestertown, Chestertown, MD, p. A296
  Chief Nursing Officer, University of Maryland Shore Medical Center at Easton, Easton, MD, p. A297
PARKER, Cindy, Chief Financial Officer and Director Human Resources, Throckmorton County Memorial Hospital, Throckmorton, TX, p. A648
PARKER, Cythia, Fiscal Director, Washington County Regional Medical Center, Sandersville, GA, p. A164
PARKER, Dan, M.D. Chief of Staff, Winona Health, Winona, MN, p. A349
PARKER, David, VP Information Technology, Magnolia Regional Health Center, Corinth, MS, p. A352
PARKER, Diana, Chief Executive Officer, Advanced Care Hospital of Montana, Billings, MT, p. A381
PARKER, Donald J., President and Chief Executive Officer, Carrier Clinic, Belle Mead, NJ, p. A409
PARKER, Grace E., R.N. Chief Nursing Officer, University of Washington Medical Center, Seattle, WA, p. A684
PARKER, Janie, Chief Financial Officer, Hardin County General Hospital, Rosiclare, IL, p. A200

Index of Health Care Professionals / Patino

Index of Health Care Professionals

PARKER, Jennifer, Director Information Systems, Delta Regional Medical Center, Greenville, MS, p. A353
PARKER, Jon–Michael, R.N. Chief Nursing Officer, Lillian M. Hudspeth Memorial Hospital, Sonora, TX, p. A644
PARKER, Judy Goforth, Ph.D., Secretary of Health, Chickasaw Nation Medical Center, Ada, OK, p. A503
PARKER, Lindy M., Interim Chief Nursing Officer and Vice President Patient Care Services, Flagstaff Medical Center, Flagstaff, AZ, p. A31
PARKER, Michael, M.D. Chief of Staff, Sharon Hospital, Sharon, CT, p. A114
PARKER, Richard, M.D., President, Marymount Hospital, Garfield Heights, OH, p. A490
PARKER, Robert, Chief Executive Officer, Meadowview Regional Medical Center, Maysville, KY, p. A263
PARKER, Rodney, Senior Associate Executive Director, Coney Island Hospital, NY, p. A439
PARKER, Sandra K., M.D. Chief Medical Officer, EastPointe Hospital, Daphne, AL, p. A18
PARKER, Thomas, Chief Executive Officer, Upper Valley Medical Center, Troy, OH, p. A499
PARKER, Tina, Director Human Resources, HEALTHSOUTH Rehabilitation Hospital Midland–Odessa, Midland, TX, p. A632
PARKER, Valerie, M.D. Clinical Director, U. S. Public Health Service Indian Hospital, Rosebud, SD, p. A571
PARKEY, Kasey, Coordinator Payroll and Benefits, Post Acute Medical Specialty Hospital of Corpus Christi, Corpus Christi, TX, p. A603
PARKHILL, Cherie, Chief Financial Officer, Crosbyton Clinic Hospital, Crosbyton, TX, p. A603
PARKHURST, James E., President and Chief Executive Officer, Newport Bay Hospital, Newport Beach, CA, p. A78
PARKINSON, Justin, M.D. President Medical Staff, Jordan Valley Medical Center–WVC Campus, West Valley City, UT, p. A659
PARKINSON, Michelle A., Director Human Resources, Prairie St. John's, Fargo, ND, p. A473
PARKS, Audrey, Senior Administrative Director Information Technology, Salinas Valley Memorial Healthcare System, Salinas, CA, p. A85
PARKS, Cary, Chief Information Resource Management, Hampton Veterans Affairs Medical Center, Hampton, VA, p. A666
PARKS, Dave, Chief Information Officer, Three Rivers Health, Three Rivers, MI, p. A331
PARKS, Ginger, Director Human Resources, Cape Fear Valley – Bladen County Hospital, Elizabethtown, NC, p. A460
PARKS, Jody, Administrator, Ottawa County Health Center, Minneapolis, KS, p. A246
PARKS, Kathi, Director of Nursing, South Lincoln Medical Center, Kemmerer, WY, p. A716
PARKS, Kyle, M.D. Chief of Staff, Evans Memorial Hospital, Claxton, GA, p. A153
PARKS, Michelle, Administrator, RiverValley Behavioral Health Hospital, Owensboro, KY, p. A264
PARKS, Richard H., FACHE, President and Chief Executive Officer, Covenant Health System, Lubbock, TX, p. B43
PARKS, Sherry, R.N. Chief Nursing Officer, Saint Alphonsus Regional Medical Center, Boise, ID, p. A172
PARKS, Vicki, Chief Financial Officer, Jackson Purchase Medical Center, Mayfield, KY, p. A262
PARLIKAR, Deven, President and Chief Executive Officer, U. S. Public Health Service Indian Hospital, San Carlos, AZ, p. A37
PARMER, David N., Chief Executive Officer, Baptist Hospitals of Southeast Texas, Beaumont, TX, p. A596
PARMER, Dennis, M.D. Chief Medical Staff, Community Hospital Long Beach, Long Beach, CA, p. A68
PARMER, Michael, Chief Medical Officer, CarePartners Health Services, Asheville, NC, p. A455
PARNEL, George, Chief Financial Officer, Clifton T. Perkins Hospital Center, Jessup, MD, p. A298
PARNELL, Brenda, Chief Executive Officer, Ferry County Memorial Hospital, Republic, WA, p. A683
PAROBY, Carmen, Administrator, West Florida Community Care Center, Milton, FL, p. A136
PAROD, Daniel A., Senior Vice President Hospital and Administrative Affairs, Rockford Memorial Hospital, Rockford, IL, p. A199
PAROSKI, Margaret, M.D. Executive Vice President and Chief Medical Officer, KALEIDA Health, Buffalo, NY, p. A430
PARR, James
Chief Financial Officer, Salem Hospital, Salem, OR, p. A526
Chief Financial Officer, West Valley Hospital, Dallas, OR, p. A520
PARR, Lynnette, Chief Financial Officer, Down East Community Hospital, Machias, ME, p. A291
PARRA, Kristin, Chief Nursing Officer, Yuma Rehabilitation Hospital, Yuma, AZ, p. A40
PARRA, Michelle, Director Human Resources, Kindred Hospital South Bay, Gardena, CA, p. A63
PARRINELLO, Kathleen M., Ph.D. Chief Operating Officer, Strong Memorial Hospital of the University of Rochester, Rochester, NY, p. A449
PARRISH, Becky, Director Human Resources, Southern Virginia Regional Medical Center, Emporia, VA, p. A664
PARRISH, Carl, Chief Fiscal Service, James E. Van Zandt Veterans Affairs Medical Center, Altoona, PA, p. A528
PARRISH, James G., FACHE, Chief Executive Officer, Humboldt General Hospital, Winnemucca, NV, p. A404
PARRISH, Pamela, Director Information Systems, Novant Health Brunswick Medical Center, Bolivia, NC, p. A456
PARRISH, Suann, Chief Financial Officer, Yoakum County Hospital, Denver City, TX, p. A608
PARROTT, Cindy, R.N. Chief Nursing Officer, St. Anthony Hospital, Lakewood, CO, p. A106
PARROTT, Keith, FACHE, President and Chief Executive Officer, Baptist Health System, Birmingham, AL, p. B20
PARRY, Mary, Vice President Operations and Chief Operating Officer, Oneida Healthcare, Oneida, NY, p. A446
PARRY, Timothy, R.N. Vice President Nursing, Highland District Hospital, Hillsboro, OH, p. A491
PARSLEY, George N., Chief Operating Officer, DeTar Healthcare System, Victoria, TX, p. A650
PARSON, Charlynne, Nurse Executive, Moccasin Bend Mental Health Institute, Chattanooga, TN, p. A575
PARSONS, Beth, R.N., Administrator, CHRISTUS Dubuis Hospital of Alexandria, Alexandria, LA, p. A268
PARSONS, Brad, FACHE, Administrator and Chief Executive Officer, NEA Baptist Memorial Hospital, Jonesboro, AR, p. A46
PARSONS, Debra, Chief Nursing Officer, Pikeville Medical Center, Pikeville, KY, p. A264
PARSONS, Jamie, Human Resources Director, Johnson City Medical Center, Johnson City, TN, p. A580
PARSONS, John, R.N. Chief Nursing Officer, TrustPoint Hospital, Lubbock, TX, p. A630
PARSONS, Lauren, M.D. Clinical Director, North Texas State Hospital, Wichita Falls Campus, Wichita Falls, TX, p. A652
PARSONS, Terri L., Administrator, Advanced Care Hospital of White County, Searcy, AR, p. A50
PARTAMIAN, Gregory A., Chief Operating Officer, Crittenton Hospital Medical Center, Rochester, MI, p. A328
PARTEE, Paris I., Associate Administrator and Director Human Resources, John H. Stroger Jr. Hospital of Cook County, Chicago, IL, p. A182
PARTENZA, John, Vice President and Treasurer, Northern Westchester Hospital, Mount Kisco, NY, p. A438
PARTHEMORE, Warrenette, Director Human Resources, Memorial Hospital, Fremont, OH, p. A490
PARTIN, James R., M.D. Chief Medical Director, Hill Country Memorial Hospital, Fredericksburg, TX, p. A614
PARTON, Scott, Director Human Resources, Oconee Regional Medical Center, Milledgeville, GA, p. A161
PARTRIDGE, Susan, Director Human Resources, Nantucket Cottage Hospital, Nantucket, MA, p. A309
PARUCH, Randy J., Director, Information Systems, Holland Hospital, Holland, MI, p. A322
PARUNGAO, Amy, Director of Nursing, Rehabilitation Hospital of the Pacific, Honolulu, HI, p. A169
PASCASCIO, Dellone, Chief Nursing Officer, LAC–Olive View–UCLA Medical Center, CA, p. A71
PASCH, Deborah, Chief Nurse Executive, University of Missouri Hospitals and Clinics, Columbia, MO, p. A366
PASCHALL, Francine, R.N. Chief Nursing Officer, Riverside Community Hospital, Riverside, CA, p. A84
PASCO, Teri, Director Human Resources, East Liverpool City Hospital, East Liverpool, OH, p. A489
PASCOE, John, M.D. Executive Medical Director, Timberlawn Mental Health System, Dallas, TX, p. A607
PASCUZZI, Robert, Chief Financial Officer, Mercy San Juan Medical Center, Carmichael, CA, p. A57
PASKERT, James, M.D. Vice President Chief Medical and Quality Officer, Kaweah Delta Medical Center, Visalia, CA, p. A97
PASLEY, Debra L., Chief Nursing Officer, OU Medical Center, Oklahoma City, OK, p. A512
PASS, Chris, Interim Chief Financial Officer, John Muir Medical Center, Concord, Concord, CA, p. A58
PASSANNANTE, Jr., Anthony, M.D. Vice President, Chief Medical Officer and Co–Chief Quality Officer, Saint Peter's University Hospital, New Brunswick, NJ, p. A415
PASSARELLI, Theresa, Human Resources Generalist, Warm Springs Medical Center, Warm Springs, GA, p. A167
PASSMANN, Frederic K., M.D. Chief of Staff, Stonewall Memorial Hospital, Aspermont, TX, p. A593
PASSMORE, Gary, Chief Information Officer, Endless Mountain Health Systems, Montrose, PA, p. A541
PASTERNAK, L. Reuven, M.P.H., Vice President for Health System and Chief Executive Officer, Stony Brook University Medical Center, Stony Brook, NY, p. A451
PASTIAN, Andre, R.N. Chief Nursing Officer, Boulder City Hospital, Boulder City, NV, p. A400
PASTORE, Raymond, M.D. Chief Medical Officer, St. John's Episcopal Hospital–South Shore, NY, p. A444
PASTRANA, Guillermo, Executive Director, Hospital Pavia–Hato Rey, San Juan, PR, p. A723
PASZTOR, Barbara J., R.N
Vice President Patient Care Services and Chief Nursing Officer, Blanchard Valley Hospital, Findlay, OH, p. A490
Vice President Nursing and Patient Care Services, Bluffton Hospital, Bluffton, OH, p. A480
PATASHNICK, Melvyn, President and Chief Executive Officer, Copley Hospital, Morrisville, VT, p. A660
PATCHELL, Lee, Lead Human Resources Business Partner, Presbyterian Hospital, Albuquerque, NM, p. A423
PATCHIN, J. Craig, Administrator, Shriners Hospitals for Children–Portland, Portland, OR, p. A525
PATE, Danny, M.D. Chief Medical Staff, Vidant Duplin Hospital, Kenansville, NC, p. A463
PATE, David C., JD, President and Chief Executive Officer, St. Luke's Health System, Boise, ID, p. B127
PATE, John, M.D. Chief Medical Officer, Tri–County Hospital, Wadena, MN, p. A348
PATE, Lois, R.N. Chief Nursing Officer, Island Hospital, Anacortes, WA, p. A676
PATEL, Amita, M.D. Medical Director, Haven Behavioral Senior Care of Dayton, Dayton, OH, p. A488
PATEL, Anil R., M.D. Medical Services Director, Kalamazoo Psychiatric Hospital, Kalamazoo, MI, p. A323
PATEL, C. N., M.D. Chief of Staff, Belmont Community Hospital, Bellaire, OH, p. A479
PATEL, Deepak, M.D. Medical Director, Cumberland Hall Hospital, Hopkinsville, KY, p. A258
PATEL, Dilip, M.D. Chief of Staff, Greater El Monte Community Hospital, South El Monte, CA, p. A93
PATEL, Fatma, M.D. Vice President Medical Affairs, Niagara Falls Memorial Medical Center, Niagara Falls, NY, p. A445
PATEL, Govind, M.D. Medical Director, HEALTHSOUTH MountainView Regional Rehabilitation Hospital, Morgantown, WV, p. A693
PATEL, Hema, Director Medical Records, RiverWoods Behavioral Health System, Riverdale, GA, p. A163
PATEL, Malini, M.D. Medical Director, Elgin Mental Health Center, Elgin, IL, p. A187
PATEL, Natu M., M.D. Chief of Staff, Phoebe Worth Medical Center, Sylvester, GA, p. A165
PATEL, Nayan, Director Information Systems, The Heart Hospital Baylor Plano, Plano, TX, p. A637
PATEL, Nirav, M.D. Interim Chief Medical Officer, SSM Health Saint Louis University Hospital, Saint Louis, MO, p. A377
PATEL, Paryus, M.D. Chief Medical Officer, Centinela Hospital Medical Center, Inglewood, CA, p. A65
PATEL, Prakash Chandra, M.D. Chief of Staff, Kindred Hospital–La Mirada, La Mirada, CA, p. A66
PATEL, Pravin, M.D. Acting President and Chief Executive Officer, Southern Virginia Mental Health Institute, Danville, VA, p. A664
PATEL, Pravinchandra, M.D. Chief Medical Officer, Barnes–Kasson County Hospital, Susquehanna, PA, p. A550
PATEL, Rajesh, M.D. Chief of Staff, Lock Haven Hospital, Lock Haven, PA, p. A539
PATEL, Rakesh, D.O. Medical Director, HEALTHSOUTH Rehabilitation Hospital of Altoona, Altoona, PA, p. A528
PATEL, Shailesh, M.D. Medical Director, Anchor Hospital, Atlanta, GA, p. A149
PATEL, Shalin, M.D. Chief Medical Officer, Memorial Hermann Rehabilitation Hospital – Katy, Katy, TX, p. A625
PATEL, Sharad, M.D. Medical Director, Florida Hospital at Connerton Long Term Acute Care, Land O'Lakes, FL, p. A131
PATEL, Suresh, M.D. Chief Medical Officer, Cavalier County Memorial Hospital, Langdon, ND, p. A475
PATEL, Vadankumar, M.D. Medical Director, Pathways of Tennessee, Jackson, TN, p. A579
PATEL, Viraj, M.D. Chief Medical Officer, Unity Medical & Surgical Hospital, Mishawaka, IN, p. A216
PATELLA, Diana, R.N. Chief Nursing Officer, Davis Medical Center, Elkins, WV, p. A690
PATER, Tom
Vice President Finance and Chief Financial Officer, RML Specialty Hospital, Chicago, IL, p. A184
Chief Financial Officer, RML Specialty Hospital, Hinsdale, IL, p. A191
PATHAK, Ajay, President, OSF Saint Anthony's Health Center, Alton, IL, p. A178
PATIL, Steve, Chief Financial Officer, W. G. (Bill) Heffner Veterans Affairs Medical Center, Salisbury, NC, p. A468
PATILLO, Laura, Manager Human Resources, Fresno Surgical Hospital, Fresno, CA, p. A62
PATINO, Beth, Chief Information Officer, DeKalb Medical at North Decatur, Decatur, GA, p. A156

Index of Health Care Professionals

Index of Health Care Professionals / Patla

PATLA, Rich
Director Information Technology, California Hospital Medical Center, Los Angeles, CA, p. A69
Site Director, St. Mary Medical Center, Long Beach, CA, p. A68
PATONAI, Steven D., Interim Chief Executive Officer, Park Plaza Hospital, Houston, TX, p. A621
PATRICK, Ann M., Vice President Human Resources, Northwest Community Hospital, Arlington Heights, IL, p. A178
PATRICK, Barbara, Director Human Resources, Chestatee Regional Hospital, Dahlonega, GA, p. A155
PATRICK, II, Calvin, Director Information Services, Bert Fish Medical Center, New Smyrna Beach, FL, p. A136
PATRICK, Chad, President and Chief Executive Officer, Orange Park Medical Center, Orange Park, FL, p. A137
PATRICK, Christian C., M.D. Chief Medical Officer, Baptist Memorial Hospital – Memphis, Memphis, TN, p. A583
PATRICK, Deborah A.
Senior Vice President Human Resources, Lehigh Valley Hospital, Allentown, PA, p. A528
Vice President Human Resources, Lehigh Valley Hospital–Muhlenberg, Bethlehem, PA, p. A529
PATRICK, Devin, Manager Human Resources, Utah State Hospital, Provo, UT, p. A657
PATRICK, Lisa, Chief Operating Officer, Caldwell Memorial Hospital, Columbia, LA, p. A271
PATRICK, Ronald, Chief Financial Officer, Northwest Medical Center, Tucson, AZ, p. A39
PATRICK, Sandra, Chief Financial Officer, Three Rivers Hospital, Waverly, TN, p. A589
PATRICK, Sean, Director Information Systems, Gifford Medical Center, Randolph, VT, p. A661
PATRICK, Wade, Senior Vice President Information Services, Indiana Regional Medical Center, Indiana, PA, p. A536
PATTEN Jr., William D., Chief Executive Officer, Holy Cross Hospital, Taos, NM, p. A427
PATTERSON, Anthony, FACHE Senior Vice President Inpatient Services, University of Alabama Hospital, Birmingham, AL, p. A17
PATTERSON, Barbara, Chief Financial Officer, Provident Hospital of Cook County, Chicago, IL, p. A184
PATTERSON, Benjamin, Chief Executive Officer, Fairway Medical Center, Covington, LA, p. A272
PATTERSON, Camie, Chief Operating Officer and Chief Financial Officer, Indiana University Health La Porte Hospital, La Porte, IN, p. A214
PATTERSON, Christina, Chief Financial Officer, Saint Thomas River Park Hospital, Mc Minnville, TN, p. A582
PATTERSON, Dave, Chief Information Officer, Memorial Hospital of Converse County, Douglas, WY, p. A716
PATTERSON, David, Director Human Resources, Parkside Psychiatric Hospital and Clinic, Tulsa, OK, p. A516
PATTERSON, Debbie, Director Health Information Management, Wesley Rehabilitation Hospital, Wichita, KS, p. A253
PATTERSON, Diane, Vice President, Chief Clinical Officer, Yakima Valley Memorial Hospital, Yakima, WA, p. A688
PATTERSON, Elmore, Chief Executive Officer, Greene County Health System, Eutaw, AL, p. A19
PATTERSON, Jan, Chief Nursing Officer, Avera St. Luke's Hospital, Aberdeen, SD, p. A567
PATTERSON, Jeffrey, Chief Operating Officer, Desert Regional Medical Center, Palm Springs, CA, p. A80
PATTERSON, Jerrie, Chief Nursing Officer, Brazosport Regional Health System, Lake Jackson, TX, p. A627
PATTERSON, Justin, Director Information Technology, OSF Saint Anthony's Health Center, Alton, IL, p. A178
PATTERSON, Karen, Deputy Director Operations, Elmira Psychiatric Center, Elmira, NY, p. A433
PATTERSON, Larry R., Deputy Commander Administration, Bayne–Jones Army Community Hospital, Fort Polk, LA, p. A273
PATTERSON, Lisa, Director Human Resources, Pointe Coupee General Hospital, New Roads, LA, p. A283
PATTERSON, Marcia, Chief Financial Officer, Valley Regional Medical Center, Brownsville, TX, p. A599
PATTERSON, Maria, Manager Health Information Management, Canyon Ridge Hospital, Chino, CA, p. A57
PATTERSON, Mark, M.D. Chief Medical Officer, Laughlin Memorial Hospital, Greeneville, TN, p. A578
PATTERSON, Melanie, R.N. Vice President Patient Care Services and Chief Nursing Officer, Children's Hospital of Orange County, Orange, CA, p. A79
PATTERSON, Melody, Chief Nurse Executive, Hawthorn Children Psychiatric Hospital, Saint Louis, MO, p. A376
PATTERSON, Michael C., Chief Executive Officer, Flint River Community Hospital, Montezuma, GA, p. A162
PATTERSON, Michael N., Chief Executive Officer, Havasu Regional Medical Center, Lake Havasu City, AZ, p. A32
PATTERSON, Mike, Director of Operations, Northside Hospital–Cherokee, Canton, GA, p. A153
PATTERSON, Philip A., President and Chief Executive Officer, Owensboro Health Regional Hospital, Owensboro, KY, p. A264
PATTERSON, Renee A., Vice President Employment and Training Services, Rogers Memorial Hospital, Oconomowoc, WI, p. A708
PATTERSON, Richard, Chief Financial Officer, TriStar Greenview Regional Hospital, Bowling Green, KY, p. A255
PATTERSON, Robert, Vice President Human Resources and Rehabilitation Services, The University of Vermont Health Network Central Vermont Medical Center, Berlin, VT, p. A660
PATTERSON, Russ, Director Information Technology, St. Rose Dominican Hospitals – Siena Campus, Henderson, NV, p. A401
PATTERSON, Sam, Chief Financial Officer, Bay Area Hospital, Coos Bay, OR, p. A520
PATTERSON, Sarah, Executive Vice President and Chief Operating Officer, Virginia Mason Medical Center, Seattle, WA, p. A684
PATTERSON, Stuart, M.D. Chief of Staff, Bartow Regional Medical Center, Bartow, FL, p. A121
PATTERSON, Tony, Chief Financial Officer, James B. Haggin Memorial Hospital, Harrodsburg, KY, p. A258
PATTI, Rosa, Chief Financial Officer, Cameron Regional Medical Center, Cameron, MO, p. A364
PATTON, Christina, Chief Financial Officer, Colorado Plains Medical Center, Fort Morgan, CO, p. A103
PATTON, Daniel, Director Information Systems, Henrico Doctors' Hospital, Richmond, VA, p. A672
PATTON, David J., President, UPMC St. Margaret, Pittsburgh, PA, p. A547
PATTON, Joy, Chief Information Services, Pampa Regional Medical Center, Pampa, TX, p. A635
PATTON, Kevin, Chief Executive Officer, Old Vineyard Behavioral Health Services, Winston–Salem, NC, p. A471
PATTON, Meghan
Vice President Human Resources, Abington Health Lansdale Hospital, Lansdale, PA, p. A538
Vice President Human Resources, Abington Memorial Hospital, Abington, PA, p. A528
PATTON, Sally K., R.N. Chief Nursing Officer, New London Hospital, New London, NH, p. A408
PATTON, William, Chief Executive Officer, Kindred Hospital–Oklahoma City, Oklahoma City, OK, p. A511
PATZEK, Dorothy, Vice President Nursing, Gnaden Huetten Memorial Hospital, Lehighton, PA, p. A538
PAUGH, David, Chief Financial Officer, Chatham Hospital, Siler City, NC, p. A468
PAUGH, J. William, FACHE, President and Chief Executive Officer, Wayne Memorial Hospital, Goldsboro, NC, p. A461
PAUL, Adam, Chief Financial Officer, Prairie Lakes Healthcare System, Watertown, SD, p. A572
PAUL, Donn, Chief Human Resources, Lackey Memorial Hospital, Forest, MS, p. A353
PAUL, John W., President and Chief Executive Officer, Allegheny Health Network, Pittsburgh, PA, p. B8
PAUL, Joseph, Chief Financial Officer, Wellington Regional Medical Center, West Palm Beach, FL, p. A147
PAUL, Lise, Vice President Reimbursement and Network Planning, Hebrew Rehabilitation Center, Boston, MA, p. A303
PAUL, Mary
Chief Information Officer, Columbia St. Mary's Hospital Milwaukee, Milwaukee, WI, p. A706
Chief Information Officer, Columbia St. Mary's Ozaukee Hospital, Mequon, WI, p. A705
Vice President and Chief Information Officer, Sacred Heart Rehabilitation Institute, Milwaukee, WI, p. A706
PAUL, Mitali, Chief Executive Officer, Select Specialty Hospital–Houston West, Houston, TX, p. A621
PAULDINE, Donna M., Deputy Commissioner, Summit Park Hospital and Nursing Care Center, Pomona, NY, p. A447
PAULEY, Clarence, Senior Vice President and Chief Human Resources Officer, University of Cincinnati Medical Center, Cincinnati, OH, p. A484
PAULK, Nicole, President, Taylor Regional Hospital, Hawkinsville, GA, p. A158
PAULK, Nikki, Chief Executive Officer, Bleckley Memorial Hospital, Cochran, GA, p. A154
PAULK, Tena, R.N. Program Director and Director Nursing, Bastrop Rehabilitation Hospital, Monroe, LA, p. A280
PAULL, Judy C., R.N. Market Chief Nursing Executive, Physicians Regional – Pine Ridge, Naples, FL, p. A136
PAULOSKY, David, Chief Financial Officer, Phoenixville Hospital, Phoenixville, PA, p. A545
PAULS, Scott, Manager Information Systems, Gundersen Boscobel Area Hospital and Clinics, Boscobel, WI, p. A698
PAULS, Scott R., Director Information Technology, Guttenberg Municipal Hospital, Guttenberg, IA, p. A228
PAULSEN, Susan, Director Human Resources, Northridge Hospital Medical Center, CA, p. A71
PAULSON, Adam, Director Finance, CentraCare Health–Melrose, Melrose, MN, p. A342
PAULSON, Erik, Director of Finance, J. D. McCarty Center for Children With Developmental Disabilities, Norman, OK, p. A510
PAULSON, Gordon, Manager Personnel, Glacial Ridge Health System, Glenwood, MN, p. A339
PAULSON, Mark E., Chief Executive Officer, Chippewa County–Montevideo Hospital, Montevideo, MN, p. A343
PAULSON, Sybil K., R.N., Administrator, North Oaks Rehabilitation Hospital, Hammond, LA, p. A274
PAULUS, Ronald A., M.D., President and Chief Executive Officer, Mission Health System, Asheville, NC, p. B92
PAULUS, Terri
Chief Nursing Officer, Banner Goldfield Medical Center, Apache Junction, AZ, p. A30
Chief Nursing Officer, Banner Ironwood Medical Center, San Tan Valley, AZ, p. A37
PAUTLER, Stephen, FACHE Chief Operating Officer, Peterson Regional Medical Center, Kerrville, TX, p. A626
PAVIA, Antoine, M.D. Medical Director, Hospital Dr. Cayetano Coll Y Toste, Arecibo, PR, p. A719
PAVIK, Sarah, Director Human Resources and Guest Services, Inova Loudoun Hospital, Leesburg, VA, p. A667
PAVILANIS, Charlotte J., R.N. Vice President of Clinical Services and Chief Nursing Officer, Sturgis Hospital, Sturgis, MI, p. A331
PAVLATOS, Thales, Medical Director, Ohio Valley Surgical Hospital, Springfield, OH, p. A497
PAWAR, Ganesh, M.D. Chief of Staff, Rusk County Memorial Hospital, Ladysmith, WI, p. A703
PAWLAK, Paul, President and Chief Executive Officer, Silver Cross Hospital, New Lenox, IL, p. A196
PAWLOWICZ, James E., Director Human Resources, Shriners Hospitals for Children–Chicago, Chicago, IL, p. A184
PAWLOWSKI, Phil, Chief Financial Officer, Glenbeigh Hospital and Outpatient Centers, Rock Creek, OH, p. A497
PAWOLA, Ken
Chief Operating Officer, RML Specialty Hospital, Chicago, IL, p. A184
Chief Operating Officer, RML Specialty Hospital, Hinsdale, IL, p. A191
PAXSON, Gary
Associate Administrator Information Systems, Stone County Medical Center, Mountain View, AR, p. A48
Chief Information Officer, White River Medical Center, Batesville, AR, p. A41
PAYNE, Angel, Clinical Director, Director of Nursing, Sonora Behavioral Health Hospital, Tucson, AZ, p. A40
PAYNE, Candyce, Chief Executive Officer, Prairie Community Hospital, Terry, MT, p. A387
PAYNE, Gary, Chief Executive Officer, Cardinal Hill Rehabilitation Hospital, Lexington, KY, p. A259
PAYNE, James, Director Information Systems, Southern Tennessee Regional Health System–Winchester, Winchester, TN, p. A589
PAYNE, Janet S.
Vice President Human Resources, Presence Covenant Medical Center, Urbana, IL, p. A202
Vice President Human Resources, Presence United Samaritans Medical Center, Danville, IL, p. A185
PAYNE, Judy, R.N. Chief Operating Officer, Turning Point Hospital, Moultrie, GA, p. A162
PAYNE, Kenneth G., Chief Financial Officer, Holzer Medical Center, Gallipolis, OH, p. A490
PAYNE, Michael, M.D. Chief of Staff, Dallas County Medical Center, Fordyce, AR, p. A44
PAYNE, Michael E., Administrator, Girard Medical Center, Girard, KS, p. A240
PAYNE, Rick, Director Information Systems, Santa Rosa Medical Center, Milton, FL, p. A135
PAYNE, Steven, Chief Financial Officer, Jordan Valley Medical Center–WVC Campus, West Valley City, UT, p. A659
PAYTON, Becky J., Vice President Human Resources, Mercy Hospital Oklahoma City, Oklahoma City, OK, p. A512
PAYTON, Melissa, Manager Human Resources, Baptist Health La Grange, La Grange, KY, p. A259
PAZDERNIK, Mary, Chief Financial Officer, Mahnomen Health Center, Mahnomen, MN, p. A341
PEA, Gary, Chief Financial Officer, Colusa Regional Medical Center, Colusa, CA, p. A58
PEA, Richard, Director Human Resources, Memorial Hospital and Health Care Center, Jasper, IN, p. A213
PEABODY, Kim, Chief Operating Officer, The Brook Hospital – KMI, Louisville, KY, p. A262
PEACE III, Lother E., President and Chief Executive Officer, Russell Medical Center, Alexander City, AL, p. A15
PEACH, Larry, Chief Financial Officer, Jefferson County Health Center, Fairfield, IA, p. A227

Index of Health Care Professionals / Perel

Index of Health Care Professionals


PEACH, Susan M., R.N., Chief Executive Officer, Sumner Regional Medical Center, Gallatin, TN, p. A578
PEACOCK, Steve, Assistant Vice President, Plaza Specialty Hospital, Houston, TX, p. A621
PEAL, Chip, Chief Executive Officer, Frankfort Regional Medical Center, Frankfort, KY, p. A257
PEARCE, Charles T.
Chief Financial and Information Officer, Kalispell Regional Medical Center, Kalispell, MT, p. A385
Chief Financial and Information Officer, The HealthCenter, Kalispell, MT, p. A385
PEARCE, Darren
Administrator and Chief Executive Officer, Medical Center of Peach County, Navicent Health, Fort Valley, GA, p. A158
Executive Director, Rehabilitation Hospital, Navicent Health, Macon, GA, p. A161
PEARCE, Margaret, R.N. Chief Nursing Officer, University of Utah Health Care – Hospital and Clinics, Salt Lake City, UT, p. A659
PEARCH, William, Chief Information Officer, Yukon–Kuskokwim Delta Regional Hospital, Bethel, AK, p. A27
PEARCY, Joetta J., Director, Human Resources, Glendive Medical Center, Glendive, MT, p. A383
PEARCY, Steve, Director Human Resources, Community Hospital North, Indianapolis, IN, p. A211
PEARLMAN, Helen, Nurse Executive, Minneapolis Veterans Affairs Health Care System, Minneapolis, MN, p. A342
PEARSALL, Cynthia, Chief Nursing Officer, Fairfield Medical Center, Lancaster, OH, p. A491
PEARSON, Bruce, Senior Vice President and Chief Executive Officer, HonorHealth Scottsdale Osborn Medical Center, Scottsdale, AZ, p. A37
PEARSON, Christine, Vice President Finance and Chief Financial Officer, AnMed Health Medical Center, Anderson, SC, p. A557
PEARSON, Dawn, Director Human Resources, HEALTHSOUTH Rehabilitation Hospital of Vineland, Vineland, NJ, p. A419
PEARSON, Debra, Chief Financial Officer, Jonathan M. Wainwright Memorial Veterans Affairs Medical Center, Walla Walla, WA, p. A687
PEARSON, Fenorris, Chief Human Resources Officer, Seton Medical Center Austin, Austin, TX, p. A594
PEARSON, Gregory, Chief Executive Officer, Merit Health River Region, Vicksburg, MS, p. A361
PEARSON, Jeff
Chief Information Officer, Mother Frances Hospital – Jacksonville, Jacksonville, TX, p. A624
Vice President and Chief Information Officer, Mother Frances Hospital – Tyler, Tyler, TX, p. A649
PEARSON, Kellie T., Director Human Resources, Lower Bucks Hospital, Bristol, PA, p. A530
PEARSON, Linnie, Coordinator Human Resources and Benefits, Baptist Medical Center Attala, Kosciusko, MS, p. A356
PEARSON, Marshall, Director Management Information Systems, St. David's North Austin Medical Center, Austin, TX, p. A595
PEARSON, Matthew Paul, Chief Executive Officer, Select Specialty Hospital – Northeast Atlanta, Atlanta, GA, p. A151
PEARSON, Susan, M.D. Chief Medical Officer, Mayo Clinic Health System in Mankato, Mankato, MN, p. A341
PEART, Carol, Chief Financial Officer, Chicago Lakeshore Hospital, Chicago, IL, p. A181
PEBURN, Eric, Chief Financial Officer, Halifax Health Medical Center of Daytona Beach, Daytona Beach, FL, p. A125
PECHOUS, Bryan, M.D. Vice President Medical Affairs, UnityPoint Health – Finley Hospital, Dubuque, IA, p. A227
PECK, Bob, Chief Financial Officer, Wesley Rehabilitation Hospital, Wichita, KS, p. A253
PECK, Charles A., M.D., Interim President and Chief Executive Officer, Athens Regional Medical Center, Athens, GA, p. A149
PECK, Darin, M.D. Chief of Staff, Charles A. Dean Memorial Hospital, Greenville, ME, p. A290
PECK, Kay E., Ph.D., Chief Executive Officer, Kindred Hospital–San Antonio, San Antonio, TX, p. A641
PECK, Lori, Vice President Finance, Aspirus Medford Hospital, Medford, WI, p. A705
PECK, Michael D., Assistant Administrator, Caribou Memorial Hospital and Living Center, Soda Springs, ID, p. A176
PECK, Robert C., M.D. Chief Medical Officer, Mayo Clinic Health System in Eau Claire, Eau Claire, WI, p. A700
PEDERSEN, Alan, Vice President Human Resources, Cayuga Medical Center at Ithaca, Ithaca, NY, p. A435
PEDERSEN, Darren, Coordinator Information Technology, Weisman Children's Rehabilitation Hospital, Marlton, NJ, p. A414
PEDERSEN, Paul E., M.D. Vice President and Chief Medical Officer, OSF St. Joseph Medical Center, Bloomington, IL, p. A179
PEDERSON, Bryan, Human Resources Manager, Tri–County Hospital, Wadena, MN, p. A348
PEDERSON, Karn, Manager Health Information Management, McKenzie County Healthcare System, Watford City, ND, p. A477
PEDERSON, Randall K., Chief Executive Officer, Tioga Medical Center, Tioga, ND, p. A476
PEDLEY, Joe, CPA Vice President and Chief Financial Officer, Lawrence Memorial Hospital, Lawrence, KS, p. A244
PEDLOW, Bernadette R., Senior Vice President Business and Chief Operating Officer, Albany Medical Center, Albany, NY, p. A428
PEDRICK, Jonathan, M.D. Medical Director, OhioHealth Rehabilitation Hospital, Columbus, OH, p. A486
PEDROZA, Fernando, Vice President Information Technology, Poudre Valley Hospital, Fort Collins, CO, p. A103
PEEBLES, Wanda V., Chief Nursing Officer, JPS Health Network, Fort Worth, TX, p. A613
PEEK, Michael Scott, Chief Executive Officer, Chambers Memorial Hospital, Danville, AR, p. A42
PEEK, Scott, FACHE, President, Baylor Medical Center at McKinney, McKinney, TX, p. A631
PEELER, Cindy K., R.N. Chief Nursing Officer, Adair County Memorial Hospital, Greenfield, IA, p. A228
PEELGREN, Jim, Chief Information Officer, Tulare Regional Medical Center, Tulare, CA, p. A95
PEEPLES, John, Senior Vice President Human Resources, Laurel Regional Hospital, Laurel, MD, p. A299
PEER, Julie, President, Penn Highlands Brookville, Brookville, PA, p. A530
PEERY, Lori, Chief Human Resource Management Services, VA Palo Alto Health Care System, Palo Alto, CA, p. A80
PEET, Carole, MSN, President and Chief Executive Officer, St. Anthony North Health Campus, Westminster, CO, p. A109
PEGE, Diane, M.D. Vice President Medical Affairs, Sutter Lakeside Hospital, Lakeport, CA, p. A67
PEHRSON, Felicia, M.D., Commanding Officer, Keller Army Community Hospital, West Point, NY, p. A453
PEIFFER, Paul, Chief Financial Officer and Vice President, Jackson Hospital and Clinic, Montgomery, AL, p. A23
PEIL, Michael, M.D. Chief Medical Director, Kindred Hospital Peoria, Peoria, IL, p. A198
PEIPERT, John, R.N. Chief Nursing Officer, HSHS St. Francis Hospital, Litchfield, IL, p. A193
PEKOFSKE, Robert, Vice President Finance, Advocate Christ Medical Center, Oak Lawn, IL, p. A196
PELACCIA, Joseph, President and Chief Executive Officer, Milford Hospital, Milford, CT, p. A113
PELFREY, Joy S., R.N. Vice President and Chief Nursing Officer, Cabell Huntington Hospital, Huntington, WV, p. A691
PELKOWSKI, Margaret, R.N. Vice President Patient Care Services, Calvary Hospital, NY, p. A439
PELLE, Fred L., FACHE Chief Operating Officer, Wellmont Holston Valley Medical Center, Kingsport, TN, p. A580
PELLERIN, Yvonne, Chief Nursing Officer, St. Elizabeth Hospital, Gonzales, LA, p. A274
PELLETIER, Stephen, Leader Guest Services, York Hospital, York, ME, p. A292
PELLICONE, John T., M.D. Chief Medical Officer, Metropolitan Hospital Center, New York, NY, p. A441
PELOT, Jeff, Interim Chief Information Officer, Denver Health, Denver, CO, p. A101
PELSMAN, Mara, Chief Executive Officer, Gateways Hospital and Mental Health Center, Los Angeles, CA, p. A69
PELTIER, Glenn, Chief Financial Officer, Mother Frances Hospital – Winnsboro, Winnsboro, TX, p. A652
PELTIER, Robert, M.D. Senior Vice President and Chief Medical Officer, North Oaks Medical Center, Hammond, LA, p. A274
PELTON, Deborah, R.N. Chief Nursing Officer, Texas Spine & Joint Hospital, Tyler, TX, p. A649
PEMBERTON, John S., Director Human Resources, Tuba City Regional Health Care Corporation, Tuba City, AZ, p. A38
PENA, Carolina, Assistant Director Administrator, Larkin Community Hospital, South Miami, FL, p. A143
PENA, Julie, Director Finance, Community Howard Specialty Hospital, Kokomo, IN, p. A213
PENA, Terry, Chief Operating Officer and Chief Nursing Officer, San Bernardino Mountains Community Hospital District, Lake Arrowhead, CA, p. A67
PENCE, Carla, President Medical Staff, Iredell Memorial Hospital, Statesville, NC, p. A469
PENCO, Kris, Director Information Systems, Coffeyville Regional Medical Center, Coffeyville, KS, p. A238
PENDER, Carol, Assistant Vice President Human Resources, Walden Psychiatric Care, Waltham, MA, p. A312
PENDER, Debra, R.N. Vice President of Nursing, Mercy Hospital Ardmore, Ardmore, OK, p. A503
PENDERGAST, Debra, Senior Vice President Patient Care Services and Chief Nursing Officer, John Muir Medical Center, Walnut Creek, Walnut Creek, CA, p. A97
PENDERGAST, Jim, Administrator Human Resources, University of New Mexico Hospitals, Albuquerque, NM, p. A423
PENDERGRAFT, Tina, Chief Nursing Officer, Satanta District Hospital and Long Term Care, Satanta, KS, p. A250
PENDLETON, Debbie, Human Resources Specialist, Weslaco Rehabilitation Hospital, Weslaco, TX, p. A651
PENDLETON, Gretchen, Chief Human Resources Officer, Mercy Suburban Hospital, Norristown, PA, p. A541
PENDLETON, Timothy, M.D. President Medical Staff, Penn Highlands Brookville, Brookville, PA, p. A530
PENICK, Lisa, R.N. Chief Nursing Officer, Carroll County Memorial Hospital, Carrollton, KY, p. A255
PENLAND, Jennifer
Controller, Kindred Hospital Tarrant County–Arlington, Arlington, TX, p. A592
Controller, Kindred Hospital–White Rock, Dallas, TX, p. A605
Controller, Kindred Rehabilitation Hospital Arlington, Arlington, TX, p. A592
PENN, Shelia, Facility Director, Bryce Hospital, Tuscaloosa, AL, p. A25
PENNACCHIO, Suzanne, Senior Vice President Patient Care Services, Brookdale Hospital Medical Center, NY, p. A439
PENNER, Jerome, Chief Executive Officer, Murray–Calloway County Hospital, Murray, KY, p. A264
PENNEY, Cindy L., R.N. Vice President Nursing, Mercy Iowa City, Iowa City, IA, p. A229
PENNEY, Jan, R.N. Vice President and Chief Nursing Officer, MidMichigan Medical Center–Midland, Midland, MI, p. A325
PENNINGTON, Brian Keith, President and Chief Executive Officer, Medical West, Bessemer, AL, p. A16
PENNINGTON, Stephen G., Chief Executive Officer, Gadsden Regional Medical Center, Gadsden, AL, p. A20
PENNINO, Jackie, Director Human Resources, Old Vineyard Behavioral Health Services, Winston–Salem, NC, p. A471
PENNISSON, Jay M., Chief Financial Officer, Atlanta Medical Center, Atlanta, GA, p. A150
PENOVICH, Carrie L., Chief Clinical Services Officer, Aurora Medical Center – Manitowoc County, Two Rivers, WI, p. A712
PENQUE, Sue, R.N. Senior Vice President and Chief Nursing Officer, South Nassau Communities Hospital, Oceanside, NY, p. A446
PENROD, Kirt, Chief Financial Officer, Shadow Mountain Behavioral Health System, Tulsa, OK, p. A517
PENROSE, Lee, President and Chief Executive Officer, St. Jude Medical Center, Fullerton, CA, p. A63
PENTON, Kelly, Chief Financial Officer, Vaughan Regional Medical Center, Selma, AL, p. A24
PENTON, Lance
Director, Information Services, Memorial Hospital Jacksonville, Jacksonville, FL, p. A129
Director, Information Services, Specialty Hospital Jacksonville, Jacksonville, FL, p. A130
PENUEL, Jennifer, Director Human Resources, Madison Medical Center, Fredericktown, MO, p. A367
PEOPLES, Diane, Director Human Resources, Two Rivers Behavioral Health System, Kansas City, MO, p. A371
PEOPLES, Kathleen K., R.N. Vice President and Nursing, St. Joseph Hospital & Health Center, Kokomo, IN, p. A214
PEOPLES, Kyle, Director Technology Management Services, Springfield Hospital, Springfield, VT, p. A661
PEOPLES, Lynn, Interim Chief Nursing Officer, Person Memorial Hospital, Roxboro, NC, p. A467
PEOPLES, Phyllis L., R.N., President and Chief Executive Officer, Terrebonne General Medical Center, Houma, LA, p. A275
PEPE, Joseph, M.D., President and Chief Executive Officer, Catholic Medical Center, Manchester, NH, p. A407
PEPPEL, David, Director Operations, Richard H. Hutchings Psychiatric Center, Syracuse, NY, p. A451
PEPPLER, Lisa, Financial Manager, Parkview Whitley Hospital, Columbia City, IN, p. A206
PERAL, Sherry, Manager Information Systems, Oak Valley Hospital District, Oakdale, CA, p. A78
PERALTA, Pennie, R.N. VP, Nursing & Chief Nursing Officer, Bon Secours St. Francis Xavier Hospital, Charleston, SC, p. A558
PERAZA, Faye, Director Human Resources, Venice Regional Bayfront Health, Venice, FL, p. A146
PERCIVAL, Steve, Director Human Resources, Washington Regional Medical Center, Fayetteville, AR, p. A44
PERDUE, Eric, Chief Human Resource Officer, Adena Medical Center, Chillicothe, OH, p. A482
PEREACE, Vicki, Manager Human Resources, William Bee Ririe Hospital, Ely, NV, p. A400
PERECKO, Gary L., President, Riddle Hospital, Media, PA, p. A540
PEREIRA, Raul Ramos, M.D. Medical Director, Ryder Memorial Hospital, Humacao, PR, p. A721
PEREL, Michael
Regional Chief Financial Officer, Kauai Veterans Memorial Hospital, Waimea, HI, p. A171
Regional Chief Financial Officer, Samuel Mahelona Memorial Hospital, Kapaa, HI, p. A170

Index of Health Care Professionals

Index of Health Care Professionals / Perez

PEREZ, Brenda, R.N. Chief Clinical Officer, Kindred Hospital–White Rock, Dallas, TX, p. A605
PEREZ, Carmen, Director Human Resources, Doctors' Center Hospital San Juan, San Juan, PR, p. A723
PEREZ, David, Vice President and Chief Information Officer, Eisenhower Medical Center, Rancho Mirage, CA, p. A82
PEREZ, Francisco, Manager Management Information Systems, Hospital de la Universidad de Puerto Rico/Dr. Federico Trilla, Carolina, PR, p. A720
PEREZ, Homar, Chief Executive Officer and Vice President Administration, Hospital Dr. Cayetano Coll Y Toste, Arecibo, PR, p. A719
PEREZ, Julie, Chief Financial Officer, St. David's Medical Center, Austin, TX, p. A595
PEREZ, Lisa, R.N. Director Nursing, Meadowbrook Rehabilitation Hospital, Gardner, KS, p. A240
PEREZ, Mercedes, Vice President Nursing, Larkin Community Hospital, South Miami, FL, p. A143
PEREZ, Miguel, Director Information Systems, Driscoll Children's Hospital, Corpus Christi, TX, p. A602
PEREZ, Nina, R.N. Chief Nursing Officer, North Okaloosa Medical Center, Crestview, FL, p. A124
PEREZ, Tony, M.D. President Medical Staff, Jewish Hospital–Shelbyville, Shelbyville, KY, p. A266
PERILLI, John, M.D., Health Services Director, Ossining Correctional Facilities Hospital, Ossining, NY, p. A447
PERIMENIS, Vasilia, Vice President Human Resources, Novant Health Medical Park Hospital, Winston–Salem, NC, p. A471
PERJON, Cindy, Associate Director, Southwest Connecticut Mental Health System, Bridgeport, CT, p. A111
PERKERSON, Robyn, R.N., Administrator, LifeCare Hospitals of North Carolina, Rocky Mount, NC, p. A467
PERKES, Neil C., Operations Officer, Logan Regional Hospital, Logan, UT, p. A655
PERKET, William, Vice President Human Resources, North Country Hospital and Health Center, Newport, VT, p. A660
PERKINS, A. William, Administrator, Atmore Community Hospital, Atmore, AL, p. A16
PERKINS, Brett, M.D. Chief Medical Staff, Madison County Memorial Hospital, Madison, FL, p. A132
PERKINS, Chris, Director Information Services, Clinch Valley Medical Center, Richlands, VA, p. A671
PERKINS, Dan
  Corporate Director Human Resources, Cornerstone Hospital–West Monroe, West Monroe, LA, p. A286
  Vice President of Human Resources, Solara Hospital Harlingen, Harlingen, TX, p. A618
PERKINS, Gary A., FACHE, President and Chief Executive Officer, Children's Hospital and Medical Center, Omaha, NE, p. A396
PERKINS, Jeanne, Vice President Nursing and Interim Manager Human Resources, Bucyrus Community Hospital, Bucyrus, OH, p. A480
PERKINS, Kathryn, M.D
  Chief Medical Officer, Banner Boswell Medical Center, Sun City, AZ, p. A38
  Chief Medical Officer, Banner Thunderbird Medical Center, Glendale, AZ, p. A32
PERKINS, Kelly, Director Human Resources, New Horizons Health Systems, Owenton, KY, p. A264
PERKINS, Mike, Vice President and Administrator, Baptist Health Extended Care Hospital, Little Rock, AR, p. A47
PERKINS, Richard, Chief Financial Officer, Baylor Scott & White Hillcrest Medical Center, Waco, TX, p. A650
PERKINS, Sherry, Ph.D. Chief Operating Officer and Chief Nursing Officer, Anne Arundel Medical Center, Annapolis, MD, p. A293
PERKINS, Tom, Chief Information Officer, Shannon Medical Center, San Angelo, TX, p. A640
PERKINS–PEPPERS, Andrea, Chief Information Officer, Forks Community Hospital, Forks, WA, p. A679
PERKINSON, B. Leonard, M.D. Chief of Staff, Humboldt General Hospital, Winnemucca, NV, p. A404
PERKO, Tina, Vice President Operations, Adena Pike Medical Center, Waverly, OH, p. A500
PERL, Lawrence, M.D. Chief Medical Officer, Columbia Memorial Hospital, Hudson, NY, p. A435
PERLA, Salvatore, President, Nashoba Valley Medical Center, Ayer, MA, p. A302
PERLICH, Gwynn, Vice President of Patient Services and Chief Nursing Officer, St. Vincent Carmel Hospital, Carmel, IN, p. A206
PERLIN, Mitch, Chief Information Officer, Interim LSU Public Hospital, New Orleans, LA, p. A282
PERLMAN, Joel A., Executive Vice President Finance, Montefiore Medical Center, NY, p. A442
PERLSTEIN, David A., M.D. Chief Medical Officer, St. Barnabas Hospital, NY, p. A444
PERMANN, Darcy, Manager Business Office, Landmann–Jungman Memorial Hospital Avera, Scotland, SD, p. A571
PERMENTER, Ethan, Chief Executive Officer, Behavioral Hospital of Bellaire, Houston, TX, p. A619
PERNICE, Paul, Vice President Finance, Beebe Healthcare, Lewes, DE, p. A117
PERONA, Lorene, Market Chief Executive Officer, Kindred Hospital Sugar Land, Sugar Land, TX, p. A645
PERRA, Scott H.
  President and Chief Executive Officer, Faxton–St. Luke's Healthcare, Utica, NY, p. A452
  Chief Executive Officer, St. Elizabeth Medical Center, Utica, NY, p. A452
PERRAS, Joseph, Chief Medical Officer, Mt. Ascutney Hospital and Health Center, Windsor, VT, p. A661
PERRATTO, Bonnie I., MSN Senior Vice President, Chief Nurse Executive, Bayhealth Medical Center, Dover, DE, p. A117
PERRIGOT, Keri, Manager Human Resources, Cassia Regional Medical Center, Burley, ID, p. A173
PERRIN, Mary R., President and Chief Executive Officer, Children's Hospital, New Orleans, LA, p. A281
PERRINE, Vicki, FACHE Chief Operating Officer, Claxton–Hepburn Medical Center, Ogdensburg, NY, p. A446
PERRITT, Daniel, Chief Financial Officer, Sunrise Hospital and Medical Center, Las Vegas, NV, p. A403
PERRON, Kirk, Interim Administrator, Jennings Senior Care Hospital, Jennings, LA, p. A276
PERRONG, Elizabeth, Vice President Human Resources, KidsPeace Children's Hospital, Orefield, PA, p. A542
PERROTTE, Kenneth, Director Operations, Rockland Children's Psychiatric Center, Orangeburg, NY, p. A446
PERROTTI, Paul R., CPA Chief Financial Officer, West Georgia Health, Lagrange, GA, p. A160
PERRY, Amy, President, Sinai Hospital of Baltimore, Baltimore, MD, p. A295
PERRY, Bill, Director Information Systems, CHI St. Vincent Hot Springs, Hot Springs, AR, p. A45
PERRY, Carol, R.N. Vice President and Chief Nursing Officer, Stormont–Vail HealthCare, Topeka, KS, p. A251
PERRY, Cheryl
  Chief Financial Officer, New Bedford Rehabilitation Hospital, New Bedford, MA, p. A309
  Director Human Resources, Paris Regional Medical Center, Paris, TX, p. A635
PERRY, Cynthia, M.D. Chief of Staff, Stephens Memorial Hospital, Breckenridge, TX, p. A598
PERRY, Doug, M.D. Chief of Staff, Baptist Medical Center Leake, Carthage, MS, p. A351
PERRY, Faye, Chief Nursing Officer, Gateway Medical Center, Clarksville, TN, p. A576
PERRY, Jan, R.N. Vice President Patient Care Services, Community Medical Center, Missoula, MT, p. A385
PERRY, Jeff
  Director Information Technology, St. John's Pleasant Valley Hospital, Camarillo, CA, p. A57
  Director Information Technology, St. John's Regional Medical Center, Oxnard, CA, p. A79
  Chief Operating Officer, UP Health System–Marquette, Marquette, MI, p. A325
PERRY, John, M.D. Chief of Staff, Wagoner Community Hospital, Wagoner, OK, p. A518
PERRY, Karen, Chief Information Resource Management Services, James H. Quillen Veterans Affairs Medical Center, Mountain Home, TN, p. A585
PERRY, Kathleen, Senior Vice President and Chief Information Officer, Mercy Medical Center, Baltimore, MD, p. A294
PERRY, Matthew, Director Information Systems, Andalusia Regional Hospital, Andalusia, AL, p. A15
PERRY, Matthew J., President and Chief Executive Officer, Genesis HealthCare System, Zanesville, OH, p. A502
PERRY, Michael, Chief Executive Officer, Michiana Behavioral Health Center, Plymouth, IN, p. A218
PERRY, Michael R., M.D., President and Chief Executive Officer, FHN Memorial Hospital, Freeport, IL, p. A188
PERRY, Nini, Chief Nursing Officer, Georgetown Behavioral Health Institute, Georgetown, TX, p. A616
PERRY, Rhonda, Chief Financial Officer, Medical Center, Navicent Health, Macon, GA, p. A160
PERRY, Sally, Chief Executive Officer, Coastal Harbor Treatment Center, Savannah, GA, p. A164
PERRY, Shaun, Chief Information Officer, McGehee–Desha County Hospital, McGehee, AR, p. A48
PERRY, Solette, Regional Director Human Resources, Kauai Veterans Memorial Hospital, Waimea, HI, p. A171
PERRY, Stacey, Director of Nursing, Beaver County Memorial Hospital, Beaver, OK, p. A504
PERRY, Teresa J., Chief Financial Officer, UP Health System–Bell, Ishpeming, MI, p. A323
PERRY, Tim, Executive Director Human Services, Baptist Health Corbin, Corbin, KY, p. A255
PERRY, V. Mark, Chief Financial Officer, Adventist Medical Center–Portland, Portland, OR, p. A524
PERRYMAN, Daniel L., President and Chief Executive Officer, HSHS St. Mary's Hospital, Decatur, IL, p. A186
PERRYMAN, Mike, Chief Financial Officer, Baptist Memorial Hospital–Union City, Union City, TN, p. A589
PERSE, David F., M.D., President and Chief Executive Officer, St. Vincent Charity Medical Center, Cleveland, OH, p. A485
PERSILY, Cynthia A., R.N., President and Chief Executive Officer, Highland Hospital, Charleston, WV, p. A690
PERSINGER, Keith D., Senior Vice President Finance and Chief Financial Officer, University of Maryland Medical Center, Baltimore, MD, p. A295
PERSON, Lisa, MSN Vice President and Chief Nursing Officer, Mercy Hospital Springfield, Springfield, MO, p. A379
PERSONS, Linda, Executive Director, Atascadero State Hospital, Atascadero, CA, p. A54
PERT, Robert M., Vice President Finance and Chief Financial Officer, United Regional Health Care System, Wichita Falls, TX, p. A652
PESCHEL, Colleen, Director Human Resources, Sutter Medical Center, Sacramento, Sacramento, CA, p. A85
PESKIN, Ted, M.D. Acute Care Medical Director, Hilo Medical Center, Hilo, HI, p. A168
PESSAGNO, Paul, Chief Financial Officer, Richard L. Roudebush Veterans Affairs Medical Center, Indianapolis, IN, p. A212
PESTLE, Janet K., R.N. Vice President Nursing and Chief Nursing Officer, SSM St. Joseph Hospital West, Lake Saint Louis, MO, p. A371
PETER, Chad
  President and Chief Executive Officer, Mercy Memorial Hospital, Urbana, OH, p. A499
  President, Mercy Hospital of Defiance, Defiance, OH, p. A488
PETER, David, M.D
  Senior Vice President Medical Affairs and Chief Medical Director, Akron General Medical Center, Akron, OH, p. A478
  Senior Vice President Medical Affairs and Chief Medical Officer, Lodi Community Hospital, Lodi, OH, p. A492
PETER, Douglas G., M.D. Chief Medical Officer, Gallup Indian Medical Center, Gallup, NM, p. A424
PETER, Jan D., Vice President Fiscal Services and Chief Financial Officer, Good Shepherd Health Care System, Hermiston, OR, p. A521
PETER, John, M.D. Vice President Medical Affairs, SSM Cardinal Glennon Children's Medical Center, Saint Louis, MO, p. A377
PETERMAN, John
  Vice President and Administrator, Riverside Shore Memorial Hospital, Nassawadox, VA, p. A668
  Vice President and Administrator, Riverside Tappahannock Hospital, Tappahannock, VA, p. A673
PETERMAN, Tammy, R.N. Executive Vice President, Chief Operating Officer and Chief Nursing Officer, The University of Kansas Hospital, Kansas City, KS, p. A243
PETERMEIER, Jill, Senior Executive Human Resources, Central Iowa Healthcare, Marshalltown, IA, p. A231
PETERS, Amy, R.N. Interim Chief Operating Officer, Truman Medical Center–Lakewood, Kansas City, MO, p. A370
PETERS, Brian, Chief Information Officer, St. Vincent Indianapolis Hospital, Indianapolis, IN, p. A212
PETERS, Bruce
  Vice President and Chief Operating Officer, Bakersfield Memorial Hospital, Bakersfield, CA, p. A55
  Chief Executive Officer, Mercy Hospitals of Bakersfield, Bakersfield, CA, p. A55
PETERS, Candace, R.N. Director of Nursing, Webster County Community Hospital, Red Cloud, NE, p. A397
PETERS, Cindy, Chief Information Officer, Oak Hill Hospital, Brooksville, FL, p. A123
PETERS, Connie, R.N., President, CHI Health Schuyler, Schuyler, NE, p. A398
PETERS, Dave, Chief Human Resources Officer, Veterans Affairs Nebraska–Western Iowa Health Care System – Lincoln, Lincoln, NE, p. A394
PETERS, Gerald, Vice President Information Technologies and Chief Information Officer, Lake Health, Concord Township, OH, p. A487
PETERS, Holli, Director Health Information Management, Holton Community Hospital, Holton, KS, p. A242
PETERS, Jan, Vice President Human Resources, Saint Vincent Hospital, Worcester, MA, p. A313
PETERS, John, Chief Financial Officer, St. Joseph's Hospital and Medical Center, Phoenix, AZ, p. A36
PETERS, Mark J., M.D., President and Chief Executive Officer, East Jefferson General Hospital, Metairie, LA, p. A280
PETERS, Pamela, Admistrator, Child and Adolescent Behavioral Health Services, Wilamar, MN, p. A349

PETERS, Patrick, Chief Executive Officer, Guthrie County Hospital, Guthrie Center, IA, p. A228

PETERS, Sue, Vice President Human Resources, Munson Medical Center, Traverse City, MI, p. A331

PETERS, Violeta, R.N., Chief Executive Officer, Specialty Hospital of Central Jersey, Lakewood, NJ, p. A413

PETERS, Wayne, Administrator, Southern Virginia Mental Health Institute, Danville, VA, p. A664

PETERS–LEWIS, Angelleen, R.N. Chief Nurse and Senior Vice President Patient Care, Women & Infants Hospital of Rhode Island, Providence, RI, p. A556

PETERSEN, Brenda, Human Resources, Sanford Wheaton Medical Center, Wheaton, MN, p. A349

PETERSEN, Debbie, R.N. Chief Operating Officer and Chief Nursing Officer, Spalding Rehabilitation Hospital, Aurora, CO, p. A99

PETERSEN, Gary, Administrator and Chief Executive Officer, Kaiser Permanente Sunnyside Medical Center, Clackamas, OR, p. A520

PETERSEN, Julie, Chief Executive Officer, PMH Medical Center, Prosser, WA, p. A682

PETERSEN, Richard W., President and Chief Executive Officer, Maine Medical Center, Portland, ME, p. A291

PETERSEN, Tina, Chief Nursing Officer, Hillcrest Hospital Cushing, Cushing, OK, p. A505

PETERSON, Alison, Vice President Medical Affairs, United Hospital, Saint Paul, MN, p. A346

PETERSON, Anne, Vice President Human Resources and Support Services, Licking Memorial Hospital, Newark, OH, p. A495

PETERSON, Bill, Director Human Resources, EASTAR Health System, Muskogee, OK, p. A510

PETERSON, Bonnie, Chief Executive Officer, Richard P. Stadter Psychiatric Center, Grand Forks, ND, p. A474

PETERSON, Brent A., Administrator, Cherry County Hospital, Valentine, NE, p. A398

PETERSON, Brett, Director of Information Services, Florida Hospital North Pinellas, Tarpon Springs, FL, p. A145

PETERSON, Bruce, Chief Information Officer, Rome Memorial Hospital, Rome, NY, p. A449

PETERSON, Chad, Chief Information Officer, Northwood Deaconess Health Center, Northwood, ND, p. A476

PETERSON, Cheryl, Business Office Manager, Surgical Institute of Reading, Wyomissing, PA, p. A554

PETERSON, Cindy, Vice President and Chief Information Officer, Henry Mayo Newhall Memorial Hospital, Valencia, CA, p. A96

PETERSON, David, Chief Information Officer, Laurel Regional Hospital, Laurel, MD, p. A299

PETERSON, Dennis, Chief Information Officer, George E. Weems Memorial Hospital, Apalachicola, FL, p. A121

PETERSON, Douglas R., President and Chief Executive Officer, Chippewa Valley Hospital and Oakview Care Center, Durand, WI, p. A699

PETERSON, Eric, Director, Ogden Regional Medical Center, Ogden, UT, p. A656

PETERSON, Erica, Chief Executive Officer, Sanford Chamberlain Medical Center, Chamberlain, SD, p. A567

PETERSON, Gary, M.D. Vice President Medical Affairs and Medical Director, St. Luke's Hospital, Duluth, MN, p. A338

PETERSON, Jeff, M.D. Chief of Staff, Essentia Health Ada, Ada, MN, p. A334

PETERSON, Jeffrey, M.D. Medical Director, Cooperstown Medical Center, Cooperstown, ND, p. A473

PETERSON, Jim, Chief Financial Officer, Steele Memorial Medical Center, Salmon, ID, p. A176

PETERSON, Josilyn, Chief Financial Officer, Ballinger Memorial Hospital, Ballinger, TX, p. A595

PETERSON, Judy, R.N. Chief Nursing Officer, East Texas Medical Center Carthage, Carthage, TX, p. A600

PETERSON, Julie, Chief Financial Officer, Sutter Delta Medical Center, Antioch, CA, p. A54

PETERSON, Kathy, Director Information Services, OSF Saint Anthony Medical Center, Rockford, IL, p. A199

PETERSON, Katie, R.N. Chief Nursing Officer, Pender Community Hospital, Pender, NE, p. A397

PETERSON, Larry, Chief Financial Officer, Allen County Regional Hospital, Iola, KS, p. A242

PETERSON, Linda, M.D. Vice President Medical Affairs, McLaren Greater Lansing, Lansing, MI, p. A324

PETERSON, Mackenzie, M.D. Chief of Staff, Anderson County Hospital, Garnett, KS, p. A240

PETERSON, Margaret R., R.N., President, California Hospital Medical Center, Los Angeles, CA, p. A69

PETERSON, Michael, M.D. Chief of Staff, Pineville Community Hospital Association, Pineville, KY, p. A265

PETERSON, Michael, Chief Operating Officer, Sebasticook Valley Health, Pittsfield, ME, p. A291

PETERSON, Natalie

Director of Human Resources, Optim Medical Center – Jenkins, Millen, GA, p. A161

Human Resources Director, Optim Medical Center – Screven, Sylvania, GA, p. A165

PETERSON, Polly, Information Technology Director, Winona Health, Winona, MN, p. A349

PETERSON, Randall, President and Chief Executive Officer, Stormont–Vail HealthCare, Topeka, KS, p. A251

PETERSON, Robert

Chief Financial Officer, Hackettstown Regional Medical Center, Hackettstown, NJ, p. A412

Chief Executive Officer, Millinocket Regional Hospital, Millinocket, ME, p. A291

PETERSON, Ron, FACHE, President and Chief Executive Officer, Baxter Regional Medical Center, Mountain Home, AR, p. A48

PETERSON, Ron, Chief Information Officer, Pottstown Memorial Medical Center, Pottstown, PA, p. A548

PETERSON, Ronald R., President, Johns Hopkins Health System, Baltimore, MD, p. B76

PETERSON, Ronald R., President, Johns Hopkins Hospital, Baltimore, MD, p. A293

PETERSON, Scott, M.D. President Medical Staff, Avera Flandreau Hospital, Flandreau, SD, p. A568

PETERSON, Scott, Vice President of People and Organizational Development, Peninsula Regional Medical Center, Salisbury, MD, p. A300

PETERSON, Scott J., Acting Chief Executive Officer, Vanderbilt Stallworth Rehabilitation Hospital, Nashville, TN, p. A586

PETERSON, Seth, Director Information Services, Coshocton County Memorial Hospital, Coshocton, OH, p. A487

PETERSON, Shelley, R.N. Vice President Patient Services and Chief Nursing Officer, St. Mary's Medical Center, Grand Junction, CO, p. A104

PETERSON, Stephen, Vice President Chief Information Officer, Garrett County Memorial Hospital, Oakland, MD, p. A299

PETERSON, Steve, M.D. Chief of Staff, CHI Health Plainview, Plainview, NE, p. A397

PETERSON, Thomas, M.D. President, Richard P. Stadter Psychiatric Center, Grand Forks, ND, p. A474

PETERSON, Tim, M.D. Chief of Staff, Meeker Memorial Hospital, Litchfield, MN, p. A341

PETERSON, Tracie, R.N. Chief Nursing Officer, Great Lakes Specialty Hospital–Grand Rapids, Grand Rapids, MI, p. A320

PETIK, Jason, ACHE, Chief Executive Officer, Sidney Regional Medical Center, Sidney, NE, p. A398

PETITT, Dorie, Chief Nursing Officer, Post Acute Medical Specialty Hospital of Milwaukee, Greenfield, WI, p. A702

PETITT, Michael

Director of Finance, Wheaton Franciscan Healthcare – Elmbrook Memorial, Brookfield, WI, p. A698

Director of Finance, Wheaton Franciscan Healthcare – St. Joseph's, Milwaukee, WI, p. A707

Director of Finance, Wheaton Franciscan Healthcare – The Wisconsin Heart Hospital, Wauwatosa, WI, p. A713

PETRE, Patrick A., Chief Executive Officer, AHMC Anaheim Regional Medical Center, Anaheim, CA, p. A53

PETRIK, Jennifer, Interim Chief Nursing Officer, Deaconess Hospital, Spokane, WA, p. A685

PETRILLO, Mary Ann, R.N. Acting Associate Director Nursing and Patient Clinical Services, Bedford Veterans Affairs Medical Center, Edith Nourse Rogers Memorial Veterans Hospital, Bedford, MA, p. A302

PETRILLO, Nancy, Director Human Resources, Matheny Medical and Educational Center, Peapack, NJ, p. A416

PETRINA, Robert, Chief Financial Officer, Alta Bates Summit Medical Center, Berkeley, CA, p. A56

PETRINO, Robert, M.D. Chief of Staff, Northwest Medical Center – Springdale, Springdale, AR, p. A51

PETRITZ, Jennifer J., Director Human Resources, University of Washington Medical Center, Seattle, WA, p. A684

PETROVICH, Lawrence, M.D. Chief Medical Officer, York Hospital, York, ME, p. A292

PETRY, Fernando, M.D. Vice President and Chief Medical Officer, Martin Health System, Stuart, FL, p. A143

PETRY, Gary, M.D. Chief of Staff, St. Vincent General Hospital District, Leadville, CO, p. A106

PETTEY, Robbie, Chief Financial Officer, National Park Medical Center, Hot Springs, AR, p. A45

PETTIGREW, Dennis, Chief Operating Officer, Saint Michael's Medical Center, Newark, NJ, p. A415

PETTIGREW, Rob, Director Information Technology, Wyoming Medical Center, Casper, WY, p. A715

PETTIJOHN, Trent, M.D. Chief Medical Officer, The Heart Hospital Baylor Plano, Plano, TX, p. A637

PETTINATO, Jim, Director Patient Care Services, Wayne Memorial Hospital, Honesdale, PA, p. A536

PETTIT, Donny, Chief Financial Officer, Coon Memorial Hospital, Dalhart, TX, p. A604

PETTITE, Shirley F., Chief Human Resources Officer, Tennessee Valley Healthcare System, Nashville, TN, p. A586

PETTREY, Lisa J., R.N., Chief Executive Officer, Regency Hospital of Columbus, Columbus, OH, p. A486

PETTY, Jane, Director Human Resources, Southern Tennessee Regional Health System–Pulaski, Pulaski, TN, p. A587

PETTY, Russ, M.D. Chief of Staff, Towner County Medical Center, Cando, ND, p. A472

PETULA, Ron

Vice President Finance, Good Shepherd Penn Partners Specialty Hospital at Rittenhouse, Philadelphia, PA, p. A543

Chief Financial Officer, Good Shepherd Rehabilitation Hospital, Allentown, PA, p. A528

PEW, Chad, Chief Operating Officer and Senior Vice President, Wyoming Medical Center, Casper, WY, p. A715

PFAFF, Joni, Chief Nursing Officer, Grisell Memorial Hospital District One, Ransom, KS, p. A249

PFAFF, Tony, Chief Executive Officer, Deer Lodge Medical Center, Deer Lodge, MT, p. A382

PFALTZGRAFF, George, Chief Medical Officer, Hansen Family Hospital, Iowa Falls, IA, p. A230

PFAU, Ben, Chief Facility and Information Officer, Bay Area Hospital, Coos Bay, OR, p. A520

PFAU, Beth, M.D. Chief Medical Officer, Larue D. Carter Memorial Hospital, Indianapolis, IN, p. A212

PFEFFER, Daniel William, Chief Nurse Executive, Weisman Children's Rehabilitation Hospital, Marlton, NJ, p. A414

PFEFFER, Stacey, Senior Vice President Human Resources, Winthrop–University Hospital, Mineola, NY, p. A437

PFEIFER, Bradley D., Chief Executive Officer, West Holt Memorial Hospital, Atkinson, NE, p. A389

PFEIFER, Mark P., M.D. Senior Vice President and Chief Medical Officer, University of Louisville Hospital, Louisville, KY, p. A262

PFEIFFER, James A., FACHE, President and Chief Executive Officer, Self Regional Healthcare, Greenwood, SC, p. A562

PFEIFFER, Margaret, R.N. Vice President Patient Care Services, Good Samaritan Hospital, Los Angeles, CA, p. A70

PFISTER, Joann M., Director Human Resources, Providence Willamette Falls Medical Center, Oregon City, OR, p. A523

PFISTER, Pam, Chief Executive Officer, Morrison Community Hospital, Morrison, IL, p. A195

PFISTER, Scott, Director Finance, Providence St. Vincent Medical Center, Portland, OR, p. A524

PFITZER, Tommy, Chief Executive Officer, Massac Memorial Hospital, Metropolis, IL, p. A194

PFRANK, Kym

Senior Vice President and Chief Operating Officer, Union Hospital, Terre Haute, IN, p. A220

Vice President Information Systems, Union Hospital Clinton, Clinton, IN, p. A206

PHAM, Bong, Chief Medical Officer, Kit Carson County Health Service District, Burlington, CO, p. A100

PHAM, K., M.D. Chief of Staff, Winkler County Memorial Hospital, Kermit, TX, p. A625

PHELAN, Cynthia, Vice President Human Resources, Lawrence General Hospital, Lawrence, MA, p. A308

PHELPS, Britton, Chief Executive Officer, Merit Health Madison, Canton, MS, p. A351

PHELPS, David E., President and Chief Executive Officer, Berkshire Health Systems, Inc., Pittsfield, MA, p. B23

PHELPS, David E., President and Chief Executive Officer, Berkshire Medical Center, Pittsfield, MA, p. A310

PHELPS, Gail, R.N. Chief Nursing Officer, Haxtun Hospital District, Haxtun, CO, p. A105

PHELPS, Joel, Chief Operating Officer, Salina Regional Health Center, Salina, KS, p. A250

PHELPS, Kathleen, Director Human Resources, Treasure Valley Hospital, Boise, ID, p. A173

PHELPS, Rick, M.D. President and Chief Operating Officer, Elliot Hospital, Manchester, NH, p. A407

PHETTEPLACE, Danial, Director Information Technology, Gundersen St. Joseph's Hospital and Clinics, Hillsboro, WI, p. A702

PHILIP, Neena S., R.N. Assistant Vice President Nursing, Hoboken University Medical Center, Hoboken, NJ, p. A412

PHILIPCHUCK, Cynthia, R.N. Executive Director of Nursing, Gibson Area Hospital and Health Services, Gibson City, IL, p. A189

PHILIPS, III, Grady W., Senior Vice President and Chief Operating Officer, Winchester Medical Center, Winchester, VA, p. A674

PHILIPS, J. Michael, Chief Strategy Officer, San Juan Regional Medical Center, Farmington, NM, p. A424

PHILLIPS, Alan M., Controller, HEALTHSOUTH Nittany Valley Rehabilitation Hospital, Pleasant Gap, PA, p. A547

PHILLIPS, Annette S., President and Chief Executive Officer, ProMedica Monroe Regional Hospital, Monroe, MI, p. A326

PHILLIPS, Barry, Executive Director Human Resources, Camden General Hospital, Camden, TN, p. A574

Index of Health Care Professionals
Index of Health Care Professionals / Phillips


PHILLIPS, Bill, Vice President Information Services, University Health System, San Antonio, TX, p. A642
PHILLIPS, Bob, Interim Chief Executive Officer, Cibola General Hospital, Grants, NM, p. A424
PHILLIPS, Bobby, Chief Nursing Officer, Medical Center Enterprise, Enterprise, AL, p. A19
PHILLIPS, Brent R., President and Chief Executive Officer, Regional Health, Rapid City, SD, p. B112
PHILLIPS, Courtney, Chief Executive Officer, South Sunflower County Hospital, Indianola, MS, p. A354
PHILLIPS, David D., Chief Executive Officer and Administrator, Barnesville Hospital, Barnesville, OH, p. A479
PHILLIPS, David L.
Chief Executive Officer, St. John Broken Arrow, Broken Arrow, OK, p. A504
President and Chief Executive Officer, St. John Owasso, Owasso, OK, p. A513
Chief Executive Officer, St. John Sapulpa, Sapulpa, OK, p. A514
PHILLIPS, Donna, President, Bryn Mawr Rehabilitation Hospital, Malvern, PA, p. A539
PHILLIPS, Eddie, M.D
Chief Medical Affairs, Baptist Health Medical Center – North Little Rock, North Little Rock, AR, p. A49
Chief Medical Officer, Baptist Health Medical Center–Arkadelphia, Arkadelphia, AR, p. A41
PHILLIPS, Frank, M.D. Chief of Staff, Mary Black Health System – Gaffney, Gaffney, SC, p. A561
PHILLIPS, Glenn, Director Information Systems, Gadsden Regional Medical Center, Gadsden, AL, p. A20
PHILLIPS, John
Chief Administrative Officer, Eastern State Hospital, Lexington, KY, p. A259
Chief of Staff, Great River Medical Center, West Burlington, IA, p. A236
Vice President Information Services, St. Joseph Regional Health Center, Bryan, TX, p. A599
PHILLIPS, John E., FACHE, President, Methodist Mansfield Medical Center, Mansfield, TX, p. A631
PHILLIPS, Kelly, M.D. Clinical Director and Chief Staff, Spring Grove Hospital Center, Baltimore, MD, p. A295
PHILLIPS, Kimberly A., Chief Financial Officer, The Children's Home of Pittsburgh, Pittsburgh, PA, p. A546
PHILLIPS, Lionel J., Vice President Financial Services, Fauquier Hospital, Warrenton, VA, p. A674
PHILLIPS, Lori, Vice President and Chief Nursing Officer, Gibson General Hospital, Princeton, IN, p. A218
PHILLIPS, Margaret, Director Human Resources, Memorial Hospital, North Conway, NH, p. A408
PHILLIPS, Michael, Chief Executive Officer, Elkhorn Valley Rehabilitation Hospital, Casper, WY, p. A715
PHILLIPS, Michael T., FACHE, Administrator, Southern California Hospital at Culver City, Culver City, CA, p. A59
PHILLIPS, Pam, Chief Human Resource Officer, Wiregrass Medical Center, Geneva, AL, p. A20
PHILLIPS, Paul, Chief Financial Officer, Taylor Regional Hospital, Campbellsville, KY, p. A255
PHILLIPS, Richard, Chief Financial Officer, Desert Regional Medical Center, Palm Springs, CA, p. A80
PHILLIPS, Robert
President, Shelby Baptist Medical Center, Alabaster, AL, p. A15
Administrator, Walker Baptist Medical Center, Jasper, AL, p. A21
PHILLIPS, Sarah, Manager Human Resources, Morgan Memorial Hospital, Madison, GA, p. A161
PHILLIPS, Steve, Information Officer, Greene County General Hospital, Linton, IN, p. A215
PHILLIPS, Tammy, Director, Information Systems, Texas Health Presbyterian Hospital Dallas, Dallas, TX, p. A606
PHILLIPS, Todd, M.D. Chief Medical Officer, Monmouth Medical Center, Southern Campus, Lakewood, NJ, p. A413
PHINNEY, Cody, Administrator, Northern Nevada Adult Mental Health Services, Sparks, NV, p. A404
PHIPPS, Bonnie, President and Chief Executive Officer, Saint Agnes Hospital, Baltimore, MD, p. A294
PHIPPS, Jackie G., Director Human Resources, Johnston Memorial Hospital, Abingdon, VA, p. A662
PIANALTO, Eric, President, Mercy Hospital Rogers, Rogers, AR, p. A50
PIATKOWSKI, Shannon, Director Information Technology, Blake Medical Center, Bradenton, FL, p. A122
PIAZZA, Tony, Director Human Resources, Titus Regional Medical Center, Mount Pleasant, TX, p. A633
PICAZA, Jose, M.D. Chief of Staff, Unicoi County Memorial Hospital, Erwin, TN, p. A577
PICCIONE, Jennifer, Chief Nursing and Clinical Services Officer, Madison Health, London, OH, p. A492
PICCONE, Robert, President, Clear Brook Manor, Wilkes–Barre, PA, p. A553
PICKARD, Bert, Chief Financial Officer, Merit Health Gilmore Memorial, Amory, MS, p. A350
PICKEL, Joseph, Director Resource Management, Walter Reed National Military Medical Center, Bethesda, MD, p. A296
PICKENS, Gayle, Chief Nursing Officer, Putnam County Memorial Hospital, Unionville, MO, p. A380
PICKENS, Ramona, Chief Operating Officer, East Cooper Medical Center, Mount Pleasant, SC, p. A563
PICKENS, Regina, Chief Financial Officer, Grafton City Hospital, Grafton, WV, p. A691
PICKENS, Roland, Interim Chief Executive Officer, San Francisco General Hospital and Trauma Center, San Francisco, CA, p. A88
PICKENS, Troy, Chief Financial Officer, Southern Palmetto Hospital, Barnwell, SC, p. A557
PICKERING, Sheridan, Chief Executive Officer, Muscogee Creek Nation Medical Center, Okmulgee, OK, p. A513
PICKETT, Beverly, R.N. Chief Nursing Officer, Atoka County Medical Center, Atoka, OK, p. A504
PICKETT, Gregory D., M.D. Chief of Staff, Jackson County Memorial Hospital, Altus, OK, p. A503
PICKETT, Lisa C., M.D. Chief Medical Officer, Duke University Hospital, Durham, NC, p. A459
PICKLER, Nancy, Director of Human Resources, HEALTHSOUTH East Valley Rehabilitation Hospital, Mesa, AZ, p. A33
PICKUL, David, M.D. Chief Medical Officer, Circle Health, Lowell General Hospital, Lowell, MA, p. A308
PICONE, Anthony, M.D. Medical Director, Roswell Park Cancer Institute, Buffalo, NY, p. A430
PICOU, Timothy, Manager Information Technology, Lower Umpqua Hospital District, Reedsport, OR, p. A525
PIEPER, Blaine, Chief Executive Officer, Ohio County Hospital, Hartford, KY, p. A258
PIEPHOFF, James, Chief Medical Officer, OSF Saint Anthony's Health Center, Alton, IL, p. A178
PIERCE, Bonnie, MSN Associate Director for Patient Care Services, Jack C. Montgomery Veterans Affairs Medical Center, Muskogee, OK, p. A510
PIERCE, Jeff M.
Manager Human Resources, Marshall Medical Center, Lewisburg, TN, p. A581
Manager Human Resources, Wayne Medical Center, Waynesboro, TN, p. A589
PIERCE, Jennifer, Administrative Director of Finance, St. Anthony Shawnee Hospital, Shawnee, OK, p. A515
PIERCE, Kenneth, Chief Financial Officer, Brookhaven Hospital, Tulsa, OK, p. A516
PIERCE, Laura, Director Human Resources, Memorial Medical Center, Las Cruces, NM, p. A425
PIERCE, Margaret H., Executive Director, Kaiser Permanente Baldwin Park Medical Center, Baldwin Park, CA, p. A55
PIERCE, Michael L., Chief Executive Officer, Post Acute Medical Specialty Hospital of Corpus Christi, Corpus Christi, TX, p. A603
PIERCE, Pamela, Deputy Chief Executive Officer, Windhaven Psychiatric Hospital, Prescott Valley, AZ, p. A36
PIERCE, Pat, Director Information Systems, Lakewood Regional Medical Center, Lakewood, CA, p. A67
PIERCE, Shelley, Chief Nursing Officer, Allegiance Specialty Hospital of Kilgore, Kilgore, TX, p. A626
PIERCE, Trent, R.N.,
Chief Executive Officer, HEALTHSOUTH City View Rehabilitation Hospital, Fort Worth, TX, p. A613
Chief Executive Officer, HEALTHSOUTH Rehabilitation Hospital of Fort Worth, Fort Worth, TX, p. A613
PIERDON, Steven, M.D. Executive Vice President and Chief Medical Officer, Geisinger Wyoming Valley Medical Center, Wilkes Barre, PA, p. A553
PIERESCHI, Giovanni
Vice President Enterprise Information and Chief Information Officer, Hospital HIMA San Pablo Caguas, Caguas, PR, p. A720
Vice President Management Information Systems, Hospital HMA de Humacao, Humacao, PR, p. A721
PIERLUISI, Guillermo, Vice President of Medical Affairs, WellStar Paulding Hospital, Hiram, GA, p. A159
PIERRE, Andre, Chief Financial Officer, Forest View Psychiatric Hospital, Grand Rapids, MI, p. A320
PIERRE, Letonia, Coordinator Human Resources, Assumption Community Hospital, Napoleonville, LA, p. A281
PIERSON, Jerome, Chief Medical Officer, Mercy Medical Center–Sioux City, Sioux City, IA, p. A234
PIERSON, Kari, Manager, Howard County Medical Center, Saint Paul, NE, p. A398
PIERSON, Kyle, Chief Financial Officer, Minnie Hamilton HealthCare Center, Grantsville, WV, p. A691
PIERSON, Lois K., Chief Financial Officer, University of Texas Harris County Psychiatric Center, Houston, TX, p. A622
PIERSON, Marc, M.D. Vice President Clinical Information and Quality, PeaceHealth St. Joseph Medical Center, Bellingham, WA, p. A676
PIETRANGELO, Steve, Director Information Services, War Memorial Hospital, Sault Sainte Marie, MI, p. A330
PIETRO, Daniel, M.D. Medical Director, Sturdy Memorial Hospital, Attleboro, MA, p. A302
PIETSCH, Al, CPA Senior Vice President and Chief Financial Officer, University of Maryland Baltimore Washington Medical Center, Glen Burnie, MD, p. A298
PIETZ, Gerald
Vice President Finance, Mercy Hospital, Coon Rapids, MN, p. A337
Vice President Finance, Unity Hospital, Fridley, MN, p. A339
PIFER, Eric, M.D. Chief Medical Officer, El Camino Hospital, Mountain View, CA, p. A77
PIFKO, Duane, Interim Director Financial Services, Daniel Drake Center for Post Acute Care, Cincinnati, OH, p. A482
PIGG, Russell, Chief Executive Officer, Eliza Coffee Memorial Hospital, Florence, AL, p. A19
PIGOTT, John, M.D. Chief Medical Officer, Tulane Medical Center, New Orleans, LA, p. A282
PIKE, David, Interim Chief Financial Officer, Memorial Hospital of Carbon County, Rawlins, WY, p. A717
PIKE, Irving, M.D. Chief Medical Officer, John Muir Medical Center, Walnut Creek, Walnut Creek, CA, p. A97
PIKE, Pauline, Chief Operating Officer, Beverly Hospital, Beverly, MA, p. A302
PIKE, Randi, Director of Nursing, Pioneer Medical Center, Big Timber, MT, p. A381
PIKE, Ronald F., M.D. Medical Director, Adcare Hospital of Worcester, Worcester, MA, p. A313
PIKE, Tim, M.D. Chief Medical Officer, Portsmouth Regional Hospital, Portsmouth, NH, p. A408
PIKER, John F., M.D. Medical Director, Villa Feliciana Medical Complex, Jackson, LA, p. A275
PIKULA, Shirley, MSN Associate Director Patient Center Care, San Francisco VA Medical Center, San Francisco, CA, p. A88
PIL, Pieter, M.D. Chief Medical Staff, Martha's Vineyard Hospital, Oak Bluffs, MA, p. A310
PILANT, Jason B., Chief Operating Officer, Roane Medical Center, Harriman, TN, p. A578
PILE, Larry, Director Human Resources, Deaconess Hospital, Evansville, IN, p. A208
PILEGGI, Anne, Chief Executive Officer, Mother Frances Hospital – Jacksonville, Jacksonville, TX, p. A624
PILEGGI, Tim
Interim Chief Financial Officer, Good Shepherd Medical Center, Longview, TX, p. A629
Interim Chief Financial Officer, Good Shepherd Medical Center–Marshall, Marshall, TX, p. A631
PILKINGTON III, Albert, Chief Executive Officer, Johnson Regional Medical Center, Clarksville, AR, p. A42
PILLION, Scott, Chief Executive Officer, Helen Newberry Joy Hospital, Newberry, MI, p. A327
PILONG Jr., Alfred E., President, Munson Medical Center, Traverse City, MI, p. A331
PILOT, Dave, Chief Financial Officer, Essentia Health St. Joseph's Medical Center, Brainerd, MN, p. A336
PIMENTEL, Joe, Chief Nursing Officer, Shenandoah Medical Center, Shenandoah, IA, p. A234
PINA, Kate, Director Human Resources, Wickenburg Community Hospital, Wickenburg, AZ, p. A40
PINDERSKI, Christopher, M.D. Medical Director of Emergency Room, Black River Medical Center, Poplar Bluff, MO, p. A374
PINE, Richard M., President and Chief Executive Officer, Livengrin Foundation, Bensalem, PA, p. A529
PINEDA, Omar, R.N. Chief Nursing Officer, Medical Center Arlington, Arlington, TX, p. A592
PINEIRO, Carlos M., President, Hospital HMA de Humacao, Humacao, PR, p. A721
PINKELMAN, Janet, Director Human Resources, Faith Regional Health Services, Norfolk, NE, p. A395
PINKOSKY, Frank
Senior Vice President, Robert Packer Hospital, Sayre, PA, p. A549
Executive Vice President, Troy Community Hospital, Troy, PA, p. A551
PINO, Elena, Chief Operating Officer and Chief Nursing Officer, Mesa Hills Specialty Hospital, El Paso, TX, p. A611
PINO, Joseph, M.D. Chief Medical Officer, Regional Medical Center Bayonet Point, Hudson, FL, p. A129
PINON, Richard, Chief Medical Officer, Eastern New Mexico Medical Center, Roswell, NM, p. A426
PINSKY, Karen, M.D. Chief Medical Information Officer, Penn Medicine Chester County Hospital, West Chester, PA, p. A552
PINSON, Charles Wright, M.D., Deputy Vice Chancellor for Health Affairs and Chief Executive Officer of Vanderbilt Health System, Vanderbilt Health, Nashville, TN, p. B149


**A940** Index of Health Care Professionals

Index of Health Care Professionals

Index of Health Care Professionals / Polivka

POLIVKA, Maureen, Chief Nursing Officer, Hill Country Memorial Hospital, Fredericksburg, TX, p. A614
POLIZZI, Arturo, President, ProMedica Toledo Hospital, Toledo, OH, p. A499
POLK, Brent, M.D. Chair Department of Pediatrics and Vice President Academic Affairs, Children's Hospital Los Angeles, Los Angeles, CA, p. A69
POLKOW, Craig, Chief Executive Officer, DeKalb Health, Auburn, IN, p. A204
POLLACK, Murray, M.D. Vice President and Chief Medical Officer, Phoenix Children's Hospital, Phoenix, AZ, p. A35
POLLACK, Neil, Senior Administrator, Terence Cardinal Cooke Health Care Center, New York, NY, p. A444
POLLACK, Richard, Vice President Information Services, VCU Medical Center, Richmond, VA, p. A672
POLLARD, Amy, R.N., President and Chief Executive Officer, Nicholas H. Noyes Memorial Hospital, Dansville, NY, p. A432
POLLARD, Anthony, D.O. Chief Medical Officer, AMG Specialty Hospital – Las Vegas, Las Vegas, NV, p. A401
POLLARD, Dennis, President, Community Memorial Hospital, Menomonee Falls, WI, p. A705
POLLMAN, Brian, Chief Medical Officer, Hutchinson Health, Hutchinson, MN, p. A340
POLLNOW, Dean, M.D. President Medical Staff, Ministry Saint Mary's Hospitals, Rhinelander, WI, p. A710
POLLOCK, Jeffrey, Chief Information Officer, Wentworth–Douglass Hospital, Dover, NH, p. A406
POLLOCK, Maureen King, Chief Executive Officer, Eagleville Hospital, Eagleville, PA, p. A533
POLO, Fabian, Chief Executive Officer, Baylor Institute for Rehabilitation, Dallas, TX, p. A604
POLONSKY, Dana, Vice President of Clinical Services, Craig Hospital, Englewood, CO, p. A103
POLSELLI, Donna, Chief Operating Officer, Franciscan Hospital for Children, Boston, MA, p. A303
POLSTER, Peggy, Manager Personnel and Administrative Assistant, Falls Community Hospital and Clinic, Marlin, TX, p. A631
POLT, Cynthia, Chief Financial Officer, Touro Infirmary, New Orleans, LA, p. A282
POLTRACK, Andrew, M.D. Chief of Staff, Margaret Mary Health, Batesville, IN, p. A204
POLZIN, Greg
Chief Financial Officer, Iowa Specialty Hospital–Belmond, Belmond, IA, p. A222
Chief Financial Officer, Iowa Specialty Hospital–Clarion, Clarion, IA, p. A224
POMA, Frank W., President, St. John River District Hospital, East China, MI, p. A318
POMPOS, Jeff, Manager Information Technology, Henry County Hospital, Napoleon, OH, p. A495
PONCE, Agustin, Supervisor Maintenance, Castaner General Hospital, Castaner, PR, p. A720
PONCE, Joseph A., Chief Information Management, Dwight David Eisenhower Army Medical Center, Fort Gordon, GA, p. A157
PONCE, Martha, Director Information Technologies and Telecommunications, Saint John's Health Center, Santa Monica, CA, p. A91
POND, Dwight, TIS Boise, Saint Alphonsus Regional Medical Center, Boise, ID, p. A172
POND–BELL, Michele, R.N. Nurse Administrator, Cassia Regional Medical Center, Burley, ID, p. A173
PONDER, Beverly K., Executive Assistant and Human Resources Coordinator, Covington County Hospital, Collins, MS, p. A352
PONDER, David, Information Technology Officer, Claremore Indian Hospital, Claremore, OK, p. A505
PONETA, Jan, Director Information Services, Mercy Hospital Jefferson, Crystal City, MO, p. A366
PONOZZO, Nancy Lynn, Chief Nursing Officer, Aspirus Iron River Hospitals and Clinics, Iron River, MI, p. A323
PONT, Allan, M.D. Vice President Medical Affairs, California Pacific Medical Center, San Francisco, CA, p. A88
PONTI, Mary–Anne D., R.N. Chief Operating Officer, McLaren Northern Michigan, Petoskey, MI, p. A327
PONTICELLO, Nat, Vice President Human Resources, Valley Children's Hospital, Madera, CA, p. A74
PONTIOUS, Becky, Human Resources/Accounting, Loring Hospital, Sac City, IA, p. A234
POOCH, Fred, Supervisor Information Technology, Johnson County Hospital, Tecumseh, NE, p. A398
POOK, Lots, Chief Information Officer, National Jewish Health, Denver, CO, p. A102
POOLE, Karen, Chief Operating Officer, Boca Raton Regional Hospital, Boca Raton, FL, p. A122
POOLE, Rob, Director, Jane Phillips Medical Center, Bartlesville, OK, p. A504
POOLE–ADAMS, Veronica, R.N. Vice President, Chief Operating Officer and Chief Nursing Executive, Cleveland Regional Medical Center, Shelby, NC, p. A468
POORE, Justin, D.O. Chief Medical Staff, Cloud County Health Center, Concordia, KS, p. A238
POORE, Luke, Administrator, Webster County Community Hospital, Red Cloud, NE, p. A397
POORE, Timothy T., Chief Executive Officer, HEALTHSOUTH Scottsdale Rehabilitation Hospital, Scottsdale, AZ, p. A37
POORTEN, Kevin P., President and Chief Executive Officer, Kish Health System, DeKalb, IL, p. B80
POOS, Joshua, M.D. President Medical Staff, Community Memorial Hospital, Staunton, IL, p. A201
POPE, Alan R., M.D
Vice President, Medical Affairs, Lourdes Medical Center of Burlington County, Willingboro, NJ, p. A420
Chief Medical Officer, Our Lady of Lourdes Medical Center, Camden, NJ, p. A410
POPE, Brad W., Vice President Human Resources, CHI Memorial, Chattanooga, TN, p. A575
POPE, Eddie, Chief Information Officer, Lackey Memorial Hospital, Forest, MS, p. A353
POPE, J. Larry, Vice President Finance, Baptist Easley Hospital, Easley, SC, p. A560
POPE, Jayne E., Chief Executive Officer, Hill Country Memorial Hospital, Fredericksburg, TX, p. A614
POPE, Lona, Director Fiscal Services, Shriners Hospitals for Children–Houston, Houston, TX, p. A622
POPE, Richard, Vice President Human Resources, Jackson County Memorial Hospital, Altus, OK, p. A503
POPE, Robert, Information Technology Director and Ministry Liaison, St. Vincent Anderson Regional Hospital, Anderson, IN, p. A204
POPHAN, Cameron, Chief Financial Officer, Spalding Regional Medical Center, Griffin, GA, p. A158
POPKIN, Steven, Chief Executive Officer, Parkview Community Hospital Medical Center, Riverside, CA, p. A83
POPLI, Anand, Medical Director, Porter–Starke Services, Valparaiso, IN, p. A221
POPOVICH, Cal, Vice President Information Technology, All Children's Hospital Johns Hopkins Medicine, Saint Petersburg, FL, p. A141
POPOVICH, John, M.D., President and Chief Executive Officer, Henry Ford Hospital, Detroit, MI, p. A317
POPOWYCZ, Alex, Senior Vice President / Chief Information Officer, Health First Palm Bay Hospital, Palm Bay, FL, p. A138
POPP, Adam, Director Information Systems, Avera St. Benedict Health Center, Parkston, SD, p. A570
POPP, Jason, Chief of Medical Staff, Rochelle Community Hospital, Rochelle, IL, p. A199
POPP, Susan, Controller, Kindred Hospital–Fort Worth, Fort Worth, TX, p. A613
POPPEN, Jeffrey, Chief Financial Officer, Sanford Aberdeen Medical Center, Aberdeen, SD, p. A567
POPPEN, Jennifer, Chief Executive Officer, Avera Creighton Hospital, Creighton, NE, p. A391
POPPERT, Dale, Chief Financial Officer, Kaiser Permanente Antioch Medical Center, Antioch, CA, p. A53
POQUETTE, Gary R., FACHE, Chief Executive Officer, Penobscot Valley Hospital, Lincoln, ME, p. A291
PORADA, John, Chief Financial Officer, TriStar Southern Hills Medical Center, Nashville, TN, p. A586
PORCO, Albert, Director Management Information Systems, Palisades Medical Center, North Bergen, NJ, p. A416
PORRAL, Azucena, M.D. Chief of Staff, Monterey Park Hospital, Monterey Park, CA, p. A76
PORTCHY, Mindy, Manager Human Resources, Summit Pacific Medical Center, Elma, WA, p. A678
PORTER, Billy, Vice President Clinical Operations, CHRISTUS Health Shreveport–Bossier, Shreveport, LA, p. A284
PORTER, Bruce, Chief Financial Officer, Red River Hospital, LLC, Wichita Falls, TX, p. A652
PORTER, Cedric, M.D. President Medical Staff, Emanuel Medical Center, Swainsboro, GA, p. A165
PORTER, Don, Senior Vice President and Chief Financial Officer, J. Arthur Dosher Memorial Hospital, Southport, NC, p. A468
PORTER, Dorothy L., Director of Compliance/Risk/Quality, Asheville Specialty Hospital, Asheville, NC, p. A455
PORTER, Glen, Vice President Human Resources, Essentia Health St. Mary's Medical Center, Duluth, MN, p. A338
PORTER, Greg, Chief Financial Officer, Rio Grande Hospital, Del Norte, CO, p. A101
PORTER, James, Chief Financial Officer, Brookdale Hospital Medical Center, NY, p. A439
PORTER, James, M.D. Vice President Medical Affairs, Deaconess Hospital, Evansville, IN, p. A208
PORTER, Jody, R.N. Senior Vice President Patient Care Services and Chief Nursing Officer, Greater Baltimore Medical Center, Baltimore, MD, p. A293
PORTER Jr., John M., President and Chief Executive Officer, Ephrata Community Hospital, Ephrata, PA, p. A534
PORTER, John T., President and Chief Executive Officer, Avera Health, Sioux Falls, SD, p. B17
PORTER, Lance, Chief Executive Officer, Payson Regional Medical Center, Payson, AZ, p. A34
PORTER, Laura, Interim Executive Director, Good Shepherd Penn Partners Specialty Hospital at Rittenhouse, Philadelphia, PA, p. A543
PORTER, Lisa, Director Human Resources, Leadership and Education, Veterans Affairs Salt Lake City Health Care System, Salt Lake City, UT, p. A659
PORTER, Patricia, Executive Director, South Oaks Hospital, Amityville, NY, p. A428
PORTER, Sharon, Chief Financial Officer, Massachusetts Hospital School, Canton, MA, p. A306
PORTER, Stephen D., President, Sentara Northern Virginia Medical Center, Woodbridge, VA, p. A674
PORTER, T. J., Director Human Resources, Bennett County Hospital and Nursing Home, Martin, SD, p. A569
PORTMAN, Angela, Chief Executive Officer, Breckinridge Memorial Hospital, Hardinsburg, KY, p. A257
PORTNER, Barry, M.D. Chief of Staff, Prowers Medical Center, Lamar, CO, p. A106
PORTNER, Michael, M.D. Chief Medical Staff, Bolivar Medical Center, Cleveland, MS, p. A352
PORWOLL, Amy, Vice President of Information Systems, St. Cloud Hospital, Saint Cloud, MN, p. A345
POSAR, Steven, M.D. Chief of Medicine, Doctors NeuroMedical Hospital, Bremen, IN, p. A205
POSCH, David R., Chief Executive Officer, Vanderbilt Hospital and Clinics, Nashville, TN, p. A586
POSCH, Tim B., Business Manager and Director Personnel, Parsons State Hospital and Training Center, Parsons, KS, p. A248
POSECAI, Scott J., Executive Vice President and Chief Financial Officer, Ochsner Medical Center, New Orleans, LA, p. A282
POSER, Samuel G., M.D. Chief of Staff, Columbus Community Hospital, Inc., Columbus, WI, p. A699
POSEY, Dawn, Chief Operating Officer, Promise Hospital of Vicksburg, Vicksburg, MS, p. A361
POSEY, M. Kenneth, FACHE, Administrator, Jasper General Hospital, Bay Springs, MS, p. A350
POSEY, Richard B., Director Human Resources, Baptist Easley Hospital, Easley, SC, p. A560
POSMOGA, Paul, Chief Financial Officer, Twin Cities Community Hospital, Templeton, CA, p. A94
POST, Eleanor, R.N. Chief Nursing Officer, Rockdale Medical Center, Conyers, GA, p. A154
POST, John, M.D. Medical Director, Morrill County Community Hospital, Bridgeport, NE, p. A390
POST, Kevin, D.O. Chief Medical Officer, Hegg Memorial Health Center Avera, Rock Valley, IA, p. A234
POST, Kimberly, R.N., Vice President and Administrator, HonorHealth Scottsdale Thompson Peak Medical Center, Scottsdale, AZ, p. A37
POSTERNACK, Charles, M.D. Vice President, Boca Raton Regional Hospital, Boca Raton, FL, p. A122
POSTLER–SLATTERY, Diane, Ph.D., President and Chief Executive Officer, MidMichigan Health, Midland, MI, p. B92
POSTLETHWAIT, Betsy, President, Princeton Baptist Medical Center, Birmingham, AL, p. A16
POSTON, Anne, Director of Human Resources/Compliance, Lake City Community Hospital, Lake City, SC, p. A563
POSTON, Sharon, President and Chief Executive Officer, Williamsburg Regional Hospital, Kingstree, SC, p. A562
POSTULKA, Carol, Administrative Coordinator, Avera Gregory Hospital, Gregory, SD, p. A569
POTEATE, Kathy, Interim Director Human Resources, Hugh Chatham Memorial Hospital, Elkin, NC, p. A460
POTEETE, Robin
Manager Human Resources, Wellmont Hancock County Hospital, Sneedville, TN, p. A588
Manager Human Resources, Wellmont Hawkins County Memorial Hospital, Rogersville, TN, p. A587
POTHAST, Joyce, Vice President Human and Environmental Services, Van Wert County Hospital, Van Wert, OH, p. A499
POTITADKUL, Wendy, Chief Information Officer, Sunrise Canyon Hospital, Lubbock, TX, p. A629
POTTENGER, Jay, Chief Executive Officer, Garfield County Public Hospital District, Pomeroy, WA, p. A682
POTTER, Carolyn
Vice President Human Resources, McLaren Bay Region, Bay City, MI, p. A315
Vice President Human Resources, McLaren Bay Special Care, Bay City, MI, p. A315
Vice President Human Resources, McLaren Central Michigan, Mount Pleasant, MI, p. A326
POTTER, Dianne P., Manager Human Resources, Parkview Whitley Hospital, Columbia City, IN, p. A206
POTTER, Joe, M.D. Chief of Staff, AllianceHealth Madill, Madill, OK, p. A509

A942 Index of Health Care Professionals

POTTER, Rhonda, Director Human Resources, De Soto Regional Health System, Mansfield, LA, p. A279

POTTER, Val, Director Human Resources, St. Vincent Salem Hospital, Salem, IN, p. A219

POTTORFF, Kelly, Chief Executive Officer, Harrison County Community Hospital, Bethany, MO, p. A363

POTTS, Kevin, M.D. Medical Director, Kindred Hospital Detroit, Detroit, MI, p. A318

POTTS, Mary Ann, Director Personnel, Community Hospitals and Wellness Centers, Bryan, OH, p. A480

POUGNAUD, Teresa, Vice President Human Resources, McLeod Loris Seacoast Hospital, Loris, SC, p. A563

POULSON, Rhonda, Chief Nursing Officer and Vice President of Clinical Operations, CHI Memorial, Chattanooga, TN, p. A575

POUND, Steve, Vice President Human Resources, St. Joseph's Hospital, Savannah, GA, p. A164

POUND, Terry, Chief Financial Officer, Hospital District One of Rice County, Lyons, KS, p. A245

POUND, Veronica, R.N., Administrator, Socorro General Hospital, Socorro, NM, p. A427

POVICH, Mark, D.O. Medical Director, OSF St. Francis Hospital and Medical Group, Escanaba, MI, p. A319

POWE, Lee, Director Management Information Systems, Hugh Chatham Memorial Hospital, Elkin, NC, p. A460

POWEL, Linda J., M.D. Medical Director, Odessa Memorial Healthcare Center, Odessa, WA, p. A681

POWELL, Candy, Administrator, Collingsworth General Hospital, Wellington, TX, p. A651

POWELL, Charles, Chief Financial Officer, Arkansas Surgical Hospital, North Little Rock, AR, p. A49

POWELL, D. Jerome, M.D
    Chief Information Officer, Highland Hospital of Rochester, Rochester, NY, p. A448
    Chief Information Officer, Strong Memorial Hospital of the University of Rochester, Rochester, NY, p. A449

POWELL, Frank R., Chief Financial Officer, Piedmont Mountainside Hospital, Jasper, GA, p. A159

POWELL, Hannah, Chief Nursing Officer, Mercy Hospital Kingfisher, Kingfisher, OK, p. A508

POWELL, Holly, Administrator, Post Acute Medical Specialty Hospital of Texarkana, Texarkana, TX, p. A647

POWELL, Jackie, Director Human Resources, Pemiscot Memorial Health System, Hayti, MO, p. A368

POWELL, Jimmy, Manager Human Resources, Harry S. Truman Memorial Veterans Hospital, Columbia, MO, p. A366

POWELL, Josh, Facility Controller, Cox Monett, Monett, MO, p. A373

POWELL, Kay, Director Human Resources, CHRISTUS Jasper Memorial Hospital, Jasper, TX, p. A624

POWELL, Lorie, Interim Chief Executive Officer, Regency Hospital of South Atlanta, East Point, GA, p. A156

POWELL, Marissa, Human Resources Director, Sistersville General Hospital, Sistersville, WV, p. A695

POWELL, Michelle, Chief Executive Officer, Select Rehabilitation Hospital of Denton, Denton, TX, p. A608

POWELL, Mike, Chief Executive Officer, Fulton Medical Center, Fulton, MO, p. A368

POWELL, Parker, Chief Executive Officer, Glendive Medical Center, Glendive, MT, p. A383

POWELL, Robyn L., Chief Financial Officer, Marion General Hospital, Marion, IN, p. A215

POWELL, Roy A., President and Chief Executive Officer, Crittenton Hospital Medical Center, Rochester, MI, p. A328

POWELL, Tammy, M.P.H., President, St. Anthony Hospital, Oklahoma City, OK, p. A513

POWELL, Traci, Director Human Resources, HEALTHSOUTH Emerald Coast Rehabilitation Hospital, Panama City, FL, p. A139

POWELL, Troy, Chief Executive Officer, HEALTHSOUTH Rehabilitation Hospital of Charleston, Charleston, SC, p. A558

POWELL, Virginia, Director Finance, Wilmington Treatment Center, Wilmington, NC, p. A470

POWELL-STAFFORD, Valerie L., Chief Operating Officer, Blake Medical Center, Bradenton, FL, p. A122

POWELSON, Jeffrey A., Chief Executive Officer, Broaddus Hospital, Philippi, WV, p. A694

POWER, Bob, Vice President Information Services, Good Samaritan Regional Medical Center, Corvallis, OR, p. A520

POWER, Robert
    Vice President Information Services, Samaritan Lebanon Community Hospital, Lebanon, OR, p. A522
    Chief Information Officer, Samaritan Pacific Communities Hospital, Newport, OR, p. A523
    Associate Executive Director Finance, Southside Hospital, Bay Shore, NY, p. A429

POWERS, Anthony, Vice President Patient Care Services, Baptist Health Corbin, Corbin, KY, p. A255

POWERS, Barbara, R.N. Chief Nursing Officer, Austin Lakes Hospital, Austin, TX, p. A593

POWERS, Brent, M.D. Vice President/Chief Medical Officer, Lexington Medical Center, West Columbia, SC, p. A566

POWERS, Charles, M.D. Administrative Medical Director, WK Bossier Health Center, Bossier City, LA, p. A271

POWERS, Donald, Chairman, President and Chief Executive Officer, Community Healthcare System, Hammond, IN, p. B41

POWERS, Jamekia, Assistant Director Human Resources, Georgia Regional Hospital at Savannah, Savannah, GA, p. A164

POWERS, Judy, Chief Nursing Officer, Singing River Health System, Pascagoula, MS, p. A359

POWERS, Kelli, Chief Financial Officer, Huntsville Hospital, Huntsville, AL, p. A21

POWERS, Marcia, Vice President Human Resources, Norwegian American Hospital, Chicago, IL, p. A183

POWERS, Mary, MS
    Senior Vice President and Chief Nursing Officer, Manchester Memorial Hospital, Manchester, CT, p. A112
    Senior Vice President Patient Care Services, Rockville General Hospital, Vernon, CT, p. A115

POWERS, Ryan J., Vice President Finance, Spectrum Health Zeeland Community Hospital, Zeeland, MI, p. A333

POWERS, Tim, Chief Executive Officer, North Canyon Medical Center, Gooding, ID, p. A174

POWRIE, Raymond, M.D. Senior Vice President Quality and Clinical Effectiveness, Women & Infants Hospital of Rhode Island, Providence, RI, p. A556

POYER, Melinda, D.O. President, Medical Staff, Memorial Hospital of Sweetwater County, Rock Springs, WY, p. A717

POYNTER, Carmen, Director Human Resources, Rockcastle Regional Hospital and Respiratory Care Center, Mount Vernon, KY, p. A263

PRABHU, Asha, M.D. Chief Medical Officer, Warren State Hospital, Warren, PA, p. A552

PRACHT, Matthew, Vice President Finance, Scotland Health Care System, Laurinburg, NC, p. A463

PRADA, Janina
    Director Information Technology, El Paso Children's Hospital, El Paso, TX, p. A610
    Director Information Services, University Medical Center of El Paso, El Paso, TX, p. A611

PRAKASH, Amitabh, M.D. Chief Medical Officer, AHMC Anaheim Regional Medical Center, Anaheim, CA, p. A53

PRANTE, Melissa
    Chief Financial Officer, Kimball Health Services, Kimball, NE, p. A393
    Chief Financial Officer, Melissa Memorial Hospital, Holyoke, CO, p. A105

PRASAD, Siripurapu, Chief of Staff, Harrison Community Hospital, Cadiz, OH, p. A480

PRATER, Marita, MS Vice President Patient Care Services, Sturdy Memorial Hospital, Attleboro, MA, p. A302

PRATER, Marsha A., Ph.D. Senior Vice President and Chief Nursing Officer, Memorial Medical Center, Springfield, IL, p. A201

PRATER, Robin, Director Human Resources, Howard A. Rusk Rehabilitation Center, Columbia, MO, p. A366

PRATHER, Jean, Director of Human Resources, Greene County General Hospital, Linton, IN, p. A215

PRATI, Richard, Chief Executive Officer, Fort Duncan Regional Medical Center, Eagle Pass, TX, p. A609

PRATT, Bailey
    Interim Chief Financial Officer, Lincoln County Health System, Fayetteville, TN, p. A577
    Chief Financial Officer, Saint Thomas Hickman Hospital, Centerville, TN, p. A575

PRATT, Dustin, M.D. Chief of Staff, Childress Regional Medical Center, Childress, TX, p. A600

PRATT, Lisa, Vice President Human Resources, Memorial Hospital of Rhode Island, Pawtucket, RI, p. A555

PRATT, Mary Ellen, FACHE, Chief Executive Officer, St. James Parish Hospital, Lutcher, LA, p. A279

PRATT, Timothy J., M.D. Vice President Medical Affairs and Chief Medical Officer, SSM St. Clare Health Center, Fenton, MO, p. A367

PRATT, Troy, Information Technology Site Director, Covenant Medical Center, Lubbock, TX, p. A629

PRAY, Jan, Coordinator Payroll and Benefits, Kindred Hospital Boston–North Shore, Peabody, MA, p. A310

PRAYWELL, Hunter, Vice President Information Technology and Chief Information Officer, Queen's Medical Center, Honolulu, HI, p. A169

PREAU, William, M.D. Medical Director, Fairway Medical Center, Covington, LA, p. A272

PREMO, Mark, Senior Director HC Intelligence, Providence Portland Medical Center, Portland, OR, p. A524

PRENOT, Traci, Chief Financial Officer, Teton Valley Health Care, Driggs, ID, p. A174

PRENTISS, Kristin, Chief Financial Officer, Specialty Hospital of Central Jersey, Lakewood, NJ, p. A413

PRESCOTT, Tina, Vice President, Hospital Services, Jackson–Madison County General Hospital, Jackson, TN, p. A579

PRESNELL, Elizabeth, Assistant Vice President of Finance, St. Luke's Hospital, Columbus, NC, p. A458

PRESS, Robert, M.D. Chief Medical Officer, NYU Langone Medical Center, New York, NY, p. A443

PRESSER, Jonathan, Vice President Finance and Operations, Norton Audubon Hospital, Louisville, KY, p. A261

PRESSMAN, Eric, D.O. Chair Department of Medicine, Englewood Community Hospital, Englewood, FL, p. A126

PREST, Craig, Director Operation Services, Humboldt General Hospital, Winnemucca, NV, p. A404

PRESTON, Tara
    Director Human Resources, Bingham Memorial Hospital, Blackfoot, ID, p. A172
    Director Human Resources, Mountain River Birthing and Surgery Center, Blackfoot, ID, p. A172

PRESTON, Troy, Director Human Resources, Schuyler Hospital, Montour Falls, NY, p. A437

PRESTRIDGE, Tim, Chief Operating Officer, Terre Haute Regional Hospital, Terre Haute, IN, p. A220

PRESUTTI, John, D.O., Chief Executive Officer, Mayo Clinic Health System in Waycross, Waycross, GA, p. A167

PRETE, Mark, M.D. Vice President Medical Affairs, The Charlotte Hungerford Hospital, Torrington, CT, p. A115

PRETTYMAN, Edgar E., PsyD, Chief Executive Officer, Rock Springs, Georgetown, TX, p. A616

PRETZLAFF, Robert, M.D
    Chief Medical Officer, St. Rose Dominican Hospitals – San Martin Campus, Las Vegas, NV, p. A402
    Chief Medical Officer, St. Rose Dominican Hospitals – Siena Campus, Henderson, NV, p. A401

PREWITT, Connie F., Chief Financial Officer, Billings Clinic, Billings, MT, p. A381

PREWITT, Margaret Elizabeth, Vice President Patient Services and Chief Nursing Officer, St. Catherine Hospital, Garden City, KS, p. A240

PRIBYL, Stephen J., FACHE, Chief Executive Officer, District One Hospital, Faribault, MN, p. A338

PRICE, Bernard J., Assistant Vice President, Medical Center, Navicent Health, Macon, GA, p. A160

PRICE, Ed, R.N. Chief Nursing Officer, Palm Beach Gardens Medical Center, Palm Beach Gardens, FL, p. A138

PRICE, James, Assistant Administrator Finance and Operations, State Hospital South, Blackfoot, ID, p. A172

PRICE, John D., Chief Financial Officer, FirstHealth Richmond Memorial Hospital, Rockingham, NC, p. A467

PRICE, Julie, Chief Financial Officer, Rooks County Health Center, Plainville, KS, p. A249

PRICE, Kelley, R.N. Chief Nursing Officer, Battle Mountain General Hospital, Battle Mountain, NV, p. A400

PRICE, Kevin A.
    Vice President and Chief Operating Officer, Sparrow Clinton Hospital, Saint Johns, MI, p. A329
    Vice President and Chief Operating Officer, Sparrow Ionia Hospital, Ionia, MI, p. A322

PRICE, Kim, Chief Executive Officer, Franklin General Hospital, Hampton, IA, p. A228

PRICE, Larry, Chief Executive Officer, Limestone Medical Center, Groesbeck, TX, p. A617

PRICE, Lawrence, M.D., President and Chief Operating Officer, Butler Hospital, Providence, RI, p. A555

PRICE, Lori, President, Gottlieb Memorial Hospital, Melrose Park, IL, p. A194

PRICE, Lorraine B., Associate Director, Hampton Veterans Affairs Medical Center, Hampton, VA, p. A666

PRICE, Manuel, Director Information Systems, Brookwood Medical Center, Birmingham, AL, p. A16

PRICE, Meredith, Vice President Fiscal Services and Chief Financial Officer, St. Joseph's Hospital Health Center, Syracuse, NY, p. A451

PRICE, Norman M., FACHE, Chief Executive Officer and Administrator, Southwest Health Systems, Mccomb, MS, p. B125

PRICE, Norman M., FACHE, Chief Executive Officer, Southwest Mississippi Regional Medical Center, McComb, MS, p. A357

PRICE, Peggy Cain, Vice President and Chief Operating Officer, Lutheran Medical Center, Wheat Ridge, CO, p. A109

PRICE, Sam, Executive Vice President Finance/Chief Financial Officer, East Alabama Medical Center, Opelika, AL, p. A23

PRICE, Shari, Director Information Services, Baptist Health Louisville, Louisville, KY, p. A260

PRICE, Sheila C., R.N. Chief Nursing Officer/Vice President of Nursing, Angel Medical Center, Franklin, NC, p. A460

PRICE, Shelby, Chief Executive Officer, Louisiana State Hospitals, Baton Rouge, LA, p. B85

PRICE, Tonya, Chief Nursing Officer, Wilson N. Jones Regional Medical Center, Sherman, TX, p. A644

---

PRICE, Walter, Director Information Technology, Newport Hospital and Health Services, Newport, WA, p. A681

PRICE–GHARZEDDINE, Karen, R.N. Chief Nursing Officer and Chief Operating Officer, San Gabriel Valley Medical Center, San Gabriel, CA, p. A89

PRICHARD, Barbara, Assistant Administrator, South Sunflower County Hospital, Indianola, MS, p. A354

PRICKEL, Trisha, Director Information Systems, Margaret Mary Health, Batesville, IN, p. A204

PRIDDY, III, Ernest C., Chief Financial Officer, Old Vineyard Behavioral Health Services, Winston–Salem, NC, p. A471

PRIDDY, Steven L., M.D. Vice President Physician Affairs and Chief Medical Officer, St. Vincent Carmel Hospital, Carmel, IN, p. A206

PRIDEAUX, Heather, Chief Financial Officer, Rawlins County Health Center, Atwood, KS, p. A237

PRIDGEN, Kim, Chief Financial Officer, Northcrest Medical Center, Springfield, TN, p. A588

PRIES, Kathleen M., Director Human Resources, Nazareth Hospital, Philadelphia, PA, p. A544

PRIEST, David, Director Information Systems, Charlevoix Area Hospital, Charlevoix, MI, p. A316

PRIEST, Geoff, M.D. Chief Medical Officer, Meriter UnityPoint Health, Madison, WI, p. A704

PRIEST, Mike, M.D. Chief of Staff, Pawhuska Hospital, Pawhuska, OK, p. A513

PRIESTLEY, Betty, Manager Business Office, Promise Hospital of Houston, Houston, TX, p. A621

PRIESTLEY, Carlos W., Chief Operating Officer, Providence Little Company of Mary Medical Center San Pedro, CA, p. A72

PRINCE, Clay, M.D. Chief Medical Officer, Madison Memorial Hospital, Rexburg, ID, p. A176

PRINCE, Gayle, Director Human Resources, Washington County Regional Medical Center, Sandersville, GA, p. A164

PRINCE, Kem, Manager of Finance, Parkview Noble Hospital, Kendallville, IN, p. A213

PRINCE, Sue, Director Information Systems, Northern Westchester Hospital, Mount Kisco, NY, p. A438

PRINCE, Thomas A., Vice President Human Resources, Northeast Rehabilitation Hospital, Salem, NH, p. A408

PRINCIPE, Hector Cintron, M.D. Director, Hospital Universitario Dr. Ramon Ruiz Arnau, Bayamon, PR, p. A720

PRINGLE, Robert W., M.D. Vice President Medical Affairs and Chief Medical Officer, Glens Falls Hospital, Glens Falls, NY, p. A434

PRINGLE–MILLER, Letitia, Administrative Director, Tuomey Healthcare System, Sumter, SC, p. A565

PRINTY, Wayne, Chief Financial Officer and Senior Vice President Finance, LincolnHealth, Damariscotta, ME, p. A290

PRIORE, Jacqueline, Chief Nursing Officer, Samaritan Hospital, Troy, NY, p. A452

PRISELAC, Thomas M., President and Chief Executive Officer, Cedars–Sinai Medical Center, Los Angeles, CA, p. A69

PRISTER, James R.
President and Chief Executive Officer, RML Specialty Hospital, Chicago, IL, p. A184
President and Chief Executive Officer, RML Specialty Hospital, Hinsdale, IL, p. A191

PRITCHARD, Jason, Chief Financial Officer, Hackensack University Medical Center at Pascack Valley, Westwood, NJ, p. A420

PRITCHARD, Jeff, Chief Executive Officer, SummitRidge Hospital, Lawrenceville, GA, p. A160

PRITCHARD, Joann, Chief Financial Officer, Erie Veterans Affairs Medical Center, Erie, PA, p. A534

PRITCHETT, Greg, Chief Financial Officer, Cuero Community Hospital, Cuero, TX, p. A603

PRITCHETT, Lynette, Chief Executive Officer, Jamestown Regional Medical Center, Jamestown, TN, p. A579

PRITT, Wayne M., Commander, U. S. Air Force Hospital, Hampton, VA, p. A666

PRIVETT, David, Deputy Director, Western New York Children's Psychiatric Center, West Seneca, NY, p. A454

PROBASCO, Brent, Chief Financial Officer, Cass Regional Medical Center, Harrisonville, MO, p. A368

PROBST, Keith, M.D. Chief of Staff, Avera Holy Family Hospital, Estherville, IA, p. A227

PROBST, Nancy, R.N. Chief Nursing Officer, Bigfork Valley Hospital, Bigfork, MN, p. A335

PROCHASKA, Jodi, Chief Financial Officer, Butler County Health Care Center, David City, NE, p. A391

PROCHILO, John F., Chief Executive Officer and Administrator, Northeast Rehabilitation Hospital, Salem, NH, p. A408

PROCHNOW, Bryan, Chief Financial Officer, Matagorda Regional Medical Center, Bay City, TX, p. A596

PROCTOR, Brandy, Director of Nursing, North Star Behavioral Health System, Anchorage, AK, p. A27

PROCTOR, Deborah A., President and Chief Executive Officer, St. Joseph Health, Irvine, CA, p. B127

PROCTOR, George M., Senior Vice President and Executive Director, Woodhull Medical and Mental Health Center, NY, p. A445

PROCTOR, Quinn, Director Human Resources, Claremore Indian Hospital, Claremore, OK, p. A505

PROCTOR, Sandra, R.N. Chief Nurse Executive, Memorial Medical Center, Modesto, CA, p. A75

PROCTOR, Scott, Chief Executive Officer, Safe Haven Hospital of Treasure Valley, Boise, ID, p. A172

PROCTOR, Stephen, Director of Human Resources/Risk, Russellville Hospital, Russellville, AL, p. A24

PROKOSCH, Brian, M.D. Vice President Medical Affairs, St. Francis Regional Medical Center, Shakopee, MN, p. A347

PRONGER, Derk, Chief Operating Officer, Munson Medical Center, Traverse City, MI, p. A331

PRONI, John, CPA Manager Finance, BayCare Alliant Hospital, Dunedin, FL, p. A126

PROPP, Elizabeth R., Vice President Finance and Chief Financial Officer, Dameron Hospital, Stockton, CA, p. A93

PROSKE, Donna, R.N., Executive Director, Staten Island University Hospital, NY, p. A444

PROSKOCIL, Danielle, Director Human Resources, Valley County Health System, Ord, NE, p. A397

PROSPER, Charles
Chief Executive Officer, Alta Bates Summit Medical Center, Berkeley, CA, p. A56
Chief Executive Officer, Alta Bates Summit Medical Center – Summit Campus, Oakland, CA, p. A78

PROSSER, Alita, Chief Financial Officer, Scott & White Memorial Hospital, Temple, TX, p. A647

PROSSER, Edna, Chief Nursing Officer, Ozark Health Medical Center, Clinton, AR, p. A42

PROSSER, Joseph, M.D
Chief Medical Officer, Texas Health Harris Methodist Hospital Fort Worth, Fort Worth, TX, p. A614
Chief Medical Officer, Texas Health Specialty Hospital, Fort Worth, TX, p. A614

PROSTKO, Michael, M.D. Chief of Staff, Rhea Medical Center, Dayton, TN, p. A577

PROUD, James, Vice President Human Resources and Marketing, Uniontown Hospital, Uniontown, PA, p. A551

PROUJANSKY, Roy, M.D., Chief Executive Officer, Alfred I. duPont Hospital for Children, Wilmington, DE, p. A118

PROULX, David R., Assistant Vice President Operations, Valley West Hospital, Sandwich, IL, p. A200

PROVENZANO, Jeff
Vice President and Chief Financial Officer, MidMichigan Medical Center–Clare, Clare, MI, p. A316
Vice President and Chief Financial Officer, MidMichigan Medical Center–Gladwin, Gladwin, MI, p. A320
Vice President and Chief Financial Officer, MidMichigan Medical Center–Gratiot, Alma, MI, p. A314

PROVINCE, Steven, Senior Vice President and Chief Operating Officer, Providence Healthcare Network, Waco, TX, p. A650

PRUESS, Mark, M.D. Chief Medical Staff, Sparta Community Hospital, Sparta, IL, p. A200

PRUETT–BAER, Karen, Senior Nurse Executive, Naval Hospital Oak Harbor, Oak Harbor, WA, p. A681

PRUITT, Jeffrey, M.D. Chief of Staff, Mercy Hospital of Defiance, Defiance, OH, p. A488

PRUITT, Michael W., Administrator and Chief Executive Officer, Coleman County Medical Center, Coleman, TX, p. A601

PRUKOP, Jeff, Director Professional Services, Jackson County Hospital District, Edna, TX, p. A610

PRUNCHUNAS, Edward M., Senior Vice President and Chief Financial Officer, Cedars–Sinai Medical Center, Los Angeles, CA, p. A69

PRUNOSKE, Mark, Chief Financial Officer and Senior Vice President Finance, F. F. Thompson Hospital, Canandaigua, NY, p. A431

PRUSATIS, Michael, Vice President Finance, Sinai–Grace Hospital, Detroit, MI, p. A318

PRYBYLO, Mary, President and Chief Executive Officer, St. Joseph Hospital, Bangor, ME, p. A288

PRYOR, David, President, Athens–Limestone Hospital, Athens, AL, p. A15

PRYOR, Dennis P., Administrator, Salem Memorial District Hospital, Salem, MO, p. A378

PRYOR, Jon, M.D., Chief Executive Officer, Hennepin County Medical Center, Minneapolis, MN, p. A342

PRYOR, Vincent, System Executive Vice President and Chief Financial Officer, Edward Hospital, Naperville, IL, p. A195

PRYOR, William B., Senior Vice President, Human Resources, Cape Fear Valley Medical Center, Fayetteville, NC, p. A460

PRZESTRZELSKI, David, Associate Director, Patient Care Services and Chief Nursing Executive, Charles George Veterans Affairs Medical Center, Asheville, NC, p. A455

PRZYBYLSKI, David, Controller, Sparrow Specialty Hospital, Lansing, MI, p. A324

PSAILA, Justin P., M.D. Vice President Medical Affairs, St. Luke's Hospital – Anderson Campus, Easton, PA, p. A533

PSCODNA, Susan, Director Human Resources, Mercy Hospital of Defiance, Defiance, OH, p. A488

PSHEA, Pam, R.N. Chief Nursing Officer, San Ramon Regional Medical Center, San Ramon, CA, p. A90

PU, Steve, D.O. Chief Medical Officer, Poplar Bluff Regional Medical Center, Poplar Bluff, MO, p. A374

PUCKETT, Clay, Assistant Administrator and Chief Information Officer, Blount Memorial Hospital, Maryville, TN, p. A582

PUCKETT, Frank, M.D. Chief Medical Officer, Pocahontas Memorial Hospital, Buckeye, WV, p. A689

PUCKETT, Kristi, Director Human Resources, Grande Ronde Hospital, La Grande, OR, p. A522

PUCKETT, Steven, Director Information Technology, Central State Hospital, Louisville, KY, p. A261

PUCLIK, Becky, Division Chief People Officer, St. John's Hospital, Springfield, IL, p. A201

PUENTES, Francisco, Human Resource Officer, San Diego County Psychiatric Hospital, San Diego, CA, p. A87

PUFFENBERGER, James, Vice President and Chief Financial Officer, Mercy Hospital of Defiance, Defiance, OH, p. A488

PUFFENBERGER, Jim, Senior Vice President Northern Region and Chief Financial Officer, Mercy St. Charles Hospital, Oregon, OH, p. A495

PUFFENBERGER, Sheila, Manager Information Technology, Hillsdale Community Health Center, Hillsdale, MI, p. A322

PUGH, Larry, Vice President and Chief Financial Officer, Beverly Hospital, Montebello, CA, p. A76

PUGH, Melodee, Director Human Resources, Navarro Regional Hospital, Corsicana, TX, p. A603

PUGH, William H., Senior Vice President Corporate Finance and Chief Financial Officer, Pinnacle Health System, Harrisburg, PA, p. A535

PUGSLEY, Tim, Chief Information Officer, Nebraska Orthopaedic Hospital, Omaha, NE, p. A396

PUHL, Cathy A., Vice President Human Resources, Chambersburg Hospital, Chambersburg, PA, p. A531

PUHY, Dorothy E., Executive VP and Chief Operating Officer, Dana–Farber Cancer Institute, Boston, MA, p. A303

PUKALA, Shirley, R.N. Assistant Administrator Operations, St. Lawrence Rehabilitation Center, Lawrenceville, NJ, p. A413

PULASKI, Jason, Controller, HEALTHSOUTH Reading Rehabilitation Hospital, Reading, PA, p. A548

PULCO, Dominic J., Executive Vice President Finance and Chief Financial Officer, VCU Medical Center, Richmond, VA, p. A672

PULEO, Mark, Vice President and Chief Human Resources Officer, Henry Mayo Newhall Memorial Hospital, Valencia, CA, p. A96

PULIDO, Michael, Chief Administrative Officer, Mosaic Life Care at St. Joseph, Saint Joseph, MO, p. A375

PULLARKAT, Sajit, Chief Executive Officer and Managing Director, Centennial Hills Hospital Medical Center, Las Vegas, NV, p. A401

PULLEN, Connie, R.N. Chief Nursing Officer, Willamette Valley Medical Center, McMinnville, OR, p. A522

PULLIAM, Elizabeth, Chief Financial Officer, Mother Frances Hospital – Jacksonville, Jacksonville, TX, p. A624

PULLIN, Dennis W., FACHE, President, MedStar Harbor Hospital, Baltimore, MD, p. A294

PULLMAN, Debbie, Director Finance, Avera Hand County Memorial Hospital, Miller, SD, p. A569

PULLMAN, Jayson, Chief Executive Officer, Hawarden Regional Healthcare, Hawarden, IA, p. A229

PULSIPHER, Gary W., President and Chief Executive Officer, Mercy Hospital Joplin, Joplin, MO, p. A369

PUNG, Margaret, R.N. Chief Nursing Officer, University of Texas Harris County Psychiatric Center, Houston, TX, p. A622

PUNJABI, Rishab
Chief Financial Officer, Kindred Hospital–La Mirada, La Mirada, CA, p. A66
Chief Financial Officer, Kindred Hospital–New Jersey Morris County, Dover, NJ, p. A411

PURCELL, Terrance J.
Vice President Support Services and Ambulatory Care, Gnaden Huetten Memorial Hospital, Lehighton, PA, p. A538
Vice President Ambulatory Care and Support Services, Palmerton Hospital, Palmerton, PA, p. A542

PURCELL, Terry, Director Information Services, Lea Regional Medical Center, Hobbs, NM, p. A424

PURDY, Bruce, M.D. Chief of Staff, Muleshoe Area Medical Center, Muleshoe, TX, p. A633

PURINGTON, Denise, Vice President and Chief Information Officer, Elliot Hospital, Manchester, NH, p. A407

PURINTON, Sandy, Chief Nursing Officer, Trego County–Lemke Memorial Hospital, Wakeeney, KS, p. A252

PURKIS, Sharon, Chief Executive Officer, Great Lakes Specialty Hospital–Muskegon, Muskegon, MI, p. A326

PUROHIT, Divyesh, M.D. Chief of Staff, Sullivan County Community Hospital, Sullivan, IN, p. A220

PUROHIT, Kumar, Chief Financial Officer, Rockford Center, Newark, DE, p. A117

PUROHIT, Shamb, Chief Financial Officer, Colquitt Regional Medical Center, Moultrie, GA, p. A162

PURRINGTON, Janice, Coordinator Medical Records, Avera Hand County Memorial Hospital, Miller, SD, p. A569

PURSLEY, Roger, Chief Executive Officer, Western Mental Health Institute, Bolivar, TN, p. A574

PURTLE, Mark, M.D
Vice President Medical Affairs, UnityPoint Health – Iowa Methodist Medical Center, Des Moines, IA, p. A226
Vice President Medical Affairs, UnityPoint Health–Iowa Lutheran Hospital, Des Moines, IA, p. A226

PURUSHOTHAM, Sanjay, Executive Director Information Systems, Bon Secours Baltimore Health System, Baltimore, MD, p. A293

PURVANCE, Clint, M.D. Chief Medical Officer, Barton Memorial Hospital, South Lake Tahoe, CA, p. A93

PURVES, Stephen A., FACHE, President and Chief Executive Officer, Maricopa Integrated Health System, Phoenix, AZ, p. A35

PURVIS, Jay, Administrator and Chief Executive Officer, Wabash General Hospital, Mount Carmel, IL, p. A195

PURVIS, Kevin, Chief Information Officer, Community Howard Regional Health, Kokomo, IN, p. A213

PURVIS, Michael L., Chief Executive Officer, Cook Medical Center–A Campus of Tift Regional Medical Center, Adel, GA, p. A149

PURVIS, Mike, Chief Administrative Officer, Sutter Santa Rosa Regional Hospital, Santa Rosa, CA, p. A92

PUSHARD, Roland, Director of Nursing, Riverview Psychiatric Center, Augusta, ME, p. A288

PUSTINA, Karl, Vice President Finance, Upland Hills Health, Dodgeville, WI, p. A699

PUSZKARSKA, Lucyna M., M.D. Medical Director, Riveredge Hospital, Forest Park, IL, p. A188

PUTHOFF, Timothy, Chief Executive Officer, Houston Northwest Medical Center, Houston, TX, p. A620

PUTNAM, Mark, M.D. Medical Director, Haven Behavioral Health of Eastern Pennsylvania, Reading, PA, p. A548

PUTNAM, Maureen M., Director Human Resources, OSS Orthopaedic Hospital, York, PA, p. A554

PUTNAM, Stewart C., Executive Vice President and Chief Operating Officer, Unity Hospital, Rochester, NY, p. A449

PUTNAM, Timothy L., FACHE, President and Chief Executive Officer, Margaret Mary Health, Batesville, IN, p. A204

PUTT, David G., FACHE,
Chief Executive Officer, University of Mississippi Medical Center Grenada, Grenada, MS, p. A353
Chief Executive Officer, University of Mississippi Medical Center Holmes County, Lexington, MS, p. A356

PUU, Linda, Hospital Administrator, Kaiser Permanente Medical Center, Honolulu, HI, p. A168

PUVOGEL, LuAnn, R.N., Administrator, Salina Surgical Hospital, Salina, KS, p. A250

PUYAU, Susan, M.D. Medical Director, Woman's Hospital, Baton Rouge, LA, p. A270

PUZO, Thomas C., President and Chief Operating Officer, Cornerstone of Medical Arts Center Hospital, Fresh Meadows, NY, p. A433

PUZZUTO, David, M.D. Vice President Medical Affairs and Chief Medical Officer, Waterbury Hospital, Waterbury, CT, p. A116

PYE, Irma L.
Chief Human Resource Officer, Valley Baptist Medical Center–Brownsville, Brownsville, TX, p. A599
Senior Vice President and Chief Human Resource Officer, Valley Baptist Medical Center–Harlingen, Harlingen, TX, p. A618

PYGON, Bernard, M.D. Chief Medical Officer, University of Illinois Hospital & Health Sciences System, Chicago, IL, p. A185

PYLE, Diana, Director Human Resources and Executive Assistant to Chief Executive Officer, Cedar County Memorial Hospital, El Dorado Springs, MO, p. A366

PYLE, Julia, R.N. Chief Nursing Officer, Newman Regional Health, Emporia, KS, p. A239

PYLE, Rick, Director Information Systems, Harrisburg Medical Center, Harrisburg, IL, p. A189

PYLE FARRELL, Martha, Vice President Human Resources and General Counsel, Massachusetts Eye and Ear Infirmary, Boston, MA, p. A304

PYNE, Mel
Chief Executive Officer, Candler County Hospital, Metter, GA, p. A161
Chief Executive Officer, Dorminy Medical Center, Fitzgerald, GA, p. A157
Chief Executive Officer, Emanuel Medical Center, Swainsboro, GA, p. A165

PYRAH, Scott, Director Information Systems, St. Luke's Rehabilitation Hospital, Boise, ID, p. A173

## Q

QUACH, Steve, M.D. Chief Medical Officer, Presbyterian–St. Luke's Medical Center, Denver, CO, p. A102

QUACKENBUSH, Kirk, M.D. Chief of Staff, Platte Valley Medical Center, Brighton, CO, p. A100

QUALIA, Leigh Ann, Director Human Resources, Val Verde Regional Medical Center, Del Rio, TX, p. A607

QUALLS, Brenda, Chief Financial Officer, Oconee Regional Medical Center, Milledgeville, GA, p. A161

QUAM, David, M.D. Area Medical Director, Kaiser Permanente Fontana Medical Center, Fontana, CA, p. A61

QUANSTROM, Julie, Director Information Systems, Wilson Medical Center, Neodesha, KS, p. A246

QUARLES, Christopher, M.D. Director Medical Services, Naval Hospital Jacksonville, Jacksonville, FL, p. A129

QUATE, Becky, R.N. Vice President Nursing and Patient Care Services, Iredell Memorial Hospital, Statesville, NC, p. A469

QUATTROCCHI, Robert, President and Chief Executive Officer, Northside Healthcare System, Atlanta, GA, p. B99

QUATTROCCHI, Robert, President and Chief Executive Officer, Northside Hospital, Atlanta, GA, p. A150

QUEBEDEAUX, Jay, Chief Executive Officer, Mena Regional Health System, Mena, AR, p. A48

QUEBODEAUX, Bryce, Chief Executive Officer, Abrom Kaplan Memorial Hospital, Kaplan, LA, p. A276

QUEEN, Sharon H., R.N. Chief Nursing Officer, Clearview Regional Medical Center, Monroe, GA, p. A161

QUENAN, James, M.D. Chief Medical Officer, Amery Hospital and Clinic, Amery, WI, p. A697

QUESNEL, Brenda, R.N. Vice President of Patient Care and Chief Nursing Officer, West Calcasieu Cameron Hospital, Sulphur, LA, p. A286

QUESNEL, Heather Iorio, Director of Nursing, Waldo County General Hospital, Belfast, ME, p. A289

QUICCI, London, Chief Operating Officer, Sinai–Grace Hospital, Detroit, MI, p. A318

QUICHOCHO, Vince, Manager Information Systems, Guam Memorial Hospital Authority, Tamuning, GU, p. A719

QUIGLEY, Scott, Director Information Services, Grays Harbor Community Hospital, Aberdeen, WA, p. A676

QUIGLEY, Stephen J., Chief Executive Officer, Southwood Psychiatric Hospital, Pittsburgh, PA, p. A546

QUILLIN, Gayla, Administrator, Parmer Medical Center, Friona, TX, p. A615

QUIN, Robert, Vice President Finance and Chief Financial Officer, UnityPoint Health – Methodist Proctor, Peoria, IL, p. A198

QUINLAN, Christine, MS Chief Nursing Officer, Alexian Brothers Behavioral Health Hospital, Hoffman Estates, IL, p. A191

QUINLAN, Patrick J., M.D. Chief Executive Officer, Ochsner Medical Center, New Orleans, LA, p. A282

QUINLIVAN, John, Chief Executive Officer, Redmond Regional Medical Center, Rome, GA, p. A163

QUINLIVAN, Kathy, Director Management Information Systems, Avera Sacred Heart Hospital, Yankton, SD, p. A573

QUINN, Brian, D.O. Chief Medical Officer, Ottumwa Regional Health Center, Ottumwa, IA, p. A233

QUINN, Clifton, Chief Executive Officer, Regency Hospital of Meridian, Meridian, MS, p. A357

QUINN, Donna, Vice President Operations and Quality, Driscoll Children's Hospital, Corpus Christi, TX, p. A602

QUINN, Jennifer, Quality and Safety Coordinator, Shawano Medical Center, Shawano, WI, p. A710

QUINN, John A.
Chief Executive Officer, Spalding Regional Medical Center, Griffin, GA, p. A158
Chief Executive Officer, Sylvan Grove Hospital, Jackson, GA, p. A159

QUINN, Judith, Vice President Patient Care Services, Cape Cod Hospital, Hyannis, MA, p. A307

QUINN, Mary Anna, Vice President, St. Jude Children's Research Hospital, Memphis, TN, p. A584

QUINN, Paul, Information Systems Manager, Kern Valley Healthcare District, Lake Isabella, CA, p. A67

QUINONES, Kathleen
Interim Vice President Finance, Berkeley Medical Center, Martinsburg, WV, p. A693
Interim Vice President Finance, Jefferson Medical Center, Ranson, WV, p. A694

QUINONES, Yolanda, Director Finance, I. Gonzalez Martinez Oncologic Hospital, PR, p. A724

QUINONEZ, Yolanda, Chief Financial Officer, Hospital de la Universidad de Puerto Rico/Dr. Federico Trilla, Carolina, PR, p. A720

QUINT–BOUZID, Marjorie, Chief Nursing Officer and Vice President Patient Care Services, Fort Washington Medical Center, Oxen Hill, MD, p. A299

QUINTANA, Francisco, Warden, Federal Medical Center, Lexington, KY, p. A259

QUINTANA, Jay, Vice President Operations, Cornerstone Hospital–West Monroe, West Monroe, LA, p. A286

QUINTANA, Sonya, R.N. Chief Nursing Officer, Osceola Regional Medical Center, Kissimmee, FL, p. A130

QUINTO, Mike, Chief Information Officer, Watauga Medical Center, Boone, NC, p. A456

QUINTON, Byron, Chief Executive Officer, Clarion Hospital, Clarion, PA, p. A531

QUINTON, J. Ben, Administrator, William Newton Hospital, Winfield, KS, p. A253

QUINTYNE, Stephen, Chief Executive Officer, The Vines, Ocala, FL, p. A137

QUIRICONI, Stephan F.
Vice President Finance, Bon Secours Memorial Regional Medical Center, Mechanicsville, VA, p. A668
Chief Financial Officer, Bon Secours St. Mary's Hospital, Richmond, VA, p. A671

QUIRKE, David, Vice President Information Services, Frederick Memorial Hospital, Frederick, MD, p. A298

QUIST, Ryan, Administrative Assistant, Orchard Hospital, Gridley, CA, p. A64

QUITO, Arturo L., M.D. Chief of Staff, Erlanger Bledsoe Hospital, Pikeville, TN, p. A587

## R

RAAUM, Elizabeth, Manger Business Office, Roosevelt Medical Center, Culbertson, MT, p. A382

RAB, Shafiq, Chief Information Officer, Orange Regional Medical Center, Middletown, NY, p. A437

RABAGO, Janie, Chief Accountant, San Antonio State Hospital, San Antonio, TX, p. A642

RABE, Robbie G., Interim Chief Executive Officer, Seton Smithville Regional Hospital, Smithville, TX, p. A644

RABIDEAU, Ray, M.D. Senior Vice President and Chief Medical Officer, Memorial Hospital, North Conway, NH, p. A408

RABIN, Barry, M.D. Medical Director, Linden Oaks Hospital, Naperville, IL, p. A195

RABINE, Traci, Vice President Clinic Operations, Prairie Lakes Healthcare System, Watertown, SD, p. A572

RABNER, Barry S., President and Chief Executive Officer, University Medical Center of Princeton at Plainsboro, Plainsboro, NJ, p. A417

RABOIN, Kirk, Chief Administrative Officer, PeaceHealth St. John Medical Center, Longview, WA, p. A680

RABON, Catherine, M.D. Chief Medical Officer, Clarendon Memorial Hospital, Manning, SC, p. A563

RABORN, Janelle, Chief Operating Officer, Lovelace Women's Hospital, Albuquerque, NM, p. A422

RACHAL, I. M., Chief Fiscal Service, South Texas Veterans Health Care System, San Antonio, TX, p. A642

RACHUIG, Sue, Director Information Services, Tulane Medical Center, New Orleans, LA, p. A282

RACKLIFFE, David, Assistant Vice President Information Services, Bristol Hospital, Bristol, CT, p. A111

RACZEK, James, M.D. Sr. Vice President of Operations and Chief Medical Officer, Eastern Maine Medical Center, Bangor, ME, p. A288

RADANDT, Jeremiah, Chief Financial Officer, Primary Children's Hospital, Salt Lake City, UT, p. A658

RADCLIFF, Joey, Chief Financial Officer, Five Rivers Medical Center, Pocahontas, AR, p. A50

RADCLIFFE, Eric, M.D. Medical Director, United Hospital Center, Bridgeport, WV, p. A689

RADCLIFFE, Kerry, JD Chief Nursing Officer, Central Texas Rehabilitation Hospital, Austin, TX, p. A594

RADEMACHER, Frank
Senior Director Information Systems, St. Joseph Mercy Ann Arbor, Ypsilanti, MI, p. A333
Director, Information Systems, St. Joseph Mercy Livingston Hospital, Howell, MI, p. A322

RADENHEIMER, Tony, Network Administrator, River Park Hospital, Huntington, WV, p. A692

RADER, Herbert, M.D. Advisor for Medical Affairs, New York Community Hospital, NY, p. A442

RADER, Michael E., M.D. Vice President and Medical Director, Nyack Hospital, Nyack, NY, p. A446

RADFORD, Jeffrey, Chief Nursing Officer, Select Specialty Hospital–Tri Cities, Bristol, TN, p. A574

RADKE, Erma, Director of Operations, Oakleaf Surgical Hospital, Eau Claire, WI, p. A700

RADKE, Sam, Interim Chief Executive Officer and Interim Chief Financial Officer, St. Vincent General Hospital District, Leadville, CO, p. A106

Index of Health Care Professionals

Index of Health Care Professionals / Radner

RADNER, Allen, M.D. Chief Medical Officer, Salinas Valley Memorial Healthcare System, Salinas, CA, p. A85
RADOTICH, Maureen, Director Human Resources, Providence Valdez Medical Center, Valdez, AK, p. A29
RADTKE, Lisa, Chief Administrative Officer, Winneshiek Medical Center, Decorah, IA, p. A226
RADU, Oana, Chief Executive Officer, Summit Oaks Hospital, Summit, NJ, p. A418
RADUNSKY, Daniel, M.D. Medical Staff President, Union County General Hospital, Clayton, NM, p. A423
RADZEVICH, Jason, Vice President Finance, Beth Israel Deaconess Hospital Plymouth, Plymouth, MA, p. A310
RADZIESKI, Shauna, Chief Executive Officer, Roxbury Treatment Center, Shippensburg, PA, p. A550
RAETHEL, Kathryn A., M.P.H., President and Chief Executive Officer, Castle Medical Center, Kailua, HI, p. A169
RAETZ, Elizabeth A., R.N. Vice President Nursing and Chief Nursing Officer, CHI Health St Elizabeth, Lincoln, NE, p. A393
RAFALA, Paula, Director, Human Resources, Memorial Medical Center, Modesto, CA, p. A75
RAFFERTY, Joyce, Vice President Finance, The University of Vermont Health Network–Champlain Valley Physicians Hospital, Plattsburgh, NY, p. A447
RAFFERTY, Patrick W., Executive Vice President and Chief Operating Officer, Community Regional Medical Center, Fresno, CA, p. A62
RAFFETY, Leannette, Administrative Generalist, Stroud Regional Medical Center, Stroud, OK, p. A515
RAFFOUL, John, Senior Vice President Finance, White Memorial Medical Center, Los Angeles, CA, p. A73
RAFFOUL, John G., President, White Memorial Medical Center, Los Angeles, CA, p. A73
RAFUS, Matthew, Chief Information Officer, White River Junction Veterans Affairs Medical Center, White River Junction, VT, p. A661
RAGAIN, Michael, M.D
Chief Medical Officer, Texas Specialty Hospital at Lubbock, Lubbock, TX, p. A630
Chief Medical Officer and Senior Vice President, University Medical Center, Lubbock, TX, p. A630
RAGAR–THOMAS, Twila, Director Health Information Management and Quality Improvement, Timberlawn Mental Health System, Dallas, TX, p. A607
RAGAS, Rene, Chief Operating Officer, Our Lady of the Angels Hospital, Bogalusa, LA, p. A270
RAGER, Claudia, R.N. Vice President Patient Care Services, Conemaugh Memorial Medical Center, Johnstown, PA, p. A537
RAGGIO, James J., Chief Executive Officer, Lompoc Valley Medical Center, Lompoc, CA, p. A68
RAGGIO, Sharon, President and Chief Executive Officer, West Springs Hospital, Grand Junction, CO, p. A104
RAGLE, Bertha, Director Personnel, CrossRidge Community Hospital, Wynne, AR, p. A52
RAGONA, Robert A., Vice President Finance, Eastern Long Island Hospital, Greenport, NY, p. A434
RAGSDALE, Jill M., Chief Human Resources Officer, Mayo Clinic Hospital – Rochester, Rochester, MN, p. A345
RAGSDALE, Sarah, R.N. Chief Nursing Officer, Smith County Memorial Hospital, Smith Center, KS, p. A250
RAGSDALE, Teri, Chief Nursing Officer, Parkland Health Center – Weber Road, Farmington, MO, p. A367
RAHAMAN, Sheer, M.D. Chief of Medical Staff, Limestone Medical Center, Groesbeck, TX, p. A617
RAHDERT, Richard, M.D. Medical Director, River Bend Hospital, West Lafayette, IN, p. A221
RAHMAN, Randy
Chief Information Officer, Miami County Medical Center, Paola, KS, p. A248
Vice President and Chief Information Officer, Olathe Medical Center, Olathe, KS, p. A247
RAHMAN, Syed, M.D. Chief of Staff, Horizon Specialty Hospital, Las Vegas, NV, p. A402
RAHN, Douglas L., President and Chief Executive Officer, Passavant Area Hospital, Jacksonville, IL, p. A191
RAHN, Kevin, President Medical Staff, Orthopaedic Hospital of Lutheran Health Network, Fort Wayne, IN, p. A208
RAICA, Dagmar, R.N. Chief Nursing Officer, UP Health System–Marquette, Marquette, MI, p. A325
RAINA, Suresh, M.D. Vice President Medical Staff and Chief Medical Officer, Palisades Medical Center, North Bergen, NJ, p. A416
RAINBOLT, Mike, Chief Financial Officer, Rivendell Behavioral Health Services of Arkansas, Benton, AR, p. A41
RAINEY, Jackie, Chief Financial Officer, Little River Memorial Hospital, Ashdown, AR, p. A41
RAINEY, Mark J., Director Human Resources, Texas Health Presbyterian Hospital Kaufman, Kaufman, TX, p. A625
RAINS, Celeste, D.O. Chief of Staff, Logan County Hospital, Oakley, KS, p. A247
RAINS, Debbie, Coordinator Health Information Management, Erlanger Bledsoe Hospital, Pikeville, TN, p. A587
RAINS, Della, Chief Nursing Officer, ContinueCare Hospital at Baptist Health Corbin, Corbin, KY, p. A255
RAINS, Gail, R.N. Director Patient Care Services, Shriners Hospitals for Children–Shreveport, Shreveport, LA, p. A285
RAINS, Jeff G., Chief Executive Officer, Baptist Medical Center East, Montgomery, AL, p. A22
RAINS, Jon Michael, Chief Executive Officer, Carrus Specialty Hospital, Sherman, TX, p. A644
RAINS, Paul, MSN, President, St. Joseph's Behavioral Health Center, Stockton, CA, p. A93
RAINS, Steve, Director Information Services, McKee Medical Center, Loveland, CO, p. A107
RAISNER, Gary, Chief Operating Officer, Norristown State Hospital, Norristown, PA, p. A542
RAJ, James, M.D. Chief Medical Officer, Wellmont Lonesome Pine Hospital, Big Stone Gap, VA, p. A662
RAJKUMAR, Anthony, Executive Director, Metropolitan Hospital Center, New York, NY, p. A441
RAJPARA, Suresh, M.D. Chief Medical Officer, Jerome Golden Center for Behavioral Health, Inc., West Palm Beach, FL, p. A147
RAJU, Ramanathan, M.D., President, New York City Health and Hospitals Corporation, New York, NY, p. B96
RAK, Roger, Director Human Resources, South Shore Hospital, Chicago, IL, p. A184
RAK, Ronald C., JD, Chief Executive Officer, Saint Peter's University Hospital, New Brunswick, NJ, p. A415
RAKES, Lori, Chief Operating Officer, Cartersville Medical Center, Cartersville, GA, p. A153
RAKES–STEPHENS, Kim, M.D. Chief Medical Staff, Colleton Medical Center, Walterboro, SC, p. A565
RAKOV, Robert, M.D. Chief Medical Officer, Cogdell Memorial Hospital, Snyder, TX, p. A644
RALPH, Chandler M., President and Chief Executive Officer, Adirondack Medical Center, Saranac Lake, NY, p. A450
RALPH, Stephen A., President and Chief Executive Officer, Huntington Memorial Hospital, Pasadena, CA, p. A80
RALSTIN, Char, Director of Nursing, Haven Senior Horizons, Phoenix, AZ, p. A35
RALSTON, Mary Beth, Human Resources Director, North Georgia Medical Center, Ellijay, GA, p. A157
RAMAGE, Debra, Director Human Resources and Payroll, Cornerstone Hospital of SouthEast Arizona, Tucson, AZ, p. A39
RAMAGE, Gary, M.D. Chief Medical Officer, McKenzie County Healthcare System, Watford City, ND, p. A477
RAMAN, Jayashree, Vice President and Chief Information Officer, Reading Hospital, West Reading, PA, p. A553
RAMAN, Reggie, M.D. Medical Director, Peninsula Hospital, Louisville, TN, p. A582
RAMAZANI, Regina, Chief Financial Officer, Garden Park Medical Center, Gulfport, MS, p. A353
RAMER, Gary, Manager Information Management, Jonathan M. Wainwright Memorial Veterans Affairs Medical Center, Walla Walla, WA, p. A687
RAMEY, Rita, Director Information Systems, Buchanan General Hospital, Grundy, VA, p. A665
RAMEY, Robert L., Interim President, Baptist Health Madisonville, Madisonville, KY, p. A262
RAMEY, Steve, Chief Financial Officer, Southampton Memorial Hospital, Franklin, VA, p. A665
RAMIREZ, Arthur L., M.D. Medical Director, University Behavioral Health of El Paso, El Paso, TX, p. A611
RAMIREZ, Corazon, M.D., Chief Executive Officer, Pine Creek Medical Center, Dallas, TX, p. A606
RAMIREZ, Eddy, Assistant Vice President Business Development, Ochsner Medical Center – Kenner, Kenner, LA, p. A276
RAMIREZ, Harvey, Chief Information Officer, Coleman County Medical Center, Coleman, TX, p. A601
RAMIREZ, Jaime, Chief Executive Officer, McCamey County Hospital District, McCamey, TX, p. A631
RAMIREZ, Marcos A., Human Resources Business Partner, Baylor Medical Center at Waxahachie, Waxahachie, TX, p. A650
RAMIREZ, Omar, Chief Executive Officer, Los Angeles Community Hospital at Los Angeles, Los Angeles, CA, p. A71
RAMIREZ, Susan, Chief Nursing Officer, HEALTHSOUTH Rehabilitation Hospital–Las Vegas, Las Vegas, NV, p. A402
RAMIREZ, Willie, Manager Labor Relations, Laguna Honda Hospital and Rehabilitation Center, San Francisco, CA, p. A88
RAMLO, Ricki, Chief Operating Officer and Vice President Operations, Jamestown Regional Medical Center, Jamestown, ND, p. A475
RAMM, Crystal, Administrator, Grady General Hospital, Cairo, GA, p. A153
RAMMLER, Linda, R.N. Chief Nursing Officer, Bonner General Hospital, Sandpoint, ID, p. A176
RAMOS, Eduardo, M.D. Medical Director, HEALTHSOUTH Rehabilitation Hospital of San Juan, San Juan, PR, p. A723
RAMOS, Eric, M.D. Division Chief Medical Officer, Southern Hills Hospital and Medical Center, Las Vegas, NV, p. A402
RAMOS, Gracie, Human Resource Generalist, East Morgan County Hospital, Brush, CO, p. A100
RAMOS, Holly, R.N. Chief Clinical Officer, Kindred Hospital–Ontario, Ontario, CA, p. A79
RAMOS, Jessie, Manager Human Resources, Skyline Hospital, White Salmon, WA, p. A687
RAMOS, Jet, Head Staff Administration, Naval Hospital Camp Pendleton, Camp Pendleton, CA, p. A57
RAMOS, Walter J., ESQ President and Chief Executive Officer, Carney Hospital, Boston, MA, p. A303
RAMPAT, Ananda, Chief Financial Officer, Northwest Medical Center, Margate, FL, p. A133
RAMPP, Randal D., M.D. Chief Medical Officer, Saint Thomas River Park Hospital, Mc Minnville, TN, p. A582
RAMSAY, Kathy, R.N. Director Communications and Development, Rooks County Health Center, Plainville, KS, p. A249
RAMSEY, Alice, M.D. Chief of Staff, Palo Pinto General Hospital, Mineral Wells, TX, p. A632
RAMSEY, David L., President and Chief Executive Officer, Charleston Area Medical Center, Charleston, WV, p. A690
RAMSEY, Lisa, Chief Financial Officer, Prairie View, Newton, KS, p. A246
RAMSEY, Lorie N., MSN Chief Nursing Executive, Merit Health Central, Jackson, MS, p. A355
RAMSEY, Paul G., M.D., Chief Executive Officer, UW Medicine, Seattle, WA, p. B149
RAMSEY, Rance, Chief Operating Officer, Martin County Hospital District, Stanton, TX, p. A645
RAMSEY, Roy M., Executive Director, Bradford Health Services at Warrior Lodge, Warrior, AL, p. A26
RAMSEY, Thomas, Chief Financial Officer, Hancock Medical Center, Bay Saint Louis, MS, p. A350
RAMTHUN, Jane, Chief Financial Officer, Story County Medical Center, Nevada, IA, p. A232
RAND, Kevin, M.D. Clinical Director, Chinle Comprehensive Health Care Facility, Chinle, AZ, p. A30
RANDALL, Bryan J.
Vice President Finance and Chief Financial Officer, Heritage Valley Health System, Beaver, PA, p. A529
Vice President Finance and Chief Financial Officer, Sewickley Valley Hospital, (A Division of Valley Medical Facilities), Sewickley, PA, p. A550
RANDALL, Cherry, Business Officer, Greater Binghamton Health Center, Binghamton, NY, p. A429
RANDALL, Kenneth W., Chief Executive Officer, Artesia General Hospital, Artesia, NM, p. A423
RANDLE, Emily, Vice President Operations, Orange Coast Memorial Medical Center, Fountain Valley, CA, p. A62
RANDOLPH, Arianne, Director Human Resources, Pikes Peak Regional Hospital, Woodland Park, CO, p. A109
RANDOLPH, Bonnie, M.D. Chief of Staff, Community Hospital, Torrington, WY, p. A718
RANDOLPH, Bruce, Chief Information Technology, Arizona State Hospital, Phoenix, AZ, p. A34
RANDOLPH, Daylashunta
Vice President Human Resources, Advocate South Suburban Hospital, Hazel Crest, IL, p. A190
Senior Vice President Human Resources, Advocate Trinity Hospital, Chicago, IL, p. A181
RANDOLPH, Geoffrey, M.D. Chief Medical Officer, Lutheran Hospital of Indiana, Fort Wayne, IN, p. A208
RANDOLPH, Joseph, M.D. Chairman Medical Executive Committee, Indiana Orthopaedic Hospital, Indianapolis, IN, p. A211
RANDOLPH, Karsten, Executive Vice President and Chief Financial Officer, Shawnee Mission Medical Center, Shawnee Mission, KS, p. A250
RANDOLPH, Jr., Leonard M., M.D. Senior Vice President and Chief Medical Officer, Mercy Health – Anderson Hospital, Cincinnati, OH, p. A483
RANDOLPH, Linda, Director Personnel Services, Washington County Hospital, Chatom, AL, p. A18
RANEY, Hollie, Director of Nursing, Dallas County Medical Center, Fordyce, AR, p. A44
RANGAVIZ, Rassoul, Chief Financial Officer, Copley Hospital, Morrisville, VT, p. A660
RANGE, Bonny, MSN Chief Nursing Officer, Holy Family Memorial, Manitowoc, WI, p. A704
RANGHELLI, Gloria, Deputy Chief Financial Officer, Henry J. Carter Specialty Hospital and Nursing Facility, New York, NY, p. A440
RANKIN, Beverley A., R.N. Vice President & Chief Nursing Officer, Alice Peck Day Memorial Hospital, Lebanon, NH, p. A406

**A946** Index of Health Care Professionals

Index of Health Care Professionals / Rector

Index of Health Care Professionals

RANKIN, Cynthia, Chief Nursing Officer, Lovelace Rehabilitation Hospital, Albuquerque, NM, p. A422
RANKIN, Kim, Chief Nursing Officer, Geisinger HEALTHSOUTH Rehabilitation Hospital, Danville, PA, p. A532
RANNEY, Timothy, M.D. Chief Medical Officer, Banner Estrella Medical Center, Phoenix, AZ, p. A34
RANSOM, Jim, Chief Executive Officer, Reliant Rehabilitation Hospital North Texas, Richardson, TX, p. A638
RANSOM, Natalie, Chief Nursing Officer, MountainView Hospital, Las Vegas, NV, p. A402
RANTZ III, August J., Founder and Chief Executive Officer, AMG Integrated Healthcare Management, Lafayette, LA, p. B10
RAO, Gutti, M.D. Medical Director, AMG Specialty Hospital–Greenwood, Greenwood, MS, p. A353
RAO, Kalapala, M.D. Medical Director, HEALTHSOUTH Western Hills Regional Rehabilitation Hospital, Parkersburg, WV, p. A694
RAO, Noel, M.D. Medical Director, Marianjoy Rehabilitation Hospital, Wheaton, IL, p. A203
RAO, Raghu, M.D. Chief of Staff, Helen Newberry Joy Hospital, Newberry, MI, p. A327
RAPENSKE, Jennifer, Manager Financial Services, Mercy Medical Center–New Hampton, New Hampton, IA, p. A232
RAPP, Catherine, R.N. Vice President Nursing, Oconomowoc Memorial Hospital, Oconomowoc, WI, p. A708
RAPP, David, Chief Information Officer, Wheeling Hospital, Wheeling, WV, p. A696
RAPP, Peter F., Executive Vice President and Executive Director, OHSU Hospital, Portland, OR, p. A524
RAPP, Ron, Controller, Cole Memorial, Coudersport, PA, p. A532
RAPPACH, Shannon, Chief Fiscal Services, Dayton Veterans Affairs Medical Center, Dayton, OH, p. A488
RAPPLEY, Marsha, M.D., Chief Executive Officer and Vice President for Health Sciences, VCU Health System, Richmond, VA, p. B149
RASCHKE, Judy, Director Human Resources, Pipestone County Medical Center Avera, Pipestone, MN, p. A344
RASHFORD, Jennifer, Manager Human Resources, LifeCare Hospitals of Mechanicsburg, Mechanicsburg, PA, p. A540
RASHID, Harun, Chief Information Officer, Magee–Womens Hospital of UPMC, Pittsburgh, PA, p. A546
RASK, Brenda, Vice President Operations, Carrington Health Center, Carrington, ND, p. A472
RASKE, Jamie, Information Technology Lead, Avera St. Mary's Hospital, Pierre, SD, p. A570
RASMUSSEN, Cassie, M.D. Chief Medical Officer, Adair County Memorial Hospital, Greenfield, IA, p. A228
RASMUSSEN, David, Chief Executive Officer, Memorial Hospital of Texas County, Guymon, OK, p. A507
RASMUSSEN, Diane, Director Human Resources, Cambridge Medical Center, Cambridge, MN, p. A336
RASMUSSEN, Jeanell, R.N. Senior Vice President and Chief Nursing Officer, Harrison Medical Center, Bremerton, WA, p. A676
RASMUSSEN, Kyle R., Chief Executive Officer, Meeker Memorial Hospital, Litchfield, MN, p. A341
RASMUSSEN, Rick, Chief Financial Officer, Northwest Specialty Hospital, Post Falls, ID, p. A176
RASMUSSEN, Scott, Director Human Resources, Lincoln Regional Center, Lincoln, NE, p. A394
RASMUSSON, Duane, Vice President Human Resources, St. Cloud Hospital, Saint Cloud, MN, p. A345
RASOOL, Chaudri, D.O. Chief of Staff, Palmer Lutheran Health Center, West Union, IA, p. A236
RASOR, Linda, R.N., Chief Executive Officer, Plains Memorial Hospital, Dimmitt, TX, p. A609
RASSIER, Mark, M.D. President Howard Young Medical Center Staff, Howard Young Medical Center, Woodruff, WI, p. A714
RASTER, Robert, M.D. Medical Director, Michiana Behavioral Health Center, Plymouth, IN, p. A218
RATAJ, Marianne, R.N. Chief Nursing Officer, Mercy Hospital Fort Smith, Fort Smith, AR, p. A44
RATCLIFF, David, M.D. Chief Medical Affairs, Washington Regional Medical Center, Fayetteville, AR, p. A44
RATCLIFF, Paul, Director Information Services, Baylor Medical Center at Carrollton, Carrollton, TX, p. A600
RATCLIFFE, Alma, M.D. Executive Vice President Medical Staff and Business Development, Saint Clare's Health System, Denville, NJ, p. A411
RATCLIFFE, Denise, Executive Vice President and Chief Operating Officer, Christian Health Care Center, Wyckoff, NJ, p. A421
RATHBUN, Lori, Chief Executive Officer, Van Diest Medical Center, Webster City, IA, p. A236
RATHBUN, Paula, Director of Nursing, Oakland Mercy Hospital, Oakland, NE, p. A395
RATLIFF, Ada, Chief Information Officer, Claiborne County Medical Center, Port Gibson, MS, p. A359
RATLIFF, Kim, Director Health Information Management, Southwestern Virginia Mental Health Institute, Marion, VA, p. A668
RATLIFF, Maggie, Vice President Information Systems, Sarah Bush Lincoln Health Center, Mattoon, IL, p. A193
RATLIFF, Steve, Director Information Technology, Guadalupe Regional Medical Center, Seguin, TX, p. A643
RATNER, Jeffrey, M.D. Senior Vice President Medical Affairs, Mount Nittany Medical Center, State College, PA, p. A550
RATTRAY, Cindy Stewart, Director Human Resources, Jewish Hospital–Shelbyville, Shelbyville, KY, p. A266
RAU, John, President and Chief Executive Officer, Stevens Community Medical Center, Morris, MN, p. A343
RAU, Robin, Chief Executive Officer, Miller County Hospital, Colquitt, GA, p. A154
RAUCH, Scott C., Vice President Human Resources, Reid Health, Richmond, IN, p. A219
RAUCH, Scott L., M.D., President, McLean Hospital, Belmont, MA, p. A302
RAUH, Bradley W., Vice President, Chief Operating Officer, Southwest General Health Center, Middleburg Heights, OH, p. A494
RAUH, Cindy, R.N. Vice President and Chief Nursing Officer, Duncan Regional Hospital, Duncan, OK, p. A505
RAUNER, Mary Ellen, R.N. Chief Nursing Officer, Mercy Suburban Hospital, Norristown, PA, p. A541
RAUPERS, Debra, MSN Chief Nursing Officer, Corning Hospital, Corning, NY, p. A432
RAVELING, Lynn, Chief Financial Officer, Pocahontas Community Hospital, Pocahontas, IA, p. A233
RAVLIN, Suzanne M., Senior Director Human Resources and Quality, Katherine Shaw Bethea Hospital, Dixon, IL, p. A186
RAWLINGS, Linda, Director Human Resources and Personnel, Three Rivers Hospital, Waverly, TN, p. A589
RAWLINGS, Sheri, Chief Information Officer, San Juan Regional Medical Center, Farmington, NM, p. A424
RAWSON, Richard L., Chief Executive Officer, Loma Linda University Medical Center–Murrieta, Murrieta, CA, p. A77
RAY, Beverly, Director Human Resources, Tennova Healthcare – Dyersburg Regional Hospital, Dyersburg, TN, p. A577
RAY, Brenda, Director Human Resources, Huntsville Memorial Hospital, Huntsville, TX, p. A623
RAY, Denise, President and Chief Executive Officer, Piedmont Mountainside Hospital, Jasper, GA, p. A159
RAY, Diane, R.N. Vice President and Chief Nursing Officer Patient Services, St. Luke's Hospital, Chesterfield, MO, p. A365
RAY, Donald, Vice President Operations, University of Maryland Medical Center Midtown Campus, Baltimore, MD, p. A295
RAY, Dwayne, Chief Financial Officer, Medical Center of McKinney, McKinney, TX, p. A632
RAY, Elaine, Administrator, Choate Mental Health Center, Anna, IL, p. A178
RAY, Evan, FACHE President, St. Vincent's Birmingham, Birmingham, AL, p. A17
RAY, Jerilyn, Manager Human Resources, St. Elizabeth Hospital, Enumclaw, WA, p. A678
RAY, Joel, MSN Vice President and Chief Nursing Officer, Rex Healthcare, Raleigh, NC, p. A467
RAY, Kirk M., Chief Executive Officer, Kosciusko Community Hospital, Warsaw, IN, p. A221
RAY, Lisa, R.N. Vice President Patient Care Services, Murray–Calloway County Hospital, Murray, KY, p. A264
RAY, Marilyn, MSN Chief Nursing Officer, Upson Regional Medical Center, Thomaston, GA, p. A165
RAY, Nancy L., R.N. Executive Vice President, Chief Nursing Executive, University Health System, San Antonio, TX, p. A642
RAY, Rachel, Chief Financial Officer, Unity Medical Center, Grafton, ND, p. A474
RAY, Roger A., M.D. Executive Vice President and Chief Medical Officer, Carolinas Medical Center, Charlotte, NC, p. A457
RAYE, Charles, M.D. Chief Medical Officer, St. Mary–Corwin Medical Center, Pueblo, CO, p. A108
RAYLS, Kim, Director Human Resources, Twin Lakes Regional Medical Center, Leitchfield, KY, p. A259
RAYMER, Chris, R.N
Chief Operating Officer and Chief Nursing Officer, Great River Medical Center, Blytheville, AR, p. A41
Chief Operating Officer and Chief Nursing Officer, South Mississippi County Regional Medical Center, Osceola, AR, p. A49
RAYMOND, Jane, Vice President and Chief Operating Officer, Reston Hospital Center, Reston, VA, p. A671
RAYMOND, Mindy, Vice President Human Resources, Boca Raton Regional Hospital, Boca Raton, FL, p. A122
RAYMOND, Scott, Director Information Systems, Orange Coast Memorial Medical Center, Fountain Valley, CA, p. A62
RAYNER, Evan J., Chief Executive Officer, Madera Community Hospital, Madera, CA, p. A74
RAYNER, Thomas J., Senior Vice President and Chief Operating Officer, Kaweah Delta Medical Center, Visalia, CA, p. A97
RAYNES, Anthony, M.D. Psychiatrist in Chief, Arbour H. R. I. Hospital, Brookline, MA, p. A305
RAYNES, Christy, R.N. Director Clinical Services, Carson Valley Medical Center, Gardnerville, NV, p. A400
RAYNES, Scott
President, Baptist Hospital, Pensacola, FL, p. A139
President, Gulf Breeze Hospital, Gulf Breeze, FL, p. A128
RAYNOR, Robert, Human Resources Director, Park Royal Hospital, Fort Myers, FL, p. A127
RAYUDU, Subbu, M.D. Chief of Staff, Alliance HealthCare System, Holly Springs, MS, p. A354
RAZMIC, Tammy, Associate Administrator Finance and Chief Financial Officer, Inova Mount Vernon Hospital, Alexandria, VA, p. A662
RAZO, Virginia, Chief Executive Officer, Curry General Hospital, Gold Beach, OR, p. A521
REA, Jerry A., Ph.D.,
Superintendent, Osawatomie State Hospital, Osawatomie, KS, p. A247
Superintendent, Parsons State Hospital and Training Center, Parsons, KS, p. A248
Interim Superintendent, Rainbow Mental Health Facility, Kansas City, KS, p. A243
READ, Eddie, Interim Chief Financial Officer, Val Verde Regional Medical Center, Del Rio, TX, p. A607
READ, John, Chief Nursing Officer, Allegiance Specialty Hospital of Greenville, Greenville, MS, p. A353
READ, Paul, R.N. Vice President and Chief Nursing Officer, Springhill Memorial Hospital, Mobile, AL, p. A22
READ, Richard
Chief Financial Officer, Central Florida Regional Hospital, Sanford, FL, p. A142
Chief Financial Officer, Regional Hospital of Jackson, Jackson, TN, p. A579
READER, G. Whitney, M.D. Chief Medical Officer, Kansas Medical Center, Andover, KS, p. A237
REAGAN Jr., James H., Ph.D., Chief Executive Officer, Morris County Hospital, Council Grove, KS, p. A239
REAGAN, Kevin, M.D. Chief Medical Officer, CHI Health Bergan Mercy, Omaha, NE, p. A395
REALE, Kelli, Vice President Human Resources, UPMC McKeesport, McKeesport, PA, p. A539
REAM, Tom, Regional Chief Information Officer, Sutter Auburn Faith Hospital, Auburn, CA, p. A54
REAMER, Roger J., Chief Executive Officer, Memorial Health Care Systems, Seward, NE, p. A398
REAMES, Jim, Director Human Resources, Bayfront Health St. Petersburg, Saint Petersburg, FL, p. A142
REANDEAU, Michael, Chief Information Officer, Mills–Peninsula Health Services, Burlingame, CA, p. A56
REANO, Paul
Chief Executive Officer, Atoka County Medical Center, Atoka, OK, p. A504
Chief Executive Officer, Pushmataha Hospital & Home Health, Antlers, OK, p. A503
REARDON, Jerry, Director Information Systems, Catawba Valley Medical Center, Hickory, NC, p. A462
REASER, Michelle, R.N. Chief Nursing Executive, Lancaster Regional Medical Center, Lancaster, PA, p. A537
REASONER, Vanessa, Chief Executive Officer, Grace Medical Center, Lubbock, TX, p. A629
REAVIS, Mack, M.D., President and Chief Medical Officer, Lakeland Regional Health, Lakeland, FL, p. A131
REBERRY, Darinda, MSN, RN, NEB Interim Chief Executive Officer, Western Missouri Medical Center, Warrensburg, MO, p. A380
REBERRY, Darinda, Chief Nursing Officer, Western Missouri Medical Center, Warrensburg, MO, p. A380
REBLOCK, Kimberly, M.D. Chief Operating Officer, The Children's Home of Pittsburgh, Pittsburgh, PA, p. A546
RECA, Sr., Thomas, Senior Vice President Finance and Chief Financial Officer, Staten Island University Hospital, NY, p. A444
RECH, Eunice A., MSN Chief Clinical Officer and Administrator of Quality Services, Tuality Healthcare, Hillsboro, OR, p. A521
RECHNER, Paula, Chief Medical Officer, War Memorial Hospital, Sault Sainte Marie, MI, p. A330
RECHSTEINER, Hans, M.D. Chief of Staff, Burnett Medical Center, Grantsburg, WI, p. A701
RECKDENWALD, Jeanine, Vice President Human Resources and Support Services, Bristol Hospital, Bristol, CT, p. A111
RECKERT, Sandy, Director Communications and Public Affairs, Johns Hopkins Bayview Medical Center, Baltimore, MD, p. A293
RECTOR, III, Fax, Director Information Technology, Sunbury Community Hospital and Outpatient Center, Sunbury, PA, p. A550


Index of Health Care Professionals A947

Index of Health Care Professionals

Index of Health Care Professionals / Rector

RECTOR, Jeanne, Chief Nursing Officer, Carroll County Memorial Hospital, Carrollton, MO, p. A365
RECUPERO, David, Chief Financial Officer, San Gorgonio Memorial Hospital, Banning, CA, p. A55
REDD, Dakota, R.N. Chief Clinical Officer, Kindred Hospital–St. Louis, Saint Louis, MO, p. A376
REDDEN, Robert, Site Director Information Technology, Community Hospital of San Bernardino, San Bernardino, CA, p. A86
REDDING, Georgia, Director Human Resources, Forbes Regional Hospital, Monroeville, PA, p. A540
REDDING, Lisa, Manager Human Resources, Morgan County ARH Hospital, West Liberty, KY, p. A266
REDDY, Challa, M.D. President Medical Staff, Mayo Regional Hospital, Dover–Foxcroft, ME, p. A290
REDDY, Lex, President and Chief Executive Officer, St. Rose Hospital, Hayward, CA, p. A64
REDDY, Prem, M.D., Interim President and Chief Executive Officer, Prime Healthcare Services, Ontario, CA, p. B107
REDDY, Sunil, Chief Executive Officer, Care Regional Medical Center, Aransas Pass, TX, p. A592
REDFIELD, Gregg, Director Finance, CentraCare Health–Paynesville, Paynesville, MN, p. A344
REDHORSE–CHARLEY, Gloria, Director Human Resources, Northern Navajo Medical Center, Shiprock, NM, p. A426
REDING, Janeen K., Director Human Resources, CHI St. Anthony Hospital, Pendleton, OR, p. A523
REDINGTON, James, M.D. Chief of Staff, Bath Community Hospital, Hot Springs, VA, p. A666
REDMAN, Sharon, Director Patient Care Services, Presbyterian Espanola Hospital, Espanola, NM, p. A424
REDMON, Gary, Chief Financial Officer, South Texas Regional Medical Center, Jourdanton, TX, p. A625
REDMOND, Michael, Senior Vice President and Chief Operating Officer, Crotched Mountain Rehabilitation Center, Greenfield, NH, p. A406
REDMOND, Paula, Controller, HEALTHSOUTH Tustin Rehabilitation Hospital, Tustin, CA, p. A95
REECE, Chuck A., President and Chief Executive Officer, Rush Foundation Hospital, Meridian, MS, p. A357
REECE, Jeff, Interim Chief Executive Officer, Venice Regional Bayfront Health, Venice, FL, p. A146
REECE, Morris A.
  EVP/COO, Laird Hospital, Union, MS, p. A361
  President and Chief Operating Officer, Rush Foundation Hospital, Meridian, MS, p. A357
REECER, Jeff, President, Texas Health Presbyterian Hospital Allen, Allen, TX, p. A590
REED, Cindy, Director Community Relations, Austin State Hospital, Austin, TX, p. A594
REED, Dianne, Director Information Systems, Higgins General Hospital, Bremen, GA, p. A152
REED, Fred, M.D. Chief of Staff, Lincoln Hospital, Davenport, WA, p. A678
REED, Gloria, Leader Human Resources, SSM DePaul Health Center, Bridgeton, MO, p. A364
REED, Helen, Director Health Information, North Mississippi Medical Center–Eupora, Eupora, MS, p. A352
REED, Jason, President and Chief Executive Officer, Oceans Healthcare, Lake Charles, LA, p. B100
REED, John E., M.D. Medical Director, Baptist Memorial Hospital–Golden Triangle, Columbus, MS, p. A352
REED, Karen, R.N
  Chief Nursing Officer, St. Charles Bend, Bend, OR, p. A519
  Chief Nursing Officer, St. Charles Redmond, Redmond, OR, p. A525
REED, Kathleen, Manager Human Resources, Missouri Baptist Sullivan Hospital, Sullivan, MO, p. A379
REED, Kirby, Director Information Systems, Franciscan Health Rensselear, Rensselear, IN, p. A219
REED, Laura, Chief Nursing Officer, University of Minnesota Medical Center, Fairview, Minneapolis, MN, p. A343
REED, Leslie, Chief Financial Officer, Wright Memorial Hospital, Trenton, MO, p. A379
REED, Lester, M.D. Vice President Medical Affairs and Acute Care, MultiCare Mary Bridge Children's Hospital and Health Center, Tacoma, WA, p. A686
REED, Linda
  Vice President and Chief Information Officer, Morristown Medical Center, Morristown, NJ, p. A414
  Vice President Information Systems and Chief Information Officer, Newton Medical Center, Newton, NJ, p. A416
  Vice President and Chief Information Officer, Overlook Medical Center, Summit, NJ, p. A418
REED, Margaret M., R.N. Chief Nursing Executive, Altru Health System, Grand Forks, ND, p. A474
REED, Renee
  Director Human Resources, Via Christi Hospital Manhattan, Inc., KS, p. A245
  Director Human Resources, Wamego Health Center, Wamego, KS, p. A252
REED, Ronald R., President and Chief Executive Officer, Mercy Iowa City, Iowa City, IA, p. A229
REED, Tim, Vice President and Chief Financial Officer, Yakima Valley Memorial Hospital, Yakima, WA, p. A688
REED, Victoria L., FACHE, Chief Executive Officer, James B. Haggin Memorial Hospital, Harrodsburg, KY, p. A258
REEDER, Carol, R.N. Chief Nursing Officer, St. Joseph Hospital, Eureka, CA, p. A60
REEDER, Wendy, R.N. Chief Nursing Officer, Harrison Memorial Hospital, Cynthiana, KY, p. A256
REEDY, James Christopher, Chief Nursing Officer, Sutter Delta Medical Center, Antioch, CA, p. A54
REEDY, Janet, Manager Human Resources, St. Thomas More Hospital, Canon City, CO, p. A100
REEFER, John C., M.D. Director, Butler Health System, Butler, PA, p. A530
REEL, Micah, Director of Bio–Med, Potomac Valley Hospital, Keyser, WV, p. A692
REEL, Stephanie L., Senior Vice President Information Services, Johns Hopkins Hospital, Baltimore, MD, p. A293
REES, Adam, President, Essentia Health St. Joseph's Medical Center, Brainerd, MN, p. A336
REES, Elizabeth, Chief Executive Officer, AMG Specialty Hospital–Albuquerque, Albuquerque, NM, p. A422
REES, Jeff, Director Information Systems, Bacharach Institute for Rehabilitation, Pomona, NJ, p. A417
REESE, Bert
  Chief Information Officer, Sentara Leigh Hospital, Norfolk, VA, p. A669
  Chief Information Officer, Sentara Norfolk General Hospital, Norfolk, VA, p. A669
  Chief Information Officer, Sentara Princess Anne Hospital, Virginia Beach, VA, p. A674
REESE, Jeff, Chief Financial Officer, Howard A. Rusk Rehabilitation Center, Columbia, MO, p. A366
REESE, Kathie
  Interim Administrator, CHRISTUS Dubuis Hospital of Beaumont, Beaumont, TX, p. A596
  Administrator, CHRISTUS Dubuis Hospital of Paris, Paris, TX, p. A635
  Interim Administrator, CHRISTUS Dubuis Hospital of Port Arthur, Port Arthur, TX, p. A637
REESE, Maryann, R.N. Chief Operating Officer, Saint Francis Medical Center, Cape Girardeau, MO, p. A364
REESE, Mike, Chief Financial Officer, OU Medical Center, Oklahoma City, OK, p. A512
REESE, Sandra, Administrator, Lower Umpqua Hospital District, Reedsport, OR, p. A525
REESE, Todd, Director Human Resources, Castle Medical Center, Kailua, HI, p. A169
REESE, Willis L., Administrator, Falls Community Hospital and Clinic, Marlin, TX, p. A631
REESE–GARDNER, Lyle, Interim Chief Executive Officer, Peak Behavioral Health Services, Santa Teresa, NM, p. A426
REETZ, Brenda, FACHE, Chief Executive Officer, Greene County General Hospital, Linton, IN, p. A215
REETZ, Renee, Director Human Resources, St. Mary's of Michigan Standish Hospital, Standish, MI, p. A330
REEVE, Jay A., President and Chief Executive Officer, Eastside Psychiatric Hospital, Tallahassee, FL, p. A144
REEVES, Cory, Chief Financial Officer, Gordon Hospital, Calhoun, GA, p. A153
REEVES, Katy, Vice President Human Resources, Fauquier Hospital, Warrenton, VA, p. A674
REEVES, Kaylene, Director, Tahoe Pacific Hospitals, Sparks, NV, p. A404
REEVES, Mike
  Vice President, St. John Medical Center, Tulsa, OK, p. A517
  Chief Information Officer, St. John Owasso, Owasso, OK, p. A513
REEVES, Pamela J., M.D., Director, John D. Dingell Veterans Affairs Medical Center, Detroit, MI, p. A318
REEVES, Rachel, Manager Human Resources, Post Acute Medical Specialty Hospital of Victoria, Victoria, TX, p. A650
REEVES, Timothy, Administrator, Bucktail Medical Center, Renovo, PA, p. A548
REEVES, Valerie
  Chief Financial Officer, Integris Baptist Regional Health Center, Miami, OK, p. A509
  Chief Financial Officer, Integris Grove Hospital, Grove, OK, p. A507
REFFNER, Gina, Chief Financial Officer, Little Colorado Medical Center, Winslow, AZ, p. A40
REFNESS, Kristen, Chief Financial Officer, Linden Oaks Hospital, Naperville, IL, p. A195
REGAL, Wendy, Director Human Resources, Providence Tarzana Medical Center, CA, p. A72
REGEHR, Stan, President and Chief Executive Officer, Nemaha Valley Community Hospital, Seneca, KS, p. A250
REGEN, Debbie, MS Vice President and Chief Nursing Officer, Saint Clare's Health System, Denville, NJ, p. A411
REGIER, Donald, M.D. Chief Medical Officer, Sedgwick County Health Center, Julesburg, CO, p. A105
REGIER, Marion, Chief Executive Officer, Hillsboro Community Hospital, Hillsboro, KS, p. A241
REGIER, Steve, Chief Financial Officer, Kearney Regional Medical Center, Kearney, NE, p. A393
REGISTER, Stephen, Chief Executive Officer, Greenleaf Center, Valdosta, GA, p. A166
REGULA, John
  Chief Information Officer, Allied Services Rehabilitation Hospital, Scranton, PA, p. A549
  Chief Information Officer, John Heinz Institute of Rehabilitation Medicine, Wilkes–Barre, PA, p. A553
REGULA, Terry, Chief Executive Officer, Aultman Specialty Hospital, Canton, OH, p. A481
REHBEIN, Beth, Chief Nursing and Quality Officer, Story County Medical Center, Nevada, IA, p. A232
REHM, Janice, Manager Human Resources, University of South Alabama Children's and Women's Hospital, Mobile, AL, p. A22
REHM, Micah, Chief Nursing Officer, Forrest General Hospital, Hattiesburg, MS, p. A354
REHN, Lindsay, Executive Director of Financial Operations, WellStar Paulding Hospital, Hiram, GA, p. A159
REHN, Ronald G.
  Chief Executive Officer, Providence Mount Carmel Hospital, Colville, WA, p. A678
  Chief Executive Officer, Providence St. Joseph's Hospital, Chewelah, WA, p. A677
REICH, David L., M.D., President, Mount Sinai Hospital, New York, NY, p. A442
REICH, Joel R., M.D
  Senior Vice President Medical Affairs, Manchester Memorial Hospital, Manchester, CT, p. A112
  Senior Vice President Medical Affairs, Rockville General Hospital, Vernon, CT, p. A115
REICHARD, Steve, Manager Information Systems, Brigham City Community Hospital, Brigham City, UT, p. A654
REICHERT, Don, Vice President Associate Chief Information Officer, MetroHealth Medical Center, Cleveland, OH, p. A485
REICHERT, James, Chief Medical Officer, Mercer Health, Coldwater, OH, p. A485
REICHFIELD, Michael L., President, OhioHealth Doctors Hospital, Columbus, OH, p. A486
REICHLE, Paula, Senior Vice President and Chief Operating Officer, Sparrow Hospital, Lansing, MI, p. A324
REICHMAN, Joseph, M.D. Vice President Medical Affairs and Clinical Effectiveness, Riverview Medical Center, Red Bank, NJ, p. A418
REID, Barbara S., Chief Executive Officer, Willingway Hospital, Statesboro, GA, p. A165
REID, Bernadette, Chief Information Officer, Torrance Memorial Medical Center, Torrance, CA, p. A94
REID, Bev, Chief Financial Officer, St. Luke Hospital and Living Center, Marion, KS, p. A245
REID, Deressa, Interim Chief Executive Officer, Hoag Orthopedic Institute, Irvine, CA, p. A65
REID, Jamie, Information Systems Director, Methodist Hospital, Henderson, KY, p. A258
REID, Jim, Vice President and Chief Information Officer, Covenant Children's Hospital, Lubbock, TX, p. A629
REID, Karl, Chief Information Officer, Minneapolis Veterans Affairs Health Care System, Minneapolis, MN, p. A342
REID, Kelly, Human Resources Director, South Mississippi State Hospital, Purvis, MS, p. A360
REID, Kenneth G., President and Chief Executive Officer, Carlinville Area Hospital, Carlinville, IL, p. A180
REID, Patricia, Director of Nursing, Marion General Hospital, Columbia, MS, p. A352
REID, Richard, Vice President Chief Finance Officer, Sparrow Carson Hospital, Carson City, MI, p. A316
REID, Stephanie, R.N. Vice President of Quality and Chief Nursing Officer, Carroll Hospital Center, Westminster, MD, p. A301
REID, Timothy, M.D. Chief Medical Staff, Carroll County Memorial Hospital, Carrollton, MO, p. A365
REIDER, Rochelle, Vice President Patient Care, Avera Queen of Peace Hospital, Mitchell, SD, p. A570
REIDER, Rodney D., President, Saint Alphonsus Regional Medical Center, Boise, ID, p. A172
REIDER, Stephen, R.N. Director of Nursing, Assistant Vice President Patient Care Services, Walden Psychiatric Care, Waltham, MA, p. A312
REIDY, Margaret, M.D. Vice President Medical Affairs, UPMC Presbyterian Shadyside, Pittsburgh, PA, p. A547

A948 Index of Health Care Professionals 

Index of Health Care Professionals / Reynolds

Index of Health Care Professionals


REIFF, Troy T., Corporate Director Operations, St. Vincent Seton Specialty Hospital, Indianapolis, IN, p. A213
REIFSNYDER, Daniel, M.D. Chief Medical Officer, Geisinger–Lewistown Hospital, Lewistown, PA, p. A539
REILLY, Brian M., Chief Financial Officer, Robert Wood Johnson University Hospital, New Brunswick, NJ, p. A415
REILLY, Dennis A., President and Chief Executive Officer, Little Company of Mary Hospital and Health Care Centers, Evergreen Park, IL, p. A188
REILLY, Jeff
Senior Vice President Operations, Bon Secours Community Hospital, Port Jervis, NY, p. A448
Senior Vice President Operations, St. Anthony Community Hospital, Warwick, NY, p. A453
REILLY, John, M.D. Vice President Medical Affairs and Chief Medical Officer, Mercy Medical Center, Rockville Centre, NY, p. A449
REILLY, Richard, Deputy Executive Director, Syosset Hospital, Syosset, NY, p. A451
REILLY, Robert, Vice President and Chief Financial Officer, Anne Arundel Medical Center, Annapolis, MD, p. A293
REILLY, Theresa, MSN Senior Vice President Patient Services and Chief Nursing Officer, Abington Memorial Hospital, Abington, PA, p. A528
REILLY, Tiffany, Director Human Resources, Childrens Care Hospital and School, Sioux Falls, SD, p. A571
REIMER, Arlo, M.D. Chief of Staff, Kearny County Hospital, Lakin, KS, p. A244
REIMER, Charm, Chief Financial Officer, Western State Hospital, Tacoma, WA, p. A686
REIMER, Randy, Chief Financial Officer, Adventist Behavioral Health Rockville, Rockville, MD, p. A299
REIMER, Ronda, R.N. Chief Nursing Officer and Assistant Administrator, Franklin General Hospital, Hampton, IA, p. A228
REIMERS, Cary, Chief Nurse Executive, CHI Health Creighton University Medical Center, Omaha, NE, p. A395
REIN, Mitchell S., M.D. Chief Medical Officer, North Shore Medical Center, Salem, MA, p. A310
REINART, Greg, Chief Financial Officer, Hereford Regional Medical Center, Hereford, TX, p. A618
REINBOTH, Thomas, Chief Financial Officer, Roxborough Memorial Hospital, Philadelphia, PA, p. A545
REINER, Scott, President and Chief Executive Officer, Adventist Health, Roseville, CA, p. B5
REINERT, Brenda, Director Human Resources, Tomah Memorial Hospital, Tomah, WI, p. A712
REINERT, Chad, Director Information Technology, Hamilton General Hospital, Hamilton, TX, p. A617
REINHARD, Diane, R.N. Vice President of Patient Care Services, Craig Hospital, Englewood, CO, p. A103
REINHARD, James S., M.D., Commissioner, Virginia Department of Mental Health, Richmond, VA, p. B151
REINHARD, Patrick, R.N. Chief Nursing Officer, Desert Valley Hospital, Victorville, CA, p. A96
REINHARD, Russ, Chief Executive, Providence Willamette Falls Medical Center, Oregon City, OR, p. A523
REINHARDT, Randy, Chief of Staff, Greenville Health System – Laurens County Memorial Hospital, Clinton, SC, p. A559
REINHART, Jeffery, M.D. Chief of Staff, Drew Memorial Hospital, Monticello, AR, p. A48
REINKE, Bradley, M.D. Vice President Medical Affairs and Chief Medical Officer, Dameron Hospital, Stockton, CA, p. A93
REINKE, N. Sue, Vice President Human Resources, Geisinger–Lewistown Hospital, Lewistown, PA, p. A539
REINKE, Peggy, R.N., Administrator, CHI Lisbon Health, Lisbon, ND, p. A475
REINKING, Cheryl, R.N. Chief Nursing Officer, El Camino Hospital, Mountain View, CA, p. A77
REISELT, Doug
Vice President and Chief Information Officer, Baptist Memorial Hospital – Memphis, Memphis, TN, p. A583
Vice President and Chief Information Officer, Baptist Memorial Hospital–Collierville, Collierville, TN, p. A576
REISMAN, Ernestine O., Vice President Human Resources, Down East Community Hospital, Machias, ME, p. A291
REISMAN, Ronald, M.D. Chief Medical Director, St. Vincent Seton Specialty Hospital, Indianapolis, IN, p. A213
REISS, Deanna, Hospital Director of Nursing, Devereux Children's Behavioral Health Center, Malvern, PA, p. A539
REISZ, Carol, Chief Financial Officer, North Caddo Medical Center, Vivian, LA, p. A286
REITER, Scott, D.O. Chief of Staff, Scheurer Hospital, Pigeon, MI, p. A327
REITZ, Brent, President, Adventist Rehabilitation Hospital of Maryland, Rockville, MD, p. A300
REITZ, Judy A., Sc.D. Executive Vice President and Chief Operating Officer, Johns Hopkins Hospital, Baltimore, MD, p. A293
REITZ, Robert, Ph.D., Chief Executive Officer, Fulton State Hospital, Fulton, MO, p. A368
REITZEL, David, Chief Information Officer, Brookdale Hospital Medical Center, NY, p. A439
RELPH, Daren, Chief Executive Officer, Wayne County Hospital, Corydon, IA, p. A225
REMALEY, Anne, Vice President Human Resources, ACMH Hospital, Kittanning, PA, p. A537
REMARK, Megan, Chief Executive Officer, Regions Hospital, Saint Paul, MN, p. A346
REMBOLD, Abbey
Human Resources Senior Generalist, Hampshire Memorial Hospital, Romney, WV, p. A695
Human Resources Senior Generalist, War Memorial Hospital, Berkeley Springs, WV, p. A689
REMIGIO, Odalys, Assistant Vice President, Finance, Baptist Health South Florida, West Kendall Baptist Hospital, Miami, FL, p. A134
REMILLARD, Jean D., M.D. Chief Medical Officer/Chief Quality Officer, Lovelace Medical Center, Albuquerque, NM, p. A422
REMILLARD, John R., President, Aurelia Osborn Fox Memorial Hospital, Oneonta, NY, p. A446
REMINGTON, Amanda
Director Human Resources, Spalding Regional Medical Center, Griffin, GA, p. A158
Director Human Resources, Sylvan Grove Hospital, Jackson, GA, p. A159
REMPHER, Kenneth, Ph.D. Chief Nursing Officer, University of Iowa Hospitals and Clinics, Iowa City, IA, p. A230
REMSPECHER, Mark, Director Human Resources, Southeast Missouri Mental Health Center, Farmington, MO, p. A367
REMSTEIN, Robert, D.O. Vice President Medical Affairs, Capital Health Medical Center–Hopewell, Pennington, NJ, p. A416
RENC, William, Chief Fiscal Officer, Summit Park Hospital and Nursing Care Center, Pomona, NY, p. A447
RENDER–LEACH, Cynthia, Director Human Resources, Highland Community Hospital, Picayune, MS, p. A359
RENDON, Eloise, Director Human Resources, Twin Cities Community Hospital, Templeton, CA, p. A94
RENEAU, John D., Medical Director, HEALTHSOUTH Rehabilitation Hospital–Las Vegas, Las Vegas, NV, p. A402
RENEY, Michael, Chief Financial Officer, Brigham and Women's Hospital, Boston, MA, p. A303
RENFREE, Mark, Chief Financial Officer, La Rabida Children's Hospital, Chicago, IL, p. A182
RENIER, Hugh, M.D
Vice President Medical Affairs, Essentia Health Duluth, Duluth, MN, p. A337
Vice President Medical Affairs, Essentia Health St. Mary's Medical Center, Duluth, MN, p. A338
RENN, Amy Katherine, Interim Administrator, Patient Care and Nursing, Via Christi Hospital Pittsburg, Pittsburg, KS, p. A249
RENNEKER, James M., MSN Vice President and Chief Nursing Officer, Loretto Hospital, Chicago, IL, p. A182
RENNER, Dianne, Director Human Resources, Logansport State Hospital, Logansport, IN, p. A215
RENO, Kelly, R.N. Chief Nursing Officer, Menorah Medical Center, Overland Park, KS, p. A248
RENO, Mike, Chief Operating Officer, Hill Country Memorial Hospital, Fredericksburg, TX, p. A614
RENO, III, William, M.D. President Medical Staff, Merit Health Wesley, Hattiesburg, MS, p. A354
RENSHAW, Dee, Chief Executive Officer, Hillcrest Hospital Henryetta, Henryetta, OK, p. A508
RENTAS, Margarita, R.N. Nursing Director, Castaner General Hospital, Castaner, PR, p. A720
RENTFRO, Donald R., Chief Executive Officer, L. V. Stabler Memorial Hospital, Greenville, AL, p. A20
RENTSCH, Richard E., President, Stroud Regional Medical Center, Stroud, OK, p. A515
RENTZ, Norman G., President and Chief Executive Officer, Cannon Memorial Hospital, Pickens, SC, p. A564
REOHR, Sara, Regional Controller, West Gables Rehabilitation Hospital, Miami, FL, p. A135
REPAC, Kimberly S., Senior Vice President and Chief Financial Officer, Western Maryland Regional Medical Center, Cumberland, MD, p. A297
REPASS, Lois, Quality Assurance Specialist and Coordinator Performance Improvement, Northern Nevada Adult Mental Health Services, Sparks, NV, p. A404
REPETTI, Gregory, Interim Chief Executive Officer, Valley Hospital, Spokane Valley, WA, p. A685
REPINO, Thomas, Executive Director Ancillary Services, Connally Memorial Medical Center, Floresville, TX, p. A612
REPIQUE, R. John, R.N., Chief Executive Officer, Friends Hospital, Philadelphia, PA, p. A543
REPKO, Keith D., Associate Medical Center Director, Veterans Affairs St. Louis Health Care System, Saint Louis, MO, p. A378
REPPERT, Joseph A., Executive Vice President and Chief Financial Officer, North Mississippi Medical Center – Tupelo, Tupelo, MS, p. A360
RESENDEZ, James R., Chief Executive Officer, South Texas Regional Medical Center, Jourdanton, TX, p. A625
RESETAR, Gayle L.
Chief Operating Officer, Tidelands Georgetown Memorial Hospital, Georgetown, SC, p. A561
Vice President and Chief Operating Officer, Tidelands Georgetown Memorial Hospital, Georgetown, SC, p. A561
Chief Operating Officer, Tidelands Waccamaw Community Hospital, Murrells Inlet, SC, p. A564
RESLER, Lori, R.N. Chief Nurse, Sullivan County Community Hospital, Sullivan, IN, p. A220
RESSLER, Dennis, Chief Financial Officer, St. Joseph Hospital & Health Center, Kokomo, IN, p. A214
RESTREPO, Macarena, Manager Business Office, Sister Emmanuel Hospital, Miami, FL, p. A135
RESTREPO, Nicolas, M.D. Vice President Medical Affairs, Winchester Medical Center, Winchester, VA, p. A674
RESTUCCIA, Michael, Chief Information Officer, Hospital of the University of Pennsylvania, Philadelphia, PA, p. A544
RESTUM, William H., Ph.D., President, Rehabilitation Institute of Michigan, Detroit, MI, p. A318
RETALIC, Tammy B., R.N. Chief Nursing Officer, Hebrew Rehabilitation Center, Boston, MA, p. A303
RETCHIN, Sheldon, M.D., Chief Executive Officer, Ohio State University Wexner Medical Center, Columbus, OH, p. A486
RETTGER, Linda, M.D. President Medical Staff, Kane Community Hospital, Kane, PA, p. A537
RETTIG, Linda, Director Financial Services, Washington County Hospital, Washington, KS, p. A252
REULAND, Charlie, Sc.D. Executive Vice President and Chief Operating Officer, Johns Hopkins Bayview Medical Center, Baltimore, MD, p. A293
REUST, Michele, Controller, Memorial Hospital of Texas County, Guymon, OK, p. A507
REVAL, Mary, R.N. Chief Nursing Officer, Gulf Coast Regional Medical Center, Panama City, FL, p. A139
REVELS, Beverly, Director Human Resources, Sutter Amador Hospital, Jackson, CA, p. A65
REVERMAN, Larry, Director Information Systems, Clark Memorial Hospital, Jeffersonville, IN, p. A213
REVIEL, Jackie, R.N., Chief Executive Officer, Allen Parish Hospital, Kinder, LA, p. A276
REWERTS, Karen
System Vice President of Finance, SSM Cardinal Glennon Children's Medical Center, Saint Louis, MO, p. A377
System Vice President Finance, SSM St. Joseph Health Center, Saint Charles, MO, p. A375
System Vice President of Finance, SSM St. Mary's Health Center, Saint Louis, MO, p. A377
REXFORD, Linda, Director Human Resources, Weeks Medical Center, Lancaster, NH, p. A406
REXWINKLE, Lori, Chief Nursing Officer, Coffeyville Regional Medical Center, Coffeyville, KS, p. A238
REYES, Arnold, Administrator, U. S. Penitentiary Infirmary, Lewisburg, PA, p. A538
REYES, Marco, Vice President of Operations, Hospital Metropolitano Dr. Tito Mattei, Yauco, PR, p. A724
REYES, Raul, M.D. Medical Director, San Juan City Hospital, San Juan, PR, p. A724
REYES, Roxanne, Director of Nursing, Cornerstone Regional Hospital, Edinburg, TX, p. A609
REYMAN, Reed, President, St. Joseph's Hospital and Health Center, Dickinson, ND, p. A473
REYNOLDS, Angela D., Chief Financial Officer, Lewis–Gale Medical Center, Salem, VA, p. A672
REYNOLDS, Denise, Chief Nursing Officer, Memorial Hospital Miramar, Miramar, FL, p. A136
REYNOLDS, Hope, Executive Director Human Resources and Support Services, Margaret R. Pardee Memorial Hospital, Hendersonville, NC, p. A462
REYNOLDS, Ian, Chief Medical Officer, Victory Surgical Hospital East Houston, Houston, TX, p. A623
REYNOLDS, James B., M.D. Medical Director, Northwest Missouri Psychiatric Rehabilitation Center, Saint Joseph, MO, p. A375
REYNOLDS, Jay, M.D. Chief Medical Officer and Chief Clinical Officer, The Aroostook Medical Center, Presque Isle, ME, p. A292
REYNOLDS, Katelyn, Manager Human Resources, Greeley County Health Services, Tribune, KS, p. A251
REYNOLDS, Lennetta M., Administrative Supervisor, Community Behavioral Health Hospital – Annandale, Annandale, MN, p. A334
REYNOLDS, Linda K., FACHE, Director, Mann–Grandstaff Veterans Affairs Medical Center, Spokane, WA, p. A685

Index of Health Care Professionals
Index of Health Care Professionals / Reynolds

REYNOLDS, Mike
Chief Financial Officer, Delta Medical Center, Memphis, TN, p. A583
Chief Financial Officer, Newberry County Memorial Hospital, Newberry, SC, p. A564
REYNOLDS, Paul, M.D. Medical Director, Coleman County Medical Center, Coleman, TX, p. A601
REYNOLDS, Phyllis, R.N. VP, Nursing, Beaumont Hospital Grosse Pointe, Grosse Pointe, MI, p. A321
REYNOLDS, Ray, Chief Executive Officer, Glen Rose Medical Center, Glen Rose, TX, p. A616
REYNOLDS, Robert, Director Information Systems, Mary Rutan Hospital, Bellefontaine, OH, p. A479
REYNOLDS, Ronald J., President, Muncy Valley Hospital, Muncy, PA, p. A541
REYNOLDS, Rose, Director Health Information, Avera Flandreau Hospital, Flandreau, SD, p. A568
REYNOLDS, Scott, Vice President Finance, Mercy Hospital Springfield, Springfield, MO, p. A379
REYNOLDS, Teresa, Chief Operating Officer, Haywood Regional Medical Center, Clyde, NC, p. A458
REYNOLDS, Todd, Chief Information Officer, Memorial Medical Center – Ashland, Ashland, WI, p. A697
REYNOLDS, Vance V., CPA, Chief Executive Officer, Aiken Regional Medical Centers, Aiken, SC, p. A557
REYNOLDS-GOSSETTE, Youdie, Controller, Wilma N. Vazquez Medical Center, Vega Baja, PR, p. A724
RHEE, Carolyn F., Chief Executive Officer, LAC–Olive View–UCLA Medical Center, CA, p. A71
RHEINHEIMER, Rick, Chief Clinical Officer, Kindred Hospital–Chattanooga, Chattanooga, TN, p. A575
RHINE, Kathleen
Regional President and Chief Executive Officer, Presence Saint Joseph Medical Center, Joliet, IL, p. A192
Regional President and Chief Executive Officer, Presence St. Mary's Hospital, Kankakee, IL, p. A192
RHINEHART, Jennie R., Administrator and Chief Executive Officer, Community Hospital, Tallassee, AL, p. A25
RHOADES, Charles E., M.D., Chief Executive Officer, Kansas City Orthopaedic Institute, Leawood, KS, p. A244
RHOADES, Mark, Vice President and Chief Human Resources Officer, Duncan Regional Hospital, Duncan, OK, p. A505
RHOADES, Shelly, Chief Financial Officer, Clarion Psychiatric Center, Clarion, PA, p. A531
RHOADS, Jack, M.D. Medical Director, Landmark Hospital of Joplin, Joplin, MO, p. A369
RHOADS, Pam, Chief Financial Officer, Fairfax Behavioral Health, Kirkland, WA, p. A680
RHODES, David, M.D. Senior Vice President Medical Affairs and Chief Medical Officer, Rapides Regional Medical Center, Alexandria, LA, p. A268
RHODES, Helen, R.N. Associate Director Operations, Veterans Affairs Northern Indiana Health Care System, Fort Wayne, IN, p. A209
RHODES, J. Gary, FACHE,
Interim President and Chief Executive Officer, Brooks Memorial Hospital, Dunkirk, NY, p. A433
Chief Executive Officer, Kane Community Hospital, Kane, PA, p. A537
RHODES, Jerome E., Chief Executive Officer, CRC Health Group, Inc., Cupertino, CA, p. B43
RHODES, Lee, Administrator and Chief Executive Officer, Greeley County Health Services, Tribune, KS, p. A251
RHODES, Pamela, R.N. Vice President Patient Services and Chief Nursing Officer, Northern Dutchess Hospital, Rhinebeck, NY, p. A448
RHODES, Tracey, Coordinator Human Resources, Evergreen Medical Center, Evergreen, AL, p. A19
RHONE, Steve, R.N. Vice President Patient Care Services, Beebe Healthcare, Lewes, DE, p. A117
RHUDY, Kenneth D., Chief Executive Officer, Brooks County Hospital, Quitman, GA, p. A162
RHYNALDS, Kayla, Interim Chief Financial Officer, Kearney County Health Services, Minden, NE, p. A394
RHYNE, Catherine A., M.P.H. Chief Nursing Officer, Gerald Champion Regional Medical Center, Alamogordo, NM, p. A422
RHYNE, Craig, M.D. Chief Medical Officer, Covenant Medical Center, Lubbock, TX, p. A629
RHYNE, Dennis, M.D. Acting Medical Director, Fairbanks, Indianapolis, IN, p. A211
RHYNE, Tim, Personnel Officer, Ventura County Medical Center, Ventura, CA, p. A96
RIAL, Joanne, Chief Financial Officer, Cumberland Hospital, New Kent, VA, p. A668
RIALS, Joe, Director Fiscal Services, North Mississippi State Hospital, Tupelo, MS, p. A361
RIALS, Loren, Chief Financial Officer, Carolinas Hospital System, Florence, SC, p. A560
RIANO, Omaira D., Chief Nursing Officer, HEALTHSOUTH Sunrise Rehabilitation Hospital, Sunrise, FL, p. A143
RIAZ, Mohammad, M.D. Chief of Staff, Raulerson Hospital, Okeechobee, FL, p. A137
RIBA, Chris, Director Human Resources, Baldwin Area Medical Center, Baldwin, WI, p. A697
RICARTTI, Rebecca R., Interim Director Human Resources, Garfield Medical Center, Monterey Park, CA, p. A76
RICCI, David A., President and Chief Executive Officer, Saint Michael's Medical Center, Newark, NJ, p. A415
RICCIO, Dustin, M.D.,
President, Clifton Springs Hospital and Clinic, Clifton Springs, NY, p. A431
Regional President Operations, Newark–Wayne Community Hospital, Newark, NY, p. A445
RICCIO, John A., M.D. Chief Medical Officer, Auburn Community Hospital, Auburn, NY, p. A429
RICCIONI, Mich
Chief Financial Officer, Petaluma Valley Hospital, Petaluma, CA, p. A81
Vice President and Chief Financial Officer, Northern California Region, Queen of the Valley Medical Center, Napa, CA, p. A77
Chief Financial Officer, Santa Rosa Memorial Hospital, Santa Rosa, CA, p. A92
Chief Financial Officer, St. Joseph Hospital, Eureka, CA, p. A60
RICCITELLI, Anthony, Chief Operating Officer, Worcester Recovery Center and Hospital, Worcester, MA, p. A313
RICCITELLI, Vincent, Vice President Finance, Hoboken University Medical Center, Hoboken, NJ, p. A412
RICE, Aimee, Human Resources Manager, Riverview Psychiatric Center, Augusta, ME, p. A288
RICE, Amy, Chief Financial Officer, Helena Regional Medical Center, Helena, AR, p. A45
RICE, Ann Madden, Chief Executive Officer, University of California, Davis Medical Center, Sacramento, CA, p. A85
RICE, Carolyn, M.D. Director Medical Services, Naval Hospital Pensacola, Pensacola, FL, p. A139
RICE, Craig, Director Information, Schneck Medical Center, Seymour, IN, p. A219
RICE, Devin, Director Information Systems, Clifton–Fine Hospital, Star Lake, NY, p. A450
RICE, Mark, CPA Controller, Jersey Shore Hospital, Jersey Shore, PA, p. A536
RICE, Mark, Administrator, Mid–Jefferson Extended Care Hospital, Nederland, TX, p. A634
RICE, Mark J., Interim Administrator, Riverside Hospital of Louisiana, Alexandria, LA, p. A268
RICE, Patricia A., Chief Executive Officer, Select Specialty Hospital–Memphis, Memphis, TN, p. A584
RICE, Peter, M.D. Medical Director, PeaceHealth Ketchikan Medical Center, Ketchikan, AK, p. A28
RICE, Thomas J., FACHE, President and Chief Executive Officer, Fawcett Memorial Hospital, Port Charlotte, FL, p. A140
RICE, Tim, President and Chief Executive Officer, Lakewood Health System, Staples, MN, p. A347
RICH, Anna, Chief Financial Officer, Complex Care Hospital at Tenaya, Las Vegas, NV, p. A401
RICH, Jeri, Assistant Administrator and Chief Financial Officer, Hunt Regional Community Hospital, Commerce, TX, p. A602
RICH, Judy F., President and Chief Executive Officer, TMC Healthcare, Tucson, AZ, p. A40
RICH, Kori, Chief Executive Officer, The Physicians Centre Hospital, Bryan, TX, p. A599
RICH, Mark, Director Information Services, Ashley Regional Medical Center, Vernal, UT, p. A659
RICH, Philip, M.D. Chief Medical Officer, West Hills Hospital, Reno, NV, p. A404
RICHARD, Brandi, Chief Nursing Officer, Michiana Behavioral Health Center, Plymouth, IN, p. A218
RICHARD, Brent, Administrative Director Information Systems, Southern Ohio Medical Center, Portsmouth, OH, p. A496
RICHARD, Christina, Administrator, Kindred Hospital Tarrant County–Arlington, Arlington, TX, p. A592
RICHARD, Larry, M.D. Chief Medical Staff, Decatur County Hospital, Leon, IA, p. A231
RICHARD, Marilyn, Director Human Resources, Daviess Community Hospital, Washington, IN, p. A221
RICHARD, Paul F., President, Sanford Medical Center Fargo, Fargo, ND, p. A474
RICHARD, Scott, Vice President Finance and Chief Financial Officer, St. Elizabeth Hospital, Gonzales, LA, p. A274
RICHARD, Thomas, Director Budget and Revenue Cycle, Redwood Area Hospital, Redwood Falls, MN, p. A345
RICHARD, Tim, IT Coordinator, Crawford Memorial Hospital, Robinson, IL, p. A199
RICHARDS, Craig A., Chief Executive Officer, Mildred Mitchell–Bateman Hospital, Huntington, WV, p. A692
RICHARDS, Frank
Chief Information Officer, Geisinger Medical Center, Danville, PA, p. A532
Chief Information Officer, Geisinger Wyoming Valley Medical Center, Wilkes Barre, PA, p. A553
RICHARDS, Jaena, Chief Financial Officer, Deer Lodge Medical Center, Deer Lodge, MT, p. A382
RICHARDS, Joan K., President and Chief Executive Officer, Crozer–Keystone Health System, Springfield, PA, p. B44
RICHARDS, Jon, Chief Financial Officer, Tennova Newport Medical Center, Newport, TN, p. A586
RICHARDS, Jonathan, Chief Financial Officer, David Grant USAF Medical Center, Travis AFB, CA, p. A94
RICHARDS, Judith, Director of Nursing, Adcare Hospital of Worcester, Worcester, MA, p. A313
RICHARDS, Mandy, R.N. Vice President Patient Care, United Hospital, Saint Paul, MN, p. A346
RICHARDS, Mark, Interim Chief Operating Officer, Seton Shoal Creek Hospital, Austin, TX, p. A594
RICHARDS, Nate, Director Information Technology, Mitchell County Hospital Health Systems, Beloit, KS, p. A238
RICHARDS, Robert J., Vice President Finance and Chief Financial Officer, The Good Samaritan Hospital, Lebanon, PA, p. A538
RICHARDS, Sheila K., Human Resources Director, Dallas Medical Center, Dallas, TX, p. A604
RICHARDS, Suzanne, FACHE, Chief Executive Officer, Integrated Healthcare, Santa Ana, CA, p. B74
RICHARDS, Suzanne, FACHE,
Chief Executive Officer, Orange County Global Medical Center, Inc., Santa Ana, CA, p. A90
Chief Executive Officer, Victor Valley Global Medical Center, Victorville, CA, p. A96
Chief Executive Officer, Western Medical Center Anaheim, Anaheim, CA, p. A53
RICHARDS, Thom
Chief Information Technology, Adair County Memorial Hospital, Greenfield, IA, p. A228
Director Information Technology, Knoxville Hospital & Clinics, Knoxville, IA, p. A230
RICHARDSON, David, M.D. Chief of Staff, Delta Medical Center, Memphis, TN, p. A583
RICHARDSON, Denise, R.N. Senior Vice President and Chief Nursing Officer, St. Barnabas Hospital, NY, p. A444
RICHARDSON, Dorothy, Director Human Resources, Van Matre HealthSouth Rehabilitation Hospital, Rockford, IL, p. A200
RICHARDSON, Dwayne, Chief Operating Officer, Placentia–Linda Hospital, Placentia, CA, p. A81
RICHARDSON, Greg H., Assistant Administrator Human Resources, Newton Medical Center, Covington, GA, p. A155
RICHARDSON, Irene, Chief Financial Officer, Memorial Hospital of Sweetwater County, Rock Springs, WY, p. A717
RICHARDSON, Jana, Chief Financial Officer, Stone County Medical Center, Mountain View, AR, p. A48
RICHARDSON, Judy, M.D. President Medical Staff, Mid–Columbia Medical Center, The Dalles, OR, p. A526
RICHARDSON, Karen K., Senior Vice President and Chief Financial Officer, Providence Healthcare Network, Waco, TX, p. A650
RICHARDSON, Keith, Chief Executive Officer, Jellico Community Hospital, Jellico, TN, p. A579
RICHARDSON, Kevin, M.D. Chief of Staff, Southwest Mississippi Regional Medical Center, McComb, MS, p. A357
RICHARDSON, Kirk, Chief Operating Officer, Bronson LakeView Hospital, Paw Paw, MI, p. A327
RICHARDSON, Kitty J., Administrator, Wilson N. Jones Regional Medical Center, Sherman, TX, p. A644
RICHARDSON, Kristy, Director of Nursing, De Queen Medical Center, De Queen, AR, p. A43
RICHARDSON, Mark D., President and Chief Executive Officer, Great River Medical Center, West Burlington, IA, p. A236
RICHARDSON Jr., Nathaniel, President, Decatur Morgan Hospital, Decatur, AL, p. A18
RICHARDSON, Robert, Information Technology Administrator, Porter Regional Hospital, Valparaiso, IN, p. A220
RICHARDSON, Sarah, Director Information Systems, Belton Regional Medical Center, Belton, MO, p. A363
RICHARDSON, Shazetta, Director of Nursing, Cypress Creek Hospital, Houston, TX, p. A619
RICHARDSON, Sonya, Chief Nursing Officer, Chillicothe Hospital District, Chillicothe, TX, p. A600
RICHARDSON, Stanley, Coordinator Human Resources and Payroll Benefits, Kindred Hospital–San Antonio, San Antonio, TX, p. A641
RICHARDSON, Terrie, Coordinator Human Resources, Select Specialty Hospital–Augusta, Augusta, GA, p. A151
RICHARDSON, Timothy J., M.D. Chief of Staff, Maine Veterans Affairs Medical Center, Augusta, ME, p. A288
RICHARDSON, William T., President and Chief Executive Officer, Tift Regional Health System, Tifton, GA, p. B134

A950 Index of Health Care Professionals

Index of Health Care Professionals / Risse

Index of Health Care Professionals


RICHARDSON, William T., President and Chief Executive Officer, Tift Regional Medical Center, Tifton, GA, p. A166
RICHARDT, Claudia, Vice President, Human Resources, Community Relations and Marketing, Dearborn County Hospital, Lawrenceburg, IN, p. A214
RICHARDVILLE, Craig D.
Senior Vice President and Chief Information Officer, Carolinas Medical Center, Charlotte, NC, p. A457
Chief Information Officer, Carolinas Rehabilitation, Charlotte, NC, p. A457
Chief Information Officer, Cleveland Regional Medical Center, Shelby, NC, p. A468
RICHASON, Amie
Vice President Human Resources, Leesburg Regional Medical Center, Leesburg, FL, p. A132
Vice President Human Resources, The Villages Regional Hospital, The Villages, FL, p. A146
RICHBOURG, Gail A., Director Human Resources, Clarendon Memorial Hospital, Manning, SC, p. A563
RICHCREEK, Keith, Manager Technical Services, Lafayette Regional Health Center, Lexington, MO, p. A372
RICHENS, Ken, Chief Information Officer, Central Valley Medical Center, Nephi, UT, p. A656
RICHER, R. David, Chief Executive Officer, Fairlawn Rehabilitation Hospital, Worcester, MA, p. A313
RICHERT, Ed, M.D. Chief of Staff, Modoc Medical Center, Alturas, CA, p. A53
RICHERT, Tadd M., CP
Senior Vice President and Chief Financial Officer, CHI St. Vincent Infirmary Medical Center, Little Rock, AR, p. A47
Senior Vice President and Chief Financial Officer, CHI St. Vincent Medical Center–North, Sherwood, AR, p. A50
RICHETTI, Michael, Chief Financial Officer, Chilton Medical Center, Pompton Plains, NJ, p. A417
RICHEY, Mark, Interim Administrator, Tippah County Hospital, Ripley, MS, p. A360
RICHHART, David, Vice President Fiscal Services, Community Medical Center, Missoula, MT, p. A385
RICHMAN, Craig, M.D. Medical Director, Meadows Psychiatric Center, Centre Hall, PA, p. A531
RICHMAN, Jonathan, M.D. Chief of Staff, Chase County Community Hospital, Imperial, NE, p. A393
RICHMAN, Timothy, President, Calumet Medical Center, Chilton, WI, p. A699
RICHMOND, Andy, Director Information Technology, Choctaw Memorial Hospital, Hugo, OK, p. A508
RICHMOND, Craig, Senior Vice President and Chief Financial Officer, MetroHealth Medical Center, Cleveland, OH, p. A485
RICHMOND, Ira, Associate Director Patient Care Services, Veterans Affairs Pittsburgh Healthcare System, Pittsburgh, PA, p. A547
RICHOUX, Jacquelyn, Chief Financial Officer, Lady of the Sea General Hospital, Cut Off, LA, p. A272
RICHTER, Daniel, M.D. Chief of Staff, CHI Health Missouri Valley, Missouri Valley, IA, p. A231
RICHTER, Thomas V., Chief Executive Officer, Pioneer Memorial Hospital and Health Services, Viborg, SD, p. A572
RICK, Bob, Vice President Information Technology, USMD Hospital at Arlington, Arlington, TX, p. A593
RICKARD, Sheryl, Chief Executive Officer, Bonner General Hospital, Sandpoint, ID, p. A176
RICKENS, Chris, R.N. Senior Vice President and Chief Nursing Officer, UPMC Altoona, Altoona, PA, p. A528
RICKETTS, Al, Director of Nursing, Jerome Golden Center for Behavioral Health, Inc., West Palm Beach, FL, p. A147
RICKS, Edward, Vice President and Chief Information Officer, Beaufort Memorial Hospital, Beaufort, SC, p. A557
RICKS, Michael R., Chief Operating Officer, St. Joseph's Medical Center, Stockton, CA, p. A93
RICO, Richard, Vice President and Chief Financial Officer, Sky Lakes Medical Center, Klamath Falls, OR, p. A522
RIDALL, Jackie, Director Human Resources, Berwick Hospital Center, Berwick, PA, p. A529
RIDDER, Terri, Director Human Resources, St. Francis Memorial Hospital, West Point, NE, p. A399
RIDDLE, Kent, Chief Executive Officer, Mary Free Bed Rehabilitation Hospital, Grand Rapids, MI, p. A320
RIDDLES, Lawrence, M.D. Executive Vice President Medical Affairs and Quality, St. Dominic–Jackson Memorial Hospital, Jackson, MS, p. A355
RIDGE, Carolyn, Chief Financial Officer, Lakeview Regional Medical Center, Covington, LA, p. A272
RIDGE, Frederick R., Chief of Staff, Greene County General Hospital, Linton, IN, p. A215
RIDGEWAY, Kerrie, R.N. Chief Nursing Officer, Pocahontas Memorial Hospital, Buckeye, WV, p. A689
RIDLEN, Deborah, CPA Vice President Fiscal Services and Chief Financial Officer, Schneck Medical Center, Seymour, IN, p. A219
RIDLEY, Pam, Director Information Systems, Henry County Medical Center, Paris, TN, p. A587
RIDLEY, Zena, Director Human Resources, Harbor Oaks Hospital, New Baltimore, MI, p. A326
RIDNER, Sheila, R.N. Director of Nursing, Behavioral HealthCare Center at Columbia, Columbia, TN, p. A576
RIEBEL, William, M.D. Vice President Medical Operations, Lakewood Hospital, Lakewood, OH, p. A491
RIEBER, Dan, Chief Financial Officer, Memorial Hospital, Colorado Springs, CO, p. A100
RIEBER, Jim, Director Information Systems, Perham Health, Perham, MN, p. A344
RIECHERS, Thomas, M.D. Chief Medical Staff, Mercy Hospital Washington, Washington, MO, p. A380
RIEDLINGER, Joann, Vice President Nursing and Manager Information Systems, Bucyrus Community Hospital, Bucyrus, OH, p. A480
RIEG, Kevin, M.D. President Medical Staff, Via Christi Rehabilitation Hospital, Wichita, KS, p. A253
RIEGE, Michael J., Administrator, Virginia Gay Hospital, Vinton, IA, p. A235
RIEGER, Bill, Chief Information Officer, Flagler Hospital, Saint Augustine, FL, p. A141
RIEGERT, Patricia, Director Fiscal Services, Danville State Hospital, Danville, PA, p. A532
RIEGLE, Tina, R.N. Chief Clinical Officer, AMG Specialty Hospital – Muncie, Muncie, IN, p. A216
RIEKE, Diane, Director Patient Care Services, Patients' Hospital of Redding, Redding, CA, p. A82
RIEKS, Katie, Chief Nursing Officer, Hansen Family Hospital, Iowa Falls, IA, p. A230
RIEMER–MATUZAK, Stephanie J., Chief Executive Officer, Munson Healthcare Grayling Hospital, Grayling, MI, p. A321
RIER, Kirk, Chief Operating Officer, Iowa Specialty Hospital–Clarion, Clarion, IA, p. A224
RIESEBERG, Eric F., President, Specialty Hospitals of America, LLC, Portsmouth, NH, p. B125
RIESER, Michael, M.D. Medical Director, Ridge Behavioral Health System, Lexington, KY, p. A260
RIESTER, Debby, Manager Human Resources, Coastal Communities Hospital, Santa Ana, CA, p. A90
RIETSEMA, Wouter, M.D. Chief Quality and Information Officer, The University of Vermont Health Network–Champlain Valley Physicians Hospital, Plattsburgh, NY, p. A447
RIEVES, S. Kathleen, M.D. Chief Medical Officer, Rangely District Hospital, Rangely, CO, p. A108
RIFFLE, Virginia, Vice President Patient Care Services, Samaritan North Lincoln Hospital, Lincoln City, OR, p. A522
RIGAS, Warren Alston, Executive Vice President and Chief Operating Officer, Floyd Medical Center, Rome, GA, p. A163
RIGDON, Alice W., Chief Financial Officer, Piedmont Medical Center, Rock Hill, SC, p. A564
RIGDON, Edward, M.D. Chief Medical Officer, Merit Health Rankin, Brandon, MS, p. A351
RIGDON, Pam, Director Nursing, Laird Hospital, Union, MS, p. A361
RIGGINS, Mark, Administrator, Bellville St. Joseph Health Center, Bellville, TX, p. A597
RIGGLE, Vikki, Director Human Resources, Eastern Louisiana Mental Health System, Jackson, LA, p. A275
RIGGS, Jen, Chief Nurse Officer, MaineGeneral Medical Center, Augusta, ME, p. A288
RIGGS, Jon, Chief Financial Officer, Medical Center Health System, Odessa, TX, p. A634
RIGNEY, Alice, Chief Human Resources Officer, Abbeville Area Medical Center, Abbeville, SC, p. A557
RIGSBEE CARROLL, Cristina, Chief Operating Officer, Granville Health System, Oxford, NC, p. A466
RIGSBY, Brent, Chief Financial Officer, Southwest Georgia Regional Medical Center, Cuthbert, GA, p. A155
RIGSBY, Diane, Chief Information Officer, Capital Hospice, Arlington, VA, p. A662
RILEY, Colleen, M.D. Medical Director, Laguna Honda Hospital and Rehabilitation Center, San Francisco, CA, p. A88
RILEY, Edward E., Chief Executive Officer and Administrator, Kingman Community Hospital, Kingman, KS, p. A243
RILEY, Jennifer, Chief of Marketing and Business Development, The Memorial Hospital at Craig, Craig, CO, p. A101
RILEY, Jim, Director Information Technology, Wagoner Community Hospital, Wagoner, OK, p. A518
RILEY, Joe B., FACHE, President and Chief Executive Officer, Jackson Hospital and Clinic, Montgomery, AL, p. A23
RILEY, Julia, M.D. Medical Director, Neshoba County General Hospital, Philadelphia, MS, p. A359
RILEY, Kenneth, Director Information Systems, Baystate Wing Hospital, Palmer, MA, p. A310
RILEY, Linzie, Interim Human Resource Manager, LifeCare Hospitals of Dallas, Dallas, TX, p. A605
RILEY, Mike, President, Novant Health Huntersville Medical Center, Huntersville, NC, p. A462
RILEY, Randy
Chief Financial Officer, Center for Behavioral Medicine, Kansas City, MO, p. A369
Fiscal and Administrative Manager, Northwest Missouri Psychiatric Rehabilitation Center, Saint Joseph, MO, p. A375
RILEY, Susan, Director Human Resources, HEALTHSOUTH Rehabilitation Hospital of Miami, Cutler Bay, FL, p. A124
RILEY, Jr., William, M.D. Chief of Staff, Memorial Hermann Sugar Land Hospital, Sugar Land, TX, p. A645
RIMAR, Stephen, M.D. Senior Vice President Medical Affairs, New York–Presbyterian/Queens, NY, p. A443
RIMEL, Jeff, Chief Financial Officer, Cibola General Hospital, Grants, NM, p. A424
RINALDI, Anthony, Executive Vice President, Fairview Hospital, Great Barrington, MA, p. A307
RINALDI, Blythe, Vice President, Mayo Clinic Health System – Northland in Barron, Barron, WI, p. A698
RINALDI, Daniel, Chief Financial Officer, Ellis Hospital, Schenectady, NY, p. A450
RINALDI, Stephen, Vice President Finance and Chief Financial Officer, Caldwell Memorial Hospital, Lenoir, NC, p. A464
RINDELS, Doris, Vice President Operations, Grinnell Regional Medical Center, Grinnell, IA, p. A228
RINDFLEISCH, Jody, Manager Human Resources, Redwood Area Hospital, Redwood Falls, MN, p. A345
RINDLISBACHER, Diane, Manager Information Systems, Orem Community Hospital, Orem, UT, p. A656
RINEHART, Linda, Director Human Resources, HEALTHSOUTH Treasure Coast Rehabilitation Hospital, Vero Beach, FL, p. A146
RINEHART, Rick, Chief Information Officer, Carle Foundation Hospital, Urbana, IL, p. A202
RINEY, Jeremy, Chief Executive Officer, San Angelo Community Medical Center, San Angelo, TX, p. A640
RING, Brian K., Chief Operating Officer, Henry County Hospital, New Castle, IN, p. A217
RING, Cynthia, Vice President Human Resources and Patient Experience, HealthAlliance Hospitals, Leominster, MA, p. A308
RING, Jackie, President and Chief Nursing Officer, Highlands–Cashiers Hospital, Highlands, NC, p. A462
RING, Melissa, M.D., Chief Executive Officer, Alaska Psychiatric Institute, Anchorage, AK, p. A27
RINGE, Kathy, Director Human Resources, Sage Rehabilitation Hospital, Baton Rouge, LA, p. A270
RINGER, Dave, M.D. Chief of Staff, St. Mary's Good Samaritan Hospital, Greensboro, GA, p. A158
RINKE, Joseph, Director Human Resources, Streamwood Behavioral Health Center, Streamwood, IL, p. A202
RINKENBERGER, Sean, Chief Financial Officer, St. Andrew's Health Center, Bottineau, ND, p. A472
RINKER, John M., Chief Medical Officer, OSF Saint James – John W. Albrecht Medical Center, Pontiac, IL, p. A198
RINTOUL, Alexander M., Chief Executive Officer, The Medical Center at Elizabeth Place, Dayton, OH, p. A488
RION, Trey, Chief Information Officer, West Calcasieu Cameron Hospital, Sulphur, LA, p. A286
RIORDAN, Michael C., President and Chief Executive Officer, Greenville Health System, Greenville, SC, p. B60
RIOS, Cindy, Chief Financial Officer, AllianceHealth Durant, Durant, OK, p. A506
RIOS, Jose C., Director Information Services, Murray Medical Center, Chatsworth, GA, p. A153
RIOS, Margot, R.N. Chief Nursing Officer, CHRISTUS Spohn Hospital Alice, Alice, TX, p. A590
RIPPE, Diana, Chief Financial Officer, Tri Valley Health System, Cambridge, NE, p. A390
RIPPERGER, Ted, Administrative Director Human Resources, Atrium Medical Center, Middletown, OH, p. A494
RIPPEY, Wesley E., M.D. Chief Medical Officer, Adventist Medical Center–Portland, Portland, OR, p. A524
RIPSCH, Sue, R.N. Vice President and Chief Nursing Officer, Mercy Hospital and Trauma Center, Janesville, WI, p. A703
RISBY, Emile, M.D. Clinical Director, Georgia Regional Hospital at Atlanta, Decatur, GA, p. A156
RISHA, Holly, Administrative Director Human Resources, College Hospital Cerritos, Cerritos, CA, p. A57
RISINGER, Jeff, Director Human Resources, UAMS Medical Center, Little Rock, AR, p. A47
RISK II, Carl W., Administrator, St. Vincent Jennings Hospital, North Vernon, IN, p. A218
RISKA, Marilouise, Chief Executive Officer, Select Specialty Hospital–Northwest Detroit, Detroit, MI, p. A318
RISLOW, Deb, Chief Information Officer, Gundersen Health System, La Crosse, WI, p. A703
RISSE, Thomas, Chief Financial Officer and Vice President Business Services, Kaiser Permanente Medical Center, Honolulu, HI, p. A168

RISSI, Daniel, M.D. Vice President, Chief Medical and Clinical Operations Officer, Lawrence + Memorial Hospital, New London, CT, p. A114

RITCHEY, Jim, Director Human Resources, Sky Ridge Medical Center, Lone Tree, CO, p. A106

RITCHIE, Ann, Director Human Resources, Ochsner St. Anne General Hospital, Raceland, LA, p. A284

RITCHIE, Bruce, Vice President of Finance and Chief Financial Officer, Peninsula Regional Medical Center, Salisbury, MD, p. A300

RITCHIE, Jim, Director Management Information Systems, South Shore Hospital, Chicago, IL, p. A184

RITCHIE, Shannan, Interim President, Lakewood Hospital, Lakewood, OH, p. A491

RITON, John, Director Information Services, Memorial Hospital of Tampa, Tampa, FL, p. A145

RITTENOUR, Melanie, Director Human Resources, Paulding County Hospital, Paulding, OH, p. A496

RITTER, Jane, R.N. Chief Nursing Officer, Lovelace Women's Hospital, Albuquerque, NM, p. A422

RITTER, Robert G., Associate Director, Harry S. Truman Memorial Veterans Hospital, Columbia, MO, p. A366

RITTMAN, Todd, Director of Nursing, Larue D. Carter Memorial Hospital, Indianapolis, IN, p. A212

RITZ, Robert P., FACHE,
President, Mercy Medical Center – West Lakes, West Des Moines, IA, p. A236
President, Mercy Medical Center–Des Moines, Des Moines, IA, p. A226

RIUS, Ana, M.D., Secretary of Health, Puerto Rico Department of Health, San Juan, PR, p. B110

RIVAS, Eloy, Director of Information Systems, Venice Regional Bayfront Health, Venice, FL, p. A146

RIVAS, Jessica, R.N. Vice President and Chief Nursing Officer, HonorHealth Deer Valley Medical Center, Phoenix, AZ, p. A35

RIVAS, Jose, M.D. Chief of Staff, Community Hospital of Huntington Park, Huntington Park, CA, p. A65

RIVAS, Ramon Rodriguez, M.D. Medical Director, Hospital San Cristobal, Coto Laurel, PR, p. A721

RIVERA, Anita, Director Human Resources, Peninsula Hospital, Louisville, TN, p. A582

RIVERA, Anthony, Director Human Resources, Hartgrove Hospital, Chicago, IL, p. A182

RIVERA, Christina, Director Human Resources, Southwest General Hospital, San Antonio, TX, p. A642

RIVERA, Cristina, Chief Executive Officer, Rio Grande Regional Hospital, McAllen, TX, p. A631

RIVERA, Enrique, Chief Financial Officer, Bella Vista Hospital, Mayaguez, PR, p. A722

RIVERA, Ivonne, Director Finance, Hospital Oriente, Humacao, PR, p. A721

RIVERA, Jamie, Chief Financial Officer, Hospital Dr. Cayetano Coll Y Toste, Arecibo, PR, p. A719

RIVERA, Joe, Chief Information Technology Officer, Laredo Medical Center, Laredo, TX, p. A627

RIVERA, Jose Garcia, Director Human Resources, Hospital Buen Samaritano, Aguadilla, PR, p. A719

RIVERA, Luis, Director Human Resources, San Juan Capestrano Hospital, San Juan, PR, p. A724

RIVERA, Maria, Director Human Resources, Westside Regional Medical Center, Plantation, FL, p. A140

RIVERA, Zamarys, R.N. Chief Nursing Officer, HEALTHSOUTH Rehabilitation Hospital of San Juan, San Juan, PR, p. A723

RIVERA–POL, Noriselle, Vice President Finance, Hospital Manati Medical Center, Manati, PR, p. A721

RIVERS, Guy, Chief Financial Officer, Columbia Memorial Hospital, Astoria, OR, p. A519

RIVERS, Jan, Director Human Resources, Ochsner Medical Center–Baton Rouge, Baton Rouge, LA, p. A269

RIVEST, Jeffrey A., FACHE, President and Chief Executive Officer, University of Maryland Medical Center, Baltimore, MD, p. A295

RIVOIRE, John, Administrator, Louisiana Extended Care Hospital of Natchitoches, Natchitoches, LA, p. A281

RIZK, Magdy, M.D. Chief of Staff, West Houston Medical Center, Houston, TX, p. A623

RIZK, Norman, M.D. Chief Medical Officer, Stanford Health Care, Palo Alto, CA, p. A80

RIZK, Rob, Director Information Technology, Good Shepherd Health Care System, Hermiston, OR, p. A521

RIZKALLA, Nasseem, M.D. Chief Medical Officer, Aspirus Iron River Hospitals and Clinics, Iron River, MI, p. A323

RIZZO, Frank, Chief Financial Officer, Central Region, North Shore University Hospital, Manhasset, NY, p. A437

RIZZO, Theresa, Administrator, Franklin County Memorial Hospital, Franklin, NE, p. A391

RIZZUTO, George, CPA Chief Financial Officer, St. Christopher's Hospital for Children, Philadelphia, PA, p. A545

ROACH, Crystal, Chief Financial Officer, TrustPoint Hospital, Lubbock, TX, p. A630

ROACH, David, Vice President Information Systems, Kadlec Regional Medical Center, Richland, WA, p. A683

ROACH, Dee A., M.D. Chief of Staff, Mitchell County Hospital, Colorado City, TX, p. A601

ROACH, Donna, Chief Information Officer, Borgess Medical Center, Kalamazoo, MI, p. A323

ROACH, Geoff, Director Human Resources, Barrett Hospital & HealthCare, Dillon, MT, p. A383

ROACH, Joseph, Chief Executive Officer, Holy Family Hospital, Methuen, MA, p. A308

ROACH, Maureen, Senior Chief Financial Officer, Kindred Hospital–St. Louis, Saint Louis, MO, p. A376

ROACH, Patricia A., R.N. Senior Vice President and Chief Nursing Officer, Faxton–St. Luke's Healthcare, Utica, NY, p. A452

ROACH, Renee, System Vice President, Human Resources, SSM St. Clare Health Center, Fenton, MO, p. A367

ROACH, Steven P., FACHE, President and Chief Executive Officer, UMass Memorial–Marlborough Hospital, Marlborough, MA, p. A308

ROADER, Charles, Vice President Finance, Edgerton Hospital and Health Services, Edgerton, WI, p. A700

ROANHORSE, Anslem, Chief Executive Officer, U. S. Public Health Service Indian Hospital, Crownpoint, NM, p. A424

ROARK, Chris, Chief Information Officer, Stillwater Medical Center, Stillwater, OK, p. A515

ROARK, Robert, Director Human Resources, Laughlin Memorial Hospital, Greeneville, TN, p. A578

ROARTY, Maureen, Executive Vice President Human Resources, Nassau University Medical Center, East Meadow, NY, p. A433

ROAT, David, D.O. Medical Director, Ancora Psychiatric Hospital, Hammonton, NJ, p. A412

ROB, Lee, Director Human Resources, Pioneer Community Hospital of Aberdeen, Aberdeen, MS, p. A350

ROBB, Joy, Vice President Human Resources, Prairie View, Newton, KS, p. A246

ROBBINS, Dan, Information Technology and Account Executive, St. Vincent Medical Center, Los Angeles, CA, p. A73

ROBBINS, Danielle A., Vice President Human Resources, St. Catherine of Siena Medical Center, Smithtown, NY, p. A450

ROBBINS, Jr., Donald, M.D. Chief Staff, Hills & Dales General Hospital, Cass City, MI, p. A316

ROBBINS, Jan, M.D. Chief of Staff, Tennova Healthcare–LaFollette Medical Center, La Follette, TN, p. A581

ROBBINS, Joe, M.D. Vice President Medical Affairs, Sentara Williamsburg Regional Medical Center, Williamsburg, VA, p. A674

ROBBINS, Shannon, Chief Operating Officer, Ohio Hospital for Psychiatry, Columbus, OH, p. A486

ROBEANO, Karen, R.N. Chief Nursing Officer and Vice President Patient Care Services, FirstHealth Moore Regional Hospital, Pinehurst, NC, p. A466

ROBERGE, Jeremy
Director Reimbursement, Androscoggin Valley Hospital, Berlin, NH, p. A405
Chief Financial Officer, Huggins Hospital, Wolfeboro, NH, p. A408

ROBERSON, Barbara, Interim Chief Financial Officer, United Medical Center, Washington, DC, p. A120

ROBERSON, Ed, Director Information Systems, Houston Northwest Medical Center, Houston, TX, p. A620

ROBERSON, Joe, Chief Executive Officer, Reliant Rehabilitation Hospital Abilene, Abilene, TX, p. A590

ROBERSON, Lynda, Senior Program Director, Rusk State Hospital, Rusk, TX, p. A639

ROBERSON, Meika, M.D. Chief Medical Officer, Hoboken University Medical Center, Hoboken, NJ, p. A412

ROBERT, Thomas W., Senior Vice President of Finance and Chief Financial Officer, Mercy Medical Center, Springfield, MA, p. A311

ROBERTS, Alden, M.D. Chief Medical Officer, PeaceHealth Southwest Medical Center, Vancouver, WA, p. A687

ROBERTS, Allyson, CPA Chief Financial Officer, Nor–Lea General Hospital, Lovington, NM, p. A425

ROBERTS, Andrew, Interim Chief Human Resources Officer, Veterans Affairs Gulf Coast Veterans Health Care System, Biloxi, MS, p. A350

ROBERTS, Barbara, Chief Financial Officer, Robley Rex Veterans Affairs Medical Center, Louisville, KY, p. A262

ROBERTS, Bert, Controller, Miracle Mile Medical Center, Los Angeles, CA, p. A71

ROBERTS, Brad, Network Administrator, Swisher Memorial Hospital District, Tulia, TX, p. A648

ROBERTS, Cathy, Vice President Mission Integration and Human Resources, Mercy Regional Medical Center, Durango, CO, p. A102

ROBERTS, Charles, M.D
Executive Vice President and Executive Medical Director, Children's Mercy Hospitals and Clinics, Kansas City, MO, p. A369
Medical Director, Children's Mercy South, Overland Park, KS, p. A248

ROBERTS, Cheryl, Chief Nursing Officer, McCamey County Hospital District, McCamey, TX, p. A631

ROBERTS, Curtis L., Chief Executive Officer, Select Specialty Hospital–Augusta, Augusta, GA, p. A151

ROBERTS, Cyndi, Director Human Resources, Plaza Medical Center of Fort Worth, Fort Worth, TX, p. A614

ROBERTS, Deborah, R.N. Chief Nursing Officer, The Surgical Hospital of Phoenix, Phoenix, AZ, p. A36

ROBERTS, Debra, Director of Human Resources, St. Luke's Lakeside Hospital, The Woodlands, TX, p. A647

ROBERTS, Greg, Superintendent, Oregon State Hospital, Salem, OR, p. A525

ROBERTS, Jack, Director Information Systems, Twin County Regional Healthcare, Galax, VA, p. A665

ROBERTS, Jeff, Director Information Technology, Pinckneyville Community Hospital, Pinckneyville, IL, p. A198

ROBERTS, Joanne, M.D. Chief Medical Officer, Providence Regional Medical Center Everett, Everett, WA, p. A679

ROBERTS, Kathryn, Director Human Resources, Mercy Medical Center–Dubuque, Dubuque, IA, p. A227

ROBERTS, Kenneth D., President, John T. Mather Memorial Hospital, Port Jefferson, NY, p. A447

ROBERTS, Kevin A., FACHE, President and Chief Executive Officer, Glendale Adventist Medical Center, Glendale, CA, p. A63

ROBERTS, Krista, Chief Operating Officer, St. Mary's Regional Medical Center, Enid, OK, p. A506

ROBERTS, Laurel, R.N., Interim Chief Executive Officer, Rolling Hills Hospital, Franklin, TN, p. A577

ROBERTS, Lisa, Chief Operating Officer, Purcell Municipal Hospital, Purcell, OK, p. A514

ROBERTS, Matthew S., Chief Executive Officer, Glenwood Regional Medical Center, West Monroe, LA, p. A286

ROBERTS, Michael, Chief Information Officer, Highlands Regional Medical Center, Prestonsburg, KY, p. A265

ROBERTS, Michele, Hospital Recruiter, Kindred Hospital–Greensboro, Greensboro, NC, p. A461

ROBERTS, Nancy, Chief Operating Officer, Providence St. Vincent Medical Center, Portland, OR, p. A524

ROBERTS, Pamela W., Chief Executive Officer, Tennova Healthcare – McNairy Regional Hospital, Selmer, TN, p. A587

ROBERTS, Phillip G., Vice President Finance and Chief Financial Officer, Columbus Community Hospital, Inc., Columbus, WI, p. A699

ROBERTS, Rob, Director Information Technology, Benson Hospital, Benson, AZ, p. A30

ROBERTS, Robert C.
Vice President, Baptist Health Extended Care Hospital, Little Rock, AR, p. A47
Senior Vice President Financial Services, Baptist Health Medical Center – North Little Rock, North Little Rock, AR, p. A49
Vice President and Chief Financial Officer, Baptist Health Medical Center–Arkadelphia, Arkadelphia, AR, p. A41
Senior Vice President Financial Services, Baptist Health Medical Center–Little Rock, Little Rock, AR, p. A47
Senior Vice President, Baptist Health Rehabilitation Institute, Little Rock, AR, p. A47

ROBERTS, Roslyn, Manager, Northside Hospital–Cherokee, Canton, GA, p. A153

ROBERTS, Stacie
Coordinator Human Resources, Baylor Specialty Hospital, Dallas, TX, p. A604
Coordinator Human Resources, Our Children's House at Baylor, Dallas, TX, p. A606

ROBERTS, Teresa, Chief Financial Officer, Ringgold County Hospital, Mount Ayr, IA, p. A232

ROBERTS, Todd, Manager Business Operations, Peninsula Hospital, Louisville, TN, p. A582

ROBERTSHAW, Hazel, R.N. Chief Nursing Officer, Vice President Patient Services, F. F. Thompson Hospital, Canandaigua, NY, p. A431

ROBERTSON, Bradley, Chief Financial Officer, Saint Francis Hospital, Memphis, TN, p. A584

ROBERTSON, Carla, Chief Operating Officer and Chief Financial Officer, Saline Memorial Hospital, Benton, AR, p. A41

ROBERTSON, Darcy, Chief Financial Officer, Page Hospital, Page, AZ, p. A34

ROBERTSON, Jr., James A., Chief Financial Officer, Bothwell Regional Health Center, Sedalia, MO, p. A378

ROBERTSON, Jean, M.D. Chief Information Officer, Fairfield Medical Center, Lancaster, OH, p. A491

ROBERTSON, John L., Administrator, West Central Georgia Regional Hospital, Columbus, GA, p. A154

ROBERTSON, Larry, President, Texas Health Center for Diagnostic & Surgery, Plano, TX, p. A637

ROBERTSON, Laura, R.N.,
Chief Executive Officer, Banner Baywood Medical Center, Mesa, AZ, p. A33
Chief Executive Officer, Banner Desert Medical Center, Mesa, AZ, p. A33
Chief Executive Officer, Banner Heart Hospital, Mesa, AZ, p. A33

ROBERTSON, Marta, Chief Medical Staff, Prevost Memorial Hospital, Donaldsonville, LA, p. A273

ROBERTSON, Michael, Chief Executive Officer, Piedmont Newnan Hospital, Newnan, GA, p. A162

ROBERTSON, Michelle, R.N., President, Seton Medical Center Williamson, Round Rock, TX, p. A639

ROBERTSON, Patricia Dianne, Chief Financial Officer, Mercy Hospital Watonga, Watonga, OK, p. A518

ROBERTSON, Steve
Vice President, Kapiolani Medical Center for Women & Children, Honolulu, HI, p. A168
Senior Vice President, Pali Momi Medical Center, Aiea, HI, p. A168
Executive Vice President and Chief Information Officer, Straub Clinic & Hospital, Honolulu, HI, p. A169
Executive Vice President Revenue Cycle Management and Chief Information Officer, Wilcox Memorial Hospital, Lihue, HI, p. A170

ROBERTSON, Tana, Chief Operating Officer, McCamey County Hospital District, McCamey, TX, p. A631

ROBERTSON, William G., President and Chief Executive Officer, MultiCare Health System, Tacoma, WA, p. B94

ROBERTSON, William G., President and Chief Executive Officer, MultiCare Tacoma General Hospital, Tacoma, WA, p. A686

ROBERTSON–KECK, Karen, Vice President Human Resources, MedStar Franklin Square Medical Center, Baltimore, MD, p. A294

ROBERTSTAD, John R., FACHE,
President, Oconomowoc Memorial Hospital, Oconomowoc, WI, p. A708
President, Waukesha Memorial Hospital, Waukesha, WI, p. A713

ROBESON, Gail, Vice President Patient Services, Huron Regional Medical Center, Huron, SD, p. A569

ROBICHEAUX, James Warren, Senior Administrator, East Texas Medical Center Pittsburg, Pittsburg, TX, p. A636

ROBINS, Scott, M.D. Chief Medical Officer, Covenant Children's Hospital, Lubbock, TX, p. A629

ROBINSON, Adam M., Acting Director, Veterans Affairs Maryland Health Care System–Baltimore Division, Baltimore, MD, p. A295

ROBINSON, Alan, Chief Financial Officer, Logan Regional Hospital, Logan, UT, p. A655

ROBINSON, Anthony, Manager, Human Resources, Mercy Hospital of Folsom, Folsom, CA, p. A61

ROBINSON, Bradley, Chief Financial Officer, Evans U. S. Army Community Hospital, Fort Carson, CO, p. A103

ROBINSON, Carol, R.N. Chief Patient Care Services Officer, University of California, Davis Medical Center, Sacramento, CA, p. A85

ROBINSON, Cliff, M.D. Chief of Staff, Central Alabama Veterans Health Care System, Montgomery, AL, p. A23

ROBINSON, David, M.D. President Medical and Dental Staff, Community Hospital, Munster, IN, p. A217

ROBINSON, David, D.O. Medical Director, St. Joseph's Behavioral Health Center, Stockton, CA, p. A93

ROBINSON, Elena, Chief Human Resources Officer, Hospital HIMA San Pablo Caguas, Caguas, PR, p. A720

ROBINSON, Eric
Chief Executive Officer, Merit Health Natchez, Natchez, MS, p. A358
Chief Executive Officer, Natchez Community Hospital, Natchez, MS, p. A358

ROBINSON, Girard, M.D. Senior Vice President Medical and Clinical Affairs, Spring Harbor Hospital, Westbrook, ME, p. A292

ROBINSON, Glenn A., Chief Executive Officer, Baylor Scott & White Hillcrest Medical Center, Waco, TX, p. A650

ROBINSON, James, Chief Financial Officer, George E. Weems Memorial Hospital, Apalachicola, FL, p. A121

ROBINSON, Jeanne, Director Human Resources, Inova Fair Oaks Hospital, Fairfax, VA, p. A664

ROBINSON, Jennifer, Administrator, Behavioral HealthCare Center at Clarksville, Clarksville, TN, p. A575

ROBINSON, Jennifer B., Vice President Human Resources, St. Petersburg General Hospital, Saint Petersburg, FL, p. A142

ROBINSON, Lance, Associate Director, Amarillo Veterans Affairs Health Care System, Amarillo, TX, p. A591

ROBINSON, Mark, FACHE, Chief Executive Officer, Capital Regional Medical Center, Tallahassee, FL, p. A144

ROBINSON, Mark, Associate Administrator and Chief Financial Officer, Hazel Hawkins Memorial Hospital, Hollister, CA, p. A65

ROBINSON, Mary, Chief Nursing Officer and Vice President Patient Care Services, Texas Health Harris Methodist Hospital Southwest Fort Worth, Fort Worth, TX, p. A614

ROBINSON, Michael
Chief Executive Officer, Bon Secours Memorial Regional Medical Center, Mechanicsville, VA, p. A668
Executive Vice President and Administrator, Bon Secours–Richmond Community Hospital, Richmond, VA, p. A671

ROBINSON, Paul H., M.D. Medical Director, American Fork Hospital, American Fork, UT, p. A654

ROBINSON, Phil, Chief Financial Officer, Saint Agnes Medical Center, Fresno, CA, p. A62

ROBINSON, Phillip D., President, Lankenau Medical Center, Wynnewood, PA, p. A554

ROBINSON, Ron, Business Partner, Lutheran Hospital, Cleveland, OH, p. A485

ROBINSON, Stephen, Chief Executive Officer, Ochsner Medical Center – Kenner, Kenner, LA, p. A276

ROBINSON, Susan Beth, Vice President Human Resources, St. Mary's Medical Center, Huntington, WV, p. A692

ROBINSON, Tim, Executive Vice President, Chief Financial and Administrative Officer and Treasurer, Nationwide Children's Hospital, Columbus, OH, p. A486

ROBINSON, Vance, Chief Information Officer, Iberia Medical Center, New Iberia, LA, p. A281

ROBINSON, William, Director Human Resources, HEALTHSOUTH Rehabilitation Hospital of Erie, Erie, PA, p. A534

ROBISCH, Christine, Senior Vice President and Area Manager, Kaiser Permanente San Francisco Medical Center, San Francisco, CA, p. A88

ROBISON, Bruce, Vice President and Chief Information Officer, Cox Medical Centers, Springfield, MO, p. A378

ROBISON, Keith, Chief Information Officer, Woman's Christian Association Hospital, Jamestown, NY, p. A435

ROBISON, Neely, Director Human Resources, The BridgeWay, North Little Rock, AR, p. A49

ROBISON, Rob, Director Information Technology, Medical Center of South Arkansas, El Dorado, AR, p. A43

ROBISON, Ryan, Chief Nursing Officer, Sanpete Valley Hospital, Mount Pleasant, UT, p. A656

ROBISON, Wendell, M.D. Chief of Staff, Sheridan Veterans Affairs Medical Center, Sheridan, WY, p. A717

ROBITAILLE, Mark E., President and Chief Executive Officer, Martin Health System, Stuart, FL, p. A143

ROBSON, Marcia, R.N. Chief Nursing Officer, Ozarks Medical Center, West Plains, MO, p. A380

ROBSON, Melissa, President, Novant Health Prince William Medical Center, Manassas, VA, p. A667

ROCA, Robert, M.D. Vice President Medical Affairs, Sheppard Pratt Health System, Baltimore, MD, p. A294

ROCCO, Carmen, M.D. Chief Medical Officer, Presence United Samaritans Medical Center, Danville, IL, p. A185

ROCHA, Israel, Chief Executive Officer, Doctor's Hospital at Renaissance, Edinburg, TX, p. A610

ROCHA, Julie, Vice President Human Resources, Mercy Medical Center Merced, Merced, CA, p. A75

ROCHE, Joseph E., Chief Executive Officer, Vibra Hospital of Charleston, Mt. Pleasant, SC, p. A563

ROCHE, Kathleen M., R.N. Executive Vice President and Chief Operating Officer, Saint Francis Hospital and Medical Center, Hartford, CT, p. A112

ROCHE, Rick, Director Human Resources and Information Systems, Lakeside Medical Center, Belle Glade, FL, p. A121

ROCHE, Sarah, Director Human Resources, Lakes Regional Healthcare, Spirit Lake, IA, p. A235

ROCHELEAU, John, Vice President Business Support and Information Technology, Bellin Memorial Hospital, Green Bay, WI, p. A701

ROCHESTER, Charmaine, Vice President Finance, Bon Secours–DePaul Medical Center, Norfolk, VA, p. A669

ROCHIER, Dennis, Chief Medical Officer, Renown South Meadows Medical Center, Reno, NV, p. A404

ROCK, Betty Ann, Vice President Nursing and Chief Nursing Officer, Uniontown Hospital, Uniontown, PA, p. A551

ROCK, Brian, Director of Information Systems, VCU Community Memorial Hospital, South Hill, VA, p. A673

ROCK, David, Executive Vice President and Chief Operating Officer, Wyckoff Heights Medical Center, NY, p. A445

ROCKSMITH, Eugenio, M.D. Medical Director, HEALTHSOUTH Rehabilitation Hospital of Vineland, Vineland, NJ, p. A419

ROCKWELL, Jane, Director Support Services, North Metro Medical Center, Jacksonville, AR, p. A46

ROCKWELL, Karla, Director of Nursing, Doctors Memorial Hospital, Bonifay, FL, p. A122

ROCKWOOD, John D., President, MedStar National Rehabilitation Hospital, Washington, DC, p. A119

RODDEN, Celeste, Chief Information Officer, Hillcrest Hospital Claremore, Claremore, OK, p. A505

RODDY, Thomas
Chief Executive Officer, HEALTHSOUTH Rehabilitation Hospital of Montgomery, Montgomery, AL, p. A23
Interim Chief Executive Officer, Riverview Regional Medical Center, Gadsden, AL, p. A20

RODDY, Tim, M.D. Vice President Medical Affairs, Swedish/Edmonds, Edmonds, WA, p. A678

RODEN, George
Vice President Human Resources, Mercy Hospital Aurora, Aurora, MO, p. A363
Vice President Human Resources, Mercy Hospital Cassville, Cassville, MO, p. A365

RODENBAUGH, Cathy, Director Human Resources, Holy Rosary Healthcare, Miles City, MT, p. A385

RODERICK, Travis W., Chief Executive Officer, Premier Surgical Institute, Galena, KS, p. A240

RODERMAN, Nicki, Chief Nursing Officer, Denton Regional Medical Center, Denton, TX, p. A608

RODGE, Mark, Director Information Systems, Eaton Rapids Medical Center, Eaton Rapids, MI, p. A319

RODGERS, April, Vice President, Human Resources, Holy Name Medical Center, Teaneck, NJ, p. A419

RODGERS, Dondie, Interim Chief Nursing Officer, Memorial Hospital of Texas County, Guymon, OK, p. A507

RODGERS, Jamie, Interim Chief Executive Officer, Choctaw Regional Medical Center, Ackerman, MS, p. A350

RODGERS, Kliff
Chief Financial Officer, ContinueCare Hospital at Baptist Health Corbin, Corbin, KY, p. A255
Vice President and Chief Financial Officer, ContinueCARE Hospital at Hendrick Medical Center, Abilene, TX, p. A590

RODGERS, Larry, Chief Executive Officer, College Station Medical Center, College Station, TX, p. A601

RODIER, James Barton, M.D. Chief Quality Officer, Health Central Hospital, Ocoee, FL, p. A137

RODOWICZ, Darlene, Chief Financial Officer, Berkshire Medical Center, Pittsfield, MA, p. A310

RODRIGUES, Pablo, M.D. Medical Director, Vibra Hospital of Amarillo, Amarillo, TX, p. A591

RODRIGUEZ, Alex
Vice President and Chief Information Officer, St. Elizabeth Edgewood, Edgewood, KY, p. A256
Vice President and Chief Information Officer, St. Elizabeth Florence, Florence, KY, p. A256
Vice President and Chief Information Officer, St. Elizabeth Fort Thomas, Fort Thomas, KY, p. A257

RODRIGUEZ, Angie, Human Resource Manager, Carson Tahoe Continuing Care Hospital, Carson City, NV, p. A400

RODRIGUEZ, Ben A., Chief Executive Officer, Hialeah Hospital, Hialeah, FL, p. A128

RODRIGUEZ, Candie, Director Human Resources, Hospital San Cristobal, Coto Laurel, PR, p. A721

RODRIGUEZ, Edgardo, Director Management Information Systems, Auxilio Mutuo Hospital, San Juan, PR, p. A723

RODRIGUEZ, Heather, Chief Nursing Officer, Fresno Heart and Surgical Hospital, Fresno, CA, p. A62

RODRIGUEZ, Jaime, Chief Financial Officer, San Juan City Hospital, San Juan, PR, p. A724

RODRIGUEZ, Jose Luis, Chief Executive Officer, Hospital Pavia–Santurce, San Juan, PR, p. A723

RODRIGUEZ, Jose O., M.D. Medical Director, Castaner General Hospital, Castaner, PR, p. A720

RODRIGUEZ, Laura, Director Medical Records, Hospital Del Maestro, San Juan, PR, p. A723

RODRIGUEZ, Lea, Chief Nursing Officer, Clara Maass Medical Center, Belleville, NJ, p. A409

RODRIGUEZ, Leticia, Chief Executive Officer, Ward Memorial Hospital, Monahans, TX, p. A633

RODRIGUEZ, Lizzette, Director Finance, Hospital San Francisco, San Juan, PR, p. A724

RODRIGUEZ, Marco, Chief Financial Officer, Valley Baptist Medical Center–Harlingen, Harlingen, TX, p. A618

RODRIGUEZ, Mario, Chief Executive Officer, Laredo Specialty Hospital, Laredo, TX, p. A627

RODRIGUEZ, Maritza, Chief Financial Officer, Hospital Metropolitan, San Juan, PR, p. A723

RODRIGUEZ, Miguel, Medical Director, Caribbean Medical Center, Fajardo, PR, p. A721

RODRIGUEZ, Oscar, Chief Fiscal Officer, Veterans Affairs Caribbean Healthcare System, San Juan, PR, p. A724

RODRIGUEZ, Patricia M., Senior Vice President and Area Manager, Kaiser Permanente South Sacramento Medical Center, Sacramento, CA, p. A84

RODRIGUEZ, Ramon J., President and Chief Executive Officer, Wyckoff Heights Medical Center, NY, p. A445

RODRIGUEZ, Rufus, M.D. Medical Director, Mayo Clinic Health System in Fairmont, Fairmont, MN, p. A338

**RODRIGUEZ, Sara**
Chief Financial Officer, Kindred Hospital Sugar Land, Sugar Land, TX, p. A645
Human Resources, Seton Smithville Regional Hospital, Smithville, TX, p. A644

**RODRIGUEZ, Susanna,** Director Human Resources, MMO WestEnd Hospital, Jennings, LA, p. A276

**RODRIGUEZ, Tammy,** Vice President of Patient Care Services, Rollins–Brook Community Hospital, Lampasas, TX, p. A627

**RODRIGUEZ, Tomas,** Chief Information Technology Officer, First Hospital Panamericano, Cidra, PR, p. A720

**RODRIGUEZ, Tony,** Director Human Resources, South Texas Rehabilitation Hospital, Brownsville, TX, p. A598

**RODRIGUEZ, Vilma,** Director Human Resources, Hospital San Pablo Del Este, Fajardo, PR, p. A721

**RODRIGUEZ, Wilfredo, M.D.** Chief of Staff, Battle Creek Veterans Affairs Medical Center, Battle Creek, MI, p. A315

**RODRIGUEZ SCHMIDT, Myriam T.,** Director Human Resources, Cardiovascular Center of Puerto Rico and the Caribbean, San Juan, PR, p. A723

**RODRIQUEZ, Daisy,** Director Human Resources, Fort Duncan Regional Medical Center, Eagle Pass, TX, p. A609

**ROE, Carolyn J., R.N.** Chief Nursing Officer, Copley Hospital, Morrisville, VT, p. A660

**ROE, Daniel, M.D.** Chief Operating Officer, Copper Queen Community Hospital, Bisbee, AZ, p. A30

**ROE, Timothy,** Chief Information Officer, Hillside Rehabilitation Hospital, Warren, OH, p. A499

**ROE, Timothy J., M.D.,** President and Chief Executive Officer, Rehabilitation Hospital of the Pacific, Honolulu, HI, p. A169

**ROEBACK, Jason,** Chief Executive Officer, Sharon Regional Health System, Sharon, PA, p. A550

**ROEBKEN, Curtis, M.D.** Chief Medical Staff, Kentfield Rehabilitation and Specialty Hospital, Kentfield, CA, p. A65

**ROEBUCK, Amanda**
Interim Chief Executive Officer, Genoa Medical Facilities, Genoa, NE, p. A392
Director Patient Care Services, Genoa Medical Facilities, Genoa, NE, p. A392

**ROEDER, Donna,** Chief Financial Officer, Jackson County Regional Health Center, Maquoketa, IA, p. A231

**ROEDER, Werner, M.D.** Vice President Medical Affairs, New York–Presbyterian/Lawrence Hospital, Bronxville, NY, p. A430

**ROEDERER, Chris,** Senior Vice President Human Resources, Tampa General Hospital, Tampa, FL, p. A145

**ROEHRLE, Andreas,** Director Finance, Sentara Williamsburg Regional Medical Center, Williamsburg, VA, p. A674

**ROEMER, Dennis,** Executive Vice President and Chief Financial Officer, Lancaster General Health, Lancaster, PA, p. A537

**ROERICK, Diane,** Interim Chief Nursing Executive, CHI Albany Area Health, Albany, MN, p. A334

**ROESER, William,** President and Chief Executive Officer, Sparrow Ionia Hospital, Ionia, MI, p. A322

**ROESLER, Bruce E., FACHE,** Chief Executive Officer, Richland Hospital, Richland Center, WI, p. A710

**ROETMAN, James D.,** President and Chief Executive Officer, Pocahontas Community Hospital, Pocahontas, IA, p. A233

**ROEVER, Judy, MSN** Chief Nursing Officer, Scenic Mountain Medical Center, Big Spring, TX, p. A597

**ROFF, Lynette A.,** Director, Veterans Affairs Eastern Colorado Health Care System, Denver, CO, p. A102

**ROFFELSEN, Michael S.,** Chief Executive Officer, Kindred Hospital South Florida–Fort Lauderdale, Fort Lauderdale, FL, p. A127

**ROGALSKI, Robert,** Chief Executive Officer, Excela Health, Greensburg, PA, p. B55

**ROGALSKI, Ted,** Administrator, Genesis Medical Center–Aledo, Aledo, IL, p. A178

**ROGAN, Edie,** Manager Human Resources, Eastern State Hospital, Williamsburg, VA, p. A674

**ROGERS, B. Carter,** Chief of Staff, Newton Medical Center, Covington, GA, p. A155

**ROGERS, Bard, M.D.** Chief of Staff, Golden Plains Community Hospital, Borger, TX, p. A598

**ROGERS, Cathy M.,** Manager Human Resources, Greenville Health System – Laurens County Memorial Hospital, Clinton, SC, p. A559

**ROGERS, David,** Chief Executive Officer, Sanford Webster Medical Center, Webster, SD, p. A573

**ROGERS, Doris,** Vice President Human Resources, Saint Luke's Hospital of Kansas City, Kansas City, MO, p. A370

**ROGERS, Gregory H.,** President, MidMichigan Medical Center–Midland, Midland, MI, p. A325

**ROGERS, Gus,** Chief Financial Officer, Coffey County Hospital, Burlington, KS, p. A238

**ROGERS, James H., FACHE,** Chief Executive Officer, Cornerstone Hospital of North Little Rock, Jacksonville, AR, p. A46

**ROGERS, Jared, M.D.,**
Interim Regional President and Chief Executive Officer, Presence Covenant Medical Center, Urbana, IL, p. A202
Interim Regional President and Chief Executive Officer, Presence United Samaritans Medical Center, Danville, IL, p. A185

**ROGERS, Joel,** Chief Operating Officer, Minidoka Memorial Hospital, Rupert, ID, p. A176

**ROGERS, Joseph E.C., M.D.** Chief of Staff, John C. Fremont Healthcare District, Mariposa, CA, p. A74

**ROGERS, Joseph J.,** Vice President and Chief Operating Officer, Redwood Memorial Hospital, Fortuna, CA, p. A61

**ROGERS, Judith, Ph.D.,** President and Chief Executive Officer, Holy Cross Hospital, Silver Spring, MD, p. A300

**ROGERS, Kathy,** Vice President Marketing, San Luis Valley Health Conejos County Hospital, La Jara, CO, p. A105

**ROGERS, Keith**
Interim Administrator, CHRISTUS Dubuis Hospital of Fort Smith, Fort Smith, AR, p. A44
Administrator, CHRISTUS Dubuis Hospital of Hot Springs, Hot Springs National Park, AR, p. A46

**ROGERS, LaDonna,** Director Human Resources, T. J. Samson Community Hospital, Glasgow, KY, p. A257

**ROGERS, Lucy,** Chief Information Resource Management Systems, Veterans Affairs North Texas Health Care System, Dallas, TX, p. A607

**ROGERS, Mark G.**
Interim Vice President Finance and Chief Financial Officer, Genesis Medical Center, Illini Campus, Silvis, IL, p. A200
Chief Financial Officer, Genesis Medical Center–Aledo, Aledo, IL, p. A178
Interim Vice President Finance and Chief Financial Officer, Genesis Medical Center–Davenport, Davenport, IA, p. A225

**ROGERS, Matt,** Chief Financial Officer, Philhaven, Mount Gretna, PA, p. A541

**ROGERS, Michael,** Vice President Fiscal Services, Brattleboro Memorial Hospital, Brattleboro, VT, p. A660

**ROGERS, Patricia,** Director of Nursing, Dahl Memorial Healthcare Association, Ekalaka, MT, p. A383

**ROGERS, Ralph, M.D.** Vice President Medical Affairs and Chief Medical Officer, Spectrum Health – Butterworth Hospital, Grand Rapids, MI, p. A321

**ROGERS, Randy, FACHE** Chief Financial Officer, Rapides Regional Medical Center, Alexandria, LA, p. A268

**ROGERS, Rhonda,** Chief Financial Officer, Des Peres Hospital, Saint Louis, MO, p. A376

**ROGERS, Richard K., FACHE** Vice President Human Resources, Wayne Memorial Hospital, Goldsboro, NC, p. A461

**ROGERS, II, Robert T., M.D.** Medical Director, Canton–Potsdam Hospital, Potsdam, NY, p. A448

**ROGERS, Selwyn O., M.D.** Vice President and Chief Medical Officer, University of Texas Medical Branch, Galveston, TX, p. A615

**ROGERS, Sherry L., MS** Chief Nursing Officer, Redington–Fairview General Hospital, Skowhegan, ME, p. A292

**ROGERS, Tammy,** Director Human Resources, Mt. San Rafael Hospital, Trinidad, CO, p. A109

**ROGERS, Valerie J.,** Director of Nursing, Cherokee Nation W.W. Hastings Indian Hospital, Tahlequah, OK, p. A515

**ROGERS, W. Kent,** Chief Executive Officer, Southwest Memorial Hospital, Cortez, CO, p. A101

**ROGERS, William,** Chief Medical Officer, Merit Health Gilmore Memorial, Amory, MS, p. A350

**ROGNESS, Robin,** Vice President and Chief Financial Officer, Mercy Hospital of Folsom, Folsom, CA, p. A61

**ROGOLS, Kevin L., FACHE,** Administrator, Kalkaska Memorial Health Center, Kalkaska, MI, p. A324

**ROGOZ, Brian,** Vice President Finance and Treasurer, The Hospital of Central Connecticut, New Britain, CT, p. A113

**ROHAN, Colleen,** Director Human Resources, Little Company of Mary Hospital and Health Care Centers, Evergreen Park, IL, p. A188

**ROHAN, Heather J.**
Chief Executive Officer, Tristar Ashland City Medical Center, Ashland City, TN, p. A574
Chief Executive Officer, TriStar Centennial Medical Center, Nashville, TN, p. A586

**ROHLEDER, Scott,** Chief Information Officer, Hays Medical Center, Hays, KS, p. A241

**ROHLOFF, William A., FACHE,** Interim Chief Executive Officer, Houston County Medical Center, Crockett, TX, p. A603

**ROHMAN, Cindy, R.N.** Vice President/Chief Nursing Officer, Lexington Medical Center, West Columbia, SC, p. A566

**ROHN, Stephen G., M.D.** Vice President and Chief Medical Officer, Hamilton Medical Center, Dalton, GA, p. A155

**ROHRBACH, Dan D.,** President and Chief Executive Officer, Southwest Health Center, Platteville, WI, p. A709

**ROHRBACH, William K.,** Chief Executive Officer, Guthrie Towanda Memorial Hospital, Towanda, PA, p. A551

**ROHRER, Harry**
Chief Financial Officer, Bascom Palmer Eye Institute–Anne Bates Leach Eye Hospital, Miami, FL, p. A134
Chief Financial Officer, University of Miami Hospital, Miami, FL, p. A135
Chief Financial Officer, University of Miami Hospital and Clinics, Miami, FL, p. A135

**ROHRER, John J.**
Acting Director, Tomah Veterans Affairs Medical Center, Tomah, WI, p. A712
Associate Director, William S. Middleton Memorial Veterans Hospital, Madison, WI, p. A704

**ROHRER, Mark, M.D.** Chief Medical Officer, Kindred Hospital–Boston, Brighton, MA, p. A304

**ROHRICH, George A., FACHE,** Chief Executive Officer, River's Edge Hospital and Clinic, Saint Peter, MN, p. A347

**ROIZ, PHR,** JoAnn, Director Human Resources, HEALTHSOUTH Tustin Rehabilitation Hospital, Tustin, CA, p. A95

**ROKOSZ, Gregory, D.O.** Senior Vice President Medical and Academic Affairs, Saint Barnabas Medical Center, Livingston, NJ, p. A413

**ROKSVAAG, George, M.D.** Chief Medical Officer, Hunterdon Medical Center, Flemington, NJ, p. A412

**ROLAND, Brian,** Chief Executive Officer, Muenster Memorial Hospital, Muenster, TX, p. A633

**ROLEK, Jim,** Chief Human Resources Officer, Clara Maass Medical Center, Belleville, NJ, p. A409

**ROLERSON, Jana,** Chief Nursing Officer, Shands Live Oak Regional Medical Center, Live Oak, FL, p. A132

**ROLEY, Margaret,** Chief Nursing Officer, South Baldwin Regional Medical Center, Foley, AL, p. A19

**ROLFE, David,** Chief Information Officer, Madonna Rehabilitation Hospital, Lincoln, NE, p. A394

**ROLFF, Christi,** Director Business Development, San Joaquin Valley Rehabilitation Hospital, Fresno, CA, p. A62

**ROLING, Robin,** Chief Executive Officer, Hot Springs County Memorial Hospital, Thermopolis, WY, p. A717

**ROLLI, Molli Martha, M.D.** Medical Director, Mendota Mental Health Institute, Madison, WI, p. A704

**ROLLING, Andy,** Director of Finance, Regina Hospital, Hastings, MN, p. A340

**ROLLINS, David,** Chief Resource Management Division, Reynolds Army Community Hospital, Fort Sill, OK, p. A507

**ROLLINS, David W.,** Chief Financial Officer, Mt. San Rafael Hospital, Trinidad, CO, p. A109

**ROLLINS, James**
Chief Financial Officer, Arbour H. R. I. Hospital, Brookline, MA, p. A305
Chief Financial Officer, Arbour–Fuller Hospital, Attleboro, MA, p. A302

**ROLLINS, Larry,** Supervisor Information Technology, McCamey County Hospital District, McCamey, TX, p. A631

**ROLOFF, Maria,** Vice President Human Resources, Mission Hospital, Asheville, NC, p. A455

**ROLON, Waleska,** Manager, Hospital Santa Rosa, Guayama, PR, p. A721

**ROMACK, Lenae,** Manager Human Resources, Baylor Institute for Rehabilitation at Fort Worth, Fort Worth, TX, p. A613

**ROMAN, Eloy, M.D.** Chief of Staff, Palmetto General Hospital, Hialeah, FL, p. A128

**ROMAN, Linda K.,** Administrator, Coast Plaza Hospital, Norwalk, CA, p. A78

**ROMAN, Marina, M.D.** Medical Director, Hospital de la Universidad de Puerto Rico/Dr. Federico Trilla, Carolina, PR, p. A720

**ROMANELLO, Marcus,** Chief Medical Officer, Fort Hamilton Hospital, Hamilton, OH, p. A491

**ROMANIA, Matt,** Director of Nursing, Soldiers and Sailors Memorial Hospital, Wellsboro, PA, p. A552

**ROMANICK, Odile,** Chief information Officer, Day Kimball Hospital, Putnam, CT, p. A114

**ROMANIELLO, Guy,** Director Fiscal Services, Belmont Center for Comprehensive Treatment, Philadelphia, PA, p. A542

**ROMANO, C. James, M.D.** Chief Medical Officer, St. Francis Medical Center, Trenton, NJ, p. A419

**ROMANO, Jana,** Manager Human Resources, Good Shepherd Penn Partners Specialty Hospital at Rittenhouse, Philadelphia, PA, p. A543

**ROMANO, Michael A., M.D.** Vice President Medical Affairs, Methodist Jennie Edmundson Hospital, Council Bluffs, IA, p. A225

**ROMANO, Sara, R.N.** Vice President, Mountain View Hospital, Gadsden, AL, p. A20

**ROMANOWSKI, Ellen,** Chief Nursing Officer, HEALTHSOUTH Rehabilitation Hospital of Miami, Cutler Bay, FL, p. A124

**ROMANS, Alan,** Director Information Technology, Ashland Health Center, Ashland, KS, p. A237

**ROMBERGER, Randall R.,** Administrator, Shriners Hospitals for Children–Greenville, Greenville, SC, p. A561

Index of Health Care Professionals / Ross

Index of Health Care Professionals

ROMEO, John, Chief Information Officer, Mercy Hospital and Medical Center, Chicago, IL, p. A183
ROMERO, Brenda, Administrator, Presbyterian Espanola Hospital, Espanola, NM, p. A424
ROMERO, Edward, Chief Financial Officer, Rehabilitation Hospital of Fort Wayne, Fort Wayne, IN, p. A209
ROMERO, Frank, M.D
Chief Medical Officer, Cox Medical Centers, Springfield, MO, p. A378
Vice President Medical Affairs and Chief Medical Officer, Cox Monett, Monett, MO, p. A373
ROMERO, Matt, Chief Financial Officer, Oak Hill Hospital, Brooksville, FL, p. A123
ROMIG, Glenn, Chief Financial Officer, Osceola Regional Medical Center, Kissimmee, FL, p. A130
ROMINE, Andy, Chief Nursing Officer, Trinity Medical Center, Birmingham, AL, p. A17
ROMINE, Donnie
Interim President and Chief Executive Officer, St. Vincent's Medical Center Riverside, Jacksonville, FL, p. A130
System Chief Operating Officer and President St. Vincent's Medical Center Riverside, St. Vincent's Medical Center Riverside, Jacksonville, FL, p. A130
Interim President and Chief Executive Officer, St. Vincent's Medical Center Southside, Jacksonville, FL, p. A130
ROMITO, Edmund J., Chief Information Officer, Genesis HealthCare System, Zanesville, OH, p. A502
ROMOFF, Jeffrey A., President and Chief Executive Officer, UPMC, Pittsburgh, PA, p. B148
RONAN, Barry P., President and Chief Executive Officer, Western Maryland Regional Medical Center, Cumberland, MD, p. A297
RONAN, John, President and Chief Executive Officer, Blue Hill Memorial Hospital, Blue Hill, ME, p. A289
RONCA, Cyndi, Director Human Resources, Twin Cities Hospital, Niceville, FL, p. A136
RONDE, Christa, Assistant Chief Financial Officer, Palo Verde Hospital, Blythe, CA, p. A56
RONE, Tom, Chief Clinical Officer, Kindred Hospital–Nashville, Nashville, TN, p. A585
RONKE, Lisa, Director Finance, St. Michael's Hospital Avera, Tyndall, SD, p. A572
RONUM, Josh, Chief of Staff, West River Regional Medical Center, Hettinger, ND, p. A474
ROODMAN, Richard D., Chief Executive Officer, UW Medicine/Valley Medical Center, Renton, WA, p. A682
ROOF, Marie, Executive Vice President Information Systems, Vibra Specialty Hospital of Portland, Portland, OR, p. A525
ROOKER, Mark, Director Information Systems, Susan B. Allen Memorial Hospital, El Dorado, KS, p. A239
ROONEY, Al, Director Information Systems, St. Vincent Healthcare, Billings, MT, p. A381
ROONEY, David, Administrator Operaitons, Winneshiek Medical Center, Decorah, IA, p. A226
ROONEY, Jeffrey, Chief Financial Officer, University of Illinois Hospital & Health Sciences System, Chicago, IL, p. A185
ROONEY, Michael T., M.D., Interim President and Chief Executive Officer, St. Joseph Regional Medical Center, Lewiston, ID, p. A174
ROONEY, Thomas, Chief Information Resource Management, Veterans Affairs Hudson Valley Health Care System, Montrose, NY, p. A438
ROOP, Terri, Director Patient Care Services, Dickenson Community Hospital, Clintwood, VA, p. A663
ROOSA, Carol, Vice President Information Services and Chief Information Officer, Athol Memorial Hospital, Athol, MA, p. A302
ROOT, Jim, Vice President Human Resources, Saint Elizabeth's Medical Center, Wabasha, MN, p. A348
ROOT, Mary Ann, Supervisor Personnel, Essex County Hospital Center, Cedar Grove, NJ, p. A410
ROOT, Rodney Mark, D.O. Vice President Medical Affairs, Bakersfield Memorial Hospital, Bakersfield, CA, p. A55
ROPER, Embra, Chief Medical Officer, Regional Hospital for Respiratory and Complex Care, Burien, WA, p. A677
ROPER, Sandra, Chief Human Resources, General Leonard Wood Army Community Hospital, Fort Leonard Wood, MO, p. A367
ROPER, William L., M.P.H., Chief Executive Officer, UNC Health Care, Chapel Hill, NC, p. B139
ROSA–TOLEDO, Luis R., M.D. Medical Director, Hospital Manati Medical Center, Manati, PR, p. A721
ROSAAEN, Nancy, Chief Executive Officer, McCone County Health Center, Circle, MT, p. A382
ROSADO, Jose, Chief Executive Officer, Hospital Metropolitan, San Juan, PR, p. A723
ROSALES, Teresa, M.D. Clinical Director, Mental Health Institute, Clarinda, IA, p. A224
ROSATI, Rosemarie, Chief Operating Officer, University Behavioral Healthcare, Piscataway, NJ, p. A417
ROSATO, Ricardo, M.D. President Medical Staff, Shands Lake Shore Regional Medical Center, Lake City, FL, p. A131
ROSBOROUGH, Brian S., M.D. Chief Medical Officer, OSF Saint Elizabeth Medical Center, Ottawa, IL, p. A197
ROSCOE, Joan, Chief Information Officer, Winchester Medical Center, Winchester, VA, p. A674
ROSE, Cheryl, Human Resources Director, Fulton County Medical Center, Mc Connellsburg, PA, p. A539
ROSE, Hugh, Vice President Fiscal Management, Palos Community Hospital, Palos Heights, IL, p. A197
ROSE, J. Anthony, President and Chief Executive Officer, Catawba Valley Medical Center, Hickory, NC, p. A462
ROSE, Julia, R.N. Director of Nursing, Braxton County Memorial Hospital, Gassaway, WV, p. A691
ROSE, Kenneth, M.D. Chief Medical Staff, Wallowa Memorial Hospital, Enterprise, OR, p. A520
ROSE, Kim, Director Information Technology, Crouse Hospital, Syracuse, NY, p. A451
ROSE, Mary R., R.N. Chief Clinical Officer, Community Health Center of Branch County, Coldwater, MI, p. A317
ROSE, May, Director Human Resources, Memorial Hospital, Chester, IL, p. A181
ROSE, Michael S., Senior Vice President Finance and Chief Financial Officer, Southern New Hampshire Medical Center, Nashua, NH, p. A407
ROSE, Regina P., R.N. Vice President Nursing Services, Mid–Columbia Medical Center, The Dalles, OR, p. A526
ROSE, Richard T., Associate Director, Manchester Veterans Affairs Medical Center, Manchester, NH, p. A407
ROSE, Robert, R.N. Senior Vice President and System Chief Nursing Officer, Mother Frances Hospital – Tyler, Tyler, TX, p. A649
ROSE, Robin, R.N. Chief Operating Officer, Gibson Area Hospital and Health Services, Gibson City, IL, p. A189
ROSE, Silvia B., R.N. Director Patient Care Services, Vidant Bertie Hospital, Windsor, NC, p. A470
ROSE, Steven P., Chief Financial Officer, Conway Regional Medical Center, Conway, AR, p. A42
ROSE, Steven A., R.N., President and Chief Executive Officer, Nanticoke Memorial Hospital, Seaford, DE, p. A117
ROSECRANS, Brenda, Executive Director Human Resources, Sentara Albemarle Medical Center, Elizabeth City, NC, p. A459
ROSEMAN, Lynda K., Area Information Officer, Kaiser Permanente Antioch Medical Center, Antioch, CA, p. A53
ROSEMORE, Michael, M.D. Medical Director, HEALTHSOUTH Lakeshore Rehabilitation Hospital, Birmingham, AL, p. A16
ROSEN, Barry, M.D. Vice President Medical Management, Advocate Good Shepherd Hospital, Barrington, IL, p. A179
ROSEN, Jules, M.D. Chief Medical Officer, West Springs Hospital, Grand Junction, CO, p. A104
ROSEN, Linda, M.D., Chief Executive Officer, Hawaii Health Systems Corporation, Honolulu, HI, p. B61
ROSEN, Michael, M.D. Chief Medical Officer, Havasu Regional Medical Center, Lake Havasu City, AZ, p. A32
ROSEN, Raymond, FACHE Vice President Operations, York Hospital, York, PA, p. A554
ROSENA, Robens, Director Information Systems, Delray Medical Center, Delray Beach, FL, p. A125
ROSENBALM, Jennifer, Manager Business Office, Veterans Affairs Nebraska–Western Iowa Health Care System, Omaha, NE, p. A397
ROSENBAUM, Victor, Chief Operating Officer, Alaska Regional Hospital, Anchorage, AK, p. A27
ROSENBERG, Steven, Chief Financial Officer, Danbury Hospital, Danbury, CT, p. A111
ROSENBERG, Stuart E., President and Chief Executive Officer, Johnson Memorial Medical Center, Stafford Springs, CT, p. A115
ROSENBERGER, Robert, Chief Financial Officer, Adena Medical Center, Chillicothe, OH, p. A482
ROSENBERGER–SLAMPACK, Janie, Market Chief Executive Officer, Kindred Hospital–Pittsburgh, Oakdale, PA, p. A542
ROSENBLATT, Michael, M.D. Medical Director, Kindred Rehabilitation Hospital Clear Lake, Webster, TX, p. A651
ROSENBURG, Deborah L., Vice President Human Resources, Chesapeake Regional Medical Center, Chesapeake, VA, p. A663
ROSENCRANCE, Daris, Chief Financial Officer, Monongalia General Hospital, Morgantown, WV, p. A693
ROSENCRANCE, Michael, Vice President Information Services, Spectrum Health – Butterworth Hospital, Grand Rapids, MI, p. A321
ROSENDAHL, Lisa, Director Human Resources, St. Cloud Veterans Affairs Health Care System, Saint Cloud, MN, p. A346
ROSENDORFF, Clive, M.D. Chief Medical Program, James J. Peters Veterans Affairs Medical Center, NY, p. A440
ROSENFELD, Merryll, Vice President, Human Resources, Catholic Medical Center, Manchester, NH, p. A407
ROSENSTEIN, Gaynor, Vice President Operations, Bon Secours Community Hospital, Port Jervis, NY, p. A448
ROSENTHAL, J. Thomas, M.D. Chief Medical Officer, Ronald Reagan UCLA Medical Center, Los Angeles, CA, p. A72
ROSENTHAL, Raul, M.D. Interim Chief of Staff, Cleveland Clinic Florida, Weston, FL, p. A147
ROSEQUIST, Helen, Manager Information Systems, Warren General Hospital, Warren, PA, p. A551
ROSETTA, Kathy, Chief Nursing Officer, Laurel Ridge Treatment Center, San Antonio, TX, p. A641
ROSHAN, Payman, Chief Operating Officer, Kaiser Permanente Baldwin Park Medical Center, Baldwin Park, CA, p. A55
ROSIAK, Michael, Chief Operating Officer, Weisman Children's Rehabilitation Hospital, Marlton, NJ, p. A414
ROSILES, Nancy, Director Human Resources, HEALTHSOUTH Rehabilitation Hospital of Arlington, Arlington, TX, p. A592
ROSKE, Jeff, D.O. Chief Medical Staff, Community Memorial Hospital, Sumner, IA, p. A235
ROSKOVSKI, Stephanie, Chief Operating Officer, Butler Health System, Butler, PA, p. A530
ROSLER, Andrea P., Vice President Human Resources, Huntsville Hospital, Huntsville, AL, p. A21
ROSNER, Neil, Area Director Human Resources, Kindred Hospital–New Jersey Morris County, Dover, NJ, p. A411
ROSS, Aletha, Vice President Human Resources, Ingalls Memorial Hospital, Harvey, IL, p. A190
ROSS, Charles, M.D. Vice President Medical Affairs, Chilton Medical Center, Pompton Plains, NJ, p. A417
ROSS, Christopher, Chief Information Technology Officer, Mayo Clinic Hospital – Rochester, Rochester, MN, p. A345
ROSS, David, Chief Executive Officer, Middle Park Medical Center–Kremmling, Kremmling, CO, p. A105
ROSS, Hoyt, Chief Executive Officer, Promise Hospital of Florida at The Villages, Oxford, FL, p. A138
ROSS, Jacqueline, Chief Human Resources Officer, Mann–Grandstaff Veterans Affairs Medical Center, Spokane, WA, p. A685
ROSS, James E.
Chief Operating Officer, Camden General Hospital, Camden, TN, p. A574
Vice President and Chief Operating Officer, Jackson–Madison County General Hospital, Jackson, TN, p. A579
ROSS, Jay
Vice President of Finance, CHI LakeWood Health, Baudette, MN, p. A335
Chief Financial Officer, CHI St. Joseph's Health, Park Rapids, MN, p. A344
ROSS, Jeffrey, M.D. Medical Director, AMG Specialty Hospital–Albuquerque, Albuquerque, NM, p. A422
ROSS, Jim
Senior Vice President and Interim Chief Operating Officer, University of Maryland Shore Medical Center at Dorchester, Cambridge, MD, p. A296
Senior Vice President and Interim Chief Operating Officer, University of Maryland Shore Medical Center at Easton, Easton, MD, p. A297
ROSS, Joan, Senior Vice President and Chief Operating Officer, St. Vincent Charity Medical Center, Cleveland, OH, p. A485
ROSS, John, Vice President, Franciscan St. Francis Health – Mooresville, Mooresville, IN, p. A216
ROSS, Johnny Shane, Executive Medical Director, HEALTHSOUTH Rehabilitation Hospital of Austin, Austin, TX, p. A594
ROSS, Joseph, Chief Financial Officer, Livingston Regional Hospital, Livingston, TN, p. A581
ROSS, Joseph P., President and Chief Executive Officer, Meritus Medical Center, Hagerstown, MD, p. A298
ROSS, Karen, Chief Executive Officer, Allegiance Specialty Hospital of Kilgore, Kilgore, TX, p. A626
ROSS, Kathy
Chief Information Officer, Providence Hospital, Mobile, AL, p. A22
Chief Information Officer, Sacred Heart Hospital of Pensacola, Pensacola, FL, p. A140
ROSS, Laurie, Chief Nursing Officer, Southampton Memorial Hospital, Franklin, VA, p. A665
ROSS, Lisa, Human Resources Officer, Greater Regional Medical Center, Creston, IA, p. A225
ROSS, Phil, Chief Executive Officer, Surgical Hospital of Oklahoma, Oklahoma City, OK, p. A513
ROSS, Robert, Chief Operating Officer, MedStar Washington Hospital Center, Washington, DC, p. A119
ROSS, Samuel Lee, MS, Chief Executive Officer, Bon Secours Baltimore Health System, Baltimore, MD, p. A293
ROSS Jr., Semmes, Administrator, Lawrence County Hospital, Monticello, MS, p. A358
ROSS, Shana, Vice President Human Resources, Bayhealth Medical Center, Dover, DE, p. A117
ROSS, Zeff, FACHE, Senior Vice President and Chief Executive Officer, Memorial Regional Hospital, FL, p. A128

ROSS–COLE, Melissa, Director Human Resources, Regency Hospital of Northwest Arkansas – Springdale, Springdale, AR, p. A51

ROSS–SPANG, Carol, Senior Vice President, Methodist Healthcare Memphis Hospitals, Memphis, TN, p. A584

ROSSDALE, Robert, Deputy Executive Director, Queens Hospital Center, NY, p. A444

ROSSER, Mary, Director Human Resources, Munson Healthcare Cadillac Hospital, Cadillac, MI, p. A315

ROSSFELD, John, Chief Executive Officer, The Memorial Hospital at Craig, Craig, CO, p. A101

ROSSI, Alfred N., M.D., Chief Executive Officer, Hopedale Medical Complex, Hopedale, IL, p. A191

ROSSI, Coleen, Director Quality Services, HEALTHSOUTH Rehabilitation Hospital of Toms River, Toms River, NJ, p. A419

ROSSI, John, Vice President Information Systems and Chief Information Officer, Stamford Hospital, Stamford, CT, p. A115

ROSSI, Lawrence, M.D. Clinical Director, Trenton Psychiatric Hospital, Trenton, NJ, p. A419

ROSSI, Linda, Vice President Human Relations, Southern New Hampshire Medical Center, Nashua, NH, p. A407

ROSSI, Mark F., Chief Operating Officer and General Counsel, Hopedale Medical Complex, Hopedale, IL, p. A191

ROSSMAN, Greg, Chief Human Resource Officer, Denver Health, Denver, CO, p. A101

ROSSMANN, Barbara, R.N., President and Chief Executive Officer, Henry Ford Macomb Hospitals, Clinton Township, MI, p. A316

ROSSOW, Scott, D.O. Chief of Staff, Atchison Hospital, Atchison, KS, p. A237

ROSVOLD, Robert, Director Finance, Virtua Voorhees, Voorhees, NJ, p. A420

ROTELLA, William, Vice President Human Resources, University of North Carolina Hospitals, Chapel Hill, NC, p. A457

ROTENBERRY–BAGGETT, Katie, Administrative Assistant and Human Resources, Yalobusha General Hospital, Water Valley, MS, p. A361

ROTERT, Angela Lynne, Chief Clinical Officer, Kindred Hospital–Indianapolis, Indianapolis, IN, p. A212

ROTGER, Lindsey, Chief Nursing Officer, HEALTHSOUTH Cane Creek Rehabilitation Hospital, Martin, TN, p. A582

ROTH, Anna M., M.P.H., Chief Executive Officer, Contra Costa Regional Medical Center, Martinez, CA, p. A74

ROTH, Chad, Director Information Services, Prairie View, Newton, KS, p. A246

ROTH, Diane, Chief Financial Officer, Rockdale Medical Center, Conyers, GA, p. A154

ROTH III, Edward J., President and Chief Executive Officer, Aultman Hospital, Canton, OH, p. A481

ROTH III, Edward J., President and Chief Executive Officer, Aultman Health Foundation, Canton, OH, p. B16

ROTH, Eugene, Vice President Information Services, Mercy Hospital St. Louis, Saint Louis, MO, p. A376

ROTH, Norman G., Chief Executive Officer, Greenwich Hospital, Greenwich, CT, p. A112

ROTH, Randy, Interim Chief Medical Officer, Singing River Health System, Pascagoula, MS, p. A359

ROTH, Steven, Vice President Informatics and Chief Information Officer, Pinnacle Health System, Harrisburg, PA, p. A535

ROTHBERGER, Richard, Corporate Executive Vice President and Chief Financial Officer, Scripps Green Hospital, La Jolla, CA, p. A66

ROTHE, Brian, Site Director Information Systems, Castle Medical Center, Kailua, HI, p. A169

ROTHERMICH, Anthony, Administrator, Mercy Hospital Lincoln, Troy, MO, p. A379

ROTHERMICH, Michael, M.D. Chief of Staff, Hermann Area District Hospital, Hermann, MO, p. A368

ROTHFIELD, Kenneth, System Vice President and Chief Medical Officer, St. Vincent's Medical Center Riverside, Jacksonville, FL, p. A130

ROTHMAN, Marc, M.D. Medical Director, Friends Hospital, Philadelphia, PA, p. A543

ROTHSCHILD, Marylee, M.D. Chief of Staff, Robley Rex Veterans Affairs Medical Center, Louisville, KY, p. A262

ROTHSTEIN, Fred C., M.D., President, University Hospitals Case Medical Center, Cleveland, OH, p. A485

ROTHSTEIN, Robert, M.D. Vice President Medical Affairs, Suburban Hospital, Bethesda, MD, p. A296

ROTY, Chris, President, Baptist Health La Grange, La Grange, KY, p. A259

ROUBIDEAUX, Yvette, M.P.H., Director, U. S. Indian Health Service, Rockville, MD, p. B137

ROULEAU, Greg, Vice President Nursing, Mercy Medical Center Merced, Merced, CA, p. A75

ROUND, Laurie, R.N. Chief Nurse Executive, Advocate BroMenn Medical Center, Normal, IL, p. A196

ROUNDS, Jason, Chief Operating Officer and Administrator, CHRISTUS St. Michael Health System, Texarkana, TX, p. A647

ROUNDY, Ann, Vice President Employee Services, Columbus Community Hospital, Inc., Columbus, WI, p. A699

ROUNSLEY, Karen, Controller, HEALTHSOUTH Chesapeake Rehabilitation Hospital, Salisbury, MD, p. A300

ROUSH, Sharon L., Chief Executive Officer, South Bay Hospital, Sun City Center, FL, p. A143

ROUSSEAU, Mickie, Director Human Resources, Terrebonne General Medical Center, Houma, LA, p. A275

ROUSSEL, Steve

  Chief Financial Officer, Baylor Medical Center at McKinney, McKinney, TX, p. A631

  Vice President Finance, Baylor Medical Center at Waxahachie, Waxahachie, TX, p. A650

ROUTH, Lori, R.N

  Nurse Administrator, Mayo Clinic Health System in Albert Lea, Albert Lea, MN, p. A334

  Nurse Administrator, Mayo Clinic Health System–Albert Lea and Austin, Austin, MN, p. A335

ROUX, Roger, Chief Financial Officer, Rady Children's Hospital – San Diego, San Diego, CA, p. A86

ROUZER, Cindy, Director Human Resources, Spooner Health System, Spooner, WI, p. A711

ROVITO, Kevin, Chief Financial Officer, Jackson Hospital, Marianna, FL, p. A133

ROW, Tracy, Manager Business Office, Fredonia Regional Hospital, Fredonia, KS, p. A240

ROWAN, Brian, Chief of Staff, North Georgia Medical Center, Ellijay, GA, p. A157

ROWAN, Cary, Chief Financial Officer, Sunnyside Community Hospital and Clinics, Sunnyside, WA, p. A686

ROWAN, R. C., Director Human Resources, Neosho Memorial Regional Medical Center, Chanute, KS, p. A238

ROWE, Aaron, Chief Financial Officer, Green Oaks Hospital, Dallas, TX, p. A605

ROWE, Chad, Human Resource Director, Aspirus Keweenaw Hospital, Laurium, MI, p. A324

ROWE, David B., Chief Executive Officer, Great Falls Clinic Medical Center, Great Falls, MT, p. A384

ROWE, Jeanne M., M.D. Chief Medical Officer, Shore Medical Center, Somers Point, NJ, p. A418

ROWE, Mike, M.D. Chief of Staff, Fayette Regional Health System, Connersville, IN, p. A206

ROWE, Paul W., Director Information Technology, St. Francis Hospital, Wilmington, DE, p. A118

ROWE, Richard, PharmD, Chief Executive Officer, Coast Plaza Hospital, Norwalk, CA, p. A78

ROWE, Scott, Chief Executive Officer, HEALTHSOUTH Chattanooga Rehabilitation Hospital, Chattanooga, TN, p. A575

ROWELL, Julie, R.N. Chief Nursing Officer, Thomas Hospital, Fairhope, AL, p. A19

ROWEN, Lisa, R.N

  Senior Vice President and Chief Nursing Officer, University of Maryland Medical Center, Baltimore, MD, p. A295

  Chief Nursing Officer, University of Maryland Medical Center Midtown Campus, Baltimore, MD, p. A295

ROWLAND, Claire, Director Human Resources, Acadia Vermilion Hospital, Lafayette, LA, p. A277

ROWLAND, Michael, M.D. Vice President Medical Affairs, Franklin Memorial Hospital, Farmington, ME, p. A290

ROWLAND, Nick, Chief Operating Officer, Pushmataha Hospital & Home Health, Antlers, OK, p. A503

ROWLAND, Robert, M.D. Medical Director, HealthSouth Rehabilitation Hospital of Tallahassee, Tallahassee, FL, p. A144

ROWLAND, Ted, Chief of Medical Staff, Atoka County Medical Center, Atoka, OK, p. A504

ROWLANDS, Dewey R., Vice President and Chief Financial Officer, Rome Memorial Hospital, Rome, NY, p. A449

ROWLEY, Charla, Chief Financial Officer, Southwest Mississippi Regional Medical Center, McComb, MS, p. A357

ROWLEY, Daniel, M.D. Chief of Medical Staff, Knoxville Hospital & Clinics, Knoxville, IA, p. A230

ROWLEY, Mike, Chief Executive Officer, Springbrook Behavioral Health System, Travelers Rest, SC, p. A565

ROY, Joel, Manager Information Systems, The Brook Hospital – KMI, Louisville, KY, p. A262

ROY, Merri, Director Information Services, Weatherford Regional Medical Center, Weatherford, TX, p. A650

ROY, Rock, Professional Services Director, Power County Hospital District, American Falls, ID, p. A172

ROY, Schindelheim, M.D. Chief of Staff, Mee Memorial Hospital, King City, CA, p. A66

ROYAL, Keli, Director Human Resources, Shenandoah Medical Center, Shenandoah, IA, p. A234

ROYAL, Shawanna, R.N. Director Nursing, Strategic Behavioral Health – Raleigh, Garner, NC, p. A460

ROYAL, Ty, Executive Director of Support Services and Human Resources, Gibson Area Hospital and Health Services, Gibson City, IL, p. A189

ROYNE, Sharon, Interim Senior Vice President Human Resources, St. Joseph Medical Center, Tacoma, WA, p. A686

ROZELL, Becky, Chief Human Resources Officer, Madison Health, London, OH, p. A492

ROZENBOOM, Steve, Chief Financial Officer, Holy Cross Hospital, Taos, NM, p. A427

ROZMUS, Mike, Director Information Systems, Sentara RMH Medical Center, Harrisonburg, VA, p. A666

ROZNOVSKY, Karen, Director Human Resources, Yoakum Community Hospital, Yoakum, TX, p. A653

RUBANO, Kathleen A., MSN Chief Nursing Officer, Corpus Christi Medical Center, Corpus Christi, TX, p. A602

RUBAR, Jackie, Administrative Assistant and Director Human Resources, Leesville Rehabilitation Hospital, Leesville, LA, p. A279

RUBE, David M., M.D. Clinical Director, New York City Children's Center, NY, p. A442

RUBEN, Wanda, R.N. Chief Nursing Officer, Garden Grove Hospital and Medical Center, Garden Grove, CA, p. A63

RUBENS, Deborah, Director Human Resources, Shriners Hospitals for Children–Northern California, Sacramento, CA, p. A84

RUBERG, Greg, Administrator, Lake View Memorial Hospital, Two Harbors, MN, p. A348

RUBERTE, Henry, Administrator, Hospital San Gerardo, San Juan, PR, p. A724

RUBERTI, Charlene, Director Information Technology Development, Ancora Psychiatric Hospital, Hammonton, NJ, p. A412

RUBIN, Amir Dan, President and Chief Executive Officer, Stanford Health Care, Palo Alto, CA, p. A80

RUBIN, Amir Dan, President and Chief Executive Officer, Stanford Health Care, Palo Alto, CA, p. B128

RUBIN, Nancy, Vice President Human Resources, Motion Picture and Television Fund Hospital and Residential Services, CA, p. A71

RUBIN, Vincent, Chief Financial Officer, Southern California Hospital at Culver City, Culver City, CA, p. A59

RUBINATE, Donna, R.N. Chief Operating Officer, Good Samaritan Medical Center, Brockton, MA, p. A305

RUBINO, Mark, M.D. Chief Medical Officer, Forbes Regional Hospital, Monroeville, PA, p. A540

RUBIO, Felipe, M.D. Medical Director, Kindred Hospital–Dayton, Dayton, OH, p. A488

RUCHTI, Robert D., Chief Executive Officer, Buchanan General Hospital, Grundy, VA, p. A665

RUCKER, Alisa, Vice President Finance and Chief Financial Officer, Washington Hospital, Washington, PA, p. A552

RUCKER, Genesia L., MSN Chief Nursing Officer, Vaughan Regional Medical Center, Selma, AL, p. A24

RUCKER, Marty, Construction/Plant Operations, Carroll County Memorial Hospital, Carrollton, MO, p. A365

RUCKER, Sheryl, Chief Information Officer, Edgerton Hospital and Health Services, Edgerton, WI, p. A700

RUCKER, William H., Administrator, Riverland Medical Center, Ferriday, LA, p. A273

RUDBERG, Susan, M.D. Chief Medical Officer, Range Regional Health Services, Hibbing, MN, p. A340

RUDD, Adam, Interim Chief Executive Officer, Southern Hills Hospital and Medical Center, Las Vegas, NV, p. A402

RUDD, Barry, Chief Information Officer, Mayo Clinic Health System in Waycross, Waycross, GA, p. A167

RUDD, John, President and Chief Executive Officer, Cayuga Medical Center at Ithaca, Ithaca, NY, p. A435

RUDDEN, Elizabeth, Vice President Human Resources, Connecticut Children's Medical Center, Hartford, CT, p. A112

RUDEK, Charles M., Chief Information Officer, UPMC St. Margaret, Pittsburgh, PA, p. A547

RUDIS, Lorrie, Vice President, Human Resources, Crotched Mountain Rehabilitation Center, Greenfield, NH, p. A406

RUDITSKY, Crystal, Interim Vice President and Chief Financial Officer, Simi Valley Hospital, Simi Valley, CA, p. A92

RUDITZ, Bettiann S., MS Chief Nursing Officer, Broward Health North, Deerfield Beach, FL, p. A125

RUDNICK, Jim, Vice President Information Technology, Navos, Seattle, WA, p. A683

RUDQUIST, Debra, FACHE, President and Chief Executive Officer, Amery Hospital and Clinic, Amery, WI, p. A697

RUDZIK, Donna, Director Human Resources, Hopkins County Memorial Hospital, Sulphur Springs, TX, p. A646

RUE, Loring, M.D. Senior Vice President, Quality Patient Safety and Clinical Effectiveness, University of Alabama Hospital, Birmingham, AL, p. A17

Index of Health Care Professionals / Ryan


RUECKERT, Sebastian, M.D
Vice President and Chief Medical Officer, Alton Memorial Hospital, Alton, IL, p. A178
Chief Medical Officer, Christian Hospital, Saint Louis, MO, p. A376
RUEDISUELI, Amy, Vice President of Finance, McKenzie Health System, Sandusky, MI, p. A330
RUELLO, Rocky, Vice President Human Resources, Mercy Hospital St. Louis, Saint Louis, MO, p. A376
RUETSCH, Rebecca, Human Resource Partner, CHI Health Creighton University Medical Center, Omaha, NE, p. A395
RUFAT, Berta, Controller, Baptist Health South Florida, South Miami Hospital, Miami, FL, p. A134
RUFF, Victoria, M.D. Medical Director, Select Specialty Hospital–Columbus, Columbus, OH, p. A487
RUFFOLO, Joseph A., President and Chief Executive Officer, Niagara Falls Memorial Medical Center, Niagara Falls, NY, p. A445
RUGE, Randy, Chief Executive Officer, Paulding County Hospital, Paulding, OH, p. A496
RUGGIERO, Taren, R.N. Vice President and Chief Nursing Officer, Holy Cross Hospital, Fort Lauderdale, FL, p. A126
RUIZ, Javier, M.D
Medical Director, Intracare North Hospital, Houston, TX, p. A620
Medical Director, Kingwood Pines Hospital, Kingwood, TX, p. A626
RUIZ, Jesus, Chief Executive Officer, Mesa Hills Specialty Hospital, El Paso, TX, p. A611
RUIZ, Kathleen, M.D. Associate Director Patient Care Services, Veterans Affairs Caribbean Healthcare System, San Juan, PR, p. A724
RUIZ, Mary, Chief Executive Officer, Manatee Glens Hospital and Addiction Center, Bradenton, FL, p. A122
RUIZ, Tony, Chief Operating Officer, Medical Center Health System, Odessa, TX, p. A634
RUKSTAD, Julie, Chief Financial Officer, Olympic Medical Center, Port Angeles, WA, p. A682
RULE, Carlton, M.D., Chief Executive Officer, O'Connor Hospital, Delhi, NY, p. A432
RUMBAUT, Michelle, Chief Strategy Officer, Guadalupe Regional Medical Center, Seguin, TX, p. A643
RUMFORD, Darren K., Chief Financial Officer, Geary Community Hospital, Junction City, KS, p. A243
RUMMEL, Jennifer
Director Human Resources, East Texas Medical Center Athens, Athens, TX, p. A593
Director Human Resources, East Texas Medical Center Fairfield, Fairfield, TX, p. A612
RUNGE, Andrew, Chief Operating Officer, CHI St. Vincent Hot Springs, Hot Springs, AR, p. A45
RUNNELS, Clay, Vice President Chief Medical Officer Washington County, Johnson City Medical Center, Johnson City, TN, p. A580
RUNT, David, Chief Information Officer, Banner Del E. Webb Medical Center, Sun City West, AZ, p. A38
RUNYAN, Duane, Chief Executive Officer and Managing Director, Willow Springs Center, Reno, NV, p. A404
RUNYAN, Mark
Director Information Systems, Jordan Valley Medical Center–WVC Campus, West Valley City, UT, p. A659
Director Information Services, Salt Lake Regional Medical Center, Salt Lake City, UT, p. A658
RUPA, Maitra, M.D. Acting Medical Director, Chester Mental Health Center, Chester, IL, p. A181
RUPERT, Chris, Chief Executive Officer, University Behavioral Health of Denton, Denton, TX, p. A608
RUPERT, Duke, President and Chief Executive Officer, Forbes Regional Hospital, Monroeville, PA, p. A540
RUPERT, James M., Chief Fiscal Services, Battle Creek Veterans Affairs Medical Center, Battle Creek, MI, p. A315
RUPERT, Michael J., Chief Financial Officer, VA Long Beach Healthcare System, Long Beach, CA, p. A68
RUPP, Robert, Chief Executive Officer, Medical Center of South Arkansas, El Dorado, AR, p. A43
RUPPERT, Jennifer, Chief Financial Officer, Iowa City Veterans Affairs Health Care System, Iowa City, IA, p. A229
RUPPERT SCHILLER, Kerri
Senior Vice President and Chief Financial Officer, Children's Hospital of Orange County, Orange, CA, p. A79
Senior Vice President and Chief Financial Officer, CHOC Children's at Mission Hospital, Mission Viejo, CA, p. A75
RUSCITTO, Kathryn H., President, St. Joseph's Hospital Health Center, Syracuse, NY, p. A451
RUSH, Andy, Senior Vice President and Chief Operating Officer, Somerset Hospital, Somerset, PA, p. A550
RUSH, Ann Marie, Chief Financial Officer, Penobscot Valley Hospital, Lincoln, ME, p. A291
RUSH, Cindy, Director Human Resources, Clay County Medical Center, Clay Center, KS, p. A238
RUSH, Ed, President and Chief Executive Officer, Iredell Memorial Hospital, Statesville, NC, p. A469
RUSH, Jeff, Chief Financial Officer, Rutherford Regional Health System, Rutherfordton, NC, p. A468
RUSH, Jeff W., Chief Financial Officer, Union Medical Center, Union, SC, p. A565
RUSH, Matthew, President and Chief Executive Officer, Hayes Green Beach Memorial Hospital, Charlotte, MI, p. A316
RUSHIN, Denise, Director Human Resources, Poplar Bluff Regional Medical Center, Poplar Bluff, MO, p. A374
RUSHING, Heath, Interim Chief Executive Officer, Memorial Hermann Northeast, Humble, TX, p. A623
RUSHING, R. Lynn, Chief Executive Officer, Brook Lane Health Services, Hagerstown, MD, p. A298
RUSHING, Richard, Chief of Staff, King's Daughters Medical Center, Brookhaven, MS, p. A351
RUSHLOW, David, Vice President Medical Affairs, Mayo Clinic Health System – Franciscan Healthcare in La Crosse, La Crosse, WI, p. A703
RUSINKO, Steve, Chief Financial Officer, Eastern Regional Medical Center, Philadelphia, PA, p. A543
RUSK, Scott, M.D. Vice President Medical Administration, Mercy Hospital of Portland, Portland, ME, p. A291
RUSNACZYK, John, Senior Vice President and Chief Financial Officer, St. Vincent Charity Medical Center, Cleveland, OH, p. A485
RUSS, Nicole L., Director Colleague Relations, Alliance Community Hospital, Alliance, OH, p. A478
RUSSEL, Kimberly A., FACHE, President and Chief Executive Officer, Bryan Health, Lincoln, NE, p. B25
RUSSELL, Bill, Senior Chief Information Officer, Mission Hospital, Mission Viejo, CA, p. A75
RUSSELL, Brant, R.N. Chief Operating Officer, St. John Hospital and Medical Center, Detroit, MI, p. A318
RUSSELL, Dardanella, Chief Human Resources Management Service, Veterans Affairs Hudson Valley Health Care System, Montrose, NY, p. A438
RUSSELL, Donald
Regional Vice President Human Resources, Adventist Hinsdale Hospital, Hinsdale, IL, p. A191
Vice President, AMITA Health Adventist GlenOaks Hospital, Glendale Heights, IL, p. A189
RUSSELL, Erin, Controller, Kindred Hospital–San Antonio, San Antonio, TX, p. A641
RUSSELL, Freda, R.N., Chief Executive Officer and Chief Nursing Officer, Three Rivers Hospital, Waverly, TN, p. A589
RUSSELL, Georgette, Vice President of Talent & Organizational Effectiveness, Sparrow Carson Hospital, Carson City, MI, p. A316
RUSSELL, John D., President and Chief Executive Officer, Columbus Community Hospital, Inc., Columbus, WI, p. A699
RUSSELL, Jon, Senior Vice President and Chief Information Officer, John Muir Medical Center, Concord, Concord, CA, p. A58
RUSSELL, Judy, Director of Nurses, Ochiltree General Hospital, Perryton, TX, p. A636
RUSSELL, Karen, Director Human Resources, Galesburg Cottage Hospital, Galesburg, IL, p. A188
RUSSELL, Kathy, R.N. Chief Nursing Officer, Bluegrass Community Hospital, Versailles, KY, p. A266
RUSSELL, Kendrick, Chief Human Resources Officer, Abrazo Scottsdale Campus, Phoenix, AZ, p. A34
RUSSELL, Kim, M.D. Chief of Staff, Scott & White Hospital – Llano, Llano, TX, p. A628
RUSSELL, Linda, Vice President and Chief Nursing Officer, Self Regional Healthcare, Greenwood, SC, p. A562
RUSSELL, Michelle, Chief Executive Officer, Lafayette Regional Rehabilitation Hospital, Lafayette, IN, p. A214
RUSSELL, Michelle L., Administrator, Community Howard Specialty Hospital, Kokomo, IN, p. A213
RUSSELL, Mila, Director of Nursing, Benewah Community Hospital, Saint Maries, ID, p. A176
RUSSELL, Nancy, Chief Financial Officer, Clifton–Fine Hospital, Star Lake, NY, p. A450
RUSSELL, Patti, Vice President Nursing, Masonicare Health Center, Wallingford, CT, p. A115
RUSSELL, Randall, Vice President and Chief Financial Officer, Memorial Hospital and Health Care Center, Jasper, IN, p. A213
RUSSELL, Robert, Chief Executive Officer, Kindred Hospital–Atlanta, Atlanta, GA, p. A150
RUSSELL, Robert J., Associate Executive Director Operations, Penn Presbyterian Medical Center, Philadelphia, PA, p. A544
RUSSELL, Shelia, Director Human Resources, Jamestown Regional Medical Center, Jamestown, TN, p. A579
RUSSELL, Shelly, Chief Executive Officer, Mitchell County Regional Health Center, Osage, IA, p. A232
RUSSELL, Sherrie
Vice President and Chief Information Officer, Alexian Brothers Behavioral Health Hospital, Hoffman Estates, IL, p. A191
Chief Information Officer, St. Alexius Medical Center, Hoffman Estates, IL, p. A191
RUSSELL, Susan, Chief Financial Officer, OCH Regional Medical Center, Starkville, MS, p. A360
RUSSELL, Tim, Administrator, Stillwater Community Hospital, Columbus, MT, p. A382
RUSSELL, William B., Chief Executive Officer, Three Rivers Health, Three Rivers, MI, p. A331
RUSSELL–JENKINS, Shane, M.D. Medical Director, Windhaven Psychiatric Hospital, Prescott Valley, AZ, p. A36
RUSSO, Arthur, M.D. Director Medical Affairs, Harrington Memorial Hospital, Southbridge, MA, p. A311
RUSSO, Kimberly, Chief Operating Officer, George Washington University Hospital, Washington, DC, p. A119
RUSSO, Mike, Vice President Information Systems, Grimes St. Joseph Health Center, Navasota, TX, p. A634
RUSSO, Paul M., FACHE, Director, Miami Veterans Affairs Healthcare System, Miami, FL, p. A134
RUST, Jeff, Information Technology Systems Site Manager, Mercy Medical Center, Williston, ND, p. A477
RUSTIN, Wayne, Vice President, Chief Human Resources Officer, St. Vincent's Medical Center, Bridgeport, CT, p. A111
RUTH, Daniel R., President and Chief Executive Officer, Jewish Home of San Francisco, San Francisco, CA, p. A88
RUTH, Joseph, Executive Vice President and Chief Operating Officer, Sparrow Hospital, Lansing, MI, p. A324
RUTHER, Randy, Vice President Finance and Chief Financial Officer, Little Company of Mary Hospital and Health Care Centers, Evergreen Park, IL, p. A188
RUTHERFORD, Dennis E., CPA Chief Financial Officer, Gilbert Hospital, Gilbert, AZ, p. A31
RUTHERFORD, Jeremiah, Chief Medical Officer, Cornerstone Hospital of Oklahoma–Muskogee, Muskogee, OK, p. A510
RUTHERFORD, Peter, M.D.,
Chief Executive Officer, Central Washington Hospital, Wenatchee, WA, p. A687
Chief Executive Officer, Wenatchee Valley Medical Center, Wenatchee, WA, p. A687
RUTHERFORD, Ronald, Chief Information Officer, Beth Israel Deaconess Hospital Plymouth, Plymouth, MA, p. A310
RUTHERFORD, Theresa, FACHE, President and Chief Executive Officer, HSHS St. Anthony's Memorial Hospital, Effingham, IL, p. A186
RUTHS, Steve, M.D. Medical Director, Vista Del Mar Hospital, Ventura, CA, p. A96
RUTKOWSKI, James C., Chief Financial Officer, Washington Health System Greene, Waynesburg, PA, p. A552
RUTKOWSKI, Jennifer, R.N. Vice President Professional Services, Grant Regional Health Center, Lancaster, WI, p. A704
RUTLEDGE, Debra K., R.N. Vice President Nursing Services, CHI Health Plainview, Plainview, NE, p. A397
RUTLEDGE, Rebel, Director Human Resources, Grady Memorial Hospital, Chickasha, OK, p. A505
RUTTER, James, M.D. Chief of Staff, Integris Grove Hospital, Grove, OK, p. A507
RUWOLDT, Steven T., Chief Operating Officer, Memorial Medical Center, Las Cruces, NM, p. A425
RUYTER, Mary J., Chief Executive Officer, Sanford Jackson Medical Center, Jackson, MN, p. A340
RYALS, Billie, Director Human Resources, Sullivan County Memorial Hospital, Milan, MO, p. A373
RYAN, Charleen, Vice President Nursing Services, Down East Community Hospital, Machias, ME, p. A291
RYAN, Chris, Chief Information Officer, Auburn Community Hospital, Auburn, NY, p. A429
RYAN, Christie, Chief Nursing Officer, HEALTHSOUTH Rehabilitation Hospital of Sewickley, Sewickley, PA, p. A550
RYAN, Christina M., R.N., Chief Executive Officer, The Women's Hospital, Newburgh, IN, p. A217
RYAN, Colleen
Director Management Information Systems, Landmark Medical Center, Woonsocket, RI, p. A556
Chief Information Officer and Vice President Professional Services, Rehabilitation Hospital of Rhode Island, North Smithfield, RI, p. A555
RYAN, Connie, Chief Nursing Officer, Select Specialty Hospital–Tulsa Midtown, Tulsa, OK, p. A517
RYAN, David P., Vice President Human Resources, Hallmark Health System, Melrose, MA, p. A308
RYAN, Debora, R.N. Vice President Patient Care, St. Francis Regional Medical Center, Shakopee, MN, p. A347
RYAN, Dennis, Senior Vice President and Chief Financial Officer, Children's Hospital of The King's Daughters, Norfolk, VA, p. A669
RYAN, Frank, Chief Financial Officer, Manchester Veterans Affairs Medical Center, Manchester, NH, p. A407


© 2015 AHA Guide Index of Health Care Professionals **A957**

Index of Health Care Professionals

Index of Health Care Professionals / Ryan

RYAN, Jacqueline, Director Human Resources, Mayo Clinic Health System in Lake City, Lake City, MN, p. A340
RYAN, John Jack, M.D. Chief Medical Officer, Oakland Regional Hospital, Southfield, MI, p. A330
RYAN, Kimberly, Administrator, Southern Regional Medical Center, Riverdale, GA, p. A163
RYAN, Lisa M., Coordinator Human Resources, Hampstead Hospital, Hampstead, NH, p. A406
RYAN, Maria, Ph.D., Chief Executive Officer, Cottage Hospital, Woodsville, NH, p. A408
RYAN, Michael J., Chief Executive Officer, Herington Municipal Hospital, Herington, KS, p. A241
RYAN, Mike, Director of Information Services, Gunnison Valley Hospital, Gunnison, UT, p. A655
RYAN, Patrice
  Vice President Human Resources, Goleta Valley Cottage Hospital, Santa Barbara, CA, p. A91
  Vice President Human Resources, Santa Barbara Cottage Hospital, Santa Barbara, CA, p. A91
  Vice President Human Resources, Santa Ynez Valley Cottage Hospital, Solvang, CA, p. A92
RYAN, Patrick, Chief Financial Officer, Christ Hospital, Jersey City, NJ, p. A413
RYAN, Patrick G., Chief Executive Officer, Promise Hospital of Fort Myers, Fort Myers, FL, p. A127
RYAN, Patrick J., Chief Human Resources Officer, Helen Hayes Hospital, West Haverstraw, NY, p. A453
RYAN, Rebecca, Interim Director Human Resources and Employee Health, Ukiah Valley Medical Center, Ukiah, CA, p. A95
RYAN, Robert, M.D. Chief Medical Officer, Guadalupe Regional Medical Center, Seguin, TX, p. A643
RYAN, Sharon, Regional Controller, Select Specialty Hospital–Macomb County, Mount Clemens, MI, p. A326
RYAN, Stacy, Corporate Director Human Resources, Warren General Hospital, Warren, PA, p. A551
RYAN, Tim, Chief Financial Officer, Centennial Peaks Hospital, Louisville, CO, p. A107
RYBA, Janice L., JD, Chief Executive Officer, St. Mary Medical Center, Hobart, IN, p. A211
RYBA, Thomas L., Chief Executive Officer, Lighthouse Care Center of Conway, Conway, SC, p. A560
RYBA, Tomi S., President and Chief Executive Officer, El Camino Hospital, Mountain View, CA, p. A77
RYBICKI, Catherine, Vice President Physician Services and Chief Operating Officer, Spectrum Health Big Rapids Hospital, Big Rapids, MI, p. A315
RYBICKI, Cathy, Chief Operating Officer, Spectrum Health Reed City Hospital, Reed City, MI, p. A328
RYBOLT, Andrew, Vice President and Chief Financial Officer, Redwood Memorial Hospital, Fortuna, CA, p. A61
RYCKMAN, George, D.O. Chief of Staff, Paul Oliver Memorial Hospital, Frankfort, MI, p. A319
RYDER, Doug, President, Holy Cross Germantown Hospital, Germantown, MD, p. A298
RYDER, Jeff, Director Information Systems, Saint Joseph Mount Sterling, Mount Sterling, KY, p. A263
RYDER, John E.
  Chief Operating Officer, Borgess–Lee Memorial Hospital, Dowagiac, MI, p. A318
  Chief Operating Officer, Borgess–Lee Memorial Hospital, Dowagiac, MI, p. A318
  Administrator and Chief Operating Officer, Borgess–Pipp Hospital, Plainwell, MI, p. A327
RYDER, Ronald, D.O. President of the Medical Staff, Robert Wood Johnson University Hospital at Hamilton, Hamilton, NJ, p. A412
RYDER, Troy, Director of Nursing, Aspire Hospital, Conroe, TX, p. A602
RYDGREN, Barbara, Administrator, Glenn Medical Center, Willows, CA, p. A98
RYKERT, Lauren P., Senior Vice President, Houston Methodist Hospital, Houston, TX, p. A620
RYLAND, Jennifer M., R.N. Chief Administrative Officer, Jackson Medical Center, Jackson, AL, p. A21
RYLE, Barry W., Chief Information Officer, Oswego Hospital, Oswego, NY, p. A447
RYLE, Deborah L., Administrator and Chief Executive Officer, St. David's Round Rock Medical Center, Round Rock, TX, p. A639
RYMER, Brandy, Coordinator Human Resources, Murray Medical Center, Chatsworth, GA, p. A153
RYON, Joel, M.D. Chief of Staff, Henry County Health Center, Mount Pleasant, IA, p. A232
RYS, Jan, Chief Operating Officer, Straith Hospital for Special Surgery, Southfield, MI, p. A330
RZENDZIAN, Michael, Chief Financial Officer, Baylor Emergency Medical Center at Aubrey, Aubrey, TX, p. A593
RZOMP, Kimberly
  Vice President and Chief Financial Officer, Chambersburg Hospital, Chambersburg, PA, p. A531
  Vice President Finance, Waynesboro Hospital, Waynesboro, PA, p. A552

# S

SAADAT, Annette, Human Resources Business Partner, Saint Joseph Mount Sterling, Mount Sterling, KY, p. A263
SAALFELD, Thomas, Senior Vice President and Chief Operating Officer, St. Elizabeth Fort Thomas, Fort Thomas, KY, p. A257
SAARI, Heidi L., Director, Human Resources, Upper Connecticut Valley Hospital, Colebrook, NH, p. A405
SAAVEDRA, JayLynn, Chief Information Officer, U. S. Public Health Service Indian Hospital, Parker, AZ, p. A34
SABA, Francis M., Chief Executive Officer, Milford Regional Medical Center, Milford, MA, p. A309
SABAHI, Hugh, M.D. President Professional Staff, Columbia Memorial Hospital, Astoria, OR, p. A519
SABANDIT, Elizabeth, Director Human Resources, Alhambra Hospital Medical Center, Alhambra, CA, p. A53
SABHARRWAL, Parajeet, Administrator, Minimally Invasive Surgery Center, Lenexa, KS, p. A245
SABIA, John, M.D. Vice President Medical Affairs, Northern Dutchess Hospital, Rhinebeck, NY, p. A448
SABIN, Margaret D., President and Chief Executive Officer, Penrose–St. Francis Health Services, Colorado Springs, CO, p. A101
SABLE, Kenneth N., M.D., President, Jersey Shore University Medical Center, Neptune, NJ, p. A414
SABOTTA, John, Director Information Systems, St. Margaret's Hospital, Spring Valley, IL, p. A201
SABUS, Matthew, Director Information Systems, Boone County Hospital, Boone, IA, p. A223
SACCO, Frank V., FACHE, President and Chief Executive Officer, Memorial Healthcare System, FL, p. B89
SACCOIO, Saria, M.D. Chief Medical Officer, Bon Secours St. Francis Health System, Greenville, SC, p. A561
SACHDEV, Aruna, M.D. Medical Director, Massachusetts Hospital School, Canton, MA, p. A306
SACHEDINA, Azeem, M.D. Chief of Staff, Broward Health Coral Springs, Coral Springs, FL, p. A124
SACHS, III, Henry T., M.D. Medical Director, Emma Pendleton Bradley Hospital, East Providence, RI, p. A555
SACHTJEN, Mistie, Chief Executive Officer, Community Memorial Hospital, Burke, SD, p. A567
SACHTLEBEN, Michael, Chief Operating Officer, MedStar Georgetown University Hospital, Washington, DC, p. A119
SACKETT, John, President, Shady Grove Adventist Hospital, Rockville, MD, p. A300
SACKETT, Walter, President, Sycamore Medical Centerf, Miamisburg, OH, p. A494
SADA, Judy, Chief Financial Officer, Memorial Hospital Miramar, Miramar, FL, p. A136
SADAU, Ernie W., Chief Executive Officer, CHRISTUS Health, Irving, TX, p. B33
SADLER, Donna, Director Human Resources, Arkansas State Hospital, Little Rock, AR, p. A47
SADLER, Joy, Director Human Resources, Bear River Valley Hospital, Tremonton, UT, p. A659
SADLER, Michele, D.O. Chief Medical Staff, Guttenberg Municipal Hospital, Guttenberg, IA, p. A228
SADOFF, Jennifer, Chief Executive Officer, Mountain View Hospital, Payson, UT, p. A657
SADR, Farrokh, M.D. Chief Medical Officer, Sacred Heart Hospital, Allentown, PA, p. A528
SADRO, Cheryl A., Executive Vice President Chief Business and Finance Officer, University of Texas Medical Branch, Galveston, TX, p. A615
SADVARY, Thomas J., FACHE, Chief Executive Officer, HonorHealth, Scottsdale, AZ, p. B71
SAENZ, Luis J Rodriquez, M.D. Medical Director, Hospital Menonita De Cayey, Cayey, PR, p. A720
SAENZ, Melanie, Regional Human Resources Officer, Presence Saints Mary & Elizabeth Medical Center, Chicago, IL, p. A183
SAFFA, Steve, Director Human Resources, St. Francis Health, Topeka, KS, p. A251
SAFLEY, Thomas, Chief Financial Officer, St. Joseph Regional Medical Center, Lewiston, ID, p. A174
SAFYER, Steven M., M.D., President and CEO, Montefiore Health System, NY, p. B93
SAFYER, Steven M., M.D., President and Chief Executive Officer, Montefiore Medical Center, NY, p. A442
SAGMIT, Rodney, Chief Information Management, VA Long Beach Healthcare System, Long Beach, CA, p. A68
SAHA, Sanjay K., Chief Operating Officer, Sibley Memorial Hospital, Washington, DC, p. A120
SAHAI, Subhosh, M.D. Chief of Staff, Van Diest Medical Center, Webster City, IA, p. A236
SAHLOLBEI, Hossain, M.D. Chief of Staff, Palo Verde Hospital, Blythe, CA, p. A56
SAHLSTROM, Christopher, M.D. Chief of Staff, Mat–Su Regional Medical Center, Palmer, AK, p. A29
SAHMAUNT, Sarabeth, Supervisory Accountant, Lawton Indian Hospital, Lawton, OK, p. A508
SAIA, Carrie L., R.N., Chief Executive Officer, Holton Community Hospital, Holton, KS, p. A242
SAINBERT, Wilmino, Chief Human Resources Management Service, Northport Veterans Affairs Medical Center, Northport, NY, p. A445
SAINTZ, Jeffrey, Vice President Human Resources, Titusville Area Hospital, Titusville, PA, p. A550
SAIYED, Ashfaq, M.D. Medical Director, Irwin County Hospital, Ocilla, GA, p. A162
SAIZ, Claudia, Chief Operating Officer, Advanced Care Hospital of Southern New Mexico, Las Cruces, NM, p. A424
SAJID, Muhammad W., M.D. Medical Director, Lincoln Trail Behavioral Health System, Radcliff, KY, p. A265
SAKALOSKY, Matt, Director Information Services and Chief Information Officer, Fremont Health, Fremont, NE, p. A391
SAKIN, Debbie, Ph.D. Interim Chief Executive Officer, Houston Methodist Willowbrook Hospital, Houston, TX, p. A620
SALADO, Martha, Interim Director Human Resources, Whittier Hospital Medical Center, Whittier, CA, p. A97
SALAKI, Jana, Regional Director Human Resources, Ephrata Community Hospital, Ephrata, PA, p. A534
SALAMANCA, Mary, Director Human Resources, HEALTHSOUTH Rehabilitation Hospital of Spring Hill, Brooksville, FL, p. A123
SALANDI, John, Chief Executive Officer, Landmark Hospital of Savannah, Savannah, GA, p. A164
SALANGER, Matthew J., President and Chief Executive Officer, United Health Services, Binghamton, NY, p. B139
SALANGER, Matthew J., President and Chief Executive Officer, United Health Services Hospitals–Binghamton, Binghamton, NY, p. A430
SALAS, Dawn, Controller, HEALTHSOUTH Rehabilitation Hospital at Martin Health, Stuart, FL, p. A143
SALAS, Victor, M.D. President Medical Staff, UnityPoint Health – Jones Regional Medical Center, Anamosa, IA, p. A222
SALAWAY, Tarek, Chief Operating Officer, University of Southern California–Norris Cancer Hospital, Los Angeles, CA, p. A73
SALAZAR, Juan, Director Human Resources, St. Luke's Episcopal Hospital, Ponce, PR, p. A722
SALAZAR, Leanne, Chief Nursing Officer, Oak Hill Hospital, Brooksville, FL, p. A123
SALAZAR, Linda C., Information Technology Leader, Kaiser Permanente Baldwin Park Medical Center, Baldwin Park, CA, p. A55
SALAZAR, Pamela, M.D. Chief of Staff, HEALTHSOUTH Walton Rehabilitation Hospital, Augusta, GA, p. A151
SALCEDO, Nydimar, Chief Human Resources Officer, Castaner General Hospital, Castaner, PR, p. A720
SALEEBY, Manhal, M.D. Chief of Staff, VCU Community Memorial Hospital, South Hill, VA, p. A673
SALEEM, David, Director Information Technology, Greystone Park Psychiatric Hospital, Morris Plains, NJ, p. A414
SALEM, Gary, M.D. Vice President Medical Affairs, McLaren Lapeer Region, Lapeer, MI, p. A324
SALEM, Michael, M.D., President and Chief Executive Officer, National Jewish Health, Denver, CO, p. A102
SALGADO, Joe, M.D. Chief of Staff, Artesia General Hospital, Artesia, NM, p. A423
SALGADO, Laura, Administrator, Baptist Emergency Hospital, San Antonio, TX, p. A640
SALIBA, K. Michael, M.D. Medical Director, Shadow Mountain Behavioral Health System, Tulsa, OK, p. A517
SALIMAN, Al, M.D. Chief Medical Officer, Valley View Hospital, Glenwood Springs, CO, p. A104
SALINAS, Amaro, Assistant Administrator and Human Resource Officer, Starr County Memorial Hospital, Rio Grande City, TX, p. A638
SALINAS, Daniel, M.D. Senior Vice President and Chief Medical Officer, Children's Healthcare of Atlanta, Atlanta, GA, p. A150
SALISBURY, Dennis, M.D. Vice President for Medical Affairs, St. James Healthcare, Butte, MT, p. A382
SALISBURY, Evelyn, M.D. Chief of Staff, Caverna Memorial Hospital, Horse Cave, KY, p. A258
SALISBURY, Renee A., Director Human Resources, OSF Saint Luke Medical Center, Kewanee, IL, p. A192
SALISBURY, Tracy
  Regional Manager Human Resources, Central State Hospital, Petersburg, VA, p. A670
  Director Human Resources, Hiram W. Davis Medical Center, Petersburg, VA, p. A670
SALLER, William, Chief Financial Officer, Rio Grande Regional Hospital, McAllen, TX, p. A631
SALLEY, Wanda, Vice President Human Resources, West Florida Hospital, Pensacola, FL, p. A140

A958 Index of Health Care Professionals

SALLIS, Tom, Director Information Systems, Sparks Regional Medical Center, Fort Smith, AR, p. A45
SALLOUM, Fadi, M.D. Medical Director, Select Specialty Hospital–Pontiac, Pontiac, MI, p. A328
SALMAN, Wael, M.D. Vice President Medical Affairs, Memorial Healthcare, Owosso, MI, p. A327
SALMANULLAH, Muhammad, Chief Medical Director, HEALTHSOUTH Rehabilitation Hospital, Concord, NH, p. A405
SALNAS, Todd
President, Petaluma Valley Hospital, Petaluma, CA, p. A81
President, Santa Rosa Memorial Hospital, Santa Rosa, CA, p. A92
SALO, Saliba, President, Northridge Hospital Medical Center, CA, p. A71
SALOME, Jenny, Chief Financial Officer and Assistant Administrator, Northwest Hills Surgical Hospital, Austin, TX, p. A594
SALOMON, Kathryn, Director Human Resources, Kona Community Hospital, Kealakekua, HI, p. A170
SALTAFORMAGGIO, Cheri, Chief Executive Officer, St. Charles Surgical Hospital, New Orleans, LA, p. A282
SALTER, Cherry B., Director of Nursing, Hardtner Medical Center, Olla, LA, p. A283
SALTONSTALL, Christine, Chief Financial Officer, Kindred Hospital–Baldwin Park, Baldwin Park, CA, p. A55
SALTZ, Catherine, Chief Financial Officer, Baptist Rehabilitation–Germantown, Germantown, TN, p. A578
SALVADOR, Ed, Chief Financial Officer, St. Jude Medical Center, Fullerton, CA, p. A63
SALVATI, Mario, Director Fiscal Services, Shriners Hospitals for Children–Philadelphia, Philadelphia, PA, p. A545
SALVINO, Sonia, Vice President Finance, University Hospitals Case Medical Center, Cleveland, OH, p. A485
SALVITTI, Alfred P., Chief Financial Officer, Eagleville Hospital, Eagleville, PA, p. A533
SALVO, Stephen, Vice President Human Resources, Anna Jaques Hospital, Newburyport, MA, p. A309
SALVO, Thomas, Associate Executive Director Human Resources, Glen Cove Hospital, Glen Cove, NY, p. A434
SALY, David, Director, Information Services, Largo Medical Center, Largo, FL, p. A132
SALYER, Steven, Senior Vice President and Chief Operating Officer, Indian River Medical Center, Vero Beach, FL, p. A146
SALZMAN, Shona, Chief Operating Officer, William Newton Hospital, Winfield, KS, p. A253
SAMBASIVAN, Venkataraman, M.D. Chief Medical Officer, Lourdes Medical Center, Pasco, WA, p. A682
SAMESS, Ronald, M.D. Chief of Staff, Fishermen's Hospital, Marathon, FL, p. A132
SAMET, Kenneth A., President and Chief Executive Officer, MedStar Health, Columbia, MD, p. B88
SAMILO, Nick, Vice President Fiscal Services and Chief Financial Officer, Stanly Regional Medical Center, Albemarle, NC, p. A455
SAMMARCO, Michael, M.D. Chief Financial Officer, Erie County Medical Center, Buffalo, NY, p. A430
SAMMONS, Craig, Chief Financial Officer, Sky Ridge Medical Center, Lone Tree, CO, p. A106
SAMMS, Caswell, Network Chief Financial Officer, Lincoln Medical and Mental Health Center, NY, p. A441
SAMORA, Martha, FACHE, Chief Executive Officer, HEALTHSOUTH Bakersfield Rehabilitation Hospital, Bakersfield, CA, p. A55
SAMPAGA, Arthur, Assistant Director Nursing, Hilo Medical Center, Hilo, HI, p. A168
SAMPSON, Arthur J., FACHE, President, Miriam Hospital, Providence, RI, p. A555
SAMPSON, Bob, Vice President Human Resources, Redwood Memorial Hospital, Fortuna, CA, p. A61
SAMPSON, Cherie L., Director Human Resources, Kaiser Permanente San Diego Medical Center, San Diego, CA, p. A86
SAMPSON, Jill, Director Human Resources, Lemuel Shattuck Hospital, Jamaica Plain, MA, p. A307
SAMS, Tricia, M.D. Medical Director, Memorial Health Care Systems, Seward, NE, p. A398
SAMSON, Ley, Director Management Information Systems, Clear Lake Regional Medical Center, Webster, TX, p. A651
SAMUDRALA, Siresha, M.D. Medical Director, Mercy Rehabilitation Hospital, Chesterfield, MO, p. A365
SAMUELS, Christopher, Chief of Staff, Skyline Hospital, White Salmon, WA, p. A687
SAMUELS, Steven, M.D. Medical Director, Kindred Hospital Indianapolis South, Greenwood, IN, p. A210
SAMUELS, Tammy, Director Human Resources, Union County Hospital, Anna, IL, p. A178
SAMUELSON, Melissa A., R.N. Chief Nurse Executive, Poplar Bluff Regional Medical Center, Poplar Bluff, MO, p. A374
SAMYN, Mike, Vice President, Finance and Chief Financial Officer, St. Mary Mercy Hospital, Livonia, MI, p. A325

SAMZ, Jeff, Chief Operating Officer, Huntsville Hospital, Huntsville, AL, p. A21
SAN FILIPPO, Bruce, M.D. Chief Medical Officer, Memorial Medical Center, Las Cruces, NM, p. A425
SANBORN, Randall, Director Information Technology, HealthSource Saginaw, Inc., Saginaw, MI, p. A329
SANCHEZ, Antonio, M.D. Chief of Staff, Veterans Affairs Caribbean Healthcare System, San Juan, PR, p. A724
SANCHEZ, Arnaldo Rodriguez, M.D. Chief Operating Officer, Hospital Episcopal San Lucas Guayama, Guayama, PR, p. A721
SANCHEZ, Emalie, Director Human Resources, Baylor Medical Center at Uptown, Dallas, TX, p. A604
SANCHEZ, Esperanza, Chief Clinical Officer, Kindred Hospital–La Mirada, La Mirada, CA, p. A66
SANCHEZ, Freddie, Director Information Systems, Fountain Valley Regional Hospital and Medical Center, Fountain Valley, CA, p. A61
SANCHEZ, John, Vice President Human Resources, White Plains Hospital Center, White Plains, NY, p. A454
SANCHEZ, Jose R., President and Chief Executive Officer, Norwegian American Hospital, Chicago, IL, p. A183
SANCHEZ, Nancy, Senior Vice President and Vice Dean Human Resources, NYU Langone Medical Center, New York, NY, p. A443
SANCHEZ, Rachel, Director Information Systems, Providence Little Company of Mary Medical Center San Pedro, CA, p. A72
SANCHEZ, Rebecca, R.N. Director of Nursing, Texas Center for Infectious Disease, San Antonio, TX, p. A642
SANCHEZ–BICKLEY, Michelle
Vice President Human Resources, Renown Regional Medical Center, Reno, NV, p. A403
Vice President Human Resources, Renown Rehabilitation Hospital, Reno, NV, p. A404
Vice President Human Resources, Renown South Meadows Medical Center, Reno, NV, p. A404
SANCHEZ–JIMENEZ, Aida, M.D. Chief Medical Officer, Osceola Regional Medical Center, Kissimmee, FL, p. A130
SANCHEZ–RICO, Gloria, Chief Nursing Officer and Vice President, Huntington Memorial Hospital, Pasadena, CA, p. A80
SAND, Michelle, R.N. Assistant Administrator Patient Care Serices and Risk Manager, Cascade Valley Hospital and Clinics, Arlington, WA, p. A676
SANDAGER, Brian, Chief Information Officer, Lowell General Hospital, Lowell, MA, p. A308
SANDBERG, Susan, R.N. Chief Operating Officer, Community Hospital North, Indianapolis, IN, p. A211
SANDBERG, Todd, Chief Executive Officer and Administrator, Ridgeview Sibley Medical Center, Arlington, MN, p. A334
SANDBULTE, Nyla H., R.N. Chief Nursing Officer, Sanford Luverne Medical Center, Luverne, MN, p. A341
SANDEFUR, Gwen L., Chief Operating Officer, Spectrum Health – Butterworth Hospital, Grand Rapids, MI, p. A321
SANDER, Cindy, Coordinator Human Resources, Kindred Hospital–St. Louis, Saint Louis, MO, p. A376
SANDERLIN, Lisa, Chief Information Officer, University Hospital McDuffie, Thomson, GA, p. A166
SANDERS, Amy, Chief Human Resources, Captain James A. Lovell Federal Health Care Center, North Chicago, IL, p. A196
SANDERS, Carolyn Lucey, Senior Vice President Patient Services and Chief Nursing Officer, University of Colorado Hospital, Aurora, CO, p. A99
SANDERS, David, Chief Financial Officer, Jackson Parish Hospital, Jonesboro, LA, p. A276
SANDERS, David S., Chief Executive Officer, Fannin Regional Hospital, Blue Ridge, GA, p. A152
SANDERS, Diane M., Chief Nursing Officer, Trios Health, Kennewick, WA, p. A680
SANDERS, Gale H., Director, Gadsden Regional Medical Center, Gadsden, AL, p. A20
SANDERS, Harv, Chief Financial Officer, Rhea Medical Center, Dayton, TN, p. A577
SANDERS, Jeff, Senior Vice President, Chief Operating Officer, Maine Medical Center, Portland, ME, p. A291
SANDERS, Jeffrey, M.D. Chief of Staff, Carson Tahoe Health, Carson City, NV, p. A400
SANDERS, Kelly B., Vice President Human Resources, Good Shepherd Health Care System, Hermiston, OR, p. A521
SANDERS, Kenneth, Interim Administrator and Chief Executive Officer, Dallas County Medical Center, Fordyce, AR, p. A44
SANDERS, Kimberly, Chief Nursing Officer, Baptist Memorial Hospital–Huntingdon, Huntingdon, TN, p. A579
SANDERS, Kyle
Chief Financial Officer, NEA Baptist Memorial Hospital, Jonesboro, AR, p. A46
Chief Operating Officer, St. Vincent's Medical Center Southside, Jacksonville, FL, p. A130

SANDERS, Laura, Manager Human Resources, Mercy Hospital Independence, Independence, KS, p. A242
SANDERS, Michael, Chief Executive Officer, AMG Specialty Hospital–Feliciana, Clinton, LA, p. A271
SANDERS, Michael B., President and Chief Executive Officer, Monroe Clinic, Monroe, WI, p. A707
SANDERS, Michael R., MS Chief Operating Officer, Promise Hospital Baton Rouge – Main Campus, Baton Rouge, LA, p. A270
SANDERS, Michael R., MS,
Administrator and Chief Operating Officer, Promise Hospital of Baton Rouge – Mid-City Campus, Baton Rouge, LA, p. A270
Administrator and Chief Operating Officer, Promise Hospital of Baton Rouge – Ochsner Campus, Baton Rouge, LA, p. A270
SANDERS, Robert, M.D. Chief Medical Officer, Texoma Medical Center, Denison, TX, p. A607
SANDERS, Ryan, Director Information Services, Midtown Medical Center West, Columbus, GA, p. A154
SANDERS, Steve, Chief Financial Officer, Washington County Hospital and Clinics, Washington, IA, p. A235
SANDERS, Susie Sherrod, Budget Officer, Cherry Hospital, Goldsboro, NC, p. A461
SANDIFER, Ron, Chief Information Officer, Community Memorial Health System, Ventura, CA, p. A96
SANDIN, James H., M.D. Assistant Administrator Medical Affairs, Hunt Regional Medical Center, Greenville, TX, p. A617
SANDIN, Karl J., M.P.H., President and Medical Director, Schwab Rehabilitation Hospital, Chicago, IL, p. A184
SANDLES, Christopher, Associate Director, Michael E. DeBakey Veterans Affairs Medical Center, Houston, TX, p. A621
SANDLIN, Keith, Chief Executive Officer, Cartersville Medical Center, Cartersville, GA, p. A153
SANDLIN, Michael, M.D. Chief of Staff, Muscogee Creek Nation Medical Center, Okmulgee, OK, p. A513
SANDMANN, Patty, Senior Director of Nursing, Burgess Health Center, Onawa, IA, p. A232
SANDS, Naomi, Administrative Assistant and Manager Human Resources, Swift County–Benson Hospital, Benson, MN, p. A335
SANDS, Sherry, R.N. Chief Nursing Officer, Southern Tennessee Regional Health System–Pulaski, Pulaski, TN, p. A587
SANDS, Tiffany, Manager Health Information, Arbuckle Memorial Hospital, Sulphur, OK, p. A515
SANDSTROM, C. Bruce, Vice President and Chief Financial Officer, The Aroostook Medical Center, Presque Isle, ME, p. A292
SANFORD, Lisa, VP Patient Care/CNO, Holy Rosary Healthcare, Miles City, MT, p. A385
SANFORD, Ricca, Director Human Resources, Regional West Garden County, Oshkosh, NE, p. A397
SANFORD, Sharon K., Director Human Resources, Jersey Community Hospital, Jerseyville, IL, p. A191
SANFORD, Stacy, Chief Executive Officer, Oceans Behavioral Hospital Abilene, Abilene, TX, p. A590
SANGANI, Bakul, M.D. President Medical Staff, Saint Luke's South Hospital, Overland Park, KS, p. A248
SANGER, David, M.D. Chief Medical Officer, Pawnee Valley Community Hospital, Larned, KS, p. A244
SANGER, Marla I., R.N., Chief Executive Officer, Wrangell Medical Center, Wrangell, AK, p. A29
SANGER, Neal, Vice President Information Services, Mayo Clinic Health System – Franciscan Healthcare in La Crosse, La Crosse, WI, p. A703
SANGHI, Harishankar, M.D. Clinical Director, St. Lawrence Psychiatric Center, Ogdensburg, NY, p. A446
SANKARAN, Jaya, M.D. Chief of Staff, St. Mary's of Michigan Standish Hospital, Standish, MI, p. A330
SANKOORIKAL, Joseph, M.D. Chief Medical Staff, Kansas Rehabilitation Hospital, Topeka, KS, p. A251
SANKOVICH, Mary Lou, MSN, Chief Executive Officer, Vibra Hospital of Mahoning Valley, Boardman, OH, p. A480
SANNUTO, John, Chief Executive Officer, Port St. Lucie Hospital, Port St. Lucie, FL, p. A141
SANSONE, John, Director Human Resources, Monadnock Community Hospital, Peterborough, NH, p. A408
SANTA ANA, Coleen F., Chief Executive Officer, Sentara Albemarle Medical Center, Elizabeth City, NC, p. A459
SANTAMARIA, Mark A., President, MidMichigan Medical Center–Gratiot, Alma, MI, p. A314
SANTANA, Leticia, Administrator Medical Records, Hospital Hermanos Melendez, Bayamon, PR, p. A720
SANTANGELO, Charles J., CPA Executive Vice President and Chief Financial Officer, Williamsport Regional Medical Center, Williamsport, PA, p. A553
SANTANGELO, John, Director Information Technology, Cleveland Clinic Florida, Weston, FL, p. A147
SANTANGELO, Linda, Ph.D., Director, Desert Willow Treatment Center, Las Vegas, NV, p. A401

Index of Health Care Professionals

Index of Health Care Professionals / Santarelli

SANTARELLI, James, M.D. President Medical Staff, Aurora Medical Center, Kenosha, WI, p. A703
SANTELLI, Lucretia, Director Human Resources, Sweetwater Hospital, Sweetwater, TN, p. A588
SANTIAGO, Alejandro, Director Finance, Doctors' Center Hospital San Juan, San Juan, PR, p. A723
SANTIAGO, Carlos T., Director Human Resources, Hospital Oncologico Andres Grillasca, Ponce, PR, p. A722
SANTIAGO, Manuel, Chief Information Officer, Hospital Metropolitan, San Juan, PR, p. A723
SANTIAGO, Orlando, Human Resources Officer, Hospital Del Maestro, San Juan, PR, p. A723
SANTIAGO, Sugehi, Director, Hospital San Francisco, San Juan, PR, p. A724
SANTIAGO, Ubaldo, M.D. Chairman, Doctors' Center Hospital San Juan, San Juan, PR, p. A723
SANTILLI, Robert J., Chief Executive Officer, Gunnison Valley Hospital, Gunnison, CO, p. A104
SANTINA, Ray, Director Information Systems, Psychiatric Institute of Washington, Washington, DC, p. A120
SANTISTEVAN, Vivian, Chief Human Resources, Tsehootsooi Medical Center, Fort Defiance, AZ, p. A31
SANTMAN, Kim D., Vice President Finance, St. Margaret's Hospital, Spring Valley, IL, p. A201
SANTORA, Judith, Human Resources Business Partner, Marymount Hospital, Garfield Heights, OH, p. A490
SANTOS, Alfred, Administrator, Lincoln County Medical Center, Ruidoso, NM, p. A426
SANTOS, Daniel, Director Ancillary Services, Pacifica Hospital of the Valley, CA, p. A72
SANTOS, David, President and Chief Executive Officer, St. Helena Hospital Clear Lake, Clearlake, CA, p. A58
SANTOS, Gloria N., R.N
Chief Nursing Officer, Florida Hospital Heartland Medical Center, Sebring, FL, p. A143
Vice President and Chief Nursing Officer, Florida Hospital Wauchula, Wauchula, FL, p. A146
SANTOS, Ismael, Director Human Resources, Valle Vista Hospital, Greenwood, IN, p. A210
SANTOS, Lori
Vice President Finance, Albany Memorial Hospital, Albany, NY, p. A428
Chief Financial Officer, St. Peter's Hospital, Albany, NY, p. A428
SANTOS, Thomas, R.N. Chief Nursing Officer, Parkview Community Hospital Medical Center, Riverside, CA, p. A83
SANTULLI, Patricia, Director Human Resources, Elmira Psychiatric Center, Elmira, NY, p. A433
SANVILLE, David, Chief Financial Officer, Mt. Ascutney Hospital and Health Center, Windsor, VT, p. A661
SANWARI, Murtaza, Chief Operating Officer, Kaiser Permanente Panorama City Medical Center, CA, p. A70
SANZ, Sean M., Chief Executive Officer, Novant Health Forsyth Medical Center, Winston–Salem, NC, p. A471
SANZONE, Frank, Manager Information Technology, Brighton Center for Recovery, Brighton, MI, p. A315
SAPIENZA, James J., Chief Administrative Officer, West Valley Hospital, Dallas, OR, p. A520
SAPORITO, Joann L., R.N. Vice President Nursing Services, Oak Valley Hospital District, Oakdale, CA, p. A78
SAPP, Tracy, Director Human Resources, HEALTHSOUTH Rehabilitation Hospital of Ocala, Ocala, FL, p. A136
SAPPENFIELD, Debra, R.N. Chief Nursing Officer, Hemphill County Hospital, Canadian, TX, p. A600
SAPPINGTON–CRITTENDEN, Shana, Chief Operating Officer, Westside Regional Medical Center, Plantation, FL, p. A140
SAPRA, Sonney, Director Information Systems and Chief Information Officer, Tuality Healthcare, Hillsboro, OR, p. A521
SARBACHER, James, Chief Information Officer, State Hospital North, Orofino, ID, p. A175
SARDANA, Sadhana, M.D. Clinical Director, Rockland Children's Psychiatric Center, Orangeburg, NY, p. A446
SARDELLA, Jeff, Director Information Technology, Terrebonne General Medical Center, Houma, LA, p. A275
SARDONE, Frank J., President and Chief Executive Officer, Bronson Battle Creek, Battle Creek, MI, p. A315
SARDONE, Frank J., President and Chief Executive Officer, Bronson Healthcare Group, Inc., Kalamazoo, MI, p. B25
SARDONE, Frank J., President and Chief Executive Officer, Bronson Methodist Hospital, Kalamazoo, MI, p. A323
SARDUY, Innette Mary, M.P.H. Associate Director Patient Care Services and Nurse Executive, Louis Stokes Cleveland Veterans Affairs Medical Center, Cleveland, OH, p. A484
SARGEANT, Marty, Chief Operating Officer, City of Hope's Helford Clinical Research Hospital, Duarte, CA, p. A60
SARGENT, Kimberly, Vice President Patient Services, St. Luke's Hospital – Miners Campus, Coaldale, PA, p. A531
SARGENT, Reed
Assistant Administrator Finance, Garfield Memorial Hospital and Clinics, Panguitch, UT, p. A657
Assistant Administrator Finance, Valley View Medical Center, Cedar City, UT, p. A654
SARGENT, Teresa, Vice President Human Resources, Saint Alphonsus Regional Medical Center, Boise, ID, p. A172
SARIDAKIS, Michael, M.D. Physician Adviser, Regional Hospital of Jackson, Jackson, TN, p. A579
SARMENTO, Joann, Manager Human Resources, Fairchild Medical Center, Yreka, CA, p. A98
SARNECKI, Adrienne, R.N. Chief Nursing Officer, Spaulding Rehabilitation Hospital Cape Cod, East Sandwich, MA, p. A306
SARNECKI, Robert (Bob), Chief Information Officer, Kingman Regional Medical Center, Kingman, AZ, p. A32
SAROFIN, Michelle, Superintendent, Albert J. Solnit Psychiatric Center – South Campus, Middletown, CT, p. A113
SARRA, Jane B., President and Chief Executive Officer, Canonsburg General Hospital, Canonsburg, PA, p. A530
SARRAFIAN, Zareh, Chief Executive Officer, Riverside County Regional Medical Center, Moreno Valley, CA, p. A76
SARROS, Steven, Vice President and Chief Information Officer, Baptist Hospital, Pensacola, FL, p. A139
SARROUI, B., M.D. Chief of Staff, Advanced Specialty Hospital of Toledo, Toledo, OH, p. A498
SARTAIN, Jarred, M.D. President Medical Staff, Marion Regional Medical Center, Hamilton, AL, p. A21
SARTAIN, Lisa M., Vice President, Human Resources, Bellevue Hospital, Bellevue, OH, p. A480
SARTOR, Frank, President and Chief Executive Officer, Ridgeview Institute, Smyrna, GA, p. A164
SARVEPALLI, Raghu, M.D. Vice President of Medical Affairs, St. Mary's of Michigan, Saginaw, MI, p. A329
SARVER, Troy, R.N. Chief Nursing Officer, Texas Orthopedic Hospital, Houston, TX, p. A622
SAS, Mary, Director of Clinical Services, Hampshire Memorial Hospital, Romney, WV, p. A695
SASS, Kevin, FACHE Senior Vice President Human Resources, Organization and Cultural Development, St. Francis Hospital, Columbus, GA, p. A154
SASSER, Kelley, Director Information Systems, Florida Hospital Zephyrhills, Zephyrhills, FL, p. A148
SASSMAN, Gregory, Interim Chief Executive Officer, Acuity Specialty Hospital of Sun City, Sun City, AZ, p. A
SATCHER, Richard H., Chief Executive Officer, Bayfront Health Port Charlotte, Port Charlotte, FL, p. A140
SATRIALE, Robert, M.D. Medical Director, LifeCare Hospitals of Chester County, West Chester, PA, p. A552
SATTAR, Parhez, Senior Director Information Technology, Grande Ronde Hospital, La Grande, OR, p. A522
SATTERWHITE, Glenda, Director of Nursing, Oklahoma Forensic Center, Vinita, OK, p. A517
SATTLER, Alan, Chief Financial Officer, ProMedica Flower Hospital, Sylvania, OH, p. A498
SAUDE, Aaron, Chief Executive Officer, Bigfork Valley Hospital, Bigfork, MN, p. A335
SAUDER, Chris, Chief Financial Officer, Frank R. Howard Memorial Hospital, Willits, CA, p. A98
SAUER, Bernie, Director Information Technology, San Gabriel Valley Medical Center, San Gabriel, CA, p. A89
SAUER, Mary R., R.N. Chief Nursing Officer, Lakewood Hospital, Lakewood, OH, p. A491
SAUERBREI, Teresa, Chief Nursing Officer, Marengo Memorial Hospital, UnityPoint Health, Marengo, IA, p. A231
SAUERS, Preston, Chief Financial Officer, Ellsworth County Medical Center, Ellsworth, KS, p. A239
SAUL, Jim, Chief Information Officer, Great Plains Health, North Platte, NE, p. A395
SAULLO, Nancy, Director Human Resources, Warren State Hospital, Warren, PA, p. A552
SAULNIER, Robert, MSN, Chief Executive Officer, Columbus Specialty Hospital, Columbus, GA, p. A154
SAUM, Anita, Director Human Resources, Rehabilitation Hospital of Tinton Falls, Tinton Falls, NJ, p. A419
SAUNDERS, Brooke, Administrator, Kindred Hospital–Westminster, Westminster, CA, p. A97
SAUNDERS, John R., M.D. Senior Vice President Medical Affairs and Chief Medical Officer, Greater Baltimore Medical Center, Baltimore, MD, p. A293
SAUNDERS, Jonathan, Chief Financial Officer, Baylor Medical Center at Trophy Club, Trophy Club, TX, p. A648
SAUNDERS, Kristi K., Director and Compliance Officer, Calais Regional Hospital, Calais, ME, p. A289
SAUNDERS, M. Patricia, R.N. Vice President Nursing, Hanover Hospital, Hanover, PA, p. A535
SAUNDERS, Ninfa, Chief Executive Officer, Medical Center, Navicent Health, Macon, GA, p. A160
SAUNDERS, Ninfa, Chief Executive Officer, Navicent Health, Macon, GA, p. B95
SAUNDERS, Theodore, Assistant Controller, Select Specialty Hospital – Northeast Atlanta, Atlanta, GA, p. A151
SAURO, Anthony, Chief Information Officer, Pointe Coupee General Hospital, New Roads, LA, p. A283
SAUS, Heather, Human Resource Generalist, Edwin Shaw Rehab, Cuyahoga Falls, OH, p. A487
SAUTER, Michael, M.D. Chief Medical Officer, St. Charles Hospital, Port Jefferson, NY, p. A448
SAVAGE, Heather, Director Human Resources, The Rehabilitation Institute of St. Louis, Saint Louis, MO, p. A378
SAVAGE, Steve, Chief Executive Officer, Stonecrest Center, Detroit, MI, p. A318
SAVAGE–TRACY, Elizabeth, Vice President and Human Resources Officer, Winchester Medical Center, Winchester, VA, p. A674
SAVINO, Linda A., MS, Chief Executive Officer, Rehabilitation Hospital of Tinton Falls, Tinton Falls, NJ, p. A419
SAVITSKY, Marian, R.N. Chief Nursing Officer, Sky Ridge Medical Center, Lone Tree, CO, p. A106
SAVOY III, F. Peter, Chief Executive Officer, Acadia–St. Landry Hospital, Church Point, LA, p. A271
SAVOY, Greg, M.D. Chief Medical Officer, Savoy Medical Center, Mamou, LA, p. A279
SAWA, Kendall, R.N., Chief Executive Officer, Ocean Beach Hospital, Ilwaco, WA, p. A679
SAWDEY, Don, M.D. Medical Director, Daniels Memorial Healthcare Center, Scobey, MT, p. A387
SAWICKI, Mitzi, Director of Nursing, Havenwyck Hospital, Auburn Hills, MI, p. A314
SAWTELLE, Bradley, M.D. President Medical Staff, Memorial Community Hospital and Health System, Blair, NE, p. A390
SAWYER, Anne, Chief Financial Officer, Wayne County Hospital, Monticello, KY, p. A263
SAWYER, Colleen A., MSN,
Executive Director, Mohawk Valley Psychiatric Center, Utica, NY, p. A452
Executive Director, Richard H. Hutchings Psychiatric Center, Syracuse, NY, p. A451
SAWYER, Dorothy, Chief Executive Officer, Eastern State Hospital, Medical Lake, WA, p. A680
SAWYER, Holly, Director and Human Resources Business Partner, Piedmont Fayette Hospital, Fayetteville, GA, p. A157
SAWYER, Regina, Vice President Chief Nursing Officer, Kaweah Delta Medical Center, Visalia, CA, p. A97
SAWYER, Robert, Senior Project Specialist, Spaulding Hospital for Continuing Medical Care North Shore, Salem, MA, p. A311
SAWYER, Scott, Chief Financial Officer, Community Medical Center, Falls City, NE, p. A391
SAWYER, Stephen, Chief Financial Officer, Norton Community Hospital, Norton, VA, p. A670
SAWYER, Steven, Chief Financial Officer, Indian Path Medical Center, Kingsport, TN, p. A580
SAXON, Kathy, R.N. Vice President Patient Care Services, Tillamook Regional Medical Center, Tillamook, OR, p. A526
SAXTON, Beth, R.N. Vice President Patient Care Services, Yuma District Hospital, Yuma, CO, p. A110
SAYAH, Assaad, M.D. Chief Medical Officer, Cambridge Health Alliance, Cambridge, MA, p. A305
SAYLER, Elizabeth, M.D. Chief of Staff, Lead–Deadwood Regional Hospital, Deadwood, SD, p. A568
SAYLER, Roger, Finance Officer, Fargo Veterans Affairs Health Care System, Fargo, ND, p. A473
SAYLER, Timothy, Chief Operating Officer, Essentia Health Fargo, Fargo, ND, p. A473
SAYLES, Debbie A., R.N. Vice President and Chief Nursing Officer, Texas Scottish Rite Hospital for Children, Dallas, TX, p. A607
SAYLOR, Craig M., Interim CEO, Somerset Hospital, Somerset, PA, p. A550
SAYLOR, Richard F., M.D. Chief Medical Officer, Pottstown Memorial Medical Center, Pottstown, PA, p. A548
SAYLORS, Julie, Controller, AnMed Health Rehabilitation Hospital, Anderson, SC, p. A557
SAYRE, Amy, Director Human Resources, General John J. Pershing Memorial Hospital, Brookfield, MO, p. A364
SAYRE, Michelle, R.N. Chief Nursing Officer, Arrowhead Regional Medical Center, Colton, CA, p. A58
SBARDELLA, Steven, M.D. Chief Medical Officer, Hallmark Health System, Melrose, MA, p. A308
SCAFIDDI, Darlene, R.N. Vice President Nursing and Patient Care Services, Pomona Valley Hospital Medical Center, Pomona, CA, p. A81
SCAFIDI, Frank
Vice President and Chief Information Officer, Tidelands Georgetown Memorial Hospital, Georgetown, SC, p. A561
Chief Information Officer, Tidelands Waccamaw Community Hospital, Murrells Inlet, SC, p. A564
SCALES, Melisa, Director of Nursing, Parkview Hospital, Wheeler, TX, p. A652

Index of Health Care Professionals

Index of Health Care Professionals / Schlatter


SCALISE, Jayne, R.N. Chief Nursing Executive, Lompoc Valley Medical Center, Lompoc, CA, p. A68
SCALISE, Paul, M.D. Chief Pulmonary Medicine and Internal Medicine, Hospital for Special Care, New Britain, CT, p. A113
SCALLION, Jessika
Administrator, Beacon Behavioral Healthcare, Lacombe, LA, p. A276
Administrator, Beacon Behavioral Hospital – New Orleans, New Orleans, LA, p. A281
SCALLON, Jean, Chief Executive Officer, Bloomington Meadows Hospital, Bloomington, IN, p. A205
SCAMARDO, II, Luke P., M.D. Chief of Staff, Grimes St. Joseph Health Center, Navasota, TX, p. A634
SCANLON, Donald
Chief Corporate Services, Mount Sinai Health System, Mount Sinai Beth Israel, New York, NY, p. A442
Chief Financial Officer, Mount Sinai Hospital, New York, NY, p. A442
Chief Corporate Services, Mount Sinai Health System, Mount Sinai St. Luke's – Roosevelt, New York, NY, p. A442
Chief Corporate Services, Mount Sinai Health System, New York Eye and Ear Infirmary of Mount Sinai, New York, NY, p. A442
SCANLON, Jill, Director Human Resources, Northern Colorado Rehabilitation Hospital, Johnstown, CO, p. A105
SCANLON, John, DPM Chief Medical Officer, Chestnut Hill Hospital, Philadelphia, PA, p. A542
SCANLON, Kerri, MSN Chief Nursing Officer, North Shore University Hospital, Manhasset, NY, p. A437
SCANZERA, Christopher A., Vice President and Chief Information Officer, AtlantiCare Regional Medical Center, Atlantic City, NJ, p. A409
SCARANO, Jenaro, M.D. Medical Director, St. Luke's Episcopal Hospital, Ponce, PR, p. A722
SCARBORO, Parrish, Chief Operating Officer, Corona Regional Medical Center, Corona, CA, p. A58
SCARBROUGH, Keith, Chief Information Officer, Saint Francis Hospital, Memphis, TN, p. A584
SCARLETT, Kamesha, Chief Information Resource Management, Veterans Affairs New Jersey Health Care System, East Orange, NJ, p. A411
SCARMATO, Victor, M.D. Acting Medical Director, Nassau University Medical Center, East Meadow, NY, p. A433
SCARPINO, David
President and Chief Executive Officer, Health Alliance Hospital – Broadway Campus, Kingston, NY, p. A436
President and Chief Executive Officer, Health Alliance Hospital – Mary's Avenue Campus, Kingston, NY, p. A436
SCARPINO, David, President and Chief Executive Officer, HealthAlliance of the Hudson Valley, Kingston, NY, p. B66
SCARROW, Alan, M/D/ President, Mercy Hospital Springfield, Springfield, MO, p. A379
SCENNA, Maria, Chief Operating Officer, St. Christopher's Hospital for Children, Philadelphia, PA, p. A545
SCEPANSKI, Theresa, Vice President People and Organizational Development, University Health System, San Antonio, TX, p. A642
SCERCY, Charles, Corporate Director, Snowden at Fredericksburg, Fredericksburg, VA, p. A665
SCHAAB, Ben, VP Fiscal Services/ Chief Financial Officer, CGH Medical Center, Sterling, IL, p. A201
SCHAACK, Gregory J., CP
Vice President and Chief Financial Officer, Candler Hospital, Savannah, GA, p. A164
Vice President and Chief Financial Officer, St. Joseph's Hospital, Savannah, GA, p. A164
SCHABERG, Dennis, M.D. Chief Medicine, VA Greater Los Angeles Healthcare System, Los Angeles, CA, p. A73
SCHACHTNER, Janet, R.N. Senior Vice President, Patient Care Services, Mount Nittany Medical Center, State College, PA, p. A550
SCHADE, Sue, Chief Information Officer, University of Michigan Hospitals and Health Centers, Ann Arbor, MI, p. A314
SCHAEF, Toby, Director Information Technology, Memorial Hospital of Carbon County, Rawlins, WY, p. A717
SCHAEFER, Becky, Chief Financial Officer, University of Utah Neuropsychiatric Institute, Salt Lake City, UT, p. A659
SCHAEFER, Debra, Chief Nursing Officer, Windsor–Laurelwood Center for Behavioral Medicine, Willoughby, OH, p. A501
SCHAEFER, Jamie, Vice President Finance, Avera Sacred Heart Hospital, Yankton, SD, p. A573
SCHAEFER, Kevin, Manager Information Services, River's Edge Hospital and Clinic, Saint Peter, MN, p. A347
SCHAEFER, Michael J., Executive Vice President and Chief Financial Officer, Methodist Charlton Medical Center, Dallas, TX, p. A605
SCHAEFER, Michelle, Chief Financial Officer, Lillian M. Hudspeth Memorial Hospital, Sonora, TX, p. A644
SCHAEFER, Stephen, Chief Executive Officer, HEALTHSOUTH Rehabilitation Hospital of Colorado Springs, Colorado Springs, CO, p. A100
SCHAEFFER, Andre, M.D. Chief of Staff, Union General Hospital, Blairsville, GA, p. A152
SCHAEFFER, Darlene, Chief Nursing Officer, Regional West Garden County, Oshkosh, NE, p. A397
SCHAEFFER, Richard, Vice President Information Systems and Chief Information Officer, St. Clair Hospital, Pittsburgh, PA, p. A546
SCHAETTI, Susan, Chief Executive Officer, Kindred Hospital–Mansfield, Mansfield, TX, p. A631
SCHAFER, Michael, Chief Executive Officer and Administrator, Spooner Health System, Spooner, WI, p. A711
SCHAFER, Mona, Regional Manager Human Resources, Milbank Area Hospital Avera, Milbank, SD, p. A569
SCHAFF, Vicki, Chief Operating Officer, Epic Medical Center, Eufaula, OK, p. A506
SCHAFFER, Arnold R., Corporate Chief Executive Officer, Avanti Hospitals, El Segundo, CA, p. B16
SCHAFFER, Megan, Administrative Assistant, Surgical Institute of Reading, Wyomissing, PA, p. A554
SCHAFFER, Renee, Coordinator Human Resources, Select Specialty Hospital–Wichita, Wichita, KS, p. A252
SCHAFFMEYER, MaryJeanne
Chief Operating Officer, Appleton Medical Center, Appleton, WI, p. A697
Chief Operating Officer, Theda Clark Medical Center, Neenah, WI, p. A707
SCHAFFNER, Leroy, Chief Executive Officer, Coon Memorial Hospital, Dalhart, TX, p. A604
SCHAFFNER, Marilyn J., Ph.D. Administrator Clinical Services and Chief Nursing Officer, MUSC Medical Center of Medical University of South Carolina, Charleston, SC, p. A558
SCHAFFNER, Randall, M.D. Chief of Staff and Medical Director, Wilbarger General Hospital, Vernon, TX, p. A650
SCHAFFNER, Richard, Senior Vice President and Chief Operating Officer, Holy Spirit – A Geisinger Affiliate, Camp Hill, PA, p. A530
SCHAFFT, Jonathan, Director Information Systems, Hunt Regional Community Hospital, Commerce, TX, p. A602
SCHAFSNITZ, Patricia, Director of Nursing Services, McKenzie Health System, Sandusky, MI, p. A330
SCHAKELAAR, Christie, Chief Financial Officer, Fairview Regional Medical Center, Fairview, OK, p. A507
SCHALES, Marion, Chief Financial Officer, Highland Hospital, Oakland, CA, p. A78
SCHALL, Dee, R.N. Chief Nursing Officer, Baptist Health Medical Center–Hot Spring County, Malvern, AR, p. A48
SCHALSKI, Paula
Director Human Resources, Atoka County Medical Center, Atoka, OK, p. A504
Director Human Resources, Pushmataha Hospital & Home Health, Antlers, OK, p. A503
SCHAMP, Cindy K., President, Baylor Medical Center at Irving, Irving, TX, p. A624
SCHANWALD, Pamela R., Chief Executive Officer, The Children's Home of Pittsburgh, Pittsburgh, PA, p. A546
SCHAPP, Susan, Vice President Finance and Treasurer, The Charlotte Hungerford Hospital, Torrington, CT, p. A115
SCHAPPER, Robert A., Chief Executive Officer, Tahoe Forest Health System, Truckee, CA, p. B130
SCHARBER, Laurel, Administrative Assistant and Coordinator Human Resources, Kindred Hospital–Ontario, Ontario, CA, p. A79
SCHARDIN, Janice, MS, Administrator and Chief Executive Officer, Avera De Smet Memorial Hospital, De Smet, SD, p. A568
SCHARENBROCK, Chris, M.D. Chief Medical Staff, David Grant USAF Medical Center, Travis AFB, CA, p. A94
SCHARFF, Tom, Director Information Services, University Hospital and Medical Center, Tamarac, FL, p. A144
SCHARLES, Susan L., Director Human Resources, Valley View Medical Center, Fort Mohave, AZ, p. A31
SCHARNBERG, Cathi Rae, R.N. Vice President Patient Services, Avera Holy Family Hospital, Estherville, IA, p. A227
SCHARNHORST, Alicia, Human Resources and Business Office Manager, Garfield County Public Hospital District, Pomeroy, WA, p. A682
SCHARR, Vickie, Chief Financial Officer, Bakersfield Heart Hospital, Bakersfield, CA, p. A54
SCHAUF, Jeffrey, Director Information Systems, Wesley Medical Center, Wichita, KS, p. A253
SCHAUF, Victoria, M.D. Chief of Staff, Ridgecrest Regional Hospital, Ridgecrest, CA, p. A83
SCHAWL, Bud, Chief Executive Officer, Kindred Hospital–Albuquerque, Albuquerque, NM, p. A422
SCHAY, Maria, Chief Information Officer, Veterans Affairs New York Harbor Healthcare System, NY, p. A445
SCHEAFFEL, Margaret, R.N. Chief Nursing Officer, Presbyterian–St. Luke's Medical Center, Denver, CO, p. A102
SCHEERER, Dan, M.D. Chief Medical Officer, Genesis HealthCare System, Zanesville, OH, p. A502
SCHEETS, Frank, Senior Vice President, NYU Lutheran, NY, p. A444
SCHEETZ, Allison, M.D. Medical Director, Rehabilitation Hospital, Navicent Health, Macon, GA, p. A161
SCHEFFLER, Robert, Chief Executive Officer, Clarion Psychiatric Center, Clarion, PA, p. A531
SCHEFFLER, Tom, Chief Fiscal Officer, Veterans Affairs Maryland Health Care System–Baltimore Division, Baltimore, MD, p. A295
SCHEHI, Jay, Chief Executive Officer, Rivendell Behavioral Health Services of Arkansas, Benton, AR, p. A41
SCHEIB, Garry L., Executive Director, Hospital of the University of Pennsylvania, Philadelphia, PA, p. A544
SCHEINBERG, Paul, M.D. Chief of Staff, Emory Saint Joseph's Hospital of Atlanta, Atlanta, GA, p. A150
SCHEINBLUM, Richard, Chief Financial Officer, Monadnock Community Hospital, Peterborough, NH, p. A408
SCHEK, Larry, M.D. Senior Vice President Chief Medical Director and Vice President Cardiology, St. Vincent's Medical Center, Bridgeport, CT, p. A111
SCHELBAR, E. Joe, M.D. Medical Director, Select Specialty Hospital–Tulsa Midtown, Tulsa, OK, p. A517
SCHELL, James, M.D. Vice President Medical Affairs, Saint Francis Medical Center, Cape Girardeau, MO, p. A364
SCHEMER, Tonia, Interim Chief Human Resources, St. Joseph Mercy Livingston Hospital, Howell, MI, p. A322
SCHENCK, Debbie, Administrator, Omega Hospital, Metairie, LA, p. A280
SCHENKER, Amy, Human Resources Director, Shriners Hospitals for Children–Tampa, Tampa, FL, p. A145
SCHEPMANN, Jane, Vice President and Chief Nursing Officer, Clara Barton Hospital, Hoisington, KS, p. A241
SCHEPPERS, Levi, Chief Executive Officer, Nebraska Orthopaedic Hospital, Omaha, NE, p. A396
SCHER, Kathleen, R.N. Chief Nursing Officer, Jamaica Hospital Medical Center, NY, p. A440
SCHERAMIC, Mychail, M.D., Chief Executive Officer, Northwest Ohio Psychiatric Hospital, Toledo, OH, p. A498
SCHERLER, Jay, Vice President Finance and Chief Information Officer, Providence Healthcare Network, Waco, TX, p. A650
SCHERNECK, Michael D., Interim Chief Executive Officer, Southeast Georgia Health System, Brunswick, GA, p. B124
SCHERNECK, Michael D.
Interim Chief Executive Officer, Southeast Georgia Health System Brunswick Campus, Brunswick, GA, p. A152
Executive Vice President and Chief Financial Officer, Southeast Georgia Health System Camden Campus, Saint Marys, GA, p. A163
SCHEVING, Travis, Chief Financial Officer, Holy Rosary Healthcare, Miles City, MT, p. A385
SCHIEBER, Steven M., Interim Chief Executive Officer, Hedrick Medical Center, Chillicothe, MO, p. A365
SCHIEFELBEIN, Shelia, Coordinator Human Resources, Northwest Florida Community Hospital, Chipley, FL, p. A123
SCHIERECK, Stacie, Director Management Services, Mendota Mental Health Institute, Madison, WI, p. A704
SCHIESL, Troy, Director Information Services, Bellin Psychiatric Center, Green Bay, WI, p. A702
SCHIFFER, Christopher, Administrator, Community Behavioral Health Hospital – St. Peter, Saint Peter, MN, p. A346
SCHILLER, Ann Mattia, Vice President Human Resources, College Medical Center, Long Beach, CA, p. A68
SCHILLING, Helen, M.D. Medical Director, Kindred Rehabilitation Hospital Northeast Houston, Humble, TX, p. A623
SCHILLING, Thomas, Chief Financial Officer and Senior Vice President Finance, ProMedica Monroe Regional Hospital, Monroe, MI, p. A326
SCHIMEROWSKI, Deborah
Vice President Finance and Chief Financial Officer, Presence Covenant Medical Center, Urbana, IL, p. A202
Chief Financial Officer, Presence United Samaritans Medical Center, Danville, IL, p. A185
SCHIMMING, Michael B., Director Financial Services, Shriners Hospitals for Children–Galveston, Galveston, TX, p. A615
SCHINDEL, Lester P., Chief Executive Officer, CharterCare Health Partners, Providence, RI, p. B32
SCHIPPER, Brad J., Chief Operating Officer, Sanford USD Medical Center, Sioux Falls, SD, p. A571
SCHIRALLI, Rocco, President/Chief Executive Officer, Porter–Starke Services, Valparaiso, IN, p. A221
SCHLABACH, Michael, M.D. Chief Medical Officer, Scott & White Hospital – Brenham, Brenham, TX, p. A598
SCHLAGER, Robert, M.D. Chief Medical Officer, Sebasticook Valley Health, Pittsfield, ME, p. A291
SCHLATTER, Christina, Chief Financial Officer, Oswego Community Hospital, Oswego, KS, p. A247

SCHLECHTER, Sandy, Chief Executive Officer, Bowdle Hospital, Bowdle, SD, p. A567

SCHLEETER, Larry C., Chief Human Resources Officer, Memorial Health, Marysville, OH, p. A493

SCHLEGEL, Patricia, Executive Director Finance, Minnesota Valley Health Center, Le Sueur, MN, p. A341

SCHLEICHER, Larry, Manager Information Services, Dr. John Warner Hospital, Clinton, IL, p. A185

SCHLEIF, John V., Senior Vice President and Chief Operating Officer, Henry Mayo Newhall Memorial Hospital, Valencia, CA, p. A96

SCHLEMMER, Tom, Chief Financial Officer, St. Mary's Medical Center, West Palm Beach, FL, p. A147

SCHLENKER, Jim, Chief Operating Officer, Good Shepherd Health Care System, Hermiston, OR, p. A521

SCHLESINGER, J. Tuerk, Chief Executive Officer, AltaPointe Health Systems, Mobile, AL, p. B10

SCHLESKE, Brenda, Interim Administrator, Community Behavioral Health Hospital – Fergus Falls, Fergus Falls, MN, p. A338

SCHLESSMAN, Alissa, Administrator, Beaver County Memorial Hospital, Beaver, OK, p. A504

SCHLEY, Kurt, Market Chief Executive Officer, CHI St. Alexius Health, Bismarck, ND, p. A472

SCHLICHTING, Nancy M., Chief Executive Officer, Henry Ford Health System, Detroit, MI, p. B70

SCHLICHTMANN, Phyllis J., Chief Executive Officer, Marlton Rehabilitation Hospital, Marlton, NJ, p. A414

SCHLOSS, William, Senior Vice President and Administrator, Laureate Psychiatric Clinic and Hospital, Tulsa, OK, p. A516

SCHLUTER, Robin M., Chief Executive Officer, Regional Health Services of Howard County, Cresco, IA, p. A225

SCHMID, Nancy, Chief Executive Officer, Healdsburg District Hospital, Healdsburg, CA, p. A64

SCHMID, Nancy A., R.N. Associate Director Patient Care Services, Coatesville Veterans Affairs Medical Center, Coatesville, PA, p. A532

SCHMIDLY, Scott, Chief Executive Officer, Eastside Medical Center, Snellville, GA, p. A164

SCHMIDT, Allen J., M.D. President, Medical Staff, Decatur Morgan Hospital, Decatur, AL, p. A18

SCHMIDT, Barbara, Chief Executive Officer, Mesa Springs, Fort Worth, TX, p. A613

SCHMIDT, Bobbi, Chief Nursing Officer, Select Specialty Hospital–Cincinnati, Cincinnati, OH, p. A483

SCHMIDT, Constance, R.N. Chief Nursing Officer, Cheyenne Regional Medical Center, Cheyenne, WY, p. A715

SCHMIDT, David, R.N. Chief Nursing Officer, Jennersville Regional Hospital, West Grove, PA, p. A552

SCHMIDT, Holly, Chief Information Officer, Hill Country Memorial Hospital, Fredericksburg, TX, p. A614

SCHMIDT, Janie, Director of Nursing, Greeley County Health Services, Tribune, KS, p. A251

SCHMIDT, Joan E., Director Human Resources, Elmwood Healthcare Center at the Springs, Green Springs, OH, p. A490

SCHMIDT, Julie, Director Human Resources, Grand Itasca Clinic and Hospital, Grand Rapids, MN, p. A339

SCHMIDT, Kristin, R.N. Chief Nursing Officer, Desert Regional Medical Center, Palm Springs, CA, p. A80

SCHMIDT, Loretta, President, Saint Joseph Regional Medical Center–Plymouth Campus, Plymouth, IN, p. A218

SCHMIDT, Mark C., President, Lead–Deadwood Regional Hospital, Deadwood, SD, p. A568

SCHMIDT, Milan, Medical Director, Cook County North Shore Hospital, Grand Marais, MN, p. A339

SCHMIDT Jr., Richard O.
President and Chief Executive Officer, United Hospital System, St. Catherine's Medical Center Campus, Pleasant Prairie, WI, p. A709
President and Chief Executive Officer, United Hospital System–Kenosha Campus, Kenosha, WI, p. A703

SCHMIDT, Robert F., Director Human Resources, Hocking Valley Community Hospital, Logan, OH, p. A492

SCHMIDT, Rosanne, R.N. Chief Nursing Officer, CHI St. Alexius Health, Bismarck, ND, p. A472

SCHMIDT, Steve, Director Information Systems, Evans Memorial Hospital, Claxton, GA, p. A153

SCHMIDT, Tim, Chief Executive Officer, Bay Area Regional Medical Center, Webster, TX, p. A651

SCHMIDT, Tressa, Administrator, CHI Albany Area Health, Albany, MN, p. A334

SCHMIDT, Veronica, President, Custer Regional Hospital, Custer, SD, p. A568

SCHMIDT, William, President and Chief Executive Officer, New London Family Medical Center, New London, WI, p. A707

SCHMIDTBERGER, Sheryl, Chief Financial Officer, AllianceHealth Blackwell, Blackwell, OK, p. A504

SCHMIEDT, Jason, Chief Financial Officer, Clinch Valley Medical Center, Richlands, VA, p. A671

SCHMIEGE, Ardis, Chief Financial Officer, Cascade Valley Hospital and Clinics, Arlington, WA, p. A676

SCHMIER, Joseph, Interim Director Human Resources, North Valley Hospital, Whitefish, MT, p. A388

SCHMIESING, Karee, Director of Nursing, Sleepy Eye Medical Center, Sleepy Eye, MN, p. A347

SCHMITS, Peggy, Director, Nursing Operations, New Braunfels Regional Rehabilitation Hospital, New Braunfels, TX, p. A634

SCHMITT, John, Senior Vice President and Chief Financial Officer, Kingsbrook Jewish Medical Center, NY, p. A441

SCHMITT, Joseph, Chief Information Officer, St. Elizabeth's Medical Center, Brighton, MA, p. A305

SCHMITT, III, Joseph, Senior Vice President Finance and Chief Financial Officer, Henry Ford Hospital, Detroit, MI, p. A317

SCHMITT, Karl, M.D. Chief of Staff, St. Elizabeth Edgewood, Edgewood, KY, p. A256

SCHMITT, Peggy, President and Chief Executive Officer, North Kansas City Hospital, North Kansas City, MO, p. A373

SCHMITT II, Robert C., Chief Executive Officer, Gibson Area Hospital and Health Services, Gibson City, IL, p. A189

SCHMITT, Thomas M., Chief Executive Officer, Kansas Spine and Specialty Hospital, Wichita, KS, p. A252

SCHMITZ, Bonnie
Vice President and Chief Financial Officer, Agnesian HealthCare, Fond Du Lac, WI, p. A700
Chief Financial Officer, Ripon Medical Center, Ripon, WI, p. A710
Chief Financial Officer, Waupun Memorial Hospital, Waupun, WI, p. A713

SCHMITZ, Christopher, Director Human Resources, Stoughton Hospital Association, Stoughton, WI, p. A711

SCHMITZ, Joseph, Chief Financial Officer, St. Cloud Veterans Affairs Health Care System, Saint Cloud, MN, p. A346

SCHMITZ, Vince, Senior Vice President and Chief Financial Officer, MultiCare Mary Bridge Children's Hospital and Health Center, Tacoma, WA, p. A686

SCHMOTZER, Dave, Chief Financial Officer, Bryn Mawr Rehabilitation Hospital, Malvern, PA, p. A539

SCHMUS, Angie, Chief Information Technology, Aleda E. Lutz Veterans Affairs Medical Center, Saginaw, MI, p. A329

SCHNACK, Tim H.
Vice President Financial Services, CHI Health Bergan Mercy, Omaha, NE, p. A395
Chief Financial Officer, CHI Health Creighton University Medical Center, Omaha, NE, p. A395
Chief Financial Officer, CHI Health Immanuel, Omaha, NE, p. A396
Chief Financial Officer, CHI Health Plainview, Plainview, NE, p. A397
Chief Financial Officer, CHI Health Schuyler, Schuyler, NE, p. A398
Vice President Operations Finance, CHI Health St. Mary's, Nebraska City, NE, p. A394

SCHNACKEL, Donald, Chief Financial Officer, Carthage Area Hospital, Carthage, NY, p. A431

SCHNEDLER, Lisa W., FACHE, President and Chief Executive Officer, Upland Hills Health, Dodgeville, WI, p. A699

SCHNEIDER, Barbara, R.N., Chief Executive Officer, Newport Specialty Hospital, Tustin, CA, p. A95

SCHNEIDER, Barry S., Chief Executive Officer, Galesburg Cottage Hospital, Galesburg, IL, p. A188

SCHNEIDER, Brenda, Chief Financial Officer, Skyline Hospital, White Salmon, WA, p. A687

SCHNEIDER, Brian, Chief Financial Officer, Dupont Hospital, Fort Wayne, IN, p. A208

SCHNEIDER, Carol L., President and Chief Executive Officer, Mercy Hospital and Medical Center, Chicago, IL, p. A183

SCHNEIDER, David R., Executive Director, Langlade Hospital, Antigo, WI, p. A697

SCHNEIDER, Doug, Director Information Systems, Raulerson Hospital, Okeechobee, FL, p. A137

SCHNEIDER, Gina, Director Human Resources, Northwest Specialty Hospital, Post Falls, ID, p. A176

SCHNEIDER, H. Frank, Chief Executive Officer, Kindred Hospital Northland, Kansas City, MO, p. A370

SCHNEIDER, Jessie, Director Human Resources, Community Memorial Healthcare, Marysville, KS, p. A246

SCHNEIDER, John, M.D. Medical Director, Milwaukee County Behavioral Health Division, Milwaukee, WI, p. A706

SCHNEIDER, John, Human Resources Director, Putnam Community Medical Center, Palatka, FL, p. A138

SCHNEIDER, Shanon, Chief Information Officer, Greeley County Health Services, Tribune, KS, p. A251

SCHNEIDER, Stacie A.
Director Human Resources, Aurora Medical Center – Manitowoc County, Two Rivers, WI, p. A712
Director Human Resources, Aurora Sheboygan Memorial Medical Center, Sheboygan, WI, p. A710

SCHNEIDER, Stephen, Manager Information Services, Alaska Psychiatric Institute, Anchorage, AK, p. A27

SCHNEIDER, Steve, Manager Behavioral Services and Director Operations, New Ulm Medical Center, New Ulm, MN, p. A344

SCHNEIDER, Steven E., M.D. Chief Medical Officer, Saint Mary's Hospital, Waterbury, CT, p. A115

SCHNEIDER, Thomas D., D.O. Chief of Staff, Jack C. Montgomery Veterans Affairs Medical Center, Muskogee, OK, p. A510

SCHNEIDER, Valerie, Director Human Resources, Gove County Medical Center, Quinter, KS, p. A249

SCHNELL, Dawn, Chief Nursing Officer, Sanford Jackson Medical Center, Jackson, MN, p. A340

SCHNELL, Julie, Interim Chief Executive Officer, Gordon Memorial Hospital, Gordon, NE, p. A392

SCHNIEDERS, Michael H., FACHE, President, CHI Health Good Samaritan, Kearney, NE, p. A393

SCHNIER, Martin, D.O. Chief of Staff, West Texas Veterans Affairs Health Care System, Big Spring, TX, p. A597

SCHNOOR, Jeff
Director Information Technology and Systems, North Suburban Medical Center, Thornton, CO, p. A109
Director Information Systems, Swedish Medical Center, Englewood, CO, p. A103

SCHOELKOPF, Lawrence, M.D. Chief Medical Officer, East Morgan County Hospital, Brush, CO, p. A100

SCHOELLER, Betsy V., Director Human Resources and Education, Mary Greeley Medical Center, Ames, IA, p. A222

SCHOEN, Greg, M.D. Regional Medical Director, Fairview Northland Medical Center, Princeton, MN, p. A345

SCHOEN, Lynn, Chief Executive Officer, Kindred Hospital–Dayton, Dayton, OH, p. A488

SCHOENECKER, Perry L., M.D. Chief of Staff, Shriners Hospitals for Children–St. Louis, Saint Louis, MO, p. A377

SCHOENER, Timothy E.
Chief Information Officer, Muncy Valley Hospital, Muncy, PA, p. A541
Senior Vice President and Chief Information Officer, Soldiers and Sailors Memorial Hospital, Wellsboro, PA, p. A552
Senior Vice President and Chief Information Officer, Williamsport Regional Medical Center, Williamsport, PA, p. A553

SCHOENIG, Thomas
Chief Information Officer, Adventist Hinsdale Hospital, Hinsdale, IL, p. A191
Chief Information Officer, Adventist La Grange Memorial Hospital, La Grange, IL, p. A192
Regional Chief Information Officer, AMITA Health Adventist GlenOaks Hospital, Glendale Heights, IL, p. A189

SCHOENIG, Tom
System Director Information Services, Desert Springs Hospital Medical Center, Las Vegas, NV, p. A401
Regional Director Information Services, Valley Hospital Medical Center, Las Vegas, NV, p. A403

SCHOENOW, David, M.D. Chief Medical Officer, Schoolcraft Memorial Hospital, Manistique, MI, p. A325

SCHOEPLEIN, Kevin D., Chief Executive Officer, OSF Healthcare System, Peoria, IL, p. B102

SCHOETTLE, Steve, M.D. Chief Medical Staff, Ozark Health Medical Center, Clinton, AR, p. A42

SCHOFIELD, Sherry, Director Human Resources, Memorial Hospital, Martinsville, VA, p. A668

SCHOLEFIELD, Robert, Chief Operating Officer, St. Elizabeth Medical Center, Utica, NY, p. A452

SCHOLZ, Suzanne, Director Medical Records, Horsham Clinic, Ambler, PA, p. A528

SCHON, John, Administrator and Chief Executive Officer, Dickinson County Healthcare System, Iron Mountain, MI, p. A322

SCHONEBERY, Jeremy, Director Information Technology, Heart of America Medical Center, Rugby, ND, p. A476

SCHONLAU, Dan
Interim President, CHI Health Nebraska Heart, Lincoln, NE, p. A393
Chief Financial Officer and Vice President of Finance, CHI Health St Elizabeth, Lincoln, NE, p. A393

SCHONS, Jeri, R.N. Chief Nursing Officer, Sanford Tracy Medical Center, Tracy, MN, p. A348

SCHOOLER, Nevelyn, Health Information Manager, Garfield County Public Hospital District, Pomeroy, WA, p. A682

SCHOOLER, Richard D., M.D. Executive Vice President and Chief Operating Officer, Freeman Hospital West, Joplin, MO, p. A369

SCHOOLER, Rick, Vice President and Chief Information Officer, Orlando Regional Medical Center, Orlando, FL, p. A138

SCHOOMAKER, Eric B., Surgeon General, Department of the Army, Office of the Surgeon General, Falls Church, VA, p. B45

SCHOPP, Mary Ellen, Senior Vice President Human Resources, Rush University Medical Center, Chicago, IL, p. A184

SCHOR, Mark, Chief Executive Officer, Belmont Center for Comprehensive Treatment, Philadelphia, PA, p. A542

Index of Health Care Professionals / Schweers

Index of Health Care Professionals


SCHORER, Emily
Senior Vice President Human Resources, Cape Cod Hospital, Hyannis, MA, p. A307
Vice President, Human Resources, Falmouth Hospital, Falmouth, MA, p. A306
SCHORI, Melissa, M.D. Medical Director, Lincoln Medical and Mental Health Center, NY, p. A441
SCHOTT, Connie, Vice President, Human Resources, Ozarks Medical Center, West Plains, MO, p. A380
SCHOTT, Lynn, Director Information Technology, Mobridge Regional Hospital, Mobridge, SD, p. A570
SCHOTTEL, Roxanne, Chief Executive Officer, Washington County Hospital, Washington, KS, p. A252
SCHOULTIES, Daniel L., M.D. Vice President Medical Affairs, Good Samaritan Hospital, Dayton, OH, p. A488
SCHOWENGERDT, Daniel, M.D. Chief of Staff, Comanche County Hospital, Coldwater, KS, p. A238
SCHRADER, Guillermo, M.D. Acting Medical Director, Eastern State Hospital, Williamsburg, VA, p. A674
SCHRAEDER, David, Director Information Systems, Russell Regional Hospital, Russell, KS, p. A249
SCHRAGE, Larry E., FACHE, Chief Executive Officer, Haxtun Hospital District, Haxtun, CO, p. A105
SCHRAMM, Michael, Chief Executive Officer, Rice Memorial Hospital, Willmar, MN, p. A349
SCHRAMM, Steven R., Chief Financial Officer, Mountain View Hospital, Payson, UT, p. A657
SCHREEG, Timothy M., President and Chief Executive Officer, Franciscan Health Rensselear, Rensselaer, IN, p. A219
SCHREFFLER, Mary Jane, Director Human Resources, Meadows Psychiatric Center, Centre Hall, PA, p. A531
SCHREIBER, Anne, Manager Human Resources, Fairfax Behavioral Health, Kirkland, WA, p. A680
SCHREIBER, Elizabeth, R.N. Director Patient Care Services, Flambeau Hospital, Park Falls, WI, p. A709
SCHREIBER, John, M.D. President and Chief Physician Executive, Baystate Medical Center, Springfield, MA, p. A311
SCHREIBER, Mary Jo, R.N. Vice President Patient Services, Winter Haven Hospital, Winter Haven, FL, p. A148
SCHREIER, Susan, R.N. Chief Nursing Executive, Rockford Memorial Hospital, Rockford, IL, p. A199
SCHREINER, David L., FACHE, President and Chief Executive Officer, Katherine Shaw Bethea Hospital, Dixon, IL, p. A186
SCHROCK, Bonnie W., FACHE Chief Operating Officer, Baptist Health Paducah, Paducah, KY, p. A264
SCHRODER, Loren D., Chief Financial Officer, Phelps Memorial Health Center, Holdrege, NE, p. A393
SCHROEDER, Brian D., M.D. Senior Vice President and Chief Medical Officer, Sparrow Hospital, Lansing, MI, p. A324
SCHROEDER, Catherine, Deputy Chief Information Officer, Brigham and Women's Faulkner Hospital, Boston, MA, p. A303
SCHROEDER, Cygnet, D.O. Medical Director, HEALTHSOUTH Rehabilitation Hospital of Fort Smith, Fort Smith, AR, p. A44
SCHROEDER, Destiny, Information Systems Director, Rawlins County Health Center, Atwood, KS, p. A237
SCHROEDER, Heather, R.N. Chief Nurse Executive and Vice President of Nursing, Aurora BayCare Medical Center, Green Bay, WI, p. A701
SCHROEDER, Larry, Chief Executive Officer, Sauk Prairie Healthcare, Prairie Du Sac, WI, p. A709
SCHROEDER, Patricia S., R.N., Administrator, Milwaukee County Behavioral Health Division, Milwaukee, WI, p. A706
SCHROEDER, Rick, Chief Executive Officer, North Big Horn Hospital District, Lovell, WY, p. A716
SCHROEDER, Russell, Chief Nursing Officer, SSM Health Saint Louis University Hospital, Saint Louis, MO, p. A377
SCHROEDER, Steve, M.D. Chief of Staff, Avera Hand County Memorial Hospital, Miller, SD, p. A569
SCHROEDL, Greg, M.D. Vice President, Medical and Chief Medical Officer, UW Medicine/Northwest Hospital & Medical Center, Seattle, WA, p. A684
SCHROEPPEL, Stacie
Director of Human Resources, Baptist Memorial Rehabilitation Hospital, Germantown, TN, p. A578
Director Human Resources, Lakeside Behavioral Health System, Memphis, TN, p. A583
SCHROYER, Amy, Vice President Administration and Senior Site Executive, Daniel Drake Center for Post Acute Care, Cincinnati, OH, p. A482
SCHROYER, Mike, Chief Operating Officer, St. Vincent Heart Center, Indianapolis, IN, p. A212
SCHRUMPF, Jason, President, Missouri Delta Medical Center, Sikeston, MO, p. A378
SCHUBACH, Michael, Director Human Resources, Carroll County Memorial Hospital, Carrollton, MO, p. A365
SCHUBERTH, Michael, Director, Fiscal Services and Plant Operations, Connecticut Valley Hospital, Middletown, CT, p. A113
SCHUCKMAN, Tim, Chief Financial Officer, Jennie M. Melham Memorial Medical Center, Broken Bow, NE, p. A390
SCHUE, Janine
Executive Vice President, Chief Human Resources Officer, Newark–Wayne Community Hospital, Newark, NY, p. A445
Senior Vice President Human Resources, Rochester General Hospital, Rochester, NY, p. A448
SCHUE, Yvonne, R.N. Chief Nursing Officer, Brownfield Regional Medical Center, Brownfield, TX, p. A598
SCHUELER, Joe, Chief Financial Officer, Morrow County Hospital, Mount Gilead, OH, p. A495
SCHUERCH, Timothy, President and Chief Executive Officer, Maniilaq Health Center, Kotzebue, AK, p. A28
SCHUESSLER, Dwight, Chief Information Officer, Iowa City Veterans Affairs Health Care System, Iowa City, IA, p. A229
SCHUETT, Susan M., Chief Information Officer, Olmsted Medical Center, Rochester, MN, p. A345
SCHUH, Jason, M.D. Chief of Staff, Wise Regional Health System, Decatur, TX, p. A607
SCHUITEMAN, Jackson, Chief Financial Officer, Sioux Center Health, Sioux Center, IA, p. A234
SCHULER, Allison, R.N. Chief Nursing Officer, Baptist Medical Center Attala, Kosciusko, MS, p. A356
SCHULER, Kathy, R.N. Vice President of Patient Care Services, Winchester Hospital, Winchester, MA, p. A313
SCHULTE, Mark, FACHE, Chief Executive Officer, Sturgis Regional Hospital, Sturgis, SD, p. A572
SCHULTEIS, Chris, Vice President/Chief Financial Officer, Southampton Hospital, Southampton, NY, p. A450
SCHULTHEIS, Hal, Director Information Systems, TriStar Hendersonville Medical Center, Hendersonville, TN, p. A578
SCHULTZ, Bradley
Chief Financial Officer, TriStar Skyline Madison Campus, Madison, TN, p. A582
Chief Financial Officer, TriStar Skyline Medical Center, Nashville, TN, p. A586
SCHULTZ, David W., FACHE,
President, Harrison Medical Center, Bremerton, WA, p. A676
President, St. Anthony Hospital, Gig Harbor, WA, p. A679
SCHULTZ, Diana, Chief Executive Officer, Kindred Hospital El Paso, El Paso, TX, p. A611
SCHULTZ, Greg, Director Health Information Management, Seven Hills Hospital, Henderson, NV, p. A401
SCHULTZ, Jacky, R.N. Chief Nurse Officer, Suburban Hospital, Bethesda, MD, p. A296
SCHULTZ, Jim, Interim Chief Executive Officer, Edgerton Hospital and Health Services, Edgerton, WI, p. A700
SCHULTZ, Kim, Senior Application Analyst, Connally Memorial Medical Center, Floresville, TX, p. A612
SCHULTZ, Kurt
Group Chief Financial Officer, Cornerstone Hospital of SouthEast Arizona, Tucson, AZ, p. A39
Chief Financial Officer, Cornerstone Hospital–West Monroe, West Monroe, LA, p. A286
Chief Financial Officer, Solara Hospital Harlingen, Harlingen, TX, p. A618
SCHULTZ, Mary Kay, Director Human Resources, Sturgis Hospital, Sturgis, MI, p. A331
SCHULTZ, Merrilee, Chief Finance, Sanford USD Medical Center, Sioux Falls, SD, p. A571
SCHULTZ, Rachelle H., President and Chief Executive Officer, Winona Health, Winona, MN, p. A349
SCHULTZ, Sharon A., MSN Chief Nurse Executive and Vice President, Tri–City Medical Center, Oceanside, CA, p. A79
SCHULTZ, Teresa L., R.N. Vice President of Patient Care, Rogers Memorial Hospital, Oconomowoc, WI, p. A708
SCHULTZ, Vince, M.D. Chief Medical Officer, Munson Healthcare Grayling Hospital, Grayling, MI, p. A321
SCHULZ, Charles K., ACHE, Chief Executive Officer, York General Hospital, York, NE, p. A399
SCHULZ, Ken, Chief Operating Officer, North Dakota State Hospital, Jamestown, ND, p. A475
SCHULZ, Larry A., Chief Executive Officer, Lake Region Healthcare, Fergus Falls, MN, p. A338
SCHULZ, Leah, Director of Nursing, North Dakota State Hospital, Jamestown, ND, p. A475
SCHULZ, Marcie, Director Patient Care, Sakakawea Medical Center, Hazen, ND, p. A474
SCHUMACHER, Ann, FACHE, President, CHI Health Immanuel, Omaha, NE, p. A396
SCHUMACHER, Debbie
Chief Human Resource Officer, Clearwater Valley Hospital and Clinics, Orofino, ID, p. A175
Chief Human Resource Officer, St. Mary's Hospital, Cottonwood, ID, p. A174
SCHUMACHER, Paul, Chief Operating Officer, Clarendon Memorial Hospital, Manning, SC, p. A563
SCHUMAN, Dawn, President, Wild Rose Community Memorial Hospital, Wild Rose, WI, p. A714
SCHUMANN, Vera, Director of Finance and Controller, Cook County North Shore Hospital, Grand Marais, MN, p. A339
SCHUMM, Herbert, M.D. Vice President Medical Affairs, St. Rita's Medical Center, Lima, OH, p. A492
SCHURKAMP, Christine, Senior Human Resources Business Partner, Spectrum Health Gerber Memorial, Fremont, MI, p. A320
SCHUSTER, Carol E., R.N. Regional Chief Nursing Officer and Vice President Patient Care Services, Franciscan St. Anthony Health – Crown Point, Crown Point, IN, p. A207
SCHUSTER, Christine C., R.N., President and Chief Executive Officer, Emerson Hospital, Concord, MA, p. A306
SCHUSTER, Emmett C., President and Chief Executive Officer, Gibson General Hospital, Princeton, IN, p. A218
SCHUSTER, Jolene, Chief Financial Officer, Grisell Memorial Hospital District One, Ransom, KS, p. A249
SCHUSTER, Lexie, Vice President Human Resources, Good Samaritan Hospital, Los Angeles, CA, p. A70
SCHWAB, Bob, M.D. Chief Medical Officer, Texas Health Presbyterian Hospital Allen, Allen, TX, p. A590
SCHWABENBAUER, Mary Ann, Director Information Technology, Penn Highlands Elk, Saint Marys, PA, p. A549
SCHWAEGEL, Glen
Vice President and Chief Financial Officer, Barnes–Jewish St. Peters Hospital, Saint Peters, MO, p. A378
Chief Financial Officer, Progress West Hospital, O'Fallon, MO, p. A374
SCHWAGER, Mary A., Director Human Resources, Antelope Memorial Hospital, Neligh, NE, p. A394
SCHWAIGER, Jim, M.D. Chief of Staff, Huron Regional Medical Center, Huron, SD, p. A569
SCHWALL, Garry, Chief Operating Officer, Winthrop–University Hospital, Mineola, NY, p. A437
SCHWAN, Joni, Director Human Resources, Excelsior Springs Hospital, Excelsior Springs, MO, p. A367
SCHWAN, Karin, Chief Nursing Officer, Vice President Patient Care Services, Samaritan Regional Health System, Ashland, OH, p. A478
SCHWANER, III, Charles, Chief Financial Officer, Doctors Hospital of Sarasota, Sarasota, FL, p. A142
SCHWANKE, Daniel, Chief Operating Officer, ProMedica St. Luke's Hospital, Maumee, OH, p. A494
SCHWARM, Tony, President, Missouri Baptist Sullivan Hospital, Sullivan, MO, p. A379
SCHWARTZ, Ave, Chief Information Officer, Austen Riggs Center, Stockbridge, MA, p. A312
SCHWARTZ, David, Chief Medical Officer, Saint Francis Hospital–Bartlett, Bartlett, TN, p. A574
SCHWARTZ, David M., D.O. Vice President, Medical Affairs, Sentara Northern Virginia Medical Center, Woodbridge, VA, p. A674
SCHWARTZ, Jonathon, M.D. Medical Director and Chief Medical Officer, Spaulding Hospital for Continuing Medical Care Cambridge, Cambridge, MA, p. A306
SCHWARTZ, Kenneth V., M.D. Medical Director, Griffin Hospital, Derby, CT, p. A112
SCHWARTZ, Kim, Assistant Administrator of Human Resources and Physician Services, Boone County Hospital, Boone, IA, p. A223
SCHWARTZ, Michael, Medical Center Director, Canandaigua Veterans Affairs Medical Center, Canandaigua, NY, p. A431
SCHWARTZ, Michael, M.D. Chief of Staff, College Hospital Costa Mesa, Costa Mesa, CA, p. A59
SCHWARTZ, Mitchell, M.D. Chief Medical Officer, Anne Arundel Medical Center, Annapolis, MD, p. A293
SCHWARTZ, Peggy, Vice President Human Resources, Wayne Hospital, Greenville, OH, p. A491
SCHWARTZ, Peter
Manager Information Services, Carrier Clinic, Belle Mead, NJ, p. A409
Director Information Systems, East Mountain Hospital, Belle Mead, NJ, p. A409
SCHWARTZ, Roberta, Executive Vice President, Houston Methodist Hospital, Houston, TX, p. A620
SCHWARTZ, Ronald, M.D. Medical Director, Masonicare Health Center, Wallingford, CT, p. A115
SCHWARTZ, Sharon, Director Medical Records, Scott & White Hospital – Brenham, Brenham, TX, p. A598
SCHWARZ–MILLER, Jan, M.D. Vice President Quality and Chief Medical Officer, Morristown Medical Center, Morristown, NJ, p. A414
SCHWARZBACH, Jerry, M.D. Medical Director, East Texas Medical Center Rehabilitation Hospital, Tyler, TX, p. A648
SCHWARZKOPF, Ruth, R.N. Chief Nursing Officer, West Boca Medical Center, Boca Raton, FL, p. A122
SCHWECHHEIMER, Betsy L., Chief Operating Officer, Tewksbury Hospital, Tewksbury, MA, p. A312
SCHWEERS, Michele, Vice President and Chief Human Resources Officer, Monmouth Medical Center, Southern Campus, Lakewood, NJ, p. A413

Index of Health Care Professionals

Index of Health Care Professionals / Schweickhardt


SCHWEICKHARDT, Mary Jo, Vice President Human Resources, MedStar Georgetown University Hospital, Washington, DC, p. A119
SCHWEIGERT, Nicole, Director Human Resources, Texas Health Presbyterian Hospital Flower Mound, Flower Mound, TX, p. A612
SCHWEIGHART, Karen, MS, Administrator, Andrew McFarland Mental Health Center, Springfield, IL, p. A201
SCHWEIKART, Jay
Chief Financial Officer, Kindred Hospital Chicago–Northlake, Northlake, IL, p. A196
Chief Financial Officer, Kindred Hospital–Sycamore, Sycamore, IL, p. A202
SCHWEITZER, Michael, M.D. Chief Medical Officer, St. Vincent Healthcare, Billings, MT, p. A381
SCHWEIZER, Brenda, Coordinator Human Resources, Kindred Hospital of Northern Indiana, Mishawaka, IN, p. A216
SCHWIEGER, Kay, Chief Human Resources Officer, Clement J. Zablocki Veterans Affairs Medical Center, Milwaukee, WI, p. A706
SCHWIND, David, Chief Financial Officer, Capital Hospice, Arlington, VA, p. A662
SCHWINGLER, Joyce, Chief Financial Officer, Eureka Community Health Services Avera, Eureka, SD, p. A568
SCHWOEBLE, Walt, Vice President Human Resources, Akron Children's Hospital, Akron, OH, p. A478
SCIARRA, Michael, M.D. Chief Medical Officer, Meadowlands Hospital Medical Center, Secaucus, NJ, p. A418
SCIARRO, Jason
President and Chief Operating Officer, Centegra Hospital – McHenry, McHenry, IL, p. A194
President and Chief Operating Officer, Centegra Hospital – Woodstock, Woodstock, IL, p. A203
SCIBELLI, Anthony, Senior Vice President Human Resources, Post Acute and Support Services, Faxton–St. Luke's Healthcare, Utica, NY, p. A452
SCIONTI, Jeff, Chief Operating Officer, Parkland Medical Center, Derry, NH, p. A405
SCIORTINO, John E., Senior Vice President and Chief Operating Officer, New York–Presbyterian/Queens, NY, p. A443
SCIOSCIA, Angela, M.D. Chief Medical Officer, UC San Diego Health, San Diego, CA, p. A87
SCIULLO, Armando, D.O. Chief of Staff, Grove City Medical Center, Grove City, PA, p. A535
SCLAMA, Tony, M.D. Vice President Medical Affairs, MedStar Franklin Square Medical Center, Baltimore, MD, p. A294
SCOBIE, Robbin, Vice President Nursing, Aurelia Osborn Fox Memorial Hospital, Oneonta, NY, p. A446
SCOFIELD, Mark, M.D. Chief Medical Officer, Shelby Baptist Medical Center, Alabaster, AL, p. A15
SCOGGIN, Terry, Chief Financial Officer, Titus Regional Medical Center, Mount Pleasant, TX, p. A633
SCOGGINS, James, Director of Nursing, Arkansas State Hospital, Little Rock, AR, p. A47
SCOGGINS, Mib, Chief Executive Officer, McLeod Health Cheraw, Cheraw, SC, p. A558
SCOGNA, Stephen, President and Chief Executive Officer, Northwest Community Hospital, Arlington Heights, IL, p. A178
SCOPELLITI, Joseph A., M.D., President and Chief Executive Officer, Guthrie Clinic, Sayre, PA, p. B60
SCORZELLI, Gerard, Chief Financial Officer, Albany Stratton Veterans Affairs Medical Center, Albany, NY, p. A428
SCOTFORD, Lucrecia, Executive Vice President and Chief Operations Officer, Bristol Bay Area Health Corporation, Dillingham, AK, p. A28
SCOTT, Alan, M.D. Chief of Staff, East Georgia Regional Medical Center, Statesboro, GA, p. A165
SCOTT, Charles F., President and Chief Executive Officer, Piedmont Henry Hospital, Stockbridge, GA, p. A165
SCOTT, Colleen M., Vice President Finance, Waterbury Hospital, Waterbury, CT, p. A116
SCOTT, Craig, Interim Director Management Information Systems, University of Miami Hospital, Miami, FL, p. A135
SCOTT, David W., President and Chief Executive Officer, Ohio Valley Hospital, McKees Rocks, PA, p. A539
SCOTT, Doug, Director Human Resources, RMC Jacksonville, Jacksonville, AL, p. A21
SCOTT, Ernie, Director Human Resources, Natchitoches Regional Medical Center, Natchitoches, LA, p. A281
SCOTT, Henry, Executive Director, Technical Services, Piedmont Newnan Hospital, Newnan, GA, p. A162
SCOTT, James, M.D
Vice President Medical Affairs, Candler Hospital, Savannah, GA, p. A164
Vice President Medical Affairs, St. Joseph's Hospital, Savannah, GA, p. A164
SCOTT, Jeffrey, Chief Information Officer, St. Joseph Hospital & Health Center, Kokomo, IN, p. A214
SCOTT, Jennifer, Director of Informatics, CarePartners Health Services, Asheville, NC, p. A455
SCOTT, Jo Ellen, R.N. Senior Vice President of Patient Care Services and Chief Nursing Officer, Indiana University Health Tipton Hospital, Tipton, IN, p. A220
SCOTT, Jon W., Chief Executive Officer, Meadowbrook Rehabilitation Hospital, Gardner, KS, p. A240
SCOTT, Joseph F., FACHE, President and Chief Executive Officer, Jersey City Medical Center, Jersey City, NJ, p. A413
SCOTT, Julie, Chief Nursing Officer, HEALTHSOUTH Rehabilitation Hospital of York, York, PA, p. A554
SCOTT, Karen M., Vice President Patient Care, Frank R. Howard Memorial Hospital, Willits, CA, p. A98
SCOTT, Lincoln, Vice President Human Resources, Southeast Hospital, Cape Girardeau, MO, p. A365
SCOTT, M Daryl, Assistant Vice President, Jefferson Regional Medical Center, Pine Bluff, AR, p. A50
SCOTT, Margie, M.D. Chief of Staff, Central Arkansas Veterans Healthcare System, Little Rock, AR, p. A47
SCOTT, Martha Lynn, Chief Patient Care Officer, Covington County Hospital, Collins, MS, p. A352
SCOTT, Matt, Chief Information Officer, Warren Memorial Hospital, Friend, NE, p. A392
SCOTT, Monica, Chief Financial Officer, Great Plains Regional Medical Center, Elk City, OK, p. A506
SCOTT, Paul, M.D. Chief of Staff, Hudson Hospital and Clinic, Hudson, WI, p. A702
SCOTT, Rhonda A., Ph.D. Chief Nursing Officer and Executive Vice President, Grady Memorial Hospital, Atlanta, GA, p. A150
SCOTT, Robert F., Vice President and Chief Human Resources Officer, Memorial Medical Center, Springfield, IL, p. A201
SCOTT, Roger, D.O. Vice President Medical Affairs and Chief Medical Officer, Cortland Regional Medical Center, Cortland, NY, p. A432
SCOTT, Seth, M.D. Chief of Staff, George Regional Hospital, Lucedale, MS, p. A356
SCOTT, Sharon, Health Information Director, Allegiance Specialty Hospital of Greenville, Greenville, MS, p. A353
SCOTT, Stacy, Director Nursing, Sabetha Community Hospital, Sabetha, KS, p. A249
SCOTT, Steve, Chief Operating Officer, Sheridan Community Hospital, Sheridan, MI, p. A330
SCOTT, Steven, Chief Operating Officer, Georgia Regents Medical Center, Augusta, GA, p. A151
SCOTT, Susan, Chief Nurse Executive, Ventura County Medical Center, Ventura, CA, p. A96
SCOTT, Thomas, Chief Operating Officer, Chilton Medical Center, Pompton Plains, NJ, p. A417
SCOTT, Thomas W., Senior Vice President and Chief Operating Officer, CentraState Healthcare System, Freehold, NJ, p. A412
SCOTT, Tina, Acting Health Director, Choctaw Health Center, Philadelphia, MS, p. A359
SCOTT, Veronica, Business Office Manager, Specialty Hospital of Midwest City, Midwest City, OK, p. A510
SCOTT, William, Chief Financial Officer, Promise Hospital of Overland Park, Overland Park, KS, p. A248
SCOTT, William, M.D. Vice President Medical Affairs, Regional Medical Center of San Jose, San Jose, CA, p. A89
SCOTT, William P., M.D. Chief of Staff, River Valley Medical Center, Dardanelle, AR, p. A43
SCOTTO, Dan, Director Data Processing, Eastern Long Island Hospital, Greenport, NY, p. A434
SCOVILL, Terry, Chief Executive Officer, Intracare North Hospital, Houston, TX, p. A620
SCOWN, Kent, Director Operations and Information Services, Jerold Phelps Community Hospital, Garberville, CA, p. A63
SCREMIN, Karen, Vice President Finance, Lutheran Medical Center, Wheat Ridge, CO, p. A109
SCRIVO, Jr., Joseph A., Director Human Resources, Mercy Hospital, Buffalo, NY, p. A430
SCROGGS, Amy, Chief Nursing Officer, Delano Regional Medical Center, Delano, CA, p. A59
SCRUGGS, Sherry, Administrator, Milan General Hospital, Milan, TN, p. A584
SCUDDER, Angela, R.N. Vice President Patient Care Services, Dearborn County Hospital, Lawrenceburg, IN, p. A214
SCUDERI, Denise, Vice President Patient Care Services, Mayo Regional Hospital, Dover–Foxcroft, ME, p. A290
SCULL, Stephen W., Vice President Ethics and Compliance officer, Rapides Regional Medical Center, Alexandria, LA, p. A268
SCULLY, Charles, Chief Information Officer, Renown Regional Medical Center, Reno, NV, p. A403
SCULLY, Kem, Chief Executive Officer, Purcell Municipal Hospital, Purcell, OK, p. A514
SCULLY, Trish
Manager Employment Services, Massachusetts Hospital School, Canton, MA, p. A306
Director Human Resources, Taunton State Hospital, Taunton, MA, p. A312
SCZYGELSKI, Sidney C., Senior Vice President Finance and Chief Financial Officer, Aspirus Wausau Hospital, Wausau, WI, p. A713
SEAGER, Jerry, Assistant Vice President and Chief Financial Officer, Inova Fair Oaks Hospital, Fairfax, VA, p. A664
SEAGO, Terri, Chief Financial Officer, Baptist Memorial Hospital–Collierville, Collierville, TN, p. A576
SEAGROVES, Matthew, Chief Financial Officer, Bayfront Health Brooksville, Brooksville, FL, p. A123
SEAHORN, Martha, R.N. Chief Nurse Office, Shelby Baptist Medical Center, Alabaster, AL, p. A15
SEAL, John, Director Human Resources, Riverside Medical Center, Franklinton, LA, p. A274
SEAL, Ronald T., Chief Executive Officer, Texoma Medical Center, Denison, TX, p. A607
SEALE, Corey A., Chief Executive Officer, Kaiser Permanente Moreno Valley Medical Center, Moreno Valley, CA, p. A76
SEALE, Edward, Chief Information Officer, New Horizons Health Systems, Owenton, KY, p. A264
SEALE, Jonathan, Chief Information Officer, Erie Veterans Affairs Medical Center, Erie, PA, p. A534
SEALS, Robert, D.O. Medical Director, Sparrow Carson Hospital, Carson City, MI, p. A316
SEAMON, Robert L., Chief Executive Officer, Clifton–Fine Hospital, Star Lake, NY, p. A450
SEARBY, Tonya L., Chief Human Resources, Marion Veterans Affairs Medical Center, Marion, IL, p. A193
SEARLE, Anne, Chief Information Officer, University Medical Center of Princeton at Plainsboro, Plainsboro, NJ, p. A417
SEARLS, Barbara, Chief Financial Officer, SEARHC MT. Edgecumbe Hospital, Sitka, AK, p. A29
SEARLS, Gary, Chief Financial Officer, Northside Hospital, Saint Petersburg, FL, p. A142
SEARS, Christopher, M.D. President Medical Staff, Mercy Tiffin Hospital, Tiffin, OH, p. A498
SEARS, Erin Clare, Associate Director of Operations, Providence Veterans Affairs Medical Center, Providence, RI, p. A556
SEARS, Marilyn, President and Chief Executive Officer, Shelby Memorial Hospital, Shelbyville, IL, p. A200
SEARS, Michelle, Director Information Systems, Helen Newberry Joy Hospital, Newberry, MI, p. A327
SEASE, Peggy
Vice President Human Resources, DCH Regional Medical Center, Tuscaloosa, AL, p. A25
Vice President Human Resources, Northport Medical Center, Northport, AL, p. A23
SEATON, Tracy, Director of Nursing, Taylorville Memorial Hospital, Taylorville, IL, p. A202
SEAVER, Roger E., President and Chief Executive Officer, Henry Mayo Newhall Memorial Hospital, Valencia, CA, p. A96
SEBASTIAN, Peggy A., R.N., President and Chief Executive Officer, HSHS St. Joseph's Hospital, Highland, IL, p. A190
SEBEK, Brenda Jean, R.N. Vice President Patient Care Services, CHI Health St. Mary's, Nebraska City, NE, p. A394
SECKINGER, Mark R., President, O'Bleness Memorial Hospital, Athens, OH, p. A479
SECOR, April, R.N. Chief Nursing Officer, Hillcrest Hospital Henryetta, Henryetta, OK, p. A508
SECOR, Diane K., Director Human Resources, Lawrence Medical Center, Moulton, AL, p. A23
SECREST, Jack, M.D. Chief Medical Officer, St. Mary's Hospital, Cottonwood, ID, p. A174
SECURRO, Matthew J., Vice President Human Resources, Conway Medical Center, Conway, SC, p. A560
SEDA, Jolene R., Administrative Director, Yakima Valley Memorial Hospital, Yakima, WA, p. A688
SEDGLEY, Don, President, Novant Health Haymarket Medical Center, Haymarket, VA, p. A666
SEDGWICK, Sally, Manager Public Relations and Marketing, Bigfork Valley Hospital, Bigfork, MN, p. A335
SEDIGHI, Hooman, M.D., President and Chief Executive Officer, GLOBALREHAB, Dallas, TX, p. B58
SEDMINIK, Vince, Chief Executive Officer, Springhill Medical Center, Springhill, LA, p. A286
SEDORE, Ann, Ph.D. Chief Nursing Officer, Crouse Hospital, Syracuse, NY, p. A451
SEEDER, Rachael, Controller, Santiam Memorial Hospital, Stayton, OR, p. A526
SEEGERS, Robert, M.D. Vice President Medical Affairs, St. Francis Medical Center, Monroe, LA, p. A280
SEEKINS, DeAnne, Director, Durham Veterans Affairs Medical Center, Durham, NC, p. A459
SEELEY, Kevin, Chief Information Officer, Mike O'Callaghan Federal Hospital, Nellis AFB, NV, p. A403
SEELEY, Pam, Chief Nursing Officer, Elmira Psychiatric Center, Elmira, NY, p. A433
SEELY, Paula, Manager Human Resources, Kossuth Regional Health Center, Algona, IA, p. A222
SEEMS, Steven, Director of Information Technology, Phillips County Hospital, Phillipsburg, KS, p. A248


A964 Index of Health Care Professionals 

Index of Health Care Professionals / Shafer

SEESE, Rebecca, Chief Operating Officer, U. S. Air Force Regional Hospital, Elmendorf AFB, AK, p. A28
SEEVER, Jennifer, Regional Chief Financial Officer, Sedan City Hospital, Sedan, KS, p. A250
SEGAL, Jonathan, Chief Financial Officer, New York State Psychiatric Institute, New York, NY, p. A443
SEGAL, Rebecca, Chief Operating Officer, Lake Cumberland Regional Hospital, Somerset, KY, p. A266
SEGAL, Stanton, M.D. Chief Medical Officer, Aria Health, Philadelphia, PA, p. A542
SEGAR–MILLER, Cindy, MS, Interim Chief Executive Officer, Williamson Memorial Hospital, Williamson, WV, p. A696
SEGELEON, Kurt, Director Health Information Management, Kindred Hospital–Pittsburgh, Oakdale, PA, p. A542
SEGER, LaDonna, Director Information Services, Saint Luke's North Hospital – Barry Road, Kansas City, MO, p. A370
SEGIN, Robert, Chief Financial Officer, Virtua Memorial, Mount Holly, NJ, p. A414
SEGLER, Randall K., FACHE, Chief Executive Officer, Comanche County Memorial Hospital, Lawton, OK, p. A508
SEGURA, Ezra, Chief Executive Officer, Utah Valley Specialty Hospital, Provo, UT, p. A657
SEGURA, Mario, Director of Nursing, Starr County Memorial Hospital, Rio Grande City, TX, p. A638
SEHRT, Lori
Associate Chief Financial Officer Northern Colorado, Banner Fort Collins Medical Center, Fort Collins, CO, p. A103
Chief Financial Officer, McKee Medical Center, Loveland, CO, p. A107
SEIBERT, Nancy, Director Human Resources, Franklin Hospital District, Benton, IL, p. A179
SEID, Lynette, Area Chief Financial Officer, Kaiser Permanente San Diego Medical Center, San Diego, CA, p. A86
SEIDE, Rob, Manager Marketing and Communications, St. Luke's Hospital, San Francisco, CA, p. A88
SEIDL, Doris A., Vice President Human Resources, McLaren Port Huron, Port Huron, MI, p. A328
SEIDLER, Richard A., FACHE,
President and Chief Executive Officer, UnityPoint Health – Trinity Bettendorf, Bettendorf, IA, p. A222
President and Chief Executive Officer, UnityPoint Health – Trinity Rock Island, Rock Island, IL, p. A199
SEIDMAN, Robert
Chief Operating Officer, Health Alliance Hospital – Broadway Campus, Kingston, NY, p. A436
Chief Operating Officer, Health Alliance Hospital – Mary's Avenue Campus, Kingston, NY, p. A436
SEIFER, Jill, Vice President Human Resources, Oaklawn Psychiatric Center, Goshen, IN, p. A210
SEIM, Lori, R.N. Director Nursing Services, First Care Health Center, Park River, ND, p. A476
SEIRER, Jeff, Interim Chief Financial Officer, Via Christi Hospital on St. Francis, Wichita, KS, p. A253
SEITZ, Stewart R., Chief Executive Officer, Gladys Spellman Specialty Hospital and Nursing Center, Cheverly, MD, p. A296
SEITZ, Tawnya, Chief Financial Officer, Lincoln County Hospital, Lincoln, KS, p. A245
SELBOVITZ, Leslie, M.D. Senior Vice President Medical Affairs, Newton–Wellesley Hospital, Newton Lower Falls, MA, p. A309
SELBY, Eric, R.N. Chief Nursing Officer, Chicot Memorial Medical Center, Lake Village, AR, p. A46
SELDEN, Thomas A., FACHE, President and Chief Executive Officer, Southwest General Health Center, Middleburg Heights, OH, p. A494
SELEY, Jim, Chief Information Officer, Clay County Medical Center, Clay Center, KS, p. A238
SELF, Debbie, Chief Financial Officer, North Georgia Medical Center, Ellijay, GA, p. A157
SELF, Joshua, Chief Executive Officer, Mary Black Health System – Gaffney, Gaffney, SC, p. A561
SELFRIDGE, Tara, Manager Human Resources, Purcell Municipal Hospital, Purcell, OK, p. A514
SELIGA, Patricia, R.N. Chief Nursing Officer, Moses Taylor Hospital, Scranton, PA, p. A549
SELIGMAN, Joel, President and Chief Executive Officer, Northern Westchester Hospital, Mount Kisco, NY, p. A438
SELIGMAN, Morris H., M.D. Chief Medical Officer and Chief Medical Information Officer, Sycamore Shoals Hospital, Elizabethton, TN, p. A577
SELIVANOFF, Paul, Chief Financial Officer, Evanston Regional Hospital, Evanston, WY, p. A716
SELL, Paula, Director Human Resources, Allen County Regional Hospital, Iola, KS, p. A242
SELLARDS, Michael G., Chief Executive Officer, Pallottine Health Services, Huntington, WV, p. B102
SELLARDS, Michael G., President and Chief Executive Officer, St. Mary's Medical Center, Huntington, WV, p. A692
SELLE, Ginger, Vice President Patient Care Services, St. Clare Hospital, Baraboo, WI, p. A697
SELLE, Justin, Chief Executive Officer, Pike County Memorial Hospital, Louisiana, MO, p. A372
SELLERS, Dan, Chief Financial Officer, Eskenazi Health, Indianapolis, IN, p. A211
SELLERS, Laura, Director Information Systems, Youth Villages Inner Harbour Campus, Douglasville, GA, p. A156
SELLERS, Liz, R.N. Chief Nursing Officer, Southwest Memorial Hospital, Cortez, CO, p. A101
SELLERS, Regena, Chief Nursing Officer, Three Rivers Behavioral Health, West Columbia, SC, p. A566
SELLERS, Robert R.
Administrator, Optim Medical Center – Jenkins, Millen, GA, p. A161
Administrator, Optim Medical Center – Screven, Sylvania, GA, p. A165
SELLHEIM, Kevin, Administrator, Sleepy Eye Medical Center, Sleepy Eye, MN, p. A347
SELLS, Matt, CPA Chief Financial Officer, Shenandoah Medical Center, Shenandoah, IA, p. A234
SELMAN, David B., FACHE, Administrator, Forks Community Hospital, Forks, WA, p. A679
SELMAN, J. Peter, FACHE, Chief Executive Officer, Baptist Medical Center South, Montgomery, AL, p. A22
SELMON, Patricia, Director Public Relations and Chief Human Resources, Jefferson County Hospital, Fayette, MS, p. A352
SELNER, Ralph, Chief Executive Officer, Kindred Hospital Central Tampa, Tampa, FL, p. A145
SELPH, Wendy, Director Human Resources, Dodge County Hospital, Eastman, GA, p. A157
SELSOR, Doug, Director Finance, Select Rehabilitation Hospital of Denton, Denton, TX, p. A608
SELTZER, Paul, M.D. Chief of Staff, West Palm Hospital, West Palm Beach, FL, p. A147
SELVAGGI, Richard, M.D. Chief of Staff, Hunt Regional Community Hospital, Commerce, TX, p. A602
SELVAM, A. Panneer, M.D. Chief of Staff, Northern Arizona Veterans Affairs Health Care System, Prescott, AZ, p. A36
SELVIDGE, Sandra, Chief Fiscal Service, Cincinnati Veterans Affairs Medical Center, Cincinnati, OH, p. A482
SELZ, Timothy P., Vice President, Orange Regional Medical Center, Middletown, NY, p. A437
SEMAR, Dale, Controller, Pauls Valley General Hospital, Pauls Valley, OK, p. A513
SEMELSBERGER, Kimberly, Vice President Financial Operations, Conemaugh Miners Medical Center, Hastings, PA, p. A535
SEMERDJIAN, Nancy, R.N. Chief Nursing Officer, NorthShore University Health System, Evanston, IL, p. A187
SEMINARO, Anthony, Chief Financial Officer, Trumbull Memorial Hospital, Warren, OH, p. A499
SEMINGSON, John H., Chief Executive Officer, Ruby Valley Hospital, Sheridan, MT, p. A387
SEMRAU, Clint, Chief of Staff, Baldwin Area Medical Center, Baldwin, WI, p. A697
SENDAYDIEGO, Fe, Director Information Systems, Sonoma Valley Hospital, Sonoma, CA, p. A92
SENELICK, Richard, M.D. Medical Director, HEALTHSOUTH Rehabilitation Institute of San Antonio, San Antonio, TX, p. A640
SENGER, Richard, Chief Financial Officer, Portsmouth Regional Hospital, Portsmouth, NH, p. A408
SENGER, Tricia, Chief Financial Officer, St. Luke's Elmore, Mountain Home, ID, p. A175
SENKER, Margaret, Chief Information Officer, Veterans Affairs Western New York Healthcare System–Buffalo Division, Buffalo, NY, p. A431
SENNEFF, Robert G., FACHE, President and Chief Executive Officer, Graham Hospital, Canton, IL, p. A180
SENNETT, Paul, Chief Financial Officer, Centinela Hospital Medical Center, Inglewood, CA, p. A65
SENNISH, James, Vice President Human Resources, Firelands Regional Health System, Sandusky, OH, p. A497
SEPP Jr., Howard W., FACHE, Vice President and Administrator, Southeast Georgia Health System Camden Campus, Saint Marys, GA, p. A163
SERAFIN, Deborah J., Vice President Human Resources, Mount St. Mary's Hospital and Health Center, Lewiston, NY, p. A436
SERAPHINE, Jeffrey G., FACHE, Division President, Duke LifePoint Healthcare, Brentwood, TN, p. B52
SERENO, Joe, Chief Financial Officer, Southwest General Hospital, San Antonio, TX, p. A642
SERENO, Joseph, Chief Financial Officer, Lovelace Women's Hospital, Albuquerque, NM, p. A422
SERFLING, G. Aubrey, President and Chief Executive Officer, Eisenhower Medical Center, Rancho Mirage, CA, p. A82
SERKETICH, Steve, Manager Information Services, Aurora Sheboygan Memorial Medical Center, Sheboygan, WI, p. A710
SERLE, John, FACHE, President and Chief Executive Officer, Lourdes Medical Center, Pasco, WA, p. A682
SERNYAK, Michael, M.D., Director, Connecticut Mental Health Center, New Haven, CT, p. A114
SERRANO, Jorge L. Matta, Administrator, Auxilio Mutuo Hospital, San Juan, PR, p. A723
SERRATT, Jim, Chief Executive Officer, Rock Prairie Behavioral Health, College Station, TX, p. A601
SESSIONS, Jerry W., M.D. Chief Medical Staff, Springhill Medical Center, Springhill, LA, p. A286
SESSIONS, Tracey, Administrator, State Hospital South, Blackfoot, ID, p. A172
SESSLER, Connie, Director Human Resources, ProMedica St. Luke's Hospital, Maumee, OH, p. A494
SESTERHENN, Steven, Vice President, UnityPoint Health – Allen Hospital, Waterloo, IA, p. A236
SETCHEL, David P., President, St. Francis Health, Topeka, KS, p. A251
SETHI, Sanjiv, M.D. Medical Director, Fulton State Hospital, Fulton, MO, p. A368
SETLIFF, Chad, Chief Executive Officer, Novant Health Medical Park Hospital, Winston–Salem, NC, p. A471
SETTELMEYER, Camille, Assistant Administrator Clinical Services, CHI Mercy Health, Valley City, ND, p. A476
SETTLE, Andrea, Director Human Resources, Taylor Regional Hospital, Campbellsville, KY, p. A255
SETTLES, April, Chief Financial Officer, Greene County General Hospital, Linton, IN, p. A215
SETTLES, Laura, Director Human Resources, Baylor Medical Center at Garland, Garland, TX, p. A616
SETZER, Jeffery, Administrator Information Systems, J. D. McCarty Center for Children With Developmental Disabilities, Norman, OK, p. A510
SETZKORN–MEYER, Marsha, Director Public Relations and Marketing, Hillsboro Community Hospital, Hillsboro, KS, p. A241
SEVCO, Mark
President, UPMC East, Monroeville, PA, p. A540
President, UPMC McKeesport, McKeesport, PA, p. A539
SEVERA, Jeff, D.O. Chief of Staff, Vidant Roanoke–Chowan Hospital, Ahoskie, NC, p. A455
SEVERANCE, Matthew J., FACHE, Chief Executive Officer, Roper Hospital, Charleston, SC, p. A558
SEVILLIAN, Clarence, President and Chief Executive Officer, McLaren Bay Region, Bay City, MI, p. A315
SEWATSKY, Mary, M.D. Chief Medical Officer, Moses Taylor Hospital, Scranton, PA, p. A549
SEWELL, Lance, Chief Financial Officer, South Lake Hospital, Clermont, FL, p. A123
SEWELL, Sue, Chief Nursing Officer, Wise Regional Health System, Decatur, TX, p. A607
SEXTON, Charles, Manager Human Resources, Cumberland Medical Center, Crossville, TN, p. A577
SEXTON, Cheryl, Director Nursing Operations, South Texas Rehabilitation Hospital, Brownsville, TX, p. A598
SEXTON, Cindy, Chief Financial Officer, St. David's Round Rock Medical Center, Round Rock, TX, p. A639
SEXTON, Kevin, Director Information Systems, Raleigh General Hospital, Beckley, WV, p. A689
SEXTON, Paul, Chief Executive Officer, Highlands Behavioral Health System, Littleton, CO, p. A106
SEXTON, William J., Administrator, Wyoming State Hospital, Evanston, WY, p. A716
SEXTON, William P., Chief Executive Officer, Prairie du Chien Memorial Hospital, Prairie Du Chien, WI, p. A709
SEYBOLD, Henry, Senior Vice President and Chief Financial Officer, Rockford Memorial Hospital, Rockford, IL, p. A199
SEYMOUR, Claudette, Director Personnel, Memphis Mental Health Institute, Memphis, TN, p. A583
SEYMOUR, Jose, Chief Information Resource Management, James A. Haley Veterans' Hospital–Tampa, Tampa, FL, p. A144
SEYMOUR, Russell, Chief Information Management Division, Reynolds Army Community Hospital, Fort Sill, OK, p. A507
SHACKELFORD, Gerald, Staff Support Specialist, Texas Center for Infectious Disease, San Antonio, TX, p. A642
SHACKELFORD, Paul, M.D. Chief Medical Officer, Vidant Medical Center, Greenville, NC, p. A461
SHACKLETON, Carol, Medical Director, Gothenburg Memorial Hospital, Gothenburg, NE, p. A392
SHADENSACK, Don, Vice President Clinical Services, OSF St. Mary Medical Center, Galesburg, IL, p. A188
SHADOWEN, Michael, M.D. Chief of Staff, T. J. Samson Community Hospital, Glasgow, KY, p. A257
SHADOWENS, Karen, Director Finance and Chief Financial Officer, West Chester Hospital, West Chester, OH, p. A500
SHADWICK, Shirley A., Administrator Human Resources, Desert Springs Hospital Medical Center, Las Vegas, NV, p. A401
SHAFER, James R., Interim Chief Executive Officer, Hamilton General Hospital, Hamilton, TX, p. A617

Index of Health Care Professionals

Index of Health Care Professionals / Shafer


SHAFER, Robert
Vice President Finance, Mercy Medical Center–Dubuque, Dubuque, IA, p. A227
Vice President Finance, Mercy Medical Center–Dyersville, Dyersville, IA, p. A227
SHAFER, Timothy, M.D. Medical Director, Grace Cottage Hospital, Townshend, VT, p. A661
SHAFICI, Khaled, M.D. President Medical Staff, Cornerstone Hospital–West Monroe, West Monroe, LA, p. A286
SHAFIU, Mohamed, M.D. Chief of Staff, Val Verde Regional Medical Center, Del Rio, TX, p. A607
SHAH, Aman Ali, M.D. Chief Medical Staff, Lake Whitney Medical Center, Whitney, TX, p. A652
SHAH, Beemal A., Chief Executive Officer, Person Memorial Hospital, Roxboro, NC, p. A467
SHAH, Girishkumar, M.D. Clinical Director, Northlake Behavioral Hospital, Mandeville, LA, p. A279
SHAH, Jay, M.D. President Medical Staff, San Antonio Community Hospital, Upland, CA, p. A95
SHAH, Jayendra H., M.D. Chief Medical Officer, Southern Arizona Veterans Affairs Health Care System, Tucson, AZ, p. A40
SHAH, Paresh, Director Information Systems, Reston Hospital Center, Reston, VA, p. A671
SHAH, Shalin, Chief Operating Officer, Regional Medical Center Bayonet Point, Hudson, FL, p. A129
SHAH, Syed, M.D. Chief of Staff, Pioneer Memorial Hospital and Health Services, Viborg, SD, p. A572
SHAH, Vital, M.D., Chief Executive Officer ad Chief Medical Officer, Central State Hospital, Louisville, KY, p. A261
SHAHAN, Mary Jo, Vice President and Chief Financial Officer, West Virginia University Hospitals, Morgantown, WV, p. A693
SHAHEEN, Jim, President, Strategic Behavioral Health, LLC, Memphis, TN, p. B128
SHAHI, Niloo, Chief Operating Officer, LAC–Olive View–UCLA Medical Center, CA, p. A71
SHAHRIARI, Sia, M.D. Chief of Staff, Great River Medical Center, Blytheville, AR, p. A41
SHAHRYAR, Syed, M.D. Medical Director, Promise Hospital of Phoenix, Mesa, AZ, p. A33
SHAHSAVARI, Mehan, M.D. Chief of Staff, Norman Specialty Hospital, Norman, OK, p. A510
SHAHZADA, Kamran, M.D. Chief Medical Staff, South Central Kansas Medical Center, Arkansas City, KS, p. A237
SHAKER, Mark S., President and Chief Executive Officer, Miami Valley Hospital, Dayton, OH, p. A488
SHALLOCK, James R., Chief Financial Officer, Memorial Hermann Northwest Hospital, Houston, TX, p. A621
SHAMBURG, Steffen, M.D. Chief of Staff, Hiawatha Community Hospital, Hiawatha, KS, p. A241
SHAMIYEH, Souhail, M.D. Chief of Staff, Mountain View Regional Medical Center, Norton, VA, p. A670
SHANAHAN, Thomas, Chief Financial Officer and Senior Vice President, Raritan Bay Medical Center, Perth Amboy, NJ, p. A417
SHAND, Natalie, M.D. Vice President Integrative Medicine and Chief Medical Officer, Freedom Pain Hospital, Scottsdale, AZ, p. A37
SHANLEY, Diane, Deputy Service Unit Director, U. S. Public Health Service Indian Hospital–Sells, Sells, AZ, p. A38
SHANLEY, Linda, Vice President and Chief Information Officer, Saint Francis Hospital and Medical Center, Hartford, CT, p. A112
SHANNON, David A., President and Chief Executive Officer, Jersey Shore Hospital, Jersey Shore, PA, p. A536
SHANNON, Greg, Director Human Resources, Golden Valley Memorial Healthcare, Clinton, MO, p. A365
SHANNON, John Jay, M.D., Chief Executive Officer, Cook County Health and Hospitals System, Chicago, IL, p. B42
SHANNON, John Jay, M.D.,
Chief Executive Officer, John H. Stroger Jr. Hospital of Cook County, Chicago, IL, p. A182
Chief Executive Officer, Provident Hospital of Cook County, Chicago, IL, p. A184
SHANNON, Richard, M.D. Chief of Staff, Montrose Memorial Hospital, Montrose, CO, p. A107
SHANNON, Scott, Director Finance, Socorro General Hospital, Socorro, NM, p. A427
SHAPE, Amy, Information Technology, North Dakota State Hospital, Jamestown, ND, p. A475
SHAPIRO, David, M.D
Vice President Medical Affairs and Chief Medical Officer, Columbia St. Mary's Hospital Milwaukee, Milwaukee, WI, p. A706
Vice President Medical Affairs and Chief Medical Officer, Columbia St. Mary's Ozaukee Hospital, Mequon, WI, p. A705
Vice President Medical Affairs and Chief Medical Officer, Sacred Heart Rehabilitation Institute, Milwaukee, WI, p. A706
SHAPIRO, Ira, M.D. Chief Medical Officer, St. Mary's Regional Medical Center, Lewiston, ME, p. A291
SHAPIRO, Louis A., President and Chief Executive Officer, Hospital for Special Surgery, New York, NY, p. A440
SHAPIRO, Marc, M.D. Chief Medical Officer, St. Helena Hospital Clear Lake, Clearlake, CA, p. A58
SHAPIRO, Robert S., Senior Vice President and Chief Financial Officer, Forest Hills Hospital, NY, p. A439
SHAPIRO, Steven D., M.D
Chief Medical Officer, Bon Secours St. Francis Xavier Hospital, Charleston, SC, p. A558
Chief Medical Officer, Mount Pleasant Hospital, Mount Pleasant, SC, p. A563
Vice President Medical Affairs, Roper Hospital, Charleston, SC, p. A558
SHARANGPANI, Rojesh, M.D. Chief of Staff, Capital Medical Center, Olympia, WA, p. A681
SHARBER–HOWELL, Sheryl, Administrator, Creek Nation Community Hospital, Okemah, OK, p. A511
SHARFSTEIN, Steven S., M.D., President and Chief Executive Officer, Sheppard Pratt Health System, Baltimore, MD, p. A294
SHARKEY, Diana, Interim Chief Information Officer, Regional Medical Center, Orangeburg, SC, p. A564
SHARKEY, Linda, R.N. Vice President Patient Care Services and Chief Nurse Executive, Fauquier Hospital, Warrenton, VA, p. A674
SHARLOW, Joseph, M.D. Chief of Staff, Ste. Genevieve County Memorial Hospital, Ste. Genevieve, MO, p. A379
SHARMA, Adhi, M.D. Chief Medical Officer, South Nassau Communities Hospital, Oceanside, NY, p. A446
SHARMA, Aika, M.D. President Medical Staff, Alameda Hospital, Alameda, CA, p. A53
SHARMA, Chandra, M.D. Chief of Staff, Welch Community Hospital, Welch, WV, p. A696
SHARMA, Roger, Chief Financial Officer, Citrus Valley Medical Center–Inter Community Campus, Covina, CA, p. A59
SHARMA, Satish C., M.D. Chief of Staff, Providence Veterans Affairs Medical Center, Providence, RI, p. A556
SHARON, Joesph P., Associate Director, Wilkes–Barre Veterans Affairs Medical Center, Wilkes–Barre, PA, p. A553
SHARON, Sandy, Senior Vice President and Area Manager, Kaiser Permanente Sacramento Medical Center, Sacramento, CA, p. A84
SHARP, Cheryl, Chief Financial Office, Miami County Medical Center, Paola, KS, p. A248
SHARP, Cindy, M.D. Chief Medical Officer, Madison Valley Medical Center, Ennis, MT, p. A383
SHARP, Gina, FACHE, President, Linden Oaks Hospital, Naperville, IL, p. A195
SHARP, John K., Chief Financial Officer, Seton Medical Center Harker Heights, Harker Heights, TX, p. A617
SHARP, Joseph, Administrator, Runnells Center for Rehabilitation and Healthcare, Berkeley Heights, NJ, p. A409
SHARP, Julie, Supervisor Human Resources, Chase County Community Hospital, Imperial, NE, p. A393
SHARP, Patrick, Senior Vice President and Chief Operating Officer, Range Regional Health Services, Hibbing, MN, p. A340
SHARP, Rebecca, Chief Financial Officer, Wagoner Community Hospital, Wagoner, OK, p. A518
SHARP, Richard, M.D. Medical Director, CHRISTUS St. Michael Rehabilitation Hospital, Texarkana, TX, p. A647
SHARP, Tanya, Vice President of Fiscal Services and Chief Financial Officer, Boone County Health Center, Albion, NE, p. A389
SHARP, Tony, Supervisor Information System, Sweetwater Hospital, Sweetwater, TN, p. A588
SHARPE, RN, Deborah, R.N. Director of Nursing, West Springs Hospital, Grand Junction, CO, p. A104
SHARPTON, Debra, Director of Nursing, Devereux Georgia Treatment Network, Kennesaw, GA, p. A159
SHARRER, Steven, Vice President Human Resources, Saint John's Health Center, Santa Monica, CA, p. A91
SHARTLE, William, Senior Vice President Human Resources, Holy Spirit – A Geisinger Affiliate, Camp Hill, PA, p. A530
SHARUM, Gary, Administrator, Mercy Hospital Tishomingo, Tishomingo, OK, p. A516
SHARUM, Melinda
Director of Human Resources, Mercy Hospital Ardmore, Ardmore, OK, p. A503
Director Human Resources, Mercy Hospital Healdton, Healdton, OK, p. A507
SHARY, Dave, Administrator Human Resources, Ridgecrest Regional Hospital, Ridgecrest, CA, p. A83
SHATRAW, Thomas, Director Human Resources, Samaritan Medical Center, Watertown, NY, p. A453
SHATTO, Leslie, Director Human Resources, Carlisle Regional Medical Center, Carlisle, PA, p. A531
SHAUGHNESSY, John, Chief Financial Officer, Clarendon Memorial Hospital, Manning, SC, p. A563
SHAUGHNESSY, Mary
Vice President Finance, Spaulding Hospital for Continuing Medical Care Cambridge, Cambridge, MA, p. A306
Vice President Finance, Spaulding Rehabilitation Hospital, Charlestown, MA, p. A306
Vice President Finance, Spaulding Rehabilitation Hospital Cape Cod, East Sandwich, MA, p. A306
SHAULL, Ty, Chief Operating Officer, Wyandot Memorial Hospital, Upper Sandusky, OH, p. A499
SHAVER, Chris
Vice President Human Resources, Covenant Medical Center, Lubbock, TX, p. A629
Vice President Human Resources, Covenant Specialty Hospital, Lubbock, TX, p. A629
SHAVER, Jennifer
Director of Nursing, Gouverneur Hospital, Gouverneur, NY, p. A434
Director of Nursing, Lewis County General Hospital, Lowville, NY, p. A436
SHAVER, John, Chief Financial Officer, Baystate Noble Hospital, Westfield, MA, p. A312
SHAVER, Robert D., M.D. Vice President Medical Affairs, The Good Samaritan Hospital, Lebanon, PA, p. A538
SHAW, Barbara, Chief Nursing Officer, Brighton Center for Recovery, Brighton, MI, p. A315
SHAW, David
Vice President Information Systems, Eskenazi Health, Indianapolis, IN, p. A211
Vice President and Chief Operating Officer, Susan B. Allen Memorial Hospital, El Dorado, KS, p. A239
SHAW, David B., Chief Executive Officer and Administrator, Nor–Lea General Hospital, Lovington, NM, p. A425
SHAW, Douglas A., Chief Executive Officer, Mad River Community Hospital, Arcata, CA, p. A54
SHAW, Gary, President, Cambridge Medical Center, Cambridge, MN, p. A336
SHAW, Gene, Chief Information Officer, Yuma Regional Medical Center, Yuma, AZ, p. A40
SHAW, Greg, Chief Financial Officer, Nevada Regional Medical Center, Nevada, MO, p. A373
SHAW, Jan, Director Personnel, River Bend Hospital, West Lafayette, IN, p. A221
SHAW, Jean, Chief Financial Officer, Valley Regional Hospital, Claremont, NH, p. A405
SHAW, John C., M.D. Medical Director, Southern Indiana Rehabilitation Hospital, New Albany, IN, p. A217
SHAW, Kathy, Chief Executive Officer, Haven Senior Horizons, Phoenix, AZ, p. A35
SHAW, Kendra, Chief Information Officer, Baldwin Area Medical Center, Baldwin, WI, p. A697
SHAW, Kimberly, Vice President Patient Care and Chief Nursing Executive, Mercy Medical Center Redding, Redding, CA, p. A82
SHAW, Mandy, M.D. Chief of Staff, Sidney Regional Medical Center, Sidney, NE, p. A398
SHAW, Michael R., Chief Executive Officer, Complex Care Hospital at Tenaya, Las Vegas, NV, p. A401
SHAW, Patrick D., Chief Executive Officer, Grafton City Hospital, Grafton, WV, p. A691
SHAW, Philip, Interim Chief Executive Officer, Frye Regional Medical Center, Hickory, NC, p. A462
SHAW, Shane, M.D. Chief of Staff, CHI St. Luke's Health Memorial Livingston, Livingston, TX, p. A628
SHAW, Violet, R.N. Director of Nursing, Grafton City Hospital, Grafton, WV, p. A691
SHAWAN, Christy, Chief Executive Officer, Black River Medical Center, Poplar Bluff, MO, p. A374
SHAWGO, Darla, Director Human Resources, Sparta Community Hospital, Sparta, IL, p. A200
SHEA, Drew, Chief Financial Officer, Doctors Hospital at White Rock Lake, Dallas, TX, p. A605
SHEA, Kevin, M.D. Chief of Staff, Carolinas Hospital System, Florence, SC, p. A560
SHEA, Natalie, Chief Nursing Officer, Central Community Hospital, Elkader, IA, p. A227
SHEA, Peggy, Human Resources Lead, Mad River Community Hospital, Arcata, CA, p. A54
SHEAFF, Charles, M.D. President Medical Staff, Passavant Area Hospital, Jacksonville, IL, p. A191
SHEAR, Larry, Administrative Assistant, Norwood Health Center, Marshfield, WI, p. A705
SHEARER, Christopher, M.D. Chief Medical Officer, HonorHealth John C. Lincoln Medical Center, Phoenix, AZ, p. A35
SHEARER, Laura, R.N. Senior Vice President and Chief Nursing Officer, Phoebe Putney Memorial Hospital, Albany, GA, p. A149
SHEARER, Ron, M.D. Regional Medical Director, PeaceHealth Peace Harbor Medical Center, Florence, OR, p. A520


A966 Index of Health Care Professionals 

Index of Health Care Professionals

Index of Health Care Professionals / Shipley

SHEARN, Daniel, R.N. Vice President Patient Services and Chief Nursing Officer, UPMC Northwest, Seneca, PA, p. A550
SHEARS, Ann Marie, Vice President Patient Care Services, Robert Wood Johnson University Hospital Rahway, Rahway, NJ, p. A417
SHEEHAN, Karen, Vice President and Chief Information Officer, Swedish Covenant Hospital, Chicago, IL, p. A185
SHEEHAN, Terrence P., M.D. Medical Director, Adventist Rehabilitation Hospital of Maryland, Rockville, MD, p. A300
SHEEHAN, William, M.D. Medical Director, Hawaii State Hospital, Kaneohe, HI, p. A170
SHEEHY, Earl N., Administrator, Ray County Memorial Hospital, Richmond, MO, p. A375
SHEEHY, Joseph, Chief Executive Officer and Managing Director, The Pavilion, Champaign, IL, p. A181
SHEERIN, Cathy, R.N. Director Patient Care Services, Glen Cove Hospital, Glen Cove, NY, p. A434
SHEERIN, Rick
Vice President Fiscal Services, Floyd Medical Center, Rome, GA, p. A163
Chief Financial Officer, Polk Medical Center, Cedartown, GA, p. A153
SHEETS, Cindy, Vice President Information Systems and Chief Information Officer, OhioHealth MedCentral Mansfield Hospital, Mansfield, OH, p. A493
SHEETS, Jim, Chief Executive Officer and Administrator, LDS Hospital, Salt Lake City, UT, p. A658
SHEFFIELD, Aubrey, Administrative Assistant Human Resources and Public Relations, Grove Hill Memorial Hospital, Grove Hill, AL, p. A20
SHEFTE, David H., Chief Executive Officer, HEALTHSOUTH Rehabilitation Hospital of Denver, Littleton, CO, p. A106
SHEGOLEV, Igor, Vice President Human Resources, Carondelet St. Joseph's Hospital, Tucson, AZ, p. A39
SHEHAN, Mary, R.N. Senior Vice President and Chief Nursing Officer, Swedish Covenant Hospital, Chicago, IL, p. A185
SHEHATA, Adel R., M.D. Medical Director, Desert Springs Hospital Medical Center, Las Vegas, NV, p. A401
SHEHATA, Nady, M.D. Vice President Medical Affairs, Sisters of Charity Hospital of Buffalo, Buffalo, NY, p. A431
SHEHI, G. Michael, M.D., Chief Executive Officer, Mountain View Hospital, Gadsden, AL, p. A20
SHELAK, Matt, Chief Operating Officer, Lower Bucks Hospital, Bristol, PA, p. A530
SHELBURNE, John D., M.D. Chief of Staff, Durham Veterans Affairs Medical Center, Durham, NC, p. A459
SHELBY, Dennis R., Chief Executive Officer, Wilson Medical Center, Neodesha, KS, p. A246
SHELBY, Joyce, Manager Human Resources, Hardin County General Hospital, Rosiclare, IL, p. A200
SHELDEN, Diana, Chief Nursing Officer, Stone County Medical Center, Mountain View, AR, p. A48
SHELDON, Donald S., M.D., President and Chief Executive Officer, University Hospitals Elyria Medical Center, Elyria, OH, p. A489
SHELDON, Ed, Warden and Chief Executive Officer, Oakwood Correctional Facility, Lima, OH, p. A492
SHELDON, Lyle Ernest, FACHE,
President and Chief Executive Officer, University of Maryland Harford Memorial Hospital, Havre De Grace, MD, p. A298
President and Chief Executive Officer, University of Maryland Upper Chesapeake Medical Center, Bel Air, MD, p. A295
SHELDON, Mo P., Chief Executive Officer and Superintendent, Odessa Memorial Healthcare Center, Odessa, WA, p. A681
SHELDON, Richard, M.D. Vice President Medical Affairs, San Gorgonio Memorial Hospital, Banning, CA, p. A55
SHELFORD, Dave, Assistant Superintendent, Richmond State Hospital, Richmond, IN, p. A219
SHELLENBERGER, David, Chief Operating Officer, St. John Vianney Hospital, Downingtown, PA, p. A532
SHELT, Elizabeth, Civilian Personnel Officer, Dwight David Eisenhower Army Medical Center, Fort Gordon, GA, p. A157
SHELTON, Amy
Vice President Patient Care Services, St. Vincent's Blount, Oneonta, AL, p. A23
Chief Nursing Officer, St. Vincent's East, Birmingham, AL, p. A17
SHELTON, Carol, Director Human Resources, Lovelace Women's Hospital, Albuquerque, NM, p. A422
SHELTON, Darlene, Coordinator Team Resources, BayCare Alliant Hospital, Dunedin, FL, p. A126
SHELTON, John
President and Chief Executive Officer, DeKalb Medical at Downtown Decatur, Decatur, GA, p. A155
Executive Vice President and Chief Operating Officer, DeKalb Medical at Downtown Decatur, Decatur, GA, p. A155
President and Chief Executive Officer, DeKalb Medical at Hillandale, Lithonia, GA, p. A160
Chief Operating Officer, DeKalb Medical at Hillandale, Lithonia, GA, p. A160
President and Chief Executive Officer, DeKalb Medical at North Decatur, Decatur, GA, p. A156
SHELTON, John, President and Chief Executive Officer, DeKalb Regional Health System, Decatur, GA, p. B45
SHELTON, Kathy, Director Human Resources, East Texas Medical Center Pittsburg, Pittsburg, TX, p. A636
SHELTON, Scott, Chief Financial Officer, Atrium Medical Center, Middletown, OH, p. A494
SHELTON, Tom, Coordinator of Nursing Services, Porterville Developmental Center, Porterville, CA, p. A81
SHELVOCK, Kathy, R.N. Assistant Administrator Patient Care Services, Fairchild Medical Center, Yreka, CA, p. A98
SHENDELL–FALIK, Nancy, R.N. Senior Vice President, Chief Operating Officer and Chief Nursing Officer, Baystate Medical Center, Springfield, MA, p. A311
SHENEFIELD, Jason, Chief Operating Officer, Cheyenne Regional Medical Center, Cheyenne, WY, p. A715
SHENGLE, Lori, Director Information Technology, Morrill County Community Hospital, Bridgeport, NE, p. A390
SHEPARD, Bridget, Director Human Resources, Wabash General Hospital, Mount Carmel, IL, p. A195
SHEPARD, Karen
Senior Vice President and Chief Financial Officer, Pioneer Memorial Hospital, Prineville, OR, p. A525
Executive Vice President Finance and Chief Financial Officer, St. Charles Bend, Bend, OR, p. A519
Senior Vice President Finance and Chief Financial Officer, St. Charles Redmond, Redmond, OR, p. A525
SHEPARD, Megan, Director Clinical Services, Odessa Memorial Healthcare Center, Odessa, WA, p. A681
SHEPARD, Sheila, Controller, HealthSouth Rehabilitation Hospital of Humble, LLC, Humble, TX, p. A623
SHEPARDSON, Dean, Chief Financial Officer, Banner Estrella Medical Center, Phoenix, AZ, p. A34
SHEPARDSON, Heather S.
Chief Human Resource Officer, Carilion Franklin Memorial Hospital, Rocky Mount, VA, p. A672
Vice President Human Resources, Carilion Roanoke Memorial Hospital, Roanoke, VA, p. A672
SHEPHARD, Bryan, Chief Financial Officer, TriStar Summit Medical Center, Hermitage, TN, p. A578
SHEPHARD, Russ, Senior Systems Analyst, Tennova Healthcare – Dyersburg Regional Hospital, Dyersburg, TN, p. A577
SHEPHERD, RN, BSN, Linda M., Chief Nursing Officer, LewisGale Hospital Pulaski, Pulaski, VA, p. A671
SHEPHERD, Thomas, Executive Vice President and Chief Operating Officer, Gwinnett Hospital System, Lawrenceville, GA, p. A160
SHEPLER, Mary, R.N. Vice President and Chief Nursing Officer, Saint Joseph Hospital, Denver, CO, p. A102
SHEPPARD, Sandy, Vice President Patient Services, Wilkes Regional Medical Center, North Wilkesboro, NC, p. A466
SHEPPARD, Sharon, Manager Human Resources, Sycamore Shoals Hospital, Elizabethton, TN, p. A577
SHEPPARD, Varinya, R.N. Chief Nursing Officer, St. Elizabeth Medical Center, Utica, NY, p. A452
SHERBONDY, Lori, Director Human Resources, Battle Mountain General Hospital, Battle Mountain, NV, p. A400
SHERER, Janet, Chief of Patient Care Services, Springfield Hospital, Springfield, VT, p. A661
SHERER, Ryan, M.D. President Medical Staff, Memorial Hospital and Health Care Center, Jasper, IN, p. A213
SHERER, Susan, Chief Information Resource Management, Dayton Veterans Affairs Medical Center, Dayton, OH, p. A488
SHERIDAN, Bridget, Chief Human Resources Officer, Beaver Dam Community Hospitals, Beaver Dam, WI, p. A698
SHERIDAN, Cheryl, R.N. Senior Vice President Patient Care Services, Rochester General Hospital, Rochester, NY, p. A448
SHERIDAN, Elizabeth
Chief Operating Officer and Chief Nursing Executive, Inspira Medical Center–Elmer, Elmer, NJ, p. A411
Chief Operating Officer and Chief Nursing Executive, Inspira Medical Center–Vineland, Vineland, NJ, p. A420
SHERIDAN, Kolbe, Chief Operating Officer, Heartland Regional Medical Center, Marion, IL, p. A193
SHERIDAN, Phil, Chief Executive Officer, Beckett Springs, West Chester, OH, p. A500
SHERIDAN, Tristen, Chief Executive Officer and Administrator, Weisbrod Memorial County Hospital, Eads, CO, p. A103
SHERMAN, Angelina, R.N. Chief Nursing Officer, The Rehabilitation Institute of St. Louis, Saint Louis, MO, p. A378
SHERMAN, Frederick C., M.D. Chief Medical Officer, The Children's Home of Pittsburgh, Pittsburgh, PA, p. A546
SHERMAN, James, President and Chief Executive Officer, Gardens Regional Hospital and Medical Center, Hawaiian Gardens, CA, p. A64
SHERMAN, Sheila, Vice President Patient Care Services, Vail Valley Medical Center, Vail, CO, p. A109
SHERMAN, Stephanie, Chief Human Resources Officer, West Boca Medical Center, Boca Raton, FL, p. A122
SHERON, William E., Chief Executive Officer, Wooster Community Hospital, Wooster, OH, p. A501
SHERRILL, Angela
Chief Information Officer, Laird Hospital, Union, MS, p. A361
Corporate Director Information System, Rush Foundation Hospital, Meridian, MS, p. A357
Corporate Director Information System, Specialty Hospital of Meridian, Meridian, MS, p. A358
SHERROD, Michael, Chief Executive Officer, TriStar Greenview Regional Hospital, Bowling Green, KY, p. A255
SHERROD, Rhonda Kay, MSN,
Administrator, Shands Lake Shore Regional Medical Center, Lake City, FL, p. A131
Interim Chief Executive Officer, Shands Starke Regional Medical Center, Starke, FL, p. A143
SHERRON, Tammy M., Vice President Finance, CarolinaEast Health System, New Bern, NC, p. A466
SHERRY, Mark A., Director Human Resources, Scott & White Hospital at Round Rock, Round Rock, TX, p. A639
SHERWIN, Charles H., Vice President of Business Development and Clinical Services, Alpena Regional Medical Center, Alpena, MI, p. A314
SHERWOOD, Matthew M., Chief Financial Officer, Unity Medical & Surgical Hospital, Mishawaka, IN, p. A216
SHETLER, Charles L., CPA Chief Financial Officer, Indiana University Health Bedford Hospital, Bedford, IN, p. A204
SHETTLESWORTH, Amanda, Director Human Resources, Bloomington Meadows Hospital, Bloomington, IN, p. A205
SHEW, Angel, Director Area Technology, Kaiser Permanente South San Francisco, South San Francisco, CA, p. A93
SHEWBRIDGE, Rick, M.D. Vice President Medical Operations, Medina Hospital, Medina, OH, p. A494
SHEYKA, Patricia, Chief Nursing Officer, Gila Regional Medical Center, Silver City, NM, p. A427
SHICKOLOVICH, William, Chief Information Officer, Tufts Medical Center, Boston, MA, p. A304
SHIELDS, Charlie
President and Chief Executive Officer, Truman Medical Center–Hospital Hill, Kansas City, MO, p. A370
President and Chief Executive Officer, Truman Medical Center–Lakewood, Kansas City, MO, p. A370
SHIELDS, Charlie, President and Chief Executive Officer, Truman Medical Centers, Kansas City, MO, p. B137
SHIELDS, Diane, Chief Human Resources Officer, Alpena Regional Medical Center, Alpena, MI, p. A314
SHIELDS, Patsy, Chief Financial Officer, Lincoln Community Hospital and Nursing Home, Hugo, CO, p. A105
SHIFF, Mary Treacy, Chief Financial Officer, Kindred Chicago–Central Hospital, Chicago, IL, p. A182
SHIFFERMILLER, William, M.D. Vice President Medical Affairs, Nebraska Methodist Hospital, Omaha, NE, p. A396
SHIHADY, Sharon, Director Human Resources, HEALTHSOUTH Cane Creek Rehabilitation Hospital, Martin, TN, p. A582
SHILKAITIS, Mary, Vice President Patient Care and Chief Nursing Officer, Rush–Copley Medical Center, Aurora, IL, p. A179
SHILLING, Angie, Chief Executive Officer, Baum Harmon Mercy Hospital, Primghar, IA, p. A233
SHILLING, Stacy, Controller, St. Vincent Rehabilitation Hospital, Sherwood, AR, p. A50
SHIM, Eunmee, R.N. Vice President Operations, Shady Grove Adventist Hospital, Rockville, MD, p. A300
SHIMABUKURO, Bert, Director Human Resources, Wahiawa General Hospital, Wahiawa, HI, p. A170
SHIMP, David, Chief Operating Officer, St. David's Medical Center, Austin, TX, p. A595
SHINER, Cindy, Manager Human Resources, Lebanon Veterans Affairs Medical Center, Lebanon, PA, p. A538
SHINGLETON, Kathy J., Ed.D. Vice President, Human Resources, Virginia Mason Medical Center, Seattle, WA, p. A684
SHINICK, Mary K., Vice President Human Resources, Nyack Hospital, Nyack, NY, p. A446
SHININGER, Kimberly R., Director Human Resources, Parkview Wabash County Hospital, Wabash, IN, p. A221
SHIPIERSKI, Sally, Controller, Geisinger HEALTHSOUTH Rehabilitation Hospital, Danville, PA, p. A532
SHIPLEY, Carolyn, Chief Nursing Officer, Roane Medical Center, Harriman, TN, p. A578

Index of Health Care Professionals

Index of Health Care Professionals / Shipley

SHIPLEY, Janice, M.D. Chief Medical Officer, Cibola General Hospital, Grants, NM, p. A424
SHIPLEY, Kurt, Chief Financial Officer, Jordan Valley Medical Center, West Jordan, UT, p. A659
SHIPLEY, Sheila, Human Resources Educator, Signature Psychiatric Hospital, Kansas City, MO, p. A370
SHIPP, Geraldine H., Director of Risk Management, Sampson Regional Medical Center, Clinton, NC, p. A458
SHIRAH, Anita, Director Human Resources, University of South Alabama Medical Center, Mobile, AL, p. A22
SHIRLEY, Christian, Director Human Resources, Geisinger HEALTHSOUTH Rehabilitation Hospital, Danville, PA, p. A532
SHIRLEY, Douglas E., Senior Executive Vice President and Chief Financial Officer, Cooper University Health Care, Camden, NJ, p. A410
SHIRLEY, Steve, Chief Information Officer, Parkview Medical Center, Pueblo, CO, p. A108
SHISLER, Catherine, Director Information Services, Baylor Medical Center at Irving, Irving, TX, p. A624
SHIVELY, Lori, Vice President of Finance, Munson Healthcare Grayling Hospital, Grayling, MI, p. A321
SHIVERY, Toni M.
Vice President Human Resources, University of Maryland Harford Memorial Hospital, Havre De Grace, MD, p. A298
Vice President Human Resources, University of Maryland Upper Chesapeake Medical Center, Bel Air, MD, p. A295
SHOBE, Franklin, Administrator and Chief Executive Officer, Black Hills Surgery Center, Rapid City, SD, p. A570
SHOBE, Susan, Director Administration and Support Services, Alton Mental Health Center, Alton, IL, p. A178
SHOCKEY, Kathryn L., Director Human Resources, Lead–Deadwood Regional Hospital, Deadwood, SD, p. A568
SHOCKLEY, Mary, Director Human Resources, Russell Medical Center, Alexander City, AL, p. A15
SHOCKNEY, Brian T., FACHE Chief Operating Officer, Indiana University Health Arnett Hospital, Lafayette, IN, p. A214
SHOEMAKER, Larry D., M.D. Chief Operating Officer, Singing River Health System, Pascagoula, MS, p. A359
SHOEMAKER, Matt, D.O. Vice President and Chief Medical Officer, Southeast Hospital, Cape Girardeau, MO, p. A365
SHOENER, Carl, Chief Information Officer, Lehigh Valley Hospital – Hazleton, Hazleton, PA, p. A536
SHOFNER, Connie, Chief Nursing Officer, Carlsbad Medical Center, Carlsbad, NM, p. A423
SHOLLER, Peter, M.D. Medical Director, Spectrum Health Special Care Hospital, Grand Rapids, MI, p. A321
SHOMAKER, Susan, Director Information Management Systems, J. Arthur Dosher Memorial Hospital, Southport, NC, p. A468
SHOOK, Susan, Interim Chief Executive officer, Murray Medical Center, Chatsworth, GA, p. A153
SHOR, Joel, M.D. Chief of Staff, Bluefield Regional Medical Center, Bluefield, WV, p. A689
SHORB, Gary S., President and Chief Executive Officer, Methodist Le Bonheur Healthcare, Memphis, TN, p. B92
SHORES, Larry, M.D. Executive Medical Director, Cedar Springs Hospital, Colorado Springs, CO, p. A100
SHORT, Jo, Director of Nursing, Fulton County Health Center, Wauseon, OH, p. A500
SHORT, Kathy, D.O. Family Practice, Carroll County Memorial Hospital, Carrollton, KY, p. A255
SHORT, M. Andrew, Vice President Information Services, Samaritan Medical Center, Watertown, NY, p. A453
SHORT, Margaret W., Coordinator Information Technology, Webster County Memorial Hospital, Webster Springs, WV, p. A695
SHORT, Penny, R.N. Chief Operating Officer, Nanticoke Memorial Hospital, Seaford, DE, p. A117
SHORT, Peter H., M.D. Senior Vice President Medical Affairs, Beverly Hospital, Beverly, MA, p. A302
SHORT, Steve, Executive Vice President Finance and Administration and Chief Financial Officer, Tampa General Hospital, Tampa, FL, p. A145
SHORT, Ted, Chief Financial Officer, Fairview Park Hospital, Dublin, GA, p. A156
SHORT, W. L., M.D. Chief Medical Officer, Memorial Health System, Abilene, KS, p. A237
SHORTT, Sheila, R.N. Human Resources Consultant, SSM St. Joseph Hospital West, Lake Saint Louis, MO, p. A371
SHOUKAIR, Sami, M.D. Chief Medical Officer, La Palma Intercommunity Hospital, La Palma, CA, p. A66
SHOUP, Emily, Director Nursing Services, Roundup Memorial Healthcare, Roundup, MT, p. A386
SHOUSE, Shellie, Chief Financial Officer, Bluegrass Community Hospital, Versailles, KY, p. A266
SHOWALTER, Will
Senior Vice President, Chief Information Officer, St. Joseph's Hospital, West Bend, WI, p. A714
Senior Vice President Information Technology, Wellmont Bristol Regional Medical Center, Bristol, TN, p. A574
Senior Vice President Information Technology, Wellmont Holston Valley Medical Center, Kingsport, TN, p. A580
SHOWALTER, William, Senior Vice President Information Systems, Chief Information Officer, Community Memorial Hospital, Menomonee Falls, WI, p. A705
SHOWS, Carla
Payroll Clerk, George Regional Hospital, Lucedale, MS, p. A356
Payroll Clerk, Greene County Hospital, Leakesville, MS, p. A356
SHREEVE, Susan
Chief Financial Officer, Belton Regional Medical Center, Belton, MO, p. A363
Chief Financial Officer, Research Medical Center, Kansas City, MO, p. A370
SHREVE, Susan, Executive Director Information Technology, Boone Memorial Hospital, Madison, WV, p. A692
SHREVES, Melissa, Director Human Resources, Monongalia General Hospital, Morgantown, WV, p. A693
SHREWSBURY, Kim, Vice President and Chief Financial Officer, Decatur Morgan Hospital, Decatur, AL, p. A18
SHRIVER, Debra, R.N. Chief Nurse Executive, UnityPoint Health – Trinity Regional Medical Center, Fort Dodge, IA, p. A228
SHROADES, David W., Vice President Technology Services, Alliance Community Hospital, Alliance, OH, p. A478
SHRODER, Robert W.
President and Chief Executive Officer, St. Elizabeth Health Center, Youngstown, OH, p. A501
President and Chief Executive Officer, St. Joseph Health Center, Warren, OH, p. A499
SHROFF, Divya, Chief Medical Officer, Tristar Ashland City Medical Center, Ashland City, TN, p. A574
SHROFF, Rajendra, M.D. Administrative Medical Director, St. Mary's Hospital, Centralia, IL, p. A180
SHROYER, Linda K., Administrator, Potomac Valley Hospital, Keyser, WV, p. A692
SHUBIN, Allan, Chief Financial Officer, Pacific Alliance Medical Center, Los Angeles, CA, p. A71
SHUEY, Keith, M.D. Chief Medical Staff, Johnson County Hospital, Tecumseh, NE, p. A398
SHUFFIELD, Sean, Regional Chief Information Officer, University of Maryland St. Joseph Medical Center, Towson, MD, p. A300
SHUFFLEBARGER, Tom, Chief Operating Officer, Children's of Alabama, Birmingham, AL, p. A16
SHUFORD, Little, Manager Medical Information, Kindred Hospital–Greensboro, Greensboro, NC, p. A461
SHUGARMAN, Mark D., Administrator, Shriners Hospitals for Children–Cincinnati Burns Hospital, Cincinnati, OH, p. A483
SHUGART, Susan C., Chief Operating Officer, Carolina Pines Regional Medical Center, Hartsville, SC, p. A562
SHUGHART, Deborah A.
Vice President and Chief Financial Officer, Fulton County Medical Center, Mc Connellsburg, PA, p. A539
Vice President and Chief Financial Officer, J. C. Blair Memorial Hospital, Huntingdon, PA, p. A536
SHUGRUE, Dianne, President and Chief Executive Officer, Glens Falls Hospital, Glens Falls, NY, p. A434
SHULER, Conrad K., M.D. Chief Medical Officer, Oconee Memorial Hospital, Seneca, SC, p. A564
SHULIK, David, Vice President and Chief Financial Officer, UPMC Horizon, Greenville, PA, p. A535
SHULL, Jennifer, R.N. Chief Nursing Officer, Florida Hospital Fish Memorial, Orange City, FL, p. A137
SHULL, Kenneth A., FACHE, Chief Executive Officer, St. Luke's Hospital, Columbus, NC, p. A458
SHULMAN, Lawrence N., M.D. Senior Vice President Medical Affairs and Chief Medical Officer, Dana–Farber Cancer Institute, Boston, MA, p. A303
SHULTS, Randi L., Chief Executive Officer, North Carolina Specialty Hospital, Durham, NC, p. A459
SHUMAN, Betty, Director Human Resources, Wesley Rehabilitation Hospital, Wichita, KS, p. A253
SHUMAN, Daniel, D.O. Chief Medical Officer, Ashland Health Center, Ashland, KS, p. A237
SHUMATE, Karen J., R.N. Chief Operating Officer, Lawrence Memorial Hospital, Lawrence, KS, p. A244
SHUMATE, Kim, Human Resources Officer, Ohio State University Wexner Medical Center, Columbus, OH, p. A486
SHUMWAY, Barbara, Director Human Resources, North Big Horn Hospital District, Lovell, WY, p. A716
SHUMWAY, Donald L., Chief Executive Officer, Crotched Mountain Rehabilitation Center, Greenfield, NH, p. A406
SHUPERT, Charlene
Director Staff Services, Carrus Rehabilitation Hospital, Sherman, TX, p. A643
Director Staff Services, Carrus Specialty Hospital, Sherman, TX, p. A644
SHUPP, Susan, Chief Human Resources Officer, Nemaha County Hospital, Auburn, NE, p. A389
SHUTE, Keith M., M.D. Senior Vice President Medical Affairs and Clinical Services, Androscoggin Valley Hospital, Berlin, NH, p. A405
SHUTE, Leonard J., Chief Financial Officer, Strong Memorial Hospital of the University of Rochester, Rochester, NY, p. A449
SHUTER, Mark H., President and Chief Executive Officer, Adena Health System, Chillicothe, OH, p. B5
SHUTER, Mark H., President and Chief Executive Officer, Adena Medical Center, Chillicothe, OH, p. A482
SIAL, Jay, Chief Financial Officer, Loyola University Medical Center, Maywood, IL, p. A193
SIBBITT, Stephen, M.D. Chief Medical Officer, Scott & White Memorial Hospital, Temple, TX, p. A647
SIBLEY, Beth, Director of Nursing, Sage Rehabilitation Hospital, Baton Rouge, LA, p. A270
SIBLEY, Cherie, R.N., Chief Executive Officer, Clark Regional Medical Center, Winchester, KY, p. A267
SIBLEY, Jeri, Director Revenue Cycle, Riverside Tappahannock Hospital, Tappahannock, VA, p. A673
SICA, Vincent A., President and Chief Executive Officer, DeSoto Memorial Hospital, Arcadia, FL, p. A121
SICHTS, Pam, Director Human Resources, Sycamore Springs Hospital, Lafayette, IN, p. A214
SICILIA, Bruce, M.D. Medical Director, HEALTHSOUTH Rehabilitation Hospital of York, York, PA, p. A554
SIDDIQI, Ather, M.D
Medical Director, Nexus Specialty Hospital, Shenandoah, TX, p. A643
Medical Director, Nexus Specialty Hospital The Woodlands, Spring, TX, p. A644
SIDDIQI, Syed, M.D. President Medical Staff, Raleigh General Hospital, Beckley, WV, p. A689
SIDDIQUI, Hugh, Senior Applications Analyst, Linden Oaks Hospital, Naperville, IL, p. A195
SIDDIQUI, Joseph, Vice President Human Resources, The Aroostook Medical Center, Presque Isle, ME, p. A292
SIDES, Tim, Chief Financial Officer, Valle Vista Hospital, Greenwood, IN, p. A210
SIDMAN, Robert, M.D. Regional Vice President, Medical Affairs, The William W. Backus Hospital, Norwich, CT, p. A114
SIEBENALER, Christopher, Chief Executive Officer, Houston Methodist Sugar Land Hospital, Sugar Land, TX, p. A645
SIEBERT, Kristy, Manager Finance, John J. Pershing Veterans Affairs Medical Center, Poplar Bluff, MO, p. A374
SIEBERT, Matt, Assistant Administrator Ancillary Services, Hermann Area District Hospital, Hermann, MO, p. A368
SIEDLECKI, Cathy, Director Human Resources, Carthage Area Hospital, Carthage, NY, p. A431
SIEGEL, Fredric, M.D. Chief of Staff, Desert View Hospital, Pahrump, NV, p. A403
SIEGEL, Lesley, M.D. Medical Director, Albert J. Solnit Psychiatric Center – South Campus, Middletown, CT, p. A113
SIEGELMAN, Gary M., M.D. Senior Vice President and Chief Medical Officer, Bayhealth Medical Center, Dover, DE, p. A117
SIEGFRIED, Carole A., MSN Campus Nurse Executive, Palmetto Health Richland, Columbia, SC, p. A559
SIEGLE, Lora, M.D. Chief Medical Officer, Morris County Hospital, Council Grove, KS, p. A239
SIEGLEN, Linda, M.D. Chief Medical Officer, Mission Hospital, Mission Viejo, CA, p. A75
SIEGMAN, Ira, M.D. Chief Medical Officer, Northside Hospital, Saint Petersburg, FL, p. A142
SIEK, Terry, MSN Chief Nursing Officer, Hays Medical Center, Hays, KS, p. A241
SIELEMAN, Sharron, R.N. VP, Nursing, Central Maine Medical Center, Lewiston, ME, p. A290
SIEMERS, Thomas R., Chief Executive Officer, J. Arthur Dosher Memorial Hospital, Southport, NC, p. A468
SIEWERT, Charles
Director Human Resources, Buffalo Psychiatric Center, Buffalo, NY, p. A430
Director Human Resources, Western New York Children's Psychiatric Center, West Seneca, NY, p. A454
SIFERS, Carl, Director Information Technology and System Services, Centerpoint Medical Center, Independence, MO, p. A368
SIFFRING, Connie K., Chief Executive Officer, Select Specialty Hospital–Quad Cities, Davenport, IA, p. A225
SIFRI, Christi, Chief Nursing Executive, Regional Hospital for Respiratory and Complex Care, Burien, WA, p. A677

SIGEL, Heather, Director of Clinical Services, War Memorial Hospital, Berkeley Springs, WV, p. A689

SIGEL, Jay, M.D. Chief Medical Staff, Crane Memorial Hospital, Crane, TX, p. A603

SIGLER, Wes, Administrator, North Mississippi Medical Center–Eupora, Eupora, MS, p. A352

SIGNOR, Kristin, Director Finance, Sunnyview Rehabilitation Hospital, Schenectady, NY, p. A450

SIGREST, Marion, M.D. Chief of Staff, Baptist Medical Center Yazoo, Yazoo City, MS, p. A362

SIGSBURY, John R., President, St. Mary's Hospital, Centralia, IL, p. A180

SILARD, Kathleen A., R.N. Executive Vice President Operations and Chief Operating Officer, Stamford Hospital, Stamford, CT, p. A115

SILBER, Steven, M.D. Senior Vice President Medical Affairs, New York Methodist Hospital, NY, p. A443

SILLS, Doug, Chief Executive Officer, Santa Rosa Medical Center, Milton, FL, p. A135

SILLS, John T., Chief Information Officer, Health Central Hospital, Ocoee, FL, p. A137

SILSBEE, Dave, Chief Information Officer, Cary Medical Center, Caribou, ME, p. A289

SILSBY, Harry, M.D. Medical Director, Intermountain Hospital, Boise, ID, p. A172

SILVA, Carmen, R.N., Interim Chief Executive Officer, Doctors Hospital of Manteca, Manteca, CA, p. A74

SILVA, Shawn, Chief Executive Officer, Heritage Oaks Hospital, Sacramento, CA, p. A84

SILVA, Tracy, Chief Financial Officer, The Heart Hospital at Deaconess Gateway, Newburgh, IN, p. A217

SILVA–STEELE, Jamie A., R.N., President and Chief Executive Officer, UNM Sandoval Regional Medical Center, Rio Rancho, NM, p. A426

SILVER, Jonathan, Chief Financial Officer, Ballard Rehabilitation Hospital, San Bernardino, CA, p. A86

SILVER, Michael R., M.D. Vice President Medical Affairs, Rush Oak Park Hospital, Oak Park, IL, p. A196

SILVER, Timothy, M.D. Medical Director, Sheltering Arms Hospital South, Midlothian, VA, p. A668

SILVERMAN, Daniel C., M.D
Chief Medical Officer, Acute Care Troy, Samaritan Hospital, Troy, NY, p. A452
Vice President and Chief Medical Officer, Sinai Hospital of Baltimore, Baltimore, MD, p. A295
Chief Medical Officer, St. Mary's Hospital, Troy, NY, p. A452

SILVERSTEIN, Douglas M., President, NorthShore University Health System, Evanston, IL, p. A187

SILVERSTEIN, Joel, M.D. Chief Medical Officer, Copley Hospital, Morrisville, VT, p. A660

SILVERTHORNE, Samuel, Chief Information Officer, U. S. Air Force Medical Center Keesler, Keesler AFB, MS, p. A355

SILVEUS, Patrick, M.D. Medical Director, Kosciusko Community Hospital, Warsaw, IN, p. A221

SILVIA, Charles B., M.D. Chief Medical Officer and Vice President Medical Affairs, Peninsula Regional Medical Center, Salisbury, MD, p. A300

SIM, Carol, President and Chief Executive Officer, Siskin Hospital for Physical Rehabilitation, Chattanooga, TN, p. A575

SIMCHUK, Cathy J., Chief Operating Officer, Providence Holy Family Hospital, Spokane, WA, p. A685

SIMIA, Greg
Chief Financial Officer, St. Mary's Hospital Medical Center, Green Bay, WI, p. A702
Chief Financial Officer, St. Nicholas Hospital, Sheboygan, WI, p. A711
Chief Financial Officer, St. Vincent Hospital, Green Bay, WI, p. A702

SIMKINS, Palma, Chief Human Resources Management Services, Battle Creek Veterans Affairs Medical Center, Battle Creek, MI, p. A315

SIMMONS, Angela L., Chief Executive Officer, HealthSouth Rehabilitation Hospital of Humble, LLC, Humble, TX, p. A623

SIMMONS, Barbara, Chief Executive Officer, Westside Regional Medical Center, Plantation, FL, p. A140

SIMMONS, Brad, Chief Operating Officer, Saint Luke's Hospital of Kansas City, Kansas City, MO, p. A370

SIMMONS, Daniel F., Senior Vice President and Treasurer, Monongahela Valley Hospital, Monongahela, PA, p. A540

SIMMONS, Dorlynn, Chief Executive Officer, Mescalero Public Health Service Indian Hospital, Mescalero, NM, p. A425

SIMMONS, Eileen
Chief Financial Officer, Magee–Womens Hospital of UPMC, Pittsburgh, PA, p. A546
Chief Financial Officer, UPMC Presbyterian Shadyside, Pittsburgh, PA, p. A547

SIMMONS, Jeanette, Chief Operating Officer, Center for Behavioral Medicine, Kansas City, MO, p. A369

SIMMONS, Leslie, R.N., President and Chief Executive Officer, Carroll Hospital Center, Westminster, MD, p. A301

SIMMONS, Linda V., President and Chief Executive Officer, Decatur County Memorial Hospital, Greensburg, IN, p. A210

SIMMONS, Nancy B., Executive Vice President and Chief Administrative Officer, Good Samaritan Hospital Medical Center, West Islip, NY, p. A453

SIMMONS, Preston M., FACHE, Chief Executive Officer, Providence Regional Medical Center Everett, Everett, WA, p. A679

SIMMONS, Steven, Chief Human Resources Officer, Hahnemann University Hospital, Philadelphia, PA, p. A543

SIMMONS, Terry E., Chief Nursing Officer, Madison County Health Care System, Winterset, IA, p. A236

SIMMONS, Tim C., Chief Executive Officer, Hopebridge Hospital, Houston, TX, p. A620

SIMMONS, William, Chief Executive Officer, St. Luke's Patients Medical Center, Pasadena, TX, p. A636

SIMMS, Sr., Michael S., Vice President Human Resources, Northeast Alabama Regional Medical Center, Anniston, AL, p. A15

SIMMS, Miquel Noelani, Chief Nursing Officer, North Hawaii Community Hospital, Kamuela, HI, p. A169

SIMON, Anha, Director Human Resources, Winnie Community Hospital, Winnie, TX, p. A652

SIMON, Ashley, Chief Financial Officer, Kansas Surgery and Recovery Center, Wichita, KS, p. A252

SIMON, Deborah R., R.N.,
President and Chief Executive Officer, UnityPoint Health – Methodist Proctor, Peoria, IL, p. A198
President and Chief Executive Officer, UnityPoint Health–Proctor, Peoria, IL, p. A198

SIMON, Joan M., R.N. Chief Nursing Officer, Kootenai Health, Coeur D'Alene, ID, p. A173

SIMON, Kenneth B., M.D. Chief of Staff, Veterans Affairs Gulf Coast Veterans Health Care System, Biloxi, MS, p. A350

SIMON, Lisa M.
Senior Vice President Chief Financial Officer, East Ohio Regional Hospital, Martins Ferry, OH, p. A493
Senior Vice President and Chief Financial Officer, Ohio Valley Medical Center, Wheeling, WV, p. A696

SIMON, Lloyd, M.D. Medical Director, Eastern Long Island Hospital, Greenport, NY, p. A434

SIMON, Patricia, Manager Information Systems, Canandaigua Veterans Affairs Medical Center, Canandaigua, NY, p. A431

SIMON, Richard, M.D. Chief of Staff, University of Connecticut Health Center, John Dempsey Hospital, Farmington, CT, p. A112

SIMON, Stuart, M.D. Medical Director, North Central Surgical Center, Dallas, TX, p. A606

SIMON, Teresa, Director Information Systems, Nacogdoches Medical Center, Nacogdoches, TX, p. A633

SIMON, Thresa, M.D. Medical Director, Poplar Springs Hospital, Petersburg, VA, p. A670

SIMONIN, Steven J., Chief Executive Officer, Iowa Specialty Hospital–Clarion, Clarion, IA, p. A224

SIMONIN, Steven J., Chief Executive Officer, Iowa Specialty Hospitals, Clarion, IA, p. B75

SIMONS, Janice, FACHE, Chief Executive Officer, Medina Regional Hospital, Hondo, TX, p. A618

SIMONSON, Paul, Vice President, Trinity Health, Minot, ND, p. A476

SIMPATICO, Thomas, M.D., Facility Director and Network System Manager, Chicago–Read Mental Health Center, Chicago, IL, p. A181

SIMPSON, Brenda, R.N. Chief Nursing Officer, Largo Medical Center, Largo, FL, p. A132

SIMPSON, Chris, Chief Executive Officer, Cornerstone Hospital–West Monroe, West Monroe, LA, p. A286

SIMPSON, Greg, Chief Nursing Officer, St. Joseph Medical Center, Kansas City, MO, p. A370

SIMPSON, Joan W., Manager Human Resources, Lauderdale Community Hospital, Ripley, TN, p. A587

SIMPSON, John, Director Information Systems, Merit Health Central, Jackson, MS, p. A355

SIMPSON, Keith J., Chief Operating Officer, Jennings American Legion Hospital, Jennings, LA, p. A275

SIMPSON, Laura, Director Human Resources, Sabine County Hospital, Hemphill, TX, p. A618

SIMPSON, Jr., Lee A., Chief Executive Officer, Post Acute Medical Specialty Hospital of Tulsa, Tulsa, OK, p. A517

SIMPSON, Linda, Vice President Human Resources, OhioHealth Grant Medical Center, Columbus, OH, p. A486

SIMPSON, Mark, Director of Nursing, Welch Community Hospital, Welch, WV, p. A696

SIMPSON, Michelle, Chief Nursing Officer and Quality Leader, Lauderdale Community Hospital, Ripley, TN, p. A587

SIMPSON, Reagan, Chief Executive Officer, Kindred Rehabilitation Hospital Northeast Houston, Humble, TX, p. A623

SIMPSON, Robert, Vice President Operations, Methodist Richardson Medical Center, Richardson, TX, p. A638

SIMPSON Jr., Robert E., M.P.H., President and Chief Executive Officer, Brattleboro Retreat, Brattleboro, VT, p. A660

SIMPSON, Ryan, Interim Chief Executive Officer, Medical Center of Aurora, Aurora, CO, p. A99

SIMPSON, Shannon, Director Information Services, St. Elizabeth Hospital, Gonzales, LA, p. A274

SIMPSON, Shawndra, Interim Chief Executive Officer, Sutter Surgical Hospital – North Valley, Yuba City, CA, p. A98

SIMPSON, Sheila, Vice President Human Resources, Palmetto Lowcountry Behavioral Health, Charleston, SC, p. A558

SIMPSON, Tanya, Chief Nursing Officer, Regional Medical Center Bayonet Point, Hudson, FL, p. A129

SIMPSON–TUGGLE, Deloris, Vice President Human Resources and Organizational Development and Chief Human Resources Officer, Greater Baltimore Medical Center, Baltimore, MD, p. A293

SIMS, Abraham, Chief Executive Officer, New England Rehabilitation Hospital, Woburn, MA, p. A313

SIMS, Anthony, M.D. Chief of Staff, DeKalb Regional Medical Center, Fort Payne, AL, p. A20

SIMS, B. Wayne, President and Chief Executive Officer, KVC Prairie Ridge Psychiatric Hospital, Kansas City, KS, p. A243

SIMS, Brian, Director Administrative Services, Knoxville Hospital & Clinics, Knoxville, IA, p. A230

SIMS, Charles, M.D. Chief of Staff, St. Luke's The Woodlands Hospital, The Woodlands, TX, p. A648

SIMS, Gregory F., Chief Executive Officer, Hamilton Memorial Hospital District, McLeansboro, IL, p. A194

SIMS, Jason, M.D. Chief Medical Officer, Cleveland Area Hospital, Cleveland, OK, p. A505

SIMS, Jason, Facility Information Security Officer, North Hills Hospital, North Richland Hills, TX, p. A634

SIMS, Jeffrey, Chief Executive Officer, Heartland Behavioral Healthcare, Massillon, OH, p. A493

SIMS, Lynn, Director Information Technology, Davis County Hospital, Bloomfield, IA, p. A223

SIMS, Mark E., Chief Executive Officer, Grand Strand Regional Medical Center, Myrtle Beach, SC, p. A564

SIMS, W. Larry, Chief Operating Officer, Colquitt Regional Medical Center, Moultrie, GA, p. A162

SINCICH, Robert, Vice President Human Resources, Trumbull Memorial Hospital, Warren, OH, p. A499

SINCLAIR, Brad, Chief Financial Officer, Merit Health River Oaks, Flowood, MS, p. A352

SINCLAIR, Elyria, Director Human Resources, Crestwood Medical Center, Huntsville, AL, p. A21

SINCLAIR, Jan, Chief Personnel Officer, Oaklawn Hospital, Marshall, MI, p. A325

SINCLAIR, Kathy, Vice President Human Resources, Spartanburg Regional Medical Center, Spartanburg, SC, p. A565

SINCLAIR, Laura, Director Human Resources, Kansas City Orthopaedic Institute, Leawood, KS, p. A244

SINCLAIR, Michael, Chief Executive Officer, Rooks County Health Center, Plainville, KS, p. A249

SINCLAIR, Nicole, Chief Financial Officer, Sierra Vista Hospital, Sacramento, CA, p. A85

SINCLAIR, Noreen, Human Resources Administrator, Connecticut Veterans Home and Hospital, Rocky Hill, CT, p. A114

SINCLAIR–CHUNG, Opal, R.N. Chief Nursing Officer, Deputy Executive Director, Kings County Hospital Center, NY, p. A440

SINCOCK, Gregory M., Information Technology Leader, Kaiser Permanente West Los Angeles Medical Center, Los Angeles, CA, p. A70

SINDELAR, David, Chief Executive Officer, St. Anthony's Medical Center, Saint Louis, MO, p. A377

SINDELAR, Michael, Vice President and Chief Financial Officer, Fremont Health, Fremont, NE, p. A391

SINDLINGER, Julie A., Director of Human Resources, Weston County Health Services, Newcastle, WY, p. A717

SINEK, James J., FACHE, President, Boone Hospital Center, Columbia, MO, p. A366

SINGAL, Manisha, M.D. Medical Director, Specialty Hospital of Washington, Washington, DC, p. A120

SINGH, Amarjit, President and Chief Executive Officer, Brunswick Psych Center, Amityville, NY, p. A428

SINGH, Armandeep, Chief Medical Officer, Monroe Hospital, Bloomfield, IN, p. A205

SINGH, Brij, Medical Staff Director, Kindred Hospital Rome, Rome, GA, p. A163

SINGH, Himanshu, M.D. Associate Director, Veterans Affairs Ann Arbor Healthcare System, Ann Arbor, MI, p. A314

SINGH, Inderjit, M.D. Clinical Director, Pilgrim Psychiatric Center, Brentwood, NY, p. A430

SINGH, Jagdeep, M.D. Chief Medical Officer, Piedmont Henry Hospital, Stockbridge, GA, p. A165

SINGLES, James L., Chief Financial Officer, Marlette Regional Hospital, Marlette, MI, p. A325

SINGLETARY–TWYMAN, Michelle, Chief Nursing Officer, Rockford Center, Newark, DE, p. A117

SINGLETON, Al, M.D. Chief Psychiatry and Chief Medical Staff, Colorado Mental Health Institute at Pueblo, Pueblo, CO, p. A108

SINGLETON, J. Knox, President and Chief Executive Officer, Inova Health System, Falls Church, VA, p. B73

SINGLETON, Roy, Director Computer Information Systems, Palmdale Regional Medical Center, Palmdale, CA, p. A80

SINHA, Sunil K., M.D. Chief Medical Officer, Bon Secours Memorial Regional Medical Center, Mechanicsville, VA, p. A668

SINIARD, Sandra, Vice President of Patient Care Services, Hutcheson Medical Center, Fort Oglethorpe, GA, p. A158

SINICKAS, Robert, Director Information Services, Marianjoy Rehabilitation Hospital, Wheaton, IL, p. A203

SINICROPE, Jr., Frank J., Vice President Financial Services, Princeton Community Hospital, Princeton, WV, p. A694

SINISI, Albert, Director Information Systems, Doctors' Hospital of Michigan, Pontiac, MI, p. A328

SINISI, Linda, Entity Information Officer, Pennsylvania Hospital, Philadelphia, PA, p. A545

SINNOTT, James, M.D. Chief Medical Staff, Coquille Valley Hospital, Coquille, OR, p. A520

SINNOTT, Lisa M., Director Human Resources, Lourdes Specialty Hospital of Southern New Jersey, Willingboro, NJ, p. A420

SINOTTE, Brian, Chief Executive Officer, Maria Parham Medical Center, Henderson, NC, p. A462

SIOSON, Stephanie
Director Human Resources, Garden Grove Hospital and Medical Center, Garden Grove, CA, p. A63
Director Human Resources, Huntington Beach Hospital, Huntington Beach, CA, p. A65
Director Human Resources, La Palma Intercommunity Hospital, La Palma, CA, p. A66
Director Human Resources, West Anaheim Medical Center, Anaheim, CA, p. A53

SIPEK, John, Supervisor Client Services, Aurora Medical Center in Washington County, Hartford, WI, p. A702

SIREK, David, Chief Information Officer, Myrtue Medical Center, Harlan, IA, p. A229

SIRIO, Carl, M.D. Professor, Vice President Medical Affairs, Associate Dean for Clinical Affairs, Chief Medical Information Officer, The University of Toledo Medical Center, Toledo, OH, p. A499

SIRK, Donald, Director Information Systems, MedStar St. Mary's Hospital, Leonardtown, MD, p. A299

SIRMAN, Gary, Chief Human Resource Officer, North Hawaii Community Hospital, Kamuela, HI, p. A169

SIROIS, Peter, Chief Executive Officer, Northern Maine Medical Center, Fort Kent, ME, p. A290

SIROTTA, Ted D., Chief Financial Officer, Northwestern Medical Center, Saint Albans, VT, p. A661

SISARCICK, Barbara, Administrator, Peterson Rehabilitation Hospital, Wheeling, WV, p. A696

SISILLO, Sabato, M.D
Chief Medical Officer, Providence Medical Center, Kansas City, KS, p. A243
Chief Medical Officer, Saint John Hospital, Leavenworth, KS, p. A244

SISK, Bryan W., Associate Director Patient and Nursing Services, Central Texas Veterans Health Care System, Temple, TX, p. A646

SISK, Glenn C., President, Coosa Valley Medical Center, Sylacauga, AL, p. A25

SISK, Jack, Chief Financial Officer, Punxsutawney Area Hospital, Punxsutawney, PA, p. A548

SISK, Lori, R.N.,
Chief Executive Officer, Sanford Canby Medical Center, Canby, MN, p. A336
Chief Executive Officer, Sanford Clear Lake Medical Center, Clear Lake, SD, p. A568

SISK, Susan, Chief Financial Officer, CHI St. Alexius Health, Bismarck, ND, p. A472

SISLER, Debbie, Director Human Resources, Vidant Roanoke–Chowan Hospital, Ahoskie, NC, p. A455

SISON, Joseph, M.D. Medical Director, Heritage Oaks Hospital, Sacramento, CA, p. A84

SISSON, Travis, Interim Chief Executive Officer, Merit Health Batesville, Batesville, MS, p. A350

SISSON, William G., President, Baptist Health Lexington, Lexington, KY, p. A259

SISTO, Steven A., Senior Vice President and Chief Operating Officer, Methodist Hospital of Southern California, Arcadia, CA, p. A54

SISTRUNK, Heather, R.N. Chief Operating Officer, Merit Health River Oaks, Flowood, MS, p. A352

SITLINGER, James, Chief Human Resources Management, Charles George Veterans Affairs Medical Center, Asheville, NC, p. A455

SITTIG, Kevin, M.D. Senior Associate Dean and Chief Medical Officer, University Health Shreveport, Shreveport, LA, p. A285

SITTLOW, Jo, Vice President Patient Care and Chief Nursing Officer, Lakeview Hospital, Stillwater, MN, p. A347

SIVAK, Steven, M.D. Chair, Department of Medicine, Einstein Medical Center Philadelphia, Philadelphia, PA, p. A543

SIVESS, Chuck, Vice President Human Resources, Providence Healthcare Network, Waco, TX, p. A650

SIVLEY, Susanna S., Chief Personnel Officer, Highlands Medical Center, Scottsboro, AL, p. A24

SIWEK, Steven M., M.D. President and Chief Executive Officer, Freedom Pain Hospital, Scottsdale, AZ, p. A37

SIX, Deborah, Coordinator Data Processing, Wayne Memorial Hospital, Jesup, GA, p. A159

SJOBERG, Rochelle, Director Human Resources, Ely–Bloomenson Community Hospital, Ely, MN, p. A338

SKABELUND, Hoyt, Chief Executive Officer, Banner Churchill Community Hospital, Fallon, NV, p. A400

SKAGGS, Lynda, Chief Nursing Officer, Fleming County Hospital, Flemingsburg, KY, p. A256

SKALA, Pat, Chief Information Officer, Laguna Honda Hospital and Rehabilitation Center, San Francisco, CA, p. A88

SKARKA, Kathy, MSN Executive Vice President Patient Care Services, Nassau University Medical Center, East Meadow, NY, p. A433

SKARULIS, Patricia, Vice President Information Systems, Memorial Sloan–Kettering Cancer Center, New York, NY, p. A441

SKARZYNSKI, Joseph, M.D. Medical Director, North Central Bronx Hospital, NY, p. A443

SKEEN, Steven, R.N. Chief Nursing Officer, Mizell Memorial Hospital, Opp, AL, p. A24

SKELDON, Timothy K., Senior Vice President and Chief Financial Officer, Parrish Medical Center, Titusville, FL, p. A146

SKELLY, Stephanie, President Medical Staff, Red Bud Regional Hospital, Red Bud, IL, p. A199

SKELTON, Jenny, System Integration Manager, The Women's Hospital, Newburgh, IN, p. A217

SKELTON, Katie, MSN Vice President Nursing and Chief Nursing Officer, St. Joseph Hospital, Orange, CA, p. A79

SKIBBA, Joshua, Chief Medical Officer, Ohio County Hospital, Hartford, KY, p. A258

SKIDMORE, Jocelyn, Director Finance, SSM Health St. Francis Hospital – Maryville, Maryville, MO, p. A372

SKIDMORE, Kim, Chief Executive Officer, Community Medical Center of Izard County, Calico Rock, AR, p. A42

SKIEM, Paul, Senior Vice President Human Resources, Presence Saint Francis Hospital, Evanston, IL, p. A188

SKILLINGS, Charles E., President and Chief Executive Officer, St. Anthony Shawnee Hospital, Shawnee, OK, p. A515

SKILLINGS, Lois N., MSN, President and Chief Executive Officer, Mid Coast Hospital, Brunswick, ME, p. A289

SKINNER, Eileen F., FACHE, President and Chief Executive Officer, Mercy Hospital of Portland, Portland, ME, p. A291

SKINNER, Gary, Director Information Technology, Rehabilitation Hospital of Indiana, Indianapolis, IN, p. A212

SKINNER, Gwendolyn, Executive Director, Devereux Georgia Treatment Network, Kennesaw, GA, p. A159

SKINNER, Jeannette, FACHE, Administrator, Shriners Hospitals for Children–Tampa, Tampa, FL, p. A145

SKINNER, Kellcie, Controller, Newman Memorial Hospital, Shattuck, OK, p. A514

SKINNER, Marjorie, Director Finance, Pershing General Hospital, Lovelock, NV, p. A403

SKINNER, Richard, Chief Information Technology Officer, University of Virginia Medical Center, Charlottesville, VA, p. A663

SKINNER, Sue, Vice President of Patient Care Services, Grand Itasca Clinic and Hospital, Grand Rapids, MN, p. A339

SKIPPER, Kymberli, Manager Human Resources, Prattville Baptist Hospital, Prattville, AL, p. A24

SKIPPER, Michelle, Director Human Resources, Kaiser Permanente Riverside Medical Center, Riverside, CA, p. A83

SKJOLDEN, Jessica, M.D. Chief of Staff, St. Andrew's Health Center, Bottineau, ND, p. A472

SKLAMBERG, Todd, President, Sunrise Hospital and Medical Center, Las Vegas, NV, p. A403

SKLAR, Joel, M.D. Chief Medical Officer, Marin General Hospital, Greenbrae, CA, p. A64

SKOCH, Michael, M.D. Chief Medical Officer, Mary Lanning Healthcare, Hastings, NE, p. A392

SKOGSBERGH, Jim H., President and Chief Executive Officer, Advocate Health Care, Downers Grove, IL, p. B7

SKORA, Lori, Chief Executive Officer, Kindred Hospital of Northern Indiana, Mishawaka, IN, p. A216

SKOW, Glenn, M.D. Chief of Staff, Fayette County Hospital, Vandalia, IL, p. A202

SKOWRON, Paul, Chief Executive Officer, Dr. John Warner Hospital, Clinton, IL, p. A185

SKRINDE, Tracie, Director Human Resources, PeaceHealth United General Medical Center, Sedro–Woolley, WA, p. A684

SKRIPPS, Michele M., R.N., Chief Executive Officer, AnMed Health Rehabilitation Hospital, Anderson, SC, p. A557

SKULA, Erika, President and Chief Executive Officer, Manchester Memorial Hospital, Manchester, KY, p. A262

SKUPIEN, Mary Beth, Director, Battle Creek Veterans Affairs Medical Center, Battle Creek, MI, p. A315

SKVARENINA, Michael, Assistant Vice President Information Systems, Holy Name Medical Center, Teaneck, NJ, p. A419

SKYLES, Jill, R.N
Vice President Patient Care Services and Chief Nurse Executive, Barnes–Jewish St. Peters Hospital, Saint Peters, MO, p. A378
Vice President Patient Care Services and Chief Nurse Executive, Progress West Hospital, O'Fallon, MO, p. A374

SLABA, Bryan, Chief Executive Officer, Wagner Community Memorial Hospital Avera, Wagner, SD, p. A572

SLABIK, Shauna, Chief Financial Officer, Sanford Mayville Medical Center, Mayville, ND, p. A475

SLACK, Randy, Chief Executive Officer, CHI St. Luke's Health Memorial Livingston, Livingston, TX, p. A628

SLADKY, Todd J., Chief Financial Officer, Great River Medical Center, West Burlington, IA, p. A236

SLAGLE, Julie A., R.N. Vice President Patient Care Services, Sidney Regional Medical Center, Sidney, NE, p. A398

SLATE, Sonny, Chief Operating Officer, Georgia Regional Hospital at Atlanta, Decatur, GA, p. A156

SLATER, Craig M., M.D. Chief Medical Officer, Carolinas Healthcare System Union, Monroe, NC, p. A465

SLATER, Mark, Director Information Systems, Lake Pointe Medical Center, Rowlett, TX, p. A639

SLATER–NESUOLD, Stephanie, Director of Nursing, Landmark Hospital of Joplin, Joplin, MO, p. A369

SLATON, Brenda, Superintendent, Rusk State Hospital, Rusk, TX, p. A639

SLATTERY, Greg, Vice President Information, Community Hospitals and Wellness Centers, Bryan, OH, p. A480

SLATTERY, Susan L., Director Human Resources, UnityPoint Health – St. Luke's Hospital, Cedar Rapids, IA, p. A223

SLATTMAN, Robin, Chief Nursing Officer, Memorial Health, Marysville, OH, p. A493

SLAVIN, Kevin J., FACHE, President and Chief Executive Officer, St. Joseph's Regional Medical Center, Paterson, NJ, p. A416

SLAVIN, Peter L., M.D., President, Massachusetts General Hospital, Boston, MA, p. A304

SLAWITSKY, Bruce, Vice President Human Resources, Hospital for Special Surgery, New York, NY, p. A440

SLAWKOWSKI, Ken, Interim Director Information Systems, Holy Cross Hospital, Chicago, IL, p. A182

SLAYDON, Cindy, Chief Nursing Executive, Sparks Regional Medical Center, Fort Smith, AR, p. A45

SLAYTON, Val, M.D. Vice President Medical Affairs, Sts. Mary & Elizabeth Hospital, Louisville, KY, p. A262

SLBERS, Craig, Vice President Patient Care and Chief Nursing Officer, Mercy St. Charles Hospital, Oregon, OH, p. A495

SLEDGE, Cynthia Moore, M.D. Medical Director, Bryce Hospital, Tuscaloosa, AL, p. A25

SLEDGE, Tasha, Director Human Resources, Texas Health Harris Methodist Hospital Southlake, Southlake, TX, p. A644

SLEEPER, Justin, Vice President Clinical Operations, Behavioral Health Network, Natchaug Hospital, Mansfield Center, CT, p. A113

SLEITER, Michelle, Chief Executive Officer, Humboldt County Memorial Hospital, Humboldt, IA, p. A229

SLENSZAK, David, Director, Information Services, Williamsburg Regional Hospital, Kingstree, SC, p. A562

SLESSOR, Steve Robert, Chief Executive Officer, Buchanan County Health Center, Independence, IA, p. A229

SLICK, Lois, Director Human Resources, CHI LakeWood Health, Baudette, MN, p. A335

SLIDER, Carol, Chief Nursing Officer, Titus Regional Medical Center, Mount Pleasant, TX, p. A633

SLIETER Jr., Richard G., Administrator, Community Behavioral Health Hospital – Baxter, Baxter, MN, p. A335

SLIGER, Susan, Director Human Resources, War Memorial Hospital, Sault Sainte Marie, MI, p. A330

SLINGERLAND, Micki J., Chief Operating Officer, TriStar Centennial Medical Center, Nashville, TN, p. A586

SLITER, Elizabeth, M.D. Chairman Medical Staff, Decatur Health Systems, Oberlin, KS, p. A247

SLIWA, James, M.D. Chief Medical Officer, Rehabilitation Institute of Chicago, Chicago, IL, p. A184

SLIWINSKI, Jeff, Chief Financial Officer, Clear Lake Regional Medical Center, Webster, TX, p. A651

SLIWINSKI, Ron, President and Chief Executive Officer, University of Wisconsin Hospital and Clinics, Madison, WI, p. A704

SLOAN, Gary, Chief Executive Officer, San Ramon Regional Medical Center, San Ramon, CA, p. A90

SLOAN, Patrick, Chief Financial Officer, Sandhills Regional Medical Center, Hamlet, NC, p. A461

SLOAN, Prudence, Coordinator Human Resources, Select Specialty Hospital–Pittsburgh/UPMC, Pittsburgh, PA, p. A546

SLOAN, Ronald A., FACHE, President, The Outer Banks Hospital, Nags Head, NC, p. A466

SLOAN, Steve, Chief Financial Officer, Lake Cumberland Regional Hospital, Somerset, KY, p. A266

SLOCUM, Brandon H., Senior Vice President and Chief Financial Officer, Medical West, Bessemer, AL, p. A16

SLOCUM, Gregg Y., Chief Financial Officer, Valley Forge Medical Center and Hospital, Norristown, PA, p. A542

SLONIM, Anthony D., Dr.PH, President and Chief Executive Officer, Renown Health, Reno, NV, p. B113

SLONIM, Sheryl A., Executive Vice President and Chief Nursing Officer, Holy Name Medical Center, Teaneck, NJ, p. A419

SLONINA, Marrianne, Director Human Resources, Georgetown Community Hospital, Georgetown, KY, p. A257

SLOPER, Carol, Manager Information Technology, Cheyenne County Hospital, Saint Francis, KS, p. A249

SLOTERBEEK, Meridell
Chief Executive Officer, Acuity Specialty Hospital of Arizona at Mesa, Mesa, AZ, p. A
Chief Executive Officer, Kindred Hospital Clear Lake, Webster, TX, p. A651

SLOUGH, Sharlet, D.O. Chief of Staff, East Texas Medical Center Jacksonville, Jacksonville, TX, p. A624

SLOVER, Christopher, Chief Executive Officer, Lakeview Specialty Hospital and Rehabilitation Center, Waterford, WI, p. A712

SLUBOWSKI, Michael A., FACHE, Chief Executive Officer, SCL Health, Broomfield, CO, p. B118

SLUCK, Jeana, R.N. Executive Director Nursing Clinical Inpatient Departments, Allied Services Rehabilitation Hospital, Scranton, PA, p. A549

SLUKA, Joseph, President and Chief Executive Officer, St. Charles Health System, Inc., Bend, OR, p. B127

SLUSHER, Carlene, Director Finance, Seneca Healthcare District, Chester, CA, p. A57

SLUSHER, Michael, Community Chief Executive Officer, Middlesboro ARH Hospital, Middlesboro, KY, p. A263

SLYTER, Mark F., FACHE, Chief Executive Officer, Baton Rouge General Medical Center, Baton Rouge, LA, p. A269

SMAJSTRLA, Julie, Director Nursing, Seymour Hospital, Seymour, TX, p. A643

SMALL, Becky, Chief Human Resources Officer, Kindred Hospital–Aurora, Aurora, CO, p. A99

SMALL, Brenda, Chief Clinical Officer, AMG Specialty Hospital–Greenwood, Greenwood, MS, p. A353

SMALL, David, M.D
Chief Medical Officer, Greene Memorial Hospital, Xenia, OH, p. A501
Chief Medical Officer, Soin Medical Center, Beavercreek, OH, p. A479

SMALL, Deborah C., R.N. Vice President Patient Care Services and Chief Nursing Officer, Fairview Hospital, Cleveland, OH, p. A484

SMALL, Donna, R.N. Chief Nursing Officer, St. Mary's Medical Center, West Palm Beach, FL, p. A147

SMALL, Jonathan
Chief Operations Information and Technology, John D. Dingell Veterans Affairs Medical Center, Detroit, MI, p. A318
Vice President, Human Resources, Memorial Health, Savannah, GA, p. A164

SMALL, Terry L., Assistant Chief Executive Officer, William R. Sharpe, Jr. Hospital, Weston, WV, p. A696

SMALLWOOD, Ravae, IS Coordinator, CHI Health Missouri Valley, Missouri Valley, IA, p. A231

SMANIK, Robert E., FACHE, President and Chief Executive Officer, Day Kimball Hospital, Putnam, CT, p. A114

SMARR, Susan, M.D. Physician–in–Chief, Kaiser Permanente Santa Clara Medical Center, Santa Clara, CA, p. A91

SMART, Dan, Chief Information Management Officer, Permian Regional Medical Center, Andrews, TX, p. A592

SMART, George J., Vice President Finance and Information Technology, Alpena Regional Medical Center, Alpena, MI, p. A314

SMART, Joanne F., M.D. Director of Medical Affairs, Indiana University Health Bedford Hospital, Bedford, IN, p. A204

SMART, Melissa, Communication ad Public Relations Specialist, Texas Health Presbyterian Hospital Denton, Denton, TX, p. A608

SMART, Paul, CPA Chief Financial Officer, Franklin County Medical Center, Preston, ID, p. A176

SMART, Robert M., Chief Executive Officer, Reliant Rehabilitation Hospital Mid–Cities, Bedford, TX, p. A596

SMEEKS, Frank C., M.D. Chief Medical Officer, Frye Regional Medical Center, Hickory, NC, p. A462

SMELSER, Scott, M.D. Chief of Staff, French Hospital Medical Center, San Luis Obispo, CA, p. A90

SMELTZER, Sharon, Chief Executive Officer, Mercy Rehabilitation Hospital Oklahoma City, Oklahoma City, OK, p. A512

SMENDIK, Douglas, M.D. Chief Medical Officer, Spectrum Health Pennock, Hastings, MI, p. A322

SMIDT, Jessica, R.N. Director of Nursing, Pipestone County Medical Center Avera, Pipestone, MN, p. A344

SMIGA, Lance, Chief Financial Officer, Jackson County Hospital District, Edna, TX, p. A610

SMILEY, Christy, Director Human Resources, SSM Health St. Mary's Hospital – Audrain, Mexico, MO, p. A372

SMILEY, Jon D., Interim Chief Executive Officer, Columbia County Health System, Dayton, WA, p. A678

SMITH, Agnes A., R.N. Chief Nursing Officer, Twin County Regional Healthcare, Galax, VA, p. A665

SMITH, Alan H.
Chief Financial Officer, Huntington Beach Hospital, Huntington Beach, CA, p. A65
Chief Financial Officer, La Palma Intercommunity Hospital, La Palma, CA, p. A66

SMITH, Andrew, Chief Information Management, Madigan Healthcare System, Tacoma, WA, p. A686

SMITH, Barbara H., Senior Vice President & Chief Operating Officer, Robert Wood Johnson University Hospital at Hamilton, Hamilton, NJ, p. A412

SMITH, Bennie, Chief Information Officer, Lady of the Sea General Hospital, Cut Off, LA, p. A272

SMITH, Bernie, Chief Financial Officer, Troy Community Hospital, Troy, PA, p. A551

SMITH, Beth, Controller, CHI Mercy Health, Valley City, ND, p. A476

SMITH, Bethany, Controller, HEALTHSOUTH Cane Creek Rehabilitation Hospital, Martin, TN, p. A582

SMITH, Beverly Bzdek, Chief Nursing Officer, Southside Regional Medical Center, Petersburg, VA, p. A670

SMITH, Bill, M.D. Chief of Staff, Cullman Regional Medical Center, Cullman, AL, p. A18

SMITH, Blythe, Administrative Assistant, Faulkton Area Medical Center, Faulkton, SD, p. A568

SMITH, Bobby, Vice President Physician Services and Quality, Illinois Valley Community Hospital, Peru, IL, p. A198

SMITH, Brad, M.D. Chief Medical Staff, Lane Regional Medical Center, Zachary, LA, p. A287

SMITH, Bradley, President and Chief Executive Officer, Rush Memorial Hospital, Rushville, IN, p. A219

SMITH, Brenda, Director Financial Services, Alliance Health Center, Meridian, MS, p. A357

SMITH, Brent, Chief Financial Officer, Comanche County Memorial Hospital, Lawton, OK, p. A508

SMITH, Brent, M.D. Chief Medical Officer and Vice President Clinical Integration, Edward Hospital, Naperville, IL, p. A195

SMITH, Brian
Executive Vice President and Chief Operating Officer, St. Rita's Medical Center, Lima, OH, p. A492
Director of Operations, Wamego Health Center, Wamego, KS, p. A252

SMITH, Carl, Director Information Systems, King's Daughters Medical Center, Brookhaven, MS, p. A351

SMITH, Carol, Vice President Patient Care and Chief Nursing Officer, Tift Regional Medical Center, Tifton, GA, p. A166

SMITH, Cheryl, Manager Human Resources, New Braunfels Regional Rehabilitation Hospital, New Braunfels, TX, p. A634

SMITH, Chris, Chief Information Officer, Falls Community Hospital and Clinic, Marlin, TX, p. A631

SMITH, Christian, Chief of Staff, Southeast Georgia Health System Camden Campus, Saint Marys, GA, p. A163

SMITH, Clifton, R.N. Interim Chief Nursing Executive, Merit Health Northwest Mississippi, Clarksdale, MS, p. A351

SMITH, Connie, President and Chief Executive Officer, Commonwealth Health Corporation, Bowling Green, KY, p. B34

SMITH, Connie, Chief Executive Officer, Medical Center at Bowling Green, Bowling Green, KY, p. A254

SMITH, Dan
Director Human Resources, Austin Lakes Hospital, Austin, TX, p. A593
Director Human Resources, Memorial Hospital, Carthage, IL, p. A180

SMITH, Daniel
Interim Chief Executive Officer, Memorial Hermann Surgical HospitalG‰(First Colony, Sugar Land, TX, p. A645
Interim Chief Executive Officer, TOPS Surgical Specialty Hospital, Houston, TX, p. A622

SMITH, Daniel B.
Vice President Finance, Good Samaritan Regional Medical Center, Corvallis, OR, p. A520
Vice President Finance, Samaritan Albany General Hospital, Albany, OR, p. A519
Vice President Finance, Samaritan Lebanon Community Hospital, Lebanon, OR, p. A522
Chief Financial Officer, Samaritan Pacific Communities Hospital, Newport, OR, p. A523

SMITH, Danny, Director Human Resources, Bryan W. Whitfield Memorial Hospital, Demopolis, AL, p. A18

SMITH, Darrin, Vice President Human Resources, Parkview Medical Center, Pueblo, CO, p. A108

SMITH, Darwin K., Vice President Human Resources, Union Hospital, Dover, OH, p. A489

SMITH, David, Chief Executive Officer, Baylor Institute for Rehabilitation at Northwest Dallas, Dallas, TX, p. A604

SMITH, David, President and Chief Executive Officer, Cornerstone Healthcare Group, Dallas, TX, p. B42

SMITH, David
President, Cornerstone Hospital of Southwest Louisiana, Sulphur, LA, p. A286
Chief Financial Officer, Memorial Regional Hospital, FL, p. A128
Manager Data Center, Texas Health Huguley Hospital Fort Worth South, Fort Worth, TX, p. A614

SMITH, Deborah S., R.N. Vice President, Chief Nursing Officer, OSF St. Joseph Medical Center, Bloomington, IL, p. A179

SMITH, Debra
Chief Executive Officer, Gundersen St. Joseph's Hospital and Clinics, Hillsboro, WI, p. A702
Chief Nursing Officer, HEALTHSOUTH Rehabilitation Hospital, Kingsport, TN, p. A580

SMITH, Denise
Director Financial Services, Florida State Hospital, Chattahoochee, FL, p. A123
Director Health Information, HEALTHSOUTH Chattanooga Rehabilitation Hospital, Chattanooga, TN, p. A575
Director Human Resources, HSHS St. Mary's Hospital, Decatur, IL, p. A186

SMITH, Dennis J., Chief Operating Officer, James Cancer Hospital and Solove Research Institute, Columbus, OH, p. A485

SMITH, Denny R., Administrator, Camden General Hospital, Camden, TN, p. A574

SMITH, Diana B., Chief Financial Officer, Promise Hospital of Dallas, Dallas, TX, p. A606

SMITH, Diane, Chief Nursing Officer, Baptist Health Extended Care Hospital, Little Rock, AR, p. A47

SMITH, Dianne, Director Personnel and Human Resources, Potomac Valley Hospital, Keyser, WV, p. A692

SMITH, Dick, Director Human Resources, West Park Hospital, Cody, WY, p. A716

SMITH, Donald, President Medical Staff, Bellevue Hospital, Bellevue, OH, p. A480

SMITH, Donna M., Chief Nursing Officer, Barstow Community Hospital, Barstow, CA, p. A56

SMITH, Donna P., R.N. Vice President Chief Operating Officer and Chief Nursing Officer, Clifton Springs Hospital and Clinic, Clifton Springs, NY, p. A431

SMITH, Donnie
Chief Human Resources Officer, Laird Hospital, Union, MS, p. A361
Director Human Resources, Rush Foundation Hospital, Meridian, MS, p. A357
Director of Human Resources, Specialty Hospital of Meridian, Meridian, MS, p. A358

SMITH, Doug
Chief Financial Officer, McKay–Dee Hospital Center, Ogden, UT, p. A656
Chief Financial Officer, Rock Prairie Behavioral Health, College Station, TX, p. A601

SMITH, Drew, Director Human Resources, Baylor Medical Center at Carrollton, Carrollton, TX, p. A600

SMITH, Edward H., President and Chief Executive Officer, St. Anthony Regional Hospital, Carroll, IA, p. A223

SMITH, Elizabeth A., Director of Nursing, John J. Pershing Veterans Affairs Medical Center, Poplar Bluff, MO, p. A374

SMITH, Ellen, Administrator, LCMH Specialty Hospital, Lake Charles, LA, p. A278

SMITH, Eric, Chief Financial Officer, Bayfront Health St. Petersburg, Saint Petersburg, FL, p. A142

SMITH, Ericka, Chief Operating Officer, Monterey Park Hospital, Monterey Park, CA, p. A76

SMITH, Eugene, Chief Information Officer, Maniilaq Health Center, Kotzebue, AK, p. A28

SMITH, Jr., Forrest Bud H., Chief Financial Officer, Fulton State Hospital, Fulton, MO, p. A368

SMITH, G. Todd, President, St. Elizabeth Community Hospital, Red Bluff, CA, p. A82

Index of Health Care Professionals

Index of Health Care Professionals / Smith


SMITH, Gene
Senior Vice President Operations, AMG Specialty Hospital–Slidell, Slidell, LA, p. A285
Interim Vice President and Chief Financial Officer, Ottumwa Regional Health Center, Ottumwa, IA, p. A233
Interim Chief Financial Officer, West Suburban Medical Center, Oak Park, IL, p. A196
SMITH, Geoffrey, Chief Financial Officer, Lebanon Veterans Affairs Medical Center, Lebanon, PA, p. A538
SMITH, Gia, Chief Executive Officer, Central Valley Specialty Hospital, Modesto, CA, p. A75
SMITH, Ginger S., Chief Nursing Officer, Claiborne Memorial Medical Center, Homer, LA, p. A275
SMITH, Greg, Chief Medical Officer, Lake Region Healthcare, Fergus Falls, MN, p. A338
SMITH, Greg, CPA Chief Financial Officer, Woman's Hospital, Baton Rouge, LA, p. A270
SMITH, Gregory
Chief Information Officer, Covenant Medical Center, Waterloo, IA, p. A235
Senior Vice President and Chief Information Officer, Midwest Orthopedic Specialty Hospital, Franklin, WI, p. A701
Senior Vice President and Chief Information Officer, Wheaton Franciscan Healthcare – Franklin, Franklin, WI, p. A701
Senior Vice President and Chief Information Officer, Wheaton Franciscan Healthcare – St. Francis, Milwaukee, WI, p. A707
Senior Vice President and Chief Information Officer, Wheaton Franciscan Healthcare – The Wisconsin Heart Hospital, Wauwatosa, WI, p. A713
SMITH, Gretchen, Vice President Nursing and Compliance and Risk, Rush Memorial Hospital, Rushville, IN, p. A219
SMITH, Hal, M.D. Chief of Staff, South Peninsula Hospital, Homer, AK, p. A28
SMITH, Harley, Chief Executive Officer, TMC Bonham Hospital, Bonham, TX, p. A598
SMITH, Heather
President, Conemaugh Meyersdale Medical Center, Meyersdale, PA, p. A540
Chief Operating Officer, Welch Community Hospital, Welch, WV, p. A696
SMITH, Holt, Chief Financial Officer, Springs Memorial Hospital, Lancaster, SC, p. A563
SMITH, Jack, Acting Chief Information Resources Management Service, Veterans Affairs Sierra Nevada Health Care System, Reno, NV, p. A404
SMITH, Jackie, R.N. Chief Nursing Officer, Holdenville General Hospital, Holdenville, OK, p. A508
SMITH, James E.
Superintendent, North Texas State Hospital, Vernon, TX, p. A649
Superintendent, North Texas State Hospital, Wichita Falls Campus, Wichita Falls, TX, p. A652
SMITH, James M., M.D. Medical Director, Bastrop Rehabilitation Hospital, Monroe, LA, p. A280
SMITH, Jamesy, D.O
Chief of Staff, Parkland Health Center – Liberty Street, Farmington, MO, p. A367
President, Medical Staff, Parkland Health Center – Weber Road, Farmington, MO, p. A367
SMITH, Jamie, Supervisor Health Information Management Systems, HEALTHSOUTH Rehabilitation Hospital of Sewickley, Sewickley, PA, p. A550
SMITH, Janet, Chief Financial Officer, Troy Regional Medical Center, Troy, AL, p. A25
SMITH, Jason, M.D. Chief of Staff, Mitchell County Hospital, Camilla, GA, p. A153
SMITH, Jason, Chief Nursing Officer, Piedmont Newnan Hospital, Newnan, GA, p. A162
SMITH, Jay, Director Information Systems, Brownwood Regional Medical Center, Brownwood, TX, p. A599
SMITH, Jeanna, Administrative Assistant and Human Resources Officer, Polk Medical Center, Cedartown, GA, p. A153
SMITH, Jeff, Chief Information Officer, Holy Cross Hospital, Fort Lauderdale, FL, p. A126
SMITH, Jeffrey, Chief Executive Officer, Kindred Hospital–Bay Area, Pasadena, TX, p. A636
SMITH, Jeffrey A., M.D. Senior Vice President and Chief Medical Officer, Aurora St. Luke's Medical Center, Milwaukee, WI, p. A706
SMITH, Jesse, Director of Nursing, Keefe Memorial Hospital, Cheyenne Wells, CO, p. A100
SMITH, Jill, Administrative Coordinator, J. Paul Jones Hospital, Camden, AL, p. A17
SMITH, Jim, Director Information Systems, Washington County Memorial Hospital, Potosi, MO, p. A374
SMITH, Jo Beth, Chief Support Services and Human Resources, Decatur County Hospital, Leon, IA, p. A231
SMITH, Joanne C., M.D., President and Chief Executive Officer, Rehabilitation Institute of Chicago, Chicago, IL, p. A184
SMITH, JoBeth, Chief Operating Officer and Director of Human Resources, Medical Arts Hospital, Lamesa, TX, p. A627
SMITH, Jodi, Administrative Assistant Human Resources, Eureka Springs Hospital, Eureka Springs, AR, p. A43
SMITH, Jon
Chief Executive Officer, Caribou Memorial Hospital and Living Center, Soda Springs, ID, p. A176
Chief Financial Officer, Lost Rivers Medical Center, Arco, ID, p. A172
SMITH, Jonathan, Assistant Administrator and Chief Financial Officer, Blount Memorial Hospital, Maryville, TN, p. A582
SMITH, Joseph S., Chief Executive Officer, Boone County Hospital, Boone, IA, p. A223
SMITH, Julia
Chief Financial Officer, Kindred Hospital Rome, Rome, GA, p. A163
Chief Financial Officer, Kindred Hospital–Chattanooga, Chattanooga, TN, p. A575
Chief Financial Officer, Vibra Hospital of Charleston, Mt. Pleasant, SC, p. A563
SMITH, Julie, Director Human Resources, HEALTHSOUTH Lakeshore Rehabilitation Hospital, Birmingham, AL, p. A16
SMITH, Julie, R.N. Director of Nursing, Jersey Community Hospital, Jerseyville, IL, p. A191
SMITH, Karen S., Director Information Services, Chilton Medical Center, Pompton Plains, NJ, p. A417
SMITH, Karyl, Director Human Resources, Harbor–UCLA Medical Center, Torrance, CA, p. A94
SMITH, Kathy A., MSN Nurse Executive, Summit Behavioral Healthcare, Cincinnati, OH, p. A483
SMITH, Kelli, M.D. Chief of Staff, Magee General Hospital, Magee, MS, p. A356
SMITH, Kelly C., Division President, Beaumont Hospital–Dearborn, Dearborn, MI, p. A317
SMITH, Kevin, D.O. Chief of Staff, Otsego Memorial Hospital, Gaylord, MI, p. A320
SMITH, Kevin, Vice President Finance and Support Services, Rehabilitation Institute of Michigan, Detroit, MI, p. A318
SMITH, Kevin E., Chief Operating Officer, Scott & White Hospital at Round Rock, Round Rock, TX, p. A639
SMITH, Kevin M., Director Human Resources, Indian Path Medical Center, Kingsport, TN, p. A580
SMITH, Kim, Director Business Office, Doctor's Hospital of Deer Creek, Leesville, LA, p. A279
SMITH, Kris, Controller, Madison St. Joseph Health Center, Madisonville, TX, p. A630
SMITH, Kyle, Director Information Systems, Iredell Memorial Hospital, Statesville, NC, p. A469
SMITH, Larry, Senior Vice President and Chief Financial Officer, UW Medicine/Valley Medical Center, Renton, WA, p. A682
SMITH, LaVonne, Director Health Information Technology, Tomah Memorial Hospital, Tomah, WI, p. A712
SMITH, Lawrence, M.D. Senior Vice President and Chief Medical Officer, Forest Hills Hospital, NY, p. A439
SMITH, Leighton, M.D. Chief Medical Officer, Florida Hospital Fish Memorial, Orange City, FL, p. A137
SMITH, Leora, Information System and Health Information Management Team Leader, Phelps Memorial Health Center, Holdrege, NE, p. A393
SMITH, Leslie, Director Human Resources, Howard County Medical Center, Saint Paul, NE, p. A398
SMITH, Lex, Chief Executive Officer, Mee Memorial Hospital, King City, CA, p. A66
SMITH, Linda C., M.D. Medical Director, HEALTHSOUTH Rehabilitation Hospital of Beaumont, Beaumont, TX, p. A596
SMITH, Linda T., Director Human Resources, Clay County Hospital, Ashland, AL, p. A15
SMITH, Linda V., Vice President Human Resources, Central Florida Regional Hospital, Sanford, FL, p. A142
SMITH, Lori, Chief Financial Officer, North Big Horn Hospital District, Lovell, WY, p. A716
SMITH, Lorie, Director Human Resources, Nason Hospital, Roaring Spring, PA, p. A549
SMITH, Lorraine, Supervisory Human Resource Specialist, Chinle Comprehensive Health Care Facility, Chinle, AZ, p. A30
SMITH, Marisa, Director, Tomball Regional Medical Center, Tomball, TX, p. A648
SMITH, Mark, M.D. Chief Medical Officer, Methodist Richardson Medical Center, Richardson, TX, p. A638
SMITH, Mark, Director Human Resources, Providence Sacred Heart Medical Center & Children's Hospital, Spokane, WA, p. A685
SMITH, Mark T., CPA, President, Fort Hamilton Hospital, Hamilton, OH, p. A491
SMITH, Marsh, Manager Health Information, University Behavioral Health of Denton, Denton, TX, p. A608
SMITH, Marshall E., Chief Executive Officer, Regency Hospital of Minneapolis, Golden Valley, MN, p. A339
SMITH, Martha, Chief Executive Officer, Kapiolani Medical Center for Women & Children, Honolulu, HI, p. A168
SMITH, Martha M., R.N. Chief Nursing Officer, Park Plaza Hospital, Houston, TX, p. A621
SMITH, Mary Clare, M.D. Medical Director, Western State Hospital, Staunton, VA, p. A673
SMITH, Mary Jo, Chief Human Resources Officer, University of Illinois Hospital & Health Sciences System, Chicago, IL, p. A185
SMITH, Marybeth
Director Human Resources, Saint Francis Hospital, Charleston, WV, p. A690
Director Human Resources, Thomas Memorial Hospital, South Charleston, WV, p. A695
SMITH, Matthew, M.D. Vice President Medical Affairs and Chief Medical Officer, Baylor Medical Center at Carrollton, Carrollton, TX, p. A600
SMITH, Megan, M.D. Chief Medical Staff, Community Memorial Hospital, Burke, SD, p. A567
SMITH, Melinda, Chief Information Systems, H. C. Watkins Memorial Hospital, Quitman, MS, p. A360
SMITH, Melissa, Controller, Select Specialty Hospital–Jackson, Jackson, MS, p. A355
SMITH, Melissa A., Deputy Director, Delaware Psychiatric Center, New Castle, DE, p. A117
SMITH, Michael, M.D. Vice President Medical Affairs, St. Joseph Mercy Oakland, Pontiac, MI, p. A328
SMITH, Michael K., D.O. Vice President Medical Affairs, McLaren Macomb, Mount Clemens, MI, p. A326
SMITH, Michelle, Coordinator Human Resources, Baton Rouge Rehabilitation Hospital, Baton Rouge, LA, p. A269
SMITH, Michelle, R.N. Chief Clinical Officer, Memorial Hospital, Colorado Springs, CO, p. A100
SMITH, Michelle T., R.N. Chief Nursing Officer, Greenville Memorial Hospital, Greenville, SC, p. A561
SMITH, Mickey, Chief Executive Officer, Oak Hill Hospital, Brooksville, FL, p. A123
SMITH, Mike
Chief Information Officer, Cape Coral Hospital, Cape Coral, FL, p. A123
Chief Information Officer, Gulf Coast Medical Center, Fort Myers, FL, p. A127
Chief Information Officer, Lee Memorial Hospital, Fort Myers, FL, p. A127
SMITH, Missy, Coordinator Human Resources, Scotland County Hospital, Memphis, MO, p. A372
SMITH, Nadine, Director Human Resources, Reeves County Hospital, Pecos, TX, p. A636
SMITH, Natalie R., R.N. Vice President Patient Care Services and Chief Nursing Officer, Portneuf Medical Center, Pocatello, ID, p. A175
SMITH, Neil, D.O., President, Fairview Hospital, Cleveland, OH, p. A484
SMITH, Nekisha, Director Health Information Systems, Riverland Medical Center, Ferriday, LA, p. A273
SMITH, Nicholas T., Chief Executive Officer, Palm Springs General Hospital, Hialeah, FL, p. A128
SMITH, Norine, Chief Executive Officer, U. S. Public Health Service Indian Hospital, Cass Lake, MN, p. A336
SMITH, Oliver, President and Chief Executive Officer, Paris Community Hospital, Paris, IL, p. A197
SMITH, Pam, Chief Nursing Officer, Reliant Rehabilitation Hospital North Texas, Richardson, TX, p. A638
SMITH, Patricia, Chief Nursing Officer, Oconee Memorial Hospital, Seneca, SC, p. A564
SMITH, Patrick, M.D. Chief Medical Officer, Arrowhead Hospital, Glendale, AZ, p. A32
SMITH, Paula
Chief Information Officer, Beaumont Hospital – Taylor, Taylor, MI, p. A331
Vice President Information Services and Chief Information Officer, Beaumont Hospital – Trenton, Trenton, MI, p. A331
Senior Vice President Chief Information Officer, Beaumont Hospital – Wayne, Wayne, MI, p. A332
Leader Information Services and Chief Information Officer, Beaumont Hospital–Dearborn, Dearborn, MI, p. A317
SMITH, Peg, Vice President and Chief Nursing Officer, Chandler Regional Medical Center, Chandler, AZ, p. A30
SMITH, Peyton A., Chief Executive Officer, Appling Healthcare System, Baxley, GA, p. A152
SMITH, Phyllis, Vice President Human Resources, Northeastern Health System, Tahlequah, OK, p. A515
SMITH, Phyllis J., Associate Director, Birmingham Veterans Affairs Medical Center, Birmingham, AL, p. A16
SMITH, Randall, Executive Vice President, Jackson Park Hospital and Medical Center, Chicago, IL, p. A182
SMITH, Rebecca, Chief Operating Officer and Vice President, Caldwell Memorial Hospital, Lenoir, NC, p. A464
SMITH, Rebekah, R.N., President and Chief Executive Officer, St. Joseph Mercy Port Huron, Port Huron, MI, p. A328
SMITH, Renee, M.D. Chief Medical Staff, Langlade Hospital, Antigo, WI, p. A697


**A972** Index of Health Care Professionals 

Index of Health Care Professionals / Sobeck

Index of Health Care Professionals


SMITH, Rhonda, Director Human Resources, Shriners Hospitals for Children–Portland, Portland, OR, p. A525
SMITH, Rhonda E., R.N
Vice President Patient Care Services and Chief Nursing Officer, Union Hospital, Terre Haute, IN, p. A220
Chief Nursing Officer, Union Hospital Clinton, Clinton, IN, p. A206
SMITH, Rich
Vice President Human Resources, Kaiser Foundation Hospital Westside Medical Center, Hillsboro, OR, p. A521
Vice President Human Resources, Kaiser Permanente Sunnyside Medical Center, Clackamas, OR, p. A520
SMITH, Richard C.
Senior Vice President and Chief Financial Officer, JFK Medical Center, Edison, NJ, p. A411
Senior Vice President Finance, Shore Rehabilitation Institute, Brick, NJ, p. A409
SMITH, Rick
Director Information Services, Cibola General Hospital, Grants, NM, p. A424
Chief Operating Officer, Health Central Hospital, Ocoee, FL, p. A137
Director Information Systems, Jamestown Regional Medical Center, Jamestown, TN, p. A579
Senior Vice President Human Resources and Chief Administrative Officer, Vail Valley Medical Center, Vail, CO, p. A109
SMITH, Robert M., M.D. Chief of Staff, VA San Diego Healthcare System, San Diego, CA, p. A87
SMITH, Robert T., M.D
Chief Medical Officer, Kettering Medical Center, Kettering, OH, p. A491
Chief Medical Officer, Sycamore Medical Center, Miamisburg, OH, p. A494
SMITH, Robin S., Chief Nursing Officer, Indiana University Health White Memorial Hospital, Monticello, IN, p. A216
SMITH, Rodney, President and Chief Executive Officer, Harrisburg Medical Center, Harrisburg, IL, p. A189
SMITH, Roy, Chief Financial Officer, Onslow Memorial Hospital, Jacksonville, NC, p. A463
SMITH, Ryan J., Administrator, Mayo Clinic Health System in Saint James, Saint James, MN, p. A346
SMITH, Ryan K., Chief Executive Officer, Memorial Hospital of Converse County, Douglas, WY, p. A716
SMITH, Scott M., Chief Executive Officer, Mercy Regional Medical Center, Ville Platte, LA, p. A286
SMITH, Sherry, Manager Human Resources, Dallas County Hospital, Perry, IA, p. A233
SMITH, Shirley M., Chief Financial Officer, Andalusia Regional Hospital, Andalusia, AL, p. A15
SMITH, Sid, Director Information Resources, Larned State Hospital, Larned, KS, p. A244
SMITH, Skip, Vice President Finance, Iredell Memorial Hospital, Statesville, NC, p. A469
SMITH, Stacy, R.N., Chief Executive Officer, Valir Rehabilitation Hospital, Oklahoma City, OK, p. A513
SMITH, Stephen, President, Selby General Hospital, Marietta, OH, p. A493
SMITH, Steve
Chief Financial Officer, CHI Albany Area Health, Albany, MN, p. A334
Assistant Vice President Finance, CHI St. Gabriel's Health, Little Falls, MN, p. A341
Chief Financial Officer, Kansas Heart Hospital, Wichita, KS, p. A252
SMITH, Steve, M.D. Chief of Staff, Providence Kodiak Island Medical Center, Kodiak, AK, p. A28
SMITH, Steven, Chief Information Officer, NorthShore University Health System, Evanston, IL, p. A187
SMITH, Steven L., Chief Executive Officer, Matagorda Regional Medical Center, Bay City, TX, p. A596
SMITH, Suzanne E., R.N. Chief Nursing Officer, San Juan Regional Medical Center, Farmington, NM, p. A424
SMITH, Tammy, Director Human Resources, St. Vincent Morrilton, Morrilton, AR, p. A48
SMITH, Teresa, Chief Financial Officer, Memorial Hospital, Carthage, IL, p. A180
SMITH, Terrance, M.D. Chairman Medical Staff, Sanford Clear Lake Medical Center, Clear Lake, SD, p. A568
SMITH, Thomas, M.D. Vice President Medical Affairs, Hutchinson Regional Medical Center, Hutchinson, KS, p. A242
SMITH, Thomas G., Administrator and Chief Executive Officer, Audubon County Memorial Hospital, Audubon, IA, p. A222
SMITH, Tiffany, Director Human Resources, Wellstone Regional Hospital, Jeffersonville, IN, p. A213
SMITH, Tim
Director Information Systems, Iroquois Memorial Hospital and Resident Home, Watseka, IL, p. A202
Senior Vice President and Chief Executive Officer, Sharp Memorial Hospital, San Diego, CA, p. A87
SMITH, Todd A., Chief Executive Officer, Aurora Charter Oak Hospital, Covina, CA, p. A59
SMITH, Tommy, Chief Executive Officer, Stroud Regional Medical Center, Stroud, OK, p. A515
SMITH, Tonya, President and Chief Executive Officer, Munson Healthcare Cadillac Hospital, Cadillac, MI, p. A315
SMITH, Tracy, Director Human Resources, Mercy St. Francis Hospital, Mountain View, MO, p. A373
SMITH, Trevor, Chief Management Information Services, Gunnison Valley Hospital, Gunnison, CO, p. A104
SMITH, Tripp, Chief Executive Officer, HEALTHSOUTH Rehabilitation Hospital, Largo, FL, p. A131
SMITH, Trisha, Chief Financial Officer, Mimbres Memorial Hospital, Deming, NM, p. A424
SMITH, Tyson, M.D. Chief Medical Officer, Haywood Regional Medical Center, Clyde, NC, p. A458
SMITH, Vicki, Director of Nursing, The Pavilion at Williamsburg Place, Williamsburg, VA, p. A674
SMITH, Vincent
Chief Information Officer, Elmhurst Hospital Center, NY, p. A439
Chief Information Officer, Queens Hospital Center, NY, p. A444
SMITH, Wayne T., Chairman, President and Chief Executive Officer, Community Health Systems, Inc., Franklin, TN, p. B35
SMITH, Wendell, Chief Operating Officer, St. James Behavioral Health Hospital, Gonzales, LA, p. A274
SMITH–HILL, Janet
Senior Vice President Human Resources, Novant Health Forsyth Medical Center, Winston–Salem, NC, p. A471
Senior Vice President Human Resources, Novant Health Presbyterian Medical Center, Charlotte, NC, p. A458
SMITH–ZUBA, Lorraina, R.N. Chief Nursing Officer, Porter Medical Center, Middlebury, VT, p. A660
SMITHERS, John, Network Specialist, River Hospital, Alexandria Bay, NY, p. A428
SMITHERS, Sandy, Director of Nursing, Wellstone Regional Hospital, Jeffersonville, IN, p. A213
SMITHHART, Paula, Director Human Resources, Coryell Memorial Hospital, Gatesville, TX, p. A616
SMITHSON, Tracey, Chief Nursing Officer, North Hills Hospital, North Richland Hills, TX, p. A634
SMOAK, Tom, Administrator, McLeod Medical Center–Darlington, Darlington, SC, p. A560
SMOCK, Tait, Manager Information Systems, Pella Regional Health Center, Pella, IA, p. A233
SMOCYNSKI, Nancy, Director Payroll, Personnel and Human Resources, Kindred Hospital–Pittsburgh, Oakdale, PA, p. A542
SMOKER, Bret, M.D. Clinical Director, PHS Santa Fe Indian Hospital, Santa Fe, NM, p. A426
SMOLIK, Chris, Chief Executive Officer, Niobrara Health and Life Center, Lusk, WY, p. A716
SMOOT, Steve, Administrator, Utah Valley Regional Medical Center, Provo, UT, p. A657
SMORRA, Colleen, Assistant Administrator, Hackensack University Medical Center at Pascack Valley, Westwood, NJ, p. A420
SMOTHERS, Carol, M.D. Chief of Staff, Pointe Coupee General Hospital, New Roads, LA, p. A283
SMOTHERS, Margaret Shawn, Administrator, Kenmare Community Hospital, Kenmare, ND, p. A475
SMOTHERS, Mark, M.D. Chief Medical Officer, University of Mississippi Medical Center Holmes County, Lexington, MS, p. A356
SMOTHERS, Stephen, Director Information Systems, Medical Center Enterprise, Enterprise, AL, p. A19
SMOTHESS, Kevin, M.D. Vice President Chief Medical Officer, Shady Grove Adventist Hospital, Rockville, MD, p. A300
SNAPP, Jeremy, Director Information Systems, Lindsborg Community Hospital, Lindsborg, KS, p. A245
SNAPP, Richard, Chief Financial Officer, Caverna Memorial Hospital, Horse Cave, KY, p. A258
SNAPP, III, William R.
Vice President and Chief Financial Officer, Ephraim McDowell Fort Logan Hospital, Stanford, KY, p. A266
Vice President Finance and Chief Financial Officer, Ephraim McDowell Regional Medical Center, Danville, KY, p. A256
SNAVELY, Gretchen, Director Human Resources, Holton Community Hospital, Holton, KS, p. A242
SNEAD, Raymond A., Chief Executive Officer and Administrator, South Georgia Medical Center, Valdosta, GA, p. A166
SNEAD, Jr., Raymond A., FACHE Interim Chief Financial Officer, South Georgia Medical Center, Valdosta, GA, p. A166
SNEATH, Roger, Chief Financial Officer, Memorial Medical Center – Neillsville, Neillsville, WI, p. A707
SNEDEGAR, Michael, Chief Financial Officer, Bourbon Community Hospital, Paris, KY, p. A264
SNEED, Farron, FACHE, Chief Executive Officer, Lovelace Westside Hospital, Albuquerque, NM, p. A422
SNEEN, Tina, Administrator, Anoka–Metropolitan Regional Treatment Center, Anoka, MN, p. A334
SNELGROVE, Steven C., President, Howard County General Hospital, Columbia, MD, p. A297
SNELL, Peggy, Chief Finance Officer, Cherry County Hospital, Valentine, NE, p. A398
SNENK, Don, Chief Financial Officer, Mercy Fitzgerald Hospital, Darby, PA, p. A532
SNIDER, Charles, Vice President Human Resources, Oak Hill Hospital, Brooksville, FL, p. A123
SNIDER, Cheryl, Director Human Resources, St. Vincent General Hospital District, Leadville, CO, p. A106
SNIDER, Glenn R., M.D., Interim Director, Louis A. Johnson Veterans Affairs Medical Center, Clarksburg, WV, p. A690
SNIDER, Tim, Senior Vice President and Chief Financial Officer, Upper Valley Medical Center, Troy, OH, p. A499
SNIDER, Timothy, Manager Information Systems, Fannin Regional Hospital, Blue Ridge, GA, p. A152
SNIDERMAN, Howard, Chief Operating Officer, Fairfield Medical Center, Lancaster, OH, p. A491
SNIPES, Rob
Chief Information Officer, Optim Medical Center – Jenkins, Millen, GA, p. A161
Chief Information Officer, Optim Medical Center – Screven, Sylvania, GA, p. A165
SNODGRASS, Liz, Chief Financial Officer, Trigg County Hospital, Cadiz, KY, p. A255
SNOOK, Joel, Chief Financial Officer, Westchester General Hospital, Miami, FL, p. A135
SNOW, David, Area Information Officer, Kaiser Permanente Woodland Hills Medical Center, CA, p. A70
SNOW, Dorothy, M.D. Chief of Staff, Veterans Affairs Maryland Health Care System–Baltimore Division, Baltimore, MD, p. A295
SNOW, Jason T., Director People Services, HSHS St. Elizabeth's Hospital, Belleville, IL, p. A179
SNOW, John, Vice President Ancillary and Support Services, Iredell Memorial Hospital, Statesville, NC, p. A469
SNOW, Meldon L., Chief Executive Officer, Logan County Hospital, Oakley, KS, p. A247
SNOW, Ryan, Director Human Resources, Habersham Medical Center, Demorest, GA, p. A156
SNOWDON, Susan, Director Information Technology, Four Winds Hospital, Saratoga Springs, NY, p. A450
SNYDER, Alice, Vice President, Chief Nursing Officer, OSF St. Mary Medical Center, Galesburg, IL, p. A188
SNYDER, Bobby, Chief Executive Officer, Specialty Hospital of Midwest City, Midwest City, OK, p. A510
SNYDER, David, M.D. Chief of Staff, DeKalb Medical at Downtown Decatur, Decatur, GA, p. A155
SNYDER, David, Chief Information Officer and Vice President Information Technology, Ellis Hospital, Schenectady, NY, p. A450
SNYDER, Jeffrey, Chief Executive Officer, Pocono Medical Center, East Stroudsburg, PA, p. A533
SNYDER, John, Executive Vice President and Chief Operating Officer, Carle Foundation Hospital, Urbana, IL, p. A202
SNYDER, Kristi, Vice President Human Resources, Charleston Area Medical Center, Charleston, WV, p. A690
SNYDER, Kristy, Director Human Resources, Fulton County Health Center, Wauseon, OH, p. A500
SNYDER, Leah, Director Health Information Services, Loring Hospital, Sac City, IA, p. A234
SNYDER, Mary E., Chief Operations Officer, Montrose Memorial Hospital, Montrose, CO, p. A107
SNYDER, Matthew, R.N. Director of Nursing, Johnson County Hospital, Tecumseh, NE, p. A398
SNYDER, Norman, M.D. Medical Director, Vantage Point of Northwest Arkansas, Fayetteville, AR, p. A44
SNYDER, Phyllis, Chief Nursing Officer, AHMC Anaheim Regional Medical Center, Anaheim, CA, p. A53
SNYDER, R. Brad, Chief Operating Officer, Torrance State Hospital, Torrance, PA, p. A551
SNYDER, Renae, Chief Financial Officer, Sakakawea Medical Center, Hazen, ND, p. A474
SNYDER, Ron, Chief Financial Officer, OhioHealth Hardin Memorial Hospital, Kenton, OH, p. A491
SNYDER, Steve, Chief Financial Officer, Ohio Hospital for Psychiatry, Columbus, OH, p. A486
SNYDER, Tony, Administrator and Chief Executive Officer, Pomerene Hospital, Millersburg, OH, p. A494
SNYDER, Vicky, Chief Operating Officer and Chief Financial Officer, Medina Hospital, Medina, OH, p. A494
SOARES, Denise C., R.N., Executive Director, Harlem Hospital Center, New York, NY, p. A439
SOARES, Jair C., M.D., Executive Director, University of Texas Harris County Psychiatric Center, Houston, TX, p. A622
SOBECK, Brenda, Director of Human Resources, Jones Memorial Hospital, Wellsville, NY, p. A453

SOBER, Joe, Chief Executive Officer, Mercy Allen Hospital, Oberlin, OH, p. A495

SOBIECK, Bridget, Director of Nursing, Cook County North Shore Hospital, Grand Marais, MN, p. A339

SODERHOLM, Jon, President, Avera Heart Hospital of South Dakota, Sioux Falls, SD, p. A571

SODERLING, Marcia, R.N. Hospital Nurse Executive, Legacy Mount Hood Medical Center, Gresham, OR, p. A521

SOEKEN, Charles
   Director Information Technology, Providence Medical Center, Kansas City, KS, p. A243
   Director Information Technology, Saint John Hospital, Leavenworth, KS, p. A244

SOEKORO, Julie, Chief Financial Officer, Trinity Medical Center, Birmingham, AL, p. A17

SOGARD, Matt, Chief Executive Officer, Lee's Summit Medical Center, Lee's Summit, MO, p. A371

SOGLIN, David, Chief Medical Officer, La Rabida Children's Hospital, Chicago, IL, p. A182

SOHN, Steven, M.D. President Medical Staff, Dallas County Hospital, Perry, IA, p. A233

SOILEAU, D. Kirk, Chief Executive Officer, Natchitoches Regional Medical Center, Natchitoches, LA, p. A281

SOK, James E., FACHE,
   President and Chief Executive Officer, Sheltering Arms Hospital South, Midlothian, VA, p. A668
   President and Chief Executive Officer, Sheltering Arms Rehabilitation Hospital, Mechanicsville, VA, p. A668

SOKOLA, Thomas P., Chief Administrative Officer, Geisinger Medical Center, Danville, PA, p. A532

SOKOLOW, Norman J., Chairman and Chief Executive Officer, Cornerstone of Medical Arts Center Hospital, Fresh Meadows, NY, p. A433

SOLAIMAN, Shereen, Vice President Human Resources, OhioHealth Riverside Methodist Hospital, Columbus, OH, p. A486

SOLARE, Frank A., Chief Executive Officer, Kindred Hospital Northwest Indiana, Hammond, IN, p. A210

SOLAZZO, Mark J.
   Senior Vice President and Chief Operating Officer, Forest Hills Hospital, NY, p. A439
   Executive Vice President and Chief Operating Officer, Franklin Hospital, Valley Stream, NY, p. A452
   Regional Chief Operating Officer, Syosset Hospital, Syosset, NY, p. A451

SOLBERG, Bradley V., FACHE, President, OSF Saint James – John W. Albrecht Medical Center, Pontiac, IL, p. A198

SOLBERG, Don, M.D. Chief Medical Officer, Kittitas Valley Healthcare, Ellensburg, WA, p. A678

SOLCHER, Barry, M.D. Chief of Staff, The Physicians Centre Hospital, Bryan, TX, p. A599

SOLDO, Stephen, M.D. Chief Medical Officer, Saint Agnes Medical Center, Fresno, CA, p. A62

SOLER, Eddie, Chief Financial Officer, Florida Hospital, Orlando, FL, p. A138

SOLES, Jason, Manager Information Systems, St. James Mercy Health System, Hornell, NY, p. A435

SOLHEIM, John H., Chief Executive Officer, Cuyuna Regional Medical Center, Crosby, MN, p. A337

SOLIE, Carol M., M.D. Chief Medical Officer, Wyoming Medical Center, Casper, WY, p. A715

SOLIMAN, Russell
   System Manager Client Services and Management Information Services, Presence Saint Joseph Medical Center, Joliet, IL, p. A192
   Director Information Services, Presence St. Mary's Hospital, Kankakee, IL, p. A192

SOLIMAN, Shawn, Manager Information Technology, OSF Saint Paul Medical Center, Mendota, IL, p. A194

SOLIN, Andrea, Chief Financial Officer, Lovelace Rehabilitation Hospital, Albuquerque, NM, p. A422

SOLINSKI, Ruth, Senior Director Human Resources, UP Health System–Marquette, Marquette, MI, p. A325

SOLIS, Gloria, R.N. Chief Operating Officer and Chief Nursing Officer, Saint Luke's East Hospital, Lee's Summit, MO, p. A371

SOLIVAN, Jose E.
   Chief Financial Officer, Hospital Menonita De Cayey, Cayey, PR, p. A720
   Chief Financial Officer, Mennonite General Hospital, Aibonito, PR, p. A719

SOLIZ, Mindy, Director Human Resources, CHRISTUS Spohn Hospital Alice, Alice, TX, p. A590

SOLLENBERGER, Donna K., Executive Vice President and Chief Executive Officer, University of Texas Medical Branch, Galveston, TX, p. A615

SOLOM, Mike, Director Information Technology, Signature Psychiatric Hospital, Kansas City, MO, p. A370

SOLOMITA, Joy B., R.N. Vice President and Chief Nursing Officer, Florida Hospital Tampa, Tampa, FL, p. A144

SOLOMON, John, M.D., Director, South Carolina Department of Corrections Hospital, Columbia, SC, p. A559

SOLOMON, Oliver, M.D. Chief Medical Officer, Glendora Community Hospital, Glendora, CA, p. A64

SOLOMON, Tina, Executive Director Finance, Winter Haven Hospital, Winter Haven, FL, p. A148

SOLOMON–OWENS, Felicia, Director Human Resources, Fayette Medical Center, Fayette, AL, p. A19

SOLORIO, Roberta, Vice President, Chief Human Resource Officer, Midland Memorial Hospital, Midland, TX, p. A632

SOLORZANO, Rosa, Interim Director Human Resources, Toppenish Community Hospital, Toppenish, WA, p. A686

SOLOW, Jodie Sartor, Director Human Resources, Chatham Hospital, Siler City, NC, p. A468

SOLTIS, Les, Director – Human Resources, St. Francis Hospital, Federal Way, WA, p. A679

SOLVERSON, Paul, Chief Information Officer, St. Luke's Lakeside Hospital, The Woodlands, TX, p. A647

SOMERVILLE, Jacqueline G., R.N. Senior Vice President for Patient Care Services and Chief Nursing Officer, Brigham and Women's Hospital, Boston, MA, p. A303

SOMERVILLE, Susan, R.N., President, Mount Sinai Beth Israel, New York, NY, p. A442

SOMMERS, Belinda, Chief Information Officer, Lake Charles Memorial Hospital, Lake Charles, LA, p. A278

SOMMERS, Dorene M., Associate Director Patient Care Services, Erie Veterans Affairs Medical Center, Erie, PA, p. A534

SOMMERS, Vickie, Director Business Office, Wellstone Regional Hospital, Jeffersonville, IN, p. A213

SONATORE, Carol, D.O. Medical Director, HEALTHSOUTH Rehabilitation Hospital of Toms River, Toms River, NJ, p. A419

SONDAG, Timothy, Senior Nursing Officer, Hopedale Medical Complex, Hopedale, IL, p. A191

SONDERMAN, Betty, Manager Human Resources, Ridgeview Institute, Smyrna, GA, p. A164

SONDERMAN, Thomas, M.D. Vice President and Chief Medical Officer, Columbus Regional Hospital, Columbus, IN, p. A206

SONEL, Ali, M.D. Chief of Staff, Veterans Affairs Pittsburgh Healthcare System, Pittsburgh, PA, p. A547

SONENREICH, Steven D., President and Chief Executive Officer, Mount Sinai Medical Center, Miami Beach, FL, p. A135

SONG, Daniel, Chief Financial Officer, Monterey Park Hospital, Monterey Park, CA, p. A76

SONGER, Lucille, Chief Nursing Officer, Athol Memorial Hospital, Athol, MA, p. A302

SONGY, David, President and Chief Executive Officer, Saint Luke Institute, Silver Spring, MD, p. A300

SONNENBERG, Martha, M.D. Chief of Staff, Southern California Hospital at Culver City, Culver City, CA, p. A59

SONNENBERG, Stephanie
   Director Information Technology, ProMedica Bixby Hospital, Adrian, MI, p. A314
   Director Information Technology, ProMedica Herrick Hospital, Tecumseh, MI, p. A331

SONNENBERG, William, M.D. President Medical Staff, Titusville Area Hospital, Titusville, PA, p. A550

SONNENSCHEIN, Silvia, M.D. Chief of Staff, Kohala Hospital, Kohala, HI, p. A170

SONTZ, Jennifer
   Director Human Resources, Evansville Psychiatric Children Center, Evansville, IN, p. A208
   Director Human Resources, Evansville State Hospital, Evansville, IN, p. A208

SOOHOO, Richard, Chief Financial Officer, Sutter Medical Center, Sacramento, Sacramento, CA, p. A85

SOPER, Brent, Chief Financial Officer, San Joaquin Community Hospital, Bakersfield, CA, p. A55

SOPIARZ, Ed, Chief Financial Officer, University Behavioral Health of Denton, Denton, TX, p. A608

SOPKO, Joseph A., M.D. Chief Medical Officer, St. Vincent Charity Medical Center, Cleveland, OH, p. A485

SOPT, Michael, M.D. Chief of Staff, Brooks County Hospital, Quitman, GA, p. A162

SORBELLO, Bud, Director Management Information Systems, New York–Presbyterian/Hudson Valley Hospital, Cortlandt Manor, NY, p. A432

SORENSEN, Bonny
   Chief Financial Officer, Wadley Regional Medical Center, Texarkana, TX, p. A647
   Chief Financial Officer, Wadley Regional Medical Center at Hope, Hope, AR, p. A45

SORENSEN, Damon
   Chief Financial Officer, McLaren Bay Region, Bay City, MI, p. A315
   Chief Financial Officer, McLaren Bay Special Care, Bay City, MI, p. A315

SORENSEN, Shannon, Chief Executive Officer, Brown County Hospital, Ainsworth, NE, p. A389

SORENSON Jr., Charles W., M.D., President and Chief Executive Officer, Intermountain Healthcare, Inc., Salt Lake City, UT, p. B74

SORENSON, Chris
   Chief Information Officer, Sheltering Arms Hospital South, Midlothian, VA, p. A668
   Chief Information Officer, Sheltering Arms Rehabilitation Hospital, Mechanicsville, VA, p. A668

SORENSON, Dennis, Supervisor Information Technology, South Haven Health System, South Haven, MI, p. A330

SORENSON, Ed, Vice President Finance and Chief Financial Officer, Community Hospital of San Bernardino, San Bernardino, CA, p. A86

SORENSON, Eric C., Chief Financial Officer, Veterans Affairs Loma Linda Healthcare System, Loma Linda, CA, p. A68

SORENSON, Euretta, R.N. Chief Nursing Officer, CentraCare Health–Monticello, Monticello, MN, p. A343

SORENSON, Tawnya, Director of Nursing, Kittson Memorial Healthcare Center, Hallock, MN, p. A340

SOREY, Sharon D., R.N., Administrator, Mercy Hospital Paris, Paris, AR, p. A49

SORG, Jamie, Chief Information Officer and Information Security Officer, Blanchard Valley Hospital, Findlay, OH, p. A490

SOROKO, Theresa, M.D. Chief Medical Officer, Hackensack University Medical Center Mountainside, Montclair, NJ, p. A414

SORRELL, Rachel, Chief Financial Officer, Tsehootsooi Medical Center, Fort Defiance, AZ, p. A31

SORRELL, Sr., Ralph W., Chief Financial Officer, Adena Greenfield Medical Center, Greenfield, OH, p. A490

SOSA, Phillip, Chief Financial Officer, University Behavioral Health of El Paso, El Paso, TX, p. A611

SOSA–GUERRERO, Sandra, Chief Executive Officer, Larkin Community Hospital, South Miami, FL, p. A143

SOSTMAN, Dirk, M.D. Executive Vice President, Chief Medical Officer and Chief Academic Officer, Houston Methodist Hospital, Houston, TX, p. A620

SOTERAKIS, Jack, M.D. Executive Vice President Medical Affairs, St. Francis Hospital, Roslyn, NY, p. A449

SOTO, Ciria, Director Human Resources, Sonora Behavioral Health Hospital, Tucson, AZ, p. A40

SOTO, Itza, MSN Nursing Executive, Ashford Presbyterian Community Hospital, San Juan, PR, p. A723

SOTO, Juan Carlos, Director Information Systems, Hospital San Carlos Borromeo, Moca, PR, p. A722

SOTO, Manuel Ramirez, M.D. Medical Director, Hospital Metropolitano Dr. Tito Mattei, Yauco, PR, p. A724

SOTOMAYOR, Eduardo, Executive Director, Caribbean Medical Center, Fajardo, PR, p. A721

SOTOS, Steven, M.D. President Medical Staff, LifeCare Hospitals of Pittsburgh, Pittsburgh, PA, p. A546

SOTTILE, Frank, M.D. Chief Medical Officer, Crittenton Hospital Medical Center, Rochester, MI, p. A328

SOUDERS, Stuart, Chief, Human Resources, William S. Middleton Memorial Veterans Hospital, Madison, WI, p. A704

SOUKUP, Paul, Chief Financial Officer, St. Luke Community Healthcare, Ronan, MT, p. A386

SOULE, Joyce M., R.N. Chief Nursing Officer, Wesley Medical Center, Wichita, KS, p. A253

SOURBEER, Jay C., Commanding Officer, Robert E. Bush Naval Hospital, Twentynine Palms, CA, p. A95

SOUTHARD, Suzanne, Director Finance, Community Hospital–Fairfax, Fairfax, MO, p. A367

SOUTHERN, Joel, MSN, Chief Executive Officer, Merit Health Northwest Mississippi, Clarksdale, MS, p. A351

SOUTHERS, Nancy J., Vice President and Chief Financial Officer, The HSC Pediatric Center, Washington, DC, p. A120

SOUTHWICK, Bill, R.N. Chief Nursing Officer, Mountain Vista Medical Center, Mesa, AZ, p. A33

SOUTHWORTH, Scott, M.D. Medical Director, South Davis Community Hospital, Bountiful, UT, p. A654

SOUZA, Darlene, Vice President, St. Joseph Health Services of Rhode Island, North Providence, RI, p. A555

SOUZA, Greg, Vice President Human Resources, Lucile Salter Packard Children's Hospital Stanford, Palo Alto, CA, p. A80

SOUZA, Jim, Chief Medical Officer, St. Luke's Regional Medical Center, Boise, ID, p. A173

SOUZA, Liz, Coordinator Nursing Services, Atascadero State Hospital, Atascadero, CA, p. A54

SOVETSKHY, Ed, Director Information Services, Portsmouth Regional Hospital, Portsmouth, NH, p. A408

SOWDERS, Dale, President and Chief Executive Officer, Holland Hospital, Holland, MI, p. A322

Index of Health Care Professionals / Spinharney

Index of Health Care Professionals


SOWELL, Ronald G.
Executive Vice President, Commonwealth Regional Specialty Hospital, Bowling Green, KY, p. A254
Executive Vice President, Medical Center at Bowling Green, Bowling Green, KY, p. A254
Executive Vice President, Medical Center at Franklin, Franklin, KY, p. A257
Chief Financial Officer, Medical Center at Scottsville, Scottsville, KY, p. A266
SOWELL, Vincent, Chief Nursing Officer, Otto Kaiser Memorial Hospital, Kenedy, TX, p. A625
SOWERS, Chuck, Vice President Finance and Chief Financial Officer, Mercy Gilbert Medical Center, Gilbert, AZ, p. A31
SOWERS, Kevin W., MSN, President, Duke University Hospital, Durham, NC, p. A459
SPACK, Paula, R.N. Vice President Nursing, Punxsutawney Area Hospital, Punxsutawney, PA, p. A548
SPACKMAN, Jared, Chief Financial Officer, Davis Hospital and Medical Center, Layton, UT, p. A655
SPACONE, Alan, M.D. Chief Medical Officer, Tuba City Regional Health Care Corporation, Tuba City, AZ, p. A38
SPACONE, Celia, M.D. Director Operations, Buffalo Psychiatric Center, Buffalo, NY, p. A430
SPADE, Ann M., Interim Chief Executive Officer, Carlisle Regional Medical Center, Carlisle, PA, p. A531
SPADONI, Robert S., Vice President of Hospital Operations, Rush Oak Park Hospital, Oak Park, IL, p. A196
SPAFFORD, Mark, Interim Chief Financial Officer, Bay Medical Center Sacred Heart Health System, Panama City, FL, p. A139
SPAHR, Kristen, Director of Marketing, DeSoto Memorial Hospital, Arcadia, FL, p. A121
SPAIN, Jeanine R., R.N. Vice President Patient and Support Services and Chief Nursing Officer, UnityPoint Health – Methodist Proctor, Peoria, IL, p. A198
SPAIN, Steve, Chief Operating Officer, Larned State Hospital, Larned, KS, p. A244
SPAIN–REMY, Claire, M.D. Senior Vice President, MultiCare Medical Associates, MultiCare Tacoma General Hospital, Tacoma, WA, p. A686
SPANBAUER, Lisa, Financial Program Supervisor, Winnebago Mental Health Institute, Winnebago, WI, p. A714
SPANGLER, Jason, Chief Operating Officer, Liberty Healthcare Systems, Bastrop, LA, p. A269
SPANGLER, Wendell J., M.D. Chief of Staff, Paulding County Hospital, Paulding, OH, p. A496
SPANN, Debbie, Director Human Resources, Morehouse General Hospital, Bastrop, LA, p. A269
SPANN, Lori, Director Human Resources, Iberia Medical Center, New Iberia, LA, p. A281
SPANO, Dennis, M.D. Medical Director, Mayo Clinic Health System in Lake City, Lake City, MN, p. A340
SPANO, Jason, Manager Information Technology, Prowers Medical Center, Lamar, CO, p. A106
SPARACINO, Michael, M.D. Chief Medical Staff, River's Edge Hospital and Clinic, Saint Peter, MN, p. A347
SPARE, John, Accountant, Parsons State Hospital and Training Center, Parsons, KS, p. A248
SPARGER, Kathy, R.N. Chief Nursing Officer, Baptist Health South Florida, South Miami Hospital, Miami, FL, p. A134
SPARKMAN, Dena C., FACHE, Community Chief Executive Officer, Whitesburg ARH Hospital, Whitesburg, KY, p. A266
SPARKMAN, Jill, Director Human Resources, Odessa Regional Medical Center, Odessa, TX, p. A635
SPARKS, Dennis, Vice President Human Resources, Saint Michael's Medical Center, Newark, NJ, p. A415
SPARKS, Gary R.
Administrator, CrossRidge Community Hospital, Wynne, AR, p. A52
Interim President, Lawrence Memorial Hospital, Walnut Ridge, AR, p. A51
SPARKS, Jason, Director, Human Resources, HEALTHSOUTH Rehabilitation Hospital at Drake, Cincinnati, OH, p. A483
SPARKS, Jennifer, Human Resources Generalist, Complex Care Hospital at Ridgelake, Sarasota, FL, p. A142
SPARKS, Lisa, R.N. Chief Nursing Officer and Vice President Patient Care Services, Indiana University Health West Hospital, Avon, IN, p. A204
SPARKS, Richard G., President and Chief Executive Officer, Appalachian Regional Healthcare System, Boone, NC, p. B10
SPARKS, Richard G., Chief Executive Officer, Watauga Medical Center, Boone, NC, p. A456
SPARKS, Rodney, M.D. Chief Staff, Down East Community Hospital, Machias, ME, p. A291
SPARKS, Wendy, Chief Operating Officer, North Colorado Medical Center, Greeley, CO, p. A104
SPARLING, Nicki, Manager Human Resources, Major Hospital, Shelbyville, IN, p. A220
SPARPANA, Eileen, Director Finance, Dickinson County Healthcare System, Iron Mountain, MI, p. A322
SPARROW, Francis D., M.D. Medical Director, Philhaven, Mount Gretna, PA, p. A541
SPARTZ, Dale A., Chief Human Resources Officer, University of Utah Health Care – Hospital and Clinics, Salt Lake City, UT, p. A659
SPARZO, John, M.D. Vice President Medical Affairs, Hendricks Regional Health, Danville, IN, p. A207
SPATH, Deborah, R.N. Associate Director Patient and Nurses Services, Albany Stratton Veterans Affairs Medical Center, Albany, NY, p. A428
SPEAK, Brent, Chief of Staff, Northeast Regional Medical Center, Kirksville, MO, p. A371
SPEARE, Mark
Senior Associate Director Human Resources, Ronald Reagan UCLA Medical Center, Los Angeles, CA, p. A72
Senior Associate Director Patient Relations and Human Resources, Santa Monica–UCLA Medical Center and Orthopaedic Hospital, Santa Monica, CA, p. A92
SPEARMAN, John, President and Chief Operating Officer, Laurel Regional Hospital, Laurel, MD, p. A299
SPEARS, David, D.O. Chief of Staff, Selby General Hospital, Marietta, OH, p. A493
SPEARS, Kevin, Chief Executive Officer, HEALTHSOUTH Rehabilitation Hospital of Memphis, Memphis, TN, p. A583
SPEARS, LaLana, Supervisor Accounting, Claremore Indian Hospital, Claremore, OK, p. A505
SPEARS, Michael, Human Resource Leader, St. Anthony Shawnee Hospital, Shawnee, OK, p. A515
SPEAS, Ryan, Director Finance, Livingston HealthCare, Livingston, MT, p. A385
SPEASE, Dorothy, Manager Business Office, Douglas County Memorial Hospital, Armour, SD, p. A567
SPECK, Michelle, Senior Vice President Human Resources, USMD Hospital at Fort Worth, Fort Worth, TX, p. A614
SPECK, Michelle A.
Vice President Human Resources, UPMC Altoona, Altoona, PA, p. A528
Vice President Human Resources, UPMC Bedford Memorial, Everett, PA, p. A534
SPEECH, Thomas, Ph.D., Director, Winnebago Mental Health Institute, Winnebago, WI, p. A714
SPEELMAN, Steven, Director Information Systems, UVA Culpeper Hospital, Culpeper, VA, p. A664
SPEER, Kevin, Chief Executive Officer, Hendricks Regional Health, Danville, IN, p. A207
SPEER–SMITH, Carol, R.N. Chief Nursing Officer, Oroville Hospital, Oroville, CA, p. A79
SPEES, M. Shane, President and Chief Executive Officer, North Mississippi Health Services, Inc., Tupelo, MS, p. B98
SPEICHER, Larry, Chief Executive Officer, Kearney Regional Medical Center, Kearney, NE, p. A393
SPEIER, Ryan, Vice President Administration, KVC Prairie Ridge Psychiatric Hospital, Kansas City, KS, p. A243
SPEIGHT, Becky, Chief Financial Officer, Lake Pointe Medical Center, Rowlett, TX, p. A639
SPEIGHT, Marianne, Vice President Information System and Chief Information Officer, Cincinnati Children's Hospital Medical Center, Cincinnati, OH, p. A482
SPEIGHTS, Shane, M.D. Vice President Medical Affairs, St. Bernards Medical Center, Jonesboro, AR, p. A46
SPELL, Kenneth R., Vice President Operations, Baptist Health South Florida, Homestead Hospital, Homestead, FL, p. A129
SPELLMAN, Warren K., Chief Executive Officer, Grady Memorial Hospital, Chickasha, OK, p. A505
SPELLS–WILSON, Debbie, R.N. Chief Nursing Officer, Trinity Hospital of Augusta, Augusta, GA, p. A151
SPENCE, Andre, Chief Medical Staff, Sanford Bagley Medical Center, Bagley, MN, p. A335
SPENCE, Ben
Chief Financial Officer, Gulf Coast Medical Center, Fort Myers, FL, p. A127
Chief Financial Officer, Lee Memorial Hospital, Fort Myers, FL, p. A127
SPENCE, Karie, Director Human Resources, Miller County Hospital, Colquitt, GA, p. A154
SPENCE, Karla, Director of Nursing, St. Andrew's Health Center, Bottineau, ND, p. A472
SPENCE, Monte, Chief Operating Officer, Rehabilitation Hospital of Indiana, Indianapolis, IN, p. A212
SPENCE, Sheldon, Director of Revenue Cycle, IT, Memorial Hospital of Texas County, Guymon, OK, p. A507
SPENCE, Terri
Chief Information Officer, Bon Secours Maryview Medical Center, Portsmouth, VA, p. A670
Chief Information Officer, Bon Secours St. Mary's Hospital, Richmond, VA, p. A671
Vice President Information Services, Mary Immaculate Hospital, Newport News, VA, p. A669
SPENCE, William, Director, Roseland Community Hospital, Chicago, IL, p. A184
SPENCER, Jill, Chief Human Resource Officer, The Memorial Hospital at Craig, Craig, CO, p. A101
SPENCER, Jim, Director Information System, McLeod Health Cheraw, Cheraw, SC, p. A558
SPENCER, Marianne, R.N. Vice President Operations and Chief Operating Officer, Edward Hospital, Naperville, IL, p. A195
SPENCER, Marie, Chief Nursing Officer and Senior Administrator, Burke Rehabilitation Hospital, White Plains, NY, p. A454
SPENCER, Mark, D.O. Chief of Staff, North Canyon Medical Center, Gooding, ID, p. A174
SPENCER, Mike, Chief Information Officer, Henry County Hospital, New Castle, IN, p. A217
SPENCER, Misti, Director Inpatient Services, Selby General Hospital, Marietta, OH, p. A493
SPENCER, Scott, Chief Financial Officer, South Shore Hospital, Chicago, IL, p. A184
SPENCER, Susan, Chief Financial Officer, Samaritan Memorial Hospital, Macon, MO, p. A372
SPENCER, Todd, M.D. Chief Medical Staff, Adventist Medical Center–Reedley, Reedley, CA, p. A83
SPENNER, Marilyn, R.N. Vice President Patient Care Services, Wheaton Franciscan Healthcare – St. Francis, Milwaukee, WI, p. A707
SPENST, Brett, Chief Executive Officer, Littleton Adventist Hospital, Littleton, CO, p. A106
SPERBER–WEISS, Doreen, Ph.D. Chief Nursing Officer, Greystone Park Psychiatric Hospital, Morris Plains, NJ, p. A414
SPERLING, Louis J., Vice President Human Resources, Rhode Island Hospital, Providence, RI, p. A556
SPERLING, Walter, M.D. Medical Director, Ellenville Regional Hospital, Ellenville, NY, p. A433
SPERRING, Jeff, M.D., Chief Executive Officer, Seattle Children's Hospital, Seattle, WA, p. A683
SPERRING, Kim
Administrator, LifeCare Hospitals of Pittsburgh, Pittsburgh, PA, p. A546
Administrator, LifeCare Hospitals of Pittsburgh – Monroeville, Monroeville, PA, p. A540
SPEZIA, Anthony, President and Chief Executive Officer, Covenant Health, Knoxville, TN, p. B43
SPICER, Charles, President and Chief Executive Officer, OU Medical Center, Oklahoma City, OK, p. A512
SPICER, Joan G., R.N. Chief Nursing Officer, San Mateo Medical Center, San Mateo, CA, p. A90
SPICER, Michael J., President and Chief Executive Officer, St. Joseph's Medical Center, Yonkers, NY, p. A454
SPICER, Sam, M.D. Vice President Medical Affairs, New Hanover Regional Medical Center, Wilmington, NC, p. A470
SPIDLE, Tara, Chief Financial Officer, Decatur County Hospital, Leon, IA, p. A231
SPIEGEL, Kevin M., FACHE, President and Chief Executive Officer, Erlanger Health System, Chattanooga, TN, p. B54
SPIEGEL, Kevin M., FACHE, Chief Executive Officer, Erlanger Medical Center, Chattanooga, TN, p. A575
SPIER, Deborah, Administrator, Oceans Behavioral Hospital of Greater New Orleans, Kenner, LA, p. A276
SPIER, Scott A., M.D. Senior Vice President Medical Affairs, Mercy Medical Center, Baltimore, MD, p. A294
SPIGEL, Michael, Executive Vice President & Chief Operating Officer, Brooks Rehabilitation Hospital, Jacksonville, FL, p. A129
SPIGNER, Jason
Vice President Human Resources, Advocate Condell Medical Center, Libertyville, IL, p. A192
Vice President Human Resources, Advocate Good Shepherd Hospital, Barrington, IL, p. A179
SPIKE, Jennifer, Director Human Resources, St. James Mercy Health System, Hornell, NY, p. A435
SPILLERS, David S., Chief Executive Officer, Huntsville Hospital, Huntsville, AL, p. A21
SPILLERS, David S., Chief Executive Officer, Huntsville Hospital Health System, Huntsville, AL, p. B72
SPILSBURY, Lauren, R.N. Vice President for Patient Care Services, Redlands Community Hospital, Redlands, CA, p. A83
SPINA, Lori, Vice President Human Resources, Good Samaritan Hospital Medical Center, West Islip, NY, p. A453
SPINA, Patricia, R.N. Director of Nursing, Runnells Center for Rehabilitation and Healthcare, Berkeley Heights, NJ, p. A409
SPINALE, Joseph W., D.O. Senior Vice President and Chief Medical Officer, Kent County Memorial Hospital, Warwick, RI, p. A556
SPINHARNEY, Sarah, Senior Vice President, Baptist Medical Center, San Antonio, TX, p. A640

Index of Health Care Professionals

Index of Health Care Professionals / Spitser

SPITSER, Christy
Vice President Finance and Business Development, Saint Joseph – London, London, KY, p. A260
Vice President Finance, Saint Joseph Berea, Berea, KY, p. A254
SPIVAK, Natalie, Director Information Services, Oaklawn Hospital, Marshall, MI, p. A325
SPIVEY, Amy, Chief Medical Officer, McCullough–Hyde Memorial Hospital/TriHealth, Oxford, OH, p. A496
SPIVEY, Courtney, Chief Nursing Officer, Hardin County General Hospital, Rosiclare, IL, p. A200
SPIVEY, David A., President and Chief Executive Officer, St. Mary Mercy Hospital, Livonia, MI, p. A325
SPIVEY, Sue, Administrator, Irwin County Hospital, Ocilla, GA, p. A162
SPOELMA, Susan G., MSN Chief Nursing Officer, Healdsburg District Hospital, Healdsburg, CA, p. A64
SPOELMAN, Roger, Interim President and Chief Executive Officer, Mount Carmel St. Ann's, Westerville, OH, p. A500
SPONSLER, Betsy A., Chief Financial Officer, Valley Hospital Medical Center, Las Vegas, NV, p. A403
SPOON, Barry, M.D. Chief of Staff, Mercy St. Francis Hospital, Mountain View, MO, p. A373
SPOONER, Allan M., President, Sacred Heart Rehabilitation Institute, Milwaukee, WI, p. A706
SPORE, Larry, Chief Financial Officer, Lawrence County Memorial Hospital, Lawrenceville, IL, p. A192
SPRADLIN, John, Information Systems Director, Franklin Foundation Hospital, Franklin, LA, p. A274
SPRAGGINS, Tommy, Director Information Services, Russell Medical Center, Alexander City, AL, p. A15
SPRAGUE, F. Remington, M.D
Chief Medical Officer, Mercy Health Hackley Campus, Muskegon, MI, p. A326
Chief Medical Officer, Mercy Health, Mercy Campus, Muskegon, MI, p. A326
SPRAGUE, Sharon, Superintendent, Dorothea Dix Psychiatric Center, Bangor, ME, p. A288
SPRAKER, Larissa, Vice President Business Development and Chief Strategy Officer, Mercy Gilbert Medical Center, Gilbert, AZ, p. A31
SPRATLIN, Larry, Chief Financial Officer, Saint Thomas Rutherford Hospital, Murfreesboro, TN, p. A585
SPRATLING, Larry, M.D. Chief Medical Officer, Banner Baywood Medical Center, Mesa, AZ, p. A33
SPRAY, William R., Chief Executive Officer, Harton Regional Medical Center, Tullahoma, TN, p. A588
SPRENGEL, Julie, Chief Executive Officer, Providence Saint Joseph Medical Center, Burbank, CA, p. A56
SPRIGGS, Larry, Controller, HEALTHSOUTH Rehabilitation Institute of San Antonio, San Antonio, TX, p. A640
SPRING, Jason A., FACHE, Chief Executive Officer, North Valley Hospital, Whitefish, MT, p. A388
SPRING, Joni, R.N. Vice President Patient Care Services and Chief Nursing Officer, Elliot Hospital, Manchester, NH, p. A407
SPRINGATE, Brian, Interim Chief Operating Officer, Logan Regional Medical Center, Logan, WV, p. A692
SPRINGER, Amy, Medical Director, Webster County Community Hospital, Red Cloud, NE, p. A397
SPRINGER, David, M.D. President Medical Staff, Sanford Rock Rapids Medical Center, Rock Rapids, IA, p. A233
SPRINGER, Diane L., MS Chief Nursing Officer, Lutheran Hospital of Indiana, Fort Wayne, IN, p. A208
SPRINGER, Madge, Director Human Resources, Florida Hospital Waterman, Tavares, FL, p. A145
SPRINGER, Theresa, Chief Financial Officer, OSF Holy Family Medical Center, Monmouth, IL, p. A194
SPRINGFIELD, Rick, Vice President Human Resources, Piedmont Hospital, Atlanta, GA, p. A151
SPRINGMAN, Kathleen, Chief Nursing Officer, Berwick Hospital Center, Berwick, PA, p. A529
SPRINGMANN, Tressa
Vice President and Chief Information Officer, Levindale Hebrew Geriatric Center and Hospital, Baltimore, MD, p. A293
Vice President and Chief Information Officer, Northwest Hospital, Randallstown, MD, p. A299
SPRINKEL, George, Chief Financial Officer, Gateway Medical Center, Clarksville, TN, p. A576
SPROTT, Kendell R., JD, Chief Executive Officer, Matheny Medical and Educational Center, Peapack, NJ, p. A416
SPROUT, Merry, R.N. Chief Nursing Officer, Antelope Memorial Hospital, Neligh, NE, p. A394
SPROWL, Chris, M.D. Vice President, PeaceHealth St. Joseph Medical Center, Bellingham, WA, p. A676
SPRUYT, James, Chief Executive Officer, Cumberland Hall Hospital, Hopkinsville, KY, p. A258
SPUHLER, Richard, Chief Executive Officer, Brigham City Community Hospital, Brigham City, UT, p. A654
SPURGEON, Sharon A., Chief Executive Officer, Coalinga Regional Medical Center, Coalinga, CA, p. A58
SPYKERMAN, Connie, Chief Nursing Officer, Pelham Medical Center, Greer, SC, p. A562
SPYROW, Florence, Interim Chief Executive Officer, Hammond–Henry Hospital, Geneseo, IL, p. A189
SQUIRE, Patricia, Director Human Resources, Jerome Golden Center for Behavioral Health, Inc., West Palm Beach, FL, p. A147
SQUIRES, Danny
Chief Financial Officer, Wake Forest Baptist Health–Davie Medical Center, Mocksville, NC, p. A465
Vice President and Chief Financial Officer, Wake Forest Baptist Health–Lexington Medical Center, Lexington, NC, p. A464
SQUIRES, Elizabeth, Chief Nursing Officer, HealthSouth Rehabilitation Hospital of Tallahassee, Tallahassee, FL, p. A144
SQUIRES, Paula C., Senior Vice President, Chief Human Resources Officer, Baystate Medical Center, Springfield, MA, p. A311
SQUIRES, Teresa, R.N. Chief Nursing Officer, Lake District Hospital, Lakeview, OR, p. A522
SREBINSKI, Ron, Chief Financial Officer, Caro Community Hospital, Caro, MI, p. A316
SRIBNICK, Wayne, M.D. Senior Vice President and Chief Medical Officer, Providence Hospital, Columbia, SC, p. A559
SRIPADA, Subra
Senior Vice President and Chief Information Officer, Beaumont Hospital – Royal Oak, Royal Oak, MI, p. A328
Senior Vice President and Chief Information Officer, Beaumont Hospital – Troy, Troy, MI, p. A331
Senior Vice President and Chief Information Officer, Beaumont Hospital Grosse Pointe, Grosse Pointe, MI, p. A321
SRIVASTAVA, Mohit, M.D. Chief of Staff, Bunkie General Hospital, Bunkie, LA, p. A271
ST CLAIR, Jeffery M., President and Chief Executive Officer, Springhill Memorial Hospital, Mobile, AL, p. A22
ST PIERRE, Jay, Chief Financial Officer, North Florida Regional Medical Center, Gainesville, FL, p. A127
ST. CLAIR, Jeffery M., President and Chief Executive Officer, Springhill Memorial Hospital, Mobile, AL, p. A22
ST. LEGER, John, Chief Executive Officer, Select Specialty Hospital–Pittsburgh/UPMC, Pittsburgh, PA, p. A546
ST. ONGE, Donald, Chief Operating Officer, Day Kimball Hospital, Putnam, CT, p. A114
ST. PETER, Colette, Senior Manager Human Resources, Mercy Hospital Carthage, Carthage, MO, p. A365
ST. PIERRE, Fran, Chief Nursing Officer, Hood Memorial Hospital, Amite, LA, p. A268
STAATS, Annie, R.N. Director Nursing, Gove County Medical Center, Quinter, KS, p. A249
STABRYLA, Della, Director of Nursing, Ellwood City Hospital, Ellwood City, PA, p. A533
STACEY, Brian, Chief Financial Officer, Queens Hospital Center, NY, p. A444
STACEY, Susan, Chief Nursing Officer, Providence Sacred Heart Medical Center & Children's Hospital, Spokane, WA, p. A685
STACHOVSKY, Jeanne M., Director Human Resources, Slidell Memorial Hospital, Slidell, LA, p. A285
STACIE, Beverly, Director Human Resources, Clifton T. Perkins Hospital Center, Jessup, MD, p. A298
STACKHOUSE, Jenni, Chief Financial Officer, River Point Behavioral Health, Jacksonville, FL, p. A129
STACKHOUSE, Sharon, Assistant Administrator and Director Risk Management, Peachford Behavioral Health System, Atlanta, GA, p. A150
STACY, Doug, Director Information Technology, UP Health System–Marquette, Marquette, MI, p. A325
STADHEIM, Barbara, Chief Nursing Officer, West River Regional Medical Center, Hettinger, ND, p. A474
STADLER, James J., M.D. Associate Administrator Medical Services, Guam Memorial Hospital Authority, Tamuning, GU, p. A719
STADLER, Thomas, M.D. Vice President Medical Affairs and Chief Medical Officer, Madonna Rehabilitation Hospital, Lincoln, NE, p. A394
STADNYK, Sheldon, M.D., Interim Chief Executive Officer, Fairbanks Memorial Hospital, Fairbanks, AK, p. A28
STAFFORD, Tom, Chief Information Officer, Halifax Health Medical Center of Daytona Beach, Daytona Beach, FL, p. A125
STAFFORD, Walt, Director Information Technology, Chatuge Regional Hospital and Nursing Home, Hiawassee, GA, p. A158
STAGG, Kevin, Executive Vice President Finance and Chief Financial Officer, Christian Health Care Center, Wyckoff, NJ, p. A421
STAGGS, Nathan, Chief Executive Officer, Pauls Valley General Hospital, Pauls Valley, OK, p. A513
STAHL, Anthony, Vice President, Florida Hospital Heartland Medical Center, Sebring, FL, p. A143
STAHL, Daniel, M.D. Medical Director, Mayo Clinic Health System in Waseca, Waseca, MN, p. A348
STAHL, Daniel, D.O. Chief of Staff, Rush Memorial Hospital, Rushville, IN, p. A219
STAHL, Marlin G., M.D. Chief Medical Officer, Nebraska Medicine – Bellevue, Bellevue, NE, p. A390
STAHL, Ronald, M.D. Chief Medical Officer, Crouse Hospital, Syracuse, NY, p. A451
STAHL, Sherri, R.N. Senior Vice President for Hospital Services, Chambersburg Hospital, Chambersburg, PA, p. A531
STAHL, Steven J., Director Human Resources, Columbia County Health System, Dayton, WA, p. A678
STAHL, William D., Chief Operating Officer, Rooks County Health Center, Plainville, KS, p. A249
STAHLKUPPE, Robert F., M.D. Chief of Staff, Chatuge Regional Hospital and Nursing Home, Hiawassee, GA, p. A158
STAIGER, Tom, M.D. Medical Director, University of Washington Medical Center, Seattle, WA, p. A684
STAIGL, Chris, Chief Nursing Officer, TriStar Southern Hills Medical Center, Nashville, TN, p. A586
STALBAUM, Angela, R.N. Chief Nursing Officer, Seton Medical Center Austin, Austin, TX, p. A594
STALCUP, Connie, Manager Information Systems, Murphy Medical Center, Murphy, NC, p. A465
STALCUP, Linda, Chief Executive Officer, Stevens County Hospital, Hugoton, KS, p. A242
STALEY, Gerald, Director Human Resources, Adventist Bolingbrook Hospital, Bolingbrook, IL, p. A180
STALKER, Neil, M.D. Chief of Staff, Dukes Memorial Hospital, Peru, IN, p. A218
STALL, Kristi, Chief Human Resources Officer, Mahnomen Health Center, Mahnomen, MN, p. A341
STALLINGS, Jay, Chief Executive Officer, Washakie Medical Center, Worland, WY, p. A718
STALLINGS, Jennifer, Chief Clinical Officer, Kindred Hospital Indianapolis South, Greenwood, IN, p. A210
STALLINGS, Terry, M.D. Chief Medical Officer, West Florida Hospital, Pensacola, FL, p. A140
STALLWORTH, David, M.D. Chief of Staff, Monroe County Hospital, Monroeville, AL, p. A22
STALLWORTH, Monica, M.D. Chief of Staff, Western Maryland Hospital Center, Hagerstown, MD, p. A298
STALLWORTH, Terresa, M.D. Clinical Director, San Antonio State Hospital, San Antonio, TX, p. A642
STALNAKER, Avah, Chief Executive Officer, Stonewall Jackson Memorial Hospital, Weston, WV, p. A696
STALNAKER, Jeffrey, M.D. Vice President, Medical Affairs, Health First Cape Canaveral Hospital, Cocoa Beach, FL, p. A124
STALNAKER, Kevin P., CPA Chief Operating Officer, Stonewall Jackson Memorial Hospital, Weston, WV, p. A696
STAMAS, Peter, M.D. Vice President Medical Affairs, Ministry Saint Joseph's Hospital, Marshfield, WI, p. A705
STAMBAUGH, Lynn E., R.N., Chief Executive Officer, Sarah D. Culbertson Memorial Hospital, Rushville, IL, p. A200
STAMM, Pam, Chief Nursing Officer, Throckmorton County Memorial Hospital, Throckmorton, TX, p. A648
STAMOS, George D., M.D. Chief Medical Officer, Overland Park Regional Medical Center, Overland Park, KS, p. A248
STAMP, John, Director Information Services, Ellett Memorial Hospital, Appleton City, MO, p. A363
STAMPS, Debbie, Vice President, Chief Nursing Officer, Newark–Wayne Community Hospital, Newark, NY, p. A445
STANCILL, Linda, Vice President and Chief Financial Officer, St. Joseph Health System, Tawas City, MI, p. A331
STANDEFFER, Luke, Administrator, Northport Medical Center, Northport, AL, p. A23
STANDER, Paul, M.D. Chief Medical Officer, Banner Good Samaritan Medical Center, Phoenix, AZ, p. A34
STANDIFORD, Steven B., M.D. Chief of Staff, Eastern Regional Medical Center, Philadelphia, PA, p. A543
STANDLEE, Cynthia, R.N. Chief Nursing Officer, Estes Park Medical Center, Estes Park, CO, p. A103
STANDRIDGE, Debra K.
President, Wheaton Franciscan Healthcare – Elmbrook Memorial, Brookfield, WI, p. A698
President, Wheaton Franciscan Healthcare – St. Joseph's, Milwaukee, WI, p. A707
STANDRIDGE, Sonya, Chief Nursing Officer, Copper Basin Medical Center, Copperhill, TN, p. A576
STANEK, Janet, Executive Vice President, Stormont–Vail HealthCare, Topeka, KS, p. A251
STANFORD, Brian, Administrator, Burleson St. Joseph Health Center, Caldwell, TX, p. A599
STANFORD, Brion, Director Human Resources, Merit Health Biloxi, Biloxi, MS, p. A350
STANFORD, Tracy, Director Human Resources, Baylor All Saints Medical Center at Fort Worth, Fort Worth, TX, p. A613

A976 Index of Health Care Professionals

STEIN, Keith L., M.D
Chief Medical Officer, Baptist Medical Center Beaches, Jacksonville Beach, FL, p. A130
Senior Vice President Medical Affairs and Chief Medical Officer, Baptist Medical Center Jacksonville, Jacksonville, FL, p. A129
STEIN, Patrick, M.D. Clinical Director, Western New York Children's Psychiatric Center, West Seneca, NY, p. A454
STEIN, Paul, Chief Operating Officer, MaineGeneral Medical Center, Augusta, ME, p. A288
STEIN, Richard, M.D. Chief Medical Officer, Bay Area Medical Center, Marinette, WI, p. A704
STEIN, Robert, M.D. Vice President Medical Management, Advocate Christ Medical Center, Oak Lawn, IL, p. A196
STEIN, Robert, Chief Executive Officer, Kindred Hospital–Houston, Houston, TX, p. A620
STEIN, Sandra, Chief Human Resources Management, Veterans Affairs Central California Health Care System, Fresno, CA, p. A63
STEIN, Sheldon J., President and Chief Executive Officer, Mt. Washington Pediatric Hospital, Baltimore, MD, p. A294
STEINBERG, James P., M.D. Chief Medical Officer, Emory University Hospital Midtown, Atlanta, GA, p. A150
STEINBLOCK, Matthew, Systems Administrator, Community Memorial Hospital, Syracuse, NE, p. A398
STEINER, Dana, R.N. Executive Director of Nursing Services, Lexington Regional Health Center, Lexington, NE, p. A393
STEINER, J. Scott, Chief Executive Officer, MacNeal Hospital, Berwyn, IL, p. A179
STEINER, Jeffrey T., Vice President Finance, Memorial Hospital at Gulfport, Gulfport, MS, p. A353
STEINES, Jeanne, D.O. Medical Director, Connecticut Mental Health Center, New Haven, CT, p. A114
STEINGALL, Patricia, R.N. Vice President, Patient Care Services, Hunterdon Medical Center, Flemington, NJ, p. A412
STEINHART, Curt, M.D. Chief Medical Officer, OU Medical Center, Oklahoma City, OK, p. A512
STEINKE, Paul, D.O., President and Chief Executive Officer, CGH Medical Center, Sterling, IL, p. A201
STEINKRUGER, Roger W., Chief Executive Officer, Community Hospital–Fairfax, Fairfax, MO, p. A367
STEINKUHLER, Diane, Administrative Assistant Human Resources, I–70 Community Hospital, Sweet Springs, MO, p. A379
STEINMANN, David R.
Administrator, Mercy Hospital Lebanon, Lebanon, MO, p. A371
Administrator, Mercy St. Francis Hospital, Mountain View, MO, p. A373
STEINMANN, Robin, Administrative Director Human Resources, Anderson Hospital, Maryville, IL, p. A193
STEINSICK, Bill, M.D. Chief Medical Staff, Asante Ashland Community Hospital, Ashland, OR, p. A519
STEITZ, David P., Chief Executive Officer, Berwick Hospital Center, Berwick, PA, p. A529
STELL, G. Max, M.D. Medical Director, Minden Medical Center, Minden, LA, p. A280
STELLER, Wayne, Vice President Chief Nursing Officer, The Acadia Hospital, Bangor, ME, p. A288
STELLING, Jonathan, M.D. Vice President Medical Affairs, CHI Health St. Mary's, Nebraska City, NE, p. A394
STELTENPOHL, Robert
Vice President and Chief Financial Officer, Frazier Rehab Institute, Louisville, KY, p. A261
Vice President, Southern Indiana Rehabilitation Hospital, New Albany, IN, p. A217
STELTER, Carolyn, M.D. Chief of Staff, Minnesota Valley Health Center, Le Sueur, MN, p. A341
STELZER, Jason, Director Human Resources, St. Clare Hospital, Baraboo, WI, p. A697
STEMMERMAN, Jill, R.N. Vice President of Patient Care and Chief Nursing Officer, Saint Anthony Hospital, Chicago, IL, p. A184
STENDEL–FREELS, Robin, Coordinator Human Resources, AMG Specialty Hospital–Albuquerque, Albuquerque, NM, p. A422
STENERSON, David, Vice President and Chief Financial Officer, OSF Saint Anthony Medical Center, Rockford, IL, p. A199
STENGER, John D., Acting Associate Director, Charlie Norwood Veterans Affairs Medical Center, Augusta, GA, p. A151
STENGER, Michael J.
President and Chief Executive Officer, Franciscan Healthcare – Munster, Munster, IN, p. A217
President and Chief Executive Officer, Franciscan St. Margaret Health – Hammond, Hammond, IN, p. A210
STENGER, Sandra, Acting Chief Human Resources, Cincinnati Veterans Affairs Medical Center, Cincinnati, OH, p. A482
STENNETT, Kevin T., M.D. Chief of Staff, W. J. Mangold Memorial Hospital, Lockney, TX, p. A628
STENSRUD, Kirk A., Chief Executive Officer, Glacial Ridge Health System, Glenwood, MN, p. A339

STEPANSKY, David, M.D. Chief Medical Officer, Phoenixville Hospital, Phoenixville, PA, p. A545
STEPHANY, Mark
Executive Director, Elmira Psychiatric Center, Elmira, NY, p. A433
Executive Director, Greater Binghamton Health Center, Binghamton, NY, p. A429
STEPHENS, Brandon, Controller, HEALTHSOUTH Deaconess Rehabilitation Hospital, Evansville, IN, p. A208
STEPHENS, Brian, Chief Financial Officer, Ministry Door County Medical Center, Sturgeon Bay, WI, p. A712
STEPHENS, Carrie, Director of Information Technology and Support Services, Saunders Medical Center, Wahoo, NE, p. A398
STEPHENS, Debra, Director Personnel, Riverland Medical Center, Ferriday, LA, p. A273
STEPHENS, Eddy, Vice President Information Technology, Mobile Infirmary Medical Center, Mobile, AL, p. A22
STEPHENS, Ellen, Vice President Information Services, Mercy Hospital Oklahoma City, Oklahoma City, OK, p. A512
STEPHENS, Jeremy, Vice President and Chief Human Resources Officer, St. Joseph Mercy Chelsea, Chelsea, MI, p. A316
STEPHENS, Kathy, Chief Financial Officer, Carl Vinson Veterans Affairs Medical Center, Dublin, GA, p. A156
STEPHENS, Larry
Chief Financial Officer, Collingsworth General Hospital, Wellington, TX, p. A651
Chief Financial Officer, Kimble Hospital, Junction, TX, p. A625
Chief Financial Officer, Sabine County Hospital, Hemphill, TX, p. A618
Chief Financial Officer, Schleicher County Medical Center, Eldorado, TX, p. A612
STEPHENS, Linda, R.N. Chief Nursing Officer, Memorial Hermann Northeast, Humble, TX, p. A623
STEPHENS, Michael R., Market Leader and President, Mercy Health – West Hospital, Cincinnati, OH, p. A483
STEPHENS, Mike, Chief Financial Officer, NCH Downtown Naples Hospital, Naples, FL, p. A136
STEPHENS, Norman F., President, St. Luke's Hospital – The Vintage Hospital, Houston, TX, p. A622
STEPHENS, Peggy, M.D., Superintendent and Medical Director, Madison State Hospital, Madison, IN, p. A215
STEPHENS, Ronald, Commander, Womack Army Medical Center, Fort Bragg, NC, p. A460
STEPHENS, Royce, Chief Financial Officer, Riverton Hospital, Riverton, UT, p. A657
STEPHENS, Terry A., Chief Executive Officer, River Park Hospital, Huntington, WV, p. A692
STEPHENS, PHR, Maria, Director Human Resources, Education and Occupational Health and Wellness, VCU Community Memorial Hospital, South Hill, VA, p. A673
STEPHENSON, Ben, M.D. Chief of Staff, Phillips County Hospital, Phillipsburg, KS, p. A248
STEPHENSON, Darlene, Chief Executive Officer, Mary Immaculate Hospital, Newport News, VA, p. A669
STEPHENSON, Melinda, Chief Executive Officer, Kingwood Medical Center, Kingwood, TX, p. A626
STEPHENSON, Penny, Chief Financial Officer, Ellinwood District Hospital, Ellinwood, KS, p. A239
STEPHENSON, Ron, Chief Operating Officer, Brookhaven Memorial Hospital Medical Center, Patchogue, NY, p. A447
STEPHENSON, Steve R., M.D. Executive Vice President and Chief Operating Officer, UnityPoint Health – Iowa Methodist Medical Center, Des Moines, IA, p. A226
STEPP, Dana, Human Resources Officer, Marcum and Wallace Memorial Hospital, Irvine, KY, p. A259
STERBACH, Maureen, Vice President Human Resources, St. Joseph's Hospital and Medical Center, Phoenix, AZ, p. A36
STERLING, Julie, Manager Information System, South Sunflower County Hospital, Indianola, MS, p. A354
STERLING, Terrie, R.N. Chief Operating Officer, Our Lady of the Lake Regional Medical Center, Baton Rouge, LA, p. A269
STERLING, Tyson, Chief Executive Officer, Wichita County Health Center, Leoti, KS, p. A245
STERN, Barry, President and Chief Executive Officer, New York Community Hospital, NY, p. A442
STERN, Robert, M.D. Medical Director, Essex County Hospital Center, Cedar Grove, NJ, p. A410
STERNARD, Cynthia, Director Human Resources, Community Memorial Hospital, Hamilton, NY, p. A434
STERNBERG, Jan, MS Senior Vice President Patient Care Services and Chief Nursing Officer, Wyoming Medical Center, Casper, WY, p. A715
STERNBERG, Paul, M.D. Professor and Chairman, Vanderbilt Hospital and Clinics, Nashville, TN, p. A586
STERNS, Brian, Director Information Systems Services, Mercy St. Charles Hospital, Oregon, OH, p. A495
STERUD, Brian, Chief Information Officer, Faith Regional Health Services, Norfolk, NE, p. A395

STESNEY–RIDENOUR, Chris, Vice President Operations, Beaumont Hospital Grosse Pointe, Grosse Pointe, MI, p. A321
STETTHEIMER, Timothy, Vice President and Chief Information Officer, St. Vincent's Birmingham, Birmingham, AL, p. A17
STEUTER, Krista, Director Human Resources, Catalina Island Medical Center, Avalon, CA, p. A54
STEVEN, Eva, Chief Financial Officer, Roosevelt General Hospital, Portales, NM, p. A425
STEVENS, Belinda, Chief Executive Officer, Access Hospital Dayton, Dayton, OH, p. A487
STEVENS, Ben, Chief Financial Officer, Buchanan County Health Center, Independence, IA, p. A229
STEVENS, Bryan N., Chief Financial Officer, Field Memorial Community Hospital, Centreville, MS, p. A351
STEVENS, Chris E., Chief Information Officer, Billings Clinic, Billings, MT, p. A381
STEVENS, Dori, Chief Executive Officer, Sutter Delta Medical Center, Antioch, CA, p. A54
STEVENS, Emily, Chief Nursing Officer, Mat–Su Regional Medical Center, Palmer, AK, p. A29
STEVENS, Eric, Chief Executive Officer, Florida Hospital Heartland Medical Center, Sebring, FL, p. A143
STEVENS, Janis, Director Human Resources, Raulerson Hospital, Okeechobee, FL, p. A137
STEVENS, Kelly, Manager Human Resources, St. Joseph Memorial Hospital, Murphysboro, IL, p. A195
STEVENS, Lisa, Chief Clinical Officer and Chief Operating Officer, Vibra Hospital of Northern California, Redding, CA, p. A82
STEVENS, Maeanne, R.N. Chief Nursing Officer, OSF Saint Elizabeth Medical Center, Ottawa, IL, p. A197
STEVENS, Mark, M.D. Chief Medical Staff, Marion General Hospital, Columbia, MS, p. A352
STEVENS, Mark
Director Human Resources, St. Luke's Jerome, Jerome, ID, p. A174
Senior Director Human Resources, St. Luke's Magic Valley Medical Center, Twin Falls, ID, p. A176
STEVENS, Rick, Chief Administrative Officer, St. Luke's Hospital, San Francisco, CA, p. A88
STEVENS, Robert, President and Chief Executive Officer, Ridgeview Medical Center, Waconia, MN, p. B113
STEVENS, Robert, President and Chief Executive Officer, Ridgeview Medical Center, Waconia, MN, p. A348
STEVENS, Shelbourn, President, Novant Health Brunswick Medical Center, Bolivia, NC, p. A456
STEVENS, Susan
Information Technology Specialist, Fallon Medical Complex, Baker, MT, p. A381
Director Human Resources, The HealthCenter, Kalispell, MT, p. A385
STEVENS, Tammy, Chief Executive Officer, Madison County Memorial Hospital, Madison, FL, p. A132
STEVENS, Tom, Director Personnel, Morehead Memorial Hospital, Eden, NC, p. A459
STEVENS, Velinda, President, Kalispell Regional Medical Center, Kalispell, MT, p. A385
STEVENS, Vicki, Human Resources Executive, Northfield Hospital, Northfield, MN, p. A344
STEVENSON, Angelia, Manager Finance, Tuscaloosa Veterans Affairs Medical Center, Tuscaloosa, AL, p. A25
STEVENSON, Brett, Controller, Kindred Hospital Kansas City, Kansas City, MO, p. A369
STEVENSON, John, M.D. Senior Vice President and Chief Medical Officer, South Shore Hospital, South Weymouth, MA, p. A311
STEVENSON, Michael, Chief Executive Officer, Murphy Medical Center, Murphy, NC, p. A465
STEVERSON, Denise, Director Human Resources, Dorminy Medical Center, Fitzgerald, GA, p. A157
STEVES, Sonja
Senior Vice President Human Resources and Marketing, Legacy Emanuel Hospital and Health Center, Portland, OR, p. A524
Vice President Marketing, Legacy Good Samaritan Hospital and Medical Center, Portland, OR, p. A524
Vice President Human Resources and Marketing, Legacy Meridian Park Medical Center, Tualatin, OR, p. A527
Senior Vice President Human Resources, Legacy Mount Hood Medical Center, Gresham, OR, p. A521
Senior Vice President Human Resources, Legacy Salmon Creek Medical Center, Vancouver, WA, p. A687
STEWARD, Rachel, Director Human Resources, Hillcrest Hospital – South, Tulsa, OK, p. A516
STEWARD, Todd E., Chief Executive Officer, St. David's South Austin Medical Center, Austin, TX, p. A595
STEWART, Charles R., Vice President Business, Finance and Corporate Compliance, MedStar Southern Maryland Hospital Center, Clinton, MD, p. A297

STONE Jr., Timothy D., Executive Vice President and Administrator, Decatur Memorial Hospital, Decatur, IL, p. A186

STONE, Wesley, D.O. Chief of Staff, Allen County Regional Hospital, Iola, KS, p. A242

STONER, Donald, M.D. Chief Medical Officer, Halifax Health Medical Center of Daytona Beach, Daytona Beach, FL, p. A125

STONER, Steve, Chief Information Officer, Richard L. Roudebush Veterans Affairs Medical Center, Indianapolis, IN, p. A212

STONESTREET, Jana S., R.N. Chief Nursing Officer, Cape Fear Valley Medical Center, Fayetteville, NC, p. A460

STOOPS, Stephens, M.D. Chief Medical Officer, St. Mary's Medical Center, Blue Springs, MO, p. A363

STOPPER, Jim, CPA Chief Financial Officer, Evangelical Community Hospital, Lewisburg, PA, p. A538

STORER, William, M.D. Medical Director, St. Vincent Heart Center, Indianapolis, IN, p. A212

STOREY, Jack, Chief Information Officer, West Georgia Health, Lagrange, GA, p. A160

STOREY, Kam, Director Human Resources, Sebastian River Medical Center, Sebastian, FL, p. A143

STOREY, Kevin, Chief Executive Officer, Golden Plains Community Hospital, Borger, TX, p. A598

STOREY, Paul, FACHE President and Chief Executive Officer, Helen Keller Hospital, Sheffield, AL, p. A25

STORFJELL, Judith, Ph.D. Senior Vice President and Chief Nursing Officer, Loma Linda University Medical Center, Loma Linda, CA, p. A67

STORM, Dave, Director Business Support, HSHS St. Anthony's Memorial Hospital, Effingham, IL, p. A186

STORR, Ambrozino, Chief Executive Officer, Haven Behavioral Senior Care of Albuquerque, Albuquerque, NM, p. A422

STORR, Katie, Director of Human Resources, Mississippi State Hospital, Whitfield, MS, p. A361

STORTO, David E., President, Spaulding Rehabilitation Hospital, Charlestown, MA, p. A306

STOTLER, Sherry, R.N. Chief Nursing Officer, Maricopa Integrated Health System, Phoenix, AZ, p. A35

STOTTLEMYRE, Georgan L., Director Human Resources, Northern Inyo Hospital, Bishop, CA, p. A56

STOTTS, Vicki, Coordinator Human Resources, Flint River Community Hospital, Montezuma, GA, p. A162

STOUGH, Robin
Chief Financial Officer, Belmont Pines Hospital, Youngstown, OH, p. A501
Chief Financial Officer, Windsor–Laurelwood Center for Behavioral Medicine, Willoughby, OH, p. A501

STOUT, Bess, Director Human Resources, Tennova Healthcare–LaFollette Medical Center, La Follette, TN, p. A581

STOUT, Deana
Vice President Financial Services, MedStar Good Samaritan Hospital, Baltimore, MD, p. A294
Vice President Finance, MedStar Union Memorial Hospital, Baltimore, MD, p. A294

STOUT, Kimberly Dawn, Chief Nursing Officer, McAlester Regional Health Center, McAlester, OK, p. A509

STOUT, Patsy, Director Personnel, Richland Parish Hospital, Delhi, LA, p. A273

STOUT–TORRES, Sherri, R.N. Chief Nursing Executive, Sutter Maternity and Surgery Center of Santa Cruz, Santa Cruz, CA, p. A91

STOVALL, Henry, President, Sacred Heart Hospital of Pensacola, Pensacola, FL, p. A140

STOVALL, Richard G., Senior Vice President Fiscal Services and Chief Financial Officer, Southern Regional Medical Center, Riverdale, GA, p. A163

STOVER, Benny, Vice President Finance, Mercy Hospital Rogers, Rogers, AR, p. A50

STOVER, George M., Chief Executive Officer, Hospital District One of Rice County, Lyons, KS, p. A245

STOVER, Nick, Director Information Systems, Plateau Medical Center, Oak Hill, WV, p. A693

STOVER, Patricia A., Administrator Nursing, Doylestown Hospital, Doylestown, PA, p. A533

STOVER, Raymond
President and Chief Executive Officer, MidMichigan Medical Center–Clare, Clare, MI, p. A316
President and Chief Executive Officer, MidMichigan Medical Center–Gladwin, Gladwin, MI, p. A320

STOVER, Rhett, Chief Executive Officer, Oklahoma State University Medical Center, Tulsa, OK, p. A516

STOVER, Ryan, Chief Executive Officer, Norton County Hospital, Norton, KS, p. A247

STOVER, Thomas L., M.D., President and Chief Executive Officer, Akron General Health System, Akron, OH, p. B7

STOVERINK, Mike, Chief Financial Officer, Richland Memorial Hospital, Olney, IL, p. A197

STOWE, Mary, R.N. Senior Vice President and Chief Nursing Officer, Children's Health System of Texas, Dallas, TX, p. A604

STOWELL, Dana A., Chief Information Officer, McCurtain Memorial Hospital, Idabel, OK, p. A508

STOWMAN, Amber, Controller, CHI Lisbon Health, Lisbon, ND, p. A475

STOY, Gale, Manager Information Systems, Mid Coast Hospital, Brunswick, ME, p. A289

STOYANOFF, Pamela
Executive Vice President and Chief Operating Officer, Methodist Charlton Medical Center, Dallas, TX, p. A605
Executive Vice President and Chief Operating Officer, Methodist Dallas Medical Center, Dallas, TX, p. A606

STRABEL, Elizabeth, M.D. Chief Medical Staff, Divine Savior Healthcare, Portage, WI, p. A709

STRACHAN, Eileen, Coordinator Human Resources, Kindred Hospital–Sycamore, Sycamore, IL, p. A202

STRACHAN, Ronald
Chief Information Officer, McLaren Bay Region, Bay City, MI, p. A315
Chief Information Officer, McLaren Flint, Flint, MI, p. A319

STRACK, Kirk, Vice President and Chief Financial Officer, Clark Memorial Hospital, Jeffersonville, IN, p. A213

STRADER, Lynn, Chief Financial Officer, Chippenham Hospital, Richmond, VA, p. A671

STRADER, Yvonne M., Chief Nursing Officer, Providence St. Mary Medical Center, Walla Walla, WA, p. A687

STRADI, Silvia, Chief Nursing Officer, Palms West Hospital, Loxahatchee, FL, p. A132

STRAHAN, Greg, Chief Operating Officer, Owensboro Health Regional Hospital, Owensboro, KY, p. A264

STRAIN, Donna, Director Human Resources, Ray County Memorial Hospital, Richmond, MO, p. A375

STRAIN, Lynn, R.N. Chief Nursing Officer, Slidell Memorial Hospital, Slidell, LA, p. A285

STRAMOWSKI, Mallary, Chief Human Resources Officer, Select Specialty Hospital–Madison, Madison, WI, p. A704

STRANATHAN, Sidney, D.O. Chief of Staff, Anthony Medical Center, Anthony, KS, p. A237

STRAND, Eric, Director Information Services, North Florida Regional Medical Center, Gainesville, FL, p. A127

STRAND, Joy A., Chief Executive Officer, McCready Foundation, Crisfield, MD, p. A297

STRANGE, John, President and Chief Executive Officer, St. Luke's Hospital, Duluth, MN, p. A338

STRANGE, Roger, Chief Information Officer, St. Vincent Heart Center, Indianapolis, IN, p. A212

STRASSER, Michael, Vice President and Chief Financial Officer, Mercy Medical Center Merced, Merced, CA, p. A75

STRASSNER III, Lawrence F., Ph.D. Senior Vice President Operations and Chief Nursing Officer, MedStar Franklin Square Medical Center, Baltimore, MD, p. A294

STRATTON, James
Regional Vice President Finance, SSM Health St. Mary's Hospital – Audrain, Mexico, MO, p. A372
Vice President Finance, SSM Health St. Mary's Hospital – Jefferson City, Jefferson City, MO, p. A369

STRATTON, Joseph, FACHE, Chief Executive Officer, Geary Community Hospital, Junction City, KS, p. A243

STRATTON, Mary, Director Human Resources, River Park Hospital, Huntington, WV, p. A692

STRATTON, Tracie, Chief Nursing Officer, Los Alamos Medical Center, Los Alamos, NM, p. A425

STRAUGHAN, Janet, Manager Human Resources, Highlands Regional Rehabilitation Hospital, El Paso, TX, p. A610

STRAUGHAN, John, Director Information Technology, Wallowa Memorial Hospital, Enterprise, OR, p. A520

STRAUMAN, Karen S., R.N. Vice President Patient Care Services, Regina Hospital, Hastings, MN, p. A340

STRAUMANIS, John P., M.D. Vice President Medical Affairs and Chief Medical Officer, University of Maryland Rehabilitation & Orthopaedic Institute, Baltimore, MD, p. A295

STRAUSBAUGH, Andy, Vice President Finance and Operations, Norton Brownsboro Hospital, Louisville, KY, p. A261

STRAUSS, Alan
Chief Financial Officer, Carondelet Holy Cross Hospital, Nogales, AZ, p. A33
Chief Financial Officer, Carondelet St. Joseph's Hospital, Tucson, AZ, p. A39
Chief Financial Officer, University Medical Center at Brackenridge, Austin, TX, p. A595

STRAUSS, Karen, Chief Human Resources Officer, ProMedica Flower Hospital, Sylvania, OH, p. A498

STRAWN, Jill, Chief Executive Officer, HEALTHSOUTH Rehabilitation Hospital of Florence, Florence, SC, p. A560

STRAWN, Keith A., Vice President Human Resources, New Hanover Regional Medical Center, Wilmington, NC, p. A470

STRAWSER, Debbie A., Director Human Resources, Lindner Center of HOPE, Mason, OH, p. A493

STRAYER, Lorna, President and Chief Executive Officer, Fisher–Titus Medical Center, Norwalk, OH, p. A495

STRAYHORN, Shelly, R.N
Chief Nursing Officer, Wadley Regional Medical Center, Texarkana, TX, p. A647
Chief Nursing Officer, Wadley Regional Medical Center at Hope, Hope, AR, p. A45

STRBICH, Steve, D.O. Chief of Staff, Spectrum Health Ludington Hospital, Ludington, MI, p. A325

STREATER, Vivian, Co–Acting Chief Executive Officer, Broughton Hospital, Morganton, NC, p. A465

STRECKER, Dede, Chief Nursing Officer, White River Medical Center, Batesville, AR, p. A41

STRECKER, Kevin, President, Via Christi Hospital on St. Teresa, Wichita, KS, p. A253

STRECKER, Robert, M.D. Chief of Staff, Colorado River Medical Center, Needles, CA, p. A77

STREDNEY, Thomas, Chief Human Resources Management Service, Aleda E. Lutz Veterans Affairs Medical Center, Saginaw, MI, p. A329

STREET, Rex, Senior Vice President and Chief Financial Officer, Alamance Regional Medical Center, Burlington, NC, p. A456

STREET, Scott, Chief Executive Officer, Nacogdoches Memorial Hospital, Nacogdoches, TX, p. A633

STREETER, Alan W., Chief Financial Officer, Beatrice Community Hospital and Health Center, Beatrice, NE, p. A390

STREETER, Matthew, Chief Financial Officer, Southwest Health Center, Platteville, WI, p. A709

STREETER, Maxine, Administrator, Reception and Medical Center, Lake Butler, FL, p. A131

STREETER, Robert, M.D. Vice President Medical Affairs, Mercy Medical Center Merced, Merced, CA, p. A75

STREICH, Rebecca, Manager Human Resources and Education Manager, Hutchinson Health, Hutchinson, MN, p. A340

STREJC, Irene T., R.N. Vice President, Nursing, Methodist Richardson Medical Center, Richardson, TX, p. A638

STRICKER, Sean, Chief Executive Officer, Select Specialty Hospital–San Antonio, San Antonio, TX, p. A642

STRICKER, Steven, M.D. Physician in Chief, Kaiser Permanente Vallejo Medical Center, Vallejo, CA, p. A96

STRICKLAND, Barrie, Chief Financial Officer, UCSF Medical Center, San Francisco, CA, p. A89

STRICKLAND, Connie, Chief Executive Officer, Select Specialty Hospital–Oklahoma City, Oklahoma City, OK, p. A512

STRICKLAND, David, Area Information Officer, Kaiser Permanente Los Angeles Medical Center, Los Angeles, CA, p. A70

STRICKLAND, Lee, Regional Director Information Technology, Park Ridge Health, Hendersonville, NC, p. A462

STRICKLAND, Morris S., Chief Financial Officer, Helen Keller Hospital, Sheffield, AL, p. A25

STRICKLAND, Wallace, President and Chief Executive Officer, Rush Health Systems, Meridian, MS, p. B115

STRICKLING, Keith
Chief Financial Officer, Atmore Community Hospital, Atmore, AL, p. A16
Chief Accountant, Jay Hospital, Jay, FL, p. A130

STRIEBICH, Shannon
Chief Operating Officer, St. Joseph Mercy Oakland, Pontiac, MI, p. A328
Chief Operating Officer, St. Mary Mercy Hospital, Livonia, MI, p. A325

STRIEBY, John F., Chief Executive Officer, Nix Health Care System, San Antonio, TX, p. A641

STRIKE, Helen J., R.N., President, Unity Hospital, Fridley, MN, p. A339

STRINDEN, William, M.D. Chief of Staff, Woodland Heights Medical Center, Lufkin, TX, p. A630

STRING, Sherrie
Senior Vice President Human Resources, Bayshore Community Hospital, Holmdel, NJ, p. A413
Senior Vice President Human Resources, Ocean Medical Center, Brick Township, NJ, p. A410
Senior Vice President Human Resources, Riverview Medical Center, Red Bank, NJ, p. A418

STRINGFELLOW, Grace, M.D. Chief of Staff, Veterans Affairs Nebraska–Western Iowa Health Care System, Omaha, NE, p. A397

STRIPLIN, Elizabeth, Chief Financial Officer, Rehabilitation Hospital of Southern New Mexico, Las Cruces, NM, p. A425

STRITTMATTER, Brenda M., Patient Services Officer, Berger Health System, Circleville, OH, p. A484

STRITTMATTER, Julie, Director Human Resources, Baylor University Medical Center, Dallas, TX, p. A604

STROBEL, Jane, Vice President and Chief Financial Officer, Mercy Regional Medical Center, Durango, CO, p. A102

STROBEL, Karli, Director Human Resources, Keefe Memorial Hospital, Cheyenne Wells, CO, p. A100

Index of Health Care Professionals / Sullivan

Index of Health Care Professionals


STROBEL, Rand
Regional Chief Information Officer, Information Technology Services, Harrison Medical Center, Bremerton, WA, p. A676
Regional Chief Information Officer, St. Francis Hospital, Federal Way, WA, p. A679
Vice President Information Technology and Compliance, St. Joseph Medical Center, Tacoma, WA, p. A686
STRODE, Marc, Chief Executive Officer, Methodist Stone Oak Hospital, San Antonio, TX, p. A641
STROEMEL, Douglas M.
President, Mercy Hospital Aurora, Aurora, MO, p. A363
Administrator, Mercy Hospital Berryville, Berryville, AR, p. A41
President, Mercy Hospital Cassville, Cassville, MO, p. A365
STROH, Rhonda, Chief Human Resources Officer, Community Memorial Hospital, Redfield, SD, p. A571
STROHE, Thomas B., Chief Executive Officer, Lafayette Physical Rehabilitation Hospital, Lafayette, LA, p. A277
STROHECKER, Sharon, R.N. Vice President Clinical Operations and Chief Nursing Officer, St. Joseph Regional Health Network, Reading, PA, p. A548
STROM, Lisa, R.N. Chief Operating Officer, MultiCare Tacoma General Hospital, Tacoma, WA, p. A686
STROM, Lisa, Director Information Systems, North Big Horn Hospital District, Lovell, WY, p. A716
STROMBERG, Audrey, Administrator, Roosevelt Medical Center, Culbertson, MT, p. A382
STROMSTAD, Darlene, FACHE, President and Chief Executive Officer, Waterbury Hospital, Waterbury, CT, p. A116
STRONG, Dana, Chief Financial Officer, Northern Cochise Community Hospital, Willcox, AZ, p. A40
STRONG, David, Chief Financial Officer/Vice President Finance, Cox Medical Center Branson, Branson, MO, p. A364
STRONG, David W., President and Chief Executive Officer, Orlando Health, Orlando, FL, p. B102
STRONG, Jim, MBA Chief Financial Officer, Regional West Medical Center, Scottsbluff, NE, p. A398
STRONG, Patricia, Interim Chief Executive Officer, Cumberland River Hospital, Celina, TN, p. A574
STRONG, Tanya, Manager Information Technology, Harney District Hospital, Burns, OR, p. A519
STROPE, Jennifer, Manager Human Resources, Hillcrest Hospital Cushing, Cushing, OK, p. A505
STROSNIDER, Preston, M.D. Vice President Medical Affairs, Conway Medical Center, Conway, SC, p. A560
STROSS, Daniel, Chief Information Officer, Genesys Regional Medical Center, Grand Blanc, MI, p. A320
STROTHER, Brad, Director Information Technology, Clay County Hospital, Ashland, AL, p. A15
STROTHKAMP, Brad, Chief Information Systems, Lakeland Behavioral Health System, Springfield, MO, p. A378
STROUCKEN, Christian, Chief Operating Officer, Carney Hospital, Boston, MA, p. A303
STROUD, Justin, Chief Financial Officer, Merit Health Northwest Mississippi, Clarksdale, MS, p. A351
STROUD, Teresa, Chief Financial Officer, Salem Township Hospital, Salem, IL, p. A200
STROUD, William, M.D. Chief Medical Officer, East Cooper Medical Center, Mount Pleasant, SC, p. A563
STROUP, Jeff, Chief Operating Officer, Oklahoma State University Medical Center, Tulsa, OK, p. A516
STRUB, Lisa, Chief Operating Officer, Centennial Peaks Hospital, Louisville, CO, p. A107
STRUTTON, Jill, Director Personnel Systems, University of Texas Harris County Psychiatric Center, Houston, TX, p. A622
STRUYK, Douglas A., CPA, President and Chief Executive Officer, Christian Health Care Center, Wyckoff, NJ, p. A421
STRZELECKI, Sarah, Ed.D. Chief Nursing Officer, Phoenixville Hospital, Phoenixville, PA, p. A545
STRZEMPKO, Stanley, M.D. Vice President Medical Affairs and Chief Medical Officer, Baystate Noble Hospital, Westfield, MA, p. A312
STUART, Conan, Director Information Services, East Georgia Regional Medical Center, Statesboro, GA, p. A165
STUART, Danna, M.D. Chief Medical Officer, Newman Memorial Hospital, Shattuck, OK, p. A514
STUART, Leslie, Chief Financial Officer, Cypress Creek Hospital, Houston, TX, p. A619
STUART, Philip J., Administrator and Chief Executive Officer, Tomah Memorial Hospital, Tomah, WI, p. A712
STUART, Robin, Chief Executive Officer, Morrill County Community Hospital, Bridgeport, NE, p. A390
STUART, Wendy, Chief Nursing Officer, Kendall Regional Medical Center, Miami, FL, p. A134
STUBBS, Don, Vice President Human Resources, Candler Hospital, Savannah, GA, p. A164
STUBBS, Kay, Chief Nursing Officer, Northwest Medical Center, Tucson, AZ, p. A39
STUBER, Joseph A., President and Chief Executive Officer, Perry County Memorial Hospital, Tell City, IN, p. A220
STUCK, Julie, R.N., Chief Executive Officer, Hocking Valley Community Hospital, Logan, OH, p. A492
STUCKY, Nancy, Director Human Resources and Public Relations, Kingman Community Hospital, Kingman, KS, p. A243
STUCZYNSKI, Joseph, Assistant Administrator Finance and Support, Memorial Hospital Pembroke, Pembroke Pines, FL, p. A139
STUDEBAKER, Shelly, Director Management Information Systems, Clinch Memorial Hospital, Homerville, GA, p. A159
STUDER, Tim, President Medical Staff, Perham Health, Perham, MN, p. A344
STUDER, Vince, Director Finance, Gundersen Tri–County Hospital and Clinics, Whitehall, WI, p. A714
STUDLEY, Jason, Chief Executive Officer, Trinity Hospital of Augusta, Augusta, GA, p. A151
STUENKEL, Kurt, FACHE, President and Chief Executive Officer, Floyd Medical Center, Rome, GA, p. A163
STUERMAN, Jason, M.D. Chief of Staff, Middle Park Medical Center–Kremmling, Kremmling, CO, p. A105
STUERSEL, Marie, Director Human Resources, Seneca Healthcare District, Chester, CA, p. A57
STUEVE, Jo W., Executive Vice President and Co–Chief Operating Officer, Children's Mercy Hospitals and Clinics, Kansas City, MO, p. A369
STUHLMILLER, Michael, Chief Financial Officer, Mann–Grandstaff Veterans Affairs Medical Center, Spokane, WA, p. A685
STULTS, Cynthia S., Executive Assistant and Human Resources Director, Rangely District Hospital, Rangely, CO, p. A108
STULTS, Kim, Director, Information Systems, Bellevue Hospital, Bellevue, OH, p. A480
STUMBO, Kathy, President, Saint Joseph – Martin, Martin, KY, p. A262
STUMME, Sarah, Director Human Resources, Owatonna Hospital, Owatonna, MN, p. A344
STUMP, Jerry, Chief Financial Officer, Good Samaritan Hospital, Vincennes, IN, p. A221
STUMP, Veronica, Chief Nursing Officer, Carilion Giles Community Hospital, Pearisburg, VA, p. A670
STUMPO, Barbara J., R.N. Vice President Patient Care Services, Griffin Hospital, Derby, CT, p. A112
STURGEON, Jim, Area Director Human Resources, Kindred Hospital Las Vegas–Sahara, Las Vegas, NV, p. A402
STURGEON, Wade, Chief Operating Officer and Chief Financial Officer, Bear Valley Community Hospital, Big Bear Lake, CA, p. A56
STURGILL, Lori
Vice President Business Partnership, Mercy Hospital Fort Scott, Fort Scott, KS, p. A240
Vice President Business Partnership, Mercy Hospital Springfield, Springfield, MO, p. A379
STURGIS, Gayle, R.N. Nurse Administrator, Heber Valley Medical Center, Heber City, UT, p. A655
STURGIS, James D., Associate Administrator, Texas Scottish Rite Hospital for Children, Dallas, TX, p. A607
STURGIS, Jonathan, Chief Financial Officer, Houston Methodist San Jacinto Hospital, Baytown, TX, p. A596
STURGIS, Paul
Vice President and Chief Human Resources Officer, Sparrow Hospital, Lansing, MI, p. A324
Chief Human Resource Officer, Sparrow Specialty Hospital, Lansing, MI, p. A324
STURLER, Kelly, Chief Nursing Officer, McKee Medical Center, Loveland, CO, p. A107
STURSA, Robin, Chief Information Officer, St. Vincent Charity Medical Center, Cleveland, OH, p. A485
STUWE, Shannon, Director of Nursing, Faulkton Area Medical Center, Faulkton, SD, p. A568
STYER, Brent
Chief Information Officer, Summers County ARH Hospital, Hinton, WV, p. A691
Director Information Technology, Whitesburg ARH Hospital, Whitesburg, KY, p. A266
STYLES, Kelly R., Vice President and Chief Information Officer, Connecticut Children's Medical Center, Hartford, CT, p. A112
STYRON, Stacie, Chief Nursing Officer, Lamb Healthcare Center, Littlefield, TX, p. A628
SUAREZ, Irma, Network Deputy Executive Director, Woodhull Medical and Mental Health Center, NY, p. A445
SUAREZ, Orlando, Director Information Technology, Larkin Community Hospital, South Miami, FL, p. A143
SUBLER, Jeffrey R., Vice President Support Services, Wayne Hospital, Greenville, OH, p. A491
SUBLETTE, Elizabeth, Director Finance, Providence Willamette Falls Medical Center, Oregon City, OR, p. A523
SUBRAMANIAN, Aarti, Vice President and Chief Financial Officer, Psychiatric Institute of Washington, Washington, DC, p. A120
SUCATO, Daniel J., M.D. Chief of Staff, Texas Scottish Rite Hospital for Children, Dallas, TX, p. A607
SUCHER, Therese O., Senior Vice President Operations, Southern Regional Medical Center, Riverdale, GA, p. A163
SUDA, Shirley, M.D. Area Medical Director, Kaiser Permanente Woodland Hills Medical Center, CA, p. A70
SUDAK, Mariellena, R.N., Interim Vice President and Chief Nursing Officer, Palomar Medical Center, Escondido, CA, p. A60
SUDDUTH, Tony, Chief Financial Officer, Trios Health, Kennewick, WA, p. A680
SUDICKY, Mary, Chief Financial Officer, St. Mary Medical Center, Hobart, IN, p. A211
SUDOLCAN, Joseph, M.D. Medical Director, Reagan Memorial Hospital, Big Lake, TX, p. A597
SUEHS, JoAnne, Manager Human Resources, Chapman Medical Center, Orange, CA, p. A79
SUEIRO, Edwin, Administrator, Hospital De Damas, Ponce, PR, p. A722
SUGAR, Bev, Associate Administrator and Director Human Resources, Inova Mount Vernon Hospital, Alexandria, VA, p. A662
SUGDEN, Elizabeth, M.D. Chief Medical Officer, St. Luke's Jerome, Jerome, ID, p. A174
SUGG, Amy, Director Human Resources, Scott Regional Hospital, Morton, MS, p. A358
SUGGS, Heather, Manager Human Resources, Jay Hospital, Jay, FL, p. A130
SUHR, Nancy, Manager Human Resources, Pender Community Hospital, Pender, NE, p. A397
SUHRE, Elizabeth, Executive Director, Rochester Psychiatric Center, Rochester, NY, p. A449
SUIRE, Bridget, Acting Administrator, MMO Rehabilitation and Wellness Center, Plaquemine, LA, p. A283
SUITTER, Marie, Chief Financial Officer, The Acadia Hospital, Bangor, ME, p. A288
SUKENIK, Richard, CPA Vice President Finance and Chief Financial Officer, Windber Medical Center, Windber, PA, p. A553
SUKSI, Eugene, Interim Chief Executive Officer, Tehachapi Valley Healthcare District, Tehachapi, CA, p. A94
SULEIMAN, Ali, M.D. Chief of Staff, Beckley ARH Hospital, Beckley, WV, p. A689
SULIK, Sandra, M.D. Vice President Medical Affairs, St. Joseph's Hospital Health Center, Syracuse, NY, p. A451
SULLINS, Jacqueline C., R.N. Chief Nursing Officer, Merit Health Rankin, Brandon, MS, p. A351
SULLIVAN, Christopher, M.D. Chief Medical Officer, Centerpoint Medical Center, Independence, MO, p. A368
SULLIVAN, Daniel, D.O. Chief Medical Officer, Vice President Medical Administration, Elmhurst Memorial Hospital, IL, p. A187
SULLIVAN, Danita S., R.N. Chief Nursing Officer, Tulane Medical Center, New Orleans, LA, p. A282
SULLIVAN, David, Director Human Resources, OhioHealth Doctors Hospital, Columbus, OH, p. A486
SULLIVAN, Denis, Chief Human Resources Management, Veterans Affairs Black Hills Health Care System, Fort Meade, SD, p. A568
SULLIVAN, Donald, M.D. Medical Director, HEALTHSOUTH Rehabilitation Hospital Memphis–North, Memphis, TN, p. A583
SULLIVAN, Gregory, Manager Human Resources, Girard Medical Center, Girard, KS, p. A240
SULLIVAN, James, M.D. Chief Medical Officer, Butler Hospital, Providence, RI, p. A555
SULLIVAN, Jennie, Chief Executive Officer, Wray Community District Hospital, Wray, CO, p. A110
SULLIVAN, Jennifer, President and Chief Executive Officer, St. James Mercy Health System, Hornell, NY, p. A435
SULLIVAN, John, President, MedStar Washington Hospital Center, Washington, DC, p. A119
SULLIVAN, Katherine, Director, Human Resources, Moab Regional Hospital, Moab, UT, p. A655
SULLIVAN, Keith, Associate Director, Chillicothe Veterans Affairs Medical Center, Chillicothe, OH, p. A482
SULLIVAN, Lowery, M.D. Chief Medical Officer, Northwestern Medical Center, Saint Albans, VT, p. A661
SULLIVAN, Martha, Chief Information Officer, Harrison Memorial Hospital, Cynthiana, KY, p. A256
SULLIVAN, Mary Patricia, R.N. Chief Nursing Officer, Overlook Medical Center, Summit, NJ, p. A418
SULLIVAN, Maurita, Vice President, Mayo Clinic Health System – Northland in Barron, Barron, WI, p. A698
SULLIVAN, Michael, M.D
Chief Medical Officer, Northern Maine Medical Center, Fort Kent, ME, p. A290
Medical Director Emergency Services, PeaceHealth Peace Island Medical Center, Friday Harbor, WA, p. A679
SULLIVAN, Michael Dean, M.D. Chief of Staff, Mercy Hospital El Reno, El Reno, OK, p. A506

Index of Health Care Professionals

Index of Health Care Professionals / Sullivan

SULLIVAN, Patrick, Interim President and Chief Executive Officer, Interfaith Medical Center, NY, p. A440
SULLIVAN, Patrick L., Chief Operating Officer, St. John's Episcopal Hospital–South Shore, NY, p. A444
SULLIVAN, Staci, MSN Chief Nursing Officer, Lane Regional Medical Center, Zachary, LA, p. A287
SULLIVAN, Tammy, R.N. Chief Nursing Officer, Baptist Health Richmond, Richmond, KY, p. A265
SULLIVAN, Theresa
Chief Operating Officer, Samaritan Healthcare, Moses Lake, WA, p. A680
Chief Operating Officer, Samaritan Healthcare, Moses Lake, WA, p. A680
Director Human Resources, Summit Park Hospital and Nursing Care Center, Pomona, NY, p. A447
SULLIVAN, Thomas, Vice President Fiscal Services, Harrington Memorial Hospital, Southbridge, MA, p. A311
SULLIVAN, Thomas, M.D. Chief of Staff, Mena Regional Health System, Mena, AR, p. A48
SULLIVAN, William, Chief Financial Officer, Mount Auburn Hospital, Cambridge, MA, p. A305
SULLIVAN SMITH, Mary, R.N. Vice President Clinical Operations and Chief Nursing Officer, New England Baptist Hospital, Boston, MA, p. A304
SULSER, Jamey, Director Human Resources, South Davis Community Hospital, Bountiful, UT, p. A654
SULU, Dorothy, Budget Analyst, Hopi Health Care Center, Keams Canyon, AZ, p. A32
SUMMER, Jay, M.D. Vice President Corporate Medical Affairs, McLaren Bay Region, Bay City, MI, p. A315
SUMMERLIN, Craig, Chief Human Resources Officer, Singing River Health System, Pascagoula, MS, p. A359
SUMMERLIN, Valerie, R.N. Chief Nursing Officer, Adventist Rehabilitation Hospital of Maryland, Rockville, MD, p. A300
SUMMERS, Andrew, Chief Financial Officer, USMD Hospital at Arlington, Arlington, TX, p. A593
SUMMERS, Barbara L., Ph.D. Vice President Nursing Practice and Chief Nursing Officer, University of Texas M.D. Anderson Cancer Center, Houston, TX, p. A622
SUMMERS, Curtis, Chief Executive Officer, Summit Medical Center, Edmond, OK, p. A506
SUMMERS, David A.
Chief Financial Officer, Tristar Ashland City Medical Center, Ashland City, TN, p. A574
Chief Financial Officer, TriStar Centennial Medical Center, Nashville, TN, p. A586
SUMMERS, Debra, Chief Nursing Officer, Calhoun–Liberty Hospital, Blountstown, FL, p. A121
SUMMERS, Jeff, M.D. Medical Director, Select Specialty Hospital–North Knoxville, Powell, TN, p. A587
SUMMERS, Kelly, Chief Information Officer, Maricopa Integrated Health System, Phoenix, AZ, p. A35
SUMMERS, Linda, Chief Operating Officer, Canton–Potsdam Hospital, Potsdam, NY, p. A448
SUMMERS, Paul, President and Chief Executive Officer, Delaware Valley Hospital, Walton, NY, p. A453
SUMMERS, Stephen M., FACHE, Chief Executive Officer, Wise Regional Health System, Decatur, TX, p. A607
SUMMERVILLE, Wendell, Chief Financial Officer, Bryce Hospital, Tuscaloosa, AL, p. A25
SUMNER, Donna, Director, Human Resources and Organizational Development, St. Joseph Medical Center, Kansas City, MO, p. A370
SUMNER, J. Andrew, M.D. Vice President Medical Affairs, MedStar Southern Maryland Hospital Center, Clinton, MD, p. A297
SUMNER, Jack R., Assistant Administrator Finance, Providence Newberg Medical Center, Newberg, OR, p. A523
SUMNER, John, Chief Executive Officer, Trigg County Hospital, Cadiz, KY, p. A255
SUMPTER, Nikki, Senior Vice President Human Resources, JPS Health Network, Fort Worth, TX, p. A613
SUMRA, K. S., M.D. Chief of Staff, Pembina County Memorial Hospital and Wedgewood Manor, Cavalier, ND, p. A473
SUMRALL, Mary Ellen, Chief Nursing Officer, Baptist Memorial Hospital–Golden Triangle, Columbus, MS, p. A352
SUMTER, Rob, Executive Vice President and Chief Operating Officer, Regional One Health, Memphis, TN, p. A584
SUND, Lynn A., R.N. Senior Vice President, Administrator and Chief Nursing Executive, Laureate Psychiatric Clinic and Hospital, Tulsa, OK, p. A516
SUND, Lynn A., MS, Senior Vice President, Administrator and Chief Nurse Executive, Saint Francis Hospital, Tulsa, OK, p. A517
SUND, Lynn A., R.N. Senior Vice President, Administrator and Chief Nurse Executive, Saint Francis Hospital, Tulsa, OK, p. A517
SUNDBERG, Nita, Director Human Resources, Three Rivers Behavioral Health, West Columbia, SC, p. A566
SUNDBLOM, Karin, Chief Nursing Officer, Saint Luke's Cushing Hospital, Leavenworth, KS, p. A244
SUNDBY, Stephen, Ph.D., Administrator and Chief Executive Officer, Cordova Community Medical Center, Cordova, AK, p. A27
SUNDERLIN, Tammy, Director of Nursing, Auburn Community Hospital, Auburn, NY, p. A429
SUNDERRAJAN, E. V., M.D. Chief of Staff, Fountain Valley Regional Hospital and Medical Center, Fountain Valley, CA, p. A61
SUNDIN, Jon, M.D. Medical Director, The Orthopedic Specialty Hospital, Murray, UT, p. A656
SUNDQUIST, Joanne, Chief Information Officer, St. John's Hospital, Maplewood, MN, p. A342
SUNDRUD, Diane
Director Human Resources, Essentia Health Fosston, Fosston, MN, p. A339
Human Resource Service Partner, Essentia Health St. Mary's – Detroit Lakes, Detroit Lakes, MN, p. A337
SUNGA, Marcos N., M.D. Chief of Staff, Hardin County General Hospital, Rosiclare, IL, p. A200
SUNKAVALLE, Krishna, M.D. Chief Medical Officer, Hamlin Memorial Hospital, Hamlin, TX, p. A617
SUNQUIST, Joanne
Information System, Senior Vice President and Chief Information Officer, St. Joseph's Hospital, Saint Paul, MN, p. A346
Chief Information Officer, Woodwinds Health Campus, Woodbury, MN, p. A349
SUNTHA, Mohan, M.D., President and Chief Executive Officer, University of Maryland St. Joseph Medical Center, Towson, MD, p. A300
SUNTRAPAK, Todd A., President and Chief Executive Officer, Valley Children's Hospital, Madera, CA, p. A74
SUPPAN, Marchelle, DPM, President and Chief Executive Officer, Aultman Orrville Hospital, Orrville, OH, p. A496
SUPPLEE, Linda, Chief Executive Officer, Select Specialty Hospital of Southeast Ohio, Zanesville, OH, p. A502
SURANI, Salim, M.D. Chief of Staff, Care Regional Medical Center, Aransas Pass, TX, p. A592
SURBER, Randy, Chief Executive Officer, Florida Hospital Zephyrhills, Zephyrhills, FL, p. A148
SURCOUF, Shelli, Chief Financial Officer, Georgetown Behavioral Health Institute, Georgetown, TX, p. A616
SURL, Deepak, Chief Information Officer, Eastern New Mexico Medical Center, Roswell, NM, p. A426
SURO, Marta R Mercado, Chief Operating Officer, Mennonite General Hospital, Aibonito, PR, p. A719
SUROWITZ, Dale, Chief Executive, Providence Tarzana Medical Center, CA, p. A72
SURRATT, Shawn, M.D. Chief of Staff, Memorial Hospital and Manor, Bainbridge, GA, p. A152
SURROCK, Lester
Chief Financial Officer, Nix Community General Hospital, Dilley, TX, p. A609
Chief Financial Officer, Nix Health Care System, San Antonio, TX, p. A641
SUSI, Jeffrey L., President and Chief Executive Officer, Indian River Medical Center, Vero Beach, FL, p. A146
SUSICK, Nancy, MSN, President, Beaumont Hospital – Troy, Troy, MI, p. A331
SUSIE–LATTNER, Debra, M.D. Vice President, Medical Management, Advocate Condell Medical Center, Libertyville, IL, p. A192
SUSSMAN, Andrew, M.D. Chief Operating Officer, UMass Memorial Medical Center, Worcester, MA, p. A313
SUSSMAN, Howard, M.D. Chief Medical Officer, St. Joseph Hospital, Bethpage, NY, p. A429
SUTER, Brian, Chief Financial Officer, Mayo Clinic Health System in Fairmont, Fairmont, MN, p. A338
SUTER, Mia, Chief Administration Officer, Owensboro Health Regional Hospital, Owensboro, KY, p. A264
SUTHERLIN, Shara, R.N. Director Patient Care Services, South Peninsula Hospital, Homer, AK, p. A28
SUTIKA, John, President, Penn Highlands DuBois, DuBois, PA, p. A533
SUTTLE, Terry, Superintendent, Richmond State Hospital, Richmond, IN, p. A219
SUTTLES, Mary Anne, Chief Nursing Officer, St. Francis Medical Center, Trenton, NJ, p. A419
SUTTON, Andrew, Chief Human Resources Officer, Coatesville Veterans Affairs Medical Center, Coatesville, PA, p. A532
SUTTON, Angie, Manager Human Resources, Genoa Medical Facilities, Genoa, NE, p. A392
SUTTON, Bob
Interim Chief Executive Officer, Avera Gettysburg Hospital, Gettysburg, SD, p. A569
President and Chief Executive Officer, Avera St. Mary's Hospital, Pierre, SD, p. A570
SUTTON, Elaine, Chief Information Officer, General John J. Pershing Memorial Hospital, Brookfield, MO, p. A364
SUTTON, Fred, M.D. Chief Medical Officer, Harris Health System, Houston, TX, p. A619
SUTTON, Janet, M.D. Medical Director, McLaren Bay Special Care, Bay City, MI, p. A315
SUTTON, Jeffrey, Chief Information Officer, Lexington Veterans Affairs Medical Center, Lexington, KY, p. A260
SUTTON, Jesse, Chief Financial Officer, Central Texas Medical Center, San Marcos, TX, p. A643
SUTTON, Julie, Director Performance Improvement, State Hospital South, Blackfoot, ID, p. A172
SUTTON, Michele K., FACHE, Administrator, North Oaks Medical Center, Hammond, LA, p. A274
SUTTON, Rhonda, Director Human Resources, Richland Hospital, Richland Center, WI, p. A710
SUTTON, Richard O., Chief Executive Officer, North Colorado Medical Center, Greeley, CO, p. A104
SUTTON, Rick, Chief Executive Officer Northern Colorado, Banner Fort Collins Medical Center, Fort Collins, CO, p. A103
SUTTON, Thomas, Associate Director, North Florida/South Georgia Veteran's Health System, Gainesville, FL, p. A127
SUTTON–WALLACE, Pamela, Chief Executive Officer, University of Virginia Medical Center, Charlottesville, VA, p. A663
SUVER, James A., FACHE, Chief Executive Officer, Ridgecrest Regional Hospital, Ridgecrest, CA, p. A83
SUZUKI, Daniel, M.D. Medical Director, Las Encinas Hospital, Pasadena, CA, p. A80
SVENDSEN, Mark Deyo, M.D. Medical Director, Mayo Clinic Health System – Red Cedar in Menomonie, Menomonie, WI, p. A705
SVIHOVEC, Angelia K., Chief Executive Officer, Mobridge Regional Hospital, Mobridge, SD, p. A570
SWAGERTY, Jill, Director Human Resources, Union County General Hospital, Clayton, NM, p. A423
SWAIN, Art, Vice President Support Services, Joint Township District Memorial Hospital, Saint Marys, OH, p. A497
SWAINE, Richard P., President, Beaumont Hospital Grosse Pointe, Grosse Pointe, MI, p. A321
SWAN, Debbie, Director Human Resources, Baptist Memorial Hospital–North Mississippi, Oxford, MS, p. A359
SWAN, Dennis A., FACHE, President and Chief Executive Officer, Sparrow Health System, Lansing, MI, p. B125
SWAN, Dennis A., FACHE, President and Chief Executive Officer, Sparrow Hospital, Lansing, MI, p. A324
SWANDAL, Dianne, R.N. Vice President Patient Care, St. Joseph Hospital, Bangor, ME, p. A288
SWANGER, Cae, Chief Information Officer, Riverside Community Hospital, Riverside, CA, p. A84
SWANGER, Carol, Chief Nursing Officer, Kansas Rehabilitation Hospital, Topeka, KS, p. A251
SWANK, Georgia, Chief Nursing Officer, Ridge Behavioral Health System, Lexington, KY, p. A260
SWANSON, Julie, Coordinator Human Resources, HEALTHSOUTH Western Hills Regional Rehabilitation Hospital, Parkersburg, WV, p. A694
SWANSON, Kerry, President, St. Mary's Janesville Hospital, Janesville, WI, p. A703
SWANSON, Margaret J., Chief Nursing Officer, Fairview Lakes Health Services, Wyoming, MN, p. A349
SWARTOUT, Paula, HR Manager, Dickinson County Healthcare System, Iron Mountain, MI, p. A322
SWARTWOOD, Philip, Director Information Systems, Grove City Medical Center, Grove City, PA, p. A535
SWARTZ, Edward, Chief Financial Officer, Spring Grove Hospital Center, Baltimore, MD, p. A295
SWARTZ, Michael J., FACHE, Medical Center Director, Bath Veterans Affairs Medical Center, Bath, NY, p. A429
SWEARINGEN, Angela, Vice President Finance, St. Mary's Medical Center, Huntington, WV, p. A692
SWEAT, Holli, Associate Administrator and Chief Nursing Officer, Mayo Clinic Health System in Waycross, Waycross, GA, p. A167
SWEENEY, Karen, MSN Vice President, Chief Nursing Officer, Mercy Hospital Ada, Ada, OK, p. A503
SWEENEY, Mary, Vice President Colleague Services and Development, St. Mary Medical Center, Langhorne, PA, p. A538
SWEENEY, Michael, Chief Information Officer, Fox Chase Cancer Center–American Oncologic Hospital, Philadelphia, PA, p. A543
SWEENY, Kevin, M.D. Vice President and Chief Medical Officer, Yakima Valley Memorial Hospital, Yakima, WA, p. A688
SWEET, Mary, Administrator, Kiowa County Memorial Hospital, Greensburg, KS, p. A241
SWEET, Renae, Chief Financial Officer, Surprise Valley Health Care District, Cedarville, CA, p. A57
SWEET, Terrance J., Director Information Technology, Winnebago Mental Health Institute, Winnebago, WI, p. A714

A982 Index of Health Care Professionals 

SWEETNICH, Ed, Vice President of Human Resources, Mercer Health, Coldwater, OH, p. A485

SWEGER, Pamela K., Director Human Resources, Atchison Hospital, Atchison, KS, p. A237

SWEHA, Amir, M.D. Vice President Medical Administration, Methodist Hospital of Sacramento, Sacramento, CA, p. A84

SWEITZER, Gregory, Chief Medical Officer, Wright Patterson Medical Center, Wright–Patterson AFB, OH, p. A501

SWENSON, Daniel J., FACHE, Administrator and Chief Executive Officer, CentraCare Health–Long Prairie, Long Prairie, MN, p. A341

SWENSON, Jennifer, President and Chief Executive Officer, Simi Valley Hospital, Simi Valley, CA, p. A92

SWENSON, Nena, Financial Manager, Tahoe Pacific Hospitals, Sparks, NV, p. A404

SWENSON, Nina, Director Business Services, Newport Bay Hospital, Newport Beach, CA, p. A78

SWENSON, Paula C., R.N. Vice President and Chief Nursing Officer, St. Catherine Hospital, East Chicago, IN, p. A207

SWENSON, Warren, Chief Financial Officer, United Medical Rehabilitation Hospital, Hammond, LA, p. A274

SWICEGOOD, Debbie
Director Human Resources, Vidant Bertie Hospital, Windsor, NC, p. A470
Director Human Resources, Vidant Chowan Hospital, Edenton, NC, p. A459

SWICK, Maureen, R.N. Senior Vice President, Chief Operating Officer, Inova Fairfax Hospital, Falls Church, VA, p. A664

SWICK, Michael D., President and Chief Executive Officer, Lima Memorial Health System, Lima, OH, p. A492

SWIDERSKI, Tom, Chief Financial Officer, Orthopaedic Hospital of Wisconsin – Glendale, Glendale, WI, p. A701

SWIFT, Brian M., Senior Administrator Plant Operations, Burke Rehabilitation Hospital, White Plains, NY, p. A454

SWIFT, Diane, Director Medical Records, I–70 Community Hospital, Sweet Springs, MO, p. A379

SWIFT, Kyle, Chief Executive Officer, Woodland Heights Medical Center, Lufkin, TX, p. A630

SWIFT, Nick, Chief Financial Officer, Maury Regional Hospital, Columbia, TN, p. A576

SWIGER, Jared, Director Information Systems, Ashtabula County Medical Center, Ashtabula, OH, p. A478

SWINDELL, Terry
Controller, Bolivar General Hospital, Bolivar, TN, p. A574
Chief Financial Officer, Camden General Hospital, Camden, TN, p. A574

SWINDLE, Patrick, Administrator, East Texas Medical Center–Quitman, Quitman, TX, p. A638

SWINGLE, Dale
Vice President Information Services, Robert Packer Hospital, Sayre, PA, p. A549
Vice President Information Services, Troy Community Hospital, Troy, PA, p. A551

SWINKO, Paul, Interim Chief Financial Officer, Penn State Milton S. Hershey Medical Center, Hershey, PA, p. A536

SWINT, Ken
Director Finance, ProMedica Defiance Regional Hospital, Defiance, OH, p. A488
Vice President Finance and Chief Financial Officer, ProMedica Fostoria Community Hospital, Fostoria, OH, p. A490

SWINT, Patricia
Director Information Management Systems, ProMedica Defiance Regional Hospital, Defiance, OH, p. A488
Director Information Technology, ProMedica St. Luke's Hospital, Maumee, OH, p. A494

SWISHER, Kay, Chief Nursing Officer, Greenville Health System – Laurens County Memorial Hospital, Clinton, SC, p. A559

SWISSHELM, Patricia, Acting Chief Fiscal Service, Lexington Veterans Affairs Medical Center, Lexington, KY, p. A260

SWITAJ, Timothy, Deputy Commander for Clinical Services, Reynolds Army Community Hospital, Fort Sill, OK, p. A507

SWITZER, Megan, Director Human Resources, Jersey Shore Hospital, Jersey Shore, PA, p. A536

SWOFFORD, William, M.D. Chief of Staff, Miller County Hospital, Colquitt, GA, p. A154

SWORDS, James, Director Human Resources, Lewis County General Hospital, Lowville, NY, p. A436

SY, Annette, R.N. Chief Nursing Officer, University of Southern California–Norris Cancer Hospital, Los Angeles, CA, p. A73

SYED, Imran, Manager Technology Information Services, Spectrum Health Zeeland Community Hospital, Zeeland, MI, p. A333

SYED, Mamoon
Vice President Human Resources, Children's Hospital of Orange County, Orange, CA, p. A79
Vice President Human Resources, CHOC Children's at Mission Hospital, Mission Viejo, CA, p. A75
Vice President Human Resources, Rady Children's Hospital – San Diego, San Diego, CA, p. A86

SYKES, Angel, Director Human Resources, Memorial Hospital and Manor, Bainbridge, GA, p. A152

SYKES, Christina, Director Human Resources, Labette Health, Parsons, KS, p. A248

SYKES, Lisa
IS/Communications Director, Carolinas HealthCare System Anson, Wadesboro, NC, p. A470
Manager, Information Services, Carolinas HealthCare System NorthEast, Concord, NC, p. A458
Director Information Services, Carolinas Healthcare System Union, Monroe, NC, p. A465

SYKES, Rebecca S., Chief Information Officer, Mercy St. Anne Hospital, Toledo, OH, p. A498

SYLVIA, John B., President, St. Luke's Hospital – Quakertown Campus, Quakertown, PA, p. A548

SYLVIA–HUTCHINSON, Doreen M., Vice President Operations and Chief Nurse Executive, Fairview Hospital, Great Barrington, MA, p. A307

SYNDER, Ron, Interim President and Chief Executive Officer, OhioHealth Hardin Memorial Hospital, Kenton, OH, p. A491

SYNDERGAARD, Christy, Vice President Nursing, Cherokee Regional Medical Center, Cherokee, IA, p. A224

SYNNESTVEDT, Eric, Director Information Technology, Southside Regional Medical Center, Petersburg, VA, p. A670

SYPIEN, Troy
Director Information Technology and Systems, Medical City Dallas Hospital, Dallas, TX, p. A605
Director Information Technology and Systems, TriStar Skyline Madison Campus, Madison, TN, p. A582
Director Information Technology and Systems, TriStar Skyline Medical Center, Nashville, TN, p. A586

SZABO, Charleen R., FACHE, Director, West Palm Beach Veterans Affairs Medical Center, West Palm Beach, FL, p. A147

SZABO, Sandor, M.D. Chief of Staff, VA Long Beach Healthcare System, Long Beach, CA, p. A68

SZCZEPANSKI, Bernadette S.
Vice President, Human Resources Development, Centegra Hospital – McHenry, McHenry, IL, p. A194
Vice President Human Resources Development, Centegra Hospital – Woodstock, Woodstock, IL, p. A203

SZCZUROWSKI, Richard, Director Human Resources, Norristown State Hospital, Norristown, PA, p. A542

SZEKELY, Lauraine, R.N. Senior Vice President, Patient Care, Northern Westchester Hospital, Mount Kisco, NY, p. A438

SZENCZY, Catherine, Senior Vice President and Chief Information Officer, MedStar Georgetown University Hospital, Washington, DC, p. A119

SZEWCZYK, Edwin, Chief Financial Officer, Wetzel County Hospital, New Martinsville, WV, p. A693

SZKLANY, Chelsea, Hospital Administrator, Southern Nevada Adult Mental Health Services, Las Vegas, NV, p. A402

SZOSTEK, Joshua, Chief Financial Officer, Specialty Hospital Jacksonville, Jacksonville, FL, p. A130

SZURA, Kathleen, R.N. Chief Nursing Officer, HEALTHSOUTH Bakersfield Rehabilitation Hospital, Bakersfield, CA, p. A55

SZYMANSKI, Michael, Chief Financial Officer, Doctors Hospital of Manteca, Manteca, CA, p. A74

# T

TAAFFE, Janette, Vice President, Human Resource, St. Luke's Hospital, Chesterfield, MO, p. A365

TABAK, Jeremy, M.D. President Medical Staff, Baptist Health South Florida, South Miami Hospital, Miami, FL, p. A134

TABB, Kevin, M.D., President and Chief Executive Officer, Beth Israel Deaconess Medical Center, Boston, MA, p. A302

TABIBI, Wasae S., M.D. President Medical Staff, Plaza Specialty Hospital, Houston, TX, p. A621

TABOADO, Ketty, Chief Financial Officer, Gladys Spellman Specialty Hospital and Nursing Center, Cheverly, MD, p. A296

TABOR, J. Britton, Senior VP and Chief Financial Officer, Erlanger Medical Center, Chattanooga, TN, p. A575

TABOR, Jeffrey, Director Human Resources, Jackson General Hospital, Ripley, WV, p. A695

TABOR, Randy, Director Fiscal Services, Shriners Hospitals for Children–Shreveport, Shreveport, LA, p. A285

TABORA, Knaya, Chief Operating Officer and Chief Nursing Officer, Colorado River Medical Center, Needles, CA, p. A77

TABUENCA, Arnold, M.D. Medical Director, Riverside County Regional Medical Center, Moreno Valley, CA, p. A76

TACHIBANA, Charleen, R.N. Senior Vice President and Chief Nursing Officer, Virginia Mason Medical Center, Seattle, WA, p. A684

TACKITT, Sue, Chief Nursing Officer, Connally Memorial Medical Center, Floresville, TX, p. A612

TADURAN, Virgilio, M.D. Chief Medical Officer, Satanta District Hospital and Long Term Care, Satanta, KS, p. A250

TAFFE, Patrick, Vice President Information Services, North Memorial Medical Center, Robbinsdale, MN, p. A345

TAFOYA, Debbie, Vice President and Chief Information Officer, Huntington Memorial Hospital, Pasadena, CA, p. A80

TAFOYA, Debra, Director Human Resources, HEALTHSOUTH Rehabilitation Hospital–Las Vegas, Las Vegas, NV, p. A402

TAFT, Kenneth L., Executive Vice President and Chief Operating Officer, Bronson Methodist Hospital, Kalamazoo, MI, p. A323

TAFUR, Mario, M.D. Chief of Staff, St. Luke's Behavioral Health Center, Phoenix, AZ, p. A36

TAGGART, Travis, Director Information Technology, RiverValley Behavioral Health Hospital, Owensboro, KY, p. A264

TAGGE, Gordon, M.D. President Medical Staff, Three Rivers Hospital, Brewster, WA, p. A677

TAHAN, Pamela S., Chief Operating Officer, Wellington Regional Medical Center, West Palm Beach, FL, p. A147

TAHBO, Robin, Financial Management Officer, U. S. Public Health Service Indian Hospital, Parker, AZ, p. A34

TAKACS, Susan, Market Chief Operating Officer, Physicians Regional – Pine Ridge, Naples, FL, p. A136

TAKES, Kay, R.N. Vice President Patient Care Services and Chief Nursing Officer, Mercy Medical Center–Dubuque, Dubuque, IA, p. A227

TAKEUCHI, Susi, Chief Human Resources Officer, UC Irvine Medical Center, Orange, CA, p. A79

TALAREK, Diane P., R.N. Chief Nursing Officer, Christiana Care Health System, Newark, DE, p. A117

TALBERT, Bradley S., FACHE, Chief Executive Officer, Coastal Carolina Hospital, Hardeeville, SC, p. A562

TALBOT, Angela, Manager Human Resources, Hamilton County Hospital, Syracuse, KS, p. A251

TALBOT, Jack, Director, Human Resources, West Chester Hospital, West Chester, OH, p. A500

TALBOT, Lisa, Director Human Resources, St. David's South Austin Medical Center, Austin, TX, p. A595

TALBOT, Tom, Chief Executive Officer, Community Mental Health Center, Lawrenceburg, IN, p. A214

TALBOTT, Ellen E., R.N. Vice President Patient Care Services, McLaren Bay Region, Bay City, MI, p. A315

TALBOTT, Sarah, Chief Nursing Officer, Sanford Chamberlain Medical Center, Chamberlain, SD, p. A567

TALENTO, Rick, Senior Vice President and Chief Financial Officer, Providence Hospital, Washington, DC, p. A120

TALLANT–BALL, Mary Jo, Director Health Information Systems, Dallas Medical Center, Dallas, TX, p. A604

TALLARICO, Dominica, President, Advocate Condell Medical Center, Libertyville, IL, p. A192

TALLEY, Cyndi, Director Information Systems, TriStar Greenview Regional Hospital, Bowling Green, KY, p. A255

TALLEY, Linda, MS Vice President and Chief Nursing Officer, Children's National Medical Center, Washington, DC, p. A119

TALLEY, Rockey, M.D. Chief Medical Officer, AllianceHealth Midwest, Midwest City, OK, p. A510

TALLEY, Stephanie S.
Director Human Resources, Centennial Medical Center, Frisco, TX, p. A615
Interim Chief Human Resource Officer, The Hospitals of Providence Memorial Campus, El Paso, TX, p. A611
Interim Chief Human Resource Officer, The Hospitals of Providence Sierra Campus, El Paso, TX, p. A611

TALLEY, Stu, Chief Nursing Officer, Carson Tahoe Continuing Care Hospital, Carson City, NV, p. A400

TALLON, Joe, Vice President Finance, Salina Regional Health Center, Salina, KS, p. A250

TALLON, Richard, Chief Financial Officer, Jefferson County Hospital, Waurika, OK, p. A518

TAM, Paulina, Vice President of Operations, Tampa Community Hospital, Tampa, FL, p. A145

TAMANAHA, Nona, Vice President Human Resources, Queen's Medical Center, Honolulu, HI, p. A169

TAMBURELLO, Leonardo, Divisional Chief Financial Officer, New York Community Hospital, NY, p. A442

TAMMINEN, John, M.D. President Medical Staff, Carilion Giles Community Hospital, Pearisburg, VA, p. A670

TAN, Bradford, M.D. Chief Medical Officer, Midwestern Regional Medical Center, Zion, IL, p. A203

TANAKA, Steven, Chief Information Officer, Pomerado Hospital, Poway, CA, p. A82

TANDON, Satwant, M.D. Director of Clinical Services, Oklahoma Forensic Center, Vinita, OK, p. A517

TANDY, Gary R., Chief Financial Officer, General John J. Pershing Memorial Hospital, Brookfield, MO, p. A364

TANEBAUM, Cynthia, Director Information Services, MedStar Harbor Hospital, Baltimore, MD, p. A294

TANEJA, K. Singh, Chief Operating Officer, Prince George's Hospital Center, Cheverly, MD, p. A296

TANG, Francis, Chief Information Officer, Rancho Los Amigos National Rehabilitation Center, Downey, CA, p. A60

Index of Health Care Professionals

Index of Health Care Professionals / Tang


TANG, Shirley, R.N. Chief Nursing Officer, Garfield Medical Center, Monterey Park, CA, p. A76

TANGEMAN, Todd, Vice President Operations, Newton Medical Center, Newton, KS, p. A246

TANGUAY, Denis, Chief Information Officer, Central Maine Medical Center, Lewiston, ME, p. A290

TANJUAKIO, Robert, Chief Information Resources Management, Edward Hines, Jr. Veterans Affairs Hospital, Hines, IL, p. A190

TANKEL, Nancy, R.N. Chief Nurse Executive, Kaiser Permanente Woodland Hills Medical Center, CA, p. A70

TANNENBAUM, Scott, M.D. Medical Director, HEALTHSOUTH Sunrise Rehabilitation Hospital, Sunrise, FL, p. A143

TANNER, Douglas, Chief Executive Officer, Washington County Hospital, Chatom, AL, p. A18

TANNER, Laureen K., FACHE, President and Chief Executive Officer, Ranken Jordan Pediatric Bridge Hospital, Maryland Heights, MO, p. A372

TANNOS, Paul, Chief Financial Officer, The Physicians Centre Hospital, Bryan, TX, p. A599

TANTHOREY, Geoff, Director Information Systems, Granville Health System, Oxford, NC, p. A466

TAPLETT, Dean, Controller, Quincy Valley Medical Center, Quincy, WA, p. A682

TAPLEY, Jahni, JD, Interim Chief Executive Officer, McCurtain Memorial Hospital, Idabel, OK, p. A508

TAPP, Gina
- Director Human Resources, Samaritan North Lincoln Hospital, Lincoln City, OR, p. A522
- Director Human Resources, Samaritan Pacific Communities Hospital, Newport, OR, p. A523

TAPPER, Shane, Director Management Information Systems, Fort Madison Community Hospital, Fort Madison, IA, p. A228

TARAMASCO, Chris, R.N. Chief Nursing Officer, Brandon Regional Hospital, Brandon, FL, p. A122

TARAR, Ahmad, M.D. Medical Director, Heartland Behavioral Health Services, Nevada, MO, p. A373

TARASOVICH, James
- Chief Financial Officer, Mayo Clinic Health System in Saint James, Saint James, MN, p. A346
- Chief Financial Officer, Mayo Clinic Health System in Springfield, Springfield, MN, p. A347

TARASOVITCH, James, Chief Financial Officer, Mayo Clinic Health System in Mankato, Mankato, MN, p. A341

TARBAY, Amy, Director Nursing Services, Naval Hospital Pensacola, Pensacola, FL, p. A139

TARBELL, Tim, Assistant Administrator Support Services, Scott & White Hospital – Taylor, Taylor, TX, p. A646

TARBET, Joyce, M.D. Chief Medical Officer, Murray County Medical Center, Slayton, MN, p. A347

TARRANT, Jeff, Chief Executive Officer, AllianceHealth Durant, Durant, OK, p. A506

TARRANT, Maureen, Chief Executive Officer, Presbyterian–St. Luke's Medical Center, Denver, CO, p. A102

TARTAGLIA, Judith C., President and Chief Executive Officer, The University of Vermont Health Network Central Vermont Medical Center, Berlin, VT, p. A660

TARULLI, Pamela, Senior Vice President Human Resources, Good Samaritan Hospital, Suffern, NY, p. A451

TARVER, Jeanette, Director of Finance, Sonoma Valley Hospital, Sonoma, CA, p. A92

TARVER, Rebecca, Chief Nursing Officer, Bates County Memorial Hospital, Butler, MO, p. A364

TARVES, Paul E., R.N. Vice President Nursing Services, Evangelical Community Hospital, Lewisburg, PA, p. A538

TARWATER, Michael C., Chief Executive Officer, Carolinas Healthcare System, Charlotte, NC, p. B28

TASSEY, Karen, FACHE Chief Operating Officer, Columbia Memorial Hospital, Hudson, NY, p. A435

TASSIN, Bruce J., President and Chief Executive Officer, CHRISTUS St. Vincent Regional Medical Center, Santa Fe, NM, p. A426

TASSO, Tina, Manager Human Resources, The Orthopedic Specialty Hospital, Murray, UT, p. A656

TATE, Charlene, M.D. Chief Medical Staff and Clinical Services, Eleanor Slater Hospital, Cranston, RI, p. A555

TATE, Charles, Director Information Technology, Lallie Kemp Medical Center, Independence, LA, p. A275

TATE, James, M.D. Chief of Staff, Patients' Hospital of Redding, Redding, CA, p. A82

TATE, Jean, Vice President Human Resources, RiverView Health, Crookston, MN, p. A337

TATE, Jodie, Director Human Resources, Westerly Hospital, Westerly, RI, p. A556

TATELBAUM, Ronald, M.D
- Interim Vice President Medical Affairs, Putnam Hospital Center, Carmel, NY, p. A431
- Chief Medical Officer – Health Quest, Vassar Brothers Medical Center, Poughkeepsie, NY, p. A448

TATRO, Chad, Supervisor Information Systems, Northeast Regional Medical Center, Kirksville, MO, p. A371

TATUM, Amber, Controller, Kindred Hospital Boston–North Shore, Peabody, MA, p. A310

TATUM, Robert, M.D. Chief of Staff, Merit Health Madison, Canton, MS, p. A351

TATUM, Stanley D., FACHE, Chief Executive Officer, St. Mary's Regional Medical Center, Enid, OK, p. A506

TAUL, Kelly, Business Manager, Meadowbrook Rehabilitation Hospital, Gardner, KS, p. A240

TAUNER, Gary, Chief Operating Officer, St. John's Medical Center and Living Center, Jackson, WY, p. A716

TAUNTON, David, M.D. Chief of Staff, Texas Health Harris Methodist Hospital Southlake, Southlake, TX, p. A644

TAUPIN, Michel, M.D. Chief Medical Officer, Abington Health Lansdale Hospital, Lansdale, PA, p. A538

TAVARY, James, Chief Executive Officer, Wickenburg Community Hospital, Wickenburg, AZ, p. A40

TAVELLA, Christopher
- Acting Executive Director, Rockland Children's Psychiatric Center, Orangeburg, NY, p. A446
- Executive Director, Rockland Psychiatric Center, Orangeburg, NY, p. A447

TAVENNER, Matt, Chief Executive Officer, Southern Virginia Regional Medical Center, Emporia, VA, p. A664

TAWNEY, Michael W., D.O. Vice President Medical Affairs, McLaren Port Huron, Port Huron, MI, p. A328

TAYLOR, Adam, Manager Information Technology, Northern Inyo Hospital, Bishop, CA, p. A56

TAYLOR, Alfred P., President and Chief Executive Officer, Stanly Regional Medical Center, Albemarle, NC, p. A455

TAYLOR, Alice, MSN, Chief Executive Officer, Broward Health Imperial Point, Fort Lauderdale, FL, p. A126

TAYLOR, Allison H., R.N. Chief Nursing Officer and Vice President Clinical Services, Sampson Regional Medical Center, Clinton, NC, p. A458

TAYLOR, Amy, Chief Financial Officer, Oklahoma Center for Orthopedic and Multi–Specialty Surgery, Oklahoma City, OK, p. A512

TAYLOR, Anthony, Manager Information Technology, Cherokee Indian Hospital, Cherokee, NC, p. A458

TAYLOR, Beth, Vice President, Human Resources, Newton–Wellesley Hospital, Newton Lower Falls, MA, p. A309

TAYLOR, Brenda, Director Information Systems, Texas Health Harris Methodist Hospital Cleburne, Cleburne, TX, p. A601

TAYLOR, Brett, M.D. Manager Information, Van Wert County Hospital, Van Wert, OH, p. A499

TAYLOR, Carol M., R.N., Regional Director Clinical Operations, Group Health Cooperative Central Hospital, Seattle, WA, p. A683

TAYLOR, Cecilia, Chief Financial Officer, Midwestern Regional Medical Center, Zion, IL, p. A203

TAYLOR, Cherie, Chief Executive Officer, Northern Rockies Medical Center, Cut Bank, MT, p. A382

TAYLOR, Cheryl, R.N. Director of Nursing, Henry Ford Kingswood Hospital, Ferndale, MI, p. A319

TAYLOR, Christina, Director Human Resources, The Brook Hospital – KMI, Louisville, KY, p. A262

TAYLOR, Clay, Chief Executive Officer, Covenant Hospital Plainview, Plainview, TX, p. A636

TAYLOR, Dana Shantel, Director Organizational Development, Fairfield Memorial Hospital, Fairfield, IL, p. A188

TAYLOR, Debra, Chief Nursing Officer, Paris Regional Medical Center, Paris, TX, p. A635

TAYLOR, Diana, Administrator, Sabine County Hospital, Hemphill, TX, p. A618

TAYLOR, Dwayne, Chief Executive Officer, Sycamore Shoals Hospital, Elizabethton, TN, p. A577

TAYLOR, Ernest Lee, M.D. Vice President Medical Affairs, St. Mary's Medical Center, Huntington, WV, p. A692

TAYLOR, Faye M., R.N. Director of Nursing, Stephens County Hospital, Toccoa, GA, p. A166

TAYLOR, Gregory W., M.D. Vice President and Chief Operating Officer, High Point Regional Health System, High Point, NC, p. A462

TAYLOR, Iris, R.N., President, Detroit Receiving Hospital/University Health Center, Detroit, MI, p. A317

TAYLOR, Janey, Chief Information and Technology, Overton Brooks Veterans Affairs Medical Center, Shreveport, LA, p. A284

TAYLOR, Jay, M.D. Chief of Staff, Pondera Medical Center, Conrad, MT, p. A382

TAYLOR, Jeff
- Senior Vice President Finance, Magnolia Regional Health Center, Corinth, MS, p. A352
- Vice President Finance, St. Luke's Regional Medical Center, Boise, ID, p. A173

TAYLOR, Jeremy, Director Information Services, Saint Francis Hospital, Charleston, WV, p. A690

TAYLOR, Jim, Chief Business Office, North Florida/South Georgia Veteran's Health System, Gainesville, FL, p. A127

TAYLOR, Joel
- Administrator, Citizens Baptist Medical Center, Talladega, AL, p. A25
- Chief Information Officer, Hoboken University Medical Center, Hoboken, NJ, p. A412

TAYLOR, Judd, Chief Financial Officer, Ogden Regional Medical Center, Ogden, UT, p. A656

TAYLOR, Julia, Area Director Human Resources, Vibra Hospital of Charleston, Mt. Pleasant, SC, p. A563

TAYLOR, Julie, FACHE, Chief Executive Officer, Alaska Regional Hospital, Anchorage, AK, p. A27

TAYLOR, Kent, Director Human Resources, Riverside Walter Reed Hospital, Gloucester, VA, p. A665

TAYLOR, Konnie, Chief Financial Officer, Carl Albert Community Mental Health Center, McAlester, OK, p. A509

TAYLOR, Kristie, Chief Financial Officer, Southern Tennessee Regional Health System–Lawrenceburg, Lawrenceburg, TN, p. A581

TAYLOR, Linda, Chief Human Resources Officer, Goodland Regional Medical Center, Goodland, KS, p. A240

TAYLOR, Lisa, Director of Nursing, Mountain View Hospital, Payson, UT, p. A657

TAYLOR, Lora, Director Human Resources and Compliance Officer, Keokuk Area Hospital, Keokuk, IA, p. A230

TAYLOR, Marc, IS Director, Mountain West Medical Center, Tooele, UT, p. A659

TAYLOR, Marcia, Chief Executive Officer, HEALTHSOUTH Rehabilitation Hospital Memphis–North, Memphis, TN, p. A583

TAYLOR, Meredith, Comptroller, South Sunflower County Hospital, Indianola, MS, p. A354

TAYLOR, Merle, Vice President Operations, UPMC St. Margaret, Pittsburgh, PA, p. A547

TAYLOR, Michael
- Chief Information Officer, Bon Secours St. Francis Xavier Hospital, Charleston, SC, p. A558
- Vice President Finance, Northridge Hospital Medical Center, CA, p. A71
- Vice President Financial Services and Chief Financial Officer, St. Rose Hospital, Hayward, CA, p. A64

TAYLOR, Michael V.
- Senior Vice President Human Resources, Sentara Leigh Hospital, Norfolk, VA, p. A669
- Vice President Human Resources, Sentara Princess Anne Hospital, Virginia Beach, VA, p. A674

TAYLOR, Mimi
- Corporate Vice President Information Technology, Baptist Health South Florida, Baptist Hospital of Miami, Miami, FL, p. A133
- Corporate Vice President Information Technology, Baptist Health South Florida, Homestead Hospital, Homestead, FL, p. A129
- Vice President Information Technology, Baptist Health South Florida, Mariners Hospital, Tavernier, FL, p. A146
- Vice President Information Technology, Baptist Health South Florida, South Miami Hospital, Miami, FL, p. A134

TAYLOR, Nathan, Director of Nursing, Heartland Behavioral Health Services, Nevada, MO, p. A373

TAYLOR, Patrick, M.D., President and Chief Executive Officer, Holy Cross Hospital, Fort Lauderdale, FL, p. A126

TAYLOR, Paul
- Administrator, Ozarks Community Hospital, Gravette, AR, p. A45
- Chief Executive Officer, Ozarks Community Hospital, Springfield, MO, p. A379

TAYLOR, Randy, Chief Information Technology Officer, Perry Memorial Hospital, Perry, OK, p. A513

TAYLOR, Renae, Chief Nursing Officer, Southeastern Health, Lumberton, NC, p. A464

TAYLOR, Richard, Chief Financial Officer, Western Mental Health Institute, Bolivar, TN, p. A574

TAYLOR, Robbie, Director Human Resources, North Sunflower Medical Center, Ruleville, MS, p. A360

TAYLOR, Robert, Director Information Services, St. Christopher's Hospital for Children, Philadelphia, PA, p. A545

TAYLOR, Ross, M.D. Clinical Director, Austin State Hospital, Austin, TX, p. A594

TAYLOR, Sarah, Chief Human Resources, National Jewish Health, Denver, CO, p. A102

TAYLOR, Scott J., President and Chief Executive Officer, St. Catherine Hospital, Garden City, KS, p. A240

TAYLOR, Scotty, Information Technology Director, East Mississippi State Hospital, Meridian, MS, p. A357

TAYLOR, Sharon, Human Resources Director, Allegiance Specialty Hospital of Greenville, Greenville, MS, p. A353

TAYLOR, Stacy, Chief Financial Officer, Nemaha County Hospital, Auburn, NE, p. A389


**A984** Index of Health Care Professionals

TAYLOR, Steve, Chief Information Officer, Anderson Regional Medical Center–South Campus, Meridian, MS, p. A357

TAYLOR, Steve, M.D. Chief Medical Officer, Sarasota Memorial Health Care System, Sarasota, FL, p. A142

TAYLOR, Steven L., Chief Executive Officer, Harrison County Hospital, Corydon, IN, p. A206

TAYLOR, Sue O., Vice President Nursing, Vidant Duplin Hospital, Kenansville, NC, p. A463

TAYLOR, Susan L., Chief Executive Officer, College Hospital Costa Mesa, Costa Mesa, CA, p. A59

TAYLOR, Todd, Chief Executive Officer, Stafford County Hospital, Stafford, KS, p. A250

TAYLOR, Tyrone, Chief Financial Officer, Veterans Affairs New Jersey Health Care System, East Orange, NJ, p. A411

TAYLOR, Venus, Director Human Resources, BHC Alhambra Hospital, Rosemead, CA, p. A84

TAYLOR–WHITEHEAD, Cheryl, Commander, Weed Army Community Hospital, Fort Irwin, CA, p. A61

TEAFORD, Carrie, Vice President Finance, Saint Thomas Midtown Hospital, Nashville, TN, p. A585

TEAGUE, Jr., David Lowell, Director Information Technology, Hood Memorial Hospital, Amite, LA, p. A268

TEAGUE, Dean, Chief Executive Officer, Calvert Memorial Hospital, Prince Frederick, MD, p. A299

TEAHL, Bradley, Director Human Resources, HEALTHSOUTH Rehabilitation Hospital of York, York, PA, p. A554

TEAL, Barbara, R.N. Associate Director Patient Care Services and Nurse Executive, Sioux Falls Veterans Affairs Health Care System, Sioux Falls, SD, p. A572

TEAL, Cydney, M.D. Vice President Medical Affairs, Union Hospital, Elkton, MD, p. A297

TEAL, Dianne P., MSN Vice President Clinical Operations, CHRISTUS St. Patrick Hospital of Lake Charles, Lake Charles, LA, p. A278

TEAL, Kelly, Chief Nursing Officer, Epic Medical Center, Eufaula, OK, p. A506

TEAS, Gregory, M.D. Chief Medical Officer, Alexian Brothers Behavioral Health Hospital, Hoffman Estates, IL, p. A191

TEASDALE, Peggy, Director Human Resources, Southeast Health Center of Ripley County, Doniphan, MO, p. A366

TEATER, Phyllis, Chief Information Officer, Ohio State University Wexner Medical Center, Columbus, OH, p. A486

TEBBE, James, M.D. Vice President Medical Affairs, Ochsner Medical Center – Kenner, Kenner, LA, p. A276

TEDDER, Cookie, Human Resources Manager, Texas Health Center for Diagnostic & Surgery, Plano, TX, p. A637

TEDESCHI, Anthony, M.P.H., Chief Executive Officer and Chief Medical Officer, Louis A. Weiss Memorial Hospital, Chicago, IL, p. A182

TEDESCO, Art, Interim Chief Financial Officer, Gaylord Hospital, Wallingford, CT, p. A115

TEETER, Richard, Chief Financial Officer, Muenster Memorial Hospital, Muenster, TX, p. A633

TEEUWEN, Pat
Director Team Resources, South Florida Baptist Hospital, Plant City, FL, p. A140
Director Team Resources, St. Joseph's Hospital, Tampa, FL, p. A145

TEFERA, Tad, Vice President Finance and Chief Financial Officer, Ohio Valley Hospital, McKees Rocks, PA, p. A539

TEFFETELLER, Scott L., President and Chief Executive Officer, Union Hospital Clinton, Clinton, IN, p. A206

TEICHMEIER, Laura, Director of Human Resources, Memorial Community Health, Aurora, NE, p. A389

TEISSONNIERE, Maria T., Director Public Relations, Hospital Oncologico Andres Grillasca, Ponce, PR, p. A722

TEITELBAUM, Karen, President and Chief Executive Officer, Sinai Health System, Chicago, IL, p. B123

TEIXEIRA, Fred, M.D. Chief of Staff, Vidant Beaufort Hospital, Washington, NC, p. A470

TEJADA, Vanessa, Director Human Resources, HEALTHSOUTH Rehabilitation Institute of San Antonio, San Antonio, TX, p. A640

TEJEDA, Nicholas R., FACHE, Chief Executive Officer, The Hospitals of Sierra Providence East Campus, El Paso, TX, p. A611

TELITZ, Rita, Chief Administrative Officer, Rusk County Memorial Hospital, Ladysmith, WI, p. A703

TELL, Marjorie, Vice President Information Technology, Aspirus Riverview Hospital and Clinics, Inc., Wisconsin Rapids, WI, p. A714

TELLOR, Tammy, Acting Director Human Resources, Choate Mental Health Center, Anna, IL, p. A178

TELTHORSTER, M.ED, CCP, Marcia M., Vice President Human Resources, University Medical Center of Princeton at Plainsboro, Plainsboro, NJ, p. A417

TEMPELMEYER, Zak, M.D. Chief Medical Staff, Community Memorial Hospital, Syracuse, NE, p. A398

TEMPEST, Wendy, Director Human Resources, Vibra Hospital of Northern California, Redding, CA, p. A82

TEMPLE, Amber L., Director Human Resources, Morrison Community Hospital, Morrison, IL, p. A195

TEMPLE, Gina, Chief Nurse Executive, Sutter Auburn Faith Hospital, Auburn, CA, p. A54

TEMPLE, Tracy, Chief Nursing Officer, Central Carolina Hospital, Sanford, NC, p. A468

TEMPLETON, Carrie E., FACHE, Chief Executive Officer, Lafayette General Surgical Hospital, Lafayette, LA, p. A277

TEMPLETON, Gary, M.D. Medical Director, Regency Hospital of Northwest Arkansas – Springdale, Springdale, AR, p. A51

TEMPLETON, Parker A., FACHE, Chief Executive Officer, Iberia Medical Center, New Iberia, LA, p. A281

TEMPLETON, Sheryl, Chief Financial Officer, Scotland County Hospital, Memphis, MO, p. A372

TEMPLETON, III, William, M.D. Medical Director, Clark Memorial Hospital, Jeffersonville, IN, p. A213

TEMPLIN, Nancy, Vice President Finance and Chief Financial Officer, All Children's Hospital Johns Hopkins Medicine, Saint Petersburg, FL, p. A141

TEN HAAF, Patricia, R.N. Associate Director of Patient Care Services, Kansas City Veterans Affairs Medical Center, Kansas City, MO, p. A369

TEN HAAF, Patricia, Ph.D., Acting Director, Veterans Affairs St. Louis Health Care System, Saint Louis, MO, p. A378

TENEWITZ, Edward, M.D. Chief of Staff, Healthmark Regional Medical Center, DeFuniak Springs, FL, p. A125

TENGERES, Michael A., Corporate Vice President and Chief Financial Officer, Bassett Medical Center, Cooperstown, NY, p. A432

TENHOUSE, Steven D., FACHE, Chief Executive Officer, Kirby Medical Center, Monticello, IL, p. A194

TENNARO, Sonja, Ed.D. Senior Vice President Clinical Operations, New York Eye and Ear Infirmary of Mount Sinai, New York, NY, p. A442

TENNEY, Ralph
Chief Information Officer, St. John Hospital and Medical Center, Detroit, MI, p. A318
Chief Information Officer, St. John Macomb–Oakland Hospital, Warren, MI, p. A332

TENNYSON, Ruby, Director Administration, Naval Hospital Jacksonville, Jacksonville, FL, p. A129

TENREIRO, Edgardo J., Executive Vice President and Chief Operating Officer, Baton Rouge General Medical Center, Baton Rouge, LA, p. A269

TEODO, Paul M., Chief Operating Officer, Holy Cross Hospital, Chicago, IL, p. A182

TEPEDINO, Miguel, M.D. Chief Medicine, Lake City Medical Center, Lake City, FL, p. A131

TEPPER, Gil, M.D., Chief Executive Officer, Miracle Mile Medical Center, Los Angeles, CA, p. A71

TER HORST, Thomas C., Vice President Human Resources, Aurora St. Luke's Medical Center, Milwaukee, WI, p. A706

TERBUSH, Jennifer, Director of Nursing, Hills & Dales General Hospital, Cass City, MI, p. A316

TERI, Anthony, Director Information Technology, Hackensack University Medical Center at Pascack Valley, Westwood, NJ, p. A420

TERNES, Howard, Chief Executive Officer, San Gabriel Valley Medical Center, San Gabriel, CA, p. A89

TERPENING, Ken, Chief Nursing Officer, Mad River Community Hospital, Arcata, CA, p. A54

TERPSTRA, Kelli, R.N
Chief Nursing Officer, Baylor Specialty Hospital, Dallas, TX, p. A604
Chief Nursing Officer, Our Children's House at Baylor, Dallas, TX, p. A606

TERRELL, Greg, Senior Vice President and Chief Operating Officer, Norman Regional Health System, Norman, OK, p. A510

TERRELL, Jay, Manager Management Information Systems, Riverview Regional Medical Center, Gadsden, AL, p. A20

TERRELL, Michael T., Chief Financial Officer, Brandon Regional Hospital, Brandon, FL, p. A122

TERRESON, Gregg, Chief Financial Officer, Cascade Behavioral Hospital, Tukwila, WA, p. A686

TERRINONI, Gary G., Chief Financial Officer and Executive Vice President Administration, Kennedy Health System, Cherry Hill, NJ, p. A410

TERRY, Sr., Darrell K., Senior Vice President Operations, Newark Beth Israel Medical Center, Newark, NJ, p. A415

TERRY, Micheal, President and Chief Executive Officer, Salina Regional Health Center, Salina, KS, p. A250

TERRY, Paula, Director of Nursing, Pathways of Tennessee, Jackson, TN, p. A579

TERRY, Randi, Site Director Management Information Systems, Munson Healthcare Cadillac Hospital, Cadillac, MI, p. A315

TERRY, Richard, Vice President & Chief Information Officer, Sparrow Carson Hospital, Carson City, MI, p. A316

TERRYBERRY, Daniel S., M.D. Vice President of Medical Affairs, Sentara Albemarle Medical Center, Elizabeth City, NC, p. A459

TERTEL, Jenifer K., Director Human Resources, Medical City Dallas Hospital, Dallas, TX, p. A605

TERWILLIGER, Michael, Chief Financial Officer, Friends Hospital, Philadelphia, PA, p. A543

TERZANO, Valerie, MS Chief Nursing Officer, Senior Vice President Nursing, Winthrop–University Hospital, Mineola, NY, p. A437

TESKE, Mark, Chief Financial Officer, Hill Crest Behavioral Health Services, Birmingham, AL, p. A16

TESKE, Tim, D.O. Chief of Staff, St. Mary's Regional Medical Center, Enid, OK, p. A506

TESSARZIK, Connie, Business Manager, Albert J. Solnit Psychiatric Center – South Campus, Middletown, CT, p. A113

TESSMAN, Lisa, Manager Information Technology, Fayette County Hospital, Vandalia, IL, p. A202

TESTA, Nick, M.D. Chief Medical Officer, Providence Saint Joseph Medical Center, Burbank, CA, p. A56

TETRAULT, Jeffrey E., Director Facilities and Construction, Crouse Hospital, Syracuse, NY, p. A451

TETTEH, Walter
Director Human Resources, Children's Hospital of Michigan, Detroit, MI, p. A317
Director Human Resources, Rehabilitation Institute of Michigan, Detroit, MI, p. A318

TETZ, Warren, Senior Vice President and Chief Operating Officer, Glendale Adventist Medical Center, Glendale, CA, p. A63

TEUBNER, Sandra, Interim Chief Executive Officer, St. Aloisius Medical Center, Harvey, ND, p. A474

TEUFEL, George, Vice President Finance, Advocate Good Shepherd Hospital, Barrington, IL, p. A179

TEVES, Alicia, Coordinator Human Resources, Molokai General Hospital, Kaunakakai, HI, p. A170

TEWKSBURY, Randy E., Vice President Finance, Geisinger–Lewistown Hospital, Lewistown, PA, p. A539

TEZANOS, Francis, Director Information Technology and Services, Kendall Regional Medical Center, Miami, FL, p. A134

THACKER, Roland, Chief Financial Officer, Northside Medical Center, Columbus, GA, p. A154

THAKOR, Pratapji, M.D. Chief of Staff, South Mississippi County Regional Medical Center, Osceola, AR, p. A49

THAMA, Todd, Chief Operating Officer, Fairfax Behavioral Health, Kirkland, WA, p. A680

THAMES, Lisa, Director of Nursing, Mesa Springs, Fort Worth, TX, p. A613

THAMES, Robert P., President and Chief Executive Officer, Northern Arizona Healthcare, Flagstaff, AZ, p. B98

THAMES, Thomas B., M.D., President, Sentara Princess Anne Hospital, Virginia Beach, VA, p. A674

THARP, Beth S., R.N., President and Chief Executive Officer, Community Hospital of Anderson and Madison County, Anderson, IN, p. A204

THARP, John Gary, M.D. Medical Director, Riverview Behavioral Health, Texarkana, AR, p. A51

THARP, Stephen, M.D. Medical Director, St. Vincent Frankfort Hospital, Frankfort, IN, p. A209

THAYER, Gilbert M., M.D. Chief Medical Staff, Hardin Medical Center, Savannah, TN, p. A587

THAYER, Kendra, Vice President Clinical and Support Services and Chief Nursing Officer, Garrett County Memorial Hospital, Oakland, MD, p. A299

THEILER, Brian, President and Chief Executive Officer, Gundersen Tri–County Hospital and Clinics, Whitehall, WI, p. A714

THEIRING, James, Chief Executive Officer, Mission Community Hospital, CA, p. A71

THEISEN, Janet
Chief Information Officer, Sanford Tracy Medical Center, Tracy, MN, p. A348
Chief Information Officer, Sanford Westbrook Medical Center, Westbrook, MN, p. A349

THELEN, Daniel, Director Information Systems, Caldwell Memorial Hospital, Lenoir, NC, p. A464

THELEN, Raymond Scott, Vice President and Chief Financial Officer, Masonicare Health Center, Wallingford, CT, p. A115

THEMELIS, Carol, Vice President Human Resources, Frisbie Memorial Hospital, Rochester, NH, p. A408

THEOBALD, Terry, Chief Information Officer, Ventura County Medical Center, Ventura, CA, p. A96

THEODOROU, Andreas, Chief Medical Officer, Banner – University Medical Center Tucson, Tucson, AZ, p. A39

THERIAC, Gary, Director Information Technology, Lawrence County Memorial Hospital, Lawrenceville, IL, p. A192

THERIOT, Lyle, Director Human Resources, Lakeview Regional Medical Center, Covington, LA, p. A272

THERIOT, Paul, Chief Operating Officer, Gadsden Regional Medical Center, Gadsden, AL, p. A20

THEROULT, Thomas N., ACHE, Chief Executive Officer, Select Specialty Hospital–Omaha, Omaha, NE, p. A396

THERRIEN, Charles D., Chief Executive Officer, Maine Coast Memorial Hospital, Ellsworth, ME, p. A290

THERRIEN, Tinna, Chief Information Officer and Director Clinical Infomatics, Gothenburg Memorial Hospital, Gothenburg, NE, p. A392

THETFORD, Carol, Chief Nursing Officer, Baptist Memorial Hospital for Women, Memphis, TN, p. A583

THEUS, Thomas L., M.D. Chief of Medicine, Midtown Medical Center West, Columbus, GA, p. A154

THEUS, Will, M.D. Chief of Staff, Gordon Hospital, Calhoun, GA, p. A153

THIBODEAU, Helene, R.N. Vice President Patient Care Services, Northeast Rehabilitation Hospital, Salem, NH, p. A408

THIBODEAU, Jan, Director Human Resources, HEALTHSOUTH Southern Hills Rehabilitation Hospital, Princeton, WV, p. A694

THIBODEAUX, Anita, Chief Nursing Officer, Beauregard Memorial Hospital, De Ridder, LA, p. A273

THIBODEAUX, Annette, Director Human Resources, Savoy Medical Center, Mamou, LA, p. A279

THIBODEAUX, Douglas, M.D. Chief Medical Officer, OakBend Medical Center, Richmond, TX, p. A638

THIEL, Stefanie
 Senior Human Resources Business Partner, Saint Alphonsus Medical Center – Nampa, Nampa, ID, p. A175
 Senior Human Resources Business Partner, Saint Alphonsus Medical Center – Ontario, Ontario, OR, p. A523

THIELE, Rosemary, Chief Executive Officer, AMG Specialty Hospital – Las Vegas, Las Vegas, NV, p. A401

THIELEMIER, Kevin, Director Human Resources, Arkansas Methodist Medical Center, Paragould, AR, p. A49

THIELEN, Kurt, Manager Business Office, Minneapolis Veterans Affairs Health Care System, Minneapolis, MN, p. A342

THIELKE, Jayne, Chief Financial Officer, Swift County–Benson Hospital, Benson, MN, p. A335

THIEME, Ron, Ph.D. Chief Knowledge and Information Officer, Community Hospital North, Indianapolis, IN, p. A211

THIESFELD RAUEN, Rebecca A., Director Human Resources, Maple Grove Hospital, Maple Grove, MN, p. A342

THILGES, Charles, Chief Financial Officer, Veterans Affairs Pittsburgh Healthcare System, Pittsburgh, PA, p. A547

THILGES, Michael, Chief Financial Officer, Clarke County Hospital, Osceola, IA, p. A232

THILL, Curtis C., M.D. Medical Staff President, Indiana University Health Paoli Hospital, Paoli, IN, p. A218

THILL, Jennifer, Chief of Staff, Mid–Valley Hospital, Omak, WA, p. A681

THIMIS, Nicholas, Chief Information Officer, West Jefferson Medical Center, Marrero, LA, p. A280

THIRUMALAREDDY, Joseph, M.D. Chief of Staff, Wishek Community Hospital and Clinics, Wishek, ND, p. A477

THOELE, Theresa, Director Human Resources, Coffey County Hospital, Burlington, KS, p. A238

THOENDEL, Victor, M.D. Chief Medical Officer, Butler County Health Care Center, David City, NE, p. A391

THOMAN, Dawn, Vice President Human Resources, Cloud County Health Center, Concordia, KS, p. A238

THOMAN, Michele, R.N. Chief Nursing Officer, NCH Downtown Naples Hospital, Naples, FL, p. A136

THOMAS, Amy, Vice President Finance, Memorial Hospital, Belleville, IL, p. A179

THOMAS, Andrew, M.D. Chief Medical Officer, Ohio State University Wexner Medical Center, Columbus, OH, p. A486

THOMAS, Brian E., Administrator, Alton Mental Health Center, Alton, IL, p. A178

THOMAS, Brian N., Senior Vice President and Chief Operating Officer, Jefferson Regional Medical Center, Pine Bluff, AR, p. A50

THOMAS, Brook, Chief Financial Officer, West Boca Medical Center, Boca Raton, FL, p. A122

THOMAS, IV, Calvin, Chief Operating Officer, St. Lucie Medical Center, Port St. Lucie, FL, p. A141

THOMAS, Charmaine, R.N. Chief Nursing Officer, Polk Medical Center, Cedartown, GA, p. A153

THOMAS, Chris, FACHE, President and Chief Executive Officer, Community Hospital, Grand Junction, CO, p. A104

THOMAS, Cristina
 Vice President and Chief Information Officer, Mercy Medical Center – West Lakes, West Des Moines, IA, p. A236
 Vice President and Chief Information Officer, Mercy Medical Center–Des Moines, Des Moines, IA, p. A226

THOMAS, Curt, Administrator, Ness County Hospital, Ness City, KS, p. A246

THOMAS, Debbie, Director Human Resources, Central Regional Hospital, Butner, NC, p. A456

THOMAS, Debora, Chief Financial Officer, Florida Hospital Memorial Medical Center, Daytona Beach, FL, p. A125

THOMAS, Debra A., Vice President of Patient Care Services and Chief Nursing Officer, Penn Highlands Brookville, Brookville, PA, p. A530

THOMAS, Denise, Chief Financial Officer, Spring View Hospital, Lebanon, KY, p. A259

THOMAS, Dennis, Chief Nursing Officer, Hardeman County Memorial Hospital, Quanah, TX, p. A638

THOMAS, Gene, Vice President, Information Systems, Chief Information Officer, Memorial Hospital at Gulfport, Gulfport, MS, p. A353

THOMAS, Jayne, Chief Nursing Officer, AllianceHealth Deaconess, Oklahoma City, OK, p. A511

THOMAS, Jeff, Chief Financial Officer, Heartland Regional Medical Center, Marion, IL, p. A193

THOMAS, Jennifer, Chief Operating Officer and Director of Public Relations, Lake Butler Hospital Hand Surgery Center, Lake Butler, FL, p. A131

THOMAS, Jill, Director of Nursing, Western State Hospital, Hopkinsville, KY, p. A258

THOMAS, Joan, Chief Financial Officer, Novant Health Brunswick Medical Center, Bolivia, NC, p. A456

THOMAS, John, Chief Operating Officer, San Mateo Medical Center, San Mateo, CA, p. A90

THOMAS, John A., M.D. Chief Medical Staff, Culberson Hospital, Van Horn, TX, p. A649

THOMAS, Karen A.
 Vice President and Chief Information Officer, Bryn Mawr Hospital, Bryn Mawr, PA, p. A530
 Chief Information Officer, Bryn Mawr Rehabilitation Hospital, Malvern, PA, p. A539
 Acting Vice President and Chief Information Officer, Lankenau Medical Center, Wynnewood, PA, p. A554
 Vice President and Chief Information Officer, Paoli Hospital, Paoli, PA, p. A542

THOMAS, Keith, M.D. Chief of Staff, Blue Mountain Hospital, John Day, OR, p. A522

THOMAS, Kirk E., Vice President Operations, Geisinger–Lewistown Hospital, Lewistown, PA, p. A539

THOMAS, Lizbeth, M.D. Vice President Medical Affairs, Fairview Ridges Hospital, Burnsville, MN, p. A336

THOMAS, Maggie, Vice President Human Resources and Practice Management, South County Hospital, Wakefield, RI, p. A556

THOMAS, Michael, Associate Administrator, Wayne County Hospital, Corydon, IA, p. A225

THOMAS, Michael S., President and Chief Administrative Officer, John Muir Medical Center, Concord, Concord, CA, p. A58

THOMAS, Michelle, Vice President Human Resources, Berkeley Medical Center, Martinsburg, WV, p. A693

THOMAS, Nicky, Director Human Resources, Baptist Memorial Hospital–Union City, Union City, TN, p. A589

THOMAS, Patric, Corporate Vice President Information Services, Scripps Green Hospital, La Jolla, CA, p. A66

THOMAS, Patricia F., Chief Nursing Officer, Sentara Halifax Regional Hospital, South Boston, VA, p. A673

THOMAS, Paula, R.N. Vice President Patient Services, UPMC Bedford Memorial, Everett, PA, p. A534

THOMAS, Russell, M.D. Chief of Staff, Rice Medical Center, Eagle Lake, TX, p. A609

THOMAS, Ruth, Chief Operating Officer, Mercy Fitzgerald Hospital, Darby, PA, p. A532

THOMAS, Sarah, Director of Human Resources, HEALTHSOUTH Rehabilitation Hospital of Denver, Littleton, CO, p. A106

THOMAS, Scott, Administrative Director Human Resources and Communications, Granville Health System, Oxford, NC, p. A466

THOMAS, Sharon, Vice President and Chief Nursing Officer, University Hospitals Parma Medical Center, Parma, OH, p. A496

THOMAS, Shawn M., Director Human Resources, Payson Regional Medical Center, Payson, AZ, p. A34

THOMAS, Stephanie, Chief Operating Officer, Denver Health, Denver, CO, p. A101

THOMAS, Sue, Manager Human Resources, Beckley ARH Hospital, Beckley, WV, p. A689

THOMAS, Sylvia, Chief Nursing Officer, Jack Hughston Memorial Hospital, Phenix City, AL, p. A24

THOMAS, Warner L., FACHE, President and Chief Executive Officer, Ochsner Health System, New Orleans, LA, p. B100

THOMAS, Jr., William, M.D. Medical Director Clinical and Internal Affairs, Molokai General Hospital, Kaunakakai, HI, p. A170

THOMAS–BOYD, Sharon L., Chief Support and Ancillary Services Officer, Oaklawn Hospital, Marshall, MI, p. A325

THOMAS–FOLDS, Lana, System Director Human Resources, Jack Hughston Memorial Hospital, Phenix City, AL, p. A24

THOMAS–WILLIAMS, Jovita, Associate Vice President Human Resources, The University of Toledo Medical Center, Toledo, OH, p. A499

THOMASON, Joe D., Chief Executive Officer, Centennial Medical Center, Frisco, TX, p. A615

THOMASON, Scott, Director of Nursing, Cumberland Hall Hospital, Hopkinsville, KY, p. A258

THOMBLEY, Stephen, M.D. Chief of Staff, Dorminy Medical Center, Fitzgerald, GA, p. A157

THOMMAN, Connie, Director of Nursing, Covenant Hospital–Levelland, Levelland, TX, p. A628

THOMPSON, Alan, M.D. President Medical Staff, Warm Springs Medical Center, Warm Springs, GA, p. A167

THOMPSON, Angela S., Vice President Human Resources and Support Services, Indiana University Health North Hospital, Carmel, IN, p. A206

THOMPSON, Becki, President, CHI Oakes Hospital, Oakes, ND, p. A476

THOMPSON, Becky, Chief Financial Officer, CHI St. Francis Health, Breckenridge, MN, p. A336

THOMPSON, Belinda, Coordinator Human Resources, HEALTHSOUTH Chesapeake Rehabilitation Hospital, Salisbury, MD, p. A300

THOMPSON, Bobby, Director Information Technology, Stephens Memorial Hospital, Breckenridge, TX, p. A598

THOMPSON, Chad
 Chief Financial Officer, Lallie Kemp Medical Center, Independence, LA, p. A275
 Interim Chief Executive Officer, Regional West Garden County, Oshkosh, NE, p. A397

THOMPSON, Charles, M.D. Chief Medical Officer, Nacogdoches Medical Center, Nacogdoches, TX, p. A633

THOMPSON, Charolette, Chief Financial Officer, Reeves Memorial Medical Center, Bernice, LA, p. A270

THOMPSON, Cheryl
 Facility Director Human Resources, Connecticut Valley Hospital, Middletown, CT, p. A113
 Chief Nursing Officer, Garden Park Medical Center, Gulfport, MS, p. A353

THOMPSON, Chris
 Chief Financial Officer, Delta Community Medical Center, Delta, UT, p. A654
 Chief Financial Officer, Fillmore Community Medical Center, Fillmore, UT, p. A654
 Chief Financial Officer, Sanpete Valley Hospital, Mount Pleasant, UT, p. A656
 Chief Financial Officer, Sevier Valley Medical Center, Richfield, UT, p. A657

THOMPSON, Cindy, Chief Financial Officer, Northwest Surgical Hospital, Oklahoma City, OK, p. A512

THOMPSON, Craig, Chief Operating Officer, Golden Valley Memorial Healthcare, Clinton, MO, p. A365

THOMPSON, Craig B., M.D., President and Chief Executive Officer, Memorial Sloan–Kettering Cancer Center, New York, NY, p. A441

THOMPSON, Dale
 Chief Financial Officer, McLaren Greater Lansing, Lansing, MI, p. A324
 Chief Operating Officer, Western State Hospital, Tacoma, WA, p. A686

THOMPSON, David, M.D. Chief of Staff, Richardson Medical Center, Rayville, LA, p. A284

THOMPSON, David
 Chief Financial Officer, St. Anthony Hospital, Lakewood, CO, p. A106
 Chief Financial Officer, St. Anthony Summit Medical Center, Frisco, CO, p. A104

THOMPSON, David M., Chief Executive Officer, Sutter Tracy Community Hospital, Tracy, CA, p. A94

THOMPSON, Debbie, Chief Financial Officer, Sweetwater Hospital, Sweetwater, TN, p. A588

THOMPSON, Donna K., Chief Executive Officer, Allegiance Health Center of Ruston, Ruston, LA, p. A284

THOMPSON, Douglas, Chief Information Officer, Upson Regional Medical Center, Thomaston, GA, p. A165

THOMPSON, Dwight, Chief Financial Officer, Altru Health System, Grand Forks, ND, p. A474

THOMPSON, Ethan, Chief Executive Officer, St. Theresa Specialty Hospital, Kenner, LA, p. A276

THOMPSON, Greg, Chief Medical Officer, Gundersen Health System, La Crosse, WI, p. A703

THOMPSON, James H., FACHE, Owner and Chief Executive Officer, Healthmark Regional Medical Center, DeFuniak Springs, FL, p. A125

THOMPSON, Jeffrey D., Chief Executive Officer, Baylor Institute for Rehabilitation at Fort Worth, Fort Worth, TX, p. A613

THOMPSON, Jeffrey E., M.D., Chief Executive Officer, Gundersen Health System, La Crosse, WI, p. A703

THOMPSON, John W., M.D. Chief of Staff, Eastern Louisiana Mental Health System, Jackson, LA, p. A275

THOMPSON, Julie
 Chief Nursing Officer, Bluffton Regional Medical Center, Bluffton, IN, p. A205
 Manager Personnel and Payroll, Mayers Memorial Hospital District, Fall River Mills, CA, p. A61

Index of Health Care Professionals / Timbers

THOMPSON, Kim, Vice President and Chief Financial Officer, Ozarks Medical Center, West Plains, MO, p. A380
THOMPSON, Linda
Chief Operating Officer, Fairfax Community Hospital, Fairfax, OK, p. A507
Vice President Human Resources, New England Baptist Hospital, Boston, MA, p. A304
THOMPSON, Lisa, MSN Director of Nursing, Hiawatha Community Hospital, Hiawatha, KS, p. A241
THOMPSON, Lisa D., Director Human Resources, Lea Regional Medical Center, Hobbs, NM, p. A424
THOMPSON, Lori L., Manager Human Resources, Nebraska Orthopaedic Hospital, Omaha, NE, p. A396
THOMPSON, Marion A., FACHE, Chief Executive Officer, Allen County Regional Hospital, Iola, KS, p. A242
THOMPSON, Mark, Vice President Finance and Chief Financial Officer, Lourdes Hospital, Paducah, KY, p. A264
THOMPSON, Mark, M.D. Chief Medical Officer, Monroe Clinic, Monroe, WI, p. A707
THOMPSON, Mark, Vice President Financial Services, Rapid City Regional Hospital, Rapid City, SD, p. A570
THOMPSON, Matthew J., Chief Executive Officer, Sparrow Carson Hospital, Carson City, MI, p. A316
THOMPSON, Michael S., Chief Executive Officer, Frio Regional Hospital, Pearsall, TX, p. A636
THOMPSON, Pamela, Chief Operations Officer, Huhukam Memorial Hospital, Sacaton, AZ, p. A37
THOMPSON, Patti, Chief Operating Officer, San Luis Valley Health, Alamosa, CO, p. A99
THOMPSON, Randell, Chief Nursing Officer, Plateau Medical Center, Oak Hill, WV, p. A693
THOMPSON, Reanna, R.N. Chief Operating Officer and Chief Nursing Officer, PIH Health Hospital–Whittier, Whittier, CA, p. A97
THOMPSON, Sarah, Director Health Information Management, Hardtner Medical Center, Olla, LA, p. A283
THOMPSON, Scott, Market Management Information System Director, Shands Live Oak Regional Medical Center, Live Oak, FL, p. A132
THOMPSON, Selva, R.N. Chief Nurse Executive, Gallup Indian Medical Center, Gallup, NM, p. A424
THOMPSON, Sherene, Director Human Resources, Houston Methodist Willowbrook Hospital, Houston, TX, p. A620
THOMPSON, Stuart, Vice President Human Resources, Memorial Hospital Jacksonville, Jacksonville, FL, p. A129
THOMPSON, Thomas R., Chief Executive Officer, Regina Hospital, Hastings, MN, p. A340
THOMPSON, Tim, Vice President Information Services, St. Anthony's Hospital, Saint Petersburg, FL, p. A142
THOMPSON, Sr., Timothy L., Senior Vice President and Chief Information Officer, Houston Methodist Hospital, Houston, TX, p. A620
THOMPSON, Tina H., Coordinator Human Resources, FirstHealth Montgomery Memorial Hospital, Troy, NC, p. A469
THOMPSON, Trinise, Director Human Resources, St. Luke's Medical Center, Phoenix, AZ, p. A36
THOMPSON, Vera, Director Human Resources, Kingsboro Psychiatric Center, NY, p. A440
THOMPSON, Wayne, Executive Vice President and Chief Information Officer, Mount Nittany Medical Center, State College, PA, p. A550
THOMPSON, Wesley, M.D. President Medical Staff, Fairfield Memorial Hospital, Fairfield, IL, p. A188
THOMPSON, William, M.D. Chief Medical Officer, Saint Thomas Midtown Hospital, Nashville, TN, p. A585
THOMPSON, William P., President and Chief Executive Officer, SSM Health, Saint Louis, MO, p. B126
THOMPSON–COOK, Timothy, Chief Operating Officer, Contra Costa Regional Medical Center, Martinez, CA, p. A74
THOMSEN, Sue
Chief Financial Officer, New Braunfels Regional Rehabilitation Hospital, New Braunfels, TX, p. A634
Chief Financial Officer, South Texas Rehabilitation Hospital, Brownsville, TX, p. A598
THOMSEN, Vicki
Director Human Resources, Aurora Behavioral Health System East, Tempe, AZ, p. A38
Director Human Resources, Aurora Behavioral Health System West, Glendale, AZ, p. A32
THOMSON, Doug, M.D. Chief Medical Officer, Commonwealth Regional Specialty Hospital, Bowling Green, KY, p. A254
THOMSON, Ken, M.D. Medical Director, Memorial Hermann Surgical HospitalG‰(First Colony, Sugar Land, TX, p. A645
THOMSON, Michael Sean, CPA Chief Financial Officer, Spotsylvania Regional Medical Center, Fredericksburg, VA, p. A665
THOMSON, Nicole, Chief Financial Officer, Saint Louise Regional Hospital, Gilroy, CA, p. A63
THOMSON, Steven, M.D. Medical Director, Heartland Behavioral Healthcare, Massillon, OH, p. A493
THOMSPON, Ormand, Administrator, Thomas Hospital, Fairhope, AL, p. A19
THONE, Tammy, M.D. Chief Medical Staff, Alleghany Memorial Hospital, Sparta, NC, p. A469
THORDARSON, G. Thor, President and Chief Executive Officer, Indiana University Health La Porte Hospital, La Porte, IN, p. A214
THORE, Joe, Chief Operating Officer, Ashe Memorial Hospital, Jefferson, NC, p. A463
THORESON, Scott D., FACHE, Administrator, Mayo Clinic Health System in Springfield, Springfield, MN, p. A347
THORMODSON, Cyndee
Chief Financial Officer, Carrington Health Center, Carrington, ND, p. A472
Assistant Vice President Finance, CHI Mercy Hospital, Devils Lake, ND, p. A473
THORN, III, Eugene A., Vice President Finance and Chief Financial Officer, Union Hospital, Dover, OH, p. A489
THORN, Margaret, Interim Director of Nursing, Red Bay Hospital, Red Bay, AL, p. A24
THORN, Mark, FACHE Executive Director, Finance, Mercy Hospital Lincoln, Troy, MO, p. A379
THORNBRUGH, Mitchell, Administrative Officer, Cherokee Nation W.W. Hastings Indian Hospital, Tahlequah, OK, p. A515
THORNE, Dana, Administrator Human Resources, Valley Hospital Medical Center, Las Vegas, NV, p. A403
THORNE Jr., William, Chief Executive Officer, Acoma–Canoncito–Laguna Hospital, Acoma, NM, p. A422
THORNELL, Timothy, FACHE, Chief Executive Officer, Lea Regional Medical Center, Hobbs, NM, p. A424
THORNSBERRY, Michael, M.D. Chief Medical Officer, Coliseum Medical Centers, Macon, GA, p. A160
THORNTON, Carol, Director Human Resources, Cherry Hospital, Goldsboro, NC, p. A461
THORNTON, Cayetano, Chief Information Officer, Walter Reed National Military Medical Center, Bethesda, MD, p. A296
THORNTON, Daryl W., Chief Operating Officer, Kansas Medical Center, Andover, KS, p. A237
THORNTON, Jan, Chief Nursing Officer, Bay Medical Center Sacred Heart Health System, Panama City, FL, p. A139
THORNTON, Jillisa, Director of Nursing, Coastal Harbor Treatment Center, Savannah, GA, p. A164
THORNTON, Laird, Director Information Systems, Alta Vista Regional Hospital, Las Vegas, NM, p. A425
THORNTON, Matt, Chief Information Officer, Liberty Dayton Regional Medical Center, Liberty, TX, p. A628
THORNTON Jr., Robert M., Chief Executive Officer, Sunlink Health Systems, Atlanta, GA, p. B129
THORNTON, Timothy J., Chief Financial Officer, Russell Medical Center, Alexander City, AL, p. A15
THORPE, Linda, Chief Executive Officer, East Morgan County Hospital, Brush, CO, p. A100
THORPE, Wendy, Area Director Information Systems, St. Joseph Hospital, Eureka, CA, p. A60
THORSEN, Erik, Chief Executive Officer, Columbia Memorial Hospital, Astoria, OR, p. A519
THORWALD, Robert, Chief Information Officer, Washington Hospital Healthcare System, Fremont, CA, p. A62
THOTAKURA, Raj, M.D. Medical Director, Old Vineyard Behavioral Health Services, Winston–Salem, NC, p. A471
THRASHER, Amanda, Director Nursing, Ellsworth County Medical Center, Ellsworth, KS, p. A239
THRASHER, Charlotte, Vice President and Chief Operating Officer, Seton Medical Center Austin, Austin, TX, p. A594
THRASHER, Kimberly, Controller, HEALTHSOUTH Lakeshore Rehabilitation Hospital, Birmingham, AL, p. A16
THRASHER, Sherri, Executive Director Human Resources, Spectrum Health Pennock, Hastings, MI, p. A322
THREEWITS, Sheree, Director Human Resources, Manatee Memorial Hospital, Bradenton, FL, p. A122
THULI, Karen, Coordinator Information Systems, Upland Hills Health, Dodgeville, WI, p. A699
THUN, Todd, Director Human Resources, Montana State Hospital, Warm Springs, MT, p. A387
THUNELL, Adam, Chief Operating Officer and Vice President Operations, Community Memorial Health System, Ventura, CA, p. A96
THURBER, Joe, Director Information Technology, Central Regional Hospital, Butner, NC, p. A456
THURMER, DeAnn, Chief Operating Officer, Waupun Memorial Hospital, Waupun, WI, p. A713
THURMOND, Jeff, Vice President Information Systems, Baptist Health Corbin, Corbin, KY, p. A255
THURSTON, Thomas, M.D. Medical Director, J. D. McCarty Center for Children With Developmental Disabilities, Norman, OK, p. A510
THYGESON, Cindy, M.D. Director Medical Affairs, Sutter Center for Psychiatry, Sacramento, CA, p. A85
THYNE, Shannon, Chief Medical Officer, LAC–Olive View–UCLA Medical Center, CA, p. A71
TIBBITS, Dick, Vice President and Chief Operating Officer, Florida Hospital Tampa, Tampa, FL, p. A144
TIBBITS, Richard M., Vice President and Chief Operating Officer, Loma Linda University Medical Center–Murrieta, Murrieta, CA, p. A77
TIBBS, E. W., President and Chief Executive Officer, Centra Health, Inc., Lynchburg, VA, p. B32
TIBBS, E. W., President and Chief Executive Officer, Centra Lynchburg General Hospital, Lynchburg, VA, p. A667
TICE, Darlette, Chief Nursing Officer, Manatee Memorial Hospital, Bradenton, FL, p. A122
TICE, Evan, Director Information Technology and Systems, Sky Ridge Medical Center, Lone Tree, CO, p. A106
TICE, Heidi, Chief Financial Officer, Cheyenne County Hospital, Saint Francis, KS, p. A249
TICE, Kirk C., President and Chief Executive Officer, Robert Wood Johnson University Hospital Rahway, Rahway, NJ, p. A417
TICE, Linda, Director Information Systems, SageWest Health Care at Riverton, Riverton, WY, p. A717
TICHENOR, Florence, Director Information Technology, Copper Basin Medical Center, Copperhill, TN, p. A576
TICHENOR, John, Chief Financial Officer, Ohio County Hospital, Hartford, KY, p. A258
TIDWELL, Joseph, Administrator, Phoenix Behavioral Hospital, Rayne, LA, p. A284
TIDWELL, Wesley, Chief Operating Officer, Memorial Hermann Northwest Hospital, Houston, TX, p. A621
TIEDE, Brad, Director Information Systems, Memorial Community Health, Aurora, NE, p. A389
TIEDT, Douglas, M.D. Chief of Staff, Springs Memorial Hospital, Lancaster, SC, p. A563
TIEDT, Jerry, Director Information Systems, Waverly Health Center, Waverly, IA, p. A236
TIEFENTHALER, MHA, BSN, Brenda Marie, R.N. Vice President Patient Care and Informatics, Spencer Hospital, Spencer, IA, p. A235
TIEMENS, Linda, Chief Executive Officer, Select Specialty Hospital–Tulsa Midtown, Tulsa, OK, p. A517
TIERNAN, Kelley, Chief Financial Officer, Claxton–Hepburn Medical Center, Ogdensburg, NY, p. A446
TIERNEY, Gregory, M.D. Office of the Chief Medical Officer, Lead, Benefis Hospitals, Great Falls, MT, p. A384
TIERNEY, Mark A., Chief Financial Officer, Manatee Memorial Hospital, Bradenton, FL, p. A122
TIFFANY, Carolyn, Deputy Commander Clinical Service, Carl R. Darnall Army Medical Center, Fort Hood, TX, p. A612
TIGGELAAR, Tom
Vice President Finance, Mayo Clinic Health System – Franciscan Healthcare in La Crosse, La Crosse, WI, p. A703
Vice President Finance ad Chief Financial Officer, Mayo Clinic Health System – Franciscan Healthcare in Sparta, Sparta, WI, p. A711
TILGHMAN, Bradley, Controller, HEALTHSOUTH Emerald Coast Rehabilitation Hospital, Panama City, FL, p. A139
TILLER, Debra, Director Personnel and Administrative Secretary, Healthmark Regional Medical Center, DeFuniak Springs, FL, p. A125
TILLER, Joni R., R.N. Chief Nursing Officer, Integris Baptist Medical Center, Oklahoma City, OK, p. A511
TILLIRSON, Mike, D.O. Executive Vice President and Chief Medical Officer, AnMed Health Medical Center, Anderson, SC, p. A557
TILLMAN, Jill, Assistant Chief Executive Officer, Brandywine Hospital, Coatesville, PA, p. A531
TILLMAN, Kanner, Chief Financial Officer, Encino Hospital Medical Center, CA, p. A69
TILLMAN, Michael C., President and Chief Executive Officer, United Hospital Center, Bridgeport, WV, p. A689
TILLMAN, Pamela P., R.N., Chief Executive Officer, Pioneer Community Hospital of Stokes, Danbury, NC, p. A458
TILLMAN, Randy, M.D. Chief Medical Staff, Promise Hospital of Miss Lou, Vidalia, LA, p. A286
TILLMAN–TAYLOR, Susan, Manager Human Resources, Southern Ocean Medical Center, Manahawkin, NJ, p. A414
TILSON, Natalie, Controller, HEALTHSOUTH Rehabilitation Hospital, Kingsport, TN, p. A580
TILTON, Colette, Vice President and Chief Nursing Officer, Southern New Hampshire Medical Center, Nashua, NH, p. A407
TILTON, David P., President and Chief Executive Officer, AtlantiCare, Egg Harbor Township, NJ, p. B16
TIMANUS, Anthony, Chief Executive Officer, Avera Gregory Hospital, Gregory, SD, p. A569
TIMBERS, Christopher, Vice President and Chief Information Officer, NorthBay Medical Center, Fairfield, CA, p. A61
TIMBERS, Christopher T., Chief Information Officer, Sibley Memorial Hospital, Washington, DC, p. A120

Index of Health Care Professionals

TIMLIN, Marie, R.N. Chief Nursing Officer, Yampa Valley Medical Center, Steamboat Springs, CO, p. A108

TIMM, Karen, R.N. Vice President Patient Services, St. Anthony Regional Hospital, Carroll, IA, p. A223

TIMM, Mark
Director Human Resources, Yavapai Regional Medical Center – East, Prescott Valley, AZ, p. A36
Director Human Resources, Yavapai Regional Medical Center, Prescott, AZ, p. A36

TIMM, Matt, M.D. Medical Director, Pender Community Hospital, Pender, NE, p. A397

TIMMER, Kari, Chief Financial Officer, Hegg Memorial Health Center Avera, Rock Valley, IA, p. A234

TIMMERMAN, Jo, Manager Accounting, Norwood Health Center, Marshfield, WI, p. A705

TIMMIS, Jonathan, Interim President and Chief Executive Officer, Saint Clare's Health System, Denville, NJ, p. A411

TIMMONS, Bret, D.O. Chief Medical Staff, Power County Hospital District, American Falls, ID, p. A172

TIMMONS, William, Chief Executive Officer, Los Ninos Hospital, Phoenix, AZ, p. A35

TIMOTHY, Promilia, Chief of Staff, Baraga County Memorial Hospital, L'Anse, MI, p. A324

TIMPE, David A., Interim President and Chief Executive Officer, Childrens Care Hospital and School, Sioux Falls, SD, p. A571

TIMPE, Ron, Chief Financial Officer, Floyd County Medical Center, Charles City, IA, p. A224

TINCHER, Pat, Director Finance, Langlade Hospital, Antigo, WI, p. A697

TINDALL, Patricia, Chief Executive Officer, Lyndon B. Johnson Tropical Medical Center, Pago Pago, AS, p. A719

TINDLE, Jeff A., Chief Executive Officer, Carroll County Memorial Hospital, Carrollton, MO, p. A365

TINDLE, Tim, Chief Information Officer, Harris Health System, Houston, TX, p. A619

TINGLE, Billy, Chief Information Officer, Dauterive Hospital, New Iberia, LA, p. A281

TINGSTAD, Jonathan, Vice President and Chief Financial Officer, Seattle Cancer Care Alliance, Seattle, WA, p. A683

TINKER, Allen, Administrator, Nix Community General Hospital, Dilley, TX, p. A609

TINKER, Peter, Chief Human Resources Officer, James J. Peters Veterans Affairs Medical Center, NY, p. A440

TINMAN, Rochelle Marie, Interim Chief Nurse Executive, Director of Nursing–Inpatient Services, UnityPoint Health – Trinity Rock Island, Rock Island, IL, p. A199

TINNERELLO, Jeremy, R.N. Chief Nursing Officer, Glenwood Regional Medical Center, West Monroe, LA, p. A286

TINNEY, Sean, FACHE Chief Operating Officer, Medical West, Bessemer, AL, p. A16

TINSA, Udom, M.D. Medical Director, Ashley Medical Center, Ashley, ND, p. A472

TINSLEY, Cassie, Director, Human Resources, Powell Valley Healthcare, Powell, WY, p. A717

TINSLEY III, Edward D., Chief Executive Officer, McLeod Loris Seacoast Hospital, Loris, SC, p. A563

TINSLEY, Nancy, President and Chief Executive Officer, University Hospitals Parma Medical Center, Parma, OH, p. A496

TIPPIN, Russell, Chief Executive Officer and Administrator, Permian Regional Medical Center, Andrews, TX, p. A592

TIPPS, Linda, Director Human Resources, Southern Tennessee Regional Health System–Winchester, Winchester, TN, p. A589

TIPTON, Maggie, Chief Information Officer, Unicoi County Memorial Hospital, Erwin, TN, p. A577

TIPTON, Peggy, Chief Operating Officer and Chief Nursing Officer, Oklahoma Heart Hospital, Oklahoma City, OK, p. A512

TIPTON, Teri, MSN Chief Nursing Officer and Vice President Patient Care Services, Nebraska Methodist Hospital, Omaha, NE, p. A396

TIRA, Cheryl, Director Information Systems, Columbus Community Hospital, Columbus, NE, p. A391

TIRADO, Norma, Vice President, Human Resources and Health Information Technology, Lakeland Hospital, Watervliet, Watervliet, MI, p. A332

TIRMAN, Kerry, President and Chief Operating Officer, Mercy St. Vincent Medical Center, Toledo, OH, p. A498

TISDALE, Willis E., Director Human Resources, Shriners Hospitals for Children–Greenville, Greenville, SC, p. A561

TISDALL, Renae, Chief Financial Officer, Mobridge Regional Hospital, Mobridge, SD, p. A570

TISSIER, Becky, Chief Fiscal Service, Veterans Affairs Illiana Health Care System, Danville, IL, p. A185

TITSWORTH, Sue, Director Human Resources, Coleman County Medical Center, Coleman, TX, p. A601

TITTLE, JoDee, Director Community and Human Resources, St. Charles Madras, Madras, OR, p. A522

TITUS, Monica, President and Chief Executive Officer, Acuity Specialty Hospital of New Jersey, Atlantic City, NJ, p. A409

TKACIK, Eileen, Vice President Information Technology and Patient Accounts, KidsPeace Children's Hospital, Orefield, PA, p. A542

TOADVINE, Stephen, M.D. Chief Medical Officer, Hardin Memorial Hospital, Elizabethtown, KY, p. A256

TOBEY, Shelley R., R.N. Chief Operating Officer and Chief Nursing Officer, Texas Health Presbyterian Hospital Flower Mound, Flower Mound, TX, p. A612

TOBIN, Hugh, Chief Financial Officer, Davis Regional Medical Center, Statesville, NC, p. A469

TOBIN, Ryan, Chief Operating Officer, Rose Medical Center, Denver, CO, p. A102

TOBLER, Randy, M.D., Chief Executive Officer, Scotland County Hospital, Memphis, MO, p. A372

TODD, Bob, Director Information Systems, Mount Auburn Hospital, Cambridge, MA, p. A305

TODD, Fred O., Senior Vice President Finance, McLeod Loris Seacoast Hospital, Loris, SC, p. A563

TODD, James, Chief Financial Officer, Acadia Vermilion Hospital, Lafayette, LA, p. A277

TODD, Nate, Chief Financial Officer, Central Arkansas Veterans Healthcare System, Little Rock, AR, p. A47

TODD, Robbie, Director Information Technology, Horn Memorial Hospital, Ida Grove, IA, p. A229

TODD, Steve J., Chief Executive Officer, St. Luke Community Healthcare, Ronan, MT, p. A386

TODD–ATKINSON, Sandra, Chief Operating Officer and Chief Nursing Officer, Broward Health Imperial Point, Fort Lauderdale, FL, p. A126

TODOROW, Thomas, Chief Financial Officer and Executive Vice President, Children's Hospital of Philadelphia, Philadelphia, PA, p. A543

TOEDT, Michael E., M.D. Director Clinical Services, Cherokee Indian Hospital, Cherokee, NC, p. A458

TOL, Daryl, Chief Executive Officer, Florida Hospital Memorial Medical Center, Daytona Beach, FL, p. A125

TOLBERT, Catherine L., R.N. Senior Vice President Nursing and Clinical Services and Chief Nurse Executive, St. Elizabeth Health Center, Youngstown, OH, p. A501

TOLBERT, James, Director Information Systems, EASTAR Health System, Muskogee, OK, p. A510

TOLEDO, Iris, Chief Nursing Officer, Hospital Dr. Cayetano Coll Y Toste, Arecibo, PR, p. A719

TOLINE, Tyler, FACHE, Interim Chief Executive Officer, Saunders Medical Center, Wahoo, NE, p. A398

TOLLEFSON, Sue, Coordinator Payroll Personnel, Granite Falls Municipal Hospital and Manor, Granite Falls, MN, p. A340

TOLLIVER, Amy, Administrator, Magee General Hospital, Magee, MS, p. A356

TOLSON, Rick, Chief Administrative Officer and Chief Human Resources Officer, Christ Hospital, Cincinnati, OH, p. A482

TOMAS, George, Director Information Services, Griffin Hospital, Derby, CT, p. A112

TOMASO, Nancy, Vice President, Patient Care Services, Milford Regional Medical Center, Milford, MA, p. A309

TOMBERLIN, Terri, Director Human Resources, Curry General Hospital, Gold Beach, OR, p. A521

TOME, Julie, M.D. Vice President North Central Region Medical Affairs, OhioHealth Marion General Hospital, Marion, OH, p. A493

TOME, Michael, M.D. Medical Director, Kaiser Permanente Los Angeles Medical Center, Los Angeles, CA, p. A70

TOMLIN, Kerry W., Associate Administrator, Clay County Hospital, Ashland, AL, p. A15

TOMLINSON, Charles M., M.D. Chief Medical Officer, Cleveland Regional Medical Center, Shelby, NC, p. A468

TOMLINSON, Daniel, Chair Human Resources, Mayo Clinic Jacksonville, Jacksonville, FL, p. A129

TOMLINSON, David
Executive Vice President Chief Financial Officer and Chief Information Officer, Centegra Hospital – McHenry, McHenry, IL, p. A194
Executive Vice President Chief Financial Officer and Chief Information Officer, Centegra Hospital – Woodstock, Woodstock, IL, p. A203

TOMLINSON, Sallie, Manager Human Resources, Arbuckle Memorial Hospital, Sulphur, OK, p. A515

TOMLON, Eric, Chief Executive Officer, The Surgical Hospital of Phoenix, Phoenix, AZ, p. A36

TOMORY, Gerald, M.D
Regional Medical Director, Kauai Veterans Memorial Hospital, Waimea, HI, p. A171
Regional Medical Director, Samuel Mahelona Memorial Hospital, Kapaa, HI, p. A170

TOMPKINS, Charles, M.D. Chief of Staff, Crenshaw Community Hospital, Luverne, AL, p. A21

TOMPKINS, Kim, Director Information Services, DeTar Healthcare System, Victoria, TX, p. A650

TONER, Tina, Director of Nursing, North Big Horn Hospital District, Lovell, WY, p. A716

TONEY, Mark, President and Chief Executive Officer, Brookdale Hospital Medical Center, NY, p. A439

TONEY, Patty, R.N. Chief Nurse Executive, CHRISTUS Santa Rosa Health System, San Antonio, TX, p. A640

TONG, Cheryl, Corporate Chief Financial Officer, Community Hospital of Huntington Park, Huntington Park, CA, p. A65

TONGATE, Scott, Chief Financial Officer, I–70 Community Hospital, Sweet Springs, MO, p. A379

TONGATE, Scott A., Chief Financial Officer, Lauderdale Community Hospital, Ripley, TN, p. A587

TONGES, Mary Crabtree, Ph.D. Senior Vice President and Chief Nursing Officer, University of North Carolina Hospitals, Chapel Hill, NC, p. A457

TONJES, Ken, Interim Chief Administrative Officer, PeaceHealth Ketchikan Medical Center, Ketchikan, AK, p. A28

TONKINSON, Robert
Chief Operating Officer and Chief Financial Officer, Mercy Allen Hospital, Oberlin, OH, p. A495
Chief Operating Officer and Chief Financial Officer, Mercy Regional Medical Center, Lorain, OH, p. A492

TONN, Deb L., Vice President Patient Care, Campbell County Memorial Hospital, Gillette, WY, p. A716

TONNU, Lannie, Senior Vice President and Chief Financial Officer, Children's Hospital Los Angeles, Los Angeles, CA, p. A69

TOOKE, Ryan, Chief Executive Officer, Rosebud Health Care Center, Forsyth, MT, p. A383

TOOKER, Deby, Director Human Resources, The Surgical Hospital of Phoenix, Phoenix, AZ, p. A36

TOOLE, LaDon, Vice President Network Operations, Mitchell County Hospital, Camilla, GA, p. A153

TOOLE, Patricia, Vice President Human Resources, East Mountain Hospital, Belle Mead, NJ, p. A409

TOOLE, Trish, Vice President Administrative Services, Carrier Clinic, Belle Mead, NJ, p. A409

TOOMEY, Richard Kirk, FACHE, President and Chief Executive Officer, Beaufort Memorial Hospital, Beaufort, SC, p. A557

TOON, William, Chief Information Officer, Baptist Hospitals of Southeast Texas, Beaumont, TX, p. A596

TOOT, Gregory P., Chief Operating Officer, Hebrew Rehabilitation Center, Boston, MA, p. A303

TOPMILLER, Darrell, Director Finance, Fulton County Health Center, Wauseon, OH, p. A500

TOPOLEWSKI, Ted, Chief Executive Officer, Madison Parish Hospital, Tallulah, LA, p. A286

TOPPEN, Jacki, Director of Nursing, Prairie St. John's, Fargo, ND, p. A473

TOPPER, David, Chief Executive Officer, Alta Healthcare System, Los Angeles, CA, p. B9

TORBETT, Russell B., Director Human Resources, Creek Nation Community Hospital, Okemah, OK, p. A511

TORCHIA, Joseph, M.D. Senior Vice President Medical Affairs and Chief Medical Officer, Holy Spirit – A Geisinger Affiliate, Camp Hill, PA, p. A530

TORCHIA, Jude, Chief Executive Officer, OrthoColorado Hospital, Lakewood, CO, p. A106

TORCHIANA, David, M.D., Chief Executive Officer, Partners HealthCare System, Inc., Boston, MA, p. B103

TORGE, Andrew, Director Human Resources, Shasta Regional Medical Center, Redding, CA, p. A82

TORGERSON, Paul, Senior Vice President Chief Administrative Officer and General Counsel, St. John's Hospital, Maplewood, MN, p. A342

TORMANEN, John, Director Mission and Human Resources, CHI St. Joseph's Health, Park Rapids, MN, p. A344

TORN, Michael, Chief Executive Officer, Edgewood Surgical Hospital, Transfer, PA, p. A551

TOROSSIAN, Lynn M., President and Chief Executive Officer, Henry Ford West Bloomfield Hospital, West Bloomfield, MI, p. A332

TORRES, Anthony, Manager Information Technology, Blue Mountain Hospital, Blanding, UT, p. A654

TORRES, Christopher John, Assistant Administrator Chief Financial Officer and Controller, Tyler County Hospital, Woodville, TX, p. A653

TORRES, Harvey, Chief Financial Officer, Valley Baptist Medical Center–Brownsville, Brownsville, TX, p. A599

TORRES, Maribel, Executive Vice President Patient Care Services and Chief Nursing Officer, United Medical Center, Washington, DC, p. A120

TORRES, Mayra, Chief Financial Officer, Ashford Presbyterian Community Hospital, San Juan, PR, p. A723

TORRES, Mike, M.D. Chief Medical Officer, Oak Hill Hospital, Brooksville, FL, p. A123

TORRES, Victor, Information Technology Specialist Administrator, University Behavioral Health of El Paso, El Paso, TX, p. A611

TORRES AYALA, Eugenio, Director Information Systems, Cardiovascular Center of Puerto Rico and the Caribbean, San Juan, PR, p. A723

Index of Health Care Professionals / Trinchetto

Index of Health Care Professionals


TORRICO, Pat, R.N. Chief Nursing Officer, Saint Mary's Regional Medical Center, Russellville, AR, p. A50
TORSCH, Peter, Chief Financial Officer, St. Charles Parish Hospital, Luling, LA, p. A279
TORTELLA, Anthony, Chief Financial Officer, Fairmount Behavioral Health System, Philadelphia, PA, p. A543
TOSI, Stephen E., M.D. Chief Medical Officer, UMass Memorial Medical Center, Worcester, MA, p. A313
TOSTEBERG, Chris, Superintendent, Mental Health Institute, Cherokee, IA, p. A224
TOSTENSON, Brad, Chief Information Officer, Essentia Health–Graceville, Graceville, MN, p. A339
TOSTI, Debra, Chief Executive Officer, Tewksbury Hospital, Tewksbury, MA, p. A312
TOUMBIS, C., M.D. Chief of Staff, Citrus Memorial Health System, Inverness, FL, p. A129
TOUPS, Sharon A., Senior Vice President and Chief Operating Officer, St. Tammany Parish Hospital, Covington, LA, p. A272
TOURIGNY, Barry, Vice President Human Resources and Organizational Development, Cabell Huntington Hospital, Huntington, WV, p. A691
TOUSIGNANT, Grace, R.N
Chief Nursing Officer, Aspirus Grand View, Ironwood, MI, p. A323
Chief Nursing Officer, Aspirus Keweenaw Hospital, Laurium, MI, p. A324
TOUVELLE, Cynthia, R.N. Senior Director Care Management and Chief Nursing Officer, Barnesville Hospital, Barnesville, OH, p. A479
TOVAR, Richard, M.D. Chief of Staff, Beaver Dam Community Hospitals, Beaver Dam, WI, p. A698
TOWERS, Darleen, Director Human Resources, Lake Whitney Medical Center, Whitney, TX, p. A652
TOWERY, O. B., M.D. Chief of Staff, John Muir Behavioral Health Center, Concord, CA, p. A58
TOWLE, Sonya, Director Human Resources, Mercy Hospital, Moose Lake, MN, p. A343
TOWN, Alex, Vice President Finance, Tri–State Memorial Hospital, Clarkston, WA, p. A677
TOWNDROW, Geraldine, R.N. Senior Vice President Nursing, Lutheran Medical Center, Wheat Ridge, CO, p. A109
TOWNE, Jana, Nurse Executive, U. S. Public Health Service Indian Hospital–Whiteriver, Whiteriver, AZ, p. A40
TOWNER, Chad, Chief Executive Officer, Dupont Hospital, Fort Wayne, IN, p. A208
TOWNER, Paul, Chief of Staff, Washington County Hospital and Clinics, Washington, IA, p. A235
TOWNES, Tim, Director Information Systems, Trinity Medical Center, Birmingham, AL, p. A17
TOWNLEY, Nancy, R.N. Senior Vice President Operations, United Regional Health Care System, Wichita Falls, TX, p. A652
TOWNSEND, Alan, Interim Chief Financial Officer, JPS Health Network, Fort Worth, TX, p. A613
TOWNSEND, Dona E., Chief Nursing Officer, Northeastern Nevada Regional Hospital, Elko, NV, p. A400
TOWNSEND, Gary, Chief Information Officer, Hurley Medical Center, Flint, MI, p. A319
TOWNSEND, Roxane A., M.D., Chief Executive Officer, UAMS Medical Center, Little Rock, AR, p. A47
TOWNSEND, Sammuel, LAN Administrator, University of Mississippi Medical Center Holmes County, Lexington, MS, p. A356
TOWNSEND, Stanley, Chief Executive Officer, Stone County Medical Center, Mountain View, AR, p. A48
TOWNSEND, Tanya, Senior Vice President, Chief Information Officer (part of LCMC), Children's Hospital, New Orleans, LA, p. A281
TOWNSEND, Theodore E., FACHE, President and Chief Executive Officer, UnityPoint Health – St. Luke's Hospital, Cedar Rapids, IA, p. A223
TOWNSLEY, Malcolm, M.D. Chief of Staff, CHI St. Anthony Hospital, Pendleton, OR, p. A523
TOWRISS, Douglas, Vice President and Chief Medical Officer, Schneck Medical Center, Seymour, IN, p. A219
TOY, Linda, Director Information Systems, Havasu Regional Medical Center, Lake Havasu City, AZ, p. A32
TOY Jr., Stanley, M.D., Chief Executive Officer, Greater El Monte Community Hospital, South El Monte, CA, p. A93
TOYE, Lawrence J., Chief Financial Officer, Kindred Hospital–Boston, Brighton, MA, p. A304
TRAC, Vincent, Chief Executive Officer, Kindred Hospital–Ontario, Ontario, CA, p. A79
TRACEY, Karen, Chief Human Resources, Select Specialty Hospital–Greensboro, Greensboro, NC, p. A461
TRACY, Allen R., Senior Vice President and Chief Financial Officer, St. John Medical Center, Westlake, OH, p. A500
TRACY Jr., Larry A., FACHE,
President, Barnes–Jewish St. Peters Hospital, Saint Peters, MO, p. A378
President, Progress West Hospital, O'Fallon, MO, p. A374
TRACY, Pat, Administrator, Ridgeview Behavioral Hospital, Middle Point, OH, p. A494
TRACY, Timothy J., Chief Executive Officer, Sanford Vermillion Medical Center, Vermillion, SD, p. A572
TRAHAN, Jennifer Lynch, Assistant Vice President Human Resources, Our Lady of Lourdes Regional Medical Center, Lafayette, LA, p. A278
TRAHAN, Leslie, Chief Executive Officer, South Cameron Memorial Hospital, Cameron, LA, p. A271
TRAHERN, Sheri, FACHE, Chief Executive Officer, St. Thomas More Hospital, Canon City, CO, p. A100
TRAHEY, Thomas F., M.D. Vice President Medical Affairs, Novant Health Rowan Medical Center, Salisbury, NC, p. A468
TRAIL, Alan, Director Information Systems, Owensboro Health Muhlenberg Community Hospital, Greenville, KY, p. A257
TRAINER, Michael, Chief Financial Officer, Akron Children's Hospital, Akron, OH, p. A478
TRAINOR, Jodee, Chief Nursing Officer, St. Thomas More Hospital, Canon City, CO, p. A100
TRAINOR, Karyn, Director Human Resources, St. Patrick Hospital, Missoula, MT, p. A386
TRAISTER, Lynne, Controller, Rehabilitation Hospital of Tinton Falls, Tinton Falls, NJ, p. A419
TRAMMELL, Patrick, Chief Operating Officer, Redmond Regional Medical Center, Rome, GA, p. A163
TRAMP, Chris, Chief of Staff, Sabetha Community Hospital, Sabetha, KS, p. A249
TRAMP, Francis G., President, Burgess Health Center, Onawa, IA, p. A232
TRAN, Ann, Chief Financial Officer, Pike County Memorial Hospital, Louisiana, MO, p. A372
TRAN, Kha H., M.D. Vice President Medical Affairs, Lima Memorial Health System, Lima, OH, p. A492
TRAN, Khiem, M.D. Acting Chief of Staff, Veterans Affairs Illiana Health Care System, Danville, IL, p. A185
TRAN, Lac, Senior Vice President Information Services, Rush University Medical Center, Chicago, IL, p. A184
TRAN, Thanh, Chief Operating Officer, North Central Surgical Center, Dallas, TX, p. A606
TRANSIER, Rhonda, Financial Officer, Rusk State Hospital, Rusk, TX, p. A639
TRANTALIS, Carolyn, R.N
Regional Vice President, Clinical Services and Operations, The William W. Backus Hospital, Norwich, CT, p. A114
Chief Operating Officer, East Region, Windham Hospital, Willimantic, CT, p. A116
TRANTHAM, Susan, Director Human Resources, HEALTHSOUTH Rehabilitation Hospital of Florence, Florence, SC, p. A560
TRAPANI, Joseph, Chief Executive Officer, Poplar Springs Hospital, Petersburg, VA, p. A670
TRAPP, John, Vice President Medical Affairs, Bryan Medical Center, Lincoln, NE, p. A393
TRAPP, Kathleen, M.D. Medical Director, Broadwater Health Center, Townsend, MT, p. A387
TRAUTMAN, Bob, Chief Executive Officer, Saline Memorial Hospital, Benton, AR, p. A41
TRAVIS, Calee, R.N. Chief Nursing Officer, Centennial Medical Center, Frisco, TX, p. A615
TRAVIS, David A.
Chief Financial Officer, East Texas Medical Center Athens, Athens, TX, p. A593
Chief Financial Officer, East Texas Medical Center Fairfield, Fairfield, TX, p. A612
TRAVIS, Dee Dee, Director Community Relations, Calais Regional Hospital, Calais, ME, p. A289
TRAVIS, Thomas, Surgeon General, Department of the Air Force, Washington, DC, p. B45
TRAXLER, Martin J., Chief Executive Officer, Robley Rex Veterans Affairs Medical Center, Louisville, KY, p. A262
TRAYLOR, Desiree, Chief Information Officer, Chickasaw Nation Medical Center, Ada, OK, p. A503
TRAYLOR, Jerri Sue, Director Human Resources and Community and Employee Wellness, The Women's Hospital, Newburgh, IN, p. A217
TRAYNOR, Karen, Chief Financial Officer, Richland Hospital, Richland Center, WI, p. A710
TRCZINSKI, Judi, Vice President and Chief Human Resources Officer, Hospital for Special Care, New Britain, CT, p. A113
TREACY, Nancy, Director Finance, Cambridge Medical Center, Cambridge, MN, p. A336
TREACY–SHIFF, Mary, Vice President Finance, Advocate Good Samaritan Hospital, Downers Grove, IL, p. A186
TREADWAY, Michael G., Controller, Trinity Mother Frances Rehabilitation Hospital, Tyler, TX, p. A649
TREADWELL, Karen, Director Human Resources, Lake Martin Community Hospital, Dadeville, AL, p. A18
TREASE, Kevin, Chief Information Officer, Antelope Memorial Hospital, Neligh, NE, p. A394
TREASURE, Martin
Director Human Resources, Schuylkill Medical Center – East Norwegian Street, Pottsville, PA, p. A548
Director Human Resources, Schuylkill Medical Center – South Jackson Street, Pottsville, PA, p. A548
TREECE, Amy, M.D. Medical Director, North Greenville Hospital, Travelers Rest, SC, p. A565
TREGLOWN, Brad, Director Information Systems, Redmond Regional Medical Center, Rome, GA, p. A163
TREHAN, Rajeev, M.D. Chief of Staff, Veterans Affairs Eastern Kansas Health Care System, Topeka, KS, p. A251
TREITLER, Scot, Chief Financial Officer and Chief Operating Officer, Cypress Pointe Surgical Hospital, Hammond, LA, p. A274
TREMAINE, Lisa, Manager Human Resources, Carson Valley Medical Center, Gardnerville, NV, p. A400
TREMBLE, John, Chief Financial Officer, St. Croix Regional Medical Center, St. Croix Falls, WI, p. A711
TREMBULAK, Frank J., Executive Vice President and Chief Operating Officer, Geisinger Medical Center, Danville, PA, p. A532
TREMONTI, Carl
Chief Financial Officer, Mease Countryside Hospital, Safety Harbor, FL, p. A141
Chief Financial Officer, Mease Dunedin Hospital, Dunedin, FL, p. A126
Chief Financial Officer, Morton Plant Hospital, Clearwater, FL, p. A123
Chief Financial Officer, Morton Plant North Bay Hospital, New Port Richey, FL, p. A136
Chief Financial Officer, South Florida Baptist Hospital, Plant City, FL, p. A140
Chief Financial Officer, St. Anthony's Hospital, Saint Petersburg, FL, p. A142
TREMONTI, Yvette, Vice President Human Resources, H. Lee Moffitt Cancer Center and Research Institute, Tampa, FL, p. A144
TRENARY, Thomas J., President, Baylor Medical Center at Garland, Garland, TX, p. A616
TRENDE, Gary D., FACHE Associate Director, Tuscaloosa Veterans Affairs Medical Center, Tuscaloosa, AL, p. A25
TRENT, Cindy, Manager Personnel, Fall River Hospital, Hot Springs, SD, p. A569
TRETINA, Mike, Senior Vice President and Chief Financial Officer, Bayhealth Medical Center, Dover, DE, p. A117
TREUTLEIN, Scott, M.D. Medical Director, Wyoming County Community Hospital, Warsaw, NY, p. A453
TREVATHAN, Dave, Director Information Systems, Rose Medical Center, Denver, CO, p. A102
TREVINO, Carlos, Chief Operating Officer, Mission Regional Medical Center, Mission, TX, p. A633
TREVINO, Chris, M.D. Chief Medical Officer, St. Elizabeth Hospital, Gonzales, LA, p. A274
TREVINO, Malissa, Director Human Resources, Pecos County Memorial Hospital, Fort Stockton, TX, p. A612
TREVINO, Paul, Chief Executive Officer, CHRISTUS Hospital–St. Elizabeth, Beaumont, TX, p. A596
TREVISANI, Michael F., M.D. Senior Vice President and Chief Medical Officer, Faxton–St. Luke's Healthcare, Utica, NY, p. A452
TREXLER, Don D., Chief Executive Officer, Cypress Pointe Surgical Hospital, Hammond, LA, p. A274
TRICE, Richard
Director Operations, University Hospitals Conneaut Medical Center, Conneaut, OH, p. A487
Director Operations, University Hospitals Geneva Medical Center, Geneva, OH, p. A490
TRICKEY, Donna, R.N. Chief Nursing Officer, Fairview Park Hospital, Dublin, GA, p. A156
TRIEBES, David G., Chief Executive Officer, Samaritan Albany General Hospital, Albany, OR, p. A519
TRIGG, Terry, Director Human Resources, Merit Health Wesley, Hattiesburg, MS, p. A354
TRIGIANI, Charles, D.O. Medical Director, Hampton Behavioral Health Center, Westampton, NJ, p. A420
TRIMBLE, Charley O., Chief Executive Officer, Lubbock Heart Hospital, Lubbock, TX, p. A629
TRIMBLE, Deborah, R.N., Chief Executive Officer, Paul B. Hall Regional Medical Center, Paintsville, KY, p. A264
TRIMBLE, Donald, CPA Chief Financial Officer, Vibra Specialty Hospital at DeSoto, Desoto, TX, p. A608
TRIMBLE, Melody, Chief Executive Officer, Johnson City Medical Center, Johnson City, TN, p. A580
TRIMMER, Mary R., Interim Chief Operating Officer, Mount Carmel, Columbus, OH, p. A486
TRIMMER, Matthew, Director Information Services, Holy Cross Hospital, Silver Spring, MD, p. A300
TRINCHETTO, Thomas, M.D. Chief Medical Officer, Doctors Hospital of Sarasota, Sarasota, FL, p. A142

TRINH, Khiet, M.D. Chief Medical Officer, Bon Secours St. Mary's Hospital, Richmond, VA, p. A671

TRIPLETT, Daniel, Acting Chief Operating Officer, Springfield Hospital Center, Sykesville, MD, p. A300

TRIPLETT, John, D.O. President Medical Staff, Saint Joseph – Martin, Martin, KY, p. A262

TRIPLETT, Robin, Chief Financial Officer, Southern Coos Hospital and Health Center, Bandon, OR, p. A519

TRIPP, Gina, Director Information Systems, TIRR Memorial Hermann, Houston, TX, p. A622

TRIPP, II, Winston, M.D. Chief Medical Officer, St. Anthony Hospital, Lakewood, CO, p. A106

TRIPPEL, Donald E., Chief Financial Officer, Hugh Chatham Memorial Hospital, Elkin, NC, p. A460

TRITTIN, Kim, Manager Human Resources, Mayo Clinic Health System in Red Wing, Red Wing, MN, p. A345

TRIVETTE, Chastity, Chief Executive Officer, Johnson County Community Hospital, Mountain City, TN, p. A584

TROCINO, Mark, Chief Information Officer, DeKalb Medical at Hillandale, Lithonia, GA, p. A160

TROGMAN, Richard, FACHE Chief Operating Officer, Kaiser Permanente Woodland Hills Medical Center, CA, p. A70

TROLLOPE, Grant, Chief Financial Officer, Northeastern Nevada Regional Hospital, Elko, NV, p. A400

TROMBLEY, Barb, Director Financial Services, Munising Memorial Hospital, Munising, MI, p. A326

TROMPETER, Dawn
  Chief Financial Officer, OSF Saint Elizabeth Medical Center, Ottawa, IL, p. A197
  Chief Financial Officer, OSF Saint Paul Medical Center, Mendota, IL, p. A194

TRONCONE, Michael T., Chief Human Resources Officer, Calvary Hospital, NY, p. A439

TROSCLAIR, Andree, Vice President Human Resources, Arkansas Children's Hospital, Little Rock, AR, p. A46

TROSIN, Jill A., R.N. Vice President Patient Care Services, Chief Nursing Officer, ProMedica St. Luke's Hospital, Maumee, OH, p. A494

TROST, Shea, D.O. Chief Medical Officer, McDonough District Hospital, Macomb, IL, p. A193

TROTTER, Kristin, Chief Nursing Officer, Lovelace Regional Hospital – Roswell, Roswell, NM, p. A426

TROTTER, Wally, Director Human Resources, Mountain View Hospital, Payson, UT, p. A657

TROTTIER, Timothy R., Chief Executive Officer, Spring View Hospital, Lebanon, KY, p. A259

TROUBLEFIELD, David, Chief Communications Officer, Hemphill County Hospital, Canadian, TX, p. A600

TROUPE, Matthew, Chief Executive Officer, Conway Regional Medical Center, Conway, AR, p. A42

TROUT, Gene, Chief Financial Officer, Weirton Medical Center, Weirton, WV, p. A696

TROUTMAN, Gary, CPA Chief Financial Officer, Baptist Hospitals of Southeast Texas, Beaumont, TX, p. A596

TROWER, Brad, Administrator, Optim Medical Center – Tattnall, Reidsville, GA, p. A163

TROWHILL, Jan, Director Health Information Management Systems, HEALTHSOUTH Cane Creek Rehabilitation Hospital, Martin, TN, p. A582

TROY, Patrick J., R.N. Associate Director Patient Care Services, Veterans Affairs New Jersey Health Care System, East Orange, NJ, p. A411

TROY, Peggy N., President and Chief Executive Officer, Children's Hospital and Health System, Milwaukee, WI, p. B32

TROY, Peggy N.
  President and Chief Executive Officer, Children's Hospital of Wisconsin, Milwaukee, WI, p. A706
  President and Chief Executive Officer, Children's Hospital of Wisconsin-Fox Valley, Neenah, WI, p. A707

TROYER, David, Chief Information Officer, Veterans Affairs Northern Indiana Health Care System, Fort Wayne, IN, p. A209

TROYER, Devin, M.D. Medical Director, HEALTHSOUTH Rehabilitation Hospital of Columbia, Columbia, SC, p. A559

TROYO–SAUVIAC, Glynda, Chief Executive Officer, Vibra Hospital of Central Dakotas, Mandan, ND, p. A475

TRUE, Terry, M.D. Chief of Staff, Shoals Hospital, Muscle Shoals, AL, p. A23

TRUEBLOOD, Susan
  Regional Hospital Administrator, Central State Hospital, Milledgeville, GA, p. A161
  Chief Executive Officer, Georgia Regional Hospital at Atlanta, Decatur, GA, p. A156

TRUELOCK, Kerri, M.D. Chief of Staff, Peterson Regional Medical Center, Kerrville, TX, p. A626

TRUESDALE, Jr., Fred A., Administrator, Tishomingo Health Services, Iuka, MS, p. A354

TRUITT, Louise, Vice President Human Resources, Capital Regional Medical Center, Tallahassee, FL, p. A144

TRUJILLO, Jesse, Chief Information Officer, St. Mark's Hospital, Salt Lake City, UT, p. A658

TRUMAN, Julia, Vice President Human Resources, Fort Walton Beach Medical Center, Fort Walton Beach, FL, p. A127

TRUMAN, Mark, Vice President of Operations, Floyd Memorial Hospital and Health Services, New Albany, IN, p. A217

TRUMAN, Michael A., Chief Executive Officer, Riverview Behavioral Health, Texarkana, AR, p. A51

TRUMBULL, Kathryn E., R.N. Chief Nursing Officer and Vice President Patient Care Services, Samaritan Healthcare, Moses Lake, WA, p. A680

TRUPP, Gary, President Medical Staff, Good Shepherd Health Care System, Hermiston, OR, p. A521

TRYON, Ellen, R.N. Chief Nursing Officer, Adventist Medical Center–Portland, Portland, OR, p. A524

TSAI, James, M.D.,  President, New York Eye and Ear Infirmary of Mount Sinai, New York, NY, p. A442

TSALATE, Cynthia, Human Resource Specialist, U. S. Public Health Service Indian Hospital, Zuni, NM, p. A427

TSAMBIRAS, Petros, M.D. Chief of Staff, Bayfront Health Dade City, Dade City, FL, p. A124

TSAO, Sean, Director Information Technology, Blue Mountain Hospital, John Day, OR, p. A522

TSCHABRUN, Dawn M., R.N.,  Chief Executive Officer, Lovelace Regional Hospital – Roswell, Roswell, NM, p. A426

TSENG, Allen, Chief Operations Officer, Memorial Hermann Memorial City Medical Center, Houston, TX, p. A621

TSO, Ronald, Chief Executive Officer, Chinle Comprehensive Health Care Facility, Chinle, AZ, p. A30

TSUI–WU, Jane, Vice President and Chief Information Officer, St. Joseph's Regional Medical Center, Paterson, NJ, p. A416

TSUNEISHI, Lani, Chief Nursing Unit, Hawaii State Hospital, Kaneohe, HI, p. A170

TUAZON, Nelson, Chief Nursing Officer, Baptist Medical Center, San Antonio, TX, p. A640

TUBBS, John, M.D
  Chief of Staff, Rock County Hospital, Bassett, NE, p. A389
  Chief of Staff, West Holt Memorial Hospital, Atkinson, NE, p. A389

TUBBS, Mary Beth, Chief Nursing Officer, Sunnyside Community Hospital and Clinics, Sunnyside, WA, p. A686

TUBERVILLE, Abby, Human Resource Manager, Fillmore County Hospital, Geneva, NE, p. A392

TUCK, Colleen, Chief Nursing Officer, Livingston Regional Hospital, Livingston, TN, p. A581

TUCK, Greg, Area Information Officer, Kaiser Permanente San Jose Medical Center, San Jose, CA, p. A89

TUCKER, Albert, Chief Financial Officer, Miami Veterans Affairs Healthcare System, Miami, FL, p. A134

TUCKER, Andy, Chief Financial Officer, South Mississippi State Hospital, Purvis, MS, p. A360

TUCKER, Cathy, Director Human Resources, Iraan General Hospital, Iraan, TX, p. A624

TUCKER, Gary C., President and Chief Executive Officer, Mount St. Mary's Hospital and Health Center, Lewiston, NY, p. A436

TUCKER, Ian, M.D. Vice President Medical Affairs, Johnson Memorial Medical Center, Stafford Springs, CT, p. A115

TUCKER, John
  Chief Nursing Executive, Center for Behavioral Medicine, Kansas City, MO, p. A369
  Chief Executive Officer, Mt. San Rafael Hospital, Trinidad, CO, p. A109

TUCKER, Joseph B., Senior Vice President and Chief Financial Officer, Fort Washington Medical Center, Oxen Hill, MD, p. A299

TUCKER, Joshua, Administrator, Mercy Hospital Logan County, Guthrie, OK, p. A507

TUCKER, Mona, Director Human Resources, Seton Medical Center Harker Heights, Harker Heights, TX, p. A617

TUCKER, Rebecca, Chief Financial Officer, Memorial Hermann Northeast, Humble, TX, p. A623

TUCKER, Ron, Business Office Manager, Kiowa County Memorial Hospital, Greensburg, KS, p. A241

TUCKER, Steven E., President, Conemaugh Memorial Medical Center, Johnstown, PA, p. A537

TUCKER, Theresa, Human Resources Officer, Sioux Center Health, Sioux Center, IA, p. A234

TUDOR, Nathan, Vice President and Chief Executive Officer, CHRISTUS Spohn Hospital Beeville, Beeville, TX, p. A597

TUELL, William J., MSN,  Facility Director, Commonwealth Center for Children and Adolescents, Staunton, VA, p. A673

TUER, Patrick, Chief Executive Officer, Select Specialty Hospital–Columbus, Columbus, OH, p. A487

TUFT, Paul R., President, Southwest Healthcare System, Scottsdale, AZ, p. B125

TULISIAK, Thomas, M.D.,  President, Medina Hospital, Medina, OH, p. A494

TULLIS, Bea, Chief Financial Officer and Budget Officer, Broughton Hospital, Morganton, NC, p. A465

TULLMAN, Stephen M., Chief Executive Officer, Phoenixville Hospital, Phoenixville, PA, p. A545

TUMA, Bonnie, Human Resources Team Lead, National Institutes of Health Clinical Center, Bethesda, MD, p. A296

TUMLIN, Richard, Chief Operating Officer, TriStar Southern Hills Medical Center, Nashville, TN, p. A586

TUMMONS, Coleen, Chief Executive Officer, Gove County Medical Center, Quinter, KS, p. A249

TUMMURU, Ramireddy K., M.D. Chief Medical Officer, Porter Regional Hospital, Valparaiso, IN, p. A220

TUNGATE, Rex A.
  Administrator, Casey County Hospital, Liberty, KY, p. A260
  Administrator, Jane Todd Crawford Hospital, Greensburg, KY, p. A257

TUNNELL, Richard, Director Information Systems Technology and Health Management Information Systems, University Hospital, Newark, NJ, p. A415

TUNNEY, Niona, Director Human Resources, Cochran Memorial Hospital, Morton, TX, p. A633

TUNSON, Lynn, Manager Medical Records, Complex Care Hospital at Tenaya, Las Vegas, NV, p. A401

TUPPER, David, Chief Executive Officer, Vibra Specialty Hospital of Portland, Portland, OR, p. A525

TUPPONCE, David, M.D.,  Chief Executive Officer, Abrazo Scottsdale Campus, Phoenix, AZ, p. A34

TURBAK, Shelly, R.N. Chief Nursing Officer, Prairie Lakes Healthcare System, Watertown, SD, p. A572

TURCO, Joseph, Director Human Resources, St. Mary Medical Center, Apple Valley, CA, p. A54

TUREK, Beth, Site Manager Information Systems, Advocate South Suburban Hospital, Hazel Crest, IL, p. A190

TUREK, Derrill Kent, R.N. Chief Nursing Officer, Blue Mountain Hospital, Blanding, UT, p. A654

TURGEON, Jim, Vice President Finance, Allegiance Behavioral Health Center of Plainview, Plainview, TX, p. A636

TURK, Edward, Vice President Finance, Scripps Mercy Hospital, San Diego, CA, p. A87

TURK, Jan, Chief Executive Officer, Kindred Hospital–New Orleans, New Orleans, LA, p. A282

TURKAL, Nick, M.D.,  President and Chief Executive Officer, Aurora Health Care, Milwaukee, WI, p. B16

TURKAL–BARRETT, Kari, Flight Commander Resource Management Officer, Mike O'Callaghan Federal Hospital, Nellis AFB, NV, p. A403

TURKEL, Brooks, Chief Executive Officer, Regional Hospital of Scranton, Scranton, PA, p. A549

TURLEY, Mary Ann, D.O. Medical Director, HonorHealth Deer Valley Medical Center, Phoenix, AZ, p. A35

TURLEY, Matt, Interim Director Information Systems, Greenbrier Valley Medical Center, Ronceverte, WV, p. A695

TURLEY, Susan S., Chief Financial Officer, Doctor's Hospital at Renaissance, Edinburg, TX, p. A610

TURMAN, Anna, Chief Operating Officer, Chadron Community Hospital and Health Services, Chadron, NE, p. A391

TURMAN, Tracy Penn, Chief Executive Officer, HEALTHSOUTH Rehabilitation Hospital of Petersburg, Petersburg, VA, p. A670

TURNA, Tarlochan, M.D. Medical Director, Mayo Clinic Health System in Cannon Falls, Cannon Falls, MN, p. A336

TURNBULL, James, Chief Information Officer, University of Utah Health Care – Hospital and Clinics, Salt Lake City, UT, p. A659

TURNBULL, Rosie, Director Human Resources, St. Lawrence Psychiatric Center, Ogdensburg, NY, p. A446

TURNER, Bill, Vice President Human Resources, Valir Rehabilitation Hospital, Oklahoma City, OK, p. A513

TURNER, Brenda C.
  Chief Human Resources Officer, Palomar Medical Center, Escondido, CA, p. A60
  Chief Human Resources Officer, Pomerado Hospital, Poway, CA, p. A82

TURNER, Carol, President and Chief Executive Officer, Atrium Medical Center, Middletown, OH, p. A494

TURNER, Chad, Chief Financial Officer, Star Valley Medical Center, Afton, WY, p. A715

TURNER, Cheryl, Administrator, Compass Behavioral Center of Houma, Houma, LA, p. A275

TURNER, Cindy R., Chief Executive Officer, Bacon County Hospital and Health System, Alma, GA, p. A149

TURNER, Dale, Chief Operating Officer, Reedsburg Area Medical Center, Reedsburg, WI, p. A710

TURNER, Dave, Chief Financial Officer, Royal Oaks Hospital, Windsor, MO, p. A380

TURNER, Eileen, Director of Nursing, Post Acute Medical Specialty Hospital of Lafayette, Lafayette, LA, p. A278

TURNER, Glenda, Director Personnel, Oakwood Correctional Facility, Lima, OH, p. A492

TURNER, Howard D., Chief Executive Officer, Perry Memorial Hospital, Perry, OK, p. A513

TURNER, Jeff, FACHE, Chief Executive Officer, Moore County Hospital District, Dumas, TX, p. A609
TURNER, Kathy, Director Human Resources, East Texas Medical Center Trinity, Trinity, TX, p. A648
TURNER, Kelly, Senior Vice President Finance and Chief Financial Officer, Glendale Adventist Medical Center, Glendale, CA, p. A63
TURNER, Laurie
  Chief Nursing Officer, TriStar Skyline Madison Campus, Madison, TN, p. A582
  Chief Nursing Officer, TriStar Skyline Medical Center, Nashville, TN, p. A586
TURNER, Lucas, Chief Financial Officer, Bowdle Hospital, Bowdle, SD, p. A567
TURNER, Mark, Director Information Systems, Beverly Hospital, Montebello, CA, p. A76
TURNER, Mark J., President and Chief Executive Officer, Memorial Hospital, Belleville, IL, p. A179
TURNER, Mark S., Chief Executive Officer, San Gorgonio Memorial Hospital, Banning, CA, p. A55
TURNER, Marquita, Chief Nursing Officer, Atrium Medical Center, Middletown, OH, p. A494
TURNER, Maurita, Team Leader Health Information Systems Services, Madison St. Joseph Health Center, Madisonville, TX, p. A630
TURNER, Melissa, Senior Vice President Human Resources, Bridgeport Hospital, Bridgeport, CT, p. A111
TURNER, Michael, M.D. Chief of Staff, Abbeville Area Medical Center, Abbeville, SC, p. A557
TURNER, Michael L., Director Human Resources, Carlsbad Medical Center, Carlsbad, NM, p. A423
TURNER, Nancy, Director Communications, Sutter Roseville Medical Center, Roseville, CA, p. A84
TURNER, Pamela, Executive Director, Bronx Psychiatric Center, NY, p. A438
TURNER, Peggy, Assistant Vice President and Director of Nursing, Unity Health White County Medical Center, Searcy, AR, p. A50
TURNER, Randy, Chief Human Resource Management Services, Boise Veterans Affairs Medical Center, Boise, ID, p. A172
TURNER, Robert L., Ph.D., Chief Executive Officer, Seven Hills Hospital, Henderson, NV, p. A401
TURNER, Sara, Director Human Resources, Alvarado Hospital Medical Center, San Diego, CA, p. A86
TURNER, Saundra G., Director Human Resources, Mercy Hospital Jefferson, Crystal City, MO, p. A366
TURNER, Scott, Co–Chief Operating Officer, University of Iowa Hospitals and Clinics, Iowa City, IA, p. A230
TURNER, Shelly, Chief Clinical Services Officer, Medical Center of Manchester, Manchester, TN, p. A582
TURNER, Sherrilyn, Director Human Resources, Southeast Colorado Hospital District, Springfield, CO, p. A108
TURNER, Spencer, Chief Executive Officer, Texas Health Presbyterian Hospital Flower Mound, Flower Mound, TX, p. A612
TURNER, Steve, Director Information Technology, Salem Township Hospital, Salem, IL, p. A200
TURNER, Teri, Chief Nursing Officer, Haskell Memorial Hospital, Haskell, TX, p. A618
TURNEY, Brian, Chief Executive Officer, Kingman Regional Medical Center, Kingman, AZ, p. A32
TURNEY, Larry, Administrator, Cochran Memorial Hospital, Morton, TX, p. A633
TURNQUIST, Carrie, Director Human Resources, Buena Vista Regional Medical Center, Storm Lake, IA, p. A235
TURO, Albert, Vice President Human Resources, St. Mary's Healthcare, Amsterdam, NY, p. A428
TURPIN, Debra, R.N. Vice President Patient Care Services and Chief Nursing Officer, Alton Memorial Hospital, Alton, IL, p. A178
TURPIN, James, Chief of Staff, Ephraim McDowell Fort Logan Hospital, Stanford, KY, p. A266
TURQUESA, Sandra
  Senior Human Resources Business Partner, Saint Joseph – London, London, KY, p. A260
  Human Resources Business Partner, Saint Joseph Berea, Berea, KY, p. A254
TURSKY, Martin, President and Chief Executive Officer, Firelands Regional Health System, Sandusky, OH, p. A497
TURSO, Janet, Controller, HEALTHSOUTH Rehabilitation Hospital of Toms River, Toms River, NJ, p. A419
TURTON, Jonathan, FACHE, Interim President, Baptist Medical Center, San Antonio, TX, p. A640
TUSA, Edward A., Chief Financial Officer, Mayo Clinic Health System in Cannon Falls, Cannon Falls, MN, p. A336
TUSCANY, Joanne E.
  Director Human Resources, St. John Hospital and Medical Center, Detroit, MI, p. A318
  Director Worklife Services, St. John Macomb–Oakland Hospital, Warren, MI, p. A332
TUSTEN, Jay, Chief Executive Officer, Stanton County Hospital, Johnson, KS, p. A242
TUTT, Michael, M.D. Chief Medical Officer, Tsehootsooi Medical Center, Fort Defiance, AZ, p. A31
TUTTLE, Casey, Director Information Technology, Sistersville General Hospital, Sistersville, WV, p. A695
TUTTLE, Kathryn, R.N. Director of Nursing, Memorial Medical Center – Ashland, Ashland, WI, p. A697
TVEIT, Charles B., Chief Executive Officer, Lake District Hospital, Lakeview, OR, p. A522
TWARDY, Cindi, Manager Human Resources, Meeker Memorial Hospital, Litchfield, MN, p. A341
TWIDALE, Margaret, Manager Information Systems, Kane Community Hospital, Kane, PA, p. A537
TWIDWELL, Lisa, Administrator, Madison Medical Center, Fredericktown, MO, p. A367
TWIGG, Nicole, Director Human Resources, Brook Lane Health Services, Hagerstown, MD, p. A298
TYE, Angie, Director Human Resources, Waverly Health Center, Waverly, IA, p. A236
TYLER, Holley, R.N. Chief Nursing Officer, Woman's Hospital of Texas, Houston, TX, p. A623
TYLER, James E., Vice President and Hospital Chief Executive Officer, Smyth County Community Hospital, Marion, VA, p. A667
TYLER, Kevin L., M.D. President Medical Staff, Penn Highlands Clearfield, Clearfield, PA, p. A531
TYLER, Philene, Chief Finance Officer, Chinle Comprehensive Health Care Facility, Chinle, AZ, p. A30
TYLER, Richard, Corporate Director Human Resources, Conway Regional Medical Center, Conway, AR, p. A42
TYLER, Rick, M.D. Vice President Medical Affairs, CHRISTUS Hospital–St. Elizabeth, Beaumont, TX, p. A596
TYLER, Rob, Chief Financial Officer, West Oaks Hospital, Houston, TX, p. A623
TYLER, Rosamond M., Administrator, Tyler Holmes Memorial Hospital, Winona, MS, p. A362
TYLER, Tanya, Vice President Human Resources, CHI St. Luke's Health Memorial Lufkin, Lufkin, TX, p. A630
TYLKOWSKI, Chester, M.D. Chief of Staff, Shriners Hospitals for Children–Lexington, Lexington, KY, p. A260
TYNER, Marilou Patalinjug, M.D. Medical Director, Highland–Clarksburg Hospital, Clarksburg, WV, p. A690
TYNER, W. Russell, President and Chief Executive Officer, Baptist Health, Montgomery, AL, p. B19
TYNES, Jr., L. Lee, M.D. Medical Director, Central Louisiana State Hospital, Pineville, LA, p. A283
TYO, Joanne, Chief Financial Officer, Carolinas ContinueCare Hospital at Pineville, Charlotte, NC, p. A457
TYRA, Diana, Director Health Information, Kentucky River Medical Center, Jackson, KY, p. A259
TYRA, J. Allen, Chief Executive, Merit Health Gilmore Memorial, Amory, MS, p. A350
TYRER, Andrew, Chief Operating Officer, TriStar StoneCrest Medical Center, Smyrna, TN, p. A588
TYRER, Ronald, Interim Chief Executive Officer, Livingston Regional Hospital, Livingston, TN, p. A581
TYRRELL, Shawn O., R.N. VP/Chief Nursing Officer, Adventist Hinsdale Hospital, Hinsdale, IL, p. A191
TYRRELL, RN, Wade Alan, Chief Nursing Officer, Sterling Regional MedCenter, Sterling, CO, p. A109
TYSLAND, Tanya, Interim Chief Executive Officer, Palmer Lutheran Health Center, West Union, IA, p. A236
TYSON, Bernard J., Chairman and Chief Executive Officer, Kaiser Foundation Hospitals, Oakland, CA, p. B76
TYSON, Charlotte C., Chief Executive Officer, LewisGale Hospital Alleghany, Low Moor, VA, p. A667
TYSON, Rhoda, Chief Information Officer, Central Alabama Veterans Health Care System, Montgomery, AL, p. A23

## U

UBER, Charlotte M., Chief Executive Officer, Warren State Hospital, Warren, PA, p. A552
UDALL, Ben, M.D. Chief of Staff, Kimble Hospital, Junction, TX, p. A625
UDISKY, John, Associate Executive Director Finance, Franklin Hospital, Valley Stream, NY, p. A452
UDOVICH, Christopher, M.D. Chief of Staff, Silver Cross Hospital, New Lenox, IL, p. A196
UFFER, Mark H., Chief Executive Officer, Corona Regional Medical Center, Corona, CA, p. A58
UGHOUWA, Ejiro, M.D. Chief of Staff, Allen Parish Hospital, Kinder, LA, p. A276
UGWUEKE, Michael O., President and Chief Executive Officer, Methodist Healthcare Memphis Hospitals, Memphis, TN, p. A584
UHARRIET, Bart, Director Information Services, Mississippi State Hospital, Whitfield, MS, p. A361
UHL, Jason, Chief Information Officer, Floyd Valley Hospital, Le Mars, IA, p. A230
UHLIK, Allen, M.D. Chief of Staff, Copper Basin Medical Center, Copperhill, TN, p. A576
UHLIR, Tricia, Chief Executive Officer, Fall River Hospital, Hot Springs, SD, p. A569
ULBRICHT, John E., Chief Operating Officer, Laredo Medical Center, Laredo, TX, p. A627
ULBRICHT, William G., President, St. Anthony's Hospital, Saint Petersburg, FL, p. A142
ULERY, Brian
  Senior Vice President and Chief Operating Officer, Saint Francis Hospital, Charleston, WV, p. A690
  Senior Vice President and Chief Operating Officer, Thomas Memorial Hospital, South Charleston, WV, p. A695
ULETT, John, Vice President and Chief Information Officer, CentraState Healthcare System, Freehold, NJ, p. A412
ULFERTS, Wendy, R.N. Chief Nursing Officer, Rice Memorial Hospital, Willmar, MN, p. A349
ULI, James, Chief Financial Officer, Loma Linda University Medical Center–Murrieta, Murrieta, CA, p. A77
ULICNY, Gary R., Ph.D., President and Chief Executive Officer, Shepherd Center, Atlanta, GA, p. A151
ULMER, Becky, R.N. Director of Nursing, Jasper General Hospital, Bay Springs, MS, p. A350
ULMER, Carlton, Chief Executive Officer, Gulf Coast Regional Medical Center, Panama City, FL, p. A139
ULMER, Carol, Chief Executive Officer, Select Specialty Hospital–Sioux Falls, Sioux Falls, SD, p. A571
ULREICH, Shawn, R.N. Vice President Clinical Operations and Chief Nursing Executive, Spectrum Health – Butterworth Hospital, Grand Rapids, MI, p. A321
ULREY, Chris, Director Management Information Systems, St. Luke's Behavioral Health Center, Phoenix, AZ, p. A36
ULRICH, Alan, Chief Financial Officer, Guam Memorial Hospital Authority, Tamuning, GU, p. A719
ULRICH Jr., James P., FACHE President and Chief Executive Officer, Community Hospital, McCook, NE, p. A394
ULSETH, Randy, Chief Executive Officer, FirstLight Health System, Mora, MN, p. A343
UMHAU, John, M.D. Clinical Director, U. S. Public Health Service Indian Hospital–Whiteriver, Whiteriver, AZ, p. A40
UNDERDAHL, Steve, Chief Executive Officer, Northfield Hospital, Northfield, MN, p. A344
UNDERHILL, Robert, Director of Business Services, Central State Hospital, Louisville, KY, p. A261
UNDERWOOD, Debbie, Manager Human Resources, Plains Memorial Hospital, Dimmitt, TX, p. A609
UNDERWOOD, Jerri C., R.N. Chief Nursing Officer, Parkridge Medical Center, Chattanooga, TN, p. A575
UNDERWOOD, Ken, Chief Executive Officer, Hazel Hawkins Memorial Hospital, Hollister, CA, p. A65
UNDERWOOD, Martha, Chief Human Resources Officer, Saint Thomas Midtown Hospital, Nashville, TN, p. A585
UNDERWOOD, Patricia A., Chief Financial Officer, Magee Rehabilitation Hospital, Philadelphia, PA, p. A544
UNDERWOOD, Vickie, Director Human Resources, Wyandot Memorial Hospital, Upper Sandusky, OH, p. A499
UNDERWOOD, Virgil, Chief Executive Officer, Boone Memorial Hospital, Madison, WV, p. A692
UNDLIN, Cassie, Chief Administrative Officer, Navos, Seattle, WA, p. A683
UNELL, Deonna, Chief Executive Officer, Irving Coppell Surgical Hospital, Irving, TX, p. A624
UNGER, Henry D., M.D. Senior Vice President and Chief Medical Officer, Holy Redeemer Hospital, Meadowbrook, PA, p. A540
UNGER, Kevin L., FACHE,
  President and Chief Executive Officer, Medical Center of the Rockies, Loveland, CO, p. A107
  President and Chief Executive Officer, Poudre Valley Hospital, Fort Collins, CO, p. A103
UNITAN, Carol, M.D. Chief Medical Officer, Kaiser Foundation Hospital Westside Medical Center, Hillsboro, OR, p. A521
UNRUH, Greg, Chief Executive Officer, Citizens Medical Center, Colby, KS, p. A238
UNZEN, John, Chief Financial Officer, Mille Lacs Health System, Onamia, MN, p. A344
UPCHURCH, Jim, M.D. Chief Medical Officer, Crow/Northern Cheyenne Hospital, Crow Agency, MT, p. A382
UPCRAFT, Jeffrey, Director Information Services, Southwest Healthcare System, Murrieta, CA, p. A77
UPFIELD, Jaclyn, Chief Operating Officer, G. Werber Bryan Psychiatric Hospital, Columbia, SC, p. A559
UPHAM, Kevin, Chief Human Resources Officer, Minneapolis Veterans Affairs Health Care System, Minneapolis, MN, p. A342
UPSHAW, Joy, Chief Nursing Officer, Oklahoma State University Medical Center, Tulsa, OK, p. A516

 

UPTON, Carol, Regional Area Practice Manager, Merit Health Gilmore Memorial, Amory, MS, p. A350

UPTON, Daniel, Vice President and Chief Financial Officer, Doylestown Hospital, Doylestown, PA, p. A533

UPTON, Kerry L., Administrative Director Human Resources, Care Regional Medical Center, Aransas Pass, TX, p. A592

UPTON, Matthew
Chief Medical Officer, Saint Francis Hospital, Charleston, WV, p. A690
Chief Medical Information Officer, Thomas Memorial Hospital, South Charleston, WV, p. A695

UPTON, Scott, Administrator, Jane Phillips Nowata Health Center, Nowata, OK, p. A510

URADNIK, Michael, Chief Executive Officer, Cascade Behavioral Hospital, Tukwila, WA, p. A686

URAIZEE, Rizwan A., Chief Financial Officer, Kedren Community Mental Health Center, Los Angeles, CA, p. A70

URBAN, Frank, Chief Financial Officer, Southwood Psychiatric Hospital, Pittsburgh, PA, p. A546

URBAN, Louise, R.N., President and Chief Executive Officer, Jefferson Hospital, Jefferson Hills, PA, p. A536

URBAN, Thomas S., Market Leader and President, Mercy Health – Fairfield Hospital, Fairfield, OH, p. A489

URBAN, Tom, Director Human Resources, Wills Memorial Hospital, Washington, GA, p. A167

URBANCSIK, Don
Director Finance, Euclid Hospital, Euclid, OH, p. A489
Director Finance, Lutheran Hospital, Cleveland, OH, p. A485

URBANIAK, Cindy, Chief Executive Officer, Kittson Memorial Healthcare Center, Hallock, MN, p. A340

URBANSKI, Joanne, President and Chief Executive Officer, South Haven Health System, South Haven, MI, p. A330

URBANSKI, Pamela A., R.N. Chief Nursing Officer, Senior Vice President, Patient Care Services, ProMedica Monroe Regional Hospital, Monroe, MI, p. A326

URBISTONDO, Lisa, Chief Financial Officer, Medical Center of Peach County, Navicent Health, Fort Valley, GA, p. A158

URDANETA, Alfonso, M.D. President Medical Staff, Washington County Hospital, Nashville, IL, p. A196

URLAUB, Charles J., President and Chief Executive Officer, Mercy Hospital, Buffalo, NY, p. A430

URQUHART, Mary, R.N. Vice President Patient Care, Brattleboro Memorial Hospital, Brattleboro, VT, p. A660

URQUHART, Mary Beth, Vice President Patient Care Services and Director of Quality, New England Sinai Hospital and Rehabilitation Center, Stoughton, MA, p. A312

URQUHART, Teresa C., Chief Operating Officer, North Fulton Regional Hospital, Roswell, GA, p. A163

USELMAN, Krista, Chief Executive Officer, HEALTHSOUTH Rehabilitation Hospital The Woodlands, Conroe, TX, p. A602

USELMAN, Melissa, Director Finance, Gundersen Boscobel Area Hospital and Clinics, Boscobel, WI, p. A698

USHER, Paul L., President and Chief Executive Officer, Marion General Hospital, Marion, IN, p. A215

USHIJIMA, Arthur A., FACHE, President and Chief Executive Officer, Queen's Health Systems, Honolulu, HI, p. B112

USHIJIMA, Arthur A., FACHE, President, Queen's Medical Center, Honolulu, HI, p. A169

UTECHT, Tom, M.D
Senior Vice President and Chief Quality Officer, Community Behavioral Health Center, Fresno, CA, p. A62
Chief Medical and Quality Officer, Community Regional Medical Center, Fresno, CA, p. A62
Corporate Chief Quality Officer, Fresno Heart and Surgical Hospital, Fresno, CA, p. A62

UTEMARK, Paul, Chief Executive Officer, Fillmore County Hospital, Geneva, NE, p. A392

UTLEY, Donna, Vice President Human Resources, Mercy San Juan Medical Center, Carmichael, CA, p. A57

UTLEY, Renee, Acting Chief Financial Officer, Hamilton Center, Terre Haute, IN, p. A220

UTTENDORFSKY, Rob, Director Information Management, Lewis County General Hospital, Lowville, NY, p. A436

UTTER, Camille, R.N. Chief Nursing Officer, Scotland Health Care System, Laurinburg, NC, p. A463

UTTERBACK, Julie, Chief Financial Officer, Roane Medical Center, Harriman, TN, p. A578

UYEMURA, Monte, M.D. Chief of Staff, Wray Community District Hospital, Wray, CO, p. A110

## V

VAAGENES, Carl P., Chief Executive Officer, Douglas County Hospital, Alexandria, MN, p. A334

VAALER, Mark, M.D
Chief Medical Officer, South Florida Baptist Hospital, Plant City, FL, p. A140
Vice President Medical Staff Affairs, St. Joseph's Hospital, Tampa, FL, p. A145

VACCARO, Michael, Chief Nursing Officer, Novant Health Presbyterian Medical Center, Charlotte, NC, p. A458

VACCARO, Stacey, Chief Operating Officer, The Children's Institute of Pittsburgh, Pittsburgh, PA, p. A546

VACHON, Scott, Director Information Technology, Littleton Regional Hospital, Littleton, NH, p. A407

VADEN, Jim, Director Information Systems, Lauderdale Community Hospital, Ripley, TN, p. A587

VAGUE, Jeff, Regional Manager Information Systems, Mercy Hospitals of Bakersfield, Bakersfield, CA, p. A55

VAHEY, Stacy Ann, Vice President, Human Resources, Thomas Jefferson University Hospitals, Philadelphia, PA, p. A545

VAHLBERG, Susan, Director Employee and Community Relations, Valor Health, Emmett, ID, p. A174

VAIL, B. J., Director Information Systems, Morehouse General Hospital, Bastrop, LA, p. A269

VAIL, Bryan, Chief Information Officer, Clement J. Zablocki Veterans Affairs Medical Center, Milwaukee, WI, p. A706

VAIL, Lisa M., R.N. Chief Nursing Officer and Vice President of Patient Care Services, Bryan Medical Center, Lincoln, NE, p. A393

VAIL, Ronald, M.D. Chief of Staff, Lower Umpqua Hospital District, Reedsport, OR, p. A525

VAILLANCOURT, Alex, Chief Information Officer, Christ Hospital, Cincinnati, OH, p. A482

VAILLANCOURT, Stacy, Vice President Marketing, Communications, Advocacy and Human Resources, Saint Agnes Medical Center, Fresno, CA, p. A62

VAIOLETI, Stephany, Administrator, Kahuku Medical Center, Kahuku, HI, p. A169

VAKHARIA, Bharat, M.D. President Medical Staff, Sturgis Hospital, Sturgis, MI, p. A331

VALBUENA, Richard, M.D. Medical Director, Latimer County General Hospital, Wilburton, OK, p. A518

VALDENEGRO, Maria, Chief Financial Officer, Meadow Wood Behavioral Health System, New Castle, DE, p. A117

VALDERA, Trummell, Senior Vice President and Chief Human Resources Officer, Jackson Health System, Miami, FL, p. A134

VALDERAZ, Leonard, Administrator, Sunrise Canyon Hospital, Lubbock, TX, p. A629

VALDESPINO, Gustavo A., President and Chief Executive Officer, Valley Presbyterian Hospital, CA, p. A73

VALDEZ, Mary, Chief Operating Officer, South Texas Rehabilitation Hospital, Brownsville, TX, p. A598

VALENCERINA, Madeline, Chief Operating Officer, Kedren Community Mental Health Center, Los Angeles, CA, p. A70

VALENTE, Anthony, M.D. Vice President Medical Affairs, Lehigh Valley Hospital – Hazleton, Hazleton, PA, p. A536

VALENTE, T. J., M.D. Medical Director, LifeStream Behavioral Center, Leesburg, FL, p. A132

VALENTI, James N., FACHE, President and Chief Executive Officer, University Medical Center of El Paso, El Paso, TX, p. A611

VALENTIN, Leonardo, Chief Executive Officer, Professional Hospital Guaynabo, Guaynabo, PR, p. A721

VALENTINE, Lisa R., Chief Operating Officer, Henrico Doctors' Hospital, Richmond, VA, p. A672

VALENTINE, Mark
President, The Heart Hospital Baylor Denton, Denton, TX, p. A608
President, The Heart Hospital Baylor Plano, Plano, TX, p. A637

VALENTINE, Robert A., President, CHI Health Missouri Valley, Missouri Valley, IA, p. A231

VALENTINI, Rudolph, M.D. Chief Medical Officer, Children's Hospital of Michigan, Detroit, MI, p. A317

VALENTO, Jessica, Director Information Systems, Range Regional Health Services, Hibbing, MN, p. A340

VALLE, Bernardo, Vice President Human Resources, USMD Hospital at Arlington, Arlington, TX, p. A593

VALLE, David, Chief Information Officer, Hospital Dr. Cayetano Coll Y Toste, Arecibo, PR, p. A719

VALLE–SMITH, Karla, Area Chief Finance Officer, Kaiser Permanente Panorama City Medical Center, CA, p. A70

VALLES, John, Senior Vice President and Chief Financial Officer, Loretto Hospital, Chicago, IL, p. A182

VALLIANT, Mary T., MS, Chief Executive Officer, Southern Palmetto Hospital, Barnwell, SC, p. A557

VALLIDO, Gabe, Chief Information Officer, Naval Hospital Camp Pendleton, Camp Pendleton, CA, p. A57

VALLIERE, George, Chief Executive Officer, Claremore Indian Hospital, Claremore, OK, p. A505

VALLIERE, Mark, M.D. Senior Vice President Medical Affairs and Chief Medical Officer, Mercy Medical Center–Cedar Rapids, Cedar Rapids, IA, p. A223

VALTAIRO, Fred, Chief Nursing Officer, Placentia–Linda Hospital, Placentia, CA, p. A81

VAMPRINE, Laurene, Senior Vice President Information Systems, Erlanger Medical Center, Chattanooga, TN, p. A575

VAN BOENING, Jon, President and Chief Executive Officer and Senior Vice President Operations Dignity Health Central Va, Bakersfield Memorial Hospital, Bakersfield, CA, p. A55

VAN BUSKIRK, George F., M.D. Chief of Staff, Bay Pines Veterans Affairs Healthcare System, Bay Pines, FL, p. A121

VAN CAMP, Keith, Vice President Information Services, St. Dominic–Jackson Memorial Hospital, Jackson, MS, p. A355

VAN CLEAVE, Bruce L., M.D. Senior Vice President and Chief Medical Officer, Aurora Medical Center of Oshkosh, Oshkosh, WI, p. A708

VAN CLEAVE, Vanetta, Chief Financial Officer, Yukon–Kuskokwim Delta Regional Hospital, Bethel, AK, p. A27

VAN DECAR, Tama, M.D. Chief Medical Officer, Fort Walton Beach Medical Center, Fort Walton Beach, FL, p. A127

VAN DEE, Keith, Director Human Resources, Drew Memorial Hospital, Monticello, AR, p. A48

VAN DER VEER, Jon, D.O. Vice President Medical Affairs, Greene County Medical Center, Jefferson, IA, p. A230

VAN DONSELAAR, Lois J., R.N. Vice President & Chief Nursing Officer, Borgess Medical Center, Kalamazoo, MI, p. A323

VAN DRIEL, Allen, FACHE, Administrator, Smith County Memorial Hospital, Smith Center, KS, p. A250

VAN EECKHOUT, Barbara, M.D. Chief of Staff, Los Alamos Medical Center, Los Alamos, NM, p. A425

VAN EPERN, Keri, Manager Human Resources, Aspirus Grand View, Ironwood, MI, p. A323

VAN GHELUWE, Betty, Chief Operating Officer, St. Luke's Elmore, Mountain Home, ID, p. A175

VAN GORDER, Chris D., FACHE, President and Chief Executive Officer, Scripps Health, San Diego, CA, p. B118

VAN GRINSVEN, Gerard, President and Chief Executive Officer, Cancer Treatment Centers of America, Schaumburg, IL, p. B26

VAN GUNDY, Dan, Director of Information Technology Systems and Hardwire, Major Hospital, Shelbyville, IN, p. A220

VAN GUNDY, Milt, M.D. President Medical Staff, Central Iowa Healthcare, Marshalltown, IA, p. A231

VAN HEUSEN, Melanie, Director Human Resources, Gateways Hospital and Mental Health Center, Los Angeles, CA, p. A69

VAN HOFF, Cynthia, Chief Financial Officer, Sutter Solano Medical Center, Vallejo, CA, p. A96

VAN HORN, Jeff, Chief Executive Officer, Mountain View Regional Hospital, Casper, WY, p. A715

VAN HOUDEN, Charles, M.D. Chief Medical Officer, Neosho Memorial Regional Medical Center, Chanute, KS, p. A238

VAN HYNING, Jill, Director Human Resources, Richland Memorial Hospital, Olney, IL, p. A197

VAN KAMPEN, Cindy, Chief Nursing Officer, North Ottawa Community Hospital, Grand Haven, MI, p. A320

VAN LUVEN, Audrey C., Senior Vice President and Chief Human Resources Officer, Christiana Care Health System, Newark, DE, p. A117

VAN MATRE, Jennifer, Director Finance, Trinity Hospital, Weaverville, CA, p. A97

VAN MEETEREN, Robert, President and Chief Executive Officer, Reedsburg Area Medical Center, Reedsburg, WI, p. A710

VAN METER, Rex, President, INTEGRIS Canadian Valley Hospital, Yukon, OK, p. A518

VAN NATTA, Timothy, M.D. Chief Medical Officer, Harbor–UCLA Medical Center, Torrance, CA, p. A94

VAN NORMAN, Steven, M.D. Medical Director, Dixie Regional Medical Center, Saint George, UT, p. A658

VAN RYBROEK, Greg, Chief Executive Officer, Mendota Mental Health Institute, Madison, WI, p. A704

VAN SCOYK, Mitch, Manager Information Systems, Delta County Memorial Hospital, Delta, CO, p. A101

VAN VICKLE, Robin, Chief Financial Officer, Bristow Medical Center, Bristow, OK, p. A504

VAN VOLKENBURG, Mark, Chief Executive Officer, HEALTHSOUTH Harmarville Rehabilitation Hospital, Pittsburgh, PA, p. A546

VAN VRANKEN, Arthur, M.D. Chief Medical Officer, Essentia Health–Graceville, Graceville, MN, p. A339

VAN VRANKEN, Ross, Executive Director, University of Utah Neuropsychiatric Institute, Salt Lake City, UT, p. A659

VAN WHY, Susan, Director Human Resources, St. Luke's Hospital – Miners Campus, Coaldale, PA, p. A531

VAN WINKLE, James, M.D. Chief of Staff, United Regional Medical Center, Manchester, TN, p. A582

VAN WINKLE, Melanie, Chief Financial Officer, Mammoth Hospital, Mammoth Lakes, CA, p. A74

VAN ZANTEN, Lorinda, MSN, Chief Executive Officer, Providence Newberg Medical Center, Newberg, OR, p. A523

Index of Health Care Professionals / Vazquez

VANASKIE, William F., Executive Vice President and Chief Operating Officer, Maricopa Integrated Health System, Phoenix, AZ, p. A35
VANBOEKEL, Tony, Director Information Systems, Shasta Regional Medical Center, Redding, CA, p. A82
VANCE, Amy, Executive Vice President and Chief Operating Officer, Novant Health Matthews Medical Center, Matthews, NC, p. A464
VANCE, Derek, Chief Executive Officer, LewisGale Hospital Pulaski, Pulaski, VA, p. A671
VANCE, Ellen B.
Chief Human Resources Officer, Sheltering Arms Hospital South, Midlothian, VA, p. A668
Chief Human Resource Officer, Sheltering Arms Rehabilitation Hospital, Mechanicsville, VA, p. A668
VANCE, Mark, M.D. Chief Medical Officer, Quincy Valley Medical Center, Quincy, WA, p. A682
VANCE, Stacie, Vice President Clinical Services, Indiana Orthopaedic Hospital, Indianapolis, IN, p. A211
VANCE, Steven, Chief Financial Officer, Dixie Regional Medical Center, Saint George, UT, p. A658
VANCONIA, R. Brent
Acting President, SSM Health St. Mary's Hospital – Audrain, Mexico, MO, p. A372
President, SSM Health St. Mary's Hospital – Jefferson City, Jefferson City, MO, p. A369
VANCOURT, Bernie, Chief Operating Officer, Bay Area Medical Center, Marinette, WI, p. A704
VANDE VEEGAETE, Cari, Human Resources Manager, Intermountain Medical Center, Murray, UT, p. A656
VANDENBARK, Heather, Human Resources Specialist, State Hospital North, Orofino, ID, p. A175
VANDENBERG, Andra, Director Human Resources, Butler County Health Care Center, David City, NE, p. A391
VANDENBOSCH, Darryl, President, St. Bernardine Medical Center, San Bernardino, CA, p. A86
VANDER, Allen, M.D. Chief Medical Staff, Thibodaux Regional Medical Center, Thibodaux, LA, p. A286
VANDER LEEST, Steven, Chief of Staff, Lakes Regional Healthcare, Spirit Lake, IA, p. A235
VANDERBEEK, Sam, Chief Information Officer, W. J. Mangold Memorial Hospital, Lockney, TX, p. A628
VANDERHOOFT, J. Eric, M.D. President Medical Staff, St. Mark's Hospital, Salt Lake City, UT, p. A658
VANDERLINDEN, Mark A., Chief Financial Officer, Greene County Medical Center, Jefferson, IA, p. A230
VANDERMARK, Jay H., Chief Financial Officer, Veterans Affairs Northern Indiana Health Care System, Fort Wayne, IN, p. A209
VANDERMEER, Nick, Director Information Systems, Payson Regional Medical Center, Payson, AZ, p. A34
VANDERPOOL, Lee, Vice President, Dominican Hospital, Santa Cruz, CA, p. A91
VANDERSLICE, Douglas M., Senior Vice President and Chief Financial Officer, Boston Children's Hospital, Boston, MA, p. A303
VANDERSTEK, Eliott R., Chief Fiscal Service, Veterans Affairs Eastern Colorado Health Care System, Denver, CO, p. A102
VANDERSTOUW, Karl, Vice President Management Information Systems, Lenoir Memorial Hospital, Kinston, NC, p. A463
VANDERVLIET, William, M.D. Vice President Medical Affairs, Holland Hospital, Holland, MI, p. A322
VANDERWEGE, Larry, Administrator, Lindsborg Community Hospital, Lindsborg, KS, p. A245
VANDETTE, Joan, Vice President Human Resources, Brooks Memorial Hospital, Dunkirk, NY, p. A433
VANDEVEER Jr., Alden M., FACHE, Chief Executive Officer, Palacios Community Medical Center, Palacios, TX, p. A635
VANDEWATER, David T., President and Chief Executive Officer, Ardent Health Services, Nashville, TN, p. B11
VANDEWEGE, Dana, Director Human Resources, Capital Medical Center, Olympia, WA, p. A681
VANDONKELAAR, Rodney
Chief Financial Officer, Carolina Pines Regional Medical Center, Hartsville, SC, p. A562
Chief Financial Officer, Saint Thomas Highlands Hospital, Sparta, TN, p. A588
VANDORT, Patti J., MSN Vice President Nursing/Chief Nursing Officer, Holland Hospital, Holland, MI, p. A322
VANDRIEL, Mary Kay
President, Spectrum Health Big Rapids Hospital, Big Rapids, MI, p. A315
President, Spectrum Health Reed City Hospital, Reed City, MI, p. A328
VANDRUFF, John, M.D. Chief of Staff, Payson Regional Medical Center, Payson, AZ, p. A34
VANEK, James, Chief Executive Officer, Columbus Community Hospital, Columbus, TX, p. A601
VANES, Wendell, Chief Financial Officer, Saint Mary's Regional Medical Center, Russellville, AR, p. A50
VANGENDEREN, Nathan, Executive Vice President and Chief Financial Officer, Mercy Medical Center–Cedar Rapids, Cedar Rapids, IA, p. A223
VANHAREN, James, M.D. Medical Director, Forest View Psychiatric Hospital, Grand Rapids, MI, p. A320
VANHOUWELING, Mason, Chief Executive Officer, University Medical Center, Las Vegas, NV, p. A403
VANNETT, Vince, Director Human Resources, Jellico Community Hospital, Jellico, TN, p. A579
VANOSDOL, Thomas J., President, St. Vincent Anderson Regional Hospital, Anderson, IN, p. A204
VANSANT, Scott, M.D. Chief Medical Officer, Central State Hospital, Milledgeville, GA, p. A161
VANTONGEREN, Teri, Director Information Services, Spectrum Health Pennock, Hastings, MI, p. A322
VANWICHEN, Ward C., Chief Executive Officer, Phillips County Hospital, Malta, MT, p. A385
VANWYHE, Brenda, Senior Vice President Finance and Chief Financial Officer, Rush–Copley Medical Center, Aurora, IL, p. A179
VARA Jr., Raymond P., President and Chief Executive Officer, Hawaii Pacific Health, Honolulu, HI, p. B61
VARELA, Alberto M., M.D., President, INSPIRA Ponce, Ponce, PR, p. A722
VARELA, Nancy, Director Human Resources, Patton State Hospital, Patton, CA, p. A80
VARGA, Patrick, Chief Operating Officer, Mercy Medical Center Redding, Redding, CA, p. A82
VARGAS, Jose L., M.D. Medical Director, West Gables Rehabilitation Hospital, Miami, FL, p. A135
VARGAS, Marisol, Director Finance, Hospital Del Maestro, San Juan, PR, p. A723
VARGAS, Nancy
Director Human Resources, Mark Twain Medical Center, San Andreas, CA, p. A85
Chief Human Resources, St. Joseph's Behavioral Health Center, Stockton, CA, p. A93
Vice President Human Resources, St. Joseph's Medical Center, Stockton, CA, p. A93
VARGAS–MAHAR, Monica, FACHE, Chief Executive Officer, The Hospitals of Providence Sierra Campus, El Paso, TX, p. A611
VARGHESE, Roy, M.D. Chief of Staff, Mary Breckinridge ARH Hospital, Hyden, KY, p. A258
VARGHESE, Shibu, Vice President Human Resources, University of Texas M.D. Anderson Cancer Center, Houston, TX, p. A622
VARIALE, Vincenzo, Chief Executive Officer, North Vista Hospital, North Las Vegas, NV, p. A403
VARIAN, Grant, M.D. Medical Director, Mary Rutan Hospital, Bellefontaine, OH, p. A479
VARK, Lawrence, M.D. Chief Medical Officer, Creek Nation Community Hospital, Okemah, OK, p. A511
VARLAND, Drew, Chief Nursing Officer and Chief Operating Officer, Pioneers Medical Center, Meeker, CO, p. A107
VARLEY, Kevin
Chief Financial Officer, Kindred Hospital South Philadelphia, Philadelphia, PA, p. A544
Chief Financial Officer, Kindred Hospital–Heritage Valley, Beaver, PA, p. A529
Chief Financial Officer, Kindred Hospital–Pittsburgh, Oakdale, PA, p. A542
VARNADO, Anjanette, M.D. Chief Medical Officer, St. Helena Parish Hospital, Greensburg, LA, p. A274
VARNADO, Darryl, Executive Vice President and Chief People Officer, Children's National Medical Center, Washington, DC, p. A119
VARNADOE, Milo, Director Information Systems, Warm Springs Medical Center, Warm Springs, GA, p. A167
VARNADOE, Tiffany G., Director Finance, Cordova Community Medical Center, Cordova, AK, p. A27
VARNER, Terry, Administrator, Yalobusha General Hospital, Water Valley, MS, p. A361
VARNEY, Tim, R.N. Chief Nursing Officer, Select Specialty Hospital–Ann Arbor, Ypsilanti, MI, p. A333
VARNUM, Daniel, President and Chief Executive Officer, Mercy Medical Center–North Iowa, Mason City, IA, p. A231
VARTELAS, Helene M., Chief Executive Officer, Connecticut Valley Hospital, Middletown, CT, p. A113
VASEK, Barbara, Director Information Technology, Yoakum Community Hospital, Yoakum, TX, p. A653
VASHISHTA, Ashok, M.D. Vice President Medical Affairs, McLaren Central Michigan, Mount Pleasant, MI, p. A326
VASIL, Kathleen, Vice President Finance, St. Charles Hospital, Port Jefferson, NY, p. A448
VASQUEZ, Alberto, Administrator, Garfield Memorial Hospital and Clinics, Panguitch, UT, p. A657
VASQUEZ, Christann
Executive Vice President and Chief Operating Officer, University Health System, San Antonio, TX, p. A642
President, University Medical Center at Brackenridge, Austin, TX, p. A595
VASQUEZ, George
Chief Technology Officer, Clovis Community Medical Center, Clovis, CA, p. A58
Vice President Information Services, Community Behavioral Health Center, Fresno, CA, p. A62
Corporate Chief Information Officer, Fresno Heart and Surgical Hospital, Fresno, CA, p. A62
VASQUEZ, J.C., M.D. Chief Medical Staff, Moab Regional Hospital, Moab, UT, p. A655
VASQUEZ, Jill, Manager Human Resources, Spectrum Health Ludington Hospital, Ludington, MI, p. A325
VASQUEZ, Kenneth, Associate Director, West Palm Hospital, West Palm Beach, FL, p. A147
VASQUEZ, Miguel, Chief Executive Officer, Sister Emmanuel Hospital, Miami, FL, p. A135
VASQUEZ, Nelson, Vice President Finance, Jackson Park Hospital and Medical Center, Chicago, IL, p. A182
VASS, Paula, Vice President Clinical Operations, Walden Psychiatric Care, Waltham, MA, p. A312
VASSALL, John, M.D
Chief Medical Officer, Swedish Medical Center–Cherry Hill Campus, Seattle, WA, p. A684
Chief Medical Officer, Swedish Medical Center–First Hill, Seattle, WA, p. A684
VASTOLA, David, Medical Director, SEARHC MT. Edgecumbe Hospital, Sitka, AK, p. A29
VASUNAGA, Amy, Chief Nurse Executive, Leahi Hospital, Honolulu, HI, p. A168
VATH, Richard, M.D. Vice President Medical Affairs, Our Lady of the Lake Regional Medical Center, Baton Rouge, LA, p. A269
VATSAVAI, Sundararama R., M.D. Medical Director, Baton Rouge Rehabilitation Hospital, Baton Rouge, LA, p. A269
VAUGHAN, Aaron, Coordinator Information Systems, Pocahontas Memorial Hospital, Buckeye, WV, p. A689
VAUGHAN, Alan, Director Information Technology, Share Medical Center, Alva, OK, p. A503
VAUGHAN, Amanda, Chief Financial Officer, St. Catherine Hospital, Garden City, KS, p. A240
VAUGHAN, Brandon, Chief Financial Officer and Vice President Finance, Jamestown Regional Medical Center, Jamestown, ND, p. A475
VAUGHAN, Page H., Chief Executive Officer, Chester Regional Medical Center, Chester, SC, p. A558
VAUGHAN, Peggy, M.D
Senior Vice President Medical Affairs, University of Maryland Harford Memorial Hospital, Havre De Grace, MD, p. A298
Senior Vice President Medical Affairs, University of Maryland Upper Chesapeake Medical Center, Bel Air, MD, p. A295
VAUGHAN, Rob, Chief Financial Officer, Carilion New River Valley Medical Center, Christiansburg, VA, p. A663
VAUGHAN, Steve, Chief Executive Officer, Pearl River County Hospital, Poplarville, MS, p. A359
VAUGHN, Anita, Administrator and Chief Executive Officer, Baptist Memorial Hospital for Women, Memphis, TN, p. A583
VAUGHN, Barbara, Chief Nursing Officer, Baylor Medical Center at Carrollton, Carrollton, TX, p. A600
VAUGHN, Kerry, Chief Information Officer, St. Mary's Health Care System, Athens, GA, p. A149
VAUGHN, Kevin P., Chief Financial Officer, Kansas Spine and Specialty Hospital, Wichita, KS, p. A252
VAUGHN, Sandy
Director Information Services, Baylor All Saints Medical Center at Fort Worth, Fort Worth, TX, p. A613
Director Information Systems, Baylor Regional Medical Center at Grapevine, Grapevine, TX, p. A616
VAUGHN, Sharma, Chief Nursing Officer, Rangely District Hospital, Rangely, CO, p. A108
VAUGHN, Ted W., Director Human Resources, UnityPoint Health – Trinity Regional Medical Center, Fort Dodge, IA, p. A228
VAUGHN, Vickie, Chief Nursing Officer, Heritage Medical Center, Shelbyville, TN, p. A588
VAVARUTSOS, Tony, Director Information Systems, Thorek Memorial Hospital, Chicago, IL, p. A185
VAZIRI, H. Kevin, President, Woodland Healthcare, Woodland, CA, p. A98
VAZQUEZ, Alfonso, Executive Director, Hospital Manati Medical Center, Manati, PR, p. A721
VAZQUEZ, Brunilda, Medical Director, Hospital de Psiquiatria, San Juan, PR, p. A723
VAZQUEZ, Emilio, M.D. Chief Medical Officer, DeKalb Health, Auburn, IN, p. A204
VAZQUEZ, Francisco, Director, Robert J. Dole Veterans Affairs Medical Center, Wichita, KS, p. A252
VAZQUEZ, Manuel J., Executive Administrator, Hospital Oncologico Andres Grillasca, Ponce, PR, p. A722

Index of Health Care Professionals

# Index of Health Care Professionals / Veach


VEACH, Jamie, Chief Operating Officer, Clay County Hospital, Flora, IL, p. A188
VEDRAL–BARON, Jennifer, Commander, Fort Belvoir Community Hospital, Fort Belvoir, VA, p. A665
VEDROS, Allyson Dill, R.N. Chief Nursing Officer, Ochsner St. Anne General Hospital, Raceland, LA, p. A284
VEERAMACHANENI, Harish, M.D. Chief of Staff, Wayne Medical Center, Waynesboro, TN, p. A589
VEESER, Tom, R.N. Chief Nursing Officer, Calumet Medical Center, Chilton, WI, p. A699
VEGA, James, Director Information Systems, Palm Beach Gardens Medical Center, Palm Beach Gardens, FL, p. A138
VEGA, Maria, Director Human Resources, Auxilio Mutuo Hospital, San Juan, PR, p. A723
VEGA, Mary, R.N. Vice President Nursing, St. Margaret's Hospital, Spring Valley, IL, p. A201
VEILLETTE, Michael D.
Senior Vice President and Chief Financial Officer, Manchester Memorial Hospital, Manchester, CT, p. A112
Senior Vice President and Chief Financial Officer, Rockville General Hospital, Vernon, CT, p. A115
VEILLEUX, Jeffrey
Senior Vice President and Chief Financial Officer, Swedish Medical Center–Cherry Hill Campus, Seattle, WA, p. A684
Executive Vice President and Chief Financial Officer, Swedish Medical Center–First Hill, Seattle, WA, p. A684
VEILLON, Paul, CP
Chief Financial Officer, CHRISTUS Dubuis Hospital of Fort Smith, Fort Smith, AR, p. A44
Chief Financial Officer, CHRISTUS Dubuis Hospital of Hot Springs, Hot Springs National Park, AR, p. A46
Chief Financial Officer, Kindred Hospital–St. Louis at Mercy, Saint Louis, MO, p. A376
VEITZ, Larry W., President, Spearfish Regional Hospital, Spearfish, SD, p. A572
VELA, Javier, Director Information Technology, Baylor Medical Center at Uptown, Dallas, TX, p. A604
VELASCO, Paul, IT Manager, Kit Carson County Health Service District, Burlington, CO, p. A100
VELASQUEZ, Alfred T., Area Information Officer, Kaiser Permanente Riverside Medical Center, Riverside, CA, p. A83
VELASQUEZ, Carol Nunley, R.N. Chief Nursing Officer, Lake Chelan Community Hospital, Chelan, WA, p. A677
VELASQUEZ, Carolina, Director Information Services, Uvalde County Hospital Authority, Uvalde, TX, p. A649
VELASQUEZ, Lin, Vice President Human Resources, Saint Louise Regional Hospital, Gilroy, CA, p. A63
VELASQUEZ, Roberto, M.D. Medical Director, Hospital Oncologico Andres Grillasca, Ponce, PR, p. A722
VELETSOS, Alex, Chief Information Officer, St. Mary's of Michigan, Saginaw, MI, p. A329
VELEZ, Luz M., Director–Administration of Nursing Services, Hospital San Carlos Borromeo, Moca, PR, p. A722
VELEZ, Pablo, Chief Executive Officer, Sharp Chula Vista Medical Center, Chula Vista, CA, p. A58
VELEZ, Raul, Director Information Systems, Huntsville Memorial Hospital, Huntsville, TX, p. A623
VELUSWAMY, Ragupathy, M.D. Vice President Medical Affairs, Wilkes–Barre General Hospital, Wilkes–Barre, PA, p. A553
VENABLE, Mark, Interim Director Human Resources, Shriners Hospitals for Children–St. Louis, Saint Louis, MO, p. A377
VENABLE, Robert, M.D. Chief Medical Staff, Washington County Hospital, Plymouth, NC, p. A466
VENDETTI, Marilouise, M.D. Chief Medical Officer, AtlantiCare Regional Medical Center, Atlantic City, NJ, p. A409
VENGCO, Joel L., M
Vice President and Chief Information Officer, Baystate Health, Baystate Mary Lane Hospital, Ware, MA, p. A312
Vice President, Chief Information Officer, Baystate Medical Center, Springfield, MA, p. A311
VENHUIZEN, Pamela, Chief Human Resources Officer, Cooperstown Medical Center, Cooperstown, ND, p. A473
VENOIT, Jon–Paul, Chief Operating Officer, Masonicare Health Center, Wallingford, CT, p. A115
VENTAMEGLIA, Tom, Director Information Systems, Crittenton Hospital Medical Center, Rochester, MI, p. A328
VENTURA, Sylvia A., R.N. Chief Nursing Officer, Olympia Medical Center, Los Angeles, CA, p. A71
VENTURELLA, James, Chief Information Officer, UPMC Presbyterian Shadyside, Pittsburgh, PA, p. A547
VENUTO, Frank, Chief Human Capital Officer, Nebraska Medicine – Nebraska Medical Center, Omaha, NE, p. A396
VENUTO, Kenneth, Chief Financial Officer, St. Anthony's Medical Center, Saint Louis, MO, p. A377
VENZANT, Shamada, Manager Health Information, Specialty Hospital of Winnfield, Winnfield, LA, p. A287
VERA, Luis F., M.D. Medical Director, Kensington Hospital, Philadelphia, PA, p. A544
VERAGIWALA, Jignesh, Chief of Staff, Mercy Hospital Logan County, Guthrie, OK, p. A507
VERBEKE, Lori, Chief Financial Officer, Timberlawn Mental Health System, Dallas, TX, p. A607
VERBUS, John R., Senior Vice President and Chief Operating Officer, Frederick Memorial Hospital, Frederick, MD, p. A298
VERCHOTA, Robert P., Vice President Support Services, Regina Hospital, Hastings, MN, p. A340
VERCRUYSSE, Craig, Chief Information Officer, California Pacific Medical Center, San Francisco, CA, p. A88
VERDEJA, Juan–Carlos, M.D. President of Medical Staff, Baptist Health South Florida, West Kendall Baptist Hospital, Miami, FL, p. A134
VERDON, Chris, Director Finance, Phillips Eye Institute, Minneapolis, MN, p. A343
VERFURTH, Larry, D.O
Chief Medical Officer and Senior Vice President, Good Shepherd Medical Center, Longview, TX, p. A629
Executive Vice President and Chief Medical Officer, Good Shepherd Medical Center–Marshall, Marshall, TX, p. A631
VERGA, Joseph P., FACHE, Chief Executive Officer, Guam Memorial Hospital Authority, Tamuning, GU, p. A719
VERGNE, Roger T., Chief Fiscal Service, Hunter Holmes McGuire Veterans Affairs Medical Center–Richmond, Richmond, VA, p. A672
VERGONIO, Merlinda, Chief Information Management and Technology, U. S. Air Force Hospital, Hampton, VA, p. A666
VERGOS, Katherine, Chief Operating Officer, Ripon Medical Center, Ripon, WI, p. A710
VERHASSELT, Helen, Chief Financial Officer, North Valley Hospital, Tonasket, WA, p. A686
VERINDER, David, Interim Chief Executive Officer, Sarasota Memorial Health Care System, Sarasota, FL, p. A142
VERMILLION, Kerry, Senior Vice President Finance and Chief Financial Officer, Gulf Breeze Hospital, Gulf Breeze, FL, p. A128
VERMULEN, Peter, Director Information Technology, Schick Shadel Hospital, Seattle, WA, p. A683
VERNON, Janice, Supervisory Information Technology Specialist, John J. Pershing Veterans Affairs Medical Center, Poplar Bluff, MO, p. A374
VERRET, Dean, Vice President Financial Services, Terrebonne General Medical Center, Houma, LA, p. A275
VERRET, Deborah, JD Chief Human Resources Officer, Baptist Hospitals of Southeast Texas, Beaumont, TX, p. A596
VERRETTE, Paul, M.D. Chief Medical Officer, St. Bernard Parish Hospital, Chalmette, LA, p. A271
VERRETTE, Paula, M.D. Senior Vice President Quality and Physician Services and Chief Medical Officer, Huntington Memorial Hospital, Pasadena, CA, p. A80
VERRILL, Alan, M.D. President Medical Staff, Bridgton Hospital, Bridgton, ME, p. A289
VERSECKES, Mike, Financial Officer, Terrell State Hospital, Terrell, TX, p. A647
VERSTEEG, Linda, Director of Nursing, Hegg Memorial Health Center Avera, Rock Valley, IA, p. A234
VERZI, Dennis, Executive Vice President and Chief Administrative Officer, St. Catherine of Siena Medical Center, Smithtown, NY, p. A450
VESSEY, Joe, Chief Financial Officer, Grays Harbor Community Hospital, Aberdeen, WA, p. A676
VETTER, Rich, M.D. Associate Chief, Essentia Health St. Mary's – Detroit Lakes, Detroit Lakes, MN, p. A337
VIALL, John, M.D. Vice President Medical Affairs, Holzer Medical Center, Gallipolis, OH, p. A490
VIALL, Sandra E., MSN Chief Nursing Officer, Hendry Regional Medical Center, Clewiston, FL, p. A124
VIBBARD, Cheryl
Manager Health Information Services, University Hospitals Conneaut Medical Center, Conneaut, OH, p. A487
Manager Health Information Systems, University Hospitals Geneva Medical Center, Geneva, OH, p. A490
VIBETO, Brett, M.D. Chief of Staff, Mercy Medical Center, Williston, ND, p. A477
VICE, Harmony, Chief Executive Officer, University General Hospital, Houston, TX, p. A622
VICE, Jeff, Chief Operating Officer, St. Joseph Hospital, Fort Wayne, IN, p. A209
VICENS–RIVERA Jr., Enrique A., JD, Chief Executive Officer, HEALTHSOUTH Hospital of Manati, Manati, PR, p. A721
VICENTE, Oscar, Chief Financial Officer, Palmetto General Hospital, Hialeah, FL, p. A128
VICENTI, Darren, M.D. Clinical Director, Hopi Health Care Center, Keams Canyon, AZ, p. A32
VICK, Dan J., M.D. Vice President of Medical Affairs and Chief Medical Officer, Oneida Healthcare, Oneida, NY, p. A446
VICKERS, Cynthia, R.N. Assistant Administrator for Nursing Services, Memorial Hospital and Manor, Bainbridge, GA, p. A152
VICKERS, Dave, Chief Financial Officer, Los Alamitos Medical Center, Los Alamitos, CA, p. A68
VICKERS, Kathy, Director Human Resources, Vantage Point of Northwest Arkansas, Fayetteville, AR, p. A44
VICKERY, Ian, Director Information Technology, D. W. McMillan Memorial Hospital, Brewton, AL, p. A17
VICKERY, Tim, Chief Information Officer, St. Mary's Sacred Heart Hospital, Lavonia, GA, p. A160
VICKROY, Joseph, M.D. Medical Director, HEALTHSOUTH Rehabilitation Hospital of Utah, Sandy, UT, p. A659
VICTORIA, Mario, M.D. Vice President, Medical Affairs, Samaritan Medical Center, Watertown, NY, p. A453
VIDONI–CLARK, Clotilde, R.N. Chief Nurse Executive, Saint Elizabeths Hospital, Washington, DC, p. A120
VIDRINE, Charmaine R., CPA Chief Financial Officer, Acadia General Hospital, Crowley, LA, p. A272
VIEIRA, Terri, President and Chief Executive Officer, Sebasticook Valley Health, Pittsfield, ME, p. A291
VIELKIND, James, Chief Financial Officer, Little Falls Hospital, Little Falls, NY, p. A436
VIENNEAU, Marie E., FACHE, President and Chief Executive Officer, Mayo Regional Hospital, Dover–Foxcroft, ME, p. A290
VIERKANT, Matthew, M.D. President Medical Staff, Mother Frances Hospital – Jacksonville, Jacksonville, TX, p. A624
VIERLING, Taryn, Chief Nursing Officer, Select Specialty Hospital of Southeast Ohio, Zanesville, OH, p. A502
VIETH, Amy, Chief Executive Officer, HEALTHSOUTH Cane Creek Rehabilitation Hospital, Martin, TN, p. A582
VIGGERS, Andreas, Director Human Resources, Providence Little Company of Mary Medical Center San Pedro, CA, p. A72
VIGIL, Kevin, Director Information Systems, Los Alamos Medical Center, Los Alamos, NM, p. A425
VILANOVA, Lynda, Director Patient Care Services, Shriners Hospitals for Children–Spokane, Spokane, WA, p. A685
VILAR, Ramon J., Administrator, Wilma N. Vazquez Medical Center, Vega Baja, PR, p. A724
VILHAUER, Beverly, Chief Executive Officer, Wishek Community Hospital and Clinics, Wishek, ND, p. A477
VILLA, Alex, Chief Executive Officer, Western Arizona Regional Medical Center, Bullhead City, AZ, p. A30
VILLANO, Jeremi, M.D. Chief of Staff, Crook County Medical Services District, Sundance, WY, p. A717
VILLANUEVA, Alice A., Senior Vice President Human Resources, John Muir Medical Center, Walnut Creek, Walnut Creek, CA, p. A97
VILLANUEVA, Andrew, M.D. Interim Chief Medical Officer, Lahey Hospital & Medical Center, Burlington, Burlington, MA, p. A305
VILLANUEVA CABRERA, Sarah I., Interim Executive Director, Hospital Buen Samaritano, Aguadilla, PR, p. A719
VILLARAZA, II, Christopher, M.D. Chief Medical Staff, Grafton City Hospital, Grafton, WV, p. A691
VILLAREAL, Xavier, Chief Operating Officer, CHRISTUS Spohn Hospital Corpus Christi Memorial, Corpus Christi, TX, p. A602
VILLARREAL, Troy, President and Chief Executive Officer, Medical City Dallas Hospital, Dallas, TX, p. A605
VILLARREAL, Xavier, Chief Executive Officer, CHRISTUS Spohn Hospital Corpus Christi Memorial, Corpus Christi, TX, p. A602
VILLARRUZ, Alex, Chief Operating Officer, Barlow Respiratory Hospital, Los Angeles, CA, p. A69
VILLEGAS, Lorraine, Manager Human Resources, Paradise Valley Hospital, National City, CA, p. A77
VILORIA, Bonnie, Chief Nursing Officer, La Paz Regional Hospital, Parker, AZ, p. A34
VINAS, Elmo, Director Human Resources, Franklin Foundation Hospital, Franklin, LA, p. A274
VINCENT, Adam, Chief Executive Officer, Mayhill Hospital, Denton, TX, p. A608
VINCENT, Ben, FACHE, Chief Executive Officer, Braxton County Memorial Hospital, Gassaway, WV, p. A691
VINCENT, Cynthia, Vice President Finance, St. Francis Regional Medical Center, Shakopee, MN, p. A347
VINCENT, David, Director Information Systems, Canonsburg General Hospital, Canonsburg, PA, p. A530
VINCENT, Larry, Director Human Resources, Delta County Memorial Hospital, Delta, CO, p. A101
VINCENT, Laurence Marie, Chief Nursing Officer, University Hospital and Clinics, Lafayette, LA, p. A278
VINCENT, Mitch, Vice President Organizational Support, Range Regional Health Services, Hibbing, MN, p. A340
VINCENT, Paula, MSN, President and Chief Operating Officer, Novant Health Presbyterian Medical Center, Charlotte, NC, p. A458
VINCENT, Sherril, Vice President Finance/CFO, Alexian Brothers Acute Care Ministries, St. Alexius Medical Center, Hoffman Estates, IL, p. A191
VINCENZ, Felix T., Ph.D. Chief Operating Officer, St. Louis Psychiatric Rehabilitation Center, Saint Louis, MO, p. A378
VINSON, Roy, Interim Chief Executive Officer, Vaughan Regional Medical Center, Selma, AL, p. A24

VINYARD, Roy G., FACHE, President and Chief Executive Officer, Asante Health System, Medford, OR, p. B12
VIOLETTE, Brenda, M.D. Director Medical Staff, Firelands Regional Health System, Sandusky, OH, p. A497
VIOLI, Ronald L., Chief Executive Officer, Wheeling Hospital, Wheeling, WV, p. A696
VIPOND, Kathleen, Assistant Administrator and Director, Abraham Lincoln Memorial Hospital, Lincoln, IL, p. A193
VIPPERMAN, Mark, President, Spectrum Health Ludington Hospital, Ludington, MI, p. A325
VIRDEN, Larkin, Chief Executive Officer, Kindred Hospital–Houston Northwest, Houston, TX, p. A620
VIRGEN, Tomas, MSN, Interim Chief Executive Officer, El Centro Regional Medical Center, El Centro, CA, p. A60
VIRGIL, Cindy L., MSN Senior Vice President Patient Care Services, Indiana Regional Medical Center, Indiana, PA, p. A536
VIRGIL–BELDING, Kathy H., Chief Nursing Officer, Banner Lassen Medical Center, Susanville, CA, p. A93
VIRJI, Ayaz, M.D. Chief of Staff, Johnson Memorial Health Services, Dawson, MN, p. A337
VIRKLER, Joe, Chief Information Officer, Carthage Area Hospital, Carthage, NY, p. A431
VISAGGIO, Stella, Chief Operating Officer, Hackettstown Regional Medical Center, Hackettstown, NJ, p. A412
VISCONI, Deborah, Director, Hospital Operations, Morristown Medical Center, Morristown, NJ, p. A414
VISH, Nancy, Ph.D., President, Baylor Jack and Jane Hamilton Heart and Vascular Hospital, Dallas, TX, p. A604
VISSERS, Robert, M.D., Interim Chief Executive Officer, Boulder Community Health, Boulder, CO, p. A99
VITAL, Dale, Chief Nursing Officer, Orange Coast Memorial Medical Center, Fountain Valley, CA, p. A62
VITALE, Nickolas A.
  Executive Vice President and Chief Financial Officer, Beaumont Hospital – Royal Oak, Royal Oak, MI, p. A328
  Senior Vice President and Chief Financial Officer, Beaumont Hospital Grosse Pointe, Grosse Pointe, MI, p. A321
VITALE–NOLEN, Roberta A., Administrator, Patient Care Services, New Hampshire Hospital, Concord, NH, p. A405
VITALI, Joe, Director Information Technology, Parkside Psychiatric Hospital and Clinic, Tulsa, OK, p. A516
VITALI, Vincent
  Chief Information Officer, RML Specialty Hospital, Chicago, IL, p. A184
  Chief Information Officer, RML Specialty Hospital, Hinsdale, IL, p. A191
VITALIS, Lee Ann, Executive Director Human Resources, St. Croix Regional Medical Center, St. Croix Falls, WI, p. A711
VITIELLO, Jon, Chief Financial Officer, Mercy Hospital Oklahoma City, Oklahoma City, OK, p. A512
VITOLAS, Victor, Acting Chief Information Technology Services, Central Texas Veterans Health Care System, Temple, TX, p. A646
VIVIANO, Paul S., President and Chief Executive Officer, Children's Hospital Los Angeles, Los Angeles, CA, p. A69
VIVIT, Romeo, Chief Surgeon, U. S. Public Health Service Indian Hospital, Rosebud, SD, p. A571
VLAHAVAS, Beth, R.N. Vice President Patient Care Services and Chief Nursing Officer, Mercy Medical Center, Rockville Centre, NY, p. A449
VLARS, Scott, Chief Information Technology Services, Wilmington Veterans Affairs Medical Center, Wilmington, DE, p. A118
VLODARCHYK, Coreen, R.N. Vice President, Patient Care Services and Chief Nursing Officer, Barnes–Jewish Hospital, Saint Louis, MO, p. A376
VLOSICH, Wade, Director, Harry S. Truman Memorial Veterans Hospital, Columbia, MO, p. A366
VOCCA, Lori A., Vice President Human Resources, Providence Regional Medical Center Everett, Everett, WA, p. A679
VOECKS, Barbara, Chief Information Officer, Ortonville Area Health Services, Ortonville, MN, p. A344
VOELKER, Dolph, Director Information Services, Indiana University Health Goshen Hospital, Goshen, IN, p. A210
VOELKER, Justin, Chief Financial Officer, Valley Hospital, Spokane Valley, WA, p. A685
VOGEL, Clay, Chief Executive Officer, Hamlin Memorial Hospital, Hamlin, TX, p. A617
VOGELSANG, Mark, Director Information Services, Providence Holy Family Hospital, Spokane, WA, p. A685
VOGENTIZ, William, M.D. Medical Director, AnMed Health Rehabilitation Hospital, Anderson, SC, p. A557
VOGT, Dennis, Director Information Technology, Madison Health, London, OH, p. A492
VOGT, Sam, Manager Human Resources, The Hospital at Hebrew Health Care, West Hartford, CT, p. A116
VOHS, Lester, Manager Information Systems, Cass Regional Medical Center, Harrisonville, MO, p. A368
VOIGT, Jordan, Administrator, Genesis Medical Center–Davenport, Davenport, IA, p. A225
VOISARD, Victor, Director Human Resources, San Gabriel Valley Medical Center, San Gabriel, CA, p. A89
VOISELLE, Dana, Director Human Resources, Baptist Medical Center Beaches, Jacksonville Beach, FL, p. A130
VOKOUN, Cory, Chief Nursing Officer, Nevada Regional Medical Center, Nevada, MO, p. A373
VOLANTO, John, Vice President and Chief Operating Officer, Nyack Hospital, Nyack, NY, p. A446
VOLGER, Helen, Director of Information Services, Aspirus Medford Hospital, Medford, WI, p. A705
VOLINSKI, Douglas R., Vice President and Chief Financial Officer, Duncan Regional Hospital, Duncan, OK, p. A505
VOLK, Charles T., M.D. Regional Chief Medical Officer, CHRISTUS Spohn Hospital Corpus Christi Memorial, Corpus Christi, TX, p. A602
VOLK, James, M.D. Chief Medical Officer, Sanford Medical Center Fargo, Fargo, ND, p. A474
VOLKERDING, Elizabeth, Director Workforce Excellence, San Juan Regional Medical Center, Farmington, NM, p. A424
VOLKERT, Brent, Director Information Technology, Ferrell Hospital, Eldorado, IL, p. A186
VOLLER, Kristi, Director of Nursing, Mobridge Regional Hospital, Mobridge, SD, p. A570
VOLLMER, Cyndy, Director Human Resources, Southern Coos Hospital and Health Center, Bandon, OR, p. A519
VOLOCH, Bill, President and Chief Executive Officer, Wesley Medical Center, Wichita, KS, p. A253
VOLPE, Buddy, Director Human Resources, Peterson Regional Medical Center, Kerrville, TX, p. A626
VOLPE, Michele M., Executive Director and Chief Executive Officer, Penn Presbyterian Medical Center, Philadelphia, PA, p. A544
VOLTAIRE, Adler, Chief Administrative Officer, Interim LSU Public Hospital, New Orleans, LA, p. A282
VON BEHREN, Rachel, Director Financial Services, UnityPoint Health – Jones Regional Medical Center, Anamosa, IA, p. A222
VONDERAU, Mary, Vice President Strategy and Operations, Presence Mercy Medical Center, Aurora, IL, p. A178
VONNIDA, Ashley Marie, Chief Nursing Officer, Coastal Carolina Hospital, Hardeeville, SC, p. A562
VOORHEES, Michael, MS, Executive Director, East Mountain Hospital, Belle Mead, NJ, p. A409
VORHEES, Nancy, Chief Administrative Officer, St. Luke's Rehabilitation Institute, Spokane, WA, p. A685
VOSBURGH, Mary M., R.N
  Vice President Nursing and Chief Nursing Officer, Arnot Ogden Medical Center, Elmira, NY, p. A433
  Vice President Nursing and Chief Nursing Officer, St. Joseph's Hospital, Elmira, NY, p. A433
VOSHELL, Shane, Director Human Resources, Adventist Medical Center–Portland, Portland, OR, p. A524
VOSKAMP, Lynne, R.N. Vice President of Nursing, Capital Region Medical Center, Jefferson City, MO, p. A368
VOSS, Daryle, FACHE, President, Mercy Hospital Ardmore, Ardmore, OK, p. A503
VOSS, Kathy, Director Human Resources, CentraCare Health–Monticello, Monticello, MN, p. A343
VOSS, Robert, Chief Financial Officer, Laredo Specialty Hospital, Laredo, TX, p. A627
VOSS, Wayne M., Chief Executive Officer, Houston Methodist West Hospital, Houston, TX, p. A620
VOSSBERG, Brad, M.D. Chief Rehabilitation, Community Howard Specialty Hospital, Kokomo, IN, p. A213
VOSSLER, Jeffrey W., Chief Financial Officer, Joint Township District Memorial Hospital, Saint Marys, OH, p. A497
VOTTO, John J., D.O., President and Chief Executive Officer, Hospital for Special Care, New Britain, CT, p. A113
VOWELL, Christy, D.O. Chief of Staff, North Mississippi Medical Center–Eupora, Eupora, MS, p. A352
VOZOS, Frank J., FACS,
  President and Chief Executive Officer, Monmouth Medical Center, Long Branch Campus, Long Branch, NJ, p. A413
  President and Chief Executive Officer, Monmouth Medical Center, Southern Campus, Lakewood, NJ, p. A413
VRABEL, Amy Z., Chief Information Officer, Mayo Clinic Hospital, Phoenix, AZ, p. A35
VRANA, Daniel A.
  Controller, HEALTHSOUTH Harmarville Rehabilitation Hospital, Pittsburgh, PA, p. A546
  Area Controller, HEALTHSOUTH Rehabilitation Hospital of Sewickley, Sewickley, PA, p. A550
VRBA, Frank, Chief Information Officer, Annie Jeffrey Memorial County Health Center, Osceola, NE, p. A397
VRBAS, Laken, R.N. Director of Nursing, Dundy County Hospital, Benkelman, NE, p. A390
VREELAND, Matthew, M.D. Chief Medical Officer, FirstHealth Richmond Memorial Hospital, Rockingham, NC, p. A467
VRONKO, Jeremy, Manager, Information Services, Spectrum Health Ludington Hospital, Ludington, MI, p. A325
VROTSOS, Darlene, R.N. Senior Vice President and Chief Nursing Officer, Virginia Hospital Center – Arlington, Arlington, VA, p. A662
VRZAK, Staci, Vice President Patient Care Services, Regional Health Services of Howard County, Cresco, IA, p. A225
VUCHAK, Jerry
  Vice President Information Systems, Barnes–Jewish Hospital, Saint Louis, MO, p. A376
  Vice President Information Systems, Barnes–Jewish West County Hospital, Saint Louis, MO, p. A376
VUKICH, David, M.D. Senior Vice President, Chief Medical Officer and Chief Quality Officer, UF Health Jacksonville, Jacksonville, FL, p. A130
VUKSTA, Jeanne, Chief Financial Officer, Bacharach Institute for Rehabilitation, Pomona, NJ, p. A417
VUTRANO, Frank A., Chief Financial Officer, Wyckoff Heights Medical Center, NY, p. A445

## W

WABAUNSEE, Gary, Chief Executive Officer, Crow/Northern Cheyenne Hospital, Crow Agency, MT, p. A382
WABLE, Chad W., President and Chief Executive Officer, Saint Mary's Hospital, Waterbury, CT, p. A115
WACHOWIAK, Darrell, Associate Vice President Operations, ProMedica Bay Park Hospital, Oregon, OH, p. A496
WACHTEL, Andrew, Chief Executive Officer, AllianceHealth Blackwell, Blackwell, OK, p. A504
WACHTEL, R. Andrew, FACHE, Chief Executive Officer, AllianceHealth Ponca City, Ponca City, OK, p. A514
WACK, Mark, Chief Financial Officer, Merit Health Biloxi, Biloxi, MS, p. A350
WADA, Takashi, Interim Director, Santa Barbara County Psychiatric Health Facility, Santa Barbara, CA, p. A91
WADDELL, Kathy, Administrator, Wayne General Hospital, Waynesboro, MS, p. A361
WADDELL, Lesa, Director Human Resources, Marengo Memorial Hospital, UnityPoint Health, Marengo, IA, p. A231
WADE, RN, BSN, Cynthia, R.N. Executive Vice President and Chief Operating Officer, LincolnHealth, Damariscotta, ME, p. A290
WADE, Donald Lee, Chief Financial Officer, Goodland Regional Medical Center, Goodland, KS, p. A240
WADE, Donna, Senior Director Human Resources, Comanche County Memorial Hospital, Lawton, OK, p. A508
WADE, Glenn, Director Information Systems, Saint Thomas Highlands Hospital, Sparta, TN, p. A588
WADE, Hong, Chief Financial Officer, Sweeny Community Hospital, Sweeny, TX, p. A646
WADE, Jonathan O., Chief Executive Officer, Jersey Community Hospital, Jerseyville, IL, p. A191
WADE, Karen, Chief Information Officer, U. S. Public Health Service Indian Hospital–Sells, Sells, AZ, p. A38
WADE, Susan, Assistant Vice President, Hendrick Health System, Abilene, TX, p. A590
WADEWITZ, Martin, Chief Operations Officer/ Vice President, Operations, Angel Medical Center, Franklin, NC, p. A460
WADLE, Don, Vice President Clinical and Support Services, Portneuf Medical Center, Pocatello, ID, p. A175
WADMAN, Timothy, Chief Executive Officer, SSM Select Rehabilitation Hospital, Richmond Heights, MO, p. A375
WADSWORTH, Barbara A., MSN Chief Nursing Officer, Bryn Mawr Hospital, Bryn Mawr, PA, p. A530
WAFFORD, Marty, Executive Officer of Support and Programs, Chickasaw Nation Medical Center, Ada, OK, p. A503
WAGENHAUSER, Missy, Director Human Resources, Cambridge Hospital in Houston, Houston, TX, p. A619
WAGERS, Rick, Senior Executive Vice President and Chief Financial Officer, Regional One Health, Memphis, TN, p. A584
WAGGENER, Yvonne, Chief Financial Officer, San Bernardino Mountains Community Hospital District, Lake Arrowhead, CA, p. A67
WAGGONER, Jeff, M.D. Chief of Staff, Weisbrod Memorial County Hospital, Eads, CO, p. A103
WAGGONER, Michelle, Chief Executive Officer, Community Memorial Hospital, Hicksville, OH, p. A491
WAGMEISTER, Lee, M.D. President Medical Staff, The Heart Hospital at Deaconess Gateway, Newburgh, IN, p. A217
WAGNER, Arthur, Senior Vice President and Executive Director, Coney Island Hospital, NY, p. A439
WAGNER, Dale, Chief Financial Officer, Kindred Hospital–Westminster, Westminster, CA, p. A97
WAGNER, David D., Chief Information Management Service, Veterans Affairs Gulf Coast Veterans Health Care System, Biloxi, MS, p. A350

Index of Health Care Professionals

Index of Health Care Professionals / Wagner


WAGNER, Elaina, Director Human Resources, Sunnyside Community Hospital and Clinics, Sunnyside, WA, p. A686
WAGNER, Fred, Chief Financial Officer, OSF St. Francis Hospital and Medical Group, Escanaba, MI, p. A319
WAGNER, Gwendolyn Dianne, R.N. Chief Nursing Officer, Mission Community Hospital, CA, p. A71
WAGNER, Janet, R.N., Chief Executive Officer, Mills–Peninsula Health Services, Burlingame, CA, p. A56
WAGNER, Jeffrey, Supervisor Information Systems, UP Health System–Bell, Ishpeming, MI, p. A323
WAGNER, Linda, Chief Financial Officer, Sanford Worthington Medical Center, Worthington, MN, p. A349
WAGNER, Linda S., FACHE, Chief Executive Officer, Seneca Healthcare District, Chester, CA, p. A57
WAGNER, Lynne, R.N. Chief Nursing Officer, Rose Medical Center, Denver, CO, p. A102
WAGNER, Michael, M.D., President and Chief Executive Officer, Tufts Medical Center, Boston, MA, p. A304
WAGNER, Randall J., Chief Operating Officer, Mercy Health Saint Mary's, Grand Rapids, MI, p. A321
WAGNER, Russell R., Executive Vice President and Chief Financial Officer, Holy Redeemer Hospital, Meadowbrook, PA, p. A540
WAGNER, Sarah, Human Resources Officer, Memorial Hospital of Texas County, Guymon, OK, p. A507
WAGNER, Sherry, Director Human Resources, Oklahoma Center for Orthopedic and Multi–Specialty Surgery, Oklahoma City, OK, p. A512
WAGNER, Suzie, Director Human Resources, HEALTHSOUTH Rehabilitation Hospital of Alexandria, Alexandria, LA, p. A268
WAGNER, Terry, R.N. Chief Operating Officer, Pocahontas Memorial Hospital, Buckeye, WV, p. A689
WAGNER, Terry, Chief Information Officer, Upstate University Hospital, Syracuse, NY, p. A451
WAGNER, Timothy, M.D. Chief Medical Staff, Yoakum Community Hospital, Yoakum, TX, p. A653
WAGNER, Tom, Interim Vice President Finance, Avera St. Mary's Hospital, Pierre, SD, p. A570
WAGNER, Vanessa, Chief Financial Officer, Lawrence Memorial Hospital, Walnut Ridge, AR, p. A51
WAGNON, LaNell, Director Medical Records, Comanche County Hospital, Coldwater, KS, p. A238
WAGNON, William, Chief Executive Officer, Henrico Doctors' Hospital, Richmond, VA, p. A672
WAGONER, Craig
  Chief Executive Officer, Community Behavioral Health Center, Fresno, CA, p. A62
  Chief Executive Officer, Community Regional Medical Center, Fresno, CA, p. A62
WAGONER, Dean, Director Human Resources, Good Samaritan Hospital, Vincennes, IN, p. A221
WAHL, Carol R., R.N. Vice President Patient Care Services, CHI Health Good Samaritan, Kearney, NE, p. A393
WAHL, Josephine Sclafani, R.N. VP, Patient Care Services & CNO, Henry Ford Wyandotte Hospital, Wyandotte, MI, p. A332
WAHL, Tony, Chief Executive Officer, Texas Spine & Joint Hospital, Tyler, TX, p. A649
WAHLERS, Brenda, M.D. Chief of Staff, Cole Memorial, Coudersport, PA, p. A532
WAHLUND, Keith, Vice President Human Resources, Essentia Health Fargo, Fargo, ND, p. A473
WAIBEL, David, M.D. Medical Director, Clarks Summit State Hospital, Clarks Summit, PA, p. A531
WAIBEL, Jason, Interim Chief Executive Officer, HEALTHSOUTH Rehabilitation Hospital of Northern Virginia, Aldie, VA, p. A662
WAIDE, Mary Beth, JD, Chief Executive Officer, Deer's Head Hospital Center, Salisbury, MD, p. A300
WAIN, Matthew, Chief Operating Officer, MUSC Medical Center of Medical University of South Carolina, Charleston, SC, p. A558
WAIND, Mark, Administrative Director Information Services, Altru Health System, Grand Forks, ND, p. A474
WAITE, Douglas, M.D. Chief Medical Officer, Saint Vincent Hospital, Worcester, MA, p. A313
WAITE, Douglas D.
  Senior Vice President and Chief Financial Officer, Seton Highland Lakes, Burnet, TX, p. A599
  Chief Financial Officer, Seton Medical Center Austin, Austin, TX, p. A594
  Senior Vice President and Chief Financial Officer, Seton Medical Center Williamson, Round Rock, TX, p. A639
  Chief Financial Officer, Seton Northwest Hospital, Austin, TX, p. A594
WAITES, Alan, Chief Financial Officer, Gove County Medical Center, Quinter, KS, p. A249
WAJDA, David
  Chief Financial Officer, Mercy Suburban Hospital, Norristown, PA, p. A541
  Chief Financial Officer, Nazareth Hospital, Philadelphia, PA, p. A544
WAKEFIELD, Brett
  Vice President Human Resources, Gottlieb Memorial Hospital, Melrose Park, IL, p. A194
  Director Human Resources, Thorek Memorial Hospital, Chicago, IL, p. A185
WAKEFIELD, Mamie
  Vice President Finance and Chief Financial Officer, Emma Pendleton Bradley Hospital, East Providence, RI, p. A555
  Chief Financial Officer, Miriam Hospital, Providence, RI, p. A555
  Senior Vice President and Chief Financial Officer, Rhode Island Hospital, Providence, RI, p. A556
WAKEMAN, Daniel L., President, ProMedica St. Luke's Hospital, Maumee, OH, p. A494
WAKIM, Tina, Vice President Information, Northside Hospital, Atlanta, GA, p. A150
WAKULCHIK, Grace, R.N. Chief Operating Officer, Akron Children's Hospital, Akron, OH, p. A478
WALAS, Steven, Chief Executive Officer, HEALTHSOUTH Chesapeake Rehabilitation Hospital, Salisbury, MD, p. A300
WALCEK, Peter, Vice President Finance, Wentworth–Douglass Hospital, Dover, NH, p. A406
WALCH, Tina, M.D. Medical Director, South Oaks Hospital, Amityville, NY, p. A428
WALCZYK–JOERS, Barbara, President and Chief Executive Officer, Gillette Children's Specialty Healthcare, Saint Paul, MN, p. A346
WALD, Barry, Chief Financial Officer, Wilkes Regional Medical Center, North Wilkesboro, NC, p. A466
WALDBART, Andy, Department Manager, Heart of the Rockies Regional Medical Center, Salida, CO, p. A108
WALDBILLIG, Karla, Director Human Resources, UnityPoint Health – Finley Hospital, Dubuque, IA, p. A227
WALDBILLIG, Kurt, Chief Executive Officer, Swift County–Benson Hospital, Benson, MN, p. A335
WALDEN, Anita, Vice President and Chief Nursing Officer, Decatur Morgan Hospital, Decatur, AL, p. A18
WALDEN, Christopher, Vice President and Chief Information Officer, HealthAlliance Hospitals, Leominster, MA, p. A308
WALDERA, John, Director Information Technology, Gundersen Tri–County Hospital and Clinics, Whitehall, WI, p. A714
WALDO, Bruce
  Chief Executive Officer, Aurora Behavioral Health System East, Tempe, AZ, p. A38
  Chief Executive Officer, Aurora Behavioral Health System West, Glendale, AZ, p. A32
WALDO, Gail, Director Information Technology, Rockdale Medical Center, Conyers, GA, p. A154
WALDOW, Dee, Chief Financial Officer, Palo Pinto General Hospital, Mineral Wells, TX, p. A632
WALDRON, Michele, Senior Vice President and Chief Financial Officer, Valley Children's Hospital, Madera, CA, p. A74
WALDRON, Ray, Director Information Technology, Gordon Memorial Hospital, Gordon, NE, p. A392
WALDRON, Sheila, Finance Manager, Providence Milwaukie Hospital, Milwaukie, OR, p. A523
WALDROP, Cathy
  Director, Hospital Nursing Services, North Mississippi Medical Center–Pontotoc, Pontotoc, MS, p. A359
  Administrator, Sterlington Rehabilitation Hospital, Bastrop, LA, p. A269
WALDRUM, Michael, M.D., Chief Executive Officer, Vidant Health, Greenville, NC, p. B151
WALI, Jyotika, M.D. Chief of Staff, Kindred Hospital–Brea, Brea, CA, p. A56
WALIGURA, R. Curtis, D.O. Vice President Medical Affairs, Chief Medical Officer, UPMC McKeesport, McKeesport, PA, p. A539
WALKENHORST, Debbie G.
  Network Vice President, SSM Cardinal Glennon Children's Medical Center, Saint Louis, MO, p. A377
  System Vice President Talent Management, SSM St. Joseph Health Center, Saint Charles, MO, p. A375
WALKER, Alene, Director Human Resources, Quincy Valley Medical Center, Quincy, WA, p. A682
WALKER, Alexander J., Executive Vice President Operations and Strategic Development, Catholic Medical Center, Manchester, NH, p. A407
WALKER, Amy, Chief Nursing Officer, Delta Regional Medical Center, Greenville, MS, p. A353
WALKER, Angela, Manager Human Resources, Aspire Hospital, Conroe, TX, p. A602
WALKER, Angela, M.D. Medical Director, HEALTHSOUTH Rehabilitation Hospital, Albuquerque, NM, p. A422
WALKER, Annette, Associate Director, John D. Dingell Veterans Affairs Medical Center, Detroit, MI, p. A318
WALKER, Austin, Accounting Manager, Kindred Hospital Northland, Kansas City, MO, p. A370
WALKER, Beth, R.N., President, FirstHealth Montgomery Memorial Hospital, Troy, NC, p. A469
WALKER, C. O., M.D. Chief of Staff, Donalsonville Hospital, Donalsonville, GA, p. A156
WALKER, Candace, Chief Financial Officer, East Central Regional Hospital, Augusta, GA, p. A151
WALKER, Carol, Chief Financial Officer, Oklahoma Heart Hospital, Oklahoma City, OK, p. A512
WALKER, Cass
  Senior Director Administrative Services, Franklin Regional Hospital, Franklin, NH, p. A406
  Senior Director, Administrative Services, Lakes Region General Hospital, Laconia, NH, p. A406
WALKER, Charity, Controller and Regional Business Officer Manager, Greenwood Regional Rehabilitation Hospital, Greenwood, SC, p. A562
WALKER, Charles, Director Information Technology, Kimball Health Services, Kimball, NE, p. A393
WALKER, Cheri, R.N. Chief Nursing Officer, King's Daughters Medical Center, Brookhaven, MS, p. A351
WALKER, Codie, Chief Financial Officer, Salem Veterans Affairs Medical Center, Salem, VA, p. A672
WALKER, Dan, Chief Nursing Officer, Lincoln Community Hospital and Nursing Home, Hugo, CO, p. A105
WALKER, Donna, Chief Nurse Executive, Weeks Medical Center, Lancaster, NH, p. A406
WALKER, Durwin, M.D. Chief Medical Officer, AMG Specialty Hospital–Denham Springs, Denham Springs, LA, p. A273
WALKER, Gale N., President and Chief Executive Officer, Avera St. Benedict Health Center, Parkston, SD, p. A570
WALKER, Gregory J., Chief Executive Officer, Wentworth–Douglass Hospital, Dover, NH, p. A406
WALKER, Jan
  Director Human Resources, Centra Lynchburg General Hospital, Lynchburg, VA, p. A667
  Director Human Resources, Glenwood Regional Medical Center, West Monroe, LA, p. A286
WALKER, Janice L., R.N
  Chief Operating Officer, Baylor All Saints Medical Center at Fort Worth, Fort Worth, TX, p. A613
  Chief Nursing Officer and Chief Operating Officer, Baylor Medical Center at Garland, Garland, TX, p. A616
WALKER, Jeremy Tyler, Vice President and Chief Financial Officer, Hendrick Health System, Abilene, TX, p. A590
WALKER, Kathy, Chief Financial Officer, Trinity Hospital, Weaverville, CA, p. A97
WALKER, Kristie, Director of Human Resources, Wythe County Community Hospital, Wytheville, VA, p. A675
WALKER, Larry D., Chief Operating Officer, Glenwood Regional Medical Center, West Monroe, LA, p. A286
WALKER, Lawrence, M.D. Chief of Staff, San Bernardino Mountains Community Hospital District, Lake Arrowhead, CA, p. A67
WALKER, LeRoy, Vice President Human Resources, DeKalb Medical at North Decatur, Decatur, GA, p. A156
WALKER, Lynette, R.N. Vice President Human Resources, Baptist Health Lexington, Lexington, KY, p. A259
WALKER, Mary, Manager Information Technology, HEALTHSOUTH Rehabilitation Hospital–Wichita Falls, Wichita Falls, TX, p. A652
WALKER, Matthew, Chief Executive Officer and Administrator, William Bee Ririe Hospital, Ely, NV, p. A400
WALKER, Melissa
  Chief Financial Officer, St. Rose Dominican Hospitals – San Martin Campus, Las Vegas, NV, p. A402
  Chief Financial Officer, St. Rose Dominican Hospitals – Siena Campus, Henderson, NV, p. A401
WALKER, Paul A., FACHE, Interim Chief Executive Officer, Tulare Regional Medical Center, Tulare, CA, p. A95
WALKER, Randy
  Chief Nursing Officer, Hillcrest Hospital Claremore, Claremore, OK, p. A505
  Vice President, Methodist Dallas Medical Center, Dallas, TX, p. A606
  Director Nursing Services, State Hospital South, Blackfoot, ID, p. A172
WALKER, Renee, Director Human Resources, Bastrop Rehabilitation Hospital, Monroe, LA, p. A280
WALKER, Rick, Network, Chief Financial Officer, Woodhull Medical and Mental Health Center, NY, p. A445
WALKER, Robert, M.D. Medical Director, HEALTHSOUTH Southern Hills Rehabilitation Hospital, Princeton, WV, p. A694
WALKER, Robert L., President and Chief Executive Officer, Texas Scottish Rite Hospital for Children, Dallas, TX, p. A607
WALKER, Robin, Chief Nursing Officer, Field Memorial Community Hospital, Centreville, MS, p. A351
WALKER, Scott, Chief Financial Officer, Southeastern Regional Medical Center, Newnan, GA, p. A162
WALKER, Scott, M.D. Chief Medical Staff, Weatherford Regional Medical Center, Weatherford, TX, p. A650
WALKER, Tim, Manager Information Services, PeaceHealth Ketchikan Medical Center, Ketchikan, AK, p. A28


**A996** Index of Health Care Professionals 

Index of Health Care Professionals / Wang

Index of Health Care Professionals


WALKER, Todd, Director Operations, Greenville Health System – Laurens County Memorial Hospital, Clinton, SC, p. A559
WALKER, Troy, Director Finance, St. Clare Hospital, Baraboo, WI, p. A697
WALKER, Tyree, Chief Human Resources Officer, Vidant Medical Center, Greenville, NC, p. A461
WALKER, Virginia, Vice President Nursing Services and Chief Nursing Officer, Kuakini Medical Center, Honolulu, HI, p. A168
WALKER Jr., William J., Chief Executive Officer, Memorial Hospital and Manor, Bainbridge, GA, p. A152
WALKUP, Jessica, Controller, HEALTHSOUTH Western Hills Regional Rehabilitation Hospital, Parkersburg, WV, p. A694
WALL, Daniel J., President and Chief Executive Officer, Emma Pendleton Bradley Hospital, East Providence, RI, p. A555
WALL, Doug, M.D. Vice President Medical Affairs, Novant Health Prince William Medical Center, Manassas, VA, p. A667
WALL, J. C., M.D. Chief of Staff, Saint Thomas Stones River Hospital, Woodbury, TN, p. A589
WALL, Kathryn S.
  Executive Vice President Human Resources and Organizational Development, Mary Washington Hospital, Fredericksburg, VA, p. A665
  Executive Vice President Human Resources and Organizational Development, Stafford Hospital, Stafford, VA, p. A673
WALL, Lorraine, Chief Nursing Officer, Olympic Medical Center, Port Angeles, WA, p. A682
WALLACE, Arthur, Chief Financial Officer, Broward Health Coral Springs, Coral Springs, FL, p. A124
WALLACE, Bernadine L., MSN Chief Nursing Officer and Chief Operating Officer, Marion General Hospital, Marion, IN, p. A215
WALLACE, Brenda, R.N. Chief Nursing Officer, Ouachita Community Hospital, West Monroe, LA, p. A287
WALLACE, Carolyn, Director Human Resources, Connecticut Mental Health Center, New Haven, CT, p. A114
WALLACE, Cynthia, M.D. Medical Director, Vibra Specialty Hospital of Portland, Portland, OR, p. A525
WALLACE, David, Chief Executive Officer, AllianceHealth Woodward, Woodward, OK, p. A518
WALLACE, Debra, M.D. Chief of Staff, Methodist Hospital Union County, Morganfield, KY, p. A263
WALLACE, Dianne, County Information Manager, Douglas County Community Mental Health Center, Omaha, NE, p. A396
WALLACE, Donna Geiken, Chief Operating Officer and Chief Financial Officer, Hopkins County Memorial Hospital, Sulphur Springs, TX, p. A646
WALLACE, Glenn
  Chief Executive Officer, Medical Center Alliance, Fort Worth, TX, p. A613
  Chief Operating Officer, Medical Center of Plano, Plano, TX, p. A637
WALLACE, Jennifer, Chief Executive Officer, AMG Specialty Hospital–Greenwood, Greenwood, MS, p. A353
WALLACE, Kelly, Senior Vice President and Chief Financial Officer, Seattle Children's Hospital, Seattle, WA, p. A683
WALLACE, Kent H., Chief Executive Officer, RegionalCare Hospital Partners, Brentwood, TN, p. B113
WALLACE, Kristina, R.N. Chief Operating Officer, OU Medical Center, Oklahoma City, OK, p. A512
WALLACE, Lisa, R.N. Chief Nursing Officer, Redmond Regional Medical Center, Rome, GA, p. A163
WALLACE, Mark A., President and Chief Executive Officer, Texas Children's Hospital, Houston, TX, p. A622
WALLACE, Mark T., Director Human Resources, Lodi Memorial Hospital, Lodi, CA, p. A67
WALLACE, Martha, Administrator, California Mens Colony Correctional Treatment Center, San Luis Obispo, CA, p. A90
WALLACE, Melanie, Manager Human Resources, Sutter Tracy Community Hospital, Tracy, CA, p. A94
WALLACE, Michael S., President and Chief Executive Officer, Fort HealthCare, Fort Atkinson, WI, p. A700
WALLACE, Nancy
  Vice President Human Resources, CHI Health Bergan Mercy, Omaha, NE, p. A395
  Vice President Human Resources, CHI Health Immanuel, Omaha, NE, p. A396
  Senior Vice President, Chief Human Resource Officer, CHI Health Lakeside, Omaha, NE, p. A396
  Senior Vice President Human Resources, CHI Health Mercy Council Bluffs, Council Bluffs, IA, p. A225
  Senior Vice President, Chief Human Resource Officer, CHI Health Midlands, Papillion, NE, p. A397
  Vice President Human Resources, CHI Health, CHI Health Saint Francis, Grand Island, NE, p. A392
  Vice President Human Resources, CHI Health Schuyler, Schuyler, NE, p. A398
  Senior Vice President, Chief Human Resources Officer, CHI Health St Elizabeth, Lincoln, NE, p. A393
WALLACE, Patrick L., Administrator, East Texas Medical Center Athens, Athens, TX, p. A593
WALLACE, Penny, Chief Financial Officer, Guadalupe Regional Medical Center, Seguin, TX, p. A643
WALLACE, Rick D., FACHE, President and Chief Executive Officer, San Juan Regional Medical Center, Farmington, NM, p. A424
WALLACE, Tabatha, Director Human Resources, Bayfront Health Dade City, Dade City, FL, p. A124
WALLACE–MOORE, Patrice, Chief Executive Officer and Executive Director, Arms Acres, Carmel, NY, p. A431
WALLEN, Carla, Manager Human Resources, Cass Regional Medical Center, Harrisonville, MO, p. A368
WALLER, Ernie, Director Information Technology, Ed Fraser Memorial Hospital and Baker Community Health Center, MacClenny, FL, p. A132
WALLER, Kenneth, Fiscal Administrator, Deer's Head Hospital Center, Salisbury, MD, p. A300
WALLER, Patricia A., R.N. Assistant Administrator Patient Care Services, Newton Medical Center, Covington, GA, p. A155
WALLER, Raymond, Director, Brighton Center for Recovery, Brighton, MI, p. A315
WALLINE, Linda K., R.N. Vice President Nursing, Columbus Community Hospital, Columbus, NE, p. A391
WALLING, Vernon, M.D. Executive Medical Director, West Oaks Hospital, Houston, TX, p. A623
WALLINGA, Joel, Chief Financial Officer, Veterans Affairs Ann Arbor Healthcare System, Ann Arbor, MI, p. A314
WALLINGA, Melvin, M.D. Medical Director, St. Michael's Hospital Avera, Tyndall, SD, p. A572
WALLIS, Carla, Director Human Resources, North Ottawa Community Hospital, Grand Haven, MI, p. A320
WALLIS, MSN, RN–, Pam B., MSN Vice President Nursing Services, Magnolia Regional Health Center, Corinth, MS, p. A352
WALLMAN, Gerald H., Administrator, Doctors Hospital of West Covina, West Covina, CA, p. A97
WALLS, Martha Delaney, R.N. Chief Nursing Officer, Crestwood Medical Center, Huntsville, AL, p. A21
WALLS, Randy, Manager Information Services, Fairbanks, Indianapolis, IN, p. A211
WALLSCHLAEGER, Erich, Chief Financial Officer, Cedar Park Regional Medical Center, Cedar Park, TX, p. A600
WALMSLEY III, George J., CPA, President and Chief Executive Officer, North Philadelphia Health System, Philadelphia, PA, p. A544
WALMUS, Adam C., Director, Michael E. DeBakey Veterans Affairs Medical Center, Houston, TX, p. A621
WALRATH, Andrea, Chief Operating Officer, Forest Health Medical Center, Ypsilanti, MI, p. A333
WALRAVEN, Jeff, Chief Executive Officer, Lindsay Municipal Hospital, Lindsay, OK, p. A509
WALSER, Bill, Coordinator Technology, Cameron Regional Medical Center, Cameron, MO, p. A364
WALSH, Brad, M.D. Chief of Staff, Ashley County Medical Center, Crossett, AR, p. A42
WALSH, Catherine
  Interim Chief Nursing Officer, Mercy Allen Hospital, Oberlin, OH, p. A495
  Interim Nursing Executive, Mercy Regional Medical Center, Lorain, OH, p. A492
WALSH, Dan, Chief Information Officer, Aria Health, Philadelphia, PA, p. A542
WALSH, Gerard, Chief Executive Officer, Western Maryland Hospital Center, Hagerstown, MD, p. A298
WALSH, John, M.D. Chief Medical Officer, Florida Hospital–Flagler, Palm Coast, FL, p. A138
WALSH, John
  Chief Executive Officer, Trumbull Memorial Hospital, Warren, OH, p. A499
  Chief Fiscal Services, Veterans Affairs Hudson Valley Health Care System, Montrose, NY, p. A438
WALSH, Kate, MPH President and Chief Executive Officer, Boston Medical Center, Boston, MA, p. A303
WALSH, Ken, Chief Financial Officer, St. Luke's Medical Center, Phoenix, AZ, p. A36
WALSH, Kim, Chief Nursing Officer, Signature Healthcare Brockton Hospital, Brockton, MA, p. A305
WALSH, Len, Executive Vice President and Chief Operating Officer, St. Barnabas Hospital, NY, p. A444
WALSH, Linda, R.N. Vice President Chief Nursing Executive, Bayshore Community Hospital, Holmdel, NJ, p. A413
WALSH, Marcia S., M.P.H. Chief Operating Officer, Community HealthCare System, Onaga, KS, p. A247
WALSH, Marilyn J., Vice President Human Resources, Kent County Memorial Hospital, Warwick, RI, p. A556
WALSH, Mary, R.N
  Vice President Patient Care Services and Chief Nursing Officer, Mount Sinai Beth Israel, New York, NY, p. A442
  Vice President Patient Care Services and Chief Nursing Officer, Mount Sinai St. Luke's – Roosevelt, New York, NY, p. A442
WALSH, Mary Beth, M.D., Chief Executive Officer, Burke Rehabilitation Hospital, White Plains, NY, p. A454
WALSH, Michael
  Senior Vice President Finance and Chief Financial Officer, Abington Health Lansdale Hospital, Lansdale, PA, p. A538
  Senior Vice President Finance and Chief Financial Officer, Abington Memorial Hospital, Abington, PA, p. A528
WALSH, Richard J., Ph.D. Chief Human Resources Officer, Duke Regional Hospital, Durham, NC, p. A459
WALSH, Ryan, M.D. Chief Medical Information Officer, UnityPoint Health – Methodist Proctor, Peoria, IL, p. A198
WALSH, Timothy J., Chief Executive Officer, Martha's Vineyard Hospital, Oak Bluffs, MA, p. A310
WALSTON, John, Chief Information Officer, Southern Arizona Veterans Affairs Health Care System, Tucson, AZ, p. A40
WALTER, Gayle, Director of Nursing, Thomas B. Finan Center, Cumberland, MD, p. A297
WALTER, Melissa, Chief Financial Officer, Clarinda Regional Health Center, Clarinda, IA, p. A224
WALTER, Stephen
  Senior Vice President and Chief Financial Officer, Community Behavioral Health Center, Fresno, CA, p. A62
  Senior Vice President and Chief Financial Officer, Community Regional Medical Center, Fresno, CA, p. A62
WALTERS, Anthony, Chief Executive Officer, Valley Behavioral Health System, Barling, AR, p. A41
WALTERS, David, D.O. Vice President and Chief Clinical Officer, Beaumont Hospital – Farmington Hills, Farmington Hills, MI, p. A319
WALTERS, Jane, Director of Nursing, Mendota Mental Health Institute, Madison, WI, p. A704
WALTERS, Janice, Executive Director, Revenue Systems and Information Technology, Cole Memorial, Coudersport, PA, p. A532
WALTERS, Julie, Chief Nursing Officer, Hillsdale Community Health Center, Hillsdale, MI, p. A322
WALTERS, Kevin, Chief Financial Officer, St. Rose Dominican Hospitals – Rose de Lima Campus, Henderson, NV, p. A401
WALTERS, Leslie, R.N. Chief Nursing Officer, Clarion Hospital, Clarion, PA, p. A531
WALTERS, Lisa, R.N. Director of Nursing, Nebraska Medicine – Bellevue, Bellevue, NE, p. A390
WALTERS, Patrick, Chief Executive Officer, Inova Loudoun Hospital, Leesburg, VA, p. A667
WALTERS, Todd, Director of UHC Information Technology Services, University Health Conway, Monroe, LA, p. A281
WALTHALL, Wayne, Vice President and Chief Financial Officer, St. John Medical Center, Tulsa, OK, p. A517
WALTHER, Diane, Controller, Henry County Hospital, Napoleon, OH, p. A495
WALTON, Carlyle L. E., FACHE,
  Chief Executive Officer, Metroplex Adventist Hospital, Killeen, TX, p. A626
  Chief Executive Officer, Rollins–Brook Community Hospital, Lampasas, TX, p. A627
WALTON, Dawn, Chief Financial Officer, Children's of Alabama, Birmingham, AL, p. A16
WALTON, Gary, M.D. Chief Medical Officer, Hill Hospital of Sumter County, York, AL, p. A26
WALTON, Georgian, Director Human Resources, Elbert Memorial Hospital, Elberton, GA, p. A157
WALTON, Greg, Chief Information Officer, El Camino Hospital, Mountain View, CA, p. A77
WALTON, Linda, R.N. Chief Nursing Officer, South Lake Hospital, Clermont, FL, p. A123
WALTZ, Brenda M., FACHE, Chief Executive Officer, Garden Park Medical Center, Gulfport, MS, p. A353
WALTZ, Dan, Vice President and Chief Information Officer, MidMichigan Medical Center–Gladwin, Gladwin, MI, p. A320
WALZ, Rachel A., Director Patient Care, CentraCare Health–Paynesville, Paynesville, MN, p. A344
WAMPLER, Beth A., R.N. Chief Nursing Officer, Fayette Regional Health System, Connersville, IN, p. A206
WAMPLER, Janice, Controller and Chief Information Technology Officer, Monroe Hospital, Bloomfield, IN, p. A205
WAMPLER, Tamara, Chief Nursing Executive, Claremore Indian Hospital, Claremore, OK, p. A505
WAMSLEY, Marie, Chief Financial Officer, Memorial Hospital of Lafayette County, Darlington, WI, p. A699
WANG, Ted, Chief Financial Officer, Providence Tarzana Medical Center, CA, p. A72
WANG, MD, Shu–Ming, Vice President Medical Affairs, CHI Health Saint Francis, Grand Island, NE, p. A392

Index of Health Care Professionals

Index of Health Care Professionals / Wangard

WANGARD, Christopher, M.D. President Medical Staff, Anderson Hospital, Maryville, IL, p. A193
WANGSMO, Gary L., Chief Financial Officer, Mee Memorial Hospital, King City, CA, p. A66
WANGSNESS, Erik, President, Washington Adventist Hospital, Takoma Park, MD, p. A300
WANNA, Fady, M.D. Chief Clinical Officer and Chief Medical Officer, Medical Center, Navicent Health, Macon, GA, p. A160
WANNER, David
Director Information Technology, Kenmare Community Hospital, Kenmare, ND, p. A475
Chief Information Officer, Trinity Health, Minot, ND, p. A476
WANNER, Joe, Chief Financial Officer, Wallowa Memorial Hospital, Enterprise, OR, p. A520
WANTLAND, Margaret, Chief Financial Officer, Kindred Hospital–Albuquerque, Albuquerque, NM, p. A422
WAPPELHORST, Andrea, Chief Nursing Officer, TOPS Surgical Specialty Hospital, Houston, TX, p. A622
WARBURTON, John B., Chief Executive Officer, Red River Hospital, LLC, Wichita Falls, TX, p. A652
WARBURTON, Kerry, Chief Financial Officer, Cheyenne Regional Medical Center, Cheyenne, WY, p. A715
WARD, Brook, Executive Vice President, Washington Hospital, Washington, PA, p. A552
WARD, Celia F., Controller and Chief Financial Officer, Doctors Memorial Hospital, Bonifay, FL, p. A122
WARD, Charlotte, Entity Financial Officer, Texas Health Harris Methodist Hospital Southwest Fort Worth, Fort Worth, TX, p. A614
WARD, Chris, Director Management Information Systems, Dorminy Medical Center, Fitzgerald, GA, p. A157
WARD, David M., Chief Financial Officer and Chief Acquisition Officer, Cabell Huntington Hospital, Huntington, WV, p. A691
WARD, Debra, Chief Operating Officer, Laurel Ridge Treatment Center, San Antonio, TX, p. A641
WARD, Dillon, Management Information Systems Specialist, Tennova Healthcare–LaFollette Medical Center, La Follette, TN, p. A581
WARD, Elizabeth S., Chief Financial Officer, University of Texas Southwestern Medical Center, Dallas, TX, p. A607
WARD, Greg, Vice President Operations, Copley Hospital, Morrisville, VT, p. A660
WARD, Julie, Vice President Finance, Northeastern Health System, Tahlequah, OK, p. A515
WARD, Julie, MSN Chief Nursing Officer, St. Joseph's Hospital and Medical Center, Phoenix, AZ, p. A36
WARD, Julie R., MSN Vice President Patient Care Services, Hutchinson Regional Medical Center, Hutchinson, KS, p. A242
WARD, Kevin, Chief Operating Officer, Jewish Home of San Francisco, San Francisco, CA, p. A88
WARD, Kevin J., Vice President and Chief Financial Officer, New York–Presbyterian/Queens, NY, p. A443
WARD, Lesli, Vice President Human Resources, UF Health Jacksonville, Jacksonville, FL, p. A130
WARD, Lisa, Director Management Information Systems, Columbus Regional Healthcare System, Whiteville, NC, p. A470
WARD, Louis James, Interim Chief Executive Officer, Mayers Memorial Hospital District, Fall River Mills, CA, p. A61
WARD, Louise, Vice President Financial and Support Services, Roane General Hospital, Spencer, WV, p. A695
WARD, Mark, M.D. Chief of Staff, Roundup Memorial Healthcare, Roundup, MT, p. A386
WARD, Michael
Director Information Services, Anderson Hospital, Maryville, IL, p. A193
Chief Executive Officer, HEALTHSOUTH Rehabilitation Hospital–Las Vegas, Las Vegas, NV, p. A402
WARD, Mike
Covenant Health, Senior Vice President and Chief Information Officer, Methodist Medical Center of Oak Ridge, Oak Ridge, TN, p. A586
Chief Information Officer, Morristown–Hamblen Healthcare System, Morristown, TN, p. A584
Senior Vice President Chief Information Officer, Roane Medical Center, Harriman, TN, p. A578
WARD, Rhonda, R.N. Chief Nursing Officer, Littleton Adventist Hospital, Littleton, CO, p. A106
WARD, Robert, Chief Executive Officer, Select Rehabilitation Hospital of San Antonio, San Antonio, TX, p. A642
WARD, Rory
Chief Financial Officer, Atoka County Medical Center, Atoka, OK, p. A504
Chief Financial Officer, Pushmataha Hospital & Home Health, Antlers, OK, p. A503
WARD, Sandy, Administrator, Johnson County Healthcare Center, Buffalo, WY, p. A715
WARD, Silva, Director Human Resources, Center for Behavioral Medicine, Kansas City, MO, p. A369
WARD, Stormy, Chief Nurse Executive, Big Spring State Hospital, Big Spring, TX, p. A597
WARD, Vaughn, Chief Executive Officer, Northwest Specialty Hospital, Post Falls, ID, p. A176
WARD, Virginia, Human Resources Officer, Robert E. Bush Naval Hospital, Twentynine Palms, CA, p. A95
WARD, Wendy, Director Human Resources, Mercy Hospital El Reno, El Reno, OK, p. A506
WARDA, Paul, Chief Financial Officer, MedStar Georgetown University Hospital, Washington, DC, p. A119
WARDELL, Patrick R., Chief Executive Officer, Cambridge Health Alliance, Cambridge, MA, p. A305
WARDEN, Michael S.
Senior Vice President Information Technology, Banner Good Samaritan Medical Center, Phoenix, AZ, p. A34
Senior Vice President and Chief Information Officer, East Morgan County Hospital, Brush, CO, p. A100
WARDROP, Kathyrn, Vice President Strategy and Operations, Gillette Children's Specialty Healthcare, Saint Paul, MN, p. A346
WARE, Bobbie K., R.N. Vice President/Patient Care/Chief Nursing Officer, Mississippi Baptist Medical Center, Jackson, MS, p. A355
WARE, Bobbie K., FACHE, Chief Executive Officer and Chief Nursing Officer, Mississippi Hospital for Restorative Care, Jackson, MS, p. A355
WARE, Dana, M.D. Chief of Staff, Seneca Healthcare District, Chester, CA, p. A57
WARE, John D., Human Resources Director, Highlands Regional Medical Center, Sebring, FL, p. A143
WARE, Judy, Director Human Resources, Johnson Memorial Hospital, Franklin, IN, p. A209
WARE, Karen, Director Human Resources, AllianceHealth Blackwell, Blackwell, OK, p. A504
WARE, Kathy, Director of Nursing, Daniels Memorial Healthcare Center, Scobey, MT, p. A387
WAREING, Colleen, Vice President Patient Care Services, Atlantic General Hospital, Berlin, MD, p. A295
WARFIELD, William, Chief Human Resources Management, Veterans Affairs Boston Healthcare System, Boston, MA, p. A304
WARING, Lance, Director Human Resources, Texas Health Harris Methodist Hospital Azle, Azle, TX, p. A595
WARLITNER, Todd, Vice President Business Operations, The Outer Banks Hospital, Nags Head, NC, p. A466
WARM, Ira, Senior Vice President Human Resources, Brooklyn Hospital Center, NY, p. A439
WARMAN, Debbie, Vice President Human Resources, MetroHealth Medical Center, Cleveland, OH, p. A485
WARMAN Jr., Harold C., FACHE, President and Chief Executive Officer, Highlands Regional Medical Center, Prestonsburg, KY, p. A265
WARMBOLD, Steve, Director Information Management Service Line, Veterans Affairs St. Louis Health Care System, Saint Louis, MO, p. A378
WARMERDAM, David, Chief Financial Officer, Brynn Marr Hospital, Jacksonville, NC, p. A463
WARNER, Grady, Director of Information Technology, Burgess Health Center, Onawa, IA, p. A232
WARNER, John, M.D., Chief Executive Officer, University of Texas Southwestern Medical Center, Dallas, TX, p. A607
WARNER, Malia, Chief Medical Staff, Holton Community Hospital, Holton, KS, p. A242
WARNER, Norma, Area Director Health Information Management, Kindred Hospital–Fort Worth, Fort Worth, TX, p. A613
WARNER, Petra, Interim Chief of Staff, Shriners Hospitals for Children–Cincinnati Burns Hospital, Cincinnati, OH, p. A483
WARNER–PACHECO, Paula, Chief Human Resources, Rio Grande Hospital, Del Norte, CO, p. A101
WARNING, Kendra, Chief Financial Officer, Davis County Hospital, Bloomfield, IA, p. A223
WARNOCK, Dawn, Director Medical Records, Taylor Regional Hospital, Hawkinsville, GA, p. A158
WARREN, Charlene, R.N. Chief Nursing Officer, Greenbrier Valley Medical Center, Ronceverte, WV, p. A695
WARREN, Danny, Chief Financial Officer, Lake Wales Medical Center, Lake Wales, FL, p. A131
WARREN, Gidgett, Director of Nursing, Westlake Regional Hospital, Columbia, KY, p. A255
WARREN, Gorman, Chief Financial Officer, Texas Health Presbyterian Hospital of Rockwall, Rockwall, TX, p. A639
WARREN, Jennifer, Chief Financial Officer, Purcell Municipal Hospital, Purcell, OK, p. A514
WARREN, Karen, Fiscal Officer, Porterville Developmental Center, Porterville, CA, p. A81
WARREN, Linda, Director Human Resources, Cogdell Memorial Hospital, Snyder, TX, p. A644
WARREN, Michael D., President, Good Samaritan Regional Health Center, Mount Vernon, IL, p. A195
WARREN, Richard, Chief Information Officer, Baylor Scott & White Hillcrest Medical Center, Waco, TX, p. A650
WARREN, Roger D., M.D., Administrator, Hanover Hospital, Hanover, KS, p. A241
WARREN, Sarah, Coordinator Human Resources, Hickory Trail Hospital, Desoto, TX, p. A608
WARREN, Seth
Interim Chief Executive Officer, Franklin Regional Hospital, Franklin, NH, p. A406
Interim Chief Executive Officer, Lakes Region General Hospital, Laconia, NH, p. A406
WARREN, Seth C. R., President and Chief Executive Officer, LRGHealthcare, Laconia, NH, p. B85
WARREN, Shanna, Director Human Resources, Medical Center of Plano, Plano, TX, p. A637
WARREN Jr., Wm. Michael, Chief Executive Officer, Children's of Alabama, Birmingham, AL, p. A16
WARRENER, Gerald, M.D. Chief Medical Officer, Parkview Noble Hospital, Kendallville, IN, p. A213
WARRINER, Ken, Market Chief Financial Officer, Physicians Regional – Pine Ridge, Naples, FL, p. A136
WARRINGTON, Sr., James E., M.D. Chief of Staff, Quitman County Hospital, Marks, MS, p. A356
WARSHAW, Leah, Coordinator Human Resources, Select Specialty Hospital–Ann Arbor, Ypsilanti, MI, p. A333
WARSING, Tracy, M.D. Site Leader Chief of Staff, Mayo Clinic Health System – Franciscan Healthcare in Sparta, Sparta, WI, p. A711
WARTENBERG, Daniel, M.P.H., Chief Executive Officer, Southwest Connecticut Mental Health System, Bridgeport, CT, p. A111
WAS, Gregory J., CPA, Chief Executive Officer, White Mountain Regional Medical Center, Springerville, AZ, p. A38
WASDEN, Mitchell L., Ed.D., Chief Executive Officer and Chief Operating Officer, University of Missouri Health Care, Columbia, MO, p. B147
WASDEN, Mitchell L., Ed.D., Chief Executive Officer and Chief Operating Officer, University of Missouri Hospitals and Clinics, Columbia, MO, p. A366
WASEF, Maha, M.D. Chief of Staff, Merit Health Northwest Mississippi, Clarksdale, MS, p. A351
WASEK, Arthur A., Director Human Resources, Merit Health Batesville, Batesville, MS, p. A350
WASHBURN, Geoffrey A., Vice President, Regional Medical Center Bayonet Point, Hudson, FL, p. A129
WASHBURN, Kimberly D., Director Human Resources, Snoqualmie Valley Hospital District, Snoqualmie, WA, p. A685
WASHBURN, Sheryl M., MSN Chief Nursing Officer, Gritman Medical Center, Moscow, ID, p. A175
WASHBURN, Tonya, M.D. Medical Director, Valir Rehabilitation Hospital, Oklahoma City, OK, p. A513
WASHECKA, James, Chief Financial Officer, Hillcrest Hospital – South, Tulsa, OK, p. A516
WASHINGTON, A. Eugene, M.D., President and Chief Executive Officer, Duke University Health System, Durham, NC, p. B52
WASHINGTON, Carolyn, Director of Human Resources, Doctor's Hospital – Tidwell, Houston, TX, p. A619
WASHINGTON, Glen A., Chief Executive Officer, Pleasant Valley Hospital, Point Pleasant, WV, p. A694
WASHINGTON, Lorraine, Vice President Human Resources, St. Dominic–Jackson Memorial Hospital, Jackson, MS, p. A355
WASHINGTON, Stephanie, Director Community Relations and Human Resources, Baptist Medical Center Yazoo, Yazoo City, MS, p. A362
WASHINGTON, Vindell, M.D. Vice President Performance Excellence and Technology, Our Lady of the Lake Regional Medical Center, Baton Rouge, LA, p. A269
WATERBURY, Brad, Director Human Resources, Bonner General Hospital, Sandpoint, ID, p. A176
WATERCUTTER, William, Director Management Information System, Upper Valley Medical Center, Troy, OH, p. A499
WATERS, Danny
Director, Information Services, Palms of Pasadena Hospital, Saint Petersburg, FL, p. A142
Director Information Technology and Systems, South Bay Hospital, Sun City Center, FL, p. A143
WATERS, Eric, Vice President Operations, Pen Bay Medical Center, Rockport, ME, p. A292
WATERS, Gina, Director Human Resources, Evans Memorial Hospital, Claxton, GA, p. A153
WATERS, Glenn D., FACHE, President, Morton Plant Mease Health Care, Clearwater, FL, p. B93
WATERS, Jerod, Chief Nursing Officer, Chickasaw Nation Medical Center, Ada, OK, p. A503
WATERS, Karen, Chief Nursing Officer, St. Mary's Warrick Hospital, Boonville, IN, p. A205
WATERS, Mickey, Director Information Technology, Conway Medical Center, Conway, SC, p. A560
WATERS, Nancy, Interim Chief Information Officer, High Point Regional Health System, High Point, NC, p. A462

Index of Health Care Professionals

Index of Health Care Professionals / Weber

WEBER, Rebecca
Senior Vice President and Chief Information Officer, Bayshore Community Hospital, Holmdel, NJ, p. A413
Senior Vice President and Chief Information Officer, Jersey Shore University Medical Center, Neptune, NJ, p. A414
Senior Vice President and Chief Information Officer, Ocean Medical Center, Brick Township, NJ, p. A410
Senior Vice President Information Technology, Riverview Medical Center, Red Bank, NJ, p. A418
Senior Vice President and Chief Information Officer, Southern Ocean Medical Center, Manahawkin, NJ, p. A414
WEBER, Robert, M.D. Chief Medical Staff, Watsonville Community Hospital, Watsonville, CA, p. A97
WEBER, Stephen, M.D. Chief Medical Officer, University of Chicago Medical Center, Chicago, IL, p. A185
WEBER, Trish, R.N. Vice President Operations and Chief Nursing Officer, Franciscan St. Anthony Health – Michigan City, Michigan City, IN, p. A216
WEBER, Wilson, Chief Operating Officer, ContinueCare Hospital at Baptist Health Corbin, Corbin, KY, p. A255
WEBSTER, Cindy, Vice President Financial Services, Licking Memorial Hospital, Newark, OH, p. A495
WEBSTER, Gwen, M.D. President Medical Staff, Texas Health Presbyterian Hospital Plano, Plano, TX, p. A637
WEBSTER, Janice, Director Human Resources, West Oaks Hospital, Houston, TX, p. A623
WEBSTER, Kathleen, R.N. Vice President Patient Services, New York–Presbyterian/Hudson Valley Hospital, Cortlandt Manor, NY, p. A432
WEBSTER, Mark
President and Chief Executive Officer, Cortland Regional Medical Center, Cortland, NY, p. A432
Vice President Finance, New York–Presbyterian/Hudson Valley Hospital, Cortlandt Manor, NY, p. A432
WEBSTER, Richard, President, Thomas Jefferson University Hospitals, Philadelphia, PA, p. A545
WEBSTER, William W., FACHE, Chief Executive Officer, Medical Center Health System, Odessa, TX, p. A634
WECKENBORG, Janet, FACHE Vice President Operations, Capital Region Medical Center, Jefferson City, MO, p. A368
WECKESSER, Kim, Director Human Resources, West Shore Medical Center, Manistee, MI, p. A325
WEDGEWORTH, Joyce, Financial Clerk, Hill Hospital of Sumter County, York, AL, p. A26
WEDO, Aaron, Manager, Human Resources, Grundy County Memorial Hospital, Grundy Center, IA, p. A228
WEE, Donald, Chief Executive Officer, Tri–State Memorial Hospital, Clarkston, WA, p. A677
WEECH, Mark, Director of Client Services for Chicago Market, MacNeal Hospital, Berwyn, IL, p. A179
WEED, III, John, M.D. Medical Director, Little River Rockdale Hospital, Rockdale, TX, p. A638
WEED, Warren
Director Human Resources, Merit Health River Oaks, Flowood, MS, p. A352
Director Associate Relations, Merit Health Woman's Hospital, Flowood, MS, p. A352
WEEKS, Ed, Manager Information Services, Paris Community Hospital, Paris, IL, p. A197
WEEKS, James, Interim Chief Information Officer, Rockville General Hospital, Vernon, CT, p. A115
WEEKS, Rolaine, R.N. Director of Nursing, Dublin Springs, Dublin, OH, p. A489
WEELDREYER, Jim, Manager Information Technology, Pershing General Hospital, Lovelock, NV, p. A403
WEEMS, Reva S., Director Human Resources, Gateway Regional Medical Center, Granite City, IL, p. A189
WEEMS, Taylor, Vice President, Chief Information Officer, Midland Memorial Hospital, Midland, TX, p. A632
WEG, Jennifer, R.N. Chief Nursing Officer, Sanford Worthington Medical Center, Worthington, MN, p. A349
WEGHORST, George, M.D. Chief Medical Officer, Providence Newberg Medical Center, Newberg, OR, p. A523
WEGLARZ, Ron, Chief Executive Officer and Managing Director, Streamwood Behavioral Health Center, Streamwood, IL, p. A202
WEGLEITNER, Theodore, Chief Executive Officer, Lakeview Hospital, Stillwater, MN, p. A347
WEGNER, Michael
Senior Vice President and Chief Financial Officer, Mercy Medical Center – West Lakes, West Des Moines, IA, p. A236
Senior Vice President and Chief Financial Officer, Mercy Medical Center–Des Moines, Des Moines, IA, p. A226
WEHE, Brad, Chief Operating Officer, Altru Health System, Grand Forks, ND, p. A474
WEHLING, Robert D., Interim Chief Financial Officer, Saint Alphonsus Medical Center – Baker City, Baker City, OR, p. A519
WEHNER, Jill, Vice President Financial Services, Harbor Beach Community Hospital, Harbor Beach, MI, p. A322
WEHRMEISTER, Erica, Chief Operating Officer, Lutheran Hospital of Indiana, Fort Wayne, IN, p. A208
WEIDER, Will
Chief Information Officer, Calumet Medical Center, Chilton, WI, p. A699
Chief Information Officer, Mercy Medical Center, Oshkosh, WI, p. A708
Chief Information Officer, Ministry Saint Joseph's Hospital, Marshfield, WI, p. A705
Chief Information Officer, Ministry Saint Michael's Hospital, Stevens Point, WI, p. A711
Chief Information Officer, St. Elizabeth Hospital, Appleton, WI, p. A697
WEIDNER, Deborah, M.D. Medical Director, Natchaug Hospital, Mansfield Center, CT, p. A113
WEIDNER, Peter, Director Information Technology, St. John's Riverside Hospital, Yonkers, NY, p. A454
WEIGEL, Cherry, Director Health Information Management, RC Hospital and Clinics, Olivia, MN, p. A344
WEIGEL, Christine H., R.N. Clinical Operating Officer, McBride Clinic Orthopedic Hospital, Oklahoma City, OK, p. A512
WEIL, David S., Senior Vice President and Administrator, Saint Francis Hospital South, Tulsa, OK, p. A517
WEILAND, David, M.D. Chief Medical Officer, Largo Medical Center, Largo, FL, p. A132
WEIMER, Linn, Chief Information Officer, Adena Medical Center, Chillicothe, OH, p. A482
WEIMER, Theresa, Director Personnel, Fallon Medical Complex, Baker, MT, p. A381
WEINBAUM, Frederic, M.D. Executive Vice President Operations and Chief Medical Officer, Southampton Hospital, Southampton, NY, p. A450
WEINBERG, Mitch, M.D. Chief of Staff, EvergreenHealth, Kirkland, WA, p. A680
WEINER, Gary
Vice President Information Technology, Chief Information Officer, Community Hospital, Munster, IN, p. A217
Chief Information Officer, St. Catherine Hospital, East Chicago, IN, p. A207
Vice President Information Technology and Chief Information Officer, St. Mary Medical Center, Hobart, IN, p. A211
WEINER, Howard, Senior Vice President Administrative Services, LifeStream Behavioral Center, Leesburg, FL, p. A132
WEINER, Jack, Ph.D., President and Chief Executive Officer, St. Joseph Mercy Oakland, Pontiac, MI, p. A328
WEINER, Jerome, M.D. Senior Vice President Medical Affairs, Good Samaritan Hospital Medical Center, West Islip, NY, p. A453
WEINER, Martin E., M.D. Chief of Staff, Seton Edgar B. Davis Hospital, Luling, TX, p. A630
WEINER, Ronald, Vice President Finance and Chief Financial Officer, Magruder Memorial Hospital, Port Clinton, OH, p. A496
WEINGART, Steve, Chief Financial Officer, Los Alamos Medical Center, Los Alamos, NM, p. A425
WEINGARTNER, Ronald, Vice President Administration, St. Charles Hospital, Port Jefferson, NY, p. A448
WEINHOLD, Robert, Chief Executive Officer, Foundations Behavioral Health, Doylestown, PA, p. A533
WEINKRANTZ, Alan, Chief Financial Officer, Finance, University Behavioral Healthcare, Piscataway, NJ, p. A417
WEINMANN, Jay, Chief Financial Officer, Bellevue Hospital Center, New York, NY, p. A438
WEINMANN, Shannon, Human Resources Manager, Community Medical Center, Falls City, NE, p. A391
WEINMEISTER, Kurt, Chief Operating Officer, St. Francis Medical Center, Lynwood, CA, p. A74
WEINREIS, Brian, Vice President Operations and Finance, Abbott Northwestern Hospital, Minneapolis, MN, p. A342
WEINSTEIN, Barry S., Chief Financial Officer, Four Winds Hospital, Katonah, NY, p. A435
WEINSTEIN, Brian, M.D. Chief of Staff, Westside Regional Medical Center, Plantation, FL, p. A140
WEINSTEIN, Freddie, M.D. Chief Medical Officer, Dominican Hospital, Santa Cruz, CA, p. A91
WEINSTEIN, Gary B., President and Chief Executive Officer, Washington Hospital, Washington, PA, p. A552
WEINSTEIN, James, MS, President and Chief Executive Officer, Dartmouth–Hitchcock Medical Center, Lebanon, NH, p. A407
WEINSTEIN, James, Chief Financial Officer, Lourdes Specialty Hospital of Southern New Jersey, Willingboro, NJ, p. A420
WEIR, Tim W., Chief Executive Officer, Olmsted Medical Center, Rochester, MN, p. A345
WEIS, Brian, M.D. Chief Medical Officer, Northwest Texas Healthcare System, Amarillo, TX, p. A591
WEIS, Charles
Chief Financial Officer, Mount Sinai Hospital, Chicago, IL, p. A183
Chief Financial Officer, Schwab Rehabilitation Hospital, Chicago, IL, p. A184
WEIS, Maurine, Vice President Nursing and Chief Nursing Officer, ProMedica Flower Hospital, Sylvania, OH, p. A498
WEIS, Robert
Director Information Systems, Bingham Memorial Hospital, Blackfoot, ID, p. A172
Director Information Technology, Mountain River Birthing and Surgery Center, Blackfoot, ID, p. A172
WEIS, Wade, Senior Director Finance, Grande Ronde Hospital, La Grande, OR, p. A522
WEISENBERGER, Scott, Administrator, Kirkbride Center, Philadelphia, PA, p. A544
WEISENFREUND, Jochanan, M.D. Senior Vice President Academic and Medical Affairs, Interfaith Medical Center, NY, p. A440
WEISER, Marcus, D.O. Chief of Staff, Community HealthCare System, Onaga, KS, p. A247
WEISFIELD, Phyllis, Chief Executive Officer and Managing Director, Horsham Clinic, Ambler, PA, p. A528
WEISHAPL, Natasha, Manager Business Office and Human Resources, Decatur Health Systems, Oberlin, KS, p. A247
WEISNER, Brad, Executive Vice President and Chief Operating Officer, Nash Health Care Systems, Rocky Mount, NC, p. A467
WEISS, Allen S., M.D., President and Chief Executive Officer, NCH Downtown Naples Hospital, Naples, FL, p. A136
WEISS, Anthony, M.D. Medical Director, Upstate University Hospital, Syracuse, NY, p. A451
WEISS, Barry J., Chairman of the Board, College Health Enterprises, Santa Fe Springs, CA, p. B34
WEISS, David, Vice President Information System, Alton Memorial Hospital, Alton, IL, p. A178
WEISS, Gary, Chief Financial Officer, NorthShore University Health System, Evanston, IL, p. A187
WEISS, Linda W., FACHE, Director, Albany Stratton Veterans Affairs Medical Center, Albany, NY, p. A428
WEISS, Mark, Executive Director Enterprise Technology Services, Nebraska Medicine – Bellevue, Bellevue, NE, p. A390
WEISS, Patrice M., Chief Medical Officer, Carilion Franklin Memorial Hospital, Rocky Mount, VA, p. A672
WEISS, Phyllis, Director Human Resources, Alameda Hospital, Alameda, CA, p. A53
WEISS, Steve, Chief Financial Officer, Washington County Memorial Hospital, Potosi, MO, p. A374
WEISS, Terri, Chief Financial Officer, Reliant Rehabilitation Hospital North Houston, Shenandoah, TX, p. A643
WEISSENBERGER, Ralf, Director Information Systems, White Memorial Medical Center, Los Angeles, CA, p. A73
WEISSER, Lisa, Supervisor Finance, Wagner Community Memorial Hospital Avera, Wagner, SD, p. A572
WEISSLER, Jonathan, M.D. Chief Medical Officer, LifeCare Hospitals of Dallas, Dallas, TX, p. A605
WEISTREICH, Tracy, Ph.D. Associate Director Patient Care Services/Nurse Executive, Veterans Affairs Roseburg Healthcare System, Roseburg, OR, p. A525
WEISUL, Jonathan, M.D. Vice President Medical Affairs and Chief Medical Officer, CHRISTUS Coushatta Health Care Center, Coushatta, LA, p. A272
WEITZELL, Kristine, Superintendent, Mental Health Institute, Clarinda, IA, p. A224
WELCH, Abbey, Director Human Resources, Harmon Memorial Hospital, Hollis, OK, p. A508
WELCH, Adam M., Interim Director, West Texas Veterans Affairs Health Care System, Big Spring, TX, p. A597
WELCH, Andrew, Director, New Mexico Veterans Affairs Health Care System – Raymond G. Murphy Medical Center, Albuquerque, NM, p. A422
WELCH, Bryant, Chief Human Resources, Washington Hospital Healthcare System, Fremont, CA, p. A62
WELCH, David, M.D. Medical Director, Clifton–Fine Hospital, Star Lake, NY, p. A450
WELCH, David, Director Information Technology, Simpson General Hospital, Mendenhall, MS, p. A357
WELCH, Denise, Chief Financial Officer, Arbuckle Memorial Hospital, Sulphur, OK, p. A515
WELCH, Donald E., Chief Operating Officer, Florida Hospital Zephyrhills, Zephyrhills, FL, p. A148
WELCH, Douglas, Chief Executive Officer, Doctors Hospital, Augusta, GA, p. A151
WELCH, Gary A., Assistant to the Chief Executive Officer and Administrative Director Support Systems, Bon Secours Memorial Regional Medical Center, Mechanicsville, VA, p. A668
WELCH, Jeffrey M., Chief Executive Officer, Palm Beach Gardens Medical Center, Palm Beach Gardens, FL, p. A138

A1000 Index of Health Care Professionals 

Index of Health Care Professionals / Westrom

Index of Health Care Professionals

WELCH, Matthew, Chief Clinical Information Officer and Director of Pharmacy, Aspirus Iron River Hospitals and Clinics, Iron River, MI, p. A323
WELCH, Melissa, Director Health Information Management, Oakdale Community Hospital, Oakdale, LA, p. A283
WELCH, Rosemary C., R.N. Vice President and Chief Nursing Officer, MedStar National Rehabilitation Hospital, Washington, DC, p. A119
WELCH, Shelly, R.N. Senior Vice President and Chief Nursing Officer, North Oaks Medical Center, Hammond, LA, p. A274
WELCH, Sherri, R.N. Chief Nursing Officer, College Station Medical Center, College Station, TX, p. A601
WELCH, Thomas, M.D. Chief Medical Officer, Mercy St. Vincent Medical Center, Toledo, OH, p. A498
WELCH, Tony
Vice President, Human Resources, Englewood Community Hospital, Englewood, FL, p. A126
Vice President Human Resources, Fawcett Memorial Hospital, Port Charlotte, FL, p. A140
Vice President Human Resources, Southeast Alabama Medical Center, Dothan, AL, p. A19
WELD, Jonathan M., Interim President and Chief Executive Officer, Brooklyn Hospital Center, NY, p. A439
WELDAY, Doug, Vice President Finance, Spectrum Health – Butterworth Hospital, Grand Rapids, MI, p. A321
WELDING, Theodore L., Chief Executive Officer, Promise Hospital of Miami, Miami, FL, p. A134
WELDON, Jim, Chief Information Officer, St. Anthony's Medical Center, Saint Louis, MO, p. A377
WELDON, William W., Ph.D., Interim Chief Executive Officer, Cogdell Memorial Hospital, Snyder, TX, p. A644
WELDY, Alan, Vice President Human Resources, Compliance and Legal Services, Indiana University Health Goshen Hospital, Goshen, IN, p. A210
WELKER, Suzanne, Chief Human Resources Officer and Vice President Marketing Strategy, Berger Health System, Circleville, OH, p. A484
WELKIE, Katy, R.N., Chief Executive Officer, Primary Children's Hospital, Salt Lake City, UT, p. A658
WELLBROCK, Jenna, Chief Nursing Officer, Gateway Rehabilitation Hospital, Florence, KY, p. A256
WELLER, Deidre, Vice President, Finance, Spectrum Health Gerber Memorial, Fremont, MI, p. A320
WELLING, Lynn, M.D. Chief Medical Officer, Sharp Chula Vista Medical Center, Chula Vista, CA, p. A58
WELLING, Michele, M.D. Chief of Staff, Bluegrass Community Hospital, Versailles, KY, p. A266
WELLMAN, James, Senior Director Information Services, Comanche County Memorial Hospital, Lawton, OK, p. A508
WELLMAN, Sonia I., R.N. Chief Operating Officer, Oak Hill Hospital, Brooksville, FL, p. A123
WELLMANN, Jane, Chief Financial Officer, Scott & White Hospital – Brenham, Brenham, TX, p. A598
WELLS, A. Shane, Chief Financial Officer, Cornerstone Hospital of Houston at Clearlake, Webster, TX, p. A651
WELLS, Benjamin, Chief Financial Officer, Red Bud Regional Hospital, Red Bud, IL, p. A199
WELLS, Carol, R.N. Chief Nursing Officer, Central Louisiana Surgical Hospital, Alexandria, LA, p. A268
WELLS, Craig, Chief Information Officer, George C Grape Community Hospital, Hamburg, IA, p. A228
WELLS, Dale W., Chief Financial and Operating Officer, Alliance Community Hospital, Alliance, OH, p. A478
WELLS, Dennis, Chief Information Officer, Syracuse Veterans Affairs Medical Center, Syracuse, NY, p. A451
WELLS, Jason, Chief Human Resources Management Service, Fargo Veterans Affairs Health Care System, Fargo, ND, p. A473
WELLS, Jonathan, Supervisor Information Technology, Kansas Surgery and Recovery Center, Wichita, KS, p. A252
WELLS, Mallory Guley, Chief Financial Officer, Richardson Medical Center, Rayville, LA, p. A284
WELLS, Mary S., R.N., Chief Executive Officer, Community Memorial Hospital, Sumner, IA, p. A235
WELLS, Mary Ellen, FACHE, Administrator, CentraCare Health–Monticello, Monticello, MN, p. A343
WELLS, Michelle, Director of Nursing, River Oaks Hospital, New Orleans, LA, p. A282
WELLS, Pamela, R.N. Chief Nursing Officer, Sharp Memorial Hospital, San Diego, CA, p. A87
WELLS, Robert, M.D. Chief Medical Officer, Providence Portland Medical Center, Portland, OR, p. A524
WELLS, Scott E., MSN Chief Nursing Officer, St. Francis Health, Topeka, KS, p. A251
WELLS, Troy R., Chief Executive Officer, Baptist Health, Little Rock, AR, p. B19
WELLS, Valerie, Manager Human Resources, HEALTHSOUTH Rehabilitation Hospital The Woodlands, Conroe, TX, p. A602
WELSH, Dennis, Chief Executive Officer, Down East Community Hospital, Machias, ME, p. A291
WELSH Jr., J. Luckey, Chief Executive Officer, Cherry Hospital, Goldsboro, NC, p. A461
WELSH, Joyce, R.N. Vice President of Clinical Services and Chief Nursing Officer, Emerson Hospital, Concord, MA, p. A306
WELTER, Matt, Chief Medical Officer, Cache Valley Hospital, North Logan, UT, p. A656
WELTON, George, Chief Executive Officer, Select Specialty Hospital–Denver, Denver, CO, p. A102
WENGER, Cheryl, Manager Health Information and Quality Assurance, Hiawatha Community Hospital, Hiawatha, KS, p. A241
WENGER–KELLER, David, M.D. Chief of Staff, Fort Madison Community Hospital, Fort Madison, IA, p. A228
WENTZ, Robert J., President and Chief Executive Officer, Oroville Hospital, Oroville, CA, p. A79
WENTZEL, Chris, M.D. Interim Medical Director, Corning Hospital, Corning, NY, p. A432
WENZEL, Matthew, President and Chief Executive Officer, Saint Luke's North Hospital – Barry Road, Kansas City, MO, p. A370
WERFT, Ronald C., President and Chief Executive Officer, Cottage Health System, Santa Barbara, CA, p. B42
WERFT, Ronald C.
President and Chief Executive Officer, Goleta Valley Cottage Hospital, Santa Barbara, CA, p. A91
President and Chief Executive Officer, Santa Barbara Cottage Hospital, Santa Barbara, CA, p. A91
President and Chief Executive Officer, Santa Ynez Valley Cottage Hospital, Solvang, CA, p. A92
WERKIN, Dave, Vice President Finance and Chief Financial Officer, Trinity Health System, Steubenville, OH, p. A498
WERKSTELL, Scott, Director Information System, T. J. Samson Community Hospital, Glasgow, KY, p. A257
WERNER, Edward, Director Human Resources, HEALTHSOUTH Reading Rehabilitation Hospital, Reading, PA, p. A548
WERNER, John W., Chief Executive Officer, Oakland Mercy Hospital, Oakland, NE, p. A395
WERNER, Julie, Chief Operating Officer, Community Memorial Hospital, Syracuse, NE, p. A398
WERNER, Kurt, M.D. Chief of Staff, Veterans Affairs Montana Health Care System, Fort Harrison, MT, p. A383
WERNER, Sandra, Director Human Resources, Simi Valley Hospital, Simi Valley, CA, p. A92
WERNER, Todd S., Chief Executive Officer, Banner Gateway Medical Center, Gilbert, AZ, p. A31
WERNICK, Joel, President and Chief Executive Officer, Phoebe Putney Health System, Albany, GA, p. B104
WERNICK, Joel, President and Chief Executive Officer, Phoebe Putney Memorial Hospital, Albany, GA, p. A149
WERNKE, Chris, Chief Operating Officer, Dominican Hospital, Santa Cruz, CA, p. A91
WERRBACH, John P., Chief Executive Officer, Alexian Brothers Medical Center, Elk Grove Village, IL, p. A187
WERTH–SWEENEY, Stacey, Facility Operating Officer, Lincoln Regional Center, Lincoln, NE, p. A394
WERTHMAN, Ronald J., Senior Vice President Finance, Chief Financial Officer and Treasurer, Johns Hopkins Hospital, Baltimore, MD, p. A293
WERTZ, Jackie, Director Human Resources, George C Grape Community Hospital, Hamburg, IA, p. A228
WERTZ, Randy S., Chief Executive Officer, Golden Valley Memorial Healthcare, Clinton, MO, p. A365
WESCOATT, Sampson, Manager Information Technology, Molokai General Hospital, Kaunakakai, HI, p. A170
WESCOTT, Lisle, President, SSM St. Joseph Hospital West, Lake Saint Louis, MO, p. A371
WESENER DIECK, Jill, Director Human Resources, Gundersen Tri–County Hospital and Clinics, Whitehall, WI, p. A714
WESLEY, Deb, MSN Chief Nursing Officer, Children's of Alabama, Birmingham, AL, p. A16
WESLEY, Jim
Senior Vice President and Chief Information Officer, John Muir Behavioral Health Center, Concord, CA, p. A58
Interim Chief Information Officer, John Muir Medical Center, Walnut Creek, Walnut Creek, CA, p. A97
WESLEY, Mary Lou, R.N. Senior Vice President and Chief Nursing Officer, Sparrow Hospital, Lansing, MI, p. A324
WESSELS, Jana, Associate Vice President Human Resources, University of Iowa Hospitals and Clinics, Iowa City, IA, p. A230
WEST, Aaron, M.D. Chief Medical Officer, Memorial Hospital Jacksonville, Jacksonville, FL, p. A129
WEST, Andrea, MS Vice President of Human Resources, Columbus Regional Healthcare System, Whiteville, NC, p. A470
WEST, Brenda, R.N. Chief Nursing Officer, Summit Pacific Medical Center, Elma, WA, p. A678
WEST, Bridgette, Director Patient Access Services, Cobleskill Regional Hospital, Cobleskill, NY, p. A432
WEST, Charles, M.D. Chief Medical Officer, Randolph Hospital, Asheboro, NC, p. A455
WEST, Darren, M.D. Interim Chief Medical Officer, Banner Ironwood Medical Center, San Tan Valley, AZ, p. A37
WEST, David, Administrator, Deckerville Community Hospital, Deckerville, MI, p. A317
WEST, James R., President and Chief Executive Officer, PIH Health, Whittier, CA, p. B104
WEST, James R.
President and Chief Executive Officer, PIH Health Hospital – Downey, Downey, CA, p. A60
President and Chief Executive Officer, PIH Health Hospital–Whittier, Whittier, CA, p. A97
WEST, Jennifer, Chief Nursing Officer, South Texas Spine and Surgical Hospital, San Antonio, TX, p. A642
WEST, Judith M., Senior Vice President Human Resources and Chief Human Resources Officer, Maine Medical Center, Portland, ME, p. A291
WEST, Karen M., Administrator Support Services, Wild Rose Community Memorial Hospital, Wild Rose, WI, p. A714
WEST, Kenneth, Chief Operating Officer, Medical Center of Trinity, Trinity, FL, p. A146
WEST, Margaret M., MS, Chief Executive Officer, Magnolia Regional Medical Center, Magnolia, AR, p. A48
WEST, Melissa, Chief Financial Officer, Cedar Crest Hospital and Residential Treatment Center, Belton, TX, p. A597
WEST, Michael, Manager Systems Account, New England Sinai Hospital and Rehabilitation Center, Stoughton, MA, p. A312
WEST, Michael C., M.D. Chief of Staff, McCurtain Memorial Hospital, Idabel, OK, p. A508
WEST, Steve, M.D. Chief Medical Officer, Capital Regional Medical Center, Tallahassee, FL, p. A144
WEST, Steven J., Chief Executive Officer, Indiana University Health Blackford Hospital, Hartford City, IN, p. A210
WEST, Tamara, R.N. Vice President Patient Care, Nicholas H. Noyes Memorial Hospital, Dansville, NY, p. A432
WEST, William, M.D. Chief of Staff, Edgerton Hospital and Health Services, Edgerton, WI, p. A700
WESTENFELDER, Grant, M.D. Chief Medical Officer, Midwest Medical Center, Galena, IL, p. A188
WESTENHOFER, Steve, Chief Executive Officer, Mimbres Memorial Hospital, Deming, NM, p. A424
WESTER, K. Scott, FACHE, President and Chief Executive Officer, Our Lady of the Lake Regional Medical Center, Baton Rouge, LA, p. A269
WESTERCHIL, Beth, Chief Nursing Officer, Byrd Regional Hospital, Leesville, LA, p. A279
WESTERHEIDE, Karen, Chief Financial Officer, Veterans Affairs St. Louis Health Care System, Saint Louis, MO, p. A378
WESTERMAN, Mandy, Chief Executive Officer, River Crest Hospital, San Angelo, TX, p. A640
WESTFALL, Gay, Senior Vice President Human Resources, Kaiser Permanente Sacramento Medical Center, Sacramento, CA, p. A84
WESTFALL, Roger, Director, Western State Hospital, Hopkinsville, KY, p. A258
WESTFIELD, Brian W., MSN, Director, Jonathan M. Wainwright Memorial Veterans Affairs Medical Center, Walla Walla, WA, p. A687
WESTIN, Robert, M.D. Chief Medical Officer, Cuyuna Regional Medical Center, Crosby, MN, p. A337
WESTMAN, Ken, Chief Executive Officer, Barrett Hospital & HealthCare, Dillon, MT, p. A383
WESTMORELAND, Penny
Chief Financial Officer, Lakeland Community Hospital, Haleyville, AL, p. A21
Chief Financial Officer, Red Bay Hospital, Red Bay, AL, p. A24
Chief Financial Officer, Russellville Hospital, Russellville, AL, p. A24
WESTON, Betty, Chief Human Resources Officer, U. S. Public Health Service Phoenix Indian Medical Center, Phoenix, AZ, p. A36
WESTON, Nancy R., R.N. Vice President Nursing Services, Memorial Hospital, Belleville, IL, p. A179
WESTON, Susan, CPA Chief Financial Officer, Mountrail County Medical Center, Stanley, ND, p. A476
WESTON, Terry, M.D. Vice President Physician Services, OhioHealth MedCentral Mansfield Hospital, Mansfield, OH, p. A493
WESTON–HALL, Patricia, Chief Executive Officer, Glenbeigh Hospital and Outpatient Centers, Rock Creek, OH, p. A497
WESTPHAL, Chris, Chief Information Technology Officer, Southeast Colorado Hospital District, Springfield, CO, p. A108
WESTPHAL, Laura R., Vice President Patient Care Services, Castle Medical Center, Kailua, HI, p. A169
WESTRICH, Christie, Administrator, Parkland Health Center – Weber Road, Farmington, MO, p. A367
WESTROM, Manda, Director of Nursing, Prairie Ridge Hospital and Health Services, Elbow Lake, MN, p. A338

Index of Health Care Professionals

Index of Health Care Professionals / Westrum


WESTRUM, Jennifer, Administrator, Community Behavioral Health Hospital – Alexandria, Alexandria, MN, p. A334
WESTWOOD, Denise P., Chief Nursing Officer, Weirton Medical Center, Weirton, WV, p. A696
WESTWOOD, John, M.D. Chief of Staff, Chambers Memorial Hospital, Danville, AR, p. A42
WETHERELL, Russell J., Senior Vice President, Administrator, Grandview Medical Center, Dayton, OH, p. A488
WETHINGTON, Bud, Chief Executive Officer, T. J. Samson Community Hospital, Glasgow, KY, p. A257
WETTON, Darlene, R.N., Chief Executive Officer, Temecula Valley Hospital, Temecula, CA, p. A94
WETZEL, James L., M.D. Vice President, Chief Medical Officer, Olathe Medical Center, Olathe, KS, p. A247
WETZEL, Lou, M.D. Chief of Staff, The University of Kansas Hospital, Kansas City, KS, p. A243
WEVER, Kurt, M.D. Chief of Staff, Pikes Peak Regional Hospital, Woodland Park, CO, p. A109
WEYMOUTH, Deborah K., FACHE, President and Chief Executive Officer, HealthAlliance Hospitals, Leominster, MA, p. A308
WEYMOUTH, Linda, Chief Financial Officer, Suncoast Behavioral Health Center, Bradenton, FL, p. A122
WHALEN, David, Chief Executive Officer, Twin Cities Hospital, Niceville, FL, p. A136
WHALEN, Patti, Manager Human Resources, Wichita County Health Center, Leoti, KS, p. A245
WHALEN, Scott, FACHE,
President and Chief Executive Officer, Saint Vincent Health Center, Erie, PA, p. A534
President and Chief Executive Officer, Westfield Memorial Hospital, Westfield, NY, p. A454
WHALEN, Thomas, Vice President Finance, Good Samaritan Medical Center, Brockton, MA, p. A305
WHALEN, Thomas, M.D
Chief Medical Officer, Lehigh Valley Hospital, Allentown, PA, p. A528
Chief Medical Officer, Lehigh Valley Hospital–Muhlenberg, Bethlehem, PA, p. A529
WHALEY, Joseph, Chief, Human Resources Management Service, Fayetteville Veterans Affairs Medical Center, Fayetteville, NC, p. A460
WHALEY, Mary, Director of Acute Care, Johnson County Healthcare Center, Buffalo, WY, p. A715
WHALEY, Shay, Administrator, Hale County Hospital, Greensboro, AL, p. A20
WHARTON, Joe H., M.D. Chief of Staff, Bradley County Medical Center, Warren, AR, p. A51
WHEAT, Ken, Senior Vice President and Chief Financial Officer, Eisenhower Medical Center, Rancho Mirage, CA, p. A82
WHEAT, Terry, R.N. Director of Patient Care Services, Shriners Hospitals for Children–Chicago, Chicago, IL, p. A184
WHEATCRAFT, Cory, Information Technology and Purchasing Officer, Windsor–Laurelwood Center for Behavioral Medicine, Willoughby, OH, p. A501
WHEATLEY, Bernard, FACHE, Chief Executive Officer, Schneider Regional Medical Center, Saint Thomas, VI, p. A725
WHEATLEY, Jane, Chief Executive Officer, Taylor Regional Hospital, Campbellsville, KY, p. A255
WHEATLEY, Richard, Chief Information Officer, Cape Regional Medical Center, Cape May Court House, NJ, p. A410
WHEATLEY, Sonya, Human Resources Manager, Central State Hospital, Louisville, KY, p. A261
WHEATLEY, Stephen J., Director of Operations, Franciscan St. Francis Health–Carmel, Carmel, IN, p. A206
WHEATON, David, Director Human Resources, Blue Hill Memorial Hospital, Blue Hill, ME, p. A289
WHEELAN, Kevin, M.D. Medical Director, Baylor Jack and Jane Hamilton Heart and Vascular Hospital, Dallas, TX, p. A604
WHEELER, Brent, Vice President Ancillary and Support Services, McLaren Flint, Flint, MI, p. A319
WHEELER, Dane, Chief Financial Officer, Adams Memorial Hospital, Decatur, IN, p. A207
WHEELER, Dawne, Chief Executive Officer, Select Specialty Hospital–Canton, Canton, OH, p. A481
WHEELER, Denise, Chief Information Officer, Star Valley Medical Center, Afton, WY, p. A715
WHEELER, Don, Director Information Systems, Twin Cities Community Hospital, Templeton, CA, p. A94
WHEELER, James A., Vice President Human Relations and Community Development, Androscoggin Valley Hospital, Berlin, NH, p. A405
WHEELER, Kevin, Information Technology Leader, Kaiser Permanente Walnut Creek Medical Center, Walnut Creek, CA, p. A97
WHEELER, Kim, R.N. Director of Nursing, Kingwood Pines Hospital, Kingwood, TX, p. A626
WHEELER, Lynette, MS
Chief Nursing Officer, Truman Medical Center–Hospital Hill, Kansas City, MO, p. A370
Chief Nursing Officer, Truman Medical Center–Lakewood, Kansas City, MO, p. A370
WHEELER, Newman, Chief Financial Officer and Chief Operating Officer, Covenant Hospital–Levelland, Levelland, TX, p. A628
WHEELER, Pamela R., Manager Human Resources, Scott County Hospital, Scott City, KS, p. A250
WHEELER, Penny Ann, M.D. President and Chief Medical Officer, Abbott Northwestern Hospital, Minneapolis, MN, p. A342
WHEELER, Penny Ann, M.D., Chief Executive Officer, Allina Health, Minneapolis, MN, p. B9
WHEELER, Philip, Director Finance, Mercy Health – Clermont Hospital, Batavia, OH, p. A479
WHEELER, Rebecca, Director Finance, Kaiser Permanente Baldwin Park Medical Center, Baldwin Park, CA, p. A55
WHEELER, Robert
Controller, HEALTHSOUTH Rehabilitation Hospital of Florence, Florence, SC, p. A560
Vice President Human Resources, South Shore Hospital, South Weymouth, MA, p. A311
WHEELER, Terry J., Chief Executive Officer, Cypress Fairbanks Medical Center, Houston, TX, p. A619
WHEELER, Tina, R.N. Director Nursing, William Newton Hospital, Winfield, KS, p. A253
WHEELER, William, M.D. Chief of Staff, Benewah Community Hospital, Saint Maries, ID, p. A176
WHEELER, Zach, Senior Vice President Human Resources, John D. Archbold Memorial Hospital, Thomasville, GA, p. A166
WHEELER–MOORE, Juanita, Director Financial Services, Four Winds Hospital, Saratoga Springs, NY, p. A450
WHEELES, Locke, Information Technology Manager, Field Memorial Community Hospital, Centreville, MS, p. A351
WHEELUS, Matthew, Chief Operating Officer, Spring Valley Hospital Medical Center, Las Vegas, NV, p. A402
WHELAN, Doris, Chief Information Officer, Moberly Regional Medical Center, Moberly, MO, p. A373
WHELAN, James, Chief Medical Officer, Munson Healthcare Cadillac Hospital, Cadillac, MI, p. A315
WHELAN, Laurie A., Senior Vice President Finance and Chief Financial Officer, Hospital for Special Care, New Britain, CT, p. A113
WHERRY, Richard, M.D. Chief of Staff, Chestatee Regional Hospital, Dahlonega, GA, p. A155
WHERRY, Robin, Risk Manager and Director Quality Assurance and Health Information Management, HEALTHSOUTH MountainView Regional Rehabilitation Hospital, Morgantown, WV, p. A693
WHICHARD, Forrest, Chief Financial Officer, Ochsner Medical Center – North Shore, Slidell, LA, p. A285
WHICHARD, Nick, Chief Information Officer, St. Luke's Hospital, Columbus, NC, p. A458
WHIDDON, William, Chief Financial Officer, Woodland Heights Medical Center, Lufkin, TX, p. A630
WHILDEN, Sean
Chief Financial Officer, Houston Medical Center, Warner Robins, GA, p. A167
Chief Financial Officer, Perry Hospital, Perry, GA, p. A162
WHILLOCK, Mary C., R.N. Associate Nursing Officer and Chief Operating Officer, Florida Hospital Carrollwood, Tampa, FL, p. A144
WHIPKEY, Jared, Chief Financial Officer, Santa Rosa Medical Center, Milton, FL, p. A135
WHIPPLE, C. Cynthia, Administrative Director and Director of Nursing, Muncy Valley Hospital, Muncy, PA, p. A541
WHIPPLE, James, Chief Executive Officer, Marshall Medical Center, Placerville, CA, p. A81
WHIPPLE, Jennifer, Director Nursing, Lane County Hospital, Dighton, KS, p. A239
WHITACRE, James, Chief Operating Officer, Select Specialty Hospital–Orlando, Orlando, FL, p. A138
WHITAKER, Bert, Interim Chief Executive Officer, Calais Regional Hospital, Calais, ME, p. A289
WHITAKER, Brittany, Chief Financial Officer, Placentia–Linda Hospital, Placentia, CA, p. A81
WHITAKER, Catherine, R.N. Vice President and Chief Nursing Officer, University of Maryland Baltimore Washington Medical Center, Glen Burnie, MD, p. A298
WHITAKER, Charles, Director Information Technology, Madison Parish Hospital, Tallulah, LA, p. A286
WHITAKER, David D., FACHE, President and Chief Executive Officer, Norman Regional Health System, Norman, OK, p. A510
WHITAKER, Dedra, R.N. Chief Nursing Officer, Morristown–Hamblen Healthcare System, Morristown, TN, p. A584
WHITAKER, Doris, Vice President and Manager, Mercy Hospital Booneville, Booneville, AR, p. A42
WHITAKER, James B., President, Circles of Care, Melbourne, FL, p. A133
WHITAKER, Jimmy, Director Information Systems, Central Carolina Hospital, Sanford, NC, p. A468
WHITAKER, Neil, M.D. Chief Medical Director, Orem Community Hospital, Orem, UT, p. A656
WHITAKER, Robert, Vice President of Operations, Southwest Medical Center, Liberal, KS, p. A245
WHITE, Al, CPA Senior Vice President Business Services, Broadlawns Medical Center, Des Moines, IA, p. A226
WHITE, Alexander, Vice President Medical Affairs, Carney Hospital, Boston, MA, p. A303
WHITE, Andrea, Chief Executive Officer, Select Specialty Hospital–Birmingham, Birmingham, AL, p. A16
WHITE, Barbara, Director Human Resources, Cascade Valley Hospital and Clinics, Arlington, WA, p. A676
WHITE, Beverly, MS, Facility Director, Mary S Harper Geriatric Psychiatry Center, Tuscaloosa, AL, p. A25
WHITE, Brian, Director Strategic Planning, Vidant Bertie Hospital, Windsor, NC, p. A470
WHITE, Brian M., President, Northwest Hospital, Randallstown, MD, p. A299
WHITE, Bruce, Administrator, Covenant Hospital–Levelland, Levelland, TX, p. A628
WHITE, Bruce D., Chief Executive Officer, Knox Community Hospital, Mount Vernon, OH, p. A495
WHITE, Catherine, Chief Financial Officer, Harney District Hospital, Burns, OR, p. A519
WHITE, Cindy, CPA Vice President of Operations, INTEGRIS Canadian Valley Hospital, Yukon, OK, p. A518
WHITE, Clifford, M.D. Chief of Staff, Uvalde County Hospital Authority, Uvalde, TX, p. A649
WHITE, Darrell, R.N. Administrator and Chief Nursing Officer, Tristar Ashland City Medical Center, Ashland City, TN, p. A574
WHITE, Darryl, M.D. Chief of Staff, East Texas Medical Center Fairfield, Fairfield, TX, p. A612
WHITE, Debbie, Chief Financial Officer, CHRISTUS St. Frances Cabrini Hospital, Alexandria, LA, p. A268
WHITE, Degie, Director Human Resources, Red River Hospital, LLC, Wichita Falls, TX, p. A652
WHITE, Denise, MS
Chief Nurse Executive, Carolinas HealthCare System Anson, Wadesboro, NC, p. A470
Chief Nurse Executive, Carolinas Healthcare System Union, Monroe, NC, p. A465
WHITE, Diane K., MSN Chief Clinical Officer, Kindred Hospital South Philadelphia, Philadelphia, PA, p. A544
WHITE, Donna, Director Human Resources, HEALTHSOUTH Rehabilitation Hospital of Charleston, Charleston, SC, p. A558
WHITE, Dudley R., Administrator and Chief Executive Officer, Concho County Hospital, Eden, TX, p. A609
WHITE, Gary B., M.D. Chief Medical Staff, Uintah Basin Medical Center, Roosevelt, UT, p. A658
WHITE, Harold, Vice Chancellor, University Health Shreveport, Shreveport, LA, p. A285
WHITE, J. B., Director Information Systems, Merit Health River Region, Vicksburg, MS, p. A361
WHITE, James P., M.D. Chief Medical Officer, Integris Baptist Medical Center, Oklahoma City, OK, p. A511
WHITE, Jason, M.D. Vice President of Medical Affairs, McLaren Flint, Flint, MI, p. A319
WHITE, Jean, Vice President Finance, Avera Heart Hospital of South Dakota, Sioux Falls, SD, p. A571
WHITE, Jeffrey L., Senior Vice President and Chief Financial Officer, Beaufort Memorial Hospital, Beaufort, SC, p. A557
WHITE, Jennifer, Chief of Staff, Mayo Clinic Health System in Springfield, Springfield, MN, p. A347
WHITE, Jim, Chief Information Officer, Lompoc Valley Medical Center, Lompoc, CA, p. A68
WHITE, Joanne, Chief Information Officer, Wood County Hospital, Bowling Green, OH, p. A480
WHITE, Joe, Chief Financial Officer, Lake Whitney Medical Center, Whitney, TX, p. A652
WHITE, Joel, Chief Operating Officer, Select Specialty Hospital–Omaha, Omaha, NE, p. A396
WHITE, John D., Chief Financial Officer, Wythe County Community Hospital, Wytheville, VA, p. A675
WHITE, John R., Administrator, Shriners Hospitals for Children–Honolulu, Honolulu, HI, p. A169
WHITE, Kay, Director Human Resources and Diversity, Carolinas Hospital System Marion, Mullins, SC, p. A563
WHITE, Kelli, Manager Human Resources, CenterPointe Hospital, Saint Charles, MO, p. A375
WHITE, Kelly Lynn, Vice President of Patient Care and Chief Nursing Officer, North Memorial Medical Center, Robbinsdale, MN, p. A345
WHITE, Kevin A., Administrator, Medicine Lodge Memorial Hospital, Medicine Lodge, KS, p. A246


**A1002** Index of Health Care Professionals

Index of Health Care Professionals / Wigman

Index of Health Care Professionals


WHITE, Knicole S., Director Human Resources, Kendall Regional Medical Center, Miami, FL, p. A134
WHITE, Linda E., President and Chief Executive Officer, Deaconess Health System, Evansville, IN, p. B44
WHITE, Lindy P., Chief Executive Officer, Franklin Woods Community Hospital, Johnson City, TN, p. A579
WHITE, Mary M., Chief Executive Officer, Swedish Medical Center, Englewood, CO, p. A103
WHITE, Mary–Louise, M.D., Chief Executive Officer, Dr. Solomon Carter Fuller Mental Health Center, Boston, MA, p. A303
WHITE, Mike, Chief Financial Officer, Hansen Family Hospital, Iowa Falls, IA, p. A230
WHITE, Nathan, Chief Information Officer, Charles A. Cannon Memorial Hospital, Linville, NC, p. A464
WHITE, Pamela K., R.N. Chief Nursing Officer, Mayo Clinic Health System in Eau Claire, Eau Claire, WI, p. A700
WHITE, Patricia, Vice President Human Resources, Seton Medical Center, Daly City, CA, p. A59
WHITE, Patty, MS, President, St. Joseph's Hospital and Medical Center, Phoenix, AZ, p. A36
WHITE, Randall, Chief Executive Officer, Fayette Regional Health System, Connersville, IN, p. A206
WHITE, Randy, Chief Nursing Officer, Baptist Memorial Hospital–Union County, New Albany, MS, p. A358
WHITE, Robert, Director Information Technology, Helena Regional Medical Center, Helena, AR, p. A45
WHITE, Ryan, Chief Financial Officer, Estes Park Medical Center, Estes Park, CO, p. A103
WHITE, Sabrina, Coordinator Human Resources, Select Specialty Hospital–Charleston, Charleston, WV, p. A690
WHITE, Sam R., Chief Nursing Officer, Gateway Regional Medical Center, Granite City, IL, p. A189
WHITE, Shelia, Director Human Resources, Bon Secours–Richmond Community Hospital, Richmond, VA, p. A671
WHITE, Shirley, Director Human Resources, Ashley County Medical Center, Crossett, AR, p. A42
WHITE, Terri, Commissioner, Oklahoma Department of Mental Health and Substance Abuse Services, Oklahoma City, OK, p. B102
WHITE, Vicki, R.N. Chief Nurse Executive, Mills–Peninsula Health Services, Burlingame, CA, p. A56
WHITE, Vickie, Director of Nursing, Keokuk Area Hospital, Keokuk, IA, p. A230
WHITE, Wendy
Vice President Human Resources, CHRISTUS Health Shreveport–Bossier, Shreveport, LA, p. A284
Regional Vice President Human Resources, CHRISTUS St. Frances Cabrini Hospital, Alexandria, LA, p. A268
Assistant Administrator Human Resources, CHRISTUS St. Patrick Hospital of Lake Charles, Lake Charles, LA, p. A278
WHITE, Willie, M.D. Director Medical Staff, J. Paul Jones Hospital, Camden, AL, p. A17
WHITE, Woody, Chief Executive Officer, Covington County Hospital, Collins, MS, p. A352
WHITE HOUSE, Judy, Vice President Human Resources, St. Mary's Medical Center, Grand Junction, CO, p. A104
WHITE–JACOBS, Mary Beth, FACHE, President and Chief Executive Officer, Black River Memorial Hospital, Black River Falls, WI, p. A698
WHITE–TREVINO, Karen, Chief Nursing Officer, West Florida Hospital, Pensacola, FL, p. A140
WHITED, Steve, Chief Executive Officer, Minnie Hamilton HealthCare Center, Grantsville, WV, p. A691
WHITEHEAD, Alva W., M.D. Vice President Medical Services, McLeod Regional Medical Center, Florence, SC, p. A561
WHITEHEAD, David A.
President, Hartford HealthCare East Region, The William W. Backus Hospital, Norwich, CT, p. A114
President, Hartford HealthCare East Region, Windham Hospital, Willimantic, CT, p. A116
WHITEHEAD, Noemi, Administrative Director Human Resources, Sutter Delta Medical Center, Antioch, CA, p. A54
WHITEHEAD, Pamela, Chief Financial Officer, Anchor Hospital, Atlanta, GA, p. A149
WHITEHORN, Jeffrey T., Chief Executive Officer, TriStar Summit Medical Center, Hermitage, TN, p. A578
WHITEHURST, Rob, Chief, Office of Information and Technology, Veterans Affairs Ann Arbor Healthcare System, Ann Arbor, MI, p. A314
WHITELEY, Earl S., FACHE, Chief Executive Officer, North Georgia Medical Center, Ellijay, GA, p. A157
WHITESEL, Carol, Vice President Patient Care Services and Chief Nursing Officer, Community Hospital of Anderson and Madison County, Anderson, IN, p. A204
WHITESIDE, Anne, Vice President Nursing, Winchester Medical Center, Winchester, VA, p. A674
WHITESIDE, John, Chief Operating Officer, Mercy Regional Medical Center, Ville Platte, LA, p. A286
WHITESIDE, Patrick, Manager Information Services, Spectrum Health Big Rapids Hospital, Big Rapids, MI, p. A315
WHITETHORNE, Priscilla, Chief Executive Officer, U. S. Public Health Service Indian Hospital–Sells, Sells, AZ, p. A38
WHITFIELD, Bruce, CPA, Chief Executive Officer and Chief Financial Officer, Cabinet Peaks Medical Center, Libby, MT, p. A385
WHITFIELD Jr., Charles H., President and Chief Executive Officer, Laughlin Memorial Hospital, Greeneville, TN, p. A578
WHITFIELD, Jay, Chief Financial Officer, Baylor University Medical Center, Dallas, TX, p. A604
WHITFIELD, Jo Ann, Business Officer, Walter B. Jones Alcohol and Drug Abuse Treatment Center, Greenville, NC, p. A461
WHITFIELD, Teresa L., MS Chief Nursing Officer, Seneca Healthcare District, Chester, CA, p. A57
WHITING, Barbara, Director Health Information Management, Promise Hospital of Vicksburg, Vicksburg, MS, p. A361
WHITING, Joseph K., FACHE, Interim Chief Executive Officer, Keokuk Area Hospital, Keokuk, IA, p. A230
WHITIS, Matt, Chief Medical Officer, Mahaska Health Partnership, Oskaloosa, IA, p. A233
WHITLATCH, Kristine, President and Chief Executive Officer, King's Daughters Medical Center, Ashland, KY, p. A254
WHITLEY, Darla, Manager Health Information Technology, Syringa Hospital and Clinics, Grangeville, ID, p. A174
WHITLEY, Myra, Director Human Resources, Columbus Specialty Hospital, Columbus, GA, p. A154
WHITLEY, Pam, R.N. Chief Operating Officer and Chief Nursing Officer, Green Oaks Hospital, Dallas, TX, p. A605
WHITMER, Carl, President and Chief Executive Officer, IASIS Healthcare, Franklin, TN, p. B72
WHITMORE, Ray B., Chief Financial Officer, McCurtain Memorial Hospital, Idabel, OK, p. A508
WHITMORE, W. Patrick, Chief Financial Officer, Medical Center of Plano, Plano, TX, p. A637
WHITNEY, Donald, Director Human Resources, Kindred Hospital–Albuquerque, Albuquerque, NM, p. A422
WHITNUM, Rhonda, Director Health Improvement Management, Prague Community Hospital, Prague, OK, p. A514
WHITSON, Charles P., CPA Senior Vice President Finance, Lake Charles Memorial Hospital, Lake Charles, LA, p. A278
WHITT, Alicia, R.N. Chief Nursing Officer, Stephens Memorial Hospital, Breckenridge, TX, p. A598
WHITT, Charles Christopher, Chief Nursing Officer, River Park Hospital, Huntington, WV, p. A692
WHITT, Stevan, M.D. Chief Medical Officer, University of Missouri Hospitals and Clinics, Columbia, MO, p. A366
WHITTAKER, Kelly, Vice President Nursing, Caro Community Hospital, Caro, MI, p. A316
WHITTAKER, Shawn, Chief Nursing Officer, Miller County Hospital, Colquitt, GA, p. A154
WHITTAKER, Sheena, M.D. President Medical Staff, Maine Coast Memorial Hospital, Ellsworth, ME, p. A290
WHITTEMORE, Marjorie, Director Human Resources, Rio Grande Regional Hospital, McAllen, TX, p. A631
WHITTEMORE, Scott
Chief Financial Officer, Merit Health Central, Jackson, MS, p. A355
Chief Financial Officer, University of Mississippi Medical Center Grenada, Grenada, MS, p. A353
Chief Financial Officer, University of Mississippi Medical Center Holmes County, Lexington, MS, p. A356
WHITTEN, Jacquelyn, R.N. Chief Nurse Executive and Vice President Nursing, Advocate Trinity Hospital, Chicago, IL, p. A181
WHITTINGTON, Bruce
Vice President Human Resources, Hays Medical Center, Hays, KS, p. A241
Vice President Human Resources, Pawnee Valley Community Hospital, Larned, KS, p. A244
WHITTINGTON, Carol, Chief Human Resources Officer, Sacred Heart Hospital of Pensacola, Pensacola, FL, p. A140
WHITTINGTON, Dorothy, Chief Financial Officer, University Health Conway, Monroe, LA, p. A281
WHITTINGTON, Hilary, Chief Financial Officer, Jefferson Healthcare, Port Townsend, WA, p. A682
WHITTINGTON, Laurie A., Chief Operating Officer, Memorial Health, Marysville, OH, p. A493
WHITTINGTON, Shane, Chief Financial Officer, Caldwell Medical Center, Princeton, KY, p. A265
WHITTON, Beth, Director Human Resources, Ocean Beach Hospital, Ilwaco, WA, p. A679
WHOLLEY, Diane, Director Fiscal Services, Bridgewater State Hospital, Bridgewater, MA, p. A304
WHORLEY, Chris, Chief Information Officer, Nashville General Hospital, Nashville, TN, p. A585
WHYBREW, Chris, Chief Operating Officer, McAlester Regional Health Center, McAlester, OK, p. A509
WHYBROW, Peter, M.D., Chief Executive Officer, Stewart & Lynda Resnick Neuropsychiatric Hospital at UCLA, Los Angeles, CA, p. A73
WIATREK, Joseph, Director Information Technology, Otto Kaiser Memorial Hospital, Kenedy, TX, p. A625
WIBBENMEYER, Christopher, Director Human Resources, Perry County Memorial Hospital, Perryville, MO, p. A374
WIBBENS, Cheryl, M.D. Vice President Medical Staff Affairs, Memorial Hospital of South Bend, South Bend, IN, p. A220
WIBBLESMAN, Christopher, M.D. Chief of Staff, Family Health West, Fruita, CO, p. A104
WIBORG, Shelley, MS Director of Nursing, OSF Holy Family Medical Center, Monmouth, IL, p. A194
WICKE, III, Julius, Vice President Finance and Hospital Financial Officer, Baylor Jack and Jane Hamilton Heart and Vascular Hospital, Dallas, TX, p. A604
WICKE, Regina, Chief Financial Officer, Columbus Community Hospital, Columbus, TX, p. A601
WICKE, Trey, Vice President, Baylor Specialty Hospital, Dallas, TX, p. A604
WICKENS, Amy Lynn, Executive Director Human Resources, Decatur County Memorial Hospital, Greensburg, IN, p. A210
WICKENS, Jeanne', Senior Vice President Finance and Strategy and Chief Financial Officer, Allegiance Health, Jackson, MI, p. A323
WICKER, Kenneth R., Chief Executive Officer, Bayfront Health Brooksville, Brooksville, FL, p. A123
WICKERSHAM, Jason, M.D. Chief of Staff, Avera St. Benedict Health Center, Parkston, SD, p. A570
WICKIZER, Jr., Boyd, M.D. Chief Medical Officer, Southside Regional Medical Center, Petersburg, VA, p. A670
WICKLANDER, Jeff, President, North Memorial Medical Center, Robbinsdale, MN, p. A345
WICKLINE, Melissa, Director Marketing, Greenbrier Valley Medical Center, Ronceverte, WV, p. A695
WICKLUND, Grant, President and Chief Executive Officer, Lutheran Medical Center, Wheat Ridge, CO, p. A109
WIDEMAN, Jeff, Director Information Systems, Merit Health Gilmore Memorial, Amory, MS, p. A350
WIDENER, Michael, Chief Financial Officer, Twin County Regional Healthcare, Galax, VA, p. A665
WIDENER, Steve, Interim Chief Executive Officer, Lackey Memorial Hospital, Forest, MS, p. A353
WIDENER, William, Administrator and Chief Executive Officer, Harper Hospital District Five, Harper, KS, p. A241
WIDGER, Judy, M.D. Chief of Staff, Healdsburg District Hospital, Healdsburg, CA, p. A64
WIDICK, Brent, Superintendent, Kansas Neurological Institute, Topeka, KS, p. A251
WIDNER, Eric W., Division President, Beaumont Hospital – Wayne, Wayne, MI, p. A332
WIDRA, Linda S., R.N., Interim Chief Executive Officer, Lakewood Ranch Medical Center, Bradenton, FL, p. A122
WIEBE, Robert, M.D. Chief Medical Officer, Mercy General Hospital, Sacramento, CA, p. A84
WIECHART, Michael, President and Chief Executive Officer, Capella Healthcare, Franklin, TN, p. B26
WIECK, Jennifer, Director Financial Services, Genoa Medical Facilities, Genoa, NE, p. A392
WIECZOREK, Pawel, Director Information Technology, BryLin Hospitals, Buffalo, NY, p. A430
WIEMANN, Michael, M.D., President, Providence – Providence Park Hospital, Southfield Campus, Southfield, MI, p. A330
WIENS, Ron, Chief Financial Officer, Shodair Children's Hospital, Helena, MT, p. A384
WIENTJES, Keri, Director Human Resources, Mobridge Regional Hospital, Mobridge, SD, p. A570
WIERZBICKI, Barb, Manager Human Resources, Select Specialty Hospital–Downriver, Wyandotte, MI, p. A332
WIESNER, Jerry, Interim Chief Executive Officer, Union County General Hospital, Clayton, NM, p. A423
WIEWORA, Ron, M.D. Chief Medical Officer, Lakeside Medical Center, Belle Glade, FL, p. A121
WIGGINS, Carla, Director Human Resources, Livingston Hospital and Healthcare Services, Salem, KY, p. A265
WIGGINS, John, Chief Financial Officer, Evans Memorial Hospital, Claxton, GA, p. A153
WIGGINS, Leslie, Director, Atlanta Veterans Affairs Medical Center, Decatur, GA, p. A155
WIGGINS, Marjorie, Senior Vice President, Chief Nursing Officer, Maine Medical Center, Portland, ME, p. A291
WIGHTMAN, Lori, FACHE, Chief Executive Officer, Mercy Hospital Ada, Ada, OK, p. A503
WIGINGTON, James, M.D. Chief of Staff, Heart of the Rockies Regional Medical Center, Salida, CO, p. A108
WIGINGTON, Yvonne, Vice President, Chief Financial Officer, Wyoming Medical Center, Casper, WY, p. A715
WIGMAN, Cathryn, Director Human Resources, Braintree Rehabilitation Hospital, Braintree, MA, p. A304

WIGNALL, Terry A., Director Human Resources, St. Vincent Seton Specialty Hospital, Indianapolis, IN, p. A213

WIIK, Jennifer, Chief Nursing Officer, Ortonville Area Health Services, Ortonville, MN, p. A344

WIJAYA, Joanne, Chief Operating Officer, Hampton Behavioral Health Center, Westampton, NJ, p. A420

WIJEWARDANE, Chamath, Director Information Technology, OCH Regional Medical Center, Starkville, MS, p. A360

WILBANKS, John F., FACH
   Chief Operating Officer, Baptist Medical Center Beaches, Jacksonville Beach, FL, p. A130
   Chief Operating Officer, Baptist Medical Center Jacksonville, Jacksonville, FL, p. A129

WILBUR, Bruce, M.D. Chief Medical Officer, Good Samaritan Hospital, San Jose, CA, p. A89

WILBUR, Thomas W., Chief Executive Officer and Superintendent, Newport Hospital and Health Services, Newport, WA, p. A681

WILBURN, Sue, Vice President Human Resources and Organizational Development, East Tennessee Children's Hospital, Knoxville, TN, p. A580

WILCHER, Greta
   Senior Vice President and Chief Financial Officer, Mercy Hospital Fort Smith, Fort Smith, AR, p. A44
   Senior Vice President and Chief Financial Officer, Mercy Hospital Waldron, Waldron, AR, p. A51

WILCHER, Kelly, Chief Executive Officer, Carson Tahoe Continuing Care Hospital, Carson City, NV, p. A400

WILCOX, Bill, Chief Information Technology Officer, Bristol Bay Area Health Corporation, Dillingham, AK, p. A28

WILCOX, Billy, Group Controller, Cornerstone Hospital of Bossier City, Bossier City, LA, p. A270

WILCOX, Jack, Chief Financial Officer, Ennis Regional Medical Center, Ennis, TX, p. A612

WILCOX, James, Chief Executive Officer, El Paso Specialty Hospital, El Paso, TX, p. A610

WILCOX, John, Chief Information Officer, Ozarks Medical Center, West Plains, MO, p. A380

WILCOX, Kyle M., Assistant Vice President Finance, Grinnell Regional Medical Center, Grinnell, IA, p. A228

WILCOX, William H., President and Chief Executive Officer, United Surgical Partners International, Addison, TX, p. B140

WILCZEK, Joseph, Chief Executive Officer, St. Elizabeth Hospital, Enumclaw, WA, p. A678

WILCZEK, Vincent Scot, Vice President and Chief Financial Officer, Pratt Regional Medical Center, Pratt, KS, p. A249

WILD, James, M.D. Medical Director, TLC Health Network – Lake Shore Hospital, Irving, NY, p. A435

WILD, Mary Lou, Vice President Patient Care Continuum and Chief Nursing Officer, Sarah Bush Lincoln Health Center, Mattoon, IL, p. A193

WILDE, Gary, President and Chief Executive Officer, Community Memorial Health System, Ventura, CA, p. A96

WILDE, Kathy R., R.N. Chief Nursing Officer, Hennepin County Medical Center, Minneapolis, MN, p. A342

WILDE, Stacy, Chief Executive Officer, AMG Specialty Hospital–Tulsa, Tulsa, OK, p. A516

WILDER, Claudia, R.N. Chief Nursing Officer, Baylor University Medical Center, Dallas, TX, p. A604

WILDER, Janet, Director Human Resources, Knox County Hospital, Barbourville, KY, p. A254

WILDER, Kathy, R.N. Chief Clinical Officer, Medical Center Barbour, Eufaula, AL, p. A19

WILDHAGEN, Quentin, Systems Administrator, Community Medical Center of Izard County, Calico Rock, AR, p. A42

WILDI, Lorri, Interim Chief Executive Officer, Coshocton County Memorial Hospital, Coshocton, OH, p. A487

WILEY, Chuck, Manager Information Systems, Harrison County Hospital, Corydon, IN, p. A206

WILEY, Donald J., President and Chief Executive Officer, St. Joseph's Medical Center, Stockton, CA, p. A93

WILEY, Eric, M.D. Chief of Staff, Brownwood Regional Medical Center, Brownwood, TX, p. A599

WILEY, George, Chief Financial Officer, North Vista Hospital, North Las Vegas, NV, p. A403

WILEY, Mark, Manager Information Systems Development, UPMC Bedford Memorial, Everett, PA, p. A534

WILFORD, Linda, CPA Senior Vice President and Chief Financial Officer, Holy Cross Hospital, Fort Lauderdale, FL, p. A126

WILHELM, Christine, Chief Operating Officer, Charlevoix Area Hospital, Charlevoix, MI, p. A316

WILHELM, Connie, Chief Financial Officer, Swisher Memorial Hospital District, Tulia, TX, p. A648

WILHELM, Jr., John O., Senior Vice President and Chief Financial Officer, Emerson Hospital, Concord, MA, p. A306

WILHELM, Paul, M.D. Chief of Staff, Kiowa District Hospital and Manor, Kiowa, KS, p. A244

WILHELMSEN Jr., Thomas E., President and Chief Executive Officer, Southern New Hampshire Medical Center, Nashua, NH, p. A407

WILHITE, James, Director Systems Information, North Mississippi State Hospital, Tupelo, MS, p. A361

WILHITE, Jerald, Administrator Human Resources, Heartland Behavioral Healthcare, Massillon, OH, p. A493

WILHOITE, David, CPA Senior Vice President Finance and Chief Financial Officer, Trousdale Medical Center, Hartsville, TN, p. A578

WILK, Leonard, President and Chief Executive Officer, St. Alexius Medical Center, Hoffman Estates, IL, p. A191

WILK, Michael, Senior President Financial Services and Chief Financial Officer, Pocono Medical Center, East Stroudsburg, PA, p. A533

WILKE, Julie, Vice President, Monroe Clinic, Monroe, WI, p. A707

WILKE, Kris, Manager Health Information, Granite Falls Municipal Hospital and Manor, Granite Falls, MN, p. A340

WILKEN, Thomas
   Senior Vice President and Chief Human Resources Officer, Mother Frances Hospital – Tyler, Tyler, TX, p. A649
   Vice President Human Resources, Seton Medical Center Williamson, Round Rock, TX, p. A639

WILKENS, Gregory, M.D. Chief of Staff, Jellico Community Hospital, Jellico, TN, p. A579

WILKER, Johnathan, Vice President Finance and Chief Financial Officer, Faith Regional Health Services, Norfolk, NE, p. A395

WILKERSON, Donald H., Chief Executive Officer, St. David's Medical Center, Austin, TX, p. A595

WILKERSON, Jacquelyn, R.N. Chief Nursing Officer, Conway Regional Medical Center, Conway, AR, p. A42

WILKERSON–UDDYBACK, Patricia, M.D. Chief Medical Officer, DMC Harper University Hospital, Detroit, MI, p. A317

WILKES, Chris, MS Director Human Resources, Blount Memorial Hospital, Maryville, TN, p. A582

WILKES, Margaret, Chief Fiscal Officer, Charles George Veterans Affairs Medical Center, Asheville, NC, p. A455

WILKIE, Chance, Information Technology Specialist, Indian Health Service – Quentin N. Burdick Memorial Health Care Facility, Belcourt, ND, p. A472

WILKIE, Paula, Chief Financial Officer, Presentation Medical Center, Rolla, ND, p. A476

WILKINS, Kate, M.D. President, Medical Staff, Carlinville Area Hospital, Carlinville, IL, p. A180

WILKINS, Michael, Chief Operating Officer, Advocate Christ Medical Center, Oak Lawn, IL, p. A196

WILKINSON, Kyle, Chief Financial Officer, Morgan Memorial Hospital, Madison, GA, p. A161

WILKINSON, Mark, M.D. Chief Medical Officer, Indian Path Medical Center, Kingsport, TN, p. A580

WILKINSON, Paul G., Chief Operating Officer, Providence St. Peter Hospital, Olympia, WA, p. A681

WILL, Charles, Chief Financial Officer, Ferrell Hospital, Eldorado, IL, p. A186

WILL, DeDe, Director Finance, Douglas County Community Mental Health Center, Omaha, NE, p. A396

WILL, Nicole, Human Resources Officer, Herington Municipal Hospital, Herington, KS, p. A241

WILL–MOWERY, Nicki L., Ph.D., Chief Executive Officer, Lower Keys Medical Center, Key West, FL, p. A130

WILLAMS, Brandon, Chief Financial Officer, East Cooper Medical Center, Mount Pleasant, SC, p. A563

WILLAMS, Kyle, Director Information Technology, Kirby Medical Center, Monticello, IL, p. A194

WILLAMS, Mike, Chief Information Officer, FHN Memorial Hospital, Freeport, IL, p. A188

WILLARD, Cheri, R.N. Chief Nursing Officer, Evanston Regional Hospital, Evanston, WY, p. A716

WILLARD, Craig, Director Information Technology and Systems, Frankfort Regional Medical Center, Frankfort, KY, p. A257

WILLARD, Ruth, Chief Nursing Officer, TriStar StoneCrest Medical Center, Smyrna, TN, p. A588

WILLE, Lesley A., Administrator and Executive Director, Kaiser Permanente South Bay Medical Center, CA, p. A70

WILLE, Matt, Chief Executive Officer, Dallas County Hospital, Perry, IA, p. A233

WILLEKE, Louis R., Administrator, Refugio County Memorial Hospital, Refugio, TX, p. A638

WILLEMSEN, Jane, Chief Administrative Officer, John Muir Medical Center, Walnut Creek, Walnut Creek, CA, p. A97

WILLERT, Todd, Chief Executive Officer, Community HealthCare System, Onaga, KS, p. A247

WILLET, Terry, Chief Financial Officer, Allen Parish Hospital, Kinder, LA, p. A276

WILLETT, Charles, Administrator and Chief Executive Officer, Fulton County Hospital, Salem, AR, p. A50

WILLETT, Richard, Chief Executive Officer, Redington–Fairview General Hospital, Skowhegan, ME, p. A292

WILLETT, Simon, Director Administrative Operations, South Texas Veterans Health Care System, San Antonio, TX, p. A642

WILLETT, Vita M., Executive Director, Kaiser Permanente Riverside Medical Center, Riverside, CA, p. A83

WILLEY, Randy, Business Manager, Lincoln Regional Center, Lincoln, NE, p. A394

WILLHITE, Jean, Director Human Resources, Sutter Solano Medical Center, Vallejo, CA, p. A96

WILLIAMS, Adrian, Chief Executive Officer, Serenity Springs Specialty Hospital, Ruston, LA, p. A284

WILLIAMS, Amber, Vice President and Chief Financial Officer, Southwest Medical Center, Liberal, KS, p. A245

WILLIAMS, Amy W., M.D. Chief Medical Officer, Mayo Clinic Hospital – Rochester, Rochester, MN, p. A345

WILLIAMS, Andrea K., Manager, Employee Relations, Winter Haven Hospital, Winter Haven, FL, p. A148

WILLIAMS, Andrew G., Chief Executive Officer and Administrator, Methodist Ambulatory Surgery Hospital – Northwest, San Antonio, TX, p. A641

WILLIAMS, Antoinette, Chief Nursing Officer, John H. Stroger Jr. Hospital of Cook County, Chicago, IL, p. A182

WILLIAMS, Arthur, M.D. Medical Director, Braintree Rehabilitation Hospital, Braintree, MA, p. A304

WILLIAMS, Ashley, Manager Human Resources, Southern Inyo Healthcare District, Lone Pine, CA, p. A68

WILLIAMS, Avilla, MS, President, INTEGRIS Health Edmond, Edmond, OK, p. A506

WILLIAMS, Beverly, R.N. Chief Nursing Officer, Washington County Memorial Hospital, Potosi, MO, p. A374

WILLIAMS, Bob, President and Chief Executive Officer, Baptist St. Anthony Health System, Amarillo, TX, p. A591

WILLIAMS, Brian, Service Leader Corporate Information Systems, St. Joseph's Hospital of Buckhannon, Buckhannon, WV, p. A690

WILLIAMS, Brian A., Chief Executive Officer, Labette Health, Parsons, KS, p. A248

WILLIAMS, Brit, M.D. President Medical Staff, Dr. John Warner Hospital, Clinton, IL, p. A185

WILLIAMS, Cara, Director Human Resources, Scripps Memorial Hospital–Encinitas, Encinitas, CA, p. A60

WILLIAMS, CarolAnn, Chief Financial Officer, Massachusetts Eye and Ear Infirmary, Boston, MA, p. A304

WILLIAMS, Carrie, R.N. Chief Nursing Officer, Henry County Hospital, New Castle, IN, p. A217

WILLIAMS, Catherine, M.D. Medical Director, Lewis County General Hospital, Lowville, NY, p. A436

WILLIAMS, Cecille, Assistant Administrator, Shamrock General Hospital, Shamrock, TX, p. A643

WILLIAMS, Dan, Vice President Finance and Support, Liberty Hospital, Liberty, MO, p. A372

WILLIAMS, Dana, Chief Financial Officer, Baptist Memorial Hospital–North Mississippi, Oxford, MS, p. A359

WILLIAMS, Dana D., Chief Executive Officer, Jennings American Legion Hospital, Jennings, LA, p. A275

WILLIAMS, Darek, Director Human Resources, Elgin Mental Health Center, Elgin, IL, p. A187

WILLIAMS, Darlene, R.N., Administrator, CHI St. Luke's Health Memorial San Augustine, San Augustine, TX, p. A643

WILLIAMS, David, Director Information Technology, Franklin Hospital District, Benton, IL, p. A179

WILLIAMS, David L., M.D. Chief Medical Officer, St. Joseph Hospital & Health Center, Kokomo, IN, p. A214

WILLIAMS, David R., Chief Executive Officer, Centerpoint Medical Center, Independence, MO, p. A368

WILLIAMS, Dionne, Director Human Resources, Vaughan Regional Medical Center, Selma, AL, p. A24

WILLIAMS, Frank L., Executive Vice President/ Medical Director, Kedren Community Mental Health Center, Los Angeles, CA, p. A70

WILLIAMS, Gary
   Administrator, Houston Hospital for Specialized Surgery, Houston, TX, p. A620
   Executive Director, The Pavilion at Williamsburg Place, Williamsburg, VA, p. A674

WILLIAMS, Ginger, FACHE, President and Chief Executive Officer, Oaklawn Hospital, Marshall, MI, p. A325

WILLIAMS, Jackie, Director Human Resources, Merit Health Madison, Canton, MS, p. A351

WILLIAMS, James, M.D. Chief of Staff, Riverside Medical Center, Waupaca, WI, p. A713

WILLIAMS, Jason, Director Information Systems, Olympia Medical Center, Los Angeles, CA, p. A71

WILLIAMS, Jennette, Interim Chief Executive Officer, Kindred Hospital Rancho, Rancho Cucamonga, CA, p. A82

WILLIAMS, Jeremy, Chief Financial Officer, Banner Boswell Medical Center, Sun City, AZ, p. A38

WILLIAMS, Jeremy, M.D. President Medical Staff, Stonewall Jackson Memorial Hospital, Weston, WV, p. A696

WILLIAMS, Jim, Chief Financial Officer, Minden Medical Center, Minden, LA, p. A280

WILLIAMS, Joan, Administrative Assistant/Human Resources, Lamb Healthcare Center, Littlefield, TX, p. A628

Index of Health Care Professionals / Wilson

Index of Health Care Professionals


WILLIAMS, John
Chief Information Officer, Bay Pines Veterans Affairs Healthcare System, Bay Pines, FL, p. A121
Administrator and Chief Executive Officer, Nell J. Redfield Memorial Hospital, Malad City, ID, p. A174
Chief Financial Officer, Upson Regional Medical Center, Thomaston, GA, p. A165
WILLIAMS, Jr., John D., Chief Financial Officer, Veterans Affairs Gulf Coast Veterans Health Care System, Biloxi, MS, p. A350
WILLIAMS Jr., John F., M.P.H., President, SUNY Downstate Medical Center University Hospital, NY, p. A444
WILLIAMS, John G., President and Chief Executive Officer, Barton Memorial Hospital, South Lake Tahoe, CA, p. A93
WILLIAMS, Joyce, Consultant Human Resources and Organizational Development, Memorial Hermann Rehabilitation Hospital – Katy, Katy, TX, p. A625
WILLIAMS, Julie, Chief Financial Officer, Smith County Memorial Hospital, Smith Center, KS, p. A250
WILLIAMS, Kathy, Chief Nursing Officer, Eastern New Mexico Medical Center, Roswell, NM, p. A426
WILLIAMS, Kenneth, Chief Information Officer, Fayetteville Veterans Affairs Medical Center, Fayetteville, NC, p. A460
WILLIAMS, Kim, R.N
Director of Nursing, Mercy Hospital Logan County, Guthrie, OK, p. A507
Chief Operating Officer, Providence Regional Medical Center Everett, Everett, WA, p. A679
WILLIAMS, L. Dale, M.D. Vice President and Chief Medical Director, High Point Regional Health System, High Point, NC, p. A462
WILLIAMS, Lana R., Chief Nursing Officer, Arkansas Methodist Medical Center, Paragould, AR, p. A49
WILLIAMS, Lauren, R.N. Vice President of Professional Services and Chief Nursing Officer, Lawrence + Memorial Hospital, New London, CT, p. A114
WILLIAMS, Linda, Director of Nursing, Villa Feliciana Medical Complex, Jackson, LA, p. A275
WILLIAMS, Lorie, R.N. Vice President Nursing, Samaritan Pacific Communities Hospital, Newport, OR, p. A523
WILLIAMS, Lynn
Vice President, Commonwealth Regional Specialty Hospital, Bowling Green, KY, p. A254
Vice President Human Resources, Medical Center at Bowling Green, Bowling Green, KY, p. A254
Vice President Human Resources, Medical Center at Scottsville, Scottsville, KY, p. A266
WILLIAMS, Margaret, Chief Financial Officer, Baptist Memorial Hospital for Women, Memphis, TN, p. A583
WILLIAMS, Margo L., R.N. Chief Nursing Officer, Anderson County Hospital, Garnett, KS, p. A240
WILLIAMS, Mark, Chief Financial Officer, Citrus Memorial Health System, Inverness, FL, p. A129
WILLIAMS, Mark, M.D. Vice President and Chief Medical Officer, Miami Valley Hospital, Dayton, OH, p. A488
WILLIAMS, Mary, Director Human Resources, Medina Memorial Hospital, Medina, NY, p. A437
WILLIAMS, Matthew, R.N. Chief Financial Officer, Olympia Medical Center, Los Angeles, CA, p. A71
WILLIAMS, Michael, Chief Information Officer, Lawrence Memorial Hospital, Lawrence, KS, p. A244
WILLIAMS, Michael D., President and Chief Executive Officer, Community Hospital Corporation, Plano, TX, p. B41
WILLIAMS, Michael L., FACHE Vice President Human Resources, Community Howard Regional Health, Kokomo, IN, p. A213
WILLIAMS, Michelle, Administrator, Sedan City Hospital, Sedan, KS, p. A250
WILLIAMS, Mickey, Manager Information Technology, Moccasin Bend Mental Health Institute, Chattanooga, TN, p. A575
WILLIAMS, Mike, Accountant, Limestone Medical Center, Groesbeck, TX, p. A617
WILLIAMS, Pam, Chief Executive Officer, Minnesota Valley Health Center, Le Sueur, MN, p. A341
WILLIAMS, Pamela G., Director Human Resources, Unity Health White County Medical Center, Searcy, AR, p. A50
WILLIAMS, Patricia, Regional VP for Behavioral Medicine and Population Health, St. Helena Hospital–Center for Behavioral Health, Vallejo, CA, p. A96
WILLIAMS Sr., Perry E., Administrator and Chief Executive Officer, Alliance HealthCare System, Holly Springs, MS, p. A354
WILLIAMS, R. D., Chief Executive Officer, Hendry Regional Medical Center, Clewiston, FL, p. A124
WILLIAMS, Randy, Director Management Information Systems, Maria Parham Medical Center, Henderson, NC, p. A462
WILLIAMS, Rich, Director Human Resources, Upson Regional Medical Center, Thomaston, GA, p. A165
WILLIAMS, Richard, Chief Operating Officer, Southwest Mississippi Regional Medical Center, McComb, MS, p. A357
WILLIAMS, Robert, R.N., Chief Executive Officer, HEALTHSOUTH Southern Hills Rehabilitation Hospital, Princeton, WV, p. A694
WILLIAMS, Robert D., Interim Chief Executive Officer, Sunbury Community Hospital and Outpatient Center, Sunbury, PA, p. A550
WILLIAMS, Robert J., M.D. Chief Medical Staff, Wills Memorial Hospital, Washington, GA, p. A167
WILLIAMS, Roberta A., Director of Nursing, U. S. Public Health Service Indian Hospital, Cass Lake, MN, p. A336
WILLIAMS, Roby D., Administrator, Hardin County General Hospital, Rosiclare, IL, p. A200
WILLIAMS, Roderick L., M.P.H., President, University Health Shreveport, Shreveport, LA, p. A285
WILLIAMS, Rodney W., M.D. Vice President Medical Affairs, Good Samaritan Hospital, Suffern, NY, p. A451
WILLIAMS, Ronald G., Administrator, Central Louisiana State Hospital, Pineville, LA, p. A283
WILLIAMS, Sandra
Chief Financial Officer, Cape Fear Valley – Bladen County Hospital, Elizabethtown, NC, p. A460
Chief Financial Officer, Cape Fear Valley Medical Center, Fayetteville, NC, p. A460
WILLIAMS, Scott, Chief Operating Officer, Cookeville Regional Medical Center, Cookeville, TN, p. A576
WILLIAMS, Sean J., President and Chief Executive Officer, Mercy Medical Center–Clinton, Clinton, IA, p. A224
WILLIAMS, Shane, Director Information Systems, Davis Hospital and Medical Center, Layton, UT, p. A655
WILLIAMS, Sharon, Vice President Finance and Information Technology, Avera Marshall Regional Medical Center, Marshall, MN, p. A342
WILLIAMS, Sheila, Vice President and Administrator, Baptist Health Medical Center–Hot Spring County, Malvern, AR, p. A48
WILLIAMS, Stephanie
Coordinator Human Resources, Kindred Rehabilitation Hospital Northeast Houston, Humble, TX, p. A623
Market Director Human Resources, Lake Norman Regional Medical Center, Mooresville, NC, p. A465
WILLIAMS, Stephanie, R.N. Chief Nursing Officer, Washington Hospital Healthcare System, Fremont, CA, p. A62
WILLIAMS, Stephen, Chief Executive Officer, Norton Healthcare, Louisville, KY, p. B99
WILLIAMS, Steve, Chief Executive Officer, Victory Medical Center Plano, Plano, TX, p. A637
WILLIAMS, Susan, R.N. Chief Nursing Officer, Baptist Health Medical Center–Stuttgart, Stuttgart, AR, p. A51
WILLIAMS, Tammy J., R.N. Chief Nursing Officer and Senior Vice President, University Medical Center, Lubbock, TX, p. A630
WILLIAMS, Teresa, R.N., Administrator and Director of Nursing, Mercy Hospital Ozark, Ozark, AR, p. A49
WILLIAMS, Thaddeus, Controller, HEALTHSOUTH Rehabilitation Hospital Memphis–North, Memphis, TN, p. A583
WILLIAMS, Tina, Chief Financial Officer, Alaska Psychiatric Institute, Anchorage, AK, p. A27
WILLIAMS, Todd, M.D. President Medical Staff, Eastern Idaho Regional Medical Center, Idaho Falls, ID, p. A174
WILLIAMS, Todd, Interim Chief Financial Officer, Forrest City Medical Center, Forrest City, AR, p. A44
WILLIAMS, Tom, Vice President Human Resources, Lake Regional Health System, Osage Beach, MO, p. A374
WILLIAMS, Tonja, R.N., President, Continuing Care Hospital, Lexington, KY, p. A259
WILLIAMS, Jr., Wendell H., M.D. Medical Director, Specialty Hospital Jacksonville, Jacksonville, FL, p. A130
WILLIAMSON, Alan, M.D. Chief Medical Officer, Eisenhower Medical Center, Rancho Mirage, CA, p. A82
WILLIAMSON, Anthony, President, Northeast Georgia Medical Center Braselton, Braselton, GA, p. A152
WILLIAMSON, Barry, President Medical Staff, Southeastern Health, Lumberton, NC, p. A464
WILLIAMSON, John, Human Resources Site Manager, Baptist Health South Florida, Mariners Hospital, Tavernier, FL, p. A146
WILLIAMSON, Johnny, M.D. Chief Medical Officer, Hartgrove Hospital, Chicago, IL, p. A182
WILLIAMSON, Judy, R.N. Chief Nursing Officer, Riverton Hospital, Riverton, UT, p. A657
WILLIAMSON, Marilyn, Chief Human Resources Officer, Rainbow Mental Health Facility, Kansas City, KS, p. A243
WILLIAMSON, Sharon, Chief Information Technology, Robert J. Dole Veterans Affairs Medical Center, Wichita, KS, p. A252
WILLIE, David, Chief Financial Officer, Yuma Regional Medical Center, Yuma, AZ, p. A40
WILLIFORD, Sandy, Chief Health Information Management and Revenue Administration, Charlie Norwood Veterans Affairs Medical Center, Augusta, GA, p. A151
WILLINGHAM, Alex, M.D. Medical Director, Post Acute/Warm Springs Rehabilitation Hospital of San Antonio, San Antonio, TX, p. A642
WILLINGHAM, John, Chief Executive Officer and Managing Director, Carolina Center for Behavioral Health, Greer, SC, p. A562
WILLIS, Bill, Director Information Technology, River Point Behavioral Health, Jacksonville, FL, p. A129
WILLIS, Brenda, Director of Nursing, Doctor's Hospital of Deer Creek, Leesville, LA, p. A279
WILLIS, Darrell, M.D. Chief of Staff, Dr. Dan C. Trigg Memorial Hospital, Tucumcari, NM, p. A427
WILLIS, Jonathon, Director Information Services, Heritage Medical Center, Shelbyville, TN, p. A588
WILLIS, Joy, Acting Chief Fiscal Service, G.V. (Sonny) Montgomery Veterans Affairs Medical Center, Jackson, MS, p. A355
WILLIS, Kathy, M.D. Medical Director, Lallie Kemp Medical Center, Independence, LA, p. A275
WILLIS, Mona M.
Director Human Resources, Landmark Medical Center, Woonsocket, RI, p. A556
Director Human Resources, Rehabilitation Hospital of Rhode Island, North Smithfield, RI, p. A555
WILLIS, Raymond, IT Manager, Choctaw Health Center, Philadelphia, MS, p. A359
WILLIS, Sandra, Manager Human Resources, Citizens Baptist Medical Center, Talladega, AL, p. A25
WILLIS, Toni, M.D. Medical Director, Reliant Rehabilitation Hospital Mid–Cities, Bedford, TX, p. A596
WILLIS, Wendy L., Vice President Human Resources, Children's Hospital, New Orleans, LA, p. A281
WILLMANN, Adam, President and Chief Executive Officer, Goodall–Witcher Hospital Authority, Clifton, TX, p. A601
WILLMON, Brian, M.D. Medical Director, Plains Regional Medical Center, Clovis, NM, p. A423
WILLMORE, Lois, Supervisor Health Information Management, Cedar County Memorial Hospital, El Dorado Springs, MO, p. A366
WILLMS, Frederick, M.D. Chief Medical Officer, Piedmont Fayette Hospital, Fayetteville, GA, p. A157
WILLS, Andrea, R.N. Chief Nursing Executive, Munising Memorial Hospital, Munising, MI, p. A326
WILLS, Andy, M.D. Medical Director, Colquitt Regional Medical Center, Moultrie, GA, p. A162
WILLS, Kim, Chief Operating Officer, Cook Medical Center–A Campus of Tift Regional Medical Center, Adel, GA, p. A149
WILLS, Laura S.
Administrator, Noland Hospital Birmingham, Birmingham, AL, p. A16
Administrator, Noland Hospital Shelby, Alabaster, AL, p. A15
WILLS, Michele, Registered Health Information Administrator, Caro Center, Caro, MI, p. A316
WILLS, Robert, M.D. Chief Medical Officer, Arise Austin Medical Center, Austin, TX, p. A593
WILLS, Shannon, Director Human Resources, Delray Medical Center, Delray Beach, FL, p. A125
WILLSHER, Jay
Chief Operating Officer, UnityPoint Health – Trinity Bettendorf, Bettendorf, IA, p. A222
Chief Operating Officer, UnityPoint Health – Trinity Rock Island, Rock Island, IL, p. A199
WILLSIE, Brett, Vice President Human Resources, Sentara Northern Virginia Medical Center, Woodbridge, VA, p. A674
WILLWERTH, Deborah J., MSN, Chief Executive Officer, Heart of Lancaster Regional Medical Center, Lititz, PA, p. A539
WILLYARD, Deborah, R.N. Senior Director Clinical Services, Mercy Medical Center – West Lakes, West Des Moines, IA, p. A236
WILMOT, Joan, Chief Finance Officer, White River Junction Veterans Affairs Medical Center, White River Junction, VT, p. A661
WILMOTH, Donna, Vice President Patient Care Services and Chief Nursing Officer, Sentara Williamsburg Regional Medical Center, Williamsburg, VA, p. A674
WILMS, Mike, Director Information Systems, Regional Medical Center Bayonet Point, Hudson, FL, p. A129
WILSON, Alice, FACHE Vice President Administration, St. Luke's Hospital – Warren Campus, Phillipsburg, NJ, p. A417
WILSON, Amy, M.D. Medical Director, Baylor Institute for Rehabilitation, Dallas, TX, p. A604
WILSON, Amy, Vice President and Chief Nursing Officer, Sacred Heart Hospital of Pensacola, Pensacola, FL, p. A140
WILSON, Bill, Chief Financial Officer, North Carolina Specialty Hospital, Durham, NC, p. A459
WILSON, Bobbie, Director Human Resources, Crete Area Medical Center, Crete, NE, p. A391
WILSON, Carolyn, R.N., President, University of Minnesota Medical Center, Fairview, Minneapolis, MN, p. A343


© 2015 AHA Guide Index of Health Care Professionals A1005

Index of Health Care Professionals

Index of Health Care Professionals / Wilson

WILSON, Charlene J., Vice President Human Resources, St. Francis Hospital, Wilmington, DE, p. A118
WILSON, Christopher, M.D. Inpatient Medical Director, South Texas Rehabilitation Hospital, Brownsville, TX, p. A598
WILSON, Christy, Chief Financial Officer, Merit Health Rankin, Brandon, MS, p. A351
WILSON, Craig, Chief Medical Officer, St. Vincent Fishers Hospital, Fishers, IN, p. A208
WILSON, David C., Chief Executive Officer, North Mississippi Medical Center – Tupelo, Tupelo, MS, p. A360
WILSON, David R., M.D. Chief of Staff, St. Vincent's Blount, Oneonta, AL, p. A23
WILSON, Deanna, VP Patient Care Services/Site Manager, Aspirus Ontonagon Hospital, Ontonagon, MI, p. A327
WILSON, Deb, Director Human Resources, Kalispell Regional Medical Center, Kalispell, MT, p. A385
WILSON, Deborah J., Senior Vice President and Chief Financial Officer, Lawrence General Hospital, Lawrence, MA, p. A308
WILSON, Debra, Vice President and Chief Nursing Officer, Saint Luke's Hospital of Kansas City, Kansas City, MO, p. A370
WILSON, Dottie D., Director Human Resources, Pickens County Medical Center, Carrollton, AL, p. A17
WILSON, Eleanor, R.N. Vice President and Chief Operating Officer, Doylestown Hospital, Doylestown, PA, p. A533
WILSON, Elizabeth, Administrator, The NeuroMedical Center Rehabilitation Hospital, Baton Rouge, LA, p. A270
WILSON, Elizabeth M., Coordinator Human Resources, Select Specialty Hospital – Cincinnati North, Cincinnati, OH, p. A483
WILSON, Hamlin J.
Senior Vice President Human Resources, Wellmont Bristol Regional Medical Center, Bristol, TN, p. A574
Senior Vice President Human Resources, Wellmont Holston Valley Medical Center, Kingsport, TN, p. A580
WILSON, Jason, Administrator, Valley View Medical Center, Cedar City, UT, p. A654
WILSON, Jim
Chief Operating Officer, Mary Free Bed Rehabilitation Hospital, Grand Rapids, MI, p. A320
Vice President Information Technology, Promise Hospital of San Diego, San Diego, CA, p. A86
WILSON, Jodi, President and Chief Operating Officer, Diley Ridge Medical Center, Canal Winchester, OH, p. A481
WILSON, John P., Chief Financial Officer, Mosaic Life Care at St. Joseph, Saint Joseph, MO, p. A375
WILSON, John R., Vice President, Human Resources, Murray–Calloway County Hospital, Murray, KY, p. A264
WILSON, Kari, R.N. Vice President Clinical Services, Chief Operating Officer and Chief Nursing Officer, SSM Health St. Mary's Hospital – Audrain, Mexico, MO, p. A372
WILSON, Kathey, Acting Chief Executive Officer, U. S. Public Health Service Indian Hospital, Rosebud, SD, p. A571
WILSON, Kim A., R.N. Chief Operating Officer, St. John's Pleasant Valley Hospital, Camarillo, CA, p. A57
WILSON, Kimberly P., Director Human Resources, University of Kentucky Albert B. Chandler Hospital, Lexington, KY, p. A260
WILSON, Kirk G., Interim Chief Executive Officer, St. Francis Hospital, Columbus, GA, p. A154
WILSON, Lawrence, M.D. Vice President, Chief Medical Officer, Midland Memorial Hospital, Midland, TX, p. A632
WILSON, Lerae, R.N. Vice President Patient Services and Chief Nursing Officer, St. Claire Regional Medical Center, Morehead, KY, p. A263
WILSON, Loretta, Administrator, Hill Hospital of Sumter County, York, AL, p. A26
WILSON, Mallory, Administrative Assistant and Human Resources Coordinator, Select Specialty Hospital–North Knoxville, Powell, TN, p. A587
WILSON, Mary L., M.D. Area Medical Director, Kaiser Permanente Panorama City Medical Center, CA, p. A70
WILSON, Maurice, Director of Nursing, Novant Health Charlotte Orthopaedic Hospital, Charlotte, NC, p. A457
WILSON, Monte, Chief Operating Officer, WellStar Kennestone Hospital, Marietta, GA, p. A161
WILSON, Nancy, Senior Vice President and Chief Financial Officer, St. Francis Medical Center, Lynwood, CA, p. A74
WILSON, Nicole, Manager Human Resources, St. Theresa Specialty Hospital, Kenner, LA, p. A276
WILSON, Owetha, Chief Information Officer, Atoka County Medical Center, Atoka, OK, p. A504
WILSON, Patricia, Senior Vice President, Human Resources, Englewood Hospital and Medical Center, Englewood, NJ, p. A412
WILSON, Regina, R.N. Director of Nursing, Share Medical Center, Alva, OK, p. A503
WILSON, Robert, D.O. Director Medical Services, Eagleville Hospital, Eagleville, PA, p. A533
WILSON, Robert E.
Vice President and Chief Information Officer, Crozer–Chester Medical Center, Upland, PA, p. A551
Vice President and Chief Information Officer, Delaware County Memorial Hospital, Drexel Hill, PA, p. A533
WILSON, Roy, M.D
Medical Director, Metropolitan St. Louis Psychiatric Center, Saint Louis, MO, p. A376
Medical Director, St. Louis Psychiatric Rehabilitation Center, Saint Louis, MO, p. A378
WILSON, Sara, Director Human Resources, Cheyenne County Hospital, Saint Francis, KS, p. A249
WILSON, Sherry, R.N. Chief Nursing Officer, Mayers Memorial Hospital District, Fall River Mills, CA, p. A61
WILSON, Stephan A., Chief Financial Officer, Montrose Memorial Hospital, Montrose, CO, p. A107
WILSON, Terrance E.
President and CEO, Franciscan St. Elizabeth Health – Crawfordsville, Crawfordsville, IN, p. A206
President and CEO, Franciscan St. Elizabeth Health – Lafayette East, Lafayette, IN, p. A214
WILSON, Vicki, Human Resources Director, Dixie Regional Medical Center, Saint George, UT, p. A658
WILSON RN, MSN,CEN, Sondra Dianne, R.N. Assistant Administrator and Chief Nursing Officer, Tyler County Hospital, Woodville, TX, p. A653
WILSON–MITCHELL, Jane, Interim Chief Executive Officer, Ten Broeck Tennessee Treatment Facility, Cookeville, TN, p. A576
WILSON–NEIL, Carla, FACHE Chief Operating Officer, Spectrum Health Pennock, Hastings, MI, p. A322
WILSON–STUBBS, Yolande, Regional Chief Operating Officer, Presence Holy Family Medical Center, Des Plaines, IL, p. A186
WILTERMOOD, Michael C., President and Chief Executive Officer, Enloe Medical Center, Chico, CA, p. A57
WILTROUT, Kristy, R.N. Chief Operating Officer, Vernon Memorial Healthcare, Viroqua, WI, p. A712
WILTROUT, Terry, President, Washington Health System Greene, Waynesburg, PA, p. A552
WIMMER, Keri, R.N. Patient Care Director, CentraCare Health–Melrose, Melrose, MN, p. A342
WIMSATT, Michael, Director Human Resources, Piedmont Geriatric Hospital, Burkeville, VA, p. A663
WINBERY, Ben, Chief Financial Officer, Vantage Point of Northwest Arkansas, Fayetteville, AR, p. A44
WINDAS, Allison Leigh, Director of Patient Care Services, Shriners Hospitals for Children–Greenville, Greenville, SC, p. A561
WINDHAM, Joel R., Director Human Resources, Trinity Medical Center, Birmingham, AL, p. A17
WINDHAM, Michael D., Chief Executive Officer, Northwest Medical Center, Winfield, AL, p. A26
WINDHAM, Vann, Chief Financial Officer, L. V. Stabler Memorial Hospital, Greenville, AL, p. A20
WINDLAND, J. Michael, M.D. Chief of Staff, Southern Tennessee Regional Health System–Pulaski, Pulaski, TN, p. A587
WINDLE, Jane, R.N. Director of Nurses, North Mississippi Medical Center–West Point, West Point, MS, p. A361
WINDOLOVICH, Winona, Director Applications, San Francisco General Hospital and Trauma Center, San Francisco, CA, p. A88
WINDROW, Matthew, M.D. Chief of Staff, Medina Regional Hospital, Hondo, TX, p. A618
WINDSOR, Bonnie, Senior Vice President Human Resources, Johns Hopkins Hospital, Baltimore, MD, p. A293
WINEGARNER, Rodney, Chief Financial Officer, Mercy Hospitals of Bakersfield, Bakersfield, CA, p. A55
WINEGEART, Steve, Chief Financial Officer, Hillcrest Medical Center, Tulsa, OK, p. A516
WINFREE, Kersey, M.D. Chief Medical Officer, St. Anthony Hospital, Oklahoma City, OK, p. A513
WING, Lilly, Chief Nursing Officer, Novant Health Franklin Medical Center, Louisburg, NC, p. A464
WING, Yakesun, Business Strategy and Finance Leader, Kaiser Permanente Walnut Creek Medical Center, Walnut Creek, CA, p. A97
WINGATE, Phyllis A., FACHE, President, Carolinas HealthCare System NorthEast, Concord, NC, p. A458
WINGET, Mary, Director Human Resources, Minden Medical Center, Minden, LA, p. A280
WINGFIELD, Gena, Senior Vice President and Chief Financial Officer, Arkansas Children's Hospital, Little Rock, AR, p. A46
WINKELMAN, Dan, President and Chief Executive Officer, Yukon–Kuskokwim Delta Regional Hospital, Bethel, AK, p. A27
WINKLE, Derek, Director Human Resources, LeConte Medical Center, Sevierville, TN, p. A588
WINKLER, Gordon W., Administrator and Chief Executive Officer, Ringgold County Hospital, Mount Ayr, IA, p. A232
WINN, Ann M., M.D. Chief Nursing Officer, Methodist Stone Oak Hospital, San Antonio, TX, p. A641
WINN, George, Chief Executive Officer, Evanston Regional Hospital, Evanston, WY, p. A716
WINN, Holly, Vice President Human Resources and Ancillary Services, Black River Memorial Hospital, Black River Falls, WI, p. A698
WINNENBERG, William
Chief Information Officer, St. Charles Bend, Bend, OR, p. A519
Chief Information Officer, St. Charles Redmond, Redmond, OR, p. A525
WINNER, Douglas, Chief Financial Officer, Providence – Providence Park Hospital, Southfield Campus, Southfield, MI, p. A330
WINNETT, Steve, Chief Executive Officer, Victory Surgical Hospital East Houston, Houston, TX, p. A623
WINNEY, Beverly, Chief Nursing Officer, Washington Regional Medical Center, Fayetteville, AR, p. A44
WINRIGHT, Donna, Director Human Resources and Senior Services, Kearny County Hospital, Lakin, KS, p. A244
WINSETT, Gracia, Chief Financial Officer, Wellstone Regional Hospital, Jeffersonville, IN, p. A213
WINSLOW, Virgil, Chief Financial Officer, Texas Orthopedic Hospital, Houston, TX, p. A622
WINSTON, Bob, M.D. Medical Director, Acadia Vermilion Hospital, Lafayette, LA, p. A277
WINT, Jesse, Director of Nursing, Hardin Medical Center, Savannah, TN, p. A587
WINTER, Jon R., D.O. Chief of Staff, Camden General Hospital, Camden, TN, p. A574
WINTER, Melissa, R.N. Chief Operating Officer and Chief Nursing Officer, Baylor Medical Center at McKinney, McKinney, TX, p. A631
WINTER–CLARK, Jan, Chief Executive Officer, Bristow Medical Center, Bristow, OK, p. A504
WINTERS, Gene, Chief Financial Officer, Northwest Texas Healthcare System, Amarillo, TX, p. A591
WINTERS, Heidi, Business Partner Human Resources, CHI Health Missouri Valley, Missouri Valley, IA, p. A231
WINTERS, Janice, Controller, Pickens County Medical Center, Carrollton, AL, p. A17
WINTHER, Mark, M.D. Medical Director, Little Falls Hospital, Little Falls, NY, p. A436
WINTHROP, Michael, President, Bellevue Hospital, Bellevue, OH, p. A480
WIRTHGEN, Doug
Chief Information Officer, VA Palo Alto Health Care System, Palo Alto, CA, p. A80
Facility Chief Information Officer, Veterans Affairs Loma Linda Healthcare System, Loma Linda, CA, p. A68
WIRTZ, David
Supervisor Information Technology, Evansville Psychiatric Children Center, Evansville, IN, p. A208
Senior LAN Administrator, Evansville State Hospital, Evansville, IN, p. A208
WISE, Dan, Manager Information Technology, Sarah D. Culbertson Memorial Hospital, Rushville, IL, p. A200
WISE, Elizabeth, R.N. Chief Nursing Officer and Vice President, Patient Care Services, Saint Peter's University Hospital, New Brunswick, NJ, p. A415
WISE, Jennifer
Chief Nurse Officer, Dauterive Hospital, New Iberia, LA, p. A281
Chief Nursing Officer, Franklin Foundation Hospital, Franklin, LA, p. A274
WISE, Jerry, Chief Executive Officer, Mercy Rehabilition Hospital Springfield, Springfield, MO, p. A379
WISE, Jerry R., Chief Executive Officer, Habersham Medical Center, Demorest, GA, p. A156
WISE, Kim, Director Human Resources, South Haven Health System, South Haven, MI, p. A330
WISE, Lori, Chief Nursing Officer and Director of Clinical Services, St. Vincent Jennings Hospital, North Vernon, IN, p. A218
WISE, Melissa, Chief Nursing Officer, Highland Community Hospital, Picayune, MS, p. A359
WISE, Robert P., FACHE, President and Chief Executive Officer, Hunterdon Medical Center, Flemington, NJ, p. A412
WISE, Toby, Chief Nursing Officer, Winn Parish Medical Center, Winnfield, LA, p. A287
WISEMANN, Jacob, Chief Financial Officer, Parkland Medical Center, Derry, NH, p. A405
WISEMORE, Donna S., Vice President and Chief Nursing Officer, DeKalb Health, Auburn, IN, p. A204
WISLER, Tam, Director Human Resources, Dublin Springs, Dublin, OH, p. A489
WISMER, Doug, Chief Financial Officer, Putnam County Memorial Hospital, Unionville, MO, p. A380
WISNER, Donna, Chief Financial Officer, Dr. John Warner Hospital, Clinton, IL, p. A185

**A1006** Index of Health Care Professionals

Index of Health Care Professionals / Wood

Index of Health Care Professionals


WISNIESKI, Thomas, FACHE, Director, North Florida/South Georgia Veteran's Health System, Gainesville, FL, p. A127
WISNIEWSKI, Cass, Interim Chief Financial Officer, Hurley Medical Center, Flint, MI, p. A319
WISNIEWSKI, Richard, Senior Vice President Finance and Chief Financial Officer, Mount Nittany Medical Center, State College, PA, p. A550
WISNOSKI, Joseph, Vice President Finance and Chief Financial Officer, John T. Mather Memorial Hospital, Port Jefferson, NY, p. A447
WISSEL, Andrew, Director Human Resources, Mount Sinai Hospital, Chicago, IL, p. A183
WISWELL, Ashleigh, Director Human Resources, Moore County Hospital District, Dumas, TX, p. A609
WITCHER–BOATENG, Bernetta, Ph.D. Director Quality Improvement Services and Compliance, Southwest Connecticut Mental Health System, Bridgeport, CT, p. A111
WITENSKE, James, Chief Information Officer, Jefferson Hospital, Jefferson Hills, PA, p. A536
WITHERSPOON, Lynn, Vice President and Chief Information Officer, Ochsner Medical Center, New Orleans, LA, p. A282
WITHIAM, Cathy, Director Human Resources, McBride Clinic Orthopedic Hospital, Oklahoma City, OK, p. A512
WITHINGTON, Amber, R.N. Chief Nursing Officer, Rawlins County Health Center, Atwood, KS, p. A237
WITKOWICZ, Victor J., Senior Vice President and Chief Financial Officer, Madonna Rehabilitation Hospital, Lincoln, NE, p. A394
WITMER, Bruce, M.D. Medical Director, Fresno Surgical Hospital, Fresno, CA, p. A62
WITT, David A., Vice President Finances, Houston Methodist St. John Hospital, Nassau Bay, TX, p. A633
WITT, Jana, Chief Executive Officer, Cedar County Memorial Hospital, El Dorado Springs, MO, p. A366
WITT, Laura, Administrator Human Resources, Banner Thunderbird Medical Center, Glendale, AZ, p. A32
WITT, Lori, Site Finance Director, Marcum and Wallace Memorial Hospital, Irvine, KY, p. A259
WITT, Michelle, Administrator, CCC at PineView Hospital, Lakeside, AZ, p. A32
WITT, Sarah, Director Human Resources, Richmond State Hospital, Richmond, IN, p. A219
WITT, Stephen, President and Chief Executive Officer, College Hospital Cerritos, Cerritos, CA, p. A57
WITT, Thomas J., M.D.,
President and Chief Executive Officer, Mayo Clinic Health System in Cannon Falls, Cannon Falls, MN, p. A336
President and Chief Executive Officer, Mayo Clinic Health System in Red Wing, Red Wing, MN, p. A345
WITTE, Kari, Director Patient Care, Windom Area Hospital, Windom, MN, p. A349
WITTE, Russell, Director Information Technology, Citizens Medical Center, Victoria, TX, p. A650
WITTENSTEIN, Robin D., Ed.D. Director and Chief Operating Officer, Penn State Milton S. Hershey Medical Center, Hershey, PA, p. A536
WITTERSTAETER, Ellen, FACHE, Chief Executive Officer, HEALTHSOUTH Rehabilitation Hospital of Ocala, Ocala, FL, p. A136
WITTHAUS, Patricia, Director Information Services, Valley Regional Hospital, Claremont, NH, p. A405
WITTMAN, Thomas, Chief Information Officer, Jewish Hospital, Louisville, KY, p. A261
WITTON, David, Manager Information Systems, St. John's Medical Center and Living Center, Jackson, WY, p. A716
WITTROCK, Edward A., Vice President Regional System, Mayo Clinic Health System – Chippewa Valley in Bloomer, Bloomer, WI, p. A698
WITTWER, Julie, Chief Financial Officer, South Texas Surgical Hospital, Corpus Christi, TX, p. A603
WODARZ, Christopher A., Chief, Resource Management Division, Tripler Army Medical Center, Honolulu, HI, p. A169
WODICKA, Mary Jo, Vice President Human Resources, Wheaton Franciscan Healthcare – All Saints, Racine, WI, p. A709
WOELKERS, Joe, Executive Vice President and Chief Staff, University of Texas Health Northeast, Tyler, TX, p. A649
WOELTJEN, Bill, Chief Financial Officer, Sarasota Memorial Health Care System, Sarasota, FL, p. A142
WOEN, Linda, Director Human Resources, Yuma Rehabilitation Hospital, Yuma, AZ, p. A40
WOERNER, Steve, President and Chief Executive Officer, Driscoll Children's Hospital, Corpus Christi, TX, p. A602
WOHLFARDT, Diana, Director Human Resources, Nashville General Hospital, Nashville, TN, p. A585
WOHLFORD, Steve, Chief Operating Officer, Johnson Memorial Hospital, Franklin, IN, p. A209
WOHLMAN, John, Manager Information Systems, Shoshone Medical Center, Kellogg, ID, p. A174
WOIRHAYE, Ted, R.N. Director of Nursing, Ruby Valley Hospital, Sheridan, MT, p. A387
WOISKE, Edward, M.D. Chief Medical Officer, Avera Marshall Regional Medical Center, Marshall, MN, p. A342
WOJNO, Kathy, Vice President Nursing Services and Chief Nursing Officer, Beverly Hospital, Montebello, CA, p. A76
WOJTALEWICZ, Jeanette, Chief Financial Officer, CHI Health Mercy Council Bluffs, Council Bluffs, IA, p. A225
WOLAK, Robert, Chief Information Resource Management Service, G.V. (Sonny) Montgomery Veterans Affairs Medical Center, Jackson, MS, p. A355
WOLCOTT, Daniel, President and Chief Executive Officer, Lodi Memorial Hospital, Lodi, CA, p. A67
WOLD, Lynn, President and Chief Executive Officer, UnityPoint Health – St. Luke's, Sioux City, IA, p. A235
WOLF, Brenda J., President and Chief Executive Officer, La Rabida Children's Hospital, Chicago, IL, p. A182
WOLF, Edward H., President and Chief Executive Officer, Lakeview Medical Center, Rice Lake, WI, p. A710
WOLF, Gregory A., Director Information Systems, Shriners Hospitals for Children–Honolulu, Honolulu, HI, p. A169
WOLF, Heidi, R.N. Chief Nursing Officer, The Medical Center of Southeast Texas, Port Arthur, TX, p. A637
WOLF, Jack, Vice President Information Systems, Montefiore Medical Center, NY, p. A442
WOLF, Kari, M.D. Medical Director, Seton Shoal Creek Hospital, Austin, TX, p. A594
WOLF, Laura J., President, Franciscan Sisters of Christian Charity Sponsored Ministries, Inc., Manitowoc, WI, p. B57
WOLF, Manuela, R.N., Chief Executive Officer, Harlan County Health System, Alma, NE, p. A389
WOLF, Marc, Assistant Vice President Human Resources, St. Barnabas Hospital, NY, p. A444
WOLF, R. Chris, Chief Executive Officer, Alta Vista Regional Hospital, Las Vegas, NM, p. A425
WOLF, Randall, Vice President Finance, Perry County Memorial Hospital, Perryville, MO, p. A374
WOLF, Robin, Chief Nursing Officer, Complex Care Hospital at Tenaya, Las Vegas, NV, p. A401
WOLF, Scott A., D.O. Senior Vice President, Medical Affairs, Chief Medical Officer and Chief Operating Officer, Mercy Medical Center, Springfield, MA, p. A311
WOLF, Stephanne, Chief Nursing Officer, Morris County Hospital, Council Grove, KS, p. A239
WOLF, Tricia, Director Information Technology, OSS Orthopaedic Hospital, York, PA, p. A554
WOLF–ROSENBLUM, Stephanie, M.D. Chief Medical Officer, Southern New Hampshire Medical Center, Nashua, NH, p. A407
WOLFE, Cathy Allyson, Chief Nursing Officer, Parkview Wabash County Hospital, Wabash, IN, p. A221
WOLFE, John, Chief Financial Officer, Saint Elizabeth's Medical Center, Wabasha, MN, p. A348
WOLFE, Lois, Director Human Resources, Geisinger–Community Medical Center, Scranton, PA, p. A549
WOLFE, Mitchell, M.D. Chief of Staff, Clay County Memorial Hospital, Henrietta, TX, p. A618
WOLFE, Philip R., President and Chief Executive Officer, Gwinnett Hospital System, Lawrenceville, GA, p. A160
WOLFE, Phillip R., Administrator, Kindred Hospital–Los Angeles, Los Angeles, CA, p. A70
WOLFE, Scott R., CPA, President, St. Luke's Hospital – Warren Campus, Phillipsburg, NJ, p. A417
WOLFE, Stephen A., President and Chief Executive Officer, Indiana Regional Medical Center, Indiana, PA, p. A536
WOLFE, Teresa E., Manager Human Resources, Kansas Heart Hospital, Wichita, KS, p. A252
WOLFENBARGER, Carol C., FACHE, President and Chief Executive Officer, McDowell Hospital, Marion, NC, p. A464
WOLFF, Cathy, Vice President Financial Services and Chief Financial Officer, Yuma District Hospital, Yuma, CO, p. A110
WOLFF, David, Director Information Technology, Newberry County Memorial Hospital, Newberry, SC, p. A564
WOLFF, Patrice P.
Director Management Information Systems, Amery Hospital and Clinic, Amery, WI, p. A697
Director Information Services, Westfields Hospital, New Richmond, WI, p. A708
WOLFF, Peter, M.D. President Medical Staff, Cascade Valley Hospital and Clinics, Arlington, WA, p. A676
WOLFGANG, Tony, Chief Financial Officer, Coatesville Veterans Affairs Medical Center, Coatesville, PA, p. A532
WOLFMAN, Barry A., Chief Executive Officer and Managing Director, George Washington University Hospital, Washington, DC, p. A119
WOLFORD, Dennis A., FACHE, Chief Executive Officer, Macon County General Hospital, Lafayette, TN, p. A581
WOLKART, Kristin, President and Chief Executive Officer, St. Francis Medical Center, Monroe, LA, p. A280
WOLLEBEN, Robert G., Chief Executive Officer, Massena Memorial Hospital, Massena, NY, p. A437
WOLLEN, Allison, Vice President Human Resources, Rutland Regional Medical Center, Rutland, VT, p. A661
WOLOSZYN, Daniel B., Chief Executive Officer, Rehabilitation Hospital of Indiana, Indianapolis, IN, p. A212
WOLTEMATH, Kelli, D.O. Chief Medical Staff, George C Grape Community Hospital, Hamburg, IA, p. A228
WOLTER, Nicholas, M.D., Chief Executive Officer, Billings Clinic, Billings, MT, p. A381
WOLTERMAN, Daniel J., President and Chief Executive Officer, Memorial Hermann Healthcare System, Houston, TX, p. B89
WOLTERMAN, Robert K., Chief Executive Officer, Ochsner Medical Center, New Orleans, LA, p. A282
WOLTHER, Eunice, Public Information Officer, Colorado Mental Health Institute at Pueblo, Pueblo, CO, p. A108
WOLTHUIZEN, Dianne, Director Human Resources, Sanford Sheldon Medical Center, Sheldon, IA, p. A234
WOLZ, John, M.D. Chief Medical Staff, Yuma District Hospital, Yuma, CO, p. A110
WOMACK, Glen, M.D. Chief of Staff, Fleming County Hospital, Flemingsburg, KY, p. A256
WOMACK, James, Administrator, Mitchell County Hospital, Camilla, GA, p. A153
WOMEODU, Robin, M.D. Chief Medical Officer, Methodist Healthcare Memphis Hospitals, Memphis, TN, p. A584
WONG, Art, Chief Financial Officer, Heritage Oaks Hospital, Sacramento, CA, p. A84
WONG, Bryan, M.D. Medical Director, Ventura County Medical Center, Ventura, CA, p. A96
WONG, Davies, M.D. Medical Director, Kindred Hospital–San Diego, San Diego, CA, p. A86
WONG, Dionne, Vice President and Chief Human Resources Officer, Broward Health Medical Center, Fort Lauderdale, FL, p. A126
WONG, Karen, Chief Human Resources Officer, Mee Memorial Hospital, King City, CA, p. A66
WONG, Wesley, M.D. Acting Vice President Medical and Academic Affairs, Community Hospital North, Indianapolis, IN, p. A211
WONSER, Matt, Director, Information Services, Providence Regional Medical Center Everett, Everett, WA, p. A679
WOOD, Aaron, Administrator, Sanpete Valley Hospital, Mount Pleasant, UT, p. A656
WOOD, Brian, Director Human Resources, Southern Hills Hospital and Medical Center, Las Vegas, NV, p. A402
WOOD, Bud, Chief Human Resources Officer, Saint Thomas West Hospital, Nashville, TN, p. A585
WOOD, Cathy, Vice President, Human Resources, Memorial Hospital at Gulfport, Gulfport, MS, p. A353
WOOD, Clyde, Chief Executive Officer, Lakeway Regional Hospital, Morristown, TN, p. A584
WOOD, David, M.D. Executive Vice President and Chief Medical Officer, Beaumont Hospital – Royal Oak, Royal Oak, MI, p. A328
WOOD, David P., FACHE, Director, Boise Veterans Affairs Medical Center, Boise, ID, p. A172
WOOD, Drew, Director Information Technology, Eureka Springs Hospital, Eureka Springs, AR, p. A43
WOOD, Erik, Chief Executive Officer, Pioneer Medical Center, Big Timber, MT, p. A381
WOOD, Gregory C., President and Chief Executive Officer, Scotland Health Care System, Laurinburg, NC, p. A463
WOOD, Jim
Chief Administrative Officer, Central Washington Hospital, Wenatchee, WA, p. A687
Chief Human Resources Officer, Wenatchee Valley Medical Center, Wenatchee, WA, p. A687
WOOD, Joann, M.D. Chief Medical Officer, Baptist Memorial Hospital–Desoto, Southaven, MS, p. A360
WOOD, John
Chief Executive Officer, Baylor Emergency Medical Center at Aubrey, Aubrey, TX, p. A593
Administrator, Scott & White Emergency Hospital– Cedar Park, Cedar Park, TX, p. A600
WOOD, Joyce, Vice President Organizational Improvement and Chief Nursing Officer, Riverview Hospital, Noblesville, IN, p. A218
WOOD, Kevin, Interim Chief Clinical Officer, Promise Hospital of San Diego, San Diego, CA, p. A86
WOOD, Lawrence, M.D. Chief Medical Officer, Littleton Adventist Hospital, Littleton, CO, p. A106
WOOD, Lisa, Chief Financial Officer, Brown County Hospital, Ainsworth, NE, p. A389
WOOD, Nancy, R.N. Nurse Executive, Swedish/Edmonds, Edmonds, WA, p. A678
WOOD, Jr., Phillip E., Chief Information Officer, Cape Fear Valley Medical Center, Fayetteville, NC, p. A460
WOOD, Richard, Chief Financial Officer, Seton Medical Center, Daly City, CA, p. A59

Index of Health Care Professionals

Index of Health Care Professionals / Wood

WOOD, Sandy, MSN Vice President Patient Services and Chief Nursing Officer, O'Bleness Memorial Hospital, Athens, OH, p. A479
WOOD, Thomas, M.D. Chief Medical Officer, Page Hospital, Page, AZ, p. A34
WOOD, Tina, Chief Financial Officer, DMC Harper University Hospital, Detroit, MI, p. A317
WOOD, William, M.D. Vice President Medical Affairs, St. Joseph Hospital, Bangor, ME, p. A288
WOOD, William E., M.D. Chief of Staff, Sequoyah Memorial Hospital, Sallisaw, OK, p. A514
WOOD–ALLEN, Diane, MS Chief Nursing Officer, Concord Hospital, Concord, NH, p. A405
WOODALL, Jay, Chief Executive Officer, Corpus Christi Medical Center, Corpus Christi, TX, p. A602
WOODALL, Lois, Director Human Resources, Lighthouse Care Center of Conway, Conway, SC, p. A560
WOODARD, Andy, Chief Financial Officer, Forrest General Hospital, Hattiesburg, MS, p. A354
WOODARD, Cathy, R.N. Chief Clinical Officer, Victory Medical Center Craig Ranch, McKinney, TX, p. A632
WOODARD, Victor, Manager Information Technology, Dodge County Hospital, Eastman, GA, p. A157
WOODBECK, Terry L., Administrator, Tulsa Spine and Specialty Hospital, Tulsa, OK, p. A517
WOODCOCK, Lisa, MBA, PHR, SHRM–CD Director Human Resources, Gordon Memorial Hospital, Gordon, NE, p. A392
WOODDELL, Mike, Director Information Services, Fairmont Regional Medical Center, Fairmont, WV, p. A691
WOODHOUSE, Janice, Director of Nursing, Missouri River Medical Center, Fort Benton, MT, p. A383
WOODIN, Joseph L., President and Chief Executive Officer, Gifford Medical Center, Randolph, VT, p. A661
WOODLIFF, Brian K., President and Chief Executive Officer Northeastern Health System, Northeastern Health System, Tahlequah, OK, p. A515
WOODLOCK, Kristin M., R.N., Acting Commissioner, New York State Office of Mental Health, Albany, NY, p. B96
WOODRICH, John T., ACHE, President and Chief Operating Officer, Bryan Medical Center, Lincoln, NE, p. A393
WOODRING, Mark, Chief Executive Officer, Coffeyville Regional Medical Center, Coffeyville, KS, p. A238
WOODRUFF, Kathy, R.N. Chief Nursing Officer, Marshall Medical Center North, Guntersville, AL, p. A20
WOODRUFF, Stephen, M.D. Chief Medical Officer, NEA Baptist Memorial Hospital, Jonesboro, AR, p. A46
WOODS, Bob, Chief Information Officer, Stanford Health Care – ValleyCare, Pleasanton, CA, p. A81
WOODS, Brian, Director Human Resources, Heritage Medical Center, Shelbyville, TN, p. A588
WOODS, Cheryl, Chief Nursing Officer, Ochsner Medical Center – North Shore, Slidell, LA, p. A285
WOODS, Dan, President, WellStar Kennestone Hospital, Marietta, GA, p. A161
WOODS, Jr., Duane L., Chief Financial Officer, Fisher–Titus Medical Center, Norwalk, OH, p. A495
WOODS, Fred, Chief Financial Officer, The BridgeWay, North Little Rock, AR, p. A49
WOODS, Jeffrey, Chief Executive Officer, TrustPoint Hospital, Murfreesboro, TN, p. A585
WOODS, Jennifer, R.N. Chief Nursing Officer, McLaren Northern Michigan, Petoskey, MI, p. A327
WOODS, Josh, Director Information Systems, Camden Clark Medical Center, Parkersburg, WV, p. A694
WOODS, Julia, R.N. Vice President and Chief Nursing Officer, Saint Luke's South Hospital, Overland Park, KS, p. A248
WOODS, Matthew, Vice President Finance, Winchester Hospital, Winchester, MA, p. A313
WOODS, Rashawn, Vice President Human Resources, Barlow Respiratory Hospital, Los Angeles, CA, p. A69
WOODS, Rebecca, Chief Information Officer, Porter Medical Center, Middlebury, VT, p. A660
WOODS, Regetta, Chief Nursing Officer and Chief Clinical Officer, Promise Hospital of Miss Lou, Vidalia, LA, p. A286
WOODS, Suzanne
President and Chief Executive Officer, Flowers Hospital, Dothan, AL, p. A18
Senior Vice President of Nursing, Memorial Hospital Jacksonville, Jacksonville, FL, p. A129
WOODS, Theresa L., MSN Chief Nursing Officer, Jennings American Legion Hospital, Jennings, LA, p. A275
WOODSON, Leslie, R.N. Chief Nursing Officer, Shasta Regional Medical Center, Redding, CA, p. A82
WOODSON, Stephen, D.O. Chief of Staff, Haskell County Community Hospital, Stigler, OK, p. A515
WOODWARD, Ashley
Interim Chief Executive Officer, Valley County Health System, Ord, NE, p. A397
Director Financial Services, Valley County Health System, Ord, NE, p. A397
WOODWARD, David E., Executive Director, Devereux Children's Behavioral Health Center, Malvern, PA, p. A539
WOODWARD, James L., President and Chief Executive Officer, Elliot Hospital, Manchester, NH, p. A407
WOODWARD, Martin D., Director Acute Care Services, Larry B. Zieverink, Sr. Alcoholism Treatment Center, Raleigh, NC, p. A467
WOODWARD, Russell, M.D. Chief Medical Officer, Methodist Hospital, San Antonio, TX, p. A641
WOODYARD, Elizabeth, MSN, Chief Executive Officer, Petersburg Medical Center, Petersburg, AK, p. A29
WOODYARD, Nancy, Chief Financial Officer, Neosho Memorial Regional Medical Center, Chanute, KS, p. A238
WOOL, Julius, Executive Director, Queens Hospital Center, NY, p. A444
WOOLDRIDGE, Joseph, Chief Financial Officer, Brownwood Regional Medical Center, Brownwood, TX, p. A599
WOOLLEN, Susan, R.N. Director of Nursing, Lafayette General Surgical Hospital, Lafayette, LA, p. A277
WOOLLEY, Diane, Vice President Human Resources, Waterbury Hospital, Waterbury, CT, p. A116
WOOLLEY, Jacqueline, Vice President Human Resources, St. Joseph Hospital, Nashua, NH, p. A407
WOOLLEY, Sheila, R.N. Vice President, Patient Care Services, Wentworth–Douglass Hospital, Dover, NH, p. A406
WOOLRIDGE, Joseph, Chief Financial Officer, Navarro Regional Hospital, Corsicana, TX, p. A603
WOOLRIDGE, Regina, Director Human Resources, Victory Medical Center – Southcross, San Antonio, TX, p. A642
WOOLSTENHULME, Daren, Chief Financial Officer, HEALTHSOUTH Rehabilitation Hospital of Utah, Sandy, UT, p. A659
WOOTEN, Scott
Senior Vice President and Chief Financial Officer, Baptist Medical Center Beaches, Jacksonville Beach, FL, p. A130
Senior Vice President and Chief Financial Officer, Baptist Medical Center Jacksonville, Jacksonville, FL, p. A129
WOOTON, Michael, Manager Information Technology Service Delivery, Wilson N. Jones Regional Medical Center, Sherman, TX, p. A644
WOOTTON, Aaron, Vice President Health Information Systems, Allegiance Health, Jackson, MI, p. A323
WORD, Jenni, R.N. Chief Nursing Officer, Wallowa Memorial Hospital, Enterprise, OR, p. A520
WORDEKEMPER, Jerry, President and Chief Executive Officer, St. Francis Memorial Hospital, West Point, NE, p. A399
WORDEN, Kieth Anne, Director Human Resources, Mildred Mitchell–Bateman Hospital, Huntington, WV, p. A692
WORKMAN, Jennifer, Director Human Resources, Jane Phillips Medical Center, Bartlesville, OK, p. A504
WORKMAN, Jessika M., Chief Nursing Officer, Wesley Rehabilitation Hospital, Wichita, KS, p. A253
WORKMAN, Mark, M.D. Chief Medical Officer, West Jefferson Medical Center, Marrero, LA, p. A280
WORLEY III, John C., Chief Executive Officer, Cache Valley Hospital, North Logan, UT, p. A656
WORLEY, Mark, Interim Director, Veterans Health Care System of the Ozarks, Fayetteville, AR, p. A44
WORLEY, Stella, Manager Revenue Cycle Team, Keefe Memorial Hospital, Cheyenne Wells, CO, p. A100
WORMAN, Scott, Chief of Staff, Tri–City Medical Center, Oceanside, CA, p. A79
WORRELL, Carl, Chief Financial Officer, Sistersville General Hospital, Sistersville, WV, p. A695
WORRELL, James W., Chief Financial Officer, Pioneers Medical Center, Meeker, CO, p. A107
WORRICK, Gerald M., President and Chief Executive Officer, Ministry Door County Medical Center, Sturgeon Bay, WI, p. A712
WORSOWICZ, Gregory, M.D. Medical Director, Howard A. Rusk Rehabilitation Center, Columbia, MO, p. A366
WORTH, Dustin, M.D. Chief Medical Staff, Gritman Medical Center, Moscow, ID, p. A175
WORTHAM, Christopher, Chief Executive Officer, HEALTHSOUTH Rehabilitation Hospital Midland–Odessa, Midland, TX, p. A632
WORTHAM, Turner, Chief Financial Officer, Grand Strand Regional Medical Center, Myrtle Beach, SC, p. A564
WORTHINGTON, Diane, Chief Human Resources Officer, Placentia–Linda Hospital, Placentia, CA, p. A81
WORTHY, David, M.D. Vice President and Chief Medical Officer, Baptist Health Corbin, Corbin, KY, p. A255
WORTMAN, Rand J., President and Chief Executive Officer, Kadlec Regional Medical Center, Richland, WA, p. A683
WOUGHTER, Andrew, Information Systems, Riverside Shore Memorial Hospital, Nassawadox, VA, p. A668
WOZNIAK, Gregory T., President and Chief Executive Officer, St. Mary Medical Center, Langhorne, PA, p. A538
WOZNIAK, Susan C., R.N. Senior Vice President and Chief Operating Officer, OSF Saint Francis Medical Center, Peoria, IL, p. A198
WOZNIKAITIS, Linda, Chief Financial Officer, Southwest Connecticut Mental Health System, Bridgeport, CT, p. A111
WRAALSTAD, Kimber L., FACHE, Administrator, Cook County North Shore Hospital, Grand Marais, MN, p. A339
WRAGGE, Jean, Director of Nurses, Limestone Medical Center, Groesbeck, TX, p. A617
WRATTEN, Carol, M.D. Vice President Medical Affairs, Seton Medical Center Austin, Austin, TX, p. A594
WRAY, Char, Vice President Chief Clinical Operations and Chief Information Officer, University Hospitals Elyria Medical Center, Elyria, OH, p. A489
WRAY, Christine R.
President and Chief Executive Officer, MedStar Southern Maryland Hospital Center, Clinton, MD, p. A297
President, MedStar St. Mary's Hospital, Leonardtown, MD, p. A299
WRAY, Dean, Vice President Finance, Southern Ohio Medical Center, Portsmouth, OH, p. A496
WRAY, Jeremy, D.O. Medical Director, Sage Memorial Hospital, Ganado, AZ, p. A31
WRAY, Thomas, Director Information, Geisinger–Bloomsburg Hospital, Bloomsburg, PA, p. A529
WREN, Mark A., M.D. Medical Director, HEALTHSOUTH Rehabilitation Hospital of Texarkana, Texarkana, TX, p. A647
WREN, Timothy, Chief Financial Officer, Abbeville Area Medical Center, Abbeville, SC, p. A557
WRIGHT, Albert, PharmD, President and Chief Executive Officer, West Virginia University Hospitals, Morgantown, WV, p. A693
WRIGHT, Ann L., R.N. Assistant Central Delivery System CNO, Presbyterian Hospital, Albuquerque, NM, p. A423
WRIGHT, April, Human Resources Officer, Collingsworth General Hospital, Wellington, TX, p. A651
WRIGHT, Bennie B., M.D. Chief of Staff, North Sunflower Medical Center, Ruleville, MS, p. A360
WRIGHT, Betsy T., President and Chief Executive Officer, Woman's Christian Association Hospital, Jamestown, NY, p. A435
WRIGHT, Brady, Information Technology Network Administrator, Washington County Hospital, Chatom, AL, p. A18
WRIGHT, Carlene, Chief Financial Officer, Vibra Hospital of Amarillo, Amarillo, TX, p. A591
WRIGHT, Charles, Chief Financial Officer, Ashe Memorial Hospital, Jefferson, NC, p. A463
WRIGHT, Charles T., President and Chief Executive Officer, St. James Healthcare, Butte, MT, p. A382
WRIGHT, Coleby, Chief Executive Officer, Parkwood Behavioral Health System, Olive Branch, MS, p. A358
WRIGHT, Dan, Vice President Human Resources, Children's Mercy South, Overland Park, KS, p. A248
WRIGHT, Daniel, Director Information Technology, Saint Alphonsus Medical Center – Nampa, Nampa, ID, p. A175
WRIGHT, Danielle, Director Human Resources, Wake Forest Baptist Health–Davie Medical Center, Mocksville, NC, p. A465
WRIGHT, Debra J., R.N., Chief Executive Officer, Howard Memorial Hospital, Nashville, AR, p. A48
WRIGHT, Dustin, Chief Executive Officer, Doctors NeuroPsychiatric Hospital and Research Institute, Bremen, IN, p. A205
WRIGHT, Fran, Director of Nursing, Broadwater Health Center, Townsend, MT, p. A387
WRIGHT, James, M.D. Chief Financial Officer, Cypress Fairbanks Medical Center, Houston, TX, p. A619
WRIGHT, Jody, Interim Chief Nursing Officer, Mercy Medical Center–New Hampton, New Hampton, IA, p. A232
WRIGHT, Joe, Chief Financial Officer, Mitchell County Hospital, Colorado City, TX, p. A601
WRIGHT, Judd, Chief Executive Officer, Southwest Idaho Advanced Care Hospital, Boise, ID, p. A172
WRIGHT, Julie M., Director Human Resources, Ridgeview Psychiatric Hospital and Center, Oak Ridge, TN, p. A587
WRIGHT, Krista, Director Human Resources, St. Vincent Frankfort Hospital, Frankfort, IN, p. A209
WRIGHT, Linda
Chief Financial Officer, HEALTHSOUTH Rehabilitation Hospital of Alexandria, Alexandria, LA, p. A268
Director Information, Ottawa County Health Center, Minneapolis, KS, p. A246
WRIGHT, Mark
Vice President, Aultman Hospital, Canton, OH, p. A481
Chief Financial Officer, Aultman Specialty Hospital, Canton, OH, p. A481
WRIGHT, Mark J., Vice President Finance, Aurelia Osborn Fox Memorial Hospital, Oneonta, NY, p. A446
WRIGHT, Mary, Vice President Nursing Services and Chief Nursing Officer, Cortland Regional Medical Center, Cortland, NY, p. A432
WRIGHT, Maura, Chief Nursing Officer, Southern Hills Hospital and Medical Center, Las Vegas, NV, p. A402
WRIGHT, Nancy, M.D. Chief Medical Staff, Alta Vista Regional Hospital, Las Vegas, NM, p. A425

**A1008** Index of Health Care Professionals 

Index of Health Care Professionals / Yi
Index of Health Care Professionals

WRIGHT, Peter J., FACHE, Chief Executive Officer, Valley Regional Hospital, Claremont, NH, p. A405
WRIGHT, Phillip L., FACHE, Chief Executive Officer, Haywood Regional Medical Center, Clyde, NC, p. A458
WRIGHT, II, Philoron A., FACHE Chief Operating Officer, Munroe Regional Medical Center, Ocala, FL, p. A137
WRIGHT, Rick, President and Chief Executive Officer, McLaren Greater Lansing, Lansing, MI, p. A324
WRIGHT, Robert
  Senior Human Resource Advisor, East Ohio Regional Hospital, Martins Ferry, OH, p. A493
  Senior Human Resource Advisor, Ohio Valley Medical Center, Wheeling, WV, p. A696
WRIGHT, Robert, M.D. Chief of Staff, Washington County Regional Medical Center, Sandersville, GA, p. A164
WRIGHT, Robert N., Chief Executive Officer, Newman Regional Health, Emporia, KS, p. A239
WRIGHT, Rory, M.D. President Medical Staff, Orthopaedic Hospital of Wisconsin – Glendale, Glendale, WI, p. A701
WRIGHT, Roy, FACHE, President and Chief Executive Officer, Louisiana Heart Hospital, Lacombe, LA, p. A277
WRIGHT, Sandra Gayle, Ed.D., Chief Executive Officer, Tyler County Hospital, Woodville, TX, p. A653
WRIGHT, Sharon, R.N. Vice President and Chief Nursing Officer, Hardin Memorial Hospital, Elizabethtown, KY, p. A256
WRIGHT, Stephanie, Director Human Resources Management, VA San Diego Healthcare System, San Diego, CA, p. A87
WRIGHT, Stuart M., CPA Chief Financial Officer, Upstate University Hospital, Syracuse, NY, p. A451
WRIGHT, Tom, Director Human Resources, Kindred Hospital Riverside, Perris, CA, p. A81
WRIGHT, Trevor, Senior Vice President and Chief Operating Officer, Shawnee Mission Medical Center, Shawnee Mission, KS, p. A250
WRIGHT, Wes, Senior Vice President and Chief Information Officer, Seattle Children's Hospital, Seattle, WA, p. A683
WRIGHT–WHITAKER, Ruth, Director Information Services, Hutcheson Medical Center, Fort Oglethorpe, GA, p. A158
WRINN, Denise, Vice President Finance and Chief Financial Officer, Cortland Regional Medical Center, Cortland, NY, p. A432
WROBBEL, Patricia A., Senior Vice President and Chief Nurse Executive, Westchester Medical Center, Valhalla, NY, p. A452
WROBLEWSKI, Edmund, M.D
  Vice President Medical Affairs and Chief Medical Officer, Goleta Valley Cottage Hospital, Santa Barbara, CA, p. A91
  Vice President Medical Affairs and Chief Medical Officer, Santa Barbara Cottage Hospital, Santa Barbara, CA, p. A91
  Vice President Medical Affairs and Chief Medical Officer, Santa Ynez Valley Cottage Hospital, Solvang, CA, p. A92
WROGG, Frank, Director Information Technology, Mayo Clinic Health System – Red Cedar in Menomonie, Menomonie, WI, p. A705
WU, Jonathan, M.D., President and Chairman, AHMC & Healthcare, Inc., Alhambra, CA, p. B7
WU, Jonathan, Vice President Human Resources, Valley Presbyterian Hospital, CA, p. A73
WU, Kenneth, M.D. Medical Director, Marlton Rehabilitation Hospital, Marlton, NJ, p. A414
WUENSCHEL, Diedra, D.O. President Medical Staff, Coryell Memorial Hospital, Gatesville, TX, p. A616
WUKITSCH, Michael
  Executive Vice President Human Resources, Northwestern Medicine Central DuPage Hospital, Winfield, IL, p. A203
  Executive Vice President Human Resources, Northwestern Medicine Delnor Hospital, Geneva, IL, p. A189
WUNDERWALD, Wendie, R.N. Vice President Patient Care Services, Samaritan Lebanon Community Hospital, Lebanon, OR, p. A522
WURGLER, Brad D., Chief Financial Officer, Perham Health, Perham, MN, p. A344
WURM, Scott, M.D. Chief Medical Officer, St. Cloud Regional Medical Center, Saint Cloud, FL, p. A141
WURTZEL, Leann, Director Human Resources, Mayo Clinic Health System – Red Cedar in Menomonie, Menomonie, WI, p. A705
WURZBURGER, Kristen, M.D. Chief of Staff, Genesis Medical Center–Aledo, Aledo, IL, p. A178
WYACO, Melissa, Chief Nurse Executive, Hopi Health Care Center, Keams Canyon, AZ, p. A32
WYATT, Basil, Chief Financial Officer, AMG Specialty Hospital–Tulsa, Tulsa, OK, p. A516
WYATT, Charles, M.D. Chief Medical Officer, Regional Medical Center of Acadiana, Lafayette, LA, p. A278
WYATT, Jana, Chief Executive Officer, Mizell Memorial Hospital, Opp, AL, p. A24
WYATT, Leslie G., Senior Vice President Children's Services and Executive Director, Children's Hospital of Richmond at VCU–Brook Road Campus, Richmond, VA, p. A671
WYATT, Robert, M.D. Chief Medical Officer, Forest Park Medical Center Frisco, Frisco, TX, p. A615
WYDICK, Sue, Director Human Resources, Ohio County Hospital, Hartford, KY, p. A258
WYDRA, Lana, Vice President Human Resources, Nathan Littauer Hospital and Nursing Home, Gloversville, NY, p. A434
WYER, Jolena, R.N. Chief Nursing Officer, Oklahoma Center for Orthopedic and Multi–Specialty Surgery, Oklahoma City, OK, p. A512
WYERS, Michael, Chief Financial Officer, Medical Center of Trinity, Trinity, FL, p. A146
WYLES, Rick, Chief Financial Officer, McLaren Flint, Flint, MI, p. A319
WYLIE, Eugene, Chief Human Resources Officer, Veterans Affairs Loma Linda Healthcare System, Loma Linda, CA, p. A68
WYLIE, Patrick, Director Information Systems, Petaluma Valley Hospital, Petaluma, CA, p. A81
WYMAN, Alan, Chief Information Officer, Providence Hospital, Washington, DC, p. A120
WYMAN, David, President and Chief Executive Officer, Gracie Square Hospital, New York, NY, p. A439
WYMER, Melanie, Director Human Resources, Highland District Hospital, Hillsboro, OH, p. A491
WYNES, Jim Bob, Director Human Resources, Southwest Memorial Hospital, Cortez, CO, p. A101
WYNN, Katherine, Director Human Resource, Oklahoma Heart Hospital, Oklahoma City, OK, p. A512
WYNN, Paige, Chief Financial Officer, Dorminy Medical Center, Fitzgerald, GA, p. A157
WYSOCKI, Greg, Chief Financial Officer, Austin Lakes Hospital, Austin, TX, p. A593
WYSONG–HARDER, Alyson, Chief Executive Officer, Heartland Behavioral Health Services, Nevada, MO, p. A373

## Y

YABLONKA, Eric, Vice President and Chief Information Officer, University of Chicago Medical Center, Chicago, IL, p. A185
YABUT, Eduardo, M.D. Medical Director, North Dakota State Hospital, Jamestown, ND, p. A475
YAEGER, Eric, M.D
  Chief Medical Officer, Kindred Hospital–Aurora, Aurora, CO, p. A99
  Medical Director, Kindred Hospital–Denver, Denver, CO, p. A102
YAHNER, Michael, Chief Financial Officer, Torrance State Hospital, Torrance, PA, p. A551
YAHYA, Zuhair, M.D. Chief Medical Officer, San Dimas Community Hospital, San Dimas, CA, p. A87
YAKE, Laurie B., Vice President Finance, Aurora Medical Center, Kenosha, WI, p. A703
YAKLIN, Shelleye, President and Chief Executive Officer, North Ottawa Community Hospital, Grand Haven, MI, p. A320
YALLOWITZ, Joseph, Vice President Medical Affairs, Valley Hospital, Ridgewood, NJ, p. A418
YAMADA, Chrissy, CPA Senior Vice President Finance, EvergreenHealth, Kirkland, WA, p. A680
YAMADA, Jeff, Vice President, Yakima Valley Memorial Hospital, Yakima, WA, p. A688
YAMAKAWA, Mark, Chief Operating Officer, Queen's Medical Center, Honolulu, HI, p. A169
YAMAN, Tonguc
  Deputy Chief Information Officer, Bellevue Hospital Center, New York, NY, p. A438
  Chief Information Officer, Metropolitan Hospital Center, New York, NY, p. A441
YANCY, Daniel, Administrator and Chief Executive Officer, Winnie Community Hospital, Winnie, TX, p. A652
YANDOW, Suzanne, M.D. Chief of Staff, Shriners Hospitals for Children–Salt Lake City, Salt Lake City, UT, p. A658
YANES, John C., Chief Executive Officer, Andalusia Regional Hospital, Andalusia, AL, p. A15
YANEZ, Maria J., Chief Financial Officer, Baptist Health South Florida, Doctors Hospital, Coral Gables, FL, p. A124
YANNI, Anthony, M.D. Vice President Medical Affairs, Regional Hospital of Scranton, Scranton, PA, p. A549
YANNI, Jason, Senior Financial Analyst, Novant Health Huntersville Medical Center, Huntersville, NC, p. A462
YAP, Elvy, Director of Finance, Rush Oak Park Hospital, Oak Park, IL, p. A196
YAP, Eric, Chief Executive Officer, OhioHealth Rehabilitation Hospital, Columbus, OH, p. A486
YARBOROUGH, Dianne, Director of Information Technology, Centennial Medical Center, Frisco, TX, p. A615
YARLING, John, M.D. Medical Director, Four County Counseling Center, Logansport, IN, p. A215
YARMEL, Jeffrey N., Chief Operating Officer, St. Mary Medical Center, Langhorne, PA, p. A538
YARN, Jayce, Director Information Technology, Marias Medical Center, Shelby, MT, p. A387
YAROCH, Julie, D.O.,
  President, ProMedica Bixby Hospital, Adrian, MI, p. A314
  Interim President, ProMedica Defiance Regional Hospital, Defiance, OH, p. A488
  President, ProMedica Herrick Hospital, Tecumseh, MI, p. A331
YARRAMSETTI, Sri
  Chief Information Officer, Chapman Medical Center, Orange, CA, p. A79
  Chief Information Officer, Orange County Global Medical Center, Inc., Santa Ana, CA, p. A90
YASKO, Joyce M., Ph.D. Chief Operating Officer, Roswell Park Cancer Institute, Buffalo, NY, p. A430
YATES, Ann C., R.N. Director Patient Care and Clinical Services, St. Vincent Mercy Hospital, Elwood, IN, p. A207
YATES, Jackie, R.N. Nurse Executive, Mississippi State Hospital, Whitfield, MS, p. A361
YATES, Randy, M.D. Chief Medical Officer, Straub Clinic & Hospital, Honolulu, HI, p. A169
YATSATTIE, Clyde, Administrative Officer, U. S. Public Health Service Indian Hospital, Zuni, NM, p. A427
YAWN, Julia K., MSN Chief Nursing Officer and Vice President for Patient Care Services, Regional Medical Center, Orangeburg, SC, p. A564
YAWORSKY, Jason
  Chief Information Officer, Bradford Regional Medical Center, Bradford, PA, p. A530
  Senior Vice President Information Systems and Chief Information Officer, Olean General Hospital, Olean, NY, p. A446
YAZAWA, Albert, M.D. Regional Medical Director, Leahi Hospital, Honolulu, HI, p. A168
YBARRA, Farra, R.N. Chief Nursing Officer, Coal County General Hospital, Coalgate, OK, p. A505
YE, Ye, Chief of Staff, York General Hospital, York, NE, p. A399
YEAGER, Angela, Director Information Technology, Palacios Community Medical Center, Palacios, TX, p. A635
YEAGER, Dianne, Chief Executive Officer, Crane Memorial Hospital, Crane, TX, p. A603
YEAGER, Kevin, Vice President Fiscal Services, Holzer Medical Center – Jackson, Jackson, OH, p. A491
YEARWOOD, Janice, Director Human Resources, W. J. Mangold Memorial Hospital, Lockney, TX, p. A628
YEASTED, G. Alan, M.D. Senior Vice President and Chief Medical Officer, St. Clair Hospital, Pittsburgh, PA, p. A546
YEATES, Alan H., Vice President Fiscal Services, Wyandot Memorial Hospital, Upper Sandusky, OH, p. A499
YEATES, Diane, Chief Operating Officer, Terrebonne General Medical Center, Houma, LA, p. A275
YEATS, Melanie, M.D. Vice President Medical Affairs, San Juan Regional Medical Center, Farmington, NM, p. A424
YECNY, Rick, Chief Executive Officer and Chief Mission Officer, PeaceHealth Peace Harbor Medical Center, Florence, OR, p. A520
YEE, Brenda, MSN, Chief Executive Officer, Chinese Hospital, San Francisco, CA, p. A88
YEE, Jr., Hal F., M.D. Interim Chief Medical Officer, LAC/University of Southern California Medical Center, Los Angeles, CA, p. A71
YEE, Martin, M.D. Medical Director, HEALTHSOUTH East Valley Rehabilitation Hospital, Mesa, AZ, p. A33
YEH, Ada, R.N. Chief Operating Officer and Chief Nursing Officer, Chapman Medical Center, Orange, CA, p. A79
YEHL, Warren, Chief Operating Officer, Eastern New Mexico Medical Center, Roswell, NM, p. A426
YEHLEN, Lorraine, R.N
  Vice President Patient Care Services, DCH Regional Medical Center, Tuscaloosa, AL, p. A25
  Chief Nursing Officer, Northport Medical Center, Northport, AL, p. A23
YELTON, Gene, Director Support Services, Keystone Newport News, Newport News, VA, p. A668
YETMAN, Robert, M.D. Medical Director, Healthbridge Children's Hospital of Houston, Houston, TX, p. A619
YETTER, Tad A., M.D. President Medical Staff, Mason District Hospital, Havana, IL, p. A190
YEUNG, Christopher A., M.D. Chief of Staff, The Surgical Hospital of Phoenix, Phoenix, AZ, p. A36
YEUNG, Diem, M.D. Medical Director, HEALTHSOUTH Rehabilitation of Gadsden, Gadsden, AL, p. A20
YHLEN, David, Chief Operating Officer, Inspira Medical Center–Elmer, Elmer, NJ, p. A411
YI, Brenda, Director Medical Resource Management and Chief Financial Officer, U. S. Air Force Medical Center Keesler, Keesler AFB, MS, p. A355


Index of Health Care Professionals **A1009**

Index of Health Care Professionals

Index of Health Care Professionals / Yim

YIM, Janet, Director Information Services, St. Mary Mercy Hospital, Livonia, MI, p. A325
YINGLING, Barbara, R.N. Vice President Patient Care Services and Chief Nursing Officer, Mercy Medical Center, Canton, OH, p. A481
YINGLING, Regina, Supervisor, Sandhills Regional Medical Center, Hamlet, NC, p. A461
YITTA, Prasad, M.D. Medical Director, River Hospital, Alexandria Bay, NY, p. A428
YOCHELSON, Michael R., M.D. Vice President and Medical Director, MedStar National Rehabilitation Hospital, Washington, DC, p. A119
YODER, Cathy, Chief Financial Officer, St. Joseph's Hospital, Tampa, FL, p. A145
YOGEL, Louis, M.D. Chief of Staff, Broward Health Medical Center, Fort Lauderdale, FL, p. A126
YON, Robin, Site Finance Director, Mercy Health – Fairfield Hospital, Fairfield, OH, p. A489
YOO, George, M.D. Chief Medical Officer, Karmanos Cancer Center, Detroit, MI, p. A318
YOON, Chris, M.D. Medical Director, HEALTHSOUTH Bakersfield Rehabilitation Hospital, Bakersfield, CA, p. A55
YORK, Ana, Coordinator Human Resources and Benefits, Harlan County Health System, Alma, NE, p. A389
YORK, Christopher, FACHE, Chief Executive Officer, Baylor Medical Center at Waxahachie, Waxahachie, TX, p. A650
YORK, Don, Vice President Human Resources, Sky Lakes Medical Center, Klamath Falls, OR, p. A522
YORK, Jack
  Chief Information Officer, Pioneer Community Hospital of Newton, Newton, MS, p. A358
  Chief Information Officer, Pioneer Community Hospital of Patrick, Stuart, VA, p. A673
  Chief Information Officer, Pioneer Community Hospital of Stokes, Danbury, NC, p. A458
YORK, Linda, Director Human Resource, Memorial Hospital of Converse County, Douglas, WY, p. A716
YORK, Robert Scott, M.D. Chief of Staff, Avoyelles Hospital, Marksville, LA, p. A279
YORK, Russell W.
  Chief Financial Officer, Mississippi Baptist Medical Center, Jackson, MS, p. A355
  Vice President and Chief Financial Officer, Mississippi Hospital for Restorative Care, Jackson, MS, p. A355
YOSHII, Brian, Vice President Information Technology, Kaiser Permanente Medical Center, Honolulu, HI, p. A168
YOSKO, Kathleen C., President and Chief Executive Officer, Marianjoy Rehabilitation Hospital, Wheaton, IL, p. A203
YOST, Gregg W., Chief Human Resources Officer, Gardens Regional Hospital and Medical Center, Hawaiian Gardens, CA, p. A64
YOUMANS, Kevin, Interim President, Genesis Medical Center, Illini Campus, Silvis, IL, p. A200
YOUNG, Aaron, Chief Information Officer, Summit Healthcare Regional Medical Center, Show Low, AZ, p. A38
YOUNG, Abby, Chief Nursing Officer, Iowa Specialty Hospital–Clarion, Clarion, IA, p. A224
YOUNG, Angela, Human Resources Officer, Chillicothe Veterans Affairs Medical Center, Chillicothe, OH, p. A482
YOUNG, Anthony, Information Services Specialist, Chester Mental Health Center, Chester, IL, p. A181
YOUNG, Anthony R., Chief Executive Officer, EASTAR Health System, Muskogee, OK, p. A510
YOUNG, Barry, Director Human Resources, Western Mental Health Institute, Bolivar, TN, p. A574
YOUNG, Bev, Director Human Resources, Frankfort Regional Medical Center, Frankfort, KY, p. A257
YOUNG, Bryce A.
  Chief Operating Officer, Hays Medical Center, Hays, KS, p. A241
  Chief Operating Officer, Pawnee Valley Community Hospital, Larned, KS, p. A244
YOUNG, C. Ray, M.D. Chief Medical Officer, Bourbon Community Hospital, Paris, KY, p. A264
YOUNG, David, M.D. Area Information Officer, Kaiser Permanente Fontana Medical Center, Fontana, CA, p. A61
YOUNG, David, Senior Vice President Planning and Technology, Trousdale Medical Center, Hartsville, TN, p. A578
YOUNG, Eric, M.D. Chief of Staff, Veterans Affairs Ann Arbor Healthcare System, Ann Arbor, MI, p. A314
YOUNG, Eric L.
  Vice President Finance and Chief Financial Officer, Marietta Memorial Hospital, Marietta, OH, p. A493
  Chief Financial Officer, Selby General Hospital, Marietta, OH, p. A493
YOUNG, J. Phillip, FACHE, Chief Executive Officer, Southern Tennessee Regional Health System–Winchester, Winchester, TN, p. A589
YOUNG, James, Senior Vice President Finance and Chief Financial Officer, Howard County General Hospital, Columbia, MD, p. A297
YOUNG, James, M.D. Chief of Staff, McGehee–Desha County Hospital, McGehee, AR, p. A48
YOUNG, Jeffrey D., Chief Information Officer, Children's Hospitals and Clinics of Minnesota, Minneapolis, MN, p. A342
YOUNG, Jeremie, M.D. Chief of Staff, Regional General Hospital, Williston, FL, p. A147
YOUNG, Joanna, R.N. Chief Nursing Officer, North Vista Hospital, North Las Vegas, NV, p. A403
YOUNG, Joyce, Ph.D
  Vice President, Patient Services and Chief Nursing Officer, St. Joseph Mercy Ann Arbor, Ypsilanti, MI, p. A333
  Vice President, Patient Services and Chief Nursing Officer, St. Joseph Mercy Livingston Hospital, Howell, MI, p. A322
YOUNG, Judy, Chief Financial Officer, Acadia–St. Landry Hospital, Church Point, LA, p. A271
YOUNG, Kathlene A., FACHE, Chief Executive Officer, Borgess Medical Center, Kalamazoo, MI, p. A323
YOUNG, Kevin, FACHE, President, Adventist Behavioral Health Rockville, Rockville, MD, p. A299
YOUNG, Martha, Director Human Resources, Cumberland County Hospital, Burkesville, KY, p. A255
YOUNG, Mary, Director Human Resources, Colorado Mental Health Institute at Pueblo, Pueblo, CO, p. A108
YOUNG, Mary C., Chief Executive Officer, Moccasin Bend Mental Health Institute, Chattanooga, TN, p. A575
YOUNG, Michael, Chief Financial Officer, Mad River Community Hospital, Arcata, CA, p. A54
YOUNG, Michael A., FACHE, President and Chief Executive Officer, Pinnacle Health System, Harrisburg, PA, p. A535
YOUNG, Pam, Director Human Resources, Davis County Hospital, Bloomfield, IA, p. A223
YOUNG, Patty, R.N. Chief Nursing Officer, Ashland Health Center, Ashland, KS, p. A237
YOUNG, Richard T., FACHE, Director, Walter P. Reuther Psychiatric Hospital, Westland, MI, p. A332
YOUNG, Roberta, Chief Nurse Executive, Sanford Medical Center Fargo, Fargo, ND, p. A474
YOUNG, Russell T., Chief Financial Officer, Riverside Community Hospital, Riverside, CA, p. A84
YOUNG, Sabrina, Administrative Support Director, South Mississippi State Hospital, Purvis, MS, p. A360
YOUNG, Sandra G., Vice President Human Resources, Missouri Baptist Medical Center, Saint Louis, MO, p. A377
YOUNG, Sheila, Vice President Human Resources, Mobile Infirmary Medical Center, Mobile, AL, p. A22
YOUNG, Stephanie, Associate Director, Aleda E. Lutz Veterans Affairs Medical Center, Saginaw, MI, p. A329
YOUNG, Stephen W., Chief Operating Officer, Doctors Hospital of Sarasota, Sarasota, FL, p. A142
YOUNG, Steven W., Director, Veterans Affairs Salt Lake City Health Care System, Salt Lake City, UT, p. A659
YOUNG, Terry, Chief Information Officer, Plains Memorial Hospital, Dimmitt, TX, p. A609
YOUNG, Tyce, Nurse Informatist, Clay County Medical Center, Clay Center, KS, p. A238
YOUNG, William, Chief Information Officer, Berkshire Medical Center, Pittsfield, MA, p. A310
YOUNG Jr., William A., President and Chief Executive Officer, St. John Medical Center, Westlake, OH, p. A500
YOUNGBLOOD, Elizabeth
  President, Baylor Specialty Hospital, Dallas, TX, p. A604
  President, Our Children's House at Baylor, Dallas, TX, p. A606
YOUNGBLOOD, Erin R., Chief Human Resources Officer, Behavioral Center of Michigan, Warren, MI, p. A332
YOUNGMAN, Darrell, D.O. Chief Medical Officer, Via Christi Hospital on St. Francis, Wichita, KS, p. A253
YOUNGS, Patsy, President, Texas Health Presbyterian Hospital Kaufman, Kaufman, TX, p. A625
YOUNT, Patrick, Director Information Services, Family Health West, Fruita, CO, p. A104
YOURTEE, Edward, M.D. Chief Medical Officer, Parkland Medical Center, Derry, NH, p. A405
YOURZEK, Tari, Chief Nursing Officer, Boundary Community Hospital, Bonners Ferry, ID, p. A173
YOUSAITIS, Zoe, Director Human Resources, Eagleville Hospital, Eagleville, PA, p. A533
YOUSO, Michael, Chief Executive Officer, Grand Itasca Clinic and Hospital, Grand Rapids, MN, p. A339
YOUSUF, Faraaz, Chief Operating Officer, Sutter Medical Center, Sacramento, Sacramento, CA, p. A85
YUHAS, Joel P., FACHE, President and Chief Executive Officer, St. Mary Medical Center, Long Beach, CA, p. A68
YUHAS, John, D.O. Medical Director, Elmwood Healthcare Center at the Springs, Green Springs, OH, p. A490
YULICH, Michael, Director Information Services, Mercy Suburban Hospital, Norristown, PA, p. A541
YUNGMANN, Michael, President, Morton Plant North Bay Hospital, New Port Richey, FL, p. A136
YUNUSOV, Ed
  Chief Information Officer, Creedmoor Psychiatric Center, NY, p. A439
  Coordinator Facility Information Center, New York City Children's Center, NY, p. A442
YUST, Randall C.
  Chief Operating Officer and Chief Financial Officer, Indiana University Health North Hospital, Carmel, IN, p. A206
  Chief Financial Officer NCR, Indiana University Health Tipton Hospital, Tipton, IN, p. A220

## Z

ZAAS, David, M.D. Chief Executive Officer, Duke Raleigh Hospital, Raleigh, NC, p. A466
ZABAWSKI, Denise, Vice President Information Services and Chief Information Officer, Nationwide Children's Hospital, Columbus, OH, p. A486
ZABEL, Sarah, Vice President, Operations, Swedish/Edmonds, Edmonds, WA, p. A678
ZABIELSKI, Gerald C., M.D. Chief Medical Staff, Wright Memorial Hospital, Trenton, MO, p. A379
ZABROWSKI, John, Chief Financial Officer, St. Mary's Medical Center of Evansville, Evansville, IN, p. A208
ZACHARIASEN, Keith, Chief Financial Officer, Wamego Health Center, Wamego, KS, p. A252
ZACHARY, Kevin, Chief Executive Officer, Logan Regional Medical Center, Logan, WV, p. A692
ZACHRICH, Jane, Chief Nursing Officer, Community Memorial Hospital, Hicksville, OH, p. A491
ZADYLAK, Robert, M.D. Vice President Medical Management, Advocate Illinois Masonic Medical Center, Chicago, IL, p. A181
ZAFEREO, Carolyn, Chief Accounting Officer, Citizens Medical Center, Victoria, TX, p. A650
ZAFONTE, Ross, D.O. Chief, Physical Medicine and Rehabilitation and Vice President Medical Affairs, Research and Education, Spaulding Rehabilitation Hospital, Charlestown, MA, p. A306
ZAGERMAN, Robert, Chief Financial Officer, Brooke Glen Behavioral Hospital, Fort Washington, PA, p. A534
ZAHN, Chip, Chief Operating Officer, Las Colinas Medical Center, Irving, TX, p. A624
ZAID, Ahmad, Chief Executive Officer, Atrium Medical Center, Stafford, TX, p. A645
ZAIDI, Syed A., M.D. Chief of Staff, Lauderdale Community Hospital, Ripley, TN, p. A587
ZAJEC, Doris A., Director Human Resources, South Pointe Hospital, Warrensville Heights, OH, p. A500
ZAJIC, Holly, Chief Operating Officer, Ivinson Memorial Hospital, Laramie, WY, p. A716
ZAJICEK, Tammy, Director of Nursing, Jackson County Hospital District, Edna, TX, p. A610
ZAKAI, Aminadav, M.D. Medical Director, Arbour–Fuller Hospital, Attleboro, MA, p. A302
ZALDIVAR, Rogelio, M.D. Medical Director, Westchester General Hospital, Miami, FL, p. A135
ZALESKI, Theodore, M.D. Vice President Clinical Effectiveness, Southern Ocean Medical Center, Manahawkin, NJ, p. A414
ZALMAN, Tisha, Chief Executive Officer, El Campo Memorial Hospital, El Campo, TX, p. A610
ZALOUDEK, Lisa, Chief Human Resources Officer, AllianceHealth Ponca City, Ponca City, OK, p. A514
ZALUD, Nicolette, Customer Site Manager, McLaren Central Michigan, Mount Pleasant, MI, p. A326
ZAMBRANA, David, R.N., Chief Executive Officer, University of Miami Hospital, Miami, FL, p. A135
ZAMBRELLO, Sally, Chief Information Officer, Carondelet St. Joseph's Hospital, Tucson, AZ, p. A39
ZAMORA DE AGUERO, Hilde, Human Resources Site Director, Baptist Health South Florida, West Kendall Baptist Hospital, Miami, FL, p. A134
ZAMPINI, Maria, Chief Operating Officer, University Medical Center of El Paso, El Paso, TX, p. A611
ZANDER, Cynthia L., Vice President and Chief Operating Officer, CGH Medical Center, Sterling, IL, p. A201
ZANE, Kristi, Chief Human Resources Officer, Crawford Memorial Hospital, Robinson, IL, p. A199
ZANI, Carl, Chief Technology Director, Memorial Health, Marysville, OH, p. A493
ZANIS, Tina
  Director Information Technology, Schuylkill Medical Center – East Norwegian Street, Pottsville, PA, p. A548
  Director Information Systems, Schuylkill Medical Center – South Jackson Street, Pottsville, PA, p. A548

**A1010** Index of Health Care Professionals

Index of Health Care Professionals / Zwanziger

ZANNI, David M., Associate Administrator, Adena Pike Medical Center, Waverly, OH, p. A500
ZANT, Dan, M.D. Chief of Staff, Morgan Memorial Hospital, Madison, GA, p. A161
ZAPARZYNSKI, Edward, Director Information Services, North Vista Hospital, North Las Vegas, NV, p. A403
ZAPATKA, Lisa, R.N. Chief Nursing Officer, Saint Vincent Hospital, Worcester, MA, p. A313
ZARAK, Tamie, Director Human Resources, Memorial Medical Center – Neillsville, Neillsville, WI, p. A707
ZARB, Karla, Chief Nursing Officer, Garden City Hospital, Garden City, MI, p. A320
ZAUNER, Janiece, Chief Nursing Officer, Providence Seaside Hospital, Seaside, OR, p. A526
ZAUNER, Mike, Chief Executive Officer, Sierra Vista Hospital, Sacramento, CA, p. A85
ZAVATCHEN, Nancy, Director Information Technology, Cullman Regional Medical Center, Cullman, AL, p. A18
ZAVODNICK, Jacquelyn, M.D. Medical Director, Devereux Children's Behavioral Health Center, Malvern, PA, p. A539
ZAWACKI, Brenda, Chief Operating Manager, Providence Kodiak Island Medical Center, Kodiak, AK, p. A28
ZDEBLICK, Mike, Chief Operating Officer, El Camino Hospital, Mountain View, CA, p. A77
ZECHMAN, David M., FACHE, President and Chief Executive Officer, McLaren Northern Michigan, Petoskey, MI, p. A327
ZEDNICEK, Allison, Chief Executive Officer, West Hills Hospital, Reno, NV, p. A404
ZEH, Gianna, Commander, U. S. Air Force Regional Hospital, Eglin AFB, FL, p. A126
ZEH, Jeffrey C., President, Indiana University Health White Memorial Hospital, Monticello, IN, p. A216
ZEHM, Laura, Vice President and Chief Financial Officer, Community Hospital of the Monterey Peninsula, Monterey, CA, p. A76
ZEHNER, Douglas A., Chief Financial Officer, Newark Beth Israel Medical Center, Newark, NJ, p. A415
ZEIGLER, Michele
Vice President and Chief Information Officer, Chambersburg Hospital, Chambersburg, PA, p. A531
Vice President Information Services, Waynesboro Hospital, Waynesboro, PA, p. A552
ZEISEL, Jeff Friant, Vice President Finance, Elmhurst Memorial Hospital, IL, p. A187
ZEITLER, Irvin, D.O. Vice President Medical Affairs, Shannon Medical Center, San Angelo, TX, p. A640
ZEITLER, Jenny, Network Administrator, North Okaloosa Medical Center, Crestview, FL, p. A124
ZELENKA, Anthony
President and Chief Operating Officer, Berkeley Medical Center, Martinsburg, WV, p. A693
Chief Executive Officer, Jefferson Medical Center, Ranson, WV, p. A694
ZELIN, Mira, D.O. Medical Director, HEALTHSOUTH Rehabilitation Hospital of Spring Hill, Brooksville, FL, p. A123
ZELL, John R., Chief Financial Officer, OSF St. Joseph Medical Center, Bloomington, IL, p. A179
ZELLA, William, Chief Executive Officer, Arbour H. R. I. Hospital, Brookline, MA, p. A305
ZELLER, April, Director Nursing, Holton Community Hospital, Holton, KS, p. A242
ZELLER, Brad, Vice President Operations, Hayward Area Memorial Hospital and Nursing Home, Hayward, WI, p. A702
ZELLER, Clifford, M.D. Chief Medical Officer, Banner Behavioral Health Hospital – Scottsdale, Scottsdale, AZ, p. A37
ZELLER, Paul, Vice President Human Resources, MedStar Southern Maryland Hospital Center, Clinton, MD, p. A297
ZELLER, Sonya, R.N. Vice President, Chief Operating Officer and Chief Nursing Officer, Indiana University Health Paoli Hospital, Paoli, IN, p. A218
ZEMAN, Brian, Chief Human Resources, Salem Veterans Affairs Medical Center, Salem, VA, p. A672
ZENDER, Dale, Regional Vice President Finance and Chief Financial Officer, PeaceHealth St. Joseph Medical Center, Bellingham, WA, p. A676
ZENGOTITA, Jamie, M.D. Chief Medical Staff, Mercy Hospital Cassville, Cassville, MO, p. A365
ZENK, Ann, Vice President Patient Care Services, Ministry Saint Mary's Hospitals, Rhinelander, WI, p. A710
ZENNA, Rita, R.N. Vice President Patient Care Services, Deborah Heart and Lung Center, Browns Mills, NJ, p. A410
ZENTY III, Thomas F., President and Chief Executive Officer, University Hospitals, Cleveland, OH, p. B145
ZEOLI, Diane, Chief Executive Officer, Kindred Hospital–Brea, Brea, CA, p. A56
ZEPHIER, Michelle, Human Resource Specialist, U. S. Public Health Service Indian Hospital, Rosebud, SD, p. A571
ZEPS, Joseph, Vice President Finance, Tomah Memorial Hospital, Tomah, WI, p. A712
ZERINGUE, Rhonda, R.N. Chief Nursing Officer, St. James Parish Hospital, Lutcher, LA, p. A279
ZERRER, Lana, M.D. Chief of Staff, Harry S. Truman Memorial Veterans Hospital, Columbia, MO, p. A366
ZETTER, David, M.D. Chief of Staff, Jackson Purchase Medical Center, Mayfield, KY, p. A262
ZEVENBERGEN, Glenn, Chief Executive Officer, Hegg Memorial Health Center Avera, Rock Valley, IA, p. A234
ZEWE, Jeff S., R.N
Senior Vice President Patient Care and Chief Nursing Officer, Bradford Regional Medical Center, Bradford, PA, p. A530
Vice President Patient Care Services and Chief Nursing Officer, Olean General Hospital, Olean, NY, p. A446
ZEYNELOGLU, Nejat, Vice President and Chief Quality Medical Officer, Brookhaven Memorial Hospital Medical Center, Patchogue, NY, p. A447
ZHANG, Jian Q., MSN Chief Operating Officer, Chinese Hospital, San Francisco, CA, p. A88
ZHIRKIN, Georgii, Chief Financial Officer, Community Mental Health Center, Lawrenceburg, IN, p. A214
ZICHAL, Frances J., Chief Executive Officer, Central Community Hospital, Elkader, IA, p. A227
ZIDANSEK, John A., President and Chief Executive Officer, Easton Hospital, Easton, PA, p. A533
ZIEGLER, John C., FACHE Vice President Human Resources, Memorial Hospital, Belleville, IL, p. A179
ZIEGLER, Peter, M.D. Acting Chief Medical Officer, U. S. Public Health Service Indian Hospital–Sells, Sells, AZ, p. A38
ZIELASKIEWICZ, Michael E., R.N. Interim Chief Nursing Officer, Johnson Regional Medical Center, Clarksville, AR, p. A42
ZIELAZINSKI, Mark, Chief Information and Technology Integration Officer, Marin General Hospital, Greenbrae, CA, p. A64
ZIELINSKI, Sharon
Manager Health Information, HEALTHSOUTH Rehabilitation Hospital of Erie, Erie, PA, p. A534
Chief Information Resource Officer, Veterans Affairs Maryland Health Care System–Baltimore Division, Baltimore, MD, p. A295
ZIEMBA, Mike, Information Technology Project Lead, Northlake Behavioral Hospital, Mandeville, LA, p. A279
ZIEMER, Patrick C., Chief Executive Officer, Alvarado Parkway Institute Behavioral Health System, La Mesa, CA, p. A66
ZIEMIANSKI, Karen, R.N. Senior Vice President Nursing, Erie County Medical Center, Buffalo, NY, p. A430
ZIENIEWICZ, Stephen P., FACHE, President and Chief Executive Officer, Saint Barnabas Medical Center, Livingston, NJ, p. A413
ZIEROLD, Bob, Senior Vice President Human Resources, Christian Health Care Center, Wyckoff, NJ, p. A421
ZIESMER, Bill, Chief Financial Officer, Skyridge Medical Center, Cleveland, TN, p. A576
ZIESMER, Valerie, Chief Financial Officer, Florida Hospital–Flagler, Palm Coast, FL, p. A138
ZIGLOR, Danyale, Assistant Director Human Resources, WellStar Douglas Hospital, Douglasville, GA, p. A156
ZILE, Ron, M.D. Chief of Staff, Highland District Hospital, Hillsboro, OH, p. A491
ZILKOW, Jon, Chief Financial Officer, Southwest Healthcare System, Murrieta, CA, p. A77
ZILLER, Andrew, M.D. Chief Medical Officer, Rose Medical Center, Denver, CO, p. A102
ZIMA, Cheryl F.
Vice President Human Resources Ministry Health Care, Ministry Saint Joseph's Hospital, Marshfield, WI, p. A705
Vice President Human Resources, Ministry Saint Michael's Hospital, Stevens Point, WI, p. A711
ZIMMEL, Robert, Senior Vice President Human Resources, St. Luke's University Hospital – Bethlehem Campus, Bethlehem, PA, p. A529
ZIMMER, Jan, R.N. Chief Nursing Officer, Regional Hospital of Jackson, Jackson, TN, p. A579
ZIMMERLY, Kara, Manager Human Resources, ProMedica Bay Park Hospital, Oregon, OH, p. A496
ZIMMERMAN, Aimee, R.N. Chief Operations Officer, Logan County Hospital, Oakley, KS, p. A247
ZIMMERMAN, David, M.D. Chief of Staff, Swain Community Hospital, Bryson City, NC, p. A456
ZIMMERMAN, Don, Director Human Resources, Morris County Hospital, Council Grove, KS, p. A239
ZIMMERMAN, Joanna, Chief Financial Officer, Carlisle Regional Medical Center, Carlisle, PA, p. A531
ZIMMERMAN, Maria, R.N. Chief Nursing Officer, Sheridan County Health Complex, Hoxie, KS, p. A242
ZIMMERMAN, Michael P., Chief Executive Officer, Sierra Vista Hospital, Truth or Consequences, NM, p. A427
ZIMMERMAN, Nancy, R.N., Administrator, Comanche County Hospital, Coldwater, KS, p. A238
ZIMMERMAN, Robert, Vice President Financial Services, Charlevoix Area Hospital, Charlevoix, MI, p. A316
ZIMMERMANN, Deb T., R.N. Chief Nursing Officer and Vice President Patient Care Services, VCU Medical Center, Richmond, VA, p. A672
ZIMMERMANN, Wayne, Chief Operating Officer, Elmhurst Hospital Center, NY, p. A439
ZINK, Jayne, Director of Nursing, Ohio Hospital for Psychiatry, Columbus, OH, p. A486
ZINKER, Dena, MSN Vice President Patient Services, Colquitt Regional Medical Center, Moultrie, GA, p. A162
ZINKULA, Lisa, Chief Financial Officer, Grundy County Memorial Hospital, Grundy Center, IA, p. A228
ZINN, David, M.D. Vice President Medical Affairs, Northeast Alabama Regional Medical Center, Anniston, AL, p. A15
ZINN, Troy, Chief Executive Officer, Little River Cameron Hospital, Cameron, TX, p. A599
ZINNER, Barbara, Chief Nursing Officer, Marymount Hospital, Garfield Heights, OH, p. A490
ZIOLKOWSKI, David
Chief Operating Officer, Petaluma Valley Hospital, Petaluma, CA, p. A81
Chief Operating Officer, Santa Rosa Memorial Hospital, Santa Rosa, CA, p. A92
ZIPPARO, Maureen, Chief Operating Officer, Putnam Hospital Center, Carmel, NY, p. A431
ZIRBSER, Glenn, Chief Financial Officer, University Medical Center of Princeton at Plainsboro, Plainsboro, NJ, p. A417
ZIRKELBACH, Mark, Chief Information Officer, Loma Linda University Medical Center, Loma Linda, CA, p. A67
ZIRKELBACK, Mark, Chief Information Officer, Loma Linda University Behavioral Medicine Center, Redlands, CA, p. A82
ZIRKLE, William, Manager Information Systems, Sentara Halifax Regional Hospital, South Boston, VA, p. A673
ZISKIN, Robert, Chief Information Officer, Northport Veterans Affairs Medical Center, Northport, NY, p. A445
ZOCH, Jeremy, Executive Vice President and Chief Operating Officer, St. Joseph Hospital, Orange, CA, p. A79
ZOGELMAN, Sharon, Director Human Resources, St. Luke Hospital and Living Center, Marion, KS, p. A245
ZOLKIWSKY, Walter R., M.D. Chief Medical Officer, Reston Hospital Center, Reston, VA, p. A671
ZOMCHEK, Daniel, M.D. Acting Director, Edward Hines, Jr. Veterans Affairs Hospital, Hines, IL, p. A190
ZOOK, Danette, Chief Financial Officer, Mercy Medical Center–North Iowa, Mason City, IA, p. A231
ZOPH, Timothy R., Senior Vice President and Chief Information Officer, Northwestern Memorial Hospital, Chicago, IL, p. A183
ZORZA, Elizabeth, Assistant Administrator, OSF St. Francis Hospital and Medical Group, Escanaba, MI, p. A319
ZOUCHA, Larry, Chief Information Officer, Boone County Health Center, Albion, NE, p. A389
ZUANICH, Elizabeth
Chief Financial Officer, Providence Little Company of Mary Medical Center – Torrance, Torrance, CA, p. A94
Chief Financial Officer, Providence Little Company of Mary Medical Center San Pedro, CA, p. A72
ZUBER, Steven, Vice President, Methodist Jennie Edmundson Hospital, Council Bluffs, IA, p. A225
ZUBRICKI, Thomas, Vice President Finance, Chief Financial Officer, Crotched Mountain Rehabilitation Center, Greenfield, NH, p. A406
ZUEL, Sally, Vice President Human Resources, Union Hospital Clinton, Clinton, IN, p. A206
ZUHD, Dajani, M.D. President Medical Staff, Punxsutawney Area Hospital, Punxsutawney, PA, p. A548
ZUINO, Matthew
Senior Vice President Hospital Services, Virtua Voorhees, Voorhees, NJ, p. A420
Senior Vice President, Hospital Services, Virtua Marlton, Marlton, NJ, p. A414
Senior Vice President Hospital Services, Virtua Memorial, Mount Holly, NJ, p. A414
ZULIANI, Michael E., Chief Executive Officer, HEALTHSOUTH Huntington Rehabilitation Hospital, Huntington, WV, p. A692
ZULTANKY, Lynne, Director Corporate Communications and Media Relations, Bon Secours–DePaul Medical Center, Norfolk, VA, p. A669
ZUMPANO, Anthony, Chief Financial Officer, Penn Presbyterian Medical Center, Philadelphia, PA, p. A544
ZUMWALT, Philip, M.D. Chief of Staff, Iroquois Memorial Hospital and Resident Home, Watseka, IL, p. A202
ZUNNO, Gerard, R.N. Vice President Patient Care Services, Peconic Bay Medical Center, Riverhead, NY, p. A448
ZUTZ–WICZEK, Sandy, Chief Operating Officer, FirstLight Health System, Mora, MN, p. A343
ZVANUT, Michelle, Vice President Human Resources, Boone Hospital Center, Columbia, MO, p. A366
ZWANZIGER, Marcia, Vice President Finance, Huron Regional Medical Center, Huron, SD, p. A569

Index of Health Care Professionals

ZWEIFEL, Mary A.
  Chief Operating Officer, Sheltering Arms Hospital South, Midlothian, VA, p. A668
  Chief Operating Officer, Sheltering Arms Rehabilitation Hospital, Mechanicsville, VA, p. A668
ZWENG, Thomas, M.D
  Senior Vice President Medical Affairs, Novant Health Matthews Medical Center, Matthews, NC, p. A464
  Executive Vice President Medical Affairs, Novant Health Presbyterian Medical Center, Charlotte, NC, p. A458
ZWICKER, Mike
  Chief Executive Officer, North Valley Hospital, Tonasket, WA, p. A686
  Chief Executive Officer, Wheatland Memorial Healthcare, Harlowton, MT, p. A384

ZWIEFEL, Laura
  Interim Chief Executive Officer, Hancock County Health System, Britt, IA, p. A223
  Chief Nursing Officer and Assistant Administration, Hancock County Health System, Britt, IA, p. A223
ZWIEG, Faye, Vice President and Chief Nursing Officer, Aurora St. Luke's Medical Center, Milwaukee, WI, p. A706
ZWINGER, Glenn, Manager Information Systems Services, Veterans Affairs Puget Sound Health Care System, Seattle, WA, p. A684
ZWINGMAN–BAGLEY, Cheryl, R.N. Chief Nursing Officer, Calais Regional Hospital, Calais, ME, p. A289
ZWIRCHITZ, Faith, Director Nursing and Professional Practice, Maple Grove Hospital, Maple Grove, MN, p. A342

ZYCH, Anita, Director of Nursing, Arrowhead Behavioral Health Hospital, Maumee, OH, p. A494
ZYLA, Jeffrey, Chief Financial Officer, Abrazo Scottsdale Campus, Phoenix, AZ, p. A34

# AHA Membership Categories

*The American Hospital Association is primarily an organization of hospitals and related institutions. Its object, according to its bylaws, is "to promote high–quality health care and health services for all the people through leadership in the development of public policy, leadership in the representation and advocacy of hospital and health care organization interests, and leadership in the provision of services to assist hospitals and health care organizations in meeting the health care needs of their communities."*

## Institutional Members

**Hospitals or health services organizations or systems which provide a continuum of integrated, community health resources and which include at least one licensed hospital that is owned, leased, managed or religiously sponsored.**

Institutional members include hospitals, health care systems, integrated delivery systems, and physician hospital organizations (PHOs) and health maintenance organizations (HMOs) wholly or partially owned by or owning a member hospital or system. An Institutional member hospital, health care system or integrated delivery system may, at its discretion and upon approval of a membership application by the Association chief executive officer, extend membership to the health care provider organizations, other than a hospital that it owns, leases, or fully controls.

### Freestanding Health Care Provider Organizations

These are health provider organizations, other than registered hospitals, that provide patient care services, including, but not limited to, ambulatory, preventive, rehabilitative, specialty, post–acute and continuing care, as well as physician groups, health insurance services, and staff and group model health maintenance organizations without a hospital component. Freestanding Health Care Provider Organizations members are not owned or controlled by an Institutional member hospital, health care system or integrated delivery system member. They may, however, be part of an organization eligible for, but not holding, Institutional membership.

### Other Organizations

This category includes organizations interested in the objectives of the American Hospital Association, but not eligible for Institutional or Freestanding Health Care Provider Organization Membership. Organizations eligible for Other membership shall include, but not be limited to, associations, societies, foundations, corporations, educational and academic institutions, companies, government agencies, international health providers, and organizations having an interest in and a desire to support the objectives of the Association.

### Provisional Members

Hospitals that are in the planning or construction stage and that, on completion, will be eligible for institutional membership. Provisional membership may also be granted to applicant institutions that cannot, at present, meet the requirements of Institutional or Freestanding Health Care Provider Organization membership.

### Government Institution Group Members

Groups of government hospitals operated by the same unit of government may obtain institutional membership under a group plan. Membership dues are based on a special schedule set forth in the bylaws of the AHA.

## Other Institutional Members

### Hospitals

*U.S. hospitals and hospitals in areas associated with the U.S. that are Institutional members of the American Hospital Association are included in the list of hospitals in section A. Canadian Institutional members of the American Hospital Association are listed below.*

## Canada

### ALBERTA

**Lamont:** LAMONT HEALTH CARE CENTRE, P.O. Bag 10, Zip T0B 2R0; tel. 780/895–2211; Harold James, Executive Director

### MANITOBA

**Winnipeg:** RIVERVIEW HEALTH CENTRE, 1 Morley Avenue East, Zip R3L 2P4; tel. 204/452–3411; Norman R. Kasian, President and Chief Executive Officer

### ONTARIO

**Renfrew:** RENFREW VICTORIA HOSPITAL, 499 Raglan Street North, Zip K7V 1P6; tel. 613/432–4851; Randy V. Penney, Executive Director

**Thornhill:** SHOULDICE HOSPITAL, 7750 Bayview Avenue, Zip L3T 4A3; tel. 905/889–1125; John Hughes, Chief Administrative Officer

### QUEBEC

**Montreal:** MOUNT SINAI HOSPITAL CENTER, 5690 Cavendish Cote St–Luc', Zip H4W 1S7; tel. 514/369–2222; Michel Amar, Executive Director

# Associated University Programs in Health Administration

## CALIFORNIA

**San Francisco:** GOLDEN GATE UNIVERSITY, 536 Mission Street, Univ Library, Zip 94105–2968; tel. 415/442–7242; James Krusling, Director Business Library and Center for Teaching and Learning Excellence

## IOWA

**Iowa City:** DEPARTMENT OF HEALTH MANAGEMENT AND POLICY, UNIVERSITY OF IOWA, 105 River Street, N232A CPHB, Zip 52246; tel. 319/384–3830; Keith Mueller, Ph.D., Professor and Head

## MARYLAND

**Bethesda:** NAVY MEDICINE PROFESSIONAL DEVELOPMENT CENTER, Naval Medicine, Education and Training Command, Zip 20889–5611; tel. 301/295–1251; Commander DuWayne Griepentrog, Director Administration

## MISSOURI

**Columbia:** UNIVERSITY OF MISSOURI, HEALTH MANAGEMENT AND INFORMATICS, CE707 Clinical Support and Education Building, DC 00600, One Hospital Drive, Zip 65212; tel. 573/882–6179; Eduardo Simoes, M.D., Chair

## TEXAS

**San Antonio:** ARMY–BAYLOR UNIVERSITY PROGRAM IN HEALTH CARE ADMINISTRATION, 3151 Scott Road, Building 2841, Zip 78234–6135; tel. 210/221–6443; Lieutenant Colonel M. Nicholas Coppola, Program Director

**Sheppard AFB:** U. S. AIR FORCE SCHOOL OF HEALTH CARE SCIENCES, Building 1900, MST/114, Academic Library, Zip 76311; tel. 817/851–2511

## PUERTO RICO

**San Juan:** SCHOOL OF PUBLIC HEALTH, P.O. Box 5067, Zip 00936; tel. 809/767–9626; Orlando Nieves, Dean

# Hospital Schools
# of Nursing

**PENNSYLVANIA**
**New Castle:** JAMESON HOSPITAL School of Nursing

# Nonhospital Preacute and Postacute Care Facilities

## CALIFORNIA

**Winterhaven:** U. S. PUBLIC HEALTH SERVICE INDIAN HOSPITAL, P.O. Box 1368, Zip 85366–1368; tel. 760/572–0217; Geniel Harrison, M.D., Clinic Director

## DELAWARE

**Newark:** HEALTH CARE CENTER AT CHRISTIANA, 200 Hygeia Drive, Zip 19714

## FLORIDA

**Jacksonville:** NEMOURS CHILDREN'S CLINIC, 807 Children's Way, Zip 32207; tel. 904/390–3600; William A. Cover, Administrator

## GEORGIA

**Calhoun:** ALLIANT HEALTH PLANS, INC., 401 South Wall Street, Suite 201, Zip 30701; tel. 706/629–8848; Judy Pair, Chief Executive Officer
GEORGIA HEALTH PLUS, 401 South Wall Street, Suite 201, Zip 30701; tel. 706/629–1833
**Rome:** CENTREX, 420 East Second Avenue, Zip 30161; tel. 706/235–1006; Dee B. Russell, M.D., Chief Executive Officer
COMMUNITY HOSPICECARE, P.O. Box 233, Zip 30162–0233; tel. 706/232–0807; Kurt Stuenkel, FACHE, President and Chief Executive Officer
FLOYD HOME HEALTH AGENCY, P.O. Box 6248, Zip 30162–6248; tel. 706/802–4600; Kurt Stuenkel, FACHE, President and Chief Executive Officer
FLOYD MEDICAL OUTPATIENT SURGERY, P.O. Box 233, Zip 30162–0233; tel. 706/802–2070; Kurt Stuenkel, FACHE, President and Chief Executive Officer
FLOYD REHABILITATION CENTER, P.O. Box 233, Zip 30162–0233; tel. 706/802–2091; Kurt Stuenkel, FACHE, President and Chief Executive Officer

## HAWAII

**Honolulu:** MALUHIA HOSPITAL, 1027 Hala Drive, Zip 96817; tel. 808/832–5874; Sally T. Ishikawa, Administrator

## ILLINOIS

**Oak Forest:** OAK FOREST HEALTH CENTER OF COOK COUNTY, 15900 South Cicero Avenue, Zip 60452–4006; tel. 708/687–7200

## INDIANA

**Martinsville:** INDIANA UNIVERSITY HEALTH MORGAN HOSPITAL, P.O. Box 1717, Zip 46151–0717; tel. 765/342–8441; Doug Puckett, President and Chief Executive Officer

## LOUISIANA

**La Place:** RIVER PARISHES HOSPITAL, 500 Rue De Sante, Zip 70068–5418; tel. 985/652–7000; Stephen Robinson, Chief Executive Officer

## MAINE

**Damariscotta:** COVE'S EDGE, 26 Schooner Street, Zip 04543; tel. 207/563–4645; Judy McGuire, Administrator
MILES MEDICAL GROUP, INC., 35 Miles Street, Zip 04543; tel. 207/563–1234; Stacey Miller–Friant, Director
**Kennebunk:** SOUTHERN MAINE HEALTH AND HOME SERVICES, P.O. Box 739, Zip 04043; tel. 207/985–4767; Elaine Brady, R.N., Executive Director

## MARYLAND

**Baltimore:** ST. AGNES HEALTH SERVICES, 900 Caton Avenue, Zip 21229; tel. 410/368–2945; Peter Clay, Senior Vice President Managed Care
ST. AGNES HOME CARE AND HOSPICE, 3421 Benson Avenue, Suite G100, Zip 21227; tel. 410/368–2825; Robin Dowell, Director
**Ellicott City:** ST. AGNES NURSING AND REHABILITATION CENTER, 3000 North Ridge Road, Zip 21043; tel. 410/461–7577; Barbara A. Gustke, R.N., Administrator Extended Care Facility

## MASSACHUSETTS

**Boston:** JOSLIN DIABETES CENTER, One Joslin Place, Zip 02215; tel. 617/732–2400; John L. Brooks, III., President and Chief Executive Officer
**Springfield:** BAY STATE VISITING NURSE ASSOCIATION AND HOSPICE, 50 Maple Street, Zip 01105; tel. 413/781–5070; Ruth Odgren, President

## MICHIGAN

**Big Rapids:** MECOSTA HEALTH SERVICES, 650 Linden Street, Zip 49307; tel. 231/796–3200; Gail Bullard, R.N., Director
**Sault Sainte Marie:** SAULT SAINTE MARIE TRIBAL HEALTH AND HUMAN SERVICES CENTER, 2864 Ashmun Street, Zip 49783; tel. 906/495–5651; Russell Vizina, Division Director Health

## MISSOURI

**Independence:** SURGI–CARE CENTER OF INDEPENDENCE, 2311 Redwood Avenue, Zip 64057; tel. 816/373–7995

## NEBRASKA

**North Platte:** GREAT PLAINS PHO, INC., P.O. Box 1167, Zip 69103; tel. 308/535–7496; Todd Hlavaty, M.D., Chairman

## NEW JERSEY

**Jersey City:** ST. FRANCIS HOSPITAL, 25 McWilliams Place, Zip 07302–1698; tel. 201/418–1000
**Millburn:** ATLANTIC HOME CARE AND HOSPICE, 33 Bleeker Street, Zip 07041; tel. 973/379–8400; Susan Quinn, Administrator
**Morristown:** ALLIANCE IMAGING CENTER, 65 Maple Street, Zip 07960; tel. 973/267–5700; Barbara Picorale, Administrator
**Succasunna:** DIALYSIS CENTER OF NORTHWEST NEW JERSEY, 170 Righter Road, Zip 07876; tel. 973/584–1117; Carol Cahill, Administrator

## NEW MEXICO

**Albuquerque:** ALBUQUERQUE IHS HEALTH CENTER, 801 Vassar Drive N.E., Zip 87106–2799; tel. 505/248–4000; Maria Rickert, Chief Executive Officer

## NEW YORK

**Tuckahoe:** HOME NURSING ASSOCIATION OF WESTCHESTER, 69 Main Street, Zip 10707; tel. 919/961–2818; Mary Wehrberger, Director

## NORTH CAROLINA

**Jefferson:** AMH SEGRAVES CARE CENTER, 200 Hospital Avenue, Zip 28640; tel. 336/246–7101
**Wilson:** WILMED NURSING CARE CENTER, 1705 Tarboro Street S.W., Zip 27893–3428; tel. 252/399–8998; Gene Fulcher, Administrator

## OHIO

**Cleveland:** METROHEALTH CENTER FOR SKILLED NURSING CARE, 4229 Pearl Road, Zip 44109; tel. 216/957–3675; Yvette Bozman, Administrator

## OKLAHOMA

**Clinton:** U. S. PUBLIC HEALTH SERVICE INDIAN HOSPITAL, Route 1, Box 3060, Zip 73601–9303; tel. 580/323–2884
**Eufaula:** EUFALA INDIAN HEALTH CENTER, 800 Forest Avenue, Zip 74432; tel. 918/689–2547; Shelly Crow, Health System Administrator
**Okmulgee:** OKMULGEE INDIAN HEALTH SYSTEM, 1313 East 20th, Zip 74447; tel. 918/758–1926; Jo Ann Skaggs, Administrator
**Sapulpa:** SAPULPA INDIAN HEALTH CENTER, 1125 East Clevelend, Zip 74066; tel. 918/224–9310

## PENNSYLVANIA

**Warminster:** ABINGTON MEMORIAL HEALTH CENTER – WARMINSTER CAMPUS, 225 Newtown Road, Zip 18974–5221; tel. 215/441–6600; Katie Farrell, Chief Executive Officer

## TEXAS

**Dallas:** SURGICARE OF TRAVIS CENTER, INC., 13355 Noel Road, Suite 650, Zip 75240–6694; tel. 713/520–1782
**Houston:** GRAMERCY OUTPATIENT SURGERY CENTER. LTD., 2727 Gramercy, Zip 77025; tel. 713/660–6900; Hamel Patel, Administrator
WEST HOUSTON SURGICARE, 970 Campbell Road, Zip 77024; tel. 713/461–3547
**Orange:** BAPTIST ORANGE HOSPITAL, 608 Strickland Drive, Zip 77630–4717; tel. 409/883–9361; Jarren Garrett, Chief Administrative Officer
**Webster:** BAY AREA SURGICARE CENTER, 502 Medical Center Boulevard, Zip 77598; tel. 281/332–2433; Carol Simons, Administrator

## WISCONSIN

**Green Bay:** UNITY HOSPICE, P.O. Box 28345, Zip 54324–8345; tel. 920/494–0225; Donald Seibel, Executive Director

![Black bar]

# Provisional Hospitals

*This listing includes organizations that, as of September 16, 2015, were in the planning or construction stage and that, on completion, will be eligible for Institutional membership. Some hospitals are granted provisional membership for reasons related to other Association requirements. Hospitals classified as provisional members for reasons other than being under construction are indicated by a bullet ( ● ).*

## TEXAS

**Houston:** BAYLOR ST. LUKE'S MEDICAL CENTER MCNAIR CAMPUS, One Baylor Plaza, BCM 100, Zip 77030–3411; tel. 713/798–4951; Paul Klotman, M.D., President

**Marble Falls:** WAYNE & EILEEN HURD REGIONAL MEDICAL CENTER – SCOTT & WHITE, 800 West Highway 71, Zip 78654; tel. 830/598–1204; Eric N. Looper, Chief Executive Officer

## GUAM

**Dededo:** GUAM REGIONAL MEDICAL CITY, P.O. Box 3830, Zip 96932; tel. 671/649–4764; Gloria Long, Chief Operating Officer

# Associate Members

## Ambulatory Centers and Home Care Agencies

### United States

**NEW HAMPSHIRE**

DARTMOUTH COLLEGE HEALTH SERVICE, 7 Rope Ferry Road, Hanover, Zip 03755–1421; tel. 603/650–1400; John H. Turco, M.D., Director

MIDTOWN SURGERY CENTER, 305 East 47th Street, New York, Zip 10017–2303; tel. 212/751–2100; Julia Ferguson, Director, Operations

WILLS EYE HOSPITAL, 840 Walnut Street, Philadelphia, Zip 19107–5109; tel. 215/928–3000; Joseph P. Bilson, Executive Director

## Blue Cross Plans

### United States

**ARIZONA**

BLUE CROSS AND BLUE SHIELD OF ARIZONA, Box 13466, Phoenix, Zip 85002–3466; tel. 602/864–4541; Vishu Jhaveri, M.D., Senior Vice President and Chief Medical Officer

# Other Members

## UNITED STATES

### Accreditation Organizations:

THE JOINT COMMISSION, One Renaissance Boulevard, Oakbrook Terrace, Illinois Zip 60181; tel. 630/792-5000; Mark Chassin, President; www.jointcommission.org

### Architecture:

CATHRYN BANG & PARTNERS ARCHITECTS AND PLANNERS, 1 Central Park South, 13th Floor, New York, New York Zip 10019-1732; tel. 646/701-4916; Cathryn H. Bang, Managing Partner; www.cbparch.com

DEVENNEY GROUP ARCHITECTS, 201 West Indian School Road, Phoenix, Arizona Zip 85013-3203; tel. 602/943-8950; Julie Barkenbush, Chief Executive Officer; www.devenneygroup.com

EARL SWENSSON ASSOCIATES, INC., 2100 West End Avenue, Suite 1200, Nashville, Tennessee Zip 37203; tel. 615/329-9445; Richard L. Miller, President; www.esarch.com

HDR ARCHITECTURE, INC., 33 West Monroe Street, Suite 1750, Chicago, Illinois Zip 60603-5662; tel. 312/470-9532; Ashley Tucker, Strategic Program Manager, Healthcare; www.hdrinc.com

MATTHEI AND COLIN ASSOCIATES, 332 South Michigan Avenue, Suite 614, Chicago, Illinois Zip 60604; tel. 312/939-4002; Ronald G. Kobold, Managing Partner

MESSER CONSTRUCTION COMPANY, 5158 Fishwick Drive, Cincinnati, Ohio Zip 45216; tel. 513/242-1541; Tiffany Witham, Director Marketing; www.messer.com

PERKINS+WILL, INC., 617 West Seventh Street, Suite 1200, Los Angeles, California Zip 90017-3830; tel. 213/270-8400; Timothy Pettigrew, Associate, Healthcare Knowledge Coordinator; www.perkinswill.com

### Bank:

**BANK OF AMERICA, 101 South Tryon Street, Charlotte, North Carolina Zip 28255-0001; tel. 704/388-2255; Gayle Higaki, Senior Vice President; www.bankofamerica.com**

TD BANK, 2130 Centre Park West Drive, 2nd Floor, West Palm Beach, Florida Zip 33409-6411; tel. 561/352-2086; Colleen Mullaney, Senior Vice President; www.tdbank.com

### Communication Systems Org:

AVAILITY, LLC, 740 East Campbell Road, Suite 1000, Richardson, Texas Zip 75081-1886; tel. 972/383-6326; Andrea Overman, Director, Marketing; www.availity.com

### Consulting Firm:

AEGIS HEALTH GROUP, 8 Cadillac Drive, Suite 450, Brentwood, Tennessee Zip 37027; tel. 800/883-0090; Philip Suiter, Chief Executive Officer; www.aegisgroup.com

AON HEWITT, 5600 West 83rd Street, 8200 Tower, Minneapolis, Minnesota Zip 55402-3721; tel. 952/807-0768; James Craig Nelson, Senior Vice President; www.stratford360.com

ARAMARK, 1101 Market Street, Philadelphia, Pennsylvania Zip 19107-2988; tel. 856/858-3822; Denise Spillane, Vice President Marketing and Communications

AVANZA HEALTHCARE STRATEGIES, LLC, 1300 West Lynn Street, Suite 207, Austin, Texas Zip 78703-3877; tel. 512/479-6700; Joan Dentler, Chief Executive Officer; www.avanzastrategies.com

BENEFIT RECOVERY ANALYSTS, INC., 403 West Fisher Avenue, Greensboro, North Carolina Zip 27401; tel. 336/273-0737; Judy Tisdale, Accounting Manager; www.benefitrecoveryanalysts.com

BEST DOCTORS, INC., 100 Federal Street, 21st Floor, Boston, Massachusetts Zip 02110-1802; tel. 617/426-3666; Ryan Schoenecker, Vice President Business Development; www.bestdoctors.com

**BMGI, 1200 17th Street, Suite 180, Denver, Colorado Zip 80202-5815; tel. 303/827-0010; Scott McAllister, Senior Performance Excellence Consultant; www.bmgi.com/default.aspx**

BOSTON CONSULTING GROUP, Exchange Place, 31st Floor, Boston, Massachusetts Zip 02109; tel. 617/973-1200; Julia Eleuteri, Lead Researcher; www.bcg.com

**BOXWOOD TECHNOLOGY, INC, 11350 McCormick Road, Suite 101, Hunt Valley, Maryland Zip 21031; tel. 888/491-8833; John Bell, Chairman; www.boxwoodtech.com**

**BURWOOD GROUP, INC., 125 South Wacker Drive, Suite 2950, Chicago, Illinois Zip 60602; tel. 312/327-4600; Mark Theoharous, President; www.burwood.com**

**CARE TECH SOLUTIONS, 901 Wilshire Drive, Suite 100, Troy, Michigan Zip 48084; tel. 248/823-0950; Jody Meehan, Vice President, Marketing, Communications, and Government Affairs; www.caretech.com/**

CBRCC INC., 4475 Morris Park Drive, Suite B., Charlotte, North Carolina Zip 28227-8254; tel. 704/573-4535; Judy B. Courtemanche, President; www.courtemanche-assocs.com

**CLEARWATER COMPLIANCE LLC, 106 Windward Point, Hendersonville, Tennessee Zip 37075-5108; tel. 615/800-7988; Kathy S. Ebbert, Chief Operating Officer; www.clearwatercompliance.com**

COMPDATA CONSULTING, 1713 East 123rd Street, Olathe, Kansas Zip 66061-5983; tel. 800/300-9570; Jessica Wahaus, Marketing Manager; www.compdataconsulting.com

CONIFER HEALTH SOLUTIONS, 2401 Internet Boulevard, Suite 201, Frisco, Texas Zip 75034-5977; tel. 972/335-6120; Vanessa Harris, Senior Market Research Specialist; www.coniferhealth.com

**DRAEGER, 3135 Quarry Road, Telford, Pennsylvania Zip 18969-1042; tel. 215/660-2310; Susan Thornton, Senior Marketing Manager, Information Technology Solutions; www.draeger.com**

**ECLIPSYS, 76 Batterson Park Road, Farmington, Connecticut Zip 06032; tel. 860/246-3000; Marvin S. Goldwasser, Vice President Product Marketing, Patient Flow and Performance Management; www.eclipsys.com**

EDIFECS INC, 2600 116th Avenue N.E., Suite 200, Bellevue, Washington Zip 98004-1468; tel. 425/452-0630; Sunny Singh, President and Chief Executive Officer; www.edifecs.com

EIDE BAILLY, LLP, 800 Nicollet Mall, Suite 1300, Minneapolis, Minnesota Zip 55402-7033; tel. 612/253-6582; Jen Dreis, Marketing Manager; www.eidebailly.com/healthcare

ELSEVIER, INC., 1600 John F. Kennedy Boulevard, Philadelphia, Pennsylvania Zip 19103-2808; tel. 215/239-3516; Peter Rush, Senior Director Customer Insight and Marketing Services; www.elsevier.com

ENSOCARE, 13808 F. Street, Omaha, Nebraska Zip 68137-1102; tel. 888/808-7807; Wayne A. Sensor, Chief Executive Officer; www.ensocare.com

ERNST & YOUNG, 150 Fourth Avenue North, Suite 1400, Nashville, Tennessee Zip 37219-2409; tel. 615/252-8254; David J. Copley, Global Leader, Health Assurance; www.ey.com

**ERNST & YOUNG, 5 Times Square, 14th Floor, New York, New York Zip 10036-6530; tel. 212/773-3000; Frank Bresz, Senior Manager; www.ey.com/global/content.nsf/us/home**

**EXECUTIVE HEALTH RESOURCES, INC., 15 Campus Boulevard, Suite 200, Newtown Square, Pennsylvania Zip 19073; tel. 610/446-6100; Michele Bowman, Vice President, Marketing and Communications; www.ehrdocs.com**

FIDELITY INVESTMENTS, 100 Magellan Way, Mail Zone KW23, Covington, Kentucky Zip 41015-1987; tel. 859/386-3117; John Campbell, Manager; www.fmr.com

GETWELLNETWORK, INC., 7920 Norfolk Avenue, 11th Floor, Bethesda, Maryland Zip 20814-2500; tel. 240/482-3200; Michael B. O'Neil, Jr., President and Chief Executive Officer; www.getwellnetwork.com

GOLDMAN, SACHS AND COMPANY, 200 West Street, New York, New York Zip 10282-2198; Cynthia Rivera, Public Sector and Infrastructure Banking

GPS HEALTHCARE CONSULTANTS, 12935 North Forty Drive, Suite 204, Saint Louis, Missouri Zip 63141; tel. 314/450-5880; Keith Petti, President and Chief Executive Officer; www.gpshealthcon.com

**H. R. S. INTERNATIONAL, 25 East Washington, 6th Floor, Chicago, Illinois Zip 60602; tel. 312/236-7770; Carrie Parks, Marketing Specialist; www.hrsolutions.com**

HEALTHCARE CHAPLAINCY NETWORK, INC., 65 Broadway, 12th Floor, New York, New York Zip 10010; tel. 212/644-1111; Father Eric J. Hall, President and Chief Executive Officer; www.healthcarechaplaincy.org

HEALTHCARE STRATEGY GROUP, LLC, 9900 Corporate Campus Drive Suite 2000, Louisville, Kentucky Zip 40223-4062; tel. 502/814-1180; Donna Russell, Marketing Director; www.healthcarestrategygroup.com

**HEALTHCARESOURCE, 100 Sylvan Road, Suite 100, Woburn, Massachusetts Zip 01801-1851; tel. 800/691-3737; Sean Gilbert, Strategic Alliances Manager; www.healthcaresource.com**

HEALTHEQUITY, INC., 15 West Scenic Pointe Drive, Suite 100, Draper, Utah Zip 84020-6120; tel. 801/727-1000; Stephen Neeleman, Founder and Vice Chairman; www.healthequity.com

HEALTHPORT, 925 North Point Parkway, Alpharetta, Georgia Zip 30005-5210; tel. 770/360-1700; Catherine Valyi, Vice President Marketing; www.healthport.com

IBM, 1 New Orchard Road, Armonk, New York Zip 10504-1722; tel. 781/575-2727; Charles Andrews, Chief Executive Officer; www.ibm.com

INTEGRATED HEALTHCARE STRATEGIES, 901 Marquette Avenue South, Suite 2100, Minneapolis, Minnesota Zip 55402-3713; tel. 612/339-0919; Julie McCauley, Senior Vice President, Corporate; www.ihstrategies.com

**KAUFMAN HALL, 5202 Old Orchard Road, Suite N700, Skokie, Illinois Zip 60077; tel. 847/441-8780; Jason H. Sussman, Partner; www.kaufmanhall.com**

KURT SALMON ASSOCIATES, 1355 Peachtree Street N.E., Suite 900, Atlanta, Georgia Zip 30309-0900; tel. 404/892-0321; Nancy Snell, Senior Research Analyst; www.kurtsalmon.com

LATHAM AND WATKINS, LLP, 633 West 5th Street, Suite 4000, Los Angeles, California Zip 90071; tel. 213/485-1234; Daniel K. Settelmayer, Partner; www.lw.com

**LEXISNEXIS, 1000 Alderman Drive, Alpharetta, Georgia Zip 30005; tel. 404/577-1779; Sarah J. Stansberry, Senior Director, Marketing; www.lexisnexis.com**

**LIVEPROCESS, 271 Grove Avenue, Building D., Verona, New Jersey Zip 07044; tel. 973/571-2500; Nathaniel Weiss, Chief Executive Officer; www.liveprocess.com**

LYRA HEALTH, 200 Park Road, Burlingame, California Zip 94010-4206; tel. 650/477-2991; David Ebersman, Chief Executive Officer; www.lyrahealth.com

MCDONALD HOPKINS, LLC, 600 Superior Avenue East, Suite 2100, Cleveland, Ohio Zip 44114-2690; tel. 216/348-5400; Richard S. Cooper, Member; www.mcdonaldhopkins.com

MCG HEALTH, LLC, 901 5th Avenue, Suite 2000, Seattle, Washington Zip 98164-2076; tel. 206/389-5300; Mara Osman, Director Government Relations; www.careguidelines.com

*The members listed in **bold** are Associate Advantage members.* © 2015 AHA Guide

MCKESSON CORPORATION, 1 Post Street, 33rd Floor, San Francisco, California Zip 94104–5203; tel. 404/338–2985; Anastasia Agapoff, Assistant Manager, Library Operations

**MEDASSETS, 100 North Pointe Center East, Suite 200, Alpharetta, Georgia Zip 30022–1506; tel. 314/579–1896; Ron DeCarlo, Senior Vice President; www.medassets.com**

**MEDICAL SIMULATION CORPORATION, 4643 South Ulster Street, Suite 650, Denver, Colorado Zip 80237–2964; tel. 888/889–5882; www.medsimulation.com**

MEDITECH INFORMATION, tel. 781/821–3000; Howard Messing, President and Chief Executive Officer; www.meditech.com

NATIONAL CENTER FOR HEALTH STATISTICS, 3311 Toledo Road, Hyattsville, Maryland Zip 20782–2064; tel. 800/232–4636; Charles Rothwell, Director; www.cdc.gov

**NAVEX GLOBAL, 6000 Meadows Road, Suite 200, Lake Oswego, Oregon Zip 97035–3172; tel. 503/924–1640; Stephen J. Molen, Vice President Strategic Solutions; www.navexglobal.com**

NORTH AMERICAN PARTNERS IN ANESTHESIA, 68 South Service Road, Suite 350, Melville, New York Zip 11747–2358; tel. 516/945–3000; Jill Aaronson, Marketing Coordinator; www.napaanesthesia.com

NUANCE, 3715 Northside Parkway, 100 Northcreek, Suite 200, Atlanta, Georgia Zip 30327; tel. 770/438–8537; Melissa Dickinson, Coordinator Marketing; www.jathomas.com

OPPENHEIMER MULTIFAMILY HOUSING AND HEALTHCARE FINANCE, 1180 Welsh Road, Suite 210, North Wales, Pennsylvania Zip 19454–2057; tel. 215/631–9151; Thomas P. Cassidy, Associate Vice President; www.opcomortgagefinance.com

PACIFIC ADR CONSULTING, 316 Occidental Avenue South, Suite 500, Seattle, Washington Zip 98104–2874; tel. 206/624–3388; Gregg Bertram, President; www.pacificadrconsulting.com

**PACKETMOTION, INC., 260 Santa Ana Court, Sunnyvale, California Zip 94085–4512; tel. 408/449–4300; Ravi Khatod, Senior Vice President, Sales and Business Development; www.packetmotion.com**

PASCAL METRICS INC., 1025 Thomas Jefferson Street N.W., Suite 420E, Washington, District of Columbia Zip 20007–5241; tel. 202/333–9090; Drew Ladner, President and Chief Executive Officer; www.pascalmetrics.com

**PEER CONSULTING, 2856 80Th Avenue S.E., Suite 200, Mercer Island, Washington Zip 98040–2984; tel. 206/236–1300; Rick Nunn, Senior Managing Partner; www.peerconsulting.net**

PHYSICIAN WELLNESS SERVICES, 5000 West 36th Street, Suite 230, Minneapolis, Minnesota Zip 55416–2771; tel. 877/731–3949; Lori Brostrom, Vice President Marketing; www.physicianwellnessservices.com

PRACTICELINK, 415 2nd Avenue, Hinton, West Virginia Zip 25951–2427; tel. 314/323–9698; Eric Martin, Physician Job Placement Services

**PREMIERE GLOBAL SERVICES, 3280 Peachtree Road N.W., Suite 1000, Atlanta, Georgia Zip 30305–2422; tel. 404/543–9449; Mark H. Horne, Vice President Marketing, Notifications and Reminders; www.premiereglobal.com**

PROFESSIONAL RESEARCH CONSULTANTS, INC., 11326 P. Street, Omaha, Nebraska Zip 68137–2316; tel. 800/428–7455; Janna Binder, Director Marketing and Public Relations; www.prconline.com

QUAMMEN HEALTH CARE CONSULTANTS, 522B Brandies Circle, Suite 4, Murfreesboro, Tennessee Zip 37128–4873; tel. 407/539–2015; Robecca Quammen, President; www.quammengroup.com

RYCAN, P.O. Box 306, Marshall, Minnesota Zip 56258–0306; tel. 800/201–3324; Marg Louwagie, Administrative Assistant; www.rycan.com

**SAMUELI INSTITUTE, 1737 King Street, Suite 600, Alexandria, Virginia Zip 22314–2764; tel. 703/299–4800; Bonnie R. Sakallaris, Vice President Optimal Healing Environments; www.siib.org**

SEERHEALTH, LLC, 1600 Parkwood Circle S.E., Suite 600, Atlanta, Georgia Zip 30339; tel. 770/767–3879; Anthony Begando, Chief Executive Officer; www.seerhealth.com

SERVICE MANAGEMENT SYSTEMS, 7135 Charlotte Pike, Nashville, Tennessee Zip 37209–5015; tel. 615/399–1839; Gary Blanks, Division Manager; www.smsclean.com

SHERIDAN HEALTHCARE, INC., 1613 North Harrison Parkway, Suite 200, Sunrise, Florida Zip 33323–2853; tel. 954/838–2749; Terri Burgess, Director Operations, Business Development; www.sheridanhealthcare.com

**SIEMENS HEALTHCARE, 51 Valley Stream Parkway, Malvern, Pennsylvania Zip 19355; tel. 610/448–4500; Amar Shah, Senior Manager, Corporate Communication; www.medical.siemens.com**

SODEXO HEALTH CARE, 86 Hopmeadow Street, Simsbury, Connecticut Zip 06089; tel. 860/325–1220; Shirley Palmieri, Director Creative Services; www.sodexo.com

SOYRING CONSULTING, 880 21st Avenue North, Saint Petersburg, Florida Zip 33704; tel. 727/822–8774; Adam Higman, Vice President; www.soyringconsulting.com

SPECIALTYCARE, 3100 West End Avenue, Suite 800, Nashville, Tennessee Zip 37203; tel. 615/345–5400; David Peterson, Senior Vice President Marketing; www.specialtycare.net

SPH ANALYTICS, 11545 Wills Road, Suite 100, Alpharetta, Georgia Zip 30009–2098; tel. 866/460–5681; Terri Davis, Vice President Marketing; www.symphonyph.com

STAKEHOLDER ADVISORY SERVICES, LLC, 56 Grayson Drive, Belle Mead, New Jersey Zip 08502–4916; tel. 609/651–8959; Jeffrey Resnick, Managing Partner

**STOCKAMP AND ASSOCIATES, INC., 6000 S.W. Meadows Road, Suite 300, Lake Oswego, Oregon Zip 97035; tel. 503/303–1200; Karen Andrews, Senior Marketing Manager; www.stockamp.com**

STROUDWATER ASSOCIATES, 50 Sewall Street, Suite 102, Portland, Maine Zip 04102–2646; tel. 207/221–8255; Marc Voyvodich, Chief Executive Officer

SULLIVAN COTTER & ASSOCIATES, INC, 200 West Madison Street, Suite 2450, Chicago, Illinois Zip 60606–3499; tel. 312/564–5883; Mary Kelley, Director of Marketing; www.sullivancotter.com

SULLIVAN, COTTER AND ASSOCIATES, INC., 1100 Peachtree Street, Suite 20, Atlanta, Georgia Zip 30309; tel. 678/551–7190; Maureen Cotter, Director Research and Information; www.sullivancotter.com

SURGICAL CARE AFFILIATES, 3000 Galleria Boulevard, Suite 500, Birmingham, Alabama Zip 35244; tel. 205/545–2759; Julie Dunn, Vice President; www.scasurgery.com

**SYSCOM SERVICES, INC, 1010 Wayne Avenue, Suite 320, Silver Spring, Maryland Zip 20910; tel. 301/768–0118; Lee Weinstein, President; www.syscomservices.com**

**TEAMHEALTH, 265 Brookview Centre Way, Suite 400, Knoxville, Tennessee Zip 37919; tel. 865/293–5486; Mike Snow, Chief Executive Officer; www.teamhealth.com**

THE CHARTIS GROUP, 220 West Kinzie Street, 5th Floor, Chicago, Illinois Zip 60654–4912; tel. 877/667–4700; Katy Pinter, Principal; www.chartis.com

THE HSM GROUP, LTD, 8777 East Via de Ventura #188, Scottsdale, Arizona Zip 85258; tel. 480/947–8078; Sheryl Bronkesh, President; www.hsmgroup.com

**THE STUDER GROUP, 8222 Douglas Avenue, Suite 780, Dallas, Texas Zip 75225–5923; tel. 972/860–0551; B. G. Porter, Chief Executive Officer and President; www.studergroup.com**

TIAA CREF, 8500 Andrew Carnegie Boulevard, B208, Charlotte, North Carolina Zip 28262–8500; tel. 704/988–8064; Kevin S. Nazworth, Managing Director; www.tiaa–cref.org

UGHS AUTIMIS BILLING INC, 7324 Southwest Freeway, Suite 700, Houston, Texas Zip 77074–2019; tel. 425/452–0630; Brandon Griffin, Chief Executive Officer; www.edifecs.com

**VECNA TECHNOLOGIES, INC., 36 Cambridgepark Drive, Cambridge, Massachusetts Zip 02140; tel. 617/864–0636; Amanda Baldi, Director, Marketing and Communications; www.vecna.com**

VENDOR CREDENTIALING SERVICE, INC., 616 Cypress Creek Parkway, Suite 800, Houston, Texas Zip 77090–3029; tel. 281/863–9500; Troy Kyle, President and Chief Executive Officer; www.vcsdatabase.com

**VERITY, INC, 5758 West Las Positas Boulevard, Suite 100, Pleasanton, California Zip 94588; tel. 925/598–3003; Michael Pliner, President; www.verity.com**

**VERRAS HEALTHCARE INTERNATIONAL, tel. 888/791–5556; Robert T. Langston, Partner**

VITAL WORKLIFE, 5000 West 36th Street, Suite 230, Minneapolis, Minnesota Zip 55416–2771; tel. 800/383–1908; Mitchell J. Best, Chief Executive Officer; www.vitalworklife.com

**WASTE MANAGEMENT, 1001 Fannin St. Suite 4000, Houston, Texas Zip 77002–6711; tel. 713/265–1352; Bill Turpin, Director Strategic Development**

WESTERN HEALTHCARE ALLIANCE, 715 Horizon Drive, Suite 401, Grand Junction, Colorado Zip 81506–8731; tel. 970/683–5223; Carolyn S. Bruce, Chief Executive Officer; www.wha1.org

XANITOS, INC., 3809 West Chester Pike, Suite 210, Newtown Square, Pennsylvania Zip 19073–2304; tel. 484/654–2300; Graeme A. Crothall, Chairman and Chief Executive Officer; www.xanitos.com

**Educational Services:**

NATIONAL RURAL HEALTH RESOURCE CENTER, 525 South Lake Avenue, Suite 320, Duluth, Minnesota Zip 55802; tel. 218/727–9390; Sally Buck, Chief Executive Officer; www.ruralcenter.org

**RAYTHEON PROFESSIONAL SERVICES, 870 Winter Street, Waltham, Massachusetts Zip 02451–1449; tel. 781/522–3000; Dave Letts, Vice President and General Manager; www.raytheon.com**

**Information Systems:**

**3M HEALTH INFORMATION SYSTEMS, 575 West Murray Boulevard, Murray, Utah Zip 84123–4611; tel. 801/265–4390; Ann Chenoweth, Senior Director, Industry Relations; www.mmm.com**

ALLSCRIPTS HEALTHCARE SOLUTIONS, 222 Merchandise Mart Plaza, Suite 2024, Chicago, Illinois Zip 60654–1010; tel. 312/447–2412; Stephanie Kowalski, Vice President Central Marketing; www.allscripts.com

CERNER CORPORATION, 2800 Rockcreek Parkway, Kansas City, Missouri Zip 64117; tel. 816/221–1024; Laurel Vine, Program Manager, Industry Events; www.cerner.com

**DESIGN CLINICALS, 5200 Southcenter Boulevard, Suite 250, Seattle, Washington Zip 98188–7911; tel. 888/633–7320; Dewey Howell, Chief Executive Officer; www.designclinicals.com**

**HEALTHLAND, 1600 Utica Avenue South, Suite 300, Minneapolis, Minnesota Zip 55416–1468; tel. 612/787–3120; Tracey Schroeder, Vice President Marketing**

**IMPRIVATA, INC., 10 Maguire Road Building 4, Lexington, Massachusetts Zip 02421–3110; tel. 781/674–2700; Ed Gaudel, Chief Marketing Officer; www.imprivata.com**

**KPMG LLP, 200 East Randolph Street, Suite 5500, Chicago, Illinois Zip 60601–6607; tel. 312/665–2073; Edward J. Giniat, National Line of Business Leader, Healthcare and Pharmaceuticals Practice**

**MEDHOST, 6100 West Plano Parkway, Suite 3100, Plano, Texas Zip 75093–8342; tel. 888/218–4678; Leslie LaFon, Departmental Segment Manager; www.medhost.com**

MPOWR, A SUPPLYCORE SOLUTION, 303 North Main Street, Suite 800, Rockford, Illinois Zip 61101–1018; tel. 815/964–7940; Bryan Davis, Director; www.mpowr.com

QGENDA, INC., 3340 Peachtree Road N.E., Suite 1100, Atlanta, Georgia Zip 30326–1043; tel. 855/399–9945; Allison Aronson, Marketing Operations Associate; www.qgenda.com

**SCC SOFT COMPUTER, 5400 Tech Data Drive, Clearwater, Florida Zip 33760–3116; tel. 727/789–0100; Gilbert Hakim, Chief Executive Officer; www.softcomputer.com**

**SHIFTWISE, 1800 S.W. 1st Avenue, Suite 510, Portland, Oregon Zip 97201–5322; tel. 503/548–2030; Nick Haselwander, Marketing Manager; www.shiftwise.com**

**VALENCE HEALTH, 600 West Jackson Boulevard, Chicago, Illinois Zip 60661–5636; tel. 312/273–6623; Kevin Weinstein, Chief Marketing Officer; www.valencehealth.com**

**Insurance Broker:**

**AMERICAN FIDELITY ASSURANCE COMPANY, 2000 North Classen Boulevard, Oklahoma City, Oklahoma Zip 73106; tel. 877/967-5748; Brian Mauck, National Sales Director; www.af-group. com**

**BOSTON MUTUAL LIFE INSURANCE COMPANY, 120 Royall Street, Canton, Massachusetts Zip 02021; tel. 781/828-7000; Peter Tillson, Vice President; www.bostonmutual.com**

**CHUBB INSURANCE, 82 Hopmeadow Street, Simsbury, Connecticut Zip 06070; tel. 860/408-2017; Kimberly Holmes, Assistant Vice President Healthcare; www.chubb.com**

**DYE & ESKIN, 1324 Vincent Place, Mc Lean, Virginia Zip 22101; tel. 703/556-0744; Rick Eskin, President**

**G. E. FINANCIAL, GE Appliance Park Building, Suite 100, Louisville, Kentucky Zip 40225; tel. 502/254-1756; Greg Miller, Director Business Development; www.ge.com**

**ING EMPLOYEE BENEFITS, 20 Washington Avenue South, Minneapolis, Minnesota Zip 55401; tel. 612/372-1122; Steve Pitzer, Vice President**

**LOYAL INSURANCE, 423 Westport Road, Suite 201, Kansas City, Missouri Zip 64111; tel. 816/841-3597; Michael Reidy, Vice President**

**MESIROW FINANCIAL, 353 North Clark Street, Chicago, Illinois Zip 60654-4704; tel. 312/595-7183; Sheila Kelly, Senior Managing Director; www.mesirowfinancial.com**

**NEBCO, 1264 Knollwood Drive West, West Chester, Pennsylvania Zip 19380; tel. 877/739-3330; James M. Mattison, Vice President; www.nebenefit. com**

**THE ALLEN J. FLOOD COMPANIES, INC., 2 Madison Avenue, Larchmont, New York Zip 10538; tel. 914/834-9326; Allen J. Flood, President; www.ajfusa.com**

**UNITED CONCORDIA COMPANY, INC., 4401 Deer Path Road, Harrisburg, Pennsylvania Zip 17110; tel. 717/260-6800; Brett Altland, Product Development Analyst; www.ucci.com**

VALIC, 2929 Allen Parkway (L6-40), Houston, Texas Zip 77019-2111; tel. 713/831-6128; Nicole Mott, Associate Director Marketing; www.valic.com

ZURICH INSURANCE GROUP, tel. 312/496-9418; Daniel R. Nash, National Healthcare Practice Leader; www. zurichna.com/healthcare

**Managed Care/Utilization:**

CENTENE CORPORATION, 111 East Capitol Street, Suite 500, Jackson, Mississippi Zip 39201; tel. 601/863-0835; K. Michael Bailey, Vice President; www.centene.com

**Manufacturer/Supplier:**

AMERISOURCE BERGEN, 1300 Morris Drive, Chesterbrook, Pennsylvania Zip 19087-5559; tel. 610/727-2441; Elisa Moxley, Director, Health Systems Market Development; www.amerisourcebergen.com

BAXTER HEALTHCARE CORPORATION, Route 120 and Wilson Road, Round Lake, Illinois Zip 60073; tel. 224/948-2000; Tom Progar, Vice President Marketing Strategy and Operations; www.baxter.com

BOEHRINGER INGELHEIM PHARMACEUTICALS, INC., 800 Ridgebury Road, Mail Stop 2D 313F, Ridgebury, Connecticut Zip 06877; tel. 203/798-9988; Michelle Jenkins-Woodman, Senior Manager, Managed Markets Marketing; www.us.boehringer-ingelheim.com

**CARDINAL HEALTH, 2215 Citygate Drive, Columbus, Ohio Zip 43219-3589; tel. 614/757-5000; Seham Yennes, Vice President, Marketing Acute; www. cardinal.com**

CARDINAL HEALTH MEDICAL DEVICE DIVISION, 7000 Cardinal Place, Dublin, Ohio Zip 43017-1091; tel. 614/553-4526; Lisa Ashby, President, Medical Devices and Diagnostics; www.cardinalhealth.com

CAREFUSION CORPORATION, 3750 Torrey View Court, San Diego, California Zip 92130-2622; tel. 858/617-2000; Jocelyn Ochinang, Market Research Manager; www. carefusion.com

CORNING OPTICAL COMMUNICATIONS WIRELESS INC., 13221 Woodland Park Road, Suite 400, Herndon, Virginia Zip 20171-5505; tel. 202/230-3306; Grace Alcivar, Director Vertical Programs, Healthcare; www. corning.com

CUVERRO – OLIN BRASS, 4801 Olympia Park Plaza, Suite 3500, Louisville, Kentucky Zip 40241-2092; tel. 877/311-2883; Anthony Kulik, Director; www. cuverro.com

DOOSAN FUEL CELL AMERICA, INC., 195 Governor's Highway, South Windsor, Connecticut Zip 06074-2419; tel. 860/727-2200; David Giordano, Federal and State Government Relations; www.doosanfuelcell.com

**EXTENSION, INC, 6435 West Jefferson Boulevard, Suite 201, Fort Wayne, Indiana Zip 46804-6203; tel. 877/207-3753; Whitney St. Pierre, Director Marketing; www.opentheredbox.com**

FOREST LABORATORIES, INC, 909 3rd Avenue, New York, New York Zip 10022-4731; tel. 212/421-7850; Elizabeth Hackworth, Associate Director Professional Relations; www.frx.com

**GE HEALTHCARE, 9900 West Innovation Drive, RP-2177, Wauwatosa, Wisconsin Zip 53226-4856; tel. 262/548-2088; Michael Becker, Director of Marketing**

HD SUPPLY FACILITIES MAINTENANCE, tel. 858/831-2646; Jim Janclaes, Manager Healthcare National Account; www.HDsupplysolutions.com

HILL-ROM, 1069 State Route 46 East, Batesville, Indiana Zip 47006-9167; tel. 812/934-7958; Thomas J. Jeffers, Director Government Relations; www.hill-rom. com

**JOHNSON & JOHNSON, 829 Williamsburg Boulevard, Downingtown, Pennsylvania Zip 19335-4124; tel. 610/518-7295; Larry Westfall, Director Healthcare Quality Alliances**

**LILLY USA, LLC, Lilly Corporate Center–DC 5021, Indianapolis, Indiana Zip 46285-4113; tel. 317/277-8173; John H. Poulin, Advisor Professional Relations; www.lilly.com**

**OTSUKA AMERICA PHARMACEUTICAL, INC., 2440 Research Boulevard, Rockville, Maryland Zip 20850; tel. 301/990-0030; Jennifer Greaney, Director; www.otsuka.com**

XEROX BUSINESS SERVICES, LLC, 2828 North Haskell Avenue, Dallas, Texas Zip 75204-2909; tel. 214/584-5964; Kirsten LeMaster, VP, Marketing and Communication, Healthcare Provider Solutions; www.services.xerox.com/healthcare-solutions/enus.html

**Metro Hospital Assn:**

HOSPITAL ASSOCIATION OF SOUTHERN CALIFORNIA, 515 South Figueroa Street, Suite 1300, Los Angeles, California Zip 90071-3300; tel. 213/538-0700; James D. Barber, President; www.hasc.org

**National Health Care Prof Assn:**

AMERICAN DENTAL ASSOCIATION, 211 East Chicago Avenue, Chicago, Illinois Zip 60611-2678; tel. 312/440-2500; Jane Grover, Director, Council on Access, Prevention and Interprofessional Relations; www.ada.org

NATIONAL ASSOCIATION FOR HEALTHCARE QUALITY, 8735 West Higgins Road, Suite 300, Chicago, Illinois Zip 60631-2738; tel. 847/375-4867; Stephanie Mercado, Executive Director

**Other:**

21ST CENTURY ONCOLOGY, 2270 Colonial Boulevard, Fort Myers, Florida Zip 33907; tel. 239/461-8584; Gheorghe Pusta, Vice President; www. 21stcenturyoncology.com

ACCENTURE, 1 North State Street, Floor 12, Chicago, Illinois Zip 60602-3314; tel. 312/693-0161; Timothy Gelman, Chief Executive Officer; www.accenture.com

**AEROSCOUT, 1300 Island Drive, Suite 202, Redwood City, California Zip 94065; tel. 650/596-2994; Gabi Daniely, Vice President Marketing and Product Strategy; www.aeroscout.com**

**AGILITY RECOVERY SOLUTIONS, 11030 Circle Point Road, Suite 450, Westminster, Colorado Zip 80020-2791; tel. 877/495-9615; Jenny Boyd, Director Marketing Account; www.agilityrecovery. com**

**AIR METHODS CORPORATION, 7211 South Peoria Street, Englewood, Colorado Zip 80112-4133; tel. 303/792-7565; Ruthie Hubka, Government Relations Specialist; www.airmethods.com**

**AMC HEALTH, INC., 39 Broadway, Suite 540, New York, New York Zip 10006; tel. 877/776-1746; Joanna Haskin, Vice President Partner Development; www.amchealth.com**

AMERICA'S BLOOD CENTERS, 725 15th Street N.W., Suite 700, Washington, District of Columbia Zip 20005; tel. 202/393-5725; Christine S. Zambricki, Chief Executive Officer

AMERICAN ACADEMY OF PHYSICIAN ASSISTANTS, 2318 Mill Road, Suite 1300, Alexandria, Virginia Zip 22314-6833; tel. 703/836-2272; Michael L. Powe, Vice President Reimbursement and Professional Advocacy; www.aapa. org

AMERICAN ASSOCIATION FOR WOUND CARE MANAGEMENT, 4109 Glenrose Street, Kensington, Maryland Zip 20895-3718; tel. 301/933-2200; Jule Crider, Executive Director; www.aawcm.org

AMERICAN ASSOCIATION OF NURSE ANESTHETISTS, 222 South Prospect Avenue, Park Ridge, Illinois Zip 60068-4001; tel. 847/655-1100; Wanda O. Wilson, Executive Director and Chief Executive Officer; www.aana.com

AMERICAN BOARD OF MEDICAL SPECIALTIES, 353 North Clark Street, Suite 1400, Chicago, Illinois Zip 60654-3454; tel. 312/436-2626; Lois Margaret Nora, President and Chief Executive Officer; www.abms. org

AMERICAN COLLEGE OF HEALTHCARE EXECUTIVES, One North Franklin, Suite 1700, Chicago, Illinois Zip 60606-4425; tel. 312/424-2800; Deborah Bowen, President and Chief Executive Officer; www.ache.org

AMERICAN DENTAL EDUCATION ASSOCIATION, 1400 K Street N.W., Suite 1100, Washington, District of Columbia Zip 20005; tel. 202/289-7201; Richard Valachovic, Executive Director; www.adea.org

AMERICAN HEALTH INFORMATION MANAGEMENT ASSOCIATION, 233 North Michigan Avenue, Suite 2150, Chicago, Illinois Zip 60601-5806; tel. 312/233-1100; David A. Sweet, Director Library Services

**AMERICAN SOCIETY OF ANESTHESIOLOGISTS, 1061 American Lane, Schaumburg, Illinois Zip 60173; tel. 847/268-9160; Paul Pomerantz, Chief Executive Officer; www.asahq.org**

**AMERINET, INC., 500 Commonwealth Drive, Warrendale, Pennsylvania Zip 15086-7516; tel. 877/711-5700; Laurie McGrath, Vice President Marketing; www.amerinet-gpo.com**

AMN HEALTHCARE, INC., 12400 High Bluff Drive, Suite 100, San Diego, California Zip 92130-3581; tel. 866/871-8519; Steve Wehn, Senior Vice President of Corporate Development

APOGEE PHYSICIANS, 2525 East Camelback Road, Suite 1100, Phoenix, Arizona Zip 85016-4282; tel. 602/778-3600; Michael Gregory, Chairman; www. apogeephysicians.com

**ARC GROUP ASSOCIATES, 330 South Warminster Road, Suite 345, Hatboro, Pennsylvania Zip 19040; tel. 215/881-9500; Eric Malakoff, Vice President Sales and Marketing; www. arcgroup.net**

**ARJOHUNTLEIGH, 2349 West Lake Street, Suite 250, Addison, Illinois Zip 60101-6183; tel. 800/323-1245; Andrew Hepburn, Vice President; www.arjohuntleigh.com**

ASSOCIATION OF PERIOPERATIVE REGISTERED NURSES, 2170 South Parker Road, Suite 400, Denver, Colorado Zip 80231; tel. 303/755-6304; Linda Kay Groah, Executive Director and Chief Executive Officer; www. aorn.org

**AVATAR SOLUTIONS, 25 East Washington Street, Suite 600, Chicago, Illinois Zip 60602; tel. 312/236-7170; Jeffrey Brady, Chief Executive Officer; www.hrsolutionsinc.com**

BACTES, 8344 Clairemont Mesa Boulevard, Suite 201, San Diego, California Zip 92111-1327; tel. 858/244-1811; Jeanie Pipitone, Senior Marketing Manager; www. bactes.com

BATTELLE MEMORIAL INSTITUTE, 505 King Avenue, Columbus, Ohio Zip 43201-2696; tel. 614/424-6424; Sean Deegan, Director; www.battelle.org

**BERNARD HODES GROUP, 220 East 42nd Street, 14th Floor, New York, New York Zip 10017; tel. 888/438-9911; Karen Hart, Senior Vice President Healthcare Division; www.hodes.com**

**BEST UPON REQUEST, 8170 Corporate Park Drive, Suite 300, Cincinnati, Ohio Zip 45242; tel. 513/605-7800; Kirsten Lecky, Vice President Business Development; www.bestuponrequest.com**

BKD, LLP, P.O. Box 1190, Springfield, Missouri Zip 65801-1900; tel. 417/831-7283; Shelbey Stockton, Marketing and Business Development; www. bkd.com

BLUE CROSS AND BLUE SHIELD ASSOCIATION, 225 North Michigan Avenue, Chicago, Illinois Zip 60601–7680; tel. 312/297–6000; Scott P. Serota, President and Chief Executive Officer; www.bcbs.com

**BOARDVANTAGE, 4300 Bohannon Drive, Suite 110, Menlo Park, California Zip 94025; tel. 650/330–2444; Virginia Portillo, Conference and Events Coordinator; www.boardvantage.com**

BOHAN ADVERTISING AND MARKETING, 124 12th Avenue S., Nashville, Tennessee Zip 37203–3146; tel. 615/327–1189; Jeremi Griggs, Group Account Director; www.bohanideas.com

BUREAU OF MEDICINE AND SURGERY, DEPARTMENT OF THE NAVY, 2300 East Street N.W., Washington, District of Columbia Zip 20372–5300; tel. 202/762–3701; Vice Admiral Matthew L. Nathan, Surgeon General

CANON SOLUTIONS AMERICA, INC., 300 Commerce Square Boulevard, Burlington, New Jersey Zip 08016–1270; tel. 847/706–3411; Paul T. Murphy, Director Strategic Contract Support; www.solutions.canon.com

**CAP SITE INC., 85 South Prospect Street, Burlington, Vermont Zip 05401–3444; tel. 802/383–0675; Gino Johnson, Senior Vice President; www.capsite.com**

**CAREERBUILDER, 200 North LaSalle Street, Suite 1100, Chicago, Illinois Zip 60601; tel. 773/353–2640; Dana Naquin, Marketing Manager– Healthcare; www.careerbuilder.com**

**CARETECH SOLUTIONS, INC., tel. 248/823–0800; Paula Gwyn, Senior Manager Business Development; www.caretechsolutions.com**

**CCM ADVISORS, LLC, 190 South La Salle Street, Suite 2800, Chicago, Illinois Zip 60603; tel. 312/444–6200; Michael Randall, Director Sales and Marketing; www.ahafunds.org**

**CERTIPHI SCREENING, INC., 1105 Industrial Highway, Southampton, Pennsylvania Zip 18966; tel. 888/260–1370; Tony D'Orazio, President; www.certiphi.com**

CHAMBERLIN EDMONDS, 14 Piedmont Center N.E., Atlanta, Georgia Zip 30305–1543; tel. 404/279–5000; Kim Williams, Chief Financial Officer; www.chamberlinedmonds.com

CHAN HEALTHCARE AUDITORS, 231 South Bemiston Avenue, Suite 300, Saint Louis, Missouri Zip 63105; tel. 314/802–2008; Dan Clayton, Director, Knowledge Management; www.chanllc.com

CHIME EDUCATION FOUNDATION, 4300 Wilson Boulevard, Suite 250, Arlington, Virginia Zip 22203–4172; tel. 734/665–0000; Russell P. Branzell, President and Chief Executive Officer

**CISCO SYSTEMS, 165 Needletree Lane, Glastonbury, Connecticut Zip 06033; tel. 860/657–8127; Michael Haymaker, Director Healthcare Industry Marketing; www.cisco.com**

**CLAREDI CORPORATION, 2525 Lake Park Boulevard, Salt Lake City, Utah Zip 84120; tel. 801/982–3001; Kepa Zubeldia, Senior Vice President; www.claredi.com**

CNA INSURANCE, 125 Broad Street, New York, New York Zip 10004–2400; tel. 212/440–7325; Glen Curley, Senior Vice President Healthcare; www.cna.com

**COMPREHENSIVE PHARMACY SERVICES, 6409 North Quail Hollow Road, Memphis, Tennessee Zip 38120–1414; tel. 901/748–0470; Walker Upshaw, Chief Development Officer; www.cpspharm.com**

**COMPUTER ASSOCIATES, One Computer Associates Plaza, Islandia, New York Zip 11749; tel. 800/225–5224; Michael McDermand, Vice President Healthcare; www.ca.com**

**CONCUITY, INCORPORATED, 200 North Fairway Drive Suite 182, Vernon Hills, Illinois Zip 60061–1861; tel. 847/465–6003; James Farrar, Vice President Sales; www.concuity.com**

CONTINUUM HEALTH ALLIANCE, LLC, 402 Lippincott Drive, Marlton, New Jersey Zip 08053–4112; tel. 856/782–3300; Sean Porrini, Chief Operating Officer; www.challc.net

CORNERSTONE ON DEMAND, 1601 Cloverfield Avenue, 6th Floor, Santa Monica, California Zip 90404; tel. 310/752–0200; Johnna Ehmke, Senior Marketing Manager; www.cornerstoneondemand.com

COVENANT HOSPICE, 5041 North 12th Avenue, Pensacola, Florida Zip 32504; tel. 850/433–2155; Dale O. Knee, President and Chief Executive Officer; www.covenanthospice.org

CRANEWARE, INC., 3340 Peachtree Road N.E. Suite 850, Atlanta, Georgia Zip 30326–1072; tel. 404/364–2037; Ann Marie Brown, Executive Vice President Marketing; www.craneware.com

CUSHMAN & WAKEFIELD, 51 West 52nd Street, New York, New York Zip 10019–6119; tel. 212/841–7748; Alistair Clement, Chief Executive Officer; www.cushwakeasia.com

**CYRACOM, 5780 North Swan Road, Tucson, Arizona Zip 85718–4527; tel. 800/713–4950; Jeremy Woan, President and Chief Executive Officer; www.cyracom.com**

DEPARTMENT OF AIR FORCE MEDICAL SERVICE, HQ USAF/SG, Bolling AFB, District of Columbia Zip 20332–6188; tel. 202/545–6700

DEPARTMENT OF THE ARMY, OFFICE OF THE SURGEON GENERAL, 5109 Leesburg Pike, Falls Church, Virginia Zip 22041–3258; tel. 202/690–6467

DISH, PO Box 5096524, Englewood, Colorado Zip 80112–5905; tel. 720/514–6019; Steven Wilson, Manager; www.dish.com

DNV HEALTHCARE, INC., 400 Techne Center Drive, Suite 100, Milford, Ohio Zip 45150–2792; tel. 513/388–4863; Shannon Walker, Team Operator and Planner; www.dnvhealthcareinc.com

DRINKER BIDDLE & REATH LLP, 191 North Wacker Drive Suite 3700, Chicago, Illinois Zip 60606–1615; tel. 312/569–1000; Elisse Lassiter, Business Development Manager; www.drinkerbiddle.com

ECRI INSTITUTE, 5200 Butler Pike, Plymouth Meeting, Pennsylvania Zip 19462–1298; tel. 610/825–6000; Amy Schwartz, Founder; www.ecri.org

**EKTRON, 542 Amherst Street, Nashua, New Hampshire Zip 03063–1016; tel. 603/594–0249; Deb Symons, Director, Field Marketing and Programs; www.ektron.com**

EMMI SOLUTIONS, 300 West Adams Street, Suite 1200, Chicago, Illinois Zip 60606–5176; tel. 312/448–5836; Michelle Collins, Director of Product Marketing; www.emmisolutions.com

**FIRST AMERICAN EQUIPMENT FINANCE, 255 Woodcliff Drive, Fairport, New York Zip 14450–4219; tel. 585/643–3266; Mike Wiedemer, Senior Vice President, Sales; www.faef.com**

FIRST DATA USA, 5565 Glenridge Connector N.E., Atlanta, Georgia Zip 30342; tel. 914/450–4545; Andrew Finck, Vice President Healthcare Segment; www.firstdata.com

GENERAL DYNAMICS HEALTH SOLUTIONS, 3060 Williams Drive, Suite 100, Fairfax, Virginia Zip 22031–4655; tel. 888/545–8477; Elena Fenton, Marketing Director; www.gdit.com/health

HEALTHCARE BUSINESS ASSOCIATES, P.O. Box 1188, Rancho Mirage, California Zip 92270–1188; tel. 888/292–6929; Jack C. Nixon, President

HEALTHTRUST PURCHASING GROUP INC, 155 Franklin Road, Suite 400, Brentwood, Tennessee Zip 37027–4693; tel. 615/344–3030; Beverly Wallace, President; www.healthtrustpg.com

**HEALTHWAYS, INC, 701 Cool Springs Boulevard, Franklin, Tennessee Zip 37067–2697; tel. 800/327–3822; Karen Meyer, Principal; www.healthways.com**

HENRY J. KAISER FAMILY FOUNDATION, 1330 G. Street N.W., Washington, District of Columbia Zip 20005–3004; tel. 202/347–5270; Drew Altman, President and Chief Executive Officer; www.kff.org

HIRERIGHT, 3349 Michelson Drive, Suite 150, Irvine, California Zip 92612–0653; tel. 800/400–2761; Bob Sparanese, Manager Product Marketing; www.hireright.com

**HMS, 355 Quartermaster Court, Jeffersonville, Indiana Zip 47130–3670; tel. 812/704–5747; Rich Flaherty, Vice President Sales and Marketing; www.hms.com**

HOOPER, LUNDY & BOOKMAN, INC., 1875 Century Park East, Suite 1600, Los Angeles, California Zip 90067; tel. 310/551–8111; Lloyd Bookman, Partner; www.health-law.com

HQ ACC/SGMS, 162 Dodd, Suite 100, Langley AFB, Virginia Zip 23665–1995

HQ AETC/SGAL, 63 Main Circle, Suite 3, Randolph AFB, Texas Zip 78150–4549

HQ AFMC/SGAR, 4225 Logistics Avenue, N–209, Dayton, Ohio Zip 45433–5761; tel. 937/656–3655; Alice Rohrbach

HQ AFSPC/SGAL, 150 Vandenberg Street, Suite 1105, Petterson AFB, Colorado Zip 80914–4550

HQ AMC/SGSL, 203 West Losey Street, Room 1180, Scott AFB, Illinois Zip 62225–5219

HQ PACAF/SGAL, 25 East Street, Suite D1, Hickam AFB, Hawaii Zip 96853–5418

HQ USAFA/SGAL, Pinion Drive, Building 4102, Suite 3, USAF Academy, Colorado Zip 80840

HURON CONSULTING GROUP, 550 West Van Buren, Chicago, Illinois Zip 60607; tel. 312/583–8700; Gordon Mountford, Executive Vice President; www.huronconsultinggroup.com

**HYLAND SOFTWARE, INC., 28500 Clemens Road, Westlake, Ohio Zip 44145; tel. 440/788–5814; Michael Kortan, Director Health Care Solutions; www.onbase.com**

**ID EXPERTS, 10300 S.W. Greenburg Road, Suite 570, Portland, Oregon Zip 97223–5410; tel. 866/726–4271; Sally Gray, Manager Sales Support; www.idexpertscorp.com**

**IDENTITY FORCE, 1257 Worcester Road, Suite 308, Framingham, Massachusetts Zip 01701; tel. 508/788–6660; Mike Lawson, Vice President; www.identityforce.com**

INFORMATICS CORPORATION OF AMERICA, 1801 West End Avenue, Suite 1000, Nashville, Tennessee Zip 37203–2540; Rodney Hamilton, Chief Medical Information Officer

INNOVATIVE CAPITAL LLC, 1489 Baltimore Pike, Building 400, Springfield, Pennsylvania Zip 19064–3958; tel. 610/543–2490; Alan P. Richman, President and Chief Executive Officer; www.innovativecapital.com

**INTERACTIVE HEALTH SOLUTIONS, 3800 North Wilke Road, Suite 155, Arlington Heights, Illinois Zip 60004–1278; tel. 847/754–2698; Joseph O'Brien, President; www.interactivesolutions.com**

INTERNATIONAL ASSOCIATION FOR HEALTHCARE SECURITY AND SAFETY, P.O. Box 5038, Glendale Heights, Illinois Zip 60139; tel. 630/529–3913; Nancy Felesena, Executive Assistant; www.iahss.org

**IRONPORT, 950 Elm Avenue, San Bruno, California Zip 94066; tel. 650/989–6500; Jeff Williams, Vice President Sales; www.ironport.com**

JANI-KING, 16885 Dallas Parkway, Addison, Texas Zip 75001; tel. 972/991–0900; Bob Carabajal, Director Healthcare Services; www.janiking.com

JEWISH GUILD HEALTHCARE, 15 West 65th Street, New York, New York Zip 10023; tel. 212/769–6200; Alan R. Morse, President and Chief Executive Officer; www.jgb.org

LANCASTER POLLARD AND CO, 65 East State Street, Columbus, Ohio Zip 43215–4213; tel. 614/224–8800; Thomas Green, Chief Executive Officer; www.lancasterpollard.com

LIFE LINE SCREENING, 6150 Oak Tree Boulevard, Suite 200, Independence, Ohio Zip 44131–2569; tel. 800/897–9177; Kellie D. Privette, Senior Vice President; www.lifelinescreening.com

LINK CAPITAL, 20 North Wacker Drive, Chicago, Illinois Zip 60606–2806; tel. 312/226–6700; Dana Ringer, Senior Vice President of Business Development; www.linkcapital.com

LITTLER MENDELSON, P.C., 1100 Superior Avenue, 20th Floor, Cleveland, Ohio Zip 44114–2530; tel. 216/623–6104; Angela Lupardus, Manager, Regional Business Development and Marketing; www.littler.com

**MAGELLAN HEALTH SERVICES, 6950 Columbia Gateway Drive, Columbia, Maryland Zip 21046; tel. 314/387–4000; Rick Lee, President Employer Solutions; www.magellanhealth.com**

MEDICAL INFORMATION TECHNOLOGY, INC., tel. 781/821–3000; Lynn Robblee, Supervisor of Event Coordination and Memberships; www.meditech.com

MEDICAL STAFFING NETWORK HEALTHCARE, LLC, 901 Yamato Road, Suite 110, Boca Raton, Florida Zip 33431–4497; tel. 561/322–1300; Brian R. Poplin, President and Chief Executive Officer; www.msnhealth.com

MEDIMPACT HEALTHCARE SYSTEMS, INC, 10680 Treena Street, San Diego, California Zip 92128; tel. 858/566–2727; Dana Felthouse, Vice President Marketing; www.medimpact.com

MEDNAX SERVICES INC., 1301 Concord Terrace, Sunrise, Florida Zip 33323–2843; tel. 954/384–0175; Roger J. Medel, President; www.mednax.com

MEDSOLUTIONS, 730 Cool Springs Boulevard, Suite 800, Franklin, Tennessee Zip 37067–7289; tel. 615/468–4116; Laura Krueger, Marketing Strategist, Bundled Payment and Business Intelligence; www.medsolutions.com

---

*The members listed in bold are Associate Advantage members.*

METLIFE RESOURCES, 300 Davidson Avenue, Somerset, New Jersey Zip 08873–4162; tel. 732/652–1268; Anthony Agentowicz, Director, New Business Acquisition, Defined Contribution Retirement Plans; www.metlife.com

MODERN HEALTHCARE, 360 North Michigan Avenue, Chicago, Illinois Zip 60601–3806; tel. 312/649–5491; Fawn Lopez, Publisher; www.modernhealthcare.com

NAVAL REGIONAL MEDICAL CENTER, PSC 1005, Box 36, FPO, Armed Forces Africa, Canada, E Zip 09593–0136

NEXTGEN HEALTHCARE, 3001 Farmington Drive Southeast, Atlanta, Georgia Zip 30339–4704; tel. 253/385–7630; Mike Swim, Vice President of Business Development; www.nextgen.com

**NOBLIS, 3150 Fairview Park South, Falls Church, Virginia Zip 22042; tel. 703/610–2255; Alan Dowling, Executive Director; www.mitretek.org**

NTRACTS, LLC., 101 West Ohio Street, Suite 400, Indianapolis, Indiana Zip 46204–1970; tel. 888/316–9805; Jeffrey W. Short, President and Chief Executive Officer; www.ntracts.com

PATIENT POINT, 8230 Montgomery Road, Suite 300, Cincinnati, Ohio Zip 45236–2292; tel. 888/479–5600; Chris Martini, President Network Solutions; www.patientpoint.com

**PILAT, 460 U.S. Highway 22 West Suite 408, Whitehouse Station, New Jersey Zip 08889–3447; tel. 908/823–9417; Travis Lupo, Director Business Development; www.pilat–nai.com**

**PINSTRIPE, 200 South Executive Drive, Suite 400, Brookfield, Wisconsin Zip 53005–4216; tel. 262/754–5061; Jill Schwieters, Executive Vice President; www.pinstripetalent.com**

PLUM HEALTHCARE GROUP, 100 East San Marcos Boulevard, Suite 200, San Marcos, California Zip 92069–2987; tel. 760/471–0388; Nanci Wilson, Vice President Research and Development; www.plumh.com

PRECISION DOCUMENT SOLUTIONS, 2452 Lacy Lane, Suite 100, Carrollton, Texas Zip 75006–6569; tel. 888/377–1325; Carolyn Inhoffer Montes, Regional Account Director; www.pdsnow.com

PRISM, 12 Estes Drive, Freeport, Maine Zip 04032–6750; tel. 207/865–6877; David Kolb, President; www.prismleaders.com

QUARLES AND BRADY LLP, 300 North LaSalle Street, Suite 4000, Chicago, Illinois Zip 60654–3422; tel. 312/715–2751; Jennifer Morrison, Senior Manager Business Development; www.quarles.com

REMEDY MEDICAL SERVICES, 1320 West Clairemont Avenue, Suite 118, Eau Claire, Wisconsin Zip 54701–6027; tel. 715/834–1555; Maria A. Fedele, Vice President Operations; www.remedymedicalservices.com

RF TECHNOLOGIES, 3125 North 126th Street, Brookfield, Wisconsin Zip 53005; tel. 800/669–9946; Glenn Jonas, President and Chief Executive Officer; www.rft.com

**RISESMART, INC., 2055 Gateway Place, Suite 150, San Jose, California Zip 95110–1015; tel. 877/384–0004; Komal Patel, Marketing Manager; www.risesmart.com**

SENTRY DATA SYSTEMS, INC., 800 Fairway Drive, Suite 400, Deerfield Beach, Florida Zip 33441–1830; tel. 806/411–4566; Tim Lantz, Senior Vice President, Data Next; www.sentryds.com

SEVEN BAR AVIATION, 2101 Cedar Springs Road, Suite 1875, Dallas, Texas Zip 75201–2152; tel. 214/468–8229; Steve Johnson, Senior Vice President Marketing; www.7bar.com

SHIPMAN & GOODWIN LLP, One Constitution Plaza, Hartford, Connecticut Zip 06103–1919; tel. 860/251–5056; Joan W. Feldman, Partner

**SIMPLEE, 480 South California Avenue, Suite 301, Palo Alto, California Zip 94306–1609; tel. 800/464–5125; Tim Holthaus, Engagement Marketing Manager; www.simplee.com**

SIMPLEX GRINNELL, 50 Technology Drive, Westminster, Massachusetts Zip 01441; tel. 978/731–8486; Suzanne Rahall, Marketing Manager, Healthcare Communications; www.simplexgrinnell.com

STRAND GENOMICS, INC., 548 Market Street, Suite 82804, San Francisco, California Zip 94104–5401; tel. 540/239–0465; Harsha K. Rajasimha, Senior Director; www.strandgenomics.com

SUBWAY, 325 Bic Drive, Milford, Connecticut Zip 06461; tel. 800/888–4848; Joanne Kilgore, Global Account Manager; www.subway.com

**TANDBERG, 29 Norfolk Avenue, Peabody, Massachusetts Zip 01960; tel. 978/531–1516; Luke Leininger, Senior Product Manager, Healthcare TelePresence; www.tandberg.com**

THE ADVISORY BOARD COMPANY, 2445 M Street N.W., Washington, District of Columbia Zip 20037–2403; tel. 202/266–5600; Kelsey Mahler, Associate Director, Information Resource Center; www.advisory.com

THE AMERICAN COLLEGE OF OBSTETRICIANS AND GYNECOLOGISTS, 409 12th Street, S.W., Washington, District of Columbia Zip 20024–2188; tel. 202/638–5577; Hal Lawrence, Executive Vice President; www.acog.org

THE BERYL INSTITUTE, 3600 Harwood Road, Suite A., Bedford, Texas Zip 76021–4011; tel. 800/833–2000; Stacy Palmer, Vice President Strategy and Member Experience; www.theberylinstitute.org

THE CPI GROUP, 7400 East Orchard Road, Suite 270, Englewood, Colorado Zip 80111; tel. 303/504–9999; John Van Gulik, Business Development Manager; www.thecpigroup.net

**THE WALKER COMPANY, 31090 S.W. Boones Bend Road, Wilsonville, Oregon Zip 97070–6412; tel. 503/694–8539; Larry W. Walker, Principal; www.walkercompany.com**

**THERMO USCS, 120 Bishop's Way, Brookfield, Wisconsin Zip 53008; tel. 262/784–5600; Christine Miller, Executive Vice President Healthcare Group; www.thermo.com**

**TRANSAMERICA RETIREMENT SOLUTIONS, 4 Manhattanville Road, Purchase, New York Zip 10577; tel. 914/697–8952; Peter Kunkel, President and Chief Executive Officer; www.https://www.trsretire.com**

**TRANSUNION, LLC, 445 Hutchinson Avenue, Suite 800, Columbus, Ohio Zip 43235; tel. 614/785–6411; Martin Callahan, Vice President Business Development; www.transunion.com**

TRAVELERS INSURANCE COMPANY, One Tower Square, 6th Floor, Hartford, Connecticut Zip 06183–1134; tel. 860/277–9830; John Truhan, Operations Manager; www.travelers.com

U. S. ARMY MEDICAL COMMAND, 2050 Worth Road, Suite 10, San Antonio, Texas Zip 78234–6010; tel. 210/221–2212; Ann Russell Potter

UNIFORM DATA SYSTEM FOR MEDICAL REHABILITATION, 270 Northpointe Parkway, Suite 300, Amherst, New York Zip 14228; tel. 716/817–7800; Troy Hillman, Manager, Analytical Services Group; www.udsmr.org

**VERGE SOLUTIONS, LLC, 710 Johnnie Dodds Boulevard, Suite 202, Mount Pleasant, South Carolina Zip 29464–3045; tel. 843/628–4168; Katie Layman, Marketing Manager; www.verge-solutions.com**

**VERISYS CORPORATION, 1001 North Fairfax Avenue, Suite 640, Alexandria, Virginia Zip 22314–1798; tel. 703/535–1471; John Benson, Chief Operating Officer; www.verisys.com/**

**VERSUS TECHNOLOGY, INC., 2600 Miller Creek Road, Traverse City, Michigan Zip 49684; tel. 231/946–5868; Stephanie Bertschy, Director Marketing; www.versustech.com**

**VERTICAL CLAIMS MANAGEMENT, L.L.C., 12300 Perry Highway, Suite 300, Wexford, Pennsylvania Zip 15090–8380; tel. 800/501–6248; Clare Bello, President; www.vcm–llc.com**

**VESTAGEN TECHNICAL TEXTILES, INC., tel. 407/781–2395; Brian Crawford, Chief Business Officer; www.vestagen.com**

**VOCERA COMMUNICATIONS, 525 Race Street, Suite 150, San Jose, California Zip 95126–3495; tel. 408/882–5100; Diana Cropley, Marketing Program Specialist; www.vocera.com**

**WALGREENS HEALTH SERVICES, 1411 Lake Cook Road, MS L414, Deerfield, Illinois Zip 60015; tel. 847/374–2640; Mariana Boggiana, Director, Payor Marketing Strategy; www.walgreens.com**

**WESTERN LITIGATION, INC, 9821 Katy Freeway, Suite 600, Houston, Texas Zip 77024–1206; tel. 800/588–0619; Robert B. Blasio, President and Chief Executive Officer; www.westernlitigation.com**

WITT/KIEFFER, 2015 Spring Road, Suite 510, Oak Brook, Illinois Zip 60523; tel. 630/990–1370; James Gauss, Chairman of Board Services

**Other Health Related:**

CENTER FOR MEDICAL INTEROPERABILITY, 618 Church Street Suite 220, Nashville, Tennessee Zip 37219–2453; tel. 202/617–6009; Kerry McDermott, Vice President for Public Policy and Communications; www.medicalinteroperability.org

**Recruitment Services:**

**B. E. SMITH, 8801 Renner Avenue, Lenexa, Kansas Zip 66219–9746; tel. 855/296–6318; Allison Murphy, Marketing Manager; www.besmith.com**

COORS HEALTHCARE SOLUTIONS, 6000 Fairview Road, Suite 1200, Charlotte, North Carolina Zip 28210–2252; tel. 704/443–2956; Cheryl Coors, Chief Executive Officer; www.coorshealthcaresolutions.com

DOCCAFE.COM, tel. 715/302–8881; Laura Fitzsimmons, Managing Member; www.doccafe.com

**FURST GROUP, 2902 McFarland Road, Rockford, Illinois Zip 61107–6801; tel. 800/642–9940; Patrick Kampert, Director of Communications; www.furstgroup.com**

**Regional Health Care Assn:**

TEXAS ORGANIZATION OF RURAL & COMMUNITY HOSPITALS, P.O. Box 203878, Austin, Texas Zip 78720–3878; tel. 512/873–0045; David Pearson, President and Chief Executive Officer; www.torchnet.org

**Other:**

COMMONWEALTH HEALTH CENTER, P.O. Box 500409, Saipan, Northern Mariana Islands Zip 96950; tel. 670/234–8950; Esther L. Muna, Chief Executive Officer; www.chcc.gov.mp

# CANADA

**Consulting Firm:**

IMPARK, 601 West Cordova Street, Suite 300, Vancouver, British Columbia Zip V6B 1G1; tel. 215/678–5040; Eric Vasterling, Director of Business Development – Healthcare; www.impark.com

**RL SOLUTIONS, INC., 1 Yonge Street, Suite 2300, Toronto, Ontario Zip M5E 1E5; tel. 416/410–8456; Sanjay Malaviya, President and CEO; www.rl–solutions.com**

**Other:**

**HALOGEN SOFTWARE CORPORATION, 495 March Road, Suite 500, Ottawa, Ontario Zip K2K 3G1; tel. 613/270–1011; Lorna Daly, Channel Manager Healthcare; www.halogensoftware.com**

**Provincial Hospital Assn:**

ONTARIO HOSPITAL ASSOCIATION, 200 Front Street West, Suite 2800, Toronto, Ontario Zip M5V 3L1; tel. 416/205–1300; Warren DiClemente, Chief Operating and Vice President Educational Services; www.oha.com

# FOREIGN

# BAHAMAS

**Other:**

PRINCESS MARGARET HOSPITAL, P.O. Box N–8200, Nassau, tel. 242/322–2861; Mary Elizabeth Lightbourne–Walker, Hospital Administrator; www.phabahamas.org

*The members listed in* **bold** *are Associate Advantage members.* © 2015 AHA Guide

## BAHRAIN

**Other:**

INTERNATIONAL HOSPITAL OF BAHRAIN, P.O. Box 1084, Manama, tel. 011/759–8222; F. S. Zeerah, President; www.ihb.net/

## BRAZIL

**Other:**

HOSPITAL SAMARITANO, Rua Conselheiro Brotero, 1486, Sao Paulo, Zip 01232–010; tel. 551/821–5300; Luiz Alberto Oliveira De Luca, Corporate Superintendent; www.samaritano.com.br

## CHINA

**Consulting Firm:**

ASSOCIATED INTERNATIONAL HOSPITAL CORPORATION CENTER, No. 1 South Street, Beijing, Gao Xingyan, Manager

## COLOMBIA

**Other:**

ASOCIACION COLOMBIANA DE HOSPITALES Y CLINICAS, Carrera 4, No 73–15, Bogota, Juan Carlos Giraldo Valencia, Director General; www.achc.org.co

## ECUADOR

**Other:**

JUNTA DE BENEFICENCIA DE GUAYAQUIL, P.O. Box 09–01–789, Guayaquil, tel. 011/432–0760; Lautaro Aspiazu Wright, Director; www.jbg.org.ec

## GEORGIA

**Other:**

MARITIME HOSPITAL JSC, Melikishrin 102B, Batumi, Zip 60100; Tamari Kachlishvili, Medical Director; www.mh.com.ge

MEDI CLUB GEORGIA, 22A, Tashkenti Street, Tbilisi, Zip 0160; tel. 995/225–1991; Nugzar Abramishvili, General Director; www.mediclubgeorgia.ge

## GERMANY

**Other:**

HQ USAFE/SGPXL, Unit 3050, Box 130, Ramstein AB, Armed Forces Africa, Canada, E Zip 09094–5001

## INDIA

**Other:**

SAMAST PATIDAR AAROGYA TRUST, Kirti Patel, Chief Executive Officer

## ISRAEL

**Other:**

HADASSAH MEDICAL ORGANIZATION, P.O. Box 12000, Jerusalem, Zip 91120; tel. 972/677–7111; Tamar Peretz–Yablonski, Interim Director General; www.hadassah.org.il

## JAPAN

**Other:**

KAMEDA MEDICAL CENTER AND CLINICS, 929 Higashi–Cho, Kamogawa City, Zip 296–8602; tel. 814/092–2211; John C. Wocher, Executive Vice President; www.kameda.com

ST. LUKE'S INTERNATIONAL HOSPITAL, 10–1 Akashi–Cho, Chuo–Ku, Tokyo 104, tel. 910/550–7091; Shigeaki Hinohara, Honorary President; www.luke.or.jp/eng/index.html

U.S. NAVAL HOSPITAL OKINAWA, U.S. Naval Base, FPO, Zip 96362; tel. 011/743–7555; Commander Martin Kerr; www.med.navy.mil/sites/nhoki/Pages/default.aspx

## JORDAN

**Other:**

SPECIALTY HOSPITAL, P.O. Box 930186, Amman, Zip 11193; Fawzi Al–Hammouri, General Manager; www.specialty–hospital.com

## LEBANON

**Other:**

SAINT GEORGE HOSPITAL UNIVERSITY MEDICAL CENTER, P.O. Box 166378, Beirut, Zip 1100–2807; tel. 961/158–5700; Ziad Kamel, Administrative Director; www.stgeorgehospital.org

## MEXICO

**Other:**

SHRINERS HOSPITAL FOR CHILDREN, Av Del Iman 257, Col Pedregal de Santa Ursula, Delegacion Coyoacan, Mexico City, Zip 04600; Araceli Nagore, Administrator

## MYANMAR

**Other:**

ASIA ROYAL GENERAL HOSPITAL, 14 Baho Street, Sanchaung Township, Yangon, Zip 11162; tel. 951/153–8055; Myat Thu, Managing Director; www.asiaroyalmedical.com

## NEPAL

**Other:**

SIDDHI VINAYAK HOSPITAL AND PRASUTI GRIHA PVT LTD, 44601 Indian SubContinent, Gongabu, Zip Kathmandu; Ram Prasad Aryal, Chairman

## PANAMA

**Other:**

CLINICA HOSPITAL SAN FERNANDO, S. A., Dept PTY 1663, P.O. Box 25207, Miami, Florida Zip 33102–5207; tel. 507/305–6399; Edgardo Fernandez, Medical Director; www.hospitalsanfernando.com

## PERU

**Other:**

BRITISH AMERICAN HOSPITAL, Avenue Alfredo Salazar 3 Era, Lima 27, tel. 511/712–3000; Gonzalo Garrido–Lecca, Director; www.angloamericana.com.pe

## PHILIPPINES

**Ambulatory Care Center:**

DEPARTMENT OF VETERANS AFFAIRS, OUTPATIENT CLINIC, Pasay City, APO, Zip 96440; tel. 632/833–4566; Artemio Arugay, Commander; www.va.gov

**Other:**

ST. LUKE'S MEDICAL CENTER, 279 East Rodriguez Sr Boulevard, Quezon City, tel. 632/723–0101; Edgardo R. Cortez, President and Chief Executive Officer; www.stluke.com.ph/home

## SAUDI ARABIA

**Other:**

ABDUL RAHMAN AL MISHARI GENERAL HOSPITAL, Olaya, P.O. Box 56929, Riyadh, Zip 11564; tel. 011/465–7700; Abdul Rahman Al Mishari, President; www.drabdulrahmanalmishari.com.sa/

MUHAMMAD SALEH BASHARAHIL HOSPITAL, P.O. Box 10505, Madinah Road, Omora Gadida, Makkah, tel. 009/520–4444; Turki M. Basharahil, General Manager; www.msbasharahil.com/

SANAD HOSPITAL, PO Box 91395, Riyadh, Khalid A. Al Ghamdi, General Manager; www.sanadhospital.com

## SPAIN

**Other:**

NEWIMAR S.A., Av De La Libertad, 24, Rota, Zip 11520; tel. 349/681–4003; Juan Miguel Margarito Monge, Project Manager, Hospital Services

## TURKEY

**Other:**

ANADOLU MEDICAL CENTER, Cumhuriyet Mahallesi 2255 Sokak Gebze, Kocaeli, Zip 41400; tel. 011/678–5400; Robert Gerard Kiely, President and Chief Executive Officer; www.anadolusaglik.org

## UNITED ARAB EMIRATES

**Other:**

AMERICAN HOSPITAL–DUBAI, Oud Metha Road, P.O. Box 5566, Dubai, tel. 011/336–7777; Saeed M. Almulla, Chairman; www.ahdubai.com/main/index.aspx

## UNITED KINGDOM

**Manufacturer/Supplier:**

PRIMAL PICTURES LTD, Christchurch Court 10–15 Newgate Street, London, tel. 442/017–5000; Peter Allan, Chief Executive Officer; www.primalpictures.com

---

# B

## Health Care Systems, Networks and Alliances

Section B

This section includes listings for networks, health care systems and alliances.

## Health Care Systems

To reflect the diversity that exists among health care organizations, this publication uses the term health care system to identify both multihospital and diversified single hospital systems.

### Multihospital Systems

A multihospital health care system is two or more hospitals owned, leased, sponsored, or contract managed by a central organization.

### Single Hospital Systems

Single, freestanding member hospitals may be categorized as health care systems by bringing into membership three or more, and at least 25 percent, of their owned or leased non–hospital preacute and postacute health care organizations. (For purposes of definition, health care delivery is the availability of professional healthcare staff during all hours of the organization's operations). Organizations provide, or provide and finance, diagnostic, therapeutic, and/or consultative patient or client services that normally precede or follow acute, inpatient, hospitalization; or that serve to prevent or substitute for such hospitalization. These services are provided in either a freestanding facility not eligible for licensure as a hospital under state statue or through one that is a subsidiary of a hospital.

The first part of this section is an alphabetical list of health care systems which are listed under the system by state. Data for this section were compiled from the 2014 *Annual Survey* and the membership information base as published in section A of the *AHA Guide.*

One of the following codes appears after the name of each system listed to indicate the type of organizational control reported by that system:

| | |
|---|---|
| **CC** | Catholic (Roman) church–related system, not–for–profit |
| **CO** | Other church–related system, not–for–profit |
| **NP** | Other not–for–profit system, including nonfederal, governmental systems |
| **IO** | Investor–owned, for profit system |
| **FG** | Federal Government |

One of the following codes appears after the name of each hospital to indicate how that hospital is related to the system:

| | |
|---|---|
| **O** | Owned |
| **L** | Leased |
| **S** | Sponsored |
| **CM** | Contract–managed |

## Health System Classification System

An identification system for Health Systems was developed jointly by the American Hospital Association's Health Research and Education Trust and Health Forum, and the University of California-Berkeley.[1] A health system is assigned to one of five categories based on how much they differentiate and centralized their hospital services, physician arrangements, and provider-based insurance products. Differentiation refers to the number of different products or services that the organization offers. Centralization refers to whether decision-making and service delivery emanate from the system level more so than individual hospitals.

## Categories:

*Centralized Health System:* A delivery system in which the system centrally organizes individual hospital service delivery, physician arrangements, and insurance product development. The number of different products/services that are offered across the system is moderate.

*Centralized Physician/Insurance Health System:* A delivery system with highly centralized physician arrangements and insurance product development. Within this group, hospital services are relatively decentralized with individual hospitals having discretion over the array of services they offer. The number of different products/services that are offered across the system is moderate.

*Moderately Centralized Health System:* A delivery system that is distinguished by the presence of both centralized and decentralized activity for hospital services, physician arrangements, and insurance product development. For example, a system within this group may have centralized care of expensive, high technology services, such as open heart surgery, but allows individual hospitals to provide an array of other health services based on local needs. The number of different products/services that are offered across the system is moderate.

*Decentralized Health System:* A delivery system with a high degree of decentralized of hospital services, physician arrangements, and insurance product development. Within this group, systems may lack an overarching structure for coordination. Service and product differentiation is high, which may explain why centralization is hard to achieve. In this group, the system may simply service a role in sharing information and providing administrative support to highly developed local delivery systems centered around hospitals.

*Independent Hospital System:* A delivery system with limited differentiation in hospital services, physician arrangements, and insurance product development. These systems are largely horizontal affiliations of autonomous hospitals.

*No Assignment:* For some systems sufficient data from the Annual Survey were not available to determine a cluster assignment.

The second part of this section lists health care systems indexed geographically by state and city. Every effort has been made to be as inclusive and accurate as possible. However, as in all efforts of this type, there may be omissions. For further information, write to the Section for Health Care Systems, American Hospital Association, 155 N. Wacker Drive, Chicago, IL 60606.

## Networks

The *AHA Guide* shows listings of networks. A network is defined as a group of hospitals, physicians, other providers, insurers and/or community agencies that work together to coordinate and deliver a broad spectrum of services to their community. Organizations listed represent the lead or hub of the network activity. Networks are listed by state, then alphabetically by name including participating partners.

The network identification process has purposely been designed to capture networks of varying organization type. Sources include but are not limited to the following: *AHA Annual Survey,* national, state and metropolitan associations, national news and periodical searches, and the networks and their health care providers themselves. Therefore, networks are included regardless of whether a hospital or healthcare system is the network lead. When an individual hospital does appear in the listing, it is indicative of the role the hospital plays as the network lead. In addition, the network listing is **not** mutually exclusive of the hospital, health care system or alliance listings within this publication.

Networks are very fluid in their composition as goals evolve and partners change. Therefore, some of the networks included in this listing may have dissolved, reformed, or simply been renamed as this section was being produced for publication.

The network identification process is an ongoing and responsive initiative. As more information is collected and validated, it will be made available in other venues, in addition to the *AHA Guide.* For more information concerning the network identification process, please contact The American Hospital Association Resource Center at 312/422–2050.

## Alliances

An alliance is a formal organization, usually owned by shareholders/members, that works on behalf of its individual members in the provision of services and products and in the promotion of activities and ventures. The organization functions under a set of bylaws or other written rules to which each member agrees to abide.

Alliances are listed alphabetically by name. Its members are listed alphabetically by state, city, and then by member name.

[1] Bazzoli, CJ; Shortell, SM; Dubbs, N; Chan, C; and Kralovec, P; ''A Taxonomy of Health networks and Systems: Bringing Order Out of Chaos'' *Health Services Research*, February; 1999

# Statistics for Health Care Systems and their Hospitals

The following tables describing health care systems refers to information in section B of the 2016 *AHA Guide*.

Table 1 shows the number of health care systems by type of control. Table 2 provides a breakdown of the number of systems that own, lease, sponsor or contract manage hospitals within each control category. Table 3 gives the number of hospitals and beds in each control category as well as total hospitals and beds. Finally, shows the percentage of hospitals and beds in each control category.

For more information on health care systems, please write to the Section for Health Care Systems, 155 N. Wacker Drive, Chicago, Illinois 60606 or call 312/422–3000.

### Table 1. Multihospital Health Care Systems, by Type of Organizaton Control

| Type of Control | Code | Number of Systems |
|---|---|---|
| Catholic (Roman) church–related | CC | 31 |
| Other church–related | CO | 7 |
| Subtotal, church–related | | 38 |
| Other not-for–profit | NP | 307 |
| Subtotal, not-for–profit | | 345 |
| Investor Owned | IO | 82 |
| Federal Government | FG | 5 |
| Total | | 432 |

### Table 2. Multihospital Health Care Systems, by Type of Ownership and Control

| Type of Ownership | Catholic Church–Related (CC) | Other Church–Related (CO) | Total Church–Related (CC + CO) | Other Not-for–Profit (NP) | Total Not-for–Profit (CC, CO, + NP) | Investor–Owned (IO) | Federal Govern–ment (FG) | All Systems |
|---|---|---|---|---|---|---|---|---|
| Systems that only own, lease or sponsor | 23 | 5 | 28 | 268 | 296 | 71 | 5 | 372 |
| Systems that only contract–manage | 0 | 0 | 0 | 3 | 3 | 3 | 0 | 6 |
| Systems that manage, own, lease, or sponsor | 8 | 2 | 10 | 34 | 44 | 8 | 0 | 52 |
| Total | 31 | 7 | 38 | 305 | 343 | 82 | 5 | 430 |

### Table 3. Hospitals and Beds in Multihospital Health Care Systems, by Type of Ownership and Control

| Type of Ownership | Catholic Church–Related (CC) | | Other Church–Related (CO) | | Total Church–Related (CC + CO) | | Other Not-for–Profit (NP) | | Total Not-for–Profit (CC, CO, + NP) | | Investor–Owned (IO) | | Federal Govern–ment (FG) | | All Systems | |
|---|---|---|---|---|---|---|---|---|---|---|---|---|---|---|---|---|
| | H | B | H | B | H | B | H | B | H | B | H | B | H | B | H | B |
| Owned, leased or sponsored | 579 | 105,147 | 74 | 16,564 | 653 | 121,711 | 1,536 | 327,830 | 2,189 | 449,541 | 1,369 | 162,067 | 212 | 40,484 | 3,770 | 652,092 |
| Contract–managed | 44 | 2,016 | 3 | 497 | 47 | 2,513 | 104 | 9,315 | 151 | 11,828 | 108 | 6,185 | 0 | 0 | 259 | 18,013 |
| Total | 623 | 107,163 | 77 | 17,061 | 700 | 124,224 | 1,640 | 337,145 | 2,340 | 461,369 | 1,477 | 168,252 | 212 | 40,484 | 4,029 | 670,105 |

H = hospitals; B = beds.

### Table 4. Hospitals and Beds in Multihospital Health Care Systems, by Type of Ownership and Control as a Percentage of All Systems

| Type of Ownership | Catholic Church–Related (CC) | | Other Church–Related (CO) | | Total Church–Related (CC + CO) | | Other Not-for–Profit (NP) | | Total Not-for–Profit (CC, CO, + NP) | | Investor–Owned (IO) | | Federal Govern–ment (FG) | | All Systems | |
|---|---|---|---|---|---|---|---|---|---|---|---|---|---|---|---|---|
| | H | B | H | B | H | B | H | B | H | B | H | B | H | B | H | B |
| Owned, leased or sponsored | 15.4 | 16.1 | 2.0 | 2.5 | 17.3 | 18.7 | 40.7 | 50.3 | 58.1 | 68.9 | 36.3 | 24.9 | 5.6 | 6.2 | 100.0 | 100.0 |
| Contract–managed | 17.0 | 11.2 | 1.2 | 2.8 | 18.1 | 14.0 | 40.2 | 51.7 | 58.3 | 65.7 | 41.7 | 34.3 | 0.0 | 0.0 | 100.0 | 100.0 |
| Total | 15.5 | 16.0 | 1.9 | 2.5 | 17.4 | 18.5 | 40.7 | 50.3 | 58.1 | 68.9 | 36.7 | 25.1 | 5.3 | 6.0 | 100.0 | 100.0 |

H = hospitals; B = beds.
*Please note that figures may not always equal the provided subtotal or total percentages due to rounding.

**0091: ACADIA HEALTHCARE COMPANY, INC.** (IO)
830 Crescent Centre Drive, Suite 610, Franklin, TN
Zip 37067–7323; tel. 615/861–6000; Joey Jacobs, Chairman and
Chief Executive Officer
**(Independent Hospital System)**

**ARIZONA:** SONORA BEHAVIORAL HEALTH HOSPITAL (O, 72 beds) 6050 North
Corona Road, #3, Tucson, AZ Zip 85704–1096; tel. 520/469–8700;
Edeli Kinsala, Chief Executive Officer

**ARKANSAS:** RIVERVIEW BEHAVIORAL HEALTH (O, 50 beds) 701 Arkansas
Boulevard, Texarkana, AR Zip 71854–2105; tel. 870/772–5028; Michael
A. Truman, Chief Executive Officer
**Web address:** www.riverviewbehavioralhealth.com

VALLEY BEHAVIORAL HEALTH SYSTEM (O, 75 beds) 10301 Mayo Drive,
Barling, AR Zip 72923–1660; tel. 479/494–5700; Anthony Walters, Chief
Executive Officer
**Web address:** www.valleybehavioral.com

VANTAGE POINT OF NORTHWEST ARKANSAS (O, 114 beds) 4253 North
Crossover Road, Fayetteville, AR Zip 72703–4596; tel. 479/521–5731;
Connie Borengasser, Chief Executive Officer
**Web address:** www.vantagepointnwa.com

**CALIFORNIA:** PACIFIC GROVE HOSPITAL (O, 68 beds) 5900 Brockton
Avenue, Riverside, CA Zip 92506–1862; tel. 951/275–8400; Brent J.
Bryson, Chief Executive Officer
**Web address:** www.pacificgrovehospital.com

**DELAWARE:** MEADOW WOOD BEHAVIORAL HEALTH SYSTEM (O, 53 beds)
575 South Dupont Highway, New Castle, DE Zip 19720–4606;
tel. 302/328–3330; Bill A. Mason, Chief Executive Officer
**Web address:** www.meadowwoodhospital.com

**FLORIDA:** NORTH TAMPA BEHAVIORAL HEALTH (O, 75 beds) 29910 State
Road 56, Wesley Chapel, FL Zip 33543–8800; tel. 813/922–3300;
Michael Ham, Chief Executive Officer
**Web address:** www.northtampabehavioralhealth.com

PARK ROYAL HOSPITAL (O, 76 beds) 9241 Park Royal Drive, Fort Myers, FL
Zip 33908–9204; tel. 239/985–2700; Michael K. Evans, Chief Executive
Officer
**Web address:** www.ParkRoyalHospital.com

**GEORGIA:** GREENLEAF CENTER (O, 50 beds) 2209 Pineview Drive, Valdosta,
GA Zip 31602–7316; tel. 229/247–4357; Stephen Register, Chief
Executive Officer
**Web address:** www.greenleafcounseling.net

RIVERWOODS BEHAVIORAL HEALTH SYSTEM (O, 75 beds) 233 Medical
Center Drive, Riverdale, GA Zip 30274–2640; tel. 770/991–8500; Kirk
Kureska, Chief Executive Officer
**Web address:** www.riverwoodsbehavioral.com

**INDIANA:** OPTIONS BEHAVIORAL HEALTH SYSTEM (O, 84 beds) 5602 Caito
Drive, Indianapolis, IN Zip 46226–1346; tel. 317/544–4340; Matthew
Love, Chief Executive Officer
**Web address:** www.optionsbehavioralhealthsystem.com/

**LOUISIANA:** ACADIA OPTIMA HOSPITAL (O, 24 beds) 1131 Rue De Belier,
Lafayette, LA Zip 70506–6532; tel. 337/991–0571; Stephanie Bonin,
Administrator
**Web address:** www.optimaspecialtyhospital.com/

ACADIA VERMILION HOSPITAL (O, 54 beds) 2520 North University Avenue,
Lafayette, LA Zip 70507–5306; tel. 337/234–5614; Eric Kennedy, Chief
Executive Officer
**Web address:** www.acadiavermilion.com

LONGLEAF HOSPITAL (O, 70 beds) 110 John Eskew Drive, Alexandria, LA
Zip 71303; tel. 318/445–5111; Cheryl Lachney, Chief Executive Officer
**Web address:** www.longleafhospital.com/

**MICHIGAN:** HARBOR OAKS HOSPITAL (O, 45 beds) 35031 23 Mile Road,
New Baltimore, MI Zip 48047–3649; tel. 586/725–5777; Sari
Abromovich, Chief Executive Officer
**Web address:** www.harboroaks.com

STONECREST CENTER (O, 81 beds) 15000 Gratiot Avenue, Detroit, MI
Zip 48205–1973; tel. 313/245–0600; Steve Savage, Chief Executive Officer
**Web address:** www.stonecrestcenter.com

**MISSOURI:** LAKELAND BEHAVIORAL HEALTH SYSTEM (O, 122 beds) 440
South Market Street, Springfield, MO Zip 65806–2026;
tel. 417/865–5581; Nathan Duncan, Chief Executive Officer
**Web address:** www.lakeland–hospital.com

**NEVADA:** SEVEN HILLS HOSPITAL (O, 94 beds) 3021 West Horizon Ridge
Parkway, Henderson, NV Zip 89052–3990; tel. 702/646–5000; Robert L.
Turner, Ph.D., Chief Executive Officer
**Web address:** www.sevenhillsbi.com

**OHIO:** OHIO HOSPITAL FOR PSYCHIATRY (O, 78 beds) 880 Greenlawn Avenue,
Columbus, OH Zip 43223–2616; tel. 614/449–9664; Stanley Frank, Chief
Executive Officer
**Web address:** www.ohiohospitalforpsychiatry.com/

TEN LAKES CENTER (O, 16 beds) 819 North First Street, 3rd Floor,
Dennison, OH Zip 44621–1003; tel. 740/922–7499; Debra C. Gardner, R.N.,
MSN, Administrator
**Web address:** www.tenlakescenter.com/

**OKLAHOMA:** ROLLING HILLS HOSPITAL (O, 44 beds) 1000 Rolling Hills Lane,
Ada, OK Zip 74820–9415; tel. 580/436–3600; Selena Stockley, Chief
Executive Officer
**Web address:** www.rollinghillshospital.com

**PENNSYLVANIA:** SOUTHWOOD PSYCHIATRIC HOSPITAL (O, 156 beds) 2575
Boyce Plaza Road, Pittsburgh, PA Zip 15241–3925; tel. 412/257–2290;
Stephen J. Quigley, Chief Executive Officer
**Web address:** www.southwoodhospital.com

**TENNESSEE:** DELTA MEDICAL CENTER (O, 173 beds) 3000 Getwell Road,
Memphis, TN Zip 38118–2299; tel. 901/369–8100; James W. Hahn,
Chief Executive Officer
**Web address:** www.deltamedcenter.com

**TEXAS:** ABILENE BEHAVIORAL HEALTH (O, 92 beds) 4225 Woods Place,
Abilene, TX Zip 79602–7991, Mailing Address: P.O. Box 5559,
Zip 79608–5559; tel. 325/698–6600; Keith Broach, Chief Executive
Officer
**Web address:** www.abilenebehavioralhealth.com/

CEDAR CREST HOSPITAL AND RESIDENTIAL TREATMENT CENTER (O, 88
beds) 3500 I–35 South, Belton, TX Zip 76513; tel. 254/939–2100; Rob
Marsh, Chief Executive Officer
**Web address:** www.cedarcresthospital.com

RED RIVER HOSPITAL, LLC (O, 74 beds) 1505 Eighth Street, Wichita Falls, TX
Zip 76301–3106; tel. 940/322–3171; John B. Warburton, Chief Executive
Officer
**Web address:** www.redriverhospital.com

**WASHINGTON:** CASCADE BEHAVIORAL HOSPITAL (O, 63 beds) 12844
Military Road South, Tukwila, WA Zip 98168–3045; tel. 206/244–0180;
Michael Uradnik, Chief Executive Officer
**Web address:** www.cascadebh.com

| | | |
|---|---|---|
| **Owned, leased, sponsored:** | 27 hospitals | 2066 beds |
| **Contract–managed:** | 0 hospitals | 0 beds |
| **Totals:** | 27 hospitals | 2066 beds |

**★0640: ACUITYHEALTHCARE, LP** (IO)
10200 Mallard Creek Road, Suite 300, Charlotte, NC
Zip 28262–9705; tel. 704/887–7280; Edwin H. Cooper, Jr., MS,
President and Chief Executive Officer
**(Independent Hospital System)**

**NEW JERSEY:** ACUITY SPECIALTY HOSPITAL OF NEW JERSEY (O, 30 beds)
1925 Pacific Avenue, 7th Floor, Atlantic City, NJ Zip 08401–6713;
tel. 609/441–2122; Monica Titus, President and Chief Executive Officer
**Web address:** www.acuityhealthcare.net

For explanation of codes following names, see page B2.
★ Indicates Type III membership in the American Hospital Association.

LOURDES SPECIALTY HOSPITAL OF SOUTHERN NEW JERSEY (O, 69 beds) 220 Sunset Road, Willingboro, NJ Zip 08046–1110; tel. 609/835–3650; Cheri Cowperthwait, R.N., Chief Executive Officer
**Web address:** www.lshnj.com

**OHIO:** ACUITY SPECIALTY HOSPITALS OHIO VALLEY (O, 40 beds) 380 Summit Avenue, 3rd Floor, Steubenville, OH Zip 43952–2667; tel. 740/283–7600; Judy K. Weaver, MS, Chief Executive Officer
**Web address:** www.acuityhealthcare.net

**TEXAS:** ACUITY HOSPITAL OF SOUTH TEXAS (O, 30 beds) 718 Lexington Avenue, San Antonio, TX Zip 78212–4768; tel. 210/572–4600; Kris Karns, Ph.D., FACHE, Chief Executive Officer
**Web address:** www.acuitysouthtexas.com

ICON HOSPITAL (C, 32 beds) 19211 McKay Boulevard, Humble, TX Zip 77338–5502; tel. 281/883–5500; Hilda Long, Chief Executive Officer
**Web address:** www.acuityhealthcare.net

| | | |
|---|---|---|
| **Owned, leased, sponsored:** | 4 hospitals | 409 beds |
| **Contract–managed:** | 1 hospital | 32 beds |
| **Totals:** | 5 hospitals | 441 beds |

**0895: ADENA HEALTH SYSTEM** (NP)
272 Hospital Road, Chillicothe, OH Zip 45601–9031; tel. 740/779–7500; Mark H. Shuter, President and Chief Executive Officer
**(Independent Hospital System)**

**OHIO:** ADENA GREENFIELD MEDICAL CENTER (O, 25 beds) 550 Mirabeau Street, Greenfield, OH Zip 45123–1617; tel. 937/981–9400; Kathy Dye, Interim Administrator
**Web address:** www.adena.org

ADENA MEDICAL CENTER (O, 209 beds) 272 Hospital Road, Chillicothe, OH Zip 45601–9031; tel. 740/779–7500; Mark H. Shuter, President and Chief Executive Officer
**Web address:** www.adena.org

ADENA PIKE MEDICAL CENTER (O, 21 beds) 100 Dawn Lane, Waverly, OH Zip 45690–9138; tel. 740/947–2186; David M. Zanni, Associate Administrator
**Web address:** www.pikecommunityhospital.org

| | | |
|---|---|---|
| **Owned, leased, sponsored:** | 3 hospitals | 255 beds |
| **Contract–managed:** | 0 hospitals | 0 beds |
| **Totals:** | 3 hospitals | 255 beds |

**★0235: ADVENTIST HEALTH** (CO)
2100 Douglas Boulevard, Roseville, CA Zip 95661–3898, Mailing Address: P.O. Box 619002, Zip 95661–9002; tel. 916/781–2000; Scott Reiner, President and Chief Executive Officer
**(Moderately Centralized Health System)**

**CALIFORNIA:** ADVENTIST MEDICAL CENTER – HANFORD (O, 199 beds) 115 Mall Drive, Hanford, CA Zip 93230–3513; tel. 559/582–9000; Wayne Ferch, President and Chief Executive Officer
**Web address:** www.adventisthealthcv.com/hospital_newhanfordhospital.aspx

ADVENTIST MEDICAL CENTER–REEDLEY (L, 49 beds) 372 West Cypress Avenue, Reedley, CA Zip 93654–2199; tel. 559/638–8155; Wayne Ferch, President and Chief Executive Officer
**Web address:** www.skdh.org

CENTRAL VALLEY GENERAL HOSPITAL (O, 49 beds) 1025 North Douty Street, Hanford, CA Zip 93230–3722, Mailing Address: P.O. Box 480, Zip 93232–2113; tel. 559/583–2100; Wayne Ferch, President and Chief Executive Officer
**Web address:** www.hanfordhealth.com

FEATHER RIVER HOSPITAL (O, 54 beds) 5974 Pentz Road, Paradise, CA Zip 95969–5593; tel. 530/877–9361; Kevin R. Erich, President and Chief Executive Officer
**Web address:** www.frhosp.org

FRANK R. HOWARD MEMORIAL HOSPITAL (L, 25 beds) One Madrone Street, Willits, CA Zip 95490–4298; tel. 707/459–6801; Rick Bockmann, Chief Executive Officer
**Web address:** www.howardhospital.com

GLENDALE ADVENTIST MEDICAL CENTER (O, 462 beds) 1509 Wilson Terrace, Glendale, CA Zip 91206–4098; tel. 818/409–8000; Kevin A. Roberts, FACHE, President and Chief Executive Officer
**Web address:** www.glendaleadventist.com

LODI MEMORIAL HOSPITAL (O, 190 beds) 975 South Fairmont Avenue, Lodi, CA Zip 95240–5118, Mailing Address: P.O. Box 3004, Zip 95241–1908; tel. 209/334–3411; Daniel Wolcott, President and Chief Executive Officer
**Web address:** www.lodihealth.org

SAN JOAQUIN COMMUNITY HOSPITAL (O, 254 beds) 2615 Chester Avenue, Bakersfield, CA Zip 93301–2014, Mailing Address: P.O. Box 2615, Zip 93303–2615; tel. 661/395–3000; Douglas Duffield, President and Chief Executive Officer
**Web address:** www.sanjoaquinhospital.org

SIMI VALLEY HOSPITAL (O, 144 beds) 2975 North Sycamore Drive, Simi Valley, CA Zip 93065–1277; tel. 805/955–6000; Jennifer Swenson, President and Chief Executive Officer
**Web address:** www.simivalleyhospital.com

SONORA REGIONAL MEDICAL CENTER (O, 152 beds) 1000 Greenley Road, Sonora, CA Zip 95370–4819; tel. 209/536–5000; Andrew Jahn, President and Chief Executive Officer
**Web address:** www.sonoramedicalcenter.org/

ST. HELENA HOSPITAL CLEAR LAKE (O, 25 beds) 15630 18th Avenue, Clearlake, CA Zip 95422–9336, Mailing Address: P.O. Box 6710, Zip 95422; tel. 707/994–6486; David Santos, President and Chief Executive Officer
**Web address:** www.adventisthealth.org

ST. HELENA HOSPITAL NAPA VALLEY (O, 116 beds) 10 Woodland Road, Saint Helena, CA Zip 94574–9554; tel. 707/963–3611; Steven Herber, M.D., FACS, President and Chief Executive Officer
**Web address:** www.sthelenahospital.org

ST. HELENA HOSPITAL–CENTER FOR BEHAVIORAL HEALTH (O, 61 beds) 525 Oregon Street, Vallejo, CA Zip 94590–3201; tel. 707/648–2200; Patricia Williams, Regional VP for Behavioral Medicine and Population Health
**Web address:** www.sthelenahospitals.org/location/center-for-behavioral-health

UKIAH VALLEY MEDICAL CENTER (O, 50 beds) 275 Hospital Drive, Ukiah, CA Zip 95482–4531; tel. 707/462–3111; Gwen Matthews, R.N., MSN, Chief Executive Officer
**Web address:** www.adventisthealth.org

WHITE MEMORIAL MEDICAL CENTER (O, 353 beds) 1720 Cesar Chavez Avenue, Los Angeles, CA Zip 90033–2414; tel. 323/268–5000; John G. Raffoul, President and Chief Executive Officer
**Web address:** www.whitememorial.com

**HAWAII:** CASTLE MEDICAL CENTER (O, 160 beds) 640 Ulukahiki Street, Kailua, HI Zip 96734–4454; tel. 808/263–5500; Kathryn A. Raethel, R.N., M.P.H., President and Chief Executive Officer
**Web address:** www.castlemed.org

**OREGON:** ADVENTIST MEDICAL CENTER–PORTLAND (O, 242 beds) 10123 S.E. Market Street, Portland, OR Zip 97216–2599; tel. 503/257–2500; Joyce Newmyer, President and Chief Executive Officer
**Web address:** www.adventisthealthnw.com

TILLAMOOK REGIONAL MEDICAL CENTER (L, 25 beds) 1000 Third Street, Tillamook, OR Zip 97141–3430; tel. 503/842–4444; David Butler, President and Chief Executive Officer
**Web address:** www.tillamookregionalmc.com

**WASHINGTON:** WALLA WALLA GENERAL HOSPITAL (O, 38 beds) 1025 South Second Avenue, Walla Walla, WA Zip 99362–4116, Mailing Address: P.O. Box 1398, Zip 99362–0309; tel. 509/525–0480; Monty E. Knittel, President and Chief Executive Officer
**Web address:** www.wwgh.com

| | | |
|---|---|---|
| **Owned, leased, sponsored:** | 19 hospitals | 2648 beds |
| **Contract–managed:** | 0 hospitals | 0 beds |
| **Totals:** | 19 hospitals | 2648 beds |

**★4165: ADVENTIST HEALTH SYSTEM SUNBELT HEALTH CARE CORPORATION** (CO)
900 Hope Way, Altamonte Springs, FL Zip 32714–1502; tel. 407/357–1000; Donald L. Jernigan, Ph.D., President and Chief Executive Officer
**(Decentralized Health System)**

---

For explanation of codes following names, see page B2.
★ Indicates Type III membership in the American Hospital Association.

**COLORADO:** AVISTA ADVENTIST HOSPITAL (O, 114 beds) 100 Health Park Drive, Louisville, CO Zip 80027–9583; tel. 303/673–1000; Dennis Barts, Chief Executive Officer
**Web address:** www.avistahospital.org

CASTLE ROCK ADVENTIST HOSPITAL (O, 48 beds) 2350 Meadows Boulevard, Castle Rock, CO Zip 80109–8405; tel. 720/455–5000; Todd Folkenberg, Chief Executive Officer
**Web address:** www.castlerockhospital.org

LITTLETON ADVENTIST HOSPITAL (O, 201 beds) 7700 South Broadway Street, Littleton, CO Zip 80122–2628; tel. 303/730–8900; Brett Spenst, Chief Executive Officer
**Web address:** www.centura.org

PARKER ADVENTIST HOSPITAL (O, 145 beds) 9395 Crown Crest Boulevard, Parker, CO Zip 80138–8573; tel. 303/269–4000; Morre Dean, Chief Executive Officer
**Web address:** www.parkerhospital.org

PORTER ADVENTIST HOSPITAL (O, 250 beds) 2525 South Downing Street, Denver, CO Zip 80210–5876; tel. 303/778–1955; Morre Dean, Chief Executive Officer
**Web address:** www.porterhospital.org/poh/home/

**FLORIDA:** FLORIDA HOSPITAL (O, 2478 beds) 601 East Rollins Street, Orlando, FL Zip 32803–1248; tel. 407/303–6611; Lars D. Houmann, President
**Web address:** www.flhosp.org

FLORIDA HOSPITAL AT CONNERTON LONG TERM ACUTE CARE (O, 50 beds) 9441 Health Center Drive, Land O'Lakes, FL Zip 34637–5837; tel. 813/903–3701; Brian Adams, President and Chief Executive Officer
**Web address:** www.elevatinghealthcare.org

FLORIDA HOSPITAL CARROLLWOOD (O, 90 beds) 7171 North Dale Mabry Highway, Tampa, FL Zip 33614–2665; tel. 813/932–2222; Joe Johnson, Chief Executive Officer
**Web address:** www.elevatinghealthcare.org/locations/carrollwood

FLORIDA HOSPITAL DELAND (O, 156 beds) 701 West Plymouth Avenue, DeLand, FL Zip 32720–3236; tel. 386/943–4522; Timothy W. Cook, President and CEO
**Web address:** www.fhdeland.org

FLORIDA HOSPITAL FISH MEMORIAL (O, 175 beds) 1055 Saxon Boulevard, Orange City, FL Zip 32763–8468; tel. 386/917–5000; Ed Noseworthy, President and Chief Executive Officer
**Web address:** www.fhfishmemorial.org

FLORIDA HOSPITAL HEARTLAND MEDICAL CENTER (O, 214 beds) 4200 Sun'n Lake Boulevard, Sebring, FL Zip 33872–1986, Mailing Address: P.O. Box 9400, Zip 33871–9400; tel. 863/314–4466; Eric Stevens, Chief Executive Officer
**Web address:** www.fhheartland.org/

FLORIDA HOSPITAL MEMORIAL MEDICAL CENTER (O, 358 beds) 301 Memorial Medical Parkway, Daytona Beach, FL Zip 32117–5167; tel. 386/676–6000; Daryl Tol, Chief Executive Officer
**Web address:** www.floridahospitalmemorial.org

FLORIDA HOSPITAL NORTH PINELLAS (O, 168 beds) 1395 South Pinellas Avenue, Tarpon Springs, FL Zip 34689–3790; tel. 727/942–5000; Bruce Bergherm, Chief Executive Officer
**Web address:** www.fhnorthpinellas.com/

FLORIDA HOSPITAL TAMPA (O, 493 beds) 3100 East Fletcher Avenue, Tampa, FL Zip 33613–4688; tel. 813/971–6000; Brian Adams, President and CEO
**Web address:** www.floridahospital.com/tampa

FLORIDA HOSPITAL WATERMAN (O, 269 beds) 1000 Waterman Way, Tavares, FL Zip 32778–5266; tel. 352/253–3333; David Ottati, Chief Executive Officer
**Web address:** www.fhwat.org

FLORIDA HOSPITAL WAUCHULA (O, 25 beds) 533 West Carlton Street, Wauchula, FL Zip 33873–3407; tel. 863/773–3101; Denise Grimsley, Administrator
**Web address:** www.fh.floridahospital.com/heartland/home.aspx

FLORIDA HOSPITAL WESLEY CHAPEL (O, 83 beds) 2600 Bruce B. Downs Bouelvard, Wesley Chapel, FL Zip 33544–9207; tel. 813/929–5000; Denyse Bales-Chubb, Chief Executive Officer
**Web address:** www.https://www.floridahospital.com/wesley–chapel

FLORIDA HOSPITAL ZEPHYRHILLS (O, 139 beds) 7050 Gall Boulevard, Zephyrhills, FL Zip 33541–1399; tel. 813/788–0411; Randy Surber, Chief Executive Officer
**Web address:** www.fhzeph.org

FLORIDA HOSPITAL–FLAGLER (O, 99 beds) 60 Memorial Medical Parkway, Palm Coast, FL Zip 32164–5980; tel. 386/586–2000; Kenneth R. Mattison, Chief Executive Officer
**Web address:** www.floridahospitalflagler.com/

**GEORGIA:** GORDON HOSPITAL (O, 85 beds) 1035 Red Bud Road, Calhoun, GA Zip 30701–2082, Mailing Address: P.O. Box 12938, Zip 30703–7013; tel. 706/629–2895; Pete M. Weber, President and Chief Executive Officer
**Web address:** www.gordonhospital.com

MURRAY MEDICAL CENTER (O, 33 beds) 707 Old Dalton Ellijay Road, Chatsworth, GA Zip 30705–2060, Mailing Address: P.O. Box 1406, Zip 30705–1406; tel. 706/695–4564; Hal Coble, Administrator
**Web address:** www.murraymedical.org/

**ILLINOIS:** ADVENTIST BOLINGBROOK HOSPITAL (O, 134 beds) 500 Remington Boulevard, Bolingbrook, IL Zip 60440–4906; tel. 630/312–5000; Rick Mace, Chief Executive Officer
**Web address:** www.keepingyouwell.com/abh/

ADVENTIST HINSDALE HOSPITAL (O, 291 beds) 120 North Oak Street, Hinsdale, IL Zip 60521–3890; tel. 630/856–9000; Michael Goebel, Vice President and Chief Executive Officer
**Web address:** www.keepingyouwell.com

ADVENTIST LA GRANGE MEMORIAL HOSPITAL (O, 158 beds) 5101 South Willow Spring Road, La Grange, IL Zip 60525–2600; tel. 708/245–9000; Michael Goebel, Vice President and Chief Executive Officer
**Web address:** www.keepingyouwell.com

AMITA HEALTH ADVENTIST GLENOAKS HOSPITAL (O, 120 beds) 701 Winthrop Avenue, Glendale Heights, IL Zip 60139–1403; tel. 630/545–8000; Bruce C. Christian, Chief Executive Officer
**Web address:** www.adventistglenoaks.com

**KANSAS:** SHAWNEE MISSION MEDICAL CENTER (O, 400 beds) 9100 West 74th Street, Shawnee Mission, KS Zip 66204–4004, Mailing Address: Box 2923, Zip 66201–1323; tel. 913/676–2000; Ken J. Bacon, President and Chief Executive Officer
**Web address:** www.shawneemission.org

**KENTUCKY:** MANCHESTER MEMORIAL HOSPITAL (O, 63 beds) 210 Marie Langdon Drive, Manchester, KY Zip 40962–6388; tel. 606/598–5104; Erika Skula, President and Chief Executive Officer
**Web address:** www.manchestermemorial.org

**NORTH CAROLINA:** PARK RIDGE HEALTH (O, 95 beds) 100 Hospital Drive, Hendersonville, NC Zip 28792–5272; tel. 828/684–8501; Jimm Bunch, President and Chief Executive Officer
**Web address:** www.parkridgehealth.org

**TENNESSEE:** TAKOMA REGIONAL HOSPITAL (C, 32 beds) 401 Takoma Avenue, Greeneville, TN Zip 37743–4647; tel. 423/639–3151; Dennis Kiley, Interim Chief Executive Officer
**Web address:** www.takoma.org

**TEXAS:** CENTRAL TEXAS MEDICAL CENTER (O, 111 beds) 1301 Wonder World Drive, San Marcos, TX Zip 78666–7544; tel. 512/353–8979; Sam Huenergardt, President and Chief Executive Officer
**Web address:** www.ctmc.org

METROPLEX ADVENTIST HOSPITAL (O, 177 beds) 2201 South Clear Creek Road, Killeen, TX Zip 76549–4110; tel. 254/526–7523; Carlyle L. E. Walton, FACHE, Chief Executive Officer
**Web address:** www.mplex.org

ROLLINS–BROOK COMMUNITY HOSPITAL (O, 35 beds) 608 North Key Avenue, Lampasas, TX Zip 76550–1106, Mailing Address: P.O. Box 589, Zip 76550–0032; tel. 512/556–3682; Carlyle L. E. Walton, FACHE, Chief Executive Officer
**Web address:** www.mplex.org

TEXAS HEALTH HUGULEY HOSPITAL FORT WORTH SOUTH (C, 197 beds) 11801 South Freeway, Fort Worth, TX Zip 76028–7021, Mailing Address: P.O. Box 6337, Zip 76115–0337; tel. 817/293–9110; Kenneth A. Finch, President and Chief Executive Officer
**Web address:** www.TexasHealthHuguley.org

---

For explanation of codes following names, see page B2.
★ Indicates Type III membership in the American Hospital Association.

**WISCONSIN:** CHIPPEWA VALLEY HOSPITAL AND OAKVIEW CARE CENTER (O, 75 beds) 1220 Third Avenue West, Durand, WI Zip 54736–1600, Mailing Address: P.O. Box 224, Zip 54736–0224; tel. 715/672–4211; Douglas R. Peterson, President and Chief Executive Officer
**Web address:** www.chippewavalleyhospital.com/

| | | |
|---|---|---|
| Owned, leased, sponsored: | 32 hospitals | 7332 beds |
| Contract–managed: | 2 hospitals | 229 beds |
| Totals: | 34 hospitals | 7561 beds |

**0214: ADVENTIST HEALTHCARE** (NP)
820 West Diamond Avenue, Suite 600, Gaithersburg, MD Zip 20878–1419; tel. 301/315–3141; Terry Forde, Interim President and Chief Executive Officer
**(Moderately Centralized Health System)**

**MARYLAND:** ADVENTIST BEHAVIORAL HEALTH ROCKVILLE (O, 220 beds) 14901 Broschart Road, Rockville, MD Zip 20850–3318; tel. 301/251–4500; Kevin Young, FACHE, President
**Web address:** www.adventistbehavioralhealth.com

ADVENTIST REHABILITATION HOSPITAL OF MARYLAND (O, 77 beds) 9909 Medical Center Drive, Rockville, MD Zip 20850–6361; tel. 240/864–6000; Brent Reitz, President
**Web address:** www.adventistrehab.com

SHADY GROVE ADVENTIST HOSPITAL (O, 331 beds) 9901 Medical Center Drive, Rockville, MD Zip 20850–3395; tel. 240/826–6000; John Sackett, President
**Web address:** www.adventisthealthcare.com

WASHINGTON ADVENTIST HOSPITAL (O, 252 beds) 7600 Carroll Avenue, Takoma Park, MD Zip 20912–6392; tel. 301/891–7600; Erik Wangsness, President
**Web address:** www.adventisthealthcare.com

**NEW JERSEY:** HACKETTSTOWN REGIONAL MEDICAL CENTER (O, 111 beds) 651 Willow Grove Street, Hackettstown, NJ Zip 07840–1799; tel. 908/852–5100; Jason C. Coe, President and Chief Executive Officer
**Web address:** www.hrmcnj.org

| | | |
|---|---|---|
| Owned, leased, sponsored: | 5 hospitals | 991 beds |
| Contract–managed: | 0 hospitals | 0 beds |
| Totals: | 5 hospitals | 991 beds |

**★0064: ADVOCATE HEALTH CARE** (NP)
3075 Highland Parkway, Suite 600, Downers Grove, IL Zip 60515–1206; tel. 630/929–8700; Jim H. Skogsbergh, President and Chief Executive Officer
**(Moderately Centralized Health System)**

**ILLINOIS:** ADVOCATE BROMENN MEDICAL CENTER (O, 203 beds) 1304 Franklin Avenue, Normal, IL Zip 61761–3558, Mailing Address: P.O. Box 2850, Bloomington, Zip 61702–2850; tel. 309/454–1400; Colleen Kannaday, FACHE, President
**Web address:** www.bromenn.org

ADVOCATE CHRIST MEDICAL CENTER (O, 659 beds) 4440 West 95th Street, Oak Lawn, IL Zip 60453–2699; tel. 708/684–8000; Kenneth W. Lukhard, President
**Web address:** www.advocatehealth.com/christ

ADVOCATE CONDELL MEDICAL CENTER (O, 277 beds) 801 South Milwaukee Avenue, Libertyville, IL Zip 60048–3199; tel. 847/362–2900; Dominica Tallarico, President
**Web address:** www.advocatehealth.com/condell/

ADVOCATE EUREKA HOSPITAL (O, 18 beds) 101 South Major Street, Eureka, IL Zip 61530–1246; tel. 309/467–2371; Colleen Kannaday, FACHE, President
**Web address:** www.advocatehealth.com/eureka/

ADVOCATE GOOD SAMARITAN HOSPITAL (O, 319 beds) 3815 Highland Avenue, Downers Grove, IL Zip 60515–1590; tel. 630/275–5900; David Fox, President
**Web address:** www.advocatehealth.com/gsam

ADVOCATE GOOD SHEPHERD HOSPITAL (O, 176 beds) 450 West Highway 22, Barrington, IL Zip 60010–1919; tel. 847/381–0123; Karen A. Lambert, President
**Web address:** www.advocatehealth.com/gshp/

ADVOCATE ILLINOIS MASONIC MEDICAL CENTER (O, 315 beds) 836 West Wellington Avenue, Chicago, IL Zip 60657–5147; tel. 773/975–1600; Susan Nordstrom Lopez, President
**Web address:** www.advocatehealth.com/masonic

ADVOCATE LUTHERAN GENERAL HOSPITAL (O, 625 beds) 1775 Dempster Street, Park Ridge, IL Zip 60068–1174; tel. 847/723–2210; Richard B. Floyd, President
**Web address:** www.advocatehealth.com/luth/

ADVOCATE SHERMAN HOSPITAL (O, 255 beds) 1425 North Randall Road, Elgin, IL Zip 60123–2300; tel. 847/742–9800; Linda Deering, MSN, R.N., President
**Web address:** www.advocatehealth.com/sherman

ADVOCATE SOUTH SUBURBAN HOSPITAL (O, 280 beds) 17800 South Kedzie Avenue, Hazel Crest, IL Zip 60429–0989; tel. 708/799–8000; Richard Heim, President
**Web address:** www.advocatehealth.com/ssub/

ADVOCATE TRINITY HOSPITAL (O, 188 beds) 2350 East 93rd Street, Chicago, IL Zip 60617; tel. 773/967–2000; Michelle Gaskill, R.N., President
**Web address:** www.advocatehealth.com/trinity

| | | |
|---|---|---|
| Owned, leased, sponsored: | 11 hospitals | 3315 beds |
| Contract–managed: | 0 hospitals | 0 beds |
| Totals: | 11 hospitals | 3315 beds |

**0312: AHMC & HEALTHCARE, INC.** (IO)
55 South Raymond Avenue, Suite 105, Alhambra, CA Zip 91801–7101; tel. 626/457–9600; Jonathan Wu, M.D., President and Chairman
**(Independent Hospital System)**

**CALIFORNIA:** AHMC ANAHEIM REGIONAL MEDICAL CENTER (O, 223 beds) 1111 West La Palma Avenue, Anaheim, CA Zip 92801–2881; tel. 714/774–1450; Patrick A. Petre, Chief Executive Officer
**Web address:** www.anaheimregionalmc.com

ALHAMBRA HOSPITAL MEDICAL CENTER (O, 144 beds) 100 South Raymond Avenue, Alhambra, CA Zip 91801–3199, Mailing Address: P.O. Box 510, Zip 91802–2510; tel. 626/570–1606; Iris Lai, Chief Executive Officer
**Web address:** www.alhambrahospital.com

GARFIELD MEDICAL CENTER (O, 210 beds) 525 North Garfield Avenue, Monterey Park, CA Zip 91754–1205; tel. 626/573–2222; David J. Batista, Chief Executive Officer
**Web address:** www.garfieldmedicalcenter.com

GREATER EL MONTE COMMUNITY HOSPITAL (O, 117 beds) 1701 Santa Anita Avenue, South El Monte, CA Zip 91733–3411; tel. 626/579–7777; Stanley Toy, Jr., M.D., Chief Executive Officer
**Web address:** www.greaterelmonte.com

MONTEREY PARK HOSPITAL (O, 101 beds) 900 South Atlantic Boulevard, Monterey Park, CA Zip 91754–4780; tel. 626/570–9000; Philip A. Cohen, Chief Executive Officer
**Web address:** www.montereyparkhosp.com

SAN GABRIEL VALLEY MEDICAL CENTER (O, 273 beds) 438 West Las Tunas Drive, San Gabriel, CA Zip 91776–1216, Mailing Address: P.O. Box 1507, Zip 91778–1507; tel. 626/289–5454; Howard Ternes, Chief Executive Officer
**Web address:** www.sgvmc.org

WHITTIER HOSPITAL MEDICAL CENTER (O, 81 beds) 9080 Colima Road, Whittier, CA Zip 90605–1600; tel. 562/945–3561; Richard Castro, Chief Executive Officer
**Web address:** www.whittierhospital.com

| | | |
|---|---|---|
| Owned, leased, sponsored: | 7 hospitals | 1149 beds |
| Contract–managed: | 0 hospitals | 0 beds |
| Totals: | 7 hospitals | 1149 beds |

**★0247: AKRON GENERAL HEALTH SYSTEM** (NP)
1 Akron General Avenue, Akron, OH Zip 44307–2433; tel. 330/344–6000; Thomas L. Stover, M.D., President and Chief Executive Officer
**(Moderately Centralized Health System)**

For explanation of codes following names, see page B2.
★ Indicates Type III membership in the American Hospital Association.

Section B

**OHIO:** AKRON GENERAL MEDICAL CENTER (O, 407 beds) 1 Akron General Avenue, Akron, OH Zip 44307–2433; tel. 330/344–6000; Alan Papa, President
**Web address:** www.akrongeneral.org

EDWIN SHAW REHAB (O, 38 beds) 330 Broadway Street East, Cuyahoga Falls, OH Zip 44221–3312; tel. 330/436–0910; Lynne Blinco, Associate Vice President
**Web address:** www.edwinshaw.com

LODI COMMUNITY HOSPITAL (O, 20 beds) 225 Elyria Street, Lodi, OH Zip 44254–1096; tel. 330/948–1222; Alan Papa, President and Chief Operating Officer
**Web address:** www.lodihospital.org

| Owned, leased, sponsored: | 3 hospitals | 465 beds |
|---|---|---|
| Contract–managed: | 0 hospitals | 0 beds |
| Totals: | 3 hospitals | 465 beds |

**0225: ALAMEDA HEALTH SYSTEM** (NP)
15400 Foothill Boulevard, San Leandro, CA Zip 94578–1009; tel. 510/677–7920; Daniel Boggan, Jr., Interim Chief Executive Officer
**(Independent Hospital System)**

**CALIFORNIA:** ALAMEDA HOSPITAL (O, 246 beds) 2070 Clinton Avenue, Alameda, CA Zip 94501–4397; tel. 510/522–3700; Bonnie Panlasigui, Chief Administrative Officer
**Web address:** www.alamedahospital.org

HIGHLAND HOSPITAL (O, 380 beds) 1411 East 31st Street, Oakland, CA Zip 94602–1018; tel. 510/437–4800; Delvecchio Finley, Chief Executive Officer
**Web address:** www.alamedahealthsystem.org

SAN LEANDRO HOSPITAL (O, 42 beds) 13855 East 14th Street, San Leandro, CA Zip 94578–2600; tel. 510/357–6500; James E. T. Jackson, M.P.H., Chief Administrative Officer
**Web address:** www.sanleandrohospital.org

| Owned, leased, sponsored: | 3 hospitals | 668 beds |
|---|---|---|
| Contract–managed: | 0 hospitals | 0 beds |
| Totals: | 3 hospitals | 668 beds |

★**0199: ALLEGHENY HEALTH NETWORK** (NP)
30 Isabella Street, Suite 300, Pittsburgh, PA Zip 15212–5862; tel. 412/359–3131; John W. Paul, President and Chief Executive Officer
**(Decentralized Health System)**

**NEW YORK:** WESTFIELD MEMORIAL HOSPITAL (O, 4 beds) 189 East Main Street, Westfield, NY Zip 14787–1195; tel. 716/326–4921; Scott Whalen, Ph.D., FACHE, President and Chief Executive Officer
**Web address:** www.wmhinc.org

**PENNSYLVANIA:** ALLEGHENY GENERAL HOSPITAL (O, 383 beds) 320 East North Avenue, Pittsburgh, PA Zip 15212–4756; tel. 412/359–3131; Michael Harlovic, R.N., President and Chief Executive Officer
**Web address:** www.wpahs.org/locations/allegheny–general–hospital

ALLEGHENY VALLEY HOSPITAL (O, 228 beds) 1301 Carlisle Street, Natrona Heights, PA Zip 15065–1152; tel. 724/224–5100; William Englert, Chief Executive Officer
**Web address:** www.wpahs.org

CANONSBURG GENERAL HOSPITAL (O, 104 beds) 100 Medical Boulevard, Canonsburg, PA Zip 15317–9762; tel. 724/745–6100; Jane B. Sarra, President and Chief Executive Officer
**Web address:** www.wpahs.org

FORBES REGIONAL HOSPITAL (O, 349 beds) 2570 Haymaker Road, Monroeville, PA Zip 15146–3513; tel. 412/858–2000; Duke Rupert, President and Chief Executive Officer
**Web address:** www.ahn.org

JEFFERSON HOSPITAL (O, 349 beds) 565 Coal Valley Road, Jefferson Hills, PA Zip 15025–3703, Mailing Address: Box 18119, Pittsburgh, Zip 15236–0119; tel. 412/469–5000; Louise Urban, R.N., President and Chief Executive Officer
**Web address:** www.jeffersonregional.com

SAINT VINCENT HEALTH CENTER (O, 413 beds) 232 West 25th Street, Erie, PA Zip 16544–0002; tel. 814/452–5000; Scott Whalen, Ph.D., FACHE, President and Chief Executive Officer
**Web address:** www.svhs.org

WEST PENN HOSPITAL (O, 308 beds) 4800 Friendship Avenue, Pittsburgh, PA Zip 15224–1722; tel. 412/578–5000; Ronald J. Andro, President and Chief Executive Officer
**Web address:** www.wpahs.org

| Owned, leased, sponsored: | 8 hospitals | 2138 beds |
|---|---|---|
| Contract–managed: | 0 hospitals | 0 beds |
| Totals: | 8 hospitals | 2138 beds |

**0413: ALLEGIANCE HEALTH MANAGEMENT** (IO)
504 Texas Street, Suite 200, Shreveport, LA Zip 71101–3526; tel. 318/226–8202; Rock Bordelon, President and Chief Executive Officer
**(Independent Hospital System)**

**ARKANSAS:** EUREKA SPRINGS HOSPITAL (O, 15 beds) 24 Norris Street, Eureka Springs, AR Zip 72632–3541; tel. 479/253–7400; Christopher L. Bariola, Chief Executive Officer
**Web address:** www.eurekaspringshospital.com

NORTH METRO MEDICAL CENTER (O, 73 beds) 1400 West Braden Street, Jacksonville, AR Zip 72076–3788; tel. 501/985–7000; Joe Farrer, Interim Administrator
**Web address:** www.northmetromed.com

RIVER VALLEY MEDICAL CENTER (O, 35 beds) 200 North Third Street, Dardanelle, AR Zip 72834–3802, Mailing Address: P.O. Box 578, Zip 72834–0578; tel. 479/229–4677; Christopher L. Bariola, Chief Executive Officer

**LOUISIANA:** ALLEGIANCE HEALTH CENTER OF RUSTON (O, 14 beds) 1401 Ezell Street, Ruston, LA Zip 71270–7218; tel. 318/255–8085; Donna K. Thompson, Chief Executive Officer
**Web address:** www.ahmgt.com

BIENVILLE MEDICAL CENTER (O, 21 beds) 1175 Pine Street, Suite 200, Arcadia, LA Zip 71001–3122; tel. 318/263–4700; Kirk Lemoine, Chief Operating Officer

SABINE MEDICAL CENTER (O, 44 beds) 240 Highland Drive, Many, LA Zip 71449–3718; tel. 318/256–5691; Chris Beddoe, Chief Executive Officer
**Web address:** www.sabinemedicalcenter.net

**MISSISSIPPI:** ALLEGIANCE SPECIALTY HOSPITAL OF GREENVILLE (O, 39 beds) 300 South Washington Avenue, 3rd Floor, Greenville, MS Zip 38701–4719; tel. 662/332–7344; Vernail Herzog, Chief Executive Officer
**Web address:** www.ahmgt.com

**TEXAS:** ALLEGIANCE BEHAVIORAL HEALTH CENTER OF PLAINVIEW (O, 20 beds) 2601 Dimmit Road, 4th Floor, Plainview, TX Zip 79072–1833; tel. 806/296–9191; Angie Alexander, Chief Executive Officer
**Web address:** www.ahmgt.com

ALLEGIANCE SPECIALTY HOSPITAL OF KILGORE (O, 60 beds) 1612 South Henderson Boulevard, Kilgore, TX Zip 75662–3594; tel. 903/984–3505; Karen Ross, Chief Executive Officer
**Web address:** www.ahmgt.com

| Owned, leased, sponsored: | 9 hospitals | 321 beds |
|---|---|---|
| Contract–managed: | 0 hospitals | 0 beds |
| Totals: | 9 hospitals | 321 beds |

**0317: ALLIANT MANAGEMENT SERVICES** (IO)
2650 Eastpoint Parkway, Suite 300, Louisville, KY Zip 40223–5164; tel. 502/992–3525; Timothy L. Jarm, President and Chief Executive Officer
**(Decentralized Health System)**

**FLORIDA:** NORTHWEST FLORIDA COMMUNITY HOSPITAL (C, 59 beds) 1360 Brickyard Road, Chipley, FL Zip 32428–6303, Mailing Address: P.O. Box 889, Zip 32428–0889; tel. 850/638–1610; Mark E. Bush, Chief Executive Officer
**Web address:** www.nfch.org

For explanation of codes following names, see page B2.
★ Indicates Type III membership in the American Hospital Association.

**ILLINOIS:** FAIRFIELD MEMORIAL HOSPITAL (C, 55 beds) 303 N.W. 11th Street, Fairfield, IL Zip 62837–1203; tel. 618/842–2611; Katherine Bunting, Chief Executive Officer
**Web address:** www.fairfieldmemorial.org

FAYETTE COUNTY HOSPITAL (O, 110 beds) 650 West Taylor Street, Vandalia, IL Zip 62471–1296; tel. 618/283–1231; Gregory D. Starnes, Chief Executive Officer
**Web address:** www.fayettecountyhospital.org

GIBSON AREA HOSPITAL AND HEALTH SERVICES (C, 67 beds) 1120 North Melvin Street, Gibson City, IL Zip 60936–1477, Mailing Address: P.O. Box 429, Zip 60936–0429; tel. 217/784–4251; Robert C. Schmitt, II, Chief Executive Officer
**Web address:** www.gibsonhospital.org

PARIS COMMUNITY HOSPITAL (C, 25 beds) 721 East Court Street, Paris, IL Zip 61944–2460; tel. 217/465–4141; Oliver Smith, President and Chief Executive Officer
**Web address:** www.pariscommunityhospital.com

WABASH GENERAL HOSPITAL (C, 25 beds) 1418 College Drive, Mount Carmel, IL Zip 62863–2638; tel. 618/262–8621; Jay Purvis, Administrator and Chief Executive Officer
**Web address:** www.wabashgeneral.com

**INDIANA:** GIBSON GENERAL HOSPITAL (C, 70 beds) 1808 Sherman Drive, Princeton, IN Zip 47670–1043; tel. 812/385–3401; Emmett C. Schuster, President and Chief Executive Officer
**Web address:** www.gibsongeneral.com

PERRY COUNTY MEMORIAL HOSPITAL (C, 25 beds) 1 Hospital Road, Tell City, IN Zip 47586–2750; tel. 812/547–7011; Joseph A. Stuber, President and Chief Executive Officer
**Web address:** www.pchospital.org

**KENTUCKY:** BRECKINRIDGE MEMORIAL HOSPITAL (C, 43 beds) 1011 Old Highway 60, Hardinsburg, KY Zip 40143–2597; tel. 270/756–7000; Angela Portman, Chief Executive Officer
**Web address:** www.breckinridgehealth.org/

CARROLL COUNTY MEMORIAL HOSPITAL (C, 25 beds) 309 11th Street, Carrollton, KY Zip 41008–1400; tel. 502/732–4321; Michael A. Kozar, Chief Executive Officer
**Web address:** www.ccmhosp.com

CAVERNA MEMORIAL HOSPITAL (C, 25 beds) 1501 South Dixie Street, Horse Cave, KY Zip 42749–1477; tel. 270/786–2191; Alan B. Alexander, Chief Executive Officer
**Web address:** www.cavernahospital.com

JAMES B. HAGGIN MEMORIAL HOSPITAL (C, 25 beds) 464 Linden Avenue, Harrodsburg, KY Zip 40330–1862; tel. 859/734–5441; Victoria L. Reed, R.N., FACHE, Chief Executive Officer
**Web address:** www.hagginhosp.org

LIVINGSTON HOSPITAL AND HEALTHCARE SERVICES (C, 25 beds) 131 Hospital Drive, Salem, KY Zip 42078–8043; tel. 270/988–2299; Mark A. Edwards, Chief Executive Officer
**Web address:** www.lhhs.org

OWENSBORO HEALTH MUHLENBERG COMMUNITY HOSPITAL (C, 105 beds) 440 Hopkinsville Street, Greenville, KY Zip 42345–1172, Mailing Address: P.O. Box 387, Zip 42345–0387; tel. 270/338–8000; Ed Heath, Chief Executive Officer
**Web address:** www.mchky.org

TWIN LAKES REGIONAL MEDICAL CENTER (C, 75 beds) 910 Wallace Avenue, Leitchfield, KY Zip 42754–2414; tel. 270/259–9400; Wayne Meriwether, Chief Executive Officer
**Web address:** www.tlrmc.com

**NORTH CAROLINA:** ALLEGHANY MEMORIAL HOSPITAL (C, 25 beds) 233 Doctors Street, Sparta, NC Zip 28675–9247; tel. 336/372–5511; Brent R. Lammers, Chief Executive Officer
**Web address:** www.amhsparta.org

HUGH CHATHAM MEMORIAL HOSPITAL (C, 208 beds) 180 Parkwood Drive, Elkin, NC Zip 28621–2430, Mailing Address: P.O. Box 560, Zip 28621–0560; tel. 336/527–7000; Paul Hammes, Chief Executive Officer
**Web address:** www.hughchatham.org

| | | |
|---|---|---|
| **Owned, leased, sponsored:** | 1 hospital | 110 beds |
| **Contract–managed:** | 16 hospitals | 882 beds |
| **Totals:** | 17 hospitals | 992 beds |

★**0041: ALLINA HEALTH** (NP)
2925 Chicago Avenue, Minneapolis, MN Zip 55407–1321, Mailing Address: P.O. Box 43, Zip 55440–0043; tel. 612/262–5000; Penny Ann Wheeler, M.D., Chief Executive Officer
**(Moderately Centralized Health System)**

**MINNESOTA:** ABBOTT NORTHWESTERN HOSPITAL (O, 674 beds) 800 East 28th Street, Minneapolis, MN Zip 55407–3799; tel. 612/863–4000; Ben Bache-Wiig, M.D., President
**Web address:** www.abbottnorthwestern.com

BUFFALO HOSPITAL (O, 44 beds) 303 Catlin Street, Buffalo, MN Zip 55313–1947; tel. 763/682–1212; Jennifer Myster, President
**Web address:** www.buffalohospital.org

CAMBRIDGE MEDICAL CENTER (O, 78 beds) 701 South Dellwood Street, Cambridge, MN Zip 55008–1920; tel. 763/689–7700; Gary Shaw, President
**Web address:** www.allina.com/ahs/cambridge.nsf

DISTRICT ONE HOSPITAL (O, 42 beds) 200 State Avenue, Faribault, MN Zip 55021–6345; tel. 507/334–6451; Stephen J. Pribyl, FACHE, Chief Executive Officer
**Web address:** www.districtonehospital.com

HUTCHINSON HEALTH (C, 57 beds) 1095 Highway 15 South, Hutchinson, MN Zip 55350–3182; tel. 320/234–5000; Steven Mulder, M.D., President and Chief Executive Officer
**Web address:** www.hutchhealth.com

MERCY HOSPITAL (O, 255 beds) 4050 Coon Rapids Boulevard, Coon Rapids, MN Zip 55433–2586; tel. 763/236–6000; Sara J. Criger, President
**Web address:** www.allinamercy.org

NEW ULM MEDICAL CENTER (O, 45 beds) 1324 Fifth Street North, New Ulm, MN Zip 56073–1553; tel. 507/217–5000; Toby Freier, President
**Web address:** www.newulmmedicalcenter.com

OWATONNA HOSPITAL (O, 43 beds) 2250 N.W. 26th Street, Owatonna, MN Zip 55060–5503; tel. 507/451–3850; David L. Albrecht, President
**Web address:** www.owatonnahospital.com

PHILLIPS EYE INSTITUTE (O, 8 beds) 2215 Park Avenue, Minneapolis, MN Zip 55404–3756; tel. 612/775–8800; Daniel S. Conrad, M.D., President
**Web address:** www.allinahealth.org/ahs/pei.nsf/

REGINA HOSPITAL (O, 55 beds) 1175 Nininger Road, Hastings, MN Zip 55033–1098; tel. 651/480–4100; Thomas R. Thompson, Chief Executive Officer
**Web address:** www.reginamedical.org

ST. FRANCIS REGIONAL MEDICAL CENTER (O, 86 beds) 1455 St. Francis Avenue, Shakopee, MN Zip 55379–3380; tel. 952/428–3000; Mike McMahan, Chief Executive Officer
**Web address:** www.stfrancis–shakopee.com

UNITED HOSPITAL (O, 364 beds) 333 North Smith Avenue, Saint Paul, MN Zip 55102–2389; tel. 651/241–8000; Thomas O'Connor, President
**Web address:** www.allina.com

UNITY HOSPITAL (O, 176 beds) 550 Osborne Road N.E., Fridley, MN Zip 55432–2799; tel. 763/236–5000; Helen J. Strike, R.N., President
**Web address:** www.allina.com

**WISCONSIN:** RIVER FALLS AREA HOSPITAL (O, 12 beds) 1629 East Division Street, River Falls, WI Zip 54022–1571; tel. 715/425–6155; David R. Miller, President
**Web address:** www.allina.com

| | | |
|---|---|---|
| **Owned, leased, sponsored:** | 13 hospitals | 1882 beds |
| **Contract–managed:** | 1 hospital | 57 beds |
| **Totals:** | 14 hospitals | 1939 beds |

**0187: ALTA HEALTHCARE SYSTEM** (IO)
10780 Santa Monica Boulevard, Suite 400, Los Angeles, CA Zip 90025–7616; tel. 310/943–4500; David Topper, Chief Executive Officer

**CALIFORNIA:** LOS ANGELES COMMUNITY HOSPITAL AT LOS ANGELES (O, 180 beds) 4081 East Olympic Boulevard, Los Angeles, CA Zip 90023–3330; tel. 323/267–0477; Omar Ramirez, Chief Executive Officer

For explanation of codes following names, see page B2.
★ Indicates Type III membership in the American Hospital Association.

SOUTHERN CALIFORNIA HOSPITAL AT HOLLYWOOD (O, 45 beds) 6245 De Longpre Avenue, Los Angeles, CA Zip 90028–9001; tel. 323/462–2271; Bruce P. Grimshaw, FACHE, Chief Executive Officer
**Web address:** www.hollywoodcommunityhospital.org/

| | | |
|---|---|---|
| Owned, leased, sponsored: | 2 hospitals | 225 beds |
| Contract–managed: | 0 hospitals | 0 beds |
| Totals: | 2 hospitals | 225 beds |

**0877: ALTAPOINTE HEALTH SYSTEMS** (IO)
5750–A Southland Drive, Mobile, AL Zip 36693–3316; tel. 251/473–4423; J. Tuerk Schlesinger, Chief Executive Officer

**ALABAMA:** BAYPOINTE BEHAVIORAL HEALTH (O, 60 beds) 5800 Southland Drive, Mobile, AL Zip 36693–3313; tel. 251/661–0153; Jack Lungu, Administrator
**Web address:** www.altapointe.org

EASTPOINTE HOSPITAL (O, 66 beds) 7400 Roper Lane, Daphne, AL Zip 36526–5274; tel. 251/378–6500; Philip L. Cusa, Administrator
**Web address:** www.altapointe.org/eastpointe.php

| | | |
|---|---|---|
| Owned, leased, sponsored: | 2 hospitals | 126 beds |
| Contract–managed: | 0 hospitals | 0 beds |
| Totals: | 2 hospitals | 126 beds |

**2295: AMERICAN PROVINCE OF LITTLE COMPANY OF MARY SISTERS** (CC)
9350 South California Avenue, Evergreen Park, IL Zip 60805–2595; tel. 708/229–5491; Sister Kathleen McIntyre, Province Leader
**(Moderately Centralized Health System)**

**ILLINOIS:** LITTLE COMPANY OF MARY HOSPITAL AND HEALTH CARE CENTERS (O, 254 beds) 2800 West 95th Street, Evergreen Park, IL Zip 60805–2795; tel. 708/422–6200; Dennis A. Reilly, President and Chief Executive Officer
**Web address:** www.lcmh.org

**INDIANA:** MEMORIAL HOSPITAL AND HEALTH CARE CENTER (O, 143 beds) 800 West Ninth Street, Jasper, IN Zip 47546–2516; tel. 812/996–2345; E. Kyle Bennett, President and Chief Executive Officer
**Web address:** www.mhhcc.org

| | | |
|---|---|---|
| Owned, leased, sponsored: | 2 hospitals | 397 beds |
| Contract–managed: | 0 hospitals | 0 beds |
| Totals: | 2 hospitals | 397 beds |

**0644: AMG INTEGRATED HEALTHCARE MANAGEMENT** (IO)
101 La Rue France, Suite 500, Lafayette, LA Zip 70508–3144; tel. 337/269–9828; August J. Rantz, III, Founder and Chief Executive Officer
**(Independent Hospital System)**

**KANSAS:** AMG SPECIALTY HOSPITAL–WICHITA (O, 26 beds) 8080 East Pawnee Street, Wichita, KS Zip 67207–5475; tel. 316/682–0004; Robert A. Loepp, Jr., FACHE, Chief Executive Officer
**Web address:** www.amgwichita.com/

**LOUISIANA:** AMG SPECIALTY HOSPITAL–DENHAM SPRINGS (O, 117 beds) 8375 Florida Boulevard, Denham Springs, LA Zip 70726–7806; tel. 225/665–2664; Karen Crayton, Administrator
**Web address:** www.amgdenham.com/

AMG SPECIALTY HOSPITAL–FELICIANA (O, 16 beds) 9725 Grace Lane, Clinton, LA Zip 70722–4925; tel. 225/683–1600; Michael Sanders, Chief Executive Officer
**Web address:** www.amgfeliciana.com/

AMG SPECIALTY HOSPITAL–HOUMA (O, 40 beds) 629 Dunn Street, Houma, LA Zip 70360–4707; tel. 985/274–0001; Keith Carruth, Chief Executive Officer
**Web address:** www.amghouma.com/

AMG SPECIALTY HOSPITAL–LAFAYETTE (O, 58 beds) 310 Youngsville Highway, Lafayette, LA Zip 70508–4524; tel. 337/839–9880; Ben Miller, Chief Executive Officer
**Web address:** www.amglafayette.com

AMG SPECIALTY HOSPITAL–SLIDELL (O, 40 beds) 1400 Lindberg Drive, Slidell, LA Zip 70458–8056; tel. 985/326–0440; Timothy Burke, Chief Executive Officer
**Web address:** www.amgslidell.com/

LAFAYETTE PHYSICAL REHABILITATION HOSPITAL (O, 32 beds) 307 Polly Lane, Lafayette, LA Zip 70508–4960; tel. 337/314–1111; Thomas R. Strohe, Chief Executive Officer
**Web address:** www.lafayettephysicalrehab.com/

THE NEUROMEDICAL CENTER REHABILITATION HOSPITAL (O, 23 beds) 10101 Park Rowe Avenue, Suite 500, Baton Rouge, LA Zip 70810–1685; tel. 225/906–2999; Elizabeth Wilson, Administrator
**Web address:** www.theneuromedicalcenter.com

**MISSISSIPPI:** AMG SPECIALTY HOSPITAL–GREENWOOD (O, 40 beds) 1401 River Road Floor 2, Greenwood, MS Zip 38930–4030; tel. 662/459–2681; Jennifer Wallace, Chief Executive Officer
**Web address:** www.amggreenwood.com/

**NEVADA:** AMG SPECIALTY HOSPITAL – LAS VEGAS (O, 24 beds) 4015 South McLeod Drive, Las Vegas, NV Zip 89121–4305; tel. 702/433–2200; William (Bill) Fox, Chief Executive Officer
**Web address:** www.amgihm.com/locations/#map_top

**NEW MEXICO:** AMG SPECIALTY HOSPITAL–ALBUQUERQUE (O, 24 beds) 235 Elm Street N.E., Albuquerque, NM Zip 87102–3672; tel. 505/842–5550; Elizabeth Rees, Chief Executive Officer
**Web address:** www.amgalbuquerque.com/

**OKLAHOMA:** AMG SPECIALTY HOSPITAL–EDMOND (O, 37 beds) 1100 East Ninth Street, Edmond, OK Zip 73034–5755; tel. 405/341–8150; Michael E. Gerten, Chief Executive Officer
**Web address:** www.amgedmond.com/

AMG SPECIALTY HOSPITAL–TULSA (O, 46 beds) 2408 East 81st Street, Suite 2800, Tulsa, OK Zip 74104–6510; tel. 918/710–3620; Stacy Wilde, Chief Executive Officer
**Web address:** www.amgihm.com

| | | |
|---|---|---|
| Owned, leased, sponsored: | 13 hospitals | 523 beds |
| Contract–managed: | 0 hospitals | 0 beds |
| Totals: | 13 hospitals | 523 beds |

**●0389: ANMED HEALTH** (NP)
800 North Fant Street, Anderson, SC Zip 29621–5793; tel. 864/512–1000; William T. Manson, III, Chief Executive Officer
**(Moderately Centralized Health System)**

**SOUTH CAROLINA:** ANMED HEALTH MEDICAL CENTER (O, 401 beds) 800 North Fant Street, Anderson, SC Zip 29621–5793; tel. 864/512–1000; William T. Manson, III, FACHE, Chief Executive Officer
**Web address:** www.anmedhealth.org

| | | |
|---|---|---|
| Owned, leased, sponsored: | 1 hospital | 401 beds |
| Contract–managed: | 0 hospitals | 0 beds |
| Totals: | 1 hospital | 401 beds |

**★0866: APPALACHIAN REGIONAL HEALTHCARE SYSTEM** (NP)
336 Deerfield Road, Boone, NC Zip 28607–5008, Mailing Address: P.O. Box 2600, Zip 28607–2600; tel. 828/262–4100; Richard G. Sparks, President and Chief Executive Officer
**(Independent Hospital System)**

**NORTH CAROLINA:** CHARLES A. CANNON MEMORIAL HOSPITAL (C, 35 beds) 434 Hospital Drive, Linville, NC Zip 28646, Mailing Address: P.O. Box 767, Zip 28646–0767; tel. 828/737–7000; Carmen Lacey, MSN, R.N., President
**Web address:** www.https://apprhs. org/locations/cannon–memorial–hospital

WATAUGA MEDICAL CENTER (C, 99 beds) 336 Deerfield Road, Boone, NC Zip 28607–5008, Mailing Address: P.O. Box 2600, Zip 28607–2600; tel. 828/262–4100; Richard G. Sparks, Chief Executive Officer
**Web address:** www.https://apprhs.org/contact–us

For explanation of codes following names, see page B2.
★ Indicates Type III membership in the American Hospital Association.
● Single hospital health care system

| Owned, leased, sponsored: | 0 hospitals | 0 beds |
| Contract–managed: | 2 hospitals | 134 beds |
| Totals: | 2 hospitals | 134 beds |

**0145: APPALACHIAN REGIONAL HEALTHCARE, INC.** (NP)
2285 Executive Drive, Suite 400, Lexington, KY Zip 40505–4810,
Mailing Address: P.O. Box 8086, Zip 40533–8086;
tel. 859/226–2440; Jerry Haynes, President and Chief Executive
Officer
**(Decentralized Health System)**

**KENTUCKY:** HARLAN ARH HOSPITAL (O, 145 beds) 81 Ball Park Road,
Harlan, KY Zip 40831–1792; tel. 606/573–8100; Donald Fields,
Community Chief Executive Officer
**Web address:** www.arh.org

HAZARD ARH REGIONAL MEDICAL CENTER (O, 308 beds) 100 Medical Center
Drive, Hazard, KY Zip 41701–9421; tel. 606/439–6600; Dan Stone, Senior
Community Chief Executive Officer
**Web address:** www.arh.org

MARY BRECKINRIDGE ARH HOSPITAL (O, 25 beds) 130 Kate Ireland Drive,
Hyden, KY Zip 41749–9071, Mailing Address: P.O. Box 447–A,
Zip 41749–0717; tel. 606/672–2901; Mallie S. Noble, Administrator
**Web address:** www.frontiernursing.org

MCDOWELL ARH HOSPITAL (O, 25 beds) Route 122, McDowell, KY
Zip 41647, Mailing Address: P.O. Box 247, Zip 41647–0247;
tel. 606/377–3400; Russell Barker, Community Chief Executive Officer
**Web address:** www.arh.org

MIDDLESBORO ARH HOSPITAL (O, 96 beds) 3600 West Cumberland Avenue,
Middlesboro, KY Zip 40965–2614, Mailing Address: P.O. Box 340,
Zip 40965–0340; tel. 606/242–1100; Michael Slusher, Community Chief
Executive Officer
**Web address:** www.arh.org/middlesboro

MORGAN COUNTY ARH HOSPITAL (L, 25 beds) 476 Liberty Road, West
Liberty, KY Zip 41472–2049, Mailing Address: P.O. Box 579,
Zip 41472–0579; tel. 606/743–3186; Stephen M. Gavalchik, FACHE,
Community Chief Executive Officer
**Web address:** www.arh.org

TUG VALLEY ARH REGIONAL MEDICAL CENTER (O, 141 beds) 260 Hospital
Drive, South Williamson, KY Zip 41503–4072; tel. 606/237–1710; Timothy
A. Hatfield, Community Chief Executive Officer
**Web address:** www.arh.org/locations/tug_valley/about_us.aspx

WHITESBURG ARH HOSPITAL (O, 87 beds) 240 Hospital Road, Whitesburg,
KY Zip 41858–7627; tel. 606/633–3600; Dena C. Sparkman, FACHE,
Community Chief Executive Officer
**Web address:** www.arh.org/whitesburg

**WEST VIRGINIA:** BECKLEY ARH HOSPITAL (O, 170 beds) 306 Stanaford
Road, Beckley, WV Zip 25801–3142; tel. 304/255–3000; Rocco K.
Massey, Community Chief Executive Officer
**Web address:** www.arh.org

SUMMERS COUNTY ARH HOSPITAL (L, 25 beds) Terrace Street, Hinton, WV
Zip 25951–2407, Mailing Address: Drawer 940, Zip 25951–0940;
tel. 304/466–1000; Wesley Dangerfield, Community Chief Executive Officer
**Web address:** www.arh.org

| Owned, leased, sponsored: | 10 hospitals | 1047 beds |
| Contract–managed: | 0 hospitals | 0 beds |
| Totals: | 10 hospitals | 1047 beds |

**★0104: ARCHBOLD MEDICAL CENTER** (NP)
910 South Broad Street, Thomasville, GA Zip 31792–6113;
tel. 229/228–2739; J. Perry Mustian, President
**(Independent Hospital System)**

**GEORGIA:** BROOKS COUNTY HOSPITAL (L, 25 beds) 903 North Court Street,
Quitman, GA Zip 31643–1315, Mailing Address: P.O. Box 5000,
Zip 31643–5000; tel. 229/263–4171; Kenneth D. Rhudy, Chief Executive
Officer
**Web address:** www.archbold.org

GRADY GENERAL HOSPITAL (L, 48 beds) 1155 Fifth Street S.E., Cairo, GA
Zip 39828–3142, Mailing Address: P.O. Box 360, Zip 39828–0360;
tel. 229/377–1150; Crystal Ramm, Administrator
**Web address:** www.archbold.org

JOHN D. ARCHBOLD MEMORIAL HOSPITAL (O, 302 beds) 915 Gordon
Avenue, Thomasville, GA Zip 31792–6614, Mailing Address: P.O. Box 1018,
Zip 31799–1018; tel. 229/228–2000; J. Perry Mustian, President and Chief
Executive Officer
**Web address:** www.archbold.org

MITCHELL COUNTY HOSPITAL (L, 181 beds) 90 East Stephens Street,
Camilla, GA Zip 31730–1836, Mailing Address: P.O. Box 639,
Zip 31730–0639; tel. 229/336–5284; James Womack, Administrator
**Web address:** www.archbold.org

| Owned, leased, sponsored: | 4 hospitals | 556 beds |
| Contract–managed: | 0 hospitals | 0 beds |
| Totals: | 4 hospitals | 556 beds |

**★0069: ARDENT HEALTH SERVICES** (IO)
1 Burton Hills Boulevard, Suite 250, Nashville, TN Zip 37215–6195;
tel. 615/296–3000; David T. Vandewater, President and Chief
Executive Officer
**(Moderately Centralized Health System)**

**NEW MEXICO:** LOVELACE MEDICAL CENTER (O, 263 beds) 601 Martin
Luther King Avenue N.E., Albuquerque, NM Zip 87102–3619;
tel. 505/727–8000; Troy Greer, Chief Executive Officer
**Web address:** www.lovelace.
com/albuquerque–hospital/lovelace–medical–center#.UDZ1laDhf48

LOVELACE REGIONAL HOSPITAL – ROSWELL (O, 26 beds) 117 East 19th
Street, Roswell, NM Zip 88201–5151; tel. 575/627–7000; Dawn M.
Tschabrun, R.N., Chief Executive Officer
**Web address:** www.lovelace.com

LOVELACE REHABILITATION HOSPITAL (O, 52 beds) 505 Elm Street N.E.,
Albuquerque, NM Zip 87102–2500; tel. 505/727–4700; Derrick Jones, Chief
Executive Officer
**Web address:** www.lovelace.com

LOVELACE WESTSIDE HOSPITAL (O, 80 beds) 10501 Golf Course Road N.W.,
Albuquerque, NM Zip 87114–5000, Mailing Address: P.O. Box 25555,
Zip 87125–0555; tel. 505/727–2000; Farron Sneed, FACHE, Chief Executive
Officer
**Web address:** www.lovelace.
com/albuquerque–hospital/lovelace–westside–hospital#.UDZ1t6Dhf48

LOVELACE WOMEN'S HOSPITAL (O, 78 beds) 4701 Montgomery Boulevard
N.E., Albuquerque, NM Zip 87109–1251, Mailing Address: P.O. Box 25555,
Zip 87125–0555; tel. 505/727–7800; Sheri Milone, Chief Executive Officer
and Administrator
**Web address:** www.lovelace.
com/albuquerque–hospital/lovelace–womens–hospital#.UDZ17KDhf48

**OKLAHOMA:** BAILEY MEDICAL CENTER (O, 37 beds) 10502 North 110th
East Avenue, Owasso, OK Zip 74055–6655; tel. 918/376–8000; Keith
Mason, Chief Executive Officer
**Web address:** www.baileymedicalcenter.com

HILLCREST HOSPITAL – SOUTH (O, 160 beds) 8801 South 101st East
Avenue, Tulsa, OK Zip 74133–5716; tel. 918/294–4000; Lynn M. Mergen,
Chief Executive Officer
**Web address:** www.southcresthospital.com

HILLCREST HOSPITAL CLAREMORE (O, 67 beds) 1202 North Muskogee
Place, Claremore, OK Zip 74017–3036; tel. 918/341–2556; David
Chaussard, Chief Executive Officer
**Web address:** www.hillcrestclaremore.com

HILLCREST HOSPITAL CUSHING (O, 95 beds) 1027 East Cherry Street,
Cushing, OK Zip 74023–4101, Mailing Address: P.O. Box 1409,
Zip 74023–1409; tel. 918/225–2915; Kevin Hawk, Chief Executive Officer
**Web address:** www.hillcrestcushing.com/

HILLCREST HOSPITAL HENRYETTA (O, 41 beds) 2401 West Main Street,
Henryetta, OK Zip 74437–3893, Mailing Address: P.O. Box 1269,
Zip 74437–1269; tel. 918/650–1100; Dee Renshaw, Chief Executive Officer
**Web address:** www.hillcresthenryetta.com/

For explanation of codes following names, see page B2.
★ Indicates Type III membership in the American Hospital Association.

Section B

HILLCREST MEDICAL CENTER (O, 557 beds) 1120 South Utica, Tulsa, OK Zip 74104–4090; tel. 918/579–1000; Kevin J. Gross, Interim Chief Executive Officer
**Web address:** www.hillcrest.com/home

**TEXAS:** BAPTIST ST. ANTHONY HEALTH SYSTEM (O, 312 beds) 1600 Wallace Boulevard, Amarillo, TX Zip 79106–1799; tel. 806/212–2000; Bob Williams, President and Chief Executive Officer
**Web address:** www.bsahs.org

PHYSICIANS SURGICAL HOSPITAL – PANHANDLE CAMPUS (O, 11 beds) 7100 West 9th Avenue, Amarillo, TX Zip 79106–1704; tel. 806/212–0247; Brad McCall, President and Chief Executive Officer
**Web address:** www.physurg.com/

PHYSICIANS SURGICAL HOSPITAL – QUAIL CREEK (O, 41 beds) 6819 Plum Creek, Amarillo, TX Zip 79124–1602; tel. 806/354–6100; Brad McCall, President and Chief Executive Officer
**Web address:** www.physurg.com

| | | |
|---|---|---|
| Owned, leased, sponsored: | 14 hospitals | 1820 beds |
| Contract–managed: | 0 hospitals | 0 beds |
| Totals: | 14 hospitals | 1820 beds |

**0809: ARNOT HEALTH** (NP)
600 Roe Avenue, Elmira, NY Zip 14905–1629; tel. 607/737–4100; Robert K. Lambert, M.D., FACHE, President and Chief Executive Officer
**(Independent Hospital System)**

**NEW YORK:** ARNOT OGDEN MEDICAL CENTER (O, 176 beds) 600 Roe Avenue, Elmira, NY Zip 14905–1629; tel. 607/737–4100; H. Fred Farley, R.N., Ph.D., FACHE, President and Chief Operating Officer
**Web address:** www.aomc.org

IRA DAVENPORT MEMORIAL HOSPITAL (O, 184 beds) 7571 State Route 54, Bath, NY Zip 14810–9590; tel. 607/776–8500; James B. Watson, President and Chief Operating Officer
**Web address:** www.arnothealth.org

ST. JOSEPH'S HOSPITAL (O, 212 beds) 555 St. Joseph's Boulevard, Elmira, NY Zip 14901–3223; tel. 607/733–6541; H. Fred Farley, R.N., Ph.D., FACHE, President and Chief Operating Officer
**Web address:** www.stjosephs.org

| | | |
|---|---|---|
| Owned, leased, sponsored: | 3 hospitals | 572 beds |
| Contract–managed: | 0 hospitals | 0 beds |
| Totals: | 3 hospitals | 572 beds |

**★0094: ASANTE HEALTH SYSTEM** (NP)
2650 Siskiyou Boulevard, Suite 200, Medford, OR Zip 97504–8170; tel. 541/789–4100; Roy G. Vinyard, FACHE, President and Chief Executive Officer
**(Moderately Centralized Health System)**

**OREGON:** ASANTE ASHLAND COMMUNITY HOSPITAL (O, 36 beds) 280 Maple Street, Ashland, OR Zip 97520–1593; tel. 541/201–4000; Sheila Clough, Chief Executive Officer
**Web address:** www.ashlandhospital.org

ASANTE ROGUE REGIONAL MEDICAL CENTER (O, 320 beds) 2825 East Barnett Road, Medford, OR Zip 97504–8332; tel. 541/789–7000; Scott A. Kelly, Chief Executive Officer
**Web address:** www.asante.org

ASANTE THREE RIVERS MEDICAL CENTER (O, 111 beds) 500 S.W. Ramsey Avenue, Grants Pass, OR Zip 97527–5554; tel. 541/472–7000; Win Howard, Chief Executive Officer
**Web address:** www.asante.org/trmc/

| | | |
|---|---|---|
| Owned, leased, sponsored: | 3 hospitals | 467 beds |
| Contract–managed: | 0 hospitals | 0 beds |
| Totals: | 3 hospitals | 467 beds |

**★0198: ASCENSION HEALTH** (CC)
101 South Hanley Road, Suite 450, Saint Louis, MO Zip 63105–3406; tel. 314/733–8000; Robert J. Henkel, FACHE, President and Chief Executive Officer
**(Decentralized Health System)**

**ALABAMA:** PROVIDENCE HOSPITAL (S, 302 beds) 6801 Airport Boulevard, Mobile, AL Zip 36608–3785, Mailing Address: P.O. Box 850429, Zip 36685–0429; tel. 251/633–1000; Todd Kennedy, President and Chief Executive Officer
**Web address:** www.providencehospital.org

ST. VINCENT'S BIRMINGHAM (S, 409 beds) 810 St. Vincent's Drive, Birmingham, AL Zip 35205–1695, Mailing Address: P.O. Box 12407, Zip 35202–2407; tel. 205/939–7000; Evan Ray, FACHE, President
**Web address:** www.stvhs.org

ST. VINCENT'S BLOUNT (S, 25 beds) 150 Gilbreath, Oneonta, AL Zip 35121–2827, Mailing Address: P.O. Box 1000, Zip 35121–0013; tel. 205/274–3000; Michael Korpiel, FACHE, President
**Web address:** www.stvhs.com

ST. VINCENT'S EAST (S, 362 beds) 50 Medical Park East Drive, Birmingham, AL Zip 35235–9987; tel. 205/838–3000; Michael Korpiel, FACHE, President and Chief Operating Officer
**Web address:** www.stvhs.com

ST. VINCENT'S ST. CLAIR (S, 40 beds) 7063 Veterans Parkway, Pell City, AL Zip 35125–1499; tel. 205/814–2105; Michael Korpiel, President
**Web address:** www.stvhs.com

**ARIZONA:** CARONDELET HOLY CROSS HOSPITAL (S, 25 beds) 1171 West Target Range Road, Nogales, AZ Zip 85621–2415; tel. 520/285–3000; Debbie Knapheide, MSN, Site Administrator, Chief Nursing Officer and Chief Operating Officer
**Web address:** www.carondelet.org

CARONDELET ST. JOSEPH'S HOSPITAL (S, 486 beds) 350 North Wilmot Road, Tucson, AZ Zip 85711–2678; tel. 520/873–3000; Tony Fonze, President and Chief Executive Officer
**Web address:** www.carondelet.org

CARONDELET ST. MARY'S HOSPITAL (S, 300 beds) 1601 West St. Mary's Road, Tucson, AZ Zip 85745–2682; tel. 520/872–3000; Amy Beiter, M.D., President and Chief Executive Officer
**Web address:** www.carondelet.org

**CONNECTICUT:** ST. VINCENT'S MEDICAL CENTER (S, 413 beds) 2800 Main Street, Bridgeport, CT Zip 06606–4292; tel. 203/576–5454; Stuart G. Marcus, M.D., FACS, President and Chief Executive Officer
**Web address:** www.stvincents.org

**DISTRICT OF COLUMBIA:** PROVIDENCE HOSPITAL (S, 438 beds) 1150 Varnum Street N.E., Washington, DC Zip 20017–2104; tel. 202/269–7000; Amy E. Freeman, President and Chief Executive Officer
**Web address:** www.provhosp.org

**FLORIDA:** SACRED HEART HOSPITAL OF PENSACOLA (S, 560 beds) 5151 North Ninth Avenue, Pensacola, FL Zip 32504–8795, Mailing Address: P.O. Box 2700, Zip 32513–2700; tel. 850/416–7000; Henry Stovall, President
**Web address:** www.sacred–heart.org

SACRED HEART HOSPITAL ON THE EMERALD COAST (S, 58 beds) 7800 Highway 98 West, Miramar Beach, FL Zip 32550; tel. 850/278–3000; Roger L. Hall, President
**Web address:** www.sacredheartemerald.org

SACRED HEART HOSPITAL ON THE GULF (S, 19 beds) 3801 East Highway 98, Port St. Joe, FL Zip 32456–5318; tel. 850/229–5600; Roger L. Hall, President
**Web address:** www.sacred–heart.org/gulf/

ST. VINCENT'S MEDICAL CENTER CLAY COUNTY (O, 64 beds) 1670 St. Vincent's Way, Middleburg, FL Zip 32068–8427, Mailing Address: 1670 St. Vincents Way, Zip 32068–8447; tel. 904/602–1000; Blain Claypool, President
**Web address:** www.jaxhealth.com/

ST. VINCENT'S MEDICAL CENTER RIVERSIDE (S, 528 beds) 1 Shircliff Way, Jacksonville, FL Zip 32204–4748, Mailing Address: P.O. Box 2982, Zip 32203–2982; tel. 904/308–7300; Donnie Romine, Interim President and Chief Executive Officer
**Web address:** www.jaxhealth.com

---

For explanation of codes following names, see page B2.
★ Indicates Type III membership in the American Hospital Association.

Section B

ST. VINCENT'S MEDICAL CENTER SOUTHSIDE (S, 288 beds) 4201 Belfort Road, Jacksonville, FL Zip 32216–1431; tel. 904/296–3700; Donnie Romine, Interim President and Chief Executive Officer
**Web address:** www.jaxhealth.com

**IDAHO:** ST. JOSEPH REGIONAL MEDICAL CENTER (S, 119 beds) 415 Sixth Street, Lewiston, ID Zip 83501–2431; tel. 208/743–2511; Michael T. Rooney, M.D., Interim President and Chief Executive Officer
**Web address:** www.sjrmc.org

**ILLINOIS:** ALEXIAN BROTHERS BEHAVIORAL HEALTH HOSPITAL (O, 141 beds) 1650 Moon Lake Boulevard, Hoffman Estates, IL Zip 60169–1010; tel. 847/882–1600; Clayton Ciha, President and Chief Executive Officer
**Web address:** www.abbhh.org

ALEXIAN BROTHERS MEDICAL CENTER (O, 371 beds) 800 Biesterfield Road, Elk Grove Village, IL Zip 60007–3397; tel. 847/437–5500; John P. Werrbach, Chief Executive Officer
**Web address:** www.alexian.org

ST. ALEXIUS MEDICAL CENTER (O, 280 beds) 1555 Barrington Road, Hoffman Estates, IL Zip 60169–1019; tel. 847/843–2000; Leonard Wilk, President and Chief Executive Officer
**Web address:** www.stalexius.org

**INDIANA:** ST. JOSEPH HOSPITAL & HEALTH CENTER (S, 138 beds) 1907 West Sycamore Street, Kokomo, IN Zip 46901–4197; tel. 765/452–5611; Margaret M. Johnson, Interim President
**Web address:** www.stvincent.org/stjoseph

ST. MARY'S WARRICK HOSPITAL (S, 35 beds) 1116 Millis Avenue, Boonville, IN Zip 47601–2204; tel. 812/897–4800; Kathy J. Hall, Administrator
**Web address:** www.stmarys.org/warrick

ST. MARY'S MEDICAL CENTER OF EVANSVILLE (S, 436 beds) 3700 Washington Avenue, Evansville, IN Zip 47714–0541; tel. 812/485–4000; Keith Jewell, President
**Web address:** www.stmarys.org

ST. VINCENT ANDERSON REGIONAL HOSPITAL (S, 141 beds) 2015 Jackson Street, Anderson, IN Zip 46016–4339; tel. 765/649–2511; Thomas J. VanOsdol, President
**Web address:** www.stvincent.org/Saint–Johns/Default.aspx

ST. VINCENT CARMEL HOSPITAL (S, 121 beds) 13500 North Meridian Street, Carmel, IN Zip 46032–1456; tel. 317/582–7000; Michael D. Chittenden, President
**Web address:** www.stvincent.org

ST. VINCENT CLAY HOSPITAL (S, 25 beds) 1206 East National Avenue, Brazil, IN Zip 47834–2797, Mailing Address: P.O. Box 489, Zip 47834–0489; tel. 812/442–2500; Jerry Laue, Administrator
**Web address:** www.stvincent.org

ST. VINCENT DUNN HOSPITAL (S, 25 beds) 1600 23rd Street, Bedford, IN Zip 47421–4704; tel. 812/275–3331; Matt Balla, Chief Executive Officer
**Web address:** www.stvincent.org/St–Vincent–Dunn/Default.aspx

ST. VINCENT FISHERS HOSPITAL (S, 46 beds) 13861 Olio Road, Fishers, IN Zip 46037–3487; tel. 317/415–9000; Gary Fammartino, Administrator
**Web address:** www.stvincent.org

ST. VINCENT FRANKFORT HOSPITAL (S, 25 beds) 1300 South Jackson Street, Frankfort, IN Zip 46041–3394; tel. 765/656–3000; Kristi Bledsoe, R.N., Administrator
**Web address:** www.stvincent.org

ST. VINCENT HEART CENTER (S, 107 beds) 10580 North Meridian Street, Indianapolis, IN Zip 46290–1028; tel. 317/583–5000; Blake A. Dye, President
**Web address:** www.bestheartcare.com/

ST. VINCENT INDIANAPOLIS HOSPITAL (S, 919 beds) 2001 West 86th Street, Indianapolis, IN Zip 46260–1991, Mailing Address: P.O. Box 40970, Zip 46240–0970; tel. 317/338–2345; Joel Feldman, M.D., President
**Web address:** www.stvincent.org

ST. VINCENT JENNINGS HOSPITAL (S, 25 beds) 301 Henry Street, North Vernon, IN Zip 47265–1097; tel. 812/352–4200; Carl W. Risk, II, Administrator
**Web address:** www.stvincent.org

ST. VINCENT MERCY HOSPITAL (S, 17 beds) 1331 South A Street, Elwood, IN Zip 46036–1942; tel. 765/552–4600; Francis G. Albarano, Administrator
**Web address:** www.stvincent.org

ST. VINCENT RANDOLPH HOSPITAL (S, 16 beds) 473 Greenville Avenue, Winchester, IN Zip 47394–9436, Mailing Address: P.O. Box 407, Zip 47394–0407; tel. 765/584–0004; Francis G. Albarano, Administrator
**Web address:** www.stvincent.org

ST. VINCENT SALEM HOSPITAL (S, 25 beds) 911 North Shelby Street, Salem, IN Zip 47167–1694; tel. 812/883–5881; Dana M. Muntz, Chief Executive Officer
**Web address:** www.stvincent.org/St–Vincent–Salem/Default.aspx

ST. VINCENT SETON SPECIALTY HOSPITAL (S, 74 beds) 8050 Township Line Road, Indianapolis, IN Zip 46260–2478; tel. 317/415–8353; Peter H. Alexander, Administrator
**Web address:** www.stvincent.org/

ST. VINCENT WILLIAMSPORT HOSPITAL (S, 16 beds) 412 North Monroe Street, Williamsport, IN Zip 47993–1049; tel. 765/762–4000; Jane Craigin, Chief Executive Officer
**Web address:** www.stvincent.org

**KANSAS:** VIA CHRISTI HOSPITAL MANHATTAN, INC. (O, 100 beds) 1823 College Avenue, Manhattan, KS Zip 66502–3346; tel. 785/776–3322; John R. Broberg, FACHE, Senior Administrator
**Web address:** www.https://www.viachristi.org/manhattan

VIA CHRISTI HOSPITAL ON ST. FRANCIS (O, 717 beds) 929 North St. Francis Street, Wichita, KS Zip 67214–3882; tel. 316/268–5000; Sherry Hausmann, Senior Administrator
**Web address:** www.via–christi.org

VIA CHRISTI HOSPITAL ON ST. TERESA (O, 58 beds) 14800 West St. Teresa, Wichita, KS Zip 67235–9602; tel. 316/796–7000; Kevin Strecker, President
**Web address:** www.via–christi.org/st–teresa

VIA CHRISTI HOSPITAL PITTSBURG (O, 120 beds) 1 Mt. Carmel Way, Pittsburg, KS Zip 66762–7587; tel. 620/231–6100; Randall R. Cason, FACHE, Senior Administrator
**Web address:** www.viachristi.org/pittsburg

VIA CHRISTI REHABILITATION HOSPITAL (O, 58 beds) 1151 North Rock Road, Wichita, KS Zip 67206–1262; tel. 316/634–3400; Cindy LaFleur, Senior Administrator
**Web address:** www.via–christi.org

**MARYLAND:** SAINT AGNES HOSPITAL (S, 367 beds) 900 Caton Avenue, Baltimore, MD Zip 21229–5201; tel. 410/368–6000; Bonnie Phipps, President and Chief Executive Officer
**Web address:** www.stagnes.org

**MICHIGAN:** BORGESS MEDICAL CENTER (S, 366 beds) 1521 Gull Road, Kalamazoo, MI Zip 49048–1640; tel. 269/226–7000; Kathlene A. Young, MS, FACHE, Chief Executive Officer
**Web address:** www.borgess.com

BORGESS–LEE MEMORIAL HOSPITAL (S, 25 beds) 420 West High Street, Dowagiac, MI Zip 49047–1943; tel. 269/782–8681; John E. Ryder, Chief Operating Officer
**Web address:** www.borgess.com

BORGESS–PIPP HOSPITAL (S, 43 beds) 411 Naomi Street, Plainwell, MI Zip 49080–1222; tel. 269/685–6811; John E. Ryder, Administrator and Chief Operating Officer
**Web address:** www.borgess.com

BRIGHTON CENTER FOR RECOVERY (S, 99 beds) 12851 Grand River Road, Brighton, MI Zip 48116–8506; tel. 810/227–1211; Raymond Waller, Director
**Web address:** www.brightonrecovery.org

GENESYS REGIONAL MEDICAL CENTER (S, 410 beds) One Genesys Parkway, Grand Blanc, MI Zip 48439–8066; tel. 810/606–5000; Elizabeth Aderholdt, President and Chief Executive Officer
**Web address:** www.genesys.org

PROVIDENCE – PROVIDENCE PARK HOSPITAL, SOUTHFIELD CAMPUS (S, 577 beds) 16001 West Nine Mile Road, Southfield, MI Zip 48075–4818, Mailing Address: P.O. Box 2043, Zip 48037–2043; tel. 248/424–3000; Michael Wiemann, M.D., President
**Web address:** www.providence–stjohnhealth.org

ST. JOHN HOSPITAL AND MEDICAL CENTER (S, 635 beds) 22101 Moross Road, Detroit, MI Zip 48236–2148; tel. 313/343–4000; Robert E. Hoban, Chief Executive Officer
**Web address:** www.stjohn.org

ST. JOHN MACOMB–OAKLAND HOSPITAL (S, 522 beds) 11800 East 12 Mile Road, Warren, MI Zip 48093–3472; tel. 586/573–5000; Terry Hamilton, President
**Web address:** www.stjohnprovidence.org/macomb–oakland/

For explanation of codes following names, see page B2.
★ Indicates Type III membership in the American Hospital Association.

Section B

ST. JOHN RIVER DISTRICT HOSPITAL (S, 68 beds) 4100 River Road, East China, MI Zip 48054-2909; tel. 810/329-7111; Frank W. Poma, President
**Web address:** www.stjohn.org

ST. JOSEPH HEALTH SYSTEM (S, 20 beds) 200 Hemlock Street, Tawas City, MI Zip 48763-9237, Mailing Address: P.O. Box 659, Zip 48764-0659; tel. 989/362-3411; Ann M. Balfour, R.N., President
**Web address:** www.sjhsys.org

ST. MARY'S OF MICHIGAN (S, 236 beds) 800 South Washington Avenue, Saginaw, MI Zip 48601-2594; tel. 989/907-8000; Elizabeth Aderholdt, President and Chief Executive Officer
**Web address:** www.stmarysofmichigan.org

ST. MARY'S OF MICHIGAN STANDISH HOSPITAL (S, 64 beds) 805 West Cedar Street, Standish, MI Zip 48658-9526; tel. 989/846-4521; Elizabeth Aderholdt, President and Chief Executive Officer
**Web address:** www.stmarysofmichigan.org/standish

**MINNESOTA:** SAINT ELIZABETH'S MEDICAL CENTER (O, 166 beds) 1200 Grant Boulevard West, Wabasha, MN Zip 55981-1042; tel. 651/565-4531; Thomas Crowley, President and Chief Executive Officer
**Web address:** www.stelizabethswabasha.org

**NEW YORK:** MOUNT ST. MARY'S HOSPITAL AND HEALTH CENTER (S, 377 beds) 5300 Military Road, Lewiston, NY Zip 14092-1903; tel. 716/297-4800; Gary C. Tucker, President and Chief Executive Officer
**Web address:** www.msmh.org

OUR LADY OF LOURDES MEMORIAL HOSPITAL, INC. (S, 154 beds) 169 Riverside Drive, Binghamton, NY Zip 13905-4246; tel. 607/798-5111; Kathryn Connerton, Chief Executive Officer
**Web address:** www.lourdes.com

ST. MARY'S HEALTHCARE (S, 290 beds) 427 Guy Park Avenue, Amsterdam, NY Zip 12010-1054; tel. 518/842-1900; Victor Giulianelli, FACHE, President and Chief Executive Officer
**Web address:** www.smha.org

**OKLAHOMA:** JANE PHILLIPS MEDICAL CENTER (O, 119 beds) 3500 East Frank Phillips Boulevard, Bartlesville, OK Zip 74006-2411; tel. 918/333-7200; Mike Moore, President and Chief Operating Officer
**Web address:** www.jpmc.org

JANE PHILLIPS NOWATA HEALTH CENTER (O, 13 beds) 237 South Locust Street, Nowata, OK Zip 74048-3660; tel. 918/273-3102; Scott Upton, Administrator
**Web address:** www.jpmc.org

ST. JOHN BROKEN ARROW (O, 44 beds) 1000 West Boise Circle, Broken Arrow, OK Zip 74012-4900; tel. 918/994-8100; David L. Phillips, Chief Executive Officer
**Web address:** www.stjohnbrokenarrow.com

ST. JOHN MEDICAL CENTER (O, 547 beds) 1923 South Utica Avenue, Tulsa, OK Zip 74104-6502; tel. 918/744-2345; Jeffrey D. Nowlin, President and Chief Operating Officer
**Web address:** www.sjmc.org

ST. JOHN OWASSO (O, 45 beds) 12451 East 100th Street North, Owasso, OK Zip 74055-4600; tel. 918/274-5000; David L. Phillips, President and Chief Executive Officer
**Web address:** www.stjohnowasso.com

ST. JOHN SAPULPA (O, 25 beds) 519 South Division Street, Sapulpa, OK Zip 74066-4501, Mailing Address: P.O. Box 1368, Zip 74067-1368; tel. 918/224-4280; David L. Phillips, Chief Executive Officer
**Web address:** www.sjmc.org

**TENNESSEE:** SAINT THOMAS DEKALB HOSPITAL (O, 56 beds) 520 West Main Street, Smithville, TN Zip 37166-1138, Mailing Address: P.O. Box 640, Zip 37166-0640; tel. 615/215-5000; Susan Conley, Chief Executive Officer
**Web address:** www.dekalbcommunityhospital.com

SAINT THOMAS HICKMAN HOSPITAL (S, 65 beds) 135 East Swan Street, Centerville, TN Zip 37033-1417; tel. 931/729-4271; Jack M. Keller, Chief Executive Officer
**Web address:** www.hickmanhospital.com

SAINT THOMAS HIGHLANDS HOSPITAL (O, 60 beds) 401 Sewell Road, Sparta, TN Zip 38583-1299; tel. 931/738-9211; William Little, Chief Executive Officer
**Web address:** www.whitecountyhospital.com

SAINT THOMAS HOSPITAL FOR SPINAL SURGERY (S, 23 beds) 2011 Murphy Avenue, Suite 400, Nashville, TN Zip 37203-2065; tel. 615/341-7500; Kathy Watson, R.N., Administrator and Chief Nursing Officer
**Web address:** www.hospitalforspinalsurgery.com

SAINT THOMAS MIDTOWN HOSPITAL (S, 425 beds) 2000 Church Street, Nashville, TN Zip 37236-0002; tel. 615/284-5555; Don King, Chief Executive Officer
**Web address:** www.sths.com

SAINT THOMAS RIVER PARK HOSPITAL (O, 85 beds) 1559 Sparta Street, Mc Minnville, TN Zip 37110-1316; tel. 931/815-4000; Timothy W. McGill, Chief Executive Officer
**Web address:** www.riverparkhospital.com

SAINT THOMAS RUTHERFORD HOSPITAL (S, 286 beds) 1700 Medical Center Parkway, Murfreesboro, TN Zip 37129-2245; tel. 615/396-4100; Gordon B. Ferguson, President and Chief Executive Officer
**Web address:** www.mtmc.org

SAINT THOMAS STONES RIVER HOSPITAL (O, 60 beds) 324 Doolittle Road, Woodbury, TN Zip 37190-1139; tel. 615/563-4001; Susan Conley, Chief Executive Officer
**Web address:** www.stonesriverhospital.com

SAINT THOMAS WEST HOSPITAL (S, 395 beds) 4220 Harding Road, Nashville, TN Zip 37205-2095, Mailing Address: P.O. Box 380, Zip 37202-0380; tel. 615/222-2111; Don King, Chief Executive Officer
**Web address:** www.stthomas.org

**TEXAS:** DELL CHILDREN'S MEDICAL CENTER OF CENTRAL TEXAS (S, 248 beds) 4900 Mueller Boulevard, Austin, TX Zip 78723-3079; tel. 512/324-0000; Robert I. Bonar, Jr., Chief Executive Officer
**Web address:** www.dellchildrens.net

PROVIDENCE HEALTHCARE NETWORK (S, 647 beds) 6901 Medical Parkway, Waco, TX Zip 76712-7998, Mailing Address: P.O. Box 2589, Zip 76702-2589; tel. 254/751-4000; Brett A. Esrock, President and Chief Executive Officer
**Web address:** www.providence.net

SETON EDGAR B. DAVIS HOSPITAL (S, 25 beds) 130 Hays Street, Luling, TX Zip 78648-3207; tel. 830/875-7000; Apryl Haynes, R.N., Vice President, Chief Operating Officer, Chief Nursing Officer and Administrator
**Web address:** www.seton.net/locations/edgar_davis/

SETON HIGHLAND LAKES (S, 23 beds) 3201 South Water Street, Burnet, TX Zip 78611-4510, Mailing Address: P.O. Box 1219, Zip 78611-7219; tel. 512/715-3000; Karen Litterer, R.N., MSN, Administrator and Chief Operating Officer
**Web address:** www.seton.net

SETON MEDICAL CENTER AUSTIN (S, 422 beds) 1201 West 38th Street, Austin, TX Zip 78705-1006; tel. 512/324-1000; Katherine Henderson, Chief Executive Officer
**Web address:** www.seton.net

SETON MEDICAL CENTER HAYS (O, 96 beds) 6001 Kyle Parkway, Kyle, TX Zip 78640-6112, Mailing Address: 6001 Kyle Prkway, Zip 78640-6112; tel. 512/504-5000; Christopher L. Hartle, President
**Web address:** www.seton.net/locations/seton_medical_center_hays/

SETON MEDICAL CENTER WILLIAMSON (S, 143 beds) 201 Seton Parkway, Round Rock, TX Zip 78665-8000; tel. 512/324-4000; Michelle Robertson, R.N., President
**Web address:** www.seton.net/williamson

SETON NORTHWEST HOSPITAL (S, 74 beds) 11113 Research Boulevard, Austin, TX Zip 78759-5236; tel. 512/324-6000; Karen Litterer, R.N., MSN, Administrator and Chief Operating Officer
**Web address:** www.seton.net

SETON SHOAL CREEK HOSPITAL (S, 92 beds) 3501 Mills Avenue, Austin, TX Zip 78731-6391; tel. 512/324-2000; William Hendricks, Vice President and Chief Operating Officer
**Web address:** www.seton.net

SETON SMITHVILLE REGIONAL HOSPITAL (O, 10 beds) 800 East Highway 71, Smithville, TX Zip 78957-1730; tel. 512/237-3214; Robbie G. Rabe, Interim Chief Executive Officer
**Web address:** www.seton.org

SETON SOUTHWEST HOSPITAL (S, 33 beds) 7900 F. M. 1826, Austin, TX Zip 78737-1407; tel. 512/324-9000; Mary Faria, FACHE, Ph.D., Vice President and Chief Operating Officer
**Web address:** www.seton.net

For explanation of codes following names, see page B2.
★ Indicates Type III membership in the American Hospital Association.

Section B

UNIVERSITY MEDICAL CENTER AT BRACKENRIDGE (S, 188 beds) 601 East 15th Street, Austin, TX Zip 78701–1996; tel. 512/324–7000; Christann Vasquez, President
**Web address:** www.seton.net

**WASHINGTON:** LOURDES COUNSELING CENTER (S, 20 beds) 1175 Carondelet Drive, Richland, WA Zip 99354–3300; tel. 509/943–9104; Barbara Mead, Executive Director
**Web address:** www.lourdeshealth.net

LOURDES MEDICAL CENTER (S, 53 beds) 520 North Fourth Avenue, Pasco, WA Zip 99301–5257, Mailing Address: P.O. Box 2568, Zip 99302–2568; tel. 509/547–7704; John Serle, FACHE, President and Chief Executive Officer
**Web address:** www.lourdeshealth.net

**WISCONSIN:** CALUMET MEDICAL CENTER (O, 15 beds) 614 Memorial Drive, Chilton, WI Zip 53014–1597; tel. 920/849–2386; Timothy Richman, President
**Web address:** www.affinityhealth.org

COLUMBIA ST. MARY'S HOSPITAL MILWAUKEE (S, 324 beds) 2301 North Lake Drive, Milwaukee, WI Zip 53211–4508; tel. 414/291–1000; Travis Andersen, President and Chief Executive Officer
**Web address:** www.columbia–stmarys.org

COLUMBIA ST. MARY'S OZAUKEE HOSPITAL (S, 116 beds) 13111 North Port Washington Road, Mequon, WI Zip 53097–2416; tel. 262/243–7300; Travis Andersen, President and Chief Executive Officer
**Web address:** www.columbia–stmarys.org

FLAMBEAU HOSPITAL (O, 25 beds) 98 Sherry Avenue, Park Falls, WI Zip 54552–1467, Mailing Address: P.O. Box 310, Zip 54552–0310; tel. 715/762–2484; David A. Grundstrom, Chief Administrative Officer
**Web address:** www.flambeauhospital.org

HOWARD YOUNG MEDICAL CENTER (O, 44 beds) 240 Maple Street, Woodruff, WI Zip 54568–9190, Mailing Address: P.O. Box 470, Zip 54568–0470; tel. 715/356–8000; Sandra L. Anderson, President and Chief Executive Officer
**Web address:** www.ministryhealth.org

MERCY MEDICAL CENTER (O, 120 beds) 500 South Oakwood Road, Oshkosh, WI Zip 54904–7944; tel. 920/223–2000; Jeremy Normington–Slay, FACHE, Chief Executive Officer
**Web address:** www.affinityhealth.org

MINISTRY DOOR COUNTY MEDICAL CENTER (O, 55 beds) 323 South 18th Avenue, Sturgeon Bay, WI Zip 54235–1495; tel. 920/743–5566; Gerald M. Worrick, President and Chief Executive Officer
**Web address:** www.ministryhealth.org

MINISTRY EAGLE RIVER MEMORIAL HOSPITAL (O, 12 beds) 201 Hospital Road, Eagle River, WI Zip 54521–8835; tel. 715/479–7411; Sandra L. Anderson, President and Chief Executive Officer
**Web address:** www.ministryhealth.org

MINISTRY GOOD SAMARITAN HEALTH CENTER (O, 10 beds) 601 South Center Avenue, Merrill, WI Zip 54452–3404; tel. 715/536–5511; Mary T. Krueger, President
**Web address:** www.ministryhealth.org

MINISTRY OUR LADY OF VICTORY HOSPITAL (O, 5 beds) 1120 Pine Street, Stanley, WI Zip 54768–1297; tel. 715/644–5571; Vanessa Freitag, President
**Web address:** www.ministryhealth.org

MINISTRY SACRED HEART HOSPITAL (O, 8 beds) 401 West Mohawk Drive, Tomahawk, WI Zip 54487–2274; tel. 715/453–7700; Sandra L. Anderson, President and Chief Executive Officer
**Web address:** www.ministryhealth.org

MINISTRY SAINT CLARE'S HOSPITAL (O, 90 beds) 3400 Ministry Parkway, Weston, WI Zip 54476–5220; tel. 715/393–3000; Mary T. Krueger, President
**Web address:** www.ministryhealth.org

MINISTRY SAINT JOSEPH'S HOSPITAL (O, 319 beds) 611 St. Joseph Avenue, Marshfield, WI Zip 54449–1898; tel. 715/387–1713; Brian Kief, Regional Vice President Ministry Health Care and President Ministry Saint Joseph's Hospital
**Web address:** www.stjosephs–marshfield.org

MINISTRY SAINT MARY'S HOSPITALS (O, 64 beds) 2251 North Shore Drive, Rhinelander, WI Zip 54501–6710; tel. 715/361–2000; Sandra L. Anderson, President and Chief Executive Officer
**Web address:** www.ministryhealth.org

MINISTRY SAINT MICHAEL'S HOSPITAL (O, 51 beds) 900 Illinois Avenue, Stevens Point, WI Zip 54481–3196; tel. 715/346–5000; Jeffrey L. Martin, President
**Web address:** www.ministryhealth.org/SMH/home.nws

SACRED HEART REHABILITATION INSTITUTE (S, 31 beds) 2323 North Lake Drive, Milwaukee, WI Zip 53211–4508; tel. 414/298–6750; Allan M. Spooner, President
**Web address:** www.columbia–stmarys.org/SHRI

ST. ELIZABETH HOSPITAL (O, 211 beds) 1506 South Oneida Street, Appleton, WI Zip 54915–1305; tel. 920/738–2000; Monica Hilt, President and Chief Executive Officer
**Web address:** www.affinityhealth.org

| | | |
|---|---|---|
| **Owned, leased, sponsored:** | 105 hospitals | 18713 beds |
| **Contract–managed:** | 0 hospitals | 0 beds |
| **Totals:** | 105 hospitals | 18713 beds |

★**0519: ASPIRUS, INC.** (NP)
425 Pine Ridge Boulevard, Wausau, WI Zip 54401–4123; tel. 715/847–2118; Matthew Heywood, Chief Executive Officer
**(Moderately Centralized Health System)**

**MICHIGAN:** ASPIRUS GRAND VIEW (O, 25 beds) N10561 Grand View Lane, Ironwood, MI Zip 49938–9622; tel. 906/932–2525; Paula L. Chermside, Chief Operating Officer
**Web address:** www.aspirusgrandview.org

ASPIRUS KEWEENAW HOSPITAL (O, 25 beds) 205 Osceola Street, Laurium, MI Zip 49913–2134; tel. 906/337–6500; Michael Hauswirth, Chief Operating Officer
**Web address:** www.aspiruskeweenaw.org

ASPIRUS ONTONAGON HOSPITAL (O, 64 beds) 601 South Seventh Street, Ontonagon, MI Zip 49953–1459; tel. 906/884–8000; Michael Hauswirth, Chief Operating Officer
**Web address:** www.aspirus–ontonagon.org

ASPIRUS IRON RIVER HOSPITALS AND CLINICS (O, 12 beds) 1400 West Ice Lake Road, Iron River, MI Zip 49935–9526; tel. 906/265–6121; Connie L. Koutouzos, R.N., MSN, Chief Executive Officer and President
**Web address:** www.northstarhs.org

**WISCONSIN:** ASPIRUS MEDFORD HOSPITAL (O, 124 beds) 135 South Gibson Street, Medford, WI Zip 54451–1696; tel. 715/748–8100; Gregory A. Olson, President and Chief Executive Officer
**Web address:** www.memhc.com

ASPIRUS RIVERVIEW HOSPITAL AND CLINICS, INC. (O, 69 beds) 410 Dewey Street, Wisconsin Rapids, WI Zip 54494–4715, Mailing Address: P.O. Box 8080, Zip 54495–8080; tel. 715/423–6060; Rick Nevers, Interim Chief Executive Officer
**Web address:** www.riverviewhospital.org

ASPIRUS WAUSAU HOSPITAL (O, 229 beds) 333 Pine Ridge Boulevard, Wausau, WI Zip 54401–4187; tel. 715/847–2121; Darrell Lentz, President
**Web address:** www.aspirus.org

| | | |
|---|---|---|
| **Owned, leased, sponsored:** | 7 hospitals | 548 beds |
| **Contract–managed:** | 0 hospitals | 0 beds |
| **Totals:** | 7 hospitals | 548 beds |

★**0865: ATLANTIC HEALTH SYSTEM** (NP)
475 South Street, Morristown, NJ Zip 07962, Mailing Address: P.O. Box 1905, Zip 07962–1905; tel. 973/660–3270; Brian A. Gragnolati, FACHE, President and Chief Executive Officer
**(Centralized Physician/Insurance Health System)**

**NEW JERSEY:** CHILTON MEDICAL CENTER (O, 199 beds) 97 West Parkway, Pompton Plains, NJ Zip 07444–1696; tel. 973/831–5000; Alan Lieber, Interim President and Chief
**Web address:** www.chiltonmemorial.org

MORRISTOWN MEDICAL CENTER (O, 678 beds) 100 Madison Avenue, Morristown, NJ Zip 07960–6136; tel. 973/971–5000; Trish O'Keefe, R.N., Ph.D., MSN, Interim President
**Web address:** www.atlantichealth.org/Morristown/

NEWTON MEDICAL CENTER (O, 148 beds) 175 High Street, Newton, NJ Zip 07860–1004; tel. 973/383–2121; Joseph DiPaolo, FACHE, President
**Web address:** www.atlantichealth.org/newton/

For explanation of codes following names, see page B2.
★ Indicates Type III membership in the American Hospital Association.

Section B

OVERLOOK MEDICAL CENTER (O, 461 beds) 99 Beauvoir Avenue, Summit, NJ Zip 07901–3533; tel. 908/522–2000; Alan R. Lieber, President
**Web address:** www.atlantichealth.org/Overlook

| | | |
|---|---|---|
| Owned, leased, sponsored: | 4 hospitals | 1486 beds |
| Contract–managed: | 0 hospitals | 0 beds |
| Totals: | 4 hospitals | 1486 beds |

● ★**0293:  ATLANTICARE** (NP)
2500 English Creek Avenue, Building 500, Suite 501, Egg Harbor Township, NJ Zip 08234; tel. 609/407–2309; David P. Tilton, President and Chief Executive Officer
**(Centralized Health System)**

ATLANTICARE REGIONAL MEDICAL CENTER (O, 540 beds) 1925 Pacific Avenue, Atlantic City, NJ Zip 08401–6713; tel. 609/441–8994; Lori Herndon, R.N., President and Chief Executive Officer
**Web address:** www.atlanticare.org

| | | |
|---|---|---|
| Owned, leased, sponsored: | 1 hospital | 540 beds |
| Contract–managed: | 0 hospitals | 0 beds |
| Totals: | 1 hospital | 540 beds |

**0894:  AUDUBON BEHAVIORAL HEALTHCARE** (IO)
100 West Hawkins, Suite D., Longview, TX Zip 75605; tel. 903/212–2930; William V. Brown, Chief Executive Officer

**TEXAS:** OCEANS BEHAVIORAL HOSPITAL LONGVIEW (O, 24 beds) 615 Clinic Drive, Longview, TX Zip 75605–5172; tel. 903/212–3105; Lauren Weber, Administrator
**Web address:** www.oceanslongview.com/

OCEANS BEHAVIORAL HOSPITAL LUFKIN (O, 24 beds) 302 Gobblers Knob, Lufkin, TX Zip 75904–5419; tel. 936/632–2276; Frances Dick, Chief Executive Officer
**Web address:** www.oceanslufkin.com/

| | | |
|---|---|---|
| Owned, leased, sponsored: | 2 hospitals | 48 beds |
| Contract–managed: | 0 hospitals | 0 beds |
| Totals: | 2 hospitals | 48 beds |

**0859:  AULTMAN HEALTH FOUNDATION** (NP)
2600 Sixth Street S.W., Canton, OH Zip 44710–1702; tel. 330/363–6192; Edward J. Roth, III, President and Chief Executive Officer
**(Moderately Centralized Health System)**

**OHIO:** AULTMAN HOSPITAL (O, 542 beds) 2600 Sixth Street S.W., Canton, OH Zip 44710–1702; tel. 330/452–9911; Edward J. Roth, III, President and Chief Executive Officer
**Web address:** www.aultman.com

AULTMAN ORRVILLE HOSPITAL (O, 25 beds) 832 South Main Street, Orrville, OH Zip 44667–2208; tel. 330/682–3010; Marchelle Suppan, DPM, President and Chief Executive Officer
**Web address:** www.aultmanorrville.org

AULTMAN SPECIALTY HOSPITAL (O, 30 beds) 2600 Sixth Street, S.W., Canton, OH Zip 44710–1702; tel. 330/363–4000; Terry Regula, Chief Executive Officer
**Web address:** www.aultman.org

| | | |
|---|---|---|
| Owned, leased, sponsored: | 3 hospitals | 597 beds |
| Contract–managed: | 0 hospitals | 0 beds |
| Totals: | 3 hospitals | 597 beds |

★**2215:  AURORA HEALTH CARE** (NP)
750 Virginia Street, Milwaukee, WI Zip 53204, Mailing Address: P.O. Box 341880, Zip 53234–1880; tel. 414/299–1631; Nick Turkal, M.D., President and Chief Executive Officer
**(Decentralized Health System)**

**WISCONSIN:** AURORA BAYCARE MEDICAL CENTER (O, 167 beds) 2845 Greenbrier Road, Green Bay, WI Zip 54311–6519, Mailing Address: P.O. Box 8900, Zip 54308–8900; tel. 920/288–8000; Daniel T. Meyer, President
**Web address:** www.aurorabaycare.com

AURORA LAKELAND MEDICAL CENTER (O, 67 beds) W3985 County Road NN, Elkhorn, WI Zip 53121–4389; tel. 262/741–2000; Lisa Just, President
**Web address:** www.aurorahealthcare.org

AURORA MEDICAL CENTER (O, 74 beds) 10400 75th Street, Kenosha, WI Zip 53142–7884; tel. 262/948–5600; Douglas E. Koch, Market President
**Web address:** www.aurorahealthcare.org

AURORA MEDICAL CENTER – MANITOWOC COUNTY (O, 63 beds) 5000 Memorial Drive, Two Rivers, WI Zip 54241–3900; tel. 920/794–5000; Cathie A. Kocourek, President
**Web address:** www.aurorahealthcare.org

AURORA MEDICAL CENTER GRAFTON (O, 107 beds) 975 Port Washington Road, Grafton, WI Zip 53024–9201; tel. 262/329–1000; Carrie Killoran, Interim President
**Web address:** www.aurorahealthcare.org

AURORA MEDICAL CENTER IN WASHINGTON COUNTY (O, 34 beds) 1032 East Sumner Street, Hartford, WI Zip 53027–1698; tel. 262/673–2300; Carrie Killoran, Interim President
**Web address:** www.aurorahealthcare.org

AURORA MEDICAL CENTER OF OSHKOSH (O, 61 beds) 855 North Westhaven Drive, Oshkosh, WI Zip 54904–7668; tel. 920/456–6000; Jeffrey Bard, President
**Web address:** www.aurorahealthcare.com

AURORA MEDICAL CENTER SUMMIT (O, 85 beds) 36500 Aurora Drive, Summit, WI Zip 53066–4899; tel. 262/434–1000; Michael Bergmann, President
**Web address:** www.aurorahealthcare.org

AURORA MEMORIAL HOSPITAL OF BURLINGTON (O, 55 beds) 252 McHenry Street, Burlington, WI Zip 53105–1828; tel. 262/767–6000; Lisa Just, President
**Web address:** www.aurorahealthcare.org

AURORA PSYCHIATRIC HOSPITAL (O, 81 beds) 1220 Dewey Avenue, Wauwatosa, WI Zip 53213–2598; tel. 414/454–6600; Peter Carlson, Administrator
**Web address:** www.aurorahealthcare.org

AURORA SHEBOYGAN MEMORIAL MEDICAL CENTER (O, 136 beds) 2629 North Seventh Street, Sheboygan, WI Zip 53083–4998; tel. 920/451–5000; David Graebner, President
**Web address:** www.aurorahealthcare.org

AURORA SINAI MEDICAL CENTER (O, 177 beds) 945 North 12th Street, Milwaukee, WI Zip 53233–1337, Mailing Address: P.O. Box 342, Zip 53201–0342; tel. 414/219–2000; Carolynn Glocka, R.N., President
**Web address:** www.aurorahealthcare.org

AURORA ST. LUKE'S MEDICAL CENTER (O, 726 beds) 2900 West Oklahoma Avenue, Milwaukee, WI Zip 53215–4330, Mailing Address: P.O. Box 2901, Zip 53201–2901; tel. 414/649–6000; Marie Golanowski, R.N., MS, President
**Web address:** www.aurorahealthcare.org

AURORA WEST ALLIS MEDICAL CENTER (O, 218 beds) 8901 West Lincoln Avenue, West Allis, WI Zip 53227–2409, Mailing Address: P.O. Box 27901, Zip 53227–0901; tel. 414/328–6000; Richard A. Kellar, President
**Web address:** www.aurorahealthcare.org

| | | |
|---|---|---|
| Owned, leased, sponsored: | 14 hospitals | 2051 beds |
| Contract–managed: | 0 hospitals | 0 beds |
| Totals: | 14 hospitals | 2051 beds |

**0869:  AVANTI HOSPITALS** (IO)
222 North Sepulveda Boulevard, Suite 950, El Segundo, CA Zip 90245–5614; tel. 310/356–0550; Arnold R. Schaffer, Corporate Chief Executive Officer
**(Independent Hospital System)**

**CALIFORNIA:** COAST PLAZA HOSPITAL (O, 123 beds) 13100 Studebaker Road, Norwalk, CA Zip 90650–2500; tel. 562/868–3751; Richard Rowe, PharmD, Chief Executive Officer
**Web address:** www.coastplaza.com

For explanation of codes following names, see page B2.
★ Indicates Type III membership in the American Hospital Association.
● Single hospital health care system

COMMUNITY HOSPITAL OF HUNTINGTON PARK (O, 81 beds) 2623 East Slauson Avenue, Huntington Park, CA Zip 90255–2926; tel. 323/583–1931; Araceli Lonergan, Chief Executive Officer
**Web address:** www.chhplax.com

EAST LOS ANGELES DOCTORS HOSPITAL (O, 127 beds) 4060 Whittier Boulevard, Los Angeles, CA Zip 90023–2526; tel. 323/268–5514; Araceli Lonergan, Chief Executive Officer
**Web address:** www.elalax.com

MEMORIAL HOSPITAL OF GARDENA (O, 172 beds) 1145 West Redondo Beach Boulevard, Gardena, CA Zip 90247–3528; tel. 310/532–4200; Josh D. Luke, Ph.D., FACHE, Interim Chief Executive Officer
**Web address:** www.mhglax.com/

| | | |
|---|---|---|
| Owned, leased, sponsored: | 4 hospitals | 503 beds |
| Contract–managed: | 0 hospitals | 0 beds |
| Totals: | 4 hospitals | 503 beds |

★**5255: AVERA HEALTH** (CC)
3900 West Avera Drive, Suite 300, Sioux Falls, SD Zip 57108–5721; tel. 605/322–4700; John T. Porter, President and Chief Executive Officer
**(Decentralized Health System)**

**IOWA:** AVERA HOLY FAMILY HOSPITAL (O, 25 beds) 826 North Eighth Street, Estherville, IA Zip 51334–1598; tel. 712/362–2631; Dale Hustedt, Administrator
**Web address:** www.avera–holyfamily.org

FLOYD VALLEY HOSPITAL (C, 25 beds) 714 Lincoln Street N.E., Le Mars, IA Zip 51031–3314; tel. 712/546–7871; Michael T. Donlin, FACHE, Administrator
**Web address:** www.floydvalleyhospital.org

HEGG MEMORIAL HEALTH CENTER AVERA (C, 85 beds) 1202 21st Avenue, Rock Valley, IA Zip 51247–1497; tel. 712/476–8000; Glenn Zevenbergen, Chief Executive Officer
**Web address:** www.hegghc.org

LAKES REGIONAL HEALTHCARE (C, 30 beds) 2301 Highway 71 South, Spirit Lake, IA Zip 51360–6810, Mailing Address: P.O. Box AB, Zip 51360–0159; tel. 712/336–1230; Jason Harrington, FACHE, President and Chief Executive Officer
**Web address:** www.lakeshealth.org

OSCEOLA COMMUNITY HOSPITAL (C, 25 beds) 600 Ninth Avenue North, Sibley, IA Zip 51249–1012, Mailing Address: P.O. Box 258, Zip 51249–0258; tel. 712/754–2574; Janet H. Dykstra, Chief Executive Officer
**Web address:** www.osceolacommunityhospital.org

SIOUX CENTER HEALTH (C, 90 beds) 1101 9th Street, S.E., Sioux Center, IA Zip 51250–1398; tel. 712/722–8107; Kayleen R. Lee, Chief Executive Officer
**Web address:** www.schospital.org

**MINNESOTA:** AVERA MARSHALL REGIONAL MEDICAL CENTER (O, 111 beds) 300 South Bruce Street, Marshall, MN Zip 56258–3900; tel. 507/532–9661; Mary B. Maertens, FACHE, President and Chief Executive Officer
**Web address:** www.averamarshall.org

PIPESTONE COUNTY MEDICAL CENTER AVERA (C, 25 beds) 916 4th Avenue S.W., Pipestone, MN Zip 56164–1890; tel. 507/825–5811; Bradley D. Burris, Chief Executive Officer
**Web address:** www.pcmchealth.org

TYLER HEALTHCARE CENTER AVERA (C, 25 beds) 240 Willow Street, Tyler, MN Zip 56178–1166; tel. 507/247–5521; Dale K. Kruger, Chief Executive Officer and Chief Financial Officer
**Web address:** www.www1.avera.org/amck/regionalfacilities/tyler/index.aspx

**NEBRASKA:** AVERA CREIGHTON HOSPITAL (O, 63 beds) 1503 Main Street, Creighton, NE Zip 68729–3007, Mailing Address: P.O. Box 186, Zip 68729–0186; tel. 402/358–5700; Jennifer Poppen, Chief Executive Officer
**Web address:** www.avera.org/creighton/

AVERA ST. ANTHONY'S HOSPITAL (O, 25 beds) 300 North Second Street, O'Neill, NE Zip 68763–1514, Mailing Address: P.O. Box 270, Oneill, Zip 68763–0270; tel. 402/336–2611; Ronald J. Cork, President and Chief Executive Officer
**Web address:** www.avera.org/st–anthonys

**SOUTH DAKOTA:** AVERA DE SMET MEMORIAL HOSPITAL (L, 6 beds) 306 Prairie Avenue S.W., De Smet, SD Zip 57231–2285, Mailing Address: P.O. Box 160, Zip 57231–0160; tel. 605/854–3329; Janice Schardin, R.N., MS, Administrator and Chief Executive Officer
**Web address:** www.desmetmemorial.org

AVERA DELLS AREA HOSPITAL (L, 23 beds) 909 North Iowa Avenue, Dell Rapids, SD Zip 57022–1231; tel. 605/428–5431; Lindsay Flannery, R.N., Administrator and Chief Executive Officer
**Web address:** www.www1.avera.org/amck/regionalfacilities/dellsareahealth/index.aspx

AVERA FLANDREAU HOSPITAL (L, 18 beds) 214 North Prairie Street, Flandreau, SD Zip 57028–1243; tel. 605/997–2433; Lindsay Flannery, R.N., Administrator and Chief Executive Officer
**Web address:** www.avera.org/flandreau–medical/

AVERA GETTYSBURG HOSPITAL (O, 55 beds) 606 East Garfield Avenue, Gettysburg, SD Zip 57442–1398; tel. 605/765–2480; Bob Sutton, Interim Chief Executive Officer
**Web address:** www.avera.org/st–marys–pierre/gettysburg–hospital/

AVERA GREGORY HOSPITAL (O, 67 beds) 400 Park Avenue, Gregory, SD Zip 57533–1302, Mailing Address: P.O. Box 408, Zip 57533–0408; tel. 605/835–8394; Anthony Timanus, Chief Executive Officer
**Web address:** www.gregoryhealthcare.org

AVERA HAND COUNTY MEMORIAL HOSPITAL (L, 9 beds) 300 West Fifth Street, Miller, SD Zip 57362–1238; tel. 605/853–2421; Bryan Breitling, Administrator
**Web address:** www.avera.org

AVERA HEART HOSPITAL OF SOUTH DAKOTA (O, 53 beds) 4500 West 69th Street, Sioux Falls, SD Zip 57108–8148; tel. 605/977–7000; Jon Soderholm, President
**Web address:** www.avera.org/heart–hospital

AVERA MCKENNAN HOSPITAL AND UNIVERSITY HEALTH CENTER (O, 400 beds) 1325 South Cliff Avenue, Sioux Falls, SD Zip 57105–1007, Mailing Address: P.O. Box 5045, Zip 57117–5045; tel. 605/322–8000; David Kapaska, D.O., Regional President and Chief Executive Officer
**Web address:** www.averamckennan.org

AVERA QUEEN OF PEACE HOSPITAL (O, 176 beds) 525 North Foster, Mitchell, SD Zip 57301–2999; tel. 605/995–2000; Thomas A. Clark, Regional President and Chief Executive Officer
**Web address:** www.averaqueenofpeace.org

AVERA SACRED HEART HOSPITAL (O, 293 beds) 501 Summit Avenue, Yankton, SD Zip 57078–3855; tel. 605/668–8000; Douglas R. Ekeren, Regional President and Chief Executive Officer
**Web address:** www.averasacredheart.com

AVERA ST. BENEDICT HEALTH CENTER (O, 99 beds) 401 West Glynn Drive, Parkston, SD Zip 57366–9605; tel. 605/928–3311; Gale N. Walker, President and Chief Executive Officer
**Web address:** www.averastbenedict.org

AVERA ST. LUKE'S HOSPITAL (O, 236 beds) 305 South State Street, Aberdeen, SD Zip 57401–4527; tel. 605/622–5000; Todd Forkel, President and Chief Executive Officer
**Web address:** www.avera.org/st–lukes–hospital/

AVERA ST. MARY'S HOSPITAL (O, 164 beds) 801 East Sioux Avenue, Pierre, SD Zip 57501–3323; tel. 605/224–3100; Bob Sutton, President and Chief Executive Officer
**Web address:** www.avera.org/st–marys–pierre/

AVERA WESKOTA MEMORIAL HOSPITAL (L, 23 beds) 604 First Street N.E., Wessington Springs, SD Zip 57382–2166; tel. 605/539–1201; Gaea Blue, R.N., Administrator and Chief Executive Officer
**Web address:** www.averaweskota.org

EUREKA COMMUNITY HEALTH SERVICES AVERA (C, 6 beds) 410 Ninth Street, Eureka, SD Zip 57437–2182, Mailing Address: P.O. Box 517, Zip 57437–0517; tel. 605/284–2661; Carmen Weber, Administrator
**Web address:** www.avera.org

LANDMANN–JUNGMAN MEMORIAL HOSPITAL AVERA (C, 17 beds) 600 Billars Street, Scotland, SD Zip 57059–2026; tel. 605/583–2226; Jonathan Moe, Chief Executive Officer
**Web address:** www.ljmh.org

MARSHALL COUNTY HEALTHCARE CENTER AVERA (C, 18 beds) 413 Ninth Street, Britton, SD Zip 57430–2274; tel. 605/448–2253; Nick Fosness, Chief Executive Officer
**Web address:** www.avera.org

For explanation of codes following names, see page B2.
★ Indicates Type III membership in the American Hospital Association.

Section B

MILBANK AREA HOSPITAL AVERA (L, 25 beds) 901 East Virgil Avenue, Milbank, SD Zip 57252–2124; tel. 605/432–4538; Natalie Gauer, Administrator
**Web address:** www.averamilbank.org

PLATTE HEALTH CENTER AVERA (C, 65 beds) 601 East Seventh, Platte, SD Zip 57369–2123, Mailing Address: P.O. Box 200, Zip 57369–0200; tel. 605/337–3364; Mark Burket, Chief Executive Officer
**Web address:** www.phcavera.org

ST. MICHAEL'S HOSPITAL AVERA (C, 25 beds) 410 West 16th Avenue, Tyndall, SD Zip 57066–2318; tel. 605/589–2152; Carol Deurmier, Chief Executive Officer
**Web address:** www.stmichaels–bhfp.org

WAGNER COMMUNITY MEMORIAL HOSPITAL AVERA (C, 20 beds) 513 Third Street S.W., Wagner, SD Zip 57380–9675, Mailing Address: P.O. Box 280, Zip 57380–0280; tel. 605/384–3611; Bryan Slaba, Chief Executive Officer
**Web address:** www.avera.org/wagnerhospital

| | | |
|---|---|---|
| **Owned, leased, sponsored:** | 19 hospitals | 1871 beds |
| **Contract–managed:** | 13 hospitals | 456 beds |
| **Totals:** | 32 hospitals | 2327 beds |

★**0633: AVITA HEALTH SYSTEM** (NP)
269 Portland Way South, Galion, OH Zip 44833–2399; tel. 419/468–4841; Jerome Morasko, President and Chief Executive Officer
**(Independent Hospital System)**

**OHIO:** AVITA GALION HOSPITAL (O, 35 beds) 269 Portland Way South, Galion, OH Zip 44833–2399; tel. 419/468–4841; Jerome Morasko, President and Chief Executive Officer
**Web address:** www.avitahs.org

BUCYRUS COMMUNITY HOSPITAL (O, 25 beds) 629 North Sandusky Avenue, Bucyrus, OH Zip 44820–1821; tel. 419/562–4677; Jerome Morasko, Chief Executive Officer
**Web address:** www.bchonline.org

| | | |
|---|---|---|
| **Owned, leased, sponsored:** | 2 hospitals | 60 beds |
| **Contract–managed:** | 0 hospitals | 0 beds |
| **Totals:** | 2 hospitals | 60 beds |

★**0194: BANNER HEALTH** (NP)
1441 North 12th Street, Phoenix, AZ Zip 85006–2837, Mailing Address: P.O. Box 25489, Zip 85002–5489; tel. 602/747–4000; Peter S. Fine, FACHE, President and Chief Executive Officer
**(Moderately Centralized Health System)**

**ALASKA:** FAIRBANKS MEMORIAL HOSPITAL (L, 217 beds) 1650 Cowles Street, Fairbanks, AK Zip 99701–5998; tel. 907/452–8181; Sheldon Stadnyk, M.D., Interim Chief Executive Officer
**Web address:** www.bannerhealth.com/locations/alaska/fairbanks+memorial+Hospital

**ARIZONA:** BANNER – UNIVERSITY MEDICAL CENTER SOUTH (O, 161 beds) 2800 East Ajo Way, Tucson, AZ Zip 85713–6289; tel. 520/874–2000; Sarah Frost, Administrator
**Web address:** www.uahealth.com

BANNER – UNIVERSITY MEDICAL CENTER TUCSON (O, 479 beds) 1501 North Campbell Avenue, Tucson, AZ Zip 85724–5128; tel. 520/694–0111; Thomas C. Dickson, Chief Executive Officer
**Web address:** www.uahealth.com

BANNER BAYWOOD MEDICAL CENTER (O, 388 beds) 6644 East Baywood Avenue, Mesa, AZ Zip 85206–1797; tel. 480/321–2000; Laura Robertson, R.N., Chief Executive Officer
**Web address:** www.bannerhealth.com/locations/Arizona/banner+baywood+medical+center

BANNER BEHAVIORAL HEALTH HOSPITAL – SCOTTSDALE (O, 95 beds) 7575 East Earll Drive, Scottsdale, AZ Zip 85251–6915; tel. 480/941–7500; Cherie Martin, R.N., MSN, FACHE, Chief Executive Officer
**Web address:** www.bannerhealth.com/Locations/Arizona/Banner+Behavioral+Health

BANNER BOSWELL MEDICAL CENTER (O, 377 beds) 10401 West Thunderbird Boulevard, Sun City, AZ Zip 85351–3004, Mailing Address: P.O. Box 1690, Zip 85372–1690; tel. 623/832–4000; David Cheney, Chief Executive Officer
**Web address:** www.bannerhealth.com/Locations/Arizona/Banner+Boswell+Medical+Center

BANNER CASA GRANDE MEDICAL CENTER (O, 87 beds) 1800 East Florence Boulevard, Casa Grande, AZ Zip 85122–5399; tel. 520/381–6300; Rona Curphy, President and Chief Executive Officer
**Web address:** www.https://www.bannerhealth.com/Locations/Arizona/Banner+Casa+Grande+Medical+Center/_Banner+Casa+Grande+Medical+Center.htm

BANNER DEL E. WEBB MEDICAL CENTER (O, 373 beds) 14502 West Meeker Boulevard, Sun City West, AZ Zip 85375–5299, Mailing Address: P.O. Box 5169, Zip 85376–5169; tel. 623/214–4000; Debbie Flores, Chief Executive Officer
**Web address:** www.bannerhealth.com/Locations/Arizona/Banner+Del+Webb+Medical+Center/

BANNER DESERT MEDICAL CENTER (O, 579 beds) 1400 South Dobson Road, Mesa, AZ Zip 85202–4707; tel. 480/412–3000; Laura Robertson, R.N., Chief Executive Officer
**Web address:** www.bannerhealth.com/Locations/Arizona/Banner+Desert+Medical+Center

BANNER ESTRELLA MEDICAL CENTER (O, 266 beds) 9201 West Thomas Road, Phoenix, AZ Zip 85037–3332; tel. 623/327–4000; Debra J. Krmpotic, R.N., Chief Executive Officer
**Web address:** www.bannerhealth.com/Locations/Arizona/Banner+Estrella+Medical+Center/

BANNER GATEWAY MEDICAL CENTER (O, 177 beds) 1900 North Higley Road, Gilbert, AZ Zip 85234–1604; tel. 480/543–2000; Todd S. Werner, Chief Executive Officer
**Web address:** www.bannerhealth.com/Locations/Arizona/Banner+Gateway+Medical+Center/

BANNER GOLDFIELD MEDICAL CENTER (O, 30 beds) 2050 West Southern Avenue, Apache Junction, AZ Zip 85120–7305; tel. 480/733–3300; Julie Nunley, R.N., Chief Executive Officer
**Web address:** www.bannerhealth.com/Locations/Arizona/Banner+Goldfield+Medical+Center/_Welcome+to+Banner+Goldfield.htm

BANNER GOOD SAMARITAN MEDICAL CENTER (O, 685 beds) 1111 East McDowell Road, Phoenix, AZ Zip 85006–2666, Mailing Address: P.O. Box 2989, Zip 85062–2989; tel. 602/239–2000; Steve Narang, M.D., Chief Executive Officer
**Web address:** www.bannerhealth.com/Locations/Arizona/Banner+Good+Samaritan+Medical+Center

BANNER HEART HOSPITAL (O, 111 beds) 6750 East Baywood Avenue, Mesa, AZ Zip 85206–1749; tel. 480/854–5000; Laura Robertson, R.N., Chief Executive Officer
**Web address:** www.bannerhealth.com/Locations/Arizona/Banner+Heart+Hospital/

BANNER IRONWOOD MEDICAL CENTER (O, 53 beds) 37000 North Gantzel Road, San Tan Valley, AZ Zip 85140–7303; tel. 480/394–4000; Julie Nunley, R.N., Chief Executive Officer
**Web address:** www.bannerhealth.com/Locations/Arizona/Banner+Ironwood/

BANNER THUNDERBIRD MEDICAL CENTER (O, 474 beds) 5555 West Thunderbird Road, Glendale, AZ Zip 85306–4696; tel. 602/865–5555; Thomas C. Dickson, Chief Executive Officer
**Web address:** www.bannerhealth.com/Locations/Arizona/Banner+Thunderbird+Medical+Center/

PAGE HOSPITAL (C, 25 beds) 501 North Navajo Drive, Page, AZ Zip 86040, Mailing Address: P.O. Box 1447, Zip 86040–1447; tel. 928/645–2424; Sandy Haryasz, R.N., Chief Executive Officer
**Web address:** www.bannerhealth.com/Locations/Arizona/Page+Hospital

**CALIFORNIA:** BANNER LASSEN MEDICAL CENTER (O, 25 beds) 1800 Spring Ridge Drive, Susanville, CA Zip 96130–6100; tel. 530/252–2000; Catherine S. Harshbarger, R.N., Chief Executive Officer
**Web address:** www.bannerhealth.com/Locations/California/Banner+Lassen+Medical+Center

**COLORADO:** BANNER FORT COLLINS MEDICAL CENTER (O, 24 beds) 4700 Lady Moon Drive, Fort Collins, CO Zip 80528–4426; tel. 970/229–4000; Rick Sutton, Chief Executive Officer Northern Colorado
**Web address:** www.bannerhealth.com/Locations/Colorado/Banner+Fort+Collins+Medical+Center

For explanation of codes following names, see page B2.
★ Indicates Type III membership in the American Hospital Association.

EAST MORGAN COUNTY HOSPITAL (L, 19 beds) 2400 West Edison Street, Brush, CO Zip 80723–1640; tel. 970/842–6200; Linda Thorpe, Chief Executive Officer
**Web address:** www.emchbrush.com

MCKEE MEDICAL CENTER (O, 105 beds) 2000 Boise Avenue, Loveland, CO Zip 80538–4281; tel. 970/669–4640; Julie Klein, Chief Operating Officer
**Web address:** www.mckeeloveland.com

NORTH COLORADO MEDICAL CENTER (L, 225 beds) 1801 16th Street, Greeley, CO Zip 80631–5154; tel. 970/352–4121; Richard O. Sutton, Chief Executive Officer
**Web address:** www.ncmcgreeley.com

STERLING REGIONAL MEDCENTER (O, 25 beds) 615 Fairhurst Street, Sterling, CO Zip 80751–4523; tel. 970/522–0122; Sharon Lind, MSN, FACHE, Interim Chief Executive Officer
**Web address:** www.bannerhealth.com/Locations/Colorado/Sterling+Regional+MedCenter

**NEBRASKA:** OGALLALA COMMUNITY HOSPITAL (L, 18 beds) 2601 North Spruce Street, Ogallala, NE Zip 69153–2465; tel. 308/284–4011; Sharon Lind, MSN, FACHE, Chief Executive Officer
**Web address:** www.bannerhealth.com/Locations/Nebraska/Ogallala+Community+Hospital

**NEVADA:** BANNER CHURCHILL COMMUNITY HOSPITAL (O, 40 beds) 801 East Williams Avenue, Fallon, NV Zip 89406–3052; tel. 775/423–3151; Hoyt Skabelund, Chief Executive Officer
**Web address:** www.bannerhealth.com/churchill

**WYOMING:** COMMUNITY HOSPITAL (O, 20 beds) 2000 Campbell Drive, Torrington, WY Zip 82240–1597; tel. 307/532–4181; Shelby Nelson, Interim Chief Executive Officer
**Web address:** www.bannerhealth.com/Locations/Wyoming/Community+Hospital/

PLATTE COUNTY MEMORIAL HOSPITAL (L, 25 beds) 201 14th Street, Wheatland, WY Zip 82201–3201, Mailing Address: P.O. Box 848, Zip 82201–0848; tel. 307/322–3636; Shelby Nelson, Chief Executive Officer
**Web address:** www.bannerhealth.com/Locations/Wyoming/Platte+County+Memorial+Hospital

WASHAKIE MEDICAL CENTER (L, 25 beds) 400 South 15th Street, Worland, WY Zip 82401–3531, Mailing Address: P.O. Box 700, Zip 82401–0700; tel. 307/347–3221; Jay Stallings, Chief Executive Officer
**Web address:** www.washakiemedicalcenter.com

| Owned, leased, sponsored: | 27 hospitals | 5103 beds |
|---|---|---|
| Contract–managed: | 1 hospital | 25 beds |
| **Totals:** | 28 hospitals | 5128 beds |

---

**★0005:  BAPTIST HEALTH** (NP)
841 Prudential Drive, Suite 1601, Jacksonville, FL Zip 32207–8202; tel. 904/202–4011; Hugh Greene, President and Chief Executive Officer
**(Moderately Centralized Health System)**

**FLORIDA:** BAPTIST MEDICAL CENTER BEACHES (O, 136 beds) 1350 13th Avenue South, Jacksonville Beach, FL Zip 32250–3205; tel. 904/627–2900; Joseph M. Mitrick, FACHE, President
**Web address:** www.community.e-baptisthealth.com/bmc/beaches/index.html

BAPTIST MEDICAL CENTER JACKSONVILLE (O, 901 beds) 800 Prudential Drive, Jacksonville, FL Zip 32207–8202; tel. 904/202–2000; Michael A. Mayo, FACHE, President
**Web address:** www.e-baptisthealth.com

BAPTIST MEDICAL CENTER NASSAU (O, 52 beds) 1250 South 18th Street, Fernandina Beach, FL Zip 32034–3098; tel. 904/321–3500; Stephen Lee, FACHE, President
**Web address:** www.baptistjax.com/locations/baptist-medical-center-nassau

| Owned, leased, sponsored: | 3 hospitals | 1089 beds |
|---|---|---|
| Contract–managed: | 0 hospitals | 0 beds |
| **Totals:** | 3 hospitals | 1089 beds |

---

**0150:  BAPTIST HEALTH** (NP)
301 Brown Springs Road, Montgomery, AL Zip 36117–7005; tel. 334/273–4400; W. Russell Tyner, President and Chief Executive Officer
**(Independent Hospital System)**

**ALABAMA:** BAPTIST MEDICAL CENTER EAST (O, 164 beds) 400 Taylor Road, Montgomery, AL Zip 36117–3512, Mailing Address: P.O. Box 241267, Zip 36124–1267; tel. 334/277–8330; Jeff G. Rains, Chief Executive Officer
**Web address:** www.baptistfirst.org

BAPTIST MEDICAL CENTER SOUTH (O, 372 beds) 2105 East South Boulevard, Montgomery, AL Zip 36116–2409, Mailing Address: Box 11010, Zip 36111–0010; tel. 334/288–2100; J. Peter Selman, FACHE, Chief Executive Officer
**Web address:** www.baptistfirst.org

PRATTVILLE BAPTIST HOSPITAL (O, 50 beds) 124 South Memorial Drive, Prattville, AL Zip 36067–3619, Mailing Address: P.O. Box 681630, Zip 36068–1638; tel. 334/365–0651; Eric Morgan, Interim Chief Executive Officer
**Web address:** www.baptistfirst.org/facilities/prattville-baptist-hospital/default.aspx

| Owned, leased, sponsored: | 3 hospitals | 586 beds |
|---|---|---|
| Contract–managed: | 0 hospitals | 0 beds |
| **Totals:** | 3 hospitals | 586 beds |

---

**★0315:  BAPTIST HEALTH** (CO)
2701 Eastpoint Parkway, Louisville, KY Zip 40223; tel. 502/896–5000; Stephen C. Hanson, Chief Executive Officer
**(Moderately Centralized Health System)**

**KENTUCKY:** BAPTIST HEALTH CORBIN (O, 273 beds) 1 Trillium Way, Corbin, KY Zip 40701–8420; tel. 606/528–1212; Larry Gray, President
**Web address:** www.baptistregional.com

BAPTIST HEALTH LA GRANGE (O, 65 beds) 1025 New Moody Lane, La Grange, KY Zip 40031–9154; tel. 502/222–5388; Chris Roty, President
**Web address:** www.baptisthealthlagrange.com

BAPTIST HEALTH LEXINGTON (O, 344 beds) 1740 Nicholasville Road, Lexington, KY Zip 40503–1499; tel. 859/260–6100; William G. Sisson, President
**Web address:** www.baptisthealthlexington.com

BAPTIST HEALTH LOUISVILLE (O, 488 beds) 4000 Kresge Way, Louisville, KY Zip 40207–4676; tel. 502/897–8100; David L. Gray, FACHE, President
**Web address:** www.baptisthealthlouisville.com

BAPTIST HEALTH MADISONVILLE (O, 186 beds) 900 Hospital Drive, Madisonville, KY Zip 42431–1694; tel. 270/825–5100; Robert L. Ramey, Interim President
**Web address:** www.baptisthealthmadisonville.com

BAPTIST HEALTH PADUCAH (O, 320 beds) 2501 Kentucky Avenue, Paducah, KY Zip 42003–3200; tel. 270/575–2100; William A. Brown, FACHE, President and CEO
**Web address:** www.baptisthealthpaducah.com

BAPTIST HEALTH RICHMOND (O, 69 beds) 801 Eastern Bypass, Richmond, KY Zip 40475–2405, Mailing Address: P.O. Box 1600, Zip 40476–2603; tel. 859/623–3131; Todd Jones, President
**Web address:** www.baptisthealthrichmond.com

HARDIN MEMORIAL HOSPITAL (C, 268 beds) 913 North Dixie Avenue, Elizabethtown, KY Zip 42701–2503; tel. 270/737–1212; Dennis B. Johnson, President & CEO
**Web address:** www.hmh.net

| Owned, leased, sponsored: | 7 hospitals | 1745 beds |
|---|---|---|
| Contract–managed: | 1 hospital | 268 beds |
| **Totals:** | 8 hospitals | 2013 beds |

---

**★0355:  BAPTIST HEALTH** (NP)
9601 Interstate 630, Exit 7, Little Rock, AR Zip 72205–7299; tel. 501/202–2000; Troy R. Wells, Chief Executive Officer
**(Centralized Physician/Insurance Health System)**

For explanation of codes following names, see page B2.
★ Indicates Type III membership in the American Hospital Association.

**ARKANSAS:** BAPTIST HEALTH EXTENDED CARE HOSPITAL (O, 55 beds) 9601 Interstate 630, Exit 7, 10th Floor, Little Rock, AR Zip 72205–7202; tel. 501/202–1070; Mike Perkins, Vice President and Administrator
**Web address:** www.baptist–health.com/maps–directions/bh_extended_care/default.aspx

BAPTIST HEALTH MEDICAL CENTER – NORTH LITTLE ROCK (O, 225 beds) 3333 Springhill Drive, North Little Rock, AR Zip 72117–2922; tel. 501/202–3000; Harrison M. Dean, FACHE, Senior Vice President and Administrator
**Web address:** www.baptist–health.com/locations/accesspoint.aspx?accessPointID=190

BAPTIST HEALTH MEDICAL CENTER–ARKADELPHIA (L, 25 beds) 3050 Twin Rivers Drive, Arkadelphia, AR Zip 71923–4299; tel. 870/245–2622; John Bowen, Assistant Vice President and Administrator
**Web address:** www.baptist–health.com/locations/accesspoint.aspx?accessPointID=187

BAPTIST HEALTH MEDICAL CENTER–HEBER SPRINGS (O, 25 beds) 1800 Bypass Road, Heber Springs, AR Zip 72543–9135; tel. 501/887–3000; Edward L. Lacy, FACHE, Vice President and Administrator
**Web address:** www.baptist–health.com/maps–directions/bhmc–heber–springs

BAPTIST HEALTH MEDICAL CENTER–HOT SPRING COUNTY (L, 72 beds) 1001 Schneider Drive, Malvern, AR Zip 72104–4811; tel. 501/332–1000; Sheila Williams, Vice President and Administrator
**Web address:** www.https://www.baptist–health.org

BAPTIST HEALTH MEDICAL CENTER–LITTLE ROCK (O, 688 beds) 9601 Interstate 630, Exit 7, Little Rock, AR Zip 72205–7299; tel. 501/202–2000; Greg Crain, FACHE, Vice President and Administrator
**Web address:** www.baptist–health.org/maps–directions/bhmc–lr

BAPTIST HEALTH MEDICAL CENTER–STUTTGART (L, 49 beds) North Buerkle Road, Stuttgart, AR Zip 72160–3420, Mailing Address: P.O. Box 1905, Zip 72160–1905; tel. 870/673–3511; Harrison M. Dean, FACHE, Interim Administrator
**Web address:** www.baptist–health.org/maps–directions/bhmc–stuttgart/default.aspx

BAPTIST HEALTH REHABILITATION INSTITUTE (O, 90 beds) 9601 Interstate 630, Exit 7, Little Rock, AR Zip 72205–7202; tel. 501/202–7000; Lee Gentry, FACHE, Vice President and Administrator
**Web address:** www.baptist–health.com/locations/accesspoint.aspx?accessPointID=202

| | | |
|---|---|---|
| Owned, leased, sponsored: | 8 hospitals | 1229 beds |
| Contract–managed: | 0 hospitals | 0 beds |
| Totals: | 8 hospitals | 1229 beds |

★**0185:** **BAPTIST HEALTH CARE CORPORATION** (NP)
1717 North E Street Suite 320, Pensacola, FL Zip 32501–6377, Mailing Address: P.O. Box 17500, Zip 32522–7500; tel. 850/434–4011; Mark T. Faulkner, President
**(Centralized Physician/Insurance Health System)**

**FLORIDA:** BAPTIST HOSPITAL (O, 339 beds) 1000 West Moreno, Pensacola, FL Zip 32501–2316, Mailing Address: P.O. Box 17500, Zip 32522–7500; tel. 850/434–4011; Scott Raynes, President
**Web address:** www.ebaptisthealthcare.org

GULF BREEZE HOSPITAL (O, 77 beds) 1110 Gulf Breeze Parkway, Gulf Breeze, FL Zip 32561–4884; tel. 850/934–2000; Scott Raynes, President
**Web address:** www.ebaptisthealthcare.org/GulfBreezeHospital/

JAY HOSPITAL (L, 49 beds) 14114 South Alabama Street, Jay, FL Zip 32565–1219; tel. 850/675–8000; Michael T. Hutchins, Administrator
**Web address:** www.bhcpns.org/jayhospital/

| | | |
|---|---|---|
| Owned, leased, sponsored: | 3 hospitals | 465 beds |
| Contract–managed: | 0 hospitals | 0 beds |
| Totals: | 3 hospitals | 465 beds |

★**0122:** **BAPTIST HEALTH SOUTH FLORIDA** (NP)
6855 Red Road, Suite 600, Coral Gables, FL Zip 33143–3632; tel. 786/662–7111; Brian E. Keeley, President and Chief Executive Officer
**(Centralized Health System)**

BAPTIST HEALTH SOUTH FLORIDA, BAPTIST HOSPITAL OF MIAMI (O, 672 beds) 8900 North Kendall Drive, Miami, FL Zip 33176–2197; tel. 786/596–1960; Albert Boulenger, Chief Executive Officer
**Web address:** www.baptisthealth.net

BAPTIST HEALTH SOUTH FLORIDA, DOCTORS HOSPITAL (O, 146 beds) 5000 University Drive, Coral Gables, FL Zip 33146–2094; tel. 786/308–3000; Nelson Lazo, Chief Executive Officer
**Web address:** www.baptisthealth.net

BAPTIST HEALTH SOUTH FLORIDA, HOMESTEAD HOSPITAL (O, 142 beds) 975 Baptist Way, Homestead, FL Zip 33033–7600; tel. 786/243–8000; William M. Duquette, Chief Executive Officer
**Web address:** www.baptisthealth.net

BAPTIST HEALTH SOUTH FLORIDA, MARINERS HOSPITAL (O, 25 beds) 91500 Overseas Highway, Tavernier, FL Zip 33070–2547; tel. 305/434–3000; Rick Freeburg, Chief Executive Officer
**Web address:** www.baptisthealth.net/en/facilities/mariners–hospital/Pages/default.aspx

BAPTIST HEALTH SOUTH FLORIDA, SOUTH MIAMI HOSPITAL (O, 335 beds) 6200 S.W. 73rd Street, Miami, FL Zip 33143–4679; tel. 786/662–4000; Lincoln S. Mendez, Chief Executive Officer
**Web address:** www.baptisthealth.net

BAPTIST HEALTH SOUTH FLORIDA, WEST KENDALL BAPTIST HOSPITAL (O, 133 beds) 9555 S.W. 162nd Avenue, Miami, FL Zip 33196–6408; tel. 786/467–2000; Javier Hernandez–Lichtl, Chief Executive Officer
**Web address:** www.baptisthealth.net/en/facilities/West–Kendall–Baptist–Hospital/Pages/default.aspx

| | | |
|---|---|---|
| Owned, leased, sponsored: | 6 hospitals | 1453 beds |
| Contract–managed: | 0 hospitals | 0 beds |
| Totals: | 6 hospitals | 1453 beds |

**0345:** **BAPTIST HEALTH SYSTEM** (CO)
3201 Fourth Avenue South, Birmingham, AL Zip 35222–1723, Mailing Address: P.O. Box 830605, Zip 35283–0605; tel. 205/715–5319; Keith Parrott, FACHE, President and Chief Executive Officer
**(Independent Hospital System)**

**ALABAMA:** CITIZENS BAPTIST MEDICAL CENTER (O, 116 beds) 604 Stone Avenue, Talladega, AL Zip 35160–2217, Mailing Address: P.O. Box 978, Zip 35161–0978; tel. 256/362–8111; Joel Taylor, Administrator
**Web address:** www.bhsala.com/home_citizens.cfm?id=38

PRINCETON BAPTIST MEDICAL CENTER (O, 295 beds) 701 Princeton Avenue S.W., Birmingham, AL Zip 35211–1303; tel. 205/783–3000; Betsy Postlethwait, President
**Web address:** www.bhsala.com

SHELBY BAPTIST MEDICAL CENTER (O, 206 beds) 1000 First Street North, Alabaster, AL Zip 35007–8703; tel. 205/620–8100; Robert Phillips, President
**Web address:** www.bhsala.com/shelby/Home.aspx

WALKER BAPTIST MEDICAL CENTER (O, 236 beds) 3400 Highway 78 East, Jasper, AL Zip 35501–8907, Mailing Address: P.O. Box 3547, Zip 35502–3547; tel. 205/387–4000; Robert Phillips, Administrator
**Web address:** www.bhsala.com

| | | |
|---|---|---|
| Owned, leased, sponsored: | 4 hospitals | 853 beds |
| Contract–managed: | 0 hospitals | 0 beds |
| Totals: | 4 hospitals | 853 beds |

★**0336:** **BAPTIST HEALTH SYSTEMS** (NP)
1225 North State Street, Jackson, MS Zip 39202–2064; tel. 601/968–1000; Chris Anderson, Chief Executive Officer
**(Moderately Centralized Health System)**

**MISSISSIPPI:** BAPTIST MEDICAL CENTER ATTALA (L, 25 beds) 220 Highway 12 West, Kosciusko, MS Zip 39090–3208, Mailing Address: P.O. Box 887, Zip 39090–0887; tel. 662/289–4311; John Dawson, Chief Executive Officer
**Web address:** www.montfortjones.com

For explanation of codes following names, see page B2.
★ Indicates Type III membership in the American Hospital Association.

BAPTIST MEDICAL CENTER LEAKE (O, 69 beds) 310 Ellis Street, Carthage, MS Zip 39051–3809, Mailing Address: P.O. Box 909, Zip 39051–0909; tel. 601/267–1100; Daryl W. Weaver, Interim Chief Executive Officer
**Web address:** www.mbhs.com/locations/baptist-medical-center-leake/

BAPTIST MEDICAL CENTER YAZOO (O, 25 beds) 823 Grand Avenue, Yazoo City, MS Zip 39194–3233; tel. 662/746–2261; Sean Johnson, Chief Executive Officer
**Web address:** www.kdhyazoo.com

MISSISSIPPI BAPTIST MEDICAL CENTER (O, 554 beds) 1225 North State Street, Jackson, MS Zip 39202–2064; tel. 601/968–1000; Chris Anderson, Chief Executive Officer
**Web address:** www.mbhs.org

MISSISSIPPI HOSPITAL FOR RESTORATIVE CARE (O, 20 beds) 1225 North State Street, Jackson, MS Zip 39202–2097, Mailing Address: P.O. Box 23695, Zip 39225–3695; tel. 601/968–1000; Bobbie K. Ware, R.N., FACHE, Chief Executive Officer and Chief Nursing Officer
**Web address:** www.mbhs.org

| | | |
|---|---|---|
| **Owned, leased, sponsored:** | 5 hospitals | 693 beds |
| **Contract–managed:** | 0 hospitals | 0 beds |
| **Totals:** | 5 hospitals | 693 beds |

---

★**1625: BAPTIST MEMORIAL HEALTH CARE CORPORATION** (NP)
350 North Humphreys Boulevard, Memphis, TN Zip 38120–2177; tel. 901/227–5117; Jason Little, President and Chief Executive Officer
**(Decentralized Health System)**

**ARKANSAS:** NEA BAPTIST MEMORIAL HOSPITAL (O, 181 beds) 4800 East Johnson Avenue, Jonesboro, AR Zip 72401–8413; tel. 870/936–1000; Brad Parsons, FACHE, Administrator and Chief Executive Officer
**Web address:** www.neabaptist.com

**MISSISSIPPI:** BAPTIST MEMORIAL HOSPITAL–BOONEVILLE (L, 66 beds) 100 Hospital Street, Booneville, MS Zip 38829–3359; tel. 662/720–5000; James Grantham, Administrator and Chief Executive Officer
**Web address:** www.bmhcc.org/booneville

BAPTIST MEMORIAL HOSPITAL–DESOTO (O, 242 beds) 7601 Southcrest Parkway, Southaven, MS Zip 38671–4742; tel. 662/772–4000; James Huffman, Chief Executive Officer and Administrator
**Web address:** www.baptistonline.org/desoto/

BAPTIST MEMORIAL HOSPITAL–GOLDEN TRIANGLE (O, 236 beds) 2520 Fifth Street North, Columbus, MS Zip 39705–2095, Mailing Address: P.O. Box 1307, Zip 39703–1307; tel. 662/244–1000; Paul Cade, Administrator and Chief Executive Officer
**Web address:** www.baptistonline.org/golden–triangle/

BAPTIST MEMORIAL HOSPITAL–NORTH MISSISSIPPI (O, 217 beds) 2301 South Lamar Boulevard, Oxford, MS Zip 38655–5373, Mailing Address: P.O. Box 946, Zip 38655–6002; tel. 662/232–8100; William C. Henning, Administrator and Chief Executive Officer
**Web address:** www.baptistonline.org/north–mississippi/

BAPTIST MEMORIAL HOSPITAL–UNION COUNTY (L, 153 beds) 200 Highway 30 West, New Albany, MS Zip 38652–3112; tel. 662/538–7631; Walter Grace, Chief Executive Officer and Administrator
**Web address:** www.baptistonline.org/union–county/

**TENNESSEE:** BAPTIST MEMORIAL HOSPITAL – MEMPHIS (O, 547 beds) 6019 Walnut Grove Road, Memphis, TN Zip 38120–2173; tel. 901/226–5000; Dana Dye, R.N., Vice President, Administrator and Chief Executive Officer
**Web address:** www.baptistonline.org/memphis/

BAPTIST MEMORIAL HOSPITAL FOR WOMEN (O, 140 beds) 6225 Humphreys Boulevard, Memphis, TN Zip 38120–2373; tel. 901/227–9000; Anita Vaughn, Administrator and Chief Executive Officer
**Web address:** www.baptistonline.org/womens/

BAPTIST MEMORIAL HOSPITAL–COLLIERVILLE (O, 61 beds) 1500 West Poplar Avenue, Collierville, TN Zip 38017–0601; tel. 901/861–9400; Kyle E. Armstrong, Administrator and Chief Executive Officer
**Web address:** www.baptistonline.org/collierville/

BAPTIST MEMORIAL HOSPITAL–HUNTINGDON (O, 33 beds) 631 R.B. Wilson Drive, Huntingdon, TN Zip 38344–1727; tel. 731/986–4461; Susan M. Breeden, Administrator and Chief Executive Officer
**Web address:** www.baptistonline.org/huntingdon/

BAPTIST MEMORIAL HOSPITAL–TIPTON (O, 44 beds) 1995 Highway 51 South, Covington, TN Zip 38019–3635; tel. 901/476–2621; Samuel Lynd, Administrator and Chief Executive Officer
**Web address:** www.baptistonline.org/tipton/

BAPTIST MEMORIAL HOSPITAL–UNION CITY (O, 85 beds) 1201 Bishop Street, Union City, TN Zip 38261–5403, Mailing Address: P.O. Box 310, Zip 38281–0310; tel. 731/885–2410; Barry Bondurant, Administrator and Chief Executive Officer
**Web address:** www.baptistonline.org/union–city/

BAPTIST MEMORIAL REHABILITATION HOSPITAL (O, 49 beds) 1240 South Germantown Road, Germantown, TN Zip 38138–2226; tel. 901/275–3300; Brian Hogan, Chief Executive Officer and Administrator
**Web address:** www.baptistrehab.com

BAPTIST MEMORIAL RESTORATIVE CARE HOSPITAL (O, 30 beds) 6019 Walnut Grove Road, Memphis, TN Zip 38120–2113; tel. 901/226–1400; Janice Hill, R.N., Administrator
**Web address:** www.baptistonline.org/restorative–care/

BAPTIST REHABILITATION–GERMANTOWN (O, 68 beds) 2100 Exeter Road, Germantown, TN Zip 38138–3978; tel. 901/757–1350; Janice Hill, R.N., President and Chief Executive Officer
**Web address:** www.baptistonline.org/germantown/

| | | |
|---|---|---|
| **Owned, leased, sponsored:** | 15 hospitals | 2152 beds |
| **Contract–managed:** | 0 hospitals | 0 beds |
| **Totals:** | 15 hospitals | 2152 beds |

---

★**0118: BARNABAS HEALTH** (NP)
95 Old Short Hills Road, West Orange, NJ Zip 07052–1008; tel. 973/322–4000; Barry Ostrowsky, President and Chief Executive Officer
**(Moderately Centralized Health System)**

**NEW JERSEY:** BARNABAS HEALTH BEHAVIORAL HEALTH CENTER (O, 40 beds) 1691 Highway 9, Toms River, NJ Zip 8754; tel. 732/914–1688; Joe Hicks, President and Chief Executive Officer
**Web address:** www.barnabashealth.org/hospitals/psychiatric/index.html

CLARA MAASS MEDICAL CENTER (O, 469 beds) One Clara Maass Drive, Belleville, NJ Zip 07109–3557; tel. 973/450–2000; Mary Ellen Clyne, Ph.D., MSN, R.N., President and Chief Executive Officer
**Web address:** www.barnabashealth.org/hospitals/clara_maass/index.html

COMMUNITY MEDICAL CENTER (O, 431 beds) 99 Route 37 West, Toms River, NJ Zip 08755–6423; tel. 732/557–8051; Michael Mimoso, FACHE, Interim Chief Executive Officer
**Web address:** www.barnabashealth.org/hospitals/community_medical/index.html

JERSEY CITY MEDICAL CENTER (O, 316 beds) 355 Grand Street, Jersey City, NJ Zip 07302–4321; tel. 201/915–2000; Joseph F. Scott, FACHE, President and Chief Executive Officer
**Web address:** www.barnabashealth.org/Jersey–City–Medical–Center.aspx

MONMOUTH MEDICAL CENTER, LONG BRANCH CAMPUS (O, 294 beds) 300 Second Avenue, Long Branch, NJ Zip 07740–6303; tel. 732/222–5200; Frank J. Vozos, M.D., FACS, President and Chief Executive Officer
**Web address:** www.barnabashealth.org/hospitals/monmouth_medical/index.html

MONMOUTH MEDICAL CENTER, SOUTHERN CAMPUS (O, 116 beds) 600 River Avenue, Lakewood, NJ Zip 08701–5237; tel. 732/363–1900; Frank J. Vozos, M.D., FACS, President and Chief Executive Officer
**Web address:** www.barnabashealth.org/hospitals/monmouth–medical–center–southern–campus.aspx

NEWARK BETH ISRAEL MEDICAL CENTER (O, 355 beds) 201 Lyons Avenue, Newark, NJ Zip 07112–2027; tel. 973/926–7000; John A. Brennan, M.D., M.P.H., President and Chief Executive Officer
**Web address:** www.barnabashealth.org/hospitals/newark_beth_israel/index.html

---

For explanation of codes following names, see page B2.
★ Indicates Type III membership in the American Hospital Association.

SAINT BARNABAS MEDICAL CENTER (O, 523 beds) 94 Old Short Hills Road, Livingston, NJ Zip 07039–5672; tel. 973/322–5000; Stephen P. Zieniewicz, FACHE, President and Chief Executive Officer
**Web address:** www.barnabashealth.org/hospitals/saint_barnabas/index.html

| Owned, leased, sponsored: | 8 hospitals | 2544 beds |
|---|---|---|
| Contract–managed: | 0 hospitals | 0 beds |
| **Totals:** | 8 hospitals | 2544 beds |

---

**★0528: BASSETT HEALTHCARE NETWORK** (NP)
1 Atwell Road, Cooperstown, NY Zip 13326–1301; tel. 607/547–3456; Vance Brown, M.D., President and Chief Executive Officer
**(Independent Hospital System)**

**NEW YORK:** AURELIA OSBORN FOX MEMORIAL HOSPITAL (O, 191 beds) 1 Norton Avenue, Oneonta, NY Zip 13820–2629; tel. 607/432–2000; John R. Remillard, President
**Web address:** www.bassett.org/ao-fox-hospital/

BASSETT MEDICAL CENTER (O, 152 beds) One Atwell Road, Cooperstown, NY Zip 13326–1394; tel. 607/547–3100; Vance Brown, M.D., President and Chief Executive Officer
**Web address:** www.bassett.org

COBLESKILL REGIONAL HOSPITAL (O, 40 beds) 178 Grandview Drive, Cobleskill, NY Zip 12043–5144; tel. 518/254–3456; Eric H. Stein, FACHE, President and Chief Executive Officer
**Web address:** www.cobleskillhospital.org

LITTLE FALLS HOSPITAL (O, 59 beds) 140 Burwell Street, Little Falls, NY Zip 13365–1725; tel. 315/823–1000; Michael L. Ogden, President and Chief Executive Officer
**Web address:** www.lfhny.org

O'CONNOR HOSPITAL (O, 16 beds) 460 Andes Road, State Route 28, Delhi, NY Zip 13753–7407; tel. 607/746–0300; Carlton Rule, M.D., Chief Executive Officer
**Web address:** www.bassett.org

| Owned, leased, sponsored: | 5 hospitals | 458 beds |
|---|---|---|
| Contract–managed: | 0 hospitals | 0 beds |
| **Totals:** | 5 hospitals | 458 beds |

---

**★0918: BAYLOR SCOTT & WHITE HEALTH** (NP)
4005 Crutcher Street, Suite 310, Dallas, TX Zip 75246–1779; tel. 214/820–0111; Joel T. Allison, Chief Executive Officer
**(Moderately Centralized Health System)**

**TEXAS:** BAYLOR ALL SAINTS MEDICAL CENTER AT FORT WORTH (O, 449 beds) 1400 Eighth Avenue, Fort Worth, TX Zip 76104–4192; tel. 817/926–2544; David G. Klein, M.D., President
**Web address:** www.baylorhealth.com/PhysiciansLocations/AllSaints/Pages/Default.aspx

BAYLOR INSTITUTE FOR REHABILITATION (O, 89 beds) 909 North Washington Avenue, Dallas, TX Zip 75246–1520; tel. 214/820–9300; Fabian Polo, Chief Executive Officer
**Web address:** www.baylorhealth.com/PhysiciansLocations/BIR/Pages/Default.aspx

BAYLOR MEDICAL CENTER AT CARROLLTON (O, 123 beds) 4343 North Josey Lane, Carrollton, TX Zip 75010–4691; tel. 972/492–1010; Mike McAllister, Interim Chief Executive Officer
**Web address:** www.baylorhealth.com

BAYLOR MEDICAL CENTER AT GARLAND (O, 185 beds) 2300 Marie Curie Drive, Garland, TX Zip 75042–5706; tel. 972/487–5000; Thomas J. Trenary, President
**Web address:** www.baylorhealth.com/PhysiciansLocations/Garland/Pages/Default.aspx

BAYLOR MEDICAL CENTER AT IRVING (L, 220 beds) 1901 North MacArthur Boulevard, Irving, TX Zip 75061–2220; tel. 972/579–8100; Cindy K. Schamp, President
**Web address:** www.baylorhealth.com/PhysiciansLocations/Irving/Pages/Default.aspx

BAYLOR MEDICAL CENTER AT MCKINNEY (O, 78 beds) 5252 West University Drive, McKinney, TX Zip 75071–7822; tel. 469/764–1000; Scott Peek, FACHE, President
**Web address:** www.baylorhealth.com/PhysiciansLocations/McKinney/Pages/Default.aspx

BAYLOR MEDICAL CENTER AT WAXAHACHIE (O, 41 beds) 2400 North I–35E, Waxahachie, TX Zip 75165; tel. 469/843–4000; Christopher York, FACHE, Chief Executive Officer
**Web address:** www.baylorhealth.com/PhysiciansLocations/Waxahachie/Pages/Default.aspx

BAYLOR REGIONAL MEDICAL CENTER AT GRAPEVINE (O, 233 beds) 1650 West College Street, Grapevine, TX Zip 76051–3565; tel. 817/481–1588; Steven R. Newton, President
**Web address:** www.https://www.baylorhealth.com/PhysiciansLocations/Grapevine/Pages/Default.aspx

BAYLOR REGIONAL MEDICAL CENTER AT PLANO (O, 110 beds) 4700 Alliance Boulevard, Plano, TX Zip 75093–5323; tel. 469/814–2000; Jerri Garison, R.N., President
**Web address:** www.baylorhealth.com/PhysiciansLocations/Plano/Pages/Default.aspx

BAYLOR SCOTT & WHITE HILLCREST MEDICAL CENTER (C, 277 beds) 100 Hillcrest Medical Boulevard, Waco, TX Zip 76712–8897, Mailing Address: P.O. Box 21146, Zip 76702–1146; tel. 254/202–2000; Glenn A. Robinson, Chief Executive Officer
**Web address:** www.hillcrest.net

BAYLOR SPECIALTY HOSPITAL (O, 57 beds) 3504 Swiss Avenue, Dallas, TX Zip 75204–6224; tel. 214/820–9700; Elizabeth Youngblood, President
**Web address:** www.baylorhealth.com/PhysiciansLocations/BSH/Pages/Default.aspx

BAYLOR UNIVERSITY MEDICAL CENTER (O, 844 beds) 3500 Gaston Avenue, Dallas, TX Zip 75246–2088; tel. 214/820–0111; John B. McWhorter, III, President
**Web address:** www.baylorhealth.com/PhysiciansLocations/Dallas/Pages/Default.aspx

OUR CHILDREN'S HOUSE AT BAYLOR (O, 54 beds) 1208 North Hall Street, Dallas, TX Zip 75204; tel. 214/820–9838; Elizabeth Youngblood, President
**Web address:** www.baylorhealth.com/PhysiciansLocations/OCH/Pages/Default.aspx

SCOTT & WHITE EMERGENCY HOSPITAL– CEDAR PARK (O, 8 beds) 900 East Whitestone Boulevard, Cedar Park, TX Zip 78613–9093; tel. 512/684–4911; John Wood, Administrator
**Web address:** www.sweh.org

SCOTT & WHITE HOSPITAL – BRENHAM (O, 60 beds) 700 Medical Parkway, Brenham, TX Zip 77833–5498; tel. 979/337–5000; Michael Pittman, Chief Operating Officer and Chief Nursing Officer
**Web address:** www.swbrenham.org

SCOTT & WHITE HOSPITAL – COLLEGE STATION (O, 95 beds) 700 Scott & White Drive, College Station, TX Zip 77845; tel. 979/207–0100; Jason Jennings, Chief Executive Officer
**Web address:** www.sw.org/location/college-station-hospital

SCOTT & WHITE HOSPITAL – LLANO (O, 20 beds) 200 West Ollie Street, Llano, TX Zip 78643–2628; tel. 325/247–5040; Eric N. Looper, Chief Executive Officer
**Web address:** www.llanomemorial.org

SCOTT & WHITE HOSPITAL – TAYLOR (O, 25 beds) 305 Mallard Lane, Taylor, TX Zip 76574–1208; tel. 512/352–7611; Jay Fox, Chief Executive Officer, Round Rock Region
**Web address:** www.swtaylor.org

SCOTT & WHITE HOSPITAL AT ROUND ROCK (O, 101 beds) 300 University Boulevard, Round Rock, TX Zip 78665–1032; tel. 512/509–0100; Jay Fox, Chief Executive Officer
**Web address:** www.sw.org

SCOTT & WHITE MEMORIAL HOSPITAL (O, 614 beds) 2401 South 31st Street, Temple, TX Zip 76508–0002; tel. 254/724–2111; Shahin Motakef, Chief Executive Officer
**Web address:** www.sw.org/location/temple-hospital

SCOTT AND WHITE CONTINUING CARE HOSPITAL (O, 50 beds) 546 North Kegley Road, Temple, TX Zip 76502–4069; tel. 254/215–0900; Kimberly K. Langston, R.N., Chief Executive Officer
**Web address:** www.sw.org/location/temple-cch

For explanation of codes following names, see page B2.
★ Indicates Type III membership in the American Hospital Association.

| Owned, leased, sponsored: | 20 hospitals | 3456 beds |
| Contract–managed: | 1 hospital | 277 beds |
| Totals: | 21 hospitals | 3733 beds |

★**1095: BAYSTATE HEALTH, INC.** (NP)
759 Chestnut Street, Springfield, MA Zip 01199–0001;
tel. 413/794–0000; Mark A. Keroack, M.D., President and Chief
Executive Officer
**(Centralized Physician/Insurance Health System)**

**MASSACHUSETTS:** BAYSTATE FRANKLIN MEDICAL CENTER (O, 90 beds)
164 High Street, Greenfield, MA Zip 01301–2613; tel. 413/773–0211;
Thomas Higgins, M.D., Interim President and Chief Executive Officer
**Web address:** www.baystatehealth.com/fmc

BAYSTATE MARY LANE HOSPITAL (O, 25 beds) 85 South Street, Ware, MA
Zip 01082–1697; tel. 413/967–6211; Charles E. Cavagnaro, III, M.D.,
President
**Web address:** www.baystatehealth.com

BAYSTATE MEDICAL CENTER (O, 710 beds) 759 Chestnut Street, Springfield,
MA Zip 01199–0001; tel. 413/794–0000; Mark A. Keroack, M.D. MPH,
President and Chief Executive Officer
**Web address:** www.baystatehealth.org/bmc

BAYSTATE NOBLE HOSPITAL (O, 97 beds) 115 West Silver Street, Westfield,
MA Zip 01085–3628; tel. 413/568–2811; Ronald Bryant, President
**Web address:** www.baystatehealth.org/locations/noble–hospital

BAYSTATE WING HOSPITAL (O, 74 beds) 40 Wright Street, Palmer, MA
Zip 01069–1138; tel. 413/283–7651; Charles E. Cavagnaro, III, M.D.,
President and Chief Executive Officer
**Web address:** www.baystatewinghospital.org/

| Owned, leased, sponsored: | 5 hospitals | 996 beds |
| Contract–managed: | 0 hospitals | 0 beds |
| Totals: | 5 hospitals | 996 beds |

★**0940: BEACON HEALTH SYSTEM** (NP)
615 North Michigan Street, South Bend, IN Zip 46601–1033;
tel. 574/647–1000; Philip A. Newbold, Chief Executive Officer
**(Centralized Physician/Insurance Health System)**

**INDIANA:** ELKHART GENERAL HEALTHCARE SYSTEM (O, 265 beds) 600 East
Boulevard, Elkhart, IN Zip 46514–2499, Mailing Address: P.O. Box 1329,
Zip 46515–1329; tel. 574/294–2621; Greg Losasso, President
**Web address:** www.egh.org

MEMORIAL HOSPITAL OF SOUTH BEND (O, 445 beds) 615 North Michigan
Street, South Bend, IN Zip 46601–1033; tel. 574/647–1000; Kreg Gruber,
President
**Web address:** www.qualityoflife.org

| Owned, leased, sponsored: | 2 hospitals | 710 beds |
| Contract–managed: | 0 hospitals | 0 beds |
| Totals: | 2 hospitals | 710 beds |

★**0953: BEAUMONT HEALTH** (NP)
2000 Town Center, Suite 1200, Southfield, MI, Zip 48075;
tel. 248/898–5000; John T. Fox, President and Chief Executive
Officer

**MICHIGAN:** BEAUMONT HOSPITAL – FARMINGTON HILLS (O, 310 beds)
28050 Grand River Avenue, Farmington Hills, MI Zip 48336–5933;
tel. 248/471–8000; Paul E. LaCasse, D.O., M.P.H., President and Chief
Executive Officer
**Web address:** www.botsford.org

BEAUMONT HOSPITAL – ROYAL OAK (O, 1070 beds) 3601 West Thirteen Mile
Road, Royal Oak, MI Zip 48073–6712; tel. 248/898–5000; Shane Cerone,
President
**Web address:** www.beaumont.edu/royal–oak–hospital–campus

BEAUMONT HOSPITAL – TAYLOR (O, 135 beds) 10000 Telegraph Road,
Taylor, MI Zip 48180–3330; tel. 313/295–5000; Lee Ann Odom, Division
President
**Web address:** www.oakwood.org

BEAUMONT HOSPITAL – TRENTON (O, 173 beds) 5450 Fort Street, Trenton,
MI Zip 48183–4625; tel. 734/671–3800; Edith M. Hughes, R.N., President
**Web address:** www.oakwood.org

BEAUMONT HOSPITAL – TROY (O, 458 beds) 44201 Dequindre Road, Troy,
MI Zip 48085–1117; tel. 248/964–5000; Nancy Susick, MSN, President
**Web address:** www.beaumont.edu/troy–hospital–campus

BEAUMONT HOSPITAL – WAYNE (O, 198 beds) 33155 Annapolis Street,
Wayne, MI Zip 48184–2405; tel. 734/467–4000; Eric W. Widner, Division
President
**Web address:** www.oakwood.org

BEAUMONT HOSPITAL GROSSE POINTE (O, 250 beds) 468 Cadieux Road,
Grosse Pointe, MI Zip 48230–1507; tel. 313/473–1000; Richard P. Swaine,
President
**Web address:** www.beaumont.edu/grosse–pointe–hospital–campus

BEAUMONT HOSPITAL-DEARBORN (O, 521 beds) 18101 Oakwood
Boulevard, Dearborn, MI Zip 48124–4089, Mailing Address: P.O. Box 2500,
Zip 48123–2500; tel. 313/593–7000; Kelly C. Smith, Division President
**Web address:** www.oakwood.org

| Owned, leased, sponsored: | 8 hospitals | 3115 beds |
| Contract–managed: | 0 hospitals | 0 beds |
| Totals: | 8 hospitals | 3115 beds |

**0538: BENEFIS HEALTH SYSTEM** (NP)
1101 26th Street South, Great Falls, MT Zip 59405–5161;
tel. 406/455–5000; John H. Goodnow, Chief Executive Officer
**(Moderately Centralized Health System)**

**MONTANA:** BENEFIS HOSPITALS (O, 441 beds) 1101 26th Street South,
Great Falls, MT Zip 59405–5104; tel. 406/455–5000; John H. Goodnow,
Chief Executive Officer
**Web address:** www.benefis.org

MISSOURI RIVER MEDICAL CENTER (C, 52 beds) 1501 St. Charles Street,
Fort Benton, MT Zip 59442–0249, Mailing Address: P.O. Box 249,
Zip 59442–0249; tel. 406/622–3331; Louie King, President, Harry Bold
Nursing Home Administrator
**Web address:** www.mrmcfb.org

| Owned, leased, sponsored: | 1 hospital | 441 beds |
| Contract–managed: | 1 hospital | 52 beds |
| Totals: | 2 hospitals | 493 beds |

★**2435: BERKSHIRE HEALTH SYSTEMS, INC.** (NP)
725 North Street, Pittsfield, MA Zip 01201–4124;
tel. 413/447–2750; David E. Phelps, President and Chief Executive
Officer
**(Independent Hospital System)**

**MASSACHUSETTS:** BERKSHIRE MEDICAL CENTER (O, 274 beds) 725 North
Street, Pittsfield, MA Zip 01201–4124; tel. 413/447–2000; David E.
Phelps, President and Chief Executive Officer
**Web address:** www.bhs1.org/body_bmc.cfm?id=43

FAIRVIEW HOSPITAL (O, 24 beds) 29 Lewis Avenue, Great Barrington, MA
Zip 01230–1713; tel. 413/528–0790; Eugene A. Dellea, President
**Web address:** www.bhs1.org/body_fh.cfm?id=39

| Owned, leased, sponsored: | 2 hospitals | 298 beds |
| Contract–managed: | 0 hospitals | 0 beds |
| Totals: | 2 hospitals | 298 beds |

★**0051: BJC HEALTHCARE** (NP)
4901 Forest Park Avenue, Suite 1200, Saint Louis, MO
Zip 63108–1402; tel. 314/747–9322; Steven H. Lipstein, President
and Chief Executive Officer
**(Centralized Health System)**

**ILLINOIS:** ALTON MEMORIAL HOSPITAL (O, 227 beds) One Memorial Drive,
Alton, IL Zip 62002–6722; tel. 618/463–7311; David A. Braasch,
President
**Web address:** www.altonmemorialhospital.org

For explanation of codes following names, see page B2.
★ Indicates Type III membership in the American Hospital Association.

**Section B**

**MISSOURI:** BARNES–JEWISH HOSPITAL (O, 1323 beds) 1 Barnes–Jewish Hospital Plaza, Saint Louis, MO Zip 63110–1003; tel. 314/747–3000; Robert W. Cannon, President
**Web address:** www.barnesjewish.org

BARNES–JEWISH ST. PETERS HOSPITAL (O, 101 beds) 10 Hospital Drive, Saint Peters, MO Zip 63376–1659; tel. 636/916–9000; Larry A. Tracy, Jr., FACHE, President
**Web address:** www.bjsph.org/

BARNES–JEWISH WEST COUNTY HOSPITAL (O, 77 beds) 12634 Olive Boulevard, Saint Louis, MO Zip 63141–6337; tel. 314/996–8000; Douglas Black, President
**Web address:** www.barnesjewishwestcounty.org

BOONE HOSPITAL CENTER (L, 304 beds) 1600 East Broadway, Columbia, MO Zip 65201–5844; tel. 573/815–8000; James J. Sinek, FACHE, President
**Web address:** www.boone.org

CHRISTIAN HOSPITAL (O, 252 beds) 11133 Dunn Road, Saint Louis, MO Zip 63136–6119; tel. 314/653–5000; Ronald B. McMullen, President
**Web address:** www.christianhospital.org

MISSOURI BAPTIST MEDICAL CENTER (O, 448 beds) 3015 North Ballas Road, Saint Louis, MO Zip 63131–2329; tel. 314/996–5000; John Antes, President
**Web address:** www.missouribaptist.org

MISSOURI BAPTIST SULLIVAN HOSPITAL (O, 35 beds) 751 Sappington Bridge Road, Sullivan, MO Zip 63080–2354; tel. 573/468–4186; Tony Schwarm, President
**Web address:** www.missouribaptistsullivan.org

PARKLAND HEALTH CENTER – LIBERTY STREET (O, 103 beds) 1101 West Liberty Street, Farmington, MO Zip 63640–1921; tel. 573/756–6451; Thomas P. Karl, President
**Web address:** www.parklandhealthcenter.org

PARKLAND HEALTH CENTER – WEBER ROAD (O, 127 beds) 1212 Weber Road, Farmington, MO Zip 63640–3325; tel. 573/756–4581; Christie Westrich, Administrator
**Web address:** www.parklandhealthcenter.org

PARKLAND HEALTH CENTER–BONNE TERRE (O, 3 beds) 7245 Raider Road, Bonne Terre, MO Zip 63628–3767; tel. 573/358–1400; Christinia Jepsen, R.N., Administrator
**Web address:** www.parklandhealthcenter.org

PROGRESS WEST HOSPITAL (O, 44 beds) Two Progress Point Parkway, O'Fallon, MO Zip 63368–2208; tel. 636/344–1000; Larry A. Tracy, Jr., FACHE, President
**Web address:** www.progresswest.org

ST. LOUIS CHILDREN'S HOSPITAL (O, 264 beds) One Children's Place, Saint Louis, MO Zip 63110–1002; tel. 314/454–6000; Joan Magruder, President
**Web address:** www.stlouischildrens.org

| Owned, leased, sponsored: | 13 hospitals | 3308 beds |
|---|---|---|
| Contract–managed: | 0 hospitals | 0 beds |
| Totals: | 13 hospitals | 3308 beds |

---

**★0852: BLANCHARD VALLEY HEALTH SYSTEM** (NP)
1900 South Main Street, Findlay, OH Zip 45840–1214; tel. 419/423–4500; Scott C. Malaney, President and Chief Executive Officer
**(Centralized Physician/Insurance Health System)**

**OHIO:** BLANCHARD VALLEY HOSPITAL (O, 159 beds) 1900 South Main Street, Findlay, OH Zip 45840–1214; tel. 419/423–4500; Scott C. Malaney, President and Chief Executive Officer
**Web address:** www.bvhealthsystem.org

BLUFFTON HOSPITAL (O, 25 beds) 139 Garau Street, Bluffton, OH Zip 45817–1027; tel. 419/358–9010; Christine Keller, Chief Administrative Officer
**Web address:** www.bvhealthsystem.org/

| Owned, leased, sponsored: | 2 hospitals | 184 beds |
|---|---|---|
| Contract–managed: | 0 hospitals | 0 beds |
| Totals: | 2 hospitals | 184 beds |

---

**★0300: BLUE MOUNTAIN HEALTH SYSTEM** (NP)
211 North 12th Street, Lehighton, PA Zip 18235–1138; tel. 610/377–1300; Andrew E. Harris, President and Chief Executive Officer
**(Independent Hospital System)**

**PENNSYLVANIA:** GNADEN HUETTEN MEMORIAL HOSPITAL (O, 183 beds) 211 North 12th Street, Lehighton, PA Zip 18235–1138; tel. 610/377–1300; Andrew E. Harris, Chief Executive Officer
**Web address:** www.blmtn.org

PALMERTON HOSPITAL (O, 60 beds) 135 Lafayette Avenue, Palmerton, PA Zip 18071–1596; tel. 610/826–3141; Andrew E. Harris, Chief Executive Officer
**Web address:** www.ghmh.org/content/palmertoncampus.htm

| Owned, leased, sponsored: | 2 hospitals | 243 beds |
|---|---|---|
| Contract–managed: | 0 hospitals | 0 beds |
| Totals: | 2 hospitals | 243 beds |

---

**★5085: BON SECOURS HEALTH SYSTEM, INC.** (CC)
1505 Marriottsville Road, Marriottsville, MD Zip 21104–1399; tel. 410/442–5511; Richard Statuto, President and Chief Executive Officer
**(Moderately Centralized Health System)**

**KENTUCKY:** OUR LADY OF BELLEFONTE HOSPITAL (O, 151 beds) St. Christopher Drive, Ashland, KY Zip 41101, Mailing Address: P.O. Box 789, Zip 41105–0789; tel. 606/833–3333; Kevin Halter, Chief Executive Officer
**Web address:** www.olbh.com

**MARYLAND:** BON SECOURS BALTIMORE HEALTH SYSTEM (O, 93 beds) 2000 West Baltimore Street, Baltimore, MD Zip 21223–1558; tel. 410/362–3000; Samuel Lee Ross, M.D., MS, Chief Executive Officer
**Web address:** www.bonsecoursbaltimore.com

**NEW YORK:** BON SECOURS COMMUNITY HOSPITAL (O, 187 beds) 160 East Main Street, Port Jervis, NY Zip 12771–2245, Mailing Address: P.O. Box 1014, Zip 12771–0268; tel. 845/858–7000; Jeff Reilly, Senior Vice President Operations
**Web address:** www.bonsecourscommunityhosp.org

GOOD SAMARITAN HOSPITAL (O, 308 beds) 255 Lafayette Avenue, Suffern, NY Zip 10901–4869; tel. 845/368–5000; Mary Leahy, M.D., Chief Executive Officer
**Web address:** www.goodsamhosp.org

ST. ANTHONY COMMUNITY HOSPITAL (O, 73 beds) 15 Maple Avenue, Warwick, NY Zip 10990–1028; tel. 845/986–2276; Jeff Reilly, Senior Vice President Operations
**Web address:** www.stanthonycommunityhosp.org

**SOUTH CAROLINA:** BON SECOURS ST. FRANCIS HEALTH SYSTEM (O, 331 beds) One St. Francis Drive, Greenville, SC Zip 29601–3207; tel. 864/255–1000; Craig McCoy, Chief Executive Officer
**Web address:** www.stfrancishealth.org

**VIRGINIA:** BON SECOURS MARYVIEW MEDICAL CENTER (O, 466 beds) 3636 High Street, Portsmouth, VA Zip 23707–3270; tel. 757/398–2200; Joseph M. Oddis, Chief Executive Officer
**Web address:** www.bonsecourshamptonroads.com

BON SECOURS MEMORIAL REGIONAL MEDICAL CENTER (O, 225 beds) 8260 Atlee Road, Mechanicsville, VA Zip 23116–1844; tel. 804/764–6000; Michael Robinson, Chief Executive Officer
**Web address:** www.bonsecours.com

BON SECOURS ST. FRANCIS MEDICAL CENTER (O, 130 beds) 13710 St. Francis Boulevard, Midlothian, VA Zip 23114–3267; tel. 804/594–7300; Mark M. Gordon, Chief Executive Officer
**Web address:** www.bonsecours.com/sfmc/default.asp

BON SECOURS ST. MARY'S HOSPITAL (O, 391 beds) 5801 Bremo Road, Richmond, VA Zip 23226–1907; tel. 804/285–2011; Toni R. Ardabell, R.N., Chief Executive Officer
**Web address:** www.bonsecours.com

BON SECOURS–DEPAUL MEDICAL CENTER (O, 204 beds) 150 Kingsley Lane, Norfolk, VA Zip 23505–4650; tel. 757/889–5000; John E. Barrett, III, Chief Executive Officer
**Web address:** www.bonsecourshamptonroads.com

---

For explanation of codes following names, see page B2.
★ Indicates Type III membership in the American Hospital Association.

Section B

BON SECOURS–RICHMOND COMMUNITY HOSPITAL (O, 85 beds) 1500 North 28th Street, Richmond, VA Zip 23223–5396, Mailing Address: P.O. Box 27184, Zip 23261–7184; tel. 804/225–1700; Michael Robinson, Executive Vice President and Administrator
**Web address:** www.bonsecours.com

MARY IMMACULATE HOSPITAL (O, 238 beds) 2 Bernardine Drive, Newport News, VA Zip 23602–4499; tel. 757/886–6000; Darlene Stephenson, Chief Executive Officer
**Web address:** www.bonsecourshamptonroads.com

RAPPAHANNOCK GENERAL HOSPITAL (O, 76 beds) 101 Harris Drive, Kilmarnock, VA Zip 22482–3880, Mailing Address: P.O. Box 1449, Zip 22482–1449; tel. 804/435–8000; James M. Holmes, Jr., President and Chief Executive Officer
**Web address:** www.rgh–hospital.com

| Owned, leased, sponsored: | 14 hospitals | 2958 beds |
|---|---|---|
| Contract–managed: | 0 hospitals | 0 beds |
| Totals: | 14 hospitals | 2958 beds |

**2455:  BRADFORD HEALTH SERVICES** (IO)
2101 Magnolia Avenue South, Suite 518, Birmingham, AL Zip 35205–2853; tel. 205/251–7753; Jerry W. Crowder, President and Chief Executive Officer

**ALABAMA:** BRADFORD HEALTH SERVICES AT HUNTSVILLE (O, 84 beds) 1600 Browns Ferry Road, Madison, AL Zip 35758–9601, Mailing Address: P.O. Box 1488, Zip 35758–0176; tel. 256/461–7272; Bob Hinds, Executive Director
**Web address:** www.bradfordhealth.com

BRADFORD HEALTH SERVICES AT WARRIOR LODGE (O, 100 beds) 1189 Allbritt Road, Warrior, AL Zip 35180, Mailing Address: P.O. Box 129, Zip 35180–0129; tel. 205/647–1945; Roy M. Ramsey, Executive Director
**Web address:** www.bradfordhealth.com

| Owned, leased, sponsored: | 2 hospitals | 184 beds |
|---|---|---|
| Contract–managed: | 0 hospitals | 0 beds |
| Totals: | 2 hospitals | 184 beds |

**★0595:  BRONSON HEALTHCARE GROUP, INC.** (NP)
301 John Street, Kalamazoo, MI Zip 49007–5295; tel. 269/341–6000; Frank J. Sardone, President and Chief Executive Officer
**(Centralized Health System)**

**MICHIGAN:** BRONSON BATTLE CREEK (O, 198 beds) 300 North Avenue, Battle Creek, MI Zip 49017–3307; tel. 269/245–8000; Frank J. Sardone, President and Chief Executive Officer
**Web address:** www.bronsonhealth.com

BRONSON LAKEVIEW HOSPITAL (O, 35 beds) 408 Hazen Street, Paw Paw, MI Zip 49079–1019, Mailing Address: P.O. Box 209, Zip 49079–0209; tel. 269/657–3141; Kirk Richardson, Chief Operating Officer
**Web address:** www.bronsonhealth.com/lakeview

BRONSON METHODIST HOSPITAL (O, 410 beds) 601 John Street, Kalamazoo, MI Zip 49007–5346; tel. 269/341–6000; Frank J. Sardone, President and Chief Executive Officer
**Web address:** www.bronsonhealth.com

| Owned, leased, sponsored: | 3 hospitals | 643 beds |
|---|---|---|
| Contract–managed: | 0 hospitals | 0 beds |
| Totals: | 3 hospitals | 643 beds |

**★3115:  BROWARD HEALTH** (NP)
303 S.E. 17th Street, Fort Lauderdale, FL Zip 33316–2523; tel. 954/355–4400; Nabil El Sanadi, M.D., President and Chief Executive Officer

**FLORIDA:** BROWARD HEALTH CORAL SPRINGS (O, 182 beds) 3000 Coral Hills Drive, Coral Springs, FL Zip 33065–4108; tel. 954/344–3000; Drew Grossman, Chief Executive Officer
**Web address:** www.browardhealth.org

BROWARD HEALTH IMPERIAL POINT (O, 180 beds) 6401 North Federal Highway, Fort Lauderdale, FL Zip 33308–1495; tel. 954/776–8500; Alice Taylor, R.N., MSN, Chief Executive Officer
**Web address:** www.browardhealth.org

BROWARD HEALTH MEDICAL CENTER (O, 648 beds) 1600 South Andrews Avenue, Fort Lauderdale, FL Zip 33316–2510; tel. 954/355–4400; Calvin E. Glidewell, Jr., Chief Executive Officer
**Web address:** www.browardhealth.org

BROWARD HEALTH NORTH (O, 334 beds) 201 East Sample Road, Deerfield Beach, FL Zip 33064–3502; tel. 954/941–8300; Pauline Grant, FACHE, Chief Executive Officer
**Web address:** www.browardhealth.org

| Owned, leased, sponsored: | 4 hospitals | 1344 beds |
|---|---|---|
| Contract–managed: | 0 hospitals | 0 beds |
| Totals: | 4 hospitals | 1344 beds |

**★0400:  BRYAN HEALTH** (NP)
1600 South 48th Street, Lincoln, NE Zip 68506–1283; tel. 402/481–1111; Kimberly A. Russel, FACHE, President and Chief Executive Officer
**(Independent Hospital System)**

**NEBRASKA:** BRYAN MEDICAL CENTER (O, 328 beds) 1600 South 48th Street, Lincoln, NE Zip 68506–1299; tel. 402/489–0200; John T. Woodrich, ACHE, President and Chief Operating Officer
**Web address:** www.bryanhealth.com

CRETE AREA MEDICAL CENTER (O, 24 beds) 2910 Betten Drive, Crete, NE Zip 68333–3084, Mailing Address: P.O. Box 220, Zip 68333–0220; tel. 402/826–2102; Rebekah Mussman, Chief Executive Officer
**Web address:** www.creteareamedicalcenter.com

SAUNDERS MEDICAL CENTER (C, 87 beds) 1760 County Road J., Wahoo, NE Zip 68066–4152; tel. 402/443–4191; Tyler Toline, FACHE, Interim Chief Executive Officer
**Web address:** www.saundersmedicalcenter.com

| Owned, leased, sponsored: | 2 hospitals | 352 beds |
|---|---|---|
| Contract–managed: | 1 hospital | 87 beds |
| Totals: | 3 hospitals | 439 beds |

**9655:  BUREAU OF MEDICINE AND SURGERY, DEPARTMENT OF THE NAVY** (FG)
2300 East Street N.W., Washington, DC Zip 20372–5300; tel. 202/762–3701; Vice Admiral Matthew L. Nathan, Surgeon General
**(Independent Hospital System)**

**CALIFORNIA:** NAVAL HOSPITAL CAMP PENDLETON (O, 72 beds) Santa Margarita Road, Building H100, Camp Pendleton, CA Zip 92055–5191, Mailing Address: P.O. Box 555191, Zip 92055–5191; tel. 760/725–1304; Captain Lisa Mulligan, Commanding Officer
**Web address:** www.cpen.med.navy.mil/

NAVAL MEDICAL CENTER SAN DIEGO (O, 285 beds) 34800 Bob Wilson Drive, San Diego, CA Zip 92134–5000; tel. 619/532–6400; Captain Jose' A. Acosta, MC, USN, Commanding Officer
**Web address:** www.med.navy.mil/sites/nmcsd/Pages/default.aspx

ROBERT E. BUSH NAVAL HOSPITAL (O, 29 beds) 1145 Sturgis Road, Twentynine Palms, CA Zip 92278, Mailing Address: Box 788250, MCAGCC, Zip 92278–8250; tel. 760/830–2190; Captain Jay C. Sourbeer, Commanding Officer
**Web address:** www.med.navy.mil/sites/nhtp/Pages/default.aspx

**FLORIDA:** NAVAL HOSPITAL JACKSONVILLE (O, 64 beds) 2080 Child Street, Jacksonville, FL Zip 32214–5000; tel. 904/542–7300; Commander Darryl Green, Director Administration
**Web address:** www.med.navy. mil/SITES/NAVALHOSPITALJAX/Pages/default.aspx

NAVAL HOSPITAL PENSACOLA (O, 28 beds) 6000 West Highway 98, Pensacola, FL Zip 32512–0003; tel. 850/505–6413; Commander Devin Morrison, Director Administration
**Web address:** www.med.navy.mil/sites/pcola/Pages/default.aspx

Section B

For explanation of codes following names, see page B2.
★ Indicates Type III membership in the American Hospital Association.

**GUAM:** U. S. NAVAL HOSPITAL GUAM (O, 55 beds) Agana, GU Zip 96910; FPO, tel. 671/344–9340; Lieutenant Commander Rona Green,
**Web address:** www.med.navy.mil/sites/usnhguam/Pages/default.aspx

**MARYLAND:** WALTER REED NATIONAL MILITARY MEDICAL CENTER (O, 247 beds) 8901 Wisconsin Avenue, Bethesda, MD Zip 20889–5600; tel. 301/295–4611; Brigadier General Jeffrey B. Clark, Director
**Web address:** www.wrnmmc.capmed.mil/SitePages/home.aspx

**NORTH CAROLINA:** NAVAL HOSPITAL CAMP LEJEUNE (O, 117 beds) 100 Brewster Boulevard, Camp Lejeune, NC Zip 28547–2538, Mailing Address: P.O. Box 10100, Zip 28547–0100; tel. 910/450–4300; Captain Rick Freedman, Commanding Officer
**Web address:** www.med.navy.mil/sites/nhcl/Pages/default.aspx

**SOUTH CAROLINA:** NAVAL HOSPITAL BEAUFORT (O, 20 beds) 1 Pinckney Boulevard, Beaufort, SC Zip 29902–6122; tel. 843/228–5301; Lieutenant Commander Willie Brown, Director Administration
**Web address:** www.med.navy.mil/sites/nhbeaufort/Pages/Welcome_Page.aspx

**VIRGINIA:** NAVAL HOSPITAL LEMOORE (O, 16 beds) 620 John Paul Jones Circle, Portsmith, VA Zip 23708, Mailing Address: 937 Franklin Avenue, Lemoore, CAZip 93246–0001; tel. 559/998–4481; Captain Mary A. Mahony, Commanding Officer
**Web address:** www.med.navy.mil/sites/nhlem/Pages/index.aspx

NAVAL MEDICAL CENTER (O, 274 beds) 620 John Paul Jones Circle, Portsmouth, VA Zip 23708–2197; tel. 757/953–1980; Commander Matthew Case, MSC, USN, Director For Administration
**Web address:** www.nmcphc.med.navy.mil/

**WASHINGTON:** NAVAL HOSPITAL BREMERTON (O, 30 beds) One Boone Road, Bremerton, WA Zip 98312–1898; tel. 360/475–4000; Commander Jeffrey Klinger, Director for Administration
**Web address:** www.med.navy.mil/sites/nhbrem/Pages/default.aspx

NAVAL HOSPITAL OAK HARBOR (O, 29 beds) 3475 North Saratoga Street, Oak Harbor, WA Zip 98278–8800; tel. 360/257–9500; Commander Frederick Joseph McDonald, Commanding Officer
**Web address:** www.med.navy.mil/sites/nhoh/Pages/default.aspx

| | | |
|---|---|---|
| **Owned, leased, sponsored:** | 13 hospitals | 1266 beds |
| **Contract–managed:** | 0 hospitals | 0 beds |
| **Totals:** | 13 hospitals | 1266 beds |

---

**0113:  CANCER TREATMENT CENTERS OF AMERICA** (IO)
1336 Basswood Road, Schaumburg, IL Zip 60173–4544; tel. 847/342–7400; Gerard van Grinsven, President and Chief Executive Officer

**ARIZONA:** WESTERN REGIONAL MEDICAL CENTER (O, 24 beds) 14200 West Celebrate Life way, Goodyear, AZ Zip 85338–3005; tel. 623/207–3000; Matthew McGuire, President and Chief Executive Officer
**Web address:** www.cancercenter.com/western–hospital.cfm

**GEORGIA:** SOUTHEASTERN REGIONAL MEDICAL CENTER (O, 50 beds) 600 Celebrate Life Parkway, Newnan, GA Zip 30265–8000; tel. 770/400–6000; Anne Meisner, MSN, President and Chief Executive Officer
**Web address:** www.cancercenter.com/southeastern–hospital.cfm

**ILLINOIS:** MIDWESTERN REGIONAL MEDICAL CENTER (O, 68 beds) 2520 Elisha Avenue, Zion, IL Zip 60099–2587; tel. 847/872–4561; Scott Jones, President and Chief Executive Officer
**Web address:** www.cancercenter.com

**OKLAHOMA:** SOUTHWESTERN REGIONAL MEDICAL CENTER (O, 40 beds) 10109 East 79th Street, Tulsa, OK Zip 74133–4564; tel. 918/286–5000; Richard Haldeman, President and Chief Executive Officer
**Web address:** www.cancercenter.com

**PENNSYLVANIA:** EASTERN REGIONAL MEDICAL CENTER (O, 74 beds) 1331 East Wyoming Avenue, Philadelphia, PA Zip 19124–3808; tel. 800/615–3055; John McNeil, President and Chief Executive Officer
**Web address:** www.cancercenter.com

| | | |
|---|---|---|
| **Owned, leased, sponsored:** | 5 hospitals | 256 beds |
| **Contract–managed:** | 0 hospitals | 0 beds |
| **Totals:** | 5 hospitals | 256 beds |

---

**★0124:   CAPE COD HEALTHCARE, INC.** (NP)
27 Park Street, Hyannis, MA Zip 02601–5230; tel. 508/862–5121; Michael K. Lauf, President and Chief Executive Officer
**(Moderately Centralized Health System)**

**MASSACHUSETTS:** CAPE COD HOSPITAL (O, 259 beds) 27 Park Street, Hyannis, MA Zip 02601–5230; tel. 508/771–1800; Michael K. Lauf, President and Chief Executive Officer
**Web address:** www.capecodhealth.org

FALMOUTH HOSPITAL (O, 95 beds) 100 Ter Heun Drive, Falmouth, MA Zip 02540–2599; tel. 508/548–5300; Michael K. Lauf, President and Chief Executive Officer
**Web address:** www.capecodhealth.org

| | | |
|---|---|---|
| **Owned, leased, sponsored:** | 2 hospitals | 354 beds |
| **Contract–managed:** | 0 hospitals | 0 beds |
| **Totals:** | 2 hospitals | 354 beds |

---

**0835:   CAPE FEAR VALLEY HEALTH SYSTEM** (NP)
1638 Owen Drive, Fayetteville, NC Zip 28304–3424, Mailing Address: P.O. Box 2000, Zip 28302–2000; tel. 910/615–4000; Michael Nagowski, President and Chief Executive Officer
**(Independent Hospital System)**

**NORTH CAROLINA:** CAPE FEAR VALLEY – BLADEN COUNTY HOSPITAL (O, 25 beds) 501 South Poplar Street, Elizabethtown, NC Zip 28337–9375, Mailing Address: P.O. Box 398, Zip 28337–0398; tel. 910/862–5100; Lisa Byrd, Interim President
**Web address:** www.bchn.org

CAPE FEAR VALLEY MEDICAL CENTER (O, 592 beds) 1638 Owen Drive, Fayetteville, NC Zip 28304–3431, Mailing Address: P.O. Box 2000, Zip 28302–2000; tel. 910/615–4000; Michael Nagowski, Chief Executive Officer
**Web address:** www.capefearvalley.com

HARNETT HEALTH SYSTEM (C, 96 beds) 800 Tilghman Drive, Dunn, NC Zip 28334–5599, Mailing Address: P.O. Box 1706, Zip 28335–1706; tel. 910/892–1000; Dan Weatherly, Chief Executive Officer
**Web address:** www.myharnetthealth.org/

HIGHSMITH–RAINEY SPECIALTY HOSPITAL (O, 66 beds) 150 Robeson Street, Fayetteville, NC Zip 28301–5570; tel. 910/615–1000; Kevin Jackson, On Site Administrator
**Web address:** www.capefearvalley.com

| | | |
|---|---|---|
| **Owned, leased, sponsored:** | 3 hospitals | 683 beds |
| **Contract–managed:** | 1 hospital | 96 beds |
| **Totals:** | 4 hospitals | 779 beds |

---

**0337:   CAPELLA HEALTHCARE** (IO)
501 Corporate Centre Drive, Suite 200, Franklin, TN Zip 37067–2662; tel. 615/764–3000; Michael Wiechart, President and Chief Executive Officer
**(Moderately Centralized Health System)**

**ARKANSAS:** NATIONAL PARK MEDICAL CENTER (O, 193 beds) 1910 Malvern Avenue, Hot Springs, AR Zip 71901–7799; tel. 501/321–1000; Jerry D. Mabry, FACHE, Chief Executive Officer
**Web address:** www.nationalparkmedical.com

SAINT MARY'S REGIONAL MEDICAL CENTER (O, 151 beds) 1808 West Main Street, Russellville, AR Zip 72801–2724; tel. 479/968–2841; Mike McCoy, Interim Chief Executive Officer
**Web address:** www.saintmarysregional.com

**OKLAHOMA:** EASTAR HEALTH SYSTEM (L, 222 beds) 300 Rockefeller Drive, Muskogee, OK Zip 74401–5081; tel. 918/682–5501; Anthony R. Young, Chief Executive Officer
**Web address:** www.eastarhealth.com

---

For explanation of codes following names, see page B2.
★ Indicates Type III membership in the American Hospital Association.

Section B

SOUTHWESTERN MEDICAL CENTER (O, 178 beds) 5602 S.W. Lee Boulevard, Lawton, OK Zip 73505–9635; tel. 580/531–4700; Stephen O. Hyde, FACHE, Chief Executive Officer
**Web address:** www.swmconline.com

**OREGON:** WILLAMETTE VALLEY MEDICAL CENTER (O, 88 beds) 2700 S.E. Stratus Avenue, McMinnville, OR Zip 97128–6255; tel. 503/472–6131; Peter A. Hofstetter, Chief Executive Officer
**Web address:** www.wvmcweb.com

**SOUTH CAROLINA:** CAROLINA PINES REGIONAL MEDICAL CENTER (O, 120 beds) 1304 West Bobo Newsom Highway, Hartsville, SC Zip 29550–4710; tel. 843/339–2100; J. Timothy Browne, FACHE, Chief Executive Officer
**Web address:** www.cprmc.com

**WASHINGTON:** CAPITAL MEDICAL CENTER (O, 85 beds) 3900 Capital Mall Drive S.W., Olympia, WA Zip 98502–5026, Mailing Address: P.O. Box 19002, Zip 98507–0013; tel. 360/754–5858; Jim Geist, Chief Executive Officer
**Web address:** www.capitalmedical.com

| Owned, leased, sponsored: | 7 hospitals | 1037 beds |
|---|---|---|
| Contract–managed: | 0 hospitals | 0 beds |
| Totals: | 7 hospitals | 1037 beds |

---

**★0297:  CAPITAL HEALTH** (NP)
750 Brunswick Avenue, Trenton, NJ Zip 08638–4143; tel. 609/394–6000; Al Maghazehe, Ph.D., FACHE, Chief Executive Officer
**(Independent Hospital System)**

**NEW JERSEY:** CAPITAL HEALTH MEDICAL CENTER–HOPEWELL (O, 197 beds) 1 Capital Way, Pennington, NJ Zip 08534–2520; tel. 609/303–4000; Al Maghazehe, Ph.D., FACHE, President and Chief Executive Officer
**Web address:** www.capitalhealth.org

CAPITAL HEALTH REGIONAL MEDICAL CENTER (O, 222 beds) 750 Brunswick Avenue, Trenton, NJ Zip 08638–4143; tel. 609/394–6000; Al Maghazehe, Ph.D., FACHE, President and Chief Executive Officer
**Web address:** www.capitalhealth.org

| Owned, leased, sponsored: | 2 hospitals | 419 beds |
|---|---|---|
| Contract–managed: | 0 hospitals | 0 beds |
| Totals: | 2 hospitals | 419 beds |

---

**★0099:  CARE NEW ENGLAND HEALTH SYSTEM** (NP)
45 Willard Avenue, Providence, RI Zip 02905–3218; tel. 401/453–7900; Dennis D. Keefe, President and Chief Executive Officer
**(Centralized Health System)**

**RHODE ISLAND:** BUTLER HOSPITAL (O, 117 beds) 345 Blackstone Boulevard, Providence, RI Zip 02906–4829; tel. 401/455–6200; Lawrence Price, M.D., President and Chief Operating Officer
**Web address:** www.butler.org

KENT COUNTY MEMORIAL HOSPITAL (O, 306 beds) 455 Tollgate Road, Warwick, RI Zip 02886–2770; tel. 401/737–7000; Michael J. Dacey, M.D., MS, President and Chief Operating Officer
**Web address:** www.kentri.org

MEMORIAL HOSPITAL OF RHODE ISLAND (O, 152 beds) 111 Brewster Street, Pawtucket, RI Zip 02860–4499; tel. 401/729–2000; James E. Fanale, M.D., Interim Chief Operating Officer and Chief Medical Officer
**Web address:** www.mhri.org

WOMEN & INFANTS HOSPITAL OF RHODE ISLAND (O, 247 beds) 101 Dudley Street, Providence, RI Zip 02905–2499; tel. 401/274–1100; Mark R. Marcantano, President and Chief Operating Officer
**Web address:** www.womenandinfants.org

| Owned, leased, sponsored: | 4 hospitals | 822 beds |
|---|---|---|
| Contract–managed: | 0 hospitals | 0 beds |
| Totals: | 4 hospitals | 822 beds |

---

**★0931:  CAREPOINT HEALTH** (IO)
10 Exchange Place, 15th Floor, Jersey City, NJ Zip 07302–3918; tel. 877/791–7000; Dennis Kelly, Chief Executive Officer

**NEW JERSEY:** BAYONNE MEDICAL CENTER (O, 178 beds) 29th Street & Avenue E., Bayonne, NJ Zip 07002–4699; tel. 201/858–5000; Paul E. Minnick, R.N., MSN, Chief Operating Officer
**Web address:** www.bayonnemedicalcenter.org/

CHRIST HOSPITAL (O, 376 beds) 176 Palisade Avenue, Jersey City, NJ Zip 07306–1196, Mailing Address: 176 Palisades Avenue, Zip 07306–1196; tel. 201/795–8200; Marie Theresa Duffy, Chief Operating Officer
**Web address:** www.christhospital.org

HOBOKEN UNIVERSITY MEDICAL CENTER (O, 333 beds) 308 Willow Avenue, Hoboken, NJ Zip 07030–3889; tel. 201/418–1000; Ann P. Logan, R.N., Ph.D., Chief Operating Officer
**Web address:** www.hobokenumc.com

| Owned, leased, sponsored: | 3 hospitals | 887 beds |
|---|---|---|
| Contract–managed: | 0 hospitals | 0 beds |
| Totals: | 3 hospitals | 887 beds |

---

**★0070:  CARILION CLINIC** (NP)
1906 Belleview Avenue S.E., Roanoke, VA Zip 24014–1838, Mailing Address: P.O. Box 13727, Zip 24036–3727; tel. 540/981–7000; Nancy Howell Agee, President and Chief Executive Officer
**(Moderately Centralized Health System)**

**VIRGINIA:** CARILION FRANKLIN MEMORIAL HOSPITAL (O, 18 beds) 180 Floyd Avenue, Rocky Mount, VA Zip 24151–1389; tel. 540/483–5277; William D. Jacobsen, Vice President and Administrator
**Web address:** www.carilionclinic.org/Carilion/Franklin+Memorial+Hospital

CARILION GILES COMMUNITY HOSPITAL (O, 16 beds) 159 Hartley Way, Pearisburg, VA Zip 24134–2471; tel. 540/921–6000; William Flattery, Vice President and Administrator Western Division
**Web address:** www.carilionclinic.org/Carilion/cgch

CARILION NEW RIVER VALLEY MEDICAL CENTER (O, 94 beds) 2900 Lamb Circle, Christiansburg, VA Zip 24073–6344, Mailing Address: P.O. Box 5, Radford, Zip 24143–0005; tel. 540/731–2000; William Flattery, Vice President and Administrator Western Division
**Web address:** www.carilionclinic.org/Carilion/cnrv

CARILION ROANOKE MEMORIAL HOSPITAL (O, 646 beds) Belleview at Jefferson Street, Roanoke, VA Zip 24014, Mailing Address: P.O. Box 13367, Zip 24033–3367; tel. 540/981–7000; Steven C. Arner, President
**Web address:** www.carilionclinic.org

CARILION STONEWALL JACKSON HOSPITAL (O, 13 beds) 1 Health Circle, Lexington, VA Zip 24450–2492; tel. 540/458–3300; Charles E. Carr, Vice President and Administrator
**Web address:** www.carilionclinic.org/Carilion/csjh

CARILION TAZEWELL COMMUNITY HOSPITAL (O, 7 beds) 141 Ben Bolt Avenue, Tazewell, VA Zip 24651–9700; tel. 276/988–8700; Kathren Dowdy, MSN, Regional Hospital Senior Director
**Web address:** www.carilionclinic.org/Carilion/Carilion+Tazewell+Community+Hospital

| Owned, leased, sponsored: | 6 hospitals | 794 beds |
|---|---|---|
| Contract–managed: | 0 hospitals | 0 beds |
| Totals: | 6 hospitals | 794 beds |

---

**★2575:  CARLE FOUNDATION** (NP)
611 West Park Street, Urbana, IL Zip 61801–2595; tel. 217/383–3311; James C. Leonard, M.D., President and Chief Executive Officer
**(Moderately Centralized Health System)**

**ILLINOIS:** CARLE FOUNDATION HOSPITAL (O, 345 beds) 611 West Park Street, Urbana, IL Zip 61801–2595; tel. 217/383–3311; James C. Leonard, M.D., President and Chief Executive Officer
**Web address:** www.carle.org

For explanation of codes following names, see page B2.
★ Indicates Type III membership in the American Hospital Association.

Section B

CARLE HOOPESTON REGIONAL HEALTH CENTER (O, 100 beds) 701 East Orange Street, Hoopeston, IL Zip 60942–1801; tel. 217/283–5531; Harry Brockus, Chief Executive Officer
**Web address:** www.carle.org

| | | |
|---|---|---|
| Owned, leased, sponsored: | 2 hospitals | 445 beds |
| Contract–managed: | 0 hospitals | 0 beds |
| **Totals:** | 2 hospitals | 445 beds |

★**0705: CAROLINAS HEALTHCARE SYSTEM** (NP)
1000 Blythe Boulevard, Charlotte, NC Zip 28203–5871, Mailing Address: P.O. Box 32861, Zip 28232–2861; tel. 704/355–2000; Michael C. Tarwater, Chief Executive Officer
**(Moderately Centralized Health System)**

**NORTH CAROLINA:** BLUE RIDGE HEALTHCARE HOSPITALS (C, 149 beds) 2201 South Sterling Street, Morganton, NC Zip 28655–4058; tel. 828/580–5000; Kathy C. Bailey, Ph.D., FACHE, President and Chief Executive Officer

CAROLINAS HEALTHCARE SYSTEM ANSON (O, 15 beds) 2301 U.S Highway 74 West, Wadesboro, NC Zip 28170; tel. 704/994–4500; Michael Lutes, President
**Web address:** www.carolinashealthcare.org/anson

CAROLINAS HEALTHCARE SYSTEM LINCOLN (O, 101 beds) 433 McAlister Road, Lincolnton, NC Zip 28092–4147, Mailing Address: PO Box 677, Zip 28093–0677; tel. 980/212–2000; Peter W. Acker, President and Chief Executive Officer
**Web address:** www.carolinashealthcare.org/lincoln

CAROLINAS HEALTHCARE SYSTEM NORTHEAST (O, 455 beds) 920 Church Street North, Concord, NC Zip 28025–2983; tel. 704/403–3000; Phyllis A. Wingate, FACHE, President
**Web address:** www.carolinashealthcare.org/northeast

CAROLINAS HEALTHCARE SYSTEM PINEVILLE (O, 229 beds) 10628 Park Road, Charlotte, NC Zip 28210–8407; tel. 704/543–2000; Christopher R. Hummer, President
**Web address:** www.carolinashealthcare.org/pineville

CAROLINAS HEALTHCARE SYSTEM UNION (L, 247 beds) 600 Hospital Drive, Monroe, NC Zip 28112–6000, Mailing Address: P.O. Box 5003, Zip 28111–5003; tel. 980/993–3100; Michael Lutes, President
**Web address:** www.carolinashealthcare.org/union

CAROLINAS MEDICAL CENTER (O, 1132 beds) 1000 Blythe Boulevard, Charlotte, NC Zip 28203–5871, Mailing Address: P.O. Box 32861, Zip 28232–2861; tel. 704/355–2000; Spencer Lilly, President
**Web address:** www.carolinashealthcare.org/cmc

CAROLINAS MEDICAL CENTER–UNIVERSITY (O, 94 beds) 8800 North Tryon Street, Charlotte, NC Zip 28262–3300, Mailing Address: P.O. Box 560727, Zip 28256–0727; tel. 704/863–6000; William H. Leonard, President
**Web address:** www.carolinashealthcare.org/university

CAROLINAS REHABILITATION (O, 157 beds) 1100 Blythe Boulevard, Charlotte, NC Zip 28203–5864; tel. 704/355–4300; Robert G. Larrison, Jr., President
**Web address:** www.carolinashealthcare.org/rehabilitation

CLEVELAND REGIONAL MEDICAL CENTER (L, 293 beds) 201 East Grover Street, Shelby, NC Zip 28150–3917; tel. 980/487–3000; Brian Gwyn, President and Chief Executive Officer
**Web address:** www.clevelandregional.org

COLUMBUS REGIONAL HEALTHCARE SYSTEM (C, 103 beds) 500 Jefferson Street, Whiteville, NC Zip 28472–3634; tel. 910/642–8011; Carla Hollis, President and Chief Executive Officer
**Web address:** www.crhealthcare.org/

KINGS MOUNTAIN HOSPITAL (O, 59 beds) 706 West King Street, Kings Mountain, NC Zip 28086–2708; tel. 980/487–5000; Brian Gwyn, President and Chief Executive Officer
**Web address:** www.clevelandregional.org/kings–mountain–hospital.html

MOSES H. CONE MEMORIAL HOSPITAL (C, 1007 beds) 1200 North Elm Street, Greensboro, NC Zip 27401–1020; tel. 336/832–7000; Mickey Foster, President
**Web address:** www.conehealth.com/locations/moses–cone–hospital/

MURPHY MEDICAL CENTER (C, 191 beds) 3990 U.S. Highway 64 East Alt, Murphy, NC Zip 28906–7917; tel. 828/837–8161; Michael Stevenson, Chief Executive Officer
**Web address:** www.murphymedical.org

SCOTLAND HEALTH CARE SYSTEM (C, 102 beds) 500 Lauchwood Drive, Laurinburg, NC Zip 28352–5599; tel. 910/291–7000; Gregory C. Wood, President and Chief Executive Officer
**Web address:** www.scotlandhealth.org

ST. LUKE'S HOSPITAL (C, 35 beds) 101 Hospital Drive, Columbus, NC Zip 28722–6418; tel. 828/894–3311; Kenneth A. Shull, FACHE, Chief Executive Officer
**Web address:** www.saintlukeshospital.com

STANLY REGIONAL MEDICAL CENTER (C, 94 beds) 301 Yadkin Street, Albemarle, NC Zip 28001–3441, Mailing Address: P.O. Box 1489, Zip 28002–1489; tel. 704/984–4000; Alfred P. Taylor, President and Chief Executive Officer
**Web address:** www.stanly.org

WILKES REGIONAL MEDICAL CENTER (C, 91 beds) 1370 West D Street, North Wilkesboro, NC Zip 28659–3506, Mailing Address: P.O. Box 609, Zip 28659–0609; tel. 336/651–8100; J. Gene Faile, Chief Executive Officer and President
**Web address:** www.wilkesregional.com/

**SOUTH CAROLINA:** BON SECOURS ST. FRANCIS XAVIER HOSPITAL (C, 172 beds) 2095 Henry Tecklenburg Drive, Charleston, SC Zip 29414–5733; tel. 843/402–1000; Allen P. Carroll, Senior Vice President and Chief Executive Officer
**Web address:** www.rsfh.com/

CANNON MEMORIAL HOSPITAL (C, 35 beds) 123 West G. Acker Drive, Pickens, SC Zip 29671–2739, Mailing Address: P.O. Box 188, Zip 29671–0188; tel. 864/878–4791; Norman G. Rentz, President and Chief Executive Officer
**Web address:** www.cannonhospital.org

ROPER ST. FRANCIS MOUNT PLEASANT HOSPITAL (C, 50 beds) 3500 Highway 17 North, Mount Pleasant, SC Zip 29466–9123, Mailing Address: 3500 North Highway 17, Zip 29466–9123; tel. 843/606–7000; Tavia Buck, Interim Chief Executive Officer
**Web address:** www.mymountpleasanthospital.com

ROPER HOSPITAL (C, 308 beds) 316 Calhoun Street, Charleston, SC Zip 29401–1125; tel. 843/724–2000; Matthew J. Severance, FACHE, Chief Executive Officer
**Web address:** www.rsfh.com/

| | | |
|---|---|---|
| Owned, leased, sponsored: | 10 hospitals | 2782 beds |
| Contract–managed: | 12 hospitals | 2337 beds |
| **Totals:** | 22 hospitals | 5119 beds |

**0656: CARRUS HOSPITALS** (IO)
1810 West U.S. Highway 82, Sherman, TX Zip 75092–7069; tel. 903/870–2600; Ronald E. Dorris, Chief Executive Officer
**(Independent Hospital System)**

**TEXAS:** CARRUS REHABILITATION HOSPITAL (O, 24 beds) 1810 West U.S. Highway 82, Suite 100, Sherman, TX Zip 75092–7069; tel. 903/870–2600; Dorothy J. Elford, Chief Executive Officer
**Web address:** www.carrushospital.com

CARRUS SPECIALTY HOSPITAL (O, 16 beds) 1810 West U.S. Highway 82, Sherman, TX Zip 75092–7069; tel. 903/870–2600; Jon Michael Rains, Chief Executive Officer
**Web address:** www.carrushospital.com

| | | |
|---|---|---|
| Owned, leased, sponsored: | 2 hospitals | 40 beds |
| Contract–managed: | 0 hospitals | 0 beds |
| **Totals:** | 2 hospitals | 40 beds |

★**0092: CATHOLIC HEALTH INITIATIVES** (CC)
198 Inverness Drive West, Suite 800, Englewood, CO Zip 80112–5202; tel. 303/298–9100; Kevin E. Lofton, FACHE, Chief Executive Officer
**(Decentralized Health System)**

**ARKANSAS:** CHI ST. VINCENT HOT SPRINGS (O, 282 beds) 300 Werner Street, Hot Springs, AR Zip 71913–6406; tel. 501/622–1000; Anthony Houston, President
**Web address:** www.chistvincent.com/Hospitals/st–vincent–hot–springs

For explanation of codes following names, see page B2.
★ Indicates Type III membership in the American Hospital Association.

CHI ST. VINCENT INFIRMARY MEDICAL CENTER (S, 447 beds) Two St. Vincent Circle, Little Rock, AR Zip 72205–5499; tel. 501/552–3000; Polly J. Davenport, FACHE, R.N., President, CHI St. Vincent Infirmary
**Web address:** www.chistvincent.com/

CHI ST. VINCENT MEDICAL CENTER–NORTH (S, 58 beds) 2215 Wildwood Avenue, Sherwood, AR Zip 72120–5089; tel. 501/552–7100; Polly J. Davenport, FACHE, R.N., President
**Web address:** www.stvincenthealth.com

CHI ST. VINCENT MORRILTON (S, 25 beds) 4 Hospital Drive, Morrilton, AR Zip 72110–4510; tel. 501/977–2300; Leslie Arnold, Chief Executive Officer and Administrator
**Web address:** www.stanthonysmorrilton.com/

**COLORADO:** MERCY REGIONAL MEDICAL CENTER (S, 82 beds) 1010 Three Springs Boulevard, Durango, CO Zip 81301–8296; tel. 970/247–4311; Thomas Gessel, FACHE, President and Chief Executive Officer
**Web address:** www.mercydurango.org

PENROSE–ST. FRANCIS HEALTH SERVICES (S, 417 beds) 2222 North Nevada Avenue, Colorado Springs, CO Zip 80907–6799, Mailing Address: P.O. Box 7021, Zip 80933–7021; tel. 719/776–5000; Margaret D. Sabin, President and Chief Executive Officer
**Web address:** www.penrosestfrancis.org

ST. ANTHONY HOSPITAL (S, 224 beds) 11600 West Second Place, Lakewood, CO Zip 80228–1527; tel. 720/321–0000; Jeffrey Brickman, FACHE, President and Chief Executive Officer
**Web address:** www.stanthonyhosp.org

ST. ANTHONY NORTH HEALTH CAMPUS (S, 122 beds) 14300 Orchard Parkway, Westminster, CO Zip 80023–9206; tel. 720/627–0000; Carole Peet, R.N., MSN, President and Chief Executive Officer
**Web address:** www.stanthonynorth.org

ST. ANTHONY SUMMIT MEDICAL CENTER (S, 34 beds) 340 Peak One Drive, Frisco, CO Zip 80443, Mailing Address: P.O. Box 738, Zip 80443–0738; tel. 970/668–3300; Paul J. Chodkowski, Chief Executive Officer
**Web address:** www.summitmedicalcenter.org

ST. MARY–CORWIN MEDICAL CENTER (S, 153 beds) 1008 Minnequa Avenue, Pueblo, CO Zip 81004–3798; tel. 719/557–4000; Brian Moore, President and Chief Executive Officer
**Web address:** www.centura.org

ST. THOMAS MORE HOSPITAL (S, 55 beds) 1338 Phay Avenue, Canon City, CO Zip 81212–2302; tel. 719/285–2000; Sheri Trahern, CPA, FACHE, Chief Executive Officer
**Web address:** www.stmhospital.org

**INDIANA:** SOUTHERN INDIANA REHABILITATION HOSPITAL (O, 60 beds) 3104 Blackiston Boulevard, New Albany, IN Zip 47150–9579; tel. 812/941–8300; Randy L. Napier, President
**Web address:** www.sirh.org

**IOWA:** CHI HEALTH MERCY CORNING (S, 22 beds) 603 Rosary Drive, Corning, IA Zip 50841–1683; tel. 641/322–3121; Debra Goldsmith, Chief Executive Officer
**Web address:** www.alegent.com

CHI HEALTH MERCY COUNCIL BLUFFS (S, 163 beds) 800 Mercy Drive, Council Bluffs, IA Zip 51503–3128, Mailing Address: P.O. Box 1C, Zip 51502–3001; tel. 712/328–5000; Marie E. Knedler, R.N., FACHE, President
**Web address:** www.alegent.com/mercy

CHI HEALTH MISSOURI VALLEY (S, 16 beds) 631 North Eighth Street, Missouri Valley, IA Zip 51555–1102; tel. 712/642–2784; Robert A. Valentine, President
**Web address:** www.alegentcreighton.com/community–memorial

KNOXVILLE HOSPITAL & CLINICS (C, 25 beds) 1002 South Lincoln Street, Knoxville, IA Zip 50138–3155; tel. 641/842–2151; Kevin Kincaid, Chief Executive Officer
**Web address:** www.knoxvillehospital.org

MADISON COUNTY HEALTH CARE SYSTEM (C, 25 beds) 300 West Hutchings Street, Winterset, IA Zip 50273–2109; tel. 515/462–2373; Marcia Hendricks, R.N., FACHE, Chief Executive Officer
**Web address:** www.madisonhealth.com

MERCY MEDICAL CENTER – WEST LAKES (O, 74 beds) 1755 59th Place, West Des Moines, IA Zip 50266–7737; tel. 515/358–8000; Robert P. Ritz, FACHE, President
**Web address:** www.mercywestlakes.org/

MERCY MEDICAL CENTER–CENTERVILLE (S, 45 beds) 1 St. Joseph's Drive, Centerville, IA Zip 52544–8055; tel. 641/437–4111; Clinton J. Christianson, FACHE, President and Chief Executive Officer
**Web address:** www.mercycenterville.com

MERCY MEDICAL CENTER–DES MOINES (S, 583 beds) 1111 6th Avenue, Des Moines, IA Zip 50314–2611; tel. 515/247–3121; Robert P. Ritz, FACHE, President
**Web address:** www.mercydesmoines.org

**KANSAS:** ST. CATHERINE HOSPITAL (S, 110 beds) 401 East Spruce Street, Garden City, KS Zip 67846–5679; tel. 620/272–2561; Scott J. Taylor, President and Chief Executive Officer
**Web address:** www.StCatherineHosp.org

**KENTUCKY:** CONTINUING CARE HOSPITAL (S, 57 beds) 150 North Eagle Creek Drive, 5th Floor, Lexington, KY Zip 40509–1805; tel. 859/967–5744; Tonja Williams, MSN, R.N., President

FLAGET MEMORIAL HOSPITAL (S, 52 beds) 4305 New Shepherdsville Road, Bardstown, KY Zip 40004–9019; tel. 502/350–5000; Beverly Sue Downs, R.N., MSN, FACHE, President
**Web address:** www.flaget.com

FRAZIER REHAB INSTITUTE (O, 79 beds) 220 Abraham Flexner Way, Louisville, KY Zip 40202–1887; tel. 502/582–7400; Randy L. Napier, President
**Web address:** www.frazierrehab.org

JEWISH HOSPITAL (O, 342 beds) 200 Abraham Flexner Way, Louisville, KY Zip 40202–1886; tel. 502/587–4011; Joseph Gilene, President
**Web address:** www.jewishhospital.org

JEWISH HOSPITAL–SHELBYVILLE (O, 47 beds) 727 Hospital Drive, Shelbyville, KY Zip 40065–1699; tel. 502/647–4000; Barry A. Papania, Interim Administrator
**Web address:** www.jhsmh.org

OUR LADY OF PEACE (O, 261 beds) 2020 Newburg Road, Louisville, KY Zip 40205–1879; tel. 502/479–4500; Jennifer Nolan, President
**Web address:** www.hopehasaplace.org

SAINT JOSEPH – LONDON (S, 114 beds) 1001 Saint Joseph Lane, London, KY Zip 40741–8345; tel. 606/330–6000; Terrence G. Deis, CPA, FACHE, Chief Executive Officer
**Web address:** www.saintjosephhealthsystem.org

SAINT JOSEPH – MARTIN (S, 25 beds) 11203 Main Street, Martin, KY Zip 41649; tel. 606/285–6400; Kathy Stumbo, President
**Web address:** www.saintjosephmartin.org

SAINT JOSEPH BEREA (S, 25 beds) 305 Estill Street, Berea, KY Zip 40403–1909; tel. 859/986–3151; Eric Gilliam, Chief Executive Officer
**Web address:** www.kentuckyonehealth.org/berea

SAINT JOSEPH EAST (S, 143 beds) 150 North Eagle Creek Drive, Lexington, KY Zip 40509–1805; tel. 859/967–5000; Eric Gilliam, President
**Web address:** www.sjhlex.org

SAINT JOSEPH HOSPITAL (S, 291 beds) One St. Joseph Drive, Lexington, KY Zip 40504–3754; tel. 859/278–3436; Beverly Sue Downs, R.N., MSN, FACHE, Interim Chief Executive Officer
**Web address:** www.sjhlex.org

SAINT JOSEPH MOUNT STERLING (S, 40 beds) 225 Falcon Drive, Mount Sterling, KY Zip 40353–1158, Mailing Address: P.O. Box 7, Zip 40353–0007; tel. 859/497–5000; Benny Nolen, President
**Web address:** www.sjhlex.org

STS. MARY & ELIZABETH HOSPITAL (O, 174 beds) 1850 Bluegrass Avenue, Louisville, KY Zip 40215–1199; tel. 502/361–6000; Jennifer Nolan, President
**Web address:** www.jhsmh.org

TAYLOR REGIONAL HOSPITAL (C, 90 beds) 1700 Old Lebanon Road, Campbellsville, KY Zip 42718–9600; tel. 270/465–3561; Jane Wheatley, Chief Executive Officer
**Web address:** www.trhosp.org

UNIVERSITY OF LOUISVILLE HOSPITAL (C, 301 beds) 530 South Jackson Street, Louisville, KY Zip 40202–3611; tel. 502/562–3000; Kenneth P. Marshall, President
**Web address:** www.ulh.org

**MINNESOTA:** CHI ALBANY AREA HEALTH (S, 17 beds) 300 Third Avenue, Albany, MN Zip 56307–9363; tel. 320/845–2121; Tressa Schmidt, Administrator
**Web address:** www.albanyareahospital.com

For explanation of codes following names, see page B2.
★ Indicates Type III membership in the American Hospital Association.

CHI LAKEWOOD HEALTH (S, 55 beds) 600 Main Avenue South, Baudette, MN Zip 56623–2855; tel. 218/634–2120; Benjamin Koppelman, Interim President
**Web address:** www.lakewoodhealthcenter.org

CHI ST. FRANCIS HEALTH (S, 105 beds) 2400 St. Francis Drive, Breckenridge, MN Zip 56520–1025; tel. 218/643–3000; David A. Nelson, President
**Web address:** www.sfcare.org

CHI ST. GABRIEL'S HEALTH (S, 25 beds) 815 Second Street S.E., Little Falls, MN Zip 56345–3596; tel. 320/632–5441; Lee Boyles, President
**Web address:** www.stgabriels.org

CHI ST. JOSEPH'S HEALTH (S, 25 beds) 600 Pleasant Avenue, Park Rapids, MN Zip 56470–1431; tel. 218/732–3311; Benjamin Koppelman, President
**Web address:** www.sjahs.org

**NEBRASKA:** CHI HEALTH BERGAN MERCY (S, 336 beds) 7500 Mercy Road, Omaha, NE Zip 68124–2319; tel. 402/398–6060; Marie E. Knedler, R.N., FACHE, President
**Web address:** www.alegent.com/bergan

CHI HEALTH CREIGHTON UNIVERSITY MEDICAL CENTER (S, 223 beds) 601 North 30th Street, Omaha, NE Zip 68131–2197; tel. 402/449–4000; Kevin J. Nokels, FACHE, President
**Web address:** www.alegentcreighton.com

CHI HEALTH GOOD SAMARITAN (S, 233 beds) 10 East 31st Street, Kearney, NE Zip 68847–2926, Mailing Address: P.O. Box 1990, Zip 68848–1990; tel. 308/865–7100; Michael H. Schnieders, FACHE, President
**Web address:** www.gshs.org

CHI HEALTH IMMANUEL (S, 289 beds) 6901 North 72nd Street, Omaha, NE Zip 68122–1799; tel. 402/572–2121; Ann Schumacher, R.N., MSN, FACHE, President
**Web address:** www.alegent.com/immanuel

CHI HEALTH LAKESIDE (S, 135 beds) 16901 Lakeside Hills Court, Omaha, NE Zip 68130–2318; tel. 402/717–8000; Cindy Alloway, President
**Web address:** www.CHIhealth.com

CHI HEALTH MIDLANDS (S, 50 beds) 11111 South 84th Street, Papillion, NE Zip 68046–4122; tel. 402/593–3000; Cindy Alloway, President
**Web address:** www.CHIhealth.com

CHI HEALTH NEBRASKA HEART (S, 52 beds) 7500 South 91st Street, Lincoln, NE Zip 68526–9437; tel. 402/327–2700; Dan Schonlau, Interim President
**Web address:** www.CHIhealthNebraskaHeart.com

CHI HEALTH PLAINVIEW (S, 16 beds) 704 North Third Street, Plainview, NE Zip 68769–2047, Mailing Address: P.O. Box 489, Zip 68769–0489; tel. 402/582–4245; Richard B. Gamel, President, Regional Hospital
**Web address:** www.alegentcreighton.com/plainview–hospital

CHI HEALTH SAINT FRANCIS (S, 192 beds) 2620 West Faidley Avenue, Grand Island, NE Zip 68803–4297, Mailing Address: P.O. Box 9804, Zip 68802–9804; tel. 308/384–4600; Daniel P. McElligott, FACHE, President
**Web address:** www.saintfrancisgi.org

CHI HEALTH SCHUYLER (S, 25 beds) 104 West 17th Street, Schuyler, NE Zip 68661–1304; tel. 402/352–2441; Connie Peters, R.N., President
**Web address:** www.alegent.com

CHI HEALTH ST ELIZABETH (S, 260 beds) 555 South 70th Street, Lincoln, NE Zip 68510–2494; tel. 402/219–8000; Kim S. Moore, FACHE, President
**Web address:** www.saintelizabethonline.com

CHI HEALTH ST. MARY'S (S, 18 beds) 1301 Grundman Boulevard, Nebraska City, NE Zip 68410; tel. 402/873–3321; Daniel J. Kelly, President
**Web address:** www.chihealthstmarys.com

NEBRASKA SPINE HOSPITAL (O, 34 beds) 6901 North 72nd Street, Suite 20300, Omaha, NE Zip 68122–1755, Mailing Address: 6901 North 72nd Street, Zip 68122–1709; tel. 402/572–3000; Cory Kruger, Interim Chief Executive Officer
**Web address:** www.nebraskaspinehospital.com

**NEW JERSEY:** SAINT CLARE'S HEALTH SYSTEM (S, 412 beds) 25 Pocono Road, Denville, NJ Zip 07834–2954; tel. 973/625–6000; Jonathan Timmis, Interim President and Chief Executive Officer
**Web address:** www.saintclares.org

**NORTH DAKOTA:** CARRINGTON HEALTH CENTER (S, 49 beds) 800 North Fourth Street, Carrington, ND Zip 58421–1217, Mailing Address: P.O. Box 461, Zip 58421–0461; tel. 701/652–3141; Mariann Doeling, R.N., President
**Web address:** www.carringtonhealthcenter.org

CHI LISBON HEALTH (S, 18 beds) 905 Main Street, Lisbon, ND Zip 58054–4334, Mailing Address: P.O. Box 353, Zip 58054–0353; tel. 701/683–5241; Peggy Reinke, R.N., Administrator
**Web address:** www.lisbonhospital.com

CHI ST. ALEXIUS HEALTH (O, 271 beds) 900 East Broadway, Bismarck, ND Zip 58501–4586, Mailing Address: P.O. Box 5510, Zip 58506–5510; tel. 701/530–7000; Kurt Schley, Market Chief Executive Officer
**Web address:** www.st.alexius.org

COMMUNITY MEMORIAL HOSPITAL (O, 25 beds) 220 Fifth Avenue, Turtle Lake, ND Zip 58575–4005, Mailing Address: P.O. Box 280, Zip 58575–0280; tel. 701/448–2331; Tod Graeber, Administrator
**Web address:** www.wrtc.com/cullum/hospital

GARRISON MEMORIAL HOSPITAL (O, 50 beds) 407 Third Avenue S.E., Garrison, ND Zip 58540–7235; tel. 701/463–2275; Tod Graeber, Administrator
**Web address:** www.garrisonmh.com

CHI MERCY HOSPITAL (S, 25 beds) 1031 Seventh Street N.E., Devils Lake, ND Zip 58301–2798; tel. 701/662–2131; Andrew Lankowicz, President
**Web address:** www.mercyhospitaldl.com

CHI MERCY HEALTH (S, 19 beds) 570 Chautauqua Boulevard, Valley City, ND Zip 58072–3199; tel. 701/845–6400; Keith E. Heuser, President
**Web address:** www.mercyhospitalvalleycity.org

MERCY MEDICAL CENTER (S, 25 beds) 1301 15th Avenue West, Williston, ND Zip 58801–3896; tel. 701/774–7400; Matthew Grimshaw, President
**Web address:** www.mercy–williston.org

CHI OAKES HOSPITAL (S, 20 beds) 1200 North Seventh Street, Oakes, ND Zip 58474–2502; tel. 701/742–3291; Becki Thompson, President
**Web address:** www.oakeshospital.com

ST. JOSEPH'S HOSPITAL AND HEALTH CENTER (S, 25 beds) 30 Seventh Street West, Dickinson, ND Zip 58601–4399; tel. 701/456–4000; Reed Reyman, President
**Web address:** www.stjoeshospital.org

**OHIO:** GOOD SAMARITAN HOSPITAL (S, 472 beds) 375 Dixmyth Avenue, Cincinnati, OH Zip 45220–2489; tel. 513/862–1400; Jamie Easterling, Executive Director, Operations
**Web address:** www.trihealth.com

TRINITY HEALTH SYSTEM (O, 312 beds) 380 Summit Avenue, Steubenville, OH Zip 43952–2699; tel. 740/283–7000; Fred B. Brower, President and Chief Executive Officer
**Web address:** www.trinityhealth.com

TRINITY HOSPITAL TWIN CITY (O, 13 beds) 819 North First Street, Dennison, OH Zip 44621–1098; tel. 740/922–2800; Joseph J. Mitchell, President
**Web address:** www.trinitytwincity.org

**OREGON:** CHI ST. ANTHONY HOSPITAL (S, 25 beds) 2801 St. Anthony Way, Pendleton, OR Zip 97801–3800; tel. 541/276–5121; Harold S. Geller, Chief Executive Officer
**Web address:** www.sahpendleton.org

MERCY MEDICAL CENTER (S, 141 beds) 2700 Stewart Parkway, Roseburg, OR Zip 97471–1281; tel. 541/673–0611; Kelly C. Morgan, President and Chief Executive Officer
**Web address:** www.mercyrose.org

**TENNESSEE:** CHI MEMORIAL (S, 336 beds) 2525 De Sales Avenue, Chattanooga, TN Zip 37404–1161; tel. 423/495–2525; James M. Hobson, Chief Executive Officer
**Web address:** www.memorial.org

**TEXAS:** BAYLOR ST. LUKE'S MEDICAL CENTER (O, 690 beds) 6720 Bertner Avenue, Houston, TX Zip 77030–2697, Mailing Address: P.O. Box 20269, Zip 77225–0269; tel. 832/355–1000; Michael H. Covert, FACHE, President and Chief Executive Officer
**Web address:** www.stlukestexas.com

BELLVILLE ST. JOSEPH HEALTH CENTER (O, 23 beds) 44 North Cummings Street, Bellville, TX Zip 77418–1347, Mailing Address: P.O. Box 977, Zip 77418–0977; tel. 979/413–7400; Mark Riggins, Administrator
**Web address:** www.st-joseph.org/body.cfm?id=773

BURLESON ST. JOSEPH HEALTH CENTER (O, 25 beds) 1101 Woodson Drive, Caldwell, TX Zip 77836–1052, Mailing Address: P.O. Box 360, Zip 77836–0360; tel. 979/567–3245; Brian Stanford, Administrator
**Web address:** www.st-joseph.org/

For explanation of codes following names, see page B2.
★ Indicates Type III membership in the American Hospital Association.

CHI ST. LUKE'S HEALTH MEMORIAL LIVINGSTON (O, 66 beds) 1717 Highway 59 Bypass, Livingston, TX Zip 77351–1257, Mailing Address: P.O. Box 1257, Zip 77351–0022; tel. 936/329–8700; Randy Slack, Chief Executive Officer
**Web address:** www.memorialhealth.org

CHI ST. LUKE'S HEALTH MEMORIAL LUFKIN (O, 217 beds) 1201 West Frank Avenue, Lufkin, TX Zip 75904–3357, Mailing Address: P.O. Box 1447, Zip 75902–1447; tel. 936/634–8111; Gary N. Looper, Chief Executive Officer
**Web address:** www.memorialhealth.us/centers/lufkin

CHI ST. LUKE'S HEALTH MEMORIAL SAN AUGUSTINE (O, 8 beds) 511 East Hospital Street, San Augustine, TX Zip 75972–2121, Mailing Address: P.O. Box 658, Zip 75972–0658; tel. 936/275–3446; Darlene Williams, R.N., Administrator
**Web address:** www.memorialhealth.org

CHI ST. LUKE'S HEALTH MEMORIAL SPECIALTY HOSPITAL (O, 20 beds) 1201 West Frank Avenue, Lufkin, TX Zip 75904–3357, Mailing Address: P.O. Box 1447, Zip 75902–1447; tel. 936/639–7530; Leslie Leach, Administrator
**Web address:** www.memorialhealth.org

GRIMES ST. JOSEPH HEALTH CENTER (O, 18 beds) 210 South Judson Street, Navasota, TX Zip 77868–3704; tel. 936/825–6585; Reed Edmundson, Regional Administrator
**Web address:** www.st-joseph.org

MADISON ST. JOSEPH HEALTH CENTER (O, 25 beds) 100 West Cross Street, Madisonville, TX Zip 77864–2432, Mailing Address: Box 698, Zip 77864–0698; tel. 936/348–2631; Reed Edmundson, Administrator
**Web address:** www.st-joseph.org

ST. JOSEPH REGIONAL HEALTH CENTER (O, 229 beds) 2801 Franciscan Drive, Bryan, TX Zip 77802–2599; tel. 979/776–3777; Kathleen R. Krusie, FACHE, Chief Executive Officer
**Web address:** www.st-joseph.org

ST. LUKE'S HOSPITAL – THE VINTAGE HOSPITAL (O, 78 beds) 20171 Chasewood Park Drive, Houston, TX Zip 77070–1437; tel. 832/534–5000; Norman F. Stephens, President
**Web address:** www.stlukesvintage.com/

ST. LUKE'S LAKESIDE HOSPITAL (O, 30 beds) 17400 St. Luke's Way, The Woodlands, TX Zip 77384–8036; tel. 936/266–9000; David Argueta, Chief Executive Officer
**Web address:** www.stlukeslakeside.com/

ST. LUKE'S PATIENTS MEDICAL CENTER (O, 61 beds) 4600 East Sam Houston Parkway South, Pasadena, TX Zip 77505–3948; tel. 713/948–7000; William Simmons, Chief Executive Officer
**Web address:** www.stlukestexas.com

ST. LUKE'S SUGAR LAND HOSPITAL (O, 58 beds) 1317 Lake Pointe Parkway, Sugar Land, TX Zip 77478–3997; tel. 281/637–7000; Robert A. Heifner, Chief Executive Officer
**Web address:** www.stlukessugarland.com

ST. LUKE'S THE WOODLANDS HOSPITAL (O, 192 beds) 17200 St. Luke's Way, The Woodlands, TX Zip 77384–8007; tel. 936/266–2000; David Argueta, President
**Web address:** www.stlukeswoodlands.com

**WASHINGTON:** HARRISON MEDICAL CENTER (O, 260 beds) 2520 Cherry Avenue, Bremerton, WA Zip 98310–4229; tel. 360/744–3911; David W. Schultz, FACHE, President
**Web address:** www.harrisonmedical.org

HIGHLINE MEDICAL CENTER (O, 128 beds) 16251 Sylvester Road S.W., Burien, WA Zip 98166–3052; tel. 206/244–9970; Mark Benedum, Chief Executive Officer
**Web address:** www.hchnet.org

ST. ANTHONY HOSPITAL (O, 80 beds) 11567 Canterwood Boulevard N.W., Gig Harbor, WA Zip 98332–5812; tel. 253/530–2000; David W. Schultz, FACHE, President
**Web address:** www.fhshealth.org/

ST. CLARE HOSPITAL (S, 105 beds) 11315 Bridgeport Way S.W., Lakewood, WA Zip 98499–3004; tel. 253/985–1711; Kathy Bressler, R.N., President
**Web address:** www.fhshealth.org

ST. ELIZABETH HOSPITAL (S, 25 beds) 1455 Battersby Avenue, Enumclaw, WA Zip 98022–3634, Mailing Address: P.O. Box 218, Zip 98022–0218; tel. 360/802–8800; Anthony McLean, Interim President
**Web address:** www.fhshealth.org

ST. FRANCIS HOSPITAL (S, 118 beds) 34515 Ninth Avenue South, Federal Way, WA Zip 98003–6799; tel. 253/944–8100; Anthony McLean, President
**Web address:** www.fhshealth.org

ST. JOSEPH MEDICAL CENTER (S, 366 beds) 1717 South J Street, Tacoma, WA Zip 98405–3004, Mailing Address: P.O. Box 2197, Zip 98401–2197; tel. 253/426–4101; Syd Bersante, R.N., President
**Web address:** www.fhshealth.org

| | | |
|---|---|---|
| **Owned, leased, sponsored:** | 89 hospitals | 11772 beds |
| **Contract–managed:** | 4 hospitals | 441 beds |
| **Totals:** | 93 hospitals | 12213 beds |

---

**0903: CATHOLIC HEALTH SERVICES** (CC)
4790 North State Road 7, Lauderdale Lakes, FL Zip 33319–5860; tel. 954/484–1515; Joseph M. Catania, President and Chief Executive Officer

**FLORIDA:** ST. ANTHONY'S REHABILITATION HOSPITAL (S, 26 beds) 3485 N.W. 30th Street, Lauderdale Lakes, FL Zip 33311–1890; tel. 954/739–6233; Joseph M. Catania, Chief Executive Officer
**Web address:** www.catholichealthservices.org

ST. CATHERINE'S REHABILITATION HOSPITAL (S, 60 beds) 1050 N.E. 125th Street, North Miami, FL Zip 33161–5881; tel. 305/357–1735; Jaime Gonzalez, Administrator
**Web address:** www.catholichealthservices.org

| | | |
|---|---|---|
| **Owned, leased, sponsored:** | 2 hospitals | 86 beds |
| **Contract–managed:** | 0 hospitals | 0 beds |
| **Totals:** | 2 hospitals | 86 beds |

---

**0233: CATHOLIC HEALTH SERVICES OF LONG ISLAND** (CC)
992 North Village Avenue, 1st Floor, Rockville Centre, NY Zip 11570–1002; tel. 516/705–3700; Alan D. Guerci, M.D., President and Chief Executive Officer
**(Moderately Centralized Health System)**

**NEW YORK:** GOOD SAMARITAN HOSPITAL MEDICAL CENTER (O, 531 beds) 1000 Montauk Highway, West Islip, NY Zip 11795–4927; tel. 631/376–3000; Nancy B. Simmons, Executive Vice President and Chief Administrative Officer
**Web address:** www.good–samaritan–hospital.org

MERCY MEDICAL CENTER (O, 191 beds) 1000 North Village Avenue, Rockville Centre, NY Zip 11570–1000; tel. 516/705–2525; Aaron Glatt, M.D., Executive Vice President and Chief Administrative Officer
**Web address:** www.mercymedicalcenter.chsli.org

ST. CATHERINE OF SIENA MEDICAL CENTER (O, 503 beds) 50 Route 25–A, Smithtown, NY Zip 11787–1348; tel. 631/862–3000; Dennis Verzi, Executive Vice President and Chief Administrative Officer
**Web address:** www.stcatherinemedicalcenter.org

ST. CHARLES HOSPITAL (O, 231 beds) 200 Belle Terre Road, Port Jefferson, NY Zip 11777–1928; tel. 631/474–6000; James O'Connor, Executive Vice President and Chief Administrative Officer
**Web address:** www.stcharleshospital.chsli.org

ST. FRANCIS HOSPITAL (O, 306 beds) 100 Port Washington Boulevard, Roslyn, NY Zip 11576–1353; tel. 516/562–6000; Ruth Hennessey, Executive Vice President and Chief Administrative Officer
**Web address:** www.stfrancisheartcenter.com/index.html

ST. JOSEPH HOSPITAL (S, 128 beds) 4295 Hempstead Turnpike, Bethpage, NY Zip 11714–5769; tel. 516/579–6000; Drew Pallas, Executive Vice President and Chief Administrative Officer
**Web address:** www.stjosephhospitalny.org

| | | |
|---|---|---|
| **Owned, leased, sponsored:** | 6 hospitals | 1890 beds |
| **Contract–managed:** | 0 hospitals | 0 beds |
| **Totals:** | 6 hospitals | 1890 beds |

---

**★0234: CATHOLIC HEALTH SYSTEM** (CC)
2121 Main Street, Suite 300, Buffalo, NY Zip 14214–2673, Mailing Address: 144 Genesee Street, Zip 14203; tel. 716/862–2410; Joseph D. McDonald, President and Chief Executive Officer
**(Centralized Physician/Insurance Health System)**

---

For explanation of codes following names, see page B2.
★ Indicates Type III membership in the American Hospital Association.

Section B

KENMORE MERCY HOSPITAL (O, 288 beds) 2950 Elmwood Avenue, Kenmore, NY Zip 14217–1390; tel. 716/447–6100; James M. Millard, President and Chief Executive Officer
**Web address:** www.chsbuffalo.org

MERCY HOSPITAL (O, 438 beds) 565 Abbott Road, Buffalo, NY Zip 14220–2095; tel. 716/826–7000; Charles J. Urlaub, President and Chief Executive Officer
**Web address:** www.chsbuffalo.org

SISTERS OF CHARITY HOSPITAL OF BUFFALO (O, 467 beds) 2157 Main Street, Buffalo, NY Zip 14214–2692; tel. 716/862–1000; Peter U. Bergmann, President and Chief Executive Officer
**Web address:** www.chsbuffalo.org

| | | |
|---|---|---|
| Owned, leased, sponsored: | 3 hospitals | 1193 beds |
| Contract–managed: | 0 hospitals | 0 beds |
| Totals: | 3 hospitals | 1193 beds |

---

★**0298:  CENTEGRA HEALTH SYSTEM** (NP)
385 Millennium Drive, Crystal Lake, IL Zip 60012–3761; tel. 815/788–5800; Michael S. Eesley, Chief Executive Officer
**(Centralized Physician/Insurance Health System)**

**ILLINOIS:** CENTEGRA HOSPITAL – MCHENRY (O, 167 beds) 4201 Medical Center Drive, McHenry, IL Zip 60050–8409; tel. 815/344–5000; Michael S. Eesley, Chief Executive Officer
**Web address:** www.centegra.org

CENTEGRA HOSPITAL – WOODSTOCK (O, 135 beds) 3701 Doty Road, Woodstock, IL Zip 60098–7509, Mailing Address: P.O. Box 1990, Zip 60098–1990; tel. 815/338–2500; Michael S. Eesley, Chief Executive Officer
**Web address:** www.centegra.org

| | | |
|---|---|---|
| Owned, leased, sponsored: | 2 hospitals | 302 beds |
| Contract–managed: | 0 hospitals | 0 beds |
| Totals: | 2 hospitals | 302 beds |

---

**2265:  CENTRA HEALTH, INC.** (NP)
1920 Atherholt Road, Lynchburg, VA Zip 24501–1104; tel. 434/200–3000; E. W. Tibbs, President and Chief Executive Officer
**(Moderately Centralized Health System)**

**VIRGINIA:** CENTRA LYNCHBURG GENERAL HOSPITAL (O, 1206 beds) 1920 Atherholt Road, Lynchburg, VA Zip 24501–1104; tel. 434/200–4700; E. W. Tibbs, President and Chief Executive Officer
**Web address:** www.centrahealth.com

CENTRA SOUTHSIDE COMMUNITY HOSPITAL (O, 86 beds) 800 Oak Street, Farmville, VA Zip 23901–1199; tel. 434/392–8811; Thomas Angelo, Chief Executive Officer
**Web address:** www.sch.centrahealth.com/

| | | |
|---|---|---|
| Owned, leased, sponsored: | 2 hospitals | 1292 beds |
| Contract–managed: | 0 hospitals | 0 beds |
| Totals: | 2 hospitals | 1292 beds |

---

★**0184:  CENTRACARE HEALTH** (NP)
1406 Sixth Avenue North, Saint Cloud, MN Zip 56303–1900; tel. 320/251–2700; Kenneth D. Holmen, M.D., President and Chief Executive Officer
**(Moderately Centralized Health System)**

**MINNESOTA:** CENTRACARE HEALTH–LONG PRAIRIE (O, 20 beds) 20 Ninth Street S.E., Long Prairie, MN Zip 56347–1404; tel. 320/732–2141; Daniel J. Swenson, FACHE, Administrator and Chief Executive Officer
**Web address:** www.centracare.com

CENTRACARE HEALTH–MELROSE (O, 93 beds) 525 Main Street West, Melrose, MN Zip 56352–1043; tel. 320/256–4231; Gerry Gilbertson, FACHE, Administrator
**Web address:** www.centracare.com

CENTRACARE HEALTH–MONTICELLO (O, 110 beds) 1013 Hart Boulevard, Monticello, MN Zip 55362–8230; tel. 763/295–2945; Mary Ellen Wells, FACHE, Administrator
**Web address:** www.newrivermedical.com

CENTRACARE HEALTH–PAYNESVILLE (O, 82 beds) 200 West 1st Street, Paynesville, MN Zip 56362–1496; tel. 320/243–3767; Dennis C. Miley, Administrator
**Web address:** www.centracare.com

CENTRACARE HEALTH–SAUK CENTRE (O, 85 beds) 425 North Elm Street, Sauk Centre, MN Zip 56378–1010; tel. 320/352–2221; Delano Christianson, Administrator
**Web address:** www.centracare.com/hospitals/sauk_centre/index.html

ST. CLOUD HOSPITAL (O, 482 beds) 1406 Sixth Avenue North, Saint Cloud, MN Zip 56303–1901; tel. 320/251–2700; Craig J. Broman, FACHE, President
**Web address:** www.centracare.com

| | | |
|---|---|---|
| Owned, leased, sponsored: | 6 hospitals | 872 beds |
| Contract–managed: | 0 hospitals | 0 beds |
| Totals: | 6 hospitals | 872 beds |

---

**0856:  CENTRAL FLORIDA HEALTH ALLIANCE** (NP)
600 East Dixie Avenue, Leesburg, FL Zip 34748–5925; tel. 352/323–5762; Donald G. Henderson, FACHE, Chief Executive Officer

**FLORIDA:** LEESBURG REGIONAL MEDICAL CENTER (O, 331 beds) 600 East Dixie Avenue, Leesburg, FL Zip 34748–5999; tel. 352/323–5762; Donald G. Henderson, FACHE, President and Chief Executive Officer
**Web address:** www.cfhalliance.com

THE VILLAGES REGIONAL HOSPITAL (O, 223 beds) 1451 El Camino Real, The Villages, FL Zip 32159–0041; tel. 352/751–8000; Donald G. Henderson, FACHE, President and Chief Executive Officer
**Web address:** www.cfhalliance.org

| | | |
|---|---|---|
| Owned, leased, sponsored: | 2 hospitals | 554 beds |
| Contract–managed: | 0 hospitals | 0 beds |
| Totals: | 2 hospitals | 554 beds |

---

**0934:  CHARTERCARE HEALTH PARTNERS** (NP)
825 Chalkstone Avenue, Providence, RI Zip 02908–4728; tel. 410/456–2001; Lester P. Schindel, Chief Executive Officer
**(Moderately Centralized Health System)**

**RHODE ISLAND:** ROGER WILLIAMS MEDICAL CENTER (O, 95 beds) 825 Chalkstone Avenue, Providence, RI Zip 02908–4735; tel. 401/456–2000; Kimberly O'Connell, President
**Web address:** www.rwmc.com

ST. JOSEPH HEALTH SERVICES OF RHODE ISLAND (O, 126 beds) 200 High Service Avenue, North Providence, RI Zip 02904–5199; tel. 401/456–3000; Thomas Hughes, President
**Web address:** www.saintjosephri.com

| | | |
|---|---|---|
| Owned, leased, sponsored: | 2 hospitals | 221 beds |
| Contract–managed: | 0 hospitals | 0 beds |
| Totals: | 2 hospitals | 221 beds |

---

**0407:  CHILDREN'S HOSPITAL AND HEALTH SYSTEM** (NP)
9000 West Wisconsin Avenue, Milwaukee, WI Zip 53226–4810, Mailing Address: P.O. Box 1997, Zip 53201–1997; tel. 414/226–2000; Peggy N. Troy, President and Chief Executive Officer
**(Independent Hospital System)**

**WISCONSIN:** CHILDREN'S HOSPITAL OF WISCONSIN (O, 306 beds) 9000 West Wisconsin Avenue, Milwaukee, WI Zip 53226–4810, Mailing Address: P.O. Box 1997, Zip 53201–1997; tel. 414/266–2000; Peggy N. Troy, President and Chief Executive Officer
**Web address:** www.chw.org

---

For explanation of codes following names, see page B2.
★ Indicates Type III membership in the American Hospital Association.

CHILDREN'S HOSPITAL OF WISCONSIN–FOX VALLEY (O, 42 beds) 130 Second Avenue, 3rd Floor South, Neenah, WI Zip 54956–2883; tel. 920/969–7900; Peggy N. Troy, President and Chief Executive Officer
**Web address:** www.chw.org

| | | |
|---|---|---|
| **Owned, leased, sponsored:** | 2 hospitals | 348 beds |
| **Contract–managed:** | 0 hospitals | 0 beds |
| **Totals:** | 2 hospitals | 348 beds |

● ★**0131: CHRISTIANA CARE HEALTH SYSTEM** (NP)
501 West 14th Street, Wilmington, DE Zip 19801–1013, Mailing Address: P.O. Box 1668, Zip 19899–1668; tel. 302/733–1000; Janice E. Nevin, M.D., M.P.H., Chief Executive Officer
**(Moderately Centralized Health System)**

**DELAWARE:** CHRISTIANA CARE HEALTH SYSTEM (O, 1007 beds) 4755 Ogletown–Stanton Road, Newark, DE Zip 19718–0002, Mailing Address: P.O. Box 6001, Zip 19714–6001; tel. 302/733–1000; Janice E. Nevin, M.D., M.P.H., Chief Executive Officer
**Web address:** www.christianacare.org

| | | |
|---|---|---|
| **Owned, leased, sponsored:** | 1 hospital | 1007 beds |
| **Contract–managed:** | 0 hospitals | 0 beds |
| **Totals:** | 1 hospital | 1007 beds |

★**0192: CHRISTUS HEALTH** (CC)
919 Hidden Ridge Drive, Irving, TX Zip 75038; tel. 469/282–2000; Ernie W. Sadau, Chief Executive Officer
**(Moderately Centralized Health System)**

**ARKANSAS:** CHRISTUS DUBUIS HOSPITAL OF FORT SMITH (C, 25 beds) 7301 Rogers Avenue, 4th Floor, Fort Smith, AR Zip 72903–4100; tel. 479/314–4900; Keith Rogers, Interim Administrator
**Web address:** www.christusdubuis.org/fortsmith

**GEORGIA:** SOUTHERN CRESCENT HOSPITAL FOR SPECIALTY CARE (C, 30 beds) 11 Upper Riverdale Road S.W., 6th Floor, Riverdale, GA Zip 30274–2615; tel. 770/897–7600; Jeff Denney, Administrator
**Web address:** www.christusdubuis.org/SouthernCrescentHospitalforSpecialtyCare

**IOWA:** CONTINUING CARE HOSPITAL AT ST. LUKE'S (C, 16 beds) 1026 A Avenue N.E., 6th Floor, Cedar Rapids, IA Zip 52402–5036; tel. 319/369–8142; Elly Steffen, Chief Executive Officer and Administrator
**Web address:** www.unitypoint.org/cedarrapids/services–continuing–care–hospital.aspx

**LOUISIANA:** CHRISTUS COUSHATTA HEALTH CARE CENTER (O, 25 beds) 1635 Marvel Street, Coushatta, LA Zip 71019–9022, Mailing Address: P.O. Box 589, Zip 71019–0589; tel. 318/932–2000; Michael Harrington, Administrator
**Web address:** www.christuscoushatta.org

CHRISTUS DUBUIS HOSPITAL OF ALEXANDRIA (O, 25 beds) 3330 Masonic Drive, 4th Floor, Alexandria, LA Zip 71301–3841; tel. 318/448–4938; Beth Parsons, R.N., Administrator
**Web address:** www.christusdubuis.org/CHRISTUSDubuisHospitalofAlexandriaLA

CHRISTUS HEALTH SHREVEPORT–BOSSIER (O, 196 beds) 1453 East Bert Koun Industrial Loop, Shreveport, LA Zip 71105–6800; tel. 318/681–5000; Isaac Palmer, Chief Executive Officer
**Web address:** www.christushealthsb.org

CHRISTUS ST. FRANCES CABRINI HOSPITAL (O, 281 beds) 3330 Masonic Drive, Alexandria, LA Zip 71301–3899; tel. 318/487–1122; Nancy R. Hellyer, R.N., FACHE, Chief Executive Officer
**Web address:** www.cabrini.org/

CHRISTUS ST. PATRICK HOSPITAL OF LAKE CHARLES (O, 160 beds) 524 Dr. Michael Debakey Drive, Lake Charles, LA Zip 70601–5799, Mailing Address: P.O. Box 3401, Zip 70602–3401; tel. 337/436–2511; Donald H. Lloyd, II, Administrator
**Web address:** www.stpatrickhospital.org

NATCHITOCHES REGIONAL MEDICAL CENTER (C, 208 beds) 501 Keyser Avenue, Natchitoches, LA Zip 71457–6036, Mailing Address: P.O. Box 2009, Zip 71457–2009; tel. 318/214–4200; D. Kirk Soileau, Chief Executive Officer
**Web address:** www.natchitocheshospital.org

**NEW MEXICO:** CHRISTUS ST. VINCENT REGIONAL MEDICAL CENTER (O, 268 beds) 455 St. Michael's Drive, Santa Fe, NM Zip 87505–7663, Mailing Address: P.O. Box 2107, Zip 87504–2107; tel. 505/983–3361; Bruce J. Tassin, President and Chief Executive Officer
**Web address:** www.stvin.org

**TEXAS:** CHRISTUS DUBUIS HOSPITAL OF BEAUMONT (O, 51 beds) 2830 Calder Avenue, 4th Floor, Beaumont, TX Zip 77702–1809; tel. 409/899–8154; Kathie Reese, Interim Administrator
**Web address:** www.christusdubuis.org/BeaumontandPortArthurSystem–CHRISTUSDubuisHospitalofBeaumont

CHRISTUS DUBUIS HOSPITAL OF BRYAN (O, 30 beds) 1600 Joseph Drive, 2nd Floor, Bryan, TX Zip 77802–1502; tel. 979/821–5000; Terry W. Kepler, Chief Executive Officer
**Web address:** www.dubuis.org/CHRISTUSDubuisHospitalofBryan

CHRISTUS DUBUIS HOSPITAL OF PARIS (C, 25 beds) 865 Deshong Drive, 5th Floor, Paris, TX Zip 75460–9313; tel. 903/782–2961; Kathie Reese, Administrator
**Web address:** www.dubuis.org/CHRISTUSDubuisHospitalofParis

CHRISTUS DUBUIS HOSPITAL OF PORT ARTHUR (C, 15 beds) 3600 Gates Boulevard, Port Arthur, TX Zip 77642–3858; tel. 409/989–5300; Kathie Reese, Interim Administrator
**Web address:** www.christusdubuis.org/CHRISTUSDubuisHospitalofPortArthur

CHRISTUS HOSPITAL–ST. ELIZABETH (O, 436 beds) 2830 Calder Avenue, Beaumont, TX Zip 77702–1809, Mailing Address: P.O. Box 5405, Zip 77726–5405; tel. 409/892–7171; Paul Trevino, Chief Executive Officer
**Web address:** www.christushospital.org

CHRISTUS JASPER MEMORIAL HOSPITAL (L, 40 beds) 1275 Marvin Hancock Drive, Jasper, TX Zip 75951–4995; tel. 409/384–5461; Lance Beus, Chief Executive Officer
**Web address:** www.christusjasper.org

CHRISTUS SANTA ROSA HEALTH SYSTEM (O, 766 beds) 333 North Santa Rosa Street, San Antonio, TX Zip 78207–3108; tel. 210/704–4184; Ken Haynes, President and Chief Executive Officer
**Web address:** www.christussantarosa.org

CHRISTUS SPOHN HOSPITAL ALICE (O, 73 beds) 2500 East Main Street, Alice, TX Zip 78332–4169; tel. 361/661–8000; Steven G. Daniel, Senior Vice President and Chief Operating Officer
**Web address:** www.christusspohn.org/locations_alice.htm

CHRISTUS SPOHN HOSPITAL BEEVILLE (L, 49 beds) 1500 East Houston Street, Beeville, TX Zip 78102–5312; tel. 361/354–2000; Nathan Tudor, Vice President and Chief Executive Officer
**Web address:** www.christusspohn.org

CHRISTUS SPOHN HOSPITAL CORPUS CHRISTI MEMORIAL (O, 710 beds) 2606 Hospital Boulevard, Corpus Christi, TX Zip 78405–1804, Mailing Address: P.O. Box 5280, Zip 78465–5280; tel. 361/902–4000; Xavier Villarreal, Chief Executive Officer
**Web address:** www.christusspohn.org

CHRISTUS SPOHN HOSPITAL KLEBERG (O, 50 beds) 1311 General Cavazos Boulevard, Kingsville, TX Zip 78363–7130; tel. 361/595–1661; David LeMonte, Vice President and Chief Operating Officer
**Web address:** www.christusspohn.org

CHRISTUS ST. MICHAEL HEALTH SYSTEM (O, 376 beds) 2600 St. Michael Drive, Texarkana, TX Zip 75503–5220; tel. 903/614–1000; Chris Karam, President and Chief Executive Officer
**Web address:** www.christusstmichael.org

CHRISTUS ST. MICHAEL REHABILITATION HOSPITAL (O, 50 beds) 2400 St. Michael Drive, Texarkana, TX Zip 75503–2374; tel. 903/614–4000; Aloma Gender, R.N., MSN, Administrator and Chief Nursing Officer
**Web address:** www.christusstmichael.org/rehab

| | | |
|---|---|---|
| **Owned, leased, sponsored:** | 17 hospitals | 3586 beds |
| **Contract–managed:** | 6 hospitals | 319 beds |
| **Totals:** | 23 hospitals | 3905 beds |

★**0101: CITRUS VALLEY HEALTH PARTNERS** (NP)
210 West San Bernardino Road, Covina, CA Zip 91723–1515; tel. 626/331–7331; Robert H. Curry, President and Chief Executive Officer

For explanation of codes following names, see page B2.
★ Indicates Type III membership in the American Hospital Association.
● Single hospital health care system

*Section B*

**CALIFORNIA:** CITRUS VALLEY MEDICAL CENTER–INTER COMMUNITY CAMPUS (O, 327 beds) 210 West San Bernadino Road, Covina, CA Zip 91723–1515, Mailing Address: P.O. Box 6108, Zip 91722–5108; tel. 626/331–7331; Robert H. Curry, President and Chief Executive Officer
**Web address:** www.cvhp.org

FOOTHILL PRESBYTERIAN HOSPITAL (O, 69 beds) 250 South Grand Avenue, Glendora, CA Zip 91741–4218; tel. 626/963–8411; Robert H. Curry, President and Chief Executive Officer
**Web address:** www.cvhp.org/Our_Facilities/Foothill_Presbyterian.aspx

| | | |
|---|---|---|
| **Owned, leased, sponsored:** | 2 hospitals | 396 beds |
| **Contract–managed:** | 0 hospitals | 0 beds |
| **Totals:** | 2 hospitals | 396 beds |

★**0212:   CLEVELAND CLINIC HEALTH SYSTEM** (NP) 9500 Euclid, Cleveland, OH Zip 44195–5108; tel. 216/444–2200; Delos Cosgrove, M.D., President and Chief Executive Officer
**(Centralized Health System)**

**FLORIDA:** CLEVELAND CLINIC FLORIDA (O, 155 beds) 2950 Cleveland Clinic Boulevard, Weston, FL Zip 33331–3602; tel. 954/659–5000; Wael Barsoum, Interim Chief Executive Officer
**Web address:** www.clevelandclinic.org/florida

**OHIO:** CLEVELAND CLINIC (O, 1278 beds) 9500 Euclid Avenue, Cleveland, OH Zip 44195–5108; tel. 216/444–2200; Delos Cosgrove, M.D., President and Chief Executive Officer
**Web address:** www.clevelandclinic.org

CLEVELAND CLINIC CHILDREN'S HOSPITAL FOR REHABILITATION (O, 25 beds) 2801 Martin Luther King Jr. Drive, Cleveland, OH Zip 44104–3865; tel. 216/448–6400; Michael J. McHugh, M.D., Medical Director
**Web address:** www.my.clevelandclinic.org/childrens–hospital/default.aspx

EUCLID HOSPITAL (O, 219 beds) 18901 Lake Shore Boulevard, Euclid, OH Zip 44119–1090; tel. 216/531–9000; Daniel Napierkowski, President
**Web address:** www.euclidhospital.org

FAIRVIEW HOSPITAL (O, 426 beds) 18101 Lorain Avenue, Cleveland, OH Zip 44111–5656; tel. 216/476–7000; Neil Smith, D.O., President
**Web address:** www.fairviewhospital.org

HILLCREST HOSPITAL (O, 438 beds) 6780 Mayfield Road, Cleveland, OH Zip 44124–2203; tel. 440/312–4500; Brian J. Harte, M.D., President
**Web address:** www.hillcresthospital.org

LAKEWOOD HOSPITAL (O, 243 beds) 14519 Detroit Avenue, Lakewood, OH Zip 44107–4383; tel. 216/521–4200; Shannan Ritchie, Interim President
**Web address:** www.lakewoodhospital.org

LUTHERAN HOSPITAL (O, 198 beds) 1730 West 25th Street, Cleveland, OH Zip 44113–3170; tel. 216/696–4300; Donald Malone, M.D., President
**Web address:** www.lutheranhospital.org

MARYMOUNT HOSPITAL (O, 284 beds) 12300 McCracken Road, Garfield Heights, OH Zip 44125–2975; tel. 216/581–0500; Richard Parker, M.D., President
**Web address:** www.marymount.org

MEDINA HOSPITAL (O, 136 beds) 1000 East Washington Street, Medina, OH Zip 44256–2170; tel. 330/725–1000; Thomas Tulisiak, M.D., President
**Web address:** www.medinahospital.org

SOUTH POINTE HOSPITAL (O, 176 beds) 20000 Harvard Road, Warrensville Heights, OH Zip 44122–6805; tel. 216/491–6000; Robert S. Juhasz, D.O., President
**Web address:** www.southpointehospital.org

| | | |
|---|---|---|
| **Owned, leased, sponsored:** | 11 hospitals | 3578 beds |
| **Contract–managed:** | 0 hospitals | 0 beds |
| **Totals:** | 11 hospitals | 3578 beds |

**0076:   COLLEGE HEALTH ENTERPRISES** (IO) 11627 Telegraph Road, Suite 200, Santa Fe Springs, CA Zip 90670–6814; tel. 562/923–9449; Barry J. Weiss, Chairman of the Board

**CALIFORNIA:** COLLEGE HOSPITAL CERRITOS (O, 157 beds) 10802 College Place, Cerritos, CA Zip 90703–1579; tel. 562/924–9581; Stephen Witt, President and Chief Executive Officer
**Web address:** www.collegehospitals.com

COLLEGE HOSPITAL COSTA MESA (O, 122 beds) 301 Victoria Street, Costa Mesa, CA Zip 92627–7131; tel. 949/642–2734; Susan L. Taylor, Chief Executive Officer
**Web address:** www.collegehospitals.com/cosHome

| | | |
|---|---|---|
| **Owned, leased, sponsored:** | 2 hospitals | 279 beds |
| **Contract–managed:** | 0 hospitals | 0 beds |
| **Totals:** | 2 hospitals | 279 beds |

**0161:   COLUMBUS REGIONAL HEALTHCARE SYSTEM** (NP) 707 Center Street, Suite 400, Columbus, GA Zip 31901–1575; tel. 706/660–6100; Scott Hill, Chief Executive Officer
**(Independent Hospital System)**

**GEORGIA:** MIDTOWN MEDICAL CENTER WEST (O, 171 beds) 616 19th Street, Columbus, GA Zip 31901–1528, Mailing Address: P.O. Box 2188, Zip 31902–2188; tel. 706/494–4262; Ryan Chandler, Chief Executive Officer
**Web address:** www.columbusregional.com

NORTHSIDE MEDICAL CENTER (O, 100 beds) 100 Frist Court, Columbus, GA Zip 31909–3578, Mailing Address: P.O. Box 7188, Zip 31908–7188; tel. 706/494–2100; Stan Hickson, FACHE, Chief Executive Officer
**Web address:** www.columbusregional.com

THE MEDICAL CENTER (O, 497 beds) 710 Center Street, Columbus, GA Zip 31901–1527, Mailing Address: P.O. Box 951, Zip 31902–0951; tel. 706/571–1000; Ryan Chandler, President and Chief Executive Officer
**Web address:** www.columbusregional.com

| | | |
|---|---|---|
| **Owned, leased, sponsored:** | 3 hospitals | 768 beds |
| **Contract–managed:** | 0 hospitals | 0 beds |
| **Totals:** | 3 hospitals | 768 beds |

**0520:   COMMONWEALTH HEALTH CORPORATION** (NP) 800 Park Street, Bowling Green, KY Zip 42101–2356; tel. 270/745–1500; Connie Smith, President and Chief Executive Officer
**(Centralized Physician/Insurance Health System)**

**KENTUCKY:** COMMONWEALTH REGIONAL SPECIALTY HOSPITAL (O, 24 beds) 250 Park Drive, 6th Floor, Bowling Green, KY Zip 42101–1760, Mailing Address: P.O. Box 90010, Zip 42102–9010; tel. 270/796–6200; Christa Atkins, Administrator
**Web address:** www.commonwealthregionalspecialtyhospital.org

MEDICAL CENTER AT BOWLING GREEN (O, 337 beds) 250 Park Street, Bowling Green, KY Zip 42101–1795, Mailing Address: P.O. Box 90010, Zip 42102–9010; tel. 270/745–1000; Connie Smith, Chief Executive Officer
**Web address:** www.themedicalcenter.org

MEDICAL CENTER AT FRANKLIN (O, 25 beds) 1100 Brookhaven Road, Franklin, KY Zip 42134–2746; tel. 270/598–4800; Eric Hagan, R.N., Vice President/Administrator
**Web address:** www.themedicalcenterfranklin.org

MEDICAL CENTER AT SCOTTSVILLE (O, 135 beds) 456 Burnley Road, Scottsville, KY Zip 42164–6355; tel. 270/622–2800; Eric Hagan, R.N., Vice President/Administrator
**Web address:** www.themedicalcenterscottsville.org/

| | | |
|---|---|---|
| **Owned, leased, sponsored:** | 4 hospitals | 521 beds |
| **Contract–managed:** | 0 hospitals | 0 beds |
| **Totals:** | 4 hospitals | 521 beds |

**0401:   COMMUNITY HEALTH NETWORK** (NP) 7330 Shadeland Station, Indianapolis, IN Zip 46256–3957; tel. 317/355–1411; Bryan A. Mills, President and Chief Executive Officer
**(Moderately Centralized Health System)**

**INDIANA:** COMMUNITY HOSPITAL EAST (O, 318 beds) 1500 North Ritter Avenue, Indianapolis, IN Zip 46219–3095; tel. 317/355–1411; Robin Ledyard, M.D., M.P.H., President
**Web address:** www.ecommunity.com/east/

For explanation of codes following names, see page B2.
★ Indicates Type III membership in the American Hospital Association.

Section B

COMMUNITY HOSPITAL NORTH (O, 314 beds) 7150 Clearvista Drive, Indianapolis, IN Zip 46256–1695; tel. 317/621–6262; Jason Fahrlander, FACHE, President
**Web address:** www.ecommunity.com/north

COMMUNITY HOSPITAL OF ANDERSON AND MADISON COUNTY (O, 140 beds) 1515 North Madison Avenue, Anderson, IN Zip 46011–3453; tel. 765/298–4242; Beth S. Tharp, R.N., President and Chief Executive Officer
**Web address:** www.communityanderson.com

COMMUNITY HOSPITAL SOUTH (O, 158 beds) 1402 East County Line Road South, Indianapolis, IN Zip 46227–0963; tel. 317/887–7000; Anthony B. Lennen, President
**Web address:** www.ecommunity.com

COMMUNITY HOWARD REGIONAL HEALTH (O, 162 beds) 3500 South Lafountain Street, Kokomo, IN Zip 46902–3803, Mailing Address: P.O. Box 9011, Zip 46904–9011; tel. 765/453–0702; Joseph Hooper, President and Chief Executive Officer
**Web address:** www.howardregional.org

COMMUNITY HOWARD SPECIALTY HOSPITAL (O, 30 beds) 829 North Dixon Road, Kokomo, IN Zip 46901–7709; tel. 765/452–6700; Michelle L. Russell, Administrator
**Web address:** www.communityhoward.org

| | | |
|---|---|---|
| **Owned, leased, sponsored:** | 6 hospitals | 1122 beds |
| **Contract–managed:** | 0 hospitals | 0 beds |
| **Totals:** | 6 hospitals | 1122 beds |

---

**★0080: COMMUNITY HEALTH SYSTEMS, INC.** (IO)
4000 Meridian Boulevard, Franklin, TN Zip 37067–6325, Mailing Address: P.O. Box 689020, Zip 37068–9020; tel. 615/465–7000; Wayne T. Smith, Chairman, President and Chief Executive Officer
**(Decentralized Health System)**

**ALABAMA:** CHEROKEE MEDICAL CENTER (O, 45 beds) 400 Northwood Drive, Centre, AL Zip 35960–1023; tel. 256/927–5531; Terry Long, Chief Executive Officer
**Web address:** www.cherokeemedicalcenter.com

CRESTWOOD MEDICAL CENTER (O, 150 beds) One Hospital Drive, Huntsville, AL Zip 35801–3403; tel. 256/429–4000; Pamela Hudson, M.D., Chief Executive Officer
**Web address:** www.crestwoodmedcenter.com

DEKALB REGIONAL MEDICAL CENTER (O, 121 beds) 200 Medical Center Drive, Fort Payne, AL Zip 35968–3458, Mailing Address: P.O. Box 680778, Zip 35968–1608; tel. 256/845–3150; Corey Ewing, FACHE, Chief Executive Officer
**Web address:** www.dekalbregional.com

FLOWERS HOSPITAL (O, 141 beds) 4370 West Main Street, Dothan, AL Zip 36305–4000, Mailing Address: P.O. Box 6907, Zip 36302–6907; tel. 334/793–5000; Suzanne Woods, President and Chief Executive Officer
**Web address:** www.flowershospital.com

GADSDEN REGIONAL MEDICAL CENTER (O, 268 beds) 1007 Goodyear Avenue, Gadsden, AL Zip 35903–1195; tel. 256/494–4000; Stephen G. Pennington, Chief Executive Officer
**Web address:** www.gadsdenregional.com

GRANDVIEW MEDICAL CENTER (O, 379 beds) 800 Montclair Road, Birmingham, AL Zip 35213–1984; tel. 205/592–1000; Keith Granger, President and Chief Executive Officer
**Web address:** www.grandviewhealth.com

L. V. STABLER MEMORIAL HOSPITAL (O, 61 beds) 29 L. V. Stabler Drive, Greenville, AL Zip 36037–3800; tel. 334/382–2671; Donald R. Rentfro, Chief Executive Officer
**Web address:** www.lvstabler.com

MEDICAL CENTER ENTERPRISE (O, 117 beds) 400 North Edwards Street, Enterprise, AL Zip 36330–2510; tel. 334/347–0584; Richard Ellis, Chief Executive Officer
**Web address:** www.mcehospital.com

SOUTH BALDWIN REGIONAL MEDICAL CENTER (L, 112 beds) 1613 North McKenzie Street, Foley, AL Zip 36535–2299; tel. 251/949–3400; Keith Newton, Chief Executive Officer
**Web address:** www.southbaldwinrmc.com

STRINGFELLOW MEMORIAL HOSPITAL (O, 75 beds) 301 East 18th Street, Anniston, AL Zip 36207–3952; tel. 256/235–8900; Jay Hinesley, Chief Executive Officer
**Web address:** www.stringfellowhealth.com

**ALASKA:** MAT–SU REGIONAL MEDICAL CENTER (O, 74 beds) 2500 South Woodworth Loop, Palmer, AK Zip 99645–8984, Mailing Address: P.O. Box 1687, Zip 99645–1687; tel. 907/861–6000; John R. Lee, Chief Executive Officer
**Web address:** www.matsuregional.com

**ARIZONA:** NORTHWEST MEDICAL CENTER (O, 270 beds) 6200 North La Cholla Boulevard, Tucson, AZ Zip 85741–3599; tel. 520/742–9000; Kevin Stockton, Chief Executive Officer
**Web address:** www.northwestmedicalcenter.com

ORO VALLEY HOSPITAL (O, 144 beds) 1551 East Tangerine Road, Oro Valley, AZ Zip 85755–6213; tel. 520/901–3500; Jae Dale, Chief Executive Officer
**Web address:** www.orovalleyhospital.com

PAYSON REGIONAL MEDICAL CENTER (L, 39 beds) 807 South Ponderosa Street, Payson, AZ Zip 85541–5599; tel. 928/474–3222; Lance Porter, Chief Executive Officer
**Web address:** www.paysonhospital.com

WESTERN ARIZONA REGIONAL MEDICAL CENTER (O, 139 beds) 2735 Silver Creek Road, Bullhead City, AZ Zip 86442–8303; tel. 928/763–2273; Alex Villa, Chief Executive Officer
**Web address:** www.warmc.com

**ARKANSAS:** FORREST CITY MEDICAL CENTER (L, 61 beds) 1601 Newcastle Road, Forrest City, AR Zip 72335–2218; tel. 870/261–0000; Kevin Decker, Chief Executive Officer
**Web address:** www.forrestcitymedicalcenter.com

HELENA REGIONAL MEDICAL CENTER (L, 105 beds) 1801 Martin Luther King Drive, Helena, AR Zip 72342, Mailing Address: P.O. Box 788, Zip 72342–0788; tel. 870/338–5800; Leah Osbahr, M.P.H., Chief Executive Officer
**Web address:** www.helenarmc.com

MEDICAL CENTER OF SOUTH ARKANSAS (L, 120 beds) 700 West Grove Street, El Dorado, AR Zip 71730–4416; tel. 870/863–2000; Robert Rupp, Chief Executive Officer
**Web address:** www.themedcenter.net

NORTHWEST MEDICAL CENTER – SPRINGDALE (O, 295 beds) 609 West Maple Avenue, Springdale, AR Zip 72764–5394, Mailing Address: P.O. Box 47, Zip 72765–0047; tel. 479/751–5711; Harrison Kiser, Interim Chief Executive Officer
**Web address:** www.northwesthealth.com

SILOAM SPRINGS REGIONAL HOSPITAL (O, 43 beds) 603 North Progress Avenue, Siloam Springs, AR Zip 72761–4352; tel. 479/524–4141; Patrick Kerwood, Chief Executive Officer,
**Web address:** www.ssrh.net/Pages/home.aspx

SPARKS MEDICAL CENTER – VAN BUREN (L, 103 beds) East Main and South 20th Streets, Van Buren, AR Zip 72956–5715, Mailing Address: P.O. Box 409, Zip 72957–0409; tel. 479/474–3401; Daniel E. McKay, Chief Executive Officer
**Web address:** www.sparkshealth.
com/locations/sparks–medical–center–van–buren

SPARKS REGIONAL MEDICAL CENTER (O, 303 beds) 100 Towson Avenue, Fort Smith, AR Zip 72901–2632, Mailing Address: P.O. Box 2406, Zip 72917–7006; tel. 479/441–4000; Daniel E. McKay, Chief Executive Officer
**Web address:** www.sparks.org

**CALIFORNIA:** BARSTOW COMMUNITY HOSPITAL (L, 30 beds) 820 East Mountain View Street, Barstow, CA Zip 92311–3004; tel. 760/256–1761; Steven Foster, Chief Executive Officer
**Web address:** www.barstowhospital.com

WATSONVILLE COMMUNITY HOSPITAL (O, 106 beds) 75 Nielson Street, Watsonville, CA Zip 95076–2468; tel. 831/724–4741; Audra Earle, FACHE, Chief Executive Officer
**Web address:** www.watsonvillehospital.com

**FLORIDA:** BARTOW REGIONAL MEDICAL CENTER (O, 72 beds) 2200 Osprey Boulevard, Bartow, FL Zip 33830–3308, Mailing Address: P.O. Box 1050, Zip 33831–1050; tel. 863/533–8111; Philip Minden, Chief Executive Officer
**Web address:** www.bartowregional.com

---

For explanation of codes following names, see page B2.
★ Indicates Type III membership in the American Hospital Association.

BAYFRONT HEALTH BROOKSVILLE (L, 120 beds) 17240 Cortez Boulevard, Brooksville, FL Zip 34601–8921, Mailing Address: P.O. Box 37, Zip 34605–0037; tel. 352/796–5111; Kenneth R. Wicker, Chief Executive Officer
**Web address:** www.brooksvilleregionalhospital.org

BAYFRONT HEALTH DADE CITY (O, 120 beds) 13100 Fort King Road, Dade City, FL Zip 33525–5294; tel. 352/521–1100; Shauna McKinnon, Chief Executive Officer
**Web address:** www.pascoregionalmc.com

BAYFRONT HEALTH PORT CHARLOTTE (O, 254 beds) 2500 Harbor Boulevard, Port Charlotte, FL Zip 33952–5000; tel. 941/766–4122; Richard H. Satcher, Chief Executive Officer
**Web address:** www.bayfrontcharlotte.com

BAYFRONT HEALTH PUNTA GORDA (O, 208 beds) 809 East Marion Avenue, Punta Gorda, FL Zip 33950–3819, Mailing Address: P.O. Box 51–1328, Zip 33951–1328; tel. 941/639–3131; Brandon W. Downey, Chief Executive Officer
**Web address:** www.bayfrontcharlotte.com

BAYFRONT HEALTH ST. PETERSBURG (O, 382 beds) 701 Sixth Street South, Saint Petersburg, FL Zip 33701–4891; tel. 727/823–1234; Kathryn Gillette, President and Chief Executive Officer
**Web address:** www.bayfrontstpete.com

HEART OF FLORIDA REGIONAL MEDICAL CENTER (O, 193 beds) 40100 Highway 27, Davenport, FL Zip 33837–5906; tel. 863/422–4971; Ann Barnhart, Chief Executive Officer
**Web address:** www.heartofflorida.com

HIGHLANDS REGIONAL MEDICAL CENTER (L, 116 beds) 3600 South Highlands Avenue, Sebring, FL Zip 33870–5495, Mailing Address: Drawer 2066, Zip 33871–2066; tel. 863/471–5800; Joseph Bernard, Chief Executive Officer
**Web address:** www.highlandsregional.com

LAKE WALES MEDICAL CENTER (O, 131 beds) 410 South 11th Street, Lake Wales, FL Zip 33853–4256; tel. 863/676–1433; Andrew Howard, Interim Chief Executive Officer
**Web address:** www.lakewalesmedicalcenter.com

LEHIGH REGIONAL MEDICAL CENTER (O, 88 beds) 1500 Lee Boulevard, Lehigh Acres, FL Zip 33936–4835; tel. 239/369–2101; Joanie Jeannette, MSN, Chief Executive Officer
**Web address:** www.lehighregional.com

LOWER KEYS MEDICAL CENTER (L, 90 beds) 5900 College Road, Key West, FL Zip 33040–4396, Mailing Address: P.O. Box 9107, Zip 33041–9107; tel. 305/294–5531; Nicki L. Will–Mowery, Ph.D., Chief Executive Officer
**Web address:** www.lkmc.com

MUNROE REGIONAL MEDICAL CENTER (O, 420 beds) 1500 S.W. 1st Avenue, Ocala, FL Zip 34471–6504, Mailing Address: P.O. Box 6000, Zip 34478–6000; tel. 352/351–7200; Bob Moore, FACHE, Chief Executive Officer
**Web address:** www.munroeregional.com

NORTH OKALOOSA MEDICAL CENTER (O, 110 beds) 151 Redstone Avenue S.E., Crestview, FL Zip 32539–6026; tel. 850/689–8100; Ronnie Daves, Chief Executive Officer
**Web address:** www.northokaloosa.com

PHYSICIANS REGIONAL – PINE RIDGE (O, 201 beds) 6101 Pine Ridge Road, Naples, FL Zip 34119–3900; tel. 239/348–4000; Scott Lowe, Interim Market Chief Executive Officer
**Web address:** www.physiciansregional.com

SANTA ROSA MEDICAL CENTER (L, 68 beds) 6002 Berryhill Road, Milton, FL Zip 32570–5062; tel. 850/626–7762; Doug Sills, Chief Executive Officer
**Web address:** www.santarosamedicalcenter.org

SEBASTIAN RIVER MEDICAL CENTER (O, 140 beds) 13695 North U.S. Highway 1, Sebastian, FL Zip 32958–3230, Mailing Address: Box 780838, Zip 32978–0838; tel. 772/589–3186; Kelly Enriquez, Chief Executive Officer
**Web address:** www.sebastianrivermedical.com

SEVEN RIVERS REGIONAL MEDICAL CENTER (O, 128 beds) 6201 North Suncoast Boulevard, Crystal River, FL Zip 34428–6712; tel. 352/795–6560; Joyce A. Brancato, Chief Executive Officer
**Web address:** www.srrmc.com

SHANDS LAKE SHORE REGIONAL MEDICAL CENTER (O, 85 beds) 368 N.E. Franklin Street, Lake City, FL Zip 32055–3047; tel. 386/292–8000; Rhonda Kay Sherrod, R.N., MSN, Administrator
**Web address:** www.shandslakeshore.com

SHANDS LIVE OAK REGIONAL MEDICAL CENTER (O, 25 beds) 1100 S.W. 11th Street, Live Oak, FL Zip 32064–3608; tel. 386/362–0800; Richard Huth, Chief Executive Officer
**Web address:** www.shandsliveoak.com/

SHANDS STARKE REGIONAL MEDICAL CENTER (O, 49 beds) 922 East Call Street, Starke, FL Zip 32091–3699; tel. 904/368–2300; Rhonda Kay Sherrod, R.N., MSN, Interim Chief Executive Officer
**Web address:** www.shands.org

ST. CLOUD REGIONAL MEDICAL CENTER (O, 84 beds) 2906 17th Street, Saint Cloud, FL Zip 34769–6099; tel. 407/892–2135; Brent Burish, Chief Executive Officer
**Web address:** www.stcloudregional.com

VENICE REGIONAL BAYFRONT HEALTH (O, 312 beds) 540 The Rialto, Venice, FL Zip 34285–2900; tel. 941/485–7711; Jeff Rece, Interim Chief Executive Officer
**Web address:** www.veniceregional.com

WUESTHOFF MEDICAL CENTER – MELBOURNE (O, 119 beds) 250 North Wickham Road, Melbourne, FL Zip 32935–8625; tel. 321/752–1200; Richard Frank, Chief Executive Officer
**Web address:** www.wuesthoff.com/locations/wuesthoff–medical–center–melbourne

WUESTHOFF MEDICAL CENTER – ROCKLEDGE (O, 298 beds) 110 Longwood Avenue, Rockledge, FL Zip 32955–2887, Mailing Address: P.O. Box 565002, Mail Stop 1, Zip 32956–5002; tel. 321/636–2211; Gary Malaer, Interim Chief Executive Officer
**Web address:** www.wuesthoff.org

**GEORGIA:** BARROW REGIONAL MEDICAL CENTER (O, 56 beds) 316 North Broad Street, Winder, GA Zip 30680–2150, Mailing Address: P.O. Box 688, Zip 30680–0688; tel. 770/867–3400; Chad Hatfield, Chief Executive Officer
**Web address:** www.barrowregional.com

CLEARVIEW REGIONAL MEDICAL CENTER (O, 77 beds) 2151 West Spring Street, Monroe, GA Zip 30655–3115, Mailing Address: PO BOX 1346, Zip 30655–1346; tel. 770/267–8461; James Machado, Chief Executive Officer
**Web address:** www.clearviewregionalmedicalcenter.com/

EAST GEORGIA REGIONAL MEDICAL CENTER (O, 149 beds) 1499 Fair Road, Statesboro, GA Zip 30458–1683, Mailing Address: P.O. Box 1048, Zip 30459–1048; tel. 912/486–1000; Robert F. Bigley, President and Chief Executive Officer
**Web address:** www.eastgeorgiaregional.com

FANNIN REGIONAL HOSPITAL (O, 50 beds) 2855 Old Highway 5, Blue Ridge, GA Zip 30513–6248; tel. 706/632–3711; David S. Sanders, Chief Executive Officer
**Web address:** www.fanninregionalhospital.com

TRINITY HOSPITAL OF AUGUSTA (O, 105 beds) 2260 Wrightsboro Road, Augusta, GA Zip 30904–4726; tel. 706/481–7000; Jason Studley, Chief Executive Officer
**Web address:** www.trinityofaugusta.com

**ILLINOIS:** CROSSROADS COMMUNITY HOSPITAL (O, 47 beds) 8 Doctors Park Road, Mount Vernon, IL Zip 62864–6224; tel. 618/244–5500; Finny Mathew, Chief Executive Officer
**Web address:** www.crossroadshospital.com

GALESBURG COTTAGE HOSPITAL (O, 119 beds) 695 North Kellogg Street, Galesburg, IL Zip 61401–2885; tel. 309/343–8131; Barry S. Schneider, Chief Executive Officer
**Web address:** www.cottagehospital.com

GATEWAY REGIONAL MEDICAL CENTER (O, 104 beds) 2100 Madison Avenue, Granite City, IL Zip 62040–4799; tel. 618/798–3000; M. Edward Cunningham, Chief Executive Officer
**Web address:** www.gatewayregional.net

HEARTLAND REGIONAL MEDICAL CENTER (O, 92 beds) 3333 West DeYoung, Marion, IL Zip 62959–5884; tel. 618/998–7000; James Flynn, Chief Executive Officer
**Web address:** www.heartlandregional.com

METROSOUTH MEDICAL CENTER (O, 285 beds) 12935 South Gregory Street, Blue Island, IL Zip 60406–2470; tel. 708/597–2000; Aaron R. Hazzard, Interim Chief Executive Officer
**Web address:** www.metrosouthmedicalcenter.com

RED BUD REGIONAL HOSPITAL (O, 140 beds) 325 Spring Street, Red Bud, IL Zip 62278–1105; tel. 618/282–3831; Shane Watson, Chief Executive Officer
**Web address:** www.redbudregional.com

For explanation of codes following names, see page B2.
★ Indicates Type III membership in the American Hospital Association.

UNION COUNTY HOSPITAL (L, 47 beds) 517 North Main Street, Anna, IL Zip 62906–1696; tel. 618/833–4511; James R. Farris, FACHE, Chief Executive Officer
**Web address:** www.unioncountyhospital.com

VISTA MEDICAL CENTER EAST (O, 190 beds) 1324 North Sheridan Road, Waukegan, IL Zip 60085–2161; tel. 847/360–3000; Barbara J. Martin, R.N., President and Chief Executive Officer
**Web address:** www.vistahealth.com

VISTA MEDICAL CENTER WEST (O, 67 beds) 2615 Washington Street, Waukegan, IL Zip 60085–4988; tel. 847/249–3900; Barbara J. Martin, R.N., President and Chief Executive Officer
**Web address:** www.vistahealth.com

**INDIANA:** BLUFFTON REGIONAL MEDICAL CENTER (O, 79 beds) 303 South Main Street, Bluffton, IN Zip 46714–2503; tel. 260/824–3210; Aaron Garofola, Chief Executive Officer
**Web address:** www.blufftonregional.com

DUKES MEMORIAL HOSPITAL (O, 25 beds) 275 West 12th Street, Peru, IN Zip 46970–1638; tel. 765/472–8000; Debra Close, Chief Executive Officer
**Web address:** www.dukesmemorialhosp.com

DUPONT HOSPITAL (O, 131 beds) 2520 East Dupont Road, Fort Wayne, IN Zip 46825–1675; tel. 260/416–3000; Chad Towner, Chief Executive Officer
**Web address:** www.thedupontdifference.com

KOSCIUSKO COMMUNITY HOSPITAL (O, 72 beds) 2101 East Dubois Drive, Warsaw, IN Zip 46580–3288; tel. 574/267–3200; Kirk M. Ray, Chief Executive Officer
**Web address:** www.kch.com

LUTHERAN HOSPITAL OF INDIANA (O, 396 beds) 7950 West Jefferson Boulevard, Fort Wayne, IN Zip 46804–4140; tel. 260/435–7001; Brian Bauer, Chief Executive Officer
**Web address:** www.lutheranhospital.com

ORTHOPAEDIC HOSPITAL OF LUTHERAN HEALTH NETWORK (O, 44 beds) 7952 West Jefferson Boulevard, Fort Wayne, IN Zip 46804–4140; tel. 260/435–2999; Lorie Ailor, Chief Executive Officer
**Web address:** www.theorthohospital.com

PORTER REGIONAL HOSPITAL (O, 276 beds) 85 East U.S. Highway 6, Valparaiso, IN Zip 46383–8947; tel. 219/983–8300; Stephen Lunn, Chief Executive Officer
**Web address:** www.porterhealth.com

REHABILITATION HOSPITAL OF FORT WAYNE (O, 36 beds) 7970 West Jefferson Boulevard, Fort Wayne, IN Zip 46804–4140; tel. 260/435–6100; Brian Bauer, Chief Executive Officer
**Web address:** www.rehabhospital.com

ST. JOSEPH HOSPITAL (O, 182 beds) 700 Broadway, Fort Wayne, IN Zip 46802–1493; tel. 260/425–3000; Kenneth Jones, Chief Executive Officer
**Web address:** www.stjoehospital.com

**KENTUCKY:** KENTUCKY RIVER MEDICAL CENTER (L, 54 beds) 540 Jett Drive, Jackson, KY Zip 41339–9622; tel. 606/666–6000; John Ballard, Ph.D., Chief Executive Officer
**Web address:** www.kentuckyrivermc.com

PAUL B. HALL REGIONAL MEDICAL CENTER (O, 72 beds) 625 James S. Trimble Boulevard, Paintsville, KY Zip 41240–0000; tel. 606/789–3511; Deborah Trimble, R.N., Chief Executive Officer
**Web address:** www.pbhrmc.com

THREE RIVERS MEDICAL CENTER (O, 80 beds) 2485 Highway 644, Louisa, KY Zip 41230–9242, Mailing Address: P.O. Box 769, Zip 41230–0769; tel. 606/638–9451; Greg Kiser, Chief Executive Officer
**Web address:** www.threeriversmedicalcenter.com

**LOUISIANA:** BYRD REGIONAL HOSPITAL (O, 60 beds) 1020 West Fertitta Boulevard, Leesville, LA Zip 71446–4645; tel. 337/239–9041; Roger C. LeDoux, Chief Executive Officer
**Web address:** www.byrdregional.com

LAKE AREA MEDICAL CENTER (O, 88 beds) 4200 Nelson Road, Lake Charles, LA Zip 70605–4118; tel. 337/474–6370; Bryan S. Bateman, Chief Executive Officer
**Web address:** www.women–childrens.com

NORTHERN LOUISIANA MEDICAL CENTER (O, 104 beds) 401 East Vaughn Avenue, Ruston, LA Zip 71270–5950; tel. 318/254–2100; Brady Dubois, Chief Executive Officer
**Web address:** www.northernlouisianamedicalcenter.com

**MISSISSIPPI:** MERIT HEALTH CENTRAL (L, 217 beds) 1850 Chadwick Drive, Jackson, MS Zip 39204–3479, Mailing Address: P.O. Box 59001, Zip 39284–9001; tel. 601/376–1000; Linda Dolan, Chief Executive Officer
**Web address:** www.centralmississippimedicalcenter.com

MERIT HEALTH RANKIN (L, 134 beds) 350 Crossgates Boulevard, Brandon, MS Zip 39042–2698; tel. 601/825–2811; Jon–Paul Croom, Chief Executive Officer
**Web address:** www.crossgatesriveroaks.com

MERIT HEALTH GILMORE MEMORIAL (O, 95 beds) 1105 Earl Frye Boulevard, Amory, MS Zip 38821–5500, Mailing Address: P.O. Box 459, Zip 38821–0459; tel. 662/256–7111; J. Allen Tyra, Chief Executive
**Web address:** www.gilmorehealth.com

MERIT HEALTH MADISON (L, 44 beds) Highway 16 East, Canton, MS Zip 39046–8823, Mailing Address: P.O. Box 1607, Zip 39046–1607; tel. 601/859–1331; Britton Phelps, Chief Executive Officer
**Web address:** www.madisonriveroaks.com

MERIT HEALTH BILOXI (L, 198 beds) 150 Reynoir Street, Biloxi, MS Zip 39530–4199, Mailing Address: P.O. Box 128, Zip 39533–0128; tel. 228/432–1571; Monte J. Bostwick, Chief Executive Officer
**Web address:** www.merithealthbiloxi.com

MERIT HEALTH WESLEY (O, 211 beds) 5001 Hardy Street, Hattiesburg, MS Zip 39402–1308, Mailing Address: P.O. Box 16509, Zip 39404–6509; tel. 601/268–8000; Michael Neuendorf, Chief Executive Officer
**Web address:** www.wesley.com

NATCHEZ COMMUNITY HOSPITAL (O, 101 beds) 129 Jefferson Davis Boulevard, Natchez, MS Zip 39120–5100, Mailing Address: P.O. Box 1203, Zip 39121–1203; tel. 601/445–6200; Eric Robinson, Chief Executive Officer
**Web address:** www.natchezcommunityhospital.com/default.aspx

MERIT HEALTH NATCHEZ (O, 155 beds) 54 Seargent S Prentiss Drive, Natchez, MS Zip 39120–4726; tel. 601/443–2100; Eric Robinson, Chief Executive Officer
**Web address:** www.natchezregional.com

MERIT HEALTH NORTHWEST MISSISSIPPI (L, 181 beds) 1970 Hospital Drive, Clarksdale, MS Zip 38614–7202, Mailing Address: P.O. Box 1218, Zip 38614–1218; tel. 662/627–3211; Joel Southern, R.N., MSN, Chief Executive Officer
**Web address:** www.northwestregional.com

MERIT HEALTH RIVER OAKS (O, 158 beds) 1030 River Oaks Drive, Flowood, MS Zip 39232–9553, Mailing Address: P.O. Box 5100, Jackson, Zip 39296–5100; tel. 601/932–1030; L. Dwayne Blaylock, Chief Executive Officer
**Web address:** www.riveroakshosp.com

MERIT HEALTH RIVER REGION (O, 317 beds) 2100 Highway 61 North, Vicksburg, MS Zip 39183–8211, Mailing Address: P.O. Box 590, Zip 39181–0590; tel. 601/883–5000; Gregory Pearson, Chief Executive Officer
**Web address:** www.riverregion.com

MERIT HEALTH BATESVILLE (O, 112 beds) 303 Medical Center Drive, Batesville, MS Zip 38606–8608; tel. 662/563–5611; Travis Sisson, Interim Chief Executive Officer
**Web address:** www.trilakesmc.com

MERIT HEALTH WOMAN'S HOSPITAL (O, 60 beds) 1026 North Flowood Drive, Flowood, MS Zip 39232–9532, Mailing Address: P.O. Box 4546, Jackson, Zip 39296–4546; tel. 601/932–1000; Sherry J. Pitts, Chief Executive Officer
**Web address:** www.womanshospitalms.com

**MISSOURI:** MOBERLY REGIONAL MEDICAL CENTER (O, 94 beds) 1515 Union Avenue, Moberly, MO Zip 65270–9449; tel. 660/263–8400; Leslie Paul Luke, Interim Chief Executive Officer
**Web address:** www.moberlyhospital.com

NORTHEAST REGIONAL MEDICAL CENTER (L, 115 beds) 315 South Osteopathy, Kirksville, MO Zip 63501–6401, Mailing Address: P.O. Box C8502, Zip 63501–8599; tel. 660/785–1000; Ranee C. Brayton, R.N., MSN, Chief Executive Officer
**Web address:** www.nermc.com

POPLAR BLUFF REGIONAL MEDICAL CENTER (O, 241 beds) 3100 Oak Grove Road, Poplar Bluff, MO Zip 63901, Mailing Address: P.O. Box 88, Zip 63902–0088; tel. 573/776–2000; Kenneth James, Chief Executive Officer
**Web address:** www.poplarbluffregional.com

Section B

TWIN RIVERS REGIONAL MEDICAL CENTER (O, 100 beds) 1301 First Street, Kennett, MO Zip 63857–2508, Mailing Address: P.O. Box 728, Zip 63857–0728; tel. 573/888–4522; Gerald Faircloth, FACHE, Chief Executive Officer
**Web address:** www.twinriversregional.com

**NEVADA:** MESA VIEW REGIONAL HOSPITAL (O, 25 beds) 1299 Bertha Howe Avenue, Mesquite, NV Zip 89027–7500; tel. 702/346–8040; Patricia Holden, Chief Executive Officer
**Web address:** www.mesaviewhospital.com

**NEW JERSEY:** MEMORIAL HOSPITAL OF SALEM COUNTY (O, 110 beds) 310 Woodstown Road, Salem, NJ Zip 08079–2080; tel. 856/935–1000; Ryan Jensen, Chief Executive Officer
**Web address:** www.salemhospitalnj.org

**NEW MEXICO:** ALTA VISTA REGIONAL HOSPITAL (O, 54 beds) 104 Legion Drive, Las Vegas, NM Zip 87701–4804; tel. 505/426–3500; R. Chris Wolf, Chief Executive Officer
**Web address:** www.altavistaregionalhospital.com

CARLSBAD MEDICAL CENTER (O, 127 beds) 2430 West Pierce Street, Carlsbad, NM Zip 88220–3597; tel. 575/887–4100; Cathy Hibbs, Chief Executive Officer
**Web address:** www.carlsbadmedicalcenter.com

EASTERN NEW MEXICO MEDICAL CENTER (O, 149 beds) 405 West Country Club Road, Roswell, NM Zip 88201–5209; tel. 575/622–8170; Maridel Acosta–Cruz, Chief Executive Officer
**Web address:** www.enmmc.com

LEA REGIONAL MEDICAL CENTER (O, 214 beds) 5419 North Lovington Highway, Hobbs, NM Zip 88240–9125, Mailing Address: P.O. Box 3000, Zip 88241–9501; tel. 575/492–5000; Timothy Thornell, FACHE, Chief Executive Officer
**Web address:** www.learegionalmedical.com

MIMBRES MEMORIAL HOSPITAL (O, 75 beds) 900 West Ash Street, Deming, NM Zip 88030–4098, Mailing Address: P.O. Box 710, Zip 88031–0710; tel. 575/546–5800; Steve Westenhofer, Chief Executive Officer
**Web address:** www.mimbresmemorial.com

MOUNTAINVIEW REGIONAL MEDICAL CENTER (O, 142 beds) 4311 East Lohman Avenue, Las Cruces, NM Zip 88011–8255; tel. 575/556–7600; Denten Park, Chief Executive Officer
**Web address:** www.mountainviewregional.com

**NORTH CAROLINA:** DAVIS REGIONAL MEDICAL CENTER (O, 131 beds) 218 Old Mocksville Road, Statesville, NC Zip 28625–1930, Mailing Address: P.O. Box 1823, Zip 28687–1823; tel. 704/873–0281; William Chad French, Chief Executive Officer
**Web address:** www.davisregional.com

LAKE NORMAN REGIONAL MEDICAL CENTER (O, 123 beds) 171 Fairview Road, Mooresville, NC Zip 28117–9500, Mailing Address: P.O. Box 3250, Zip 28117–3250; tel. 704/660–4000; Stephen L. Midkiff, Chief Executive Officer
**Web address:** www.lnrmc.com

MARTIN GENERAL HOSPITAL (L, 49 beds) 310 South McCaskey Road, Williamston, NC Zip 27892–2150, Mailing Address: P.O. Box 1128, Zip 27892–1128; tel. 252/809–6300; Taffy J. Arias, Chief Executive Officer
**Web address:** www.martingeneral.com

SANDHILLS REGIONAL MEDICAL CENTER (O, 64 beds) 1000 West Hamlet Avenue, Hamlet, NC Zip 28345–4522, Mailing Address: P.O. Box 1109, Zip 28345–1109; tel. 910/205–8000; David Clay, Chief Executive Officer
**Web address:** www.sandhillsregional.com

**OHIO:** AFFINITY MEDICAL CENTER (O, 112 beds) 875 Eighth Street N.E., Massillon, OH Zip 44646–8503, Mailing Address: P.O. Box 4805, Zip 44648–0805; tel. 330/832–8761; Ronald L. Bierman, Chief Executive Officer
**Web address:** www.affinitymedicalcenter.com

HILLSIDE REHABILITATION HOSPITAL (O, 65 beds) 8747 Squires Lane N.E., Warren, OH Zip 44484–1649; tel. 330/841–3700; Ian Cooper, Chief Executive Officer
**Web address:** www.valleycarehealth.net

NORTHSIDE MEDICAL CENTER (O, 373 beds) 500 Gypsy Lane, Youngstown, OH Zip 44504–1315; tel. 330/884–1000; W. Trent Crable, Chief Executive Officer
**Web address:** www.northsidemedicalcenter.net

TRUMBULL MEMORIAL HOSPITAL (O, 292 beds) 1350 East Market Street, Warren, OH Zip 44483–6628; tel. 330/841–9011; John Walsh, Chief Executive Officer
**Web address:** www.vchs.net

**OKLAHOMA:** ALLIANCEHEALTH BLACKWELL (O, 49 beds) 710 South 13th Street, Blackwell, OK Zip 74631–3700; tel. 580/363–2311; Andrew Wachtel, Chief Executive Officer
**Web address:** www.integris–health.com

ALLIANCEHEALTH CLINTON (O, 49 beds) 100 North 30th Street, Clinton, OK Zip 73601–3117, Mailing Address: P.O. Box 1569, Zip 73601–1569; tel. 580/323–2363; Cameron Lewis, Chief Executive Officer
**Web address:** www.alliancehealthclinton.com

ALLIANCEHEALTH DEACONESS (O, 238 beds) 5501 North Portland Avenue, Oklahoma City, OK Zip 73112–2099; tel. 405/604–6000; Devon Hyde, Chief Executive Officer
**Web address:** www.deaconessokc.com

ALLIANCEHEALTH DURANT (O, 148 beds) 1800 University Boulevard, Durant, OK Zip 74701–3006, Mailing Address: P.O. Box 1207, Zip 74702–1207; tel. 580/924–3080; Jeff Tarrant, Chief Executive Officer
**Web address:** www.mymcso.com

ALLIANCEHEALTH MADILL (O, 21 beds) 1 Hospital Drive, Madill, OK Zip 73446, Mailing Address: P.O. Box 827, Zip 73446–0827; tel. 580/795–3384; Minnie Burkhardt, Administrator
**Web address:** www.integrismarshallcounty.com

ALLIANCEHEALTH MIDWEST (L, 255 beds) 2825 Parklawn Drive, Midwest City, OK Zip 73110–4258; tel. 405/610–4411; Damon Brown, Chief Executive Officer
**Web address:** www.midwestregional.com

ALLIANCEHEALTH PONCA CITY (O, 72 beds) 1900 North 14th Street, Ponca City, OK Zip 74601–2099; tel. 580/765–3321; R. Andrew Wachtel, FACHE, Chief Executive Officer
**Web address:** www.poncamedcenter.com

ALLIANCEHEALTH PRYOR (O, 24 beds) 111 North Bailey Street, Pryor, OK Zip 74361–4201, Mailing Address: P.O. Box 278, Zip 74362–0278; tel. 918/825–1600; Douglas K. Weaver, FACHE, President
**Web address:** www.integrismayescounty.com

ALLIANCEHEALTH SEMINOLE (O, 32 beds) 2401 Wrangler Boulevard, Seminole, OK Zip 74868–1917; tel. 405/303–4000; Benjamin Heath, Interim Chief Executive Officer
**Web address:** www.hma.com

ALLIANCEHEALTH WOODWARD (L, 40 beds) 900 17th Street, Woodward, OK Zip 73801–2448; tel. 580/256–5511; David Wallace, Chief Executive Officer
**Web address:** www.woodwardhospital.com

**OREGON:** MCKENZIE–WILLAMETTE MEDICAL CENTER (O, 113 beds) 1460 G Street, Springfield, OR Zip 97477–4197; tel. 541/726–4400; Chad Campbell, Chief Executive Officer
**Web address:** www.mckweb.com

**PENNSYLVANIA:** BERWICK HOSPITAL CENTER (O, 341 beds) 701 East 16th Street, Berwick, PA Zip 18603–2397; tel. 570/759–5000; David P. Steitz, Chief Executive Officer
**Web address:** www.berwick–hospital.com

BRANDYWINE HOSPITAL (O, 169 beds) 201 Reeceville Road, Coatesville, PA Zip 19320–1536; tel. 610/383–8000; W. Jeffrey Hunt, Chief Executive Officer
**Web address:** www.brandywinehospital.com

CARLISLE REGIONAL MEDICAL CENTER (O, 165 beds) 361 Alexander Spring Road, Carlisle, PA Zip 17015–6940; tel. 717/249–1212; Ann M. Spade, Interim Chief Executive Officer
**Web address:** www.carlislermc.com/default.aspx

CHESTNUT HILL HOSPITAL (O, 212 beds) 8835 Germantown Avenue, Philadelphia, PA Zip 19118–2718; tel. 215/248–8200; John D. Cacciamani, M.D., Chief Executive Officer
**Web address:** www.chhealthsystem.com

EASTON HOSPITAL (O, 224 beds) 250 South 21st Street, Easton, PA Zip 18042–3892; tel. 610/250–4000; John A. Zidansek, President and Chief Executive Officer
**Web address:** www.easton–hospital.com

FIRST HOSPITAL WYOMING VALLEY (O, 127 beds) 562 Wyoming Avenue, Kingston, PA Zip 18704–3721; tel. 570/552–3900; Rhonda Moffitt Sod, Interim Chief Executive Officer
**Web address:** www.commonwealthhealth.net/locations/first–hospital

For explanation of codes following names, see page B2.
★ Indicates Type III membership in the American Hospital Association.

HEART OF LANCASTER REGIONAL MEDICAL CENTER (O, 148 beds) 1500 Highlands Drive, Lititz, PA Zip 17543–7694; tel. 717/625–5000; Deborah J. Willwerth, R.N., MSN, Chief Executive Officer
**Web address:** www.heartoflancaster.com

JENNERSVILLE REGIONAL HOSPITAL (O, 63 beds) 1015 West Baltimore Pike, West Grove, PA Zip 19390–9459; tel. 610/869–1000; Andrew Guz, Chief Executive Officer
**Web address:** www.jennersville.com

LANCASTER REGIONAL MEDICAL CENTER (O, 150 beds) 250 College Avenue, Lancaster, PA Zip 17603–3363, Mailing Address: P.O. Box 3434, Zip 17604–3434; tel. 717/291–8211; Russell Baxley, Chief Executive Officer
**Web address:** www.lancasterregional.com

LOCK HAVEN HOSPITAL (O, 137 beds) 24 Cree Drive, Lock Haven, PA Zip 17745–2699; tel. 570/893–5000; Steven T. Davis, Chief Executive Officer
**Web address:** www.lockhavenhospital.com

MEMORIAL HOSPITAL (O, 100 beds) 325 South Belmont Street, York, PA Zip 17403–2609, Mailing Address: P.O. Box 15118, Zip 17405–7118; tel. 717/843–8623; Sally J. Dixon, Chief Executive Officer
**Web address:** www.mhyork.org

MOSES TAYLOR HOSPITAL (O, 217 beds) 700 Quincy Avenue, Scranton, PA Zip 18510–1724; tel. 570/770–5000; Justin Davis, Chief Executive Officer
**Web address:** www.mth.org

PHOENIXVILLE HOSPITAL (O, 113 beds) 140 Nutt Road, Phoenixville, PA Zip 19460–3900, Mailing Address: P.O. Box 3001, Zip 19460–0916; tel. 610/983–1000; Stephen M. Tullman, Chief Executive Officer
**Web address:** www.phoenixvillehospital.com

POTTSTOWN MEMORIAL MEDICAL CENTER (O, 232 beds) 1600 East High Street, Pottstown, PA Zip 19464–5093; tel. 610/327–7000; Rich Newell, Chief Executive Officer
**Web address:** www.pottstownmemorial.com

REGIONAL HOSPITAL OF SCRANTON (O, 192 beds) 746 Jefferson Avenue, Scranton, PA Zip 18510–1624; tel. 570/348–7100; Brooks Turkel, Chief Executive Officer
**Web address:** www.regionalhospitalofscranton.net

SHARON REGIONAL HEALTH SYSTEM (O, 256 beds) 740 East State Street, Sharon, PA Zip 16146–3395; tel. 724/983–3911; Jason Roeback, Chief Executive Officer
**Web address:** www.sharonregional.com

SUNBURY COMMUNITY HOSPITAL AND OUTPATIENT CENTER (O, 76 beds) 350 North Eleventh Street, Sunbury, PA Zip 17801–1611; tel. 570/286–3333; Robert D. Williams, Interim Chief Executive Officer
**Web address:** www.sunburyhospital.com

TYLER MEMORIAL HOSPITAL (O, 48 beds) 5950 State Route 6, Tunkhannock, PA Zip 18657–7905; tel. 570/836–2161; Diane Ljungquist, R.N., MS, Chief Executive Officer
**Web address:** www.tylermemorialhospital.net

WILKES–BARRE GENERAL HOSPITAL (O, 374 beds) 575 North River Street, Wilkes–Barre, PA Zip 18764–0001; tel. 570/829–8111; Cornelio R. Catena, President and Chief Executive Officer
**Web address:** www.wvhc.org

**SOUTH CAROLINA:** CAROLINAS HOSPITAL SYSTEM (O, 429 beds) 805 Pamplico Highway, Florence, SC Zip 29505–6050, Mailing Address: P.O. Box 100550, Zip 29502–0550; tel. 843/674–5000; Darcy Craven, Chief Executive Officer
**Web address:** www.carolinashospital.com

CAROLINAS HOSPITAL SYSTEM MARION (O, 216 beds) 2829 East Highway 76, Mullins, SC Zip 29574–6035, Mailing Address: P.O. Drawer 1150, Marion, Zip 29571–1150; tel. 843/431–2000; Parkes Coggins, Interim Chief Executive Officer
**Web address:** www.carolinashospitalmarion.com/Pages/Home.aspx

CHESTER REGIONAL MEDICAL CENTER (L, 36 beds) 1 Medical Park Drive, Chester, SC Zip 29706–9769; tel. 803/581–3151; Page H. Vaughan, Chief Executive Officer
**Web address:** www.chesterregional.com

MARY BLACK HEALTH SYSTEM—GAFFNEY (O, 125 beds) 1530 North Limestone Street, Gaffney, SC Zip 29340–4738; tel. 864/487–4271; Joshua Self, Chief Executive Officer
**Web address:** www.upstatecarolina.org

MARY BLACK HEALTH SYSTEM—SPARTANSBURG (O, 181 beds) 1700 Skylyn Drive, Spartanburg, SC Zip 29307–1061, Mailing Address: P.O. Box 3217, Zip 29304–3217; tel. 864/573–3000; Sean T. Dardeau, Chief Executive Officer
**Web address:** www.maryblackhealthsystem.com

SPRINGS MEMORIAL HOSPITAL (O, 168 beds) 800 West Meeting Street, Lancaster, SC Zip 29720–2298; tel. 803/286–1214; Janice Dabney, Chief Executive Officer
**Web address:** www.springsmemorial.com

**TENNESSEE:** TENNOVA HEALTHCARE—DYERSBURG REGIONAL HOSPITAL (O, 120 beds) 400 East Tickle Street, Dyersburg, TN Zip 38024–3120; tel. 731/285–2410; Reba Celsor, Chief Executive Officer
**Web address:** www.dyersburgregionalmc.com

GATEWAY MEDICAL CENTER (O, 247 beds) 651 Dunlop Lane, Clarksville, TN Zip 37040–5015, Mailing Address: P.O. Box 31629, Zip 37040–0028; tel. 931/502–1000; Mark A. Marsh, Chief Executive Officer
**Web address:** www.ghsystem.com

HARTON REGIONAL MEDICAL CENTER (O, 104 beds) 1801 North Jackson Street, Tullahoma, TN Zip 37388–8259; tel. 931/393–3000; William R. Spray, Chief Executive Officer
**Web address:** www.hartonmedicalcenter.com

HENDERSON COUNTY COMMUNITY HOSPITAL (O, 45 beds) 200 West Church Street, Lexington, TN Zip 38351–2038; tel. 731/968–3646; Dale Humphrey, Chief Executive Officer
**Web address:** www.hendersoncchospital.com

HERITAGE MEDICAL CENTER (O, 70 beds) 2835 Highway 231 North, Shelbyville, TN Zip 37160–7327; tel. 931/685–5433; David V. Bunch, Chief Executive Officer
**Web address:** www.heritagemedicalcenter.com

JAMESTOWN REGIONAL MEDICAL CENTER (O, 85 beds) 436 Central Avenue W., Jamestown, TN Zip 38556–3031, Mailing Address: P.O. Box 1500, Zip 38556–1500; tel. 931/879–8171; Lynette Pritchett, Chief Executive Officer
**Web address:** www.jamestownregional.org

LAKEWAY REGIONAL HOSPITAL (O, 135 beds) 726 McFarland Street, Morristown, TN Zip 37814–3990; tel. 423/586–2302; Clyde Wood, Chief Executive Officer
**Web address:** www.tennova.com

MCKENZIE REGIONAL HOSPITAL (O, 35 beds) 161 Hospital Drive, McKenzie, TN Zip 38201–1636; tel. 731/352–5344; Michael G. Morrical, Chief Executive Officer
**Web address:** www.mckenzieregionalhospital.com

TENNOVA HEALTHCARE—MCNAIRY REGIONAL HOSPITAL (O, 45 beds) 705 East Poplar Avenue, Selmer, TN Zip 38375–1828; tel. 731/645–3221; Pamela W. Roberts, Chief Executive Officer
**Web address:** www.mcnairyregionalhospital.com

TENOVA HEALTHCARE—REGIONAL HOSPITAL OF JACKSON (O, 129 beds) 367 Hospital Boulevard, Jackson, TN Zip 38305–2080; tel. 731/661–2000; Charles F. Miller, Chief Executive Officer
**Web address:** www.regionalhospitaljackson.com/Pages/Home.aspx

SKYRIDGE MEDICAL CENTER (O, 186 beds) 2305 Chambliss Avenue N.W., Cleveland, TN Zip 37311–3847, Mailing Address: P.O. Box 3060, Zip 37320–3060; tel. 423/559–6000; R. Coleman Foss, Chief Executive Officer
**Web address:** www.skyridgemedicalcenter.net

TENNOVA HEALTHCARE–JEFFERSON MEMORIAL HOSPITAL (L, 54 beds) 110 Hospital Drive, Jefferson City, TN Zip 37760–5281; tel. 865/471–2500; Colin McRae, Chief Executive Officer
**Web address:** www.tennova.com/

TENNOVA HEALTHCARE–LAFOLLETTE MEDICAL CENTER (O, 164 beds) 923 East Central Avenue, La Follette, TN Zip 37766–2768, Mailing Address: P.O. Box 1301, Zip 37766–1301; tel. 423/907–1200; Mark Cain, Chief Executive Officer
**Web address:** www.tennova.com

TENNOVA NEWPORT MEDICAL CENTER (O, 47 beds) 435 Second Street, Newport, TN Zip 37821–3799; tel. 423/625–2200; Trevor Castaneda, Chief Executive Officer
**Web address:** www.tennova.com

TENNOVA PHYSICIANS REGIONAL MEDICAL CENTER (O, 233 beds) 900 East Oak Hill Avenue, Knoxville, TN Zip 37917–4556; tel. 865/545–8000; Neil Heatherly, Interim Chief Executive Officer
**Web address:** www.hma.com/content/physicians–regional–medical–center

For explanation of codes following names, see page B2.
★ Indicates Type III membership in the American Hospital Association.

UNIVERSITY MEDICAL CENTER (O, 245 beds) 1411 Baddour Parkway, Lebanon, TN Zip 37087–2513; tel. 615/444–8262; Matthew T. Caldwell, Chief Executive Officer
**Web address:** www.universitymedicalcenter.com

TENNOVA HEALTHCARE—VOLUNTEER COMMUNITY HOSPITAL (O, 65 beds) 161 Mount Pelia Road, Martin, TN Zip 38237–3811; tel. 731/587–4261; Darrell Blaylock, Chief Executive Officer
**Web address:** www.volunteercommunityhospital.com

**TEXAS:** ABILENE REGIONAL MEDICAL CENTER (O, 205 beds) 6250 U.S. Highway 83, Abilene, TX Zip 79606–5299; tel. 325/428–1000; Michael D. Murphy, Chief Executive Officer
**Web address:** www.abileneregional.com

BIG BEND REGIONAL MEDICAL CENTER (O, 25 beds) 2600 Highway 118 North, Alpine, TX Zip 79830–2002; tel. 432/837–3447; John Hughson, Chief Executive Officer
**Web address:** www.bigbendhealthcare.com

BROWNWOOD REGIONAL MEDICAL CENTER (O, 168 beds) 1501 Burnet Road, Brownwood, TX Zip 76801–8520, Mailing Address: P.O. Box 760, Zip 76804–0760; tel. 325/646–8541; Claude E. Chip Camp, III, FACHE, Chief Executive Officer
**Web address:** www.brmc–cares.com

CEDAR PARK REGIONAL MEDICAL CENTER (O, 93 beds) 1401 Medical Parkway, Cedar Park, TX Zip 78613–7763; tel. 512/528–7000; Brad D. Holland, Chief Executive Officer
**Web address:** www.cedarparkregional.com

COLLEGE STATION MEDICAL CENTER (O, 148 beds) 1604 Rock Prairie Road, College Station, TX Zip 77845–8345, Mailing Address: P.O. Box 10000, Zip 77842–3500; tel. 979/764–5100; Larry Rodgers, Chief Executive Officer
**Web address:** www.csmedcenter.com

DETAR HEALTHCARE SYSTEM (O, 245 beds) 506 East San Antonio Street, Victoria, TX Zip 77901–6060, Mailing Address: P.O. Box 2089, Zip 77902–2089; tel. 361/575–7441; William R. Blanchard, Chief Executive Officer
**Web address:** www.detar.com

HILL REGIONAL HOSPITAL (O, 66 beds) 101 Circle Drive, Hillsboro, TX Zip 76645–2670; tel. 254/580–8500; Michael J. Ellis, Chief Executive Officer
**Web address:** www.chs.net

LAKE GRANBURY MEDICAL CENTER (L, 83 beds) 1310 Paluxy Road, Granbury, TX Zip 76048–5655; tel. 817/573–2273; Derrick Cuenca, Chief Executive Officer
**Web address:** www.lakegranburymedicalcenter.com

LAREDO MEDICAL CENTER (O, 326 beds) 1700 East Saunders Avenue, Laredo, TX Zip 78041–5474, Mailing Address: P.O. Box 2068, Zip 78044–2068; tel. 956/796–5000; Enrique Gallegos, Chief Executive Officer
**Web address:** www.laredomedical.com

LONGVIEW REGIONAL MEDICAL CENTER (O, 198 beds) 2901 North Fourth Street, Longview, TX Zip 75605–5191, Mailing Address: P.O. Box 14000, Zip 75607–4000; tel. 903/758–1818; Jim R. Kendrick, Chief Executive Officer
**Web address:** www.longviewregional.com

NAVARRO REGIONAL HOSPITAL (O, 148 beds) 3201 West State Highway 22, Corsicana, TX Zip 75110–2469; tel. 903/654–6800; Michael K. Stewart, Chief Executive Officer
**Web address:** www.navarrohospital.com

SAN ANGELO COMMUNITY MEDICAL CENTER (O, 131 beds) 3501 Knickerbocker Road, San Angelo, TX Zip 76904–7698; tel. 325/949–9511; Jeremy Riney, Chief Executive Officer
**Web address:** www.sacmc.com

SCENIC MOUNTAIN MEDICAL CENTER (O, 75 beds) 1601 West 11th Place, Big Spring, TX Zip 79720–4198; tel. 432/263–1211; Emma Krabill, Interim Chief Executive Officer
**Web address:** www.smmccares.com

SOUTH TEXAS REGIONAL MEDICAL CENTER (O, 67 beds) 1905 Highway 97 East, Jourdanton, TX Zip 78026–1504; tel. 830/769–3515; James R. Resendez, Chief Executive Officer
**Web address:** www.strmc.com

TOMBALL REGIONAL MEDICAL CENTER (O, 160 beds) 605 Holderrieth Street, Tomball, TX Zip 77375–6445; tel. 281/401–7500; Thomas W. Jackson, Chief Executive Officer
**Web address:** www.tomballregionalmedicalcenter.com

WEATHERFORD REGIONAL MEDICAL CENTER (O, 86 beds) 713 East Anderson Street, Weatherford, TX Zip 76086–5705; tel. 817/596–8751; David Orcutt, Chief Executive Officer
**Web address:** www.weatherfordregional.com

WOODLAND HEIGHTS MEDICAL CENTER (O, 115 beds) 505 South John Redditt Drive, Lufkin, TX Zip 75904–3157, Mailing Address: P.O. Box 150610, Zip 75904; tel. 936/634–8311; Kyle Swift, Chief Executive Officer
**Web address:** www.woodlandheights.net

**UTAH:** MOUNTAIN WEST MEDICAL CENTER (O, 31 beds) 2055 North Main Street, Tooele, UT Zip 84074–9819; tel. 435/843–3600; Philip Eaton, Interim Chief Executive Officer
**Web address:** www.mountainwestmc.com

**VIRGINIA:** SOUTHAMPTON MEMORIAL HOSPITAL (O, 72 beds) 100 Fairview Drive, Franklin, VA Zip 23851–1238, Mailing Address: P.O. Box 817, Zip 23851–0817; tel. 757/569–6100; Kimberly W. Marks, Interim Chief Executive Officer
**Web address:** www.smhfranklin.com

SOUTHERN VIRGINIA REGIONAL MEDICAL CENTER (O, 80 beds) 727 North Main Street, Emporia, VA Zip 23847–1274; tel. 434/348–4400; Matt Tavenner, Chief Executive Officer
**Web address:** www.svrmc.com

SOUTHSIDE REGIONAL MEDICAL CENTER (O, 300 beds) 200 Medical Park Boulevard, Petersburg, VA Zip 23805–9274; tel. 804/765–5000; Douglas J. Moyer, Chief Executive Officer
**Web address:** www.srmconline.com

**WASHINGTON:** DEACONESS HOSPITAL (O, 352 beds) 800 West Fifth Avenue, Spokane, WA Zip 99204–2803, Mailing Address: P.O. Box 248, Zip 99210–0248; tel. 509/458–5800; Maurine Cate, Chief Executive Officer
**Web address:** www.deaconessspokane.com/Deaconess–Hospital/home. aspx

TOPPENISH COMMUNITY HOSPITAL (O, 48 beds) 502 West Fourth Avenue, Toppenish, WA Zip 98948–1616, Mailing Address: P.O. Box 672, Zip 98948–0672; tel. 509/865–3105; Perry Gay, Chief Executive Officer
**Web address:** www.toppenishhospital.com

VALLEY HOSPITAL (O, 123 beds) 12606 East Mission Avenue, Spokane Valley, WA Zip 99216–1090; tel. 509/924–6650; Gregory Repetti, Interim Chief Executive Officer
**Web address:** www.valleyhospital.org

YAKIMA REGIONAL MEDICAL AND CARDIAC CENTER (O, 167 beds) 110 South Ninth Avenue, Yakima, WA Zip 98902–3315; tel. 509/575–5000; Veronica Knudson, Chief Executive Officer
**Web address:** www.yakimaregional.net

**WEST VIRGINIA:** BLUEFIELD REGIONAL MEDICAL CENTER (O, 102 beds) 500 Cherry Street, Bluefield, WV Zip 24701–3390; tel. 304/327–1100; Gigi Fergus, Interim Chief Executive Officer
**Web address:** www.bluefield.org

GREENBRIER VALLEY MEDICAL CENTER (O, 113 beds) 202 Maplewood Avenue, Ronceverte, WV Zip 24970–1334, Mailing Address: P.O. Box 497, Zip 24970–0497; tel. 304/647–4411; Robert Calhoun, Chief Executive Officer
**Web address:** www.gvmc.com

PLATEAU MEDICAL CENTER (O, 25 beds) 430 Main Street, Oak Hill, WV Zip 25901–3455; tel. 304/469–8600; Derek W. Cimala, Interim Chief Executive Officer
**Web address:** www.plateaumedicalcenter.com

WILLIAMSON MEMORIAL HOSPITAL (O, 76 beds) 859 Alderson Street, Williamson, WV Zip 25661–3215, Mailing Address: P.O. Box 1980, Zip 25661–1980; tel. 304/235–2500; Cindy Segar–Miller, R.N., MS, Interim Chief Executive Officer
**Web address:** www.williamsonmemorial.net

**WYOMING:** EVANSTON REGIONAL HOSPITAL (O, 42 beds) 190 Arrowhead Drive, Evanston, WY Zip 82930–9266; tel. 307/789–3636; George Winn, Chief Executive Officer
**Web address:** www.evanstonregionalhospital.com

| | | |
|---|---|---|
| **Owned, leased, sponsored:** | 193 hospitals | 26398 beds |
| **Contract–managed:** | 0 hospitals | 0 beds |
| **Totals:** | 193 hospitals | 26398 beds |

For explanation of codes following names, see page B2.
★ Indicates Type III membership in the American Hospital Association.

**0249: COMMUNITY HEALTHCARE SYSTEM** (NP)
901 MacArthur Boulevard, Hammond, IN Zip 46321–2959;
tel. 219/836–1600; Donald Powers, Chairman, President and Chief
Executive Officer
**(Independent Hospital System)**

**INDIANA:** COMMUNITY HOSPITAL (O, 473 beds) 901 Macarthur Boulevard,
Munster, IN Zip 46321–2959; tel. 219/836–1600; Donald P. Fesko, Chief
Executive Officer and Administrator
**Web address:** www.comhs.org

ST. CATHERINE HOSPITAL (O, 189 beds) 4321 Fir Street, East Chicago, IN
Zip 46312–3097; tel. 219/392–1700; JoAnn Birdzell, Chief Executive Officer
and Administrator
**Web address:** www.stcatherinehospital.org

ST. MARY MEDICAL CENTER (O, 195 beds) 1500 South Lake Park Avenue,
Hobart, IN Zip 46342–6699; tel. 219/942–0551; Janice L. Ryba, JD, Chief
Executive Officer
**Web address:** www.comhs.org

| | | |
|---|---|---|
| Owned, leased, sponsored: | 3 hospitals | 857 beds |
| Contract–managed: | 0 hospitals | 0 beds |
| Totals: | 3 hospitals | 857 beds |

**★0384: COMMUNITY HOSPITAL CORPORATION** (NP)
7800 North Dallas Parkway, Suite 200, Plano, TX Zip 75024–6116;
tel. 972/943–6400; Michael D. Williams, President and Chief
Executive Officer
**(Independent Hospital System)**

**KENTUCKY:** CONTINUECARE HOSPITAL AT BAPTIST HEALTH CORBIN (L, 32
beds) 1 Trillium Way, Lower Level, Corbin, KY Zip 40701–8727;
tel. 606/523–5150; R. Alan Coppock, FACHE, President
**Web address:** www.continuecare.org

**NORTH CAROLINA:** CAROLINAS CONTINUECARE HOSPITAL AT KINGS
MOUNTAIN (L, 28 beds) 706 West King Street, 2nd Floor, Kings Mountain,
NC Zip 28086–2708, Mailing Address: P.O. Box 159, Zip 28086–0159;
tel. 980/487–5520; Denise R. Murray, Chief Executive Officer
**Web address:** www.continuecare.org/kings–mountain/

CAROLINAS CONTINUECARE HOSPITAL AT PINEVILLE (L, 40 beds) 10648
Park Road, Charlotte, NC Zip 28210; tel. 704/667–8050; Daniel C. Dunmyer,
Chief Executive Officer
**Web address:** www.cshnc.com

**TENNESSEE:** JELLICO COMMUNITY HOSPITAL (L, 31 beds) 188 Hospital
Lane, Jellico, TN Zip 37762–4400; tel. 423/784–7252; Keith Richardson,
Chief Executive Officer
**Web address:** www.jellicohospital.com

**TEXAS:** BAPTIST HOSPITALS OF SOUTHEAST TEXAS (O, 349 beds) 3080
College Street, Beaumont, TX Zip 77701–4689, Mailing Address: P.O.
Box 1591, Zip 77704–1591; tel. 409/212–5000; David N. Parmer, Chief
Executive Officer
**Web address:** www.bhset.net

BAPTIST ORANGE HOSPITAL (O, 35 beds) 608 Strickland Drive, Orange, TX
Zip 77630–4717; tel. 409/883–9361; Jarren Garrett, Chief Administrative
Officer

CONTINUECARE HOSPITAL AT HENDRICK MEDICAL CENTER (L, 19 beds)
1900 Pine Street, Abilene, TX Zip 79601–2432; tel. 325/670–6251; Thomas
P. Harlan, Chief Executive Officer
**Web address:** www.continuecare.org/hendrick/

CONTINUECARE HOSPITAL AT MIDLAND MEMORIAL (L, 29 beds) 4214
Andrews Highway, 3rd Floor, Midland, TX Zip 79703–4822;
tel. 432/221–3563; ,
**Web address:** www.continuecare.org/midland/

ST. MARK'S MEDICAL CENTER (O, 44 beds) One St. Mark's Place, La Grange,
TX Zip 78945; tel. 979/242–2200; Shane Kernell, Chief Executive Officer
**Web address:** www.smmctx.org

TYLER CONTINUECARE HOSPITAL AT MOTHER FRANCES (L, 51 beds) 800
East Dawson, 4th Floor, Tyler, TX Zip 75701–2036; tel. 903/531–4080;
Stephanie Hyde, Chief Executive Officer
**Web address:** www.continuecare.org

YOAKUM COMMUNITY HOSPITAL (L, 25 beds) 1200 Carl Ramert Drive,
Yoakum, TX Zip 77995–4868; tel. 361/293–2321; Karen Barber, R.N., Chief
Executive Officer
**Web address:** www.yoakumhospital.org

| | | |
|---|---|---|
| Owned, leased, sponsored: | 11 hospitals | 683 beds |
| Contract–managed: | 0 hospitals | 0 beds |
| Totals: | 11 hospitals | 683 beds |

**1085: COMMUNITY MEDICAL CENTERS** (NP)
Fresno and Maddy Drive, Fresno, CA Zip 93721, Mailing Address:
P.O. Box 1232, Zip 93715–1232; tel. 559/459–6000; Tim A. Joslin,
President and Chief Executive Officer
**(Moderately Centralized Health System)**

**CALIFORNIA:** CLOVIS COMMUNITY MEDICAL CENTER (O, 109 beds) 2755
Herndon Avenue, Clovis, CA Zip 93611–6801; tel. 559/324–4000; Craig
Castro, Chief Executive Officer
**Web address:** www.communitymedical.org

COMMUNITY BEHAVIORAL HEALTH CENTER (O, 61 beds) 7171 North Cedar
Avenue, Fresno, CA Zip 93720–3311; tel. 559/449–8000; Craig Wagoner,
Chief Executive Officer
**Web address:** www.communitymedical.org

COMMUNITY REGIONAL MEDICAL CENTER (O, 793 beds) 2823 Fresno
Street, Fresno, CA Zip 93721–1324, Mailing Address: P.O. Box 1232,
Zip 93715–1232; tel. 559/459–6000; Craig Wagoner, Chief Executive
Officer
**Web address:** www.communitymedical.org

FRESNO HEART AND SURGICAL HOSPITAL (O, 60 beds) 15 East Audubon
Drive, Fresno, CA Zip 93720–1542; tel. 559/433–8000; Wanda Holderman,
R.N., Chief Executive Officer
**Web address:** www.fresnoheartandsurgical.org

| | | |
|---|---|---|
| Owned, leased, sponsored: | 4 hospitals | 1023 beds |
| Contract–managed: | 0 hospitals | 0 beds |
| Totals: | 4 hospitals | 1023 beds |

**0909: COMPASS HEALTH** (NP)
426 North Avenue G., Crowley, LA Zip 70526–2434;
tel. 337/788–3330; Mark J. Cullen, Chief Executive Officer
**(Independent Hospital System)**

**LOUISIANA:** COMPASS BEHAVIORAL CENTER OF ALEXANDRIA (O, 16 beds)
6410 Masonic Drve, Alexandria, LA Zip 71301–2319;
tel. 318/442–3163; Phillip Maxwell, Administrator
**Web address:** www.compasshealthcare.com/site191.php

COMPASS BEHAVIORAL CENTER OF CROWLEY (O, 34 beds) 1526 North
Avenue I., Crowley, LA Zip 70526–2434; tel. 337/788–3380; Allison Kidder,
Administrator
**Web address:** www.compasshealthcare.com

COMPASS BEHAVIORAL CENTER OF HOUMA (O, 20 beds) 4701 West Park
Avenue, Houma, LA Zip 70364–4426; tel. 985/876–1715; Cheryl Turner,
Administrator
**Web address:** www.compasshealthcare.com/site83.php

| | | |
|---|---|---|
| Owned, leased, sponsored: | 3 hospitals | 70 beds |
| Contract–managed: | 0 hospitals | 0 beds |
| Totals: | 3 hospitals | 70 beds |

**0950: CONE HEALTH** (NP)
1200 North Elm Street, Greensboro, NC Zip 27401–1004;
tel. 336/832–7000; Terry Akin, President and Chief Executive Officer

| | | |
|---|---|---|
| Owned, leased, sponsored: | 0 hospitals | 0 beds |
| Contract–managed: | 0 hospitals | 0 beds |
| Totals: | 0 hospitals | 0 beds |

Section B

For explanation of codes following names, see page B2.
★ Indicates Type III membership in the American Hospital Association.

**0014: CONNECTICUT DEPARTMENT OF MENTAL HEALTH AND ADDICTION SERVICES** (NP)
410 Capitol Avenue, Hartford, CT Zip 06106–1367, Mailing Address: P.O. Box 341431, Zip 06134–1431; tel. 860/418–7000; Miriam Delphin–Rittmon, Ph.D., Commissioner
**(Independent Hospital System)**

**CONNECTICUT:** CONNECTICUT MENTAL HEALTH CENTER (O, 39 beds) 34 Park Street, New Haven, CT Zip 06519–1109, Mailing Address: P.O. Box 1842, Zip 06508–1842; tel. 203/974–7144; Michael Sernyak, M.D., Director
**Web address:** www.ct.gov/dmhas/cwp/view.asp?a=2906&q=334596

CONNECTICUT VALLEY HOSPITAL (O, 596 beds) Eastern Drive, Middletown, CT Zip 06457–3947, Mailing Address: P.O. Box 351, Zip 06457–3947; tel. 860/262–5000; Helene M. Vartelas, Chief Executive Officer
**Web address:** www.ct.gov/dmhas/cwp/view.asp?a=3519&q=416778

SOUTHWEST CONNECTICUT MENTAL HEALTH SYSTEM (O, 62 beds) 1635 Central Avenue, Bridgeport, CT Zip 06610–2717; tel. 203/551–7400; Daniel Wartenberg, PsyD, M.P.H., Chief Executive Officer
**Web address:** www.ct.gov/dmhas/cwp/view.asp?a=2946&q=378936

| | | |
|---|---|---|
| Owned, leased, sponsored: | 3 hospitals | 697 beds |
| Contract–managed: | 0 hospitals | 0 beds |
| Totals: | 3 hospitals | 697 beds |

**0016: COOK COUNTY HEALTH AND HOSPITALS SYSTEM** (NP)
1900 West Polk Street, Suite 220, Chicago, IL Zip 60612–3723; tel. 312/864–6820; John Jay Shannon, M.D., Chief Executive Officer
**(Independent Hospital System)**

**ILLINOIS:** JOHN H. STROGER JR. HOSPITAL OF COOK COUNTY (O, 448 beds) 1969 West Ogden Avenue, Chicago, IL Zip 60612–3714; tel. 312/864–6000; John Jay Shannon, M.D., Chief Executive Officer
**Web address:** www.cookcountyhealth.net

PROVIDENT HOSPITAL OF COOK COUNTY (O, 25 beds) 500 East 51st Street, Chicago, IL Zip 60615–2494; tel. 312/572–2000; John Jay Shannon, M.D., Chief Executive Officer
**Web address:** www.ccbhs.org/pages/ProvidentHospitalofCookCounty.htm

| | | |
|---|---|---|
| Owned, leased, sponsored: | 2 hospitals | 473 beds |
| Contract–managed: | 0 hospitals | 0 beds |
| Totals: | 2 hospitals | 473 beds |

**0905: CORNERSTONE HEALTHCARE GROUP** (IO)
2200 Ross Avenue, Suite 5400, Dallas, TX Zip 75201–7984; tel. 469/621–6700; David Smith, President and Chief Executive Officer
**(Independent Hospital System)**

**ARIZONA:** CORNERSTONE HOSPITAL OF SOUTHEAST ARIZONA (O, 34 beds) 7220 East Rosewood Drive, Tucson, AZ Zip 85710–1350; tel. 520/546–4595; Louise Cassidy, Chief Executive Officer
**Web address:** www.chghospitals.com

**ARKANSAS:** CORNERSTONE HOSPITAL OF NORTH LITTLE ROCK (O, 40 beds) 9601 Interstate 630, Exit 7, 10th Floor, Jacksonville, AR Zip 72076–3721; Little Rock, tel. 501/265–0600; James H. Rogers, FACHE, Chief Executive Officer
**Web address:** www.chghospitals.com/littlerock/

**LOUISIANA:** CORNERSTONE HOSPITAL OF BOSSIER CITY (O, 54 beds) 4900 Medical Drive, Bossier City, LA Zip 71112–4521; tel. 318/747–9500; Sheri Burnette, R.N., Chief Executive Officer and Administrator
**Web address:** www.chghospitals.com/

CORNERSTONE HOSPITAL OF SOUTHWEST LOUISIANA (O, 30 beds) 703 Cypress Street, Sulphur, LA Zip 70663–5053; tel. 337/310–6000; David Smith, President
**Web address:** www.chghospitals.com/sulphur/

CORNERSTONE HOSPITAL–WEST MONROE (O, 40 beds) 6198 Cypress Street, West Monroe, LA Zip 71291–9010; tel. 318/396–5600; Chris Simpson, Chief Executive Officer
**Web address:** www.chghospitals.com/chwm.html

**OKLAHOMA:** CORNERSTONE HOSPITAL OF OKLAHOMA–MUSKOGEE (O, 64 beds) 351 South 40th Street, Muskogee, OK Zip 74401–4916; tel. 918/682–6161; Craig Koele, Chief Executive Officer
**Web address:** www.chghospitals.com/muskogee/

CORNERSTONE HOSPITAL OF OKLAHOMA–SHAWNEE (O, 34 beds) 1900 Gordon Cooper Drive, 2nd Floor, Shawnee, OK Zip 74801–8603, Mailing Address: PO BOX 1245, Zip 74802–1245; tel. 405/395–5800; Elizabeth Waytula, Chief Executive Officer
**Web address:** www.chghospitals.com/shawnee/

**TEXAS:** CORNERSTONE HOSPITAL OF AUSTIN (O, 118 beds) 4207 Burnet Road, Austin, TX Zip 78756–3396; tel. 512/706–1900; Scott Galliardt, Chief Executive Officer
**Web address:** www.chghospitals.com/austin/

CORNERSTONE HOSPITAL OF HOUSTON AT CLEARLAKE (O, 130 beds) 709 Medical Center Boulevard, Webster, TX Zip 77598; tel. 281/332–3322; Amy Stasney, Chief Executive Officer
**Web address:** www.cornerstonehealthcaregroup.com

CORNERSTONE HOSPITAL–MEDICAL CENTER OF HOUSTON (O, 35 beds) 2001 Hermann Drive, Houston, TX Zip 77004; tel. 832/649–6200; Michael Higginbotham, Chief Executive Officer
**Web address:** www.chghospitals.com

SOLARA HOSPITAL CONROE (O, 41 beds) 1500 Grand Lake Drive, Conroe, TX Zip 77304–2891; tel. 936/523–1800; Suzanne Kretschmer, Interim Hospital Administrator
**Web address:** www.chghospitals.com/conroe/

SOLARA HOSPITAL HARLINGEN (O, 82 beds) 508 Victoria Lane, Harlingen, TX Zip 78550–3225; tel. 956/425–9600; Cary L. Montalvo, Chief Executive Officer
**Web address:** www.chghospitals.com/harlingen/

SOLARA HOSPITAL MCALLEN (O, 71 beds) 301 West Expressway 83, McAllen, TX Zip 78503–3045; tel. 956/632–4880; Chris Chizek, Chief Executive Officer
**Web address:** www.chghospitals.com/mcallen/

**WEST VIRGINIA:** CORNERSTONE HOSPITAL OF HUNTINGTON (O, 25 beds) 2900 First Avenue, Two East, Huntington, WV Zip 25702–1241; tel. 304/399–2600; Cynthia Isaacs, Chief Executive Officer
**Web address:** www.chghospitals.com

| | | |
|---|---|---|
| Owned, leased, sponsored: | 14 hospitals | 798 beds |
| Contract–managed: | 0 hospitals | 0 beds |
| Totals: | 14 hospitals | 798 beds |

**★0103: COTTAGE HEALTH** (NP)
400 West Pueblo Street, Santa Barbara, CA Zip 93105–4353, Mailing Address: P.O. Box 689, Zip 93102–0689; tel. 805/569–7290; Ronald C. Werft, President and Chief Executive Officer
**(Independent Hospital System)**

**CALIFORNIA:** GOLETA VALLEY COTTAGE HOSPITAL (O, 80 beds) 351 South Patterson Avenue, Santa Barbara, CA Zip 93111–2496, Mailing Address: Box 6306, Zip 93160–6306; tel. 805/967–3411; Ronald C. Werft, President and Chief Executive Officer
**Web address:** www.sbch.org

SANTA BARBARA COTTAGE HOSPITAL (O, 351 beds) 400 West Pueblo Street, Santa Barbara, CA Zip 93105–4390, Mailing Address: P.O. Box 689, Zip 93102–0689; tel. 805/682–7111; Ronald C. Werft, President and Chief Executive Officer
**Web address:** www.cottagehealthsystem.org

SANTA YNEZ VALLEY COTTAGE HOSPITAL (O, 11 beds) 2050 Viborg Road, Solvang, CA Zip 93463–2295; tel. 805/688–6431; Ronald C. Werft, President and Chief Executive Officer
**Web address:** www.cottagehealthsystem.org

| | | |
|---|---|---|
| Owned, leased, sponsored: | 3 hospitals | 442 beds |
| Contract–managed: | 0 hospitals | 0 beds |
| Totals: | 3 hospitals | 442 beds |

For explanation of codes following names, see page B2.
★ Indicates Type III membership in the American Hospital Association.

★0123:  **COVENANT HEALTH** (NP)
100 Fort Sanders West Boulevard, Knoxville, TN Zip 37922–3353; tel. 865/531–5555; Anthony Spezia, President and Chief Executive Officer
**(Centralized Health System)**

**TENNESSEE:** CLAIBORNE MEDICAL CENTER (L, 62 beds) 1850 Old Knoxville Road, Tazewell, TN Zip 37879–3625; tel. 423/626–4211; Patricia P. Ketterman, R.N., President and Chief Administrative Officer
**Web address:** www.claibornehospital.org

CUMBERLAND MEDICAL CENTER (O, 110 beds) 421 South Main Street, Crossville, TN Zip 38555–5031; tel. 931/484–9511; Jeremy Biggs, President and Chief Administrative Officer
**Web address:** www.cmchealthcare.org

FORT LOUDOUN MEDICAL CENTER (L, 30 beds) 550 Fort Loudoun Medical Center Drive, Lenoir City, TN Zip 37772–5673; tel. 865/271–6000; Jeffrey Feike, President and Chief Administrative Officer
**Web address:** www.covenanthealth.com

FORT SANDERS REGIONAL MEDICAL CENTER (O, 384 beds) 1901 West Clinch Avenue, Knoxville, TN Zip 37916–2307; tel. 865/541–1111; Keith Altshuler, President and Chief Administrative Officer
**Web address:** www.covenanthealth.com

LECONTE MEDICAL CENTER (O, 129 beds) 742 Middle Creek Road, Sevierville, TN Zip 37862–5019, Mailing Address: P.O. Box 8005, Zip 37864–8005; tel. 865/446–7000; Jennifer Hanson, MS, R.N., President and Chief Administrative Officer
**Web address:** www.lecontemedicalcenter.com

METHODIST MEDICAL CENTER OF OAK RIDGE (O, 210 beds) 990 Oak Ridge Turnpike, Oak Ridge, TN Zip 37830–6976, Mailing Address: P.O. Box 2529, Zip 37831–2529; tel. 865/835–1000; Michael Belbeck, President and Chief Administrative Officer
**Web address:** www.mmcoakridge.com

MORRISTOWN–HAMBLEN HEALTHCARE SYSTEM (O, 131 beds) 908 West Fourth North Street, Morristown, TN Zip 37814–3894, Mailing Address: P.O. Box 1178, Zip 37816–1178; tel. 423/492–9000; Gordon Lintz, Chief Administrative Officer
**Web address:** www.mhhs1.org

PARKWEST MEDICAL CENTER (O, 297 beds) 9352 Park West Boulevard, Knoxville, TN Zip 37923–4325, Mailing Address: P.O. Box 22993, Zip 37933–0993; tel. 865/373–1000; Rick Lassiter, President and Chief Administrative Officer
**Web address:** www.yesparkwest.com

ROANE MEDICAL CENTER (O, 54 beds) 8045 Roane Medical Center Drive, Harriman, TN Zip 37748–8333; tel. 865/316–1000; Gaye Jolly, FACHE, President/Chief Administrative Officer
**Web address:** www.roanemedical.com

| Owned, leased, sponsored: | 9 hospitals | 1407 beds |
|---|---|---|
| Contract–managed: | 0 hospitals | 0 beds |
| **Totals:** | 9 hospitals | 1407 beds |

★5885:  **COVENANT HEALTH** (CC)
100 Ames Pond Drive, Suite 102, Tewksbury, MA Zip 01876–1240; tel. 978/654–6363; David R. Lincoln, FACHE, President and Chief Executive Officer
**(Moderately Centralized Health System)**

**MAINE:** ST. JOSEPH HOSPITAL (O, 84 beds) 360 Broadway, Bangor, ME Zip 04401–3979, Mailing Address: P.O. Box 403, Zip 04402–0403; tel. 207/262–1000; Mary Prybylo, President and Chief Executive Officer
**Web address:** www.sjhhealth.com

ST. MARY'S REGIONAL MEDICAL CENTER (O, 171 beds) 318 Sabattus Street, Lewiston, ME Zip 04240–5553, Mailing Address: P.O. Box 291, Zip 04243–0291; tel. 207/777–8100; Christopher Chekouras, President and Chief Executive Officer
**Web address:** www.stmarysmaine.com

**NEW HAMPSHIRE:** ST. JOSEPH HOSPITAL (O, 126 beds) 172 Kinsley Street, Nashua, NH Zip 03060–3648; tel. 603/882–3000; Richard Boehler, M.D., President and Chief Executive Officer
**Web address:** www.stjosephhospital.com

| Owned, leased, sponsored: | 3 hospitals | 381 beds |
|---|---|---|
| Contract–managed: | 0 hospitals | 0 beds |
| **Totals:** | 3 hospitals | 381 beds |

★0036:  **COVENANT HEALTH SYSTEM** (NP)
3615 19th Street, Lubbock, TX Zip 79410–1203; tel. 806/725–0447; Richard H. Parks, FACHE, President and Chief Executive Officer
**(Centralized Health System)**

**TEXAS:** COVENANT CHILDREN'S HOSPITAL (O, 73 beds) 4015 22nd Place, Lubbock, TX Zip 79410; tel. 806/725–1011; Christopher J. Dougherty, Chief Executive Officer
**Web address:** www.covenanthealth.org/About–Us/Facilities/Childrens–Hospital.aspx

COVENANT HOSPITAL PLAINVIEW (L, 68 beds) 2601 Dimmitt Road, Plainview, TX Zip 79072–1833; tel. 806/296–5531; Clay Taylor, Chief Executive Officer
**Web address:** www.covenantplainview.org

COVENANT HOSPITAL–LEVELLAND (L, 26 beds) 1900 South College Avenue, Levelland, TX Zip 79336–6508; tel. 806/894–4963; Bruce White, Administrator
**Web address:** www.covenanthospitallevelland.com/

COVENANT MEDICAL CENTER (O, 551 beds) 3615 19th Street, Lubbock, TX Zip 79410–1203, Mailing Address: P.O. Box 1201, Zip 79408–1201; tel. 806/725–0000; Walt Cathey, Chief Executive Officer
**Web address:** www.covenanthealth.org

COVENANT SPECIALTY HOSPITAL (O, 56 beds) 3815 20th Street, Lubbock, TX Zip 79410–1235; tel. 806/725–9200; Stuart Oertli, Executive Director
**Web address:** www.covenanthealth.org/view/Facilities/Specialty_Hospital

| Owned, leased, sponsored: | 5 hospitals | 774 beds |
|---|---|---|
| Contract–managed: | 0 hospitals | 0 beds |
| **Totals:** | 5 hospitals | 774 beds |

0179:  **COXHEALTH** (NP)
1423 North Jefferson Avenue, Springfield, MO Zip 65802–1988; tel. 417/269–3108; Steven D. Edwards, President and Chief Executive Officer
**(Centralized Physician/Insurance Health System)**

**MISSOURI:** COX MEDICAL CENTER BRANSON (O, 119 beds) 251 Skaggs Road, Branson, MO Zip 65616–2031, Mailing Address: P.O. Box 650, Zip 65615–0650; tel. 417/335–7000; William K. Mahoney, President and Chief Executive Officer
**Web address:** www.skaggs.net

COX MEDICAL CENTERS (O, 660 beds) 1423 North Jefferson Street, Springfield, MO Zip 65802–1988; tel. 417/269–3000; Steven D. Edwards, President and Chief Executive Officer
**Web address:** www.coxhealth.com

COX MONETT (O, 25 beds) 801 North Lincoln Avenue, Monett, MO Zip 65708–1641; tel. 417/235–3144; Darren Bass, President
**Web address:** www.coxhealth.com

| Owned, leased, sponsored: | 3 hospitals | 804 beds |
|---|---|---|
| Contract–managed: | 0 hospitals | 0 beds |
| **Totals:** | 3 hospitals | 804 beds |

0930:  **CRC HEALTH GROUP, INC.** (IO)
20400 Stevens Creek Boulevard, Suite 600, Cupertino, CA Zip 95014–2217; tel. 866/540–5240; Jerome E. Rhodes, Chief Executive Officer
**(Independent Hospital System)**

**ARIZONA:** SIERRA TUCSON (O, 139 beds) 39580 South Lago Del Oro Parkway, Tucson, AZ Zip 85739–1091; tel. 520/624–4000; Stephen P. Fahey, Executive Director
**Web address:** www.sierratucson.com

For explanation of codes following names, see page B2.
★ Indicates Type III membership in the American Hospital Association.

Section B

**NORTH CAROLINA:** WILMINGTON TREATMENT CENTER (O, 44 beds) 2520 Troy Drive, Wilmington, NC Zip 28401–7643; tel. 910/762–2727; Robert Pitts, Executive Director
**Web address:** www.wilmtreatment.com

| | | |
|---|---|---|
| Owned, leased, sponsored: | 2 hospitals | 183 beds |
| Contract–managed: | 0 hospitals | 0 beds |
| Totals: | 2 hospitals | 183 beds |

★**0008: CROZER–KEYSTONE HEALTH SYSTEM** (NP)
100 West Sproul Road, Springfield, PA Zip 19064–2033; tel. 610/338–8205; Joan K. Richards, President and Chief Executive Officer
**(Moderately Centralized Health System)**

**PENNSYLVANIA:** CROZER–CHESTER MEDICAL CENTER (O, 400 beds) One Medical Center Boulevard, Upland, PA Zip 19013–3995; tel. 610/447–2000; Patrick J. Gavin, President
**Web address:** www.crozer.org

DELAWARE COUNTY MEMORIAL HOSPITAL (O, 209 beds) 501 North Lansdowne Avenue, Drexel Hill, PA Zip 19026–1114; tel. 610/284–8100; Robert Haffey, R.N., President
**Web address:** www.crozer.org

| | | |
|---|---|---|
| Owned, leased, sponsored: | 2 hospitals | 609 beds |
| Contract–managed: | 0 hospitals | 0 beds |
| Totals: | 2 hospitals | 609 beds |

**0960: CURAE HEALTH** (NP)
121 Leinart Street, Clinton, TN Zip 37716–3632, Mailing Address: P.O. Box 358, Zip 37717–0358; tel. 865/269–4074; Steve Clapp, President and Chief Executive Officer

**ALABAMA:** LAKELAND COMMUNITY HOSPITAL (O, 56 beds) Highway 195 East, Haleyville, AL Zip 35565–9536, Mailing Address: P.O. Box 780, Zip 35565–0780; tel. 205/486–5213; Cynthia Nichols, R.N., MSN, Chief Executive Officer
**Web address:** www.lakelandcommunityhospital.com/

NORTHWEST MEDICAL CENTER (O, 66 beds) 1530 U.S. Highway 43, Winfield, AL Zip 35594–5056; tel. 205/487–7000; Michael D. Windham, Chief Executive Officer
**Web address:** www.northwestmedcenter.com

RUSSELLVILLE HOSPITAL (O, 92 beds) 15155 Highway 43, Russellville, AL Zip 35653–1975, Mailing Address: P.O. Box 1089, Zip 35653–1089; tel. 256/332–1611; Christine R. Stewart, FACHE, Chief Executive Officer
**Web address:** www.russellvillehospital.com

| | | |
|---|---|---|
| Owned, leased, sponsored: | 3 hospitals | 214 beds |
| Contract–managed: | 0 hospitals | 0 beds |
| Totals: | 3 hospitals | 214 beds |

★**1075: DAUGHTERS OF CHARITY HEALTH SYSTEM** (CC)
26000 Altamont Road, Los Altos Hills, CA Zip 94022–4317; tel. 650/917–4500; Robert Issai, President and Chief Executive Officer
**(Independent Hospital System)**

**CALIFORNIA:** O'CONNOR HOSPITAL (O, 202 beds) 2105 Forest Avenue, San Jose, CA Zip 95128–1471; tel. 408/947–2500; Sister Margaret Keaveney, President and Chief Executive Officer
**Web address:** www.oconnorhospital.org

SAINT LOUISE REGIONAL HOSPITAL (O, 93 beds) 9400 No Name Uno, Gilroy, CA Zip 95020–3528; tel. 408/848–2000; Sister Margaret Keaveney, Chief Executive Officer
**Web address:** www.dochs.org

SETON MEDICAL CENTER (O, 423 beds) 1900 Sullivan Avenue, Daly City, CA Zip 94015–2229; tel. 650/992–4000; John Ferrelli, President and Chief Executive Officer
**Web address:** www.setonmedicalcenter.org

ST. FRANCIS MEDICAL CENTER (O, 323 beds) 3630 East Imperial Highway, Lynwood, CA Zip 90262–2636; tel. 310/900–8900; Gerald T. Kozai, President and Chief Executive Officer
**Web address:** www.dochs.org

ST. VINCENT MEDICAL CENTER (O, 271 beds) 2131 West Third Street, Los Angeles, CA Zip 90057–1901, Mailing Address: P.O. Box 57992, Zip 90057–0992; tel. 213/484–7111; Catherine Fickes, R.N., President and Chief Executive Officer
**Web address:** www.stvincentmedicalcenter.com

| | | |
|---|---|---|
| Owned, leased, sponsored: | 5 hospitals | 1312 beds |
| Contract–managed: | 0 hospitals | 0 beds |
| Totals: | 5 hospitals | 1312 beds |

★**0864: DAVIS HEALTH SYSTEM** (NP)
Reed Street and Gorman Avenue, Elkins, WV Zip 26241, Mailing Address: P.O. Box 1697, Zip 26241–1697; tel. 304/636–3300; Mark Doak, President and Chief Executive Officer
**(Independent Hospital System)**

**WEST VIRGINIA:** BROADDUS HOSPITAL (O, 72 beds) 1 Healthcare Drive, Philippi, WV Zip 26416–9405, Mailing Address: P.O. Box 930, Zip 26416–0930; tel. 304/457–1760; Jeffrey A. Powelson, Chief Executive Officer
**Web address:** www.davishealthsystem.org/

DAVIS MEDICAL CENTER (O, 80 beds) Gorman Avenue and Reed Street, Elkins, WV Zip 26241, Mailing Address: P.O. Box 1484, Zip 26241–1484; tel. 304/636–3300; Vance Jackson, Chief Executive Officer
**Web address:** www.davishealthsystem.com

| | | |
|---|---|---|
| Owned, leased, sponsored: | 2 hospitals | 152 beds |
| Contract–managed: | 0 hospitals | 0 beds |
| Totals: | 2 hospitals | 152 beds |

**1825: DCH HEALTH SYSTEM** (NP)
809 University Boulevard East, Tuscaloosa, AL Zip 35401–2029; tel. 205/759–7111; Bryan N. Kindred, FACHE, President and Chief Executive Officer
**(Moderately Centralized Health System)**

**ALABAMA:** DCH REGIONAL MEDICAL CENTER (O, 684 beds) 809 University Boulevard East, Tuscaloosa, AL Zip 35401–2029; tel. 205/759–7111; William H. Cassels, Administrator
**Web address:** www.dchsystem.com

FAYETTE MEDICAL CENTER (L, 167 beds) 1653 Temple Avenue North, Fayette, AL Zip 35555–1314, Mailing Address: P.O. Drawer 710, Zip 35555–0710; tel. 205/932–5966; Donald J. Jones, FACHE, Administrator
**Web address:** www.dchsystem.com

NORTHPORT MEDICAL CENTER (O, 196 beds) 2700 Hospital Drive, Northport, AL Zip 35476–3360; tel. 205/333–4500; Luke Standeffer, Administrator
**Web address:** www.dchsystem.com

| | | |
|---|---|---|
| Owned, leased, sponsored: | 3 hospitals | 1047 beds |
| Contract–managed: | 0 hospitals | 0 beds |
| Totals: | 3 hospitals | 1047 beds |

★**0313: DEACONESS HEALTH SYSTEM** (NP)
600 Mary Street, Evansville, IN Zip 47710–1658; tel. 812/450–5000; Linda E. White, President and Chief Executive Officer
**(Centralized Health System)**

**INDIANA:** DEACONESS HOSPITAL (O, 484 beds) 600 Mary Street, Evansville, IN Zip 47710–1658; tel. 812/450–5000; Shawn W. McCoy, Chief Administrative Officer
**Web address:** www.deaconess.com

THE HEART HOSPITAL AT DEACONESS GATEWAY (O, 24 beds) 4007 Gateway Boulevard, Newburgh, IN Zip 47630–8947; tel. 812/842–4784; Rebecca Malotte, Executive Director and Chief Nursing Officer
**Web address:** www.deaconess.com/

For explanation of codes following names, see page B2.
★ Indicates Type III membership in the American Hospital Association.

THE WOMEN'S HOSPITAL (O, 74 beds) 4199 Gateway Boulevard, Newburgh, IN Zip 47630–8940; tel. 812/842–4200; Christina M. Ryan, R.N., Chief Executive Officer
**Web address:** www.deaconess.com

| Owned, leased, sponsored: | 3 hospitals | 582 beds |
| --- | --- | --- |
| Contract–managed: | 0 hospitals | 0 beds |
| Totals: | 3 hospitals | 582 beds |

## 0330: DEKALB REGIONAL HEALTH SYSTEM (NP)
2701 North Decatur Road, Decatur, GA Zip 30033–5918; tel. 404/501–1000; John Shelton, President and Chief Executive Officer
**(Independent Hospital System)**

**GEORGIA:** DEKALB MEDICAL AT DOWNTOWN DECATUR (O, 44 beds) 450 North Candler Street, Decatur, GA Zip 30030–2671; tel. 404/501–6700; John Shelton, President and Chief Executive Officer
**Web address:** www.dekalbmedicalcenter.org

DEKALB MEDICAL AT HILLANDALE (O, 80 beds) 2801 DeKalb Medical Parkway, Lithonia, GA Zip 30058–4996; tel. 404/501–8700; John Shelton, President and Chief Executive Officer
**Web address:** www.dekalbmedical.org

DEKALB MEDICAL AT NORTH DECATUR (O, 417 beds) 2701 North Decatur Road, Decatur, GA Zip 30033–5995; tel. 404/501–1000; John Shelton, President and Chief Executive Officer
**Web address:** www.dekalbmedical.org

| Owned, leased, sponsored: | 3 hospitals | 541 beds |
| --- | --- | --- |
| Contract–managed: | 0 hospitals | 0 beds |
| Totals: | 3 hospitals | 541 beds |

## 9495: DEPARTMENT OF THE AIR FORCE (FG)
1420 Pentagon, Room 4E1084, Washington, DC Zip 20330–1420; tel. 202/767–4765; Lieutenant General Thomas Travis, Surgeon General
**(Independent Hospital System)**

**ALASKA:** U. S. AIR FORCE REGIONAL HOSPITAL (O, 64 beds) 5955 Zeamer Avenue, Elmendorf AFB, AK Zip 99506–3702; tel. 907/580–3006; Major Mark Lamey, Commander
**Web address:** www.elmendorf.af.mil/

**CALIFORNIA:** DAVID GRANT USAF MEDICAL CENTER (O, 116 beds) 101 Bodin Circle, Travis AFB, CA Zip 94535–1809; tel. 707/423–7300; Colonel Brian T. Hayes, Commander
**Web address:** www.travis.af.mil/units/dgmc/index.asp

**FLORIDA:** U. S. AIR FORCE REGIONAL HOSPITAL (O, 57 beds) 307 Boatner Road, Suite 114, Eglin AFB, FL Zip 32542–1282; tel. 850/883–8221; Colonel Gianna Zeh, Commander
**Web address:** www.eglin.af.mil

**IDAHO:** U. S. AIR FORCE CLINIC (O, 10 beds) 90 Hope Drive, Building 600, Mountain Home AFB, ID Zip 83648–1057; tel. 208/828–7610; Lieutenant Colonel Gregory W. Carson, Administrator

**MISSISSIPPI:** U. S. AIR FORCE MEDICAL CENTER KEESLER (O, 56 beds) 301 Fisher Street, Room 1A132, Keesler AFB, MS Zip 39534–2519; tel. 228/376–2550; Colonel Thomas Harrell, M.D., Commander
**Web address:** www.keesler.af.mil

**NEVADA:** MIKE O'CALLAGHAN FEDERAL HOSPITAL (O, 46 beds) 4700 Las Vegas Boulevard North, Suite 2419, Nellis AFB, NV Zip 89191–6600; tel. 702/653–2000; Colonel Christian Benjamin, USAF, MC, Commander
**Web address:** www.lasvegas.va.gov/

**OHIO:** WRIGHT PATTERSON MEDICAL CENTER (O, 62 beds) 4881 Sugar Maple Drive, Wright–Patterson AFB, OH Zip 45433–5529; tel. 937/257–9144; Colonel Brent J. Erickson, Administrator
**Web address:** www.wpafb.af.mil/units/wpmc/

**VIRGINIA:** U. S. AIR FORCE HOSPITAL (O, 65 beds) 77 Nealy Avenue, Hampton, VA Zip 23665–2040; tel. 757/764–6969; Colonel Wayne M. Pritt, Commander
**Web address:** www.jble.af.mil

| Owned, leased, sponsored: | 8 hospitals | 476 beds |
| --- | --- | --- |
| Contract–managed: | 0 hospitals | 0 beds |
| Totals: | 8 hospitals | 476 beds |

## 9395: DEPARTMENT OF THE ARMY, OFFICE OF THE SURGEON GENERAL (FG)
5109 Leesburg Pike, Falls Church, VA Zip 22041–3215; tel. 703/681–3000; Lieutenant General Eric B. Schoomaker, Surgeon General
**(Moderately Centralized Health System)**

**ALASKA:** BASSETT ARMY COMMUNITY HOSPITAL (O, 24 beds) 1060 Gaffney Road, Box 7400, Fort Wainwright, AK Zip 99703–5001, Mailing Address: 1060 Gaffney Road, Box 7440, Zip 99703–5001; tel. 907/361–4000; Timothy Bergeron, Deputy Commander, Administration
**Web address:** www.alaska.amedd.army.mil

**CALIFORNIA:** WEED ARMY COMMUNITY HOSPITAL (O, 27 beds) Inner Loop Road and 4th Street, Building 166, Fort Irwin, CA Zip 92310–5065, Mailing Address: P.O. Box 105109, Zip 92310–5109; tel. 760/380–3108; Colonel Cheryl Taylor–Whitehead, Commander
**Web address:** www.irwin.amedd.army.mil

**COLORADO:** EVANS U. S. ARMY COMMUNITY HOSPITAL (O, 69 beds) 1650 Cochrane Circle, Building 7500, Fort Carson, CO Zip 80913–4613; tel. 719/526–7200; Colonel Dennis P. LeMaster, Commander
**Web address:** www.evans.amedd.army.mil

**GEORGIA:** DWIGHT DAVID EISENHOWER ARMY MEDICAL CENTER (O, 107 beds) 300 West Hospital Road, Fort Gordon, GA Zip 30905–5741; tel. 706/787–5811; Colonel John P. Lamoureux, Commander
**Web address:** www.ddeamc.amedd.army.mil

MARTIN ARMY COMMUNITY HOSPITAL (O, 57 beds) 7950 Martin Loop, Fort Benning, GA Zip 31905–5648, Mailing Address: 7950 Martin Loop, B9200, Room 010, Zip 31905–5648; tel. 706/544–2516; Colonel Scott B. Avery, Commander
**Web address:** www.martin.amedd.army.mil

WINN ARMY COMMUNITY HOSPITAL (O, 37 beds) 1061 Harmon Avenue, Hinesville, GA Zip 31314–5641, Mailing Address: 1061 Harmon Avenue, Suite 2311B, Zip 31314–5641; tel. 912/435–6965; Colonel Kirk W. Eggleston, Commanding Officer
**Web address:** www.winn.amedd.army.mil/

**HAWAII:** TRIPLER ARMY MEDICAL CENTER (O, 194 beds) 1 Jarret White Road, Honolulu, HI Zip 96859–5001; tel. 808/433–6661; Colonel David K. Dunning, Commanding Officer
**Web address:** www.tamc.amedd.army.mil

**KANSAS:** IRWIN ARMY COMMUNITY HOSPITAL (O, 44 beds) 600 Caisson Hill Road, Junction City, KS Zip 66442–7037; tel. 785/239–7000; Colonel Barry R. Pockrandt, Commander
**Web address:** www.iach.amedd.army.mil

**KENTUCKY:** COLONEL FLORENCE A. BLANCHFIELD ARMY COMMUNITY HOSPITAL (O, 66 beds) 650 Joel Drive, Fort Campbell, KY Zip 42223–5318; tel. 270/798–8040; Colonel Paul Cordts, Commander
**Web address:** www.campbell.amedd.army.mil/

IRELAND ARMY COMMUNITY HOSPITAL (O, 33 beds) 289 Ireland Avenue, Fort Knox, KY Zip 40121–5111; tel. 502/624–9333; Colonel Robert Cornes, Commander
**Web address:** www.iach.knox.amedd.army.mil/

**LOUISIANA:** BAYNE–JONES ARMY COMMUNITY HOSPITAL (O, 13 beds) 1585 3rd Street, Fort Polk, LA Zip 71459–5102; tel. 337/531–3928; Colonel Carlene Blanding, Commander
**Web address:** www.polk.amedd.army.mil

**MARSHALL ISLANDS:** KWAJALEIN HOSPITAL (O, 14 beds) U.S. Army Kwajalein Atoll, Kwajalein Island, MH Zip 96960, Mailing Address: Box 1702, APO, UNITZip 96555–5000; tel. 805/355–2225; Elaine McMahon, Administrator

**MISSOURI:** GENERAL LEONARD WOOD ARMY COMMUNITY HOSPITAL (O, 42 beds) 126 Missouri Avenue, Fort Leonard Wood, MO Zip 65473–8952; tel. 573/596–0414; Colonel Peter Nielsen, M.D., Commander
**Web address:** www.glwach.amedd.army.mil/

For explanation of codes following names, see page B2.
★ Indicates Type III membership in the American Hospital Association.

**NEW YORK:** KELLER ARMY COMMUNITY HOSPITAL (O, 20 beds) 900 Washington Road, West Point, NY Zip 10996–1197, Mailing Address: U.S. Military Academy, Building 900, Zip 10996–1197; tel. 845/938–5169; Colonel Felicia Pehrson, M.D., Commanding Officer
**Web address:** www.kach.amedd.army.mil/

**NORTH CAROLINA:** WOMACK ARMY MEDICAL CENTER (O, 156 beds) Normandy Drive, Fort Bragg, NC Zip 28307–5000; tel. 910/907–6000; Colonel Ronald Stephens, Commander
**Web address:** www.wamc.amedd.army.mil/

**OKLAHOMA:** REYNOLDS ARMY COMMUNITY HOSPITAL (O, 24 beds) 4301 Wilson Street, Fort Sill, OK Zip 73503–4472; tel. 580/558–3000; Colonel Noel J. Cardenas, FACHE, Commander and Chief Executive Officer
**Web address:** www.rach.sill.amedd.army.mil

**SOUTH CAROLINA:** MONCRIEF ARMY COMMUNITY HOSPITAL (O, 60 beds) 4500 Stuart Street, Fort Jackson, SC Zip 29207–5700; tel. 803/751–2160; Colonel Traci Crawford, R.N., Commander
**Web address:** www.moncrief.amedd.army.mil

**TEXAS:** BROOKE ARMY MEDICAL CENTER (O, 226 beds) 3851 Roger Brookes Drive, Fort Sam Houston, TX Zip 78234–4501; tel. 210/916–4141; Colonel Kyle D. Campbell, Commander
**Web address:** www.bamc.amedd.army.mil

CARL R. DARNALL ARMY MEDICAL CENTER (O, 109 beds) 36000 Darnall Loop, Fort Hood, TX Zip 76544–5095; tel. 254/288–8000; Colonel Patricia Darnauer, Medical Center Commander
**Web address:** www.crdamc.amedd.army.mil

WILLIAM BEAUMONT ARMY MEDICAL CENTER (O, 209 beds) 5005 North Piedras Street, El Paso, TX Zip 79920–5001; tel. 915/742–2121; Colonel Michael S. Heimall, Commander
**Web address:** www.wbamc.amedd.army.mil

**VIRGINIA:** FORT BELVOIR COMMUNITY HOSPITAL (O, 46 beds) 9300 Dewitt Loop, Fort Belvoir, VA Zip 22060–5285; tel. 571/231–3224; Captain Jennifer Vedral–Baron, Commander
**Web address:** www.fbch.capmed.mil/SitePages/Home.aspx

**WASHINGTON:** MADIGAN HEALTHCARE SYSTEM (O, 227 beds) Fitzsimmons Drive, Building 9040, Tacoma, WA Zip 98431–1100; tel. 253/968–1110; Colonel Ramona Fiorey, MSN, M.P.H., Commander
**Web address:** www.mamc.amedd.army.mil

| | | |
|---|---|---|
| Owned, leased, sponsored: | 22 hospitals | 1804 beds |
| Contract–managed: | 0 hospitals | 0 beds |
| Totals: | 22 hospitals | 1804 beds |

**9295:  DEPARTMENT OF VETERANS AFFAIRS** (FG)
810 Vermont Avenue N.W., Washington, DC Zip 20420–0001; tel. 202/273–5781; Robert A. McDonald, Secretary, Veterans Affairs
**(Decentralized Health System)**

**ALABAMA:** BIRMINGHAM VETERANS AFFAIRS MEDICAL CENTER (O, 151 beds) 700 South 19th Street, Birmingham, AL Zip 35233–1927; tel. 205/933–8101; William F. Harper, M.D., Acting Director
**Web address:** www.birmingham.va.gov/

CENTRAL ALABAMA VETERANS HEALTH CARE SYSTEM (O, 261 beds) 215 Perry Hill Road, Montgomery, AL Zip 36109–3798; tel. 334/272–4670; Robin Jackson, Ph.D., Interim Director
**Web address:** www.centralalabama.va.gov/

TUSCALOOSA VETERANS AFFAIRS MEDICAL CENTER (O, 366 beds) 3701 Loop Road East, Tuscaloosa, AL Zip 35404–5015; tel. 205/554–2000; John F. Merkle, Acting Medical Center Director
**Web address:** www.tuscaloosa.va.gov

**ARIZONA:** NORTHERN ARIZONA VETERANS AFFAIRS HEALTH CARE SYSTEM (O, 147 beds) 500 Highway 89 North, Prescott, AZ Zip 86313–5000; tel. 928/445–4860; Donna K. Jacobs, FACHE, Director
**Web address:** www.prescott.va.gov/

PHOENIX VETERANS AFFAIRS HEALTH CARE SYSTEM (O, 197 beds) 650 East Indian School Road, Phoenix, AZ Zip 85012–1892; tel. 602/277–5551; Glen W. Grippen, Interim Medical Center Director
**Web address:** www.phoenix.va.gov/

SOUTHERN ARIZONA VETERANS AFFAIRS HEALTH CARE SYSTEM (O, 285 beds) 3601 South 6th Avenue, Tucson, AZ Zip 85723–0002; tel. 520/792–1450; Jonathan H. Gardner, FACHE, Director
**Web address:** www.tucson.va.gov

**ARKANSAS:** CENTRAL ARKANSAS VETERANS HEALTHCARE SYSTEM (O, 551 beds) 4300 West Seventh Street, Little Rock, AR Zip 72205–5446; tel. 501/257–1000; Cyril Ekeh, Interim Director
**Web address:** www.littlerock.va.gov

VETERANS HEALTH CARE SYSTEM OF THE OZARKS (O, 72 beds) 1100 North College Avenue, Fayetteville, AR Zip 72703–1944; tel. 479/443–4301; Mark Worley, Interim Director
**Web address:** www.fayettevillear.va.gov

**CALIFORNIA:** SAN FRANCISCO VA MEDICAL CENTER (O, 244 beds) 4150 Clement Street, San Francisco, CA Zip 94121–1545; tel. 415/221–4810; Bonnie S. Graham, Director
**Web address:** www.sanfrancisco.va.gov/

VA GREATER LOS ANGELES HEALTHCARE SYSTEM (O, 1087 beds) 11301 Wilshire Boulevard, Los Angeles, CA Zip 90073–1003; tel. 310/478–3711; Donna M. Beiter, R.N., MSN, Director
**Web address:** www.losangeles.va.gov/

VA LONG BEACH HEALTHCARE SYSTEM (O, 356 beds) 5901 East 7th Street, Long Beach, CA Zip 90822–5201; tel. 562/826–8000; Michael W. Fisher, Director
**Web address:** www.longbeach.va.gov/

VA PALO ALTO HEALTH CARE SYSTEM (O, 808 beds) 3801 Miranda Avenue, Palo Alto, CA Zip 94304–1207; tel. 650/493–5000; Elizabeth Joyce Freeman, FACHE, Director
**Web address:** www.paloalto.va.gov/

VA SAN DIEGO HEALTHCARE SYSTEM (O, 216 beds) 3350 LaJolla Village Drive, San Diego, CA Zip 92161–0002; tel. 858/552–8585; Jeffrey T. Gering, FACHE, Director
**Web address:** www.sandiego.va.gov

VETERANS AFFAIRS CENTRAL CALIFORNIA HEALTH CARE SYSTEM (O, 117 beds) 2615 East Clinton Avenue, Fresno, CA Zip 93703–2223; tel. 559/225–6100; Wessel H. Meyer, M.D., Acting Director
**Web address:** www.fresno.va.gov/

VETERANS AFFAIRS LOMA LINDA HEALTHCARE SYSTEM (O, 270 beds) 11201 Benton Street, Loma Linda, CA Zip 92357–1000; tel. 909/825–7084; Barbara Fallen, FACHE, Director
**Web address:** www.lomalinda.va.gov

**COLORADO:** GRAND JUNCTION VETERANS HEALTH CARE SYSTEM (O, 23 beds) 2121 North Avenue, Grand Junction, CO Zip 81501–6428; tel. 970/242–0731; Marc Magill, Medical Center Director
**Web address:** www.grandjunction.va.gov/

VETERANS AFFAIRS EASTERN COLORADO HEALTH CARE SYSTEM (O, 271 beds) 1055 Clermont Street, Denver, CO Zip 80220–3877; tel. 303/399–8020; Lynette A. Roff, Director
**Web address:** www.denver.va.gov/

**CONNECTICUT:** VETERANS AFFAIRS CONNECTICUT HEALTHCARE SYSTEM (O, 197 beds) 950 Campbell Avenue, West Haven, CT Zip 06516–2770; tel. 203/932–5711; Gerald F. Culliton, Medical Center Director
**Web address:** www.connecticut.va.gov

**DELAWARE:** WILMINGTON VETERANS AFFAIRS MEDICAL CENTER (O, 60 beds) 1601 Kirkwood Highway, Wilmington, DE Zip 19805–4989; tel. 302/994–2511; Robin C. Aube–Warren, Director
**Web address:** www.va.gov/wilmington

**DISTRICT OF COLUMBIA:** WASHINGTON DC VETERANS AFFAIRS MEDICAL CENTER (O, 291 beds) 50 Irving Street N.W., Washington, DC Zip 20422–0002; tel. 202/745–8000; Brian A. Hawkins, Director
**Web address:** www.washingtondc.va.gov/

**FLORIDA:** BAY PINES VETERANS AFFAIRS HEALTHCARE SYSTEM (O, 396 beds) 10000 Bay Pines Boulevard, Bay Pines, FL Zip 33744–8200, Mailing Address: P.O. Box 5005, Zip 33744–5005; tel. 727/398–6661; Suzanne M. Klinker, Director
**Web address:** www.baypines.va.gov/

JAMES A. HALEY VETERANS' HOSPITAL–TAMPA (O, 499 beds) 13000 Bruce B. Downs Boulevard, Tampa, FL Zip 33612–4745; tel. 813/972–2000; Kathleen R. Fogarty, Director
**Web address:** www.tampa.va.gov/

MIAMI VETERANS AFFAIRS HEALTHCARE SYSTEM (O, 401 beds) 1201 N.W. 16th Street, Miami, FL Zip 33125–1624; tel. 305/575–7000; Paul M. Russo, FACHE, Director
**Web address:** www.miami.va.gov/

For explanation of codes following names, see page B2.
★ Indicates Type III membership in the American Hospital Association.

Section B

NORTH FLORIDA/SOUTH GEORGIA VETERAN'S HEALTH SYSTEM (O, 623 beds) 1601 S.W. Archer Road, Gainesville, FL Zip 32608–1135; tel. 352/376–1611; Thomas Wisnieski, FACHE, Director
**Web address:** www.northflorida.va.gov

WEST PALM BEACH VETERANS AFFAIRS MEDICAL CENTER (O, 300 beds) 7305 North Military Trail, West Palm Beach, FL Zip 33410–6400; tel. 561/422–8262; Charleen R. Szabo, FACHE, Director
**Web address:** www.westpalmbeach.va.gov/

**GEORGIA:** ATLANTA VETERANS AFFAIRS MEDICAL CENTER (O, 239 beds) 1670 Clairmont Road, Decatur, GA Zip 30033–4004; tel. 404/321–6111; Leslie Wiggins, Director
**Web address:** www.atlanta.va.gov/

CARL VINSON VETERANS AFFAIRS MEDICAL CENTER (O, 178 beds) 1826 Veterans Boulevard, Dublin, GA Zip 31021–3620; tel. 478/272–1210; Captain Maryalice Morro, Director
**Web address:** www.dublin.va.gov/

CHARLIE NORWOOD VETERANS AFFAIRS MEDICAL CENTER (O, 338 beds) 1 Freedom Way, Augusta, GA Zip 30904–6285; tel. 706/733–0188; Maria R. Andrews, Director
**Web address:** www.augusta.va.gov/

**HAWAII:** VETERANS AFFAIRS PACIFIC ISLANDS HEALTH CARE SYSTEM (O, 0 beds) 459 Patterson Road, Honolulu, HI Zip 96819; tel. 808/433–0600; James E. Hastings, M.D., Director
**Web address:** www.hawaii.va.gov/

**IDAHO:** BOISE VETERANS AFFAIRS MEDICAL CENTER (O, 89 beds) 500 West Fort Street, Boise, ID Zip 83702–4598; tel. 208/422–1000; David P. Wood, FACHE, Director
**Web address:** www.boise.va.gov/

**ILLINOIS:** CAPTAIN JAMES A. LOVELL FEDERAL HEALTH CARE CENTER (O, 103 beds) 3001 Green Bay Road, North Chicago, IL Zip 60064–3049; tel. 847/688–1900; Stephen R. Holt, M.D., Director
**Web address:** www.lovell.fhcc.va.gov/

EDWARD HINES, JR. VETERANS AFFAIRS HOSPITAL (O, 485 beds) 5000 South Fifth Avenue, Hines, IL Zip 60141–3030, Mailing Address: P.O. Box 5000, Zip 60141–5000; tel. 708/202–8387; Daniel Zomchek, MD, Acting Director
**Web address:** www.hines.va.gov/

JESSE BROWN VETERANS AFFAIRS MEDICAL CENTER (O, 198 beds) 820 South Damen, Chicago, IL Zip 60612–3776; tel. 312/569–8387; Ann R. Brown, FACHE, Director
**Web address:** www.chicago.va.gov/

MARION VETERANS AFFAIRS MEDICAL CENTER (O, 225 beds) 2401 West Main Street, Marion, IL Zip 62959–1188; tel. 618/997–5311; Donald Hutson, Director
**Web address:** www.marion.va.gov

VETERANS AFFAIRS ILLIANA HEALTH CARE SYSTEM (O, 221 beds) 1900 East Main Street, Danville, IL Zip 61832–5198; tel. 217/554–3000; Diana Carranza, Interim Director
**Web address:** www.danville.va.gov/

**INDIANA:** RICHARD L. ROUDEBUSH VETERANS AFFAIRS MEDICAL CENTER (O, 209 beds) 1481 West Tenth Street, Indianapolis, IN Zip 46202–2884; tel. 317/554–0000; Ginny L. Creasman, Acting Director
**Web address:** www.indianapolis.va.gov

VETERANS AFFAIRS NORTHERN INDIANA HEALTH CARE SYSTEM (O, 26 beds) 2121 Lake Avenue, Fort Wayne, IN Zip 46805–5100; tel. 260/426–5431; Denise M. Deitzen, Director
**Web address:** www.northernindiana.va.gov/

**IOWA:** IOWA CITY VETERANS AFFAIRS HEALTH CARE SYSTEM (O, 68 beds) 601 Highway 6 West, Iowa City, IA Zip 52246–2208; tel. 319/338–0581; Judith Johnson–Mekota, Director
**Web address:** www.iowacity.va.gov/

VETERANS AFFAIRS CENTRAL IOWA HEALTH CARE SYSTEM (O, 256 beds) 3600 30th Street, Des Moines, IA Zip 50310–5753; tel. 515/699–5999; Lavonne Liversage, Acting Director
**Web address:** www.centraliowa.va.gov/

**KANSAS:** ROBERT J. DOLE VETERANS AFFAIRS MEDICAL CENTER (O, 41 beds) 5500 East Kellogg, Wichita, KS Zip 67218–1607; tel. 316/685–2221; Francisco Vazquez, Director
**Web address:** www.wichita.va.gov

VETERANS AFFAIRS EASTERN KANSAS HEALTH CARE SYSTEM (O, 213 beds) 2200 South West Gage Boulevard, Topeka, KS Zip 66622–0002; tel. 785/350–3111; Anthony Rudy Klopfer, FACHE, Director
**Web address:** www.topeka.va.gov/

**KENTUCKY:** LEXINGTON VETERANS AFFAIRS MEDICAL CENTER (O, 199 beds) 1101 Veterans Drive, Lexington, KY Zip 40502–2235; tel. 859/281–4901; Emma Metcalf, MSN, R.N., Director
**Web address:** www.lexington.va.gov/

ROBLEY REX VETERANS AFFAIRS MEDICAL CENTER (O, 116 beds) 800 Zorn Avenue, Louisville, KY Zip 40206–1499; tel. 502/287–4000; Martin J. Traxler, Chief Executive Officer
**Web address:** www.louisville.va.gov

**LOUISIANA:** ALEXANDRIA VETERANS AFFAIRS HEALTH CARE SYSTEM (O, 143 beds) 2495 Shreveport Highway, 71 N., Pineville, LA Zip 71360–4044, Mailing Address: P.O. Box 69004, Alexandria, Zip 71306–9004; tel. 318/473–0010; Peter P. Henry, FACHE, Interim Director
**Web address:** www.alexandria.va.gov/

OVERTON BROOKS VETERANS AFFAIRS MEDICAL CENTER (O, 100 beds) 510 East Stoner Avenue, Shreveport, LA Zip 71101–4295; tel. 318/221–8411; Toby T. Mathew, Medical Center Director
**Web address:** www.shreveport.va.gov/

**MAINE:** MAINE VETERANS AFFAIRS MEDICAL CENTER (O, 181 beds) 1 VA Center, Augusta, ME Zip 04330–6719; tel. 207/623–8411; Ryan S. Lilly, Director
**Web address:** www.maine.va.gov/

**MARYLAND:** VETERANS AFFAIRS MARYLAND HEALTH CARE SYSTEM–BALTIMORE DIVISION (O, 727 beds) 10 North Greene Street, Baltimore, MD Zip 21201–1524; tel. 410/605–7001; Adam M. Robinson, Acting Director
**Web address:** www.maryland.va.gov/

**MASSACHUSETTS:** BEDFORD VETERANS AFFAIRS MEDICAL CENTER, EDITH NOURSE ROGERS MEMORIAL VETERANS HOSPITAL (O, 147 beds) 200 Springs Road, Bedford, MA Zip 01730–1198; tel. 781/687–2000; Christine Croteau, MBA, Director
**Web address:** www.bedford.va.gov

VETERANS AFFAIRS BOSTON HEALTHCARE SYSTEM (O, 361 beds) 1400 VFW Parkway, Boston, MA Zip 02132–4927; tel. 617/323–7700; Vincent Ng, Director
**Web address:** www.boston.va.gov/

VETERANS AFFAIRS BOSTON HEALTHCARE SYSTEM BROCKTON DIVISION (O, 375 beds) 940 Belmont Street, Brockton, MA Zip 02301–5596; tel. 508/583–4500; Vincent Ng, Interim Director
**Web address:** www.boston.va.gov/

VETERANS AFFAIRS CENTRAL WESTERN MASSACHUSETTS HEALTHCARE SYSTEM (O, 101 beds) 421 North Main Street, Leeds, MA Zip 01053–9764; tel. 413/582–3000; John P. Collins, Medical Center Director
**Web address:** www.centralwesternmass.va.gov/

**MICHIGAN:** ALEDA E. LUTZ VETERANS AFFAIRS MEDICAL CENTER (O, 89 beds) 1500 Weiss Street, Saginaw, MI Zip 48602–5298; tel. 989/497–2500; Peggy W. Kearns, MS, FACHE, Medical Center Director
**Web address:** www.saginaw.va.gov/

BATTLE CREEK VETERANS AFFAIRS MEDICAL CENTER (O, 242 beds) 5500 Armstrong Road, Battle Creek, MI Zip 49037–7314; tel. 269/966–5600; Mary Beth Skupien, Director
**Web address:** www.battlecreek.va.gov/

JOHN D. DINGELL VETERANS AFFAIRS MEDICAL CENTER (O, 157 beds) 4646 John R Street, Detroit, MI Zip 48201–1932; tel. 313/576–1000; Pamela J. Reeves, M.D., Director
**Web address:** www.detroit.va.gov/

OSCAR G. JOHNSON VETERANS AFFAIRS MEDICAL CENTER (O, 17 beds) 325 East H Street, Iron Mountain, MI Zip 49801–4792; tel. 906/774–3300; Andrea Collins, Acting Director
**Web address:** www.ironmountain.va.gov/

VETERANS AFFAIRS ANN ARBOR HEALTHCARE SYSTEM (O, 109 beds) 2215 Fuller Road, Ann Arbor, MI Zip 48105–2399; tel. 734/769–7100; Robert P. McDivitt, FACHE, Director
**Web address:** www.annarbor.va.gov

Section B

For explanation of codes following names, see page B2.
★ Indicates Type III membership in the American Hospital Association.

**MINNESOTA:** MINNEAPOLIS VETERANS AFFAIRS HEALTH CARE SYSTEM (O, 279 beds) One Veterans Drive, Minneapolis, MN Zip 55417–2399; tel. 612/725–2000; Patrick J. Kelly, FACHE, Director
**Web address:** www.minneapolis.va.gov

ST. CLOUD VETERANS AFFAIRS HEALTH CARE SYSTEM (O, 388 beds) 4801 Veterans Drive, Saint Cloud, MN Zip 56303–2099; tel. 320/252–1670; Barry I. Bahl, Director
**Web address:** www.stcloud.va.gov

**MISSISSIPPI:** G.V. (SONNY) MONTGOMERY VETERANS AFFAIRS MEDICAL CENTER (O, 323 beds) 1500 East Woodrow Wilson Drive, Jackson, MS Zip 39216–5199; tel. 601/362–4471; Joe Battle, Director
**Web address:** www.jackson.va.gov/

VETERANS AFFAIRS GULF COAST VETERANS HEALTH CARE SYSTEM (O, 392 beds) 400 Veterans Avenue, Biloxi, MS Zip 39531–2410; tel. 228/523–5000; Anthony L. Dawson, FACHE, Director
**Web address:** www.biloxi.va.gov/

**MISSOURI:** HARRY S. TRUMAN MEMORIAL VETERANS HOSPITAL (O, 123 beds) 800 Hospital Drive, Columbia, MO Zip 65201–5275; tel. 573/814–6000; Wade Vlosich, Director
**Web address:** www.columbiamo.va.gov

JOHN J. PERSHING VETERANS AFFAIRS MEDICAL CENTER (O, 58 beds) 1500 North Westwood Boulevard, Poplar Bluff, MO Zip 63901–3318; tel. 573/686–4151; Michael Moore, Ph.D., Acting Medical Center Director
**Web address:** www.poplarbluff.va.gov

KANSAS CITY VETERANS AFFAIRS MEDICAL CENTER (O, 157 beds) 4801 East Linwood Boulevard, Kansas City, MO Zip 64128–2226; tel. 816/861–4700; Kevin Inkley, Acting Medical Center Director
**Web address:** www.kansascity.va.gov/

VETERANS AFFAIRS ST. LOUIS HEALTH CARE SYSTEM (O, 356 beds) 915 North Grand, Saint Louis, MO Zip 63106–1621; tel. 314/652–4100; Patricia Ten Haaf, R.N., MSN, Ph.D., Acting Director
**Web address:** www.stlouis.va.gov/

**MONTANA:** VETERANS AFFAIRS MONTANA HEALTH CARE SYSTEM (O, 94 beds) 3687 Veterans Drive, Fort Harrison, MT Zip 59636–9703, Mailing Address: P.O. Box 1500, Zip 59636–1500; tel. 406/442–6410; John Ginnity, Interim Director
**Web address:** www.montana.va.gov/

**NEBRASKA:** VETERANS AFFAIRS NEBRASKA–WESTERN IOWA HEALTH CARE SYSTEM (O, 137 beds) 4101 Woolworth Avenue, Omaha, NE Zip 68105–1873; tel. 402/346–8800; Don Burman, Director
**Web address:** www.nebraska.va.gov/

VETERANS AFFAIRS NEBRASKA–WESTERN IOWA HEALTH CARE SYSTEM – LINCOLN (O, 162 beds) 600 South 70th Street, Lincoln, NE Zip 68510–2493; tel. 402/489–3802; Don Burman, Director
**Web address:** www.nebraska.va.gov/

**NEVADA:** VETERANS AFFAIRS SIERRA NEVADA HEALTH CARE SYSTEM (O, 124 beds) 975 Kirman Avenue, Reno, NV Zip 89502–0993; tel. 775/786–7200; Lisa M. Howard, Acting Director
**Web address:** www.reno.va.gov/

VETERANS AFFAIRS SOUTHERN NEVADA HEALTHCARE SYSTEM (O, 58 beds) 6900 North Pecos Road, North Las Vegas, NV tel. 702/791–9000; Isabel Duff, MS, Director
**Web address:** www.lasvegas.va.gov/

**NEW HAMPSHIRE:** MANCHESTER VETERANS AFFAIRS MEDICAL CENTER (O, 90 beds) 718 Smyth Road, Manchester, NH Zip 03104–4098; tel. 603/624–4366; Tammy A. Krueger, Acting Director
**Web address:** www.manchester.va.gov/

**NEW JERSEY:** VETERANS AFFAIRS NEW JERSEY HEALTH CARE SYSTEM (O, 439 beds) 385 Tremont Avenue, East Orange, NJ Zip 07018–1095; tel. 973/676–1000; Kenneth H. Mizrach, Director
**Web address:** www.newjersey.va.gov/

**NEW MEXICO:** NEW MEXICO VETERANS AFFAIRS HEALTH CARE SYSTEM – RAYMOND G. MURPHY MEDICAL CENTER (O, 203 beds) 1501 San Pedro S.E., Albuquerque, NM Zip 87108–5153; tel. 505/265–1711; Andrew Welch, Director
**Web address:** www.albuquerque.va.gov/

**NEW YORK:** ALBANY STRATTON VETERANS AFFAIRS MEDICAL CENTER (O, 149 beds) 113 Holland Avenue, Albany, NY Zip 12208–3473; tel. 518/626–5000; Linda W. Weiss, MS, FACHE, Director
**Web address:** www.albany.va.gov/

BATH VETERANS AFFAIRS MEDICAL CENTER (O, 371 beds) 76 Veterans Avenue, Bath, NY Zip 14810–0842; tel. 607/664–4000; Michael J. Swartz, FACHE, Medical Center Director
**Web address:** www.bath.va.gov

CANANDAIGUA VETERANS AFFAIRS MEDICAL CENTER (O, 196 beds) 400 Fort Hill Avenue, Canandaigua, NY Zip 14424–1159; tel. 585/394–2000; Michael Schwartz, Medical Center Director
**Web address:** www.canandaigua.va.gov/

JAMES J. PETERS VETERANS AFFAIRS MEDICAL CENTER (O, 325 beds) 130 West Kingsbridge Road, Bronx, NY Zip 10468–3904; tel. 718/584–9000; Erik Langhoff, M.D., Ph.D., Director
**Web address:** www.bronx.va.gov/

NORTHPORT VETERANS AFFAIRS MEDICAL CENTER (O, 502 beds) 79 Middleville Road, Northport, NY Zip 11768–2200; tel. 631/261–4400; Philip C. Moschitta, Director
**Web address:** www.northport.va.gov/index.asp

SYRACUSE VETERANS AFFAIRS MEDICAL CENTER (O, 235 beds) 800 Irving Avenue, Syracuse, NY Zip 13210–2716; tel. 315/425–4400; James Cody, Director
**Web address:** www.syracuse.va.gov/

VETERANS AFFAIRS HUDSON VALLEY HEALTH CARE SYSTEM (O, 403 beds) 2094 Albany Post Road, Montrose, NY Zip 10548–1454, Mailing Address: P.O. Box 100, Zip 10548–0100; tel. 914/737–4400; Margaret B. Caplan, Director
**Web address:** www.hudsonvalley.va.gov/

VETERANS AFFAIRS NEW YORK HARBOR HEALTHCARE SYSTEM (O, 522 beds) 800 Poly Place, Brooklyn, NY Zip 11209–7104; tel. 718/630–3500; Martina A. Parauda, Director
**Web address:** www.nyharbor.va.gov

VETERANS AFFAIRS WESTERN NEW YORK HEALTHCARE SYSTEM–BATAVIA DIVISION (O, 128 beds) 222 Richmond Avenue, Batavia, NY Zip 14020–1288; tel. 585/297–1000; Brian G. Stiller, Director Medical Center
**Web address:** www.buffalo.va.gov/batavia.asp

VETERANS AFFAIRS WESTERN NEW YORK HEALTHCARE SYSTEM–BUFFALO DIVISION (O, 113 beds) 3495 Bailey Avenue, Buffalo, NY Zip 14215–1129; tel. 716/834–9200; Brian G. Stiller, Director Medical Center
**Web address:** www.buffalo.va.gov/index.asp

**NORTH CAROLINA:** CHARLES GEORGE VETERANS AFFAIRS MEDICAL CENTER (O, 257 beds) 1100 Tunnel Road, Asheville, NC Zip 28805–2087; tel. 828/298–7911; Cynthia Breyfogle, FACHE, Director
**Web address:** www.asheville.va.gov/

DURHAM VETERANS AFFAIRS MEDICAL CENTER (O, 265 beds) 508 Fulton Street, Durham, NC Zip 27705–3897; tel. 919/286–0411; DeAnne Seekins, Director
**Web address:** www.durham.va.gov/

FAYETTEVILLE VETERANS AFFAIRS MEDICAL CENTER (O, 58 beds) 2300 Ramsey Street, Fayetteville, NC Zip 28301–3899; tel. 910/488–2120; Elizabeth Goolsby, Director
**Web address:** www.fayettevillenc.va.gov

W. G. (BILL) HEFFNER VETERANS AFFAIRS MEDICAL CENTER (O, 171 beds) 1601 Brenner Avenue, Salisbury, NC Zip 28144–2559; tel. 704/638–9000; Kaye Green, FACHE, Director
**Web address:** www.salisbury.va.gov

**NORTH DAKOTA:** FARGO VETERANS AFFAIRS HEALTH CARE SYSTEM (O, 42 beds) 2101 Elm Street North, Fargo, ND Zip 58102–2498; tel. 701/232–3241; Lavonne Liversage, Director
**Web address:** www.fargo.va.gov/

**OHIO:** CHILLICOTHE VETERANS AFFAIRS MEDICAL CENTER (O, 303 beds) 17273 State Route 104, Chillicothe, OH Zip 45601–9718; tel. 740/773–1141; Wendy J. Hepker, FACHE, Director
**Web address:** www.chillicothe.va.gov/

CINCINNATI VETERANS AFFAIRS MEDICAL CENTER (O, 268 beds) 3200 Vine Street, Cincinnati, OH Zip 45220–2288; tel. 513/475–6300; John Gennaro, FACHE, Director
**Web address:** www.cincinnati.va.gov/

DAYTON VETERANS AFFAIRS MEDICAL CENTER (O, 460 beds) 4100 West Third Street, Dayton, OH Zip 45428–9000; tel. 937/268–6511; Glenn A. Costie, FACHE, Director
**Web address:** www.dayton.va.gov/

For explanation of codes following names, see page B2.
★ Indicates Type III membership in the American Hospital Association.

LOUIS STOKES CLEVELAND VETERANS AFFAIRS MEDICAL CENTER (O, 585 beds) 10701 East Boulevard, Cleveland, OH Zip 44106–1702; tel. 216/791–3800; Susan Fuehrer, Director
**Web address:** www.cleveland.va.gov/

**OKLAHOMA:** JACK C. MONTGOMERY VETERANS AFFAIRS MEDICAL CENTER (O, 99 beds) 1011 Honor Heights Drive, Muskogee, OK Zip 74401–1318; tel. 918/577–3000; Richard Crockett, Acting Medical Center Director
**Web address:** www.muskogee.va.gov

OKLAHOMA CITY VETERANS AFFAIRS MEDICAL CENTER (O, 192 beds) 921 N.E. 13th Street, Oklahoma City, OK Zip 73104–5028; tel. 405/456–1000; Gerald K. Darnell, PsyD, Acting Medical Center Director
**Web address:** www.oklahoma.va.gov

**OREGON:** PORTLAND VETERANS AFFAIRS MEDICAL CENTER (O, 303 beds) 3710 S.W. U.S. Veterans Hospital Road, Portland, OR Zip 97239–2964, Mailing Address: P.O. Box 1034, Zip 97207–1034; tel. 503/220–8262; Joanne Krumberger, R.N., FACHE, Director
**Web address:** www.portland.va.gov/

VETERANS AFFAIRS ROSEBURG HEALTHCARE SYSTEM (O, 88 beds) 913 N.W. Garden Valley Boulevard, Roseburg, OR Zip 97471–6513; tel. 541/440–1000; Carol Bogedain, FACHE, Director
**Web address:** www.roseburg.va.gov/

**PENNSYLVANIA:** COATESVILLE VETERANS AFFAIRS MEDICAL CENTER (O, 145 beds) 1400 Black Horse Hill Road, Coatesville, PA Zip 19320–2040; tel. 610/384–7711; Gary W. Devansky, Director
**Web address:** www.coatesville.va.gov/

ERIE VETERANS AFFAIRS MEDICAL CENTER (O, 78 beds) 135 East 38th Street, Erie, PA Zip 16504–1559; tel. 814/860–2576; David Cord, Director
**Web address:** www.erie.va.gov/

JAMES E. VAN ZANDT VETERANS AFFAIRS MEDICAL CENTER (O, 68 beds) 2907 Pleasant Valley Boulevard, Altoona, PA Zip 16602–4305; tel. 877/626–2500; William H. Mills, Director
**Web address:** www.altoona.va.gov/

LEBANON VETERANS AFFAIRS MEDICAL CENTER (O, 213 beds) 1700 South Lincoln Avenue, Lebanon, PA Zip 17042–7529; tel. 717/272–6621; Robert W. Callahan, Jr., Director
**Web address:** www.lebanon.va.gov

PHILADELPHIA VETERANS AFFAIRS MEDICAL CENTER (O, 280 beds) 3900 Woodland Avenue, Philadelphia, PA Zip 19104–4594; tel. 215/823–5800; Daniel Hendee, Director
**Web address:** www.philadelphia.va.gov/

VETERANS AFFAIRS BUTLER HEALTHCARE (O, 126 beds) 325 New Castle Road, Butler, PA Zip 16001–2480; tel. 724/287–4781; Timothy R. Burke, M.D., Acting Director

VETERANS AFFAIRS PITTSBURGH HEALTHCARE SYSTEM (O, 582 beds) University Drive, Pittsburgh, PA Zip 15240–1001; tel. 866/482–7488; David S. Macpherson, M.D., M.P.H., Acting Director
**Web address:** www.pittsburgh.va.gov/

WILKES–BARRE VETERANS AFFAIRS MEDICAL CENTER (O, 161 beds) 1111 East End Boulevard, Wilkes–Barre, PA Zip 18711–0030; tel. 570/824–3521; Michael Adelman, M.D., Medical Center Director
**Web address:** www.va.gov/vamcwb

**PUERTO RICO:** VETERANS AFFAIRS CARIBBEAN HEALTHCARE SYSTEM (O, 330 beds) 10 Casia Street, San Juan, PR Zip 00921–3201; tel. 787/641–7582; DeWayne Hamlin, Director
**Web address:** www.caribbean.va.gov

**RHODE ISLAND:** PROVIDENCE VETERANS AFFAIRS MEDICAL CENTER (O, 73 beds) 830 Chalkstone Avenue, Providence, RI Zip 02908–4799; tel. 401/273–7100; Susan MacKenzie, Director
**Web address:** www.providence.va.gov/

**SOUTH CAROLINA:** RALPH H. JOHNSON VETERANS AFFAIRS MEDICAL CENTER (O, 98 beds) 109 Bee Street, Charleston, SC Zip 29401–5799; tel. 843/577–5011; Scott R. Isaacks, FACHE, Interim Director
**Web address:** www.charleston.va.gov/

WM. JENNINGS BRYAN DORN VETERANS AFFAIRS MEDICAL CENTER (O, 216 beds) 6439 Garners Ferry Road, Columbia, SC Zip 29209–1639; tel. 803/776–4000; Timothy McMurry, Director
**Web address:** www.columbiasc.va.gov/

**SOUTH DAKOTA:** SIOUX FALLS VETERANS AFFAIRS HEALTH CARE SYSTEM (O, 98 beds) 2501 West 22nd Street, Sioux Falls, SD Zip 57105–1305, Mailing Address: P.O. Box 5046, Zip 57117–5046; tel. 605/336–3230; Darwin Goodspeed, Director
**Web address:** www.siouxfalls.va.gov

VETERANS AFFAIRS BLACK HILLS HEALTH CARE SYSTEM (O, 243 beds) 113 Comanche Road, Fort Meade, SD Zip 57741–1099; tel. 605/347–2511; Stephen R. DiStasio, Director
**Web address:** www.blackhills.va.gov/

**TENNESSEE:** JAMES H. QUILLEN VETERANS AFFAIRS MEDICAL CENTER (O, 98 beds) Corner of Lamont & Veterans Way, Mountain Home, TN Zip 37684, Mailing Address: P.O. Box 4000, Zip 37684–4000; tel. 423/926–1171; Charlene S. Ehret, FACHE, Director
**Web address:** www.mountainhome.va.gov/

MEMPHIS VETERANS AFFAIRS MEDICAL CENTER (O, 251 beds) 1030 Jefferson Avenue, Memphis, TN Zip 38104–2193; tel. 901/523–8990; C. Diane Knight, M.D., Director and Chief Executive Officer
**Web address:** www.memphis.va.gov

TENNESSEE VALLEY HEALTHCARE SYSTEM (O, 546 beds) 1310 24th Avenue South, Nashville, TN Zip 37212–2637; tel. 615/327–4751; Juan A. Morales, R.N., MSN, Health System Director
**Web address:** www.tennesseevalley.va.gov

**TEXAS:** AMARILLO VETERANS AFFAIRS HEALTH CARE SYSTEM (O, 55 beds) 6010 West Amarillo Boulevard, Amarillo, TX Zip 79106–1992; tel. 806/355–9703; Walt Dannenberg, Interim Director
**Web address:** www.amarillo.va.gov/

CENTRAL TEXAS VETERANS HEALTH CARE SYSTEM (O, 1532 beds) 1901 Veterans Memorial Drive, Temple, TX Zip 76504–7493; tel. 254/778–4811; Sallie Houser–Hanfelder, FACHE, Director
**Web address:** www.centraltexas.va.gov/

MICHAEL E. DEBAKEY VETERANS AFFAIRS MEDICAL CENTER (O, 479 beds) 2002 Holcombe Boulevard, Houston, TX Zip 77030–4298; tel. 713/791–1414; Adam C. Walmus, Director
**Web address:** www.houston.va.gov

SOUTH TEXAS VETERANS HEALTH CARE SYSTEM (O, 838 beds) 7400 Merton Minter Boulevard, San Antonio, TX Zip 78229–4404; tel. 210/617–5300; Julianne Flynn, M.D., Acting Director
**Web address:** www.southtexas.va.gov

VETERANS AFFAIRS NORTH TEXAS HEALTH CARE SYSTEM (O, 875 beds) 4500 South Lancaster Road, Dallas, TX Zip 75216–7167; tel. 214/742–8387; Jeffrey Milligan, Director
**Web address:** www.northtexas.va.gov/

WEST TEXAS VETERANS AFFAIRS HEALTH CARE SYSTEM (O, 149 beds) 300 Veterans Boulevard, Big Spring, TX Zip 79720–5500; Big Springs, tel. 432/263–7361; Adam M. Welch, Interim Director
**Web address:** www.bigspring.va.gov/about/

**UTAH:** VETERANS AFFAIRS SALT LAKE CITY HEALTH CARE SYSTEM (O, 121 beds) 500 Foothill Drive, Salt Lake City, UT Zip 84148–0002; tel. 801/582–1565; Steven W. Young, Director
**Web address:** www.saltlakecity.va.gov/

**VERMONT:** WHITE RIVER JUNCTION VETERANS AFFAIRS MEDICAL CENTER (O, 60 beds) 215 North Main Street, White River Junction, VT Zip 05009–0001; tel. 802/295–9363; Deborah Amdur, Director
**Web address:** www.whiteriver.va.gov/

**VIRGINIA:** HAMPTON VETERANS AFFAIRS MEDICAL CENTER (O, 468 beds) 100 Emancipation Drive, Hampton, VA Zip 23667–0001; tel. 757/722–9961; Michael H. Dunfee, Director
**Web address:** www.hampton.va.gov/

HUNTER HOLMES MCGUIRE VETERANS AFFAIRS MEDICAL CENTER–RICHMOND (O, 389 beds) 1201 Broad Rock Boulevard, Richmond, VA Zip 23249–0002; tel. 804/675–5000; John A. Brandecker, Director
**Web address:** www.richmond.va.gov/

SALEM VETERANS AFFAIRS MEDICAL CENTER (O, 200 beds) 1970 Roanoke Boulevard, Salem, VA Zip 24153–6478; tel. 540/982–2463; Miguel H. LaPuz, M.D., Director
**Web address:** www.salem.va.gov

**WASHINGTON:** JONATHAN M. WAINWRIGHT MEMORIAL VETERANS AFFAIRS MEDICAL CENTER (O, 14 beds) 77 Wainwright Drive, Walla Walla, WA Zip 99362–3994; tel. 509/525–5200; Brian W. Westfield, MSN, Director
**Web address:** www.wallawalla.va.gov

For explanation of codes following names, see page B2.
★ Indicates Type III membership in the American Hospital Association.

Section B

MANN–GRANDSTAFF VETERANS AFFAIRS MEDICAL CENTER (O, 46 beds) 4815 North Assembly Street, Spokane, WA Zip 99205–6197; tel. 509/434–7000; Linda K. Reynolds, FACHE, Director
**Web address:** www.spokane.va.gov/

VETERANS AFFAIRS PUGET SOUND HEALTH CARE SYSTEM (O, 358 beds) 1660 South Columbian Way, Seattle, WA 98108–1597; tel. 206/762–1010; Michael J. Murphy, FACHE, Director
**Web address:** www.pugetsound.va.gov/

**WEST VIRGINIA:** BECKLEY VETERANS AFFAIRS MEDICAL CENTER (O, 40 beds) 200 Veterans Avenue, Beckley, WV Zip 25801–6499; tel. 304/255–2121; Karin L. McGraw, MSN, FACHE, Director
**Web address:** www.beckley.va.gov/

HUNTINGTON VETERANS AFFAIRS MEDICAL CENTER (O, 80 beds) 1540 Spring Valley Drive, Huntington, WV Zip 25704–9300; tel. 304/429–6741; Brian Nimmo, Director
**Web address:** www.huntington.va.gov/

LOUIS A. JOHNSON VETERANS AFFAIRS MEDICAL CENTER (O, 71 beds) 1 Medical Center Drive, Clarksburg, WV Zip 26301–4199; tel. 304/623–3461; Glenn R. Snider, M.D., Interim Director
**Web address:** www.clarksburg.va.gov

MARTINSBURG VETERANS AFFAIRS MEDICAL CENTER (O, 449 beds) 510 Butler Avenue, Martinsburg, WV Zip 25405–9990; tel. 304/263–0811; Timothy J. Cooke, Medical Center Director and Chief Executive Officer
**Web address:** www.martinsburg.va.gov

**WISCONSIN:** CLEMENT J. ZABLOCKI VETERANS AFFAIRS MEDICAL CENTER (O, 637 beds) 5000 West National Avenue, Milwaukee, WI Zip 53295–0001; tel. 414/384–2000; Robert H. Beller, FACHE, Director
**Web address:** www.milwaukee.va.gov/

TOMAH VETERANS AFFAIRS MEDICAL CENTER (O, 71 beds) 500 East Veterans Street, Tomah, WI Zip 54660–3105; tel. 608/372–3971; John J. Rohrer, Acting Director
**Web address:** www.tomah.va.gov

WILLIAM S. MIDDLETON MEMORIAL VETERANS HOSPITAL (O, 87 beds) 2500 Overlook Terrace, Madison, WI Zip 53705–2286; tel. 608/256–1901; Judy McKee, FACHE, Director
**Web address:** www.madison.va.gov

**WYOMING:** CHEYENNE VETERANS AFFAIRS MEDICAL CENTER (O, 61 beds) 2360 East Pershing Boulevard, Cheyenne, WY Zip 82001–5392; tel. 307/778–7550; Cynthia McCormack, MS, Director
**Web address:** www.cheyenne.va.gov/

SHERIDAN VETERANS AFFAIRS MEDICAL CENTER (O, 185 beds) 1898 Fort Road, Sheridan, WY Zip 82801–8320; tel. 307/672–3473; Kathy Berger, R.N., Acting Director
**Web address:** www.sheridan.va.gov/

| | | |
|---|---|---|
| Owned, leased, sponsored: | 135 hospitals | 34431 beds |
| Contract–managed: | 0 hospitals | 0 beds |
| **Totals:** | **135 hospitals** | **34431 beds** |

**0845: DEVEREUX** (NP)
444 Devereux Drive, Villanova, PA Zip 19085–1932, Mailing Address: P.O. Box 638, Zip 19085–0638; tel. 610/520–3000; Robert Q. Kreider, President and Chief Executive Officer
**(Independent Hospital System)**

**FLORIDA:** DEVEREUX HOSPITAL AND CHILDREN'S CENTER OF FLORIDA (O, 100 beds) 8000 Devereux Drive, Melbourne, FL Zip 32940–7907; tel. 321/242–9100; Steven Murphy, Executive Director
**Web address:** www.devereux.org

**GEORGIA:** DEVEREUX GEORGIA TREATMENT NETWORK (O, 100 beds) 1291 Stanley Road N.W., Kennesaw, GA Zip 30152–4359; tel. 770/427–0147; Gwendolyn Skinner, Executive Director
**Web address:** www.devereuxga.org

**PENNSYLVANIA:** DEVEREUX CHILDREN'S BEHAVIORAL HEALTH CENTER (O, 49 beds) 655 Sugartown Road, Malvern, PA Zip 19355–3303, Mailing Address: 655 Sugartown Road, Zip 19355–3303; tel. 800/345–1292; David E. Woodward, Executive Director
**Web address:** www.devereux.org

**TEXAS:** DEVEREUX TEXAS TREATMENT NETWORK (O, 39 beds) 1150 Devereux Drive, League City, TX Zip 77573–2043; tel. 281/335–1000; Pamela E. Helm, Executive Director
**Web address:** www.devereux.org

| | | |
|---|---|---|
| Owned, leased, sponsored: | 4 hospitals | 288 beds |
| Contract–managed: | 0 hospitals | 0 beds |
| **Totals:** | **4 hospitals** | **288 beds** |

★**5205: DIGNITY HEALTH** (CC)
185 Berry Street, Suite 300, San Francisco, CA Zip 94107–1773; tel. 415/438–5500; Lloyd H. Dean, President and Chief Executive Officer
**(Decentralized Health System)**

**ARIZONA:** CHANDLER REGIONAL MEDICAL CENTER (O, 243 beds) 1955 West Frye Road, Chandler, AZ Zip 85224–6282; tel. 480/728–3000; Tim Bricker, President and Chief Executive Officer
**Web address:** www.chandlerregional.com

MERCY GILBERT MEDICAL CENTER (S, 220 beds) 3555 South Val Vista Road, Gilbert, AZ Zip 85297–7323; tel. 480/728–8000; Tim Bricker, President and Chief Executive Officer
**Web address:** www.mercygilbert.org

ST. JOSEPH'S HOSPITAL AND MEDICAL CENTER (S, 595 beds) 350 West Thomas Road, Phoenix, AZ Zip 85013–4496, Mailing Address: P.O. Box 2071, Zip 85001–2071; tel. 602/406–3000; Patty White, R.N., MS, President
**Web address:** www.stjosephs–phx.org

**CALIFORNIA:** ARROYO GRANDE COMMUNITY HOSPITAL (O, 67 beds) 345 South Halcyon Road, Arroyo Grande, CA Zip 93420–3896; tel. 805/489–4261; Kenneth Dalebout, Administrator and Chief Executive Officer
**Web address:** www.arroyograndehospital.org

BAKERSFIELD MEMORIAL HOSPITAL (O, 406 beds) 420 34th Street, Bakersfield, CA Zip 93301–2237; tel. 661/327–1792; Jon Van Boening, President and Chief Executive Officer and Senior Vice President Operations Dignity Health Central Valley Service Area
**Web address:** www.bakersfieldmemorial.org

CALIFORNIA HOSPITAL MEDICAL CENTER (O, 318 beds) 1401 South Grand Avenue, Los Angeles, CA Zip 90015–3010; tel. 213/748–2411; Margaret R. Peterson, Ph.D., R.N., President
**Web address:** www.chmcla.org

COMMUNITY HOSPITAL OF SAN BERNARDINO (O, 379 beds) 1805 Medical Center Drive, San Bernardino, CA Zip 92411–1214; tel. 909/887–6333; June Collison, President
**Web address:** www.chsb.org

DOMINICAN HOSPITAL (S, 223 beds) 1555 Soquel Drive, Santa Cruz, CA Zip 95065–1794; tel. 831/462–7700; Nanette Mickiewicz, M.D., President
**Web address:** www.dominicanhospital.org

FRENCH HOSPITAL MEDICAL CENTER (O, 112 beds) 1911 Johnson Avenue, San Luis Obispo, CA Zip 93401–4197; tel. 805/543–5353; Alan Iftiniuk, Chief Executive Officer
**Web address:** www.frenchmedicalcenter.org

GLENDALE MEMORIAL HOSPITAL AND HEALTH CENTER (O, 334 beds) 1420 South Central Avenue, Glendale, CA Zip 91204–2594; tel. 818/502–1900; Jack Ivie, President
**Web address:** www.glendalememorial.com

MARIAN REGIONAL MEDICAL CENTER (S, 286 beds) 1400 East Church Street, Santa Maria, CA Zip 93454–5906; tel. 805/739–3000; Charles J. Cova, President and Chief Executive Officer
**Web address:** www.marianmedicalcenter.org

MARK TWAIN MEDICAL CENTER (O, 25 beds) 768 Mountain Ranch Road, San Andreas, CA Zip 95249–9998; tel. 209/754–3521; Craig J. Marks, FACHE, President
**Web address:** www.marktwainhospital.com

MERCY GENERAL HOSPITAL (S, 394 beds) 4001 J Street, Sacramento, CA Zip 95819–3600; tel. 916/453–4545; Edmundo Castaneda, President
**Web address:** www.mercygeneral.org

MERCY HOSPITAL OF FOLSOM (S, 106 beds) 1650 Creekside Drive, Folsom, CA Zip 95630–3400; tel. 916/983–7400; Edmundo Castaneda, President
**Web address:** www.mercyfolsom.org

For explanation of codes following names, see page B2.
★ Indicates Type III membership in the American Hospital Association.

MERCY HOSPITALS OF BAKERSFIELD (S, 222 beds) 2215 Truxtun Avenue, Bakersfield, CA Zip 93301–3698, Mailing Address: P.O. Box 119, Zip 93302–0119; tel. 661/632–5000; Bruce Peters, Chief Executive Officer
**Web address:** www.mercybakersfield.org

MERCY MEDICAL CENTER MERCED (S, 186 beds) 333 Mercy Avenue, Merced, CA Zip 95340–8319; tel. 209/564–5000; Charles Kassis, President
**Web address:** www.mercymercedcares.org

MERCY MEDICAL CENTER MOUNT SHASTA (S, 33 beds) 914 Pine Street, Mount Shasta, CA Zip 96067–2143; tel. 530/926–6111; Kenneth E. S. Platou, President
**Web address:** www.mercymtshasta.org

MERCY MEDICAL CENTER REDDING (S, 267 beds) 2175 Rosaline Avenue, Redding, CA Zip 96001–2549, Mailing Address: P.O. Box 496009, Zip 96049–6009; tel. 530/225–6000; Mark D. Korth, President
**Web address:** www.mercy.org

MERCY SAN JUAN MEDICAL CENTER (S, 370 beds) 6501 Coyle Avenue, Carmichael, CA Zip 95608–0306, Mailing Address: P.O. Box 479, Zip 95609–0479; tel. 916/537–5000; Brian K. Ivie, President
**Web address:** www.mercysanjuan.org

METHODIST HOSPITAL OF SACRAMENTO (O, 281 beds) 7500 Hospital Drive, Sacramento, CA Zip 95823–5477; tel. 916/423–3000; Brian K. Ivie, President and Chief Executive Officer
**Web address:** www.methodistsacramento.org

NORTHRIDGE HOSPITAL MEDICAL CENTER (O, 371 beds) 18300 Roscoe Boulevard, Northridge, CA Zip 91328–4167; tel. 818/885–8500; Saliba Salo, President
**Web address:** www.northridgehospital.org

SAINT FRANCIS MEMORIAL HOSPITAL (O, 239 beds) 900 Hyde Street, San Francisco, CA Zip 94109–4899, Mailing Address: P.O. Box 7726, Zip 94120–7726; tel. 415/353–6000; James P. Houser, Interim Chief Executive Officer
**Web address:** www.saintfrancismemorial.org

SEQUOIA HOSPITAL (O, 131 beds) 170 Alameda De Las Pulgas, Redwood City, CA Zip 94062–2799; tel. 650/369–5811; Bill Graham, President
**Web address:** www.sequoiahospital.org

SIERRA NEVADA MEMORIAL HOSPITAL (O, 121 beds) 155 Glasson Way, Grass Valley, CA Zip 95945–5723, Mailing Address: P.O. Box 1029, Zip 95945–1029; tel. 530/274–6000; Katherine A. Medeiros, President and Chief Executive Officer
**Web address:** www.snmh.org

ST. BERNARDINE MEDICAL CENTER (S, 342 beds) 2101 North Waterman Avenue, San Bernardino, CA Zip 92404–4855; tel. 909/883–8711; Darryl VandenBosch, President
**Web address:** www.stbernardinemedicalcenter.com

ST. ELIZABETH COMMUNITY HOSPITAL (S, 65 beds) 2550 Sister Mary Columba Drive, Red Bluff, CA Zip 96080–4397; tel. 530/529–8000; G. Todd Smith, President
**Web address:** www.mercy.org

ST. JOHN'S PLEASANT VALLEY HOSPITAL (S, 127 beds) 2309 Antonio Avenue, Camarillo, CA Zip 93010–1414; tel. 805/389–5800; Darren W. Lee, President and Chief Executive Officer
**Web address:** www.stjohnshealth.org

ST. JOHN'S REGIONAL MEDICAL CENTER (S, 266 beds) 1600 North Rose Avenue, Oxnard, CA Zip 93030–3723; tel. 805/988–2500; Darren W. Lee, President and Chief Executive Officer
**Web address:** www.stjohnshealth.org

ST. JOSEPH'S BEHAVIORAL HEALTH CENTER (S, 35 beds) 2510 North California Street, Stockton, CA Zip 95204–5568; tel. 209/461–2000; Paul Rains, R.N., MSN, President
**Web address:** www.stjosephscanhelp.org

ST. JOSEPH'S MEDICAL CENTER (S, 273 beds) 1800 North California Street, Stockton, CA Zip 95204–6019, Mailing Address: P.O. Box 213008, Zip 95213–9008; tel. 209/943–2000; Donald J. Wiley, President and Chief Executive Officer
**Web address:** www.stjosephsCARES.org

ST. MARY MEDICAL CENTER (S, 135 beds) 1050 Linden Avenue, Long Beach, CA Zip 90813–3321, Mailing Address: P.O. Box 887, Zip 90801–0887; tel. 562/491–9000; Joel P. Yuhas, FACHE, President and Chief Executive Officer
**Web address:** www.stmarymedicalcenter.org

ST. MARY'S MEDICAL CENTER (S, 232 beds) 450 Stanyan Street, San Francisco, CA Zip 94117–1079; tel. 415/668–1000; Anna Cheung, President
**Web address:** www.stmarysmedicalcenter.com

WOODLAND HEALTHCARE (O, 111 beds) 1325 Cottonwood Street, Woodland, CA Zip 95695–5199; tel. 530/662–3961; H. Kevin Vaziri, President
**Web address:** www.woodlandhealthcare.org

**NEVADA:** ST. ROSE DOMINICAN HOSPITALS – ROSE DE LIMA CAMPUS (S, 109 beds) 102 East Lake Mead Parkway, Henderson, NV Zip 89015–5524; tel. 702/616–5000; Teressa Conley, President and Chief Executive Officer
**Web address:** www.strosehospitals.org

ST. ROSE DOMINICAN HOSPITALS – SAN MARTIN CAMPUS (O, 147 beds) 8280 West Warm Springs Road, Las Vegas, NV Zip 89113–3612; tel. 702/492–8000; Lawrence Barnard, President and Chief Executive Officer
**Web address:** www.strosehospitals.org

ST. ROSE DOMINICAN HOSPITALS – SIENA CAMPUS (S, 230 beds) 3001 St. Rose Parkway, Henderson, NV Zip 89052; tel. 702/616–5000; Brian G. Brannman, President and Chief Executive Officer
**Web address:** www.strosehospitals.com

| | | |
|---|---|---|
| Owned, leased, sponsored: | 36 hospitals | 8001 beds |
| Contract–managed: | 0 hospitals | 0 beds |
| Totals: | 36 hospitals | 8001 beds |

**0029: DIMENSIONS HEALTHCARE SYSTEM** (NP)
3001 Hospital Drive, 3rd Floor, Cheverly, MD Zip 20785–1189; tel. 301/583–4000; Neil J. Moore, President and Chief Executive Officer
**(Moderately Centralized Health System)**

**MARYLAND:** LAUREL REGIONAL HOSPITAL (O, 166 beds) 7300 Van Dusen Road, Laurel, MD Zip 20707–9463; tel. 301/725–4300; John Spearman, President and Chief Operating Officer
**Web address:** www.laurelregionalhospital.org

PRINCE GEORGE'S HOSPITAL CENTER (O, 158 beds) 3001 Hospital Drive, Cheverly, MD Zip 20785–1189; tel. 301/618–2000; K. Singh Taneja, Chief Operating Officer
**Web address:** www.princegeorgeshospital.org

| | | |
|---|---|---|
| Owned, leased, sponsored: | 2 hospitals | 324 beds |
| Contract–managed: | 0 hospitals | 0 beds |
| Totals: | 2 hospitals | 324 beds |

**0010: DIVISION OF MENTAL HEALTH AND ADDICTION SERVICES, DEPARTMENT OF HUMAN SERVICES, STATE OF NEW JERSEY** (NP)
222 South Warren Street, Trenton, NJ Zip 08608–2306, Mailing Address: P.O. Box 700, Zip 08625–0700; tel. 609/777–0702; Lynn Kovich, Assistant Commissioner
**(Independent Hospital System)**

**NEW JERSEY:** ANCORA PSYCHIATRIC HOSPITAL (O, 500 beds) 301 Spring Garden Road, Hammonton, NJ Zip 08037–9699; tel. 609/561–1700; John Lubitsky, Chief Executive Officer
**Web address:** www.state.nj.us/humanservices/dmhs/oshm/aph/

GREYSTONE PARK PSYCHIATRIC HOSPITAL (O, 506 beds) 59 Koch Avenue, Morris Plains, NJ Zip 07950–4400; tel. 973/538–1800; Janet J. Monroe, R.N., Chief Executive Officer
**Web address:** www.state.nj.us/humanservices/dmhs/oshm/gpph/

TRENTON PSYCHIATRIC HOSPITAL (O, 430 beds) Route 29 and Sullivan Way, Trenton, NJ Zip 08628–3425, Mailing Address: P.O. Box 7500, West Trenton, Zip 08628–0500; tel. 609/633–1500; Teresa A. McQuaide, Chief Executive Officer
**Web address:** www.state.nj.us/humanservices/dmhs/oshm/tph/

| | | |
|---|---|---|
| Owned, leased, sponsored: | 3 hospitals | 1436 beds |
| Contract–managed: | 0 hospitals | 0 beds |
| Totals: | 3 hospitals | 1436 beds |

**Section B**

For explanation of codes following names, see page B2.
★ Indicates Type III membership in the American Hospital Association.

**0536:   DIVISION OF MENTAL HEALTH, DEPARTMENT OF HUMAN SERVICES** (NP)
319 East Madison Street, S–3B, Springfield, IL Zip 62701–1035; tel. 217/785–6023; Lorrie Rickman Jones, Ph.D., Director
**(Independent Hospital System)**

**ILLINOIS:** ALTON MENTAL HEALTH CENTER (O, 165 beds) 4500 College Avenue, Alton, IL Zip 62002–5099; tel. 618/474–3800; Brian E. Thomas, Administrator

ANDREW MCFARLAND MENTAL HEALTH CENTER (O, 118 beds) 901 East Southwind Road, Springfield, IL Zip 62703–5125; tel. 217/786–6994; Karen Schweighart, R.N., MS, Administrator

CHESTER MENTAL HEALTH CENTER (O, 245 beds) Chester Road, Chester, IL Zip 62233–0031, Mailing Address: Box 31, Zip 62233–0031; tel. 618/826–4571; Leah Hammel, Acting Administrator

CHICAGO–READ MENTAL HEALTH CENTER (O, 200 beds) 4200 North Oak Park Avenue, Chicago, IL Zip 60634–1457; tel. 773/794–4000; Thomas Simpatico, M.D., Facility Director and Network System Manager

CHOATE MENTAL HEALTH CENTER (O, 79 beds) 1000 North Main Street, Anna, IL Zip 62906–1699; tel. 618/833–5161; Elaine Ray, Administrator

ELGIN MENTAL HEALTH CENTER (O, 500 beds) 750 South State Street, Elgin, IL Zip 60123–7692; tel. 847/742–1040; Amparo Lopez, Region Executive Director
**Web address:** www.dhs.state.il.us

JOHN J. MADDEN MENTAL HEALTH CENTER (O, 125 beds) 1200 South First Avenue, Hines, IL Zip 60141–0800; tel. 708/338–7202; Edith Newman, Interim Administrator

| | | |
|---|---|---|
| Owned, leased, sponsored: | 7 hospitals | 1432 beds |
| Contract–managed: | 0 hospitals | 0 beds |
| Totals: | 7 hospitals | 1432 beds |

**★0861:   DUKE LIFEPOINT HEALTHCARE** (IO)
103 Powell Court, Brentwood, TN Zip 37027–5079; tel. 615/372–8540; Jeffrey G. Seraphine, FACHE, Division President
**(Moderately Centralized Health System)**

**MICHIGAN:** UP HEALTH SYSTEM–MARQUETTE (O, 268 beds) 580 West College Avenue, Marquette, MI Zip 49855–2736; tel. 906/228–9440; James Bogan, FACHE, Interim Chief Executive Officer
**Web address:** www.mgh.org

**NORTH CAROLINA:** HARRIS REGIONAL HOSPITAL (O, 86 beds) 68 Hospital Road, Sylva, NC Zip 28779–2722; tel. 828/586–7000; Steve Heatherly, Chief Executive Officer
**Web address:** www.westcare.org

HAYWOOD REGIONAL MEDICAL CENTER (O, 146 beds) 262 Leroy George Drive, Clyde, NC Zip 28721–7430; tel. 828/456–7311; Phillip L. Wright, FACHE, Chief Executive Officer
**Web address:** www.haymed.org

MARIA PARHAM MEDICAL CENTER (O, 102 beds) 566 Ruin Creek Road, Henderson, NC Zip 27536–2927; tel. 252/438–4143; Brian Sinotte, Chief Executive Officer
**Web address:** www.mariaparham.com

PERSON MEMORIAL HOSPITAL (O, 106 beds) 615 Ridge Road, Roxboro, NC Zip 27573–4629; tel. 336/599–2121; Beemal A. Shah, Chief Executive Officer
**Web address:** www.personhospital.com

RUTHERFORD REGIONAL HEALTH SYSTEM (O, 112 beds) 288 South Ridgecrest Avenue, Rutherfordton, NC Zip 28139–2838; tel. 828/286–5000; Cindy D. Buck, Chief Executive Officer
**Web address:** www.rutherfordhosp.org

SWAIN COMMUNITY HOSPITAL (O, 25 beds) 45 Plateau Street, Bryson City, NC Zip 28713–4200; tel. 828/488–2155; Steve Heatherly, Chief Executive Officer
**Web address:** www.westcare.org

WILSON MEDICAL CENTER (O, 294 beds) 1705 Tarboro Street, S.W., Wilson, NC Zip 27893–3428; tel. 252/399–8040; William E. Caldwell, Jr., Chief Executive Officer
**Web address:** www.wilmed.org

**PENNSYLVANIA:** CONEMAUGH MEMORIAL MEDICAL CENTER (O, 539 beds) 1086 Franklin Street, Johnstown, PA Zip 15905–4398; tel. 814/534–9000; Steven E. Tucker, President
**Web address:** www.conemaugh.org

CONEMAUGH MEYERSDALE MEDICAL CENTER (O, 20 beds) 200 Hospital Drive, Meyersdale, PA Zip 15552–1249; tel. 814/634–5911; Heather Smith, President
**Web address:** www.conemaugh.org

CONEMAUGH MINERS MEDICAL CENTER (O, 30 beds) 290 Haida Avenue, Hastings, PA Zip 16646–5610, Mailing Address: P.O. Box 689, Zip 16646–0689; tel. 814/247–3100; William R. Crowe, President
**Web address:** www.minersmedicalcenter.org

**VIRGINIA:** TWIN COUNTY REGIONAL HEALTHCARE (O, 141 beds) 200 Hospital Drive, Galax, VA Zip 24333–2227; tel. 276/236–8181; Jon D. Applebaum, Chief Executive Officer
**Web address:** www.tcrh.org

| | | |
|---|---|---|
| Owned, leased, sponsored: | 12 hospitals | 1869 beds |
| Contract–managed: | 0 hospitals | 0 beds |
| Totals: | 12 hospitals | 1869 beds |

**★0190:   DUKE UNIVERSITY HEALTH SYSTEM** (NP)
201 Trent Drive, Durham, NC Zip 27710–3037, Mailing Address: P.O. Box 3701, Zip 27710–3701; tel. 919/684–2255; A. Eugene Washington, M.D., President and Chief Executive Officer
**(Centralized Health System)**

**NORTH CAROLINA:** DUKE RALEIGH HOSPITAL (O, 148 beds) 3400 Wake Forest Road, Raleigh, NC Zip 27609–7373; tel. 919/954–3000; David Zaas, MD, Chief Executive Officer
**Web address:** www.dukehealthraleigh.org

DUKE REGIONAL HOSPITAL (L, 210 beds) 3643 North Roxboro Road, Durham, NC Zip 27704–2763; tel. 919/470–4000; Kathleen B. Galbraith, President
**Web address:** www.dukeregional.org/

DUKE UNIVERSITY HOSPITAL (O, 919 beds) 2301 Erwin Road, Durham, NC Zip 27705–4699, Mailing Address: P.O. Box 3708, Zip 27710–3708; tel. 919/684–8111; Kevin W. Sowers, R.N., MSN, President
**Web address:** www.dukehealth.org

| | | |
|---|---|---|
| Owned, leased, sponsored: | 3 hospitals | 1277 beds |
| Contract–managed: | 0 hospitals | 0 beds |
| Totals: | 3 hospitals | 1277 beds |

**★1895:   EAST TEXAS MEDICAL CENTER REGIONAL HEALTHCARE SYSTEM** (NP)
1000 South Beckham Street, Tyler, TX Zip 75701–1908, Mailing Address: P.O. Box 6400, Zip 75711–6400; tel. 903/535–6211; Elmer G. Ellis, FACHE, President and Chief Executive Officer
**(Independent Hospital System)**

**TEXAS:** EAST TEXAS MEDICAL CENTER ATHENS (L, 127 beds) 2000 South Palestine Street, Athens, TX Zip 75751–5610; tel. 903/676–1000; Patrick L. Wallace, Administrator
**Web address:** www.etmc.org

EAST TEXAS MEDICAL CENTER CARTHAGE (L, 25 beds) 409 Cottage Road, Carthage, TX Zip 75633–1466; tel. 903/693–3841; Gary Mikeal Hudson, Administrator
**Web address:** www.etmc.org

EAST TEXAS MEDICAL CENTER FAIRFIELD (L, 44 beds) 125 Newman Street, Fairfield, TX Zip 75840–1499; tel. 903/389–2121; Ruth Cook, Administrator
**Web address:** www.etmc.org

EAST TEXAS MEDICAL CENTER HENDERSON (O, 41 beds) 300 Wilson Street, Henderson, TX Zip 75652–5956; tel. 903/657–7541; Mark Leitner, Administrator
**Web address:** www.etmc.org/etmchenderson/

EAST TEXAS MEDICAL CENTER JACKSONVILLE (O, 38 beds) 501 South Ragsdale Street, Jacksonville, TX Zip 75766–2413; tel. 903/541–5000; Jack R. Endres, JD, FACHE, Administrator
**Web address:** www.etmc.org

For explanation of codes following names, see page B2.
★ Indicates Type III membership in the American Hospital Association.

**B52**  Health Care Systems, Networks and Alliances

© 2015 AHA Guide

Section B

EAST TEXAS MEDICAL CENTER PITTSBURG (L, 25 beds) 2701 Highway 271 North, Pittsburg, TX Zip 75686–1032; tel. 903/946–5000; James Warren Robicheaux, Senior Administrator
**Web address:** www.etmc.org/newpittsburg.htm

EAST TEXAS MEDICAL CENTER REHABILITATION HOSPITAL (O, 49 beds) 701 Olympic Plaza Circle, Tyler, TX Zip 75701–1950, Mailing Address: P.O. Box 7530, Zip 75711–7530; tel. 903/596–3000; Eddie L. Howard, Vice President and Chief Operating Officer
**Web address:** www.etmc.org

EAST TEXAS MEDICAL CENTER SPECIALTY HOSPITAL (O, 36 beds) 1000 South Beckham, 5th Floor, Tyler, TX Zip 75701–1908, Mailing Address: P.O. Box 7018, Zip 75711–7018; tel. 903/596–3600; Eddie L. Howard, Vice President and Chief Operating Officer
**Web address:** www.etmc.org

EAST TEXAS MEDICAL CENTER TRINITY (L, 22 beds) 317 Prospect Drive, Trinity, TX Zip 75862–6202, Mailing Address: P.O. Box 3169, Zip 75862–3169; tel. 936/744–1100; Ruth Cook, Chief Executive Officer and Administrator
**Web address:** www.etmc.org

EAST TEXAS MEDICAL CENTER TYLER (O, 437 beds) 1000 South Beckham Street, Tyler, TX Zip 75701–1908, Mailing Address: Box 6400, Zip 75711–6400; tel. 903/597–0351; Robert B. Evans, Administrator and Chief Executive Officer
**Web address:** www.etmc.org

EAST TEXAS MEDICAL CENTER–QUITMAN (L, 25 beds) 117 Winnsboro Street, Quitman, TX Zip 75783–2144, Mailing Address: P.O. Box 1000, Zip 75783–1000; tel. 903/763–6300; Patrick Swindle, Administrator
**Web address:** www.etmc.org/etmcquitman/

HOUSTON COUNTY MEDICAL CENTER (L, 46 beds) 1100 Loop 304 East, Crockett, TX Zip 75835–1810; tel. 936/546–3862; William A. Rohloff, FACHE, Interim Chief Executive Officer

| | | |
|---|---|---|
| Owned, leased, sponsored: | 11 hospitals | 869 beds |
| Contract–managed: | 0 hospitals | 0 beds |
| Totals: | 11 hospitals | 869 beds |

---

★**0270:  EASTERN CONNECTICUT HEALTH NETWORK** (NP)
71 Haynes Street, Manchester, CT Zip 06040–4131; tel. 860/533–3400; Peter J. Karl, President and Chief Executive Officer
**(Centralized Physician/Insurance Health System)**

**CONNECTICUT:** MANCHESTER MEMORIAL HOSPITAL (O, 156 beds) 71 Haynes Street, Manchester, CT Zip 06040–4188; tel. 860/646–1222; Peter J. Karl, President and Chief Executive Officer
**Web address:** www.echn.org

ROCKVILLE GENERAL HOSPITAL (O, 47 beds) 31 Union Street, Vernon, CT Zip 06066–3160; tel. 860/872–0501; Peter J. Karl, President and Chief Executive Officer
**Web address:** www.echn.org

| | | |
|---|---|---|
| Owned, leased, sponsored: | 2 hospitals | 203 beds |
| Contract–managed: | 0 hospitals | 0 beds |
| Totals: | 2 hospitals | 203 beds |

---

★**0555:  EASTERN MAINE HEALTHCARE SYSTEMS** (NP)
43 Whiting Hill Road, Brewer, ME Zip 04412–1005; tel. 207/973–7045; M. Michelle Hood, FACHE, President and Chief Executive Officer
**(Moderately Centralized Health System)**

**MAINE:** BLUE HILL MEMORIAL HOSPITAL (O, 23 beds) 57 Water Street, Blue Hill, ME Zip 04614–5231; tel. 207/374–3400; John Ronan, President and Chief Executive Officer
**Web address:** www.bhmh.org

CHARLES A. DEAN MEMORIAL HOSPITAL (O, 36 beds) 364 Pritham Avenue, Greenville, ME Zip 04441–1395, Mailing Address: P.O. Box 1129, Zip 04441–1129; tel. 207/695–5200; Geno Murray, President and Chief Executive Officer
**Web address:** www.cadean.org

EASTERN MAINE MEDICAL CENTER (O, 361 beds) 489 State Street, Bangor, ME Zip 04401–6674, Mailing Address: P.O. Box 404, Zip 04402–0404; tel. 207/973–7000; Deborah Carey Johnson, R.N., President and Chief Executive Officer
**Web address:** www.emh.org

INLAND HOSPITAL (O, 46 beds) 200 Kennedy Memorial Drive, Waterville, ME Zip 04901–4595; tel. 207/861–3000; John Dalton, President and Chief Executive Officer
**Web address:** www.inlandhospital.org

MERCY HOSPITAL OF PORTLAND (O, 148 beds) 144 State Street, Portland, ME Zip 04101–3795; tel. 207/879–3000; Eileen F. Skinner, FACHE, President and Chief Executive Officer
**Web address:** www.mercyhospital.org

SEBASTICOOK VALLEY HEALTH (O, 25 beds) 447 North Main Street, Pittsfield, ME Zip 04967–3707; tel. 207/487–4000; Terri Vieira, President and Chief Executive Officer
**Web address:** www.sebasticookvalleyhealth.org

THE ACADIA HOSPITAL (O, 68 beds) 268 Stillwater Avenue, Bangor, ME Zip 04401–3945, Mailing Address: P.O. Box 422, Zip 04402–0422; tel. 207/973–6100; Daniel B. Coffey, President and Chief Executive Officer
**Web address:** www.acadiahospital.org

THE AROOSTOOK MEDICAL CENTER (O, 122 beds) 140 Academy Street, Presque Isle, ME Zip 04769–3171, Mailing Address: P.O. Box 151, Zip 04769–0151; tel. 207/768–4000; Sylvia Getman, President and Chief Executive Officer
**Web address:** www.tamc.org

| | | |
|---|---|---|
| Owned, leased, sponsored: | 8 hospitals | 829 beds |
| Contract–managed: | 0 hospitals | 0 beds |
| Totals: | 8 hospitals | 829 beds |

---

★**0926:  EDWARD–ELMHURST HEALTHCARE** (NP)
801 South Washington Street, Naperville, IL Zip 60540–7430; tel. 630/527–3000; Pamela M. Davis, System President and Chief Executive Officer
**(Centralized Health System)**

**ILLINOIS:** EDWARD HOSPITAL (O, 311 beds) 801 South Washington Street, Naperville, IL Zip 60540–7499; tel. 630/527–3000; Pamela M. Davis, System President and Chief Executive Officer
**Web address:** www.edward.org

ELMHURST MEMORIAL HOSPITAL (O, 259 beds) 155 East Brush Hill Road, Elmhurst, IL Zip 60126–5658; tel. 331/221–1000; Mary Lou Mastro, President and Chief Executive Officer
**Web address:** www.emhc.org

LINDEN OAKS HOSPITAL (O, 108 beds) 852 West Street, Naperville, IL Zip 60540–6400; tel. 630/305–5500; Gina Sharp, FACHE, President
**Web address:** www.edward.org

| | | |
|---|---|---|
| Owned, leased, sponsored: | 3 hospitals | 678 beds |
| Contract–managed: | 0 hospitals | 0 beds |
| Totals: | 3 hospitals | 678 beds |

---

**1685:  EINSTEIN HEALTHCARE NETWORK** (NP)
5501 Old York Road, Philadelphia, PA Zip 19141–3098; tel. 215/456–7890; Barry R. Freedman, President and Chief Executive Officer

**PENNSYLVANIA:** BELMONT CENTER FOR COMPREHENSIVE TREATMENT (O, 147 beds) 4200 Monument Road, Philadelphia, PA Zip 19131–1625; tel. 215/877–2000; Mark Schor, Chief Executive Officer
**Web address:** www.einstein.edu/locations/belmont–behavioral–health/

EINSTEIN MEDICAL CENTER MONTGOMERY (O, 170 beds) 559 West Germantown Pike, East Norriton, PA Zip 19403–4250; tel. 484/622–1000; Beth Duffy, Chief Operating Officer

For explanation of codes following names, see page B2.
★ Indicates Type III membership in the American Hospital Association.

EINSTEIN MEDICAL CENTER PHILADELPHIA (O, 489 beds) 5501 Old York Road, Philadelphia, PA Zip 19141–3098; tel. 215/456–7890; Barry R. Freedman, President and Chief Executive Officer
**Web address:** www.einstein.edu

| Owned, leased, sponsored: | 3 hospitals | 806 beds |
|---|---|---|
| Contract–managed: | 0 hospitals | 0 beds |
| **Totals:** | 3 hospitals | 806 beds |

**0879: EMERUS** (IO)
10077 Grogan's Mill, Suite 100, The Woodlands, TX Zip 77380–1022; tel. 281/292–2450; Toby Hamilton, Chief Executive Officer

**TEXAS:** BAYLOR EMERGENCY MEDICAL CENTER AT AUBREY (O, 32 beds) 26791 Highway 380, Aubrey, TX Zip 76227; tel. 972/347–2525; John Wood, Chief Executive Officer
**Web address:** www.bemcataubrey.com

EMERUS (O, 7 beds) 16000 Southwest Freeway, Suite 100, Sugar Land, TX Zip 77479–2674; tel. 281/277–0911; Mike Kohler, Chief Executive Officer
**Web address:** www.emerus.com

| Owned, leased, sponsored: | 2 hospitals | 39 beds |
|---|---|---|
| Contract–managed: | 0 hospitals | 0 beds |
| **Totals:** | 2 hospitals | 39 beds |

★**0256: EMORY HEALTHCARE** (NP)
1440 Clifton Road N.E., Suite 309, Atlanta, GA Zip 30322–1102; tel. 404/778–5000; Michael J. Mandl, President and Chief Executive Officer
**(Centralized Health System)**

**GEORGIA:** EMORY JOHNS CREEK HOSPITAL (O, 113 beds) 6325 Hospital Parkway, Johns Creek, GA Zip 30097–5775; tel. 678/474–7000; Marilyn Margolis, Chief Executive Officer
**Web address:** www.emoryjohnscreek.com

EMORY REHABILITATION HOSPITAL (O, 56 beds) 1441 Clifton Road N.E., Atlanta, GA Zip 30322–1004; tel. 404/712–5512; Michael Eric Garrard, Chief Executive Officer
**Web address:** www.emoryhealthcare.org/rehabilitation

EMORY SAINT JOSEPH'S HOSPITAL OF ATLANTA (O, 250 beds) 5665 Peachtree Dunwoody Road N.E., Atlanta, GA Zip 30342–1701; tel. 678/843–7001; Craig McCoy, Chief Executive Officer
**Web address:** www.stjosephsatlanta.org

EMORY UNIVERSITY HOSPITAL (O, 550 beds) 1364 Clifton Road N.E., atlanta, GA Zip 30322; tel. 404/712–2000; Bryce Gartland, Chief Executive Officer
**Web address:** www.emoryhealthcare.org

EMORY UNIVERSITY HOSPITAL MIDTOWN (O, 458 beds) 550 Peachtree Street N.E., Atlanta, GA Zip 30308–2247; tel. 404/686–4411; Daniel Owens, Chief Executive Officer
**Web address:** www.emoryhealthcare.org

| Owned, leased, sponsored: | 5 hospitals | 1427 beds |
|---|---|---|
| Contract–managed: | 0 hospitals | 0 beds |
| **Totals:** | 5 hospitals | 1427 beds |

**0647: ENCORE HEALTHCARE** (IO)
7150 Columbia Gateway Drove, Suite J., Columbia, MD Zip 21046–2974; tel. 443/539–2350; Tim Nicholson, Chief Executive Officer
**(Independent Hospital System)**

**OKLAHOMA:** SPECIALTY HOSPITAL OF MIDWEST CITY (O, 31 beds) 8210 National Avenue, Midwest City, OK Zip 73110–8518; tel. 405/739–0800; Bobby Snyder, Chief Executive Officer

**TEXAS:** MESA HILLS SPECIALTY HOSPITAL (O, 32 beds) 2311 North Oregon Street, El Paso, TX Zip 79902–3216; tel. 915/545–1823; Jesus Ruiz, Chief Executive Officer
**Web address:** www.mesahillsspecialtyhospital.com/mesa_hills/index.aspx
PLANO SPECIALTY HOSPITAL (O, 43 beds) 1621 Coit Road, Plano, TX Zip 75075–6141; tel. 972/758–5200; Jay Lindsey, Chief Executive Officer
**Web address:** www.specialtyhospital–plano.com

PLUM CREEK SPECIALTY HOSPITAL (O, 47 beds) 5601 Plum Creek Drive, Amarillo, TX Zip 79124–1801; tel. 806/351–1000; Timothy Deaton, Chief Executive Officer
**Web address:** www.plumcreekspecialtyhosp.com/

| Owned, leased, sponsored: | 4 hospitals | 153 beds |
|---|---|---|
| Contract–managed: | 0 hospitals | 0 beds |
| **Totals:** | 4 hospitals | 153 beds |

★**0959: EPHRAIM MCDOWELL HEALTH** (NP)
217 South Third Street, Danville, KY Zip 40422–1823; tel. 859/239–1000; Vicki A. Darnell, R.N., MSN, President and Chief Executive Officer

**KENTUCKY:** EPHRAIM MCDOWELL FORT LOGAN HOSPITAL (O, 25 beds) 110 Metker Trail, Stanford, KY Zip 40484–1020; tel. 606/365–4600; Vicki A. Darnell, R.N., MSN, Chief Executive Officer
**Web address:** www.fortloganhospital.org

EPHRAIM MCDOWELL REGIONAL MEDICAL CENTER (O, 159 beds) 217 South Third Street, Danville, KY Zip 40422–1823; tel. 859/239–1000; Vicki A. Darnell, R.N., MSN, President and Chief Executive Officer
**Web address:** www.emrmc.org

| Owned, leased, sponsored: | 2 hospitals | 184 beds |
|---|---|---|
| Contract–managed: | 0 hospitals | 0 beds |
| **Totals:** | 2 hospitals | 184 beds |

**0525: ERLANGER HEALTH SYSTEM** (NP)
975 East Third Street, Chattanooga, TN Zip 37403–2147; tel. 423/778–7000; Kevin M. Spiegel, FACHE, President and Chief Executive Officer
**(Moderately Centralized Health System)**

**GEORGIA:** HUTCHESON MEDICAL CENTER (C, 185 beds) 100 Gross Crescent Circle, Fort Oglethorpe, GA Zip 30742–3669; tel. 706/858–2000; Farrell Hayes, President and Chief Executive Officer
**Web address:** www.hutcheson.org

**TENNESSEE:** ERLANGER BLEDSOE HOSPITAL (C, 25 beds) 71 Wheeler Avenue, Pikeville, TN Zip 37367, Mailing Address: P.O. Box 699, Zip 37367–0699; tel. 423/447–2112; Stephanie Boynton, Administrator
**Web address:** www.erlanger.org

ERLANGER MEDICAL CENTER (O, 540 beds) 975 East Third Street, Chattanooga, TN Zip 37403–2147; tel. 423/778–7000; Kevin M. Spiegel, FACHE, Chief Executive Officer
**Web address:** www.erlanger.org

| Owned, leased, sponsored: | 1 hospital | 540 beds |
|---|---|---|
| Contract–managed: | 2 hospitals | 210 beds |
| **Totals:** | 3 hospitals | 750 beds |

**0382: ERNEST HEALTH, INC.** (IO)
7770 Jefferson Street N.E., Suite 320, Albuquerque, NM Zip 87109–4386; tel. 505/856–5300; Darby Brockette, Chief Executive Officer
**(Independent Hospital System)**

**ARIZONA:** MOUNTAIN VALLEY REGIONAL REHABILITATION HOSPITAL (O, 16 beds) 3700 North Windsong Drive, Prescott Valley, AZ Zip 86314–1253; tel. 928/759–8800; Judy Baum, Chief Executive Officer
**Web address:** www.mvrrh.ernesthealth.com

**COLORADO:** NORTHERN COLORADO LONG TERM ACUTE HOSPITAL (O, 40 beds) 4401 Union Street, Johnstown, CO Zip 80534; tel. 970/619–3663; Lamar McBride, Chief Operating Officer
**Web address:** www.ncltah.ernesthealth.com/

NORTHERN COLORADO REHABILITATION HOSPITAL (O, 40 beds) 4401 Union Street, Johnstown, CO Zip 80534–2800; tel. 970/619–3400; Elizabeth Bullard, Chief Operating Officer
**Web address:** www.ncrh.ernesthealth.com

**IDAHO:** NORTHERN IDAHO ADVANCED CARE HOSPITAL (O, 40 beds) 600 North Cecil Road, Post Falls, ID Zip 83854–6200; tel. 208/262–2800; Maria Godley, R.N., Chief Executive Officer
**Web address:** www.niach.ernesthealth.com

For explanation of codes following names, see page B2.
★ Indicates Type III membership in the American Hospital Association.

SOUTHWEST IDAHO ADVANCED CARE HOSPITAL (O, 40 beds) 6651 West Franklin Road, Boise, ID Zip 83709–0914; tel. 208/376–5700; Judd Wright, Chief Executive Officer
**Web address:** www.siach.ernesthealth.com/

**INDIANA:** LAFAYETTE REGIONAL REHABILITATION HOSPITAL (O, 40 beds) 950 Park East Boulevard, Lafayette, IN Zip 47905–0792; tel. 765/447–4040; Michelle Russell, Chief Executive Officer
**Web address:** www.lrrh.ernesthealth.com

**MONTANA:** ADVANCED CARE HOSPITAL OF MONTANA (O, 40 beds) 3528 Gabel Road, Billings, MT Zip 59102–7307; tel. 406/373–8000; Diana Parker, Chief Executive Officer
**Web address:** www.achm.ernesthealth.com

**NEW MEXICO:** ADVANCED CARE HOSPITAL OF SOUTHERN NEW MEXICO (O, 40 beds) 4451 East Lohman Avenue, Las Cruces, NM Zip 88011–8267; tel. 575/521–6600; Claudia Saiz, Chief Operating Officer
**Web address:** www.achsnm.ernesthealth.com

REHABILITATION HOSPITAL OF SOUTHERN NEW MEXICO (O, 40 beds) 4441 East Lohman Avenue, Las Cruces, NM Zip 88011–8267; tel. 575/521–6400; Sabrina Martin, Chief Executive Officer
**Web address:** www.rhsnm.ernesthealth.com

**SOUTH CAROLINA:** GREENWOOD REGIONAL REHABILITATION HOSPITAL (O, 49 beds) 1530 Parkway, Greenwood, SC Zip 29646–4027; tel. 864/330–9070; Kristin Manske, Chief Executive Officer
**Web address:** www.grrh.ernesthealth.com

**TEXAS:** LAREDO SPECIALTY HOSPITAL (O, 40 beds) 2005 Bustamente Street, Laredo, TX Zip 78041–5470; tel. 956/753–5353; Mario Rodriguez, Chief Executive Officer
**Web address:** www.lsh.ernesthealth.com

MESQUITE REHABILITATION INSTITUTE (O, 20 beds) 1023 North Belt Line Road, Mesquite, TX Zip 75149–1788; tel. 972/216–2400; Brian Abraham, Chief Executive Officer
**Web address:** www.mesquiterehab.ernesthealth.com/

MESQUITE SPECIALTY HOSPITAL (O, 40 beds) 1024 North Galloway Avenue, Mesquite, TX Zip 75149–2434; tel. 972/216–2300; Louis Bradley, Chief Executive Officer
**Web address:** www.msh.ernesthealth.com

NEW BRAUNFELS REGIONAL REHABILITATION HOSPITAL (O, 40 beds) 2041 Sundance Parkway, New Braunfels, TX Zip 78130–2779; tel. 830/625–6700; Jennifer Malatek, Chief Executive Officer
**Web address:** www.nbrrh.ernesthealth.com

SOUTH TEXAS REHABILITATION HOSPITAL (O, 40 beds) 425 East Alton Gloor Boulevard, Brownsville, TX Zip 78526–3361; tel. 956/554–6000; Jessie Eason Smedley, Chief Executive Officer
**Web address:** www.strh.ernesthealth.com

**UTAH:** UTAH VALLEY SPECIALTY HOSPITAL (O, 40 beds) 306 River Bend Lane, Provo, UT Zip 84604–5625; tel. 801/226–8880; Ezra Segura, Chief Executive Officer
**Web address:** www.uvsh.ernesthealth.com

**WYOMING:** ELKHORN VALLEY REHABILITATION HOSPITAL (O, 40 beds) 5715 East 2nd Street, Casper, WY Zip 82609–4322; tel. 307/265–0005; Michael Phillips, Chief Executive Officer
**Web address:** www.evrh.ernesthealth.com/

| | | |
|---|---|---|
| **Owned, leased, sponsored:** | 17 hospitals | 645 beds |
| **Contract–managed:** | 0 hospitals | 0 beds |
| **Totals:** | 17 hospitals | 645 beds |

---

★**0396: ESSENTIA HEALTH** (NP)
502 East Second Street, Duluth, MN Zip 55805–1913; tel. 218/786–8376; David C. Herman, M.D., Chief Executive Officer
**(Moderately Centralized Health System)**

**IDAHO:** CLEARWATER VALLEY HOSPITAL AND CLINICS (O, 23 beds) 301 Cedar, Orofino, ID Zip 83544–9029; tel. 208/476–4555; Lenne Bonner, Interim President
**Web address:** www.smh–cvhc.org

ST. MARY'S HOSPITAL (O, 28 beds) Lewiston and North Streets, Cottonwood, ID Zip 83522–9750, Mailing Address: P.O. Box 137, Zip 83522–0137; tel. 208/962–3251; Lenne Bonner, Interim President
**Web address:** www.smh–cvhc.org/getpage.php?name=index

**MINNESOTA:** ESSENTIA HEALTH ADA (O, 14 beds) 201 9th Street West, Ada, MN Zip 56510–1279; tel. 218/784–5000; Ryan Hill, Chief Executive Officer
**Web address:** www.essentiahealth.org

ESSENTIA HEALTH DULUTH (O, 154 beds) 502 East Second Street, Duluth, MN Zip 55805–1982; tel. 218/727–8762; James Garvey, Administrator
**Web address:** www.smdcmedicalcenter.org

ESSENTIA HEALTH FOSSTON (O, 75 beds) 900 Hilligoss Boulevard S.E., Fosston, MN Zip 56542–1599; tel. 218/435–1133; Kevin Gish, Administrator and Vice President
**Web address:** www.essentiahealth.org

ESSENTIA HEALTH NORTHERN PINES MEDICAL CENTER (O, 58 beds) 5211 Highway 110, Aurora, MN Zip 55705–1599; tel. 218/229–2211; Laura Ackman, Chief Operating Officer and Administrator
**Web address:** www.essentiahealth. org/NorthernPines/FindaClinic/Essentia–HealthNorthern–Pines–36.aspx

ESSENTIA HEALTH SANDSTONE (O, 56 beds) 109 Court Avenue South, Sandstone, MN Zip 55072–5120; tel. 320/245–2212; Michael D. Hedrix, Administrator and President
**Web address:** www.pinemedicalcenter.org

ESSENTIA HEALTH ST. JOSEPH'S MEDICAL CENTER (O, 162 beds) 523 North Third Street, Brainerd, MN Zip 56401–3098; tel. 218/829–2861; Adam Rees, President
**Web address:** www.essentiahealth.org

ESSENTIA HEALTH ST. MARY'S – DETROIT LAKES (O, 131 beds) 1027 Washington Avenue, Detroit Lakes, MN Zip 56501–3409; tel. 218/847–5611; Peter Jacobson, President
**Web address:** www.essentiahealth.org

ESSENTIA HEALTH ST. MARY'S MEDICAL CENTER (O, 306 beds) 407 East Third Street, Duluth, MN Zip 55805–1984; tel. 218/786–4000; James Garvey, Executive Vice President, Operations and Administrator
**Web address:** www.essentiahealth.org/StMarysMedicalCenter/FindaClinic/ Essentia–HealthSt–Marys–Medical–Center–46.aspx

ESSENTIA HEALTH–DEER RIVER (O, 52 beds) 115 10th Avenue N.E., Deer River, MN Zip 56636–8795; tel. 218/246–2900; Marsha Green, Chief Executive Officer
**Web address:** www.essentiahealth.org

ESSENTIA HEALTH–GRACEVILLE (O, 60 beds) 115 West Second Street, Graceville, MN Zip 56240–4845, Mailing Address: P.O. Box 157, Zip 56240–0157; tel. 320/748–7223; John Campion, Administrator
**Web address:** www.essentiahealth. org/HolyTrinityHospital/FindaClinic/Essentia–HealthHoly–Trinity–Hospital–96. aspx

ESSENTIA HEALTH–VIRGINIA (L, 150 beds) 901 Ninth Street North, Virginia, MN Zip 55792–2398; tel. 218/741–3340; Daniel Milbridge, Administrator and Chief Operating Officer
**Web address:** www.essentiahealth.org

MINNESOTA VALLEY HEALTH CENTER (O, 64 beds) 621 South Fourth Street, Le Sueur, MN Zip 56058–2298; tel. 507/665–3375; Pam Williams, Chief Executive Officer
**Web address:** www.mvhc.org

**NORTH DAKOTA:** ESSENTIA HEALTH FARGO (O, 94 beds) 3000 32nd Avenue South, Fargo, ND Zip 58103–6132; tel. 701/364–8000; Timothy Sayler, Chief Operating Officer
**Web address:** www.essentiahealth.com

**WISCONSIN:** ESSENTIA HEALTH ST. MARY'S HOSPITAL OF SUPERIOR (O, 25 beds) 3500 Tower Avenue, Superior, WI Zip 54880–5395; tel. 715/817–7000; Terry Jacobson, Administrator and Chief Executive Officer
**Web address:** www.essentiahealth. org/EssentiaHealthStMarysHospitalofSuperiorFoundation/overview.aspx

| | | |
|---|---|---|
| **Owned, leased, sponsored:** | 16 hospitals | 1452 beds |
| **Contract–managed:** | 0 hospitals | 0 beds |
| **Totals:** | 16 hospitals | 1452 beds |

---

**2395: EXCELA HEALTH** (NP)
532 West Pittsburgh Street, Greensburg, PA Zip 15601, Mailing Address: 134 Industrial Park Road, Zip 15601–7328; tel. 724/832–5050; Robert Rogalski, Chief Executive Officer
**(Centralized Health System)**

For explanation of codes following names, see page B2.
★ Indicates Type III membership in the American Hospital Association.

**PENNSYLVANIA:** EXCELA FRICK HOSPITAL (O, 33 beds) 508 South Church Street, Mount Pleasant, PA Zip 15666–1790; tel. 724/547–1500; Ronald H. Ott, President
**Web address:** www.excelahealth.
org/PatientsandVisitors/HospitalsFacilities/Hospitals/Frick.aspx

EXCELA HEALTH WESTMORELAND HOSPITAL (O, 284 beds) 532 West Pittsburg Street, Greensburg, PA Zip 15601–2282; tel. 724/832–4000; Ronald H. Ott, President
**Web address:** www.excelahealth.org

EXCELA LATROBE AREA HOSPITAL (O, 114 beds) One Mellon Way, Latrobe, PA Zip 15650–1096; tel. 724/537–1000; Michael D. Busch, Executive Vice President and Chief Operating Officer
**Web address:** www.excelahealth.org

| | | |
|---|---|---|
| Owned, leased, sponsored: | 3 hospitals | 431 beds |
| Contract–managed: | 0 hospitals | 0 beds |
| Totals: | 3 hospitals | 431 beds |

---

**★1325:   FAIRVIEW HEALTH SERVICES** (NP)
2450 Riverside Avenue, Minneapolis, MN Zip 55454–1400; tel. 612/672–6141; David Murphy, Interim Chief Executive Officer
**(Centralized Physician/Insurance Health System)**

**MINNESOTA:** FAIRVIEW LAKES HEALTH SERVICES (O, 49 beds) 5200 Fairview Boulevard, Wyoming, MN Zip 55092–8013; tel. 651/982–7000; John W. Herman, Chief Executive Officer
**Web address:** www.fairview.org/

FAIRVIEW NORTHLAND MEDICAL CENTER (O, 37 beds) 911 Northland Drive, Princeton, MN Zip 55371–2173; tel. 763/389–1313; John W. Herman, Chief Executive Officer
**Web address:** www.northland.fairview.org

FAIRVIEW RIDGES HOSPITAL (O, 157 beds) 201 East Nicollet Boulevard, Burnsville, MN Zip 55337–5799; tel. 952/892–2000; Patrick Belland, President and Chief Executive Officer
**Web address:** www.fairview.org

FAIRVIEW SOUTHDALE HOSPITAL (O, 338 beds) 6401 France Avenue South, Edina, MN Zip 55435–2199; tel. 952/924–5000; Bradley Beard, Regional President
**Web address:** www.fairview.org

RANGE REGIONAL HEALTH SERVICES (O, 53 beds) 750 East 34th Street, Hibbing, MN Zip 55746–4600; tel. 218/262–4881; Debra K. Boardman, FACHE, President and Chief Executive Officer
**Web address:** www.range.fairview.org

UNIVERSITY OF MINNESOTA MEDICAL CENTER, FAIRVIEW (O, 839 beds) 2450 Riverside Avenue, Minneapolis, MN Zip 55454–1400; tel. 612/672–6000; Carolyn Wilson, R.N., President
**Web address:** www.fairview.org

| | | |
|---|---|---|
| Owned, leased, sponsored: | 6 hospitals | 1473 beds |
| Contract–managed: | 0 hospitals | 0 beds |
| Totals: | 6 hospitals | 1473 beds |

---

**0814:   FAITH REGIONAL HEALTH SERVICES** (NP)
2700 West Norfolk Avenue, Norfolk, NE Zip 68701–4438, Mailing Address: P.O. Box 869, Zip 68702–0869; tel. 402/644–7201; Mark D. Klosterman, FACHE, President and Chief Executive Officer
**(Independent Hospital System)**

**NEBRASKA:** FAITH REGIONAL HEALTH SERVICES (O, 146 beds) 2700 West Norfolk Avenue, Norfolk, NE Zip 68701–4438, Mailing Address: P.O. Box 869, Zip 68702–0869; tel. 402/644–7201; Mark D. Klosterman, FACHE, President and Chief Executive Officer
**Web address:** www.frhs.org

NIOBRARA VALLEY HOSPITAL (C, 20 beds) 401 South Fifth Street, Lynch, NE Zip 68746–0118, Mailing Address: P.O. Box 118, Zip 68746–0118; tel. 402/569–2451; Kelly Kalkowski, Chief Executive Officer
**Web address:** www.nvhcares.org

WEST HOLT MEMORIAL HOSPITAL (C, 18 beds) 406 West Neely Street, Atkinson, NE Zip 68713–4801; tel. 402/925–2811; Bradley D. Pfeifer, Chief Executive Officer
**Web address:** www.westholtmed.org

| | | |
|---|---|---|
| Owned, leased, sponsored: | 1 hospital | 146 beds |
| Contract–managed: | 2 hospitals | 38 beds |
| Totals: | 3 hospitals | 184 beds |

---

**0397:   FINGER LAKES HEALTH** (NP)
196 North Street, Geneva, NY Zip 14456–1651; tel. 315/787–4000; Jose Acevedo, M.D., President and Chief Executive Officer
**(Independent Hospital System)**

**NEW YORK:** GENEVA GENERAL HOSPITAL (O, 132 beds) 196 North Street, Geneva, NY Zip 14456–1694; tel. 315/787–4000; Jose Acevedo, M.D., President and Chief Executive Officer
**Web address:** www.flhealth.org

SOLDIERS AND SAILORS MEMORIAL HOSPITAL OF YATES COUNTY (O, 186 beds) 418 North Main Street, Penn Yan, NY Zip 14527–1085; tel. 315/531–2000; Jose Acevedo, M.D., President and Chief Executive Officer
**Web address:** www.flhealth.org

| | | |
|---|---|---|
| Owned, leased, sponsored: | 2 hospitals | 318 beds |
| Contract–managed: | 0 hospitals | 0 beds |
| Totals: | 2 hospitals | 318 beds |

---

**★0243:   FIRSTHEALTH OF THE CAROLINAS** (NP)
155 Memorial Drive, Pinehurst, NC Zip 28374–8710, Mailing Address: P.O. Box 3000, Zip 28374–3000; tel. 910/715–1000; David J. Kilarski, Chief Executive Officer
**(Centralized Physician/Insurance Health System)**

**NORTH CAROLINA:** FIRSTHEALTH MONTGOMERY MEMORIAL HOSPITAL (O, 25 beds) 520 Allen Street, Troy, NC Zip 27371–2802; tel. 910/571–5000; Beth Walker, R.N., President
**Web address:** www.firsthealth.org

FIRSTHEALTH MOORE REGIONAL HOSPITAL (O, 371 beds) 155 Memorial Drive, Pinehurst, NC Zip 28374–8710, Mailing Address: P.O. Box 3000, Zip 28374–3000; tel. 910/715–1000; David J. Kilarski, Chief Executive Officer
**Web address:** www.firsthealth.org

FIRSTHEALTH RICHMOND MEMORIAL HOSPITAL (O, 91 beds) 925 Long Drive, Rockingham, NC Zip 28379–4835; tel. 910/417–3000; John J. Jackson, President
**Web address:** www.firsthealth.org

| | | |
|---|---|---|
| Owned, leased, sponsored: | 3 hospitals | 487 beds |
| Contract–managed: | 0 hospitals | 0 beds |
| Totals: | 3 hospitals | 487 beds |

---

**0378:   FIVE STAR QUALITY CARE** (IO)
400 Centre Street, Newton, MA Zip 02458–2094; tel. 617/796–8387; Bruce J. Mackey, Jr., President and Chief Executive Officer
**(Independent Hospital System)**

**MASSACHUSETTS:** BRAINTREE REHABILITATION HOSPITAL (O, 187 beds) 250 Pond Street, Braintree, MA Zip 02184–5351; tel. 781/348–2500; Randy Doherty, CPA, Chief Executive Officer
**Web address:** www.braintreerehabhospital.com

NEW ENGLAND REHABILITATION HOSPITAL (O, 210 beds) Two Rehabilitation Way, Woburn, MA Zip 01801–6098; tel. 781/935–5050; Abraham Sims, Chief Executive Officer
**Web address:** www.newenglandrehab.com

| | | |
|---|---|---|
| Owned, leased, sponsored: | 2 hospitals | 397 beds |
| Contract–managed: | 0 hospitals | 0 beds |
| Totals: | 2 hospitals | 397 beds |

---

For explanation of codes following names, see page B2.
★ Indicates Type III membership in the American Hospital Association.

Section B

**0900: FOUNDATION SURGICAL HOSPITAL AFFILIATES** (IO)
14000 North Portland Avenue, Suite 204, Oklahoma City, OK
Zip 73134–4002; tel. 405/608–1700; Thomas A. Michaud, Chief
Executive Officer
**(Independent Hospital System)**

**TEXAS:** FOUNDATION SURGICAL HOSPITAL OF EL PASO (O, 20 beds) 1416
George Dieter Drive, El Paso, TX Zip 79936–7601; tel. 915/598–4240;
Don Burris, Chief Executive Officer
**Web address:** www.physiciansmedcenter.com

FOUNDATION SURGICAL HOSPITAL OF SAN ANTONIO (O, 20 beds) 9522
Huebner Road, San Antonio, TX Zip 78240–1548; tel. 210/478–5400;
Kenneth Crouch, Chief Executive Officer
**Web address:** www.fshsanantonio.com/bariatric–foundation–surgical.html

HERITAGE PARK SURGICAL HOSPITAL (O, 10 beds) 3601 North Calais Street,
Sherman, TX Zip 75090–1785; tel. 903/870–0999; Marc Devorsetz, Chief
Executive Officer
**Web address:** www.heritageparksurgicalhospital.com

HOUSTON ORTHOPEDIC AND SPINE HOSPITAL (O, 64 beds) 5410 West Loop
South, Bellaire, TX Zip 77401–2103; tel. 713/314–4500; Andrew Knizley,
Chief Executive Officer
**Web address:** www.foundationsurgicalhospital.com

| | | |
|---|---|---|
| Owned, leased, sponsored: | 4 hospitals | 114 beds |
| Contract–managed: | 0 hospitals | 0 beds |
| Totals: | 4 hospitals | 114 beds |

**5345: FRANCISCAN ALLIANCE** (CC)
1515 Dragoon Trail, Mishawaka, IN Zip 46544–4710, Mailing
Address: P.O. Box 1290, Zip 46546–1290; tel. 574/256–3935;
Kevin D. Leahy, President and Chief Executive Officer
**(Moderately Centralized Health System)**

**ILLINOIS:** FRANCISCAN ST. JAMES HOSPITAL AND HEALTH CENTERS (O,
329 beds) 20201 South Crawford Avenue, Olympia Fields, IL
Zip 60461–1010; tel. 708/747–4000; Arnold Kimmel, Chief Executive
Officer
**Web address:** www.franciscanalliance.
org/hospitals/olympiafields/pages/default.aspx

**INDIANA:** FRANCISCAN HEALTHCARE – MUNSTER (O, 32 beds) 701 Superior
Avenue, Munster, IN Zip 46321–4037; tel. 219/924–1300; Michael J.
Stenger, President and Chief Executive Officer
**Web address:** www.franciscanphysicianshospital.org

FRANCISCAN ST. ANTHONY HEALTH – CROWN POINT (O, 254 beds) 1201
South Main Street, Crown Point, IN Zip 46307–8483; tel. 219/738–2100;
Barbara M. Anderson, President and Chief Executive Officer
**Web address:** www.franciscanalliance.org

FRANCISCAN ST. ANTHONY HEALTH – MICHIGAN CITY (O, 171 beds) 301
West Homer Street, Michigan City, IN Zip 46360–4358; tel. 219/879–8511;
Gene Diamond, Interim President
**Web address:** www.franciscanalliance.org

FRANCISCAN ST. ELIZABETH HEALTH – CRAWFORDSVILLE (O, 42 beds)
1710 Lafayette Road, Crawfordsville, IN Zip 47933–1099;
tel. 765/362–2800; Terrance E. Wilson, President and CEO
**Web address:** www.stclaremedical.org

FRANCISCAN ST. ELIZABETH HEALTH – LAFAYETTE EAST (O, 187 beds)
1701 South Creasy Lane, Lafayette, IN Zip 47905–4972;
tel. 765/502–4000; Terrance E. Wilson, President and CEO
**Web address:** www.ste.org

FRANCISCAN ST. FRANCIS HEALTH – INDIANAPOLIS (O, 485 beds) 8111
South Emerson Avenue, Indianapolis, IN Zip 46237–8601;
tel. 317/528–5000; James Callaghan, III, M.D., President and Chief Executive
Officer
**Web address:** www.stfrancishospitals.org

FRANCISCAN ST. FRANCIS HEALTH – MOORESVILLE (O, 115 beds) 1201
Hadley Road, Mooresville, IN Zip 46158–1789; tel. 317/831–1160; Peter J.
Murphy, Senior Vice President and Chief Operating Officer
**Web address:** www.franciscanalliance.
org/hospitals/mooresville/Pages/default.aspx

FRANCISCAN ST. FRANCIS HEALTH–CARMEL (O, 6 beds) 12188B North
Meridian Street, Carmel, IN Zip 46032–4840; tel. 317/705–4500; Stephen J.
Wheatley, Director of Operations
**Web address:** www.franciscanalliance.org/hospitals/carmel/Pages/default.
aspx

FRANCISCAN ST. MARGARET HEALTH – HAMMOND (O, 500 beds) 5454
Hohman Avenue, Hammond, IN Zip 46320–1999; tel. 219/932–2300;
Michael J. Stenger, President and Chief Executive Officer
**Web address:** www.smmhc.com

| | | |
|---|---|---|
| Owned, leased, sponsored: | 10 hospitals | 2121 beds |
| Contract–managed: | 0 hospitals | 0 beds |
| Totals: | 10 hospitals | 2121 beds |

**★1475: FRANCISCAN MISSIONARIES OF OUR LADY HEALTH
SYSTEM, INC.** (CC)
4200 Essen Lane, Baton Rouge, LA Zip 70809–2158;
tel. 225/923–2701; John J. Finan, Jr., FACHE, President and Chief
Executive Officer
**(Moderately Centralized Health System)**

**LOUISIANA:** ASSUMPTION COMMUNITY HOSPITAL (O, 6 beds) 135 Highway
402, Napoleonville, LA Zip 70390–2217; tel. 985/369–3600; Wayne M.
Arboneaux, Chief Executive Officer
**Web address:** www.ololrmc.com

OUR LADY OF LOURDES REGIONAL MEDICAL CENTER (O, 186 beds) 4801
Ambassador Caffery Parkway, Lafayette, LA Zip 70508–6917;
tel. 337/470–2000; William F. Barrow, II, President and Chief Executive
Officer
**Web address:** www.lourdesrmc.com

OUR LADY OF THE ANGELS HOSPITAL (O, 57 beds) 433 Plaza Street,
Bogalusa, LA Zip 70427–3793; tel. 985/730–6700; Rene Ragas, Chief
Operating Officer
**Web address:** www.oloah.org

OUR LADY OF THE LAKE REGIONAL MEDICAL CENTER (O, 1093 beds) 5000
Hennessy Boulevard, Baton Rouge, LA Zip 70808–4375; tel. 225/765–6565;
K. Scott Wester, FACHE, President and Chief Executive Officer
**Web address:** www.ololrmc.com

ST. ELIZABETH HOSPITAL (O, 46 beds) 1125 West Highway 30, Gonzales, LA
Zip 70737–5004; tel. 225/647–5000; Robert L. Burgess, President and
Chief Executive Officer
**Web address:** www.steh.com

ST. FRANCIS MEDICAL CENTER (O, 343 beds) 309 Jackson Street, Monroe,
LA Zip 71201–7407, Mailing Address: P.O. Box 1901, Zip 71210–1901;
tel. 318/966–4000; Kristin Wolkart, President and Chief Executive Officer
**Web address:** www.stfran.com

| | | |
|---|---|---|
| Owned, leased, sponsored: | 6 hospitals | 1731 beds |
| Contract–managed: | 0 hospitals | 0 beds |
| Totals: | 6 hospitals | 1731 beds |

**★1455: FRANCISCAN SISTERS OF CHRISTIAN CHARITY
SPONSORED MINISTRIES, INC.** (CC)
1415 South Rapids Road, Manitowoc, WI Zip 54220–9302;
tel. 920/684–7071; Sister Laura J. Wolf, President
**(Moderately Centralized Health System)**

**NEBRASKA:** ST. FRANCIS MEMORIAL HOSPITAL (O, 92 beds) 430 North
Monitor Street, West Point, NE Zip 68788–1555; tel. 402/372–2404;
Jerry Wordekemper, President and Chief Executive Officer
**Web address:** www.fcswp.org

**OHIO:** GENESIS HEALTHCARE SYSTEM (O, 298 beds) 2951 Maple Avenue,
Zanesville, OH Zip 43701–1406; tel. 740/454–5000; Matthew J. Perry,
President and Chief Executive Officer
**Web address:** www.genesishcs.org

For explanation of codes following names, see page B2.
★ Indicates Type III membership in the American Hospital Association.

Section B

**WISCONSIN:** HOLY FAMILY MEMORIAL (O, 67 beds) 2300 Western Avenue, Manitowoc, WI Zip 54220–3712, Mailing Address: P.O. Box 1450, Zip 54221–1450; tel. 920/320–2011; Mark P. Herzog, President and Chief Executive Officer
**Web address:** www.hfmhealth.org

| Owned, leased, sponsored: | 3 hospitals | 457 beds |
|---|---|---|
| Contract–managed: | 0 hospitals | 0 beds |
| Totals: | 3 hospitals | 457 beds |

---

**★0271: FREEMAN HEALTH SYSTEM** (NP)
1102 West 32nd Street, Joplin, MO Zip 64804–3503; tel. 417/347–1111; Paula F. Baker, President and Chief Executive Officer
**(Centralized Health System)**

**MISSOURI:** FREEMAN HOSPITAL WEST (O, 396 beds) 1102 West 32nd Street, Joplin, MO Zip 64804–3503; tel. 417/347–1111; Paula F. Baker, President and Chief Executive Officer
**Web address:** www.freemanhealth.com

FREEMAN NEOSHO HOSPITAL (O, 25 beds) 113 West Hickory Street, Neosho, MO Zip 64850–1705; tel. 417/455–4352; Paula F. Baker, President and Chief Executive Officer
**Web address:** www.freemanhealth.com

| Owned, leased, sponsored: | 2 hospitals | 421 beds |
|---|---|---|
| Contract–managed: | 0 hospitals | 0 beds |
| Totals: | 2 hospitals | 421 beds |

---

**0182: FUNDAMENTAL LONG TERM CARE HOLDINGS, LLC** (IO)
930 Ridgebrook Road, Sparks Glencoe, MD Zip 21152–9390; tel. 410/773–1000; W. Bradley Bennett, President and Chief Executive Officer
**(Independent Hospital System)**

**NEVADA:** HARMON MEDICAL AND REHABILITATION HOSPITAL (O, 118 beds) 2170 East Harmon Avenue, Las Vegas, NV Zip 89119–7840; tel. 702/794–0100; Bonnie Essex Hillegass, Chief Executive Officer

HORIZON SPECIALTY HOSPITAL (O, 49 beds) 640 Desert Lane, Las Vegas, NV Zip 89106–4207; tel. 702/382–3155; William Fox, Chief Executive Officer and Administrator
**Web address:** www.horizonspecialtyhosp.com/

**TEXAS:** TEXAS SPECIALTY HOSPITAL AT LUBBOCK (O, 25 beds) 4302 Princeton Street, Lubbock, TX Zip 79415–1304; tel. 806/723–8700; Deanna Graves, Chief Executive Officer

| Owned, leased, sponsored: | 3 hospitals | 267 beds |
|---|---|---|
| Contract–managed: | 0 hospitals | 0 beds |
| Totals: | 3 hospitals | 267 beds |

---

**★5570: GEISINGER HEALTH SYSTEM** (NP)
100 North Academy Avenue, Danville, PA Zip 17822–9800; tel. 570/271–6211; David T. Feinberg, M.D., President and Chief Executive Officer
**(Independent Hospital System)**

**PENNSYLVANIA:** GEISINGER MEDICAL CENTER (O, 545 beds) 100 North Academy Avenue, Danville, PA Zip 17822–2201; tel. 570/271–6211; Thomas P. Sokola, Chief Administrative Officer
**Web address:** www.geisinger.org

GEISINGER WYOMING VALLEY MEDICAL CENTER (O, 238 beds) 1000 East Mountain Boulevard, Wilkes Barre, PA Zip 18711–0027; tel. 570/808–7300; Ronald R. Beer, FACHE, Vice President, Clinical Operations
**Web address:** www.geisinger.org

GEISINGER–BLOOMSBURG HOSPITAL (O, 72 beds) 549 Fair Street, Bloomsburg, PA Zip 17815–1419; tel. 570/387–2100; Lissa Bryan–Smith, Chief Administrative Officer
**Web address:** www.bloomhealth.net

GEISINGER–COMMUNITY MEDICAL CENTER (O, 248 beds) 1800 Mulberry Street, Scranton, PA Zip 18510–2369; tel. 570/703–8000; David T. Feinberg, MD, Chief Executive Officer
**Web address:** www.cmccare.org/

GEISINGER–LEWISTOWN HOSPITAL (O, 123 beds) 400 Highland Avenue, Lewistown, PA Zip 17044–1198; tel. 717/248–5411; Kay A. Hamilton, R.N., MS, Chief Administrative Officer
**Web address:** www.geisinger.org

| Owned, leased, sponsored: | 5 hospitals | 1226 beds |
|---|---|---|
| Contract–managed: | 0 hospitals | 0 beds |
| Totals: | 5 hospitals | 1226 beds |

---

**★0311: GENESIS HEALTH SYSTEM** (NP)
1227 East Rusholme Street, Davenport, IA Zip 52803–2498; tel. 563/421–1000; Douglas P. Cropper, President and Chief Executive Officer
**(Centralized Physician/Insurance Health System)**

**ILLINOIS:** GENESIS MEDICAL CENTER, ILLINI CAMPUS (O, 135 beds) 801 Illini Drive, Silvis, IL Zip 61282–1893; tel. 309/281–4000; Kevin Youmans, Interim President
**Web address:** www.genesishealth.com

GENESIS MEDICAL CENTER–ALEDO (O, 22 beds) 409 N.W. Ninth Avenue, Aledo, IL Zip 61231–1296; tel. 309/582–9100; Ted Rogalski, Administrator
**Web address:** www.genesishealth.com

**IOWA:** GENESIS MEDICAL CENTER, DEWITT (O, 86 beds) 1118 11th Street, De Witt, IA Zip 52742–1296; tel. 563/659–4200; Curt Coleman, FACHE, Chief Executive Officer
**Web address:** www.genesishealth.com

GENESIS MEDICAL CENTER–DAVENPORT (O, 352 beds) 1227 East Rusholme Street, Davenport, IA Zip 52803–2498; tel. 563/421–1000; Jordan Voigt, Administrator
**Web address:** www.genesishealth.com

JACKSON COUNTY REGIONAL HEALTH CENTER (C, 25 beds) 700 West Grove Street, Maquoketa, IA Zip 52060–2163; tel. 563/652–2474; Curt Coleman, FACHE, Administrator
**Web address:** www.jcrhc.org

| Owned, leased, sponsored: | 4 hospitals | 595 beds |
|---|---|---|
| Contract–managed: | 1 hospital | 25 beds |
| Totals: | 5 hospitals | 620 beds |

---

**0283: GILLIARD HEALTH SERVICES** (IO)
3091 Carter Hill Road, Montgomery, AL Zip 36111–1801; tel. 334/265–5009; William G. McKenzie, President, Chief Executive Officer and Chairman

**ALABAMA:** EVERGREEN MEDICAL CENTER (O, 44 beds) 101 Crestview Avenue, Evergreen, AL Zip 36401–3333, Mailing Address: P.O. Box 706, Zip 36401–0706; tel. 251/578–2480; Tom McLendon, Administrator
**Web address:** www.evergreenmedical.org

JACKSON MEDICAL CENTER (O, 26 beds) 220 Hospital Drive, Jackson, AL Zip 36545–2459, Mailing Address: P.O. Box 428, Zip 36545–0428; tel. 251/246–9021; Amy Gibson, Chief Executive Officer
**Web address:** www.jacksonmedicalcenter.org

| Owned, leased, sponsored: | 2 hospitals | 70 beds |
|---|---|---|
| Contract–managed: | 0 hospitals | 0 beds |
| Totals: | 2 hospitals | 70 beds |

---

**0654: GLOBALREHAB** (IO)
1420 West Mockingbird Lane, Suite 100, Dallas, TX Zip 75247–4932, Mailing Address: 1340 Empire Central Drive, Zip 75247–4022; tel. 214/879–7500; Hooman Sedighi, M.D., President and Chief Executive Officer
**(Independent Hospital System)**

**TEXAS:** BAYLOR INSTITUTE FOR REHABILITATION AT FORT WORTH (O, 42 beds) 6601 Harris Parkway, Fort Worth, TX Zip 76132–6108; tel. 817/433–9600; Jeffrey D. Thompson, Chief Executive Officer
**Web address:** www.globalrehabhospitals.com

---

For explanation of codes following names, see page B2.
★ Indicates Type III membership in the American Hospital Association.

BAYLOR INSTITUTE FOR REHABILITATION AT NORTHWEST DALLAS (O, 42 beds) 1340 Empire Central Drive, Dallas, TX Zip 75247–4022; tel. 214/879–7300; David Smith, Chief Executive Officer
**Web address:** www.baylorhealth.com/bir

SELECT REHABILITATION HOSPITAL OF SAN ANTONIO (O, 42 beds) 19126 Stonehue Road, San Antonio, TX Zip 78258–3490; tel. 210/482–3400; Robert Ward, Chief Executive Officer
**Web address:** www.globalrehabhospitals.com

| | | |
|---|---|---|
| Owned, leased, sponsored: | 3 hospitals | 126 beds |
| Contract–managed: | 0 hospitals | 0 beds |
| Totals: | 3 hospitals | 126 beds |

## 0522: GOOD SHEPHERD HEALTH SYSTEM (NP)
700 East Marshall Avenue, Longview, TX Zip 75601–5580; tel. 903/315–2000; Steve Altmiller, President and Chief Executive Officer
**(Independent Hospital System)**

GOOD SHEPHERD MEDICAL CENTER (O, 393 beds) 700 East Marshall Avenue, Longview, TX Zip 75601–5580; tel. 903/315–2000; Steve Altmiller, President and Chief Executive Officer
**Web address:** www.gsmc.org

GOOD SHEPHERD MEDICAL CENTER–MARSHALL (O, 140 beds) 811 South Washington Avenue, Marshall, TX Zip 75670–5336, Mailing Address: P.O. Box 1599, Zip 75671–1599; tel. 903/927–6000; Russell J. Collier, FACHE, President and Chief Executive Officer
**Web address:** www.gsmcmarshall.org

| | | |
|---|---|---|
| Owned, leased, sponsored: | 2 hospitals | 533 beds |
| Contract–managed: | 0 hospitals | 0 beds |
| Totals: | 2 hospitals | 533 beds |

## 0648: GOOD SHEPHERD REHABILITATION NETWORK (IO)
850 South Fifth Street, Allentown, PA Zip 18103–3308; tel. 610/776–3100; John Kristel, President and Chief Executive Officer
**(Independent Hospital System)**

**PENNSYLVANIA:** GOOD SHEPHERD REHABILITATION HOSPITAL (O, 106 beds) 850 South 5th Street, Allentown, PA Zip 18103–3308; tel. 610/776–3299; John Kristel, President and Chief Executive Officer
**Web address:** www.goodshepherdrehab.org

GOOD SHEPHERD SPECIALTY HOSPITAL (O, 32 beds) 2545 Schoenersville Road, 3rd Floor, Bethlehem, PA Zip 18017–7300; tel. 484/884–5051; John Kristel, President and Chief Executive Officer
**Web address:** www.goodshepherdrehab.org

| | | |
|---|---|---|
| Owned, leased, sponsored: | 2 hospitals | 138 beds |
| Contract–managed: | 0 hospitals | 0 beds |
| Totals: | 2 hospitals | 138 beds |

## ★1535: GREAT PLAINS HEALTH ALLIANCE, INC. (NP)
250 North Rock Road, Suite 160, Wichita, KS Zip 67206–2241; tel. 316/685–1523; Dave Dellasega, President and Chief Executive Officer
**(Decentralized Health System)**

**KANSAS:** ASHLAND HEALTH CENTER (C, 45 beds) 709 Oak Street, Ashland, KS Zip 67831–0188, Mailing Address: P.O. Box 188, Zip 67831–0188; tel. 620/635–2241; Roger Barnhart, Chief Executive Officer
**Web address:** www.ashlandhc.org

CHEYENNE COUNTY HOSPITAL (L, 16 beds) 210 West First Street, Saint Francis, KS Zip 67756–3540, Mailing Address: P.O. Box 547, Zip 67756–0547; tel. 785/332–2104; Scott Jenkins, Administrator
**Web address:** www.cheyennecountyhospital.com

COMANCHE COUNTY HOSPITAL (C, 12 beds) 202 South Frisco Street, Coldwater, KS Zip 67029–9101, Mailing Address: HC 65, Box 8A, Zip 67029–9500; tel. 620/582–2144; Nancy Zimmerman, R.N., Administrator
**Web address:** www.gpha.com

ELLINWOOD DISTRICT HOSPITAL (L, 25 beds) 605 North Main Street, Ellinwood, KS Zip 67526–1440; tel. 620/564–2548; Kile Magner, Administrator
**Web address:** www.ellinwooddistricthospital.org

FREDONIA REGIONAL HOSPITAL (C, 34 beds) 1527 Madison Street, Fredonia, KS Zip 66736–1751, Mailing Address: P.O. Box 579, Zip 66736–0579; tel. 620/378–2121; John Hart, Chief Executive Officer
**Web address:** www.fredoniaregionalhospital.org

GRISELL MEMORIAL HOSPITAL DISTRICT ONE (C, 46 beds) 210 South Vermont Avenue, Ransom, KS Zip 67572–9525; tel. 785/731–2231; David Caudill, Administrator
**Web address:** www.grisellmemorialhospital.org

KIOWA COUNTY MEMORIAL HOSPITAL (L, 15 beds) 721 West Kansas Avenue, Greensburg, KS Zip 67054–1633; tel. 620/723–3341; Mary Sweet, Administrator
**Web address:** www.kcmh.net

LANE COUNTY HOSPITAL (C, 31 beds) 235 West Vine, Dighton, KS Zip 67839–0969, Mailing Address: P.O. Box 969, Zip 67839–0969; tel. 620/397–5321; Donna McGowan, Administrator

MEDICINE LODGE MEMORIAL HOSPITAL (C, 25 beds) 710 North Walnut Street, Medicine Lodge, KS Zip 67104–1019; tel. 620/886–3771; Kevin A. White, Administrator
**Web address:** www.mlmh.net/

MINNEOLA DISTRICT HOSPITAL (C, 54 beds) 212 Main Street, Minneola, KS Zip 67865–8511, Mailing Address: P.O. Box 127, Zip 67865–0127; tel. 620/885–4264; Deborah Bruner, Chief Executive Officer and Administrator
**Web address:** www.minneolahealthcare.com

OSBORNE COUNTY MEMORIAL HOSPITAL (C, 25 beds) 424 West New Hampshire Street, Osborne, KS Zip 67473–2314, Mailing Address: P.O. Box 70, Zip 67473–0070; tel. 785/346–2121; Kiley Floyd, Administrator
**Web address:** www.ocmh.org

OTTAWA COUNTY HEALTH CENTER (L, 42 beds) 215 East Eighth, Minneapolis, KS Zip 67467–1902, Mailing Address: P.O. Box 290, Zip 67467–0290; tel. 785/392–2122; Jody Parks, Administrator
**Web address:** www.ottawacountyhealthcenter.com

PHILLIPS COUNTY HOSPITAL (L, 25 beds) 1150 State Street, Phillipsburg, KS Zip 67661–1743, Mailing Address: P.O. Box 607, Zip 67661–0607; tel. 785/543–5226; David Engel, Chief Executive Officer
**Web address:** www.phillipshospital.org

RAWLINS COUNTY HEALTH CENTER (C, 24 beds) 707 Grant Street, Atwood, KS Zip 67730–1526, Mailing Address: P.O. Box 47, Zip 67730–0047; tel. 785/626–3211; Sharon K. Cox, FACHE, Chief Executive Officer
**Web address:** www.rchc.us

REPUBLIC COUNTY HOSPITAL (L, 63 beds) 2420 G Street, Belleville, KS Zip 66935–2400; tel. 785/527–2254; Blaine K. Miller, Administrator
**Web address:** www.rphospital.org

SABETHA COMMUNITY HOSPITAL (L, 25 beds) 14th and Oregon Streets, Sabetha, KS Zip 66534–0229, Mailing Address: P.O. Box 229, Zip 66534–0229; tel. 785/284–2121; Lora Key, Chief Executive Officer
**Web address:** www.sabethahospital.com

SATANTA DISTRICT HOSPITAL AND LONG TERM CARE (C, 57 beds) 401 South Cheyenne Street, Satanta, KS Zip 67870–0159, Mailing Address: P.O. Box 159, Zip 67870–0159; tel. 620/649–2761; Jeremy Clingenpeel, Administrator
**Web address:** www.satantahospital.org

SMITH COUNTY MEMORIAL HOSPITAL (L, 53 beds) 614 South Main Street, Smith Center, KS Zip 66967–3001; tel. 785/282–6845; Allen Van Driel, FACHE, Administrator
**Web address:** www.gpha.com

TREGO COUNTY–LEMKE MEMORIAL HOSPITAL (C, 62 beds) 320 North 13th Street, Wakeeney, KS Zip 67672–2099; tel. 785/743–2182; David Augustine, Chief Executive Officer
**Web address:** www.tclmh.org

For explanation of codes following names, see page B2.
★ Indicates Type III membership in the American Hospital Association.

**NEBRASKA:** HARLAN COUNTY HEALTH SYSTEM (C, 19 beds) 717 North Brown Street, Alma, NE Zip 68920–2132, Mailing Address: P.O. Box 836, Zip 68920–0836; tel. 308/928–2151; Manuela Wolf, R.N., Chief Executive Officer
**Web address:** www.harlancountyhealth.com

| | | |
|---|---|---|
| Owned, leased, sponsored: | 8 hospitals | 264 beds |
| Contract–managed: | 12 hospitals | 434 beds |
| Totals: | 20 hospitals | 698 beds |

**0144: GREATER HUDSON VALLEY HEALTH SYSTEM** (NP)
60 Prospect Avenue, Middletown, NY Zip 10940–4133; tel. 845/568–6050; Scott Batulis, President and Chief Executive Officer
**(Moderately Centralized Health System)**

**NEW YORK:** CATSKILL REGIONAL MEDICAL CENTER (O, 184 beds) 68 Harris Bushville Road, Harris, NY Zip 12742–5030, Mailing Address: P.O. Box 800, Zip 12742–0800; tel. 845/794–3300; Gerard Galarneau, M.D., Chief Executive Officer and Chief Medical Officer
**Web address:** www.crmcny.org

GROVER M. HERMANN HOSPITAL (O, 25 beds) 8881 Route 97, Callicoon, NY Zip 12723; tel. 845/887–5530; Rolland Bojo, R.N., Administrator
**Web address:** www.crmcny.org

ORANGE REGIONAL MEDICAL CENTER (O, 301 beds) 707 East Main Street, Middletown, NY Zip 10940–2650; tel. 845/333–1000; Scott Batulis, President and Chief Executive Officer
**Web address:** www.ormc.org

| | | |
|---|---|---|
| Owned, leased, sponsored: | 3 hospitals | 510 beds |
| Contract–managed: | 0 hospitals | 0 beds |
| Totals: | 3 hospitals | 510 beds |

**★1555: GREENVILLE HEALTH SYSTEM** (NP)
701 Grove Road, Greenville, SC Zip 29605–5611; tel. 864/455–7000; Michael C. Riordan, President and Chief Executive Officer
**(Centralized Health System)**

**SOUTH CAROLINA:** GREENVILLE HEALTH SYSTEM – LAURENS COUNTY MEMORIAL HOSPITAL (L, 50 beds) 22725 Highway 76 East, Clinton, SC Zip 29325–7527, Mailing Address: P.O. Drawer 976, Zip 29325–0976; tel. 864/833–9100; Richard E. D'Alberto, FACHE, Campus President
**Web address:** www.ghs.org/laurens

GREENVILLE MEMORIAL HOSPITAL (O, 759 beds) 701 Grove Road, Greenville, SC Zip 29605–4295; tel. 864/455–7000; Paul F. Johnson, President
**Web address:** www.ghs.org

GREER MEMORIAL HOSPITAL (O, 35 beds) 830 South Bumcombe Road, Greer, SC Zip 29650–2400; tel. 864/797–8000; John F. Mansure, FACHE, President
**Web address:** www.ghs.org

HILLCREST MEMORIAL HOSPITAL (O, 19 beds) 729 S.E. Main Street, Simpsonville, SC Zip 29681–3280; tel. 864/454–6100; Eric Bour, M.D., FACS, President
**Web address:** www.ghs.org

OCONEE MEMORIAL HOSPITAL (L, 248 beds) 298 Memorial Drive, Seneca, SC Zip 29672–9499; tel. 864/882–3351; Hunter Kome, Campus President
**Web address:** www.oconeemed.org

PATEWOOD MEMORIAL HOSPITAL (O, 16 beds) 175 Patewood Drive, Greenville, SC Zip 29615–3570; tel. 864/797–1000; Beverly J. Haines, R.N., President
**Web address:** www.ghs.org/patewood

| | | |
|---|---|---|
| Owned, leased, sponsored: | 6 hospitals | 1127 beds |
| Contract–managed: | 0 hospitals | 0 beds |
| Totals: | 6 hospitals | 1127 beds |

**★0675: GUTHRIE CLINIC** (NP)
Guthrie Square, Sayre, PA Zip 18840; tel. 570/887–4312; Joseph A. Scopelliti, M.D., President and Chief Executive Officer
**(Moderately Centralized Health System)**

**NEW YORK:** CORNING HOSPITAL (O, 82 beds) One Guthrie Drive, Corning, NY Zip 14830–3696; tel. 607/937–7200; Garrett W. Hoover, FACHE, Senior Vice President, President and Chief Operating Officer
**Web address:** www.corninghospital.com

**PENNSYLVANIA:** GUTHRIE TOWANDA MEMORIAL HOSPITAL (O, 103 beds) 91 Hospital Drive, Towanda, PA Zip 18848–9702; tel. 570/265–2191; William K. Rohrbach, Chief Executive Officer
**Web address:** www.memorialhospital.org

ROBERT PACKER HOSPITAL (O, 251 beds) 1 Guthrie Square, Sayre, PA Zip 18840–1698; tel. 570/888–6666; Marie T. Droege, President
**Web address:** www.guthrie.org

TROY COMMUNITY HOSPITAL (O, 25 beds) 275 Guthrie Drive, Troy, PA Zip 16947; tel. 570/297–2121; Staci Covey, R.N., MS, President
**Web address:** www.guthrie.org

| | | |
|---|---|---|
| Owned, leased, sponsored: | 4 hospitals | 461 beds |
| Contract–managed: | 0 hospitals | 0 beds |
| Totals: | 4 hospitals | 461 beds |

**● ★0908: HACKENSACK UNIVERSITY HEALTH NETWORK** (NP)
30 Prospect Avenue, Hackensack, NJ Zip 07601–1914; tel. 201/996–2000; Robert C. Garrett, FACHE, President and Chief Executive Officer

**NEW JERSEY:** HACKENSACK UNIVERSITY MEDICAL CENTER (O, 710 beds) 30 Prospect Avenue, Hackensack, NJ Zip 07601–1914; tel. 201/996–2000; Robert C. Garrett, FACHE, President and Chief Executive Officer
**Web address:** www.hackensackumc.org

| | | |
|---|---|---|
| Owned, leased, sponsored: | 1 hospital | 710 beds |
| Contract–managed: | 0 hospitals | 0 beds |
| Totals: | 1 hospital | 710 beds |

**★0541: HARTFORD HEALTHCARE** (NP)
One State Street, 19th Floor, Hartford, CT Zip 06103; tel. 860/263–4100; Elliot T. Joseph, President and Chief Executive Officer
**(Centralized Health System)**

**CONNECTICUT:** HARTFORD HOSPITAL (O, 898 beds) 80 Seymour Street, Hartford, CT Zip 06102–8000, Mailing Address: P.O. Box 5037, Zip 06102–5037; tel. 860/545–5000; Stuart Markowitz, M.D., President
**Web address:** www.harthosp.org

MIDSTATE MEDICAL CENTER (O, 98 beds) 435 Lewis Avenue, Meriden, CT Zip 06451–2101; tel. 203/694–8200; Lucille A. Janatka, President and Chief Executive Officer, Hartford HealthCare Central Region
**Web address:** www.midstatemedical.org

NATCHAUG HOSPITAL (O, 57 beds) 189 Storrs Road, Mansfield Center, CT Zip 06250–1683; tel. 860/456–1311; Stephen W. Larcen, Ph.D., President
**Web address:** www.natchaug.org

THE HOSPITAL OF CENTRAL CONNECTICUT (O, 188 beds) 100 Grand Street, New Britain, CT Zip 06052–2017, Mailing Address: P.O. Box 100, Zip 06052–2017; tel. 860/224–5011; Lucille A. Janatka, President and Chief Executive Officer, Hartford HealthCare Central Region
**Web address:** www.thocc.org

THE WILLIAM W. BACKUS HOSPITAL (O, 184 beds) 326 Washington Street, Norwich, CT Zip 06360–2740; tel. 860/889–8331; David A. Whitehead, President, Hartford HealthCare East Region
**Web address:** www.backushospital.org

WINDHAM HOSPITAL (O, 56 beds) 112 Mansfield Avenue, Willimantic, CT Zip 06226–2040; tel. 860/456–9116; David A. Whitehead, President, Hartford HealthCare East Region
**Web address:** www.windhamhospital.org

For explanation of codes following names, see page B2.
★ Indicates Type III membership in the American Hospital Association.
● Single hospital health care system

| | | |
|---|---|---|
| **Owned, leased, sponsored:** | 6 hospitals | 1481 beds |
| **Contract–managed:** | 0 hospitals | 0 beds |
| **Totals:** | 6 hospitals | 1481 beds |

---

### 0637: HAVEN BEHAVIORAL HEALTHCARE (IO)
652 West Iris Drive, Nashville, TN Zip 37204–3191;
tel. 615/250–9500; Michael Lindley, Chief Executive Officer

**ARIZONA:** HAVEN SENIOR HORIZONS (O, 30 beds) 1201 South 7th Avenue, Suite 200, Phoenix, AZ Zip 85007–4076; tel. 623/236–2000; Kathy Shaw, Chief Executive Officer
**Web address:** www.havenbehavioral.com

**COLORADO:** HAVEN BEHAVIORAL WAR HEROES HOSPITAL (O, 20 beds) 1008 Minnequa Avenue, Suite 6100, Pueblo, CO Zip 81004–3733; tel. 719/546–6000; Carrin Harper, M.D., Chief Executive Officer

**OHIO:** HAVEN BEHAVIORAL SENIOR CARE OF DAYTON (O, 32 beds) One Elizabeth Place, 4th Floor Southwest Tower, Dayton, OH Zip 45417–3445; tel. 937/234–0100; Keith Kuhn, Chief Executive Officer
**Web address:** www.havenbehavioraldayton.com/

**PENNSYLVANIA:** HAVEN BEHAVIORAL HEALTH OF EASTERN PENNSYLVANIA (O, 48 beds) 145 North 6th Street, 3rd Floor, Reading, PA Zip 19601–3096; tel. 610/406–4340; John Baker, Interim Chief Executive Officer
**Web address:** www.havenbehavioralhospital.com

| | | |
|---|---|---|
| **Owned, leased, sponsored:** | 4 hospitals | 130 beds |
| **Contract–managed:** | 0 hospitals | 0 beds |
| **Totals:** | 4 hospitals | 130 beds |

---

### ★3555: HAWAII HEALTH SYSTEMS CORPORATION (NP)
3675 Kilauea Avenue, Honolulu, HI Zip 96816–2333;
tel. 808/733–4151; Linda Rosen, M.D., Chief Executive Officer
**(Independent Hospital System)**

**HAWAII:** HALE HO'OLA HAMAKUA (O, 52 beds) 45–547 Plumeria Street, Honokaa, HI Zip 96727–6902; tel. 808/932–4100; David Culbreth, Administrator
**Web address:** www.hhh.hhsc.org/

HILO MEDICAL CENTER (O, 276 beds) 1190 Waianuenue Avenue, Hilo, HI Zip 96720–2089; tel. 808/932–3000; Dan Brinkman, R.N., Interim Chief Executive Officer
**Web address:** www.hmc.hhsc.org

KAU HOSPITAL (O, 21 beds) 1 Kamani Street, Pahala, HI Zip 96777, Mailing Address: P.O. Box 40, Zip 96777–0040; tel. 808/932–4200; Merilyn Harris, Administrator
**Web address:** www.hhsc.org

KAUAI VETERANS MEMORIAL HOSPITAL (O, 45 beds) Waimea Canyon Road, Waimea, HI Zip 96796, Mailing Address: P.O. Box 337, Zip 96796–0337; tel. 808/338–9431; Peter Klune, Chief Executive Officer
**Web address:** www.kvmh.hhsc.org

KOHALA HOSPITAL (O, 28 beds) 54–383 Hospital Road, Kohala, HI Zip 96755, Mailing Address: P.O. Box 10, Kapaau, Zip 96755–0010; tel. 808/889–6211; Eugene Amar, Jr., Administrator
**Web address:** www.koh.hhsc.org

KONA COMMUNITY HOSPITAL (O, 94 beds) 79–1019 Haukapila Street, Kealakekua, HI Zip 96750–7920; tel. 808/322–9311; Jay E. Kreuzer, FACHE, Chief Executive Officer
**Web address:** www.kch.hhsc.org

KULA HOSPITAL (O, 6 beds) 100 Keokea Place, Kula, HI Zip 96790–7450; tel. 808/878–1221; Darren Kasai, Assistant Administrator
**Web address:** www.hhsc.org

LANAI COMMUNITY HOSPITAL (O, 24 beds) 628 Seventh Street, Lanai City, HI Zip 96763–0650, Mailing Address: P.O. Box 630650, Zip 96763–0650; tel. 808/565–8450; Darren Kasai, Assistant Administrator
**Web address:** www.lch.hhsc.org

LEAHI HOSPITAL (O, 164 beds) 3675 Kilauea Avenue, Honolulu, HI Zip 96816–2398; tel. 808/733–8000; Reid Kondo, Interim Chief Executive Officer
**Web address:** www.hhsc.org

MAUI MEMORIAL MEDICAL CENTER (O, 213 beds) 221 Mahalani Street, Wailuku, HI Zip 96793–2581; tel. 808/244–9056; Wesley Lo, Regional Chief Executive Officer
**Web address:** www.mmmc.hhsc.org

SAMUEL MAHELONA MEMORIAL HOSPITAL (O, 80 beds) 4800 Kawaihau Road, Kapaa, HI Zip 96746–1971; tel. 808/822–4961; Peter Klune, Chief Executive Officer
**Web address:** www.smmh.hhsc.org

| | | |
|---|---|---|
| **Owned, leased, sponsored:** | 11 hospitals | 1003 beds |
| **Contract–managed:** | 0 hospitals | 0 beds |
| **Totals:** | 11 hospitals | 1003 beds |

---

### 0266: HAWAII PACIFIC HEALTH (NP)
55 Merchant Street, Honolulu, HI Zip 96813–4306;
tel. 808/949–9355; Raymond P. Vara, Jr., President and Chief Executive Officer
**(Independent Hospital System)**

KAPIOLANI MEDICAL CENTER FOR WOMEN & CHILDREN (O, 225 beds) 1319 Punahou Street, Honolulu, HI Zip 96826–1001; tel. 808/983–6000; Martha Smith, Chief Executive Officer
**Web address:** www.kapiolani.org

PALI MOMI MEDICAL CENTER (O, 128 beds) 98–1079 Moanalua Road, Aiea, HI Zip 96701–4713; tel. 808/486–6000; Art Gladstone, R.N., President and Chief Executive Officer
**Web address:** www.palimomi.org

STRAUB CLINIC & HOSPITAL (O, 129 beds) 888 South King Street, Honolulu, HI Zip 96813–3097; tel. 808/522–4000; Art Gladstone, R.N., Chief Executive Officer
**Web address:** www.straubhealth.org

WILCOX MEMORIAL HOSPITAL (O, 65 beds) 3–3420 Kuhio Highway, Lihue, HI Zip 96766–1099; tel. 808/245–1100; Jen Chahanovich, President and Chief Executive Officer
**Web address:** www.wilcoxhealth.org

| | | |
|---|---|---|
| **Owned, leased, sponsored:** | 4 hospitals | 547 beds |
| **Contract–managed:** | 0 hospitals | 0 beds |
| **Totals:** | 4 hospitals | 547 beds |

---

### ★0048: HCA (IO)
One Park Plaza, Nashville, TN Zip 37203–1548; tel. 615/344–9551; R. Milton Johnson, President and Chief Executive Officer
**(Decentralized Health System)**

**ALASKA:** ALASKA REGIONAL HOSPITAL (O, 132 beds) 2801 Debarr Road, Anchorage, AK Zip 99508–2997, Mailing Address: P.O. Box 143889, Zip 99514–3889; tel. 907/264–1754; Julie Taylor, FACHE, Chief Executive Officer
**Web address:** www.alaskaregional.com

**CALIFORNIA:** GOOD SAMARITAN HOSPITAL (O, 332 beds) 2425 Samaritan Drive, San Jose, CA Zip 95124–3997, Mailing Address: P.O. Box 240002, Zip 95154–2402; tel. 408/559–2011; Paul Beaupre, M.D., Chief Executive Officer
**Web address:** www.goodsamsanjose.com

LOS ROBLES HOSPITAL AND MEDICAL CENTER (O, 367 beds) 215 West Janss Road, Thousand Oaks, CA Zip 91360–1899; tel. 805/497–2727; Natalie Mussi, President and Chief Executive Officer
**Web address:** www.losrobleshospital.com

REGIONAL MEDICAL CENTER OF SAN JOSE (O, 193 beds) 225 North Jackson Avenue, San Jose, CA Zip 95116–1603; tel. 408/259–5000; Michael T. Johnson, FACHE, President and Chief Executive Officer
**Web address:** www.regionalmedicalsanjose.com

RIVERSIDE COMMUNITY HOSPITAL (O, 373 beds) 4445 Magnolia Avenue, Riverside, CA Zip 92501–4199, Mailing Address: P.O. Box 1669, Zip 92502–1669; tel. 951/788–3000; Patrick D. Brilliant, President and Chief Executive Officer
**Web address:** www.riversidecommunityhospital.com

WEST HILLS HOSPITAL AND MEDICAL CENTER (O, 225 beds) 7300 Medical Center Drive, West Hills, CA Zip 91307–1900; tel. 818/676–4000; Douglas Long, President and Chief Executive Officer
**Web address:** www.westhillshospital.com

---

**COLORADO:** MEDICAL CENTER OF AURORA (O, 303 beds) 1501 South Potomac Street, Aurora, CO Zip 80012–5411; tel. 303/695–2600; Ryan Simpson, Interim Chief Executive Officer
**Web address:** www.auroramed.com

NORTH SUBURBAN MEDICAL CENTER (O, 115 beds) 9191 Grant Street, Thornton, CO Zip 80229–4341; tel. 303/451–7800; Jennifer Alderfer, Chief Executive Officer
**Web address:** www.northsuburban.com

PRESBYTERIAN–ST. LUKE'S MEDICAL CENTER (O, 399 beds) 1719 East 19th Avenue, Denver, CO Zip 80218–1281; tel. 303/839–6000; Maureen Tarrant, Chief Executive Officer
**Web address:** www.pslmc.com

ROSE MEDICAL CENTER (O, 262 beds) 4567 East Ninth Avenue, Denver, CO Zip 80220–3941; tel. 303/320–2121; Kenneth H. Feiler, Chief Executive Officer
**Web address:** www.rosebabies.com

SKY RIDGE MEDICAL CENTER (O, 275 beds) 10101 Ridge Gate Parkway, Lone Tree, CO Zip 80124–5522; tel. 720/225–1000; Susan Hicks, Chief Executive Officer
**Web address:** www.skyridgemedcenter.com

SPALDING REHABILITATION HOSPITAL (O, 40 beds) 900 Potomac Steet, Aurora, CO Zip 80011–6716; tel. 303/367–1166; Mark S. Deno, Chief Executive Officer
**Web address:** www.spaldingrehab.com

SWEDISH MEDICAL CENTER (O, 363 beds) 501 East Hampden Avenue, Englewood, CO Zip 80113–2702; tel. 303/788–5000; Mary M. White, Chief Executive Officer
**Web address:** www.swedishhospital.com

**FLORIDA:** AVENTURA HOSPITAL AND MEDICAL CENTER (O, 359 beds) 20900 Biscayne Boulevard, Aventura, FL Zip 33180–1407; tel. 305/682–7000; Dianne Goldenberg, Chief Executive Officer
**Web address:** www.aventurahospital.com

BLAKE MEDICAL CENTER (O, 377 beds) 2020 59th Street West, Bradenton, FL Zip 34209–4669; tel. 941/792–6611; Daniel J. Friedrich, III, Chief Executive Officer
**Web address:** www.blakemedicalcenter.com

BRANDON REGIONAL HOSPITAL (O, 407 beds) 119 Oakfield Drive, Brandon, FL Zip 33511–5779; tel. 813/681–5551; Bland Eng, Chief Executive Officer
**Web address:** www.brandonhospital.com

CAPITAL REGIONAL MEDICAL CENTER (O, 198 beds) 2626 Capital Medical Boulevard, Tallahassee, FL Zip 32308–4499; tel. 850/325–5000; Mark Robinson, FACHE, Chief Executive Officer
**Web address:** www.capitalregionalmedicalcenter.com

CENTRAL FLORIDA REGIONAL HOSPITAL (O, 226 beds) 1401 West Seminole Boulevard, Sanford, FL Zip 32771–6764; tel. 407/321–4500; Wendy H. Brandon, Chief Executive Officer
**Web address:** www.centralfloridaregional.com

CITRUS MEMORIAL HEALTH SYSTEM (O, 198 beds) 502 West Highland Boulevard, Inverness, FL Zip 34452–4754; tel. 352/726–1551; Ralph A. Aleman, President and Chief Executive Officer
**Web address:** www.citrusmh.com

DOCTORS HOSPITAL OF SARASOTA (O, 168 beds) 5731 Bee Ridge Road, Sarasota, FL Zip 34233–5056; tel. 941/342–1100; Robert C. Meade, Chief Executive Officer
**Web address:** www.doctorsofsarasota.com

ENGLEWOOD COMMUNITY HOSPITAL (O, 100 beds) 700 Medical Boulevard, Englewood, FL Zip 34223–3978; tel. 941/475–6571; Dale Alward, Chief Executive Officer
**Web address:** www.englewoodcommunityhospital.com

FAWCETT MEMORIAL HOSPITAL (O, 238 beds) 21298 Olean Boulevard, Port Charlotte, FL Zip 33952–6765; tel. 941/629–1181; Thomas J. Rice, FACHE, President and Chief Executive Officer
**Web address:** www.fawcetthospital.com

FORT WALTON BEACH MEDICAL CENTER (O, 257 beds) 1000 Mar–Walt Drive, Fort Walton Beach, FL Zip 32547–6795; tel. 850/862–1111; Mitchell P. Mongell, FACHE, Chief Executive Officer
**Web address:** www.fwbmc.com

GULF COAST REGIONAL MEDICAL CENTER (O, 176 beds) 449 West 23rd Street, Panama City, FL Zip 32405–4593, Mailing Address: P.O. Box 15309, Zip 32406–5309; tel. 850/769–8341; Carlton Ulmer, Chief Executive Officer
**Web address:** www.egulfcoastmedical.com

JFK MEDICAL CENTER (O, 424 beds) 5301 South Congress Avenue, Atlantis, FL Zip 33462–1197; tel. 561/965–7300; Gina Melby, Chief Executive Officer
**Web address:** www.jfkmc.com

KENDALL REGIONAL MEDICAL CENTER (O, 300 beds) 11750 Bird Road, Miami, FL Zip 33175–3530; tel. 305/223–3000; Scott A. Cihak, Chief Executive Officer
**Web address:** www.kendallmed.com

LAKE CITY MEDICAL CENTER (O, 67 beds) 340 N.W. Commerce Drive, Lake City, FL Zip 32055–4709; tel. 386/719–9000; Mark Miller, FACHE, Chief Executive Officer
**Web address:** www.lakecitymedical.com

LARGO MEDICAL CENTER (O, 243 beds) 201 14th Street S.W., Largo, FL Zip 33770–3133; tel. 727/588–5200; Anthony M. Degina, President and Chief Executive Officer
**Web address:** www.largomedical.com

LAWNWOOD REGIONAL MEDICAL CENTER & HEART INSTITUTE (O, 331 beds) 1700 South 23rd Street, Fort Pierce, FL Zip 34950–4803; tel. 772/461–4000; Greg Lowe, Chief Executive Officer
**Web address:** www.lawnwoodmed.com

MEDICAL CENTER OF TRINITY (O, 282 beds) 9330 State Road 54, Trinity, FL Zip 34655–1808; tel. 727/834–4900; Leigh Massengill, Chief Executive Officer
**Web address:** www.medicalcentertrinity.com

MEMORIAL HOSPITAL JACKSONVILLE (O, 418 beds) 3625 University Boulevard South, Jacksonville, FL Zip 32216–4207, Mailing Address: P.O. Box 16325, Zip 32245–6325; tel. 904/399–6111; James F. O'Loughlin, President and Chief Executive Officer
**Web address:** www.memorialhospitaljax.com

MEMORIAL HOSPITAL OF TAMPA (O, 139 beds) 2901 Swann Avenue, Tampa, FL Zip 33609–4057; tel. 813/873–6400; Ward Boston, III, Chief Executive Officer
**Web address:** www.memorialhospitaltampa.com

NORTH FLORIDA REGIONAL MEDICAL CENTER (O, 432 beds) 6500 Newberry Road, Gainesville, FL Zip 32605–4392, Mailing Address: P.O. Box 147006, Zip 32614–7006; tel. 352/333–4000; Brian Cook, Chief Executive Officer
**Web address:** www.nfrmc.com

NORTHSIDE HOSPITAL (O, 227 beds) 6000 49th Street North, Saint Petersburg, FL Zip 33709–2145; tel. 727/521–4411; Dia Nichols, Chief Executive Officer
**Web address:** www.northsidehospital.com

NORTHWEST MEDICAL CENTER (O, 223 beds) 2801 North State Road 7, Margate, FL Zip 33063–5727; tel. 954/974–0400; Erica Gulrich, Chief Executive Officer
**Web address:** www.northwestmed.com

OAK HILL HOSPITAL (O, 262 beds) 11375 Cortez Boulevard, Brooksville, FL Zip 34613–5409; tel. 352/596–6632; Mickey Smith, Chief Executive Officer
**Web address:** www.oakhillhospital.com

OCALA REGIONAL MEDICAL CENTER (O, 270 beds) 1431 S.W. First Avenue, Ocala, FL Zip 34471–6500, Mailing Address: P.O. Box 2200, Zip 34478–2200; tel. 352/401–1000; Randy McVay, Chief Executive Officer
**Web address:** www.ocalaregional.com

ORANGE PARK MEDICAL CENTER (O, 297 beds) 2001 Kingsley Avenue, Orange Park, FL Zip 32073–5156; tel. 904/639–8500; Chad Patrick, President and Chief Executive Officer
**Web address:** www.opmedical.com

OSCEOLA REGIONAL MEDICAL CENTER (O, 235 beds) 700 West Oak Street, Kissimmee, FL Zip 34741–4996; tel. 407/846–2266; Robert M. Krieger, Chief Executive Officer
**Web address:** www.osceolaregional.com

PALMS OF PASADENA HOSPITAL (O, 307 beds) 1501 Pasadena Avenue South, Saint Petersburg, FL Zip 33707–3798; tel. 727/381–1000; Sharon Hayes, Chief Executive Officer
**Web address:** www.palmspasadena.com

PALMS WEST HOSPITAL (O, 204 beds) 13001 Southern Boulevard, Loxahatchee, FL Zip 33470–9203; tel. 561/798–3300; Eric Goldman, Chief Executive Officer
**Web address:** www.palmswesthospital.com

PLANTATION GENERAL HOSPITAL (O, 264 beds) 401 N.W. 42nd Avenue, Plantation, FL Zip 33317–2882; tel. 954/587–5010; Randy Gross, Chief Executive Officer
**Web address:** www.plantationgeneral.com

For explanation of codes following names, see page B2.
★ Indicates Type III membership in the American Hospital Association.

POINCIANA MEDICAL CENTER (O, 24 beds) 325 Cypress Parkway, Kissimmee, FL Zip 34758; tel. 407/530–2000; Joanna J. Conley, FACHE, Chief Executive Officer
**Web address:** www.poincianamedicalcenter.com

RAULERSON HOSPITAL (O, 100 beds) 1796 Highway 441 North, Okeechobee, FL Zip 34972–1918, Mailing Address: P.O. Box 1307, Zip 34973–1307; tel. 863/763–2151; Robert H. Lee, President
**Web address:** www.raulersonhospital.com

REGIONAL MEDICAL CENTER BAYONET POINT (O, 290 beds) 14000 Fivay Road, Hudson, FL Zip 34667–7199; tel. 727/869–5400; Shayne George, Chief Executive Officer
**Web address:** www.rmchealth.com

SOUTH BAY HOSPITAL (O, 112 beds) 4016 Sun City Center Boulevard, Sun City Center, FL Zip 33573–5298; tel. 813/634–3301; Sharon L. Roush, Chief Executive Officer
**Web address:** www.southbayhospital.com

SPECIALTY HOSPITAL JACKSONVILLE (O, 62 beds) 4901 Richard Street, Jacksonville, FL Zip 32207–7328; tel. 904/737–3120; Barbara McCarthy, Chief Executive Officer
**Web address:** www.specialtyhospitaljax.com

ST. LUCIE MEDICAL CENTER (O, 194 beds) 1800 S.E. Tiffany Avenue, Port St. Lucie, FL Zip 34952–7521; tel. 772/335–4000; Jay Finnegan, Chief Executive Officer
**Web address:** www.stluciemed.com

ST. PETERSBURG GENERAL HOSPITAL (O, 219 beds) 6500 38th Avenue North, Saint Petersburg, FL Zip 33710–1629; tel. 727/384–1414; Janice Balzano, Chief Executive Officer
**Web address:** www.stpetegeneral.com

TAMPA COMMUNITY HOSPITAL (O, 201 beds) 6001 Webb Road, Tampa, FL Zip 33615–3291; tel. 813/888–7060; Jacob Fisher, Chief Executive Officer
**Web address:** www.tampacommunityhospital.com/

TWIN CITIES HOSPITAL (O, 65 beds) 2190 Highway 85 North, Niceville, FL Zip 32578–1045; tel. 850/678–4131; David Whalen, Chief Executive Officer
**Web address:** www.tchealthcare.com

UNIVERSITY HOSPITAL AND MEDICAL CENTER (O, 317 beds) 7201 North University Drive, Tamarac, FL Zip 33321–2996; tel. 954/721–2200; Joseph D. Melchiode, Chief Executive Officer
**Web address:** www.uhmchealth.com

WEST FLORIDA HOSPITAL (O, 339 beds) 8383 North Davis Highway, Pensacola, FL Zip 32514–6088; tel. 850/494–4000; Brian Baumgardner, Chief Executive Officer
**Web address:** www.westfloridahospital.com

WEST PALM HOSPITAL (O, 245 beds) 2201 45th Street, West Palm Beach, FL Zip 33407–2047; tel. 561/842–6141; Dana Oaks, Chief Executive Officer
**Web address:** www.westpalmhospital.com

WESTSIDE REGIONAL MEDICAL CENTER (O, 215 beds) 8201 West Broward Boulevard, Plantation, FL Zip 33324–2701; tel. 954/473–6600; Barbara Simmons, Chief Executive Officer
**Web address:** www.westsideregional.com

**GEORGIA:** CARTERSVILLE MEDICAL CENTER (O, 80 beds) 960 Joe Frank Harris Parkway, Cartersville, GA Zip 30120–2129; tel. 770/382–1530; Keith Sandlin, Chief Executive Officer
**Web address:** www.cartersvillemedical.com

COLISEUM MEDICAL CENTERS (O, 227 beds) 350 Hospital Drive, Macon, GA Zip 31217–3871; tel. 478/765–7000; Lance Jones, Chief Executive Officer
**Web address:** www.coliseumhealthsystem.com

COLISEUM NORTHSIDE HOSPITAL (O, 103 beds) 400 Charter Boulevard, Macon, GA Zip 31210–4853, Mailing Address: P.O. Box 4627, Zip 31208–4627; tel. 478/757–8200; Stephen J. Daugherty, Chief Executive Officer
**Web address:** www.coliseumhealthsystem.com

DOCTORS HOSPITAL (O, 307 beds) 3651 Wheeler Road, Augusta, GA Zip 30909–6426; tel. 706/651–3232; Douglas Welch, Chief Executive Officer
**Web address:** www.doctors–hospital.net

EASTSIDE MEDICAL CENTER (O, 247 beds) 1700 Medical Way, Snellville, GA Zip 30078–2195; tel. 770/979–0200; Scott Schmidly, Chief Executive Officer
**Web address:** www.eastsidemedical.com

FAIRVIEW PARK HOSPITAL (O, 168 beds) 200 Industrial Boulevard, Dublin, GA Zip 31021–2997, Mailing Address: P.O. Box 1408, Zip 31040–1408; tel. 478/275–2000; Donald R. Avery, FACHE, President and Chief Executive Officer
**Web address:** www.fairviewparkhospital.com

REDMOND REGIONAL MEDICAL CENTER (O, 230 beds) 501 Redmond Road, Rome, GA Zip 30165–1415, Mailing Address: P.O. Box 107001, Zip 30165–7001; tel. 706/291–0291; John Quinlivan, Chief Executive Officer
**Web address:** www.redmondregional.com

**IDAHO:** EASTERN IDAHO REGIONAL MEDICAL CENTER (O, 309 beds) 3100 Channing Way, Idaho Falls, ID Zip 83404–7533, Mailing Address: P.O. Box 2077, Zip 83403–2077; tel. 208/529–6111; Douglas Crabtree, Chief Executive Officer
**Web address:** www.eirmc.com

WEST VALLEY MEDICAL CENTER (O, 86 beds) 1717 Arlington, Caldwell, ID Zip 83605–4802; tel. 208/459–4641; Elizabeth Hunsicker, Chief Executive Officer
**Web address:** www.westvalleymedctr.com

**INDIANA:** TERRE HAUTE REGIONAL HOSPITAL (O, 208 beds) 3901 South Seventh Street, Terre Haute, IN Zip 47802–5709; tel. 812/232–0021; Mary Ann Conroy, Chief Executive Officer
**Web address:** www.regionalhospital.com

**KANSAS:** MENORAH MEDICAL CENTER (O, 158 beds) 5721 West 119th Street, Overland Park, KS Zip 66209–3722; tel. 913/498–6000; Charles Laird, Chief Executive Officer
**Web address:** www.menorahmedicalcenter.com

OVERLAND PARK REGIONAL MEDICAL CENTER (O, 277 beds) 10500 Quivira Road, Overland Park, KS Zip 66215–2306, Mailing Address: P.O. Box 15959, Zip 66215–5959; tel. 913/541–5000; Kevin J. Hicks, President and CEO
**Web address:** www.oprmc.com

WESLEY MEDICAL CENTER (O, 548 beds) 550 North Hillside, Wichita, KS Zip 67214–4976; tel. 316/962–2000; Bill Voloch, President and Chief Executive Officer
**Web address:** www.wesleymc.com

**KENTUCKY:** FRANKFORT REGIONAL MEDICAL CENTER (O, 103 beds) 299 King's Daughters Drive, Frankfort, KY Zip 40601–4186; tel. 502/875–5240; Chip Peal, Chief Executive Officer
**Web address:** www.frankfortregional.com

TRISTAR GREENVIEW REGIONAL HOSPITAL (O, 167 beds) 1801 Ashley Circle, Bowling Green, KY Zip 42104–3362; tel. 270/793–1000; Michael Sherrod, Chief Executive Officer
**Web address:** www.greenviewhospital.com

**LOUISIANA:** LAKEVIEW REGIONAL MEDICAL CENTER (O, 172 beds) 95 Judge Tanner Boulevard, Covington, LA Zip 70433–7507; tel. 985/867–3800; Bret G. Kolman, CPA, FACHE, Chief Executive Officer
**Web address:** www.lakeviewregional.com

RAPIDES REGIONAL MEDICAL CENTER (O, 357 beds) 211 Fourth Street, Alexandria, LA Zip 71301–8421; tel. 318/473–3000; Jason E. Cobb, FACHE, Chief Executive Officer
**Web address:** www.rapidesregional.com

REGIONAL MEDICAL CENTER OF ACADIANA (O, 289 beds) 2810 Ambassador Caffery Parkway, Lafayette, LA Zip 70506–5906; tel. 337/981–2949; Kathy Bobbs, FACHE, President and Chief Executive Officer
**Web address:** www.medicalcenterofacadiana.com

TULANE MEDICAL CENTER (O, 362 beds) 1415 Tulane Avenue, New Orleans, LA Zip 70112–2600; tel. 504/988–5263; William Lunn, M.D., Chief Executive Officer
**Web address:** www.tuhc.com

**MISSISSIPPI:** GARDEN PARK MEDICAL CENTER (O, 130 beds) 15200 Community Road, Gulfport, MS Zip 39503–3085, Mailing Address: P.O. Box 1240, Zip 39502–1240; tel. 228/575–7000; Brenda M. Waltz, FACHE, Chief Executive Officer
**Web address:** www.gpmedical.com

**MISSOURI:** BELTON REGIONAL MEDICAL CENTER (O, 46 beds) 17065 South 71 Highway, Belton, MO Zip 64012–4631; tel. 816/348–1200; Todd Krass, Chief Executive Officer
**Web address:** www.beltonregionalmedicalcenter.com

CENTERPOINT MEDICAL CENTER (O, 221 beds) 19600 East 39th Street, Independence, MO Zip 64057–2301; tel. 816/698–7000; David R. Williams, Chief Executive Officer
**Web address:** www.centerpointmedical.com

For explanation of codes following names, see page B2.
★ Indicates Type III membership in the American Hospital Association.

LAFAYETTE REGIONAL HEALTH CENTER (O, 25 beds) 1500 State Street, Lexington, MO Zip 64067–1107; tel. 660/259–2203; Darrel Box, Chief Executive Officer
**Web address:** www.lafayetteregionalhealthcenter.com

LEE'S SUMMIT MEDICAL CENTER (O, 64 beds) 2100 S.E. Blue Parkway, Lee's Summit, MO Zip 64063–1007; tel. 816/282–5000; Matt Sogard, Chief Executive Officer
**Web address:** www.leessummitmedicalcenter.com

RESEARCH MEDICAL CENTER (O, 450 beds) 2316 East Meyer Boulevard, Kansas City, MO Zip 64132–1136; tel. 816/276–4000; Jacqueline DeSouza, Chief Executive Officer
**Web address:** www.researchmedicalcenter.com

**NEVADA:** MOUNTAINVIEW HOSPITAL (O, 340 beds) 3100 North Tenaya Way, Las Vegas, NV Zip 89128–0436; tel. 702/255–5000; Chris Mowan, Chief Executive Officer
**Web address:** www.mountainview–hospital.com

SOUTHERN HILLS HOSPITAL AND MEDICAL CENTER (O, 134 beds) 9300 West Sunset Road, Las Vegas, NV Zip 89148–4844; tel. 702/880–2100; Adam Rudd, Interim Chief Executive Officer
**Web address:** www.southernhillshospital.com

SUNRISE HOSPITAL AND MEDICAL CENTER (O, 664 beds) 3186 Maryland Parkway, Las Vegas, NV Zip 89109–2306, Mailing Address: P.O. Box 98530, Zip 89193; tel. 702/731–8000; Todd Sklamberg, President
**Web address:** www.sunrisehospital.com

**NEW HAMPSHIRE:** PARKLAND MEDICAL CENTER (O, 82 beds) One Parkland Drive, Derry, NH Zip 03038–2750; tel. 603/432–1500; Chris Accashian, Chief Executive Officer
**Web address:** www.parklandmedicalcenter.com

PORTSMOUTH REGIONAL HOSPITAL (O, 165 beds) 333 Borthwick Avenue, Portsmouth, NH Zip 03801–7128; tel. 603/436–5110; Dean Carucci, Interim Chief Executive Officer
**Web address:** www.portsmouthhospital.com

**OKLAHOMA:** OU MEDICAL CENTER (O, 724 beds) 1200 Everett Drive, Oklahoma City, OK Zip 73104–5047, Mailing Address: P.O. Box 26307, Zip 73126–0307; tel. 405/271–3636; Charles Spicer, President and Chief Executive Officer
**Web address:** www.oumedicine.com/oumedicalcenter

**SOUTH CAROLINA:** COLLETON MEDICAL CENTER (O, 131 beds) 501 Robertson Boulevard, Walterboro, SC Zip 29488–5714; tel. 843/782–2000; Brad Griffin, Chief Executive Officer
**Web address:** www.colletonmedical.com

GRAND STRAND REGIONAL MEDICAL CENTER (O, 271 beds) 809 82nd Parkway, Myrtle Beach, SC Zip 29572–4607; tel. 843/692–1000; Mark E. Sims, Chief Executive Officer
**Web address:** www.grandstrandmed.com

TRIDENT MEDICAL CENTER (O, 421 beds) 9330 Medical Plaza Drive, Charleston, SC Zip 29406–9195; tel. 843/797–7000; Todd Gallati, FACHE, President and Chief Executive Officer
**Web address:** www.tridenthealthsystem.com

**TENNESSEE:** PARKRIDGE MEDICAL CENTER (O, 513 beds) 2333 McCallie Avenue, Chattanooga, TN Zip 37404–3258; tel. 423/698–6061; Darrell W. Moore, Chief Executive Officer
**Web address:** www.parkridgemedicalcenter.com

TRISTAR ASHLAND CITY MEDICAL CENTER (O, 12 beds) 313 North Main Street, Ashland City, TN Zip 37015–1347; tel. 615/792–3030; Heather J. Rohan, Chief Executive Officer
**Web address:** www.tristarashlandcity.com/

TRISTAR CENTENNIAL MEDICAL CENTER (O, 641 beds) 2300 Patterson Street, Nashville, TN Zip 37203–1528; tel. 615/342–1000; Heather J. Rohan, Chief Executive Officer
**Web address:** www.tristarcentennial.com

TRISTAR HENDERSONVILLE MEDICAL CENTER (O, 70 beds) 355 New Shackle Island Road, Hendersonville, TN Zip 37075–2479; tel. 615/338–1000; Regina Bartlett, Chief Executive Officer
**Web address:** www.hendersonvillemedicalcenter.com

TRISTAR HORIZON MEDICAL CENTER (O, 130 beds) 111 Highway 70 East, Dickson, TN Zip 37055–2080; tel. 615/446–0446; Dustin Greene, Chief Executive Officer
**Web address:** www.horizonmedicalcenter.com

TRISTAR SKYLINE MADISON CAMPUS (O, 284 beds) 500 Hospital Drive, Madison, TN Zip 37115–5032; tel. 615/769–5000; Steve Otto, Chief Executive Officer
**Web address:** www.skylinemadison.com

TRISTAR SKYLINE MEDICAL CENTER (O, 295 beds) 3441 Dickerson Pike, Nashville, TN Zip 37207–2539; tel. 615/769–2000; Steve Otto, Chief Executive Officer
**Web address:** www.skylinemedicalcenter.com

TRISTAR SOUTHERN HILLS MEDICAL CENTER (O, 87 beds) 391 Wallace Road, Nashville, TN Zip 37211–4859; tel. 615/781–4000; Thomas H. Ozburn, Chief Executive Officer
**Web address:** www.tristarsouthernhills.com

TRISTAR STONECREST MEDICAL CENTER (O, 101 beds) 200 StoneCrest Boulevard, Smyrna, TN Zip 37167–6810; tel. 615/768–2000; Louis Caputo, Chief Executive Officer
**Web address:** www.stonecrestmedical.com

TRISTAR SUMMIT MEDICAL CENTER (O, 196 beds) 5655 Frist Boulevard, Hermitage, TN Zip 37076–2053; tel. 615/316–3000; Jeffrey T. Whitehorn, Chief Executive Officer
**Web address:** www.summitmedctr.com

**TEXAS:** BAYSHORE MEDICAL CENTER (O, 451 beds) 4000 Spencer Highway, Pasadena, TX Zip 77504–1202; tel. 713/359–2000; Jeanna Barnard, Chief Executive Officer
**Web address:** www.bayshoremedical.com

CLEAR LAKE REGIONAL MEDICAL  CENTER (O, 680 beds) 500 Medical Center Boulevard, Webster, TX Zip 77598–4220; tel. 281/332–2511; Stephen K. Jones, Jr., FACHE, Chief Executive Officer
**Web address:** www.clearlakermc.com

CONROE REGIONAL MEDICAL CENTER (O, 312 beds) 504 Medical Boulevard, Conroe, TX Zip 77304, Mailing Address: P.O. Box 1538, Zip 77305–1538; tel. 936/539–1111; Matt Davis, Chief Executive Officer
**Web address:** www.conroeregional.com/

CORPUS CHRISTI MEDICAL CENTER (O, 436 beds) 3315 South Alameda Street, Corpus Christi, TX Zip 78411–1883, Mailing Address: P.O. Box 8991, Zip 78468–8991; tel. 361/761–1400; Jay Woodall, Chief Executive Officer
**Web address:** www.ccmedicalcenter.com

DENTON REGIONAL MEDICAL CENTER (O, 185 beds) 3535 South 1–35 East, Denton, TX Zip 76210; tel. 940/384–3535; Caleb F. O'Rear, Chief Executive Officer
**Web address:** www.dentonregional.com

GREEN OAKS HOSPITAL (O, 124 beds) 7808 Clodus Fields Drive, Dallas, TX Zip 75251–2206; tel. 972/991–9504; Thomas M. Collins, President, Chairman and Chief Executive Officer
**Web address:** www.greenoakspsych.com

KINGWOOD MEDICAL CENTER (O, 345 beds) 22999 U.S. Highway 59 North, Kingwood, TX Zip 77339; tel. 281/348–8000; Melinda Stephenson, Chief Executive Officer
**Web address:** www.kingwoodmedical.com

LAS COLINAS MEDICAL CENTER (O, 90 beds) 6800 North MacArthur Boulevard, Irving, TX Zip 75039–2422; tel. 972/969–2000; Daniela Decell, Chief Executive Officer
**Web address:** www.lascolinasmedical.com

LAS PALMAS MEDICAL CENTER (O, 570 beds) 1801 North Oregon Street, El Paso, TX Zip 79902–3591; tel. 915/521–1200; Don Karl, Interim Chief Executive Officer
**Web address:** www.laspalmashealth.com

MEDICAL CENTER ARLINGTON (O, 265 beds) 3301 Matlock Road, Arlington, TX Zip 76015–2908; tel. 817/465–3241; Winston Borland, FACHE, President and Chief Executive Officer
**Web address:** www.medicalcenterarlington.com

MEDICAL CENTER ALLIANCE, (O, 55 beds) 3101 North Tarrant Parkway, Forth Worth, TX Zip 76177; tel. 871/639–1000; Glenn Wallace, Chief Executive Officer
**Web address:** http://mcalliancemob.com

MEDICAL CENTER OF LEWISVILLE (O, 166 beds) 500 West Main, Lewisville, TX Zip 75057–3699; tel. 972/420–1000; LaSharndra Barbarin, Chief Executive Officer and Chief Operating Officer
**Web address:** www.lewisvillemedical.com

MEDICAL CENTER OF MCKINNEY (O, 219 beds) 4500 Medical Center Drive, McKinney, TX Zip 75069–1650; tel. 972/547–8000; Ernest C. Lynch, III, President and Chief Executive Officer
**Web address:** www.medicalcenterofmckinney.com

For explanation of codes following names, see page B2.
★ Indicates Type III membership in the American Hospital Association.

MEDICAL CENTER OF PLANO (O, 362 beds) 3901 West 15th Street, Plano, TX Zip 75075–7738; tel. 972/596–6800; Charles Gressle, Chief Executive Officer
**Web address:** www.medicalcenterplano.com

MEDICAL CITY DALLAS HOSPITAL (O, 534 beds) 7777 Forest Lane, Dallas, TX Zip 75230–2598; tel. 972/566–7000; Troy Villarreal, President and Chief Executive Officer
**Web address:** www.medicalcityhospital.com

METHODIST AMBULATORY SURGERY HOSPITAL – NORTHWEST (O, 23 beds) 9150 Huebner Road, Suite 100, San Antonio, TX Zip 78240–1545; tel. 210/575–5000; Andrew G. Williams, Chief Executive Officer and Administrator
**Web address:** www.sahealth.com

METHODIST HOSPITAL (O, 1585 beds) 7700 Floyd Curl Drive, San Antonio, TX Zip 78229–3993; tel. 210/575–4000; Gay Nord, Chief Executive Officer
**Web address:** www.sahealth.com

METHODIST STONE OAK HOSPITAL (O, 140 beds) 1139 East Sonterra Boulevard, San Antonio, TX Zip 78258–4347; tel. 210/638–2100; Marc Strode, Chief Executive Officer
**Web address:** www.sahealth.com/locations/methodist–stone–oak–hospital/

NORTH HILLS HOSPITAL (O, 176 beds) 4401 Booth Calloway Road, North Richland Hills, TX Zip 76180–7399; tel. 817/255–1000; Randy Moresi, Chief Executive Officer
**Web address:** www.northhillshospital.com

PEARLAND MEDICAL CENTER (O, 33 beds) 11100 Shadow Creek Parkway, Pearland, TX Zip 77584–7285; tel. 713/770–7000; Matt Dixon, Chief Executive Officer
**Web address:** www.pearlandmc.com

PLAZA MEDICAL CENTER OF FORT WORTH (O, 212 beds) 900 Eighth Avenue, Fort Worth, TX Zip 76104–3902; tel. 817/336–2100; Clay Franklin, Chief Executive Officer
**Web address:** www.plazamedicalcenter.com

RIO GRANDE REGIONAL HOSPITAL (O, 320 beds) 101 East Ridge Road, McAllen, TX Zip 78503–1299; tel. 956/632–6000; Cristina Rivera, Chief Executive Officer
**Web address:** www.riohealth.com

ST. DAVID'S MEDICAL CENTER (O, 553 beds) 919 East 32nd Street, Austin, TX Zip 78705–2709, Mailing Address: P.O. Box 4039, Zip 78765–4039; tel. 512/476–7111; Donald H. Wilkerson, Chief Executive Officer
**Web address:** www.stdavids.com

ST. DAVID'S NORTH AUSTIN MEDICAL CENTER (O, 363 beds) 12221 North MoPac Expressway, Austin, TX Zip 78758–2496; tel. 512/901–1000; Allen Harrison, Chief Executive Officer
**Web address:** www.northaustin.com

ST. DAVID'S ROUND ROCK MEDICAL CENTER (O, 148 beds) 2400 Round Rock Avenue, Round Rock, TX Zip 78681–4097; tel. 512/341–1000; Deborah L. Ryle, Administrator and Chief Executive Officer
**Web address:** www.stdavids.com

ST. DAVID'S SOUTH AUSTIN MEDICAL CENTER (O, 266 beds) 901 West Ben White Boulevard, Austin, TX Zip 78704–6903; tel. 512/447–2211; Todd E. Steward, Chief Executive Officer
**Web address:** www.southaustinmc.com

TEXAS ORTHOPEDIC HOSPITAL (O, 49 beds) 7401 South Main Street, Houston, TX Zip 77030–4509; tel. 713/799–8600; Trent Lind, Chief Executive Officer
**Web address:** www.texasorthopedic.com

VALLEY REGIONAL MEDICAL CENTER (O, 214 beds) 100A Alton Gloor Boulevard, Brownsville, TX Zip 78526–3354, Mailing Address: P.O. Box 3710, Zip 78523–3710; tel. 956/350–7101; Art Garza, Interim Chief Executive Officer
**Web address:** www.valleyregionalmedicalcenter.com

WEST HOUSTON MEDICAL CENTER (O, 238 beds) 12141 Richmond Avenue, Houston, TX Zip 77082–2499; tel. 281/558–3444; Todd Caliva, Chief Executive Officer
**Web address:** www.westhoustonmedical.com

WOMAN'S HOSPITAL OF TEXAS (O, 345 beds) 7600 Fannin Street, Houston, TX Zip 77054–1906; tel. 713/790–1234; Ashley McClellan, Chief Executive Officer
**Web address:** www.womanshospital.com

**UTAH:** BRIGHAM CITY COMMUNITY HOSPITAL (O, 39 beds) 950 South Medical Drive, Brigham City, UT Zip 84302–4724; tel. 435/734–9471; Richard Spuhler, Chief Executive Officer
**Web address:** www.brighamcityhospital.com

CACHE VALLEY HOSPITAL (O, 22 beds) 2380 North 400 East, North Logan, UT Zip 84341–6000; tel. 435/713–9700; John C. Worley, III, Chief Executive Officer
**Web address:** www.cachevalleyhospital.com/

LAKEVIEW HOSPITAL (O, 119 beds) 630 East Medical Drive, Bountiful, UT Zip 84010–4908; tel. 801/299–2200; Rand Kerr, Chief Executive Officer
**Web address:** www.lakeviewhospital.com

LONE PEAK HOSPITAL (O, 32 beds) 1925 South State Street, Draper, UT Zip 84020; tel. 801/545–8000; Mark Meadows, Chief Executive Officer
**Web address:** www.lonepeakhospital.com

MOUNTAIN VIEW HOSPITAL (O, 114 beds) 1000 East 100 North, Payson, UT Zip 84651–1600; tel. 801/465–7000; Kevin Johnson, Chief Executive Officer
**Web address:** www.mvhpayson.com

OGDEN REGIONAL MEDICAL CENTER (O, 167 beds) 5475 South 500 East, Ogden, UT Zip 84405–6905; tel. 801/479–2111; Mark B. Adams, Chief Executive Officer
**Web address:** www.ogdenregional.com

ST. MARK'S HOSPITAL (O, 277 beds) 1200 East 3900 South, Salt Lake City, UT Zip 84124–1390; tel. 801/268–7111; Steven B. Bateman, Chief Executive Officer
**Web address:** www.stmarkshospital.com

TIMPANOGOS REGIONAL HOSPITAL (O, 105 beds) 750 West 800 North, Orem, UT Zip 84057–3660; tel. 801/714–6000; Kimball Anderson, FACHE, Chief Executive Officer
**Web address:** www.timpanogosregionalhospital.com

**VIRGINIA:** CHIPPENHAM HOSPITAL (O, 667 beds) 7101 Jahnke Road, Richmond, VA Zip 23225–4044; tel. 804/320–3911; Tim McManus, President and Chief Executive Officer
**Web address:** www.cjwmedical.com

DOMINION HOSPITAL (O, 100 beds) 2960 Sleepy Hollow Road, Falls Church, VA Zip 22044–2030; tel. 703/536–2000; C. Alan Eaks, Chief Executive Officer
**Web address:** www.dominionhospital.com

HENRICO DOCTORS' HOSPITAL (O, 559 beds) 1602 Skipwith Road, Richmond, VA Zip 23229–5205; tel. 804/289–4500; William Wagnon, Chief Executive Officer
**Web address:** www.henricodoctorshospital.com

JOHN RANDOLPH MEDICAL CENTER (O, 112 beds) 411 West Randolph Road, Hopewell, VA Zip 23860–2938; tel. 804/541–1600; Suzanne B. Jackson, FACHE, Chief Executive Officer
**Web address:** www.johnrandolphmed.com

LEWIS–GALE MEDICAL CENTER (O, 521 beds) 1900 Electric Road, Salem, VA Zip 24153–7494; tel. 540/776–4000; Jonathan L. Bartlett, Chief Executive Officer
**Web address:** www.lewis–gale.com

LEWISGALE HOSPITAL ALLEGHANY (O, 146 beds) One ARH Lane, Low Moor, VA Zip 24457, Mailing Address: P.O. Box 7, Zip 24457–0007; tel. 540/862–6011; Charlotte C. Tyson, Chief Executive Officer
**Web address:** www.alleghanyregional.com

LEWISGALE HOSPITAL MONTGOMERY (O, 89 beds) 3700 South Main Street, Blacksburg, VA Zip 24060–7081, Mailing Address: P.O. Box 90004, Zip 24062–9004; tel. 540/951–1111; Alan J. Fabian, Chief Executive Officer
**Web address:** www.lewisgale.com

LEWISGALE HOSPITAL PULASKI (O, 54 beds) 2400 Lee Highway, Pulaski, VA Zip 24301–2326, Mailing Address: P.O. Box 759, Zip 24301–0759; tel. 540/994–8100; Derek Vance, Chief Executive Officer
**Web address:** www.lewisgale.com/

RESTON HOSPITAL CENTER (O, 147 beds) 1850 Town Center Parkway, Reston, VA Zip 20190–3219; tel. 703/689–9000; John A. Deardorff, Chief Executive Officer
**Web address:** www.restonhospital.com

**Section B**

For explanation of codes following names, see page B2.
★ Indicates Type III membership in the American Hospital Association.

SPOTSYLVANIA REGIONAL MEDICAL CENTER (O, 100 beds) 4600 Spotsylvania Parkway, Fredericksburg, VA Zip 22408–7762; tel. 540/498–4000; Greg T. Madsen, Chief Executive Officer
**Web address:** www.spotsrmc.com

| | | |
|---|---|---|
| **Owned, leased, sponsored:** | 147 hospitals | 36815 beds |
| **Contract–managed:** | 0 hospitals | 0 beds |
| **Totals:** | 147 hospitals | 36815 beds |

**0328: HEALTH FIRST, INC.** (NP)
6450 U.S. Highway 1, Rockledge, FL Zip 32955–5747; tel. 321/434–7000; Steven P. Johnson, Ph.D., President and Chief Executive Officer
**(Centralized Physician/Insurance Health System)**

**FLORIDA:** HEALTH FIRST CAPE CANAVERAL HOSPITAL (O, 145 beds) 701 West Cocoa Beach Causeway, Cocoa Beach, FL Zip 32931–5595, Mailing Address: P.O. Box 320069, Zip 32932–0069; tel. 321/799–7111; William Calhoun, President, Community Hospitals
**Web address:** www.health–first.org

HEALTH FIRST HOLMES REGIONAL MEDICAL CENTER (O, 514 beds) 1350 South Hickory Street, Melbourne, FL Zip 32901–3224; tel. 321/434–7000; Sean Gregory, President
**Web address:** www.health–first.org

HEALTH FIRST PALM BAY HOSPITAL (O, 119 beds) 1425 Malabar Road N.E., Palm Bay, FL Zip 32907–2506; tel. 321/434–8000; William Calhoun, President, Community Hospitals
**Web address:** www.health–first.org/hospitals_services/pbch/index.cfm

HEALTH FIRST VIERA HOSPITAL (O, 84 beds) 8745 North Wickham Road, Melbourne, FL Zip 32940–5997; tel. 321/434–9164; William Calhoun, President, Community Hospitals
**Web address:** www.vierahospital.org

| | | |
|---|---|---|
| **Owned, leased, sponsored:** | 4 hospitals | 862 beds |
| **Contract–managed:** | 0 hospitals | 0 beds |
| **Totals:** | 4 hospitals | 862 beds |

**0307: HEALTH QUEST SYSTEMS, INC.** (NP)
1351 Route 55, LaGrangeville, NY Zip 12540–5108; tel. 845/475–9500; Luke McGuinness, President and CEO
**(Independent Hospital System)**

**NEW YORK:** NORTHERN DUTCHESS HOSPITAL (O, 68 beds) 6511 Springbrook Avenue, Rhinebeck, NY Zip 12572–3709, Mailing Address: P.O. Box 5002, Zip 12572–5002; tel. 845/876–3001; Denise George, R.N., President
**Web address:** www.health–quest.org/home_nd.cfm?id=9

PUTNAM HOSPITAL CENTER (O, 164 beds) 670 Stoneleigh Avenue, Carmel, NY Zip 10512–3997; tel. 845/279–5711; James Caldas, President
**Web address:** www.health–quest.org

VASSAR BROTHERS MEDICAL CENTER (O, 365 beds) 45 Reade Place, Poughkeepsie, NY Zip 12601–3947; tel. 845/454–8500; Robert Friedberg, President
**Web address:** www.health–quest.org

| | | |
|---|---|---|
| **Owned, leased, sponsored:** | 3 hospitals | 597 beds |
| **Contract–managed:** | 0 hospitals | 0 beds |
| **Totals:** | 3 hospitals | 597 beds |

**0534: HEALTHALLIANCE OF THE HUDSON VALLEY** (NP)
396 Broadway, Kingston, NY Zip 12401–4626; tel. 845/331–3131; David Scarpino, President and Chief Executive Officer
**(Independent Hospital System)**

HEALTH ALLIANCE HOSPITAL – BROADWAY CAMPUS (O, 150 beds) 396 Broadway, Kingston, NY Zip 12401–4692; tel. 845/331–3131; David Scarpino, President and Chief Executive Officer
**Web address:** www.hahv.org

HEALTH ALLIANCE HOSPITAL – MARY'S AVENUE CAMPUS (O, 120 beds) 105 Marys Avenue, Kingston, NY Zip 12401–5894; tel. 845/338–2500; David Scarpino, President and Chief Executive Officer
**Web address:** www.hahv.org

MARGARETVILLE HOSPITAL (O, 15 beds) 42084 State Highway 28, Margaretville, NY Zip 12455–2820; tel. 845/586–2631; Sandra A. Horan, Executive Director
**Web address:** www.margaretvillehospital.org

| | | |
|---|---|---|
| **Owned, leased, sponsored:** | 3 hospitals | 285 beds |
| **Contract–managed:** | 0 hospitals | 0 beds |
| **Totals:** | 3 hospitals | 285 beds |

**★2185: HEALTHEAST CARE SYSTEM** (NP)
559 Capitol Boulevard, 6–South, Saint Paul, MN Zip 55103–0000; tel. 651/232–2300; Kathryn G. Correia, President and Chief Executive Officer
**(Centralized Health System)**

**MINNESOTA:** BETHESDA HOSPITAL (O, 126 beds) 559 Capitol Boulevard, Saint Paul, MN Zip 55103–2101; tel. 651/232–2000; Catherine Barr, Senior Vice President and President, Bethesda Hospital
**Web address:** www.healtheast.org

ST. JOHN'S HOSPITAL (O, 192 beds) 1575 Beam Avenue, Maplewood, MN Zip 55109–1126; tel. 651/232–7000; Scott L. North, FACHE, Senior Vice President and President, Acute Care Hospitals
**Web address:** www.stjohnshospital–mn.org

ST. JOSEPH'S HOSPITAL (O, 234 beds) 45 West 10th Street, Saint Paul, MN Zip 55102–1053; tel. 651/232–3000; Scott L. North, FACHE, Senior Vice President and President, Acute Care Hospitals
**Web address:** www.healtheast.org

WOODWINDS HEALTH CAMPUS (O, 86 beds) 1925 Woodwinds Drive, Woodbury, MN Zip 55125–4445; tel. 651/232–0228; Scott L. North, FACHE, Senior Vice President and President, Acute Care Hospitals
**Web address:** www.woodwinds.org

| | | |
|---|---|---|
| **Owned, leased, sponsored:** | 4 hospitals | 638 beds |
| **Contract–managed:** | 0 hospitals | 0 beds |
| **Totals:** | 4 hospitals | 638 beds |

**0342: HEALTHPARTNERS** (NP)
8170 33rd Avenue South, Bloomington, MN Zip 55425–4516; tel. 952/883–7600; Mary K. Brainerd, President and Chief Executive Officer
**(Moderately Centralized Health System)**

GLENCOE REGIONAL HEALTH SERVICES (C, 135 beds) 1805 Hennepin Avenue North, Glencoe, MN Zip 55336–1416; tel. 320/864–3121; Jon D. Braband, FACHE, President and Chief Executive Officer
**Web address:** www.grhsonline.org

LAKEVIEW HOSPITAL (O, 54 beds) 927 Churchill Street West, Stillwater, MN Zip 55082–6605; tel. 651/439–5330; Theodore Wegleitner, Chief Executive Officer
**Web address:** www.lakeview.org

PARK NICOLLET METHODIST HOSPITAL (O, 411 beds) 6500 Excelsior Boulevard, Saint Louis Park, MN Zip 55426–4702; Minneapolis, tel. 952/993–5000; David Abelson, M.D., President and Chief Executive Officer
**Web address:** www.parknicollet.com

REGIONS HOSPITAL (O, 451 beds) 640 Jackson Street, Saint Paul, MN Zip 55101–2595; tel. 651/254–3456; Megan Remark, Chief Executive Officer
**Web address:** www.regionshospital.com

**WISCONSIN:** AMERY HOSPITAL AND CLINIC (O, 12 beds) 265 Griffin Street East, Amery, WI Zip 54001–1439; tel. 715/268–8000; Debra Rudquist, FACHE, President and Chief Executive Officer
**Web address:** www.amerymedicalcenter.org

HUDSON HOSPITAL AND CLINIC (O, 7 beds) 405 Stageline Road, Hudson, WI Zip 54016–7848; tel. 715/531–6000; Marian M. Furlong, R.N., FACHE, Chief Executive Officer
**Web address:** www.hudsonhospital.org

WESTFIELDS HOSPITAL (O, 25 beds) 535 Hospital Road, New Richmond, WI Zip 54017–1449; tel. 715/243–2600; Steven Massey, President and Chief Executive Officer
**Web address:** www.westfieldshospital.com

For explanation of codes following names, see page B2.
★ Indicates Type III membership in the American Hospital Association.

| | | |
|---|---|---|
| Owned, leased, sponsored: | 6 hospitals | 960 beds |
| Contract–managed: | 1 hospital | 135 beds |
| Totals: | 7 hospitals | 1095 beds |

★**0023: HEALTHSOUTH CORPORATION** (IO)
3660 Grandview Parkway, Suite 200, Birmingham, AL
Zip 35243–3332; tel. 205/967–7116; Jay F. Grinney, President and
Chief Executive Officer
**(Independent Hospital System)**

**ALABAMA:** HEALTHSOUTH LAKESHORE REHABILITATION HOSPITAL (O, 100
beds) 3800 Ridgeway Drive, Birmingham, AL Zip 35209–5599;
tel. 205/868–2000; Vickie Demers, Chief Executive Officer
**Web address:** www.healthsouthlakeshorerehab.com

HEALTHSOUTH REHABILITATION HOSPITAL (O, 39 beds) 1736 East Main
Street, Dothan, AL Zip 36301–3040, Mailing Address: P.O. Box 6708,
Zip 36302–6708; tel. 334/712–6333; Margaret A. Futch, Chief Executive
Officer
**Web address:** www.healthsouthdothan.com

HEALTHSOUTH REHABILITATION HOSPITAL OF MONTGOMERY (O, 70 beds)
4465 Narrow Lane Road, Montgomery, AL Zip 36116–2900;
tel. 334/284–7700; Thomas Roddy, Chief Executive Officer
**Web address:** www.healthsouthmontgomery.com

HEALTHSOUTH REHABILITATION HOSPITAL OF NORTH ALABAMA (O, 70 beds)
107 Governors Drive S.W., Huntsville, AL Zip 35801–4326;
tel. 256/535–2300; Douglas H. Beverly, Chief Executive Officer
**Web address:** www.healthsouthhuntsville.com

HEALTHSOUTH REHABILITATION OF GADSDEN (O, 44 beds) 801 Goodyear
Avenue, Gadsden, AL Zip 35903–1133; tel. 256/439–5000; Kayla Feazell,
Chief Executive Officer
**Web address:** www.healthsouthgadsden.com

REGIONAL REHABILITATION HOSPITAL (O, 48 beds) 3715 Highway 280/431
North, Phenix City, AL Zip 36867; tel. 334/732–2200; Michael Bartell, CEO,
**Web address:** www.regionalrehabhospital.com

**ARIZONA:** HEALTHSOUTH EAST VALLEY REHABILITATION HOSPITAL (O, 60
beds) 5652 East Baseline Road, Mesa, AZ Zip 85206–4713;
tel. 480/567–0350; Jerry Gray, Interim Chief Executive Officer
**Web address:** www.healthsoutheastvalley.com

HEALTHSOUTH REHABILITATION HOSPITAL OF SOUTHERN ARIZONA (O, 60
beds) 1921 West Hospital Drive, Tucson, AZ Zip 85704–7806;
tel. 520/742–2800; Donna Beifus, Chief Executive Officer
**Web address:** www.healthsouthsouthernarizona.com

HEALTHSOUTH REHABILITATION INSTITUTE OF TUCSON (O, 80 beds) 2650
North Wyatt Drive, Tucson, AZ Zip 85712–6108; tel. 520/325–1300; Jeffrey
Christensen, Chief Executive Officer
**Web address:** www.rehabinstituteoftucson.com

HEALTHSOUTH SCOTTSDALE REHABILITATION HOSPITAL (O, 60 beds) 9630
East Shea Boulevard, Scottsdale, AZ Zip 85260–6267; tel. 480/551–5400;
Timothy T. Poore, Chief Executive Officer
**Web address:** www.healthsouthscottsdale.com

HEALTHSOUTH VALLEY OF THE SUN REHABILITATION HOSPITAL (O, 75 beds)
13460 North 67th Avenue, Glendale, AZ Zip 85304–1042;
tel. 623/878–8800; Beth Bacher, Chief Executive Officer
**Web address:** www.healthsouthvalleyofthesun.com

YUMA REHABILITATION HOSPITAL (O, 41 beds) 901 West 24th Street, Yuma,
AZ Zip 85364–6384; tel. 928/726–5000;
**Web address:** www.yumarehabhospital.com

**ARKANSAS:** HEALTHSOUTH REHABILITATION HOSPITAL (O, 60 beds) 153
East Monte Painter Drive, Fayetteville, AR Zip 72703–4002;
tel. 479/444–2200; Jack C. Mitchell, FACHE, Chief Executive Officer
**Web address:** www.healthsouthfayetteville.com

HEALTHSOUTH REHABILITATION HOSPITAL OF FORT SMITH (O, 60 beds)
1401 South J Street, Fort Smith, AR Zip 72901–5155; tel. 479/785–3300;
Dawn Watts, Chief Executive Officer
**Web address:** www.healthsouthfortsmith.com

HEALTHSOUTH REHABILITATION HOSPITAL OF JONESBORO (O, 67 beds)
1201 Fleming Avenue, Jonesboro, AR Zip 72401–4311, Mailing Address:
P.O. Box 1680, Zip 72403–1680; tel. 870/932–0440; Donna Harris, Chief
Executive Officer
**Web address:** www.healthsouthjonesboro.com

ST. VINCENT REHABILITATION HOSPITAL (O, 60 beds) 2201 Wildwood
Avenue, Sherwood, AR Zip 72120–5074; tel. 501/834–1800; Lisa Watson,
Chief Executive Officer
**Web address:** www.stvincenthealth.com/svrehabhospital/index.html

**CALIFORNIA:** HEALTHSOUTH BAKERSFIELD REHABILITATION HOSPITAL (O,
66 beds) 5001 Commerce Drive, Bakersfield, CA Zip 93309–0689;
tel. 661/323–5500; Martha Samora, R.N., FACHE, Chief Executive Officer
**Web address:** www.healthsouthbakersfield.com

HEALTHSOUTH TUSTIN REHABILITATION HOSPITAL (O, 48 beds) 14851
Yorba Street, Tustin, CA Zip 92780–2925; tel. 714/832–9200; Diana C.
Hanyak, Chief Executive Officer
**Web address:** www.tustinrehab.com

**COLORADO:** HEALTHSOUTH REHABILITATION HOSPITAL OF COLORADO
SPRINGS (O, 56 beds) 325 Parkside Drive, Colorado Springs, CO
Zip 80910–3134; tel. 719/630–8000; Stephen Schaefer, Chief Executive
Officer
**Web address:** www.healthsouthcoloradosprings.com

HEALTHSOUTH REHABILITATION HOSPITAL OF DENVER (O, 40 beds) 1001
West Mineral Avenue, Littleton, CO Zip 80120–4507; tel. 303/334–1100;
David H. Shefte, Chief Executive Officer
**Web address:** www.healthsouthdenver.com

**FLORIDA:** HEALTHSOUTH EMERALD COAST REHABILITATION HOSPITAL (O,
75 beds) 1847 Florida Avenue, Panama City, FL Zip 32405–4640;
tel. 850/914–8600; Tony N. Bennett, Chief Executive Officer
**Web address:** www.healthsouthpanamacity.com

HEALTHSOUTH REHABILITATION HOSPITAL (O, 70 beds) 901 North
Clearwater–Largo Road, Largo, FL Zip 33770–4126; tel. 727/586–2999;
Tripp Smith, Chief Executive Officer
**Web address:** www.healthsouthlargo.com

HEALTHSOUTH REHABILITATION HOSPITAL AT MARTIN HEALTH (O, 34 beds)
5850 S.E. Community Drive, Stuart, FL Zip 34997–6420;
tel. 772/324–3500; Ivette Miranda, Chief Executive Officer
**Web address:** www.healthsouthmartin.com

HEALTHSOUTH REHABILITATION HOSPITAL OF ALTAMONTE SPRINGS (O, 50
beds) 831 South State Road 434, Altamonte Springs, FL Zip 32714–3502;
tel. 407/587–8600; Jill Jordan, Chief Executive Officer
**Web address:** www.healthsouthaltamontesprings.com

HEALTHSOUTH REHABILITATION HOSPITAL OF MIAMI (O, 60 beds) 20601 Old
Cutler Road, Cutler Bay, FL Zip 33189–2400; tel. 305/251–3800; Elizabeth
L. Izquierdo, CPA, Chief Executive Officer
**Web address:** www.healthsouthmiami.com

HEALTHSOUTH REHABILITATION HOSPITAL OF OCALA (O, 40 beds) 2275
S.W. 22nd Lane, Ocala, FL Zip 34471–7710; tel. 352/282–4000; Ellen
Witterstaeter, FACHE, Chief Executive Officer
**Web address:** www.healthsouthocala.com

HEALTHSOUTH REHABILITATION HOSPITAL OF SARASOTA (O, 96 beds) 6400
Edgelake Drive, Sarasota, FL Zip 34240–8813; tel. 941/921–8600; Marcus
Braz, Chief Executive Officer
**Web address:** www.healthsouthsarasota.com

HEALTHSOUTH REHABILITATION HOSPITAL OF SPRING HILL (O, 80 beds)
12440 Cortez Boulevard, Brooksville, FL Zip 34613–2628;
tel. 352/592–4250; Lori Bedard, Chief Executive Officer
**Web address:** www.healthsouthspringhill.com

HEALTHSOUTH REHABILITATION HOSPITAL OF TALLAHASSEE (O, 76 beds)
1675 Riggins Road, Tallahassee, FL Zip 32308–5315; tel. 850/656–4800;
K. Dale Neely, FACHE, Chief Executive Officer
**Web address:** www.healthsouthtallahassee.com

HEALTHSOUTH SEA PINES REHABILITATION HOSPITAL (O, 90 beds) 101 East
Florida Avenue, Melbourne, FL Zip 32901–8301; tel. 321/984–4600; Denise
B. McGrath, Chief Executive Officer
**Web address:** www.healthsouthseapines.com

HEALTHSOUTH SUNRISE REHABILITATION HOSPITAL (O, 126 beds) 4399
North Nob Hill Road, Sunrise, FL Zip 33351–5899; tel. 954/749–0300;
Stacy Modlin, Chief Executive Officer
**Web address:** www.healthsouthsunrise.com

HEALTHSOUTH TREASURE COAST REHABILITATION HOSPITAL (O, 80 beds)
1600 37th Street, Vero Beach, FL Zip 32960–4863; tel. 772/778–2100;
Michael Kissner, Chief Executive Officer
**Web address:** www.healthsouthtreasurecoast.com

Section B

For explanation of codes following names, see page B2.
★ Indicates Type III membership in the American Hospital Association.

**GEORGIA:** HEALTHSOUTH WALTON REHABILITATION HOSPITAL (O, 58 beds) 1355 Independence Drive, Augusta, GA Zip 30901–1037; tel. 706/724–7746; Eric Crossan, Chief Executive Officer
**Web address:** www.healthsouthwalton.com/

**ILLINOIS:** VAN MATRE HEALTHSOUTH REHABILITATION HOSPITAL (O, 53 beds) 950 South Mulford Road, Rockford, IL Zip 61108–4274; tel. 815/381–8500; Ken Bowman, Chief Executive Officer
**Web address:** www.healthsouth.com

**INDIANA:** HEALTHSOUTH DEACONESS REHABILITATION HOSPITAL (O, 85 beds) 4100 Covert Avenue, Evansville, IN Zip 47714–5567, Mailing Address: P.O. Box 5349, Zip 47716–5349; tel. 812/476–9983; Blake Bunner, Chief Executive Officer
**Web address:** www.healthsouthdeaconess.com

**KANSAS:** KANSAS REHABILITATION HOSPITAL (O, 59 beds) 1504 S.W. Eighth Avenue, Topeka, KS Zip 66606–1632; tel. 785/235–6600; William J. Overbey, Chief Executive Officer
**Web address:** www.kansasrehabhospital.com

MID–AMERICA REHABILITATION HOSPITAL (O, 98 beds) 5701 West 110th Street, Shawnee Mission, KS Zip 66211–2503; tel. 913/491–2400; Troy DeDecker, FACHE, Chief Executive Officer
**Web address:** www.midamericarehabhospital.com

WESLEY REHABILITATION HOSPITAL (O, 65 beds) 8338 West 13th Street North, Wichita, KS Zip 67212–2984; tel. 316/729–9999; James F. Grocholski, FACHE, Chief Executive Officer
**Web address:** www.wesleyrehabhospital.com

**KENTUCKY:** Cardinal Hill Rehabilitation Hospital (O, 158 beds) 2050 Versailles Road, Lexington, KY Zip 40504–1405 tel. 859/254-5701; Gary Payne, Chief Executive Officer
**Web address:** cardinalhillhealthsouth.com

HEALTHSOUTH LAKEVIEW REHABILITATION HOSPITAL (O, 40 beds) 134 Heartland Drive, Elizabethtown, KY Zip 42701–2778; tel. 270/769–3100; Lori Jarboe, Chief Executive Officer
**Web address:** www.healthsouthlakeview.com

HEALTHSOUTH NORTHERN KENTUCKY REHABILITATION HOSPITAL (O, 40 beds) 201 Medical Village Drive, Edgewood, KY Zip 41017–3407; tel. 859/341–2044; Richard R. Evens, Chief Executive Officer
**Web address:** www.healthsouthkentucky.com

**LOUISIANA:** HEALTHSOUTH REHABILITATION HOSPITAL OF ALEXANDRIA (O, 47 beds) 104 North Third Street, Alexandria, LA Zip 71301–8581; tel. 318/449–1370; James W. McClung, Chief Executive Officer
**Web address:** www.healthsouthalexandria.com

**MAINE:** NEW ENGLAND REHABILITATION HOSPITAL OF PORTLAND (O, 90 beds) 335 Brighton Avenue, Portland, ME Zip 04102–2363; tel. 207/775–4000; Jeanine Chesley, Chief Executive Officer
**Web address:** www.nerhp.org

**MARYLAND:** HEALTHSOUTH CHESAPEAKE REHABILITATION HOSPITAL (O, 54 beds) 220 Tilghman Road, Salisbury, MD Zip 21804–1921; tel. 410/546–4600; Steven Walas, Chief Executive Officer
**Web address:** www.healthsouthchesapeake.com

**MASSACHUSETTS:** FAIRLAWN REHABILITATION HOSPITAL (O, 110 beds) 189 May Street, Worcester, MA Zip 01602–4339; tel. 508/791–6351; R. David Richer, Chief Executive Officer
**Web address:** www.fairlawnrehab.org

HEALTHSOUTH REHABILITATION HOSPITAL OF WESTERN MASSACHUSETTS (O, 53 beds) 222 State Street, Ludlow, MA Zip 01056–3437; tel. 413/308–3300; Victoria Healy, Chief Executive Officer
**Web address:** www.healthsouthrehab.org

**MISSOURI:** HOWARD A. RUSK REHABILITATION CENTER (O, 60 beds) 315 Business Loop 70 West, Columbia, MO Zip 65203–3248; tel. 573/817–2703; Larry Meeker, Chief Executive Officer
**Web address:** www.ruskrehab.com

THE REHABILITATION INSTITUTE OF ST. LOUIS (O, 96 beds) 4455 Duncan Avenue, Saint Louis, MO Zip 63110–1111; tel. 314/658–3800; Tara Diebling, Chief Executive Officer
**Web address:** www.rehabinstitutestl.com

**NEVADA:** HEALTHSOUTH DESERT CANYON REHABILITATION HOSPITAL (O, 50 beds) 9175 West Oquendo Road, Las Vegas, NV Zip 89148–1234; tel. 702/252–7342; Andrea Davis, Chief Executive Officer
**Web address:** www.healthsouthdesertcanyon.com

HEALTHSOUTH REHABILITATION HOSPITAL – HENDERSON (O, 90 beds) 10301 Jeffreys Street, Henderson, NV Zip 89052–3922; tel. 702/939–9400; Samantha Billing, Chief Executive Officer
**Web address:** www.hendersonrehabhospital.com

HEALTHSOUTH REHABILITATION HOSPITAL–LAS VEGAS (O, 79 beds) 1250 South Valley View Boulevard, Las Vegas, NV Zip 89102–1861; tel. 702/877–8898; Michael Ward, Chief Executive Officer
**Web address:** www.healthsouthlasvegas.com

**NEW HAMPSHIRE:** HEALTHSOUTH REHABILITATION HOSPITAL (O, 50 beds) 254 Pleasant Street, Concord, NH Zip 03301–2508; tel. 603/226–9800; Catherine Devaney, Chief Executive Officer
**Web address:** www.healthsouthrehabconcordnh.com

**NEW JERSEY:** HEALTHSOUTH REHABILITATION HOSPITAL OF TOMS RIVER (O, 92 beds) 14 Hospital Drive, Toms River, NJ Zip 08755–6470; tel. 732/244–3100; Patricia Ostaszewski, MS, Chief Executive Officer
**Web address:** www.rehabnjtomsriver.com/

HEALTHSOUTH REHABILITATION HOSPITAL OF VINELAND (O, 41 beds) 1237 West Sherman Avenue, Vineland, NJ Zip 08360–6920; tel. 856/696–7100; Tammy Feuer, Chief Executive Officer
**Web address:** www.healthsouthvineland.com

REHABILITATION HOSPITAL OF TINTON FALLS (O, 60 beds) 2 Centre Plaza, Tinton Falls, NJ Zip 07724–9744; tel. 732/460–5320; Linda A. Savino, MS, Chief Executive Officer
**Web address:** www.rehabnj.com

**NEW MEXICO:** HEALTHSOUTH REHABILITATION HOSPITAL (O, 87 beds) 7000 Jefferson Street N.E., Albuquerque, NM Zip 87109–4313; tel. 505/344–9478; Byron Aten, Interim Chief Executive Officer
**Web address:** www.healthsouthnewmexico.com

**OHIO:** HEALTHSOUTH REHABILITATION HOSPITAL AT DRAKE (O, 60 beds) 151 West Galbraith Road, Cincinnati, OH Zip 45216–1015; tel. 513/418–5600; Brad Kennedy, Chief Executive Officer
**Web address:** www.healthsouthatdrake.com

**PENNSYLVANIA:** GEISINGER HEALTHSOUTH REHABILITATION HOSPITAL (O, 42 beds) 2 Rehab Lane, Danville, PA Zip 17821–8498; tel. 570/271–6733; Lorie Dillon, Chief Executive Officer
**Web address:** www.geisingerhealthsouth.com

HEALTHSOUTH HARMARVILLE REHABILITATION HOSPITAL (O, 162 beds) Guys Run Road, Pittsburgh, PA Zip 15238–0460, Mailing Address: P.O. Box 11460, Zip 15238–0460; tel. 412/828–1300; Mark Van Volkenburg, Chief Executive Officer
**Web address:** www.healthsouthharmarville.com

HEALTHSOUTH NITTANY VALLEY REHABILITATION HOSPITAL (O, 73 beds) 550 West College Avenue, Pleasant Gap, PA Zip 16823–7401; tel. 814/359–3421; Susan Hartman, Chief Executive Officer
**Web address:** www.nittanyvalleyrehab.com

HEALTHSOUTH READING REHABILITATION HOSPITAL (O, 60 beds) 1623 Morgantown Road, Reading, PA Zip 19607–9455; tel. 610/796–6000; Richard Kruczek, Chief Executive Officer
**Web address:** www.healthsouthreading.com

HEALTHSOUTH REHABILITATION HOSPITAL OF ALTOONA (O, 80 beds) 2005 Valley View Boulevard, Altoona, PA Zip 16602–4598; tel. 814/944–3535; Scott Filler, Chief Executive Officer
**Web address:** www.healthsouthaltoona.com

HEALTHSOUTH REHABILITATION HOSPITAL OF ERIE (O, 100 beds) 143 East Second Street, Erie, PA Zip 16507–1501; tel. 814/878–1200; John Papalia, Chief Executive Officer
**Web address:** www.healthsoutherie.com

HEALTHSOUTH REHABILITATION HOSPITAL OF MECHANICSBURG (O, 75 beds) 175 Lancaster Boulevard, Mechanicsburg, PA Zip 17055–3562; tel. 717/691–3700; Mark Freeburn, Chief Executive Officer
**Web address:** www.healthsouthpa.com

HEALTHSOUTH REHABILITATION HOSPITAL OF SEWICKLEY (O, 44 beds) 303 Camp Meeting Road, Sewickley, PA Zip 15143–8322; tel. 412/741–9500; Leah Laffey, R.N., Chief Executive Officer
**Web address:** www.healthsouthsewickley.com

HEALTHSOUTH REHABILITATION HOSPITAL OF YORK (O, 90 beds) 1850 Normandie Drive, York, PA Zip 17408–1534; tel. 717/767–6941; Steven Alwine, Chief Executive Officer
**Web address:** www.healthsouthyork.com

For explanation of codes following names, see page B2.
★ Indicates Type III membership in the American Hospital Association.

Section B

**PUERTO RICO:** HEALTHSOUTH HOSPITAL OF MANATI (O, 40 beds) Carretera 2, Kilometro 47 7, Manati, PR Zip 674; tel. 787/621–3800; Enrique A. Vicens–Rivera, Jr., JD, Chief Executive Officer
**Web address:** www.healthsouth.com

HEALTHSOUTH REHABILITATION HOSPITAL OF SAN JUAN (O, 32 beds) University Hospital, 3rd Floor, San Juan, PR Zip 923, Mailing Address: P.O. Box 70344, Zip 923; tel. 787/274–5100; Daniel Del Castillo, Chief Executive Officer
**Web address:** www.healthsouthsanjuan.com

**SOUTH CAROLINA:** ANMED HEALTH REHABILITATION HOSPITAL (O, 55 beds) 1 Spring Back Way, Anderson, SC Zip 29621–2676; tel. 864/716–2600; Michele M. Skripps, R.N., Chief Executive Officer
**Web address:** www.anmedrehab.com

HEALTHSOUTH REHABILITATION HOSPITAL OF CHARLESTON (O, 49 beds) 9181 Medcom Street, Charleston, SC Zip 29406–9168; tel. 843/820–7777; Troy Powell, Chief Executive Officer
**Web address:** www.healthsouthcharleston.com

HEALTHSOUTH REHABILITATION HOSPITAL OF COLUMBIA (O, 96 beds) 2935 Colonial Drive, Columbia, SC Zip 29203–6811; tel. 803/254–7777; W. Anthony Jackson, Chief Executive Officer
**Web address:** www.healthsouthcolumbia.com

HEALTHSOUTH REHABILITATION HOSPITAL OF FLORENCE (O, 88 beds) 900 East Cheves Street, Florence, SC Zip 29506–2704; tel. 843/679–9000; Jill Strawn, Chief Executive Officer
**Web address:** www.healthsouthflorence.com

HEALTHSOUTH REHABILITATION HOSPITAL OF ROCK HILL (O, 50 beds) 1795 Dr. Frank Gaston Boulevard, Rock Hill, SC Zip 29732–1190; tel. 803/326–3500; Deanna Martin, Chief Executive Officer
**Web address:** www.healthsouthrockhill.com

**TENNESSEE:** HEALTHSOUTH CANE CREEK REHABILITATION HOSPITAL (O, 40 beds) 180 Mount Pelia Road, Martin, TN Zip 38237–3812; tel. 731/587–4231; Amy Vieth, Chief Executive Officer
**Web address:** www.healthsouthcanecreek.com

HEALTHSOUTH CHATTANOOGA REHABILITATION HOSPITAL (O, 69 beds) 2412 McCallie Avenue, Chattanooga, TN Zip 37404–3398; tel. 423/698–0221; Scott Rowe, Chief Executive Officer
**Web address:** www.healthsouthchattanooga.com

HEALTHSOUTH REHABILITATION HOSPITAL (O, 50 beds) 113 Cassel Drive, Kingsport, TN Zip 37660–3775; tel. 423/246–7240; Troy Clark, Chief Executive Officer
**Web address:** www.healthsouthkingsport.com

HEALTHSOUTH REHABILITATION HOSPITAL MEMPHIS–NORTH (O, 40 beds) 4100 Austin Peay Highway, Memphis, TN Zip 38128–2502; tel. 901/213–5400; Marcia Taylor, Chief Executive Officer
**Web address:** www.healthsouthnorthmemphis.com

HEALTHSOUTH REHABILITATION HOSPITAL OF MEMPHIS (O, 72 beds) 1282 Union Avenue, Memphis, TN Zip 38104–3414; tel. 901/722–2000; Kevin Spears, Chief Executive Officer
**Web address:** www.healthsouthmemphis.com

QUILLEN REHABILITATION HOSPITAL (O, 60 beds) 2511 Wesley Street, Johnson City, TN Zip 37601–1723; tel. 423/283–0700; Brian Luff, Chief Executive Officer
**Web address:** www.quillenrehabilitationhospital.com/

VANDERBILT STALLWORTH REHABILITATION HOSPITAL (O, 80 beds) 2201 Childrens Way, Nashville, TN Zip 37212–3165; tel. 615/320–7600; Scott J. Peterson, Acting Chief Executive Officer
**Web address:** www.vanderbiltstallworthrehab.com

**TEXAS:** HEALTHSOUTH CITY VIEW REHABILITATION HOSPITAL (O, 62 beds) 6701 Oakmont Boulevard, Fort Worth, TX Zip 76132–2957; tel. 817/370–4700; Trent Pierce, R.N., Chief Executive Officer
**Web address:** www.healthsouthcityview.com

HEALTHSOUTH PLANO REHABILITATION HOSPITAL (O, 83 beds) 2800 West 15th Street, Plano, TX Zip 75075–7526; tel. 972/612–9000; Jennifer Lynn Brewer, Chief Executive Officer
**Web address:** www.healthsouthplano.com

HEALTHSOUTH REHABILITATION HOSPITAL MIDLAND–ODESSA (O, 60 beds) 1800 Heritage Boulevard, Midland, TX Zip 79707–9750; tel. 432/520–1600; Christopher Wortham, Chief Executive Officer
**Web address:** www.healthsouthmidland.com

HEALTHSOUTH REHABILITATION HOSPITAL OF ARLINGTON (O, 85 beds) 3200 Matlock Road, Arlington, TX Zip 76015–2911; tel. 817/468–4000; Sheryl Appel, Chief Executive Officer
**Web address:** www.healthsoutharlington.com

HEALTHSOUTH REHABILITATION HOSPITAL OF AUSTIN (O, 40 beds) 1215 Red River Street, Austin, TX Zip 78701–1921; tel. 512/474–5700; Sandra Hegland, Chief Executive Officer
**Web address:** www.healthsouthaustin.com

HEALTHSOUTH REHABILITATION HOSPITAL OF BEAUMONT (O, 61 beds) 3340 Plaza 10 Boulevard, Beaumont, TX Zip 77707–2551; tel. 409/835–0835; H. J. Gaspard, Chief Executive Officer
**Web address:** www.healthsouthbeaumont.com

HEALTHSOUTH REHABILITATION HOSPITAL OF CYPRESS (O, 60 beds) 13031 Wortham Center Drive, Houston, TX Zip 77065–5662; tel. 832/280–2500; Sheila A. Bollier, Chief Executive Officer
**Web address:** www.healthsouthcypress.com

HEALTHSOUTH REHABILITATION HOSPITAL OF FORT WORTH (O, 60 beds) 1212 West Lancaster Avenue, Fort Worth, TX Zip 76102–4510; tel. 817/870–2336; Trent Pierce, R.N., Chief Executive Officer
**Web address:** www.healthsouthfortworth.com

HEALTHSOUTH REHABILITATION HOSPITAL OF HUMBLE, LLC (O, 60 beds) 19002 McKay Drive, Humble, TX Zip 77338–5701; tel. 281/446–6148; Angela L. Simmons, Chief Executive Officer
**Web address:** www.healthsouthhumble.com

HEALTHSOUTH REHABILITATION HOSPITAL OF TEXARKANA (O, 60 beds) 515 West 12th Street, Texarkana, TX Zip 75501–4416; tel. 903/735–5000; Harlo McCall, Chief Executive Officer
**Web address:** www.healthsouthtexarkana.com

HEALTHSOUTH REHABILITATION HOSPITAL THE WOODLANDS (O, 84 beds) 18550 'IH' 45 South, Conroe, TX Zip 77384; tel. 281/364–2000; Krista Uselman, Chief Executive Officer
**Web address:** www.healthssouththewoodlands.com

HEALTHSOUTH REHABILITATION HOSPITAL–WICHITA FALLS (O, 63 beds) 3901 Armory Road, Wichita Falls, TX Zip 76302–2204; tel. 940/720–5700; Michael L. Bullitt, Chief Executive Officer
**Web address:** www.healthsouthwichitafalls.com

HEALTHSOUTH REHABILITATION INSTITUTE OF SAN ANTONIO (O, 96 beds) 9119 Cinnamon Hill, San Antonio, TX Zip 78240–5401; tel. 210/691–0737; Scott Butcher, Chief Executive Officer
**Web address:** www.hsriosa.com

HEALTHSOUTH SUGAR LAND REHABILITATION HOSPITAL (O, 50 beds) 1325 Highway 6, Sugar Land, TX Zip 77478–4906; tel. 281/276–7574; Nicholas Hardin, Chief Executive Officer
**Web address:** www.healthsouthsugarland.com

TRINITY MOTHER FRANCES REHABILITATION HOSPITAL (O, 74 beds) 3131 Troup Highway, Tyler, TX Zip 75701–8352; tel. 903/510–7000; Sharla Anderson, Chief Executive Officer
**Web address:** www.tmfrehabhospital.com

**UTAH:** HEALTHSOUTH REHABILITATION HOSPITAL OF UTAH (O, 105 beds) 8074 South 1300 East, Sandy, UT Zip 84094–0743; tel. 801/561–3400; Jeff Frandsen, Chief Executive Officer
**Web address:** www.healthsouthutah.com

**VIRGINIA:** HEALTHSOUTH REHABILITATION HOSPITAL OF FREDERICKSBURG (O, 40 beds) 300 Park Hill Drive, Fredericksburg, VA Zip 22401–3387; tel. 540/368–7300; Gary J. Herbek, Chief Executive Officer
**Web address:** www.fredericksburgrehabhospital.com

HEALTHSOUTH REHABILITATION HOSPITAL OF NORTHERN VIRGINIA (O, 40 beds) 24430 Millstream Drive, Aldie, VA Zip 20105–3098; tel. 703/957–2000; Jason Waibel, Interim Chief Executive Officer
**Web address:** www.healthsouthnorthernvirginia.com

HEALTHSOUTH REHABILITATION HOSPITAL OF PETERSBURG (O, 53 beds) 95 Medical Park Boulevard, Petersburg, VA Zip 23805–9233; tel. 804/504–8100; Tracy Penn Turman, Chief Executive Officer
**Web address:** www.healthsouthpetersburg.com

HEALTHSOUTH REHABILITATION HOSPITAL OF VIRGINIA (O, 40 beds) 5700 Fitzhugh Avenue, Richmond, VA Zip 23226–1800; tel. 804/288–5700; David Cashwell, Chief Executive Officer
**Web address:** www.healthsouthrichmond.com

REHABILITATION HOSPITAL OF SOUTHWEST VIRGINIA (O, 25 beds) 103 North Street, Bristol, VA Zip 24201–3201; tel. 276/642–7900; Georgeanne Cole, Chief Executive Officer
**Web address:** www.rehabilitationhospitalswvirginia.com

Section B

For explanation of codes following names, see page B2.
★ Indicates Type III membership in the American Hospital Association.

UVA–HEALTHSOUTH REHABILITATION HOSPITAL (O, 50 beds) 515 Ray C. Hunt Drive, Charlottesville, VA Zip 22903–2981; tel. 434/244–2000; Thomas J. Cook, Chief Executive Officer
**Web address:** www.uvahealthsouth.com

**WEST VIRGINIA:** HEALTHSOUTH HUNTINGTON REHABILITATION HOSPITAL (O, 50 beds) 6900 West Country Club Drive, Huntington, WV Zip 25705–2000; tel. 304/733–1060; Michael E. Zuliani, Chief Executive Officer
**Web address:** www.healthsouthhuntington.com

HEALTHSOUTH MOUNTAINVIEW REGIONAL REHABILITATION HOSPITAL (O, 96 beds) 1160 Van Voorhis Road, Morgantown, WV Zip 26505–3437; tel. 304/598–1100; Lou Little, Chief Executive Officer
**Web address:** www.healthsouthmountainview.com

HEALTHSOUTH SOUTHERN HILLS REHABILITATION HOSPITAL (O, 45 beds) 120 Twelfth Street, Princeton, WV Zip 24740–2352; tel. 304/487–8000; Robert Williams, R.N., Chief Executive Officer
**Web address:** www.healthsouthsouthernhills.com

HEALTHSOUTH WESTERN HILLS REGIONAL REHABILITATION HOSPITAL (O, 40 beds) 3 Western Hills Drive, Parkersburg, WV Zip 26105–8122; tel. 304/420–1300; Alvin R. Lawson, JD, FACHE, Chief Executive Officer
**Web address:** www.healthsouthwesternhills.com

| Owned, leased, sponsored: | 106 hospitals | 6985 beds |
|---|---|---|
| Contract–managed: | 0 hospitals | 0 beds |
| Totals: | 106 hospitals | 6985 beds |

★**0585:  HEALTHTECH MANAGEMENT SERVICES** (IO)
5110 Maryland Way Suite 200, Brentwood, TN Zip 37027–2307; tel. 615/309–6053; Derek Morkel, Chief Executive Officer
**(Decentralized Health System)**

**ARIZONA:** COBRE VALLEY REGIONAL MEDICAL CENTER (C, 25 beds) 5880 South Hospital Drive, Globe, AZ Zip 85501–9454; tel. 928/425–3261; Neal Jensen, Chief Executive Officer
**Web address:** www.cvrmc.org

**GEORGIA:** UPSON REGIONAL MEDICAL CENTER (C, 77 beds) 801 West Gordon Street, Thomaston, GA Zip 30286–3426, Mailing Address: P.O. Box 1059, Zip 30286–0027; tel. 706/647–8111; David L. Castleberry, FACHE, Chief Executive Officer
**Web address:** www.urmc.org

**ILLINOIS:** CARLINVILLE AREA HOSPITAL (C, 25 beds) 20733 North Broad Street, Carlinville, IL Zip 62626–1499; tel. 217/854–3141; Kenneth G. Reid, President and Chief Executive Officer
**Web address:** www.cahcare.com

HAMMOND–HENRY HOSPITAL (C, 61 beds) 600 North College Avenue, Geneseo, IL Zip 61254–1099; tel. 309/944–4625; Florence Spyrow, Interim Chief Executive Officer
**Web address:** www.hammondhenry.com

HILLSBORO AREA HOSPITAL (C, 25 beds) 1200 East Tremont Street, Hillsboro, IL Zip 62049–1900; tel. 217/532–6111; Rex H. Brown, President and Chief Executive Officer
**Web address:** www.hillsborohealth.org

**LOUISIANA:** IBERIA MEDICAL CENTER (C, 84 beds) 2315 East Main Street, New Iberia, LA Zip 70560–4031, Mailing Address: P.O. Box 13338, Zip 70562–3338; tel. 337/364–0441; Parker A. Templeton, FACHE, Chief Executive Officer
**Web address:** www.iberiamedicalcenter.com

**MONTANA:** BARRETT HOSPITAL & HEALTHCARE (C, 18 beds) 600 State Highway 91 South, Dillon, MT Zip 59725–7379; tel. 406/683–3000; Ken Westman, Chief Executive Officer
**Web address:** www.barretthospital.org

**NEBRASKA:** TRI VALLEY HEALTH SYSTEM (C, 48 beds) 1305 West Highway 6 and 34, Cambridge, NE Zip 69022–0488, Mailing Address: P.O. Box 488, Zip 69022–0488; tel. 308/697–3329; Deborah L. Herzberg, R.N., MS, FACHE, Chief Executive Officer
**Web address:** www.trivalleyhealth.com

**NEW YORK:** ADIRONDACK MEDICAL CENTER (C, 200 beds) 2233 State Route 86, Saranac Lake, NY Zip 12983–5644, Mailing Address: P.O. Box 471, Zip 12983–0471; tel. 518/891–4141; Chandler M. Ralph, President and Chief Executive Officer
**Web address:** www.adirondackhealth.org

**OREGON:** BLUE MOUNTAIN HOSPITAL (C, 45 beds) 170 Ford Road, John Day, OR Zip 97845–2009; tel. 541/575–1311; Randall L. Mee, FACHE, Chief Executive Officer
**Web address:** www.bluemountainhospital.org

**WASHINGTON:** SUNNYSIDE COMMUNITY HOSPITAL AND CLINICS (C, 25 beds) 1016 Tacoma Avenue, Sunnyside, WA Zip 98944–2263, Mailing Address: P.O. Box 719, Zip 98944–0719; tel. 509/837–1500; John Gallagher, Chief Executive Officer
**Web address:** www.sunnysidehospital.com

**WISCONSIN:** GRANT REGIONAL HEALTH CENTER (C, 9 beds) 507 South Monroe Street, Lancaster, WI Zip 53813–2054; tel. 608/723–2143; Nicole Clapp, R.N., MSN, FACHE, President and Chief Executive Officer
**Web address:** www.grantregional.com

SPOONER HEALTH SYSTEM (C, 25 beds) 819 Ash Street, Spooner, WI Zip 54801–1299; tel. 715/635–2111; Michael Schafer, Chief Executive Officer and Administrator
**Web address:** www.spoonerhealthsystem.com

TOMAH MEMORIAL HOSPITAL (C, 25 beds) 321 Butts Avenue, Tomah, WI Zip 54660–1412; tel. 608/372–2181; Philip J. Stuart, Administrator and Chief Executive Officer
**Web address:** www.tomahhospital.org

**WYOMING:** HOT SPRINGS COUNTY MEMORIAL HOSPITAL (C, 25 beds) 150 East Arapahoe Street, Thermopolis, WY Zip 82443–2498; tel. 307/864–3121; Robin Roling, Chief Executive Officer
**Web address:** www.hscmh.org

POWELL VALLEY HEALTHCARE (C, 125 beds) 777 Avenue H, Powell, WY Zip 82435–2296; tel. 307/754–2267; Terry Odom, Chief Executive Officer
**Web address:** www.pvhc.org

| Owned, leased, sponsored: | 0 hospitals | 0 beds |
|---|---|---|
| Contract–managed: | 16 hospitals | 842 beds |
| Totals: | 16 hospitals | 842 beds |

★**9505:  HENRY FORD HEALTH SYSTEM** (NP)
One Ford Place, Detroit, MI Zip 48202–3450; tel. 313/876–8708; Nancy M. Schlichting, Chief Executive Officer
**(Centralized Health System)**

**MICHIGAN:** HENRY FORD HOSPITAL (O, 673 beds) 2799 West Grand Boulevard, Detroit, MI Zip 48202–2608; tel. 313/916–2600; John Popovich, M.D., President and Chief Executive Officer
**Web address:** www.henryfordhealth.org

HENRY FORD KINGSWOOD HOSPITAL (O, 80 beds) 10300 West Eight Mile Road, Ferndale, MI Zip 48220–2100; tel. 248/398–3200; DoreeAnn V. Espiritu, M.D., Interim Chair, Behavioral Health Services
**Web address:** www.henryford.com

HENRY FORD MACOMB HOSPITALS (O, 420 beds) 15855 19 Mile Road, Clinton Township, MI Zip 48038–6324; tel. 586/263–2300; Barbara Rossmann, R.N., President and Chief Executive Officer
**Web address:** www.henryfordmacomb.com

HENRY FORD WEST BLOOMFIELD HOSPITAL (O, 191 beds) 6777 West Maple Road, West Bloomfield, MI Zip 48322–3013; tel. 248/661–4100; Lynn M. Torossian, President and Chief Executive Officer
**Web address:** www.henryford.com

HENRY FORD WYANDOTTE HOSPITAL (O, 353 beds) 2333 Biddle Avenue, Wyandotte, MI Zip 48192–4668; tel. 734/246–6000; Denise Brooks–Williams, President and Chief Executive Officer
**Web address:** www.henryfordhealth.org

| Owned, leased, sponsored: | 5 hospitals | 1717 beds |
|---|---|---|
| Contract–managed: | 0 hospitals | 0 beds |
| Totals: | 5 hospitals | 1717 beds |

**0309:  HERITAGE VALLEY HEALTH SYSTEM** (NP)
1000 Dutch Ridge Road, Beaver, PA Zip 15009–9727; tel. 724/773–2024; Norman F. Mitry, President and Chief Executive Officer
**(Independent Hospital System)**

For explanation of codes following names, see page B2.
★ Indicates Type III membership in the American Hospital Association.

**PENNSYLVANIA:** HERITAGE VALLEY HEALTH SYSTEM (O, 273 beds) 1000 Dutch Ridge Road, Beaver, PA Zip 15009–9727; tel. 724/728–7000; Norman F. Mitry, President and Chief Executive Officer
**Web address:** www.heritagevalley.org

SEWICKLEY VALLEY HOSPITAL, (A DIVISION OF VALLEY MEDICAL FACILITIES) (O, 179 beds) 720 Blackburn Road, Sewickley, PA Zip 15143–1459; tel. 412/741–6600; Norman F. Mitry, President and Chief Executive Officer
**Web address:** www.heritagevalley.org

| | | |
|---|---|---|
| Owned, leased, sponsored: | 2 hospitals | 452 beds |
| Contract–managed: | 0 hospitals | 0 beds |
| Totals: | 2 hospitals | 452 beds |

★**0963:**   **HONORHEALTH** (IO)
8125 North Hayden Road, Scottsdale, AZ Zip 85258–2463; tel. 623/580–5800; Thomas J. Sadvary, FACHE, Chief Executive Officer

**ARIZONA:** HONORHEALTH DEER VALLEY MEDICAL CENTER (O, 204 beds) 19829 North 27th Avenue, Phoenix, AZ Zip 85027–4002; tel. 623/879–6100; John L. Harrington, Jr., FACHE, Chief Executive Officer
**Web address:** www.jcl.com

HONORHEALTH JOHN C. LINCOLN MEDICAL CENTER (O, 262 beds) 250 East Dunlap Avenue, Phoenix, AZ Zip 85020–2825; tel. 602/943–2381; Margaret Elizabeth Griffin, Chief Executive Officer
**Web address:** www.jcl.com

HONORHEALTH SCOTTSDALE OSBORN MEDICAL CENTER (O, 347 beds) 7400 East Osborn Road, Scottsdale, AZ Zip 85251–6403; tel. 480/882–4000; Bruce Pearson, Senior Vice President and Chief Executive Officer
**Web address:** www.shc.org

HONORHEALTH SCOTTSDALE SHEA MEDICAL CENTER (O, 409 beds) 9003 East Shea Boulevard, Scottsdale, AZ Zip 85260–6771; tel. 480/323–3000; Gary E. Baker, Senior Vice President and Chief Executive Officer
**Web address:** www.shc.org

HONORHEALTH SCOTTSDALE THOMPSON PEAK MEDICAL CENTER (O, 64 beds) 7400 East Thompson Peak Parkway, Scottsdale, AZ Zip 85255–4109; tel. 480/324–7000; Kimberly Post, R.N., Vice President and Administrator
**Web address:** www.shc.org

| | | |
|---|---|---|
| Owned, leased, sponsored: | 5 hospitals | 1286 beds |
| Contract–managed: | 0 hospitals | 0 beds |
| Totals: | 5 hospitals | 1286 beds |

★**5355:**   **HOSPITAL SISTERS HEALTH SYSTEM** (CC)
4936 LaVerna Road, Springfield, IL Zip 62707–9797, Mailing Address: P.O. Box 19456, Zip 62794–9456; tel. 217/523–4747; Mary Starmann–Harrison, FACHE, President and Chief Executive Officer
**(Moderately Centralized Health System)**

**ILLINOIS:** HSHS ST. ANTHONY'S MEMORIAL HOSPITAL (O, 133 beds) 503 North Maple Street, Effingham, IL Zip 62401–2099; tel. 217/342–2121; Theresa Rutherford, R.N., MS, FACHE, President and Chief Executive Officer
**Web address:** www.stanthonyshospital.org

HSHS ST. ELIZABETH'S HOSPITAL (O, 260 beds) 211 South Third Street, Belleville, IL Zip 62220–1998; tel. 618/234–2120; Shelley Harris, MSN, R.N., Interim Chief Executive Officer
**Web address:** www.steliz.org

HSHS ST. FRANCIS HOSPITAL (O, 25 beds) 1215 Franciscan Drive, Litchfield, IL Zip 62056–1799, Mailing Address: P.O. Box 1215, Zip 62056–0999; tel. 217/324–2191; Patricia Fischer, President and Chief Executive Officer
**Web address:** www.stfrancis–litchfield.org

HSHS ST. JOSEPH'S HOSPITAL (O, 49 beds) 9515 Holy Cross Lane, Breese, IL Zip 62230–3618, Mailing Address: PO Box 99, Zip 62230–0099; tel. 618/526–4511; Paulette Evans, R.N., MSN, President and Chief Executive Officer
**Web address:** www.stjoebreese.com

HSHS ST. JOSEPH'S HOSPITAL (O, 25 beds) 12866 Troxler Avenue, Highland, IL Zip 62249–1698; tel. 618/654–7421; Peggy A. Sebastian, MSN, R.N., President and Chief Executive Officer
**Web address:** www.stjosephshighland.com

HSHS ST. MARY'S HOSPITAL (O, 244 beds) 1800 East Lake Shore Drive, Decatur, IL Zip 62521–3883; tel. 217/464–2966; Daniel L. Perryman, President and Chief Executive Officer
**Web address:** www.stmarysdecatur.com

HSHS ST. MARY'S HOSPITAL (O, 68 beds) 111 Spring Street, Streator, IL Zip 61364–3399; tel. 815/673–2311; John T. Flanders, MS, R.N., President and Chief Executive Officer
**Web address:** www.stmaryshospital.org

ST. JOHN'S HOSPITAL (O, 431 beds) 800 East Carpenter Street, Springfield, IL Zip 62769–0002; tel. 217/544–6464; Charles Lucore, M.D., President and Chief Executive Officer
**Web address:** www.st–johns.org

**WISCONSIN:** HSHS ST. JOSEPH'S HOSPITAL (O, 102 beds) 2661 County Highway I., Chippewa Falls, WI Zip 54729–5407; tel. 715/723–1811; Joan M. Coffman, President and Chief Executive Officer
**Web address:** www.stjoeschipfalls.com

SACRED HEART HOSPITAL (O, 216 beds) 900 West Clairemont Avenue, Eau Claire, WI Zip 54701–6122; tel. 715/717–4121; Julie Manas, President and Chief Executive Officer
**Web address:** www.sacredhearteauclaire.org

ST. MARY'S HOSPITAL MEDICAL CENTER (O, 83 beds) 1726 Shawano Avenue, Green Bay, WI Zip 54303–3282; tel. 920/498–4200; Therese B. Pandl, President and Chief Executive Officer
**Web address:** www.stmgb.org

ST. NICHOLAS HOSPITAL (O, 53 beds) 3100 Superior Avenue, Sheboygan, WI Zip 53081–1948; tel. 920/459–8300; Andrew Bagnall, President and Chief Executive Officer
**Web address:** www.stnicholashospital.org

ST. VINCENT HOSPITAL (O, 255 beds) 835 South Van Buren Street, Green Bay, WI Zip 54301–3526, Mailing Address: P.O. Box 13508, Zip 54307–3508; tel. 920/433–0111; Therese B. Pandl, President and Chief Executive Officer
**Web address:** www.stvincenthospital.org

| | | |
|---|---|---|
| Owned, leased, sponsored: | 13 hospitals | 1944 beds |
| Contract–managed: | 0 hospitals | 0 beds |
| Totals: | 13 hospitals | 1944 beds |

★**0642:**   **HOUSTON HEALTHCARE SYSTEM** (NP)
1601 Watson Boulevard, Warner Robins, GA Zip 31093–3431, Mailing Address: P.O. Box 2886, Zip 31099–2886; tel. 478/922–4281; Cary Martin, Chief Executive Officer
**(Independent Hospital System)**

**GEORGIA:** HOUSTON MEDICAL CENTER (O, 237 beds) 1601 Watson Boulevard, Warner Robins, GA Zip 31093–3431, Mailing Address: P.O. Box 2886, Zip 31099–2886; tel. 478/922–4281; Cary Martin, Chief Executive Officer
**Web address:** www.hhc.org

PERRY HOSPITAL (O, 39 beds) 1120 Morningside Drive, Perry, GA Zip 31069–2906; tel. 478/987–3600; David Campbell, Administrator
**Web address:** www.hhc.org

| | | |
|---|---|---|
| Owned, leased, sponsored: | 2 hospitals | 276 beds |
| Contract–managed: | 0 hospitals | 0 beds |
| Totals: | 2 hospitals | 276 beds |

★**7235:**   **HOUSTON METHODIST** (CO)
6565 Fannin Street, D–200, Houston, TX Zip 77030–2707; tel. 713/441–2221; Marc L. Boom, M.D., Chief Executive Officer
**(Moderately Centralized Health System)**

**TEXAS:** HOUSTON METHODIST HOSPITAL (O, 856 beds) 6565 Fannin Street, Houston, TX Zip 77030–2707; tel. 713/790–3311; Roberta Schwartz, Executive Vice President
**Web address:** www.methodisthealth.com

For explanation of codes following names, see page B2.
★ Indicates Type III membership in the American Hospital Association.

Section B

HOUSTON METHODIST SAN JACINTO HOSPITAL (O, 275 beds) 4401 Garth Road, Baytown, TX Zip 77521–2122; tel. 281/420–8600; David P. Bernard, Administrator
**Web address:** www.houstonmethodist.org

HOUSTON METHODIST ST. CATHERINE HOSPITAL (O, 30 beds) 701 Fry Road, Katy, TX Zip 77450–2255; tel. 281/599–5700; Gary L. Kempf, R.N., Administrator
**Web address:** www.houstonmethodist.org/katy–st–catherine–hospital

HOUSTON METHODIST ST. JOHN HOSPITAL (O, 137 beds) 18300 St. John Drive, Nassau Bay, TX Zip 77058–6302; tel. 281/333–5503; Dan Newman, Chief Executive Officer
**Web address:** www.houstonmethodist.org/st–john–clear–lake

HOUSTON METHODIST SUGAR LAND HOSPITAL (O, 243 beds) 16655 S.W. Freeway, Sugar Land, TX Zip 77479–2329; tel. 281/274–7000; Christopher Siebenaler, Chief Executive Officer
**Web address:** www.methodisthealth.com

HOUSTON METHODIST WEST HOSPITAL (O, 176 beds) 18500 Katy Freeway, Houston, TX Zip 77094–1110; tel. 832/522–1000; Wayne M. Voss, Chief Executive Officer
**Web address:** www.methodisthealth.com

HOUSTON METHODIST WILLOWBROOK HOSPITAL (O, 261 beds) 18220 Tomball Parkway, Houston, TX Zip 77070–4347; tel. 281/477–1000; Debbie Sakin, PhD, Interim Chief Executive Officer
**Web address:** www.methodisthealth.com

| Owned, leased, sponsored: | 7 hospitals | 1978 beds |
| Contract–managed: | 0 hospitals | 0 beds |
| **Totals:** | 7 hospitals | 1978 beds |

**0907: HUNT REGIONAL HEALTHCARE** (NP)
4215 Joe Ramsey Boulevard, Greenville, TX Zip 75401–7852, Mailing Address: P.O. Box 1059, Zip 75403–1059; tel. 903/408–5000; Richard Carter, Chief Executive Officer
**(Independent Hospital System)**

HUNT REGIONAL COMMUNITY HOSPITAL (O, 15 beds) 2900 Sterling Hart Drive, Commerce, TX Zip 75428–3912; tel. 903/886–3161; Michael R. Klepin, Associate Administrator
**Web address:** www.huntregional.org

HUNT REGIONAL MEDICAL CENTER (O, 225 beds) 4215 Joe Ramsey Boulevard, Greenville, TX Zip 75401–7899, Mailing Address: P.O. Box 1059, Zip 75403–1059; tel. 903/408–5000; Richard Carter, District Chief Executive Officer
**Web address:** www.huntregional.org

| Owned, leased, sponsored: | 2 hospitals | 240 beds |
| Contract–managed: | 0 hospitals | 0 beds |
| **Totals:** | 2 hospitals | 240 beds |

**0117: HUNTSVILLE HOSPITAL HEALTH SYSTEM** (NP)
101 Sivley Road S.W., Huntsville, AL Zip 35801–4421; tel. 265/256–1000; David S. Spillers, Chief Executive Officer
**(Moderately Centralized Health System)**

**ALABAMA:** ATHENS–LIMESTONE HOSPITAL (C, 101 beds) 700 West Market Street, Athens, AL Zip 35611–2457, Mailing Address: P.O. Box 999, Zip 35612–0999; tel. 256/233–9292; David Pryor, President
**Web address:** www.athenslimestonehospital.com

DECATUR MORGAN HOSPITAL (O, 132 beds) 1201 Seventh Street S.E., Decatur, AL Zip 35601–3303, Mailing Address: P.O. Box 2239, Zip 35609–2239; tel. 256/341–2000; Nathaniel Richardson, Jr., President
**Web address:** www.decaturgeneral.org

HELEN KELLER HOSPITAL (C, 145 beds) 1300 South Montgomery Avenue, Sheffield, AL Zip 35660–6334, Mailing Address: P.O. Box 610, Zip 35660–0610; tel. 256/386–4196; Paul Storey, FACHE, President and Chief Executive Officer
**Web address:** www.helenkeller.com

HUNTSVILLE HOSPITAL (O, 877 beds) 101 Sivley Road S.W., Huntsville, AL Zip 35801–4470; tel. 256/265–1000; David S. Spillers, Chief Executive Officer
**Web address:** www.huntsvillehospital.org

LAWRENCE MEDICAL CENTER (C, 43 beds) 202 Hospital Street, Moulton, AL Zip 35650–1218, Mailing Address: P.O. Box 39, Zip 35650–0039; tel. 256/974–2200; Kyle Buchanan, Chief Executive Officer
**Web address:** www.lawrencemedicalcenter.com

RED BAY HOSPITAL (C, 25 beds) 211 Hospital Road, Red Bay, AL Zip 35582–3858, Mailing Address: P.O. Box 490, Zip 35582–0490; tel. 256/356–9532; Glen M. Jones, FACHE, Administrator
**Web address:** www.redbayhospital.com

| Owned, leased, sponsored: | 2 hospitals | 1009 beds |
| Contract–managed: | 4 hospitals | 314 beds |
| **Totals:** | 6 hospitals | 1323 beds |

**0201: IASIS HEALTHCARE** (IO)
117 Seaboard Lane, Building E., Franklin, TN Zip 37067–2855; tel. 615/844–2747; Carl Whitmer, President and Chief Executive Officer
**(Moderately Centralized Health System)**

**ARIZONA:** MOUNTAIN VISTA MEDICAL CENTER (O, 172 beds) 1301 South Crismon Road, Mesa, AZ Zip 85209–3767; tel. 480/358–6100; Anthony Marinello, Chief Executive Officer
**Web address:** www.mvmedicalcenter.com

ST. LUKE'S BEHAVIORAL HEALTH CENTER (O, 85 beds) 1800 East Van Buren, Phoenix, AZ Zip 85006–3742; tel. 602/251–8546; Gregory L. Jahn, R.N., Chief Executive Officer
**Web address:** www.iasishealthcare.com

ST. LUKE'S MEDICAL CENTER (O, 284 beds) 1800 East Van Buren Street, Phoenix, AZ Zip 85006–3742; tel. 602/251–8100; Christopher Hill, Chief Executive Officer
**Web address:** www.stlukesmedcenter.com

**ARKANSAS:** WADLEY REGIONAL MEDICAL CENTER AT HOPE (O, 79 beds) 2001 South Main Street, Hope, AR Zip 71801–8194; tel. 870/722–3800; Thomas D. Gilbert, FACHE, Chief Executive Officer
**Web address:** www.wadleyhealthathope.com

**COLORADO:** PIKES PEAK REGIONAL HOSPITAL (O, 15 beds) 16420 West Highway 24, Woodland Park, CO Zip 80863; tel. 719/687–9999; Terry Buckner, Chief Executive Officer
**Web address:** www.pprmc.org

**LOUISIANA:** GLENWOOD REGIONAL MEDICAL CENTER (O, 268 beds) 503 McMillan Road, West Monroe, LA Zip 71291–5327; tel. 318/329–4200; Matthew S. Roberts, Chief Executive Officer
**Web address:** www.grmc.com

OUACHITA COMMUNITY HOSPITAL (O, 10 beds) 1275 Glenwood Drive, West Monroe, LA Zip 71291–5539; tel. 318/322–1339; Robert L. Colvin, Administrator
**Web address:** www.ouachitacommunityhospital.com

**NEVADA:** NORTH VISTA HOSPITAL (O, 198 beds) 1409 East Lake Mead Boulevard, North Las Vegas, NV Zip 89030–7197; tel. 702/649–7711; Vincenzo Variale, Chief Executive Officer
**Web address:** www.northvistahospital.com

**TEXAS:** ODESSA REGIONAL MEDICAL CENTER (O, 213 beds) 520 East Sixth Street, Odessa, TX Zip 79761–4565, Mailing Address: P.O. Box 4859, Zip 79760–4859; tel. 432/582–8000; Stacey L. Gerig, Chief Executive Officer
**Web address:** www.odessaregionalmedicalcenter.com

SOUTHWEST GENERAL HOSPITAL (O, 253 beds) 7400 Barlite Boulevard, San Antonio, TX Zip 78224–1399; tel. 210/921–2000; P. Craig Desmond, Chief Executive Officer
**Web address:** www.swgeneralhospital.com

ST. JOSEPH MEDICAL CENTER (O, 374 beds) 1401 St. Joseph Parkway, Houston, TX Zip 77002–8301; tel. 713/757–1000; Mark L. Bernard, Chief Executive Officer
**Web address:** www.sjmctx.com

THE MEDICAL CENTER OF SOUTHEAST TEXAS (O, 185 beds) 2555 Jimmy Johnson Boulevard, Port Arthur, TX Zip 77640–2007; tel. 409/724–7389; Richard Gonzalez, Chief Executive Officer
**Web address:** www.medicalcentersetexas.com

For explanation of codes following names, see page B2.
★ Indicates Type III membership in the American Hospital Association.

WADLEY REGIONAL MEDICAL CENTER (O, 179 beds) 1000 Pine Street, Texarkana, TX Zip 75501–5170; tel. 903/798–8000; Thomas D. Gilbert, FACHE, Chief Executive Officer
**Web address:** www.wadleyhealth.com

**UTAH:** DAVIS HOSPITAL AND MEDICAL CENTER (O, 200 beds) 1600 West Antelope Drive, Layton, UT Zip 84041–1142; tel. 801/807–1000; Michael E. Jensen, Chief Executive Officer
**Web address:** www.davishospital.com

JORDAN VALLEY MEDICAL CENTER (O, 183 beds) 3580 West 9000 South, West Jordan, UT Zip 84088–8812; tel. 801/561–8888; Steven Anderson, Chief Executive Officer
**Web address:** www.jordanvalleymc.com

JORDAN VALLEY MEDICAL CENTER—WVC CAMPUS (O, 101 beds) 3460 South Pioneer Parkway, West Valley City, UT Zip 84120–2049; tel. 801/561–8888; Steven Anderson, Chief Executive Officer
**Web address:** www.pioneervalleyhospital.com

SALT LAKE REGIONAL MEDICAL CENTER (O, 132 beds) 1050 East South Temple, Salt Lake City, UT Zip 84102–1507; tel. 801/350–4111; Dale Johns, Chief Executive Officer
**Web address:** www.saltlakeregional.com

| | | |
|---|---|---|
| **Owned, leased, sponsored:** | 17 hospitals | 2931 beds |
| **Contract–managed:** | 0 hospitals | 0 beds |
| **Totals:** | 17 hospitals | 2931 beds |

★**0231: INDIANA UNIVERSITY HEALTH** (NP)
340 West 10th Street, Suite 6100, Indianapolis, IN Zip 46202–3082, Mailing Address: P.O. Box 1367, Zip 46206–1367; tel. 317/962–5900; Daniel F. Evans, Jr., JD, President and Chief Executive Officer
**(Moderately Centralized Health System)**

**INDIANA:** INDIANA UNIVERSITY HEALTH ARNETT HOSPITAL (O, 191 beds) 5165 McCarty Lane, Lafayette, IN Zip 47905–8764, Mailing Address: P.O. Box 5545, Zip 47903–5545; tel. 765/448–8000; Alfonso W. Gatmaitan, Chief Executive Officer
**Web address:** www.iuhealth.org

INDIANA UNIVERSITY HEALTH BALL MEMORIAL HOSPITAL (O, 322 beds) 2401 University Avenue, Muncie, IN Zip 47303–3499; tel. 765/747–3111; Michael E. Haley, President and Chief Executive Officer
**Web address:** www.iuhealth.org

INDIANA UNIVERSITY HEALTH BEDFORD HOSPITAL (O, 25 beds) 2900 West 16th Street, Bedford, IN Zip 47421–3583; tel. 812/275–1200; Bradford W. Dykes, President and Chief Executive Officer
**Web address:** www.iuhealth.com

INDIANA UNIVERSITY HEALTH BLACKFORD HOSPITAL (O, 15 beds) 410 Pilgrim Boulevard, Hartford City, IN Zip 47348–1897; tel. 765/348–0300; Steven J. West, Chief Executive Officer
**Web address:** www.iuhealth.org/blackford

INDIANA UNIVERSITY HEALTH BLOOMINGTON HOSPITAL (O, 306 beds) 601 West Second Street, Bloomington, IN Zip 47403–2317, Mailing Address: P.O. Box 1149, Zip 47402–1149; tel. 812/336–6821; Mark E. Moore, President and Chief Executive Officer
**Web address:** www.iuhealth.org

INDIANA UNIVERSITY HEALTH GOSHEN HOSPITAL (O, 122 beds) 200 High Park Avenue, Goshen, IN Zip 46526–4899, Mailing Address: P.O. Box 139, Zip 46527–0139; tel. 574/533–2141; Randal Christophel, President and Chief Executive Officer
**Web address:** www.iuhealth.org

INDIANA UNIVERSITY HEALTH LA PORTE HOSPITAL (O, 129 beds) 1007 Lincolnway, La Porte, IN Zip 46350–3201, Mailing Address: P.O. Box 250, Zip 46352–0250; tel. 219/326–1234; G. Thor Thordarson, President and Chief Executive Officer
**Web address:** www.iuhealth.org

INDIANA UNIVERSITY HEALTH NORTH HOSPITAL (O, 161 beds) 11700 North Meridian Avenue, Carmel, IN Zip 46032–4656; tel. 317/688–2000; Jonathan R. Goble, FACHE, President and Chief Executive Officer
**Web address:** www.iuhealth.org

INDIANA UNIVERSITY HEALTH PAOLI HOSPITAL (O, 24 beds) 642 West Hospital Road, Paoli, IN Zip 47454–9672, Mailing Address: P.O. Box 499, Zip 47454–0499; tel. 812/723–2811; Larry Bailey, Chief Executive Officer
**Web address:** www.iuhealth.org/paoli

INDIANA UNIVERSITY HEALTH STARKE HOSPITAL (O, 15 beds) 102 East Culver Road, Knox, IN Zip 46534–2216, Mailing Address: P.O. Box 339, Zip 46534–0339; tel. 574/772–6231; Craig Felty, Chief Executive Officer
**Web address:** www.iuhealth.org/starke/

INDIANA UNIVERSITY HEALTH TIPTON HOSPITAL (O, 25 beds) 1000 South Main Street, Tipton, IN Zip 46072–9799; tel. 765/675–8500; Michael Harlowe, President and Chief Executive Officer
**Web address:** www.iuhealth.org

INDIANA UNIVERSITY HEALTH UNIVERSITY HOSPITAL (O, 1243 beds) 550 University Boulevard, Indianapolis, IN Zip 46202–5149, Mailing Address: P.O. Box 1367, Zip 46206–1367; tel. 317/944–5000; Herbert Buchanan, President
**Web address:** www.iuhealth.org

INDIANA UNIVERSITY HEALTH WEST HOSPITAL (O, 127 beds) 1111 North Ronald Reagan Parkway, Avon, IN Zip 46123–7085; tel. 317/217–3000; Matthew D. Bailey, FACHE, President and Chief Executive Officer
**Web address:** www.iuhealth.org

INDIANA UNIVERSITY HEALTH WHITE MEMORIAL HOSPITAL (O, 25 beds) 720 South Sixth Street, Monticello, IN Zip 47960–8182; tel. 574/583–7111; Jeffrey C. Zeh, President
**Web address:** www.iuhealth.org/white–memorial

JAY COUNTY HOSPITAL (C, 35 beds) 500 West Votaw Street, Portland, IN Zip 47371–1322; tel. 260/726–7131; David W. Hyatt, Chief Executive Officer
**Web address:** www.jaycountyhospital.com

REHABILITATION HOSPITAL OF INDIANA (O, 83 beds) 4141 Shore Drive, Indianapolis, IN Zip 46254–2607; tel. 317/329–2000; Daniel B. Woloszyn, Chief Executive Officer
**Web address:** www.rhin.com

| | | |
|---|---|---|
| **Owned, leased, sponsored:** | 15 hospitals | 2813 beds |
| **Contract–managed:** | 1 hospital | 35 beds |
| **Totals:** | 16 hospitals | 2848 beds |

**2025: INFIRMARY HEALTH SYSTEM** (NP)
5 Mobile Infirmary Circle, Mobile, AL Zip 36607–3513; tel. 251/435–5500; D. Mark Nix, President and Chief Executive Officer

**ALABAMA:** INFIRMARY LONG TERM ACUTE CARE HOSPITAL (L, 38 beds) 5 Mobile Infirmary Circle, Mobile, AL Zip 36607–3513, Mailing Address: P.O. Box 2226, Zip 36652–2226; tel. 251/660–5239; Susanne Marmande, Administrator
**Web address:** www.theinfirmary.com/

MOBILE INFIRMARY MEDICAL CENTER (O, 517 beds) 5 Mobile Infirmary Drive North, Mobile, AL Zip 36607–3513, Mailing Address: P.O. Box 2144, Zip 36652–2144; tel. 251/435–2400; Jennifer Eslinger, M.D., Administrator
**Web address:** www.infirmaryhealth.org

NORTH BALDWIN INFIRMARY (L, 50 beds) 1815 Hand Avenue, Bay Minette, AL Zip 36507–4110, Mailing Address: P.O. Box 1409, Zip 36507–1409; tel. 251/937–5521; Bed K. Hansart, Administrator
**Web address:** www.mobileinfirmary.org

THOMAS HOSPITAL (L, 136 beds) 750 Morphy Avenue, Fairhope, AL Zip 36532–1812, Mailing Address: P.O. Box 929, Zip 36533–0929; tel. 251/928–2375; Ormand Thompson, Administrator
**Web address:** www.thomashospital.com

| | | |
|---|---|---|
| **Owned, leased, sponsored:** | 4 hospitals | 741 beds |
| **Contract–managed:** | 0 hospitals | 0 beds |
| **Totals:** | 4 hospitals | 741 beds |

★**1305: INOVA HEALTH SYSTEM** (NP)
8110 Gatehouse Road, Suite 200 East, Falls Church, VA Zip 22042–1252; tel. 703/289–2069; J. Knox Singleton, President and Chief Executive Officer
**(Centralized Health System)**

**VIRGINIA:** INOVA ALEXANDRIA HOSPITAL (O, 334 beds) 4320 Seminary Road, Alexandria, VA Zip 22304–1535; tel. 703/504–3167; Susan Carroll, Chief Executive Officer
**Web address:** www.inova.org

For explanation of codes following names, see page B2.
★ Indicates Type III membership in the American Hospital Association.

Section B

INOVA FAIR OAKS HOSPITAL (O, 196 beds) 3600 Joseph Siewick Drive, Fairfax, VA Zip 22033–1798; tel. 703/391–3600; John L. Fitzgerald, Chief Executive Officer
**Web address:** www.inova.org

INOVA FAIRFAX HOSPITAL (O, 926 beds) 3300 Gallows Road, Falls Church, VA Zip 22042–3300; tel. 703/776–4001; Patrick Christiansen, Ph.D., Chief Executive Officer
**Web address:** www.inova.org

INOVA LOUDOUN HOSPITAL (O, 286 beds) 44045 Riverside Parkway, Leesburg, VA Zip 20176–5101, Mailing Address: P.O. Box 6000, Zip 20177–0600; tel. 703/858–6000; Patrick Walters, Chief Executive Officer
**Web address:** www.inova.org

INOVA MOUNT VERNON HOSPITAL (O, 237 beds) 2501 Parker's Lane, Alexandria, VA Zip 22306–3209; tel. 703/664–7000; Deborah Addo–Samuels, Chief Executive Officer
**Web address:** www.inova.org

| | | |
|---|---|---|
| **Owned, leased, sponsored:** | 5 hospitals | 1979 beds |
| **Contract–managed:** | 0 hospitals | 0 beds |
| **Totals:** | 5 hospitals | 1979 beds |

---

★**0151:  INSPIRA HEALTH NETWORK** (NP)
165 Bridgeton Pike, Mullica Hill, NJ Zip 08062; tel. 856/641–8000; John A. DiAngelo, President and Chief Executive Officer
**(Moderately Centralized Health System)**

**NEW JERSEY:** INSPIRA MEDICAL CENTER–ELMER (O, 88 beds) 501 West Front Street, Elmer, NJ Zip 08318–2101; tel. 856/363–1000; John A. DiAngelo, President and Chief Executive Officer
**Web address:** www.inspirahealthnetwork.org/?id=5281&sid=1

INSPIRA MEDICAL CENTER–VINELAND (O, 335 beds) 1505 West Sherman Avenue, Vineland, NJ Zip 08360–6912; tel. 856/641–8000; John A. DiAngelo, President and Chief Executive Officer
**Web address:** www.inspirahealthnetwork.org/?id=5280&sid=1

INSPIRA MEDICAL CENTER–WOODBURY (O, 256 beds) 509 North Broad Street, Woodbury, NJ Zip 08096–1697; tel. 856/845–0100; Eileen K. Cardile, R.N., MS, Executive Vice President, Inspira Health Network and President and Chief Executive Officer, Inspira Medical Center–Woodb
**Web address:** www.inspirahealthnetwork.org/?id=5282&sid=1

| | | |
|---|---|---|
| **Owned, leased, sponsored:** | 3 hospitals | 679 beds |
| **Contract–managed:** | 0 hospitals | 0 beds |
| **Totals:** | 3 hospitals | 679 beds |

---

**0333:  INTEGRATED HEALTHCARE** (IO)
1301 North Tustin Avenue, Santa Ana, CA Zip 92705–8619; tel. 714/953–3652; Suzanne Richards, R.N., M.P.H., FACHE, Chief Executive Officer
**(Independent Hospital System)**

**CALIFORNIA:** CHAPMAN MEDICAL CENTER (O, 100 beds) 2601 East Chapman Avenue, Orange, CA Zip 92869–3296; tel. 714/633–0011; Don Kreitz, Chief Executive Officer
**Web address:** www.chapmanmedicalcenter.com

COASTAL COMMUNITIES HOSPITAL (O, 178 beds) 2701 South Bristol Street, Santa Ana, CA Zip 92704–6278; tel. 714/754–5454; Don Kreitz, Interim Chief Executive Officer
**Web address:** www.coastalcommhospital.com

ORANGE COUNTY GLOBAL MEDICAL CENTER, INC. (O, 282 beds) 1001 North Tustin Avenue, Santa Ana, CA Zip 92705–3577; tel. 714/953–3500; Suzanne Richards, R.N., M.P.H., FACHE, Chief Executive Officer
**Web address:** www.orangecounty–gmc.com

WESTERN MEDICAL CENTER ANAHEIM (O, 188 beds) 1025 South Anaheim Boulevard, Anaheim, CA Zip 92805–5806; tel. 714/533–6220; Suzanne Richards, R.N., M.P.H., FACHE, Chief Executive Officer
**Web address:** www.westernmedanaheim.com

| | | |
|---|---|---|
| **Owned, leased, sponsored:** | 4 hospitals | 748 beds |
| **Contract–managed:** | 0 hospitals | 0 beds |
| **Totals:** | 4 hospitals | 748 beds |

---

★**0305:  INTEGRIS HEALTH** (NP)
3366 N.W. Expressway, Suite 800, Oklahoma City, OK Zip 73112–9756; tel. 405/949–6066; Bruce Lawrence, President and Chief Executive Officer
**(Moderately Centralized Health System)**

**OKLAHOMA:** INTEGRIS BAPTIST MEDICAL CENTER (O, 528 beds) 3300 N.W. Expressway, Oklahoma City, OK Zip 73112–4418; tel. 405/949–3011; Timothy J. Johnsen, MS, President
**Web address:** www.integrisok.com

INTEGRIS BAPTIST REGIONAL HEALTH CENTER (O, 84 beds) 200 Second Street S.W., Miami, OK Zip 74354–6830; tel. 918/542–6611; Jordan Cash, President
**Web address:** www.integris–health.com

INTEGRIS BASS BAPTIST HEALTH CENTER (O, 167 beds) 600 South Monroe Street, Enid, OK Zip 73701–7211, Mailing Address: P.O. Box 3168, Zip 73702–3168; tel. 580/233–2300; Edward Herrman, R.N., FACHE, President
**Web address:** www.integris–health.com

INTEGRIS CANADIAN VALLEY HOSPITAL (O, 75 beds) 1201 Health Center Parkway, Yukon, OK Zip 73099–6381; tel. 405/717–6800; Rex Van Meter, President
**Web address:** www.integris–health.com

INTEGRIS GROVE HOSPITAL (O, 58 beds) 1001 East 18th Street, Grove, OK Zip 74344–2907; tel. 918/786–2243; Tim Bowen, President
**Web address:** www.integris–health.com

INTEGRIS HEALTH EDMOND (O, 40 beds) 4801 Integris Parkway, Edmond, OK Zip 73034–8864; tel. 405/657–3000; Avilla Williams, MS, President
**Web address:** www.integrisok.com/edmond

INTEGRIS SOUTHWEST MEDICAL CENTER (O, 335 beds) 4401 South Western, Oklahoma City, OK Zip 73109–3413; tel. 405/636–7000; James D. Moore, FACHE, President
**Web address:** www.integris–health.com

LAKESIDE WOMEN'S HOSPITAL (O, 23 beds) 11200 North Portland Avenue, Oklahoma City, OK Zip 73120–5045; tel. 405/936–1500; Kelley Brewer, R.N., MSN, President
**Web address:** www.lakeside–wh.net

| | | |
|---|---|---|
| **Owned, leased, sponsored:** | 8 hospitals | 1310 beds |
| **Contract–managed:** | 0 hospitals | 0 beds |
| **Totals:** | 8 hospitals | 1310 beds |

---

★**1815:  INTERMOUNTAIN HEALTHCARE, INC.** (NP)
36 South State Street, 22nd Floor, Salt Lake City, UT Zip 84111–1453; tel. 801/442–2000; Charles W. Sorenson, Jr., M.D., President and Chief Executive Officer
**(Moderately Centralized Health System)**

**IDAHO:** CASSIA REGIONAL MEDICAL CENTER (O, 25 beds) 1501 Hiland Avenue, Burley, ID Zip 83318–2688; tel. 208/678–4444; Rod Barton, Administrator
**Web address:** www.cassiaregional.org

**UTAH:** ALTA VIEW HOSPITAL (O, 69 beds) 9660 South 1300 East, Sandy, UT Zip 84094–3793; tel. 801/501–2600; Bryan L. Johnson, Administrator
**Web address:** www.intermountainhealthcare.org

AMERICAN FORK HOSPITAL (O, 90 beds) 170 North 1100 East, American Fork, UT Zip 84003–2096; tel. 801/855–3300; Michael R. Olson, Administrator
**Web address:** www.intermountainhealthcare.org

BEAR RIVER VALLEY HOSPITAL (O, 14 beds) 905 North 1000 West, Tremonton, UT Zip 84337–2497; tel. 435/207–4500; Eric Packer, Administrator
**Web address:** www.intermountainhealthcare.org/hospitals/bearriver

DELTA COMMUNITY MEDICAL CENTER (O, 18 beds) 126 South White Sage Avenue, Delta, UT Zip 84624–8937; tel. 435/864–5591; Lenny Lyons, Administrator
**Web address:** www.ihc.com

DIXIE REGIONAL MEDICAL CENTER (O, 261 beds) 1380 East Medical Center Drive, Saint George, UT Zip 84790–2123; tel. 435/251–1000; Terri Kane, Chief Executive Officer
**Web address:** www.intermountainhealthcare.org

---

For explanation of codes following names, see page B2.
★ Indicates Type III membership in the American Hospital Association.

FILLMORE COMMUNITY MEDICAL CENTER (O, 19 beds) 674 South Highway 99, Fillmore, UT Zip 84631–5013; tel. 435/743–5591; Lenny Lyons, Administrator
**Web address:** www.ihc.com

GARFIELD MEMORIAL HOSPITAL AND CLINICS (C, 41 beds) 200 North 400 East, Panguitch, UT Zip 84759, Mailing Address: P.O. Box 389, Zip 84759–0389; tel. 435/676–8811; Alberto Vasquez, Administrator
**Web address:** www.ihc.com/hospitals/garfield

HEBER VALLEY MEDICAL CENTER (O, 19 beds) 1485 South Highway 40, Heber City, UT Zip 84032–3522; tel. 435/654–2500; Shawn Morrow, Administrator
**Web address:** www.intermountainhealthcare.org

INTERMOUNTAIN MEDICAL CENTER (O, 464 beds) 5121 South Cottonwood Street, Murray, UT Zip 84107–5701; tel. 801/507–7000; David Grauer, Chief Executive Officer and Administrator
**Web address:** www.intermountainhealthcare.org

LDS HOSPITAL (O, 262 beds) Eighth Avenue and C Street, Salt Lake City, UT Zip 84143–0001; tel. 801/408–1100; Jim Sheets, Chief Executive Officer and Administrator
**Web address:** www.intermountainhealthcare.org

LOGAN REGIONAL HOSPITAL (O, 139 beds) 1400 North 500 East, Logan, UT Zip 84341–2455; tel. 435/716–1000; Kyle A. Hansen, Chief Executive Officer
**Web address:** www.loganregionalhospital.org

MCKAY–DEE HOSPITAL CENTER (O, 312 beds) 4401 Harrison Boulevard, Ogden, UT Zip 84403–3195; tel. 801/387–2800; Michael A. Clark, Administrator
**Web address:** www.mckay–dee.org

OREM COMMUNITY HOSPITAL (O, 18 beds) 331 North 400 West, Orem, UT Zip 84057–1999; tel. 801/224–4080; Scott Mortensen, Administrator
**Web address:** www.intermountainhealthcare.org

PARK CITY MEDICAL CENTER (O, 26 beds) 900 Round Valley Drive, Park City, UT Zip 84060–7552; tel. 435/658–7000; Si Hutt, Administrator
**Web address:** www.intermountainhealthcare.org

PRIMARY CHILDREN'S HOSPITAL (O, 289 beds) 100 North Mario Capecchi Drive, Salt Lake City, UT Zip 84113–1100; tel. 801/662–1000; Katy Welkie, R.N., Chief Executive Officer
**Web address:** www.intermountainhealthcare.org

RIVERTON HOSPITAL (O, 88 beds) 3741 West 12600 South, Riverton, UT Zip 84065–7215; tel. 801/285–4000; Blair Kent, Administrator
**Web address:** www.intermountainhealthcare.org/

SANPETE VALLEY HOSPITAL (O, 18 beds) 1100 South Medical Drive, Mount Pleasant, UT Zip 84647–2222; tel. 435/462–2441; Aaron Wood, Administrator
**Web address:** www.intermountainhealthcare.com

SEVIER VALLEY MEDICAL CENTER (O, 27 beds) 1000 North Main Street, Richfield, UT Zip 84701–1857; tel. 435/893–4100; Gary E. Beck, Administrator
**Web address:** www.sevierhospital.org

THE ORTHOPEDIC SPECIALTY HOSPITAL (O, 40 beds) 5848 South 300 East, Murray, UT Zip 84107–6121; tel. 801/314–4100; Barbara Ohm, Administrator
**Web address:** www.intermountainhealthcare.org

UTAH VALLEY REGIONAL MEDICAL CENTER (O, 375 beds) 1034 North 500 West, Provo, UT Zip 84604–3337; tel. 801/357–7850; Steve Smoot, Administrator
**Web address:** www.utahvalleyregional.org

VALLEY VIEW MEDICAL CENTER (O, 48 beds) 1303 North Main Street, Cedar City, UT Zip 84721–9746; tel. 435/868–5000; Jason Wilson, Administrator
**Web address:** www.ihc.com

| | | |
|---|---|---|
| **Owned, leased, sponsored:** | 21 hospitals | 2621 beds |
| **Contract–managed:** | 1 hospital | 41 beds |
| **Totals:** | 22 hospitals | 2662 beds |

---

**★0902: IOWA SPECIALTY HOSPITALS** (NP)
1316 South Main Street, Clarion, IA Zip 50525–2019; tel. 515/532–2811; Steven J. Simonin, Chief Executive Officer
**(Independent Hospital System)**

**IOWA:** IOWA SPECIALTY HOSPITAL–BELMOND (C, 22 beds) 403 First Street S.E., Belmond, IA Zip 50421–1201; tel. 641/444–3223; Amy McDaniel, Administrator and Chief Executive Officer
**Web address:** www.iowaspecialtyhospital.com

IOWA SPECIALTY HOSPITAL–CLARION (C, 25 beds) 1316 South Main Street, Clarion, IA Zip 50525–2019; tel. 515/532–2811; Steven J. Simonin, Chief Executive Officer
**Web address:** www.iowaspecialtyhospital.com

| | | |
|---|---|---|
| **Owned, leased, sponsored:** | 0 hospitals | 0 beds |
| **Contract–managed:** | 2 hospitals | 47 beds |
| **Totals:** | 2 hospitals | 47 beds |

---

**7775: JEFFERSON HEALTH** (NP)
259 Radnor–Chester Road, Suite 290, Radnor, PA Zip 19087–5288, Mailing Address: 111 South 11th Street, Philadelphia, Zip 19107; tel. 610/225–6200; Stephen K. Klasko, M.D., Chief Executive Officer
**(Centralized Health System)**

**PENNSYLVANIA:** ABINGTON HEALTH LANSDALE HOSPITAL (O, 139 beds) 100 Medical Campus Drive, Lansdale, PA Zip 19446–1200; tel. 215/368–2100; Gary R. Candia, Ph.D., FACHE, Chief Administrative Officer
**Web address:** www.amh.org/lansdale/index.aspx

ABINGTON MEMORIAL HOSPITAL (O, 598 beds) 1200 Old York Road, Abington, PA Zip 19001–3720; tel. 215/481–2000; Margaret M. McGoldrick, President
**Web address:** www.abingtonhealth.org

THOMAS JEFFERSON UNIVERSITY HOSPITALS (O, 937 beds) 111 South 11th Street, Philadelphia, PA Zip 19107–5084; tel. 215/955–6000; Richard Webster, President
**Web address:** www.jefferson.edu

| | | |
|---|---|---|
| **Owned, leased, sponsored:** | 3 hospitals | 1674 beds |
| **Contract–managed:** | 0 hospitals | 0 beds |
| **Totals:** | 3 hospitals | 1674 beds |

---

**★8855: JFK HEALTH SYSTEM** (NP)
80 James Street, 2nd Floor, Edison, NJ Zip 08820–3938; tel. 732/632–1503; Raymond F. Fredericks, President and Chief Executive Officer

**NEW JERSEY:** JFK JOHNSON REHABILITATION INSTITUTE (O, 94 beds) 65 James Street, Edison, NJ Zip 8818; tel. 732/321–7050; Anthony Cuzzola, Vice President Administrator
**Web address:** www.njrehab.org

JFK MEDICAL CENTER (O, 334 beds) 65 James Street, Edison, NJ Zip 8818; tel. 732/321–7000; Raymond F. Fredericks, President and CEO
**Web address:** www.jfkmc.org

| | | |
|---|---|---|
| **Owned, leased, sponsored:** | 2 hospitals | 428 beds |
| **Contract–managed:** | 0 hospitals | 0 beds |
| **Totals:** | 2 hospitals | 428 beds |

---

**★0324: JOHN MUIR HEALTH** (NP)
1400 Treat Boulevard, Walnut Creek, CA Zip 94597–2142; tel. 925/941–2100; Calvin K. Knight, President and Chief Executive Officer
**(Moderately Centralized Health System)**

**CALIFORNIA:** JOHN MUIR BEHAVIORAL HEALTH CENTER (O, 70 beds) 2740 Grant Street, Concord, CA Zip 94520–2265; tel. 925/674–4100; Cindy Bolter, Chief Nursing and Operations Officer
**Web address:** www.johnmuirhealth.com

JOHN MUIR MEDICAL CENTER, CONCORD (O, 183 beds) 2540 East Street, Concord, CA Zip 94520–1906; tel. 925/682–8200; Michael S. Thomas, President and Chief Administrative Officer
**Web address:** www.johnmuirhealth.com

**Section B**

For explanation of codes following names, see page B2.
★ Indicates Type III membership in the American Hospital Association.

JOHN MUIR MEDICAL CENTER, WALNUT CREEK (O, 383 beds) 1601 Ygnacio Valley Road, Walnut Creek, CA Zip 94598–3194; tel. 925/939–3000; Jane Willemsen, Chief Administrative Officer
**Web address:** www.jmmdhs.com/index.php/jmmdhs_jmmc.html

| | | |
|---|---|---|
| Owned, leased, sponsored: | 3 hospitals | 636 beds |
| Contract–managed: | 0 hospitals | 0 beds |
| **Totals:** | 3 hospitals | 636 beds |

★**1015: JOHNS HOPKINS HEALTH SYSTEM** (NP)
733 North Broadway, BRB 104, Baltimore, MD Zip 21205–1832; tel. 410/955–5000; Ronald R. Peterson, President
**(Centralized Health System)**

**DISTRICT OF COLUMBIA:** SIBLEY MEMORIAL HOSPITAL (O, 246 beds) 5255 Loughboro Road N.W., Washington, DC Zip 20016–2633; tel. 202/537–4000; Richard O. Davis, Ph.D., President
**Web address:** www.sibley.org

**FLORIDA:** ALL CHILDREN'S HOSPITAL JOHNS HOPKINS MEDICINE (O, 259 beds) 501 6th Avenue South, Saint Petersburg, FL Zip 33701–4634; tel. 727/898–7451; Jonathan M. Ellen, M.D., President
**Web address:** www.allkids.org

**MARYLAND:** HOWARD COUNTY GENERAL HOSPITAL (O, 256 beds) 5755 Cedar Lane, Columbia, MD Zip 21044–2999; tel. 410/740–7890; Steven C. Snelgrove, President
**Web address:** www.hcgh.org

JOHNS HOPKINS BAYVIEW MEDICAL CENTER (O, 428 beds) 4940 Eastern Avenue, Baltimore, MD Zip 21224–2780; tel. 410/550–0100; Richard G. Bennett, M.D., President
**Web address:** www.hopkinsbayview.org

JOHNS HOPKINS HOSPITAL (O, 998 beds) 733 North Broadway MRB 104, Baltimore, MD Zip 21205–1832; tel. 410/955–5000; Ronald R. Peterson, President
**Web address:** www.hopkinsmedicine.org

SUBURBAN HOSPITAL (O, 235 beds) 8600 Old Georgetown Road, Bethesda, MD Zip 20814–1497; tel. 301/896–3100; Gene E. Green, M.D., President
**Web address:** www.suburbanhospital.org

| | | |
|---|---|---|
| Owned, leased, sponsored: | 6 hospitals | 2422 beds |
| Contract–managed: | 0 hospitals | 0 beds |
| **Totals:** | 6 hospitals | 2422 beds |

★**2105: KAISER FOUNDATION HOSPITALS** (NP)
One Kaiser Plaza, Oakland, CA Zip 94612–3600; tel. 510/271–5910; Bernard J. Tyson, Chairman and Chief Executive Officer
**(Decentralized Health System)**

**CALIFORNIA:** FREMONT MEDICAL CENTER (O, 106 beds) 39400 Paseo Padre Parkway, Fremont, CA Zip 94538–2310; tel. 510/248–3000; Victoria O'Gorman, Administrator
**Web address:** www.kp.org

KAISER PERMANENTE ANTIOCH MEDICAL CENTER (O, 150 beds) 4501 Sand Creek Road, Antioch, CA Zip 94531–8687; tel. 925/813–6500; Colleen McKeown, Senior Vice President and Area Manager
**Web address:** www.https://health.kaiserpermanente. org/wps/portal/facility/100382

KAISER PERMANENTE BALDWIN PARK MEDICAL CENTER (O, 254 beds) 1011 Baldwin Park Boulevard, Baldwin Park, CA Zip 91706–5806; tel. 626/851–1011; Margaret H. Pierce, Executive Director
**Web address:** www.kp.org

KAISER PERMANENTE DOWNEY MEDICAL CENTER (O, 342 beds) 9333 Imperial Highway, Downey, CA Zip 90242–2812; tel. 562/657–9000; James Branchick, R.N., MS, Executive Director
**Web address:** www.kaiserpermanente.org

KAISER PERMANENTE FONTANA MEDICAL CENTER (O, 490 beds) 9961 Sierra Avenue, Fontana, CA Zip 92335–6794; tel. 909/427–5000; Greg Christian, Executive Director
**Web address:** www.kaiserpermanente.org

KAISER PERMANENTE FRESNO MEDICAL CENTER (O, 169 beds) 7300 North Fresno Street, Fresno, CA Zip 93720–2942; tel. 559/448–4500; Debbie Hemker, Senior Vice President and Area Manager
**Web address:** www.kaiserpermanente.org

KAISER PERMANENTE LOS ANGELES MEDICAL CENTER (O, 528 beds) 4867 Sunset Boulevard, Los Angeles, CA Zip 90027–5961; tel. 323/783–4011; William N. Grice, Executive Director
**Web address:** www.kaiserpermanente.org

KAISER PERMANENTE MANTECA MEDICAL CENTER (O, 184 beds) 1777 West Yosemite Avenue, Manteca, CA Zip 95337–5187; tel. 209/825–3700; Deborah G. Friberg, Interim Senior Vice President and Area Manager
**Web address:** www.kaiserpermanente.org

KAISER PERMANENTE MORENO VALLEY MEDICAL CENTER (O, 71 beds) 27300 Iris Avenue, Moreno Valley, CA Zip 92555–4800; tel. 951/243–0811; Corey A. Seale, Chief Executive Officer

KAISER PERMANENTE OAKLAND MEDICAL CENTER (O, 267 beds) 3600 Broadway, Oakland, CA Zip 94611–5693; tel. 510/752–1000; Odette Bolano, R.N., Senior Vice President and Area Manager
**Web address:** www.kaiserpermanente.org

KAISER PERMANENTE ORANGE COUNTY ANAHEIM MEDICAL CENTER (O, 436 beds) 3440 East La Palma Avenue, Anaheim, CA Zip 92806–2020; tel. 714/644–2000; Mark E. Costa, Executive Director
**Web address:** www.kp.org

KAISER PERMANENTE PANORAMA CITY MEDICAL CENTER (O, 154 beds) 13652 Cantara Street, Panorama City, CA Zip 91402–5497; tel. 818/375–2000; Dennis C. Benton, Executive Director
**Web address:** www.kaiserpermanente.org

KAISER PERMANENTE REDWOOD CITY MEDICAL CENTER (O, 213 beds) 1150 Veterans Boulevard, Redwood City, CA Zip 94063–2087; tel. 650/299–2000; Frank T. Beirne, FACHE, Senior Vice President and Area Manager
**Web address:** www.kaiserpermanente.org

KAISER PERMANENTE RIVERSIDE MEDICAL CENTER (O, 226 beds) 10800 Magnolia Avenue, Riverside, CA Zip 92505–3000; tel. 951/353–2000; Vita M. Willett, Executive Director
**Web address:** www.kaiserpermanente.org

KAISER PERMANENTE ROSEVILLE MEDICAL CENTER (O, 340 beds) 1600 Eureka Road, Roseville, CA Zip 95661–3027; tel. 916/784–4000; Jeffrey A. Collins, M.D., Senior Vice President and Area Manager
**Web address:** www.kp.org

KAISER PERMANENTE SACRAMENTO MEDICAL CENTER (O, 287 beds) 2025 Morse Avenue, Sacramento, CA Zip 95825–2100; tel. 916/973–5000; Sandy Sharon, Senior Vice President and Area Manager
**Web address:** www.kp.org

KAISER PERMANENTE SAN DIEGO MEDICAL CENTER (O, 414 beds) 4647 Zion Avenue, San Diego, CA Zip 92120–2507; tel. 619/528–5000; E. Jane Finley, Senior Vice President and Executive Director
**Web address:** www.kaiserpermanente.org

KAISER PERMANENTE SAN FRANCISCO MEDICAL CENTER (O, 215 beds) 2425 Geary Boulevard, San Francisco, CA Zip 94115–3358; tel. 415/833–2000; Christine Robisch, Senior Vice President and Area Manager
**Web address:** www.kaiserpermanente.org

KAISER PERMANENTE SAN JOSE MEDICAL CENTER (O, 217 beds) 250 Hospital Parkway, San Jose, CA Zip 95119–1199; tel. 408/972–7000; Irene Chavez, Senior Vice President and Area Manager

KAISER PERMANENTE SAN LEANDRO MEDICAL CENTER (O, 264 beds) 2500 Merced Street, San Leandro, CA Zip 94577–4201; tel. 510/454–1000; Thomas S. Hanenburg, Senior Vice President and Area Manager
**Web address:** www.kaiserpermanente.org

KAISER PERMANENTE SAN RAFAEL MEDICAL CENTER (O, 116 beds) 99 Montecillo Road, San Rafael, CA Zip 94903–3397; tel. 415/444–2000; Judy Coffey, R.N., Senior Vice President and Area Manager
**Web address:** www.kaiserpermanente.org

KAISER PERMANENTE SANTA CLARA MEDICAL CENTER (O, 327 beds) 700 Lawrence Expressway, Santa Clara, CA Zip 95051–5173; tel. 408/851–1000; Christopher L. Boyd, Senior Vice President and Area Manager
**Web address:** www.kaiserpermanente.org

For explanation of codes following names, see page B2.
★ Indicates Type III membership in the American Hospital Association.

**B76** Health Care Systems, Networks and Alliances

© 2015 AHA Guide

KAISER PERMANENTE SANTA ROSA MEDICAL CENTER (O, 117 beds) 401 Bicentennial Way, Santa Rosa, CA Zip 95403–2192; tel. 707/571–4000; Judy Coffey, R.N., Senior Vice President and Area Manager
**Web address:** www.kaiserpermanente.org

KAISER PERMANENTE SOUTH BAY MEDICAL CENTER (O, 180 beds) 25825 Vermont Avenue, Harbor City, CA Zip 90710–3599; tel. 310/325–5111; Lesley A. Wille, Administrator and Executive Director
**Web address:** www.kaiserpermanente.org

KAISER PERMANENTE SOUTH SACRAMENTO MEDICAL CENTER (O, 181 beds) 6600 Bruceville Road, Sacramento, CA Zip 95823–4691; tel. 916/688–2430; Patricia M. Rodriguez, Senior Vice President and Area Manager
**Web address:** www.kp.org

KAISER PERMANENTE SOUTH SAN FRANCISCO (O, 120 beds) 1200 El Camino Real, South San Francisco, CA Zip 94080–3208; tel. 650/742–2000; Frank T. Beirne, FACHE, Senior Vice President and Area Manager
**Web address:** www.kaiserpermanente.org

KAISER PERMANENTE VACAVILLE MEDICAL CENTER (O, 64 beds) 1 Quality Drive, Vacaville, CA Zip 95688–9494; tel. 707/624–4000; Corwin N. Harper, Senior Vice President and Area Manager
**Web address:** www.kp.org

KAISER PERMANENTE VALLEJO MEDICAL CENTER (O, 287 beds) 975 Sereno Drive, Vallejo, CA Zip 94589–2441; tel. 707/651–1000; Corwin N. Harper, Senior Vice President and Area Manager
**Web address:** www.kaiserpermanente.org

KAISER PERMANENTE WALNUT CREEK MEDICAL CENTER (O, 233 beds) 1425 South Main Street, Walnut Creek, CA Zip 94596–5300; tel. 925/295–4000; Colleen McKeown, Senior Vice President and Area Manager
**Web address:** www.kaiserpermanente.org

KAISER PERMANENTE WEST LOS ANGELES MEDICAL CENTER (O, 130 beds) 6041 Cadillac Avenue, Los Angeles, CA Zip 90034–1700; tel. 323/857–2201; Georgina R. Garcia, R.N., Executive Director
**Web address:** www.kaiserpermanente.org

KAISER PERMANENTE WOODLAND HILLS MEDICAL CENTER (O, 158 beds) 5601 DeSoto Avenue, Woodland Hills, CA Zip 91367–6798; tel. 818/719–2000; Michael C. Carter, Executive Director
**Web address:** www.kaiserpermanente.org

**HAWAII:** KAISER PERMANENTE MEDICAL CENTER (O, 235 beds) 3288 Moanalua Road, Honolulu, HI Zip 96819–1469; tel. 808/432–0000; Linda Puu, Hospital Administrator
**Web address:** www.kaiserpermanente.org

**OREGON:** KAISER FOUNDATION HOSPITAL WESTSIDE MEDICAL CENTER (O, 122 beds) 2875 N.W. Stucki Avenue, Hillsboro, OR Zip 97124–5806; tel. 971/310–1000; Cindy Davis, R.N., Chief Operating Officer
**Web address:** www.kp.org

KAISER PERMANENTE SUNNYSIDE MEDICAL CENTER (O, 299 beds) 10180 S.E. Sunnyside Road, Clackamas, OR Zip 97015–8970; tel. 503/652–2880; Gary Petersen, Administrator and Chief Operating Officer
**Web address:** www.kaiserpermanente.org

| | | |
|---|---|---|
| Owned, leased, sponsored: | 34 hospitals | 7896 beds |
| Contract–managed: | 0 hospitals | 0 beds |
| Totals: | 34 hospitals | 7896 beds |

## 0954:  KECK MEDICINE OF USC (NP)

1500 San Pablo Street, Los Angeles, CA Zip 90033–5313; tel. 323/442–8500; Paul A. Craig, R.N., JD, Interim Chief Executive Officer

**CALIFORNIA:** KECK HOSPITAL OF USC (O, 240 beds) 1500 San Pablo Street, Los Angeles, CA Zip 90033–5313; tel. 323/442–8500; Rodney Hanners, Chief Executive Officer
**Web address:** www.keckhospitalofusc.org

UNIVERSITY OF SOUTHERN CALIFORNIA–NORRIS CANCER HOSPITAL (O, 60 beds) 1441 Eastlake Avenue, Los Angeles, CA Zip 90089–0112; tel. 323/865–3000; Rodney Hanners, Chief Executive Officer
**Web address:** www.uscnorriscancerhospital.org

USC VERDUGO HILLS HOSPITAL (O, 75 beds) 1812 Verdugo Boulevard, Glendale, CA Zip 91208–1409; tel. 818/790–7100; Paul A. Craig, R.N., JD, Chief Executive Officer
**Web address:** www.uscvhh.org

| | | |
|---|---|---|
| Owned, leased, sponsored: | 3 hospitals | 375 beds |
| Contract–managed: | 0 hospitals | 0 beds |
| Totals: | 3 hospitals | 375 beds |

## ★0258:  KETTERING HEALTH NETWORK (NP)

3965 Southern Boulevard, Dayton, OH Zip 45429–1229; tel. 937/395–8150; Fred M. Manchur, Chief Executive Officer
**(Independent Hospital System)**

**OHIO:** FORT HAMILTON HOSPITAL (O, 166 beds) 630 Eaton Avenue, Hamilton, OH Zip 45013–2770; tel. 513/867–2000; Mark T. Smith, JD, CPA, President
**Web address:** www.khnetwork.org/forthamilton

GRANDVIEW MEDICAL CENTER (O, 278 beds) 405 West Grand Avenue, Dayton, OH Zip 45405–4796; tel. 937/723–3200; Russell J. Wetherell, Senior Vice President, Administrator
**Web address:** www.ketteringhealth.org/grandview/

GREENE MEMORIAL HOSPITAL (O, 49 beds) 1141 North Monroe Drive, Xenia, OH Zip 45385–1600; tel. 937/352–2000; Terry M. Burns, President
**Web address:** www.ketteringhealth.org/greene

KETTERING MEDICAL CENTER (O, 388 beds) 3535 Southern Boulevard, Kettering, OH Zip 45429–1221; tel. 937/298–4331; Roy G. Chew, Ph.D., President
**Web address:** www.ketteringhealth.org/kettering

SOIN MEDICAL CENTER (O, 102 beds) 3535 Pentagon Boulevard, Beavercreek, OH Zip 45431–1705; tel. 937/702–4000; Terry M. Burns, Administrator, Senior Vice President of KHN
**Web address:** www.khnetwork.org/soin

SYCAMORE  MEDICAL CENTER (O, 172 beds) 4000 Miamisburg–Centerville Road, Miamisburg, OH Zip 45342–7615; tel. 937/866–0551; Walter Sackett, President
**Web address:** www.khnetwork.org/sycamore

| | | |
|---|---|---|
| Owned, leased, sponsored: | 6 hospitals | 1155 beds |
| Contract–managed: | 0 hospitals | 0 beds |
| Totals: | 6 hospitals | 1155 beds |

## ★0026:  KINDRED HEALTHCARE (IO)

680 South Fourth Street, Louisville, KY Zip 40202–2412; tel. 502/596–7300; Benjamin Breier, Chief Executive Officer
**(Independent Hospital System)**

**ARIZONA:** KINDRED HOSPITAL ARIZONA–PHOENIX (O, 166 beds) 40 East Indianola Avenue, Phoenix, AZ Zip 85012–2059; tel. 602/280–7000; Karen Cawley, Chief Executive Officer
**Web address:** www.khphoenix.com/

KINDRED HOSPITAL–TUCSON (O, 51 beds) 355 North Wilmot Road, Tucson, AZ Zip 85711–2601; tel. 520/584–4500; Marc Lemon, Chief Executive Officer
**Web address:** www.khtucson.com

**CALIFORNIA:** KINDRED HOSPITAL RANCHO (O, 55 beds) 10841 White Oak Avenue, Rancho Cucamonga, CA Zip 91730–3811; tel. 909/581–6400; Jeanette Williams, Interim Chief Executive Officer
**Web address:** www.khrancho.com

KINDRED HOSPITAL RIVERSIDE (O, 40 beds) 2224 Medical Center Drive, Perris, CA Zip 92571–2638; tel. 951/436–3535; Jonathan Jean–Marie, Administrator and Chief Executive Officer
**Web address:** www.khriverside.com

KINDRED HOSPITAL SOUTH BAY (O, 84 beds) 1246 West 155th Street, Gardena, CA Zip 90247–4062; tel. 310/323–5330; Lourene Money, R.N., Interim Chief Executive Officer
**Web address:** www.khsouthbay.com/

KINDRED HOSPITAL–BALDWIN PARK (C, 91 beds) 14148 Francisquito Avenue, Baldwin Park, CA Zip 91706–6120; tel. 626/388–2700; Fiona Basa–Reyes, Chief Executive Officer
**Web address:** www.khbaldwinpark.com

For explanation of codes following names, see page B2.
★ Indicates Type III membership in the American Hospital Association.

Section B

KINDRED HOSPITAL–BREA (O, 48 beds) 875 North Brea Boulevard, Brea, CA Zip 92821–2699; tel. 714/529–6842; Diane Zeoli, Chief Executive Officer
**Web address:** www.kindredhospitalbrea.com/

KINDRED HOSPITAL–LA MIRADA (O, 216 beds) 14900 East Imperial Highway, La Mirada, CA Zip 90638–2172; tel. 562/944–1900; April Myers, Administrator
**Web address:** www.kindredlamirada.com/

KINDRED HOSPITAL–LOS ANGELES (O, 81 beds) 5525 West Slauson Avenue, Los Angeles, CA Zip 90056–1067; tel. 310/642–0325; Phillip R. Wolfe, Administrator
**Web address:** www.kindredhospitalla.com/

KINDRED HOSPITAL–ONTARIO (O, 91 beds) 550 North Monterey Avenue, Ontario, CA Zip 91764–3399; tel. 909/391–0333; Vincent Trac, Chief Executive Officer
**Web address:** www.khontario.com/

KINDRED HOSPITAL–SAN DIEGO (O, 70 beds) 1940 El Cajon Boulevard, San Diego, CA Zip 92104–1096; tel. 619/543–4500; Natalie Germuska, R.N., MSN, Market Chief Executive Officer
**Web address:** www.kindredsandiego.com

KINDRED HOSPITAL–SAN FRANCISCO BAY AREA (O, 99 beds) 2800 Benedict Drive, San Leandro, CA Zip 94577–6840; tel. 510/357–8300; Jacob M. McCarty, Chief Executive Officer
**Web address:** www.kindredhospitalsfba.com

KINDRED HOSPITAL–WESTMINSTER (O, 109 beds) 200 Hospital Circle, Westminster, CA Zip 92683–3910; tel. 714/893–4541; Brooke Saunders, Administrator
**Web address:** www.khwestminster.com/

**COLORADO:** KINDRED HOSPITAL–AURORA (O, 37 beds) 700 Potomac Street 2nd Floor, Aurora, CO Zip 80011–6844; tel. 720/857–8333; Adolphe Edward, Market Chief Executive Officer
**Web address:** www.khaurora.com/

KINDRED HOSPITAL–DENVER (O, 68 beds) 1920 High Street, Denver, CO Zip 80218–1213; tel. 303/320–5871; Adolphe Edward, Market Chief Executive Officer
**Web address:** www.kh–denver.com

**FLORIDA:** KINDRED HOSPITAL BAY AREA–TAMPA (O, 73 beds) 4555 South Manhattan Avenue, Tampa, FL Zip 33611–2397; tel. 813/839–6341; Sandra Morgan, Chief Executive Officer
**Web address:** www.khtampa.com/

KINDRED HOSPITAL CENTRAL TAMPA (O, 102 beds) 4801 North Howard Avenue, Tampa, FL Zip 33603–1411; tel. 813/874–7575; Ralph Selner, Chief Executive Officer
**Web address:** www.kindredcentraltampa.com/

KINDRED HOSPITAL MELBOURNE (O, 60 beds) 765 West Nasa Boulevard, Melbourne, FL Zip 32901–1815; tel. 321/733–5725; Joyce Baldrica, Chief Executive Officer
**Web address:** www.khmelbourne.com

KINDRED HOSPITAL NORTH FLORIDA (O, 80 beds) 801 Oak Street, Green Cove Springs, FL Zip 32043–4317; tel. 904/284–9230; Susan Drago, R.N., Chief Executive Officer
**Web address:** www.khnorthflorida.com

KINDRED HOSPITAL OCALA (O, 31 beds) 1500 S.W. 1st Avenue, Ocala, FL Zip 34471–6504; tel. 352/369–0513; Merlene Bhoorasingh, Administrator
**Web address:** www.kindredocala.com/

KINDRED HOSPITAL SOUTH FLORIDA–FORT LAUDERDALE (O, 123 beds) 1516 East Las Olas Boulevard, Fort Lauderdale, FL Zip 33301–2399; tel. 954/764–8900; Michael S. Roffelsen, Chief Executive Officer
**Web address:** www.khfortlauderdale.com/

KINDRED HOSPITAL THE PALM BEACHES (O, 70 beds) 5555 West Blue Heron Boulevard, Riviera Beach, FL Zip 33418–7813; tel. 561/840–0754; Timothy Page, Chief Executive Officer
**Web address:** www.khthepalmbeaches.com/

**GEORGIA:** KINDRED HOSPITAL ROME (O, 45 beds) 304 Turner McCall Boulevard, Rome, GA Zip 30165–5621; tel. 706/378–6800; Chad Lovett, Chief Executive Officer
**Web address:** www.kindredrome.com

KINDRED HOSPITAL–ATLANTA (O, 70 beds) 705 Juniper Street N.E., Atlanta, GA Zip 30308–1307; tel. 404/873–2871; Robert Russell, Chief Executive Officer
**Web address:** www.kindredatlanta.com/

**ILLINOIS:** KINDRED CHICAGO–CENTRAL HOSPITAL (O, 187 beds) 4058 West Melrose Street, Chicago, IL Zip 60641–4797; tel. 773/736–7000; Bruce Carey, Chief Executive Officer
**Web address:** www.khchicagocentral.com

KINDRED HOSPITAL CHICAGO–NORTHLAKE (O, 94 beds) 365 East North Avenue, Northlake, IL Zip 60164–2628; tel. 708/345–8100; Beverly Foster, Chief Executive Officer
**Web address:** www.kindrednorthlake.com/

KINDRED HOSPITAL PEORIA (O, 50 beds) 500 West Romeo B. Garrett Avenue, Peoria, IL Zip 61605–2301; tel. 309/680–1500; Ted Paarlberg, Chief Executive Officer
**Web address:** www.khpeoria.com/

KINDRED HOSPITAL–SYCAMORE (O, 69 beds) 225 Edward Street, Sycamore, IL Zip 60178–2137; tel. 815/895–2144; Jim Cohick, Chief Executive Officer
**Web address:** www.kindredhospitalsyc.com/

**INDIANA:** KINDRED HOSPITAL INDIANAPOLIS SOUTH (O, 52 beds) 607 Greenwood Springs Drive, Greenwood, IN Zip 46143–6377; tel. 317/888–8155; Matthew Keppler, Market Chief Executive Officer
**Web address:** www.khindysouth.com/

KINDRED HOSPITAL NORTHWEST INDIANA (O, 70 beds) 5454 Hohman Avenue, 5th Floor, Hammond, IN Zip 46320–1931; tel. 219/937–9900; Frank A. Solare, Chief Executive Officer
**Web address:** www.khnwindiana.com

KINDRED HOSPITAL OF NORTHERN INDIANA (O, 32 beds) 215 West Fourth Street, Suite 200, Mishawaka, IN Zip 46544–1917; tel. 574/252–2000; Lori Skora, Chief Executive Officer
**Web address:** www.khnorthernindiana.com/

KINDRED HOSPITAL–INDIANAPOLIS (O, 59 beds) 1700 West 10th Street, Indianapolis, IN Zip 46222–3802; tel. 317/636–4400; Bryan Chatterton, Chief Executive Officer
**Web address:** www.kindredhospitalindy.com/

**KENTUCKY:** KINDRED HOSPITAL–LOUISVILLE (O, 164 beds) 1313 Saint Anthony Place, Louisville, KY Zip 40204–1740; tel. 502/587–7001; Wayne D. Blanchard, Chief Executive Officer
**Web address:** www.kindredlouisville.com/

**LOUISIANA:** KINDRED HOSPITAL–NEW ORLEANS (O, 80 beds) 3601 Coliseum Street, New Orleans, LA Zip 70115–3606; tel. 504/899–1555; Jan Turk, Chief Executive Officer
**Web address:** www.kindredhospitalnola.com

**MASSACHUSETTS:** KINDRED HOSPITAL BOSTON–NORTH SHORE (O, 50 beds) 15 King Street, Peabody, MA Zip 01960–4379; tel. 978/531–2900; Amber Hester, Chief Executive Officer
**Web address:** www.kindredbns.com/

KINDRED HOSPITAL NORTHEAST–STOUGHTON (O, 111 beds) 909 Sumner Street, 1st Floor, Stoughton, MA Zip 02072–3396; tel. 781/297–8200; Robert A. Gundersen, Market Chief Executive Officer
**Web address:** www.khstoughton.com

KINDRED HOSPITAL–BOSTON (O, 59 beds) 1515 Commonwealth Avenue, Brighton, MA Zip 02135–3617; tel. 617/254–1100; Susan Downey, R.N., MS, Chief Executive Officer
**Web address:** www.kindredbos.com/

**MICHIGAN:** KINDRED HOSPITAL DETROIT (O, 77 beds) 4777 East Outer Drive, Detroit, MI Zip 48234–3241; tel. 313/369–5800; Mary Hoskins, Chief Executive Officer
**Web address:** www.kindreddetroit.com/

**MISSOURI:** KINDRED HOSPITAL KANSAS CITY (O, 130 beds) 8701 Troost Avenue, Kansas City, MO Zip 64131–2767; tel. 816/995–2000; Alexander Gill, Chief Executive Officer
**Web address:** www.kindredhospitalkc.com

KINDRED HOSPITAL NORTHLAND (O, 35 beds) 500 Northwest 68th Street, Kansas City, MO Zip 64118–2455; tel. 816/420–6300; H. Frank Schneider, Chief Executive Officer
**Web address:** www.khnorthland.com

KINDRED HOSPITAL–ST. LOUIS (O, 98 beds) 4930 Lindell Boulevard, Saint Louis, MO Zip 63108–1510; tel. 314/361–8700; Stephanie Bridges, Chief Executive Officer
**Web address:** www.kindredstlouis.com/

KINDRED HOSPITAL–ST. LOUIS AT MERCY (O, 54 beds) 615 South New Ballas Road, 7th Floor, Saint Louis, MO Zip 63141–8221; tel. 314/567–4326; Robert S. Adcock, Chief Executive Officer
**Web address:** www.kindredstlouismercy.com

For explanation of codes following names, see page B2.
★ Indicates Type III membership in the American Hospital Association.

Section B

MERCY REHABILITATION HOSPITAL (O, 90 beds) 14561 North Outer Forty Road, Chesterfield, MO Zip 63017; tel. 314/881–4000; Donna M. Flannery, Chief Executive Officer
**Web address:** www.stjohnsmercyrehab.com

MERCY REHABILITION HOSPITAL SPRINGFIELD (O, 60 beds) 5904 South Southwood Road, Springfield, MO Zip 65804–5234; tel. 417/227–9000; Jerry Wise, Chief Executive Officer
**Web address:** www.mercy.net

ST. LUKE'S REHABILITATION HOSPITAL (O, 35 beds) 14709 Olive Boulevard, Chesterfield, MO Zip 63017–2221; tel. 314/317–5700; Christopher Baechle, Chief Executive Officer
**Web address:** www.khrehabstluke.com

**NEVADA:** KINDRED HOSPITAL LAS VEGAS–SAHARA (O, 238 beds) 5110 West Sahara Avenue, Las Vegas, NV Zip 89146–3406; tel. 702/871–1418; Doug McCoy, Chief Executive Officer
**Web address:** www.kindredhospitallvs.com/

**NEW JERSEY:** KINDRED HOSPITAL–NEW JERSEY MORRIS COUNTY (O, 117 beds) 400 West Blackwell Street, Dover, NJ Zip 07801–2525; tel. 973/537–3818; Jonathan Cohee, Chief Executive Officer
**Web address:** www.khmorriscounty.com/

**NEW MEXICO:** KINDRED HOSPITAL–ALBUQUERQUE (O, 61 beds) 700 High Street N.E., Albuquerque, NM Zip 87102–2565; tel. 505/242–4444; Bud Schawl, Chief Executive Officer
**Web address:** www.kindredalbuquerque.com/

**NORTH CAROLINA:** KINDRED HOSPITAL–GREENSBORO (O, 124 beds) 2401 Southside Boulevard, Greensboro, NC Zip 27406–3311; tel. 336/271–2800; Christopher Haynes, Chief Executive Officer
**Web address:** www.khgreensboro.com

**OHIO:** KINDRED HOSPITAL CLEVELAND–GATEWAY (O, 153 beds) 2351 East 22nd Street, 7th Floor, Cleveland, OH Zip 44115–3111; tel. 216/363–2671; Prentice Lipsey, Chief Executive Officer
**Web address:** www.kindredgateway.com

KINDRED HOSPITAL LIMA (O, 26 beds) 730 West Market Street, 6th Floor, Lima, OH Zip 45801–4602; tel. 419/224–1888; Susan Krinke, Chief Executive Officer
**Web address:** www.khlima.com

KINDRED HOSPITAL OF CENTRAL OHIO (O, 33 beds) 335 Glessner Avenue, 5th Floor, Mansfield, OH Zip 44903–2269; tel. 419/526–0777; Pamela A. Edson, Chief Executive Officer
**Web address:** www.khcentralohio.com/

KINDRED HOSPITAL–DAYTON (O, 67 beds) 707 South Edwin C. Moses Boulevard, Dayton, OH Zip 45417–3462; tel. 937/222–5963; Lynn Schoen, Chief Executive Officer
**Web address:** www.khdayton.com

**OKLAHOMA:** KINDRED HOSPITAL– OKLAHOMA CITY (O, 93 beds) 1407 North Robinson Avenue, Oklahoma City, OK Zip 73103–4823; tel. 405/232–8000; William Patton, Chief Executive Officer
**Web address:** www.kindredoklahoma.com

MERCY REHABILITATION HOSPITAL OKLAHOMA CITY (O, 50 beds) 5401 West Memorial Road, Oklahoma City, OK Zip 73142–2026; tel. 405/752–3935; Sharon Smeltzer, Chief Executive Officer

**PENNSYLVANIA:** KINDRED HOSPITAL SOUTH PHILADELPHIA (O, 58 beds) 1930 South Broad Street, Philadelphia, PA Zip 19145–2328; tel. 267/570–5200; Deborah Karn, Chief Executive Officer
**Web address:** www.khsouthphilly.com

KINDRED HOSPITAL–HERITAGE VALLEY (O, 35 beds) 1000 Dutch Ridge Road, Beaver, PA Zip 15009–9727; tel. 724/773–8480; Dusty Bowers, Chief Executive Officer
**Web address:** www.kindredhospitalhv.com/

KINDRED HOSPITAL–PHILADELPHIA (O, 52 beds) 6129 Palmetto Street, Philadelphia, PA Zip 19111–5729; tel. 215/722–8555; Sandra Larson, Interim Chief Executive Officer
**Web address:** www.kindredphila.com/

KINDRED HOSPITAL–PITTSBURGH (O, 63 beds) 7777 Steubenville Pike, Oakdale, PA Zip 15071–3409; tel. 412/494–5500; Janie Rosenberger–Slampack, Market Chief Executive Officer
**Web address:** www.kindredhospitalpittsburgh.com/

LANCASTER REHABILITATION HOSPITAL (O, 10 beds) 675 Good Drive, Lancaster, PA Zip 17601–2426; tel. 717/406–3000; Tammy L. Ober, Chief Executive Officer
**Web address:** www.lancastergeneral.org

**TENNESSEE:** KINDRED HOSPITAL–CHATTANOOGA (O, 44 beds) 709 Walnut Street, Chattanooga, TN Zip 37402–1916; tel. 423/266–7721; Gigi Johnson, Interim Chief Executive Officer
**Web address:** www.kindredchattanooga.com/

KINDRED HOSPITAL–NASHVILLE (O, 58 beds) 1412 County Hospital Road, Nashville, TN Zip 37218–3007; tel. 615/687–2600; William P. Macri, Chief Executive Officer
**Web address:** www.khnashville.com/

**TEXAS:** CENTRAL TEXAS REHABILITATION HOSPITAL (O, 50 beds) 700 West 45th Street, Austin, TX Zip 78751–2800; tel. 512/407–2111; Peggy Barrett, R.N., Chief Executive Officer
**Web address:** www.khrehabcentraltexas.com/

KINDRED HOSPITAL CLEAR LAKE (O, 110 beds) 350 Blossom Street, Webster, TX Zip 77598; tel. 281/316–7800; Meridell Sloterbeek, Chief Executive Officer
**Web address:** www.khclearlake.com

KINDRED HOSPITAL DALLAS CENTRAL (O, 60 beds) 8050 Meadows Road, Dallas, TX Zip 75231–3406; tel. 469/232–6500; Stephanie Madrid, Chief Executive Officer
**Web address:** www.khdallascentral.com/

KINDRED HOSPITAL EL PASO (O, 72 beds) 1740 Curie Drive, El Paso, TX Zip 79902–2901; tel. 915/351–9044; Diana Schultz, Chief Executive Officer
**Web address:** www.khelpaso.com

KINDRED HOSPITAL SUGAR LAND (O, 171 beds) 1550 First Colony Boulevard, Sugar Land, TX Zip 77479–4000; tel. 281/275–6000; Lorene Perona, Market Chief Executive Officer
**Web address:** www.khsugarland.com

KINDRED HOSPITAL TARRANT COUNTY–ARLINGTON (O, 55 beds) 1000 North Cooper Street, Arlington, TX Zip 76011–5540; tel. 817/548–3400; Christina Richard, Administrator
**Web address:** www.kindredhospitalarl.com/

KINDRED HOSPITAL TOMBALL (O, 74 beds) 505 Graham Drive, Tomball, TX Zip 77375–3368; tel. 281/255–5600; Eric Cantrell, Chief Executive Officer
**Web address:** www.khtomball.com/

KINDRED HOSPITAL–BAY AREA (O, 74 beds) 4801 East Sam Houston Parkway South, Pasadena, TX Zip 77505–3955; tel. 281/991–5463; Jeffrey Smith, Chief Executive Officer
**Web address:** www.khbayareahouston.com/

KINDRED HOSPITAL–DALLAS (O, 50 beds) 9525 Greenville Avenue, Dallas, TX Zip 75243–4116; tel. 214/355–2600; James Mendez, Chief Executive Officer
**Web address:** www.khdallas.com

KINDRED HOSPITAL–FORT WORTH (O, 54 beds) 815 Eighth Avenue, Fort Worth, TX Zip 76104–2609; tel. 817/332–4812; Angela Harris, Chief Executive Officer
**Web address:** www.kindredfortworth.com/

KINDRED HOSPITAL–HOUSTON (O, 105 beds) 6441 Main Street, Houston, TX Zip 77030–1596; tel. 713/790–0500; Robert Stein, Chief Executive Officer
**Web address:** www.khhouston.com/

KINDRED HOSPITAL–HOUSTON NORTHWEST (O, 84 beds) 11297 Fallbrook Drive, Houston, TX Zip 77065–4292; tel. 281/897–8114; Larkin Virden, Chief Executive Officer
**Web address:** www.khhoustonnw.com/

KINDRED HOSPITAL–MANSFIELD (O, 55 beds) 1802 Highway 157 North, Mansfield, TX Zip 76063–3923; tel. 817/473–6101; Susan Schaetti, Chief Executive Officer
**Web address:** www.kindredmansfield.com

KINDRED HOSPITAL–SAN ANTONIO (O, 59 beds) 3636 Medical Drive, San Antonio, TX Zip 78229–2183; tel. 210/616–0616; Kay E. Peck, Ph.D., Chief Executive Officer
**Web address:** www.khsanantonio.com/

KINDRED HOSPITAL–WHITE ROCK (O, 25 beds) 9440 Poppy Drive, 5th Floor, Dallas, TX Zip 75218–3652; tel. 214/324–6562; Kelly Bailey, Administrator
**Web address:** www.khwhiterock.com

KINDRED REHABILITATION HOSPITAL ARLINGTON (O, 24 beds) 2601 West Randol Mill Road, Arlington, TX Zip 76012–4289; tel. 817/804–4400; Amy Hoffner, Administrator
**Web address:** www.khrehabarlington.com

KINDRED REHABILITATION HOSPITAL CLEAR LAKE (O, 60 beds) 655 East Medical Center Boulevard, Webster, TX Zip 77598–4328; tel. 281/286–1500; Dale R. Mulder, Chief Executive Officer
**Web address:** www.khrehabclearlake.com/

Section B

For explanation of codes following names, see page B2.
★ Indicates Type III membership in the American Hospital Association.

KINDRED REHABILITATION HOSPITAL NORTHEAST HOUSTON (O, 46 beds) 18839 McKay Road, Humble, TX Zip 77338–5721; tel. 281/964–6600; Reagan Simpson, Chief Executive Officer
**Web address:** www.khrehabnortheasthouston.com

TEXAS REHABILITATION HOSPITAL OF FORT WORTH (O, 66 beds) 425 Alabama Avenue, Fort Worth, TX Zip 76104–1022; tel. 817/820–3400; Russell Bailey, Chief Executive Officer
**Web address:** www.texasrehabhospital.com/

**WASHINGTON:** KINDRED HOSPITAL SEATTLE–NORTHGATE (O, 80 beds) 10631 8th Avenue N.E., Seattle, WA Zip 98125–7213; tel. 206/364–2050; Jean Clark, Administrator
**Web address:** www.kindredhospitalseattle.com/

**WISCONSIN:** REHABILITATION HOSPITAL OF WISCONSIN (O, 40 beds) 1625 Coldwater Creek Drive, Waukesha, WI Zip 53188–8028; tel. 262/521–8800; Linda Newberry–Ferguson, Chief Executive Officer
**Web address:** www.rehabhospitalwi.com

| | | |
|---|---|---|
| Owned, leased, sponsored: | 82 hospitals | 6221 beds |
| Contract–managed: | 1 hospital | 91 beds |
| Totals: | 83 hospitals | 6312 beds |

---

★**0149:  KISH HEALTH SYSTEM** (NP)
1 Kish Hospital Drive, DeKalb, IL Zip 60115–9602, Mailing Address: P.O. Box 707, Zip 60115–0707; tel. 815/756–1521; Kevin P. Poorten, President and Chief Executive Officer
**(Independent Hospital System)**

**ILLINOIS:** KISHWAUKEE HOSPITAL (O, 98 beds) 1 Kish Hospital Drive, DeKalb, IL Zip 60115–9602, Mailing Address: P.O. Box 707, Zip 60115–0707; tel. 815/756–1521; Brad Copple, President
**Web address:** www.kishhospital.org

VALLEY WEST HOSPITAL (O, 25 beds) 1302 North Main Street, Sandwich, IL Zip 60548–2587; tel. 815/786–8484; Brad Copple, President
**Web address:** www.kishhealth.org

| | | |
|---|---|---|
| Owned, leased, sponsored: | 2 hospitals | 123 beds |
| Contract–managed: | 0 hospitals | 0 beds |
| Totals: | 2 hospitals | 123 beds |

---

★**0904:  L+M HEALTHCARE** (NP)
365 Montauk Avenue, New London, CT Zip 06320–4700; tel. 860/442–0711; Bruce D. Cummings, President and Chief Executive Officer
**(Independent Hospital System)**

**CONNECTICUT:** LAWRENCE + MEMORIAL HOSPITAL (O, 256 beds) 365 Montauk Avenue, New London, CT Zip 06320–4769; tel. 860/442–0711; Bruce D. Cummings, President and Chief Executive Officer
**Web address:** www.lmhospital.org

**RHODE ISLAND:** WESTERLY HOSPITAL (O, 100 beds) 25 Wells Street, Westerly, RI Zip 02891–2934; tel. 401/596–6000; Bruce D. Cummings, President and Chief Executive Officer
**Web address:** www.westerlyhospital.org

| | | |
|---|---|---|
| Owned, leased, sponsored: | 2 hospitals | 356 beds |
| Contract–managed: | 0 hospitals | 0 beds |
| Totals: | 2 hospitals | 356 beds |

---

**0911:  LAFAYETTE GENERAL HEALTH** (NP)
1214 Coolidge Boulevard, Lafayette, LA Zip 70503–2621; tel. 337/289–7991; David L. Callecod, FACHE, President and CEO
**(Independent Hospital System)**

**LOUISIANA:** ABROM KAPLAN MEMORIAL HOSPITAL (C, 35 beds) 1310 West Seventh Street, Kaplan, LA Zip 70548–2910; tel. 337/643–8300; Bryce Quebodeaux, Chief Executive Officer
**Web address:** www.lafayettegeneral.com

ACADIA GENERAL HOSPITAL (C, 178 beds) 1305 Crowley Rayne Highway, Crowley, LA Zip 70526–8202; tel. 337/783–3222; Heather L. Harper, Chief Executive Officer
**Web address:** www.acadiageneral.com

LAFAYETTE GENERAL MEDICAL CENTER (O, 324 beds) 1214 Coolidge Avenue, Lafayette, LA Zip 70503–2696, Mailing Address: P.O. Box 52009 OCS, Zip 70505–2009; tel. 337/289–7991; Patrick W. Gandy, CPA, Executive Vice President and Chief Executive Officer
**Web address:** www.lafayettegeneral.org

LAFAYETTE GENERAL SURGICAL HOSPITAL (C, 10 beds) 1000 West Pinhook Road, Lafayette, LA Zip 70503–2460; tel. 337/289–8088; Carrie E. Templeton, FACHE, Chief Executive Officer
**Web address:** www.lgsh.us

ST. MARTIN HOSPITAL (C, 25 beds) 210 Champagne Boulevard, Breaux Bridge, LA Zip 70517–3700, Mailing Address: P.O. Box 357, Zip 70517–0357; tel. 337/332–2178; Bryan Laperouse, Interim Administrator
**Web address:** www.stmartinhospital.org

UNIVERSITY HOSPITAL AND CLINICS (L, 105 beds) 2390 West Congress Street, Lafayette, LA Zip 70506–4298; tel. 337/261–6000; Jared Stark, Chief Executive Officer
**Web address:** www.lafayettegeneral.com

| | | |
|---|---|---|
| Owned, leased, sponsored: | 2 hospitals | 429 beds |
| Contract–managed: | 4 hospitals | 248 beds |
| Totals: | 6 hospitals | 677 beds |

---

**0891:  LAHEY HEALTH** (NP)
41 Mall Road, Burlington, MA Zip 01805–0001; tel. 781/744–7100; Howard R. Grant, JD, M.D., President and Chief Executive Officer
**(Centralized Health System)**

**MASSACHUSETTS:** BEVERLY HOSPITAL (O, 320 beds) 85 Herrick Street, Beverly, MA Zip 01915–1777; tel. 978/922–3000; Philip M. Cormier, Chief Executive Officer
**Web address:** www.beverlyhospital.org

LAHEY HOSPITAL & MEDICAL CENTER, BURLINGTON (O, 345 beds) 41 Mall Road, Burlington, MA Zip 01805–0001; tel. 781/744–5100; Joanne Conroy, M.D., Chief Executive Officer
**Web address:** www.lahey.org

WINCHESTER HOSPITAL (O, 198 beds) 41 Highland Avenue, Winchester, MA Zip 01890–1496; tel. 781/729–9000; Dale M. Lodge, Chief Executive Officer
**Web address:** www.winchesterhospital.org

| | | |
|---|---|---|
| Owned, leased, sponsored: | 3 hospitals | 863 beds |
| Contract–managed: | 0 hospitals | 0 beds |
| Totals: | 3 hospitals | 863 beds |

---

**0056:  LAKELAND HEALTH** (NP)
1234 Napier Avenue, Saint Joseph, MI Zip 49085–2158; tel. 269/983–8300; Loren Hamel, M.D., President and Chief Executive Officer
**(Independent Hospital System)**

**MICHIGAN:** LAKELAND HOSPITAL, WATERVLIET (O, 38 beds) 400 Medical Park Drive, Watervliet, MI Zip 49098–9225; tel. 269/463–3111; Ray Cruse, Chief Executive Officer

LAKELAND MEDICAL CENTER, ST. JOSEPH (O, 250 beds) 1234 Napier Avenue, Saint Joseph, MI Zip 49085–2158; tel. 269/983–8300; Loren Hamel, M.D., President and Chief Executive Officer
**Web address:** www.lakelandhealth.org

| | | |
|---|---|---|
| Owned, leased, sponsored: | 2 hospitals | 288 beds |
| Contract–managed: | 0 hospitals | 0 beds |
| Totals: | 2 hospitals | 288 beds |

---

**0393:  LANDMARK HOSPITALS** (IO)
3255 Independence Street, Cape Girardeau, MO Zip 63701–4914; tel. 573/335–1091; William K. Kapp, III, M.D., President and Chief Executive Officer
**(Independent Hospital System)**

---

For explanation of codes following names, see page B2.
★ Indicates Type III membership in the American Hospital Association.

**FLORIDA:** LANDMARK HOSPITAL OF SOUTHWEST FLORIDA (O, 50 beds) 1285 Creekside Boulevard East, Naples, FL Zip 34108; tel. 239/529–1800; Jimmy Dascani, Chief Executive Officer
**Web address:** www.landmarkhospitals.com/naples.aspx

**GEORGIA:** LANDMARK HOSPITAL OF ATHENS (O, 42 beds) 775 Sunset Drive, Athens, GA Zip 30606–2211; tel. 706/425–1500; Tommy Jackson, Chief Executive Officer
**Web address:** www.landmarkhospitals.com

LANDMARK HOSPITAL OF SAVANNAH (O, 50 beds) 800 East 68th Street, Savannah, GA Zip 31405–4710; tel. 912/298–1000; John Salandi, Chief Executive Officer
**Web address:** www.landmarkhospitals.com/savannah

**MISSOURI:** LANDMARK HOSPITAL OF CAPE GIRARDEAU (O, 30 beds) 3255 Independence Street, Cape Girardeau, MO Zip 63701–4914; tel. 573/335–1091; Rodney Brown, Chief Executive Officer
**Web address:** www.landmarkhospitals.com

LANDMARK HOSPITAL OF COLUMBIA (O, 42 beds) 604 Old 63 North, Columbia, MO Zip 65201–6308; tel. 573/499–6600; Mindy S. Moore, Chief Executive Officer
**Web address:** www.landmarkhospitals.com

LANDMARK HOSPITAL OF JOPLIN (O, 30 beds) 2040 West 32nd Street, Joplin, MO Zip 64804–3512; tel. 417/627–1300; Kevin J. Clement, Chief Executive Officer
**Web address:** www.landmarkhospitals.com

**UTAH:** LANDMARK HOSPITAL OF SALT LAKE CITY (O, 38 beds) 4252 South Birkhill Boulevard, Murray, UT Zip 84107–5715; tel. 801/268–5400; Ken D'Amico, Chief Executive Officer
**Web address:** www.landmarkhospitals.com/utah.aspx

| Owned, leased, sponsored: | 7 hospitals | 282 beds |
|---|---|---|
| Contract–managed: | 0 hospitals | 0 beds |
| Totals: | 7 hospitals | 282 beds |

**0932: LCMC HEALTH** (NP)
200 Henry Clay Avenue, New Orleans, LA Zip 70118–5720; tel. 504/899–9511; Greg Feirn, CPA, President and Chief Executive Officer
**(Centralized Health System)**

**LOUISIANA:** CHILDREN'S HOSPITAL (O, 200 beds) 200 Henry Clay Avenue, New Orleans, LA Zip 70118–5720; tel. 504/899–9511; Mary R. Perrin, President and Chief Executive Officer
**Web address:** www.chnola.org

INTERIM LSU PUBLIC HOSPITAL (O, 390 beds) 2021 Perdido Street, New Orleans, LA Zip 70112–1396; tel. 504/903–3000; Cindy Nuesslein, Chief Executive Officer
**Web address:** www.umcno.org

NEW ORLEANS EAST HOSPITAL (C, 34 beds) 5620 Read Boulevard, New Orleans, LA Zip 70127–3106, Mailing Address: 5620 Read Boulevard, Zip 70127–3106; tel. 504/592–6600; Charlotte Parent, R.N., Interim Chief Executive Officer
**Web address:** www.noehospital.org

TOURO INFIRMARY (O, 539 beds) 1401 Foucher Street, New Orleans, LA Zip 70115–3593; tel. 504/897–7011; Susan E. Andrews, Chief Executive Officer
**Web address:** www.touro.com

UNIVERSITY CAMPUS (O, 272 beds) 2000 Canal Street, New Orleans, LA Zip 70112–1396, Mailing Address: 2021 Perdido Street, Zip 70112–1396; tel. 504/588–3000; Cindy Nuesslein, Interim Chief Executive Officer
**Web address:** www.umcno.org

| Owned, leased, sponsored: | 4 hospitals | 1401 beds |
|---|---|---|
| Contract–managed: | 1 hospital | 34 beds |
| Totals: | 5 hospitals | 1435 beds |

**★0369: LEE MEMORIAL HEALTH SYSTEM** (NP)
2776 Cleveland Avenue, Fort Myers, FL Zip 33901–5856, Mailing Address: P.O. Box 2218, Zip 33902–2218; tel. 239/343–2000; James R. Nathan, President and Chief Executive Officer
**(Centralized Health System)**

**FLORIDA:** CAPE CORAL HOSPITAL (O, 291 beds) 636 Del Prado Boulevard, Cape Coral, FL Zip 33990–2695; tel. 239/424–2000; James R. Nathan, President and Chief Executive Officer
**Web address:** www.leememorial.org

GULF COAST MEDICAL CENTER (O, 349 beds) 13681 Doctor's Way, Fort Myers, FL Zip 33912–4300; tel. 239/343–1000; James R. Nathan, President and Chief Executive Officer
**Web address:** www.leememorial.org

LEE MEMORIAL HOSPITAL (O, 835 beds) 2776 Cleveland Avenue, Fort Myers, FL Zip 33901–5855, Mailing Address: P.O. Box 2218, Zip 33902–2218; tel. 239/332–1111; James R. Nathan, President and Chief Executive Officer
**Web address:** www.leememorial.org

| Owned, leased, sponsored: | 3 hospitals | 1475 beds |
|---|---|---|
| Contract–managed: | 0 hospitals | 0 beds |
| Totals: | 3 hospitals | 1475 beds |

**★2755: LEGACY HEALTH** (NP)
1919 N.W. Lovejoy Street, Portland, OR Zip 97209–1503; tel. 503/415–5600; George J. Brown, M.D., President and Chief Executive Officer
**(Centralized Health System)**

**OREGON:** LEGACY EMANUEL HOSPITAL AND HEALTH CENTER (O, 427 beds) 2801 North Gantenbein Avenue, Portland, OR Zip 97227–1674; tel. 503/413–2200; Lori Morgan, M.D., Chief Administrative Officer
**Web address:** www.legacyhealth.org

LEGACY GOOD SAMARITAN HOSPITAL AND MEDICAL CENTER (O, 247 beds) 1015 N.W. 22nd Avenue, Portland, OR Zip 97210–3099; tel. 503/413–7711; Jonathan Avery, Chief Administrative Officer
**Web address:** www.legacyhealth.org

LEGACY MERIDIAN PARK MEDICAL CENTER (O, 130 beds) 19300 S.W. 65th Avenue, Tualatin, OR Zip 97062–9741; tel. 503/692–1212; Allyson Anderson, Chief Administrative Officer
**Web address:** www.legacyhealth.org

LEGACY MOUNT HOOD MEDICAL CENTER (O, 91 beds) 24800 S.E. Stark, Gresham, OR Zip 97030–3378; tel. 503/667–1122; Gretchen Nichols, R.N., Chief Administrative Officer
**Web address:** www.legacyhealth.org

**WASHINGTON:** LEGACY SALMON CREEK MEDICAL CENTER (O, 214 beds) 2211 N.E. 139th Street, Vancouver, WA Zip 98686–2742; tel. 360/487–1000; Bryce R. Helgerson, Chief Administrative Officer
**Web address:** www.legacyhealth.org

| Owned, leased, sponsored: | 5 hospitals | 1109 beds |
|---|---|---|
| Contract–managed: | 0 hospitals | 0 beds |
| Totals: | 5 hospitals | 1109 beds |

**★0370: LEHIGH VALLEY HEALTH NETWORK** (NP)
1200 South Cedar Crest Boulevard, Allentown, PA Zip 18103–6202, Mailing Address: P.O. Box 689, Zip 18105–1556; tel. 610/402–8000; Brian Nester, D.O., President and Chief Executive Officer
**(Moderately Centralized Health System)**

**PENNSYLVANIA:** LEHIGH VALLEY HOSPITAL (O, 784 beds) 1200 South Cedar Crest Boulevard, Allentown, PA Zip 18103–6248, Mailing Address: P.O. Box 689, Zip 18105–1556; tel. 610/402–8000; Brian Nester, D.O., Interim President and Chief Executive Officer
**Web address:** www.lvhhn.org

LEHIGH VALLEY HOSPITAL – HAZLETON (O, 116 beds) 700 East Broad Street, Hazleton, PA Zip 18201–6897; tel. 570/501–4000; John R. Fletcher, President
**Web address:** www.lvhn.org/hazleton/

For explanation of codes following names, see page B2.
★ Indicates Type III membership in the American Hospital Association.

LEHIGH VALLEY HOSPITAL–MUHLENBERG (O, 162 beds) 2545 Schoenersville Road, Bethlehem, PA Zip 18017–7300; tel. 484/884–2201; Brian Nester, D.O., Interim President and Chief Executive Officer
**Web address:** www.lvhhn.org

| | | |
|---|---|---|
| Owned, leased, sponsored: | 3 hospitals | 1062 beds |
| Contract–managed: | 0 hospitals | 0 beds |
| Totals: | 3 hospitals | 1062 beds |

## 0632:  LHC GROUP (IO)
420 West Pinhook Road, Lafayette, LA Zip 70503–2131; tel. 337/223–1307; Keith G. Myers, Chairman and Chief Executive Officer

**LOUISIANA:** LOUISIANA EXTENDED CARE HOSPITAL OF LAFAYETTE (O, 42 beds) 1214 Coolidge Boulevard, Floors 9 & 10, Lafayette, LA Zip 70503–2621; tel. 337/289–8180; Kevin Frank, Administrator
**Web address:** www.lhcgroup.com

LOUISIANA EXTENDED CARE HOSPITAL OF NATCHITOCHES (O, 21 beds) 501 Keyser Avenue, Natchitoches, LA Zip 71457–6018; tel. 318/354–2044; John Rivoire, Administrator
**Web address:** www.lhcgroup.com

LOUISIANA EXTENDED CARE HOSPITAL WEST MONROE (O, 18 beds) 503 McMillan Road, 3rd Floor, West Monroe, LA Zip 71291–5327; tel. 318/329–4378; Cleta Munholland, Administrator

OCHSNER EXTENDED CARE HOSPITAL OF KENNER (O, 32 beds) 180 West Esplanade Avenue, 5th Floor, Kenner, LA Zip 70065–2467; tel. 504/464–8658; Frederick Nelson, Administrator
**Web address:** www.lhcgroup.com/

SPECIALTY HOSPITAL (O, 32 beds) 309 Jackson Street, 7th Floor, Monroe, LA Zip 71201–7407, Mailing Address: P.O. Box 1532, Zip 71210–1532; tel. 318/966–7045; Cleta Munholland, Administrator
**Web address:** www.lhcgroup.com

ST. LANDRY EXTENDED CARE HOSPITAL (O, 41 beds) 3983 1–49 South Service Road, 2nd Floor, Opelousas, LA Zip 70570; tel. 337/948–2251; Biff David, R.N., Administrator
**Web address:** www.lhcgroup.com

| | | |
|---|---|---|
| Owned, leased, sponsored: | 6 hospitals | 186 beds |
| Contract–managed: | 0 hospitals | 0 beds |
| Totals: | 6 hospitals | 186 beds |

## ★0394:  LHP HOSPITAL GROUP (IO)
2400 North Dallas Parkway, Suite 450, Plano, TX Zip 75093–5994; tel. 866/465–9222; John F. Holland, Chief Executive Officer
**(Centralized Physician/Insurance Health System)**

**FLORIDA:** BAY MEDICAL CENTER SACRED HEART HEALTH SYSTEM (O, 273 beds) 615 North Bonita Avenue, Panama City, FL Zip 32401–3600, Mailing Address: P.O. Box 59515, Zip 32412–0515; tel. 850/769–1511; Stephen Grubbs, Chief Executive Officer
**Web address:** www.baymedical.org

**IDAHO:** PORTNEUF MEDICAL CENTER (O, 175 beds) 777 Hospital Way, Pocatello, ID Zip 83201–5175; tel. 208/239–1000; Daniel Ordyna, Chief Executive Officer
**Web address:** www.portmed.org

**NEW JERSEY:** HACKENSACK UNIVERSITY MEDICAL CENTER AT PASCACK VALLEY (O, 128 beds) 250 Old Hook Road, Westwood, NJ Zip 07675–3123; tel. 201/383–1035; Emily L. Holliman, Chief Executive Officer
**Web address:** www.hackensackumcpv.com/

HACKENSACK UNIVERSITY MEDICAL CENTER MOUNTAINSIDE (O, 218 beds) 1 Bay Avenue, Montclair, NJ Zip 07042–4898; tel. 973/429–6000; John A. Fromhold, FACHE, Chief Executive Officer
**Web address:** www.mountainsidenow.com

**TEXAS:** SETON MEDICAL CENTER HARKER HEIGHTS (O, 60 beds) 850 West Central Texas Expressway, Harker Heights, TX Zip 76548–1890; tel. 254/690–0900; Matt T. Maxfield, FACHE, Chief Executive Officer
**Web address:** www.setonharkerheights.net

| | | |
|---|---|---|
| Owned, leased, sponsored: | 5 hospitals | 854 beds |
| Contract–managed: | 0 hospitals | 0 beds |
| Totals: | 5 hospitals | 854 beds |

## 0158:  LIFEBRIDGE HEALTH (NP)
2401 West Belvedere Avenue, Baltimore, MD Zip 21215–5216; tel. 410/601–5134; Neil M. Meltzer, President and Chief Executive Officer
**(Centralized Health System)**

**MARYLAND:** CARROLL HOSPITAL CENTER (O, 151 beds) 200 Memorial Avenue, Westminster, MD Zip 21157–5799; tel. 410/848–3000; Leslie Simmons, R.N., FACHE, R.N., President and Chief Executive Officer
**Web address:** www.carrollhospitalcenter.org

LEVINDALE HEBREW GERIATRIC CENTER AND HOSPITAL (O, 481 beds) 2434 West Belvedere Avenue, Baltimore, MD Zip 21215–5267; tel. 410/601–2400; Barry Eisenberg, FACHE, Chief Operating Officer and Executive Director
**Web address:** www.sinai–balt.com

NORTHWEST HOSPITAL (O, 244 beds) 5401 Old Court Road, Randallstown, MD Zip 21133–5185; tel. 410/521–2200; Brian M. White, President
**Web address:** www.lifebridgehealth.org

| | | |
|---|---|---|
| Owned, leased, sponsored: | 3 hospitals | 876 beds |
| Contract–managed: | 0 hospitals | 0 beds |
| Totals: | 3 hospitals | 876 beds |

## ★0191:  LIFECARE MANAGEMENT SERVICES (IO)
5340 Legacy Drive, Suite 150, Plano, TX Zip 75024–3131; tel. 469/241–2100; Phillip B. Douglas, Chairman and Chief Executive Officer
**(Independent Hospital System)**

**COLORADO:** COLORADO ACUTE LONG TERM HOSPITAL (O, 63 beds) 1690 North Meade Street, Denver, CO Zip 80204–1552; tel. 303/264–6900; Craig Bailey, MS, Administrator
**Web address:** www.lifecare–hospitals.com/hospital/colorado

**FLORIDA:** COMPLEX CARE HOSPITAL AT RIDGELAKE (O, 40 beds) 6150 Edgelake Drive, Sarasota, FL Zip 34240–8803; tel. 941/342–3000; Danny R. Edwards, Administrator
**Web address:** www.lifecare–hospitals.com/hospital.php?id=23

**LOUISIANA:** LIFECARE HOSPITALS OF SHREVEPORT (O, 119 beds) 9320 Linwood Avenue, Shreveport, LA Zip 71106–7003; tel. 318/688–8504; Keith Cox, Administrator
**Web address:** www.lifecare–hospitals.com

LIFECARE SPECIALTY HOSPITAL OF NORTH LOUISIANA (O, 70 beds) 1401 Ezell Street, Ruston, LA Zip 71270–7218; tel. 318/251–3126; Brent Martin, Administrator
**Web address:** www.lifecare–hospitals.com/hospital.php?id=19

**NEVADA:** COMPLEX CARE HOSPITAL AT TENAYA (O, 70 beds) 2500 North Tenaya, Las Vegas, NV Zip 89128–0482; tel. 702/562–2021; Michael R. Shaw, Chief Executive Officer
**Web address:** www.lifecare–hospitals.com

TAHOE PACIFIC HOSPITALS (O, 60 beds) 2375 East Prater Way, Sparks, NV Zip 89434; tel. 775/355–5600; Derrick Glum, Chief Executive Officer
**Web address:** www.lifecare–hospitals.com

**NORTH CAROLINA:** LIFECARE HOSPITALS OF NORTH CAROLINA (O, 41 beds) 1051 Noell Lane, Rocky Mount, NC Zip 27804–1761; tel. 252/451–2300; Robyn Perkerson, R.N., Administrator
**Web address:** www.lifecare–hospitals.com

**OHIO:** LIFECARE HOSPITAL OF DAYTON (O, 44 beds) 4000 Miamisburg–Centerville Road, Miamisburg, OH Zip 45342–7615; tel. 937/384–8300; William Bryant, Chief Executive Officer
**Web address:** www.lifecare–hospitals.com

**PENNSYLVANIA:** LIFECARE HOSPITALS OF CHESTER COUNTY (O, 39 beds) 400 East Marshall Street, West Chester, PA Zip 19380–5412; tel. 484/826–0400; Garrett Arneson, Chief Executive Officer
**Web address:** www.lifecare–hospitals.com

For explanation of codes following names, see page B2.
★ Indicates Type III membership in the American Hospital Association.

LIFECARE HOSPITALS OF MECHANICSBURG (O, 68 beds) 4950 Wilson Lane, Mechanicsburg, PA Zip 17055–4442; tel. 717/697–7706; Mary Ellen Kable, Chief Executive Officer
**Web address:** www.lifecare–hospitals.com/hospital.php?id=20

LIFECARE HOSPITALS OF PITTSBURGH (O, 236 beds) 225 Penn Avenue, Pittsburgh, PA Zip 15221–2148; tel. 412/247–2424; Kim Sperring, Administrator
**Web address:** www.lifecare–hospitals.com

LIFECARE HOSPITALS OF PITTSBURGH – MONROEVILLE (O, 87 beds) 2380 McGinley Road, Monroeville, PA Zip 15146–4400; tel. 412/856–2400; Kim Sperring, Administrator
**Web address:** www.lifecare–hospitals.com/hospital.php?id=8

**TEXAS:** LIFECARE HOSPITALS OF DALLAS (O, 173 beds) 1950 Record Crossing Road, Dallas, TX Zip 75235–6223; tel. 214/640–9600; Kevin S. Cooper, R.N., Chief Executive Officer
**Web address:** www.lifecare–hospitals.com/hospital/dallas

LIFECARE HOSPITALS OF SAN ANTONIO (O, 62 beds) 8902 Floyd Curl Drive, San Antonio, TX Zip 78240–1681; tel. 210/690–7000; Randell G. Stokes, Chief Executive Officer
**Web address:** www.lifecare–hospitals.com

LIFECARE HOSPITALS OF SOUTH TEXAS–NORTH MCALLEN (O, 84 beds) 5101 North Jackson, McAllen, TX Zip 78504–6343; tel. 956/926–7000; Angel Lozano, Chief Executive Officer
**Web address:** www.lifecare–hospitals.com/hospital/southtexas

**WISCONSIN:** LIFECARE HOSPITALS OF WISCONSIN (O, 30 beds) 2400 Golf Road, Pewaukee, WI Zip 53072–5590; tel. 262/524–2600; Gayla Campbell, Interim Chief Executive Officer
**Web address:** www.lifecare–hospitals.com

| | | |
|---|---|---|
| **Owned, leased, sponsored:** | 16 hospitals | 1286 beds |
| **Contract–managed:** | 0 hospitals | 0 beds |
| **Totals:** | 16 hospitals | 1286 beds |

---

**★0180:   LIFEPOINT HEALTH** (IO)
330 Seven Springs Way, Brentwood, TN Zip 37027–4536; tel. 615/920–7000; William F. Carpenter, III, Chairman and Chief Executive Officer
**(Decentralized Health System)**

**ALABAMA:** ANDALUSIA REGIONAL HOSPITAL (O, 88 beds) 849 South Three Notch Street, Andalusia, AL Zip 36420–5325, Mailing Address: P.O. Box 760, Zip 36420–1214; tel. 334/222–8466; John C. Yanes, Chief Executive Officer
**Web address:** www.andalusiaregionalhospital.com

VAUGHAN REGIONAL MEDICAL CENTER (O, 175 beds) 1015 Medical Center Parkway, Selma, AL Zip 36701–6352; tel. 334/418–4100; Roy Vinson, Interim Chief Executive Officer
**Web address:** www.vaughanregional.com

**ARIZONA:** HAVASU REGIONAL MEDICAL CENTER (O, 162 beds) 101 Civic Center Lane, Lake Havasu City, AZ Zip 86403–5683; tel. 928/855–8185; Michael N. Patterson, Chief Executive Officer
**Web address:** www.havasuregional.com

VALLEY VIEW MEDICAL CENTER (O, 90 beds) 5330 South Highway 95, Fort Mohave, AZ Zip 86426–9225; tel. 928/788–2273; Fred Capozello, Jr., Chief Executive Officer
**Web address:** www.valleyviewmedicalcenter.net

**COLORADO:** COLORADO PLAINS MEDICAL CENTER (L, 50 beds) 1000 Lincoln Street, Fort Morgan, CO Zip 80701–3298; tel. 970/867–3391; Gene L. O'Hara, Interim Chief Executive Officer
**Web address:** www.coloradoplainsmedicalcenter.com

**FLORIDA:** PUTNAM COMMUNITY MEDICAL CENTER (O, 99 beds) Highway 20 West, Palatka, FL Zip 32177–8118, Mailing Address: P.O. Box 778, Zip 32178–0778; tel. 386/328–5711; Christopher J. Mosley, Chief Executive Officer
**Web address:** www.pcmcfl.com

**GEORGIA:** ROCKDALE MEDICAL CENTER (O, 138 beds) 1412 Milstead Avenue N.E., Conyers, GA Zip 30012–3877; tel. 770/918–3000; Deborah Armstrong, Chief Executive Officer
**Web address:** www.rockdalemedicalcenter.org

**INDIANA:** SCOTT MEMORIAL HOSPITAL (O, 25 beds) 1415 North Gardner Street, Scottsburg, IN Zip 47170, Mailing Address: Box 430, Zip 47170–0430; tel. 812/752–3456; Michael Everett, Chief Executive Officer
**Web address:** www.scottmemorial.com

**KANSAS:** WESTERN PLAINS MEDICAL COMPLEX (O, 89 beds) 3001 Avenue A, Dodge City, KS Zip 67801–6508, Mailing Address: P.O. Box 1478, Zip 67801–1478; tel. 620/225–8400; Michael R. Burroughs, FACHE, Chief Executive Officer
**Web address:** www.westernplainsmc.com

**KENTUCKY:** BLUEGRASS COMMUNITY HOSPITAL (O, 16 beds) 360 Amsden Avenue, Versailles, KY Zip 40383–1286; tel. 859/873–3111; Tommy Haggard, Chief Executive Officer
**Web address:** www.bluegrasscommunityhospital.com

BOURBON COMMUNITY HOSPITAL (O, 58 beds) 9 Linville Drive, Paris, KY Zip 40361–2196; tel. 859/987–3600; Joseph G. Koch, Chief Executive Officer
**Web address:** www.bourbonhospital.com

CLARK REGIONAL MEDICAL CENTER (O, 79 beds) 175 Hospital Drive, Winchester, KY Zip 40391–9591; tel. 859/745–3500; Cherie Sibley, R.N., Chief Executive Officer
**Web address:** www.clarkregional.org

FLEMING COUNTY HOSPITAL (O, 52 beds) 55 Foundation Drive, Flemingsburg, KY Zip 41041–9815, Mailing Address: P.O. Box 388, Zip 41041–0388; tel. 606/849–5000; Michael Clark, Interim Chief Executive Officer
**Web address:** www.flemingcountyhospital.org

GEORGETOWN COMMUNITY HOSPITAL (O, 58 beds) 1140 Lexington Road, Georgetown, KY Zip 40324–9362; tel. 502/868–1100; William Haugh, Administrator
**Web address:** www.georgetowncommunityhospital.com

JACKSON PURCHASE MEDICAL CENTER (O, 227 beds) 1099 Medical Center Circle, Mayfield, KY Zip 42066–1159; tel. 270/251–4100; David Anderson, Chief Executive Officer
**Web address:** www.jacksonpurchase.com

LAKE CUMBERLAND REGIONAL HOSPITAL (O, 295 beds) 305 Langdon Street, Somerset, KY Zip 42503–2750, Mailing Address: P.O. Box 620, Zip 42502–0620; tel. 606/679–7441; Timothy A. Bess, Chief Executive Officer
**Web address:** www.lakecumberlandhospital.com

LOGAN MEMORIAL HOSPITAL (O, 53 beds) 1625 South Nashville Road, Russellville, KY Zip 42276–8834, Mailing Address: P.O. Box 10, Zip 42276–0010; tel. 270/726–4011; James Bills, Chief Executive Officer
**Web address:** www.loganmemorial.com

MEADOWVIEW REGIONAL MEDICAL CENTER (O, 101 beds) 989 Medical Park Drive, Maysville, KY Zip 41056–8750; tel. 606/759–5311; Robert Parker, Chief Executive Officer
**Web address:** www.meadowviewregional.com

SPRING VIEW HOSPITAL (O, 75 beds) 320 Loretto Road, Lebanon, KY Zip 40033–1300; tel. 270/692–3161; Timothy R. Trottier, Chief Executive Officer
**Web address:** www.springviewhospital.com

**LOUISIANA:** MERCY REGIONAL MEDICAL CENTER (O, 109 beds) 800 East Main Street, Ville Platte, LA Zip 70586–4618; tel. 337/363–5684; Scott M. Smith, Chief Executive Officer
**Web address:** www.mercyregionalmedicalcenter.com

MINDEN MEDICAL CENTER (O, 161 beds) 1 Medical Plaza, Minden, LA Zip 71055–3330, Mailing Address: P.O. Box 5003, Zip 71058–5003; tel. 318/377–2321; George E. French, III, FACHE, Chief Executive Officer
**Web address:** www.mindenmedicalcenter.com

TECHE REGIONAL MEDICAL CENTER (L, 165 beds) 1125 Marguerite Street, Morgan City, LA Zip 70380–1855, Mailing Address: P.O. Box 2308, Zip 70381–2308; tel. 985/384–2200; James P. Frazier, III, Chief Executive Officer
**Web address:** www.techeregional.com

**MICHIGAN:** UP HEALTH SYSTEM–BELL (O, 25 beds) 901 Lakeshore Drive, Ishpeming, MI Zip 49849–1367; tel. 906/486–4431; Mitchell D. Leckelt, Chief Executive Officer
**Web address:** www.bellhospital.org

For explanation of codes following names, see page B2.
★ Indicates Type III membership in the American Hospital Association.

UP HEALTH SYSTEM–MARQUETTE (O, 268 beds) 580 West College Avenue, Marquette, MI Zip 49855–2736; tel. 906/228–9440; James Bogan, FACHE, Interim Chief Executive Officer
**Web address:** www.mgh.org

UP HEALTH SYSTEM–PORTAGE (O, 96 beds) 500 Campus Drive, Hancock, MI Zip 49930–1569; tel. 906/483–1000; Jeff Lang, President
**Web address:** www.portagehealth.org

**MISSISSIPPI:** BOLIVAR MEDICAL CENTER (L, 127 beds) 901 East Sunflower Road, Cleveland, MS Zip 38732–2833, Mailing Address: P.O. Box 1380, Zip 38732–1380; tel. 662/846–0061; Robert L. Marshall, Jr., FACHE, Chief Executive Officer
**Web address:** www.bolivarmedical.com

**NEVADA:** NORTHEASTERN NEVADA REGIONAL HOSPITAL (O, 50 beds) 2001 Errecart Boulevard, Elko, NV Zip 89801–8333; tel. 775/738–5151; Richard L. Palagi, Chief Executive Officer
**Web address:** www.nnrhospital.com

**NEW MEXICO:** LOS ALAMOS MEDICAL CENTER (O, 29 beds) 3917 West Road, Los Alamos, NM Zip 87544–2293; tel. 505/661–9500; Feliciano Jiron, Chief Executive Officer
**Web address:** www.losalamosmedicalcenter.com

MEMORIAL MEDICAL CENTER (L, 224 beds) 2450 South Telshor Boulevard, Las Cruces, NM Zip 88011–5076; tel. 575/522–8641; John Harris, Chief Executive Officer
**Web address:** www.mmclc.org

**NORTH CAROLINA:** HARRIS REGIONAL HOSPITAL (O, 86 beds) 68 Hospital Road, Sylva, NC Zip 28779–2722; tel. 828/586–7000; Steve Heatherly, Chief Executive Officer
**Web address:** www.westcare.org

HAYWOOD REGIONAL MEDICAL CENTER (O, 146 beds) 262 Leroy George Drive, Clyde, NC Zip 28721–7430; tel. 828/456–7311; Phillip L. Wright, FACHE, Chief Executive Officer
**Web address:** www.haymed.org

MARIA PARHAM MEDICAL CENTER (O, 102 beds) 566 Ruin Creek Road, Henderson, NC Zip 27536–2927; tel. 252/438–4143; Brian Sinotte, Chief Executive Officer
**Web address:** www.mariaparham.com

PERSON MEMORIAL HOSPITAL (O, 106 beds) 615 Ridge Road, Roxboro, NC Zip 27573–4629; tel. 336/599–2121; Beemal A. Shah, Chief Executive Officer
**Web address:** www.personhospital.com

RUTHERFORD REGIONAL HEALTH SYSTEM (O, 112 beds) 288 South Ridgecrest Avenue, Rutherfordton, NC Zip 28139–2838; tel. 828/286–5000; Cindy D. Buck, Chief Executive Officer
**Web address:** www.rutherfordhosp.org

SWAIN COMMUNITY HOSPITAL (O, 25 beds) 45 Plateau Street, Bryson City, NC Zip 28713–4200; tel. 828/488–2155; Steve Heatherly, Chief Executive Officer
**Web address:** www.westcare.org

WILSON MEDICAL CENTER (O, 294 beds) 1705 Tarboro Street, S.W., Wilson, NC Zip 27893–3428; tel. 252/399–8040; William E. Caldwell, Jr., Chief Executive Officer
**Web address:** www.wilmed.org

**PENNSYLVANIA:** CONEMAUGH MEMORIAL MEDICAL CENTER (O, 539 beds) 1086 Franklin Street, Johnstown, PA Zip 15905–4398; tel. 814/534–9000; Steven E. Tucker, President
**Web address:** www.conemaugh.org

CONEMAUGH MEYERSDALE MEDICAL CENTER (O, 20 beds) 200 Hospital Drive, Meyersdale, PA Zip 15552–1249; tel. 814/634–5911; Heather Smith, President
**Web address:** www.conemaugh.org

CONEMAUGH MINERS MEDICAL CENTER (O, 30 beds) 290 Haida Avenue, Hastings, PA Zip 16646–5610, Mailing Address: P.O. Box 689, Zip 16646–0689; tel. 814/247–3100; William R. Crowe, President
**Web address:** www.minersmedicalcenter.org

NASON HOSPITAL (O, 45 beds) 105 Nason Drive, Roaring Spring, PA Zip 16673–1202; tel. 814/224–2141; Richard Grogan, Interim Chief Executive Officer
**Web address:** www.nasonhospital.org

**TENNESSEE:** LIVINGSTON REGIONAL HOSPITAL (O, 114 beds) 315 Oak Street, Livingston, TN Zip 38570–1728, Mailing Address: P.O. Box 550, Zip 38570–0550; tel. 931/823–5611; Ronald Tyrer, Interim Chief Executive Officer
**Web address:** www.MyLivingstonHospital.com

RIVERVIEW REGIONAL MEDICAL CENTER (O, 35 beds) 158 Hospital Drive, Carthage, TN Zip 37030–1096; tel. 615/735–1560; Rod Harkleroad, R.N., Administrator
**Web address:** www.myriverviewmedical.com/

SOUTHERN TENNESSEE REGIONAL HEALTH SYSTEM–LAWRENCEBURG (O, 99 beds) 1607 South Locust Avenue, Lawrenceburg, TN Zip 38464–4011, Mailing Address: P.O. Box 847, Zip 38464–0847; tel. 931/762–6571; Jeff Noblin, FACHE, Chief Executive Officer
**Web address:** www.crocketthospital.com

SOUTHERN TENNESSEE REGIONAL HEALTH SYSTEM–PULASKI (O, 95 beds) 1265 East College Street, Pulaski, TN Zip 38478–4541; tel. 931/363–7531; James H. Edmondson, Chief Executive Officer
**Web address:** www.hillsidehospital.com

SOUTHERN TENNESSEE REGIONAL HEALTH SYSTEM–WINCHESTER (O, 198 beds) 185 Hospital Road, Winchester, TN Zip 37398–2404; tel. 931/967–8200; J. Phillip Young, FACHE, Chief Executive Officer
**Web address:** www.southerntennessee.com

STARR REGIONAL MEDICAL CENTER (O, 190 beds) 1114 West Madison Avenue, Athens, TN Zip 37303–4150, Mailing Address: P.O. Box 250, Zip 37371–0250; tel. 423/745–1411; Mark Nichols, FACHE, Chief Executive Officer
**Web address:** www.starrregional.com

SUMNER REGIONAL MEDICAL CENTER (O, 155 beds) 555 Hartsville Pike, Gallatin, TN Zip 37066–2400, Mailing Address: P.O. Box 1558, Zip 37066–1558; tel. 615/452–4210; Susan M. Peach, R.N., Chief Executive Officer
**Web address:** www.mysumnermedical.com

TROUSDALE MEDICAL CENTER (O, 25 beds) 500 Church Street, Hartsville, TN Zip 37074–1744; tel. 615/374–2221; Rod Harkleroad, R.N., Chief Executive Officer
**Web address:** www.mytrousdalemedical.com

**TEXAS:** ENNIS REGIONAL MEDICAL CENTER (L, 58 beds) 2201 West Lampasas Street, Ennis, TX Zip 75119–5644; tel. 972/875–0900; Alan Daugherty, Interim Chief Executive Officer
**Web address:** www.ennisregional.com

PALESTINE REGIONAL MEDICAL CENTER (O, 12 beds) 2900 South Loop 256, Palestine, TX Zip 75801–6958; tel. 903/731–1000; Alan E. George, Chief Executive Officer
**Web address:** www.palestineregional.com

PALESTINE REGIONAL MEDICAL CENTER–EAST (O, 139 beds) 2900 South Loop 256, Palestine, TX Zip 75801–6958; tel. 903/731–1000; Alan E. George, Chief Executive Officer
**Web address:** www.palestineregional.com

PARKVIEW REGIONAL HOSPITAL (L, 58 beds) 600 South Bonham, Mexia, TX Zip 76667–3603; tel. 254/562–5332; Alan Daugherty, Interim Chief Executive Officer
**Web address:** www.parkviewregional.com

**UTAH:** ASHLEY REGIONAL MEDICAL CENTER (O, 39 beds) 150 West 100 North, Vernal, UT Zip 84078–2036; tel. 435/789–3342; Ben Cluff, Chief Executive Officer
**Web address:** www.ashleyregional.com

CASTLEVIEW HOSPITAL (O, 49 beds) 300 North Hospital Drive, Price, UT Zip 84501–4200; tel. 435/637–4800; Mark Holyoak, Chief Executive Officer
**Web address:** www.castleviewhospital.net

**VIRGINIA:** CLINCH VALLEY MEDICAL CENTER (O, 111 beds) 6801 Governor G. C. Peery Highway, Richlands, VA Zip 24641–2194; tel. 276/596–6000; Peter Mulkey, Chief Executive Officer
**Web address:** www.clinchvalleymedicalcenter.com

DANVILLE REGIONAL MEDICAL CENTER (O, 250 beds) 142 South Main Street, Danville, VA Zip 24541–2922; tel. 434/799–2100; Alan Larson, Chief Executive Officer
**Web address:** www.danvilleregional.org

FAUQUIER HOSPITAL (O, 97 beds) 500 Hospital Drive, Warrenton, VA Zip 20186–3099; tel. 540/316–5000; Rodger H. Baker, President and Chief Executive Officer
**Web address:** www.fauquierhospital.org

For explanation of codes following names, see page B2.
★ Indicates Type III membership in the American Hospital Association.

MEMORIAL HOSPITAL (O, 220 beds) 320 Hospital Drive, Martinsville, VA Zip 24112–1981, Mailing Address: P.O. Box 4788, Zip 24115–4788; tel. 276/666–7200; Michael Ehrat, Chief Executive Officer
**Web address:** www.martinsvillehospital.com

TWIN COUNTY REGIONAL HEALTHCARE (O, 141 beds) 200 Hospital Drive, Galax, VA Zip 24333–2227; tel. 276/236–8181; Jon D. Applebaum, Chief Executive Officer
**Web address:** www.tcrh.org

WYTHE COUNTY COMMUNITY HOSPITAL (L, 70 beds) 600 West Ridge Road, Wytheville, VA Zip 24382–1099; tel. 276/228–0200; Chad Melton, Chief Executive Officer
**Web address:** www.wcchcares.com

**WEST VIRGINIA:** LOGAN REGIONAL MEDICAL CENTER (O, 129 beds) 20 Hospital Drive, Logan, WV Zip 25601–3452; tel. 304/831–1101; Kevin Zachary, Chief Executive Officer
**Web address:** www.loganregionalmedicalcenter.com

RALEIGH GENERAL HOSPITAL (O, 229 beds) 1710 Harper Road, Beckley, WV Zip 25801–3397; tel. 304/256–4100; David B. Darden, Chief Executive Officer
**Web address:** www.raleighgeneral.com

**WYOMING:** SAGEWEST HEALTH CARE AT RIVERTON (O, 71 beds) 2100 West Sunset Drive, Riverton, WY Zip 82501–2274; tel. 307/856–4161; Stephen M. Erixon, Chief Executive Officer
**Web address:** www.sagewesthealthcare.com

| | | |
|---|---|---|
| **Owned, leased, sponsored:** | 51 hospitals | 5404 beds |
| **Contract–managed:** | 0 hospitals | 0 beds |
| **Totals:** | 51 hospitals | 5404 beds |

**0060: LIFESPAN CORPORATION** (NP)
167 Point Street, Providence, RI Zip 02903–4771; tel. 401/444–3500; Timothy J. Babineau, M.D., President and Chief Executive Officer
**(Centralized Health System)**

**RHODE ISLAND:** EMMA PENDLETON BRADLEY HOSPITAL (O, 60 beds) 1011 Veterans Memorial Parkway, East Providence, RI Zip 02915–5099; tel. 401/432–1000; Daniel J. Wall, President and Chief Executive Officer
**Web address:** www.lifespan.org

MIRIAM HOSPITAL (O, 247 beds) 164 Summit Avenue, Providence, RI Zip 02906–2853; tel. 401/793–2500; Arthur J. Sampson, FACHE, President
**Web address:** www.lifespan.org

NEWPORT HOSPITAL (O, 119 beds) 11 Friendship Street, Newport, RI Zip 02840–2299; tel. 401/846–6400; Crista F. Durand, President
**Web address:** www.newporthospital.org

RHODE ISLAND HOSPITAL (O, 640 beds) 593 Eddy Street, Providence, RI Zip 02903–4900; tel. 401/444–4000; Timothy J. Babineau, M.D., President and Chief Executive Officer
**Web address:** www.rhodeislandhospital.org/

| | | |
|---|---|---|
| **Owned, leased, sponsored:** | 4 hospitals | 1066 beds |
| **Contract–managed:** | 0 hospitals | 0 beds |
| **Totals:** | 4 hospitals | 1066 beds |

**2175: LOMA LINDA UNIVERSITY ADVENTIST HEALTH SCIENCES CENTER** (NP)
11175 Campus Street, Loma Linda, CA Zip 92350–1700; tel. 909/558–7572; Richard H. Hart, M.D., President and Chief Executive Officer
**(Moderately Centralized Health System)**

**CALIFORNIA:** LOMA LINDA UNIVERSITY BEHAVIORAL MEDICINE CENTER (O, 89 beds) 1710 Barton Road, Redlands, CA Zip 92373–5304; tel. 909/558–9200; Edward Field, Administrator
**Web address:** www.llu.edu

LOMA LINDA UNIVERSITY MEDICAL CENTER (O, 850 beds) 11234 Anderson Street, Loma Linda, CA Zip 92354–2804, Mailing Address: P.O. Box 2000, Zip 92354–0200; tel. 909/558–4000; Kerry Heinrich, JD, Chief Executive Officer
**Web address:** www.llumc.edu

LOMA LINDA UNIVERSITY MEDICAL CENTER–MURRIETA (O, 106 beds) 28062 Baxter Road, Murrieta, CA Zip 92563–1401; tel. 951/290–4000; Richard L. Rawson, Chief Executive Officer
**Web address:** www.llumcmurrieta.org

| | | |
|---|---|---|
| **Owned, leased, sponsored:** | 3 hospitals | 1045 beds |
| **Contract–managed:** | 0 hospitals | 0 beds |
| **Totals:** | 3 hospitals | 1045 beds |

**5755: LOS ANGELES COUNTY–DEPARTMENT OF HEALTH SERVICES** (NP)
313 North Figueroa Street, Room 912, Los Angeles, CA Zip 90012–2691; tel. 213/240–8101; Mitchell H. Katz, M.D., Director
**(Independent Hospital System)**

HARBOR–UCLA MEDICAL CENTER (O, 397 beds) 1000 West Carson Street, Torrance, CA Zip 90502–2059; tel. 310/222–2345; Delvecchio Finley, Chief Executive Officer
**Web address:** www.humc.edu

LAC–OLIVE VIEW–UCLA MEDICAL CENTER (O, 190 beds) 14445 Olive View Drive, Sylmar, CA Zip 91342–1438; tel. 818/364–1555; Carolyn F. Rhee, Chief Executive Officer
**Web address:** www.ladhs.org

LAC/UNIVERSITY OF SOUTHERN CALIFORNIA MEDICAL CENTER (O, 664 beds) 1200 North State Street, Los Angeles, CA Zip 90033–1029; tel. 323/226–2622; Dan Castillo, Chief Executive Officer
**Web address:** www.lacusc.org

RANCHO LOS AMIGOS NATIONAL REHABILITATION CENTER (O, 207 beds) 7601 East Imperial Highway, Downey, CA Zip 90242–3496; tel. 562/401–7111; Jorge Orozco, Chief Executive Officer
**Web address:** www.rancho.org

| | | |
|---|---|---|
| **Owned, leased, sponsored:** | 4 hospitals | 1458 beds |
| **Contract–managed:** | 0 hospitals | 0 beds |
| **Totals:** | 4 hospitals | 1458 beds |

**0047: LOUISIANA STATE HOSPITALS** (NP)
628 North 4th Street, Baton Rouge, LA Zip 70802–5342, Mailing Address: P.O. Box 629, Zip 70821–0628; tel. 225/342–9500; Shelby Price, Chief Executive Officer
**(Independent Hospital System)**

**LOUISIANA:** CENTRAL LOUISIANA STATE HOSPITAL (O, 128 beds) 242 West Shamrock Avenue, Pineville, LA Zip 71360–6439, Mailing Address: P.O. Box 5031, Zip 71361–5031; tel. 318/484–6200; Ronald G. Williams, Administrator
**Web address:** www.dhh.louisiana.gov/index.cfm/directory/detail/217

EASTERN LOUISIANA MENTAL HEALTH SYSTEM (O, 473 beds) 4502 Highway 951, Jackson, LA Zip 70748–5842, Mailing Address: P.O. Box 498, Zip 70748–0498; tel. 225/634–0100; Hampton P. S. Lea, Acting Chief Executive Officer
**Web address:** www.wwprd.doa.louisiana.gov/laservices/publicpages/ServiceDetail.cfm?service_id=2445

| | | |
|---|---|---|
| **Owned, leased, sponsored:** | 2 hospitals | 601 beds |
| **Contract–managed:** | 0 hospitals | 0 beds |
| **Totals:** | 2 hospitals | 601 beds |

**★0320: LRGHEALTHCARE** (NP)
80 Highland Street, Laconia, NH Zip 03246–3298; tel. 603/524–3211; Seth Warren, President and Chief Executive Officer
**(Independent Hospital System)**

**NEW HAMPSHIRE:** FRANKLIN REGIONAL HOSPITAL (O, 35 beds) 15 Aiken Avenue, Franklin, NH Zip 03235–1299; tel. 603/934–2060; Charles K. Van Sluyter, Interim Chief Executive Officer
**Web address:** www.lrgh.org

Section B

For explanation of codes following names, see page B2.
★ Indicates Type III membership in the American Hospital Association.

LAKES REGION GENERAL HOSPITAL (O, 88 beds) 80 Highland Street, Laconia, NH Zip 03246–3298; tel. 603/524–3211; Seth Warren, Interim Chief Executive Officer
**Web address:** www.lrgh.org

| Owned, leased, sponsored: | 2 hospitals | 123 beds |
|---|---|---|
| Contract–managed: | 0 hospitals | 0 beds |
| Totals: | 2 hospitals | 123 beds |

---

**0614: MAINEHEALTH** (NP)
110 Free Street, Portland, ME Zip 04101–3537; William L. Caron, Jr., President
**(Moderately Centralized Health System)**

**MAINE:** LINCOLNHEALTH (O, 79 beds) 35 Miles Street, Damariscotta, ME Zip 04543–4047; tel. 207/563–1234; James W. Donovan, President and Chief Executive Officer
**Web address:** www.lchcare.org

MAINE MEDICAL CENTER (O, 637 beds) 22 Bramhall Street, Portland, ME Zip 04102–3175; tel. 207/662–0111; Richard W. Petersen, President and Chief Executive Officer
**Web address:** www.mmc.org

PEN BAY MEDICAL CENTER (O, 165 beds) 6 Glen Cove Drive, Rockport, ME Zip 04856–4240; tel. 207/921–8000; Mark A. Biscone, Chief Executive Officer
**Web address:** www.penbayhealthcare.org

SPRING HARBOR HOSPITAL (O, 88 beds) 123 Andover Road, Westbrook, ME Zip 04092–3850; tel. 207/761–2200; Mary Jane Krebs, Chief Executive Officer
**Web address:** www.springharbor.org

STEPHENS MEMORIAL HOSPITAL (O, 25 beds) 181 Main Street, Norway, ME Zip 04268–5664; tel. 207/743–5933; Timothy A. Churchill, President
**Web address:** www.wmhcc.com

WALDO COUNTY GENERAL HOSPITAL (O, 25 beds) 118 Northport Avenue, Belfast, ME Zip 04915–6072, Mailing Address: P.O. Box 287, Zip 04915–0287; tel. 207/338–2500; Mark A. Biscone, Chief Executive Officer
**Web address:** www.wcgh.org

**NEW HAMPSHIRE:** MEMORIAL HOSPITAL (O, 70 beds) 3073 White Mountain Highway, North Conway, NH Zip 03860–7101; tel. 603/356–5461; Scott McKinnon, President and Chief Executive Officer
**Web address:** www.memorialhospitalnh.org

| Owned, leased, sponsored: | 7 hospitals | 1089 beds |
|---|---|---|
| Contract–managed: | 0 hospitals | 0 beds |
| Totals: | 7 hospitals | 1089 beds |

---

**1975: MARSHALL HEALTH SYSTEM** (NP)
227 Britany Road, Guntersville, AL Zip 35976–5766; tel. 256/894–6615; Gary R. Gore, Chief Executive Officer
**(Independent Hospital System)**

**ALABAMA:** MARSHALL MEDICAL CENTER NORTH (O, 90 beds) 8000 Alabama Highway 69, Guntersville, AL Zip 35976; tel. 256/753–8000; Cheryl M. Hays, FACHE, Administrator
**Web address:** www.mmcenters.com

MARSHALL MEDICAL CENTER SOUTH (O, 114 beds) U.S. Highway 431 North, Boaz, AL Zip 35957–0999, Mailing Address: P.O. Box 758, Zip 35957–0758; tel. 256/593–8310; John D. Anderson, FACHE, Administrator
**Web address:** www.mmcenters.com//index.php/facilities/marshall_south

| Owned, leased, sponsored: | 2 hospitals | 204 beds |
|---|---|---|
| Contract–managed: | 0 hospitals | 0 beds |
| Totals: | 2 hospitals | 204 beds |

---

**★0523: MARY WASHINGTON HEALTHCARE** (NP)
2300 Fall Hill Avenue, Suite 308, Fredericksburg, VA Zip 22401–3343; tel. 540/741–3100; Michael McDermott, M.D., President and Chief Executive Officer
**(Independent Hospital System)**

**VIRGINIA:** MARY WASHINGTON HOSPITAL (O, 437 beds) 1001 Sam Perry Boulevard, Fredericksburg, VA Zip 22401–3354; tel. 540/741–1100; Michael McDermott, M.D., President and Chief Executive Officer
**Web address:** www.marywashingtonhealthcare.com

STAFFORD HOSPITAL (O, 100 beds) 101 Hospital Center Boulevard, Stafford, VA Zip 22554–6200; tel. 540/741–9000; Michael McDermott, M.D., President and Chief Executive Officer
**Web address:** www.mwhc.com

| Owned, leased, sponsored: | 2 hospitals | 537 beds |
|---|---|---|
| Contract–managed: | 0 hospitals | 0 beds |
| Totals: | 2 hospitals | 537 beds |

---

**0013: MASSACHUSETTS DEPARTMENT OF MENTAL HEALTH** (NP)
25 Staniford Street, Boston, MA Zip 02114–2575; tel. 617/626–8123; Joan Mikula, Interim Commissioner

**MASSACHUSETTS:** DR. J. CORRIGAN MENTAL HEALTH CENTER (O, 16 beds) 49 Hillside Street, Fall River, MA Zip 02720–5266; tel. 508/235–7200; Roberta H. Guez, Director

TAUNTON STATE HOSPITAL (O, 45 beds) 60 Hodges Avenue Extension, Taunton, MA Zip 02780–3034, Mailing Address: PO Box 4007, Zip 02780–0997; tel. 508/977–3000; Joyce O. Connor, Chief Operating Officer

WORCESTER RECOVERY CENTER AND HOSPITAL (O, 126 beds) 305 Belmont Street, Worcester, MA Zip 01604–1695; tel. 508/368–3300; Anthony Riccitelli, Chief Operating Officer

| Owned, leased, sponsored: | 3 hospitals | 187 beds |
|---|---|---|
| Contract–managed: | 0 hospitals | 0 beds |
| Totals: | 3 hospitals | 187 beds |

---

**0280: MASSACHUSETTS DEPARTMENT OF PUBLIC HEALTH** (NP)
250 Washington Street, Boston, MA Zip 02108–4619; tel. 617/624–6000; Sandra Akers, Bureau Director, Public Health Hospitals
**(Independent Hospital System)**

LEMUEL SHATTUCK HOSPITAL (O, 260 beds) 170 Morton Street, Jamaica Plain, MA Zip 02130–3735; tel. 617/522–8110; Rosette Martinez, Acting Chief Executive Officer
**Web address:** www.mass.gov/shattuckhospital

MASSACHUSETTS HOSPITAL SCHOOL (O, 80 beds) 3 Randolph Street, Canton, MA Zip 02021–2351; tel. 781/828–2440; Brian V. Devin, Chief Executive Officer
**Web address:** www.mhsf.us/

TEWKSBURY HOSPITAL (O, 381 beds) 365 East Street, Tewksbury, MA Zip 01876–1998; tel. 978/851–7321; Debra Tosti, Chief Executive Officer
**Web address:** www.mass.gov

WESTERN MASSACHUSETTS HOSPITAL (O, 70 beds) 91 East Mountain Road, Westfield, MA Zip 01085–1801; tel. 413/562–4131; Valenda M. Liptak, Chief Executive Officer
**Web address:** www.mass.gov/eohhs/gov/departments/dph/programs/western–massachusetts–hospital.html

| Owned, leased, sponsored: | 4 hospitals | 791 beds |
|---|---|---|
| Contract–managed: | 0 hospitals | 0 beds |
| Totals: | 4 hospitals | 791 beds |

---

**★0882: MAURY REGIONAL HEALTH SYSTEM** (NP)
1224 Trotwood Avenue, Columbia, TN Zip 38401–4802; tel. 931/381–1111; H. Alan Watson, FACHE, Chief Executive Officer
**(Independent Hospital System)**

**TENNESSEE:** MARSHALL MEDICAL CENTER (O, 12 beds) 1080 North Ellington Parkway, Lewisburg, TN Zip 37091–2227, Mailing Address: P.O. Box 1609, Zip 37091–1609; tel. 931/359–6241; Phyllis Brown, Chief Executive Officer
**Web address:** www.mauryregional.com

For explanation of codes following names, see page B2.
★ Indicates Type III membership in the American Hospital Association.

MAURY REGIONAL HOSPITAL (O, 211 beds) 1224 Trotwood Avenue, Columbia, TN Zip 38401–4802; tel. 931/381–1111; H. Alan Watson, FACHE, Chief Executive Officer
**Web address:** www.mauryregional.com

WAYNE MEDICAL CENTER (L, 78 beds) 103 J. V. Mangubat Drive, Waynesboro, TN Zip 38485–2440, Mailing Address: P.O. Box 580, Zip 38485–0580; tel. 931/722–5411; Teresa Grimmett, Chief Executive Officer
**Web address:** www.mauryregional.com

| | | |
|---|---|---|
| **Owned, leased, sponsored:** | 3 hospitals | 301 beds |
| **Contract–managed:** | 0 hospitals | 0 beds |
| **Totals:** | 3 hospitals | 301 beds |

---

★**1875: MAYO CLINIC** (NP)
200 First Street S.W., Rochester, MN Zip 55905–0002; tel. 507/284–2511; John H. Noseworthy, MD, M.D., President and Chief Executive Officer
**(Decentralized Health System)**

**ARIZONA:** MAYO CLINIC HOSPITAL (O, 268 beds) 5777 East Mayo Boulevard, Phoenix, AZ Zip 85054–4502; tel. 480/515–6296; Darin Goss, Administrator
**Web address:** www.mayoclinic.org/arizona/

**FLORIDA:** MAYO CLINIC JACKSONVILLE (O, 249 beds) 4500 San Pablo Road South, Jacksonville, FL Zip 32224–1865; tel. 904/953–2000; Gianrico Farrugia, M.D., Vice President and Chief Executive Officer
**Web address:** www.mayoclinic.org/jacksonville/

**GEORGIA:** MAYO CLINIC HEALTH SYSTEM IN WAYCROSS (O, 199 beds) 410 Darling Avenue, Waycross, GA Zip 31501–6357, Mailing Address: P.O. Box 139, Zip 31502–0139; tel. 912/283–3030; John Presutti, D.O., Chief Executive Officer
**Web address:** www.mayoclinichealthsystem.org

**IOWA:** FLOYD COUNTY MEDICAL CENTER (C, 25 beds) 800 Eleventh Street, Charles City, IA Zip 50616–3499; tel. 641/228–6830; Bill D. Faust, Administrator
**Web address:** www.fcmc.us.com/

WINNESHIEK MEDICAL CENTER (C, 25 beds) 901 Montgomery Street, Decorah, IA Zip 52101–2325; tel. 563/382–2911; Lisa Radtke, Chief Administrative Officer
**Web address:** www.winmedical.org

**MINNESOTA:** MAYO CLINIC HEALTH SYSTEM IN ALBERT LEA (O, 129 beds) 404 West Fountain Street, Albert Lea, MN Zip 56007–2473; tel. 507/373–2384; Mark Ciota, M.D., Chief Executive Officer
**Web address:** www.almedcenter.org

MAYO CLINIC HEALTH SYSTEM IN CANNON FALLS (O, 21 beds) 1116 West Mill Street, Cannon Falls, MN Zip 55009–1898; tel. 507/263–4221; Thomas J. Witt, M.D., President and Chief Executive Officer
**Web address:** www.mayoclinichealthsystem.org/locations/cannon–falls

MAYO CLINIC HEALTH SYSTEM IN FAIRMONT (O, 96 beds) 800 Medical Center Drive, Fairmont, MN Zip 56031–4575; tel. 507/238–8100; Robert Bartingale, Administrator
**Web address:** www.fairmontmedicalcenter.org

MAYO CLINIC HEALTH SYSTEM IN LAKE CITY (O, 108 beds) 500 West Grant Street, Lake City, MN Zip 55041–1143; tel. 651/345–3321; Susan M. Stiene, R.N., MS, Interim Chief Administrative Officer
**Web address:** www.lakecitymedicalcenter.org

MAYO CLINIC HEALTH SYSTEM IN MANKATO (O, 166 beds) 1025 Marsh Street, Mankato, MN Zip 56001–4752; tel. 507/625–4031; Gregory Kutcher, M.D., President and Chief Executive Officer
**Web address:** www.isj–mhs.org

MAYO CLINIC HEALTH SYSTEM IN NEW PRAGUE (O, 25 beds) 301 Second Street N.E., New Prague, MN Zip 56071–1799; tel. 952/758–4431; Mary J. Klimp, FACHE, Administrator
**Web address:** www.mayoclinichealthsystem.org/locations/new–prague

MAYO CLINIC HEALTH SYSTEM IN RED WING (O, 134 beds) 701 Hewitt Boulevard, Red Wing, MN Zip 55066–2848, Mailing Address: P.O. Box 95, Zip 55066–0095; tel. 651/267–5000; Thomas J. Witt, M.D., President and Chief Executive Officer
**Web address:** www.mayoclinichealthsystem.org/locations/red–wing

MAYO CLINIC HEALTH SYSTEM IN SAINT JAMES (O, 13 beds) 1101 Moulton and Parsons Drive, Saint James, MN Zip 56081–5550; tel. 507/375–3261; Ryan J. Smith, Administrator
**Web address:** www.mayoclinichealthsystem.org/locations/st–james

MAYO CLINIC HEALTH SYSTEM IN SPRINGFIELD (O, 23 beds) 625 North Jackson Avenue, Springfield, MN Zip 56087–1714, Mailing Address: P.O. Box 146, Zip 56087–0146; tel. 507/723–6201; Scott D. Thoreson, FACHE, Administrator
**Web address:** www.mayoclinichealthsystem.org

MAYO CLINIC HEALTH SYSTEM IN WASECA (O, 25 beds) 501 North State Street, Waseca, MN Zip 56093–2811; tel. 507/835–1210; Thomas Borowski, Administrator
**Web address:** www.mayoclinichealthsystem.org

MAYO CLINIC HEALTH SYSTEM–ALBERT LEA AND AUSTIN (O, 82 beds) 1000 First Drive N.W., Austin, MN Zip 55912–2904; tel. 507/433–7351; Mark Ciota, M.D., Chief Executive Officer
**Web address:** www.austinmedicalcenter.org

MAYO CLINIC HOSPITAL – ROCHESTER (O, 1243 beds) 1216 Second Street S.W., Rochester, MN Zip 55902–1906; tel. 507/255–5123; F. Kenneth Ackerman, Chair, Hospital Operations
**Web address:** www.mayoclinic.org

**WISCONSIN:** MAYO CLINIC HEALTH SYSTEM – CHIPPEWA VALLEY IN BLOOMER (O, 54 beds) 1501 Thompson Street, Bloomer, WI Zip 54724–1299; tel. 715/568–2000; Edward A. Wittrock, Vice President Regional System
**Web address:** www.bloomermedicalcenter.org

MAYO CLINIC HEALTH SYSTEM – FRANCISCAN HEALTHCARE IN LA CROSSE (O, 152 beds) 700 West Avenue South, La Crosse, WI Zip 54601–4783; tel. 608/785–0940; Timothy J. Johnson, President and Chief Executive Officer
**Web address:** www.franciscanskemp.org

MAYO CLINIC HEALTH SYSTEM – FRANCISCAN HEALTHCARE IN SPARTA (O, 10 beds) 310 West Main Street, Sparta, WI Zip 54656–2171; tel. 608/269–2132; Kimberly Hawthorne, Administrator
**Web address:** www.mayoclinichealthsystem.org

MAYO CLINIC HEALTH SYSTEM – NORTHLAND IN BARRON (O, 35 beds) 1222 Woodland Avenue, Barron, WI Zip 54812–1798; tel. 715/537–3186; Maurita Sullivan, Vice President
**Web address:** www.luthermidelfortnorthland.org

MAYO CLINIC HEALTH SYSTEM – OAKRIDGE IN OSSEO (O, 39 beds) 13025 Eighth Street, Osseo, WI Zip 54758–7634, Mailing Address: P.O. Box 70, Zip 54758–0070; tel. 715/597–3121; Dean Eide, Vice President
**Web address:** www.mayoclinichealthsystem.org/locations/osseo

MAYO CLINIC HEALTH SYSTEM – RED CEDAR IN MENOMONIE (O, 23 beds) 2321 Stout Road, Menomonie, WI Zip 54751–2397; tel. 715/235–5531; Steven Lindberg, Chief Administrative Officer
**Web address:** www.rcmc–mhs.org

MAYO CLINIC HEALTH SYSTEM IN EAU CLAIRE (O, 185 beds) 1221 Whipple Street, Eau Claire, WI Zip 54703–5270, Mailing Address: P.O. Box 4105, Zip 54702–4105; tel. 715/838–3311; Randall L. Linton, M.D., President and Chief Executive Officer
**Web address:** www.mhs.mayo.edu

| | | |
|---|---|---|
| **Owned, leased, sponsored:** | 22 hospitals | 3279 beds |
| **Contract–managed:** | 2 hospitals | 50 beds |
| **Totals:** | 24 hospitals | 3329 beds |

---

**0252: MCLAREN HEALTH CARE CORPORATION** (NP)
G3235 Beecher Road, Suite B., Flint, MI Zip 48532–3650; tel. 810/342–1100; Philip A. Incarnati, President and Chief Executive Officer
**(Centralized Physician/Insurance Health System)**

**MICHIGAN:** MCLAREN BAY REGION (O, 338 beds) 1900 Columbus Avenue, Bay City, MI Zip 48708–6831; tel. 989/894–3000; Clarence Sevillian, President and Chief Executive Officer
**Web address:** www.bayregional.org

MCLAREN BAY SPECIAL CARE (O, 26 beds) 3250 East Midland Road, Suite 1, Bay City, MI Zip 48706–2835; tel. 989/667–6802; Cheryl A. Burzynski, President
**Web address:** www.bayspecialcare.org

For explanation of codes following names, see page B2.
★ Indicates Type III membership in the American Hospital Association.

MCLAREN CENTRAL MICHIGAN (O, 78 beds) 1221 South Drive, Mount Pleasant, MI Zip 48858–3257; tel. 989/772–6700; William P. Lawrence, President and Chief Executive Officer
**Web address:** www.cmch.org

MCLAREN FLINT (O, 336 beds) 401 South Ballenger Highway, Flint, MI Zip 48532–3685; tel. 810/342–2000; Donald C. Kooy, President and Chief Executive Officer
**Web address:** www.mclarenregional.org

MCLAREN GREATER LANSING (O, 321 beds) 401 West Greenlawn Avenue, Lansing, MI Zip 48910–2819; tel. 517/975–6000; Rick Wright, President and Chief Executive Officer
**Web address:** www.irmc.org

MCLAREN LAPEER REGION (O, 159 beds) 1375 North Main Street, Lapeer, MI Zip 48446–1350; tel. 810/667–5500; Barton Buxton, Ed.D., President and Chief Executive Officer
**Web address:** www.lapeerregional.org

MCLAREN MACOMB (O, 288 beds) 1000 Harrington Boulevard, Mount Clemens, MI Zip 48043–2992; tel. 586/493–8000; Thomas M. Brisse, President and Chief Executive Officer
**Web address:** www.mclaren.org/macomb/macomb.aspx

MCLAREN OAKLAND (O, 269 beds) 50 North Perry Street, Pontiac, MI Zip 48342–2253; tel. 248/338–5000; Chad M. Grant, President and Chief Executive Officer
**Web address:** www.pohmedical.org

MCLAREN PORT HURON (O, 186 beds) 1221 Pine Grove Avenue, Port Huron, MI Zip 48060–3511; tel. 810/987–5000; Thomas D. DeFauw, FACHE, President and Chief Executive Officer
**Web address:** www.porthuronhospital.org

| | | |
|---|---|---|
| **Owned, leased, sponsored:** | 10 hospitals | 2189 beds |
| **Contract–managed:** | 0 hospitals | 0 beds |
| **Totals:** | 10 hospitals | 2189 beds |

---

**0874:  MCLEOD HEALTH** (NP)
555 East Cheves Street, Florence, SC Zip 29506–2617, Mailing Address: P.O. Box 100551, Zip 29502–0551; tel. 843/777–2000; Robert L. Colones, President and Chief Executive Officer
**(Centralized Health System)**

**SOUTH CAROLINA:** MCLEOD HEALTH CHERAW (O, 59 beds) 711 Chesterfield Highway, Cheraw, SC Zip 29520–7002; tel. 843/537–7881; Mib Scoggins, Chief Executive Officer
**Web address:** www.chesterfieldgeneral.com

MCLEOD LORIS SEACOAST HOSPITAL (O, 193 beds) 3655 Mitchell Street, Loris, SC Zip 29569–2827; tel. 843/716–7000; Edward D. Tinsley, III, Chief Executive Officer
**Web address:** www.mcleodhealth.org

MCLEOD MEDICAL CENTER DILLON (O, 58 beds) 301 East Jackson Street, Dillon, SC Zip 29536–2509, Mailing Address: P.O. Box 1327, Zip 29536–1327; tel. 843/774–4111; Joan Gruin, RN, MN, Administrator
**Web address:** www.mcleodhealth.org

MCLEOD MEDICAL CENTER–DARLINGTON (O, 72 beds) 701 Cashua Ferry Road, Darlington, SC Zip 29532–8488, Mailing Address: P.O. Box 1859, Zip 29540; tel. 843/395–1100; Tim Smoak, Administrator
**Web address:** www.mcleodhealth.org

MCLEOD REGIONAL MEDICAL CENTER (O, 493 beds) 555 East Cheves Street, Florence, SC Zip 29506–2617, Mailing Address: P.O. Box 100551, Zip 29502–0551; tel. 843/777–2000; Robert L. Colones, President and Chief Executive Officer
**Web address:** www.mcleodhealth.org

| | | |
|---|---|---|
| **Owned, leased, sponsored:** | 5 hospitals | 875 beds |
| **Contract–managed:** | 0 hospitals | 0 beds |
| **Totals:** | 5 hospitals | 875 beds |

---

**★0971:  MEDISYS HEALTH NETWORK** (NP)
8900 Van Wyck Expressway, Jamaica, NY Zip 11418–2832; tel. 718/206–6000; Bruce J. Flanz, President and Chief Executive Officer

**NEW YORK:** FLUSHING HOSPITAL MEDICAL CENTER (C, 299 beds) 4500 Parsons Boulevard, Flushing, NY Zip 11355–2205; tel. 718/670–5000; Bruce J. Flanz, President and Chief Executive Officer
**Web address:** www.flushinghospital.org

JAMAICA HOSPITAL MEDICAL CENTER (C, 650 beds) 8900 Van Wyck Expressway, Jamaica, NY Zip 11418–2832; tel. 718/206–6000; Bruce J. Flanz, President and Chief Executive Officer
**Web address:** www.Jamaicahospital.org

| | | |
|---|---|---|
| **Owned, leased, sponsored:** | 0 hospitals | 0 beds |
| **Contract–managed:** | 2 hospitals | 949 beds |
| **Totals:** | 2 hospitals | 949 beds |

---

**★0154:  MEDSTAR HEALTH** (NP)
5565 Sterrett Place, 5th Floor, Columbia, MD Zip 21044–2665; tel. 410/772–6500; Kenneth A. Samet, President and Chief Executive Officer
**(Centralized Health System)**

**DISTRICT OF COLUMBIA:** MEDSTAR GEORGETOWN UNIVERSITY HOSPITAL (O, 399 beds) 3800 Reservoir Road N.W., Washington, DC Zip 20007–2197; tel. 202/444–2000; Richard L. Goldberg, M.D., President
**Web address:** www.georgetownuniversityhospital.org

MEDSTAR NATIONAL REHABILITATION HOSPITAL (O, 137 beds) 102 Irving Street N.W., Washington, DC Zip 20010–2949; tel. 202/877–1000; John D. Rockwood, President
**Web address:** www.medstarnrh.org

MEDSTAR WASHINGTON HOSPITAL CENTER (O, 763 beds) 110 Irving Street N.W., Washington, DC Zip 20010–3017; tel. 202/877–7000; John Sullivan, President
**Web address:** www.whcenter.org

**MARYLAND:** MEDSTAR FRANKLIN SQUARE MEDICAL CENTER (O, 401 beds) 9000 Franklin Square Drive, Baltimore, MD Zip 21237–3901; tel. 443/777–7000; Samuel E. Moskowitz, President
**Web address:** www.medstarfranklin.org

MEDSTAR GOOD SAMARITAN HOSPITAL (O, 287 beds) 5601 Loch Raven Boulevard, Baltimore, MD Zip 21239–2995; tel. 443/444–8000; Bradley Chambers, President and Chief Executive Officer
**Web address:** www.goodsam-md.org

MEDSTAR HARBOR HOSPITAL (O, 150 beds) 3001 South Hanover Street, Baltimore, MD Zip 21225–1290; tel. 410/350–3200; Dennis W. Pullin, FACHE, President
**Web address:** www.harborhospital.org

MEDSTAR MONTGOMERY MEDICAL CENTER (O, 149 beds) 18101 Prince Philip Drive, Olney, MD Zip 20832–1512; tel. 301/774–8882; Peter W. Monge, President
**Web address:** www.medstarmontgomery.org

MEDSTAR SOUTHERN MARYLAND HOSPITAL CENTER (O, 275 beds) 7503 Surratts Road, Clinton, MD Zip 20735–3358; tel. 301/868–8000; Christine R. Wray, President and Chief Executive Officer
**Web address:** www.smhchealth.org

MEDSTAR ST. MARY'S HOSPITAL (O, 89 beds) 25500 Point Lookout Road, Leonardtown, MD Zip 20650–2015, Mailing Address: P.O. Box 527, Zip 20650–0527; tel. 301/475–6001; Christine R. Wray, President
**Web address:** www.medstarstmarys.org

MEDSTAR UNION MEMORIAL HOSPITAL (O, 231 beds) 201 East University Parkway, Baltimore, MD Zip 21218–2895; tel. 410/554–2000; Bradley Chambers, President
**Web address:** www.medstarunionmemorial.org

| | | |
|---|---|---|
| **Owned, leased, sponsored:** | 10 hospitals | 2881 beds |
| **Contract–managed:** | 0 hospitals | 0 beds |
| **Totals:** | 10 hospitals | 2881 beds |

---

**★0086:  MEMORIAL HEALTH SYSTEM** (NP)
701 North First Street, Springfield, IL Zip 62781–0001; tel. 217/788–3000; Edgar J. Curtis, FACHE, President and Chief Executive Officer
**(Centralized Health System)**

---

For explanation of codes following names, see page B2.
★ Indicates Type III membership in the American Hospital Association.

**ILLINOIS:** ABRAHAM LINCOLN MEMORIAL HOSPITAL (O, 25 beds) 200 Stahlhut Drive, Lincoln, IL Zip 62656–5066; tel. 217/732–2161; Dolan Dalpoas, President and Chief Executive Officer
**Web address:** www.almh.org

MEMORIAL MEDICAL CENTER (O, 473 beds) 701 North First Street, Springfield, IL Zip 62781–0001; tel. 217/788–3000; Edgar J. Curtis, FACHE, President and Chief Executive Officer
**Web address:** www.memorialmedical.com

PASSAVANT AREA HOSPITAL (O, 108 beds) 1600 West Walnut Street, Jacksonville, IL Zip 62650–1136; tel. 217/245–9541; Douglas L. Rahn, President and Chief Executive Officer
**Web address:** www.passavanthospital.com

TAYLORVILLE MEMORIAL HOSPITAL (O, 45 beds) 201 East Pleasant Street, Taylorville, IL Zip 62568–1597; tel. 217/824–3331; Kimberly L. Bourne, Chief Executive Officer
**Web address:** www.taylorvillememorial.org

| | | |
|---|---|---|
| Owned, leased, sponsored: | 4 hospitals | 651 beds |
| Contract–managed: | 0 hospitals | 0 beds |
| Totals: | 4 hospitals | 651 beds |

★**0083:  MEMORIAL HEALTHCARE SYSTEM** (NP)
3501 Johnson Street, Hollywood, FL Zip 33021–5421; tel. 954/265–5805; Frank V. Sacco, FACHE, President and Chief Executive Officer
**(Centralized Health System)**

**FLORIDA:** MEMORIAL HOSPITAL MIRAMAR (O, 178 beds) 1901 S.W. 172nd Avenue, Miramar, FL Zip 33029–5592; tel. 954/538–5000; Leah A. Carpenter, Administrator and Chief Executive Officer
**Web address:** www.mhs.net

MEMORIAL HOSPITAL PEMBROKE (L, 149 beds) 7800 Sheridan Street, Pembroke Pines, FL Zip 33024–2536; tel. 954/883–8482; Mark Doyle, Chief Executive Officer
**Web address:** www.memorialpembroke.com/

MEMORIAL HOSPITAL WEST (O, 384 beds) 703 North Flamingo Road, Pembroke Pines, FL Zip 33028–1014; tel. 954/436–5000; C. Kennon Hetlage, FACHE, Administrator and Chief Executive Officer
**Web address:** www.mhs.net

MEMORIAL REGIONAL HOSPITAL (O, 1037 beds) 3501 Johnson Street, Hollywood, FL Zip 33021–5421; tel. 954/987–2000; Zeff Ross, FACHE, Senior Vice President and Chief Executive Officer
**Web address:** www.mhs.net

| | | |
|---|---|---|
| Owned, leased, sponsored: | 4 hospitals | 1748 beds |
| Contract–managed: | 0 hospitals | 0 beds |
| Totals: | 4 hospitals | 1748 beds |

★**2645:  MEMORIAL HERMANN HEALTHCARE SYSTEM** (NP)
929 Gessner, Suite 2700, Houston, TX Zip 77024–2593; tel. 713/242–2700; Daniel J. Wolterman, President and Chief Executive Officer
**(Centralized Health System)**

**TEXAS:** MEMORIAL HERMANN – TEXAS MEDICAL CENTER (O, 877 beds) 6411 Fannin Street, Houston, TX Zip 77030–1501; tel. 713/704–4000; Craig Cordola, Chief Executive Officer
**Web address:** www.mhhs.org

MEMORIAL HERMANN KATY HOSPITAL (O, 142 beds) 23900 Katy Freeway, Katy, TX Zip 77494–1323; tel. 281/644–7000; James Parisi, Chief Executive Officer
**Web address:** www.memorialhermann.org/locations/katy/

MEMORIAL HERMANN MEMORIAL CITY MEDICAL CENTER (L, 383 beds) 921 Gessner Road, Houston, TX Zip 77024–2501; tel. 713/242–3000; Paul O'Sullivan, Chief Executive Officer
**Web address:** www.memorialhermann.org

MEMORIAL HERMANN NORTHEAST (L, 216 beds) 18951 North Memorial Drive, Humble, TX Zip 77338–4297; tel. 281/540–7700; Heath Rushing, Interim Chief Executive Officer
**Web address:** www.memorialhermann.org

MEMORIAL HERMANN NORTHWEST HOSPITAL (O, 1217 beds) 1635 North Loop West, Houston, TX Zip 77008–1532; tel. 713/867–3380; Susan Jadlowski, MSN, R.N., Chief Executive Officer
**Web address:** www.mhbh.org

MEMORIAL HERMANN REHABILITATION HOSPITAL – KATY (O, 35 beds) 21720 Kingsland Boulevard, Katy, TX Zip 77450–2550; tel. 281/579–5555; Carl E. Josehart, Chief Executive Officer
**Web address:** www.memorialhermann.com

MEMORIAL HERMANN SUGAR LAND HOSPITAL (O, 81 beds) 17500 West Grand Parkway South, Sugar Land, TX Zip 77479–2562; tel. 281/725–5000; Gregory Haralson, Chief Executive Officer
**Web address:** www.memorialhermann.org

MEMORIAL HERMANN SURGICAL HOSPITAL – FIRST COLONY (O, 6 beds) 16906 Southwest Freeway, Sugar Land, TX Zip 77479–2350; tel. 281/243–1000; Daniel Smith, Interim Chief Executive Officer
**Web address:** www.memorialhermannfirstcolony.com

TIRR MEMORIAL HERMANN (O, 134 beds) 1333 Moursund Street, Houston, TX Zip 77030–3405; tel. 713/799–5000; Carl E. Josehart, Chief Executive Officer
**Web address:** www.memorialhermann.org/locations/tirr.html

| | | |
|---|---|---|
| Owned, leased, sponsored: | 9 hospitals | 3091 beds |
| Contract–managed: | 0 hospitals | 0 beds |
| Totals: | 9 hospitals | 3091 beds |

**0084:  MEMORIALCARE** (NP)
17360 Brookhurst Street, Fountain Valley, CA Zip 92708–3720, Mailing Address: P.O. Box 1428, Long Beach, Zip 90801–1428; tel. 714/377–2900; Barry S. Arbuckle, Ph.D., President and Chief Executive Officer
**(Centralized Health System)**

**CALIFORNIA:** COMMUNITY HOSPITAL LONG BEACH (O, 148 beds) 1720 Termino Avenue, Long Beach, CA Zip 90804–2104; tel. 562/498–1000; Diana Hendel, PharmD, Chief Executive Officer
**Web address:** www.memorialcare.org

LONG BEACH MEMORIAL MEDICAL CENTER (O, 458 beds) 2801 Atlantic Avenue, Long Beach, CA Zip 90806–1701, Mailing Address: P.O. Box 1428, Zip 90801–1428; tel. 562/933–2000; Tammie McMann Brailsford, Interim Chief Executive Officer
**Web address:** www.memorialcare.org/LongBeach

MILLER CHILDREN'S & WOMEN'S HOSPITAL LONG BEACH (O, 371 beds) 2801 Atlantic Avenue, Long Beach, CA Zip 90806–1701; tel. 562/933–5437; Diana Hendel, PharmD, Chief Executive Officer
**Web address:** www.memorialcare.org

ORANGE COAST MEMORIAL MEDICAL CENTER (O, 218 beds) 9920 Talbert Avenue, Fountain Valley, CA Zip 92708–5115; tel. 714/378–7000; Marcia Manker, Chief Executive Officer
**Web address:** www.memorialcare.org

SADDLEBACK MEMORIAL MEDICAL CENTER (O, 313 beds) 24451 Health Center Drive, Laguna Hills, CA Zip 92653–3689; tel. 949/837–4500; Steve Geidt, Chief Executive Officer
**Web address:** www.memorialcare.org

| | | |
|---|---|---|
| Owned, leased, sponsored: | 5 hospitals | 1508 beds |
| Contract–managed: | 0 hospitals | 0 beds |
| Totals: | 5 hospitals | 1508 beds |

★**5155:  MERCY HEALTH** (CC)
615 Elsinore Place, Cincinnati, OH Zip 45202–1459; tel. 513/639–2800; Michael D. Connelly, President and Chief Executive Officer
**(Decentralized Health System)**

**KENTUCKY:** LOURDES HOSPITAL (O, 264 beds) 1530 Lone Oak Road, Paducah, KY Zip 42003–7900, Mailing Address: P.O. Box 7100, Zip 42002–7100; tel. 270/444–2444; Steven Grinnell, Chief Executive Officer
**Web address:** www.lourdes–pad.org

For explanation of codes following names, see page B2.
★ Indicates Type III membership in the American Hospital Association.

Section B

MARCUM AND WALLACE MEMORIAL HOSPITAL (O, 25 beds) 60 Mercy Court, Irvine, KY Zip 40336–1331; tel. 606/723–2115; Susan Starling, President and Chief Executive Officer
**Web address:** www.marcumandwallace.org

**OHIO:** INSTITUTE FOR ORTHOPAEDIC SURGERY (O, 3 beds) 801 Medical Drive, Suite B., Lima, OH Zip 45804–4030; tel. 419/224–7586; Mark McDonald, M.D., President and Chief Executive Officer
**Web address:** www.ioshospital.com

MERCY ALLEN HOSPITAL (O, 25 beds) 200 West Lorain Street, Oberlin, OH Zip 44074–1077; tel. 440/775–1211; Joe Sober, President
**Web address:** www.mercyonline.org/mercy_allen_hospital.aspx

MERCY HEALTH – ANDERSON HOSPITAL (O, 188 beds) 7500 State Road, Cincinnati, OH Zip 45255–2492; tel. 513/624–4500; Jeff Graham, Market Leader and President
**Web address:** www.e-mercy.com

MERCY HEALTH – CLERMONT HOSPITAL (O, 119 beds) 3000 Hospital Drive, Batavia, OH Zip 45103–1921; tel. 513/732–8200; Jeff Graham, Market Leader and President
**Web address:** www.e-mercy.com

MERCY HEALTH – FAIRFIELD HOSPITAL (O, 229 beds) 3000 Mack Road, Fairfield, OH Zip 45014–5335; tel. 513/870–7000; Thomas S. Urban, Market Leader and President
**Web address:** www.e-mercy.com

MERCY HEALTH – WEST HOSPITAL (O, 250 beds) 3300 Mercy Health Boulevard, Cincinnati, OH Zip 45211; tel. 513/215–5000; Michael R. Stephens, Market Leader and President
**Web address:** www.e-mercy.com/west-hospital

MERCY HOSPITAL OF DEFIANCE (O, 23 beds) 1404 East Second Street, Defiance, OH Zip 43512–2440; tel. 419/782–8444; Chad Peter, President
**Web address:** www.ehealthconnection.com/regions/toledo/

MERCY MEMORIAL HOSPITAL (O, 25 beds) 904 Scioto Street, Urbana, OH Zip 43078–2200; tel. 937/653–5231; Paul Hiltz, President and Chief Executive Officer
**Web address:** www.health-partners.org

MERCY REGIONAL MEDICAL CENTER (O, 259 beds) 3700 Kolbe Road, Lorain, OH Zip 44053–1697; tel. 440/960–4000; Edwin M. Oley, President and Chief Executive Officer
**Web address:** www.community-health-partners.com

MERCY ST. ANNE HOSPITAL (O, 96 beds) 3404 West Sylvania Avenue, Toledo, OH Zip 43623–4467; tel. 419/407–2663; Bradley J. Bertke, President
**Web address:** www.mercyweb.org

MERCY ST. CHARLES HOSPITAL (O, 265 beds) 2600 Navarre Avenue, Oregon, OH Zip 43616–3297; tel. 419/696–7200; Jeffrey Dempsey, President and Chief Executive Officer
**Web address:** www.mercyweb.org

MERCY ST. VINCENT MEDICAL CENTER (O, 409 beds) 2213 Cherry Street, Toledo, OH Zip 43608–2691; tel. 419/251–3232; Kerry Tirman, President
**Web address:** www.mercyweb.org

MERCY TIFFIN HOSPITAL (O, 51 beds) 45 St. Lawrence Drive, Tiffin, OH Zip 44883–8310; tel. 419/455–7000; B. Lynn Detterman, President
**Web address:** www.mercyweb.org

MERCY WILLARD HOSPITAL (O, 20 beds) 1100 Neal Zick Road, Willard, OH Zip 44890–9287; tel. 419/964–5000; B. Lynn Detterman, President and Chief Executive Officer
**Web address:** www.mercyweb.org

SPRINGFIELD REGIONAL MEDICAL CENTER (O, 259 beds) 100 Medical Center Drive, Springfield, OH Zip 45504–2687; tel. 937/523–1000; Paul C. Hiltz, FACHE, Market President and Chief Executive Officer
**Web address:** www.community-mercy.org

ST. ELIZABETH BOARDMAN HEALTH CENTER (O, 169 beds) 8401 Market Street, Boardman, OH Zip 44512–6777; tel. 330/729–2929; Eugenia Aubel, President
**Web address:** www.ehealthconnection.com/regions/youngstown/content/show_facility.asp?facility_id=190

ST. ELIZABETH HEALTH CENTER (O, 362 beds) 1044 Belmont Avenue, Youngstown, OH Zip 44504–1096, Mailing Address: P.O. Box 1790, Zip 44501–1790; tel. 330/746–7211; Robert W. Shroder, President and Chief Executive Officer
**Web address:** www.mercy.com

ST. JOSEPH HEALTH CENTER (O, 136 beds) 667 Eastland Avenue S.E., Warren, OH Zip 44484–4531; tel. 330/841–4000; Kathy Cook, R.N., MSN, President
**Web address:** www.hmpartners.org

ST. RITA'S MEDICAL CENTER (O, 415 beds) 730 West Market Street, Lima, OH Zip 45801–4602; tel. 419/227–3361; Robert O. Baxter, President and Chief Executive Officer
**Web address:** www.stritas.org

THE JEWISH HOSPITAL – MERCY HEALTH (O, 209 beds) 4777 East Galbraith Road, Cincinnati, OH Zip 45236–2725; tel. 513/686–3000; Patricia Davis-Hagens, R.N., Market Leader and President
**Web address:** www.jewishhospitalcincinnati.com/

| | | |
|---|---|---|
| Owned, leased, sponsored: | 22 hospitals | 3801 beds |
| Contract–managed: | 0 hospitals | 0 beds |
| Totals: | 22 hospitals | 3801 beds |

---

★**5185:  MERCY HEALTH** (CC)
14528 South Outer 40, Suite 100, Chesterfield, MO Zip 63017–5743; tel. 314/579–6100; Lynn Britton, President and Chief Executive Officer
**(Decentralized Health System)**

**ARKANSAS:** MERCY HOSPITAL BERRYVILLE (O, 25 beds) 214 Carter Street, Berryville, AR Zip 72616–4303; tel. 870/423–3355; Douglas M. Stroemel, Administrator
**Web address:** www.mercy.net/berryvillear

MERCY HOSPITAL BOONEVILLE (O, 25 beds) 880 West Main Street, Booneville, AR Zip 72927–3443, Mailing Address: P.O. Box 290, Zip 72927–0290; tel. 479/675–2800; David Hill, Regional Administrator
**Web address:** www.mercy.net

MERCY HOSPITAL FORT SMITH (O, 344 beds) 7301 Rogers Avenue, Fort Smith, AR Zip 72903–4189, Mailing Address: P.O. Box 17000, Zip 72917–7000; tel. 479/314–6000; Ryan Gehrig, President
**Web address:** www.mercy.net/fortsmithar

MERCY HOSPITAL OZARK (O, 25 beds) 801 West River Street, Ozark, AR Zip 72949–3023; tel. 479/667–4138; Teresa Williams, R.N., Administrator and Director of Nursing
**Web address:** www.mercy.net/northwestarar/practice/mercy-hospital-ozark

MERCY HOSPITAL PARIS (O, 16 beds) 500 East Academy, Paris, AR Zip 72855–4040; tel. 479/963–6101; Sharon D. Sorey, R.N., Administrator
**Web address:** www.mercy.net/fortsmithar

MERCY HOSPITAL ROGERS (O, 162 beds) 2710 Rife Medical Lane, Rogers, AR Zip 72758–1452; tel. 479/338–8000; Eric Pianalto, President
**Web address:** www.mercyhealthnwa.smhs.com

MERCY HOSPITAL WALDRON (O, 24 beds) 1341 West 6th Street, Waldron, AR Zip 72958–7642; tel. 479/637–4135; Dorothy O'Bar, R.N., Administrator
**Web address:** www.stedwardmercy.com

MERCY ORTHOPEDIC HOSPITAL FORT SMITH (O, 24 beds) 3601 South 79th Street, Fort Smith, AR Zip 72903–6255; tel. 479/709–8500; Ryan Gehrig, President
**Web address:** www.mercy.net/practice/mercy-orthopedic-hospital-fort-smith

**KANSAS:** MERCY HOSPITAL FORT SCOTT (O, 61 beds) 401 Woodland Hills Boulevard, Fort Scott, KS Zip 66701–8797; tel. 620/223–2200; Reta K. Baker, President
**Web address:** www.mercykansas.com

MERCY HOSPITAL INDEPENDENCE (O, 40 beds) 800 West Myrtle Street, Independence, KS Zip 67301–3240, Mailing Address: P.O. Box 388, Zip 67301–0388; tel. 620/331–2200; Kim Day, Interim President
**Web address:** www.mercy.net/independenceks

MERCY MAUDE NORTON HOSPITAL (O, 18 beds) 220 North Pennsylvania Avenue, Columbus, KS Zip 66725–1110; tel. 620/429–2545; Cindy Neely, Administrator
**Web address:** www.mercy.net/newsroom-mercy-maude-norton-hospital-quick-facts

**MISSOURI:** MERCY HOSPITAL AURORA (L, 25 beds) 500 Porter Street, Aurora, MO Zip 65605–2365; tel. 417/678–2122; Douglas M. Stroemel, President
**Web address:** www.stjohns.com/aboutus/aurora.aspx

For explanation of codes following names, see page B2.
★ Indicates Type III membership in the American Hospital Association.

MERCY HOSPITAL CARTHAGE (L, 49 beds) 3125 Drive Russell Smith Way, Carthage, MO Zip 64836–7402; tel. 417/358–8121; Robert Watson, JD, Administrator
**Web address:** www.mercy.net

MERCY HOSPITAL CASSVILLE (L, 18 beds) 94 Main Street, Cassville, MO Zip 65625–1610; tel. 417/847–6000; Douglas M. Stroemel, President
**Web address:** www.mercy.net/northwestarar/practice/mercy–hospital–cassville

MERCY HOSPITAL JEFFERSON (O, 213 beds) Highway 61 South, Crystal City, MO Zip 63019, Mailing Address: P.O. Box 350, Zip 63019–0350; tel. 636/933–1000; Eric Ammons, President
**Web address:** www.mercy.net/crystalcitymo

MERCY HOSPITAL JOPLIN (O, 179 beds) 100 Mercy Way, Joplin, MO Zip 64804–1626; tel. 417/781–2727; Gary W. Pulsipher, President and Chief Executive Officer
**Web address:** www.mercy.net/joplinmo

MERCY HOSPITAL LEBANON (O, 58 beds) 100 Hospital Drive, Lebanon, MO Zip 65536–9210; tel. 417/533–6100; David R. Steinmann, Administrator
**Web address:** www.mercy.net/practice/mercy–hospital–lebanon

MERCY HOSPITAL LINCOLN (L, 25 beds) 1000 East Cherry Street, Troy, MO Zip 63379–1513; tel. 636/528–8551; Anthony Rothermich, Administrator
**Web address:** www.mercy.net

MERCY HOSPITAL SPRINGFIELD (O, 628 beds) 1235 East Cherokee Street, Springfield, MO Zip 65804–2263; tel. 417/820–2000; Dr. Alan Scarrow, MD, President
**Web address:** www.mercy.net/springfieldmo

MERCY HOSPITAL ST. LOUIS (O, 979 beds) 615 South New Ballas Road, Saint Louis, MO Zip 63141–8277; tel. 314/569–6000; Jeffrey A. Johnston, President
**Web address:** www.mercy.net/stlouismo

MERCY HOSPITAL WASHINGTON (O, 166 beds) 901 East Fifth Street, Washington, MO Zip 63090–3127; tel. 636/239–8000; Terri L. McLain, FACHE, President
**Web address:** www.mercy.net

MERCY ST. FRANCIS HOSPITAL (O, 20 beds) 100 West Highway 60, Mountain View, MO Zip 65548–7125; tel. 417/934–7000; David R. Steinmann, Administrator
**Web address:** www.stjohns.com/aboutus/stfrancis.aspx

**OKLAHOMA:** ARBUCKLE MEMORIAL HOSPITAL (C, 13 beds) 2011 West Broadway Street, Sulphur, OK Zip 73086–4221; tel. 580/622–2161; Darin Farrell, Chief Executive Officer
**Web address:** www.arbucklehospital.com/

MERCY HEALTH LOVE COUNTY (C, 35 beds) 300 Wanda Street, Marietta, OK Zip 73448–1200; tel. 580/276–3347; Richard Barker, Administrator
**Web address:** www.mercyhealthlovecounty.com

MERCY HOSPITAL ADA (C, 156 beds) 430 North Monte Vista, Ada, OK Zip 74820–4610; tel. 580/332–2323; Lori Wightman, R.N., MSN, FACHE, Chief Executive Officer
**Web address:** www.mercy.net/ada

MERCY HOSPITAL ARDMORE (O, 190 beds) 1011 14th Avenue N.W., Ardmore, OK Zip 73401–1828; tel. 580/223–5400; Daryle Voss, FACHE, President
**Web address:** www.mercyok.net

MERCY HOSPITAL EL RENO (L, 48 beds) 2115 Parkview Drive, El Reno, OK Zip 73036–2199, Mailing Address: P.O. Box 129, Zip 73036–0129; tel. 405/262–2640; Doug Danker, Administrator
**Web address:** www.mercyok.net

MERCY HOSPITAL HEALDTON (L, 22 beds) 918 South 8th Street, Healdton, OK Zip 73438–0928, Mailing Address: P.O. Box 928, Zip 73438–0928; tel. 580/229–0701; Jeremy A. Jones, Administrator
**Web address:** www.mercyok.net

MERCY HOSPITAL KINGFISHER (C, 25 beds) 1000 Kingfisher Regional Hospital Drive, Kingfisher, OK Zip 73750–3528, Mailing Address: P.O. Box 59, Zip 73750–0059; tel. 405/375–3141; Brian Denton, Administrator
**Web address:** www.kingfisherhospital.com

MERCY HOSPITAL LOGAN COUNTY (O, 25 beds) 200 South Academy Road, Guthrie, OK Zip 73044–8727, Mailing Address: P.O. Box 1017, Zip 73044–1017; tel. 405/282–6700; Joshua Tucker, Administrator
**Web address:** www.mercy.net

MERCY HOSPITAL OKLAHOMA CITY (O, 369 beds) 4300 West Memorial Road, Oklahoma City, OK Zip 73120–8362; tel. 405/755–1515; Jim Gebhart, Jr., FACHE, President
**Web address:** www.mercyok.net

MERCY HOSPITAL TISHOMINGO (L, 25 beds) 1000 South Byrd Street, Tishomingo, OK Zip 73460–3299; tel. 580/371–2327; Gary Sharum, Administrator
**Web address:** www.mercy.net/

MERCY HOSPITAL WATONGA (L, 17 beds) 500 North Clarence Nash Boulevard, Watonga, OK Zip 73772–2845, Mailing Address: P.O. Box 370, Zip 73772–0370; tel. 580/623–7211; Bobby Stitt, R.N., Administrator
**Web address:** www.mercy.net/watongaok/practice/mercy–hospital–watonga

SEILING MUNICIPAL HOSPITAL (C, 18 beds) Highway 60 N.E., Seiling, OK Zip 73663, Mailing Address: P.O. Box 720, Zip 73663–0720; tel. 580/922–7361; Bobby Stitt, R.N., Chief Executive Officer
**Web address:** www.seilinghospital.com

| | | |
|---|---|---|
| Owned, leased, sponsored: | 29 hospitals | 3820 beds |
| Contract–managed: | 5 hospitals | 247 beds |
| Totals: | 34 hospitals | 4067 beds |

---

**0649: MERCY HEALTH SYSTEM** (NP)
1000 Mineral Point Avenue, Janesville, WI Zip 53548–2940, Mailing Address: P.O. Box 5003, Zip 53547–5003; tel. 608/756–6000; Javon R. Bea, President and Chief Executive Officer
**(Centralized Physician/Insurance Health System)**

**ILLINOIS:** MERCY HARVARD HOSPITAL (O, 45 beds) 901 Grant Street, Harvard, IL Zip 60033–1898, Mailing Address: P.O. Box 850, Zip 60033–0850; tel. 815/943–5431; Javon R. Bea, Chief Executive Officer
**Web address:** www.mercyhealthsystem.org

**WISCONSIN:** MERCY HOSPITAL AND TRAUMA CENTER (O, 132 beds) 1000 Mineral Point Avenue, Janesville, WI Zip 53548–2982, Mailing Address: P.O. Box 5003, Zip 53547–5003; tel. 608/756–6000; Javon R. Bea, President and Chief Executive Officer
**Web address:** www.mercyhealthsystem.org

MERCY WALWORTH HOSPITAL AND MEDICAL CENTER (O, 15 beds) N2950 State Road 67, Lake Geneva, WI Zip 53147–2655; tel. 262/245–0535; Jennifer Hallatt, Chief Operating Officer
**Web address:** www.mercyhealthsystem.org

| | | |
|---|---|---|
| Owned, leased, sponsored: | 3 hospitals | 192 beds |
| Contract–managed: | 0 hospitals | 0 beds |
| Totals: | 3 hospitals | 192 beds |

---

**★0257: MERIDIAN HEALTH** (NP)
1350 Campus Parkway, Neptune, NJ Zip 07753–6821; tel. 732/751–7510; John K. Lloyd, President and Chief Executive Officer
**(Centralized Physician/Insurance Health System)**

**NEW JERSEY:** BAYSHORE COMMUNITY HOSPITAL (O, 152 beds) 727 North Beers Street, Holmdel, NJ Zip 07733–1598; tel. 732/739–5900; Timothy J. Hogan, FACHE, Regional President
**Web address:** www.bchs.com

JERSEY SHORE UNIVERSITY MEDICAL CENTER (O, 544 beds) 1945 Route 33, Neptune, NJ Zip 07754–0397; tel. 732/775–5500; Kenneth N. Sable, M.D., President
**Web address:** www.meridianhealth.com

OCEAN MEDICAL CENTER (O, 271 beds) 425 Jack Martin Boulevard, Brick Township, NJ Zip 08724–7732; tel. 732/840–2200; Dean Q. Lin, FACHE, President
**Web address:** www.meridianhealth.com

RIVERVIEW MEDICAL CENTER (O, 301 beds) 1 Riverview Plaza, Red Bank, NJ Zip 07701–1864; tel. 732/741–2700; Timothy J. Hogan, FACHE, Regional President
**Web address:** www.riverviewmedicalcenter.com

Section B

For explanation of codes following names, see page B2.
★ Indicates Type III membership in the American Hospital Association.

SOUTHERN OCEAN MEDICAL CENTER (O, 139 beds) 1140 Route 72 West, Manahawkin, NJ Zip 08050–2499; tel. 609/597–6011; Joseph P. Coyle, President and Chief Executive Officer
**Web address:** www.soch.com

| Owned, leased, sponsored: | 5 hospitals | 1407 beds |
|---|---|---|
| Contract–managed: | 0 hospitals | 0 beds |
| Totals: | 5 hospitals | 1407 beds |

---

★**2735: METHODIST HEALTH SYSTEM** (NP)
1441 North Beckley Avenue, Dallas, TX Zip 75203–1201, Mailing Address: P.O. Box 655999, Zip 75265–5999; tel. 214/947–8181; Stephen L. Mansfield, Ph.D., FACHE, President and Chief Executive Officer
**(Centralized Physician/Insurance Health System)**

**TEXAS:** METHODIST CHARLTON MEDICAL CENTER (O, 304 beds) 3500 West Wheatland Road, Dallas, TX Zip 75237–3460, Mailing Address: P.O. Box 225357, Zip 75222–5357; tel. 214/947–7777; Fran Laukaitis, R.N., Interim Chief Executive Officer and Chief Nursing Officer
**Web address:** www.methodisthealthsystem.org/charlton

METHODIST DALLAS MEDICAL CENTER (O, 408 beds) 1441 North Beckley Avenue, Dallas, TX Zip 75203–1201, Mailing Address: P.O. Box 655999, Zip 75265–5999; tel. 214/947–8181; David D. Clark, President
**Web address:** www.methodisthealthsystem.org/Dallas

METHODIST MANSFIELD MEDICAL CENTER (O, 175 beds) 2700 East Broad Street, Mansfield, TX Zip 76063–5899; tel. 682/622–2000; John E. Phillips, FACHE, President
**Web address:** www.methodisthealthsystem.org/mansfield

METHODIST RICHARDSON MEDICAL CENTER (O, 164 beds) 2831 East President George Bush Highway, Richardson, TX Zip 75082–3561; tel. 469/204–1000; E. Kenneth Hutchenrider, President and Chief Executive Officer
**Web address:** www.methodisthealthsystem.org/richardson

| Owned, leased, sponsored: | 4 hospitals | 1051 beds |
|---|---|---|
| Contract–managed: | 0 hospitals | 0 beds |
| Totals: | 4 hospitals | 1051 beds |

---

**9345: METHODIST LE BONHEUR HEALTHCARE** (CO)
1211 Union Avenue, Suite 700, Memphis, TN Zip 38104–6600; tel. 901/516–0791; Gary S. Shorb, President and Chief Executive Officer
**(Centralized Health System)**

**MISSISSIPPI:** METHODIST OLIVE BRANCH HOSPITAL (O, 44 beds) 4250 Bethel Road, Olive Branch, MS Zip 38654–8737; tel. 662/932–9000; David G. Baytos, Chief Executive Officer
**Web address:** www.methodisthealth.org/olivebranch

**TENNESSEE:** METHODIST EXTENDED CARE HOSPITAL (O, 36 beds) 225 South Claybrook Street, Memphis, TN Zip 38104–3537; tel. 901/516–2595; Sandra Bailey–DeLeeuw, Chief Executive Officer
**Web address:** www.methodisthealth.org

METHODIST HEALTHCARE MEMPHIS HOSPITALS (O, 1446 beds) 1265 Union Avenue, Memphis, TN Zip 38104–3415; tel. 901/516–7000; Michael O. Ugwueke, President and Chief Executive Officer
**Web address:** www.methodisthealth.org

| Owned, leased, sponsored: | 3 hospitals | 1526 beds |
|---|---|---|
| Contract–managed: | 0 hospitals | 0 beds |
| Totals: | 3 hospitals | 1526 beds |

---

★**0001: MIDMICHIGAN HEALTH** (NP)
4000 Wellness Drive, Midland, MI Zip 48670–0001; tel. 989/839–3000; Diane Postler–Slattery, Ph.D., President and Chief Executive Officer
**(Independent Hospital System)**

**MICHIGAN:** MIDMICHIGAN MEDICAL CENTER–CLARE (O, 49 beds) 703 North McEwan Street, Clare, MI Zip 48617–1440; tel. 989/802–5000; Raymond Stover, President and Chief Executive Officer
**Web address:** www.midmichigan.org

MIDMICHIGAN MEDICAL CENTER–GLADWIN (O, 25 beds) 515 Quarter Street, Gladwin, MI Zip 48624–1959; tel. 989/426–9286; Raymond Stover, President and Chief Executive Officer
**Web address:** www.midmichigan.org

MIDMICHIGAN MEDICAL CENTER–GRATIOT (O, 79 beds) 300 East Warwick Drive, Alma, MI Zip 48801–1014; tel. 989/463–1101; Mark A. Santamaria, President
**Web address:** www.midmichigan.org/gratiot

MIDMICHIGAN MEDICAL CENTER–MIDLAND (O, 265 beds) 4000 Wellness Drive, Midland, MI Zip 48670–2000; tel. 989/839–3000; Gregory H. Rogers, President
**Web address:** www.midmichigan.org

| Owned, leased, sponsored: | 4 hospitals | 418 beds |
|---|---|---|
| Contract–managed: | 0 hospitals | 0 beds |
| Totals: | 4 hospitals | 418 beds |

---

**0368: MINNESOTA DEPARTMENT OF HUMAN SERVICES** (NP)
540 Cedar Street, Saint Paul, MN Zip 55101–2208, Mailing Address: P.O. Box 64998, Zip 55164–0998; tel. 651/431–3212; Anne Barry, Deputy Commissioner
**(Independent Hospital System)**

**MINNESOTA:** ANOKA–METROPOLITAN REGIONAL TREATMENT CENTER (O, 200 beds) 3301 Seventh Avenue, Anoka, MN Zip 55303–4516; tel. 651/431–5000; Tina Sneen, Administrator
**Web address:** www.health.state.mn.us

COMMUNITY BEHAVIORAL HEALTH HOSPITAL – ALEXANDRIA (O, 16 beds) 1610 8th Avenue East, Alexandria, MN Zip 56308–2472; tel. 320/335–6201; Jennifer Westrum, Administrator
**Web address:** www.health.state.mn.us

COMMUNITY BEHAVIORAL HEALTH HOSPITAL – ANNANDALE (O, 16 beds) 400 Annandale Boulevard, Annandale, MN Zip 55302–3141; tel. 651/259–3850; Pamela R. Bajari, R.N., Interim Administrator
**Web address:** www.health.state.mn.us

COMMUNITY BEHAVIORAL HEALTH HOSPITAL – BAXTER (O, 16 beds) 14241 Grand Oaks Drive, Baxter, MN Zip 56425–8749; tel. 218/316–3101; Richard G. Slieter, Jr., Administrator

COMMUNITY BEHAVIORAL HEALTH HOSPITAL – BEMIDJI (O, 16 beds) 800 Bemidji Avenue North, Bemidji, MN Zip 56601–3054; tel. 218/308–2400; Larry A. Laudon, Administrator

COMMUNITY BEHAVIORAL HEALTH HOSPITAL – FERGUS FALLS (O, 16 beds) 1801 West Alcott Avenue, Fergus Falls, MN Zip 56537–2661, Mailing Address: P.O. Box 478, Zip 56538–0478; tel. 218/332–5001; Brenda Schleske, Interim Administrator

COMMUNITY BEHAVIORAL HEALTH HOSPITAL – ROCHESTER (O, 16 beds) 251 Wood Lake Drive S.E., Rochester, MN Zip 55904–5530; tel. 507/206–2561; Stephanie Juhl, Administrator
**Web address:** www.health.state.mn.us

COMMUNITY BEHAVIORAL HEALTH HOSPITAL – ST. PETER (O, 16 beds) 2000 Klein Street, Saint Peter, MN Zip 56082–5800; tel. 507/933–5001; Christopher Schiffer, Administrator
**Web address:** www.health.state.mn.us

| Owned, leased, sponsored: | 8 hospitals | 312 beds |
|---|---|---|
| Contract–managed: | 0 hospitals | 0 beds |
| Totals: | 8 hospitals | 312 beds |

---

★**0143: MISSION HEALTH SYSTEM** (NP)
509 Biltmore Avenue, Asheville, NC Zip 28801–4601; tel. 828/213–1111; Ronald A. Paulus, M.D., President and Chief Executive Officer
**(Moderately Centralized Health System)**

**NORTH CAROLINA:** ANGEL MEDICAL CENTER (O, 25 beds) 120 Riverview Street, Franklin, NC Zip 28734–2612, Mailing Address: P.O. Box 1209, Zip 28744–0569; tel. 828/524–8411; James B. Bross, President
**Web address:** www.angelmed.org

ASHEVILLE SPECIALTY HOSPITAL (O, 32 beds) 428 Biltmore Avenue, 4th Floor, Asheville, NC Zip 28801–4502; tel. 828/213–5400; Robert C. Desotelle, President and Chief Executive Officer
**Web address:** www.missionhospitals.org/acute–care

---

For explanation of codes following names, see page B2.
★ Indicates Type III membership in the American Hospital Association.

BLUE RIDGE REGIONAL HOSPITAL (O, 42 beds) 125 Hospital Drive, Spruce Pine, NC Zip 28777–3035, Mailing Address: P.O. Drawer 9, Zip 28777–0009; tel. 828/765–4201; Rebecca W. Carter, MSN, R.N., FACHE, Chief Executive Officer and Chief Nursing Officer
**Web address:** www.spchospital.org

HIGHLANDS–CASHIERS HOSPITAL (O, 104 beds) 190 Hospital Drive, Highlands, NC Zip 28741–7600, Mailing Address: P.O. Drawer 190, Zip 28741–0190; tel. 828/526–1200; Jackie Ring, President and Chief Nursing Officer
**Web address:** www.hchospital.org

MCDOWELL HOSPITAL (O, 49 beds) 430 Rankin Drive, Marion, NC Zip 28752–6568, Mailing Address: P.O. Box 730, Zip 28752–0730; tel. 828/659–5000; Carol C. Wolfenbarger, R.N., MSN, FACHE, President and Chief Executive Officer
**Web address:** www.mcdhospital.org

MISSION HOSPITAL (O, 763 beds) 509 Biltmore Avenue, Asheville, NC Zip 28801–4690; tel. 828/213–1111; Jill Hoggard Green, R.N., Ph.D., President
**Web address:** www.missionhospitals.org

TRANSYLVANIA REGIONAL HOSPITAL (O, 52 beds) 260 Hospital Drive, Brevard, NC Zip 28712–3378; tel. 828/884–9111; Catherine Landis, R.N., President and Chief Nursing Officer
**Web address:** www.trhospital.org

| | | |
|---|---|---|
| **Owned, leased, sponsored:** | 7 hospitals | 1067 beds |
| **Contract–managed:** | 0 hospitals | 0 beds |
| **Totals:** | 7 hospitals | 1067 beds |

---

**2475: MISSISSIPPI COUNTY HOSPITAL SYSTEM** (NP)
1520 North Division Street, Blytheville, AR Zip 72315–1448, Mailing Address: P.O. Box 108, Zip 72316–0108; tel. 870/838–7300; Ralph E. Beaty, Chief Executive Officer
**(Independent Hospital System)**

| | | |
|---|---|---|
| **Owned, leased, sponsored:** | 0 hospitals | 0 beds |
| **Contract–managed:** | 0 hospitals | 0 beds |
| **Totals:** | 0 hospitals | 0 beds |

---

**0017: MISSISSIPPI STATE DEPARTMENT OF MENTAL HEALTH** (NP)
1101 Robert East Lee Building, 239 North Lamar Street, Jackson, MS Zip 39201–1101; tel. 601/359–1288; Edwin C. LeGrand, III, Executive Director
**(Independent Hospital System)**

**MISSISSIPPI:** EAST MISSISSIPPI STATE HOSPITAL (O, 181 beds) 1818 College Drive, Meridian, MS Zip 39307, Mailing Address: Box 4128, West Station, Zip 39304–4128; tel. 601/482–6186; Charles Carlisle, Director
**Web address:** www.emsh.state.ms.us

MISSISSIPPI STATE HOSPITAL (O, 899 beds) 3550 Highway 468 West, Whitfield, MS Zip 39193–5529, Mailing Address: P.O. Box 157–A, Zip 39193–0157; tel. 601/351–8000; James G. Chastain, FACHE, Director
**Web address:** www.msh.state.ms.us

NORTH MISSISSIPPI STATE HOSPITAL (O, 50 beds) 1937 Briar Ridge Road, Tupelo, MS Zip 38804–5963; tel. 662/690–4200; Paul A. Callens, Ph.D., Director
**Web address:** www.nmsh.state.ms.us

SOUTH MISSISSIPPI STATE HOSPITAL (O, 50 beds) 823 Highway 589, Purvis, MS Zip 39475–4194; tel. 601/794–0100; Clint Ashley, Director
**Web address:** www.smsh.state.ms.us

| | | |
|---|---|---|
| **Owned, leased, sponsored:** | 4 hospitals | 1180 beds |
| **Contract–managed:** | 0 hospitals | 0 beds |
| **Totals:** | 4 hospitals | 1180 beds |

---

**★0970: MONONGALIA HEALTH SYSTEM** (NP)
1200 J. D. Anderson Drive, Morgantown, WV Zip 26505–3494; tel. 304/598–1200; Darryl L. Duncan, President and Chief Executive Officer

**WEST VIRGINIA:** MONONGALIA GENERAL HOSPITAL (O, 175 beds) 1200 J. D. Anderson Drive, Morgantown, WV Zip 26505–3486; tel. 304/598–1200; Darryl L. Duncan, President and Chief Executive Officer
**Web address:** www.mongeneral.com

PRESTON MEMORIAL HOSPITAL (O, 25 beds) 150 Memorial Drive, Kingwood, WV Zip 26537–1495; tel. 304/329–1400; Melissa Lockwood, Chief Executive Officer
**Web address:** www.prestonmemorial.org

| | | |
|---|---|---|
| **Owned, leased, sponsored:** | 2 hospitals | 200 beds |
| **Contract–managed:** | 0 hospitals | 0 beds |
| **Totals:** | 2 hospitals | 200 beds |

---

**0343: MONTEFIORE HEALTH SYSTEM** (NP)
111 East 210th Street, Bronx, NY Zip 10467–2490; tel. 718/920–4321; Steven M. Safyer, M.D., President and CEO
**(Centralized Health System)**

**NEW YORK:** MONTEFIORE MEDICAL CENTER (O, 1512 beds) 111 East 210th Street, Bronx, NY Zip 10467–2401; tel. 718/920–4321; Steven M. Safyer, M.D., President and Chief Executive Officer
**Web address:** www.montefiore.org

MONTEFIORE MOUNT VERNON (O, 83 beds) 12 North Seventh Avenue, Mount Vernon, NY Zip 10550–2098; tel. 914/664–8000; Susan Green–Lorenzen, Senior Vice President Operations
**Web address:** www.montefiorehealthsystem.org/landing.cfm?id=17

MONTEFIORE NEW ROCHELLE (O, 253 beds) 16 Guion Place, New Rochelle, NY Zip 10801–5502; tel. 914/632–5000; Anthony Alfano, Vice President Executive Director
**Web address:** www.montefiorehealthsystem.org

| | | |
|---|---|---|
| **Owned, leased, sponsored:** | 3 hospitals | 1848 beds |
| **Contract–managed:** | 0 hospitals | 0 beds |
| **Totals:** | 3 hospitals | 1848 beds |

---

**1335: MORTON PLANT MEASE HEALTH CARE** (NP)
300 Pinellas Street, Clearwater, FL Zip 33756–3804, Mailing Address: P.O. Box 210, Zip 33757–0210; tel. 727/462–7000; Glenn D. Waters, FACHE, President

**FLORIDA:** MEASE COUNTRYSIDE HOSPITAL (O, 311 beds) 3231 McMullen–Booth Road, Safety Harbor, FL Zip 34695–6607, Mailing Address: P.O. Box 1098, Zip 34695–1098; tel. 727/725–6222; Lou Galdieri, R.N., President
**Web address:** www.mpmhealth.com

MEASE DUNEDIN HOSPITAL (O, 120 beds) 601 Main Street, Dunedin, FL Zip 34698–5891, Mailing Address: P.O. Box 760, Zip 34697–0760; tel. 727/733–1111; Lou Galdieri, R.N., President
**Web address:** www.mpmhealth.com

MORTON PLANT HOSPITAL (O, 662 beds) 300 Pinellas Street, Clearwater, FL Zip 33756–3804, Mailing Address: P.O. Box 210, Zip 33757–0210; tel. 727/462–7000; N. Kristopher Hoce, President
**Web address:** www.mortonplant.com

MORTON PLANT NORTH BAY HOSPITAL (O, 226 beds) 6600 Madison Street, New Port Richey, FL Zip 34652–1900; tel. 727/842–8468; Michael Yungmann, President
**Web address:** www.mpmhealth.com

| | | |
|---|---|---|
| **Owned, leased, sponsored:** | 4 hospitals | 1319 beds |
| **Contract–managed:** | 0 hospitals | 0 beds |
| **Totals:** | 4 hospitals | 1319 beds |

---

**★0917: MOUNT SINAI HEALTH SYSTEM** (NP)
One Gustave L. Levy Place, New York, NY Zip 10029; tel. 212/659–8888; Kenneth L. Davis, M.D., President and Chief Executive
**(Centralized Health System)**

For explanation of codes following names, see page B2.
★ Indicates Type III membership in the American Hospital Association.

**NEW YORK:** MOUNT SINAI BETH ISRAEL (O, 989 beds) First Avenue and 16th Street, New York, NY Zip 10003–3803; tel. 212/420–2000; Susan Somerville, R.N., President
**Web address:** www.bethisraelny.org

MOUNT SINAI HOSPITAL (O, 1183 beds) One Gustave L. Levy Place, New York, NY Zip 10029–6574; tel. 212/241–6500; David L. Reich, M.D., President
**Web address:** www.mountsinai.org

MOUNT SINAI ST. LUKE'S – ROOSEVELT (O, 685 beds) 1111 Amsterdam Avenue, New York, NY Zip 10025–1716; tel. 212/523–4000; Arthur A. Gianelli, M.P.H., President
**Web address:** www.stlukeshospitalnyc.org

NEW YORK EYE AND EAR INFIRMARY OF MOUNT SINAI (O, 32 beds) 310 East 14th Street, New York, NY Zip 10003–4201; tel. 212/979–4000; James Tsai, M.D., President
**Web address:** www.nyee.edu

| Owned, leased, sponsored: | 4 hospitals | 2889 beds |
|---|---|---|
| Contract–managed: | 0 hospitals | 0 beds |
| **Totals:** | 4 hospitals | 2889 beds |

---

**0167: MOUNTAIN STATES HEALTH ALLIANCE** (NP)
400 North State of Franklin Road, Johnson City, TN Zip 37604–6035; tel. 423/302–3423; Alan M. Levine, President and Chief Executive Officer
**(Centralized Health System)**

**TENNESSEE:** FRANKLIN WOODS COMMUNITY HOSPITAL (O, 80 beds) 300 MedTech Parkway, Johnson City, TN Zip 37604–2277; tel. 423/302–1000; Lindy P. White, Chief Executive Officer
**Web address:** www.msha.com

INDIAN PATH MEDICAL CENTER (O, 239 beds) 2000 Brookside Drive, Kingsport, TN Zip 37660–4627; tel. 423/857–7000; Monty E. McLaurin, President and Chief Executive Officer
**Web address:** www.msha.com

JOHNSON CITY MEDICAL CENTER (O, 658 beds) 400 North State of Franklin Road, Johnson City, TN Zip 37604–6094; tel. 423/431–6111; Melody Trimble, Chief Executive Officer
**Web address:** www.msha.com

JOHNSON COUNTY COMMUNITY HOSPITAL (O, 2 beds) 1901 South Shady Street, Mountain City, TN Zip 37683–2271; tel. 423/727–1100; Chastity Trivette, Chief Executive Officer
**Web address:** www.msha.com

SYCAMORE SHOALS HOSPITAL (O, 121 beds) 1501 West Elk Avenue, Elizabethton, TN Zip 37643–2874; tel. 423/542–1300; Dwayne Taylor, Chief Executive Officer
**Web address:** www.msha.com

**VIRGINIA:** DICKENSON COMMUNITY HOSPITAL (O, 25 beds) 312 Hospital Drive, Clintwood, VA Zip 24228, Mailing Address: P.O. Box 1440, Zip 24228–1440; tel. 276/926–0300; Mark T. Leonard, Chief Executive Officer
**Web address:** www.msha.com/dch

JOHNSTON MEMORIAL HOSPITAL (O, 116 beds) 16000 Johnston Memorial Drive, Abingdon, VA Zip 24211–7659; tel. 276/676–7000; Sean S. McMurray, FACHE, Vice President and Chief Executive Officer
**Web address:** www.jmh.org

NORTON COMMUNITY HOSPITAL (O, 129 beds) 100 15th Street N.W., Norton, VA Zip 24273–1616; tel. 276/679–9600; Mark T. Leonard, Chief Executive Officer
**Web address:** www.msha.com/nch

RUSSELL COUNTY MEDICAL CENTER (O, 78 beds) 58 Carroll Street, Lebanon, VA Zip 24266, Mailing Address: P.O. Box 3600, Zip 24266–0200; tel. 276/883–8000; Stephen K. Givens, Assistant Vice President and Administrator
**Web address:** www.msha.com/rcmc

SMYTH COUNTY COMMUNITY HOSPITAL (O, 153 beds) 245 Medical Park Drive, Marion, VA Zip 24354, Mailing Address: P.O. Box 880, Zip 24354–0880; tel. 276/378–1000; James E. Tyler, Vice President and Hospital Chief Executive Officer
**Web address:** www.msha.com/scch

| Owned, leased, sponsored: | 10 hospitals | 1601 beds |
|---|---|---|
| Contract–managed: | 0 hospitals | 0 beds |
| **Totals:** | 10 hospitals | 1601 beds |

---

**6555: MULTICARE HEALTH SYSTEM** (NP)
315 Martin Luther King Jr. Way, Tacoma, WA Zip 98405–4234, Mailing Address: P.O. Box 5299, Zip 98415–0299; tel. 253/403–1000; William G. Robertson, President and Chief Executive Officer
**(Centralized Physician/Insurance Health System)**

**WASHINGTON:** MULTICARE AUBURN MEDICAL CENTER (O, 173 beds) 202 North Division, Plaza One, Auburn, WA Zip 98001–4908; tel. 253/833–7711; David Nicewonger, Chief Operating Officer
**Web address:** www.auburnregional.com

MULTICARE GOOD SAMARITAN HOSPITAL (O, 282 beds) 401 15th Avenue S.E., Puyallup, WA Zip 98372–3770, Mailing Address: P.O. Box 1247, Zip 98371–0192; tel. 253/697–4000; Marcia L. Johnson, R.N., Chief Operating Officer
**Web address:** www.goodsamhealth.org

MULTICARE MARY BRIDGE CHILDREN'S HOSPITAL AND HEALTH CENTER (O, 75 beds) 317 Martin Luther King Jr. Way, Tacoma, WA Zip 98405–4234, Mailing Address: P.O. Box 5299, Zip 98415–0299; tel. 253/403–1400; Robert Lenza, Chief Operating Officer and Administrator
**Web address:** www.multicare.org/marybridge

MULTICARE TACOMA GENERAL HOSPITAL (O, 381 beds) 315 Martin Luther King Jr. Way, Tacoma, WA Zip 98405–4234, Mailing Address: P.O. Box 5299, Zip 98415–0299; tel. 253/403–1000; William G. Robertson, President and Chief Executive Officer
**Web address:** www.multicare.org

| Owned, leased, sponsored: | 4 hospitals | 911 beds |
|---|---|---|
| Contract–managed: | 0 hospitals | 0 beds |
| **Totals:** | 4 hospitals | 911 beds |

---

**★1465: MUNSON HEALTHCARE** (NP)
1105 Sixth Street, Traverse City, MI Zip 49684–2386; tel. 231/935–6703; Edwin Ness, President and Chief Executive Officer
**(Centralized Health System)**

**MICHIGAN:** KALKASKA MEMORIAL HEALTH CENTER (O, 92 beds) 419 South Coral Street, Kalkaska, MI Zip 49646–2503; tel. 231/258–7500; Kevin L. Rogols, FACHE, Administrator
**Web address:** www.munsonhealthcare.org

MUNSON HEALTHCARE CADILLAC HOSPITAL (O, 65 beds) 400 Hobart Street, Cadillac, MI Zip 49601–2389; tel. 231/876–7200; Tonya Smith, President and Chief Executive Officer
**Web address:** www.mercyhealthcadillac.com/welcome–cadillac

MUNSON HEALTHCARE GRAYLING HOSPITAL (O, 94 beds) 1100 East Michigan Avenue, Grayling, MI Zip 49738–1312; tel. 989/348–5461; Stephanie J. Riemer–Matuzak, Chief Executive Officer
**Web address:** www.mercygrayling.munsonhealthcare.org/

MUNSON MEDICAL CENTER (O, 391 beds) 1105 Sixth Street, Traverse City, MI Zip 49684–2386; tel. 231/935–5000; Alfred E. Pilong, Jr., President
**Web address:** www.munsonhealthcare.org

PAUL OLIVER MEMORIAL HOSPITAL (O, 47 beds) 224 Park Avenue, Frankfort, MI Zip 49635–9658; tel. 231/352–2200; Peter Marinoff, President
**Web address:** www.munsonhealthcare.org

| Owned, leased, sponsored: | 5 hospitals | 689 beds |
|---|---|---|
| Contract–managed: | 0 hospitals | 0 beds |
| **Totals:** | 5 hospitals | 689 beds |

---

**0261: NATIONAL SURGICAL HEALTHCARE** (IO)
250 South Wacker Drive, Suite 500, Chicago, IL Zip 60606–5897; tel. 312/627–8400; David Crane, Chief Executive Officer
**(Independent Hospital System)**

---

For explanation of codes following names, see page B2.
★ Indicates Type III membership in the American Hospital Association.

Section B

**ARIZONA:** ARIZONA SPINE AND JOINT HOSPITAL (O, 23 beds) 4620 East Baseline Road, Mesa, AZ Zip 85206–4624; tel. 480/832–4770; Todd Greene, Chief Executive Officer
**Web address:** www.azspineandjoint.com

**GEORGIA:** OPTIM MEDICAL CENTER – JENKINS (O, 25 beds) 931 East Winthrope Avenue, Millen, GA Zip 30442–1839; tel. 478/982–4221; Robert R. Sellers, Administrator
**Web address:** www.optimhealth.com

OPTIM MEDICAL CENTER – SCREVEN (O, 25 beds) 215 Mims Road, Sylvania, GA Zip 30467–2097; tel. 912/564–7426; Robert R. Sellers, Administrator
**Web address:** www.optimhealth.com

OPTIM MEDICAL CENTER – TATTNALL (O, 25 beds) 247 South Main Street, Reidsville, GA Zip 30453–4605; tel. 912/557–1000; Brad Trower, Administrator
**Web address:** www.tattnallhospital.com

**IDAHO:** NORTHWEST SPECIALTY HOSPITAL (O, 34 beds) 1593 East Polston Avenue, Post Falls, ID Zip 83854–5326; tel. 208/262–2300; Vaughn Ward, Chief Executive Officer
**Web address:** www.northwestspecialtyhospital.com

**LOUISIANA:** LAFAYETTE SURGICAL SPECIALTY HOSPITAL (O, 20 beds) 1101 Kaliste Saloom Road, Lafayette, LA Zip 70508–5705; tel. 337/769–4100; Buffy Domingue, Chief Executive Officer
**Web address:** www.lafayettesurgical.com

**MICHIGAN:** SOUTHEAST MICHIGAN SURGICAL HOSPITAL (O, 13 beds) 21230 Dequindre, Warren, MI Zip 48091–2287; tel. 586/427–1000; Yvonne Kughn, Chief Executive Officer
**Web address:** www.nshinc.com

**NORTH CAROLINA:** NORTH CAROLINA SPECIALTY HOSPITAL (O, 18 beds) 3916 Ben Franklin Boulevard, Durham, NC Zip 27704–2383, Mailing Address: PO Box 15819, Zip 27704–2383; tel. 919/956–9300; Randi L. Shults, Chief Executive Officer
**Web address:** www.ncspecialty.com

**TEXAS:** EL PASO SPECIALTY HOSPITAL (O, 27 beds) 1755 Curie Drive, El Paso, TX Zip 79902–2919; tel. 915/544–3636; James Wilcox, Chief Executive Officer
**Web address:** www.elpasospecialtyhospital.com

SOUTH TEXAS SPINE AND SURGICAL HOSPITAL (O, 30 beds) 18600 Hardy Oak Boulevard, San Antonio, TX Zip 78258–4206; tel. 210/507–4090; Debbie Kelly, Chief Executive Officer
**Web address:** www.southtexassurgical.com

SOUTH TEXAS SURGICAL HOSPITAL (O, 20 beds) 6130 Parkway Drive, Corpus Christi, TX Zip 78414–2455; tel. 361/993–2000; James Murphy, Chief Executive Officer
**Web address:** www.southtexassurgicalhospital.com

**WISCONSIN:** OAKLEAF SURGICAL HOSPITAL (O, 13 beds) 3802 West Oakwood Mall Drive, Eau Claire, WI Zip 54701–3016; tel. 715/831–8130; Anne Hargrave–Thomas, Chief Executive Officer
**Web address:** www.oakleafmedical.com

**WYOMING:** MOUNTAIN VIEW REGIONAL HOSPITAL (O, 23 beds) 6550 East Second Street, Casper, WY Zip 82609–4321, Mailing Address: P.O. Box 51888, Zip 82605–1888; tel. 307/995–8100; Jeff Van Horn, Chief Executive Officer
**Web address:** www.mountainviewregionalhospital.com

| | | |
|---|---|---|
| Owned, leased, sponsored: | 13 hospitals | 296 beds |
| Contract–managed: | 0 hospitals | 0 beds |
| Totals: | 13 hospitals | 296 beds |

**0923: NAVICENT HEALTH** (NP)
777 Hemlock Street, Macon, GA Zip 31201–2155; tel. 478/633–1000; Ninfa Saunders, Chief Executive Officer
**(Centralized Health System)**

**GEORGIA:** MEDICAL CENTER OF PEACH COUNTY, NAVICENT HEALTH (O, 25 beds) 601 Blue Bird Boulevard, Fort Valley, GA Zip 31030–4599, Mailing Address: P.O. Box 1799, Zip 31030–1799; tel. 478/825–8691; Darren Pearce, Administrator and Chief Executive Officer
**Web address:** www.navicenthealth.org

MEDICAL CENTER, NAVICENT HEALTH (O, 659 beds) 777 Hemlock Street, Macon, GA Zip 31201–2155; tel. 478/633–1000; Ninfa Saunders, Chief Executive Officer
**Web address:** www.mccg.org

REHABILITATION HOSPITAL, NAVICENT HEALTH (O, 58 beds) 3351 Northside Drive, Macon, GA Zip 31210–2587; tel. 478/201–6500; Elbert T. McQueen, President and Chief Executive Officer
**Web address:** www.centralgarehab.com

| | | |
|---|---|---|
| Owned, leased, sponsored: | 3 hospitals | 742 beds |
| Contract–managed: | 0 hospitals | 0 beds |
| Totals: | 3 hospitals | 742 beds |

**★9265: NEBRASKA METHODIST HEALTH SYSTEM, INC.** (CO)
8511 West Dodge Road, Omaha, NE Zip 68114–3403; tel. 402/354–5411; John M. Fraser, FACHE, President and Chief Executive Officer
**(Centralized Physician/Insurance Health System)**

**IOWA:** METHODIST JENNIE EDMUNDSON HOSPITAL (O, 114 beds) 933 East Pierce Street, Council Bluffs, IA Zip 51503–4652, Mailing Address: P.O. Box 2C, Zip 51502–3002; tel. 712/396–6000; Steven P. Baumert, President and Chief Executive Officer
**Web address:** www.bestcare.org

**NEBRASKA:** NEBRASKA METHODIST HOSPITAL (O, 368 beds) 8303 Dodge Street, Omaha, NE Zip 68114–4199; tel. 402/354–4000; Stephen L. Goeser, FACHE, President and Chief Executive Officer
**Web address:** www.bestcare.org

| | | |
|---|---|---|
| Owned, leased, sponsored: | 2 hospitals | 482 beds |
| Contract–managed: | 0 hospitals | 0 beds |
| Totals: | 2 hospitals | 482 beds |

**0892: NEMOURS** (NP)
10140 Centurion Parkway North, Jacksonville, FL Zip 32256–0532; tel. 904/697–4100; David J. Bailey, M.D., President and Chief Executive Officer
**(Independent Hospital System)**

**DELAWARE:** ALFRED I. DUPONT HOSPITAL FOR CHILDREN (O, 196 beds) 1600 Rockland Road, Wilmington, DE Zip 19803–3616, Mailing Address: Box 269, Zip 19899–0269; tel. 302/651–4000; Roy Proujansky, M.D., Chief Executive Officer
**Web address:** www.nemours.org

**FLORIDA:** NEMOURS CHILDREN'S HOSPITAL (O, 64 beds) 13535 Nemours Parkway, Orlando, FL Zip 32827–7402; tel. 407/567–4000; Roger A. Oxendale, Chief Executive Officer
**Web address:** www.nemours.org

| | | |
|---|---|---|
| Owned, leased, sponsored: | 2 hospitals | 260 beds |
| Contract–managed: | 0 hospitals | 0 beds |
| Totals: | 2 hospitals | 260 beds |

**0620: NEUROPSYCHIATRIC HOSPITALS** (IO)
1625 East Jefferson Boulevard, Mishawaka, IN Zip 46545–7103; tel. 574/255–1400; Cameron R. Gilbert, Ph.D., President and Chief Executive Officer

**INDIANA:** DOCTORS NEUROMEDICAL HOSPITAL (O, 20 beds) 411 South Whitlock Street, Bremen, IN Zip 46506–1626, Mailing Address: P.O. Box 36, Zip 46506–0036; tel. 574/546–3830; Alan Fisher, Chief Executive Officer
**Web address:** www.physicianshospitalsystem.net

DOCTORS NEUROPSYCHIATRIC HOSPITAL AND RESEARCH INSTITUTE (O, 20 beds) 417 South Whitlock Street, Bremen, IN Zip 46506–1626; tel. 574/546–0330; Cameron R. Gilbert, Ph.D., President and Chief Executive Officer

**Section B**

For explanation of codes following names, see page B2.
★ Indicates Type III membership in the American Hospital Association.

RIVERCREST SPECIALTY HOSPITAL (O, 30 beds) 1625 East Jefferson Boulevard, Mishawaka, IN Zip 46545–7103; tel. 574/255–1400; Cameron R. Gilbert, Ph.D., President and Chief Executive Officer
**Web address:** www.physicianshospitalsystem.net/

| Owned, leased, sponsored: | 3 hospitals | 70 beds |
|---|---|---|
| Contract–managed: | 0 hospitals | 0 beds |
| **Totals:** | 3 hospitals | 70 beds |

---

★**0213: NEW HANOVER REGIONAL MEDICAL CENTER** (NP)
2131 South 17th Street, Wilmington, NC Zip 28401–7407; tel. 910/343–7040; John K. Barto, Jr., President and Chief Executive Officer
**(Moderately Centralized Health System)**

**NORTH CAROLINA:** NEW HANOVER REGIONAL MEDICAL CENTER (O, 692 beds) 2131 South 17th Street, Wilmington, NC Zip 28401–7483, Mailing Address: P.O. Box 9000, Zip 28402–9000; tel. 910/343–7000; John K. Barto, Jr., President and Chief Executive Officer
**Web address:** www.nhrmc.org

PENDER MEMORIAL HOSPITAL (C, 68 beds) 507 East Freemont Street, Burgaw, NC Zip 28425–5131; tel. 910/259–5451; Ruth Glaser, President
**Web address:** www.pendermemorial.org

| Owned, leased, sponsored: | 1 hospital | 692 beds |
|---|---|---|
| Contract–managed: | 1 hospital | 68 beds |
| **Totals:** | 2 hospitals | 760 beds |

---

★**3075: NEW YORK CITY HEALTH AND HOSPITALS CORPORATION** (NP)
125 Worth Street, Room 514, New York, NY Zip 10013–4006; tel. 212/788–3321; Ramanathan Raju, M.D., President
**(Decentralized Health System)**

**NEW YORK:** BELLEVUE HOSPITAL CENTER (O, 827 beds) 462 First Avenue, New York, NY Zip 10016–9198; tel. 212/562–4141; Steven Alexander, Executive Director
**Web address:** www.nyc.gov/bellevue

CONEY ISLAND HOSPITAL (O, 371 beds) 2601 Ocean Parkway, Brooklyn, NY Zip 11235–7795; tel. 718/616–3000; Arthur Wagner, Senior Vice President and Executive Director
**Web address:** www.nyc.gov/html/hhc/html/facilities/coneyisland.shtml

ELMHURST HOSPITAL CENTER (O, 532 beds) 79–01 Broadway, Elmhurst, NY Zip 11373–1329; tel. 718/334–4000; Chris D. Constantino, Senior Vice President and Executive Director
**Web address:** www.nyc.gov/html/hhc/ehc/html/home/home.shtml

HARLEM HOSPITAL CENTER (O, 279 beds) 506 Lenox Avenue, New York, NY Zip 10037–1802; tel. 212/939–1000; Denise C. Soares, R.N., Executive Director
**Web address:** www.nyc.gov/html/hhc/harlem

HENRY J. CARTER SPECIALTY HOSPITAL AND NURSING FACILITY (O, 2016 beds) 1752 Park Avenue, New York, NY Zip 10035; tel. 646/686–0000; Robert K. Hughes, Executive Director
**Web address:** www.coler-goldwater.org

JACOBI MEDICAL CENTER (O, 457 beds) 1400 Pelham Parkway South, Bronx, NY Zip 10461–1197; tel. 718/918–5000; Chris Fugazy, Acting Executive Director
**Web address:** www.nyc.gov/html/hhc/jacobi/home.html

KINGS COUNTY HOSPITAL CENTER (O, 599 beds) 451 Clarkson Avenue, Brooklyn, NY Zip 11203–2097; tel. 718/245–3131; Ernest Baptiste, Executive Director
**Web address:** www.nyc.gov/html/hhc/kchc/html/home/home.shtml

LINCOLN MEDICAL AND MENTAL HEALTH CENTER (O, 355 beds) 234 East 149th Street, Bronx, NY Zip 10451–5504; tel. 718/579–5700; Milton Nunez, Executive Director
**Web address:** www.nyc.gov/html/hhc/lincoln/

METROPOLITAN HOSPITAL CENTER (O, 317 beds) 1901 First Avenue, New York, NY Zip 10029–7404; tel. 212/423–6262; Anthony Rajkumar, Executive Director
**Web address:** www.nyc.gov/html/hhc/mhc/html/home/home.shtml

NORTH CENTRAL BRONX HOSPITAL (O, 207 beds) 3424 Kossuth Avenue, Bronx, NY Zip 10467–2489; tel. 718/519–3500; Gregory Calliste, PhD, Acting Executive Director
**Web address:** www.nyc.gov/html/hhc/ncbh/html/home/home.shtml

QUEENS HOSPITAL CENTER (O, 281 beds) 82–68 164th Street, Jamaica, NY Zip 11432–1104; tel. 718/883–3000; Julius Wool, Executive Director
**Web address:** www.nyc.gov/html/hhc/qhc/html/home/home.shtml

WOODHULL MEDICAL AND MENTAL HEALTH CENTER (O, 323 beds) 760 Broadway, Brooklyn, NY Zip 11206–5383; tel. 718/963–8000; George M. Proctor, Senior Vice President and Executive Director
**Web address:** www.nyc.gov/html/hhc

| Owned, leased, sponsored: | 12 hospitals | 6564 beds |
|---|---|---|
| Contract–managed: | 0 hospitals | 0 beds |
| **Totals:** | 12 hospitals | 6564 beds |

---

**0142: NEW YORK PRESBYTERIAN HEALTHCARE SYSTEM** (NP)
525 East 68th Street, Box 182, New York, NY Zip 10065; tel. 212/746–3745; Steven J. Corwin, M.D., Chief Executive Officer
**(Moderately Centralized Health System)**

NEW YORK–PRESBYTERIAN HOSPITAL (O, 2328 beds) 525 East 68th Street, New York, NY Zip 10065–4870; tel. 212/746–5454; Steven J. Corwin, M.D., Chief Executive Officer
**Web address:** www.nyp.org

NEW YORK–PRESBYTERIAN/HUDSON VALLEY HOSPITAL (O, 128 beds) 1980 Crompond Road, Cortlandt Manor, NY Zip 10567–4182; tel. 914/737–9000; John C. Federspiel, President and Chief Executive Officer
**Web address:** www.hvhc.org

NEW YORK–PRESBYTERIAN/LAWRENCE HOSPITAL (O, 187 beds) 55 Palmer Avenue, Bronxville, NY Zip 10708–3403; tel. 914/787–1000; Michael Fossina, President and Chief Executive Officer
**Web address:** www.lawrencehealth.org

NEW YORK–PRESBYTERIAN/QUEENS (O, 559 beds) 56–45 Main Street, Flushing, NY Zip 11355–5045; tel. 718/670–1231; Stephen S. Mills, President and Chief Executive Officer
**Web address:** www.nyhq.org

| Owned, leased, sponsored: | 4 hospitals | 3202 beds |
|---|---|---|
| Contract–managed: | 0 hospitals | 0 beds |
| **Totals:** | 4 hospitals | 3202 beds |

---

**0009: NEW YORK STATE OFFICE OF MENTAL HEALTH** (NP)
44 Holland Avenue, Albany, NY Zip 12208–3411; tel. 518/474–7056; Kristin M. Woodlock, R.N., Acting Commissioner
**(Independent Hospital System)**

BRONX PSYCHIATRIC CENTER (O, 450 beds) 1500 Waters Place, Bronx, NY Zip 10461–2796; tel. 718/931–0600; Pamela Turner, Executive Director
**Web address:** www.omh.ny.gov

BUFFALO PSYCHIATRIC CENTER (O, 240 beds) 400 Forest Avenue, Buffalo, NY Zip 14213–1298; tel. 716/885–2261; Thomas Dodson, Executive Director
**Web address:** www.omh.ny.gov

CAPITAL DISTRICT PSYCHIATRIC CENTER (O, 200 beds) 75 New Scotland Avenue, Albany, NY Zip 12208–3474; tel. 518/447–9611; William Dickson, Acting Executive Director
**Web address:** www.omh.ny.gov/omhweb/facilities/cdpc/facility.htm

CENTRAL NEW YORK PSYCHIATRIC CENTER (O, 226 beds) 9005 Old River Road, Marcy, NY Zip 13403–3000, Mailing Address: P.O. Box 300, Zip 13403–0300; tel. 315/765–3600; Maureen Bosco, Executive Director
**Web address:** www.omh.ny.gov

CREEDMOOR PSYCHIATRIC CENTER (O, 380 beds) 79–25 Winchester Boulevard, Jamaica, NY Zip 11427–2128; tel. 718/264–3600; Ann Marie Barbarotta, Executive Director
**Web address:** www.omh.ny.gov

ELMIRA PSYCHIATRIC CENTER (O, 100 beds) 100 Washington Street, Elmira, NY Zip 14901–2898; tel. 607/737–4739; Mark Stephany, Executive Director
**Web address:** www.omh.ny.gov/omhweb/facilities/elpc/facility.htm

For explanation of codes following names, see page B2.
★ Indicates Type III membership in the American Hospital Association.

GREATER BINGHAMTON HEALTH CENTER (O, 101 beds) 425 Robinson Street, Binghamton, NY Zip 13904–1735; tel. 607/724–1391; Mark Stephany, Executive Director
**Web address:** www.omh.ny.gov/omhweb/facilities/bipc/facility.htm

KINGSBORO PSYCHIATRIC CENTER (O, 290 beds) 681 Clarkson Avenue, Brooklyn, NY Zip 11203–2125; tel. 718/221–7395; Deborah Parchment, Executive Director
**Web address:** www.omh.ny.gov/omhweb/facilities/kbpc/facility/htm

MANHATTAN PSYCHIATRIC CENTER–WARD'S ISLAND (O, 745 beds) 600 East 125th Street, New York, NY Zip 10035–6000; tel. 646/672–6767; Vinny Miccoli, Executive Director
**Web address:** www.omh.ny.gov

MID–HUDSON FORENSIC PSYCHIATRIC CENTER (O, 169 beds) Route 17M, New Hampton, NY Zip 10958, Mailing Address: P.O. Box 158, Zip 10958–0158; tel. 845/374–8700; Joseph Freebern, Executive Director
**Web address:** www.omh.ny.gov

MOHAWK VALLEY PSYCHIATRIC CENTER (O, 614 beds) 1400 Noyes Street, Utica, NY Zip 13502–3854; tel. 315/738–3800; Colleen A. Sawyer, R.N., MSN, Executive Director
**Web address:** www.omh.ny.gov/omhweb/facilities/mvpc/facility.htm

NEW YORK CITY CHILDREN'S CENTER (O, 84 beds) 74–03 Commonwealth Boulevard, Jamaica, NY Zip 11426–1890; tel. 718/264–4506; Anita Daniels, Executive Director
**Web address:** www.omh.ny.gov/omhweb/facilities/nyccc/

NEW YORK STATE PSYCHIATRIC INSTITUTE (O, 58 beds) 1051 Riverside Drive, New York, NY Zip 10032–1007; tel. 212/543–5000; Jeffrey A. Lieberman, M.D., Executive Director
**Web address:** www.nyspi.org

PILGRIM PSYCHIATRIC CENTER (O, 569 beds) 998 Crooked Hill Road, Brentwood, NY Zip 11717–1019; tel. 631/761–3500; Kathy O'Keefe, Executive Director
**Web address:** www.omh.ny.gov/omhweb/facilities/pgpc/facility.htm

RICHARD H. HUTCHINGS PSYCHIATRIC CENTER (O, 131 beds) 620 Madison Street, Syracuse, NY Zip 13210–2319; tel. 315/426–3632; Colleen A. Sawyer, R.N., MSN, Executive Director
**Web address:** www.omh.ny.gov

ROCHESTER PSYCHIATRIC CENTER (O, 180 beds) 1111 Elmwood Avenue, Rochester, NY Zip 14620–3005; tel. 585/241–1200; Elizabeth Suhre, Executive Director
**Web address:** www.omh.ny.gov/omhweb/facilities/ropc/facility.htm

ROCKLAND CHILDREN'S PSYCHIATRIC CENTER (O, 54 beds) 599 Convent Road, Orangeburg, NY Zip 10962–1162; tel. 845/359–7400; Christopher Tavella, Acting Executive Director
**Web address:** www.omh.ny.gov/

ROCKLAND PSYCHIATRIC CENTER (O, 525 beds) 140 Old Orangeburg Road, Orangeburg, NY Zip 10962–1157; tel. 845/359–1000; Christopher Tavella, Executive Director
**Web address:** www.omh.ny.gov/

SAGAMORE CHILDREN'S PSYCHIATRIC CENTER (O, 69 beds) 197 Half Hollow Road, Dix Hills, NY Zip 11746–5861; tel. 631/370–1700; Kathy O'Keefe, Interim Executive Director
**Web address:** www.omh.ny.gov

SOUTH BEACH PSYCHIATRIC CENTER (O, 340 beds) 777 Seaview Avenue, Staten Island, NY Zip 10305–3409; tel. 718/667–2300; Rosanne Gaylor, M.D., Acting Executive Director
**Web address:** www.omh.ny.gov/omhweb/facilities/sbpc/facility.htm

ST. LAWRENCE PSYCHIATRIC CENTER (O, 146 beds) 1 Chimney Point Drive, Ogdensburg, NY Zip 13669–2291; tel. 315/541–2001; Timothy Farrell, Executive Director
**Web address:** www.omh.ny.gov/omhweb/facilities/slpc/facility.htm

WESTERN NEW YORK CHILDREN'S PSYCHIATRIC CENTER (O, 46 beds) 1010 East and West Road, West Seneca, NY Zip 14224–3602; tel. 716/677–7000; Kathe Hayes, Executive Director
**Web address:** www.omh.ny.gov

| | | |
|---|---|---|
| **Owned, leased, sponsored:** | 22 hospitals | 5717 beds |
| **Contract–managed:** | 0 hospitals | 0 beds |
| **Totals:** | 22 hospitals | 5717 beds |

**0353:  NEXUS HEALTH SYSTEMS** (IO)
One Riverway, Suite 600, Houston, TX Zip 77056–1993; tel. 713/355–6111; John W. Cassidy, M.D., President, Chief Executive Officer and Chief Medical Officer
**(Independent Hospital System)**

**CALIFORNIA:** HEALTHBRIDGE CHILDREN'S HOSPITAL (O, 27 beds) 393 South Tustin Street, Orange, CA Zip 92866–2501; tel. 714/289–2400; Brian Cotter, Chief Executive Officer
**Web address:** www.HealthBridgeOrange.com

**TEXAS:** HEALTHBRIDGE CHILDREN'S HOSPITAL OF HOUSTON (O, 37 beds) 2929 Woodland Park Drive, Houston, TX Zip 77082–2687; tel. 281/293–7774; Tony Bonilla, Chief Executive Officer
**Web address:** www.healthbridgehouston.com/

NEXUS SPECIALTY HOSPITAL (O, 75 beds) 123 Vision Park Boulevard, Shenandoah, TX Zip 77384–3001; tel. 281/364–0317; Judith Butryn, Chief Executive Officer
**Web address:** www.nexusspecialty.com

| | | |
|---|---|---|
| **Owned, leased, sponsored:** | 3 hospitals | 139 beds |
| **Contract–managed:** | 0 hospitals | 0 beds |
| **Totals:** | 3 hospitals | 139 beds |

**0349:  NOLAND HEALTH SERVICES, INC.** (NP)
600 Corporate Parkway, Suite 100, Birmingham, AL Zip 35242–5451; tel. 205/783–8484; Gary M. Glasscock, President and Chief Executive Officer

**ALABAMA:** NOLAND HOSPITAL ANNISTON (O, 38 beds) 400 East 10th Street, 4th Floor, Anniston, AL Zip 36207–4716; tel. 256/741–6141; Bill Mitchell, Administrator
**Web address:** www.nolandhealth.com

NOLAND HOSPITAL BIRMINGHAM (O, 45 beds) 50 Medical Park East Drive, 8th Floor, Birmingham, AL Zip 35235; tel. 205/808–5100; Laura S. Wills, Administrator
**Web address:** www.nolandhealth.com

NOLAND HOSPITAL DOTHAN (O, 35 beds) 1108 Ross Clark Circle, 4th Floor, Dothan, AL Zip 36301–3022; tel. 334/699–4300; Kaye Burke, Administrator
**Web address:** www.nolandhealth.com

NOLAND HOSPITAL MONTGOMERY (O, 65 beds) 1725 Pine Street, 5 North, Montgomery, AL Zip 36106–1109; tel. 334/240–0532; Susan E. Legg, Interim Administrator
**Web address:** www.nolandhealth.com

NOLAND HOSPITAL SHELBY (O, 52 beds) 1000 First Street North, 3rd Floor, Alabaster, AL Zip 35007–8703; tel. 205/620–8641; Laura S. Wills, Administrator
**Web address:** www.nolandhospitals.com

NOLAND HOSPITAL TUSCALOOSA (O, 32 beds) 809 University Boulevard E, 4th Floor, Tuscaloosa, AL Zip 35401–2029; tel. 205/759–7241; Dale Jones, Administrator
**Web address:** www.nolandhealth.com

| | | |
|---|---|---|
| **Owned, leased, sponsored:** | 6 hospitals | 267 beds |
| **Contract–managed:** | 0 hospitals | 0 beds |
| **Totals:** | 6 hospitals | 267 beds |

**★0887:  NORTH MEMORIAL HEALTH CARE** (NP)
3300 Oakdale Avenue North, Robbinsdale, MN Zip 55422–2926; tel. 763/520–5200; J. Kevin Croston, M.D., Chief Executive Officer
**(Centralized Physician/Insurance Health System)**

**MINNESOTA:** MAPLE GROVE HOSPITAL (C, 108 beds) 9875 Hospital Drive, Maple Grove, MN Zip 55369–4648; tel. 763/581–1000; Andrew S. Cochrane, Chief Executive Officer
**Web address:** www.maplegrovehospital.org

For explanation of codes following names, see page B2.
★ Indicates Type III membership in the American Hospital Association.

Section B

NORTH MEMORIAL MEDICAL CENTER (O, 355 beds) 3300 Oakdale Avenue North, Robbinsdale, MN Zip 55422–2926; tel. 763/520–5200; Jeff Wicklander, President
**Web address:** www.northmemorial.com

| | | |
|---|---|---|
| **Owned, leased, sponsored:** | 1 hospital | 355 beds |
| **Contract–managed:** | 1 hospital | 108 beds |
| **Totals:** | 2 hospitals | 463 beds |

---

**★0032:   NORTH MISSISSIPPI HEALTH SERVICES, INC.** (NP)
830 South Gloster Street, Tupelo, MS Zip 38801–4996; tel. 662/377–3136; M. Shane Spees, President and Chief Executive Officer
**(Centralized Physician/Insurance Health System)**

**ALABAMA:** MARION REGIONAL MEDICAL CENTER (O, 36 beds) 1256 Military Street South, Hamilton, AL Zip 35570–5003; tel. 205/921–6200; Tanya Brasher, Administrator
**Web address:** www.nmhs.net

**MISSISSIPPI:** CALHOUN HEALTH SERVICES (C, 150 beds) 140 Burke–Calhoun City Road, Calhoun City, MS Zip 38916–9690; tel. 662/628–6611; James P. Franklin, Administrator
**Web address:** www.nmhs.net/calhoun_city

NORTH MISSISSIPPI MEDICAL CENTER – TUPELO (O, 747 beds) 830 South Gloster Street, Tupelo, MS Zip 38801–4934; tel. 662/377–3000; David C. Wilson, Chief Executive Officer
**Web address:** www.nmhs.net

NORTH MISSISSIPPI MEDICAL CENTER–EUPORA (O, 73 beds) 70 Medical Plaza, Eupora, MS Zip 39744–4018; tel. 662/258–6221; Wes Sigler, Administrator
**Web address:** www.nmhs.net/eupora

TISHOMINGO HEALTH SERVICES (O, 48 beds) 1777 Curtis Drive, Iuka, MS Zip 38852–1001, Mailing Address: P.O. Box 860, Zip 38852–0860; tel. 662/423–6051; Fred A. Truesdale, Jr., Administrator
**Web address:** www.nmhs.net

NORTH MISSISSIPPI MEDICAL CENTER–PONTOTOC (L, 69 beds) 176 South Main Street, Pontotoc, MS Zip 38863–3311, Mailing Address: P.O. Box 790, Zip 38863–0790; tel. 662/488–7640; Leslia Carter, Administrator
**Web address:** www.nmhs.net

NORTH MISSISSIPPI MEDICAL CENTER–WEST POINT (O, 60 beds) 835 Medical Center Drive, West Point, MS Zip 39773–9320; tel. 662/495–2300; Barry L. Keel, Chief Executive Officer
**Web address:** www.nmhs.net/westpoint

| | | |
|---|---|---|
| **Owned, leased, sponsored:** | 6 hospitals | 1033 beds |
| **Contract–managed:** | 1 hospital | 150 beds |
| **Totals:** | 7 hospitals | 1183 beds |

---

**0867:   NORTH OAKS HEALTH SYSTEM** (NP)
15790 Paul Vega MD Drive, Hammond, LA Zip 70403–1436, Mailing Address: P.O. Box 2668, Zip 70404–2668; tel. 985/345–2700; Julie Hughs, Administrative Operations Support Analyst
**(Independent Hospital System)**

**LOUISIANA:** NORTH OAKS MEDICAL CENTER (O, 278 beds) 15790 Paul Vega, MD, Drive, Hammond, LA Zip 70403–1436, Mailing Address: P.O. Box 2668, Zip 70404–2668; tel. 985/345–2700; Michele K. Sutton, FACHE, Administrator
**Web address:** www.northoaks.org

NORTH OAKS REHABILITATION HOSPITAL (O, 27 beds) 1900 South Morrison Boulevard, Hammond, LA Zip 70403–5742; tel. 985/345–2700; Sybil K. Paulson, R.N., Administrator
**Web address:** www.northoaks.org

| | | |
|---|---|---|
| **Owned, leased, sponsored:** | 2 hospitals | 305 beds |
| **Contract–managed:** | 0 hospitals | 0 beds |
| **Totals:** | 2 hospitals | 305 beds |

---

**★0062:   NORTH SHORE–LONG ISLAND JEWISH HEALTH SYSTEM** (NP)
145 Community Drive, Great Neck, NY Zip 11021–5502; tel. 516/465–8100; Michael J. Dowling, President and Chief Executive Officer
**(Centralized Health System)**

**NEW YORK:** FOREST HILLS HOSPITAL (O, 235 beds) 102–01 66th Road, Forest Hills, NY Zip 11375–2029; tel. 718/830–4000; Susan Browning, Executive Director
**Web address:** www.northshorelij.com

FRANKLIN HOSPITAL (O, 330 beds) 900 Franklin Avenue, Valley Stream, NY Zip 11580–2190; tel. 516/256–6000; Catherine Hottendorf, R.N., MS, Executive Director
**Web address:** www.northshorelij.com

GLEN COVE HOSPITAL (O, 140 beds) 101 St. Andrews Lane, Glen Cove, NY Zip 11542–2254; tel. 516/674–7300; Susan Kwiatek, R.N., Executive Director
**Web address:** www.northshorelij.com

HUNTINGTON HOSPITAL (O, 290 beds) 270 Park Avenue, Huntington, NY Zip 11743–2799; tel. 631/351–2200; Gerard Brogan, Jr., M.D., Executive Director
**Web address:** www.hunthosp.org

LENOX HILL HOSPITAL (O, 441 beds) 100 East 77th Street, New York, NY Zip 10075–1850; tel. 212/434–2000; Dennis Connors, Executive Director
**Web address:** www.lenoxhillhospital.org

LONG ISLAND JEWISH MEDICAL CENTER (O, 900 beds) 270–05 76th Avenue, New Hyde Park, NY Zip 11040–1496; tel. 718/470–7000; Michael Goldberg, Executive Director
**Web address:** www.lij.edu

NORTH SHORE UNIVERSITY HOSPITAL (O, 764 beds) 300 Community Drive, Manhasset, NY Zip 11030–3816; tel. 516/562–0100; Alessandro Bellucci, M.D., Executive Director
**Web address:** www.northshorelij.com

PECONIC BAY MEDICAL CENTER (O, 94 beds) 1300 Roanoke Avenue, Riverhead, NY Zip 11901–2031; tel. 631/548–6000; Andrew J. Mitchell, President and Chief Executive Officer
**Web address:** www.pbmchealth.org

PLAINVIEW HOSPITAL (O, 189 beds) 888 Old Country Road, Plainview, NY Zip 11803–4978; tel. 516/719–3000; Michael Fener, Executive Director
**Web address:** www.northshorelij.com

SOUTH OAKS HOSPITAL (O, 260 beds) 400 Sunrise Highway, Amityville, NY Zip 11701–2508; tel. 631/264–4000; Patricia Porter, Executive Director
**Web address:** www.longislandhome.org

SOUTHSIDE HOSPITAL (O, 300 beds) 301 East Main Street, Bay Shore, NY Zip 11706–8458; tel. 631/968–3000; Donna Moravick, R.N., MSN, Executive Director
**Web address:** www.southsidehospital.org

STATEN ISLAND UNIVERSITY HOSPITAL (O, 663 beds) 475 Seaview Avenue, Staten Island, NY Zip 10305–3436; tel. 718/226–9000; Donna Proske, MS, R.N., Executive Director
**Web address:** siuh.edu

SYOSSET HOSPITAL (O, 75 beds) 221 Jericho Turnpike, Syosset, NY Zip 11791–4515; tel. 516/496–6500; Michael Fener, Executive Director
**Web address:** www.northshorelij.com

| | | |
|---|---|---|
| **Owned, leased, sponsored:** | 13 hospitals | 4681 beds |
| **Contract–managed:** | 0 hospitals | 0 beds |
| **Totals:** | 13 hospitals | 4681 beds |

---

**★0281:   NORTHERN ARIZONA HEALTHCARE** (NP)
1200 North Beaver Street, Flagstaff, AZ Zip 86001–3118; tel. 928/779–3366; Robert P. Thames, President and Chief Executive Officer
**(Moderately Centralized Health System)**

**ARIZONA:** FLAGSTAFF MEDICAL CENTER (O, 267 beds) 1200 North Beaver Street, Flagstaff, AZ Zip 86001–3118; tel. 928/779–3366; Richard Langosch, President and Chief Executive Officer
**Web address:** www.flagstaffmedicalcenter.com

For explanation of codes following names, see page B2.
★ Indicates Type III membership in the American Hospital Association.

Section B

VERDE VALLEY MEDICAL CENTER (O, 110 beds) 269 South Candy Lane, Cottonwood, AZ Zip 86326–4170; tel. 928/639–6000; Susanne Maiden, Interim Administrator
**Web address:** www.nahealth.com

| | | |
|---|---|---|
| **Owned, leased, sponsored:** | 2 hospitals | 377 beds |
| **Contract–managed:** | 0 hospitals | 0 beds |
| **Totals:** | 2 hospitals | 377 beds |

---

**★0410:  NORTHSIDE HEALTHCARE SYSTEM** (NP)
1000 Johnson Ferry Road N.E., Atlanta, GA Zip 30342–1611; tel. 404/851–8000; Robert Quattrocchi, President and Chief Executive Officer

**GEORGIA:** NORTHSIDE HOSPITAL (O, 587 beds) 1000 Johnson Ferry Road N.E., Atlanta, GA Zip 30342–1611; tel. 404/851–8000; Robert Quattrocchi, President and Chief Executive Officer
**Web address:** www.northside.com

NORTHSIDE HOSPITAL–CHEROKEE (O, 88 beds) 201 Hospital Road, Canton, GA Zip 30114–2408, Mailing Address: P.O. Box 906, Zip 30169–0906; tel. 770/720–5100; William M. Hayes, Chief Executive Officer
**Web address:** www.northside.com

NORTHSIDE HOSPITAL–FORSYTH (O, 252 beds) 1200 Northside Forsyth Drive, Cumming, GA Zip 30041–7659; tel. 770/844–3200; Lynn Jackson, Administrator
**Web address:** www.northside.com

| | | |
|---|---|---|
| **Owned, leased, sponsored:** | 3 hospitals | 927 beds |
| **Contract–managed:** | 0 hospitals | 0 beds |
| **Totals:** | 3 hospitals | 927 beds |

---

**★0024:  NORTHWESTERN MEMORIAL HEALTHCARE** (NP)
251 East Huron Street, Chicago, IL Zip 60611–2908; tel. 312/926–2000; Dean M. Harrison, President and Chief Executive Officer
**(Centralized Health System)**

**ILLINOIS:** NORTHWESTERN MEDICINE CENTRAL DUPAGE HOSPITAL (O, 378 beds) 25 North Winfield Road, Winfield, IL Zip 60190; tel. 630/933–1600; Brian J. Lemon, President
**Web address:** www.cdh.org

NORTHWESTERN MEDICINE DELNOR HOSPITAL (O, 159 beds) 300 Randall Road, Geneva, IL Zip 60134–4200; tel. 630/208–3000; Maureen A. Bryant, FACHE, President
**Web address:** www.cadencehealth.org

NORTHWESTERN LAKE FOREST HOSPITAL (O, 181 beds) 660 North Westmoreland Road, Lake Forest, IL Zip 60045–1696; tel. 847/234–5600; Thomas J. McAfee, President, North Market
**Web address:** www.lfh.org

NORTHWESTERN MEMORIAL HOSPITAL (O, 885 beds) 251 East Huron Street, Chicago, IL Zip 60611–2908; tel. 312/926–2000; Dean M. Harrison, President and Chief Executive Officer
**Web address:** www.nmh.org

| | | |
|---|---|---|
| **Owned, leased, sponsored:** | 4 hospitals | 1603 beds |
| **Contract–managed:** | 0 hospitals | 0 beds |
| **Totals:** | 4 hospitals | 1603 beds |

---

**★2285:  NORTON HEALTHCARE** (NP)
4967 U.S. Highway 42, Suite 100, Louisville, KY Zip 40222–6363, Mailing Address: P.O. Box 35070, Zip 40232–5070; tel. 502/629–8000; Stephen Williams, Chief Executive Officer
**(Centralized Health System)**

**KENTUCKY:** KOSAIR CHILDREN'S HOSPITAL (O, 267 beds) 231 East Chestnut Street, Louisville, KY Zip 40202–1821; tel. 502/629–6000; Thomas D. Kmetz, Division President
**Web address:** www.kosairchildrens.com/

NORTON AUDUBON HOSPITAL (O, 288 beds) One Audubon Plaza Drive, Louisville, KY Zip 40217–1300, Mailing Address: P.O. Box 17550, Zip 40217–0550; tel. 502/636–7111; Jon Cooper, Chief Administrative Officer
**Web address:** www.nortonhealthcare.com/NortonAudubonHospital

NORTON BROWNSBORO HOSPITAL (O, 118 beds) 4960 Norton Healthcare Boulevard, Louisville, KY Zip 40241–2831; tel. 502/446–8000; John D. Harryman, Chief Administrative Officer
**Web address:** www.nortonhealthcare.com/nortonbrownsborohospital

NORTON HOSPITAL (O, 379 beds) 200 East Chestnut Street, Louisville, KY Zip 40202–1800, Mailing Address: P.O. Box 35070, Zip 40232–5070; tel. 502/629–8000; Matthew Ayers, Chief Administrative Officer
**Web address:** www.nortonhealthcare.com/nortonhospital

NORTON WOMEN'S AND KOSAIR CHILDREN'S HOSPITAL (O, 368 beds) 4001 Dutchmans Lane, Louisville, KY Zip 40207–4799; tel. 502/893–1000; Charlotte Ipsan, Chief Administrative Officer
**Web address:** www.nortonhealthcare.com/nortonsuburbanhospital

| | | |
|---|---|---|
| **Owned, leased, sponsored:** | 5 hospitals | 1420 beds |
| **Contract–managed:** | 0 hospitals | 0 beds |
| **Totals:** | 5 hospitals | 1420 beds |

---

**★0139:  NOVANT HEALTH** (NP)
2085 Frontis Plaza Boulevard, Winston Salem, NC Zip 27103–5614; tel. 336/718–5600; Carl S. Armato, President and Chief Executive Officer
**(Moderately Centralized Health System)**

**NORTH CAROLINA:** ASHE MEMORIAL HOSPITAL (C, 25 beds) 200 Hospital Avenue, Jefferson, NC Zip 28640–9244; tel. 336/846–7101; Laura Lambeth, Chief Executive Officer
**Web address:** www.ashememorial.org

HALIFAX REGIONAL MEDICAL CENTER (C, 142 beds) 250 Smith Church Road, Roanoke Rapids, NC Zip 27870–4914, Mailing Address: P.O. Box 1089, Zip 27870–1089; tel. 252/535–8011; William Mahone, President and Chief Executive Officer
**Web address:** www.halifaxmedicalcenter.org

NOVANT HEALTH BRUNSWICK MEDICAL CENTER (O, 52 beds) 240 Hospital Drive N.E., Bolivia, NC Zip 28422–8346; tel. 910/721–1000; Shelbourn Stevens, President
**Web address:** www.brunswicknovant.org

NOVANT HEALTH CHARLOTTE ORTHOPAEDIC HOSPITAL (O, 33 beds) 1901 Randolph Road, Charlotte, NC Zip 28207–1195; tel. 704/316–2000; Jason Bernd, Vice President
**Web address:** www.novanthealth.org

NOVANT HEALTH FORSYTH MEDICAL CENTER (O, 689 beds) 3333 Silas Creek Parkway, Winston–Salem, NC Zip 27103–3090; tel. 336/718–5000; Sean M. Sanz, Chief Executive Officer
**Web address:** www.forsythmedicalcenter.org

NOVANT HEALTH FRANKLIN MEDICAL CENTER (O, 17 beds) 100 Hospital Drive, Louisburg, NC Zip 27549–2256, Mailing Address: P.O. Box 609, Zip 27549–0609; tel. 919/497–8401; Jody Morris, President and Chief Operating Officer
**Web address:** www.https://www.novanthealth.org/franklin–medical–center.aspx

NOVANT HEALTH HUNTERSVILLE MEDICAL CENTER (O, 78 beds) 10030 Gilead Road, Huntersville, NC Zip 28078–7545, Mailing Address: P.O. Box 3508, Zip 28070–3508; tel. 704/316–4000; Mike Riley, President
**Web address:** www.novanthealth.org

NOVANT HEALTH MATTHEWS MEDICAL CENTER (O, 102 beds) 1500 Matthews Township Parkway, Matthews, NC Zip 28105–4656, Mailing Address: P.O. Box 3310, Zip 28106–3310; tel. 704/384–6500; Roland R. Bibeau, FACHE, President
**Web address:** www.presbyterian.org

NOVANT HEALTH MEDICAL PARK HOSPITAL (O, 16 beds) 1950 South Hawthorne Road, Winston–Salem, NC Zip 27103–3993; tel. 336/718–0600; Chad Setliff, Chief Executive Officer
**Web address:** www.novanthealth.org

NOVANT HEALTH PRESBYTERIAN MEDICAL CENTER (O, 416 beds) 200 Hawthorne Lane, Charlotte, NC Zip 28204–2528, Mailing Address: P.O. Box 33549, Zip 28233–3549; tel. 704/384–4000; Paula Vincent, MSN, President and Chief Operating Officer
**Web address:** www.novanthealth.org

---

For explanation of codes following names, see page B2.
★ Indicates Type III membership in the American Hospital Association.

Section B

NOVANT HEALTH ROWAN MEDICAL CENTER (O, 148 beds) 612 Mocksville Avenue, Salisbury, NC Zip 28144–2799; tel. 704/210–5000; Dari Caldwell, R.N., Ph.D., FACHE, President and Chief Operating Officer
**Web address:** www.https://www.novanthealth.org/rowan–medical–center.aspx

NOVANT HEALTH THOMASVILLE MEDICAL CENTER (O, 75 beds) 207 Old Lexington Road, Thomasville, NC Zip 27360–3428, Mailing Address: P.O. Box 789, Zip 27361–0789; tel. 336/472–2000; Kathie A. Johnson, R.N., MS, Ph.D., Chief Executive Officer
**Web address:** www.thomasvillemedicalcenter.org

**VIRGINIA:** NOVANT HEALTH HAYMARKET MEDICAL CENTER (O, 14 beds) 15225 Heathcote Boulevard, Haymarket, VA Zip 20155–4023, Mailing Address: 14535 John Marshall Highway, Gainesville, Zip 20155–4023; tel. 571/284–1000; Don Sedgley, President
**Web address:** www.novanthealth.org

NOVANT HEALTH PRINCE WILLIAM MEDICAL CENTER (O, 93 beds) 8700 Sudley Road, Manassas, VA Zip 20110–4418, Mailing Address: P.O. Box 2610, Zip 20108–0867; tel. 703/369–8000; Melissa Robson, President
**Web address:** www.pwhs.org

| | | |
|---|---|---|
| Owned, leased, sponsored: | 12 hospitals | 1733 beds |
| Contract–managed: | 2 hospitals | 167 beds |
| Totals: | 14 hospitals | 1900 beds |

---

**0966: NYU LANGONE HEALTH SYSTEM** (NP)
550 First Avenue, New York, NY Zip 10016–6402; tel. 212/263–7300; Robert I. Grossman, M.D., Chief Executive Officer

**NEW YORK:** NYU LANGONE MEDICAL CENTER (O, 718 beds) 550 First Avenue, New York, NY Zip 10016–6402; tel. 212/263–7300; Robert I. Grossman, M.D., Chief Executive Officer
**Web address:** www.nyumedicalcenter.org

NYU LUTHERAN (O, 400 beds) 150 55th Street, Brooklyn, NY Zip 11220–2559; tel. 718/630–7000; Wendy Z. Goldstein, Chief Executive Officer
**Web address:** www.lmcmc.com

| | | |
|---|---|---|
| Owned, leased, sponsored: | 2 hospitals | 1118 beds |
| Contract–managed: | 0 hospitals | 0 beds |
| Totals: | 2 hospitals | 1118 beds |

---

**0616: OCEANS HEALTHCARE** (IO)
2720 Rue de Jardin, Suite 100, Lake Charles, LA Zip 70605–4050; tel. 337/721–1900; Jason Reed, President and Chief Executive Officer

**LOUISIANA:** OCEANS BEHAVIORAL HOSPITAL OF ALEXANDRIA (O, 24 beds) 2621 North Bolton Avenue, Alexandria, LA Zip 71303–4506; tel. 318/448–8473; Nicholas D. Guillory, MSN, Interim Administrator
**Web address:** www.obha.info/

OCEANS BEHAVIORAL HOSPITAL OF BATON ROUGE (O, 20 beds) 11135 Florida Boulevard, Baton Rouge, LA Zip 70815–2013; tel. 225/356–7030; Valerie Dalton, R.N., Administrator
**Web address:** www.obhbr.info/

OCEANS BEHAVIORAL HOSPITAL OF BROUSSARD (O, 38 beds) 418 Albertson Parkway, Broussard, LA Zip 70518–4971; tel. 337/237–6444; Amy Dysart–Credeur, Administrator
**Web address:** www.obhb.info/

OCEANS BEHAVIORAL HOSPITAL OF DE RIDDER (O, 20 beds) 1420 Blankenship Drive, Deridder, LA Zip 70634–4604; tel. 337/460–9472; Sheila Langston, Administrator
**Web address:** www.obhd.info/

OCEANS BEHAVIORAL HOSPITAL OF GREATER NEW ORLEANS (O, 30 beds) 716 Village Road, Kenner, LA Zip 70065–2751; tel. 504/464–8895; Deborah Spier, Administrator
**Web address:** www.obhgno.info/

OCEANS BEHAVIORAL HOSPITAL OF KENTWOOD (O, 18 beds) 921 Avenue G., Kentwood, LA Zip 70444–2636; tel. 985/229–0717; Gina Isbell, Administrator
**Web address:** www.obhk.info/

OCEANS BEHAVIORAL HOSPITAL OF LAKE CHARLES (O, 20 beds) 302 West Mcneese Street, Lake Charles, LA Zip 70605–5604; tel. 337/474–7581; Dena Jules, Administrator
**Web address:** www.obhlc.info/

OCEANS BEHAVIORAL HOSPITAL OF OPELOUSAS (O, 20 beds) 1310 Heather Drive, Opelousas, LA Zip 70570–7714; tel. 337/948–8820; Theresa Fontenot, Executive Director
**Web address:** www.obho.info/

**TEXAS:** OCEANS BEHAVIORAL HEALTH CENTER PERMIAN BASIN (O, 48 beds) 3300 South FM 1788, Midland, TX Zip 79706–2601; tel. 432/561–5915; Kristin Harris, Interim Chief Executive Officer
**Web address:** www.oceanspermianbasin.com/

| | | |
|---|---|---|
| Owned, leased, sponsored: | 9 hospitals | 238 beds |
| Contract–managed: | 0 hospitals | 0 beds |
| Totals: | 9 hospitals | 238 beds |

---

**★0359: OCHSNER HEALTH SYSTEM** (NP)
1514 Jefferson Highway, New Orleans, LA Zip 70121–2429; tel. 800/874–8984; Warner L. Thomas, FACHE, President and Chief Executive Officer
**(Moderately Centralized Health System)**

**LOUISIANA:** LEONARD J. CHABERT MEDICAL CENTER (C, 72 beds) 1978 Industrial Boulevard, Houma, LA Zip 70363–7094; tel. 985/873–2200; Timothy J. Allen, FACHE, Chief Executive Officer
**Web address:** www.ochsner.org/locations/leonard_j_chabert_medical_center/

OCHSNER MEDICAL CENTER (O, 789 beds) 1514 Jefferson Highway, New Orleans, LA Zip 70121–2429; tel. 504/842–3000; Robert K. Wolterman, Chief Executive Officer
**Web address:** www.ochsner.org

OCHSNER MEDICAL CENTER – KENNER (O, 110 beds) 180 West Esplanade Avenue, Kenner, LA Zip 70065–6001; tel. 504/468–8600; Stephen Robinson, Chief Executive Officer
**Web address:** www.ochsner.org/locations/ochsner_health_center_kenner_w_esplanade_ave/

OCHSNER MEDICAL CENTER – NORTH SHORE (L, 110 beds) 100 Medical Center Drive, Slidell, LA Zip 70461–5520; tel. 985/649–7070; Bradley R. Goodson, Chief Executive Officer
**Web address:** www.ochsner.org/locations/northshore

OCHSNER MEDICAL CENTER–BATON ROUGE (O, 155 beds) 17000 Medical Center Drive, Baton Rouge, LA Zip 70816–3224; tel. 225/752–2470; Eric McMillen, Chief Executive Officer
**Web address:** www.ochsner.org/page.cfm?id=103

OCHSNER ST. ANNE GENERAL HOSPITAL (O, 35 beds) 4608 Highway 1, Raceland, LA Zip 70394–2623; tel. 985/537–6841; Timothy J. Allen, FACHE, Chief Executive Officer
**Web address:** www.ochsnerstanne.org

ST. CHARLES PARISH HOSPITAL (C, 59 beds) 1057 Paul Maillard Road, Luling, LA Zip 70070–4349, Mailing Address: P.O. Box 87, Zip 70070–0087; tel. 985/785–6242; Anthony DiGerolamo, R.N., MSN, Chief Executive Officer
**Web address:** www.ochsner.org/locations/st_charles_parish_hospital/

**MISSISSIPPI:** HANCOCK MEDICAL CENTER (C, 102 beds) 149 Drinkwater Boulevard, Bay Saint Louis, MS Zip 39520–1658, Mailing Address: 149 Drinkwater Road, Zip 39520–1658; tel. 228/467–8600; Alan Hodges, Chief Executive Officer
**Web address:** www.hmc.org

| | | |
|---|---|---|
| Owned, leased, sponsored: | 5 hospitals | 1199 beds |
| Contract–managed: | 3 hospitals | 233 beds |
| Totals: | 8 hospitals | 1432 beds |

---

**0388: OCONEE REGIONAL HEALTH SYSTEMS** (NP)
821 North Cobb Street, Milledgeville, GA Zip 31061–2343; tel. 478/454–3505; Jean Aycock, President and Chief Executive Officer
**(Independent Hospital System)**

For explanation of codes following names, see page B2.
★ Indicates Type III membership in the American Hospital Association.

**GEORGIA:** JASPER MEMORIAL HOSPITAL (O, 67 beds) 898 College Street, Monticello, GA Zip 31064–1258; tel. 706/468–6411; Jan Gaston, Administrator
**Web address:** www.jaspermemorialhospital.org

OCONEE REGIONAL MEDICAL CENTER (O, 90 beds) 821 North Cobb Street, Milledgeville, GA Zip 31061–2351, Mailing Address: P.O. Box 690, Zip 31059–0690; tel. 478/454–3505; RANDY HOOVER, Interim President and Chief Executive Officer
**Web address:** www.oconeeregional.com

| | | |
|---|---|---|
| Owned, leased, sponsored: | 2 hospitals | 157 beds |
| Contract–managed: | 0 hospitals | 0 beds |
| Totals: | 2 hospitals | 157 beds |

---

**0537: OHIO DEPARTMENT OF MENTAL HEALTH** (NP)
30 East Broad Street, 8th Floor, Columbus, OH Zip 43215–3430; tel. 614/466–2297; Tracy Plouck, Director
**(Independent Hospital System)**

**OHIO:** APPALACHIAN BEHAVIORAL HEALTHCARE (O, 224 beds) 100 Hospital Drive, Athens, OH Zip 45701–2301; tel. 740/594–5000; Jane E. Krason, R.N., Chief Executive Officer
**Web address:** www.mh.state.oh.us

HEARTLAND BEHAVIORAL HEALTHCARE (O, 130 beds) 3000 Erie Stree South, Massillon, OH Zip 44646–7993, Mailing Address: 3000 Erie Street South, Zip 44646–7976; tel. 330/833–3135; Jeffrey Sims, Chief Executive Officer
**Web address:** www.mh.state.oh.us/ibhs/bhos/hoh.html

NORTHCOAST BEHAVIORAL HEALTHCARE SYSTEM (O, 260 beds) 1756 Sagamore Road, Northfield, OH Zip 44067–1086; tel. 330/467–7131; Douglas W. Kern, Chief Executive Officer
**Web address:** www.mha.ohio.gov

NORTHWEST OHIO PSYCHIATRIC HOSPITAL (O, 114 beds) 930 Detroit Avenue, Toledo, OH Zip 43614–2701; tel. 419/381–1881; Mychail Scheramic, M.D., Chief Executive Officer
**Web address:** www.mh.state.oh.us/

SUMMIT BEHAVIORAL HEALTHCARE (O, 291 beds) 1101 Summit Road, Cincinnati, OH Zip 45237–2652; tel. 513/948–3600; Elizabeth Banks, Chief Executive Officer
**Web address:** www.mh.state.oh.us/

TWIN VALLEY BEHAVIORAL HEALTHCARE (O, 248 beds) 2200 West Broad Street, Columbus, OH Zip 43223–1297; tel. 614/752–0333; Veronica Lofton, Acting Chief Executive Officer
**Web address:** www.mh.state.oh.us/ibhs/bhos/tvbh.html

| | | |
|---|---|---|
| Owned, leased, sponsored: | 6 hospitals | 1267 beds |
| Contract–managed: | 0 hospitals | 0 beds |
| Totals: | 6 hospitals | 1267 beds |

---

**★0251: OHIO STATE UNIVERSITY HEALTH SYSTEM** (NP)
370 West Ninth Avenue, Columbus, OH Zip 43210–1238; tel. 614/685–9015; Peter E. Geier, Chief Executive Officer
**(Centralized Physician/Insurance Health System)**

JAMES CANCER HOSPITAL AND SOLOVE RESEARCH INSTITUTE (O, 236 beds) 300 West Tenth Avenue, Columbus, OH Zip 43210–1280; tel. 614/293–3300; Michael Caligiuri, Chief Executive Officer
**Web address:** www.jamesline.com

OHIO STATE UNIVERSITY WEXNER MEDICAL CENTER (O, 962 beds) 370 West 9th Avenue, Columbus, OH Zip 43210–1238; tel. 614/293–8000; Sheldon Retchin, M.D., Chief Executive Officer
**Web address:** www.medicalcenter.osu.edu

| | | |
|---|---|---|
| Owned, leased, sponsored: | 2 hospitals | 1198 beds |
| Contract–managed: | 0 hospitals | 0 beds |
| Totals: | 2 hospitals | 1198 beds |

---

**3315: OHIO VALLEY HEALTH SERVICES AND EDUCATION CORPORATION** (NP)
2000 Eoff Street, Wheeling, WV Zip 26003–3823; tel. 304/234–8383; Michael J. Caruso, President and Chief Executive Officer
**(Moderately Centralized Health System)**

EAST OHIO REGIONAL HOSPITAL (O, 139 beds) 90 North Fourth Street, Martins Ferry, OH Zip 43935–1648; tel. 740/633–1100; Michael J. Caruso, President and Chief Executive Officer
**Web address:** www.ovmc–eorh.com

**WEST VIRGINIA:** OHIO VALLEY MEDICAL CENTER (O, 189 beds) 2000 Eoff Street, Wheeling, WV Zip 26003–3870; tel. 304/234–0123; Michael J. Caruso, President and Chief Executive Officer
**Web address:** www.ovmc–eorh.com

| | | |
|---|---|---|
| Owned, leased, sponsored: | 2 hospitals | 328 beds |
| Contract–managed: | 0 hospitals | 0 beds |
| Totals: | 2 hospitals | 328 beds |

---

**★0162: OHIOHEALTH** (NP)
180 East Broad Street, Columbus, OH Zip 43215–3707; tel. 614/544–4455; David P. Blom, President and Chief Executive Officer
**(Centralized Physician/Insurance Health System)**

**OHIO:** MORROW COUNTY HOSPITAL (C, 22 beds) 651 West Marion Road, Mount Gilead, OH Zip 43338–1027; tel. 419/946–5015; Chad J. Miller, President and Chief Executive Officer
**Web address:** www.morrowcountyhospital.com

O'BLENESS MEMORIAL HOSPITAL (O, 64 beds) 55 Hospital Drive, Athens, OH Zip 45701–2302; tel. 740/593–5551; Mark R. Seckinger, President
**Web address:** www.obleness.org

OHIOHEALTH DOCTORS HOSPITAL (O, 243 beds) 5100 West Broad Street, Columbus, OH Zip 43228–1607; tel. 614/544–1000; Michael L. Reichfield, President
**Web address:** www.ohiohealth.com

OHIOHEALTH DUBLIN METHODIST HOSPITAL (O, 100 beds) 7500 Hospital Drive, Dublin, OH Zip 43016–8518; tel. 614/544–8000; Steve Bunyard, President
**Web address:** www.ohiohealth.com

OHIOHEALTH GRADY MEMORIAL HOSPITAL (O, 61 beds) 561 West Central Avenue, Delaware, OH Zip 43015–1410; tel. 740/615–1000; Steve Bunyard, President
**Web address:** www.ohiohealth.com

OHIOHEALTH GRANT MEDICAL CENTER (O, 427 beds) 111 South Grant Avenue, Columbus, OH Zip 43215–1898; tel. 614/566–9000; Michael Lawson, President and Chief Operating Officer
**Web address:** www.ohiohealth.com

OHIOHEALTH HARDIN MEMORIAL HOSPITAL (O, 25 beds) 921 East Franklin Street, Kenton, OH Zip 43326–2099; tel. 419/673–0761; Ron Snyder, Interim President and Chief Executive Officer
**Web address:** www.hardinmemorial.org

OHIOHEALTH MARION GENERAL HOSPITAL (O, 204 beds) 1000 McKinley Park Drive, Marion, OH Zip 43302–6397; tel. 740/383–8400; Bruce P. Hagen, President
**Web address:** www.ohiohealth.com/mariongeneral

OHIOHEALTH MEDCENTRAL MANSFIELD HOSPITAL (O, 232 beds) 335 Glessner Avenue, Mansfield, OH Zip 44903–2265; tel. 419/526–8000; Jean Halpin, President
**Web address:** www.medcentral.org

OHIOHEALTH MEDCENTRAL SHELBY HOSPITAL (O, 25 beds) 199 West Main Street, Shelby, OH Zip 44875–1490; tel. 419/342–5015; Jean Halpin, President
**Web address:** www.medcentral.org/body.cfm?id=153

---

For explanation of codes following names, see page B2.
★ Indicates Type III membership in the American Hospital Association.

OHIOHEALTH RIVERSIDE METHODIST HOSPITAL (O, 756 beds) 3535 Olentangy River Road, Columbus, OH Zip 43214–3998; tel. 614/566–5000; Brian Jepson, President
**Web address:** www.ohiohealth.com

| | | |
|---|---|---|
| **Owned, leased, sponsored:** | 10 hospitals | 2137 beds |
| **Contract–managed:** | 1 hospital | 22 beds |
| **Totals:** | 11 hospitals | 2159 beds |

**0018: OKLAHOMA DEPARTMENT OF MENTAL HEALTH AND SUBSTANCE ABUSE SERVICES** (NP)
1200 N.E. 13th Street, Oklahoma City, OK Zip 73117–1022, Mailing Address: P.O. Box 53277, Zip 73152–3277; tel. 405/522–3908; Terri White, Commissioner
**(Independent Hospital System)**

**OKLAHOMA:** GRIFFIN MEMORIAL HOSPITAL (O, 120 beds) 900 East Main Street, Norman, OK Zip 73071–5305, Mailing Address: P.O. Box 151, Zip 73070–0151; tel. 405/321–4880; Lori Jordan, Executive Director
**Web address:** www.odmhsas.org

NORTHWEST CENTER FOR BEHAVIORAL HEALTH (O, 28 beds) 1 Mi East Highway 270, Fort Supply, OK Zip 73841; tel. 580/766–2311; Trudy Hoffman, Executive Director
**Web address:** www.ncbhok.org/

OKLAHOMA FORENSIC CENTER (O, 200 beds) 24800 South 4420 Road, Vinita, OK Zip 74301–5544, Mailing Address: P.O. Box 69, Zip 74301–0069; tel. 918/256–7841; Kevan Finley, Chief Executive Officer
**Web address:** www.odmhsas.org

| | | |
|---|---|---|
| **Owned, leased, sponsored:** | 3 hospitals | 348 beds |
| **Contract–managed:** | 0 hospitals | 0 beds |
| **Totals:** | 3 hospitals | 348 beds |

**3355: ORLANDO HEALTH** (NP)
1414 Kuhl Avenue, Orlando, FL Zip 32806–2093; tel. 321/843–7000; David W. Strong, President and Chief Executive Officer
**(Centralized Physician/Insurance Health System)**

**FLORIDA:** HEALTH CENTRAL HOSPITAL (O, 399 beds) 10000 West Colonial Drive, Ocoee, FL Zip 34761–3499; tel. 407/296–1000; Gregory P. Ohe, President
**Web address:** www.healthcentral.org

ORLANDO REGIONAL MEDICAL CENTER (O, 1468 beds) 1414 Kuhl Avenue, Orlando, FL Zip 32806–2093; tel. 407/841–5111; Mark A. Jones, President
**Web address:** www.orlandohealth. com/facilities/orlando–regional–medical–center

SOUTH LAKE HOSPITAL (O, 122 beds) 1900 Don Wickham Drive, Clermont, FL Zip 34711–1979; tel. 352/394–4071; John Moore, President
**Web address:** www.southlakehospital.com

| | | |
|---|---|---|
| **Owned, leased, sponsored:** | 3 hospitals | 1989 beds |
| **Contract–managed:** | 0 hospitals | 0 beds |
| **Totals:** | 3 hospitals | 1989 beds |

**★5335: OSF HEALTHCARE SYSTEM** (CC)
800 N.E. Glen Oak Avenue, Peoria, IL Zip 61603–3200; tel. 309/655–2850; Kevin D. Schoeplein, Chief Executive Officer
**(Moderately Centralized Health System)**

**ILLINOIS:** OSF HOLY FAMILY MEDICAL CENTER (O, 23 beds) 1000 West Harlem Avenue, Monmouth, IL Zip 61462–1007; tel. 309/734–3141; Patricia A. Luker, President
**Web address:** www.osfholyfamily.org

OSF SAINT ANTHONY MEDICAL CENTER (O, 235 beds) 5666 East State Street, Rockford, IL Zip 61108–2425; tel. 815/226–2000; Paula A. Carynski, MS, R.N., President
**Web address:** www.osfhealth.com

OSF SAINT ANTHONY'S HEALTH CENTER (O, 203 beds) 1 Saint Anthony's Way, Alton, IL Zip 62002–4579, Mailing Address: PO Box 340, Zip 62002–0340; tel. 618/465–2571; Ajay Pathak, President
**Web address:** www.osfsaintanthonys.org

OSF SAINT ELIZABETH MEDICAL CENTER (O, 87 beds) 1100 East Norris Drive, Ottawa, IL Zip 61350–1687; tel. 815/433–3100; Kenneth Beutke, President
**Web address:** www.osfsaintelizabeth.org

OSF SAINT FRANCIS MEDICAL CENTER (O, 609 beds) 530 N.E. Glen Oak Avenue, Peoria, IL Zip 61637–0001; tel. 309/655–2000; Michael A. Cruz, M.D., President
**Web address:** www.osfsaintfrancis.org

OSF SAINT JAMES – JOHN W. ALBRECHT MEDICAL CENTER (O, 42 beds) 2500 West Reynolds, Pontiac, IL Zip 61764–9774; tel. 815/842–2828; Bradley V. Solberg, FACHE, President
**Web address:** www.osfsaintjames.org

OSF SAINT LUKE MEDICAL CENTER (O, 25 beds) 1051 West South Street, Kewanee, IL Zip 61443–8354, Mailing Address: P.O. Box 747, Zip 61443–0747; tel. 309/852–7500; Lynn Fulton, President
**Web address:** www.osfsaintluke.org

OSF ST. JOSEPH MEDICAL CENTER (O, 149 beds) 2200 East Washington Street, Bloomington, IL Zip 61701–4323; tel. 309/662–3311; Chad Boore, President
**Web address:** www.osfstjoseph.org

OSF ST. MARY MEDICAL CENTER (O, 81 beds) 3333 North Seminary Street, Galesburg, IL Zip 61401–1299; tel. 309/344–3161; Roxanna Crosser, President
**Web address:** www.osfstmary.org

**MICHIGAN:** OSF ST. FRANCIS HOSPITAL AND MEDICAL GROUP (O, 25 beds) 3401 Ludington Street, Escanaba, MI Zip 49829–1377; tel. 906/786–3311; David Lord, President
**Web address:** www.osfstfrancis.org

| | | |
|---|---|---|
| **Owned, leased, sponsored:** | 10 hospitals | 1479 beds |
| **Contract–managed:** | 0 hospitals | 0 beds |
| **Totals:** | 10 hospitals | 1479 beds |

**0367: PACER HEALTH CORPORATION** (IO)
14100 Palmetto Frontage Road, Suite 110, Miami Lakes, FL Zip 33016; tel. 305/828–7660; Rainier Gonzalez, Chairman and Chief Executive Officer

**KENTUCKY:** KNOX COUNTY HOSPITAL (O, 25 beds) 80 Hospital Drive, Barbourville, KY Zip 40906–7363, Mailing Address: P.O. Box 10, Zip 40906–0010; tel. 606/546–4175; Ray B. Canady, Chief Executive Officer and Administrator
**Web address:** www.knoxcohospital.com

**LOUISIANA:** CALCASIEU OAKS GERIATRIC PSYCHIATRIC HOSPITAL (O, 24 beds) 2837 Ernest Street, Lake Charles, LA Zip 70601–8785; tel. 337/439–8111; Charles Getwood, Assistant Chief Executive Officer

| | | |
|---|---|---|
| **Owned, leased, sponsored:** | 2 hospitals | 49 beds |
| **Contract–managed:** | 0 hospitals | 0 beds |
| **Totals:** | 2 hospitals | 49 beds |

**★5235: PALLOTTINE HEALTH SERVICES** (CC)
2900 First Avenue, Huntington, WV Zip 25702–1241; tel. 304/526–1234; Michael G. Sellards, Chief Executive Officer
**(Independent Hospital System)**

**WEST VIRGINIA:** ST. JOSEPH'S HOSPITAL OF BUCKHANNON (O, 51 beds) 1 Amalia Drive, Buckhannon, WV Zip 26201–2276; tel. 304/473–2000; Sue E. Johnson–Phillippe, FACHE, President and Chief Executive Officer
**Web address:** www.stj.net

ST. MARY'S MEDICAL CENTER (O, 393 beds) 2900 First Avenue, Huntington, WV Zip 25702–1272; tel. 304/526–1234; Michael G. Sellards, President and Chief Executive Officer
**Web address:** www.st–marys.org

| | | |
|---|---|---|
| **Owned, leased, sponsored:** | 2 hospitals | 444 beds |
| **Contract–managed:** | 0 hospitals | 0 beds |
| **Totals:** | 2 hospitals | 444 beds |

For explanation of codes following names, see page B2.
★ Indicates Type III membership in the American Hospital Association.

Section B

**★4155:  PALMETTO HEALTH** (NP)
1301 Taylor Street, Suite 9–A, Columbia, SC Zip 29201–2942,
Mailing Address: P.O. Box 2266, Zip 29202–2266;
tel. 803/296–2100; Charles D. Beaman, Jr., Chief Executive Officer
**(Moderately Centralized Health System)**

**SOUTH CAROLINA:** BAPTIST EASLEY HOSPITAL (O, 89 beds) 200 Fleetwood
Drive, Easley, SC Zip 29640–2022, Mailing Address: P.O. Box 2129,
Zip 29641–2129; tel. 864/442–7200; Michael Batchelor, Chief Executive
Officer
**Web address:** www.baptisteasley.org

PALMETTO HEALTH BAPTIST (O, 404 beds) Taylor at Marion Street,
Columbia, SC Zip 29220–0001; tel. 803/296–5010; Gregory B. Gattman,
Acute Care Executive
**Web address:** www.palmettohealth.org

PALMETTO HEALTH BAPTIST PARKRIDGE (O, 75 beds) 400 Palmetto Health
Parkway, Columbia, SC Zip 29212–1760, Mailing Address: P.O. BOX 2266,
Zip 29202–2266; tel. 803/907–7000; Sarah Kirby, R.N., MSN, FACHE,
Acute Care Executive
**Web address:** www.palmettohealth.org

PALMETTO HEALTH RICHLAND (O, 694 beds) Five Richland Medical Park
Drive, Columbia, SC Zip 29203–6897; tel. 803/434–7000; Jay Hamm, R.N.,
FACHE, Chief Acute Care Executive
**Web address:** www.palmettohealth.org

| Owned, leased, sponsored: | 4 hospitals | 1262 beds |
|---|---|---|
| Contract–managed: | 0 hospitals | 0 beds |
| Totals: | 4 hospitals | 1262 beds |

**★7555:  PALOMAR HEALTH** (NP)
456 East Grand Avenue, Escondido, CA Zip 92025–3319;
tel. 760/740–6393; Robert Hemker, President and Chief Executive
Officer
**(Moderately Centralized Health System)**

**CALIFORNIA:** PALOMAR MEDICAL CENTER (O, 287 beds) 2185 West
Citracado Parkway, Escondido, CA Zip 92029–4159; tel. 760/739–3000;
Mariellena Sudak, R.N., Interim Vice President and Chief Nursing Officer
**Web address:** www.palomarhealth.org

POMERADO HOSPITAL (O, 201 beds) 15615 Pomerado Road, Poway, CA
Zip 92064–2460; tel. 858/613–4000; Cheryl Olson, Chief Administrative
Officer
**Web address:** www.pph.org

| Owned, leased, sponsored: | 2 hospitals | 488 beds |
|---|---|---|
| Contract–managed: | 0 hospitals | 0 beds |
| Totals: | 2 hospitals | 488 beds |

**★0159:  PARKVIEW HEALTH** (NP)
10501 Corporate Drive, Fort Wayne, IN Zip 46845–1700;
tel. 260/373–7001; Michael J. Packnett, President and Chief
Executive Officer
**(Centralized Physician/Insurance Health System)**

**INDIANA:** PARKVIEW ORTHO HOSPITAL (O, 37 beds) 11130 Parkview Circle
Drive, Fort Wayne, IN Zip 46845–1735; tel. 260/672–5000; Julie Fleck,
Chief Operating Officer
**Web address:** www.parkview.com

PARKVIEW HUNTINGTON HOSPITAL (O, 36 beds) 2001 Stults Road,
Huntington, IN Zip 46750–1291; tel. 260/355–3000; Juli Johnson, R.N.,
President
**Web address:** www.parkview.com

PARKVIEW LAGRANGE HOSPITAL (O, 25 beds) 207 North Townline Road,
LaGrange, IN Zip 46761–1325; tel. 260/463–9000; Robert T. Myers,
President
**Web address:** www.parkview.com

PARKVIEW NOBLE HOSPITAL (O, 31 beds) 401 Sawyer Road, Kendallville, IN
Zip 46755–2568; tel. 260/347–8700; Gary W. Adkins, Chief Executive
Officer
**Web address:** www.parkview.com

PARKVIEW REGIONAL MEDICAL CENTER (O, 678 beds) 11109 Parkview Plaza
Drive, Fort Wayne, IN Zip 46845–1701; tel. 260/373–4000; Ben Miles,
President
**Web address:** www.parkview.com

PARKVIEW WABASH COUNTY HOSPITAL (O, 25 beds) 710 North East Street,
Wabash, IN Zip 46992–1924, Mailing Address: P.O. Box 548,
Zip 46992–0548; tel. 260/563–3131; Marilyn J. Custer–Mitchell, President
**Web address:** www.wchospital.org

PARKVIEW WHITLEY HOSPITAL (O, 97 beds) 1260 East State Road 205,
Columbia City, IN Zip 46725–9492; tel. 260/248–9000; Scott F. Gabriel,
President
**Web address:** www.parkview.com

| Owned, leased, sponsored: | 7 hospitals | 929 beds |
|---|---|---|
| Contract–managed: | 0 hospitals | 0 beds |
| Totals: | 7 hospitals | 929 beds |

**★1785:  PARTNERS HEALTHCARE SYSTEM, INC.** (NP)
800 Boylston Street, Suite 1150, Boston, MA Zip 02199–8123;
tel. 617/278–1004; David Torchiana, M.D., Chief Executive Officer
**(Moderately Centralized Health System)**

**MASSACHUSETTS:** BRIGHAM AND WOMEN'S FAULKNER HOSPITAL (O, 117
beds) 1153 Centre Street, Boston, MA Zip 02130–3446;
tel. 617/983–7000; Michael Gustafson, M.D., President
**Web address:** www.brighamandwomensfaulkner.org/index.asp

BRIGHAM AND WOMEN'S HOSPITAL (O, 757 beds) 75 Francis Street, Boston,
MA Zip 02115–6110; tel. 617/732–5500; Elizabeth Nabel, M.D., President
**Web address:** www.brighamandwomens.org

COOLEY DICKINSON HOSPITAL (O, 93 beds) 30 Locust Street, Northampton,
MA Zip 01060–2093, Mailing Address: P.O. Box 5001, Zip 01061–5001;
tel. 413/582–2000; Joanne Marqusee, President and Chief Executive Officer
**Web address:** www.cooley–dickinson.org

MARTHA'S VINEYARD HOSPITAL (O, 25 beds) One Hospital Road, Oak Bluffs,
MA Zip 2557, Mailing Address: P.O. Box 1477, Zip 02557–1477;
tel. 508/693–0410; Timothy J. Walsh, Chief Executive Officer
**Web address:** www.marthasvineyardhospital.org

MASSACHUSETTS GENERAL HOSPITAL (O, 999 beds) 55 Fruit Street,
Boston, MA Zip 02114–2696; tel. 617/726–2000; Peter L. Slavin, M.D.,
President
**Web address:** www.massgeneral.org

MCLEAN HOSPITAL (O, 177 beds) 115 Mill Street, Belmont, MA
Zip 02478–1064; tel. 617/855–2000; Scott L. Rauch, M.D., President
**Web address:** www.mclean.harvard.edu

NANTUCKET COTTAGE HOSPITAL (O, 19 beds) 57 Prospect Street,
Nantucket, MA Zip 02554–2799; tel. 508/825–8100; Margot Hartmann,
M.D., Ph.D., President and Chief Executive Officer
**Web address:** www.nantuckethospital.org

NEWTON–WELLESLEY HOSPITAL (O, 252 beds) 2014 Washington Street,
Newton Lower Falls, MA Zip 02462–1699; tel. 617/243–6000; Kerry
Watson, President
**Web address:** www.nwh.org

NORTH SHORE MEDICAL CENTER (O, 406 beds) 81 Highland Avenue, Salem,
MA Zip 01970–2714; tel. 978/741–1200; Robert G. Norton, President
**Web address:** www.nsmc.partners.org

SPAULDING HOSPITAL FOR CONTINUING MEDICAL CARE NORTH SHORE (O,
160 beds) 1 Dove Avenue, Salem, MA Zip 01970–2999; tel. 978/825–8900;
Maureen Banks, R.N., FACHE, President
**Web address:** www.shaughnessy–kaplan.org

SPAULDING HOSPITAL FOR CONTINUING MEDICAL CARE CAMBRIDGE (O, 180
beds) 1575 Cambridge Street, Cambridge, MA Zip 02138–4308;
tel. 617/876–4344; Maureen Banks, R.N., FACHE, President
**Web address:** www.spauldingnetwork.org

SPAULDING REHABILITATION HOSPITAL (O, 132 beds) 300 First Avenue,
Charlestown, MA Zip 02129–3109; tel. 617/573–7000; David E. Storto,
President
**Web address:** www.spauldingrehab.org

For explanation of codes following names, see page B2.
★ Indicates Type III membership in the American Hospital Association.

SPAULDING REHABILITATION HOSPITAL CAPE COD (O, 60 beds) 311 Service Road, East Sandwich, MA Zip 02537–1370; tel. 508/833–4000; Maureen Banks, R.N., FACHE, President
**Web address:** www.spauldingrehab.org

| | | |
|---|---|---|
| **Owned, leased, sponsored:** | 13 hospitals | 3377 beds |
| **Contract–managed:** | 0 hospitals | 0 beds |
| **Totals:** | 13 hospitals | 3377 beds |

---

**★5415:  PEACEHEALTH** (CC)
1115 S.E. 164th Avenue, Vancouver, WA Zip 98683; tel. 360/729–1000; Elizabeth Dunne, President and Chief Executive Officer
**(Moderately Centralized Health System)**

**ALASKA:** PEACEHEALTH KETCHIKAN MEDICAL CENTER (L, 54 beds) 3100 Tongass Avenue, Ketchikan, AK Zip 99901–5746; tel. 907/225–5171; Ken Tonjes, Interim Chief Administrative Officer
**Web address:** www.peacehealth.org

**OREGON:** PEACEHEALTH COTTAGE GROVE COMMUNITY MEDICAL CENTER (O, 14 beds) 1515 Village Drive, Cottage Grove, OR Zip 97424–9700; tel. 541/942–0511; Tim Herrmann, R.N., Administrator
**Web address:** www.peacehealth.org

PEACEHEALTH PEACE HARBOR MEDICAL CENTER (O, 21 beds) 400 Ninth Street, Florence, OR Zip 97439–7398; tel. 541/997–8412; Rick Yecny, Chief Executive Officer and Chief Mission Officer
**Web address:** www.peacehealth.org

PEACEHEALTH SACRED HEART MEDICAL CENTER AT RIVERBEND (O, 379 beds) 3333 Riverbend Drive, Springfield, OR Zip 97477–8800; tel. 541/222–7300; Rand O'Leary, Chief Administrative Officer
**Web address:** www.peacehealth.org

PEACEHEALTH SACRED HEART MEDICAL CENTER UNIVERSITY DISTRICT (O, 104 beds) 1255 Hilyard Street, Eugene, OR Zip 97401–3700, Mailing Address: P.O. Box 10905, Zip 97440–2905; tel. 541/686–7300; Rand O'Leary, Chief Executive Officer
**Web address:** www.peacehealth.org

**WASHINGTON:** PEACEHEALTH PEACE ISLAND MEDICAL CENTER (O, 10 beds) 1117 Spring Street, Friday Harbor, WA Zip 98250–9782; tel. 360/378–2141; James R. Barnhart, Chief Administrator Officer
**Web address:** www.peacehealth.org

PEACEHEALTH SOUTHWEST MEDICAL CENTER (O, 450 beds) 400 N.E. Mother Joseph Place, Vancouver, WA Zip 98664–3200, Mailing Address: P.O. Box 1600, Zip 98668–1600; tel. 360/256–2000; ,
**Web address:** www.swmedicalcenter.org

PEACEHEALTH ST. JOHN MEDICAL CENTER (O, 200 beds) 1615 Delaware Street, Longview, WA Zip 98632–2367, Mailing Address: P.O. Box 3002, Zip 98632–0302; tel. 360/414–2000; Kirk Raboin, Chief Administrative Officer
**Web address:** www.peacehealth.org

PEACEHEALTH ST. JOSEPH MEDICAL CENTER (O, 253 beds) 2901 Squalicum Parkway, Bellingham, WA Zip 98225–1851; tel. 360/734–5400; Nancy Steiger, R.N., FACHE, Chief Executive Officer and Chief Mission Officer, Northwest Network
**Web address:** www.peacehealth.org

PEACEHEALTH UNITED GENERAL MEDICAL CENTER (C, 25 beds) 2000 Hospital Drive, Sedro–Woolley, WA Zip 98284–4327; tel. 360/856–6021; James R. Barnhart, Chief Administrative Officer
**Web address:** www.peacehealth.org/united–general/Pages/default.aspx

| | | |
|---|---|---|
| **Owned, leased, sponsored:** | 9 hospitals | 1485 beds |
| **Contract–managed:** | 1 hospital | 25 beds |
| **Totals:** | 10 hospitals | 1510 beds |

---

**★0314:  PHOEBE PUTNEY HEALTH SYSTEM** (NP)
417 Third Avenue, Albany, GA Zip 31701–1943; tel. 229/312–1000; Joel Wernick, President and Chief Executive Officer
**(Independent Hospital System)**

**GEORGIA:** PHOEBE SUMTER MEDICAL CENTER (O, 45 beds) 126 Highway 280 West, Americus, GA Zip 31719; tel. 229/924–6011; Brandi Lunneborg, Chief Executive Officer
**Web address:** www.phoebesumter.org

PHOEBE WORTH MEDICAL CENTER (O, 25 beds) 807 South Isabella Street, Sylvester, GA Zip 31791–7554, Mailing Address: P.O. Box 545, Zip 31791–0545; tel. 229/776–6961; Kim Gilman, Chief Executive Officer
**Web address:** www.phoebeputney.com

SOUTHWEST GEORGIA REGIONAL MEDICAL CENTER (O, 105 beds) 361 Randolph Street, Cuthbert, GA Zip 39840–6127; tel. 229/732–2181; Kim Gilman, Chief Executive Officer and Chief Nursing Officer
**Web address:** www.phoebeputney.com/

| | | |
|---|---|---|
| **Owned, leased, sponsored:** | 3 hospitals | 175 beds |
| **Contract–managed:** | 0 hospitals | 0 beds |
| **Totals:** | 3 hospitals | 175 beds |

---

**0043:  PHYSICIANS FOR HEALTHY HOSPITALS** (IO)
1117 East Devonshire Avenue, Hemet, CA Zip 92543–3083; tel. 951/652–2811; Joel M. Bergenfeld, Chief Executive Officer

**CALIFORNIA:** HEMET VALLEY MEDICAL CENTER (O, 238 beds) 1117 East Devonshire Avenue, Hemet, CA Zip 92543–3083; tel. 951/652–2811; Joel M. Bergenfeld, Chief Hospital Executive Officer
**Web address:** www.physiciansforhealthyhospitals.com

MENIFEE VALLEY MEDICAL CENTER (O, 74 beds) 28400 McCall Boulevard, Sun City, CA Zip 92585–9537; tel. 951/679–8888; Joel M. Bergenfeld, Chief Hospital Executive Officer
**Web address:** www.valleyhealthsystem.com

| | | |
|---|---|---|
| **Owned, leased, sponsored:** | 2 hospitals | 312 beds |
| **Contract–managed:** | 0 hospitals | 0 beds |
| **Totals:** | 2 hospitals | 312 beds |

---

**★0310:  PIEDMONT HEALTHCARE** (NP)
1800 Howell Mill Road N.W., Suite 850, Atlanta, GA Zip 30318–0923; tel. 404/425–1314; Kevin Brown, President and Chief Executive Officer
**(Independent Hospital System)**

**GEORGIA:** PIEDMONT FAYETTE HOSPITAL (O, 172 beds) 1255 Highway 54 West, Fayetteville, GA Zip 30214–4526; tel. 770/719–7000; Michael Burnett, Chief Executive Officer
**Web address:** www.piedmont.org

PIEDMONT HENRY HOSPITAL (L, 214 beds) 1133 Eagle's Landing Parkway, Stockbridge, GA Zip 30281–5099; tel. 678/604–1000; Charles F. Scott, President and Chief Executive Officer
**Web address:** www.piedmonthenry.org

PIEDMONT HOSPITAL (O, 510 beds) 1968 Peachtree Road N.W., Atlanta, GA Zip 30309–1281; tel. 404/605–5000; Leslie A. Donahue, President and Chief Executive Officer
**Web address:** www.piedmonthospital.org

PIEDMONT MOUNTAINSIDE HOSPITAL (O, 52 beds) 1266 Highway 515 South, Jasper, GA Zip 30143–4872; tel. 706/692–2441; Denise Ray, President and Chief Executive Officer
**Web address:** www.piedmontmountainsidehospital.org

PIEDMONT NEWNAN HOSPITAL (O, 130 beds) 745 Poplar Road, Newnan, GA Zip 30265–1618; tel. 770/400–1000; Michael Robertson, Chief Executive Officer
**Web address:** www.piedmontnewnan.org

| | | |
|---|---|---|
| **Owned, leased, sponsored:** | 5 hospitals | 1078 beds |
| **Contract–managed:** | 0 hospitals | 0 beds |
| **Totals:** | 5 hospitals | 1078 beds |

---

**★0958:  PIH HEALTH** (NP)
12401 Washington Boulevard, Whittier, CA Zip 90602–1006; tel. 562/698–0811; James R. West, President and Chief Executive Officer

**CALIFORNIA:** PIH HEALTH HOSPITAL – DOWNEY (O, 192 beds) 11500 Brookshire Avenue, Downey, CA Zip 90241–4917; tel. 562/904–5000; James R. West, President and Chief Executive Officer
**Web address:** www.PIHHealth.org

For explanation of codes following names, see page B2.
★ Indicates Type III membership in the American Hospital Association.

PIH HEALTH HOSPITAL–WHITTIER (O, 242 beds) 12401 Washington Boulevard, Whittier, CA Zip 90602–1099; tel. 562/698–0811; James R. West, President and Chief Executive Officer
**Web address:** www.PIHHealth.org

| | | |
|---|---|---|
| Owned, leased, sponsored: | 2 hospitals | 434 beds |
| Contract–managed: | 0 hospitals | 0 beds |
| Totals: | 2 hospitals | 434 beds |

---

**★0326:  PIONEER HEALTH SERVICES** (IO)
110 Pioneer Way, Magee, MS Zip 39111–5501, Mailing Address: P.O. Box 1100, Zip 39111–1100; tel. 601/849–6440; Joseph S. McNulty, III, President and Chief Executive Officer
**(Independent Hospital System)**

**GEORGIA:** PIONEER COMMUNITY HOSPITAL OF EARLY (L, 25 beds) 11740 Columbia Street, Blakely, GA Zip 39823–2574; tel. 229/723–4241; Allen J. Gamble, Chief Executive Officer
**Web address:** www.pchearly.com

**MISSISSIPPI:** LACKEY MEMORIAL HOSPITAL (C, 55 beds) 330 Broad Street, Forest, MS Zip 39074–3508, Mailing Address: P.O. Box 428, Zip 39074–0428; tel. 601/469–4151; Steve Widener, Interim Chief Executive Officer
**Web address:** www.lackeymemorialhospital.com

PIONEER COMMUNITY HOSPITAL OF ABERDEEN (L, 35 beds) 400 South Chestnut Street, Aberdeen, MS Zip 39730–3335, Mailing Address: P.O. Box 548, Zip 39730–0548; tel. 662/369–2455; Christopher Chandler, Chief Executive Officer
**Web address:** www.pchaberdeen.com

PIONEER COMMUNITY HOSPITAL OF NEWTON (O, 30 beds) 9421 Eastside Drive, Newton, MS Zip 39345–8063; tel. 601/683–2031; Mark Norman, Administrator
**Web address:** www.pchnewton.com

**NORTH CAROLINA:** PIONEER COMMUNITY HOSPITAL OF STOKES (L, 25 beds) 1570 Highway 8 and 89 North, Danbury, NC Zip 27016, Mailing Address: P.O. Box 10, Zip 27016–0010; tel. 336/593–2831; Pamela P. Tillman, R.N., Chief Executive Officer
**Web address:** www.pchstokes.com

**VIRGINIA:** PIONEER COMMUNITY HOSPITAL OF PATRICK (O, 25 beds) 18688 Jeb Stuart Highway, Stuart, VA Zip 24171–1559; tel. 276/694–3151; Jeanette Filpi, Chief Executive Officer
**Web address:** www.pchpatrick.com

| | | |
|---|---|---|
| Owned, leased, sponsored: | 5 hospitals | 140 beds |
| Contract–managed: | 1 hospital | 55 beds |
| Totals: | 6 hospitals | 195 beds |

---

**0899:  POLARIS HOSPITAL COMPANY** (IO)
10 Cadillac Drive, Suite 470, Brentwood, TN Zip 37027–1045; tel. 615/577–1111; Kevin D. Lee, Director and Chief Executive Officer
**(Independent Hospital System)**

**TENNESSEE:** TRUSTPOINT HOSPITAL (O, 60 beds) 1009 North Thompson Lane, Murfreesboro, TN Zip 37129–4351; tel. 615/867–1111; Jeffrey Woods, Chief Executive Officer
**Web address:** www.trustpointhospital.com

**TEXAS:** TRUSTPOINT HOSPITAL (O, 67 beds) 4302 Princeton Street, Lubbock, TX Zip 79415–1304; tel. 806/749–2222; Craig Bragg, Chief Executive Officer
**Web address:** www.trustpointhospital.com/

| | | |
|---|---|---|
| Owned, leased, sponsored: | 2 hospitals | 127 beds |
| Contract–managed: | 0 hospitals | 0 beds |
| Totals: | 2 hospitals | 127 beds |

---

**★0617:  POST ACUTE MEDICAL, LLC** (IO)
1828 Good Hope Road, Suite 102, Enola, PA Zip 17025–1233; tel. 717/731–9660; Anthony F. Misitano, President and Chief Executive Officer
**(Independent Hospital System)**

**LOUISIANA:** POST ACUTE MEDICAL SPECIALTY HOSPITAL OF LAFAYETTE (O, 50 beds) 204 Energy Parkway, Lafayette, LA Zip 70508–3816; tel. 337/232–1905; Brian Holt, Chief Executive Officer
**Web address:** www.postacutemedical.com

POST ACUTE NORTHSHORE SPECIALTY HOSPITAL (O, 58 beds) 20050 Crestwood Boulevard, Covington, LA Zip 70433–5207; tel. 985/875–7525; Stephanie Morvant, Chief Executive Officer
**Web address:** www.northshoreltach.com

POST ACUTE SPECIALTY HOSPITAL OF HAMMOND (O, 40 beds) 42074 Veterans Avenue, Hammond, LA Zip 70403–1408; tel. 985/902–8148; Jerry Elenbaas, Administrator
**Web address:** www.warmsprings.org/locations/hos/h2/

**OKLAHOMA:** POST ACUTE MEDICAL SPECIALTY HOSPITAL OF TULSA (O, 60 beds) 3219 South 79th East Avenue, Tulsa, OK Zip 74145–1343; tel. 918/663–8183; Lee A. Simpson, Jr., Chief Executive Officer
**Web address:** www.postacutetulsa.com

**TEXAS:** POST ACUTE MEDICAL SPECIALTY HOSPITAL OF CORPUS CHRISTI (O, 22 beds) 600 Elizabeth Street, 3rd Floor, Corpus Christi, TX Zip 78404–2235; tel. 361/881–3223; Hector Bernal, Chief Executive Officer
**Web address:** www.postacutemedical.com/our-facilities/hospitals/post-acute–medical–specialty–hospital–corpus–christi/

POST ACUTE MEDICAL SPECIALTY HOSPITAL OF CORPUS CHRISTI (O, 74 beds) 6226 Saratoga Boulevard, Corpus Christi, TX Zip 78414–3421; tel. 361/986–1600; Michael L. Pierce, Chief Executive Officer
**Web address:** www.postacutemedical.com

POST ACUTE MEDICAL SPECIALTY HOSPITAL OF TEXARKANA (O, 49 beds) 2400 St. Michael Drive, 2nd Floor, Texarkana, TX Zip 75503–2372; tel. 903/614–7600; Holly Powell, Administrator
**Web address:** www.postacutemedical.com

POST ACUTE MEDICAL SPECIALTY HOSPITAL OF VICTORIA (O, 23 beds) 506 East San Antonio Street, 3rd Floor, Victoria, TX Zip 77901–6060; tel. 361/575–1445; Portlyn Brogger, Chief Executive Officer
**Web address:** www.khvictoria.com

POST ACUTE/WARM SPRINGS REHABILITATION HOSPITAL OF ALLEN (O, 39 beds) 1001 Raintree Circle, Allen, TX Zip 75013–4912; tel. 972/908–2015; Bill Kaupas, Chief Executive Officer
**Web address:** www.warmsprings.org

POST ACUTE/WARM SPRINGS REHABILITATION HOSPITAL OF SAN ANTONIO (O, 138 beds) 5101 Medical Drive, San Antonio, TX Zip 78229–4801; tel. 210/616–0100; Kasondra Kistner, Chief Executive Officer
**Web address:** www.postacutemedical.com/our-facilities/hospitals/warm–springs–rehabilitation–hospital–san–antonio/

POST ACUTE/WARM SPRINGS SPECIALTY HOSPITAL OF LULING (O, 34 beds) 200 Memorial Drive, Luling, TX Zip 78648–3213; tel. 830/875–8400; Jana Kuykendall, Chief Executive Officer
**Web address:** www.warmsprings.org

POST ACUTE/WARM SPRINGS SPECIALTY HOSPITAL OF NEW BRAUNFELS (O, 40 beds) 1445 Hanz Drive, New Braunfels, TX Zip 78130–2567; tel. 830/627–7600; Shayne Goode, Administrator
**Web address:** www.warmsprings.org/locations/hos/h1/

POST ACUTE/WARM SPRINGS SPECIALTY HOSPITAL OF SAN ANTONIO (O, 26 beds) 7400 Barlite Boulevard, 2nd Floor, San Antonio, TX Zip 78224–1308; tel. 210/921–3550; Karen Pitcher, Chief Executive Officer and Vice President
**Web address:** www.postacutemedical.com

POST ACUTE/WARM SPRINGS SPECIALTY HOSPITAL OF VICTORIA (O, 26 beds) 102 Medical Drive, Victoria, TX Zip 77904–3101; tel. 361/576–6200; Portlyn Brogger, Chief Executive Officer
**Web address:** www.warmsprings.org

**WISCONSIN:** POST ACUTE MEDICAL SPECIALTY HOSPITAL OF MILWAUKEE (O, 56 beds) 5017 South 110Th Street, Greenfield, WI Zip 53228–3131; tel. 414/427–8282; Christine Ninu, Chief Executive Officer
**Web address:** www.postacutemedical.com/

| | | |
|---|---|---|
| Owned, leased, sponsored: | 15 hospitals | 735 beds |
| Contract–managed: | 0 hospitals | 0 beds |
| Totals: | 15 hospitals | 735 beds |

---

For explanation of codes following names, see page B2.
★ Indicates Type III membership in the American Hospital Association.

Section B

**0240: PREFERRED MANAGEMENT CORPORATION** (IO)
120 West MacArthur, Suite 121, Shawnee, OK Zip 74804–2005;
tel. 405/878–0202; Donald Freeman, President and Chief Executive
Officer
**(Independent Hospital System)**

**TEXAS:** COLEMAN COUNTY MEDICAL CENTER (L, 25 beds) 310 South Pecos
Street, Coleman, TX Zip 76834–4159; tel. 325/625–2135; Michael W.
Pruitt, Administrator and Chief Executive Officer
**Web address:** www.colemantexas.org/hospital.html

COLLINGSWORTH GENERAL HOSPITAL (L, 13 beds) 1013 15th Street,
Wellington, TX Zip 79095–3703, Mailing Address: P.O. Box 1112,
Zip 79095–1112; tel. 806/447–2521; Candy Powell, Administrator
**Web address:** www.collingsworthgeneral.net

CULBERSON HOSPITAL (L, 14 beds) Eisenhower–Farm Market Road 2185,
Van Horn, TX Zip 79855, Mailing Address: P.O. Box 609, Zip 79855–0609;
tel. 432/283–2760; Jared Chanski, Administrator
**Web address:** www.culbersonhospital.org

KIMBLE HOSPITAL (O, 15 beds) 349 Reid Road, Junction, TX
Zip 76849–3049; tel. 325/446–3321; Steve Bowen, Administrator
**Web address:** www.kimblehospital.org/

PARMER MEDICAL CENTER (C, 15 beds) 1307 Cleveland Avenue, Friona, TX
Zip 79035–1121; tel. 806/250–2754; Gayla Quillin, Administrator
**Web address:** www.parmermedicalcenter.com

SABINE COUNTY HOSPITAL (L, 25 beds) 2301 Worth Street, Hemphill, TX
Zip 75948–7216, Mailing Address: P.O. Box 750, Zip 75948–0750;
tel. 409/787–3300; Diana Taylor, Administrator
**Web address:** www.sabinecountyhospital.com/

SCHLEICHER COUNTY MEDICAL CENTER (L, 14 beds) 400 West Murchison,
Eldorado, TX Zip 76936, Mailing Address: P.O. Box V., Zip 76936–1246;
tel. 325/853–2507; Paul Burke, Administrator
**Web address:** www.scmc.us

| | | |
|---|---|---|
| **Owned, leased, sponsored:** | 6 hospitals | 106 beds |
| **Contract–managed:** | 1 hospital | 15 beds |
| **Totals:** | 7 hospitals | 121 beds |

---

**0977: PREMIER HEALTH** (NP)
110 North Main Street Suite 390, Dayton, OH Zip 45402–3720;
tel. 937/499–9401; James R. Pancoast, President and Chief
Executive Officer

**OHIO:** ATRIUM MEDICAL CENTER (O, 302 beds) One Medical Center Drive,
Middletown, OH Zip 45005–1066; tel. 513/424–2111; Carol Turner,
President and Chief Executive Officer
**Web address:** www.atriummedcenter.org

GOOD SAMARITAN HOSPITAL (O, 346 beds) 2222 Philadelphia Drive, Dayton,
OH Zip 45406–1813; tel. 937/734–2612; Eloise Broner, President and Chief
Executive Officer
**Web address:** www.goodsamdayton.com

MIAMI VALLEY HOSPITAL (O, 870 beds) One Wyoming Street, Dayton, OH
Zip 45409–2793; tel. 937/208–8000; Mark S. Shaker, President and Chief
Executive Officer
**Web address:** www.miamivalleyhospital.org

UPPER VALLEY MEDICAL CENTER (O, 168 beds) 3130 North County Road
25A, Troy, OH Zip 45373–1309; tel. 937/440–4000; Thomas Parker, Chief
Executive Officer
**Web address:** www.uvmc.com

| | | |
|---|---|---|
| **Owned, leased, sponsored:** | 4 hospitals | 1686 beds |
| **Contract–managed:** | 0 hospitals | 0 beds |
| **Totals:** | 4 hospitals | 1686 beds |

---

**★3505: PRESBYTERIAN HEALTHCARE SERVICES** (NP)
2501 Buena Vista Drive, S.E., Albuquerque, NM Zip 87106–4260,
Mailing Address: P.O. Box 26666, Zip 87125–6666;
tel. 505/841–1234; James H. Hinton, President and Chief Executive
Officer
**(Centralized Physician/Insurance Health System)**

**NEW MEXICO:** DR. DAN C. TRIGG MEMORIAL HOSPITAL (L, 10 beds) 301
East Miel De Luna Avenue, Tucumcari, NM Zip 88401–3810, Mailing
Address: P.O. Box 608, Zip 88401–0608; tel. 575/461–7000; Lance C.
Labine, Administrator
**Web address:** www.phs.org

LINCOLN COUNTY MEDICAL CENTER (L, 25 beds) 211 Sudderth Drive,
Ruidoso, NM Zip 88345–6043, Mailing Address: P.O. Box 8000,
Zip 88355–8000; tel. 575/257–8200; Alfred Santos, Administrator
**Web address:** www.phs.org

PLAINS REGIONAL MEDICAL CENTER (O, 50 beds) 2100 Martin Luther King
Boulevard, Clovis, NM Zip 88101–9412, Mailing Address: P.O. Box 1688,
Zip 88102–1688; tel. 575/769–2141; Vincent B. DiFranco, Chief Executive
Officer
**Web address:** www.phs.org

PRESBYTERIAN ESPANOLA HOSPITAL (O, 42 beds) 1010 Spruce Street,
Espanola, NM Zip 87532–2746; tel. 505/753–7111; Brenda Romero,
Administrator
**Web address:** www.phs.org

PRESBYTERIAN HOSPITAL (O, 409 beds) 1100 Central Avenue S.E.,
Albuquerque, NM Zip 87106–4934, Mailing Address: P.O. Box 26666,
Zip 87125–6666; tel. 505/841–1234; Sandra C. Podley, Administrator
**Web address:** www.phs.org

PRESBYTERIAN KASEMAN HOSPITAL (O, 90 beds) 8300 Constitution Avenue
N.E., Albuquerque, NM Zip 87110–7624, Mailing Address: P.O. Box 26666,
Zip 87125–6666; tel. 505/291–2000; Doyle Boykin, R.N., MSN,
Administrator
**Web address:** www.phs.org

SOCORRO GENERAL HOSPITAL (O, 14 beds) 1202 Highway 60 West,
Socorro, NM Zip 87801–3914, Mailing Address: P.O. Box 1009,
Zip 87801–1009; tel. 505/835–1140; Veronica Pound, R.N., Administrator
**Web address:** www.phs.org

| | | |
|---|---|---|
| **Owned, leased, sponsored:** | 7 hospitals | 640 beds |
| **Contract–managed:** | 0 hospitals | 0 beds |
| **Totals:** | 7 hospitals | 640 beds |

---

**★0851: PRESENCE HEALTH** (CC)
200 South Wacker Drive, Chicago, IL Zip 60606–5829;
tel. 312/308–3200; Sandra B. Bruce, FACHE, President and Chief
Executive Officer
**(Moderately Centralized Health System)**

**ILLINOIS:** PRESENCE COVENANT MEDICAL CENTER (O, 181 beds) 1400
West Park Street, Urbana, IL Zip 61801–2396; tel. 217/337–2000; Jared
Rogers, M.D., Interim Regional President and Chief Executive Officer
**Web address:** www.provena.org/covenant

PRESENCE HOLY FAMILY MEDICAL CENTER (O, 128 beds) 100 North River
Road, Des Plaines, IL Zip 60016–1255; tel. 847/297–1800; Yolande
Wilson–Stubbs, Regional Chief Operating Officer
**Web address:** www.presencehealth.org

PRESENCE MERCY MEDICAL CENTER (O, 170 beds) 1325 North Highland
Avenue, Aurora, IL Zip 60506–1449; tel. 630/859–2222; Michael L. Brown,
Regional President and Chief Executive Officer
**Web address:** www.provena.org/mercy/

PRESENCE RESURRECTION MEDICAL CENTER (O, 199 beds) 7435 West
Talcott Avenue, Chicago, IL Zip 60631–3746; tel. 773/774–8000; Lowell W.
Johnson, LFACHE, Chief Executive Officer
**Web address:** www.presencehealth.org

PRESENCE SAINT FRANCIS HOSPITAL (O, 192 beds) 355 Ridge Avenue,
Evanston, IL Zip 60202–3399; tel. 847/316–4000; Roberta Luskin–Hawk,
M.D., Chief Executive Officer
**Web address:** www.reshealth.org

PRESENCE SAINT JOSEPH HOSPITAL (O, 310 beds) 2900 North Lake Shore
Drive, Chicago, IL Zip 60657–6274; tel. 773/665–3000; Roberta
Luskin–Hawk, M.D., President and Chief Executive Officer
**Web address:** www.reshealth.org

PRESENCE SAINT JOSEPH HOSPITAL (O, 184 beds) 77 North Airlite Street,
Elgin, IL Zip 60123–4912; tel. 847/695–3200; Michael L. Brown, Regional
President and Chief Executive Officer
**Web address:** www.provena.org

Section B

PRESENCE SAINT JOSEPH MEDICAL CENTER (O, 443 beds) 333 North Madison Street, Joliet, IL Zip 60435–8200; tel. 815/725–7133; Kathleen Rhine, Regional President and Chief Executive Officer
**Web address:** www.provena.org/stjoes

PRESENCE SAINTS MARY & ELIZABETH MEDICAL CENTER (O, 476 beds) 2233 West Division Street, Chicago, IL Zip 60622–3086; tel. 312/770–2000; Martin H. Judd, Regional President and Chief Executive Officer
**Web address:** www.presencehealth. org/presence–saints–mary–and–elizabeth–medical–center–chicago

PRESENCE ST. MARY'S HOSPITAL (O, 156 beds) 500 West Court Street, Kankakee, IL Zip 60901–3661; tel. 815/937–2400; Kathleen Rhine, Regional President and Chief Executive Officer
**Web address:** www.provena.org/stmarys/

PRESENCE UNITED SAMARITANS MEDICAL CENTER (O, 117 beds) 812 North Logan, Danville, IL Zip 61832–3788; tel. 217/443–5000; Jared Rogers, M.D., Interim Regional President and Chief Executive Officer
**Web address:** www.provena.org/usmc

| | | |
|---|---|---|
| **Owned, leased, sponsored:** | 11 hospitals | 2556 beds |
| **Contract–managed:** | 0 hospitals | 0 beds |
| **Totals:** | 11 hospitals | 2556 beds |

---

**0357: PRIME HEALTHCARE SERVICES** (IO)
3300 East Guasti Road, Ontario, CA Zip 91761–8655; tel. 909/235–4400; Prem Reddy, M.D., Interim President and Chief Executive Officer
**(Moderately Centralized Health System)**

**ALABAMA:** RIVERVIEW REGIONAL MEDICAL CENTER (O, 175 beds) 600 South Third Street, Gadsden, AL Zip 35901–5399; tel. 256/543–5200; Thomas Roddy, Interim Chief Executive Officer
**Web address:** www.riverviewregional.com

**CALIFORNIA:** ALVARADO HOSPITAL MEDICAL CENTER (O, 83 beds) 6655 Alvarado Road, San Diego, CA Zip 92120–5208; tel. 619/287–3270; Robin Gomez, R.N., MSN, Administrator
**Web address:** www.alvaradohospital.com

CENTINELA HOSPITAL MEDICAL CENTER (O, 353 beds) 555 East Hardy Street, Inglewood, CA Zip 90301–4011, Mailing Address: P.O. Box 720, Zip 90312–6720; tel. 310/673–4660; Linda Bradley, Chief Executive Officer
**Web address:** www.centinelamed.com

CHINO VALLEY MEDICAL CENTER (O, 112 beds) 5451 Walnut Avenue, Chino, CA Zip 91710–2672; tel. 909/464–8600; James M. Lally, D.O., President and Chief Medical Officer
**Web address:** www.cvmc.com

DESERT VALLEY HOSPITAL (O, 110 beds) 16850 Bear Valley Road, Victorville, CA Zip 92395–5795; tel. 760/241–8000; Fred Hunter, R.N., Chief Executive Officer
**Web address:** www.dvmc.com

ENCINO HOSPITAL MEDICAL CENTER (O, 66 beds) 16237 Ventura Boulevard, Encino, CA Zip 91436–2272; tel. 818/995–5000; Bockhi Park, Chief Executive Officer
**Web address:** www.encinomed.com

GARDEN GROVE HOSPITAL AND MEDICAL CENTER (O, 167 beds) 12601 Garden Grove Boulevard, Garden Grove, CA Zip 92843–1959; tel. 714/537–5160; Edward Mirzabegian, Chief Executive Officer
**Web address:** www.gardengrovehospital.com

HUNTINGTON BEACH HOSPITAL (O, 131 beds) 17772 Beach Boulevard, Huntington Beach, CA Zip 92647–6896; tel. 714/843–5000; Kevan Metcalfe, Chief Executive Officer
**Web address:** www.hbhospital.com

LA PALMA INTERCOMMUNITY HOSPITAL (O, 141 beds) 7901 Walker Street, La Palma, CA Zip 90623–1764; tel. 714/670–7400; Virgis Narbutas, Chief Executive Officer
**Web address:** www.lapalmaintercommunityhospital.com

MONTCLAIR HOSPITAL MEDICAL CENTER (O, 102 beds) 5000 San Bernardino Street, Montclair, CA Zip 91763–2326; tel. 909/625–5411; Gregory Brentano, Chief Executive Officer
**Web address:** www.montclair–hospital.com

PARADISE VALLEY HOSPITAL (O, 205 beds) 2400 East Fourth Street, National City, CA Zip 91950–2099; tel. 619/470–4321; Neerav Jadeja, Administrator
**Web address:** www.paradisevalleyhospital.org

SAN DIMAS COMMUNITY HOSPITAL (O, 101 beds) 1350 West Covina Boulevard, San Dimas, CA Zip 91773–3219; tel. 909/599–6811; Gregory Brentano, Chief Executive Officer
**Web address:** www.sandimashospital.com/

SHASTA REGIONAL MEDICAL CENTER (O, 120 beds) 1100 Butte Street, Redding, CA Zip 96001–0853, Mailing Address: P.O. Box 496072, Zip 96049–6072; tel. 530/244–5400; Cynthia Gordon, R.N., Chief Executive Officer
**Web address:** www.shastaregional.com

SHERMAN OAKS HOSPITAL (O, 91 beds) 4929 Van Nuys Boulevard, Sherman Oaks, CA Zip 91403–1777; tel. 818/981–7111; Bockhi Park, Chief Executive Officer
**Web address:** www.shermanoakshospital.com

WEST ANAHEIM MEDICAL CENTER (O, 219 beds) 3033 West Orange Avenue, Anaheim, CA Zip 92804–3183; tel. 714/827–3000; Virgis Narbutas, Chief Executive Officer
**Web address:** www.westanaheimmedctr.com

**INDIANA:** MONROE HOSPITAL (O, 32 beds) 5811 East Slick Rock lane, Bloomfield, IN Zip 47424, Mailing Address: 4011 South Monroe Medical Park Boulevard, Bloomington, Zip 47403–8000; tel. 812/825–1111; Phillip W. Lowe, Chief Executive Officer
**Web address:** www.monroehospital.com

**KANSAS:** PROVIDENCE MEDICAL CENTER (O, 162 beds) 8929 Parallel Parkway, Kansas City, KS Zip 66112–1689; tel. 913/596–4000; Randall G. Nyp, FACHE, Chief Executive Officer
**Web address:** www.providencekc.com

SAINT JOHN HOSPITAL (O, 40 beds) 3500 South Fourth Street, Leavenworth, KS Zip 66048–5043; tel. 913/680–6000; Randall G. Nyp, FACHE, President and Chief Executive Officer
**Web address:** www.providence–health.org/sjh

**MICHIGAN:** GARDEN CITY HOSPITAL (O, 170 beds) 6245 Inkster Road, Garden City, MI Zip 48135–4001; tel. 734/421–3300; Saju George, Chief Executive Officer
**Web address:** www.gch.org

ST. JOSEPH MERCY PORT HURON (O, 119 beds) 2601 Electric Avenue, Port Huron, MI Zip 48060–6518; tel. 810/985–1500; Rebekah Smith, R.N., President and Chief Executive Officer
**Web address:** www.mymercy.us

**MISSOURI:** ST. JOSEPH MEDICAL CENTER (O, 187 beds) 1000 Carondelet Drive, Kansas City, MO Zip 64114–4673; tel. 816/942–4400; Robert J. Erickson, Chief Executive Officer
**Web address:** www.carondelethealth.org

ST. MARY'S MEDICAL CENTER (O, 90 beds) 201 West R. D. Mize Road, Blue Springs, MO Zip 64014–2518; tel. 816/228–5900; Debra Ohnoutka, Chief Executive Officer
**Web address:** www.carondelethealth.org

**NEVADA:** SAINT MARY'S REGIONAL MEDICAL CENTER (O, 272 beds) 235 West Sixth Street, Reno, NV Zip 89503–4548; tel. 775/770–3000; Helen Lidholm, Chief Executive Officer
**Web address:** www.saintmarysreno.org

**NEW JERSEY:** ST. MARY'S GENERAL HOSPITAL (O, 221 beds) 350 Boulevard, Passaic, NJ Zip 07055–2840; tel. 973/365–4300; Edward Condit, President and Chief Executive Officer
**Web address:** www.smh–passaic.org

**PENNSYLVANIA:** LOWER BUCKS HOSPITAL (O, 150 beds) 501 Bath Road, Bristol, PA Zip 19007–3190; tel. 215/785–9200; Peter J. Adamo, Chief Executive Officer
**Web address:** www.lowerbuckshosp.com

ROXBOROUGH MEMORIAL HOSPITAL (O, 140 beds) 5800 Ridge Avenue, Philadelphia, PA Zip 19128–1737; tel. 215/483–9900; Peter J. Adamo, Chief Executive Officer
**Web address:** www.roxboroughmemorial.com

**RHODE ISLAND:** LANDMARK MEDICAL CENTER (O, 140 beds) 115 Cass Avenue, Woonsocket, RI Zip 02895–4731; tel. 401/769–4100; Richard Charest, President
**Web address:** www.landmarkmedical.org

Section B

REHABILITATION HOSPITAL OF RHODE ISLAND (O, 40 beds) 116 Eddie Dowling Highway, North Smithfield, RI Zip 02896–7327; tel. 401/766–0800; Richard Charest, Chief Executive Officer
**Web address:** www.rhri.net

**TEXAS:** DALLAS MEDICAL CENTER (O, 83 beds) Seven Medical Parkway, Dallas, TX Zip 75234–7823, Mailing Address: P.O. Box 819094, Zip 75381–9094; tel. 972/247–1000; Raji Kumar, Chief Executive Officer
**Web address:** www.dallasmedcenter.com

DALLAS REGIONAL MEDICAL CENTER (O, 100 beds) 1011 North Galloway Avenue, Mesquite, TX Zip 75149–2433; tel. 214/320–7000; Raji Kumar, Regional Chief Executive Officer
**Web address:** www.dallasregionalmedicalcenter.com

HARLINGEN MEDICAL CENTER (O, 88 beds) 5501 South Expressway 77, Harlingen, TX Zip 78550–3213; tel. 956/365–1000; Brenda Ivory, Chief Executive Officer
**Web address:** www.harlingenmedicalcenter.com

KNAPP MEDICAL CENTER (O, 192 beds) 1401 East Eighth Street, Weslaco, TX Zip 78596–6640, Mailing Address: P.O. Box 1110, Zip 78599–1110; tel. 956/968–8567; William D. Adams, Chief Executive Officer
**Web address:** www.knappmed.org

PAMPA REGIONAL MEDICAL CENTER (O, 72 beds) One Medical Plaza, Pampa, TX Zip 79065; tel. 806/665–3721; Brad S. Morse, Chief Executive Officer
**Web address:** www.prmctx.com

| | | |
|---|---|---|
| **Owned, leased, sponsored:** | 33 hospitals | 4474 beds |
| **Contract–managed:** | 0 hospitals | 0 beds |
| **Totals:** | 33 hospitals | 4474 beds |

---

**★0153: PROHEALTH CARE, INC.** (NP)
N17 W24100 Riverwood Drive, Suite 130, Waukesha, WI Zip 53188; tel. 262/928–2242; Susan A. Edwards, President and Chief Executive Officer
**(Centralized Health System)**

**WISCONSIN:** OCONOMOWOC MEMORIAL HOSPITAL (O, 58 beds) 791 Summit Avenue, Oconomowoc, WI Zip 53066–3896; tel. 262/569–9400; John R. Robertstad, FACHE, President
**Web address:** www.prohealthcare.org/locations/locations–v2–detail/?id= 1123

WAUKESHA MEMORIAL HOSPITAL (O, 287 beds) 725 American Avenue, Waukesha, WI Zip 53188–5099; tel. 262/928–1000; John R. Robertstad, FACHE, President
**Web address:** www.prohealthcare.org/locations/locations–v2–detail/?id= 1119

| | | |
|---|---|---|
| **Owned, leased, sponsored:** | 2 hospitals | 345 beds |
| **Contract–managed:** | 0 hospitals | 0 beds |
| **Totals:** | 2 hospitals | 345 beds |

---

**★0197: PROMEDICA HEALTH SYSTEM** (NP)
1801 Richards Road, Toledo, OH Zip 43607–1037; tel. 419/469–3800; Randall D. Oostra, FACHE, President and Chief Executive Officer
**(Centralized Physician/Insurance Health System)**

**MICHIGAN:** PROMEDICA BIXBY HOSPITAL (O, 66 beds) 818 Riverside Avenue, Adrian, MI Zip 49221–1446; tel. 517/265–0900; Julie Yaroch, D.O., President
**Web address:** www.promedica.org

PROMEDICA HERRICK HOSPITAL (O, 60 beds) 500 East Pottawatamie Street, Tecumseh, MI Zip 49286–2018; tel. 517/424–3000; Julie Yaroch, D.O., President
**Web address:** www.promedica.org

PROMEDICA MONROE REGIONAL HOSPITAL (O, 179 beds) 718 North Macomb Street, Monroe, MI Zip 48162–7815; tel. 734/240–8400; Annette S. Phillips, President and Chief Executive Officer
**Web address:** www.mercymemorial.org

**OHIO:** PROMEDICA BAY PARK HOSPITAL (O, 77 beds) 2801 Bay Park Drive, Oregon, OH Zip 43616–4920; tel. 419/690–7900; Holly L. Bristoll, President
**Web address:** www.promedica.org

PROMEDICA DEFIANCE REGIONAL HOSPITAL (O, 35 beds) 1200 Ralston Avenue, Defiance, OH Zip 43512–1396; tel. 419/783–6955; Julie Yaroch, D.O., Interim President
**Web address:** www.promedica.org

PROMEDICA FLOWER HOSPITAL (O, 273 beds) 5200 Harroun Road, Sylvania, OH Zip 43560–2196; tel. 419/824–1444; Neeraj Kanwal, M.D., President
**Web address:** www.promedica.org

PROMEDICA FOSTORIA COMMUNITY HOSPITAL (O, 25 beds) 501 Van Buren Street, Fostoria, OH Zip 44830–1534, Mailing Address: P.O. Box 907, Zip 44830–0907; tel. 419/435–7734; Holly L. Bristoll, President
**Web address:** www.promedica.org

PROMEDICA ST. LUKE'S HOSPITAL (O, 172 beds) 5901 Monclova Road, Maumee, OH Zip 43537–1899; tel. 419/893–5911; Daniel L. Wakeman, President
**Web address:** www.stlukeshospital.com

PROMEDICA TOLEDO HOSPITAL (O, 649 beds) 2142 North Cove Boulevard, Toledo, OH Zip 43606–3896; tel. 419/291–4000; Arturo Polizzi, President
**Web address:** www.promedica.org

| | | |
|---|---|---|
| **Owned, leased, sponsored:** | 9 hospitals | 1536 beds |
| **Contract–managed:** | 0 hospitals | 0 beds |
| **Totals:** | 9 hospitals | 1536 beds |

---

**0230: PROMISE HEALTHCARE** (IO)
999 Yamato Road, 3rd Floor, Boca Raton, FL Zip 33431–4477; tel. 561/869–3100; Peter R. Baronoff, Chief Executive Officer
**(Independent Hospital System)**

**ARIZONA:** PROMISE HOSPITAL OF PHOENIX (L, 40 beds) 433 East 6th Street, Mesa, AZ Zip 85203–7104; tel. 480/427–3000; Scott Floden, Chief Executive Officer
**Web address:** www.promise–phoenix.com

**CALIFORNIA:** PROMISE HOSPITAL OF EAST LOS ANGELES (L, 199 beds) 443 South Soto Street, Los Angeles, CA Zip 90033–4398; tel. 323/261–1181; Michael D. Kerr, Chief Executive Officer
**Web address:** www.promiseeastla.com

PROMISE HOSPITAL OF SAN DIEGO (O, 100 beds) 5550 University Avenue, San Diego, CA Zip 92105–2307; tel. 619/582–3800; Chuck Smith, Interim Chief Executive Officer
**Web address:** www.promisesandiego.com

**FLORIDA:** PROMISE HOSPITAL OF FLORIDA AT THE VILLAGES (O, 40 beds) 5050 County Road, Oxford, FL Zip 34484; tel. 352/689–6400; Hoyt Ross, Chief Executive Officer
**Web address:** www.promise–villages.com

PROMISE HOSPITAL OF FORT MYERS (O, 60 beds) 3050 Champion Ring Road, Fort Myers, FL Zip 33905–5599; tel. 239/313–2900; Patrick G. Ryan, Chief Executive Officer
**Web address:** www.promisefortmyers.om

PROMISE HOSPITAL OF MIAMI (O, 60 beds) 14001 N.W. 82nd Avenue, Miami, FL Zip 33158; tel. 786/609–9200; Theodore L. Welding, Chief Executive Officer
**Web address:** www.promise–miami.com

**KANSAS:** PROMISE HOSPITAL OF OVERLAND PARK (O, 104 beds) 6509 West 103rd Street, Overland Park, KS Zip 66212–1728; tel. 913/649–3701; Karen Leverich, Chief Executive Officer
**Web address:** www.promise–overlandpark.com

**LOUISIANA:** PROMISE HOSPITAL BATON ROUGE – MAIN CAMPUS (L, 54 beds) 5130 Mancuso Lane, Baton Rouge, LA Zip 70809–3583; tel. 225/490–9600; Kiley P. Cedotal, Chief Executive Officer
**Web address:** www.promise–batonrouge.com

PROMISE HOSPITAL OF BATON ROUGE – MID–CITY CAMPUS (O, 57 beds) 3600 Florida Boulevard, 4th Floor, Baton Rouge, LA Zip 70806–3842; tel. 225/387–7770; Michael R. Sanders, MS, Administrator and Chief Operating Officer
**Web address:** www.promise–batonrougemidcity.com

PROMISE HOSPITAL OF BATON ROUGE – OCHSNER CAMPUS (O, 29 beds) 17000 Medical Center Drive, 3rd Floor, Baton Rouge, LA Zip 70816–3246; tel. 225/236–5440; Michael R. Sanders, MS, Administrator and Chief Operating Officer
**Web address:** www.promise–batonrougeochsner.com

---

For explanation of codes following names, see page B2.
★ Indicates Type III membership in the American Hospital Association.

PROMISE HOSPITAL OF LOUISIANA – SHREVEPORT CAMPUS (O, 146 beds) 1800 Irving Place, Shreveport, LA Zip 71101–4608; tel. 318/425–4096; Rick Stockton, Chief Executive Officer
**Web address:** www.promise–shreveport.com

PROMISE HOSPITAL OF MISS LOU (O, 40 beds) 209 Front Street, Vidalia, LA Zip 71373–2837; tel. 318/336–6500; Benny Costello, Chief Executive Officer
**Web address:** www.promise–misslou.com

**MISSISSIPPI:** PROMISE HOSPITAL OF VICKSBURG (L, 33 beds) 1111 North Frontage Road, 2nd Floor, Vicksburg, MS Zip 39180–5102; tel. 601/619–3526; Michael Harrell, Chief Executive Officer
**Web address:** www.promise–vicksburg.com

**TEXAS:** PROMISE HOSPITAL OF DALLAS (O, 62 beds) 7955 Harry Hines Boulevard, Dallas, TX Zip 75235–3305; tel. 214/637–0000; Mary Alexander, Interim Chief Executive Officer
**Web address:** www.promise–dallas.com/

PROMISE HOSPITAL OF HOUSTON (O, 35 beds) 6160 South Loop East, Houston, TX Zip 77087–1010; tel. 713/640–2400; Tom Omondi, Interim Chief Executive Officer
**Web address:** www.promise–houston.com

PROMISE HOSPITAL OF WICHITA FALLS (O, 31 beds) 1103 Grace Street, Wichita Falls, TX Zip 76301–4414; tel. 940/720–6633; Delnita Bray, Administrator
**Web address:** www.promise–wichitafalls.com

**UTAH:** PROMISE HOSPITAL OF SALT LAKE (O, 32 beds) 8 Avenue, C. Street, Salt Lake City, UT Zip 84143; tel. 801/408–7110; Wayne Kinsey, Chief Executive Officer
**Web address:** www.promise–saltlake.com

| | | |
|---|---|---|
| Owned, leased, sponsored: | 17 hospitals | 1122 beds |
| Contract–managed: | 0 hospitals | 0 beds |
| Totals: | 17 hospitals | 1122 beds |

---

★**0344: PROVIDENCE HEALTH & SERVICES** (CC) 1801 Lind Avenue S.W., 9016, Renton, WA Zip 98057–9016; tel. 425/525–3698; Rodney F. Hochman, M.D., President and Chief Executive Officer
**(Decentralized Health System)**

**ALASKA:** PROVIDENCE ALASKA MEDICAL CENTER (O, 401 beds) 3200 Providence Drive, Anchorage, AK Zip 99508–4615, Mailing Address: P.O. Box 196604, Zip 99519–6604; tel. 907/562–2211; Richard Mandsager, M.D., Executive Officer
**Web address:** www.providence.org/alaska/pamc/default.htm

PROVIDENCE KODIAK ISLAND MEDICAL CENTER (L, 25 beds) 1915 East Rezanof Drive, Kodiak, AK Zip 99615–6602; tel. 907/486–3281; Barbara Bigelow, Administrator
**Web address:** www.providence.org

PROVIDENCE SEWARD MEDICAL CENTER (L, 46 beds) 417 First Avenue, Seward, AK Zip 99664, Mailing Address: P.O. Box 365, Zip 99664–0365; tel. 907/224–5205; Joseph Fong, Administrator
**Web address:** www.providence.org

PROVIDENCE VALDEZ MEDICAL CENTER (C, 21 beds) 911 Meals Avenue, Valdez, AK Zip 99686–0550, Mailing Address: P.O. Box 550, Zip 99686–0550; tel. 907/835–2249; Barbara Bigelow, Administrator
**Web address:** www.providence.org/alaska

**CALIFORNIA:** PROVIDENCE HOLY CROSS MEDICAL CENTER (O, 377 beds) 15031 Rinaldi Street, Mission Hills, CA Zip 91345–1207; tel. 818/365–8051; Bernard Klein, M.D., Chief Executive
**Web address:** www.https://california.providence.org/holy–cross/Pages/default.aspx

PROVIDENCE LITTLE COMPANY OF MARY MEDICAL CENTER – TORRANCE (O, 376 beds) 4101 Torrance Boulevard, Torrance, CA Zip 90503–4664; tel. 310/540–7676; Elizabeth Dunne, Chief Executive
**Web address:** www.lcmweb.org

PROVIDENCE LITTLE COMPANY OF MARY MEDICAL CENTER SAN PEDRO (O, 307 beds) 1300 West Seventh Street, San Pedro, CA Zip 90732–3505; tel. 310/832–3311; Mary Kingston, Chief Executive Officer
**Web address:** www.https://california.providence.org/san–pedro

PROVIDENCE SAINT JOSEPH MEDICAL CENTER (O, 383 beds) 501 South Buena Vista Street, Burbank, CA Zip 91505–4866; tel. 818/843–5111; Julie Sprengel, Chief Executive Officer
**Web address:** www.providence.org

PROVIDENCE TARZANA MEDICAL CENTER (O, 249 beds) 18321 Clark Street, Tarzana, CA Zip 91356–3521; tel. 818/881–0800; Dale Surowitz, Chief Executive
**Web address:** www.providence.org/tarzana.com

SAINT JOHN'S HEALTH CENTER (O, 234 beds) 2121 Santa Monica Boulevard, Santa Monica, CA Zip 90404–2091; tel. 310/829–5511; Marcel C. Loh, FACHE, Chief Executive Officer
**Web address:** www.newstjohns.org/home.aspx

**MONTANA:** COMMUNITY HOSPITAL OF ANACONDA (C, 87 beds) 401 West Pennsylvania Street, Anaconda, MT Zip 59711; tel. 406/563–8500; Steve McNeece, Chief Executive Officer
**Web address:** www.communityhospitalofanaconda.org

PROVIDENCE ST. JOSEPH MEDICAL CENTER (S, 22 beds) 6 Thirteenth Avenue East, Polson, MT Zip 59860–5315, Mailing Address: P.O. Box 1010, Zip 59860–1010; tel. 406/883–5377; James R. Kiser, II, Chief Executive Officer
**Web address:** www.saintjoes.org

ST. PATRICK HOSPITAL (S, 193 beds) 500 West Broadway, Missoula, MT Zip 59802–4096, Mailing Address: P.O. Box 4587, Zip 59806–4587; tel. 406/543–7271; Jeff Fee, Chief Executive Officer
**Web address:** www.saintpatrick.org

**OREGON:** PROVIDENCE HOOD RIVER MEMORIAL HOSPITAL (O, 25 beds) 810 12th Street, Hood River, OR Zip 97031–1587, Mailing Address: P.O. Box 149, Zip 97031–0055; tel. 541/386–3911; Edward E. Freysinger, Chief Executive Officer
**Web address:** www.providence.org/hoodriver

PROVIDENCE MEDFORD MEDICAL CENTER (O, 142 beds) 1111 Crater Lake Avenue, Medford, OR Zip 97504–6241; tel. 541/732–5000; Cindy Mayo, R.N., FACHE, Chief Executive Officer
**Web address:** www.providence.org

PROVIDENCE MILWAUKIE HOSPITAL (O, 51 beds) 10150 S.E. 32nd Avenue, Milwaukie, OR Zip 97222–6516; tel. 503/513–8300; Keith Hyde, Chief Executive Officer
**Web address:** www.providence.org

PROVIDENCE NEWBERG MEDICAL CENTER (O, 40 beds) 1001 Providence Drive, Newberg, OR Zip 97132–7485; tel. 503/537–1555; Lorinda Van Zanten, MSN, Chief Executive Officer
**Web address:** www.phsor.org

PROVIDENCE PORTLAND MEDICAL CENTER (O, 417 beds) 4805 N.E. Glisan Street, Portland, OR Zip 97213–2933; tel. 503/215–5526; Paul Gaden, Chief Executive Officer
**Web address:** www.providence.org

PROVIDENCE SEASIDE HOSPITAL (L, 25 beds) 725 South Wahanna Road, Seaside, OR Zip 97138–7735; tel. 503/717–7000; Debbie Glass, Interim Chief Executive Officer
**Web address:** www.providence.org

PROVIDENCE ST. VINCENT MEDICAL CENTER (O, 552 beds) 9205 S.W. Barnes Road, Portland, OR Zip 97225–6661; tel. 503/216–1234; Janice Burger, Chief Executive
**Web address:** www.providence.org/portland/hospitals

PROVIDENCE WILLAMETTE FALLS MEDICAL CENTER (O, 111 beds) 1500 Division Street, Oregon City, OR Zip 97045–1597; tel. 503/656–1631; Russ Reinhard, Chief Executive
**Web address:** www.providence.org/pwfmc

**WASHINGTON:** KADLEC REGIONAL MEDICAL CENTER (O, 254 beds) 888 Swift Boulevard, Richland, WA Zip 99352–3514; tel. 509/946–4611; Rand J. Wortman, President and Chief Executive Officer
**Web address:** www.kadlecmed.org

PROVIDENCE CENTRALIA HOSPITAL (O, 91 beds) 914 South Scheuber Road, Centralia, WA Zip 98531–9027; tel. 360/736–2803; Medrice Coluccio, R.N., Southwest Region Chief Executive
**Web address:** www.providence.org

PROVIDENCE HOLY FAMILY HOSPITAL (S, 191 beds) 5633 North Lidgerwood Street, Spokane, WA Zip 99208–1224; tel. 509/482–0111; Alex Jackson, Chief Executive
**Web address:** www.providence.org

**Section B**

---

For explanation of codes following names, see page B2.
★ Indicates Type III membership in the American Hospital Association.

PROVIDENCE MOUNT CARMEL HOSPITAL (S, 25 beds) 982 East Columbia Avenue, Colville, WA Zip 99114–3352; tel. 509/685–5100; Ronald G. Rehn, Chief Executive Officer
**Web address:** www.mtcarmelhospital.org

PROVIDENCE REGIONAL MEDICAL CENTER EVERETT (O, 501 beds) 1321 Colby Avenue, Everett, WA Zip 98201–1665, Mailing Address: P.O. Box 1147, Zip 98206–1147; tel. 425/261–2000; Preston M. Simmons, FACHE, Chief Executive Officer
**Web address:** www.providence.org

PROVIDENCE SACRED HEART MEDICAL CENTER & CHILDREN'S HOSPITAL (S, 668 beds) 101 West Eighth Avenue, Spokane, WA Zip 99204–2364, Mailing Address: P.O. Box 2555, Zip 99220–2555; tel. 509/474–3131; Alex Jackson, Chief Executive
**Web address:** www.shmc.org

PROVIDENCE ST. JOSEPH'S HOSPITAL (S, 65 beds) 500 East Webster Street, Chewelah, WA Zip 99109–9523; tel. 509/935–8211; Ronald G. Rehn, Chief Executive Officer
**Web address:** www.washington.providence.org/hospitals/st-josephs–hospital/

PROVIDENCE ST. MARY MEDICAL CENTER (S, 80 beds) 401 West Poplar Street, Walla Walla, WA Zip 99362–2846, Mailing Address: P.O. Box 1477, Zip 99362–0312; tel. 509/525–3320; Steven A. Burdick, Chief Executive Officer
**Web address:** www.washington.providence.org/hospitals/st-mary/

PROVIDENCE ST. PETER HOSPITAL (O, 347 beds) 413 Lilly Road N.E., Olympia, WA Zip 98506–5166; tel. 360/491–9480; Medrice Coluccio, R.N., Chief Executive Officer
**Web address:** www.providence.org/swsa/facilities/st_peter_hospital

ST. LUKE'S REHABILITATION INSTITUTE (O, 72 beds) 711 South Cowley Street, Spokane, WA Zip 99202–1388; tel. 509/473–6000; Nancy Vorhees, Chief Administrative Officer
**Web address:** www.st-lukes.org

SWEDISH MEDICAL CENTER–CHERRY HILL CAMPUS (O, 198 beds) 500 17th Avenue, Seattle, WA Zip 98122–5711; tel. 206/320–2000; June Altaras, R.N., Chief Executive Officer
**Web address:** www.swedish.org

SWEDISH MEDICAL CENTER–FIRST HILL (O, 631 beds) 747 Broadway, Seattle, WA Zip 98122–4307; tel. 206/386–6000; June Altaras, R.N., Chief Executive Officer
**Web address:** www.swedish.org

SWEDISH/EDMONDS (O, 164 beds) 21601 76th Avenue West, Edmonds, WA Zip 98026–7506; tel. 425/640–4000; Jennifer Graves, R.N., MS, Chief Executive
**Web address:** www.swedish.org

SWEDISH/ISSAQUAH (O, 80 beds) 751 N.E. Blakely Drive, Issaquah, WA Zip 98029–6201; tel. 425/313–4000; Rayburn Lewis, M.D., Chief Executive Officer
**Web address:** www.swedish.org/issaquah

WHITMAN HOSPITAL AND MEDICAL CENTER (C, 25 beds) 1200 West Fairview Street, Colfax, WA Zip 99111–9579; tel. 509/397–3435; Hank Hanigan, Administrator and Chief Executive Officer
**Web address:** www.whitmanhospital.com

| | | |
|---|---|---|
| Owned, leased, sponsored: | 33 hospitals | 7343 beds |
| Contract–managed: | 3 hospitals | 133 beds |
| **Totals:** | 36 hospitals | 7476 beds |

---

**★0011: PUERTO RICO DEPARTMENT OF HEALTH** (NP)
Building A – Medical Center, San Juan, PR Zip 00936, Mailing Address: Call Box 70184, Zip 00936; tel. 787/765–2929; Ana Rius, M.D., Secretary of Health
**(Independent Hospital System)**

**PUERTO RICO:** CARDIOVASCULAR CENTER OF PUERTO RICO AND THE CARIBBEAN (O, 146 beds) Americo Miranda Centro Medico, San Juan, PR Zip 936, Mailing Address: P.O. Box 366528, Zip 00936–6528; tel. 787/754–8500; Waleska Crespo, Executive Director
**Web address:** www.cardiovascular.gobierno.pr

HOSPITAL UNIVERSITARIO DR. RAMON RUIZ ARNAU (O, 101 beds) Avenue Laurel, Santa Juanita, Bayamon, PR Zip 956; tel. 787/787–5151; Humberto M. Monserrate, Chief Executive Officer

UNIVERSITY HOSPITAL (O, 262 beds) Nineyas 869 Rio Piedras, San Juan, PR Zip 922, Mailing Address: P.O. Box 2116, Zip 922; tel. 787/754–0101; Jorge Matta Gonzalez, Executive Director

UNIVERSITY PEDIATRIC HOSPITAL (O, 145 beds) Barrio Monacenno, Carretera 22, Rio Piedras, PR Zip 935, Mailing Address: P.O. Box 191079, San Juan, Zip 00910–1070; tel. 787/777–3535; Gloria Hernandez, Executive Director
**Web address:** www.md.rcm.upr.edu/pediatrics/university_pediatric_hospital.php

| | | |
|---|---|---|
| Owned, leased, sponsored: | 4 hospitals | 654 beds |
| Contract–managed: | 0 hospitals | 0 beds |
| **Totals:** | 4 hospitals | 654 beds |

---

**★0002: QHR** (IO)
105 Continental Place, Brentwood, TN Zip 37027–1052; tel. 800/233–1470; Mickey Bilbrey, President and Chief Executive Officer
**(Decentralized Health System)**

**ARKANSAS:** GREAT RIVER MEDICAL CENTER (C, 73 beds) 1520 North Division Street, Blytheville, AR Zip 72315–1448, Mailing Address: P.O. Box 108, Zip 72316–0108; tel. 870/838–7300; Ralph E. Beaty, Chief Executive Officer
**Web address:** www.mchsys.org

SOUTH MISSISSIPPI COUNTY REGIONAL MEDICAL CENTER (C, 25 beds) 611 West Lee Avenue, Osceola, AR Zip 72370–3001, Mailing Address: P.O. Box 108, Blytheville, Zip 72316–0108; tel. 870/563–7000; Ralph E. Beaty, Chief Executive Officer
**Web address:** www.mchsys.org

**COLORADO:** ARKANSAS VALLEY REGIONAL MEDICAL CENTER (C, 163 beds) 1100 Carson Avenue, La Junta, CO Zip 81050–2799; tel. 719/383–6000; Lynn Crowell, Chief Executive Officer
**Web address:** www.avrmc.org

COMMUNITY HOSPITAL (C, 42 beds) 2021 North 12th Street, Grand Junction, CO Zip 81501–2999; tel. 970/242–0920; Chris Thomas, FACHE, President and Chief Executive Officer
**Web address:** www.yourcommunityhospital.com

MONTROSE MEMORIAL HOSPITAL (C, 69 beds) 800 South Third Street, Montrose, CO Zip 81401–4212; tel. 970/249–2211; Steven Hannah, Chief Executive Officer
**Web address:** www.montrosehospital.com

PIONEERS MEDICAL CENTER (C, 40 beds) 345 Cleveland Street, Meeker, CO Zip 81641–3238; tel. 970/878–5047; Kenneth Harman, Chief Executive Officer
**Web address:** www.pioneershospital.org

PROWERS MEDICAL CENTER (C, 25 beds) 401 Kendall Drive, Lamar, CO Zip 81052–3993; tel. 719/336–4343; Craig Loveless, Chief Executive Officer
**Web address:** www.prowersmedical.com

THE MEMORIAL HOSPITAL AT CRAIG (C, 25 beds) 750 Hospital Loop, Craig, CO Zip 81625–8750; tel. 970/824–9411; John Rossfeld, Chief Executive Officer
**Web address:** www.thememorialhospital.com

**FLORIDA:** FISHERMEN'S HOSPITAL (C, 25 beds) 3301 Overseas Highway, Marathon, FL Zip 33050–2329; tel. 305/743–5533; Hal W. Leftwich, FACHE, Chief Executive Officer
**Web address:** www.fishermenshospital.org

HENDRY REGIONAL MEDICAL CENTER (C, 25 beds) 524 West Sagamore Avenue, Clewiston, FL Zip 33440–3514; tel. 863/902–3000; R. D. Williams, Chief Executive Officer
**Web address:** www.hendryregional.org

JACKSON HOSPITAL (C, 68 beds) 4250 Hospital Drive, Marianna, FL Zip 32446–1917, Mailing Address: P.O. Box 1608, Zip 32447–5608; tel. 850/526–2200; Larry Meese, Chief Executive Officer
**Web address:** www.jacksonhosp.com

**IDAHO:** GRITMAN MEDICAL CENTER (C, 25 beds) 700 South Main Street, Moscow, ID Zip 83843–3056; tel. 208/882–4511; Kara Besst, President and Chief Executive Officer
**Web address:** www.gritman.org

---

For explanation of codes following names, see page B2.
★ Indicates Type III membership in the American Hospital Association.

STEELE MEMORIAL MEDICAL CENTER (C, 18 beds) 203 South Daisy Street, Salmon, ID Zip 83467–4709; tel. 208/756–5600; Jeff Hill, Chief Executive Officer
**Web address:** www.steelemh.org

**ILLINOIS:** CRAWFORD MEMORIAL HOSPITAL (C, 63 beds) 1000 North Allen Street, Robinson, IL Zip 62454–1167; tel. 618/544–3131; Donald E. Annis, Chief Executive Officer
**Web address:** www.crawfordmh.org

LAWRENCE COUNTY MEMORIAL HOSPITAL (C, 25 beds) 2200 West State Street, Lawrenceville, IL Zip 62439–1852; tel. 618/943–1000; Doug Florkowski, Chief Executive Officer
**Web address:** www.lcmhosp.org

PEKIN HOSPITAL (C, 125 beds) 600 South 13th Street, Pekin, IL Zip 61554–4936; tel. 309/347–1151; Bob J. Haley, Chief Executive Officer
**Web address:** www.pekinhospital.org

**INDIANA:** DAVIESS COMMUNITY HOSPITAL (C, 48 beds) 1314 East Walnut Street, Washington, IN Zip 47501–2860, Mailing Address: P.O. Box 760, Zip 47501–0760; tel. 812/254–2760; David Bixler, Chief Executive Officer
**Web address:** www.dchosp.org

SULLIVAN COUNTY COMMUNITY HOSPITAL (C, 25 beds) 2200 North Section Street, Sullivan, IN Zip 47882–7523, Mailing Address: P.O. Box 10, Zip 47882–0010; tel. 812/268–4311; Michelle Franklin, Chief Executive Officer
**Web address:** www.schosp.com

**IOWA:** BOONE COUNTY HOSPITAL (C, 39 beds) 1015 Union Street, Boone, IA Zip 50036–4821; tel. 515/432–3140; Joseph S. Smith, Chief Executive Officer
**Web address:** www.boonehospital.com

FORT MADISON COMMUNITY HOSPITAL (C, 50 beds) 5445 Avenue O, Fort Madison, IA Zip 52627–9611, Mailing Address: P.O. Box 174, Zip 52627–0174; tel. 319/372–6530; C. James Platt, Chief Executive Officer
**Web address:** www.fmchosp.com

**KANSAS:** GREELEY COUNTY HEALTH SERVICES (C, 50 beds) 506 Third Street, Tribune, KS Zip 67879–9684, Mailing Address: P.O. Box 338, Zip 67879–0338; tel. 620/376–4221; Lee Rhodes, Administrator and Chief Executive Officer
**Web address:** www.mygchs.com

NEOSHO MEMORIAL REGIONAL MEDICAL CENTER (C, 25 beds) 629 South Plummer, Chanute, KS Zip 66720–1928, Mailing Address: P.O. Box 426, Zip 66720–0426; tel. 620/431–4000; Dennis Franks, FACHE, Chief Executive Officer
**Web address:** www.nmrmc.com

ST. LUKE HOSPITAL AND LIVING CENTER (C, 37 beds) 535 South Freeborn, Marion, KS Zip 66861–1256; tel. 620/382–2177; Jeremy Ensey, Chief Executive Officer
**Web address:** www.slhmarion.org

WILSON MEDICAL CENTER (C, 15 beds) 2600 Ottawa Road, Neodesha, KS Zip 66757–1897, Mailing Address: P.O. Box 360, Zip 66757–0360; tel. 620/325–2611; Dennis R. Shelby, Chief Executive Officer
**Web address:** www.wilsonmedical.org

**KENTUCKY:** CALDWELL MEDICAL CENTER (C, 25 beds) 100 Medical Center Drive, Princeton, KY Zip 42445–2430, Mailing Address: P.O. Box 410, Zip 42445–0410; tel. 270/365–0300; Charles D. Lovell, Jr., FACHE, President and Chief Executive Officer
**Web address:** www.caldwellhosp.org

JENNIE STUART MEDICAL CENTER (C, 139 beds) 320 West 18th Street, Hopkinsville, KY Zip 42240–1965, Mailing Address: P.O. Box 2400, Zip 42241–2400; tel. 270/887–0100; Eric A. Lee, President and Chief Executive Officer
**Web address:** www.jsmc.org

MONROE COUNTY MEDICAL CENTER (C, 49 beds) 529 Capp Harlan Road, Tompkinsville, KY Zip 42167–1840; tel. 270/487–9231; Vicky McFall, Chief Executive Officer
**Web address:** www.mcmccares.com

OHIO COUNTY HOSPITAL (C, 25 beds) 1211 Main Street, Hartford, KY Zip 42347–1619; tel. 270/298–7411; Blaine Pieper, Chief Executive Officer
**Web address:** www.ohiocountyhospital.com

**LOUISIANA:** CLAIBORNE MEMORIAL MEDICAL CENTER (C, 57 beds) 620 East College Street, Homer, LA Zip 71040–3202; tel. 318/927–2024; Derrick A. Frazier, Chief Executive Officer
**Web address:** www.claibornemedical.com/

FRANKLIN FOUNDATION HOSPITAL (C, 22 beds) 1097 Northwest Boulevard, Franklin, LA Zip 70538–3407, Mailing Address: P.O. Box 577, Zip 70538–0577; tel. 337/828–0760; Craig R. Cudworth, Chief Executive Officer
**Web address:** www.franklinfoundation.org

**MAINE:** CALAIS REGIONAL HOSPITAL (C, 25 beds) 24 Hospital Lane, Calais, ME Zip 04619–1398; tel. 207/454–7521; Bert Whitaker, Interim Chief Executive Officer
**Web address:** www.calaishospital.com

CARY MEDICAL CENTER (C, 49 beds) 163 Van Buren Road, Suite 1, Caribou, ME Zip 04736–3567; tel. 207/498–3111; Kris A. Doody, R.N., Chief Executive Officer
**Web address:** www.carymedicalcenter.org

PENOBSCOT VALLEY HOSPITAL (C, 25 beds) 7 Transalpine Road, Lincoln, ME Zip 04457–4222, Mailing Address: P.O. Box 368, Zip 04457–0368; tel. 207/794–3321; Gary R. Poquette, FACHE, Chief Executive Officer
**Web address:** www.pvhme.org

**MICHIGAN:** ALLEGAN GENERAL HOSPITAL (C, 25 beds) 555 Linn Street, Allegan, MI Zip 49010–1524; tel. 269/673–8424; Gerald J. Barbini, President and Chief Executive Officer
**Web address:** www.aghosp.org

HAYES GREEN BEACH MEMORIAL HOSPITAL (C, 25 beds) 321 East Harris Street, Charlotte, MI Zip 48813–1629; tel. 517/543–1050; Matthew Rush, President and Chief Executive Officer
**Web address:** www.hgbhealth.com

STURGIS HOSPITAL (C, 49 beds) 916 Myrtle Street, Sturgis, MI Zip 49091–2326; tel. 269/651–7824; Robert J. LaBarge, President and Chief Executive Officer
**Web address:** www.sturgishospital.com

THREE RIVERS HEALTH (C, 35 beds) 701 South Health Parkway, Three Rivers, MI Zip 49093–8352; tel. 269/278–1145; William B. Russell, Chief Executive Officer
**Web address:** www.threerivershealth.org

**MISSISSIPPI:** KING'S DAUGHTERS MEDICAL CENTER (C, 122 beds) 427 Highway 51 North, Brookhaven, MS Zip 39601–2350, Mailing Address: P.O. Box 948, Zip 39602–0948; tel. 601/833–6011; Alvin Hoover, FACHE, Chief Executive Officer
**Web address:** www.kdmc.org

**MISSOURI:** NEVADA REGIONAL MEDICAL CENTER (C, 71 beds) 800 South Ash Street, Nevada, MO Zip 64772–3223; tel. 417/667–3355; Kevin Leeper, Chief Executive Officer
**Web address:** www.nrmchealth.com

**MONTANA:** CENTRAL MONTANA MEDICAL CENTER (C, 90 beds) 408 Wendell Avenue, Lewistown, MT Zip 59457–2261; tel. 406/535–7711; Christopher Noland, Interim Chief Executive Officer
**Web address:** www.cmmccares.com

NORTH VALLEY HOSPITAL (C, 25 beds) 1600 Hospital Way, Whitefish, MT Zip 59937–7849; tel. 406/863–3500; Jason A. Spring, FACHE, Chief Executive Officer
**Web address:** www.nvhosp.org

**NEBRASKA:** PHELPS MEMORIAL HEALTH CENTER (C, 25 beds) 1215 Tibbals Street, Holdrege, NE Zip 68949–1255; tel. 308/995–2211; Mark Harrel, Chief Executive Officer
**Web address:** www.phelpsmemorial.com

**NEW MEXICO:** CIBOLA GENERAL HOSPITAL (C, 25 beds) 1016 East Roosevelt Avenue, Grants, NM Zip 87020–2118; tel. 505/287–4446; Bob Phillips, Interim Chief Executive Officer
**Web address:** www.cibolahospital.com

HOLY CROSS HOSPITAL (C, 29 beds) 1397 Weimer Road, Taos, NM Zip 87571–6253; tel. 575/758–8883; William D. Patten, Jr., Chief Executive Officer
**Web address:** www.taoshospital.org

**NORTH CAROLINA:** NORTHERN HOSPITAL OF SURRY COUNTY (C, 108 beds) 830 Rockford Street, Mount Airy, NC Zip 27030–5365, Mailing Address: P.O. Box 1101, Zip 27030–1101; tel. 336/719–7000; Ned Hill, President and Chief Executive Officer
**Web address:** www.northernhospital.com

For explanation of codes following names, see page B2.
★ Indicates Type III membership in the American Hospital Association.

Section B

**OHIO:** KNOX COMMUNITY HOSPITAL (C, 61 beds) 1330 Coshocton Road, Mount Vernon, OH Zip 43050–1495; tel. 740/393–9000; Bruce D. White, Chief Executive Officer
**Web address:** www.knoxcommhosp.org

WOOSTER COMMUNITY HOSPITAL (C, 152 beds) 1761 Beall Avenue, Wooster, OH Zip 44691–2342; tel. 330/263–8100; William E. Sheron, Chief Executive Officer
**Web address:** www.woosterhospital.org

**OKLAHOMA:** PERRY MEMORIAL HOSPITAL (C, 26 beds) 501 North 14th Street, Perry, OK Zip 73077–5099; tel. 580/336–3541; Howard D. Turner, Chief Executive Officer
**Web address:** www.pmh–ok.org

**PENNSYLVANIA:** CLARION HOSPITAL (C, 77 beds) One Hospital Drive, Clarion, PA Zip 16214–8501; tel. 814/226–9500; Byron Quinton, Chief Executive Officer
**Web address:** www.clarionhospital.org

JERSEY SHORE HOSPITAL (C, 25 beds) 1020 Thompson Street, Jersey Shore, PA Zip 17740–1794; tel. 570/398–0100; David A. Shannon, President and Chief Executive Officer
**Web address:** www.jsh.org

**SOUTH CAROLINA:** ABBEVILLE AREA MEDICAL CENTER (C, 25 beds) 420 Thomson Circle, Abbeville, SC Zip 29620–5656, Mailing Address: P.O. Box 887, Zip 29620–0887; tel. 864/366–5011; Richard D. Osmus, Chief Executive Officer
**Web address:** www.abbevilleareamc.com

NEWBERRY COUNTY MEMORIAL HOSPITAL (C, 52 beds) 2669 Kinard Street, Newberry, SC Zip 29108–2911, Mailing Address: P.O. Box 497, Zip 29108–0497; tel. 803/276–7570; Bruce A. Baldwin, Chief Executive Officer
**Web address:** www.newberryhospital.org

REGIONAL MEDICAL CENTER (C, 283 beds) 3000 St. Matthews Road, Orangeburg, SC Zip 29118–1442; tel. 803/395–2200; Thomas C. Dandridge, FACHE, President and Chief Executive Officer
**Web address:** www.trmchealth.org

TIDELANDS GEORGETOWN MEMORIAL HOSPITAL (C, 136 beds) 606 Black River Road, Georgetown, SC Zip 29440–3368, Mailing Address: Drawer 421718, Zip 29442–4203; tel. 843/527–7000; Gayle L. Resetar, Chief Operating Officer
**Web address:** www.georgetownhospitalsystem.org

TIDELANDS WACCAMAW COMMUNITY HOSPITAL (C, 169 beds) 4070 Highway 17 Bypass, Murrells Inlet, SC Zip 29576–5033, Mailing Address: P.O. Drawer 3350, Zip 29576–2673; tel. 843/652–1000; Gayle L. Resetar, Chief Operating Officer
**Web address:** www.tidelandshealth.org

**SOUTH DAKOTA:** HURON REGIONAL MEDICAL CENTER (C, 25 beds) 172 Fourth Street S.E., Huron, SD Zip 57350–2590; tel. 605/353–6200; David Dick, Chief Executive Officer
**Web address:** www.huronregional.org

**TENNESSEE:** LINCOLN COUNTY HEALTH SYSTEM (C, 323 beds) 106 Medical Center Boulevard, Fayetteville, TN Zip 37334–2684; tel. 931/438–1100; John Harding, Interim Chief Executive Officer
**Web address:** www.lchealthsystem.com

MACON COUNTY GENERAL HOSPITAL (C, 25 beds) 204 Medical Drive, Lafayette, TN Zip 37083–1799, Mailing Address: P.O. Box 378, Zip 37083–0378; tel. 615/666–2147; Dennis A. Wolford, FACHE, Chief Executive Officer
**Web address:** www.mcgh.net

RHEA MEDICAL CENTER (C, 25 beds) 9400 Rhea County Highway, Dayton, TN Zip 37321–7922; tel. 423/775–1121; Kennedy L. Croom, Jr., Administrator and Chief Executive Officer
**Web address:** www.rheamedical.org

**TEXAS:** BRAZOSPORT REGIONAL HEALTH SYSTEM (C, 103 beds) 100 Medical Drive, Lake Jackson, TX Zip 77566–5674; tel. 979/297–4411; Al Guevara, FACHE, President and Chief Executive Officer
**Web address:** www.brhstx.org

GRAHAM REGIONAL MEDICAL CENTER (C, 25 beds) 1301 Montgomery Road, Graham, TX Zip 76450–4240, Mailing Address: P.O. Box 1390, Zip 76450–1390; tel. 940/549–3400; Scott M. Landrum, Interim Administrator
**Web address:** www.grahamrmc.com

MATAGORDA REGIONAL MEDICAL CENTER (C, 58 beds) 104 7th Street, Bay City, TX Zip 77414–4853; tel. 979/245–6383; Steven L. Smith, Chief Executive Officer
**Web address:** www.matagordaregional.org

MEMORIAL HOSPITAL (C, 33 beds) 1110 Sarah Dewitt Drive, Gonzales, TX Zip 78629–3311, Mailing Address: P.O. Box 587, Zip 78629–0587; tel. 830/672–7581; Charles Norris, Chief Executive Officer
**Web address:** www.gonzaleshealthcare.com

**VERMONT:** NORTHWESTERN MEDICAL CENTER (C, 55 beds) 133 Fairfield Street, Saint Albans, VT Zip 05478–1726; tel. 802/524–5911; Jill Berry Bowen, President and Chief Executive Officer
**Web address:** www.northwesternmedicalcenter.org

**WYOMING:** MEMORIAL HOSPITAL OF CARBON COUNTY (C, 25 beds) 2221 West Elm Street, Rawlins, WY Zip 82301–5108, Mailing Address: P.O. Box 460, Zip 82301–0460; tel. 307/324–2221; Dana Barnett, Chief Executive Officer
**Web address:** www.imhcc.com

WEST PARK HOSPITAL (C, 112 beds) 707 Sheridan Avenue, Cody, WY Zip 82414–3409; tel. 307/527–7501; Douglas A. McMillan, Administrator and Chief Executive Officer
**Web address:** www.westparkhospital.org

| Owned, leased, sponsored: | 0 hospitals | 0 beds |
|---|---|---|
| Contract–managed: | 66 hospitals | 3985 beds |
| **Totals:** | 66 hospitals | 3985 beds |

---

★**0040:  QUEEN'S HEALTH SYSTEMS** (NP)
1301 Punchbowl Street, Honolulu, HI Zip 96813–2402; tel. 808/535–5448; Arthur A. Ushijima, FACHE, President and Chief Executive Officer
**(Moderately Centralized Health System)**

**HAWAII:** MOLOKAI GENERAL HOSPITAL (O, 15 beds) 280 Home Olu Place, Kaunakakai, HI Zip 96748–0408, Mailing Address: P.O. Box 408, Zip 96748–0408; tel. 808/553–5331; Janice Kalanihuia, President
**Web address:** www.queens.org

NORTH HAWAII COMMUNITY HOSPITAL (O, 35 beds) 67–1125 Mamalahoa Highway, Kamuela, HI Zip 96743–8496; tel. 808/885–4444; Kenneth D. Graham, FACHE, President
**Web address:** www.nhch.com

QUEEN'S MEDICAL CENTER (O, 512 beds) 1301 Punchbowl Street, Honolulu, HI Zip 96813–2499; tel. 808/691–5100; Arthur A. Ushijima, FACHE, President
**Web address:** www.queensmedicalcenter.org

| Owned, leased, sponsored: | 3 hospitals | 562 beds |
|---|---|---|
| Contract–managed: | 0 hospitals | 0 beds |
| **Totals:** | 3 hospitals | 562 beds |

---

★**8495:  REGIONAL HEALTH** (NP)
353 Fairmont Boulevard, Rapid City, SD Zip 57701–7375, Mailing Address: P.O. Box 6000, Zip 57709–6000; tel. 605/719–1000; Brent R. Phillips, President and Chief Executive Officer
**(Moderately Centralized Health System)**

**SOUTH DAKOTA:** CUSTER REGIONAL HOSPITAL (L, 87 beds) 1039 Montgomery Street, Custer, SD Zip 57730–1397; tel. 605/673–2229; Veronica Schmidt, President
**Web address:** www.regionalhealth.com

LEAD–DEADWOOD REGIONAL HOSPITAL (O, 8 beds) 61 Charles Street, Deadwood, SD Zip 57732–1303; tel. 605/717–6000; Mark C. Schmidt, President
**Web address:** www.regionalhealth.com

PHILIP HEALTH SERVICES (C, 48 beds) 503 West Pine Street, Philip, SD Zip 57567–3300, Mailing Address: P.O. Box 790, Zip 57567–0790; tel. 605/859–2511; Kent Olson, Administrator and Chief Executive Officer

RAPID CITY REGIONAL HOSPITAL (O, 369 beds) 353 Fairmont Boulevard, Rapid City, SD Zip 57701–7393, Mailing Address: P.O. Box 6000, Zip 57709–6000; tel. 605/755–1000; Mick Gibbs, President
**Web address:** www.regionalhealth.com

---

For explanation of codes following names, see page B2.
★ Indicates Type III membership in the American Hospital Association.

SPEARFISH REGIONAL HOSPITAL (O, 35 beds) 1440 North Main Street, Spearfish, SD Zip 57783–1504; tel. 605/644–4000; Larry W. Veitz, President
**Web address:** www.regionalhealth.com/Our–Locations/Regional–Hospitals/Spearfish–Regional–Hospital.aspx

STURGIS REGIONAL HOSPITAL (O, 109 beds) 949 Harmon Street, Sturgis, SD Zip 57785–2452; tel. 605/720–2400; Mark Schulte, FACHE, Chief Executive Officer
**Web address:** www.regionalhealth.com/Our–Locations/Regional–Hospitals/Sturgis–Regional–Hospital.aspx

| | | |
|---|---|---|
| **Owned, leased, sponsored:** | 5 hospitals | 608 beds |
| **Contract–managed:** | 1 hospitals | 55 beds |
| **Totals:** | 6 hospitals | 663 beds |

---

**0622: REGIONALCARE HOSPITAL PARTNERS** (IO)
103 Continental Place, Suite 200, Brentwood, TN Zip 37027–1042; tel. 615/844–9800; Kent H. Wallace, Chief Executive Officer
**(Moderately Centralized Health System)**

**ALABAMA:** ELIZA COFFEE MEMORIAL HOSPITAL (O, 278 beds) 205 Marengo Street, Florence, AL Zip 35630–6033, Mailing Address: P.O. Box 818, Zip 35631–0818; tel. 256/768–9191; Russell Pigg, Chief Executive Officer
**Web address:** www.chgroup.org

SHOALS HOSPITAL (O, 137 beds) 201 Avalon Avenue, Muscle Shoals, AL Zip 35661–2805, Mailing Address: P.O. Box 3359, Zip 35662–3359; tel. 256/386–1600; Jeff Jennings, FACHE, Chief Executive Officer
**Web address:** www.shoalshospital.com

**ARIZONA:** CANYON VISTA MEDICAL CENTER (L, 83 beds) 5700 East Highway 90, Sierra Vista, AZ Zip 85635–9110; tel. 520/263–2000; Jeff Egbert, Interim Executive Officer
**Web address:** www.svrhc.org

**CONNECTICUT:** SHARON HOSPITAL (O, 78 beds) 50 Hospital Hill Road, Sharon, CT Zip 06069–2096, Mailing Address: P.O. Box 789, Zip 06069–0789; tel. 860/364–4000; Kim Lumia, President and Chief Executive Officer
**Web address:** www.sharonhospital.com

**IOWA:** OTTUMWA REGIONAL HEALTH CENTER (O, 101 beds) 1001 Pennsylvania Avenue, Ottumwa, IA Zip 52501–2186; tel. 641/684–2300; Philip J. Noel, III, Chief Executive Officer
**Web address:** www.ottumwaregionalhealth.com

**OHIO:** CLINTON MEMORIAL HOSPITAL (O, 102 beds) 610 West Main Street, Wilmington, OH Zip 45177–2125; tel. 937/382–6611; Gregory A. Nielsen, FACHE, Chief Executive Officer
**Web address:** www.cmhregional.com

**TEXAS:** PARIS REGIONAL MEDICAL CENTER (O, 192 beds) 865 Deshong Drive, Paris, TX Zip 75460–9313, Mailing Address: P.O. Box 9070, Zip 75461–9070; tel. 903/785–4521; Patti Monczewski, Interim Chief Executive Officer
**Web address:** www.parisrmc.com

| | | |
|---|---|---|
| **Owned, leased, sponsored:** | 7 hospitals | 971 beds |
| **Contract–managed:** | 0 hospitals | 0 beds |
| **Totals:** | 7 hospitals | 971 beds |

---

**0411: RELIANT HEALTHCARE PARTNERS** (IO)
1300 East Lookout Drive, Suite 115, Richardson, TX Zip 75082–4114; tel. 469/298–1400; Chester Crouch, Chief Executive Officer
**(Independent Hospital System)**

**OHIO:** DAYTON REHABILITATION INSTITUTE (O, 50 beds) One Elizabeth Place, Dayton, OH Zip 45417–3445; tel. 937/424–8200; Randy J. Kitchen, Chief Executive Officer
**Web address:** www.reliantdayton.com

**TEXAS:** RELIANT REHABILITATION HOSPITAL ABILENE (O, 30 beds) 6401 Directors Parkway, Abilene, TX Zip 79606–5869; tel. 325/691–1600; Joe Roberson, Chief Executive Officer
**Web address:** www.reliantabilene.com

RELIANT REHABILITATION HOSPITAL CENTRAL TEXAS (O, 75 beds) 1400 Hester's Crossing, Round Rock, TX Zip 78681–8025; tel. 512/244–4400; Eric Mueller, Chief Executive Officer
**Web address:** www.reliantcentraltx.com/

RELIANT REHABILITATION HOSPITAL NORTH HOUSTON (O, 60 beds) 117 Vision Park Boulevard, Shenandoah, TX Zip 77384–3001; tel. 936/444–1700; Jeff Crawford, Chief Executive Officer
**Web address:** www.reliantnorthhouston.com/

RELIANT REHABILITATION HOSPITAL NORTH TEXAS (O, 50 beds) 3351 Waterview Parkway, Richardson, TX Zip 75080–1449; tel. 972/398–5700; Jim Ransom, Chief Executive Officer
**Web address:** www.relianthcp.com

| | | |
|---|---|---|
| **Owned, leased, sponsored:** | 5 hospitals | 265 beds |
| **Contract–managed:** | 0 hospitals | 0 beds |
| **Totals:** | 5 hospitals | 265 beds |

---

**★2625: RENOWN HEALTH** (NP)
1155 Mill Street, Reno, NV Zip 89502–1576; tel. 775/982–4100; Anthony D. Slonim, M.D., Dr.PH, President and Chief Executive Officer
**(Centralized Health System)**

**NEVADA:** RENOWN REGIONAL MEDICAL CENTER (O, 643 beds) 1155 Mill Street, Reno, NV Zip 89502–1576; tel. 775/982–4100; Erik Olson, Chief Executive Officer
**Web address:** www.renown.org

RENOWN REHABILITATION HOSPITAL (O, 62 beds) 1495 Mill Street, Reno, NV Zip 89502–1479; tel. 775/982–3500; Erik Olson, Chief Executive Officer
**Web address:** www.renown.org

RENOWN SOUTH MEADOWS MEDICAL CENTER (O, 76 beds) 10101 Double R Boulevard, Reno, NV Zip 89521–5931; tel. 775/982–7000; Mark Behl, Chief Executive Officer
**Web address:** www.renown.org

| | | |
|---|---|---|
| **Owned, leased, sponsored:** | 3 hospitals | 781 beds |
| **Contract–managed:** | 0 hospitals | 0 beds |
| **Totals:** | 3 hospitals | 781 beds |

---

**★0964: RIDGEVIEW MEDICAL CENTER** (IO)
500 South Maple Street, Waconia, MN Zip 55387–1752; tel. 952/442–2191; Robert Stevens, President and Chief Executive Officer

**MINNESOTA:** RIDGEVIEW MEDICAL CENTER (O, 102 beds) 500 South Maple Street, Waconia, MN Zip 55387–1791; tel. 952/442–2191; Robert Stevens, President and Chief Executive Officer
**Web address:** www.ridgeviewmedical.org

RIDGEVIEW SIBLEY MEDICAL CENTER (L, 16 beds) 601 West Chandler Street, Arlington, MN Zip 55307–2127; tel. 507/964–2271; Todd Sandberg, Chief Executive Officer and Administrator
**Web address:** www.sibleymedical.org

| | | |
|---|---|---|
| **Owned, leased, sponsored:** | 2 hospitals | 118 beds |
| **Contract–managed:** | 0 hospitals | 0 beds |
| **Totals:** | 2 hospitals | 118 beds |

---

**4810: RIVERSIDE HEALTH SYSTEM** (NP)
701 Town Center Drive, Suite 1000, Newport News, VA Zip 23606–4286; tel. 757/534–7000; William B. Downey, President and Chief Executive Officer
**(Centralized Physician/Insurance Health System)**

**VIRGINIA:** HAMPTON ROADS SPECIALTY HOSPITAL (O, 25 beds) 245 Chesapeake Avenue, Newport News, VA Zip 23607–6038; tel. 757/534–5000; Courtney Detwiler, R.N., Administrator
**Web address:** www.hamptonroadsspecialtyhospital.com

RIVERSIDE BEHAVIORAL HEALTH CENTER (O, 79 beds) 2244 Executive Drive, Hampton, VA Zip 23666–2430; tel. 757/827–1001; Debra Campbell, R.N., Administrator
**Web address:** www.riversideonline.com

For explanation of codes following names, see page B2.
★ Indicates Type III membership in the American Hospital Association.

Section B

RIVERSIDE DOCTORS' HOSPITAL (O, 40 beds) 1500 Commonwealth Avenue, Williamsburg, VA Zip 23185–5229; tel. 757/585–2200; Steve C. McCary, Administrator
**Web address:** www.riversideonline.com

RIVERSIDE REGIONAL MEDICAL CENTER (O, 293 beds) 500 J. Clyde Morris Boulevard, Newport News, VA Zip 23601–1929; tel. 757/594–2000; Michael J. Doucette, Senior Vice President and Administrator
**Web address:** www.riverside–online.com

RIVERSIDE REHABILITATION INSTITUTE (O, 32 beds) 245 Chesapeake Avenue, Newport News, VA Zip 23607–6038; tel. 757/928–8000; Edward Heckler, Administrator
**Web address:** www.riverside–online.com

RIVERSIDE SHORE MEMORIAL HOSPITAL (O, 51 beds) 9507 Hospital Avenue, Nassawadox, VA Zip 23413–1821, Mailing Address: P.O. Box 17, Zip 23413–0017; tel. 757/414–8000; John Peterman, Vice President and Administrator
**Web address:** www.riversideonline.com

RIVERSIDE TAPPAHANNOCK HOSPITAL (O, 16 beds) 618 Hospital Road, Tappahannock, VA Zip 22560–5000; tel. 804/443–3311; John Peterman, Vice President and Administrator
**Web address:** www.riverside–online.com

RIVERSIDE WALTER REED HOSPITAL (O, 32 beds) 7519 Hospital Drive, Gloucester, VA Zip 23061–4178, Mailing Address: P.O. Box 1130, Zip 23061–1130; tel. 804/693–8800; Megan Kleckner, Vice President and Administrator
**Web address:** www.riversideonline.com

| Owned, leased, sponsored: | 8 hospitals | 568 beds |
|---|---|---|
| Contract–managed: | 0 hospitals | 0 beds |
| Totals: | 8 hospitals | 568 beds |

---

**0268:  ROBERT WOOD JOHNSON HEALTH SYSTEM & NETWORK** (NP)
1 Robert Wood Johnson Place, New Brunswick, NJ Zip 08901–1928; tel. 732/828–3000; Stephen K. Jones, FACHE, President and Chief Executive Officer
**(Moderately Centralized Health System)**

**NEW JERSEY:** CHILDREN'S SPECIALIZED HOSPITAL–PSE&G (O, 140 beds) 200 Somerset Street, New Brunswick, NJ Zip 08901–1942; tel. 732/258–7000; Amy B. Mansue, President and Chief Executive Officer
**Web address:** www.childrens–specialized.org

ROBERT WOOD JOHNSON UNIVERSITY HOSPITAL (O, 610 beds) 1 Robert Wood Johnson Place, New Brunswick, NJ Zip 08901–1928; tel. 732/828–3000; Stephen K. Jones, FACHE, President and Chief Executive Officer
**Web address:** www.rwjuh.edu

ROBERT WOOD JOHNSON UNIVERSITY HOSPITAL AT HAMILTON (O, 213 beds) One Hamilton Health Place, Hamilton, NJ Zip 08690–3599; tel. 609/586–7900; Richard Freeman, President and Chief Executive Officer
**Web address:** www.rwjhamilton.org

ROBERT WOOD JOHNSON UNIVERSITY HOSPITAL RAHWAY (O, 147 beds) 865 Stone Street, Rahway, NJ Zip 07065–2797; tel. 732/381–4200; Kirk C. Tice, President and Chief Executive Officer
**Web address:** www.rwjuhr.com

| Owned, leased, sponsored: | 4 hospitals | 1110 beds |
|---|---|---|
| Contract–managed: | 0 hospitals | 0 beds |
| Totals: | 4 hospitals | 1110 beds |

---

★**0046:  ROCHESTER REGIONAL HEALTH** (NP)
1425 Portland Avenue, 5th Floor, Rochester, NY Zip 14621–3001; tel. 585/922–4000; Eric Bieber, M.D., President and Chief Executive Officer
**(Moderately Centralized Health System)**

**NEW YORK:** CLIFTON SPRINGS HOSPITAL AND CLINIC (O, 214 beds) 2 Coulter Road, Clifton Springs, NY Zip 14432–1189; tel. 315/462–9561; Dustin Riccio, M.D., President
**Web address:** www.cliftonspringshospital.org

NEWARK–WAYNE COMMUNITY HOSPITAL (O, 280 beds) 1200 Driving Park Avenue, Newark, NY Zip 14513–1057, Mailing Address: P.O. Box 111, Zip 14513–0111; tel. 315/332–2022; Dustin Riccio, M.D., Regional President Operations
**Web address:** www.rochesterregional.org

ROCHESTER GENERAL HOSPITAL (O, 520 beds) 1425 Portland Avenue, Rochester, NY Zip 14621–3099; tel. 585/922–4000; Douglas Stewart, PsyD, President
**Web address:** www.rochestergeneral.org

UNITED MEMORIAL MEDICAL CENTER (O, 131 beds) 127 North Street, Batavia, NY Zip 14020–1631; tel. 585/343–6030; Daniel P. Ireland, FACHE, President
**Web address:** www.ummc.org

UNITY HOSPITAL (O, 487 beds) 1555 Long Pond Road, Rochester, NY Zip 14626–4182; tel. 585/723–7000; Douglas Stewart, PsyD, President
**Web address:** www.unityhealth.org

| Owned, leased, sponsored: | 5 hospitals | 1632 beds |
|---|---|---|
| Contract–managed: | 0 hospitals | 0 beds |
| Totals: | 5 hospitals | 1632 beds |

---

**0348:  RURAL COMMUNITY HOSPITALS OF AMERICA** (IO)
1100 Main Street, Suite 2350, Kansas City, MO Zip 64105–5186; tel. 816/474–7800; Lawrence J. Arthur, President
**(Independent Hospital System)**

**KANSAS:** HILLSBORO COMMUNITY HOSPITAL (O, 10 beds) 701 South Main Street, Hillsboro, KS Zip 67063–1553; tel. 620/947–3114; Marion Regier, Chief Executive Officer
**Web address:** www.hchks.com

HORTON COMMUNITY HOSPITAL (O, 25 beds) 240 West 18th Street, Horton, KS Zip 66439–1245; tel. 785/486–2642; James D. Noble, Chief Executive Officer
**Web address:** www.horton–hospital.com

OSWEGO COMMUNITY HOSPITAL (O, 12 beds) 800 Barker Drive, Oswego, KS Zip 67356–9014; tel. 620/795–2921; Daniel Hiben, Chief Executive Officer
**Web address:** www.oswegocommunityhospital.com

**MISSOURI:** COOPER COUNTY MEMORIAL HOSPITAL (C, 32 beds) 17651 B Highway, Boonville, MO Zip 65233–2839, Mailing Address: P.O. Box 88, Zip 65233–0088; tel. 660/882–7461; Danielle Gearhart, Chief Executive Officer
**Web address:** www.coopercmh.com

I–70 COMMUNITY HOSPITAL (O, 15 beds) 105 Hospital Drive, Sweet Springs, MO Zip 65351–2229; tel. 660/335–4700; Jeff Bloemker, Chief Executive Officer
**Web address:** www.i70medcenter.com

**NORTH CAROLINA:** WASHINGTON COUNTY HOSPITAL (O, 25 beds) 958 U.S. Highway 64 East, Plymouth, NC Zip 27962–9591; tel. 252/793–4135; Cameron Highsmith, Chief Executive Officer

**OKLAHOMA:** DRUMRIGHT REGIONAL HOSPITAL (O, 15 beds) 610 West Bypass, Drumright, OK Zip 74030–5957; tel. 918/382–2300; William Holland, Chief Executive Officer
**Web address:** www.drumrighthospital.com/

FAIRFAX COMMUNITY HOSPITAL (O, 15 beds) 40 Hospital Road, Fairfax, OK Zip 74637–5084; tel. 918/642–3291; Tina Steele, Chief Executive Officer and Chief Financial Officer

HASKELL COUNTY COMMUNITY HOSPITAL (O, 18 beds) 401 Northwest H Street, Stigler, OK Zip 74462–1625; tel. 918/967–4682; Donald E. Buchanan, Interim Chief Executive Officer
**Web address:** www.haskellhospital.com

PRAGUE COMMUNITY HOSPITAL (O, 19 beds) 1322 Klabzuba Avenue, Prague, OK Zip 74864–9005, Mailing Address: P.O. Box S., Zip 74864–1090; tel. 405/567–4922; William Holland, Chief Executive Officer
**Web address:** www.praguehospital.com

**TENNESSEE:** LAUDERDALE COMMUNITY HOSPITAL (O, 25 beds) 326 Asbury Avenue, Ripley, TN Zip 38063–5577; tel. 731/221–2200; Tammie H. Hardy, Chief Executive Officer
**Web address:** www.lauderdalehospital.com/

---

For explanation of codes following names, see page B2.
★ Indicates Type III membership in the American Hospital Association.

| Owned, leased, sponsored: | 10 hospitals | 179 beds |
|---|---|---|
| Contract–managed: | 1 hospital | 32 beds |
| Totals: | 11 hospitals | 211 beds |

★**0109:  RURAL HEALTH GROUP** (IO)
48 West 1500 North, Nephi, UT Zip 84648–8900;
tel. 435/623–4924; Mark R. Stoddard, President and Chairman
**(Independent Hospital System)**

**NEVADA:** DESERT VIEW HOSPITAL (O, 25 beds) 360 South Lola Lane,
Pahrump, NV Zip 89048–0884; tel. 775/751–7500; Kelly H. Adams,
Chief Executive Officer
**Web address:** www.desertviewhospital.com

**UTAH:** CENTRAL VALLEY MEDICAL CENTER (L, 27 beds) 48 West 1500
North, Nephi, UT Zip 84648–8900; tel. 435/623–3000; Mark R.
Stoddard, President
**Web address:** www.cvmed.net

| Owned, leased, sponsored: | 2 hospitals | 52 beds |
|---|---|---|
| Contract–managed: | 0 hospitals | 0 beds |
| Totals: | 2 hospitals | 52 beds |

★**0220:  RUSH HEALTH SYSTEMS** (NP)
1314 19th Avenue, Meridian, MS Zip 39301–4116;
tel. 601/483–0011; Wallace Strickland, President and Chief
Executive Officer
**(Independent Hospital System)**

**ALABAMA:** CHOCTAW GENERAL HOSPITAL (O, 25 beds) 401 Vanity Fair
Avenue, Butler, AL Zip 36904–3032; tel. 205/459–9100; J. W. Cowan,
Administrator
**Web address:** www.choctawgeneral.com/cgh/

**MISSISSIPPI:** H. C. WATKINS MEMORIAL HOSPITAL (O, 25 beds) 605 South
Archusa Avenue, Quitman, MS Zip 39355–2331; tel. 601/776–6925;
Clinton Eaves, Administrator
**Web address:** www.watkinsmemorialhospital.com/hcwmh/

JOHN C. STENNIS MEMORIAL HOSPITAL (O, 25 beds) 14365 Highway 16
West, De Kalb, MS Zip 39328–7974; tel. 769/486–1000; Michael Nester,
Administrator
**Web address:** www.johncstennismemorialhospital.com/jcsmh/

LAIRD HOSPITAL (O, 25 beds) 25117 Highway 15, Union, MS
Zip 39365–9099; tel. 601/774–8214; Thomas G. Bartlett, III, Administrator
**Web address:** www.lairdhospital.com/lh/

RUSH FOUNDATION HOSPITAL (O, 182 beds) 1314 19th Avenue, Meridian,
MS Zip 39301–4195; tel. 601/483–0011; Chuck A. Reece, President and
Chief Executive Officer
**Web address:** www.rushhealthsystems.org/rfh/

SCOTT REGIONAL HOSPITAL (O, 25 beds) 317 Highway 13 South, Morton,
MS Zip 39117–3353, Mailing Address: P.O. Box 259, Zip 39117–0259;
tel. 601/732–6301; Michael R. Edwards, Administrator
**Web address:** www.scottregional.org/srh/

SPECIALTY HOSPITAL OF MERIDIAN (O, 49 beds) 1314 19th Avenue,
Meridian, MS Zip 39301–4116; tel. 601/703–4211; Elizabeth C. Mitchell,
Vice President and Administrator
**Web address:** www.specialtyhospitalofmeridian.com/shm/

| Owned, leased, sponsored: | 7 hospitals | 356 beds |
|---|---|---|
| Contract–managed: | 0 hospitals | 0 beds |
| Totals: | 7 hospitals | 356 beds |

★**3855:  RUSH UNIVERSITY MEDICAL CENTER** (NP)
1653 West Congress Parkway, Chicago, IL Zip 60612–3864;
tel. 312/942–5000; Larry J. Goodman, M.D., Chief Executive Officer
**(Moderately Centralized Health System)**

**ILLINOIS:** RUSH OAK PARK HOSPITAL (O, 96 beds) 520 South Maple Avenue,
Oak Park, IL Zip 60304–1097; tel. 708/383–9300; Bruce M. Elegant,
FACHE, President and Chief Executive Officer
**Web address:** www.roph.org

RUSH UNIVERSITY MEDICAL CENTER (O, 677 beds) 1653 West Congress
Parkway, Chicago, IL Zip 60612–3833; tel. 312/942–5000; Larry J.
Goodman, M.D., Chief Executive Officer
**Web address:** www.rush.edu

RUSH–COPLEY MEDICAL CENTER (O, 210 beds) 2000 Ogden Avenue,
Aurora, IL Zip 60504–7222; tel. 630/978–6200; Barry C. Finn, President
and Chief Executive Officer
**Web address:** www.rushcopley.com

| Owned, leased, sponsored: | 3 hospitals | 983 beds |
|---|---|---|
| Contract–managed: | 0 hospitals | 0 beds |
| Totals: | 3 hospitals | 983 beds |

**0912:  SAFE HAVEN HEALTH CARE** (IO)
2520 South 5th Avenue, Pocatello, ID Zip 83204–1923;
tel. 800/261–2443; Scott Burpee, President

**IDAHO:** SAFE HAVEN HOSPITAL OF POCATELLO (O, 87 beds) 1200 Hospital
Way, Pocatello, ID Zip 83201–2708; tel. 208/232–2570; Josiah
Dahlstrom, Administrator
**Web address:** www.safehavenhealthcare.org/safehaven_hospital/index.
html

SAFE HAVEN HOSPITAL OF TREASURE VALLEY (O, 22 beds) 8050 Northview
Street, Boise, ID Zip 83704–7126; tel. 208/327–0504; Scott Proctor, Chief
Executive Officer
**Web address:** www.boisepsychhospital.com

| Owned, leased, sponsored: | 2 hospitals | 109 beds |
|---|---|---|
| Contract–managed: | 0 hospitals | 0 beds |
| Totals: | 2 hospitals | 109 beds |

★**0318:  SAINT FRANCIS CARE, INC.** (NP)
114 Woodland Street, Hartford, CT Zip 06105–1208;
tel. 860/714–5541; Christopher M. Dadlez, President and Chief
Executive Officer
**(Independent Hospital System)**

**CONNECTICUT:** MOUNT SINAI REHABILITATION HOSPITAL (O, 30 beds) 490
Blue Hills Avenue, Hartford, CT Zip 06112–1513; tel. 860/714–3500;
Robert J. Krug, M.D., Chief Executive Officer
**Web address:** www.stfranciscare.org

SAINT FRANCIS HOSPITAL AND MEDICAL CENTER (O, 612 beds) 114
Woodland Street, Hartford, CT Zip 06105–1208; tel. 860/714–4000;
Christopher M. Dadlez, President and Chief Executive Officer
**Web address:** www.saintfranciscare.com

| Owned, leased, sponsored: | 2 hospitals | 642 beds |
|---|---|---|
| Contract–managed: | 0 hospitals | 0 beds |
| Totals: | 2 hospitals | 642 beds |

★**0254:  SAINT FRANCIS HEALTH SYSTEM** (NP)
6161 South Yale Avenue, Tulsa, OK Zip 74136–1902;
tel. 918/494–8454; Jake Henry, Jr., President and Chief Executive
Officer
**(Centralized Health System)**

**OKLAHOMA:** LAUREATE PSYCHIATRIC CLINIC AND HOSPITAL (O, 75 beds)
6655 South Yale Avenue, Tulsa, OK Zip 74136–3329;
tel. 918/481–4000; William Schloss, Senior Vice President and
Administrator
**Web address:** www.laureate.com

SAINT FRANCIS HOSPITAL (O, 833 beds) 6161 South Yale Avenue, Tulsa, OK
Zip 74136–1902; tel. 918/494–2200; Lynn A. Sund, R.N., MS, Senior Vice
President, Administrator and Chief Nurse Executive
**Web address:** www.saintfrancis.com

For explanation of codes following names, see page B2.
★ Indicates Type III membership in the American Hospital Association.

SAINT FRANCIS HOSPITAL SOUTH (O, 81 beds) 10501 East 91St. Streeet, Tulsa, OK Zip 74133–5790; tel. 918/455–3535; David S. Weil, Senior Vice President and Administrator
**Web address:** www.saintfrancis.com/south/

| Owned, leased, sponsored: | 3 hospitals | 989 beds |
|---|---|---|
| Contract–managed: | 0 hospitals | 0 beds |
| **Totals:** | 3 hospitals | 989 beds |

### ★0120: SAINT LUKE'S HEALTH SYSTEM (NP)
901 East 104th Street, Mailstop 900N, Kansas City, MO Zip 64131–4517, Mailing Address: 901 East 104th Street, Zip 64131–4517; tel. 816/932–2000; Melinda Estes, M.D., President and Chief Executive Officer
**(Centralized Health System)**

**KANSAS:** ANDERSON COUNTY HOSPITAL (L, 40 beds) 421 South Maple, Garnett, KS Zip 66032–1334, Mailing Address: P.O. Box 309, Zip 66032–0309; tel. 785/448–3131; Dennis A. Hachenberg, FACHE, Chief Executive Officer
**Web address:** www.saint–lukes.org

SAINT LUKE'S CUSHING HOSPITAL (O, 25 beds) 711 Marshall Street, Leavenworth, KS Zip 66048–3235; tel. 913/684–1100; Adele Ducharme, R.N., MSN, Chief Executive Officer
**Web address:** www.https://www.saintlukeshealthsystem.org/location/cushing–memorial–hospital

SAINT LUKE'S SOUTH HOSPITAL (O, 110 beds) 12300 Metcalf Avenue, Overland Park, KS Zip 66213–1324; tel. 913/317–7000; Bobby Olm–Shipman, Chief Executive Officer
**Web address:** www.saintlukeshealthsystem.org/south

**MISSOURI:** CRITTENTON CHILDREN'S CENTER (O, 46 beds) 10918 Elm Avenue, Kansas City, MO Zip 64134–4108; tel. 816/765–6600; Janine Hron, Chief Executive Officer
**Web address:** www.crittentonkc.org

HEDRICK MEDICAL CENTER (L, 25 beds) 2799 North Washington Street, Chillicothe, MO Zip 64601–2902; tel. 660/646–1480; Steven M. Schieber, Interim Chief Executive Officer
**Web address:** www.saintlukeskc.org

SAINT LUKE'S EAST HOSPITAL (O, 161 beds) 100 N.E. Saint Luke's Boulevard, Lee's Summit, MO Zip 64086–6000; tel. 816/347–5000; Ronald L. Baker, Chief Executive Officer
**Web address:** www.saintlukeskc.org

SAINT LUKE'S HOSPITAL OF KANSAS CITY (O, 431 beds) 4401 Wornall Road, Kansas City, MO Zip 64111–3220; tel. 816/932–3800; Jani L. Johnson, R.N., MSN, Chief Executive Officer
**Web address:** www.saint–lukes.org

SAINT LUKE'S NORTH HOSPITAL – BARRY ROAD (O, 142 beds) 5830 N.W. Barry Road, Kansas City, MO Zip 64154–2778; tel. 816/891–6000; Matthew Wenzel, President and Chief Executive Officer
**Web address:** www.saint–lukes.org

WRIGHT MEMORIAL HOSPITAL (L, 25 beds) 191 Iowa Boulevard, Trenton, MO Zip 64683–8343; tel. 660/358–5700; Gary W. Jordan, FACHE, Chief Executive Officer
**Web address:** www.saintlukeshealthsystem.org

| Owned, leased, sponsored: | 9 hospitals | 1005 beds |
|---|---|---|
| Contract–managed: | 0 hospitals | 0 beds |
| **Totals:** | 9 hospitals | 1005 beds |

### 0403: SALEM HEALTH (NP)
890 Oak Street Building B. POB 14001, Salem, OR Zip 97309–5014; tel. 503/561–5200; Norman F. Gruber, President and Chief Executive Officer
**(Independent Hospital System)**

**OREGON:** SALEM HOSPITAL (O, 428 beds) 890 Oak Street S.E., Salem, OR Zip 97301–3959, Mailing Address: P.O. Box 14001, Zip 97309–5014; tel. 503/561–5200; Norman F. Gruber, President and Chief Executive Officer
**Web address:** www.salemhealth.org

WEST VALLEY HOSPITAL (O, 6 beds) 525 S.E. Washington Street, Dallas, OR Zip 97338–2834, Mailing Address: P.O. Box 378, Zip 97338–0378; tel. 503/623–8301; James J. Sapienza, Chief Administrative Officer
**Web address:** www.salemhealth.org/wvh/

| Owned, leased, sponsored: | 2 hospitals | 434 beds |
|---|---|---|
| Contract–managed: | 0 hospitals | 0 beds |
| **Totals:** | 2 hospitals | 434 beds |

### ★0186: SAMARITAN HEALTH SERVICES (NP)
3600 N.W. Samaritan Drive, Corvallis, OR Zip 97330–3737, Mailing Address: P.O. Box 1068, Zip 97339–1068; tel. 541/768–5001; Larry A. Mullins, FACHE, President and Chief Executive Officer
**(Centralized Physician/Insurance Health System)**

GOOD SAMARITAN REGIONAL MEDICAL CENTER (O, 165 beds) 3600 N.W. Samaritan Drive, Corvallis, OR Zip 97330–3737, Mailing Address: P.O. Box 1068, Zip 97339–1068; tel. 541/768–5111; Larry A. Mullins, FACHE, Chief Executive Officer
**Web address:** www.samhealth.org

SAMARITAN ALBANY GENERAL HOSPITAL (O, 70 beds) 1046 Sixth Avenue, S.W., Albany, OR Zip 97321–1999; tel. 541/812–4000; David G. Triebes, Chief Executive Officer
**Web address:** www.samhealth.org

SAMARITAN LEBANON COMMUNITY HOSPITAL (O, 25 beds) 525 North Santiam Highway, Lebanon, OR Zip 97355–4363, Mailing Address: P.O. Box 739, Zip 97355–0739; tel. 541/258–2101; Becky A. Pape, R.N., Chief Executive Officer
**Web address:** www.samhealth.org

SAMARITAN NORTH LINCOLN HOSPITAL (C, 25 beds) 3043 N.E. 28th Street, Lincoln City, OR Zip 97367–4518, Mailing Address: P.O. Box 767, Zip 97367–0767; tel. 541/994–3661; Marty Cahill, Chief Executive Officer
**Web address:** www.samhealth.org

SAMARITAN PACIFIC COMMUNITIES HOSPITAL (C, 25 beds) 930 S.W. Abbey Street, Newport, OR Zip 97365–4820, Mailing Address: P.O. Box 945, Zip 97365–0072; tel. 541/265–2244; David C. Bigelow, PharmD, Chief Executive Officer
**Web address:** www.samhealth.org

| Owned, leased, sponsored: | 3 hospitals | 260 beds |
|---|---|---|
| Contract–managed: | 2 hospitals | 50 beds |
| **Totals:** | 5 hospitals | 310 beds |

### ★0914: SAN LUIS VALLEY HEALTH (NP)
106 Blanca Avenue, Alamosa, CO Zip 81101–2340; tel. 719/589–2511; Konnie Martin, Chief Executive Officer
**(Independent Hospital System)**

**COLORADO:** SAN LUIS VALLEY HEALTH (O, 44 beds) 106 Blanca Avenue, Alamosa, CO Zip 81101–2393; tel. 719/589–2511; Konnie Martin, Chief Executive Officer
**Web address:** www.slvrmc.org

SAN LUIS VALLEY HEALTH CONEJOS COUNTY HOSPITAL (O, 17 beds) 19021 U.S. Highway 285, La Jara, CO Zip 81140–0639, Mailing Address: P.O. Box 639, Zip 81140–0639; tel. 719/274–5121; Kelly Gallegos, Administrator
**Web address:** www.sanluisvalleyhealth.org/locations/conejos–county–hospital

| Owned, leased, sponsored: | 2 hospitals | 61 beds |
|---|---|---|
| Contract–managed: | 0 hospitals | 0 beds |
| **Totals:** | 2 hospitals | 61 beds |

### ★0530: SANFORD HEALTH (NP)
2301 East 60th Street North, Sioux Falls, SD Zip 57104–0569, Mailing Address: PO Box 5039, Zip 57117–5039; tel. 605/333–1000; Kelby K. Krabbenhoft, President and Chief Executive Officer
**(Decentralized Health System)**

**IOWA:** ORANGE CITY AREA HEALTH SYSTEM (C, 108 beds) 1000 Lincoln Circle S.E., Orange City, IA Zip 51041–1862; tel. 712/737–4984; Martin W. Guthmiller, Chief Executive Officer
**Web address:** www.ochealthsystem.org

For explanation of codes following names, see page B2.
★ Indicates Type III membership in the American Hospital Association.

SANFORD ROCK RAPIDS MEDICAL CENTER (L, 14 beds) 801 South Greene Street, Rock Rapids, IA Zip 51246–1998; tel. 712/472–2591; Tammy Loosbrock, Chief Executive Officer
**Web address:** www.sanfordmerrill.org

SANFORD SHELDON MEDICAL CENTER (O, 95 beds) 118 North Seventh Avenue, Sheldon, IA Zip 51201–1235, Mailing Address: P.O. Box 250, Zip 51201–0250; tel. 712/324–5041; Richard E. Nordahl, Chief Executive Officer
**Web address:** www.sanfordsheldon.org

**MINNESOTA:** MAHNOMEN HEALTH CENTER (C, 68 beds) 414 West Jefferson Avenue, Mahnomen, MN Zip 56557–4912, Mailing Address: P.O. Box 396, Zip 56557–0396; tel. 218/935–2511; Susan K. Klassen, Chief Executive Officer
**Web address:** www.mahnomenhealthcenter.com

MURRAY COUNTY MEDICAL CENTER (C, 18 beds) 2042 Juniper Avenue, Slayton, MN Zip 56172–1017; tel. 507/836–6111; Dennis Goebel, Chief Executive Officer
**Web address:** www.murraycountymed.org

ORTONVILLE AREA HEALTH SERVICES (C, 89 beds) 450 Eastvold Avenue, Ortonville, MN Zip 56278–1133; tel. 320/839–2502; Kevin Benson, Interim Chief Executive Officer
**Web address:** www.oahs.us

PERHAM HEALTH (C, 121 beds) 1000 Coney Street West, Perham, MN Zip 56573–1108; tel. 218/347–4500; Chuck Hofius, Chief Executive Officer
**Web address:** www.perhamhealth.org

SANFORD BAGLEY MEDICAL CENTER (O, 25 beds) 203 Fourth Street N.W., Bagley, MN Zip 56621–8307; tel. 218/694–6501; Sammi Davidson, Administrative Director
**Web address:** www.sanfordhealth.org

SANFORD BEMIDJI MEDICAL CENTER (O, 196 beds) 1300 Anne Street N.W., Bemidji, MN Zip 56601–5103; tel. 218/751–5430; Dan Olson, President
**Web address:** www.nchs.com

SANFORD CANBY MEDICAL CENTER (L, 93 beds) 112 St. Olaf Avenue South, Canby, MN Zip 56220–1433; tel. 507/223–7277; Lori Sisk, R.N., Chief Executive Officer
**Web address:** www.sanfordcanby.org

SANFORD JACKSON MEDICAL CENTER (O, 16 beds) 1430 North Highway, Jackson, MN Zip 56143–1093; tel. 507/847–2420; Mary J. Ruyter, Chief Executive Officer
**Web address:** www.sanfordjackson.org

SANFORD LUVERNE MEDICAL CENTER (O, 25 beds) 1600 North Kniss Avenue, Luverne, MN Zip 56156–1067; tel. 507/283–2321; Tammy Loosbrock, Chief Executive Officer
**Web address:** www.sanfordluverne.org

SANFORD THIEF RIVER FALLS MEDICAL CENTER (O, 35 beds) 120 LaBree Avenue South, Thief River Falls, MN Zip 56701–2840; tel. 218/681–4240; Brian J. Carlson, FACHE, Chief Executive Officer
**Web address:** www.sanfordhealth.org

SANFORD TRACY MEDICAL CENTER (L, 25 beds) 251 Fifth Street East, Tracy, MN Zip 56175–1536; tel. 507/629–3200; Stacy Barstad, Chief Executive Officer
**Web address:** www.sanfordtracy.org

SANFORD WESTBROOK MEDICAL CENTER (L, 6 beds) 920 Bell Avenue, Westbrook, MN Zip 56183–9669, Mailing Address: P.O. Box 188, Zip 56183–0188; tel. 507/274–6121; Stacy Barstad, Chief Executive Officer
**Web address:** www.sanfordwestbrook.org

SANFORD WHEATON MEDICAL CENTER (O, 15 beds) 401 12th Street North, Wheaton, MN Zip 56296–1099; tel. 320/563–8226; JoAnn M. Foltz, R.N., Chief Executive Officer
**Web address:** www.sanfordhealth.org

SANFORD WORTHINGTON MEDICAL CENTER (O, 48 beds) 1018 Sixth Avenue, Worthington, MN Zip 56187–2202, Mailing Address: P.O. Box 997, Zip 56187–0997; tel. 507/372–2941; Michael Hammer, Chief Executive Officer
**Web address:** www.sanfordhealth.org

WINDOM AREA HOSPITAL (C, 25 beds) 2150 Hospital Drive, Windom, MN Zip 56101–0339, Mailing Address: P.O. Box 339, Zip 56101–0339; tel. 507/831–2400; Geraldine F. Burmeister, FACHE, Chief Executive Officer
**Web address:** www.windomareahospital.com

**NORTH DAKOTA:** NORTHWOOD DEACONESS HEALTH CENTER (O, 73 beds) 4 North Park Street, Northwood, ND Zip 58267–4102, Mailing Address: P.O. Box 190, Zip 58267–0190; tel. 701/587–6060; Pete Antonson, Chief Executive Officer
**Web address:** www.ndhc.net

SANFORD BISMARCK (O, 208 beds) 300 North Seventh Street, Bismarck, ND Zip 58501–4439, Mailing Address: P.O. Box 5525, Zip 58506–5525; tel. 701/323–6000; Craig Lambrecht, M.D., President
**Web address:** www.bismarck.sanfordhealth.org/

SANFORD HILLSBORO MEDICAL CENTER (C, 52 beds) 12 Third Street S.E., Hillsboro, ND Zip 58045–4840, Mailing Address: P.O. Box 609, Zip 58045–0609; tel. 701/636–3200; Jac McTaggart, Chief Executive Officer
**Web address:** www.hillsboromedicalcenter.com

SANFORD MAYVILLE MEDICAL CENTER (O, 18 beds) 42 Sixth Avenue S.E., Mayville, ND Zip 58257–1598; tel. 701/786–3800; Roger Baier, Chief Executive Officer
**Web address:** www.unionhospital.com

SANFORD MEDICAL CENTER FARGO (O, 486 beds) 801 Broadway North, Fargo, ND Zip 58122–3641; tel. 701/234–2000; Paul F. Richard, President
**Web address:** www.sanfordhealth.org

**SOUTH DAKOTA:** COMMUNITY MEMORIAL HOSPITAL (C, 16 beds) 809 Jackson Street, Burke, SD Zip 57523–2065, Mailing Address: P.O. Box 319, Zip 57523–0319; tel. 605/775–2621; Mistie Sachtjen, Executive Officer
**Web address:** www.sanfordhealth.org

PIONEER MEMORIAL HOSPITAL AND HEALTH SERVICES (C, 64 beds) 315 North Washington Street, Viborg, SD Zip 57070–2002, Mailing Address: P.O. Box 368, Zip 57070–0368; tel. 605/326–5161; Thomas V. Richter, Chief Executive Officer
**Web address:** www.pioneermemorial.org

SANFORD ABERDEEN MEDICAL CENTER (O, 48 beds) 2905 3rd Avenue S.E., Aberdeen, SD Zip 57401–5420; tel. 605/626–4200; Ashley M. Erickson, Chief Executive Officer
**Web address:** www.sanfordaberdeen.org/

SANFORD CANTON–INWOOD MEDICAL CENTER (O, 16 beds) 440 North Hiawatha Drive, Canton, SD Zip 57013–5800; tel. 605/764–1400; Scott C. Larson, Chief Executive Officer
**Web address:** www.sanfordcantoninwood.org

SANFORD CHAMBERLAIN MEDICAL CENTER (O, 69 beds) 300 South Byron Boulevard, Chamberlain, SD Zip 57325–9741; tel. 605/234–5511; Erica Peterson, Chief Executive Officer
**Web address:** www.sanfordmiddakota.org

SANFORD CLEAR LAKE MEDICAL CENTER (L, 10 beds) 701 Third Avenue South, Clear Lake, SD Zip 57226–2016; tel. 605/874–2141; Lori Sisk, R.N., Chief Executive Officer
**Web address:** www.sanforddeuelcounty.org

SANFORD USD MEDICAL CENTER (O, 511 beds) 1305 West 18th Street, Sioux Falls, SD Zip 57105–0496, Mailing Address: P.O. Box 5039, Zip 57117–5039; tel. 605/333–1000; Paul A. Hanson, FACHE, President
**Web address:** www.sanfordhealth.org

SANFORD VERMILLION MEDICAL CENTER (L, 114 beds) 20 South Plum Street, Vermillion, SD Zip 57069–3346; tel. 605/624–2611; Timothy J. Tracy, Chief Executive Officer
**Web address:** www.sanfordvermillion.org

SANFORD WEBSTER MEDICAL CENTER (L, 25 beds) 1401 West 1st Street, Webster, SD Zip 57274–1054, Mailing Address: P.O. Box 489, Zip 57274–0489; tel. 605/345–3336; David Rogers, Chief Executive Officer
**Web address:** www.sanfordhealth.org

WINNER REGIONAL HEALTHCARE CENTER (C, 104 beds) 745 East Eighth Street, Winner, SD Zip 57580–2631; tel. 605/842–7100; Kevin Coffey, Chief Executive Officer
**Web address:** www.winnerregional.org

| | | |
|---|---|---|
| Owned, leased, sponsored: | 23 hospitals | 2171 beds |
| Contract–managed: | 10 hospitals | 665 beds |
| **Totals:** | 33 hospitals | 2836 beds |

For explanation of codes following names, see page B2.
★ Indicates Type III membership in the American Hospital Association.

Section B

**0412:  SCHUYLKILL HEALTH SYSTEM** (NP)
420 South Jackson Street, Pottsville, PA Zip 17901–3625;
tel. 570/621–5000; Marc H. Lory, Interim Chief Executive Officer
**(Independent Hospital System)**

**PENNSYLVANIA:** SCHUYLKILL MEDICAL CENTER – EAST NORWEGIAN
STREET (O, 109 beds) 700 East Norwegian Street, Pottsville, PA
Zip 17901–2710; tel. 570/621–4000; Mark H. Lory, Chief Executive
Officer
**Web address:** www.schuylkillhealth.com

SCHUYLKILL MEDICAL CENTER – SOUTH JACKSON STREET (O, 190 beds)
420 South Jackson Street, Pottsville, PA Zip 17901–3625;
tel. 570/621–5000; Mark H. Lory, Chief Executive Officer
**Web address:** www.schuylkillhealth.com

| | | |
|---|---|---|
| Owned, leased, sponsored: | 2 hospitals | 299 beds |
| Contract–managed: | 0 hospitals | 0 beds |
| Totals: | 2 hospitals | 299 beds |

★**5095:  SCL HEALTH** (CC)
500 Eldorado Boulevard, Suite 100–D, Broomfield, CO Zip 80021;
tel. 303/813–5180; Michael A. Slubowski, FACHE, Chief Executive
Officer
**(Moderately Centralized Health System)**

**COLORADO:** GOOD SAMARITAN MEDICAL CENTER (S, 183 beds) 200
Exempla Circle, Lafayette, CO Zip 80026–3370; tel. 303/689–4000;
David Hamm, President and Chief Executive Officer
**Web address:** www.exempla.org

LUTHERAN MEDICAL CENTER (S, 475 beds) 8300 West 38th Avenue, Wheat
Ridge, CO Zip 80033–6005; tel. 303/425–4500; Grant Wicklund, President
and Chief Executive Officer
**Web address:** www.exempla.org

SAINT JOSEPH HOSPITAL (S, 400 beds) 1835 Franklin Street, Denver, CO
Zip 80218–1126; tel. 303/837–7111; Bain J. Farris, President and Chief
Executive Officer
**Web address:** www.exempla.org

ST. MARY'S MEDICAL CENTER (O, 346 beds) 2635 North 7th Street, Grand
Junction, CO Zip 81501–8209, Mailing Address: P.O. Box 1628,
Zip 81502–1628; tel. 970/298–2273; Michael J. McBride, FACHE, President
and Chief Executive Officer
**Web address:** www.stmarygj.com

**KANSAS:** ST. FRANCIS HEALTH (O, 259 beds) 1700 S.W. 7th Street, Topeka,
KS Zip 66606–1690; tel. 785/295–8000; David P. Setchel, President
**Web address:** www.stfrancistopeka.org

**MONTANA:** HOLY ROSARY HEALTHCARE (O, 90 beds) 2600 Wilson Street,
Miles City, MT Zip 59301–5094; tel. 406/233–2600; Paul Lewis, Chief
Executive Officer
**Web address:** www.holyrosaryhealthcare.org

ST. JAMES HEALTHCARE (O, 67 beds) 400 South Clark Street, Butte, MT
Zip 59701–2328; tel. 406/723–2500; Charles T. Wright, President and Chief
Executive Officer
**Web address:** www.stjameshealthcare.org

ST. VINCENT HEALTHCARE (O, 221 beds) 1233 North 30th Street, Billings,
MT Zip 59101–0165, Mailing Address: P.O. Box 35200, Zip 59107–5200;
tel. 406/237–7000; Steve Loveless, President and Chief Executive Officer
**Web address:** www.svh-mt.org

| | | |
|---|---|---|
| Owned, leased, sponsored: | 8 hospitals | 2041 beds |
| Contract–managed: | 0 hospitals | 0 beds |
| Totals: | 8 hospitals | 2041 beds |

★**1505:  SCRIPPS HEALTH** (NP)
4275 Campus Point Court, San Diego, CA Zip 92121–1513;
tel. 858/678–7200; Chris D. Van Gorder, FACHE, President and
Chief Executive Officer
**(Centralized Health System)**

**CALIFORNIA:** SCRIPPS GREEN HOSPITAL (O, 173 beds) 10666 North Torrey
Pines Road, La Jolla, CA Zip 92037–1093; tel. 858/455–9100; Robin
Brown, Chief Executive, Senior Vice President
**Web address:** www.scrippshealth.org

SCRIPPS MEMORIAL HOSPITAL–ENCINITAS (O, 194 beds) 354 Santa Fe
Drive, Encinitas, CA Zip 92024–5182, Mailing Address: P.O. Box 230817,
Zip 92023–0817; tel. 760/633–6501; Carl J. Etter, Chief Executive and
Senior Vice President
**Web address:** www.scripps.org

SCRIPPS MEMORIAL HOSPITAL–LA JOLLA (O, 194 beds) 9888 Genesee
Avenue, La Jolla, CA Zip 92037–1200, Mailing Address: P.O. Box 28,
Zip 92038–0028; tel. 858/626–4123; Gary G. Fybel, Chief Executive, Senior
Vice President
**Web address:** www.scripps.org/locations/hospitals__
scripps–memorial–hospital–la–jolla

SCRIPPS MERCY HOSPITAL (O, 436 beds) 4077 Fifth Avenue, San Diego, CA
Zip 92103–2105; tel. 619/294–8111; Thomas A. Gammiere, Chief
Executive, Senior Vice President
**Web address:** www.scrippshealth.org

| | | |
|---|---|---|
| Owned, leased, sponsored: | 4 hospitals | 997 beds |
| Contract–managed: | 0 hospitals | 0 beds |
| Totals: | 4 hospitals | 997 beds |

★**0181:  SELECT MEDICAL CORPORATION** (IO)
4714 Gettysburg Road, Mechanicsburg, PA Zip 17055–4325;
tel. 717/972–1100; David S. Chernow, President and Chief
Executive Officer
**(Independent Hospital System)**

**ALABAMA:** SELECT SPECIALTY HOSPITAL–BIRMINGHAM (O, 38 beds) 800
Montclair Road, 9th Floor, Birmingham, AL Zip 35213–1908;
tel. 205/599–4600; Andrea White, Chief Executive Officer
**Web address:** www.selectspecialtyhospitals.
com/company/locations/birmingham.aspx

**ARIZONA:** HONORHEALTH REHABILITATION HOSPITAL (O, 50 beds) 8850
East Pima Center Parkway, Scottsdale, AZ Zip 85258–4619;
tel. 480/800–3900; Scott R. Keen, Chief Executive Officer
**Web address:** www.scottsdale–rehab.com/

SELECT SPECIALTY HOSPITAL–PHOENIX (O, 48 beds) 350 West Thomas
Road, 3rd Floor Main, Phoenix, AZ Zip 85013–4409; tel. 602/406–6802;
Sharon Anthony, Interim Chief Executive Officer
**Web address:** www.selectspecialtyhospitals.
com/company/locations/phoenix.aspx

SELECT SPECIALTY HOSPITAL–SCOTTSDALE (O, 62 beds) 7400 East Osborn
Road, 3 West, Scottsdale, AZ Zip 85251–6432; tel. 480/882–4360; Anthony
Martino, Chief Executive Officer
**Web address:** www.selectspecialtyhospitals.
com/company/locations/scottsdale.aspx

**ARKANSAS:** REGENCY HOSPITAL OF NORTHWEST ARKANSAS – SPRINGDALE
(O, 25 beds) 609 West Maple Avenue, 6th Floor, Springdale, AR
Zip 72764; tel. 479/757–2600; Jerry Alexander, Chief Executive Officer
**Web address:** www.regencyhospital.com

SELECT SPECIALTY HOSPITAL–FORT SMITH (O, 34 beds) 1001 Towson
Avenue, 6 Central, Fort Smith, AR Zip 72901–4921; tel. 479/441–3960;
Cindy McLain, Chief Executive Officer
**Web address:** www.selectspecialtyhospitals.
com/company/locations/fortsmith.aspx

**COLORADO:** SELECT LONG TERM CARE HOSPITAL – COLORADO SPRINGS
(O, 30 beds) 6001 East Woodmen Road, 6th Floor, Colorado Springs, CO
Zip 80923–2601; tel. 719/571–6000; Kent Helwig, Chief Executive
Officer
**Web address:** www.coloradosprings.selectspecialtyhospitals.com/

SELECT SPECIALTY HOSPITAL–DENVER (O, 22 beds) 1719 East 19th
Avenue, 5B, Denver, CO Zip 80218–1235; tel. 303/563–3700; George
Welton, Chief Executive Officer
**Web address:** www.selectspecialtyhospitals.com/company/locations/denver.
aspx

**DELAWARE:** SELECT SPECIALTY HOSPITAL–WILMINGTON (O, 35 beds) 701
North Clayton Street, 5th Floor, Wilmington, DE Zip 19805–3948;
tel. 302/421–4545; Donna Gares, R.N., FACHE, MSN, Chief Executive
Officer
**Web address:** www.wilmington.selectspecialtyhospitals.com

For explanation of codes following names, see page B2.
★ Indicates Type III membership in the American Hospital Association.

**FLORIDA:** SELECT SPECIALTY HOSPITAL DAYTONA BEACH (O, 34 beds) 301 Memorial Medical Parkway, 11th Floor, Daytona Beach, FL Zip 32117–5167; tel. 386/231–3436; Adrianne Lutes, Chief Executive Officer
**Web address:** www.daytonabeach.selectspecialtyhospitals.com

SELECT SPECIALTY HOSPITAL–GAINESVILLE (O, 44 beds) 2708 S.W. Archer Road, Gainesville, FL Zip 32608–1316; tel. 352/337–3240; Kristopher Kitzke, Chief Executive Officer
**Web address:** www.selectspecialtyhospitals. com/company/locations/gainesville.aspx

SELECT SPECIALTY HOSPITAL–MIAMI (O, 47 beds) 955 N.W. 3rd Street, Miami, FL Zip 33128–1274; tel. 305/416–5700; Dionisio Bencomo, Chief Executive Officer
**Web address:** www.selectspecialtyhospitals.com/company/locations/miami. aspx

SELECT SPECIALTY HOSPITAL–ORLANDO (O, 75 beds) 2250 Bedford Road, Orlando, FL Zip 32803–1443; tel. 407/303–7869; Nellie Castroman, Chief Executive Officer
**Web address:** www.selectspecialtyhospitals. com/company/locations/orlando.aspx

SELECT SPECIALTY HOSPITAL–PALM BEACH (O, 60 beds) 3060 Melaleuca Lane, Lake Worth, FL Zip 33461–5174; tel. 561/357–7200; Larry Melby, Chief Executive Officer
**Web address:** www.selectspecialtyhospitals. com/company/locations/palmbeach.aspx

SELECT SPECIALTY HOSPITAL–PANAMA CITY (O, 30 beds) 615 North Bonita Avenue, 3rd Floor, Panama City, FL Zip 32401–3623; tel. 850/767–3180; Randal S. Hamilton, Chief Executive Officer
**Web address:** www.selectspecialtyhospitals. com/company/locations/panamacity.aspx

SELECT SPECIALTY HOSPITAL–PENSACOLA (O, 75 beds) 7000 Cobble Creek Drive, Pensacola, FL Zip 32504–8638; tel. 850/473–4800; David Goodson, Chief Executive Officer
**Web address:** www.selectspecialtyhospitals. com/company/locations/pensacola.aspx

SELECT SPECIALTY HOSPITAL–TALLAHASSEE (O, 29 beds) 1554 Surgeons Drive, Tallahassee, FL Zip 32308–4631; tel. 850/219–6800; Lora Davis, Chief Executive Officer
**Web address:** www.tallahassee.selectspecialtyhospitals.com/

WEST GABLES REHABILITATION HOSPITAL (O, 60 beds) 2525 S.W. 75th Avenue, Miami, FL Zip 33155–2800; tel. 305/262–6800; Walter Concepcion, Chief Executive Officer
**Web address:** www.westgablesrehabhospital.com/

**GEORGIA:** REGENCY HOSPITAL OF CENTRAL GEORGIA (O, 60 beds) 535 Coliseum Drive, Macon, GA Zip 31217–0104; tel. 478/803–7300; Michael S. Boggs, Chief Executive Officer
**Web address:** www.regencyhospital.com

REGENCY HOSPITAL OF SOUTH ATLANTA (O, 40 beds) 1170 Cleveland Avenue, 4th Floor, East Point, GA Zip 30344–3615; tel. 404/466–6250; Lorie Powell, Interim Chief Executive Officer
**Web address:** www.regencyhospital.com

SELECT SPECIALTY HOSPITAL – NORTHEAST ATLANTA (O, 18 beds) 1821 Clifton Road N.E., 2nd Floor, Atlanta, GA Zip 30329–4021; tel. 404/728–6200; Matthew Paul Pearson, Chief Executive Officer
**Web address:** www.selectspecialtyhospitals.com/

SELECT SPECIALTY HOSPITAL–ATLANTA (O, 30 beds) 550 Peachtree Street N.E., Atlanta, GA Zip 30308–2247; tel. 404/815–0348; Dwayne Hooks, Jr., R.N., Chief Executive Officer
**Web address:** www.selectspecialtyhospitals.com/company/locations/atlanta. aspx

SELECT SPECIALTY HOSPITAL–AUGUSTA (O, 80 beds) 1537 Walton Way, Augusta, GA Zip 30904–3764; tel. 706/731–1200; Curtis L. Roberts, Chief Executive Officer
**Web address:** www.augusta.selectspecialtyhospitals.com

SELECT SPECIALTY HOSPITAL–SAVANNAH (O, 40 beds) 5353 Reynolds Street, 4 South, Savannah, GA Zip 31405–6015; tel. 912/819–7972; Patrick McVey, Chief Executive Officer
**Web address:** www.selectspecialtyhospitals. com/company/locations/savannah.aspx

**INDIANA:** REGENCY HOSPITAL OF NORTHWEST INDIANA (O, 61 beds) 4321 Fir Street, 4th Floor, East Chicago, IN Zip 46312–3049; tel. 219/392–7799; Cheryl G. Gentry, Chief Executive Officer
**Web address:** www.regencyhospital. com/company/locations/indiana–northwest–indiana.aspx

SELECT SPECIALTY HOSPITAL–EVANSVILLE (O, 60 beds) 400 S.E. 4th Street, Evansville, IN Zip 47713–1206; tel. 812/421–2500; Mike Carney, Chief Executive Officer
**Web address:** www.selectspecialtyhospitals. com/company/locations/evansville.aspx

SELECT SPECIALTY HOSPITAL–FORT WAYNE (O, 32 beds) 700 Broadway, 7th Floor, Fort Wayne, IN Zip 46802–1402; tel. 260/425–3810; Teresa R. Detano, M.P.H., Chief Executive Officer
**Web address:** www.fortwayne.selectspecialtyhospitals.com

SELECT SPECIALTY HOSPITAL–INDIANAPOLIS (O, 45 beds) 8060 Knue Road, Indianapolis, IN Zip 46250–1976; tel. 317/783–8985; Rick Ament, Chief Executive Officer
**Web address:** www.indianapolis.selectspecialtyhospitals.com/

**IOWA:** SELECT SPECIALTY HOSPITAL–DES MOINES (O, 30 beds) 1111 6th Avenue, 4th Floor Main, Des Moines, IA Zip 50314–2610; tel. 515/247–4400; Glen Griesheim, Chief Executive Officer
**Web address:** www.selectspecialtyhospitals.com

SELECT SPECIALTY HOSPITAL–QUAD CITIES (O, 48 beds) 1111 West Kimberly Road, Davenport, IA Zip 52806–5711; tel. 563/468–2000; Connie K. Siffring, Chief Executive Officer
**Web address:** www.selectmedicalcorp.com

**KANSAS:** SELECT SPECIALTY HOSPITAL–KANSAS CITY (O, 40 beds) 1731 North 90th Street, Kansas City, KS Zip 66112–1515; tel. 913/732–5900; Brian Jones, Interim Chief Executive Officer
**Web address:** www.selectspecialtyhospitals.com

SELECT SPECIALTY HOSPITAL–WICHITA (O, 48 beds) 929 North St. Francis Street, Wichita, KS Zip 67214–3821; tel. 316/261–8303; Peggy Cliffe, Chief Executive Officer
**Web address:** www.selectspecialtyhospitals.com/company/locations/wichita. aspx

**KENTUCKY:** SELECT SPECIALTY HOSPITAL–LEXINGTON (O, 41 beds) 310 South Limestone Street, 3rd Floor, Lexington, KY Zip 40508–3008; tel. 859/226–7096; Mary Lou Guinle, FACHE, Chief Executive Officer
**Web address:** www.lexington.selectspecialtyhospitals.com/

SELECT SPECIALTY HOSPITAL–NORTHERN KENTUCKY (O, 33 beds) 85 North Grand Avenue, Fort Thomas, KY Zip 41075–1793; tel. 859/572–3880; Victor J. Galfano, FACHE, Chief Executive Officer
**Web address:** www.selectspecialtyhospitals. com/company/locations/northern–kentucky.aspx

**LOUISIANA:** REGENCY HOSPITAL OF COVINGTON (O, 38 beds) 195 Highland Park Entrance, Covington, LA Zip 70433–7164; tel. 985/867–3977; Racheal Z. Fischer, Interim Chief Executive Officer
**Web address:** www.regencyhospital.com

**MICHIGAN:** GREAT LAKES SPECIALTY HOSPITAL–GRAND RAPIDS (O, 20 beds) 200 S.E. Jefferson Avenue, 5th Floor, Grand Rapids, MI Zip 49503–4502; tel. 616/965–8650; Jevne Conover, Chief Executive Officer
**Web address:** www.selectmedicalcorp.com

GREAT LAKES SPECIALTY HOSPITAL–MUSKEGON (O, 31 beds) 1700 Clinton Street, 3 South, Muskegon, MI Zip 49442–5502; tel. 231/728–5811; Sharon Purkis, Chief Executive Officer
**Web address:** www.greatlakesspecialtyhospital.com

SELECT SPECIALTY HOSPITAL–ANN ARBOR (O, 36 beds) 5301 East Huron River Drive, 5th Floor, Ypsilanti, MI Zip 48197–1051; tel. 734/712–0111; John F. O'Malley, FACHE, Chief Executive Officer
**Web address:** www.selectspecialtyhospitals. com/company/locations/annarbor.aspx

SELECT SPECIALTY HOSPITAL–BATTLE CREEK (O, 25 beds) 300 North Avenue, Battle Creek, MI Zip 49017–3307; tel. 269/245–4675; Salvatore Iweimrin, R.N., Chief Executive Officer
**Web address:** www.battlecreek.selectspecialtyhospitals.com/

SELECT SPECIALTY HOSPITAL–DOWNRIVER (O, 35 beds) 2333 Biddle Avenue, 8th Floor, Wyandotte, MI Zip 48192–4668; tel. 734/246–5500; Douglas R. Dascenzo, MSN, R.N., Chief Executive Officer
**Web address:** www.downriver.selectspecialtyhospitals.com/

Section B

For explanation of codes following names, see page B2.
★ Indicates Type III membership in the American Hospital Association.

SELECT SPECIALTY HOSPITAL–FLINT (O, 26 beds) 401 South Ballenger Highway, 5th Floor Central, Flint, MI Zip 48532–3638; tel. 810/342–4500; Patricia Adams, Chief Executive Officer
**Web address:** www.selectspecialtyhospitals.com/company/locations/flint. aspx

SELECT SPECIALTY HOSPITAL–GROSSE POINTE (O, 30 beds) 468 Cadieux Road, 3 North East, Grosse Pointe, MI Zip 48230–1507; tel. 313/473–6131; Miriam Deemer, Chief Executive Officer
**Web address:** www.grossepointe.selectspecialtyhospitals.com/

SELECT SPECIALTY HOSPITAL–MACOMB COUNTY (O, 36 beds) 215 North Avenue, Mount Clemens, MI Zip 48043–1700; tel. 586/307–9000; Jon P. O'Malley, Chief Executive Officer
**Web address:** www.macomb.selectspecialtyhospitals.com/

SELECT SPECIALTY HOSPITAL–NORTHWEST DETROIT (O, 36 beds) 6071 West Outer Drive, Detroit, MI Zip 48235–2624; tel. 313/966–4747; Marilouise Riska, Chief Executive Officer
**Web address:** www.selectspecialtyhospitals. com/company/locations/northwestdetroit.aspx

SELECT SPECIALTY HOSPITAL–PONTIAC (O, 30 beds) 44405 Woodward Avenue, 8th Floor, Pontiac, MI Zip 48341–5023; tel. 248/452–5252; Peggy Kingston, Chief Executive Officer
**Web address:** www.selectspecialtyhospitals. com/company/locations/pontiac.aspx

SELECT SPECIALTY HOSPITAL–SAGINAW (O, 32 beds) 1447 North Harrison Street, 8th Floor, Saginaw, MI Zip 48602–4785; tel. 989/583–4235; Matthew Cannon, Chief Executive Officer
**Web address:** www.selectspecialtyhospitals. com/company/locations/saginaw.aspx

**MINNESOTA:** REGENCY HOSPITAL OF MINNEAPOLIS (O, 92 beds) 1300 Hidden Lakes Parkway, Golden Valley, MN Zip 55422–4286; tel. 763/588–2750; Marshall E. Smith, Chief Executive Officer
**Web address:** www.regencyhospital.com

**MISSISSIPPI:** REGENCY HOSPITAL OF HATTIESBURG (O, 33 beds) 6051 U.S. Highway 495, 5th Floor, Hattiesburg, MS Zip 39401–6031; tel. 601/288–8510; Rachael Fisher, Chief Executive Officer
**Web address:** www.regencyhospital.com/hattiesburg

REGENCY HOSPITAL OF JACKSON (O, 36 beds) 969 Lakeland Drive, 6th Floor, Jackson, MS Zip 39216–4643; tel. 601/364–6200; R. Shannon Canard, Chief Executive Officer
**Web address:** www.regencyhospital.com

REGENCY HOSPITAL OF MERIDIAN (O, 40 beds) 1102 Constitution Avenue, 2nd Floor, Meridian, MS Zip 39301–4001; tel. 601/484–7900; Clifton Quinn, Chief Executive Officer
**Web address:** www.regencyhospital.com

SELECT SPECIALTY HOSPITAL–GULFPORT (O, 61 beds) 1520 Broad Avenue, Suite 300, Gulfport, MS Zip 39501–3601; tel. 228/575–7500; John O'Keefe, Chief Executive Officer
**Web address:** www.selectspecialtyhospitals. com/company/locations/gulfcoast.aspx

SELECT SPECIALTY HOSPITAL–JACKSON (O, 53 beds) 5903 Ridgewood Road, Suite 100, Jackson, MS Zip 39211–3700; tel. 601/899–3800; Chandler Ewing, Chief Executive Officer
**Web address:** www.selectspecialtyhospitals. com/company/locations/jackson.aspx

**MISSOURI:** SELECT SPECIALTY HOSPITAL–SPRINGFIELD (O, 44 beds) 1630 East Primrose Street, Springfield, MO Zip 65804–7929; tel. 417/885–4700; Mark S. Brodeur, FACHE, Chief Executive Officer
**Web address:** www.selectspecialtyhospitals. com/company/locations/springfield.aspx

SELECT SPECIALTY HOSPITAL–ST. LOUIS (O, 33 beds) 300 First Capitol Drive, Unit 1, Saint Charles, MO Zip 63301–2844; tel. 636/947–5010; Patrice L. Komoroski, Ph.D., R.N., Chief Executive Officer
**Web address:** www.selectspecialtyhospitals.com/company/locations/stlouis. aspx

SELECT SPECIALTY HOSPITAL–WESTERN MISSOURI (O, 34 beds) 2316 East Meyer Boulevard, 3 West, Kansas City, MO Zip 64132–1136; tel. 816/276–3300; Jeffrey Alexander, Chief Executive Officer
**Web address:** www.selectspecialtyhospitals. com/company/locations/westernmissouri.aspx

SSM SELECT REHABILITATION HOSPITAL (O, 95 beds) 1027 Bellevue Avenue, 3rd Floor, Richmond Heights, MO Zip 63117–1851, Mailing Address: 1027 Bellevue Avenue, Zip 63117–1851; tel. 314/768–5300; Timothy Wadman, Chief Executive Officer
**Web address:** www.ssm–select.com

**NEBRASKA:** SELECT SPECIALTY HOSPITAL – LINCOLN (O, 24 beds) 2300 South 16th Street, 7th Floor, Lincoln, NE Zip 68502–3704; tel. 402/483–8444; Scott Butterfield, Chief Executive Officer

SELECT SPECIALTY HOSPITAL–OMAHA (O, 52 beds) 1870 South 75th Street, Omaha, NE Zip 68124–1700; tel. 402/361–5700; Thomas N. Theroult, ACHE, Chief Executive Officer
**Web address:** www.selectspecialtyhospitals. com/company/locations/omahacentral.aspx

**NEW JERSEY:** KESSLER INSTITUTE FOR REHABILITATION (O, 336 beds) 1199 Pleasant Valley Way, West Orange, NJ Zip 07052–1424; tel. 973/731–3600; Robert Brehm, President
**Web address:** www.kessler-rehab.com

SELECT SPECIALTY HOSPITAL–NORTHEAST NEW JERSEY (O, 62 beds) 96 Parkway, Rochelle Park, NJ Zip 07662–4200; tel. 201/221–2358; Barbara E. Hannan, MS, R.N., Chief Executive Officer
**Web address:** www.selectspecialtyhospitals. com/company/locations/northeastnewjersey.aspx

**NORTH CAROLINA:** SELECT SPECIALTY HOSPITAL–DURHAM (O, 30 beds) 3643 North Roxboro Road, 6th Floor, Durham, NC Zip 27704–2702; tel. 919/470–9137; Theresa Hunkins, R.N., Chief Executive Officer
**Web address:** www.selectspecialtyhospitals. com/company/locations/durham.aspx

SELECT SPECIALTY HOSPITAL–GREENSBORO (O, 30 beds) 1200 North Elm Street, 5th Floor, Greensboro, NC Zip 27401–1004; tel. 336/832–8571; Deana Knight, Chief Executive Officer
**Web address:** www.selectspecialtyhospitals. com/company/locations/greensboro.aspx

SELECT SPECIALTY HOSPITAL–WINSTON–SALEM (O, 42 beds) 3333 Silas Creek Parkway, 6th Floor, Winston–Salem, NC Zip 27103–3013; tel. 336/718–6300; Leslie Deane, Chief Executive Officer
**Web address:** www.selectspecialtyhospitals. com/company/locations/winston–salem.aspx

**OHIO:** OHIOHEALTH REHABILITATION HOSPITAL (O, 43 beds) 1087 Dennison Avenue, 4th Floor, Columbus, OH Zip 43201–3201; tel. 614/484–9600; Eric Yap, Chief Executive Officer
**Web address:** www.ohiohealth–rehab.com

REGENCY HOSPITAL CLEVELAND EAST (O, 132 beds) 4200 Interchange Corporate Center Road, Warrensville Heights, OH Zip 44128–5631; tel. 216/910–3800; Thomas Knoske, Chief Executive Officer
**Web address:** www.regencyhospital.com/

REGENCY HOSPITAL OF COLUMBUS (O, 43 beds) 1430 South High Street, Columbus, OH Zip 43207–1045; tel. 614/456–0300; Lisa J. Pettrey, MSN, R.N., Chief Executive Officer
**Web address:** www.regencyhospital.com/

REGENCY HOSPITAL OF TOLEDO (O, 45 beds) 5220 Alexis Road, Sylvania, OH Zip 43560–2504; tel. 419/318–5700; Matt Cannon, Chief Executive Officer
**Web address:** www.regencyhospital.com

SELECT SPECIALTY HOSPITAL – CINCINNATI NORTH (O, 41 beds) 10500 Montgomery Road, Cincinnati, OH Zip 45242–4402; tel. 513/865–5300; Susan Glen, Chief Executive Officer
**Web address:** www.cincinnatinorth.selectspecialtyhospitals.com/

SELECT SPECIALTY HOSPITAL – YOUNGSTOWN (O, 56 beds) 8401 Market Street, 7 South, Boardman, OH Zip 44512–6725; tel. 330/729–1750; Sharon Noro, Interim Chief Executive Officer

SELECT SPECIALTY HOSPITAL–AKRON (O, 60 beds) 200 East Market Street, Akron, OH Zip 44308–2015; tel. 330/761–7500; Sonda Burns, Chief Executive Officer
**Web address:** www.selectspecialtyhospitals.com/company/locations/akron. aspx

SELECT SPECIALTY HOSPITAL–CANTON (O, 30 beds) 1320 Mercy Drive N.W., 6th Floor, Canton, OH Zip 44708–2614; tel. 330/489–8189; Dawne Wheeler, Chief Executive Officer
**Web address:** www.selectspecialtyhospitals.com/company/locations/canton. aspx

For explanation of codes following names, see page B2.
★ Indicates Type III membership in the American Hospital Association.

SELECT SPECIALTY HOSPITAL–CINCINNATI (O, 36 beds) 375 Dixmyth Avenue, 15th Floor, Cincinnati, OH Zip 45220–2475; tel. 513/872–4444; Curtis Ohashi, Chief Executive Officer
**Web address:** www.selectspecialtyhospitals.com/company/locations/cincinnati.aspx

SELECT SPECIALTY HOSPITAL–COLUMBUS (O, 186 beds) 1087 Dennison Avenue, Columbus, OH Zip 43201–3201; tel. 614/458–9000; Patrick Tuer, Chief Executive Officer
**Web address:** www.selectspecialtyhospitals.com/company/locations/columbus.aspx

SELECT SPECIALTY HOSPITAL–YOUNGSTOWN (O, 51 beds) 1044 Belmont Avenue, Youngstown, OH Zip 44504–1006; tel. 330/480–2349; Sharon Noro, Chief Executive Officer
**Web address:** www.selectspecialtyhospitals.com/company/locations/youngstown.aspx

SELECT SPECIALTY HOSPITAL OF SOUTHEAST OHIO (O, 35 beds) 800 Forest Avenue, 6th Floor, Zanesville, OH Zip 43701–2882; tel. 740/588–7888; Linda Supplee, Chief Executive Officer
**Web address:** www.selectspecialtyhospitals.com/company/locations/zanesville.aspx

**OKLAHOMA:** SELECT SPECIALTY HOSPITAL–OKLAHOMA CITY (O, 72 beds) 3524 N.W. 56th Street, Oklahoma City, OK Zip 73112–4518; tel. 405/606–6700; Connie Strickland, Chief Executive Officer
**Web address:** www.selectspecialtyhospitals.com/company/locations/oklahomacity.aspx

SELECT SPECIALTY HOSPITAL–TULSA MIDTOWN (O, 56 beds) 1125 South Trenton Avenue, 3rd Floor, Tulsa, OK Zip 74120–5418; tel. 918/579–7300; Linda Tiemens, Chief Executive Officer
**Web address:** www.selectmedical.com

**PENNSYLVANIA:** HELEN M. SIMPSON REHABILITATION HOSPITAL (C, 55 beds) 4300 Londonderry Road, Harrisburg, PA Zip 17109–5317; tel. 717/920–4300; Melissa Gillis, Chief Executive Officer

PENN STATE HERSHEY REHABILITATION HOSPITAL (O, 32 beds) 1135 Old West Chocolate Avenue, Hummelstown, PA Zip 17036; tel. 717/832–2600; Scott Guevin, Chief Executive Officer
**Web address:** www.psh–rehab.com

SELECT SPECIALTY HOSPITAL–CENTRAL PENNSYLVANIA (O, 61 beds) 503 North 21st Street, 5th Floor, Camp Hill, PA Zip 17011–2204; tel. 717/972–4575; Tom Mullin, Chief Executive Officer
**Web address:** www.selectspecialtyhospitals.com/company/locations/camphill.aspx

SELECT SPECIALTY HOSPITAL–DANVILLE (O, 30 beds) 100 North Academy Avenue, 3rd Floor, Danville, PA Zip 17822–3050; tel. 570/214–9653; Brian Mann, Chief Executive Officer
**Web address:** www.selectspecialtyhospitals.com/company/locations/danville.aspx

SELECT SPECIALTY HOSPITAL–ERIE (O, 50 beds) 252 West 11th Street, Erie, PA Zip 16501–1702; tel. 814/874–5300; Randy Neiswonger, Chief Executive Officer
**Web address:** www.erie.selectspecialtyhospitals.com/

SELECT SPECIALTY HOSPITAL–JOHNSTOWN (O, 39 beds) 320 Main Street, 3rd Floor, Johnstown, PA Zip 15901–1601; tel. 814/534–7300; Kelly Blake, Chief Executive Officer
**Web address:** www.selectspecialtyhospitals.com/company/locations/johnstown.aspx

SELECT SPECIALTY HOSPITAL–LAUREL HIGHLANDS (O, 40 beds) One Mellon Way, 3rd Floor, Latrobe, PA Zip 15650–1197; tel. 724/539–3230; Laurie Kozorosky, Chief Executive Officer
**Web address:** www.selectspecialtyhospitals.com/company/locations/laurelhighlands.aspx

SELECT SPECIALTY HOSPITAL–MCKEESPORT (O, 30 beds) 1500 Fifth Avenue, 6th Floor, McKeesport, PA Zip 15132–2422; tel. 412/664–2900; Angela Merryman, Chief Executive Officer
**Web address:** www.mckeesport.selectspecialtyhospitals.com/

SELECT SPECIALTY HOSPITAL–PITTSBURGH/UPMC (O, 32 beds) 200 Lothrop Street, E824, Pittsburgh, PA Zip 15213–2536; tel. 412/586–9800; John St. Leger, Chief Executive Officer
**Web address:** www.selectspecialtyhospitals.com/company/locations/pittsburghupmc.aspx

**SOUTH CAROLINA:** REGENCY HOSPITAL OF FLORENCE (O, 40 beds) 121 East Cedar Street, 4th Floor, Florence, SC Zip 29506–2576; tel. 843/661–3471; Amy Metz, Chief Executive Officer
**Web address:** www.regencyhospital.com

REGENCY HOSPITAL OF GREENVILLE (O, 32 beds) One St. Francis Drive, 4th Floor, Greenville, SC Zip 29601–3955; tel. 864/255–1438; Stephanie James, Chief Executive Officer
**Web address:** www.regencyhospital.com

**SOUTH DAKOTA:** SELECT SPECIALTY HOSPITAL–SIOUX FALLS (O, 24 beds) 1305 West 18th Street, Sioux Falls, SD Zip 57105–0401; tel. 605/312–9500; Carol Ulmer, Chief Executive Officer
**Web address:** www.selectspecialtyhospitals.com/company/locations/siouxfalls.aspx

**TENNESSEE:** SELECT SPECIALTY HOSPITAL–KNOXVILLE (O, 35 beds) 1901 Clinch Avenue, 4th Floor North, Knoxville, TN Zip 37916–2307; tel. 865/541–2615; Steve Plumlee, Interim Chief Executive Officer
**Web address:** www.knoxville.selectspecialtyhospitals.com/

SELECT SPECIALTY HOSPITAL–MEMPHIS (O, 39 beds) 5959 Park Avenue, 12th Floor, Memphis, TN Zip 38119–5200; tel. 901/765–1245; Patricia A. Rice, Chief Executive Officer
**Web address:** www.selectspecialtyhospitals.com/company/locations/memphis.aspx

SELECT SPECIALTY HOSPITAL–NASHVILLE (O, 47 beds) 2000 Hayes Street, Nashville, TN Zip 37203–2318; tel. 615/284–4599; Jennifer Causey, Chief Executive Officer
**Web address:** www.selectspecialtyhospitals.com/company/locations/nashville.aspx

SELECT SPECIALTY HOSPITAL–NORTH KNOXVILLE (O, 33 beds) 7557B Dannaher Drive, Suite 145, Powell, TN Zip 37849–3568; tel. 865/512–2450; Steve Plumlee, Chief Executive Officer
**Web address:** www.northknoxville.selectspecialtyhospitals.com/

SELECT SPECIALTY HOSPITAL–TRI CITIES (O, 33 beds) One Medical Park Boulevard, 5th Floor, Bristol, TN Zip 37620–8964; tel. 423/844–5900; ,
**Web address:** www.selectspecialtyhospitals.com/company/locations/tricities.aspx

**TEXAS:** BAYLOR INSTITUTE FOR REHABILITATION AT FRISCO (O, 44 beds) 2990 Legacy Drive, Frisco, TX Zip 75034–6066; tel. 469/888–5100; Mark D. Boles, Chief Executive Officer
**Web address:** www.baylorhealth.com/bir

REGENCY HOSPITAL OF FORT WORTH (O, 44 beds) 6801 Oakmont Boulevard, Fort Worth, TX Zip 76132–3918; tel. 817/840–2500; Natalie D. Lamberton, Chief Executive Officer
**Web address:** www.regencyhospital.com

SELECT REHABILITATION HOSPITAL OF DENTON (O, 44 beds) 2620 Scripture Street, Denton, TX Zip 76201–4315; tel. 940/297–6500; Michelle Powell, Chief Executive Officer
**Web address:** www.selectrehab–denton.com/

SELECT SPECIALTY HOSPITAL – DALLAS DOWNTOWN (O, 46 beds) 3500 Gaston Avenue, Floors 3&4 Jonnson, Dallas, TX Zip 75246–2017; tel. 409/801–4500; Melody Nagel, Chief Executive Officer
**Web address:** www.dallasdowntown.selectspecialtyhospitals.com/

SELECT SPECIALTY HOSPITAL – DALLAS GARLAND (O, 40 beds) 2300 Marie Curie Drive, Floors 3E and 3W, Garland, TX Zip 75042–5706; tel. 469/440–5800; Ron Norris, Chief Executive Officer
**Web address:** www.dallasgarland.selectspecialtyhospitals.com/

SELECT SPECIALTY HOSPITAL–DALLAS (O, 60 beds) 2329 West Parker Road, Carrollton, TX Zip 75010–4713; tel. 469/892–1400; John M. Griffes, Chief Executive Officer
**Web address:** www.selectspecialtyhospitals.com/company/locations/dallas.aspx

SELECT SPECIALTY HOSPITAL–HOUSTON WEST (O, 72 beds) 9430 Old Katy Road, Houston, TX Zip 77055; tel. 713/984–2273; Mitali Paul, Chief Executive Officer
**Web address:** www.selectmedicalcorp.com

SELECT SPECIALTY HOSPITAL–LONGVIEW (O, 32 beds) 700 East Marshall Avenue, 1st Floor, Longview, TX Zip 75601–5580; tel. 903/315–1100; Dennis Baker, Chief Executive Officer
**Web address:** www.selectspecialtyhospitals.com/company/locations/longview.aspx

Section B

For explanation of codes following names, see page B2.
★ Indicates Type III membership in the American Hospital Association.

SELECT SPECIALTY HOSPITAL–SAN ANTONIO (O, 44 beds) 111 Dallas Street, 4th Floor, San Antonio, TX Zip 78205–1201; tel. 210/297–7185; Sean Stricker, Chief Executive Officer
**Web address:** www.selectspecialtyhospitals. com/company/locations/sanantonio.aspx

SELECT SPECIALTY HOSPITAL–SOUTH DALLAS (O, 69 beds) 3500 West Wheatland Road, 4th Floor, Dallas, TX Zip 75237–3460; tel. 972/780–6500; Richard Knowland, Chief Executive Officer
**Web address:** www.selectspecialtyhospitals. com/company/locations/southdallas.aspx

**WEST VIRGINIA:** SELECT SPECIALTY HOSPITAL–CHARLESTON (O, 32 beds) 333 Laidley Street, 3rd Floor East, Charleston, WV Zip 25301–1614; tel. 304/720–7234; Frank Weber, Chief Executive Officer
**Web address:** www.selectspecialtyhospitals. com/company/locations/charleston.aspx

**WISCONSIN:** SELECT SPECIALTY HOSPITAL–MADISON (O, 58 beds) 801 Braxton Place, 2nd Floor, Madison, WI Zip 53715–1415; tel. 608/260–2700; Raymond F. Carnevale, Chief Executive Officer
**Web address:** www.madison.selectspecialtyhospitals.com

SELECT SPECIALTY HOSPITAL–MILWAUKEE (O, 34 beds) 8901 West Lincoln Avenue, 2nd Floor, Milwaukee, WI Zip 53227–2409; tel. 414/328–7700; Richard Keddington, Chief Executive Officer
**Web address:** www.selectspecialtyhospitals. com/company/locations/milwaukee.aspx

| | | |
|---|---|---|
| **Owned, leased, sponsored:** | 106 hospitals | 5078 beds |
| **Contract–managed:** | 1 hospital | 55 beds |
| **Totals:** | 107 hospitals | 5133 beds |

---

**★2565: SENTARA HEALTHCARE** (NP)
6015 Poplar Hall Drive, Norfolk, VA Zip 23502–3819; tel. 757/455–7000; David L. Bernd, Chief Executive Officer
**(Centralized Health System)**

**NORTH CAROLINA:** SENTARA ALBEMARLE MEDICAL CENTER (L, 83 beds) 1144 North Road Street, Elizabeth City, NC Zip 27909–3473, Mailing Address: P.O. Box 1587, Zip 27906–1587; tel. 252/335–0531; Coleen F. Santa Ana, Chief Executive Officer
**Web address:** www.albemarlehealth.org

**VIRGINIA:** MARTHA JEFFERSON HOSPITAL (O, 139 beds) 500 Martha Jefferson Drive, Charlottesville, VA Zip 22911–4668; tel. 434/654–7000; Jonathan S. Davis, FACHE, President
**Web address:** www.marthajefferson.org

SENTARA CAREPLEX HOSPITAL (O, 136 beds) 3000 Coliseum Drive, Hampton, VA Zip 23666–5963; tel. 757/736–1000; Debra A. Flores, R.N., MS, President and Administrator
**Web address:** www.sentara.com

SENTARA HALIFAX REGIONAL HOSPITAL (O, 438 beds) 2204 Wilborn Avenue, South Boston, VA Zip 24592–1638; tel. 434/517–3100; Chris A. Lumsden, Chief Executive Officer
**Web address:** www.hrhs.org

SENTARA LEIGH HOSPITAL (O, 238 beds) 830 Kempsville Road, Norfolk, VA Zip 23502–3920; tel. 757/261–6000; Teresa L. Edwards, President and Administrator
**Web address:** www.sentara.com

SENTARA NORFOLK GENERAL HOSPITAL (O, 495 beds) 600 Gresham Drive, Norfolk, VA Zip 23507–1904; tel. 757/388–3000; Kurt T. Hofelich, President
**Web address:** www.sentara.com

SENTARA NORTHERN VIRGINIA MEDICAL CENTER (O, 181 beds) 2300 Opitz Boulevard, Woodbridge, VA Zip 22191–3399; tel. 703/523–1000; Stephen D. Porter, President
**Web address:** www.sentara.com/northernvirginia

SENTARA OBICI HOSPITAL (O, 176 beds) 2800 Godwin Boulevard, Suffolk, VA Zip 23434–8038; tel. 757/934–4000; Steve Julian, M.D., President
**Web address:** www.sentara.com

SENTARA PRINCESS ANNE HOSPITAL (O, 160 beds) 2025 Glenn Mitchell Drive, Virginia Beach, VA Zip 23456–0178; tel. 757/507–1000; Thomas B. Thames, M.D., President
**Web address:** www.sentara.com

SENTARA RMH MEDICAL CENTER (O, 244 beds) 2010 Health Campus Drive, Harrisonburg, VA Zip 22801–3293; tel. 540/689–1000; James D. Krauss, President
**Web address:** www.rmhonline.com

SENTARA VIRGINIA BEACH GENERAL HOSPITAL (O, 259 beds) 1060 First Colonial Road, Virginia Beach, VA Zip 23454–3002; tel. 757/395–8000; Elwood Bernard Boone, III, FACHE, President
**Web address:** www.sentara.com

SENTARA WILLIAMSBURG REGIONAL MEDICAL CENTER (O, 145 beds) 100 Sentara Circle, Williamsburg, VA Zip 23188–5713; tel. 757/984–6000; David J. Masterson, President
**Web address:** www.sentara.com

| | | |
|---|---|---|
| **Owned, leased, sponsored:** | 12 hospitals | 2694 beds |
| **Contract–managed:** | 0 hospitals | 0 beds |
| **Totals:** | 12 hospitals | 2694 beds |

---

**★2065: SHARP HEALTHCARE** (NP)
8695 Spectrum Center Boulevard, San Diego, CA Zip 92123–1489; tel. 858/499–4000; Michael Murphy, CPA, President & Chief Executive Officer
**(Centralized Health System)**

**CALIFORNIA:** SHARP CHULA VISTA MEDICAL CENTER (O, 343 beds) 751 Medical Center Court, Chula Vista, CA Zip 91911–6699, Mailing Address: P.O. Box 1297, Zip 91912–1297; tel. 619/502–5800; Pablo Velez, Chief Executive Officer
**Web address:** www.sharp.com

SHARP CORONADO HOSPITAL AND HEALTHCARE CENTER (L, 181 beds) 250 Prospect Place, Coronado, CA Zip 92118–1999; tel. 619/522–3600; Susan Stone, R.N., Ph.D., Senior Vice President and Chief Executive Officer
**Web address:** www.sharp.com

SHARP GROSSMONT HOSPITAL (L, 490 beds) 5555 Grossmont Center Drive, La Mesa, CA Zip 91942–3019, Mailing Address: P.O. Box 158, Zip 91944–0158; tel. 619/740–6000; Scott Evans, FACHE, PharmD, Senior Vice President and Chief Executive Officer
**Web address:** www.sharp.com

SHARP MEMORIAL HOSPITAL (O, 394 beds) 7901 Frost Street, San Diego, CA Zip 92123–2701; tel. 858/939–3400; Tim Smith, Senior Vice President and Chief Executive Officer
**Web address:** www.sharp.com

SHARP MESA VISTA HOSPITAL (O, 163 beds) 7850 Vista Hill Avenue, San Diego, CA Zip 92123–2717; tel. 858/278–4110; Kathi Lencioni, Senior Vice President and Chief Executive Officer
**Web address:** www.sharp.com

| | | |
|---|---|---|
| **Owned, leased, sponsored:** | 5 hospitals | 1571 beds |
| **Contract–managed:** | 0 hospitals | 0 beds |
| **Totals:** | 5 hospitals | 1571 beds |

---

**4125: SHRINERS HOSPITALS FOR CHILDREN** (NP)
2900 Rocky Point Drive, Tampa, FL Zip 33607–1435, Mailing Address: P.O. Box 31356, Zip 33631–3356; tel. 813/281–0300; John P. McCabe, Executive Vice President
**(Independent Hospital System)**

SHRINERS HOSPITALS FOR CHILDREN–LOS ANGELES (O, 60 beds) 3160 Geneva Street, Los Angeles, CA Zip 90020–1199; tel. 213/388–3151; Lou Lazatin, Administrator
**Web address:** www.shrinershospitalsforchildren. org/Hospitals/Locations/Losangeles.aspx

SHRINERS HOSPITALS FOR CHILDREN–NORTHERN CALIFORNIA (O, 70 beds) 2425 Stockton Boulevard, Sacramento, CA Zip 95817–2215; tel. 916/453–2000; Margaret Bryan, Administrator
**Web address:** www.shrinershospitalsforchildren. org/Hospitals/Locations/NorthernCalifornia.aspx

**FLORIDA:** SHRINERS HOSPITALS FOR CHILDREN–TAMPA (O, 60 beds) 12502 USF Pine Drive, Tampa, FL Zip 33612–9499; tel. 813/972–2250; Jeannette Skinner, R.N., FACHE, Administrator
**Web address:** www.shrinershospitalsforchildren. org/Hospitals/Locations/Tampa.aspx

---

For explanation of codes following names, see page B2.
★ Indicates Type III membership in the American Hospital Association.

Section B

**HAWAII:** SHRINERS HOSPITALS FOR CHILDREN–HONOLULU (O, 16 beds) 1310 Punahou Street, Honolulu, HI Zip 96826–1099; tel. 808/941–4466; John R. White, Administrator
**Web address:** www.shrinershospitalsforchildren. org/Hospitals/Locations/Honolulu.aspx

**ILLINOIS:** SHRINERS HOSPITALS FOR CHILDREN–CHICAGO (O, 36 beds) 2211 North Oak Park Avenue, Chicago, IL Zip 60707–3392; tel. 773/622–5400; Mark L. Niederpruem, FACHE, Administrator
**Web address:** www.shrinershospitalsforchildren. org/Hospitals/Locations/Chicago.aspx

**KENTUCKY:** SHRINERS HOSPITALS FOR CHILDREN–LEXINGTON (O, 50 beds) 1900 Richmond Road, Lexington, KY Zip 40502–1298; tel. 859/266–2101; Tony Lewgood, Administrator
**Web address:** www.shrinershospitalsforchildren. org/Hospitals/Locations/Lexington.aspx

**LOUISIANA:** SHRINERS HOSPITALS FOR CHILDREN–SHREVEPORT (O, 45 beds) 3100 Samford Avenue, Shreveport, LA Zip 71103–4289; tel. 318/222–5704; Garry Kim Green, FACHE, Administrator
**Web address:** www.shrinershospitalsforchildren. org/Hospitals/Locations/Shreveport.aspx

**MASSACHUSETTS:** SHRINERS HOSPITALS FOR CHILDREN–BOSTON (O, 18 beds) 51 Blossom Street, Boston, MA Zip 02114–2601; tel. 617/722–3000; John Patrick O'Neill, FACHE, Administrator
**Web address:** www.shrinershospitalsforchildren. org/Hospitals/Locations/Boston

SHRINERS HOSPITALS FOR CHILDREN–SPRINGFIELD (O, 20 beds) 516 Carew Street, Springfield, MA Zip 01104–2396; tel. 413/787–2000; H. Lee Kirk, Jr., FACHE, Administrator
**Web address:** www.shrinershospitalsforchildren. org/Hospitals/Locations/Springfield.aspx

**MINNESOTA:** SHRINERS HOSPITALS FOR CHILDREN–TWIN CITIES (O, 40 beds) 2025 East River Parkway, Minneapolis, MN Zip 55414–3696; tel. 612/596–6100; Charles C. Lobeck, Administrator
**Web address:** www.shrinershospitalsforchildren. org/Hospitals/Locations/twincities.aspx

**MISSOURI:** SHRINERS HOSPITALS FOR CHILDREN–ST. LOUIS (O, 42 beds) 4400 Clayton Avenue, Saint Louis, MO Zip 63110–1624; tel. 314/432–3600; John Gloss, FACHE, Administrator
**Web address:** www.shrinershospitalsforchildren. org/Hospitals/Locations/Stlouis.aspx

**OHIO:** SHRINERS HOSPITALS FOR CHILDREN–CINCINNATI BURNS HOSPITAL (O, 30 beds) 3229 Burnet Avenue, Cincinnati, OH Zip 45229–3095; tel. 513/872–6000; Mark D. Shugarman, Administrator
**Web address:** www.shrinershospitalsforchildren. org/Hospitals/Locations/Cincinnati.aspx

**OREGON:** SHRINERS HOSPITALS FOR CHILDREN–PORTLAND (O, 8 beds) 3101 S.W. Sam Jackson Park Road, Portland, OR Zip 97239–3009; tel. 503/241–5090; J. Craig Patchin, Administrator
**Web address:** www.shrinershospitalsforchildren. org/Hospitals/Locations/Portland.aspx

**PENNSYLVANIA:** SHRINERS HOSPITALS FOR CHILDREN–PHILADELPHIA (O, 39 beds) 3551 North Broad Street, Philadelphia, PA Zip 19140–4160; tel. 215/430–4000; Ed Myers, Administrator
**Web address:** www.shrinershospitalsforchildren. org/Hospitals/Locations/Philadelphia.aspx

**SOUTH CAROLINA:** SHRINERS HOSPITALS FOR CHILDREN–GREENVILLE (O, 15 beds) 950 West Faris Road, Greenville, SC Zip 29605–4277; tel. 864/271–3444; Randall R. Romberger, Administrator
**Web address:** www.greenvilleshrinershospital.org

**TEXAS:** SHRINERS HOSPITALS FOR CHILDREN–GALVESTON (O, 15 beds) 815 Market Street, Galveston, TX Zip 77550–2725; tel. 409/770–6600; Mary Jaco, R.N., MSN, Administrator
**Web address:** www.shrinershospitalsforchildren. org/Hospitals/Locations/Galveston.aspx

SHRINERS HOSPITALS FOR CHILDREN–HOUSTON (O, 40 beds) 6977 Main Street, Houston, TX Zip 77030–3701; tel. 713/797–1616; David A. Ferrell, Regional Administrator
**Web address:** www.shrinershospitalsforchildren. org/Hospitals/Locations/Houston.aspx

**UTAH:** SHRINERS HOSPITALS FOR CHILDREN–SALT LAKE CITY (O, 40 beds) Fairfax Road & Virginia Street, Salt Lake City, UT Zip 84103–4399; tel. 801/536–3500; Kevin Martin, M.P.H., R.N., Administrator
**Web address:** www.shrinershospitalsforchildren. org/Hospitals/Locations/SaltLakeCity.aspx

**WASHINGTON:** SHRINERS HOSPITALS FOR CHILDREN–SPOKANE (O, 30 beds) 911 West Fifth Avenue, Spokane, WA Zip 99204–2901, Mailing Address: P.O. Box 2472, Zip 99210–2472; tel. 509/455–7844; Peter G. Brewer, Administrator
**Web address:** www.shrinershospitalsforchildren. org/Hospitals/Locations/Spokane.aspx

| | | |
|---|---|---|
| Owned, leased, sponsored: | 19 hospitals | 674 beds |
| Contract–managed: | 0 hospitals | 0 beds |
| **Totals:** | 19 hospitals | 674 beds |

---

**0360: SIGNATURE HEALTHCARE SERVICES** (IO)
4238 Green River Road, Corona, CA Zip 92880–1669; tel. 951/549–8032; Soon K. Kim, M.D., President and Chief Executive Officer
**(Independent Hospital System)**

**ARIZONA:** AURORA BEHAVIORAL HEALTH SYSTEM EAST (O, 70 beds) 6350 South Maple Street, Tempe, AZ Zip 85283–2857; tel. 480/345–5400; Bruce Waldo, Chief Executive Officer
**Web address:** www.auroraarizona.com

AURORA BEHAVIORAL HEALTH SYSTEM WEST (O, 90 beds) 6015 West Peoria Avenue, Glendale, AZ Zip 85302–1213; tel. 623/344–4400; Bruce Waldo, Chief Executive Officer
**Web address:** www.aurorabehavioral.com

**CALIFORNIA:** AURORA CHARTER OAK HOSPITAL (O, 146 beds) 1161 East Covina Boulevard, Covina, CA Zip 91724–1599; tel. 626/966–1632; Todd A. Smith, Chief Executive Officer
**Web address:** www.charteroakhospital.com

AURORA SAN DIEGO HOSPITAL (O, 80 beds) 11878 Avenue of Industry, San Diego, CA Zip 92128–3490; tel. 858/487–3200; James S. Plummer, Chief Executive Officer
**Web address:** www.sandiego.aurorabehavioral.com/

LAS ENCINAS HOSPITAL (O, 138 beds) 2900 East Del Mar Boulevard, Pasadena, CA Zip 91107–4399; tel. 626/795–9901; Gerard Conway, Chief Executive Officer
**Web address:** www.lasencinashospital.com

VISTA DEL MAR HOSPITAL (O, 87 beds) 801 Seneca Street, Ventura, CA Zip 93001–1411; tel. 805/653–6434; Mayla Krebsbach, Chief Executive Officer
**Web address:** www.vistadelmarhospital.com

**ILLINOIS:** CHICAGO LAKESHORE HOSPITAL (O, 115 beds) 4840 North Marine Drive, Chicago, IL Zip 60640–4296; tel. 773/878–9700; Patrick Moallemian, Chief Executive Officer
**Web address:** www.chicagolakeshorehospital.com

**TEXAS:** DALLAS BEHAVIORAL HEALTHCARE HOSPITAL (O, 44 beds) 800 Kirnwood Drive, Desoto, TX Zip 75115–2000; tel. 855/982–0897; Selene Q. Hammon, Chief Executive Officer
**Web address:** www.dallasbehavioral.com

GEORGETOWN BEHAVIORAL HEALTH INSTITUTE (O, 118 beds) 3101 South Austin Avenue, Georgetown, TX Zip 78626–7541; tel. 512/819–1100; Sheila McDermott-Lord, Chief Executive Officer
**Web address:** www.georgetownbehavioral.co

| | | |
|---|---|---|
| Owned, leased, sponsored: | 9 hospitals | 888 beds |
| Contract–managed: | 0 hospitals | 0 beds |
| **Totals:** | 9 hospitals | 888 beds |

---

**★0284: SINAI HEALTH SYSTEM** (NP)
1500 South California Avenue, Chicago, IL Zip 60608–1729; tel. 773/542–2000; Karen Teitelbaum, President and Chief Executive Officer
**(Independent Hospital System)**

For explanation of codes following names, see page B2.
★ Indicates Type III membership in the American Hospital Association.

**ILLINOIS:** HOLY CROSS HOSPITAL (O, 160 beds) 2701 West 68th Street, Chicago, IL Zip 60629–1882; tel. 773/884–9000; Lori Pacura, R.N., MSN, President
**Web address:** www.holycrosshospital.org

MOUNT SINAI HOSPITAL (O, 290 beds) California Avenue at 15th Street, Chicago, IL Zip 60608–1729; tel. 773/542–2000; Loren Chandler, President
**Web address:** www.sinai.org

SCHWAB REHABILITATION HOSPITAL (O, 21 beds) 1401 South California Avenue, Chicago, IL Zip 60608–1858; tel. 773/522–2010; Karl J. Sandin, M.D., M.P.H., President and Medical Director
**Web address:** www.schwabrehab.org

| Owned, leased, sponsored: | 3 hospitals | 471 beds |
|---|---|---|
| Contract–managed: | 0 hospitals | 0 beds |
| Totals: | 3 hospitals | 471 beds |

**5125:  SISTERS OF CHARITY HEALTH SYSTEM** (CC)
2475 East 22nd Street, Cleveland, OH Zip 44115–3221; tel. 216/363–2797; Terrence Kessler, President and Chief Executive Officer
**(Moderately Centralized Health System)**

**OHIO:** MERCY MEDICAL CENTER (O, 322 beds) 1320 Mercy Drive N.W., Canton, OH Zip 44708–2641; tel. 330/489–1000; Thomas E. Cecconi, President and Chief Executive Officer
**Web address:** www.cantonmercy.org

ST. JOHN MEDICAL CENTER (O, 191 beds) 29000 Center Ridge Road, Westlake, OH Zip 44145–5293; tel. 440/835–8000; William A. Young, Jr., President and Chief Executive Officer
**Web address:** www.sjws.net

ST. VINCENT CHARITY MEDICAL CENTER (O, 199 beds) 2351 East 22nd Street, Cleveland, OH Zip 44115–3111; tel. 216/861–6200; David F. Perse, M.D., President and Chief Executive Officer
**Web address:** www.stvincentcharity.com/

**SOUTH CAROLINA:** PROVIDENCE HOSPITAL (O, 314 beds) 2435 Forest Drive, Columbia, SC Zip 29204–2098; tel. 803/865–4500; Terrence Kessler, Interim Chief Executive Officer
**Web address:** www.sistersofcharityhealth.org/health–care/providence–hospitals/

| Owned, leased, sponsored: | 4 hospitals | 1026 beds |
|---|---|---|
| Contract–managed: | 0 hospitals | 0 beds |
| Totals: | 4 hospitals | 1026 beds |

**5805:  SISTERS OF MARY OF THE PRESENTATION HEALTH SYSTEM** (CC)
1202 Page Drive S.W., Fargo, ND Zip 58103–2340, Mailing Address: P.O. Box 10007, Zip 58106–0007; tel. 701/237–9290; Aaron K. Alton, President and Chief Executive Officer
**(Independent Hospital System)**

**ILLINOIS:** ST. MARGARET'S HOSPITAL (O, 54 beds) 600 East First Street, Spring Valley, IL Zip 61362–1512; tel. 815/664–5311; Tim Muntz, President and Chief Executive Officer
**Web address:** www.aboutsmh.org

**NORTH DAKOTA:** PRESENTATION MEDICAL CENTER (O, 25 beds) 213 Second Avenue N.E., Rolla, ND Zip 58367–7153, Mailing Address: P.O. Box 759, Zip 58367–0759; tel. 701/477–3161; Mark Kerr, Chief Executive Officer
**Web address:** www.pmc–rolla.com

ST. ALOISIUS MEDICAL CENTER (O, 120 beds) 325 East Brewster Street, Harvey, ND Zip 58341–1653; tel. 701/324–4651; Sandra Teubner, Interim Chief Executive Officer
**Web address:** www.staloisius.com

ST. ANDREW'S HEALTH CENTER (O, 25 beds) 316 Ohmer Street, Bottineau, ND Zip 58318–1045; tel. 701/228–9300; Jodi Atkinson, President and Chief Executive Officer
**Web address:** www.standrewshealth.com

| Owned, leased, sponsored: | 4 hospitals | 224 beds |
|---|---|---|
| Contract–managed: | 0 hospitals | 0 beds |
| Totals: | 4 hospitals | 224 beds |

**●5955:  SISTERS OF SAINT FRANCIS** (CC)
2500 Grant Boulevard, Syracuse, NY Zip 13208–1782; tel. 315/634–7000; Sister Geraldine Ching, Assistant General Minister
**(Moderately Centralized Health System)**

**NEW YORK:** ST. ELIZABETH MEDICAL CENTER (S, 181 beds) 2209 Genesee Street, Utica, NY Zip 13501–5999; tel. 315/798–8100; Scott H. Perra, Chief Executive Officer
**Web address:** www.stemc.org

| Owned, leased, sponsored: | 1 hospital | 181 beds |
|---|---|---|
| Contract–managed: | 0 hospitals | 0 beds |
| Totals: | 1 hospital | 181 beds |

**★0253:  SOUTHEAST GEORGIA HEALTH SYSTEM** (NP)
2415 Parkwood Drive, Brunswick, GA Zip 31520–4722, Mailing Address: P.O. Box 1518, Zip 31521–1518; tel. 912/466–7000; Michael D. Scherneck, Interim Chief Executive Officer

**GEORGIA:** SOUTHEAST GEORGIA HEALTH SYSTEM BRUNSWICK CAMPUS (O, 469 beds) 2415 Parkwood Drive, Brunswick, GA Zip 31520–4722, Mailing Address: P.O. Box 1518, Zip 31521–1518; tel. 912/466–7000; Michael D. Scherneck, Interim Chief Executive Officer
**Web address:** www.sghs.org

SOUTHEAST GEORGIA HEALTH SYSTEM CAMDEN CAMPUS (O, 40 beds) 2000 Dan Proctor Drive, Saint Marys, GA Zip 31558–3810; tel. 912/576–6200; Howard W. Sepp, Jr., FACHE, Vice President and Administrator
**Web address:** www.sghs.org

| Owned, leased, sponsored: | 2 hospitals | 509 beds |
|---|---|---|
| Contract–managed: | 0 hospitals | 0 beds |
| Totals: | 2 hospitals | 509 beds |

**0628:  SOUTHEASTHEALTH** (NP)
1701 Lacey Street, Cape Girardeau, MO Zip 63701–5230; tel. 573/334–4822; Kenneth Bateman, CPA, Chief Executive Officer
**(Independent Hospital System)**

**MISSOURI:** SOUTHEAST HEALTH CENTER OF REYNOLDS COUNTY (L, 8 beds) 100 Highway 21 South, Ellington, MO Zip 63638, Mailing Address: Rural Route 4, Box 4269, Zip 63638–9409; tel. 573/663–2511; Cheryl Barton, RN, Chief Executive Officer

SOUTHEAST HEALTH CENTER OF RIPLEY COUNTY (L, 8 beds) 109 Plum Street, Doniphan, MO Zip 63935–1299; tel. 573/996–2141; Cheryl Barton, R.N., Chief Executive Officer
**Web address:** www.sehealth.org/southeast–health–center–of–ripley–county/SoutheastHEALTH.aspx?nd=41

SOUTHEAST HEALTH CENTER OF STODDARD COUNTY (L, 16 beds) 1200 North One Mile Road, Dexter, MO Zip 63841–1000; tel. 573/624–5566; Adam Bracks, Chief Executive Officer
**Web address:** www.sehealth.org

SOUTHEAST HOSPITAL (O, 221 beds) 1701 Lacey Street, Cape Girardeau, MO Zip 63701–5230; tel. 573/334–4822; Kenneth Bateman, CPA, Chief Executive Officer
**Web address:** www.sehealth.org/

| Owned, leased, sponsored: | 4 hospitals | 253 beds |
|---|---|---|
| Contract–managed: | 0 hospitals | 0 beds |
| Totals: | 4 hospitals | 253 beds |

**4175:  SOUTHERN ILLINOIS HOSPITAL SERVICES** (NP)
1239 East Main Street, Carbondale, IL Zip 62901–3114, Mailing Address: P.O. Box 3988, Zip 62902–3988; tel. 618/457–5200; Rex P. Budde, President and Chief Executive Officer
**(Independent Hospital System)**

For explanation of codes following names, see page B2.
★ Indicates Type III membership in the American Hospital Association.
● Single hospital health care system

**B124** Health Care Systems, Networks and Alliances

© 2015 AHA Guide

Section B

**ILLINOIS:** HERRIN HOSPITAL (O, 114 beds) 201 South 14th Street, Herrin, IL Zip 62948–3631; tel. 618/942–2171; Terence Farrell, Vice President and Administrator
**Web address:** www.sih.net

MEMORIAL HOSPITAL OF CARBONDALE (O, 159 beds) 405 West Jackson Street, Carbondale, IL Zip 62901–1467, Mailing Address: P.O. Box 10000, Zip 62902–9000; tel. 618/549–0721; Bart Millstead, Administrator
**Web address:** www.sih.net

ST. JOSEPH MEMORIAL HOSPITAL (O, 25 beds) 2 South Hospital Drive, Murphysboro, IL Zip 62966–3333; tel. 618/684–3156; Susan Odle, Administrator
**Web address:** www.sih.net

| | | |
|---|---|---|
| **Owned, leased, sponsored:** | 3 hospitals | 298 beds |
| **Contract–managed:** | 0 hospitals | 0 beds |
| **Totals:** | 3 hospitals | 298 beds |

**0346: SOUTHERN PLAINS MEDICAL GROUP** (IO)
4323 N.W. 63rd Street Suite 232, Oklahoma City, OK Zip 73116–1546; tel. 405/753–6770; Margie Homer, President

**OKLAHOMA:** PHYSICIANS' HOSPITAL IN ANADARKO (O, 25 beds) 1002 Central Boulevard East, Anadarko, OK Zip 73005–4496; tel. 405/247–2551; Drew Flowers, Interim Administrator
**Web address:** www.anadarkohospital.com

STROUD REGIONAL MEDICAL CENTER (O, 25 beds) Highway 66 West, Stroud, OK Zip 74079, Mailing Address: P.O. Box 530, Zip 74079–0530; tel. 918/968–3571; Tommy Smith, Chief Executive Officer
**Web address:** www.stroudhospital.com/

| | | |
|---|---|---|
| **Owned, leased, sponsored:** | 2 hospitals | 50 beds |
| **Contract–managed:** | 0 hospitals | 0 beds |
| **Totals:** | 2 hospitals | 50 beds |

**0652: SOUTHWEST HEALTH SYSTEMS** (NP)
215 Marion Avenue, Mccomb, MS Zip 39648–2705, Mailing Address: P.O. Box 1307, Zip 39649–1307; tel. 601/249–5500; Norman M. Price, FACHE, Chief Executive Officer and Administrator
**(Independent Hospital System)**

**MISSISSIPPI:** LAWRENCE COUNTY HOSPITAL (O, 25 beds) Highway 84 East, Monticello, MS Zip 39654–0788, Mailing Address: P.O. Box 788, Zip 39654–0788; tel. 601/587–4051; Semmes Ross, Jr., Administrator
**Web address:** www.smrmc.com

SOUTHWEST MISSISSIPPI REGIONAL MEDICAL CENTER (O, 143 beds) 215 Marion Avenue, McComb, MS Zip 39648–2705, Mailing Address: P.O. Box 1307, Zip 39649–1307; tel. 601/249–5500; Norman M. Price, FACHE, Chief Executive Officer
**Web address:** www.smrmc.com

| | | |
|---|---|---|
| **Owned, leased, sponsored:** | 2 hospitals | 168 beds |
| **Contract–managed:** | 0 hospitals | 0 beds |
| **Totals:** | 2 hospitals | 168 beds |

**●0164: SOUTHWEST HEALTHCARE SYSTEM** (IO)
4400 North Scottsdale Road, Suite 9347, Scottsdale, AZ Zip 85251–3331; tel. 480/348–9800; Paul R. Tuft, President
**(Independent Hospital System)**

**TEXAS:** GULF COAST MEDICAL CENTER (O, 159 beds) 10141 Highway 59, Wharton, TX Zip 77488–3004; tel. 979/282–6100; Loretta Flynn, Chief Executive Officer
**Web address:** www.gulfcoastmedical.com

| | | |
|---|---|---|
| **Owned, leased, sponsored:** | 1 hospital | 159 beds |
| **Contract–managed:** | 0 hospitals | 0 beds |
| **Totals:** | 1 hospital | 159 beds |

**★1245: SPARROW HEALTH SYSTEM** (NP)
1215 East Michigan Avenue, Lansing, MI Zip 48912–1811; tel. 517/364–1000; Dennis A. Swan, JD, FACHE, President and Chief Executive Officer
**(Centralized Health System)**

**MICHIGAN:** SPARROW CARSON HOSPITAL (O, 62 beds) 406 East Elm Street, Carson City, MI Zip 48811–9693, Mailing Address: P.O. Box 879, Zip 48811–0879; tel. 989/584–3131; Matthew J. Thompson, Chief Executive Officer
**Web address:** www.carsoncityhospital.com

SPARROW CLINTON HOSPITAL (O, 25 beds) 805 South Oakland Street, Saint Johns, MI Zip 48879–2253; tel. 989/227–3400; Edward Bruun, President and Chief Executive Officer
**Web address:** www.sparrowclinton.org

SPARROW HOSPITAL (O, 655 beds) 1215 East Michigan Avenue, Lansing, MI Zip 48912–1811; tel. 517/364–1000; Dennis A. Swan, JD, FACHE, President and Chief Executive Officer
**Web address:** www.sparrow.org

SPARROW IONIA HOSPITAL (O, 25 beds) 3565 South State Road, Ionia, MI Zip 48846–1870, Mailing Address: Box 1001, Zip 48846–6001; tel. 616/523–1400; William Roeser, President and Chief Executive Officer
**Web address:** www.sparrow.org/sparrowionia

SPARROW SPECIALTY HOSPITAL (O, 36 beds) 8 West Sparrow Hospital Tower, Lansing, MI Zip 48912; tel. 517/364–4840; Kira Carter–Robertson, FACHE, President and Chief Executive Officer
**Web address:** www.sparrowspecialty.org

| | | |
|---|---|---|
| **Owned, leased, sponsored:** | 5 hospitals | 803 beds |
| **Contract–managed:** | 0 hospitals | 0 beds |
| **Totals:** | 5 hospitals | 803 beds |

**★4195: SPARTANBURG REGIONAL HEALTHCARE SYSTEM** (NP)
101 East Wood Street, Spartanburg, SC Zip 29303–3040; tel. 864/560–6000; Bruce Holstien, President and Chief Executive Officer
**(Centralized Health System)**

**SOUTH CAROLINA:** PELHAM MEDICAL CENTER (O, 39 beds) 250 Westmoreland Road, Greer, SC Zip 29651–9013; tel. 864/530–6000; Anthony Kouskolekas, FACHE, President
**Web address:** www.villageatpelham.com

SPARTANBURG HOSPITAL FOR RESTORATIVE CARE (O, 116 beds) 389 Serpentine Drive, Spartanburg, SC Zip 29303–3026; tel. 864/560–3280; Anita M. Butler, Chief Executive Officer
**Web address:** www.srhs.com

SPARTANBURG REGIONAL MEDICAL CENTER (O, 539 beds) 101 East Wood Street, Spartanburg, SC Zip 29303–3040; tel. 864/560–6000; Bruce Holstien, President and Chief Executive Officer
**Web address:** www.spartanburgregional.com

UNION MEDICAL CENTER (O, 59 beds) 322 West South Street, Union, SC Zip 29379–2857, Mailing Address: P.O. Box 789, Zip 29379–0789; tel. 864/427–0351; Paul R. Newhouse, Chief Executive Officer
**Web address:** www.wallacethomson.com

| | | |
|---|---|---|
| **Owned, leased, sponsored:** | 4 hospitals | 753 beds |
| **Contract–managed:** | 0 hospitals | 0 beds |
| **Totals:** | 4 hospitals | 753 beds |

**0352: SPECIALTY HOSPITALS OF AMERICA, LLC** (IO)
155 Fleet Street, Portsmouth, NH Zip 03801–4050; tel. 603/570–4888; Eric F. Rieseberg, President
**(Independent Hospital System)**

**DISTRICT OF COLUMBIA:** SPECIALTY HOSPITAL OF WASHINGTON (O, 177 beds) 700 Constitution Avenue N.E., Washington, DC Zip 20002–6058; tel. 202/546–5700; Susan P. Bailey, R.N., Chief Executive Officer
**Web address:** www.specialtyhospitalofwashington.com

For explanation of codes following names, see page B2.
★ Indicates Type III membership in the American Hospital Association.
● Single hospital health care system

© 2015 AHA Guide                    Health Care Systems, Networks and Alliances    **B125**

Section B

SPECIALTY HOSPITAL OF WASHINGTON–HADLEY (O, 82 beds) 4601 Martin Luther King Jr. Avenue, S.W., Washington, DC Zip 20032–1131; tel. 202/574–5700; Cathy Borris–Hale, Chief Executive Officer

| | | |
|---|---|---|
| Owned, leased, sponsored: | 2 hospitals | 259 beds |
| Contract–managed: | 0 hospitals | 0 beds |
| Totals: | 2 hospitals | 259 beds |

---

★0177:  **SPECTRUM HEALTH** (NP)
100 Michigan Street N.E., Grand Rapids, MI Zip 49503–2551; tel. 616/391–1774; Richard C. Breon, President and Chief Executive Officer
**(Moderately Centralized Health System)**

**MICHIGAN:** SPECTRUM HEALTH – BUTTERWORTH HOSPITAL (O, 1102 beds) 100 Michigan Street N.E., Grand Rapids, MI Zip 49503–2560; tel. 616/774–7444; Christina Freese–Decker, President, Spectrum Health Hospital Group
**Web address:** www.spectrumhealth.org

SPECTRUM HEALTH BIG RAPIDS HOSPITAL (O, 53 beds) 605 Oak Street, Big Rapids, MI Zip 49307–2099; tel. 231/796–8691; Mary Kay VanDriel, President
**Web address:** www.mcmcbr.com

SPECTRUM HEALTH GERBER MEMORIAL (O, 40 beds) 212 South Sullivan Avenue, Fremont, MI Zip 49412–1548; tel. 231/924–3300; Randall Stasik, President and Chief Executive Officer
**Web address:** www.spectrumhealth.org

SPECTRUM HEALTH LUDINGTON HOSPITAL (O, 52 beds) One Atkinson Drive, Ludington, MI Zip 49431–1906; tel. 231/843–2591; Mark Vipperman, President
**Web address:** www.mmcwm.com

SPECTRUM HEALTH PENNOCK (O, 58 beds) 1009 West Green Street, Hastings, MI Zip 49058–1710; tel. 269/945–3451; Sheryl Lewis Blake, FACHE, President
**Web address:** www.pennockhealth.com

SPECTRUM HEALTH REED CITY HOSPITAL (O, 75 beds) 300 North Patterson Road, Reed City, MI Zip 49677–8041, Mailing Address: P.O. Box 75, Zip 49677–0075; tel. 231/832–3271; Mary Kay VanDriel, President
**Web address:** www.reedcity.spectrum–health.org

SPECTRUM HEALTH SPECIAL CARE HOSPITAL (O, 36 beds) 750 Fuller Avenue N.E., Grand Rapids, MI Zip 49503–1995; tel. 616/486–3000; Jennifer Groeneweg, R.N., Interim Chief Executive Officer and Chief Nurse Executive
**Web address:** www.spectrum–health.org

SPECTRUM HEALTH UNITED HOSPITAL (O, 116 beds) 615 South Bower Street, Greenville, MI Zip 48838–2614; tel. 616/754–4691; Brian Brasser, President
**Web address:** www.spectrumhealth.org/

SPECTRUM HEALTH ZEELAND COMMUNITY HOSPITAL (O, 50 beds) 8333 Felch Street, Zeeland, MI Zip 49464–2608; tel. 616/772–4644; Ron Lewis, President
**Web address:** www.spectrumhealth.org/zeeland

| | | |
|---|---|---|
| Owned, leased, sponsored: | 9 hospitals | 1582 beds |
| Contract–managed: | 0 hospitals | 0 beds |
| Totals: | 9 hospitals | 1582 beds |

---

★5455:  **SSM HEALTH** (CC)
10101 Woodfield Lane, Saint Louis, MO Zip 63132–2937; tel. 314/994–7800; William P. Thompson, President and Chief Executive Officer
**(Decentralized Health System)**

**ILLINOIS:** CLAY COUNTY HOSPITAL (C, 22 beds) 911 Stacy Burk Drive, Flora, IL Zip 62839–3241, Mailing Address: P.O. Box 280, Zip 62839–0280; tel. 618/662–2131; Amanda J. Basso, President
**Web address:** www.claycountyhospital.org

GOOD SAMARITAN REGIONAL HEALTH CENTER (O, 134 beds) 1 Good Samaritan Way, Mount Vernon, IL Zip 62864–2402; tel. 618/242–4600; Michael D. Warren, President
**Web address:** www.smgsi.com

ST. MARY'S HOSPITAL (O, 113 beds) 400 North Pleasant Avenue, Centralia, IL Zip 62801–3056; tel. 618/436–8000; John R. Sigsbury, President
**Web address:** www.smgsi.com

**MISSOURI:** SSM CARDINAL GLENNON CHILDREN'S MEDICAL CENTER (O, 176 beds) 1465 South Grand Boulevard, Saint Louis, MO Zip 63104–1095; tel. 314/577–5600; Damon R. Harbison, MBA, Interim Chief Executive Officer
**Web address:** www.cardinalglennon.com

SSM DEPAUL HEALTH CENTER (O, 474 beds) 12303 De Paul Drive, Bridgeton, MO Zip 63044–2512; tel. 314/344–6000; Sean Hogan, President
**Web address:** www.ssmdepaul.com

SSM HEALTH SAINT LOUIS UNIVERSITY HOSPITAL (O, 356 beds) 3635 Vista at Grand Boulevard, Saint Louis, MO Zip 63110–0250, Mailing Address: P.O. Box 15250, Zip 63110–0250; tel. 314/577–8000; Kathleen R. Becker, MPH, JD, President
**Web address:** www.sluhospital.com

SSM HEALTH ST. FRANCIS HOSPITAL – MARYVILLE (O, 56 beds) 2016 South Main Street, Maryville, MO Zip 64468–2655; tel. 660/562–2600; Michael A. Baumgartner, President
**Web address:** www.ssmhealthstfrancis.com

SSM HEALTH ST. MARY'S HOSPITAL – AUDRAIN (O, 49 beds) 620 East Monroe Street, Mexico, MO Zip 65265–2919; tel. 573/582–5000; R. Brent VanConia, Acting President
**Web address:** www.audrainmedicalcenter.com

SSM HEALTH ST. MARY'S HOSPITAL – JEFFERSON CITY (O, 152 beds) 2505 Mission Drive, Jefferson City, MO Zip 65109; tel. 573/681–3000; R. Brent VanConia, President
**Web address:** www.lethealingbegin.com

SSM ST. CLARE HEALTH CENTER (O, 184 beds) 1015 Bowles Avenue, Fenton, MO Zip 63026–2394; tel. 636/496–2000; Ellis Hawkins, President
**Web address:** www.ssmstclare.com

SSM ST. JOSEPH HEALTH CENTER (O, 331 beds) 300 First Capitol Drive, Saint Charles, MO Zip 63301–2844; tel. 636/947–5000; Michael E. Bowers, President
**Web address:** www.ssmstjoseph.com

SSM ST. JOSEPH HOSPITAL WEST (O, 119 beds) 100 Medical Plaza, Lake Saint Louis, MO Zip 63367–1366; tel. 636/625–5200; Lisle Wescott, President
**Web address:** www.ssmstjoseph.com

SSM ST. MARY'S HEALTH CENTER (O, 381 beds) 6420 Clayton Road, Saint Louis, MO Zip 63117–1811; tel. 314/768–8000; Candice Jennings, FACHE, President
**Web address:** www.stmarys–stlouis.com

**OKLAHOMA:** ST. ANTHONY HOSPITAL (O, 565 beds) 1000 North Lee Street, Oklahoma City, OK Zip 73102–1080, Mailing Address: P.O. Box 205, Zip 73101–0205; tel. 405/272–7000; Tammy Powell, FACHE, M.P.H., President
**Web address:** www.saintsok.com

ST. ANTHONY SHAWNEE HOSPITAL (O, 76 beds) 1102 West MacArthur Street, Shawnee, OK Zip 74804–1744; tel. 405/273–2270; Charles E. Skillings, President and Chief Executive Officer
**Web address:** www.stanthonyshawnee.com

**WISCONSIN:** ST. CLARE HOSPITAL (O, 60 beds) 707 14th Street, Baraboo, WI Zip 53913–1597; tel. 608/356–1400; Laura Jelle, President
**Web address:** www.stclare.com

ST. MARY'S HOSPITAL (O, 364 beds) 700 South Park Street, Madison, WI Zip 53715–1830; tel. 608/251–6100; Damond Boatwright, Interim President
**Web address:** www.stmarysmadison.com

ST. MARY'S JANESVILLE HOSPITAL (O, 50 beds) 3400 East Racine Steeet, Janesville, WI Zip 53546–2344; tel. 608/373–8000; Kerry Swanson, President
**Web address:** www.stmarysjanesville.com

| | | |
|---|---|---|
| Owned, leased, sponsored: | 17 hospitals | 3640 beds |
| Contract–managed: | 1 hospital | 22 beds |
| Totals: | 18 hospitals | 3662 beds |

---

For explanation of codes following names, see page B2.
★ Indicates Type III membership in the American Hospital Association.

**★0250: ST. CHARLES HEALTH SYSTEM, INC.** (NP)
2500 N.E. Neff Road, Bend, OR Zip 97701–6015;
tel. 541/382–4321; Joseph Sluka, President and Chief Executive
Officer
**(Centralized Physician/Insurance Health System)**

**OREGON:** PIONEER MEMORIAL HOSPITAL (L, 25 beds) 1201 N.E. Elm Street,
Prineville, OR Zip 97754–1206; tel. 541/447–6254; Jeanine Gentry, Chief
Executive Officer
**Web address:** www.stcharleshealthcare.org

ST. CHARLES BEND (O, 250 beds) 2500 N.E. Neff Road, Bend, OR
Zip 97701–6015; tel. 541/382–4321; Robert Gomes, FACHE, Chief
Executive Officer
**Web address:** www.scmc.org

ST. CHARLES MADRAS (O, 25 beds) 470 N.E. A Street, Madras, OR
Zip 97741–1844; tel. 541/475–3882; Jeanine Gentry, Chief Executive
Officer
**Web address:** www.mvhd.org

ST. CHARLES REDMOND (O, 48 beds) 1253 N.W. Canal Boulevard, Redmond,
OR Zip 97756–1395; tel. 541/548–8131; Robert Gomes, FACHE, Chief
Executive Officer
**Web address:** www.stcharleshealthcare.org

| Owned, leased, sponsored: | 4 hospitals | 348 beds |
|---|---|---|
| Contract–managed: | 0 hospitals | 0 beds |
| **Totals:** | 4 hospitals | 348 beds |

**0618: ST. ELIZABETH HEALTHCARE** (NP)
1 Medical Village Drive, Edgewood, KY Zip 41017–3403;
tel. 859/301–2000; Garren Colvin, Chief Executive Officer
**(Independent Hospital System)**

**KENTUCKY:** ST. ELIZABETH EDGEWOOD (O, 499 beds) 1 Medical Village
Drive, Edgewood, KY Zip 41017–3403; tel. 859/301–2000; Garren
Colvin, Chief Executive Officer
**Web address:** www.stelizabeth.com

ST. ELIZABETH FLORENCE (O, 169 beds) 4900 Houston Road, Florence, KY
Zip 41042–4824; tel. 859/212–5200; Garren Colvin, Chief Executive Officer
**Web address:** www.stelizabeth.com

ST. ELIZABETH FORT THOMAS (O, 171 beds) 85 North Grand Avenue, Fort
Thomas, KY Zip 41075–1796; tel. 859/572–3100; Garren Colvin, Chief
Executive Officer
**Web address:** www.stelizabeth.com

ST. ELIZABETH GRANT (O, 16 beds) 238 Barnes Road, Williamstown, KY
Zip 41097–9482; tel. 859/824–8240; Garren Colvin, Chief Executive Officer
**Web address:** www.stelizabeth.com

| Owned, leased, sponsored: | 4 hospitals | 855 beds |
|---|---|---|
| Contract–managed: | 0 hospitals | 0 beds |
| **Totals:** | 4 hospitals | 855 beds |

**★5425: ST. JOSEPH HEALTH** (CC)
3345 Michelson Drive, Suite 100, Irvine, CA Zip 92612;
tel. 949/381–4000; Deborah A. Proctor, President and Chief
Executive Officer
**(Moderately Centralized Health System)**

**CALIFORNIA:** MISSION HOSPITAL (O, 228 beds) 27700 Medical Center Road,
Mission Viejo, CA Zip 92691–6474; tel. 949/364–1400; Kenneth D.
McFarland, President and Chief Executive Officer
**Web address:** www.mission4health.com

PETALUMA VALLEY HOSPITAL (L, 38 beds) 400 North McDowell Boulevard,
Petaluma, CA Zip 94954–2366; tel. 707/778–1111; Todd Salnas, President
**Web address:** www.stjosephhealth.
org/About–Us/Facilities/Petaluma–Valley–Hospital.aspx

QUEEN OF THE VALLEY MEDICAL CENTER (O, 174 beds) 1000 Trancas
Street, Napa, CA Zip 94558–2906, Mailing Address: P.O. Box 2340,
Zip 94558–0688; tel. 707/252–4411; Walt Mickens, FACHE, President and
Chief Executive Officer
**Web address:** www.thequeen.org

REDWOOD MEMORIAL HOSPITAL (O, 25 beds) 3300 Renner Drive, Fortuna,
CA Zip 95540–3198; tel. 707/725–3361; David O'Brien, M.D., President
**Web address:** www.redwoodmemorial.org/

SANTA ROSA MEMORIAL HOSPITAL (O, 278 beds) 1165 Montgomery Drive,
Santa Rosa, CA Zip 95405–4897, Mailing Address: P.O. Box 522,
Zip 95402–0522; tel. 707/546–3210; Todd Salnas, President
**Web address:** www.stjosephhealth.com

ST. JOSEPH HOSPITAL (O, 153 beds) 2700 Dolbeer Street, Eureka, CA
Zip 95501–4799; tel. 707/445–8121; David O'Brien, M.D., President
**Web address:** www.stjosepheureka.org

ST. JOSEPH HOSPITAL (O, 379 beds) 1100 West Stewart Drive, Orange, CA
Zip 92868–3849, Mailing Address: P.O. Box 5600, Zip 92863–5600;
tel. 714/633–9111; Steven C. Moreau, President and Chief Executive Officer
**Web address:** www.sjo.org

ST. JUDE MEDICAL CENTER (O, 329 beds) 101 East Valencia Mesa Drive,
Fullerton, CA Zip 92835–3875; tel. 714/992–3000; Lee Penrose, President
and Chief Executive Officer
**Web address:** www.stjudemedicalcenter.org

ST. MARY MEDICAL CENTER (O, 210 beds) 18300 Highway 18, Apple Valley,
CA Zip 92307–2206, Mailing Address: P.O. Box 7025, Zip 92307–0725;
tel. 760/242–2311; Alan H. Garrett, Chief Executive Officer
**Web address:** www.stmaryapplevalley.com/

| Owned, leased, sponsored: | 9 hospitals | 1814 beds |
|---|---|---|
| Contract–managed: | 0 hospitals | 0 beds |
| **Totals:** | 9 hospitals | 1814 beds |

**0928: ST. LAWRENCE HEALTH SYSTEM** (NP)
50 Leroy Street, Potsdam, NY Zip 13676–1799;
tel. 315/265–3300; David B. Acker, FACHE, President and CEO
**(Independent Hospital System)**

**NEW YORK:** CANTON–POTSDAM HOSPITAL (O, 94 beds) 50 Leroy Street,
Potsdam, NY Zip 13676–1799; tel. 315/265–3300; David B. Acker,
FACHE, President and CEO
**Web address:** www.cphospital.org

GOUVERNEUR HOSPITAL (O, 25 beds) 77 West Barney Street, Gouverneur,
NY Zip 13642–1040; tel. 315/287–1000; Marlinda L. LaValley, Chief
Executive Officer
**Web address:** www.gvnrhospital.org

| Owned, leased, sponsored: | 2 hospitals | 119 beds |
|---|---|---|
| Contract–managed: | 0 hospitals | 0 beds |
| **Totals:** | 2 hospitals | 119 beds |

**★0356: ST. LUKE'S HEALTH SYSTEM** (NP)
420 West Idaho Street, Boise, ID Zip 83702–6041;
tel. 208/381–4200; David C. Pate, M.D., JD, President and Chief
Executive Officer
**(Moderately Centralized Health System)**

**IDAHO:** NORTH CANYON MEDICAL CENTER (C, 15 beds) 267 North Canyon
Drive, Gooding, ID Zip 83330–5500; tel. 208/934–4433; Tim Powers,
Chief Executive Officer
**Web address:** www.ncm–c.org

ST. LUKE'S ELMORE (O, 63 beds) 895 North Sixth East Street, Mountain
Home, ID Zip 83647–2207, Mailing Address: P.O. Box 1270,
Zip 83647–1270; tel. 208/587–8401; Michael Blauer, Administrator
**Web address:** www.stlukesonline.org/elmore/

ST. LUKE'S JEROME (O, 25 beds) 709 North Lincoln Street, Jerome, ID
Zip 83338–1851, Mailing Address: 709 North Lincoln Avenue,
Zip 83338–1851; tel. 208/324–4301; James L. Angle, FACHE, Chief
Executive Officer
**Web address:** www.stlukesonline.org/jerome/

ST. LUKE'S MAGIC VALLEY MEDICAL CENTER (O, 224 beds) 801 Pole Line
Road West, Twin Falls, ID Zip 83301–5810, Mailing Address: P.O. Box 409,
Zip 83303–0409; tel. 208/814–1000; James L. Angle, FACHE, Regional
Chief Executive Officer
**Web address:** www.stlukesonline.org

ST. LUKE'S MCCALL (O, 15 beds) 1000 State Street, McCall, ID
Zip 83638–3704; tel. 208/634–2221; Michael A. Fenello, Administrator
**Web address:** www.mccallhosp.org

For explanation of codes following names, see page B2.
★ Indicates Type III membership in the American Hospital Association.

ST. LUKE'S REGIONAL MEDICAL CENTER (O, 574 beds) 190 East Bannock Street, Boise, ID Zip 83712–6241; tel. 208/381–2222; Kathy D. Moore, Chief Executive Officer
**Web address:** www.stlukesonline.org/boise

ST. LUKE'S REHABILITATION HOSPITAL (O, 31 beds) 600 North Robbins Road, Boise, ID Zip 83702–4565, Mailing Address: P.O. Box 1100, Zip 83701–1100; tel. 208/489–4444; Nolan Hoffer, Senior Director
**Web address:** www.idahoelksrehab.org

ST. LUKE'S WOOD RIVER MEDICAL CENTER (O, 25 beds) 100 Hospital Drive, Ketchum, ID Zip 83340, Mailing Address: P.O. Box 100, Zip 83340–0100; tel. 208/727–8800; Cody Langbehn, Administrator
**Web address:** www.slrmc.org

WEISER MEMORIAL HOSPITAL (C, 25 beds) 645 East Fifth Street, Weiser, ID Zip 83672–2202; tel. 208/549–0370; Tom Murphy, Chief Executive Officer
**Web address:** www.weisermemorialhospital.org

| | | |
|---|---|---|
| Owned, leased, sponsored: | 7 hospitals | 957 beds |
| Contract–managed: | 2 hospitals | 40 beds |
| **Totals:** | 9 hospitals | 997 beds |

---

**0862:  ST. LUKE'S UNIVERSITY HEALTH NETWORK** (NP)
801 Ostrum Street, Bethlehem, PA Zip 18015–1000; tel. 610/954–4000; Richard A. Anderson, President and Chief Executive Officer
**(Moderately Centralized Health System)**

**NEW JERSEY:** ST. LUKE'S HOSPITAL – WARREN CAMPUS (O, 140 beds) 185 Roseberry Street, Phillipsburg, NJ Zip 08865–1690; tel. 908/859–6700; Scott R. Wolfe, CPA, President
**Web address:** www.slhn.org

**PENNSYLVANIA:** ST. LUKE'S HOSPITAL – ANDERSON CAMPUS (O, 78 beds) 1872 Riverside Circle, Easton, PA Zip 18045–5669; tel. 484/503–3000; Edward Nawrocki, President
**Web address:** www.mystlukesonline.org

ST. LUKE'S HOSPITAL – MINERS CAMPUS (O, 92 beds) 360 West Ruddle Street, Coaldale, PA Zip 18218–1027; tel. 570/645–2131; William E. Moyer, President
**Web address:** www.slhn.org

ST. LUKE'S HOSPITAL – QUAKERTOWN CAMPUS (O, 57 beds) 1021 Park Avenue, Quakertown, PA Zip 18951–1573; tel. 215/538–4500; John B. Sylvia, President
**Web address:** www.slhhn.org

ST. LUKE'S UNIVERSITY HOSPITAL – BETHLEHEM CAMPUS (O, 550 beds) 801 Ostrum Street, Bethlehem, PA Zip 18015–1065; tel. 484/526–4000; Carol R. Kupler, President and Chief Executive Officer
**Web address:** www.slhn-lehighvalley.org

| | | |
|---|---|---|
| Owned, leased, sponsored: | 5 hospitals | 917 beds |
| Contract–managed: | 0 hospitals | 0 beds |
| **Totals:** | 5 hospitals | 917 beds |

---

**★0156:  STANFORD HEALTH CARE** (NP)
300 Pasteur Drive, Palo Alto, CA Zip 94304–2299; tel. 650/723–4000; Amir Dan Rubin, President and Chief Executive Officer
**(Moderately Centralized Health System)**

**CALIFORNIA:** LUCILE SALTER PACKARD CHILDREN'S HOSPITAL STANFORD (O, 302 beds) 725 Welch Road, Palo Alto, CA Zip 94304–1614; tel. 650/497–8000; Christopher G. Dawes, President and Chief Executive Officer
**Web address:** www.stanfordchildrens.org

STANFORD HEALTH CARE (O, 481 beds) 300 Pasteur Drive, Suite H3200, Palo Alto, CA Zip 94304–2203; tel. 650/723–4000; Amir Dan Rubin, President and Chief Executive Officer
**Web address:** www.stanfordhealthcare.org

STANFORD HEALTH CARE – VALLEYCARE (O, 207 beds) 5555 West Las Positas Boulevard, Pleasanton, CA Zip 94588–4000; tel. 925/847–3000; Scott Gregerson, President and Chief Executive Officer
**Web address:** www.valleycare.com

| | | |
|---|---|---|
| Owned, leased, sponsored: | 3 hospitals | 990 beds |
| Contract–managed: | 0 hospitals | 0 beds |
| **Totals:** | 3 hospitals | 990 beds |

---

**0141:  STEWARD HEALTH CARE SYSTEM, LLC** (IO)
500 Boylston Street, 5th Floor, Boston, MA Zip 02116–3740; tel. 617/419–4700; Ralph de la Torre, M.D., Chairman and Chief Executive Officer
**(Independent Hospital System)**

**MASSACHUSETTS:** CARNEY HOSPITAL (O, 81 beds) 2100 Dorchester Avenue, Boston, MA Zip 02124–5615; tel. 617/296–4000; Walter J. Ramos, ESQ, President and Chief Executive Officer
**Web address:** www.carneyhospital.org

GOOD SAMARITAN MEDICAL CENTER (O, 190 beds) 235 North Pearl Street, Brockton, MA Zip 02301–1794; tel. 508/427–3000; John A. Jurczyk, FACHE, Interim President
**Web address:** www.stewardhealth.org/Good–Samaritan

HOLY FAMILY HOSPITAL (O, 329 beds) 70 East Street, Methuen, MA Zip 01844–4597; tel. 978/687–0151; Joseph Roach, Chief Executive Officer
**Web address:** www.stewardhealth.org/Holy–Family–Hospital

MORTON HOSPITAL AND MEDICAL CENTER (O, 153 beds) 88 Washington Street, Taunton, MA Zip 02780–2465; tel. 508/828–7000; Kimberly S. Bassett, R.N., President
**Web address:** www.mortonhospital.org

NASHOBA VALLEY MEDICAL CENTER (O, 42 beds) 200 Groton Road, Ayer, MA Zip 01432–3300; tel. 978/784–9000; Salvatore Perla, President
**Web address:** www.nashobamed.org

NEW ENGLAND SINAI HOSPITAL AND REHABILITATION CENTER (O, 212 beds) 150 York Street, Stoughton, MA Zip 02072–1881; tel. 781/344–0600; Judith C. Waterston, R.N., MS, President and Chief Executive Officer
**Web address:** www.newenglandsinai.org

NORWOOD HOSPITAL (O, 188 beds) 800 Washington Street, Norwood, MA Zip 02062–3487; tel. 781/769–4000; Kimberly S. Bassett, R.N., Interim President
**Web address:** www.stewardhealth.org/Norwood–Hospital

SAINT ANNE'S HOSPITAL (O, 160 beds) 795 Middle Street, Fall River, MA Zip 02721–1798; tel. 508/674–5741; Craig A. Jesiolowski, FACHE, President
**Web address:** www.saintanneshospital.org

ST. ELIZABETH'S MEDICAL CENTER (O, 338 beds) 736 Cambridge Street, Brighton, MA Zip 02135–2997; tel. 617/789–3000; Roger Mitty, Interim Chief Executive Officer
**Web address:** www.stewardhealth.org/St_Elizabeths

| | | |
|---|---|---|
| Owned, leased, sponsored: | 9 hospitals | 1693 beds |
| Contract–managed: | 0 hospitals | 0 beds |
| **Totals:** | 9 hospitals | 1693 beds |

---

**0858:  STRATEGIC BEHAVIORAL HEALTH, LLC** (IO)
8295 Tournament Drive, Suite 201, Memphis, TN Zip 38125–8913; tel. 901/969–3100; Jim Shaheen, President

**COLORADO:** PEAK VIEW BEHAVIORAL HEALTH (O, 92 beds) 7353 Sisters Grove, Colorado Springs, CO Zip 80923–2615; tel. 719/444–8484; Lana Currance, R.N., MSN, Chief Executive Officer
**Web address:** www.strategicbh.com/peakview.html

**NEVADA:** MONTEVISTA HOSPITAL (O, 90 beds) 5900 West Rochelle Avenue, Las Vegas, NV Zip 89103–3327; tel. 702/364–1111; Richard Failla, Chief Executive Officer
**Web address:** www.montevistahospital.com

RED ROCK BEHAVIORAL HOSPITAL (O, 21 beds) 5975 West Twain Avenue, Las Vegas, NV Zip 89103–1237; tel. 702/214–8099; Toby Davis, Chief Executive Officer
**Web address:** www.redrockhospital.com

**NEW MEXICO:** PEAK BEHAVIORAL HEALTH SERVICES (O, 36 beds) 5065 McNutt Road, Santa Teresa, NM Zip 88008–9442; tel. 575/589–3000; Lyle Reese–Gardner, Interim Chief Executive Officer
**Web address:** www.peakbehavioral.com/

For explanation of codes following names, see page B2.
★ Indicates Type III membership in the American Hospital Association.

**NORTH CAROLINA:** STRATEGIC BEHAVIORAL HEALTH – CHARLOTTE (O, 60 beds) 1715 Sharon Road West, Charlotte, NC Zip 28210–5663; tel. 704/944–0650; Mercy Estevez, Chief Executive Officer
**Web address:** www.sbccharlotte.com/

STRATEGIC BEHAVIORAL HEALTH – RALEIGH (O, 50 beds) 3200 Waterfield Drive, Garner, NC Zip 27529–7727; tel. 919/573–4163; Robert Eklofe, Chief Executive Officer
**Web address:** www.sbcraleigh.com/

STRATEGIC BEHAVIORAL HEALTH – WILMINGTON (O, 92 beds) 2050 Mercantile Drive, Leland, NC Zip 28451–4053; tel. 910/371–2500; Daniel Kern, Chief Executive Officer
**Web address:** www.sbcwilmington.com/

**TEXAS:** ROCK PRAIRIE BEHAVIORAL HEALTH (O, 72 beds) 3550 Normand Drive, College Station, TX Zip 77845–6399; tel. 979/703–8848; Jim Serratt, Chief Executive Officer

| | | |
|---|---|---|
| **Owned, leased, sponsored:** | 8 hospitals | 513 beds |
| **Contract–managed:** | 0 hospitals | 0 beds |
| **Totals:** | 8 hospitals | 513 beds |

---

**0517:   SUCCESS HEALTHCARE** (IO)
999 Yamato Road, 3rd Floor, Boca Raton, FL Zip 33431–4477; tel. 561/869–6300; Peter R. Baronoff, President and Chief Executive Officer
**(Independent Hospital System)**

**CALIFORNIA:** SILVER LAKE MEDICAL CENTER (O, 150 beds) 1711 West Temple Street, Los Angeles, CA Zip 90026–5421; tel. 213/989–6100; Brent A. Cope, Chief Executive Officer
**Web address:** www.silverlakemc.com

**MISSOURI:** ST. ALEXIUS HOSPITAL – BROADWAY CAMPUS (O, 189 beds) 3933 South Broadway, Saint Louis, MO Zip 63118–4601; tel. 314/865–7000; Michael J. Motte, Chief Executive Officer
**Web address:** www.stalexiushospital.com

| | | |
|---|---|---|
| **Owned, leased, sponsored:** | 2 hospitals | 339 beds |
| **Contract–managed:** | 0 hospitals | 0 beds |
| **Totals:** | 2 hospitals | 339 beds |

---

**0399:   SUMMA HEALTH SYSTEM** (NP)
1077 Gorge Boulevard, Akron, OH Zip 44310; tel. 330/375–3000; Thomas Malone, M.D., President and Chief Executive Officer
**(Centralized Physician/Insurance Health System)**

**OHIO:** SUMMA AKRON CITY HOSPITAL (O, 436 beds) 525 East Market Street, Akron, OH Zip 44304–1619; tel. 330/375–3000; Thomas Malone, M.D., President and Chief Executive Officer
**Web address:** www.summahealth.org

SUMMA BARBERTON CITIZENS HOSPITAL (O, 192 beds) 155 Fifth Street N.E., Barberton, OH Zip 44203–3332; tel. 330/615–3000; Jason Niehaus, Senior Vice President Operations and Administrator
**Web address:** www.summahealth.org/locations/hospitals/barberton

SUMMA REHAB HOSPITAL (O, 60 beds) 29 North Adams Street, Akron, OH Zip 44304–1641; tel. 330/572–7300; Cheryl Henthorn, Chief Executive Officer
**Web address:** www.summarehabhospital.com/

SUMMA WESTERN RESERVE HOSPITAL (O, 65 beds) 1900 23rd Street, Cuyahoga Falls, OH Zip 44223–1499; tel. 330/971–7000; Robert Kent, D.O., President and Chief Executive Officer
**Web address:** www.westernreservehospital.org

| | | |
|---|---|---|
| **Owned, leased, sponsored:** | 4 hospitals | 753 beds |
| **Contract–managed:** | 0 hospitals | 0 beds |
| **Totals:** | 4 hospitals | 753 beds |

---

**★0189:   SUMMIT HEALTH** (NP)
112 North Seventh Street, Chambersburg, PA Zip 17201–1720; tel. 717/267–7138; Patrick W. O'Donnell, CPA, President and Chief Executive Officer
**(Independent Hospital System)**

**PENNSYLVANIA:** CHAMBERSBURG HOSPITAL (O, 248 beds) 112 North Seventh Street, Chambersburg, PA Zip 17201–1720; tel. 717/267–3000; Patrick W. O'Donnell, CPA, President and Chief Executive Officer
**Web address:** www.summithealth.org

WAYNESBORO HOSPITAL (O, 56 beds) 501 East Main Street, Waynesboro, PA Zip 17268–2394; tel. 717/765–4000; Melissa Dubrow, Chief Operating Officer
**Web address:** www.summithealth.org

| | | |
|---|---|---|
| **Owned, leased, sponsored:** | 2 hospitals | 304 beds |
| **Contract–managed:** | 0 hospitals | 0 beds |
| **Totals:** | 2 hospitals | 304 beds |

---

**0237:   SUNLINK HEALTH SYSTEMS** (IO)
900 Circle 75 Parkway, Suite 1120, Atlanta, GA Zip 30339–3005; tel. 770/933–7000; Robert M. Thornton, Jr., Chief Executive Officer
**(Independent Hospital System)**

**GEORGIA:** CHESTATEE REGIONAL HOSPITAL (O, 49 beds) 227 Mountain Drive, Dahlonega, GA Zip 30533–1606; tel. 706/864–6136; Jason Cox, Chief Executive Officer
**Web address:** www.chestateeregionalhospital.com

NORTH GEORGIA MEDICAL CENTER (O, 135 beds) 1362 South Main Street, Ellijay, GA Zip 30540–5410, Mailing Address: P.O. Box 2239, Zip 30540–0025; tel. 706/276–4741; Earl S. Whiteley, FACHE, Chief Executive Officer
**Web address:** www.northgeorgiamedicalcenter.com

**MISSISSIPPI:** TRACE REGIONAL HOSPITAL (O, 84 beds) Highway 8 East, Houston, MS Zip 38851–9396, Mailing Address: P.O. Box 626, Zip 38851–0626; tel. 662/456–3700; Gary L. Staten, Chief Executive Officer
**Web address:** www.traceregional.com

| | | |
|---|---|---|
| **Owned, leased, sponsored:** | 3 hospitals | 268 beds |
| **Contract–managed:** | 0 hospitals | 0 beds |
| **Totals:** | 3 hospitals | 268 beds |

---

**★0066:   SUSQUEHANNA HEALTH SYSTEM** (NP)
700 High Street, Williamsport, PA Zip 17701–3100; tel. 570/321–1000; Steven P. Johnson, FACHE, President and Chief Executive Officer
**(Centralized Health System)**

**PENNSYLVANIA:** DIVINE PROVIDENCE HOSPITAL (O, 31 beds) 1100 Grampian Boulevard, Williamsport, PA Zip 17701–1995; tel. 570/326–8000; Robert E. Kane, President
**Web address:** www.susquehannahealth.org

MUNCY VALLEY HOSPITAL (O, 156 beds) 215 East Water Street, Muncy, PA Zip 17756–8700; tel. 570/546–8282; Ronald J. Reynolds, President
**Web address:** www.susquehannahealth.org

SOLDIERS AND SAILORS MEMORIAL HOSPITAL (O, 83 beds) 32–36 Central Avenue, Wellsboro, PA Zip 16901–1899; tel. 570/724–1631; Janie Hilfiger, President
**Web address:** www.susquehannahealth.org

WILLIAMSPORT REGIONAL MEDICAL CENTER (O, 203 beds) 700 High Street, Williamsport, PA Zip 17701–3100; tel. 570/321–1000; Jan E. Fisher, President
**Web address:** www.susquehannahealth.org

| | | |
|---|---|---|
| **Owned, leased, sponsored:** | 4 hospitals | 473 beds |
| **Contract–managed:** | 0 hospitals | 0 beds |
| **Totals:** | 4 hospitals | 473 beds |

---

**★8795:   SUTTER HEALTH** (NP)
2200 River Plaza Drive, Sacramento, CA Zip 95833–4134; tel. 916/733–8800; Patrick E. Fry, President and Chief Executive Officer
**(Centralized Health System)**

---

For explanation of codes following names, see page B2.
★ Indicates Type III membership in the American Hospital Association.

Section B

**CALIFORNIA:** ALTA BATES SUMMIT MEDICAL CENTER (O, 441 beds) 2450 Ashby Avenue, Berkeley, CA Zip 94705–2067; tel. 510/204–4444; Charles Prosper, Chief Executive Officer
**Web address:** www.altabates.com

ALTA BATES SUMMIT MEDICAL CENTER – SUMMIT CAMPUS (O, 326 beds) 350 Hawthorne Avenue, Oakland, CA Zip 94609–3100; tel. 510/655–4000; Charles Prosper, Chief Executive Officer
**Web address:** www.altabatessummit.com

CALIFORNIA PACIFIC MEDICAL CENTER (O, 644 beds) 2333 Buchanan Street, San Francisco, CA Zip 94115–1925, Mailing Address: P.O. Box 7999, Zip 94120–7999; tel. 415/600–6000; Warren S. Browner, M.D., M.P.H., Chief Executive Officer
**Web address:** www.cpmc.org

EDEN MEDICAL CENTER (O, 130 beds) 20103 Lake Chabot Road, Castro Valley, CA Zip 94546–5305; tel. 510/537–1234; Theresa Glubka, R.N., Chief Executive Officer
**Web address:** www.edenmedcenter.org

MEMORIAL HOSPITAL LOS BANOS (O, 36 beds) 520 West I Street, Los Banos, CA Zip 93635–3498; tel. 209/826–0591; Ash Gokli, M.D., Chief Executive Officer
**Web address:** www.memoriallosbanos.org/

MEMORIAL MEDICAL CENTER (O, 230 beds) 1700 Coffee Road, Modesto, CA Zip 95355–2869, Mailing Address: P.O. Box 942, Zip 95353–0942; tel. 209/526–4500; Daryn J. Kumar, Chief Executive Officer
**Web address:** www.memorialmedicalcenter.org

MENLO PARK SURGICAL HOSPITAL (O, 12 beds) 570 Willow Road, Menlo Park, CA Zip 94025–2617; tel. 650/324–8500; Kathleen Palange, R.N., Chief Administrative Officer
**Web address:** www.pamf.org/mpsh

MILLS–PENINSULA HEALTH SERVICES (O, 320 beds) 1501 Trousdale Drive, Burlingame, CA Zip 94010–3282; tel. 650/696–5400; Janet Wagner, R.N., Chief Executive Officer
**Web address:** www.mills–peninsula.org

NOVATO COMMUNITY HOSPITAL (O, 40 beds) 180 Rowland Way, Novato, CA Zip 94945–5009, Mailing Address: P.O. Box 1108, Zip 94948–1108; tel. 415/209–1300; Brian Alexander, Chief Administrative Officer
**Web address:** www.novatocommunity.sutterhealth.org

ST. LUKE'S HOSPITAL (O, 175 beds) 3555 Cesar Chavez Street, San Francisco, CA Zip 94110–4403; tel. 415/600–6000; Warren S. Browner, M.D., M.P.H., Chief Executive Officer
**Web address:** www.stlukes–sf.org

SUTTER AMADOR HOSPITAL (O, 52 beds) 200 Mission Boulevard, Jackson, CA Zip 95642–2564; tel. 209/223–7500; Anne Platt, Chief Executive Officer
**Web address:** www.sutteramador.org

SUTTER AUBURN FAITH HOSPITAL (O, 72 beds) 11815 Education Street, Auburn, CA Zip 95602–2410; tel. 530/888–4500; Mitchell J. Hanna, Chief Executive Officer
**Web address:** www.sutterhealth.org

SUTTER CENTER FOR PSYCHIATRY (O, 71 beds) 7700 Folsom Boulevard, Sacramento, CA Zip 95826–2608; tel. 916/386–3000; John W. Boyd, PsyD, Chief Administrative Officer
**Web address:** www.sutterpsychiatry.org

SUTTER COAST HOSPITAL (O, 49 beds) 800 East Washington Boulevard, Crescent City, CA Zip 95531–8359; tel. 707/464–8511; Mitchell J. Hanna, Interim Chief Executive Officer
**Web address:** www.sutterhealth.org

SUTTER DAVIS HOSPITAL (O, 48 beds) 2000 Sutter Place, Davis, CA Zip 95616–6201, Mailing Address: P.O. Box 1617, Zip 95617–1617; tel. 530/756–6440; Jennifer Maher, Chief Executive Officer
**Web address:** www.sutterhealth.org

SUTTER DELTA MEDICAL CENTER (O, 132 beds) 3901 Lone Tree Way, Antioch, CA Zip 94509–6253; tel. 925/779–7200; Dori Stevens, Chief Executive Officer
**Web address:** www.sutterdelta.org

SUTTER LAKESIDE HOSPITAL (O, 25 beds) 5176 Hill Road East, Lakeport, CA Zip 95453–6300; tel. 707/262–5000; Siri Nelson, Chief Administrative Officer
**Web address:** www.sutterlakeside.org

SUTTER MATERNITY AND SURGERY CENTER OF SANTA CRUZ (O, 30 beds) 2900 Chanticleer Avenue, Santa Cruz, CA Zip 95065–1816; tel. 831/477–2200; Stephen Gray, Chief Administrative Officer
**Web address:** www.suttersantacruz.org

SUTTER MEDICAL CENTER, SACRAMENTO (O, 512 beds) 2801 L Street, Sacramento, CA Zip 95816–5680; tel. 916/454–3333; Carrie Owen–Plietz, Chief Executive Officer
**Web address:** www.sutterhealth.org

SUTTER ROSEVILLE MEDICAL CENTER (O, 328 beds) One Medical Plaza Drive, Roseville, CA Zip 95661–3037; tel. 916/781–1000; Patrick R. Brady, Chief Executive Officer
**Web address:** www.sutterroseville.org

SUTTER SANTA ROSA REGIONAL HOSPITAL (O, 84 beds) 30 Mark West Springs Road, Santa Rosa, CA Zip 95403; tel. 707/576–4000; Mike Purvis, Chief Administrative Officer
**Web address:** www.sutterhealth.org

SUTTER SOLANO MEDICAL CENTER (O, 102 beds) 300 Hospital Drive, Vallejo, CA Zip 94589–2574, Mailing Address: P.O. Box 3189, Zip 94590–0669; tel. 707/554–4444; John W. Boyd, PsyD, Chief Executive Officer
**Web address:** www.suttersolano.org

SUTTER TRACY COMMUNITY HOSPITAL (O, 78 beds) 1420 North Tracy Boulevard, Tracy, CA Zip 95376–3497; tel. 209/835–1500; David M. Thompson, Chief Executive Officer
**Web address:** www.suttertracy.org

**HAWAII:** KAHI MOHALA BEHAVIORAL HEALTH (O, 76 beds) 91–2301 Old Fort Weaver Road, Ewa Beach, HI Zip 96706–3602; tel. 808/671–8511; Leonard Licina, Chief Executive Officer
**Web address:** www.kahimohala.org

| | | |
|---|---|---|
| **Owned, leased, sponsored:** | 24 hospitals | 4013 beds |
| **Contract–managed:** | 0 hospitals | 0 beds |
| **Totals:** | 24 hospitals | 4013 beds |

---

★**0871:  SWEDISH HEALTH SERVICES** (NP)
747 Broadway, Seattle, WA Zip 98122–4379; tel. 206/386–6000; Anthony A. Armada, Senior Vice President, Chief Executive Officer of Swedish Health Services and Providence Health and Services **(Independent Hospital System)**

**WASHINGTON:** SWEDISH MEDICAL CENTER–CHERRY HILL CAMPUS (O, 198 beds) 500 17th Avenue, Seattle, WA Zip 98122–5711; tel. 206/320–2000; June Altaras, R.N., Chief Executive Officer
**Web address:** www.swedish.org

SWEDISH MEDICAL CENTER–FIRST HILL (O, 631 beds) 747 Broadway, Seattle, WA Zip 98122–4307; tel. 206/386–6000; June Altaras, R.N., Chief Executive Officer
**Web address:** www.swedish.org

SWEDISH/EDMONDS (O, 164 beds) 21601 76th Avenue West, Edmonds, WA Zip 98026–7506; tel. 425/640–4000; Jennifer Graves, R.N., MS, Chief Executive
**Web address:** www.swedish.org

SWEDISH/ISSAQUAH (O, 80 beds) 751 N.E. Blakely Drive, Issaquah, WA Zip 98029–6201; tel. 425/313–4000; Rayburn Lewis, M.D., Chief Executive Officer
**Web address:** www.swedish.org/issaquah

| | | |
|---|---|---|
| **Owned, leased, sponsored:** | 4 hospitals | 1073 beds |
| **Contract–managed:** | 0 hospitals | 0 beds |
| **Totals:** | 4 hospitals | 1073 beds |

---

★**0379:  TAHOE FOREST HEALTH SYSTEM** (NP)
10121 Pine Avenue, Truckee, CA Zip 96161–4835; tel. 530/587–6011; Robert A. Schapper, Chief Executive Officer

**CALIFORNIA:** TAHOE FOREST HOSPITAL DISTRICT (O, 62 beds) 10121 Pine Avenue, Truckee, CA Zip 96161–4856, Mailing Address: P.O. Box 759, Zip 96160–0759; tel. 530/587–6011; Jake Dorst, Interim Chief Executive Officer
**Web address:** www.tfhd.com

**NEVADA:** INCLINE VILLAGE COMMUNITY HOSPITAL (O, 6 beds) 880 Alder Avenue, Incline Village, NV Zip 89451–8335; tel. 775/833–4100; Judy Newland, R.N., Chief Nursing Officer
**Web address:** www.tfhd.com

---

For explanation of codes following names, see page B2.
★ Indicates Type III membership in the American Hospital Association.

| Owned, leased, sponsored: | 2 hospitals | 68 beds |
|---|---|---|
| Contract–managed: | 0 hospitals | 0 beds |
| Totals: | 2 hospitals | 68 beds |

**★0341:  TANNER HEALTH SYSTEM** (NP)
705 Dixie Street, Carrollton, GA Zip 30117–3818;
tel. 770/836–9580; Loy M. Howard, President and Chief Executive Officer

**GEORGIA:** HIGGINS GENERAL HOSPITAL (L, 25 beds) 200 Allen Memorial Drive, Bremen, GA Zip 30110–2012; tel. 770/824–2000; Michael D. Alexander, MS, Administrator
**Web address:** www.tanner.org/Main/HigginsGeneralHospitalBremen.aspx

TANNER MEDICAL CENTER–CARROLLTON (O, 201 beds) 705 Dixie Street, Carrollton, GA Zip 30117–3818; tel. 770/836–9666
**Web address:** www.tanner.org

TANNER MEDICAL CENTER–VILLA RICA (O, 39 beds) 601 Dallas Road, Villa Rica, GA Zip 30180–1202; tel. 770/456–3000; Bonnie Boles, M.D., Administrator
**Web address:** www.tanner.org

| Owned, leased, sponsored: | 3 hospitals | 265 beds |
|---|---|---|
| Contract–managed: | 0 hospitals | 0 beds |
| Totals: | 3 hospitals | 265 beds |

**★0169:  TEMPLE UNIVERSITY HEALTH SYSTEM** (NP)
3509 North Broad Street, 9th Floor, Philadelphia, PA Zip 19140–4105; tel. 215/707–0900; Larry Kaiser, M.D., President and Chief Executive Officer
**(Moderately Centralized Health System)**

**PENNSYLVANIA:** FOX CHASE CANCER CENTER–AMERICAN ONCOLOGIC HOSPITAL (O, 100 beds) 333 Cottman Avenue, Philadelphia, PA Zip 19111–2434; tel. 215/728–6900; Richard Fisher, President and Chief Executive Officer
**Web address:** www.fccc.edu

JEANES HOSPITAL (O, 146 beds) 7600 Central Avenue, Philadelphia, PA Zip 19111–2499; tel. 215/728–2000; Marc P. Hurowitz, D.O., President and Chief Executive Officer
**Web address:** www.jeanes.com

TEMPLE UNIVERSITY HOSPITAL (O, 665 beds) 3401 North Broad Street, Philadelphia, PA Zip 19140–5103; tel. 215/707–2000; John N. Kastanis, Chief Executive Officer
**Web address:** www.tuh.templehealth.org/content/default.htm

| Owned, leased, sponsored: | 3 hospitals | 911 beds |
|---|---|---|
| Contract–managed: | 0 hospitals | 0 beds |
| Totals: | 3 hospitals | 911 beds |

**★0919:  TENET HEALTHCARE CORPORATION** (IO)
1445 Ross Avenue, Suite 1400, Dallas, TX Zip 75202–2703, Mailing Address: P.O. Box 1390369, Zip 75313–9036; tel. 469/893–2200; Trevor Fetter, President and Chief Executive Officer
**(Decentralized Health System)**

**ALABAMA:** BROOKWOOD MEDICAL CENTER (O, 645 beds) 2010 Brookwood Medical Center Drive, Birmingham, AL Zip 35209–6875; tel. 205/877–1000; Charles A. Stark, FACHE, President and Chief Executive Officer
**Web address:** www.bwmc.com

**ARIZONA:** ABRAZO MARYVALE CAMPUS (O, 100 beds) 5102 West Campbell Avenue, Phoenix, AZ Zip 85031–1799; tel. 623/848–5000; Crystal Hamilton, R.N., Chief Executive Officer
**Web address:** www.maryvalehospital.com

ABRAZO SCOTTSDALE CAMPUS (O, 142 beds) 3929 East Bell Road, Phoenix, AZ Zip 85032–2196; tel. 602/923–5000; David Tupponce, M.D., Chief Executive Officer
**Web address:** www.abrazoscottsdale.com

ARROWHEAD HOSPITAL (O, 234 beds) 18701 North 67th Avenue, Glendale, AZ Zip 85308–7100; tel. 623/561–1000; Frank L. Molinaro, Chief Executive Officer
**Web address:** www.arrowheadhospital.com

PHOENIX BAPTIST HOSPITAL (O, 215 beds) 2000 West Bethany Home Road, Phoenix, AZ Zip 85015–2443; tel. 602/249–0212; Danny L. Jones, Jr., FACHE, Chief Executive Officer
**Web address:** www.phoenixbaptisthospital.com

WEST VALLEY HOSPITAL (O, 106 beds) 13677 West McDowell Road, Goodyear, AZ Zip 85395–2635; tel. 623/882–1500; Stan V. Holm, FACHE, Chief Executive Officer
**Web address:** www.wvhospital.com

**CALIFORNIA:** DESERT REGIONAL MEDICAL CENTER (L, 382 beds) 1150 North Indian Canyon Drive, Palm Springs, CA Zip 92262–4872, Mailing Address: P.O. Box 2739, Zip 92263–2739; tel. 760/323–6511; Carolyn P. Caldwell, Chief Executive Officer
**Web address:** www.desertregional.com

DOCTORS HOSPITAL OF MANTECA (O, 73 beds) 1205 East North Street, Manteca, CA Zip 95336–4900; tel. 209/823–3111; Carmen Silva, R.N., Interim Chief Executive Officer
**Web address:** www.doctorsmanteca.com

DOCTORS MEDICAL CENTER (O, 455 beds) 1441 Florida Avenue, Modesto, CA Zip 95350–4418, Mailing Address: P.O. Box 4138, Zip 95352–4138; tel. 209/578–1211; Warren J. Kirk, Chief Executive Officer
**Web address:** www.dmc–modesto.com

EMANUEL MEDICAL CENTER (O, 209 beds) 825 Delbon Avenue, Turlock, CA Zip 95382–2016, Mailing Address: P.O. Box 819005, Zip 95381–9005; tel. 209/667–4200; Susan C. Micheletti, Chief Executive Officer
**Web address:** www.emanuelmed.org

FOUNTAIN VALLEY REGIONAL HOSPITAL AND MEDICAL CENTER (O, 242 beds) 17100 Euclid Street, Fountain Valley, CA Zip 92708–4043; tel. 714/966–7200; B. Joseph Badalian, Chief Executive Officer
**Web address:** www.fountainvalleyhospital.com

HI–DESERT MEDICAL CENTER (O, 179 beds) 6601 White Feather Road, Joshua Tree, CA Zip 92252–6607; tel. 760/366–3711; Randall L. Kelley, FACHE, Interim Chief Executive Officer
**Web address:** www.hdmc.org

JOHN F. KENNEDY MEMORIAL HOSPITAL (O, 112 beds) 47111 Monroe Street, Indio, CA Zip 92201–6799; tel. 760/347–6191; Gary Honts, Chief Executive Officer
**Web address:** www.jfkmemorialhosp.com

LAKEWOOD REGIONAL MEDICAL CENTER (O, 153 beds) 3700 East South Street, Lakewood, CA Zip 90712–1498, Mailing Address: P.O. Box 6070, Zip 90714–6070; tel. 562/531–2550; Timothy P. Menton, Interim Chief Executive Officer
**Web address:** www.lakewoodregional.com

LOS ALAMITOS MEDICAL CENTER (O, 167 beds) 3751 Katella Avenue, Los Alamitos, CA Zip 90720–3164; tel. 562/598–1311; Kent G. Clayton, Chief Executive Officer
**Web address:** www.losalamitosmedctr.com

PLACENTIA–LINDA HOSPITAL (O, 114 beds) 1301 North Rose Drive, Placentia, CA Zip 92870–3899; tel. 714/993–2000; Audrey Gregory, R.N., MSN, Chief Executive Officer
**Web address:** www.placentialinda.com

SAN RAMON REGIONAL MEDICAL CENTER (O, 123 beds) 6001 Norris Canyon Road, San Ramon, CA Zip 94583–5400; tel. 925/275–9200; Gary Sloan, Chief Executive Officer
**Web address:** www.sanramonmedctr.com

SIERRA VISTA REGIONAL MEDICAL CENTER (O, 164 beds) 1010 Murray Avenue, San Luis Obispo, CA Zip 93405–1806, Mailing Address: P.O. Box 1367, Zip 93406–1367; tel. 805/546–7600; Joseph DeSchryver, Chief Executive Officer
**Web address:** www.sierravistaregional.com

TWIN CITIES COMMUNITY HOSPITAL (O, 89 beds) 1100 Las Tablas Road, Templeton, CA Zip 93465–9796; tel. 805/434–3500; Mark P. Lisa, FACHE, Chief Executive Officer
**Web address:** www.twincitieshospital.com

**FLORIDA:** CORAL GABLES HOSPITAL (O, 256 beds) 3100 Douglas Road, Coral Gables, FL Zip 33134–6914; tel. 305/445–8461; Patrick Downes, Chief Executive Officer
**Web address:** www.coralgableshospital.com

For explanation of codes following names, see page B2.
★ Indicates Type III membership in the American Hospital Association.

Section B

DELRAY MEDICAL CENTER (O, 439 beds) 5352 Linton Boulevard, Delray Beach, FL Zip 33484–6580; tel. 561/498–4440; Mark Bryan, Chief Executive Officer
**Web address:** www.delraymedicalctr.com

FLORIDA MEDICAL CENTER – A CAMPUS OF NORTH SHORE (O, 459 beds) 5000 West Oakland Park Boulevard, Fort Lauderdale, FL Zip 33313–1585; tel. 954/735–6000; Gabrielle Finley–Hazle, Chief Executive Officer
**Web address:** www.fmc–campus.com

GOOD SAMARITAN MEDICAL CENTER (O, 174 beds) 1309 North Flagler Drive, West Palm Beach, FL Zip 33401–3499; tel. 561/655–5511; Mark Nosacka, Chief Executive Officer
**Web address:** www.goodsamaritanmc.com

HIALEAH HOSPITAL (O, 172 beds) 651 East 25th Street, Hialeah, FL Zip 33013–3878; tel. 305/693–6100; Ben A. Rodriguez, Chief Executive Officer
**Web address:** www.hialeahhosp.com

NORTH SHORE MEDICAL CENTER (O, 357 beds) 1100 N.W. 95th Street, Miami, FL Zip 33150–2098; tel. 305/835–6000; Manuel Linares, Chief Executive Officer
**Web address:** www.northshoremedical.com

PALM BEACH GARDENS MEDICAL CENTER (L, 199 beds) 3360 Burns Road, Palm Beach Gardens, FL Zip 33410–4323; tel. 561/622–1411; Jeffrey M. Welch, Chief Executive Officer
**Web address:** www.pbgmc.com

PALMETTO GENERAL HOSPITAL (O, 360 beds) 2001 West 68th Street, Hialeah, FL Zip 33016–1898; tel. 305/823–5000; Ana J. Mederos, Chief Executive Officer
**Web address:** www.palmettogeneral.com

ST. MARY'S MEDICAL CENTER (O, 464 beds) 901 45th Street, West Palm Beach, FL Zip 33407–2495; tel. 561/844–6300; Joey Bulfin, R.N., Interim Chief Executive Officer
**Web address:** www.stmarysmc.com

WEST BOCA MEDICAL CENTER (O, 195 beds) 21644 State Road 7, Boca Raton, FL Zip 33428–1899; tel. 561/488–8000; Mitchell S. Feldman, Chief Executive Officer
**Web address:** www.westbocamedctr.com

**GEORGIA:** ATLANTA MEDICAL CENTER (O, 403 beds) 303 Parkway Drive N.E., Atlanta, GA Zip 30312–1212; tel. 404/265–4000; Thomas E. Casaday, Chief Executive Officer
**Web address:** www.atlantamedcenter.com

NORTH FULTON REGIONAL HOSPITAL (L, 196 beds) 3000 Hospital Boulevard, Roswell, GA Zip 30076–3899; tel. 770/751–2500; Deborah C. Keel, Chief Executive Officer
**Web address:** www.northfultonregional.com

SPALDING REGIONAL MEDICAL CENTER (O, 160 beds) 601 South Eighth Street, Griffin, GA Zip 30224–4294, Mailing Address: P.O. Drawer V, Zip 30224–1168; tel. 770/228–2721; John A. Quinn, Chief Executive Officer
**Web address:** www.spaldingregional.com

SYLVAN GROVE HOSPITAL (L, 24 beds) 1050 McDonough Road, Jackson, GA Zip 30233–1599; tel. 770/775–7861; John A. Quinn, Chief Executive Officer
**Web address:** www.sylvangrovehospital.com

**ILLINOIS:** LOUIS A. WEISS MEMORIAL HOSPITAL (O, 184 beds) 4646 North Marine Drive, Chicago, IL Zip 60640–5759; tel. 773/878–8700; Anthony Tedeschi, M.D., M.P.H., Chief Executive Officer and Chief Medical Officer
**Web address:** www.weisshospital.com

MACNEAL HOSPITAL (O, 371 beds) 3249 South Oak Park Avenue, Berwyn, IL Zip 60402–0715; tel. 708/783–9100; J. Scott Steiner, Chief Executive Officer
**Web address:** www.macneal.com

WEST SUBURBAN MEDICAL CENTER (O, 172 beds) 3 Erie Court, Oak Park, IL Zip 60302–2599; tel. 708/383–6200; Patrick J. Maloney, Chief Executive Officer
**Web address:** www.westsuburbanmc.com/Home.aspx

WESTLAKE HOSPITAL (O, 181 beds) 1225 Lake Street, Melrose Park, IL Zip 60160–4000; tel. 708/681–3000; Patrick J. Maloney, Chief Executive Officer
**Web address:** www.westlakehosp.com

**MASSACHUSETTS:** METROWEST MEDICAL CENTER (O, 148 beds) 115 Lincoln Street, Framingham, MA Zip 01702–6342; tel. 508/383–1000; Barbara J. Doyle, R.N., MS, Chief Executive Officer
**Web address:** www.mwmc.com

SAINT VINCENT HOSPITAL (O, 283 beds) 123 Summer Street, Worcester, MA Zip 01608–1216; tel. 508/363–5000; Steven MacLauchlan, President and CEO
**Web address:** www.stvincenthospital.com

**MICHIGAN:** CHILDREN'S HOSPITAL OF MICHIGAN (O, 222 beds) 3901 Beaubien Street, Detroit, MI Zip 48201–2119; tel. 313/745–5437; Larry M. Gold, Chief Executive Officer
**Web address:** www.chmkids.org

DETROIT RECEIVING HOSPITAL/UNIVERSITY HEALTH CENTER (O, 210 beds) 4201 Saint Antoine Street, Detroit, MI Zip 48201–2153; tel. 313/745–3000; Iris Taylor, Ph.D., R.N., President
**Web address:** www.dmc.org

DMC HARPER UNIVERSITY HOSPITAL (O, 412 beds) 3990 John R Street, Detroit, MI Zip 48201–2018; tel. 313/745–8040; Reginald J. Eadie, M.D., Chief Executive Officer
**Web address:** www.harperhospital.org

DMC HURON VALLEY–SINAI HOSPITAL (O, 145 beds) 1 William Carls Drive, Commerce Township, MI Zip 48382–2201; tel. 248/937–3300; Karen Fordham, President
**Web address:** www.hvsh.org

REHABILITATION INSTITUTE OF MICHIGAN (O, 69 beds) 261 Mack Avenue, Detroit, MI Zip 48201–2495; tel. 313/745–1203; William H. Restum, Ph.D., President
**Web address:** www.rimrehab.org

SINAI–GRACE HOSPITAL (O, 304 beds) 6071 West Outer Drive, Detroit, MI Zip 48235–2679; tel. 313/966–3300; Paula R. Autry, FACHE, Chief Executive Officer
**Web address:** www.sinaigrace.org

**MISSOURI:** DES PERES HOSPITAL (O, 143 beds) 2345 Dougherty Ferry Road, Saint Louis, MO Zip 63122–3313; tel. 314/966–9100; John A. Grah, JD, FACHE, Chief Executive Officer
**Web address:** www.despereshospital.com

**NORTH CAROLINA:** CENTRAL CAROLINA HOSPITAL (O, 116 beds) 1135 Carthage Street, Sanford, NC Zip 27330–4162; tel. 919/774–2100; David E. Loving, Chief Executive Officer
**Web address:** www.centralcarolinahosp.com

FRYE REGIONAL MEDICAL CENTER (L, 279 beds) 420 North Center Street, Hickory, NC Zip 28601–5049; tel. 828/322–6070; Philip Shaw, Interim Chief Executive Officer
**Web address:** www.fryemedctr.com

**PENNSYLVANIA:** HAHNEMANN UNIVERSITY HOSPITAL (O, 496 beds) Broad and Vine Streets, Philadelphia, PA Zip 19102–1192; tel. 215/762–7000; Michael P. Halter, Chief Executive Officer
**Web address:** www.hahnemannhospital.com

ST. CHRISTOPHER'S HOSPITAL FOR CHILDREN (O, 189 beds) 3601 A. Street, Philadelphia, PA Zip 19134–1043; tel. 215/427–5000; J. Mark McLoone, FACHE, Chief Executive Officer
**Web address:** www.stchristophershospital.com

**SOUTH CAROLINA:** COASTAL CAROLINA HOSPITAL (O, 35 beds) 1000 Medical Center Drive, Hardeeville, SC Zip 29927–3446; tel. 843/784–8000; Bradley S. Talbert, FACHE, Chief Executive Officer
**Web address:** www.coastalhospital.com

EAST COOPER MEDICAL CENTER (O, 140 beds) 2000 Hospital Drive, Mount Pleasant, SC Zip 29464–3764; tel. 843/881–0100; Jason P. Alexander, FACHE, Chief Executive Officer
**Web address:** www.eastcoopermedctr.com

HILTON HEAD HOSPITAL (O, 93 beds) 25 Hospital Center Boulevard, Hilton Head Island, SC Zip 29926–2738; tel. 843/681–6122; Jeremy Clark, President and Chief Executive Officer
**Web address:** www.hiltonheadregional.com

PIEDMONT MEDICAL CENTER (O, 280 beds) 222 Herlong Avenue, Rock Hill, SC Zip 29732–1234; tel. 803/329–1234; William Masterton, Chief Executive Officer
**Web address:** www.piedmontmedicalcenter.com

**TENNESSEE:** SAINT FRANCIS HOSPITAL (O, 511 beds) 5959 Park Avenue, Memphis, TN Zip 38119–5198, Mailing Address: P.O. Box 171808, Zip 38187–1808; tel. 901/765–1000; David L. Archer, Chief Executive Officer
**Web address:** www.saintfrancishosp.com

For explanation of codes following names, see page B2.
★ Indicates Type III membership in the American Hospital Association.

SAINT FRANCIS HOSPITAL–BARTLETT (O, 156 beds) 2986 Kate Bond Road, Bartlett, TN Zip 38133–4003; tel. 901/820–7000; Christopher Locke, Chief Executive Officer
**Web address:** www.saintfrancisbartlett.com

**TEXAS:** BAPTIST MEDICAL CENTER (O, 1672 beds) 111 Dallas Street, San Antonio, TX Zip 78205–1230; tel. 210/297–7000; Jonathan Turton, FACHE, Interim President
**Web address:** www.baptisthealthsystem.com

CENTENNIAL MEDICAL CENTER (O, 118 beds) 12505 Lebanon Road, Frisco, TX Zip 75035–8298; tel. 972/963–3333; Joe D. Thomason, Chief Executive Officer
**Web address:** www.centennialmedcenter.com

CYPRESS FAIRBANKS MEDICAL CENTER (O, 181 beds) 10655 Steepletop Drive, Houston, TX Zip 77065–4297; tel. 281/890–4285; Terry J. Wheeler, Chief Executive Officer
**Web address:** www.cyfairhospital.com

DOCTORS HOSPITAL AT WHITE ROCK LAKE (O, 151 beds) 9440 Poppy Drive, Dallas, TX Zip 75218–3694; tel. 214/324–6100; Jaikumar Krishnaswamy, Chief Executive Officer
**Web address:** www.doctorshospitaldallas.com

HOUSTON NORTHWEST MEDICAL CENTER (O, 339 beds) 710 FM 1960 Road West, Houston, TX Zip 77090–3402; tel. 281/440–1000; Timothy Puthoff, Chief Executive Officer
**Web address:** www.hnmc.com

LAKE POINTE MEDICAL CENTER (O, 112 beds) 6800 Scenic Drive, Rowlett, TX Zip 75088–4552, Mailing Address: P.O. Box 1550, Zip 75030–1550; tel. 972/412–2273; Brett D. Lee, Chief Executive Officer
**Web address:** www.lakepointemedical.com

NACOGDOCHES MEDICAL CENTER (O, 109 beds) 4920 N.E. Stallings Drive, Nacogdoches, TX Zip 75965–1200; tel. 936/569–9481; Gary L. Stokes, Chief Executive Officer
**Web address:** www.nacmedicalcenter.com

PARK PLAZA HOSPITAL (O, 157 beds) 1313 Hermann Drive, Houston, TX Zip 77004–7092; tel. 713/527–5000; Steven D. Patonai, Interim Chief Executive Officer
**Web address:** www.parkplazahospital.com

PLAZA SPECIALTY HOSPITAL (O, 39 beds) 1300 Binz, Houston, TX Zip 77004–7016; tel. 713/285–1000; Richard Pletz, Chief Executive Officer
**Web address:** www.plazaspecialtyhospital.com

RESOLUTE HEALTH (O, 54 beds) 555 Creekside Crossing, New Braunfels, TX Zip 78130–2594; tel. 830/500–6000; Matt Stone, Chief Executive Officer
**Web address:** www.resolutehealth.com

THE HOSPITALS OF PROVIDENCE MEMORIAL CAMPUS (O, 351 beds) 2001 North Oregon Street, El Paso, TX Zip 79902–3368; tel. 915/577–6625; Sally A. Hurt–Deitch, FACHE, Chief Executive Officer
**Web address:** www.sphn.com

THE HOSPITALS OF PROVIDENCE SIERRA CAMPUS (O, 349 beds) 1625 Medical Center Drive, El Paso, TX Zip 79902–5044; tel. 915/747–4000; Monica Vargas–Mahar, FACHE, Chief Executive Officer
**Web address:** www.sphn.com

THE HOSPITALS OF SIERRA PROVIDENCE EAST CAMPUS (O, 170 beds) 3280 Joe Battle Boulevard, El Paso, TX Zip 79938–2622; tel. 915/832–2000; Nicholas R. Tejeda, FACHE, Chief Executive Officer
**Web address:** www.sphn.com

VALLEY BAPTIST MEDICAL CENTER–BROWNSVILLE (O, 262 beds) 1040 West Jefferson Street, Brownsville, TX Zip 78520–6338, Mailing Address: P.O. Box 3590, Zip 78523–3590; tel. 956/698–5400; Leslie Bingham, Senior Vice President and Chief Executive Officer
**Web address:** www.valleybaptist.net/brownsville/index.htm

VALLEY BAPTIST MEDICAL CENTER–HARLINGEN (O, 416 beds) 2101 Pease Street, Harlingen, TX Zip 78550–8307, Mailing Address: P.O. Drawer 2588, Zip 78551–2588; tel. 956/389–1100; Todd Mann, Senior Vice President and Chief Executive Officer
**Web address:** www.valleybaptist.net/harlingen/index.htm

| Owned, leased, sponsored: | 71 hospitals | 17381 beds |
|---|---|---|
| Contract–managed: | 0 hospitals | 0 beds |
| Totals: | 71 hospitals | 17381 beds |

**0876: TENNESSEE HEALTH MANAGEMENT** (IO)
52 West Eighth Street, Parsons, TN Zip 38363–4656, Mailing Address: PO Box 10, Zip 38363–0010; tel. 731/847–6343; Dennis Berry, Chief Executive Officer

**ALABAMA:** BEHAVIORAL HEALTHCARE CENTER AT HUNTSVILLE (O, 20 beds) 5315 Millennium Drive N.W., Huntsville, AL Zip 35806–2458; tel. 256/964–6700; Bradley Moss, Administrator
**Web address:** www.tnhealthmanagement.com/bhc/huntsville

**TENNESSEE:** BEHAVIORAL HEALTHCARE CENTER AT CLARKSVILLE (O, 26 beds) 930 Professional Park Drive, Clarksville, TN Zip 37040–5136; tel. 931/538–6420; Jennifer Robinson, Administrator
**Web address:** www.bhcclarksville.com

BEHAVIORAL HEALTHCARE CENTER AT COLUMBIA (O, 16 beds) 1400 Rosewood Drive, Columbia, TN Zip 38401–4878; tel. 931/388–6573; Paula Chennault, Administrator
**Web address:** www.bhccolumbia.com

BEHAVIORAL HEALTHCARE CENTER AT MARTIN (O, 16 beds) 458 Hannings Lane, Martin, TN Zip 38237–3308; tel. 731/588–2830; Carrie Brawley, Administrator
**Web address:** www.tnhealthmanagement.com/BHC/martin/

| Owned, leased, sponsored: | 4 hospitals | 78 beds |
|---|---|---|
| Contract–managed: | 0 hospitals | 0 beds |
| Totals: | 4 hospitals | 78 beds |

**0020: TEXAS DEPARTMENT OF STATE HEALTH SERVICES** (NP)
1100 West 49th Street, Austin, TX Zip 78756–3199; tel. 512/458–7111; Kirk Cole, Interim Commissioner
**(Independent Hospital System)**

**TEXAS:** AUSTIN STATE HOSPITAL (O, 314 beds) 4110 Guadalupe Street, Austin, TX Zip 78751–4296; tel. 512/452–0381; Cathy Nottebart, Acting Superintendent
**Web address:** www.dshs.state.tx.us/mhhospitals/austinsh/default.shtm

BIG SPRING STATE HOSPITAL (O, 200 beds) 1901 North Highway 87, Big Spring, TX Zip 79720–0283; tel. 432/267–8216; Lorie Dunnam, Superintendent
**Web address:** www.dshs.state.tx.us/mhhospitals/BigSpringSH/default.shtm

EL PASO PSYCHIATRIC CENTER (O, 74 beds) 4615 Alameda Avenue, El Paso, TX Zip 79905–2702; tel. 915/532–2202; Zulema Carrillo, Superintendent
**Web address:** www.dshs.state.tx.us/mhhospitals/ElPasoPC/default.shtm

KERRVILLE STATE HOSPITAL (O, 202 beds) 721 Thompson Drive, Kerrville, TX Zip 78028–5154; tel. 830/896–2211; Leigh Ann Fitzpatrick, Superintendent
**Web address:** www.dshs.state.tx.us/mhhospitals/KerrvilleSH/default.shtm

NORTH TEXAS STATE HOSPITAL (O, 640 beds) Highway 70 Northwest, Vernon, TX Zip 76384, Mailing Address: P.O. Box 2231, Zip 76385–2231; tel. 940/552–9901; James E. Smith, Superintendent
**Web address:** www.dshs.state.tx.us/mhhospitals/NorthTexasSH/default.shtm

RIO GRANDE STATE CENTER/SOUTH TEXAS HEALTH CARE SYSTEM (O, 128 beds) 1401 South Rangerville Road, Harlingen, TX Zip 78552–7638; tel. 956/364–8000; Sonia Hernandez–Keeble, Superintendent
**Web address:** www.dshs.state.tx.us/mhhospitals/RioGrandeSC/default.shtm

RUSK STATE HOSPITAL (O, 325 beds) 805 North Dickinson, Rusk, TX Zip 75785–2333, Mailing Address: P.O. Box 318, Zip 75785–0318; tel. 903/683–3421; Brenda Slaton, Superintendent
**Web address:** www.dshs.state.tx.us/mhhospitals/RuskSH/default.shtm

SAN ANTONIO STATE HOSPITAL (O, 302 beds) 6711 South New Braunfels, Suite 100, San Antonio, TX Zip 78223–3006; tel. 210/531–7711; Robert C. Arizpe, Superintendent
**Web address:** www.dshs.state.tx.us/mhhospitals/SanAntonioSH/default.shtm

TERRELL STATE HOSPITAL (O, 288 beds) 1200 East Brin Street, Terrell, TX Zip 75160–2938, Mailing Address: P.O. Box 70, Zip 75160–9000; tel. 972/524–6452; Dorothy Floyd, Ph.D., Superintendent
**Web address:** www.dshs.state.tx.us/mhhospitals/terrellsh

For explanation of codes following names, see page B2.
★ Indicates Type III membership in the American Hospital Association.

TEXAS CENTER FOR INFECTIOUS DISEASE (O, 40 beds) 2303 S.E. Military Drive, San Antonio, TX Zip 78223–3597; tel. 210/534–8857; James N. Elkins, FACHE, Superintendent
**Web address:** www.dshs.state.tx.us/tcid/default.shtm

| | | |
|---|---|---|
| Owned, leased, sponsored: | 10 hospitals | 2513 beds |
| Contract–managed: | 0 hospitals | 0 beds |
| Totals: | 10 hospitals | 2513 beds |

---

★**0129: TEXAS HEALTH RESOURCES** (NP)
612 East Lamar Boulevard, Suite 900, Arlington, TX Zip 76011–4130; tel. 682/236–7900; Barclay E. Berdan, FACHE, Chief Executive Officer
**(Moderately Centralized Health System)**

TEXAS HEALTH ARLINGTON MEMORIAL HOSPITAL (O, 266 beds) 800 West Randol Mill Road, Arlington, TX Zip 76012–2503; tel. 817/548–6100; Blake Kretz, President
**Web address:** www.arlingtonmemorial.org

TEXAS HEALTH HARRIS METHODIST HOSPITAL ALLIANCE (O, 58 beds) 10864 Texas Health Trail, Fort Worth, TX Zip 76244–4897; tel. 682/212–2000; Clint Abernathy, Interim Chief Executive Officer

TEXAS HEALTH HARRIS METHODIST HOSPITAL AZLE (O, 31 beds) 108 Denver Trail, Azle, TX Zip 76020–3614; tel. 817/444–8600; Bob S. Ellzey, FACHE, President
**Web address:** www.texashealth.org/Azle

TEXAS HEALTH HARRIS METHODIST HOSPITAL CLEBURNE (O, 85 beds) 201 Walls Drive, Cleburne, TX Zip 76033–4007; tel. 817/641–2551; Lorrie Normand, R.N., Interim Chief Executive Officer
**Web address:** www.texashealth.org

TEXAS HEALTH HARRIS METHODIST HOSPITAL FORT WORTH (O, 641 beds) 1301 Pennsylvania Avenue, Fort Worth, TX Zip 76104–2122; tel. 817/250–2000; Lillie Biggins, RN, R.N., President
**Web address:** www.texashealth.org

TEXAS HEALTH HARRIS METHODIST HOSPITAL HURST–EULESS–BEDFORD (O, 210 beds) 1600 Hospital Parkway, Bedford, TX Zip 76022–6913, Mailing Address: P.O. Box 669, Zip 76095–0669; tel. 817/685–4000; Deborah Paganelli, President
**Web address:** www.texashealth.org

TEXAS HEALTH HARRIS METHODIST HOSPITAL SOUTHWEST FORT WORTH (O, 199 beds) 6100 Harris Parkway, Fort Worth, TX Zip 76132–4199; tel. 817/433–5000; Joseph DeLeon, President
**Web address:** www.texashealth.org

TEXAS HEALTH HARRIS METHODIST HOSPITAL STEPHENVILLE (O, 54 beds) 411 North Belknap Street, Stephenville, TX Zip 76401–3415; tel. 254/965–1500; Christopher Leu, President
**Web address:** www.texashealth.org/landing.cfm?id=108

TEXAS HEALTH PRESBYTERIAN HOSPITAL ALLEN (O, 73 beds) 1105 Central Expressway North, Allen, TX Zip 75013–6103; tel. 972/747–1000; Jeff Reecer, President
**Web address:** www.texashealth.org

TEXAS HEALTH PRESBYTERIAN HOSPITAL DALLAS (O, 644 beds) 8200 Walnut Hill Lane, Dallas, TX Zip 75231–4426; tel. 214/345–6789; James Berg, FACHE, President
**Web address:** www.texashealth.org

TEXAS HEALTH PRESBYTERIAN HOSPITAL DENTON (O, 208 beds) 3000 North I–35, Denton, TX Zip 76201–5119; tel. 940/898–7000; Stan C. Morton, FACHE, President
**Web address:** www.dentonhospital.com

TEXAS HEALTH PRESBYTERIAN HOSPITAL KAUFMAN (O, 68 beds) 850 Ed Hall Drive, Kaufman, TX Zip 75142–1861, Mailing Address: P.O. Box 1108, Zip 75142–5401; tel. 972/932–7200; Patsy Youngs, President
**Web address:** www.texashealth.org/Kaufman

TEXAS HEALTH PRESBYTERIAN HOSPITAL PLANO (O, 307 beds) 6200 West Parker Road, Plano, TX Zip 75093–8185; tel. 972/981–8000; Joshua Floren, Interim President
**Web address:** www.texashealth.org

TEXAS HEALTH SPECIALTY HOSPITAL (O, 10 beds) 1301 Pennsylvania Avenue, 4th Floor, Fort Worth, TX Zip 76104–2190; tel. 817/250–5500; Cheryl Mobley, FACHE, President
**Web address:** www.texashealth.org

| | | |
|---|---|---|
| Owned, leased, sponsored: | 14 hospitals | 2854 beds |
| Contract–managed: | 0 hospitals | 0 beds |
| Totals: | 14 hospitals | 2854 beds |

---

**2445: THEDACARE, INC.** (NP)
122 East College Avenue, Appleton, WI Zip 54911–5794, Mailing Address: P.O. Box 8025, Zip 54912–8025; tel. 920/830–5889; Dean Gruner, M.D., President and Chief Executive Officer
**(Moderately Centralized Health System)**

**WISCONSIN:** APPLETON MEDICAL CENTER (O, 149 beds) 1818 North Meade Street, Appleton, WI Zip 54911–3496; tel. 920/731–4101; Brian Burmeister, Senior Vice President
**Web address:** www.thedacare.org

BERLIN MEMORIAL HOSPITAL (O, 75 beds) 225 Memorial Drive, Berlin, WI Zip 54923–1295; tel. 920/361–1313; John Feeney, President and Chief Executive Officer
**Web address:** www.chnwi.org

NEW LONDON FAMILY MEDICAL CENTER (O, 25 beds) 1405 Mill Street, New London, WI Zip 54961–2155, Mailing Address: P.O. Box 307, Zip 54961–0307; tel. 920/531–2000; William Schmidt, President and Chief Executive Officer
**Web address:** www.thedacare.org

RIVERSIDE MEDICAL CENTER (O, 25 beds) 800 Riverside Drive, Waupaca, WI Zip 54981–1999; tel. 715/258–1000; Craig A. Kantos, Chief Executive Officer
**Web address:** www.riversidemedical.org

SHAWANO MEDICAL CENTER (O, 25 beds) 309 North Bartlette Street, Shawano, WI Zip 54166–2127; tel. 715/526–2111; Dorothy Erdmann, Chief Executive Officer
**Web address:** www.shawanomed.org

THEDA CLARK MEDICAL CENTER (O, 151 beds) 130 Second Street, Neenah, WI Zip 54956–2883, Mailing Address: P.O. Box 2021, Zip 54957–2021; tel. 920/729–3100; Brian Burmeister, Senior Vice President, ThedaCare Hospitals
**Web address:** www.thedacare.org

WILD ROSE COMMUNITY MEMORIAL HOSPITAL (O, 25 beds) 601 Grove Avenue, Wild Rose, WI Zip 54984–6903, Mailing Address: P.O. Box 243, Zip 54984–0243; tel. 920/622–3257; Dawn Schuman, President
**Web address:** www.wildrosehospital.org

| | | |
|---|---|---|
| Owned, leased, sponsored: | 7 hospitals | 475 beds |
| Contract–managed: | 0 hospitals | 0 beds |
| Totals: | 7 hospitals | 475 beds |

---

★**0643: THOMAS HEALTH SYSTEM, INC.** (NP)
4605 MacCorkle Avenue S.W., South Charleston, WV Zip 25309–1311; tel. 304/766–3600; Daniel Lauffer, FACHE, President and Chief Executive Officer
**(Centralized Health System)**

**WEST VIRGINIA:** SAINT FRANCIS HOSPITAL (O, 118 beds) 333 Laidley Street, Charleston, WV Zip 25301–1628, Mailing Address: P.O. Box 471, Zip 25322–0471; tel. 304/347–6500; Daniel Lauffer, FACHE, President and Chief Executive Officer
**Web address:** www.stfrancishospital.com

THOMAS MEMORIAL HOSPITAL (O, 215 beds) 4605 MacCorkle Avenue S.W., South Charleston, WV Zip 25309–1398; tel. 304/766–3600; Daniel Lauffer, FACHE, President and Chief Executive Officer
**Web address:** www.thomaswv.org

| | | |
|---|---|---|
| Owned, leased, sponsored: | 2 hospitals | 333 beds |
| Contract–managed: | 0 hospitals | 0 beds |
| Totals: | 2 hospitals | 333 beds |

---

★**0910: TIFT REGIONAL HEALTH SYSTEM** (NP)
901 East 18th Street, Tifton, GA Zip 31794–3648; tel. 229/353–6100; William T. Richardson, President and Chief Executive Officer
**(Independent Hospital System)**

For explanation of codes following names, see page B2.
★ Indicates Type III membership in the American Hospital Association.

Section B

**GEORGIA:** COOK MEDICAL CENTER–A CAMPUS OF TIFT REGIONAL MEDICAL CENTER (O, 155 beds) 706 North Parrish Avenue, Adel, GA Zip 31620–1511; tel. 229/896–8000; Michael L. Purvis, Chief Executive Officer
**Web address:** www.cookmedicalcenter.com

TIFT REGIONAL MEDICAL CENTER (O, 191 beds) 901 East 18th Street, Tifton, GA Zip 31794–3648, Mailing Address: Drawer 747, Zip 31793–0747; tel. 229/382–7120; William T. Richardson, President and Chief Executive Officer
**Web address:** www.tiftregional.com

| Owned, leased, sponsored: | 2 hospitals | 346 beds |
|---|---|---|
| Contract–managed: | 0 hospitals | 0 beds |
| Totals: | 2 hospitals | 346 beds |

---

**★0906: TRINITY HEALTH** (CC)
20555 Victor Parkway, Livonia, MI Zip 48152–7031; tel. 734/343–1000; Richard J. Gilfillan, M.D., President and Chief Executive Officer
**(Decentralized Health System)**

**CALIFORNIA:** SAINT AGNES MEDICAL CENTER (O, 436 beds) 1303 East Herndon Avenue, Fresno, CA Zip 93720–3397; tel. 559/450–3000; Nancy Hollingsworth, R.N., MSN, President and Chief Executive Officer
**Web address:** www.samc.com

**DELAWARE:** ST. FRANCIS HOSPITAL (O, 214 beds) Seventh and Clayton Streets, Wilmington, DE Zip 19805–0500, Mailing Address: P.O. Box 2500, Zip 19805–0500; tel. 302/421–4100; Brian E. Dietz, FACHE, Interim President and Chief Executive officer
**Web address:** www.stfrancishealthcare.org

**FLORIDA:** HOLY CROSS HOSPITAL (O, 359 beds) 4725 North Federal Highway, Fort Lauderdale, FL Zip 33308–4668, Mailing Address: P.O. Box 23460, Zip 33307–3460; tel. 954/771–8000; Patrick Taylor, M.D., President and Chief Executive Officer
**Web address:** www.holy–cross.com

SOUTH FLORIDA BAPTIST HOSPITAL (S, 115 beds) 301 North Alexander Street, Plant City, FL Zip 33563–4303; tel. 813/757–1200; Karen Kerr, R.N., President and Chief Executive Officer
**Web address:** www.sjbhealth.org

ST. ANTHONY'S HOSPITAL (S, 393 beds) 1200 Seventh Avenue North, Saint Petersburg, FL Zip 33705–1388, Mailing Address: P.O. Box 12588, Zip 33733–2588; tel. 727/825–1100; William G. Ulbricht, President
**Web address:** www.stanthonys.com/

ST. JOSEPH'S HOSPITAL (S, 1006 beds) 3001 West Martin Luther King Jr. Boulevard, Tampa, FL Zip 33607–6387, Mailing Address: P.O. Box 4227, Zip 33677–4227; tel. 813/870–4000; Lorraine Lutton, President
**Web address:** www.sjbhealth.org

**GEORGIA:** ST. MARY'S GOOD SAMARITAN HOSPITAL (O, 25 beds) 5401 Lake Oconee Parkway, Greensboro, GA Zip 30642–4232; tel. 706/453–7331; D. Montez Carter, President
**Web address:** www.stmarysgoodsam.org

ST. MARY'S HEALTH CARE SYSTEM (O, 179 beds) 1230 Baxter Street, Athens, GA Zip 30606–3791; tel. 706/389–3000; Donald McKenna, President and Chief Executive Officer
**Web address:** www.stmarysathens.com

ST. MARY'S SACRED HEART HOSPITAL (O, 35 beds) 367 Clear Creek Parkway, Lavonia, GA Zip 30553–4173; tel. 706/356–7800; Jeff English, Interim Chief Executive Officer
**Web address:** www.stmaryssacredheart.org/

**IDAHO:** SAINT ALPHONSUS MEDICAL CENTER – NAMPA (O, 142 beds) 1512 12th Avenue Road, Nampa, ID Zip 83686–6008; tel. 208/463–5000; Karl Keeler, Chief Executive Officer
**Web address:** www.mercynampa.org

SAINT ALPHONSUS REGIONAL MEDICAL CENTER (O, 399 beds) 1055 North Curtis Road, Boise, ID Zip 83706–1309, Mailing Address: 1055 North Curtis Road, Zip 83706–1309; tel. 208/367–2121; Rodney D. Reider, President
**Web address:** www.saintalphonsus.org

**ILLINOIS:** GOTTLIEB MEMORIAL HOSPITAL (O, 205 beds) 701 West North Avenue, Melrose Park, IL Zip 60160–1612; tel. 708/681–3200; Lori Price, President
**Web address:** www.gottliebhospital.org

LOYOLA UNIVERSITY MEDICAL CENTER (O, 509 beds) 2160 South First Avenue, Maywood, IL Zip 60153–3328; tel. 708/216–9000; Larry M. Goldberg, President and Chief Executive Officer
**Web address:** www.loyolamedicine.org/Medical_Services/index.cfm

MERCY HOSPITAL AND MEDICAL CENTER (O, 189 beds) 2525 South Michigan Avenue, Chicago, IL Zip 60616–2333; tel. 312/567–2000; Carol L. Schneider, President and Chief Executive Officer
**Web address:** www.mercy–chicago.org

**INDIANA:** SAINT JOSEPH REGIONAL MEDICAL CENTER (O, 294 beds) 5215 Holy Cross Parkway, Mishawaka, IN Zip 46545–1469; tel. 574/335–5000; Albert Gutierrez, FACHE, President and Chief Executive Officer
**Web address:** www.sjmed.com

SAINT JOSEPH REGIONAL MEDICAL CENTER–PLYMOUTH CAMPUS (O, 48 beds) 1915 Lake Avenue, Plymouth, IN Zip 46563–9366, Mailing Address: P.O. Box 670, Zip 46563–0670; tel. 574/948–4000; Loretta Schmidt, President
**Web address:** www.sjmed.com

**IOWA:** BAUM HARMON MERCY HOSPITAL (O, 11 beds) 255 North Welch Avenue, Primghar, IA Zip 51245–7765, Mailing Address: P.O. Box 528, Zip 51245–0528; tel. 712/957–2300; Angie Shilling, Chief Executive Officer
**Web address:** www.baumharmon.org

CENTRAL COMMUNITY HOSPITAL (C, 25 beds) 901 Davidson Street N.W., Elkader, IA Zip 52043–9015; tel. 563/245–7000; Frances J. Zichal, Chief Executive Officer
**Web address:** www.centralcommunityhospital.com

FRANKLIN GENERAL HOSPITAL (C, 77 beds) 1720 Central Avenue East, Suite A., Hampton, IA Zip 50441–1867; tel. 641/456–5000; Kim Price, Chief Executive Officer
**Web address:** www.franklingeneral.com

HANCOCK COUNTY HEALTH SYSTEM (C, 25 beds) 532 First Street N.W., Britt, IA Zip 50423–1227; tel. 641/843–5000; Laura Zwiefel, Interim Chief Executive Officer
**Web address:** www.trusthchs.com/hancock–county–health–system

HANSEN FAMILY HOSPITAL (C, 21 beds) 920 South Oak, Iowa Falls, IA Zip 50126–9506; tel. 641/648–4631; Cherelle Montanye–Ireland, Chief Executive Officer
**Web address:** www.hansenfamilyhospital.com

HAWARDEN REGIONAL HEALTHCARE (C, 18 beds) 1111 11th Street, Hawarden, IA Zip 51023–1999; tel. 712/551–3100; Jayson Pullman, Chief Executive Officer
**Web address:** www.hawardenregionalhealthcare.com/

KOSSUTH REGIONAL HEALTH CENTER (C, 23 beds) 1515 South Phillips Street, Algona, IA Zip 50511–3649; tel. 515/295–2451; Scott A. Curtis, Administrator and Chief Executive Officer
**Web address:** www.krhc.com

MERCY MEDICAL CENTER–CLINTON (O, 290 beds) 1410 North Fourth Street, Clinton, IA Zip 52732–2940; tel. 563/244–5555; Sean J. Williams, President and Chief Executive Officer
**Web address:** www.mercyclinton.com

MERCY MEDICAL CENTER–DUBUQUE (O, 235 beds) 250 Mercy Drive, Dubuque, IA Zip 52001–7360; tel. 563/589–8000; Russell M. Knight, President and Chief Executive Officer
**Web address:** www.mercydubuque.com

MERCY MEDICAL CENTER–DYERSVILLE (O, 20 beds) 1111 Third Street S.W., Dyersville, IA Zip 52040–1725; tel. 563/875–7101; Russell M. Knight, President and Chief Executive Officer
**Web address:** www.mercydubuque.com/mercy–dyersville

MERCY MEDICAL CENTER–NEW HAMPTON (O, 18 beds) 308 North Maple Avenue, New Hampton, IA Zip 50659–1142; tel. 641/394–4121; Aaron Flugum, Chief Executive Officer
**Web address:** www.mercynewhampton.com

MERCY MEDICAL CENTER–NORTH IOWA (O, 206 beds) 1000 Fourth Street S.W., Mason City, IA Zip 50401–2800; tel. 641/428–7000; Daniel Varnum, President and Chief Executive Officer
**Web address:** www.mercynorthiowa.com

MERCY MEDICAL CENTER–SIOUX CITY (O, 192 beds) 801 Fifth Street, Sioux City, IA Zip 51101–1326, Mailing Address: P.O. Box 3168, Zip 51102–3168; tel. 712/279–2010; James G. Fitzpatrick, FACHE, Chief Executive Officer
**Web address:** www.mercysiouxcity.com

For explanation of codes following names, see page B2.
★ Indicates Type III membership in the American Hospital Association.

---

MITCHELL COUNTY REGIONAL HEALTH CENTER (C, 25 beds) 616 North Eighth Street, Osage, IA Zip 50461–1498; tel. 641/732–6000; Shelly Russell, Chief Executive Officer
**Web address:** www.mitchellcohospital–clinics.com

PALO ALTO COUNTY HEALTH SYSTEM (C, 47 beds) 3201 First Street, Emmetsburg, IA Zip 50536–2516; tel. 712/852–5500; Desiree Einsweiler, Chief Executive Officer
**Web address:** www.pachs.com

REGIONAL HEALTH SERVICES OF HOWARD COUNTY (C, 20 beds) 235 Eighth Avenue West, Cresco, IA Zip 52136–1098; tel. 563/547–2101; Robin M. Schluter, Chief Executive Officer
**Web address:** www.rhshc.com

**MARYLAND:** HOLY CROSS HOSPITAL (O, 425 beds) 1500 Forest Glen Road, Silver Spring, MD Zip 20910–1487; tel. 301/754–7000; Judith Rogers, R.N., Ph.D., President and Chief Executive Officer
**Web address:** www.holycrosshealth.org

**MASSACHUSETTS:** MERCY MEDICAL CENTER (O, 336 beds) 271 Carew Street, Springfield, MA Zip 01104–2398, Mailing Address: P.O. Box 9012, Zip 01102–9012; tel. 413/748–9000; Daniel P. Moen, President and Chief Executive Officer
**Web address:** www.mercycares.com

**MICHIGAN:** MERCY HEALTH HACKLEY CAMPUS (O, 213 beds) 1700 Clinton Street, Muskegon, MI Zip 49442–5502, Mailing Address: P.O. Box 3302, Zip 49443–3302; tel. 231/726–3511; Greg Loomis, President
**Web address:** www.mercyhealthmuskegon.com

MERCY HEALTH SAINT MARY'S (O, 334 beds) 200 Jefferson Avenue S.E., Grand Rapids, MI Zip 49503–4598; tel. 616/685–5000; Bill Manns, President
**Web address:** www.mercyhealthsaintmarys.org

MERCY HEALTH, LAKESHORE CAMPUS (O, 24 beds) 72 South State Street, Shelby, MI Zip 49455–1299; tel. 231/861–2156; Jay Bryan, President and Chief Executive Officer
**Web address:** www.mercyhealthmuskegon.com

MERCY HEALTH, MERCY CAMPUS (O, 188 beds) 1500 East Sherman Boulevard, Muskegon, MI Zip 49444–1849; tel. 231/672–2000; Greg Loomis, President
**Web address:** www.mercyhealth.com

ST. JOSEPH MERCY ANN ARBOR (O, 481 beds) 5301 Mcauley Drive, Ypsilanti, MI Zip 48197–1051, Mailing Address: P.O. Box 995, Ann Arbor, Zip 48106–0995; tel. 734/712–3456; Robert F. Casalou, President and Chief Executive Officer
**Web address:** www.sjmercyhealth.org

ST. JOSEPH MERCY CHELSEA (O, 113 beds) 775 South Main Street, Chelsea, MI Zip 48118–1383; tel. 734/593–6000; Nancy Kay Graebner, President and Chief Executive Officer
**Web address:** www.cch.org

ST. JOSEPH MERCY LIVINGSTON HOSPITAL (O, 42 beds) 620 Byron Road, Howell, MI Zip 48843–1093; tel. 517/545–6000; Robert F. Casalou, President and Chief Executive Officer
**Web address:** www.stjoeslivingston.org/livingston

ST. JOSEPH MERCY OAKLAND (O, 443 beds) 44405 Woodward Avenue, Pontiac, MI Zip 48341–5023; tel. 248/858–3000; Jack Weiner, Ph.D., President and Chief Executive Officer
**Web address:** www.stjoesoakland.com

ST. MARY MERCY HOSPITAL (O, 301 beds) 36475 Five Mile Road, Livonia, MI Zip 48154–1988; tel. 734/655–4800; David A. Spivey, President and Chief Executive Officer
**Web address:** www.stmarymercy.org

**NEBRASKA:** OAKLAND MERCY HOSPITAL (O, 18 beds) 601 East Second Street, Oakland, NE Zip 68045–1499; tel. 402/685–5601; John W. Werner, Chief Executive Officer
**Web address:** www.oaklandhospital.org

PENDER COMMUNITY HOSPITAL (C, 67 beds) 100 Hospital Drive, Pender, NE Zip 68047–0100, Mailing Address: P.O. Box 100, Zip 68047–0100; tel. 402/385–3083; Melissa Kelly, Administrator
**Web address:** www.pendercommunityhospital.com

**NEW JERSEY:** LOURDES MEDICAL CENTER OF BURLINGTON COUNTY (O, 169 beds) 218–A Sunset Road, Willingboro, NJ Zip 08046–1162; tel. 609/835–2900; Mark Nessel, Executive Vice President and Chief Operating Officer
**Web address:** www.lourdesnet.org

OUR LADY OF LOURDES MEDICAL CENTER (O, 350 beds) 1600 Haddon Avenue, Camden, NJ Zip 08103–3117; tel. 856/757–3500; Alexander J. Hatala, FACHE, President and Chief Executive Officer
**Web address:** www.lourdesnet.org

SAINT MICHAEL'S MEDICAL CENTER (O, 147 beds) 111 Central Avenue, Newark, NJ Zip 07102–1909; tel. 973/877–5350; David A. Ricci, President and Chief Executive Officer
**Web address:** www.smmcnj.org

ST. FRANCIS MEDICAL CENTER (O, 163 beds) 601 Hamilton Avenue, Trenton, NJ Zip 08629–1986; tel. 609/599–5000; Vincent Costantino, Chief Administrative Officer
**Web address:** www.stfrancismedical.com

**NEW YORK:** ALBANY MEMORIAL HOSPITAL (O, 74 beds) 600 Northern Boulevard, Albany, NY Zip 12204–1083; tel. 518/471–3221; Ann Errichetti, M.D., Chief Executive Officer
**Web address:** www.nehealth.com

SAMARITAN HOSPITAL (O, 212 beds) 2215 Burdett Avenue, Troy, NY Zip 12180–2475; tel. 518/271–3300; Norman E. Dascher, Jr., Chief Executive Officer
**Web address:** www.nehealth.com

ST. JAMES MERCY HEALTH SYSTEM (O, 222 beds) 411 Canisteo Street, Hornell, NY Zip 14843–2197; tel. 607/324–8000; Jennifer Sullivan, President and Chief Executive Officer
**Web address:** www.stjamesmercy.org

ST. JOSEPH'S HOSPITAL HEALTH CENTER (O, 431 beds) 301 Prospect Avenue, Syracuse, NY Zip 13203–1807; tel. 315/448–5111; Kathryn H. Ruscitto, President
**Web address:** www.sjhsyr.org

ST. MARY'S HOSPITAL (O, 173 beds) 1300 Massachusetts Avenue, Troy, NY Zip 12180–1695; tel. 518/268–5000; Norman E. Dascher, Jr., Chief Executive Officer
**Web address:** www.setonhealth.org

ST. PETER'S HOSPITAL (O, 442 beds) 315 South Manning Boulevard, Albany, NY Zip 12208–1789; tel. 518/525–1550; Ann Errichetti, M.D., Chief Executive Officer
**Web address:** www.sphcs.org

SUNNYVIEW REHABILITATION HOSPITAL (O, 115 beds) 1270 Belmont Avenue, Schenectady, NY Zip 12308–2104; tel. 518/382–4500; Edward Eisenman, Chief Executive Officer
**Web address:** www.sunnyview.org

**OHIO:** FAYETTE COUNTY MEMORIAL HOSPITAL (C, 25 beds) 1430 Columbus Avenue, Washington Court House, OH Zip 43160–1791; tel. 740/335–1210; John DesMarais, M.D., President and Chief Executive Officer
**Web address:** www.fcmh.org

MOUNT CARMEL (O, 747 beds) 793 West State Street, Columbus, OH Zip 43222–1551; tel. 614/234–5000; Sean McKibben, President and Chief Operating Officer
**Web address:** www.mountcarmelhealth.com

MOUNT CARMEL NEW ALBANY SURGICAL HOSPITAL (O, 60 beds) 7333 Smith's Mill Road, New Albany, OH Zip 43054–9291; tel. 614/775–6600; Diane Douchette, MBA, RN, President
**Web address:** www.mountcarmelhealth.com

MOUNT CARMEL ST. ANN'S (O, 281 beds) 500 South Cleveland Avenue, Westerville, OH Zip 43081–8998; tel. 614/898–4000; Roger Spoelman, Interim President and Chief Executive Officer
**Web address:** www.mountcarmelhealth.com

**OREGON:** SAINT ALPHONSUS MEDICAL CENTER – BAKER CITY (S, 55 beds) 3325 Pocahontas Road, Baker City, OR Zip 97814–1464; tel. 541/523–6461; H. Ray Gibbons, FACHE, Chief Executive Officer
**Web address:** www.saintalphonsus.org/bakercity

SAINT ALPHONSUS MEDICAL CENTER – ONTARIO (S, 49 beds) 351 S.W. Ninth Street, Ontario, OR Zip 97914–2693; tel. 541/881–7000; Karl Keeler, Chief Executive Officer
**Web address:** www.saintalphonsus.org/ontario

**PENNSYLVANIA:** MERCY FITZGERALD HOSPITAL (O, 382 beds) 1500 Lansdowe Avenue, Darby, PA Zip 19023–1200; tel. 610/237–4000; Kathryn Conallen, Chief Executive Officer
**Web address:** www.mercyhealth.org

For explanation of codes following names, see page B2.
★ Indicates Type III membership in the American Hospital Association.

MERCY SUBURBAN HOSPITAL (O, 126 beds) 2701 DeKalb Pike, Norristown, PA Zip 19401–1820; tel. 610/278–2000; Kathryn Conallen, Interim Chief Executive Officer
**Web address:** www.mercyhealth.org

NAZARETH HOSPITAL (O, 231 beds) 2601 Holme Avenue, Philadelphia, PA Zip 19152–2096; tel. 215/335–6000; Nancy Cherone, Executive Director and Administrator
**Web address:** www.nazarethhospital.org

ST. MARY MEDICAL CENTER (O, 323 beds) 1201 Langhorne–Newtown Road, Langhorne, PA Zip 19047–1201; tel. 215/710–2000; Gregory T. Wozniak, President and Chief Executive Officer
**Web address:** www.stmaryhealthcare.org

| | | |
|---|---|---|
| **Owned, leased, sponsored:** | 55 hospitals | 13190 beds |
| **Contract–managed:** | 11 hospitals | 373 beds |
| **Totals:** | 66 hospitals | 13563 beds |

**0540: TRINITY MOTHER FRANCES HOSPITALS AND CLINICS** (NP)
910 East Houston, Tyler, TX Zip 75702–8369; tel. 903/593–8441; J. Lindsey Bradley, Jr., FACHE, President
**(Centralized Physician/Insurance Health System)**

**TEXAS:** MOTHER FRANCES HOSPITAL – JACKSONVILLE (O, 21 beds) 2026 South Jackson, Jacksonville, TX Zip 75766–5822; tel. 903/541–4500; Anne Pileggi, Chief Executive Officer
**Web address:** www.tmfhs.org/jacksonville

MOTHER FRANCES HOSPITAL – TYLER (O, 458 beds) 800 East Dawson Street, Tyler, TX Zip 75701–2036; tel. 903/593–8441; John McGreevy, Chief Executive Officer
**Web address:** www.tmfhc.org

MOTHER FRANCES HOSPITAL – WINNSBORO (O, 23 beds) 719 West Coke Road, Winnsboro, TX Zip 75494–3011, Mailing Address: P.O. Box 628, Zip 75494–0628; tel. 903/342–5227; Janet E. Coates, R.N., President and Chief Executive Officer
**Web address:** www.tmfhs.org

| | | |
|---|---|---|
| **Owned, leased, sponsored:** | 3 hospitals | 502 beds |
| **Contract–managed:** | 0 hospitals | 0 beds |
| **Totals:** | 3 hospitals | 502 beds |

**★9255: TRUMAN MEDICAL CENTERS** (NP)
2301 Holmes Street, Kansas City, MO Zip 64108–2677; tel. 816/404–1000; Charlie Shields, President and Chief Executive Officer
**(Independent Hospital System)**

**MISSOURI:** TRUMAN MEDICAL CENTER–HOSPITAL HILL (O, 232 beds) 2301 Holmes Street, Kansas City, MO Zip 64108–2640; tel. 816/404–1000; Charlie Shields, President and Chief Executive Officer
**Web address:** www.trumed.org

TRUMAN MEDICAL CENTER–LAKEWOOD (O, 296 beds) 7900 Lee's Summit Road, Kansas City, MO Zip 64139–1236; tel. 816/404–7000; Charlie Shields, President and Chief Executive Officer
**Web address:** www.trumed.org

| | | |
|---|---|---|
| **Owned, leased, sponsored:** | 2 hospitals | 528 beds |
| **Contract–managed:** | 0 hospitals | 0 beds |
| **Totals:** | 2 hospitals | 528 beds |

**9195: U. S. INDIAN HEALTH SERVICE** (FG)
801 Thompson Avenue, Rockville, MD Zip 20852–1627; tel. 301/443–1083; Yvette Roubideaux, M.D., M.P.H., Director
**(Moderately Centralized Health System)**

**ARIZONA:** CHINLE COMPREHENSIVE HEALTH CARE FACILITY (O, 60 beds) Highway 191, Chinle, AZ Zip 86503, Mailing Address: P.O. Drawer PH, Zip 86503–8000; tel. 928/674–7011; Ronald Tso, Chief Executive Officer
**Web address:** www.ihs.gov

HOPI HEALTH CARE CENTER (O, 15 beds) Highway 264 Mile Marker 388, Keams Canyon, AZ Zip 86042, Mailing Address: P.O. Box 4000, Polacca, Zip 86042–4000; tel. 928/737–6000; Daryl Melvin, Chief Executive Officer
**Web address:** www.ihs.gov/index.asp

TSEHOOTSOOI MEDICAL CENTER (O, 39 beds) Highway 12 & Bonito Drive, Fort Defiance, AZ Zip 86504, Mailing Address: P.O. Box 649, Zip 86504–0649; tel. 928/729–8000; Leland Leonard, Ph.D., Chief Executive Officer
**Web address:** www.fdihb.org

U. S. PUBLIC HEALTH SERVICE INDIAN HOSPITAL (O, 20 beds) 12033 Agency Road, Parker, AZ Zip 85344–7718; tel. 928/669–2137; Ronald Milford, Chief Executive Officer
**Web address:** www.ihs.gov

U. S. PUBLIC HEALTH SERVICE INDIAN HOSPITAL (O, 8 beds) 238 Cibeque Circle, San Carlos, AZ Zip 85550, Mailing Address: P.O. Box 208, Zip 85550–0208; tel. 928/475–2371; Deven Parlikar, President and Chief Executive Officer
**Web address:** www.ihs.gov

U. S. PUBLIC HEALTH SERVICE INDIAN HOSPITAL–SELLS (O, 12 beds) Highway 86 & Topawa Road, Sells, AZ Zip 85634, Mailing Address: P.O. Box 548, Zip 85634–0548; tel. 520/383–7251; Priscilla Whitethorne, Chief Executive Officer
**Web address:** www.ihs.gov

U. S. PUBLIC HEALTH SERVICE INDIAN HOSPITAL–WHITERIVER (O, 35 beds) 200 West Hospital Drive, Whiteriver, AZ Zip 85941–0860, Mailing Address: State Route 73, Box 860, Zip 85941–0860; tel. 928/338–4911; Michelle Martinez, Chief Executive Officer
**Web address:** www.ihs.gov

U. S. PUBLIC HEALTH SERVICE PHOENIX INDIAN MEDICAL CENTER (O, 127 beds) 4212 North 16th Street, Phoenix, AZ Zip 85016–5389; tel. 602/263–1200; Captain Michael Weahkee, Chief Executive Officer
**Web address:** www.ihs.gov

**MARYLAND:** NATIONAL INSTITUTES OF HEALTH CLINICAL CENTER (O, 146 beds) 9000 Rockville Pike, Building 10, Room 6–2551, Bethesda, MD Zip 20892–1504; tel. 301/496–4000; John I. Gallin, M.D., Director
**Web address:** www.clinicalcenter.nih.gov

**MINNESOTA:** RED LAKE INDIAN HEALTH SERVICE HOSPITAL (O, 19 beds) 24760 Hospital Drive, Red Lake, MN Zip 56671, Mailing Address: P.O. Box 497, Zip 56671–0497; tel. 218/679–3912; Louis P. Erdrich, Interim Chief Executive Officer
**Web address:** www.rlnnredlakehospital.com/

U. S. PUBLIC HEALTH SERVICE INDIAN HOSPITAL (O, 13 beds) 7th Street & Grant Utley Avenue N.W., Cass Lake, MN Zip 56633, Mailing Address: Rural Route 3, Box 211, Zip 56633; tel. 218/335–3200; Norine Smith, Chief Executive Officer
**Web address:** www.ihs.gov

**MONTANA:** CROW/NORTHERN CHEYENNE HOSPITAL (O, 24 beds) 10110 South 7650 East, Crow Agency, MT Zip 59022–0009, Mailing Address: P.O. Box 9, Zip 59022–0009; tel. 406/638–2626; Gary Wabaunsee, Chief Executive Officer
**Web address:** www.ihs. gov/facilitiesservices/areaoffices/billings/crow/index.asp

FORT BELKNAP U. S. PUBLIC HEALTH SERVICE INDIAN HOSPITAL (O, 6 beds) 669 Agency Main Street, Harlem, MT Zip 59526–9455; tel. 406/353–3100; Steve Fox, Chief Executive Officer
**Web address:** www.ihs.gov

U. S. PUBLIC HEALTH SERVICE BLACKFEET COMMUNITY HOSPITAL (O, 25 beds) 760 New Hospital Circle, Saint Mary, MT Zip 59417–0760, Mailing Address: P.O. Box 760, Browning, Zip 59417–0760; tel. 406/338–6100; Merlin Gilham, Chief Executive Officer
**Web address:** www.ihs.gov

**NEBRASKA:** U. S. PUBLIC HEALTH SERVICE INDIAN HOSPITAL (O, 30 beds) Highway 7577, Winnebago, NE Zip 68071; tel. 402/878–2231; Patricia Medina, Service Unit Director
**Web address:** www.ihs.gov

**NEW MEXICO:** ACOMA–CANONCITO–LAGUNA HOSPITAL (O, 25 beds) 80B Veterans Boulevard, Acoma, NM Zip 87034, Mailing Address: P.O. Box 130, San Fidel, Zip 87049–0130; tel. 505/552–5300; William Thorne, Jr., Chief Executive Officer
**Web address:** www.ihs.gov/albuquerque/index.cfm?module=dsp_abq_acoma_canoncito_laguna

---

For explanation of codes following names, see page B2.
★ Indicates Type III membership in the American Hospital Association.

GALLUP INDIAN MEDICAL CENTER (O, 84 beds) 516 East Nizhoni Boulevard, Gallup, NM Zip 87301–5748, Mailing Address: P.O. Box 1337, Zip 87305–1337; tel. 505/722–1000; Vida J. Khow, Chief Executive Officer
**Web address:** www.ihs.gov/navajo/index.cfm?module=nao_hcc_gallup

MESCALERO PUBLIC HEALTH SERVICE INDIAN HOSPITAL (O, 13 beds) 318 Abalone Loop, Mescalero, NM Zip 88340, Mailing Address: Box 210, Zip 88340–0210; tel. 505/671–4441; Dorlynn Simmons, Chief Executive Officer
**Web address:** www.ihs.gov

NORTHERN NAVAJO MEDICAL CENTER (O, 62 beds) Highway 491 North, Shiprock, NM Zip 87420–0160, Mailing Address: P.O. Box 160, Zip 87420–0160; tel. 505/368–6001; Fannessa Comer, Chief Executive Officer
**Web address:** www.ihs.gov/

PHS SANTA FE INDIAN HOSPITAL (O, 39 beds) 1700 Cerrillos Road, Santa Fe, NM Zip 87505–3554; tel. 505/988–9821; Robert J. Lyon, Chief Executive Officer

U. S. PUBLIC HEALTH SERVICE INDIAN HOSPITAL (O, 12 beds) Route 9 and State Road 371, Crownpoint, NM Zip 87313, Mailing Address: P.O. Box 358, Zip 87313–0358; tel. 505/786–5291; Anslem Roanhorse, Chief Executive Officer
**Web address:** www.ihs.gov

U. S. PUBLIC HEALTH SERVICE INDIAN HOSPITAL (O, 32 beds) Route 301 North B. Street, Zuni, NM Zip 87327, Mailing Address: P.O. Box 467, Zip 87327–0467; tel. 505/782–4431; Jean Othole, Chief Executive Officer
**Web address:** www.ihs.gov

**NORTH DAKOTA:** INDIAN HEALTH SERVICE – QUENTIN N. BURDICK MEMORIAL HEALTH CARE FACILITY (O, 27 beds) 1300 Hospital Loop, Belcourt, ND Zip 58316, Mailing Address: P.O. Box 160, Zip 58316–0160; tel. 701/477–6111; Shelly Harris, Chief Executive Officer
**Web address:** www.ihs.gov

STANDING ROCK SERVICE UNIT, FORT YATES HOSPITAL, INDIAN HEALTH SERVICE, DHHS (O, 14 beds) 10 North River Road, Fort Yates, ND Zip 58538, Mailing Address: P.O. Box J, Zip 58538; tel. 701/854–3831; Jana Gipp, Chief Executive Officer
**Web address:** www.ihs.gov

**OKLAHOMA:** CHEROKEE NATION W.W. HASTINGS INDIAN HOSPITAL (O, 58 beds) 100 South Bliss Avenue, Tahlequah, OK Zip 74464–2512; tel. 918/458–3100; Brian Hail, Chief Executive Officer
**Web address:** www.cherokee.org

CLAREMORE INDIAN HOSPITAL (O, 44 beds) 101 South Moore Avenue, Claremore, OK Zip 74017–5091; tel. 918/342–6200; George Valliere, Chief Executive Officer
**Web address:** www.ihs.gov

LAWTON INDIAN HOSPITAL (O, 26 beds) 1515 Lawrie Tatum Road, Lawton, OK Zip 73507–3099; tel. 580/353–0350; Greg Ketcher, Administrator
**Web address:** www.ihs.gov

**SOUTH DAKOTA:** INDIAN HEALTH SERVICE HOSPITAL (O, 9 beds) 3200 Canyon Lake Drive, Rapid City, SD Zip 57702–8197; tel. 605/355–2280; Kevin J. Stiffarm, Chief Executive Officer
**Web address:** www.ihs.gov

U. S. PUBLIC HEALTH SERVICE INDIAN HOSPITAL (O, 11 beds) 317 Main Street, Eagle Butte, SD Zip 57625–1012, Mailing Address: P.O. Box 1012, Zip 57625–1012; tel. 605/964–7724; Charles Fisher, Chief Executive Officer
**Web address:** www.ihs.gov

U. S. PUBLIC HEALTH SERVICE INDIAN HOSPITAL (O, 45 beds) East Highway 18, Pine Ridge, SD Zip 57770, Mailing Address: P.O. Box 1201, Zip 57770–1201; tel. 605/867–5131; Ellen Davis, Service Unit Director
**Web address:** www.ihs.gov

U. S. PUBLIC HEALTH SERVICE INDIAN HOSPITAL (O, 35 beds) Highway 18, Soldier Creek Road, Rosebud, SD Zip 57570; tel. 605/747–2231; Kathey Wilson, Acting Chief Executive Officer
**Web address:** www.ihs.gov

| | | |
|---|---|---|
| **Owned, leased, sponsored:** | 31 hospitals | 1115 beds |
| **Contract–managed:** | 0 hospitals | 0 beds |
| **Totals:** | 31 hospitals | 1115 beds |

★**9105:** **UAB HEALTH SYSTEM** (NP)
500 22nd Street South, Suite 408, Birmingham, AL Zip 35233–3110; tel. 205/975–5362; William Ferniany, Ph.D., Chief Executive Officer
**(Centralized Physician/Insurance Health System)**

**ALABAMA:** MEDICAL WEST (O, 231 beds) 995 Ninth Avenue S.W., Bessemer, AL Zip 35022–4527; tel. 205/481–7000; Brian Keith Pennington, President and Chief Executive Officer
**Web address:** www.medicalwesthospital.org

UNIVERSITY OF ALABAMA HOSPITAL (O, 1191 beds) 619 19th Street South, Birmingham, AL Zip 35249–1900; tel. 205/934–4011; Anthony Patterson, FACHE, Senior Vice President Inpatient Services
**Web address:** www.uabmedicine.org

| | | |
|---|---|---|
| **Owned, leased, sponsored:** | 2 hospitals | 1422 beds |
| **Contract–managed:** | 0 hospitals | 0 beds |
| **Totals:** | 2 hospitals | 1422 beds |

★**0082:** **UC HEALTH** (NP)
3200 Burnet Avenue, Cincinnati, OH Zip 45229–3019; tel. 513/585–6000; Richard P. Lofgren, M.D., M.P.H., President and CEO
**(Moderately Centralized Health System)**

**OHIO:** DANIEL DRAKE CENTER FOR POST ACUTE CARE (O, 202 beds) 151 West Galbraith Road, Cincinnati, OH Zip 45216–1015; tel. 513/418–2500; Amy Schroyer, Vice President Administration and Senior Site Executive
**Web address:** www.uchealth.com/danieldrakecenter/

UNIVERSITY OF CINCINNATI MEDICAL CENTER (O, 605 beds) 234 Goodman Street, Cincinnati, OH Zip 45219–2316; tel. 513/584–1000; Lee Ann Liska, President and Chief Executive Officer
**Web address:** www.uchealth.com/university–of–cincinnati–medical–center/

WEST CHESTER HOSPITAL (O, 181 beds) 7700 University Drive, West Chester, OH Zip 45069–2505; tel. 513/298–3000; Kevin Joseph, M.D., Chief Executive Officer
**Web address:** www.uchealth.com/westchesterhospital

| | | |
|---|---|---|
| **Owned, leased, sponsored:** | 3 hospitals | 988 beds |
| **Contract–managed:** | 0 hospitals | 0 beds |
| **Totals:** | 3 hospitals | 988 beds |

★**0111:** **UF HEALTH SHANDS** (NP)
1600 S.W. Archer Road, Gainesville, FL Zip 32610–0326; tel. 352/733–1500; Edward Jimenez, Chief Executive Officer
**(Moderately Centralized Health System)**

**FLORIDA:** UF HEALTH JACKSONVILLE (O, 620 beds) 655 West Eighth Street, Jacksonville, FL Zip 32209–6595; tel. 904/244–0411; Russell Armistead, Chief Executive Officer
**Web address:** www.ufhealthjax.org/

UF HEALTH SHANDS HOSPITAL (O, 973 beds) 1600 S.W. Archer Road, Gainesville, FL Zip 32610–3003, Mailing Address: P.O. Box 100326, Zip 32610–0326; tel. 352/265–0111; Edward Jimenez, Chief Executive Officer
**Web address:** www.https://ufhealth.org/

| | | |
|---|---|---|
| **Owned, leased, sponsored:** | 2 hospitals | 1593 beds |
| **Contract–managed:** | 0 hospitals | 0 beds |
| **Totals:** | 2 hospitals | 1593 beds |

★**0224:** **UMASS MEMORIAL HEALTH CARE, INC.** (NP)
1 Biotech Park, Worcester, MA Zip 01605–2982; tel. 508/334–0100; Eric Dickson, M.D., President and Chief Executive Officer
**(Moderately Centralized Health System)**

**MASSACHUSETTS:** CLINTON HOSPITAL (O, 41 beds) 201 Highland Street, Clinton, MA Zip 01510–1096; tel. 978/368–3000; Sheila Daly, R.N., MS, President and Chief Executive Officer
**Web address:** www.clintonhospital.org

---

For explanation of codes following names, see page B2.
★ Indicates Type III membership in the American Hospital Association.

Section B

HEALTHALLIANCE HOSPITALS (O, 97 beds) 60 Hospital Road, Leominster, MA Zip 01453–2205; tel. 978/466–2000; Deborah K. Weymouth, FACHE, President and Chief Executive Officer
**Web address:** www.healthalliance.com

UMASS MEMORIAL MEDICAL CENTER (O, 807 beds) 119 Belmont Street, Worcester, MA Zip 01605–2982; tel. 508/334–1000; Patrick L. Muldoon, FACHE, President and CEO
**Web address:** www.umassmemorial.org

UMASS MEMORIAL–MARLBOROUGH HOSPITAL (O, 67 beds) 157 Union Street, Marlborough, MA Zip 01752–1297; tel. 508/481–5000; Steven P. Roach, FACHE, President and Chief Executive Officer
**Web address:** www.marlboroughhospital.org

| Owned, leased, sponsored: | 4 hospitals | 1012 beds |
|---|---|---|
| Contract–managed: | 0 hospitals | 0 beds |
| Totals: | 4 hospitals | 1012 beds |

---

**★0901:  UNC HEALTH CARE** (NP)
101 Manning Drive, Chapel Hill, NC Zip 27514–4220; tel. 919/966–4131; William L. Roper, M.D., M.P.H., Chief Executive Officer
**(Moderately Centralized Health System)**

**NORTH CAROLINA:** CALDWELL MEMORIAL HOSPITAL (O, 76 beds) 321 Mulberry Street S.W., Lenoir, NC Zip 28645–5720, Mailing Address: P.O. Box 1890, Zip 28645–1890; tel. 828/757–5100; Laura J. Easton, R.N., President and Chief Executive Officer
**Web address:** www.caldwellmemorial.org

CHATHAM HOSPITAL (O, 25 beds) 475 Progress Boulevard, Siler City, NC Zip 27344–6787, Mailing Address: P.O. Box 649, Zip 27344–0649; tel. 919/799–4000; Robert A. Enders, Jr., President
**Web address:** www.chathamhospital.org

HIGH POINT REGIONAL HEALTH SYSTEM (O, 335 beds) 601 North Elm Street, High Point, NC Zip 27262–4398, Mailing Address: P.O. Box HP–5, Zip 27261–1899; tel. 336/878–6000; Ernest L. Bovio, Jr., Chief Executive Officer
**Web address:** www.highpointregional.com

JOHNSTON HEALTH (C, 145 beds) 509 North Bright Leaf Boulevard, Smithfield, NC Zip 27577–4407, Mailing Address: P.O. Box 1376, Zip 27577–1376; tel. 919/934–8171; Charles W. Elliott, Jr., Chief Executive Officer
**Web address:** www.johnstonhealth.org

MARGARET R. PARDEE MEMORIAL HOSPITAL (C, 138 beds) 800 North Justice Street, Hendersonville, NC Zip 28791–3410; tel. 828/696–1000; James M. Kirby, II, President and Chief Executive Officer
**Web address:** www.pardeehospital.org

NASH HEALTH CARE SYSTEMS (O, 303 beds) 2460 Curtis Ellis Drive, Rocky Mount, NC Zip 27804–2237; tel. 252/443–8000; Larry H. Chewning, III, President and Chief Executive Officer
**Web address:** www.nhcs.org

REX HEALTHCARE (O, 660 beds) 4420 Lake Boone Trail, Raleigh, NC Zip 27607–6599; tel. 919/784–3100; Steve W. Burriss, Interim President
**Web address:** www.rexhealth.com

UNIVERSITY OF NORTH CAROLINA HOSPITALS (O, 830 beds) 101 Manning Drive, Chapel Hill, NC Zip 27514–4220; tel. 919/966–4131; Gary L. Park, President
**Web address:** www.unchealthcare.org

| Owned, leased, sponsored: | 6 hospitals | 2229 beds |
|---|---|---|
| Contract–managed: | 2 hospitals | 283 beds |
| Totals: | 8 hospitals | 2512 beds |

---

**0922:  UNION GENERAL HOSPITAL, INC.** (NP)
35 Hospital Road, Blairsville, GA Zip 30512–3139; tel. 706/745–2111; Mike Gowder, Chief Executive Officer

**GEORGIA:** CHATUGE REGIONAL HOSPITAL AND NURSING HOME (O, 137 beds) 110 Main Street, Hiawassee, GA Zip 30546–3408, Mailing Address: P.O. Box 509, Zip 30546–0509; tel. 706/896–2222; John Mark Gordon, Administrator
**Web address:** www.chatugeregionalhospital.org

UNION GENERAL HOSPITAL (O, 195 beds) 35 Hospital Road, Blairsville, GA Zip 30512–3139; tel. 706/745–2111; Mike Gowder, Chief Executive Officer
**Web address:** www.uniongeneralhospital.org

| Owned, leased, sponsored: | 2 hospitals | 332 beds |
|---|---|---|
| Contract–managed: | 0 hospitals | 0 beds |
| Totals: | 2 hospitals | 332 beds |

---

**0288:  UNITED HEALTH SERVICES** (NP)
10–42 Mitchell Avenue, Binghamton, NY Zip 13903–1617; tel. 607/762–2200; Matthew J. Salanger, President and Chief Executive Officer
**(Independent Hospital System)**

**NEW YORK:** CHENANGO MEMORIAL HOSPITAL (O, 138 beds) 179 North Broad Street, Norwich, NY Zip 13815–1097; tel. 607/337–4111; Drake M. Lamen, M.D., President and Chief Executive Officer
**Web address:** www.uhs.net/cmh

DELAWARE VALLEY HOSPITAL (O, 25 beds) 1 Titus Place, Walton, NY Zip 13856–1498; tel. 607/865–2100; Paul Summers, President and Chief Executive Officer
**Web address:** www.uhs.net

UNITED HEALTH SERVICES HOSPITALS–BINGHAMTON (O, 465 beds) 10–42 Mitchell Avenue, Binghamton, NY Zip 13903–1678; tel. 607/763–6000; Matthew J. Salanger, President and Chief Executive Officer
**Web address:** www.uhs.net

| Owned, leased, sponsored: | 3 hospitals | 628 beds |
|---|---|---|
| Contract–managed: | 0 hospitals | 0 beds |
| Totals: | 3 hospitals | 628 beds |

---

**9605:  UNITED MEDICAL CORPORATION** (IO)
603 Main Street, Windermere, FL Zip 34786–3548, Mailing Address: P.O. Box 1100, Zip 34786–1100; tel. 407/876–2200; Donald R. Dizney, Chairman and Chief Executive Officer

**PUERTO RICO:** HOSPITAL PAVIA–HATO REY (O, 180 beds) 435 Ponce De Leon Avenue, San Juan, PR Zip 00917–3428; tel. 787/641–2323; Guillermo Pastrana, Executive Director
**Web address:** www.paviahealth.com

HOSPITAL PAVIA–SANTURCE (O, 198 beds) 1462 Asia Street, San Juan, PR Zip 00909–2143, Mailing Address: Box 11137, Santurce Station, Zip 00910–1137; tel. 787/727–6060; Jose Luis Rodriguez, Chief Executive Officer
**Web address:** www.paviahealth.com

HOSPITAL PEREA (O, 103 beds) 15 Basora Street, Mayaguez, PR Zip 681, Mailing Address: P.O. Box 170, Zip 681; tel. 787/834–0101; Jorge I. Martinez, Executive Director
**Web address:** www.paviahealth.com/perea_hospital.htm

SAN JORGE CHILDREN'S HOSPITAL (O, 125 beds) 252 San Jorge Street, Santurce, San Juan, PR Zip 00912–3310; tel. 787/727–1000; Domingo Cruz, Senior Vice President Operations
**Web address:** www.sanjorgechildrenshospital.com

**TENNESSEE:** TEN BROECK TENNESSEE TREATMENT FACILITY (O, 32 beds) 1 Medical Center Boulevard, 5 West, Cookeville, TN Zip 38501; tel. 931/783–2570; Jane Wilson–Mitchell, Interim Chief Executive Officer
**Web address:** www.tenbroeck.com

| Owned, leased, sponsored: | 5 hospitals | 638 beds |
|---|---|---|
| Contract–managed: | 0 hospitals | 0 beds |
| Totals: | 5 hospitals | 638 beds |

---

**0937:  UNITED MEDICAL REHABILITATION HOSPITALS** (IO)
3201 Wall Boulevard, Suite B., Gretna, LA Zip 70056–7755; tel. 504/433–5551; John E.H. Mills, President & Chief Executive Officer

**LOUISIANA:** UNITED MEDICAL HEALTHWEST–NEW ORLEANS (O, 15 beds) 3201 Wall Boulevard, Suite B., Gretna, LA Zip 70056–7755; tel. 504/433–5551; John E.H. Mills, President and Chief Executive Officer
**Web address:** www.umrhospital.com/

---

For explanation of codes following names, see page B2.
★ Indicates Type III membership in the American Hospital Association.

Section B

UNITED MEDICAL REHABILITATION HOSPITAL (O, 20 beds) 15717 Belle Drive, Hammond, LA Zip 70403–1439; tel. 985/340–5998; Cyrilia Bonds, Administrator
**Web address:** www.umrhospital.com

| Owned, leased, sponsored: | 2 hospitals | 35 beds |
|---|---|---|
| Contract–managed: | 0 hospitals | 0 beds |
| Totals: | 2 hospitals | 35 beds |

---

**0322: UNITED SURGICAL PARTNERS INTERNATIONAL** (IO)
15305 Dallas Parkway, Suite 1600, Addison, TX Zip 75001–6491; tel. 972/713–3500; William H. Wilcox, President and Chief Executive Officer
**(Independent Hospital System)**

**ARIZONA:** ARIZONA ORTHOPEDIC SURGICAL HOSPITAL (O, 24 beds) 2905 West Warner Road, Chandler, AZ Zip 85224–1674; tel. 480/603–9000; Patricia Alice, Chief Executive Officer
**Web address:** www.azosh.com

**OKLAHOMA:** OKLAHOMA CENTER FOR ORTHOPEDIC AND MULTI–SPECIALTY SURGERY (O, 10 beds) 8100 South Walker, Suite C., Oklahoma City, OK Zip 73139–9402, Mailing Address: P.O. Box 890609, Zip 73189–0609; tel. 405/602–6500; Mike Kimzey, Chief Executive Officer and Administrator
**Web address:** www.ocomhospital.com

**TEXAS:** BAYLOR MEDICAL CENTER AT FRISCO (O, 68 beds) 5601 Warren Parkway, Frisco, TX Zip 75034–4069; tel. 214/407–5000; William A. Keaton, Chief Executive Officer
**Web address:** www.bmcf.com

BAYLOR MEDICAL CENTER AT UPTOWN (O, 24 beds) 2727 East Lemmon Avenue, Dallas, TX Zip 75204–2895; tel. 214/443–3000; Jon Duckert, Chief Executive Officer
**Web address:** www.bmcuptown.com

IRVING COPPELL SURGICAL HOSPITAL (O, 12 beds) 400 West Interstate 635, Irving, TX Zip 75063; tel. 972/868–4000; Deonna Unell, Chief Executive Officer
**Web address:** www.ic–sh.com

TOPS SURGICAL SPECIALTY HOSPITAL (O, 15 beds) 17080 Red Oak Drive, Houston, TX Zip 77090–2602; tel. 281/539–2900; Daniel Smith, Interim Chief Executive Officer
**Web address:** www.tops–hospital.com

| Owned, leased, sponsored: | 6 hospitals | 153 beds |
|---|---|---|
| Contract–managed: | 0 hospitals | 0 beds |
| Totals: | 6 hospitals | 153 beds |

---

**★0061: UNITYPOINT HEALTH** (NP)
1776 Westlakes Parkway, Suite 400, West Des Moines, IA Zip 50266–8239; tel. 515/241–6161; William B. Leaver, President and Chief Executive Officer
**(Decentralized Health System)**

**ILLINOIS:** UNITYPOINT HEALTH – METHODIST PROCTOR (O, 288 beds) 221 N.E. Glen Oak Avenue, Peoria, IL Zip 61636–4310; tel. 309/672–5522; Deborah R. Simon, R.N., President and Chief Executive Officer
**Web address:** www.mymethodist.net

UNITYPOINT HEALTH – TRINITY ROCK ISLAND (O, 345 beds) 2701 17th Street, Rock Island, IL Zip 61201–5393; tel. 309/779–5000; Richard A. Seidler, FACHE, President and Chief Executive Officer
**Web address:** www.trinityqc.com

**IOWA:** BUENA VISTA REGIONAL MEDICAL CENTER (C, 35 beds) 1525 West Fifth Street, Storm Lake, IA Zip 50588–3027, Mailing Address: P.O. Box 309, Zip 50588–0309; tel. 712/732–4030; Steven Colerick, Chief Executive Officer
**Web address:** www.bvrmc.org

CLARKE COUNTY HOSPITAL (C, 25 beds) 800 South Fillmore Street, Osceola, IA Zip 50213–1619; tel. 641/342–2184; Brian G. Evans, FACHE, Chief Executive Officer
**Web address:** www.clarkehosp.org

COMMUNITY MEMORIAL HOSPITAL (C, 16 beds) 909 West First Street, Sumner, IA Zip 50674–1203, Mailing Address: P.O. Box 148, Zip 50674–0148; tel. 563/578–3275; Dustin Wright, Chief Executive Officer
**Web address:** www.cmhsumner.org

GREATER REGIONAL MEDICAL CENTER (C, 25 beds) 1700 West Townline Street Suite 3, Creston, IA Zip 50801–1099; tel. 641/782–7091; Monte Neitzel, Chief Executive Officer
**Web address:** www.greaterregional.org

GREENE COUNTY MEDICAL CENTER (C, 90 beds) 1000 West Lincolnway, Jefferson, IA Zip 50129–1645; tel. 515/386–2114; Carl P. Behne, Administrator and Chief Executive Officer
**Web address:** www.gcmchealth.com

GRUNDY COUNTY MEMORIAL HOSPITAL (C, 80 beds) 201 East J Avenue, Grundy Center, IA Zip 50638–2096; tel. 319/824–5421; Jennifer Havens, Director of Nursing and Chief Executive Officer
**Web address:** www.grundycountyhospital.com

GUTHRIE COUNTY HOSPITAL (C, 17 beds) 710 North 12th Street, Guthrie Center, IA Zip 50115–1544; tel. 641/332–2201; Patrick Peters, Chief Executive Officer
**Web address:** www.guthriecountyhospital.org

GUTTENBERG MUNICIPAL HOSPITAL (C, 20 beds) 200 Main Street, Guttenberg, IA Zip 52052–9108, Mailing Address: P.O. Box 550, Zip 52052–0550; tel. 563/252–1121; Kimberley A. Gau, FACHE, Chief Executive Officer
**Web address:** www.guttenberghospital.org

HUMBOLDT COUNTY MEMORIAL HOSPITAL (C, 49 beds) 1000 North 15th Street, Humboldt, IA Zip 50548–1008; tel. 515/332–4200; Michelle Sleiter, Chief Executive Officer
**Web address:** www.humboldthospital.org

LORING HOSPITAL (C, 25 beds) 211 Highland Avenue, Sac City, IA Zip 50583–2424; tel. 712/662–7105; James Beck, Interim Chief Executive Officer
**Web address:** www.loringhospital.org

MARENGO MEMORIAL HOSPITAL, UNITYPOINT HEALTH (O, 25 beds) 300 West May Street, Marengo, IA Zip 52301–1261, Mailing Address: P.O. Box 228, Zip 52301–0228; tel. 319/642–5543; Barry Goettsch, FACHE, Chief Executive Officer
**Web address:** www.marengohospital.org

POCAHONTAS COMMUNITY HOSPITAL (C, 20 beds) 606 N.W. Seventh Street, Pocahontas, IA Zip 50574–1099; tel. 712/335–3501; James D. Roetman, President and Chief Executive Officer
**Web address:** www.pocahontashospital.org

STEWART MEMORIAL COMMUNITY HOSPITAL (C, 25 beds) 1301 West Main, Lake City, IA Zip 51449–1585; tel. 712/464–3171; Heather L. Cain, Chief Executive Officer
**Web address:** www.stewartmemorial.org

STORY COUNTY MEDICAL CENTER (C, 77 beds) 640 South 19th Street, Nevada, IA Zip 50201–2902; tel. 515/382–2111; Timothy Ahlers, FACHE, Chief Executive Officer
**Web address:** www.storymedical.org

UNITYPOINT HEALTH – ALLEN HOSPITAL (O, 201 beds) 1825 Logan Avenue, Waterloo, IA Zip 50703–1916; tel. 319/235–3941; Pamela K. Delagardelle, President and Chief Executive Officer
**Web address:** www.allenhospital.org

UNITYPOINT HEALTH – FINLEY HOSPITAL (O, 109 beds) 350 North Grandview Avenue, Dubuque, IA Zip 52001–6392; tel. 563/582–1881; David R. Brandon, President and Chief Executive Officer
**Web address:** www.unitypoint.org

UNITYPOINT HEALTH – IOWA METHODIST MEDICAL CENTER (O, 429 beds) 1200 Pleasant Street, Des Moines, IA Zip 50309–1406; tel. 515/241–6212; Eric T. Crowell, President and Chief Executive Officer
**Web address:** www.iowahealth.org

UNITYPOINT HEALTH – JONES REGIONAL MEDICAL CENTER (O, 22 beds) 1795 Highway 64 East, Anamosa, IA Zip 52205–2112; tel. 319/462–6131; Eric Briesemeister, Chief Executive Officer
**Web address:** www.jonesregional.org

UNITYPOINT HEALTH – ST. LUKE'S (O, 146 beds) 2720 Stone Park Boulevard, Sioux City, IA Zip 51104–3734; tel. 712/279–3500; Lynn Wold, President and Chief Executive Officer
**Web address:** www.stlukes.org

For explanation of codes following names, see page B2.
★ Indicates Type III membership in the American Hospital Association.

UNITYPOINT HEALTH – ST. LUKE'S HOSPITAL (O, 346 beds) 1026 A Avenue N.E., Cedar Rapids, IA Zip 52402–3026, Mailing Address: P.O. Box 3026, Zip 52406–3026; tel. 319/369–7211; Theodore E. Townsend, FACHE, President and Chief Executive Officer
**Web address:** www.unitypoint.org

UNITYPOINT HEALTH – TRINITY BETTENDORF (O, 82 beds) 4500 Utica Ridge Road, Bettendorf, IA Zip 52722–1626; tel. 563/742–5000; Richard A. Seidler, FACHE, President and Chief Executive Officer
**Web address:** www.trinityqc.com

UNITYPOINT HEALTH – TRINITY MUSCATINE (O, 48 beds) 1518 Mulberry Avenue, Muscatine, IA Zip 52761–3499; tel. 563/264–9100; James M. Hayes, Chief Executive Officer
**Web address:** www.unitypoint.org/quadcities/trinity–muscatine.aspx

UNITYPOINT HEALTH – TRINITY REGIONAL MEDICAL CENTER (O, 106 beds) 802 Kenyon Road, Fort Dodge, IA Zip 50501–5795; tel. 515/573–3101; Mike Dewerff, President and Chief Executive Officer
**Web address:** www.trmc.org

UNITYPOINT HEALTH–IOWA LUTHERAN HOSPITAL (O, 205 beds) 700 East University Avenue, Des Moines, IA Zip 50316–2392; tel. 515/263–5612; Eric T. Crowell, President and Chief Executive Officer
**Web address:** www.iowahealth.org

| | | |
|---|---|---|
| Owned, leased, sponsored: | 13 hospitals | 2352 beds |
| Contract–managed: | 13 hospitals | 504 beds |
| **Totals:** | 26 hospitals | 2856 beds |

---

**9555: UNIVERSAL HEALTH SERVICES, INC.** (IO)
367 South Gulph Road, King of Prussia, PA Zip 19406–3121, Mailing Address: P.O. Box 61558, Zip 19406–0958; tel. 610/768–3300; Alan B. Miller, Chairman and Chief Executive Officer
**(Decentralized Health System)**

**ALABAMA:** HILL CREST BEHAVIORAL HEALTH SERVICES (O, 89 beds) 6869 Fifth Avenue South, Birmingham, AL Zip 35212–1866; tel. 205/833–9000; Steve McCabe, Chief Executive Officer
**Web address:** www.hillcrestbhs.com

LAUREL OAKS BEHAVIORAL HEALTH CENTER (O, 38 beds) 700 East Cottonwood Road, Dothan, AL Zip 36301–3644; tel. 334/794–7373; Derek Johnson, Chief Executive Officer
**Web address:** www.laureloaksbhc.com

**ALASKA:** NORTH STAR BEHAVIORAL HEALTH SYSTEM (O, 200 beds) 2530 DeBarr Circle, Anchorage, AK Zip 99508–2948; tel. 907/258–7575; Andrew Mayo, Ph.D., Chief Executive Officer and Managing Director
**Web address:** www.northstarbehavioral.com

**ARIZONA:** PALO VERDE MENTAL BEHAVIORAL HEALTH (O, 48 beds) 2695 North Craycroft Road, Tucson, AZ Zip 85712–2244; tel. 520/322–2888; P. Jay Frayser, Chief Executive Officer
**Web address:** www.paloverdebh.com/

VALLEY HOSPITAL PHOENIX (O, 122 beds) 3550 East Pinchot Avenue, Phoenix, AZ Zip 85018–7434; tel. 602/957–4000; Michelle David, Chief Executive Officer
**Web address:** www.valleyhospital–phoenix.com

**ARKANSAS:** PINNACLE POINTE HOSPITAL (O, 124 beds) 11501 Financial Center Parkway, Little Rock, AR Zip 72211–3715; tel. 501/223–3322; Shane Frazier, Chief Executive Officer
**Web address:** www.pinnaclepointehospital.com

RIVENDELL BEHAVIORAL HEALTH SERVICES OF ARKANSAS (O, 77 beds) 100 Rivendell Drive, Benton, AR Zip 72019–9100; tel. 501/316–1255; Jay Schehi, Chief Executive Officer
**Web address:** www.rivendellofarkansas.com

THE BRIDGEWAY (L, 103 beds) 21 Bridgeway Road, North Little Rock, AR Zip 72113–9516; tel. 501/771–1500; Jason Miller, M.P.H., Chief Executive Officer
**Web address:** www.thebridgeway.com

**CALIFORNIA:** BHC ALHAMBRA HOSPITAL (O, 97 beds) 4619 North Rosemead Boulevard, Rosemead, CA Zip 91770–1478, Mailing Address: P.O. Box 369, Zip 91770–0369; tel. 626/286–1191; Peggy Minnick, R.N., Chief Executive Officer
**Web address:** www.bhcalhambra.com

CANYON RIDGE HOSPITAL (O, 106 beds) 5353 G Street, Chino, CA Zip 91710–5250; tel. 909/590–3700; Jeff McDonald, Chief Executive Officer
**Web address:** www.canyonridgehospital.com

CORONA REGIONAL MEDICAL CENTER (O, 238 beds) 800 South Main Street, Corona, CA Zip 92882–3400; tel. 951/737–4343; Mark H. Uffer, Chief Executive Officer
**Web address:** www.coronaregional.com

DEL AMO HOSPITAL (O, 70 beds) 23700 Camino Del Sol, Torrance, CA Zip 90505–5000; tel. 310/530–1151; Lisa K. Montes, Chief Executive Officer
**Web address:** www.delamohospital.com

FREMONT HOSPITAL (O, 96 beds) 39001 Sundale Drive, Fremont, CA Zip 94538–2005; tel. 510/796–1100; John C. Cooper, Chief Executive Officer
**Web address:** www.fremonthospital.com

HERITAGE OAKS HOSPITAL (O, 120 beds) 4250 Auburn Boulevard, Sacramento, CA Zip 95841–4164; tel. 916/489–3336; Shawn Silva, Chief Executive Officer
**Web address:** www.heritageoakshospital.com

PALMDALE REGIONAL MEDICAL CENTER (O, 157 beds) 38600 Medical Center Drive, Palmdale, CA Zip 93551–4483; tel. 661/382–5000; Richard Allen, Chief Executive Officer
**Web address:** www.palmdaleregional.com

SIERRA VISTA HOSPITAL (O, 120 beds) 8001 Bruceville Road, Sacramento, CA Zip 95823–2329; tel. 916/288–0300; Mike Zauner, Chief Executive Officer
**Web address:** www.sierravistahospital.com

SOUTHWEST HEALTHCARE SYSTEM (O, 252 beds) 25500 Medical Center Drive, Murrieta, CA Zip 92562–5965; tel. 951/696–6000; Bradley D. Neet, FACHE, Chief Executive Officer
**Web address:** www.swhealthcaresystem.com/

TEMECULA VALLEY HOSPITAL (O, 140 beds) 31700 Temecula Parkway, Temecula, CA Zip 92592–5896; tel. 951/331–2216; Darlene Wetton, R.N., Chief Executive Officer
**Web address:** www.temeculavalleyhospital.com

**COLORADO:** CEDAR SPRINGS HOSPITAL (O, 110 beds) 2135 Southgate Road, Colorado Springs, CO Zip 80906–2693; tel. 719/633–4114; A. Elaine Crnkovic, Chief Executive Officer
**Web address:** www.cedarspringsbhs.com

CENTENNIAL PEAKS HOSPITAL (O, 72 beds) 2255 South 88th Street, Louisville, CO Zip 80027–9716; tel. 303/673–9990; Elicia Bunch, Chief Executive Officer
**Web address:** www.centennialpeaks.com

HIGHLANDS BEHAVIORAL HEALTH SYSTEM (O, 86 beds) 8565 South Poplar Way, Littleton, CO Zip 80130–3602; tel. 720/348–2800; Paul Sexton, Chief Executive Officer
**Web address:** www.highlandsbhs.com

**DELAWARE:** DOVER BEHAVIORAL HEALTH SYSTEM (O, 72 beds) 725 Horsepond Road, Dover, DE Zip 19901–7232; tel. 302/741–0140; Jean–Charles Constant, Administrator
**Web address:** www.doverbehavioral.com

ROCKFORD CENTER (O, 118 beds) 100 Rockford Drive, Newark, DE Zip 19713–2121; tel. 302/996–5480; John F. McKenna, Chief Executive Officer and Managing Director
**Web address:** www.rockfordcenter.com

**DISTRICT OF COLUMBIA:** GEORGE WASHINGTON UNIVERSITY HOSPITAL (O, 363 beds) 900 23rd Street N.W., Washington, DC Zip 20037–2342; tel. 202/715–4000; Barry A. Wolfman, Chief Executive Officer and Managing Director
**Web address:** www.gwhospital.com

**FLORIDA:** ATLANTIC SHORES HOSPITAL (O, 72 beds) 4545 North Federal Highway, Fort Lauderdale, FL Zip 33308–5274; tel. 954/771–2711; Manuel R. Llano, Chief Executive Officer
**Web address:** www.atlanticshoreshospital.com

CENTRAL FLORIDA BEHAVIORAL HOSPITAL (O, 126 beds) 6601 Central Florida Parkway, Orlando, FL Zip 32821–8064; tel. 407/370–0111; Vickie Lewis, Chief Executive Officer
**Web address:** www.centralfloridabehavioral.com

Section B

---

For explanation of codes following names, see page B2.
★ Indicates Type III membership in the American Hospital Association.

EMERALD COAST BEHAVIORAL HOSPITAL (O, 86 beds) 1940 Harrison Avenue, Panama City, FL Zip 32405–4542; tel. 850/763–0017; Tim Bedford, Chief Executive Officer
**Web address:** www.emeraldcoastbehavioral.com

FORT LAUDERDALE HOSPITAL (L, 100 beds) 1601 East Las Olas Boulevard, Fort Lauderdale, FL Zip 33301–2393; tel. 954/463–4321; Manuel R. Llano, Chief Executive Officer
**Web address:** www.fortlauderdalehospital.org

LAKEWOOD RANCH MEDICAL CENTER (O, 120 beds) 8330 Lakewood Ranch Boulevard, Bradenton, FL Zip 34202–5174; tel. 941/782–2100; Linda S. Widra, FACHE, Ph.D., R.N., Interim Chief Executive Officer
**Web address:** www.lakewoodranchmedicalcenter.com

MANATEE MEMORIAL HOSPITAL (O, 319 beds) 206 Second Street East, Bradenton, FL Zip 34208–1000; tel. 941/746–5111; Kevin DiLallo, Chief Executive Officer
**Web address:** www.manateememorial.com

RIVER POINT BEHAVIORAL HEALTH (O, 92 beds) 6300 Beach Boulevard, Jacksonville, FL Zip 32216–2782; tel. 904/724–9202; Kevin McGee, Chief Executive Officer
**Web address:** www.riverpointbehavioral.com

SUNCOAST BEHAVIORAL HEALTH CENTER (O, 60 beds) 4480 51st Street West, Bradenton, FL Zip 34210–2855; tel. 941/251–5000; Brandy Hamilton, Chief Executive Officer
**Web address:** www.suncoastbhc.com

THE VINES (O, 64 beds) 3130 S.W. 27th Avenue, Ocala, FL Zip 34471–4306; tel. 352/671–3130; Stephen Quintyne, Chief Executive Officer
**Web address:** www.thevineshospital.com

WEKIVA SPRINGS (O, 60 beds) 3947 Salisbury Road, Jacksonville, FL Zip 32216–6115; tel. 904/296–3533; Sheila Carr, Chief Executive Officer
**Web address:** www.wekivacenter.com

WELLINGTON REGIONAL MEDICAL CENTER (L, 108 beds) 10101 Forest Hill Boulevard, West Palm Beach, FL Zip 33414–6199; tel. 561/798–8500; Robbin Lee, Chief Executive Officer
**Web address:** www.wellingtonregional.com

WINDMOOR HEALTHCARE OF CLEARWATER (O, 100 beds) 11300 U.S. 19 North, Clearwater, FL Zip 33764; tel. 727/541–2646; Wendy Merson, Chief Executive Officer
**Web address:** www.windmoor.com

**GEORGIA:** ANCHOR HOSPITAL (O, 122 beds) 5454 Yorktowne Drive, Atlanta, GA Zip 30349–5317; tel. 770/991–6044; Jason McPherson, Chief Executive Officer and Managing Director
**Web address:** www.anchorhospital.com

COASTAL HARBOR TREATMENT CENTER (O, 193 beds) 1150 Cornell Avenue, Savannah, GA Zip 31406–2702; tel. 912/354–3911; Sally Perry, Chief Executive Officer
**Web address:** www.coastalharbor.com

PEACHFORD BEHAVIORAL HEALTH SYSTEM (O, 246 beds) 2151 Peachford Road, Atlanta, GA Zip 30338–6599; tel. 770/455–3200; Matthew Crouch, Chief Executive Officer and Managing Director
**Web address:** www.peachfordhospital.com

SAINT SIMONS BY-THE-SEA HOSPITAL (O, 101 beds) 2927 Demere Road, Saint Simons Island, GA Zip 31522–1620; tel. 912/638–1999; Tim Merritt, Chief Executive Officer
**Web address:** www.ssbythesea.com

TURNING POINT HOSPITAL (O, 59 beds) 3015 Veterans Parkway South, Moultrie, GA Zip 31788–6705, Mailing Address: P.O. Box 1177, Zip 31776–1177; tel. 229/985–4815; Ben Marion, Chief Executive Officer and Managing Director
**Web address:** www.turningpointcare.com

**IDAHO:** INTERMOUNTAIN HOSPITAL (O, 140 beds) 303 North Allumbaugh Street, Boise, ID Zip 83704–9208; tel. 208/377–8400; Jeffrey F. Morrell, Chief Executive Officer
**Web address:** www.intermountainhospital.com

**ILLINOIS:** GARFIELD PARK HOSPITAL (O, 88 beds) 520 North Ridgeway Avenue, Chicago, IL Zip 60624–1232; tel. 773/265–3700; Len Kirby, Chief Executive Officer
**Web address:** www.garfieldparkhospital.com

HARTGROVE HOSPITAL (O, 128 beds) 5730 West Roosevelt Road, Chicago, IL Zip 60644–1580; tel. 773/413–1700; Steven Airhart, Chief Executive Officer
**Web address:** www.hartgrovehospital.com

LINCOLN PRAIRIE BEHAVIORAL HEALTH CENTER (O, 97 beds) 5230 South Sixth Street, Springfield, IL Zip 62703–5128; tel. 217/585–1180; Mark Littrell, Chief Executive Officer
**Web address:** www.lincolnprairiebhc.com/

RIVEREDGE HOSPITAL (O, 224 beds) 8311 West Roosevelt Road, Forest Park, IL Zip 60130–2500; tel. 708/771–7000; Carey Carlock, Chief Executive Officer
**Web address:** www.riveredgehospital.com

STREAMWOOD BEHAVIORAL HEALTH CENTER (O, 178 beds) 1400 East Irving Park Road, Streamwood, IL Zip 60107–3203; tel. 630/837–9000; Ron Weglarz, Chief Executive Officer and Managing Director
**Web address:** www.streamwoodhospital.com

THE PAVILION (O, 46 beds) 809 West Church Street, Champaign, IL Zip 61820–3399; tel. 217/373–1700; Joseph Sheehy, Chief Executive Officer and Managing Director
**Web address:** www.pavilionhospital.com

**INDIANA:** BLOOMINGTON MEADOWS HOSPITAL (O, 67 beds) 3600 North Prow Road, Bloomington, IN Zip 47404–1616; tel. 812/331–8000; Jean Scallon, Chief Executive Officer
**Web address:** www.bloomingtonmeadows.com

MICHIANA BEHAVIORAL HEALTH CENTER (O, 75 beds) 1800 North Oak Drive, Plymouth, IN Zip 46563–3492; tel. 574/936–3784; Michael Perry, Chief Executive Officer
**Web address:** www.michianabhc.com

VALLE VISTA HOSPITAL (O, 102 beds) 898 East Main Street, Greenwood, IN Zip 46143–1400; tel. 317/887–1348; Sherri R. Jewett, Chief Executive Officer
**Web address:** www.vallevistahospital.com

WELLSTONE REGIONAL HOSPITAL (O, 100 beds) 2700 Vissing Park Road, Jeffersonville, IN Zip 47130–5989; tel. 812/284–8000; Greg Stewart, Chief Executive Officer
**Web address:** www.wellstonehospital.com

**KENTUCKY:** CUMBERLAND HALL HOSPITAL (O, 97 beds) 270 Walton Way, Hopkinsville, KY Zip 42240–6808; tel. 270/886–1919; James Spruyt, Chief Executive Officer
**Web address:** www.cumberlandhallhospital.com

LINCOLN TRAIL BEHAVIORAL HEALTH SYSTEM (O, 67 beds) 3909 South Wilson Road, Radcliff, KY Zip 40160–8944, Mailing Address: P.O. Box 369, Zip 40159–0369; tel. 270/351–9444; Charles L. Webb, Jr., Chief Executive Officer
**Web address:** www.lincolnbehavioral.com

RIDGE BEHAVIORAL HEALTH SYSTEM (O, 110 beds) 3050 Rio Dosa Drive, Lexington, KY Zip 40509–1540; tel. 859/269–2325; Nina W. Eisner, Chief Executive Officer and Managing Director
**Web address:** www.ridgebhs.com

RIVENDELL BEHAVIORAL HEALTH (O, 125 beds) 1035 Porter Pike, Bowling Green, KY Zip 42103–9581; tel. 270/843–1199; Matt Ours, Chief Executive Officer and Managing Director
**Web address:** www.rivendellbehavioral.com

THE BROOK AT DUPONT (O, 66 beds) 1405 Browns Lane, Louisville, KY Zip 40207–4608; tel. 502/896–0495; Paul Andrews, Chief Executive Officer
**Web address:** www.thebrookhospitals.com/

THE BROOK HOSPITAL – KMI (O, 94 beds) 8521 Old LaGrange Road, Louisville, KY Zip 40242–3800; tel. 502/426–6380; Paul Andrews, Chief Executive Officer
**Web address:** www.thebrookhospitals.com

**LOUISIANA:** BRENTWOOD HOSPITAL (O, 172 beds) 1006 Highland Avenue, Shreveport, LA Zip 71101–4103; tel. 318/678–7500; William Weaver, Chief Executive Officer
**Web address:** www.brentwoodbehavioral.com

RIVER OAKS HOSPITAL (O, 126 beds) 1525 River Oaks Road West, New Orleans, LA Zip 70123–2162; tel. 504/734–1740; Evelyn Nolting, Chief Executive Officer and Managing Director
**Web address:** www.riveroakshospital.com

**MASSACHUSETTS:** ARBOUR H. R. I. HOSPITAL (O, 68 beds) 227 Babcock Street, Brookline, MA Zip 02446–6799; tel. 617/731–3200; William Zella, Chief Executive Officer
**Web address:** www.arbourhealth.com

ARBOUR HOSPITAL (O, 118 beds) 49 Robinwood Avenue, Boston, MA Zip 02130–2156; tel. 617/522–4400; Laura Ames, Chief Executive Officer
**Web address:** www.arbourhealth.com

For explanation of codes following names, see page B2.
★ Indicates Type III membership in the American Hospital Association.

ARBOUR–FULLER HOSPITAL (O, 46 beds) 200 May Street, Attleboro, MA Zip 02703–5520; tel. 508/761–8500; Kevin Burchill, Chief Executive Officer
**Web address:** www.arbourhealth.com

PEMBROKE HOSPITAL (O, 80 beds) 199 Oak Street, Pembroke, MA Zip 02359–1953; tel. 781/829–7000; Thomas P. Hickey, Chief Executive Officer and Managing Director
**Web address:** www.arbourhealth.com/organizations/pembroke–hospital/

WESTWOOD LODGE HOSPITAL (O, 130 beds) 45 Clapboardtree Street, Westwood, MA Zip 02090–2903; tel. 781/762–7764; Gregory Brownstein, Chief Executive Officer
**Web address:** www.arbourhealth.com

**MICHIGAN:** FOREST VIEW PSYCHIATRIC HOSPITAL (O, 82 beds) 1055 Medical Park Drive S.E., Grand Rapids, MI Zip 49546–3607; tel. 616/942–9610; Andrew Hotaling, Chief Executive Officer
**Web address:** www.forestviewhospital.com

HAVENWYCK HOSPITAL (O, 235 beds) 1525 University Drive, Auburn Hills, MI Zip 48326–2673; tel. 248/373–9200; Diane Henneman, Chief Executive Officer
**Web address:** www.havenwyckhospital.com

**MISSISSIPPI:** ALLIANCE HEALTH CENTER (O, 134 beds) 5000 Highway 39 North, Meridian, MS Zip 39301–1021; tel. 601/483–6211; James Miller, Interim Chief Executive Officer
**Web address:** www.alliancehealthcenter.com

BRENTWOOD BEHAVIORAL HEALTHCARE OF MISSISSIPPI (O, 105 beds) 3531 East Lakeland Drive, Jackson, MS Zip 39232–8839; tel. 601/936–2024; Michael J. Carney, Chief Executive Officer
**Web address:** www.brentwoodjackson.com

PARKWOOD BEHAVIORAL HEALTH SYSTEM (O, 148 beds) 8135 Goodman Road, Olive Branch, MS Zip 38654–2103; tel. 662/895–4900; Coleby Wright, Chief Executive Officer
**Web address:** www.parkwoodbhs.com

**MISSOURI:** HEARTLAND BEHAVIORAL HEALTH SERVICES (O, 69 beds) 1500 West Ashland Street, Nevada, MO Zip 64772–1710; tel. 417/667–2666; Alyson Wysong–Harder, Chief Executive Officer
**Web address:** www.heartlandbehavioral.com

TWO RIVERS BEHAVIORAL HEALTH SYSTEM (O, 105 beds) 5121 Raytown Road, Kansas City, MO Zip 64133–2141; tel. 816/382–6300; Cara Macaleer, Chief Executive Officer/Managing Director
**Web address:** www.tworivershospital.com

**NEVADA:** CENTENNIAL HILLS HOSPITAL MEDICAL CENTER (O, 165 beds) 6900 North Durango Drive, Las Vegas, NV Zip 89149–4409; tel. 702/835–9700; Sajit Pullarkat, Chief Executive Officer and Managing Director
**Web address:** www.centennialhillshospital.com

DESERT SPRINGS HOSPITAL MEDICAL CENTER (O, 346 beds) 2075 East Flamingo Road, Las Vegas, NV Zip 89119–5121; tel. 702/733–8800; Samuel Kaufman, Chief Executive Officer and Managing Director
**Web address:** www.desertspringshospital.com

NORTHERN NEVADA MEDICAL CENTER (O, 108 beds) 2375 East Prater Way, Sparks, NV Zip 89434–9641; tel. 775/331–7000; Alan C. Olive, Chief Executive Officer
**Web address:** www.nnmc.com

SPRING MOUNTAIN SAHARA (O, 30 beds) 5460 West Sahara, Las Vegas, NV Zip 89146–3307; tel. 702/216–8900; Darryl S. Dubroca, Chief Executive Officer and Managing Director
**Web address:** www.springmountainsahara.com

SPRING MOUNTAIN TREATMENT CENTER (L, 82 beds) 7000 West Spring Mountain Road, Las Vegas, NV Zip 89117–3816; tel. 702/873–2400; Darryl S. Dubroca, Chief Executive Officer and Managing Director
**Web address:** www.springmountaintreatmentcenter.com/

SPRING VALLEY HOSPITAL MEDICAL CENTER (O, 169 beds) 5400 South Rainbow Boulevard, Las Vegas, NV Zip 89118–1859; tel. 702/853–3000; Leonard Freehof, Chief Executive Officer and Managing Director
**Web address:** www.springvalleyhospital.com

SUMMERLIN HOSPITAL MEDICAL CENTER (O, 148 beds) 657 Town Center Drive, Las Vegas, NV Zip 89144–6367; tel. 702/233–7000; Robert S. Freymuller, Chief Executive Officer
**Web address:** www.summerlinhospital.com

VALLEY HOSPITAL MEDICAL CENTER (O, 365 beds) 620 Shadow Lane, Las Vegas, NV Zip 89106–4119; tel. 702/388–4000; Elaine Glaser, Chief Executive Officer, Managing Director
**Web address:** www.valleyhospital.net

WEST HILLS HOSPITAL (O, 190 beds) 1240 East Ninth Street, Reno, NV Zip 89512–2964; tel. 775/323–0478; Allison Zednicek, Chief Executive Officer
**Web address:** www.westhillshospital.net

**NEW JERSEY:** HAMPTON BEHAVIORAL HEALTH CENTER (O, 110 beds) 650 Rancocas Road, Westampton, NJ Zip 08060–5613; tel. 609/267–7000; Craig Hilton, Chief Executive Officer
**Web address:** www.hamptonhospital.com

SUMMIT OAKS HOSPITAL (O, 90 beds) 19 Prospect Street, Summit, NJ Zip 07901–2530; tel. 908/522–7000; Oana Radu, Chief Executive Officer
**Web address:** www.summitoakshospital.com/

**NEW MEXICO:** MESILLA VALLEY HOSPITAL (O, 120 beds) 3751 Del Rey Boulevard, Las Cruces, NM Zip 88012–8526; tel. 575/382–3500; Robert Mansfield, Chief Executive Officer
**Web address:** www.mesillavalleyhospital.com

**NORTH CAROLINA:** BRYNN MARR HOSPITAL (O, 99 beds) 192 Village Drive, Jacksonville, NC Zip 28546–7299; tel. 910/577–1400; Jay Kortemeyer, Chief Executive Officer
**Web address:** www.brynnmarr.org

HOLLY HILL HOSPITAL (O, 205 beds) 3019 Falstaff Road, Raleigh, NC Zip 27610–1812; tel. 919/250–7000; Michael S. McDonald, Jr., Chief Executive Officer
**Web address:** www.hollyhillhospital.com

OLD VINEYARD BEHAVIORAL HEALTH SERVICES (O, 104 beds) 3637 Old Vineyard Road, Winston–Salem, NC Zip 27104–4842; tel. 336/794–3550; Kevin Patton, Chief Executive Officer
**Web address:** www.oldvineyardbhs.com

**NORTH DAKOTA:** PRAIRIE ST. JOHN'S (O, 94 beds) 510 4th Street South, Fargo, ND Zip 58103–1914; tel. 701/476–7200; Jeff Herman, Chief Executive Officer
**Web address:** www.prairie–stjohns.com

**OHIO:** ARROWHEAD BEHAVIORAL HEALTH HOSPITAL (O, 42 beds) 1725 Timber Line Road, Maumee, OH Zip 43537–4015; tel. 419/891–9333; Joseph Denicola, Chief Executive Officer and Managing Director
**Web address:** www.arrowheadbehavioral.com

BELMONT PINES HOSPITAL (O, 96 beds) 615 Churchill–Hubbard Road, Youngstown, OH Zip 44505–1379; tel. 330/759–2700; Lisa Cocca, Chief Executive Officer
**Web address:** www.belmontpines.com

WINDSOR–LAURELWOOD CENTER FOR BEHAVIORAL MEDICINE (O, 159 beds) 35900 Euclid Avenue, Willoughby, OH Zip 44094–4648; tel. 440/953–3000; Ric McAllister, Chief Executive Officer
**Web address:** www.windsorlaurelwood.com

**OKLAHOMA:** CEDAR RIDGE HOSPITAL (O, 116 beds) 6501 N.E. 50th Street, Oklahoma City, OK Zip 73141–9118; tel. 405/605–6111; Diane Bedell, R.N., Chief Executive Officer
**Web address:** www.cedarridgebhs.com

SHADOW MOUNTAIN BEHAVIORAL HEALTH SYSTEM (O, 226 beds) 6262 South Sheridan Road, Tulsa, OK Zip 74133–4055; tel. 918/492–8200; Mike Kistler, Chief Executive Officer
**Web address:** www.shadowmountainbhs.com

ST. MARY'S REGIONAL MEDICAL CENTER (O, 149 beds) 305 South Fifth Street, Enid, OK Zip 73701–5899, Mailing Address: P.O. Box 232, Zip 73702–0232; tel. 580/233–6100; Stanley D. Tatum, FACHE, Chief Executive Officer
**Web address:** www.stmarysregional.com

**OREGON:** CEDAR HILLS HOSPITAL (O, 78 beds) 10300 S.W. Eastridge Street, Portland, OR Zip 97225–5004; tel. 503/944–5000; Elizabeth Hutter, Chief Executive Officer
**Web address:** www.cedarhillshospital.com

**PENNSYLVANIA:** BROOKE GLEN BEHAVIORAL HOSPITAL (O, 146 beds) 7170 Lafayette Avenue, Fort Washington, PA Zip 19034–2301; tel. 215/641–5300; Neil Callahan, Chief Executive Officer
**Web address:** www.brookeglenhospital.com

**Section B**

For explanation of codes following names, see page B2.
★ Indicates Type III membership in the American Hospital Association.

CLARION PSYCHIATRIC CENTER (O, 74 beds) 2 Hospital Drive, Clarion, PA Zip 16214–8502; tel. 814/226–9545; Robert Scheffler, Chief Executive Officer
**Web address:** www.clarioncenter.com

FAIRMOUNT BEHAVIORAL HEALTH SYSTEM (O, 235 beds) 561 Fairthorne Avenue, Philadelphia, PA Zip 19128–2499; tel. 215/487–4000; Lisa McConlogue, PhD, Managing Director
**Web address:** www.fairmountbhs.com

FOUNDATIONS BEHAVIORAL HEALTH (O, 58 beds) 833 East Butler Avenue, Doylestown, PA Zip 18901–2280; tel. 215/345–0444; Robert Weinhold, Chief Executive Officer
**Web address:** www.fbh.com

FRIENDS HOSPITAL (O, 192 beds) 4641 Roosevelt Boulevard, Philadelphia, PA Zip 19124–2343; tel. 215/831–4600; R. John Repique, MS, R.N., Chief Executive Officer
**Web address:** www.friendshospital.com

HORSHAM CLINIC (O, 138 beds) 722 East Butler Pike, Ambler, PA Zip 19002–2310; tel. 215/643–7800; Phyllis Weisfield, Chief Executive Officer and Managing Director
**Web address:** www.horshamclinic.com

MEADOWS PSYCHIATRIC CENTER (O, 107 beds) 132 The Meadows Drive, Centre Hall, PA Zip 16828–9231; tel. 814/364–2161; Ann Wayne, Interim Chief Executive Officer
**Web address:** www.themeadows.net

ROXBURY TREATMENT CENTER (O, 94 beds) 601 Roxbury Road, Shippensburg, PA Zip 17257–9302; tel. 800/648–4673; Shauna Radzieski, Chief Executive Officer
**Web address:** www.roxburyhospital.com

**PUERTO RICO:** FIRST HOSPITAL PANAMERICANO (O, 153 beds) State Road 787 KM 1 5, Cidra, PR Zip 739, Mailing Address: P.O. Box 1400, Zip 739; tel. 787/739–5555; Astro Munoz, Executive Director
**Web address:** www.hospitalpanamericano.com

**SOUTH CAROLINA:** AIKEN REGIONAL MEDICAL CENTERS (O, 271 beds) 302 University Parkway, Aiken, SC Zip 29801–6302; tel. 803/641–5000; Vance V. Reynolds, FACHE, CPA, Chief Executive Officer
**Web address:** www.aikenregional.com

CAROLINA CENTER FOR BEHAVIORAL HEALTH (O, 112 beds) 2700 East Phillips Road, Greer, SC Zip 29650–4816; tel. 864/235–2335; John Willingham, Chief Executive Officer and Managing Director
**Web address:** www.thecarolinacenter.com

LIGHTHOUSE CARE CENTER OF CONWAY (O, 72 beds) 152 Waccamaw Medical Park Drive, Conway, SC Zip 29526–8901; tel. 843/347–8871; Thomas L. Ryba, Chief Executive Officer
**Web address:** www.lighthousecarecenterofconway.com/

PALMETTO LOWCOUNTRY BEHAVIORAL HEALTH (O, 84 beds) 2777 Speissegger Drive, Charleston, SC Zip 29405–8229; tel. 843/747–5830; Shari Baker, Chief Executive Officer
**Web address:** www.palmettobehavioralhealth.com

THREE RIVERS BEHAVIORAL HEALTH (O, 118 beds) 2900 Sunset Boulevard, West Columbia, SC Zip 29169–3422; tel. 803/796–9911; Nannette M. Lewis, Chief Executive Officer
**Web address:** www.threeriversbehavioral.org

**TENNESSEE:** LAKESIDE BEHAVIORAL HEALTH SYSTEM (O, 319 beds) 2911 Brunswick Road, Memphis, TN Zip 38133–4199; tel. 901/377–4700; Joy Golden, Chief Executive Officer
**Web address:** www.lakesidebhs.com

ROLLING HILLS HOSPITAL (O, 80 beds) 2014 Quail Hollow Circle, Franklin, TN Zip 37067–5967; tel. 615/628–5700; Laurel Roberts, R.N., Interim Chief Executive Officer
**Web address:** www.rollinghillshospital.org/

**TEXAS:** AUSTIN LAKES HOSPITAL (O, 58 beds) 1025 East 32nd Street, Austin, TX Zip 78705–2714; tel. 512/544–5253; Rick Buckelew, Chief Executive Officer
**Web address:** www.austinlakeshospital.com

AUSTIN OAKS HOSPITAL (O, 80 beds) 1407 West Stassney Lane, Austin, TX Zip 78745–2947; tel. 512/440–4800; Steve Kelly, Interim Chief Executive Officer
**Web address:** www.austinoakshospital.com

BEHAVIORAL HOSPITAL OF BELLAIRE (O, 84 beds) 5314 Dashwood Drive, Houston, TX Zip 77081–4603; tel. 713/600–9500; Ethan Permenter, Chief Executive Officer
**Web address:** www.bhbhospital.com

CORNERSTONE REGIONAL HOSPITAL (L, 14 beds) 2302 Cornerstone Boulevard, Edinburg, TX Zip 78539–8471; tel. 956/618–4444; Roxanna M. Godinez, Chief Executive Officer
**Web address:** www.cornerstoneregional.com

CYPRESS CREEK HOSPITAL (O, 96 beds) 17750 Cali Drive, Houston, TX Zip 77090–2700; tel. 281/586–7600; Brian Brooker, Chief Executive Officer
**Web address:** www.cypresscreekhospital.com

DOCTORS HOSPITAL OF LAREDO (O, 183 beds) 10700 McPherson Road, Laredo, TX Zip 78045–6268; tel. 956/523–2000; Rene Lopez, Chief Executive Officer
**Web address:** www.doctorshoslaredo.com

FORT DUNCAN REGIONAL MEDICAL CENTER (O, 101 beds) 3333 North Foster Maldonado Boulevard, Eagle Pass, TX Zip 78852–5893; tel. 830/773–5321; Richard Prati, Chief Executive Officer
**Web address:** www.fortduncanmedicalcenter.com

GLEN OAKS HOSPITAL (O, 54 beds) 301 Division Street, Greenville, TX Zip 75401–4101; tel. 903/454–6000; Greg Garland, Interim Chief Executive Officer
**Web address:** www.glenoakshospital.com

HICKORY TRAIL HOSPITAL (O, 86 beds) 2000 Old Hickory Trail, Desoto, TX Zip 75115–2242; tel. 972/298–7323; Lance Folske, Chief Executive Officer
**Web address:** www.hickorytrail.com

KINGWOOD PINES HOSPITAL (O, 116 beds) 2001 Ladbrook Drive, Kingwood, TX Zip 77339–3004; tel. 281/404–1001; James Burroughs, Chief Executive Officer
**Web address:** www.kingwoodpines.com

LAUREL RIDGE TREATMENT CENTER (O, 208 beds) 17720 Corporate Woods Drive, San Antonio, TX Zip 78259–3500; tel. 210/491–9400; Jacob Cuellar, M.D., Chief Executive Officer
**Web address:** www.laurelridgetc.com

MAYHILL HOSPITAL (O, 59 beds) 2809 South Mayhill Road, Denton, TX Zip 76208–5910; tel. 940/239–3000; Adam Vincent, Chief Executive Officer
**Web address:** www.mayhillhospital.com

MILLWOOD HOSPITAL (O, 122 beds) 1011 North Cooper Street, Arlington, TX Zip 76011–5517; tel. 817/261–3121; Dwight A. Lacy, Chief Executive Officer
**Web address:** www.millwoodhospital.com

NORTHWEST TEXAS HEALTHCARE SYSTEM (O, 417 beds) 1501 South Coulter Avenue, Amarillo, TX Zip 79106–1770, Mailing Address: P.O. Box 1110, Zip 79105–1110; tel. 806/354–1000; Mark W. Crawford, Chief Executive Officer
**Web address:** www.nwtexashealthcare.com

RIVER CREST HOSPITAL (O, 80 beds) 1636 Hunters Glen Road, San Angelo, TX Zip 76901–5016; tel. 325/949–5722; Mandy Westerman, Chief Executive Officer
**Web address:** www.rivercresthospital.com

SOUTH TEXAS HEALTH SYSTEM (O, 788 beds) 1102 West Trenton Road, Edinburg, TX Zip 78539–9105; tel. 956/388–6000; Jennifer Garza, Chief Executive Officer
**Web address:** www.southtexashealthsystem.com

TEXAS NEUROREHAB CENTER (O, 47 beds) 1106 West Dittmar, Austin, TX Zip 78745–6328, Mailing Address: P.O. Box 150459, Zip 78715–0459; tel. 512/444–4835; Cindy Mostaffa, Chief Executive Officer
**Web address:** www.texasneurorehab.com

TEXOMA MEDICAL CENTER (O, 294 beds) 5016 South U.S. Highway 75, Denison, TX Zip 75020–4584, Mailing Address: P.O. Box 890, Zip 75021–0890; tel. 903/416–4000; Ronald T. Seal, Chief Executive Officer
**Web address:** www.texomamedicalcenter.net

TIMBERLAWN MENTAL HEALTH SYSTEM (O, 144 beds) 4600 Samuell Boulevard, Dallas, TX Zip 75228–6800; tel. 214/381–7181; Shelah Adams, Chief Executive Officer
**Web address:** www.timberlawn.com

UNIVERSITY BEHAVIORAL HEALTH OF DENTON (O, 104 beds) 2026 West University Drive, Denton, TX Zip 76201–0644; tel. 940/320–8100; Chris Rupert, Chief Executive Officer
**Web address:** www.ubhdenton.com

---

For explanation of codes following names, see page B2.
★ Indicates Type III membership in the American Hospital Association.

UNIVERSITY BEHAVIORAL HEALTH OF EL PASO (O, 163 beds) 1900 Denver Avenue, El Paso, TX Zip 79902–3008; tel. 915/544–4000; David W. Morris, Chief Executive Officer
**Web address:** www.ubhelpaso.com/

WEST OAKS HOSPITAL (O, 144 beds) 6500 Hornwood Drive, Houston, TX Zip 77074–5095; tel. 713/995–0909; Gregory Drummond, Chief Executive Officer
**Web address:** www.westoakshospital.com

**UTAH:** PROVO CANYON BEHAVIORAL HOSPITAL (O, 80 beds) 1350 East 750 North, Orem, UT Zip 84097–4345; tel. 801/852–2273; Jeremy Cottle, Ph.D., Chief Executive Officer
**Web address:** www.pcbh.com

SALT LAKE BEHAVIORAL HEALTH (O, 118 beds) 3802 South 700 East, Salt Lake City, UT Zip 84106–1182; tel. 801/264–6000; Kreg Gillman, Chief Executive Officer
**Web address:** www.saltlakebehavioralhealth.com

**VIRGINIA:** CUMBERLAND HOSPITAL (O, 132 beds) 9407 Cumberland Road, New Kent, VA Zip 23124–2029; tel. 804/966–2242; Patrice Gay Brooks, Chief Executive Officer
**Web address:** www.cumberlandhospital.com

POPLAR SPRINGS HOSPITAL (O, 180 beds) 350 Poplar Drive, Petersburg, VA Zip 23805–9367; tel. 804/733–6874; Joseph Trapani, Chief Executive Officer
**Web address:** www.poplarsprings.com

VIRGINIA BEACH PSYCHIATRIC CENTER (O, 100 beds) 1100 First Colonial Road, Virginia Beach, VA Zip 23454–2403; tel. 757/496–6000; Dustin Davis, Chief Executive Officer
**Web address:** www.vbpcweb.com

**WASHINGTON:** FAIRFAX BEHAVIORAL HEALTH (O, 157 beds) 10200 N.E. 132nd Street, Kirkland, WA Zip 98034–2899; tel. 425/821–2000; Ron Escarda, Chief Executive Officer
**Web address:** www.fairfaxhospital.com

**WEST VIRGINIA:** RIVER PARK HOSPITAL (O, 173 beds) 1230 Sixth Avenue, Huntington, WV Zip 25701–2312, Mailing Address: P.O. Box 1875, Zip 25719–1875; tel. 304/526–9111; Terry A. Stephens, Chief Executive Officer
**Web address:** www.riverparkhospital.net

**WYOMING:** WYOMING BEHAVIORAL INSTITUTE (O, 130 beds) 2521 East 15th Street, Casper, WY Zip 82609–4126; tel. 307/237–7444; Joseph Gallagher, Chief Executive Officer
**Web address:** www.wbihelp.com

| Owned, leased, sponsored: | 141 hospitals | 18524 beds |
|---|---|---|
| Contract–managed: | 0 hospitals | 0 beds |
| **Totals:** | 141 hospitals | 18524 beds |

---

**★0896: UNIVERSITY HEALTH CARE SYSTEM** (NP)
1350 Walton Way, Augusta, GA Zip 30901–2629; tel. 706/722–9011; James R. Davis, President and Chief Executive Officer
**(Independent Hospital System)**

**GEORGIA:** UNIVERSITY HOSPITAL (O, 477 beds) 1350 Walton Way, Augusta, GA Zip 30901–2629; tel. 706/722–9011; James R. Davis, Chief Executive Officer
**Web address:** www.universityhealth.org

UNIVERSITY HOSPITAL MCDUFFIE (O, 25 beds) 2460 Washington Road, N.E., Thomson, GA Zip 30824; tel. 706/595–1411; Sandra I. McVicker, R.N., MSN, President and Chief Nursing Officer
**Web address:** www.universityhealth.org/mcduffie

| Owned, leased, sponsored: | 2 hospitals | 502 beds |
|---|---|---|
| Contract–managed: | 0 hospitals | 0 beds |
| **Totals:** | 2 hospitals | 502 beds |

---

**0961: UNIVERSITY HEALTH SYSTEM** (NP)
1501 Kings Highway, Shreveport, LA Zip 71103–4228; tel. 318/675–5000; Richard C. Cascio, Interim Chief Executive Officer

**LOUISIANA:** UNIVERSITY HEALTH CONWAY (O, 105 beds) 4864 Jackson Street, Monroe, LA Zip 71202–6497, Mailing Address: P.O. Box 1881, Zip 71210–8005; tel. 318/330–7000; Larry Donner, Administrator
**Web address:** www.uhsystem.com

UNIVERSITY HEALTH SHREVEPORT (O, 459 beds) 1501 Kings Highway, Shreveport, LA Zip 71103–4228, Mailing Address: P.O. Box 33932, Zip 71130–3932; tel. 318/675–5000; Roderick L. Williams, M.P.H., President
**Web address:** www.lsuhscshreveport.edu

| Owned, leased, sponsored: | 2 hospitals | 564 beds |
|---|---|---|
| Contract–managed: | 0 hospitals | 0 beds |
| **Totals:** | 2 hospitals | 564 beds |

---

**★0112: UNIVERSITY HOSPITALS** (NP)
11100 Euclid Avenue, Cleveland, OH Zip 44106–5000; tel. 216/844–1000; Thomas F. Zenty, III, President and Chief Executive Officer
**(Moderately Centralized Health System)**

**OHIO:** UH REGIONAL HOSPITALS (O, 101 beds) 27100 Chardon Road, Cleveland, OH Zip 44143–1116; tel. 440/585–6500; Robert G. David, President
**Web address:** www.uhhospitals.org

UH ROBINSON MEDICAL CENTER (O, 141 beds) 6847 North Chestnut Street, Ravenna, OH Zip 44266–3929, Mailing Address: P.O. Box 1204, Zip 44266–1204; tel. 330/297–0811; Stephen Colecchi, President and Chief Executive Officer
**Web address:** www.robinsonmemorial.org

UNIVERSITY HOSPITALS AHUJA MEDICAL CENTER (O, 144 beds) 3999 Richmond Road, Beachwood, OH Zip 44122–6046; tel. 216/593–5500; Susan V. Juris, President
**Web address:** www.uhhospitals.org/ahuja/tabid/7051/uhahujamedicalcenter.aspx

UNIVERSITY HOSPITALS CASE MEDICAL CENTER (O, 790 beds) 11100 Euclid Avenue, Cleveland, OH Zip 44106–1716; tel. 216/844–1000; Fred C. Rothstein, M.D., President
**Web address:** www.UHhospitals.org

UNIVERSITY HOSPITALS CONNEAUT MEDICAL CENTER (O, 25 beds) 158 West Main Road, Conneaut, OH Zip 44030–2039; tel. 440/593–1131; M. Steven Jones, President
**Web address:** www.uhhospitals.org

UNIVERSITY HOSPITALS ELYRIA MEDICAL CENTER (O, 237 beds) 630 East River Street, Elyria, OH Zip 44035–5902; tel. 440/329–7500; Donald S. Sheldon, M.D., President and Chief Executive Officer
**Web address:** www.emh–healthcare.org

UNIVERSITY HOSPITALS GEAUGA MEDICAL CENTER (O, 126 beds) 13207 Ravenna Road, Chardon, OH Zip 44024–7032; tel. 440/269–6000; M. Steven Jones, President
**Web address:** www.uhhospitals.org/geauga/

UNIVERSITY HOSPITALS GENEVA MEDICAL CENTER (O, 25 beds) 870 West Main Street, Geneva, OH Zip 44041–1295; tel. 440/466–1141; M. Steven Jones, President
**Web address:** www.uhhs.com

UNIVERSITY HOSPITALS PARMA MEDICAL CENTER (O, 255 beds) 7007 Powers Boulevard, Parma, OH Zip 44129–5495; tel. 440/743–3000; Nancy Tinsley, President and Chief Executive Officer
**Web address:** www.parmahospital.org

| Owned, leased, sponsored: | 9 hospitals | 1844 beds |
|---|---|---|
| Contract–managed: | 0 hospitals | 0 beds |
| **Totals:** | 9 hospitals | 1844 beds |

---

**★0915: UNIVERSITY HOSPITALS AND HEALTH SYSTEM** (NP)
2500 North State Street, Jackson, MS Zip 39216–4500; tel. 601/984–1000; Kevin S. Cook, Chief Executive Officer
**(Decentralized Health System)**

**MISSISSIPPI:** UNIVERSITY OF MISSISSIPPI MEDICAL CENTER (O, 684 beds) 2500 North State Street, Jackson, MS Zip 39216–4505; tel. 601/984–1000; Kevin S. Cook, Chief Executive Officer
**Web address:** www.umc.edu

For explanation of codes following names, see page B2.
★ Indicates Type III membership in the American Hospital Association.

UNIVERSITY OF MISSISSIPPI MEDICAL CENTER GRENADA (C, 107 beds) 960 Avent Drive, Grenada, MS Zip 38901–5230; tel. 662/227–7000; David G. Putt, FACHE, Chief Executive Officer
**Web address:** www.glmc.net

UNIVERSITY OF MISSISSIPPI MEDICAL CENTER HOLMES COUNTY (O, 25 beds) 239 Bowling Green Road, Lexington, MS Zip 39095–5167; tel. 601/496–5200; David G. Putt, FACHE, Chief Executive Officer
**Web address:** www.ummchealth.com/holmes/

| | | |
|---|---|---|
| **Owned, leased, sponsored:** | 2 hospitals | 709 beds |
| **Contract–managed:** | 1 hospital | 107 beds |
| **Totals:** | 3 hospitals | 816 beds |

**★6405:   UNIVERSITY OF CALIFORNIA SYSTEMWIDE ADMINISTRATION** (NP)
1111 Franklin Street, 11th Floor, Oakland, CA Zip 94607–5200; tel. 510/987–9071; John D. Stobo, M.D., Executive Vice President and Chief Executive Officer
**(Moderately Centralized Health System)**

**CALIFORNIA:** RONALD REAGAN UCLA MEDICAL CENTER (O, 466 beds) 757 Westwood Plaza, Los Angeles, CA Zip 90095–8358; tel. 310/825–9111; James Atkinson, M.D., Interim President
**Web address:** www.uclahealth.org

SANTA MONICA–UCLA MEDICAL CENTER AND ORTHOPAEDIC HOSPITAL (O, 265 beds) 1250 16th Street, Santa Monica, CA Zip 90404–1249; tel. 310/319–4000; Paul Watkins, Chief Administrative Officer
**Web address:** www.healthcare.ucla.edu

STEWART & LYNDA RESNICK NEUROPSYCHIATRIC HOSPITAL AT UCLA (O, 74 beds) 150 UCLA Medical Plaza, Los Angeles, CA Zip 90095–8353; tel. 310/825–9989; Peter Whybrow, M.D., Chief Executive Officer
**Web address:** www.semel.ucla.edu/resnick

UC IRVINE MEDICAL CENTER (O, 411 beds) 101 The City Drive South, Orange, CA Zip 92868–3298; tel. 714/456–6011; Terry A. Belmont, Chief Executive Officer
**Web address:** www.ucihealth.com

UC SAN DIEGO HEALTH (O, 530 beds) 200 West Arbor Drive, San Diego, CA Zip 92103–9000; tel. 619/543–6222; Patty Maysent, Interim Chief Executive Officer
**Web address:** www.health.ucsd.edu

UCSF MEDICAL CENTER (O, 650 beds) 500 Parnassus Avenue, San Francisco, CA Zip 94143–0296, Mailing Address: 500 Parnassus Avenue, Box 0296, Zip 94143–0296; tel. 415/476–1000; Mark R. Laret, Chief Executive Officer
**Web address:** www.ucsfhealth.org

UNIVERSITY OF CALIFORNIA, DAVIS MEDICAL CENTER (O, 581 beds) 2315 Stockton Boulevard, Sacramento, CA Zip 95817–2282; tel. 916/734–2011; Ann Madden Rice, Chief Executive Officer
**Web address:** www.ucdmc.ucdavis.edu

| | | |
|---|---|---|
| **Owned, leased, sponsored:** | 7 hospitals | 2977 beds |
| **Contract–managed:** | 0 hospitals | 0 beds |
| **Totals:** | 7 hospitals | 2977 beds |

**★0381:   UNIVERSITY OF COLORADO HEALTH** (NP)
2315 East Harmony Road, Suite 200, Fort Collins, CO Zip 80528–8620; tel. 970/848–0000; Elizabeth B. Concordia, President and Chief Executive Officer
**(Independent Hospital System)**

**COLORADO:** MEDICAL CENTER OF THE ROCKIES (O, 166 beds) 2500 Rocky Mountain Avenue, Loveland, CO Zip 80538–9004; tel. 970/624–2500; Kevin L. Unger, FACHE, President and Chief Executive Officer
**Web address:** www.medctrrockies.org

MEMORIAL HOSPITAL (L, 448 beds) 1400 East Boulder Street, Colorado Springs, CO Zip 80909–5599; tel. 719/365–9888; George E. Hayes, FACHE, President and Chief Executive Officer
**Web address:** www.uchealth.org/southerncolorado

POUDRE VALLEY HOSPITAL (O, 226 beds) 1024 South Lemay Avenue, Fort Collins, CO Zip 80524–3998; tel. 970/495–7000; Kevin L. Unger, FACHE, President and Chief Executive Officer
**Web address:** www.uchealth.org

UNIVERSITY OF COLORADO HOSPITAL (O, 648 beds) 12605 East 16th Avenue, Aurora, CO Zip 80045–2545; tel. 720/848–0000; Elizabeth B. Concordia, Interim President and Chief Executive Officer
**Web address:** www.uch.edu

| | | |
|---|---|---|
| **Owned, leased, sponsored:** | 4 hospitals | 1488 beds |
| **Contract–managed:** | 0 hospitals | 0 beds |
| **Totals:** | 4 hospitals | 1488 beds |

**★0216:   UNIVERSITY OF MARYLAND MEDICAL SYSTEM** (NP)
250 West Pratt Street, 24th Floor, Baltimore, MD Zip 21201–1595; tel. 410/328–8667; Robert A. Chrencik, President and Chief Executive Officer
**(Moderately Centralized Health System)**

**MARYLAND:** MT. WASHINGTON PEDIATRIC HOSPITAL (O, 61 beds) 1708 West Rogers Avenue, Baltimore, MD Zip 21209–4545; tel. 410/578–8600; Sheldon J. Stein, President and Chief Executive Officer
**Web address:** www.mwph.org

UNIVERSITY OF MARYLAND BALTIMORE WASHINGTON MEDICAL CENTER (O, 323 beds) 301 Hospital Drive, Glen Burnie, MD Zip 21061–5899; tel. 410/787–4000; Karen E. Olscamp, President and Chief Executive Officer
**Web address:** www.bwmc.umms.org

UNIVERSITY OF MARYLAND CHARLES REGIONAL MEDICAL CENTER (O, 121 beds) 5 Garrett Avenue, La Plata, MD Zip 20646–5960, Mailing Address: P.O. Box 1070, Zip 20646–1070; tel. 301/609–4000; Noel A. Cervino, President and Chief Executive Officer
**Web address:** www.charlesregional.org

UNIVERSITY OF MARYLAND HARFORD MEMORIAL HOSPITAL (O, 79 beds) 501 South Union Avenue, Havre De Grace, MD Zip 21078–3493; tel. 443/843–5000; Lyle Ernest Sheldon, FACHE, President and Chief Executive Officer
**Web address:** www.uchs.org

UNIVERSITY OF MARYLAND MEDICAL CENTER (O, 725 beds) 22 South Greene Street, Baltimore, MD Zip 21201–1595; tel. 410/328–8667; Jeffrey A. Rivest, FACHE, President and Chief Executive Officer
**Web address:** www.umm.edu

UNIVERSITY OF MARYLAND MEDICAL CENTER MIDTOWN CAMPUS (O, 220 beds) 827 Linden Avenue, Baltimore, MD Zip 21201–4606; tel. 410/225–8000; John W. Ashworth, Interim President and Chief Executive Officer
**Web address:** www.ummidtown.org/

UNIVERSITY OF MARYLAND REHABILITATION & ORTHOPAEDIC INSTITUTE (O, 144 beds) 2200 Kernan Drive, Baltimore, MD Zip 21207–6697; tel. 410/448–2500; Cynthia Kelleher, M.P.H., President and Chief Executive Officer
**Web address:** www.umrehabortho.org

UNIVERSITY OF MARYLAND SHORE MEDICAL CENTER AT CHESTERTOWN (O, 41 beds) 100 Brown Street, Chestertown, MD Zip 21620–1499; tel. 410/778–3300; Kenneth D. Kozel, FACHE, President and Chief Executive Officer
**Web address:** www.umms.org/hospitals/shore–health–system.htm

UNIVERSITY OF MARYLAND SHORE MEDICAL CENTER AT DORCHESTER (O, 41 beds) 300 Byrn Street, Cambridge, MD Zip 21613–1908; tel. 410/228–5511; Kenneth D. Kozel, FACHE, President and Chief Executive Officer
**Web address:** www.shorehealth.org

UNIVERSITY OF MARYLAND SHORE MEDICAL CENTER AT EASTON (O, 132 beds) 219 South Washington Street, Easton, MD Zip 21601–2996; tel. 410/822–1000; Kenneth D. Kozel, FACHE, President and Chief Executive Officer
**Web address:** www.shorehealth.org

UNIVERSITY OF MARYLAND ST. JOSEPH MEDICAL CENTER (O, 314 beds) 7601 Osler Drive, Towson, MD Zip 21204–7582; tel. 410/337–1000; Mohan Suntha, M.D., President and Chief Executive Officer
**Web address:** www.sjmcmd.org

UNIVERSITY OF MARYLAND UPPER CHESAPEAKE MEDICAL CENTER (O, 162 beds) 500 Upper Chesapeake Drive, Bel Air, MD Zip 21014–4324; tel. 443/643–1000; Lyle Ernest Sheldon, FACHE, President and Chief Executive Officer
**Web address:** www.uchs.org

For explanation of codes following names, see page B2.
★ Indicates Type III membership in the American Hospital Association.

Section B

| Owned, leased, sponsored: | 12 hospitals | 2363 beds |
|---|---|---|
| Contract–managed: | 0 hospitals | 0 beds |
| Totals: | 12 hospitals | 2363 beds |

**0881:  UNIVERSITY OF MIAMI HEALTH SYSTEM** (NP)
1400 N.W. 12th Avenue, Miami, FL Zip 33136–1003;
tel. 305/243–4000; Pascal J. Goldschmidt, M.D., Chief Executive Officer
**(Centralized Health System)**

**FLORIDA:** BASCOM PALMER EYE INSTITUTE–ANNE BATES LEACH EYE HOSPITAL (O, 56 beds) 900 N.W. 17th Street, Miami, FL Zip 33136–1199, Mailing Address: Box 016880, Zip 33101–6880; tel. 305/326–6000; Michael B. Gittelman, Administrator
**Web address:** www.bascompalmer.org

UNIVERSITY OF MIAMI HOSPITAL (O, 514 beds) 1400 N.W. 12th Avenue, Miami, FL Zip 33136–1003; tel. 305/325–5511; David Zambrana, R.N., Chief Executive Officer
**Web address:** www.umiamihospital.com

UNIVERSITY OF MIAMI HOSPITAL AND CLINICS (O, 40 beds) 1475 N.W. 12th Avenue, Miami, FL Zip 33136–1002; tel. 305/243–4000; Richard R. Ballard, Chief Executive Officer and Administrator
**Web address:** www.uhealthsystem.com

| Owned, leased, sponsored: | 3 hospitals | 610 beds |
|---|---|---|
| Contract–managed: | 0 hospitals | 0 beds |
| Totals: | 3 hospitals | 610 beds |

**★0227:  UNIVERSITY OF MISSOURI HEALTH CARE** (NP)
One Hospital Drive, DC 031, Columbia, MO Zip 65212–0001;
tel. 573/884–8738; Mitchell L. Wasden, Ed.D., Chief Executive Officer and Chief Operating Officer
**(Moderately Centralized Health System)**

**MISSOURI:** FULTON MEDICAL CENTER (O, 37 beds) 10 South Hospital Drive, Fulton, MO Zip 65251–2510; tel. 573/642–3376; Mike Powell, Chief Executive Officer
**Web address:** www.mycallaway.org

CAPITAL REGION MEDICAL CENTER (O, 114 beds) 1125 Madison Street, Jefferson City, MO Zip 65101–5200, Mailing Address: P.O. Box 1128, Zip 65102–1128; tel. 573/632–5000; Gaspare Calvaruso, President
**Web address:** www.crmc.org

UNIVERSITY OF MISSOURI HOSPITALS AND CLINICS (O, 477 beds) One Hospital Drive, Columbia, MO Zip 65212–0001; tel. 573/882–4141; Mitchell L. Wasden, Ed.D., Chief Executive Officer and Chief Operating Officer
**Web address:** www.muhealth.org

| Owned, leased, sponsored: | 3 hospitals | 628 beds |
|---|---|---|
| Contract–managed: | 0 hospitals | 0 beds |
| Totals: | 3 hospitals | 628 beds |

**0021:  UNIVERSITY OF NEW MEXICO HOSPITALS** (NP)
915 Camino De Salud, Albuquerque, NM Zip 87131–0001;
tel. 505/272–5849; Stephen W. McKernan, Chief Executive Officer
**(Moderately Centralized Health System)**

**NEW MEXICO:** UNIVERSITY OF NEW MEXICO HOSPITALS (O, 537 beds) 2211 Lomas Boulevard N.E., Albuquerque, NM Zip 87106–2745; tel. 505/272–2111; Stephen W. McKernan, Chief Executive Officer
**Web address:** www.unm.edu

UNM SANDOVAL REGIONAL MEDICAL CENTER (O, 72 beds) 3001 Broadmoor Boulevard N.E., Rio Rancho, NM Zip 87144–2100; tel. 505/994–7000; Jamie A. Silva-Steele, R.N., President and Chief Executive Officer
**Web address:** www.hospitals.unm.edu/

| Owned, leased, sponsored: | 2 hospitals | 609 beds |
|---|---|---|
| Contract–managed: | 0 hospitals | 0 beds |
| Totals: | 2 hospitals | 609 beds |

**★0168:  UNIVERSITY OF PENNSYLVANIA HEALTH SYSTEM** (NP)
3400 Civic Center Bouelvard, Philadelphia, PA Zip 19104–5127;
tel. 215/662–2203; Ralph W. Muller, President and Chief Executive Officer
**(Centralized Physician/Insurance Health System)**

**PENNSYLVANIA:** HOSPITAL OF THE UNIVERSITY OF PENNSYLVANIA (O, 789 beds) 3400 Spruce Street, Philadelphia, PA Zip 19104–4206; tel. 215/662–4000; Garry L. Scheib, Executive Director
**Web address:** www.pennhealth.com

LANCASTER GENERAL HEALTH (O, 630 beds) 555 North Duke Street, Lancaster, PA Zip 17602–2250, Mailing Address: P.O. Box 3555, Zip 17604–3555; tel. 717/544–5511; Jan L. Bergen, President and Chief Executive Officer
**Web address:** www.lghealth.org

PENN MEDICINE CHESTER COUNTY HOSPITAL (O, 211 beds) 701 East Marshall Street, West Chester, PA Zip 19380–4412; tel. 610/431–5000; Michael J. Duncan, President and Chief Executive Officer
**Web address:** www.chestercountyhospital.org

PENN PRESBYTERIAN MEDICAL CENTER (O, 331 beds) 51 North 39th Street, Philadelphia, PA Zip 19104–2699; tel. 215/662–8000; Michele M. Volpe, Executive Director and Chief Executive Officer
**Web address:** www.pennmedicine.org/pmc/

PENNSYLVANIA HOSPITAL (O, 415 beds) 800 Spruce Street, Philadelphia, PA Zip 19107–6192; tel. 215/829–3000; Theresa M. Larivee, Executive Director
**Web address:** www.pahosp.com

| Owned, leased, sponsored: | 5 hospitals | 2376 beds |
|---|---|---|
| Contract–managed: | 0 hospitals | 0 beds |
| Totals: | 5 hospitals | 2376 beds |

**★0223:  UNIVERSITY OF ROCHESTER MEDICAL CENTER** (NP)
601 Elmwood Avenue Box 623, Rochester, NY Zip 14642–0002,
Mailing Address: 601 Elmwood Avenue, Zip 14642–0002;
tel. 585/275–2100; Steven I. Goldstein, General Director and Chief Executive Officer
**(Centralized Health System)**

**NEW YORK:** F. F. THOMPSON HOSPITAL (O, 251 beds) 350 Parrish Street, Canandaigua, NY Zip 14424–1731; tel. 585/396–6000; Michael Stapleton, President and Chief Executive Officer
**Web address:** www.thompsonhealth.com

HIGHLAND HOSPITAL OF ROCHESTER (O, 261 beds) 1000 South Avenue, Rochester, NY Zip 14620–2733; tel. 585/473–2200; Steven I. Goldstein, President and Chief Executive Officer
**Web address:** www.stronghealth.com

STRONG MEMORIAL HOSPITAL OF THE UNIVERSITY OF ROCHESTER (O, 815 beds) 601 Elmwood Avenue, Rochester, NY Zip 14642–0002; tel. 585/275–2100; Steven I. Goldstein, President and Chief Executive Officer
**Web address:** www.urmc.rochester.edu

| Owned, leased, sponsored: | 3 hospitals | 1327 beds |
|---|---|---|
| Contract–managed: | 0 hospitals | 0 beds |
| Totals: | 3 hospitals | 1327 beds |

**★0057:  UNIVERSITY OF SOUTH ALABAMA HOSPITALS** (NP)
2451 Fillingim Street, Mobile, AL Zip 36617–2238;
tel. 251/471–7000; Stanley K. Hammack, Chief Executive Officer
**(Independent Hospital System)**

**ALABAMA:** UNIVERSITY OF SOUTH ALABAMA CHILDREN'S AND WOMEN'S HOSPITAL (O, 198 beds) 1700 Center Street, Mobile, AL Zip 36604–3301; tel. 251/415–1000; Owen Bailey, FACHE, Administrator
**Web address:** www.usahealthsystem.com/usacwh

---

For explanation of codes following names, see page B2.
★ Indicates Type III membership in the American Hospital Association.

Section B

UNIVERSITY OF SOUTH ALABAMA MEDICAL CENTER (O, 132 beds) 2451 Fillingim Street, Mobile, AL Zip 36617–2293; tel. 251/471–7000; A. Elizabeth Anderson, Administrator
**Web address:** www.usahealthsystem.com/usamc

| | | |
|---|---|---|
| **Owned, leased, sponsored:** | 2 hospitals | 330 beds |
| **Contract–managed:** | 0 hospitals | 0 beds |
| **Totals:** | 2 hospitals | 330 beds |

---

### ★0033: UNIVERSITY OF TEXAS SYSTEM (NP)
601 Colorado Street, Suite 205, Austin, TX Zip 78701–2904; tel. 512/499–4224; Raymond Greenberg, M.D., Executive Vice Chancellor
**(Moderately Centralized Health System)**

**TEXAS:** UNIVERSITY OF TEXAS HARRIS COUNTY PSYCHIATRIC CENTER (C, 204 beds) 2800 South MacGregor Way, Houston, TX Zip 77021–1000, Mailing Address: P.O. Box 20249, Zip 77225–0249; tel. 713/741–7870; Jair C. Soares, M.D., Executive Director
**Web address:** www.hcpc.uth.tmc.edu

UNIVERSITY OF TEXAS HEALTH NORTHEAST (O, 111 beds) 11937 Highway 271, Tyler, TX Zip 75708–3154; tel. 903/877–7777; Kirk A. Calhoun, M.D., President
**Web address:** www.uthct.edu

UNIVERSITY OF TEXAS M.D. ANDERSON CANCER CENTER (O, 654 beds) 1515 Holcombe Boulevard, Box 91, Houston, TX Zip 77030–4000; tel. 713/792–2121; Ronald A. DePinho, M.D., President
**Web address:** www.mdanderson.org

UNIVERSITY OF TEXAS MEDICAL BRANCH (O, 437 beds) 301 University Boulevard, Galveston, TX Zip 77555–0128; tel. 409/772–1011; Donna K. Sollenberger, Executive Vice President and Chief Executive Officer
**Web address:** www.utmb.edu

| | | |
|---|---|---|
| **Owned, leased, sponsored:** | 3 hospitals | 1202 beds |
| **Contract–managed:** | 1 hospital | 204 beds |
| **Totals:** | 4 hospitals | 1406 beds |

---

### 0137: UPMC (NP)
600 Grant Street, U.S. Steel Tower, Suite 6262, Pittsburgh, PA Zip 15219–2702; tel. 412/647–8762; Jeffrey A. Romoff, President and Chief Executive Officer
**(Centralized Physician/Insurance Health System)**

**PENNSYLVANIA:** CHILDREN'S HOSPITAL OF PITTSBURGH OF UPMC (O, 304 beds) 4401 Penn Avenue, Pittsburgh, PA Zip 15224–1334; tel. 412/692–5325; Christopher Gessner, President
**Web address:** www.chp.edu

MAGEE–WOMENS HOSPITAL OF UPMC (O, 327 beds) 300 Halket Street, Pittsburgh, PA Zip 15213–3108; tel. 412/641–1000; Leslie C. Davis, President
**Web address:** www.magee.edu

UPMC ALTOONA (O, 380 beds) 620 Howard Avenue, Altoona, PA Zip 16601–4804; tel. 814/889–2011; Gerald Murray, President
**Web address:** www.altoonaregional.org

UPMC BEDFORD MEMORIAL (O, 27 beds) 10455 Lincoln Highway, Everett, PA Zip 15537–7046; tel. 814/623–6161; Gerald Murray, President
**Web address:** www.upmcbedfordmemorial.com

UPMC EAST (O, 155 beds) 2775 Mosside Boulevard, Monroeville, PA Zip 15146–2760; tel. 412/357–3000; Mark Sevco, President
**Web address:** www.upmc.com/locations/hospitals/east/Pages/default.aspx

UPMC HAMOT (O, 311 beds) 201 State Street, Erie, PA Zip 16550–0002; tel. 814/877–6000; V. James Fiorenzo, President
**Web address:** www.hamot.org

UPMC HORIZON (O, 184 beds) 110 North Main Street, Greenville, PA Zip 16125–1726; tel. 724/588–2100; Donald R. Owrey, President
**Web address:** www.horizon.upmc.com

UPMC MCKEESPORT (O, 208 beds) 1500 Fifth Avenue, McKeesport, PA Zip 15132–2422; tel. 412/664–2000; Mark Sevco, President
**Web address:** www.mckeesport.upmc.com

UPMC MERCY (O, 482 beds) 1400 Locust Street, Pittsburgh, PA Zip 15219–5166; tel. 412/232–8111; Michael Grace, President
**Web address:** www.upmc.com/HospitalsFacilities/HFHome/Hospitals/Mercy/

UPMC NORTHWEST (O, 180 beds) 100 Fairfield Drive, Seneca, PA Zip 16346–2130; tel. 814/676–7600; David Gibbons, President
**Web address:** www.upmc.com/locations/hospitals/northwest/Pages/default. aspx

UPMC PASSAVANT (O, 425 beds) 9100 Babcock Boulevard, Pittsburgh, PA Zip 15237–5815; tel. 412/748–6700; David T. Martin, President
**Web address:** www.upmc.edu/passavant

UPMC PRESBYTERIAN SHADYSIDE (O, 1517 beds) 200 Lothrop Street, Pittsburgh, PA Zip 15213–2536; tel. 412/647–2345; John Innocenti, Sr., President and Chief Executive Officer
**Web address:** www.upmc.edu

UPMC ST. MARGARET (O, 249 beds) 815 Freeport Road, Pittsburgh, PA Zip 15215–3301; tel. 412/784–4000; David J. Patton, President
**Web address:** www.upmc. com/locations/hospitals/st–margaret/Pages/default.aspx

| | | |
|---|---|---|
| **Owned, leased, sponsored:** | 13 hospitals | 4749 beds |
| **Contract–managed:** | 0 hospitals | 0 beds |
| **Totals:** | 13 hospitals | 4749 beds |

---

### 0816: UPPER ALLEGHENY HEALTH SYSTEM (NP)
130 South Union Street, Suite 300, Olean, NY Zip 14760–3676; tel. 716/375–6190; Timothy J. Finan, FACHE, President and Chief Executive Officer
**(Independent Hospital System)**

**NEW YORK:** OLEAN GENERAL HOSPITAL (O, 186 beds) 515 Main Street, Olean, NY Zip 14760–1513; tel. 716/373–2600; Timothy J. Finan, FACHE, President and Chief Executive Officer
**Web address:** www.ogh.org

**PENNSYLVANIA:** BRADFORD REGIONAL MEDICAL CENTER (O, 182 beds) 116 Interstate Parkway, Bradford, PA Zip 16701–1036; tel. 814/368–4143; Timothy J. Finan, FACHE, President and Chief Executive Officer
**Web address:** www.brmc.com

| | | |
|---|---|---|
| **Owned, leased, sponsored:** | 2 hospitals | 368 beds |
| **Contract–managed:** | 0 hospitals | 0 beds |
| **Totals:** | 2 hospitals | 368 beds |

---

### 0868: USMD INC. (IO)
6333 North State Highway 161 Suite 200, Irving, TX Zip 75038–2229; tel. 214/493–4000; Karen A. Fiducia, FACHE, President, Hospital Division
**(Independent Hospital System)**

**TEXAS:** USMD HOSPITAL AT ARLINGTON (O, 34 beds) 801 West Interstate 20, Arlington, TX Zip 76017–5851; tel. 817/472–3400; Marcia Crim, R.N., MSN, Chief Executive Officer
**Web address:** www.usmdarlington.com

USMD HOSPITAL AT FORT WORTH (O, 8 beds) 5900 Altamesa Boulevard, Fort Worth, TX Zip 76132–5473; tel. 817/433–9100; Stephanie Atkins–Guidry, Administrator and Chief Nursing Officer
**Web address:** www.usmdfortworth.com/

| | | |
|---|---|---|
| **Owned, leased, sponsored:** | 2 hospitals | 42 beds |
| **Contract–managed:** | 0 hospitals | 0 beds |
| **Totals:** | 2 hospitals | 42 beds |

---

### 0860: UVA HEALTH SYSTEM (NP)
1215 Lee Street, Charlottesville, VA Zip 22908–0816; tel. 434/924–0211; R. Edward Howell, Vice President and Chief Executive Officer
**(Centralized Health System)**

**VIRGINIA:** UNIVERSITY OF VIRGINIA MEDICAL CENTER (O, 584 beds) 1215 Lee Street, Charlottesville, VA Zip 22908–0001, Mailing Address: P.O. Box 800809, Zip 22908–0809; tel. 434/924–0211; Pamela Sutton–Wallace, Chief Executive Officer
**Web address:** www.healthsystem.virginia.edu

For explanation of codes following names, see page B2.
★ Indicates Type III membership in the American Hospital Association.

Section B

UVA CULPEPER HOSPITAL (O, 68 beds) 501 Sunset Lane, Culpeper, VA Zip 22701–3917, Mailing Address: P.O. Box 592, Zip 22701–0500; tel. 540/829–4100; Greg Napps, Chief Executive Officer
**Web address:** www.culpeperhealth.org

UVA TRANSITIONAL CARE HOSPITAL (O, 40 beds) 2965 Ivy Road (250 West), Charlottesville, VA Zip 22903–9330; tel. 434/924–7897; Michelle Hereford, Chief
**Web address:** www.uvahealth.com/services/transitional–care–hospital

| | | |
|---|---|---|
| **Owned, leased, sponsored:** | 3 hospitals | 692 beds |
| **Contract–managed:** | 0 hospitals | 0 beds |
| **Totals:** | 3 hospitals | 692 beds |

---

★**6415:  UW MEDICINE** (NP)
1959 N.E. Pacific Street, Seattle, WA Zip 98195–0001, Mailing Address: P.O. Box 356350, Zip 98195–6350; tel. 206/543–7718; Paul G. Ramsey, M.D., Chief Executive Officer
**(Independent Hospital System)**

**WASHINGTON:** UNIVERSITY OF WASHINGTON MEDICAL CENTER (O, 428 beds) 1959 N.E. Pacific Street, Seattle, WA Zip 98195–6151; tel. 206/598–3300; Geoff Austin, Interim Executive Director
**Web address:** www.uwmedicine.
org/Patient–Care/Locations/UWMC/Pages/default.aspx

UW MEDICINE/HARBORVIEW MEDICAL CENTER (C, 413 beds) 325 Ninth Avenue, Seattle, WA Zip 98104–2499, Mailing Address: P.O. Box 359717, Zip 98195–9717; tel. 206/744–3000; Paul Hayes, Executive Director
**Web address:** www.uwmedicine.
org/Patient–Care/Locations/HMC/Pages/default.aspx

UW MEDICINE/NORTHWEST HOSPITAL & MEDICAL CENTER (C, 176 beds) 1550 North 115th Street, Seattle, WA Zip 98133–8401; tel. 206/364–0500; Cynthia Hecker, R.N., Executive Director
**Web address:** www.uwmedicine.
org/Patient–Care/Locations/nwh/Pages/default.aspx

UW MEDICINE/VALLEY MEDICAL CENTER (C, 187 beds) 400 South 43rd Street, Renton, WA Zip 98055–5714, Mailing Address: P.O. Box 50010, Zip 98058–5010; tel. 425/228–3450; Richard D. Roodman, Chief Executive Officer
**Web address:** www.valleymed.org

| | | |
|---|---|---|
| **Owned, leased, sponsored:** | 1 hospital | 428 beds |
| **Contract–managed:** | 3 hospitals | 776 beds |
| **Totals:** | 4 hospitals | 1204 beds |

---

★**0128:  VALLEY HEALTH SYSTEM** (NP)
220 Campus Boulevard, Suite 420, Winchester, VA Zip 22601–2889, Mailing Address: P.O. Box 3340, Zip 22604–2540; tel. 540/536–8024; Mark H. Merrill, President and Chief Executive Officer
**(Moderately Centralized Health System)**

**VIRGINIA:** PAGE MEMORIAL HOSPITAL (O, 25 beds) 200 Memorial Drive, Luray, VA Zip 22835–1005; tel. 540/743–4561; N. Travis Clark, President
**Web address:** www.valleyhealthlink.com/page

SHENANDOAH MEMORIAL HOSPITAL (O, 25 beds) 759 South Main Street, Woodstock, VA Zip 22664–1127; tel. 540/459–1100; Floyd Heater, President
**Web address:** www.valleyhealthlink.com/shenandoah

WARREN MEMORIAL HOSPITAL (O, 166 beds) 1000 North Shenandoah Avenue, Front Royal, VA Zip 22630–3598; tel. 540/636–0300; Floyd Heater, Interim President and Chief Executive Officer
**Web address:** www.valleyhealthlink.com/WMH

WINCHESTER MEDICAL CENTER (O, 475 beds) 1840 Amherst Street, Winchester, VA Zip 22601–2808, Mailing Address: P.O. Box 3340, Zip 22604–2540; tel. 540/536–8000; Mark H. Merrill, President
**Web address:** www.valleyhealthlink.com/WMC

**WEST VIRGINIA:** HAMPSHIRE MEMORIAL HOSPITAL (O, 44 beds) 363 Sunrise Boulevard, Romney, WV Zip 26757–4607; tel. 304/822–4561; Neil R. McLaughlin, R.N., President
**Web address:** www.valleyhealthlink.com/hampshire

WAR MEMORIAL HOSPITAL (O, 41 beds) One Healthy Way, Berkeley Springs, WV Zip 25411–7463; tel. 304/258–1234; Neil R. McLaughlin, R.N., President
**Web address:** www.valleyhealthlink.com/war

| | | |
|---|---|---|
| **Owned, leased, sponsored:** | 6 hospitals | 776 beds |
| **Contract–managed:** | 0 hospitals | 0 beds |
| **Totals:** | 6 hospitals | 776 beds |

---

● ★**0387:  VANDERBILT HEALTH** (NP)
1211 22nd Avenue South, Nashville, TN Zip 37232; tel. 615/322–5000; Charles Wright Pinson, M.D., Deputy Vice Chancellor for Health Affairs and Chief Executive Officer of Vanderbilt Health System
**(Moderately Centralized Health System)**

**TENNESSEE:** VANDERBILT HOSPITAL AND CLINICS (O, 1004 beds) 1211 22nd Avenue North, Nashville, TN Zip 37232–2102; tel. 615/322–5000; David R. Posch, Chief Executive Officer
**Web address:** www.mc.vanderbilt.edu

| | | |
|---|---|---|
| **Owned, leased, sponsored:** | 1 hospital | 1004 beds |
| **Contract–managed:** | 0 hospitals | 0 beds |
| **Totals:** | 1 hospital | 1004 beds |

---

**0939:  VCU HEALTH SYSTEM** (NP)
1250 East Marshall Street, Richmond, VA Zip 23298–5051, Mailing Address: P.O. Box 980510, Zip 23298–0510; tel. 804/828–9000; Marsha Rappley, M.D., Chief Executive Officer and Vice President for Health Sciences
**(Moderately Centralized Health System)**

**VIRGINIA:** CHILDREN'S HOSPITAL OF RICHMOND AT VCU–BROOK ROAD CAMPUS (O, 36 beds) 2924 Brook Road, Richmond, VA Zip 23220–1298; tel. 804/321–7474; Leslie G. Wyatt, Senior Vice President Children's Services and Executive Director
**Web address:** www.chrichmond.org

VCU COMMUNITY MEMORIAL HOSPITAL (O, 178 beds) 125 Buena Vista Circle, South Hill, VA Zip 23970–1431, Mailing Address: P.O. Box 90, Zip 23970–0090; tel. 434/447–3151; W. Scott Burnette, Chief Executive Officer
**Web address:** www.cmh–sh.org

VCU MEDICAL CENTER (O, 774 beds) 1250 East Marshall Street, Richmond, VA Zip 23298–5051, Mailing Address: P.O. Box 980510, Zip 23298–0510; tel. 804/828–9000; John Duval, Chief Executive Officer
**Web address:** www.vcuhealth.org

| | | |
|---|---|---|
| **Owned, leased, sponsored:** | 3 hospitals | 988 beds |
| **Contract–managed:** | 0 hospitals | 0 beds |
| **Totals:** | 3 hospitals | 988 beds |

---

★**0299:  VIBRA HEALTHCARE** (IO)
4550 Lena Drive, Suite 225, Mechanicsburg, PA Zip 17055–4920; tel. 717/591–5700; Brad Hollinger, Chairman and Chief Executive Officer
**(Independent Hospital System)**

**CALIFORNIA:** BALLARD REHABILITATION HOSPITAL (O, 45 beds) 1760 West 16th Street, San Bernardino, CA Zip 92411–1160; tel. 909/473–1200; Mary Miles Hunt, Chief Executive Officer
**Web address:** www.ballardrehab.com

KENTFIELD REHABILITATION AND SPECIALTY HOSPITAL (O, 48 beds) 1125 Sir Francis Drake Boulevard, Kentfield, CA Zip 94904–1455; tel. 415/456–9680; Ann Gors, Chief Executive Officer
**Web address:** www.kentfieldrehab.com

SAN JOAQUIN VALLEY REHABILITATION HOSPITAL (O, 62 beds) 7173 North Sharon Avenue, Fresno, CA Zip 93720–3329; tel. 559/436–3600; Mary Jo Jacobson, Chief Executive Officer
**Web address:** www.sanjoaquinrehab.com

---

For explanation of codes following names, see page B2.
★ Indicates Type III membership in the American Hospital Association.
● Single hospital health care system

VIBRA HOSPITAL OF NORTHERN CALIFORNIA (O, 88 beds) 2801 Eureka Way, Redding, CA Zip 96001–0222; tel. 530/246–9000; Chris Jones, Chief Executive Officer
**Web address:** www.norcalrehab.com

VIBRA HOSPITAL OF SACRAMENTO (O, 37 beds) 330 Montrose Drive, Folsom, CA Zip 95630–2720; tel. 916/351–9151; Janet Biedron, R.N., Chief Executive Officer
**Web address:** www.vhsacramento.com

VIBRA HOSPITAL OF SAN DIEGO (O, 110 beds) 555 Washington Street, San Diego, CA Zip 92103–2294; tel. 619/260–8300; Yameeka Jones, Chief Executive Officer
**Web address:** www.vhsandiego.com/

**COLORADO:** VIBRA HOSPITAL OF DENVER (O, 71 beds) 8451 Pearl Street, Thornton, CO Zip 80229–4804; tel. 303/288–3000; Austin B. Cleveland, Chief Executive Officer
**Web address:** www.vhdenver.com

**IDAHO:** VIBRA HOSPITAL OF BOISE (O, 60 beds) 2131 South Bonito Way, Meridian, ID Zip 83642–1659; tel. 877/801–2244; James Elton, Chief Executive Officer
**Web address:** www.vhboise.com

**ILLINOIS:** VIBRA HOSPITAL OF SPRINGFIELD (O, 30 beds) 701 North Walnut Street, Springfield, IL Zip 62702–4931; tel. 217/528–1217; Charles Nordyke, Chief Executive Officer
**Web address:** www.222.vhspringfield.com

**INDIANA:** VIBRA HOSPITAL OF FORT WAYNE (O, 24 beds) 2200 Randallia Drive, Fort Wayne, IN Zip 46805–4638; tel. 260/399–2900; Ryan Cassedy, Chief Executive Officer
**Web address:** www.vhfortwayne.com

VIBRA HOSPITAL OF NORTHWESTERN INDIANA (O, 40 beds) 9509 Georgia Street, Crown Point, IN Zip 46307–6518; tel. 219/472–2200; Charles Nordyke, Interim Chief Executive Officer
**Web address:** www.vhnwindiana.com/

**KENTUCKY:** GATEWAY REHABILITATION HOSPITAL (C, 40 beds) 5940 Merchant Street, Florence, KY Zip 41042–1158; tel. 859/426–2400; Elizabeth Cooley, Chief Executive Officer
**Web address:** www.gatewayflorence.com/

SOUTHERN KENTUCKY REHABILITATION HOSPITAL (O, 60 beds) 1300 Campbell Lane, Bowling Green, KY Zip 42104–4162; tel. 270/782–6900; Stuart Locke, Chief Executive Officer
**Web address:** www.skyrehab.com

**MASSACHUSETTS:** NEW BEDFORD REHABILITATION HOSPITAL (O, 90 beds) 4499 Acushnet Avenue, New Bedford, MA Zip 02745–4707; tel. 508/995–6900; Edward B. Leary, Chief Executive Officer
**Web address:** www.newbedfordrehab.com

VIBRA HOSPITAL OF WESTERN MASSACHUSETTS (O, 202 beds) 1400 State Street, Springfield, MA Zip 01109–2550; tel. 413/726–6700; Daniel Mitchell, Chief Executive Officer
**Web address:** www.vhwmass.com

**MICHIGAN:** VIBRA HOSPITAL OF SOUTHEASTERN MICHIGAN, LLC (O, 220 beds) 26400 West Outer Drive, Lincoln Park, MI Zip 48146–2088; tel. 313/386–2000; Denise Wayne, Chief Executive Officer
**Web address:** www.vhsemichigan.com/

**NEW JERSEY:** MARLTON REHABILITATION HOSPITAL (O, 61 beds) 92 Brick Road, Marlton, NJ Zip 08053–2177; tel. 856/988–8778; Phyllis J. Schlichtmann, Chief Executive Officer
**Web address:** www.marltonrehab.com

**NORTH DAKOTA:** VIBRA HOSPITAL OF CENTRAL DAKOTAS (O, 41 beds) 1000 18th Street N.W., Mandan, ND Zip 58554–1612; tel. 701/667–2000; Glynda Troyo-Sauviac, Chief Executive Officer
**Web address:** www.vhcentraldakotas.com

VIBRA HOSPITAL OF FARGO (O, 31 beds) 1720 University Drive South, Fargo, ND Zip 58103–4940; tel. 701/241–9099; Custer Huseby, Chief Executive Officer
**Web address:** www.vhfargo.com

**OHIO:** VIBRA HOSPITAL OF MAHONING VALLEY (O, 42 beds) 8049 South Avenue, Boardman, OH Zip 44512–6154; tel. 330/726–5000; Mary Lou Sankovich, R.N., MSN, Chief Executive Officer
**Web address:** www.vhmvalley.com

**OREGON:** VIBRA SPECIALTY HOSPITAL OF PORTLAND (O, 73 beds) 10300 N.E. Hancock Street, Portland, OR Zip 97220–3831; tel. 503/257–5500; David Tupper, Chief Executive Officer
**Web address:** www.vshportland.com

**SOUTH CAROLINA:** VIBRA HOSPITAL OF CHARLESTON (O, 94 beds) 1200 Hospital Drive, Mt. Pleasant, SC Zip 29464; tel. 843/375–4000; Joseph E. Roche, Chief Executive Officer
**Web address:** www.vhcharleston.com

**TEXAS:** VIBRA HOSPITAL OF AMARILLO (O, 72 beds) 7501 Wallace Boulevard, Amarillo, TX Zip 79124–2150; tel. 806/467–7000; Jerry Jasper, Chief Executive Officer
**Web address:** www.vhamarillo.com

VIBRA REHABILITATION HOSPITAL LAKE TRAVIS (O, 36 beds) 2000 Medical Drive, Lakeway, TX Zip 78734–4200; tel. 512/263–4500; Deborah Hopps, Chief Executive Officer
**Web address:** www.vrhlaketravis.com

VIBRA REHABILITATION HOSPITAL OF AMARILLO (O, 44 beds) 7200 West 9th Avenue, Amarillo, TX Zip 79106–1703; tel. 806/468–2900; Jerry Jasper, Chief Executive Officer
**Web address:** www.vrhamarillo.com

VIBRA SPECIALTY HOSPITAL AT DESOTO (O, 40 beds) 2700 Walker Way, Desoto, TX Zip 75115–2088; tel. 972/298–1100; Thomas Alexander, Chief Executive Officer
**Web address:** www.vshdesoto.com

**VIRGINIA:** VIBRA HOSPITAL OF RICHMOND (O, 60 beds) 2220 Edward Holland Drive, Richmond, VA Zip 23230–2519; tel. 804/678–7000; Peter Miller, Interim Chief Executive Officer
**Web address:** www.vhrichmond.com

| | | |
|---|---|---|
| **Owned, leased, sponsored:** | 26 hospitals | 1781 beds |
| **Contract–managed:** | 1 hospital | 40 beds |
| **Totals:** | 27 hospitals | 1821 beds |

---

**0920: VIBRANT HEALTHCARE** (IO)
12222 North Central Expressway, Suite 440, Dallas, TX Zip 75243–3767; tel. 469/330–6745; Wilton M. Burt, Chief Executive Officer
**(Independent Hospital System)**

**TEXAS:** FOREST PARK MEDICAL CENTER (C, 84 beds) 11990 North Central Expressway, Dallas, TX Zip 75243–3714; tel. 972/234–1900; Cindy Bledsoe, Chief Executive Officer
**Web address:** www.forestparkmc.com/

FOREST PARK MEDICAL CENTER FRISCO (C, 54 beds) 5500 Frisco Square Boulevard, Frisco, TX Zip 75034–3305; tel. 214/618–0500; Julie A. Camp, R.N., Chief Executive Officer
**Web address:** www.forestparkfrisco.com/default.aspx

FOREST PARK MEDICAL CENTER–SOUTHLAKE (C, 18 beds) 421 East State Highway 114, Southlake, TX Zip 76092; tel. 817/865–4400; Dawn Beljin, R.N., Chief Operating Officer
**Web address:** www.forestparksouthlake.com

| | | |
|---|---|---|
| **Owned, leased, sponsored:** | 0 hospitals | 0 beds |
| **Contract–managed:** | 3 hospitals | 156 beds |
| **Totals:** | 3 hospitals | 156 beds |

---

**0897: VICTORY HEALTHCARE** (IO)
2201 Timberloch Place, Suite 200, The Woodlands, TX Zip 77380; tel. 281/863–2100; Robert N. Helms, Jr., Board Chair, President and Chief Executive Officer
**(Independent Hospital System)**

VICTORY MEDICAL CENTER – SOUTHCROSS (O, 9 beds) 5330 N. Loop 1604 W., San Antonio, TX Zip 78249; tel. 210/877–8000; Louis O. Garcia, Chief Executive Officer
**Web address:** www.victory–healthcare.com/san–antonio–location/

VICTORY MEDICAL CENTER BEAUMONT (O, 17 beds) 6025 Metropolitan Drive, Beaumont, TX Zip 77706–2407; tel. 409/617–7700; Becky Ames, Chief Executive Officer
**Web address:** www.victory–healthcare.com/beaumont

---

For explanation of codes following names, see page B2.
★ Indicates Type III membership in the American Hospital Association.

VICTORY MEDICAL CENTER CRAIG RANCH (O, 24 beds) 6045 Alma Road, McKinney, TX Zip 75070–2188; tel. 972/908–1215; Ashley Anson, Chief Executive Officer
**Web address:** www.victory–healthcare.com/craig–ranch/

VICTORY MEDICAL CENTER HOUSTON (O, 25 beds) 2001 Hermann Drive, Houston, TX Zip 77004–7643; tel. 713/285–5500; Nicholas Crafts, Chief Executive Officer
**Web address:** www.victory–healthcare.com

VICTORY MEDICAL CENTER LANDMARK (O, 25 beds) 5330 North Loop 1604 West, San Antonio, TX Zip 78249–1371; tel. 210/877–8000; Alex Garcia, Chief Executive Officer
**Web address:** www.victory–healthcare.com/sanantoniolandmark

VICTORY MEDICAL CENTER MID–CITIES (O, 16 beds) 1612 Hurst Town Center Drive, Hurst, TX Zip 76054–6236; tel. 817/345–4100; Barbara Millwood, Chief Executive Officer
**Web address:** www.victory–healthcare.com

VICTORY MEDICAL CENTER PLANO (O, 26 beds) 2301 Marsh Lane, Plano, TX Zip 75093–8497; tel. 972/820–2600; Steve Williams, Chief Executive Officer
**Web address:** www.victory–healthcare.com/plano

VICTORY SURGICAL HOSPITAL EAST HOUSTON (O, 4 beds) 12950 East Freeway, Houston, TX Zip 77015–5710; tel. 713/330–3887; Steve Winnett, Chief Executive Officer
**Web address:** www.victory–healthcare.com/easthouston

| | | |
|---|---|---|
| **Owned, leased, sponsored:** | 8 hospitals | 146 beds |
| **Contract–managed:** | 0 hospitals | 0 beds |
| **Totals:** | 8 hospitals | 146 beds |

---

★**0217: VIDANT HEALTH** (NP)
2100 Stantonsburg Road, Greenville, NC Zip 27834–2818, Mailing Address: P.O. Box 6028, Zip 27835–6028; tel. 252/847–4100; Michael Waldrum, M.D., Chief Executive Officer
**(Moderately Centralized Health System)**

**NORTH CAROLINA:** THE OUTER BANKS HOSPITAL (O, 21 beds) 4800 South Croatan Highway, Nags Head, NC Zip 27959–9704; tel. 252/449–4511; Ronald A. Sloan, FACHE, President
**Web address:** www.theouterbankshospital.com

VIDANT BEAUFORT HOSPITAL (L, 43 beds) 628 East 12th Street, Washington, NC Zip 27889–3409; tel. 252/975–4100; Harvey Case, President
**Web address:** www.vidanthealth.com

VIDANT BERTIE HOSPITAL (L, 6 beds) 1403 South King Street, Windsor, NC Zip 27983–9666, Mailing Address: P.O. Box 40, Zip 27983–0040; tel. 252/794–6600; Jeffery Dial, President
**Web address:** www.vidanthealth.com

VIDANT CHOWAN HOSPITAL (L, 19 beds) 211 Virginia Road, Edenton, NC Zip 27932–9668, Mailing Address: P.O. Box 629, Zip 27932–0629; tel. 252/482–8451; Jeffery Dial, President
**Web address:** www.vidanthealth.com

VIDANT DUPLIN HOSPITAL (L, 48 beds) 401 North Main Street, Kenansville, NC Zip 28349–8801, Mailing Address: P.O. Box 278, Zip 28349–0278; tel. 910/296–0941; Jay Briley, President
**Web address:** www.vidanthealth.com

VIDANT EDGECOMBE HOSPITAL (O, 59 beds) 111 Hospital Drive, Tarboro, NC Zip 27886–2011; tel. 252/641–7700; Wendell H. Baker, Jr., President
**Web address:** www.https://www.vidanthealth.com/edgecombe/default.aspx

VIDANT MEDICAL CENTER (O, 909 beds) 2100 Stantonsburg Road, Greenville, NC Zip 27834–2818, Mailing Address: P.O. Box 6028, Zip 27835–6028; tel. 252/847–4100; Brian Floyd, President Emeritus
**Web address:** www.https://www.vidanthealth.com/

VIDANT ROANOKE–CHOWAN HOSPITAL (L, 70 beds) 500 South Academy Street, Ahoskie, NC Zip 27910–3261, Mailing Address: P.O. Box 1385, Zip 27910–1385; tel. 252/209–3000; Susan S. Lassiter, FACHE, President and Chief Executive Officer
**Web address:** www.vidanthealth.com

| | | |
|---|---|---|
| **Owned, leased, sponsored:** | 8 hospitals | 1175 beds |
| **Contract–managed:** | 0 hospitals | 0 beds |
| **Totals:** | 8 hospitals | 1175 beds |

**0012: VIRGINIA DEPARTMENT OF MENTAL HEALTH** (NP)
1220 Bank Street, Richmond, VA Zip 23219–3645, Mailing Address: P.O. Box 1797, Zip 23218–1797; tel. 804/786–3921; James S. Reinhard, M.D., Commissioner
**(Independent Hospital System)**

**VIRGINIA:** CATAWBA HOSPITAL (O, 110 beds) 5525 Catawba Hospital Drive, Catawba, VA Zip 24070–2115, Mailing Address: P.O. Box 200, Zip 24070–0200; tel. 540/375–4200; Walton F. Mitchell, III, Director
**Web address:** www.catawba.dbhds.virginia.gov

CENTRAL STATE HOSPITAL (O, 277 beds) 26317 West Washington Street, Petersburg, VA Zip 23803–2727, Mailing Address: P.O. Box 4030, Zip 23803–0030; tel. 804/524–7000; Vicki Montgomery, Director and Chief Executive Officer
**Web address:** www.csh.dbhds.virginia.gov

CENTRAL VIRGINIA TRAINING CENTER (O, 1112 beds) 210 East Colony Road, Madison Heights, VA Zip 24572–2005, Mailing Address: P.O. Box 1098, Lynchburg, Zip 24505–1098; tel. 434/947–6326; Denise D. Micheletti, R.N., Director
**Web address:** www.cvtc.dmhmrsas.virginia.gov/

COMMONWEALTH CENTER FOR CHILDREN AND ADOLESCENTS (O, 60 beds) 1355 Richmond Road, Staunton, VA Zip 24401–9146, Mailing Address: Box 4000, Zip 24402–4000; tel. 540/332–2100; William J. Tuell, MSN, Facility Director
**Web address:** www.ccca.dbhds.virginia.gov

EASTERN STATE HOSPITAL (O, 334 beds) 4601 Ironbound Road, Williamsburg, VA Zip 23188–2652; tel. 757/253–5161; John M. Favret, Director
**Web address:** www.esh.dmhmrsas.virginia.gov/

HIRAM W. DAVIS MEDICAL CENTER (O, 10 beds) 26317 West Washington Street, Petersburg, VA Zip 23803–2727, Mailing Address: P.O. Box 4030, Zip 23803–0030; tel. 804/524–7344; Brenda Buenvenida, Director

NORTHERN VIRGINIA MENTAL HEALTH INSTITUTE (O, 134 beds) 3302 Gallows Road, Falls Church, VA Zip 22042–3398; tel. 703/207–7110; James R. Newton, Facility Director
**Web address:** www.nvmhi.dmhmrsas.virginia.gov

PIEDMONT GERIATRIC HOSPITAL (O, 150 beds) 5001 East Patrick Henry Highway, Burkeville, VA Zip 23922–3460, Mailing Address: P.O. Box 427, Zip 23922–0427; tel. 434/767–4401; Stephen M. Herrick, Ph.D., Director
**Web address:** www.pgh.dmhmrsas.virginia.gov

SOUTHERN VIRGINIA MENTAL HEALTH INSTITUTE (O, 72 beds) 382 Taylor Drive, Danville, VA Zip 24541–4023; tel. 434/799–6220; William Cook, Director
**Web address:** www.svmhi.dbhds.virginia.gov

SOUTHWESTERN VIRGINIA MENTAL HEALTH INSTITUTE (O, 166 beds) 340 Bagley Circle, Marion, VA Zip 24354–3390; tel. 276/783–1200; Cynthia McClaskey, Ph.D., Director
**Web address:** www.swvmhi.dmhmrsas.virginia.gov/

WESTERN STATE HOSPITAL (O, 260 beds) 1301 Richmond Avenue, Staunton, VA Zip 24401–9146, Mailing Address: P.O. Box 2500, Zip 24402–2500; tel. 540/332–8000; Jack W. Barber, M.D., Director
**Web address:** www.dbhds.virginia.gov

| | | |
|---|---|---|
| **Owned, leased, sponsored:** | 11 hospitals | 2685 beds |
| **Contract–managed:** | 0 hospitals | 0 beds |
| **Totals:** | 11 hospitals | 2685 beds |

---

★**6725: VIRTUA HEALTH** (NP)
50 Lake Center Executive Drive, Suite 401, Marlton, NJ Zip 08053; tel. 856/355–0010; Richard P. Miller, Chief Executive Officer
**(Centralized Health System)**

**NEW JERSEY:** VIRTUA MARLTON (O, 192 beds) 90 Brick Road, Marlton, NJ Zip 08053–2177; tel. 856/355–6000; Matthew Zuino, Senior Vice President. Hospital Services
**Web address:** www.virtua.org

VIRTUA MEMORIAL (O, 334 beds) 175 Madison Avenue, Mount Holly, NJ Zip 08060–2099; tel. 609/267–0700; Matthew Zuino, Senior Vice President Hospital Services
**Web address:** www.virtua.org

For explanation of codes following names, see page B2.
★ Indicates Type III membership in the American Hospital Association.

Section B

VIRTUA VOORHEES (O, 398 beds) 100 Bowman Drive, Voorhees, NJ
Zip 08043–9612; tel. 856/325–3000; Matthew Zuino, Senior Vice President.
Hospital Services
**Web address:** www.virtua.org

| | | |
|---|---|---|
| **Owned, leased, sponsored:** | 3 hospitals | 924 beds |
| **Contract–managed:** | 0 hospitals | 0 beds |
| **Totals:** | 3 hospitals | 924 beds |

★**0221: WAKE FOREST BAPTIST HEALTH** (NP)
Medical Center Boulevard, Winston–Salem, NC Zip 27157;
tel. 336/716–2011; John D. McConnell, M.D., Chief Executive Officer
**(Moderately Centralized Health System)**

**NORTH CAROLINA:** WAKE FOREST BAPTIST HEALTH–DAVIE MEDICAL
CENTER (O, 25 beds) 223 Hospital Street, Mocksville, NC
Zip 27028–2038, Mailing Address: 329 NC Highway 801 North, Bermuda
Run, Zip 27006; tel. 336/998–1300; Chad J. Brown, M.P.H., President
**Web address:** www.wakehealth.edu/Davie–Medical–Center

WAKE FOREST BAPTIST HEALTH–LEXINGTON MEDICAL CENTER (O, 76 beds)
250 Hospital Drive, Lexington, NC Zip 27292–6728, Mailing Address: P.O.
Box 1817, Zip 27293–1817; tel. 336/248–5161; William B. James, FACHE,
Chief Executive Officer
**Web address:** www.lexingtonmemorial.com

WAKE FOREST BAPTIST MEDICAL CENTER (O, 831 beds) Medical Center
Boulevard, Winston–Salem, NC Zip 27157–0001; tel. 336/716–2011; John
D. McConnell, M.D., Chief Executive Officer
**Web address:** www.wakehealth.edu

| | | |
|---|---|---|
| **Owned, leased, sponsored:** | 3 hospitals | 932 beds |
| **Contract–managed:** | 0 hospitals | 0 beds |
| **Totals:** | 3 hospitals | 932 beds |

★**6705: WAKEMED HEALTH & HOSPITALS** (NP)
3000 New Bern Avenue, Raleigh, NC Zip 27610–1231;
tel. 919/350–8000; Donald R. Gintzig, President and Chief Executive
Officer
**(Moderately Centralized Health System)**

WAKEMED CARY HOSPITAL (O, 192 beds) 1900 Kildaire Farm Road, Cary,
NC Zip 27518–6616; tel. 919/350–2300; Donald R. Gintzig, President and
Chief Executive Officer
**Web address:** www.wakemed.org

WAKEMED RALEIGH CAMPUS (O, 704 beds) 3000 New Bern Avenue, Raleigh,
NC Zip 27610–1295; tel. 919/350–8000; Donald R. Gintzig, President and
Chief Executive Officer
**Web address:** www.wakemed.org

| | | |
|---|---|---|
| **Owned, leased, sponsored:** | 2 hospitals | 896 beds |
| **Contract–managed:** | 0 hospitals | 0 beds |
| **Totals:** | 2 hospitals | 896 beds |

★**0979: WASHINGTON HEALTH SYSTEM, INC.** (IO)
155 Wilson Avenue, Washington, PA Zip 15301-3336; tel. 724/225-
7000; Gary B. Weinstein, Chief Executive Officer (Independent
Hospital System)

**PENNSYLVANIA:** WASHINGTON HEALTH SYSTEM GREENE (O, 77 beds) 350
Bonar Avenue, Waynesburg, PA Zip 15370-1608; tel. 724/627-3101;
Terry Wiltrout, President
**Web address:** http://southwestregionalmedical.com

WASHINGTON HOSPITAL, (O, 260 beds) 155 Wilson Avenue, Washington, PA
Zip 15301-3336; tel. 724/225-7000; Gary B. Weinstein, President and Chief
Executive Officer
**Web address:** www.washingtonhospital.org

| | | |
|---|---|---|
| **Owned, leased, sponsored:** | 2 hospitals | 337 beds |
| **Contract-managed:** | 0 hospitals | 0 beds |
| **Totals:** | 2 hospitals | 337 beds |

★**0188: WELLMONT HEALTH SYSTEM** (NP)
1905 American Way, Kingsport, TN Zip 37660–5882;
tel. 423/230–8200; Barton A. Hove, President and Chief Executive
Officer
**(Centralized Physician/Insurance Health System)**

**TENNESSEE:** WELLMONT BRISTOL REGIONAL MEDICAL CENTER (O, 312
beds) 1 Medical Park Boulevard, Bristol, TN Zip 37620–7430;
tel. 423/844–1121; Greg Neal, President
**Web address:** www.wellmont.org

WELLMONT HANCOCK COUNTY HOSPITAL (O, 10 beds) 1519 Main Street,
Sneedville, TN Zip 37869–3657; tel. 423/733–5000; Rebecca Beck,
President
**Web address:** www.wellmont.org/Hospitals/Hancock–County–Hospital.aspx

WELLMONT HAWKINS COUNTY MEMORIAL HOSPITAL (L, 20 beds) 851
Locust Street, Rogersville, TN Zip 37857–2407, Mailing Address: P.O. Box
130, Zip 37857–0130; tel. 423/921–7000; Rebecca Beck, President
**Web address:** www.wellmont.org

WELLMONT HOLSTON VALLEY MEDICAL CENTER (O, 345 beds) 130 West
Ravine Street, Kingsport, TN Zip 37660–3837, Mailing Address: P.O. Box
238, Zip 37662–0238; tel. 423/224–4000; Tim Attebery, Chief Executive
Officer
**Web address:** www.wellmont.org

**VIRGINIA:** MOUNTAIN VIEW REGIONAL MEDICAL CENTER (O, 72 beds) 310
Third Street N.E., Norton, VA Zip 24273–1137; tel. 276/679–9100; Dale
Clark, President
**Web address:** www.wellmont.org

WELLMONT LONESOME PINE HOSPITAL (O, 30 beds) 1990 Holton Avenue
East, Big Stone Gap, VA Zip 24219–3350; tel. 276/523–3111; Dale Clark,
President
**Web address:** www.wellmont.org

| | | |
|---|---|---|
| **Owned, leased, sponsored:** | 6 hospitals | 789 beds |
| **Contract–managed:** | 0 hospitals | 0 beds |
| **Totals:** | 6 hospitals | 789 beds |

★**0068: WELLSPAN HEALTH** (NP)
45 Monument Road, Suite 200, York, PA Zip 17403–5071;
tel. 717/851–2121; Kevin H. Mosser, M.D., President and Chief
Executive Officer
**(Centralized Physician/Insurance Health System)**

**PENNSYLVANIA:** EPHRATA COMMUNITY HOSPITAL (O, 130 beds) 169 Martin
Avenue, Ephrata, PA Zip 17522–1724, Mailing Address: P.O. Box 1002,
Zip 17522–1002; tel. 717/733–0311; John M. Porter, Jr., President and
Chief Executive Officer
**Web address:** www.wellspan.org

GETTYSBURG HOSPITAL (O, 76 beds) 147 Gettys Street, Gettysburg, PA
Zip 17325–2534; tel. 717/334–2121; Jane E. Hyde, President
**Web address:** www.wellspan.org

THE GOOD SAMARITAN HOSPITAL (O, 151 beds) Fourth and Walnut Streets,
Lebanon, PA Zip 17042–1281, Mailing Address: P.O. Box 1281,
Zip 17042–1281; tel. 717/270–7500; Robert J. Longo, FACHE, President
and Chief Executive Officer
**Web address:** www.gshleb.org

YORK HOSPITAL (O, 556 beds) 1001 South George Street, York, PA
Zip 17403–3645; tel. 717/851–2345; Keith D. Noll, President
**Web address:** www.wellspan.org

| | | |
|---|---|---|
| **Owned, leased, sponsored:** | 4 hospitals | 913 beds |
| **Contract–managed:** | 0 hospitals | 0 beds |
| **Totals:** | 4 hospitals | 913 beds |

★**0995: WELLSTAR HEALTH SYSTEM** (NP)
805 Sandy Plains Road, Marietta, GA Zip 30066–6340;
tel. 770/792–5012; Reynold J. Jennings, Chief Executive Officer
**(Centralized Health System)**

**GEORGIA:** WELLSTAR COBB HOSPITAL (O, 362 beds) 3950 Austell Road,
Austell, GA Zip 30106–1121; tel. 770/732–4000; Kem Mullins, FACHE,
Senior Vice President and Hospital President
**Web address:** www.wellstar.org

For explanation of codes following names, see page B2.
★ Indicates Type III membership in the American Hospital Association.

Section B

WELLSTAR DOUGLAS HOSPITAL (O, 108 beds) 8954 Hospital Drive, Douglasville, GA Zip 30134–2282; tel. 770/949–1500; Craig A. Owens, President
**Web address:** www.wellstar.org

WELLSTAR KENNESTONE HOSPITAL (O, 633 beds) 677 Church Street, Marietta, GA Zip 30060–1148; tel. 770/793–5000; Dan Woods, President
**Web address:** www.wellstar.org

WELLSTAR PAULDING HOSPITAL (O, 238 beds) 2518 Jimmy Lee Smith Parkway, Hiram, GA Zip 30141; tel. 470/644–7000; Mark Haney, President
**Web address:** www.wellstar.org

WELLSTAR WINDY HILL HOSPITAL (O, 55 beds) 2540 Windy Hill Road, Marietta, GA Zip 30067–8632; tel. 770/644–1000; Kem Mullins, FACHE, President
**Web address:** www.wellstar.org

| Owned, leased, sponsored: | 5 hospitals | 1396 beds |
|---|---|---|
| Contract–managed: | 0 hospitals | 0 beds |
| Totals: | 5 hospitals | 1396 beds |

★**0004:  WEST TENNESSEE HEALTHCARE** (NP)
620 Skyline Drive, Jackson, TN Zip 38301–3923; tel. 731/541–5000; Bobby Arnold, President and Chief Executive Officer
**(Centralized Physician/Insurance Health System)**

**TENNESSEE:** BOLIVAR GENERAL HOSPITAL (O, 15 beds) 650 Nuckolls Road, Bolivar, TN Zip 38008–1532, Mailing Address: PO Box 509, Zip 38008–0509; tel. 731/658–3100; Ruby Kirby, Administrator
**Web address:** www.wth.net

CAMDEN GENERAL HOSPITAL (O, 25 beds) 175 Hospital Drive, Camden, TN Zip 38320–1617; tel. 731/584–6135; Denny R. Smith, Administrator
**Web address:** www.wth.net

JACKSON–MADISON COUNTY GENERAL HOSPITAL (O, 635 beds) 620 Skyline Drive, Jackson, TN Zip 38301–3923; tel. 731/541–5000; Bobby Arnold, President and Chief Executive Officer
**Web address:** www.wth.org

MILAN GENERAL HOSPITAL (O, 28 beds) 4039 Highland Street, Milan, TN Zip 38358–3483; tel. 731/686–1591; Sherry Scruggs, Administrator
**Web address:** www.wth.org

PATHWAYS OF TENNESSEE (O, 25 beds) 238 Summar Drive, Jackson, TN Zip 38301–3906; tel. 731/541–8200; Pam Henson, Executive Director
**Web address:** www.wth.net/pathways

| Owned, leased, sponsored: | 5 hospitals | 728 beds |
|---|---|---|
| Contract–managed: | 0 hospitals | 0 beds |
| Totals: | 5 hospitals | 728 beds |

★**0119:  WEST VIRGINIA UNITED HEALTH SYSTEM** (NP)
1000 Technology Drive, Suite 2320, Fairmont, WV Zip 26554–8834; tel. 304/368–2700; Christopher Colenda, M.D., M.P.H., President and Chief Executive Officer
**(Centralized Physician/Insurance Health System)**

**WEST VIRGINIA:** BERKELEY MEDICAL CENTER (O, 174 beds) 2500 Hospital Drive, Martinsburg, WV Zip 25401–3402; tel. 304/264–1000; Anthony Zelenka, President and Chief Operating Officer
**Web address:** www.cityhospital.org

CAMDEN CLARK MEDICAL CENTER (O, 240 beds) 800 Garfield Avenue, Parkersburg, WV Zip 26101–5378, Mailing Address: P.O. Box 718, Zip 26102–0718; tel. 304/424–2111; David K. McClure, President and Chief Executive Officer
**Web address:** www.camdenclark.org

JEFFERSON MEDICAL CENTER (O, 25 beds) 300 South Preston Street, Ranson, WV Zip 25438–1631; tel. 304/728–1600; Anthony Zelenka, Chief Executive Officer
**Web address:** www.wvuniversityhealthcare. com/locations/Jefferson–Medical–Center.aspx

POTOMAC VALLEY HOSPITAL (O, 25 beds) 100 Pin Oak Lane, Keyser, WV Zip 26726–5908; tel. 304/597–3500; Linda K. Shroyer, Administrator
**Web address:** www.potomacvalleyhospital.com

UNITED HOSPITAL CENTER (O, 264 beds) 327 Medical Park Drive, Bridgeport, WV Zip 26330–9006; tel. 681/342–1000; Michael C. Tillman, President and Chief Executive Officer
**Web address:** www.thenewuhc.com

WEST VIRGINIA UNIVERSITY HOSPITALS (O, 514 beds) 1 Medical Center Drive, Morgantown, WV Zip 26506–4749; tel. 304/598–4000; Albert Wright, PharmD, President and Chief Executive Officer
**Web address:** www.health.wvu.edu

| Owned, leased, sponsored: | 6 hospitals | 1242 beds |
|---|---|---|
| Contract–managed: | 0 hospitals | 0 beds |
| Totals: | 6 hospitals | 1242 beds |

● ★**0811:  WESTERN CONNECTICUT HEALTH NETWORK** (NP)
24 Hospital Avenue, Danbury, CT Zip 06810–6099; tel. 203/739–7066; John M. Murphy, M.D., President
**(Centralized Health System)**

**CONNECTICUT:** DANBURY HOSPITAL (O, 342 beds) 24 Hospital Avenue, Danbury, CT Zip 06810–6099; tel. 203/739–7000; John M. Murphy, M.D., President and Chief Executive Officer, Western Connecticut Health Network
**Web address:** www.danburyhospital.org

| Owned, leased, sponsored: | 1 hospital | 342 beds |
|---|---|---|
| Contract–managed: | 0 hospitals | 0 beds |
| Totals: | 1 hospital | 342 beds |

★**6745:  WHEATON FRANCISCAN HEALTHCARE** (CC)
26W171 Roosevelt Road, Wheaton, IL Zip 60187–6002, Mailing Address: P.O. Box 667, Zip 60187–0667; tel. 630/909–6900; John D. Oliverio, President and Chief Executive Officer
**(Moderately Centralized Health System)**

**ILLINOIS:** MARIANJOY REHABILITATION HOSPITAL (O, 128 beds) 26 West 171 Roosevelt Road, Wheaton, IL Zip 60187–0795, Mailing Address: P.O. Box 795, Zip 60187–0795; tel. 630/909–8000; Kathleen C. Yosko, President and Chief Executive Officer
**Web address:** www.marianjoy.org

**IOWA:** COVENANT MEDICAL CENTER (O, 229 beds) 3421 West Ninth Street, Waterloo, IA Zip 50702–5401; tel. 319/272–8000; Jack Dusenbery, FACHE, President and Chief Executive Officer
**Web address:** www.wheatoniowa.org

MERCY HOSPITAL OF FRANCISCAN SISTERS (O, 64 beds) 201 Eighth Avenue S.E., Oelwein, IA Zip 50662–2447; tel. 319/283–6000; Terri Derflinger, Administrator
**Web address:** www.covhealth.com

SARTORI MEMORIAL HOSPITAL (O, 50 beds) 515 College Street, Cedar Falls, IA Zip 50613–2500; tel. 319/268–3000; MaryJo Kavalier, Administrator
**Web address:** www.wheatoniowa.org

**WISCONSIN:** MIDWEST ORTHOPEDIC SPECIALTY HOSPITAL (O, 16 beds) 10101 South 27th Street, 2nd Floor, Franklin, WI Zip 53132–7209; tel. 414/817–5800; Coreen Dicus–Johnson, President
**Web address:** www.mymosh.com/

UNITED HOSPITAL SYSTEM, ST. CATHERINE'S MEDICAL CENTER CAMPUS (O, 202 beds) 9555 76th Street, Pleasant Prairie, WI Zip 53158–1984; tel. 262/656–2011; Richard O. Schmidt, Jr., President and Chief Executive Officer
**Web address:** www.uhsi.org

WHEATON FRANCISCAN HEALTHCARE – ALL SAINTS (O, 405 beds) 3801 Spring Street, Racine, WI Zip 53405–1690; tel. 262/687–4011; Susan Boland, R.N., MSN, President and Chief Executive Officer
**Web address:** www.allsaintshealth.com

WHEATON FRANCISCAN HEALTHCARE – ELMBROOK MEMORIAL (O, 100 beds) 19333 West North Avenue, Brookfield, WI Zip 53045–4198; tel. 262/785–2000; Debra K. Standridge, President
**Web address:** www.wfhealthcare.org

WHEATON FRANCISCAN HEALTHCARE – FRANKLIN (O, 37 beds) 10101 South 27th Street, Franklin, WI Zip 53132–7209; tel. 414/325–4700; Coreen Dicus–Johnson, President
**Web address:** www.mywheaton.org/

For explanation of codes following names, see page B2.
★ Indicates Type III membership in the American Hospital Association.
● Single hospital health care system

WHEATON FRANCISCAN HEALTHCARE – ST. FRANCIS (S, 177 beds) 3237 South 16th Street, Milwaukee, WI Zip 53215–4592; tel. 414/647–5000; Coreen Dicus–Johnson, President
**Web address:** www.mywheaton.org/stfrancis

WHEATON FRANCISCAN HEALTHCARE – ST. JOSEPH'S (O, 189 beds) 5000 West Chambers Street, Milwaukee, WI Zip 53210–1650; tel. 414/447–2000; Debra K. Standridge, President
**Web address:** www.mywheaton.org/stjoseph

WHEATON FRANCISCAN HEALTHCARE – THE WISCONSIN HEART HOSPITAL (O, 30 beds) 10000 West Bluemound Road, Wauwatosa, WI Zip 53226–4321; tel. 414/778–7800; Coreen Dicus–Johnson, President
**Web address:** www.mywheaton.org/hearthospital

| | | |
|---|---|---|
| **Owned, leased, sponsored:** | 12 hospitals | 1627 beds |
| **Contract–managed:** | 0 hospitals | 0 beds |
| **Totals:** | 12 hospitals | 1627 beds |

★**0468:  WHITE RIVER HEALTH SYSTEM** (NP)
1710 Harrison Street, Batesville, AR Zip 72501–7303; tel. 870/262–1200; Gary Bebow, FACHE, Administrator and Chief Executive Officer
**(Independent Hospital System)**

**ARKANSAS:** STONE COUNTY MEDICAL CENTER (O, 25 beds) 2106 East Main Street, Mountain View, AR Zip 72560–6439, Mailing Address: P.O. Box 510, Zip 72560–0510; tel. 870/269–4361; Stanley Townsend, Chief Executive Officer
**Web address:** www.whiteriverhealthsystem.com

WHITE RIVER MEDICAL CENTER (O, 210 beds) 1710 Harrison Street, Batesville, AR Zip 72501–7303, Mailing Address: P.O. Box 2197, Zip 72503–2197; tel. 870/262–1200; Gary Bebow, FACHE, Administrator and Chief Executive Officer
**Web address:** www.whiteriverhealthsystem.com

| | | |
|---|---|---|
| **Owned, leased, sponsored:** | 2 hospitals | 235 beds |
| **Contract–managed:** | 0 hospitals | 0 beds |
| **Totals:** | 2 hospitals | 235 beds |

**0646:  WHITTIER HEALTH NETWORK** (IO)
25 Railroad Square, Haverhill, MA Zip 01832–5721; tel. 978/556–5858; Alfred L. Arcidi, M.D., President
**(Independent Hospital System)**

**MASSACHUSETTS:** WHITTIER PAVILION (O, 65 beds) 76 Summer Street, Haverhill, MA Zip 01830–5814; tel. 978/373–8222; Alfred L. Arcidi, M.D., Chief Executive Officer
**Web address:** www.whittierhealth.com

WHITTIER REHABILITATION HOSPITAL (O, 74 beds) 150 Flanders Road, Westborough, MA Zip 01581–1017; tel. 508/871–2000; Alfred J. Arcidi, M.D., Senior Vice President
**Web address:** www.whittierhealth.com

WHITTIER REHABILITATION HOSPITAL (O, 60 beds) 145 Ward Hill Avenue, Bradford, MA Zip 01835–6928; tel. 978/372–8000; Alfred J. Arcidi, M.D., Senior Vice President
**Web address:** www.whittierhealth.com

| | | |
|---|---|---|
| **Owned, leased, sponsored:** | 3 hospitals | 199 beds |
| **Contract–managed:** | 0 hospitals | 0 beds |
| **Totals:** | 3 hospitals | 199 beds |

**1945:  WILLIS–KNIGHTON HEALTH SYSTEM** (NP)
2600 Greenwood Road, Shreveport, LA Zip 71103–3908; tel. 318/212–4000; James K. Elrod, FACHE, President and Chief Executive Officer
**(Centralized Health System)**

**LOUISIANA:** DE SOTO REGIONAL HEALTH SYSTEM (C, 12 beds) 207 Jefferson Street, Mansfield, LA Zip 71052–2603, Mailing Address: P.O. Box 1636, Zip 71052–1636; tel. 318/871–3100; Todd Eppler, FACHE, Chief Executive Officer
**Web address:** www.desotoregional.com

SPRINGHILL MEDICAL CENTER (C, 58 beds) 2001 Doctors Drive, Springhill, LA Zip 71075–4526, Mailing Address: P.O. Box 920, Zip 71075–0920; tel. 318/539–1000; Vince Sedminik, Chief Executive Officer
**Web address:** www.smccare.com

WILLIS–KNIGHTON MEDICAL CENTER (O, 720 beds) 2600 Greenwood Road, Shreveport, LA Zip 71103–3908, Mailing Address: P.O. Box 32600, Zip 71130–2600; tel. 318/212–4600; James K. Elrod, FACHE, Chief Executive Officer
**Web address:** www.wkhs.com

WK BOSSIER HEALTH CENTER (O, 166 beds) 2400 Hospital Drive, Bossier City, LA Zip 71111–2385; tel. 318/212–7000; Clifford M. Broussard, FACHE, Administrator
**Web address:** www.wkhs.com/wkb/

| | | |
|---|---|---|
| **Owned, leased, sponsored:** | 2 hospitals | 886 beds |
| **Contract–managed:** | 2 hospitals | 70 beds |
| **Totals:** | 4 hospitals | 956 beds |

★**0157:  YALE NEW HAVEN HEALTH SYSTEM** (NP)
789 Howard Avenue, New Haven, CT Zip 06519–1304; tel. 203/688–4608; Marna P. Borgstrom, President and Chief Executive Officer
**(Centralized Physician/Insurance Health System)**

**CONNECTICUT:** BRIDGEPORT HOSPITAL (O, 357 beds) 267 Grant Street, Bridgeport, CT Zip 06610–2805, Mailing Address: P.O. Box 5000, Zip 06610–0120; tel. 203/384–3000; William M. Jennings, President and Chief Executive Officer
**Web address:** www.bridgeporthospital.org

GREENWICH HOSPITAL (O, 184 beds) 5 Perryridge Road, Greenwich, CT Zip 06830–4697; tel. 203/863–3000; Norman G. Roth, Chief Executive Officer
**Web address:** www.greenhosp.org

YALE–NEW HAVEN HOSPITAL (O, 1576 beds) 20 York Street, New Haven, CT Zip 06510–3202; tel. 203/688–4242; Marna P. Borgstrom, Chief Executive Officer
**Web address:** www.ynhh.org

| | | |
|---|---|---|
| **Owned, leased, sponsored:** | 3 hospitals | 2117 beds |
| **Contract–managed:** | 0 hospitals | 0 beds |
| **Totals:** | 3 hospitals | 2117 beds |

For explanation of codes following names, see page B2.
★ Indicates Type III membership in the American Hospital Association.

**B154** / Health Care Systems, Networks and Alliances © 2015 AHA Guide

Section B

## Geographically

### United States

#### ALABAMA

**Birmingham:** BAPTIST HEALTH SYSTEM 3201 Fourth Avenue South, Zip 35222–1723, Mailing Address: P.O. Box 830605, Zip 35283–0605; tel. 205/715–5319; Keith Parrott, FACHE, President and Chief Executive Officer, p. B20

BRADFORD HEALTH SERVICES 2101 Magnolia Avenue South, Suite 518, Zip 35205–2853; tel. 205/251–7753; Jerry W. Crowder, President and Chief Executive Officer, p. B25

★ HEALTHSOUTH CORPORATION 3660 Grandview Parkway, Suite 200, Zip 35243–3332; tel. 205/967–7116; Jay F. Grinney, President and Chief Executive Officer, p. B67

NOLAND HEALTH SERVICES, INC. 600 Corporate Parkway, Suite 100, Zip 35242–5451; tel. 205/783–8484; Gary M. Glasscock, President and Chief Executive Officer, p. B97

★ UAB HEALTH SYSTEM 500 22nd Street South, Suite 408, Zip 35233–3110; tel. 205/975–5362; William Ferniany, Ph.D., Chief Executive Officer, p. B138

**Guntersville:** MARSHALL HEALTH SYSTEM 227 Britany Road, Zip 35976–5766; tel. 256/894–6615; Gary R. Gore, Chief Executive Officer, p. B86

**Huntsville:** HUNTSVILLE HOSPITAL HEALTH SYSTEM 101 Sivley Road S.W., Zip 35801–4421; tel. 265/256–1000; David S. Spillers, Chief Executive Officer, p. B72

**Mobile:** ALTAPOINTE HEALTH SYSTEMS 5750–A Southland Drive, Zip 36693–3316; tel. 251/473–4423; J. Tuerk Schlesinger, Chief Executive Officer, p. B10

INFIRMARY HEALTH SYSTEM 5 Mobile Infirmary Circle, Zip 36607–3513; tel. 251/435–5500; D. Mark Nix, President and Chief Executive Officer, p. B73

★ UNIVERSITY OF SOUTH ALABAMA HOSPITALS 2451 Fillingim Street, Zip 36617–2238; tel. 251/471–7000; Stanley K. Hammack, Chief Executive Officer, p. B147

**Montgomery:** BAPTIST HEALTH 301 Brown Springs Road, Zip 36117–7005; tel. 334/273–4400; W. Russell Tyner, President and Chief Executive Officer, p. B19

GILLIARD HEALTH SERVICES 3091 Carter Hill Road, Zip 36111–1801; tel. 334/265–5009; William G. McKenzie, President, Chief Executive Officer and Chairman, p. B58

**Tuscaloosa:** DCH HEALTH SYSTEM 809 University Boulevard East, Zip 35401–2029; tel. 205/759–7111; Bryan N. Kindred, FACHE, President and Chief Executive Officer, p. B44

#### ARIZONA

**Flagstaff:** ★ NORTHERN ARIZONA HEALTHCARE 1200 North Beaver Street, Zip 86001–3118; tel. 928/779–3366; Robert P. Thames, President and Chief Executive Officer, p. B98

**Phoenix:** ★ BANNER HEALTH 1441 North 12th Street, Zip 85006–2837, Mailing Address: P.O. Box 25489, Zip 85002–5489; tel. 602/747–4000; Peter S. Fine, FACHE, President and Chief Executive Officer, p. B18

**Scottsdale:** ★ HONORHEALTH 8125 North Hayden Road, Zip 85258–2463; tel. 623/580–5800; Thomas J. Sadvary, FACHE, Chief Executive Officer, p. B71

SOUTHWEST HEALTHCARE SYSTEM 4400 North Scottsdale Road, Suite 9347, Zip 85251–3331; tel. 480/348–9800; Paul R. Tuft, President, p. B125

#### ARKANSAS

**Batesville:** ★ WHITE RIVER HEALTH SYSTEM 1710 Harrison Street, Zip 72501–7303; tel. 870/262–1200; Gary Bebow, FACHE, Administrator and Chief Executive Officer, p. B154

**Blytheville:** MISSISSIPPI COUNTY HOSPITAL SYSTEM 1520 North Division Street, Zip 72315–1448, Mailing Address: P.O. Box 108, Zip 72316–0108; tel. 870/838–7300; Ralph E. Beaty, Chief Executive Officer, p. B93

**Little Rock:** ★ BAPTIST HEALTH 9601 Interstate 630, Exit 7, Zip 72205–7299; tel. 501/202–2000; Troy R. Wells, Chief Executive Officer, p. B19

#### CALIFORNIA

**Alhambra:** AHMC & HEALTHCARE, INC. 55 South Raymond Avenue, Suite 105, Zip 91801–7101; tel. 626/457–9600; Jonathan Wu, M.D., President and Chairman, p. B7

**Corona:** SIGNATURE HEALTHCARE SERVICES 4238 Green River Road, Zip 92880–1669; tel. 951/549–8032; Soon K. Kim, M.D., President and Chief Executive Officer, p. B123

**Covina:** ★ CITRUS VALLEY HEALTH PARTNERS 210 West San Bernardino Road, Zip 91723–1515; tel. 626/331–7331; Robert H. Curry, President and Chief Executive Officer, p. B33

**Cupertino:** CRC HEALTH GROUP, INC. 20400 Stevens Creek Boulevard, Suite 600, Zip 95014–2217; tel. 866/540–5240; Jerome E. Rhodes, Chief Executive Officer, p. B43

**El Segundo:** AVANTI HOSPITALS 222 North Sepulveda Boulevard, Suite 950, Zip 90245–5614; tel. 310/356–0550; Arnold R. Schaffer, Corporate Chief Executive Officer, p. B16

**Escondido:** ★ PALOMAR HEALTH 456 East Grand Avenue, Zip 92025–3319; tel. 760/740–6393; Robert Hemker, President and Chief Executive Officer, p. B103

**Fountain Valley:** MEMORIALCARE 17360 Brookhurst Street, Zip 92708–3720, Mailing Address: P.O. Box 1428, Long Beach, Zip 90801–1428; tel. 714/377–2900; Barry S. Arbuckle, Ph.D., President and Chief Executive Officer, p. B89

**Fresno:** COMMUNITY MEDICAL CENTERS Fresno and Maddy Drive, Zip 93721, Mailing Address: P.O. Box 1232, Zip 93715–1232; tel. 559/459–6000; Tim A. Joslin, President and Chief Executive Officer, p. B41

**Hemet:** PHYSICIANS FOR HEALTHY HOSPITALS 1117 East Devonshire Avenue, Zip 92543–3083; tel. 951/652–2811; Joel M. Bergenfeld, Chief Executive Officer, p. B104

**Irvine:** ★ ST. JOSEPH HEALTH 3345 Michelson Drive, Suite 100, Zip 92612; tel. 949/381–4000; Deborah A. Proctor, President and Chief Executive Officer, p. B127

**Loma Linda:** LOMA LINDA UNIVERSITY ADVENTIST HEALTH SCIENCES CENTER 11175 Campus Street, Zip 92350–1700; tel. 909/558–7572; Richard H. Hart, M.D., President and Chief Executive Officer, p. B85

**Los Altos Hills:** ★ DAUGHTERS OF CHARITY HEALTH SYSTEM 26000 Altamont Road, Zip 94022–4317; tel. 650/917–4500; Robert Issai, President and Chief Executive Officer, p. B44

**Los Angeles:** ALTA HEALTHCARE SYSTEM 10780 Santa Monica Boulevard, Suite 400, Zip 90025–7616; tel. 310/943–4500; David Topper, Chief Executive Officer, p. B9

KECK MEDICINE OF USC 1500 San Pablo Street, Zip 90033–5313; tel. 323/442–8500; Paul A. Craig, R.N., JD, Interim Chief Executive Officer, p. B77

LOS ANGELES COUNTY–DEPARTMENT OF HEALTH SERVICES 313 North Figueroa Street, Room 912, Zip 90012–2691; tel. 213/240–8101; Mitchell H. Katz, M.D., Director, p. B85

**Oakland:** ★ KAISER FOUNDATION HOSPITALS One Kaiser Plaza, Zip 94612–3600; tel. 510/271–5910; Bernard J. Tyson, Chairman and Chief Executive Officer, p. B76

★ UNIVERSITY OF CALIFORNIA SYSTEMWIDE ADMINISTRATION 1111 Franklin Street, 11th Floor, Zip 94607–5200; tel. 510/987–9071; John D. Stobo, M.D., Executive Vice President and Chief Executive Officer, p. B146

**Ontario:** PRIME HEALTHCARE SERVICES 3300 East Guasti Road, Zip 91761–8655; tel. 909/235–4400; Prem Reddy, M.D., Interim President and Chief Executive Officer, p. B107

**Palo Alto:** ★ STANFORD HEALTH CARE 300 Pasteur Drive, Zip 94304–2299; tel. 650/723–4000; Amir Dan Rubin, President and Chief Executive Officer, p. B128

**Roseville:** ★ ADVENTIST HEALTH 2100 Douglas Boulevard, Zip 95661–3898, Mailing Address: P.O. Box 619002, Zip 95661–9002; tel. 916/781–2000; Scott Reiner, President and Chief Executive Officer, p. B5

**Sacramento:** ★ SUTTER HEALTH 2200 River Plaza Drive, Zip 95833–4134; tel. 916/733–8800; Patrick E. Fry, President and Chief Executive Officer, p. B129

**San Diego:** ★ SCRIPPS HEALTH 4275 Campus Point Court, Zip 92121–1513; tel. 858/678–7200; Chris D. Van Gorder, FACHE, President and Chief Executive Officer, p. B118

★ SHARP HEALTHCARE 8695 Spectrum Center Boulevard, Zip 92123–1489; tel. 858/499–4000; Michael Murphy, CPA, President & Chief Executive Officer, p. B122

**San Francisco:** ★ DIGNITY HEALTH 185 Berry Street, Suite 300, Zip 94107–1773; tel. 415/438–5500; Lloyd H. Dean, President and Chief Executive Officer, p. B50

**San Leandro:** ALAMEDA HEALTH SYSTEM 15400 Foothill Boulevard, Zip 94578–1009; tel. 510/677–7920; Daniel Boggan, Jr., Interim Chief Executive Officer, p. B8

**Santa Ana:** INTEGRATED HEALTHCARE 1301 North Tustin Avenue, Zip 92705–8619; tel. 714/953–3652; Suzanne Richards, R.N., M.P.H., FACHE, Chief Executive Officer, p. B74

**Santa Barbara:** ★ COTTAGE HEALTH 400 West Pueblo Street, Zip 93105–4353, Mailing Address: P.O. Box 689, Zip 93102–0689; tel. 805/569–7290; Ronald C. Werft, President and Chief Executive Officer, p. B42

**Santa Fe Springs:** COLLEGE HEALTH ENTERPRISES 11627 Telegraph Road, Suite 200, Zip 90670–6814; tel. 562/923–9449; Barry J. Weiss, Chairman of the Board, p. B34

**Truckee:** ★ TAHOE FOREST HEALTH SYSTEM 10121 Pine Avenue, Zip 96161–4835; tel. 530/587–6011; Robert A. Schapper, Chief Executive Officer, p. B130

**Walnut Creek:** ★ JOHN MUIR HEALTH 1400 Treat Boulevard, Zip 94597–2142; tel. 925/941–2100; Calvin K. Knight, President and Chief Executive Officer, p. B75

**Whittier:** ★ PIH HEALTH 12401 Washington Boulevard, Zip 90602–1006; tel. 562/698–0811; James R. West, President and Chief Executive Officer, p. B104

## COLORADO

**Alamosa:** ★ SAN LUIS VALLEY HEALTH 106 Blanca Avenue, Zip 81101–2340; tel. 719/589–2511; Konnie Martin, Chief Executive Officer, p. B116

**Broomfield:** ★ SCL HEALTH 500 Eldorado Boulevard, Suite 100–D, Zip 80021; tel. 303/813–5180; Michael A. Slubowski, FACHE, Chief Executive Officer, p. B118

**Englewood:** ★ CATHOLIC HEALTH INITIATIVES 198 Inverness Drive West, Suite 800, Zip 80112–5202; tel. 303/298–9100; Kevin E. Lofton, FACHE, Chief Executive Officer, p. B28

**Fort Collins:** ★ UNIVERSITY OF COLORADO HEALTH 2315 East Harmony Road, Suite 200, Zip 80528–8620; tel. 970/848–0000; Elizabeth B. Concordia, President and Chief Executive Officer, p. B146

## CONNECTICUT

**Danbury:** ★ WESTERN CONNECTICUT HEALTH NETWORK 24 Hospital Avenue, Zip 06810–6099; tel. 203/739–7066; John M. Murphy, M.D., President, p. B153

**Hartford:** CONNECTICUT DEPARTMENT OF MENTAL HEALTH AND ADDICTION SERVICES 410 Capitol Avenue, Zip 06106–1367, Mailing Address: P.O. Box 341431, Zip 06134–1431; tel. 860/418–7000; Miriam Delphin–Rittmon, Ph.D., Commissioner, p. B42

★ HARTFORD HEALTHCARE One State Street, 19th Floor, Zip 06103; tel. 860/263–4100; Elliot T. Joseph, President and Chief Executive Officer, p. B60

★ SAINT FRANCIS CARE, INC. 114 Woodland Street, Zip 06105–1208; tel. 860/714–5541; Christopher M. Dadlez, President and Chief Executive Officer, p. B115

**Manchester:** ★ EASTERN CONNECTICUT HEALTH NETWORK 71 Haynes Street, Zip 06040–4131; tel. 860/533–3400; Peter J. Karl, President and Chief Executive Officer, p. B53

**New Haven:** ★ YALE NEW HAVEN HEALTH SYSTEM 789 Howard Avenue, Zip 06519–1304; tel. 203/688–4608; Marna P. Borgstrom, President and Chief Executive Officer, p. B154

**New London:** ★ L+M HEALTHCARE 365 Montauk Avenue, Zip 06320–4700; tel. 860/442–0711; Bruce D. Cummings, President and Chief Executive Officer, p. B80

## DELAWARE

**Wilmington:** ★ CHRISTIANA CARE HEALTH SYSTEM 501 West 14th Street, Zip 19801–1013, Mailing Address: P.O. Box 1668, Zip 19899–1668; tel. 302/733–1000; Janice E. Nevin, M.D., M.P.H., Chief Executive Officer, p. B33

## DISTRICT OF COLUMBIA

**Washington:** BUREAU OF MEDICINE AND SURGERY, DEPARTMENT OF THE NAVY 2300 East Street N.W., Zip 20372–5300; tel. 202/762–3701; Vice Admiral Matthew L. Nathan, Surgeon General, p. B25

DEPARTMENT OF THE AIR FORCE 1420 Pentagon, Room 4E1084, Zip 20330–1420; tel. 202/767–4765; Lieutenant General Thomas Travis, Surgeon General, p. B45

DEPARTMENT OF VETERANS AFFAIRS 810 Vermont Avenue N.W., Zip 20420–0001; tel. 202/273–5781; Robert A. McDonald, Secretary, Veterans Affairs, p. B46

## FLORIDA

**Altamonte Springs:** ★ ADVENTIST HEALTH SYSTEM SUNBELT HEALTH CARE CORPORATION 900 Hope Way, Zip 32714–1502; tel. 407/357–1000; Donald L. Jernigan, Ph.D., President and Chief Executive Officer, p. B5

**Boca Raton:** PROMISE HEALTHCARE 999 Yamato Road, 3rd Floor, Zip 33431–4477; tel. 561/869–3100; Peter R. Baronoff, Chief Executive Officer, p. B108

SUCCESS HEALTHCARE 999 Yamato Road, 3rd Floor, Zip 33431–4477; tel. 561/869–6300; Peter R. Baronoff, President and Chief Executive Officer, p. B129

**Clearwater:** MORTON PLANT MEASE HEALTH CARE 300 Pinellas Street, Zip 33756–3804, Mailing Address: P.O. Box 210, Zip 33757–0210; tel. 727/462–7000; Glenn D. Waters, FACHE, President, p. B93

**Coral Gables:** ★ BAPTIST HEALTH SOUTH FLORIDA 6855 Red Road, Suite 600, Zip 33143–3632; tel. 786/662–7111; Brian E. Keeley, President and Chief Executive Officer, p. B20

**Fort Lauderdale:** ★ BROWARD HEALTH 303 S.E. 17th Street, Zip 33316–2523; tel. 954/355–4400; Nabil El Sanadi, M.D., President and Chief Executive Officer, p. B25

**Fort Myers:** ★ LEE MEMORIAL HEALTH SYSTEM 2776 Cleveland Avenue, Zip 33901–5856, Mailing Address: P.O. Box 2218, Zip 33902–2218; tel. 239/343–2000; James R. Nathan, President and Chief Executive Officer, p. B81

**Gainesville:** ★ UF HEALTH SHANDS 1600 S.W. Archer Road, Zip 32610–0326; tel. 352/733–1500; Edward Jimenez, Chief Executive Officer, p. B138

**Hollywood:** ★ MEMORIAL HEALTHCARE SYSTEM 3501 Johnson Street, Zip 33021–5421; tel. 954/265–5805; Frank V. Sacco, FACHE, President and Chief Executive Officer, p. B89

**Jacksonville:** ★ BAPTIST HEALTH 841 Prudential Drive, Suite 1601, Zip 32207–8202; tel. 904/202–4011; Hugh Greene, President and Chief Executive Officer, p. B19

NEMOURS 10140 Centurion Parkway North, Zip 32256–0532; tel. 904/697–4100; David J. Bailey, M.D., President and Chief Executive Officer, p. B95

**Lauderdale Lakes:** CATHOLIC HEALTH SERVICES 4790 North State Road 7, Zip 33319–5860; tel. 954/484–1515; Joseph M. Catania, President and Chief Executive Officer, p. B31

**Leesburg:** CENTRAL FLORIDA HEALTH ALLIANCE 600 East Dixie Avenue, Zip 34748–5925; tel. 352/323–5762; Donald G. Henderson, FACHE, Chief Executive Officer, p. B32

**Miami:** UNIVERSITY OF MIAMI HEALTH SYSTEM 1400 N.W. 12th Avenue, Zip 33136–1003; tel. 305/243–4000; Pascal J. Goldschmidt, M.D., Chief Executive Officer, p. B147

**Miami Lakes:** PACER HEALTH CORPORATION 14100 Palmetto Frontage Road, Suite 110, Zip 33016; tel. 305/828–7660; Rainier Gonzalez, Chairman and Chief Executive Officer, p. B102

**Orlando:** ORLANDO HEALTH 1414 Kuhl Avenue, Zip 32806–2093; tel. 321/843–7000; David W. Strong, President and Chief Executive Officer, p. B102

**Pensacola:** ★ BAPTIST HEALTH CARE CORPORATION 1717 North E Street Suite 320, Zip 32501–6377, Mailing Address: P.O. Box 17500, Zip 32522–7500; tel. 850/434–4011; Mark T. Faulkner, President, p. B20

**Rockledge:** HEALTH FIRST, INC. 6450 U.S. Highway 1, Zip 32955–5747; tel. 321/434–7000; Steven P. Johnson, Ph.D., President and Chief Executive Officer, p. B66

**Tampa:** SHRINERS HOSPITALS FOR CHILDREN 2900 Rocky Point Drive, Zip 33607–1435, Mailing Address: P.O. Box 31356, Zip 33631–3356; tel. 813/281–0300; John P. McCabe, Executive Vice President, p. B122

**Windermere:** UNITED MEDICAL CORPORATION 603 Main Street, Zip 34786–3548, Mailing Address: P.O. Box 1100, Zip 34786–1100; tel. 407/876–2200; Donald R. Dizney, Chairman and Chief Executive Officer, p. B139

## GEORGIA

**Albany:** ★ PHOEBE PUTNEY HEALTH SYSTEM 417 Third Avenue, Zip 31701–1943; tel. 229/312–1000; Joel Wernick, President and Chief Executive Officer, p. B104

**Atlanta:** ★ EMORY HEALTHCARE 1440 Clifton Road N.E., Suite 309, Zip 30322–1102; tel. 404/778–5000; Michael J. Mandl, President and Chief Executive Officer, p. B54

★ NORTHSIDE HEALTHCARE SYSTEM 1000 Johnson Ferry Road N.E., Zip 30342–1611; tel. 404/851–8000; Robert Quattrocchi, President and Chief Executive Officer, p. B99

★ PIEDMONT HEALTHCARE 1800 Howell Mill Road N.W., Suite 850, Zip 30318–0923; tel. 404/425–1314; Kevin Brown, President and Chief Executive Officer, p. B104

SUNLINK HEALTH SYSTEMS 900 Circle 75 Parkway, Suite 1120, Zip 30339–3005; tel. 770/933–7000; Robert M. Thornton, Jr., Chief Executive Officer, p. B129

**Augusta:** ★ UNIVERSITY HEALTH CARE SYSTEM 1350 Walton Way, Zip 30901–2629; tel. 706/722–9011; James R. Davis, President and Chief Executive Officer, p. B145

**Blairsville:** UNION GENERAL HOSPITAL, INC. 35 Hospital Road, Zip 30512–3139; tel. 706/745–2111; Mike Gowder, Chief Executive Officer, p. B139

**Brunswick:** ★ SOUTHEAST GEORGIA HEALTH SYSTEM 2415 Parkwood Drive, Zip 31520–4722, Mailing Address: P.O. Box 1518, Zip 31521–1518; tel. 912/466–7000; Michael D. Scherneck, Interim Chief Executive Officer, p. B124

**Carrollton:** ★ TANNER HEALTH SYSTEM 705 Dixie Street, Zip 30117–3818; tel. 770/836–9580; Loy M. Howard, President and Chief Executive Officer, p. B131

**Columbus:** COLUMBUS REGIONAL HEALTHCARE SYSTEM 707 Center Street, Suite 400, Zip 31901–1575; tel. 706/660–6100; Scott Hill, Chief Executive Officer, p. B34

**Decatur:** DEKALB REGIONAL HEALTH SYSTEM 2701 North Decatur Road, Zip 30033–5918; tel. 404/501–1000; John Shelton, President and Chief Executive Officer, p. B45

**Macon:** NAVICENT HEALTH 777 Hemlock Street, Zip 31201–2155; tel. 478/633–1000; Ninfa Saunders, Chief Executive Officer, p. B95

**Marietta:** ★ WELLSTAR HEALTH SYSTEM 805 Sandy Plains Road, Zip 30066–6340; tel. 770/792–5012; Reynold J. Jennings, Chief Executive Officer, p. B152

**Milledgeville:** OCONEE REGIONAL HEALTH SYSTEMS 821 North Cobb Street, Zip 31061–2343; tel. 478/454–3505; Jean Aycock, President and Chief Executive Officer, p. B100

**Tifton:** ★ TIFT REGIONAL HEALTH SYSTEM 901 East 18th Street, Zip 31794–3648; tel. 229/353–6100; William T. Richardson, President and Chief Executive Officer, p. B134

**Warner Robins:** ★ HOUSTON HEALTHCARE SYSTEM 1601 Watson Boulevard, Zip 31093–3431, Mailing Address: P.O. Box 2886, Zip 31099–2886; tel. 478/922–4281; Cary Martin, Chief Executive Officer, p. B71

## HAWAII

**Honolulu:** ★ HAWAII HEALTH SYSTEMS CORPORATION 3675 Kilauea Avenue, Zip 96816–2333; tel. 808/733–4151; Linda Rosen, M.D., Chief Executive Officer, p. B61

HAWAII PACIFIC HEALTH 55 Merchant Street, Zip 96813–4306; tel. 808/949–9355; Raymond P. Vara, Jr., President and Chief Executive Officer, p. B61

★ QUEEN'S HEALTH SYSTEMS 1301 Punchbowl Street, Zip 96813–2402; tel. 808/535–5448; Arthur A. Ushijima, FACHE, President and Chief Executive Officer, p. B112

## IDAHO

**Boise:** ★ ST. LUKE'S HEALTH SYSTEM 420 West Idaho Street, Zip 83702–6041; tel. 208/381–4200; David C. Pate, M.D., JD, President and Chief Executive Officer, p. B127

**Pocatello:** SAFE HAVEN HEALTH CARE 2520 South 5th Avenue, Zip 83204–1923; tel. 800/261–2443; Scott Burpee, President, p. B115

## ILLINOIS

**Carbondale:** SOUTHERN ILLINOIS HOSPITAL SERVICES 1239 East Main Street, Zip 62901–3114, Mailing Address: P.O. Box 3988, Zip 62902–3988; tel. 618/457–5200; Rex P. Budde, President and Chief Executive Officer, p. B124

**Chicago:** COOK COUNTY HEALTH AND HOSPITALS SYSTEM 1900 West Polk Street, Suite 220, Zip 60612–3723; tel. 312/864–6820; John Jay Shannon, M.D., Chief Executive Officer, p. B42

NATIONAL SURGICAL HEALTHCARE 250 South Wacker Drive, Suite 500, Zip 60606–5897; tel. 312/627–8400; David Crane, Chief Executive Officer, p. B94

★ NORTHWESTERN MEMORIAL HEALTHCARE 251 East Huron Street, Zip 60611–2908; tel. 312/926–2000; Dean M. Harrison, President and Chief Executive Officer, p. B99

★ PRESENCE HEALTH 200 South Wacker Drive, Zip 60606–5829; tel. 312/308–3200; Sandra B. Bruce, FACHE, President and Chief Executive Officer, p. B106

★ RUSH UNIVERSITY MEDICAL CENTER 1653 West Congress Parkway, Zip 60612–3864; tel. 312/942–5000; Larry J. Goodman, M.D., Chief Executive Officer, p. B115

★ SINAI HEALTH SYSTEM 1500 South California Avenue, Zip 60608–1729; tel. 773/542–2000; Karen Teitelbaum, President and Chief Executive Officer, p. B123

**Crystal Lake:** ★ CENTEGRA HEALTH SYSTEM 385 Millennium Drive, Zip 60012–3761; tel. 815/788–5800; Michael S. Eesley, Chief Executive Officer, p. B32

**DeKalb:** ★ KISH HEALTH SYSTEM 1 Kish Hospital Drive, Zip 60115–9602, Mailing Address: P.O. Box 707, Zip 60115–0707; tel. 815/756–1521; Kevin P. Poorten, President and Chief Executive Officer, p. B80

**Downers Grove:** ★ ADVOCATE HEALTH CARE 3075 Highland Parkway, Suite 600, Zip 60515–1206; tel. 630/929–8700; Jim H. Skogsbergh, President and Chief Executive Officer, p. B7

**Evergreen Park:** AMERICAN PROVINCE OF LITTLE COMPANY OF MARY SISTERS 9350 South California Avenue, Zip 60805–2595; tel. 708/229–5491; Sister Kathleen McIntyre, Province Leader, p. B10

**Naperville:** ★ EDWARD–ELMHURST HEALTHCARE 801 South Washington Street, Zip 60540–7430; tel. 630/527–3000; Pamela M. Davis, System President and Chief Executive Officer, p. B53

**Peoria:** ★ OSF HEALTHCARE SYSTEM 800 N.E. Glen Oak Avenue, Zip 61603–3200; tel. 309/655–2850; Kevin D. Schoeplein, Chief Executive Officer, p. B102

**Schaumburg:** CANCER TREATMENT CENTERS OF AMERICA 1336 Basswood Road, Zip 60173–4544; tel. 847/342–7400; Gerard van Grinsven, President and Chief Executive Officer, p. B26

**Springfield:** DIVISION OF MENTAL HEALTH, DEPARTMENT OF HUMAN SERVICES 319 East Madison Street, S–3B, Zip 62701–1035; tel. 217/785–6023; Lorrie Rickman Jones, Ph.D., Director, p. B52

★ HOSPITAL SISTERS HEALTH SYSTEM 4936 LaVerna Road, Zip 62707–9797, Mailing Address: P.O. Box 19456, Zip 62794–9456; tel. 217/523–4747; Mary Starmann–Harrison, FACHE, President and Chief Executive Officer, p. B71

★ MEMORIAL HEALTH SYSTEM 701 North First Street, Zip 62781–0001; tel. 217/788–3000; Edgar J. Curtis, FACHE, President and Chief Executive Officer, p. B88

**Urbana:** ★ CARLE FOUNDATION 611 West Park Street, Zip 61801–2595; tel. 217/383–3311; James C. Leonard, M.D., President and Chief Executive Officer, p. B27

**Wheaton:** ★ WHEATON FRANCISCAN HEALTHCARE 26W171 Roosevelt Road, Zip 60187–6002, Mailing Address: P.O. Box 667, Zip 60187–0667; tel. 630/909–6900; John D. Oliverio, President and Chief Executive Officer, p. B153

## INDIANA

**Evansville:** ★ DEACONESS HEALTH SYSTEM 600 Mary Street, Zip 47710–1658; tel. 812/450–5000; Linda E. White, President and Chief Executive Officer, / p. B44

**Fort Wayne:** ★ PARKVIEW HEALTH 10501 Corporate Drive, Zip 46845–1700; tel. 260/373–7001; Michael J. Packnett, President and Chief Executive Officer, p. B103

**Hammond:** COMMUNITY HEALTHCARE SYSTEM 901 MacArthur Boulevard, Zip 46321–2959; tel. 219/836–1600; Donald Powers, Chairman, President and Chief Executive Officer, p. B41

**Indianapolis:** COMMUNITY HEALTH NETWORK 7330 Shadeland Station, Zip 46256–3957; tel. 317/355–1411; Bryan A. Mills, President and Chief Executive Officer, p. B34

★ INDIANA UNIVERSITY HEALTH 340 West 10th Street, Suite 6100, Zip 46202–3082, Mailing Address: P.O. Box 1367, Zip 46206–1367; tel. 317/962–5900; Daniel F. Evans, Jr., JD, President and Chief Executive Officer, p. B73

**Mishawaka:** FRANCISCAN ALLIANCE 1515 Dragoon Trail, Zip 46544–4710, Mailing Address: P.O. Box 1290, Zip 46546–1290; tel. 574/256–3935; Kevin D. Leahy, President and Chief Executive Officer, p. B57

NEUROPSYCHIATRIC HOSPITALS 1625 East Jefferson Boulevard, Zip 46545–7103; tel. 574/255–1400; Cameron R. Gilbert, Ph.D., President and Chief Executive Officer, p. B95

**South Bend:** ★ BEACON HEALTH SYSTEM 615 North Michigan Street, Zip 46601–1033; tel. 574/647–1000; Philip A. Newbold, Chief Executive Officer, p. B23

## IOWA

**Clarion:** ★ IOWA SPECIALTY HOSPITALS 1316 South Main Street, Zip 50525–2019; tel. 515/532–2811; Steven J. Simonin, Chief Executive Officer, p. B75

**Davenport:** ★ GENESIS HEALTH SYSTEM 1227 East Rusholme Street, Zip 52803–2498; tel. 563/421–1000; Douglas P. Cropper, President and Chief Executive Officer, p. B58

**West Des Moines:** ★ UNITYPOINT HEALTH 1776 Westlakes Parkway, Suite 400, Zip 50266–8239; tel. 515/241–6161; William B. Leaver, President and Chief Executive Officer, p. B140

## KANSAS

**Wichita:** ★ GREAT PLAINS HEALTH ALLIANCE, INC. 250 North Rock Road, Suite 160, Zip 67206–2241; tel. 316/685–1523; Dave Dellasega, President and Chief Executive Officer, p. B59

## KENTUCKY

**Bowling Green:** COMMONWEALTH HEALTH CORPORATION 800 Park Street, Zip 42101–2356; tel. 270/745–1500; Connie Smith, President and Chief Executive Officer, p. B34

**Danville:** ★ EPHRAIM MCDOWELL HEALTH 217 South Third Street, Zip 40422–1823; tel. 859/239–1000; Vicki A. Darnell, R.N., MSN, President and Chief Executive Officer, p. B54

**Edgewood:** ST. ELIZABETH HEALTHCARE 1 Medical Village Drive, Zip 41017–3403; tel. 859/301–2000; Garren Colvin, Chief Executive Officer, p. B127

**Lexington:** APPALACHIAN REGIONAL HEALTHCARE, INC. 2285 Executive Drive, Suite 400, Zip 40505–4810, Mailing Address: P.O. Box 8086, Zip 40533–8086; tel. 859/226–2440; Jerry Haynes, President and Chief Executive Officer, p. B11

**Louisville:** ALLIANT MANAGEMENT SERVICES 2650 Eastpoint Parkway, Suite 300, Zip 40223–5164; tel. 502/992–3525; Timothy L. Jarm, President and Chief Executive Officer, p. B8

★ BAPTIST HEALTH 2701 Eastpoint Parkway, Zip 40223; tel. 502/896–5000; Stephen C. Hanson, Chief Executive Officer, p. B19

★ KINDRED HEALTHCARE 680 South Fourth Street, Zip 40202–2412; tel. 502/596–7300; Benjamin Breier, Chief Executive Officer, p. B77

★ NORTON HEALTHCARE 4967 U.S. Highway 42, Suite 100, Zip 40222–6363, Mailing Address: P.O. Box 35070, Zip 40232–5070; tel. 502/629–8000; Stephen Williams, Chief Executive Officer, p. B99

## LOUISIANA

**Baton Rouge:** ★ FRANCISCAN MISSIONARIES OF OUR LADY HEALTH SYSTEM, INC. 4200 Essen Lane, Zip 70809–2158; tel. 225/923–2701; John J. Finan, Jr., FACHE, President and Chief Executive Officer, p. B57

LOUISIANA STATE HOSPITALS 628 North 4th Street, Zip 70802–5342, Mailing Address: P.O. Box 629, Zip 70821–0628; tel. 225/342–9500; Shelby Price, Chief Executive Officer, p. B85

**Crowley:** COMPASS HEALTH 426 North Avenue G., Zip 70526–2434; tel. 337/788–3330; Mark J. Cullen, Chief Executive Officer, p. B41

**Gretna:** UNITED MEDICAL REHABILITATION HOSPITALS 3201 Wall Boulevard, Suite B., Zip 70056–7755; tel. 504/433–5551; John E.H. Mills, President & Chief Executive Officer, p. B139

**Hammond:** NORTH OAKS HEALTH SYSTEM 15790 Paul Vega MD Drive, Zip 70403–1436, Mailing Address: P.O. Box 2668, Zip 70404–2668; tel. 985/345–2700; Julie Hughs, Administrative Operations Support Analyst, p. B98

**Lafayette:** AMG INTEGRATED HEALTHCARE MANAGEMENT 101 La Rue France, Suite 500, Zip 70508–3144; tel. 337/269–9828; August J. Rantz, III, Founder and Chief Executive Officer, p. B10

LAFAYETTE GENERAL HEALTH 1214 Coolidge Boulevard, Zip 70503–2621; tel. 337/289–7991; David L. Callecod, FACHE, President and CEO, p. B80

LHC GROUP 420 West Pinhook Road, Zip 70503–2131; tel. 337/223–1307; Keith G. Myers, Chairman and Chief Executive Officer, p. B82

**Lake Charles:** OCEANS HEALTHCARE 2720 Rue de Jardin, Suite 100, Zip 70605–4050; tel. 337/721–1900; Jason Reed, President and Chief Executive Officer, p. B100

**New Orleans:** LCMC HEALTH 200 Henry Clay Avenue, Zip 70118–5720; tel. 504/899–9511; Greg Feirn, CPA, President and Chief Executive Officer, p. B81

★ OCHSNER HEALTH SYSTEM 1514 Jefferson Highway, Zip 70121–2429; tel. 800/874–8984; Warner L. Thomas, FACHE, President and Chief Executive Officer, p. B100

**Shreveport:** ALLEGIANCE HEALTH MANAGEMENT 504 Texas Street, Suite 200, Zip 71101–3526; tel. 318/226–8202; Rock Bordelon, President and Chief Executive Officer, p. B8

UNIVERSITY HEALTH SYSTEM 1501 Kings Highway, Zip 71103–4228; tel. 318/675–5000; Richard C. Cascio, Interim Chief Executive Officer, p. B145

WILLIS–KNIGHTON HEALTH SYSTEM 2600 Greenwood Road, Zip 71103–3908; tel. 318/212–4000; James K. Elrod, FACHE, President and Chief Executive Officer, p. B154

## MAINE

**Brewer:** ★ EASTERN MAINE HEALTHCARE SYSTEMS 43 Whiting Hill Road, Zip 04412–1005; tel. 207/973–7045; M. Michelle Hood, FACHE, President and Chief Executive Officer, p. B53

**Portland:** MAINEHEALTH 110 Free Street, Zip 04101–3537; William L. Caron, Jr., President, p. B86

## MARYLAND

**Baltimore:** ★ JOHNS HOPKINS HEALTH SYSTEM 733 North Broadway, BRB 104, Zip 21205–1832; tel. 410/955–5000; Ronald R. Peterson, President, p. B76

LIFEBRIDGE HEALTH 2401 West Belvedere Avenue, Zip 21215–5216; tel. 410/601–5134; Neil M. Meltzer, President and Chief Executive Officer, p. B82

★ UNIVERSITY OF MARYLAND MEDICAL SYSTEM 250 West Pratt Street, 24th Floor, Zip 21201–1595; tel. 410/328–8667; Robert A. Chrencik, President and Chief Executive Officer, p. B146

**Cheverly:** DIMENSIONS HEALTHCARE SYSTEM 3001 Hospital Drive, 3rd Floor, Zip 20785–1189; tel. 301/583–4000; Neil J. Moore, President and Chief Executive Officer, p. B51

**Columbia:** ENCORE HEALTHCARE 7150 Columbia Gateway Drove, Suite J., Zip 21046–2974; tel. 443/539–2350; Tim Nicholson, Chief Executive Officer, p. B54

★ MEDSTAR HEALTH 5565 Sterrett Place, 5th Floor, Zip 21044–2665; tel. 410/772–6500; Kenneth A. Samet, President and Chief Executive Officer, p. B88

**Gaithersburg:** ADVENTIST HEALTHCARE 820 West Diamond Avenue, Suite 600, Zip 20878–1419; tel. 301/315–3141; Terry Forde, Interim President and Chief Executive Officer, p. B7

**Marriottsville:** ★ BON SECOURS HEALTH SYSTEM, INC. 1505 Marriottsville Road, Zip 21104–1399; tel. 410/442–5511; Richard Statuto, President and Chief Executive Officer, p. B24

**Rockville:** U. S. INDIAN HEALTH SERVICE 801 Thompson Avenue, Zip 20852–1627; tel. 301/443–1083; Yvette Roubideaux, M.D., M.P.H., Director, p. B137

**Sparks Glencoe:** FUNDAMENTAL LONG TERM CARE HOLDINGS, LLC 930 Ridgebrook Road, Zip 21152–9390; tel. 410/773–1000; W. Bradley Bennett, President and Chief Executive Officer, p. B58

## MASSACHUSETTS

**Boston:** MASSACHUSETTS DEPARTMENT OF MENTAL HEALTH 25 Staniford Street, Zip 02114–2575; tel. 617/626–8123; Joan Mikula, Interim Commissioner, p. B86

MASSACHUSETTS DEPARTMENT OF PUBLIC HEALTH 250 Washington Street, Zip 02108–4619; tel. 617/624–6000; Sandra Akers, Bureau Director, Public Health Hospitals, p. B86

★ PARTNERS HEALTHCARE SYSTEM, INC. 800 Boylston Street, Suite 1150, Zip 02199–8123; tel. 617/278–1004; David Torchiana, M.D., Chief Executive Officer, p. B103

STEWARD HEALTH CARE SYSTEM, LLC 500 Boylston Street, 5th Floor, Zip 02116–3740; tel. 617/419–4700; Ralph de la Torre, M.D., Chairman and Chief Executive Officer, p. B128

**Burlington:** LAHEY HEALTH 41 Mall Road, Zip 01805–0001; tel. 781/744–7100; Howard R. Grant, JD, M.D., President and Chief Executive Officer, p. B80

**Haverhill:** WHITTIER HEALTH NETWORK 25 Railroad Square, Zip 01832–5721; tel. 978/556–5858; Alfred L. Arcidi, M.D., President, p. B154

**Hyannis:** ★ CAPE COD HEALTHCARE, INC. 27 Park Street, Zip 02601–5230; tel. 508/862–5121; Michael K. Lauf, President and Chief Executive Officer, p. B26

**Newton:** FIVE STAR QUALITY CARE 400 Centre Street, Zip 02458–2094; tel. 617/796–8387; Bruce J. Mackey, Jr., President and Chief Executive Officer, p. B56

**Pittsfield:** ★ BERKSHIRE HEALTH SYSTEMS, INC. 725 North Street, Zip 01201–4124; tel. 413/447–2750; David E. Phelps, President and Chief Executive Officer, p. B23

**Springfield:** ★ BAYSTATE HEALTH, INC. 759 Chestnut Street, Zip 01199–0001; tel. 413/794–0000; Mark A. Keroack, M.D., President and Chief Executive Officer, p. B23

**Tewksbury:** ★ COVENANT HEALTH 100 Ames Pond Drive, Suite 102, Zip 01876–1240; tel. 978/654–6363; David R. Lincoln, FACHE, President and Chief Executive Officer, p. B43

**Worcester:** ★ UMASS MEMORIAL HEALTH CARE, INC. 1 Biotech Park, Zip 01605–2982; tel. 508/334–0100; Eric Dickson, M.D., President and Chief Executive Officer, p. B138

### MICHIGAN

**Detroit:** ★ HENRY FORD HEALTH SYSTEM One Ford Place, Zip 48202–3450; tel. 313/876–8708; Nancy M. Schlichting, Chief Executive Officer, p. B70

**Flint:** MCLAREN HEALTH CARE CORPORATION G3235 Beecher Road, Suite B., Zip 48532–3650; tel. 810/342–1100; Philip A. Incarnati, President and Chief Executive Officer, p. B87

**Grand Rapids:** ★ SPECTRUM HEALTH 100 Michigan Street N.E., Zip 49503–2551; tel. 616/391–1774; Richard C. Breon, President and Chief Executive Officer, p. B126

**Kalamazoo:** ★ BRONSON HEALTHCARE GROUP, INC. 301 John Street, Zip 49007–5295; tel. 269/341–6000; Frank J. Sardone, President and Chief Executive Officer, p. B25

**Lansing:** ★ SPARROW HEALTH SYSTEM 1215 East Michigan Avenue, Zip 48912–1811; tel. 517/364–1000; Dennis A. Swan, JD, FACHE, President and Chief Executive Officer, p. B125

**Livonia:** ★ TRINITY HEALTH 20555 Victor Parkway, Zip 48152–7031; tel. 734/343–1000; Richard J. Gilfillan, M.D., President and Chief Executive Officer, p. B135

**Midland:** ★ MIDMICHIGAN HEALTH 4000 Wellness Drive, Zip 48670–0001; tel. 989/839–3000; Diane Postler–Slattery, Ph.D., President and Chief Executive Officer, p. B92

**Royal Oak:** ★ BEAUMONT HEALTH 3711 West 13 Mile Road, Zip 48073–6712, Mailing Address: 44201 Dequindre Road, Troy, Zip 48085–1117; tel. 248/898–5000; John T. Fox, President and Chief Executive Officer, p. B23

**Saint Joseph:** LAKELAND HEALTH 1234 Napier Avenue, Zip 49085–2158; tel. 269/983–8300; Loren Hamel, M.D., President and Chief Executive Officer, p. B80

**Traverse City:** ★ MUNSON HEALTHCARE 1105 Sixth Street, Zip 49684–2386; tel. 231/935–6703; Edwin Ness, President and Chief Executive Officer, p. B94

### MINNESOTA

**Bloomington:** HEALTHPARTNERS 8170 33rd Avenue South, Zip 55425–4516; tel. 952/883–7600; Mary K. Brainerd, President and Chief Executive Officer, p. B66

**Duluth:** ★ ESSENTIA HEALTH 502 East Second Street, Zip 55805–1913; tel. 218/786–8376; David C. Herman, M.D., Chief Executive Officer, p. B55

**Minneapolis:** ★ ALLINA HEALTH 2925 Chicago Avenue, Zip 55407–1321, Mailing Address: P.O. Box 43, Zip 55440–0043; tel. 612/262–5000; Penny Ann Wheeler, M.D., Chief Executive Officer, p. B9

★ FAIRVIEW HEALTH SERVICES 2450 Riverside Avenue, Zip 55454–1400; tel. 612/672–6141; David Murphy, Interim Chief Executive Officer, p. B56

**Robbinsdale:** ★ NORTH MEMORIAL HEALTH CARE 3300 Oakdale Avenue North, Zip 55422–2926; tel. 763/520–5200; J. Kevin Croston, M.D., Chief Executive Officer, p. B97

**Rochester:** ★ MAYO CLINIC 200 First Street S.W., Zip 55905–0002; tel. 507/284–2511; John H. Noseworthy, MD, M.D., President and Chief Executive Officer, p. B87

**Saint Cloud:** ★ CENTRACARE HEALTH 1406 Sixth Avenue North, Zip 56303–1900; tel. 320/251–2700; Kenneth D. Holmen, M.D., President and Chief Executive Officer, p. B32

**Saint Paul:** ★ HEALTHEAST CARE SYSTEM 559 Capitol Boulevard, 6–South, Zip 55103–0000; tel. 651/232–2300; Kathryn G. Correia, President and Chief Executive Officer, p. B66

MINNESOTA DEPARTMENT OF HUMAN SERVICES 540 Cedar Street, Zip 55101–2208, Mailing Address: P.O. Box 64998, Zip 55164–0998; tel. 651/431–3212; Anne Barry, Deputy Commissioner, p. B92

**Waconia:** ★ RIDGEVIEW MEDICAL CENTER 500 South Maple Street, Zip 55387–1752; tel. 952/442–2191; Robert Stevens, President and Chief Executive Officer, p. B113

### MISSISSIPPI

**Jackson:** ★ BAPTIST HEALTH SYSTEMS 1225 North State Street, Zip 39202–2064; tel. 601/968–1000; Chris Anderson, Chief Executive Officer, p. B20

MISSISSIPPI STATE DEPARTMENT OF MENTAL HEALTH 1101 Robert East Lee Building, 239 North Lamar Street, Zip 39201–1101; tel. 601/359–1288; Edwin C. LeGrand, III, Executive Director, p. B93

★ UNIVERSITY HOSPITALS AND HEALTH SYSTEM 2500 North State Street, Zip 39216–4500; tel. 601/984–1000; Kevin S. Cook, Chief Executive Officer, p. B145

**Magee:** ★ PIONEER HEALTH SERVICES 110 Pioneer Way, Zip 39111–5501, Mailing Address: P.O. Box 1100, Zip 39111–1100; tel. 601/849–6440; Joseph S. McNulty, III, President and Chief Executive Officer, p. B105

**Mccomb:** SOUTHWEST HEALTH SYSTEMS 215 Marion Avenue, Zip 39648–2705, Mailing Address: P.O. Box 1307, Zip 39649–1307; tel. 601/249–5500; Norman M. Price, FACHE, Chief Executive Officer and Administrator, p. B125

**Meridian:** ★ RUSH HEALTH SYSTEMS 1314 19th Avenue, Zip 39301–4116; tel. 601/483–0011; Wallace Strickland, President and Chief Executive Officer, p. B115

**Tupelo:** ★ NORTH MISSISSIPPI HEALTH SERVICES, INC. 830 South Gloster Street, Zip 38801–4996; tel. 662/377–3136; M. Shane Spees, President and Chief Executive Officer, p. B98

### MISSOURI

**Cape Girardeau:** LANDMARK HOSPITALS 3255 Independence Street, Zip 63701–4914; tel. 573/335–1091; William K. Kapp, III, M.D., President and Chief Executive Officer, p. B80

SOUTHEASTHEALTH 1701 Lacey Street, Zip 63701–5230; tel. 573/334–4822; Kenneth Bateman, CPA, Chief Executive Officer, p. B124

**Chesterfield:** ★ MERCY HEALTH 14528 South Outer 40, Suite 100, Zip 63017–5743; tel. 314/579–6100; Lynn Britton, President and Chief Executive Officer, p. B90

**Columbia:** ★ UNIVERSITY OF MISSOURI HEALTH CARE One Hospital Drive, DC 031, Zip 65212–0001; tel. 573/884–8738; Mitchell L. Wasden, Ed.D., Chief Executive Officer and Chief Operating Officer, p. B147

**Joplin:** ★ FREEMAN HEALTH SYSTEM 1102 West 32nd Street, Zip 64804–3503; tel. 417/347–1111; Paula F. Baker, President and Chief Executive Officer, p. B58

**Kansas City:** RURAL COMMUNITY HOSPITALS OF AMERICA 1100 Main Street, Suite 2350, Zip 64105–5186; tel. 816/474–7800; Lawrence J. Arthur, President, p. B114

★ SAINT LUKE'S HEALTH SYSTEM 901 East 104th Street, Mailstop 900N, Zip 64131–4517, Mailing Address: 901 East 104th Street, Zip 64131–4517; tel. 816/932–2000; Melinda Estes, M.D., President and Chief Executive Officer, p. B116

★ TRUMAN MEDICAL CENTERS 2301 Holmes Street, Zip 64108–2677; tel. 816/404–1000; Charlie Shields, President and Chief Executive Officer, p. B137

**Saint Louis:** ★ ASCENSION HEALTH 101 South Hanley Road, Suite 450, Zip 63105–3406; tel. 314/733–8000; Robert J. Henkel, FACHE, President and Chief Executive Officer, p. B12

★ BJC HEALTHCARE 4901 Forest Park Avenue, Suite 1200, Zip 63108–1402; tel. 314/747–9322; Steven H. Lipstein, President and Chief Executive Officer, p. B23

★ SSM HEALTH 10101 Woodfield Lane, Zip 63132–2937; tel. 314/994–7800; William P. Thompson, President and Chief Executive Officer, p. B126

**Springfield:** COXHEALTH 1423 North Jefferson Avenue, Zip 65802–1988; tel. 417/269–3108; Steven D. Edwards, President and Chief Executive Officer, p. B43

### MONTANA

**Great Falls:** BENEFIS HEALTH SYSTEM 1101 26th Street South, Zip 59405–5161; tel. 406/455–5000; John H. Goodnow, Chief Executive Officer, p. B23

### NEBRASKA

**Lincoln:** ★ BRYAN HEALTH 1600 South 48th Street, Zip 68506–1283; tel. 402/481–1111; Kimberly A. Russel, FACHE, President and Chief Executive Officer, p. B25

**Norfolk:** FAITH REGIONAL HEALTH SERVICES 2700 West Norfolk Avenue, Zip 68701–4438, Mailing Address: P.O. Box 869, Zip 68702–0869; tel. 402/644–7201; Mark D. Klosterman, FACHE, President and Chief Executive Officer, p. B56

**Omaha:** ★ NEBRASKA METHODIST HEALTH SYSTEM, INC. 8511 West Dodge Road, Zip 68114–3403; tel. 402/354–5411; John M. Fraser, FACHE, President and Chief Executive Officer, p. B95

## NEVADA

**Reno:** ★ RENOWN HEALTH 1155 Mill Street, Zip 89502–1576; tel. 775/982–4100; Anthony D. Slonim, M.D., Dr.PH, President and Chief Executive Officer, p. B113

## NEW HAMPSHIRE

**Laconia:** ★ LRGHEALTHCARE 80 Highland Street, Zip 03246–3298; tel. 603/524–3211; Seth C. R. Warren, President and Chief Executive Officer, p. B85

**Portsmouth:** SPECIALTY HOSPITALS OF AMERICA, LLC 155 Fleet Street, Zip 03801–4050; tel. 603/570–4888; Eric F. Rieseberg, President, p. B125

## NEW JERSEY

**Edison:** ★ JFK HEALTH SYSTEM 80 James Street, 2nd Floor, Zip 08820–3938; tel. 732/632–1503; Raymond F. Fredericks, President and Chief Executive Officer, p. B75

**Egg Harbor Township:** ★ ATLANTICARE 2500 English Creek Avenue, Building 500, Suite 501, Zip 08234; tel. 609/407–2309; David P. Tilton, President and Chief Executive Officer, p. B16

**Hackensack:** ★ HACKENSACK UNIVERSITY HEALTH NETWORK 30 Prospect Avenue, Zip 07601–1914; tel. 201/996–2000; Robert C. Garrett, FACHE, President and Chief Executive Officer, p. B60

**Jersey City:** ★ CAREPOINT HEALTH 10 Exchange Place, 15th Floor, Zip 07302–3918; tel. 877/791–7000; Dennis Kelly, Chief Executive Officer, p. B27

**Marlton:** ★ VIRTUA HEALTH 50 Lake Center Executive Drive, Suite 401, Zip 08053; tel. 856/355–0010; Richard P. Miller, Chief Executive Officer, p. B151

**Morristown:** ★ ATLANTIC HEALTH SYSTEM 475 South Street, Zip 07962, Mailing Address: P.O. Box 1905, Zip 07962–1905; tel. 973/660–3270; Brian A. Gragnolati, FACHE, President and Chief Executive Officer, p. B15

**Mullica Hill:** ★ INSPIRA HEALTH NETWORK 165 Bridgeton Pike, Zip 08062; tel. 856/641–8000; John A. DiAngelo, President and Chief Executive Officer, p. B74

**Neptune:** ★ MERIDIAN HEALTH 1350 Campus Parkway, Zip 07753–6821; tel. 732/751–7510; John K. Lloyd, President and Chief Executive Officer, p. B91

**New Brunswick:** ROBERT WOOD JOHNSON HEALTH SYSTEM & NETWORK 1 Robert Wood Johnson Place, Zip 08901–1928; tel. 732/828–3000; Stephen K. Jones, FACHE, President and Chief Executive Officer, p. B114

**Trenton:** ★ CAPITAL HEALTH 750 Brunswick Avenue, Zip 08638–4143; tel. 609/394–6000; Al Maghazehe, Ph.D., FACHE, Chief Executive Officer, p. B27

DIVISION OF MENTAL HEALTH AND ADDICTION SERVICES, DEPARTMENT OF HUMAN SERVICES, STATE OF NEW JERSEY 222 South Warren Street, Zip 08608–2306, Mailing Address: P.O. Box 700, Zip 08625–0700; tel. 609/777–0702; Lynn Kovich, Assistant Commissioner, p. B51

**West Orange:** ★ BARNABAS HEALTH 95 Old Short Hills Road, Zip 07052–1008; tel. 973/322–4000; Barry Ostrowsky, President and Chief Executive Officer, p. B21

## NEW MEXICO

**Albuquerque:** ERNEST HEALTH, INC. 7770 Jefferson Street N.E., Suite 320, Zip 87109–4386; tel. 505/856–5300; Darby Brockette, Chief Executive Officer, p. B54

★ PRESBYTERIAN HEALTHCARE SERVICES 2501 Buena Vista Drive, S.E., Zip 87106–4260, Mailing Address: P.O. Box 26666, Zip 87125–6666; tel. 505/841–1234; James H. Hinton, President and Chief Executive Officer, p. B106

UNIVERSITY OF NEW MEXICO HOSPITALS 915 Camino De Salud, Zip 87131–0001; tel. 505/272–5849; Stephen W. McKernan, Chief Executive Officer, p. B147

## NEW YORK

**Albany:** NEW YORK STATE OFFICE OF MENTAL HEALTH 44 Holland Avenue, Zip 12208–3411; tel. 518/474–7056; Kristin M. Woodlock, R.N., Acting Commissioner, p. B96

**Binghamton:** UNITED HEALTH SERVICES 10–42 Mitchell Avenue, Zip 13903–1617; tel. 607/762–2200; Matthew J. Salanger, President and Chief Executive Officer, p. B139

**Bronx:** MONTEFIORE HEALTH SYSTEM 111 East 210th Street, Zip 10467–2490; tel. 718/920–4321; Steven M. Safyer, M.D., President and CEO, p. B93

**Buffalo:** ★ CATHOLIC HEALTH SYSTEM 2121 Main Street, Suite 300, Zip 14214–2673, Mailing Address: 144 Genesee Street, Zip 14203; tel. 716/862–2410; Joseph D. McDonald, President and Chief Executive Officer, p. B31

**Cooperstown:** ★ BASSETT HEALTHCARE NETWORK 1 Atwell Road, Zip 13326–1301; tel. 607/547–3456; Vance Brown, M.D., President and Chief Executive Officer, p. B22

**Elmira:** ARNOT HEALTH 600 Roe Avenue, Zip 14905–1629; tel. 607/737–4100; Robert K. Lambert, M.D., FACHE, President and Chief Executive Officer, p. B12

**Geneva:** FINGER LAKES HEALTH 196 North Street, Zip 14456–1651; tel. 315/787–4000; Jose Acevedo, M.D., President and Chief Executive Officer, p. B56

**Great Neck:** ★ NORTH SHORE–LONG ISLAND JEWISH HEALTH SYSTEM 145 Community Drive, Zip 11021–5502; tel. 516/465–8100; Michael J. Dowling, President and Chief Executive Officer, p. B98

**Jamaica:** ★ MEDISYS HEALTH NETWORK 8900 Van Wyck Expressway, Zip 11418–2832; tel. 718/206–6000; Bruce J. Flanz, President and Chief Executive Officer, p. B88

**Kingston:** HEALTHALLIANCE OF THE HUDSON VALLEY 396 Broadway, Zip 12401–4626; tel. 845/331–3131; David Scarpino, President and Chief Executive Officer, p. B66

**LaGrangeville:** HEALTH QUEST SYSTEMS, INC. 1351 Route 55, Zip 12540–5108; tel. 845/475–9500; Luke McGuinness, President and CEO, p. B66

**Middletown:** GREATER HUDSON VALLEY HEALTH SYSTEM 60 Prospect Avenue, Zip 10940–4133; tel. 845/568–6050; Scott Batulis, President and Chief Executive Officer, p. B60

**New York:** ★ MOUNT SINAI HEALTH SYSTEM One Gustave L. Levy Place, Zip 10029; tel. 212/659–8888; Kenneth L. Davis, M.D., President and Chief Executive, p. B93

★ NEW YORK CITY HEALTH AND HOSPITALS CORPORATION 125 Worth Street, Room 514, Zip 10013–4006; tel. 212/788–3321; Ramanathan Raju, M.D., President, p. B96

NEW YORK PRESBYTERIAN HEALTHCARE SYSTEM 525 East 68th Street, Box 182, Zip 10065; tel. 212/746–3745; Steven J. Corwin, M.D., Chief Executive Officer, p. B96

NYU LANGONE HEALTH SYSTEM 550 First Avenue, Zip 10016–6402; tel. 212/263–7300; Robert I. Grossman, M.D., Chief Executive Officer, p. B100

**Olean:** UPPER ALLEGHENY HEALTH SYSTEM 130 South Union Street, Suite 300, Zip 14760–3676; tel. 716/375–6190; Timothy J. Finan, FACHE, President and Chief Executive Officer, p. B148

**Potsdam:** ST. LAWRENCE HEALTH SYSTEM 50 Leroy Street, Zip 13676–1799; tel. 315/265–3300; David B. Acker, FACHE, President and CEO, p. B127

**Rochester:** ★ ROCHESTER REGIONAL HEALTH 1425 Portland Avenue, 5th Floor, Zip 14621–3001; tel. 585/922–4000; Eric Bieber, M.D., President and Chief Executive Officer, p. B114

★ UNIVERSITY OF ROCHESTER MEDICAL CENTER 601 Elmwood Avenue Box 623, Zip 14642–0002, Mailing Address: 601 Elmwood Avenue, Zip 14642–0002; tel. 585/275–2100; Steven I. Goldstein, General Director and Chief Executive Officer, p. B147

**Rockville Centre:** CATHOLIC HEALTH SERVICES OF LONG ISLAND 992 North Village Avenue, 1st Floor, Zip 11570–1002; tel. 516/705–3700; Alan D. Guerci, M.D., President and Chief Executive Officer, p. B31

**Syracuse:** SISTERS OF SAINT FRANCIS 2500 Grant Boulevard, Zip 13208–1782; tel. 315/634–7000; Sister Geraldine Ching, Assistant General Minister, p. B124

## NORTH CAROLINA

**Asheville:** ★ MISSION HEALTH SYSTEM 509 Biltmore Avenue, Zip 28801–4601; tel. 828/213–1111; Ronald A. Paulus, M.D., President and Chief Executive Officer, p. B92

**Boone:** ★ APPALACHIAN REGIONAL HEALTHCARE SYSTEM 336 Deerfield Road, Zip 28607–5008, Mailing Address: P.O. Box 2600, Zip 28607–2600; tel. 828/262–4100; Richard G. Sparks, President and Chief Executive Officer, p. B10

**Chapel Hill:** ★ UNC HEALTH CARE 101 Manning Drive, Zip 27514–4220; tel. 919/966–4131; William L. Roper, M.D., M.P.H., Chief Executive Officer, p. B139

**Charlotte:** ★ ACUITYHEALTHCARE, LP 10200 Mallard Creek Road, Suite 300, Zip 28262–9705; tel. 704/887–7280; Edwin H. Cooper, Jr., MS, President and Chief Executive Officer, p. B4

★ CAROLINAS HEALTHCARE SYSTEM 1000 Blythe Boulevard, Zip 28203–5871, Mailing Address: P.O. Box 32861, Zip 28232–2861; tel. 704/355–2000; Michael C. Tarwater, Chief Executive Officer, p. B28

**Durham:** ★ DUKE UNIVERSITY HEALTH SYSTEM 201 Trent Drive, Zip 27710–3037, Mailing Address: P.O. Box 3701, Zip 27710–3701; tel. 919/684–2255; A. Eugene Washington, M.D., President and Chief Executive Officer, p. B52

**Fayetteville:** CAPE FEAR VALLEY HEALTH SYSTEM 1638 Owen Drive, Zip 28304–3424, Mailing Address: P.O. Box 2000, Zip 28302–2000; tel. 910/615–4000; Michael Nagowski, President and Chief Executive Officer, p. B26

**Greensboro:** CONE HEALTH 1200 North Elm Street, Zip 27401–1004; tel. 336/832–7000; Terry Akin, President and Chief Executive Officer, p. B41

**Greenville:** ★ VIDANT HEALTH 2100 Stantonsburg Road, Zip 27834–2818, Mailing Address: P.O. Box 6028, Zip 27835–6028; tel. 252/847–4100; Michael Waldrum, M.D., Chief Executive Officer, p. B151

**Pinehurst:** ★ FIRSTHEALTH OF THE CAROLINAS 155 Memorial Drive, Zip 28374–8710, Mailing Address: P.O. Box 3000, Zip 28374–3000; tel. 910/715–1000; David J. Kilarski, Chief Executive Officer, p. B56

**Raleigh:** ★ WAKEMED HEALTH & HOSPITALS 3000 New Bern Avenue, Zip 27610–1231; tel. 919/350–8000; Donald R. Gintzig, President and Chief Executive Officer, p. B152

**Wilmington:** ★ NEW HANOVER REGIONAL MEDICAL CENTER 2131 South 17th Street, Zip 28401–7407; tel. 910/343–7040; John K. Barto, Jr., President and Chief Executive Officer, p. B96

**Winston Salem:** ★ NOVANT HEALTH 2085 Frontis Plaza Boulevard, Zip 27103–5614; tel. 336/718–5600; Carl S. Armato, President and Chief Executive Officer, p. B99

**Winston–Salem:** ★ WAKE FOREST BAPTIST HEALTH Medical Center Boulevard, Zip 27157; tel. 336/716–2011; John D. McConnell, M.D., Chief Executive Officer, p. B152

### NORTH DAKOTA

**Fargo:** SISTERS OF MARY OF THE PRESENTATION HEALTH SYSTEM 1202 Page Drive S.W., Zip 58103–2340, Mailing Address: P.O. Box 10007, Zip 58106–0007; tel. 701/237–9290; Aaron K. Alton, President and Chief Executive Officer, p. B124

### OHIO

**Akron:** ★ AKRON GENERAL HEALTH SYSTEM 1 Akron General Avenue, Zip 44307–2433; tel. 330/344–6000; Thomas L. Stover, M.D., President and Chief Executive Officer, p. B7

SUMMA HEALTH SYSTEM 1077 Gorge Boulevard, Zip 44310; tel. 330/375–3000; Thomas Malone, M.D., President and Chief Executive Officer, p. B129

**Canton:** AULTMAN HEALTH FOUNDATION 2600 Sixth Street S.W., Zip 44710–1702; tel. 330/363–6192; Edward J. Roth, III, President and Chief Executive Officer, p. B16

**Chillicothe:** ADENA HEALTH SYSTEM 272 Hospital Road, Zip 45601–9031; tel. 740/779–7500; Mark H. Shuter, President and Chief Executive Officer, p. B5

**Cincinnati:** ★ MERCY HEALTH 615 Elsinore Place, Zip 45202–1459; tel. 513/639–2800; Michael D. Connelly, President and Chief Executive Officer, p. B89

★ UC HEALTH 3200 Burnet Avenue, Zip 45229–3019; tel. 513/585–6000; Richard P. Lofgren, M.D., M.P.H., President and CEO, p. B138

**Cleveland:** ★ CLEVELAND CLINIC HEALTH SYSTEM 9500 Euclid, Zip 44195–5108; tel. 216/444–2200; Delos Cosgrove, M.D., President and Chief Executive Officer, p. B34

SISTERS OF CHARITY HEALTH SYSTEM 2475 East 22nd Street, Zip 44115–3221; tel. 216/363–2797; Terrence Kessler, President and Chief Executive Officer, p. B124

★ UNIVERSITY HOSPITALS 11100 Euclid Avenue, Zip 44106–5000; tel. 216/844–1000; Thomas F. Zenty, III, President and Chief Executive Officer, p. B145

**Columbus:** OHIO DEPARTMENT OF MENTAL HEALTH 30 East Broad Street, 8th Floor, Zip 43215–3430; tel. 614/466–2297; Tracy Plouck, Director, p. B101

★ OHIO STATE UNIVERSITY HEALTH SYSTEM 370 West Ninth Avenue, Zip 43210–1238; tel. 614/685–9015; Peter E. Geier, Chief Executive Officer, p. B101

★ OHIOHEALTH 180 East Broad Street, Zip 43215–3707; tel. 614/544–4455; David P. Blom, President and Chief Executive Officer, p. B101

**Dayton:** ★ KETTERING HEALTH NETWORK 3965 Southern Boulevard, Zip 45429–1229; tel. 937/395–8150; Fred M. Manchur, Chief Executive Officer, p. B77

PREMIER HEALTH 110 North Main Street Suite 390, Zip 45402–3720; tel. 937/499–9401; James R. Pancoast, President and Chief Executive Officer, p. B106

**Findlay:** ★ BLANCHARD VALLEY HEALTH SYSTEM 1900 South Main Street, Zip 45840–1214; tel. 419/423–4500; Scott C. Malaney, President and Chief Executive Officer, p. B24

**Galion:** ★ AVITA HEALTH SYSTEM 269 Portland Way South, Zip 44833–2399; tel. 419/468–4841; Jerome Morasko, President and Chief Executive Officer, p. B18

**Toledo:** ★ PROMEDICA HEALTH SYSTEM 1801 Richards Road, Zip 43607–1037; tel. 419/469–3800; Randall D. Oostra, FACHE, President and Chief Executive Officer, p. B108

### OKLAHOMA

**Oklahoma City:** FOUNDATION SURGICAL HOSPITAL AFFILIATES 14000 North Portland Avenue, Suite 204, Zip 73134–4002; tel. 405/608–1700; Thomas A. Michaud, Chief Executive Officer, p. B57

★ INTEGRIS HEALTH 3366 N.W. Expressway, Suite 800, Zip 73112–9756; tel. 405/949–6066; Bruce Lawrence, President and Chief Executive Officer, p. B74

OKLAHOMA DEPARTMENT OF MENTAL HEALTH AND SUBSTANCE ABUSE SERVICES 1200 N.E. 13th Street, Zip 73117–1022, Mailing Address: P.O. Box 53277, Zip 73152–3277; tel. 405/522–3908; Terri White, Commissioner, p. B102

SOUTHERN PLAINS MEDICAL GROUP 4323 N.W. 63rd Street Suite 232, Zip 73116–1546; tel. 405/753–6770; Margie Homer, President, p. B125

**Shawnee:** PREFERRED MANAGEMENT CORPORATION 120 West MacArthur, Suite 121, Zip 74804–2005; tel. 405/878–0202; Donald Freeman, President and Chief Executive Officer, p. B106

**Tulsa:** ★ SAINT FRANCIS HEALTH SYSTEM 6161 South Yale Avenue, Zip 74136–1902; tel. 918/494–8454; Jake Henry, Jr., President and Chief Executive Officer, p. B115

### OREGON

**Bend:** ★ ST. CHARLES HEALTH SYSTEM, INC. 2500 N.E. Neff Road, Zip 97701–6015; tel. 541/382–4321; Joseph Sluka, President and Chief Executive Officer, p. B127

**Corvallis:** ★ SAMARITAN HEALTH SERVICES 3600 N.W. Samaritan Drive, Zip 97330–3737, Mailing Address: P.O. Box 1068, Zip 97339–1068; tel. 541/768–5001; Larry A. Mullins, FACHE, President and Chief Executive Officer, p. B116

**Medford:** ★ ASANTE HEALTH SYSTEM 2650 Siskiyou Boulevard, Suite 200, Zip 97504–8170; tel. 541/789–4100; Roy G. Vinyard, FACHE, President and Chief Executive Officer, p. B12

**Portland:** ★ LEGACY HEALTH 1919 N.W. Lovejoy Street, Zip 97209–1503; tel. 503/415–5600; George J. Brown, M.D., President and Chief Executive Officer, p. B81

**Salem:** SALEM HEALTH 890 Oak Street Building B. POB 14001, Zip 97309–5014; tel. 503/561–5200; Norman F. Gruber, President and Chief Executive Officer, p. B116

### PENNSYLVANIA

**Allentown:** GOOD SHEPHERD REHABILITATION NETWORK 850 South Fifth Street, Zip 18103–3308; tel. 610/776–3100; John Kristel, President and Chief Executive Officer, p. B59

★ LEHIGH VALLEY HEALTH NETWORK 1200 South Cedar Crest Boulevard, Zip 18103–6202, Mailing Address: P.O. Box 689, Zip 18105–1556; tel. 610/402–8000; Brian Nester, D.O., President and Chief Executive Officer, p. B81

**Beaver:** HERITAGE VALLEY HEALTH SYSTEM 1000 Dutch Ridge Road, Zip 15009–9727; tel. 724/773–2024; Norman F. Mitry, President and Chief Executive Officer, p. B70

**Bethlehem:** ST. LUKE'S UNIVERSITY HEALTH NETWORK 801 Ostrum Street, Zip 18015–1000; tel. 610/954–4000; Richard A. Anderson, President and Chief Executive Officer, p. B128

**Chambersburg:** ★ SUMMIT HEALTH 112 North Seventh Street, Zip 17201–1720; tel. 717/267–7138; Patrick W. O'Donnell, CPA, President and Chief Executive Officer, p. B129

**Danville:** ★ GEISINGER HEALTH SYSTEM 100 North Academy Avenue, Zip 17822–9800; tel. 570/271–6211; David T. Feinberg, M.D., President and Chief Executive Officer, p. B58

**Enola:** ★ POST ACUTE MEDICAL, LLC 1828 Good Hope Road, Suite 102, Zip 17025–1233; tel. 717/731–9660; Anthony F. Misitano, President and Chief Executive Officer, p. B105

**Greensburg:** EXCELA HEALTH 532 West Pittsburgh Street, Zip 15601, Mailing Address: 134 Industrial Park Road, Zip 15601–7328; tel. 724/832–5050; Robert Rogalski, Chief Executive Officer, p. B55

**King of Prussia:** UNIVERSAL HEALTH SERVICES, INC. 367 South Gulph Road, Zip 19406–3121, Mailing Address: P.O. Box 61558, Zip 19406–0958; tel. 610/768–3300; Alan B. Miller, Chairman and Chief Executive Officer, p. B141

**Lehighton:** ★ BLUE MOUNTAIN HEALTH SYSTEM 211 North 12th Street, Zip 18235–1138; tel. 610/377–1300; Andrew E. Harris, President and Chief Executive Officer, p. B24

**Mechanicsburg:** ★ SELECT MEDICAL CORPORATION 4714 Gettysburg Road, Zip 17055–4325; tel. 717/972–1100; David S. Chernow, President and Chief Executive Officer, p. B118

★ VIBRA HEALTHCARE 4550 Lena Drive, Suite 225, Zip 17055–4920; tel. 717/591–5700; Brad Hollinger, Chairman and Chief Executive Officer, p. B149

**Philadelphia:** EINSTEIN HEALTHCARE NETWORK 5501 Old York Road, Zip 19141–3098; tel. 215/456–7890; Barry R. Freedman, President and Chief Executive Officer, p. B53

★ TEMPLE UNIVERSITY HEALTH SYSTEM 3509 North Broad Street, 9th Floor, Zip 19140–4105; tel. 215/707–0900; Larry Kaiser, M.D., President and Chief Executive Officer, p. B131

★ UNIVERSITY OF PENNSYLVANIA HEALTH SYSTEM 3400 Civic Center Bouelvard, Zip 19104–5127; tel. 215/662–2203; Ralph W. Muller, President and Chief Executive Officer, p. B147

**Pittsburgh:** ★ ALLEGHENY HEALTH NETWORK 30 Isabella Street, Suite 300, Zip 15212–5862; tel. 412/359–3131; John W. Paul, President and Chief Executive Officer, p. B8

UPMC 600 Grant Street, U.S. Steel Tower, Suite 6262, Zip 15219–2702; tel. 412/647–8762; Jeffrey A. Romoff, President and Chief Executive Officer, p. B148

**Pottsville:** SCHUYLKILL HEALTH SYSTEM 420 South Jackson Street, Zip 17901–3625; tel. 570/621–5000; Marc H. Lory, Interim Chief Executive Officer, p. B118

**Radnor:** JEFFERSON HEALTH 259 Radnor–Chester Road, Suite 290, Zip 19087–5288, Mailing Address: 111 South 11th Street, Philadelphia, Zip 19107; tel. 610/225–6200; Stephen K. Klasko, M.D., Chief Executive Officer, p. B75

**Sayre:** ★ GUTHRIE CLINIC Guthrie Square, Zip 18840; tel. 570/887–4312; Joseph A. Scopelliti, M.D., President and Chief Executive Officer, p. B60

**Springfield:** ★ CROZER–KEYSTONE HEALTH SYSTEM 100 West Sproul Road, Zip 19064–2033; tel. 610/338–8205; Joan K. Richards, President and Chief Executive Officer, p. B44

**Villanova:** DEVEREUX 444 Devereux Drive, Zip 19085–1932, Mailing Address: P.O. Box 638, Zip 19085–0638; tel. 610/520–3000; Robert Q. Kreider, President and Chief Executive Officer, p. B50

**Washington:** ★ WASHINGTON HEALTH SYSTEM, INC. 155 Wilson Avenue, Zip 15301–3336; tel. 724/225–7000; Gary B. Weinstein, Chief Executive Officer, p. B152

**Williamsport:** ★ SUSQUEHANNA HEALTH SYSTEM 700 High Street, Zip 17701–3100; tel. 570/321–1000; Steven P. Johnson, FACHE, President and Chief Executive Officer, p. B129

**York:** ★ WELLSPAN HEALTH 45 Monument Road, Suite 200, Zip 17403–5071; tel. 717/851–2121; Kevin H. Mosser, M.D., President and Chief Executive Officer, p. B152

### PUERTO RICO

**San Juan:** ★ PUERTO RICO DEPARTMENT OF HEALTH Building A – Medical Center, Zip 00936, Mailing Address: Call Box 70184, Zip 00936; tel. 787/765–2929; Ana Rius, M.D., Secretary of Health, p. B110

### RHODE ISLAND

**Providence:** ★ CARE NEW ENGLAND HEALTH SYSTEM 45 Willard Avenue, Zip 02905–3218; tel. 401/453–7900; Dennis D. Keefe, President and Chief Executive Officer, p. B27

CHARTERCARE HEALTH PARTNERS 825 Chalkstone Avenue, Zip 02908–4728; tel. 410/456–2001; Lester P. Schindel, Chief Executive Officer, p. B32

LIFESPAN CORPORATION 167 Point Street, Zip 02903–4771; tel. 401/444–3500; Timothy J. Babineau, M.D., President and Chief Executive Officer, p. B85

### SOUTH CAROLINA

**Anderson:** ANMED HEALTH 800 North Fant Street, Zip 29621–5793; tel. 864/512–1000; William T. Manson, III, Chief Executive Officer, p. B10

**Columbia:** ★ PALMETTO HEALTH 1301 Taylor Street, Suite 9–A, Zip 29201–2942, Mailing Address: P.O. Box 2266, Zip 29202–2266; tel. 803/296–2100; Charles D. Beaman, Jr., Chief Executive Officer, p. B103

**Florence:** MCLEOD HEALTH 555 East Cheves Street, Zip 29506–2617, Mailing Address: P.O. Box 100551, Zip 29502–0551; tel. 843/777–2000; Robert L. Colones, President and Chief Executive Officer, p. B88

**Greenville:** ★ GREENVILLE HEALTH SYSTEM 701 Grove Road, Zip 29605–5611; tel. 864/455–7000; Michael C. Riordan, President and Chief Executive Officer, p. B60

**Spartanburg:** ★ SPARTANBURG REGIONAL HEALTHCARE SYSTEM 101 East Wood Street, Zip 29303–3040; tel. 864/560–6000; Bruce Holstien, President and Chief Executive Officer, p. B125

### SOUTH DAKOTA

**Rapid City:** ★ REGIONAL HEALTH 353 Fairmont Boulevard, Zip 57701–7375, Mailing Address: P.O. Box 6000, Zip 57709–6000; tel. 605/719–1000; Brent R. Phillips, President and Chief Executive Officer, p. B112

**Sioux Falls:** ★ AVERA HEALTH 3900 West Avera Drive, Suite 300, Zip 57108–5721; tel. 605/322–4700; John T. Porter, President and Chief Executive Officer, p. B17

★ SANFORD HEALTH 2301 East 60th Street North, Zip 57104–0569, Mailing Address: PO Box 5039, Zip 57117–5039; tel. 605/333–1000; Kelby K. Krabbenhoft, President and Chief Executive Officer, p. B116

### TENNESSEE

**Brentwood:** ★ DUKE LIFEPOINT HEALTHCARE 103 Powell Court, Zip 37027–5079; tel. 615/372–8540; Jeffrey G. Seraphine, FACHE, Division President, p. B52

★ HEALTHTECH MANAGEMENT SERVICES 5110 Maryland Way Suite 200, Zip 37027–2307; tel. 615/309–6053; Derek Morkel, Chief Executive Officer, p. B70

★ LIFEPOINT HEALTH 330 Seven Springs Way, Zip 37027–4536; tel. 615/920–7000; William F. Carpenter, III, Chairman and Chief Executive Officer, p. B83

POLARIS HOSPITAL COMPANY 10 Cadillac Drive, Suite 470, Zip 37027–1045; tel. 615/577–1111; Kevin D. Lee, Director and Chief Executive Officer, p. B105

★ QHR 105 Continental Place, Zip 37027–1052; tel. 800/233–1470; Mickey Bilbrey, President and Chief Executive Officer, p. B110

REGIONALCARE HOSPITAL PARTNERS 103 Continental Place, Suite 200, Zip 37027–1042; tel. 615/844–9800; Kent H. Wallace, Chief Executive Officer, p. B113

**Chattanooga:** ERLANGER HEALTH SYSTEM 975 East Third Street, Zip 37403–2147; tel. 423/778–7000; Kevin M. Spiegel, FACHE, President and Chief Executive Officer, p. B54

**Clinton:** CURAE HEALTH 121 Leinart Street, Zip 37716–3632, Mailing Address: P.O. Box 358, Zip 37717–0358; tel. 865/269–4074; Steve Clapp, President and Chief Executive Officer, p. B44

**Columbia:** ★ MAURY REGIONAL HEALTH SYSTEM 1224 Trotwood Avenue, Zip 38401–4802; tel. 931/381–1111; H. Alan Watson, FACHE, Chief Executive Officer, p. B86

**Franklin:** ACADIA HEALTHCARE COMPANY, INC. 830 Crescent Centre Drive, Suite 610, Zip 37067–7323; tel. 615/861–6000; Joey Jacobs, Chairman and Chief Executive Officer, p. B4

CAPELLA HEALTHCARE 501 Corporate Centre Drive, Suite 200, Zip 37067–2662; tel. 615/764–3000; Michael Wiechart, President and Chief Executive Officer, p. B26

★ COMMUNITY HEALTH SYSTEMS, INC. 4000 Meridian Boulevard, Zip 37067–6325, Mailing Address: P.O. Box 689020, Zip 37068–9020; tel. 615/465–7000; Wayne T. Smith, Chairman, President and Chief Executive Officer, p. B35

IASIS HEALTHCARE 117 Seaboard Lane, Building E., Zip 37067–2855; tel. 615/844–2747; Carl Whitmer, President and Chief Executive Officer, p. B72

**Jackson:** ★ WEST TENNESSEE HEALTHCARE 620 Skyline Drive, Zip 38301–3923; tel. 731/541–5000; Bobby Arnold, President and Chief Executive Officer, p. B153

**Johnson City:** MOUNTAIN STATES HEALTH ALLIANCE 400 North State of Franklin Road, Zip 37604–6035; tel. 423/302–3423; Alan M. Levine, President and Chief Executive Officer, p. B94

**Kingsport:** ★ WELLMONT HEALTH SYSTEM 1905 American Way, Zip 37660–5882; tel. 423/230–8200; Barton A. Hove, President and Chief Executive Officer, p. B152

**Knoxville:** ★ COVENANT HEALTH 100 Fort Sanders West Boulevard, Zip 37922–3353; tel. 865/531–5555; Anthony Spezia, President and Chief Executive Officer, p. B43

**Memphis:** ★ BAPTIST MEMORIAL HEALTH CARE CORPORATION 350 North Humphreys Boulevard, Zip 38120–2177; tel. 901/227–5117; Jason Little, President and Chief Executive Officer, p. B21

METHODIST LE BONHEUR HEALTHCARE 1211 Union Avenue, Suite 700, Zip 38104–6600; tel. 901/516–0791; Gary S. Shorb, President and Chief Executive Officer, p. B92

STRATEGIC BEHAVIORAL HEALTH, LLC 8295 Tournament Drive, Suite 201, Zip 38125–8913; tel. 901/969–3100; Jim Shaheen, President, p. B128

**Nashville:** ★ ARDENT HEALTH SERVICES 1 Burton Hills Boulevard, Suite 250, Zip 37215–6195; tel. 615/296–3000; David T. Vandewater, President and Chief Executive Officer, p. B11

© 2015 AHA Guide

HAVEN BEHAVIORAL HEALTHCARE 652 West Iris Drive, Zip 37204–3191; tel. 615/250–9500; Michael Lindley, Chief Executive Officer, p. B61

★ HCA One Park Plaza, Zip 37203–1548; tel. 615/344–9551; R. Milton Johnson, President and Chief Executive Officer, p. B61

★ VANDERBILT HEALTH 1211 22nd Avenue South, Zip 37232; tel. 615/322–5000; Charles Wright Pinson, M.D., Deputy Vice Chancellor for Health Affairs and Chief Executive Officer of Vanderbilt Health System, p. B149

**Parsons:** TENNESSEE HEALTH MANAGEMENT 52 West Eighth Street, Zip 38363–4656, Mailing Address: PO Box 10, Zip 38363–0010; tel. 731/847–6343; Dennis Berry, Chief Executive Officer, p. B133

## TEXAS

**Addison:** UNITED SURGICAL PARTNERS INTERNATIONAL 15305 Dallas Parkway, Suite 1600, Zip 75001–6491; tel. 972/713–3500; William H. Wilcox, President and Chief Executive Officer, p. B140

**Arlington:** ★ TEXAS HEALTH RESOURCES 612 East Lamar Boulevard, Suite 900, Zip 76011–4130; tel. 682/236–7900; Barclay E. Berdan, FACHE, Chief Executive Officer, p. B134

**Austin:** TEXAS DEPARTMENT OF STATE HEALTH SERVICES 1100 West 49th Street, Zip 78756–3199; tel. 512/458–7111; Kirk Cole, Interim Commissioner, p. B133

★ UNIVERSITY OF TEXAS SYSTEM 601 Colorado Street, Suite 205, Zip 78701–2904; tel. 512/499–4224; Raymond Greenberg, M.D., Executive Vice Chancellor, p. B148

**Dallas:** ★ BAYLOR SCOTT & WHITE HEALTH 4005 Crutcher Street, Suite 310, Zip 75246–1779; tel. 214/820–0111; Joel T. Allison, Chief Executive Officer, p. B22

CORNERSTONE HEALTHCARE GROUP 2200 Ross Avenue, Suite 5400, Zip 75201–7984; tel. 469/621–6700; David Smith, President and Chief Executive Officer, p. B42

GLOBALREHAB 1420 West Mockingbird Lane, Suite 100, Zip 75247–4932, Mailing Address: 1340 Empire Central Drive, Zip 75247–4022; tel. 214/879–7500; Hooman Sedighi, M.D., President and Chief Executive Officer, p. B58

★ METHODIST HEALTH SYSTEM 1441 North Beckley Avenue, Zip 75203–1201, Mailing Address: P.O. Box 655999, Zip 75265–5999; tel. 214/947–8181; Stephen L. Mansfield, Ph.D., FACHE, President and Chief Executive Officer, p. B92

★ TENET HEALTHCARE CORPORATION 1445 Ross Avenue, Suite 1400, Zip 75202–2703, Mailing Address: P.O. Box 1390369, Zip 75313–9036; tel. 469/893–2200; Trevor Fetter, President and Chief Executive Officer, p. B131

VIBRANT HEALTHCARE 12222 North Central Expressway, Suite 440, Zip 75243–3767; tel. 469/330–6745; Wilton M. Burt, Chief Executive Officer, p. B150

**Greenville:** HUNT REGIONAL HEALTHCARE 4215 Joe Ramsey Boulevard, Zip 75401–7852, Mailing Address: P.O. Box 1059, Zip 75403–1059; tel. 903/408–5000; Richard Carter, Chief Executive Officer, p. B72

**Houston:** ★ HOUSTON METHODIST 6565 Fannin Street, D–200, Zip 77030–2707; tel. 713/441–2221; Marc L. Boom, M.D., Chief Executive Officer, p. B71

★ MEMORIAL HERMANN HEALTHCARE SYSTEM 929 Gessner, Suite 2700, Zip 77024–2593; tel. 713/242–2700; Daniel J. Wolterman, President and Chief Executive Officer, p. B89

NEXUS HEALTH SYSTEMS One Riverway, Suite 600, Zip 77056–1993; tel. 713/355–6111; John W. Cassidy, M.D., President, Chief Executive Officer and Chief Medical Officer, p. B97

**Irving:** ★ CHRISTUS HEALTH 919 Hidden Ridge Drive, Zip 75038; tel. 469/282–2000; Ernie W. Sadau, Chief Executive Officer, p. B33

USMD INC. 6333 North State Highway 161 Suite 200, Zip 75038–2229; tel. 214/493–4000; Karen A. Fiducia, FACHE, President, Hospital Division, p. B148

**Longview:** AUDUBON BEHAVIORAL HEALTHCARE 100 West Hawkins, Suite D., Zip 75605; tel. 903/212–2930; William V. Brown, Chief Executive Officer, p. B16

GOOD SHEPHERD HEALTH SYSTEM 700 East Marshall Avenue, Zip 75601–5580; tel. 903/315–2000; Steve Altmiller, President and Chief Executive Officer, p. B59

**Lubbock:** ★ COVENANT HEALTH SYSTEM 3615 19th Street, Zip 79410–1203; tel. 806/725–0447; Richard H. Parks, FACHE, President and Chief Executive Officer, p. B43

**Plano:** ★ COMMUNITY HOSPITAL CORPORATION 7800 North Dallas Parkway, Suite 200, Zip 75024–6116; tel. 972/943–6400; Michael D. Williams, President and Chief Executive Officer, p. B41

★ LHP HOSPITAL GROUP 2400 North Dallas Parkway, Suite 450, Zip 75093–5994; tel. 866/465–9222; John F. Holland, Chief Executive Officer, p. B82

★ LIFECARE MANAGEMENT SERVICES 5340 Legacy Drive, Suite 150, Zip 75024–3131; tel. 469/241–2100; Phillip B. Douglas, Chairman and Chief Executive Officer, p. B82

**Richardson:** RELIANT HEALTHCARE PARTNERS 1300 East Lookout Drive, Suite 115, Zip 75082–4114; tel. 469/298–1400; Chester Crouch, Chief Executive Officer, p. B113

**Sherman:** CARRUS HOSPITALS 1810 West U.S. Highway 82, Zip 75092–7069; tel. 903/870–2600; Ronald E. Dorris, Chief Executive Officer, p. B28

**The Woodlands:** EMERUS 10077 Grogan's Mill, Suite 100, Zip 77380–1022; tel. 281/292–2450; Toby Hamilton, Chief Executive Officer, p. B54

VICTORY HEALTHCARE 2201 Timberloch Place, Suite 200, Zip 77380; tel. 281/863–2100; Robert N. Helms, Jr., Board Chair, President and Chief Executive Officer, p. B150

**Tyler:** ★ EAST TEXAS MEDICAL CENTER REGIONAL HEALTHCARE SYSTEM 1000 South Beckham Street, Zip 75701–1908, Mailing Address: P.O. Box 6400, Zip 75711–6400; tel. 903/535–6211; Elmer G. Ellis, FACHE, President and Chief Executive Officer, p. B52

TRINITY MOTHER FRANCES HOSPITALS AND CLINICS 910 East Houston, Zip 75702–8369; tel. 903/593–8441; J. Lindsey Bradley, Jr., FACHE, President, p. B137

## UTAH

**Nephi:** ★ RURAL HEALTH GROUP 48 West 1500 North, Zip 84648–8900; tel. 435/623–4924; Mark R. Stoddard, President and Chairman, p. B115

**Salt Lake City:** ★ INTERMOUNTAIN HEALTHCARE, INC. 36 South State Street, 22nd Floor, Zip 84111–1453; tel. 801/442–2000; Charles W. Sorenson, Jr., M.D., President and Chief Executive Officer, p. B74

## VIRGINIA

**Charlottesville:** UVA HEALTH SYSTEM 1215 Lee Street, Zip 22908–0816; tel. 434/924–0211; R. Edward Howell, Vice President and Chief Executive Officer, p. B148

**Falls Church:** DEPARTMENT OF THE ARMY, OFFICE OF THE SURGEON GENERAL 5109 Leesburg Pike, Zip 22041–3215; tel. 703/681–3000; Lieutenant General Eric B. Schoomaker, Surgeon General, p. B45

★ INOVA HEALTH SYSTEM 8110 Gatehouse Road, Suite 200 East, Zip 22042–1252; tel. 703/289–2069; J. Knox Singleton, President and Chief Executive Officer, p. B73

**Fredericksburg:** ★ MARY WASHINGTON HEALTHCARE 2300 Fall Hill Avenue, Suite 308, Zip 22401–3343; tel. 540/741–3100; Michael McDermott, M.D., President and Chief Executive Officer, p. B86

**Lynchburg:** CENTRA HEALTH, INC. 1920 Atherholt Road, Zip 24501–1104; tel. 434/200–3000; E. W. Tibbs, President and Chief Executive Officer, p. B32

**Newport News:** RIVERSIDE HEALTH SYSTEM 701 Town Center Drive, Suite 1000, Zip 23606–4286; tel. 757/534–7000; William B. Downey, President and Chief Executive Officer, p. B113

**Norfolk:** ★ SENTARA HEALTHCARE 6015 Poplar Hall Drive, Zip 23502–3819; tel. 757/455–7000; David L. Bernd, Chief Executive Officer, p. B122

**Richmond:** VCU HEALTH SYSTEM 1250 East Marshall Street, Zip 23298–5051, Mailing Address: P.O. Box 980510, Zip 23298–0510; tel. 804/828–9000; Marsha Rappley, M.D., Chief Executive Officer and Vice President for Health Sciences, p. B149

VIRGINIA DEPARTMENT OF MENTAL HEALTH 1220 Bank Street, Zip 23219–3645, Mailing Address: P.O. Box 1797, Zip 23218–1797; tel. 804/786–3921; James S. Reinhard, M.D., Commissioner, p. B151

**Roanoke:** ★ CARILION CLINIC 1906 Belleview Avenue S.E., Zip 24014–1838, Mailing Address: P.O. Box 13727, Zip 24036–3727; tel. 540/981–7000; Nancy Howell Agee, President and Chief Executive Officer, p. B27

**Winchester:** ★ VALLEY HEALTH SYSTEM 220 Campus Boulevard, Suite 420, Zip 22601–2889, Mailing Address: P.O. Box 3340, Zip 22604–2540; tel. 540/536–8024; Mark H. Merrill, President and Chief Executive Officer, p. B149

## WASHINGTON

**Renton:** ★ PROVIDENCE HEALTH & SERVICES 1801 Lind Avenue S.W., 9016, Zip 98057–9016; tel. 425/525–3698; Rodney F. Hochman, M.D., President and Chief Executive Officer, p. B109

**Seattle:** ★ SWEDISH HEALTH SERVICES 747 Broadway, Zip 98122–4379; tel. 206/386–6000; Anthony A. Armada, Senior Vice President, Chief Executive Officer of Swedish Health Services and Providence Health and Services, p. B130

★ UW MEDICINE 1959 N.E. Pacific Street, Zip 98195–0001, Mailing Address: P.O. Box 356350, Zip 98195–6350; tel. 206/543–7718; Paul G. Ramsey, M.D., Chief Executive Officer, p. B149

**Tacoma:** MULTICARE HEALTH SYSTEM 315 Martin Luther King Jr. Way, Zip 98405–4234, Mailing Address: P.O. Box 5299, Zip 98415–0299; tel. 253/403–1000; William G. Robertson, President and Chief Executive Officer, p. B94

**Vancouver:** ★ PEACEHEALTH 1115 S.E. 164th Avenue, Zip 98683; tel. 360/729–1000; Elizabeth Dunne, President and Chief Executive Officer, p. B104

**WEST VIRGINIA**

**Elkins:** ★ DAVIS HEALTH SYSTEM Reed Street and Gorman Avenue, Zip 26241, Mailing Address: P.O. Box 1697, Zip 26241–1697; tel. 304/636–3300; Mark Doak, President and Chief Executive Officer, p. B44

**Fairmont:** ★ WEST VIRGINIA UNITED HEALTH SYSTEM 1000 Technology Drive, Suite 2320, Zip 26554–8834; tel. 304/368–2700; Christopher Colenda, M.D., M.P.H., President and Chief Executive Officer, p. B153

**Huntington:** ★ PALLOTTINE HEALTH SERVICES 2900 First Avenue, Zip 25702–1241; tel. 304/526–1234; Michael G. Sellards, Chief Executive Officer, p. B102

**Morgantown:** ★ MONONGALIA HEALTH SYSTEM 1200 J. D. Anderson Drive, Zip 26505–3494; tel. 304/598–1200; Darryl L. Duncan, President and Chief Executive Officer, p. B93

**South Charleston:** ★ THOMAS HEALTH SYSTEM, INC. 4605 MacCorkle Avenue S.W., Zip 25309–1311; tel. 304/766–3600; Daniel Lauffer, FACHE, President and Chief Executive Officer, p. B134

**Wheeling:** OHIO VALLEY HEALTH SERVICES AND EDUCATION CORPORATION 2000 Eoff Street, Zip 26003–3823; tel. 304/234–8383; Michael J. Caruso, President and Chief Executive Officer, p. B101

**WISCONSIN**

**Appleton:** THEDACARE, INC. 122 East College Avenue, Zip 54911–5794, Mailing Address: P.O. Box 8025, Zip 54912–8025; tel. 920/830–5889; Dean Gruner, M.D., President and Chief Executive Officer, p. B134

**Janesville:** MERCY HEALTH SYSTEM 1000 Mineral Point Avenue, Zip 53548–2940, Mailing Address: P.O. Box 5003, Zip 53547–5003; tel. 608/756–6000; Javon R. Bea, President and Chief Executive Officer, p. B91

**Manitowoc:** ★ FRANCISCAN SISTERS OF CHRISTIAN CHARITY SPONSORED MINISTRIES, INC. 1415 South Rapids Road, Zip 54220–9302; tel. 920/684–7071; Sister Laura J. Wolf, President, p. B57

**Milwaukee:** ★ AURORA HEALTH CARE 750 Virginia Street, Zip 53204, Mailing Address: P.O. Box 341880, Zip 53234–1880; tel. 414/299–1631; Nick Turkal, M.D., President and Chief Executive Officer, p. B16

CHILDREN'S HOSPITAL AND HEALTH SYSTEM 9000 West Wisconsin Avenue, Zip 53226–4810, Mailing Address: P.O. Box 1997, Zip 53201–1997; tel. 414/226–2000; Peggy N. Troy, President and Chief Executive Officer, p. B32

**Waukesha:** ★ PROHEALTH CARE, INC. N17 W24100 Riverwood Drive, Suite 130, Zip 53188; tel. 262/928–2242; Susan A. Edwards, President and Chief Executive Officer, p. B108

**Wausau:** ★ ASPIRUS, INC. 425 Pine Ridge Boulevard, Zip 54401–4123; tel. 715/847–2118; Matthew Heywood, Chief Executive Officer, p. B15

## ARIZONA

**HONORHEALTH**
**8125 North Hayden Road, Scottsdale, AZ 85258–2463;**
**tel. 480/882–4000; Thomas J. Sadvary, FACHE, Chief Executive Officer**

HONORHEALTH DEER VALLEY MEDICAL CENTER, 19829 North 27th Avenue, Phoenix, AZ, Zip 85027–4002; tel. 623/879–6100; John L. Harrington, Jr., FACHE, Chief Executive Officer

HONORHEALTH JOHN C. LINCOLN MEDICAL CENTER, 250 East Dunlap Avenue, Phoenix, AZ, Zip 85020–2825; tel. 602/943–2381; Margaret Elizabeth Griffin, Chief Executive Officer

HONORHEALTH REHABILITATION HOSPITAL, 8850 East Pima Center Parkway, Scottsdale, AZ, Zip 85258–4619; tel. 480/800–3900; Scott R. Keen, Chief Executive Officer

HONORHEALTH SCOTTSDALE OSBORN MEDICAL CENTER, 7400 East Osborn Road, Scottsdale, AZ, Zip 85251–6403; tel. 480/882–4000; Bruce Pearson, Senior Vice President and Chief Executive Officer

HONORHEALTH SCOTTSDALE SHEA MEDICAL CENTER, 9003 East Shea Boulevard, Scottsdale, AZ, Zip 85260–6771; tel. 480/323–3000; Gary E. Baker, Senior Vice President and Chief Executive Officer

HONORHEALTH SCOTTSDALE THOMPSON PEAK MEDICAL CENTER, 7400 East Thompson Peak Parkway, Scottsdale, AZ, Zip 85255–4109; tel. 480/324–7000; Kimberly Post, R.N., Vice President and Administrator

**NORTHERN ARIZONA HEALTHCARE**
**1200 North Beaver Street, Flagstaff, AZ 86001–3118;**
**tel. 928/779–3366; Robert P. Thames, President and Chief Executive**
**Officer**

FLAGSTAFF MEDICAL CENTER, 1200 North Beaver Street, Flagstaff, AZ, Zip 86001–3118; tel. 928/779–3366; Richard Langosch, Interim President and Chief Executive Officer

VERDE VALLEY MEDICAL CENTER, 269 South Candy Lane, Cottonwood, AZ, Zip 86326–4170; tel. 928/639–6000; Susanne Maiden, Interim Administrator

## CALIFORNIA

**NORTHERN CALIFORNIA NETWORK**
**821 South St. Helena Highway Suite 208, St. Helena, CA 95661–3804;**
**tel. 707/967–7515; Terry Newmyer, President and Chief Executive**
**Officer**

FRANK R. HOWARD MEMORIAL HOSPITAL, One Madrone Street, Willits, CA, Zip 95490–4298; tel. 707/459–6801; Rick Bockmann, Chief Executive Officer

ST. HELENA HOSPITAL CLEAR LAKE, 15630 18th Avenue, Clearlake, CA, Zip 95422–9336, Mailing Address: P.O. Box 6710, Zip 95422; tel. 707/994–6486; David Santos, President and Chief Executive Officer

ST. HELENA HOSPITAL NAPA VALLEY, 10 Woodland Road, Saint Helena, CA, Zip 94574–9554; tel. 707/963–3611; Steven Herber, M.D., FACS, President and Chief Executive Officer

ST. HELENA HOSPITAL–CENTER FOR BEHAVIORAL HEALTH, 525 Oregon Street, Vallejo, CA, Zip 94590–3201; tel. 707/648–2200; Patricia Williams, Regional VP for Behavioral Medicine and Population Health

UKIAH VALLEY MEDICAL CENTER, 275 Hospital Drive, Ukiah, CA, Zip 95482–4531; tel. 707/462–3111; Gwen Matthews, R.N., MSN, Chief Executive Officer

**PROVIDENCE HEALTH AND SERVICES – SOUTHERN CALIFORNIA**
**501 South Buena Vista Street, Burbank, CA 91505–4809;**
**tel. 818/843–5111; Julie Sprengel, Chief Executive Officer**

PROVIDENCE HOLY CROSS MEDICAL CENTER, 15031 Rinaldi Street, Mission Hills, CA, Zip 91345–1207; tel. 818/365–8051; Bernard Klein, M.D., Chief Executive

PROVIDENCE LITTLE COMPANY OF MARY MEDICAL CENTER – TORRANCE, 4101 Torrance Boulevard, Torrance, CA, Zip 90503–4664; tel. 310/540–7676; Elizabeth Dunne, Chief Executive

PROVIDENCE LITTLE COMPANY OF MARY MEDICAL CENTER SAN PEDRO, 1300 West Seventh Street, San Pedro, CA, Zip 90732–3505; tel. 310/832–3311; Elizabeth Dunne, Chief Executive

PROVIDENCE SAINT JOSEPH MEDICAL CENTER, 501 South Buena Vista Street, Burbank, CA, Zip 91505–4866; tel. 818/843–5111; Julie Sprengel, Chief Executive Officer

PROVIDENCE TARZANA MEDICAL CENTER, 18321 Clark Street, Tarzana, CA, Zip 91356–3521; tel. 818/881–0800; Dale Surowitz, Chief Executive

**ST. JOSEPH HOAG HEALTH**
**3345 Michelson Drive, Suite 100, Irvine, CA 92612–0693;**
**tel. 949/381–4019; Richard Afable, M.D., M.P.H., President and Chief**
**Executive Officer**

HOAG MEMORIAL HOSPITAL PRESBYTERIAN, One Hoag Drive, Newport Beach, CA, Zip 92663–4120, Mailing Address: P.O. Box 6100, Zip 92658–6100; tel. 949/764–4624; Robert Braithwaite, President and Chief Executive Officer

MISSION HOSPITAL, 27700 Medical Center Road, Mission Viejo, CA, Zip 92691–6474; tel. 949/364–1400; Kenneth D. McFarland, President and Chief Executive Officer

ST. JOSEPH HOSPITAL, 1100 West Stewart Drive, Orange, CA, Zip 92868–3849, Mailing Address: P.O. Box 5600, Zip 92863–5600; tel. 714/633–9111; Steven C. Moreau, President and Chief Executive Officer

ST. JUDE MEDICAL CENTER, 101 East Valencia Mesa Drive, Fullerton, CA, Zip 92835–3875; tel. 714/992–3000; Lee Penrose, President and Chief Executive Officer

ST. MARY MEDICAL CENTER, 18300 Highway 18, Apple Valley, CA, Zip 92307–2206, Mailing Address: P.O. Box 7025, Zip 92307–0725; tel. 760/242–2311; Alan H. Garrett, Chief Executive Officer

## COLORADO

**CENTURA HEALTH**
**188 Inverness Drive West, Suite 500, Englewood, CO 80112–5204;**
**tel. 303/290–6500; Gary Campbell, Chief Executive Officer**

AVISTA ADVENTIST HOSPITAL, 100 Health Park Drive, Louisville, CO, Zip 80027–9583; tel. 303/673–1000; Dennis Barts, Chief Executive Officer

CASTLE ROCK ADVENTIST HOSPITAL, 2350 Meadows Boulevard, Castle Rock, CO, Zip 80109–8405; tel. 720/455–5000; Todd Folkenberg, Chief Executive Officer

LITTLETON ADVENTIST HOSPITAL, 7700 South Broadway Street, Littleton, CO, Zip 80122–2628; tel. 303/730–8900; Brett Spenst, Chief Executive Officer

PARKER ADVENTIST HOSPITAL, 9395 Crown Crest Boulevard, Parker, CO, Zip 80138–8573; tel. 303/269–4000; Morre Dean, Chief Executive Officer

PENROSE–ST. FRANCIS HEALTH SERVICES, 2222 North Nevada Avenue, Colorado Springs, CO, Zip 80907–6799, Mailing Address: P.O. Box 7021, Zip 80933–7021; tel. 719/776–5000; Margaret D. Sabin, President and Chief Executive Officer

PORTER ADVENTIST HOSPITAL, 2525 South Downing Street, Denver, CO, Zip 80210–5876; tel. 303/778–1955; Morre Dean, Chief Executive Officer

ST. ANTHONY HOSPITAL, 11600 West Second Place, Lakewood, CO, Zip 80228–1527; tel. 720/321–0000; Jeffrey Brickman, FACHE, President and Chief Executive Officer

ST. ANTHONY NORTH HEALTH CAMPUS, 14300 Orchard Parkway, Westminster, CO, Zip 80023–9206; tel. 720/627–0000; Carole Peet, R.N., MSN, President and Chief Executive Officer

ST. ANTHONY SUMMIT MEDICAL CENTER, 340 Peak One Drive, Frisco, CO, Zip 80443, Mailing Address: P.O. Box 738, Zip 80443–0738; tel. 970/668–3300; Paul J. Chodkowski, Chief Executive Officer

ST. MARY–CORWIN MEDICAL CENTER, 1008 Minnequa Avenue, Pueblo, CO, Zip 81004–3798; tel. 719/557–4000; Brian Moore, President and Chief Executive Officer

ST. THOMAS MORE HOSPITAL, 1338 Phay Avenue, Canon City, CO, Zip 81212–2302; tel. 719/285–2000; Sheri Trahern, CPA, FACHE, Chief Executive Officer

ST. VINCENT GENERAL HOSPITAL DISTRICT, 822 West 4th Street, Leadville, CO, Zip 80461–3897; tel. 719/486–0230; Sam Radke, Interim Chief Executive Officer and Interim Chief Financial Officer

**COMMUNITY HEALTH PROVIDERS ORGANIZATION**
**2021 North 12th Street, Grand Junction, CO 81501–2980;**
**tel. 970/256–6200; Chris Thomas, FACHE, President and Chief**
**Executive Officer**

COMMUNITY HOSPITAL, 2021 North 12th Street, Grand Junction, CO, Zip 81501–2999; tel. 970/242–0920; Chris Thomas, FACHE, President and Chief Executive Officer

**HCA HEALTHONE, LLC**
**4900 South Monaco Street, Suite 380, Denver, CO 80237–3487;**
**tel. 303/788–2500; Sylvia Young, President**

MEDICAL CENTER OF AURORA, 1501 South Potomac Street, Aurora, CO, Zip 80012–5411; tel. 303/695–2600; Ryan Simpson, Interim Chief Executive Officer

NORTH SUBURBAN MEDICAL CENTER, 9191 Grant Street, Thornton, CO, Zip 80229–4341; tel. 303/451–7800; Jennifer Alderfer, Chief Executive Officer

PRESBYTERIAN–ST. LUKE'S MEDICAL CENTER, 1719 East 19th Avenue, Denver, CO, Zip 80218–1281; tel. 303/839–6000; Maureen Tarrant, Chief Executive Officer

ROSE MEDICAL CENTER, 4567 East Ninth Avenue, Denver, CO, Zip 80220–3941; tel. 303/320–2121; Kenneth H. Feiler, Chief Executive Officer

SKY RIDGE MEDICAL CENTER, 10101 Ridge Gate Parkway, Lone Tree, CO, Zip 80124–5522; tel. 720/225–1000; Susan Hicks, Chief Executive Officer

**Section B**

SPALDING REHABILITATION HOSPITAL, 900 Potomac Steet, Aurora, CO, Zip 80011–6716; tel. 303/367–1166; Mark S. Deno, Chief Executive Officer

SWEDISH MEDICAL CENTER, 501 East Hampden Avenue, Englewood, CO, Zip 80113–2702; tel. 303/788–5000; Mary M. White, Chief Executive Officer

## CONNECTICUT

**EASTERN CONNECTICUT HEALTH NETWORK**
**71 Haynes Street, Manchester, CT 06040–4131; tel. 860/533–3400; Peter J. Karl, President and Chief Executive Officer**

MANCHESTER MEMORIAL HOSPITAL, 71 Haynes Street, Manchester, CT, Zip 06040–4188; tel. 860/646–1222; Peter J. Karl, President and Chief Executive Officer

ROCKVILLE GENERAL HOSPITAL, 31 Union Street, Vernon, CT, Zip 06066–3160; tel. 860/872–0501; Peter J. Karl, President and Chief Executive Officer

## FLORIDA

**BAYCARE HEALTH SYSTEM**
**16255 Bay Vista Drive, Clearwater, FL 33760–3127; tel. 877/692–2922; Stephen R. Mason, President and Chief Executive Officer**

BAYCARE ALLIANT HOSPITAL, 601 Main Street, Dunedin, FL, Zip 34698–5848; tel. 727/736–9999; Jacqueline Arocho, Administrator

MEASE COUNTRYSIDE HOSPITAL, 3231 McMullen–Booth Road, Safety Harbor, FL, Zip 34695–6607, Mailing Address: P.O. Box 1098, Zip 34695–1098; tel. 727/725–6222; Lou Galdieri, R.N., President

MEASE DUNEDIN HOSPITAL, 601 Main Street, Dunedin, FL, Zip 34698–5891, Mailing Address: P.O. Box 760, Zip 34697–0760; tel. 727/733–1111; Lou Galdieri, R.N., President

MORTON PLANT HOSPITAL, 300 Pinellas Street, Clearwater, FL, Zip 33756–3804, Mailing Address: P.O. Box 210, Zip 33757–0210; tel. 727/462–7000; N. Kristopher Hoce, President

MORTON PLANT NORTH BAY HOSPITAL, 6600 Madison Street, New Port Richey, FL, Zip 34652–1900; tel. 727/842–8468; Michael Yungmann, President

SOUTH FLORIDA BAPTIST HOSPITAL, 301 North Alexander Street, Plant City, FL, Zip 33563–4303; tel. 813/757–1200; Karen Kerr, R.N., President and Chief Executive Officer

ST. ANTHONY'S HOSPITAL, 1200 Seventh Avenue North, Saint Petersburg, FL, Zip 33705–1388, Mailing Address: P.O. Box 12588, Zip 33733–2588; tel. 727/825–1100; William G. Ulbricht, President

ST. JOSEPH'S HOSPITAL, 3001 West Martin Luther King Jr. Boulevard, Tampa, FL, Zip 33607–6387, Mailing Address: P.O. Box 4227, Zip 33677–4227; tel. 813/870–4000; Lorraine Lutton, President

WINTER HAVEN HOSPITAL, 200 Avenue F. N.E., Winter Haven, FL, Zip 33881–4193; tel. 863/293–1121; Stephen A. Nierman, President

## GEORGIA

**ST. JOSEPH'S/CANDLER HEALTH SYSTEM, INC.**
**5353 Reynolds Street, Savannah, GA 31405–6015; tel. 912/819–6000; Paul P. Hinchey, President and Chief Executive Officer**

APPLING HEALTHCARE SYSTEM, 163 East Tollison Street, Baxley, GA, Zip 31513–0120; tel. 912/367–9841; Peyton A. Smith, Chief Executive Officer

CANDLER HOSPITAL, 5353 Reynolds Street, Savannah, GA, Zip 31405–6015; tel. 912/819–6000; Paul P. Hinchey, President and Chief Executive Officer

EFFINGHAM HOSPITAL, 459 Highway 119 South, Springfield, GA, Zip 31329–3021, Mailing Address: P.O. Box 386, Zip 31329–0386; tel. 912/754–6451; Norma J. Morgan, Chief Executive Officer

EMORY UNIVERSITY HOSPITAL, 1364 Clifton Road N.E., atlanta, GA, Zip 30322; tel. 404/712–2000; Robert J. Bachman, Chief Executive Officer

LIBERTY REGIONAL MEDICAL CENTER, 462 Elma G. Miles Parkway, Hinesville, GA, Zip 31313–4000, Mailing Address: P.O. Box 919, Zip 31310–0919; tel. 912/369–9400; H. Scott Kroell, Jr., Chief Executive Officer

MEADOWS REGIONAL MEDICAL CENTER, One Meadows Parkway, Vidalia, GA, Zip 30474–8759, Mailing Address: P.O. Box 1048, Zip 30475–1048; tel. 912/535–5555; Alan Kent, Chief Executive Officer

ST. JOSEPH'S HOSPITAL, 11705 Mercy Boulevard, Savannah, GA, Zip 31419–1791; tel. 912/819–4100; Paul P. Hinchey, President and Chief Executive Officer

WILLINGWAY HOSPITAL, 311 Jones Mill Road, Statesboro, GA, Zip 30458–4765; tel. 912/764–6236; Barbara S. Reid, Chief Executive Officer

## IDAHO

**SOUTHWEST IDAHO COMMUNITY HEALTH NETWORK**
**PO Box 607, Boise, ID 83701–0607; tel. 208/473–3006; Stephen R. Stoddard, FACHE, Executive Director**

CASCADE MEDICAL CENTER, 402 Lake Cascade Parkway, Cascade, ID, Zip 83611–7702, Mailing Address: P.O. Box 1330, Zip 83611–1330; tel. 208/382–4242; Virgil Boss, Chief Executive Officer

NORTH CANYON MEDICAL CENTER, 267 North Canyon Drive, Gooding, ID, Zip 83330–5500; tel. 208/934–4433; Tim Powers, Chief Executive Officer

ST. LUKE'S ELMORE, 895 North Sixth East Street, Mountain Home, ID, Zip 83647–2207, Mailing Address: P.O. Box 1270, Zip 83647–1270; tel. 208/587–8401; Michael Blauer, Administrator

ST. LUKE'S JEROME, 709 North Lincoln Street, Jerome, ID, Zip 83338–1851, Mailing Address: 709 North Lincoln Avenue, Zip 83338–1851; tel. 208/324–4301; James L. Angle, FACHE, Chief Executive Officer

ST. LUKE'S MAGIC VALLEY MEDICAL CENTER, 801 Pole Line Road West, Twin Falls, ID, Zip 83301–5810, Mailing Address: P.O. Box 409, Zip 83303–0409; tel. 208/814–1000; James L. Angle, FACHE, Regional Chief Executive Officer

ST. LUKE'S MCCALL, 1000 State Street, McCall, ID, Zip 83638–3704; tel. 208/634–2221; Michael A. Fenello, Administrator

ST. LUKE'S REHABILITATION HOSPITAL, 600 North Robbins Road, Boise, ID, Zip 83702–4565, Mailing Address: P.O. Box 1100, Zip 83701–1100; tel. 208/489–4444; Nolan Hoffer, Senior Director

ST. LUKE'S WOOD RIVER MEDICAL CENTER, 100 Hospital Drive, Ketchum, ID, Zip 83340, Mailing Address: P.O. Box 100, Zip 83340–0100; tel. 208/727–8800; Cody Langbehn, Chief Executive Officer

SYRINGA HOSPITAL AND CLINICS, 607 West Main Street, Grangeville, ID, Zip 83530–1396; tel. 208/983–1700; Joseph Cladouhos, Chief Executive Officer

VALOR HEALTH, 1202 East Locust Street, Emmett, ID, Zip 83617–2715; tel. 208/365–3561; Wade C. Johnson, MS, FACHE, Chief Executive Officer

WEISER MEMORIAL HOSPITAL, 645 East Fifth Street, Weiser, ID, Zip 83672–2202; tel. 208/549–0370; Tom Murphy, Chief Executive Officer

**THE HOSPITAL COOPERATIVE**
**500 South 11th Avenue Suite 503, Pocatello, ID 83201–4881; tel. 208/239–1951; Jon Smith, Executive Director**

BEAR LAKE MEMORIAL HOSPITAL, 164 South Fifth Street, Montpelier, ID, Zip 83254–1597; tel. 208/847–1630; Rodney D. Jacobson, Administrator

BINGHAM MEMORIAL HOSPITAL, 98 Poplar Street, Blackfoot, ID, Zip 83221–1799; tel. 208/785–4100; Louis D. Kraml, FACHE, Chief Executive Officer

CARIBOU MEMORIAL HOSPITAL AND LIVING CENTER, 300 South Third West, Soda Springs, ID, Zip 83276–1598; tel. 208/547–3341; Jon Smith, Chief Executive Officer

EASTERN IDAHO REGIONAL MEDICAL CENTER, 3100 Channing Way, Idaho Falls, ID, Zip 83404–7533, Mailing Address: P.O. Box 2077, Zip 83403–2077; tel. 208/529–6111; Douglas Crabtree, Chief Executive Officer

FRANKLIN COUNTY MEDICAL CENTER, 44 North First East Street, Preston, ID, Zip 83263–1399; tel. 208/852–0137; Alan Bird, Chief Executive Officer

LOST RIVERS MEDICAL CENTER, 551 Highland Drive, Arco, ID, Zip 83213–9771, Mailing Address: P.O. Box 145, Zip 83213–0145; tel. 208/527–8206; Brad Huerta, Chief Executive Officer and Administrator

MADISON MEMORIAL HOSPITAL, 450 East Main Street, Rexburg, ID, Zip 83440–2048, Mailing Address: P.O. Box 310, Zip 83440–0310; tel. 208/359–6900; Rachel Ann Gonzales, M.D., Chief Executive Officer

MINIDOKA MEMORIAL HOSPITAL, 1224 Eighth Street, Rupert, ID, Zip 83350–1599; tel. 208/436–0481; Carl Hanson, Administrator

NELL J. REDFIELD MEMORIAL HOSPITAL, 150 North 200 West, Malad City, ID, Zip 83252–1239, Mailing Address: Box 126, Zip 83252–0126; tel. 208/766–2231; John Williams, Administrator and Chief Executive Officer

PORTNEUF MEDICAL CENTER, 777 Hospital Way, Pocatello, ID, Zip 83201–5175; tel. 208/239–1000; Daniel Ordyna, Chief Executive Officer

POWER COUNTY HOSPITAL DISTRICT, 510 Roosevelt Road, American Falls, ID, Zip 83211–1362, Mailing Address: P.O. Box 420, Zip 83211–0420; tel. 208/226–3200; Dallas Clinger, Administrator

STAR VALLEY MEDICAL CENTER, 901 Adams Street, Afton, WY, Zip 83110–9621, Mailing Address: P.O. Box 579, Zip 83110–0579; tel. 307/885–5800; Charlie A. Button, President and Chief Executive Officer

STEELE MEMORIAL MEDICAL CENTER, 203 South Daisy Street, Salmon, ID, Zip 83467–4709; tel. 208/756–5600; Jeff Hill, Chief Executive Officer

TETON VALLEY HEALTH CARE, 120 East Howard Street, Driggs, ID, Zip 83422–5112; tel. 208/354–2383; Keith Gnagey, Chief Executive Officer

## ILLINOIS

**FELICIAN SERVICES, INC.**
**3800 West Peterson Avenue, Chicago, IL 60659–3116; tel. 773/463–3806; Sister Mary Clarette Stryzewski, President and Chief Executive Officer**

ST. MARY'S HOSPITAL, 400 North Pleasant Avenue, Centralia, IL, Zip 62801–3056; tel. 618/436–8000; John R. Sigsbury, President

WHEATON FRANCISCAN HEALTHCARE – ST. FRANCIS, 3237 South 16th Street, Milwaukee, WI, Zip 53215–4592; tel. 414/647–5000; Coreen Dicus–Johnson, President

## INDIANA

### LUTHERAN HEALTH NETWORK
**7950 West Jefferson Boulevard, Fort Wayne, IN 46804–4140; tel. 260/435–7001; Brian Bauer, Chief Executive Officer**

BLUFFTON REGIONAL MEDICAL CENTER, 303 South Main Street, Bluffton, IN, Zip 46714–2503; tel. 260/824–3210; Aaron Garofola, Chief Executive Officer

DUKES MEMORIAL HOSPITAL, 275 West 12th Street, Peru, IN, Zip 46970–1638; tel. 765/472–8000; Debra Close, Chief Executive Officer

DUPONT HOSPITAL, 2520 East Dupont Road, Fort Wayne, IN, Zip 46825–1675; tel. 260/416–3000; Chad Towner, Chief Executive Officer

KOSCIUSKO COMMUNITY HOSPITAL, 2101 East Dubois Drive, Warsaw, IN, Zip 46580–3288; tel. 574/267–3200; Stephen R. Miller, Chief Executive Officer

LUTHERAN HOSPITAL OF INDIANA, 7950 West Jefferson Boulevard, Fort Wayne, IN, Zip 46804–4140; tel. 260/435–7001; Brian Bauer, Chief Executive Officer

ORTHOPAEDIC HOSPITAL OF LUTHERAN HEALTH NETWORK, 7952 West Jefferson Boulevard, Fort Wayne, IN, Zip 46804–4140; tel. 260/435–2999; Lorie Ailor, Chief Executive Officer

REHABILITATION HOSPITAL OF FORT WAYNE, 7970 West Jefferson Boulevard, Fort Wayne, IN, Zip 46804–4140; tel. 260/435–6100; Brian Bauer, Chief Executive Officer

ST. JOSEPH HOSPITAL, 700 Broadway, Fort Wayne, IN, Zip 46802–1493; tel. 260/425–3000; Kenneth Jones, Chief Executive Officer

### ST. VINCENT HEALTH
**10330 North Meridian Street, Indianapolis, IN 46290–1024; tel. 317/338–2273; Jonathan Nalli, Chief Executive Officer**

ST. JOSEPH HOSPITAL & HEALTH CENTER, 1907 West Sycamore Street, Kokomo, IN, Zip 46901–4197; tel. 765/452–5611; Margaret M. Johnson, Interim President

ST. MARY'S WARRICK HOSPITAL, 1116 Millis Avenue, Boonville, IN, Zip 47601–2204; tel. 812/897–4800; Kathy J. Hall, Administrator

ST. MARY'S MEDICAL CENTER OF EVANSVILLE, 3700 Washington Avenue, Evansville, IN, Zip 47714–0541; tel. 812/485–4000; Keith Jewell, President

ST. VINCENT ANDERSON REGIONAL HOSPITAL, 2015 Jackson Street, Anderson, IN, Zip 46016–4339; tel. 765/649–2511; Thomas J. VanOsdol, President

ST. VINCENT CARMEL HOSPITAL, 13500 North Meridian Street, Carmel, IN, Zip 46032–1456; tel. 317/582–7000; Michael D. Chittenden, President

ST. VINCENT CLAY HOSPITAL, 1206 East National Avenue, Brazil, IN, Zip 47834–2797, Mailing Address: P.O. Box 489, Zip 47834–0489; tel. 812/442–2500; Jerry Laue, Administrator

ST. VINCENT DUNN HOSPITAL, 1600 23rd Street, Bedford, IN, Zip 47421–4704; tel. 812/275–3331; Matt Balla, Chief Executive Officer

ST. VINCENT FISHERS HOSPITAL, 13861 Olio Road, Fishers, IN, Zip 46037–3487; tel. 317/415–9000; Gary Fammartino, Administrator

ST. VINCENT FRANKFORT HOSPITAL, 1300 South Jackson Street, Frankfort, IN, Zip 46041–3394; tel. 765/656–3000; Kristi Bledsoe, R.N., Administrator

ST. VINCENT HEART CENTER, 10580 North Meridian Street, Indianapolis, IN, Zip 46290–1028; tel. 317/583–5000; Blake A. Dye, President

ST. VINCENT INDIANAPOLIS HOSPITAL, 2001 West 86th Street, Indianapolis, IN, Zip 46260–1991, Mailing Address: P.O. Box 40970, Zip 46240–0970; tel. 317/338–2345; Joel Feldman, M.D., President

ST. VINCENT JENNINGS HOSPITAL, 301 Henry Street, North Vernon, IN, Zip 47265–1097; tel. 812/352–4200; Carl W. Risk, II, Administrator

ST. VINCENT MERCY HOSPITAL, 1331 South A Street, Elwood, IN, Zip 46036–1942; tel. 765/552–4600; Francis G. Albarano, Administrator

ST. VINCENT RANDOLPH HOSPITAL, 473 Greenville Avenue, Winchester, IN, Zip 47394–9436, Mailing Address: P.O. Box 407, Zip 47394–0407; tel. 765/584–0004; Francis G. Albarano, Administrator

ST. VINCENT SALEM HOSPITAL, 911 North Shelby Street, Salem, IN, Zip 47167–1694; tel. 812/883–5881; Dana M. Muntz, Chief Executive Officer

ST. VINCENT SETON SPECIALTY HOSPITAL, 8050 Township Line Road, Indianapolis, IN, Zip 46260–2478; tel. 317/415–8353; Peter H. Alexander, Administrator

ST. VINCENT WILLIAMSPORT HOSPITAL, 412 North Monroe Street, Williamsport, IN, Zip 47993–1049; tel. 765/762–4000; Jane Craigin, Chief Executive Officer

### SUBURBAN HEALTH ORGANIZATION
**2780 Waterfront Parkway East Drive, Suite 300, Indianapolis, IN 46214; tel. 317/692–5222; Dave Lippincott, President**

HANCOCK REGIONAL HOSPITAL, 801 North State Street, Greenfield, IN, Zip 46140–1270, Mailing Address: P.O. Box 827, Zip 46140–0827; tel. 317/462–5544; Steven V. Long, FACHE, President and Chief Executive Officer

HENDRICKS REGIONAL HEALTH, 1000 East Main Street, Danville, IN, Zip 46122–1948, Mailing Address: P.O. Box 409, Zip 46122–0409; tel. 317/745–4451; Kevin Speer, Chief Executive Officer

HENRY COUNTY HOSPITAL, 1000 North 16th Street, New Castle, IN, Zip 47362–4319, Mailing Address: P.O. Box 490, Zip 47362–0490; tel. 765/521–0890; Paul Janssen, President and Chief Executive Officer

JOHNSON MEMORIAL HOSPITAL, 1125 West Jefferson Street, Franklin, IN, Zip 46131–2140, Mailing Address: P.O. Box 549, Zip 46131–0549; tel. 317/736–3300; Larry Heydon, President and Chief Executive Officer

MAJOR HOSPITAL, 150 West Washington Street, Shelbyville, IN, Zip 46176–1236; tel. 317/392–3211; John M. Horner, Chief Executive Officer

MARGARET MARY HEALTH, 321 Mitchell Avenue, Batesville, IN, Zip 47006–8909, Mailing Address: P.O. Box 226, Zip 47006–0226; tel. 812/934–6624; Timothy L. Putnam, FACHE, President and Chief Executive Officer

RIVERVIEW HOSPITAL, 395 Westfield Road, Noblesville, IN, Zip 46060–1425, Mailing Address: P.O. Box 220, Zip 46061–0220; tel. 317/773–0760; Patricia K. Fox, President and Chief Executive Officer

RUSH MEMORIAL HOSPITAL, 1300 North Main Street, Rushville, IN, Zip 46173–1198, Mailing Address: P.O. Box 608, Zip 46173–0608; tel. 765/932–4111; Bradley Smith, President and Chief Executive Officer

WITHAM MEMORIAL HOSPITAL, 2605 North Lebanon Street, Lebanon, IN, Zip 46052–1476, Mailing Address: P.O. Box 1200, Zip 46052–3005; tel. 765/485–8000; Raymond V. Ingham, Ph.D., President and Chief Executive Officer

## IOWA

### GENESIS HEALTH SYSTEM
**1227 East Rusholme Street, Davenport, IA 52803–2498; tel. 563/421–1000; Douglas P. Cropper, President and Chief Executive Officer**

GENESIS MEDICAL CENTER, DEWITT, 1118 11th Street, De Witt, IA, Zip 52742–1296; tel. 563/659–4200; Curt Coleman, FACHE, Chief Executive Officer

GENESIS MEDICAL CENTER, ILLINI CAMPUS, 801 Illini Drive, Silvis, IL, Zip 61282–1893; tel. 309/281–4000; Kevin Youmans, Interim President

GENESIS MEDICAL CENTER–ALEDO, 409 N.W. Ninth Avenue, Aledo, IL, Zip 61231–1296; tel. 309/582–9100; Ted Rogalski, Administrator

GENESIS MEDICAL CENTER–DAVENPORT, 1227 East Rusholme Street, Davenport, IA, Zip 52803–2498; tel. 563/421–1000; Jordan Voigt, Administrator

### MERCY HEALTH NETWORK – CENTRAL IOWA
**1111 6th Avenue, Des Moines, IA 50314–2611; tel. 515/358–8023; Jim FitzPatrick, Senior Vice President, Network Development**

ADAIR COUNTY MEMORIAL HOSPITAL, 609 S.E. Kent Street, Greenfield, IA, Zip 50849–9454; tel. 641/743–2123; Angela Mortoza, Administrator

AUDUBON COUNTY MEMORIAL HOSPITAL, 515 Pacific Street, Audubon, IA, Zip 50025–1056; tel. 712/563–2611; Thomas G. Smith, Administrator and Chief Executive Officer

BOONE COUNTY HOSPITAL, 1015 Union Street, Boone, IA, Zip 50036–4821; tel. 515/432–3140; Joseph S. Smith, Chief Executive Officer

CLARINDA REGIONAL HEALTH CENTER, 220 Essie Davison Drive, Clarinda, IA, Zip 51632–2915, Mailing Address: P.O. Box 217, Zip 51632–0217; tel. 712/542–2176; Christopher R. Stipe, FACHE, Chief Executive Officer

DALLAS COUNTY HOSPITAL, 610 10th Street, Perry, IA, Zip 50220–2221; tel. 515/465–3547; Matt Wille, Chief Executive Officer

DAVIS COUNTY HOSPITAL, 509 North Madison Street, Bloomfield, IA, Zip 52537–1271; tel. 641/664–2145; Kirby Johnson, Chief Executive Officer

DECATUR COUNTY HOSPITAL, 1405 N.W. Church Street, Leon, IA, Zip 50144–1299; tel. 641/446–4871; Suzanne Cooner, R.N., MSN, Chief Executive Officer

GRINNELL REGIONAL MEDICAL CENTER, 210 Fourth Avenue, Grinnell, IA, Zip 50112–1898; tel. 641/236–2300; Todd C. Linden, President and Chief Executive Officer

KNOXVILLE HOSPITAL & CLINICS, 1002 South Lincoln Street, Knoxville, IA, Zip 50138–3155; tel. 641/842–2151; Kevin Kincaid, Chief Executive Officer

MADISON COUNTY HEALTH CARE SYSTEM, 300 West Hutchings Street, Winterset, IA, Zip 50273–2109; tel. 515/462–2373; Marcia Hendricks, R.N., FACHE, Chief Executive Officer

MANNING REGIONAL HEALTHCARE CENTER, 1550 6th Street, Manning, IA, Zip 51455–1093; tel. 712/655–2072; John O'Brien, Chief Executive Officer

MERCY MEDICAL CENTER–CENTERVILLE, 1 St. Joseph's Drive, Centerville, IA, Zip 52544–8055; tel. 641/437–4111; Clinton J. Christianson, FACHE, President and Chief Executive Officer

MERCY MEDICAL CENTER–DES MOINES, 1111 6th Avenue, Des Moines, IA, Zip 50314–2611; tel. 515/247–3121; Robert P. Ritz, FACHE, President

MONROE COUNTY HOSPITAL AND CLINICS, 6580 165th Street, Albia, IA, Zip 52531–8793; tel. 641/932–2134; Veronica Fuhs, Chief Executive Officer

RINGGOLD COUNTY HOSPITAL, 504 North Cleveland Street, Mount Ayr, IA, Zip 50854–2201; tel. 641/464–3226; Gordon W. Winkler, Administrator and Chief Executive Officer

VAN DIEST MEDICAL CENTER, 2350 Hospital Drive, Webster City, IA, Zip 50595–6600; tel. 515/832–9400; Lori Rathbun, Chief Executive Officer

WAYNE COUNTY HOSPITAL, 417 South East Street, Corydon, IA, Zip 50060–1860, Mailing Address: P.O. Box 305, Zip 50060–0305; tel. 641/872–2260; Daren Relph, Chief Executive Officer

**MERCY HEALTH NETWORK – NORTH IOWA**
**1000 4th Street S.W., Mason City, IA 50401–2800; tel. 641/428–7000;**
**Daniel Varnum, Chief Executive Officer**

FRANKLIN GENERAL HOSPITAL, 1720 Central Avenue East, Suite A., Hampton, IA, Zip 50441–1867; tel. 641/456–5000; Kim Price, Chief Executive Officer

HANCOCK COUNTY HEALTH SYSTEM, 532 First Street N.W., Britt, IA, Zip 50423–1227; tel. 641/843–5000; Vance Jackson, FACHE, Administrator and Chief Executive Officer

HANSEN FAMILY HOSPITAL, 920 South Oak, Iowa Falls, IA, Zip 50126–9506; tel. 641/648–4631; Cherelle Montanye–Ireland, Chief Executive Officer

KOSSUTH REGIONAL HEALTH CENTER, 1515 South Phillips Street, Algona, IA, Zip 50511–3649; tel. 515/295–2451; Scott A. Curtis, Administrator and Chief Executive Officer

MERCY MEDICAL CENTER–NEW HAMPTON, 308 North Maple Avenue, New Hampton, IA, Zip 50659–1142; tel. 641/394–4121; Aaron Flugum, Chief Executive Officer

MITCHELL COUNTY REGIONAL HEALTH CENTER, 616 North Eighth Street, Osage, IA, Zip 50461–1498; tel. 641/732–6000; Shelly Russell, Chief Executive Officer

PALO ALTO COUNTY HEALTH SYSTEM, 3201 First Street, Emmetsburg, IA, Zip 50536–2516; tel. 712/852–5500; Desiree Einsweiler, Chief Executive Officer

REGIONAL HEALTH SERVICES OF HOWARD COUNTY, 235 Eighth Avenue West, Cresco, IA, Zip 52136–1098; tel. 563/547–2101; Robin M. Schluter, Chief Executive Officer

# KANSAS

**COTTONWOOD HEALTH ALLIANCE**
**1100 Columbine Drive, Holton, KS, Zip 66436–8824;**
**tel. 785/364–2116; Sara A. Larison, Director**

F. W. HUSTON MEDICAL CENTER, 408 Delaware Street, Winchester, KS, Zip 66097–4003; tel. 913/774–4340; LaMont Cook, Adminstrator

HIAWATHA COMMUNITY HOSPITAL, 300 Utah Street, Hiawatha, KS 66434–2314; tel. 785/742–2131; John Moore, Administrator

HOLTON COMMUNITY HOSPITAL, 1100 Columbine Drive, Holton KS, Zxip 66436–8824; tel. 785/364–2116; Carrie L. Saia, RN, Chief Executive Officer

NEMAHA VALLEY COMMUNITY HOSPITAL, 1600 Community Drive, Seneca, KS, Zip 66538–9739; tel. 785/336–6181; Stan Regehr, President and Chief Executive Officer

ST. FRANCIS HEALTH, 1700 SW 7th Street, Topeka, KS, Zip 66606–1690; tel. 785/295–8000; David P. Setchel, President

**HAYS MEDICAL CENTER**
**2220 Canterbury Drive, Hays, KS 67601–2370; tel. 785/623–2300;**
**John H. Jeter, M.D., President and Chief Executive Officer**

PAWNEE VALLEY COMMUNITY HOSPITAL, 923 Carroll Avenue, Larned, KS 67550–2429; tel. 620/285–3161; John Hughes, Adminstrator

**HEALTH INNOVATIONS NETWORK OF KANSAS**
**1500 S.W. 10th Avenue, Topeka, KS 66604–1301; tel. 785/354–6137;**
**Kristi Gosser, Network Operations Director**

ATCHISON HOSPITAL, 800 Raven Hill Drive, Atchison, KS, Zip 66002–9204; tel. 913/367–2131; John L. Jacobson, Chief Executive Officer

CLAY COUNTY MEDICAL CENTER, 617 Liberty Street, Clay Center, KS, Zip 67432–1564, Mailing Address: P.O. Box 512, Zip 67432–0512; tel. 785/632–2144; Austin M. Gillard, Chief Executive Officer

COFFEY COUNTY HOSPITAL, 801 North Fourth Street, Burlington, KS, Zip 66839–2602; tel. 620/364–2121; Thomas W. Laux, Interim Chief Executive Officer

COMMUNITY HEALTHCARE SYSTEM, 120 West Eighth Street, Onaga, KS, Zip 66521–9574; tel. 785/889–4272; Todd Willert, Chief Executive Officer

F. W. HUSTON MEDICAL CENTER, 408 Delaware Street, Winchester, KS, Zip 66097–4003; tel. 913/774–4340; LaMont Cook, Administrator

GEARY COMMUNITY HOSPITAL, 1102 St. Mary's Road, Junction City, KS, Zip 66441–4196, Mailing Address: P.O. Box 490, Zip 66441–0490; tel. 785/238–4131; Joseph Stratton, FACHE, Chief Executive Officer

HERINGTON MUNICIPAL HOSPITAL, 100 East Helen Street, Herington, KS, Zip 67449–1606; tel. 785/258–2207; Michael J. Ryan, Chief Executive Officer

HIAWATHA COMMUNITY HOSPITAL, 300 Utah Street, Hiawatha, KS, Zip 66434–2314; tel. 785/742–2131; John Moore, Administrator

IRWIN ARMY COMMUNITY HOSPITAL, 600 Caisson Hill Road, Junction City, KS, Zip 66442–7037; tel. 785/239–7000; Colonel Barry R. Pockrandt, Commander

KANSAS REHABILITATION HOSPITAL, 1504 S.W. Eighth Avenue, Topeka, KS, Zip 66606–1632; tel. 785/235–6600; William J. Overbey, Chief Executive Officer

MORRIS COUNTY HOSPITAL, 600 North Washington Street, Council Grove, KS, Zip 66846–1422; tel. 620/767–6811; James H. Reagan, Jr., Ph.D., Chief Executive Officer

NEMAHA VALLEY COMMUNITY HOSPITAL, 1600 Community Drive, Seneca, KS, Zip 66538–9739; tel. 785/336–6181; Stan Regehr, President and Chief Executive Officer

NEWMAN REGIONAL HEALTH, 1201 West 12th Avenue, Emporia, KS, Zip 66801–2597; tel. 620/343–6800; Robert N. Wright, Chief Executive Officer

SABETHA COMMUNITY HOSPITAL, 14th and Oregon Streets, Sabetha, KS, Zip 66534–0229, Mailing Address: P.O. Box 229, Zip 66534–0229; tel. 785/284–2121; Lora Key, Chief Executive Officer

STORMONT–VAIL HEALTHCARE, 1500 S.W. Tenth Avenue, Topeka, KS, Zip 66604–1353; tel. 785/354–6000; Randall Peterson, President and Chief Executive Officer

VIA CHRISTI HOSPITAL MANHATTAN, INC., 1823 College Avenue, Manhattan, KS, Zip 66502–3346; tel. 785/776–3322; John R. Broberg, FACHE, Senior Administrator

WAMEGO HEALTH CENTER, 711 Genn Drive, Wamego, KS, Zip 66547–1179; tel. 785/456–2295; Shannan Flach, Chief Executive Officer

WASHINGTON COUNTY HOSPITAL, 304 East Third Street, Washington, KS, Zip 66968–2033; tel. 785/325–2211; Roxanne Schottel, Chief Executive Officer

**MED–OP, INC.**
**205 East 7th Street, Hays, KS 67601–4907; tel. 785/621–4510; David**
**Brittain, Executive Director**

CITIZENS MEDICAL CENTER, 100 East College Drive, Colby, KS, Zip 67701–3799; tel. 785/462–7511; Greg Unruh, Chief Executive Officer

CLARA BARTON HOSPITAL, 250 West Ninth Street, Hoisington, KS, Zip 67544–1706; tel. 620/653–2114; James Blackwell, Chief Executive Officer

GOODLAND REGIONAL MEDICAL CENTER, 220 West Second Street, Goodland, KS, Zip 67735–1602; tel. 785/890–3625; Donald Lee Wade, Chief Financial Officer

GOVE COUNTY MEDICAL CENTER, 520 West Fifth Street, Quinter, KS, Zip 67752–0129, Mailing Address: P.O. Box 129, Zip 67752–0129; tel. 785/754–3341; Coleen Tummons, Chief Executive Officer

GRAHAM COUNTY HOSPITAL, 304 West Prout Street, Hill City, KS, Zip 67642–1435; tel. 785/421–2121; Melissa Atkins, CPA, Chief Executive Officer

HAYS MEDICAL CENTER, 2220 Canterbury Drive, Hays, KS, Zip 67601–2370, Mailing Address: P.O. Box 8100, Zip 67601–8100; tel. 785/623–5000; John H. Jeter, M.D., President and Chief Executive Officer

LOGAN COUNTY HOSPITAL, 211 Cherry Street, Oakley, KS, Zip 67748–1201; tel. 785/672–3211; Meldon L. Snow, Chief Executive Officer

NESS COUNTY HOSPITAL, 312 Custer Street, Ness City, KS, Zip 67560–1654; tel. 785/798–2291; Curt Thomas, Administrator

NORTON COUNTY HOSPITAL, 102 East Holme, Norton, KS, Zip 67654–1406, Mailing Address: P.O. Box 250, Zip 67654–0250; tel. 785/877–3351; Ryan Stover, Chief Executive Officer

ROOKS COUNTY HEALTH CENTER, 1210 North Washington Street, Plainville, KS, Zip 67663–1632, Mailing Address: P.O. Box 389, Zip 67663–0389; tel. 785/434–4553; Michael Sinclair, Chief Executive Officer

RUSH COUNTY MEMORIAL HOSPITAL, 801 Locust Street, La Crosse, KS, Zip 67548–9673, Mailing Address: P.O. Box 520, Zip 67548–0520; tel. 785/222–2545; Brenda Legleiter, R.N., Chief Executive Officer

RUSSELL REGIONAL HOSPITAL, 200 South Main Street, Russell, KS, Zip 67665–2920; tel. 785/483–3131; Harold Courtois, Chief Executive Officer

SCOTT COUNTY HOSPITAL, 201 East Albert Avenue, Scott City, KS, Zip 67871–1203; tel. 620/872–5811; Mark Burnett, President and Chief Executive Officer

SHERIDAN COUNTY HEALTH COMPLEX, 826 18th Street, Hoxie, KS, Zip 67740–0167, Mailing Address: P.O. Box 167, Zip 67740–0167; tel. 785/675–3281; Niceta Farber, Chief Executive Officer

**PIONEER HEALTH NETWORK, INC.**
**310 East Walnut Street, Suite 210, Garden City, KS 67846–5565;**
**tel. 620/276–6100; Mary Adam, Executive Director**

BOB WILSON MEMORIAL GRANT COUNTY HOSPITAL, 415 North Main Street, Ulysses, KS, Zip 67880–2133; tel. 620/356–1266; Arthur H. Frable, Chief Executive Officer

CITIZENS MEDICAL CENTER, 100 East College Drive, Colby, KS, Zip 67701–3799; tel. 785/462–7511; Greg Unruh, Chief Executive Officer

EDWARDS COUNTY HOSPITAL AND HEALTHCARE CENTER, 620 West Eighth Street, Kinsley, KS, Zip 67547–2329, Mailing Address: P.O. Box 99, Zip 67547–0099; tel. 620/659–3621; Jimmie W. Hansel, Ph.D., Chief Executive Officer

GREELEY COUNTY HEALTH SERVICES, 506 Third Street, Tribune, KS, Zip 67879–9684, Mailing Address: P.O. Box 338, Zip 67879–0338; tel. 620/376–4221; Lee Rhodes, Administrator and Chief Executive Officer

HAMILTON COUNTY HOSPITAL, 700 North Huser Street, Syracuse, KS, Zip 67878–0948, Mailing Address: P.O. Box 948, Zip 67878–0948; tel. 620/384–7461; Rob Nahmensen, Chief Executive Officer

HODGEMAN COUNTY HEALTH CENTER, 809 Bramley Street, Jetmore, KS, Zip 67854–9320, Mailing Address: P.O. Box 310, Zip 67854–0310; tel. 620/357–8361; Teresa L. Deuel, Chief Executive Officer

KEARNY COUNTY HOSPITAL, 500 Thorpe Street, Lakin, KS, Zip 67860–9625; tel. 620/355–7111; Benjamin Anderson, Chief Executive Officer and Administrator

LANE COUNTY HOSPITAL, 235 West Vine, Dighton, KS, Zip 67839–0969, Mailing Address: P.O. Box 969, Zip 67839–0969; tel. 620/397–5321; Donna McGowan, Administrator

LOGAN COUNTY HOSPITAL, 211 Cherry Street, Oakley, KS, Zip 67748–1201; tel. 785/672–3211; Meldon L. Snow, Chief Executive Officer

MEADE DISTRICT HOSPITAL, 510 East Carthage Street, Meade, KS, Zip 67864–6401, Mailing Address: P.O. Box 820, Zip 67864–0820; tel. 620/873–2141; Steve Stewart, Administrator

MINNEOLA DISTRICT HOSPITAL, 212 Main Street, Minneola, KS, Zip 67865–8511, Mailing Address: P.O. Box 127, Zip 67865–0127; tel. 620/885–4264; Deborah Bruner, Chief Executive Officer and Administrator

MORTON COUNTY HEALTH SYSTEM, 445 Hilltop Street, Elkhart, KS, Zip 67950–0937, Mailing Address: P.O. Box 937, Zip 67950–0937; tel. 620/697–2141; Richard Q. Bergling, Interim Chief Executive Officer

SATANTA DISTRICT HOSPITAL AND LONG TERM CARE, 401 South Cheyenne Street, Satanta, KS, Zip 67870–0159, Mailing Address: P.O. Box 159, Zip 67870–0159; tel. 620/649–2761; Jeremy Clingenpeel, Administrator

SCOTT COUNTY HOSPITAL, 201 East Albert Avenue, Scott City, KS, Zip 67871–1203; tel. 620/872–5811; Mark Burnett, President and Chief Executive Officer

SOUTHWEST MEDICAL CENTER, 315 West 15th Street, Liberal, KS, Zip 67901–2455, Mailing Address: Box 1340, Zip 67905–1340; tel. 620/624–1651; William Ermann, President and Chief Executive Officer

ST. CATHERINE HOSPITAL, 401 East Spruce Street, Garden City, KS, Zip 67846–5679; tel. 620/272–2561; Scott J. Taylor, President and Chief Executive Officer

STANTON COUNTY HOSPITAL, 404 North Chestnut Street, Johnson, KS, Zip 67855–5001, Mailing Address: P.O. Box 779, Zip 67855–0779; tel. 620/492–6250; Jay Tusten, Chief Executive Officer

STEVENS COUNTY HOSPITAL, 1006 South Jackson Street, Hugoton, KS, Zip 67951–2858, Mailing Address: P.O. Box 10, Zip 67951–0010; tel. 620/544–8511; Linda Stalcup, Chief Executive Officer

WICHITA COUNTY HEALTH CENTER, 211 East Earl Street, Leoti, KS, Zip 67861–9620; tel. 620/375–2233; Tyson Sterling, Chief Executive Officer

**SOUTHERN PLAINS HEALTH NETWORK**
**203 South Main, Pratt, KS, Zip 67124; tel. 620/672–6411; DeWayne Bryan, Executive Director**

ASHLAND HEALTH CENTER 709 Oak Street, Ashland, KS, Zip 67831–0188; tel. 620/635–2241; Roger Barnhart, Chief Executive Officer

COMANCHE COUNTY HOSPITAL, 202 South Frisco Street, Coldwater, KS, Zip 67029–9500; Mailing address: HC 65, Box 8A, Zip 67029–9500; tel. 620/582–2144; Nancy Zimmerman, RN, Administrator

KIOWA DISTRICT HOSPITAL AND MAJOR, 819 Drumm Street, Kiowa, KS, Zip 67070–1626; Mailing address: P.O. Box 184, Zip 67070–0184; tel. 620/825–4131; Margaret Grisner, Chief Executive Officer

MEDICINE LODGE MEMORIAL HOSPITAL, 719 North Walnut Street, Medicine Lodge, KS, Zp 67104–1019; tel. 620/886–3771; Kevin A. White, Administrator

PRATT REGIONAL MEDICAL CENTER, 200 Commodore Street, Pratt, KS, Zip 67124–2903; tel. 620/672–7451; Susan M. Page, President and Chief Executive Officer

STAFFORD COUNTY HOSPITAL, 502 South Buckeye Street, Stafford, KS, Zip 67578–2035; Mailing address: P.O. Box 190, Zip 67578–0190; tel. 620/234–5221; Todd Taylor, Chief Executive Officer

**SUNFLOWER HEALTH NETWORK**
**400 South Santa Fe Avenue, Salina, KS 67401–4144; tel. 785/452–6102; Heather Fuller, Executive Director**

ANTHONY MEDICAL CENTER, 1101 East Spring Street, Anthony, KS, Zip 67003–2122; tel. 620/842–5111; J. Bryant Anderson, Administrator and Chief Executive Officer

CLAY COUNTY MEDICAL CENTER, 617 Liberty Street, Clay Center, KS, Zip 67432–1564, Mailing Address: P.O. Box 512, Zip 67432–0512; tel. 785/632–2144; Austin M. Gillard, Chief Executive Officer

CLOUD COUNTY HEALTH CENTER, 1100 Highland Drive, Concordia, KS, Zip 66901–3923; tel. 785/243–1234; Don Bates, President and Chief Executive Officer

ELLSWORTH COUNTY MEDICAL CENTER, 1604 Aylward Street, Ellsworth, KS, Zip 67439–0087, Mailing Address: P.O. Box 87, Zip 67439–0087; tel. 785/472–3111; Roger A. Masse, FACHE, Chief Executive Officer

HERINGTON MUNICIPAL HOSPITAL, 100 East Helen Street, Herington, KS, Zip 67449–1606; tel. 785/258–2207; Michael J. Ryan, Chief Executive Officer

HILLSBORO COMMUNITY HOSPITAL, 701 South Main Street, Hillsboro, KS, Zip 67063–1553; tel. 620/947–3114; Marion Regier, Chief Executive Officer

HOSPITAL DISTRICT ONE OF RICE COUNTY, 619 South Clark Street, Lyons, KS, Zip 67554–3003, Mailing Address: P.O. Box 828, Zip 67554–0828; tel. 620/257–5173; George M. Stover, Chief Executive Officer

JEWELL COUNTY HOSPITAL, 100 Crestvue Avenue, Mankato, KS, Zip 66956–2407, Mailing Address: P.O. Box 327, Zip 66956–0327; tel. 785/378–3137; Doyle L. McKimmy, FACHE, Chief Executive Officer

LINCOLN COUNTY HOSPITAL, 624 North Second Street, Lincoln, KS, Zip 67455–1738, Mailing Address: P.O. Box 406, Zip 67455–0406; tel. 785/524–4403; Steven L. Granzow, Chief Executive Officer

LINDSBORG COMMUNITY HOSPITAL, 605 West Lincoln Street, Lindsborg, KS, Zip 67456–2328; tel. 785/227–3308; Larry VanDerWege, Administrator

MEMORIAL HEALTH SYSTEM, 511 N.E. Tenth Street, Abilene, KS, Zip 67410–2153; tel. 785/263–2100; Mark A. Miller, FACHE, Chief Executive Officer

MITCHELL COUNTY HOSPITAL HEALTH SYSTEMS, 400 West Eighth, Beloit, KS, Zip 67420–1605, Mailing Address: P.O. Box 399, Zip 67420–0399; tel. 785/738–2266; Jeremy Armstrong, FACHE, Chief Executive Officer

OSBORNE COUNTY MEMORIAL HOSPITAL, 424 West New Hampshire Street, Osborne, KS, Zip 67473–2314, Mailing Address: P.O. Box 70, Zip 67473–0070; tel. 785/346–2121; Kiley Floyd, Administrator

OTTAWA COUNTY HEALTH CENTER, 215 East Eighth, Minneapolis, KS, Zip 67467–1902, Mailing Address: P.O. Box 290, Zip 67467–0290; tel. 785/392–2122; Jody Parks, Administrator

REPUBLIC COUNTY HOSPITAL, 2420 G Street, Belleville, KS, Zip 66935–2400; tel. 785/527–2254; Blaine K. Miller, Administrator

SALINA REGIONAL HEALTH CENTER, 400 South Santa Fe Avenue, Salina, KS, Zip 67401–4198, Mailing Address: P.O. Box 5080, Zip 67402–5080; tel. 785/452–7000; Micheal Terry, President and Chief Executive Officer

SMITH COUNTY MEMORIAL HOSPITAL, 614 South Main Street, Smith Center, KS, Zip 66967–3001; tel. 785/282–6845; Allen Van Driel, FACHE, Administrator

## KENTUCKY

**COMMONWEALTH HEALTH CORPORATION**
**800 Park Street, Bowling Green, KY 42101–2356; tel. 270/745–1500; Connie Smith, President and Chief Executive Officer**

COMMONWEALTH REGIONAL SPECIALTY HOSPITAL, 250 Park Drive, 6th Floor, Bowling Green, KY, Zip 42101–1760, Mailing Address: P.O. Box 90010, Zip 42102–9010; tel. 270/796–6200; Emily Howard Martin, Administrator

MEDICAL CENTER AT BOWLING GREEN, 250 Park Street, Bowling Green, KY, Zip 42101–1795, Mailing Address: P.O. Box 90010, Zip 42102–9010; tel. 270/745–1000; Connie Smith, Chief Executive Officer

MEDICAL CENTER AT FRANKLIN, 1100 Brookhaven Road, Franklin, KY, Zip 42134–2746; tel. 270/598–4800; Eric Hagan, R.N., Vice President/Administrator

MEDICAL CENTER AT SCOTTSVILLE, 456 Burnley Road, Scottsville, KY, Zip 42164–6355; tel. 270/622–2800; Eric Hagan, R.N., Vice President/Administrator

**COMMUNITY CARE NETWORK**
**110 A. Second Street, Henderson, KY 42420; tel. 619/278–2273; Roberta Alexander, Director**

BAPTIST HEALTH MADISONVILLE, 900 Hospital Drive, Madisonville, KY, Zip 42431–1694; tel. 270/825–5100; Robert L. Ramey, Interim President

BAPTIST HEALTH PADUCAH, 2501 Kentucky Avenue, Paducah, KY, Zip 42003–3200; tel. 270/575–2100; William A. Brown, FACHE, President and CEO

CALDWELL MEDICAL CENTER, 100 Medical Center Drive, Princeton, KY, Zip 42445–2430, Mailing Address: P.O. Box 410, Zip 42445–0410; tel. 270/365–0300; Charles D. Lovell, Jr., FACHE, President and Chief Executive Officer

CRITTENDEN COUNTY HOSPITAL, 520 West Gum Street, Marion, KY, Zip 42064–1516, Mailing Address: P.O. Box 386, Zip 42064–0386; tel. 270/965–5281; Greg R. McNeil, Chief Executive Officer

HEALTHSOUTH DEACONESS REHABILITATION HOSPITAL, 4100 Covert Avenue, Evansville, IN, Zip 47714–5567, Mailing Address: P.O. Box 5349, Zip 47716–5349; tel. 812/476–9983; Blake Bunner, Chief Executive Officer

JENNIE STUART MEDICAL CENTER, 320 West 18th Street, Hopkinsville, KY, Zip 42240–1965, Mailing Address: P.O. Box 2400, Zip 42241–2400; tel. 270/887–0100; Eric A. Lee, President and Chief Executive Officer

KOSAIR CHILDREN'S HOSPITAL, 231 East Chestnut Street, Louisville, KY, Zip 40202–1821; tel. 502/629–6000; Thomas D. Kmetz, Division President

LINCOLN TRAIL BEHAVIORAL HEALTH SYSTEM, 3909 South Wilson Road, Radcliff, KY, Zip 40160–8944, Mailing Address: P.O. Box 369, Zip 40159–0369; tel. 270/351–9444; Charles L. Webb, Jr., Chief Executive Officer

LIVINGSTON HOSPITAL AND HEALTHCARE SERVICES, 131 Hospital Drive, Salem, KY, Zip 42078–8043; tel. 270/988–2299; Mark A. Edwards, Chief Executive Officer

MEDICAL CENTER AT FRANKLIN, 1100 Brookhaven Road, Franklin, KY, Zip 42134–2746; tel. 270/598–4800; Eric Hagan, R.N., Vice President/Administrator

METHODIST HOSPITAL, 1305 North Elm Street, Henderson, KY, Zip 42420–2775, Mailing Address: P.O. Box 48, Zip 42419–0048; tel. 270/827–7700; Bruce D. Begley, Executive Director

METHODIST HOSPITAL UNION COUNTY, 4604 Highway 60 West, Morganfield, KY, Zip 42437–9570; tel. 270/389–5000; Patrick Donahue, Vice President and Administrator

MUHLENBERG COMMUNITY HOSPITAL, 440 Hopkinsville Street, Greenville, KY, Zip 42345–1172, Mailing Address: P.O. Box 387, Zip 42345–0387; tel. 270/338–8000; Ed Heath, Chief Executive Officer

MURRAY–CALLOWAY COUNTY HOSPITAL, 803 Poplar Street, Murray, KY, Zip 42071–2432; tel. 270/762–1100; Colonel Jerome Penner, Chief Executive Officer

NORTON AUDUBON HOSPITAL, One Audubon Plaza Drive, Louisville, KY, Zip 40217–1300, Mailing Address: P.O. Box 17550, Zip 40217–0550; tel. 502/636–7111; Jon Cooper, Chief Administrative Officer

NORTON HOSPITAL, 200 East Chestnut Street, Louisville, KY, Zip 40202–1800, Mailing Address: P.O. Box 35070, Zip 40232–5070; tel. 502/629–8000; Matthew Ayers, Chief Administrative Officer

NORTON WOMEN'S AND KOSAIR CHILDREN'S HOSPITAL, 4001 Dutchmans Lane, Louisville, KY, Zip 40207–4799; tel. 502/893–1000; Charlotte Ipsan, Chief Administrative Officer

OHIO COUNTY HOSPITAL, 1211 Main Street, Hartford, KY, Zip 42347–1619; tel. 270/298–7411; Blaine Pieper, Chief Executive Officer

RIVERVALLEY BEHAVIORAL HEALTH HOSPITAL, 1000 Industrial Drive, Owensboro, KY, Zip 42301–8715; tel. 270/689–6500; Gayle DiCesare, President and Chief Executive Officer

SAINT THOMAS WEST HOSPITAL, 4220 Harding Road, Nashville, TN, Zip 37205–2095, Mailing Address: P.O. Box 380, Zip 37202–0380; tel. 615/222–2111; Don King, Chief Executive Officer

ST. MARY'S MEDICAL CENTER OF EVANSVILLE, 3700 Washington Avenue, Evansville, IN, Zip 47714–0541; tel. 812/485–4000; Keith Jewell, President

STS. MARY & ELIZABETH HOSPITAL, 1850 Bluegrass Avenue, Louisville, KY, Zip 40215–1199; tel. 502/361–6000; Jennifer Nolan, President

TRIGG COUNTY HOSPITAL, 254 Main Street, Cadiz, KY, Zip 42211–9153, Mailing Address: P.O. Box 312, Zip 42211–0312; tel. 270/522–3215; John Sumner, Chief Executive Officer

### KENTUCKYONE
**200 Abraham Flexner Way, Louisville, KY 40202–2877; tel. 502/587–4011; Ruth W. Brinkley, R.N., MSN, F, President and Chief Executive Officer**

CONTINUING CARE HOSPITAL, 150 North Eagle Creek Drive, 5th Floor, Lexington, KY, Zip 40509–1805; tel. 859/967–5744; Tonja Williams, MSN, R.N., President

FLAGET MEMORIAL HOSPITAL, 4305 New Shepherdsville Road, Bardstown, KY, Zip 40004–9019; tel. 502/350–5000; Beverly Sue Downs, R.N., MSN, FACHE, President

FRAZIER REHAB INSTITUTE, 220 Abraham Flexner Way, Louisville, KY, Zip 40202–1887; tel. 502/582–7400; Randy L. Napier, President

JEWISH HOSPITAL, 200 Abraham Flexner Way, Louisville, KY, Zip 40202–1886; tel. 502/587–4011; Joseph Gilene, President

JEWISH HOSPITAL–SHELBYVILLE, 727 Hospital Drive, Shelbyville, KY, Zip 40065–1699; tel. 502/647–4000; Barry A. Papania, Interim Administrator

OUR LADY OF PEACE, 2020 Newburg Road, Louisville, KY, Zip 40205–1879; tel. 502/479–4500; Jennifer Nolan, President

SAINT JOSEPH – LONDON, 1001 Saint Joseph Lane, London, KY, Zip 40741–8345; tel. 606/330–6000; Terrence G. Deis, CPA, FACHE, Chief Executive Officer

SAINT JOSEPH – MARTIN, 11203 Main Street, Martin, KY, Zip 41649; tel. 606/285–6400; Kathy Stumbo, President

SAINT JOSEPH BEREA, 305 Estill Street, Berea, KY, Zip 40403–1909; tel. 859/986–3151; Eric Gilliam, Chief Executive Officer

SAINT JOSEPH EAST, 150 North Eagle Creek Drive, Lexington, KY, Zip 40509–1805; tel. 859/967–5000; Eric Gilliam, President

SAINT JOSEPH HOSPITAL, One St. Joseph Drive, Lexington, KY, Zip 40504–3754; tel. 859/278–3436; Beverly Sue Downs, R.N., MSN, FACHE, Interim Chief Executive Officer

SAINT JOSEPH MOUNT STERLING, 225 Falcon Drive, Mount Sterling, KY, Zip 40353–1158, Mailing Address: P.O. Box 7, Zip 40353–0007; tel. 859/497–5000; Benny Nolen, President

SOUTHERN INDIANA REHABILITATION HOSPITAL, 3104 Blackiston Boulevard, New Albany, IN, Zip 47150–9579; tel. 812/941–8300; Randy L. Napier, President

STS. MARY & ELIZABETH HOSPITAL, 1850 Bluegrass Avenue, Louisville, KY, Zip 40215–1199; tel. 502/361–6000; Jennifer Nolan, President

UNIVERSITY OF LOUISVILLE HOSPITAL, 530 South Jackson Street, Louisville, KY, Zip 40202–3611; tel. 502/562–3000; Kenneth P. Marshall, President

### ST. ELIZABETH HEALTHCARE
**1 Medical Village Drive, Edgewood, KY 41017–3403; tel. 859/301–2000; Garren Colvin, Chief Executive Officer**

ST. ELIZABETH EDGEWOOD, 1 Medical Village Drive, Edgewood, KY, Zip 41017–3403; tel. 859/301–2000; Garren Colvin, Chief Executive Officer

ST. ELIZABETH FLORENCE, 4900 Houston Road, Florence, KY, Zip 41042–4824; tel. 859/212–5200; Garren Colvin, Chief Executive Officer

ST. ELIZABETH FORT THOMAS, 85 North Grand Avenue, Fort Thomas, KY, Zip 41075–1796; tel. 859/572–3100; Garren Colvin, Chief Executive Officer

ST. ELIZABETH GRANT, 238 Barnes Road, Williamstown, KY, Zip 41097–9482; tel. 859/824–8240; Garren Colvin, Chief Executive Officer

## MAINE

### MAINE NETWORK FOR HEALTH
**Key Plaza, 23 Water Street, Bangor, ME 04401; tel. 207/942–2844; Stephen A. Ryan, President and Chief Executive Officer**

BLUE HILL MEMORIAL HOSPITAL, 57 Water Street, Blue Hill, ME, Zip 04614–5231; tel. 207/374–3400; John Ronan, President and Chief Executive Officer

CHARLES A. DEAN MEMORIAL HOSPITAL, 364 Pritham Avenue, Greenville, ME, Zip 04441–1395, Mailing Address: P.O. Box 1129, Zip 04441–1129; tel. 207/695–5200; Geno Murray, President and Chief Executive Officer

EASTERN MAINE MEDICAL CENTER, 489 State Street, Bangor, ME, Zip 04401–6674, Mailing Address: P.O. Box 404, Zip 04402–0404; tel. 207/973–7000; Deborah Carey Johnson, R.N., President and Chief Executive Officer

HOULTON REGIONAL HOSPITAL, 20 Hartford Street, Houlton, ME, Zip 04730–1891; tel. 207/532–9471; Thomas J. Moakler, Chief Executive Officer

INLAND HOSPITAL, 200 Kennedy Memorial Drive, Waterville, ME, Zip 04901–4595; tel. 207/861–3000; John Dalton, President and Chief Executive Officer

MAYO REGIONAL HOSPITAL, 897 West Main Street, Dover–Foxcroft, ME, Zip 04426–1099; tel. 207/564–8401; Marie E. Vienneau, FACHE, President and Chief Executive Officer

MILLINOCKET REGIONAL HOSPITAL, 200 Somerset Street, Millinocket, ME, Zip 04462–1298; tel. 207/723–5161; Robert Peterson, Chief Executive Officer

MOUNT DESERT ISLAND HOSPITAL, 10 Wayman Lane, Bar Harbor, ME, Zip 04609–1625, Mailing Address: P.O. Box 8, Zip 04609–0008; tel. 207/288–5081; Arthur J. Blank, President and Chief Executive Officer

NORTHERN MAINE MEDICAL CENTER, 194 East Main Street, Fort Kent, ME, Zip 04743–1497; tel. 207/834–3155; Peter Sirois, Chief Executive Officer

SEBASTICOOK VALLEY HEALTH, 447 North Main Street, Pittsfield, ME, Zip 04967–3707; tel. 207/487–4000; Terri Vieira, President and Chief Executive Officer

THE ACADIA HOSPITAL, 268 Stillwater Avenue, Bangor, ME, Zip 04401–3945, Mailing Address: P.O. Box 422, Zip 04402–0422; tel. 207/973–6100; Daniel B. Coffey, President and Chief Executive Officer

THE AROOSTOOK MEDICAL CENTER, 140 Academy Street, Presque Isle, ME, Zip 04769–3171, Mailing Address: P.O. Box 151, Zip 04769–0151; tel. 207/768–4000; Sylvia Getman, President and Chief Executive Officer

## MASSACHUSETTS

### LAHEY HEALTH
**41 Mall Road, Burlington, MA 01805–0001; tel. 781/744–7100; Howard R. Grant, JD, M.D., President and Chief Executive Officer**

BEVERLY HOSPITAL, 85 Herrick Street, Beverly, MA, Zip 01915–1777; tel. 978/922–3000; Philip M. Cormier, Chief Executive Officer

LAHEY HOSPITAL & MEDICAL CENTER, BURLINGTON, 41 Mall Road, Burlington, MA, Zip 01805–0001; tel. 781/744–5100; Joanne Conroy, M.D., Chief Executive Officer

WINCHESTER HOSPITAL, 41 Highland Avenue, Winchester, MA, Zip 01890–1496; tel. 781/729–9000; Dale M. Lodge, Chief Executive Officer

### WELLFORCE
**16 New England Executive Park, Suite 125, Burlington, MA 01803–5217; tel. 978/942–2220; Normand E. Deschene, FACHE, Chief Executive Officer**

LOWELL GENERAL HOSPITAL, 295 Varnum Avenue, Lowell, MA, Zip 01854–2134; tel. 978/937–6000; Normand E. Deschene, FACHE, Chief Executive Officer

TUFTS MEDICAL CENTER, 800 Washington Street, Boston, MA, Zip 02111–1552; tel. 617/636–5000; Michael Wagner, M.D., President and Chief Executive Officer

## MICHIGAN

### GENESYS HEALTH SYSTEM
**1 Genesys Parkway, Grand Blanc, MI 48439–8065; tel. 810/606–5000; Elizabeth Aderholdt, Chief Executive Officer**

ST. JOHN MACOMB–OAKLAND HOSPITAL, 11800 East 12 Mile Road, Warren, MI, Zip 48093–3472; tel. 586/573–5000; Terry Hamilton, Chief Executive Officer

ST. JOSEPH HEALTH SYSTEM, 200 Hemlock Street, Tawas City, MI, Zip 48763–9237, Mailing Address: P.O. Box 659, Zip 48764–0659; tel. 989/362–3411; Ann M. Balfour, R.N., President

ST. MARY'S OF MICHIGAN, 800 South Washington Avenue, Saginaw, MI, Zip 48601–2594; tel. 989/907–8000; Elizabeth Aderholdt, President and Chief Executive Officer

### LAKELAND REGIONAL HEALTH SYSTEM
**1234 Napier Avenue, Saint Joseph, MI 49085–2112; tel. 269/983–8300; Loren Hamel, M.D., President and Chief Executive Officer**

LAKELAND HOSPITAL, WATERVLIET, 400 Medical Park Drive, Watervliet, MI, Zip 49098–9225; tel. 269/463–3111; Ray Cruse, Chief Executive Officer

LAKELAND MEDICAL CENTER, ST. JOSEPH, 1234 Napier Avenue, Saint Joseph, MI, Zip 49085–2158; tel. 269/983–8300; Loren Hamel, M.D., President and Chief Executive Officer

**ST. JOHN PROVIDENCE HEALTH SYSTEM**
**28000 Dequindre Drive, Warren, MI 48092; tel. 866/501–3627; Jean Meyer, President and Chief Executive Officer**

BRIGHTON CENTER FOR RECOVERY, 12851 Grand River Road, Brighton, MI, Zip 48116–8506; tel. 810/227–1211; Raymond Waller, Director

PROVIDENCE – PROVIDENCE PARK HOSPITAL, SOUTHFIELD CAMPUS, 16001 West Nine Mile Road, Southfield, MI, Zip 48075–4818, Mailing Address: P.O. Box 2043, Zip 48037–2043; tel. 248/424–3000; Michael Wiemann, M.D., President

ST. JOHN HOSPITAL AND MEDICAL CENTER, 22101 Moross Road, Detroit, MI, Zip 48236–2148; tel. 313/343–4000; Robert E. Hoban, Chief Executive Officer

ST. JOHN MACOMB–OAKLAND HOSPITAL, 11800 East 12 Mile Road, Warren, MI, Zip 48093–3472; tel. 586/573–5000; Terry Hamilton, President

ST. JOHN RIVER DISTRICT HOSPITAL, 4100 River Road, East China, MI, Zip 48054–2909; tel. 810/329–7111; Frank W. Poma, President

**UPPER PENINSULA HEALTH CARE NETWORK (UPHCN)**
**228 West Washington Street, Marquette, MI 49855–4330; tel. 906/225–3146; Dennis Smith, Chief Executive Officer**

ASPIRUS GRAND VIEW, N10561 Grand View Lane, Ironwood, MI, Zip 49938–9622; tel. 906/932–2525; Paula L. Chermside, Chief Operating Officer

ASPIRUS KEWEENAW HOSPITAL, 205 Osceola Street, Laurium, MI, Zip 49913–2134; tel. 906/337–6500; Michael Hauswirth, Chief Operating Officer

ASPIRUS ONTONAGON HOSPITAL, 601 South Seventh Street, Ontonagon, MI, Zip 49953–1459; tel. 906/884–8000; Michael Hauswirth, Chief Operating Officer

BARAGA COUNTY MEMORIAL HOSPITAL, 18341 U.S. Highway 41, L'Anse, MI, Zip 49946–8024; tel. 906/524–3300; Margie Hale, R.N., MSN, Chief Operating Officer

DICKINSON COUNTY HEALTHCARE SYSTEM, 1721 South Stephenson Avenue, Iron Mountain, MI, Zip 49801–3637; tel. 906/774–1313; John Schon, Administrator and Chief Executive Officer

HELEN NEWBERRY JOY HOSPITAL, 502 West Harrie Street, Newberry, MI, Zip 49868–1209; tel. 906/293–9200; Scott Pillion, Chief Executive Officer

MACKINAC STRAITS HEALTH SYSTEM, INC., 1140 North State Street, Saint Ignace, MI, Zip 49781–1048; tel. 906/643–8585; Rodney M. Nelson, Chief Executive Officer

MUNISING MEMORIAL HOSPITAL, 1500 Sand Point Road, Munising, MI, Zip 49862–1406; tel. 906/387–4110; Kevin P. Calhoun, Chief Executive Officer

NORTHSTAR HEALTH SYSTEM, 1400 West Ice Lake Road, Iron River, MI, Zip 49935–9526; tel. 906/265–6121; Connie L. Koutouzos, R.N., MSN, Chief Executive Officer and President

SCHOOLCRAFT MEMORIAL HOSPITAL, 7870W U.S. Highway 2, Manistique, MI, Zip 49854–8992; tel. 906/341–3200; Tanya Hoar, Chief Executive Officer and Chief Financial Officer

UP HEALTH SYSTEM–BELL, 901 Lakeshore Drive, Ishpeming, MI, Zip 49849–1367; tel. 906/486–4431; Mitchell D. Leckelt, Chief Executive Officer

UP HEALTH SYSTEM–PORTAGE, 500 Campus Drive, Hancock, MI, Zip 49930–1569; tel. 906/483–1000; Jeff Lang, President

WAR MEMORIAL HOSPITAL, 500 Osborn Boulevard, Sault Sainte Marie, MI, Zip 49783–1884; tel. 906/635–4460; David B. Jahn, President and Chief Executive Officer

## MISSOURI

**HEALTH NETWORK OF MISSOURI**
**One Hospital Drive, Room C1213, DC 079.00, Columbia, MO 65212; tel. 573/815–8000; Marty McCormick, Chief Executive Officer**

BOTHWELL REGIONAL HEALTH CENTER, 601 East 14th Street, Sedalia, MO, Zip 65301–5972, Mailing Address: P.O. Box 1706, Zip 65302–1706; tel. 660/826–8833; John M. Dawes, FACHE, Chief Executive Officer

CAPITAL REGION MEDICAL CENTER, 1125 Madison Street, Jefferson City, MO, Zip 65101–5200, Mailing Address: P.O. Box 1128, Zip 65102–1128; tel. 573/632–5000; Gaspare Calvaruso, President

HANNIBAL REGIONAL HOSPITAL, 6000 Hospital Drive, Hannibal, MO, Zip 63401–6887, Mailing Address: P.O. Box 551, Zip 63401–0551; tel. 573/248–1300; Lynn W. Olson, President and Chief Executive Officer

LAKE REGIONAL HEALTH SYSTEM, 54 Hospital Drive, Osage Beach, MO, Zip 65065–3050; tel. 573/348–8000; Michael E. Henze, Chief Executive Officer

SAINT FRANCIS MEDICAL CENTER, 211 St. Francis Drive, Cape Girardeau, MO, Zip 63703–5049; tel. 573/331–3000; Steven C. Bjelich, President and Chief Executive Officer

UNIVERSITY OF MISSOURI HOSPITALS AND CLINICS, One Hospital Drive, Columbia, MO, Zip 65212–0001; tel. 573/882–4141; Mitchell L. Wasden, Ed.D., Chief Executive Officer and Chief Operating Officer

**MERCY HEALTH EAST**
**615 South New Ballas Road, Saint Louis, MO 63141–8221; tel. 314/364–3000; Donn Sorensen, President, East Region**

MERCY HOSPITAL JEFFERSON, Highway 61 South, Crystal City, MO, Zip 63019, Mailing Address: P.O. Box 350, Zip 63019–0350; tel. 636/933–1000; Eric Ammons, President

MERCY HOSPITAL ST. LOUIS, 615 South New Ballas Road, Saint Louis, MO, Zip 63141–8277; tel. 314/569–6000; Jeffrey A. Johnston, President

MERCY HOSPITAL WASHINGTON, 901 East Fifth Street, Washington, MO, Zip 63090–3127; tel. 636/239–8000; Terri L. McLain, FACHE, President

**MOSAIC LIFE CARE**
**5325 Faraon Street, Saint Joseph, MO 64506–3488; tel. 816/271–6000; Samuel Mark Laney, M.D., President and Chief Executive Officer**

LONG–TERM ACUTE CARE HOSPITAL, MOSAIC LIFE CARE AT ST. JOSEPH, 5325 Faraon Street, Saint Joseph, MO, Zip 64506–3488; tel. 816/271–6000; Dana Anderson, Interim Administrator

MOSAIC LIFE CARE AT ST. JOSEPH, 5325 Faraon Street, Saint Joseph, MO, Zip 64506–3488; tel. 816/271–6000; Samuel Mark Laney, M.D., President and Chief Executive Officer

NORTHWEST MEDICAL CENTER, 705 North College Street, Albany, MO, Zip 64402–1433; tel. 660/726–3941; Jon D. Doolittle, President and Chief Executive Officer

## MONTANA

**MONTANA HEALTH NETWORK**
**11 South 7th Street, Suite 241, Miles City, MT 59301; tel. 406/234–1420; Janet Bastian, Chief Executive Officer**

BEARTOOTH BILLINGS CLINIC, 2525 North Broadway Avenue, Red Lodge, MT, Zip 59068–9222, Mailing Address: P.O. Box 590, Zip 59068–0590; tel. 406/446–2345; Deborah Agnew, M.D., Chief Executive Officer

BILLINGS CLINIC, 2800 10th Avenue North, Billings, MT, Zip 59101–0703, Mailing Address: P.O. Box 37000, Zip 59107–7000; tel. 406/657–4000; Nicholas Wolter, M.D., Chief Executive Officer

CENTRAL MONTANA MEDICAL CENTER, 408 Wendell Avenue, Lewistown, MT, Zip 59457–2261; tel. 406/535–7711; Christopher Noland, Interim Chief Executive Officer

DANIELS MEMORIAL HEALTHCARE CENTER, 105 Fifth Avenue East, Scobey, MT, Zip 59263, Mailing Address: P.O. Box 400, Zip 59263–0400; tel. 406/487–2296; David Hubbard, Chief Executive Officer

FALLON MEDICAL COMPLEX, 202 South 4th Street West, Baker, MT, Zip 59313–9156, Mailing Address: P.O. Box 820, Zip 59313–0820; tel. 406/778–3331; David Espeland, Chief Executive Officer

FRANCES MAHON DEACONESS HOSPITAL, 621 Third Street South, Glasgow, MT, Zip 59230–2699; tel. 406/228–3500; Randall G. Holom, Chief Executive Officer

GLENDIVE MEDICAL CENTER, 202 Prospect Drive, Glendive, MT, Zip 59330–1999; tel. 406/345–3306; Parker Powell, Chief Executive Officer

HOLY ROSARY HEALTHCARE, 2600 Wilson Street, Miles City, MT, Zip 59301–5094; tel. 406/233–2600; Paul Lewis, Chief Executive Officer

MCCONE COUNTY HEALTH CENTER, 605 Sullivan Avenue, Circle, MT, Zip 59215, Mailing Address: P.O. Box 48, Zip 59215–0048; tel. 406/485–3381; Nancy Rosaaen, Chief Executive Officer

PHILLIPS COUNTY HOSPITAL, 417 South Fourth East, Malta, MT, Zip 59538–8825, Mailing Address: P.O. Box 640, Zip 59538–0640; tel. 406/654–1100; Ward C. VanWichen, Chief Executive Officer

ROOSEVELT MEDICAL CENTER, 818 Second Avenue East, Culbertson, MT, Zip 59218, Mailing Address: P.O. Box 419, Zip 59218–0419; tel. 406/787–6401; Audrey Stromberg, Administrator

ROUNDUP MEMORIAL HEALTHCARE, 1202 Third Street West, Roundup, MT, Zip 59072–1816, Mailing Address: P.O. Box 40, Zip 59072–0040; tel. 406/323–2301; Bradley Howell, Chief Executive Officer

SHERIDAN MEMORIAL HOSPITAL, 440 West Laurel Avenue, Plentywood, MT, Zip 59254–1596; tel. 406/765–3700; Gregory L. Maurer, Chief Executive Officer

SIDNEY HEALTH CENTER, 216 14th Avenue S.W., Sidney, MT, Zip 59270–3586; tel. 406/488–2100; Richard Haraldson, Chief Executive Officer

STILLWATER COMMUNITY HOSPITAL, 44 West Fourth Avenue North, Columbus, MT, Zip 59019–0959, Mailing Address: P.O. Box 959, Zip 59019–0959; tel. 406/322–5316; Tim Russell, Administrator

## NEBRASKA

**BLUE RIVER VALLEY HEALTH NETWORK**
**2222 North Lincoln Avenue, York, NE 68467–1030; tel. 402/362–0445; Charles K. Schulz, FACHE, President**

Section B

ANNIE JEFFREY MEMORIAL COUNTY HEALTH CENTER, 531 Beebe Street, Osceola, NE, Zip 68651–5537, Mailing Address: P.O. Box 428, Zip 68651–0428; tel. 402/747–2031; Joseph W. Lohrman, FACHE, Chief Executive Officer

BOONE COUNTY HEALTH CENTER, 723 West Fairview Street, Albion, NE, Zip 68620–1725, Mailing Address: P.O. Box 151, Zip 68620–0151; tel. 402/395–2191; Victor N. Lee, FACHE, President and Chief Executive Officer

BRODSTONE MEMORIAL HOSPITAL, 520 East Tenth Street, Superior, NE, Zip 68978–1225, Mailing Address: P.O. Box 187, Zip 68978–0187; tel. 402/879–3281; John E. Keelan, Administrator and Chief Executive Officer

BUTLER COUNTY HEALTH CARE CENTER, 372 South Ninth Street, David City, NE, Zip 68632–2116; tel. 402/367–1200; Donald T. Naiberk, Administrator

COMMUNITY MEMORIAL HOSPITAL, 1579 Midland Street, Syracuse, NE, Zip 68446–9732, Mailing Address: P.O. Box N., Zip 68446–0518; tel. 402/269–2011; Michael Harvey, President and Chief Executive Officer

CRETE AREA MEDICAL CENTER, 2910 Betten Drive, Crete, NE, Zip 68333–3084, Mailing Address: P.O. Box 220, Zip 68333–0220; tel. 402/826–2102; Rebekah Mussman, Chief Executive Officer

FILLMORE COUNTY HOSPITAL, 1900 F Street, Geneva, NE, Zip 68361–1325, Mailing Address: P.O. Box 193, Zip 68361–0193; tel. 402/759–3167; Paul Utemark, Chief Executive Officer

HENDERSON HEALTH CARE SERVICES, 1621 Front Street, Henderson, NE, Zip 68371–8902; tel. 402/723–4512; Cheryl Brown, Administrator

HOWARD COUNTY MEDICAL CENTER, 1113 Sherman Street, Saint Paul, NE, Zip 68873–1546, Mailing Address: P.O. Box 406, Zip 68873–0406; tel. 308/754–4421; Arlan D. Johnson, FACHE, Chief Executive Officer

JEFFERSON COMMUNITY HEALTH CENTER, 2200 H Street, Fairbury, NE, Zip 68352–1119, Mailing Address: P.O. Box 277, Zip 68352–0277; tel. 402/729–3351; Chad Jurgens, Chief Executive Officer

JOHNSON COUNTY HOSPITAL, 202 High Street, Tecumseh, NE, Zip 68450–2443, Mailing Address: P.O. Box 599, Zip 68450–0599; tel. 402/335–3361; Diane Newman, FACHE, Administrator

LITZENBERG MEMORIAL COUNTY HOSPITAL, 1715 26th Street, Central City, NE, Zip 68826–9620; tel. 308/946–3015; Julie Murray, Chief Executive Officer

MEMORIAL COMMUNITY HEALTH, 1423 Seventh Street, Aurora, NE, Zip 68818–1197; tel. 402/694–3171; Diane R. Keller, Chief Executive Officer

MEMORIAL HEALTH CARE SYSTEMS, 300 North Columbia Avenue, Seward, NE, Zip 68434–2228; tel. 402/643–2971; Roger J. Reamer, Chief Executive Officer

THAYER COUNTY HEALTH SERVICES, 120 Park Avenue, Hebron, NE, Zip 68370–2019, Mailing Address: P.O. Box 49, Zip 68370–0049; tel. 402/768–6041; Michael G. Burcham, Sr., FACHE, Chief Executive Officer

VALLEY COUNTY HEALTH SYSTEM, 2707 L. Street, Ord, NE, Zip 68862–1275; tel. 308/728–4200; William T. Sugg, President and Chief Executive Officer

WARREN MEMORIAL HOSPITAL, 905 Second Street, Friend, NE, Zip 68359–1133; tel. 402/947–2541; Christopher R. Bjornberg, Chief Executive Officer

YORK GENERAL HOSPITAL, 2222 North Lincoln Avenue, York, NE, Zip 68467–1095; tel. 402/362–6671; Charles K. Schulz, FACHE, Chief Executive Officer

**CHI HEALTH**
  **12809 West Dodge Road, Omaha, NE 68154–2155; tel. 402/343–4000; Cliff Robertson, M.D., President and Chief Executive Officer**

CHI HEALTH BERGAN MERCY, 7500 Mercy Road, Omaha, NE, Zip 68124–2319; tel. 402/398–6060; Marie E. Knedler, R.N., FACHE, President

CHI HEALTH CREIGHTON UNIVERSITY MEDICAL CENTER, 601 North 30th Street, Omaha, NE, Zip 68131–2197; tel. 402/449–4000; Kevin J. Nokels, FACHE, President

CHI HEALTH GOOD SAMARITAN, 10 East 31st Street, Kearney, NE, Zip 68847–2926, Mailing Address: P.O. Box 1990, Zip 68848–1990; tel. 308/865–7100; Michael H. Schnieders, FACHE, President

CHI HEALTH IMMANUEL, 6901 North 72nd Street, Omaha, NE, Zip 68122–1799; tel. 402/572–2121; Ann Schumacher, R.N., MSN, FACHE, President

CHI HEALTH LAKESIDE, 16901 Lakeside Hills Court, Omaha, NE, Zip 68130–2318; tel. 402/717–8000; Cindy Alloway, President

CHI HEALTH MERCY CORNING, 603 Rosary Drive, Corning, IA, Zip 50841–1683; tel. 641/322–3121; Debra Goldsmith, Chief Executive Officer

CHI HEALTH MERCY COUNCIL BLUFFS, 800 Mercy Drive, Council Bluffs, IA, Zip 51503–3128, Mailing Address: P.O. Box 1C, Zip 51502–3001; tel. 712/328–5000; Marie E. Knedler, R.N., FACHE, President

CHI HEALTH MIDLANDS, 11111 South 84th Street, Papillion, NE, Zip 68046–4122; tel. 402/593–3000; Cindy Alloway, President

CHI HEALTH MISSOURI VALLEY, 631 North Eighth Street, Missouri Valley, IA, Zip 51555–1102; tel. 712/642–2784; Robert A. Valentine, President

CHI HEALTH NEBRASKA HEART, 7500 South 91st Street, Lincoln, NE, Zip 68526–9437; tel. 402/327–2700; Dan Schonlau, Interim President

CHI HEALTH PLAINVIEW, 704 North Third Street, Plainview, NE, Zip 68769–2047, Mailing Address: P.O. Box 489, Zip 68769–0489; tel. 402/582–4245; Richard B. Gamel, President, Regional Hospital

CHI HEALTH SAINT FRANCIS, 2620 West Faidley Avenue, Grand Island, NE, Zip 68803–4297, Mailing Address: P.O. Box 9804, Zip 68802–9804; tel. 308/384–4600; Daniel P. McElligott, FACHE, President

CHI HEALTH SCHUYLER, 104 West 17th Street, Schuyler, NE, Zip 68661–1304; tel. 402/352–2441; Connie Peters, R.N., President

CHI HEALTH ST ELIZABETH, 555 South 70th Street, Lincoln, NE, Zip 68510–2494; tel. 402/219–8000; Kim S. Moore, FACHE, President

CHI HEALTH ST. MARY'S, 1301 Grundman Boulevard, Nebraska City, NE, Zip 68410; tel. 402/873–3321; Daniel J. Kelly, President

**NEBRASKA MEDICINE**
  **987400 Nebraska Medical Center, Omaha, NE 68198–7400; tel. 877/763–0000; Rosanna D. Morris, R.N., Interim Chief Executive Officer**

NEBRASKA MEDICINE – BELLEVUE, 2500 Bellevue Medical Center Drive, Bellevue, NE, Zip 68123–1591; tel. 402/763–3000; Rosanna D. Morris, R.N., Interim Chief Executive Officer

NEBRASKA MEDICINE – NEBRASKA MEDICAL CENTER, 987400 Nebraska Medical Center, Omaha, NE, Zip 68198–7400; tel. 402/552–2000; Rosanna D. Morris, R.N., Interim Chief Executive Officer

**NORTHEAST HEALTH SERVICES**
  **PO Box 186, Creighton, NE 68729–0186; tel. 402/358–5700; Jennifer Poppen, Chief Executive Officer**

AVERA CREIGHTON HOSPITAL, 1503 Main Street, Creighton, NE, Zip 68729–3007, Mailing Address: P.O. Box 186, Zip 68729–0186; tel. 402/358–5700; Jennifer Poppen, Chief Executive Officer

CHI HEALTH PLAINVIEW, 704 North Third Street, Plainview, NE, Zip 68769–2047, Mailing Address: P.O. Box 489, Zip 68769–0489; tel. 402/582–4245; Richard B. Gamel, President, Regional Hospital

OSMOND GENERAL HOSPITAL, 402 North Maple Street, Osmond, NE, Zip 68765–5726, Mailing Address: P.O. Box 429, Zip 68765–0429; tel. 402/748–3393; Lon Knievel, Chief Executive Officer

**NEW HAMPSHIRE**

**CARING COMMUNITY NETWORK OF THE TWIN RIVERS**
  **c/o First Health, 841 Central Street, Franklin, NH 03235–2026; tel. 603/934–0177; Rick Silverberg, Managing Director**

FRANKLIN REGIONAL HOSPITAL, 15 Aiken Avenue, Franklin, NH, Zip 03235–1299; tel. 603/934–2060; Charles K. Van Sluyter, Interim Chief Executive Officer

**NEW JERSEY**

**QUALCARE, INC.**
  **242 Old New Brunswick Road, Piscataway, NJ 08854–3754; tel. 732/562–2800; Jerry Eisenberg, Network Contact**

CAPITAL HEALTH MEDICAL CENTER–HOPEWELL, 1 Capital Way, Pennington, NJ, Zip 08534–2520; tel. 609/303–4000; Al Maghazehe, Ph.D., FACHE, President and Chief Executive Officer

CHILTON MEDICAL CENTER, 97 West Parkway, Pompton Plains, NJ, Zip 07444–1696; tel. 973/831–5000; Alan Lieber, Interim President and Chief Executive Officer

CHRIST HOSPITAL, 176 Palisade Avenue, Jersey City, NJ, Zip 07306–1196, Mailing Address: 176 Palisades Avenue, Zip 07306–1196; tel. 201/795–8200; Marie Theresa Duffy, Chief Operating Officer

CLARA MAASS MEDICAL CENTER, One Clara Maass Drive, Belleville, NJ, Zip 07109–3557; tel. 973/450–2000; Mary Ellen Clyne, Ph.D., MSN, R.N., President and Chief Executive Officer

DEBORAH HEART AND LUNG CENTER, 200 Trenton Road, Browns Mills, NJ, Zip 08015–1705; tel. 609/893–6611; Joseph Chirichella, President and Chief Executive Officer

ENGLEWOOD HOSPITAL AND MEDICAL CENTER, 350 Engle Street, Englewood, NJ, Zip 07631–1898; tel. 201/894–3000; Warren Geller, President and Chief Executive Officer

HACKENSACK UNIVERSITY MEDICAL CENTER, 30 Prospect Avenue, Hackensack, NJ, Zip 07601–1914; tel. 201/996–2000; Robert C. Garrett, FACHE, President and Chief Executive Officer

HACKETTSTOWN REGIONAL MEDICAL CENTER, 651 Willow Grove Street, Hackettstown, NJ, Zip 07840–1799; tel. 908/852–5100; Jason C. Coe, President and Chief Executive Officer

INSPIRA MEDICAL CENTER–VINELAND, 1505 West Sherman Avenue, Vineland, NJ, Zip 08360–6912; tel. 856/641–8000; John A. DiAngelo, President and Chief Executive Officer

JFK MEDICAL CENTER, 65 James Street, Edison, NJ, Zip 08818; tel. 732/321–7000; Raymond F. Fredericks, President and CEO

MEMORIAL HOSPITAL OF SALEM COUNTY, 310 Woodstown Road, Salem, NJ, Zip 08079–2080; tel. 856/935–1000; Ryan Jensen, Chief Executive Officer

OCEAN MEDICAL CENTER, 425 Jack Martin Boulevard, Brick Township, NJ, Zip 08724–7732; tel. 732/840–2200; Dean Q. Lin, FACHE, President

PIEDMONT MOUNTAINSIDE HOSPITAL, 1266 Highway 515 South, Jasper, GA, Zip 30143–4872; tel. 706/692–2441; Denise Ray, President and Chief Executive Officer

RARITAN BAY MEDICAL CENTER, 530 New Brunswick Avenue, Perth Amboy, NJ, Zip 08861–3654; tel. 732/442–3700; Michael R. D'Agnes, FACHE, President and Chief Executive Officer

RIVERVIEW MEDICAL CENTER, 1 Riverview Plaza, Red Bank, NJ, Zip 07701–1864; tel. 732/741–2700; Timothy J. Hogan, FACHE, Regional President

ROBERT WOOD JOHNSON UNIVERSITY HOSPITAL, 1 Robert Wood Johnson Place, New Brunswick, NJ, Zip 08901–1928; tel. 732/828–3000; Stephen K. Jones, FACHE, President and Chief Executive Officer

SAINT MICHAEL'S MEDICAL CENTER, 111 Central Avenue, Newark, NJ, Zip 07102–1909; tel. 973/877–5350; David A. Ricci, President and Chief Executive Officer

ST. MARY'S GENERAL HOSPITAL, 350 Boulevard, Passaic, NJ, Zip 07055–2840; tel. 973/365–4300; Edward Condit, President and Chief Executive Officer

UNIVERSITY HOSPITAL, 150 Bergen Street, Newark, NJ, Zip 07103–2496; tel. 973/972–4300; Nancy Hamstra, Interim President and Chief Executive Officer

UNIVERSITY MEDICAL CENTER OF PRINCETON AT PLAINSBORO, One Plainsboro Road, Plainsboro, NJ, Zip 08536–1913; tel. 609/853–7100; Barry S. Rabner, President and Chief Executive Officer

VIRTUA MARLTON, 90 Brick Road, Marlton, NJ, Zip 08053–2177; tel. 856/355–6000; Matthew Zuino, Senior Vice President

## NEW YORK

### ARDENT SOLUTIONS, INC.
**85 North Main Street, Suite 4, Wellsville, NY 14895–1254; tel. 585/593–5223; Carrie Whitwood, Executive Director**

JONES MEMORIAL HOSPITAL, 191 North Main Street, Wellsville, NY, Zip 14895–1150, Mailing Address: P.O. Box 72, Zip 14895–0072; tel. 585/593–1100; Eva Benedict, R.N., President and Chief Executive Officer

ST. JAMES MERCY HEALTH SYSTEM, 411 Canisteo Street, Hornell, NY, Zip 14843–2197; tel. 607/324–8000; Jennifer Sullivan, President and Chief Executive Officer

### ARNOT HEALTH
**600 Roe Avenue, Elmira, NY 14905–1629; tel. 607/737–4100; Robert K. Lambert, M.D., FACHE, President and Chief Executive Officer**

ARNOT OGDEN MEDICAL CENTER, 600 Roe Avenue, Elmira, NY, Zip 14905–1629; tel. 607/737–4100; H. Fred Farley, R.N., Ph.D., FACHE, President and Chief Operating Officer

IRA DAVENPORT MEMORIAL HOSPITAL, 7571 State Route 54, Bath, NY, Zip 14810–9590; tel. 607/776–8500; James B. Watson, President and Chief Operating Officer

ST. JOSEPH'S HOSPITAL, 555 St. Joseph's Boulevard, Elmira, NY, Zip 14901–3223; tel. 607/733–6541; H. Fred Farley, R.N., Ph.D., FACHE, President and Chief Operating Officer

### BASSETT HEALTHCARE NETWORK
**1 Atwell Road, Cooperstown, NY 13326–1301; tel. 607/547–3456; Vance Brown, M.D., President and Chief Executive Officer**

AURELIA OSBORN FOX MEMORIAL HOSPITAL, 1 Norton Avenue, Oneonta, NY, Zip 13820–2629; tel. 607/432–2000; John R. Remillard, President

BASSETT MEDICAL CENTER, One Atwell Road, Cooperstown, NY, Zip 13326–1394; tel. 607/547–3100; Vance Brown, M.D., President and Chief Executive Officer

COBLESKILL REGIONAL HOSPITAL, 178 Grandview Drive, Cobleskill, NY, Zip 12043–5144; tel. 518/254–3456; Eric H. Stein, FACHE, President and Chief Executive Officer

LITTLE FALLS HOSPITAL, 140 Burwell Street, Little Falls, NY, Zip 13365–1725; tel. 315/823–1000; Michael L. Ogden, President and Chief Executive Officer

O'CONNOR HOSPITAL, 460 Andes Road, State Route 28, Delhi, NY, Zip 13753–7407; tel. 607/746–0300; Carlton Rule, M.D., Chief Executive Officer

### GREAT LAKES HEALTH SYSTEM OF WESTERN NEW YORK
**726 Exchange Street, Suite 522, Buffalo, NY 14210–1485; tel. 716/859–8820; Jody Lomeo, Interim Chief Executive Officer**

ERIE COUNTY MEDICAL CENTER, 462 Grider Street, Buffalo, NY, Zip 14215–3098; tel. 716/898–3000; Richard C. Cleland, FACHE, President and Chief Operating Officer and Interim Chief Executive Officer

KALEIDA HEALTH, 100 High Street, Buffalo, NY, Zip 14203–1154; tel. 716/859–5600; Jody Lomeo, Chief Executive Officer

### LAKE ERIE REGIONAL HEALTH SYSTEM OF NEW YORK
**529 Central Avenue, Dunkirk, NY 14048–2514; tel. 716/366–1111; J. Gary Rhodes, FACHE, Interim Chief Executive Officer**

BROOKS MEMORIAL HOSPITAL, 529 Central Avenue, Dunkirk, NY, Zip 14048–2599; tel. 716/366–1111; J. Gary Rhodes, FACHE, Interim President and Chief Executive Officer

TLC HEALTH NETWORK – LAKE SHORE HOSPITAL, 845 Route 5 and 20, Irving, NY, Zip 14081–9716; tel. 716/951–7000; John P. Galati, Chief Executive Officer

### MOHAWK VALLEY NETWORK, INC.
**1710 Burrstone Road, New Hartford, NY 13413–1002; tel. 315/624–6001; Scott H. Perra, President and Chief Executive Officer**

FAXTON–ST. LUKE'S HEALTHCARE, 1656 Champlin Avenue, Utica, NY, Zip 13502–4830, Mailing Address: P.O. Box 479, Zip 13503–0479; tel. 315/624–6000; Scott H. Perra, President and Chief Executive Officer

ST. ELIZABETH MEDICAL CENTER, 2209 Genesee Street, Utica, NY, Zip 13501–5999; tel. 315/798–8100; Scott H. Perra, Chief Executive Officer

### MOUNT SINAI NYU HEALTH NETWORK
**One Gustave L. Levy Place, New York, NY 10029; tel. 212/659–8888; Arthur A. Klein, M.D., President**

ELMHURST HOSPITAL CENTER, 79–01 Broadway, Elmhurst, NY, Zip 11373–1329; tel. 718/334–4000; Chris D. Constantino, Senior Vice President and Executive Director

ENGLEWOOD HOSPITAL AND MEDICAL CENTER, 350 Engle Street, Englewood, NJ, Zip 07631–1898; tel. 201/894–3000; Warren Geller, President and Chief Executive Officer

JAMES J. PETERS VETERANS AFFAIRS MEDICAL CENTER, 130 West Kingsbridge Road, Bronx, NY, Zip 10468–3904; tel. 718/584–9000; Erik Langhoff, M.D., Ph.D., Director

JERSEY CITY MEDICAL CENTER, 355 Grand Street, Jersey City, NJ, Zip 07302–4321; tel. 201/915–2000; Joseph F. Scott, FACHE, President and Chief Executive Officer

MEADOWLANDS HOSPITAL MEDICAL CENTER, 55 Meadowlands Parkway, Secaucus, NJ, Zip 07094–2977; tel. 201/392–3100; Felicia Karsos, R.N., President and Chief Executive Officer

MORRISTOWN MEDICAL CENTER, 100 Madison Avenue, Morristown, NJ, Zip 07960–6136; tel. 973/971–5000; Trish O'Keefe, R.N., Ph.D., MSN, Interim President

MOUNT SINAI HOSPITAL, One Gustave L. Levy Place, New York, NY, Zip 10029–6574; tel. 212/241–6500; David L. Reich, M.D., President

NYU LUTHERAN, 150 55th Street, Brooklyn, NY, Zip 11220–2559; tel. 718/630–7000; Wendy Z. Goldstein, Chief Executive Officer

OVERLOOK MEDICAL CENTER, 99 Beauvoir Avenue, Summit, NJ, Zip 07901–3533; tel. 908/522–2000; Alan R. Lieber, President

PHELPS MEMORIAL HOSPITAL CENTER, 701 North Broadway, Sleepy Hollow, NY, Zip 10591–1020; tel. 914/366–3000; Daniel Blum, President

QUEENS HOSPITAL CENTER, 82–68 164th Street, Jamaica, NY, Zip 11432–1104; tel. 718/883–3000; Julius Wool, Executive Director

ST. JOHN'S RIVERSIDE HOSPITAL, 967 North Broadway, Yonkers, NY, Zip 10701–1399; tel. 914/964–4444; Ronald J. Corti, President and Chief Executive Officer

ST. JOSEPH'S REGIONAL MEDICAL CENTER, 703 Main Street, Paterson, NJ, Zip 07503–2691; tel. 973/754–2000; Kevin J. Slavin, FACHE, President and Chief Executive Officer

ST. LUKE'S CORNWALL HOSPITAL, 70 Dubois Street, Newburgh, NY, Zip 12550–4851; tel. 845/561–4400; Joan Cusack–McGuirk, Interim President and Chief Executive Officer

VASSAR BROTHERS MEDICAL CENTER, 45 Reade Place, Poughkeepsie, NY, Zip 12601–3947; tel. 845/454–8500; Robert Friedberg, President

### NEW YORK PRESBYTERIAN HEALTHCARE SYSTEM
**525 East 68th Street, Box 182, New York, NY 10065; tel. 212/746–3745; Steven J. Corwin, M.D., Chief Executive Officer**

GRACIE SQUARE HOSPITAL, 420 East 76th Street, New York, NY, Zip 10021–3396; tel. 212/988–4400; David Wyman, President and Chief Executive Officer

NEW YORK COMMUNITY HOSPITAL, 2525 Kings Highway, Brooklyn, NY, Zip 11229–1705; tel. 718/692–5300; Barry Stern, President and Chief Executive Officer

NEW YORK METHODIST HOSPITAL, 506 Sixth Street, Brooklyn, NY, Zip 11215–3609; tel. 718/780–3000; Mark J. Mundy, President and Chief Executive Officer

### NORTHERN NY RURAL HEALTH CARE ALLIANCE
**800 Starbuck Avenue, Suite A–5, Watertown, NY 13601; tel. 212/584–7676; James R. Knickman, President and Chief Executive Officer**

### NYU LUTHERAN HEALTHCARE
**150 55th Street, Brooklyn, NY 11220–2508; tel. 718/630–7000; Wendy Z. Goldstein, President and Chief Executive Officer**

NYU LUTHERAN, 150 55th Street, Brooklyn, NY, Zip 11220–2559; tel. 718/630–7000; Wendy Z. Goldstein, Chief Executive Officer

### RURAL HEALTH NETWORK OF OSWEGO COUNTY
**10 George Street, Oswego, NY 13126; tel. 315/592–0827; Brian Coleman, Coordinator**

OSWEGO HOSPITAL, 110 West Sixth Street, Oswego, NY, Zip 13126–2507; tel. 315/349–5511; Charles Gijanto, President and Chief Executive Officer

### STELLARIS HEALTH
**135 Bedford Road, Armonk, NY 10504–1945; tel. 914/273–5454; Sharon A. Lucian, President and Chief Executive Officer**

NEW YORK–PRESBYTERIAN/LAWRENCE HOSPITAL, 55 Palmer Avenue, Bronxville, NY, Zip 10708–3403; tel. 914/787–1000; Michael Fosina, President and Chief Executive Officer

NORTHERN WESTCHESTER HOSPITAL, 400 East Main Street, Mount Kisco, NY, Zip 10549–3477; tel. 914/666–1200; Joel Seligman, President and Chief Executive Officer

PHELPS MEMORIAL HOSPITAL CENTER, 701 North Broadway, Sleepy Hollow, NY, Zip 10591–1020; tel. 914/366–3000; Daniel Blum, President

WHITE PLAINS HOSPITAL CENTER, 41 East Post Road, White Plains, NY, Zip 10601–4699; tel. 914/681–0600; Susan Fox, President

## NORTH CAROLINA

**COASTAL CAROLINAS HEALTH ALLIANCE**
**5305–M Wrightsville Avenue, Wilmington, NC 28403;**
**tel. 910/332–8012; Yvonne Hughes, Chief Executive Officer**

CAPE FEAR VALLEY – BLADEN COUNTY HOSPITAL, 501 South Poplar Street, Elizabethtown, NC, Zip 28337–9375, Mailing Address: P.O. Box 398, Zip 28337–0398; tel. 910/862–5100; Lisa Byrd, Interim President

COLUMBUS REGIONAL HEALTHCARE SYSTEM, 500 Jefferson Street, Whiteville, NC, Zip 28472–3634; tel. 910/642–8011; Carla Hollis, President and Chief Executive Officer

J. ARTHUR DOSHER MEMORIAL HOSPITAL, 924 North Howe Street, Southport, NC, Zip 28461–3099; tel. 910/457–3800; Thomas R. Siemers, Chief Executive Officer

MCLEOD LORIS SEACOAST HOSPITAL, 3655 Mitchell Street, Loris, SC, Zip 29569–2827; tel. 843/716–7000; Edward D. Tinsley, III, Chief Executive Officer

MCLEOD REGIONAL MEDICAL CENTER, 555 East Cheves Street, Florence, SC, Zip 29506–2617, Mailing Address: P.O. Box 100551, Zip 29502–0551; tel. 843/777–2000; Robert L. Colones, President and Chief Executive Officer

NEW HANOVER REGIONAL MEDICAL CENTER, 2131 South 17th Street, Wilmington, NC, Zip 28401–7483, Mailing Address: P.O. Box 9000, Zip 28402–9000; tel. 910/343–7000; John K. Barto, Jr., President and Chief Executive Officer

PENDER MEMORIAL HOSPITAL, 507 East Freemont Street, Burgaw, NC, Zip 28425–5131; tel. 910/259–5451; Ruth Glaser, President

SAMPSON REGIONAL MEDICAL CENTER, 607 Beaman Street, Clinton, NC, Zip 28328–2697, Mailing Address: P.O. Box 260, Zip 28329–0260; tel. 910/592–8511; Shawn Howerton, M.D., Chief Executive Officer and President, Medical Staff

SCOTLAND HEALTH CARE SYSTEM, 500 Lauchwood Drive, Laurinburg, NC, Zip 28352–5599; tel. 910/291–7000; Gregory C. Wood, President and Chief Executive Officer

SOUTHEASTERN HEALTH, 300 West 27th Street, Lumberton, NC, Zip 28358–3075, Mailing Address: P.O. Box 1408, Zip 28359–1408; tel. 910/671–5000; Joann Anderson, President and Chief Executive Officer

VIDANT DUPLIN HOSPITAL, 401 North Main Street, Kenansville, NC, Zip 28349–8801, Mailing Address: P.O. Box 278, Zip 28349–0278; tel. 910/296–0941; Jay Briley, President

VIDANT MEDICAL CENTER, 2100 Stantonsburg Road, Greenville, NC, Zip 27834–2818, Mailing Address: P.O. Box 6028, Zip 27835–6028; tel. 252/847–4100; Stephen Lawler, President Emeritus

**MISSION HEALTH SYSTEM**
**509 Biltmore Avenue, Asheville, NC 28801–4601; tel. 828/213–1111;**
**Ronald A. Paulus, M.D., President and Chief Executive Officer**

ANGEL MEDICAL CENTER, 120 Riverview Street, Franklin, NC, Zip 28734–2612, Mailing Address: P.O. Box 1209, Zip 28744–0569; tel. 828/524–8411; James B. Bross, President

ASHEVILLE SPECIALTY HOSPITAL, 428 Biltmore Avenue, 4th Floor, Asheville, NC, Zip 28801–4502; tel. 828/213–5400; Robert C. Desotelle, President and Chief Executive Officer

BLUE RIDGE REGIONAL HOSPITAL, 125 Hospital Drive, Spruce Pine, NC, Zip 28777–3035, Mailing Address: P.O. Drawer 9, Zip 28777–0009; tel. 828/765–4201; Rebecca W. Carter, MSN, R.N., FACHE, Chief Executive Officer and Chief Nursing Officer

CAREPARTNERS HEALTH SERVICES, 68 Sweeten Creek Road, Asheville, NC, Zip 28803–2318, Mailing Address: P.O. Box 15025, Zip 28813–0025; tel. 828/277–4800; Tracy Buchanan, Chief Executive Officer / President

HIGHLANDS–CASHIERS HOSPITAL, 190 Hospital Drive, Highlands, NC, Zip 28741–7600, Mailing Address: P.O. Drawer 190, Zip 28741–0190; tel. 828/526–1200; Jackie Ring, President and Chief Nursing Officer

MCDOWELL HOSPITAL, 430 Rankin Drive, Marion, NC, Zip 28752–6568, Mailing Address: P.O. Box 730, Zip 28752–0730; tel. 828/659–5000; Carol C. Wolfenbarger, R.N., MSN, FACHE, President and Chief Executive Officer

MISSION HOSPITAL, 509 Biltmore Avenue, Asheville, NC, Zip 28801–4690; tel. 828/213–1111; Jill Hoggard Green, R.N., Ph.D., President

TRANSYLVANIA REGIONAL HOSPITAL, 260 Hospital Drive, Brevard, NC, Zip 28712–3378; tel. 828/884–9111; Catherine Landis, R.N., President and Chief Nursing Officer

**WNC HEALTH NETWORK, INC.**
**1200 Ridgefield Boulevard Suite 200, Asheville, NC 28806–2280;**
**tel. 828/667–8220; Heather Gates, Executive Director**

ANGEL MEDICAL CENTER, 120 Riverview Street, Franklin, NC, Zip 28734–2612, Mailing Address: P.O. Box 1209, Zip 28744–0569; tel. 828/524–8411; James B. Bross, President

BLUE RIDGE REGIONAL HOSPITAL, 125 Hospital Drive, Spruce Pine, NC, Zip 28777–3035, Mailing Address: P.O. Drawer 9, Zip 28777–0009; tel. 828/765–4201; Rebecca W. Carter, MSN, R.N., FACHE, Chief Executive Officer and Chief Nursing Officer

CAREPARTNERS HEALTH SERVICES, 68 Sweeten Creek Road, Asheville, NC, Zip 28803–2318, Mailing Address: P.O. Box 15025, Zip 28813–0025; tel. 828/277–4800; Tracy Buchanan, Chief Executive Officer / President

CHARLES GEORGE VETERANS AFFAIRS MEDICAL CENTER, 1100 Tunnel Road, Asheville, NC, Zip 28805–2087; tel. 828/298–7911; Cynthia Breyfogle, FACHE, Director

CHEROKEE INDIAN HOSPITAL, 1 Hospital Road, Cherokee, NC, Zip 28719; tel. 828/497–9163; Casey Cooper, Chief Executive Officer

HARRIS REGIONAL HOSPITAL, 68 Hospital Road, Sylva, NC, Zip 28779–2722; tel. 828/586–7000; Steve Heatherly, Chief Executive Officer

HAYWOOD REGIONAL MEDICAL CENTER, 262 Leroy George Drive, Clyde, NC, Zip 28721–7430; tel. 828/456–7311; Phillip L. Wright, FACHE, Chief Executive Officer

HIGHLANDS–CASHIERS HOSPITAL, 190 Hospital Drive, Highlands, NC, Zip 28741–7600, Mailing Address: P.O. Drawer 190, Zip 28741–0190; tel. 828/526–1200; Jackie Ring, President and Chief Nursing Officer

MARGARET R. PARDEE MEMORIAL HOSPITAL, 800 North Justice Street, Hendersonville, NC, Zip 28791–3410; tel. 828/696–1000; James M. Kirby, II, President and Chief Executive Officer

MCDOWELL HOSPITAL, 430 Rankin Drive, Marion, NC, Zip 28752–6568, Mailing Address: P.O. Box 730, Zip 28752–0730; tel. 828/659–5000; Carol C. Wolfenbarger, R.N., MSN, FACHE, President and Chief Executive Officer

MISSION HOSPITAL, 509 Biltmore Avenue, Asheville, NC, Zip 28801–4690; tel. 828/213–1111; Jill Hoggard Green, R.N., Ph.D., President

MURPHY MEDICAL CENTER, 3990 U.S. Highway 64 East Alt, Murphy, NC, Zip 28906–7917; tel. 828/837–8161; Michael Stevenson, Chief Executive Officer

PARK RIDGE HEALTH, 100 Hospital Drive, Hendersonville, NC, Zip 28792–5272; tel. 828/684–8501; Jimm Bunch, President and Chief Executive Officer

RUTHERFORD REGIONAL HEALTH SYSTEM, 288 South Ridgecrest Avenue, Rutherfordton, NC, Zip 28139–2838; tel. 828/286–5000; Cindy D. Buck, Chief Executive Officer

ST. LUKE'S HOSPITAL, 101 Hospital Drive, Columbus, NC, Zip 28722–6418; tel. 828/894–3311; Kenneth A. Shull, FACHE, Chief Executive Officer

SWAIN COMMUNITY HOSPITAL, 45 Plateau Street, Bryson City, NC, Zip 28713–4200; tel. 828/488–2155; Steve Heatherly, Chief Executive Officer

TRANSYLVANIA REGIONAL HOSPITAL, 260 Hospital Drive, Brevard, NC, Zip 28712–3378; tel. 828/884–9111; Catherine Landis, R.N., President and Chief Nursing Officer

## NORTH DAKOTA

**NORTHLAND HEALTHCARE ALLIANCE**
**3811 Lockport Street Suite 3, Bismarck, ND 58503–5554;**
**tel. 701/250–0709; Timothy Cox, Director**

ASHLEY MEDICAL CENTER, 612 North Center Avenue, Ashley, ND, Zip 58413–7013, Mailing Address: P.O. Box 450, Zip 58413–0450; tel. 701/288–3433; Jerry Lepp, Chief Executive Officer

CHI ST. ALEXIUS HEALTH, 900 East Broadway, Bismarck, ND, Zip 58501–4586, Mailing Address: P.O. Box 5510, Zip 58506–5510; tel. 701/530–7000; Kurt Schley, Market Chief Executive Officer

COMMUNITY MEMORIAL HOSPITAL, 220 Fifth Avenue, Turtle Lake, ND, Zip 58575–4005, Mailing Address: P.O. Box 280, Zip 58575–0280; tel. 701/448–2331; Tod Graeber, Administrator

GARRISON MEMORIAL HOSPITAL, 407 Third Avenue S.E., Garrison, ND, Zip 58540–7235; tel. 701/463–2275; Tod Graeber, Administrator

LINTON HOSPITAL, 518 North Broadway, Linton, ND, Zip 58552–7308, Mailing Address: P.O. Box 850, Zip 58552–0850; tel. 701/254–4511; Robert O. Black, Chief Executive Officer

MCKENZIE COUNTY HEALTHCARE SYSTEM, 516 North Main Street, Watford City, ND, Zip 58854–7310; tel. 701/842–3000; Daniel R. Kelly, Chief Executive Officer

MOBRIDGE REGIONAL HOSPITAL, 1401 Tenth Avenue West, Mobridge, SD, Zip 57601–1106, Mailing Address: P.O. Box 580, Zip 57601–0580; tel. 605/845–3692; Angelia K. Svihovec, Chief Executive Officer

PRESENTATION MEDICAL CENTER, 213 Second Avenue N.E., Rolla, ND, Zip 58367–7153, Mailing Address: P.O. Box 759, Zip 58367–0759; tel. 701/477–3161; Mark Kerr, Chief Executive Officer

SAKAKAWEA MEDICAL CENTER, 510 Eighth Avenue N.E., Hazen, ND, Zip 58545–4637; tel. 701/748–2225; Darrold Bertsch, Chief Executive Officer

SOUTHWEST HEALTHCARE SERVICES, 802 2nd Street Northwest, Bowman, ND, Zip 58623–4483, Mailing Address: P.O. Drawer C, Zip 58623; tel. 701/523–5265; Becky Hansen, Chief Executive Officer

ST. ALOISIUS MEDICAL CENTER, 325 East Brewster Street, Harvey, ND, Zip 58341–1653; tel. 701/324–4651; Sandra Teubner, Interim Chief Executive Officer

ST. ANDREW'S HEALTH CENTER, 316 Ohmer Street, Bottineau, ND,
Zip 58318–1045; tel. 701/228–9300; Jodi Atkinson, President and Chief
Executive Officer

ST. JOSEPH'S HOSPITAL AND HEALTH CENTER, 30 Seventh Street West,
Dickinson, ND, Zip 58601–4399; tel. 701/456–4000; Reed Reyman,
President

WEST RIVER REGIONAL MEDICAL CENTER, 1000 Highway 12, Hettinger, ND,
Zip 58639–7530; tel. 701/567–4561; James K. Long, CPA, Administrator
and Chief Executive Officer

WISHEK COMMUNITY HOSPITAL AND CLINICS, 1007 Fourth Avenue South,
Wishek, ND, Zip 58495–7527, Mailing Address: P.O. Box 647,
Zip 58495–0647; tel. 701/452–2326; Beverly Vilhauer, Chief Executive
Officer

## OHIO

### CLEVELAND HEALTH NETWORK
**6000 West Creek Road, Suite 20, Independence, OH 44131–2139;
tel. 216/986–1100; Fred M. DeGrandis, President**

AKRON CHILDREN'S HOSPITAL, One Perkins Square, Akron, OH,
Zip 44308–1063; tel. 330/543–1000; William H. Considine, President

ASHTABULA COUNTY MEDICAL CENTER, 2420 Lake Avenue, Ashtabula, OH,
Zip 44004–4954; tel. 440/997–2262; Michael J. Habowski, President and
Chief Executive Officer

CLEVELAND CLINIC, 9500 Euclid Avenue, Cleveland, OH, Zip 44195–5108;
tel. 216/444–2200; Delos Cosgrove, M.D., President and Chief Executive
Officer

CLEVELAND CLINIC CHILDREN'S HOSPITAL FOR REHABILITATION, 2801 Martin
Luther King Jr. Drive, Cleveland, OH, Zip 44104–3865; tel. 216/448–6400;
Michael J. McHugh, M.D., Medical Director

EUCLID HOSPITAL, 18901 Lake Shore Boulevard, Euclid, OH, Zip 44119–1090;
tel. 216/531–9000; Daniel Napierkowski, Chief Executive Officer

FAIRVIEW HOSPITAL, 18101 Lorain Avenue, Cleveland, OH, Zip 44111–5656;
tel. 216/476–7000; Neil Smith, D.O., President

FIRELANDS REGIONAL HEALTH SYSTEM, 1111 Hayes Avenue, Sandusky, OH,
Zip 44870–3323; tel. 419/557–7400; Martin Tursky, President and Chief
Executive Officer

FISHER–TITUS MEDICAL CENTER, 272 Benedict Avenue, Norwalk, OH,
Zip 44857–2374; tel. 419/668–8101; Lorna Strayer, President and Chief
Executive Officer

HILLCREST HOSPITAL, 6780 Mayfield Road, Cleveland, OH, Zip 44124–2203;
tel. 440/312–4500; Brian J. Harte, M.D., President

LAKEWOOD HOSPITAL, 14519 Detroit Avenue, Lakewood, OH, Zip 44107–4383;
tel. 216/521–4200; Shannan Ritchie, Interim President

LUTHERAN HOSPITAL, 1730 West 25th Street, Cleveland, OH, Zip 44113–3170;
tel. 216/696–4300; Donald Malone, M.D., President

MARYMOUNT HOSPITAL, 12300 McCracken Road, Garfield Heights, OH,
Zip 44125–2975; tel. 216/581–0500; Richard Parker, M.D., President

MEDINA HOSPITAL, 1000 East Washington Street, Medina, OH, Zip 44256–2170;
tel. 330/725–1000; Thomas Tulisiak, M.D., President

METROHEALTH MEDICAL CENTER, 2500 MetroHealth Drive, Cleveland, OH,
Zip 44109–1998; tel. 216/778–7800; Akram Boutros, M.D., FACHE,
President and Chief Executive Officer

SOUTH POINTE HOSPITAL, 20000 Harvard Road, Warrensville Heights, OH,
Zip 44122–6805; tel. 216/491–6000; Robert S. Juhasz, D.O., President

SUMMA AKRON CITY HOSPITAL, 525 East Market Street, Akron, OH,
Zip 44304–1619; tel. 330/375–3000; Thomas Malone, M.D., President and
Chief Executive Officer

SUMMA BARBERTON CITIZENS HOSPITAL, 155 Fifth Street N.E., Barberton, OH,
Zip 44203–3332; tel. 330/615–3000; Jason Niehaus, Senior Vice President
Operations and Administrator

SUMMA WESTERN RESERVE HOSPITAL, 1900 23rd Street, Cuyahoga Falls, OH,
Zip 44223–1499; tel. 330/971–7000; Robert Kent, D.O., President and
Chief Executive Officer

UNIVERSITY HOSPITALS ELYRIA MEDICAL CENTER, 630 East River Street, Elyria,
OH, Zip 44035–5902; tel. 440/329–7500; Donald S. Sheldon, M.D.,
President and Chief Executive Officer

UNIVERSITY HOSPITALS PARMA MEDICAL CENTER, 7007 Powers Boulevard,
Parma, OH, Zip 44129–5495; tel. 440/743–3000; Nancy Tinsley, President
and Chief Executive Officer

### COMPREHENSIVE HEALTHCARE OF OHIO, INC.
**630 East River Street, Elyria, OH 44035–5902; tel. 440/329–7700;
Donald S. Sheldon, M.D., President and Chief Executive Officer**

UNIVERSITY HOSPITALS ELYRIA MEDICAL CENTER, 630 East River Street, Elyria,
OH, Zip 44035–5902; tel. 440/329–7500; Donald S. Sheldon, M.D.,
President and Chief Executive Officer

### MERCY HEALTH – SOUTHWEST OHIO
**4600 McAuley Place, Cincinnati, OH 45242; tel. 513/981–6000; John
M. Starcher, President and Chief Executive Officer**

MERCY HEALTH – ANDERSON HOSPITAL, 7500 State Road, Cincinnati, OH,
Zip 45255–2492; tel. 513/624–4500; Jeff Graham, Market Leader and
President

MERCY HEALTH – CLERMONT HOSPITAL, 3000 Hospital Drive, Batavia, OH,
Zip 45103–1921; tel. 513/732–8200; Jeff Graham, Market Leader and
President

MERCY HEALTH – FAIRFIELD HOSPITAL, 3000 Mack Road, Fairfield, OH,
Zip 45014–5335; tel. 513/870–7000; Thomas S. Urban, Market Leader and
President

MERCY HEALTH – WEST HOSPITAL, 3300 Mercy Health Boulevard, Cincinnati, OH,
Zip 45211; tel. 513/215–5000; Michael R. Stephens, Market Leader and
President

THE JEWISH HOSPITAL – MERCY HEALTH, 4777 East Galbraith Road, Cincinnati,
OH, Zip 45236–2725; tel. 513/686–3000; Patricia Davis–Hagens, R.N.,
Chief Executive Officer

### OHIO STATE HEALTH NETWORK
**660 Ackerman Road, Suite 601F, Columbus, OH 43202–4500;
tel. 614/293–3785; Joann Ort, Executive Director**

BARNESVILLE HOSPITAL, 639 West Main Street, Barnesville, OH,
Zip 43713–1039, Mailing Address: P.O. Box 309, Zip 43713–0309;
tel. 740/425–3941; David D. Phillips, Chief Executive Officer and
Administrator

MADISON HEALTH, 210 North Main Street, London, OH, Zip 43140–1115;
tel. 740/845–7000; Dana E. Engle, Chief Executive Officer

MARY RUTAN HOSPITAL, 205 Palmer Avenue, Bellefontaine, OH,
Zip 43311–2281; tel. 937/592–4015; Mandy C. Goble, President and Chief
Executive Officer

MERCER HEALTH, 800 West Main Street, Coldwater, OH, Zip 45828–1698;
tel. 419/678–2341; Lisa R. Klenke, R.N., Chief Executive Officer and Chief
Nursing Officer

OHIO STATE UNIVERSITY WEXNER MEDICAL CENTER, 370 West 9th Avenue,
Columbus, OH, Zip 43210–1238; tel. 614/293–8000; Sheldon Retchin,
M.D., Chief Executive Officer

OHIO VALLEY MEDICAL CENTER, 2000 Eoff Street, Wheeling, WV,
Zip 26003–3870; tel. 304/234–0123; Michael J. Caruso, President and
Chief Executive Officer

TRINITY HOSPITAL TWIN CITY, 819 North First Street, Dennison, OH,
Zip 44621–1098; tel. 740/922–2800; Joseph J. Mitchell, President

WILSON MEMORIAL HOSPITAL, 915 West Michigan Street, Sidney, OH,
Zip 45365–2491; tel. 937/498–2311; Mark J. Dooley, Chief Executive
Officer

WYANDOT MEMORIAL HOSPITAL, 885 North Sandusky Avenue, Upper Sandusky,
OH, Zip 43351–1098; tel. 419/294–4991; Joseph A. D'Ettorre, Chief
Executive Officer

### PREMIER HEALTH
**110 North Main Street, Suite 390, Dayton, OH 45402–3720;
tel. 937/499–9401; James R. Pancoast, President and Chief Executive
Officer**

ATRIUM MEDICAL CENTER, One Medical Center Drive, Middletown, OH,
Zip 45005–1066; tel. 513/424–2111; Carol Turner, President and Chief
Executive Officer

GOOD SAMARITAN HOSPITAL, 2222 Philadelphia Drive, Dayton, OH,
Zip 45406–1813; tel. 937/734–2612; Eloise Broner, President and Chief
Executive Officer

MIAMI VALLEY HOSPITAL, One Wyoming Street, Dayton, OH, Zip 45409–2793;
tel. 937/208–8000; Mark S. Shaker, President and Chief Executive Officer

UPPER VALLEY MEDICAL CENTER, 3130 North County Road 25A, Troy, OH,
Zip 45373–1309; tel. 937/440–4000; Thomas Parker, Chief Executive
Officer

### TRIHEALTH
**619 Oak Street, Cincinnati, OH 45206; tel. 513/569–6507; John S.
Prout, Chief Executive Officer**

BETHESDA NORTH HOSPITAL, 10500 Montgomery Road, Cincinnati, OH,
Zip 45242–4402; tel. 513/865–1111; Barbara Boyne, Executive Director,
Operations

GOOD SAMARITAN HOSPITAL, 375 Dixmyth Avenue, Cincinnati, OH,
Zip 45220–2489; tel. 513/862–1400; Jamie Easterling, Executive Director,
Operations

MCCULLOUGH–HYDE MEMORIAL HOSPITAL/TRIHEALTH, 110 North Poplar Street,
Oxford, OH, Zip 45056–1292; tel. 513/523–2111; Bryan D. Hehemann,
President and Chief Executive Officer

TRIHEALTH EVENDALE HOSPITAL, 3155 Glendale Milford Road, Cincinnati, OH,
Zip 45241–3134; tel. 513/454–2222; Kelvin Hanger, Chief Executive Officer

### WEST CENTRAL OHIO REGIONAL HEALTHCARE ALLIANCE
**2615 Fort Amanda Road, Lima, OH, Zip 45804–3704;
tel. 419/226–9085; Robin Johnson, Executive Director**

JOINT TOWNSHIP DISTRICT MEMORIAL HSOPITAL, 200 St. Clair Street, Saint
Marys, OH, Zip 45885–2400; tel. 419/394–3335; Kevin W. Harlan,
President

MARY RUTAN HOSPITAL, 205 Palmer Avenue, Bellefontaine, OH,
Zip 43311–2281; tel. 937/592–4015; Mandy C. Goble, President and Chief
Executive Officer

MERCER HEALTH, 800 West Main Street, Coldwater, OH, Zip 45828–1698;
tel. 419/678–2341; Lisa R. Klenke, RN, Chief Executive Officer and Chief
Nursing Officer

ST. RITA'S MEDICAL CENTER, 730 West Market Street, Lima, OH, Zip 45801–4602; tel. 419/227–3361; Robert O. Baxter, President and Chief Executive Officer

VAN WERT COUNTY HOSPITAL, 1250 South Washington Street, Van Wert, OH, Zip 45891–2599; tel. 419/238–2390; Mark J. Minick, President and Chief Executive Officer

## OKLAHOMA

**MERCY HEALTH SYSTEM OF OKLAHOMA**
**4300 West Memorial Road, Oklahoma City, OK 73120–8304; tel. 405/752–3756; Diana Smalley, President and Chief Executive Officer**

ARBUCKLE MEMORIAL HOSPITAL, 2011 West Broadway Street, Sulphur, OK, Zip 73086–4221; tel. 580/622–2161; Darin Farrell, Chief Executive Officer

MERCY HEALTH LOVE COUNTY, 300 Wanda Street, Marietta, OK, Zip 73448–1200; tel. 580/276–3347; Richard Barker, Administrator

MERCY HOSPITAL ADA, 430 North Monte Vista, Ada, OK, Zip 74820–4610; tel. 580/332–2323; Lori Wightman, R.N., MSN, FACHE, Chief Executive Officer

MERCY HOSPITAL ARDMORE, 1011 14th Avenue N.W., Ardmore, OK, Zip 73401–1828; tel. 580/223–5400; Daryle Voss, FACHE, President

MERCY HOSPITAL EL RENO, 2115 Parkview Drive, El Reno, OK, Zip 73036–2199, Mailing Address: P.O. Box 129, Zip 73036–0129; tel. 405/262–2640; Doug Danker, Administrator

MERCY HOSPITAL HEALDTON, 918 South 8th Street, Healdton, OK, Zip 73438–0928, Mailing Address: P.O. Box 928, Zip 73438–0928; tel. 580/229–0701; Jeremy A. Jones, Administrator

MERCY HOSPITAL KINGFISHER, 1000 Kingfisher Regional Hospital Drive, Kingfisher, OK, Zip 73750–3528, Mailing Address: P.O. Box 59, Zip 73750–0059; tel. 405/375–3141; Brian Denton, Administrator

MERCY HOSPITAL LOGAN COUNTY, 200 South Academy Road, Guthrie, OK, Zip 73044–8727, Mailing Address: P.O. Box 1017, Zip 73044–1017; tel. 405/282–6700; Joshua Tucker, Administrator

MERCY HOSPITAL OKLAHOMA CITY, 4300 West Memorial Road, Oklahoma City, OK, Zip 73120–8362; tel. 405/755–1515; Jim Gebhart, Jr., FACHE, President

MERCY HOSPITAL TISHOMINGO, 1000 South Byrd Street, Tishomingo, OK, Zip 73460–3299; tel. 580/371–2327; Gary Sharum, Administrator

MERCY HOSPITAL WATONGA, 500 North Clarence Nash Boulevard, Watonga, OK, Zip 73772–2845, Mailing Address: P.O. Box 370, Zip 73772–0370; tel. 580/623–7211; Bobby Stitt, R.N., Administrator

MERCY REHABILITATION HOSPITAL OKLAHOMA CITY, 5401 West Memorial Road, Oklahoma City, OK, Zip 73142–2026; tel. 405/752–3935; Sharon Smeltzer, Chief Executive Officer

OKLAHOMA HEART HOSPITAL, 4050 West Memorial Road, Oklahoma City, OK, Zip 73120–8382; tel. 405/608–3200; John Harvey, M.D., President and Chief Executive Officer

OKLAHOMA HEART HOSPITAL SOUTH CAMPUS, 5200 East I–240 Service Road, Oklahoma City, OK, Zip 73135; tel. 405/628–6000; John Harvey, M.D., President and Chief Executive Officer

OKLAHOMA STATE UNIVERSITY MEDICAL CENTER, 744 West Ninth Street, Tulsa, OK, Zip 74127–9020; tel. 918/599–1000; Rhett Stover, Chief Executive Officer

SEILING MUNICIPAL HOSPITAL, Highway 60 N.E., Seiling, OK, Zip 73663, Mailing Address: P.O. Box 720, Zip 73663–0720; tel. 580/922–7361; Bobby Stitt, R.N., Chief Executive Officer

## OREGON

**HEALTH FUTURE, LLC**
**711 Medford Center #105, Medford, OR 97504–6772; tel. 541/772–3062; Leslie A. Flick, Executive Director**

ASANTE ASHLAND COMMUNITY HOSPITAL, 280 Maple Street, Ashland, OR, Zip 97520–1593; tel. 541/201–4000; Sheila Clough, Chief Executive Officer

ASANTE ROGUE REGIONAL MEDICAL CENTER, 2825 East Barnett Road, Medford, OR, Zip 97504–8332; tel. 541/789–7000; Scott A. Kelly, Chief Executive Officer

ASANTE THREE RIVERS MEDICAL CENTER, 500 S.W. Ramsey Avenue, Grants Pass, OR, Zip 97527–5554; tel. 541/472–7000; Win Howard, Chief Executive Officer

BAY AREA HOSPITAL, 1775 Thompson Road, Coos Bay, OR, Zip 97420–2198; tel. 541/269–8111; Paul Janke, FACHE, President and Chief Executive Officer

MID–COLUMBIA MEDICAL CENTER, 1700 East 19th Street, The Dalles, OR, Zip 97058–3317; tel. 541/296–1111; Duane Francis, President and Chief Executive Officer

PIONEER MEMORIAL HOSPITAL, 1201 N.E. Elm Street, Prineville, OR, Zip 97754–1206; tel. 541/447–6254; Jeanine Gentry, Chief Executive Officer

SKY LAKES MEDICAL CENTER, 2865 Daggett Avenue, Klamath Falls, OR, Zip 97601–1106; tel. 541/882–6311; Paul R. Stewart, President and Chief Executive Officer

ST. CHARLES BEND, 2500 N.E. Neff Road, Bend, OR, Zip 97701–6015; tel. 541/382–4321; Robert Gomes, FACHE, Chief Executive Officer

ST. CHARLES MADRAS, 470 N.E. A Street, Madras, OR, Zip 97741–1844; tel. 541/475–3882; Jeanine Gentry, Chief Executive Officer

ST. CHARLES REDMOND, 1253 N.W. Canal Boulevard, Redmond, OR, Zip 97756–1395; tel. 541/548–8131; Robert Gomes, FACHE, Chief Executive Officer

## PENNSYLVANIA

**ALLEGHENY HEALTH NETWORK**
**120 Fifth Avenue, Suite 2901, Pittsburgh, PA 15222–3002; tel. 412/544–3075; John W. Paul, President and Chief Executive Officer**

ALLEGHENY GENERAL HOSPITAL, 320 East North Avenue, Pittsburgh, PA, Zip 15212–4756; tel. 412/359–3131; Michael Harlovic, R.N., President and Chief Executive Officer

ALLEGHENY VALLEY HOSPITAL, 1301 Carlisle Street, Natrona Heights, PA, Zip 15065–1152; tel. 724/224–5100; William Englert, Chief Executive Officer

CANONSBURG GENERAL HOSPITAL, 100 Medical Boulevard, Canonsburg, PA, Zip 15317–9762; tel. 724/745–6100; Jane B. Sarra, President and Chief Executive Officer

FORBES REGIONAL HOSPITAL, 2570 Haymaker Road, Monroeville, PA, Zip 15146–3513; tel. 412/858–2000; Duke Rupert, President and Chief Executive Officer

JEFFERSON HOSPITAL, 565 Coal Valley Road, Jefferson Hills, PA, Zip 15025–3703, Mailing Address: Box 18119, Pittsburgh, Zip 15236–0119; tel. 412/469–5000; Louise Urban, R.N., President and Chief Executive Officer

SAINT VINCENT HEALTH CENTER, 232 West 25th Street, Erie, PA, Zip 16544–0002; tel. 814/452–5000; Scott Whalen, Ph.D., FACHE, President and Chief Executive Officer

WEST PENN HOSPITAL, 4800 Friendship Avenue, Pittsburgh, PA, Zip 15224–1722; tel. 412/578–5000; Ronald J. Andro, President and Chief Executive Officer

**COMMONWEALTH HEALTH**
**575 North River Street, Wilkes Barre, PA 18764–0999; tel. 570/829–8111; Cornelio R. Catena, Chief Executive Officer**

BERWICK HOSPITAL CENTER, 701 East 16th Street, Berwick, PA, Zip 18603–2397; tel. 570/759–5000; David P. Steitz, Chief Executive Officer

FIRST HOSPITAL WYOMING VALLEY, 562 Wyoming Avenue, Kingston, PA, Zip 18704–3721; tel. 570/552–3900; Rhonda Moffitt Sod, Interim Chief Executive Officer

MOSES TAYLOR HOSPITAL, 700 Quincy Avenue, Scranton, PA, Zip 18510–1724; tel. 570/770–5000; Justin Davis, Chief Executive Officer

REGIONAL HOSPITAL OF SCRANTON, 746 Jefferson Avenue, Scranton, PA, Zip 18510–1624; tel. 570/348–7100; Brooks Turkel, Chief Executive Officer

TYLER MEMORIAL HOSPITAL, 5950 State Route 6, Tunkhannock, PA, Zip 18657–7905; tel. 570/836–2161; Diane Ljungquist, R.N., MS, Chief Executive Officer

WILKES–BARRE GENERAL HOSPITAL, 575 North River Street, Wilkes–Barre, PA, Zip 18764–0001; tel. 570/829–8111; Cornelio R. Catena, President and Chief Executive Officer

**PENN HIGHLANDS HEALTHCARE**
**204 Hospital Avenue, DuBois, PA 15801–1442; tel. 814/371–2200; Raymond A. Graeca, Chief Executive Officer**

PENN HIGHLANDS BROOKVILLE, 100 Hospital Road, Brookville, PA, Zip 15825–1367; tel. 814/849–2312; Julie Peer, President

PENN HIGHLANDS CLEARFIELD, 809 Turnpike Avenue, Clearfield, PA, Zip 16830–1232, Mailing Address: P.O. Box 992, Zip 16830–0992; tel. 814/765–5341; Gary Macioce, President

PENN HIGHLANDS DUBOIS, 100 Hospital Avenue, DuBois, PA, Zip 15801–1440, Mailing Address: P.O. Box 447, Zip 15801–0447; tel. 814/371–2200; John Sutika, President

PENN HIGHLANDS ELK, 763 Johnsonburg Road, Saint Marys, PA, Zip 15857–3498; tel. 814/788–8000; Rose Campbell, R.N., President

**VANTAGE HEALTHCARE NETWORK, INC.**
**18282 Technology Drive, Suite 202, Meadville, PA 16335; tel. 814/337–0000; David Petrarca, Director Retail Operations**

BRADFORD REGIONAL MEDICAL CENTER, 116 Interstate Parkway, Bradford, PA, Zip 16701–1036; tel. 814/368–4143; Timothy J. Finan, FACHE, President and Chief Executive Officer

CLARION HOSPITAL, One Hospital Drive, Clarion, PA, Zip 16214–8501; tel. 814/226–9500; Byron Quinton, Chief Executive Officer

JAMESON HOSPITAL, 1211 Wilmington Avenue, New Castle, PA, Zip 16105–2516; tel. 724/658–9001; Douglas Danko, President and Chief Executive Officer

KANE COMMUNITY HOSPITAL, 4372 Route 6, Kane, PA, Zip 16735–3060; tel. 814/837–8585; J. Gary Rhodes, FACHE, Chief Executive Officer

Section B

MEADVILLE MEDICAL CENTER, 751 Liberty Street, Meadville, PA,
Zip 16335–2559; tel. 814/333–5000; Philip Pandolph, Chief Executive
Officer

PENN HIGHLANDS BROOKVILLE, 100 Hospital Road, Brookville, PA,
Zip 15825–1367; tel. 814/849–2312; Julie Peer, President

PENN HIGHLANDS ELK, 763 Johnsonburg Road, Saint Marys, PA,
Zip 15857–3498; tel. 814/788–8000; Rose Campbell, R.N., President

PUNXSUTAWNEY AREA HOSPITAL, 81 Hillcrest Drive, Punxsutawney, PA,
Zip 15767–2616; tel. 814/938–1800; Daniel D. Blough, Jr., Chief Executive
Officer

TITUSVILLE AREA HOSPITAL, 406 West Oak Street, Titusville, PA,
Zip 16354–1404; tel. 814/827–1851; Anthony J. Nasralla, FACHE,
President and Chief Executive Officer

UPMC BEDFORD MEMORIAL, 10455 Lincoln Highway, Everett, PA,
Zip 15537–7046; tel. 814/623–6161; Gerald Murray, President

UPMC HAMOT, 201 State Street, Erie, PA, Zip 16550–0002; tel. 814/877–6000;
V. James Fiorenzo, President

UPMC MCKEESPORT, 1500 Fifth Avenue, McKeesport, PA, Zip 15132–2422;
tel. 412/664–2000; Mark Sevco, President

UPMC NORTHWEST, 100 Fairfield Drive, Seneca, PA, Zip 16346–2130;
tel. 814/676–7600; David Gibbons, President

UPMC PASSAVANT, 9100 Babcock Boulevard, Pittsburgh, PA, Zip 15237–5815;
tel. 412/748–6700; David T. Martin, President

UPMC ST. MARGARET, 815 Freeport Road, Pittsburgh, PA, Zip 15215–3301;
tel. 412/784–4000; David J. Patton, President

WARREN GENERAL HOSPITAL, Two Crescent Park West, Warren, PA,
Zip 16365–0068, Mailing Address: P.O. Box 68, Zip 16365–0068;
tel. 814/723–4973; Richard Allen, Chief Executive Officer

## SOUTH DAKOTA

### REGIONAL HEALTH
**353 Fairmont Boulevard, Rapid City, SD 57701–7375;
tel. 605/719–1000; Brent R. Phillips, President and Chief Executive
Officer**

CUSTER REGIONAL HOSPITAL, 1039 Montgomery Street, Custer, SD,
Zip 57730–1397; tel. 605/673–2229; Veronica Schmidt, President

LEAD–DEADWOOD REGIONAL HOSPITAL, 61 Charles Street, Deadwood, SD,
Zip 57732–1303; tel. 605/717–6000; Mark C. Schmidt, President

PHILIP HEALTH SERVICES, 503 West Pine Street, Philip, SD, Zip 57567–3300,
Mailing Address: P.O. Box 790, Zip 57567–0790; tel. 605/859–2511; Kent
Olson, Administrator and Chief Executive Officer

RAPID CITY REGIONAL HOSPITAL, 353 Fairmont Boulevard, Rapid City, SD,
Zip 57701–7393, Mailing Address: P.O. Box 6000, Zip 57709–6000;
tel. 605/755–1000; Mick Gibbs, President

SPEARFISH REGIONAL HOSPITAL, 1440 North Main Street, Spearfish, SD,
Zip 57783–1504; tel. 605/644–4000; Larry W. Veitz, President

STURGIS REGIONAL HOSPITAL, 949 Harmon Street, Sturgis, SD,
Zip 57785–2452; tel. 605/720–2400; Mark Schulte, FACHE, Chief Executive
Officer

WESTON COUNTY HEALTH SERVICES, 1124 Washington Boulevard, Newcastle,
WY, Zip 82701–2972; tel. 307/746–4491; Maureen K. Cadwell, Chief
Executive Officer

## TENNESSEE

### TRISTAR HEALTH
**110 Winners Circle, First Floor, Brentwood, TN 37027–5070;
tel. 615/886–4900; Stephen Corbeil, President**

CARTERSVILLE MEDICAL CENTER, 960 Joe Frank Harris Parkway, Cartersville,
GA, Zip 30120–2129; tel. 770/382–1530; Keith Sandlin, Chief Executive
Officer

EASTSIDE MEDICAL CENTER, 1700 Medical Way, Snellville, GA, Zip 30078–2195;
tel. 770/979–0200; Scott Schmidly, Chief Executive Officer

PARKRIDGE MEDICAL CENTER, 2333 McCallie Avenue, Chattanooga, TN,
Zip 37404–3258; tel. 423/698–6061; Darrell W. Moore, Chief Executive
Officer

REDMOND REGIONAL MEDICAL CENTER, 501 Redmond Road, Rome, GA,
Zip 30165–1415, Mailing Address: P.O. Box 107001, Zip 30165–7001;
tel. 706/291–0291; John Quinlivan, Chief Executive Officer

TRISTAR CENTENNIAL MEDICAL CENTER, 2300 Patterson Street, Nashville, TN,
Zip 37203–1528; tel. 615/342–1000; Heather J. Rohan, Chief Executive
Officer

TRISTAR CENTENNIAL MEDICAL CENTER AT ASHLAND CITY, 313 North Main
Street, Ashland City, TN, Zip 37015–1347; tel. 615/792–3030; Heather J.
Rohan, Chief Executive Officer

TRISTAR GREENVIEW REGIONAL HOSPITAL, 1801 Ashley Circle, Bowling Green,
KY, Zip 42104–3362; tel. 270/793–1000; Michael Sherrod, Chief Executive
Officer

TRISTAR HENDERSONVILLE MEDICAL CENTER, 355 New Shackle Island Road,
Hendersonville, TN, Zip 37075–2479; tel. 615/338–1000; Regina Bartlett,
Chief Executive Officer

TRISTAR HORIZON MEDICAL CENTER, 111 Highway 70 East, Dickson, TN,
Zip 37055–2080; tel. 615/446–0446; Dustin Greene, Chief Executive
Officer

TRISTAR SKYLINE MADISON CAMPUS, 500 Hospital Drive, Madison, TN,
Zip 37115–5032; tel. 615/769–5000; Steve Otto, Chief Executive Officer

TRISTAR SKYLINE MEDICAL CENTER, 3441 Dickerson Pike, Nashville, TN,
Zip 37207–2539; tel. 615/769–2000; Steve Otto, Chief Executive Officer

TRISTAR SOUTHERN HILLS MEDICAL CENTER, 391 Wallace Road, Nashville, TN,
Zip 37211–4859; tel. 615/781–4000; Thomas H. Ozburn, Chief Executive
Officer

TRISTAR STONECREST MEDICAL CENTER, 200 StoneCrest Boulevard, Smyrna,
TN, Zip 37167–6810; tel. 615/768–2000; Louis Caputo, Chief Executive
Officer

TRISTAR SUMMIT MEDICAL CENTER, 5655 Frist Boulevard, Hermitage, TN,
Zip 37076–2053; tel. 615/316–3000; Jeffrey T. Whitehorn, Chief Executive
Officer

## TEXAS

### LITTLE RIVER HEALTHCARE
**1700 Brazos Avenue, Rockdale, TX 76567–2517; tel. 512/446–4500;
Jeffrey Madison, Chief Executive Officer**

LITTLE RIVER CAMERON HOSPITAL, 806 North Crockett Avenue, Cameron, TX,
Zip 76520–2553; tel. 254/605–1300; Troy Zinn, Chief Executive Officer

LITTLE RIVER ROCKDALE HOSPITAL, 1700 Brazos Street, Rockdale, TX,
Zip 76567–2517, Mailing Address: Drawer 1010, Zip 76567–1010;
tel. 512/446–4500; Jeffrey Madison, Chief Executive Officer

### METHODIST HEALTHCARE SYSTEM
**8109 Fredericksburg Road, San Antonio, TX 78229–3311;
tel. 210/575–0355; Jaime Wesolowski, President and Chief Executive
Officer**

METHODIST AMBULATORY SURGERY HOSPITAL – NORTHWEST, 9150 Huebner
Road, Suite 100, San Antonio, TX, Zip 78240–1545; tel. 210/575–5000;
Andrew G. Williams, Chief Executive Officer and Administrator

METHODIST HOSPITAL, 7700 Floyd Curl Drive, San Antonio, TX,
Zip 78229–3993; tel. 210/575–4000; Gay Nord, Chief Executive Officer

METHODIST STONE OAK HOSPITAL, 1139 East Sonterra Boulevard, San Antonio,
TX, Zip 78258–4347; tel. 210/638–2100; Marc Strode, Chief Executive
Officer

### REGIONAL HEALTHCARE ALLIANCE
**530 South Beckham Avenue, Tyler, TX 75702–8310;
tel. 903/531–4449; John Webb, President**

ALLEGIANCE SPECIALTY HOSPITAL OF KILGORE, 1612 South Henderson
Boulevard, Kilgore, TX, Zip 75662–3594; tel. 903/984–3505; Karen Ross,
Chief Executive Officer

BAYLOR UNIVERSITY MEDICAL CENTER, 3500 Gaston Avenue, Dallas, TX,
Zip 75246–2088; tel. 214/820–0111; John B. McWhorter, III, President

CHILDREN'S HEALTH SYSTEM OF TEXAS, 1935 Medical District Drive, Dallas, TX,
Zip 75235; tel. 214/456–7000; Christopher J. Durovich, President and Chief
Executive Officer

EAST TEXAS MEDICAL CENTER HENDERSON, 300 Wilson Street, Henderson, TX,
Zip 75652–5956; tel. 903/657–7541; Mark Leitner, Administrator

GOOD SHEPHERD MEDICAL CENTER, 700 East Marshall Avenue, Longview, TX,
Zip 75601–5580; tel. 903/315–2000; Steve Altmiller, President and Chief
Executive Officer

HOPKINS COUNTY MEMORIAL HOSPITAL, 115 Airport Road, Sulphur Springs, TX,
Zip 75482–2105; tel. 903/885–7671; Michael McAndrew, Chief Executive
Officer

MOTHER FRANCES HOSPITAL – JACKSONVILLE, 2026 South Jackson,
Jacksonville, TX, Zip 75766–5822; tel. 903/541–4500; Anne Pileggi, Chief
Executive Officer

MOTHER FRANCES HOSPITAL – TYLER, 800 East Dawson Street, Tyler, TX,
Zip 75701–2036; tel. 903/593–8441; John McGreevy, Chief Executive
Officer

NACOGDOCHES MEDICAL CENTER, 4920 N.E. Stallings Drive, Nacogdoches, TX,
Zip 75965–1200; tel. 936/569–9481; Gary L. Stokes, Chief Executive
Officer

PALESTINE REGIONAL MEDICAL CENTER–EAST, 2900 South Loop 256, Palestine,
TX, Zip 75801–6958; tel. 903/731–1000; Alan E. George, Chief Executive
Officer

PARIS REGIONAL MEDICAL CENTER, 865 Deshong Drive, Paris, TX,
Zip 75460–9313, Mailing Address: P.O. Box 9070, Zip 75461–9070;
tel. 903/785–4521; Patti Monczewski, Interim Chief Executive Officer

TITUS REGIONAL MEDICAL CENTER, 2001 North Jefferson Avenue, Mount
Pleasant, TX, Zip 75455–2398; tel. 903/577–6000; John P. Allen, Chief
Executive Officer

TRINITY MOTHER FRANCES REHABILITATION HOSPITAL, 3131 Troup Highway,
Tyler, TX, Zip 75701–8352; tel. 903/510–7000; Sharla Anderson, Chief
Executive Officer

TYLER CONTINUECARE HOSPITAL AT MOTHER FRANCES, 800 East Dawson, 4th
Floor, Tyler, TX, Zip 75701–2036; tel. 903/531–4080; Stephanie Hyde,
Chief Executive Officer

UNIVERSITY OF TEXAS HEALTH NORTHEAST, 11937 Highway 271, Tyler, TX, Zip 75708-3154; tel. 903/877-7777; Kirk A. Calhoun, M.D., President

**ST. DAVID'S HEALTH NETWORK**
**98 San Jacinto Boulevard, Austin, TX 78701-4082; tel. 512/708-9700; David Huffstutler, President and Chief Executive Officer**

ST. DAVID'S MEDICAL CENTER, 919 East 32nd Street, Austin, TX, Zip 78705-2709, Mailing Address: P.O. Box 4039, Zip 78765-4039; tel. 512/476-7111; Donald H. Wilkerson, Chief Executive Officer

ST. DAVID'S NORTH AUSTIN MEDICAL CENTER, 12221 North MoPac Expressway, Austin, TX, Zip 78758-2496; tel. 512/901-1000; Allen Harrison, Chief Executive Officer

ST. DAVID'S ROUND ROCK MEDICAL CENTER, 2400 Round Rock Avenue, Round Rock, TX, Zip 78681-4097; tel. 512/341-1000; Deborah L. Ryle, Administrator and Chief Executive Officer

ST. DAVID'S SOUTH AUSTIN MEDICAL CENTER, 901 West Ben White Boulevard, Austin, TX, Zip 78704-6903; tel. 512/447-2211; Todd E. Steward, Chief Executive Officer

**THE HOSPITALS OF PROVIDENCE**
**1625 Medical Center Drive, El Paso, TX 79902-5005; tel. 915/577-7746; Sally A. Hurt-Deitch, FACHE, Market Chief Executive Officer**

THE HOSPITALS OF PROVIDENCE MEMORIAL CAMPUS, 2001 North Oregon Street, El Paso, TX, Zip 79902-3368; tel. 915/577-6625; Sally A. Hurt-Deitch, FACHE, Chief Executive Officer

THE HOSPITALS OF PROVIDENCE SIERRA CAMPUS, 1625 Medical Center Drive, El Paso, TX, Zip 79902-5044; tel. 915/747-4000; Monica Vargas-Mahar, FACHE, Chief Executive Officer

THE HOSPITALS OF SIERRA PROVIDENCE EAST CAMPUS, 3280 Joe Battle Boulevard, El Paso, TX, Zip 79938-2622; tel. 915/832-2000; Nicholas R. Tejeda, FACHE, Chief Executive Officer

## VERMONT

**THE UNIVERSITY OF VERMONT HEALTH NETWORK**
**111 Colchester Avenue, Burlington, VT 05401-1473; tel. 802/847-3983; John R. Brumsted, M.D., President and Chief Executive Officer**

THE UNIVERSITY OF VERMONT HEALTH NETWORK CENTRAL VERMONT MEDICAL CENTER, 130 Fisher Road, Berlin, VT, Zip 05602-9516, Mailing Address: P.O. Box 547, Barre, Zip 05641-0547; tel. 802/371-4100; Judith C. Tartaglia, President and Chief Executive Officer

THE UNIVERSITY OF VERMONT HEALTH NETWORK ELIZABETHTOWN COMMUNITY HOSPITAL, Park Street, Elizabethtown, NY, Zip 12932-0277, Mailing Address: P.O. Box 277, Zip 12932-0277; tel. 518/873-6377; Rodney C. Boula, Administrator and Chief Executive Officer

THE UNIVERSITY OF VERMONT HEALTH NETWORK UNIVERSITY OF VERMONT MEDICAL CENTER, 111 Colchester Avenue, Burlington, VT, Zip 05401-1473; tel. 802/847-0000; John R. Brumsted, M.D., President and Chief Executive Officer

THE UNIVERSITY OF VERMONT HEALTH NETWORK–CHAMPLAIN VALLEY PHYSICIANS HOSPITAL, 75 Beekman Street, Plattsburgh, NY, Zip 12901-1438; tel. 518/561-2000; Stephens M. Mundy, President and Chief Executive Officer

## VIRGINIA

**CENTRAL VIRGINIA HEALTH NETWORK**
**2201 West Broad Street, Suite 202, Richmond, VA 23220-2022; tel. 804/359-4500; Michael Matthews, Chief Executive Officer**

BON SECOURS MEMORIAL REGIONAL MEDICAL CENTER, 8260 Atlee Road, Mechanicsville, VA, Zip 23116-1844; tel. 804/764-6000; Michael Robinson, Chief Executive Officer

BON SECOURS ST. FRANCIS MEDICAL CENTER, 13710 St. Francis Boulevard, Midlothian, VA, Zip 23114-3267; tel. 804/594-7300; Mark M. Gordon, Chief Executive Officer

BON SECOURS ST. MARY'S HOSPITAL, 5801 Bremo Road, Richmond, VA, Zip 23226-1907; tel. 804/285-2011; Toni R. Ardabell, R.N., Chief Executive Officer

BON SECOURS–RICHMOND COMMUNITY HOSPITAL, 1500 North 28th Street, Richmond, VA, Zip 23223-5396, Mailing Address: P.O. Box 27184, Zip 23261-7184; tel. 804/225-1700; Michael Robinson, Executive Vice President and Administrator

CENTRA SOUTHSIDE COMMUNITY HOSPITAL, 800 Oak Street, Farmville, VA, Zip 23901-1199; tel. 434/392-8811; Thomas Angelo, Chief Executive Officer

MARY IMMACULATE HOSPITAL, 2 Bernardine Drive, Newport News, VA, Zip 23602-4499; tel. 757/886-6000; Darlene Stephenson, Chief Executive Officer

RAPPAHANNOCK GENERAL HOSPITAL, 101 Harris Drive, Kilmarnock, VA, Zip 22482-3880, Mailing Address: P.O. Box 1449, Zip 22482-1449; tel. 804/435-8000; James M. Holmes, Jr., President and Chief Executive Officer

SHELTERING ARMS REHABILITATION HOSPITAL, 8254 Atlee Road, Mechanicsville, VA, Zip 23116-1844; tel. 804/764-1000; James E. Sok, FACHE, President and Chief Executive Officer

UNIVERSITY OF VIRGINIA MEDICAL CENTER, 1215 Lee Street, Charlottesville, VA, Zip 22908-0001, Mailing Address: P.O. Box 800809, Zip 22908-0809; tel. 434/924-0211; Pamela Sutton-Wallace, Chief Executive Officer

VCU COMMUNITY MEMORIAL HOSPITAL, 125 Buena Vista Circle, South Hill, VA, Zip 23970-1431, Mailing Address: P.O. Box 90, Zip 23970-0090; tel. 434/447-3151; W. Scott Burnette, Chief Executive Officer

**VIRGINIA HEALTH NETWORK**
**7400 Beaufont Springs Drive, Suite 505, Richmond, VA 23225-5521; tel. 804/320-3837; James Brittain, President**

AUGUSTA HEALTH, 78 Medical Center Drive, Fishersville, VA, Zip 22939-2332, Mailing Address: P.O. Box 1000, Zip 22939-1000; tel. 540/932-4000; Mary N. Mannix, FACHE, President and Chief Executive Officer

BATH COMMUNITY HOSPITAL, 83 Park Drive, Hot Springs, VA, Zip 24445-2788, Mailing Address: P.O. Box Z., Zip 24445-0750; tel. 540/839-7000; Kathy Landreth, Interim Chief Executive Officer

BEDFORD MEMORIAL HOSPITAL, 1613 Oakwood Street, Bedford, VA, Zip 24523-1213, Mailing Address: P.O. Box 688, Zip 24523-0688; tel. 540/586-2441; Patti Jurkus, Chief Executive Officer

BON SECOURS MARYVIEW MEDICAL CENTER, 3636 High Street, Portsmouth, VA, Zip 23707-3270; tel. 757/398-2200; Joseph M. Oddis, Chief Executive Officer

BON SECOURS MEMORIAL REGIONAL MEDICAL CENTER, 8260 Atlee Road, Mechanicsville, VA, Zip 23116-1844; tel. 804/764-6000; Michael Robinson, Chief Executive Officer

BON SECOURS ST. FRANCIS MEDICAL CENTER, 13710 St. Francis Boulevard, Midlothian, VA, Zip 23114-3267; tel. 804/594-7300; Mark M. Gordon, Chief Executive Officer

BON SECOURS ST. MARY'S HOSPITAL, 5801 Bremo Road, Richmond, VA, Zip 23226-1907; tel. 804/285-2011; Toni R. Ardabell, R.N., Chief Executive Officer

BON SECOURS–DEPAUL MEDICAL CENTER, 150 Kingsley Lane, Norfolk, VA, Zip 23505-4650; tel. 757/889-5000; John E. Barrett, III, Chief Executive Officer

BON SECOURS–RICHMOND COMMUNITY HOSPITAL, 1500 North 28th Street, Richmond, VA, Zip 23223-5396, Mailing Address: P.O. Box 27184, Zip 23261-7184; tel. 804/225-1700; Michael Robinson, Executive Vice President and Administrator

BUCHANAN GENERAL HOSPITAL, 1535 Slate Creek Road, Grundy, VA, Zip 24614-6974; tel. 276/935-1000; Robert D. Ruchti, Chief Executive Officer

CARILION FRANKLIN MEMORIAL HOSPITAL, 180 Floyd Avenue, Rocky Mount, VA, Zip 24151-1389; tel. 540/483-5277; William D. Jacobsen, Vice President and Administrator

CARILION GILES COMMUNITY HOSPITAL, 159 Hartley Way, Pearisburg, VA, Zip 24134-2471; tel. 540/921-6000; William Flattery, Vice President and Administrator Western Division

CARILION NEW RIVER VALLEY MEDICAL CENTER, 2900 Lamb Circle, Christiansburg, VA, Zip 24073-6344, Mailing Address: P.O. Box 5, Radford, Zip 24143-0005; tel. 540/731-2000; William Flattery, Vice President and Administrator Western Division

CARILION ROANOKE MEMORIAL HOSPITAL, Belleview at Jefferson Street, Roanoke, VA, Zip 24014, Mailing Address: P.O. Box 13367, Zip 24033-3367; tel. 540/981-7000; Steven C. Arner, President

CARILION STONEWALL JACKSON HOSPITAL, 1 Health Circle, Lexington, VA, Zip 24450-2492; tel. 540/458-3300; Charles E. Carr, Vice President and Administrator

CARILION TAZEWELL COMMUNITY HOSPITAL, 141 Ben Bolt Avenue, Tazewell, VA, Zip 24651-9700; tel. 276/988-8700; Kathren Dowdy, MSN, Regional Hospital Senior Director

CENTRA SOUTHSIDE COMMUNITY HOSPITAL, 800 Oak Street, Farmville, VA, Zip 23901-1199; tel. 434/392-8811; Thomas Angelo, Chief Executive Officer

CHESAPEAKE REGIONAL MEDICAL CENTER, 736 Battlefield Boulevard North, Chesapeake, VA, Zip 23320-4941, Mailing Address: P.O. Box 2028, Zip 23327-2028; tel. 757/312-8121; Peter F. Bastone, Chief Executive Officer

CHILDREN'S HOSPITAL OF RICHMOND AT VCU–BROOK ROAD CAMPUS, 2924 Brook Road, Richmond, VA, Zip 23220-1298; tel. 804/321-7474; Leslie G. Wyatt, Senior Vice President Children's Services and Executive Director

CHILDREN'S HOSPITAL OF THE KING'S DAUGHTERS, 601 Children's Lane, Norfolk, VA, Zip 23507-1910; tel. 757/668-7000; James D. Dahling, President and Chief Executive Officer

CHIPPENHAM HOSPITAL, 7101 Jahnke Road, Richmond, VA, Zip 23225-4044; tel. 804/320-3911; Tim McManus, President and Chief Executive Officer

CLINCH VALLEY MEDICAL CENTER, 6801 Governor G. C. Peery Highway, Richlands, VA, Zip 24641-2194; tel. 276/596-6000; Peter Mulkey, Chief Executive Officer

DOMINION HOSPITAL, 2960 Sleepy Hollow Road, Falls Church, VA, Zip 22044-2030; tel. 703/536-2000; C. Alan Eaks, Chief Executive Officer

FAUQUIER HOSPITAL, 500 Hospital Drive, Warrenton, VA, Zip 20186-3099; tel. 540/316-5000; Rodger H. Baker, President and Chief Executive Officer

Section B

HEALTHSOUTH REHABILITATION HOSPITAL OF VIRGINIA, 5700 Fitzhugh Avenue, Richmond, VA, Zip 23226–1800; tel. 804/288–5700; David Cashwell, Chief Executive Officer

HENRICO DOCTORS' HOSPITAL, 1602 Skipwith Road, Richmond, VA, Zip 23229–5205; tel. 804/289–4500; William Wagnon, Chief Executive Officer

INOVA ALEXANDRIA HOSPITAL, 4320 Seminary Road, Alexandria, VA, Zip 22304–1535; tel. 703/504–3167; Susan Carroll, Chief Executive Officer

INOVA FAIR OAKS HOSPITAL, 3600 Joseph Siewick Drive, Fairfax, VA, Zip 22033–1798; tel. 703/391–3600; John L. Fitzgerald, Chief Executive Officer

INOVA FAIRFAX HOSPITAL, 3300 Gallows Road, Falls Church, VA, Zip 22042–3300; tel. 703/776–4001; Patrick Christiansen, Ph.D., Chief Executive Officer

INOVA LOUDOUN HOSPITAL, 44045 Riverside Parkway, Leesburg, VA, Zip 20176–5101, Mailing Address: P.O. Box 6000, Zip 20177–0600; tel. 703/858–6000; Patrick Walters, Chief Executive Officer

INOVA MOUNT VERNON HOSPITAL, 2501 Parker's Lane, Alexandria, VA, Zip 22306–3209; tel. 703/664–7000; Deborah Addo–Samuels, Chief Executive Officer

JOHN RANDOLPH MEDICAL CENTER, 411 West Randolph Road, Hopewell, VA, Zip 23860–2938; tel. 804/541–1600; Suzanne B. Jackson, FACHE, Chief Executive Officer

JOHNSTON MEMORIAL HOSPITAL, 16000 Johnston Memorial Drive, Abingdon, VA, Zip 24211–7659; tel. 276/676–7000; Sean S. McMurray, FACHE, Vice President and Chief Executive Officer

LEWISGALE HOSPITAL ALLEGHANY, One ARH Lane, Low Moor, VA, Zip 24457, Mailing Address: P.O. Box 7, Zip 24457–0007; tel. 540/862–6011; Charlotte C. Tyson, Chief Executive Officer

LEWISGALE HOSPITAL PULASKI, 2400 Lee Highway, Pulaski, VA, Zip 24301–2326, Mailing Address: P.O. Box 759, Zip 24301–0759; tel. 540/994–8100; Derek Vance, Chief Executive Officer

MARTHA JEFFERSON HOSPITAL, 500 Martha Jefferson Drive, Charlottesville, VA, Zip 22911–4668; tel. 434/654–7000; Jonathan S. Davis, FACHE, President

MARY IMMACULATE HOSPITAL, 2 Bernardine Drive, Newport News, VA, Zip 23602–4499; tel. 757/886–6000; Darlene Stephenson, Chief Executive Officer

MARY WASHINGTON HOSPITAL, 1001 Sam Perry Boulevard, Fredericksburg, VA, Zip 22401–3354; tel. 540/741–1100; Michael McDermott, M.D., President and Chief Executive Officer

MEMORIAL HOSPITAL, 320 Hospital Drive, Martinsville, VA, Zip 24112–1981, Mailing Address: P.O. Box 4788, Zip 24115–4788; tel. 276/666–7200; Michael Ehrat, Chief Executive Officer

MOUNTAIN VIEW REGIONAL MEDICAL CENTER, 310 Third Street N.E., Norton, VA, Zip 24273–1137; tel. 276/679–9100; Dale Clark, President

NORTHERN HOSPITAL OF SURRY COUNTY, 830 Rockford Street, Mount Airy, NC, Zip 27030–5365, Mailing Address: P.O. Box 1101, Zip 27030–1101; tel. 336/719–7000; Ned Hill, President and Chief Executive Officer

NOVANT HEALTH PRINCE WILLIAM MEDICAL CENTER, 8700 Sudley Road, Manassas, VA, Zip 20110–4418, Mailing Address: P.O. Box 2610, Zip 20108–0867; tel. 703/369–8000; Melissa Robson, President

PIONEER COMMUNITY HOSPITAL OF PATRICK, 18688 Jeb Stuart Highway, Stuart, VA, Zip 24171–1559; tel. 276/694–3151; Jeanette Filpi, Chief Executive Officer

RAPPAHANNOCK GENERAL HOSPITAL, 101 Harris Drive, Kilmarnock, VA, Zip 22482–3880, Mailing Address: P.O. Box 1449, Zip 22482–1449; tel. 804/435–8000; James M. Holmes, Jr., President and Chief Executive Officer

RESTON HOSPITAL CENTER, 1850 Town Center Parkway, Reston, VA, Zip 20190–3219; tel. 703/689–9000; John A. Deardorff, Chief Executive Officer

RIVERSIDE BEHAVIORAL HEALTH CENTER, 2244 Executive Drive, Hampton, VA, Zip 23666–2430; tel. 757/827–1001; Debra Campbell, R.N., Administrator

RIVERSIDE REGIONAL MEDICAL CENTER, 500 J. Clyde Morris Boulevard, Newport News, VA, Zip 23601–1929; tel. 757/594–2000; Michael J. Doucette, Senior Vice President and Administrator

RIVERSIDE REHABILITATION INSTITUTE, 245 Chesapeake Avenue, Newport News, VA, Zip 23607–6038; tel. 757/928–8000; Edward Heckler, Administrator

RIVERSIDE SHORE MEMORIAL HOSPITAL, 9507 Hospital Avenue, Nassawadox, VA, Zip 23413–1821, Mailing Address: P.O. Box 17, Zip 23413–0017; tel. 757/414–8000; John Peterman, Vice President and Administrator

RIVERSIDE TAPPAHANNOCK HOSPITAL, 618 Hospital Road, Tappahannock, VA, Zip 22560–5000; tel. 804/443–3311; John Peterman, Vice President and Administrator

RIVERSIDE WALTER REED HOSPITAL, 7519 Hospital Drive, Gloucester, VA, Zip 23061–4178, Mailing Address: P.O. Box 1130, Zip 23061–1130; tel. 804/693–8800; Megan Kleckner, Vice President and Administrator

RUSSELL COUNTY MEDICAL CENTER, 58 Carroll Street, Lebanon, VA, Zip 24266, Mailing Address: P.O. Box 3600, Zip 24266–0200; tel. 276/883–8000; Stephen K. Givens, Assistant Vice President and Administrator

SENTARA CAREPLEX HOSPITAL, 3000 Coliseum Drive, Hampton, VA, Zip 23666–5963; tel. 757/736–1000; Debra A. Flores, R.N., MS, President and Administrator

SENTARA LEIGH HOSPITAL, 830 Kempsville Road, Norfolk, VA, Zip 23502–3920; tel. 757/261–6000; Teresa L. Edwards, President and Administrator

SENTARA NORFOLK GENERAL HOSPITAL, 600 Gresham Drive, Norfolk, VA, Zip 23507–1904; tel. 757/388–3000; Kurt T. Hofelich, President

SENTARA NORTHERN VIRGINIA MEDICAL CENTER, 2300 Opitz Boulevard, Woodbridge, VA, Zip 22191–3399; tel. 703/523–1000; Stephen D. Porter, President

SENTARA OBICI HOSPITAL, 2800 Godwin Boulevard, Suffolk, VA, Zip 23434–8038; tel. 757/934–4000; Steve Julian, M.D., President

SENTARA PRINCESS ANNE HOSPITAL, 2025 Glenn Mitchell Drive, Virginia Beach, VA, Zip 23456–0178; tel. 757/507–1000; Thomas B. Thames, M.D., President

SENTARA VIRGINIA BEACH GENERAL HOSPITAL, 1060 First Colonial Road, Virginia Beach, VA, Zip 23454–3002; tel. 757/395–8000; Elwood Bernard Boone, III, FACHE, President

SENTARA WILLIAMSBURG REGIONAL MEDICAL CENTER, 100 Sentara Circle, Williamsburg, VA, Zip 23188–5713; tel. 757/984–6000; David J. Masterson, President

SHELTERING ARMS REHABILITATION HOSPITAL, 8254 Atlee Road, Mechanicsville, VA, Zip 23116–1844; tel. 804/764–1000; James E. Sok, FACHE, President and Chief Executive Officer

SMYTH COUNTY COMMUNITY HOSPITAL, 245 Medical Park Drive, Marion, VA, Zip 24354, Mailing Address: P.O. Box 880, Zip 24354–0880; tel. 276/378–1000; James E. Tyler, Vice President and Hospital Chief Executive Officer

SOUTHAMPTON MEMORIAL HOSPITAL, 100 Fairview Drive, Franklin, VA, Zip 23851–1238, Mailing Address: P.O. Box 817, Zip 23851–0817; tel. 757/569–6100; Kimberly W. Marks, Interim Chief Executive Officer

SOUTHERN VIRGINIA REGIONAL MEDICAL CENTER, 727 North Main Street, Emporia, VA, Zip 23847–1274; tel. 434/348–4400; Matt Tavenner, Chief Executive Officer

SOUTHSIDE REGIONAL MEDICAL CENTER, 200 Medical Park Boulevard, Petersburg, VA, Zip 23805–9274; tel. 804/765–5000; Douglas J. Moyer, Chief Executive Officer

TWIN COUNTY REGIONAL HEALTHCARE, 200 Hospital Drive, Galax, VA, Zip 24333–2227; tel. 276/236–8181; Jon D. Applebaum, Chief Executive Officer

UNIVERSITY OF VIRGINIA MEDICAL CENTER, 1215 Lee Street, Charlottesville, VA, Zip 22908–0001, Mailing Address: P.O. Box 800809, Zip 22908–0809; tel. 434/924–0211; Pamela Sutton–Wallace, Chief Executive Officer

UVA CULPEPER HOSPITAL, 501 Sunset Lane, Culpeper, VA, Zip 22701–3917, Mailing Address: P.O. Box 592, Zip 22701–0500; tel. 540/829–4100; Greg Napps, Chief Executive Officer

UVA–HEALTHSOUTH REHABILITATION HOSPITAL, 515 Ray C. Hunt Drive, Charlottesville, VA, Zip 22903–2981; tel. 434/244–2000; Thomas J. Cook, Chief Executive Officer

VCU COMMUNITY MEMORIAL HOSPITAL, 125 Buena Vista Circle, South Hill, VA, Zip 23970–1431, Mailing Address: P.O. Box 90, Zip 23970–0090; tel. 434/447–3151; W. Scott Burnette, Chief Executive Officer

VCU MEDICAL CENTER, 1250 East Marshall Street, Richmond, VA, Zip 23298–5051, Mailing Address: P.O. Box 980510, Zip 23298–0510; tel. 804/828–9000; John Duval, Chief Executive Officer

VIRGINIA HOSPITAL CENTER – ARLINGTON, 1701 North George Mason Drive, Arlington, VA, Zip 22205–3698; tel. 703/558–5000; James B. Cole, Chief Executive Officer

WYTHE COUNTY COMMUNITY HOSPITAL, 600 West Ridge Road, Wytheville, VA, Zip 24382–1099; tel. 276/228–0200; Chad Melton, Chief Executive Officer

## WASHINGTON

**GROUP HEALTH COOPERATIVE**
**320 Westlake Avenue North, Suite 100, Seattle, WA 98109–5233; tel. 206/448–5083; Scott Armstrong, Chief Executive Officer**

CASCADE VALLEY HOSPITAL AND CLINICS, 330 South Stillaguamish Avenue, Arlington, WA, Zip 98223–1642; tel. 360/435–2133; W. Clark Jones, Superintendent and Administrator

COLUMBIA COUNTY HEALTH SYSTEM, 1012 South Third Street, Dayton, WA, Zip 99328–1696; tel. 509/382–2531; Jon D. Smiley, Interim Chief Executive Officer

DEACONESS HOSPITAL, 800 West Fifth Avenue, Spokane, WA, Zip 99204–2803, Mailing Address: P.O. Box 248, Zip 99210–0248; tel. 509/458–5800; Maurine Cate, Chief Executive Officer

GROUP HEALTH COOPERATIVE CENTRAL HOSPITAL, 201 16th Avenue East, Seattle, WA, Zip 98112–5226; tel. 206/326–3000; Carol M. Taylor, R.N., Regional Director Clinical Operations

HARRISON MEDICAL CENTER, 2520 Cherry Avenue, Bremerton, WA, Zip 98310–4229; tel. 360/744–3911; David W. Schultz, FACHE, President

ISLAND HOSPITAL, 1211 24th Street, Anacortes, WA, Zip 98221–2562; tel. 360/299–1300; Vincent Oliver, Administrator

KADLEC REGIONAL MEDICAL CENTER, 888 Swift Boulevard, Richland, WA, Zip 99352–3514; tel. 509/946–4611; Rand J. Wortman, President and Chief Executive Officer

KITTITAS VALLEY HEALTHCARE, 603 South Chestnut Street, Ellensburg, WA, Zip 98926–3875; tel. 509/962–7302; Paul E. Nurick, Chief Executive Officer

Section B

KOOTENAI HEALTH, 2003 Kootenai Health Way, Coeur D'Alene, ID, Zip 83814–2677; tel. 208/625–4000; Jon Ness, Chief Executive Officer

LOURDES MEDICAL CENTER, 520 North Fourth Avenue, Pasco, WA, Zip 99301–5257, Mailing Address: P.O. Box 2568, Zip 99302–2568; tel. 509/547–7704; John Serle, FACHE, President and Chief Executive Officer

MULTICARE MARY BRIDGE CHILDREN'S HOSPITAL AND HEALTH CENTER, 317 Martin Luther King Jr. Way, Tacoma, WA, Zip 98405–4234, Mailing Address: P.O. Box 5299, Zip 98415–0299; tel. 253/403–1400; Robert Lenza, Chief Operating Officer and Administrator

NORTHWEST SPECIALTY HOSPITAL, 1593 East Polston Avenue, Post Falls, ID, Zip 83854–5326; tel. 208/262–2300; Vaughn Ward, Chief Executive Officer

OVERLAKE MEDICAL CENTER, 1035 116th Avenue N.E., Bellevue, WA, Zip 98004–4604; tel. 425/688–5000; J. Michael Marsh, President and Chief Executive Officer

PEACEHEALTH ST. JOSEPH MEDICAL CENTER, 2901 Squalicum Parkway, Bellingham, WA, Zip 98225–1851; tel. 360/734–5400; Nancy Steiger, R.N., FACHE, Chief Executive Officer and Chief Mission Officer, Northwest Network

PEACEHEALTH UNITED GENERAL MEDICAL CENTER, 2000 Hospital Drive, Sedro–Woolley, WA, Zip 98284–4327; tel. 360/856–6021; James R. Barnhart, Chief Administrative Officer

PMH MEDICAL CENTER, 723 Memorial Street, Prosser, WA, Zip 99350–1593; tel. 509/786–2222; Julie Petersen, Chief Executive Officer

PROVIDENCE CENTRALIA HOSPITAL, 914 South Scheuber Road, Centralia, WA, Zip 98531–9027; tel. 360/736–2803; Medrice Coluccio, R.N., Southwest Region Chief Executive

PROVIDENCE HOLY FAMILY HOSPITAL, 5633 North Lidgerwood Street, Spokane, WA, Zip 99208–1224; tel. 509/482–0111; Alex Jackson, Chief Executive

PROVIDENCE REGIONAL MEDICAL CENTER EVERETT, 1321 Colby Avenue, Everett, WA, Zip 98201–1665, Mailing Address: P.O. Box 1147, Zip 98206–1147; tel. 425/261–2000; Preston M. Simmons, FACHE, Chief Executive Officer

PROVIDENCE SACRED HEART MEDICAL CENTER & CHILDREN'S HOSPITAL, 101 West Eighth Avenue, Spokane, WA, Zip 99204–2364, Mailing Address: P.O. Box 2555, Zip 99220–2555; tel. 509/474–3131; Alex Jackson, Chief Executive

PROVIDENCE ST. MARY MEDICAL CENTER, 401 West Poplar Street, Walla Walla, WA, Zip 99362–2846, Mailing Address: P.O. Box 1477, Zip 99362–0312; tel. 509/525–3320; Steven A. Burdick, Chief Executive Officer

PULLMAN REGIONAL HOSPITAL, 835 S.E. Bishop Boulevard, Pullman, WA, Zip 99163–5512; tel. 509/332–2541; Scott K. Adams, Chief Executive Officer

SEATTLE CHILDREN'S HOSPITAL, 4800 Sand Point Way N.E., Seattle, WA, Zip 98105–3901, Mailing Address: P.O. Box 5371, Zip 98145–5005; tel. 206/987–2000; Jeff Sperring, M.D., Chief Executive Officer

SKAGIT VALLEY HOSPITAL, 1415 East Kincaid Street, Mount Vernon, WA, Zip 98274–4126, Mailing Address: P.O. Box 1376, Zip 98273–1376; tel. 360/424–4111; Gregg Agustin Davidson, FACHE, Chief Executive Officer

ST. FRANCIS HOSPITAL, 34515 Ninth Avenue South, Federal Way, WA, Zip 98003–6799; tel. 253/944–8100; Anthony McLean, President

ST. JOSEPH MEDICAL CENTER, 1717 South J Street, Tacoma, WA, Zip 98405–3004, Mailing Address: P.O. Box 2197, Zip 98401–2197; tel. 253/426–4101; Syd Bersante, R.N., President

SUNNYSIDE COMMUNITY HOSPITAL AND CLINICS, 1016 Tacoma Avenue, Sunnyside, WA, Zip 98944–2263, Mailing Address: P.O. Box 719, Zip 98944–0719; tel. 509/837–1500; John Gallagher, Chief Executive Officer

TOPPENISH COMMUNITY HOSPITAL, 502 West Fourth Avenue, Toppenish, WA, Zip 98948–1616, Mailing Address: P.O. Box 672, Zip 98948–0672; tel. 509/865–3105; Perry Gay, Chief Executive Officer

TRIOS HEALTH, 900 South Auburn Street, Kennewick, WA, Zip 99336–5621; Mailing Address: P.O. Box 6128, Zip 99336–0128; tel. 509/586–6111; Glen Marshall, Chief Executive Officer

VALLEY HOSPITAL, 12606 East Mission Avenue, Spokane Valley, WA, Zip 99216–1090; tel. 509/924–6650; Gregory Repetti, Interim Chief Executive Officer

VIRGINIA MASON MEDICAL CENTER, 1100 Ninth Avenue, Seattle, WA, Zip 98101–2756, Mailing Address: P.O. Box 900, Zip 98111–0900; tel. 206/223–6600; Gary Kaplan, M.D., FACHE, Chairman and Chief Executive Officer

WALLA WALLA GENERAL HOSPITAL, 1025 South Second Avenue, Walla Walla, WA, Zip 99362–4116, Mailing Address: P.O. Box 1398, Zip 99362–0309; tel. 509/525–0480; Monty E. Knittel, President and Chief Executive Officer

WHIDBEY GENERAL HOSPITAL, 101 North Main Street, Coupeville, WA, Zip 98239–3413; tel. 360/678–5151; Geri Forbes, Chief Executive Officer

WHITMAN HOSPITAL AND MEDICAL CENTER, 1200 West Fairview Street, Colfax, WA, Zip 99111–9579; tel. 509/397–3435; Hank Hanigan, Administrator and Chief Executive Officer

YAKIMA REGIONAL MEDICAL AND CARDIAC CENTER, 110 South Ninth Avenue, Yakima, WA, Zip 98902–3315; tel. 509/575–5000; Veronica Knudson, Chief Executive Officer

YAKIMA VALLEY MEMORIAL HOSPITAL, 2811 Tieton Drive, Yakima, WA, Zip 98902–3761; tel. 509/575–8000; Russ Myers, Chief Executive Officer

**LINCOLN COUNTY HEALTH DEPARTMENT**
  **90 Nichols Street, Davenport, WA 99122–9729; tel. 509/725–1001; Ed Dzedzy, Public Health Administration**

LINCOLN HOSPITAL, 10 Nicholls Street, Davenport, WA, Zip 99122–9729; tel. 509/725–7101; Thomas J. Martin, Administrator

ODESSA MEMORIAL HEALTHCARE CENTER, 502 East Amende Drive, Odessa, WA, Zip 99159–7003, Mailing Address: P.O. Box 368, Zip 99159–0368; tel. 509/982–2611; Mo P. Sheldon, Chief Executive Officer and Superintendent

## WEST VIRGINIA

**HEALTH PARTNERS NETWORK, INC.**
  **1000 Technology Drive, Suite 2320, Fairmont, WV 26554–8834; tel. 304/368–2740; William G. MacLean, Executive Director**

BROADDUS HOSPITAL, 1 Healthcare Drive, Philippi, WV, Zip 26416–9405, Mailing Address: P.O. Box 930, Zip 26416–0930; tel. 304/457–1760; Jeffrey A. Powelson, Chief Executive Officer

CAMDEN CLARK MEDICAL CENTER, 800 Garfield Avenue, Parkersburg, WV, Zip 26101–5378, Mailing Address: P.O. Box 718, Zip 26102–0718; tel. 304/424–2111; David K. McClure, President and Chief Executive Officer

DAVIS MEDICAL CENTER, Gorman Avenue and Reed Street, Elkins, WV, Zip 26241, Mailing Address: P.O. Box 1484, Zip 26241–1484; tel. 304/636–3300; Mark Doak, Chief Executive Officer

GRAFTON CITY HOSPITAL, 1 Hospital Plaza, Grafton, WV, Zip 26354–1283; tel. 304/265–0400; Patrick D. Shaw, Chief Executive Officer

HEALTHSOUTH MOUNTAINVIEW REGIONAL REHABILITATION HOSPITAL, 1160 Van Voorhis Road, Morgantown, WV, Zip 26505–3437; tel. 304/598–1100; Lou Little, Chief Executive Officer

MINNIE HAMILTON HEALTHCARE CENTER, 186 Hospital Drive, Grantsville, WV, Zip 26147–7100; tel. 304/354–9244; Steve Whited, Chief Executive Officer

ST. JOSEPH'S HOSPITAL OF BUCKHANNON, 1 Amalia Drive, Buckhannon, WV, Zip 26201–2276; tel. 304/473–2000; Sue E. Johnson–Phillippe, FACHE, President and Chief Executive Officer

STONEWALL JACKSON MEMORIAL HOSPITAL, 230 Hospital Plaza, Weston, WV, Zip 26452–8558; tel. 304/269–8000; Avah Stalnaker, Chief Executive Officer

UNITED HOSPITAL CENTER, 327 Medical Park Drive, Bridgeport, WV, Zip 26330–9006; tel. 681/342–1000; Michael C. Tillman, President and Chief Executive Officer

WEBSTER COUNTY MEMORIAL HOSPITAL, 324 Miller Mountain Drive, Webster Springs, WV, Zip 26288–1087, Mailing Address: P.O. Box 312, Zip 26288–0312; tel. 304/847–5682; Robert Mace, M.D., Interim Chief Executive Officer

WEST VIRGINIA UNIVERSITY HOSPITALS, 1 Medical Center Drive, Morgantown, WV, Zip 26506–4749; tel. 304/598–4000; Albert Wright, PharmD, President and Chief Executive Officer

**PARTNERS IN HEALTH NETWORK, INC.**
  **405 Capitol Street, Suite 505, Charleston, WV 25301–1783; tel. 304/388–7385; Robert D. Whitler, Executive Director**

BOONE MEMORIAL HOSPITAL, 701 Madison Avenue, Madison, WV, Zip 25130–1699; tel. 304/369–1230; Virgil Underwood, Chief Executive Officer

BRAXTON COUNTY MEMORIAL HOSPITAL, 100 Hoylman Drive, Gassaway, WV, Zip 26624–9318; tel. 304/364–5156; Ben Vincent, FACHE, Chief Executive Officer

CHARLESTON AREA MEDICAL CENTER, 501 Morris Street, Charleston, WV, Zip 25301–1300, Mailing Address: P.O. Box 1547, Zip 25326–1547; tel. 304/388–5432; David L. Ramsey, President and Chief Executive Officer

EYE AND EAR CLINIC OF CHARLESTON, 1306 Kanawha Boulevard East, Charleston, WV, Zip 25301–3001, Mailing Address: P.O. Box 2271, Zip 25328–2271; tel. 304/343–4371; Christina Arvon, Administrator and Chief Executive Officer

HIGHLAND HOSPITAL, 300 56th Street S.E., Charleston, WV, Zip 25304–2361, Mailing Address: P.O. Box 4107, Zip 25364–4107; tel. 304/926–1600; Cynthia A. Persily, Ph.D., R.N., President and Chief Executive Officer

JACKSON GENERAL HOSPITAL, 122 Pinnell Street, Ripley, WV, Zip 25271–9101, Mailing Address: P.O. Box 720, Zip 25271–0720; tel. 304/372–2731; Stephanie McCoy, President and Chief Executive Officer

MINNIE HAMILTON HEALTHCARE CENTER, 186 Hospital Drive, Grantsville, WV, Zip 26147–7100; tel. 304/354–9244; Steve Whited, Chief Executive Officer

MONTGOMERY GENERAL HOSPITAL, 401 Sixth Avenue, Montgomery, WV, Zip 25136–2116, Mailing Address: P.O. Box 270, Zip 25136–0270; tel. 304/442–5151; Vickie Gay, Chief Executive Officer

POCAHONTAS MEMORIAL HOSPITAL, 150 Duncan Road, Buckeye, WV, Zip 24924, Mailing Address: Rural Route 2, Box 52 W, Zip 24924; tel. 304/799–7400; Barbara Lay, Chief Executive Officer

ROANE GENERAL HOSPITAL, 200 Hospital Drive, Spencer, WV, Zip 25276–1050; tel. 304/927–4444; Douglas E. Bentz, Chief Executive Officer

STONEWALL JACKSON MEMORIAL HOSPITAL, 230 Hospital Plaza, Weston, WV, Zip 26452–8558; tel. 304/269–8000; Avah Stalnaker, Chief Executive Officer

SUMMERSVILLE REGIONAL MEDICAL CENTER, 400 Fairview Heights Road, Summersville, WV, Zip 26651–9308; tel. 304/872–2891; Daniel M. Ayres, President and Chief Executive Officer

WEBSTER COUNTY MEMORIAL HOSPITAL, 324 Miller Mountain Drive, Webster Springs, WV, Zip 26288–1087, Mailing Address: P.O. Box 312, Zip 26288–0312; tel. 304/847–5682; Robert Mace, M.D., Interim Chief Executive Officer

## WISCONSIN

### AFFINITY HEALTH SYSTEM
**1570 Midway Place, Menasha, WI 54952–1165; tel. 920/720–1713; Monica Hilt, President and Chief Executive Officer**

CALUMET MEDICAL CENTER, 614 Memorial Drive, Chilton, WI, Zip 53014–1597; tel. 920/849–2386; Timothy Richman, President

MERCY MEDICAL CENTER, 500 South Oakwood Road, Oshkosh, WI, Zip 54904–7944; tel. 920/223–2000; Jeremy Normington–Slay, FACHE, Chief Executive Officer

ST. ELIZABETH HOSPITAL, 1506 South Oneida Street, Appleton, WI, Zip 54915–1305; tel. 920/738–2000; Monica Hilt, President and Chief Executive Officer

### ASPIRUS, INC.
**425 Pine Ridge Boulevard, Wausau, WI 54401–4123; tel. 715/847–2118; Matthew Heywood, Chief Executive Officer**

ASPIRUS GRAND VIEW, N10561 Grand View Lane, Ironwood, MI, Zip 49938–9622; tel. 906/932–2525; Paula L. Chermside, Chief Operating Officer

ASPIRUS KEWEENAW HOSPITAL, 205 Osceola Street, Laurium, MI, Zip 49913–2134; tel. 906/337–6500; Michael Hauswirth, Chief Operating Officer

ASPIRUS MEDFORD HOSPITAL, 135 South Gibson Street, Medford, WI, Zip 54451–1696; tel. 715/748–8100; Gregory A. Olson, President and Chief Executive Officer

ASPIRUS ONTONAGON HOSPITAL, 601 South Seventh Street, Ontonagon, MI, Zip 49953–1459; tel. 906/884–8000; Michael Hauswirth, Chief Operating Officer

ASPIRUS RIVERVIEW HOSPITAL AND CLINICS, INC., 410 Dewey Street, Wisconsin Rapids, WI, Zip 54494–4715, Mailing Address: P.O. Box 8080, Zip 54495–8080; tel. 715/423–6060; Celse A. Berard, President

ASPIRUS WAUSAU HOSPITAL, 333 Pine Ridge Boulevard, Wausau, WI, Zip 54401–4187; tel. 715/847–2121; Darrell Lentz, Interim President

LANGLADE HOSPITAL, 112 East Fifth Avenue, Antigo, WI, Zip 54409–2796; tel. 715/623–2331; David R. Schneider, Executive Director

NORTHSTAR HEALTH SYSTEM, 1400 West Ice Lake Road, Iron River, MI, Zip 49935–9526; tel. 906/265–6121; Connie L. Koutouzos, R.N., MSN, Chief Executive Officer and President

### COLUMBIA ST. MARY'S
**2025 East Newport Avenue, Milwaukee, WI 53211–2906; tel. 414/961–3300; Travis Andersen, President and Chief Executive Officer**

COLUMBIA ST. MARY'S HOSPITAL MILWAUKEE, 2301 North Lake Drive, Milwaukee, WI, Zip 53211–4508; tel. 414/291–1000; Travis Andersen, President and Chief Executive Officer

COLUMBIA ST. MARY'S OZAUKEE HOSPITAL, 13111 North Port Washington Road, Mequon, WI, Zip 53097–2416; tel. 262/243–7300; Travis Andersen, President and Chief Executive Officer

SACRED HEART REHABILITATION INSTITUTE, 2323 North Lake Drive, Milwaukee, WI, Zip 53211–4508; tel. 414/298–6750; Allan M. Spooner, President

### COMMUNITY HEALTH NETWORK, INC.
**225 Memorial Drive, Berlin, WI 54923–1243; tel. 920/361–5580; John Feeney, President and Chief Executive Officer**

BERLIN MEMORIAL HOSPITAL, 225 Memorial Drive, Berlin, WI, Zip 54923–1295; tel. 920/361–1313; John Feeney, President and Chief Executive Officer

WILD ROSE COMMUNITY MEMORIAL HOSPITAL, 601 Grove Avenue, Wild Rose, WI, Zip 54984–6903, Mailing Address: P.O. Box 243, Zip 54984–0243; tel. 920/622–3257; Dawn Schuman, President

### FROEDTERT HEALTH
**9200 West Wisconsin Avenue, Milwaukee, WI 53226–3596; tel. 414/805–3000; Catherine A. Jacobson, President and Chief Executive Officer**

COMMUNITY MEMORIAL HOSPITAL, W180 N8085 Town Hall Road, Menomonee Falls, WI, Zip 53051–3518, Mailing Address: P.O. Box 408, Zip 53052–0408; tel. 262/251–1000; Dennis Pollard, President

FROEDTERT MEMORIAL LUTHERAN HOSPITAL, 9200 West Wisconsin Avenue, Milwaukee, WI, Zip 53226–3596, Mailing Address: P.O. Box 26099, Zip 53226–0099; tel. 414/805–3000; Catherine Buck, President

ST. JOSEPH'S HOSPITAL, 3200 Pleasant Valley Road, West Bend, WI, Zip 53095–9274; tel. 262/334–5533; Allen Ericson, President

### GUNDERSON HEALTH SYSTEM
**1900 South Avenue, La Crosse, WI 54601–5467; tel. 608/782–7300; Jeffrey E. Thompson, M.D., Chief Executive Officer**

GUNDERSEN BOSCOBEL AREA HOSPITAL AND CLINICS, 205 Parker Street, Boscobel, WI, Zip 53805–1698; tel. 608/375–4112; David Hartberg, Administrator

GUNDERSEN HEALTH SYSTEM, 1900 South Avenue, La Crosse, WI, Zip 54601–5467; tel. 608/782–7300; Jeffrey E. Thompson, M.D., Chief Executive Officer

GUNDERSEN ST. JOSEPH'S HOSPITAL AND CLINICS, 400 Water Avenue, Hillsboro, WI, Zip 54634–9054, Mailing Address: P.O. Box 527, Zip 54634–0527; tel. 608/489–8000; Debra Smith, Chief Executive Officer

GUNDERSEN TRI–COUNTY HOSPITAL AND CLINICS, 18601 Lincoln Street, Whitehall, WI, Zip 54773–8605; tel. 715/538–4361; Brian Theiler, President and Chief Executive Officer

PALMER LUTHERAN HEALTH CENTER, 112 Jefferson Street, West Union, IA, Zip 52175–1022; tel. 563/422–3811; Tanya Tysland, Interim Chief Executive Officer

### MERCY ALLIANCE, INC.
**1000 Mineral Point Avenue, Janesville, WI 53548–2940; tel. 608/756–6000; Javon R. Bea, President and Chief Executive Officer**

MERCY HARVARD HOSPITAL, 901 Grant Street, Harvard, IL, Zip 60033–1898, Mailing Address: P.O. Box 850, Zip 60033–0850; tel. 815/943–5431; Javon R. Bea, Chief Executive Officer

MERCY HOSPITAL AND TRAUMA CENTER, 1000 Mineral Point Avenue, Janesville, WI, Zip 53548–2982, Mailing Address: P.O. Box 5003, Zip 53547–5003; tel. 608/756–6000; Javon R. Bea, President and Chief Executive Officer

MERCY WALWORTH HOSPITAL AND MEDICAL CENTER, N2950 State Road 67, Lake Geneva, WI, Zip 53147–2655; tel. 262/245–0535; Jennifer Hallatt, Chief Operating Officer

### MINISTRY HEALTH CARE
**11925 West Lake Park Drive, Milwaukee, WI 53224–3002; tel. 414/359–1060; Daniel Neufelder, President and Chief Executive Officer**

CALUMET MEDICAL CENTER, 614 Memorial Drive, Chilton, WI, Zip 53014–1597; tel. 920/849–2386; Timothy Richman, President

FLAMBEAU HOSPITAL, 98 Sherry Avenue, Park Falls, WI, Zip 54552–1467, Mailing Address: P.O. Box 310, Zip 54552–0310; tel. 715/762–2484; David A. Grundstrom, Chief Administrative Officer

HOWARD YOUNG MEDICAL CENTER, 240 Maple Street, Woodruff, WI, Zip 54568–9190, Mailing Address: P.O. Box 470, Zip 54568–0470; tel. 715/356–8000; Sandra L. Anderson, President and Chief Executive Officer

MERCY MEDICAL CENTER, 500 South Oakwood Road, Oshkosh, WI, Zip 54904–7944; tel. 920/223–2000; Jeremy Normington–Slay, FACHE, Chief Executive Officer

MINISTRY DOOR COUNTY MEDICAL CENTER, 323 South 18th Avenue, Sturgeon Bay, WI, Zip 54235–1495; tel. 920/743–5566; Gerald M. Worrick, President and Chief Executive Officer

MINISTRY EAGLE RIVER MEMORIAL HOSPITAL, 201 Hospital Road, Eagle River, WI, Zip 54521–8835; tel. 715/479–7411; Sandra L. Anderson, President and Chief Executive Officer

MINISTRY GOOD SAMARITAN HEALTH CENTER, 601 South Center Avenue, Merrill, WI, Zip 54452–3404; tel. 715/536–5511; Mary T. Krueger, President

MINISTRY OUR LADY OF VICTORY HOSPITAL, 1120 Pine Street, Stanley, WI, Zip 54768–1297; tel. 715/644–5571; Vanessa Freitag, President

MINISTRY SACRED HEART HOSPITAL, 401 West Mohawk Drive, Tomahawk, WI, Zip 54487–2274; tel. 715/453–7700; Sandra L. Anderson, President and Chief Executive Officer

MINISTRY SAINT CLARE'S HOSPITAL, 3400 Ministry Parkway, Weston, WI, Zip 54476–5220; tel. 715/393–3000; Mary T. Krueger, President

MINISTRY SAINT JOSEPH'S HOSPITAL, 611 St. Joseph Avenue, Marshfield, WI, Zip 54449–1898; tel. 715/387–1713; Brian Kief, Regional Vice President Ministry Health Care and President Ministry Saint Joseph's Hospital

MINISTRY SAINT MARY'S HOSPITALS, 2251 North Shore Drive, Rhinelander, WI, Zip 54501–6710; tel. 715/361–2000; Sandra L. Anderson, President and Chief Executive Officer

MINISTRY SAINT MICHAEL'S HOSPITAL, 900 Illinois Avenue, Stevens Point, WI, Zip 54481–3196; tel. 715/346–5000; Jeffrey L. Martin, President

SAINT ELIZABETH'S MEDICAL CENTER, 1200 Grant Boulevard West, Wabasha, MN, Zip 55981–1042; tel. 651/565–4531; Thomas Crowley, President and Chief Executive Officer

ST. ELIZABETH HOSPITAL, 1506 South Oneida Street, Appleton, WI, Zip 54915–1305; tel. 920/738–2000; Monica Hilt, President and Chief Executive Officer

### WHEATON FRANCISCAN HEALTHCARE
**400 West River Woods Parkway, Glendale, WI 53212–1060; tel. 414/465–3000; John D. Oliverio, President and Chief Executive Officer**

MIDWEST ORTHOPEDIC SPECIALTY HOSPITAL, 10101 South 27th Street, 2nd Floor, Franklin, WI, Zip 53132–7209; tel. 414/817–5800; Coreen Dicus–Johnson, President

WHEATON FRANCISCAN HEALTHCARE – ALL SAINTS, 3801 Spring Street, Racine, WI, Zip 53405–1690; tel. 262/687–4011; Susan Boland, R.N., MSN, President and Chief Executive Officer

WHEATON FRANCISCAN HEALTHCARE – ELMBROOK MEMORIAL, 19333 West North Avenue, Brookfield, WI, Zip 53045–4198; tel. 262/785–2000; Debra K. Standridge, President

WHEATON FRANCISCAN HEALTHCARE – FRANKLIN, 10101 South 27th Street, Franklin, WI, Zip 53132–7209; tel. 414/325–4700; Coreen Dicus–Johnson, President

WHEATON FRANCISCAN HEALTHCARE – ST. FRANCIS, 3237 South 16th Street, Milwaukee, WI, Zip 53215–4592; tel. 414/647–5000; Coreen Dicus–Johnson, President

WHEATON FRANCISCAN HEALTHCARE – ST. JOSEPH'S, 5000 West Chambers Street, Milwaukee, WI, Zip 53210–1650; tel. 414/447–2000; Debra K. Standridge, President

WHEATON FRANCISCAN HEALTHCARE – THE WISCONSIN HEART HOSPITAL, 10000 West Bluemound Road, Wauwatosa, WI, Zip 53226–4321; tel. 414/778–7800; Coreen Dicus–Johnson, President

## ALLIANCE OF INDEPENDENT ACADEMIC MEDICAL CENTERS

233 East Erie Street, Ste 306, Chicago, IL Zip 60611; tel. 312/836–3712; Kimberly Pierce–Boggs, Executive Director

### ARIZONA
**Phoenix**
Member
  Maricopa Integrated Health System

**Scottsdale**
Member
  HonorHealth Scottsdale Osborn Medical Center

### CALIFORNIA
**Los Angeles**
Member
  Cedars–Sinai Medical Center

**Oakland**
Member
  Kaiser Permanente Oakland Medical Center

### CONNECTICUT
**Danbury**
Member
  Danbury Hospital

**Hartford**
Member
  Saint Francis Hospital and Medical Center

### DELAWARE
**Newark**
Member
  Christiana Care Health System

### FLORIDA
**Orlando**
Member
  Florida Hospital

### ILLINOIS
**Chicago**
Member
  Advocate Illinois Masonic Medical Center

**Oak Lawn**
Member
  Advocate Christ Medical Center

**Park Ridge**
Member
  Advocate Lutheran General Hospital

**Peoria**
Member
  OSF Saint Francis Medical Center

### KENTUCKY
**Louisville**
Member
  Kosair Children's Hospital
  Norton Audubon Hospital
  Norton Brownsboro Hospital
  Norton Hospital
  Norton Women's and Kosair Children's Hospital

### LOUISIANA
**Baton Rouge**
Member
  Baton Rouge General Medical Center
  Our Lady of the Lake Regional Medical Center

### MAINE
**Portland**
Member
  Maine Medical Center

### MARYLAND
**Annapolis**
Member
  Anne Arundel Medical Center

**Baltimore**
Member
  Sinai Hospital of Baltimore

### MASSACHUSETTS
**Burlington**
Member
  Lahey Hospital & Medical Center, Burlington

### MICHIGAN
**Grand Rapids**
Member
  Mercy Health Saint Mary's

**Lansing**
Member
  Sparrow Hospital

**Rochester**
Member
  Crittenton Hospital Medical Center

**Royal Oak**
Member
  Beaumont Hospital – Royal Oak

### MONTANA
**Billings**
Member
  Billings Clinic

### NEW JERSEY
**Brick Township**
Member
  Ocean Medical Center

**Holmdel**
Member
  Bayshore Community Hospital

**Livingston**
Member
  Saint Barnabas Medical Center

**Long Branch**
Member
  Monmouth Medical Center, Long Branch Campus

**Manahawkin**
Member
  Southern Ocean Medical Center

**Neptune**
Member
  Jersey Shore University Medical Center

**Newark**
Member
  Newark Beth Israel Medical Center

**Phillipsburg**
Member
  St. Luke's Hospital – Warren Campus

**Red Bank**
Member
  Riverview Medical Center

### NEW YORK
**Brooklyn**
Member
  Maimonides Medical Center

**Cooperstown**
Member
  Bassett Medical Center

**Mineola**
Member
  Winthrop–University Hospital

### NORTH CAROLINA
**Charlotte**
Member
  Carolinas Medical Center

**Greensboro**
Member
  Moses H. Cone Memorial Hospital

### OHIO
**Akron**
Member
  Akron General Medical Center

**Cincinnati**
Member
  Christ Hospital
  TriHealth Evendale Hospital

**Columbus**
Member
  Mount Carmel
  OhioHealth Grant Medical Center
  OhioHealth Riverside Methodist Hospital

### PENNSYLVANIA
**Bethlehem**
Member
  St. Luke's University Hospital – Bethlehem Campus

**Bryn Mawr**
Member
  Bryn Mawr Hospital

**Johnstown**
Member
  Conemaugh Memorial Medical Center

**Philadelphia**
Member
  Einstein Medical Center Philadelphia

**Sayre**
Member
  Robert Packer Hospital

**West Reading**
Member
  Reading Hospital

**Wynnewood**
Member
  Lankenau Medical Center

**York**
Member
  York Hospital

### TEXAS
**Dallas**
Member
  Parkland Health & Hospital System

**Fort Worth**
Member
  JPS Health Network

**Garland**
Member
  Baylor Medical Center at Garland

### WASHINGTON
**Seattle**
Member
  Swedish Medical Center–Cherry Hill Campus
  Swedish Medical Center–First Hill
  Virginia Mason Medical Center

### WISCONSIN
**Marshfield**
Member
  Ministry Saint Joseph's Hospital

**Milwaukee**
Member
  Aurora Sinai Medical Center
  Aurora St. Luke's Medical Center

## CAPSTONE HEALTH ALLIANCE

1200 Ridgefield Boulevard, Suite 200, Asheville, NC Zip 28806; tel. 828/418–5050; Tim Bugg, President and Chief Executive Officer

### ALABAMA
**Dothan**
Member
  Southeast Alabama Medical Center

**Opelika**
Member
  East Alabama Medical Center

### GEORGIA
**Bremen**
Member
  Higgins General Hospital

**Carrollton**
Member
  Tanner Medical Center–Carrollton

**Lagrange**
Member
West Georgia Health

**Villa Rica**
Member
Tanner Medical Center–Villa Rica

## KENTUCKY
**Bowling Green**
Member
Commonwealth Regional Specialty Hospital
Medical Center at Bowling Green

**Franklin**
Member
Medical Center at Franklin

**Scottsville**
Member
Medical Center at Scottsville

## NORTH CAROLINA
**Asheboro**
Member
Randolph Hospital

**Asheville**
Member
Asheville Specialty Hospital
CarePartners Health Services
Mission Hospital

**Blowing Rock**
Member
Blowing Rock Rehabilitation & Davant Extended Care
Center

**Boone**
Member
Watauga Medical Center

**Brevard**
Member
Transylvania Regional Hospital

**Bryson City**
Member
Swain Community Hospital

**Cherokee**
Member
Cherokee Indian Hospital

**Clyde**
Member
Haywood Regional Medical Center

**Columbus**
Member
St. Luke's Hospital

**Elizabeth City**
Member
Sentara Albemarle Medical Center

**Elizabethtown**
Member
Cape Fear Valley – Bladen County Hospital

**Fayetteville**
Member
Cape Fear Valley Medical Center
Highsmith–Rainey Specialty Hospital

**Franklin**
Member
Angel Medical Center

**Gastonia**
Member
CaroMont Regional Medical Center

**Goldsboro**
Member
Wayne Memorial Hospital

**Hendersonville**
Member
Margaret R. Pardee Memorial Hospital
Park Ridge Health

**Hickory**
Member
Catawba Valley Medical Center

**Highlands**
Member
Highlands–Cashiers Hospital

**Kinston**
Member
Lenoir Memorial Hospital

**Linville**
Member
Charles A. Cannon Memorial Hospital

**Lumberton**
Member
Southeastern Health

**Marion**
Member
McDowell Hospital

**Morehead City**
Member
Carteret Health Care

**Oxford**
Member
Granville Health System

**Pinehurst**
Member
FirstHealth Moore Regional Hospital

**Roanoke Rapids**
Member
Halifax Regional Medical Center

**Rockingham**
Member
FirstHealth Richmond Memorial Hospital

**Rutherfordton**
Member
Rutherford Regional Health System

**Spruce Pine**
Member
Blue Ridge Regional Hospital

**Statesville**
Member
Iredell Memorial Hospital

**Sylva**
Member
Harris Regional Hospital

**Troy**
Member
FirstHealth Montgomery Memorial Hospital

## PENNSYLVANIA
**Erie**
Member
Millcreek Community Hospital

**Kittanning**
Member
ACMH Hospital

**Meadville**
Member
Meadville Medical Center

## SOUTH CAROLINA
**Barnwell**
Member
Southern Palmetto Hospital

**Conway**
Member
Conway Medical Center

**Dillon**
Member
McLeod Medical Center Dillon

**Florence**
Member
McLeod Regional Medical Center

**Greenwood**
Member
Self Regional Healthcare

**Loris**
Member
McLeod Loris Seacoast Hospital

**Seneca**
Member
Oconee Memorial Hospital

**West Columbia**
Member
Lexington Medical Center

**Winnsboro**
Member
Fairfield Memorial Hospital

## TENNESSEE
**Crossville**
Member
Cumberland Medical Center

**Elizabethton**
Member
Sycamore Shoals Hospital

**Erwin**
Member
Unicoi County Memorial Hospital

**Greeneville**
Member
Laughlin Memorial Hospital

**Johnson City**
Member
Franklin Woods Community Hospital
Johnson City Medical Center

**Kingsport**
Member
Indian Path Medical Center

**Knoxville**
Member
University of Tennessee Medical Center

**Maryville**
Member
Blount Memorial Hospital

**Mountain City**
Member
Johnson County Community Hospital

## VIRGINIA
**Abingdon**
Member
Johnston Memorial Hospital

**Bedford**
Member
Bedford Memorial Hospital

**Chesapeake**
Member
Chesapeake Regional Medical Center

**Christiansburg**
Member
Carilion New River Valley Medical Center

**Clintwood**
Member
Dickenson Community Hospital

**Gloucester**
Member
Riverside Walter Reed Hospital

**Grundy**
Member
Buchanan General Hospital

**Lebanon**
Member
Russell County Medical Center

**Lexington**
Member
Carilion Stonewall Jackson Hospital

**Marion**
Member
Smyth County Community Hospital

**Nassawadox**
Member
Riverside Shore Memorial Hospital

**Newport News**
Member
Riverside Regional Medical Center

**Norton**
Member
Norton Community Hospital

**Pearisburg**
Member
Carilion Giles Community Hospital

**Roanoke**
Member
Carilion Roanoke Memorial Hospital

**Rocky Mount**
Member
Carilion Franklin Memorial Hospital

South Hill
Member
VCU Community Memorial Hospital

**Tappahannock**
Member
Riverside Tappahannock Hospital

**Williamsburg**
Member
Riverside Doctors' Hospital

## CATHOLIC CEO HEALTHCARE CONNECTION
3333 Warrenville Rd, Ste 200, Lisle, IL Zip 60532; tel. 630/799–8315; Roger N. Butler, Executive Director

### CALIFORNIA
**Irvine**
Member
St. Joseph Health

**San Francisco**
Member
Dignity Health

### COLORADO
**Broomfield**
Member
SCL Health

**Englewood**
Member
Catholic Health Initiatives

### ILLINOIS
**Chicago**
Member
Presence Health

**Peoria**
Member
OSF Healthcare System

**Springfield**
Member
Hospital Sisters Health System

**Wheaton**
Member
Wheaton Franciscan Healthcare

### LOUISIANA
**Baton Rouge**
Member
Franciscan Missionaries of Our Lady Health System, Inc.

### MARYLAND
**Marriottsville**
Member
Bon Secours Health System, Inc.

### MASSACHUSETTS
**Tewksbury**
Member
Covenant Health

### MISSOURI
**Chesterfield**
Member
Mercy Health

**Saint Louis**
Member
Ascension Health
SSM Health

### OHIO
**Cincinnati**
Member
Mercy Health

### SOUTH DAKOTA
**Sioux Falls**
Member
Avera Health

### TEXAS
**Irving**
Member
CHRISTUS Health

### WASHINGTON
**Renton**
Member
Providence Health & Services

**Vancouver**
Member
PeaceHealth

### WISCONSIN
**Manitowoc**
Member
Franciscan Sisters of Christian Charity Sponsored Ministries, Inc.

## COMMUNITY HEALTH COLLABORATIVE, LLC
630 East River Street, Elyria, OH Zip 44035–5902; tel. 440/329–7500; Frank L. Lordeman, President and Chief Executive Officer

### OHIO
**Elyria**
Member
University Hospitals Elyria Medical Center

**Middleburg Heights**
Member
Southwest General Health Center

**Parma**
Member
University Hospitals Parma Medical Center

## CONFLUENCE HEALTH
820 North Chelan Avenue, Wenatchee, WA Zip 98801–2028; tel. 509/663–8711; Peter Rutherford M.D., Chief Executive Officer

### WASHINGTON
**Wenatchee**
Member
Central Washington Hospital
Wenatchee Valley Medical Center

## HEALTH ENTERPRISES OF IOWA
5825 Dry Creek Lane NE, Cedar Rapids, IA Zip 52402–1225; tel. 319/368–3619; Judy L. Sadler, President and Chief Executive Officer

### IOWA
**Ames**
Member
Mary Greeley Medical Center

**Chariton**
Member
Lucas County Health Center

**Charles City**
Member
Floyd County Medical Center

**Cherokee**
Affiliate
Cherokee Regional Medical Center

**Davenport**
Member
Genesis Health System

**Denison**
Member
Crawford County Memorial Hospital

**Des Moines**
Affiliate
Broadlawns Medical Center

**Fairfield**
Member
Jefferson County Health Center

**Guthrie Center**
Member
Guthrie County Hospital

**Humboldt**
Member
Humboldt County Memorial Hospital

**Ida Grove**
Affiliate
Horn Memorial Hospital

**Independence**
Member
Buchanan County Health Center

**Iowa City**
Member
Mercy Iowa City

**Manchester**
Member
Regional Medical Center

**Maquoketa**
Member
Jackson County Regional Health Center

**Marshalltown**
Member
Central Iowa Healthcare

**Mount Pleasant**
Member
Henry County Health Center

**Oskaloosa**
Member
Mahaska Health Partnership

**Pella**
Member
Pella Regional Health Center

**Pocahontas**
Member
Pocahontas Community Hospital

**Sac City**
Member
Loring Hospital

**Waukon**
Affiliate
Veterans Memorial Hospital

**Waverly**
Member
Waverly Health Center

**West Burlington**
Member
Great River Medical Center

## HOSPITAL NETWORK VENTURES, LLC
6212 American Avenue, Portage, MI Zip 49002; tel. 269/329–3200; Gregory L. Hedegore, President and Chief Executive Officer

### MICHIGAN
**Allegan**
Partner
Allegan General Hospital

**Hastings**
Partner
Spectrum Health Pennock

**Kalamazoo**
Partner
Bronson Methodist Hospital

**Marshall**
Partner
Oaklawn Hospital

**Sturgis**
Partner
Sturgis Hospital

## HOSPITAL SHARED SERVICES ASSOCIATION
P O Box 19741, Seattle, WA Zip 98109–6741; tel. 425/899–2753; Joe McNamee, Executive Director

### OREGON
**Salem**
Member
Oregon State Hospital

### WASHINGTON
**Bellevue**
Member
Overlake Medical Center

**Burien**
Member
Highline Medical Center

**Chelan**
Member
Lake Chelan Community Hospital

**Clarkston**
Member
Tri–State Memorial Hospital

**Davenport**
Member
Lincoln Hospital

**Edmonds**
Member
Swedish/Edmonds

**Ephrata**
Member
Columbia Basin Hospital

**Grand Coulee**
Member
Coulee Medical Center

**Kirkland**
Member
EvergreenHealth

**Medical Lake**
Member
Eastern State Hospital

**Moses Lake**
Member
Samaritan Healthcare

**Mount Vernon**
Member
Skagit Valley Hospital

**Newport**
Member
Newport Hospital and Health Services

**Odessa**
Member
Odessa Memorial Healthcare Center

**Othello**
Member
Othello Community Hospital

**Prosser**
Member
PMH Medical Center

**Pullman**
Member
Pullman Regional Hospital

**Quincy**
Member
Quincy Valley Medical Center

**Republic**
Member
Ferry County Memorial Hospital

**Ritzville**
Member
East Adams Rural Hospital

**Tacoma**
Member
Western State Hospital

**Tonasket**
Member
North Valley Hospital

## MEDI–SOTA, INC.
1280 Locust Street Suite 16, Dawson,
MN Zip 56232–2375;
tel. 320/769–2269; Deb Ranallo,
Executive Director

### MINNESOTA
**Appleton**
Member
Appleton Area Health Services

**Arlington**
Member
Ridgeview Sibley Medical Center

**Benson**
Member
Swift County–Benson Hospital

**Canby**
Member
Sanford Canby Medical Center

**Dawson**
Member
Johnson Memorial Health Services

**Elbow Lake**
Member
Prairie Ridge Hospital and Health Services

**Glencoe**
Member
Glencoe Regional Health Services

**Glenwood**
Member
Glacial Ridge Health System

**Graceville**
Member
Essentia Health–Graceville

**Granite Falls**
Member
Granite Falls Municipal Hospital and Manor

**Hendricks**
Member
Hendricks Community Hospital Association

**Litchfield**
Member
Meeker Memorial Hospital

**Long Prairie**
Member
CentraCare Health–Long Prairie

**Madelia**
Member
Madelia Community Hospital

**Mahnomen**
Member
Mahnomen Health Center

**Marshall**
Member
Avera Marshall Regional Medical Center

**Montevideo**
Member
Chippewa County–Montevideo Hospital

**Olivia**
Member
RC Hospital and Clinics

**Ortonville**
Member
Ortonville Area Health Services

**Paynesville**
Member
CentraCare Health–Paynesville

**Perham**
Member
Perham Health

**Pipestone**
Member
Pipestone County Medical Center Avera

**Redwood Falls**
Member
Redwood Area Hospital

**Saint Peter**
Member
River's Edge Hospital and Clinic

**Slayton**
Member
Murray County Medical Center

**Sleepy Eye**
Member
Sleepy Eye Medical Center

**Staples**
Member
Lakewood Health System

**Tracy**
Member
Sanford Tracy Medical Center

**Tyler**
Member
Tyler Healthcare Center Avera

**Wadena**
Member
Tri–County Hospital

**Willmar**
Member
Rice Memorial Hospital

**Windom**
Member
Windom Area Hospital

## NORTHWEST KANSAS HEALTH ALLIANCE
2220 Canterbury Drive, Hays, KS
Zip 67601–2370; tel. 785/623–2300;
John H. Jeter M.D., President and Chief
Executive Officer

### KANSAS
**Ashland**
Member
Ashland Health Center

**Atwood**
Member
Rawlins County Health Center

**Beloit**
Member
Mitchell County Hospital Health Systems

**Colby**
Member
Citizens Medical Center

**Dighton**
Member
Lane County Hospital

**Dodge City**
Member
Western Plains Medical Complex

**Ellsworth**
Member
Ellsworth County Medical Center

**Garden City**
Member
St. Catherine Hospital

**Goodland**
Member
Goodland Regional Medical Center

**Great Bend**
Member
Great Bend Regional Hospital

**Greensburg**
Member
Kiowa County Memorial Hospital

**Hill City**
Member
Graham County Hospital

**Hoisington**
Member
Clara Barton Hospital

**Hoxie**
Member
Sheridan County Health Complex

**Hutchinson**
Member
Hutchinson Regional Medical Center

**Jetmore**
Member
Hodgeman County Health Center

**Kinsley**
Member
Edwards County Hospital and Healthcare Center

**La Crosse**
Member
Rush County Memorial Hospital

**Larned**
Member
Pawnee Valley Community Hospital

**Lawrence**
Member
Lawrence Memorial Hospital

**Leoti**
Member
Wichita County Health Center

**Lincoln**
Member
Lincoln County Hospital

**Lyons**
Member
Hospital District One of Rice County

**Minneola**
Member
Minneola District Hospital

**Ness City**
Member
Ness County Hospital

**Norton**
Member
Norton County Hospital

**Oakley**
Member
Logan County Hospital

**Oberlin**
Member
Decatur Health Systems

**Osborne**
Member
Osborne County Memorial Hospital

**Ottawa**
Member
Ransom Memorial Hospital

**Phillipsburg**
Member
Phillips County Hospital

**Plainville**
Member
Rooks County Health Center

**Quinter**
Member
Gove County Medical Center

**Ransom**
Member
Grisell Memorial Hospital District One

**Russell**
Member
Russell Regional Hospital

**Saint Francis**
Member
Cheyenne County Hospital

**Salina**
Member
Salina Regional Health Center

**Satanta**
Member
Satanta District Hospital and Long Term Care

**Scott City**
Member
Scott County Hospital

**Smith Center**
Member
Smith County Memorial Hospital

**Stafford**
Member
Stafford County Hospital

**Tribune**
Member
Greeley County Health Services

**Wakeeney**
Member
Trego County–Lemke Memorial Hospital

## PENNANT HEALTH ALLIANCE
2122 Health Drive SW Suite 100,
Wyoming, MI Zip 49519–9698;
tel. 616/252–6800; Michael D. Faas,
Chief Executive Officer

### MICHIGAN
**Ann Arbor**
Member
University of Michigan Hospitals and Health Centers

**Cadillac**
Member
Munson Healthcare Cadillac Hospital

**Grand Rapids**
Member
Mary Free Bed Rehabilitation Hospital
Mercy Health Saint Mary's

**Grayling**
Member
Munson Healthcare Grayling Hospital

**Muskegon**
Member
Mercy Health, Mercy Campus

**Wyoming**
Member
Metro Health Hospital

## PREMIER, INC.
13034 Ballantyne Corporate Place,
Charlotte, NC Zip 28277–1498;
tel. 704/816–5353; Susan DeVore,
President and Chief Executive Officer

### ALABAMA
**Dothan**
Owner
Southeast Alabama Medical Center

**Opelika**
Owner
East Alabama Medical Center

### ARKANSAS
**Pine Bluff**
Owner
Jefferson Regional Medical Center

### CALIFORNIA
**Long Beach**
St. Mary Medical Center

**Mountain View**
El Camino Hospital

**Oceanside**
Tri–City Medical Center

**Rancho Mirage**
Owner
Eisenhower Medical Center

### CONNECTICUT
**Hartford**
Owner
Saint Francis Hospital and Medical Center

**Waterbury**
Saint Mary's Hospital

### DELAWARE
**Dover**
Owner
Bayhealth Medical Center

**Lewes**
Owner
Beebe Healthcare

### DISTRICT OF COLUMBIA
**Washington**
Owner
Sibley Memorial Hospital

### FLORIDA
**Clearwater**
BayCare Health System

**Miami Beach**
Owner
Mount Sinai Medical Center

**Saint Petersburg**
Member
Bayfront Health St. Petersburg

**Tampa**
Member
H. Lee Moffitt Cancer Center and Research Institute

**Vero Beach**
Owner
Indian River Medical Center

**Winter Haven**
Owner
Winter Haven Hospital

### GEORGIA
**Carrollton**
Tanner Medical Center–Carrollton

**Columbus**
Owner
St. Francis Hospital

**Lagrange**
Owner
West Georgia Health

**Savannah**
St. Joseph's Hospital
Owner
Memorial Health

### HAWAII
**Honolulu**
Owner
Kuakini Medical Center

### ILLINOIS
**Chicago**
Owner
Mount Sinai Hospital

**Harvey**
Ingalls Memorial Hospital

**Naperville**
Edward Hospital

**Peoria**
UnityPoint Health – Methodist Proctor

**Urbana**
Owner
Carle Foundation Hospital

### INDIANA
**Gary**
Owner
Methodist Hospitals

### IOWA
**Davenport**
Member
Genesis Medical Center–Davenport

**De Witt**
Member
Genesis Medical Center, DeWitt

### KENTUCKY
**Ashland**
King's Daughters Medical Center

**Bowling Green**
Commonwealth Regional Specialty Hospital

**Danville**
Ephraim McDowell Regional Medical Center

**Edgewood**
St. Elizabeth Edgewood

**Glasgow**
Owner
T. J. Samson Community Hospital

**Henderson**
Owner
Methodist Hospital

**Louisville**
Member
University of Louisville Hospital

**Murray**
Owner
Murray–Calloway County Hospital

### LOUISIANA
**Baton Rouge**
Baton Rouge General Medical Center
Member
Woman's Hospital

**Columbia**
Caldwell Memorial Hospital

**Houma**
Owner
Terrebonne General Medical Center

**Lafayette**
Owner
Lafayette General Medical Center

**Marrero**
Owner
West Jefferson Medical Center

### MAINE
**Lewiston**
Central Maine Medical Center

## MARYLAND

**Annapolis**
Owner
  Anne Arundel Medical Center

**Baltimore**
  Greater Baltimore Medical Center
Member
  Mercy Medical Center
  Sinai Hospital of Baltimore

**Bethesda**
Owner
  Suburban Hospital

**Columbia**
Owner
  Howard County General Hospital

**Elkton**
Owner
  Union Hospital

**Frederick**
Owner
  Frederick Memorial Hospital

**Hagerstown**
  Western Maryland Hospital Center
Owner
  Meritus Medical Center

**Lanham**
Owner
  Doctors Community Hospital

**Randallstown**
Member
  Northwest Hospital

**Salisbury**
Owner
  Peninsula Regional Medical Center

**Westminster**
Owner
  Carroll Hospital Center

## MASSACHUSETTS

**Boston**
  Tufts Medical Center

## MICHIGAN

**Jackson**
  Allegiance Health

**Lansing**
Owner
  Sparrow Hospital

**Rochester**
Member
  Crittenton Hospital Medical Center

## MISSISSIPPI

**Laurel**
Owner
  South Central Regional Medical Center

## MISSOURI

**Saint Louis**
  St. Anthony's Medical Center

## MONTANA

**Billings**
  Billings Clinic

## NEW YORK

**Rochester**
Owner
  Seagate Alliance

## NORTH CAROLINA

**Asheboro**
Owner
  Randolph Hospital

**Boone**
Owner
  Watauga Medical Center

**Burlington**
Owner
  Alamance Regional Medical Center

**Clyde**
Owner
  Haywood Regional Medical Center

**Fayetteville**
  Cape Fear Valley Medical Center

**Gastonia**
Owner
  CaroMont Regional Medical Center

**Goldsboro**
Owner
  Wayne Memorial Hospital

**Hendersonville**
Owner
  Margaret R. Pardee Memorial Hospital

**Hickory**
Owner
  Catawba Valley Medical Center

**Kinston**
Owner
  Lenoir Memorial Hospital

**Lumberton**
Owner
  Southeastern Health

**Morehead City**
  Carteret Health Care

**Roanoke Rapids**
Owner
  Halifax Regional Medical Center

**Statesville**
Owner
  Iredell Memorial Hospital

**Wilson**
Owner
  Wilson Medical Center

## OHIO

**Akron**
Owner
  Summa Akron City Hospital

**Cincinnati**
Owner
  Bethesda North Hospital

**Cleveland**
Owner
  Cleveland Clinic

**Elyria**
Member
  University Hospitals Elyria Medical Center

**Kettering**
  Kettering Medical Center

**Parma**
Member
  University Hospitals Parma Medical Center

## OKLAHOMA

**Tulsa**
Owner
  Saint Francis Hospital

## OREGON

**Salem**
Member
  Salem Hospital

## PENNSYLVANIA

**Washington**
  Washington Hospital

## SOUTH CAROLINA

**Anderson**
Owner
  AnMed Health Medical Center

**Conway**
Owner
  Conway Medical Center

**Florence**
Owner
  McLeod Regional Medical Center

**Greenwood**
Owner
  Self Regional Healthcare

**West Columbia**
Owner
  Lexington Medical Center

## SOUTH DAKOTA

**Rapid City**
Owner
  Rapid City Regional Hospital

## TENNESSEE

**Crossville**
  Cumberland Medical Center

**Greeneville**
  Laughlin Memorial Hospital

**Knoxville**
  University of Tennessee Medical Center

**Maryville**
Owner
  Blount Memorial Hospital

## TEXAS

**Dallas**
  University of Texas Southwestern Medical Center

**Galveston**
  University of Texas Medical Branch

**Houston**
  Harris Health System
Owner
  University of Texas M.D. Anderson Cancer Center

**Lubbock**
Owner
  University Medical Center

**Nacogdoches**
Owner
  Nacogdoches Memorial Hospital

## VIRGINIA

**Abingdon**
Owner
  Johnston Memorial Hospital

**Chesapeake**
Owner
  Chesapeake Regional Medical Center

**Marion**
Owner
  Smyth County Community Hospital

**South Hill**
Owner
  VCU Community Memorial Hospital

**Winchester**
Member
  Winchester Medical Center

## WASHINGTON

**Seattle**
  Group Health Cooperative Central Hospital

## WEST VIRGINIA

**Elkins**
Owner
  Davis Medical Center

**Huntington**
  Cabell Huntington Hospital

**Morgantown**
Owner
  Monongalia General Hospital

**Parkersburg**
Owner
  Camden Clark Medical Center

**Point Pleasant**
Owner
  Pleasant Valley Hospital

**South Charleston**
Owner
  Thomas Memorial Hospital

**Weirton**
Owner
  Weirton Medical Center

## SEAGATE ALLIANCE
  3445 Winton Place, Sute 222, Rochester,
  NY Zip 14623–2950;
  tel. 888/732–4284; Diane H. Ashley,
  President and Chief Executive Officer

## NEW JERSEY

**Newark**
Member
  Columbus Hospital LTACH

## NEW YORK

**Bath**
Member
Bath Veterans Affairs Medical Center
Ira Davenport Memorial Hospital

**Buffalo**
Member
BryLin Hospitals
Catholic Health System
Erie County Medical Center
Roswell Park Cancer Institute

**Canandaigua**
Member
F. F. Thompson Hospital

**Carthage**
Member
Carthage Area Hospital

**Clifton Springs**
Member
Clifton Springs Hospital and Clinic

**Corning**
Member
Corning Hospital

**Cuba**
Member
Cuba Memorial Hospital

**Dansville**
Member
Nicholas H. Noyes Memorial Hospital

**Dunkirk**
Member
Brooks Memorial Hospital

**Elmira**
Member
Arnot Ogden Medical Center
Elmira Psychiatric Center
St. Joseph's Hospital

**Geneva**
Member
Geneva General Hospital

**Hornell**
Member
St. James Mercy Health System

**Kenmore**
Member
Kenmore Mercy Hospital

**Lockport**
Member
Eastern Niagara Hospital

**Montour Falls**
Member
Schuyler Hospital

**Newark**
Member
Newark–Wayne Community Hospital

**Olean**
Member
Olean General Hospital

**Penn Yan**
Member
Soldiers and Sailors Memorial Hospital of Yates
County

**Rochester**
Member
Highland Hospital of Rochester
Rochester General Hospital
Rochester Psychiatric Center
Strong Memorial Hospital of the University of
Rochester
Unity Hospital

**Springville**
Member
Bertrand Chaffee Hospital

**Syracuse**
Member
Upstate University Hospital

**Wellsville**
Member
Jones Memorial Hospital

## PENNSYLVANIA

**Bradford**
Member
Bradford Regional Medical Center

**Coudersport**
Member
Cole Memorial

## SYNERNET, INC.
110 Free Street, Portland, ME
Zip 04101–3908; tel. 207/771–3456;
Gerry Vicenzi, President and Chief
Executive Officer

## MAINE

**Augusta**
Affiliate
MaineGeneral Medical Center

**Bangor**
Affiliate
St. Joseph Hospital

**Bar Harbor**
Affiliate
Mount Desert Island Hospital

**Brunswick**
Affiliate
Mid Coast Hospital

**Damariscotta**
LincolnHealth

**Farmington**
Owner
Franklin Memorial Hospital

**Fort Kent**
Affiliate
Northern Maine Medical Center

**Norway**
Owner
Stephens Memorial Hospital

**Portland**
Member
Mercy Hospital of Portland
Owner
Maine Medical Center
New England Rehabilitation Hospital of Portland

**Rockport**
Affiliate
Pen Bay Medical Center

**Skowhegan**
Affiliate
Redington–Fairview General Hospital

**Westbrook**
Owner
Spring Harbor Hospital

## THE NEW JERSEY COUNCIL OF
## TEACHING HOSPITALS
154 West State Street, Trenton, NJ
Zip 08608; tel. 609/656–9600; Deborah
S. Briggs, President

## NEW JERSEY

**Camden**
Member
Cooper University Health Care

**Hackensack**
Member
Hackensack University Medical Center

**Marlton**
Member
Weisman Children's Rehabilitation Hospital

**Montclair**
Member
Hackensack University Medical Center Mountainside

**Morristown**
Member
Atlantic Health System
Morristown Medical Center

**Neptune**
Member
Meridian Health

**New Brunswick**
Member
Children's Specialized Hospital–PSE&G

**North Bergen**
Member
Palisades Medical Center

**Paterson**
Member
St. Joseph's Regional Medical Center

**Summit**
Member
Overlook Medical Center

## UNITED IROQUOIS SHARED SERVICES,
## INC.
15 Executive Park Drive, Clifton Park, NY
Zip 12065–5631; tel. 518/383–5060;
Gary J. Fitzgerald, President

## NEW YORK

**Albany**
Member
Albany Memorial Hospital
St. Peter's Hospital

**Alexandria Bay**
Member
River Hospital

**Amsterdam**
Member
St. Mary's Healthcare

**Auburn**
Member
Auburn Community Hospital

**Binghamton**
Member
Our Lady of Lourdes Memorial Hospital, Inc.
United Health Services Hospitals–Binghamton

**Buffalo**
Member
Roswell Park Cancer Institute

**Carthage**
Member
Carthage Area Hospital

**Cobleskill**
Member
Cobleskill Regional Hospital

**Cooperstown**
Member
Bassett Medical Center

**Cortland**
Member
Cortland Regional Medical Center

**Cuba**
Member
Cuba Memorial Hospital

**Delhi**
Member
O'Connor Hospital

**Elizabethtown**
Member
The University of Vermont Health Network
Elizabethtown Community Hospital

**Glens Falls**
Member
Glens Falls Hospital

**Glenville**
Member
Conifer Park

**Gloversville**
Member
Nathan Littauer Hospital and Nursing Home

**Hamilton**
Member
Community Memorial Hospital

**Hudson**
Member
Columbia Memorial Hospital

**Ithaca**
Member
Cayuga Medical Center at Ithaca

**Little Falls**
Member
   Little Falls Hospital

**Lowville**
Member
   Lewis County General Hospital

**Malone**
Member
   Alice Hyde Medical Center

**Margaretville**
Member
   Margaretville Hospital

**Massena**
Member
   Massena Memorial Hospital

**Norwich**
Member
   Chenango Memorial Hospital

**Ogdensburg**
Member
   Claxton–Hepburn Medical Center

**Olean**
Member
   Olean General Hospital

**Oneida**
Member
   Oneida Healthcare

**Oneonta**
Member
   Aurelia Osborn Fox Memorial Hospital

**Oswego**
Member
   Oswego Hospital

**Plattsburgh**
Member
   The University of Vermont Health Network–Champlain
     Valley Physicians Hospital

**Potsdam**
Member
   Canton–Potsdam Hospital

**Rome**
Member
   Rome Memorial Hospital

**Saranac Lake**
Member
   Adirondack Medical Center

**Saratoga Springs**
Member
   Saratoga Hospital

**Schenectady**
Member
   Ellis Hospital
   Sunnyview Rehabilitation Hospital

**Springville**
Member
   Bertrand Chaffee Hospital

**Star Lake**
Member
   Clifton–Fine Hospital

**Syracuse**
Member
   Crouse Hospital
   Upstate University Hospital

**Troy**
Member
   Samaritan Hospital
   St. Mary's Hospital

**Utica**
Member
   Faxton–St. Luke's Healthcare
   St. Elizabeth Medical Center

**Walton**
Member
   Delaware Valley Hospital

**Watertown**
Member
   Samaritan Medical Center

## UNIVERSITY HEALTHSYSTEM CONSORTIUM, INC.
155 North Wacker Drive, Chicago, IL
Zip 60606–1787; tel. 312/775–4100;
Curtis W. Nonomaque, President and
Chief Executive Officer

### ALABAMA
**Alexander City**
Member
   Russell Medical Center

**Bessemer**
Member
   Medical West

**Birmingham**
Member
   University of Alabama Hospital

**Mobile**
Member
   University of South Alabama Children's and Women's
     Hospital
   University of South Alabama Medical Center

### ARIZONA
**Phoenix**
Member
   Maricopa Integrated Health System

**Tucson**
Member
   Banner – University Medical Center South
   Banner – University Medical Center Tucson

### ARKANSAS
**Little Rock**
Member
   UAMS Medical Center

### CALIFORNIA
**Bakersfield**
Member
   Kern Medical Center

**Colton**
Member
   Arrowhead Regional Medical Center

**Downey**
Member
   Rancho Los Amigos National Rehabilitation Center

**Duarte**
Member
   City of Hope's Helford Clinical Research Hospital

**French Camp**
Member
   San Joaquin General Hospital

**Joshua Tree**
Member
   Hi–Desert Medical Center

**Los Angeles**
Member
   Cedars–Sinai Medical Center
   Keck Hospital of USC
   LAC/University of Southern California Medical Center
   Ronald Reagan UCLA Medical Center
   Stewart & Lynda Resnick Neuropsychiatric Hospital at
     UCLA
   University of Southern California–Norris Cancer
     Hospital

**Martinez**
Member
   Contra Costa Regional Medical Center

**Moreno Valley**
Member
   Riverside County Regional Medical Center

**Oakland**
Member
   Highland Hospital

**Orange**
Member
   UC Irvine Medical Center

**Palo Alto**
Member
   Lucile Salter Packard Children's Hospital Stanford
   Stanford Health Care

**Portola**
Member
   Eastern Plumas Health Care

**Sacramento**
Member
   University of California, Davis Medical Center

**San Diego**
Member
   UC San Diego Health

**San Francisco**
Member
   Laguna Honda Hospital and Rehabilitation Center
   San Francisco General Hospital and Trauma Center
   UCSF Medical Center

**San Jose**
Member
   Santa Clara Valley Medical Center

**Santa Monica**
Member
   Santa Monica–UCLA Medical Center and Orthopaedic
     Hospital

**Stockton**
Member
   Dameron Hospital

**Sylmar**
Member
   LAC–Olive View–UCLA Medical Center

**Torrance**
Member
   Harbor–UCLA Medical Center

### COLORADO
**Aurora**
Member
   University of Colorado Hospital

**Colorado Springs**
Member
   Memorial Hospital

**Denver**
Member
   Denver Health
   National Jewish Health

**Fort Collins**
Member
   Poudre Valley Hospital

**Loveland**
Member
   Medical Center of the Rockies

### CONNECTICUT
**Bridgeport**
Member
   Bridgeport Hospital

**Farmington**
Member
   University of Connecticut Health Center, John
     Dempsey Hospital

**Greenwich**
Member
   Greenwich Hospital

**New Haven**
Member
   Yale–New Haven Hospital

**Stamford**
Member
   Stamford Hospital

### DELAWARE
**Newark**
Member
   Christiana Care Health System

### DISTRICT OF COLUMBIA
**Washington**
Member
   Howard University Hospital
   MedStar Georgetown University Hospital
   MedStar Washington Hospital Center

### FLORIDA
**Gainesville**
Member
   UF Health Shands
   UF Health Shands Hospital

**Jacksonville**
Member
  Mayo Clinic Jacksonville
  UF Health Jacksonville

**Miami**
Member
  Jackson Health System

**Tampa**
Member
  H. Lee Moffitt Cancer Center and Research Institute
  Tampa General Hospital

**Weston**
Member
  Cleveland Clinic Florida

## GEORGIA

**Atlanta**
Member
  Emory Healthcare
  Emory Saint Joseph's Hospital of Atlanta
  Emory University Hospital
  Emory University Hospital Midtown
  Grady Memorial Hospital

**Augusta**
Member
  Georgia Regents Medical Center

**Johns Creek**
Member
  Emory Johns Creek Hospital

**Waycross**
Member
  Mayo Clinic Health System in Waycross

## ILLINOIS

**Alton**
Member
  Alton Memorial Hospital

**Aurora**
Member
  Rush–Copley Medical Center

**Chicago**
Member
  Cook County Health and Hospitals System
  John H. Stroger Jr. Hospital of Cook County
  La Rabida Children's Hospital
  Northwestern Memorial Hospital
  Provident Hospital of Cook County
  Rush University Medical Center
  University of Chicago Medical Center
  University of Illinois Hospital & Health Sciences
    System

**Geneva**
Member
  Delnor Hospital

**Hinsdale**
Member
  RML Specialty Hospital

**Lake Forest**
Member
  Northwestern Lake Forest Hospital

**Maywood**
Member
  Loyola University Medical Center

**Melrose Park**
Member
  Gottlieb Memorial Hospital

**Oak Forest**
Member
  Oak Forest Health Center of Cook County

**Oak Park**
Member
  Rush Oak Park Hospital

**Winfield**
Member
  Central DuPage Hospital

## INDIANA

**Avon**
Member
  Indiana University Health West Hospital

**Bedford**
Member
  Indiana University Health Bedford Hospital

**Bloomington**
Member
  Indiana University Health Bloomington Hospital

**Carmel**
Member
  Indiana University Health North Hospital

**Goshen**
Member
  Indiana University Health Goshen Hospital

**Hartford City**
Member
  Indiana University Health Blackford Hospital

**Indianapolis**
Member
  Eskenazi Health
  Indiana University Health

**Knox**
Member
  Indiana University Health Starke Hospital

**La Porte**
Member
  Indiana University Health La Porte Hospital

**Lafayette**
Member
  Indiana University Health Arnett Hospital

**Martinsville**
Member
  Indiana University Health Morgan Hospital

**Monticello**
Member
  Indiana University Health White Memorial Hospital

**Muncie**
Member
  Indiana University Health Ball Memorial Hospital

**Paoli**
Member
  Indiana University Health Paoli Hospital

**Seymour**
Member
  Schneck Medical Center

**Tipton**
Member
  Indiana University Health Tipton Hospital

## IOWA

**Belmond**
Member
  Iowa Specialty Hospital–Belmond

**Clarion**
Member
  Iowa Specialty Hospital–Clarion

**Iowa City**
Member
  University of Iowa Hospitals and Clinics

**Keosauqua**
Member
  Van Buren County Hospital

**Marengo**
Member
  Marengo Memorial Hospital, UnityPoint Health

**Shenandoah**
Member
  Shenandoah Medical Center

**Sigourney**
Member
  Keokuk County Health Center

**Waverly**
Member
  Waverly Health Center

## KANSAS

**Kansas City**
Member
  The University of Kansas Hospital

**Overland Park**
Member
  Saint Luke's South Hospital

## KENTUCKY

**Cynthiana**
Member
  Harrison Memorial Hospital

**Lexington**
Member
  University of Kentucky Albert B. Chandler Hospital

**Louisville**
Member
  University of Louisville Hospital

**Morehead**
Member
  St. Claire Regional Medical Center

**Mount Vernon**
Member
  Rockcastle Regional Hospital and Respiratory Care
    Center

## LOUISIANA

**Monroe**
Member
  University Health Conway

**Shreveport**
Member
  University Health Shreveport

## MAINE

**Portland**
Member
  Maine Medical Center

## MARYLAND

**Baltimore**
Member
  Johns Hopkins Bayview Medical Center
  Johns Hopkins Hospital
  MedStar Franklin Square Medical Center
  MedStar Good Samaritan Hospital
  MedStar Harbor Hospital
  MedStar Union Memorial Hospital
  Mt. Washington Pediatric Hospital
  University of Maryland Medical Center
  University of Maryland Medical Center Midtown
    Campus
  University of Maryland Rehabilitation & Orthopaedic
    Institute

**Bel Air**
Member
  University of Maryland Upper Chesapeake Medical
    Center

**Cambridge**
Member
  University of Maryland Shore Medical Center at
    Dorchester

**Chestertown**
Member
  University of Maryland Shore Medical Center at
    Chestertown

**Clinton**
Member
  MedStar Southern Maryland Hospital Center

**Easton**
Member
  University of Maryland Shore Medical Center at
    Easton

**Glen Burnie**
Member
  University of Maryland Baltimore Washington Medical
    Center

**Havre De Grace**
Member
  University of Maryland Harford Memorial Hospital

**La Plata**
Member
  University of Maryland Charles Regional Medical
    Center

**Leonardtown**
Member
  MedStar St. Mary's Hospital

**Olney**
Member
  MedStar Montgomery Medical Center

**Towson**
Member
  University of Maryland St. Joseph Medical Center

## MASSACHUSETTS

**Ayer**
Member
  Nashoba Valley Medical Center

**Section B**

**Boston**
Member
Beth Israel Deaconess Medical Center
Boston Medical Center
Brigham and Women's Faulkner Hospital
Brigham and Women's Hospital
Carney Hospital
Dana–Farber Cancer Institute
Massachusetts General Hospital
Partners HealthCare System, Inc.
Steward Health Care System, LLC
Tufts Medical Center

**Brighton**
Member
St. Elizabeth's Medical Center

**Brockton**
Member
Good Samaritan Medical Center

**Burlington**
Member
Lahey Hospital & Medical Center, Burlington

**Cambridge**
Member
Cambridge Health Alliance

**Clinton**
Member
Clinton Hospital

**Concord**
Member
Emerson Hospital

**Fall River**
Member
Saint Anne's Hospital

**Greenfield**
Member
Baystate Franklin Medical Center

**Holyoke**
Member
Holyoke Medical Center

**Leominster**
Member
HealthAlliance Hospitals

**Marlborough**
Member
UMass Memorial–Marlborough Hospital

**Melrose**
Member
Hallmark Health System

**Methuen**
Member
Holy Family Hospital

**Milton**
Member
Beth Israel Deaconess Hospital–Milton

**Nantucket**
Member
Nantucket Cottage Hospital

**Newton Lower Falls**
Member
Newton–Wellesley Hospital

**Norwood**
Member
Norwood Hospital

**Palmer**
Member
Baystate Wing Hospital

**Quincy**
Member
Steward Satellite Emergency Facility – Quincy

**Salem**
Member
North Shore Medical Center

**Springfield**
Member
Baystate Medical Center

**Taunton**
Member
Morton Hospital and Medical Center

**Ware**
Member
Baystate Mary Lane Hospital

**Winchester**
Member
Winchester Hospital

**Worcester**
Member
UMass Memorial Medical Center

## MICHIGAN

**Ann Arbor**
Member
University of Michigan Hospitals and Health Centers

**Dearborn**
Member
Beaumont Hospital–Dearborn

**Farmington Hills**
Member
Beaumont Hospital – Farmington Hills

**Flint**
Member
Hurley Medical Center

**Grosse Pointe**
Member
Beaumont Hospital Grosse Pointe

**Midland**
Member
MidMichigan Medical Center–Midland

**Royal Oak**
Member
Beaumont Hospital – Royal Oak

**Taylor**
Member
Beaumont Hospital – Taylor

**Troy**
Member
Beaumont Hospital – Troy

**Wayne**
Member
Beaumont Hospital – Wayne

## MINNESOTA

**Albert Lea**
Member
Mayo Clinic Health System in Albert Lea

**Austin**
Member
Mayo Clinic Health System–Albert Lea and Austin

**Burnsville**
Member
Fairview Ridges Hospital

**Edina**
Member
Fairview Southdale Hospital

**Fairmont**
Member
Mayo Clinic Health System in Fairmont

**Hibbing**
Member
Range Regional Health Services

**Mankato**
Member
Mayo Clinic Health System in Mankato

**Minneapolis**
Member
Hennepin County Medical Center
University of Minnesota Medical Center, Fairview

**Princeton**
Member
Fairview Northland Medical Center

**Red Wing**
Member
Mayo Clinic Health System in Red Wing

**Rochester**
Member
Mayo Clinic Hospital – Rochester

**Saint Paul**
Member
Regions Hospital

**Stillwater**
Member
Lakeview Hospital

**Wyoming**
Member
Fairview Lakes Health Services

## MISSISSIPPI

**Jackson**
Member
University Hospital

**Lexington**
Member
University of Mississippi Medical Center Holmes County

## MISSOURI

**Columbia**
Member
Boone Hospital Center
University of Missouri Health Care
University of Missouri Hospitals and Clinics

**Farmington**
Member
Parkland Health Center – Liberty Street
Parkland Health Center – Weber Road

**Jefferson City**
Member
Capital Region Medical Center

**Kansas City**
Member
Saint Luke's Hospital of Kansas City
Saint Luke's North Hospital – Barry Road
Truman Medical Center–Hospital Hill
Truman Medical Center–Lakewood

**Lee's Summit**
Member
Saint Luke's East Hospital

**Milan**
Member
Sullivan County Memorial Hospital

**O'Fallon**
Member
Progress West Hospital

**Saint Louis**
Member
Barnes–Jewish Hospital
Barnes–Jewish West County Hospital
Christian Hospital
Missouri Baptist Medical Center

**Saint Peters**
Member
Barnes–Jewish St. Peters Hospital

**Sullivan**
Member
Missouri Baptist Sullivan Hospital

## NEBRASKA

**Bellevue**
Member
Nebraska Medicine – Bellevue

**O'Neill**
Member
Avera St. Anthony's Hospital

**Omaha**
Member
Nebraska Medicine – Nebraska Medical Center
Nebraska Orthopaedic Hospital

## NEVADA

**Las Vegas**
Member
University Medical Center

## NEW HAMPSHIRE

**Lebanon**
Member
Dartmouth–Hitchcock Medical Center

## NEW JERSEY

**Hamilton**
Member
Robert Wood Johnson University Hospital at Hamilton

**Morristown**
Member
Atlantic Health System
Morristown Medical Center

Section B

**Neptune**
Member
Meridian Health

**New Brunswick**
Member
Robert Wood Johnson University Hospital

**Newark**
Member
University Hospital

**Newton**
Member
Newton Medical Center

**Pompton Plains**
Member
Chilton Medical Center

**Rahway**
Member
Robert Wood Johnson University Hospital Rahway

**Summit**
Member
Overlook Medical Center

## NEW MEXICO

**Albuquerque**
Member
University of New Mexico Hospitals

**Rio Rancho**
Member
UNM Sandoval Regional Medical Center

## NEW YORK

**Albany**
Member
Albany Medical Center

**Bay Shore**
Member
Southside Hospital

**Bronx**
Member
Jacobi Medical Center
Lincoln Medical and Mental Health Center
Montefiore Medical Center
North Central Bronx Hospital

**Bronxville**
Member
New York–Presbyterian/Lawrence Hospital

**Brooklyn**
Member
Coney Island Hospital
New York Community Hospital
New York Methodist Hospital
SUNY Downstate Medical Center University Hospital
Woodhull Medical and Mental Health Center

**Buffalo**
Member
Roswell Park Cancer Institute

**Canandaigua**
Member
F. F. Thompson Hospital

**Cooperstown**
Member
Bassett Medical Center

**Cortlandt Manor**
Member
New York–Presbyterian/Hudson Valley Hospital

**Elmhurst**
Member
Elmhurst Hospital Center

**Flushing**
Member
New York–Presbyterian/Queens

**Forest Hills**
Member
Forest Hills Hospital

**Glen Cove**
Member
Glen Cove Hospital

**Great Neck**
Member
North Shore–Long Island Jewish Health System

**Greenport**
Member
Eastern Long Island Hospital

**Huntington**
Member
Huntington Hospital

**Jamaica**
Member
Queens Hospital Center

**Manhasset**
Member
North Shore University Hospital

**Mineola**
Member
Winthrop–University Hospital

**New Hyde Park**
Member
Long Island Jewish Medical Center

**New York**
Member
Henry J. Carter Specialty Hospital and Nursing Facility
Mount Sinai Hospital
New York City Health and Hospitals Corporation
New York–Presbyterian Hospital
NYU Langone Medical Center

**Plainview**
Member
Plainview Hospital

**Plattsburgh**
Member
The University of Vermont Health Network–Champlain
Valley Physicians Hospital

**Riverhead**
Member
Peconic Bay Medical Center

**Rochester**
Member
Highland Hospital of Rochester
Strong Memorial Hospital of the University of
Rochester

**Stony Brook**
Member
Stony Brook University Medical Center

**Syosset**
Member
Syosset Hospital

**Syracuse**
Member
Upstate University Hospital

**Valley Stream**
Member
Franklin Hospital

## NORTH CAROLINA

**Ahoskie**
Member
Vidant Roanoke–Chowan Hospital

**Chapel Hill**
Member
University of North Carolina Hospitals

**Durham**
Member
Duke Regional Hospital
Duke University Hospital

**Edenton**
Member
Vidant Chowan Hospital

**Greenville**
Member
Vidant Medical Center

**Kenansville**
Member
Vidant Duplin Hospital

**Lexington**
Member
Wake Forest Baptist Health–Lexington Medical Center

**Mocksville**
Member
Wake Forest Baptist Health–Davie Medical Center

**Nags Head**
Member
The Outer Banks Hospital

**Raleigh**
Member
Duke Raleigh Hospital
Rex Healthcare

**Siler City**
Member
Chatham Hospital

**Tarboro**
Member
Vidant Edgecombe Hospital

**Washington**
Member
Vidant Beaufort Hospital

**Windsor**
Member
Vidant Bertie Hospital

**Winston–Salem**
Member
Wake Forest Baptist Health
Wake Forest Baptist Medical Center

## OHIO

**Ashtabula**
Member
Ashtabula County Medical Center

**Barnesville**
Member
Barnesville Hospital

**Bellefontaine**
Member
Mary Rutan Hospital

**Bucyrus**
Member
Bucyrus Community Hospital

**Cadiz**
Member
Harrison Community Hospital

**Chardon**
Member
University Hospitals Geauga Medical Center

**Cincinnati**
Member
Cincinnati Children's Hospital Medical Center
Daniel Drake Center for Post Acute Care
University of Cincinnati Medical Center

**Cleveland**
Member
Cleveland Clinic
Fairview Hospital
Hillcrest Hospital
Lutheran Hospital
MetroHealth Medical Center

**Coldwater**
Member
Mercer Health

**Columbus**
Member
Ohio State University Wexner Medical Center

**Conneaut**
Member
University Hospitals Conneaut Medical Center

**Euclid**
Member
Euclid Hospital

**Galion**
Member
Avita Galion Hospital

**Garfield Heights**
Member
Marymount Hospital

**Geneva**
Member
University Hospitals Geneva Medical Center

**Lakewood**
Member
Lakewood Hospital

**London**
Member
  Madison Health

**Martins Ferry**
Member
  East Ohio Regional Hospital

**Medina**
Member
  Medina Hospital

**Middleburg Heights**
Member
  Southwest General Health Center

**Sidney**
Member
  Wilson Memorial Hospital

**Toledo**
Member
  The University of Toledo Medical Center

**Upper Sandusky**
Member
  Wyandot Memorial Hospital

**Warrensville Heights**
Member
  South Pointe Hospital

**Washington Court House**
Member
  Fayette County Memorial Hospital

**West Chester**
Member
  West Chester Hospital

**Westlake**
Member
  St. John Medical Center

## OREGON

**Grants Pass**
Member
  Asante Three Rivers Medical Center

**Medford**
Member
  Asante Health System
  Asante Rogue Regional Medical Center

**Portland**
Member
  OHSU Hospital

## PENNSYLVANIA

**Allentown**
Member
  Lehigh Valley Hospital

**Bryn Mawr**
Member
  Bryn Mawr Hospital

**Hershey**
Member
  Penn State Milton S. Hershey Medical Center

**Media**
Member
  Riddle Hospital

**Paoli**
Member
  Paoli Hospital

**Philadelphia**
Member
  Children's Hospital of Philadelphia
  Fox Chase Cancer Center–American Oncologic
    Hospital
  Hospital of the University of Pennsylvania
  Jeanes Hospital
  Penn Presbyterian Medical Center
  Pennsylvania Hospital
  Temple University Hospital
  Thomas Jefferson University Hospitals

**Pittsburgh**
Member
  UPMC Presbyterian Shadyside

**Wynnewood**
Member
  Lankenau Medical Center

## RHODE ISLAND

**Newport**
Member
  Newport Hospital

**Providence**
Member
  Miriam Hospital
  Rhode Island Hospital

## SOUTH CAROLINA

**Camden**
Member
  KershawHealth

**Charleston**
Member
  MUSC Medical Center of Medical University of South
    Carolina

**Clinton**
Member
  Greenville Health System – Laurens County Memorial
    Hospital

**Columbia**
Member
  Palmetto Health
  Palmetto Health Baptist
  Palmetto Health Baptist Parkridge
  Palmetto Health Richland

**Easley**
Member
  Baptist Easley Hospital

**Greenville**
Member
  Greenville Health System
  Greenville Memorial Hospital
  Patewood Memorial Hospital

**Greer**
Member
  Greer Memorial Hospital

**Seneca**
Member
  Oconee Memorial Hospital

**Simpsonville**
Member
  Hillcrest Memorial Hospital

**Travelers Rest**
Member
  North Greenville Hospital

## TENNESSEE

**Knoxville**
Member
  University of Tennessee Medical Center

**Nashville**
Member
  Vanderbilt Hospital and Clinics

## TEXAS

**Baytown**
Member
  Houston Methodist San Jacinto Hospital

**Dallas**
Member
  Parkland Health & Hospital System
  University of Texas Southwestern Medical Center

**Fort Worth**
Member
  JPS Health Network

**Galveston**
Member
  University of Texas Medical Branch

**Houston**
Member
  Baylor St. Luke's Medical Center
  Harris Health System
  Houston Methodist Hospital
  Houston Methodist West Hospital
  Houston Methodist Willowbrook Hospital
  Memorial Hermann – Texas Medical Center
  St. Luke's Hospital – The Vintage Hospital
  TIRR Memorial Hermann
  University of Texas M.D. Anderson Cancer Center

**Katy**
Member
  Houston Methodist St. Catherine Hospital

**Nassau Bay**
Member
  Houston Methodist St. John Hospital

**Pasadena**
Member
  St. Luke's Patients Medical Center

**Sugar Land**
Member
  Houston Methodist Sugar Land Hospital
  St. Luke's Sugar Land Hospital

**The Woodlands**
Member
  St. Luke's Lakeside Hospital
  St. Luke's The Woodlands Hospital

**Tyler**
Member
  University of Texas Health Northeast

## UTAH

**Gunnison**
Member
  Gunnison Valley Hospital

**Salt Lake City**
Member
  University of Utah Health Care – Hospital and Clinics

## VERMONT

**Brattleboro**
Member
  Brattleboro Retreat

**Burlington**
Member
  The University of Vermont Health Network University
    of Vermont Medical Center

## VIRGINIA

**Charlottesville**
Member
  University of Virginia Medical Center
  UVA–HEALTHSOUTH Rehabilitation Hospital

**Culpeper**
Member
  UVA Culpeper Hospital

**Norfolk**
Member
  Sentara Norfolk General Hospital

**Richmond**
Member
  VCU Medical Center

## WASHINGTON

**Renton**
Member
  UW Medicine/Valley Medical Center

**Seattle**
Member
  Seattle Cancer Care Alliance
  University of Washington Medical Center
  UW Medicine/Harborview Medical Center
  UW Medicine/Northwest Hospital & Medical Center

## WEST VIRGINIA

**Martinsburg**
Member
  Berkeley Medical Center

**Morgantown**
Member
  West Virginia University Hospitals

**Ranson**
Member
  Jefferson Medical Center

**Wheeling**
Member
  Ohio Valley Medical Center

## WISCONSIN

**Eau Claire**
Member
  Mayo Clinic Health System in Eau Claire

**Friendship**
Member
  Moundview Memorial Hospital & Clinics

**Hudson**
Member
  Hudson Hospital and Clinic

**La Crosse**
Member
Mayo Clinic Health System – Franciscan Healthcare in La Crosse

**Madison**
Member
University of Wisconsin Hospital and Clinics

**Medford**
Member
Aspirus Medford Hospital

**Milwaukee**
Member
Froedtert Memorial Lutheran Hospital

**New Richmond**
Member
Westfields Hospital

**Oconto Falls**
Member
HSHS St. Clare Memorial Hospital

**Portage**
Member
Divine Savior Healthcare

**Wausau**
Member
Aspirus Wausau Hospital

**West Bend**
Member
St. Joseph's Hospital

**Wisconsin Rapids**
Member
Aspirus Riverview Hospital and Clinics, Inc.

**WYOMING**
**Laramie**
Member
Ivinson Memorial Hospital

## UNIVERSITY OF IOWA HEALTH ALLIANCE
1755 59th Place, West Des Moines, IA Zip 50266–7737; tel. 515/643–4000; Dan Kueter, Chief Executive Officer

**ILLINOIS**
**Aledo**
Member
Genesis Medical Center–Aledo

**Silvis**
Member
Genesis Medical Center, Illini Campus

**IOWA**
**Albia**
Member
Monroe County Hospital and Clinics

**Algona**
Member
Kossuth Regional Health Center

**Audubon**
Member
Audubon County Memorial Hospital

**Belmond**
Member
Iowa Specialty Hospital–Belmond

**Bloomfield**
Member
Davis County Hospital

**Britt**
Member
Hancock County Health System

**Cedar Falls**
Member
Sartori Memorial Hospital

**Cedar Rapids**
Member
Mercy Medical Center–Cedar Rapids

**Centerville**
Member
Mercy Medical Center–Centerville

**Clarinda**
Member
Clarinda Regional Health Center

**Clarion**
Member
Iowa Specialty Hospital–Clarion

**Clinton**
Member
Mercy Medical Center–Clinton

**Corydon**
Member
Wayne County Hospital

**Cresco**
Member
Regional Health Services of Howard County

**Davenport**
Member
Genesis Medical Center–Davenport

**De Witt**
Member
Genesis Medical Center, DeWitt

**Des Moines**
Member
Mercy Medical Center–Des Moines

**Dubuque**
Member
Mercy Medical Center–Dubuque

**Dyersville**
Member
Mercy Medical Center–Dyersville

**Elkader**
Member
Central Community Hospital

**Emmetsburg**
Member
Palo Alto County Health System

**Fairfield**
Member
Jefferson County Health Center

**Greenfield**
Member
Adair County Memorial Hospital

**Grinnell**
Member
Grinnell Regional Medical Center

**Hampton**
Member
Franklin General Hospital

**Hawarden**
Member
Hawarden Regional Healthcare

**Iowa City**
Member
University of Iowa Hospitals and Clinics

**Iowa Falls**
Member
Hansen Family Hospital

**Keosauqua**
Member
Van Buren County Hospital

**Knoxville**
Member
Knoxville Hospital & Clinics

**Leon**
Member
Decatur County Hospital

**Manning**
Member
Manning Regional Healthcare Center

**Maquoketa**
Member
Jackson County Regional Health Center

**Mason City**
Member
Mercy Medical Center–North Iowa

**Mount Ayr**
Member
Ringgold County Hospital

**Mount Pleasant**
Member
Henry County Health Center

**New Hampton**
Member
Mercy Medical Center–New Hampton

**Oelwein**
Member
Mercy Hospital of Franciscan Sisters

**Osage**
Member
Mitchell County Regional Health Center

**Pella**
Member
Pella Regional Health Center

**Perry**
Member
Dallas County Hospital

**Primghar**
Member
Baum Harmon Mercy Hospital

**Sigourney**
Member
Keokuk County Health Center

**Sioux City**
Member
Mercy Medical Center–Sioux City

**Vinton**
Member
Virginia Gay Hospital

**Washington**
Member
Washington County Hospital and Clinics

**Waterloo**
Member
Covenant Medical Center

**Waverly**
Member
Waverly Health Center

**Webster City**
Member
Van Diest Medical Center

**West Des Moines**
Member
Mercy Medical Center – West Lakes

**Winterset**
Member
Madison County Health Care System

**NEBRASKA**
**Oakland**
Member
Oakland Mercy Hospital

**Pender**
Member
Pender Community Hospital

## VANTAGE HEALTHCARE NETWORK, INC.
18282 Technology Drive, Suite 202, Meadville, PA Zip 16335; tel. 814/337–0000; David Petrarca, Director Retail Operations

## VHA, INC.
290 East John Carpenter Freeway, Irving, TX Zip 75062–2730; tel. 972/830–0000; Edward Goodman, Executive Vice President Policy

**ALABAMA**
**Alabaster**
Shelby Baptist Medical Center

**Anniston**
Partner
Northeast Alabama Regional Medical Center

**Athens**
Partner
Athens–Limestone Hospital

**Atmore**
Atmore Community Hospital

**Bay Minette**
Member
North Baldwin Infirmary

**Birmingham**
Princeton Baptist Medical Center
Shareholder
Baptist Health System

**Boaz**
Marshall Medical Center South

**Brewton**
D. W. McMillan Memorial Hospital

**Carrollton**
Pickens County Medical Center

**Decatur**
Decatur Morgan Hospital

**Fairhope**
Thomas Hospital

**Fayette**
Fayette Medical Center

**Guntersville**
Marshall Medical Center North
Partner
Marshall Health System

**Huntsville**
Huntsville Hospital

**Jasper**
Walker Baptist Medical Center

**Mobile**
Member
Mobile Infirmary Medical Center

**Montgomery**
Baptist Medical Center East
Shareholder
Baptist Medical Center South

**Northport**
Northport Medical Center

**Opp**
Mizell Memorial Hospital

**Ozark**
Dale Medical Center

**Prattville**
Prattville Baptist Hospital

**Red Bay**
Member
Red Bay Hospital

**Scottsboro**
Partner
Highlands Medical Center

**Sheffield**
Member
Helen Keller Hospital

**Sylacauga**
Coosa Valley Medical Center

**Talladega**
Citizens Baptist Medical Center

**Tuscaloosa**
DCH Regional Medical Center
Partner
DCH Health System

**Union Springs**
Bullock County Hospital

## ALASKA

**Anchorage**
Shareholder
Providence Alaska Medical Center
St. Elias Specialty Hospital

**Cordova**
Shareholder
Cordova Community Medical Center

**Kodiak**
Shareholder
Providence Kodiak Island Medical Center

**Seward**
Shareholder
Providence Seward Medical Center

**Valdez**
Shareholder
Providence Valdez Medical Center

**Wrangell**
Shareholder
Wrangell Medical Center

## ARIZONA

**Bisbee**
Copper Queen Community Hospital

**Kingman**
Member
Kingman Regional Medical Center

**Phoenix**
Mayo Clinic Hospital

**Safford**
Mt. Graham Regional Medical Center

**Scottsdale**
Unit_of
HonorHealth Scottsdale Osborn Medical Center

**Tucson**
TMC Healthcare

## ARKANSAS

**Arkadelphia**
Baptist Health Medical Center–Arkadelphia

**Booneville**
Mercy Hospital Booneville

**Clinton**
Ozark Health Medical Center

**Conway**
Partner
Conway Regional Medical Center

**Fayetteville**
Partner
Washington Regional Medical Center

**Heber Springs**
Baptist Health Medical Center–Heber Springs

**Jonesboro**
NEA Baptist Memorial Hospital
Partner
St. Bernards Medical Center

**Little Rock**
Baptist Health Medical Center–Little Rock
Member
Baptist Health Extended Care Hospital
Shareholder
Baptist Health

**Malvern**
Member
Baptist Health Medical Center–Hot Spring County

**North Little Rock**
Baptist Health Medical Center – North Little Rock

**Paragould**
Partner
Arkansas Methodist Medical Center

**Piggott**
Piggott Community Hospital

**Stuttgart**
Baptist Health Medical Center–Stuttgart

**Walnut Ridge**
Lawrence Memorial Hospital

**Wynne**
CrossRidge Community Hospital

## CALIFORNIA

**Alameda**
Alameda Hospital

**Arcadia**
Methodist Hospital of Southern California

**Auburn**
Sutter Auburn Faith Hospital

**Berkeley**
Alta Bates Medical Center–Herrick Campus
Alta Bates Summit Medical Center

**Burbank**
Providence Saint Joseph Medical Center

**Burlingame**
Mills–Peninsula Health Services

**Castro Valley**
Eden Medical Center

**Clovis**
Clovis Community Medical Center

**Concord**
John Muir Medical Center, Concord

**Covina**
Citrus Valley Health Partners
Member
Citrus Valley Medical Center–Inter Community Campus

**Crescent City**
Sutter Coast Hospital

**Davis**
Sutter Davis Hospital

**Downey**
Member
PIH Health Hospital – Downey

**El Centro**
El Centro Regional Medical Center

**Encinitas**
Scripps Memorial Hospital–Encinitas

**Escondido**
Palomar Health
Palomar Medical Center

**Fairfield**
Member
NorthBay Medical Center

**Fremont**
Member
Washington Hospital Healthcare System

**Fresno**
Shareholder
Community Medical Centers

**Glendora**
Foothill Presbyterian Hospital

**Jackson**
Sutter Amador Hospital

**King City**
Member
Mee Memorial Hospital

**Lakeport**
Sutter Lakeside Hospital

**Lancaster**
Partner
Antelope Valley Hospital

**Los Angeles**
Shareholder
Cedars–Sinai Medical Center

**Los Banos**
Member
Memorial Hospital Los Banos

**Mariposa**
John C. Fremont Healthcare District

**Menlo Park**
Menlo Park Surgical Hospital

**Mission Hills**
Providence Holy Cross Medical Center

**Modesto**
Partner
Memorial Medical Center

**Monterey**
Community Hospital of the Monterey Peninsula

**Novato**
Novato Community Hospital

**Oakland**
Alta Bates Summit Medical Center – Summit Campus

**Oceanside**
Member
Tri–City Medical Center

**Pleasanton**
Stanford Health Care – ValleyCare

**Pomona**
Partner
Pomona Valley Hospital Medical Center

**Porterville**
Member
Sierra View Medical Center

**Poway**
Pomerado Hospital

**Redlands**
Member
Redlands Community Hospital

**Roseville**
Sutter Roseville Medical Center

**Sacramento**
Sutter Medical Center, Sacramento
Shareholder
Sutter Health

**Salinas**
Member
Natividad Medical Center

**San Diego**
Scripps Health
Scripps Mercy Hospital

**San Francisco**
California Pacific Medical Center–Davies Campus
Chinese Hospital
St. Luke's Hospital
Shareholder
California Pacific Medical Center

**San Pedro**
Providence Little Company of Mary Medical Center
San Pedro

**Santa Barbara**
Cottage Health System
Goleta Valley Cottage Hospital
Partner
Santa Barbara Cottage Hospital

**Santa Cruz**
Sutter Maternity and Surgery Center of Santa Cruz

**Santa Rosa**
Sutter Santa Rosa Regional Hospital

**Solvang**
Santa Ynez Valley Cottage Hospital

**Tarzana**
Providence Tarzana Medical Center

**Torrance**
Providence Little Company of Mary Medical Center –
Torrance
Partner
Torrance Memorial Medical Center

**Tracy**
Sutter Tracy Community Hospital

**Vallejo**
Sutter Solano Medical Center

**Walnut Creek**
John Muir Health
John Muir Medical Center, Walnut Creek

**Whittier**
Partner
PIH Health Hospital–Whittier

**COLORADO**

**Boulder**
Partner
Boulder Community Health

**Englewood**
Craig Hospital

**Gunnison**
Partner
Gunnison Valley Hospital

**Kremmling**
Middle Park Medical Center–Kremmling

**La Jara**
San Luis Valley Health Conejos County Hospital

**Longmont**
Partner
Longmont United Hospital

**Steamboat Springs**
Partner
Yampa Valley Medical Center

**CONNECTICUT**

**Bridgeport**
Bridgeport Hospital

**Bristol**
Member
Bristol Hospital

**Danbury**
Partner
Danbury Hospital

**Greenwich**
Partner
Greenwich Hospital

**Manchester**
Eastern Connecticut Health Network
Manchester Memorial Hospital

**Milford**
Member
Milford Hospital

**New Haven**
Yale New Haven Health System
Yale–New Haven Hospital

**New London**
Member
Lawrence + Memorial Hospital

**Norwalk**
Norwalk Hospital

**Putnam**
Day Kimball Hospital

**Torrington**
Partner
The Charlotte Hungerford Hospital

**Vernon**
Rockville General Hospital

**DISTRICT OF COLUMBIA**

**Washington**
MedStar Georgetown University Hospital
MedStar Washington Hospital Center

**FLORIDA**

**Apalachicola**
George E. Weems Memorial Hospital

**Boca Raton**
Partner
Boca Raton Regional Hospital

**Boynton Beach**
Partner
Bethesda Hospital East

**Clermont**
South Lake Hospital

**Cocoa Beach**
Health First Cape Canaveral Hospital

**Coral Gables**
Member
Baptist Health South Florida, Doctors Hospital

**Daytona Beach**
Shareholder
Halifax Health Medical Center of Daytona Beach

**Gulf Breeze**
Gulf Breeze Hospital

**Homestead**
Member
Baptist Health South Florida, Homestead Hospital

**Jacksonville**
Mayo Clinic Jacksonville

**Jay**
Jay Hospital

**Lakeland**
Shareholder
Lakeland Regional Health

**Leesburg**
Leesburg Regional Medical Center

**Melbourne**
Shareholder
Health First Holmes Regional Medical Center

**Miami**
Member
Baptist Health South Florida, Baptist Hospital of Miami
Baptist Health South Florida, West Kendall Baptist
Hospital

**Milton**
Member
West Florida Community Care Center

**Naples**
Member
NCH Downtown Naples Hospital

**New Smyrna Beach**
Bert Fish Medical Center

**Ocoee**
Health Central Hospital

**Orlando**
Orlando Regional Medical Center
Shareholder
Orlando Health

**Palm Bay**
Member
Health First Palm Bay Hospital

**Panama City**
Bay Medical Center Sacred Heart Health System

**Pensacola**
Baptist Hospital
Shareholder
Baptist Health Care Corporation

**Perry**
Member
Doctor's Memorial Hospital

**Rockledge**
Health First, Inc.

**Stuart**
Martin Health System

**Tallahassee**
Shareholder
Tallahassee Memorial HealthCare

**Tavernier**
Member
Baptist Health South Florida, Mariners Hospital

**The Villages**
Member
The Villages Regional Hospital

**Titusville**
Partner
Parrish Medical Center

**Weston**
Member
Cleveland Clinic Florida

**GEORGIA**

**Adel**
Member
Cook Medical Center–A Campus of Tift Regional
Medical Center

**Albany**
Phoebe Putney Health System
Member
Phoebe Putney Memorial Hospital

**Americus**
Phoebe Sumter Medical Center

**Athens**
Partner
Athens Regional Medical Center

**Atlanta**
Partner
Northside Hospital

**Augusta**
University Hospital

**Austell**
WellStar Cobb Hospital

**Braselton**
Member
Northeast Georgia Medical Center Braselton

**Brunswick**
Southeast Georgia Health System
Southeast Georgia Health System Brunswick Campus

**Cairo**
Grady General Hospital

**Camilla**
Mitchell County Hospital

**Canton**
Northside Hospital–Cherokee

**Cedartown**
Member
Polk Medical Center

**Claxton**
Member
Evans Memorial Hospital

**Columbus**
Columbus Regional Healthcare System
Columbus Specialty Hospital
Northside Medical Center
Partner
The Medical Center

**Cordele**
Crisp Regional Hospital

**Cumming**
Northside Hospital–Forsyth

**Cuthbert**
Southwest Georgia Regional Medical Center

**Dalton**
Partner
Hamilton Medical Center

**Decatur**
DeKalb Medical at Downtown Decatur
Partner
DeKalb Medical at North Decatur

**Douglas**
Coffee Regional Medical Center

Section B

**Douglasville**
WellStar Douglas Hospital
**Eatonton**
Member
Putnam General Hospital
**Fitzgerald**
Dorminy Medical Center
**Fort Valley**
Member
Medical Center of Peach County, Navicent Health
**Gainesville**
Northeast Georgia Medical Center
**Hiram**
WellStar Paulding Hospital
**Homerville**
Clinch Memorial Hospital
**Lakeland**
South Georgia Medical Center Lanier Campus
**Lawrenceville**
Partner
Gwinnett Hospital System
**Lithonia**
DeKalb Medical at Hillandale
**Macon**
Member
Rehabilitation Hospital, Navicent Health
Partner
Medical Center, Navicent Health
**Marietta**
WellStar Health System
WellStar Windy Hill Hospital
Partner
WellStar Kennestone Hospital
**Moultrie**
Colquitt Regional Medical Center
**Nashville**
Member
South Georgia Medical Center Berrien Campus
**Perry**
Perry Hospital
**Quitman**
Brooks County Hospital
**Riverdale**
Partner
Southern Regional Medical Center
**Rome**
Kindred Hospital Rome
Partner
Floyd Medical Center
**Saint Marys**
Southeast Georgia Health System Camden Campus
**Sylvester**
Phoebe Worth Medical Center
**Thomasville**
Partner
Archbold Medical Center
John D. Archbold Memorial Hospital
**Thomson**
Member
University Hospital McDuffie
**Tifton**
Tift Regional Medical Center
**Valdosta**
Partner
South Georgia Medical Center
**Warner Robins**
Houston Medical Center
**Waycross**
Mayo Clinic Health System in Waycross

**HAWAII**
**Ewa Beach**
Member
Kahi Mohala Behavioral Health
**Honolulu**
Queen's Health Systems
Queen's Medical Center
**Kamuela**
Member
North Hawaii Community Hospital
**Kaunakakai**
Molokai General Hospital

**Wahiawa**
Wahiawa General Hospital
**IDAHO**
**American Falls**
Power County Hospital District
**Arco**
Lost Rivers Medical Center
**Blackfoot**
Bingham Memorial Hospital
**Boise**
St. Luke's Health System
St. Luke's Rehabilitation Hospital
Shareholder
St. Luke's Regional Medical Center
**Bonners Ferry**
Boundary Community Hospital
**Cascade**
Cascade Medical Center
**Coeur D'Alene**
Partner
Kootenai Health
**Cottonwood**
Member
St. Mary's Hospital
**Emmett**
Valor Health
**Gooding**
North Canyon Medical Center
**Grangeville**
Syringa Hospital and Clinics
**Jerome**
St. Luke's Jerome
**Ketchum**
St. Luke's Wood River Medical Center
**Malad City**
Nell J. Redfield Memorial Hospital
**McCall**
St. Luke's McCall
**Montpelier**
Bear Lake Memorial Hospital
**Mountain Home**
St. Luke's Elmore
**Orofino**
Clearwater Valley Hospital and Clinics
**Preston**
Franklin County Medical Center
**Rupert**
Minidoka Memorial Hospital
**Sandpoint**
Partner
Bonner General Hospital
**Twin Falls**
Partner
St. Luke's Magic Valley Medical Center
**Weiser**
Weiser Memorial Hospital
**ILLINOIS**
**Alton**
Alton Memorial Hospital
**Belleville**
Partner
Memorial Hospital
**Canton**
Graham Hospital
**Carbondale**
Memorial Hospital of Carbondale
Partner
Southern Illinois Hospital Services
**Chester**
Memorial Hospital
**Chicago**
Partner
Swedish Covenant Hospital
**Decatur**
Decatur Memorial Hospital
**DeKalb**
Kish Health System
**Eldorado**
Member
Ferrell Hospital

**Elgin**
Partner
Advocate Sherman Hospital
**Elmhurst**
Partner
Elmhurst Memorial Hospital
**Evanston**
NorthShore University Health System
**Evergreen Park**
Partner
Little Company of Mary Hospital and Health Care Centers
**Freeport**
Partner
FHN Memorial Hospital
**Herrin**
Herrin Hospital
**Jacksonville**
Partner
Passavant Area Hospital
**Jerseyville**
Jersey Community Hospital
**Lincoln**
Abraham Lincoln Memorial Hospital
**Macomb**
Partner
McDonough District Hospital
**Maryville**
Partner
Anderson Hospital
**Mattoon**
Sarah Bush Lincoln Health Center
**Monticello**
Kirby Medical Center
**Murphysboro**
St. Joseph Memorial Hospital
**New Lenox**
Partner
Silver Cross Hospital
**Palos Heights**
Member
Palos Community Hospital
**Pittsfield**
Illini Community Hospital
**Quincy**
Partner
Blessing Hospital
**Rock Island**
Member
UnityPoint Health – Trinity Rock Island
**Rockford**
SwedishAmerican Hospital, A Division of UW Health
**Rushville**
Sarah D. Culbertson Memorial Hospital
**Salem**
Salem Township Hospital
**Shelbyville**
Shelby Memorial Hospital
**Springfield**
Memorial Health System
Shareholder
Memorial Medical Center
**Taylorville**
Taylorville Memorial Hospital
**INDIANA**
**Anderson**
Community Hospital of Anderson and Madison County
**Angola**
Member
Cameron Memorial Community Hospital
**Auburn**
Member
DeKalb Health
**Avon**
Indiana University Health West Hospital
**Batesville**
Margaret Mary Health
**Bedford**
Indiana University Health Bedford Hospital

**Bloomington**
Partner
    Indiana University Health Bloomington Hospital

**Bremen**
    Doctors NeuroMedical Hospital

**Carmel**
    Indiana University Health North Hospital

**Clinton**
    Union Hospital Clinton

**Columbia City**
    Parkview Whitley Hospital

**Columbus**
Partner
    Columbus Regional Hospital

**Danville**
Partner
    Hendricks Regional Health

**Elkhart**
Partner
    Elkhart General Healthcare System

**Evansville**
    Deaconess Health System
Shareholder
    Deaconess Hospital

**Fort Wayne**
    Parkview Health
Member
    Parkview Ortho Hospital
    Parkview Regional Medical Center

**Franklin**
    Johnson Memorial Hospital

**Goshen**
    Indiana University Health Goshen Hospital

**Hartford City**
    Indiana University Health Blackford Hospital

**Huntington**
    Parkview Huntington Hospital

**Indianapolis**
    Community Health Network
    Community Hospital East
    Community Hospital North
    Community Hospital South
    Indiana University Health Methodist Hospital
Shareholder
    Indiana University Health University Hospital

**Jasper**
Member
    Memorial Hospital and Health Care Center

**Jeffersonville**
Member
    Clark Memorial Hospital

**Kendallville**
    Parkview Noble Hospital

**Knox**
    Indiana University Health Starke Hospital

**Kokomo**
Partner
    Community Howard Regional Health

**La Porte**
Partner
    Indiana University Health La Porte Hospital

**Lafayette**
    Indiana University Health Arnett Hospital

**LaGrange**
    Parkview LaGrange Hospital

**Logansport**
Member
    Logansport Memorial Hospital

**Madison**
Partner
    King's Daughters' Health

**Marion**
Partner
    Marion General Hospital

**Martinsville**
    Indiana University Health Morgan Hospital

**Monticello**
Member
    Indiana University Health White Memorial Hospital

**Muncie**
Shareholder
    Indiana University Health Ball Memorial Hospital

**New Albany**
Member
    Southern Indiana Rehabilitation Hospital
Partner
    Floyd Memorial Hospital and Health Services

**New Castle**
    Henry County Hospital

**Newburgh**
Member
    The Heart Hospital at Deaconess Gateway
    The Women's Hospital

**Noblesville**
Partner
    Riverview Hospital

**Paoli**
    Indiana University Health Paoli Hospital

**Portland**
    Jay County Hospital

**Richmond**
Partner
    Reid Health

**Seymour**
    Schneck Medical Center

**Shelbyville**
    Major Hospital

**South Bend**
    Healthwin Hospital
    Memorial Hospital of South Bend

**Terre Haute**
Partner
    Union Hospital

**Tipton**
    Indiana University Health Tipton Hospital

**Vincennes**
Partner
    Good Samaritan Hospital

**Wabash**
Member
    Parkview Wabash County Hospital

## IOWA

**Anamosa**
Member
    UnityPoint Health – Jones Regional Medical Center

**Atlantic**
Shareholder
    Cass County Memorial Hospital

**Bettendorf**
Member
    UnityPoint Health – Trinity Bettendorf

**Cedar Rapids**
Member
    UnityPoint Health – St. Luke's Hospital

**Clarinda**
Member
    Clarinda Regional Health Center

**Council Bluffs**
Shareholder
    Methodist Jennie Edmundson Hospital

**Decorah**
    Winneshiek Medical Center

**Des Moines**
Member
    UnityPoint Health–Iowa Lutheran Hospital

**Dubuque**
Member
    UnityPoint Health – Finley Hospital

**Fort Dodge**
Member
    UnityPoint Health – Trinity Regional Medical Center

**Grundy Center**
Member
    Grundy County Memorial Hospital

**Guttenberg**
Member
    Guttenberg Municipal Hospital

**Hamburg**
    George C Grape Community Hospital

**Harlan**
Partner
    Myrtue Medical Center

**Jefferson**
Member
    Greene County Medical Center

**Keokuk**
Shareholder
    Keokuk Area Hospital

**Lake City**
Member
    Stewart Memorial Community Hospital

**Le Mars**
Partner
    Floyd Valley Hospital

**Marengo**
Member
    Marengo Memorial Hospital, UnityPoint Health

**Muscatine**
    UnityPoint Health – Trinity Muscatine

**Nevada**
Member
    Story County Medical Center

**Orange City**
    Orange City Area Health System

**Osceola**
Member
    Clarke County Hospital

**Red Oak**
Shareholder
    Montgomery County Memorial Hospital

**Rock Rapids**
    Sanford Rock Rapids Medical Center

**Sheldon**
    Sanford Sheldon Medical Center

**Sioux City**
Shareholder
    UnityPoint Health – St. Luke's

**Sumner**
Member
    Community Memorial Hospital

**West Des Moines**
Member
    UnityPoint Health – Methodist West Hospital

**West Union**
    Palmer Lutheran Health Center

## KANSAS

**Abilene**
    Memorial Health System

**Anthony**
    Anthony Medical Center

**Atchison**
Shareholder
    Atchison Hospital

**Atwood**
    Rawlins County Health Center

**Belleville**
    Republic County Hospital

**Beloit**
    Mitchell County Hospital Health Systems

**Clay Center**
    Clay County Medical Center

**Colby**
Shareholder
    Citizens Medical Center

**Coldwater**
    Comanche County Hospital

**Concordia**
    Cloud County Health Center

**Dighton**
    Lane County Hospital

**El Dorado**
    Susan B. Allen Memorial Hospital

**Ellinwood**
    Ellinwood District Hospital

**Ellsworth**
    Ellsworth County Medical Center

**Emporia**
Member
    Newman Regional Health

Section B

**Fredonia**
Fredonia Regional Hospital
**Garnett**
Anderson County Hospital
**Goodland**
Goodland Regional Medical Center
**Great Bend**
Member
Great Bend Regional Hospital
**Greensburg**
Kiowa County Memorial Hospital
**Hays**
Shareholder
Hays Medical Center
**Herington**
Herington Municipal Hospital
**Hiawatha**
Partner
Hiawatha Community Hospital
**Hill City**
Graham County Hospital
**Hoisington**
Clara Barton Hospital
**Hoxie**
Sheridan County Health Complex
**Junction City**
Geary Community Hospital
**La Crosse**
Rush County Memorial Hospital
**Larned**
Member
Pawnee Valley Community Hospital
**Lawrence**
Lawrence Memorial Hospital
**Leavenworth**
Saint Luke's Cushing Hospital
**Lincoln**
Lincoln County Hospital
**Lindsborg**
Lindsborg Community Hospital
**Mankato**
Jewell County Hospital
**Medicine Lodge**
Medicine Lodge Memorial Hospital
**Minneapolis**
Ottawa County Health Center
**Minneola**
Minneola District Hospital
**Ness City**
Ness County Hospital
**Norton**
Norton County Hospital
**Oakley**
Logan County Hospital
**Overland Park**
Saint Luke's South Hospital
**Parsons**
Partner
Labette Health
**Phillipsburg**
Phillips County Hospital
**Plainville**
Rooks County Health Center
**Pratt**
Shareholder
Pratt Regional Medical Center
**Quinter**
Gove County Medical Center
**Ransom**
Grisell Memorial Hospital District One
**Russell**
Russell Regional Hospital
**Sabetha**
Sabetha Community Hospital
**Saint Francis**
Cheyenne County Hospital
**Salina**
Salina Surgical Hospital
Partner
Salina Regional Health Center

**Satanta**
Satanta District Hospital and Long Term Care
**Scott City**
Scott County Hospital
**Smith Center**
Smith County Memorial Hospital
**Stafford**
Stafford County Hospital
**Topeka**
Shareholder
Stormont–Vail HealthCare
**Wakeeney**
Trego County–Lemke Memorial Hospital
**Wichita**
Shareholder
Great Plains Health Alliance, Inc.

## KENTUCKY
**Owensboro**
Member
Owensboro Health Regional Hospital
**Pikeville**
Pikeville Medical Center

## LOUISIANA
**Baton Rouge**
Franciscan Missionaries of Our Lady Health System, Inc.
Ochsner Medical Center–Baton Rouge
Member
Our Lady of the Lake Regional Medical Center
Partner
Woman's Hospital
**Bogalusa**
Member
Our Lady of the Angels Hospital
**Bossier City**
WK Bossier Health Center
**Church Point**
Acadia–St. Landry Hospital
**Covington**
Partner
St. Tammany Parish Hospital
**De Ridder**
Partner
Beauregard Memorial Hospital
**Ferriday**
Riverland Medical Center
**Franklinton**
Member
Riverside Medical Center
**Gonzales**
St. Elizabeth Hospital
**Jennings**
Jennings American Legion Hospital
**Kenner**
Ochsner Medical Center – Kenner
**Lafayette**
Partner
Our Lady of Lourdes Regional Medical Center
**Lake Charles**
Member
LCMH Specialty Hospital
Partner
Lake Charles Memorial Hospital
**Mansfield**
De Soto Regional Health System
**Monroe**
Partner
St. Francis Medical Center
**Napoleonville**
Assumption Community Hospital
**Natchitoches**
Natchitoches Regional Medical Center
**New Iberia**
Iberia Medical Center
**New Orleans**
Member
Touro Infirmary
Shareholder
Ochsner Medical Center
**Raceland**
Ochsner St. Anne General Hospital

**Shreveport**
Willis–Knighton Health System
Shareholder
Willis–Knighton Medical Center
**Slidell**
Member
Ochsner Medical Center – North Shore
**Springhill**
Springhill Medical Center
**Sulphur**
Partner
West Calcasieu Cameron Hospital
**Vivian**
North Caddo Medical Center

## MAINE
**Augusta**
MaineGeneral Medical Center–Augusta Campus
Shareholder
MaineGeneral Medical Center
**Bangor**
Eastern Maine Medical Center
The Acadia Hospital
**Bar Harbor**
Mount Desert Island Hospital
**Belfast**
Waldo County General Hospital
**Biddeford**
Member
Southern Maine Health Care – Biddeford Medical Center
**Blue Hill**
Blue Hill Memorial Hospital
**Brewer**
Partner
Eastern Maine Healthcare Systems
**Brunswick**
Mid Coast Hospital
**Damariscotta**
LincolnHealth
**Dover-Foxcroft**
Mayo Regional Hospital
**Ellsworth**
Maine Coast Memorial Hospital
**Farmington**
Member
Franklin Memorial Hospital
**Fort Kent**
Member
Northern Maine Medical Center
**Greenville**
Charles A. Dean Memorial Hospital
**Houlton**
Houlton Regional Hospital
**Machias**
Down East Community Hospital
**Millinocket**
Member
Millinocket Regional Hospital
Unit_of
Millinocket Regional Hospital
**Norway**
Stephens Memorial Hospital
**Pittsfield**
Sebasticook Valley Health
**Portland**
Shareholder
Maine Medical Center
**Presque Isle**
The Aroostook Medical Center
**Rockport**
Pen Bay Medical Center
**Skowhegan**
Redington–Fairview General Hospital
**Waterville**
Inland Hospital
**Westbrook**
Spring Harbor Hospital

## MARYLAND
**Baltimore**
MedStar Franklin Square Medical Center
MedStar Good Samaritan Hospital
MedStar Harbor Hospital
MedStar Union Memorial Hospital

**Bel Air**
  University of Maryland Upper Chesapeake Medical
    Center
Partner
  Upper Chesapeake Health System
**Clinton**
Member
  MedStar Southern Maryland Hospital Center
**Columbia**
  MedStar Health
**Havre De Grace**
  University of Maryland Harford Memorial Hospital
**Leonardtown**
  MedStar St. Mary's Hospital
**Olney**
  MedStar Montgomery Medical Center
**Prince Frederick**
  Calvert Memorial Hospital
**MASSACHUSETTS**
**Athol**
Member
  Athol Memorial Hospital
**Belmont**
  McLean Hospital
**Boston**
  Brigham and Women's Faulkner Hospital
  Brigham and Women's Hospital
  Dana–Farber Cancer Institute
  Massachusetts General Hospital
Member
  Beth Israel Deaconess Medical Center
Partner
  Massachusetts Eye and Ear Infirmary
Shareholder
  Partners HealthCare System, Inc.
**Brockton**
Member
  Signature Healthcare Brockton Hospital
**Cambridge**
  Spaulding Hospital for Continuing Medical Care
    Cambridge
Member
  Cambridge Health Alliance
Partner
  Mount Auburn Hospital
**Charlestown**
  Spaulding Rehabilitation Hospital
**East Sandwich**
  Spaulding Rehabilitation Hospital Cape Cod
**Gardner**
Partner
  Heywood Hospital
**Hyannis**
  Cape Cod Healthcare, Inc.
**Lawrence**
Owner
  Lawrence General Hospital
**Melrose**
  Hallmark Health System
Partner
  Melrose–Wakefield Hospital
**Milton**
Member
  Beth Israel Deaconess Hospital–Milton
**Nantucket**
  Nantucket Cottage Hospital
**Northampton**
  Cooley Dickinson Hospital
**Oak Bluffs**
  Martha's Vineyard Hospital
**Plymouth**
Member
  Beth Israel Deaconess Hospital Plymouth
**Salem**
  North Shore Medical Center
  Spaulding Hospital for Continuing Medical Care North
    Shore
**South Weymouth**
Partner
  South Shore Hospital
**Southbridge**
Partner
  Harrington Memorial Hospital

**MICHIGAN**
**Alpena**
  Alpena Regional Medical Center
**Battle Creek**
Member
  Bronson Battle Creek
**Bay City**
Member
  McLaren Bay Region
  McLaren Bay Special Care
**Big Rapids**
  Spectrum Health Big Rapids Hospital
**Carson City**
Member
  Sparrow Carson Hospital
**Cass City**
  Hills & Dales General Hospital
**Coldwater**
  Community Health Center of Branch County
**Dearborn**
Partner
  Beaumont Hospital–Dearborn
**Flint**
Member
  McLaren Flint
**Fremont**
  Spectrum Health Gerber Memorial
**Grand Haven**
  North Ottawa Community Hospital
**Grand Rapids**
  Mary Free Bed Rehabilitation Hospital
  Spectrum Health
  Spectrum Health – Butterworth Hospital
Member
  Pine Rest Christian Mental Health Services
**Greenville**
  Spectrum Health United Hospital
**Hastings**
  Spectrum Health Pennock
**Holland**
Partner
  Holland Hospital
**Ionia**
Member
  Sparrow Ionia Hospital
**Iron River**
Member
  NORTHSTAR Health System
**Ironwood**
Member
  Aspirus Grand View
**Jackson**
  Allegiance Health
**Kalamazoo**
Partner
  Bronson Healthcare Group, Inc.
  Bronson Methodist Hospital
**Lansing**
Member
  Sparrow Hospital
  Sparrow Specialty Hospital
**Laurium**
  Aspirus Keweenaw Hospital
**Ludington**
  Spectrum Health Ludington Hospital
**Marlette**
Member
  Marlette Regional Hospital
**Marshall**
  Oaklawn Hospital
**Mount Clemens**
Member
  McLaren Macomb
**Mount Pleasant**
Member
  McLaren Central Michigan
**Ontonagon**
  Aspirus Ontonagon Hospital
**Paw Paw**
  Bronson LakeView Hospital

**Petoskey**
  McLaren Northern Michigan
**Pontiac**
Member
  McLaren Oakland
**Port Huron**
  McLaren Port Huron
**Reed City**
  Spectrum Health Reed City Hospital
**Royal Oak**
Shareholder
  Beaumont Hospital – Royal Oak
**Saginaw**
  Covenant Healthcare
**Saint Johns**
Member
  Sparrow Clinton Hospital
**Saint Joseph**
  Lakeland Health
  Lakeland Medical Center, St. Joseph
**Sheridan**
Member
  Sheridan Community Hospital
**South Haven**
  South Haven Health System
**Taylor**
  Beaumont Hospital – Taylor
**Trenton**
  Beaumont Hospital – Trenton
**Troy**
  Beaumont Hospital – Troy
**Vicksburg**
  Bronson Vicksburg Hospital
**Watervliet**
Member
  Lakeland Hospital, Watervliet
**Wayne**
  Beaumont Hospital – Wayne
**West Branch**
Partner
  West Branch Regional Medical Center
**Wyoming**
  Metro Health Hospital
**Zeeland**
  Spectrum Health Zeeland Community Hospital
**MINNESOTA**
**Ada**
  Essentia Health Ada
**Albert Lea**
  Mayo Clinic Health System in Albert Lea
**Arlington**
  Ridgeview Sibley Medical Center
**Aurora**
Member
  Essentia Health Northern Pines Medical Center
**Austin**
  Mayo Clinic Health System–Albert Lea and Austin
**Bagley**
Member
  Sanford Bagley Medical Center
**Bemidji**
Partner
  Sanford Bemidji Medical Center
**Benson**
  Swift County–Benson Hospital
**Blue Earth**
  United Hospital District
**Brainerd**
  Essentia Health St. Joseph's Medical Center
**Buffalo**
  Buffalo Hospital
**Cambridge**
  Cambridge Medical Center
**Canby**
  Sanford Canby Medical Center
**Cannon Falls**
  Mayo Clinic Health System in Cannon Falls
**Coon Rapids**
  Mercy Hospital

Section B

# Alliances

**Crookston**
Member
RiverView Health

**Deer River**
Member
Essentia Health–Deer River

**Detroit Lakes**
Essentia Health St. Mary's – Detroit Lakes

**Duluth**
Essentia Health
Essentia Health Duluth
Essentia Health St. Mary's Medical Center
Partner
St. Luke's Hospital

**Fairmont**
Mayo Clinic Health System in Fairmont

**Faribault**
Member
District One Hospital

**Fergus Falls**
Partner
Lake Region Healthcare

**Fosston**
Essentia Health Fosston

**Fridley**
Unity Hospital

**Graceville**
Essentia Health–Graceville

**Grand Rapids**
Grand Itasca Clinic and Hospital

**Granite Falls**
Member
Granite Falls Municipal Hospital and Manor

**Hallock**
Kittson Memorial Healthcare Center

**Hastings**
Member
Regina Hospital

**Hutchinson**
Hutchinson Health

**Jackson**
Sanford Jackson Medical Center

**Lake City**
Mayo Clinic Health System in Lake City

**Le Sueur**
Minnesota Valley Health Center

**Long Prairie**
CentraCare Health–Long Prairie

**Luverne**
Sanford Luverne Medical Center

**Madelia**
Madelia Community Hospital

**Mahnomen**
Mahnomen Health Center

**Mankato**
Partner
Mayo Clinic Health System in Mankato

**Maple Grove**
Maple Grove Hospital

**Melrose**
CentraCare Health–Melrose

**Minneapolis**
Abbott Northwestern Hospital
Member
Hennepin County Medical Center
Shareholder
Allina Health

**Monticello**
Member
CentraCare Health–Monticello

**New Prague**
Member
Mayo Clinic Health System in New Prague

**New Ulm**
New Ulm Medical Center

**Ortonville**
Ortonville Area Health Services

**Owatonna**
Owatonna Hospital

**Paynesville**
CentraCare Health–Paynesville

**Perham**
Perham Health

**Red Wing**
Member
Mayo Clinic Health System in Red Wing

**Redwood Falls**
Redwood Area Hospital

**Robbinsdale**
North Memorial Medical Center

**Rochester**
Mayo Clinic
Member
Mayo Clinic Hospital – Rochester

**Saint Cloud**
CentraCare Health
Partner
St. Cloud Hospital

**Saint James**
Mayo Clinic Health System in Saint James

**Saint Paul**
United Hospital
Shareholder
HealthEast Care System

**Saint Peter**
River's Edge Hospital and Clinic

**Sandstone**
Essentia Health Sandstone

**Sauk Centre**
Member
CentraCare Health–Sauk Centre

**Shakopee**
St. Francis Regional Medical Center

**Slayton**
Murray County Medical Center

**Springfield**
Mayo Clinic Health System in Springfield

**Thief River Falls**
Sanford Thief River Falls Medical Center

**Tracy**
Sanford Tracy Medical Center

**Two Harbors**
Member
Lake View Memorial Hospital

**Virginia**
Member
Essentia Health–Virginia

**Waconia**
Partner
Ridgeview Medical Center

**Warren**
North Valley Health Center

**Waseca**
Mayo Clinic Health System in Waseca

**Westbrook**
Sanford Westbrook Medical Center

**Wheaton**
Member
Sanford Wheaton Medical Center

**Willmar**
Partner
Rice Memorial Hospital

**Windom**
Windom Area Hospital

**Worthington**
Sanford Worthington Medical Center

## MISSISSIPPI

**Booneville**
Baptist Memorial Hospital–Booneville

**Columbia**
Member
Marion General Hospital

**Columbus**
Baptist Memorial Hospital–Golden Triangle

**Corinth**
Magnolia Regional Health Center

**Greenville**
Delta Regional Medical Center

**Greenwood**
Partner
Greenwood Leflore Hospital

**Gulfport**
Partner
Memorial Hospital at Gulfport

**Hattiesburg**
Partner
Forrest General Hospital

**Indianola**
Member
South Sunflower County Hospital

**Jackson**
Partner
St. Dominic–Jackson Memorial Hospital

**Leakesville**
Member
Greene County Hospital

**Lucedale**
Member
George Regional Hospital

**McComb**
Partner
Southwest Mississippi Regional Medical Center

**Meridian**
Member
Anderson Regional Medical Center–South Campus
Partner
Anderson Regional Medical Center

**Monticello**
Lawrence County Hospital

**New Albany**
Baptist Memorial Hospital–Union County

**Oxford**
Baptist Memorial Hospital–North Mississippi

**Pascagoula**
Singing River Health System

**Philadelphia**
Member
Neshoba County General Hospital

**Picayune**
Highland Community Hospital

**Prentiss**
Lease
Jefferson Davis Community Hospital

**Southaven**
Baptist Memorial Hospital–Desoto

**Starkville**
OCH Regional Medical Center

**Tupelo**
North Mississippi Health Services, Inc.

**Tylertown**
Walthall County General Hospital

## MISSOURI

**Bolivar**
Partner
Citizens Memorial Hospital

**Bonne Terre**
Parkland Health Center–Bonne Terre

**Branson**
Partner
Cox Medical Center Branson

**Brookfield**
General John J. Pershing Memorial Hospital

**Cameron**
Partner
Cameron Regional Medical Center

**Cape Girardeau**
Partner
Saint Francis Medical Center

**Chillicothe**
Hedrick Medical Center

**Clinton**
Golden Valley Memorial Healthcare

**Columbia**
Boone Hospital Center

**Farmington**
Parkland Health Center – Liberty Street
Member
Parkland Health Center – Weber Road

**Joplin**
    Freeman Health System
    Freeman Hospital East
  Lease
    Freeman Hospital West

**Kansas City**
    Crittenton Children's Center
    Saint Luke's North Hospital – Barry Road
  Member
    Truman Medical Center–Hospital Hill
    Truman Medical Center–Lakewood
  Shareholder
    Saint Luke's Health System
    Saint Luke's Hospital of Kansas City

**Lamar**
    Barton County Memorial Hospital

**Lee's Summit**
    Saint Luke's East Hospital

**Liberty**
  Partner
    Liberty Hospital

**Macon**
    Samaritan Memorial Hospital

**Marshall**
    Fitzgibbon Hospital

**Monett**
    Cox Monett

**Neosho**
    Freeman Neosho Hospital

**O'Fallon**
  Member
    Progress West Hospital

**Poplar Bluff**
  Member
    Black River Medical Center

**Potosi**
    Washington County Memorial Hospital

**Saint Louis**
    Barnes–Jewish Hospital
    Barnes–Jewish West County Hospital
    Christian Hospital
    Missouri Baptist Medical Center
    St. Louis Children's Hospital
  Shareholder
    BJC HealthCare

**Saint Peters**
    Barnes–Jewish St. Peters Hospital

**Salem**
    Salem Memorial District Hospital

**Sikeston**
    Missouri Delta Medical Center

**Springfield**
    Cox Medical Center North
    CoxHealth
  Shareholder
    Cox Medical Centers

**Ste Genevieve**
    Ste. Genevieve County Memorial Hospital

**Sullivan**
    Missouri Baptist Sullivan Hospital

**Trenton**
    Wright Memorial Hospital

**Warrensburg**
    Western Missouri Medical Center

## MONTANA

**Anaconda**
    Community Hospital of Anaconda

**Bozeman**
  Partner
    Bozeman Deaconess Hospital

**Columbus**
  Unit_of
    Stillwater Community Hospital

**Conrad**
  Member
    Pondera Medical Center

**Deer Lodge**
  Member
    Deer Lodge Medical Center

**Ennis**
  Member
    Madison Valley Medical Center

**Hamilton**
  Partner
    Marcus Daly Memorial Hospital

**Helena**
  Partner
    St. Peter's Hospital

**Kalispell**
    The HealthCenter
  Member
    Kalispell Regional Medical Center

**Libby**
  Member
    Cabinet Peaks Medical Center

**Missoula**
    St. Patrick Hospital

**Philipsburg**
  Member
    Granite County Medical Center

**Plains**
    Clark Fork Valley Hospital

**Polson**
    Providence St. Joseph Medical Center

**Ronan**
  Partner
    St. Luke Community Healthcare

**Sidney**
  Partner
    Sidney Health Center

**Townsend**
  Member
    Broadwater Health Center

**White Sulphur Springs**
  Member
    Mountainview Medical Center

## NEBRASKA

**Alliance**
    Box Butte General Hospital

**Alma**
    Harlan County Health System

**Atkinson**
    West Holt Memorial Hospital

**Beatrice**
  Partner
    Beatrice Community Hospital and Health Center

**Bellevue**
  Member
    Madonna Rehabilitation Specialty Hospital

**Bridgeport**
    Morrill County Community Hospital

**Broken Bow**
    Jennie M. Melham Memorial Medical Center

**Columbus**
  Partner
    Columbus Community Hospital

**Crete**
    Crete Area Medical Center

**Falls City**
    Community Medical Center

**Franklin**
    Franklin County Memorial Hospital

**Gordon**
    Gordon Memorial Hospital

**Hastings**
  Partner
    Mary Lanning Healthcare

**Lexington**
  Partner
    Lexington Regional Health Center

**Lincoln**
    Bryan Health
    Bryan Medical Center
  Partner
    Madonna Rehabilitation Hospital

**Lynch**
    Niobrara Valley Hospital

**Minden**
    Kearney County Health Services

**Neligh**
    Antelope Memorial Hospital

**Norfolk**
  Partner
    Faith Regional Health Services

**Omaha**
    Nebraska Methodist Health System, Inc.
  Shareholder
    Nebraska Methodist Hospital

**Ord**
    Valley County Health System

**Oshkosh**
    Regional West Garden County

**Osmond**
    Osmond General Hospital

**Scottsbluff**
  Partner
    Regional West Medical Center

**York**
  Partner
    York General Hospital

## NEW HAMPSHIRE

**Claremont**
    Valley Regional Hospital

**Colebrook**
    Upper Connecticut Valley Hospital

**Dover**
  Partner
    Wentworth–Douglass Hospital

**Keene**
  Partner
    Cheshire Medical Center

**Lancaster**
    Weeks Medical Center

**Lebanon**
    Alice Peck Day Memorial Hospital
    Dartmouth–Hitchcock Medical Center

**Nashua**
  Partner
    Southern New Hampshire Medical Center

**New London**
    New London Hospital

**North Conway**
  Member
    Memorial Hospital

**Peterborough**
    Monadnock Community Hospital

**Plymouth**
  Member
    Speare Memorial Hospital

**Woodsville**
    Cottage Hospital

## NEW JERSEY

**Atlantic City**
    AtlantiCare Regional Medical Center

**Cape May Court House**
  Member
    Cape Regional Medical Center

**Edison**
    JFK Health System
    JFK Medical Center

**Egg Harbor Township**
    AtlantiCare

**Elmer**
    Inspira Medical Center–Elmer

**Flemington**
  Partner
    Hunterdon Medical Center

**Marlton**
  Member
    Virtua Marlton

**Mount Holly**
  Member
    Virtua Memorial

**Mullica Hill**
    Inspira Health Network

**Pomona**
    Bacharach Institute for Rehabilitation

**Ridgewood**
    Valley Hospital

Section B

**Somers Point**
Partner
Shore Medical Center

**Trenton**
Capital Health

**Vineland**
Inspira Medical Center–Vineland

**Voorhees**
Member
Virtua Voorhees

**Woodbury**
Partner
Inspira Medical Center–Woodbury

**NEW MEXICO**

**Farmington**
Partner
San Juan Regional Medical Center

**Gallup**
Partner
Rehoboth McKinley Christian Health Care Services

**NEW YORK**

**Binghamton**
Shareholder
United Health Services Hospitals–Binghamton

**Bronxville**
New York–Presbyterian/Lawrence Hospital

**Brooklyn**
New York Community Hospital
New York Methodist Hospital
Member
Brooklyn Hospital Center

**Buffalo**
Erie County Medical Center
Roswell Park Cancer Institute

**Corning**
Corning Hospital

**Flushing**
New York–Presbyterian/Queens

**Geneva**
Finger Lakes Health

**Hamilton**
Community Memorial Hospital

**Ithaca**
Partner
Cayuga Medical Center at Ithaca

**Jamestown**
Woman's Christian Association Hospital

**Mineola**
Winthrop–University Hospital

**Montour Falls**
Member
Schuyler Hospital

**New York**
New York–Presbyterian Hospital
Member
Gracie Square Hospital
Rockefeller University Hospital
Shareholder
New York–Presbyterian/Columbia University Medical
Center

**Norwich**
Chenango Memorial Hospital

**Nyack**
Nyack Hospital

**Ogdensburg**
Claxton–Hepburn Medical Center

**Rochester**
Unity Hospital
University of Rochester Medical Center

**Sleepy Hollow**
Phelps Memorial Hospital Center

**Syracuse**
Partner
Crouse Hospital

**Walton**
Delaware Valley Hospital

**NORTH CAROLINA**

**Ahoskie**
Vidant Roanoke–Chowan Hospital

**Bolivia**
Novant Health Brunswick Medical Center

**Cary**
WakeMed Cary Hospital

**Charlotte**
Novant Health Charlotte Orthopaedic Hospital
Novant Health Presbyterian Medical Center
Shareholder
Carolinas Healthcare System

**Clinton**
Sampson Regional Medical Center

**Dunn**
Harnett Health System

**Eden**
Member
Morehead Memorial Hospital

**Edenton**
Vidant Chowan Hospital

**Elizabeth City**
Member
Sentara Albemarle Medical Center

**Elkin**
Member
Hugh Chatham Memorial Hospital

**Greenville**
Shareholder
Vidant Medical Center

**Huntersville**
Novant Health Huntersville Medical Center

**Jefferson**
Member
Ashe Memorial Hospital

**Kenansville**
Vidant Duplin Hospital

**Lexington**
Wake Forest Baptist Health–Lexington Medical Center

**Lincolnton**
Carolinas HealthCare System Lincoln

**Louisburg**
Novant Health Franklin Medical Center

**Matthews**
Novant Health Matthews Medical Center

**Nags Head**
The Outer Banks Hospital

**New Bern**
Member
CarolinaEast Health System

**Raleigh**
WakeMed Health & Hospitals
Partner
WakeMed Raleigh Campus

**Roanoke Rapids**
Member
Halifax Regional Medical Center

**Rocky Mount**
Partner
Nash Health Care Systems

**Salisbury**
Partner
Novant Health Rowan Medical Center

**Tarboro**
Vidant Edgecombe Hospital

**Thomasville**
Partner
Novant Health Thomasville Medical Center

**Washington**
Member
Vidant Beaufort Hospital

**Wilson**
Member
Wilson Medical Center

**Windsor**
Vidant Bertie Hospital

**Winston Salem**
Novant Health

**Winston–Salem**
Novant Health Forsyth Medical Center
Novant Health Medical Park Hospital

**NORTH DAKOTA**

**Bismarck**
Partner
Sanford Bismarck

**Fargo**
Sanford Medical Center Fargo

**Grafton**
Unity Medical Center

**Grand Forks**
Partner
Altru Health System

**Hillsboro**
Sanford Hillsboro Medical Center

**Jamestown**
Partner
Jamestown Regional Medical Center

**Kenmare**
Kenmare Community Hospital

**Mayville**
Sanford Mayville Medical Center

**Mcville**
Nelson County Health System

**Minot**
Trinity Health

**Northwood**
Member
Northwood Deaconess Health Center

**OHIO**

**Akron**
Akron General Health System
Shareholder
Akron General Medical Center

**Alliance**
Member
Alliance Community Hospital

**Ashland**
Samaritan Regional Health System

**Ashtabula**
Member
Ashtabula County Medical Center

**Athens**
O'Bleness Memorial Hospital

**Bellaire**
Belmont Community Hospital

**Bluffton**
Member
Bluffton Hospital

**Cambridge**
Partner
Southeastern Ohio Regional Medical Center

**Canton**
Member
Aultman Hospital

**Cincinnati**
UC Health
Shareholder
Christ Hospital

**Circleville**
Member
Berger Health System

**Cleveland**
Member
Cleveland Clinic
Fairview Hospital
Hillcrest Hospital
Lutheran Hospital

**Columbus**
OhioHealth Doctors Hospital
OhioHealth Grant Medical Center
OhioHealth Riverside Methodist Hospital
Member
OhioHealth

**Concord Township**
Partner
Lake Health

**Coshocton**
Member
Coshocton County Memorial Hospital

**Cuyahoga Falls**
Edwin Shaw Rehab

**Dayton**
Miami Valley Hospital
Partner
Good Samaritan Hospital

**Delaware**
OhioHealth Grady Memorial Hospital

**Dover**
Partner
Union Hospital

**Dublin**
OhioHealth Dublin Methodist Hospital

**Euclid**
Member
Euclid Hospital

**Findlay**
Blanchard Valley Hospital

**Garfield Heights**
Member
Marymount Hospital

**Kenton**
OhioHealth Hardin Memorial Hospital

**Lakewood**
Member
Lakewood Hospital

**Lima**
Partner
Lima Memorial Health System

**Lodi**
Lodi Community Hospital

**Mansfield**
OhioHealth MedCentral Mansfield Hospital

**Marion**
OhioHealth Marion General Hospital

**Maumee**
Partner
ProMedica St. Luke's Hospital

**Medina**
Member
Medina Hospital

**Middletown**
Partner
Atrium Medical Center

**Millersburg**
Member
Pomerene Hospital

**Mount Gilead**
Morrow County Hospital

**Newark**
Partner
Licking Memorial Hospital

**Norwalk**
Fisher–Titus Medical Center

**Orrville**
Member
Aultman Orrville Hospital

**Oxford**
McCullough–Hyde Memorial Hospital/TriHealth

**Paulding**
Member
Paulding County Hospital

**Portsmouth**
Southern Ohio Medical Center

**Rock Creek**
Member
Glenbeigh Hospital and Outpatient Centers

**Shelby**
OhioHealth MedCentral Shelby Hospital

**Steubenville**
Partner
Trinity Health System

**Toledo**
ProMedica Health System

**Troy**
Partner
Upper Valley Medical Center

**Van Wert**
Member
Van Wert County Hospital

**Warrensville Heights**
Member
South Pointe Hospital

**Zanesville**
Partner
Genesis HealthCare System

## OKLAHOMA

**Altus**
Partner
Jackson County Memorial Hospital

**Antlers**
Member
Pushmataha Hospital & Home Health

**Atoka**
Member
Atoka County Medical Center

**Bethany**
Member
The Children's Center Rehabilitation Hospital

**Carnegie**
Carnegie Tri–County Municipal Hospital

**Chickasha**
Partner
Grady Memorial Hospital

**Duncan**
Partner
Duncan Regional Hospital

**Edmond**
Member
INTEGRIS Health Edmond

**Elk City**
Great Plains Regional Medical Center

**Enid**
Integris Bass Baptist Health Center
Integris Bass Pavilion

**Frederick**
Memorial Hospital and Physician Group

**Grove**
Integris Grove Hospital

**Hobart**
Elkview General Hospital

**Hugo**
Member
Choctaw Memorial Hospital

**Lawton**
Partner
Comanche County Memorial Hospital

**McAlester**
Partner
McAlester Regional Health Center

**Miami**
Integris Baptist Regional Health Center

**Norman**
Norman Regional Health System
Member
Norman Specialty Hospital

**Oklahoma City**
Integris Baptist Medical Center
INTEGRIS Health
Member
Lakeside Women's Hospital

**Stillwater**
Partner
Stillwater Medical Center

**Tahlequah**
Northeastern Health System

**Waurika**
Jefferson County Hospital

**Yukon**
INTEGRIS Canadian Valley Hospital

## OREGON

**Forest Grove**
Member
Tuality Forest Grove Hospital

**Hillsboro**
Partner
Tuality Healthcare

**Hood River**
Providence Hood River Memorial Hospital

**Medford**
Providence Medford Medical Center

**Milwaukie**
Providence Milwaukie Hospital

**Newberg**
Providence Newberg Medical Center

**Oregon City**
Providence Willamette Falls Medical Center

**Portland**
Providence Portland Medical Center
Providence St. Vincent Medical Center

**Seaside**
Providence Seaside Hospital

**Silverton**
Silverton Hospital

## PENNSYLVANIA

**Abington**
Partner
Abington Memorial Hospital

**Allentown**
Shareholder
Lehigh Valley Hospital

**Bethlehem**
Lehigh Valley Hospital–Muhlenberg

**Brookville**
Penn Highlands Brookville

**Bryn Mawr**
Member
Bryn Mawr Hospital

**Butler**
Partner
Butler Health System

**Chambersburg**
Chambersburg Hospital
Summit Health

**Clearfield**
Penn Highlands Clearfield

**Drexel Hill**
Delaware County Memorial Hospital

**DuBois**
Penn Highlands DuBois

**East Stroudsburg**
Pocono Medical Center

**Ephrata**
Partner
Ephrata Community Hospital

**Gettysburg**
Gettysburg Hospital

**Greensburg**
Member
Excela Health Westmoreland Hospital

**Hanover**
Hanover Hospital

**Harrisburg**
Community Hospital
Pinnacle Health System

**Hazleton**
Member
Lehigh Valley Hospital – Hazleton

**Huntingdon**
Member
J. C. Blair Memorial Hospital

**Indiana**
Indiana Regional Medical Center

**Jefferson Hills**
Jefferson Hospital

**Lancaster**
Partner
Lancaster General Health

**Lansdale**
Member
Abington Health Lansdale Hospital

**Latrobe**
Member
Excela Latrobe Area Hospital

**Lebanon**
The Good Samaritan Hospital

**Lehighton**
Blue Mountain Health System
Gnaden Huetten Memorial Hospital

**Malvern**
Member
Bryn Mawr Rehabilitation Hospital

**Meadowbrook**
Holy Redeemer Hospital

**Media**
Member
Riddle Hospital

**Monongahela**
Monongahela Valley Hospital

**Mount Pleasant**
Member
Excela Frick Hospital

**Muncy**
Member
Muncy Valley Hospital

**New Castle**
Jameson Hospital

**Palmerton**
Palmerton Hospital

**Paoli**
Member
Paoli Hospital

**Philadelphia**
Hospital of the University of Pennsylvania
Penn Presbyterian Medical Center
University of Pennsylvania Health System
Shareholder
Pennsylvania Hospital

**Pittsburgh**
Partner
St. Clair Hospital

**Pottsville**
Member
Schuylkill Medical Center – East Norwegian Street
Schuylkill Medical Center – South Jackson Street

**Saint Marys**
Penn Highlands Elk

**Sayre**
Robert Packer Hospital
Shareholder
Guthrie Clinic

**Sellersville**
Partner
Grand View Health

**Springfield**
Crozer–Keystone Health System

**Towanda**
Member
Guthrie Towanda Memorial Hospital

**Troy**
Troy Community Hospital

**Uniontown**
Partner
Uniontown Hospital

**Upland**
Crozer–Chester Medical Center

**Waynesboro**
Waynesboro Hospital

**Wellsboro**
Soldiers and Sailors Memorial Hospital

**West Chester**
Partner
Penn Medicine Chester County Hospital

**West Reading**
Reading Hospital

**Williamsport**
Divine Providence Hospital
Lease
Williamsport Regional Medical Center
Partner
Susquehanna Health System

**Windber**
Windber Medical Center

**Wynnewood**
Member
Lankenau Medical Center

**York**
Partner
WellSpan Health
Shareholder
York Hospital

**RHODE ISLAND**

**Newport**
Newport Hospital

**Pawtucket**
Memorial Hospital of Rhode Island

**Providence**
Butler Hospital
Care New England Health System
Miriam Hospital
Women & Infants Hospital of Rhode Island
Shareholder
Lifespan Corporation
Rhode Island Hospital

**Warwick**
Kent County Memorial Hospital

**Westerly**
Westerly Hospital

**SOUTH DAKOTA**

**Aberdeen**
Member
Sanford Aberdeen Medical Center

**Armour**
Douglas County Memorial Hospital

**Burke**
Community Memorial Hospital

**Canton**
Member
Sanford Canton–Inwood Medical Center

**Chamberlain**
Sanford Chamberlain Medical Center

**Clear Lake**
Sanford Clear Lake Medical Center

**Sioux Falls**
Sanford Health
Shareholder
Sanford USD Medical Center

**Vermillion**
Sanford Vermillion Medical Center

**Viborg**
Pioneer Memorial Hospital and Health Services

**Watertown**
Prairie Lakes Healthcare System

**Webster**
Sanford Webster Medical Center

**Winner**
Winner Regional Healthcare Center

**TENNESSEE**

**Chattanooga**
Erlanger Health System
Erlanger North Hospital

**Collierville**
Baptist Memorial Hospital–Collierville

**Columbia**
Partner
Maury Regional Hospital

**Covington**
Baptist Memorial Hospital–Tipton

**Franklin**
Williamson Medical Center

**Germantown**
Member
Baptist Memorial Rehabilitation Hospital

**Harriman**
Roane Medical Center

**Huntingdon**
Baptist Memorial Hospital–Huntingdon

**Knoxville**
Covenant Health
Fort Sanders Regional Medical Center
Parkwest Medical Center

**Lenoir City**
Fort Loudoun Medical Center

**Lewisburg**
Marshall Medical Center

**Louisville**
Peninsula Hospital

**Memphis**
Baptist Memorial Health Care Corporation
Baptist Memorial Hospital for Women

Baptist Memorial Hospital – Memphis

**Morristown**
Member
Morristown–Hamblen Healthcare System

**Oak Ridge**
Partner
Methodist Medical Center of Oak Ridge

**Sevierville**
LeConte Medical Center

**Tazewell**
Member
Claiborne Medical Center

**Trenton**
Trenton Medical Center

**Union City**
Baptist Memorial Hospital–Union City

**Waynesboro**
Wayne Medical Center

**TEXAS**

**Andrews**
Permian Regional Medical Center

**Bellville**
Bellville St. Joseph Health Center

**Dallas**
Methodist Health System
Shareholder
Baylor Scott & White Health

**Houston**
Memorial Hermann – Texas Medical Center
Memorial Hermann Healthcare System
Memorial Hermann Northwest Hospital

**Humble**
Memorial Hermann Northeast

**Katy**
Memorial Hermann Katy Hospital

**Lubbock**
Covenant Medical Center–Lakeside
Shareholder
Covenant Health System

**Midland**
Midland Memorial Hospital

**Pearsall**
Frio Regional Hospital

**Plano**
Community Hospital Corporation

**Sherman**
Partner
Wilson N. Jones Regional Medical Center

**Sugar Land**
Memorial Hermann Sugar Land Hospital

**Sulphur Springs**
Hopkins County Memorial Hospital

**Sweeny**
Sweeny Community Hospital

**Wichita Falls**
Partner
United Regional Health Care System–Eighth Street
Campus

**VERMONT**

**Bennington**
Southwestern Vermont Medical Center

**Berlin**
Partner
The University of Vermont Health Network Central
Vermont Medical Center

**Brattleboro**
Member
Brattleboro Memorial Hospital

**Burlington**
Member
The University of Vermont Health Network University
of Vermont Medical Center

**Morrisville**
Copley Hospital

**Newport**
North Country Hospital and Health Center

**Rutland**
Partner
Rutland Regional Medical Center

**Saint Johnsbury**
Northeastern Vermont Regional Hospital

**Springfield**
Member
Springfield Hospital

**Townshend**
Member
  Grace Cottage Hospital

**Windsor**
  Mt. Ascutney Hospital and Health Center

**VIRGIN ISLANDS**

**Saint Thomas**
  Schneider Regional Medical Center

**VIRGINIA**

**Bedford**
Member
  Bedford Memorial Hospital

**Charlottesville**
Partner
  Martha Jefferson Hospital

**Farmville**
  Centra Southside Community Hospital

**Fishersville**
Member
  Augusta Health

**Fredericksburg**
  Mary Washington Hospital
Member
  Snowden at Fredericksburg

**Hampton**
  Sentara CarePlex Hospital

**Harrisonburg**
Partner
  Sentara RMH Medical Center

**Haymarket**
Member
  Novant Health Haymarket Medical Center

**Lynchburg**
  Centra Lynchburg General Hospital

**Manassas**
  Novant Health Prince William Medical Center

**Norfolk**
  Hospital for Extended Recovery
  Sentara Leigh Hospital
  Sentara Norfolk General Hospital
Shareholder
  Sentara Healthcare

**South Boston**
Member
  Sentara Halifax Regional Hospital

**Stafford**
Member
  Stafford Hospital

**Suffolk**
  Sentara Obici Hospital

**Virginia Beach**
  Sentara Princess Anne Hospital
  Sentara Virginia Beach General Hospital

**Williamsburg**
  Sentara Williamsburg Regional Medical Center

**Woodbridge**
  Sentara Northern Virginia Medical Center

**WASHINGTON**

**Aberdeen**
  Grays Harbor Community Hospital

**Auburn**
Member
  MultiCare Auburn Medical Center

**Centralia**
  Providence Centralia Hospital

**Chewelah**
  Providence St. Joseph's Hospital

**Colfax**
  Whitman Hospital and Medical Center

**Colville**
  Providence Mount Carmel Hospital

**Dayton**
Member
  Columbia County Health System

**Edmonds**
Member
  Swedish/Edmonds

**Everett**
  Providence Regional Medical Center Everett

**Issaquah**
Member
  Swedish/Issaquah

**Morton**
  Morton General Hospital

**Olympia**
  Providence St. Peter Hospital

**Pomeroy**
Member
  Garfield County Public Hospital District

**Port Angeles**
Member
  Olympic Medical Center

**Puyallup**
  MultiCare Good Samaritan Hospital

**Renton**
  Providence Health & Services

**Richland**
Member
  Kadlec Regional Medical Center

**Seattle**
  Swedish Medical Center–Cherry Hill Campus
Member
  Swedish Medical Center–First Hill

**Spokane**
  Providence Holy Family Hospital
Member
  Providence Sacred Heart Medical Center & Children's
    Hospital
  St. Luke's Rehabilitation Institute

**Tacoma**
  MultiCare Tacoma General Hospital
Shareholder
  MultiCare Health System

**Walla Walla**
  Providence St. Mary Medical Center

**Yakima**
Partner
  Yakima Valley Memorial Hospital

**WEST VIRGINIA**

**Charleston**
  CAMC Women and Children's Hospital
  Charleston Area Medical Center

**Gassaway**
  Braxton County Memorial Hospital

**Madison**
  Boone Memorial Hospital

**Montgomery**
  Montgomery General Hospital

**Princeton**
Partner
  Princeton Community Hospital

**Ripley**
  Jackson General Hospital

**Spencer**
  Roane General Hospital

**Wheeling**
Partner
  Wheeling Hospital

**WISCONSIN**

**Antigo**
  Langlade Hospital

**Appleton**
  Appleton Medical Center
Shareholder
  ThedaCare, Inc.

**Barron**
  Mayo Clinic Health System – Northland in Barron

**Beaver Dam**
Partner
  Beaver Dam Community Hospitals

**Beloit**
Partner
  Beloit Health System

**Berlin**
Member
  Berlin Memorial Hospital

**Bloomer**
  Mayo Clinic Health System – Chippewa Valley in
    Bloomer

**Boscobel**
Member
  Gundersen Boscobel Area Hospital and Clinics

**Eau Claire**
Partner
  Mayo Clinic Health System in Eau Claire

**Fond Du Lac**
Member
  Agnesian HealthCare

**Green Bay**
Member
  Bellin Psychiatric Center
Partner
  Bellin Memorial Hospital

**Hillsboro**
Member
  Gundersen St. Joseph's Hospital and Clinics

**La Crosse**
  Mayo Clinic Health System – Franciscan Healthcare in
    La Crosse
Member
  Gundersen Health System

**Madison**
Shareholder
  Meriter UnityPoint Health

**Marinette**
  Bay Area Medical Center

**Medford**
  Aspirus Medford Hospital

**Menomonee Falls**
Partner
  Community Memorial Hospital

**Menomonie**
  Mayo Clinic Health System – Red Cedar in Menomonie

**Milwaukee**
Partner
  Froedtert Memorial Lutheran Hospital

**Neenah**
  Theda Clark Medical Center

**Neillsville**
  Memorial Medical Center – Neillsville

**New London**
  New London Family Medical Center

**Oconomowoc**
  Oconomowoc Memorial Hospital

**Oconto**
  Bellin Health Oconto Hospital

**Osseo**
  Mayo Clinic Health System – Oakridge in Osseo

**Ripon**
Member
  Ripon Medical Center

**River Falls**
  River Falls Area Hospital

**Shawano**
Member
  Shawano Medical Center

**Sparta**
  Mayo Clinic Health System – Franciscan Healthcare in
    Sparta

**Superior**
  Essentia Health St. Mary's Hospital of Superior

**Watertown**
Partner
  Watertown Regional Medical Center

**Waukesha**
  ProHealth Care, Inc.
  Waukesha Memorial Hospital

**Waupaca**
  Riverside Medical Center

**Waupun**
Member
  Waupun Memorial Hospital

**Wausau**
  Aspirus Wausau Hospital
Member
  North Central Health Care

**West Bend**
Partner
  St. Joseph's Hospital

**Section B**

**Whitehall**
Gundersen Tri–County Hospital and Clinics
**Wild Rose**
Member
Wild Rose Community Memorial Hospital
**Wisconsin Rapids**
Aspirus Riverview Hospital and Clinics, Inc.

**WYOMING**
**Buffalo**
Johnson County Healthcare Center
**Casper**
Partner
Wyoming Medical Center
**Cheyenne**
Partner
Cheyenne Regional Medical Center
**Douglas**
Memorial Hospital of Converse County
**Gillette**
Campbell County Memorial Hospital
**Jackson**
St. John's Medical Center and Living Center
**Lusk**
Niobrara Health and Life Center
**Sheridan**
Sheridan Memorial Hospital

**YANKEE ALLIANCE**
138 River Road, Andover, MA
Zip 01810–1083; tel. 978/470–2000;
James W. Oliver, President and Chief
Executive Officer

**CALIFORNIA**
**Long Beach**
Member
College Medical Center
**Oceanside**
Member
Tri–City Medical Center

**CONNECTICUT**
**Derby**
Member
Griffin Hospital
**Hartford**
Member
Saint Francis Hospital and Medical Center
**New London**
Member
Lawrence + Memorial Hospital
**Stafford Springs**
Member
Johnson Memorial Medical Center

**FLORIDA**
**Boca Raton**
Member
Promise Healthcare
**Coral Gables**
Member
Baptist Health South Florida, Doctors Hospital
**Homestead**
Member
Baptist Health South Florida, Homestead Hospital
**Miami**
Member
Baptist Health South Florida, Baptist Hospital of Miami
Baptist Health South Florida, South Miami Hospital
Baptist Health South Florida, West Kendall Baptist
  Hospital
**Miami Beach**
Member
Mount Sinai Medical Center
**Miramar**
Member
Memorial Hospital Miramar
**Pembroke Pines**
Member
Memorial Hospital Pembroke
Memorial Hospital West

**South Miami**
Member
Larkin Community Hospital
**Tavernier**
Member
Baptist Health South Florida, Mariners Hospital

**ILLINOIS**
**Geneva**
Member
Delnor Hospital
**Winfield**
Member
Central DuPage Hospital

**INDIANA**
**Gary**
Member
Methodist Hospitals
**Mishawaka**
Member
Unity Medical & Surgical Hospital

**KENTUCKY**
**Ashland**
Member
King's Daughters Medical Center
**Benton**
Member
Marshall County Hospital
**Corbin**
Member
Baptist Health Corbin
**Elizabethtown**
Member
Hardin Memorial Hospital
**La Grange**
Member
Baptist Health La Grange
**Lexington**
Member
Baptist Health Lexington
**Louisville**
Member
Baptist Health Louisville
**Madisonville**
Member
Baptist Health Madisonville
**Paducah**
Member
Baptist Health Paducah
**Prestonsburg**
Member
Highlands Regional Medical Center
**Richmond**
Member
Baptist Health Richmond

**MAINE**
**Bangor**
Member
St. Joseph Hospital
**Lewiston**
Member
St. Mary's Regional Medical Center

**MASSACHUSETTS**
**Attleboro**
Member
Sturdy Memorial Hospital
**Boston**
Member
Boston Medical Center
New England Baptist Hospital
Tufts Medical Center
**Brockton**
Member
Signature Healthcare Brockton Hospital
**Burlington**
Member
Lahey Hospital & Medical Center, Burlington
**Fall River**
Member
Southcoast Hospitals Group

**Great Barrington**
Member
Fairview Hospital
**Lowell**
Member
Lowell General Hospital
**Milford**
Member
Milford Regional Medical Center
**Newburyport**
Member
Anna Jaques Hospital
**Oak Bluffs**
Member
Martha's Vineyard Hospital
**Pittsfield**
Member
Berkshire Medical Center
**Westfield**
Member
Baystate Noble Hospital
**Winchester**
Member
Winchester Hospital

**NEW HAMPSHIRE**
**Concord**
Member
Concord Hospital
**Exeter**
Member
Exeter Hospital
**Franklin**
Member
Franklin Regional Hospital
**Laconia**
Member
Lakes Region General Hospital
**Manchester**
Member
Catholic Medical Center
Elliot Hospital
**Nashua**
Member
St. Joseph Hospital
**North Conway**
Member
Memorial Hospital
**Rochester**
Member
Frisbie Memorial Hospital
**Salem**
Member
Northeast Rehabilitation Hospital

**NEW YORK**
**Batavia**
Member
United Memorial Medical Center
**Bath**
Member
Ira Davenport Memorial Hospital
**Elizabethtown**
Member
The University of Vermont Health Network
  Elizabethtown Community Hospital
**Elmira**
Member
Arnot Ogden Medical Center
St. Joseph's Hospital
**Glens Falls**
Member
Glens Falls Hospital
**Gloversville**
Member
Nathan Littauer Hospital and Nursing Home
**Plattsburgh**
Member
The University of Vermont Health Network–Champlain
  Valley Physicians Hospital

**Warsaw**
Member
  Wyoming County Community Hospital

## OHIO
**Logan**
Member
  Hocking Valley Community Hospital

**Montpelier**
Member
  Community Hospitals and Wellness
    Centers–Montpelier

**Salem**
Member
  Salem Regional Medical Center

**Seaman**
Member
  Adams County Regional Medical Center

**Sidney**
Member
  Wilson Memorial Hospital

**Steubenville**
Member
  Life Line Hospital

## OKLAHOMA
**Hugo**
Member
  Lane Frost Health and Rehabilitation Center

## PENNSYLVANIA
**Honesdale**
Member
  Wayne Memorial Hospital

**Langhorne**
Member
  Barix Clinics of Pennsylvania

**Washington**
Member
  Advanced Surgical Hospital

## RHODE ISLAND
**Pawtucket**
Member
  Memorial Hospital of Rhode Island

**Providence**
Member
  Roger Williams Medical Center

**Wakefield**
Member
  South County Hospital

**Westerly**
Member
  Westerly Hospital

## SOUTH CAROLINA
**Columbia**
Member
  Providence Hospital

**Fairfax**
Member
  Allendale County Hospital

## TEXAS
**Aransas Pass**
Member
  Care Regional Medical Center

**Austin**
Member
  Arise Austin Medical Center

**Houston**
Member
  Healthbridge Children's Hospital of Houston

**New Braunfels**
Member
  Post Acute/Warm Springs Specialty Hospital of New
    Braunfels

**Plainview**
Member
  Covenant Hospital Plainview

## WEST VIRGINIA
**New Martinsville**
Member
  Wetzel County Hospital

**Section B**

# Abbreviations Used in the AHA Guide

**AB,** Army Base
**ACSW,** Academy of Certified Social Workers
**AEC,** Atomic Energy Commission
**AFB,** Air Force Base
**AHA,** American Hospital Association
**AK,** Alaska
**AL,** Alabama
**AODA,** Alcohol and Other Drug Abuse
**APO,** Army Post Office
**AR,** Arkansas
**A.R.T.,** Accredited Record Technician
**A.S.C.,** Ambulatory Surgical Center
**A.T.C.,** Alcoholism Treatment Center
**Ave.,** Avenue
**AZ,** Arizona

**B.A.,** Bachelor of Arts
**B.B.A.,** Bachelor of Business Administration
**B.C.,** British Columbia
**Blvd.,** Boulevard
**B.S.,** Bachelor of Science
**B.S.Ed.,** Bachelor of Science in Education
**B.S.H.S.,** Bachelor of Science in Health Studies
**B.S.N.,** Bachelor of Science in Nursing
**B.S.W.,** Bachelor of Science and Social Worker
**CA,** California; Controller of Accounts

**C.A.A.D.A.C.,** Certified Alcohol and Drug Abuse Counselor
**CAC,** Certified Alcoholism Counselor
**CAE,** Certified Association Executive
**CAP,** College of American Pathologists
**CAPA,** Certified Ambulatory Post Anesthesia
**C.A.S.,** Certificate of Advanced Study
**CCDC,** Certified Chemical Dependency Counselor
**C.D.,** Commander of the Order of Distinction
**CDR,** Commander
**CDS,** Chemical Dependency Specialist
**CFACHE,** Certified Fellow American College of Healthcare Executives
**CFRE,** Certified Fund Raising Executive
**C.G.,** Certified Gastroenterology
**CHC,** Certified Health Consultant
**CHE,** Certified Healthcare Executive
**C.L.D.,** Clinical Laboratory Director
**CLU,** Certified Life Underwriter, Chartered Life Underwriter
**CMA,** Certified Medical Assistant
**C.M.H.A.,** Certified Mental Health Administrator
**CNHA,** Certified Nursing Home Administrator
**CNM,** Certified Nurse Midwife
**CNOR,** Certified Operating Room Nurse
**C.N.S.,** Clinical Nurse Specialist
**CO,** Colorado; Commanding Officer
**COA,** Certified Ophthalmic Assistant
**COMT,** Commandant
**C.O.M.T.,** Certified Ophthalmic Medical Technician
**Conv.,** Conventions
**Corp.,** Corporation; Corporate
**C.O.T.,** Certified Ophthalmic Technician
**CPA,** Certified Public Accountant
**C.P.H.Q.,** Certified Professional in Health Care Quality
**CPM,** Certified Public Manager
**CRNA,** Certified Registered Nurse Anesthetist
**CRNH,** Certified Registered Nurse Hospice
**C.S.J.B.,** Catholic Saint John the Baptist
**CSW,** Certified Social Worker
**CT,** Connecticut
**CWO,** Chief Warrant Officer

**D.B.A.,** Doctor of Business Administration
**DC,** District of Columbia
**D.D.,** Doctor of Divinity
**D.D.S.,** Doctor of Dental Surgery
**DE,** Delaware
**Diet,** Dietitian; Dietary; Dietetics
**D.M.D.,** Doctor of Dental Medicine
**D.MIN.,** Doctor of Ministry
**D.O.,** Doctor of Osteopathic Medicine and Surgery, Doctor of Osteopathy
**DPA,** Doctorate Public Administration
**D.P.M.,** Doctor of Podiatric Medicine
**Dr.,** Drive
**Dr.Ph.,** Doctor of Public Health
**D.Sc.,** Doctor of Science
**D.S.W.,** Doctor of Social Welfare
**D.V.M.,** Doctor of Veterinary Medicine

**E.,** East
**Ed.D.,** Doctor of Education
**Ed.S.,** Specialist in Education
**ENS,** Ensign
**Esq.,** Esquire
**Expwy.,** Expressway
**ext.,** extension

**FAAN,** Fellow of the American Academy of Nursing
**FACATA,** Fellow of the American College of Addiction Treatment Administrators
**FACHE,** Fellow of the American College of Healthcare Executives
**FACMGA,** Fellow of the American College of Medical Group Administrators
**FACP,** Fellow of the American College of Physicians
**FACS,** Fellow of the American College of Surgeons
**FAX,** Facsimile
**FL,** Florida
**FPO,** Fleet Post Office
**FRCPSC,** Fellow of the Royal College of Physicians and Surgeons of Canada
**FT,** Full-time

**GA,** Georgia
**Govt.,** Government; Governmental

**HHS,** Department of Health and Human Services
**HI,** Hawaii
**HM,** Helmsman
**HMO,** Health Maintenance Organization
**Hon.,** Honorable; Honorary
**H.S.A.,** Health System Administrator
**Hts.,** Heights
**Hwy.,** Highway

**IA,** Iowa
**ID,** Idaho
**IL,** Illinois
**IN,** Indiana
**Inc.,** Incorporated

**J.D.,** Doctor of Law
**J.P.,** Justice of the Peace
**Jr.,** Junior

**KS,** Kansas
**KY,** Kentucky

**LA,** Louisiana
**LCDR,** Lieutenant Commander
**LCSW,** Licensed Certified Social Worker
**L.H.D.,** Doctor of Humanities

**L.I.S.W.,** Licensed Independent Social Worker
**LL.D.,** Doctor of Laws
**L.L.P.,** Limited Licensed Practitioner
**L.M.H.C.,** Licensed Master of Health Care
**L.M.S.W.,** Licensed Master of Social Work
**L.N.H.A.,** Licensed Nursing Home Administrator
**L.P.C.,** Licensed Professional Counselor
**LPN,** Licensed Practical Nurse
**L.P.N.,** Licensed Practical Nurse
**L.S.W.,** Licensed Social Worker
**Lt.,** Lieutenant
**LTC,** Lieutenant Colonel
**Ltd.,** Limited
**LT.GEN.,** Lieutenant General
**LTJG,** Lieutenant (junior grade)

**MA,** Massachusetts
**M.A.,** Master of Arts
**Maj.,** Major
**M.B.,** Bachelor of Medicine
**M.B.A.,** Masters of Business Administration
**MC,** Medical Corps; Marine Corps
**M.C.,** Member of Congress
**MD,** Maryland
**M.D.,** Doctor of Medicine
**ME,** Maine
**M.Ed.,** Master of Education
**MFCC,** Marriage/Family/Child Counselor
**MHA,** Mental Health Association
**M.H.S.,** Masters in Health Science; Masters in Human Service
**MI,** Michigan
**MM,** Masters of Management
**MN,** Minnesota
**M.N.,** Master of Nursing
**MO,** Missouri
**M.P.A.,** Master of Public Administration; Master Public Affairs
**M.P.H.,** Master of Public Health
**M.P.S.,** Master of Professional Studies; Master of Public Science
**MS,** Mississippi
**M.S.,** Master of Science
**MSC,** Medical Service Corps
**M.S.D.,** Doctor of Medical Science
**MSHSA,** Master of Science Health Service Administration
**M.S.N.,** Master of Science in Nursing
**M.S.P.H.,** Master of Science in Public Health
**M.S.S.W.,** Master of Science in Social Work
**M.S.W.,** Master of Social Work
**MT,** Montana
**Mt.,** Mount

**N.,** North
**NC,** North Carolina
**N.C.A.D.C.,** National Certification of Alcohol and Drug Counselors
**ND,** North Dakota
**NE,** Nebraska
**NH,** New Hampshire
**NHA,** National Hearing Association; Nursing Home Administrator
**NJ,** New Jersey
**NM,** New Mexico
**NPA,** National Perinatal Association
**NV,** Nevada
**NY,** New York

**OCN,** Oncology Certified Nurse
**O.D.,** Doctor of Optometry
**O.F.M.,** Order Franciscan Monks, Order of Friars Minor
**OH,** Ohio
**OK,** Oklahoma
**OR,** Oregon
**O.R.,** Operating Room

**O.R.S.,** Operating Room Supervisor
**OSF,** Order of St. Francis

**PA,** Pennsylvania
**P.A.,** Professional Association
**P.C.,** Professional Corporation
**Pharm.D.,** Doctor of Pharmacy
**Ph.B.,** Bachelor of Philosophy
**Ph.D.,** Doctor of Philosophy
**PHS,** Public Health Service
**Pkwy.,** Parkway
**Pl.,** Place
**PR,** Puerto Rico
**PS,** Professional Services
**PSRO,** Professional Standards Review Organization

**RADM,** Rear Admiral
**RD,** Rural Delivery
**Rd.,** Road
**R.F.D.,** Rural Free Delivery
**RI,** Rhode Island
**R.M.,** Risk Manager
**R.N.,** Registered Nurse
**RNC,** Republican National Committee; Registered Nurse or Board Certified
**R.Ph.,** Registered Pharmacist
**RRA,** Registered Record Administrator
**R.S.M.,** Religious Sisters of Mercy
**Rte.,** Route

**S.,** South
**SC,** South Carolina
**S.C.,** Surgery Center
**SCAC,** Senior Certified Addiction Counselor
**Sc.D.,** Doctor of Science
**Sci.,** Science, Scientific
**SD,** South Dakota
**SHCC,** Statewide Health Coordinating Council
**Sgt.,** Sergeant
**SNA,** Surgical Nursing Assistant
**SNF,** Skilled Nursing Facility
**Sq.,** Square
**Sr.,** Senior, Sister
**St.,** Saint, Street
**Sta.,** Station
**Ste.,** Saint; Suite

**Tel.,** Telephone
**Terr.,** Terrace
**TN,** Tennessee
**Tpke,** Turnpike
**Twp.,** Township
**TX,** Texas

**USA,** United States Army
**USAF,** United States Air Force
**USMC,** United States Marine Corps
**USN,** United States Navy
**USPHS,** United States Public Health Service
**UT,** Utah

**VA,** Virginia
**VADM,** Vice Admiral
**VI,** Virgin Islands
**Vlg.,** Village
**VT,** Vermont

**W.,** West
**WA,** Washington
**WI,** Wisconsin
**WV,** West Virginia
**WY,** Wyoming

# Index

# Notes

# Notes

# Notes

# Notes

# Notes

# Notes

# Notes

# Notes

# Notes

# Notes

# Notes

**Notes**

# AHA Guide® to the Health Care Field

2016 Edition

AHA Members $255
Nonmembers $380
AHA Item Number 010016
Telephone ORDERS 1–800–AHA–2626

ISSN 0094–8969
ISBN–13: 978–0–87258–962–9